Directory
1995/96

Crockford's Clerical Directory

1995/96

Ninety-fourth edition
First issue 1858

*A Directory of the Clergy
of the Church of England
the Church in Wales
the Scottish Episcopal Church
the Church of Ireland*

Published for The Church Commissioners for England
and The Central Board of Finance of The Church of England
by Church House Publishing

Crockford's Clerical Directory
94th edition (1995/96) © The Church Commissioners for England and
The Central Board of Finance of the Church of England 1995

Published December 1995 by
Church House Publishing
Church House
Great Smith Street
London SW1P 3NZ

ISBN 0 7151 8087 8 (hardback)
     0 7151 8088 6 (paperback)

Jacket and cover design by Drummond and Peggy Chapman

Typeset by Create Publishing Services Ltd
(Bath Press Manufacturing Group) and
Datix International Limited, Bungay, Suffolk

Printed and bound by
The Bath Press
Lower Bristol Road
Bath BA2 3BL

CONTENTS

Index to advertisements   6
Introduction   41
John Crockford   43
A user's guide to *Crockford*   44
How to address the clergy   47
Abbreviations   49

Biographies of clergy and deaconesses
Clergy of the Church of England, the Church in Wales,
    the Scottish Episcopal Church and the Church of Ireland   1
Deaconesses of the Church of England, the Church in
    Wales, the Scottish Episcopal Church and the Church of
    Ireland   789

Indexes
Diocesan, area, suffragan and assistant bishops, and
    provincial episcopal visitors   791
Succession of archbishops and bishops   793
Cathedrals   824
Royal Peculiars, the Chapel Royal and College of Chaplains   826
Diocesan offices   827
Archdeaconries, deaneries and rural deans   830
English benefices and churches   838
Central London churches   1015
Welsh benefices and churches   1017
Scottish incumbencies   1033
Irish benefices and churches   1037
Chaplains of the Diocese of Gibraltar in Europe   1051
Chaplains to Her Majesty's Services   1053
Prison chaplains   1055
Hospital chaplains   1057
Educational chaplains   1059
Theological colleges and courses   1063

The Anglican Communion
Bishops of Anglican dioceses overseas   1064
Bishops of united churches   1074
Provincial offices   1076
Directories of the Anglican provinces   1077

Supplementary information
Addresses unknown   1078
Ordinations to the diaconate at Michaelmas 1995   1079
Clergy who have died since the last edition   1081

Maps
England and Wales   1086
Scotland   1088
Ireland   1089

INDEX TO ADVERTISEMENTS

Advertisements can be found on the following pages

CHURCH AND BENEVOLENT SOCIETIES

Additional Curates Society, *30*
Bible Lands Trading Ltd, *24*
Central Board of Finance, *32*
The Children's Society, *27*
Church of England Pensions Board, *29*
Church Lads' and Church Girls' Brigade, *34*
Church Society, *30*
Church Union, *34*
College of St Barnabas, *24*
Corporation of the Sons of the Clergy, *33*
Corrymeela Link, *28*
The English Clergy Association, *26*
The Friends of the Clergy Corporation, *8*
GFS Platform, *28*
The Leprosy Mission, *28*
London City Mission, *8*
The Missions to Seamen, *31*
The Mothers' Union, *24*
The Prayer Book Society, *7*
St Luke's Hospital for the Clergy, *35*

CHURCH FURNISHERS AND ROBES

James Chase & Son (Furnishings) Ltd, *17*
Charles Farris Ltd, *40*
Pruden & Smith, *18*
St Martin Vestment Ltd, *14*
The House of Vanheems Ltd, *15*
Vanpoulles Ltd, *9*
Watts & Company Ltd, *19*
J Wippell & Co Ltd, *16*

CHURCH BELL FOUNDERS

John Taylor Bellfounders Ltd, *25*
Whitechapel Bell Foundry, *12*

CARS

Autosave (UK) Ltd, *11*

HEATING

Emberheat, *23*
Multibeton Ltd, *18*

FINANCE AND INSURANCE

Church Finance Supplies Ltd, *10*
Ecclesiastical Insurance, *62*
Lockie Envelopes, *10*

PASTORAL REORGANISATION

David E Gillman, *22*

PUBLISHERS, PUBLICATIONS AND BOOKSELLERS

Canterbury Press Norwich, *37*
Church House Bookshop, 1090
Church House Publishing, *61*
Church Times, *39*
Church Pulpit Year Book, *36*
The Sign, *21*
SPCK, *38*

ALTAR BREADS

F A Dumont Ltd, *14*

SCHOOLS AND COLLEGES

Dean Close School, Cheltenham, *36*
King Edward's School, Witley, *22*
Marlborough College, Marlborough, *36*
St Lawrence College, Ramsgate, *20*
St Mary's Hall, Brighton, *22*

STAINED GLASS, CLOCKS AND CHURCH CONSERVATION

Church Conservation Ltd, *20*
Cliff Durant & Son, *20*
Smith of Derby, *18*

TRAVEL AND HOLIDAYS

McCabe Travel, *42*
Maranatha Tours, *13*

The Book of Common Prayer

contains some of the most majestic and beautiful prose in the English language. Over the centuries it has been the repository of doctrine from which Anglican beliefs could be learned. A devotional power-house, the Book of Common Prayer is a deeply valued means of communication with our Maker.

The Prayer Book Society

⋆ seeks to defend and uphold that doctrine and to promote the worship enshrined in the Book of Common Prayer

⋆ does NOT propagate Prayer Book fundamentalism but believes a modest amount of flexibility in usage is both sensible and to be desired

The Prayer Book Society aims

⋆ To encourage the use of the Book of Common Prayer for the training of Ordinands and Confirmands

⋆ To spread knowledge of the Book of Common Prayer and the doctrine contained therein.

⋆ To encourage use of the Book of Common Prayer for public worship.

ARE YOU A REGULAR READER OF THE SOCIETY'S TWO MAGAZINES?

ISSUES OF "FAITH AND HERITAGE" ALTERNATE WITH "FAITH AND WORSHIP"

Please support
THE PRAYER BOOK SOCIETY *write now to:*
PBS OFFICE, ST JAMES GARLICKHYTHE, GARLICK HILL, LONDON EC4V 2AL

Bells bring people together!

Their call to worship proclaims the Christian message to the world. And the bellringers themselves, developing their skills, become united as a team.

The team that works at the Whitechapel Bell Foundry, casting and tuning, installing and restoring church bells of every kind, is deploying skills that have been developed over four hundred years. Today, our technical expertise, and our reputation for the highest standards of craftsmanship and service, stand unrivalled.

Bells and bellringers make an important contribution to the Church's witness in the world. We are proud to be a part of it.

WHITECHAPEL
The World's most famous Bellfoundry
32 & 34 Whitechapel Road, London E1 1DY.
Tel: (0171) 247 2599.   Fax: (0171) 375 1979.

Visiting The Biblical World

Tailor-made itineraries for group visits to

THE HOLY LAND

Jordan - Egypt - Syria - Turkey - Greece - Italy

Our formula for success

ASK FOR OUR BROCHURE NOW

0345 125488

Calls charged at local rate

M A N U F A C T U R I N G • P R E C I S E L Y

OUR RANGE INCLUDES

CHAIRS • TABLES • PULPITS • ALTARS • KNEELERS

 JAMES CHASE & SON (FURNISHINGS) LTD

191 Thornton Road, Bradford BD1 2JT. Telephone: 01274 738282 Fax: 01274 737836

18

YOUR LOVE IS A POWERFUL FORCE

The Children's Society wishes to thank its fundraising volunteers and supporters for their continued love, parish prayers and help throughout this year. We rely on your dedication to raise those vital funds which enable us to continue to help thousands of children, young people and families in need throughout England and Wales. In many areas community development is undertaken with dioceses.

So if you would like more information about the work of the Society, a collecting box, or to find out more about how you can help,

WE'D LOVE TO HEAR FROM YOU

The Children's Society
MAKING LIVES WORTH LIVING
A VOLUNTARY SOCIETY OF THE CHURCH OF ENGLAND
AND THE CHURCH IN WALES

Edward Rudolf House, Margery Street, London WC1X 0JL. Telephone: 0171 837 4299.
Charity Registration No. 221124

© Robert Walker

CYCLE OF PRAYER 1995/96 is available, free of charge from Judith Seaward at The Children's Society's Head Office.

AP9035

OUR WORK IS CARING . . .

The Church of England Pensions Board offers support to retired clergy and their spouses, the widows or widowers of clergy, and church workers retired from full time ministry.

Our greatest concern is for the welfare of our older pensioners, who because of age or infirmity need sheltered accommodation and some special care. The Pensions Board runs nine residential and nursing homes offering security and peace of mind to those who have given their lives towards helping others in the name of Christ. Assistance can also be given towards the fees payable for accommodation in homes run by other organisations.

The Board receives no help from central Church funds towards the cost of its residential and nursing care, and must rely on support from donations, deeds of covenant, and legacies in order to continue this much needed work. Please help us in any way you can.

For further information about ways to help, a form of words for inclusion in a Will, or more details about our work, please write to:

The Secretary, Freepost CD,
The Church of England Pensions Board
7 LITTLE COLLEGE STREET
WESTMINSTER, LONDON SW1P 3SF

Reg. Charity No. 236627

For the nation-wide work of the Church of England

The Central Church Fund is unique. It is the *only* fund available for the general purposes of the Church of England as a whole.

It helps parishes and dioceses with imaginative and innovative projects of all kinds – and especially those that meet the needs of local communities.

It provides for training for ministry in the Church (donations and bequests can be directed specifically for this purpose).

It makes money available for those unexpected and urgent needs which cannot be budgeted for.

As a general purpose Fund, its flexibility allows it to provide, without delay, for a host of needs that no other fund is geared to cope with, and its value in this way to the Church of England is incalculable.

There are inevitably many calls upon it and funds are always urgently needed. Please help with your donation, covenanted subscription or bequest – or find out more from the Secretary.

Charity No. 248711

The Central Church Fund

The Central Board of Finance of the Church of England, Church House, Great Smith Street, Westminster, London SW1P 3NZ. Tel: 0171-222 9011.

CORPORATION OF THE

SONS OF THE CLERGY

Founded A.D. 1655   Incorporated by Royal Charter 1678

For assisting Clergymen of the Anglican Church and their Widows and Dependants, and for providing Grants for Education, Maintenance or Apprenticeship of Children of the Clergy of the Dioceses of the United Kingdom, Ireland and the Mission Field

Office: 1 DEAN TRENCH STREET, WESTMINSTER
LONDON, SW1P 3HB
Telephone: 0171-799 3696 & 0171-222 5887
(Charity registration number: 207736)

THE COURT OF ASSISTANTS

President:

THE ARCHBISHOP OF CANTERBURY

Vice-President:

The Right Honourable The LORD TEMPLEMAN, M.B.E.

TREASURERS:
CANON J. ROBINSON BD FKC
L.H.G. TRIMM Esq BSc ACII FREconS
T.D. BAXENDALE Esq

ASSISTANTS

The Archbishop of Armagh
R.J. Askwith Esq BA FRGS
Rear Admiral D.W. Bazalgette CB
Dr. J.A. Birch MA DMus FRCM FRCO (CHM)
P.W. Boorman Esq MA
D.W. Brewer Esq JP, FCII
The Reverend D. Burgess MA
C.B. Byford Esq CBE ATI
C.P.G. Chavasse Esq MA
The Viscount Churchill
Major Sir Peter Clarke KCVO
Brigadier GB Curtis OBE MC
R H N Dashwood Esq JP DL

The Most Reverend The Bishop of Edinburgh and Primus
The Venerable K Gibbons BSc
A H P Gillett Esq MA FRICS
P Griffin Esq MBE MA
N R J James Esq MA JP
Alderman Sir Brian Jenkins GBE
The Venerable F Johnston CB
The Honourable A C St J Lawson Johnston BA FRSA DL
P Locke Esq
I S Lockhart Esq MA
The Bishop of London
The Right Reverend L E Luscombe LLD CA

Mrs J C Manuel JP
M L J Marshall Esq MA FRICS
The Venerable J A Morrison
Major General J I H Owen OBE
Prebendary A R Royall MA
Mrs D M Stanesby BA MEd MSc
D N Vermont Esq MA
The Archbishop of Wales
Alderman C R Walford MA
Doctor E M Webb MB BS MRCGP
A E Woodall Esq
The Archbishop of York

The Corporation distributed over £1,237,000 in 1994 by way of grants to 2500 clergymen, their widows and dependants. Education and maintenance help was given to 200 ordinands and 500 boys and girls.

The ANNUAL FESTIVAL SERVICE in St Paul's Cathedral is held in May and tickets may be obtained from the Registrar at the address given above.

Donors of not less than £100 may be elected to be Governors of the Corporation.

SUBSCRIPTIONS, DONATIONS, CHURCH and SCHOOL COLLECTIONS, and LEGACIES, in aid of funds or towards the extension of any of the above branches of work, are requested, and will be gratefully acknowledged by the Registrar, who will provide any information required.

R. C. F. LEACH, Registrar.

SPCK BOOKSHOPS

If we don't stock a book you want, we will happily order it for you,
or you can call our Mail Order Department.

BATH
Tel: 01225 466092

BIRMINGHAM
Tel: 0121 643 2617

BRADFORD ✶✶
Tel: 01274 728669

BRIGHTON
Tel: 01273 328767

BRISTOL ✶✶
Tel: 01179 273461

CAMBRIDGE
Tel: 01223 358452

CANTERBURY ✶✶
Tel/Fax: 01227 462881

CARDIFF
Tel/Fax: 01222 227736

CARLISLE
Tel/Fax: 01228 43498

CHESTER ✶✶
Tel/Fax: 01244 323753

CHICHESTER
Tel: 01243 782790

DURHAM CATHEDRAL
Tel: 0191 386 2972

EXETER ✶✶
1/2 Catherine Street, Exeter
Tel/ Fax: 01392 73640

GLOUCESTER CATHEDRAL
Tel: 01452 522805

GUILDFORD
Tel: 01483 60316

HEREFORD
Tel/Fax: 01432 266785

LEEDS
Tel/Fax: 01132 442488

LEICESTER ✶✶
Tel: 01162 626161

LINCOLN ✶✶
Tel: 01522 527486

LIVERPOOL CATHEDRAL
Tel: 0151 709 1897

LIVERPOOL
Tel/Fax: 0151 7222784

LONDON
Tel: 0171 388 1659

MANCHESTER
Tel: 0161 834 0257

NEWCASTLE
Tel: 0191 232 3466

NORWICH ✶✶
Tel/Fax: 01603 627332

SALISBURY
Tel/Fax: 01722 334535

SHEFFIELD
Tel: 01142 723454

TRURO ✶✶
Tel/Fax: 01872 72771

WINCHESTER ✶✶
Tel/Fax: 01962 866617

WORCESTER
Tel/Fax: 01905 24396

YORK
Tel: 01904 654176

HEAD OFFICE
Tel: 0171 387 5282
Fax: 0171 388 2352

*✶✶ - indicates branches with
secondhand departments*

Would you like to buy or sell secondhand books?

If you are wishing to buy secondhand and antiquarian theological books, or to sell them, why not contact the experts? SPCK has several bookshops which buy and sell second-hand theological books. Our main specialist branch is located at: Charles Higham (SPCK), Holy Trinity Church, Marylebone Road, London NW1 4DU (0171 383 3097), where we operate a booksearch service for out of print and hard to find titles. Please contact Mr Pickering at Charles Higham for further details.

SPCK MAIL ORDER

CHRISTIAN BOOKS DELIVERED DIRECT TO YOUR HOME

Most major credit and debit cards accepted including Switch, Mastercard and Visa.
Call 0345 626747 (All UK calls charged at the local rate)

For all your Christian books, gifts and resources

INTRODUCTION

This, the ninety-fourth edition of *Crockford's Clerical Directory*, provides details as at 31 July 1995 of 25,614 clergy and deaconesses in the Church of England (including the Diocese of Gibraltar in Europe), the Church in Wales, the Scottish Episcopal Church and the Church of Ireland.

It is the sixth edition for which the Central Board of Finance and the Church Commissioners have had joint responsibility. Church House Publishing, with its considerable experience of providing many different kinds of resources for the Church of England (not least *The Church of England Year Book*, to which *Crockford* is complementary), deals with publishing, selling, advertising and distributing the directory, while the Commissioners have responsibility for maintaining and updating the computer database from which the directory is compiled every other year. This partnership enables the Church to have access to detailed records of its clergy at a reasonable price without the need for any subsidy from central Church funds. This is possible because most clergy are paid centrally and any changes to their payroll details (for example when they move or retire) are automatically reflected on the *Crockford* database.

Around 7,000, or just under 30%, of the clergy included in *Crockford* are not on the central payroll. Details of these clergy – principally non-stipendiary ministers, those engaged in some form of ministry outside the parochial system and those serving in Wales, Scotland or Ireland – are obtained from other sources. We are particularly grateful to those clergy who have taken the trouble to inform us of new appointments and changes of address. We also make extensive use of diocesan directories and year books, as well as gleaning information from the *Church Times* and *The Church of England Newspaper*. The central authorities of the Church in Wales, the Scottish Episcopal Church and the Church of Ireland kindly provide information on a regular basis. We also receive considerable assistance from bishops' secretaries, the offices of diocesan registrars, the Home Office, the General Synod Board of Education, the Diocese of Gibraltar in Europe, the Ministry of Defence and the Hospital Chaplaincies Council and should like to put on record our gratitude to all of those who have provided us with information.

Despite the extensive work that goes into its compilation, it is not possible for *Crockford* to be a complete record. For reasons of time, space and consistency, we are unable to include all the information that clergy request us to publish. Although we endeavour to keep omissions and errors to a minimum, they are inevitable in a volume of this size. We are, however, always glad to be informed so that we can correct them in future editions and particularly appreciate any information that users of *Crockford* are able to provide about clergy whose addresses are not currently known (see list on page 1078).

Changes to the scope of this edition have been relatively modest. The list of bishops now includes all diocesan, area, suffragan and assistant bishops, and the provincial episcopal visitors. We have revised the order of some of the shorter sections at the back of the book in the hope that this will make them easier to locate.

For archival information from previous editions of *Crockford*, please write to the Church of England Record Centre, 15 Galleywall Road, South Bermondsey, London SE6 3PB (tel 0171 222 7010 extension 4155). Comments and suggestions on how *Crockford* might be improved are always welcomed by the Crockford Working Party, Church Commissioners, 1 Millbank, London SW1P 3JZ.

Church Commissioners
1 Millbank
London SW1P 3JZ

Central Board of Finance
Church House
Great Smith Street
London SW1P 3NZ

September 1995

JOHN CROCKFORD

John Crockford, publisher (?1823–1865) is best remembered for his association with the clerical directory that bears his name. His origins and parentage are obscure. No baptism can be traced, though his marriage certificate records him as the son of John Crockford, schoolmaster. By his early twenties he was in business as a printer and publisher at 29 Essex Street, Strand; and it was from that address that *Crockford* was first published in 1858. On 6 December of the same year, John Crockford moved to new business premises at 346 Strand and 19 Wellington Street North.

His private address at that time was 16 Oakley Square, Hampstead Road; though by 1865 he had moved to 10 Park Road, Haverstock Hill.

Crockford's business association of more than two decades with Edward William Cox (1809–1879) had begun in 1843, when the *Law Times* first appeared. Both men are claimed as publisher – Crockford by Boase in *Modern English Biography*; Cox by the *Athenaeum* and by *Notes and Queries*. There is similar lack of agreement over other publications, such as the ill-fated *Critic*. "[Crockford] tried to establish a literary paper, the *Critic*. To this he brought all his great ability, but after fifteen years he gave it up in despair" (*Notes and Queries*): whereas the *DNB* has it that Cox became "proprietor of . . . two other papers called respectively 'The Critic' and 'The Royal Exchange'."

The truth appears to be that the two men, who shared the same business address in Essex Street, were joint founders of a number of projects. Cox – the elder, more established and richer man – was often the financier and named publisher, with Crockford as the manager of the undertaking. Each had his own specialities: Cox, called to the bar in 1843, and successively Recorder of Helston & Falmouth (1857–1868) and of Portsmouth (1868–1879) was no doubt the leader in the establishment of the *Law Times*, to which, in *DNB*'s words, he "thenceforth devoted . . . the larger portion of his time and attention." But the legend which has arisen that Cox, restrained by professional ethics from using his own name, chose, almost at random, the name of one of his clerks to bear the title of his new clerical directory in 1858 – thus, in the words of the first postwar editor (probably Newman) bestowing "a more than tomb-stone meed of remembrance" – cannot be substantiated. As the jubilee account of the *Field* notes, Crockford was an equal partner in the success of the joint enterprises: "It was John Crockford who purchased the paper for Mr Cox. He obtained it from Mr Benjamin Webster for a trifling sum . . . In a short time the net profits amounted to 20,000*l.* a year. The management was placed under Crockford's control. He was a splendid man of business" (*Notes and Queries*).

The first *Clerical Directory* (1858), "A Biographical and Statistical Book of Reference for facts relating to the clergy and the Church", seems to have been assembled in a very haphazard fashion, with names added "as fast as they could be obtained", out of alphabetical order and with an unreliable index. By 1860 the *Directory* had become a very much more useful work of reference; and by 1917, with the absorption of its only serious rival, the *Clergy List*, reigned supreme.

No more than glimpses survive of Crockford's personality, and those mostly from the account of him given by John C. Francis, in the *Field* jubilee article already referred to. "I had occasion to call upon him a short time before his death, when we joined in a hearty laugh over his former furious attacks upon the *Athenaeum*. 'Dilke's Drag' he used to call it, and would accuse it of 'vulgar insolence and coxcombry' and 'the coarsest vulgarity'. As we parted he said, 'You have the *Athenaeum* to be proud of, and we have the *Field*.'"

John Crockford died suddenly at his home on 13 January 1865, at the age of 41. He left a widow, Annie (née Ellam) whom he married on 24 December 1847 at St Pancras Old Church. No children are recorded. His very brief will, proved 6 February 1865 at the Principal Probate Registry, left everything to his widow. His personal effects were valued at less than £1,000, but the family must have lived in some style, since one of the witnesses to the will was the resident coachman.

BRENDA HOUGH

A request from the *Dictionary of National Biography* for a notice of the life of John Crockford led to the preparation of this article, a shorter version of which appeared in *The Dictionary of National Biography: Mission Persons*, 1993.

A USER'S GUIDE TO CROCKFORD

Who is included in *Crockford*?
Crockford includes details of over 25,000 clergy and deaconesses of the Church of England, the Church in Wales, the Scottish Episcopal Church and the Church of Ireland. Clergy currently serving overseas do not automatically qualify for inclusion (see Overseas clergy), although those who have substantial past service in the British Isles are included. Clergy who have died since the last edition are listed on p.1081. Clergy who have resigned their offices (but not their orders) are included unless they are known to have been received into another Church. A small number of clergy are excluded at their own request.

Readers and lay workers are not included: please consult diocesan directories. The *Who's Who* section of *The Church of England Year Book* lists members of General Synod and principal members of staff of the Church's central organisations.

Addressing the clergy
See p.47.

Appointment details in the *Biographies* section
These reflect the legal pastoral situation prevailing at 31 July 1995, the date of the compilation of this edition of *Crockford*. Conventional districts, proprietary chapels and local ecumenical projects are also recorded. Benefice names are only recorded once in a biographical entry when they apply to successive appointments.

Crockford does not record group ministries, informal local arrangements, areas of special responsibility, emeritus appointments (except as reflected in the style of address), licence or permission to officiate when held in conjunction with another appointment from the same diocese, commissary appointments, examining chaplaincies, or secular appointments (except for educational or charitable posts).

Appointments before ordination are not included (apart from service as a deaconess) unless they straddle the date of ordination.

Archdeaconries
See *Archdeaconries, deaneries and rural deans* on p.830.

Archdeacons
Look up the place name in *Biographies*: this is cross-referenced to a personal name.

Bishops (diocesan, area, suffragan)
Look up the place name in *Biographies*: this is cross-referenced to a personal name. See also p.791 which lists the diocesan, area, suffragan and assistant bishops by diocese.

Bishops (assistant)
See *Diocesan, area, suffragan and assistant bishops* on p.791.

Bishops in the House of Lords
See *The Church of England Year Book*, published annually by Church House Publishing and covering most aspects of the life and institutions of the Church of England.

Bishops overseas
See *Bishops of Anglican dioceses overseas* on p.1064, and Bishops of united churches on p.1074. Further information about the Anglican Communion can be found in *The Church of England Year Book*.

Bishops and archbishops, former
A list of former archbishops and bishops (diocesan and suffragan) dating back to Eborius, Bishop of York in 314, will be found on p.793.

Boundaries, provincial and diocesan
Maps of England and Wales, Scotland and Ireland showing provincial, diocesan and county boundaries and cathedral cities will be found on p.1086.

Cathedral clergy
See *Cathedrals* on p.824 for full-time cathedral clergy. The list does not include honorary appointments.

Chapel Royal
See *Royal Peculiars* on p.826.

Christian names
The name by which a person prefers to be known, if not the first Christian name, is underlined (e.g. David John Smith prefers to be called John). Names 'in religion' or names not part of a person's legal name are shown in parentheses.

Church: how to find the names of clergy responsible for a particular church
Look up the place name in the appropriate *Benefices and churches* section, see pp.838-1050: if the entry is in bold type the names of all clergy are listed and can be cross-referenced in the *Biographies* section. If the place name is not in bold type the name of the benefice is given where the names of all clergy will be found.

Church: how to find the names of clergy responsible for a particular church when there is a vacancy
If the benefice is vacant the telephone number of the clergy house is usually given in the appropriate *Benefices and churches* section to enable contact to be made with a new incumbent or priest-in-charge. The deanery reference (e.g. *Guildf 2*) following the benefice name cross-refers to *Archdeaconries, deaneries and rural deans* on p.830 by means of which the name of the rural dean responsible for the vacant benefice can be found.

College chaplains
See p.1059 for chaplains at universities, colleges of further education, colleges of higher education, and schools (England only).

Crockford
The full title is *Crockford's Clerical Directory*; *Crockford* (not *Crockford's*) is an accepted abbreviation. See also the biography of John Crockford on p.*43*.

Deaconesses
See separate section on p.789.

Deacons
See *Biographies* section.

Deaneries
See Rural or area deans below.

Deans
Look up the place name in *Biographies*: this is cross-referenced to a personal name. See also *Cathedrals* on p.824, and *Royal Peculiars* on p.826.

Diocesan offices
Details of the diocesan offices in England, Wales, Scotland and Ireland can be found on p.827.

Europe, chaplains in
See *Chaplains of the Diocese of Gibraltar in Europe* on p.1051.

Fax numbers
The exchange number is only given if different from that of the preceding telephone number.

Honours and education
The order of these items in a biography is normally: honours, professional qualifications and membership of learned societies, education (that is academic qualifications including theological degrees from universities, normally in date order), and ministerial training detailing college or course with qualification (if any) or year of entry. Dr is inserted before the Christian name when clergy with appropriate qualifications request this.

Hospital chaplains
Full-time hospital chaplains at their base hospitals (as defined by the Hospital Chaplaincies Council) are listed on p.1057.

Lay workers
Lay workers are not included in *Crockford*: please consult diocesan directories.

London churches
See p.1015 for an index of central London churches (with street names) listed by postal district. For further details consult *English benefices and churches* on p.838.

Married or single?
Crockford does not provide information on marital status. However, where a woman priest, deacon or deaconess has requested the form of address Miss, Mrs or Ms this is included. Where there has been a change of surname following marriage a cross-reference may be found from the previous name.

Non-stipendiary clergy
Non-stipendiary clergy are listed in the main *Biographies* section.

Ordination courses
See *Theological colleges and courses* on p.1063.

Overseas clergy
Clergy currently serving overseas do not automatically qualify for inclusion in *Crockford*, although clergy who are native to the British Isles or have substantial past service there but who now work or reside overseas are included. Service overseas is recorded by country only, but higher office (e.g. as bishop or archdeacon) is also noted.

Overseas addresses and telephone numbers are given as required by a user in the UK. Where area codes are not applicable (e.g. France) the country code is given. In other cases, the area code is listed and the country code will need to be obtained from international directory enquiries (telephone 153). The international access code (00) will be required in all cases.

Patronage
The patron of each benefice is listed under the benefice name in *English benefices and churches*, see p.838.

Prison chaplains
See p.1055.

Proprietary chapels
See *English benefices and churches* on p.838.

Provosts
Look up the place name in *Biographies*: this is cross-referenced to a personal name. See also *Cathedrals* on p.824.

Queen's Chaplains
See *Royal Peculiars* on p.826.

Readers
Readers are not included in *Crockford*: please consult diocesan directories.

Religious orders
For members of religious orders where the Christian name alone is commonly used (e.g. Brother Aidan) a cross-reference is provided to the surname. Names 'in religion' not forming part of a person's legal name will be shown in parentheses. Details of religious communities are provided in *The Church of England Year Book*.

Retired clergy
Appointments are recorded which ended after 1970. Full biographies are included for retired bishops.

Rural or area deans
See *Archdeaconries, deaneries and rural deans* on p.830. To find who is the rural dean of a particular church, look up the place or benefice name in the appropriate *Benefices* section: the deanery reference (e.g. *Guildf 2*) following the benefice name cross-refers to *Archdeaconries, deaneries and rural deans on* p.830 where the name of the rural dean responsible can be found.

School chaplains
See p.1060 for chaplains in schools (England only).

Service chaplains
See p.1053.

Theological colleges and courses
See p.1063.

University chaplains
See p.1059.

HOW TO ADDRESS THE CLERGY

In offering the advice below, we do not intend to imply that other practices are necessarily to be discouraged (for example, the use of Father as in 'Father Smith'). A good deal depends on circumstances, and, where a personal preference is known, it is usually good practice to follow it.

The following notes show acceptable current usage

- (a) on an envelope or formal listing
- (b) in starting a social letter or in speech, and
- (c) when referring to a member of the clergy

Category (a) is not open to much variation, owing to the formality of the context, but categories (b) and (c) will often vary according to circumstances. It is always acceptable to use the appropriate Christian name in place of initials (for example, the Revd Alice Smith). In the absence of any style or title conferred by a post, all deacons and priests are styled 'The Reverend', and all who have been consecrated bishop are styled 'The Right Reverend'.

For abbreviations, see paragraph 12 below.

1 Deacons and Priests

- (a) The Reverend A B Smith
- (b) Mr/Mrs/Miss/Ms Smith (unless it is known that some other style is preferred – the title Vicar or Rector is acceptable only if the person so addressed really is the incumbent of the parish where you live or worship)
- (c) The Reverend A B Smith at the first mention, and Mr/Mrs/Miss/Ms Smith thereafter

Note The form 'Reverend Smith' or 'The Reverend Smith' should *never* be used this side of the Atlantic. If the Christian name or initials are not known, the correct forms are
- (a) The Reverend—Smith, *or* The Reverend Mr/Mrs/Miss/Ms Smith
- (b) Mr/Mrs/Miss/Ms Smith
- (c) The Reverend Mr/Mrs/Miss/Ms Smith at the first mention, and Mr/Mrs/Miss/Ms Smith thereafter

2 Prebendaries

- (a) The Reverend Prebendary A B Smith
- (b) Prebendary Smith
- (c) Prebendary Smith

3 Canons (both Residentiary and Honorary)

- (a) The Reverend Canon A B Smith
- (b) Canon Smith
- (c) Canon Smith

4 Archdeacons

- (a) The Venerable the Archdeacon of X
- (b) Archdeacon, *or more formally* Mr Archdeacon
- (c) The Archdeacon of X at the first mention, and the Archdeacon thereafter

Notes 1 In the case of an archdeacon (or dean/provost, bishop, or archbishop) in office, the style above is to be preferred. The personal name should be used only for the purpose of identification.
2 For an archdeacon emeritus, the correct forms are
- (a) The Venerable A B Smith
- (b) Archdeacon
- (c) Archdeacon Smith

5 Deans and Provosts

- (a) The very Reverend the Dean/Provost of X
- (b) Dean/Provost, *or more formally* Mr Dean/Provost
- (c) The Dean/Provost of X at the first mention, and the Dean thereafter (see also note 1 to paragraph 4 above)

6 Bishops, Diocesan and Suffragan

- (a) The Right Reverend the Bishop of X, *or* The Right Reverend the Lord Bishop of X
- (b) Bishop, *or more formally* My Lord
- (c) The Bishop of X at the first mention, and the Bishop thereafter (see also note 1 to paragraph 4 above)

Notes 1 The use of 'Lord' before 'Bishop' is diminishing. It is a matter of individual preference whether it should be used.

2 The Bishop of London is a Privy Councillor, and has the style 'The Right Reverend and Right Honourable the Lord Bishop of London'.

3 The Bishop of Meath and Kildare is styled 'The Most Reverend'.

7 Assistant and Retired Bishops

(a) The Right Reverend A B Smith
(b) Bishop
(c) Bishop Smith

8 Archbishops

(a) The Most Reverend the Lord Archbishop of X
(b) Archbishop, *or more formally* Your Grace
(c) The Archbishop of X at the first mention, and the Archbishop thereafter (see also note 1 to paragraph 4 above)

Notes 1 The Archbishops of Canterbury and York, being Privy Councillors, also have 'Right Honourable' included in their style (for example, The Most Reverend and Right Honourable the Lord Archbishop of Canterbury).

2 The presiding bishop of the Scottish Episcopal Church is the Primus, and the correct forms are
    (a) The Most Reverend the Primus
    (b) Primus
    (c) Primus

3 Retired archbishops properly revert to the status of bishop, but may be given as a courtesy the style of an archbishop.

9 Chaplains to the Armed Services

(a) The Reverend A B Smith RN (*or* CF *or* RAF)
(b) Padre, *or* Padre Smith
(c) The Padre, *or* Padre Smith

10 Ordained Members of Religious Orders

(a) The Reverend Alan/Alice Smith XYZ; The Reverend Brother Alan/Sister Alice XYZ
(b) Father, Father Smith, *or* Father Alan; Brother Alan/Sister Alice
(c) The Reverend Alan/Alice Smith; Father Alan Smith; Father Smith; Brother Alan/Sister Alice

Notes 1 A name 'in religion', shown in parentheses in the biographical entry, should be used in preference to the baptismal name or initials. Sometimes the surname is not used. In this Directory, however, the entry will be found under the surname, whether it is normally used or not, and, if appropriate, a cross-reference is given under the Christian name.

2 Some orders use 'Brother' and 'Sister' for lay and ordained members without distinction, along with Christian names.

3 It is customary to specify the religious order by giving the appropriate letters after the name.

11 Academics

When a member of the clergy holds more than one title, the ecclesiastical one is normally used.

Professor	(a) The Reverend Canon A B Smith
also Canon	(b) Canon Smith, *or* Professor Smith, according to context
	(c) Canon Smith, *or* Professor Smith, according to context
Canon	(a) The Reverend Canon A B Smith (degree)
also Doctor	(b) Canon Smith, *or* Dr Smith, according to context
	(c) Canon Smith, *or* Dr Smith, according to context

12 Abbreviations

The following abbreviations are in common use

Reverend:	Revd *or* Rev
Father:	Fr
Right Reverend:	Rt Revd *or* Rt Rev
Prebendary:	Preb
Venerable:	Ven

Reverend, Right Reverend, and Venerable, whether abbreviated or not, should always be preceded by the definite article.

ABBREVIATIONS USED IN CROCKFORD'S CLERICAL DIRECTORY

A

AAAI .... Associate of the Institute of Administrative Accountants

AACCA .... Associate of the Association of Certified and Corporate Accountants (now see ACCA)

AB .... Bachelor of Arts (USA)

ABAF............... Associate of the British Academy of Fencing

ABIA .... Associate of the Bankers' Institute of Australasia

ABIST.............. Associate of the British Institute of Surgical Technology

ABM .... Advisory Board of Ministry (formerly ACCM and CACTM)

ABPsS .... Associate of the British Psychological Society (now see AFBPsS)

ABSM .... Associate of the Birmingham and Midland Institute School of Music

ACA................ Associate of the Institute of Chartered Accountants

ACC................ Anglican Consultative Council

ACCA .... Associate of the Chartered Assn of Certified Accountants (formerly AACCA)

ACCM .... Advisory Council for the Church's Ministry (formerly CACTM; now see ABM)

ACCS.............. Associate of the Corporation of Secretaries

ACF................ Army Cadet Force

ACGI .... Associate of the City and Guilds of London

ACIArb .... Associate of the Chartered Institute of Arbitrators

ACIB............... Associate of the Chartered Institute of Bankers (formerly AIB)

ACII................ Associate of the Chartered Insurance Institute

ACIS .... Associate of the Institute of Chartered Secretaries and Administrators

ACIT............... Associate of the Chartered Institute of Transport

ACMA .... Associate of the Institute of Cost and Management Accountants (formerly ACWA)

ACORA .... Archbisbops' Commission on Rural Areas

ACP .... Associate of the College of Preceptors

ACS .... Additional Curates Society

ACSM .... Associate of Camborne School of Mines

ACT................ Australian Capital Territory Australian College of Theology

ACTVR........... Advanced Certificate in Television and Radio

ACUPA........... Archbishops' Commission on Urban Priority Areas

ACWA .... Associate of the Institute of Cost and Works Accountants (now see ACMA)

ACertCM .... Archbishop of Canterbury's Certificate in Church Music

ACertEd .... Advanced Certificate of Education

AD .... Area Dean

ADB................ Associate of the Drama Board

ADC .... Advanced Diploma in Counselling

ADCM .... Archbishop of Canterbury's Diploma in Church Music

ADEDC .... Advanced Diploma in Education of the Deaf and Partially Hearing Children

ADEd .... Advanced Diploma in Education

ADME .... Advanced Diploma in Maths Education

ADMT .... Advanced Diploma in Ministerial Theology

ADPS .... Advanced Diploma in Pastoral Studies

ADipR .... Archbishop's Diploma for Readers

ADipRE .... Advanced Diploma in Religious Education

ADipTh .... Advanced Diploma in Theology

AEdRD .... Associateship in Educational Research and Development

AFAIM .... Associate Fellow of the Australian Institute of Management

AFBPsS........... Associate Fellow of the British Psychological Society (formerly ABPsS)

AFC................ Air Force Cross

AFIMA .... Associate Fellow of the Institute of Mathematics and its Applications

AGSM.............. Associate of the Guildhall School of Music and Drama

AHSM or AHA . Associate, Institute of Health Service Management (formerly Administrators)

AIA................. Associate of the Institute of Actuaries

AIAS............... Associate of the Incorporated Association of Architects and Surveyors

AIAT .... Associate of the Institute of Animal Technicians

AIB .... Associate of the Institute of Bankers (now see ACIB)

AIDS............... Acquired Immunity Deficiency Syndrome (also see HIV)

AIFST............. Associate of the Institute of Food Science and Technology

AIGCM............ Associate of the Incorporated Guild of Church Musicians

AIIM............... Associate of the Institute of Investment Management

AIL .... Associate of the Institute of Linguists

AIMLS............ Associate of the Institute of Medical Laboratory Sciences

AIMarE........... Associate of the Institute of Marine Engineering

AIPM.............. Associate of the Institute of Personnel Management

AITI................ Associate of the Institute of Taxation in Ireland

AKC .... Associate of King's College, London

ALA................. Associate of the Library Association

ALAM .... Associate of the London Academy of Music

ALBC.............. Associate of the London Bible College

ALCD .... Associate of the London College of Divinity

ALCM............. Associate of the London College of Music

ALSM .... Associate of the Lancashire School of Music

AM .... Albert Medal Master of Arts (USA)

AMA................ Associate of the Museums Association

AMBIM .... Associate Member of the British Institute of Management (later MBIM; now see FBIM)

AMCST........... Associate of the Manchester College of Science and Technology

AMCT............. Associate of the Manchester College of Technology

AMGAS.......... Associate Member of the Group-Analytic Society

AMIBF .... Associate Member of the Institute of British Foundrymen

AMIC.............. Associate Member of the Institute of Counselling

AMICE .... Associate Member of the Institution of Civil Engineers (now see MICE)

AMIDHE......... Associate Member of the Institute of Domestic Heating Engineers

AMIEE .... Associate Member of the Institution of Electrical Engineers (now see MIEE)

AMIEHO .... Associate Member of the Institution of Environmental Health Officers

AMIM.............. Associate Member of the Institute of Metals

AMIMechE ...... Associate of the Institution of Mechanical Engineers (now see MIMechE)

AMIMinE .... Associate Member of the Institute of Mining Engineers

AMITD........... Associate Member of the Institute of Training and Development

AMIWO.......... Associate Member of the Institute of Welfare Officers

AMInstTA........ Associate Member of the Institute of Transport Administration

AMP .... Advanced Management Program

AMRSH .... Associate Member of the Royal Society of Health

AMSIA .... Associate Member of the Society of Investment Analysts

AMusTCL .... Associate in Music of Trinity College of Music, London

ANCA .... Advanced National Certificate in Agriculture

AP.................... Assistant Priest

APM .... Auxiliary Pastoral Minister (or Ministry)

APhS................ Associate of the Philosophical Society of England

ARAM .... Associate of the Royal Academy of Music

ARCA.............. Associate of the Royal College of Art

ARCIC............. Anglican-Roman Catholic International Commission

ARCM .... Associate of the Royal College of Music
ARCO .... Associate of the Royal College of Organists
ARCS .... Associate of the Royal College of Science
ARCST .... Associate of the Royal College of Science and Technology (Glasgow)
ARCUK .... Architects' Registration Council of the United Kingdom
ARHistS .... Associate of the Royal Historical Society
ARIBA .... Associate of the Royal Institute of British Architects (now see RIBA)
ARIC .... Associate of the Royal Institute of Chemistry (later MRIC; now see MRSC)
ARICS .... Associate of the Royal Institute of Chartered Surveyors
ARMCM .... Associate of the Royal Manchester College of Music
ARSM .... Associate of the Royal School of Mines
AS .... Associate in Science (USA)
ASCA .... Associate of the Society of Company and Commercial Accountants
ASCAT .... All Souls' College of Applied Theology
ASEEDip .... Association of Supervising Electrical Engineers Diploma
ATC .... Air Training Corps
ATCL .... Associate of Trinity College of Music, London
ATD .... Art Teacher's Diploma
ATI .... Associate of the Textile Institute
ATII .... Associate Member of the Institute of Taxation
ATPL .... Airline Transport Pilot's Licence
ATV .... Associated Television
ATh(SA) .... Associate in Theology (South Africa)
AV .... Associate Vicar
Ab .... (Diocese of) Aberdeen and Orkney
Aber .... Aberdeen
Abp .... Archbishop
Abth .... Aberystwyth
AcDipEd .... Academic Diploma in Education
Admin .... Administration Administrative Administrator
Adn .... Archdeacon
Adnry .... Archdeaconry
Adv .... Adviser Advisory
AdvDipCrim ...... Advanced Diploma in Criminology
Agric .... Agricultural Agriculture
Aid .... Aidan Aidan's
alt..................... alternate
Andr................. Andrew Andrew's Andrews
Angl .... Anglican Anglicans
Ant.................. Anthony Anthony's
Appt................. Appointment
Arg.................. (Diocese of) Argyll and The Isles
Arm.................. (Diocese of) Armagh
Assn .... Association
Assoc................ Associate
Asst................. Assistant
Aug .... Augustine Augustine's
Aus.................. Australia Australian
Aux .... Auxiliary

B

b...................... Born
B & W .... (Diocese of) Bath and Wells
B or Bapt........... Baptist Baptist's
BA .... Bachelor of Arts
BA(Econ)........... Bachelor of Arts in Economics
BA(Ed)............. Bachelor of Arts in Education
BA(Theol)......... Bachelor of Arts in Theology
BAC Accred...... British Accreditation Council Accredit
BAI .... Bachelor of Engineering (also see BE and BEng)
BAO .... Bachelor of Obstetrics
BAOR .... British Army of (formerly on) the Rhine
BASc .... Bachelor of Applied Science
BAdmin .... Bachelor of Administration
BAgr .... Bachelor of Agriculture
BArch............... Bachelor of Architecture
BBA .... Bachelor of Business Administration
BBC .... British Broadcasting Corporation
BBS .... Bachelor of Business Studies
BC................... British Columbia (Canada)
BCC .... British Council of Churches (now see CCBI)
BCL .... Bachelor of Civil Law
BCMS .... Bible Churchmen's Missionary Society (now Crosslinks)
BCh or BChir..... Bachelor of Surgery (also see BS and ChB)
BCom .... Bachelor of Commerce
BCombStuds...... Bachelor of Combined Studies
BD .... Bachelor of Divinity
BDQ................. Bachelor of Divinity Qualifying Examination
BDS .... Bachelor of Dental Surgery
BDip .... Bible Diploma
BE.................... Bachelor of Engineering (also see BAI and BEng)
BEM .... British Empire Medal
BEcon............... Bachelor of Economics (USA)
BEd .... Bachelor of Education
BEng .... Bachelor of Engineering (also see BAI and BE)
BFBS................ British and Foreign Bible Society
BFPO .... British Forces Post Office
BIE................... Bachelor of Industrial Engineering (USA)
BL................... Bachelor of Law
BLitt................. Bachelor of Letters
BM .... Bachelor of Medicine (also see MB)
BMMF .... Bible and Medical Missionary Fellowship (now Intersave)
BMU .... Board for Mission and Unity
BMedSci........... Bachelor of Medical Science
BMet .... Bachelor of Metallurgy
BMin .... Bachelor of Ministry
BMus .... Bachelor of Music (also see MusB or MusBac)
BMusEd .... Bachelor of Music Education
BN .... Bachelor of Nursing
BNC................. Brasenose College
BPaed .... Bachelor of Paediatrics
BPh or BPhil...... Bachelor of Philosophy
BPharm .... Bachelor of Pharmacy
BPhil(Ed)........... Bachelor of Philosophy (Education)
BRE .... Bachelor of Religious Education (USA)
BRF .... Bible Reading Fellowship
BS .... Bachelor of Science (also see BSc)
Bachelor of Surgery (also see BCh or BChir and ChB)

BSA.................. Bachelor of Scientific Agriculture
BSB.................. Brotherhood of St Barnabas
BSE.................. Bachelor of Science in Engineering (also see BScEng)
BSEd .... Bachelor of Science in Education (USA)
BSP.................. Brotherhood of St Paul
BSSc................. Bachelor of Social Science (also see BSocSc)
BSW................. Bachelor of Social Work
BSc.................. Bachelor of Science (also see BS)
BSc(Econ)......... Bachelor of Science in Economics
BSc(Soc)........... Bachelor of Science (Sociology)
BScAgr .... Bachelor of Science in Agriculture
BScEng............. Bachelor of Science in Engineering (also see BSE)
BScFor .... Bachelor of Science in Forestry
BScTech .... Bachelor of Technical Science
BSocAdmin .... Bachelor of Social Administration
BSocSc .... Bachelor of Social Science (also see BSSc)
BSocStuds......... Bachelor of Social Studies
BT.................... Bachelor of Teaching
BTA .... British Tuberculosis Association Certificate
BTEC HNC ...... Business and Technician Education Council Higher National Certificate
BTEC NC.......... Business and Technician Education Council National Certificate
BTEC ND .... Business and Technician Education Council National Diploma
BTS.................. Bachelor of Theological Studies
BTech............... Bachelor of Technology
BTh.................. Bachelor of Theology (also see STB)
BVSc .... Bachelor of Veterinary Science
BVetMed .... Bachelor of Veterinary Medicine (also see VetMB)
Ball................... Balliol
Ban................... (Diocese of) Bangor
Barn .... Barnabas Barnabas's
Bart .... Bartholomew Bartholomew's
Bd .... Board
Bedf................. Bedford
Beds .... Bedfordshire
Belf.................. Belfast
Berks .... Berkshire
BesL .... Bachelier es Lettres
Bibl .... Biblical
Birkb................ Birkbeck
Birm................. (Diocese of) Birmingham
Blackb .... (Diocese of) Blackburn
Boro .... Borough
Bp .... Bishop
Br..................... British
Bradf................. (Diocese of) Bradford
Bre .... (Diocese of) Brechin
Brig.................. Brigadier
Bris................... (Diocese of) Bristol
Bt..................... Baronet
Buckm.............. Buckingham
Bucks .... Buckinghamshire

C

C...................... Curate
c...................... Consecrated
C & O.............. (Diocese of) Cashel and Ossory (united dioceses of Cashel, Waterford, Lismore, Ossory, Ferns and Leighlin)
C of E.............. Church of England
C&G .... City and Guilds
C, C & R .... (Diocese of) Cork, Cloyne and Ross
C-in-c .... Curate-in-charge

c/o .... Care of
CA .... Church Army
                     Member of the Institute of
                     Chartered Accountants of
                     Scotland
CA(Z) .... Member of the Institute of
                     Chartered Accountants of
                     Zimbabwe
CACP .... Certificate in Advanced
                     Counselling Practice
CACTM .... Central Advisory Council
                     for the Ministry (later
                     ACCM; now see ABM)
CANDL .... Church and
                     Neighbourhood
                     Development in London
CANP .... Certificate in Advanced
                     Nursery Practices
CARA .... Care and Resources for
                     people affected by
                     AIDS/HIV
CARE .... Christian Action Research
                     and Education
CASA .... Anglican Church of the
                     Southern Cone of America
CASS .... Certificate in Applied
                     Social Studies
CB .... Companion of the Bath
CBE .... Commander of the Order
                     of the British Empire
CBIM .... Companion of the British
                     Institute of Management
CBTS .... Certificate in Biblical and
                     Theological Studies
CBiol .... Chartered Biologist
CCBI .... Council of Churches for
                     Britain and Ireland
                     (formerly BCC)
CCC .... Corpus Christi College
                     Council for the Care of
                     Churches
CCCS .... Commonwealth and
                     Continental Church
                     Society
CCSk .... Certificate in Counselling
                     Skills
CCT .... Certificate in Clinical
                     Teaching
CChem .... Chartered Chemist
CCouns .... Certificate in Counselling
CD .... Canadian Forces
                     Decoration
                     Conventional District (also
                     see ED)
CD (US Air) ...... Commercial Diver (US Air
                     Force)
CDRS .... Certificate in Divinity and
                     Religious Studies
CDipAF .... Certified Diploma in
                     Accounting and Finance
CECD .... Church of England
                     Council for the Deaf
CECM .... Certificate of Education
                     for the Church's Ministry
CECS .... Church of England
                     Children's Society (now
                     known as the Children's
                     Society)
CEIR .... Certificate in Economics
                     and Industrial Relations
CEMS .... Church of England Men's
                     Society
CES .... Certificate in Ecumenical
                     Studies
CEng .... Chartered Engineer
CEurStuds .... Certificate in European
                     Studies
CF .... Chaplain to the Forces
CFTV .... Certificate in Film and
                     Television
CGA .... Community of the
                     Glorious Ascension
CIO .... Church Information Office
CIPFA .... Chartered Institute of
                     Public Finance and
                     Accountancy
CITC .... Church of Ireland
                     Theological College
CLHist .... Certificate in Local
                     History
CLJ .... Commander of the Order
                     of St Lazarus of Jerusalem

CLRHist .... Certificate in Local and
                     Regional History
CM .... Carnegie Medal
CMBHI .... Craft Member of the
                     British Horological
                     Institute
CMD .... Cambridge Mission to
                     Delhi (now see USPG)
CME .... Continuing Ministerial
                     Education
CMG .... Companion of St Michael
                     and St George
CMJ .... Church's Ministry among
                     the Jews
CMM .... Certificate in Ministry and
                     Mission
CMS .... Church Mission Society
                     Church Missionary Society
CMT .... Certificate in Ministerial
                     Theology
CMinlEd .... Certificate in Ministerial
                     Education
CMinlStuds .... Certificate in Ministerial
                     Studies
CNAA .... Council for National
                     Academic Awards
COPEC .... Conference on Politics,
                     Economics and
                     Community
CORAT .... Christian Organizations
                     Research and Advisory
                     Trust
CORE .... City Outreach through
                     Renewal Evangelism
CP .... Community Priest
CPA .... Chartered Patent Agent
                     (formerly FCIPA)
CPAS .... Church Pastoral Aid
                     Society
CPC .... Certificate of Professional
                     Competence (Road
                     Transport)
CPES .... Certificate in Post
                     Excavation Studies
CPM .... Colonial Police Medal
CPPS .... Certificate of Proficiency in
                     Pastoral Studies
CPS .... Certificate in Pastoral
                     Studies
CPSS .... Certificate in Pastoral and
                     Social Studies
CPT .... Certificate in Pastoral
                     Theology
CPTS .... Certificate in Pastoral and
                     Theological Studies
CPhys .... Chartered Physicist of the
                     Institute of Physics
CPsychol .... Chartered Psychologist
CQSW .... Certificate of Qualification
                     in Social Work
CR .... Community of the
                     Resurrection (Mirfield)
CSA .... Community of St Andrew
CSD .... Co-operative Societies'
                     Diploma
CSF .... Community of St Francis
CSG .... Company of the Servants
                     of God
CSS .... Certificate in Social Service
CSSM .... Children's Special Service
                     Mission
CSWG .... Community of the
                     Servants of the Will of
                     God
CSocSc .... Certificate in Social
                     Science
CSocStuds .... Certificate in Social
                     Studies
CStJ .... Commander, the Most
                     Venerable Order of the
                     Hospital of St John of
                     Jerusalem
CTM .... Certificate in Theology
                     and Mission
CTMin .... Certificate in Theology
                     and Ministry
CTOSc .... Certificate in the Teaching
                     of Science
CTPS .... Certificate in Theological
                     and Pastoral Studies
CTUS .... Certificate in Trades
                     Union Studies

CUF .... Church Urban Fund
CV .... Clerical Vicar
CVO .... Commander of the Royal
                     Victorian Order
CWME .... Commission on World
                     Mission and Evangelism
CWWCh .... Certificate of Women's
                     Work in the Church
CYCW .... Certificate in Youth and
                     Community Work
CYFA .... Church Youth Fellowships
                     Association
CYPECS .... Christian Youth
                     Fellowship, Pathfinders,
                     Explorers, Climbers and
                     Scramblers
Cam .... Cambridge
Cambs .... Cambridgeshire
Can .... Canon
Cand .... Candidate
                     Candidate's
                     Candidates'
Cant .... (Diocese of) Canterbury
Capt .... Captain
Carl .... (Diocese of) Carlisle
Cath .... Catharine/Catherine
                     Catharine's/Catherine's
Cathl .... Cathedral
Cdre .... Commodore
Cen .... Centre
                     Center
                     Central
Cert .... Certificate
CertAnPsych ...... Certificate in Analytical
                     Psychology
CertBS .... Certificate in Bible Studies
CertCC .... Certificate of Child Care
CertCEd .... Certificate for Leadership
                     in Christian Education
CertCS .... Certificate in Christian
                     Studies
CertCT .... Certificate in Ceramic
                     Technology
CertComp .... Certificate in Computing
CertDiv .... Certificate in Divinity
CertEd .... Certificate of Education
CertEdD .... Certificate in the
                     Education of the Deaf
CertFAI .... Certificate in French,
                     Arabic and Islamic Studies
CertFE .... Certificate of Further
                     Education
CertFSW .... Certificate in Family Social
                     Work of the NSPCC
CertFT .... Certificate in Family
                     Therapy
CertHE .... Certificate in Health
                     Education
CertHist .... Certificate in History
CertJourn .... Certificate in Journalism
CertMBiol .... Certificate of Microbiology
CertMS .... Certificate in Management
                     Studies
CertPsych .... Certificate in Psychology
CertRE .... Certificate in Religious
                     Education
CertRK .... Certificate in Religious
                     Knowledge
CertRS .... Certificate in Religious
                     Studies
CertSc .... Certificate of Science
CertTESLA .... Certificate in Teaching
                     English as a Second
                     Language to Adults
CertTESOL .... Certificate in Teaching
                     English to Speakers of
                     Other Languages
CertTS .... Certificate in Timber
                     Surveying
CertYS .... Certificate in Youth
                     Service
Ch .... Christ
                     Christ's
                     Church
Ch Ch .... Christ Church
ChB .... Bachelor of Surgery (also
                     see BCh or BChir and BS)
ChStJ .... Chaplain, the Most
                     Venerable Order of the
                     Hospital of St John of
                     Jerusalem
Chan .... Chancellor
Chapl .... Chaplain
                     Chaplaincy
Chas .... Charles
                     Charles's

Chelmsf .... (Diocese of) Chelmsford
Ches .... (Diocese of) Chester
Chich .... (Diocese of) Chichester
Chmn .... Chairman
      Chairwoman
Chpl .... Chapel
Chr .... Christian
      Christians
Chris .... Christopher
      Christopher's
Chrys .... Chrysostom
      Chrysostom's
Chu .... Churchill
Cl-in-c .... Cleric-in-charge
Clem .... Clement
      Clement's
Cllr .... Councillor
Clogh .... (Diocese of) Clogher
Co .... Company
      County
      Counties
Co-ord .... Co-ordinator
      Co-ordinating
Col .... Colonel
Coll .... College
Colleg .... Collegiate
Comdr .... Commander
Commn .... Commission
Commr .... Commissioner
Comp .... Comprehensive
Conf .... Confederation
      Conference
Congr .... Congregation
      Congregational
Conn .... (Diocese of) Connor
Corp .... Corporation
Coun .... Council
Cov .... (Diocese of) Coventry
Cttee .... Committee
Cust .... Custodian
      Custody
Cuth .... Cuthbert
      Cuthbert's
Cypr .... Cyprian
      Cyprian's

D

d .... Ordained Deacon
D & D .... (Diocese of) Down and Dromore
D & G .... (Diocese of) Dublin and Glendalough
D & R .... (Diocese of) Derry and Raphoe
D&C .... Dean and Chapter
DA .... Diploma in Anaesthetics
DAA .... Diploma in Archive Administration
DAC .... Diploma in Adult Counselling
DAES .... Diploma in Advanced Educational Studies
DAM .... Diploma in Archives Management
DAPC .... Diploma in Advanced Psychological Counselling
DASAE .... Diploma of Advanced Study in Adult Education
DASE .... Diploma in the Advanced Study of Education
DASS .... Diploma in Applied Social Studies
DASSc .... Diploma in Applied Social Science
DATh .... Diploma of the Arts in Theology
DAVM .... Diploma in Audio Visual Media
DB .... Bachelor of Divinity (USA)
DBF .... Diocesan Board of Finance
DBMS .... Diploma in Biblical and Mission Studies
DBO .... Diploma of the British Orthoptic Society
DBP .... Diocesan Board of Patronage
DBRS .... Diploma in Biblical and Religious Studies
DBS .... Diploma in Biblical Studies
DC .... Diocesan Certificate

      District of Columbia (USA)
DCAe .... Diploma of the College of Aeronautics
DCC .... Diploma in Crisis Counselling of the Institute of Counselling
DCE .... Diploma in Careers Education
DCEG .... Diploma in Careers Education and Guidance
DCEd .... Diploma in Community Education
DCG .... Diploma in Careers Guidance
DCH .... Diploma in Child Health
DCHospC .... Diploma in Counselling and Hospital Chaplaincy
DCL .... Doctor of Civil Law
DCM .... Diploma in Christian Ministry
DCR .... Diploma of the College of Radiographers
DCR, MU .... Diploma of the College of Radiographers in Medical Ultra Sound
DCS .... Diploma in Community Studies
DCTM .... Diploma in Christian Theology and Ministry
DCYW .... Diploma in Community and Youth Work
DChCD .... Diploma in Church Community Development
DChemEng .... Diploma in Chemical Engineering
DCnL .... Doctor of Canon Law
DCouns .... Diploma in Counselling
DD .... Doctor of Divinity
DDEd .... Diploma in Distance Education
DDW .... Diploma in Deaf Welfare
DEd .... Doctor of Education (also see EdD)
DEdin Cert .... Duke of Edinburgh's Awards Certificate of Recognition
DFC .... Distinguished Flying Cross
DFM .... Distinguished Flying Medal (Canada)
DFStuds .... Diploma in French Studies
DGA .... Diploma in Government Administration
DHA .... District Health Authority
DHL .... Doctor of Humane Letters
DHRK .... Diploma in Humanities and Religious Knowledge
DHSA .... Diploma in Health Services Administration
DHistA .... Diploma in the History of Art
DIC .... Diploma of Imperial College
DIH .... Diploma in Industrial Health
DIL .... Diploma of the Institute of Linguists
DIM .... Diploma in Industrial Management
DIS .... Diploma in Industrial Studies
DIT .... Diploma in Interpreting and Translating
DL .... Deputy Lieutenant
DLC .... Diploma of Loughborough College
DLIS .... Diploma in Library and Information Studies
DLLP .... Diploma in Law and Legal Practice
DLO .... Diploma in Laryngology and Otology
DLSc .... Doctor of Legal Science
DLitt .... Doctor of Letters (also see LittD)
DLitt et Phil ...... Doctor of Letters and Philosophy
DM .... Diploma in Management
DMA .... Diploma in Municipal Administration
DMEd .... Diploma of Management in Education
DMS .... Diploma in Management Studies
DMSchM .... Diploma of the Mission School of Medicine, London

DMin .... Doctor of Ministry
DMinlStuds .... Diploma in Ministerial Studies
DMinlTh .... Diploma in Ministerial Theology
DMusEd .... Diploma in Music Education
DN .... Diploma in Nursing
DNEd .... Diploma in Nursery Education
DNM .... Diploma in Nuclear Medicine
DOE .... Department of the Environment
DOMS .... Diploma in Ophthalmic Medicine and Surgery
DON .... Diploma in Ophthalmic Nursing
DObstRCOG ..... Diploma in Obstetrics, Royal College of Obstetricians and Gynaecologists
DPA .... Diploma in Public Administration
DPEd .... Diploma in Primary Education
DPH .... Diploma in Public Health
DPM .... Diploma in Psychological Medicine
DPMSA .... Diploma in Philosophy of Medicine, Society of Apothecaries
DPS .... Diploma in Pastoral Studies
DPSE .... Diploma in Professional Studies in Education
DPSN .... Diploma in Professional Studies in Nursing
DPST .... Diploma in Pastoral and Social Theology
DPT .... Diploma in Pastoral Theology
DPastMin .... Diploma in Pastoral Ministry
DPhil .... Doctor of Philosophy (also see PhD)
DRBS .... Diploma in Religious and Biblical Studies
DRCOG .... Diploma of the Royal College of Obstetricians and Gynaecologists
DRI .... Diploma in Radionuclide Imaging
DRS .... Diploma in Rural Studies
DRSS .... Diploma in Religious and Social Studies
DSA .... Diploma in Social Administration
DSC .... Distinguished Service Cross
DSCE .... Diploma in Social and Community Education
DSM .... Distinguished Service Medal
DSMS .... Diploma in Sales Management Studies
DSO .... Companion of the Distinguished Service Order
DSPT .... Diploma in Social and Pastoral Theology
DSRS .... Diploma in Social and Religious Studies
DST .... Doctor of Sacred Theology (also see STD)
DSc .... Doctor of Science (also see ScD)
DSocSc .... Doctor of Social Science
DSocStuds .... Diploma in Social Studies
DSpEd .... Diploma in Special Education
DTEd .... Diploma in Tertiary Education
DTI .... Department of Trade and Industry
DTM .... Diploma in Tropical Medicine
DTM&H .... Diploma in Tropical Medicine and Hygiene
DTPH .... Diploma in Tropical Public Health
DTPS .... Diploma in Theological and Pastoral Studies

DTS	Diploma in Theological Studies
DTechM	Diploma in Technical Mining
DTh	Doctor of Theology (also see ThD)
DUP	Docteur de l'Universite de Paris
DUniv	Doctor of the University
Darw	Darwin
Dav	David David's
Dep	Deputy
Dept	Department
DesL	Docteur es Lettres
Det	Detention
Dio	Diocese
Dioc	Diocesan
Dip	Diploma
DipA&CE	Diploma in Adult and Continuing Education
DipAD	Diploma in Art and Design
DipAE	Diploma in Adult Education
DipAI	Diploma in Artificial Insemination
DipAct	Diploma in Acting
DipAdEd	Diploma in Advanced Education
DipAgr	Diploma in Agriculture
DipAnChem	Diploma in Analytical Chemistry
DipAnPsych	Diploma in Analytical Psychology
DipAnth	Diploma in Anthropology
DipApEc	Diploma in Applied Economics
DipApSc	Diploma of Applied Science
DipApTh	Diploma in Applied Theology
DipArch	Diploma in Architecture
DipBBSS	Diploma in Bilingual Business and Secretarial Studies
DipBS	Diploma in Business Studies
DipC&G	Diploma in Counselling and Guidance
DipC&S	Diploma in Counselling and Supervision
DipCD	Diploma in Church Development
DipCH	Diploma in Clinical Hypnotherapy
DipCK	Diploma in Christian Knowledge
DipCL	Diploma in Christian Leadership
DipCMus	Diploma in Church Music
DipCOT	Diploma of the College of Occupational Therapists
DipCSM	Diploma of the Cork School of Music
DipChD	Diploma of Chaplains to the Deaf
DipCivEng	Diploma in Civil Engineering
DipCombStuds	Diploma in Combined Studies
DipContEd	Diploma in Continuing Education
DipDA	Diploma in Dramatic Art
DipDiet	Diploma in Dietetics
DipEEngD	Diploma in Environmental Engineering and Design
DipEH	Diploma in Environmental Health
DipEM	Diploma in Estate Management
DipEcon	Diploma in Economics
DipEcum	Diploma in Ecumenicalism
DipEd	Diploma in Education
DipEdG	Diploma in Educational Guidance
DipEdHChild	Diploma in the Education of Handicapped Children
DipEdMan	Diploma in Educational Management
DipEvang	Diploma in Evangelism
DipFD	Diploma in Funeral Directing
DipFE	Diploma in Further Education
DipFL	Diploma in Foreign Languages
DipG&C	Diploma in Guidance and Counselling
DipGD	Diploma in Graphic Design
DipGL	Diploma in German Language
DipGeochem	Diploma in Geochemistry
DipHCM	Diploma in Hotel and Catering Management
DipHE	Diploma in Higher Education
DipHP	Diploma in Human Purposes
DipHRel	Diploma in Human Relations
DipHV	Diploma in Health Visiting
DipHort	Diploma in Horticulture
DipHums	Diploma in Humanities
DipHyp	Diploma in Hypnotherapy
DipIR	Diploma in Industrial Relations
DipInstAM	Diploma of the Institute of Administrative Management
DipInstBM	Diploma of the Institution of Merchanting (Builders)
DipInstHSM	Diploma of the Institute of Health Service Management
DipInstM	Diploma of the Institute of Marketing
DipL&A	Diploma in Liturgy and Architecture
DipLib	Diploma of Librarianship
DipLit	Diploma in Liturgy
DipM	Diploma in Marketing
DipMA	Diploma of the Museums Association
DipMM	Diploma in Mission and Ministry
DipMan	Diploma for Management
DipMathEd	Diploma in Maths Education
DipMaths	Postgraduate Diploma in Mathematics
DipMechEng	Diploma in Mechanical Engineering
DipMentH	Diploma in Mental Health
DipMin	Diploma in Ministry
DipMiss	Diploma in Mission
DipMus	Diploma in Music
DipNCTD	Diploma of the National College of Teachers of the Deaf
DipNuc	Diploma in Nuclear Technology
DipOAS	Diploma in Oriental and African Studies
DipOH&S	Diploma in Occupational Health and Safety
DipOT	Diploma in Occupational Therapy
DipP&C	Diploma in Psychology and Counselling
DipPC	Diploma in Pastoral Counselling
DipPE	Diploma in Physical Education
DipPM	Diploma in Personnel Management
DipPSA	Diploma in Public and Social Administration
DipPSE	Diploma in Personal and Social Education
DipPTh	Diploma in Practical Theology
DipPh	Diploma in Physiotherapy
DipPhil	Diploma in Philosophy
DipPs	Diploma in Psychotherapy
DipPsych	Diploma in Psychology
DipRCM	Diploma of the Royal College of Music
DipRD	Diploma in Reading Development
DipRE	Diploma in Religious Education
DipREM	Diploma in Rural Estate Management
DipRIPH&H	Diploma of the Royal Institute of Public Health and Hygiene
DipRJ	Diploma of Retail Jewellery
DipRK	Diploma in Religious Knowledge
DipRS	Diploma in Religious Studies
DipRSAMDA	Diploma of the Royal Scottish Academy of Music and Dramatic Art
DipSC	Diploma in Student Counselling
DipSM	Diploma in Sales Marketing of the Managing and Marketing Sales Association
DipSMan	Diploma in School Management
DipSoc	Diploma in Sociology
DipSocAnth	Diploma in Social Anthropology
DipSocSc	Diploma in Social Sciences
DipSocWork	Diploma in Social Work
DipSurg	Diploma in Surgery
DipT	Diploma in Teaching
DipTE	Diploma in Transportation Engineering
DipTHPsych	Diploma in Therapeutic Hypnosis and Psychology
DipTM	Diploma in Training Management
DipTP	Diploma in Town Planning
DipTS	Diploma in Transport Studies
DipTSM	Diploma in the Techniques of Safety Management
DipTh	Diploma in Theology
DipThe	Diploma in Theatre
DipVG	Diploma in Vocational Guidance
DipYESTB	Diploma of the Youth Employment Service Training Board
DipYL	Diploma in Youth Leadership
DipYW	Diploma in Youth Work
Dipl-Reg	Diplom-Regiesseur fuer Musiktheater
Dir	Director
Distr	District
Div	Divinity
Div Test	Divinity Testimonium
Dn-in-c	Deacon-in-charge
Dom	Domestic
Down	Downing
Dr	Doctor
DrTheol	Doctor of Theology (Germany)
Dss	Deaconess
dss	Admitted Deaconess
Dub	Dublin
Dur	(Diocese of) Durham

E

Abbreviation	Meaning
E	East Eastern
EC	Emergency Commission
ED	Ecclesiastical District (also see CD) Efficiency Decoration
EKD	Evangelische Kirche Deutschland
EN(G)	Enrolled Nurse (General)
EN(M)	Enrolled Nurse (Mental)
ERD	Emergency Reserve Decoration
ESC	Ecole Superievre de Commerce
ESMI	Elderley, Sick and Mentally Infirm
Ecum	Ecumenical Ecumenics Ecumenism
Ed	Editor Editorial
EdD	Doctor of Education (also see DEd)
Edin	(Diocese of) Edinburgh

Edm .... Edmund
Edmund's
Educn............... Education
Educational
Edw.................. Edward
Edward's
Eliz.................... Elizabeth
Elizabeth's
Em .... Emmanuel
Emb .... Embassy
EngTech .... Engineering Technician
Episc .... Episcopal
Episcopalian
Esq.................. Esquire
etc .... et cetera
Eur .... (Diocese of) Gibraltar in
Europe
Europe
European
Ev .... Evangelist
Evangelists
Evangelist's
Evang............... Evangelical
Evangelism
Ex .... (Diocese of) Exeter
Ex-paroch.......... Extra-parochial
Exam............... Examining
Exec .... Executive
Exors................ Executors
Exper................. Experimental
Ext .... Extension

F

F&HE .... Further and Higher
Education
FAA.................. Fellow of the Institution of
Administrative
Accountants
FACC................ Fellow of the American
College of Cardiology
FACCA............. Fellow of the Association
of Certified and Corporate
Accountants (now see
FCCA)
FACOG .... Fellow of the American
College of Obstetricians
and Gynaecologists
FAEB................ Fellow of the Academy of
Environmental Biology
(India)
FAIW............... Fellow of the Australian
Institute of Welfare and
Community Workers
FASI .... Fellow of the Architects'
and Surveyors' Institute
FBA .... Fellow of the British
Academy
FBCO............... Fellow of the British
College of Ophthalmic
Opticians (Optometrists)
FBCS .... Fellow of the British
Computer Society
FBDO .... Fellow of the Association
of British Dispensing
Opticians
FBIM .... Fellow of the British
Institute of Management
(formerly MBIM)
FBIS................. Fellow of the British
Interplanetary Society
FBOA............... Fellow of the British
Optical Association
FBPICS .... Fellow of the British
Production and Inventory
Control Society
FBPsS.............. Fellow of the British
Psychological Society
FCA .... Fellow of the Institute of
Chartered Accountants
FCCA............... Fellow of the Chartered
Association of Certified
Accountants (formerly
FACCA)
FCFI .... Fellow of the Clothing and
Footwear Institute
FCIArb .... Fellow of the Chartered
Institute of Arbitrators
FCIB .... Fellow of the Corporation
of Insurance Brokers
FCII .... Fellow of the Chartered
Insurance Institute
FCILA .... Fellow of the Chartered
Institute of Loss Adjusters
FCIM .... Fellow of the Chartered
Institute of Marketing
(formerly FInstM)

FCIPA.............. Fellow of the Chartered
Institute of Patent Agents
(now see CPA)
FCIS .... Fellow of the Institute of
Chartered Secretaries and
Administrators
FCIT .... Fellow of the Chartered
Institute of Transport
FCMA............... Fellow of the Institute of
Cost and Management
Accountants
FCO.................. Foreign and
Commonwealth Office
FCP.................. Fellow of the College of
Preceptors
FCollP.............. Ordinary Fellow of the
College of Preceptors
FDS .... Fellow in Dental Surgery
FDSRCS .... Fellow in Dental Surgery
of the Royal College of
Surgeons of England
FE .... Further Education
FEPA .... Fellow of the Evangelical
Preachers' Association
FETC .... Further Education
Teacher's Certificate
FEng .... Fellow of the Royal
Academy (formerly
Fellowship) of Engineering
FFARCS .... Fellow of the Faculty of
Anaesthetists, Royal
College of Surgeons of
England
FFChM .... Fellow of the Faculty of
Church Music
FFPHM .... Fellow of the Faculty of
Public Health Medicine
FFS .... Full Faith Society
FGA.................. Fellow of the
Gemmalogical Association
FGS.................. Fellow of the Geological
Society of London
FHSM or FHA .. Fellow, Institute of Health
Service Management
(formerly Administrators)
FIA .... Fellow of the Institute of
Actuaries
FIBD................. Fellow of the Institute of
British Decorators
FIBiol.............. Fellow of the Institute of
Biology
FICE................. Fellow of the Institution of
Civil Engineers
FICM .... Fellow of the Institution of
Commercial Managers
FIChemE.......... Fellow of the Institution of
Chemical Engineers
FIDiagE .... Fellow of the Institute of
Diagnostic Engineers
FIED................. Fellow of the Institution of
Engineering Designers
FIEE .... Fellow of the Institution of
Electrical Engineers
(formerly FIERE)
FIEEE.............. Fellow of the Institute of
Electrical and Electronics
Engineers (NY)
FIERE.............. Fellow of the Institution of
Electronic and Radio
Engineers (now see FIEE)
FIFireE .... Fellow of the Institution of
Fire Engineers
FIHospE........... Fellow of the Institute of
Hospital Engineering
FIIM .... Fellow of the Institution of
Industrial Managers
(formerly FIPlantE)
FIL .... Fellow of the Institute of
Linguists
FILEx .... Fellow of the Institute of
Legal Executives
FIMA............... Fellow of the Institute of
Mathematics and its
Applications
FIMEMME....... Fellow of the Institution of
Mining Electrical and
Mining Mechanical
Engineers
FIMI .... Fellow of the Institute of
the Motor Industry
FIMLS .... Fellow of the Institute of
Medical Laboratory
Sciences

FIMM .... Fellow of the Institution of
Mining and Metallurgy
FIMS .... Fellow of the Institute of
Management Specialists
FIMSSA........... Fellow of the Institute of
Mine Surveyors of South
Africa
FIMarE .... Fellow of the Institute of
Marine Engineers
FIMechE .... Fellow of the Institution of
Mechanical Engineers
FIMgt............... Fellow of the Institute of
Management
FIPM .... Fellow of the Institute of
Personnel Management
FIPlantE........... Fellow of the Institution of
Plant Engineers (now see
FIIM)
FIQA .... Fellow of the Institute of
Quality Assurance
FIST................. Fellow of the Institute of
Science and Technology
FIStructE.......... Fellow of the Institution of
Structural Engineers
FITD................. Fellow of the Institute of
Training and Development
FIWSc .... Fellow of the Institute of
Wood Science
FInstD............. Fellow of the Institute of
Directors
FInstE .... Fellow of the Institute of
Energy
FInstFF............ Fellow of the Institute of
Freight Forwarders
Limited
FInstM .... Fellow of the Institute of
Marketing (now see
FCIM)
FInstP .... Fellow of the Institute of
Physics
FInstSMM........ Fellow of the Institute of
Sales and Marketing
Management
FKC.................. Fellow of King's College,
London
FLA .... Fellow of the Library
Association
FLAME .... Family Life and Marriage
Education
FLAS .... Fellow of the Chartered
Land Agents' Society (now
see FRICS)
FLCM............... Fellow of the London
College of Music
FLIA .... Fellow of the Life
Insurance Association
FLS.................. Fellow of the Linnean
Society
FMA .... Fellow of the Museums
Association
FPACert........... Family Planning
Association Certificate
FPS .... Fellow of the
Pharmaceutical Society of
Great Britain
FPWI .... Fellow of the Permanent
Way Institute
FPhS .... Fellow of the
Philosophical Society of
England
FRACI .... Fellow of the Royal
Australian Chemical
Institute
FRAI .... Fellow of the Royal
Anthropological Institute
FRAM .... Fellow of the Royal
Academy of Music
FRAS .... Fellow of the Royal
Asiatic Society
Fellow of the Royal
Astronomical Society
FRAeS .... Fellow of the Royal
Aeronautical Society
FRCGP .... Fellow of the Royal
College of General
Practitioners
FRCM.............. Fellow of the Royal
College of Music
FRCO .... Fellow of the Royal
College of Organists
FRCOG .... Fellow of the Royal
College of Obstetricians
and Gynaecologists

FRCP .... Fellow of the Royal College of Physicians, London

FRCPEd .... Fellow of the Royal College of Physicians, Edinburgh

FRCPGlas .... Fellow, Royal College of Physicians and Surgeons, Glasgow (also see FRCSGlas)

FRCPath .... Fellow of the Royal College of Pathologists

FRCPsych .... Fellow of the Royal College of Psychiatrists

FRCR .... Fellow of the Royal College of Radiologists

FRCS .... Fellow of the Royal College of Physicians and Surgeons of England

FRCSE or
FRCSEd .... Fellow of the Royal College of Surgeons of Edinburgh

FRCSGlas .... Fellow of the Royal College of Physicians and Surgeons, Glasgow (also see FRCPGlas)

FRCVS .... Fellow of the Royal College of Veterinary Surgeons

FRGS .... Fellow of the Royal Geographical Society

FRHistS .... Fellow of the Royal Historical Society

FRIAS .... Fellow of the Royal Incorporation of Architects of Scotland

FRIBA .... Fellow of the Royal Institute of British Architects

FRIC .... Fellow of the Royal Institute of Chemistry (now see FRSC)

FRICS .... Fellow of the Royal Institute of Chartered Surveyors (formerly FLAS and FSI)

FRIN .... Fellow of the Royal Institute of Navigation

FRINA .... Fellow of the Royal Institution of Naval Architects

FRIPHH .... Fellow of the Royal Institute of Public Health and Hygiene

FRMetS .... Fellow of the Royal Meteorological Society

FRS .... Fellow of the Royal Society

FRSA .... Fellow of the Royal Society of Arts

FRSC .... Fellow of the Royal Society of Canada
Fellow of the Royal Society of Chemistry (formerly FRIC)

FRSE .... Fellow of the Royal Society of Edinburgh

FRSH .... Fellow of the Royal Society for the Promotion of Health

FRSL .... Fellow of the Royal Society of Literature

FRSM .... Fellow of the Royal Society of Medicine

FRTPI .... Fellow of the Royal Town Planning Institute

FSA .... Fellow of the Society of Antiquaries

FSAScot .... Fellow of the Royal Society of Antiquaries of Scotland

FSCA .... Fellow of the Royal Society of Company and Commercial Accountants

FSI .... Fellow of the Chartered Surveyors' Institution (now see FRICS)

FSJ .... Fellowship of St John the Evangelist

FSMC .... Freeman of the Spectacle-Makers' Company

FSR .... Fellowship Diploma of the Society of Radiographers

FSS .... Fellow of the Royal Statistical Society

FTC .... Flying Training Command Full Technological Certificate, City and Guilds of the London Institute

FTCD .... Fellow of Trinity College, Dublin

FTCL .... Fellow of Trinity College of Music, London

FTII .... Fellow of the Institute of Taxation

FTSC .... Fellow of the Tonic sol-fa College

FVCM .... Fellow of the Victoria College of Music

FWeldI .... Fellow of the Institute of Welding

Fell .... Fellow

Fitzw .... Fitzwilliam

Foundn .... Foundation

Fran .... Francis
Francis's

G

G&C .... Gonville and Caius

GB .... Great Britain

GBSM .... Graduate of the Birmingham School of Music

GDip .... Gemmology Diploma

GDipGP .... Graduate Diploma in Gestalt Psychotherapy

GDipP .... Graduate Diploma in Physiotherapy

GFS .... Girls' Friendly Society

GGSM .... Graduate Diploma of the Guildhall School of Music and Drama

GIBiol .... Graduate of the Institute of Biology

GIFireE .... Graduate of the Institute of Fire Engineers

GIMechE .... Graduate of the Institution of Mechanical Engineers

GIPE .... Graduate of the Institution of Production Engineers

GLCM .... Graduate Diploma of the London College of Music

GM .... George Medal

GNSM .... Graduate of the Northern School of Music

GRIC .... Graduate Membership of the Royal Institute of Chemistry

GRNCM .... Graduate of the Royal Northern College of Music

GRSC .... Graduate of the Royal School of Chemistry

GRSM .... Graduate of the Royal Schools of Music

GSM .... (Member of) the Guildhall School of Music and Drama

GSSR .... Graduate of the Scottish School of Reflexology

GTCL .... Graduate Diploma of Trinity College of Music, London

Gabr .... Gabriel
Gabriel's

Gd .... Good

Gen .... General

Geo .... George
George's

Gib .... Gibraltar

Glam .... Glamorgan

Glas .... (Diocese of) Glasgow and Galloway
Glasgow

Glos .... Gloucestershire

Glouc .... (Diocese of) Gloucester

Golds .... Goldsmiths'

Gov .... Governor

Gp .... Group

Gr .... Grammar

Grad LI .... Graduate of the Landscape Institute

GradCertEd(FE) Graduate Certificate in Education (Further Education)

GradDipEd .... Postgraduate Diploma of Education (Australia)

GradIEE .... Graduate of the Institution of Electrical Engineers

GradIMI .... Graduate of the Institute of the Motor Industry

GradIPM .... Graduate of the Institute of Personnel Management

GradIT .... Graduate of the Institute of Transport

Greg .... Gregory
Gregory's

Gt .... Great

Gtr .... Greater

Guildf .... (Diocese of) Guildford

H

H .... Holy

H&FE .... Higher and Further Education

HA .... Health Authority

HDipABiol .... Higher Diploma in Applied Biology

HDipEd .... Higher Diploma in Education

HDipHV .... Higher Diploma in Health Visit Studies

HDipRE .... Higher Diploma in Religious Education

HE .... Higher Education

HIV .... Human Immunodeficiency Virus (also see AIDS)

HM .... Her (or His) Majesty

HMI .... Her (or His) Majesty's Inspector (or Inspectorate)

HMS .... Her (or His) Majesty's Ship

HNC .... Higher National Certificate

HND .... Higher National Diploma

HND(IMechE)... Higher National Diploma, Institution of Mechanical Engineers

HQ .... Headquarters

HTC .... Higher Technical Certificate

HTV .... Harlech Television

HVCert .... Health Visitor's Certificate

Hants .... Hampshire

Hatf .... Hatfield

Hd .... Head

Heref .... (Diocese of) Hereford

Hertf .... Hertford

Herts .... Hertfordshire

Hist .... Historical
History

Ho .... House

Hon .... Honorary
Honourable

Hon RCM .... Honorary Member of the Royal College of Music

HonFChS .... Honorary Fellow of the Society of Chiropodists

HonLMStJ .... Honorary Life Member of the St John's Ambulance Association

Hosp .... Hospital

HospCC .... Hospital Chaplaincy Certificate

Hunts .... Huntingdonshire

I

I .... Incumbent

IAAP .... International Association for Analytical Psychology

IBA .... Independent Broadcasting Authority

ICF .... Industry Churches Forum (formerly Industrial Christian Fellowship)

ICM .... Irish Church Missions

ICS .... Intercontinental Church Society

IDC .... Inter-Diocesan Certificate

IDWAL .... Inter-Diocesan West African Link

IEng .... Incorporated Engineer (formerly TEng(CEI))

IGAP .... Independent Group of Analytical Psychology

ILEA .... Inner London Education Authority

IMinE .... Institution of Mining Engineers
IPFA .... Member of the Chartered Institute of Public Finance and Accountancy
ISM .... Imperial Service Medal
ISO .... Imperial Service Order
ITV .... Independent Television
IVF .... Inter-Varsity Fellowship of Evangelical Unions (now see UCCF)
IVS .... International Voluntary Service
Imp .... Imperial
Inc .... Incorporated
Ind .... Industrial
     Industry
Info .... Information
Insp .... Inspector
Inst .... Institute
     Institution
Intercon .... Intercontinental
Internat .... International
Interpr .... Interpretation
Is .... Island
     Islands
     Isle
     Isles

J

JCL .... Licentiate in Canon Law
JD .... Doctor of Jurisprudence
JEM .... Jerusalem and the East Mission (now see JMECA)
JMECA .... Jerusalem and Middle East Church Association (formerly JEM)
JP .... Justice of the Peace
Jas .... James
     James's
Jes .... Jesus
Jo .... John
     John's
Jos .... Joseph
     Joseph's
Jt or jt .... Joint
Jun .... Junior

K

K .... King
     King's
K, E & A .... (Diocese of) Kilmore, Elphin and Ardagh
KBE .... Knight Commander of the Order of the British Empire
KCB .... Knight Commander of the Order of the Bath
KCMG .... Knight Commander of the Order of St Michael and St George
KCT .... Knight Commander of the Order of the Templars
KCVO .... Knight Commander of the Royal Victorian Order
KIAD .... Kent Institute of Art and Design
KLJ .... Knight of the Order of St Lazarus of Jerusalem
KPM .... King's Police Medal
Kath .... Katharine/Katherine Katharine's/Katherine's
Kt .... Knight

L

L & K .... (Diocese of) Limerick and Killaloe (united dioceses of Limerick, Ardfert, Aghadoe, Killaloe, Kilfenora, Clonfert, Kilmacduagh and Emly)
LASI .... Licentiate of the Ambulance Service Institute
LBIPP .... Licentiate of the British Institute of Professional Photography
LCC .... London County Council
LCP .... Licentiate of the College of Preceptors
LCST .... Licentiate of the College of Speech Therapists

LDS .... Licentiate in Dental Surgery
LDSRCSEng ..... Licentiate in Dental Surgery of the Royal College of Surgeons of England
LDiv .... Licentiate in Divinity
LEA .... Local Education Authority
LEP .... Local Ecumenical Project
LGCM .... Lesbian and Gay Christian Movement
LGSM .... Licentiate of the Guildhall School of Music and Drama
LHSM .... Licentiate of the Institute of Health Services Management
LICeram .... Licentiate of the Institute of Ceramics
LLA .... Lady Literate in Arts
LLAM .... Licentiate of the London Academy of Music and Dramatic Art
LLB .... Bachelor of Laws
LLCM .... Licentiate of the London College of Music
LLD .... Doctor of Laws
LLM .... Master of Laws
LMH .... Lady Margaret Hall
LMPA .... Licentiate Master of the Photographers' Association
LNSM .... Local Non-stipendiary Minister (or Ministry)
LRAM .... Licentiate of the Royal Academy of Music
LRCP .... Licentiate of the Royal College of Physicians
LRCPI .... Licentiate of the Royal College of Physicians of Ireland
LRSC .... Licentiate of the Royal Society of Chemistry
LSE .... London School of Economics and Political Science
LSHTM .... London School of Hygiene and Tropical Medicine
LSIAD .... Licentiate of the Society of Industrial Artists and Designers
LSMF .... Licentiate of the State Medical Faculty
LST .... Licentiate in Theology (also see LTh)
LTCL .... Licentiate of the Trinity College of Music, London
LTh .... Licentiate in Theology (also see LST)
LVCM .... Licentiate of the Victoria College of Music
LVO .... Lieutenant of the Royal Victorian Order
LWCMD .... Licentiate of the Welsh College of Music and Drama
Lamp .... Lampeter
Lanc .... Lancaster
Lancs .... Lancashire
Laur .... Laurence
     Laurence's
Lawr .... Lawrence
     Lawrence's
Ld .... Lord
Ldr .... Leader
Lect .... Lecturer
Leic .... (Diocese of) Leicester
Leics .... Leicestershire
Leon .... Leonard
     Leonard's
LesL .... Licencie es Lettres
Lib .... Librarian
     Library
Lic .... Licensed
     Licentiate
LicIM&C .... Licentiate of the Institute of Measurement and Control
LicSTh .... Licentiate in Sacred Theology
LicScCat .... Licence en Sciences Catechetiques
Lich .... (Diocese of) Lichfield
Linc .... (Diocese of) Lincoln

Lincs .... Lincolnshire
Lit .... Literature
LittD .... Doctor of Letters (also see DLitt)
Liturg .... Liturgical
Liv .... (Diocese of) Liverpool
Llan .... (Diocese of) Llandaff
Lon .... (Diocese of) London
Loughb .... Loughborough
Lt .... Lieutenant
     Little
Ltd .... Limited
Luth .... Lutheran

M

M .... Mid
M & K .... (Diocese of) Meath and Kildare
MA .... Master of Arts
MA(Ed) .... Master of Arts in Education
MA(Theol) .... Master of Arts in Theology
MAAIS .... Member of the Association of Archaeological Illustrators and Surveyors
MAAR .... Member of the American Academy of Religion
MAAT .... Member of the Association of Accounting Technicians
MACC .... Member of the Australian College of Chaplains
MACE .... Member of the Australian College of Education
MACT .... Member of the Association of Corporate Treasurers
MAJA .... Member of the Association of Jungian Analysts
MAMIT .... Member of the Associate of Meat Inspectors Trust
MAOT .... Member of the Association of Occupational Therapists (now see MBAOT)
MAPCC .... Member of the Association for Pastoral Care and Counselling
MASCH .... Member of the Australian Society of Clinical Hypnotherapists
MATA .... Member of the Animal Technicians' Association
MATCA .... Member of the Air Traffic Control Association
MArch .... Master of Architecture
MB .... Bachelor of Medicine (also see BM)
MB,BS or
MB,ChB .... Conjoint degree of Bachelor of Medicine, Bachelor of Surgery
MBA .... Master of Business Administration
MBAC .... Member of the British Association for Counselling
MBAOT .... Member of the British Association of Occupational Therapists (formerly MAOT)
MBAP .... Member of the British Association of Psychotherapists
MBASW .... Member of the British Association of Social Workers
MBATOD .... Member of the British Association of Teachers of the Deaf
MBC .... Metropolitan (or Municipal) Borough Council
MBCS .... Member of the British Computer Society
MBE .... Member of the Order of the British Empire
MBHI .... Member of the British Horological Institute
MBIM .... Member of the British Institute of Management (formerly AMBIM; now see FBIM)
MBKSTS .... Member of the British Kinematograph, Sound and Television Society
MBPsS .... Member of the British Psychological Society

MBTI .... Licensed Administrator of the Myers Briggs Type Indicator
MC.................. Military Cross
MCA............... Member of the Institute of Chartered Accountants
MCB .... Master in Clinical Biochemistry
MCBiblAA .... Member of the Catholic Biblical Association of America
MCCEd .... Member of the Craft College of Education
MCD............... Master of Civic Design
MCE .... Master of Civil Engineering
MCIBSE .... Member of the Chartered Institute of Building Service Engineers
MCIM............. Member of the Chartered Institute of Marketing (formerly MInstM)
MCIMA .... Member of the Chartered Institute of Management Accountants
MCIOB .... Member of the Chartered Institute of Building
MCIT.............. Member of the Chartered Institute of Transport
MCS................ Master of Christian Studies
MCSD............. Member of the Chartered Society of Designers
MCSP............. Member of the Chartered Society of Physiotherapy
MCST .... Member of the College of Speech Therapists
MCThA........... Member of the Clinical Theology Association
MChS............. Member of the Society of Chiropodists
MChemA.......... Master in Chemical Analysis
MCollP............ Member of the College of Preceptors
MCom............. Master of Commerce
MD................. Doctor of Medicine
MDCT .... Manager's Diploma in Ceramic Technology
MDiv.............. Master of Divinity
MEHS.............. Member of the Ecclesiastical History Society
MESB.............. Member of the English Speaking Board
MEd................ Master of Education
MEng.............. Master of Engineering
MFA .... Master of Fine Art
MFBA.............. Member of the Freshwater Biological Association
MFCM .... Member of the Faculty of Community Medicine
MHCIMA .... Member of the Hotel, Catering and Institutional Management Association
MHSA.............. Member of the Hymn Society of America
MHSGBI........... Member of the Hymn Society of Great Britain and Ireland
MHums .... Master of Humanities
MIA .... Malawi Institute of Architects
MIAAP .... Member of the International Association for Analytical Psychology
MIAAS .... Member of the Incorporated Association of Architects and Surveyors
MIBC............... Member of the Institute of Business Counsellors
MIBCO .... Member of the Institution of Building Control Officers
MIBF .... Member of the Institute of British Foundrymen
MIBiol.............. Member of the Institute of Biology
MICA............... Member of the International Cartographic Association
MICE................ Member of the Institution of Civil Engineers (formerly AMICE)

MICFM .... Member of the Institute of Charity Fundraising Managers
MICFRM.......... Member of the Institute of Charity Fund Raising Managers
MICFor............ Member of the Institute of Chartered Foresters
MICS .... Member of the Institute of Chartered Shipbrokers
MIChemE.......... Member of the Institution of Chemical Engineers
MICorrST .... Member of the Institution of Corrosion Science and Technology
MIDPM .... Member of the Institute of Data Processing Management
MIE .... Member of the Institute of Engineers and Technicians
MIEE .... Member of the Institution of Electrical Engineers (formerly AMIEE & MIERE)
MIEEE.............. Member of the Institute of Electrical and Electronics Engineers (NY)
MIEH............... Member of the Institute of Environmental Health
MIERE .... Member of the Institute of Electronic and Radio Engineers (now see MIEE)
MIEIecIE .... Corporate Member of the Institution of Electrical and Electronics Incorporated Engineers
MIEx................ Member of the Institute of Export
MIGasE .... Member of the Institution of Gas Engineers
MIH.................. Member of the Institute of Housing
MIHE................ Member of the Institute of Health Education
MIHT............... Member of the Institution of Highways and Transportation
MIHospE .... Member of the Institute of Hospital Engineers
MIIExE .... Member of the Institute of Incorporated Executive Engineers
MIIM .... Member of the Institution of Industrial Managers
MIL .... Member of the Institute of Linguists
MIM .... Member of the Institute of Metals (formerly Institution of Metallurgists)
MIMA.............. Member of the Institute of Management Accountants
MIMC.............. Member of the Institute of Management Consultants
MIMI............... Member of the Institute of the Motor Industry
MIMM............. Member of the Institution of Mining and Metallurgy
MIMarE............ Member of the Institute of Marine Engineers
MIMechE .... Member of the Institution of Mechanical Engineers (formerly AMIMechE)
MIMfgE .... Member of the Institution of Manufacturing Engineers
MIMgt .... Member of the Institute of Management
MIMunE .... Member of the Institution of Municipal Engineers
MINucE .... Member of the Institute of Nuclear Engineers
MIOSH .... Member of the Institution of Occupational Safety and Health
MIOT............... Member of the Institute of Operating Theatre Technicians
MIPD................ Member of the Institute of Personnel and Development
MIPI .... Member of the Institute of Private Investigators
MIPR .... Member of the Institute of Public Relations
MIProdE .... Member of the Institution of Production Engineers

MIQA .... Member of the Institute of Quality Assurance
MISE .... Member of the Institute of Sales Engineers
MISM .... Member of the Institute of Supervisory Management
MISW .... Member of the Institute of Social Welfare
MIStructE .... Member of the Institute of Structural Engineers
MITD............... Member of the Institute of Training and Development
MITE .... Member of the Institution of Electrical and Electronics Technician Engineers
MITSA.............. Member of the Institute of Trading Standards Administration
MIWEM........... Member of the Institution of Water and Environmental Management
MInstAM .... Member of the Institute of Administrative Management
MInstC(Glas)..... Member of the Institute of Counselling (Glasgow)
MInstE .... Member of the Institute of Energy
MInstGA.......... Member of the Institute of Group Analysis
MInstM .... Member of the Institute of Marketing (now see MCIM)
MInstP .... Member of the Institute of Physics
MInstPC........... Member of the Institute of Psychotherapy and Counselling
MInstPS .... Corporate Member of the Institute of Purchasing and Supply
MInstPkg.......... Member of the Institute of Packaging
MLS................. Master of Library Studies
MLawSoc .... Member of the Law Society
MLitt............... Master of Letters
MM.................. Military Medal
MMCET........... Martyrs' Memorial and Church of England Trust
MMS................ Member of the Institute of Management Services
MMin................ Master of Ministry
MMus .... Master of Music (also see MusM)
MNAAL........... Member of the North American Academy of Liturgy
MNACH .... Member of the National Association of Clergy Hypnotherapists
MNFSH .... Member of the National Federation of Spiritual Healers
MOD................ Ministry of Defence
MPS................. Member of the Pharmaceutical Society (now see MRPharmS)
MPhil .... Master of Philosophy
MPsychSc .... Master of Psychological Science
MRAC .... Member of the Royal Agricultural College
MRAeS .... Member of the Royal Aeronautical Society
MRCGP........... Member of the Royal College of General Practitioners
MRCO .... Member of the Royal College of Organists
MRCOG .... Member of the Royal College of Obstetricians and Gynaecologists
MRCP.............. Member of the Royal College of Physicians
MRCPath .... Member of the Royal College of Pathologists
MRCPsych .... Member of the Royal College of Psychiatrists
MRCS.............. Member of the Royal College of Surgeons

MRCSE .... Member of the Royal College of Surgeons of Edinburgh
MRCVS .... Member of the Royal College of Veterinary Surgeons
MRHS .... Member of the Royal Horticultural Society
MRIA .... Member of the Royal Irish Academy
MRIC .... Member of the Royal Institute of Chemistry (formerly ARIC; now see MRSC)
MRIN .... Member of the Royal Institute of Navigation
MRINA .... Member of the Royal Institution of Naval Architects
MRIPHH .... Member of the Royal Institute of Public Health and Hygiene
MRPharmS ...... Member of the Royal Pharmaceutical Society (formerly MPS)
MRSC .... Member of the Royal Society of Chemistry (formerly MRIC)
MRSH .... Member of the Royal Society for the Promotion of Health
MRSL .... Member of the Order of the Republic of Sierra Leone
MRST .... Member of the Royal Society of Teachers
MRTPI .... Member of the Royal Town Planning Institute
MRTS .... Member of the Royal Television Society
MS .... Master of Science (USA) Master of Surgery
MSAICE .... Member of the South African Institution of Civil Engineers
MSAPP .... Member of the Society of Advanced Psychotherapy Practitioners
MSAnPsych ...... Member of the Society of Analytical Psychology
MSBC .... Member of the Society of British Cartographers
MSBiblLit .... Member of the Society of Biblical Literature
MSE .... Minister (or Ministers) in Secular Employment
MSERT .... Member of the Society of Electronic and Radio Technicians
MSHAA .... Member of the Society of Hearing Aid Audiologists
MSIAD .... Member of the Society of Industrial Artists and Designers
MSLS .... Member of the Society of Liturgical Study
MSOSc .... Member of the Society of Ordained Scientists
MSOTS .... Member of the Society for Old Testament Study
MSR .... Member of the Society of Radiographers
MSSCLE .... Member of the Society for the Study of the Crusades and the Latin East
MSSCh .... Member of the School of Surgical Chiropody
MSSTh .... Member of the Society for the Study of Theology
MSTSD .... Member of the Society of Teachers of Speech and Drama
MSUC .... Member of the Society of (University) Cartographers
MSW .... Master of Social Work
MSacMus .... Master of Sacred Music
MSc .... Master of Science
MSc(Econ) .... Master of Science in Economics
MSocSc .... Master of Social Sciences
MSocWork .... Master of Social Work (USA)

MTD .... Master of Transport Design Midwife Teacher's Diploma
MTS .... Master of Theological Studies
MTech .... Master of Technology
MTh or MTheol. Master of Theology (also see STM and ThM)
MU .... Mothers' Union
MVI .... Member of the Victoria Institute
MVO .... Member of the Royal Victorian Order
MYPS .... Member of the Yorkshire Philosophical Society
Magd .... Magdalen/Magdalene Magdalen's/Magdalene's
Man .... (Diocese of) Manchester
Man Dir .... Managing Director
Mansf .... Mansfield
Marg .... Margaret Margaret's
Mass .... Massachusetts (USA)
Matt .... Matthew Matthew's
Mert .... Merton
MesL .... Lettres Modernes
Meth .... Methodist
Metrop .... Metropolitan
Mich .... Michael Michael's Michael and All Angels
Middlesb .... Middlesbrough
Middx .... Middlesex
Midl .... Midlands
Mil .... Military
Min .... Minister Ministries Ministry Minor
Minl .... Ministerial
Miss .... Mission Missions Missionary
Missr .... Missioner
Mon .... (Diocese of) Monmouth
Mor .... (Diocese of) Moray, Ross and Caithness
Mt .... Mount
MusB or MusBac .... Bachelor of Music (also see BMus)
MusD or MusDoc .... Doctor of Music
MusM .... Master of Music (also see MMus)

N

N .... North Northern
NACRO .... National Association for the Care and Rehabilitation of Offenders
NC(BS) .... National Certificate in Business Studies (Irish Republic)
NCA .... National Certificate in Agriculture
NCEC .... National Christian Education Council
NCTJ .... National Certificate for the Training of Journalists
NDA .... National Diploma in Agriculture
NDAD .... National Diploma in Art and Design
NDD .... National Diploma in Design
NDFOM .... National Diploma in Farm Organisation and Management
NDH .... National Diploma in Horticulture
NDN .... National District Nurse Certificate
NDTJ .... National Diploma in the Training of Journalists
NE .... North East
NHS .... National Health Service
NIDA .... National Institute of Dramatic Art
NNEB .... National Nursery Examination Board

NRD .... National Registered Designer
NS .... Nova Scotia (Canada)
NSM .... Non-stipendiary Minister (or Ministry)
NSPCC .... National Society for the Prevention of Cruelty to Children
NSW .... New South Wales (Australia)
NT .... New Testament
NUI .... National University of Ireland
NUU .... New University of Ulster
NW .... North West/Northwestern
NWT .... North West Territories (Canada)
NY .... New York (USA)
NZ .... New Zealand
Nat .... National
Nath .... Nathanael/Nathaniel Nathanael's/Nathaniel's
nee .... Maiden name
Newc .... (Diocese of) Newcastle
Nic .... Nicholas/Nicolas Nicholas's/Nicolas's
Nor .... (Diocese of) Norwich
Northants .... Northamptonshire
Northd .... Northumberland
Northn .... Northampton
Nottm .... Nottingham
Notts .... Nottinghamshire
Nuff .... Nuffield

O

OBE .... (Officer of) the Order of the British Empire
OBI .... Order of British India
OCF .... Officiating Chaplain to the Forces
OGS .... Oratory of the Good Shepherd
OHP .... Order of the Holy Paraclete
OM(Ger) .... Order of Merit of Germany
OMF .... Overseas Missionary Fellowship
ONC .... Ordinary National Certificate
OND .... Ordinary National Diploma
OSB .... Order of St Benedict
OSJM .... (Prelate of) the Order of St John of Malta
OSP .... Order of St Paul
OStJ .... (Officer of) the Most Venerable Order of the Hospital of St John of Jerusalem
OT .... Old Testament
Offg .... Officiating
Offic .... Officiate
Or .... Oriel
Ord .... Ordained Ordinands Ordination
Org .... Organizer Organizing
Ox .... (Diocese of) Oxford
Oxon .... Oxfordshire

P

P .... Patron Patrons
p .... Ordained Priest
P in O .... Priest in Ordinary
P-in-c .... Priest-in-charge
PACTA .... Professional Associate of the Clinical Theology Association
PBS .... Pengeran Bintang Sarawak (Companion of the Order of the Star, Sarawak)
PC .... Perpetual Curate Privy Counsellor
PCC .... Parochial Church Council
PCVG .... Postgraduate Certificate of Vocational Guidance
PEV .... Provincial Episcopal Visitor
PGCE .... Postgraduate Certificate in Education
PGDE .... Postgraduate Diploma in Education

PM .... Priest Missioner
PO .... Post Office
PPAC .... Post Professional Award in Counselling
PQCSW .... Post-Qualifying Certificate in Social Work
PV .... Priest Vicar
Par .... Parish
 Parishes
Paroch .... Parochial
Past .... Pastoral
Patr .... Patrick
 Patrick's
 Patronage
Pb .... Presbyterian
PdipEM .... Post Diploma in Early Music
Pemb .... Pembroke
Penn .... Pennsylvania (USA)
Perm .... Permission
Pet .... (Diocese of) Peterborough
 Peter
 Peter's
Peterho .... Peterhouse
PhC .... Pharmaceutical Chemist
PhD .... Doctor of Philosophy (also see DPhil)
PhL .... Licentiate of Philosophy
Phil .... Philip
 Philip's
plc .... public limited company
Poly .... Polytechnic
Portsm .... (Diocese of) Portsmouth
Preb .... Prebendary
Prec .... Precentor
Prep .... Preparatory
Pres .... President
Prin .... Principal
Pris .... Prison
 Prisons
Prof .... Professor
Progr .... Programme
 Programmes
Prop .... Proprietary
Prov .... Province
 Provincial
Pt .... Point

Q

QC .... Queen's Counsel
QFSM .... Queen's Fire Service Medal for Distinguished Service
QGM .... Queen's Gallantry Medal
QHC .... Queen's Honorary Chaplain
QN .... Queen's Nurse
QPFF .... Qualified Professional Fire-Fighter
QPM .... Queen's Police Medal
QSM .... Queen's Service Medal
QUB .... The Queen's University of Belfast
Qu .... Queen
 Queen's
 Queens'

R

R .... Rector
 Royal
R and D .... Research and Development
R of O .... Reserve of Officers
R&SChTrust ...... Rochester and Southwark Church Trust
RAAF .... Royal Australian Air Force
RAChD .... Royal Army Chaplains' Department
RAD or RADD .. Royal Association in Aid of Deaf People (formerly Deaf and Dumb)
RAEC .... Royal Army Educational Corps
RAF .... Royal Air Force
RAFVR .... Royal Air Force Volunteer Reserve
RAM .... (Member of) the Royal Academy of Music
RC .... Roman Catholic
RCA .... Royal College of Art
RCAF .... Royal Canadian Air Force

RCM .... Royal College of Music
RCN .... Royal Canadian Navy
 Royal College of Nursing
RCS .... Royal College of Surgeons of England
RCSE .... Royal College of Surgeons of Edinburgh
RD .... Royal Navy Reserve Decoration
 Rural Dean
RE .... Religious Education
RGN .... Registered General Nurse
RHV .... Registered Health Visitor
RIA .... Royal Irish Academy
RIBA .... (Member of) the Royal Institute of British Architects (formerly ARIBA)
RM .... Registered Midwife
RMA or RMC ... Royal Military Academy (formerly College), Sandhurst
RMCM .... Royal Manchester College of Music
RMCS .... Royal Military College of Science, Shrivenham
RMN .... Registered Mental Nurse
RN .... Registered Nurse (Canada)
 Royal Navy
RNIB .... Royal National Institute for the Blind
RNLI .... Royal National Lifeboat Institution
RNR .... Royal Naval Reserve
RNT .... Registered Nurse Tutor
RNVR .... Royal Naval Volunteer Reserve
RSCM .... Royal School of Church Music
RSCN .... Registered Sick Children's Nurse
RTC .... Religious Teaching Certificate
RTE .... Radio Telefis Eireann
RVC .... Royal Veterinary College
RVO .... Royal Victorian Order
Relig .... Religious
Relns .... Relations
Rem .... Remand
Rep .... Representative
Res .... Residence
 Resident
 Residential
 Residentiary
Resp .... Responsibility
Resurr .... Resurrection
Rev .... Reverend
Rich .... Richard
 Richard's
Rob .... Robinson
Roch .... (Diocese of) Rochester
Rt .... Right
Rtd or rtd .... Retired

S

S .... South
 Southern
S & B .... (Diocese of) Swansea and Brecon
S & M .... (Diocese of) Sodor and Man
S'wark .... (Diocese of) Southwark
S'well .... (Diocese of) Southwell
SACert .... Social Administration Certificate
SAMS .... South American Mission Society
SBStJ .... Serving Brother, the Most Ven Order of the Hospital of St John of Jerusalem
SCM .... State Certified Midwife
 Student Christian Movement
SDES .... Special Diploma in Educational Studies
SE .... South East
SEAN .... Study by Extension to All Nations
SEN .... State Enrolled Nurse
SHARE .... Shelter Housing and Renewal Experiment
SMF .... Society for the Maintenance of the Faith

SOAS .... School of Oriental and African Studies
SOMA .... Sharing of Ministries Abroad
SOSc .... Society of Ordained Scientists
SPCK .... Society for Promoting Christian Knowledge
SPG .... Society for the Propagation of the Gospel (now see USPG)
SRD .... State Registered Dietician
SRN .... State Registered Nurse
SRP .... State Registered Physiotherapist
SS .... Saints
 Saints'
 Sidney Sussex
SSC .... Secretarial Studies Certificate
 Societas Sanctae Crucis (Society of the Holy Cross)
 Solicitor before the Supreme Court (Scotland)
SSF .... Society of St Francis
SSJ .... Society of St John of Jerusalem
SSJE .... Society of St John the Evangelist
SSM .... Society of the Sacred Mission
STB .... Bachelor of Theology (also see BTh)
STD .... Doctor of Sacred Theology (also see DST)
STDip .... Sister-Tutor's Diploma
STL .... Reader (or Professor) of Sacred Theology
STM .... Master of Theology (also see MTh or MTheol and ThM)
STV .... Scottish Television
STh .... Scholar in Theology (also see ThSchol)
SW .... South West
SWJ .... Servants with Jesus
Sacr .... Sacrist
 Sacristan
Sarum .... (Diocese of) Salisbury
Sav .... Saviour
 Saviour's
ScD .... Doctor of Science (also see DSc)
Sch .... School
Sec .... Secretary
Selw .... Selwyn
Sem .... Seminary
Sen .... Senior
Sheff .... (Diocese of) Sheffield
Shep .... Shepherd
So .... Souls
 Souls'
Soc .... Social
 Society
Southn .... Southampton
Sqn Ldr .... Squadron Leader
St .... Saint
St Alb .... (Diocese of) St Albans
 St Alban
 St Alban's
St And .... (Diocese of) St Andrews, Dunkeld and Dunblane
St As .... (Diocese of) St Asaph
St D .... (Diocese of) St Davids
St E .... (Diocese of) St Edmundsbury and Ipswich
Staffs .... Staffordshire
Ste .... Sainte
Steph .... Stephen
 Stephen's
Sub .... Substitute
Succ .... Succentor
Suff .... Suffragan
Supt .... Superindendent
Switz .... Switzerland
Syn .... Synod

T

T, K & A .... (Diocese of) Tuam, Killala and Achonry
TA .... Territorial Army
TAVR .... Territorial and Army Volunteer Reserve
TC .... Technician Certificate

TCD	Trinity College, Dublin
TCert	Teacher's Certificate
TD	Territorial Efficiency Decoration
TDDSc	Technical Diploma in Domestic Science
TDip	Teacher's Diploma
TEAR	The Evangelical Alliance Relief
TEM	Territorial Efficiency Medal
TEng	Senior Technician Engineer
TEng(CEI)	Technician Engineer (now see IEng)
TM	Team Minister (or Ministry)
TNC	Thoracic Nursing Certificate
TP	Team Priest
TR	Team Rector
TS	Training Ship
TSB	Trustee Savings Bank
TV	Team Vicar Television
TVS	Television South
Tech	Technical Technology
temp	temporarily
Th	Theologian Theological Theology
ThA	Associate of Theology
ThB	Bachelor of Theology (USA)
ThD	Doctorate in Theology (also see DTh)
ThDip	Theology Diploma (Australia)
ThL	Theological Licentiate
ThM	Master of Theology (also see MTh or MTheol and STM)

ThSchol	Scholar in Theology (also see STh)
Thos	Thomas Thomas's
Tim	Timothy Timothy's
Tr	Trainer Training
TransDip	Translator's Diploma
Treas	Treasurer
Trin	Trinity

U

UAE	United Arab Emirates
UCCF	Universities and Colleges Christian Fellowship of Evangelical Unions (formerly IVF)
UCD	University College, Dublin
UEA	University of East Anglia
UK	United Kingdom
UMCA	Universities' Mission to Central Africa (now see USPG)
UMIST	University of Manchester Institute of Science and Technology
UNISA	University of South Africa
UPA	Urban Priority Area (or Areas)
URC	United Reformed Church
US or USA	United States (of America)
USCL	United Society for Christian Literature
USPG	United Society for the Propagation of the Gospel (formerly SPG, UMCA and CMD)
UWIST	University of Wales Institute of Science and Technology
Univ	University

V

V	Vicar Virgin Virgin's
VC	Vicar Choral
VRD	Royal Naval Volunteer Reserve Officers' Decoration
Ven	Venerable
VetMB	Bachelor of Veterinary Medicine (also see BVetMed)
Vin	Vincent Vincent's
Voc	Vocational Vocations

W

W	West Western
w	with
WCC	World Council of Churches
WEC	Worldwide Evangelism Crusade
WRAF	Women's Royal Air Force
Wadh	Wadham
Wakef	(Diocese of) Wakefield
Warks	Warwickshire
Warw	Warwick
Westf	Westfield
Westmr	Westminster
Wg Comdr	Wing Commander
Wilts	Wiltshire
Win	(Diocese of) Winchester
Wm	William
Wolfs	Wolfson
Wolv	Wolverhampton
Worc	(Diocese of) Worcester
Worcs	Worcestershire

Y

YMCA	Young Men's Christian Association

A

AAGAARD, Angus Robert. b 64. Moray Ho Coll of Educn CQSW86 DipSocWork86. Ripon Coll Cuddesdon BTh93. **d** 93 **p** 94. C Taunton St Andr *B & W* from 93. *2 Rosebery Street, Taunton, Somerset TA2 6NF* Taunton (01823) 289500

ABAYOMI-COLE, Bimbisara Alfred (Bimbi). b 58. CCC Ox BA80 MA85. Trin Coll Bris BA94. **d** 94 **p** 95. C Deptford St Pet *S'wark* from 94. *31A Crescent Way, London SE4 1QL* 0181-469 0898

ABBEY, Canon Anthony James. b 36. ARCO61 Selw Coll Cam BA59 MA63. Ely Th Coll 59. **d** 61 **p** 62. C Wanstead St Mary *Chelmsf* 61-63; C Laindon w Basildon 63-67; R Sandon 67-76; V Epping St Jo 76-92; Hon Can Chelmsf Cathl from 85; P-in-c Doddinghurst and Mountnessing from 92. *The Rectory, Church Lane, Doddinghurst, Brentwood, Essex CM15 0NJ* Brentwood (01277) 821366

ABBOTT, Barry Ingle. b 31. Sarum Th Coll 65. **d** 67 **p** 68. C Wilton w Netherhampton *Sarum* 69-71; V Warminster Ch Ch 71-76; Lic to Offic 76-77; P-in-c Figheldean w Milston 77-79; P-in-c Bulford 77-79; Lic to Offic *B & W* 79-88; Lic to Offic *Ex* 80-88; Perm to Offic *Sarum* from 88; rtd 91. *Fern Cottage, Berwick Lane, Steeple Langford, Salisbury SP3 4NB* Salisbury (01722) 790348

ABBOTT, Barry Joseph. b 59. MIEH Newc Coll of Arts DipEH81 DipOH&S83 DipTSM83. NE Ord Course 89. **d** 92 **p** 93. NSM Bishopwearmouth Ch Ch *Dur* from 92. *3 Greetlands Road, Sunderland SR2 9EB* 0191-520 0577

ABBOTT, Charles Peter. b 25. Maryland Univ 60. Pecusa Ord Course. **d** 62 **p** 62. C Oxhey St Matt *St Alb* 66-70; Asst Chapl Alleyn's Foundn Dulwich 70-72; C Dulwich St Barn *S'wark* 70-72; V Southway *Ex* 72-78; V Whitgift w Adlingfleet and Eastoft *Sheff* 78-79; rtd 86. *21 Lychgates Close, Bexhill-on-Sea, E Sussex TN40 2EW*

ABBOTT, Christopher Ralph (Chris). b 38. Univ of Wales (Lamp) BA59. Wells Th Coll 59. **d** 61 **p** 62. C Camberwell St Giles *S'wark* 61-67; C Portsea St Mary *Portsm* 67-70; V Portsea St Cuth 70-87; P-in-c Gt Milton *Ox* 87-88; P-in-c Lt Milton 87-88; R Gt w Lt Milton and Gt Haseley 88-93; R Chailey *Chich* from 93. *Chailey Rectory, East Grinstead Road, North Chailey, Lewes, E Sussex BN8 4DA* Newick (01825) 722286

ABBOTT, David John. b 52. CertEd. St Jo Coll Nottm LTh. **d** 87 **p** 88. C Biddulph *Lich* 87-90; C Tunbridge Wells St Jas *Roch* 90-92; TV Tunbridge Wells St Jas w St Phil from 92. *St Philip's House, Birken Road, Tunbridge Wells, Kent TN2 3TE* Tunbridge Wells (01892) 531031

ABBOTT, David Robert. b 49. Edin Univ BD72 Birm Univ DipTh73. Qu Coll Birm 72. **d** 74 **p** 75. C Kirkby *Liv* 74-78; C Ditton St Mich 78-80; R Ashton-in-Makerfield H Trin from 80. *The Rectory, North Ashton, Wigan, Lancs WN4 0QF* Ashton-in-Makerfield (01942) 727241

ABBOTT, Miss Geraldine (Mary). b 33. SRN55 SCM58 Open Univ BA77 Lon Univ MTh85. Oak Hill Th Coll BA82. **dss** 86 **d** 87 **p** 94. Tutor Oak Hill Th Coll from 86; St Alb St Paul *St Alb* 86-87; Hon Par Dn 87-94; Hon C from 94. *2 Wheatleys, St Albans, Herts AL4 9UE* St Albans (01727) 860869 Fax 0181-441 5996

ABBOTT, Leslie Leonard. b 24. ARICS47 FRICS83. Wycliffe Hall Ox 55. **d** 56 **p** 56. V Attenborough w Chilwell *S'well* 67-73; Perm to Offic *Chich* 73-83; C Patcham from 83; rtd 89. *32 Brangwyn Avenue, Brighton BN1 8XG* Brighton (01273) 553864

ABBOTT, Michael Reginald. b 40. Hull Univ BSc64. Cuddesdon Coll 64. **d** 66 **p** 67. C Workington St Jo *Carl* 66-68; C Ambleside w Rydal and Brathay 68-70; Hong Kong 70-71; Chapl RN 71-72; C Dalton-in-Furness *Carl* 72-73; V Stanbridge w Tilsworth *St Alb* 73-78; TV Dunstable 78-83; TR Chambersbury (Hemel Hempstead) from 83. *The Rectory, 14 Pancake Lane, Hemel Hempstead, Herts HP2 4NB* Hemel Hempstead (01442) 64860

ABBOTT, Nigel Douglas Blayney. b 37. Open Univ BA87. Bps' Coll Cheshunt 58. **d** 61 **p** 62. C Northn St Mich *Pet* 61-64; C Wanstead St Mary *Chelmsf* 64-66; Chapl St Jo Sch Tiffield Northants 66-69; V Earls Barton *Pet* 69-73; V Cov H Trin *Cov* 73-80; Provost St Jo Cathl Oban *Arg* 80-86; R Oban St Jo 80-86; TR Hemel Hempstead *St Alb* from 86; Chmn BSR from 94. *The Rectory, 40 High Street, Hemel Hempstead, Herts HP1 3AE* Hemel Hempstead (01442) 213838

ABBOTT, Stephen Anthony. b 43. K Coll Cam BA65 MA69 Edin Univ BD68 Harvard Univ ThM69. Edin Th Coll 65. **d** 69 **p** 70. C Deal St Leon *Cant* 69-72; Chapl K Coll Cam 72-75; C Cam St Matt *Ely* 75-76; Asst Chapl Bris Univ *Bris* 77-80; Hon C Clifton St Paul 77-80; Perm to Offic from 81. *29 Withleigh Road, Knowle, Bristol BS4 2LG* Bristol (0117) 977 9270

ABBOTT, Stephen John. b 62. Qu Mary Coll Lon LLB83. Linc Th Coll BTh92. **d** 92 **p** 93. C E Dereham and Scarning *Nor* from 92. *15 George Eliot Way, Toftwood, Dereham, Norfolk NR19 1EX* Dereham (01362) 692982

ABDY, John Channing. b 38. Nottm Univ BA63. Cuddesdon Coll 63. **d** 65 **p** 66. C Leagrave *St Alb* 65-69; C N Mymms 69-72; V Kings Walden 72-79; V S Woodham Ferrers *Chelmsf* 79-85; V Walthamstow St Pet 85-91; V Burrington and Churchill *B & W* from 91. *The Parsonage, Bristol Road, Langford, Bristol BS18 7JE* Churchill (01934) 852295

ABEL, David John. b 31. S'wark Ord Course 71. **d** 74 **p** 75. NSM Crowhurst *S'wark* 74-85; NSM Lingfield and Crowhurst 85-92; Perm to Offic from 92. *Tye Copse Cottage, South Park Lane, Bletchingley, Redhill, Surrey RH1 4NF* Godstone (01883) 743370

ABELL, Brian. b 37. Nottm Univ BA61 DipEd. Cuddesdon Coll 61. **d** 63 **p** 64. C Lightcliffe *Wakef* 63-66; C-in-c Mixenden CD 66-68; Lect Linc Coll of Tech 68-69; Chapl Trent Coll Nottm 70-74; V Thorner *Ripon* 74-82; V Far Headingley St Chad 82-86; Deputation Appeals Org CECS 86-89; V Masham and Healey *Ripon* from 89. *The Vicarage, Rodney Terrace, Masham, Ripon, N Yorkshire HG4 4JA* Ripon (01765) 689255 Fax as telephone

ABELL, George Derek. b 31. Selw Coll Cam BA54 MA68. Qu Coll Birm 54. **d** 56 **p** 57. R Bridgnorth St Mary *Heref* 64-70; P-in-c Oldbury 64-70; Australia 70-73; R Withington w Westhide and Weston Beggard *Heref* 73-81; R Withington w Westhide 81-83; P-in-c Sutton St Nicholas w Sutton St Michael 76-81; R 81-83; Preb Heref Cathl 82-83; V Basing *Win* 83-88; rtd 88. *51 Buckfield Road, Leominster, Herefordshire HR6 8SF* Leominster (01568) 614564

ABELL, Peter John. b 45. Chich Th Coll 67. **d** 70 **p** 71. C Churchdown St Jo *Glouc* 70-74; Chapl RAF from 74. *Chaplaincy Services (RAF), HQ, Personnel and Training Command, RAF Innsworth, Gloucester GL3 1EZ* Gloucester (01452) 712612 Ext 5164 Fax 510828

ABERDEEN AND ORKNEY, Bishop of. See CAMERON, Rt Rev Andrew Bruce

ABERDEEN AND ORKNEY, Dean of. See STRANRAER-MULL, Very Rev Gerald Hugh

ABERDEEN, Provost of. See WIGHTMAN, Very Rev William David

ABERNETHY, Alan Francis. b 57. QUB BA78. CITC 81. **d** 81 **p** 82. C Dundonald *D & D* 81-84; C Lecale Gp 84-86; I Helen's Bay 86-90; I Ballyholme from 90. *Ballyholme Rectory, 3 Ward Avenue, Bangor, Co Down BT20 5JW* Bangor (01247) 274912 or 274901

ABERNETHY, David Terence Phillips (Terry). b 42. St D Coll Lamp 61. **d** 65 **p** 66. C Abergele *St As* 65-72; Bermuda 72-84; V Beaulieu and Exbury and E Boldre *Win* from 84. *The Vicarage, Palace Lane, Beaulieu, Hants SO4 7YG* Beaulieu (01590) 612242

ABINGTON, David John Barringer. b 48. E Anglian Minl Tr Course 91. **d** 94 **p** 95. C Newport w Longford and Chetwynd *Lich* from 94. *9 Mere Close, Newport, Shropshire TF10 7SL* Newport (01952) 825209

ABLETT, Edwin John. b 37. Clifton Th Coll 64. **d** 67 **p** 68. C Sneinton St Chris w St Phil *S'well* 67-70; R High and Gd Easter w Margaret Roding *Chelmsf* 70-73; Chile 73-75; C Gt Baddow *Chelmsf* 75-78; V Newchapel *Lich* 78-82; V S Westoe *Dur* 82-86; V Tibshelf *Derby* from 86. *The Vicarage, 67 High Street, Tibshelf, Alfreton, Derbyshire DE55 5NU* Ripley (01773) 872243

ABLEWHITE, John Leslie Charles. b 43. K Coll Lon BA66. Coll of Resurr Mirfield 84. **d** 86 **p** 87. C E Dereham *Nor* 86-88; C E Dereham and Scarning 89; P-in-c S Lynn 89-95; V New Brompton St Luke *Roch* from 95. *St Luke's Vicarage, Sidney Road, Gillingham, Kent ME7 1PA* Medway (01634) 853060

ABLEWHITE, Stanley Edward. b 30. Birm Univ BSocScn59 LSE CASS60. Tyndale Hall Bris 64 Wycliffe Hall Ox 73. **d** 73 **p** 74.

1

C Much Woolton *Liv* 73-77; V Brough w Stainmore *Carl* 77-84; Min Aldridge *Lich* 84-90; P-in-c Swindon from 90; P-in-c Himley from 90. *The Vicarage, 12 St John's Close, Swindon, Dudley, W Midlands DY3 4PG* Kingswinford (01384) 278532

ABRAHAM, Canon David Alexander. b 37. AKC61. **d** 62 **p** 63. C Oswestry St Oswald *Lich* 62-63; C Gt Wyrley 63-65; C Sprowston *Nor* 65-67; V Ormesby w Scratby 67-81; R Oxborough w Foulden and Caldecote 81-87; R Cockley Cley w Gooderstone 81-87; V Didlington 81-87; R Gt and Lt Cressingham w Threxton 81-87; R Hilborough w Bodney 81-87; P-in-c Nor St Giles from 87; Chapl Asst Norfolk and Nor Hosp 87-91; Hon Can Nor Cathl *Nor* from 95. *St Giles's Vicarage, Heigham Road, Norwich NR2 3AU* Norwich (01603) 623724

ABRAHAM, Richard James. b 42. Liv Univ BA63. Ridley Hall Cam 64. **d** 66 **p** 67. C Warrington St Ann *Liv* 66-70; C Golborne 70-73; V Bickershaw 73-78; V Ewerby w Evedon *Linc* 78-82; R Kirkby Laythorpe w Asgarby 78-82; R Kirkby Laythorpe from 82. *The Rectory, Kirkby Laythorpe, Sleaford, Lincs NG34 9NY* Sleaford (01529) 304804

ABRAHAMS, Peter William. b 42. Southn Univ BA77. Sarum Th Coll 77. **d** 78 **p** 79. C Bitterne Park *Win* 78-82; C Old Brumby *Linc* 82-84; V Mitcham Ascension *S'wark* 84-91; TV Riverside *Ox* from 91. *The Vicarage, Mill Street, Colnbrook, Slough SL3 0JJ* Slough (01753) 682156 Fax as telephone

ABRAM, Paul Robert Carrington. b 36. Keble Coll Ox BA62 MA65. Chich Th Coll 60. **d** 62 **p** 63. C Redcar *York* 62-65; CF 65-89; V Salcombe *Ex* from 89; Miss to Seamen from 89. *The Vicarage, Devon Road, Salcombe, Devon TQ8 8HJ* Salcombe (01548) 842626

ABRAM, Steven James. b 50. Lon Univ DipTh74 BD76. Oak Hill Th Coll 71. **d** 76 **p** 77. C Biddulph *Lich* 76-79; C Heatherlands St Jo *Sarum* 79-83; Libya 83-84; C Stratford-on-Avon w Bishopton *Cov* 84; V Alderholt *Sarum* 84-90; V Daubhill *Man* from 90. *St George's Vicarage, Roseberry Street, Bolton BL3 4AR* Bolton (01204) 61067

ABREY, Mark Evans John. b 66. Ripon Coll Cuddesdon BTh93. **d** 93 **p** 94. C W Derby St Mary *Liv* from 93. *2 The Village, West Derby, Liverpool L12 5HW* 0151-256 6600

ABREY, Philip James. b 51. N Ord Course 82. **d** 85 **p** 86. NSM Hindley All SS *Liv* 85-90; C Caversham and Mapledurham *Ox* from 90; Min Caversham Park LEP from 90. *51 Galsworthy Drive, Caversham Park, Reading RG4 0PR* Reading (01734) 475152

ABSALOM, Alexander James David Edward (Alex). b 69. St Jo Coll Dur BA91. Cranmer Hall Dur DMinlStuds94. **d** 94 **p** 95. C Cranham *Chelmsf* from 94. *72 Marlborough Gardens, Upminster, Essex RM14 1SG* Romford (01708) 225604

ABSALOM, Hugh Pryse. b 10. Fitzw Ho Cam BA31 MA36 Lon Univ BD56. **d** 36 **p** 37. Chapl and Sen Lect St Hild's Tr Coll Dur 61-73; R Walton W w Talbenny and Haroldston W *St D* 73-77; rtd 77. *34 Ruther Park, Haverfordwest, Dyfed SA61 1DH* Haverfordwest (01437) 765950

ABSOLON, Canon Peter Chambers. b 27. St Jo Coll Cam BA50 MA55. Linc Th Coll 50. **d** 53 **p** 54. TV Strood *Roch* 67-80; Hon Can Roch Cathl 79-91; C Strood St Nic w St Mary 80-81; V Gillingham H Trin 81-91; RD Gillingham 90-91; rtd 91. *Holly Tree Cottage, 1 Itlay, Daglingworth, Cirencester, Glos GL7 7HZ* Cirencester (01285) 654225

ACHESON, James Malcolm. b 48. BNC Ox BA70 MA73. Sarum & Wells Th Coll 83. **d** 85 **p** 86. C Highgate St Mich *Lon* 85-88; TV Tisbury *Sarum* 88-94; Offg Chapl RAF from 88; R Storrington *Chich* from 94. *The Rectory, Storrington, Pulborough, W Sussex RH20 4EF* Storrington (01903) 742888

ACHESON, Canon Russell Robert. b 16. Univ Coll Ox BA39 MA45 DipTh47. Wells Th Coll 45. **d** 47 **p** 48. V Much Wenlock w Bourton *Heref* 66-79; P-in-c Hughley w Church Preen 69-79; RD Condover 72-78; P-in-c Harley w Kenley 73-75; Preb Heref Cathl 74-79; P-in-c Shipton 76-79; P-in-c Easthope w Long Stanton 76-79; Can Res Heref Cathl 79-83; rtd 83; Perm to Offic *Heref* from 83. *1 Penras, Newborough, Anglesey, Gwynedd LL61 6RS* Newborough (0124879) 325

ACHONRY, Dean of. *Vacant*

ACKERLEY, Glyn James. b 57. HNC83. Cranmer Hall Dur 84. **d** 87 **p** 88. C Tonbridge SS Pet and Paul *Roch* 87-90; R Willingham *Ely* 90-94; R Rampton 90-94; V Chatham St Phil and St Jas *Roch* from 94. *The Vicarage, 139 Sussex Drive, Walderslade, Chatham, Kent ME5 0NE* Medway (01634) 862498

ACKERLEY, Herbert. b 20. St Deiniol's Hawarden 60. **d** 61 **p** 63. R Longsight St Matt w St Clem *Man* 64-71; R Longsight St Luke 71-85; rtd 85; Perm to Offic *Man* from 85; Perm to Offic *Ches* from 86. *42 Newboult Road, Cheadle, Cheshire SK8 2AH* 0161-428 5801

ACKLAM, Leslie Charles. b 46. Birm Univ BEd71. Ripon Coll Cuddesdon 78. **d** 80 **p** 81. C Chingford St Anne *Chelmsf* 80-83;

C Spalding *Linc* 83-85; V Spalding St Paul 85-93; P-in-c Linc St Faith and St Martin w St Pet from 93. *165C Carholme Road, Lincoln LN1 1RU* Lincoln (01522) 531477

ACKLAND, John Robert Warwick. b 47. **d** 82 **p** 83. Lic to Offic *S'wark* 82-88; Hon C Mottingham St Andr 88-94; Hon C Woolwich St Thos from 94. *Priory Cottage, 39 Upton Road, Bexleyheath, Kent DA6 8LW* 0181-301 0718

ACKROYD, Dennis. b 36. Cranmer Hall Dur 67. **d** 70 **p** 71. C Newc w Butterton *Lich* 70-73; C Horsell *Guildf* 73-77; P-in-c Moreton and Woodsford w Tincleton *Sarum* 77-82; R 82-86; RD Dorchester 79-85; R Ewhurst *Guildf* 86-94; V Cleckheaton St Luke and Whitechapel *Wakef* from 94. *The Vicarage, 62 Whitcliffe Road, Cleckheaton, W Yorkshire BD19 3BY* Cleckheaton (01274) 873964

ACKROYD, Eric. b 29. Leeds Univ BA51 Liv Univ MA71 Leic Univ MA(Ed)86. St Jo Coll Dur DipTh54. **d** 55 **p** 56. Lect Kirkby Fields Tr Coll Liv 67-72; Sen Lect Nene Coll of HE Northn 72-85; rtd 85. *1 Beech Avenue, Northampton NN3 2HE* Northampton (01604) 717848

ACKROYD, John Michael. b 32. Lon Univ BSc53. Ripon Hall Ox 71. **d** 73 **p** 74. C Keighley *Bradf* 73-76; TV 76-81; V Keighley All SS 81; V Whalley *Blackb* from 81; Chapl Calderstones Hosp Blackb from 81. *The Vicarage, 40 The Sands, Whalley, Clitheroe, Lancs BB7 9TL* Whalley (01254) 823943 or 823249

ACKROYD, Peter Michael. b 60. Jes Coll Cam BA82 MA86 Fontainebleau MBA87. Wycliffe Hall Ox BA93 DipTh94. **d** 94 **p** 95. C Denton Holme *Carl* from 94. *118 Dalston Road, Carlisle CA2 5PJ* Carlisle (01228) 22938 or 810616

ACKROYD, Prof Peter Runham. b 17. Down Coll Cam BA38 Trin Coll Cam MA42 PhD45 Lon Univ MTh42 DD70 St Andr Univ Hon DD70. Westcott Ho Cam 57. **d** 57 **p** 58. Prof OT Studies Lon Univ 61-82; FKC from 69; rtd 82; Perm to Offic *St E* from 86. *Lavender Cottage, Middleton, Saxmundham, Suffolk IP17 3NQ* Westleton (0172873) 458

ACKROYD, William Lancelot. b 1900. Egerton Hall Man 31. **d** 33 **p** 34. V Eastleach w Southrop *Glouc* 64-68; rtd 68; C Stokenham w Sherford *Ex* 69-71; Perm to Offic *Truro* from 72. *2 Trelawney Road, Callington, Cornwall PL17 7EE* Liskeard (01579) 83150

ACLAND, Simon Henry Harper. b 41. Westcott Ho Cam 65. **d** 67 **p** 68. C Prestwich St Marg *Man* 67-69; New Zealand 69-71 and 75-85; Singapore 71-74; C Kensington St Mary Abbots w St Geo *Lon* 85-87; C Chelsea Ch Ch 87; C Chelsea St Luke and Ch Ch 87-93; Dir Post-Ord Tr 87-94; C Kensington St Mary Abbots w St Geo 93-94. *183 Kennington Road, London SE11 6ST* 0171-820 3787

ACOTT, David. b 32. Clifton Th Coll 54. **d** 58 **p** 59. C Streatham Park St Alb *S'wark* 58-60; C Maidstone St Faith *Cant* 60-64; R Pettaugh and Winston *St E* 64-76; R Pettaugh and Winston w Framsden 76-77; Area Sec (Dios Cant and Roch) CMS 77-85; C-in-c Hove H Trin CD *Chich* 86-93; TV Hove from 93. *Holy Trinity Parsonage, Blatchington Road, Hove, E Sussex BN3 3TA* Brighton (01273) 739870

ACREMAN, John. b 53. Oak Hill Th Coll 86. **d** 88 **p** 89. C Iver *Ox* 88-92; R Hook Norton w Gt Rollright, Swerford etc from 92. *Hook Norton Rectory, Banbury, Oxon OX15 5QQ* Hook Norton (01608) 737223

ACWORTH, Oswald Roney. b 10. SS Coll Cam BA33 MA37. Westcott Ho Cam. **d** 46 **p** 47. V Chobham w Valley End *Guildf* 56-79; rtd 79; Perm to Offic *B & W* from 82; Perm to Offic *Sarum* from 82. *Farrs, Chapel Lane, Zeals, Warminster, Wilts BA12 6NP* Bourton (01747) 840128

ACWORTH, Ven Richard Foote (Dick). b 36. SS Coll Cam BA62 MA65. Cuddesdon Coll 61. **d** 63 **p** 64. C Fulham St Etheldreda *Lon* 63-64; C Langley All SS and Martyrs *Man* 64-66; C Bridgwater St Mary w Chilton Trinity *B & W* 66-69; V Yatton 69-81; V Yatton Moor 81; P-in-c Taunton St Jo 81-85; P-in-c Taunton St Mary 81-85; V 85-93; Preb Wells Cathl 87-93; Adn Wells, Can Res and Preb Wells Cathl from 93. *The Old Rectory, The Crescent, Croscombe, Wells, Somerset BA5 3QN* Shepton Mallet (01749) 342242 Fax 330060

ACWORTH, Richard John Philip. b 30. Ch Ch Ox BA52 MA56 Paris Univ DesL70. **d** 63 **p** 63. In RC Ch 63-67; C Walthamstow St Mary w St Steph *Chelmsf* 68-70; P-in-c Lt Sampford 70-76; P-in-c Gt Sampford 74-76; Lect Bath Coll of HE 76-77; Lect Th Derby Lonsdale Coll *Derby* 77-83; Derbyshire Coll of HE 83-88; P-in-c Newton Tracey, Alverdiscott, Huntshaw etc *Ex* from 88; RD Torrington from 94. *The Rectory, Newton Tracey, Barnstaple, Devon EX31 3PL* Newton Tracey (01271) 858292

ADAIR, Raymond (Ray). b 33. Ripon Hall Ox 70. **d** 72 **p** 73. C Knottingley *Wakef* 72-75; C Sandal St Helen 75-77; V Sandal St Cath 77-87; V Brownhill from 87. *The Vicarage, 24 Intake Lane, Batley, W Yorkshire WF17 0QQ* Batley (01924) 471999

ADAIR, William Matthew. b 52. Open Univ BA. CITC 77. **d** 77 **p** 78. C Portadown St Mark *Arm* 77-78; Asst Chapl Miss to

Seamen 78-80; C Lisburn Ch Ch Cathl *Conn* 80-84; I Kildress w Altedesert *Arm* 84-92; I Portadown St Columba from 92. *St Columba's Rectory, 81 Loughgall Road, Portadown, Craigavon, Co Armagh BT62 4EG* Portadown (01762) 332746

ADAM, Canon David. b 36. Kelham Th Coll 54. **d** 59 **p** 60. C Auckland St Helen *Dur* 59-63; C Owton Manor CD 63-67; V Danby *York* 67-90; Can and Preb York Minster 89-90; V Holy Is *Newc* from 90. *The Vicarage, Holy Island, Berwick-upon-Tweed TD15 2RX* Berwick-upon-Tweed (01289) 89216

ADAM, Canon John Marshall William. b 09. Or Coll Ox BA31 MA36. Wycliffe Hall Ox 31. **d** 33 **p** 34. Hon Can Blackb Cathl *Blackb* 64-74; RD Preston 67-70; V Broughton 69-74; rtd 74; Lic to Offic *Blackb* from 74. *7 Caton Green Road, Brookhouse, Lancaster LA2 9JL* Caton (01524) 770030

ADAM, Lawrence (Lawrie). b 38. N Ord Course 82. **d** 82 **p** 83. C Thornton-le-Fylde *Blackb* 82-86; Dioc Video Production Co-ord from 85; P-in-c Scorton 86-91; C W Burnley from 91. *Cranleigh House, 242A Burnley Road, Padiham, Burnley, Lancs BB12 8SS* Padiham (01282) 779291 Fax Blackburn (01254) 824955

ADAM, Michael MacIntosh (Mike). b 48. Sarum & Wells Th Coll. **d** 84 **p** 85. C Stamford Hill St Thos *Lon* 84-87; rtd 88. *Flat 1, 112 Millfields Road, London E5 0AP*

ADAM, William Jonathan (Will). b 69. Man Univ BA91. Westcott Ho Cam 92 Bossey Ecum Inst Geneva CES94. **d** 94 **p** 95. C Beaconsfield *Ox* from 94. *35 Maxwell Road, Beaconsfield, Bucks HP9 1RG* Beaconsfield (01494) 674506

✠**ADAMS, Rt Rev Albert James.** b 15. K Coll Lon 39. St Andr Whittlesford 41. **d** 42 **p** 43 **c** 75. C Walkley *Sheff* 42-44; Succ Sheff Cathl 44; Prec 45-47; Chapl Bermondsey Medical Miss 47-55; R Bermondsey St Mary w St Olave and St Jo *S'wark* 47-55; RD Bermondsey 55; R Stoke Damerel *Ex* 55-63; R Wanstead St Mary *Chelms* 63-71; Adn W Ham 71-75; Suff Bp Barking 75-83; rtd 83; C Ridgeway *Sarum* 84-87. *89 Hardens Mead, Chippenham, Wilts SN15 3AQ* Chippenham (01249) 660728

ADAMS, Anthony John. b 42. St Jo Coll Nottm 83. **d** 85 **p** 86. C Wellesbourne *Cov* 85-89; R Weddington and Caldecote from 89. *The Rectory, Weddington, Nuneaton, Warks CV10 0EX* Nuneaton (01203) 353400

ADAMS, Arthur White. b 12. Sheff Univ BA35 MA36 Ox Univ MA49 BD50 DD67. Ripon Hall Ox 35. **d** 36 **p** 37. Fell and Dean of Div Magd Coll Ox 49-79; rtd 79. *30 Frenchay Road, Oxford OX2 6TG* Oxford (01865) 515092

ADAMS, Brian Hugh. b 32. Pemb Coll Ox BA54 MA57 Lon Univ DipTh56. Sarum & Wells Th Coll 77. **d** 79 **p** 80. Hon C Crediton *Ex* 79-81; Chapl St Brandon's Sch Clevedon 81-85; C Street w Walton *B & W* 86-88; RD Glastonbury 86-92 and from 93; V Baltonsborough w Butleigh and W Bradley from 88. *The Vicarage, Church Close, Butleigh, Glastonbury, Somerset BA6 8SH* Baltonsborough (01458) 50409

ADAMS, Brian Peter. b 47. FInstD FRSA Avery Hill Coll CertEd70 Lon Univ CertRS92 DipRS93. S'wark Ord Course 90. **d** 93 **p** 94. NSM Tonbridge SS Pet and Paul *Roch* from 93. *16 Dry Hill Road, Tonbridge, Kent TN9 1LX* Tonbridge (01732) 350053 Fax 362600

ADAMS, Mrs Celia. b 39. R Holloway Coll Lon BSc60 Cam Univ CertEd61. Sarum & Wells Th Coll 86. **d** 88 **p** 94. NSM Canley *Cov* 88-91; NSM Cov N Deanery 91-92; C Cov Caludon from 92; Asst to Dioc Dir of Educn from 92. *Holy Cross Vicarage, 14 St Austell Road, Coventry CV2 5AE* Coventry (01203) 635734

ADAMS, Ven Charles Alexander. b 29. MBE73 CBE82 JP. AKC59. **d** 60 **p** 61. C Bishopwearmouth St Mich w St Hilda *Dur* 60-63; C Ox SS Phil and Jas *Ox* 63-66; C Tunbridge Wells St Barn *Roch* 66-68; St Vincent from 68; Miss to Seamen from 68; Can Kingstown Cathl from 73; Adn St Vincent & The Grenadines from 76. *St Mary's Rectory, Bequia, Northern Grenadines, Windward Islands* St Vincent (1809) 458-3234

ADAMS, David John Anthony. b 46. BSc. Bris Sch of Min. **d** 84 **p** 85. NSM Sea Mills *Bris* from 84. *31 Elberton Road, Bristol BS9 2PZ* Bristol (0117) 968 4625

ADAMS, Denis Leslie. b 23. Ox NSM Course 78. **d** 81 **p** 82. NSM Reading All SS *Ox* 81-82; C Wargrave 82-83; C Skegness and Winthorpe *Linc* 83-85; V Gainsborough St Jo 85-89; rtd 89; Perm to Offic *Linc* from 89. *4 Collum Gardens, Ashby, Scunthorpe, S Humberside DN16 2SY* Scunthorpe (01724) 842554

ADAMS, Donald John. b 46. St Jo Coll Nottm 86. **d** 88 **p** 89. C Byfleet *Guildf* 88-93; P-in-c E Molesey St Mary from 93. *The Vicarage, St Mary's Road, East Molesey, Surrey KT8 0ST* 0181-979 1441

ADAMS, Douglas George. b 39. St Luke's Coll Ex CertEd69 MEd87. ALBC65 SW Minl Tr Course 86. **d** 89 **p** 90. NSM Bude Haven and Marhamchurch *Truro* 89-93; P-in-c St Mewan from 93; Chapl Mt Edgcumbe Hospice from 93. *The Rectory, St Mewan, St Austell, Cornwall PL26 7DP* St Austell (01726) 72679

ADAMS, Canon Douglass Arthur. b 04. Dur Univ LTh33. Bp Wilson Coll 29. **d** 32 **p** 33. V Market Harborough *Leic* 54-73; Hon Can Leic Cathl 59-73; RD Gartree I (Harborough) 69-73; rtd 73; Lic to Offic *Leic* 73-81; Perm to Offic from 81. *32 The Hawthorns, Holly Drive, Lutterworth, Leics LE17 4UL* Lutterworth (01455) 554709

ADAMS, George Ernest. b 12. Sarum Th Coll 37. **d** 39 **p** 40. V Arlesey w Astwick *St Alb* 66-70; R Gillingham w Geldeston and Stockton *Nor* 70-80; rtd 80; Perm to Offic *Nor* from 82; Perm to Offic *St E* from 87. *4 Malthouse Court, London Road, Harleston, Norfolk IP20 9BU* Harleston (01379) 853445

ADAMS, Gillian. *See* WILTON, Mrs Gillian Linda

ADAMS, Godfrey Bernard. b 47. Local Minl Tr Course. **d** 93 **p** 94. NSM Saddleworth *Man* from 93. *11 Springmeadow Lane, Uppermill, Oldham OL3 6EP* Saddleworth (01457) 875126

ADAMS, James Michael. b 49. LLB. St Jo Coll Nottm DipTh CertEd. **d** 82 **p** 83. C Luton St Mary *St Alb* 82-85; TV Cove St Jo *Guildf* 85-92; V Chislehurst Ch Ch *Roch* from 92. *Christ Church Vicarage, 62 Lubbock Road, Chislehurst, Kent BR7 5JX* 0181-467 3185

ADAMS, John. b 38. Lon Univ DipEd66 Open Univ BA79. Linc Th Coll 68. **d** 70 **p** 71. C Skipton H Trin *Bradf* 70-72; C Bassingham *Linc* 72-73; Chapl Lingfield Hosp Sch 73-74; Hon C Keighley *Bradf* 76-79; P-in-c Bredenbury and Wacton w Grendon Bishop *Heref* 79-84; P-in-c Edwyn Ralph and Collington w Thornbury 79-84; P-in-c Pencombe w Marston Stannett and Lt Cowarne 79-84; V Macclesfield St Jo *Ches* 84-87; R Wimblington *Ely* 87-90; V Manea 87-90; R Hallaton w Horninghold, Allexton, Tugby etc *Leic* from 90. *The Rectory, Churchgate, Hallaton, Market Harborough, Leics LE16 8TY* Hallaton (01858) 555363

ADAMS, John Richard. b 38. St D Coll Lamp BA62 Lich Th Coll 62. **d** 64 **p** 65. C Falmouth K Chas *Truro* 64-68; C Bath Twerton-on-Avon *B & W* 68-72; V Milton *Win* 72-79; P-in-c Weymouth St Edm *Sarum* 79-90; V 90-95; Chapl Westhaven Hosp Weymouth 79-94; P-in-c The Winterbournes and Compton Valence from 95. *The Rectory, Martinstown, Dorchester, Dorset DT2 9JZ* Martinstown (01305) 588241

ADAMS, John David Andrew. b 37. TCD BA60 Div Test61 MA64 BD69 Reading Univ MEd74. **d** 62 **p** 63. C Belf St Steph *Conn* 62-65; Teacher 65-74; Hd Master St Paul's Secondary Sch Addlestone 74-82; Weydon Secondary Sch Farnham from 82; NSM Bourne *Guildf* 80-85; Chapl to The Queen from 94. *Brookside Farm, Oast House Crescent, Farnham, Surrey GU9 0NP* Farnham (01252) 726888

ADAMS, John Peregrine. b 25. Magd Coll Ox BA46 MA50. Wells Th Coll 48. **d** 49 **p** 50. V Stapleford w Berwick St James *Sarum* 57-91; RD Wylye and Wilton 77-85; rtd 91. *12 Harcourt Terrace, Salisbury SP2 7SA* Salisbury (01722) 336061

ADAMS, John Peter. b 42. Lon Univ BD69. Oak Hill Th Coll 65. **d** 70 **p** 71. C Whitnash *Cov* 70-74; Chapl Davos *Eur* 74-75; Chapl Dusseldorf 75-76; C Gt Baddow *Chelmsf* 77-80; Asst Chapl Zurich w St Gallen and Winterthur *Eur* 91-93; Asst Chapl Zurich w Winterthur 93-95; P-in-c Harmondsworth *Lon* from 95. *St Mary's Vicarage, Harmondsworth, West Drayton, Middx UB7 0AQ* 0181-897 2385

ADAMS, Jonathan Henry. b 48. St Andr Univ MA73. Cranmer Hall Dur 73. **d** 76 **p** 77. C Upperby St Jo *Carl* 76-78; C Sunderland St Chad *Dur* 78-82; Soc Resp Officer 83-91; TV Willington Team *Newc* from 91; Local Min Development Officer from 91. *47 Norman Terrace, Wallsend, Tyne & Wear NE28 6SP* 0191-262 3574

ADAMS, Margaret Anne. *See* FREEMAN, Mrs Margaret Anne

ADAMS, Martin Philip. b 57. Sarum & Wells Th Coll 88. **d** 90 **p** 91. C Sandringham w W Newton *Nor* 90-93; P-in-c Docking w The Birchams and Stanhoe w Barwick 93-95; V Docking, The Birchams, Stanhoe and Sedgeford from 95. *The Vicarage, Sedgeford Road, Docking, King's Lynn, Norfolk PE31 8PN* Docking (01485) 518247

ADAMS, Michael John. b 48. St Jo Coll Dur BA77. Ripon Coll Cuddesdon 77. **d** 79 **p** 80. C Falmouth K Chas *Truro* 79-81; C St Buryan, St Levan and Sennen 81-83; P-in-c Lanlivery w Luxulyan 83-84; V 84-88; V St Agnes from 88; RD Powder from 90; Perm to Offic *Ex* from 94. *The Vicarage, Trevaunance Road, St Agnes, Cornwall TR5 0SE* St Agnes (01872) 552328

ADAMS, Nigel David. b 40. Sarum & Wells Th Coll 86. **d** 88 **p** 89. C Tile Hill *Cov* 88-91; C Cov Caludon 91-92; TV from 92; Asst Chapl HM Young Offender Inst Onley from 92. *Holy Cross Vicarage, 14 St Austell Road, Coventry CV2 5AE* Coventry (01203) 635734

ADAMS, Peter. Bris Univ CertEd52 Lon Univ ADEd81. Oak Hill Th Coll. **d** 91 **p** 92. NSM Towcester w Easton Neston *Pet* 91-95; Perm to Offic *Ex* from 95. *3 Copperwood Close, Ashburton, Newton Abbot, Devon TQ13 7JQ* Ashburton (01364) 654261

ADAMS, Peter. b 37. Trin Coll Cam MA70. AKC65 St Boniface Warminster 65. **d** 66 **p** 67. C Clapham H Trin *S'wark* 66-70; Chapl Trin Coll Cam 70-75; Warden Trin Coll Cen Camberwell 75-83; V Camberwell St Geo *S'wark* 75-83; RD Camberwell 80-83; V W Dulwich All SS and Em 83-92; V Addington from 92. *Addington Vicarage, Spout Hill, Croydon CR0 5AN* Lodge Hill (01689) 842167 or 841838

ADAMS, Peter Anthony. b 48. K Coll Lon BD70 AKC70 MTh72. **d** 72 **p** 74. Lic to Offic *Eur* 72-73; C Ashford *Cant* 73-79; P-in-c Ramsgate H Trin 79-86; P-in-c Ramsgate St Geo 84-86; R Ramsgate H Trin and St Geo from 86. *Holy Trinity Rectory, Winterstoke Way, Ramsgate, Kent CT11 8AG* Thanet (01843) 593593

ADAMS, Peter Harrison. b 41. Tyndale Hall Bris 63. **d** 68 **p** 69. C Kendal St Thos *Carl* 68-71; C W Bromwich Gd Shep w St Jo *Lich* 71-75; R Aldham *Chelmsf* 76-81; R Marks Tey 76-81; R Marks Tey w Aldham and Lt Tey 81-85; NSM Colchester St Jo from 85; Dioc Missr from 85. *4 St Jude's Gardens, St John's Estate, Colchester CO4 4PP* Colchester (01206) 854041

ADAMS, Canon Raymond Michael (Ray). b 41. Lon Univ BD67. ALCD66. **d** 67 **p** 68. C Old Hill H Trin *Worc* 67-73; TR Ipsley from 73; Hon Can Worc Cathl from 84. *The Rectory, Icknield Street, Ipsley, Redditch, Worcs B98 0AN* Redditch (01527) 523307

ADAMS, Raymond William. b 58. Reading Univ BA79. Oak Hill Th Coll BA85. **d** 85 **p** 86. C Blackpool St Thos *Blackb* 85-88; C Padiham 88-90; TV Rodbourne Cheney *Bris* from 90. *The Vicarage, 54 Furlong Close, Haydon Wick, Swindon SN2 3QP* Swindon (01793) 726378

ADAMS, Richard. b 10. TCD BA32 MA35 BD44 PhD46. **d** 33 **p** 34. Dean Conn 63-75; rtd 75. *c/o R W Adams Esq, 15 Lenaghan Avenue, Belfast BT8 4JF*

ADAMS, Robin Thomas. b 54. QUB BSc76. Oak Hill Th Coll BA79. **d** 79 **p** 80. C Magheralin *D & D* 79-82; C Coleraine *Conn* 82-86; I Belf St Aid 86-89; USA from 89. *332 North Union Street, Tecumseh, Michigan, 49286, USA* Tecumseh (517) 423-3233

ADAMS, Roger Charles. b 36. Em Coll Cam BA60 MA64. Tyndale Hall Bris 60. **d** 62 **p** 63. C Longfleet *Sarum* 62-65; C Uphill *B & W* 66-71; R Ramsden Crays w Ramsden Bellhouse *Chelmsf* 71-78; SW Area Sec BFBS 78-84; P-in-c Plymouth St Aug *Ex* 84-85; TV Plymouth Em w Efford 85-90; V Paignton Ch Ch from 90. *Christ Church Vicarage, 133 Torquay Road, Paignton, Devon TQ3 2AG* Paignton (01803) 556311

ADAMS, Stephen Paul. b 56. Ex Univ BSc78. Sarum & Wells Th Coll 85. **d** 87 **p** 88. C Swansea St Nic *S & B* 87-88; C Llwynderw 88-91; R Badby w Newham and Charwelton w Fawsley etc *Pet* from 91. *The Vicarage, Vicarage Hill, Badby, Daventry, Northants NN11 6AP* Daventry (01327) 310239

ADAMSON, Anthony Scott (Tony). b 49. Newc Univ BA70. St Jo Coll Dur 75. **d** 78 **p** 79. C High Elswick St Paul *Newc* 78-86; C Benwell Team 86-92; V Tweedmouth from 92; Miss to Seamen from 92. *The Vicarage, Main Street, Tweedmouth, Berwick-upon-Tweed TD15 2AW* Berwick-upon-Tweed (01289) 306409

ADAMSON, Arthur John. b 38. Keble Coll Ox BA61 MA65. Tyndale Hall Bris 61. **d** 63 **p** 64. C Redhill H Trin *S'wark* 63-66; Chapl Trent Park Coll of Educn 66-69; C Enfield Ch Ch Trent Park *Lon* 66-70; Ind Chapl *S'wark* 70-74; C Battersea St Geo w St Andr 70-74; R Reedham *Nor* 74-80; Min Beighton and Moulton 75-80; P-in-c Cantley w Limpenhoe and Southwood 77-80; R Oulton St Mich 80-90; Chapl Lothingland Hosp 80-90; R Laceby *Linc* from 90. *3 Butterfield Close, Laceby, Grimsby, S Humberside DN37 7BG* Grimsby (01472) 870884

ADAMSON, Paul. b 35. Leeds Univ BA58. Coll of Resurr Mirfield. **d** 60 **p** 61. C Southwick St Columba *Dur* 60-63; Br Guiana 63-66; Guyana 66-75; C Benwell St Jas *Newc* 75-77; V Cowgate 77-83; V Prudhoe 83-93; TV N Tyne and Redesdale Team from 93. *Falstone Rectory, Hexham, Northd NE48 1AE* Hexham (01434) 240213

ADAMSON, Richard Edwin Aidan. b 56. Pepperdine Univ BA76 Hamburg Univ Dipl-Reg86. Coll of Resurr Mirfield 89 Sarum & Wells Th Coll 90. **d** 91 **p** 92. C Reddish *Man* 91-93; Chapl Bryanston Sch Blandford from 93. *Bryanston School, Blandford Forum, Dorset DH11 0PX* Blandford (01258) 452411

ADAMSON, Warren Joseph. b 43. St Jo Coll Nottm. **d** 82 **p** 83. C S Croydon Em *Cant* 82-85; TV Folkestone H Trin and St Geo w Ch Ch 85-90; R Folkestone St Geo 90-91; V Douglas St Ninian *S & M* 91-93; V Potters Green *Cov* from 93. *St Philip's Vicarage, Ringwood Highway, Coventry CV2 2GF* Coventry (01203) 617568

ADDENBROOKE, Peter Homfray. b 38. Trin Coll Cam BA59 MA. Lich Th Coll 61. **d** 63 **p** 64. C Bakewell *Derby* 63-67; C Horsham *Chich* 67-73; P-in-c Colgate from 73; Adv for Past Care and Counselling from 73. *The Vicarage, Colgate, Horsham, W Sussex RH12 4SZ* Faygate (01293) 851362

ADDINGTON HALL, Gerald Richard. b 38. Qu Coll Ox BA62 MA67 Birm Univ MA69. Qu Coll Birm 62. **d** 65 **p** 66. C Leeds St Sav *Ripon* 65-69; Tanzania 69-75; V Ipswich St Fran *St E* 75-81; V Pakenham w Norton and Tostock 81-91; V Charsfield w Debach, Monewden, Hoo etc from 91; Warden of Readers from 91. *The Vicarage, Charsfield, Woodbridge, Suffolk IP13 7PY* Charsfield (0147337) 740

ADDIS, Arthur Lewis. b 11. TD. Worc Ord Coll 62. **d** 64 **p** 65. R W Dean w E Grimstead *Sarum* 66-70; V Stratford sub Castle 70-79; rtd 79. *78 Park Street, Salisbury SP1 3AU* Salisbury (01722) 335476

ADDISON, Bernard Michael Bruce. b 31. Cam Univ MA73. Oak Hill Th Coll 58. **d** 61 **p** 62. Australia 70-72; C Catford St Andr *S'wark* 72-73; Chapl Ch Coll Cam 73-78; Chapl Bonn w Cologne *Eur* 79-82; R Kegworth *Leic* 82-89; V Market Harborough 89-94; rtd 94; Spain from 94. *Calle Madrid 28, Piso 4, PTA 8, 46700 Gandia, Valencia, Spain*

ADDISON, David John Frederick. b 37. DipMA73 K Coll Dur BA60 DipEd62 Birm Univ MA79 Bris Univ MLitt93. Wells Th Coll 64. **d** 66 **p** 71. C Rastrick St Matt *Wakef* 66-67; Perm to Offic *Bradf* 67-71; Hon C Manningham St Luke 71-73; Perm to Offic *Glouc* 77-79; Hon C Bisley w Oakridge 79-81; V Newland and Redbrook w Clearwell from 81; Chapl R Forest of Dean Coll from 89. *The Vicarage, Newland, Coleford, Glos GL16 8NP* Dean (01594) 833777

ADDISON, Philip Ives. b 29. Dur Univ BA49. Ely Th Coll 59. **d** 61 **p** 62. C Waltham Cross *St Alb* 61-64; C Belf St Paul 64-66; Chapl RN 66-70; V Foleshill St Laur *Cov* 70-74; P-in-c Halsham *York* 74-78; V Owthorne and Rimswell w Withernsea from 74. *The Vicarage, 28 Park Avenue, Withernsea, N Humberside HU19 2JU* Withernsea (01964) 613598

ADDISON SMITH, Canon Anthony Cecil. b 18. Keble Coll Ox BA48 MA53. Linc Th Coll 48. **d** 49 **p** 50. V Easingwold w Raskelfe *York* 66-78; RD Easingwold 70-77; Can York Minster 76-83; V Selby Abbey 78-83; rtd 83; Perm to Offic *Ox* 83-85 and from 87; C Cookham 85-86; C Hambleden Valley 87. *5 Tierney Court, Marlow, Bucks SL7 2BL* Marlow (01628) 483288

ADDLEY, David Bernard. b 41. St Paul's Cheltenham CertEd64 Leic Univ DipEd69 Bradf Univ MSc73. Ox Min Course 91. **d** 92 **p** 93. NSM Claydon w Mollington *Ox* from 92; Perm to Offic *Pet* from 95. *66 Main Road, Middleton Cheney, Banbury, Oxon OX17 2LT* Banbury (01295) 710313 Fax Shipston-on-Stour (01608) 663291

ADENEY, Dr Harold Walter. b 14. OBE76. Qu Coll Cam BA35 MB BChir38 MA53. Trin Coll Bris. **d** 75 **p** 76. Burundi 75-82; Perm to Offic *St Alb* from 83; Perm to Offic *Nor* 86-92. *5 Coles Way, Reepham, Norwich NR10 4LW* Norwich (01603) 871932

ADENEY, Canon Ronald Edward. b 19. OBE79. Qu Coll Cam BA40 MA44 Birm Univ PGCE71. Ridley Hall Cam 41. **d** 42 **p** 43. Jerusalem 47-73 and 75-80; Perm to Offic *Birm* 73-75; Hon Can Jerusalem 77-80; P-in-c Fulmer *Ox* 81-85; rtd 85; Perm to Offic *Ox* 85-87; Perm to Offic Jerusalem 86-92. *28 Trafford Road, Oxford OX3 8BE* Oxford (01865) 68538

ADEY, John Douglas. b 33. Man Univ BSc54. Coll of Resurr Mirfield 56. **d** 58 **p** 59. C Forton *Portsm* 58-64; C Northolt St Mary *Lon* 64-67; V Snibston *Leic* 67-72; V Outwood *Wakef* 72-78; V Clifton 78; V Upton Priory *Ches* 79-81; V Hyde St Thos 81-82; V Newton in Mottram 82-89; R Roos and Garton in Holderness w Tunstall etc *York* 89-92; C Woodchurch *Ches* from 92. *23 Mavis Drive, Upton, Wirral, Merseyside L49 0UN* 0151-677 7578

ADFIELD, Richard Ernest. b 31. Oak Hill Th Coll 62. **d** 64 **p** 65. V Whitehall Park St Andr Hornsey Lane *Lon* 67-77; V Kensington St Helen w H Trin 77-86; V Turnham Green Ch Ch 86-92; rtd 92. *363 Hangleton Road, Hove, E Sussex BN3 7LQ* Brighton (01273) 732538

✠**ADIE, Rt Rev Michael Edgar.** b 29. CBE94. St Jo Coll Ox BA52 MA56. Westcott Ho Cam 52. **d** 54 **p** 55 c 83. C Pallion *Dur* 54-57; Abp's Dom Chapl *Cant* 57-60; V Sheff St Mark Broomhall *Sheff* 60-69; RD Hallam 66-69; R Louth w Welton-le-Wold *Linc* 69-75; P-in-c N w S Elkington 69-75; TR Louth 75-76; V Morton w Hacconby 76-83; Adn Linc 77-83; Can and Preb Linc Cathl 77-83; Bp Guildf 83-94; rtd 95. *Greenslade, Froxfield, Petersfield, Hants GU32 1EB* Petersfield (01730) 827266

ADKINS, Canon Harold. b 20. Lon Univ BA41. Wycliffe Hall Ox. **d** 43 **p** 44. Jerusalem 54-73; Can Res Jerusalem 65-70; Dean Jerusalem 70-73; V Barkby *Leic* 74-83; RD Goscote II 82-84; V Barkby and Queniborough 83-85; rtd 85; Perm to Offic *Leic* from 85. *14 Spinney Drive, Quorn, Loughborough, Leics LE12 8HB* Quorn (01509) 416080

ADKINS, Peter Vincent Alexander (Alex). b 44. Lon Univ DipTh68 Lanc Univ BA71 Lon Inst of Educn CertEd78.

Kelham Th Coll 63. **d** 69 **p** 70. SSM 67-73; Tutor Kelham Th Coll 71-73; Jerusalem 73-75; Hon C Cam St Giles w St Pet *Ely* 76-78; Hon C Northolt St Mary *Lon* 81-83; P-in-c Hanworth St Geo 83-86; R 86-88; Adult Educn Officer 83-86; Priory of Our Lady Burford 89-93; Perm to Offic *Ox* 89-93; Warden Edw K Ho *Linc* from 93. *Edward King House, The Old Palace, Lincoln LN2 1PU* Lincoln (01522) 528778 Fax 527308

ADLER, Thomas Payne. b 07. Selw Coll Cam BA29 MA36. Wells Th Coll 29. **d** 30 **p** 31. R Castor *Pet* 47-74; R Marholm 47-74; rtd 74; Perm to Offic *Glouc* 75-94; Perm to Offic *Worc* from 85. *Hill Cottage, Cottons Lane, Ashton-under-Hill, Evesham, Worcs WR11 6SS* Evesham (01386) 881431

ADLEY, Ernest George. b 38. Leeds Univ BA61. Wells Th Coll 62. **d** 64 **p** 65. C Bideford *Ex* 64-67; C Yeovil St Mich *B & W* 67-70; V Taunton Lyngford 70-79; R Skegness and Winthorpe *Linc* 79-91; R Wantage Downs *Ox* from 91. *The Rectory, Church Street, East Hendred, Wantage, Oxon OX12 8LA* Abingdon (01235) 833235

ADLINGTON, David John. b 51. AKC73. **d** 74 **p** 75. C Clapham St Paul *S'wark* 74-77; C Bethnal Green St Matt *Lon* 77-80; P-in-c Stepney St Pet w St Benet 80-84; Succ S'wark Cathl *S'wark* 84-87; Min Llan w Capel Llanilltern *Llan* 88-91; PV and Succ Llan Cathl 88-91; Dioc Dir of Educn from 91; V St Hilary 91-94; TV Cowbridge 94-95; C Whitchurch from 95. *Pendinas, The Cathedral Green, Llandaff, Cardiff CF5 2EB* Cardiff (01222) 562649

ADLINGTON, Kenneth Leonard. b 27. Launde Abbey. **d** 74 **p** 75. C Braunstone *Leic* 74-76; C Eyres Monsell 76-78; V Whetstone 78-83; V Old Dalby and Nether Broughton 83-85; R Waltham on the Wolds, Stonesby, Saxby etc 85-89; rtd 89; Perm to Offic *Linc* from 89. *3 Fleetwood Gardens, Market Harborough, Leics LE16 9LX* Market Harborough (01858) 461331

ADNETT, Roy Gumley. b 14. Tyndale Hall Bris 39. **d** 42 **p** 43. V Chilcompton *B & W* 55-80; RD Midsomer Norton 78-81; R Chilcompton w Downside and Stratton on the Fosse 80-81; rtd 81; Perm to Offic *Leic* from 81. *129 Harrowgate Drive, Birstall, Leicester LE4 3GS* Leicester (0116) 267 5315

ADOYO, Miss Eugeniah Ombwayo. b 54. Lon Bible Coll 84 Westmr Coll Ox BA86 MPhil90. **dss** 82 **d** 91 **p** 91. Kenya 82-94; Internat Sec Crosslinks from 94; NSM Hatcham St Jas *S'wark* from 94. *12 Redstart Close, Southern Gateway, London SE14 6DE* 0181-469 3840 or 691 6111

ADU-BOACHIE, Francis. b 60. Oak Hill Th Coll DipTh95. **d** 95. C Stonebridge St Mich *Lon* from 95. *6 The Green, Southgate, London N14 7GE*

AEGEAN AND THE DANUBE, Archdeacon of the. *See* PEAKE, Ven Simon Jeremy Brinsley

AELRED, Brother. *See* ARNESEN, Raymond Halfdan

AFFLECK, John. b 20. Liv Univ LLB48. K Coll Lon 68 St Aug Coll Cant 71. **d** 71 **p** 72. C Hutton *Chelmsf* 71-74; P-in-c Hawkchurch, Fishpond, Bettiscombe, Marshwood etc *Sarum* 74-80; R Marshwood Vale 80-86; rtd 86. *3 St George's Close, Lower Street, Harnham, Salisbury SP2 8HA* Salisbury (01722) 334659

AFFLECK, Stuart John. b 47. AKC69. St Aug Coll Cant. **d** 70 **p** 71. C Prittlewell St Mary *Chelmsf* 70-75; Asst Chapl Charterhouse Godalming 75-78; Chapl 78-80; Warden Pilsdon Community Salisbury from 80. *Pilsdon Community, Pilsdon, Bridport, Dorset DT6 5NZ* Broadwindsor (01308) 868308

AGAR, George. b 40. Edin Univ BSc63 Ox Univ PGCE64. N Ord Course 92. **d** 94 **p** 95. NSM Sandbach *Ches* from 94; Head Buddulph High Sch Stoke-on-Trent from 94. *128 Middlewich Road, Sandbach, Cheshire CW11 9EA* Crewe (01270) 760191

AGASSIZ, David John Lawrence. b 42. St Pet Hall Ox BA64 MA68 Imp Coll Lon PhD94. Ripon Hall Ox 64. **d** 66 **p** 67. C Southn St Mary Extra *Win* 66-71; V Enfield St Jas *Lon* 71-80; P-in-c Grays Thurrock *Chelmsf* 80-83; P-in-c Grays All SS 81-84; P-in-c Lt Thurrock St Mary 81-84; P-in-c W Thurrock 81-83; P-in-c Grays SS Pet and Paul, S Stifford and W Thurrock 83-84; TR Grays Thurrock 84-90; Hon Can Chelmsf Cathl 90-93; Dioc Development Rep 90-93; Perm to Offic 93-94. *23 St James's Road, Gravesend, Kent DA11 0HF* Gravesend (01474) 332193

AGGETT, Miss Vivienne Cecilia. b 33. Sarum & Wells Th Coll 86. **d** 88 **p** 94. C Binley *Cov* 88-91; C Hednesford *Lich* from 91. *St Saviour's Vicarage, 76 Highmount Street, Hednesford, Cannock, Staffs WS12 4BN* Shenstone (01543) 878928

AGGREY, Dr Solomon Samuel. b 49. BSc76. Immanuel Coll Ibadan MA84 Internat Bibl Inst Florida DMin86. **d** 80 **p** 82. Nigeria 80-88; Miss Partner CMS from 88; C Gorton Em *Man* from 93; C Gorton St Jas from 93. *St James's Rectory, 44 Wellington Street, Gorton, Manchester M18 8LJ* 0161-223 0708

AGLEN, Miss Elizabeth Senga. b 15. Cam Univ MA. Lambeth STh49. **dss** 59 **d** 87. Oxton *Ches* 72-76; rtd 76; Perm to Offic *Sarum* 76-84; Perm to Offic *Ex* from 84. *4 Gracey Court, Woodland Road, Broadclyst, Exeter EX5 3LP* Exeter (01392) 461714

AGNEW, Kenneth David. b 33. Jes Coll Cam BA58 MA62. Clifton Th Coll 58. **d** 60 **p** 61. C Lozells St Silas *Birm* 60-63; C Skellingthorpe *Linc* 63-68; C Birchwood 68-72; R Willand *Ex* from 72; RD Cullompton 89-95. *Willand Rectory, Cullompton, Devon EX15 2RH* Cullompton (01884) 32247

AGNEW, Kevin Raymond Christopher. b 59. Chich Th Coll. **d** 94 **p** 95. C Eastbourne St Mary *Chich* from 94. *6 Bay Pond Road, Eastbourne, E Sussex BN21 1HX* Eastbourne (01323) 728680

AGNEW, Stephen Mark. b 54. Univ of Wales BSc76 Southn Univ BTh81. Sarum & Wells Th Coll 76. **d** 79 **p** 80. C Wilmslow *Ches* 79-84; V Crewe St Jo 84-90; Chapl Bromsgrove Sch Worcs from 90. *Willow Cottage, 14 Ednall Lane, Bromsgrove, Worcs B60 2BZ* Bromsgrove (01527) 575048

AIDAN, Brother. *See* THOMPSON, Barry

AIKEN, Nicholas John. b 58. Sheff Univ BA. Wycliffe Hall Ox 80. **d** 82 **p** 83. C Ashtead *Guildf* 82-86; Dioc Youth Officer 86-93; R Wisley w Pyrford from 93. *The Rectory, Aviary Road, Woking, Surrey GU22 8TH* Byfleet (01932) 352914

AIKEN, Simon Mark. b 62. St Andr Univ MTh85. Ripon Coll Cuddesdon 86. **d** 88 **p** 89. C Burnley (Habergham Eaves) St Matt w H Trin *Blackb* 88-91; C Heyhouses on Sea 91-94; V Musbury from 94. *St Thomas's Vicarage, 1 Flaxmoss Close, Haslingden, Rossendale, Lancs BB4 4PX* Rossendale (01706) 213302

AIKMAN, Michael Alexander. b 64. St Andr Univ MA85 Rolle Coll PGCE86. Linc Th Coll BTh94. **d** 94 **p** 95. C Andover w Foxcott *Win* from 94. *2 Madrid Road, Andover, Hants SP10 1JR* Andover (01264) 359625

AINGE, David Stanley. b 47. Brasted Place Coll 68 Lon Univ DipTh74. Oak Hill Th Coll 70. **d** 73 **p** 74. C Bitterne Win 73-77; C Castle Church *Lich* 77-79; P-in-c Becontree St Alb *Chelmsf* 79-89; P-in-c Becontree St Jo 85-89; RD Barking and Dagenham 86-91; TR Becontree S 89-91; V Leyton St Mary w St Edw from 91; P-in-c Leyton St Luke from 91; RD Waltham Forest from 94. *St Mary's Vicarage, 4 Vicarage Road, London E10 5EA* 0181-539 7882

AINSCOUGH, Malcolm Ralph. b 52. Liv Univ BEd76 Liv Inst of Educn DASE85 Univ of Wales (Cardiff) DipTh87. St Mich Coll Llan 85. **d** 87 **p** 88. C Fleur-de-Lis *Mon* 87-90; C Chepstow 90-91; TV Cwmbran 91-95; V Newport St Steph and H Trin from 95. *St Stephen's Vicarage, Adeline Street, Newport, Gwent NP9 2HA* Newport (01633) 265192

AINSLEY, Canon Anthony Dixon. b 29. Or Coll Ox BA52 MA57 Univ of S Africa BA74. St Steph Ho Ox 53. **d** 55 **p** 56. S Africa 60-80; Adn All SS 73-80; Can St Jo Cathl Umtata 73-80; Hon Can from 81; Chapl Bordeaux w Riberac, Cahors, Duras etc Eur 81; V Blackpool St Steph *Blackb* 81-94; rtd 94. *The Reader's House, Slaidburn Road, Waddington, Clitheroe, Lancs BB7 3JA*

AINSLEY, John Alwyn. b 32. Univ of Wales (Lamp) BA53. St Mich Coll Llan 53. **d** 55 **p** 56. Dir Lay Tr & Community Service Worcs 72-76; Officer Gen Syn Bd of Educn 69-72; Dioc Youth and Community Officer *Ox* 76-90; rtd 94. *21 York Place, Worcester WR1 3DR* Worcester (01905) 612747

AINSLEY, Peter Dixon. b 32. OBE87. St Steph Ho Ox 58. **d** 60 **p** 61. C Bury St Thos *Man* 60-62; Chapl RN 62-87; Chapl HM Pris Liv 87-88; Chapl HM Pris Garth from 88. *HM Prison, Garth, Ulnes Walton Lane, Leyland, Lancs PR5 3NE* Preston (01772) 622722 Fax 622276

AINSWORTH, Canon David Lawrence. b 28. AKC54. **d** 55 **p** 56. R Northrepps *Nor* 63-93; R Sidestrand 63-93; P-in-c Roughton 75-79; Hon Can Nor Cathl 92-93; rtd 93; Perm to Offic *Nor* from 93. *36 Vicarage Street, North Walsham, Norfolk NR28 9DQ* North Walsham (01692) 405501

AINSWORTH, Mark John. b 64. Lon Univ MTh92. Wycliffe Hall Ox 86. **d** 89 **p** 90. C Chipping Barnet w Arkley *St Alb* 89-93; USA 93-95; TV Hemel Hempstead *St Alb* from 95. *St Mary's Vicarage, 51 Walnut Grove, Hemel Hempstead, Herts HP2 4AP* Hemel Hempstead (01442) 256708

AINSWORTH, Michael Ronald. b 50. K Coll Lon LLB71 LLM72 Trin Hall Cam BA74 MA79. Westcott Ho Cam 72. **d** 75 **p** 76. C Scotforth *Blackb* 75-78; Chapl St Martin's Coll of Educn 78-82; Chapl N Ord Course 82-89; Lic to Offic *Man* 82-89; R Withington 89-94; TR Worsley from 94. *The Rectory, Walkden Road, Worsley, Manchester M28 2WH* 0161-790 2362

AINSWORTH, Paul Henry. b 46. JP. Man Poly BA81. N Ord Course 85. **d** 88 **p** 89. NSM Salterhebble All SS *Wakef* 88-92; C Golcar from 92. *40 Longcroft Street, Golcar, Huddersfield, W Yorkshire HD7 4EA* Huddersfield (01484) 650480

AINSWORTH, Peter. b 34. Lon Univ BD57. Coll of Resurr Mirfield 69. **d** 70 **p** 71. C Leeds St Wilfrid *Ripon* 70-74; TV Tong *Bradf* 74-77; V Fairweather Green 77-94; rtd 94. *21 Park Avenue, Royston, Barnsley, S Yorkshire S71 4AD* Barnsley (01226) 726435

AINSWORTH-SMITH, Canon Ian Martin. b 41. Selw Coll Cam BA64 MA68. Westcott Ho Cam 64. **d** 66 **p** 67. C Mill Hill Jo Keble Ch *Lon* 66-69; USA 69-71; C Purley St Mark Woodcote *S'wark* 71-73; Chapl St Geo Hosp *Lon* from 73; Chapl Atkinson Morley Hosp *Lon* from 73; Hon Can *S'wark* Cathl *S'wark* from 95. *107 West Side, London SW4 9AZ* 0171-223 5302 or 0181-672 1255

AIRD, Donald Allan Ross. b 33. BSc84. AKC55. **d** 56 **p** 57. C N Wembley St Cuth *Lon* 56-59; C Sidmouth, Woolbrook and Salcombe Regis *Ex* 59-62; Youth Chapl *Ely* 62-68; V Swaffham Bulbeck 62-69; V Preston Ascension *Lon* 69-79; V St Marylebone St Mark Hamilton Terrace from 79. *St Mark's Vicarage, 114 Hamilton Terrace, London NW8 9UT* 0171-328 4373

AIRD, Robert Malcolm. b 31. Lon Univ BSc54. Westcott Ho Cam 75. **d** 77 **p** 78. C Burnham *B & W* 77-79; P-in-c Taunton Lyngford 79-84; V 84-87; R Dulverton and Brushford 87-94. *Arran Cottage, East Street, Chulmleigh, Devon EX18 7DD* Chulmleigh (01769) 581042

AIREY, Simon Christopher. b 60. Trin Coll Bris BA87. **d** 87 **p** 88. C Wilton *B & W* 87-90; Chapl Scargill Ho 90-93; TV Kingswood *Bris* from 93. *60 Lavers Close, Bristol BS15 2ZG* Bristol (0117) 935 2658

AISBITT, Joanne. *See* LISTER, Mrs Joanne

AISBITT, Michael. b 60. St Pet Coll Ox BA81 MA84. Westcott Ho Cam 81. **d** 84 **p** 85. C Norton St Mary *Dur* 84-87; C Kirkleatham *York* 87-90; V S Bank from 90. *The Vicarage, Normanby Road, South Bank, Middlesbrough, Cleveland TS6 6TB* Middlesbrough (01642) 453679

AISBITT, Osmond John. b 35. St Chad's Coll *Dur* BA57 DipTh61. **d** 61 **p** 62. C Ashington *Newc* 61-64; C Blyth St Mary 64-68; V Cleckheaton St Jo *Wakef* 68-75; V Horbury 75-78; V Horbury w Horbury Bridge from 78. *St Peter's Vicarage, Horbury, Wakefield, W Yorkshire WF4 6AS* Wakefield (01924) 273477

AISH, Canon Norman Cyril Roslyn. b 20. St Steph Ho Ox 52. **d** 54 **p** 55. V Hyde Common *Win* 62-73; Adv Soc Resp 73-85; Hon Can *Win* Cathl 83-85; rtd 85; Perm to Offic *Win* from 85. *51 Pearce Avenue, Poole, Dorset BH14 8EL* Parkstone (01202) 742077

AITCHISON, Charles Baillie. b 45. ACP69 Bede Coll *Dur* TCert67 Newc Univ DAES74 New Coll *Dur* BEd85. Local NSM Course 85. **d** 93 **p** 93. NSM Peebles *Edin* from 93; NSM Innerleithen from 93. *Milestone Cottage, Princes Street, Innerleithen, Peeblesshire EH44 6JT* Innerleithen (01896) 831491

AITCHISON, John Frederick. b 13. Ripon Hall Ox 66. **d** 67 **p** 68. C Boldmere *Birm* 67-70; C Pembury *Roch* 70-73; V Bassingbourn *Ely* 73-92; V Whaddon 74-92; rtd 93. *Merlewood, Henham Road, Debden Green, Saffron Walden, Essex CB11 3LX* Thaxted (01371) 831412

AITKEN, Christopher William Mark. b 53. *Dur* Univ BA75. Westcott Ho Cam 76. **d** 79 **p** 80. C Finchley St Mary *Lon* 79-82; C Radlett *St Alb* 82-85; V Sprowston *Nor* 85-90; R Beeston St Andr 85-90; R Sprowston w Beeston 90-93; Chapl Sherborne Sch *Dorset* from 93. *Rosslyn House, Acreman Street, Sherborne, Dorset DT9 3NU* Sherborne (01935) 813846

AITKEN, Leslie Robert. b 19. MBE76. St Aid Coll *Dur.* **d** 46 **p** 47. R Alvechurch *Worc* 64-84; rtd 84; Perm to Offic *Cant* from 84. *36 Ethelbert Road, Birchington, Kent CT7 9PY* Thanet (01843) 41877

AITKEN, Leslie St John Robert. b 41. Open Univ BA75. Cranmer Hall *Dur* 62. **d** 65 **p** 66. C Worc St Barn w Ch Ch *Worc* 65-69; C Halesowen 69-73; P-in-c Wyche 73-80; R Blackley St Pet *Man* from 80; Chapl Booth Hall Hosp *Man* from 80. *St Peter's Rectory, 1161 Rochdale Road, Manchester M9 2FP* 0161-740 2124

AITKEN, William Stuart. b 35. FCFI MSIAD CertEd. Cant Sch of Min 79. **d** 82 **p** 83. NSM Roch 82-86; C Orpington All SS 86-88; R Burham and Wouldham from 88; Dioc Communications Officer from 88. *The Rectory, 266 Rochester Road, Burham, Rochester, Kent ME1 3RJ* Medway (01634) 666862 Fax 868749

AITON, Robert Neilson (Bob). b 36. Univ of Wales BA59 DipEd60. Chich Th Coll 74. **d** 76 **p** 77. C E Grinstead St Swithun *Chich* 76-83; R Lavant 83-90; V Durrington from 90; Chapl St Barn Hospice Worthing from 90. *The Vicarage, Bramble Lane, Worthing, W Sussex BN13 3JE* Worthing (01903) 693499

AIZLEWOOD, Geoffrey Rymer. b 27. St Aid Birkenhead. **d** 61 **p** 62. V Liv St Mark Edge Lane *Liv* 69-75; rtd 75. *c/o Mrs L Threlfall, 20 Brereton Avenue, Wavertree, Liverpool L15 6TJ* 0151-228 5728 or 733 5199

AJETUNMOBI, Jacob Ademola. b 48. Lon Bible Coll BA80. Igbaja Sem Nigeria BTh73. **d** 83 **p** 83. Nigeria 83-89; Chapl to Nigerian Students in UK (CMS) from 89; Miss Partner CMS from 89. *82 Keslake Road, London NW6 6DG* 0181-969 2379 or 0171-793 8257 Fax 0171-401 3215

AKEHURST, Peter Russell. b 16. Reading Univ BSc38 Trin Hall Cam. Wycliffe Hall Ox. **d** 48 **p** 49. S Africa 51-70; R Didsbury St Jas *Man* 70-74; V Totland Bay *Portsm* 75-81; rtd 81; Perm to Offic *Bris* 86-89; Perm to Offic *Ox* 89-90. *20 Emmbrook Court, Woolacombe Drive, Reading RG6 5TZ* Reading (01734) 862946

AKERMAN, Roy. b 37. ALCD63. **d** 63 **p** 64. C E Ham St Paul *Chelmsf* 63-67; C Hornchurch St Andr 67-69; Area Sec (Dios Ox and Win) CMS 69-75; V Ollerton *S'well* 75-79; V Boughton 76-79; V N and S Leverton from 79. *The Vicarage, South Gore Lane, North Leverton, Retford, Notts DN22 0AA* Gainsborough (01427) 880882

AKIN-FLENLEY, Kenneth Bernard. b 17. TD62 and Bar 69. St Pet Hall Ox BA41 MA43. Wycliffe Hall Ox 44. **d** 45 **p** 46. CF (TA) 49-80; V Bathford *B & W* 50-79; Perm to Offic from 79; rtd 82. *Mudros, 85 Dovers Park, Bathford, Bath BA1 7UE* Bath (01225) 858763

AKKER, Derek Alexander. b 46. Bradf Univ MA83. N Ord Course 85. **d** 88 **p** 89. C Mossley *Man* 88-90; C Bury St Pet 90-92; V Lever Bridge from 92. *St Stephen's Vicarage, Radcliffe Road, Bolton BL2 1NZ* Bolton (01204) 28300

ALBAN-JONES, Timothy Morris. b 64. Warw Univ BA85. Ripon Coll Cuddesdon 83. **d** 88 **p** 89. C Tupsley *Heref* 88-93; P-in-c Weston-under-Penyard w Hope Mansel and The Lea 93; TV Ross w Brampton Abbotts, Bridstow, Peterstow etc from 93. *The Rectory, Weston under Penyard, Ross-on-Wye, Herefordshire HR9 7QA* Ross-on-Wye (01989) 62926

ALBANY, Edric George. b 06. Local Minl Tr Course. **d** 39 **p** 41. V Goff's Oak St Jas *St Alb* 56-59; Australia from 59; rtd 73. *258 Moline House, Jeanes Road, Karrinyup, W Australia 6018* Perth (9) 341-3099

ALBANY, John Brian. b 10. ALCD40. **d** 40 **p** 41. Australia from 49; Hon Can Perth 76-78; rtd 79. *48 Parry House, Lesmurdie, W Australia 6076* Perth (9) 291-7177

ALBIN, Colin Leslie. b 51. Cov Poly BA75 DCG78. Cranmer Hall *Dur* 89. **d** 91 **p** 92. C Chadderton Ch Ch *Man* 91-94; V Witton *Blackb* from 94; Bp's Adv on Inter-Faith Relns from 94. *St Mark's Vicarage, Buncer Lane, Blackburn BB2 6SY* Blackburn (01254) 676615

ALBON, Lionel Frederick Shapland. b 31. CEng MIMechE60. St Alb Minl Tr Scheme 80. **d** 83 **p** 84. NSM Bromham w Oakley *St Alb* 83-88; NSM Bromham w Oakley and Stagsden 88-89; Ind Chapl from 89. *10 Turnberry Walk, Bedford MK41 8AZ* Bedford (01234) 346668

ALBY, Harold Oriel. b 45. Witwatersrand Univ BA68 MA77. Sarum Th Coll 68. **d** 71 **p** 72. S Africa 71-89; P-in-c Forton *Portsm* from 89. *The Vicarage, 10 Spring Garden Lane, Gosport, Hants PO12 1HY* Gosport (01705) 581965

ALCOCK, Edwin James. b 31. AKC57. **d** 58 **p** 59. C Old St Pancras w Bedf New Town St Matt *Lon* 58-62; C Hillingdon St Andr 62-81; V N Acton St Gabr from 81. *The Vicarage, 15 Balfour Road, London W3 0DG* 0181-992 5938

ALDCROFT, Malcolm Charles. b 44. Lon Univ DSocSc68 Liv Univ DASS71 Leeds Univ MA94. N Ord Course 79. **d** 82 **p** 83. NSM Alverthorpe *Wakef* 82-85; NSM Horbury Junction from 85; Perm to Offic from 93; Sub Chapl HM Pris New Hall from 94. *47 Stannard Well Lane, Horbury, Wakefield, W Yorkshire WF4 6BL* Wakefield (01924) 261977

ALDER, Eric Reginald Alfred. b 23. St Luke's Coll *Ex* 47 Lon Univ BA55 Cam Inst of Educn 64. Chich Th Coll 70. **d** 71 **p** 72. C Deal St Leon w Sholden *Cant* 72-80; P-in-c Woodnesborough 80-83; P-in-c Worth 80-83; P-in-c Staple 80-83; V Woodnesborough w Worth and Staple 83-90; rtd 90. *3 Hackington Terrace, Canterbury, Kent CT2 7HE* Canterbury (01227) 766783

ALDER, William. b 09. Ripon Hall Ox. **d** 55 **p** 56. R Silchester *Win* 59-81; rtd 81; Perm to Offic *Ox* from 81. *17 Isis Close, Long Hanborough, Oxford OX8 8JN* Freeland (01993) 882198

ALDERMAN, John David. b 49. Man Univ BA71 Selw Coll Cam BA79. Ridley Hall Cam 77. **d** 80 **p** 81. C Hartley Wintney, Elvetham, Winchfield etc *Win* 80-83; V Bursledon 83-92; R Dibden from 92. *The Rectory, Beaulieu Road, Dibden Purlieu, Southampton SO4 5PT* Hythe (01703) 843204

ALDERSLEY, Ian. b 42. AIMLS65 FIMLS68. Wycliffe Hall Ox 89. **d** 91 **p** 92. C Allestree *Derby* 91-94; R Brailsford w Shirley and Osmaston w Edlaston from 94. *The Rectory, Church Lane, Brailsford, Derby DE6 3BX* Ashbourne (01335) 360362

ALDERSON, Albert George. b 22. K Coll Lon 46. **d** 50 **p** 51. P-in-c S Shields St Fran *Dur* 69-72; V S Shields St Jude 69-72; R Penshaw 72-79; P-in-c Bilsdale Midcable *York* 79-80; P-in-c Hawnby w Old Byland 79-80; P-in-c Scawton w Cold Kirby 79-80; R Upper Ryedale 80-91; rtd 91. *11 Bells Court, Helmsley, York YO6 5BA* Helmsley (01439) 712631

ALDERSON, Christopher Derek. b 21. AKC55. **d** 55 **p** 56. V Dunster *B & W* 67-82; P-in-c Brompton Regis w Upton and Skilgate 82-83; R 83-86; rtd 86; Perm to Offic *B & W* 86-90. *377 Old Commercial Road, Portsmouth PO1 4QL* Portsmouth (01705) 821032

ALDERSON, Mrs Maureen. b 40. W Midl Minl Tr Course 90. **d** 93 **p** 94. NSM Yardley St Cypr Hay Mill *Birm* from 93. *70 Thurlston Avenue, Solihull, W Midlands B92 7NZ* 0121-742 7363

ALDERSON, Roger James. b 47. Lon Univ BD70 AKC71. **d** 71 **p** 72. C Lawton Moor *Man* 71-75; C Barton w Peel Green 75-76; R Heaton Norris St Thos 76-85; V Bedf Leigh 85-92. *St Joseph's College Farm, Stony Brow, Roby Mill, Upholland, Skelmersdale, Lancs WN8 0QD* Up Holland (01695) 627474

ALDERTON-FORD, Jonathan Laurence. b 57. Nottm Univ BTh85. St Jo Coll Nottm 82. **d** 85 **p** 86. C Gaywood, Bawsey and Mintlyn *Nor* 85-87; C Herne Bay Ch Ch *Cant* 87-90; Min Bury St Edmunds St Mary *St E* 90-91; Min Moreton Hall Estate St Edm CD 91-94; V Bury St Edmunds Ch Ch from 94. *18 Heldhaw Road, Bury St Edmunds, Suffolk IP32 7ER* Bury St Edmunds (01284) 769956

ALDIS, Canon John Arnold. b 43. Univ of Wales BA65 Lon Univ BD67. Clifton Th Coll 68. **d** 69 **p** 70. C Tonbridge SS Pet and Paul *Roch* 69-72; C St Marylebone All So w SS Pet and Jo *Lon* 72-77; Overseas Service Adv and Under Sec CMS 77-80; C Welling *Roch* 77-80; V Leic H Trin w St Jo *Leic* 80-89; Hon Can Leic Cathl 88-89; Hong Kong from 89. *St Andrew's Church, 138 Nathan Road, Tsim Sha Tsui, Kowloon, Hong Kong* Hong Kong (852) 367-1478 Fax 367-6562

ALDIS, Preb John Steadman. b 07. Magd Coll Cam BA28 MA42. Cuddesdon Coll 42. **d** 43 **p** 44. Preb St Paul's Cathl *Lon* 63-75; Chapl to Bp Edmonton 71-75; Hon C Edmonton St Mary w St Jo from 72; rtd 75; Perm to Offic *Chich* from 92. *College of St Barnabas, Blackberry Lane, Lingfield, Surrey RH7 6NJ* Dormans Park (01342) 870648

ALDOUS, Alexander Charles Victor. b 56. Southn Univ BA81 K Alfred's Coll Win PGCE83. S Dios Minl Tr Scheme 91. **d** 94 **p** 95. Chapl Oundle Sch Pet from 94. *Oundle School, New Street, Oundle, Peterborough PE8 4EN* Oundle (01832) 273536

ALDRIDGE, Christopher John. b 35. Trin Hall Cam BA57 MA61. Ripon Hall Ox 59. **d** 60 **p** 61. C Coalville *Leic* 60-64; P-in-c Clifton St Fran *S'well* 64-72; V Gospel Lane St Mich *Birm* 72-90; V Selly Oak St Mary from 90. *St Mary's Vicarage, Bristol Road, Birmingham B29 6ND* 0121-472 0250

ALDRIDGE, Harold. b 35. Keble Coll Ox BA61 MA71. Chich Th Coll 60. **d** 62 **p** 63. C Notting Hill All SS w St Columb *Lon* 62-65; C Kensington St Mary Abbots w St Geo 65-69; Chapl Beech Hill Sch Macclesfield 69-82; TV Staveley and Barrow Hill *Derby* 82-86; P-in-c Longford 86-89; P-in-c Radbourne 86-89; P-in-c Dalbury, Long Lane and Trusley 86-89; V Braddan *S & M* 89-94. *21 Windermere Drive, Onchan, Douglas, Isle of Man* Douglas (01624) 626201

ALDRIDGE, Harold John. b 42. Lon Univ DipTh67. Oak Hill Th Coll 65. **d** 69 **p** 70. C Rawtenstall St Mary *Man* 69-76; CMJ 72-76; C Woodford Wells *Chelmsf* 76-79; TV Washfield, Stoodleigh, Withleigh etc *Ex* 79-86; V Burton *Ches* 86-90; Chapl Clatterbridge Hosp Wirral from 86; P-in-c Shotwick *Ches* 90; V Burton and Shotwick from 91; Dioc Clergy Widows and Retirement Officer from 91. *The Vicarage, Vicarage Lane, Burton, South Wirral L64 5TJ* 0151-336 4070

ALDRIDGE, Mark Richard. b 58. Oak Hill Th Coll BA89. **d** 89 **p** 90. C Come Down w Monkton Combe and S Stoke *B & W* 89-90; C Woodside Park St Barn *Lon* 90-94; P-in-c Cricklewood St Gabr and St Mich from 94. *St Gabriel's Vicarage, 156 Anson Road, London NW2 6BH* 0181-452 6305

ALEXANDER, David Graham. b 61. Ridley Hall Cam 87. **d** 89 **p** 90. C New Barnet St Jas *St Alb* 89-93; C Northwood H Trin *Lon* from 93. *74 Knoll Crescent, Northwood, Middx HA6 1HY* Northwood (01923) 829375

ALEXANDER, Douglas Keith. b 45. Ripon Coll Cuddesdon 87. **d** 89 **p** 90. C Thorpe St Matt *Nor* 89-92; P-in-c Lakenham St Alb from 92; Chapl Nor City Coll from 92. *St Alban's Vicarage, Eleanor Road, Norwich NR1 2RE* Norwich (01603) 621843

ALEXANDER, Hugh Crighton. b 03. Qu Coll Cam BA24 MA30. Ridley Hall Cam 29. **d** 30 **p** 31. R Hazelbury Bryan w Stoke Wake etc *Sarum* 64-71; rtd 71. *The Vicarage Flat, 99 Water Lane, Oakington, Cambridge CB4 5AL* Cambridge (01223) 232396

ALEXANDER, James Crighton. b 43. Qu Coll Cam BA65 MA69. Cuddesdon Coll 68. **d** 68 **p** 69. C Much Wenlock w

Bourton *Heref* 68-72; V Oakington *Ely* from 72; P-in-c Dry Drayton 85-95. *The Vicarage, 99 Water Lane, Oakington, Cambridge CB4 5AL* Cambridge (01223) 232396

ALEXANDER, Canon James Douglas (Jim). b 27. Linc Th Coll 57. **d** 58 **p** 59. C Frodingham *Linc* 58-61; V Alvingham w N and S Cockerington 61-65; V Keddington 61-65; R Gunhouse w Burringham 65-70; R Peterhead *Ab* 70-76; R Aber St Mary from 76; Miss to Seamen from 76; Can St Andr Cathl *Ab* from 79; Chapl HM Pris Aber from 82; P-in-c Cove Bay *Ab* 85-90. *St Mary's Rectory, 28 Stanley Street, Aberdeen AB1 6UR* Aberdeen (01224) 584123

ALEXANDER, Jane Louise. See MACLAREN, Mrs Jane Louise

ALEXANDER, Julius Erik Louis. b 66. Guildf Co Coll of Tech BTEC NC84 BTEC HNC86. Wycliffe Hall Ox 89. **d** 92 **p** 93. C Hoole *Ches* 92-94; C Offerton from 94. *11 Martham Drive, Offerton, Stockport, Cheshire SK2 5XZ* 0161-487 2861

ALEXANDER, Michael George. b 47. Sarum & Wells Th Coll 74. **d** 77 **p** 78. C Wednesfield *Lich* 77-80; C Tettenhall Wood 80-83; Distr Min Tettenhall Wood (Ecum Ch) 83-85; Dioc Adv in Adult and Youth Educn *Derby* 85-89; V Hazelwood 85-89; V Turnditch 85-89; Par Educn Adv (Laity Development) from 89. *14 Chevin Road, Duffield, Belper, Derbyshire DE56 4DS* Derby (01332) 840817

ALEXANDER, Norman William. b 27. Chich Th Coll 54. **d** 56 **p** 57. R Mutford w Rushmere w Gisleham w N Cove w Barnby *Nor* 69-74; R W Winch 74-81; V Frensham *Guildf* 81-84; V Hemsby *Nor* 84-89; RD Flegg (Gt Yarmouth) 87-89; rtd 89. *12 Planters Grove, Oulton Broad, Lowestoft, Suffolk NR33 9QL* Lowestoft (01502) 562144

ALEXANDER, Peter John. b 36. CQSW73 DMA74. Oak Hill Th Coll 92. **d** 95. NSM Aspenden, Buntingford and Westmill *St Alb* from 95. *14 Meadow View, Buntingford, Herts SG9 9SQ* Royston (01763) 272882

ALEXANDER, Robert. b 37. Lon Univ LLB60 St Cath Coll Ox BA62. St Steph Ho Ox 60. **d** 63 **p** 64. C Kensington St Mary Abbots w St Geo *Lon* 63-68; C Notting Hill 71-74; TV 74-79; Australia from 79. *5/31 Alexandra Street, Drummoyne, NSW, Australia 2047* Sydney (2) 232-3592

ALEXANDER, Wilfred Robert Donald. b 35. TCD BA58 MA80. **d** 63 **p** 63. C Raheny w Coolock *D & G* 63-67; Min Can St Patr Cathl Dub 65-67; Hon C Herne Hill St Paul *S'wark* 68-70; Asst Master Gosforth Gr Sch 71-76; Hon C Long Benton St Mary *Newc* 74-76; Chapl SS Mary and Anne's Sch Abbots Bromley 76-80; V Cauldon *Lich* 80-83; V Waterfall 80-83; P-in-c Calton 80-83; P-in-c Grindon 80-83; V Blackb St Luke w St Phil *Blackb* 83-89; V Rainhill *Liv* 89-92; R Croft w Southworth from 92. *The Rectory, 76 New Lane, Croft, Warrington WA3 0ES* Culcheth (01925) 762294

ALFLATT, Malcolm Edward. b 35. FBA68 Bp's Univ Lennoxville BA64 Lon Univ BD69 Univ of New Brunswick MA74. Wells Th Coll 64. **d** 66 **p** 68. C Leeds St Marg *Ripon* 66-67; Canada 67-81; C Sheff St Oswald *Sheff* 81-83; V Sheff Abbeydale St Pet 83-93. *1 Farndon Cottages, Romanby, Northallerton, N Yorkshire DL7 8HE* Northallerton (01609) 771637

ALFORD, John. b 35. Nottm Univ BSc58 NDA59 DipEd76. Qu Coll Birm 74. **d** 77 **p** 78. NSM Edgmond *Lich* 77-87; C Cheadle 87-88; C Cheadle w Freehay 88-89; Chapl to RD Alcester 89-95; P-in-c Wootton Wawen *Cov* 89-95; P-in-c Ellington *Ely* from 95; P-in-c Grafham from 95; P-in-c Easton from 95; P-in-c Spaldwick w Barham and Woolley from 95. *The Vicarage, Parson's Drive, Ellington, Huntingdon, Cambs PE18 0AB* Huntingdon (01480) 891695

ALGAR, John Herbert. b 29. Tyndale Hall Bris 54. **d** 57 **p** 58. C Stapenhill w Cauldwell *Derby* 57-61; C Willesborough w Hinxhill *Cant* 61-69; V Tipton St Martin *Lich* 69-89; P-in-c Tipton St Paul 86-89; V Tipton St Martin and St Paul from 89. *St Martin's Vicarage, Tipton, W Midlands DY4 7PR* 0121-557 1902

ALKER, Adrian. b 49. Wadh Coll Ox BA70 Lanc Univ MA71. Ripon Coll Cuddesdon 77. **d** 79 **p** 80. C W Derby St Mary *Liv* 79-83; Dioc Youth Officer *Carl* 83-88; V Sheff St Mark Broomhall 88-92; V Sheff St Mark Broomhill from 92; Dioc Dir of In-Service Tr from 90. *St Mark's Vicarage, 4 St Mark's Crescent, Sheffield S10 2SG* Sheffield (0114) 267 0362

ALLABY, Miss Mary Dorothea. b 60. Bedf Coll Lon BA82 W Sussex Inst of HE PGCE83. Trin Coll Bris DipHE90 ADPS92. **d** 92 **p** 94. Par Dn Ipsley *Worc* 92-94; C from 94. *31 Kinnersley Close, Redditch, Worcs B98 0LB* Redditch (01527) 521552

ALLABY, Simon Arnold Kenworthy. b 65. St Chad's Coll Dur BA88. Trin Coll Bris 88. **d** 90 **p** 91. C Preston on Tees *Dur* 90-93; C Ches le Street from 93. *16 Park Road North, Chester le Street, Co Durham DH3 3SD* 0191-388 6801

ALLAIN CHAPMAN, Ms Justine Penelope Heathcote. b 67. K Coll Lon BA88 PGCE89 Nottm Univ MDiv93. Linc Th

Coll 91. **d** 93 **p** 94. Par Dn Forest Hill *S'wark* 93-94; C from 94. *12 Ewelme Road, London SE23 3BH* 0181-699 1588

ALLAN, Andrew John. b 47. Westcott Ho Cam 76. **d** 79 **p** 80. C Whitstable All SS w St Pet *Cant* 79-84; C Whitstable 84-86; P-in-c Littlebourne 86-87; P-in-c Ickham w Wickhambreaux and Stodmarsh 86-87; R Littlebourne and Ickham w Wickhambreaux etc from 87. *The Vicarage, Church Road, Littlebourne, Canterbury, Kent CT3 1UA* Canterbury (01227) 721233

ALLAN, Canon Archibald Blackie. b 35. Edin Th Coll 57. **d** 60 **p** 61. C Aber St Jo *Ab* 60-63; R from 82; Chapl St Paul's Cathl Dundee *Bre* 63-68; P-in-c Aber St Clem *Ab* 68-76; Vice-Provost St Andr Cathl 76-82; Can St Andr Cathl from 88. *15 Ashley Road, Aberdeen AB1 6RU* Aberdeen (01224) 591527

ALLAN, Arthur Ashford. b 18. Kelham Th Coll. **d** 44 **p** 45. V Brislington St Luke *Bris* 67-76; P-in-c Coalpit Heath 76-80; rtd 80; Perm to Offic *Ex* from 83. *4 Homer Close, Bratton Fleming, Barnstaple, Devon EX31 4TD* Brayford (01598) 710556

ALLAN, Donald James. b 35. Sarum & Wells Th Coll 63. **d** 65 **p** 66. C Royton St Paul *Man* 65-71; V Middleton Junction 71-78; P-in-c Finmere w Mixbury *Ox* 78-83; R Finmere w Mixbury, Cottisford, Hardwick etc 83; Chapl Westcliff Hosp 83-87; V Westcliff St Andr *Chelmsf* 83-87; R Goldhanger w Lt Totham from 87. *The Rectory, Church Street, Goldhanger, Maldon, Essex CM9 8AR* Maldon (01621) 88740

ALLAN, Jeanette Winifred. b 40. ALA63. St And Dioc Tr Course 79. **dss** 81 **d** 86 **p** 94. Hillfoot's Team Min 81-86; NSM Bridge of Allan *St And* 86-88; NSM Dunblane from 88. *Pernettya, Sinclairs Street, Dunblane, Perthshire FK15 0AH* Dunblane (01786) 822037

ALLAN, John William. b 58. St Olaf Coll Minnesota BA80 Bris Univ PhD90. Trin Luth Sem Ohio MDiv84 Qu Coll Birm 90. **d** 91 **p** 92. In Luth Ch (USA) 84-86; C Newport w Longford and Chetwynd *Lich* 91-94; P-in-c Longdon from 94; Lich Local Min Adv from 94. *The Vicarage, Longdon, Rugeley, Staffs WS15 4PS* Armitage (01543) 490307

ALLAN, Peter Burnaby. b 52. Clare Coll Cam BA74 MA78 St Jo Coll Dur BA82. Cranmer Hall Dur 80. **d** 83 **p** 84. C Chaddesden St Mary *Derby* 83-86; C Brampton St Thos 86-89; TV Halesworth w Linstead, Chediston, Holton etc *St E* 89-94; TR Trunch *Nor* from 94. *The Rectory, 1 Gimingham Road, Mundesley, Norwich NR11 8DG* Mundesley (01263) 720520

ALLAN, Peter George. b 50. Wadh Coll Ox BA72 MA76 Leeds Univ DipTh74. Coll of Resurr Mirfield 72. **d** 75 **p** 76. C Stevenage St Geo *St Alb* 75-78; Chapl Wadh Coll Ox 78-82; C Ox St Mary V w St Cross and St Pet *Ox* 78-82; CR from 85. *House of the Resurrection, Mirfield, W Yorkshire WF14 0BN* Mirfield (01924) 494318

ALLANDER, William Edward Morgell Kidd. b 15. TCD BA37 MA40. CITC 37. **d** 38 **p** 39. C Atherstone *Cov* 64-73; I Rathcooney Union *C, C & R* 73-88; rtd 88. *12 Richmond Estate, Blackrock, Cork, Irish Republic* Cork (21) 293352

ALLARD, John Ambrose. b 30. Bps' Coll Cheshunt 63. **d** 65 **p** 66. P-in-c Rawreth w Rettendon *Chelmsf* 69-70; R 70-72; V Barkingside St Fran 73-84; V E Ham St Geo 84-86; V St Osyth 86-95; rtd 95. *3 John Shepherd Road, Fressingfield, Eye, Suffolk IP21 5SW* Eye (01379) 586627

ALLARD, Roy Frank. b 38. E Anglian Minl Tr Course 86. **d** 89 **p** 90. NSM Ipswich All Hallows *St E* from 89. *6 Mandy Close, Ipswich IP4 5JE* Ipswich (01473) 724470

ALLARD, Victor James. b 13. S'wark Ord Course 65. **d** 68 **p** 69. Hd Master Isleworth C of E Primary Sch 59-73; C Isleworth All SS *Lon* 68-73; C Stansted Mountfitchet *Chelmsf* 73-80; C Mayfield *Chich* 80-83; rtd 83; Perm to Offic *Leic* from 83. *1 Oakley Close, Shepshed, Loughborough, Leics LE12 9AS* Shepshed (01509) 502745

ALLARDICE, Alexander Edwin. b 49. SRN. Chich Th Coll 73. **d** 76 **p** 77. C Rugeley *Lich* 76-79; C Felixstowe St Jo *St E* 79-81; TV Ipswich St Fran 81-87; C Lostwithiel *Truro* 87-90; C Boconnoc w Bradoc 87-90; C St Veep 87-90; C St Winnow 87-90; R Lostwithiel, St Winnow w St Nectan's Chpl etc from 90. *The Rectory, 3 Springfield Close, Lostwithiel, Cornwall PL22 0ER* Bodmin (01208) 873448

ALLBERRY, William Alan John. b 49. Ch Coll Cam BA70 MA71. Ripon Coll Cuddesdon 84. **d** 86 **p** 87. C Brixton St Matt *S'wark* 86-90; V Wandsworth St Paul from 90. *St Paul's Vicarage, Augustus Road, London SW19 6EW* 0181-788 2024

ALLCHIN, Canon Arthur Macdonald (Donald). b 30. Ch Ch Ox BA51 MA55 BLitt56 Univ of Wales 93. Bucharest Th Inst Hon DD77 Cuddesdon Coll 54. **d** 56 **p** 57. Warden Community of Sisters of the Love of God Ox 72-73; Can Res and Lib Cant Cathl *Cant* 73-87; Dir St Theosevia Cen for Chr Spirituality 87-94; Hon Prof Univ of N Wales Ban from 93; rtd 94. *1 Tremt Y Wyddfa, Bangor, Gwynedd LL57 2ER* Bangor (01248) 353744

ALLCHIN, Miss Maureen Ann. b 50. Edge Hill Coll of HE CertEd71 Sussex Univ MA93. S Dios Minl Tr Scheme 88. **d** 91

p 94. Hd of Faculty Steyning Gr Sch 79-92; NSM Southwick *Chich* 91-92; C Storrington 93-95; TV Bridport *Sarum* from 95. *The Vicarage, King's Head Hill, Bridport, Dorset DT6 3DZ* Bridport (01308) 458788

ALLCOCK, David. b 28. Coll of Resurr Mirfield. **d** 66 **p** 67. C Shrewsbury St Chad *Lich* 66-70; Chapl K Coll Taunton 70-78; Chapl Shrewsbury Sch 78-93; rtd 93. *Elwy House, Dalydd Terrace, Betws y Coed, Gwynedd LL24 0BU* Betws-y-Coed (01690) 710146

ALLCOCK, Jeremy Robert. b 63. Trin Coll Bris BA92. **d** 92 **p** 93. C Walthamstow St Luke *Chelmsf* from 92. *23 Russell Road, London E17 6QY* 0181-521 3573

ALLCOCK, Peter Michael. b 37. Oak Hill Th Coll 65. **d** 68 **p** 69. C Upper Tulse Hill St Matthias *S'wark* 68-71; C Dunkeswell and Dunkeswell Abbey *Ex* 71-72; P-in-c Luppitt 72-75; P-in-c Monkton 72-75; V Okehampton w Inwardleigh 75-80; TV Solihull *Birm* 80-85; V Highbury New Park St Aug *Lon* from 85. *St Augustine's Vicarage, 108 Highbury New Park, London N5 2DR* 0171-226 6870

ALLDRIT, Nicolas Sebastian Fitz-Ansculf. b 41. St Edm Hall Ox BA63 MA69 DPhil69. Cuddesdon Coll 72. **d** 72 **p** 73. C Limpsfield and Titsey *S'wark* 72-81; Tutor Linc Th Coll from 81; Sub-Warden from 88. *The Theological College, Drury Lane, Lincoln LN1 3BP* Lincoln (01522) 537339

ALLEN, Andrew Stephen. b 55. MPS Nottm Univ BPharm77. St Steph Ho Ox 78. **d** 81 **p** 82. C Gt Ilford St Mary *Chelmsf* 81-83; C Luton All SS w St Pet *St Alb* 83-86; TV Chambersbury (Hemel Hempstead) 86-91; TV Brixham w Churston Ferrers and Kingswear *Ex* from 91. *The Vicarage, 41 Greenway Road, Galmpton, Brixham, Devon TQ5 0LZ* Churston (01803) 846127

ALLEN, Brian. b 58. Oak Hill NSM Course 90. **d** 93 **p** 94. Hon C Norwood *S'wark* 93-94; Hon C W Norwood, St Luke from 94. *11A Queen Mary Road, London SE19 3NN* 0181-670 2227

ALLEN, Brian Stanley. b 24. Roch Th Coll 65. **d** 67 **p** 68. C Roch 67-74; P-in-c Drypool St Jo *York* 74-80; TV Drypool 80; V Marlpool *Derby* 80-87; rtd 87. *22 Sycamore Terrace, York YO3 7DN* York (01904) 653418

ALLEN, Bruce Owen. b 14. Lon Univ BA37. Clifton Th Coll 37. **d** 39 **p** 40. V Topcliffe w Dalton and Dishforth *York* 65-81; rtd 81; Perm to Offic *Linc* from 81. *Minerva, Bormans Lane, North Thoresby, Grimsby, S Humberside DN36 5RQ* Grimsby (01472) 840425

ALLEN, Christopher Dennis. b 50. Fitzw Coll Cam BA73 MA77. Cuddesdon Coll 74. **d** 76 **p** 77. C Kettering St Andr *Pet* 76-79; C Pet H Spirit Bretton 79-82; R Bardney *Linc* 82-87; V Knighton St Mary Magd *Leic* from 87. *The Vicarage, Church Lane, Knighton, Leicester LE2 3WG* Leicester (0116) 270 5730

ALLEN, Christopher Leslie. b 56. Leeds Univ BA78. St Jo Coll Nottm 79. **d** 80 **p** 81. C Birm St Martin *Birm* 80-85; Tr and Ed Pathfinders 85-89; Hd 89-92; Midl Youth Dept Co-ord CPAS 85-89; Hon C Selly Park St Steph and St Wulstan *Birm* 86-92; V Hamstead St Bernard 92-95. *33 Endwood Court, Handsworth Wood Road, Birmingham B20 2RZ* 0121-515 2959

ALLEN, David. b 38. Llan Dioc Tr Scheme. **d** 76 **p** 77. C Fairwater *Llan* 76-84; Lic to Offic from 84; Chapl The Bp of Llan High Sch from 84. *16 Restways Close, Llandaff, Cardiff CF5 2SB* Cardiff (01222) 554334

ALLEN, David Edward. b 70. Van Mildert Coll Dur BSc91. Ripon Coll Cuddesdon BA94. **d** 95. C Grantham *Linc* from 95. *26 Castlegate, Grantham, Lincs NG31 6SW* Grantham (01476) 64351

ALLEN, Derek Milton. b 45. Bradf Univ BTech67 Man Univ BD80. Oak Hill Th Coll 80. **d** 81 **p** 82. C Chadderton Ch Ch *Man* 81-84; V Roundthorn 84-94. *47 Malvern Avenue, Redcar, Cleveland TS10 4AJ* Redcar (01642) 488023

ALLEN, Preb Donovan Bawden. b 14. Keble Coll Ox BA36 MA40. Westcott Ho Cam 36. **d** 38 **p** 39. Chapl Cross Ho Hosp Shropshire 68-80; R Berrington and Betton Strange *Heref* 68-80; Preb Heref Cathl 73-80; rtd 80; Perm to Offic *Lich* from 80; Perm to Offic *Heref* from 81. *13 Swan Hill, Shrewsbury SY1 1NL* Shrewsbury (01743) 352412

ALLEN, Edward Charles. b 16. Bps' Coll Cheshunt 47. **d** 50 **p** 51. V E Molesey St Mary *Guildf* 60-87; rtd 87. *11 Cootham Green, Storrington, Pulborough, W Sussex RH20 4JW* Storrington (01903) 745932

ALLEN, Frank Brian. b 47. K Coll Lon BD AKC71. **d** 71 **p** 72. C Leam Lane *Dur* 71-74; C Tynemouth Ch Ch *Newc* 74-78; Chapl Newc Poly 78-84; V Newc St Hilda 84-88; Chapl Nottm Mental Illness & Psychiatric Unit 88-89; Chapl St Nic Hosp Newc from 89; Chapl Newc Mental Health Unit from 89. *43 Cherryburn Gardens, Newcastle upon Tyne NE4 9UQ* 0191-274 9335 or 213 0151

ALLEN, Frank John. b 17. FRIC58 Aston Univ BSc66 Birm Univ DipTh75. Qu Coll Birm 75. **d** 76 **p** 76. NSM Hobs Moat *Birm* 76-79; Perm to Offic *Heref* from 79. *Haresfield, Luston,*

Leominster, Herefordshire HR6 0EB   Leominster (01568) 615735

ALLEN, Ven Geoffrey Gordon. b 39. Sarum Th Coll 64. **d** 66 **p** 67. C Langley Marish *Ox* 66-70; Miss to Seamen from 70; Chapl Rotterdam w Schiedam *Eur* 78-82; Asst Chapl The Hague 84-93; Chapl Voorschoten 84-93; Can Brussels Cathl from 89; Chapl E Netherlands from 93; Adn NW Eur from 93; Chapl Haarlem from 95. *IJsselsingel 86, 6991 ZT Rheden, The Netherlands*   Rheden (26) 495-3800   Fax 495-4922

ALLEN, Giles David. b 70. BMus91. Coll of Resurr Mirfield 92. **d** 95. C Palmers Green St Jo *Lon* from 95. *19 Pembroke Road, London N13 5NR*   0181-807 4283

ALLEN, Gordon Richard. b 29. St Jo Coll Dur BA54 DipTh55 MA58. **d** 55 **p** 56. V Lathom *Liv* 64-68; USA from 68; rtd 94. *17 Monroe Street Ext, Portsmouth, New Hampshire, USA*

ALLEN, Hugh Edward. b 47. Sarum & Wells Th Coll 79. **d** 81 **p** 82. C Frome St Jo *B & W* 81-85; R Old Cleeve, Leighland and Treborough from 85; RD Exmoor from 92. *The Rectory, Old Cleeve, Minehead, Somerset TA24 6HN*   Washford (01984) 40576

ALLEN, John Catling. b 25. Leeds Univ BA50. Coll of Resurr Mirfield 50. **d** 52 **p** 53. V Linc St Jo *Linc* 66-84; C Tynemouth Ch Ch w H Trin *Newc* 85-87; C N Shields 87-89; rtd 89. *St Giles's House, Little Torrington, Devon EX38 8PS* Torrington (01805) 622497

ALLEN, John Clement. b 32. K Coll Lon 54. **d** 58 **p** 59. C Middlesb St Martin *York* 58-60; C Northallerton w Kirby Sigston 60-64; V Larkfield *Roch* 64-70; R Ash 70-79; R Ridley 70-79; RD Cobham 76-79; R Chislehurst St Nic from 79. *The Rectory, The Glebe, Chislehurst, Kent BR7 5PX*   0181-467 0196

ALLEN, Very Rev John Edward. b 32. Univ Coll Ox BA56 MA63 Fitzw Coll Cam BA68. Westcott Ho Cam 66. **d** 68 **p** 69. C Deal St Leon *Cant* 68-71; P-in-c Clifton St Paul *Bris* 71-78; Chapl Bris Univ 71-78; P-in-c Chippenham St Andr w Tytherton Lucas 78-82; Provost Wakef from 82. *1 Cathedral Close, Margaret Street, Wakefield, W Yorkshire WF1 2DQ* Wakefield (01924) 372402   Fax 383842

ALLEN, John Michael. b 27. Cuddesdon Coll 71. **d** 72 **p** 73. C Shrewsbury St Giles *Lich* 72-75; V Hengoed w Gobowen 75-82; V Burghill *Heref* 82-85; RD Heref Rural 83-85; TV Bracknell *Ox* 85-92; rtd 92. *15 Mill Street, Ludlow, Shropshire SY8 1BE*   Ludlow (01584) 877679

ALLEN, Mrs Kathleen. b 46. N Ord Course 88. **d** 91 **p** 94. NSM Colne H Trin *Blackb* from 91. *St Mary's Vicarage, Burnley Road, Trawden, Colne, Lancs BB8 8PN*   Colne (01282) 864046

ALLEN, Michael Edward Gerald. b 26. Selw Coll Cam BA50 MA53. Chich Th Coll 50. **d** 52 **p** 53. V Baswich (or Berkswich) *Lich* 60-75; V Highbrook and W Hoathly *Chich* 75-91; RD Cuckfield 77-88; rtd 91. *Michell House, 6 Chatsworth Gardens, Eastbourne, E Sussex BN20 7JP*   Eastbourne (01323) 638688

ALLEN, Michael Stephen. b 37. Nottm Univ BA60. Cranmer Hall Dur 60. **d** 62 **p** 63. C Sandal St Helen *Wakef* 62-66; Hon C Tile Cross *Birm* 66-70; V 72-84; Hon C Bletchley *Ox* 70-72; Vice-Prin Aston Tr Scheme 84-91; P-in-c Colton and Marlingford *Nor* 91-93; Local Min Officer 91-93; Dioc Adv in Adult Educn *S'well* from 93. *8 Grenville Rise, Arnold, Nottingham NG5 8EW* Nottingham (0115) 981 4504

ALLEN, Michael Tarrant. b 30. St Cath Coll Cam BA56 MA61. Ely Th Coll 56. **d** 58 **p** 59. V Harston w Hauxton *Ely* 65-91; rtd 91. *13 Church End, Rampton, Cambridge CB4 4QA*   Rampton (01945) 250434

ALLEN, Noel Stephen (Brother Noel). b 38. Kelham Th Coll. **d** 63 **p** 64. C Nuneaton St Mary *Cov* 63-67; Australia from 67. *23 Scott Avenue, Flinders Park, S Australia 5025*   Adelaide (8) 340-3231 or 222-6000

ALLEN, Patrick Charles Benedict. b 55. St Steph Ho Ox 83. **d** 86 **p** 87. C Bethnal Green St Matt w St Jas the Gt *Lon* 86-90; C Kenton 90-92; V Plumstead St Nic *S'wark* 92-94. *229 Wilmot Street, London E2 0BY*   0171-729 4846

ALLEN, Peter Henry. b 34. Nottm Univ BA66. Kelham Th Coll 58. **d** 66 **p** 67. C Salisbury St Martin *Sarum* 66-70; C Melksham 70-73; C Paignton Ch Ch *Ex* 73-76; P-in-c W Holt St Dav *Lon* 76-77; V Barnsbury St Dav w St Clem 77-84; P-in-c Brentford St Faith 84-87; TV Brentford 87-91; TV Catford (Southend) and Downham *S'wark* from 91. *St Luke's House, Northover, Bromley BR1 5JR*   0181-698 1354

ALLEN, Peter John. b 34. HNC72 Leic Coll of Educn CertEd74 Leic Univ BEd75 MA79. E Anglian Minl Tr Course 89. **d** 92 **p** 93. NSM Ketton w Tinwell *Pet* 92-94; NSM Easton on the Hill, Collyweston w Duddington etc from 94. *St John's, Gretton Road, Harringworth, Corby, Northants NN17 3AD*

ALLEN, Peter John Douglas. b 35. Jes Coll Cam BA61 MA64. Westcott Ho Cam 60. **d** 62 **p** 63. C Wyken *Cov* 62-65; USA 65-66; Chapl Jes Coll Cam 66-72; Chapl K Sch Cant 72-87; Hon Min Can Cant Cathl *Cant* from 73; Second Master and Sen Chapl Sedbergh Sch Cumbria 87-93; P-in-c Edin St

Ninian *Edin* 93-94; Can St Mary's Cathl from 94; Prec from 94. *147 Comely Bank Road, Edinburgh EH4 1BH*   0131-332 6226

ALLEN, Philip Gerald. b 48. Lon Univ DipTh71. Trin Coll Bris 71. **d** 73 **p** 74. C Portsea St Luke *Portsm* 73-75; C-in-c 75-79; C Southsea St Jude 75-79; P-in-c Gatten St Paul 79-85; V from 85. *St Paul's Vicarage, St Paul's Crescent, Shanklin, Isle of Wight PO37 7AW*   Isle of Wight (01983) 862027

ALLEN, Richard James. b 46. Wells Th Coll 69. **d** 71 **p** 72. C Upholland *Liv* 71-75; TV 76-79; TV Padgate 79-85; V Weston-super-Mare St Andr Bournville *B & W* 85-93; V Williton from 93. *The Vicarage, 16 Bridge Street, Williton, Taunton, Somerset TA4 4NR*   Williton (01984) 632626

ALLEN, Richard Lee. b 41. Liv Inst of Educn TCert67. N Ord Course 80. **d** 83 **p** 84. NSM Colne Ch Ch *Blackb* 83-90; P-in-c Trawden from 91. *The Vicarage, Burnley Road, Trawden, Colne, Lancs BB8 8PN*   Colne (01282) 864046

ALLEN, Roger Charles Brews. b 44. Solicitor 77 Loughb Univ BTech66. Local NSM Course 89. **d** 92 **p** 93. NSM S Elmham and Ilketshall *St E* 92-93; NSM Wainford from 93. *The Old Rectory, Ilketshall St Mary, Bungay, Suffolk NR35 1QZ* Ilketshall (01986) 781429

ALLEN, Roy Vernon. b 43. Open Univ BA81 Birm Univ MA84. Sarum Th Coll 67. **d** 70 **p** 71. C Hall Green Ascension *Birm* 70-74; V Temple Balsall 74-78; P-in-c Smethwick St Steph 78-81; V Smethwick St Mich 78-81; V Smethwick SS Steph and Mich 81-86; V Marston Green from 86. *The Vicarage, Elmdon Road, Birmingham B37 7BT*   0121-779 2492

ALLEN, Samuel Joseph. b 25. CITC. **d** 65 **p** 66. C Bray *D & G* 65-75; P-in-c Carbury *M & K* 75-84; rtd 84. *2 Coastguard Terrace, Putland Road, Bray, Co Wicklow, Irish Republic* Dublin (1) 282-8476

ALLEN, Canon Stanley Leonard Sidney. b 26. K Coll Lon BD52 AKC52. **d** 53 **p** 54. Warden Roch Th Coll 66-70; Can Res Roch Cathl *Roch* 66-70; Hon Can Roch Cathl 70-95; V Sidcup St Jo 70-95; Chapl Qu Mary's Hosp Sidcup 70-95; RD Sidcup *Roch* 75-93; rtd 95. *55 Manor Road, Dersingham, King's Lynn, Norfolk PE31 6LH*   Dersingham (01485) 543425

ALLEN, Steven. b 49. Nottm Univ BA73. St Jo Coll Nottm 73. **d** 75 **p** 76. C Gt Horton *Bradf* 75-80; V from 89; V Upper Armley *Ripon* 80-89. *The Vicarage, 30 Bartle Close, Bradford, W Yorkshire BD7 4QH*   Bradford (01274) 521456

ALLEN, Thomas Davidson. b 49. Greenwich Univ MA BTh QUB BA. **d** 84 **p** 85. C Magheralin w Dollingstown *D & D* 84-86; I Kilwarlin Upper w Kilwarlin Lower 86-91; I Maghera w Killelagh *D & R* from 91. *20 Church Street, Maghera, Co Londonderry BT46 5EA*   Maghera (01648) 42252

ALLEN, Thomas Henry (Tom). b 42. N Ord Course 87. **d** 90 **p** 91. C Upholland *Liv* 90-93; TV Walton-on-the-Hill from 93. *138 Queens Drive, Walton, Liverpool L4 6XD*   0151-521 5276

ALLEN, William Charles Ralph. b 09. Clifton Th Coll 46. **d** 47 **p** 48. V Bris St Leon Redfield *Bris* 53-74; rtd 74; Perm to Offic *Bris* from 74. *17 Creswicke Avenue, Bristol BS15 3HD*   Bristol (0117) 967 0955

ALLEN, Zachary Edward. b 52. Warw Univ BA74. Ripon Coll Cuddesdon 78. **d** 81 **p** 82. C Bognor *Chich* 81-84; C Rusper 84-86; C Roughey (or Roffey) 84-86; TV Carl H Trin and St Barn *Carl* 86-90; Chapl Strathclyde Ho Hosp Carl 86-90; V Findon w Clapham and Patching *Chich* from 90. *The Vicarage, School Hill, Findon, Worthing, W Sussex BN14 0TR* Findon (01903) 873601

ALLEYNE, Sir John Olpherts Campbell, Bt. b 28. Jes Coll Cam BA50 MA55. **d** 55 **p** 56. Area Sec (SW England) Toc H 68-71; V Speke All SS *Liv* 71-73; TR Speke St Aid 73-76; R Win St Matt *Win* 76-93; rtd 93. *2 Ash Grove, Guildford, Surrey GU2 5UT*   Guildford (01483) 573824

ALLFORD, Judith Mary. b 55. Sheff Univ BA Lon Univ BD. Trin Coll Bris 77. **dss** 86 **d** 87 **p** 94. Par Dn Deptford St Jo w H Trin *S'wark* 87-91; Asst Chapl Dulwich Hosp 91-93; Asst Chapl K Coll Hosp Lon from 91; Asst Chapl King's Healthcare NHS Trust from 93. *Kings Healthcare NHS Trust (Dulwich), East Dulwich Grove, London SE22 3PT*   0171-737 4000 ext 6054

ALLIN, Philip Ronald. b 43. Lich Th Coll 71. **d** 71 **p** 72. C Sutton in Ashfield St Mary *S'well* 71-74; Chapl to Sutton Cen 74-76; Lic to Offic 74-76; P-in-c Grove 76-77; R Ordsall 76-80; V Mansf St Mark 81-83; TR Hermitage and Hampstead Norreys, Cold Ash etc *Ox* from 83; OCF from 83. *The Rectory, High Street, Hermitage, Newbury, Berks RG16 9ST* Hermitage (01635) 200448

ALLINGTON, Andrew William. b 57. ACA81 Sheff Univ BA78. Cranmer Hall Dur BA95. **d** 95. C Clifton *York* from 95. *5 Manor Park Close, Rawcliffe, York YO3 6UZ*   York (01904) 624241

ALLINGTON-SMITH, Canon Richard. b 28. Lon Univ BA49 MA52. Wells Th Coll 54. **d** 56 **p** 57. V Rainham *Roch* 67-79; V

Gt Yarmouth *Nor* 79-89; TR 89-91; Hon Can Nor Cathl from 86; rtd 91; P-in-c Nor St Andr *Nor* from 91. *14 Yare Court, Yarmouth Road, Norwich NR7 0EJ* Norwich (01603) 37185

ALLINSON, Capt Paul Timothy. b 63. Edin Th Coll 89. **d** 91 **p** 92. C Peterlee *Dur* 91-94; Dio Children's Adv from 94; C Shadforth from 94; C Sherburn w Pittington from 94. *The Rectory, 1 Rectory View, Shadforth, Durham DH6 1LF* 0191-372 0223

ALLISON, Elliott Desmond. b 36. Univ of S Africa BA64 K Coll Lon MTh74. S Africa Federal Th Coll. **d** 69 **p** 70. *294 Reinwood Road, Huddersfield HD3 4DS* Huddersfield (01484) 461109

ALLISON, James Timothy. b 61. Man Univ BSc83. Oak Hill Th Coll BA89. **d** 89 **p** 90. C Walkden Moor *Man* 89-93; Chapl Huddersfield Univ *Wakef* from 93. *85 New North Road, Huddersfield HD1 5ND* Huddersf'd (0484) 530655 or 422288

ALLISON, Keith. b 34. Dur Univ BA59. Ely Th Coll 59. **d** 61 **p** 62. C Sculcoates *York* 61-64; C Stainton-in-Cleveland 64-65; C Leeds St Pet *Ripon* 65-70; V Micklefield *York* 70-74; V Appleton-le-Street w Amotherby 74-78; P-in-c Barton le Street 77-78; P-in-c Salton 77-80; R Amotherby w Appleton and Barton-le-Street 78-82; Chapl Lister Hosp Stevenage 82-90; P-in-c St Ippolyts *St Alb* 82-85; V 85-90; Chapl Hitchin Hosp 86-90; Chapl Shotley Bridge Gen Hosp from 90; Chapl Dur HA from 90. *Chaplain's Office, General Hospital, Shotley Bridge, Consett, Co Durham DH8 0NB* Consett (01207) 503456 or 503863

ALLISON, Canon Roger Grant. b 10. MBE54. Jes Coll Cam BA33 MA36. Ridley Hall Cam 32. **d** 34 **p** 35. Jerusalem 41-75; rtd 75; Perm to Offic *Chich* from 76. *Shalom, 11 Gloucester Avenue, Bexhill-on-Sea, E Sussex TN40 2LA* Bexhill-on-Sea (01424) 218786

ALLISTER, Donald Spargo. b 52. Peterho Cam BA74 MA77. Trin Coll Bris 74. **d** 76 **p** 77. C Hyde St Geo *Ches* 76-79; C Sevenoaks St Nic *Roch* 79-83; V Birkenhead Ch Ch *Ches* 83-89; R Cheadle from 89. *The Rectory, 1 Depleach Road, Cheadle, Cheshire SK8 1DZ* 0161-428 3440

ALLISTON, Cyril John. b 11. Fitzw Ho Cam BA33 MA37. Cuddesdon Coll 33. **d** 35 **p** 36. V Penponds *Truro* 63-70; S Africa from 71; rtd 76. *Huis Lettie Theron, Private Bag X03, Hermanus 7200, South Africa*

ALLON-SMITH, Roderick David. b 51. Leic Univ BA PhD Cam Univ MA. Ridley Hall Cam 79. **d** 82 **p** 83. C Kinson *Sarum* 82-86; V Westwood *Cov* from 86; RD Cov S from 92. *St John's Vicarage, Westwood Heath Road, Coventry CV4 7DD* Coventry (01203) 466227

ALLPORT, David Jack. b 55. Ox Univ BA Birm Univ DPS. Qu Coll Birm 78. **d** 80 **p** 81. C Abingdon w Shippon *Ox* 80-83; C-in-c Woodgate Valley CD *Birm* 83-91; Perm to Offic *Lich* from 91. *122 Cherry Tree Avenue, Walsall, W Midlands WS5 4JL* 0121-353 2292

ALLRED, Frank. b 23. Tyndale Hall Bris 62. **d** 64 **p** 65. V Ravenhead *Liv* 67-75; R Chadwell *Chelmsf* 75-82; TV Heworth *York* 82-86; rtd 87. *12 Viking Road, Bridlington, N Humberside YO16 5TW* Bridlington (01262) 677321

ALLSOP, Anthony James. b 37. AKC62. **d** 63 **p** 64. C Leytonstone St Marg w St Columba *Chelmsf* 63-68; V Gt Ilford St Alb 68-80; V Gainsborough St Jo *Linc* 80-85; V Hockerill *St Alb* from 85; Chapl Herts and Essex Gen Hosp Bp's Stortford from 85. *Hockerill Vicarage, All Saints' Close, Bishop's Stortford, Herts CM23 2EA* Bishop's Stortford (01279) 654930

ALLSOP, Patrick Leslie Fewtrell. b 52. Fitzw Coll Cam BA74 MA78. Ripon Coll Cuddesdon BA78 MA83. **d** 79 **p** 80. C Barrow St Matt *Carl* 79-82; Chapl Eton Coll Windsor 82-88; Chapl K Sch Roch from 89; Hon PV Roch Cathl *Roch* from 89. *49 Holcombe Road, Rochester, Kent ME1 2HX* Medway (01634) 400184

ALLSOP, Peter William. b 33. Kelham Th Coll 58. **d** 58 **p** 59. C Woodford St Barn *Chelmsf* 58-61; C Upholland *Liv* 61-65; V Wigan St Geo 65-71; P-in-c Marham *Ely* 71-72; TV Fincham 72-76; V Trawden *Blackb* 76-90; C Marton 90-92; C S Shore H Trin from 92. *31 Lomond Avenue, Blackpool FY3 9QL* Blackpool (01253) 696624

ALLSOP, Mrs Christine. b 47. Aston Univ BSc68. S Dios Minl Tr Scheme 86. **d** 89 **p** 94. C Caversham and Mapledurham *Ox* 89-94; C Bracknell 94; TV from 94. *St Paul's Vicarage, 58 Harmanswater Road, Bracknell, Berks RG12 9PT* Bracknell (01344) 422819

ALLSOPP, Edmund Gibson. b 16. Dur Univ LTh41. St Pet Coll Jamaica 38. **d** 41 **p** 42. Jamaica 41-73; R Lansallos *Truro* 73-80; V Talland 73-80; V St Neot 80-88; RD W Wivelshire 81-87; rtd 89. *4 Mews Court, Menheniot, Liskeard, Cornwall PL14 3QW* Liskeard (01579) 347729

ALLSOPP, Dr Stephen Robert. b 50. BSc71 MSc72 PhD75. Mon Dioc Tr Scheme 81. **d** 84 **p** 85. NSM Trevethin *Mon* 84-88; Asst Chapl K Sch Roch from 88; Hon PV Roch Cathl

Roch from 89. *33 St Margarets Street, Rochester, Kent ME1 1UF* Medway (01634) 409878

ALLSWORTH, Peter Thomas. b 44. St Mich Coll Llan DMinlStuds93. **d** 93 **p** 94. C Prestatyn *St As* from 93. *The Parsonage, High Street, Prestatyn, Clwyd LL19 9AR* Prestatyn (01745) 889363

ALLTON, Canon Paul Irving. b 38. Man Univ BA60 Dur Univ DipTh62. **d** 63 **p** 64. C Kibworth Beauchamp *Leic* 63-66; C Reading St Mary V *Ox* 66-70; R Caston *Nor* 70-75; R Caston w Griston, Mert and Thompson 70-75; P-in-c Sturston w Thompson and Tottington 70-75; V Holme-next-the-Sea 75-80; V Hunstanton St Mary w Lt Ringstead 75-80; V Hunstanton St Mary w Ringstead Parva, Holme etc 80-85; RD Heacham and Rising 81-85; Hon Can Nor Cathl 85-93; TR Lowestoft and Kirkley 85-93; TR Keynsham *B & W* from 93. *The Rectory, 1 The Park, Keynsham, Bristol BS18 2BL* Bristol (0117) 986 3354

ALLUM, Jeremy Warner. b 32. Wycliffe Hall Ox 60. **d** 62 **p** 63. C Hornchurch St Andr *Chelmsf* 62-67; P-in-c W Derby St Luke *Liv* 67-69; V 69-75; P-in-c Boulton *Derby* 75-90; RD Melbourne 86-90; V Hathersage from 90. *The Vicarage, Hathersage, Sheffield S30 1AB* Hope Valley (01433) 650215

ALLUM, Peter Drage. b 11. Univ Coll Dur LTh35 BA36 MA42. Sarum Th Coll 32. **d** 36 **p** 37. V Sheepscombe *Glouc* 51-77; rtd 77; Perm to Offic *Glouc* from 78; Perm to Offic *Heref* 82-94. *Rose Cottage, Kempley, Dymock, Glos GL18 2BN* Dymock (01531) 890571

ALLWRIGHT, Mrs Janet Margaret. b 40. Oak Hill Th Coll 87. **d** 90 **p** 94. NSM Galleywood Common *Chelmsf* 90-93; NSM Downham w S Hanningfield from 93; NSM Ramsden Crays w Ramsden Bellhouse from 95. *26 Chaplin Close, Chelmsford CM2 8QW* Chelmsford (01245) 265499

ALMOND, Kenneth Alfred. b 36. E Midl Min Tr Course 76 Linc Th Coll 78. **d** 79 **p** 80. C Boston *Linc* 79-82; V Surfleet 82-87; RD Elloe W from 86; V Spalding St Jo w Deeping St Nicholas from 87. *St John's Vicarage, 66A Hawthorn Bank, Spalding, Lincs PE11 1JQ* Spalding (01775) 722816

ALPIAR, Ronald. b 29. Pemb Coll Cam BA52. Ely Th Coll 52. **d** 54 **p** 55. SSF 54-57; rtd 79. *84 Dudsbury Road, Ferndown, Dorset BH22 8RG* Bournemouth (01202) 590314

ALSBURY, Colin. b 56. Ch Ch Ox BA77 MA81. Ripon Coll Cuddesdon 77. **d** 80 **p** 81. C Oxton *Ches* 80-84; V Crewe All SS and St Paul 84-92; Ind Chapl from 92. *The Vicarage, Crewe Green, Crewe CW1 1UN* Crewe (01270) 580118

ALSOP, Eric George. b 12. Dorchester Miss Coll 34. **d** 37 **p** 38. P-in-c Bodiam *Chich* 69-72; V Burwash Weald 72-77; rtd 77; Perm to Offic *Chich* from 77. *Jacob's Well Farm House, 125 London Road, Hurst Green, Etchingham, E Sussex TN19 7PN* Hurst Green (01580) 860591

ALTHAM, Donald. b 40. Liv Univ BA62. N Ord Course 87. **d** 90 **p** 91. NSM Ramsbottom St Jo and St Paul *Man* from 90. *387 Whalley Road, Ramsbottom, Bury, Lancs BL0 0ER* Ramsbottom (01706) 822025

ALWAY, Cecil William. b 24. Glouc Th Course 67. **d** 69 **p** 70. C Wotton-under-Edge *Glouc* 69-73; P-in-c Pauntley w Upleadon 74-76; V Quinton w Marston Sicca 76-82; P-in-c Lower Cam 82-83; V Lower Cam w Coaley 83-90; rtd 90; Lic to Offic *Glouc* from 90; Cl Widows Officer Adnry Glouc from 94. *Middlecot, 116A Parklands, Wotton-under-Edge, Glos GL12 7NR* Dursley (01453) 844346

AMBANI, Stephen Frederick. b 45. Univ of Wales (Lamp) BA90. St Jo Coll Nottm 86 CA Tr Coll Nairobi 70. **d** 83 **p** 83. Kenya 83-93; C Glan Ely *Llan* 93-95; C Whitchurch from 95. *47 Penydre, Rhiwbina, Cardiff CF4 6EJ* Cardiff (01222) 592129

AMBROSE, Edgar. b 22. N Ord Course 80. **d** 81 **p** 82. NSM Broughton *Blackb* 81-94; Perm to Offic from 94. *76 Conway Drive, Fulwood, Preston PR2 3EQ* Preston (01772) 717530

AMBROSE, Canon Frederick Lee Giles. b 12. Kelham Th Coll 28. **d** 36 **p** 37. C Nottm St Geo w St Jo *S'well* 36-39; S Africa 39-63 and from 70; Lic to Offic *S'well* 63-70; Hon Can Pretoria from 92. *PO Box 11026, Queenswood, Pretoria, 0121 South Africa* Pretoria (12) 731379

AMBROSE, James Field. b 51. Newc Univ BA73. Cranmer Hall Dur DipTh80. **d** 80 **p** 81. C Barrow St Geo w St Luke *Carl* 80-83; C Workington St Jo 83-85; Ch Radio Officer BBC Radio Shropshire 85-88; R Montford w Shrawardine and Fitz *Lich* 85-88; Chapl RAF 88-92; Voc and Min Adv CPAS from 92; Perm to Offic *Cov* from 92. *c/o CPAS, Athena Drive, Tachbrook Park, Warwick CV34 6NG* Warwick (01926) 334242 Fax 337613

AMBROSE, John George. b 30. Ox Univ PGCE Lon Univ BD. **d** 74 **p** 75. C Rayleigh *Chelmsf* 74-79; V Hadleigh St Barn 79-95; rtd 95. *St Barnabas' Vicarage, 169 Church Road, Hadleigh, Essex SS7 2EJ* Southend-on-Sea (01702) 558591

AMBROSE, Dr Thomas (Tom). b 47. Sheff Univ BSc69 PhD73 Em Coll Cam BA77. Westcott Ho Cam 75. **d** 78 **p** 79. C

Morpeth *Newc* 78-81; C N Gosforth 81-84; R March St Jo *Ely* 84-93; RD March 89-93; P-in-c Witchford w Wentworth from 93; Dioc Dir of Communications from 93; Chapl K Sch Ely from 94. *The Vicarage, Main Street, Witchford, Ely, Cambs CB6 2HQ* Ely (01353) 669420 Fax 669609

AMES, Henry George. b 33. Em Coll Cam BA56 MA60 Lon Univ BD58. Tyndale Hall Bris 56. **d** 59 **p** 60. Chapl Highbury Coll of Tech Portsm 66-88; Lic to Offic *Portsm* from 66; rtd 88. *49 Carmarthen Avenue, Cosham, Portsmouth PO6 2AG*

AMES, Jeremy Peter. b 49. K Coll Lon BD71 AKC71. **d** 72 **p** 73. C Kennington St Jo *S'wark* 72-75; Chapl RN from 75; RN Engineering Coll from 86; RN Dir of Studies RAF Chapl Sch from 89. *Directorate Gen, RN Chapl Services, Room 203, Victory Building, HM Naval Base, Portsmouth PO1 3LS* Portsmouth (01705) 727903 Fax 727112

AMES, Reginald John. b 27. Bps' Coll Cheshunt 51. **d** 54 **p** 55. V Northwood Hills St Edm *Lon* 64-92; rtd 92; Hon C Moffat *Glas* from 92. *Oakbank, Lochwood, Beattock, Moffat, Dumfriesshire DG10 9PS* Beattock (016833) 381

AMES-LEWIS, Richard. b 45. Em Coll Cam BA66 MA70. Westcott Ho Cam 76. **d** 78 **p** 79. C Bromley St Mark *Roch* 78-81; C Edenbridge 81-84; V 84-91; P-in-c Crockham Hill H Trin 84-91; P-in-c Barnes St Mary *S'wark* from 91; RD Richmond and Barnes from 94. *The Rectory, 25 Glebe Road, London SW13 0DZ* 0181-878 6982 or 741 5422

AMEY, Graham George. b 44. Lon Univ BD70. Tyndale Hall Bris 67. **d** 71 **p** 72. C Hornsey Rise St Mary *Lon* 71-74; C St Helens St Helen *Liv* 74-79; V Liv All So Springwood 79-91; V Whiston from 91. *The Vicarage, 90 Windy Arbor Road, Prescot, Merseyside L35 3SG* 0151-426 6329

AMIS, Ronald. b 37. Linc Th Coll 74. **d** 76 **p** 77. C Grantham w Manthorpe *Linc* 76-78; C Grantham 78-79; P-in-c Holbeach Hurn 79-81; V Long Bennington w Foston 81-91; V Corby Glen 91-93; RD Grantham 90-92; rtd 93. *35 Huntly Grove, Peterborough PE1 2QW*

✠AMOORE, Rt Rev Frederick Andrew. b 13. Leeds Univ BA34. Coll of Resurr Mirfield 34. **d** 36 **p** 37 **c** 67. C Clapham H Trin *S'wark* 36-39; S Africa from 39; Dean Pretoria 50-61; Adn Pretoria 60-61; Can Pretoria 62-67; Hon Can Pretoria from 67; Bp Bloemfontein 67-82. *503 Salwood Court, Arbor Road, Rondebosch, 7700 South Africa* Cape Town (21) 685-7259

AMOR, Peter David Card. b 28. AKC53. **d** 54 **p** 55. V Bingley H Trin *Bradf* 65-72; V The Collingbournes *Sarum* 72-75; R The Collingbournes and Everleigh 75-77; V Thorpe *Guildf* 77-85; P-in-c Monks Risborough *Ox* 85-89; R 89-94; rtd 94. *1 Murren Croft, Crowmarsh Gifford, Wallingford, Oxon OX10 8EZ* Wallingford (01491) 826580

AMOS, Alan John. b 44. OBE79. K Coll Lon BD66 AKC67 MTh67. St Steph Ho Ox 68. **d** 69 **p** 70. C Hoxton H Trin w St Mary *Lon* 69-72; Lebanon 73-82; Lect Liturg Studies Westcott Ho Cam 82-85; Vice-Prin 85-89; Prin Cant Sch of Min 89-94; Co-Prin SE Inst for Th Educn from 94. *SE Inst for Theological Education, Deanery Gate, The Precinct, Rochester, Kent ME1 1SJ* Medway (01634) 832299

AMOS, Brother. See YONGE, James Mohun

AMOS, Colin James. b 62. Univ of Wales (Lamp) BA83 Univ of Wales (Cardiff) CQSW85 DipSocWork85. Ridley Hall Cam CTMin93. **d** 93 **p** 94. C Aberdare St Jo *Llan* from 93. *19 Willow Grove, Glandare, Aberdare, M Glam CF44 8BS* Aberdare (01685) 884334

AMOS, Gerald. b 31. St Mich Coll Llan. **d** 58 **p** 62. C Rhosymedre *St As* 58-59; C Peckham St Andr w All SS *S'wark* 62-65; C Walworth 65-72; C S Wimbledon H Trin 72-74; C S Wimbledon H Trin and St Pet 74-75; C Warlingham w Chelsham and Farleigh 75-78; TV Speke St Aid *Liv* 78-88; P-in-c Fazakerley St Nath 88-92; TV Walton-on-the-Hill from 92. *St Nathanael's Vicarage, 65 Fazakerley Road, Liverpool L9 2AJ* 0151-525 7720

AMOS, Patrick Henry. b 31. Roch Th Coll 63. **d** 65 **p** 66. C Polegate *Chich* 68-71; V Horam 71-83; R Chiddingly w E Hoathly 83-93; rtd 93; Clergy Widows Officer Maidstone Adnry *Cant* from 95. *20 Fauchons Close, Bearsted, Maidstone, Kent ME14 4BB* Maidstone (01622) 736725

AMYS, Richard James Rutherford. b 58. Trin Coll Bris BA90. **d** 90 **p** 91. C Whitnash *Cov* 90-93; P-in-c Gravesend H Family w Ifield *Roch* 93-95; R from 95. *The Rectory, 2 Wilberforce Way, Gravesend, Kent DA12 5DQ* Gravesend (01474) 363038

ANCRUM, John. b 28. Clifton Th Coll 55. **d** 58 **p** 59. V Tibshelf *Derby* 63-70; Canada 70-74; P-in-c Salwarpe *Worc* 74-75; P-in-c Tibberton w Bredicot and Warndon 75-76; P-in-c Hadzor w Oddingley 76-78; Lic to Offic *Chelmsf* 78-81; Chapl HM Pris Stafford 81-82; Chapl HM Pris Dartmoor 82-89; Lic to Offic *Ex* from 88; rtd 89. *14 Merrivale View Road, Dousland, Yelverton, Devon PL20 6NS* Yelverton (01822) 853909

ANDERS, Jonathan Cyril. b 36. Wycliffe Hall Ox 69. **d** 71 **p** 72. C Prescot *Liv* 71-74; C-in-c 74-76; R Wavertree St Mary 76-81; V Aigburth from 81. *St Anne's Vicarage, 389 Aigburth Road, Liverpool L17 6BH* 0151-727 1101

ANDERS, Roger John. b 38. Man Univ LLB61. Nor Ord Course 91. **d** 94 **p** 95. NSM New Mills *Derby* from 94. *Bowden Head Farmhouse, Bowden Lane, Chapel-en-le-Frith, Stockport, Cheshire SK12 6QP* Chapel-en-le-Frith (01298) 813332

ANDERS-RICHARDS, Dr Donald. b 28. Dur Univ BA60 MA62 Leic Univ MEd72 Sheff Univ PhD76. Coll of Resurr Mirfield 60. **d** 62 **p** 63. Lic to Offic *Derby* from 68; Sen Lect Sheff Poly 75-88; rtd 88; Perm to Offic *Lich* from 88. *Laburnum Cottage, Gwern-y-Brenin, Oswestry, Shropshire SY10 8AS* Oswestry (01691) 653528

ANDERSON, Albert Geoffrey (Geoff). b 42. Ex Univ BA65 MA67. Qu Coll Birm DipTh75. **d** 75 **p** 76. C Helsby and Ince *Ches* 75-77; C Helsby and Dunham-on-the-Hill 77-78; TV Gleadless *Sheff* 78-85; V Thorpe Hesley 85-92; R Ribbesford w Bewdley and Dowles *Worc* from 92. *The Rectory, 57 Park Lane, Bewdley, Worcs DY12 2HA* Bewdley (01299) 402275

ANDERSON, Alice Calder. b 50. Moray Ho Coll of Educn DipEd76. Local Minl Tr Course 90. **d** 93. NSM Edin St Barn *Edin* from 93. *7 Mactaggart Loan, Newtongrange, Dalkeith, Midlothian EH22 4QZ* Prestonpans (01875) 821135

ANDERSON, Brian Arthur. b 42. Sarum Th Coll 75. **d** 78 **p** 79. C Plymouth St Jas Ham *Ex* 78-80; Org Sec (Dios B & W, Ex and Truro) CECS 80-89; Perm to Offic *B & W* from 86; TV Saltash *Truro* 89-94; RD E Wivelshire 91-94; P-in-c St Breoke and Egloshayle from 94. *The Rectory, 31 Trevanion Road, Wadebridge, Cornwall PL27 7NZ* Wadebridge (01208) 812460

ANDERSON, Brian Glaister (Jeremy). b 35. SSF. K Coll Lon 57. **d** 79 **p** 79. Chapl St Fran Sch Hooke 79; C Croydon *Cant* 80-83; Asst Chapl HM Youth Cust Cen Glen Parva 83-84; Chapl HM Young Offender Inst Hewell Grange 84-89; Chapl HM Rem Cen Brockhill 84-89; Chapl HM Pris Parkhurst from 89. *HM Prison Parkhurst, Newport, Isle of Wight PO30 5NX* Isle of Wight (01983) 523855 Fax 524861

ANDERSON, David. b 19. Selw Coll Cam BA41 MA45. Wycliffe Hall Ox 47. **d** 49 **p** 50. Lic to Offic *St Alb* 71-84; Prin Lect Wall Hall Coll Aldenham 74-84; rtd 84. *6 Flassburn Road, Durham DH1 4LX* 0191-384 3063

ANDERSON, David Graham. b 33. MICE MIStructE. St Mich Coll Llan 85. **d** 88 **p** 89. C Llanishen and Lisvane *Llan* 88-90; C Fazeley *Lich* 90-94. *Buddleia, Wrigglesbrook Lane, Kingsthorne, Hereford HR2 8AD* Hereford (01981) 540424

ANDERSON, Digby Carter. b 44. PhD. **d** 85 **p** 86. NSM Luton St Sav *St Alb* from 85. *17 Hardwick Place, Woburn Sands, Milton Keynes MK17 8QQ* Milton Keynes (01908) 584526

ANDERSON, Donald Whimbey. b 31. Trin Coll Toronto BA54 LTh57 STB57 MA58 ThD71. **d** 56 **p** 57. Canada 57-59 and 75-88; Japan 59-74; The Philippines 74-75; Assoc Sec Ecum Affairs ACC from 88. *c/o ACC, Partnership House, 157 Waterloo Road, London SE1 8UT* 0171-928 8681

ANDERSON, Francis Hindley. b 20. Ch Coll Cam BA43 MA47. Wycliffe Hall Ox. **d** 44 **p** 45. V Upper Chelsea St Sav *Lon* 59-91; rtd 92; P-in-c Linchmere *Chich* from 93. *35 Oaklands, Haslemere, Surrey GU27 3RD* Haslemere (01428) 642133

ANDERSON, Canon Gordon Fleming. b 19. TCD BA41 MA46. **d** 42 **p** 43. I Cumber Lower *D & R* 61-72; I Cumber Lower w Banagher 72-94; Can Derry Cathl 76-94; Preb Howth St Patr Cathl Dub 86-94; rtd 94. *Silversprings, 85 Dunboe Road, Ardiclave, Coleraine, Co Londonderry BT51 4JR*

ANDERSON, Gordon Roy. b 30. FCA58. Ox NSM Course 83. **d** 86 **p** 87. NSM Beaconsfield *Ox* from 86. *9 Mynchen Road, Beaconsfield, Bucks HP9 2AS* Beaconsfield (01494) 676617

ANDERSON, Gordon Stuart. b 49. St Jo Coll Nottm **d** 82 **p** 83. C Hattersley *Ches* 82-86; C Dagenham *Chelmsf* 86-91; TV Mildenhall *St E* from 91. *The Vicarage, 103 Melbourne Drive, Mildenhall, Bury St Edmunds, Suffolk IP28 7BP* Mildenhall (01638) 718840

ANDERSON, Hugh Richard Oswald. b 35. Roch Th Coll 68. **d** 70 **p** 71. C Minehead *B & W* 70-76; C Darley w S Darley *Derby* 76-80; R Hasland 80-94; V Temple Normanton 80-94; rtd 94. *32 Barry Road, Brimington, Chesterfield, Derbyshire S43 1PX* Chesterfield (01246) 551020

ANDERSON, James Frederick Wale. b 34. G&C Coll Cam BA58 MA62. Cuddesdon Coll 60. **d** 62 **p** 63. C Leagrave *St Alb* 62-65; C Eastleigh *Win* 65-70; R Sherfield-on-Loddon 70-86; P-in-c Stratfield Saye w Hartley Wespall 75-86; R Sherfield-on-Loddon and Stratfield Saye etc 86-87; R Newton Valence, Selborne and E Tisted w Colemore from 87. *The Vicarage, The Plestor, Selborne, Alton, Hants GU34 3JQ* Alton (01420) 511242

ANDERSON, Canon James Raffan. b 33. FRSA90 Edin Univ MA54. Edin Th Coll 56. **d** 58 **p** 59. Chapl Lucton Sch Herefordshire 69-71; Chapl Barnard Castle Sch 71-74; Asst Dir of Educn *Blackb* 74-78; P-in-c Whitechapel 74-78; Bp's Officer for Min *Cov* 78-87; Hon Can Cov Cathl 83-87; Miss Sec Gen Syn Bd for Miss and Unity 87-92; rtd 92. *15 Cotswold Drive, Coventry CV3 6EZ* Coventry (01203) 411985

ANDERSON (nee FLAHERTY), Mrs Jane Venitia. b 68. Oak Hill Th Coll DipHE91 BA92. d 93 p 94. C Timperley *Ches* from 93. *57 Heyes Lane, Timperley, Altrincham, Cheshire WA15 6DZ* 0161-976 1145

ANDERSON, Jeremy Dudgeon. b 41. Edin Univ BSc63. Trin Coll Bris 75. d 77 p 78. C Bitterne *Win* 77-81; TV Wexcombe *Sarum* 81-91; Evang Enabler (Reading Deanery) *Ox* from 91. *6 Scholars Close, Reading RG4 7DN* Reading (01734) 548396

ANDERSON, Joanna Elisabeth. b 53. St Andr Univ MTh75. E Midl Min Tr Course 85. d 88 p 95. Par Dn Crosby *Linc* 88-92; Warden Iona Community *Arg* from 92. *Iona Abbey, Isle of Iona PA76 6SN* Iona (016817) 404 Fax 460

ANDERSON, John Michael. b 17. Madras Univ BA38. St Aug Coll Cant 59. d 60 p 61. Trinidad and Tobago 69-73; V Leic St Sav *Leic* 74-82; rtd 82; Perm to Offic *Leic* from 82. *4 Cooden Avenue, West End, Leicester LE3 0JS* Leicester (0116) 255 7112

ANDERSON, Canon Keith Bernard. b 36. Qu Coll Cam BA60 MA64. Tyndale Hall Bris 60. d 62 p 63. C Bootle St Leon *Liv* 62-65; Burundi 66-74; Kenya 74-83; Hon Can Mt Kenya E from 82; P-in-c Doddington w Wychling *Cant* 83-88; P-in-c Newnham 83-88; Chapl Cannes w Grasse *Eur* 88-94; Dir and Chapl Mulberry Ho High Ongar 94-95. *17 Dorset House, 6 Hastings Road, Bexhill-on-Sea, E Sussex TN40 2HH* Bexhill-on-Sea (01424) 214673

ANDERSON, Keith Edward. b 42. MRCS83 Fitzw Coll Cam BA77 MA83. Ridley Hall Cam 74. d 77 p 78. C Goodmayes All SS *Chelmsf* 77-80; Lic to Offic *Truro* 80-87; Chapl Coll of St Mark and St Jo Plymouth *Ex* 80-87; RD Plymouth Moorside 83-86; V Northn H Sepulchre w St Andr and St Lawr *Pet* from 87; RD Northn from 92. *The Vicarage, Campbell Square, Northampton NN1 3EB* Northampton (01604) 230563

ANDERSON, Kenneth. b 38. G&C Coll Cam BA62 MA66. Westcott Ho Cam 63. d 65 p 66. C Nor St Steph *Nor* 65-68; Chapl Norfolk and Nor Hosp 65-68; C Wareham w Arne *Sarum* 68-71; Chapl Sherborne Sch Dorset 71-83; Zimbabwe 83-94; Chapl Van Mildert and Trevelyan Coll Dur from 95. *Trevelyan College, Elvet Hill Road, Durham DH1 3LN* 0191-374 3770 Fax 374 3789

ANDERSON, Mark Jonathan David. b 59. Ruskin Coll Ox 81 Univ of Wales (Cardiff) BSc(Econ)86. St Steph Ho Ox 86. d 89 p 90. C Deptford St Paul *S'wark* 89-92; C Battersea Ch Ch and St Steph 92-93. *Address temp unknown*

ANDERSON, Canon Michael Garland. b 42. Clifton Th Coll 62. d 66 p 67. C Fareham St Jo *Portsm* 66-69; C Worting *Win* 69-74; V Hordle from 74; RD Lyndhurst from 82; Hon Can Win Cathl from 92. *The Vicarage, Stopples Lane, Hordle, Lymington, Hants SO41 0HX* New Milton (01425) 614428

ANDERSON, Michael John Austen. b 35. AKC60. d 66 p 67. C Southall Ch Redeemer *Lon* 66-69; C Hampstead Garden Suburb 69-73; V S Mimms St Giles 73-80; V S Mymms *St Alb* 80; V The Brents and Davington w Oare and Luddenham *Cant* 80-86; V Margate All SS from 86. *All Saints' Vicarage, All Saints' Avenue, Margate, Kent CT9 5QL* Thanet (01843) 220795

ANDERSON, Nicholas Patrick. b 53. BA. d 81 p 82. In RC Ch 81-89; C Gt Crosby St Faith *Liv* 89-92; C Walton-on-the-Hill 92-95; V Pemberton St Fran Kitt Green from 95. *The Vicarage, 42 Sherbourne Road, Kitt Green, Wigan, Lancs WN5 0JA* Wigan (01942) 213227

ANDERSON, Olaf Emanuel. b 64. Queensland Univ BA88. St Fran Coll Queensland 84. d 87 p 88. Australia 87-90; C Petersfield *Portsm* 91-93; C Buriton from 91. *42 Heath Road, Petersfield, Hants GU31 4EH* Petersfield (01730) 263190

ANDERSON, Mrs Pearl Ann. b 46. MIPM74 St Andr Univ MA68. Cant Sch of Min 90. d 93. Par Dn Epping St Jo *Chelmsf* 93-95; Adv to Coun for Soc Resp (Dios Cant and Roch) *Cant* from 95. *1 Gibbs Hill, Headcorn, Ashford, Kent TN27 9UD* Headcorn (01622) 890043

ANDERSON, Peter Scott. b 49. Nottm Univ BTh72 CertEd. Kelham Th Coll 68. d 74 p 75. C Sheff Parson Cross St Cecilia *Sheff* 74-77; C Leytonstone St Marg w St Columba *Chelmsf* 77-81; P-in-c Forest Gate St Edm 81-89; V 89-90; P-in-c Plaistow 90-94; V Willesden Green St Andr and St Fran of Assisi *Lon* from 94. *The Clergy House, St Andrew's Road, London NW10 2QS* 0181-459 2670

ANDERSON, Peter John. b 44. Nottm Univ BA65 BA73. St Jo Coll Nottm DPS. d 74 p 75. C Otley *Bradf* 74-77; TV Marfleet *York* 77-84; V Greasbrough *Sheff* 84-95; I Clonmel Union C, C & R from 95. *The Rectory, Lake Road, Cobh, Co Cork, Irish Republic* Cobh (21) 811790

ANDERSON, Canon Dr Roderick Stephen (Rod). b 43. Cant Univ (NZ) BSc63 PhD67 New Coll Ox BA72. Wycliffe Hall Ox 70. d 73 p 74. C Bradf Cathl *Bradf* 73-75; C Allerton 76-78; V Cottingley 78-94; RD Airedale 88-95; Hon Can Bradf Cathl from 94; V Heaton St Barn from 94. *The Vicarage, Parsons Road, Heaton, Bradford, W Yorkshire BD9 4AY* Bradford (01274) 496712

ANDERSON, Mrs Rosemary Ann. b 36. Ex Univ BA59. N Ord Course 83. dss 86 d 87 p 94. Oldham St Paul *Man* 86-87; Hon Par Dn 87-89; Bp's Adv for Women's Min from 88; Par Dn Roughtown 93-94; P-in-c from 94. *St John's Vicarage, Carrhill Road, Mossley, Newcastle-under-Lyne, Lancs OL5 0BL* Mossley (01457) 832250

ANDERSON, Stuart. b 31. Dur Univ BA52. Linc Th Coll 52. d 54 p 55. C Billingham St Cuth *Dur* 54-57; C Fulham St Etheldreda *Lon* 57-61; New Zealand from 61. *61 McHardy Street, Havelock North, Hawkes Bay, New Zealand* Hastings (6) 877-8567

ANDERSON, Thomas. b 07. Dorchester Miss Coll 32. d 36 p 37. V Appleton-le-Street w Amotherby *York* 57-70; rtd 72. *Hillside Cottage, Appleton-le-Street, Malton, N Yorkshire YO17 0PG* Malton (01653) 693681

ANDERSON, Timothy George. b 59. Ealing Coll of HE BA82. Wycliffe Hall Ox 83. d 86 p 87. C Harold Wood *Chelmsf* 86-90; C Whitfield *Derby* 90-95; P-in-c Wolv St Luke *Lich* from 95. *St Luke's Vicarage, 122 Goldthorn Hill, Wolverhampton WV2 3HQ* Wolverhampton (01902) 340261

ANDERSON, Timothy James Lane. b 59. Pemb Coll Ox BA80 MA90. St Jo Coll Nottm DTS92. d 93 p 94. C Reigate St Mary *S'wark* from 93. *11 Monk's Court, Reigate, Surrey RH2 0SR* Reigate (01737) 224441

ANDERTON, Frederic Michael. b 31. IAAP IGAP Pemb Coll Cam MA57 Jung Institut Zurich DipAnPsych86. Westcott Ho Cam 64. d 66 p 67. C St Jo Wood *Lon* 66-69; C All Hallows by the Tower etc 70-77; C St Giles Cripplegate w St Bart Moor Lane etc 77-82; C Zurich *Eur* 82-86; Perm to Offic *Lon* from 94. *100 Harvist Road, London NW6 6HZ* 0171-960 4780

ANDERTON, Peter. b 45. Sarum & Wells Th Coll 80. d 82 p 83. C Adel *Ripon* 82-86; P-in-c Dacre w Hartwith 86-90; P-in-c Thornthwaite w Thruscross and Darley 88-90; V Dacre w Hartwith and Darley w Thornthwaite 90-91; V Owton Manor *Dur* from 91. *The Vicarage, 18 Rossmere Way, Hartlepool, Cleveland TS25 5EF* Hartlepool (01429) 273938

ANDREW, Brian. b 31. Oak Hill Th Coll 75. d 77 p 78. C Broadwater St Mary *Chich* 77-81; R Nettlebed w Bix and Highmore *Ox* 81-87; V Shenstone *Lich* from 87. *The Vicarage, Shenstone, Lichfield, Staffs WS14 0JB* Shenstone (01543) 480286

ANDREW, Dr David Neil. b 62. Down Coll Cam BA83 MA87 PhD84. Ridley Hall Cam CTMin93. d 93 p 94. C Heatherlands St Jo *Sarum* from 93. *91 Churchill Road, Poole, Dorset BH12 2LR* Poole (01202) 748754

ANDREW, Donald. b 35. Tyndale Hall Bris 63. d 66 p 67. C Croydon Ch Ch Broad Green *Cant* 66-69; C Ravenhead *Liv* 69-72; Scripture Union 72-77; V Rushen *S & M* 77-82; TR Heworth *York* from 82. *Heworth Rectory, Melrosegate, York YO3 0RP* York (01904) 422958

ANDREW, Frank. b 17. St D Coll Lamp BA49 Ely Th Coll 50. d 51 p 52. R March St Jo *Ely* 69-77; R March St Mary 71-77; RD March 73-77; R Catworth Magna 77-83; R Covington 77-83; R Tilbrook 77-83; rtd 83; Perm to Offic *Chich* from 83. *11 Romney Close, Seaford, E Sussex BN25 3TR* Seaford (01323) 897352

ANDREW, Michael Paul. b 51. SSC Leic Univ CertEd73. Chich Th Coll 80. d 83 p 84. C Par *Truro* 83-86; Hon Chapl Miss to Seamen 86; P-in-c Salford Ordsall St Clem *Man* 86-91; P-in-c Hammersmith St Jo *Lon* from 91. *St John's Vicarage, Iffley Road, London W6 0PA* 0181-748 0079 Fax 741-1825 or 741 8933

ANDREW, Ronald Arthur. b 27. Sarum Th Coll 64. d 65 p 66. C Padiham *Blackb* 69-71; V Colne H Trin 71-76; V Adlington 76-85; V Goosnargh w Whittingham 85-92; rtd 92; Perm to Offic *Blackb* from 92. *7 Windsor Gardens, Garstang, Preston PR3 1EG* Garstang (01995) 600273

ANDREW, Sydney William. b 55. Cranmer Hall Dur 82. d 85 p 86. C Horncastle w Low Toynton *Linc* 85-88; V Worlaby 88-93; V Bonby 88-93; V Elsham 88-93; rtd 93; Lic to Offic *Linc* 93-95; Hon C Gt Limber w Brocklesby from 95. *10 Bentley Lane, Grasby, Barnetby, S Humberside DN38 6AW* Barnetby (01652) 62586

ANDREW, Canon William Hugh (Bill). b 32. Selw Coll Cam BA56 MA60. Ridley Hall Cam 56. d 58 p 59. C Woking St Mary *Guildf* 58-61; C Farnborough 61-64; V Gatten St Paul *Portsm* 64-71; R Weymouth St Mary *Sarum* 71-76; V Heatherlands St Jo 76-82; Can and Preb Sarum Cathl 81-86; R Alderbury and W Grimstead 82-86; Perm to Offic *Bris* 86-88; Communications Dir Bible Soc 86-94; Communications Consultant from 94; Hon C The Lydiards *Bris* 88-94; C from 94. *20 Chudleigh, Freshbrook, Swindon SN5 8NQ* Swindon (01793) 695313 or 418100

ANDREWES UTHWATT, Henry. b 25. Jes Coll Cam BA49 MA51. Wells Th Coll 49. d 51 p 52. V W Wimbledon Ch Ch *S'wark* 61-73; V Yeovil St Jo w Preston Plucknett *B & W* 73-76; TR Yeovil 76-82; V Burrington and Churchill 82-90; RD Locking 87-90; rtd 90; Perm to Offic *B & W* from 90;

Chapl Partis Coll Bath from 91; Chapl St Martin's Hosp Bath from 91. *71 Mount Road, Bath BA2 1LJ* Bath (01225) 482220

ANDREWS, Canon Alan Robert Williams. b 14. AKC37. **d** 37 **p** 38. V Quarndon *Derby* 58-79; Hon Can Derby Cathl 77-79; rtd 79; Perm to Offic *Derby* from 79. *4 Orchard Court, Hawthorn Close, Doveridge, Ashbourne, Derbyshire DE6 5ND*

ANDREWS, Alfred Vincent. b 14. St D Coll Lamp 54. **d** 56 **p** 57. C Westmr St Sav and St Jas Less *Lon* 58-79; rtd 79. *3 Coast View, Bude, Cornwall EX23 8AG* Bude (01288) 352609

ANDREWS, Anthony Brian. b 33. Lon Univ BA54 AKC58. Coll of Resurr Mirfield 56. **d** 58 **p** 59. C Haggerston St Columba *Lon* 58-60; C N Hammersmith St Kath 60-63; V Goldthorpe *Sheff* 63-74; V Notting Hill St Mich and Ch Ch *Lon* from 74. *St Michael's Vicarage, 35 St Lawrence Terrace, London W10 5SR* 0181-969 0776

ANDREWS, Anthony Bryan de Tabley. b 20. K Coll Lon BA42. Linc Th Coll 42. **d** 44 **p** 45. V Babbacombe *Ex* 59-75; R Worth *Chich* 75-82; RD E Grinstead 77-82; P-in-c Exton and Winsford and Cutcombe w Luxborough *B & W* 82-83; R 83-85; rtd 85; Perm to Offic *Ex* from 86. *Cordwainers, Iddesleigh, Winkleigh, Devon EX19 8BG* Winkleigh (01837) 810116

ANDREWS, Anthony Frederick. b 25. K Coll Lon 54. **d** 55 **p** 56. C Bridgwater St Mary w Chilton Trinity *B & W* 69-70; R Cossington 70-73; C Highworth w Sevenhampton and Inglesham etc *Bris* 75-84; P-in-c Bishopstone w Hinton Parva 84-88; rtd 88. *Burford House, Highworth, Swindon SN6 7AD* Swindon (01793) 762796

ANDREWS, Anthony John. b 35. S'wark Ord Course 75. **d** 80 **p** 81. NSM Cheam *S'wark* 80-83; C Epsom St Martin *Guildf* 83-86; V Barton *Portsm* 86-89; Chapl Northwick Park Hosp Harrow from 90; Chapl Harrow Hosp from 90. *9 The Terrace, Northwick Park Hospital, Watford Road, Harrow, Middx HA1 3UJ* 0181-869 3923 or 864 3232

ANDREWS, Canon Brian Keith. b 39. Keble Coll Ox BA62 MA69. Coll of Resurr Mirfield 62. **d** 64 **p** 65. C Is of Dogs Ch Ch and St Jo w St Luke *Lon* 64-68; C Hemel Hempstead *St Alb* 68-71; TV 71-79; V Abbots Langley from 79; RD Watford 88-94; Hon Can St Alb from 94. *The Vicarage, High Street, Abbots Langley, Herts WD5 0AS* Kings Langley (01923) 263013/261795 Fax 261795

ANDREWS, Christopher Paul. b 47. Fitzw Coll Cam BA70 MA73. Westcott Ho Cam 69. **d** 72 **p** 73. C Croydon *Cant* 72-75; C Gosforth All SS *Newc* 75-79; TV Newc Epiphany 80-87; RD Newc Cen 82-87; V Alnwick St Mich and St Paul from 87; Chapl Alnwick Infirmary from 87. *The Vicarage, Alnwick, Northd NE66 1LT* Alnwick (01665) 602184

ANDREWS, Clive Francis. b 50. K Coll Lon BD72 AKC72. **d** 73 **p** 74. C Clapham H Trin *S'wark* 73-75; C Kidbrooke St Jas 76-78; Youth Officer 79-84; V Forest Hill St Aug 84-89; Perm to Offic *Sarum* from 89. *Cross River Cottage, Donhead St Andrew, Shaftesbury, Dorset SP7 9EQ* Donhead (01747) 828126

ANDREWS, Clive Frederick. b 43. St Jo Coll Nottm 81. **d** 83 **p** 84. C Leic St Jas *Leic* 83-86; Ind Chapl 86-90; Hon TV Melton Gt Framland 89-90; TV Clifton *S'well* 90-92; P-in-c Elkesley w Bothamsall 92-94; P-in-c Gamston w Eaton and W Drayton 92-94; R from 94. *The Vicarage, 3 Maple Drive, Elkesley, Retford, Notts DN22 8AX* Gamston (01777) 838293

ANDREWS, Edward Robert. b 33. St Mich Coll Llan 62. **d** 64 **p** 65. C Kingswinford St Mary *Lich* 64-69; Chapl RAF 69-88; R St Just in Roseland w Philleigh *Truro* from 88. *The Rectory, St Just in Roseland, Truro, Cornwall TR2 5JD* St Mawes (01326) 270248

ANDREWS, Eric Charles. b 17. AKC41. **d** 41 **p** 42. V Eastbourne St Andr *Chich* 63-73; R E Blatchington 73-83; rtd 83; Perm to Offic *Chich* from 83. *3 The Spinney, Bexhill-on-Sea, E Sussex TN39 3SW* Cooden (01424) 843864

ANDREWS, Eric Keith. b 11. Tyndale Hall Bris 36. **d** 38 **p** 39. Kenya 66-70; R Staunton *St E* 70-76; rtd 76; Perm to Offic *Heref* from 76. *79 Bearcroft, Weobley, Hereford HR4 8TD* Weobley (01544) 318114

ANDREWS, Frances. b 24. E Midl Min Tr Course 73. **dss** 78 **d** 87 **p** 94. Porchester *S'well* 78-86; Asst Chapl Nottm City Hosp 86-88; Hon C Gedling *S'well* 88-92; NSM Epperstone 92-95; NSM Gonalston 92-95; NSM Oxton 92-95; rtd 95. *1 Cromford Avenue, Nottingham NG4 3RU* Nottingham (0115) 961 3857

ANDREWS, John Colin. b 47. Sarum & Wells Th Coll 78. **d** 80 **p** 81. C Burnham *B & W* 80-84; V Williton 84-92; P-in-c Ashwick w Oakhill and Binegar from 92; Bp's Research and Dioc Communications Officer from 92. *The Rectory, Fosse Road, Oakhill, Bath BA3 5HU* Oakhill (01749) 841341 Fax 841098

ANDREWS, Preb John Douglas. b 19. Keble Coll Ox BA39 MA44. Chich Th Coll 40. **d** 42 **p** 43. V Penkhull *Lich* 68-80; P-in-c Ellenhall w Ranton 80-86; P-in-c Chebsey 80-86; Preb

Lich Cathl 81-86; rtd 86; Perm to Offic *Lich* from 86. *The Bungalow, 1 Belgrave Place, Shrewsbury SY2 5LT* Shrewsbury (01743) 240270

ANDREWS, John Elfric. b 35. Ex Coll Ox BA59 MA63. Wycliffe Hall Ox 59. **d** 61 **p** 62. C Cheltenham All SS *Glouc* 61-66; Cand Sec Lon City Miss 66-92; Lic to Offic *S'wark* 66-92; R Kingham w Churchill, Daylesford and Sarsden *Ox* from 92. *The Rectory, 6 The Moat, Kingham, Oxford OX7 4XZ* Kingham (01608) 658230

ANDREWS, John Francis. b 34. Jes Coll Cam BA58 MA62. S'wark Ord Course 78. **d** 81 **p** 82. C Norwood All SS *Cant* 81-82; NSM Upper Norwood All SS w St Marg 82-85; NSM Upper Norwood All SS *S'wark* 85-87; NSM Dulwich St Barn 89-92; NSM S Dulwich St Steph 92-95; Perm to Offic from 95. *46 Cypress Road, London SE25 4AU* 0181-653 5620

ANDREWS, John George William. b 42. Qu Coll Birm 65. **d** 68 **p** 69. C Smethwick St Matt w St Chad *Birm* 68-71; CF from 71. *c/o MOD (Army), Bagshot Park, Bagshot, Surrey GU19 5PL* Bagshot (01276) 471717 Fax 412834

ANDREWS, John Viccars. b 31. St Edm Hall Ox BA55. St Steph Ho Ox 55. **d** 58 **p** 59. C Clerkenwell H Redeemer w St Phil *Lon* 58-63; C Tilehurst St Mich *Ox* 63-69; P-in-c Abingdon w Shippon 69-76; R Cranwich *Nor* 76-86; R Ickburgh w Langford 76-86; R Mundford w Lynford 76-86; R Seaton Ross Gp of Par *York* from 86; RD S Wold from 90. *The Rectory, Everingham, York YO4 4JA* Market Weighton (01430) 860602

ANDREWS, Keith. b 47. St Mich Coll Llan 79. **d** 81 **p** 82. C Penarth w Lavernock *Llan* 81-85; V Nantymoel w Wyndham 85-91; RD Bridgend 89-93; R Coychurch w Llangan and St Mary Hill from 91. *The Rectory, Coychurch, Bridgend, M Glam CF35 5HF* Bridgend (01656) 860785

ANDREWS, Major Paul Rodney Gwyther. b 16. GM41. Mon Dioc Tr Scheme 74. **d** 77 **p** 78. NSM Goetre w Llanover and Llanfair Kilgeddin *Mon* 77-80; Lic to Offic *S & B* from 81. *Bromelys, Llangorse, Brecon, Powys LD3 7UG* Llangorse (0187484) 296

ANDREWS, Peter Alwyne. b 44. Lon Univ BSc67. Westcott Ho Cam 70. **d** 73 **p** 74. C Barnoldswick w Bracewell *Bradf* 73-76; C Maltby *Sheff* 76-78; V Bradf St Oswald Chapel Green *Bradf* 78-85; V Hanwell St Thos *Lon* from 85. *St Thomas's Vicarage, 182 Boston Road, London W7 2AD* 0181-567 5280

ANDREWS, Peter Douglas. b 52. SEN72 SRN78. St Steph Ho Ox 86. **d** 88 **p** 89. C Perry Barr *Birm* 88-92; TV Swindon New Town *Bris* from 92. *St Saviour's Vicarage, 6 Hillcrest Close, Hillside Avenue, Swindon SN1 4LX* Swindon (01793) 617681

ANDREWS, Richard John. b 57. Bris Univ BA78 CertEd79. Ripon Coll Cuddesdon 82. **d** 84 **p** 85. C Kidderminster St Mary and All SS etc *Worc* 84-87; Hon C Derby Cathl *Derby* 87-89; Chapl Derbyshire Coll of HE 87-89; V Chellaston *Derby* 89-93; V Spondon from 93. *St Werburgh's Vicarage, Gascoigne Drive, Spondon, Derby DE21 7LH* Derby (01332) 673573

ANDREWS, Walford Brian (Wally). b 34. Univ of Wales (Lamp) BA54. St Mich Coll Llan 54. **d** 57 **p** 58. C Canton St Jo *Llan* 57-62; Miss to Seamen from 62; India 62-65; Chapl Rotterdam Miss to Seamen *Eur* 65-66 and 70-77; Australia 66-69; Chapl Hull Miss to Seamen 77-83; Regional Chapl Hong Kong Miss to Seamen 83-92; Chapl Avonmouth Miss to Seamen from 92. *Avonmouth Seafarer's Centre, Gloucester Road, Bristol BS11 9AQ, or 4 Penlea Court, Bristol BS11 0BY* Bristol (0117) 982 2335 or 982 6107

ANGEL, Gervais Thomas David. b 36. Ch Ch Ox BA59 MA62 Bris Univ MEd78. **d** 61 **p** 62. C Abth St Mich *St D* 61-65; Tutor Clifton Th Coll 65-72; Dean Studies Trin Coll Bris 72-81; Dir Studies 81-90; Hon C Clifton H Trin, St Andr and St Pet *Bris* 82-90; Area Sec (W England) SAMS from 90; Th Consultant SAMS from 90; Perm to Offic *Ex* from 90; NSM Stoke Gifford *Bris* from 92. *82 Oak Close, Little Stoke, Bristol BS12 6RD* Chipping Sodbury (01454) 618081 Fax Bristol (01272) 236053

ANGEL, Robin Alan. b 41. St Mich Coll Llan. **d** 89 **p** 90. C Whitchurch *Llan* 89-94; V Abperpergwm and Blaengwrach from 94. *The Vicarage, 11 Roberts Close, Glyn Neath, Neath, W Glam SA11 5HR* Neath (01639) 721964

ANGELO, Brother. *See* DEACON, Donald

ANGLE, John Edwin George. b 42. Liv Univ ADEd73 Univ of Wales MEd75 Univ of the W of England, Bris DipEdMan85. Lon Bible Coll BD65 W of England Minl Tr Course 92. **d** 94 **p** 95. NSM Clevedon St Andr and Ch Ch *B & W* from 94. *19 Pyne Point, Clevedon, Avon BS21 7RL* Clevedon (01275) 872630 Fax as telephone

ANGUS, Edward. b 39. Man Univ BA60. Qu Coll Birm DipTh61. **d** 62 **p** 63. C Chorley St Geo *Blackb* 62-65; C S Shore H Trin 65-68; R Bretherton 68-76; V Altham w Clayton le Moors 76-90; V Preesall from 90. *St Oswald's Vicarage, Lancaster Road, Poulton-le-Fylde, Lancs FY6 0DU* Knott End (01253) 810297

ANGWIN, Richard Paul. b 25. ACA49 FCA60 AKC56. d 56 p 57. V Wanstead H Trin Hermon Hill *Chelmsf* 69-75; Chapl Wanstead Hosp Lon 69-75; Chapl Halstead Hosp 75-87; V Halstead St Andr *Chelmsf* 75-78; P-in-c Greenstead Green 75-78; V Halstead St Andr w H Trin 78-79; V Halstead St Andr w H Trin and Greenstead Green 79-87; RD Halstead and Coggeshall 84-87; rtd 87. *2 Seckham Road, Lichfield, Staffs WS13 7AN* Lichfield (01543) 250848

ANIDO, John David Forsdyke. b 16. Ox Univ BA38 MA41 McGill Univ Montreal PhD75. Westcott Ho Cam 39. d 40 p 41. Canada 47-51 and 57-76; V Auckland St Andr and St Anne *Dur* 76-83; rtd 83; Perm to Offic *York* from 83. *The Spinney, 2 Park Road, Malton, N Yorkshire YO17 9EA* Malton (01653) 696338

ANKER, George William. b 10. AKC51. d 51 p 52. V Brockley Hill St Sav *S'wark* 68-72; C Sanderstead All SS 72-76; rtd 76; Perm to Offic *S'wark* from 76. *St Barnabas College, Blackberry Lane, Lingfield, Surrey RH7 6NJ* Dormans Park (01342) 870260

ANKER, Malcolm. b 39. Univ of Wales BA61. Bps' Coll Cheshunt 61. d 63 p 64. C Marfleet *York* 63-66; C Cottingham 66-69; V Skirlaugh w Long Riston 69-74; V Elloughton and Brough w Brantingham 74-84; V Tadcaster 84-86; V Tadcaster w Newton Kyme 86-91; V Oatlands *Guildf* from 91. *The Vicarage, 5 Beechwood Avenue, Weybridge, Surrey KT13 9TE* Weybridge (01932) 847963

ANKER-PETERSEN, Robert Brian. b 52. Aber Univ MTh88. Wycliffe Hall Ox BA79 MA88. d 93 p 94. C Perth St Ninian *St And* from 93. *53 Grange Road, Alloa, Clackmannanshire FK10 1LU* Alloa (01259) 212322

ANKERS, Charles William (Bill). b 42. FIMI. NE Ord Course 89. d 93. NSM York St Luke *York* from 93. *85 Burton Stone Lane, York YO3 6BZ* York (01904) 634145

ANKETELL, Jeyarajan. b 41. MInstP Lon Univ BSc62 PhD67. Coll of Resurr Mirfield 69. d 73 p 74. Asst Chapl Newc Univ *Newc* 73-75; Asst Chapl Lon Univ *Lon* 75-77; Teacher from 78; Lic to Offic *S'wark* 81-83; Chasetown High Sch from 85; NSM Lich St Mary w St Mich *Lich* from 86. *7 Wissage Lane, Lichfield, Staffs WS13 6DQ* Lichfield (01543) 262032

ANNACEY, Felix. b 62. Hull Univ DipTh87. d 87 p 88. C Fenton *Lich* 87-88; Ghana from 88. *PO Box 248, Koforidva, Ghana*

ANNAS, Geoffrey Peter. b 53. Sarum & Wells Th Coll. d 83 p 84. C S'wark H Trin w St Matt *S'wark* 83-87; TV Walworth 87-94; Warden Pemb Coll Miss Walworth 87-94; V Southn Thornhill St Chris *Win* from 94. *St Christopher's Vicarage, 402 Hinkler Road, Southampton SO2 6DF* Southampton (01703) 448537

ANNEAR, Hubert Tours. b 24. Dur Univ BA49 Leeds Univ MA58. Linc Th Coll 49. d 51 p 52. USPG 65-71; V Bierley *Bradf* 71-76; V Morley St Paul *Wakef* 76-87; rtd 88. *112 Asquith Avenue, Morley, Leeds LS27 9QN* Leeds (0113) 253 7880

ANNELY, Maurice James Leonard. b 22. Qu Coll Birm 77. d 80 p 82. NSM Tettenhall Regis *Lich* 81-83; NSM Midsomer Norton w Clandown *B & W* 83-86; NSM Selworthy and Timberscombe and Wootton Courtenay 86-88; NSM Luccombe 86-88; rtd 88. *26 Jay Park Crescent, Kidderminster, Worcs DY10 4JP* Kidderminster (01562) 69821

ANNET, John Thomas. b 20. TD66. Selw Coll Cam BA49 MA53. Westcott Ho Cam 49. d 51 p 52. R Didsbury Ch Ch *Man* 66-75; V Gt Budworth *Ches* 75-86; rtd 86; Perm to Offic *Ex* from 86. *58 Lydgates Road, Seaton, Devon EX12 2BX* Seaton (01297) 23495

ANNIS, Herman North. b 28. Lich Th Coll 62. d 64 p 65. C Toxteth Park St Agnes *Liv* 67-70; V 70-82; V Hempton and Pudding Norton *Nor* 82-84; P-in-c Sculthorpe w Dunton and Doughton 82-84; V Northn H Trin *Pet* 84-95; rtd 95; NSM Brighton St Bart *Chich* from 95. *45 Orchard Avenue, Worthing, W Sussex BN14 7PY* Worthing (01903) 205683

ANNIS, Jennifer Mary. b 49. d 95. NSM Digswell and Panshanger *St Alb* from 95. *261 Knightsfield, Welwyn Garden City, Herts AL8 7RA* Welwyn Garden (01707) 329599

ANNIS, Rodney James. b 43. Ex Univ BA75 MA79 PhD86. Ripon Coll Cuddesdon 75. d 76 p 77. C Brixham *Ex* 76-77; Asst Chapl Ex Univ 77-80; Chapl Ex Sch 77-80; C Boston *Linc* 80-84; Chapl Trin Hall Cam 84-87; V Bush Hill Park St Steph *Lon* from 87. *St Stephen's Vicarage, Village Road, Bush Hill Park, Enfield, Middx EN1 2ET* 0181-360 1407

ANNS, Pauline Mary. See HIGHAM, Mrs Pauline Mary

ANSAH, Kwesi Gyebi Ababio (George). b 54. DipSM87. Simon of Cyrene Th Inst 90 Oak Hill Th Coll DipHE93. d 93 p 94. C Peckham St Mary Magd *S'wark* from 93. *2 Wroxton Road, London SE15 2BN* 0171-652 4874

ANSCOMBE, John Thomas. b 51. Ex Univ BA72. Cranmer Hall Dur DipTh73. d 74 p 75. C Upper Armley *Ripon* 74-77; C Leeds St Geo 78-81; Exec Producer Scripture Union from 81;

Hon C Beckenham Ch Ch *Roch* from 82. *26 Wimborne Way, Beckenham, Kent BR3 4DJ* 0181-658 4037 or 0171-782 0013 Fax 0171-782 0014

ANSCOMBE, Canon Thomas. b 15. Qu Coll Cam BA37 MA41. Ridley Hall Cam 37. d 39 p 40. R Kirkheaton *Wakef* 64-80; Hon Can Wakef Cathl 77-80; rtd 80; Perm to Offic *Bradf* from 80; Perm to Offic *Wakef* from 80. *c/o Milton House, Marton Road, Gargrave, Skipton, N Yorkshire BD23 3NN* Skipton (01756) 749289

ANSDELL-EVANS, Peter. b 25. Liv Univ BArch51. S'wark Ord Course 89. d 91 p 92. NSM Kennington St Jo w St Jas *S'wark* from 91. *9 Dalmore Road, London SE21 8HD* 0181-670 8046

ANSELL, Antony Michael. b 40. St Jo Coll Nottm 78. d 80 p 81. C Harrow Weald St Mich *Lon* 80-84; C Trin St Mich, Harrow 84; Hon C Ches Square St Mich w St Phil 86-88; Hon C Mayfair Ch Ch from 88. *10 Durand Gardens, London SW9 0PP* 0171-587 0997

ANSELL, Howard. b 36. St Jo Coll Cam BA59 MA62. NW Ord Course 73. d 76 p 77. C Chapeltown *Sheff* 76-79; V Worsbrough St Thos and St Jas 79-83; R Lt Waltham *Chelmsf* from 83; P-in-c Gt Leighs from 92. *The Rectory, Brook Hill, Little Waltham, Chelmsford CM3 3LJ* Chelmsford (01245) 360241

ANSELL, John Christopher. b 49. DipAD. Sarum & Wells Th Coll 79. d 81 p 82. C Dartford St Alb *Roch* 81-84; C Leybourne 84-88; C Larkfield 84-88; TV Mortlake w E Sheen *S'wark* from 88. *17 Sheen Gate Gardens, London SW14 7PD* 0181-876 5002

ANSELL, Philip Harding. b 67. LMH Ox BA89 Rob Coll Cam BA92. Ridley Hall Cam CTM93. d 93 p 94. C Rainham w Wennington *Chelmsf* from 93. *34 Warwick Road, Rainham, Essex RM13 9XU* Rainham (01708) 555810

ANSELM, Brother. See SMYTH, Robert Andrew Laine

ANSON, Harry. b 35. FInstFF79. St Jo Coll Nottm 83. d 88. NSM Ayr *Glas* 88-93; Miss to Seamen 91-93. *Bridgend House, Patna, Ayr KA6 7LP* Ayr (01292) 531238

ANSTEY, Christopher Robin Paul. b 25. Trin Coll Ox BA49 MA50. St Steph Ho Ox 49. d 51 p 52. V Headington *Ox* 64-71; Lic to Offic *Ches* 72-75; Lic to Offic *Worc* 76-79; Hon Min Can Pet Cathl *Pet* 79-90; Chapl Westwood Ho Sch Pet 79-83; V Gretton w Rockingham and Caldecote *Pet* 83-90; rtd 90; Hon C Warton St Oswald w Yealand Conyers *Blackb* from 91. *The Parsonage, Upphall Lane, Priest Hutton, Carnforth, Lancs LA6 1JL* Carnforth (01524) 781264

ANSTEY, Nigel John. b 55. Cranmer Hall Dur 84. d 87 p 88. C Plumstead St Jo w St Jas and St Paul *S'wark* 87-91; TV Ipswich St Fran *St E* from 91. *St Clare's Vicarage, 92 Belmont Road, Ipswich IP8 3RP* Ipswich (01473) 687847

ANSTICE, John Neville. b 39. Lon Univ BSc63. Cuddesdon Coll 69. d 71 p 72. C Stonebridge St Mich *Lon* 71-74; Chapl Woodbridge Sch Suffolk 74-76; TV Droitwich *Worc* 76-80; P-in-c Salwarpe 76-79; Perm to Offic *Chich* from 80. *2 Fernhurst Close, Ifield, Crawley, W Sussex RH11 0AW* Crawley (01293) 535654

ANTHONY, Brother. See WILLIAMS, Howard Graham

ANTHONY, Charles William. b 15. St Cath Coll Cam BA38 MA42 Leeds Univ DipEd. Ely Th Coll 38. d 39 p 40. P-in-c Airmyn *Sheff* 59-78; V Hook 60-78; V Hook w Airmyn 78-86; rtd 86; Perm to Offic *Sheff* from 86; Perm to Offic *S'well* from 87. *The Old Rectory, Top Street, North Wheatley, Retford, Notts DN22 9OA* Gainsborough (01427) 880959

ANTHONY, Canon David Ivor Morgan. b 04. Dur Univ LTh32. St Aug Coll Cant 26. d 31 p 32. C Leic St Matt *Leic* 31-34; Australia from 34; Hon Can Bendigo 74-75. *52 Frodsham Street, Albion, Queensland, Australia 4010* Brisbane (7) 262-3040

ANTHONY, Gerald Caldecott. b 18. Down Coll Cam BA41 MA44. Wycliffe Hall Ox 41. d 43 p 44. R Bulmer *York* 66-72; V Broughton-in-Furness w Woodland *Carl* 72-75; P-in-c Seathwaite w Ulpha 73-75; V Broughton and Duddon 75-83; rtd 83; Perm to Offic *Worc* from 83. *2 Coppice Close, Malvern, Worcs WR14 1LE* Leigh Sinton (01886) 832930

ANTHONY, Ian Charles. b 47. NW Ord Course 76. d 79 p 80. NSM Lt Lever *Man* from 79. *36 Meadow Close, Little Lever, Bolton BL3 1LG* Farnworth (01204) 791437

ANTONY-ROBERTS, Gelert Roderick. b 43. Southn Univ BEd78 Reading Univ MA84. Sarum & Wells Th Coll. d 90 p 91. C Alton St Lawr *Win* 90-94. *c/o Harborne Vicarage, Old Church Road, Birmingham B17 0BB* 0121-427 1949

ap GWILYM, Gwynn. b 50. Univ of Wales (Ban) BA71 MA76. Wycliffe Hall Ox BA84 MA. d 84 p 85. C Ynyscynhaearn w Penmorfa and Porthmadog *Ban* 84-86; R Penegoes and Darowen w Llanbryn-Mair from 86. *The Rectory, Penegoes, Machynlleth, Powys SY20 8LW* Machynlleth (01654) 703214

ap IORWERTH, Geraint. b 50. Univ of Wales (Lamp) DipTh72 Univ of Wales (Cardiff) DPS73 MPhil90 Open Univ BA78. Burgess Hall Lamp 69 Westmr Past Foundn 73 St Mich Coll

Llan 73. **d** 74 **p** 75. C Holyhead w Rhoscolyn *Ban* 74-78; R Pennal w Corris and Esgairgeiliog from 78; Founder and Ldr Order of Sancta Sophia from 87. *The Rectory, Pennal, Machynlleth, Powys SY20 9JS* Pennal (01654) 791216

APPELBE, Frederick Charles. b 52. TCD DipTh87. CITC 87. **d** 87 **p** 88. C Waterford w Killea, Drumcannon and Dunhill *C & O* 87-90; C Taney *D & G* 90-92; I Rathmichael from 92. *Rathmichael Rectory, Shankill, Co Dublin, Irish Republic* Dublin (1) 282-2803

APPLEBY, Anthony Robert Nightingale (Tony). b 40. K Coll Lon AKC62. St Boniface Warminster 62. **d** 63 **p** 64. C Cov St Mark *Cov* 63-67; CF 67-95; R Dulverton and Brushford *B & W* from 95. *The Vicarage, High Street, Dulverton, Somerset TA22 9DW* Dulverton (01398) 323425

APPLEBY, Miss Janet Mohr (Jan). b 32. Lon Univ TCert53 BA79 Sussex Univ MA(Ed)74. Chich Th Coll 90. **d** 91. NSM Rottingdean *Chich* 91-95; NSM Stantonbury and Willen *Ox* from 95. *28 Lodge Gate, Great Linford, Milton Keynes MK14 5EW* Milton Keynes (01908) 676993

APPLEFORD, Kenneth Henry (Ken). b 30. ISM90. Portsm Dioc Tr Course 91. **d** 92. NSM Portsea St Mary *Portsm* from 92. *124 Stride Avenue, Portsmouth PO3 6HN* Portsmouth (01705) 814685

APPLEFORD, Canon Patrick Robert. b 25. Trin Coll Cam BA49 MA54. Chich Th Coll 50. **d** 52 **p** 53. Dean Lusaka Cath 66-72; P-in-c Sutton St Nicholas w Sutton St Michael *Heref* 73-75; Dir of Educn *Chelmsf* 75-90; Can Chelmsf Cathl 78-90; rtd 90. *35 Sowerberry Close, Chelmsford, Essex CM1 4YB* Chelmsford (01245) 443508

APPLEGARTH, Anthony Edgar (Tony). b 44. Chich Th Coll 82. **d** 84 **p** 85. C Cannington, Otterhampton, Combwich and Stockland *B & W* 84-86; C Bridgwater St Mary, Chilton Trinity and Durleigh 86-89; R Stogursey w Fiddington from 89. *The Rectory, High Street, Stogursey, Bridgwater, Somerset TA5 1PL* Nether Stowey (01278) 732884

APPLEGATE, John. b 56. Bris Univ BSc75. Trin Coll Bris DipHE PhD. **d** 84 **p** 85. C Collyhurst *Man* 84-87; C Broughton 87-92; C Higher Broughton 87-92; C Lower Broughton St Clem w St Matthias 87-92; C Broughton St Jas w St Clem and St Matthias 92-94; R Broughton from 94. *237 Great Clowes Street, Higher Broughton, Salford M7 9DZ* 0161-792 9161

APPLETON, Mrs Bonita (Bonnie). b 55. St Jo Coll Nottm DCM93. **d** 93 **p** 94. C Camberley St Paul *Guildf* from 93. *Cornerways, 3 Upper Gordon Road, Camberley, Surrey GU15 2HJ* Camberley (01276) 64699

APPLETON, John Bearby. b 42. Linc Th Coll 74. **d** 76 **p** 77. C Selby Abbey *York* 76-79; C Epsom St Barn *Guildf* 79-82; V Linc All SS *Linc* 82-94. *33 South End, Osmotherley, Northallerton, N Yorkshire DL6 3BN*

APPLETON, Canon Paul Valentine. b 19. LRAM ARCM K Coll Cam BA42 MA46. Lich Th Coll 42. **d** 44 **p** 45. Hd Master Linc Cathl Sch 60-70; Succ Linc Cathl *Linc* 60-85; V Owmby w Normanby 70-75; P-in-c Spridlington w Saxby and Firsby 73-90; R Owmby and Normanby w Glentham 75-90; Can and Preb Linc Cathl 77-90; rtd 90. *2 Eastfield Lane, Welton, Lincoln LN2 3NA* Welton (01673) 860667

APPLETON, Canon Ronald Percival. b 15. St Pet Hall Ox BA36 MA40. Ridley Hall Cam 36. **d** 38 **p** 39. V Winchcombe, Gretton, Sudeley Manor etc *Glouc* 62-86; RD Winchcombe 63-86; Hon Can Glouc Cathl 80-86; rtd 86. *1 Abbey Croft, Pershore, Worcs WR10 1JQ* Pershore (01386) 553023

APPLETON, Stanley Basil. b 04. Wycliffe Hall Ox 66. **d** 66 **p** 66. Lic to Offic *Ox* 66-74; Hon C Welford w Wickham and Gt Shefford 74-86; Hon C Welford w Wickham and Gt Shefford, Boxford etc from 86. *Leigh Cottage, Wickham, Newbury, Berks RG16 8HD* Boxford (0148838) 239

APPLETON, Dr Timothy Charles. b 36. Selw Coll Cam BA60 MA65 K Coll Lon PhD67 Cam Univ DSc81. S'wark Ord Course 69. **d** 72 **p** 73. NSM Harston w Hauxton *Ely* 72-76; Lect Cam Univ 73-88; Lic to Offic *Ely* 76-79 and from 84; P-in-c w Lt Eversden 79-84; Chapl and Counsellor Bourn Hall Clinic from 88. *44 Eversden Road, Harlton, Cambridge CB3 7ET* Cambridge (01223) 262226

APPLEYARD, Edward. b 19. OBE75 RD68. Kelham Th Coll 37. **d** 43 **p** 44. V Gt Ayton w Easby and Newton in Cleveland *York* 68-78; RD Stokesley 70-77; P-in-c Middlesb St Columba w St Paul 78-84; Dioc Rtd Clergy and Widows Officer *York* from 87. *16 Linden Road, Great Ayton, Middlesbrough, Cleveland TS9 6AN* Middlesbrough (01642) 722488

APPLIN, David Edward. b 39. Oak Hill Th Coll 63. **d** 65 **p** 66. C Ox St Clem *Ox* 65-69; C Felixstowe SS Pet and Paul *St E* 69-71; Lic to Offic *Win* 71-91; Travelling Sec Rwanda Miss 71-74; Home Sec 74-77; Gen Sec 77-81; Dir Overseas Personnel Dept TEAR Fund 82-87; Overseas Dir 87-92; Hon C Kempshott *Win* 91-92; R Awbridge w Sherfield English from 92. *The Rectory, Sherfield English, Romsey, Hants SO51 6FP* West Wellow (01794) 322152

APPS, Anthony Howard. b 22. Ch Coll Cam BA47 MA51. **d** 49 **p** 50. V Myddleton Square St Mark *Lon* 66-82; rtd 82. *18 Longworth Way, Guisborough, Cleveland TS14 6DG* Guisborough (01287) 637939

APPS, Bryan Gerald. b 37. Univ of Wales (Lamp) BA59 St Cath Coll Ox BA61 MA65. Wycliffe Hall Ox 59. **d** 61 **p** 62. C Southn St Alb *Win* 61-65; C Andover w Foxcott 65-69; P-in-c Freemantle 69-72; R 73-78; V Pokesdown All SS from 78. *All Saints' Vicarage, 14 Stourwood Road, Bournemouth BH6 3QP* Bournemouth (01202) 423747

APPS, David Ronald. b 34. Univ of Wales (Lamp) BA57. Sarum Th Coll 57. **d** 59 **p** 60. C Southbourne St Chris *Win* 59-62; C Weeke 62-67; V Alton All SS 67-80; V Charlestown *Truro* from 80; Miss to Seamen from 80. *The Vicarage, Charlestown, St Austell, Cornwall PL25 3PG* Par (01726) 812824

APPS, Canon Michael John (Brother Bernard). b 28. Pemb Coll Cam BA52 MA56. Cuddesdon Coll 53. **d** 55 **p** 56. C Spalding *Linc* 55-58; SSF from 58; Perm to Offic *Chelmsf* 59-63 and 67-69; P-in-c Plaistow 63-67; Australia 69-75; Guardian St Nic Friary Harbledown 77-78; Guardian Hilfield Friary Dorchester 78-89; Can and Preb Sarum Cathl *Sarum* 81-89. *10 Halcrow Street, London E1 2EP* 0171-247 6233

APTHORP, Ven Arthur Norman. b 24. Pemb Coll Cam BA47 MA50. Chich Th Coll 48. **d** 50 **p** 51. C Henfield *Chich* 50-52; C Hove All SS 52-56; Australia from 56; Hon Can Perth 73-77 and from 79; Adn of the Country (Perth) 82-89. *2 Brookton Highway, Brookton, W Australia 6306* Brookton (96) 421046

ARBER, Gerald Kenneth. b 37. Open Univ BA87. Oak Hill NSM Course. **d** 84 **p** 85. NSM Romford St Edw *Chelmsf* from 84. *5 Hill Grove, Romford RM1 4JP* Romford (01708) 750070

ARBERY, Canon Richard Neil. b 25. AKC49. **d** 50 **p** 51. V Hindley All SS *Liv* 59-78; RD Wigan 75-89; Hon Can Liv Cathl 77-92; V Wigan St Andr 78-92; rtd 92; Asst Chapl HM Young Offender Inst Hindley from 92. *11 Gillan Road, Wigan, Lancs WN6 7HQ* Wigan (01942) 491734 or 866255 Fax 867442

ARBUCKLE, Canon James Hugh. b 19. AKC49. **d** 49 **p** 50. V Barnetby le Wold *Linc* 54-76; P-in-c Bigby 64-76; Can and Preb Linc Cathl from 70; RD Yarborough 70-76; P-in-c Somerby w Humby 74-76; Sec Linc Dioc Syn and Past Cttee 76-84; rtd 85. *26 St Clare's Walk, Brigg, S Humberside DN20 8JS* Brigg (01652) 655594

ARBUTHNOT, Andy. b 26. S'wark Ord Course 71. **d** 74 **p** 75. NSM Mortlake w E Sheen *S'wark* 74-77; Lic to Offic *Guildf* 77-83; Missr Lon Healing Miss from 83. *20 Dawson Place, London W2 4TJ* 0171-229 3641

ARBUTHNOT, Canon James. b 19. QUB BA42. CITC 44. **d** 44 **p** 45. I Belf St Phil *Conn* 60-70; I Belf St Paul 70-87; Can Conn Cathl 83-87; rtd 87. *6 St Elizabeth's Court, Ballyregan Road, Dundonald, Belfast BT16 0HX* Belfast (01232) 487951

ARCHER, Alan Robert. b 38. AKC56. Lich Th Coll 65. **d** 68 **p** 69. C Lower Mitton *Worc* 68-71; C Foley Park 71-74; V Warndon 74-79; P-in-c Clifton upon Teme 79-81; P-in-c Lower Sapey 79-81; P-in-c The Shelsleys 79-81; V Malvern Wells and Wyche 81-83; TV Braunstone *Leic* 83-91; P-in-c Bemerton *Sarum* from 91; Dioc Link Officer for ACUPA from 92. *St Michael's Rectory, St Michael's Road, Salisbury SP2 9EQ* Salisbury (01722) 333750

ARCHER, Frederick John. b 06. Clifton Th Coll 29. **d** 33 **p** 38. V Corse and Staunton *Glouc* 61-73; rtd 73; Perm to Offic *Glouc* from 75. *c/o 194 Silverdale Road, Earley, Reading RG6 2NB* Reading (01734) 264494

ARCHER, Graham John. b 58. Lanc Univ BSc79. St Jo Coll Nottm DipTh. **d** 85 **p** 86. C Ipswich St Matt *St E* 85-89; C Walton 89-95; P-in-c from 95. *2 Blyford Way, Felixstowe, Suffolk IP11 8FW* Felixstowe (01394) 282204

ARCHER, John Thomas. b 28. Birm Coll of Commerce GIMechE68 Birm Poly CQSW83. E Midl Min Tr Course 79. **d** 80 **p** 81. NSM Derby St Thos *Derby* 80-86; V Edlington *Sheff* from 87. *The Vicarage, Broomhouse Lane, Edlington, Doncaster, S Yorkshire DN12 1LN* Rotherham (01709) 863148

ARCHER, Keith Malcolm. b 40. Man Univ BA61 MA80 Magd Coll Cam BA67 MA72. Ridley Hall Cam 66. **d** 68 **p** 69. C Newland St Jo *York* 68-70; Hon C Kersal Moor *Man* 72-79; Ind Chapl 72-93; V Weaste from 93. *The Vicarage, Derby Road, Salford M6 5BA* 0161-736 5819

ARCHER, Michael James (Mike). b 67. St Jo Coll Dur BA90. Ridley Hall Cam CTM92. **d** 94 **p** 95. C Littleover *Derby* from 94. *8 Thornhill Road, Littleover, Derby DE23 6FZ* Derby (01332) 763263

ARCHER, Michael John. b 37. Trin Coll Bris 76. **d** 78 **p** 79. C Kinson *Sarum* 78-81; C Harpenden St Nic *St Alb* 81-88; P-in-c Rashcliffe and Lockwood *Wakef* from 88. *The Vicarage, 42 Beaumont Park Road, Huddersfield HD4 5JS* Huddersfield (01484) 514968

ARCHER, Stanley Edwin. b 21. St Jo Coll Dur 80. **d** 81 **p** 82. C Upper Nidderdale *Ripon* 81-83; P-in-c Wensley 83-89; P-in-c

W Witton 83-89; rtd 89. *40 The Oaks, Masham, Ripon, N Yorkshire HG4 4DT* Ripon (01765) 689685

ARCUS, Jeffrey. b 40. NW Ord Course 72. **d** 75 **p** 76. C Halliwell St Thos *Man* 75-78; C Walmsley 78-81; P-in-c Bury Ch King 81-82; TV Bury Ch King w H Trin 82-93; V Ramsbottom St Jo and St Paul from 93. *St Paul's Vicarage, Maple Grove, Ramsbottom, Bury, Lancs BL0 0AN* Ramsbottom (01706) 821036

ARDAGH-WALTER, Christopher Richard. b 35. Univ of Wales (Lamp) BA58. Chich Th Coll 58. **d** 60 **p** 61. C Heavitree *Ex* 60-64; C Redcar *York* 64-67; C King's Worthy *Win* 67-69; C-in-c Four Marks CD 70-73; V Four Marks 73-76; P-in-c Eling, Testwood and Marchwood 76-78; TR Totton 76-84; R The Sherbornes w Pamber 84-88; V Froyle and Holybourne from 88. *The Vicarage, Church Lane, Holybourne, Alton, Hants GU34 4HD* Alton (01420) 83240

✠**ARDEN, Rt Rev Donald Seymour.** b 16. CBE81. Leeds Univ BA37. Coll of Resurr Mirfield 37. **d** 39 **p** 40 **c** 61. C Hatcham St Cath *S'wark* 39-40; C Potten End w Nettleden *St Alb* 41-43; S Africa 44-61; Can Zululand 59-61; Bp Nyasaland 61-64; Bp Malawi 64-81; Bp S Malawi & Abp Cen Africa 71-80; Asst Bp Willesden *Lon* from 81; P-in-c Uxbridge St Marg 81-86; rtd 86; Hon C N Harrow St Alb *Lon* from 86. *6 Frobisher Close, Pinner, Middx HA5 1NN* 0181-866 6009 Fax as telephone

ARDFERT AND AGHADOE, Archdeacon of. See SHANNON, Ven Malcolm James Douglas

ARDILL, Robert William Brian. b 40. QUB BSc63 PhD67. Ox NSM Course 80 St Jo Coll Nottm 84. **d** 83 **p** 85. NSM Sunninghill *Ox* 83-85; C Lenton *S'well* 85-87; Lic to Offic *Leic* from 94; NSM Loughb Em from 94. *6 Bramcote Road, Loughborough, Leics LE11 2SA* Loughborough (01509) 266340

ARDING, Richard. b 52. ACIB84. Oak Hill Th Coll DipHE92. **d** 92 **p** 93. C Bromley Common St Aug *Roch* from 92. *40 Rolleston Avenue, Orpington, Kent BR5 1AH* 0181-467 3877

ARDIS, Very Rev Edward George. b 54. CITC 76. **d** 78 **p** 79. C Dub Drumcondra w N Strand and St Barn *D & G* 78-81; C Dub St Bart w Ch Ch Leeson Park 81-84; I Ardamine w Kiltennel, Glascarrig etc *C & O* 84-89; Can Tuam Cathl *T, K & A* from 89; Dean Killala from 89; I Killala w Dunfeeny, Crossmolina etc 89-94; I Killala w Dunfeeny, Crossmolina, Kilmoremoy etc from 94; Dir of Ords from 95. *The Rectory, Ballina, Co Mayo, Irish Republic* Ballina (96) 216547

ARDLEY, Canon John Owen. b 39. Lon Univ BD70. S'wark Ord Course 70. **d** 72 **p** 73. C Caterham Valley *S'wark* 72-76; V Abbey Wood 76-84; Sub-Dean Woolwich 77-84; P-in-c Lower Sydenham St Mich from 84; P-in-c Sydenham All SS from 84; RD W Lewisham from 87; Hon Can S'wark Cathl from 95. *41 Trewsbury Road, London SE26 5DP* 0181-778 3065

ARGUILE, Roger Henry William. b 43. Dur Univ LLB64 Keble Coll Ox BA70 MA75. Ripon Hall Ox 70. **d** 71 **p** 72. C Walsall *Lich* 71-76; TV Blakenall Heath 76-83; TV Stafford 83-95; P-in-c St Neots *Ely* from 95. *The Vicarage, Church Street, St Neots, Huntingdon, Cambs PE19 2BU* Huntingdon (01480) 472297

ARGYLE, Douglas Causer. b 17. St Jo Coll Cam BA39 MA43. Ridley Hall Cam 39. **d** 41 **p** 42. Chapl Gresham's Sch Holt 59-74; P-in-c Eastleach w Southrop *Glouc* 74-82; rtd 82; Perm to Offic *Glouc* from 82. *East Lynn, London Road, Fairford, Glos GL7 4AR* Cirencester (01285) 713235

ARGYLE, Canon Edward Charles. b 55. ACT DipTh80. **d** 80 **p** 80. Australia 80-83; C Gt Yarmouth *Nor* 83-85; I Kilcooley w Littleon, Crohane and Fertagh *C & O* 85-94; Preb Ossory and Leighlin Cathls 92-94; rtd 94. *The Rectory, Grange Barna, Thurles, Co Tipperary, Irish Republic* Thurles (56) 34147

ARGYLL AND THE ISLES, Bishop of. See CAMERON, Rt Rev Douglas MacLean

ARGYLL AND THE ISLES, Dean of. See MACLEAY, Very Rev John Henry James

ARIES, William Albert. b 28. ACT ThL61 Bps' Coll Cheshunt 59. **d** 60 **p** 61. C-in-c Ringwood St Ive and St Leon CD *Win* 66-70; V St Leonards and St Ives 70-75; V Bournemouth St Clem 75-91; rtd 92; Perm to Offic *Win* from 92. *Avon View, 15 Beatty Road, Bournemouth BH9 3RG* Bournemouth (01202) 351128

ARKELL, Kevin Paul. b 53. Preston Poly DipSocWork81 BTh86. Sarum & Wells Th Coll 84. **d** 86 **p** 87. C S Petherton w the Seavingtons *B & W* 86-88; P-in-c Gt Harwood St Bart *Blackb* 88-90; V from 90. *St Bartholomew's Vicarage, 1 Church Lane, Great Harwood, Blackburn BB6 7PU* Great Harwood (01254) 884039

ARLOW, Canon William James. b 26. Edin Th Coll 59. **d** 59 **p** 60. I Newry St Patr *D & D* 66-70; I Belf St Donard 70-74; Dep Sec Irish Coun of Chs 74-75; Sec 75-79; Can for Ecum Affairs Belf

Cathl from 79; Treas 85-89; P-in-c Ballyphilip w Ardquin 86-89; rtd 89; Lic to Offic *D & D* from 90. *13 Ashford Park, Bangor, Co Down BT19 6DD* Bangor (01247) 469758

ARMAGH, Archbishop of. See EAMES, Most Rev Robert Henry Alexander

ARMAGH, Archdeacon of. See HOEY, Ven Raymond George

ARMAGH, Dean of. See CASSIDY, Very Rev Herbert

ARMAN, Brian Robert. b 54. St Jo Coll Dur BA77 LTh78. Cranmer Hall Dur 74. **d** 78 **p** 79. C Lawrence Weston *Bris* 78-82; C Bishopston 82-88; R Filton from 88. *The Rectory, Station Road, Bristol BS12 7BX* Bristol (0117) 979 1128

ARMES, John Andrew. b 55. SS Coll Cam BA77 MA81. Sarum & Wells Th Coll 77. **d** 79 **p** 80. C Walney Is *Carl* 79-82; Chapl to Agric 82-86; TV Greystoke, Matterdale and Mungrisdale 82-86; TV Watermillock 84-86; TV Man Whitworth *Man* 86-88; TR 88-94; Chapl Man Univ 86-94; P-in-c Goodshaw and Crawshawbooth from 94; AD Rossendale from 94. *Goodshaw Vicarage, Goodshawfold Road, Rossendale, Lancs BB4 8QN* Rossendale (01706) 213969

ARMFELT, Julian Roger. b 31. K Coll Cam BA53. Wells Th Coll 54. **d** 56 **p** 58. C Corringham *Linc* 69-73; TV Fincham *Ely* 73-75; V Freckleton *Blackb* 75-79; P-in-c Sherburn *York* 79-80; P-in-c W and E Heslerton w Knapton 79-80; P-in-c Yedingham 79-80; R Sherburn and W and E Heslerton w Yedingham 80-83; TV York All SS Pavement w St Crux and St Martin etc 83-84; P-in-c York St Mary Bishophill Junior w All SS 83-84; C Howden TM 84-86; P-in-c Laughton w Throapham *Sheff* 86-88; rtd 88. *Meadow Haven Cottage, Pier Road, Berwick-upon-Tweed TD15 1JB* Berwick-upon-Tweed (01289) 307241

ARMITAGE, Bryan Ambrose. b 28. K Coll Lon AKC55 BD58. **d** 56 **p** 57. C High Harrogate St Pet *Ripon* 56-59; S Africa 59-61; Uganda 61-73; Chapl Sutton Valence Sch Kent 73-75; Chapl Qu Ethelburga's Sch Harrogate 76-91; V Weaverthorpe w Helperthorpe, Luttons Ambo etc *York* from 91. *The Vicarage, Helperthorpe, Malton, N Yorkshire YO17 8TJ* Lutton (01944) 738213

ARMITAGE, Michael Stanley. b 45. Jes Coll Cam BA67 MA71. Cuddesdon Coll 67. **d** 69 **p** 70. C Sanderstead All SS *S'wark* 69-70; C Battersea St Mary 70-71; Hon C Kingston St Jo 72-73; Chapl Kingston Poly 72-73; V Angell Town St Jo from 73. *St John's Vicarage, Wiltshire Road, London SW9 7NF* 0171-733 0585

ARMITAGE, Richard Norris. b 51. AKC. St Aug Coll Cant 73. **d** 74 **p** 75. C Chapelthorpe *Wakef* 74-77; C W Bromwich All SS *Lich* 77-82; P-in-c Ketley 82-83; V Oakengates 82-83; V Ketley and Oakengates 83-89; V Evesham *Worc* from 89. *The Vicarage, 5 Croft Road, Evesham, Worcs WR11 4NE* Evesham (01386) 446219

ARMSON, Canon John Moss. b 39. Selw Coll Cam BA61 MA64 St Andr Univ PhD65. Coll of Resurr Mirfield 64. **d** 66 **p** 67. C Notting Hill St Jo *Lon* 66-69; Chapl Down Coll Cam 69-73; Fell 70-73; Chapl Westcott Ho Cam 73-76; Vice-Prin 76-82; Prin Edin Th Coll 82-89; Can St Mary's Cathl 82-89; Can Res Roch Cathl *Roch* from 89. *Easter Garth, King's Orchard, Rochester, Kent ME1 1SX* Medway (01634) 406992

ARMSTEAD, Geoffrey Malcolm. b 32. K Coll Lon BD56 AKC56 Nottm Univ ADEd73. St Boniface Warminster 56. **d** 57 **p** 57. C Weymouth H Trin *Sarum* 57-60; C Mortlake w E Sheen *S'wark* 60-63; Chapl Em Sch Wandsworth 63-74; Dep Hd Master Harriet Costello Sch 74-91; Acting Hd Master 91-92; Perm to Offic *Win* 74-92; V Win St Bart from 92. *Hyde Vicarage, 1 Abbey Hill Close, Winchester, Hants SO23 7AZ* Winchester (01962) 852032

ARMSTEAD, Gordon. b 33. Oak Hill Th Coll DPS74. **d** 74 **p** 75. C Woodside *Ripon* 74-76; C Heaton Ch Ch *Man* 76-79; Australia 79-81; R Levenshulme St Mark *Man* 81-86; V Borth and Eglwys-fach w Llangynfelyn *St D* 86-92; rtd 93. *27 Parkside Road, St Annes, Lytham St Annes, Lancs FY8 3SZ* St Annes (01253) 727647

ARMSTRONG, Dr Adrian Christopher. b 48. LSE BSc70 K Coll Lon PhD80. E Anglian Minl Tr Course 84. **d** 87 **p** 88. NSM Linton *Ely* 87-95; NSM N and S Muskham *S'well* from 95; NSM Averham w Kelham from 95. *St Wilfrid's Vicarage, Marsh Lane, North Muskham, Newark, Notts NG23 6HG* Newark (01636) 702655

ARMSTRONG, Alexander Milford. b 57. Local Minl Tr Course 87. **d** 95. NSM Livingston LEP *Edin* from 95. *6 Herd Green, Livingston, West Lothian EH54 8PU* Livingston (01506) 436524

ARMSTRONG, Christopher John. b 47. Nottm Univ BTh75. Kelham Th Coll 72. **d** 76 **p** 76. C Maidstone All SS w St Phil and H Trin *Cant* 76-79; Chapl St Hild and St Bede Coll Dur 79-84; Dir of Ords *York* from 85; Abp's Dom Chapl 85-91; V Scarborough St Martin from 91. *St Martin's Vicarage, Craven Street, Scarborough, N Yorkshire YO11 2BY* Scarborough (01723) 360437

ARMSTRONG, Christopher John Richard. b 35. Fribourg Univ LTh60 Ch Coll Cam BA64 MA68 PhD79. Edin Th Coll 74. **d** 59 **p** 59. In RC Ch 59-71; Lect Aber Univ 68-74; C Ledbury *Heref* 74-76; P-in-c Bredenbury and Wacton w Grendon Bishop 76-79; P-in-c Edwyn Ralph and Collington w Thornbury 76-79; P-in-c Pencombe w Marston Stannett and Lt Cowarne 76-79; R Cherry Burton *York* 79-80; Tutor Westcott Ho Cam 80-85; V Bottisham *Ely* 85-89; P-in-c Lode and Longmeadow 85-89; P-in-c Cropthorne w Charlton *Worc* 89-93; Dioc Local Min Sec 89-93; R Aberdaron w Rhiw and Llanfaelrhys etc *Ban* from 93. *The Rectory, Llangwnnadl, Pwllheli, Gwynedd LL53 8NU* Tudweiliog (01758) 770250

ARMSTRONG, Colin John. b 32. St Cath Soc Ox BA59 MA65. Wells Th Coll 59. **d** 61 **p** 62. C Acomb St Steph *York* 61-64; C Newland St Jo 64-67; Chapl and Tutor All SS Coll Tottenham 67-78; Chapl and Tutor Middx Poly 78-85. *Mead House, The Street, Preston St Mary, Sudbury, Suffolk CO10 9NQ* Sudbury (01787) 248218

ARMSTRONG, Edwin. b 23. TCD BA45 MA69. **d** 46 **p** 47. I Gilford *D & D* 57-85; rtd 85. *3 St Elizabeth's Court, Ballyregan Road, Dundonald, Belfast BT16 0HX* Belfast (01232) 487629

ARMSTRONG, Canon George. b 09. Clifton Th Coll 29. **d** 32 **p** 33. R Layer Marney *Chelmsf* 46-82; R Gt w Lt Birch and Layer Breton 47-82; RD Coggeshall and Tey 68-79; Hon Can Chelmsf Cathl 77-82; rtd 82; Perm to Offic *Chelmsf* from 82; Perm to Offic *St E* from 82. *11 The Westerings, Nayland, Colchester CO6 4LJ* Colchester (01206) 262952

ARMSTRONG, Guy Lionel Walter. b 18. OBE93. Wycliffe Hall Ox 60. **d** 61 **p** 62. V Bagshot *Guildf* 65-73; V Ripley 73-77; rtd 77; Perm to Offic *Portsm* from 81. *The Briary, 3 Wood Street, Ryde, Isle of Wight PO33 2DH* Isle of Wight (01983) 562454

ARMSTRONG, John Edwin. b 51. Leic Univ CertEd73 BEd74 Homerton Coll Cam AEdRD87. Ridley Hall Cam CTM93. **d** 93 **p** 94. C Gt Wilbraham *Ely* from 93. *The Vicarage, 5 Benstead's End, Great Wilbraham, Cambridge CB1 5JS* Cambridge (01223) 880332

ARMSTRONG, Canon John Hammond. b 24. Dur Univ BA47 DipTh49. **d** 49 **p** 50. R Sutton upon Derwent *York* 63-71; Dioc Stewardship Adv 63-75; P-in-c York All SS and St Crux w St Sav etc 71-72; R 72-76; Can and Preb York Minster 72-91; P-in-c York St Denys 74-76; RD City of York 76-86; TR York All SS Pavement w St Crux and St Denys 76-77; TR York All SS Pavement w St Crux and St Martin etc 77-91; rtd 91. *20 Hempland Avenue, Stockton Lane, York YO3 0DE* York (01904) 421312

ARMSTRONG, John James. b 15. TCD BA38 MA42 Div Test40. **d** 40 **p** 41. Miss to Seamen 58-77; Sudan 58-59; Dunkirk 60-62; Belf 75-77; C Derriaghy *Conn* 71-77; C Seagoe *D & D* 71-73; Hd of S Ch Miss Belf 73-75; C Belf St Simon w St Phil *Conn* 77-80; rtd 80. *60 The Green, Dunmurry, Belfast BT17 0QA* Belfast (01232) 623032

ARMSTRONG, Mrs Margaret Betty. b 48. Westcott Ho Cam 89. **d** 92 **p** 94. NSM Linton *Ely* 92-95; NSM Shudy Camps 92-95; NSM Castle Camps 92-95; NSM Bartlow 92-95; NSM N and S Muskham *S'well* from 95; NSM Averham w Kelham from 95. *St Wilfrid's Vicarage, Marsh Lane, North Muskham, Newark, Notts NG23 6HG* Newark (01636) 702655

ARMSTRONG, Maurice Alexander. b 62. Ulster Poly BA84 TCD DipTh87. CITC 84. **d** 87 **p** 88. C Portadown St Mark *Arm* 87-90; I Sixmilecross w Termonmaguirke 90-95; I Richhill from 95. *The Rectory, 15 Annareagh Road, Richhill, Armagh BT61 9JT* Richhill (01762) 871232

ARMSTRONG, Nicholas Paul (Nick). b 58. Bris Univ BSc79. Trin Coll Bris DipHE93. **d** 93 **p** 94. C Filey *York* from 93. *7 Elm Close, Filey, N Yorkshire YO14 9NN* Scarborough (01723) 514469

ARMSTRONG, Canon Robert Charles (Robin). b 24. TCD BA46 HDipEd52 MA57. CITC 47. **d** 47 **p** 48. I Dun Laoghaire *D & G* 67-94; RD Newc 71-76; Dir of Ords (Dub) 74-88; USPG Area Sec 77-94; Can Ch Ch Cathl Dub 84-88; Treas 88-94; rtd 94. *1 Glenageary Terrace, Dun Laoghaire, Co Dublin, Irish Republic* Dublin (1) 284-6941

ARMSTRONG, Ronald. b 09. St Jo Coll Dur BA38 MA42. **d** 38 **p** 39. Chapl Whipps Cross Hosp Lon 65-79; rtd 79. *Nether Barr, Newton Stewart, Wigtownshire DG8 6AU* Newton Stewart (01671) 2236

ARMSTRONG, Samuel David. b 48. BD MTh. **d** 86 **p** 87. C Cam H Trin w St Andr Gt *Ely* 86-89; V Cam St Martin from 89. *33 Rustat Road, Cambridge CB1 3QR* Cambridge (01223) 248648

ARMSTRONG, Samuel George (Sammie). b 39. Ox Univ Inst of Educn TCert65 CYCW65 ACertEd71 Open Univ BA72 Reading Univ MSc89. S Dios Minl Tr Scheme 90. **d** 93 **p** 94. NSM N Tadley St Mary *Win* from 93. *The Cedars, Blakes Lane, Tadley, Basingstoke, Hants RG26 6PU* Reading (01734) 816593

ARMSTRONG, William. b 29. Sarum Th Coll 52. **d** 54 **p** 55. Australia 66-81; Asst Dir of Educn *Liv* 81-90; V Aintree St Pet 81-88; TV Speke St Aid 88-90; rtd 90. *10 Blenheim Court, Horn Lane, Woodford Green, Essex IG8 9AQ* 0181-504 1874

ARMSTRONG-MacDONNELL (nee BROOKES), Mrs Vivienne Christine. b 42. Open Univ BA89. Ripon Coll Cuddesdon 88. **d** 90 **p** 94. C Crediton and Shobrooke *Ex* 90-93; Dioc Adv in Adult Tr from 93. *Strand House, Woodbury, Exeter EX5 1LZ* Woodbury (01395) 232790

ARNAUD, John Charles Stanley. b 23. Aber Univ MA48 DipEd49. **d** 78 **p** 79. Hon C Huntly *Mor* 78-91; Hon C Aberchirder 78-91; Hon C Keith 78-91; rtd 91; Perm to Offic *Mor* from 91. *Rosemount, 19 Kynoch Terrace, Keith, Banffshire AB5 3EX* Keith (015422) 2240

ARNESEN, Christopher Paul. b 48. Lon Univ BA70. Sarum & Wells Th Coll 78. **d** 80 **p** 81. C Dalton-in-Furness *Carl* 80-83; C Ranmoor *Sheff* 83-86; R Distington *Carl* 86-93; TV Sheff Manor *Sheff* from 93. *St Paul's Vicarage, East Bank Road, Sheffield S2 2AD* Sheffield (0114) 239 8533

ARNESEN, Raymond Halfdan (Brother Ælred). b 25. Qu Coll Cam BA49 MA54. Linc Th Coll 50. **d** 52 **p** 53. C Newc St Fran *Newc* 52-55; SSF 55-66; Cistercian Monk from 66. *Ewell Monastery, West Malling, Kent ME19 6HH* West Malling (01732) 843089

ARNOLD, Alan Roy. b 33. Lon Univ BD79. S'wark Ord Course 75. **d** 78 **p** 79. C Fleet *Guildf* 78-81; V Hinchley Wood 81-84; C Cobham 84-89; C Addlestone 89-92; rtd 93; Perm to Offic *Guildf* 92-94; Perm to Offic *Win* from 94. *Flat 9, 68 West Cliff Road, Bournemouth BH4 8BE* Bournemouth (01202) 752018

ARNOLD, Arthur Philip. b 46. Em Coll Cam BA67 MA71. Qu Coll Birm DipTh69. **d** 70 **p** 71. C Failsworth H Family CD *Man* 70-74; Asst Chapl Hurstpierpoint Coll Hassocks 74-77; Chapl K Coll Cam 77-80; Chapl St Chad's Coll Dur 80-82; Chapl Plymouth Coll from 83; Lic to Offic *Ex* from 83. *Mannamead Flat, Plymouth College, Ford Park, Plymouth PL4 6RE* Plymouth (01752) 228239

ARNOLD, Brother. See NODDER, Thomas Arthur

ARNOLD, Elisabeth Anne Truyens. b 44. TCert66. Local NSM Course 88. **d** 91 **p** 94. NSM Ipswich St Thos *St E* from 91. *66 Bromeswell Road, Ipswich IP4 3AT* Ipswich (01473) 257406

ARNOLD, Ernest Stephen. b 27. **d** 64 **p** 65. V Ferndale *Llan* 68-74; Cyprus 81-85; rtd 94. *Barn Cottage, Apse Manor Road, Shanklin, Isle of Wight PO37 7PN* Isle of Wight (01983) 866324

ARNOLD, George Innes. b 22. Roch Th Coll. **d** 61 **p** 62. Egypt 68-70; V Croydon St Jas *Cant* 71-80; P-in-c Dullingham *Ely* 80-91; P-in-c Stetchworth 80-91; RD Linton 81-88; rtd 91. *5 Bridge Place, Rye, E Sussex TN31 7LN* Rye (01797) 224509

ARNOLD, Graham Thomas. b 62. S Kent Coll of Tech OND80. Aston Tr Scheme 87 Ripon Coll Cuddesdon 89. **d** 92 **p** 93. C Margate St Jo *Cant* from 92. *173 Ramsgate Road, Margate, Kent CT9 4EY* Thanet (01843) 294621

ARNOLD, Very Rev John Robert. b 33. SS Coll Cam BA57 MA61. Westcott Ho Cam 58. **d** 60 **p** 61. C Millhouses H Trin *Sheff* 60-63; Chapl and Lect Southn Univ *Win* 63-72; Gen Sec Gen Syn Bd for Miss and Unity 72-78; Hon Can Win Cathl *Win* 74-78; Dean Roch 78-89; Dean Dur from 89. *The Deanery, The College, Durham DH1 3EQ* 0191-384 7500

✠**ARNOLD, Rt Rev Keith Appleby.** b 26. Trin Coll Cam BA50 MA55. Westcott Ho Cam 50. **d** 52 **p** 53 **c** 80. C Haltwhistle *Newc* 52-55; C Edin St Jo *Edin* 55-61; R 61-69; CF (TA) 58-62; V Kirkby Lonsdale w Mansergh *Carl* 69-73; RD Berkhamsted *St Alb* 73-80; TR Hemel Hempstead 73-80; Suff Bp Warw *Cov* 80-90; Hon Can Cov Cathl 80-90; rtd 90. *White Lodge, Dunstan, Alnwick, Northd NE66 3TB* Alnwick (01665) 76485

ARNOLD, Paul Maxwell. b 53. Or Coll Ox BA74 MA78. Ripon Coll Cuddesdon 79. **d** 82 **p** 83. C Kensington St Mary Abbots w St Geo *Lon* 82-86; C Wokingham St Paul *Ox* 86-90; C Fingringhoe w E Donyland and Abberton etc *Chelmsf* 90-94. *5 Cope Place, London W8 6AA* 0171-937 6806

ARNOLD, Richard Nicholas. b 54. AKC76. S'wark Ord Course 76. **d** 77 **p** 78. C Nunhead St Antony *S'wark* 77-80; C Walworth 80-82; P-in-c Streatham Hill St Marg 82-84; V 84-89; P-in-c Oseney Crescent St Luke *Lon* 89-93; P-in-c Kentish Town St Jo 89-93; P-in-c Kentish Town St Benet and All SS 89-93; V Kentish Town from 93. *Kentish Town Vicarage, 43 Lady Margaret Road, London NW5 2NH* 0171-485 4231 Fax 482 7222

ARNOLD, Roy. b 36. St D Coll Lamp BA62 DipTh63. **d** 63 **p** 64. C Brislington St Luke *Bris* 63-66; C Ches St Mary *Ches* 67-70; V Brinnington w Portwood 71-75; V Sale St Paul 75-82; R Dodleston 82-84; V Sheff St Oswald *Sheff* 84-90; Dioc Communications Officer from 84; Chapl w the Deaf from 90. *10 Devonshire Road, Sheffield S17 3NT* Sheffield (0114) 236 1972 Fax 262 1189

ARNOLD, Victor Norman. b 45. Oak Hill Th Coll 91. **d** 94 **p** 95. NSM Chigwell and Chigwell Row *Chelmsf* from 94. *Spring Cottage, 6 Spring Grove, Loughton, Essex IG10 4QA* 0181-508 6572

ARNOTT, David. b 44. Em Coll Cam BA66. Qu Coll Birm 68. **d** 69 **p** 70. C Old Charlton *S'wark* 69-73; C S Beddington St Mich 73-78; Chapl Liv Poly *Liv* 78-82; V Bridgwater St Fran *B & W* from 86. *The Vicarage, Saxon Green, Bridgwater, Somerset TA6 4HZ* Bridgwater (01278) 422744

ARNOTT, Eric William. b 12. Cranmer Hall Dur 67. **d** 68 **p** 69. C Gosforth St Nic *Newc* 68-71; C Wooler 71-74; TV Wooler Gp 74-78; rtd 78. *Forge Cottage, Hoopers Lane, Puncknowle, Dorchester, Dorset DT2 9BE* Burton Bradstock (01308) 897768

ARNOTT, Thomas Grenfell. b 11. Solicitor. NE Ord Course 61 Cranmer Hall Dur 68. **d** 68 **p** 69. C Ryton *Dur* 68-71; V Weston-super-Mare Em *B & W* 71-73; R Brandesburton *York* 73-78; RD N Holderness 76-78; rtd 78. *1 Mulrany Manor, Graham Crescent, Scarborough, N Yorkshire YO12 5DG* Scarborough (01723) 363133

ARRAND, Ven Geoffrey William. b 44. K Coll Lon BD66 AKC66. **d** 67 **p** 68. C Washington *Dur* 67-70; C S Ormsby w Ketsby, Calceby and Driby *Linc* 70-73; TV Gt Grimsby St Mary and St Jas 73-79; TR Halesworth w Linstead and Chediston *St E* 79-80; TR Halesworth w Linstead, Chediston, Holton etc 80-85; R Hadleigh w Layham and Shelley 85-94; Dean Bocking 85-94; RD Hadleigh 86-94; Can Soc St E Cathl from 91; Adn Suffolk from 94. *38 Saxmundham Road, Aldeburgh, Suffolk IP15 5JE* Aldeburgh (01728) 454034 Fax as telephone

ARRANDALE, Richard Paul Matthew. b 63. BA87. Chich Th Coll 87. **d** 90 **p** 91. C E Grinstead St Swithun *Chich* 90-94; C Crawley 94. *6 Main Drive, Bognor Regis, W Sussex PO22 7TN*

ARRANTASH, Canon Reginald Thomas. b 12. Linc Th Coll 33. **d** 36 **p** 37. C Kennington St Jo *S'wark* 36-37; Australia 37-48 and from 52; R Kenchester and Bridge Sollers *Heref* 48-52; R Bishopstone 48-52. *51 Sundowner Centre, 416 Stirling Highway, Cottesloe, W Australia 6011* Perth (9) 385-2318

ARRIDGE, Leonard Owen. b 22. Univ of Wales (Ban) BA51. St Deiniol's Hawarden 64. **d** 67 **p** 68. Tutor Ches Coll of FE 67-79; Hon C Wrexham *St As* 69-79; Min Can Ban Cathl *Ban* 79-87; C Ban Cathl Par 79-87; rtd 87. *8 Ffordd Islwyn, Bangor, Gwynedd LL57 1AR* Bangor (01248) 362233

ARSCOTT, Barry James. b 36. AKC59. **d** 60 **p** 61. C Walthamstow St Andr *Chelmsf* 60-65; P-in-c Leyton St Luke 65-67; V 67-77; P-in-c Lt Ilford St Barn 77-86; R from 86. *St Barnabas' Vicarage, Browning Road, London E12 6PB* 0181-472 2777

ARTHINGTON, Sister Muriel. b 23. dss 67 **d** 87. St Etheldreda's Children's Home Bedf 64-84; rtd 84; Hon Par Dn Bedf St Paul *St Alb* 87-94; Perm to Offic from 94. *12 Christie House, Newnham Road, Bedford MK40 3NZ*

ARTHUR, Graeme Richard. b 52. Univ of NSW BCom78. Linc Th Coll CMinlStuds93. **d** 93 **p** 94. C Witney *Ox* from 93. *111 Thorney Leys, Witney, Oxon OX8 7AY* Witney (01993) 772191

ARTHUR, Ian Willoughby. b 40. Lon Univ BA63 BA66 PGCE64. Ripon Coll Cuddesdon 78. **d** 80 **p** 81. C Kempston Transfiguration *St Alb* 80-83; R Potton w Sutton and Cockayne Hatley from 83. *The Rectory, Hatley Road, Potton, Sandy, Beds SG19 2DX* Potton (01767) 260782

ARTISS, Joseph Sturge. b 28. Dur Univ BSc52. Cranmer Hall Dur DipTh67. **d** 67 **p** 68. C Ches le Street *Dur* 68-70; V Walsall St Pet *Lich* 71-94; rtd 94. *89 Bloxwich Road, Walsall WS2 8BP* Walsall (01922) 23995

ARTLEY, Clive Mansell. b 30. St Jo Coll Dur BA56. Cranmer Hall Dur DipTh58. **d** 58 **p** 59. CF 64-73; Teacher 73-93; Perm to Offic *York* from 73; rtd 93. *56 High Street, Castleton, Whitby, N Yorkshire YO21 2DA* Guisborough (01287) 660470

ARTLEY, Harold Leslie. b 37. N Ord Course 79. **d** 82 **p** 83. NSM Flamborough *York* 82-89; R Bainton w N Dalton, Middleton-on-the-Wolds etc from 89. *The New Rectory, West End, Bainton, Driffield, N Humberside YO25 9NR* Middleton-on-the-Wolds (01377) 217622

ARTUS, Stephen James. b 60. Man Poly BA82 W Midl Coll of Educn PGCE84. St Jo Coll Nottm MA95. **d** 95. C Altrincham St Geo *Ches* from 95. *18 Hawarden Road, Altrincham, Cheshire WA14 1NG* 0161-928 5897

ARUNDEL, Canon Michael. b 36. Qu Coll Ox BA60 MA64. Linc Th Coll 60. **d** 62 **p** 63. C Hollinwood *Man* 62-65; C Leesfield 65-69; R Newton Heath All SS 69-80; RD N Man 75-80; P-in-c Eccles St Mary 80-81; TR Eccles 81-91; Hon Can Man Cathl from 82; R Man St Ann from 91. *The Rectory, 449 Wilbraham Road, Chorlton-cum-Hardy, Manchester M21 1US* 0161-881 1229

ARVIDSSON, Karl Fredrik. b 66. Independent Bible Coll DipTh91. **d** 92 **p** 93. OSB from 92; C Southsea H Spirit *Portsm* 92-94; C Botley from 94; C Curdridge from 94; C Durley from 94. *1 Rectory Court, Botley, Southampton SO3 2SJ* Botley (01489) 787715

ASBRIDGE, Preb John Hawell. b 26. Dur Univ BA47. Bps' Coll Cheshunt 47. **d** 49 **p** 50. C Barrow St Geo *Carl* 49-52; C Fort William *Arg* 52-54; C Lon Docks St Pet w Wapping St Jo *Lon* 54-55; C Kilburn St Aug 55-59; V Northolt Park St Barn 59-66; V Shepherd's Bush St Steph w St Thos from 66; Preb St Paul's Cathl from 89. *St Stephen's Vicarage, Coverdale Road, London W12 8JJ* 0181-743 3166

ASBRIDGE, Nigel Henry. b 58. Bris Univ BA80. Chich Th Coll 87. **d** 89 **p** 90. C Tottenham St Paul *Lon* 89; C W Hampstead St Jas 89-94; P-in-c Hornsey H Innocents from 94. *99 Hillfield Avenue, London N8 7DG* 0171-340 1300

ASH, Arthur Edwin. b 44. St Jo Coll Nottm 85. **d** 87 **p** 88. C Attleborough *Cov* 87-91; V Garretts Green *Birm* from 91. *The Vicarage, 112 Rotherfield Road, Birmingham B26 2SH* 0121-743 2971

ASH, Brian John. b 32. ALCD62. **d** 62 **p** 63. C Plymouth St Andr *Ex* 62-66; Area Sec (Dios Cant and Roch) CMS 66-73; V Bromley Common St Aug *Roch* from 73. *St Augustine's Vicarage, Southborough Lane, Bromley BR2 8AT* 0181-467 1351

ASH, Christopher Brian Garton. b 53. Trin Hall Cam MA76. Wycliffe Hall Ox BA92. **d** 93 **p** 94. C Cam H Sepulchre *Ely* from 93. *1 Pretoria Road, Cambridge CB4 1HD* Cambridge (01223) 355165

ASH, Nicholas John. b 59. Bath Univ BSc81 Nottm Univ BTh88. Linc Th Coll 85. **d** 88 **p** 89. C Hersham *Guildf* 88-93; P-in-c Flookburgh *Carl* from 93; Dioc Officer for Stewardship from 94. *The Vicarage, Flookburgh, Grange-over-Sands, Cumbria LA11 7JY* Grange-over-Sands (015395) 58245

ASHBURNER, David Barrington. b 26. Ch Coll Cam BA51 MA55. Wycliffe Hall Ox 51. **d** 53 **p** 54. V Bucklebury w Marlston *Ox* 58-70; V Belton *Leic* 70-75; P-in-c Osgathorpe 73-75; R Belton and Osgathorpe 75-79; V Frisby-on-the-Wreake w Kirby Bellars 79-82; V Uffington w Woolstone and Baulking *Ox* 82-91; P-in-c Shellingford 83-91; RD Vale of White Horse 87-91; rtd 91; Perm to Offic *Glouc* from 91; Perm to Offic *Ox* from 91. *Rose Cottage, Bourton on the Hill, Moreton-in-Marsh, Glos GL56 9AE* Evesham (01386) 700682

ASHBY, Eric. b 37. E Midl Min Tr Course 78. **d** 81 **p** 82. C Hucknall Torkard *S'well* 81-85; V Lowdham 85-93; V Lowdham w Caythorpe, and Gunthorpe from 93. *The Vicarage, Lowdham, Notts NG14 7BU* Nottingham (0115) 966 3069

✠**ASHBY, Rt Rev Godfrey William Ernest Candler.** b 30. Lon Univ AKC53 BD54 PhD69. **d** 55 **p** 56 **c** 80. C St Helier *S'wark* 55-57; S Africa 57-88; Can Grahamstown Cathl 69-75; Dean and Adn Grahamstown 75-80; Bp St John's 80-85; Asst Bp Leic from 88; P-in-c Newtown Linford from 92; Hon Can Leic Cathl from 93. *Bishopsmead, 554 Bradgate Road, Newtown Linford, Leicester LE6 0HB* Markfield (01530) 242955 Fax 243563

ASHBY, John Robert Patrick. b 36. Lon Univ BSc57. Coll of Resurr Mirfield 58. **d** 60 **p** 61. C Northolt St Mary *Lon* 60-64; Tanzania 64-66; C W Brompton St Mary *Lon* 66-68; V N Acton St Gabr 68-80; R Arlington, Folkington and Wilmington *Chich* 80-88; V Willingdon from 88. *The Vicarage, 35A Church Street, Willingdon, Eastbourne, E Sussex BN20 9HR* Eastbourne (01323) 502079

ASHBY, Kevin Patrick. b 53. Jes Coll Ox BA76 MA80. Wycliffe Hall Ox 76. **d** 78 **p** 79. C Market Harborough *Leic* 78-82; C Horwich H Trin *Man* 82-84; C Horwich 84; TV 84-90; R Gt w Lt Billing *Pet* from 90. *The Rectory, 25 Church Walk, Great Billing, Northampton NN3 4ED* Northampton (01604) 784870

ASHBY, Norman. b 13. Man Egerton Hall. **d** 39 **p** 40. Warden Ripon Dioc Retreat Ho 62-70; P-in-c Pickhill *Ripon* 70-72; V 72-84; R Kirkby Wiske 77-84; rtd 84. *8 Southolme Drive, York YO3 6RL* York (01904) 638422

ASHBY, Peter George. b 49. Univ of Wales (Cardiff) BSc(Econ)70 Nottm Univ DipTh71. Linc Th Coll 70. **d** 73 **p** 74. C Bengeo *St Alb* 73-75; Chapl Hatf Poly 76-79; C Apsley End 80; TV Chambersbury (Hemel Hempstead) 80-82; Zimbabwe 82-87; Adn N Harare 84-87; V Eskdale, Irton, Muncaster and Waberthwaite *Carl* 87-93; V Sedgley All SS Lich 93; TR Sedgley All SS *Worc* from 93. *All Saints' Vicarage, Vicar Street, Sedgley, Dudley, W Midlands DY3 3SD* Sedgley (01902) 883255

ASHCROFT, Mrs Ann Christine. b 46. Cov Coll of Educn TCert68. N Ord Course 82. **d** 87 **p** 94. Chapl Trin High Sch Man 86-91; Burnage St Nic *Man* 86-87; Hon Par Dn St Nic Dio Adv Man Coun for Educn 91-95; TV Wareham *Sarum* from 95; Chapl Purbeck Sch Wareham from 95. *St Martin's Vicarage, Keysworth Road, Sandford, Wareham, Dorset BH20 7DD* Wareham (01929) 552756

ASHCROFT, Ven Lawrence. b 01. Univ Coll Dur 22. Lich Th Coll 24. **d** 26 **p** 27. Adn Stow *Linc* 54-62; V Flixborough w Burton upon Stather 54-62; rtd 62. *44 George Street, St Catherines, Ontario, Canada, L2R 5N6*

ASHCROFT, Mark David. b 54. Worc Coll Ox BA77 MA82 Fitzw Coll Cam BA81. Ridley Hall Cam 79. **d** 82 **p** 83. C Burnage St Marg *Man* 82-85; CMS from 86; Kenya from 86. *St Paul's School of Divinity, PO Box 18, Kapsabet, Kenya*

ASHDOWN, Andrew William Harvey. b 64. K Coll Lon BD88 AKC88. Sarum & Wells Th Coll 88. **d** 90 **p** 91. C Cranleigh *Guildf* 90-94; V Ryhill *Wakef* from 94. *The Vicarage, 20 School Lane, Ryhill, Wakefield, W Yorkshire WF4 2DW* Barnsley (01226) 722363

ASHDOWN, Anthony Hughes. b 37. AKC63. **d** 64 **p** 65. C Tettenhall Regis *Lich* 64-67; P-in-c Bassaley *Mon* 67-70; Rhodesia 70-77; P-in-c Longton St Jas *Lich* 77-78; P-in-c Longton St Jo 77-78; R Longton 78-80; TR Cove St Jo *Guildf* 80-87; Chapl Lisbon *Eur* 87-90; V Wanstead H Trin Hermon Hill *Chelmsf* from 90. *Holy Trinity Vicarage, Hermon Hill, London E18 1QQ* 0181-989 0912

ASHDOWN, Barry Frederick. b 42. St Pet Coll Ox BA65 MA69. Ridley Hall Cam 66. **d** 68 **p** 69. C Shipley St Pet *Bradf* 68-71; C Rushden w Newton Bromswold *Pet* 71-74; R Haworth *Bradf* 74-82; V Ore Ch Ch *Chich* 82-87; C Southwick 91-93. *47 Kipling Court, Bradford, W Yorkshire BD10 9BQ* Bradford (01274) 617484

ASHDOWN, Dr Philip David. b 57. ARCS79 AFIMA87 Imp Coll Lon BSc79 NW Univ Chicago MS80 Cranfield Inst of Tech PhD85. Ripon Coll Cuddesdon DipMin93. **d** 93 **p** 94. C Houghton le Spring *Dur* from 93. *Kepier Flat, Church Street, Houghton le Spring, Tyne & Wear DH4 4DN* 0191-584 8970

ASHE, Francis John. b 53. Sheff Univ BMet74. Ridley Hall Cam 77. **d** 79 **p** 80. C Ashtead *Guildf* 79-82; S Africa 82-87; R Wisley w Pyrford *Guildf* 87-93; V Godalming from 93. *The Vicarage, Westbrook Road, Godalming, Surrey GU7 1ET* Godalming (01483) 414135

ASHE, Francis Patrick Bellesme. b 15. St Jo Coll Cam BA37 MA41. Westcott Ho Cam 37. **d** 40 **p** 41. V Leamington Priors St Mary *Cov* 64-72; R Church Stretton *Heref* 72-74; Chmn Admin Project Vietnam Orphanage 75-81; rtd 80; Perm to Offic *Guildf* from 81. *62 Busbridge Lane, Godalming, Surrey GU7 1QQ* Godalming (01483) 422435

ASHENDEN, Gavin Roy Pelham. b 54. Bris Univ LLB76 Heythrop Coll Lon MTh89. Oak Hill Th Coll BA80. **d** 80 **p** 81. C Bermondsey St Jas w Ch Ch *S'wark* 80-83; TV Sanderstead All SS 83-89; Chapl and Lect Sussex Univ from 89. *The Meeting House, University of Sussex, Brighton BN1 9QN* Brighton (01273) 678217

ASHFOLD, Sidney Sayer. b 10. St Jo Coll Morpeth. **d** 42 **p** 43. V Henlow *St Alb* 68-77; rtd 77. *Flamstead, 27 Boanyo Avenue, Kiama, NSW, Australia 2533*

ASHFORD, Ven Percival Leonard. b 27. Tyndale Hall Bris 49. **d** 54 **p** 55. Chapl HM Pris Dur 69-71; Chapl HM Pris Wandsworth 71-75; Chapl HM Pris Win 75-85; SW Regional Chapl of Pris and Borstals 77-81; Chapl Gen of Pris 81-85; Chapl to The Queen from 82; V Hambledon *Portsm* 85-87; rtd 87; Chmn Selectors ACCM 87-88. *45 Windsor Way, Alderholt, Fordingbridge, Hants SP6 3BN* Fordingbridge (01425) 655493

ASHFORTH, David Edward. b 37. ARCS59 Lon Univ BSc Birm Univ DipTh61. Qu Coll Birm. **d** 61 **p** 62. C Scarborough St Columba *York* 61-65; C Northallerton w Kirby Sigston 65-67; V Keyingham 67-73; Chapl Imp Coll *Lon* 73-89; V Balderstone *Blackb* from 89; Dir of Post-Ord Tr from 89. *The Vicarage, Commons Lane, Balderstone, Blackburn BB2 7LL* Mellor (01254) 812232

ASHLEY, Brian. b 36. S'wark Ord Course 75. **d** 77 **p** 78. NSM Horsell *Guildf* from 77. *Starston, Church Hill, Horsell, Woking, Surrey GU21 4QE* Woking (01483) 761232

ASHLEY, Brian Christenson. b 33. Roch Th Coll 68. **d** 70 **p** 71. C New Sleaford *Linc* 70-72; Min Basegreen CD 72-74; TV Gleadless *Sheff* 74-77; R Dinnington 77-85; RD Laughton 82-85; V Mosborough 85-88; P-in-c Curbar and Stoney Middleton *Derby* 88-91; rtd 91. *15 Eliot Close, Saxon Fields, Kettering, Northants NN16 9XR* Kettering (01536) 524457

ASHLEY, Clive Ashley. b 54. SRN80 RGN81 Croydon Coll of Art and Design LSIAD75 E Ham Coll of Tech FETC82 NE Lon Poly NDN83. Aston Tr Scheme 81 Cranmer Hall Dur 84. **d** 86 **p** 87. C Withington St Paul *Man* 86-89; Asst Chapl Freeman Hosp Newc 89-92; Chapl St Rich Hosp Chich from 92; Chapl Graylingwell Hosp Chich from 92; Chapl R W Sussex Hosp Chich from 92. *St Richard's Hospital, Spitalfield Lane, Chichester, W Sussex PO19 4SE* Chichester (01243) 788122

ASHLEY, John Michael. b 28. Worc Coll Ox BA51 MA54. Linc Th Coll 50. **d** 54 **p** 55. R Woolsthorpe *Linc* 66-93; R W E Allington and Sedgebrook 66-93; CF (TAVR) 79-93; rtd 93; Perm to Offic *Linc* from 93. *35 Gregory Close, Harlaxton, Grantham, Lincs NG32 1JG* Grantham (01476) 61846

ASHLEY-ROBERTS, James. b 53. Lon Univ BD77. Oak Hill Th Coll 75 Wycliffe Hall Ox 79. **d** 80 **p** 81. C Gt Warley Ch Ch *Chelmsf* 80-83; C E Ham St Paul 83-85; TV Holyhead w

Rhoscolyn w Llanfair-yn-Neubwll *Ban* 85-88; R 88-91; V Penrhyndeudraeth w Llanfrothen w Beddgelert from 91. *The Vicarage, Penrhyndeudraeth, Gwynedd LL48 6LG* Penrhyndeudraeth (01766) 770677

ASHLING, Raymond Charles. b 32. Dur Univ BA58. Linc Th Coll 58. **d** 60 **p** 61. Rhodesia 65-71; Chapl Rishworth Sch Ripponden 71-75; Lesotho 75-85; V Somercotes *Linc* 85-88; Ethiopia 88-89; R Gt w Lt Snoring w Kettlestone and Pensthorpe *Nor* 89-94; rtd 94. *14 Abbey Court, Norwich NR1 2AW*

ASHMAN, Peter Nicholas. b 52. CSS81 SEN73. Sarum & Wells Th Coll 87. **d** 89 **p** 90. C Stafford *Lich* 89-93; R Dymchurch w Burmarsh and Newchurch *Cant* from 93. *The New Rectory, 135 High Street, Dymchurch, Romney Marsh, Kent TN29 0LD* Dymchurch (01303) 872150

ASHTON, Anthony Joseph. b 37. Oak Hill Th Coll 62. **d** 65 **p** 66. C Heeley *Sheff* 68-73; V Bowling St Steph *Bradf* 73-78; R Chesterfield H Trin *Derby* 78-92; rtd 93. *118 Newbold Road, Chesterfield, Derbyshire S41 7BG* Chesterfield (01246) 279604

ASHTON, Canon Cyril Guy. b 42. Lanc Univ MA86. Oak Hill Th Coll 64. **d** 67 **p** 68. C Blackpool St Thos *Blackb* 67-70; Voc Sec CPAS 70-74; V Lanc St Thos 74-91; Lanc Almshouses 76-90; Dioc Dir of Tr *Blackb* from 91; Hon Can Blackb Cathl from 91. *1 Picaddilly Grove, Scotforth, Lancaster LA1 4PP* Lancaster (01524) 841495

ASHTON, David William. b 51. Reading Univ BA74 Lanc Univ PGCE75. Wycliffe Hall Ox 79. **d** 82 **p** 83. C Shipley St Pet *Bradf* 82-85; C Tadley St Pet *Win* 85-88; V Sinfin *Derby* 88-91; Chapl Sophia Antipolis *Eur* 91-94; P-in-c Swanwick and Pentrich *Derby* from 95. *The Vicarage, 4 Broom Avenue, Broadway, Swanwick, Alfreton, Derbyshire DE55 1DQ* Leabrooks (01773) 602684 or 541458 Fax 602684

✠**ASHTON, Rt Rev Jeremy Claude.** b 30. Trin Coll Cam BA53 MA57. Westcott Ho Cam 53. **d** 55 **p** 56 **c** 76. C Bury St Mary *Man* 55-60; CF (TA) 57-60; CF (TA - R of O) 60-70; Papua New Guinea 60-86; Asst Bp Papua 76-77; Bp Aipo Rongo 77-86; rtd 86; Australia from 86. *PO Box 113, Maldon, Victoria, Australia 3463*

ASHTON, Miss Joan Elizabeth. b 54. Eaton Hall Coll of Educn CertEd76. Cranmer Hall Dur CTMin93. **d** 93 **p** 94. Par Dn Darnall-cum-Attercliffe *Sheff* 93-94; C Hillsborough and Wadsley Bridge from 94. *10 Welney Place, Sheffield S6 1JX* Sheffield (0114) 231 3876

ASHTON, Joseph Patrick Bankes (Pat). b 27. Jes Coll Cam BA49 MA52. Wells Th Coll 53. **d** 55 **p** 56. R Eyke w Bromeswell and Rendlesham *St E* 66-76; R Eyke w Bromeswell, Rendlesham, Tunstall etc 76-86; Chapl Seckford Foundn 86-92; Hon C Woodbridge St Mary 86-92; rtd 92. *Drift Cottage, Church Lane, Rendlesham, Woodbridge, Suffolk IP12 2SF* Eyke (01394) 461511

✠**ASHTON, Rt Rev Leonard James.** b 15. CB70. Tyndale Hall Bris 40. **d** 42 **p** 43 **c** 74. C Cheadle *Ches* 42-45; Chapl RAF 45-62; Asst Chapl-in-Chief RAF 62-65; Chapl St Clem Danes (RAF Ch) 65-69; Chapl-in-Chief RAF 69-73; QHC 67-83; Can and Preb Linc Cathl *Linc* 69-73; Asst Bp Jerusalem 74-76; Can from 76; Bp Cyprus and the Gulf 76-83; rtd 83; Asst Bp Ox from 84; Can Cyprus from 89. *60 Lowndes Avenue, Chesham, Bucks HP5 2HJ* Chesham (01494) 782952

ASHTON, Mrs Margaret Lucie. b 40. St Jo Coll Nottm DPS79. dss 83 **d** 87 **p** 94. Billericay and Lt Burstead *Chelmsf* 83-87; NSM from 87. *The Rectory, 40 Laindon Road, Billericay, Essex CM12 9LD* Billericay (01277) 622837

ASHTON, Mark Hewett. b 48. Ch Ch Ox BA70 MA74 Trin Coll Cam BA72. Ridley Hall Cam 71. **d** 73 **p** 74. C Beckenham Ch Ch *Roch* 73-77; Win Coll 78-81; Lic to Offic *S'wark* 81-87; Hd of CYFA (CPAS) 81-87; V Cam H Sepulchre w All SS *Ely* 87-92; V Cam H Sepulchre from 92. *The Parsonage, Manor Street, Cambridge CB1 1LK* Cambridge (01223) 327331

ASHTON, Neville Anthony. b 45. Sarum & Wells Th Coll 78. **d** 80 **p** 81. C Hattersley *Ches* 80-82; C Lanc Ch Ch w St Jo and St Anne *Blackb* 82-84; R Church Kirk from 84. *Church Kirk Rectory, 434 Blackburn Road, Accrington, Lancs BB5 0DE* Accrington (01254) 236946

ASHTON, Nigel Charles. b 49. SW Minl Tr Course. **d** 78 **p** 79. NSM St Stephen by Saltash *Truro* 78-94; Lic to Offic *Ex* from 94. *Stabbacks, Parsonage Way, Woodbury, Exeter EX5 1JD* Woodbury (01395) 233686

ASHTON, Canon Peter Donald. b 34. Lon Univ BD62. ALCD61. **d** 62 **p** 63. C Walthamstow St Mary *Chelmsf* 62-68; V Girlington *Bradf* 68-73; Dir Past Studies St Jo Coll Nottm 73-80; TR Billericay and Lt Burstead *Chelmsf* from 80; Chapl Mayflower Hosp Billericay from 80; Chapl St Andr Hosp Billericay from 80; RD Basildon *Chelmsf* from 89; Hon Can Chelmsf Cathl from 92. *The Rectory, 40 Laindon Road, Billericay, Essex CM12 9LD* Billericay (01277) 622837

ASHTON, Samuel Rupert. b 42. Sarum & Wells Th Coll. **d** 83 **p** 84. C Ledbury w Eastnor *Heref* 83-86; R St Weonards w

Orcop, Garway, Tretire etc from 86; RD Ross and Archenfield 91-95. *The Vicarage, St Weonards, Hereford HR2 8NU* St Weonards (01981) 580307

ASHTON, Stephen Robert. b 55. BA BPhil. Sarum & Wells Th Coll. **d** 84 **p** 85. C Penzance St Mary w St Paul *Truro* 84-86; C Tewkesbury w Walton Cardiff *Glouc* 86-89; P-in-c Newton Heath St Wilfrid and St Anne *Man* 89-92; V Breage w Germoe *Truro* 92-94. *20 Tregarrick Close, Helston, Cornwall TR13 8YA* Helston (01326) 573449

ASHTON, Thomas Eyre Maunsell (Tom). b 13. St Edm Hall Ox BA36 MA39. Wycliffe Hall Ox 36. **d** 38 **p** 39. R Lee St Marg *S'wark* 67-75; Chapl Morden Coll Blackheath 75-83; rtd 83; Perm to Offic *S'wark* from 83. *7 The Quadrangle, Mordon College, London SE3 0PW* 0181-853 1576

ASHTON, William Grant. b 57. St Chad's Coll Dur BA79. Oak Hill Th Coll BA85. **d** 85 **p** 86. C Lanc St Thos *Blackb* 85-89; CF from 89. *c/o MOD (Army), Bagshot Park, Bagshot, Surrey GU19 5PL* Bagshot (01276) 471717 Fax 412834

ASHWELL, Anthony John. b 42. CChem74 MRSC74 St Andr Univ BSc65. Sarum & Wells Th Coll 86. **d** 88 **p** 89. C Plymstock *Ex* 88-91; C Axminster, Chardstock, Combe Pyne and Rousdon 91-92; TV from 92. *The Vicarage, Chardstock, Axminster, Devon EX13 7BY* South Chard (01460) 220005

ASHWIN, Vincent George. b 42. Worc Coll Ox BA65. Coll of Resurr Mirfield 65. **d** 67 **p** 68. C Shildon *Dur* 67-70; V 79-85; C Newc St Fran *Newc* 70-72; Swaziland 72-79; V Fenham St Jas and St Basil *Newc* from 85; RD Newc W from 89. *The Vicarage, Wingrove Road, Newcastle upon Tyne NE4 9EJ* 0191-274 5078

ASHWORTH, Canon David. b 40. Nottm Univ BPharm62. Linc Th Coll 63. **d** 65 **p** 66. C Halliwell St Thos *Man* 65-69; C Heywood St Jas 69-72; C-in-c Heywood St Marg CD 72-78; V Hale *Ches* 78-87; RD Bowdon from 87; V Hale and Ashley from 87; Hon Can Ches Cathl from 94. *1 Harrop Road, Hale, Altrincham, Cheshire WA15 9BU* 0161-928 4182

ASHWORTH, Edward James. b 33. Clifton Th Coll 60. **d** 63 **p** 64. C Spitalfields Ch Ch w All SS *Lon* 63-65; C Pennycross *Ex* 65-69; C Blackb Ch Ch *Blackb* 69-72; V Camerton H Trin W Seaton *Carl* 72-79; V Tunstead *Man* from 79. *The Vicarage, 33 Booth Road, Bacup, Lancs OL13 0QP* Bacup (01706) 874508

ASHWORTH, James Nigel. b 55. York Univ BA77. Cranmer Hall Dur CTMin93. **d** 93 **p** 94. C Rothwell *Ripon* from 93. *17 Haighside, Rothwell, Leeds LS26 0UF* Leeds (0113) 282 9291

ASHWORTH, John Russell. b 33. Lich Th Coll 57. **d** 60 **p** 61. C Castleford All SS *Wakef* 60-62; C Luton St Sav *St Alb* 63-67; V Clipstone *S'well* 67-70; V Bolton-upon-Dearne *Sheff* 70-82; V Thornhill Lees *Wakef* from 82. *The Vicarage, Thornhill Lees, Dewsbury, W Yorkshire WF12 9PD* Dewsbury (01924) 461269

ASHWORTH, Keith Benjamin. b 33. NW Ord Course 76. **d** 79 **p** 80. C Pennington *Man* 79-83; P-in-c Bolton St Bede 83-88; V 88-95; V Hillock from 95. *St Andrew's Vicarage, Mersey Drive, Whitefield, Manchester M25 6LA* 0161-766 5561

ASHWORTH, Martin. b 41. AKC63. **d** 64 **p** 65. C-in-c Wythenshawe Wm Temple Ch CD *Man* 64-71; R Haughton St Anne 71-83; V Prestwich St Marg from 83. *St Margaret's Vicarage, St Margaret's Road, Prestwich, Manchester M25 5QB* 0161-773 2698

ASHWORTH, Timothy (Tim). b 52. Worc Coll of Educn CertEd73. Trin Coll Bris DipHE79 Oak Hill Th Coll BA81. **d** 82 **p** 83. C Tonbridge St Steph *Roch* 82-85; C Whittle-le-Woods *Blackb* 85-90; Chapl Scargill Ho from 90. *Scargill House, Kettlewell, Skipton, N Yorkshire BD23 5HU* Kettlewell (01756) 760234

ASHWORTH, Mrs Vivien (Viv). b 52. Worc Coll of Educn CertEd73. Trin Coll Bris 79 Oak Hill Th Coll BA82. **dss** 82 **d** 87 **p** 94. Tonbridge St Steph *Roch* 82-85; Whittle-le-Woods *Blackb* 85-87; Hon Par Dn 87-90; Chapl Scargill Ho from 90. *Scargill House, Kettlewell, Skipton, N Yorkshire BD23 5HU* Kettlewell (01756) 760234

ASKE, Sir Conan, Bt. b 12. Ball Coll Ox BA33 MA39. Wycliffe Hall Ox 69. **d** 70 **p** 71. C Hagley *Worc* 70-72; C St Jo in Bedwardine 72-80; rtd 80; Perm to Offic *Worc* from 80. *167 Malvern Road, Worcester WR2 4NN* Worcester (01905) 422817

ASKEW, Alison Jane. Dur Univ BA PGCE. S Dios Minl Tr Scheme. **d** 95. NSM Kingsclere *Win* from 95; Chapl N Hants Hosp from 95. *5 Essex Block, North Hampshire Hospital, Basingstoke, Hants RG24 9NA*

ASKEW, Canon Dennis. b 30. Open Univ BA76. Kelham Th Coll 45 Lich Th Coll 55. **d** 58 **p** 59. C Garforth *Ripon* 58-61; C Seacroft 61-64; V Holland Fen *Linc* 64-69; R Folkingham w Laughton 69-77; V Aswarby w Swarby 69-77; R Osbournby w Scott Willoughby 69-77; R Pickworth w Walcot 69-77; V Threckingham 69-77; P-in-c Newton w Haceby 72-77; P-in-c Aunsby w Dembleby 72-77; R S Lafford 77-87; Hon Can Linc

Cathl from 86; R Ruskington from 87. *The Rectory, Ruskington, Sleaford, Lincs NG34 9AE* Ruskington (01526) 832463

ASKEW, Canon Reginald James Albert. b 28. CCC Cam BA51 MA55. Linc Th Coll 55. **d** 57 **p** 58. V Paddington Ch Ch *Lon* 69-73; Member Corrymeela Community from 71; Prin Sarum & Wells Th Coll 73-87; Chmn S Dios Minl Tr Scheme 73-87; Can and Preb Sarum Cathl *Sarum* 75-87; Dean K Coll Lon 88-93; rtd 93; Perm to Offic *B & W* from 93. *Carters Cottage, North Wootton, Shepton Mallet, Somerset BA4 4AF* Pilton (01749) 890728

ASKEW, Preb Richard George. b 35. BNC Ox BA59 MA63. Ridley Hall Cam 62. **d** 64 **p** 65. C Chesham St Mary Ox 64-66; C Mossley Hill St Matt and St Jas *Liv* 66-67; Chapl Ox Pastorate 67-72; Asst Chapl BNC Ox 67-71; R Ashtead *Guildf* 72-83; RD Leatherhead 80-83; Can Res and Treas Sarum Cathl *Sarum* 83-90; Dioc Adv on Miss and Min *B & W* 83-90; R Bath Abbey w St Jas from 90; Preb Wells Cathl from 92. *The Abbey Rectory, Redwood House, Trossachs Drive, Bath BA2 6RP* Bath (01225) 464930 or 422462 Fax 429990

ASKEW, Sydney Derek. b 29. Roch Th Coll 66. **d** 68 **p** 69. C Kirkstall *Ripon* 68-73; V Markington w S Stainley and Bishop Thornton 73-94; rtd 94. *6 Mallorie Close, Ripon, N Yorkshire HG4 2QE* Ripon (01765) 603309

ASKEY, Gary Simon. b 64. St Steph Ho Ox 88. **d** 91 **p** 92. SSM from 87; C Middlesb All SS *York* 91-94; Sub-Chapl HM Pris Holme Ho 92-94; C Whitby from 94; Missr Whitby Missr and Seafarer's Trust from 94. *St Mary's House, Spital Bridge, Whitby, N Yorkshire YO22 4EF* Whitby (01947) 601341 Fax 602404

ASKEY, John Stuart. b 39. Chich Th Coll 63. **d** 66 **p** 67. C Feltham *Lon* 66-69; C Epsom Common Ch Ch *Guildf* 69-72; C Chesterton Gd Shep *Ely* 72-74; R Stretham w Thetford 74-93; Dioc Youth Officer from 80; P-in-c Brinkley, Burrough Green and Carlton from 93; P-in-c Westley Waterless from 93; P-in-c Dullingham from 93; P-in-c Stetchworth from 93. *The Rectory, Brinkley, Newmarket, Suffolk CB8 0SE* Newmarket (01638) 507263

ASLACHSEN, Grosvenor Trevelyan. b 03. Lich Th Coll 24. **d** 28 **p** 29. R Halstead *Roch* 40-68; rtd 68. *Bishopsdown Corner, 4 Manor Park, Tunbridge Wells, Kent TN4 8XP* Tunbridge Wells (01892) 531535

ASPDEN, Peter George. b 28. Univ of Wales (Lamp) BA50. Ely Th Coll 52. **d** 53 **p** 54. V St Annes St Marg *Blackb* 66-75; V Lanc Ch Ch 75-79; R Eccleston 79-94; rtd 94. *21 Glencoyne Drive, Southport, Merseyside PR9 9TS*

ASPINALL, Philip Norman. b 51. Cam Univ MA ATI. W Midl Minl Tr Course 86. **d** 89 **p** 90. NSM Cov E *Cov* from 89. *139 Wiltshire Court, Nod Rise, Mount Nod, Coventry CV5 7JP* Coventry (01203) 467509

ASQUITH, Eric Lees. b 24. St Aid Birkenhead 55. **d** 56 **p** 57. V Netherthong *Wakef* 59-68; rtd 89. *15 Heycroft Way, Nayland, Colchester CO6 4LN* Nayland (01206) 262593

ASQUITH, Michael John. b 60. St D Coll Lamp BA82 MPhil91 Ch Ch Coll Cant PGCE83. Cant Sch of Min 91. **d** 94 **p** 95. C S Ashford Ch Ch *Cant* from 94. *112 Beaver Road, Ashford, Kent TN23 7SR* Ashford (01233) 620600

ASSON, Geoffrey Ormrod. b 34. Univ of Wales BA54 St Cath Coll Ox BA56 MA61. St Steph Ho Ox 54. **d** 57 **p** 58. C Aberdare St Jo *Llan* 57-59; C Roath St Marg 59-61; R Hagworthingham w Asgarby and Lusby *Linc* 61-65; P-in-c Mavis Enderby w Raithby 62-65; V Friskney 65-69; R S Ormsby w Ketsby, Calceby and Driby 69-74; R Harrington w Brinkhill 69-74; R Oxcombe 69-74; R Ruckland w Farforth and Maidenwell 69-74; R Somersby w Bag Enderby 69-74; R Tetford and Salmonby 69-74; P-in-c Belchford 71-74; P-in-c W Ashby 71-74; V Riverhead w Dunton Green *Roch* 75-80; R Kington w Huntington *Heref* 80-82; RD Kington and Weobley 80-86; P-in-c Almeley 81-82; P-in-c Knill 81-82; P-in-c Old Radnor 81-82; R Kington w Huntington, Old Radnor, Kinnerton etc 82-86; V Mathry w St Edren's and Grandston etc *St D* from 86. *The Rectory, St Nicholas, Goodwick, Dyfed SA64 0LG* St Nicholas (01348) 891230

ASTILL, Cyril John. b 33. Lon Univ DipTh64. Oak Hill Th Coll 62. **d** 65 **p** 66. C Carl St Jo *Carl* 65-68; C St Helens St Helen *Liv* 68-71; V Blackb Sav *Blackb* 71-85; P-in-c Blackb Ch w St Matt 81-83; TR N Ferriby *York* from 85. *The Rectory, 20 Aston Hall Drive, North Ferriby, N Humberside HU14 3EB* Hull (01482) 631306

ASTIN, Alfred Ronald. b 18. St Pet Hall Ox BA43 MA45. Ridley Hall Cam. **d** 47 **p** 48. V Earlham St Anne *Nor* 57-70; V Sheringham 70-84; rtd 84; Perm to Offic *Nor* from 84. *9 Cromer Road, Overstrand, Cromer, Norfolk NR27 0NU* Overstrand (0126378) 201

ASTIN, Howard Keith. b 51. Warw Univ LLB DipHE. Trin Coll Bris 83. **d** 83 **p** 84. C Kirkheaton *Wakef* 83-88; V Bowling St Jo *Bradf* from 88. *St John's Vicarage, 96 Lister Avenue, Bradford, W Yorkshire BD4 7QS* Bradford (01274) 720660

ASTIN, Mrs Moira Anne Elizabeth. b 65. Clare Coll Cam BA86 MA90. Wycliffe Hall Ox BA94 DipMin95. d 95. C Newbury Ox from 95. *241 Oxford Road, Reading RG1 7PX* Reading (01734) 560827

ASTIN, Dr Timothy Robin. b 58. St Edm Hall Ox BA79 Darw Coll Cam PhD82. Ox Min Course CBTS93. d 93 p 94. NSM Reading St Jo Ox from 93. *241 Oxford Road, Reading RG1 7PX* Reading (01734) 560827

ASTLEY, Dr Jeffrey. b 47. Down Coll Cam BA68 MA72 Birm Univ DipTh69 Dur Univ PhD79. Qu Coll Birm 68. d 70 p 71. C Cannock *Lich* 70-73; Lect and Chapl St Hild Coll Dur 73-75; Sen Lect and Chapl SS Hild & Bede Coll Dur 75-77; Prin Lect & Hd Relig Studies Bp Grosseteste Coll 77-81; Lic to Offic *Linc* 78-81; Dir N England Inst for Chr Educn from 81. *Carter House, Pelaw Leazes Place, Durham DH1 1TB* 0191-384 1034 or 386 4466 Fax 384 7529

ASTON, Glyn. b 29. Univ of Wales (Abth) BA54. d 79 p 80. Hon C Newport Maindee St Jo Ev *Mon* 79-85; C 85-86; P-in-c Llangwm Uchaf w Llangwm Isaf w Gwernesney etc 86; V from 86. *The Rectory, Gwernesney, Usk, Gwent NP5 1HF* Usk (01291) 672518

ASTON, John Bernard. b 34. Leeds Univ BA55 PGCE56. Qu Coll Birm 72. d 75 p 76. NSM Shenstone *Lich* from 75; Chapl HM Young Offender Inst Swinfen Hall from 90. *21 Wordsworth Close, Lichfield, Staffs WS14 9BY* Lichfield (01543) 264960 Fax 480138

ASTON, John Leslie. b 47. Oak Hill Th Coll 77. d 80 p 81. C Trentham *Lich* 80-83; C Meir Heath 83-85; V Upper Tean 85-91; CF from 91. *c/o MOD (Army), Bagshot Park, Bagshot, Surrey GU19 5PL* Bagshot (01276) 471717 Fax 412834

ASTON SMITH, Dr Anthony. b 29. CEng MIM FIDiagE MICorrST AMIMechE Trin Coll Cam BA2 MA56 PhD56. Ox NSM Course 86. d 93 p 94. NSM Ox St Giles and SS Phil and Jas w St Marg *Ox* from 93. *32 Chalfont Road, Oxford OX2 6TH* Oxford (01865) 57090

ASTON, Archdeacon of. See BARTON, Ven Charles John Greenwood

ASTON, Suffragan Bishop of. See AUSTIN, Rt Rev John Michael

ATACK, John Philip. b 49. Linc Th Coll 86. d 88 p 89. C Cleveleys *Blackb* 88-92; V Appley Bridge from 92. *The Vicarage, Finch Lane, Appley Bridge, Wigan, Lancs WN6 9DT* Appley Bridge (01257) 252875

ATFIELD, Gladys. Univ Coll Lon BSc53 DipTh76. Gilmore Course. dss 79 d 87 p 94. Bexley St Mary *Roch* 79-87; Hon C from 87. *7 Clarendon Mews, High Street, Bexley, Kent DA5 1JS* Crayford (01322) 551741

ATHERFOLD, Mrs Evelyne Sara (Eve). b 43. Leeds Inst of Educn CertEd64. N Ord Course 82. dss 85 d 92 p 94. Kirk Sandall and Edenthorpe *Sheff* 85-87; Fishlake w Sykehouse, Kirk Bramwith, Fenwick etc 87-92; NSM from 92. *Padley House, Hawkeshouse Green, Moss, Doncaster, S Yorkshire DN6 0DL* Doncaster (01302) 700452 Fax 707221

ATHERLEY, Keith Philip. b 56. St Steph Ho Ox 77. d 80 p 81. C St Bart Armley w St Mary New Wortley *Ripon* 80-82; C Harrogate St Wilfrid and St Luke 82-85; V Forcett and Stanwick w Aldbrough 85-89; CF from 89. *c/o MOD (Army), Bagshot Park, Bagshot, Surrey GU19 5PL* Bagshot (01276) 471717 Fax 412834

ATHERSTONE, Castell Hugh. b 45. Natal Univ BA67 St Chad's Coll Dur DipTh69 MA79. d 70 p 70. S Africa 70-83; Dioc Stewardship Adv *Ely* 83-87; P-in-c Doddington w Benwick 83-87; R Frant w Eridge *Chich* 87-95; RD Rotherfield 90-94; V Seaford w Sutton from 95. *The Vicarage, Sutton Road, Seaford, E Sussex BN25 1SH* Seaford (01323) 893508

ATHERTON, Albert. b 26. CQSW71. St Aid Birkenhead 60. d 62 p 63. V Patricroft *Man* 66-70; Lic to Offic 71-72; V Mossley 77-83; V Ockbrook *Derby* 83-86; P-in-c Newall Green *Man* 86-91; V 91-94; rtd 94. *50 Belmont Drive, Bury, Lancs BL8 2HU* 0161-764 8397

ATHERTON, Graham Bryson. b 47. GRSM69 FTCL69. Edin Th Coll 77. d 79 p 80. C Orford St Marg *Liv* 79-82; V Warrington St Barn 82-88; V Leeds Halton St Wilfrid *Ripon* 88-95; RD Whitkirk 92-95; TR Guiseley w Esholt *Bradf* from 95. *The Rectory, The Green, Guiseley, Leeds LS20 9BT* Guiseley (01943) 874321

ATHERTON, Henry Anthony. b 44. FGS68 Univ of Wales BSc67 DipEd68 Fitzw Coll Cam BA72 MA75. Westcott Ho Cam 70. d 72 p 73. C Leamington Priors All SS *Cov* 72-75; C Orpington All SS *Roch* 75-78; V Gravesend St Mary 78-87; Chapl St Jas Hosp Gravesend 82-87; V Bromley St Andr *Roch* from 87. *The Vicarage, 1 Lake Avenue, Bromley BR1 4EN* 0181-460 0481

ATHERTON, Canon John Robert. b 39. Lon Univ BA60 Man Univ MA74 PhD79. Coll of Resurr Mirfield 60. d 62 p 63. C Aber St Marg *Ab* 62-64; C Bury St Mark *Man* 64-67; P-in-c Glas St Marg *Glas* 67-68; R Hulme St Geo *Man* 68-74; Ind

Chapl 68-74; Asst Dir Wm Temple Foundn 74-79; Dir from 79; Lic to Offic 74-84; Can Res Man Cathl from 84. *Latham, Myrtle Grove, Whitefield, Manchester M25 7RR* 0161-766 9296 or 833 2220

ATHERTON, Lionel Thomas. b 45. Univ of Wales (Ban) BA74 St Luke's Coll Ex. St Steph Ho Ox 74. d 76 p 77. C Chenies and Lt Chalfont *Ox* 76-79; C Fleet *Guildf* 79-84; V S Farnborough 84-89; TR Alston Team *Newc* from 89. *The Vicarage, Front Street, Alston, Cumbria CA9 3RE* Alston (01434) 381317

ATHERTON, Paul Christopher. b 56. Chich Th Coll. d 82 p 83. C Orford St Marg *Liv* 82-86; Chapl Univ of Wales (Cardiff) *Llan* 88-89; TV Walton St Mary *Liv* 89-92; C Westmr St Matt *Lon* from 92. *20 Great Peter Street, London SW1P 2BU* 0171-222 7484

ATHERTON, Percy Francis. b 22. Man Univ BA47 PGCE48 Univ of Minnesota MA56. Seabury-Western Th Sem 52. d 52 p 53. Lic to Offic *Ex* 66-75; HMI of Schs 70-75; Peru 75-76; Singapore 76-77; P-in-c Zeal Monachorum *Ex* 78-79; R Bow w Broad Nymet 78-79; V Colebrooke 78-79; Perm to Offic from 79; Algeria 80-81; rtd 89. *The Old Dame's Cottage, Cove, Tiverton, Devon EX16 7RX* Bampton (01398) 331489

ATHERTON, Philip Andrew. b 51. Wycliffe Hall Ox. d 84 p 85. C Ox St Clem *Ox* 84-87; Ind Missr *Man* from 87. *192 Windsor Road, Oldham OL8 1RG* 0161-652 2684

ATHERTON, Timothy Edward John. b 60. Middx Poly DipHE83. Cranmer Hall Dur 83. d 86 p 87. C S Molton w Nymet St George, High Bray etc *Ex* 86-89; Canada from 89. *St John's Anglican Mission, PO Box 240, Tuktoyaktuk, NWT, Canada, X0E 1C0* Tuktoyaktuk (403) 977-2216

ATKIN, Arthur Courtney Qu'appelle. b 19. Dur Univ BA44. Lich Th Coll 59. d 59 p 60. Chapl R Hosp Sch Holbrook 69-72; P-in-c Brixham *Ex* 72-74; Chapl Colston's Sch Bris 74-79; P-in-c Pitcombe w Shepton Montague and Bratton St Maur *B & W* 79-85; rtd 86; Perm to Offic *B & W* 86-93. *Newlands Court, Victoria Road, Ledbury, Herefordshire HR8 2DD* Ledbury (01531) 634526

ATKIN, John Anthony. b 33. Glouc Th Course 70. d 72 p 73. NSM Leamington Priors All SS *Cov* 72-77; NSM Barford 77-78; NSM Barford w Wasperton and Sherbourne 78-80; P-in-c Exford w Exmoor *B & W* 80-82; P-in-c Hawkridge w Withypool 80-82; P-in-c Exford, Exmoor, Hawkridge and Withypool 82-83; R 83-92; RD Exmoor 86-92; rtd 93. *Halsgrove Farm, Withypool, Minehead, Somerset TA24 7RX* Exford (0164383) 388

ATKIN, Mrs Stephanie. b 23. d 87. Boreham Wood St Mich *St Alb* 78-79; Borehamwood 79-81; Dunstable 81-87; Par Dn 87-90; rtd 90. *11 Mount Street, Lincoln LN1 3JE* Lincoln (01522) 560428

ATKINS, Anthony John. b 58. Nottm Univ BSc80 SS Paul & Mary Coll Cheltenham PGCE82. Cranmer Hall Dur 87. d 90 p 91. C Shipley St Paul and Frizinghall *Bradf* 90-92; C Baildon 92-93; Chapl Asst Hope Hosp Salford from 93; Chapl Asst Ladywell Hosp from 93. *3 Charlton Avenue, Eccles, Manchester M30 0JQ or, Hope Hospital, Stott Lane, Salford M6 8HD* 0161-789 1674 or 789 7373

ATKINS, Austen Shaun. b 55. St Pet Coll Ox MA82 Selw Coll Cam MA85. Ridley Hall Cam 79. d 82 p 83. C S Mimms Ch Ch *Lon* 82-86; C Fulham St Matt 86-91; P-in-c Fulham St Dionis Parson's Green from 91. *St Dionis' Vicarage, 18 Parson's Green, London SW6 4UH* 0171-736 2585

ATKINS, Christopher Leigh. b 33. Keble Coll Ox BA55 MA58. Wells Th Coll 57. d 59 p 60. C Foley Park *Worc* 59-62; C Eastleigh *Win* 62-69; TV Lord's Hill 69-81; V 81-85; R Church Oakley and Wootton St Lawrence from 85. *The Rectory, 9 The Drive, Oakley, Basingstoke, Hants RG23 7DA* Basingstoke (01256) 780825

ATKINS, David John. b 43. Lon Univ DipTh68. Kelham Th Coll 64. d 68 p 69. C Lewisham St Mary *S'wark* 68-72; Min Motspur Park 72-77; P-in-c Mitcham Ascension 77-82; V 82-83; P-in-c Downham w S Hanningfield *Chelmsf* 83-88; R from 88; Asst RD Chelmsf 88-93; RD Chelmsf S from 93; P-in-c W Hanningfield 90-93. *The Rectory, Castledon Road, Billericay, Essex CM11 1LD* Basildon (01268) 710370

ATKINS, Mrs Diana. b 31. K Coll Lon BD54 DipEd55. Qu Coll Birm 81. dss 83 d 87. De Beauvoir Town St Pet *Lon* 83-85; Gleadless *Sheff* 85-87; Par Dn 87-93; rtd 93; Perm to Offic *Sheff* from 93. *27 Stannington Glen, Sheffield S6 6NA* Sheffield (0114) 234 0543

ATKINS, Forrest William (Bill). b 59. Ch Coll Cam MA85 Lon Univ BD84. Ridley Hall Cam 83. d 86 p 87. C Normanton *Derby* 86-90; C Stratford St Jo and Ch Ch w Forest Gate St Jas *Chelmsf* from 90. *2 St James's Road, London E15 1RL* 0181-503 1476

ATKINS, Francis John. b 47. CEng MIStructE. S Dios Minl Tr Scheme. d 89 p 90. NSM Studley *Sarum* 89-92; Lic to RD Bradford from 92. *Church Cottage, 344 Frome Road, Trowbridge, Wilts BA14 0EF* Trowbridge (01225) 761757

ATKINS, Graham Anthony Hazlewood. b 28. Selw Coll Cam BA52 MA57. Coll of Resurr Mirfield 52. **d** 54 **p** 55. Chapl Prestfelde Sch Shrewsbury 58-76; P-in-c Ash *Lich* 76-77; P-in-c Tenbury St Mich *Heref* 77-84; R Hinstock and Sambrook *Lich* 85-94; rtd 94. *The Rectory, Ellerton Road, Hinstock, Market Drayton, Shropshire TF9 0NH* Sambrook (01952) 550783

ATKINS, Canon John Hamilton. b 15. AKC42. **d** 42 **p** 43. V Cuddington *Guildf* 63-72; Hon Can Guildf Cathl 71-80; R Walton-on-the-Hill 72-80; rtd 80; Perm to Offic *Sarum* from 81; Perm to Offic *B & W* from 86. *1 Elizabeth Court, High Street, Bembridge, Isle of Wight PO35 5SN* Isle of Wight (01983) 873008

ATKINS, Nicholas Steven (Nick). b 60. Oak Hill Th Coll BA88. **d** 88 **p** 89. C Shepton Mallet w Doulting *B & W* 88-91; C Combe Down w Monkton Combe and S Stoke 91-93; TV N Wingfield, Clay Cross and Pilsley *Derby* from 93. *The Vicarage, Stretton Road, Clay Cross, Chesterfield, Derbyshire S45 9AQ* Chesterfield (01246) 866908

ATKINS, Canon Paul Henry. b 38. Univ of Wales DipTh65. St Mich Coll Llan 62. **d** 65 **p** 66. C Sheringham *Nor* 65-68; V Southtown 68-84; RD Flegg (Gt Yarmouth) 78-84; R Aylmerton w Runton from 84; RD Repps 86-95; Hon Can Nor Cathl from 88. *The Rectory, West Runton, Cromer, Norfolk NR27 9QT* West Runton (01263) 837279

ATKINS, Peter. b 29. Edin Univ MA52. Edin Th Coll 52. **d** 54 **p** 55. C Edin Old St Paul *Edin* 54-59; P-in-c Edin St Dav 59-64; Chapl Fulbourn Hosp Cam 64-66; R Galashiels *Edin* 66-69; Perm to Offic 69-72; Divisional Dir Soc Services Brighton 72-83; Asst Dir Soc Services E Sussex from 83. *11 South Street, Lewes, E Sussex BN7 2BT* Lewes (01273) 476230

ATKINS, Roger Francis. b 30. AKC54. **d** 55 **p** 56. Australia 62-71; V Wolverley *Worc* 71-76; V S Hackney St Mich w Haggerston St Paul *Lon* 76-85; TV Gleadless *Sheff* 85-93; rtd 93; Perm to Offic *Sheff* from 93. *27 Stannington Glen, Sheffield S6 6NA* Sheffield (0114) 234 0543

ATKINS, Timothy David. b 45. Ridley Hall Cam 71. **d** 74 **p** 75. C Stoughton *Guildf* 74-79; C Stillwell *S'well* 79-84; R Eastwood 84-91; V Finchley Ch Ch *Lon* from 91; Chapl Finchley Memorial Hosp from 92. *Christ Church Vicarage, 616 High Road, London N12 0AA* 0181-445 2377 or 445 2532

ATKINS, Timothy James (Tim). b 38. Worc Coll Ox BA62. Cuddesdon Coll 62. **d** 64 **p** 65. C Stafford St Mary *Lich* 64-67; C Loughb St Pet *Leic* 67-69; C Usworth *Dur* 69-71; Lic to Offic *Newc* 71-76; P-in-c Slaley 76-87; P-in-c Shotley from 87. *St John's Vicarage, Snods Edge, Consett, Co Durham DH8 9TL* Edmundbyers (01207) 55665

ATKINS, Timothy Samuel. b 22. DSC44. Em Coll Cam BA46 MA52. Ridley Hall Cam 47. **d** 49 **p** 50. V Bunbury *Ches* 63-87; RD Malpas 85-87; rtd 87; Perm to Offic *Ches* from 87. *Lime Tree Cottage, Barton Road, Farndon, Chester CH3 6NL* Farndon (01829) 270183

ATKINS, William Maynard. b 11. FSA TCD BA33 MA41. **d** 35 **p** 36. C Dundalk *Arm* 35-40; I Clonfeacle 40-46; Dep Min Can St Paul's Cathl *Lon* 46-49; Min Can 49-55; Hon Min Can from 55; C St Sepulchre w Ch Ch Greyfriars etc 49-55; Chapl Mercers' Sch Holborn 54-59; R Hanover Square St Geo 55-74; Chapl City of Lon Sch 62-67; P-in-c N Audley Street St Mark *Lon* 68-74; R Hanover Square St Geo w St Mark from 74. *St George's Vestry, 2A Mill Street, London W1R 9LB* 0171-629 0874

ATKINSON, Albert Edward. b 35. St Deiniol's Hawarden 79. **d** 79 **p** 80. C Ellesmere Port *Ches* 79-81; TV 81-84; P-in-c Kirkby Malzeard w Grewelthorpe and Mickley etc *Ripon* 84-88; P-in-c Fountains 88-90; R Fountains Gp 90-92; V Aysgarth and Bolton cum Redmire from 92. *The Vicarage, Carperby, Leyburn, N Yorkshire DL8 4DQ* Aysgarth (01969) 663235

ATKINSON, Brian Colin. b 49. Sarum & Wells Th Coll 85. **d** 87 **p** 88. C Up Hatherley *Glouc* 87-90; R Upper Stour *Sarum* from 90. *The Rectory, Zeals, Warminster, Wilts BA12 6PG* Warminster (01985) 840221

ATKINSON, Christopher John (Chris). b 57. Man Univ BA80 DipTh84. Qu Coll Birm 82. **d** 85 **p** 86. C Stalybridge *Man* 85-88; P-in-c Westhall w Brampton and Stoven *St E* 88-89; P-in-c Sotterley, Willingham, Shadingfield, Ellough etc 88-90; P-in-c Hundred River Gp of Par 90-92; R Hundred River from 92. *The Rectory, Moll's Lane, Brampton, Beccles, Suffolk NR34 8DB* Brampton (01502) 575859

ATKINSON, Canon Christopher Lionel Varley. b 39. K Coll Lon 63. Chich Th Coll 65. **d** 67 **p** 68. C Sowerby Bridge w Norland *Wakef* 67-70; P-in-c Flushing *Truro* 70-73; Dioc Adv in RE 70-73; Perm to Offic *Worc* 74-78; TR Halesowen 78-88; RD Dudley 79-87; Hon Can Worc Cathl 83-88; V Cartmel *Carl* from 88; RD Windermere from 94; Hon Can Carl Cathl from 94. *Priory Vicarage, Cartmel, Grange-over-Sands, Cumbria LA11 6PU* Cartmel (015395) 36261

ATKINSON, Clive James. b 68. QUB BA90. CITC 90. **d** 93 **p** 94. C Belf H Trin and Ardoyne *Conn* from 93. *27 Wheatfield Gardens, Crumlin Road, Belfast BT14 7HU* Belfast (01232) 715478

ATKINSON, Canon David James. b 41. Lon Univ BD AKC63 Selw Coll Cam BA65 MA72. Linc Th Coll 65. **d** 66 **p** 67. C Linc St Giles *Linc* 66-70; Asst Chapl Newc Univ *Newc* 70-73; Adult Educn Officer *Lich* 73-75; P-in-c Adbaston 73-80; Dir of Educn 75-82; Preb Lich Cathl 79-82; Chapl Hull Univ *York* 82-87; Dir of Educn *Linc* 87-94; Hon Can Linc Cathl from 89; P-in-c Bishop Norton, Wadingham and Snitterby from 94. *The Rectory, Church Road, Waddingham, Gainsborough, Lincs DN21 4SU* Bishop Norton (01673) 818551

ATKINSON, Canon David John. b 43. MSOScK Coll Lon BSc65 AKC65 PhD69 Bris Univ DipTh70 MLitt73 Ox Univ MA85. Trin Coll Bris and Tyndale Hall Bris 69. **d** 72 **p** 73. C Halliwell St Pet *Man* 72-74; C Harborne Heath *Birm* 74-77; Lib Latimer Ho Ox 77-80; Chapl and Lect CCC Ox 80-93; Fell from 84; Visiting Lect Wycliffe Hall Ox 84-93; Can Res and Chan S'wark Cathl *S'wark* from 93. *7 Temple West Mews, West Square, London SE11 4TJ* 0171-735 5924 or 403 8686

ATKINSON, Derek Arthur. b 31. K Coll Lon BD59 AKC59. **d** 60 **p** 61. R E w W Ogwell *Ex* 68-81; Asst Dir of RE 68-78; Dep Dir and Children's Adv 78-88; R Ogwell and Denbury 81-84; R Kenton w Mamhead and Powderham 84-88; rtd 88; Perm to Offic *Ex* 88-93. *clo 6 Hudson Close, Harthill, Sheffield S31 8WB* Worksop (01909) 771149

ATKINSON, Ian. b 33. BNC Ox BA58 MA63. Coll of Resurr Mirfield 56. **d** 58 **p** 59. C Welling *S'wark* 58-62; C Camberwell St Giles 62-63; V Wandsworth Common St Mary 63-67; S Africa 67-68; C Oxted *S'wark* 68-69; Asst Chapl Ch Hosp Horsham 70-85; NSM Dalmahoy *Edin* 85-91; Asst Master Clifton Hall Sch 85-91; NSM Dunkeld *St And* from 92. *2 Pinel Lodge, Murthly, Perth PH1 4ES* Perth (01738) 710561

ATKINSON, Canon Prof James. b 14. St Jo Coll Dur BA36 MA39 MLitt50 Univ of Munster DTh55. **d** 37 **p** 38. Prof Bibl Studies Sheff Univ 67-79; Lic to Offic *Sheff* from 68; Can Th Sheff Cathl 70-93; rtd 79; Latimer Ho Ox 81-84. *Leach House, Hathersage, Sheffield S30 1BA* Hope Valley (01433) 650570

ATKINSON, John Dudley. b 38. ACA60 FCA71. Qu Coll Birm 63. **d** 66 **p** 67. C Bishop's Stortford St Mich *St Alb* 66-70; C Norton 70-73; V Markyate Street 73-80; R Baldock w Bygrave 80-94; RD Stevenage 83-89; TR Bride Valley *Sarum* from 94. *The Rectory, Church Street, Burton Bradstock, Bridport, Dorset DT6 4QS* Burton Bradstock (01308) 897359

ATKINSON, Kenneth. b 24. Qu Coll Birm 74. **d** 77 **p** 77. C Olton *Birm* 77-82; Perm to Offic *York* 83-93; Perm to Offic *Birm* from 93. *98 Fabian Crescent, Shirley, Solihull, W Midlands B90 2AB* 0121-744 4044

ATKINSON, Lewis Malcolm. b 34. St Jo Coll Dur. **d** 82 **p** 83. C Chapeltown *Sheff* 82-85; V Sheff St Paul Wordsworth Avenue 85-93; Ind Chapl from 85; RD Ecclesfield 90-93; V Oughtibridge from 93. *The Vicarage, Church Street, Oughtibridge, Sheffield S30 3FU* Sheffield (0114) 286 2317

ATKINSON, Marianne Rose. b 39. Girton Coll Cam BA61 CertEd62 MA64. Linc Th Coll 86. **d** 88 **p** 94. C S w N Hayling *Portsm* 88-91; Par Dn Rainham *Roch* 91-92; Asst Chapl Salford R Hosps NHS Trust from 92; Hon C Prestwich St Marg *Man* from 94. *Hope Hospital, Stott Lane, Salford M6 8HD, or 42 Kendall Road, Manchester M8 4NF* 0161-789 7373 or 740 1335

ATKINSON, Michael Hubert. b 33. Qu Coll Ox BA57 MA60. Ripon Hall Ox 56. **d** 58 **p** 59. C Attercliffe w Carbrook *Sheff* 58-60; Ind Chapl 60-66; C Sheff Sharrow 60-66; Ind Chapl *Pet* 66-71; Sen Ind Chapl *Cant* 71-79; Research Officer Gen Syn Bd for Soc Resp 79-87; Representation Sec USPG 88-92; TV High Wycombe *Ox* from 92. *St James's Vicarage, Plomer Hill, Downley, High Wycombe, Bucks HP13 5NB* High Wycombe (01494) 525346

ATKINSON, Michael James. b 38. AKC62. **d** 63 **p** 64. C Leeds Halton St Wilfrid *Ripon* 63-65; C Luton St Hugh Lewsey CD *St Alb* 65-67; V Luton Lewsey St Hugh 67-71; C Caversham *Ox* 71-73; P-in-c N Woolwich *Chelmsf* 73-74; V N Woolwich w Silvertown 74-78; V Clavering w Langley and Arkesden 78-89; V Chelmsf All SS 89-92; P-in-c Gt and Lt Bardfield 92-94; V Gt and Lt Bardfield w Gt and Saling from 94. *The Vicarage, Braintree Road, Great Bardfield, Braintree, Essex CM7 4RN* Great Dunmow (01371) 810267

ATKINSON, Nigel Terence. b 60. Sheff Univ BA82. Westmr Th Sem (USA) MDiv87 Cranmer Hall Dur 87. **d** 89 **p** 90. C Oakwood St Thos *Lon* 89-92; P-in-c Dalton *Ex* 92-95; P-in-c Iddesleigh w Dowland 92-95; P-in-c Monkokehampton 92-95; Warden Latimer Ho Ox from 95. *Latimer House, 131 Banbury Road, Oxford OX2 7AJ* Oxford (01865) 513879

ATKINSON, Mrs Patricia Anne. b 47. Local NSM Course. **d** 89. NSM Nor St Steph *Nor* 89-94; Lic to Offic from 94. *32 Berryfields, Brundall, Norwich NR13 5QE* Norwich (01603) 714720

ATKINSON, Peter Duncan. b 41. Univ Coll Dur BA62. Linc Th Coll 63. **d** 65 **p** 66. C Beckenham St Geo *Roch* 65-69; C Caversham *Ox* 69-75; P-in-c Millfield St Mark *Dur* 76-86; V Dedworth *Ox* 86-93; TV Aylesbury w Bierton and Hulcott from 93. *4 Cubb Field, Aylesbury, Bucks HP21 8SH* Aylesbury (01296) 25008

ATKINSON, Peter Geoffrey. b 50. Sarum & Wells Th Coll 81. **d** 83 **p** 84. C Aylesbury *Ox* 83-86; C Dorchester 86-87; TV 87-91; V Cropredy w Gt Bourton and Wardington from 91. *The Vicarage, High Street, Cropredy, Banbury, Oxon OX17 1NG* Cropredy (01295) 750799

ATKINSON, Canon Peter Gordon. b 52. St Jo Coll Ox BA74 MA78. Westcott Ho Cam 77. **d** 79 **p** 80. C Clapham Old Town *S'wark* 79-83; P-in-c Tatsfield 83-90; R Bath H Trin *B & W* 90-91; Prin Chich Th Coll 91-94; Can and Preb Chich Cathl *Chich* from 91; R Lavant from 94. *The Rectory, Lavant, Chichester, W Sussex PO18 0AH* Chichester (01243) 527313

ATKINSON, Philip Charles. b 50. Hull Univ BA71 PhD76 Chorley Coll of Educn CertEd77. N Ord Course 81. **d** 84 **p** 85. NSM Bolton SS Simon and Jude *Man* 84-87; Chapl R Wolv Sch from 87. *5A Claremont Road, Wolverhampton WV3 0EA* Wolverhampton (01902) 330706

ATKINSON, Philip Stephen. b 58. K Coll Lon BD80 AKC80. Ridley Hall Cam. **d** 83 **p** 84. C Barrow St Matt *Carl* 83-86; C Kirkby Lonsdale 86-89; R Redmarshall *Dur* from 89; V Bishopton w Gt Stainton from 89. *The Rectory, Redmarshall, Stockton-on-Tees, Cleveland TS21 1EP* Sedgefield (01740) 30810

ATKINSON, Richard William Bryant. b 58. Magd Coll Cam MA. Ripon Coll Cuddesdon. **d** 84 **p** 85. C Abingdon w Shippon *Ox* 84-87; TV Sheff Manor *Sheff* 87-91; TR from 91. *The Vicarage, Cary Road, Sheffield S2 1JP* Sheffield (0114) 239 8360/253 0518

ATKINSON, Canon Samuel Charles Donald. b 30. TCD BA54. **d** 55 **p** 56. C Belf St Simon *Conn* 55-62; I Ballynaclough *L & K* 62-68; I Cloughjordan w Modreeny 68-87; Dioc Youth Adv (Killaloe) 75-83; Dioc Info Officer (Limerick and Killaloe) 76-88; Can Killaloe Cathl 76-82; Chan from 82; I Cloughjordan w Borrisokane etc from 87. *Modreeny Rectory, Cloughjordan, Co Tipperary, Irish Republic* Cloughjordan (505) 42183

ATKINSON, Simon James. b 71. St Chad's Coll Dur BA93. St Steph Ho Ox 93. **d** 95. C Norton St Mary *Dur* from 95. *71 The Glebe, Stockton-on-Tees, Cleveland TS20 1ND* Stockton (01642) 361300

ATKINSON, Terence Harry. b 52. Coll of Resurr Mirfield 88. **d** 90 **p** 91. C Bottesford w Ashby *Linc* 90-93; TV Cleethorpes from 93. *St Francis House, Sandringham Road, Cleethorpes, S Humberside DN35 9HA* Cleethorpes (01472) 691215

ATTFIELD, David George. b 31. Magd Coll Ox BA54 MA58 BD61 K Coll Lon MPhil72 Dur Univ MA81. Westcott Ho Cam 57. **d** 58 **p** 59. C Edgbaston St Aug *Birm* 58-61; C Ward End 61-62; Lect Div St Kath Coll Tottenham 62-64; All SS Coll Tottenham 64-68; Sen Lect St Bede Coll Dur 68-75; St Hild and St Bede Coll 75-80; TV Drypool *York* 80-86; R Newton Heath All SS *Man* from 86. *All Saints' Rectory, 2 Culcheth Lane, Newton Heath, Manchester M10 6LR* 0161-681 3102

ATTLEY, Ronald (Ron). b 46. Open Univ BA87. Chich Th Coll 68. **d** 70 **p** 71. C Heworth St Mary *Dur* 70-73; C Hulme Ascension *Man* 73-75; Belize 76-79; V Leadgate *Dur* 79-84; Chapl HM Rem Cen Ashford 84-87; Chapl HM Pris Ashwell and Stocken 87-89; Chapl HM Pris Frankland 89-92; Chapl HM Young Offender Inst Deerbolt from 92. *HM Young Offender Institution, Deerbolt, Bowes Road, Barnard Castle, Co Durham DL12 9BG* Teesdale (01833) 37561 Fax 31736

ATTRILL, Norman Edmund Charles. b 16. K Coll Lon BA37. Wm Temple Coll Rugby 65 Ripon Hall Ox 67. **d** 68 **p** 69. C Portsea St Mary *Portsm* 68-72; V Sea View 72-80; rtd 81; Perm to Offic *Ox* from 83. *27 Church Street, Henley-on-Thames, Oxon RG9 1SE* Henley-on-Thames (01491) 574268

ATTWATER, Mrs Sallyanne (Sally). b 48. **d** 94 **p** 95. Chapl Asst Eastbourne Distr Gen Hosp 94-95; Asst Chapl Princess Alice Hosp and All SS Hosp 94-95; C E Grinstead St Swithun *Chich* from 95. *11 Gardenhouse Lane, East Grinstead, W Sussex RH19 4JT* East Grinstead (01342) 328306

ATTWATER, Stephen Philip. b 47. ALCM67. Linc Th Coll 85. **d** 87 **p** 88. C Warrington St Elphin *Liv* 87-90; P-in-c Eccleston St Thos 90-94; V from 94. *St Thomas' Vicarage, 21 St George's Road, St Helens, Merseyside WA10 4LH* St Helens (01744) 22295

ATTWOOD, Anthony Norman (Tony). b 47. Univ of Wales (Abth) BSc(Econ)69 Birm Univ DipTh71 Hull Univ MA82. Qu Coll Birm 69. **d** 72 **p** 73. C Greenhill *Sheff* 72-75; V Elsecar 76-81; Ind Missr from 81; TV Maltby 81-86; Ind Chapl from 86; RD Adwick 89-95. *5 Daw Wood, Bentley, Doncaster, S Yorkshire DN5 0PU* Doncaster (01302) 875904 Fax as telephone

ATTWOOD, Carl Norman Harry. b 53. Bris Univ BA74 Ox Univ BA76 MA80. Cuddesdon Coll 74. **d** 77 **p** 78. C Tupsley *Heref* 77-82; R Colwall w Upper Colwall and Coddington from 82; Bp's Voc Officer 83-89; Chapl St Jas and the Abbey Sch W Malvern from 86; RD Ledbury *Heref* from 90. *The Rectory, Colwall, Malvern, Worcs WR13 6EG* Colwall (01684) 540330 Fax 540083

ATTWOOD, David John Edwin. b 51. Dur Univ BA76 Em Coll Cam BA73 MA74. Cranmer Hall Dur 74. **d** 77 **p** 78. C Rodbourne Cheney *Bris* 77-79; C Lydiard Millicent w Lydiard Tregoz 79-85; Lect Trin Coll Bris from 85. *13 St Andrews Road, Bristol BS19 3NR* Chew Magna (01275) 463864

ATTY, Canon Norman Hughes. b 40. Dur Univ BA62. Cranmer Hall Dur 62. **d** 65 **p** 66. C Blackb Sch *Blackb* 65-67; Asst Master Billinge Sch Blackb 67-71; City of Leic Boys' Sch 71-73; P-in-c Elmley Lovett w Hampton Lovett *Worc* 73-78; P-in-c Elmbridge w Rushock 74-78; R Elmley Lovett w Hampton Lovett and Elmbridge etc 78-85; Hon Can Worc Cathl 81-85. *3 Gilbertstone Road, Redditch, Worcs B98 7NQ*

ATWELL, Very Rev James Edgar. b 46. Ex Coll Ox BA68 MA73 Harvard Univ ThM70. Cuddesdon Coll 68. **d** 70 **p** 71. C E Dulwich St Jo *S'wark* 70-74; C Cam Gt St Mary w St Mich *Ely* 74-77; Chapl Jes Coll Cam 77-81; V Towcester w Easton Neston *Pet* 81-95; RD Towcester 83-91; Provost St E from 95. *The Provost's House, Bury St Edmunds, Suffolk IP33 1RS* Bury St Edmunds (01284) 754852

ATWELL, Brother Robert Ronald. b 54. St Jo Coll Dur BA75 Dur Univ MLitt79. Westcott Ho Cam 76. **d** 78 **p** 79. C Mill Hill Jo Keble Ch *Lon* 78-81; Chapl Trin Coll Cam 81-87; OSB from 87; Lic to Offic *Ox* from 87. *Burford Priory, Priory Lane, Burford, Oxford OX18 4SQ* Burford (01993) 823605

AUBREY, Canon John Watkin. b 17. Ch Coll Cam BA39 MA43. Westcott Ho Cam 39. **d** 40 **p** 41. S Africa 48-76; R Collyweston w Duddington and Tixover *Pet* 76-82; rtd 82. *St Barnabas, Beauchamp Community, The Quadrangle, Newland, Malvern, Worcs WR13 5AX* Malvern (01684) 892187

AUCHMUTY, John Robert. b 67. ACCA Athlone Regional Tech Coll NC(BS)89. CITC 89. **d** 92 **p** 93. C Dundela *D & D* from 92. *2A Sydenham Avenue, Belfast BT4 2DR* Belfast (01232) 655969

AUCKLAND, Canon Allan Frank. b 13. K Coll Lon 49. **d** 49 **p** 50. V Hatcham St Cath *S'wark* 56-74; RD Lewisham 65-70; Hon Can S'wark Cathl 67-81; R Burstow 74-81; rtd 81; Perm to Offic *Cant* from 81. *14 The Pavement, Front Road, Woodchurch, Ashford, Kent TN26 3QE* Woodchurch (01233) 861231

AUCKLAND, Archdeacon of. See GIBSON, Ven George Granville

AUDEN, Lawson Philip. b 45. Qu Coll Birm 73. **d** 78 **p** 81. C Spalding *Linc* 78-81; TV Wordsley *Lich* 81-82; TV Kidderminster St Mary and All SS etc *Worc* 82-87; Ind Chapl 82-87; Perm to Offic *Worc* and *Cov* from 87; Perm to Offic *Birm* and *Lich* from 90; Perm to Offic *Glouc* from 94. *Willowbrook, Willersley Fields, Badsey, Evesham, Worcs WR11 5HF* Evesham (01386) 858263

AUGUSTINE, Brother. See MORRIS, David Freestone

AULD, Mrs Sheila Edith. b 38. Newc Poly BA87. NE Ord Course 91. **d** 94 **p** 95. NSM Newc St Gabr *Newc* from 94. *5 Plessey Terrace, Newcastle upon Tyne NE7 7DJ* 0191-281 8647

AUST, Arthur John. b 14. St Aug Coll Cant 62. **d** 63 **p** 64. R Theddlethorpe w Mablethorpe *Linc* 67-71; Nigeria 71-74; S Africa 77-79; TV Clyst St George, Aylesbeare, Clyst Honiton etc *Ex* 79-81; rtd 81; Perm to Offic *Cant* from 81. *Overhill House, Upper Street, Kingsdown, Deal, Kent CT14 8DR* Deal (01304) 361583

AUSTEN, Glyn. b 54. UEA BA MPhil Ox Univ MA. Ripon Coll Cuddesdon 79. **d** 82 **p** 83. C Newport w Longford and Chetwynd *Lich* 82-85; C Hawley H Trin *Guildf* 85-87; R Barnack w Ufford and Bainton *Pet* from 87. *The Rectory, Barnack, Stamford, Lincs PE9 3ET* Stamford (01780) 740234

AUSTEN, John. b 46. St Cath Coll Cam BA69 MA72. Qu Coll Birm DipTh70. **d** 71 **p** 72. C Thornaby on Tees *York* 71-74; C Aston St Jas *Birm* 74-82; Chapl Aston Univ 82-88; C Handsworth St Andr from 88. *151 Church Lane, Birmingham B20 2RU* 0121-554 8882

AUSTEN, Simon Neil. b 67. Warw Univ BSc88. Wycliffe Hall Ox BA93 DipMin94. **d** 94 **p** 95. C Gt Chesham *Ox* from 94. *31 Chapmans Crescent, Chesham, Bucks HP5 2QT* Chesham (01494) 783629

AUSTERBERRY, David Naylor. b 35. Birm Univ BA58. Wells Th Coll 58. **d** 60 **p** 61. C Leek St Edw *Lich* 60-63; Iran 64-70; Chapl CMS Foxbury 70-73; V Walsall Pleck and Bescot *Lich* 73-82; R Brierley Hill 82-88; R Kinnerley w Melverley and Knockin w Maesbrook from 88; RD Oswestry from 92. *The Rectory, Kinnerley, Oswestry, Shropshire SY10 8DE* Knockin (01691) 682233

AUSTERBERRY, John Maurice. b 62. Birm Univ BA83. Sarum & Wells Th Coll 84. **d** 86 **p** 87. C Clayton *Lich* 86-90; Asst Chapl Withington Hosp Man from 89. *The Chaplain's Office, Withington Hospital, West Didsbury, Manchester M20 8LR* 0161-445 8111 or 881 3864

AUSTERBERRY, Ven Sidney Denham. b 08. Man Egerton Hall 30. **d** 31 **p** 33. Adn Salop *Lich* 59-79; V Gt Ness 59-77; V Lt Ness 73-77; rtd 80. *6 Honeysuckle Row, Shrewsbury SY3 7TW* Shrewsbury (01743) 368080

AUSTIN, Ven George Bernard. b 31. St D Coll Lamp BA53 Chich Th Coll 53. **d** 55 **p** 56. C Chorley St Pet *Blackb* 55-57; C Notting Hill St Clem *Lon* 57-60; Asst Chapl Lon Univ 60-61; C Dunstable *St Alb* 61-64; V Eaton Bray 64-70; V Bushey Heath 70-88; Hon Can St Alb 78-88; Adn York from 88. *7 Lang Road, Bishopthorpe, York YO2 1QJ* York (01904) 709541 Fax 701685

AUSTIN, Miss Jane. b 43. SRN64 SCM66. Trin Coll Bris DipTh81. **dss** 81 **d** 87 **p** 94. Tonbridge SS Pet and Paul *Roch* 81-87; Par Dn 87-94; C from 94. *48 Longmead Way, Tonbridge, Kent TN10 3TG* Tonbridge (01732) 367765

✠**AUSTIN, Rt Rev John Michael.** b 39. St Edm Hall Ox BA63. St Steph Ho Ox 62. **d** 64 **p** 65 **c** 92. C E Dulwich St Jo *S'wark* 64-68; USA 68-69; Warden Pemb Ho and Missr Walworth St Chris CD *S'wark* 69-76; TV Walworth 75-76; Soc Resp Adv *St Alb* 76-84; Dir Dioc Bd for Soc Resp *Lon* 84-92; Preb St Paul's Cathl 89-92; Suff Bp Aston *Birm* from 92. *Strensham House, 8 Strensham Hill, Birmingham B13 8AG* 0121-449 0675 Fax 428 1114

AUSTIN, Leslie Ernest. b 46. Trin Coll Bris 72. **d** 74 **p** 75. C Paddock Wood *Roch* 74-79; C Upper Armley *Ripon* 79-81; V Horton *Bradf* 81-85; V Long Preston w Tosside from 85. *The Vicarage, Long Preston, Skipton, N Yorkshire BD23 4NH* Long Preston (01729) 840513

AUSTIN, Canon Michael Ridgwell. b 33. FRHistS Lon Univ BD57 PhD69 Birm Univ MA66. Lon Coll of Div ALCD56 LTh. **d** 57 **p** 58. C Ward End *Birm* 57-60; V Derby St Andr *Derby* 60-66; Lect Th Derbyshire Coll of HE 66-73; Chapl Derby Cathl *Derby* 66-81; Prin Lect 73-85; Can Res Derby Cathl 81-85; Bp's Tr Adv *S'well* 85-88; Dir of Post-Ord Tr 86-94; Can Res S'well Minster 88-94; Dioc Dir of Tr 88-94; Abps' Adv for Bps' Min *Cant* from 94. *22 Marlock Close, Fiskerton, Southwell, Notts NG25 0UB* Southwell (01636) 830074

AUSTIN, Raymond Charles. b 23. St Edm Hall Ox BA48 MA53 Lon Univ BD70 DipEd74. Linc Th Coll 48. **d** 50 **p** 51. V Chapel-en-le-Frith *Derby* 57-66; Perm to Offic *Mon* 66-84; V Llantilio Crossenny w Penrhos, Llanvetherine etc 84-91; rtd 88. *Glanmor, Hardwick Hill, Chepstow, Gwent NP6 5PN* Chepstow (01291) 620079

AUSTIN, Ronald Glyn. b 52. Llan Dioc Tr Scheme 88. **d** 90 **p** 91. C Llangynwyd w Maesteg *Llan* 90-91; C Barry All SS 91-93; V Nantymoel w Wyndham from 93. *The Vicarage, Wyndham, Ogmore Vale, Bridgend, M Glam CF32 7HE* Ogmore Valley (01656) 840248

AUSTIN, Mrs Susan Frances. b 47. Open Univ BA81. Cant Sch of Min 87. **d** 92 **p** 94. Chapl Ashford Sch 90-94; C Gt Chart *Cant* 92-94; C Ashford 92-94; C Estover *Ex* from 94. *14 Dover Road, Plymouth PL6 8ST* Plymouth (01752) 780683

AUTTON, Canon Norman William James. b 20. Selw Coll Cam BA42 MA46. St Mich Coll Llan 42. **d** 44 **p** 45. Dir of Tr Gen Syn Hosp Chapls Coun 67-72; Chapl Univ Hosp of Wales Cardiff 72-85; Can Llan Cathl *Llan* 77-85; Chan 85-92; rtd 85. *112 St Anthony Road, Cardiff CF4 4DJ* Cardiff (01222) 625788

AVANN, Canon Penelope Joyce (Penny). b 46. Trin Coll Bris DipTh71. **dss** 83 **d** 87. Southborough St Pet w Ch Ch and St Matt *Roch* 83-89; Par Dn 87-89; Warden Past Assts from 89; Par Dn Beckenham St Jo 89-94; C from 94; Hon Can Roch Cathl from 94. *21 Glanfield Road, Beckenham, Kent BR3 3JS* 0181-650 4061

AVENT, Raymond John. b 28. St D Coll Lamp BA55 Coll of Resurr Mirfield 55. **d** 57 **p** 58. V Tottenham St Paul *Lon* 67-77; RD E Haringey 73-77; V Kilburn St Aug w St Jo 77-87; AD Westmr Paddington 79-84; R St Vedast w St Mich-le-Querne etc 87-94; rtd 94. *124 Midhurst Road, London W13 9TP* 0181-567 8964

AVERY, Richard Julian. b 52. Keble Coll Ox BA73. St Jo Coll Nottm 74. **d** 77 **p** 78. C Macclesfield St Mich *Ches* 77-80; Canada 82-83 and from 87; C Becontree St Mary *Chelmsf* 84-87. *5984 Rothwell Place, Duncan, British Columbia, Canada, V9L 3B7* Duncan (604) 748-5729

AVERY, Robert Edward. b 69. Magd Coll Cam BA90. Ripon Coll Cuddesdon 90. **d** 93 **p** 94. C Cen Telford *Lich* from 93. *19 Dodmoor Grange, Telford, Shropshire TF3 2AW* Telford (01952) 597278

AVES, John Albert. b 51. K Coll Lon AKC73 BD74 CertEd79 MA82. **d** 75 **p** 76. C Plaistow St Andr *Chelmsf* 75-77; Perm to Offic *Lon* 77-79; C Nor St Pet Mancroft *Nor* 79-82; R Attleborough w Besthorpe from 82. *The Rectory, Surrogate Street, Attleborough, Norfolk NR17 2AW* Attleborough (01953) 453185

AVES, Peter Colin. b 57. Qu Mary Coll Lon BSc79 CertEd80. Wycliffe Hall Ox 85. **d** 88 **p** 89. C Thames Ditton *Guildf* 88-90; C Chertsey 90-93; R Stockbridge and Longstock and Leckford *Win* from 93. *The Rectory, 11 Trafalgar Way, Stockbridge, Hants SO20 6ET* Andover (01264) 810810

AVEYARD, Ian. b 46. Liv Univ BSc68. ALCD72 St Jo Coll Nottm 71. **d** 71 **p** 72. C Bradley *Wakef* 71-74; C Knowle *Birm* 74-79; P-in-c Cofton Hackett 79; P-in-c Barnt Green 79; V Cofton Hackett w Barnt Green 80-94; Dioc Dir of Reader Tr 85-94; Dioc Warden of Readers 91-94. *19 Darley Avenue, Beeston, Nottingham NG9 6JP* Nottingham (0115) 973 1367

AVIS, Preb Paul David Loup. b 47. Lon Univ BD70 PhD76. Westcott Ho Cam 73. **d** 75 **p** 76. C S Molton, Nymet St George, High Bray etc *Ex* 75-80; V Stoke Canon, Poltimore w Huxham and Rewe etc from 80; Preb Ex Cathl from 92. *The Vicarage, Stoke Canon, Exeter EX5 4AS* Exeter (01392) 841583

AWDRY, Wilbert Vere. b 11. St Pet Hall Ox BA32 MA36. Wycliffe Hall Ox 32. **d** 36 **p** 37. V Emneth *Ely* 53-65; Perm to Offic *Glouc* 65-89; rtd 76. *Sodor, 30 Rodborough Avenue, Stroud, Glos GL5 3RS* Stroud (01453) 762321

AWRE, Edward Francis Wintour. b 11. St Jo Coll Dur BA37 DipTh38 MA40. **d** 38 **p** 39. V Nether Stowey *B & W* 56-70; P-in-c Over Stowey w Aisholt 69-70; rtd 71; Hon C Burnham *B & W* 72-81; Perm to Offic from 81. *3 Seaview Road, Burnham-on-Sea, Somerset TA8 2AJ* Burnham-on-Sea (01278) 782493

AWRE, Richard William Esgar. b 56. Univ of Wales BA78. Wycliffe Hall Ox 78. **d** 81 **p** 82. C Blackpool St Jo *Blackb* 81-84; Asst Dir of Ords and Voc Adv 84-89; C Altham w Clayton le Moors 84-89; V Longridge from 89. *The Vicarage, Church Street, Longridge, Preston PR3 3WA* Longridge (01772) 783281

AXFORD, Robert Henry. b 50. CEng85 Univ of Wales BEng72. Sarum & Wells Th Coll 89. **d** 91 **p** 92. C Castle Cary w Ansford *B & W* from 91. *35 Hallett Road, Castle Cary, Somerset BA7 7LG* Castle Cary (01963) 51286

AXTELL, Ronald Arthur John. b 33. Lon Univ BSc54 St Cath Soc Ox BA58 MA62. Wycliffe Hall Ox 56. **d** 58 **p** 59. C Walton Breck *Liv* 58-61; Iran 63-78; Chr Witness to Israel Miss in Man 78-82; Perm to Offic *Man* 79-82; TV Man Resurr 82; TV Man Gd Shep 82-88; R Levenshulme St Pet from 88. *29A Ardwick Green North, Manchester M12 6FZ* 0161-273 5020

AYAD, Karl. b 25. Cairo Univ BSc48 Lon Univ MSc53 PhD55. St Steph Ho Ox 80. **d** 81 **p** 82. C Allerton *Liv* 81-83; V Knowsley 83-90; rtd 90. *2 Stanley House, 46 Stanley Road, Hoylake, Wirral, Merseyside L47 1HY* 0151-632 5519

AYERS, Canon John. b 40. FCollP Bris Univ BEd75 Newton Park Coll Bath MEd89 FRSA94. **d** 77 **p** 78. NSM Corsham *Bris* 77-79; NSM Gtr Corsham 79-88; NSM Ditteridge 88-92; NSM Box w Hazlebury and Ditteridge from 93; Hon Can Bris Cathl from 94. *Toad Hall, Middlehill, Box, Corsham, Wilts SN13 8QP* Box (01225) 742123

AYERS, Paul Nicholas. b 61. St Pet Coll Ox BA82 MA86. Trin Coll Bris 83. **d** 85 **p** 86. C Clayton *Bradf* 85-88; C Keighley St Andr 88-91; V Wrose from 91. *St Cuthbert's Vicarage, 71 Wrose Road, Bradford, W Yorkshire BD2 1LN* Bradford (01274) 611631

AYERST, Edward Richard. b 25. Leeds Univ BA51. Coll of Resurr Mirfield 51. **d** 53 **p** 54. R Whippingham w E Cowes *Portsm* 66-77; V Bridgwater St Mary w Chilton Trinity *B & W* 77-84; V Durleigh 77-84; V Bridgwater St Mary, Chilton Trinity and Durleigh 84-90; Chapl to The Queen from 87; rtd 90; Perm to Offic *B & W* from 90. *56 Maple Drive, Burham-on-Sea, Somerset TA8 1DH* Burnham-on-Sea (01278) 780701

AYKROYD, Harold Allan. b 22. DFC. Man Univ BA48. Qu Coll Birm 73. **d** 76 **p** 76. NSM Moseley St Agnes *Birm* 76-82; NSM Bournville from 82. *108 Middleton Hall Road, Birmingham B30 1DG* 0121-451 1365 or 569 4687

AYLEN, George Richard. b 24. Chich Th Coll 48. **d** 52 **p** 53. V Whitstable St Pet *Cant* 67-75; R Petham w Waltham and Lower Hardres w Nackington 75-78; rtd 78; Perm to Offic *Cant* from 80. *20 Seymour Place, Canterbury, Kent CT1 3SF* Canterbury (01227) 456243

AYLETT, Graham Peter. b 59. Qu Coll Cam BA81 MA84 PhD85 St Jo Coll Dur BA88. Cranmer Hall Dur 86. **d** 90 **p** 91. C Wilton *B & W* 90-94; C Runcorn All SS *Ches* from 94. *145 Greenway Road, Runcorn, Cheshire WA7 4NR* Runcorn (01928) 576168

AYLETT, Mrs Nicola Jane. b 63. St Anne's Coll Ox BA84 St Jo Coll Dur BA89. Cranmer Hall Dur 87. **d** 90 **p** 94. C Wilton *B & W* 90-93; NSM 93-94; NSM Runcorn All SS *Ches* from 94. *145 Greenway Road, Runcorn, Cheshire WA7 4NR* Runcorn (01928) 576168

AYLING, Arnold Paul. b 38. Ball Coll Ox BA61. Wells Th Coll 65. **d** 67 **p** 68. C Weymouth H Trin *Sarum* 67-70; Chapl K Alfred Coll *Win* 70-73; Miss to Seamen 73-84; Dunkirk 73; Nigeria 74-82; S Africa 82-84; Perm to Offic *Sarum* 85-86; Perm to Offic *Chich* from 85; Chapl Leybourne Grange Hosp W Malling from 86; Chapl Pembury Hosp Tunbridge Wells from 86; Chapl Kent and Sussex Hosp Tunbridge Wells from 86; Distr Chapl Tunbridge Wells HA from 86. *Pembury Hospital, Pembury, Tunbridge Wells, Kent TN2 4QJ* Pembury (01892) 824954 or 823535

AYLING, Preb John Charles. b 02. St Jo Coll Dur BA29. **d** 29 **p** 30. R Myddle *Lich* 59-70; V Broughton 59-70; P-in-c Grinshill 59-65; Dioc Dir RE 59-75; Preb Lich Cathl 61-75; rtd 70. *10 Church Close, Bicton, Shrewsbury SY3 8EN* Shrewsbury (01743) 850491

AYLING, John Michael. b 37. St Cath Coll Cam BA60 MA64. Linc Th Coll 60. **d** 62 **p** 63. C Stoke upon Trent *Lich* 62-66; C Codsall 66-67; Australia 67-71; Solomon Is 71-72; Lic to Offic *St Alb* 72-91; TR Boscastle w Davidstow *Truro* from 91. *The Rectory, Boscastle, Cornwall PL35 0DJ* Boscastle (01840) 250359

AYNSLEY, Ernest Edgar. b 02. FRIC Dur Univ BSc23 MSc24 PhD34 DSc62. Westcott Ho Cam 42. **d** 42 **p** 43. Lic to Offic *Newc* from 63; Prof Chemistry Newc Univ 63-67; rtd 67. *7 Manor Court, Ulgham, Morpeth, Northd NE61 3BG* Morpeth (01670) 790197

AYRES, Anthony Lawrence. b 47. Trin Coll Bris 69. **d** 73 **p** 74. C Plumstead All SS *S'wark* 73-77; Hon C from 77; Member of Counselling Team CA from 83. *37 Donaldson Road, London SE18 4JZ* 0181-856 1542

B

BABB, Charles Thomas. b 47. Newfoundland Univ BA70. Qu Coll Newfoundland 64. **d** 70 **p** 72. Canada 70-80; Miss to Seamen 80-94; Chapl Antwerp Seafarers' Cen *Eur* 80-94; Chapl Hull Miss to Seamen from 94. *Hull Missions to Seamen, 900 Hendon Road, Hull HU9 5LZ* Hull (01482) 76322

BABB, Canon Geoffrey. b 42. Man Univ BSc64 MA74 Linacre Coll Ox BA67. Ripon Hall Ox 65. **d** 68 **p** 69. C Heywood St Luke *Man* 68-71; P-in-c Loundsley Green Ascension CD *Derby* 71-76; TV Old Brampton and Loundsley Green 76-77; TV Stafford St Mary and St Chad *Lich* 77-79; Soc Resp Officer 77-88; TV Stafford 79-88; Preb Lich Cathl 87-88; P-in-c Salford Sacred Trin *Man* from 88; Dir of Continuing Min Educn from 88; Hon Can Man Cathl from 89. *197A Lancaster Road, Salford M6 8NB* 0161-788 7077 or 832 5785

BABINGTON, Canon Gervase Hamilton. b 30. Keble Coll Ox BA57 MA57. Wells Th Coll 55. **d** 57 **p** 58. R Waddington *Linc* 65-81; RD Graffoe 74-81; Can and Preb Linc Cathl 77-95; V Gainsborough All SS 81-90; RD Corringham 82-87; R Walesby 90-95; rtd 95. *15 Highfields, Nettleham, Lincoln LN2 2ST* Lincoln (01522) 595702

BACH, Frances Mary. b 48. Open Univ BA AIL. CITC BTh. **d** 94 **p** 95. NSM Ballynure and Ballyeaston *Conn* from 94. *c/o 18 Straid Road, Ballynure, Co Antrim BT39 9PY* Antrim (01960) 341083

BACH, John Edward Goulden. b 40. JP. Dur Univ BA66 DipTh69. Cranmer Hall Dur 66. **d** 69 **p** 70. C Bradf Cathl *Bradf* 69-72; Chapl and Lect NUU 73-84; Chapl Ulster Univ from 84. *The Anglican Chaplaincy, 70 Hopefield Avenue, Portrush, Co Antrim BT56 8HE* Portrush (01265) 823348 or 44141 Fax 40908

BACHE, Edward Cyril Forbes. b 07. Dur Univ BA33 MA56. **d** 34 **p** 35. Chapl St Felix Sch Southwold 71-74; Lic to Offic *St E* 71-75; TV Halesworth w Linstead and Chediston 76-77; rtd 77; C Hardwick w Tusmore *Ox* 77-80; C Cottisford 77-80; Perm to Offic *St E* from 81. *Brook Cottage, Newbourn, Woodbridge, Suffolk IP12 4NY* Waldringfield (0147336) 702

BACHELL, Kenneth George. b 22. Lon Univ BD49. K Coll Lon 55. **d** 56 **p** 57. V Southn St Alb *Win* 68-76; Warden Dioc Conf Ho Crawshawbooth *Man* 76-79; P-in-c Crawshawbooth 76-79; V Holdenhurst *Win* 79-83; V Froyle and Holybourne 83-87; rtd 87; Perm to Offic *Blackb* from 88. *8 Hazelwood, Silverdale, Carnforth, Lancs LA5 0TQ* Silverdale (01524) 701181

BACK, Christopher George. b 46. St Chad's Coll Dur BA69 Linacre Coll Ox BA71 MA. St Steph Ho Ox 69. **d** 72 **p** 73. C Hoxton H Trin w St Mary *Lon* 72-75; C Kenton 75-83; V Noel Park St Mark 83-94. *6A Bushwood, London E11 3AY* 0181-989 9076

BACK, Edward James. b 24. Regent St Poly Lon BScEng49 MIEE53 CEng85. ALCD65. **d** 65 **p** 66. Teacher Rutland Ho Sch Uxbridge 69-70; Lect Harrow Coll Middx 70-89; rtd 94. *8 Wolsey Road, Northwood, Middlesex HA6 2HW* Northwood (01923) 825332

BACK, Miss Esther Elaine. b 52. Saffron Walden Coll CertEd74. Trin Coll Bris 79 Oak Hill Th Coll BA81. **dss** 81 **d** 87 **p** 94. Collyhurst *Man* 81-84; Upton (or Overchurch) *Ches* 84-87; Par Dn 87-88; Par Dn Upper Holloway St Pet w St Jo *Lon* 88-94; C from 94. *4 Anatola Road, London N19 5HN* 0171-263 8473

BACKHOUSE, Alan Eric. b 37. Keble Coll Ox BA61 MA67. Tyndale Hall Bris 61. **d** 64 **p** 65. C Burnage St Marg *Man* 64-67; C Cheadle Hulme St Andr *Ches* 67-70; V Buglawton 70-80; V New Ferry 80-87; V Tarvin 87-93; V Knypersley *Lich* from 93. *St John's Vicarage, 62 Park Lane, Knypersley, Stoke-on-Trent ST8 7AU* Stoke-on-Trent (01782) 512240

BACKHOUSE, Colin. b 41. MCSD82 Birm Poly BA67. Oak Hill Th Coll DipHE87. **d** 87 **p** 88. C Branksome St Clem *Sarum* 87-91; P-in-c Bluntisham cum Earith w Colne and Woodhurst *Ely* 91-92; R from 92. *The Rectory, Bluntisham, Huntingdon, Cambs PE17 3LN* Ramsey (01487) 740456

BACKHOUSE, John. b 30. Univ Coll Southn BA50. Wycliffe Hall Ox 51. **d** 53 **p** 54. Area Sec CMS 64-78; Dios Linc and Ely 64-71; Leic 72-78; Pet 72-75; Cov 75-78; V Dishley and Thorpe Acre *Leic* 78-83; R Ab Kettleby Gp 83-89; P-in-c Bitteswell 89-94; RD Guthlaxton II (Lutterworth) 90-94; rtd 94. *29 Peashill Close, Sileby, Loughborough, Leics LE12 7PT* Loughborough (01509) 812016

BACON, David Gary. b 62. Leic Univ BA83 Southn Univ BTh88. Sarum & Wells Th Coll 85. **d** 88 **p** 89. C Bromley St Mark *Roch* 88-92; C Lynton, Brendon, Countisbury, Lynmouth etc *Ex* 92; TV 92-95; P-in-c Lapford, Nymet Rowland and Coldridge from 95. *The Rectory, Lapford, Crediton, Devon EX17 6PX* Lapford (01363) 83321

BACON, Derek Robert Alexander. b 44. Birkb Coll Lon DAC87 CACP89 BA92 MSc94. TCD Div Sch 69. **d** 71 **p** 72. C Templeroan *D & R* 71-73; VC Derry Cathl 72-73; C Heeley *Sheff* 74-76; V Sheff Abbeydale St Pet 76-82; Chapl Gt Ormond Street Hosp for Children NHS Trust from 82. *Great Ormond Street Hospital for Children NHS Trust, Great Ormond Street, London WC1N 3JH* 0171-813 8232 or 405 9200

BACON, Eric Arthur. b 23. Qu Coll Birm 68. **d** 69 **p** 70. C Linc St Pet-at-Gowts and St Andr *Linc* 69-71; C Asterby Gp 71-74; V Anwick 74-78; V S Kyme 74-78; P-in-c Kirkby Laythorpe w Asgarby 76-78; P-in-c Ewerby w Evedon 76-78; P-in-c Burton Pedwardine 76-78; V Messingham 78-89; rtd 89; Perm to Offic *Linc* from 89. *23 Londesborough Way, Metheringham, Lincoln LN4 3HW* Metheringham (01526) 320418

BACON, John Martindale. b 22. St Aid Birkenhead 54. **d** 57 **p** 58. C-in-c Clifton Green St Thos CD *Man* 59-71; V Astley Bridge 71-87; rtd 87. *21 Lichen Close, Charnock Richard, Chorley, Lancs PR7 5TT* Chorley (01257) 792535

BACON, Lionel William Rupert. b 06. Univ Coll Dur LTh31 BA32 MA40. St Paul's Coll Burgh 27. **d** 33 **p** 34. V Ancaster *Linc* 59-73; V Honington 59-73; rtd 73; Perm to Offic *Chich* from 77. *Lomas House, 43 Wordsworth Road, Worthing, W Sussex BN11 3JA* Worthing (01903) 213667

BADDELEY, Canon Martin James. b 36. Keble Coll Ox BA60 MA64. Linc Th Coll 60. **d** 62 **p** 63. C Stretford St Matt *Man* 62-64; Lic to Offic *Linc* 65-69; Lect Linc Th Coll 65-66; Tutor 66-69; Chapl 68-69; Chapl Fitzw Coll and New Hall Cam 69-74; Can Res Roch Cathl *Roch* 74-80; Hon Can from 80; Prin S'wark Ord Course 80-94; Co-Prin SE Inst for Th Educn from 94. *27 Blackfriars Road, London SE1 8NY* 0171-928 4793 or (01634) 832299

BADDELEY, Very Rev William Pye. b 14. St Chad's Coll Dur BA40. Cuddesdon Coll 40. **d** 41 **p** 42. R Westmr St Jas *Lon* 67-80; ChStJ from 70; RD Westmr St Marg *Lon* 74-80; Visiting Chapl Westmr Abbey from 80; rtd 80; Perm to Offic *St E* from 81. *Cumberland House, 17 Cumberland Street, Woodbridge, Suffolk IP12 4AH* Woodbridge (01394) 384104

BADEN, Peter Michael. b 35. CCC Cam BA59 MA62. Cuddesdon Coll 58. **d** 60 **p** 61. C Hunslet St Mary and Stourton *Ripon* 60-63; Lic to Offic *Wakef* 63-64; C E Grinstead St Swithun *Chich* 65-68; V Brighton St Martin 68-74; TR Brighton Resurr 74-76; R Westbourne 76-84; V Stansted 76-84; V Copthorne 84-91; V Clifton *Carl* from 91; R Dean from 91. *The Vicarage, 1 Clifton Gardens, Great Clifton, Workington, Cumbria CA14 1TT* Workington (01900) 603886

BADGER, Canon Edwin. b 09. Bris Univ BA32 MA86 Lon Univ BD57. St Boniface Warminster 28. **d** 34 **p** 35. C Kidderminster

St Jo *Worc* 34-36; Australia from 36; Hon Can Wangaratta 69-76. *6 Malcolm Street, Bacchus Marsh, Victoria, Australia 3340* Ballarat (53) 672316

BADHAM, Canon Herbert William. b 09. Hatf Coll Dur LTh30 BA31. St Boniface Warminster 27. **d** 32 **p** 33. V Bournemouth St Clem w St Mary *Win* 68-75; rtd 75; Perm to Offic *Win* from 75. *2 Northover, Dunbar Road, Bournemouth BH3 7AZ* Bournemouth (01202) 295781

BADHAM, Prof Paul Brian Leslie. b 42. Jes Coll Ox BA65 MA69 Jes Coll Cam BA68 MA72 Birm Univ PhD73. Westcott Ho Cam. **d** 68 **p** 69. C Edgbaston St Bart *Birm* 68-69; C Rubery 69-73; Lic to Offic *St D* from 73; Lect Th Univ of Wales (Lamp) 73-83; Sen Lect 83-88; Reader 88-91; Prof Th from 91. *St David's College, Lampeter, Dyfed SA48 7ED* Lampeter (01570) 422351

BAELZ, Very Rev Peter Richard. b 23. Ch Coll Cam BA44 MA48 BD71 Ox Univ DD79 Dur Univ Hon DD93. Westcott Ho Cam 44. **d** 47 **p** 50. Dean Jes Coll Cam 60-72; Lic to Offic *Ely* 61-72; Lect Th Cam Univ 66-72; Can Res Ch Ch *Ox* 72-79; Regius Prof Moral and Past Th Ox Univ 72-79; Dean Dur 80-88; rtd 88; Perm to Offic *S & B* from 88. *36 Brynteg, Llandrindod Wells, Powys LD1 5NB* Llandrindod Wells (01597) 825404

BAGGALEY, Canon Dennis. b 31. Dur Univ BA53 Liv Univ MA79 St Jo Coll Dur DipTh56. **d** 56 **p** 57. C Pennington *Man* 56-59; C N Meols *Liv* 59-60; V Bacup Ch Ch *Man* 60-65; R Burnage St Nic 65-71; V Onchan *S & M* from 71; Can St German's Cathl 80-89; RD Douglas 82-86. *The Vicarage, Onchan, Douglas, Isle of Man IM3 1BF* Douglas (01624) 675797

BAGGALEY, John Roger Pocklington. b 14. MC45. Keble Coll Ox BA36 MA45. Westcott Ho Cam. **d** 47 **p** 48. R Badger *Lich* 69-83; R Ryton 69-83; R Beckbury 69-83; rtd 83. *21 Swanston Drive, Fairmilehead, Edinburgh EH10 7BP* 0131-445 1331

BAGGLEY, John Samuel. b 40. Dur Univ BA62. Kelham Th Coll 62. **d** 66 **p** 67. C Poplar *Lon* 66-71; TV 71-72; V De Beauvoir Town St Pet 72-82; TR Bicester w Bucknell, Caversfield and Launton *Ox* from 82. *St Edburg's Vicarage, Victoria Road, Bicester, Oxon OX6 7PQ* Bicester (01869) 253222

BAGGOTT, Michael. b 30. FVCM91 ADipR92. Chich Th Coll DipTh94. **d** 94 **p** 95. NSM Southbourne w W Thorney *Chich* from 94. *14 Orchard Lane, Hermitage, Emsworth, Hants PO10 8BH* Emsworth (01243) 377778

BAGLEY, Canon John Marmaduke Erskine. b 08. G&C Coll Cam BA30 MA36. Ely Th Coll 30. **d** 32 **p** 33. V Ely 63-74; Chapl Ely Cathl 63-74; Hon Can Ely Cathl 68-74; P-in-c Chettisham 68-74; rtd 74; Perm to Offic *St E* 74-77; Perm to Offic *Ely* from 77; Perm to Offic *Nor* from 91. *Old House Cottage, Church Road, Aylmerton, Norwich NR11 8PZ* West Runton (01263) 837685

BAGNALL, Harry. b 30. OBE82. S'wark Ord Course 64. **d** 67 **p** 68. C Goole *Sheff* 67-70; C Doncaster St Leon and St Jude 70-72; C-in-c New Cantley CD 72-79; Falkland Is 79-86; V Hook w Airmyn *Sheff* from 86. *The Vicarage, Church Lane, Hook, Goole, N Humberside DN14 5PN* Goole (01405) 763654

BAGNALL, Canon John Thomas. b 12. Leeds Univ BA34. Coll of Resurr Mirfield 34. **d** 36 **p** 37. V Bournemouth St Luke *Win* 71-79; rtd 79; Perm to Offic *Win* from 80. *57A Wentworth Avenue, Bournemouth BH5 2EH* Bournemouth (01202) 422356

BAGNALL, Roger. b 15. St Edm Hall Ox BA37 MA41. Linc Th Coll 37. **d** 39 **p** 40. V Ticknall *Derby* 66-84; RD Melbourne 68-78; V Smisby 69-84; P-in-c Stanton-by-Bridge and Swarkestone 80-84; V Ticknall, Smisby and Stanton by Bridge 84-86; rtd 86. *4 Westfield Rise, Withernsea, N Humberside HU19 2NS* Withernsea (01964) 613305

BAGOTT, Paul Andrew. b 61. Leeds Univ BA85. Westcott Ho Cam 86. **d** 88 **p** 89. C Chingford SS Pet and Paul *Chelmsf* 88-91; C Pimlico St Sav *Lon* 91-95; P-in-c Clerkenwell H Redeemer and St Mark from 95. *Holy Redeemer Clergy House, 24 Exmouth Market, London EC1R 4QE* 0171-837 1861

BAGOTT, Robert Blakeway. b 25. St Aid Birkenhead 51. **d** 54 **p** 55. R Luton Ch Ch *Roch* 66-77; Chapl All SS Hosp Chatham 70-77; R Dowlishwake w Chaffcombe, Knowle St Giles etc *B & W* 77-82; R E w W Harptree and Hinton Blewett 82-90; Co-ord Retirement Officer from 89; rtd 90. *12 Hawkers Lane, Wells, Somerset BA5 3JL* Wells (01749) 674086

BAGSHAW, Paul Stanley. b 55. Selw Coll Cam BA78 MA81 Man Univ CQSW80. N Ord Course 85. **d** 88 **p** 89. Ind Missr *Sheff* 86-90; C Handsworth Woodhouse 88-90; NSM 91-93; C Newark-upon-Trent *S'well* from 93. *82 Appletongate, Newark, Notts NG24 1LR* Newark (01636) 702339

BAGSHAWE, John Allen. b 45. Dur Univ BA70 DipTh71. Cranmer Hall Dur 67. **d** 71 **p** 72. C Bridlington Priory *York* 71-75; C N Ferriby 75-79; V Kingston upon Hull St Matt w St

Barn from 79. *St Matthew's Vicarage, Boulevard, Hull HU3 2TA* Hull (01482) 26573

BAGULEY, Henry. b 23. Qu Coll Birm 55. **d** 58 **p** 59. V Kelsall *Ches* 61-75; V New Brighton St Jas 75-88; rtd 88. *The Meadows, Nantwich Road, Whitchurch, Shropshire SY13 4AA* Whitchurch (01948) 662692

BAILES, Dr Kenneth. b 35. Dur Univ BA69 DipTh71 DPhil. **d** 71 **p** 72. C Redcar *York* 71-73; TV Redcar w Kirkleatham 73-74; P-in-c Appleton Roebuck w Acaster Selby 74-80; P-in-c Sutton on the Forest 80-82; R Stamford Bridge Gp of Par 82-90; V Healaugh w Wighill, Bilbrough and Askham Richard from 90. *The Rectory, Back Lane, Bilbrough, York YO2 3PL* Tadcaster (01937) 833527

BAILEY, Adrian Richard. b 57. St Jo Coll Dur 89. **d** 91 **p** 92. C Oswestry St Oswald *Lich* 91-94; C Oswestry 94; C Shobnall from 94. *114 Shobnall Road, Burton-on-Trent, Staffs DE14 2BB* Burton-on-Trent (01283) 530910

BAILEY, Alan George. b 40. Ripon Hall Ox 62. **d** 64 **p** 65. C Formby H Trin *Liv* 64-67; C Upholland 67-70; P-in-c Edge Hill St Dunstan 70-74; V 74-81; RD Toxteth 78-81; Perm to Offic 81-83; Asst Chapl Liv Cathl 83-85; C Liv Our Lady and St Nic w St Anne 85-89; V Waddington *Bradf* from 89. *The Vicarage, Waddington, Clitheroe, Lancs BB7 3JQ* Clitheroe (01200) 23589

BAILEY, Andrew Henley. b 57. AKC78. Sarum & Wells Th Coll 79. **d** 80 **p** 81. C Romsey *Win* 80-83; V Bournemouth St Alb 83-93; R Milton from 93. *The Rectory, New Milton, Hants BH25 6QN* New Milton (01425) 615150

BAILEY, Andrew John. b 37. Trin Coll Cam BA61 MA. Ridley Hall Cam 60. **d** 63 **p** 64. C Drypool *York* 63-66; C Melton Mowbray w Thorpe Arnold *Leic* 66-69; C-in-c Skelmersdale Ecum Cen *Liv* 69-79; V Langley Mill *Derby* 79-90; V Gt Faringdon w Lt Coxwell *Ox* from 90. *The Vicarage, Coach Lane, Faringdon, Oxon SN7 8AB* Faringdon (01367) 240106

BAILEY, Ms Angela. b 61. Kent Univ BA82. Qu Coll Birm 83. dss 85 **d** 87 **p** 94. Reculver and Herne Bay St Bart *Cant* 85-87; Par Dn 87-88; Asst Chapl Hull Univ *York* 88-92; Chapl (Sen) from 94; Perm to Offic 92-94. *Kingston, 21 Southwood Road, Cottingham, N Humberside HU15 5AE* Hull (01482) 847151

BAILEY, Anthony. b 27. Univ of Wales (Lamp) BA51. Ely Th Coll 51. **d** 53 **p** 54. Min Can Bris Cathl *Bris* 66-84; Chapl Bris Cathl Sch 66-84; Succ Bris Cathl *Bris* 68-82; P-in-c Maenclochog w Henry's Moat and Mynachlogddu etc *St D* 83-90; V 90-92; rtd 92. *The Village Stores, Charing Cross, Llangolman, Clunderwen, Dyfed SA66 7XN* Maenclochog (01991) 532430

BAILEY, Bertram Arthur. b 20. Tyndale Hall Bris 65. **d** 67 **p** 68. C Bath St Luke *B & W* 67-72; C Bickenhill w Elmdon *Birm* 72-73; R N Tawton *Ex* 73-79; R N Tawton and Bondleigh 79-87; rtd 87; Perm to Offic *B & W* 87-89; Clergy Retirement and Widows' Officer from 89. *4 Uphill Road South, Uphill, Weston-super-Mare, Avon BS23 4SD* Weston-super-Mare (01934) 633552

BAILEY, Brendan John. b 61. Strathclyde Univ BSc83. Ripon Coll Cuddesdon BTh93. **d** 94. C Purley *Ox* from 94. *10 Knowsley Road, Tilehurst, Reading RG3 6FA* Reading (01734) 451411

BAILEY, Canon Brian Constable. b 36. AKC62. **d** 63 **p** 64. C Mill Hill Jo Keble Ch *Lon* 63-66; C Gt Stanmore 66-69; C Gt Marlow *Ox* 69-72; R Burghfield 72-81; R Wokingham All SS from 81; Hon Can Ch Ch from 94. *All Saints' Rectory, 5 Wiltshire Road, Wokingham, Berks RG11 1TP* Wokingham (01734) 792999

BAILEY, Darren Stephen. b 65. Wales Poly BA87 Sheff Poly CertTESOL89 Nottm Univ BTh. Linc Th Coll. **d** 95. C Mexborough *Sheff* from 95. *49 Tennyson Avenue, Mexborough, S Yorkshire S64 0AX* Mexborough (01709) 582675

BAILEY, David Charles. b 52. Linc Coll Ox BA75 MA78 MSc77. St Jo Coll Nottm BA79. **d** 80 **p** 81. C Worksop St Jo *S'well* 80-83; C Edgware *Lon* 83-87; V S Cave and Ellerker w Broomfleet *York* from 87; RD Howden from 91. *The Vicarage, 10 Station Road, South Cave, Brough, N Humberside HU15 2AA* Howden (01430) 423693

BAILEY, Dennis. b 53. Man Univ BEd74 BMus74. St Jo Coll Nottm BTh79. **d** 79 **p** 80. C Netherley Ch Ch CD *Liv* 79-83; S Africa from 83. *PO Box 635, Hilton, 3245 South Africa*

BAILEY, Derek Gilbert. b 42. Div Hostel Dub 65. **d** 68 **p** 69. C Cork St Luke w St Ann *C, C & R* 68-72; CF from 72. *c/o MOD (Army), Bagshot Park, Bagshot, Surrey GU19 5PL* Bagshot (01276) 471717 Fax 412834

BAILEY, Derek William. b 39. Lon Univ DipTh64. Cranmer Hall Dur 64. **d** 67 **p** 68. C Sutton *Liv* 67-69; C Chapel-en-le-Frith *Derby* 69-73; V Hadfield 73-90; R Collyhurst *Man* from 90. *The Rectory, Eggington Street, Collyhurst, Manchester M10 7RN* 0161-205 2808

BAILEY, Canon Dr Edward Ian. b 35. CCC Cam BA59 MA63 Bris Univ MA69 PhD77. United Th Coll Bangalore 59 Westcott Ho Cam 61. **d** 63 **p** 64. C Newc St Jo *Newc* 63-65; Asst Chapl Marlborough Coll Wilts 65-68; Perm to Offic *Bris* 69-70; R Winterbourne from 70; P-in-c Winterbourne Down 75-81; RD Stapleton 77-83; Hon Can Bris Cathl from 84. *The Rectory, 58 High Street, Winterbourne, Bristol BS17 1JQ* Winterbourne (01454) 772131/776518

BAILEY, Edward Peter. b 35. Nottm Univ MA93. Qu Coll Birm. **d** 62 **p** 63. C Ordsall *S'well* 62-66; C Clifton w Glapton 66-71; V Lady Bay 71-83; Relig Affairs Adv to Radio Trent 83-85; C Gedling 86-89; C Bilborough St Jo from 89; Chapl Bilborough Coll from 89. *32 Crosslands Meadow, Colwick, Nottingham NG4 2DJ* Nottingham (0115) 940 1074

BAILEY, Mrs Elizabeth Carmen. b 45. E Anglian Minl Tr Course 89. **d** 93 **p** 94. Hon C Roughton and Felbrigg, Metton, Sustead etc *Nor* from 93. *5 Warren Road, Southrepps, Norwich NR11 8UN* Southrepps (01263) 833785

BAILEY, Eric Arthur. b 14. AKC37. **d** 37 **p** 38. V Stonegate *Chich* 65-79; rtd 79; Perm to Offic *St E* 81-88. *Hill End, Sapiston, Bury St Edmunds, Suffolk IP31 1RR* Honington (01359) 269638

BAILEY, Frederick Hugh. b 18. Keble Coll Ox BA40. Linc Th Coll 40. **d** 42 **p** 43. Chapl Rauceby Hosp Lincs from 49; R Quarrington w Old Sleaford *Linc* 49-84; R Silk Willoughby 57-84; rtd 84. *1 Willow Close, Scopwick, Lincoln LN4 3PJ* Lincoln (01522) 321127

BAILEY, Canon Ivan John. b 33. Keble Coll Ox BA57 MA65. St Steph Ho Ox DipTh59. **d** 59 **p** 60. C Ipswich All Hallows *St E* 59-62; Clerical Sec CEMS 62-66; V Cringleford *Nor* 66-81; RD Humbleyard 73-81; R Colney 80-81; Relig Adv Anglia TV 81-91; P-in-c Kirby Bedon w Bixley and Whitlingham *Nor* 81-92; Hon Can Nor Cathl from 84; Chapl St Andr Hosp Norwich 92-94; Chapl Mental Health Unit Nor HA from 92; Chapl Hellesdon Hosp Nor from 94. *21 Cranleigh Rise, Norwich NR4 6PQ, or Hellesdon Hospital, Drayton High Road, Norwich NR6 5BE* Norwich (01603) 53565 or 421421

BAILEY, John Ernest. b 32. Leeds Univ BA57. Coll of Resurr Mirfield 57. **d** 59 **p** 60. V Uffington w Woolstone and Baulking *Ox* 63-70; P-in-c Gt w Lt Oakley *Pet* 70-72; TV Corby SS Pet and Andr w Gt and Lt Oakley 70-72; Chapl Cen Hosp Warw 72-95; Chapl Cen Weston and Abbeyfields 82-90; Chapl Cen Weston 90-95; rtd 94. *22 Hill Wootton Road, Leek Wootton, Warwick CV35 7QL* Kenilworth (01926) 53528

BAILEY, John Robert. b 40. St Jo Coll Cam BA62 MA66 Nottm Univ MEd77. S'wark Ord Course 68. **d** 69 **p** 70. NSM Plumstead Wm Temple Ch Abbey Wood CD *S'wark* 69-70; Lon Sec Chr Educn Movement 69-71; NSM Markyate Street *St Alb* 70-71; RE Adv *Linc* 72-80; Perm to Offic *Man* 80-83; Perm to Offic *St Alb* 84-92; Perm to Offic *Linc* from 92. *Juniper Cottage, Vicarage Lane, Wellingore, Lincoln LN5 0JP* Lincoln (01522) 810317

✠**BAILEY, Rt Rev Jonathan Sansbury.** b 40. Trin Coll Cam BA61 MA65. Ridley Hall Cam 62. **d** 65 **p** 66 **c** 92. C Sutton *Liv* 65-68; C Warrington St Paul 68-71; Warden Marrick Priory *Ripon* 71-76; V Wetherby 76-82; Adn Southend *Chelmsf* 82-92; Suff Bp Dunwich *St E* 92-95; Bp Derby from 95. *The Bishop's House, 6 King Street, Duffield, Belper, Derbyshire DE56 4EY* Derby (01332) 840132 or 346744   Fax 295810

BAILEY, Joyce Mary Josephine. *See* OUTEN, Mrs Joyce Mary Josephine

BAILEY, Justin Mark. b 55. Birm Univ BA77 Wolv Poly PGCE78. Ripon Coll Cuddesdon 90. **d** 92 **p** 93. C Oakdale St Geo *Sarum* from 92. *328 Wimborne Road, Poole, Dorset BH15 3EG* Poole (01202) 673296

BAILEY, Mark David. b 62. Ripon Coll Cuddesdon 87. **d** 90 **p** 91. C Leigh Park *Portsm* 90-93; C Fleet *Guildf* 93-95; TV Basingstoke *Win* from 95. *The Vicarage, 75 Cumberland Avenue, Basingstoke, Hants RG22 4BQ* Basingstoke (01256) 465666

BAILEY, Mark Robert. b 60. Trin Coll Bris BA89. **d** 89 **p** 90. C Heigham H Trin *Nor* 89-94; TV Cheltenham St Mary, St Matt, St Paul and H Trin *Glouc* from 94. *100 Hewlett Road, Cheltenham, Glos GL52 6AR* Cheltenham (01242) 582396

BAILEY, Martin Tristram. b 57. BA79. Oak Hill Th Coll DipHE91. **d** 91 **p** 92. C Brundall w Braydeston and Postwick *Nor* 91-95; TV Plymouth St Andr and St Paul Stonehouse *Ex* from 95. *28 Durnford Street, Plymouth PL1 3QW* Plymouth (01752) 228114

BAILEY, Nicholas Andrew. b 55. Nottm Univ CertEd80 Open Univ BA84. Ripon Coll Cuddesdon 88. **d** 90 **p** 91. C Guisborough *York* 90-92; Chapl Foremark Prep Sch from 92. *Sycamore Cottage, Foremark, Milton, Derby DE65 6TB* Repton (01283) 703558

BAILEY, Norman Gerald. b 25. **d** 83 **p** 84. Hon C Kingswood *Bris* 83-90; Hon C E Bris from 90. *71 Lincombe Road, Bristol BS16 5LL* Bristol (0117) 957 2822

BAILEY, Peter Robin. b 43. St Jo Coll Dur BA64. Trin Coll Bris 72. **d** 74 **p** 75. C Corby St Columba *Pet* 74-77; C Bishopsworth *Bris* 77-82; V Sea Mills from 82; RD Westbury and Severnside from 91. *St Edyth's Vicarage, Avon Leaze, Bristol BS9 2HV* Bristol (0117) 968 1912 or 968 6965

BAILEY, Richard William. b 38. Man Univ BSc59. Ripon Hall Ox 63. **d** 65 **p** 66. C Tonge *Man* 65-68; C Stretford St Matt 68-71; R Abbey Hey 71-80; V E Crompton 80-86; V Chadderton St Matt from 86. *St Matthew's Vicarage, Mill Brow, Chadderton, Oldham OL1 2RT* 0161-624 8600

BAILEY, Richard William. b 47. All Nations Chr Coll DBMS75 Oak Hill Th Coll BA84. **d** 84 **p** 85. C Huyton St Geo *Liv* 84-87; V Wombridge *Lich* from 87. *Wombridge Vicarage, Wombridge Road, Telford, Shropshire TF2 6HT* Telford (01952) 613334

BAILEY, Robert William. b 49. Lich Th Coll 69. **d** 72 **p** 73. C Stoke *Cov* 72-75; Chapl RAF from 75. *Chaplaincy Services (RAF), HQ, Personnel and Training Command, RAF Innsworth, Gloucester GL3 1EZ* Gloucester (01452) 712612 Ext 5164   Fax 510828

BAILEY, Canon Ronald George Bainton. b 07. Trin Coll Cam BA28 MA37. Wycliffe Hall Ox 30. **d** 32 **p** 33. V Wray w Tatham Fells *Blackb* 69-73; rtd 73; Perm to Offic *Guildf* 81-94; Perm to Offic *Portsm* from 86. *Flat 20, Manormead, Tilford Road, Hindhead, Surrey GU26 6RA* Hindhead (01428) 607151

BAILEY, Ronald William. b 12. Linc Coll Ox BA35 BSc36 MA45. Ripon Hall Ox 57. **d** 58 **p** 59. V Lamberhurst *Roch* 61-77; rtd 77. *Tamarisk, Wagg Drove, Huish Episcopi, Langport, Somerset TA10 9ER* Langport (01458) 250103

BAILEY, Simon. b 56. Man Univ MusB Nottm Univ BCombStuds. Linc Th Coll. **d** 83 **p** 84. C St Bart Armley w St Mary New Wortley *Ripon* 83-86; C Harrogate St Wilfrid and St Luke 86-90; R Harby, Long Clawson and Hose *Leic* 90-94; V Woodhall *Bradf* from 94. *St James's Vicarage, Galloway Lane, Pudsey, W Yorkshire LS28 8JR* Bradford (01274) 662735

BAILEY, Simon Paul. b 55. Ox Univ BA77 MA81 Em Coll Cam BA80 MA. Westcott Ho Cam 78. **d** 81 **p** 82. C Norton *Sheff* 81-85; R Dinnington from 85. *The Rectory, 217 Nursery Road, Dinnington, Sheffield S31 7QU* Dinnington (01909) 562335

BAILEY, Stephen. b 39. Leic Univ BA61. Clifton Th Coll 61. **d** 62 **p** 63. C Wellington w Eyton *Lich* 62-66; C Rainham *Chelmsf* 66-69; V Ercall Magna *Lich* 69-75; V Rowton 69-75; RD Wrockwardine 72-75; V W Bromwich Gd Shep w St Jo 75-83; P-in-c W Bromwich St Phil 80-81; V 81-83; R Chadwell *Chelmsf* from 83; Area Warden Ords Brentwood, Basildon & Thurrock from 91; RD Thurrock from 92. *The Rectory, Rigby Gardens, Grays, Essex RM16 4JJ* Tilbury (01375) 842176

BAILEY, Stephen John. b 57. NE Surrey Coll of Tech HNC78. Sarum & Wells Th Coll 88. **d** 90 **p** 91. C Redhill H Trin *S'wark* from 90; Chapl E Surrey Coll 91-93. *3 Ringwood Avenue, Redhill, Surrey RH1 2DY* Redhill (01737) 762593

BAILEY, Mrs Susan Mary. b 40. F L Calder Coll Liv CertEd61. E Anglian Minl Tr Course 89. **d** 92 **p** 94. NSM Chelmsf Cathl *Chelmsf* 92-93; NSM Needham Market w Badley *St E* 93-95. *6 King Street, Duffield, Derby DE56 4EY* Derby (01332) 840132

BAILLIE, Alistair Hope Pattison. b 50. Loughb Univ BSc73 Ox Univ DipTh. Ripon Coll Cuddesdon 73. **d** 76 **p** 77. C Aylestone *Leic* 76-79; C Leic All SS 79-82; C Leic H Spirit 82-83; TV Heavitree w Ex St Paul *Ex* 83-84; C 84-86; Asst Chapl N Gen Hosp Sheff 86-88; C Sheff St Cuth *Sheff* 86-88; Chapl Broadgreen Hosp Liv from 88. *Broadgreen Hospital, Thomas Drive, Liverpool L14 3LB* 0151-228 4878 or 228 1616

BAILLIE, Canon Frederick Alexander. b 21. FRGS Open Univ BA75 QUB MA86 PhD87. CITC 53. **d** 55 **p** 56. I Belf Whiterock *Conn* 69-74; Hd of S Ch Miss Ballymacarrett 74-79; I Magheraculmoney *Clogh* 79-87; Dioc Info Officer 80-86; RD Kesh 85-87; Can Clogh Cathl 85-87; rtd 87. *2 St Elizabeth's Court, Ballyregan Road, Dundonald, Belfast BT16 0HX* Belfast (01232) 487642

BAILLIE, Iain Robert Cullen. b 28. St Pet Hall Ox BA54 MA58. Wycliffe Hall Ox 54. **d** 56 **p** 57. C Penge Lane H Trin *Roch* 56-58; CF 58-83; Perm to Offic *Cant* from 92. *8 The Precincts, Canterbury, Kent CT1 2EE* Canterbury (01227) 768206

BAILLIE, John Launcelot. b 16. AKC47. **d** 47 **p** 48. V Milborne St Andrew w Dewlish *Sarum* 59-70; Peru 70-74; V Felkirk w Brierley *Wakef* 75-79; R Orford w Sudbourne, Chillesford, Butley and Iken *St E* 79-82; rtd 82; Perm to Offic *St E* from 82. *Long Walk, 99 Abbey Road, Leiston, Suffolk IP16 4TA* Leiston (01728) 830365

BAILLIE, Terence John. b 46. New Coll Ox BA69 MA78 Man Univ MSc72. St Jo Coll Nottm 74. **d** 77 **p** 78. C Chadwell *Chelmsf* 77-80; C Bickenhill w Elmdon *Birm* 80-84; V Bedminster St Mich *Bris* from 84. *St Michael's Vicarage, 153 St John's Lane, Bedminster, Bristol BS3 5AE* Bristol (0117) 977 6132

BAILY, Canon Robert Spencer Canning. b 21. G&C Coll Cam BA42 MA46. Westcott Ho Cam 42. **d** 44 **p** 45. P-in-c Perlethorpe *S'well* 69-87; Dir of Educn 69-87; Hon Can S'well Minster 80-87; rtd 87. *17 Ravendale Close, Grantham, Lincs NG31 8BS* Grantham (01476) 68614

BAILY, Rodney Alexander. b 39. Bris Univ LLB61. Westcott Ho Cam 76. **d** 78 **p** 79. C Monkseaton St Mary *Newc* 78-81; C Hexham 81-83; TV Cullercoats St Geo 83-93; R Allendale w Whitfield from 93. *Allendale Rectory, 16 Forstersteads, Allendale, Hexham, Northd NE47 9DA* Hexham (01434) 683336

BAIN, Alan. b 48. Thames Poly BSc72. St Jo Coll Nottm DipTh75. **d** 77 **p** 78. C Wakef St Andr and St Mary *Wakef* 77-81; V Bath Odd Down *B & W* 81-82; P-in-c Combe Hay 81-82; V Bath Odd Down w Combe Hay from 82. *The Vicarage, 39 Frome Road, Bath BA2 2QF* Combe Down (01225) 832838

BAIN, Andrew John. b 55. Newc Poly BA77 Edin Univ MTh89. Edin Th Coll 86. **d** 88 **p** 89. Chapl St Mary's Cathl *Edin* 88-91; C Edin St Mary 88-91; R Edin St Jas from 91; P-in-c Edin St Marg from 93. *29 Dudley Gardens, Edinburgh EH6 4PU* 0131-554 3520

BAIN, David Roualeyn Findlater (Roly). b 54. Bris Univ BA75. Ripon Coll Cuddesdon 76. **d** 78 **p** 79. C Perry Hill St Geo *S'wark* 78-81; Chapl Asst Guy's Hosp Lon 81-84; Succ S'wark Cathl *S'wark* 81-84; V Streatham St Paul 84-90; Perm to Offic *Bris* from 90. *285 North Street, Bedminster, Bristol BS3 1JP* Bristol (0117) 963 6490

BAIN, John Stuart. b 55. Van Mildert Coll Dur BA77. Westcott Ho Cam 78. **d** 80 **p** 81. C Washington *Dur* 80-84; C Dunston 84-86; V Shiney Row 86-92; V Herrington 86-92; P-in-c Whitworth w Spennymoor from 92. *The Vicarage, Horswell Gardens, Spennymoor, Co Durham DL16 7AA* Spennymoor (01388) 814522

BAINBRIDGE, David George. b 42. Wadh Coll Ox BA63 MA67 Lon Univ CertEd67. Ridley Hall Cam 84. **d** 86 **p** 87. C Downend *Bris* 86-90; TV Yate New Town from 90. *The Vicarage, 57 Brockworth, Yate, Bristol BS17 4SJ* Chipping Sodbury (01454) 322921

BAINBRIDGE, Mrs Jean Waite. b 29. ALA54 Birm Univ BA77 DipL&A79. Qu Coll Birm 78. **dss** 79 **d** 87 **p** 94. Worc St Barn w Ch Ch *Worc* 79-82; Catshill and Dodford 82-87; Par Dn 87-90; rtd 90; Hon Par Dn Hallow *Worc* 90-94; Hon C Worc St Wulstan from 94. *7 St Catherine's Hill, Worcester WR5 2EA* Worcester (01905) 748593

BAINBRIDGE, John Richard. b 35. Pemb Coll Cam BA59 MA63. Clifton Th Coll 65. **d** 67 **p** 68. C Ex St Leon w H Trin *Ex* 67-70; P-in-c Penge St Paul *Roch* 70-73; Chapl Uppingham Sch Leics 73-87; Lic to Offic *Pet* 73-87; V Stevenage St Nic St Alb from 87. *St Nicholas House, 2A North Road, Stevenage, Herts SG1 4AT* Stevenage (01438) 354355

BAINBRIDGE, Norman Harold. b 15. St Jo Coll Dur LTh38. ALCD38. **d** 38 **p** 39. V Boscombe St Jo *Win* 66-80; rtd 80; Perm to Offic *Sarum* 81-93; Perm to Offic *Win* 81-93; Perm to Offic *Ex* from 95. *1 Gracey Court, Woodland Road, Broadclyst, Exeter EX5 3LP* Exeter (01392) 460492

BAINBRIDGE, Richard Densham. b 49. Ch Coll Cam BA71 MA75 Edge Hill Coll of HE PGCE72 Roehampton Inst DipC&CD91. S'wark Ord Course 91. **d** 94. C Bermondsey St Jas w Ch Ch *S'wark* from 94. *3 Fenwick Grove, London SE15 4HT* 0171-732 1659

BAINES, Alan William. b 50. S Bank Poly BSc72. Trin Coll Bris DipHE94. **d** 94 **p** 95. C Chenies and Lt Chalfont, Latimer and Flaunden *Ox* from 94. *St George's Parsonage, White Lion Road, Amersham, Bucks HP7 9LW* Little Chalfont (01494) 763244

BAINES, Bernard Frederick. b 20. JP. ACP. St Jo Coll Nottm 83. **d** 84 **p** 85. NSM Nottm All SS *S'well* 84-90; rtd 90; Perm to Offic *S'well* from 90. *18 Forest Road East, Nottingham NG1 4HH* Nottingham (0115) 978 4191

BAINES, John Edmund. b 22. Down Coll Cam BA47 MA50 Lon Univ BD51. New Coll Lon. **d** 58 **p** 59. V Cawthorne *Wakef* 69-89; rtd 89. *3 Huskar Close, Silkstone, Barnsley, S Yorkshire S75 4SX* Barnsley (01226) 791088

BAINES, Nicholas. b 57. Bradf Univ BA80. Trin Coll Bris BA87. **d** 87 **p** 88. C Kendal St Thos *Carl* 87-91; C Leic H Trin w St Jo *Leic* 91-92; V Rothley from 92. *The Vicarage, 128 Hallfields Lane, Rothley, Leicester LE7 7NG* Leicester (0116) 230 2241

BAINES, Noel Edward (Ted). b 29. St Jo Coll Dur BSc52 DipTh54 MA62. **d** 54 **p** 55. V Beckenham St Jo *Roch* 67-74; Hd RE Taunton Manor High Sch Caterham 74-83; Keston Coll 85-91; Perm to Offic *Roch* 74-91; Hon C Bromley Ch Ch from 91; rtd 94. *10 Bromley Avenue, Bromley BR1 4BQ* 0181-460 8256

BAINES, Canon Roger Holford. b 07. St Jo Coll Cam BA29 MA32. Westcott Ho Cam 29. **d** 30 **p** 31. V High Harrogate St

Pet *Ripon* 47-66; Lic to Offic *Heref* 68-80; rtd 72. *Barn House, Ashford Bowdler, Ludlow, Shropshire SY8 4DJ* Richards Castle (0158474) 602

BAIRD, Dr Edward Simpson. b 17. Lon Univ BD58 MLitt65 DLitt68 Newc Univ 62. Yorkshire United Th Coll 42 Selly Oak Coll 47 Sarum Th Coll 54. **d** 55 **p** 56. R Harrington *Carl* 66-75; V Barton w Peel Green *Man* 75-80; R Jarrow Grange *Dur* 80-83; rtd 83. *5 Hemsley Road, South Shields, Tyne & Wear N34 6HW* 0191-456 1389

BAIRD, Paul Drummond. b 48. Newc Univ CertEd71 Open Univ BA85. Ripon Coll Cuddesdon 88. **d** 90 **p** 91. C Chandler's Ford *Win* 90-93; V Hythe from 93. *The Vicarage, 14 Atheling Road, Hythe, Southampton SO4 6BR* Hythe (01703) 842461

BAIRD, Robert Douglas. b 21. ERD56. Cam Univ MA64. Ripon Coll Cuddesdon. **d** 85 **p** 86. NSM Charlbury w Shorthampton *Ox* 85-87; Asst Chapl HM Pris Grendon and Spring Hill 85; Lic to Offic *Ox* from 87. *Glebe House, Ibstone, High Wycombe, Bucks HP14 3XZ* Turville Heath (01491) 638642

BAIRD, Canon William Stanley. b 33. TCD BA54 Div Test. **d** 56 **p** 57. C Carlow *C & O* 56-59; I Dunganstown *D & G* 59-64; C Knock *D & D* 64-69; P-in-c Kilwarlin Upper w Kilwarlin Lower 69-71; I 71-72; Warden Ch Min of Healing (Ireland) 72-79; I Dub Drumcondra w N Strand *D & G* 79-91; Dir of Ords (Dub) from 84; Can Ch Ch Cathl Dub 88-92; Preb from 92; I Swords w Donabate and Killsallaghan from 91. *The Rectory, Swords, Co Dublin, Irish Republic* Dublin (1) 840-2308

BAISLEY, Mrs Barbara Pauline. b 47. DipAD69. S Dios Minl Tr Scheme 79. **dss** 82 **d** 87 **p** 94. Glouc St Geo w Whaddon *Glouc* 82-83; Welford w Weston and Clifford Chambers 83-87; Chapl Warw Univ *Cov* 87-94; Dioc Adv for Women's Min from 90; C Kenilworth St Nic from 94. *The Rectory, Meriden Road, Berkswell, Coventry CV7 7BE* Berkswell (01676) 533605

BAISLEY, George. b 45. Sarum & Wells Th Coll 78. **d** 80 **p** 81. C Glouc St Geo w Whaddon *Glouc* 80-83; R Welford w Weston and Clifford Chambers 83-87; Chapl Myton Hamlet Hospice from 87; Chapl Warw Univ *Cov* 87-91; R Berkswell from 91. *The Rectory, Meriden Road, Berkswell, Coventry CV7 7BE* Berkswell (01676) 533605

BAKER, Albert George. b 30. Qu Coll Birm. **d** 61 **p** 62. R Odd Rode *Ches* 68-76; V Holme Cultram St Mary *Carl* 76-78; R Blofield w Hemblington *Nor* 78-94; rtd 94. *240 Raedwald Drive, Bury St Edmunds, Suffolk IP32 7DN* Bury St Emunds (01284) 701802

BAKER, Angela. b 42. **d** 91. Par Dn Battersea St Sav and St Geo w St Andr *S'wark* 91-94; C from 94. *89 Ambergate Street, London SE17 3RZ* 0171-820 0786

BAKER, Anne-Marie Clare. *See* BIRD, Mrs Anne-Marie Clare

BAKER, Anthony Peter (Tony). b 38. Hertf Coll Ox BA59 MA63. Clifton Th Coll 60. **d** 63 **p** 64. C Ox St Ebbe w St Pet *Ox* 63-66; C Welling *Roch* 66-70; V Redland *Bris* 70-79; Lect Tyndale Hall Bris 70-71; Lect Trin Coll Bris 71-77; V Beckenham Ch Ch *Roch* 79-94; Chapl Beckenham Hosp 79-94; V Hove Bp Hannington Memorial Ch *Chich* from 94. *82 Holmes Avenue, Hove, E Sussex BN3 7LD* Brighton (01273) 732821

BAKER, Miss Barbara Ann. b 36. Linc Th Coll 85. **d** 87 **p** 94. Par Dn Hornchurch St Andr *Chelmsf* 87-94; C from 94. *St Matthew's Bungalow, 55A Chelmsford Drive, Upminster, Essex RM14 2PH* Hornchurch (01708) 452705

BAKER, Canon Bernard George Coleman. b 36. Lon Univ BD61. Oak Hill Th Coll 61. **d** 63 **p** 64. C Broadwater St Mary *Chich* 63-66; Tanzania 66-84; Hon Can Morogoro from 77; C-in-c Ryde St Jas Prop Chpl *Portsm* from 84. *77 Argyll Street, Ryde, Isle of Wight PO33 3BY* Isle of Wight (01983) 564893

BAKER, Brian Ernest Harry. b 38. Sarum & Wells Th Coll 74. **d** 76 **p** 77. C Cannock *Lich* 76-79; C Penkridge w Stretton 79-80; C Dunston w Coppenhall 79-80; P-in-c Earl Stonham w Stonham Parva and Creeting St Pet *St E* 80-89; V Staincliffe *Wakef* 89-93. *Address temp unknown*

BAKER, Charles Edward. b 47. **d** 87 **p** 88. NSM Dub Clontarf *D & G* 87-90; NSM Delgany 90-94; NSM Dub Sandford w Milltown from 94. *12 Aranleigh Vale, Rathfarnham, Dublin 14, Irish Republic* Dublin (1) 494-6465

BAKER, Christopher James. b 54. MRAeS83 MICE83 CEng83 St Cath Coll Cam BA75 MA78 PhD78. E Midl Min Tr Course 85. **d** 88 **p** 89. NSM Matlock Bath *Derby* 88-95; NSM Matlock Bath and Cromford from 95. *31 Clifton Road, Matlock Bath, Derbyshire DE4 3PW* Matlock (01629) 582500

BAKER, Christopher Richard (Chris). b 61. Man Univ BA83 Southn Univ BTh90 Heythrop Coll Lon MTh92. Sarum & Wells Th Coll 86. **d** 89 **p** 93. C Dulwich St Barn *S'wark* 89-92; Tutor Sarum & Wells Th Coll 92-94; Dir Chr Tr Milton Keynes *Ox* from 94. *The Vicarage, 2 Hooper Gate, Willen, Milton Keynes MK15 9JR* Milton Keynes (01908) 662092

BAKER, David Clive. b 47. Sarum & Wells Th Coll 76. **d** 78 **p** 79. C Shirley *Birm* 78-82; P-in-c Croft *Linc* 82-83; R Wainfleet All

SS w St Thos 82-83; P-in-c Wainfleet St Mary 82-83; R The Wainfleets and Croft 83-86; V Stirchley *Birm* from 86. *The Vicarage, 18 Pineapple Grove, Birmingham B30 2TJ*

BAKER, David Frederick. b 32. Clifton Th Coll 67. **d** 69 **p** 70. C Bilton *Ripon* 69-71; C Heworth w Peasholme St Cuth *York* 71-75; V Sand Hutton w Gate and Upper Helmsley 75-77; P-in-c Bossall w Buttercrambe 75-77; V Sand Hutton 77-80; R Preston in Holderness 80; P-in-c Sproatley 80; R Preston and Sproatley in Holderness 80-89; C Topcliffe w Dalton and Dishforth 89; V Baldersby w Dalton, Dishforth etc from 89. *The New Vicarage, Baldersby St James, Thirsk, N Yorkshire YO7 4PT* Melmerby (01765) 640471

BAKER, David John. b 27. LRAM50 GRSM51. Ely Th Coll 53. **d** 55 **p** 56. C Swanley St Mary *Roch* 55-58; C Guildf St Nic *Guildf* 58-63; Prec St Alb Abbey *St Alb* 63-67; P-in-c Colney St Pet 67-68; V 68-73; V Tattenham Corner and Burgh Heath *Guildf* 73-84; R Fetcham from 84. *Fetcham Rectory, 10A The Ridgeway, Leatherhead, Surrey KT22 9AZ* Leatherhead (01372) 372598

BAKER, David Jordan. b 35. Univ of Wales (Lamp) BA59. Ely Th Coll 59. **d** 61 **p** 62. C Spalding *Linc* 61-66; C Gainsborough All SS 66-70; V Wrawby 69-78; V Melton Ross w New Barnetby 70-78; V Linc St Pet-at-Gowts and St Andr 78-94. *Fartherwell, The Paddock, Canwick, Lincoln LN4 2RX* Lincoln (01522) 526903

BAKER, Elsie. b 13. dss 38 **d** 87 **p** 94. Blackheath Ascension *S'wark* 68-83; NSM Lewisham St Swithun from 87. *24 Princes Rise, London SE13 7PP* 0181-852 2169

BAKER, Frank Thomas. b 36. Selw Coll Cam BA61. Coll of Resurr Mirfield. **d** 63 **p** 64. C Leeds St Pet *Ripon* 66-73; P-in-c Stanley *Dur* 73-74; R Crook 73-74; Chapl Bucharest *Eur* 74-75; C Tewkesbury w Walton Cardiff *Glouc* 75-81; Min Can Windsor 81-86; rtd 86; Perm to Offic *Ox* from 86. *St Anne's House, Hatch Lane, Windsor, Berks SL4 3QP* Windsor (01753) 865757

BAKER, Frederick Peter. b 24. Bps' Coll Cheshunt 58. **d** 60 **p** 61. P-in-c Northn St Lawr *Pet* 69-71; V Northn St Edm 71-78; V Spratton 78-83; R Walgrave w Hannington and Wold 83-89; rtd 89. *1A Malvern Close, Bournemouth BH9 3BN* Bournemouth (01202) 512862

BAKER, Geoffrey Gorton. b 26. Chich Th Coll 63. **d** 65 **p** 66. V Jersey St Mark *Win* 66-73; Lic to Offic from 73; Chapl HM Pris Jersey 80-91; rtd 91. *La Rousse, Le Bourg, St Clement, Jersey, Channel Islands JE2 6SP* Jersey (01534) 854735

BAKER, Gillian Devonald. b 40. S Dios Minl Tr Scheme 88. **d** 91 **p** 94. NSM Redhorn *Sarum* from 91; Chapl HM Young Offender Inst Erlestoke Ho from 94. *11 The Street, Chirton, Devizes, Wilts SN10 3QS* Devizes (01380) 848170

BAKER, Very Rev Graham Brinkworth. b 26. AKC54. **d** 55 **p** 56. C Wandsworth St Anne *S'wark* 55-58; Canada from 58. *1280 Tracksell Avenue, Victoria, British Columbia, Canada, V8P 2C9*

BAKER, Harry Hallas. b 16. Bps' Coll Cheshunt 51. **d** 53 **p** 54. V Howdon Panns *Newc* 63-73; C Alnwick St Mich 73-74; C Alnwick St Mich and St Paul 74-84; rtd 84. *16 Canongate, Alnwick, Northd NE66 1NE* Alnwick (01665) 604716

BAKER, Henry Blandford Benedict. b 26. Univ of NZ BA49 MA50. Coll of Resurr Mirfield 51. **d** 53 **p** 54. Perm to Offic *Chich* 81-86; R Beckington w Standerwick, Berkley, Rodden etc *B & W* 86-92; rtd 92. *Coed Glas, Talgarth Road, Bronllys, Brecon, Powys LD3 0HN* Talgarth (01874) 711964

BAKER, Henry Edward (Ted). b 09. Bris Univ BA31. Sarum Th Coll 31. **d** 32 **p** 33. C Kingswood *Bris* 69-74; rtd 74. *26 Henley Court, Spencer Road, Lichfield, Staffs WS14 9AT* Lichfield (01543) 256520

BAKER, Ms Hilary Mary (Dilly). b 61. Man Univ BA83 Univ of Wales (Cardiff) CQSW86. Sarum & Wells Th Coll 86. **d** 89 **p** 94. Par Dn E Dulwich St Jo *S'wark* 89-92; Tutor Sarum & Wells Th Coll 92-94; TV Stantonbury and Willen *Ox* from 94. *The Vicarage, 2 Hooper gate, Willen, Milton keynes MK15 9JR* Milton Keynes (01908) 662092

BAKER, Hugh Crispin. b 58. Open Univ BA92. Linc Th Coll CMinlStuds95. **d** 95. C Birstall and Wanlip *Leic* from 95. *33 Walker Road, Birstall, Leicester LE4 4DJ* Leicester (0116) 267 7572

BAKER, Hugh John. b 46. Birm Univ BSocSc68 Nottm Univ DipTh69. Cuddesdon Coll 69. **d** 71 **p** 72. C Binley *Cov* 71-74; C Pemberton St Mark Newtown *Liv* 74-78; TV Sutton 78-90; V Fazeley *Lich* from 90; R Drayton Bassett from 90; V Canwell from 90; P-in-c Hints from 90. *St Paul's Vicarage, 9 West Drive, Bonehill, Tamworth, Staffs B78 3HR* Tamworth (01827) 287701

BAKER, Ivon Robert. b 28. St Aug Coll Cant 59. **d** 60 **p** 61. V Gringley-on-the-Hill *S'well* 62-94; Chapl HM Young Offender Inst Gringley 82-91; RD Bawtry *S'well* 85-90; rtd 94. *2 Willowgate, Pickering, N Yorkshire YO18 7BE*

BAKER, James Henry. b 39. Lon Univ DipTh66. Kelham Th Coll 62. **d** 67 **p** 68. C Sheff Arbourthorne *Sheff* 67-70; C

Pemberton St Jo *Liv* 70-71; Chapl and Prec St Mary's Cathl *Edin* 71-74; R Lochgelly *St And* 74-84; P-in-c Rosyth 76-84; P-in-c Inverkeithing 76-84; Can St Ninian's Cathl Perth 83-84; V Whitehaven *Carl* from 84. *The Vicarage, Oakbank, Whitehaven, Cumbria CA28 6HY* Whitehaven (01946) 692630 or 62572

BAKER, Jean Margaret. b 47. Sheff Univ BSc69 DipEd70 Lon Univ DipTh75 BD78. All Nations Chr Coll 75 Gilmore Course 81. dss 82 **d** 87. Liv Our Lady and St Nic w St Anne *Liv* 82-87; Chapl Huyton Coll 87; Chapl SS Mary and Anne's Sch Abbots Bromley 87-91; Chapl Howell's Sch Denbigh from 91. *9 Woodcroft Lane, Bebington, Wirral, Merseyside L63 8NL* 0151-645 7934

BAKER, John Albert. b 29. St Edm Hall Ox BA52 MA56 Lon Univ BSc68 S Bank Poly MSc76. Cuddesdon Coll 52. **d** 54 **p** 55. Hon C Battersea St Luke *S'wark* from 84; V Battersea Park All SS 62-83; Tutor Roehampton Inst 83-91; rtd 94. *44 Wroughton Road, London SW11 6BG* 0171-585 2492

✝**BAKER, Rt Rev John Austin.** b 28. Or Coll Ox BA52 MA55 BLitt55 MLitt. Lambeth DD91 Cuddesdon Coll 52. **d** 54 **p** 55 c 82. C Cuddesdon *Ox* 54-57; Tutor Cuddesdon Coll 54-57; C Hatch End St Anselm *Lon* 57-59; Lect K Coll Lon 57-59; Chapl CCC Ox 59-73; Lect Th Ox Univ 59-73; Can Westmr Abbey 73-82; Sub-Dean Westmr 78-82; R Westmr St Marg 78-82; Chapl to Speaker of Ho of Commons 78-82; Bp Sarum 82-93; Can and Preb Sarum Cathl 82-93; rtd 93. *4 Mede Villas, Kingsgate Road, Winchester, Hants SO23 9QQ* Winchester (01962) 861388

BAKER, John Carl. b 55. Chich Th Coll 77. **d** 80 **p** 81. C Wigan St Andr *Liv* 80-83; V Hollinfare 83-85; TV Seacroft *Ripon* 85-89; TV Bottesford w Ashby *Linc* 89-94; V Liv St Paul Stoneycroft *Liv* from 94. *St Paul's Vicarage, Carlton Lane, Liverpool L13 6QS* 0151-228 1041

BAKER, John Reginald. b 62. Hatf Coll Dur BSc83. Wycliffe Hall Ox 86. **d** 89 **p** 90. C Amersham *Ox* 89-92; C Greenford H Cross *Lon* from 92. *St Edward's House, Medway Drive, Greenford, Middx UB6 8LN* 0181-997 4953

BAKER, Jonathan Mark Richard. b 66. St Jo Coll Ox BA88 MPhil90. St Steph Ho Ox BA92. **d** 93 **p** 94. C Ascot Heath *Ox* from 93. *The Parsonage, King Edward's Road, Ascot, Berks SL5 8PD* Ascot (01344) 885500

BAKER, Jonathan William. b 61. SS Coll Cam MA85. Wycliffe Hall Ox BA91. **d** 92 **p** 93. C Sanderstead All SS *S'wark* from 92. *285 Limpsfield Road, South Croydon, Surrey CR2 9DG* 0181-657 0613

BAKER, Canon Michael Robert Henry. b 39. Keele Univ MA88. Lich Th Coll 63. **d** 66 **p** 67. C Wellingborough All SS *Pet* 66-68; C Pet All SS 68-73; V Earls Barton 73-87; RD Wellingborough 76-87; P-in-c Gt Doddington 77-82; Can Pet Cathl from 85; TR Kingsthorpe w St Dav Northn from 87. *The Rectory, 16 Green End, Kingsthorpe, Northampton NN2 6RD* Northampton (01604) 717133

BAKER, Michael William. b 38. Roch Th Coll 68. **d** 70 **p** 71. C Woodmansterne *S'wark* 70-75; TV Danbury *Chelmsf* 75-78; P-in-c Barrington *Ely* 78-90; V from 90; P-in-c Shepreth 78-90; V from 90. *The Vicarage, 4 Church Road, Shepreth, Royston, Herts SG8 6RG* Royston (01763) 260172

BAKER, Canon Neville Duff. b 35. St Aid Birkenhead 60. **d** 63 **p** 64. C Stranton *Dur* 63-66; C Houghton le Spring 66-68; V Tudhoe Grange from 68; RD Auckland 83-94; Hon Can Dur Cathl from 90; P-in-c Merrington from 91. *St Andrew's Vicarage, Tudhoe Grange, Spennymoor, Co Durham DL16 6NE* Spennymoor (01388) 814817

BAKER, Noel Edward Lloyd. b 37. Sarum & Wells Th Coll 73. **d** 75 **p** 76. C Charlton Kings St Mary *Glouc* 75-79; V Clearwell 79-81; R Eastington and Frocester from 81; RD Stonehouse 90-94. *The Rectory, Mill End Lane, Eastington, Stonehouse, Glos GL10 3SG* Stonehouse (01453) 822437

BAKER, Paul Anthony. b 64. St Chad's Coll Dur BA85. St Steph Ho Ox BA88. **d** 89 **p** 90. C Hartlepool St Aid Dur 89-93; TV Jarrow from 93. *St Mark's House, Randolph Street, Jarrow, Tyne & Wear NE32 3AQ* 0191-483 2092

BAKER, Peter Colin. b 43. Sarum & Wells Th Coll. **d** 82 **p** 83. C Bridgemary *Portsm* 82-86; V Ash Vale *Guildf* from 86. *The Vicarage, 203 Vale Road, Ash Vale, Aldershot, Hants GU12 5JE* Aldershot (01252) 25295

BAKER, Peter Graham. b 55. MA PhD. St Steph Ho Ox. **d** 82 **p** 83. C Ches H Trin *Ches* 82-86; C Holborn St Alb w Saffron Hill St Pet *Lon* 86-91; V Golders Green 91-94; V Golders Green from 94; AD W Barnet from 95. *The Vicarage, 3 St Alban's Close, North End Road, London NW11 7RA* 0181-455 4525

BAKER, Canon Peter Malcolm. b 21. Lich Th Coll 40. **d** 43 **p** 45. CF (TA) 53-75; V Inkberrow *Worc* 67-75; P-in-c Kington w Dormston 74-75; R Inkberrow w Cookhill and Kington w Dormston 75-77; P-in-c Wilden 77-80; R Mamble w Bayton

80-82; RD Stourport 80-88; R Teme Valley N 82-88; Hon Can Worc Cathl 84-88; rtd 88. *The Ryelands, Menith Wood, Worcester WR6 6UG* Eardiston (01584) 881227

BAKER, Robert John Kenneth. b 50. MICE79 Southn Univ BSc71. Oak Hill Th Coll 88. **d** 90 **p** 91. C Cromer *Nor* 90-94; P-in-c Pakefield 94; R from 94. *The Rectory, Pakefield, Lowestoft, Suffolk NR33 0JZ* Lowestoft (01502) 574040

BAKER, Canon Robert Mark. b 50. Bris Univ BA73. St Jo Coll Nottm 74. **d** 76 **p** 77. C Portswood Ch Ch *Win* 76-80; R Witton w Brundall and Braydeston *Nor* 80-89; P-in-c Buckenham w Hassingham and Strumpshaw 80-86; R Brundall w Braydeston and Postwick from 89; RD Blofield 89-94; Hon Can Nor Cathl from 93. *The Rectory, 73 The Street, Brundall, Norwich NR13 5LZ* Norwich (01603) 715136

BAKER, Canon Robin Henry. b 31. Man Univ BA52. Cuddesdon Coll 54. **d** 56 **p** 57. C Swinton St Pet *Man* 56-59; C Birch St Jas 59-61; R Stretford All SS 61-66; Chapl High Royds Hosp Menston 66-72; P-in-c Simpson w Woughton on the Green *Ox* 72-73; P-in-c Woughton 74; TR 74-79; RD Milton Keynes 78-86; C-in-c Milton Keynes City Cen 79-80; V Milton Keynes 80-86; Hon Can Ch Ch 84-91; TR Banbury 86-91; P-in-c Scorton *Blackb* from 91; Bp's Adv on Healing from 91. *St Peter's Vicarage, Scorton, Preston PR3 1AY* Forton (01524) 791229

BAKER, Ronald Harry. b 21. Ely Th Coll 62. **d** 64 **p** 65. R Thornbury *Ex* 66-73; R Black Torrington, Bradf and Thornbury 73-77; P-in-c Broadhempston and Woodland 77-78; P-in-c Lt Hempston 77-78; P-in-c Berry Pomeroy 77-78; V Broadhempston, Woodland, Berry Pomeroy etc 78-86; rtd 86; Chapl Marseille w St Raphael Aix-en-Provence etc *Eur* 87-88; Perm to Offic *Ex* from 88. *95 Barton Avenue, Paignton, Devon TQ3 3HY* Totnes (01803) 557462

BAKER, Ronald Kenneth (Ron). b 43. Open Univ BA80 LTh. St Jo Coll Nottm 85. **d** 87 **p** 88. C Paddock Wood *Roch* 87-90; V Ramsgate St Mark *Cant* 90-95; P-in-c Ewhurst *Chich* from 95; P-in-c Bodiam from 95. *The Rectory, Ewhurst Green, Robertsbridge, E Sussex TN32 5TB* Robertsbridge (01580) 830268

BAKER, Roy David. b 36. Lon Univ DipTh61. St Aid Birkenhead 59. **d** 62 **p** 63. C Garston *Liv* 62-64; C N Meols 64-68; V Newton-le-Willows 68-73; V Crossens 73-82; V Blundellsands St Nic from 82. *St Nicholas' Vicarage, Nicholas Road, Blundellsands, Liverpool L23 6TS* 0151-924 3551

BAKER, Simon Nicholas Hartland. b 57. K Coll Lon BD78 Trin Hall Cam DipTh79. Qu Coll Birm 79. **d** 81 **p** 82. C Tupsley *Heref* 81-85; V Shinfield *Ox* from 85; Prin Berks Chr Tr Scheme from 93. *The Vicarage, Church Lane, Shinfield, Reading RG2 9BY* Reading (01734) 883363

BAKER, Stephen Anthony. b 55. St Luke's Coll Ex BEd80. Sarum & Wells Th Coll 88. **d** 91 **p** 92. C Guildf H Trin w St Mary *Guildf* from 91; Chapl Guildf Coll of Tech from 91. *27 Pewley Way, Guildford, Surrey GU1 3PX* Guildford (01483) 68477

BAKER, Stuart. b 44. MATA63 AIAT65. Spurgeon's Coll DipTh61 Bapt Tr Coll DipMin75 Ripon Coll Cuddesdon 92. **d** 93 **p** 94. C Whitchurch *Bris* from 93. *127 Bristol Road, Bristol BS14 0PU* Bristol (0117) 983 4992

BAKER, Very Rev Thomas George Adames. b 20. Ex Coll Ox BA43 MA50. Linc Th Coll 43. **d** 44 **p** 45. Preb Wells Cathl *B & W* 60-71; Prin Wells Th Coll 60-71; Adn Bath and Preb Wells Cathl *B & W* 71-75; Dean Worc 75-86; rtd 86; Perm to Offic *B & W* 86-94. *Charterhouse, Charterhouse Square, London EC1M 6AN* 0171-250 3578

BAKER, Walter Donald. b 06. FRSA LTCL. St Aid Birkenhead 42. **d** 44 **p** 45. V Upper Holloway St Steph *Lon* 69-80; rtd 80; Hon C St Jas Garlickhythe w St Mich Queenhithe etc *Lon* from 80. *Charterhouse, Charterhouse Square, London EC1M 6AH* 0171-253 2728

BAKER, William Alfred Douglas. b 21. Lon Univ BSc52 MSc56. Qu Coll Birm 72. **d** 75 **p** 76. Hon C Bridgnorth w Tasley *Heref* 75-78; Hon C Bridgnorth, Tasley, Astley Abbotts, Oldbury etc from 78. *Oaklea, Astley Abbotts, Bridgnorth, Shropshire WV16 4SW* Bridgnorth (01746) 762980

BAKER, William Douglas Willson. b 19. Linc Th Coll 79. **d** 80 **p** 81. NSM Mablethorpe w Trusthorpe *Linc* 80-84; NSM Sutton le Marsh 84-90; NSM Sutton, Huttoft and Anderby 90-94; Perm to Offic from 94. *7 Grove Road, Sutton-on-Sea, Mablethorpe, Lincs LN12 2LP* Mablethorpe (01507) 441506

BAKER, William George. b 07. St Cath Coll Cam BTh. **d** 38 **p** 42. V Moreton *Lich* 53-76; rtd 76. *Fidelis, 39 Lime Tree Road, Matlock, Derbyshire DE4 3EJ* Matlock (01629) 582717

BAKER, William John (Bill). b 45. FCII80. Cranmer Hall Dur 87. **d** 89 **p** 90. C Sale St Anne *Ches* 89-93; V Crewe St Andr 93-94; P-in-c Crewe St Jo 93-94; V Crewe St Andr w St Jo the Baptist from 94. *St John's Vicarage, 14 Dane Bank Avenue, Crewe CW2 8AA* Crewe (01270) 68835

BAKERE, Very Rev Ronald Duncan. b 35. TCD BA58 HDipEd60 MA61 BD62 Ch Ch Ox MA66 FRSA68 FBIM79. CITC 59. **d** 59 **p** 60. C Knockbreda *D & D* 59-61; C Dub Zion Ch *D & G* 61-63; Min Can St Patr Cathl Dub 62-64; CF (TA) 65-67; Lect Th Plymouth Univ 67-72; Nigeria 73-77; Cen Org Ex Red Cross 78-81; Perm to Offic *Ex* 82-85; P-in-c Chew Magna w Dundry *B & W* 86-87; Hd Relig Studies Sir Jo Cass Foundn Lon 88-93; Perm to Offic *Lon* 88-93; Dean Port Moresby from 93; ChStJ from 95. *St John's Cathedral, PO Box 6, Port Moresby, Papua New Guinea* Papua New Guinea (675) 214525 Fax 232493

BALCH, John Robin. b 37. Lon Univ BSc61 Bris Univ CertEd62. ALCD82. **d** 68 **p** 69. C Bath Walcot *B & W* 68-71; C Fulwood *Sheff* 71-76; V Erith St Paul *Roch* 76-93; RD Erith 90-93; P-in-c Fairlight *Chich* 93-94; R Fairlight, Guestling and Pett from 94. *The Rectory, Pett, Hastings, E Sussex TN35 4HG* Hastings (01424) 813234

BALCHIN, Michael John. b 38. Selw Coll Cam BA60 MA64. Wells Th Coll 60. **d** 62 **p** 63. C Bournemouth H Epiphany *Win* 62-65; C Bris St Mary Redcliffe w Temple etc *Bris* 65-69; R Norton sub Hamdon *B & W* 69-70; P-in-c Chiselborough w W Chinnock 69-70; R Norton sub Hamdon w Chiselborough 70-77; P-in-c Chipstable w Huish Champflower and Clatworthy 77-82; R 82-88; Rural Ministers Officer 87-88; Perm to Offic *Ban* from 88. *Glyntwymyn, Commins Coch, Machynlleth, Powys SY20 8LS* Cemmaes Road (01650) 511659

BALDOCK, Charles William Martin. b 52. Nottm Univ BPharm73. St Jo Coll Nottm LTh. **d** 85 **p** 86. C Nailsea Ch Ch *B & W* 85-89; V Brampton Bierlow *Sheff* from 89; RD Wath from 95. *The Vicarage, Christchurch Road, Wath-upon-Dearne, Rotherham, S Yorkshire S63 6NW* Rotherham (01709) 873210

BALDOCK, Canon Norman. b 29. K Coll Lon BD52 AKC52. **d** 53 **p** 54. V Sheerness H Trin w St Paul *Cant* 67-75; V Margate St Jo 75-94; RD Thanet 80-86; Hon Can Cant Cathl 82-94; Chapl Margate Gen Hosp 82-94; rtd 94. *9 Beach Avenue, Birchington, Kent CT7 9VS* Thanet (01843) 841173

BALDOCK, Reginald David. b 48. Oak Hill Th Coll 72. **d** 75 **p** 76. C Plymouth St Jude *Ex* 75-79; C Ardsley *Sheff* 79-85; V Rawthorpe *Wakef* from 85. *The Vicarage, 138 Rawthorpe Lane, Huddersfield HD5 9PB* Huddersfield (01484) 428045

BALDRY, John Netherway. b 19. Lon Univ BA53. **d** 79 **p** 80. Hon C Brighton St Paul *Chich* from 79. *26 Braybon Avenue, Brighton BN1 8HG* Brighton (01273) 501268

BALDRY, Ralph Yorke. b 18. St Jo Coll Ox BA40 MA44. Wycliffe Hall Ox 40. **d** 41 **p** 42. V Finchley St Luke *Lon* 64-72; V Golders Green St Alb 72-80; P-in-c Golders Green St Mich 77-80; V Golders Green 80-83; rtd 84. *159 Falloden Way, London NW11 6LG* 0181-455 6926

BALDWICK, Frank Eric. b 24. Ripon Hall Ox 54. **d** 55 **p** 56. R Gt Leaver *Man* 65-78; V Hindsford 78-81; TV Clifton *S'well* 81-89; rtd 89; Perm to Offic *S'well* from 89. *35 Ladybay Road, Nottingham NG2 5BJ* Nottingham (0115) 982 1273

BALDWIN, David Frederick Beresford. b 57. Wolv Univ 91. Ripon Coll Cuddesdon DipMin95. **d** 95. C Uttoxeter w Bramshall *Lich* from 95. *5 Beech Close, Uttoxeter, Staffs ST14 7DZ* Uttoxeter (01889) 567677

BALDWIN, Derek Wilfred Walter. b 23. Lon Univ LTh74. ALCD56. **d** 52 **p** 53. Org Sec (Dios B & W, Ex and Truro) CECS 66-72; Lic to Offic *Ex* 67-72; R Morchard Bishop 72-73; Org Sec (Dios St Alb and Ox) CECS 73-77; C Portishead *B & W* 77-79; R Wymondham w Edmondthorpe *Leic* 79-80; P-in-c St Mewan *Truro* 80-81; V Crowan w Godolphin 81-83; C Cockington *Ex* 83-87; rtd 87; Perm to Offic *Ex* from 90. *Belfry Cottage, Sidmouth, Devon EX10 8SY*

BALDWIN, Dr John Charles. b 39. FBCS CEng Bris Univ BSc63 Sussex Univ DPhil65. St Steph Ho Ox 82. **d** 83 **p** 84. C Llan w Capel Llanilltern *Llan* 83-90; R Ewenny w St Brides Major 90-92; Lic to Offic from 92. *60 Llantrisant Road, Llandaff, Cardiff CF5 2PX* Cardiff (01222) 560081

BALDWIN, Jonathan Michael. b 58. Chich Th Coll 92. **d** 94 **p** 95. C Crawley *Chich* from 94. *54 Dovedale Crescent, Crawley, W Sussex RH11 8SG* Crawley (01293) 539552

BALDWIN, Joyce Gertrude. See CAINE, Mrs Joyce Gertrude

BALDWIN, Peter Alan. b 48. Bede Coll Dur BA70 Birm Univ DipTh72. Qu Coll Birm 72. **d** 73 **p** 74. C Hartlepool St Oswald *Dur* 73-75; C Darlington H Trin 75-78; OGS from 77; C-in-c Bishop Auckland Woodhouse Close CD *Dur* 78-82; V Ferryhill 82-88; P-in-c Charlestown *Man* 88-89; V Pendleton St Thos 88-89; TR Pendleton St Thos w Charlestown 89-90; TR Newton Aycliffe *Dur* from 90. *St Clare's Rectory, St Cuthbert's Way, Newton Aycliffe, Co Durham DL5 5NT* Aycliffe (01325) 313613

BALDWIN, William. b 48. RMN73 FRSH83. NW Ord Course 75. **d** 78 **p** 79. C Royton St Anne *Man* 78-82; V Halliwell St

Thos 82-87; TR Atherton from 87; OStJ from 88. *Atherton Rectory, Bee Fold Lane, Atherton, Manchester M29 0BL* Atherton (01942) 874666

BALE, Edward William Carre. b 22. ABAF74 AKC55 Leic Univ DSRS67. **d** 55 **p** 56. V Wollaston and Strixton *Pet* 69-87; rtd 88; Perm to Offic *Ox* from 88; Perm to Offic *Pet* from 89. *49 Kilpin Green, North Crawley, Newport Pagnell, Bucks MK16 9LZ* North Crawley (01234) 391443

BALE, James Henry. b 30. St Pet Hall Ox BA53 DipEd54 MA57 CQSW81. Oak Hill Th Coll 56. **d** 58 **p** 59. C Walcot St Sav *B & W* 58-61; C Kinson *Sarum* 61-64; Sudan 64-75; Hon C Prestwick *Glas* 75-89; Brazil from 89. *CxP 2024, 30161 Belo Horizinti, MG Brazil*

BALE, Kenneth John. b 34. Univ of Wales (Lamp) BA58. Qu Coll Birm DipTh60. **d** 60 **p** 61. C Mitcham St Olave *S'wark* 60-63; C Warlingham w Chelsham and Farleigh 63-67; V Battersea Rise St Mark 67-85; Perm to Offic 85-88; Hon C Balham St Mary and St Jo 88-90; V S Wimbledon All SS from 90; Dioc Adv Min of Healing from 91. *All Saints' Vicarage, De Burgh Road, London SW19 1DX* 0181-542 5514

BALES, Charles Noel. b 07. Dorchester Miss Coll 31. **d** 35 **p** 36. V Marshland St James *Ely* 42-84; P-in-c 84-92; rtd 84. *5 St Edmund's Terrace, Downham Market, Norfolk PE38 9LR* Downham Market (01366) 386072

BALFOUR, Andrew Crispin Roxburgh. b 49. Coll of Resurr Mirfield 93. **d** 95. C S Lafford *Linc* from 95. *The Vicarage, 1 The Drove, Osbournby, Sleaford, Lincs NG34 0DH* Sleaford (01529) 455630

BALFOUR, Hugh Rowlatt. b 54. SS Coll Cam BA76. Ridley Hall Cam 78. **d** 81 **p** 82. C Bedf Ch Ch *St Alb* 81-86; P-in-c Camberwell Ch Ch *S'wark* 86-90; V from 90. *Christ Church Vicarage, 79 Asylum Road, London SE15 2RJ* 0171-639 5662

BALFOUR, Mrs Penelope Mary (Penny). b 47. St Andr Univ MA69 St Jo Coll York DipEd72. Coates Hall Edin 89 St Jo Coll Nottm 84. **d** 88 **p** 95. C Dundee St Marg *Bre* from 88; Dioc AIDS Officer 90-94; NSM Invergowrie from 94; Chapl Abertay Univ from 94. *10 Strathaird Place, Dundee DD2 4TN* Dundee (01382) 643114

BALKWILL, Michael Robert. b 67. Univ of Wales (Lamp) BD89 Univ of Wales (Cardiff) DPS90 MTh92. St Mich Coll Llan 89 Bp Tucker Coll Mukono 91. **d** 91 **p** 92. C Llanrhos *St As* from 91; Dioc RE Adv from 94. *The Parsonage, All Saints' Avenue, Deganwy, Conwy, Gwynedd LL31 9DZ* Deganwy (01492) 583260

BALKWILL, Roger Bruce. b 41. Univ of Wales DipTh64 DPS66. St Mich Coll Llan 61. **d** 64 **p** 65. C Llantrisant *Llan* 64-68; C Caerphilly 68-73; Rhodesia 73-76; P-in-c Ilam w Blore Ray and Okeover *Lich* 76-81; P-in-c Albrighton 81-82; V from 82; P-in-c Beckbury 89-90; P-in-c Badger 89-90; P-in-c Ryton 89-90; P-in-c Kemberton, Sutton Maddock and Stockton 89-90; RD Shifnal from 89. *The Vicarage, High Street, Albrighton, Wolverhampton WV7 3EQ* Albrighton (01902) 372701

BALL, Alan. b 26. Qu Coll Birm 72. **d** 75 **p** 75. NSM Hamstead St Paul *Birm* 75-93; rtd 93. *23 Tebourba Drive, Sovereign Green, Alverstoke, Gosport, Hants PO12 2NT* Gosport (01705) 601694

BALL, Albert Bernard. b 15. Coll of Resurr Mirfield. **d** 62 **p** 63. V Oldham St Jo *Man* 71-80; rtd 80. *4 Holly Mount, Seymour Grove, Stretford, Manchester M16 0ET* 0161-860 7289

BALL, Andrew Thomas. b 54. K Coll Lon BD75 AKC75. Sarum & Wells Th Coll 76. **d** 77 **p** 78. C Ribbleton *Blackb* 77-80; C Sedgley All SS *Lich* 80-84; V Pheasey 84-90; Chapl Gd Hope Distr Gen Hosp Sutton Coldfield from 90. *Chaplain's Office, Good Hope Hospital, Rectory Road, Sutton Coldfield, W Midlands B75 7RR* 0121-378 2211

BALL, Anthony Charles. b 46. Lon Univ BD71. Chich Th Coll 72. **d** 73 **p** 74. C Heref St Martin *Heref* 73-76; C Ealing St Pet Mt Park *Lon* 76-82; V Ruislip Manor St Paul from 82. *St Paul's Vicarage, Thurlstone Road, Ruislip, Middx HA4 0BP* Ruislip (01895) 633499

BALL, Anthony Michael (Tony). b 46. Kelham Th Coll 66. **d** 70 **p** 71. C Kingswinford St Mary *Lich* 70-74; C W Bromwich All SS 74-76; P-in-c Priorslee 76-80; V 80-82; Asst Chapl HM Pris Liv 82-83; Chapl 88-95; Chapl HM Pris Lewes 83-88; Chapl HM Pris Featherstone from 95. *HM Prison, New Road, Featherstone, Wolverhampton WV10 7PN* Standeford (01902) 790991

BALL, Christopher Rowland. b 40. Wycliffe Hall Ox. **d** 82 **p** 83. C Heysham *Blackb* 82-86; TV Swanborough *Sarum* 86-90; R Llanyblodwel and Trefonen *Lich* from 90. *The Rectory, School Lane, Trefonen, Oswestry, Shropshire SY10 9DY* Oswestry (01691) 654184

BALL, Canon Frank. b 21. Lambeth BA47. Coll of Resurr Mirfield 46. **d** 48 **p** 49. V Sheff Norwood St Leon *Sheff* 61-87; RD Ecclesfield 80-87; Hon Can Sheff Cathl 85-93; rtd 87; Gov and Chapl Shrewsbury Hosp Sheff 87-93. *40 Seagrave Road, Sheffield S12 2JS* Sheffield (0114) 264 4931

BALL, Geoffrey Williams. b 32. FLIA80 FInstSMM81. SW Minl Tr Course 82. **d** 85 **p** 86. NSM Sampford Spiney w Horrabridge *Ex* 85-87; TV Yelverton, Meavy, Sheepstor and Walkhampton 87-91; V Marystowe, Coryton, Stowford, Lewtrenchard etc from 91. *The Rectory, Lewdown, Okehampton, Devon EX20 4NU* Lewdown (01566) 783493

BALL, George Raymond. b 15. Univ of Wales (Lamp) BA40. St Mich Coll Llan 40. **d** 42 **p** 43. R Bosherston w St Twynells *St D* 50-85; rtd 85. *1 Meadowbank, St Twynnells, Pembroke, Dyfed SA71 5HZ* Castlemartin (01646) 661432

BALL, Glynne Howell James. b 47. ACIS DMA. Llan Dioc Tr Scheme. **d** 90 **p** 91. NSM Llangynwyd w Maesteg *Llan* from 90. *7 Bridgend Road, Llangynwyd, Maesteg, M Glam CF34 9SW* Maesteg (01656) 734805

BALL, Ian Raymond. b 45. CertEd Univ of Wales MPhil. Glouc Th Course 81. **d** 85 **p** 87. NSM Churchstoke w Hyssington and Sarn *Heref* from 85; Lic to Bp Ludlow from 87; Lic to Offic *St As* from 93. *Bachaethlon Cottage, Sarn, Newtown, Powys SY16 4HH* Kerry (01686) 670505 Fax as telephone

BALL, John Roy. b 47. Fitzw Coll Cam MA71. Wycliffe Hall Ox 83. **d** 85 **p** 86. C Stockport St Mary *Ches* 85-88; C Fazeley *Lich* 88-94; Min Drayton Bassett 89-94; Chapl Grenoble *Eur* from 94. *34 Quai de France, 3800 Grenoble, France* France (33) 76 85 46 07

BALL, John Kenneth. b 42. Lon Univ BSc64 AKC64. Linc Th Coll 69. **d** 71 **p** 72. C Garston *Liv* 71-74; C Eastham *Ches* 74-75; C Barnston 75-77; V Over St Jo 77-82; V Helsby and Dunham-on-the-Hill 82-94; RD Frodsham 88-94; P-in-c Alvanley 92-94; V Hoylake from 94. *The Vicarage, Stanley Road, Hoylake, Wirral, Merseyside L47 1HW* 0151-632 3897

✠**BALL, Rt Rev John Martin.** b 34. Univ of Wales BA55. Tyndale Hall Bris. **d** 59 **p** 60 **c** 95. C Blackb St Jude *Blackb* 59-63; Kenya 63-79; Dep Gen Sec BCMS 79-81; Gen Sec 81-93; Gen Sec Crosslinks 93-95; Hon C Sidcup Ch Ch *Roch* 81-95; Hon Can Karamoja from 88; Asst Bp Tanzania from 95. *PO Box 15, Dodoma, Tanzania* Dodoma (61) 23025 or 21777

BALL, Jonathan. b 63. BNC Ox BA85 Leeds Univ BA87. Coll of Resurr Mirfield 85. **d** 88 **p** 89. C Blakenall Heath *Lich* 88-92; TV Rugeley from 92. *4 Cardigan Avenue, Rugeley, Staffs WS15 1LG* Rugeley (01889) 576401

BALL, Kevin Harry. b 55. Linc Th Coll 92. **d** 94 **p** 95. C New Mills *Derby* from 94. *St George's House, 32 Church Road, New Mills, Stockport, Cheshire SK12 4NJ* New Mills (01663) 746301

BALL, Michael Gordon. b 12. St Aid Birkenhead 45. **d** 48 **p** 49. R Newington Bagpath w Kingscote and Ozleworth *Glouc* 70-74; P-in-c Boxwell w Leighterton 71-72; R Withington and Compton Abdale w Haselton 75-77; rtd 77; Perm to Offic *Ex* from 77. *5 Instow House, Marine Parade, Instow, Bideford, Devon EX39 4JJ* Instow (01271) 860593

✠**BALL, Rt Rev Michael Thomas.** b 32. Qu Coll Cam BA55 MA59. **d** 71 **p** 71 **c** 80. CGA from 60; Prior Stroud Priory 64-76; C Whiteshill *Glouc* 71-76; Lic to Offic 76; P-in-c Stanmer w Falmer *Chich* 76-80; Chapl Sussex Univ 76-80; Suff Bp Jarrow *Dur* 80-90; Angl Adv Tyne Tees TV 84-90; Bp Truro from 90. *Lis Escop, Feock, Truro, Cornwall TR3 6QQ* Truro (01872) 862657 Fax 862037

BALL, Nicholas Edward. b 54. Man Univ BA75 Ox Univ MA85. Ripon Coll Cuddesdon 79. **d** 80 **p** 81. C Yardley Wood *Birm* 80-83; C Moseley St Mary 83-86; Chapl Cen 13 83-85; V Bartley Green 86-95; P-in-c Hall Green St Pet from 95. *St Peter's Vicarage, 33 Paradise Lane, Birmingham B28 0DY* 0121-777 1935

BALL, Norman. b 41. Liv Univ BA63. Cuddesdon Coll 67. **d** 68 **p** 69. C Broseley w Benthall *Heref* 68-72; Lic to Offic *Ches* 72-75; V Plemstall w Guilden Sutton 75-79; Perm to Offic 79-88; NSM Dodleston 88-94; R Hawarden *St As* from 94. *White Cottage, Lower Mountain Road, Penyffordd, Chester CH4 0EX* Kinnerton (01244) 661132

BALL, Peter Edwin. b 44. Lon Univ BD65 DipEd. Wycliffe Hall Ox 75. **d** 77 **p** 78. C Prescot *Liv* 77-80; R Lawford *Chelmsf* from 80; RD Harwich from 91. *The Rectory, Church Hill, Lawford, Manningtree, Essex CO11 2JX* Colchester (01206) 392659

✠**BALL, Rt Rev Peter John.** b 32. Qu Coll Cam BA54 MA58. Wells Th Coll 54. **d** 56 **p** 57 **c** 77. C Rottingdean *Chich* 56-58; Novice SSM 58-60; CGA from 60; Prior CGA 60-77; Lic to Offic 65-66; P-in-c Hoar Cross *Lich* 66-69; Lic to Offic *B & W* 69-77; Suff Bp Lewes *Chich* 77-84; Area Bp Lewes 84-92; Can and Preb Chich Cathl 78-92; Bp Glouc 92-93; rtd 93. *c/o Lis Escop, Feock, Truro, Cornwall TR3 6QQ* Truro (01872) 862657 Fax 862037

BALL, Canon Peter Prior. b 25. St Jo Coll Ox BA50 MA55. Ridley Hall Cam 51. **d** 53 **p** 54. Chapl RN 60-76; Chapl Cannes *Eur* 76-80; Visiting Chapl (Eur & N Africa) Intercon Ch Soc 80-86; Eur Rep SOMA from 86; rtd 90; Hon Can Malta Cathl *Eur* from 91. *Chateau d'Azur, 44 Boulevard d'Italie, Monte Carlo MC98000, Monaco* Monaco (3393) 303079

BALL, Canon Peter William. b 30. Worc Coll Ox BA53 MA57. Cuddesdon Coll 53. **d** 55 **p** 56. R Shepperton *Lon* 68-84; RD Staines 72-74; RD Spelthorne 74-83; Preb St Paul's Cathl 76-84; Can Res and Chan 84-90; Perm to Offic *Sarum* from 90; rtd 95. *Whittonedge, Whittonditch Road, Ramsbury, Marlborough, Wilts SN8 2PX* Marlborough (01672) 20259

BALL, Philip John. b 52. Bris Univ BEd75. Ripon Coll Cuddesdon 79. **d** 82 **p** 83. C Norton St Mich *Dur* 82-84; C Greenford H Cross *Lon* 84-88; V Hayes St Edm from 88; AD Hillingdon from 94. *St Edmund's Vicarage, 1 Edmund's Close, Hayes, Middx UB4 0HA* 0181-573 6913

BALL, Vernon. b 34. Ox Min Course 87. **d** 90 **p** 91. NSM Banbury *Ox* from 90. *15 Crouch Street, Banbury, Oxon OX16 9PP* Banbury (01295) 259839

BALLAMAN, Ms Pauline Margaret. b 54. Golds Coll Lon BA89 Lon Univ MA90. Oak Hill Th Coll 93 Ridley Hall Cam CTM95. **d** 95. C New Addington *S'wark* from 95. *126 Fairchildes Avenue, New Addington, Croydon CR0 0AN*

BALLANTINE, Peter Sinclair. b 46. Nottm Univ MTh85. K Coll Lon BA68 AKC68 St Jo Coll Nottm 70 Lon Coll of Div ALCD71 BD73 LTh74. **d** 73 **p** 74. C Rainham *Chelmsf* 73-77; C Wennington 73-77; TV Barton Mills *St E* 77-80; TV Barton Mills, Beck Row w Kenny Hill etc 80-82; Chapl Liv Poly *Liv* 83-86; Tr Officer Rugby Deanery *Cov* from 86; P-in-c Churchover w Willey from 86; P-in-c Clifton upon Dunsmore and Newton from 86. *The Rectory, Churchover, Rugby, Warks CV23 0EH* Rugby (01788) 832420

BALLANTINE, Roderic Keith. b 44. Chich Th Coll 66. **d** 69 **p** 70. C Nunhead St Antony *S'wark* 69-72; C S Hackney St Jo w Ch Ch *Lon* 72-75; P-in-c Kensal Town St Thos w St Andr and St Phil 75-79; V Stoke Newington St Andr from 79. *St Andrew's Vicarage, 106 Bethune Road, London N16 5DU* 0181-800 2900

BALLANTYNE, Jane Elizabeth. See KENCHINGTON, Mrs Jane Elizabeth Ballantyne

BALLARD, Andrew Edgar. b 44. Dur Univ BA66. Westcott Ho Cam 66. **d** 68 **p** 69. C St Marylebone St Mary *Lon* 68-72; C Portsea St Mary *Portsm* 72-76; V Haslingden w Haslingden Grane *Blackb* 76-82; V Walkden Moor *Man* 82-93; TR Walkden Moor St Paul w Lt Hulton St Jo the Bapt from 93; Chapl Salford Coll 82-92; AD Farnworth *Man* from 90. *St Paul's Vicarage, Manchester Road, Worsley, Manchester M28 5LN* 0161-790 2483

BALLARD, Miss Anne Christina. b 54. LRAM76 Hon RCM93 ARAM94. Wycliffe Hall Ox 82. **dss** 85 **d** 87 **p** 94. Hove By Hannington Memorial Ch *Chich* 85-87; Chapl St Mich Sch Burton Park 87-89; Chapl RCM *Lon* 89-93; Chapl Imp Coll 89-93; Prec Ch Ch *Ox* from 93. *Christ Church, Oxford OX1 1DP* Oxford (01865) 276214 Fax as telephone

BALLARD, Anthony James. E Midl Min Tr Course 86. **d** 89 **p** 90. Hon Chapl Woodbank Gr Sch Leic from 89; Hon C Clarendon Park St Jo w Knighton St Mich *Leic* from 89. *Flat 7, 51 Evington Road, Leicester LE2 1QG* Leicester (0116) 255 8086

BALLARD, Charles Martin. b 29. Jes Coll Cam BA52 MA56. **d** 58 **p** 59. V Balne *Sheff* 61-62; rtd 94. *35 Abbey Road, Cambridge CB5 8HH*

BALLARD, Canon Michael Arthur. b 44. Lon Univ BA66. Westcott Ho Cam 68. **d** 70 **p** 71. C Harrow Weald All SS *Lon* 70-73; C Aylesbury *Ox* 73-78; V Eastwood *Chelmsf* 78-90; RD Hadleigh 83-90; Hon Can Chelmsf Cathl from 89; R Southchurch H Trin from 90; RD Southend-on-Sea from 94. *The Rectory, 8 Pilgrims Close, Southend-on-Sea SS2 4XF* Southend-on-Sea (01702) 466423

BALLARD, Nigel Humphrey. b 48. Linc Th Coll 92. **d** 94 **p** 95. C Old Brumby *Linc* 94; C Bottesford w Ashby from 94. *111 Ashby High Street, Scunthorpe, S Humberside DN16 2JX* Scunthorpe (01724) 860573

BALLARD, Peter James. b 55. St Hild & Bede Coll Dur BEd78 Lon Univ DipTh85. Sarum & Wells Th Coll 85. **d** 87 **p** 88. C Grantham *Linc* 87-90 and 91; Australia 90; V Lanc Ch Ch w St Jo and St Anne *Blackb* from 91; RD Lanc from 94. *Christ Church Vicarage, 1 East Road, Lancaster LA1 3EE* Lancaster (01524) 34430

BALLARD, Richard Ernest. b 37. Linc Coll Ox BA60 MA66 Lon Univ BD68. Wells Th Coll 60. **d** 62 **p** 63. C Farnham *Guildf* 62-67; Chapl Pierrepont Sch Frensham 67-69; Asst Chapl Eton Coll Windsor 69-74; P-in-c Fiddington *B & W* 74-76; P-in-c Stogursey 74-76; R Stogursey w Fiddington 76-78; R Trull w Angersleigh 78-80; Chapl Qu Coll Taunton 78-80; Chapl Wells Cathl Sch 81-86; Chapl Haileybury Coll Herts 86-91; Chapl Westmr Sch from 91; PV Westmr Abbey from 91; Hon C Westmr St Matt *Lon* from 94. *8 Gayfere Street, London SW1P 3HN* 0171-799 2620 or 222 2831

BALLARD, Steven Peter. b 52. Man Univ BA73 MA74. St Steph Ho Ox 76. **d** 78 **p** 79. C Lanc St Mary *Blackb* 78-81; C Blackpool St Mich 81-84; V Brierfield 84-94. *1 St Catherine's Court, Drover's Lane, Penrith, Cumbria CA11 9EF* Penrith (01768) 890976

BALLENTINE, Ian Clarke. b 46. Aston Univ BSc71 CEng. BTh. **d** 91 **p** 92. C Lurgan St Jo *D & D* 91-95; I Mallusk *Conn* from 95. *The Rectory, Carwood Drive, Glengormley, Newtownabbey, Co Antrim BT36 8LP* Glengormley (01232) 833773

BALLEY, John Frederick. b 05. ALCD41. **d** 41 **p** 42. Lic to Offic *Ex* 65-70; Chapl Torbay Hosp Torquay 65-70; rtd 70. *Hornsey Rise Memorial Home, Main Road, Wellsborough, Nuneaton, Warks CV13 6PA* Market Bosworth (01455) 290219

BALLINGER, Francis James. b 43. AKC70. **d** 71 **p** 85. C Weston-super-Mare St Sav *B & W* 71-72; Dir Bd Soc Resp *Leic* 85-88; Hon C Bringhurst w Gt Easton 85-88; TV Melksham *Sarum* 88-93; P-in-c Spernall, Morton Bagot and Oldberrow *Cov* from 93; P-in-c Coughton from 93; Dioc Rural Adv from 93. *The Parsonage, Sambourne Lane, Sambourne, Redditch, Worcs B96 6PA* Redditch (01527) 892372

BALMER, Walter Owen. b 30. N Ord Course 83. **d** 86 **p** 87. NSM Gateacre *Liv* 86-91; NSM Hale from 91. *38 Grangemeadow Road, Liverpool L25 4SU* 0151-421 1189

BALMFORTH, Ven Anthony James. b 26. BNC Ox BA50 MA51. Linc Th Coll 50. **d** 52 **p** 53. V Kings Norton *Birm* 65-72; TR 73-79; RD Kings Norton 73-79; Hon Can Birm Cathl 75-79; Hon Can Bris Cathl *Bris* from 79; Adn Bris 79-90; rtd 90. *Slipper Cottage, Stag Hill, Yorkley, Lydney, Glos GL15 4TB* Dean (01594) 564016

BAMBER, David Beverley. b 51. Univ of Wales (Lamp) BA75. St Steph Ho Ox 75. **d** 77 **p** 78. C Altrincham St Geo *Ches* 77-80; C Oxton 80-81; Perm to Offic *Derby* 85-87; C Staveley and Barrow Hill 87-88; C W Retford *S'well* 89-90; C E Retford 89-90 and 91-92. *97 Grove Lane, Retford, Notts DN22 6ND* Retford (01777) 701317

BAMFORD, Mrs Marion. b 35. K Coll Lon BA56 AKC56. N Ord Course 81. **dss** 84 **d** 90 **p** 94. Baildon *Bradf* 84-85; S Kirkby *Wakef* 85-90; Chapl Pontefract Gen Infirmary Wakef from 89; D-in-c Brotherton *Wakef* 90-94; P-in-c from 94. *Brotherton Vicarage, North Road, Byram, Knottingley, W Yorkshire WF11 9ED* Knottingley (01977) 672370

BAMFORTH, Marvin John. b 48. N Ord Course 78. **d** 81 **p** 82. C Barnoldswick w Bracewell *Bradf* 81-84; V Cullingworth 84-88; New Zealand 88-89; V Thornton in Lonsdale w Burton in Lonsdale *Bradf* from 89; Dioc Chapl MU from 91; P-in-c Bentham St Jo from 93. *The Vicarage, Low Street, Burton in Lonsdale, Carnforth, Lancs LA6 3LF* Bentham (015242) 61579

BAMFORTH, Stuart Michael. b 35. Hertf Coll Ox BA58 MA61. Sarum Th Coll 60. **d** 62 **p** 63. C Adel *Ripon* 62-67; V Hempton and Pudding Norton *Nor* 67-71; V Toftrees w Shereford 67-71; P-in-c Pensthorpe 67-71; P-in-c Colkirk 69-70; Lic to Offic *Derby* 72-77; Lic to Offic *Ripon* from 77. *36 Gainsborough Avenue, Leeds LS16 7PQ*

BANBURY, David Paul. b 62. Coll of Ripon & York St Jo BA84. Ridley Hall Cam 85. **d** 88 **p** 89. C Blackb St Jas *Blackb* 88-90; C Preston St Cuth 90-95; P-in-c Bradf St Clem *Bradf* from 95. *St Clement's Vicarage, 294A Barkerend Road, Bradford, W Yorkshire BD3 9DF* Bradford (01274) 665109

BANFIELD, Andrew Henry. b 48. AKC71. St Aug Coll Cant 72. **d** 73 **p** 74. C Crayford *Roch* 73-76; Youth Chapl *Glouc* 77-89; Soc Services Development Officer Glos Co Coun from 89. *Rosemary Cottage, Oakwood Close, Bream, Lydney, Glos GL15 6HS*

BANFIELD, Ven David John. b 33. ALCD56. **d** 57 **p** 58. C Middleton *Man* 57-62; Chapl Scargill Ho 62-65; Asst Warden 65-67; V Addiscombe St Mary *Cant* 67-80; V Luton St Mary *St Alb* 80-90; Hon Can St Alb 89-90; RD Luton 89-90; Adn Bris from 90. *10 Great Brockeridge, Westbury-on-Trym, Bristol BS9 3TY* Bristol (0117) 962 2438 Fax as telephone

BANGAY (formerly REAST), Mrs Eileen Joan. b 40. Open Univ BA93. E Midl Min Tr Course 81. **dss** 84 **d** 87 **p** 94. Linc St Mary-le-Wigford w St Benedict etc *Linc* 80-87; C 87-90; C Stamford All SS w St Jo 90-93; NSM Walesby 93-95; P-in-c Sutton Bridge from 95. *The Vicarage, 79 Bridge Road, Sutton Bridge, Spalding, Lincs PE12 9SD* Holbeach (01406) 351503

BANGERT, Henry Alfred. b 07. ALCD33. **d** 33 **p** 34. Chapl Knowle Hosp Fareham 67-75; rtd 76; Hon C E Preston w Kingston *Chich* 76-80. *Davenham, 148 Graham Road, Malvern, Worcs WR14 2HY* Malvern (01684) 567179

BANGOR, Archdeacon of. See ROBERTS, Ven Elwyn

BANGOR, Bishop of. See MORGAN, Rt Rev Dr Barry Cennydd

BANGOR, Dean of. See EDWARDS, Very Rev Thomas Erwyd Pryse

BANISTER, Martin John. b 39. Worc Coll Ox BA62 MA68. Chich Th Coll 62. **d** 64 **p** 65. C Wellingborough All Hallows *Pet* 64-67; C Heene *Chich* 67-70; V Denford w Ringstead *Pet* 70-78; P-in-c Wilshamstead *St Alb* 78-80; P-in-c Houghton Conquest 78-80; V Wilshamstead and Houghton Conquest

80-89; RD Elstow 86-89; V Waltham Cross from 89. *The Vicarage, 5 Longlands Close, Waltham Cross, Herts EN8 8LW* Waltham Cross (01992) 633243

BANKS, Aleck George. b 18. Lon Univ BD42 AKC42. **d** 42 **p** 43. V S Benfleet *Chelmsf* 61-83; rtd 83; Perm to Offic *Chelmsf* from 83; Perm to Offic *St E* from 85. *5 Gosford Close, Clare, Sudbury, Suffolk CO10 8PT* Clare (01787) 277088

BANKS, Brian William Eric. b 35. Lon Univ DipTh65 BD69 Birm Univ DPS70. Wycliffe Hall Ox 63. **d** 65 **p** 66. C Swindon Ch Ch *Bris* 65-68; C Halesowen *Worc* 68-71; R Wychbold and Upton Warren 71-77; V Bengeworth 77-87; RD Evesham 81-86; R Freshwater *Portsm* from 87. *The Rectory, Afton Road, Freshwater, Isle of Wight PO40 9TS* Isle of Wight (01983) 752010

BANKS, Ernest Leslie. b 10. Oak Hill Th Coll 53. **d** 55 **p** 56. R Kimberley *S'well* 60-83; rtd 83; Perm to Offic *Derby* from 83. *32 King's Drive, Littleover, Derby DE23 6EY* Derby (01332) 360706

BANKS, Geoffrey Alan. b 43. St Andr Univ MA66. N Ord Course 84. **d** 87 **p** 88. NSM Shelley and Shepley *Wakef* 87-89; C Halifax 89-91; V Holmfield from 91. *St Andrew's Vicarage, Beechwood Road, Holmfield, Halifax, W Yorkshire HX2 9AR* Halifax (01422) 244586

BANKS, John Alan. b 32. Hertf Coll Ox BA54 MA58. Westcott Ho Cam 56. **d** 58 **p** 59. V Ollerton *S'well* 54-75; V Boughton 64-75; R Wollaton 75-83; RD Beeston 77-81; rtd 83-85; Lic to Offic *S'well* 83-85; C Bramcote 85-86; C Arnold from 86. *247 Oxclose Lane, Arnold, Nottingham NG5 6FB* Nottingham (0115) 926 6814

BANKS, Joseph. b 23. CEng65 MIMechE65 FBIM70. **d** 80 **p** 81. NSM Bollington St Jo *Ches* 80-84; R New Galloway *Glas* 84-93; rtd 93. *Castlebank House, Castlebank Road, Cupar, Fife KY15 4HL* Cupar (01334) 54090

BANKS, Michael Lawrence. b 40. Open Univ BA72 Brunel Univ MA82. Westcott Ho Cam 84. **d** 86 **p** 87. C Cheshunt *St Alb* 86-89; Chapl HM Pris Blundeston 89-90; V Leagrave *St Alb* 90-94; Asst RD Luton 91-94; V Hatf Hyde St Mary from 95. *Church House, Hollybush Lane, Welwyn Garden City, Herts AL7 4JS* Welwyn Garden (01707) 323214

BANKS, Canon Michael Thomas Harvey. b 35. Ushaw Coll Dur 58 Open Univ BA75. **d** 63 **p** 64. In RC Ch 63-69; C Winlaton *Dur* 69-71; P-in-c Bishopwearmouth Gd Shep 71-75; TV Melton Mowbray w Thorpe Arnold *Leic* 75-80; R Loughb Em 80-88; Dir of Ords 83-87; Hon Can Leic Cathl 83-87; Can Res and Chan from 87; RD Christianity (Leic) S from 93. *Chancellor's House, 3 Morland Avenue, Leicester LE2 2PF* Leicester (0116) 270 8078

BANKS, Norman. b 54. Or Coll Ox BA76 MA80. St Steph Ho Ox 79. **d** 82 **p** 83. C Newc Ch Ch w St Ann *Newc* 82-87; P-in-c 87-90; V Tynemouth Cullercoats St Paul from 90. *The Vicarage, 53 Grosvenor Drive, Whitley Bay, Tyne & Wear NE26 2JR* 0191-252 4916

BANKS, Philip Charles. b 61. ARICS87 NE Lon Poly BSc85 Nottm Univ BTh93. Linc Th Coll 90. **d** 93 **p** 94. C Chelmsf Ascension *Chelmsf* 93-94; C Brentwood St Thos from 94. *25 St Thomas Road, Brentwood, Essex CM14 4DS* Brentwood (01277) 210323

BANKS, Miss Susan Angela. b 61. St Jo Coll Nottm BTh94. **d** 94 **p** 95. C Ingrow cum Hainworth *Bradf* from 94. *Endlich, 2 Prospect Drive, Keighley, W Yorkshire BD22 6DD* Keighley (01535) 602682

BANNARD-SMITH, Dennis Ronald. b 22. Birm Univ BSc42. St Alb Minl Tr Scheme. **d** 83 **p** 84. NSM Pavenham *St Alb* 83-88; NSM Odell and Pavenham from 88. *Goodly Heritage, 10 The Bury, Pavenham, Bedford MK43 7PX* Oakley (01234) 822992

BANNER, John William. b 36. Open Univ BA78. Tyndale Hall Bris 61. **d** 64 **p** 65. C Bootle St Leon *Liv* 64-66; C Wigan St Jas 66-69; C Stapleton *Bris* 69-70; Australia 70-72; V Liv Ch Ch Norris Green *Liv* 72-82; V Tunbridge Wells H Trin w Ch Ch *Roch* from 82. *The Vicarage, 63 Claremont Road, Tunbridge Wells, Kent TN1 1TE* Tunbridge Wells (01892) 526644

BANNER, Prof Michael Charles. b 61. Ball Coll Ox BA83 MA86 DPhil87. **d** 86 **p** 87. Fell St Pet Coll Ox 85-88; Dean Peterho Cam 88-94; Prof Moral and Soc Th K Coll Lon from 94. *King's College, Strand, London WC2R 2LS* 0171-873 2073 Fax 873 2255

BANNISTER, Anthony Peter. b 40. Ex Univ BA62. Clifton Th Coll 63. **d** 65 **p** 66. C Uphill *B & W* 65-69; C Hove Bp Hannington Memorial Ch *Chich* 69-74; V Wembdon *B & W* 74-91; Youth Chapl 80-83; RD Bridgwater 80-89; V Taunton St Jas from 91. *St James's Vicarage, 3 Richmond Road, Taunton, Somerset TA1 1EN* Taunton (01823) 333194

BANNISTER, Clifford John. b 53. Hatf Coll Dur BA76. Ripon Coll Cuddesdon 84. **d** 86 **p** 87. C Weymouth H Trin *Sarum* 86-89; TV Basingstoke *Win* 89-94; V Hedge End from 94. *The Vicarage, Vicarage Drive, Hedge End, Southampton SO3 4DF* Botley (01489) 782288

BANNISTER, Edward. b 06. Lich Th Coll 27. **d** 29 **p** 30. V Sparsholt w Lainston *Win* 56-73; rtd 73; Warden Morley Coll 76-95. *c/o E A Bannister Esq, 19A Adam and Eve Mews, London W8 6UG* 0171-938 1636

BANNISTER, Grattan Eric McGillycuddy Colm Brendon. b 01. TCD BA50 MA53. **d** 52 **p** 57. P-in-c Schull *C, C & R* 63-75; rtd 75. *Schull, Co Cork, Irish Republic*

BANNISTER, John. b 24. Westcott Ho Cam 68. **d** 69 **p** 70. Hon C Rye *Chich* 69-73; Hon C Playden w E Guldeford 69-73; Hon C Rye w Rye Harbour and Playden 73-79; Hon C Rye, Rye Harbour and Playden and Iden 79-80; Hon C Rye 80-94; rtd 94. *Wynfields, Grove Lane, Iden, Rye, E Sussex TN31 7PX* Iden (01797) 280229

BANNISTER, Peter Edward. b 38. Leeds Univ BSc60. Linc Th Coll 72. **d** 74 **p** 75. C Norbury St Steph *Cant* 74-77; C Allington and Maidstone St Pet 77-80; R Temple Ewell w Lydden 80-86; TV Bracknell *Ox* 86-93; P-in-c Swallowfield from 93. *The Vicarage, Swallowfield Street, Swallowfield, Reading RG7 1QY* Reading (01734) 883786

BANNISTER, Canon Simon Monro. b 38. St Jo Coll Ox BA62 MA69. Linc Th Coll 61. **d** 63 **p** 64. C Prestwich St Marg *Man* 63-66; C Farnborough *Roch* 66-70; V Bury St Mark *Man* 70-78; V Oldham St Mary w St Pet 78; TR Oldham 78-81; Hon Can Man Cathl 81-87; V Hatf Hyde St Mary *St Alb* 87-94; P-in-c Brasted *Roch* from 94; Dioc Adv on Cont Minl Educn from 94. *The Rectory, Brasted, Westerham, Kent TN16 1NH* Westerham (01959) 563491

BANNOCKS, David George. b 64. Trin Coll Bris DipHE84 Lon Bible Coll BA85 Dur Univ MA94. Cranmer Hall Dur 88. **d** 90 **p** 91. C Stapleford *S'well* 90-93; C Southport Ch Ch *Liv* 93-95; Chapl Imp Coll *Lon* from 95; Chapl R Coll of Art from 95. *Imperial College, London SW7 2BX* 0171-589 5111

BANNON, Canon Richard Babington. b 20. TCD BA42 MA47. CITC 48. **d** 48 **p** 49. I Ardclinis w Tickmacrevan *Conn* 55-86; Can Belf Cathl 85-86; rtd 86. *Dean's Cottage, 7 Whin Road, Ballygally, Larne, Co Antrim BT40 2QJ* Ballygally (01574) 583230

BANTING, David Percy. b 51. Magd Coll Cam MA74. Wycliffe Hall Ox MA79. **d** 80 **p** 81. C Ox St Ebbe w H Trin and St Pet Ox 80-83; Min St Jos Merry Hill CD *Lich* 83-90; V Chadderton Ch Ch *Man* from 90. *Christ Church Vicarage, Block Lane, Chadderton, Oldham OL9 7QB* 0161-624 2326

BANTING, Kenneth Mervyn Lancelot Hadfield. b 37. Pemb Coll Cam BA61 MA65. Cuddesdon Coll 64. **d** 65 **p** 66. Asst Chapl Win Coll 65-70; C Leigh Park *Portsm* 70-72; TV Hemel Hempstead *St Alb* 73-79; V Goldington 79-88; P-in-c Renhold 80-82; RD Bedf 84-87; V Portsea St Cuth *Portsm* from 88; RD Portsm from 94. *St Cuthbert's Vicarage, 2 Lichfield Road, Portsmouth PO3 6DE* Portsmouth (01705) 827071

BANYARD, Douglas Edward. b 21. S'wark Ord Course 69. **d** 71 **p** 72. NSM Selsdon St Jo w St Fran *Cant* 71-77; Perm to Offic *Portsm* from 77. *22 Lower Wardown, Petersfield, Hants GU31 4NY* Petersfield (01730) 261004

BANYARD, Peter Vernon. b 35. Sarum Th Coll 57. **d** 59 **p** 60. V Chesterfield St Aug *Derby* 68-74; TV Grantham w Manthorpe *Linc* 74-78; TV Grantham 78-79; Chapl Warminster Sch Wilts 79-85; V Hykeham *Linc* 85-88; rtd 88; Perm to Offic *Linc* from 88. *56 Western Avenue, Lincoln LN6 7SY*

BANYARD (or BRUNSKILL), Sheila Kathryn. b 53. Univ of Wales (Ban) BA75 K Coll Lon MA83. Cranmer Hall Dur 76. dss 82 **d** 92 **p** 94. Sunbury Lon 82-85; Asst Chapl Ch Hosp Horsham 85-90; Chapl Malvern Girls' Coll Worcs 90-95; TV Droitwich Spa *Worc* from 95. *The Vicarage, 205 Worcester Road, Droitwich, Worcs WR9 8AS* Droitwich (01905) 773134

BARBER, Charles William Walters. b 60. Pemb Coll Cam BA81 MA85. Wycliffe Hall Ox 83. **d** 86 **p** 87. C Wolv St Matt *Lich* 86-90; C Hornsey St Mary w St Geo *Lon* 90-94; C Hornsey Rise Whitehall Park Team 90-94. *94 Mowatt Close, London N19 3XZ* 0171-272 3160

BARBER, Canon Christopher Albert (Chris). b 33. Ch Coll Cam BA53 MA57. Coll of Resurr Mirfield 56. **d** 58 **p** 59. C Cov St Pet *Cov* 58-61; C Stokenchurch and Cadmore End *Ox* 61-64; V Royton St Paul *Man* 64-70; V Stapleford *Ely* 70-80; RD Shelford 76-80; V Cherry Hinton St Andr 80-88; Hon Can Ely Cathl from 88; R Cottenham 88-92; RD N Stowe 90-92; V Terrington St John from 92; V Tilney All Saints from 92. *The Vicarage, Church Road, Terrington St John, Wisbech, Cambs PE14 7SA* Wisbech (01945) 880259

BARBER, Garth Antony. b 48. FRAS MSOSc Southn Univ BSc69 Lon Univ MSc79. St Jo Coll Nottm LTh76. **d** 76 **p** 77. C Hounslow H Trin *Lon* 76-79; Chapl City of Lon Poly 79-86; P-in-c Twickenham All Hallows from 86; Chapl Richmond-upon-Thames Coll from 87. *All Hallows' Vicarage, 138 Chertsey Road, Twickenham TW1 1EW* 0181-892 1322

BARBER, Geoffrey Thomas. b 23. Univ of Wales (Lamp) BA51. Ridley Hall Cam 51. **d** 53 **p** 54. V Rushden St Pet 66-75;

V Leyton Em *Chelmsf* 75-81; rtd 81. *22 Longacre Drive, Ferndown, Wimborne, Dorset BH22 9EE* Ferndown (01202) 873626

BARBER, John Eric Michael. b 30. Wycliffe Hall Ox 63. **d** 65 **p** 66. C Lupset *Wakef* 65-68; C Halifax St Jo Bapt 68-70; V Dewsbury St Matt and St Jo 70-80; V Perry Common *Birm* from 80. *St Martin's Vicarage, 148 Witton Lodge Road, Birmingham B23 5AP* 0121-382 7666

BARBER, Mrs Margaret Ann. b 31. GTCL52. Dalton Ho Bris 55 Sarum & Wells Th Coll 82. **dss** 83 **d** 87 **p** 94. Wimborne Minster and Holt *Sarum* 83-90; Par Dn 87-90; rtd 90; Hon Par Dn Hampreston *Sarum* 90-94; Hon C from 94. *22 Longacre Drive, Ferndown, Wimborne, Dorset BH22 9EE* Ferndown (01202) 873626

BARBER, Martin John. b 35. Lon Univ BA61. Linc Th Coll 61. **d** 63 **p** 64. Chapl K Sch Bruton 67-93; rtd 93. *1 Plox Green, Bruton, Somerset BA10 0EY* Bruton (01749) 812290

BARBER, Michael. b 40. Open Univ BA83. Oak Hill Th Coll 69. **d** 71 **p** 72. C Rothley *Leic* 71-74; C Leic Martyrs 74-76; V Queniborough 76-82; V Monkwearmouth All SS *Dur* 82-92; V Mirehouse *Carl* from 92. *The Vicarage, Hollins Close, Mirehouse, Whitehaven, Cumbria CA28 8EX* Whitehaven (01946) 693565

✠**BARBER, Rt Rev Paul Everard.** b 35. St Jo Coll Cam BA58 MA66. Wells Th Coll 58. **d** 60 **p** 61 **c** 89. C Westborough *Guildf* 60-66; V York Town St Mich 66-73; V Bourne 73-80; RD Farnham 74-79; Hon Can Guildf Cathl 80-89; Adn Surrey 80-89; Suff Bp Brixworth *Pet* from 89. *4 The Avenue, Dallington, Northampton NN5 7AN* Northampton (01604) 759423 Fax 750925

BARBER, Philip Kenneth. b 43. St Jo Coll Dur BA65. NW Ord Course 74. **d** 76 **p** 77. NSM Burscough Bridge *Liv* 76-84; P-in-c Brigham *Carl* 84-85; V 85-89; P-in-c Mosser 84-85; V 85-89; P-in-c Borrowdale 89-94; Chapl Keswick Sch 89-94; P-in-c Beetham *Carl* from 94; Educn Adv from 94. *The Old Parsonage, Stanley Street, Beetham, Milnthorpe, Cumbria LA7 7AL* Milnthorpe (015395) 62216

BARBER, Royston Henry (Roy). b 38. Univ of Wales (Abth) BD86. United Th Coll Abth 83. **d** 86 **p** 87. NSM Tywyn w Aberdyfi *Ban* 86-92; NSM Cannington, Otterhampton, Combwich and Stockland *B & W* from 93. *4 Collingwood Court, Bridgwater, Somerset TA6 3TE* Bridgwater (01278) 446910

BARBER, William Ewart Worsley. b 15. Leeds Univ BA38. Coll of Resurr Mirfield 38. **d** 40 **p** 41. V Tuffley *Glouc* 67-74; R Huntley 74-79; Hon C Bromsberrow 79-90; rtd 79; Hon C Redmarley D'Abitot, Bromsberrow w Pauntley etc *Glouc* from 79. *37 St Mary's Square, Gloucester GL1 2QT* Gloucester (01452) 330842

BARBOUR, Mrs Jennifer Louise. b 32. JP67. Barrister-at-Law 55 St Hugh's Coll Ox BA54 MA57. Gilmore Course 80. **dss** 81 **d** 87 **p** 94. Bray and Braywood *Ox* 81-84; Hermitage and Hampstead Norreys, Cold Ash etc 84-87; Chapl Leeds Poly *Ripon* 87-92; Chapl Leeds Metrop Univ 92-95; rtd 95; NSM Shipton Moyne w Westonbirt and Lasborough *Glouc* from 95. *The Rectory, Shipton Moyne, Tetbury, Glos GL8 8PW* Tetbury (01666) 880244

BARBOUR, Walter Iain. b 28. FICE65 Pemb Coll Cam BA48 MA53. Ox NSM Course 78. **d** 81 **p** 82. NSM Bray and Braywood *Ox* 81-84; NSM Thatcham 84-87; TV Moor Allerton *Ripon* 87-95; rtd 95; NSM Shipton Moyne w Westonbirt and Lasborough *Glouc* from 95. *The Rectory, Shipton Moyne, Tetbury, Glos GL8 8PW* Tetbury (01666) 880244

BARBY, Mrs Sheana Braidwood. b 38. Bedf Coll Lon BA59. E Midl Min Tr Course 81. **dss** 84 **d** 87 **p** 94. Derby St Paul *Derby* 84-87; NSM Derby Cathl from 87; Dioc Dir of Female Ords from 90; Par Educn Adv from 93. *2 Margaret Street, Derby DE1 3FE* Derby (01332) 383301

BARCLAY, Ian Newton. b 33. Clifton Th Coll 58. **d** 61 **p** 62. C St Helen Bishopsgate w St Martin Outwich *Lon* 70-73; V Prestonville St Luke *Chich* 73-81; Lic to Offic 82-93; rtd 93. *35 Marine Avenue, Hove, E Sussex BN3 4LH* Brighton (01273) 421628

BARCLAY, Mrs Susan Molly. d 87. Hon Par Dn March St Wendreda *Ely* from 87. *42 Greystoke Road, Cambridge CB1 4DS* Cambridge (01223) 246877

BARCROFT, Ambrose William Edgar. b 17. TCD BA40 MA46. TCD Div Sch Div Test41. **d** 41 **p** 42. Chapl RN 46-70; R Pitlochry *St And* 70-82; rtd 82; Perm to Offic *St And* from 82. *The Old School House, Calvine, Pitlochry, Perthshire PH18 5UD* Calvine (0179683) 224

BARCROFT, Ian David. b 60. UMIST BSc83 Edin Univ BD88. Edin Th Coll 85. **d** 88 **p** 89. Prec St Ninian's Cathl Perth *St And* 88-92; Min Perth St Ninian 88-92; P-in-c Aber St Clem *Ab* from 92. *St Clement's Church House, Mastrick Drive, Aberdeen AB2 6UF* Aberdeen (01224) 662247

BARD, Christopher Frederick Jesse (Chris). b 52. AKC75 Open Univ BA88. St Aug Coll Cant 75. **d** 76 **p** 77. C Billingham St Cuth *Dur* 76-79; Chapl to Arts and Recreation 79-81; C Egglescliffe 79-81; P-in-c Epping Upland *Chelmsf* 81-95; Dioc Communications Officer 81-91; BBC Essex Relig Producer from 89; Bp's Adv on Satellite Broadcasting from 91; TV Epping Distr from 95. *The Vicarage, Epping Green, Epping, Essex CM16 6PN* Epping (01992) 572949 Fax 578892

BARDELL, Alan George. Local NSM Course. **d** 92 **p** 93. NSM Addlestone *Guildf* from 92; NSM Byfleet from 92. *14 Dickens Drive, Addlestone, Surrey KT15 1AW* Weybridge (01932) 847524

BARDELL, Frank Stanley. b 04. ARIBA38 Lon Univ BA24. Oak Hill Th Coll 54. **d** 55 **p** 56. R Maresfield *Chich* 59-73; rtd 73; Perm to Offic *Win* from 73. *Sanctuary Cottage, 13 Orchard Way, Dibden Purlieu, Southampton SO4 5AP* Hythe (01703) 845612

BARDSLEY, Edwin Roy. b 24. St Jo Coll Cam BA47 MA52. Wells Th Coll 48. **d** 49 **p** 50. V Moulsham St Jo *Chelmsf* 58-74; Chapl Chelmsf and Essex Hosp 58-74; V Bittadon *Ex* 74-77; R Marwood 74-77; P-in-c Littleham 77-80; P-in-c Monkleigh 77-80; P-in-c Weare Giffard w Landcross 77-80; RD Hartland 79-80; V Tiverton St Andr 80-86; rtd 86; Perm to Offic *Ex* 87-90; Perm to Offic *Blackb* from 90. *10 Nickleby Road, Chelmsford CM1 4UL* Chelmsford (01245) 443332

BARDSLEY, Warren Nigel Antony. b 52. AKC74. St Aug Coll Cant 74. **d** 75 **p** 76. C Leeds St Aid *Ripon* 75-78; C Cov St Jo Cov 78-80; P-in-c Stoke Golding w Dadlington *Leic* 80-89; TV Swinton and Pendlebury *Man* 90-94. *68 High Road, Wortwell, Harleston, Norfolk IP20 2EF* Harleston (01986) 788365

BARDWELL, Edward Mercer. b 12. ALCD41 LTh74. **d** 41 **p** 43. R Cranworth w Letton and Southbergh *Nor* 59-78; rtd 79; Perm to Offic *Ely* from 79; Perm to Offic *St E* from 89. *6 Cromwell Road, Weeting, Brandon, Suffolk IP27 0QT* Thetford (01842) 810582

BARDWELL, Mrs Elaine Barbara. b 60. K Coll Lon BA81 AKC81. St Steph Ho Ox BA85 MA90. **dss** 86 **d** 87 **p** 95. Heref H Trin *Heref* 86-87; C 87-89; Dir Past Studies St Steph Ho Ox from 89. *1 Moberly Close, 134C Cowley Road, Oxford OX4 1HX* Oxford (01865) 251500

BARDWELL, John Edward. b 53. Jes Coll Cam BA75 MA79 Ox Univ BA85 MA90. St Steph Ho Ox BA38 MA42. **d** 86 **p** 87. C Heref H Trin *Heref* 86-89; Perm to Offic *Ox* from 90. *1 Moberly Close, 134C Cowley Road, Oxford OX4 1HX* Oxford (01865) 251500

BAREHAM, Miss Sylvia Alice. b 36. Hockerill Coll Cam CertEd59 Open Univ BA83 Ox Univ DipEd84. Ox Min Course 86. **d** 89 **p** 94. NSM N Leigh *Ox* 89-93; NSM Bampton w Clanfield from 93. *St Edmund's, East End, North Leigh, Witney, Oxon OX8 6PX* Freeland (01993) 881383

BARFETT, Ven Thomas. b 16. Keble Coll Ox BA38 MA42. Wells Th Coll 38. **d** 39 **p** 40. R Falmouth K Chas *Truro* 55-77; Asst ChStJ 63-71; Sub ChStJ from 71; Chapl to The Queen 75-86; Adn Heref 77-82; Can Res and Treas Heref Cathl 77-82; rtd 82; Bermuda 84; Chapl Menton w San Remo *Eur* 86. *Treberveth, 57 Falmouth Road, Truro, Cornwall TR1 2HL* Truro (01872) 73726

BARFF, John Robert. b 43. Ch Coll Cam BA66 MA70 K Coll Lon MTh69. ALCD68. **d** 69 **p** 70. C Fulham St Mary N End *Lon* 69-73; CMS 73-83; Sudan 75-83; P-in-c Compton Greenfield *Bris* 83-85; P-in-c Pilning 83-85; V Pilning w Compton Greenfield 85-92; rtd 92; Perm to Offic *Bris* from 92. *10 Cote Park, Stoke Bishop, Bristol BS9 2AD* Bristol (0117) 968 5889

BARFORD, Mrs Valerie Anne. b 43. Man Univ BSc64 MPS65. St Alb Minl Tr Scheme 80. **d** 87 **p** 94. Par Dn Weston Favell *Pet* 87-90; Lic to Northn Deanery 90-94; Chapl Cynthia Spencer Unit Manfield Hosp 90-94; NSM Kingsthorpe w St Dav Northn *Pet* from 94. *27 Elmhurst Avenue, Northampton NN3 2LD* Northampton (01604) 405743

BARGH, George Edward Norman. b 25. St Jo Coll Cam BA48 MA53 Leeds Univ LLB51. Carl Dioc Tr Course 80. **d** 83 **p** 84. NSM Ulverston St Mary w H Trin *Carl* 83-86; P-in-c Egton w Newland 86-87; P-in-c Blawith w Lowick 86-87; P-in-c Egton-cum-Newland and Lowick 87-89; rtd 90. *2 Woodheads, Grange Fell Road, Grange-over-Sands, Cumbria LA11 6AF* Grange-over-Sands (015395) 35151

BARHAM, Ian Harold. b 40. Clifton Th Coll 64. **d** 66 **p** 67. C Broadwater St Mary *Chich* 66-69 and 72-76; Burundi 71-72; R Beyton and Hessett *St E* 76-79; Perm to Offic 79-81; Hon C Bury St Edmunds St Mary 81-84; Chapl St Aubyn's Sch Tiverton from 84; Lic to Offic *Ex* from 84. *Emmaus, 53 Sylvan Road, Exeter EX4 6EY* Exeter (01392) 51643

BARHAM, Mrs Jennifer Mary (Jen). b 43. RN65. Oak Hill Th Coll 92. **d** 95. NSM Leigh-on-Sea St Aid *Chelmsf* from 95. *47 Walker Drive, Leigh-on-Sea, Essex SS9 3QT* Hadleigh (01702) 558766

✠**BARHAM, Rt Rev Kenneth Lawrence (Ken).** b 36. Clifton Th Coll BD63. **d** 63 **p** 64 **c** 93. C Worthing St Geo *Chich* 63-65; C Sevenoaks St Nic *Roch* 65-67; C Cheltenham St Mark *Glouc* 67-70; V Maidstone St Luke *Cant* 70-79; S Area Sec Rwanda Miss 79-84; P-in-c Ashburnham w Penhurst *Chich* from 84; Asst Bp Cyangugu (Rwanda) from 93. *Rosewood, Canadia Road, Battle, E Sussex TN33 0LR*   Battle (01424) 773073 Fax as telephone

BARHAM, Peter. b 62. Selw Coll Cam MA83. Linc Th Coll BTh94. **d** 94 **p** 95. C Fornham All SS and St Martin w Timworth *St E* from 94. *The Rectory, Rectory Meadow, Fornham All Saints, Bury St Edmunds, Suffolk IP28 6JR* Bury St Edmunds (01284) 760027

BARKER, Arthur John Willoughby. b 10. Lon Coll of Div 46. **d** 48 **p** 49. V Dent w Cowgill *Bradf* 61-76; rtd 76; Perm to Offic *Bradf* from 76. *West Banks, Dent, Sedbergh, Cumbria LA10 5QT*   Dent (015396) 25355

BARKER, Arundel Charles. b 24. Tyndale Hall Bris 54. **d** 56 **p** 57. R Passenham *Pet* 65-90; P-in-c Cosgrove 65-66; rtd 90. *7 Bull Farm Mews, Bull Lane, Matlock, Derbyshire DE4 5NB* Matlock (01629) 580321

BARKER, Brian Wallwork. b 26. G&C Coll Cam BA50 MA55. Wells Th Coll 51. **d** 52 **p** 53. V Ashton St Jas *Man* 65-71; R Burnage St Nic 71-85; R Heaton Reddish 85-91; rtd 91. *105 Crossfield Road, Cheadle Hulme, Cheadle, Cheshire SK8 5PD*   0161-486 0334

BARKER, Charles Gordon. b 19. St Aug Coll Cant 60. **d** 61 **p** 62. Lic to Offic *Heref* 70-78; P-in-c Hopesay w Edgton 78-80; P-in-c Lydbury N 78-80; rtd 83. *25 Lydbury North, Shropshire SY7 8AU*   Clun (01588) 640257

✠**BARKER, Rt Rev Clifford Conder.** b 26. TD71. Or Coll Ox BA50 MA55. St Chad's Coll Dur DipTh52. **d** 52 **p** 53 **c** 76. C Falsgrave *York* 52-55; C Redcar 55-57; V Sculcoates 57-63; CF (TA) 58-74; P-in-c Sculcoates St Silas *York* 59-61; V Rudby in Cleveland w Middleton 63-70; RD Stokesley 65-70; V York St Olave w St Giles 70-76; RD City of York 71-75; Can and Preb York Minster 73-76; Suff Bp Whitby 76-83; Suff Bp Selby 83-91; rtd 91. *15 Oak Tree Cose, Strensall, York YO3 5TE*   York (01904) 490406

BARKER, David Robert. b 45. Worc Coll Ox BA67 MA70. Virginia Th Sem BD72. **d** 72 **p** 73. C Roehampton H Trin *S'wark* 72-75; Chapl Golds Coll Lon 75-79; Min Tr Officer *Cov* 79-85; Selection Sec ACCM 85-90; Sec for Continuing Minl Educn ACCM 85-90; V Sutton Valence w E Sutton and Chart Sutton *Cant* from 90. *The Vicarage, Chart Road, Sutton Valence, Maidstone, Kent ME17 3AW*   Maidstone (01622) 843156

BARKER, Donald Charles. b 05. St Edm Hall Ox BA29 MA67. Ely Th Coll 27. **d** 28 **p** 29. V Haggerston St Paul *Lon* 60-67; Master Hugh Sexey's Hosp Bruton 67-85; Hon C Bruton w Lamyatt, Wyke and Redlynch *B & W* 67-85; rtd 72; Hon C Bruton and Distr *B & W* from 85. *Denhams, Higher Backway, Bruton, Somerset BA10 0DW*   Bruton (01749) 812218

BARKER, Francis Howard. b 41. St Deiniol's Hawarden. **d** 84 **p** 85. NSM Capesthorne w Siddington and Marton *Ches* 84-86; NSM Wilmslow 86-93; C from 93. *The Cedars, Butley Town, Prestbury, Macclesfield, Cheshire SK10 4DZ* Prestbury (01625) 829409

BARKER, Mrs Gillian Ann (Gill). b 52. Portsm Dioc Tr Course 91. **d** 92. NSM Alverstoke *Portsm* 92-95; NSM Bridgemary from 95. *3 Blackbird Way, Lee-on-the-Solent, Hants PO13 8HJ*   Lee-on-the-Solent (01705) 552515

BARKER, Gordon. d 94. NSM Malew *S & M* from 94. *Ingleton House, Shore Road, Castletown, Isle of Man IM9 1BF* Castletown (01624) 822941

BARKER, Canon Hugh Remington. b 19. Pemb Coll Cam BA41 MA45. Chich Th Coll 41. **d** 43 **p** 44. V Wisbech St Mary *Ely* 62-75; RD Wisbech 72-75; P-in-c Walpole St Andrew 75-77; V 77-84; P-in-c Walpole St Peter 75-77; R 77-84; RD Lynn Marshland 76-84; Hon Can Ely Cathl 81-84; rtd 84; Perm to Offic *Ely* from 84. *39 Dowgate Road, Leverington, Wisbech, Cambs PE13 5DJ*   Wisbech (01945) 585385

BARKER, James Gavin. b 33. Kelham Th Coll 54. **d** 58 **p** 59. C Greenford H Cross *Lon* 58-61; C Bournemouth St Clem w St Mary *Win* 61-66; C Pokesdown St Jas 66-70; V Stanmore 70-77; Chapl Besselsleigh Sch Abingdon 77-86; Hon C Hinksey *Ox* 77-79; Hon C Wootton (Boars Hill) 79-86; V Southbourne St Chris *Win* from 86. *St Christopher's Vicarage, 81 Watcombe Road, Bournemouth BH6 3LX*   Bournemouth (01202) 424886

BARKER, Canon John Howard. b 36. Southn Univ BA58. Ripon Coll Cuddesdon 80. **d** 82 **p** 83. C W Leigh *Portsm* 82-84; V Cosham 84-88; Bp's Dom Chapl from 88; Hon Can Portsm Cathl from 93. *46 Blackbrook Park Avenue, Fareham, Hants PO15 5JL*   Fareham (01329) 280247 or 221326

BARKER, John Frederic Waller. b 18. MBE45. Selw Coll Cam BA49 MA53. Linc Th Coll 49. **d** 51 **p** 52. Chapl Univ Coll

Hosp Lon 56-83; rtd 83. *Brambles, East Boldre, Brockenhurst, Hants SO42 7WT*   East End (01590) 650679

BARKER, John Lawrence. b 26. Middx Poly BA74 NE Lon Poly MSc84. Oak Hill NSM Course 86. **d** 88 **p** 89. NSM Prittlewell *Chelmsf* 88-91; Perm to Offic *Linc* from 91. *Rose Cottage, Back Lane, Bilsby, Alford, Lincs LN13 9PT* Alford (01507) 462644

BARKER, John Stuart. b 30. Keele Univ BA55. Wells Th Coll 55. **d** 57 **p** 58. V Chew Magna w Dundry *B & W* 70-85; rtd 94. *9 West Street, Axbridge, Somerset BS26 2AA*   Axbridge (01934) 732740

BARKER, Jonathan. b 55. Hull Univ BA79. Westcott Ho Cam 79. **d** 83 **p** 84. C Sketty *S & B* 83-86; Chapl Sport & Leisure 83-86; C Swansea St Mary w H Trin 85-86; Bermuda 86-90; TV Liv Our Lady and St Nic w St Anne *Liv* 90-93; P-in-c S Shore St Pet *Blackb* from 93; Chapl Qu Victoria's Hosp Morecambe from 93. *St Peter's Vicarage, 19 Windermere Road, Blackpool FY4 2BX*   Blackpool (01253) 41231

BARKER, Julian Roland Palgrave. b 37. Magd Coll Cam BA61 MA65. Westcott Ho Cam 61. **d** 63 **p** 64. C Stafford St Mary *Lich* 63-66; Chapl Clare Hall Cam 66-69; Chapl Clare Coll Cam 66-70; Lic to Offic *Cant* 70-71; Tutor St Aug Coll Cant 70-71; TV Raveningham *Nor* 71-78; TR 78-82; V Foremark *Derby* from 82; V Repton from 82; RD Repton from 91. *St Wystan's Vicarage, Repton, Derby DE65 6FH*   Burton-on-Trent (01283) 703317

BARKER, Leonard Ralph. b 11. ALCD39. **d** 39 **p** 40. R Linby w Papplewick *S'well* 63-78; rtd 78. *53 Lancaster Drive, Long Sutton, Spalding, Lincs PE12 9BD*   Holbeach (01406) 363422

BARKER, Canon Leonard Roy. b 24. Selw Coll Cam BA49 MA53. Ridley Hall Cam 49. **d** 51 **p** 52. V Upton (or Overchurch) *Ches* 62-80; Hon Can Ches Cathl 78-80; Dir Past Studies Ridley Hall Cam 80-84; Dir of Ords Ches 84-90; Can Res Ches Cathl 84-89; rtd 90. *Parkgate, 1 Dee Hills Park, Chester CH3 5AR*   Chester (01244) 314662

BARKER, Mark. b 62. ACIB90. St Jo Coll Nottm BTh95. **d** 95. C Barking St Marg w St Patr *Chelmsf* from 95. *48 Sunningdale Avenue, Barking, Essex IG11 7QF*

BARKER, Neil Anthony. b 52. St Andr Univ BSc73. Ridley Hall Cam 74. **d** 77 **p** 78. C Leic H Apostles *Leic* 77-81; C Camberley St Paul *Guildf* 81-86; R Bradfield *Ox* 86-88; P-in-c Stanford Dingley 88; R Bradfield and Stanford Dingley 88-92; R Woodmansterne *S'wark* from 92. *The Rectory, Woodmansterne, Banstead, Surrey SM7 3NL*   Burgh Heath (01737) 352849

BARKER, Nicholas John Willoughby (Nick). b 49. Or Coll Ox BA73 BTh75 MA77. Trin Coll Bris 75. **d** 77 **p** 78. C Watford *St Alb* 77-80; TV Didsbury St Jas and Em *Man* 80-86; TR Kidderminster St Geo *Worc* from 86. *The Rectory, 30 Leswell Street, Kidderminster, Worcs DY10 1RP*   Kidderminster (01562) 822131

BARKER, Canon Roy Thomas. b 33. K Coll Lon BD57 AKC57. **d** 58 **p** 59. C Headingley *Ripon* 58-62; C Hawksworth Wood 62-66; S Africa 66-92; Sub-Dean Cape Town Cathl 73-80; Can 74-80; Dean and Adn Grahamstown 80-92; Hon Can from 92; V Southmead *Bris* from 92. *St Stephen's Vicarage, Wigton Crescent, Bristol BS10 6DR*   Bristol (0117) 950 7164

BARKER, Stephen Luke Remington. b 20. Cant St Aug Coll of Min. **d** 82 **p** 83. NSM Cranbrook *Cant* 82-90; rtd 90. *St Damian's, High Street, Cranbrook, Kent TN17 3LH*   Cranbrook (01580) 712048

BARKER, Timothy Reed (Tim). b 56. Qu Coll Cam BA79 MA82. Westcott Ho Cam 78. **d** 80 **p** 81. C Nantwich *Ches* 80-83; V Norton 83-88; V Runcorn All SS 88-94; Urban Officer 88-90; Dioc Communications Officer from 91; Bp's Chapl from 94. *11 Abbey Street, Chester CH1 2JF*   Chester (01244) 347811 or 350864

BARKER, Walter Frederick. b 25. Lon Univ BD48 ALCD48. St Jo Coll Lon 44. **d** 51 **p** 52. Home Sec CMJ 66-71; Gen Sec CMJ 71-86; Min at Large CMJ 86-89; rtd 89. *72 Lime Grove, Ruislip, Middx HA4 8RY*   0181-866 6941

BARKER, William Edward. b 28. Kelham Th Coll 49. **d** 54 **p** 55. V Barrow St Jas *Carl* 64-70; V Applethwaite 70-93; P-in-c Troutbeck 78-93; rtd 93. *114 Burneside Road, Kendal, Cumbria LA9 4RZ*   Kendal (01539) 734787

BARKING, Area Bishop of. See SAINSBURY, Rt Rev Roger Frederick

BARKS, Jeffrey Stephen. b 45. Cranmer Hall Dur 66. **d** 71 **p** 72. C Wootton *St Alb* 71-74; C Boscombe St Jo *Win* 74-76; C Ringwood 76-80; P-in-c Spaxton w Charlynch *B & W* 80; P-in-c Enmore w Goathurst 80; P-in-c Spaxton w Goathurst, Enmore and Charlynch 80-81; R 81-92; RD Bridgwater 89-94; V Wembdon from 92. *The Vicarage, 12 Greenacre, Wembdon, Bridgwater, Somerset TA6 7RD*   Bridgwater (01278) 423468

BARLEY, Ann Christine. b 47. Local NSM Course 91. **d** 93 **p** 94. NSM Walton *St E* from 93. *Carmel, 143 Melford Way, Felixstowe, Suffolk IP11 8UH*   Felixstowe (01394) 283752

BARLEY, Christopher James. b 56. St Steph Ho Ox DipMin93. **d** 93 **p** 94. C Upton cum Chalvey *Ox* from 93. *134 Albert Street, Slough SL1 2AU* Slough (01753) 694083

BARLEY, Ivan William. b 48. CEng74 MIEE74 Suffolk Poly DMS80. Local NSM Course 91. **d** 93 **p** 94. NSM Walton *St E* from 93. *Carmel, 143 Melford Way, Felixstowe, Suffolk IP11 8UH* Felixstowe (01394) 283752

BARLING, Michael Keith. b 38. Oak Hill Th Coll 63. **d** 66 **p** 67. C Portman Square St Paul *Lon* 66-70; C Enfield Ch Ch Trent Park 70-74; V Sidcup St Andr *Roch* 74-78; Dir Fountain Trust 78-81; Lic to Offic *Guildf* 78-81; Chapl Bethany Fellowship and Roffey Place Tr Cen 81-88; Lic to Offic *Chich* 81-88; Hon C Kennington St Mark *S'wark* from 88. *Roffey Place, Faygate, Horsham, W Sussex RH12 4SA* Faygate (01293) 851543

BARLOW, Alan David. b 36. Worc Coll Ox BA59 MA65. Wycliffe Hall Ox 59. **d** 61 **p** 62. C Wealdstone H Trin *Lon* 61-67; V Neasden cum Kingsbury St Cath 67-73; Chapl Cranleigh Sch Surrey 73-81; Chapl Cheltenham Ladies' Coll from 82. *22 Moorend Road, Leckhampton, Cheltenham, Glos GL53 0EU* Cheltenham (01242) 584668

BARLOW, Arthur Stanley. b 06. Bp Wilson Coll 39. **d** 39 **p** 41. V Runcorn St Mich *Ches* 58-77; rtd 77; Perm to Offic *Ches* from 77. *26 Hallastone Road, Helsby, Warrington WA6 0PR* Helsby (01928) 723115

BARLOW, Charles William Moore. b 32. ALCM50 Man Univ BA57. Cuddesdon Coll 56. **d** 58 **p** 59. C Atherton *Man* 58-61; C Swinton St Pet 61-64; V Dobcross 64-76; V Dobcross w Scouthead from 76. *The Vicarage, Woods Lane, Dobcross, Oldham OL3 5AN* Saddleworth (01457) 872342

BARLOW, Clive Christopher. b 42. Lich Th Coll 67. **d** 70 **p** 71. C Surbiton St Mark *S'wark* 70-74; C Spring Park *Cant* 74-77; V Ash w Westmarsh 77-92; RD E Bridge 86-92; R Chartham from 92. *The Rectory, The Green, Chartham, Canterbury, Kent CT4 7JW* Canterbury (01227) 738256

BARLOW, David. b 50. Leeds Univ BA71 MA. Wycliffe Hall Ox 71. **d** 73 **p** 74. C Horninglow *Lich* 73-75; C Wednesfield St Thos 75-77; C Bloxwich 77-78; Chapl RN from 78. *Directorate Gen, RN Chapl Services, Room 203, Victory Building, HM Naval Base, Portsmouth PO1 3LS* Portsmouth (01705) 727903 Fax 727112

BARLOW, Canon Edward Burnley. b 29. St Aid Birkenhead 56. **d** 58 **p** 59. C Lenton Abbey *S'well* 58-61; C Ipswich All SS *St E* 61-63; R Fishtoft *Linc* 63-76; V Linc St Giles from 76; Can Linc Cathl from 92. *The Vicarage, Shelley Drive, Lincoln LN2 4BY* Lincoln (01522) 527655

BARLOW, Paul Andrew. b 59. Imp Coll Lon BSc80 UMIST PhD84 Bolton Inst of HE PGCE85. Aston Tr Scheme 89 Chich Th Coll 91. **d** 93 **p** 94. C Hale *Guildf* from 93. *195 Eton Place, Farnham, Surrey GU9 0EG* Farnham (01252) 713826

BARLOW, Paul Benson. b 31. Fitzw Coll Cam BA73 MA77. **d** 64 **p** 65. C Bath Abbey w St Jas *B & W* 64-74; Dep Hd Master Leys High Sch Redditch 74-81; Hd Master Jo Kyrle High Sch Ross-on-Wye from 82; Perm to Offic *Heref* 82-85; Lic to Offic 85-92; NSM Walford and Saint John, w Bishopswood etc from 92. *The Coach House, Hentland, Ross-on-Wye, Herefordshire HR9 6LP*

BARLOW, Robert Mark. b 53. St Jo Coll Nottm. **d** 86 **p** 87. C Colwich w Gt Haywood *Lich* 86-91; R Crick and Yelvertoft w Clay Coton and Lilbourne *Pet* from 91. *The Rectory, Crick, Northants NN6 7TU* Crick (01788) 822147

BARLOW, Thomas Frank. b 24. W Midl Minl Tr Course. **d** 84 **p** 85. NSM Dudley St Jas *Worc* 84-88; NSM Belbroughton w Fairfield and Clent 88-93; Perm to Offic from 93. *30 The Glebe, Belbroughton, Stourbridge, W Midlands DY9 9TH* Belbroughton (01562) 730426

BARLOW, Timothy David. b 46. Univ Coll Ox BA67 MA71 Lon Univ BD71. Oak Hill Th Coll 71. **d** 71 **p** 72. C Marple All SS *Ches* 71-74; C Northwood Em *Lon* 74-78; Chapl Vevey w Chateau d'Oex and Villars *Eur* 78-84; Switzerland 84-89; V Chadkirk *Ches* from 89. *St Chad's Vicarage, Chadkirk Road, Romiley, Stockport, Cheshire SK6 3JY* 0161-430 4652

BARLOW, William George. b 40. Liv Univ BSc62 Univ of Wales BD65. St Mich Coll Llan 76. **d** 76 **p** 77. C Roath St Marg *Llan* 76-79; TV Cyncoed *Mon* 79-83; R Radyr *Llan* from 83. *The Rectory, Radyr, Cardiff CF4 8DY* Cardiff (01222) 842417

BARNACLE, Ronald William. b 20. Wells Th Coll 66. **d** 66 **p** 67. C Camp Hill w Galley Common *Cov* 69-70; R Etton w Dalton Holme *York* 70-76; R Hinderwell w Roxby 76-78; P-in-c Buckland Newton *Sarum* 78-80; P-in-c Wootton Glanville and Holnest 78-80; P-in-c Pulham 78-80; R Radwinter w Hempstead *Chelmsf* 80-83; V Blackfordby *Leic* 83-84; rtd 84; Perm to Offic *Worc* 84-92; Perm to Offic *Cov* from 92. *12 Larch Close, Bilton, Rugby CV22 7PJ* Rugby (01788) 810390

BARNARD, Canon Anthony Nevin. b 36. St Jo Coll Cam BA60 MA64. Wells Th Coll 61. **d** 63 **p** 64. C Cheshunt *St Alb* 63-65; Tutor Wells Th Coll 65-66; Chapl 66-69; Vice-Prin 69-71;

Dep Prin Sarum & Wells Th Coll 71-77; Dir S Dios Minl Tr Scheme 74-77; Can Res and Chan Lich Cathl *Lich* from 77; Warden of Readers 77-91; Dir of Tr 86-91. *13 The Close, Lichfield, Staffs WS13 7LD* Lichfield (01543) 255168 or 250300

BARNARD, Catherine Elizabeth. b 54. York Univ BA76 Dur Univ BA79. Cranmer Hall Dur 77. **dss** 80 **d** 87 **p** 94. Mexborough *Sheff* 80-83; Sheff Manor 83-90; Hon Par Dn 87-90; Hon Par Dn Bolsterstone 90-94; C from 94. *The Vicarage, Stonemoor Road, Bolsterstone, Sheffield S30 5ZN* Sheffield (0114) 288 2149

BARNARD, Canon Harold Reginald. b 07. AKC35. **d** 35 **p** 36. V Fishponds St Mary *Bris* 49-75; RD Stapleton 65-76; Hon Can Bris Cathl 67-81; rtd 75. *68 Oldbury Court Road, Bristol BS16 2JG* Bristol (0117) 965 9105

BARNARD, Canon John Stuart. b 19. Em Coll Cam BA41 MA45. Ridley Hall Cam 41. **d** 43 **p** 44. V Bromley Common St Aug *Roch* 58-73; Hon Can Roch Cathl 70-82; V Seal St Pet 73-82; Perm to Offic *Chich* from 82; rtd 84. *3 Chanctonbury Close, Rustington, Littlehampton, W Sussex BN16 2JB* Rustington (01903) 771351

BARNARD, Jonathan Dixon. b 46. St Cath Coll Cam BA68. Cuddesdon Coll 69. **d** 71 **p** 72. C Silksworth *Dur* 71-74; C Hatf Hyde St Mary *St Alb* 74-78; TV Hitchin 78-86; TR Penrith w Newton Reigny and Plumpton Wall *Carl* 86-91; rtd 91. *4 Hallin Croft, Penrith, Cumbria CA11 8AA* Penrith (01768) 63000

BARNARD, Kevin James. b 52. Keble Coll Ox BA77 MA79. Cranmer Hall Dur 77. **d** 79 **p** 80. C Swinton *Sheff* 79-83; TV Sheff Manor 83-90; V Bolsterstone from 90. *The Vicarage, Stonemoor Road, Bolsterstone, Sheffield S30 5ZN* Sheffield (0114) 288 2149

BARNARD, Leslie William. b 24. St Cath Coll Ox BA50 MA55 Southn Univ PhD70. Cuddesdon Coll 51. **d** 51 **p** 52. Sen Lect Leeds Univ 69-83; Dioc Dir of Tr *Ripon* 70-76; Chapl Harrogate Gen Hosp 83-89; rtd 89. *68 Park Place, Park Parade, Harrogate, N Yorkshire HG1 4NS* Harrogate (01423) 560038

BARNARD, Robert James. b 15. Lich Th Coll 54. **d** 55 **p** 56. R Clenchwarton *Ely* 65-77; P-in-c Hinxton 77-80; rtd 80; Perm to Offic *Roch* from 80. *Flat 23, Bromley College, London Road, Bromley BR1 1PE* 0181-290 1280

BARNARD, Canon William Henry (Bill). b 09. Dorchester Miss Coll 37. **d** 39 **p** 40. R Hinton Martel *Sarum* 53-93; RD Wimborne 75-79; Can and Preb Sarum Cathl 79-93; rtd 93; Perm to Offic *B & W* from 94. *Halcyon, 94 Park Road, Congresbury, Bristol BS19 5HH*

BARNBY, Canon Bertram Louis. b 13. Ch Coll Cam BA35 MA39. Ridley Hall Cam 36. **d** 38 **p** 39. P-in-c Wilmslow *Ches* 69-72; R 72-76; Hon Can Ches Cathl 74-82; R W Kirby St Andr 76-82; rtd 82. *7 Holbeck Road, Scarborough, N Yorkshire YO11 2XF* Scarborough (01723) 378282

BARNES, Alan Duff. b 42. St Steph Ho Ox 75. **d** 77 **p** 78. C Wanstead H Trin Hermon Hill *Chelmsf* 77-80; C Clacton St Jas 80-82; R Cranham 82-89; V Calcot *Ox* from 89. *St Birinus' House, Langley Hill, Reading RG3 5QX* Reading (01734) 422828

BARNES, Brian. b 42. Sussex Univ MA82. Cant Sch of Min 79. **d** 82 **p** 83. NSM Maidstone All SS and St Phil w Tovil *Cant* 82-89; C 89-92; FE Adv Gen Syn Bd of Educn 86-92; R Staplehurst *Cant* from 92. *The Rectory, Frittenden Road, Staplehurst, Tonbridge, Kent TN12 0DH* Staplehurst (01580) 891258

BARNES, Brian. b 49. St Mich Coll Llan DMinlStuds93. **d** 93 **p** 94. C Betws St Dav w Ammanford *St D* from 93. *44 Maes y Coed, Ammanford, Dyfed SA18 2JB* Ammanford (01269) 591035

BARNES, Bruce Roy. b 52. FRSA. St Steph Ho Ox 73. **d** 76 **p** 77. C Birm St Pet *Birm* 76-81; C Portsea St Mary *Portsm* 81-87; V Paulsgrove 87-92. *Peterhouse, St Peter Street, Winchester, Hants SO23 8BW* Winchester (01962) 866036

BARNES, Canon Bryan Peter. b 24. Leeds Univ BA50. Coll of Resurr Mirfield 50. **d** 52 **p** 53. V Moorfields *Bris* 66-71; P-in-c Winterbourne Down 71-75; V Fishponds St Mary 75-87; Hon Can Bris Cathl 84-87; rtd 87; NSM Duloe w Herodsfoot *Truro* 91-95; Warden Jes Hosp Cant from 95. *The Warden's Lodge, Jesus Hospital, Canterbury, Kent CT1 1BS* Canterbury (01227) 463771

BARNES, Canon Charles Peter Kentish. b 19. Ch Coll Cam BA40 MA44. Ridley Hall Cam 40. **d** 42 **p** 43. R Stratford-on-Avon w Bishopton *Cov* 69-75; TR 75-81; V Priors Hardwick, Priors Marston and Wormleighton 81-84; rtd 84; Perm to Offic *Cov* from 84; Perm to Offic *Glouc* from 84. *5 Willow Bank, Welford on Avon, Stratford-upon-Avon, Warks CV37 8HB* Stratford-upon-Avon (01789) 750780

BARNES, Colin. b 33. St Jo Coll York CertEd58. St Aid Birkenhead 61. **d** 64 **p** 65. C Eccles St Mary *Man* 64-66; C Barrow St Geo w St Luke *Carl* 66-68; V Goodshaw *Man*

68-80; P-in-c Wythenshawe St Martin 80-83; New Zealand from 83. *St Matthew's Vicarage, 16 Pearce Crescent, Taita, Lower Hutt, New Zealand*   Wellington (4) 677655

BARNES, Very Rev Cyril Arthur. b 26. Edin Th Coll 47. **d** 50 **p** 51. R Huntly *Mor* 67-83; R Aberchirder 67-83; Hon Can St Andr Cathl Inverness 71-80; Dioc Sec 71-83; R Keith 74-83; Syn Clerk 77-80; Dean Mor 80-83; rtd 83; Perm to Offic *Ab* from 83; Perm to Offic *Mor* from 90. *Tillyartmont Cottage, Bridge of Isla, Huntly, Aberdeenshire AB54 4SP*   Rothiemay (01466) 81370   Fax as telephone

BARNES, David John. b 37. Lon Univ DipRS65. Chich Th Coll 65. **d** 68 **p** 69. C Crayford *Roch* 68-71; Chapl RAF 71-75; Chapl Sutton Valence Sch Kent 75-87; C Minster in Sheppey *Cant* 87-93; V Ash w Westmarsh from 93. *The Vicarage, Queen's Road, Ash, Canterbury, Kent CT3 2BG*   Ash (01304) 812296

BARNES, David Keith. b 53. Linc Th Coll. **d** 89 **p** 90. C E Crompton *Man* 89-93; V Belfield from 93. *St Ann's Vicarage, 310 Milnrow Road, Rochdale, Lancs OL16 5BT*   Rochdale (01706) 46173

BARNES, Derek Ian. b 44. Leeds Univ BA66. Westcott Ho Cam 66. **d** 68 **p** 69. C Far Headingley St Chad *Ripon* 68-71; Chapl Qu Eliz Coll *Lon* 72-77; Warden Lee Abbey Internat Students' Club Kensington 77-81; Hon C Willesden Green St Gabr *Lon* 81-83; P-in-c Southall H Trin from 84; P-in-c Southall St Geo 89-92. *Holy Trinity Vicarage, 41 Park View Road, Southall, Middx UB1 3HJ*   0181-574 3762

BARNES, Preb Donald Edward. b 26. K Coll Lon BD51 AKC51. **d** 52 **p** 53. C Willesden St Matt *Lon* 52-59; V Cricklewood St Pet 59-79; Lect Bps' Coll Cheshunt 63-68; V Belsize Park *Lon* from 79; Preb St Paul's Cathl from 84; AD N Camden (Hampstead) 83-88. *St Peter's Parsonage, Belsize Square, London NW3 4HY*   0171-794 4020

BARNES, Duncan Christopher. b 64. Warw Univ BA90. Trin Coll Bris BA93. **d** 93 **p** 94. C Hornchurch St Andr *Chelmsf* from 93. *49 Burnway, Hornchurch, Essex RM11 3SN*   Hornchurch (01708) 443358

✠**BARNES, Rt Rev Edwin Ronald.** b 35. Pemb Coll Ox BA58 MA62. Cuddesdon Coll 58. **d** 60 **p** 61 **c** 95. C Portsea N End St Mark *Portsm* 60-64; C Woodham *Guildf* 64-67; R Farncombe 67-78; V Hessle *York* 78-87; AD W Hull 85-87; Prin St Steph Ho Ox 87-95; Hon Can Ch Ch *Ox* 94-95; Suff Bp Richborough (PEV) *Cant* from 95. *St Stephen's House, 16 Marston Street, Oxford OX4 1JX*   Oxford (01865) 247874   Fax 794338

BARNES, Mrs Enid Mabel. b 38. Homerton Coll Cam DipT58. W Midl Minl Tr Course 87. **d** 90 **p** 94. Par Dn Walsall St Paul *Lich* 90-94; C from 94. *Emmanuel Vicarage, Bentley, Walsall WS2 0HP*   Walsall (01922) 24200

BARNES, Esdaile Lenox. b 13. ALCD40. **d** 40 **p** 41. Australia 70-72; C Folkestone H Trin w Ch Ch *Cant* 72-74; R Grimston w Congham *Nor* 74-75; R Roydon All SS 74-75; rtd 75. *84 Upper Street, Tamworth, NSW, Australia 2340*

BARNES, James Barrie. b 27. Bps' Coll Cheshunt 51. **d** 53 **p** 54. V Blackfordby *Leic* 59-76; RD Akeley W (Ashby) 69-76; V Broom Leys 76-92; rtd 93. *15 Diamond Avenue, Sherwood Park, Rainsworth, Mansfield, Notts NG21 0FF*   Mansfield (01623) 796601

BARNES, Canon John Barwick. b 32. AKC58. **d** 59 **p** 60. C Brentwood St Thos *Chelmsf* 59-65; R Arkesden w Wicken Bonhunt 65-71; V Gt Ilford St Mary from 71; Hon Can Chelmsf Cathl from 95. *26 South Park Road, Ilford, Essex IG1 1SS*   0181-478 0546

BARNES, John Christopher. b 43. MA ATI DMS. Linc Th Coll 78. **d** 80 **p** 81. C Guiseley *Bradf* 80-83; TV Guiseley w Esholt 83-86; V Rawdon 86-92; R Armthorpe *Sheff* from 92. *The Rectory, Church Street, Armthorpe, Doncaster, S Yorkshire DN3 3AD*   Doncaster (01302) 831231

BARNES, John Kenneth. b 04. Jes Coll Ox BA27 MA35. Ripon Hall Ox 34. **d** 36 **p** 37. R Kinnersley w Norton Canon *Heref* 57-74; rtd 74; Perm to Offic *Heref* from 74. *12 Falstaff Road, Hereford HR2 7QF*

BARNES, John Seymour. b 30. Qu Coll Birm 58. **d** 61 **p** 62. C Bromsgrove St Jo *Worc* 61-64; C Kingsthorpe *Pet* 64-66; C Styvechale *Cov* 66-69; P-in-c Avon Dassett w Farnborough 69-75; P-in-c Cov St Alb 75-84; R Weddington and Caldecote 84-89; P-in-c Wilnecote *Lich* 89-90; V Bentley from 90. *The Vicarage, Bentley, Walsall WS2 0HP*   Walsall (01922) 242000

BARNES, Katrina Crawford. b 52. Oak Hill NSM Course 90. **d** 93 **p** 94. NSM Bromley H Trin *Roch* from 93. *39 The Fairway, Bromley BR1 2JZ*   0181-467 0338

BARNES, Dr Neal Duncan. b 63. Leeds Univ BSc84 Cranfield Inst of Tech PhD92. Oak Hill Th Coll DipHE95. **d** 95. C Biggleswade *St Alb* from 95. *46 Wilsheres Road, Beggleswade, Beds SG18 0DN*   Biggleswade (01767) 314240

BARNES, Neil. b 42. Kelham Th Coll 61 Bps' Coll Cheshunt 65. **d** 68 **p** 69. C Poulton-le-Fylde *Blackb* 68-72; C Ribbleton 72-75; V Knuzden 75-81; Chapl Prestwich Hosp Man 81-88; Chapl Salford Mental Health Services (NHS Trust) from 88.

Mental Health Services of Salford, Bury New Road, Prestwich, Manchester M25 3BL*   0161-772 3675 or 773 9121

BARNES, Paul Nicholas. b 58. Qu Coll Birm 89. **d** 91 **p** 92. C Weymouth H Trin *Sarum* 91-95; P-in-c Studley from 95. *The Vicarage, 340 Frome Road, Trowbridge, Wilts BA14 0ED*   Trowbridge (01225) 753162

BARNES, Peter Frank. b 52. St Jo Coll Nottm LTh81. **d** 81 **p** 82. C Colne St Bart *Blackb* 81-83; C Melton Mowbray w Thorpe Arnold *Leic* 83-86; P-in-c Barlestone 86-89; V Broughton and Duddon *Carl* from 89. *The Vicarage, Broughton-in-Furness, Cumbria LA20 6HS*   Broughton-in-Furness (01229) 716305

BARNES, Ms Sheena Elizabeth. b 56. Reading Univ MFA Cant Coll of Art BA78 Ox Univ BA85. Ripon Coll Cuddesdon 83. **dss** 86 **d** 87. Westmr St Jas *Lon* 86-89; Par Dn 87-89; rtd 89. *14H Sussex Street, London SW1V 4RS*   0171-931 8318

BARNES, Stephen. b 46. Hull Univ BA69 Bris Univ DipTh71. Clifton Th Coll 69. **d** 72 **p** 73. C Girlington *Bradf* 72-74; TV Glyncorrwg w Afan Vale and Cymmer Afan *Llan* 74-79; R 79-86; V Aberavon from 86. *The Vicarage, 68 Pentyla, Aberavon, Port Talbot, W Glam SA12 8AD*   Port Talbot (01639) 883824

BARNES, Stephen John. b 59. Univ of Wales (Cardiff) BSc80. Chich Th Coll 83. **d** 86 **p** 87. C Neath w Llantwit *Llan* 86-89; C Coity w Nolton from 89. *Y Lletty, Heol-yr-Ysgol, Coity, Bridgend, M Glam CF35 6BL*   Bridgend (01656) 652540

BARNES, Stephen William. b 53. Man Univ BSc. St Jo Coll Nottm DipTh82. **d** 83 **p** 84. C Chadwell Heath *Chelmsf* 83-87; C Becontree St Alb 88-89; Deanery Youth Chapl 88-91; C Becontree S 89-91; TV Worth *Chich* from 91. *St Barnabas's Vicarage, 2 Crawley Lane, Crawley, W Sussex RH10 4EB*   Crawley (01293) 513398

BARNES, William (Billy). b 54. RGN89 St Andr Univ MTh84. Westcott Ho Cam CTM92. **d** 92 **p** 93. C S Bank *York* 92-95; C Northallerton w Kirby Sigston from 95. *26 Helmsley Way, Northallerton, N Yorkshire DL7 8SX*   Northallerton (01609) 780975

BARNES, William Thomas. b 39. Dur Univ BA60. Wycliffe Hall Ox 60. **d** 62 **p** 63. C Scotforth *Blackb* 62-66; C Cleveleys 66-67; V Colne Ch Ch 67-74; V Bamber Bridge St Sav from 74. *St Saviour's Vicarage, Bamber Bridge, Preston PR5 6AJ*   Preston (01772) 35374

BARNES-CEENEY, Brian. b 35. St Aid Birkenhead 59. **d** 62 **p** 63. C Plaistow St Andr *Chelmsf* 62-64; C Waltham Abbey 64-66; V Falfield *Glouc* 66-71; R Rockhampton 66-71; Chapl HM Det Cen Eastwood Park 68-71; Chapl HM Youth Cust Cen Everthorpe 71-76; Chapl HM Pris Coldingley 76-79; Chapl HM Pris Bris 79-87; Chapl HM Pris Ford from 87. *HM Prison, Arundel, W Sussex BN18 0BX*   Littlehampton (01903) 717261   Fax 726060

BARNES-CLAY, Peter John Granger. b 43. MCollP Cam Univ CertEd69. Chich Th Coll 72. **d** 75 **p** 82. C Earlham St Anne *Nor* 75-76; Asst Master Hewett Sch Nor 76-83; Hon C Eaton 81-83; C 83-87; R Winterton w E and W Somerton and Horsey 87-92; R Weybourne Gp from 92; RD Holt from 95. *The Rectory, Weybourne, Holt, Norfolk NR25 7SY*   Weybourne (0126370) 268

BARNETT, Alec James Leon. b 44. Em Coll Cam BA66 MA70. Cuddesdon Coll. **d** 69 **p** 70. C Preston St Jo *Blackb* 69-72; Asst Chapl Uppingham Sch Leics 72-80; Hd of RE 73-80; Dir of Farmington/Ampleforth Project 79-83; C Witney *Ox* 80-84; P-in-c Lt Compton w Chastleton, Cornwell etc 84-88; Prin Ox Chr Tr Scheme 84-88; P-in-c St Michael Penkevil *Truro* 88-95; P-in-c Lamorran and Merther 88-95; Dioc Tr Officer 88-95; Chapl Strasbourg *Eur* from 95. *16 rue Riehl, 67100 Strasbourg-Neuhof, France*   France (33) 88 40 36 15   Fax 88 39 07 58

BARNETT, David John. b 33. Magd Coll Ox BA56 BTh58 MA61. St Steph Ho Ox 56. **d** 59 **p** 60. C Styvechale *Cov* 59-62; S Africa 62-69; Rhodesia 70-76; V Colindale St Matthias *Lon* 77-90; R Finchley St Mary from 90. *St Mary's Rectory, Rectory Close, London N3 1TS*   0181-346 4600

BARNETT, Dudley Graham. b 36. Ch Ch Ox BA62 MA65. St Steph Ho Ox 62. **d** 64 **p** 65. C Abbey Hey *Man* 64-68; V Swinton H Rood 68-90; R Old Trafford St Hilda from 90. *St Hilda's Rectory, 255 Kings Road, Manchester M16 0JD*   0161-881 9332

BARNETT, Miss Jessica Dorothy Anne. b 18. St Paul's Coll Limuru. **dss** 69 **d** 87. Halifax St Jo Bapt *Wakef* 72-80; rtd 80; Perm to Offic *Ox* from 80. *Cotswold Cottage, Thames Street, Charlbury, Chipping Norton, Oxon OX7 3QL*   Charlbury (01608) 810234

BARNETT, John Raymond. b 51. Lon Univ LLB74 BD86. Westcott Ho Cam 74. **d** 77 **p** 78. C Northfield *Birm* 77-81; V Hamstead St Bernard 81-91; R The Quinton from 91. *The Rectory, 773 Hagley Road West, Birmingham B32 1AJ*   0121-422 2031

BARNETT, John Richard. b 28. FCIS72. Portsm Dioc Tr Course 86. **d** 88. NSM Droxford *Portsm* 88-91; NSM Meonstoke w Corhampton cum Exton 88-91; NSM W Meon and Warnford from 91. *Pinfarthings, Coombe Lane, West Meon, Petersfield, Hants GU32 1NB* West Meon (01730) 829380

BARNETT, Canon Norman. b 19. Univ of Wales BA41. St Mich Coll Llan 41. **d** 43 **p** 44. R Liss *Portsm* 53-85; RD Petersfield 70-75; Hon Can Portsm Cathl 76-85; rtd 85. *Banbury House, Burton Street, Marnhull, Sturminster Newton, Dorset DT10 1PS* Sturminster Newton (01258) 820260

BARNETT, Miss Patricia Ann. b 38. Whitelands Coll Lon CertEd. St Jo Coll Dur 75. **dss** 78 **d** 87 **p** 94. Gateacre *Liv* 78-82; Litherland St Paul Hatton Hill 82-87; Par Dn 87-88; Par Dn Platt Bridge 88-94; C 94-95; V Skelmersdale Ch at Cen from 95. *10 Ferndale, Skelmersdale, Lancs WN8 6PZ*

BARNETT, Peter Geoffrey. b 46. AKC71. St Aug Coll Cant 71. **d** 72 **p** 73. C Wolv *Lich* 72-77; P-in-c Caldmore 77-83; TR Bris St Agnes and St Simon w St Werburgh *Bris* 83-87; P-in-c Bris St Paul w St Barn 83-87; TR Bris St Paul's 87-94; Warden Pilsdon Community Salisbury from 94. *The Pilsdon Comminity, Pilsdon Manor, Bridport, Dorset DT6 5NZ* Bridport (01308) 868308

BARNETT, Peter John. b 36. N Ord Course 82. **d** 85 **p** 86. C New Bury *Man* 85-87; TV 87-94; P-in-c Clifton from 94. *St Anne's Vicarage, Manchester Road, Manchester M27 6PP* 0161-794 1939

BARNETT, Preb Raymond Michael. b 31. Man Univ BA54. Wells Th Coll 54. **d** 56 **p** 57. C Fallowfield *Man* 56-59; Madagascar 59-60; V Blackrod *Man* 60-67; V Woolavington *B & W* 67-76; RD Bridgwater 72-76; V St Decumans from 76; RD Quantock 78-86 and 93-95; Preb Wells Cathl from 89. *St Decuman's Vicarage, 47A Brendon Road, Watchet, Somerset TA23 0HU* Watchet (01984) 631228

BARNETT, Russell Scott. b 20. Oak Hill Th Coll 56. **d** 58 **p** 59. V Salterhebble All SS *Wakef* 67-77; R Aikton *Carl* 77-85; R Orton St Giles 77-85; rtd 86; Perm to Offic *Carl* from 86. *8 Jackson Road, Houghton, Carlisle CA3 0NW* Carlisle (01228) 31721

BARNEY, Michael Frank. b 29. New Coll Ox BA53 MA58. Chich Th Coll 53. **d** 55 **p** 56. C Kensington St Mary Abbots w St Geo *Lon* 68-75; V Chiswick St Mich 75-93; rtd 94; Perm to Offic *Lon* from 95; Perm to Offic *S'wark* from 95. *58 Deanhill Court, Upper Richmond Road West, London SW14 7DL* 0181-878 2668

BARNFATHER, Thomas Fenwick. b 52. Linc Th Coll 86. **d** 88 **p** 89. C Sedgefield *Dur* 88-91; TV E Darlington 91-92; CF from 92. *c/o MOD (Army), Bagshot Park, Bagshot, Surrey GU19 5PL* Bagshot (01276) 471717 Fax 412834

BARNSLEY, Mrs Angela Vera. b 47. St Hild Coll Dur BA70. St Alb Minl Tr Scheme 90. **d** 93. NSM Codicote *St Alb* 93-94. *1 Marquis Close, Weymouth, Dorset DT4 9TA* Weymouth (01305) 770406

BARNSLEY, Melvyn. b 46. Dur Univ BA67 DipTh69 CertEd. St Chad's Coll Dur 64. **d** 71 **p** 72. C Cov St Thos *Cov* 71-74; C Cov St Jo 71-75; V New Bilton 75-82; R Stevenage St Andr and St Geo *St Alb* from 82; RD Stevenage from 89. *The Rectory, Cuttys Lane, Stevenage, Herts SG1 1UP* Stevenage (01438) 351631

BARNSLEY, Mrs Valerie Anne. b 48. Sussex Univ BEd71. W Midl Minl Tr Course 91. **d** 94 **p** 95. NSM Tettenhall Regis *Lich* from 94. *3 Highlands Road, Finchfield, Wolverhampton WV3 8AG* Wolverhampton (01902) 344115

BARNSTAPLE, Archdeacon of. *See* LLOYD, Ven Bertram Trevor

BARON, Noel Spencer Peter. b 15. K Coll Cam BA39 MA42. Linc Th Coll 40. **d** 41 **p** 42. V W Malvern *Worc* 52-83; rtd 83; Perm to Offic *Heref* from 85. *Brindley, 21 The Crescent, Colwall, Malvern, Worcs WR13 6QN* Colwall (01684) 40477

BARON, Peter Murray. b 56. New Coll Ox MA78. Cranmer Hall Dur 91. **d** 93 **p** 94. C Monkseaton St Pet *Newc* from 93. *30 Paignton Avenue, Whitley Bay, Tyne & Wear NE25 8EX* 0191-251 7587

BARON, Thomas Michael. b 63. St Steph Ho Ox 85. **d** 88 **p** 89. C Hartlepool St Paul *Dur* 88-92; Chapl Asst Hartlepool Gen Hosp 89-92; Asst Chapl Whittington Hosp Lon 92-95; Chapl Chase Farm Hosp Enfield from 95. *Chase Farm Hospital, 127 The Ridgeway, Enfield, Middx EN2 8JL* 0181-366 6600

BARON, Mrs Vanessa Lilian. b 57. SRN79 City Univ BSc79 Fitzw Coll Cam MA85. Ridley Hall Cam 83. **dss** 86 **d** 87 **p** 94. Roxbourne St Andr *Lon* 86-87; Par Dn 87-89; NSM Roxeth from 94. *4 Peterborough House, Grove Hill, Harrow, Middx HA1 3HF* 0181-869 1203

BARR, Canon David James Osborne (Ossie). b 23. TCD BA45 MA. CITC 46. **d** 46 **p** 47. I Dub Booterstown *D & G* 65-92; RD Monkstown 83-92; Can Ch Ch Cathl Dub 84-92; rtd 92. *26 Woodlands Avenue, Stillorgan, Co Dublin, Irish Republic* Dublin (1) 288-4275

BARR, John Gourlay Crichton. b 23. Edin Univ BL46. Edin Dioc NSM Course 81. **d** 84 **p** 85. NSM Edin St Mark *Edin* 84-91; rtd

91. *22 Grove House, 22 St Andrew Street, Brechin, Angus DD9 6JJ* Brechin (01356) 624412

BARR (nee HAYTER), Dr Mary Elizabeth. b 58. Jes Coll Ox BA80 CertEd81 MA84 DPhil85. Ridley Hall Cam 84. **dss** 86 **d** 87 **p** 94. Chapl Cam Univ Pastorate 86-91; Cam H Trin w St Andr Gt *Ely* 86-87; Par Dn 87-91; Perm to Offic 91-92; Perm to Offic *Ex* 92-94; NSM Torquay St Luke from 94. *St Luke's Vicarage, 1 Mead Road, Torquay TQ2 6TE* Torquay (01803) 605097

BARR, Michael John Alexander. b 60. Qu Coll Ox BA82 MA86 Pemb Coll Cam BA86 MA90. Ridley Hall Cam 84. **d** 87 **p** 88. C Earley St Pet *Ox* 87-89; C Cam Gt St Mary w St Mich *Ely* 89-92; Chapl Girton Coll Cam 90-92; P-in-c Torquay St Luke *Ex* from 92; Dioc Communications Officer from 92. *St Luke's Vicarage, 1 Mead Road, Torquay TQ2 6TE* Torquay (01803) 605097 Fax as telephone

BARR, Very Rev William Norman Cochrane. b 20. TCD BA44 MA50 BD50. CITC 45. **d** 46 **p** 46. Bp's Dom Chapl *Conn* 56-71; I Derriaghy w Colin 61-90; RD Derriaghy 72-82; Can Conn Cathl 80-82; Dean Conn 82-90; rtd 90. *45 Killeaton Crescent, Dunmurry, Belfast BT17 9HB* Belfast (01232) 621746

BARR JOHNSTON, Charles Walter. b 38. BSc61. Oak Hill Th Coll 62. **d** 64 **p** 65. C Tollington Park St Mark w St Anne *Lon* 64-68; SAMS 68-95; Argentina 68-95; Perm to Offic *Cov* from 95. *34 Almond Avenue, Leamington Spa, Warks CV32 6QD* Leamington Spa (01926) 330832

BARRACLOUGH, Dennis. b 35. LCP62 FCP74 CertEd58. Lambeth STh68 Ripon Hall Ox 66. **d** 68 **p** 69. C Woodhouse *Wakef* 68-71; V Gildersome 71-83; V Kirkburton from 83; RD Kirkburton from 92. *The Vicarage, 3B Shelley Lane, Kirkburton, Huddersfield HD8 0SJ* Huddersfield (01484) 602188

BARRACLOUGH, Canon Owen Conrad. b 32. Pemb Coll Cam BA55 MA59. Westcott Ho Cam 56. **d** 57 **p** 58. C Chippenham St Andr w Tytherton Lucas *Bris* 57-62; V Harringay St Paul *Lon* 62-70; Bp's Chapl for Community Relns *Cov* 70-77; P-in-c Baginton 72-77; V Swindon Ch Ch *Bris* from 77; Chapl Princess Marg Hosp Swindon 77-89; Hon Can Bris Cathl *Bris* from 87. *Christ Church Vicarage, 26 Cricklade Street, Swindon SN1 3HG* Swindon (01793) 522832

BARRALL, John Henry. b 31. BEd. Bps' Coll Cheshunt. **d** 61 **p** 62. C Digswell *St Alb* 61-65; C Aldershot St Mich *Guildf* 65-70; TV Hemel Hempstead *St Alb* 70-82; Perm to Offic 83-91; R Meppershall w Campton and Stondon from 91. *The Rectory, Church Road, Meppershall, Shefford, Beds SG17 5NA* Hitchin (01462) 813334

BARRAND, George William. b 33. Lon Coll of Div 59. **d** 62 **p** 63. C Bucknall and Bagnall *Lich* 62-65; C Parr *Liv* 65-70; Australia from 70. *33 Little Yara Road, Yarra Junction, Warburton, Victoria, Australia 3799* Warburton (59) 671166

BARRATT, Ven Anthony John. b 19. Glas Univ MRCVS. Bible Churchmen's Coll. **d** 49 **p** 50. Argentina 70-84; Adn Tucuman 73-84; rtd 84. *Couchill Villa, Couchill Farm Lane, Seaton, Devon EX12 3AL* Seaton (01297) 21118

BARRATT, Mrs Elizabeth June. b 32. ACP65. Trin Coll Bris 75. **dss** 78 **d** 87 **p** 94. W Kilburn St Luke w St Simon and St Jude *Lon* 78-87; Par Dn 87-94; C from 94. *Flat 1, St Luke's Church Centre, Fernhead Road, London W9 3EH* 0181-969 9338

BARRATT, Peter. b 29. Down Coll Cam BA53 MA57. Ridley Hall Cam 53. **d** 55 **p** 56. V Rawtenstall St Mary *Man* 68-83; AD Rossendale 80-83; V Bosley and N Rode w Wincle and Wildboarclough *Ches* 83-94; rtd 94. *10 Snab Wood Close, Little Neston, South Wirral L64 0UP* 0151-336 6641

BARRATT, Philip Norman. b 62. Aston Tr Scheme 87 St Steph Ho Ox 89 Coll of Resurr Mirfield 90. **d** 92 **p** 93. C Heywood St Luke w All So *Man* from 92. *All Souls' Vicarage, 173 Rochdale Road East, Heywood, Lancs OL10 1QU* Heywood (01706) 626008 Fax as telephone

BARRETT, Alan. b 48. Southn Univ BA69. Wycliffe Hall Ox 74. **d** 77 **p** 78. C Conisbrough *Sheff* 77-80; C Lower Homerton St Paul *Lon* 80-81; C Homerton St Barn w St Paul 81; C-in-c Hounslow Gd Shep Beavers Lane CD 81-87; R Langdon Hills *Chelmsf* from 87. *The Rectory, 105A Berry Lane, Langdon Hills, Basildon, Essex SS16 6AP* Basildon (01268) 542156

BARRETT, Brian William. b 28. Lon Univ BA60. Ox NSM Course 72. **d** 75 **p** 76. Hd Master St Edw's Sch Reading 73-88; Hon C Goring *Ox* 75-84; Hon C Goring w S Stoke 84-90; rtd 88; C Blewbury *Ox* 89-90; C Hagbourne 89-90; C Blewbury, Hagbourne and Upton 90-93. *3 Chestnut Cottages, Wallingford Road, Streatley, Reading RG8 9JQ* Goring-on-Thames (01491) 873337

BARRETT, Christopher Paul. b 49. AKC71 St Aug Coll Cant 71. **d** 72 **p** 73. C Tupsley *Heref* 72-75; C Ex St Thos *Ex* 75-79; R Atherington and High Bickington 79-83; V Burrington 79-83; Asst Dir of Educn 79-87; P-in-c Sticklepath 83-85; P-in-c

Barnstaple 83-85; TV 85-90; V Whipton from 90. *The Vicarage, 19 The Mede, Exeter EX4 8ED*   Exeter (01392) 467552

BARRETT, Clive. b 55. MA CertEd. St Steph Ho Ox. **d** 83 **p** 84. C Wakef Cathl *Wakef* 83-87; Chapl Leeds Univ *Ripon* from 87; Dioc Development Rep from 89. *81 Becketts Park Drive, Leeds LS6 3PJ*   Leeds (0113) 275 5497 or 233 5071

BARRETT, Dr David Brian. b 27. Clare Coll Cam BA48 MA50 BD69 Columbia Univ (NY) PhD65. Union Th Sem (NY) STM63 PhD65 Ridley Hall Cam 52. **d** 54 **p** 55. CMS 57-92; Kenya 65-85; Research Sec ACC 70-87; Lic to Offic *Lon* 70-87; USA from 87; rtd 92. *2503 Prestwick Circle, Richmond, Virginia 23294, USA*   Richmond (804) 747-7455   Fax 358-0504

BARRETT, Canon Derek Leonard. b 25. St Fran Coll Brisbane ThL57. **d** 57 **p** 58. V Kidderminster St Jo *Worc* 67-77; V Stourbridge St Thos 77-90; RD Stourbridge 83-89; Hon Can Worc Cathl 87-90; rtd 90. *Barton Cottage, Bourton-on-the-Water, Glos GL54 2AR*   Cotswold (01451) 821777

BARRETT, Gary John. b 46. Sarum & Wells Th Coll 87. **d** 90 **p** 91. NSM Guernsey St Peter Port *Win* from 90; Chapl Eliz Coll Guernsey from 93. *Berachah, Les Ozouets Close, St Peter Port, Guernsey, Channel Islands GY1 1FT*   Guernsey (01481) 720405

BARRETT, Graham Crichton. b 51. IEng76 FIMEMME78. Linc Th Coll 88. **d** 90 **p** 91. C Torpoint *Truro* 90-94; Dio Youth and Voc Officer from 94; C St Columb Major w St Wenn 94-95. *6 Carloggas Close, St Mawgan, Newquay, Cornwall TR8 4HJ*   Newquay (01637) 860139

BARRETT, Very Rev John Alan Gardiner. b 29. CITC 57. **d** 59 **p** 60. C Bray *D & G* 59-63; I Kingscourt *M & K* 63-69; I Navan 69-84; RD Ardnurcher and Clonmacnoise 78-84; Can Meath 81-84; I Rathdrum w Glenealy, Derralossary and Laragh *D & G* 84-89; Dean Clonmacnoise *M & K* from 89; I Trim w Bective and Galtrim from 89; Dioc Registrar (Meath) from 90. *St Patrick's Deanery, Trim, Co Meath, Irish Republic*   Trim (46) 36698

BARRETT, John Edward. b 40. Cam Inst of Educn DipEd72. E Anglian Minl Tr Course 78. **d** 81 **p** 82. NSM Everton w Tetworth *Ely* 81-86; TV Stanground and Farcet 86-91; V Friday Bridge from 91; V Coldham from 91; V Elm from 91. *The Vicarage, Friday Bridge, Wisbech, Cambs PE14 0HJ*   Wisbech (01945) 860382

BARRETT, John Joseph James. b 38. Lon Univ BD65. Sarum & Wells Th Coll. **d** 78 **p** 78. C Danbury *Chelmsf* 78-80; Ind Chapl 80-89; C Dovercourt 80-83; TV Dovercourt and Parkeston 83-89; V Rubery *Birm* from 89. *St Chad's Vicarage, 160A New Road, Rednal, Birmingham B45 9JA*   0121-453 3255

BARRETT, Kenneth. b 42. Univ of Wales (Lamp) BA64. St Steph Ho Ox 65. **d** 67 **p** 68. C Poulton-le-Fylde *Blackb* 67-69; C S Shore H Trin 69-72; V Brierfield 72-83; V Chorley St Geo from 83. *St George's Vicarage, Letchworth Place, Chorley, Lancs PR7 2HJ*   Chorley (01257) 263064

BARRETT, Mrs Marion Lily. b 54. SRN75. SW Minl Tr Course 91. **d** 94 **p** 95. C St Mawgan w St Ervan and St Eval *Truro* from 94. *6 Carloggas Close, St Mawgan, Newquay, Cornwall TR8 4HJ*   Newquay (01637) 860139

BARRETT, Peter Francis. b 56. TCD BA78 MA81 DipTh81 MPhil84. CITC. **d** 81 **p** 82. C Drumachose *D & R* 81-83; C Dub St Ann *D & G* 83-85; I Conwal Union w Gartan *D & R* 85-90; RD Kilmacrenan E and W 88-90; I Belf St Geo *Conn* 90-94; Chapl Actors' Ch Union from 93; Chapl TCD from 94; Min Can Dublin from 94. *The Chaplaincy, 27 Trinity College, Dublin 2, Irish Republic*   Dublin (1) 702-1402   Fax 679-0335

BARRETT, Philip Leslie Sibborn. b 47. FRHistS88 Ex Coll Ox BA68 MA72 BD90 Univ of Wales (Cardiff) LLM95. Cuddesdon Coll 68. **d** 70 **p** 71. C Pershore w Wick *Worc* 70-73; C Bournemouth St Pet w St Swithun, St Steph etc *Win* 74-76; VC Heref Cathl *Heref* 76-86; P-in-c Otterbourne *Win* 86-87; R Compton and Otterbourne from 87; Hon Chapl Win Cathl from 90. *The Rectory, Kiln Lane, Otterbourne, Winchester, Hants SO21 2EU*   Twyford (01962) 713400

BARRETT, Raymond William. b 23. St Mich Coll Llan 72. **d** 73 **p** 74. C Cheltenham St Luke and St Jo *Glouc* 73-75; P-in-c Holbeach Hurn *Linc* 75-78; V Baston 78-83; rtd 83; Perm to Offic *Glouc* from 83. *2 Millhouse Drive, Wymans Brook, Cheltenham, Glos GL50 4RG*   Cheltenham (01242) 575434

BARRETT, Ronald Reginald. b 30. Roch Th Coll 61. **d** 64 **p** 65. V Greengates *Bradf* 68-73; V Shelf 73-79; V Embsay w Eastby 79-87; V Farndon and Coddington *Ches* 87-92; rtd 92. *12 Craigmore Drive, Ben Rhydding, Ilkley, W Yorkshire LS29 8PG*   Ilkley (01943) 609713

BARRETT, Stephen David Norman. b 54. Aber Univ BSc75 Edin Univ BD78. Edin Th Coll 75. **d** 78 **p** 79. C Ardrossan *Glas* 78-80; R Peterhead *Ab* 80-81; Chapl HM Pris Peterhead 80-81; R Renfrew *Glas* 81-87; R Bishopbriggs 87-94; Chapl HM Pris Glas (Barlinnie) from 87; Chapl Stobhill Gen Hosp from 87; P-in-c Port Glas from 94. *The Rectory, Bardrainney Avenue,*

Port Glasgow, Renfrewshire PA14 6HB   Port Glasgow (01475) 707444

BARRETT, Mrs Thelma. b 29. S'wark Ord Course 80. **dss** 82 **d** 87 **p** 94. Newington St Mary *S'wark* 82-84; Chapl Asst St Pet Hosp Chertsey 84-90; Chertsey *Guildf* 84-87; C 87-90; rtd 91; Perm to Offic *Guildf* from 91; NSM Worplesdon 94-95. *9 Danses Close, Guildford, Surrey GU4 7EE*   Guildford (01483) 505215

BARRETT, Wilfred. b 19. Dur Univ BA46 MA49. Wycliffe Hall Ox 55. **d** 57 **p** 58. V Wilmington *Roch* 60-72; Perm to Offic *Chelmsf* from 76; rtd 84. *204 Hockley Road, Rayleigh, Essex SS6 8EU*   Rayleigh (01268) 770364

BARRIBAL, Richard James Pitt. b 45. Trin Coll Bris DipTh80. **d** 80 **p** 81. C Northn St Giles *Pet* 80-82; V Long Buckby w Watford 82-86; Perm to Offic from 86. *166 Abington Avenue, Northampton NN1 4QD*   Northampton (01604) 27734

BARRIE, John Arthur. b 38. K Coll Lon 58 Bps' Coll Cheshunt 59. **d** 63 **p** 64. C Southgate St Mich *Lon* 63-66; CF 66-88; Sen CF 88-93; QHC 91-93; P-in-c Heref H Trin *Heref* from 93. *Holy Trinity Vicarage, 164 Whitecross Road, Hereford HR4 0DH*   Hereford (01432) 273086

BARRINGTON, Dominic Matthew Jesse. b 62. Hatf Coll Dur BA84 MSc85. Ripon Coll Cuddesdon BA94 Berkeley Div Sch MTS95. **d** 95. C Mortlake w E Sheen *S'wark* from 95. *5 Vernon Road, London SW14 8NH*   0181-876 6364

✠**BARRINGTON-WARD, Rt Rev Simon.** b 30. Magd Coll Cam BA53 MA57. Wycliffe Coll Toronto Hon DD Westcott Ho Cam 54. **d** 56 **p** 57 **c** 85. Chapl Magd Coll Cam 56-60; Nigeria 60-63; Fell and Dean of Chpl Magd Coll Cam 63-69; Prin Crowther Hall CMS Tr Coll Selly Oak 69-74; Gen Sec CMS 75-85; Hon Can Derby Cathl *Derby* 75-85; Chapl to The Queen 84-85; Bp Cov from 85. *The Bishop's House, 23 Davenport Road, Coventry CV5 6PW*   Coventry (01203) 672244   Fax 713271

BARRODALE, George Bryan. b 44. Univ of Wales (Ban) DipTh DipMin88. St Mich Coll Llan 67. **d** 69 **p** 70. C Newport Maindee St Jo Ev *Mon* 69-72; TV Merthyr Tydfil and Cyfarthfa *Llan* 72-76; R Cotgrave *S'well* from 76; P-in-c Owthorpe from 76; CF (TA) 76-86; RD Bingham *S'well* from 94. *The Rectory, Thurman Drive, Cotgrave, Nottingham NG12 3HT*   Nottingham (0115) 989 2223

BARRON, Kurt Karl. b 60. Chich Th Coll BTh92. **d** 92 **p** 93. C Bulwell St Mary *S'well* from 92. *123 Squares Avenue, Nottingham NG6 8GL*   Nottingham (0115) 976 1130

BARRON, Leslie Gill. b 44. ACII69. Lich Th Coll 67. **d** 70 **p** 71. C Bishopwearmouth Ch Ch *Dur* 70-72; C Bishopwearmouth St Mary V w St Pet Cdp 72-75; C Harton 75-77; V Lumley 77-88; P-in-c Hendon and Sunderland 88-90; R Hendon 90-94; P-in-c Ushaw Moor 94-95; TR Bearpark and Ushaw Moor from 95. *The Vicarage, 8 Woodland Close, Bearpark, Durham DH7 7EB*   0191-373 3886

BARRON, Richard Davidson. b 51. Lon Univ BSc74. Trin Coll Bris 75. **d** 78 **p** 79. C Bradley *Wakef* 78-81; C Heworth *York* 81-82; TV 82-89; Chapl York Distr Hosp 82-86; R Greenhithe St Mary *Roch* from 89. *The Rectory, Mounts Road, Greenhithe, Kent DA9 9ND*   Greenhithe (01322) 842031

BARRON, Victor Robert. b 45. Ex Univ CertEd70. Trin Coll Bris 76. **d** 78 **p** 79. C Rainham *Chelmsf* 78-81; V Easton H Trin w St Gabr and St Lawr *Bris* 81-82; V Easton H Trin w St Gabr and St Lawr and St Jude 82-89; TR Kinson *Sarum* from 89. *The Rectory, 51 Millham's Road, Bournemouth BH10 7LJ*   Bournemouth (01202) 571996

BARROW, Sqn Ldr Wilfrid Edward Lewis. b 10. Worc Ord Coll 60. **d** 62 **p** 63. V Heath and Reach *St Alb* 66-86; rtd 86; Perm to Offic *Ox* from 86; Perm to Offic *St Alb* from 86. *High Tree House, 5 Leopold Road, Leighton Buzzard, Beds LU7 7QU*   Leighton Buzzard (01525) 377122

BARRY, Herbert Brian. b 25. QUB 46. Edin Th Coll 46. **d** 48 **p** 49. C Northolt Park St Barn *Lon* 69-72; P-in-c S Acton All SS 72-82; V Acton Green St Alb 75-82; V Acton St Alb w All SS 82-88; V Acton Green 88-90; Sub-Warden Guild of St Raphael from 85; rtd 90; Perm to Offic *Ex* from 90. *9 Livery Dole, Magdalen Road, Exeter EX2 5DT*   Exeter (01392) 427835

BARRY, Canon John. b 15. TCD BA38 MA41. CITC 38. **d** 38 **p** 39. I Hillsborough *D & D* 49-83; Preb St Patr Cathl Dub 73-83; rtd 83. *16 West Park, Lisburn, Co Antrim BT28 2BQ*   Lisburn (01846) 670664

BARRY, Jonathan Peter Oulton. b 47. TCD BA70 MA73 Hull Univ BA73 QUB PhD84. Ripon Hall Ox 73. **d** 74 **p** 75. C Dundela *D & D* 74-79; I Ballyphilip w Ardquin 79-85; Dioc Info Officer 80-90; I Comber from 85. *12 Windmill Hill, High Street, Comber, Newtownards, Co Down BT23 5HJ*   Comber (01247) 872283

BARRY, Keith Gordon. b 67. TCD BA92. CITC 92. **d** 94 **p** 95. C Templemore *D & R* from 94; VC Derry Cathl from 94. *4 St Columb's Court, Londonderry BT48 6PT*   Londonderry (01504) 267539

BARRY

BARRY, Nicholas Brian Paul. b 61. Leic Univ BA83. St Steph Ho Ox 84. **d** 87 **p** 88. C St Jo Wood *Lon* 87-90; Chapl RAF from 90. *Chaplaincy Services (RAF), HQ, Personnel and Training Command, RAF Innsworth, Gloucester GL3 1EZ* Gloucester (01452) 712612 Ext 5164 Fax 510828

BARRYMORE, Arthur Norman. b 38. Lon Univ DipTh67. Kelham Th Coll 61. **d** 67 **p** 68. C Guildf St Nic *Guildf* 67-69; P-in-c Burgess Hill St Jo *Chich* 69-74; P-in-c Portslade Gd Shep Mile Oak CD 74-79; Dir Sussex Dioc Assn for the Deaf 80-93; USA from 93. *Redeemer Rectory, Madison Street, Eagle Path, Texas 78852, USA*

BARSLEY, Anthony Noel. b 11. St Aid Birkenhead 46. **d** 47 **p** 48. V Chebsey *Lich* 61-76; rtd 76. *5 Brookside Close, Bedale, N Yorkshire DL8 2DR* Bedale (01677) 422087

BARSLEY, Ms Margaret Ann. b 39. E Midl Min Tr Course 79. **dss** 83 **d** 87 **p** 94. Kirton in Holland *Linc* 83-87; NSM 87-89; NSM Skirbeck Quarter from 89. *44 Sentance Crescent, Boston, Lincs PE20 1XF* Boston (01205) 722307

BARTER, Christopher Stuart. b 49. Chich Th Coll. **d** 84 **p** 85. C Margate St Jo *Cant* 84-88; R Whitwood *Wakef* from 88; Chapl Castleford, Normanton & Distr Hosp 88-95; AIDS Counsellor W Yorkshire Health Authority from 95. *The Rectory, 10A Lumley Street, Castleford, W Yorkshire WF10 5LB* Castleford (01977) 559215

BARTER, Very Rev Donald. b 34. St Fran Coll Brisbane ThL69 ACT ThSchol74. **d** 69 **p** 70. Australia 69-90; Adn of the W 81-86; Dean Townsville 86-90; Appeals Dir SPCK 90-93; Lic to Offic *Leic* 90-93; Australia from 93. *Address temp unknown*

BARTER, Geoffrey Roger. b 41. Bris Univ BSc63. Clifton Th Coll 65. **d** 67 **p** 68. C Normanton *Derby* 67-70; C Rainham *Chelmsf* 70-75; V Plumstead St Jo w St Jas and St Paul *S'wark* 75-82; V Frogmore H Trin *St Alb* from 82. *Holy Trinity Vicarage, 39 Frogmore, St Albans, Herts AL2 2JU* Park Street (01727) 872172

BARTHOLOMEW, David Grant. b 50. Univ of Wales (Lamp) BA77 Brighton Poly DMS78. Chich Th Coll 91. **d** 93 **p** 94. C Petersfield *Portsm* from 93. *42 Heath Road, Petersfield, Hants GU31 4EH* Petersfield (01730) 263190

BARTLAM, Alan Thomas. b 51. Bris Univ BEd74. Linc Th Coll 88. **d** 90 **p** 91. C Longdon-upon-Tern, Rodington, Uppington etc *Lich* 90-92; C Tilstock and Whixall 92-95; V Tilstock, Edstaston and Whixall from 95. *The Vicarage, Tilstock, Whitchurch, Shropshire SY13 3JL* Whixall (01948) 880552

BARTLAM, Graham Frederick. b 37. Lon Univ BA63. Oak Hill Th Coll 59. **d** 64 **p** 65. C Hawkwell *Chelmsf* 64-68; C Gt Warley Ch 68-74; R High and Gd Easter w Margaret Roding from 74. *Good Easter Vicarage, Chelmsford CM1 4RU* Good Easter (01245) 231429

BARTLE, Alan. b 45. Ridley Hall Cam 82. **d** 84 **p** 85. C Ely 84-88; V 87-93; V Chettisham 87-93; V Prickwillow 87-93; P-in-c Thorney Abbey 93-95. *Address temp unknown*

BARTLE, Canon David Colin. b 29. Em Coll Cam BA53 MA57. Ridley Hall Cam 53. **d** 55 **p** 56. V Lowestoft St Jo *Nor* 60-70; P-in-c Thetford St Cuth w H Trin 70-72; TR Thetford 72-75; P-in-c Kilverstone 70-75; P-in-c Croxton 70-75; Teacher Bournemouth Sch 75-83; R Brantham w Stutton *St E* 83-90; RD Samford 86-90; P-in-c Roxwell *Chelmsf* 90-93; Dioc Dir of Ords 90-93; Dioc Lay Min Adv 90-93; Hon Can Chelmsf Cathl 91-93; rtd 93. *8 River Way, Christchurch, Dorset BH23 2QW* Christchurch (01202) 482919

BARTLE, Reginald Stephen. b 24. K Coll Lon AKC51 BD52. **d** 52 **p** 53. SAMS 55-79; Chile 55-79; Adn Chile and Can St Andr Cathl Santiago 64-70; C Tunbridge Wells St Jas *Roch* 80-83; rtd 83; Perm to Offic *St D* 84-94. *28 Blacksmith Close, Pump Lane, Chelmsford CM1 5SY* Chelmsford (01245) 462249

BARTLE-JENKINS, Canon Leonard Christmas. b 13. Univ of Wales (Lamp) BA35. Lich Th Coll 35. **d** 38 **p** 39. V Bassaleg *Mon* 55-73; Can St Woolos Cathl 64-82; RD Bassaleg 67-82; R Michaelston-y-Fedw and Rudry 74-82; rtd 82; Lic to Offic *Mon* from 85. *3 St Teilo's Court, Sturminster Road, Roath, Cardiff CF2 5AX* Cardiff (01222) 489378

BARTLE-JENKINS, Paul. b 43. Bris & Glouc Tr Course. **d** 84 **p** 86. NSM Bris St Agnes and St Simon w St Werburgh *Bris* 84-87; NSM Bris St Paul's from 87. *51 Henleaze Park Drive, Westbury-on-Trym, Bristol BS9 4LN* Bristol (0117) 962 4689

✠**BARTLEET, Rt Rev David Henry.** b 29. St Pet Hall Ox BA55 MA61. Westcott Ho Cam 55. **d** 57 **p** 58 **c** 82. C Ipswich St Mary le Tower *St E* 57-60; C Doncaster St Geo *Sheff* 60-64; V Edenbridge *Roch* 64-73; V Bromley SS Pet and Paul 73-82; Hon Can Roch Cathl 79-93; Suff Bp Tonbridge 82-93; rtd 93. *21 Leaf Road, Aldeburgh, Suffolk IP15 5EY* Aldeburgh (01728) 452724

BARTLES-SMITH, Ven Douglas Leslie. b 37. St Edm Hall Ox BA61 MA65. Wells Th Coll 61. **d** 63 **p** 64. C Westmr St Steph w St Jo *Lon* 63-68; P-in-c Camberwell St Mich w All So w Em

S'wark 68-72; V 72-75; V Battersea St Luke 75-85; RD Battersea 81-85; Adn S'wark from 85. *1A Dog Kennel Hill, London SE22 8AA* 0171-274 6767

BARTLETT, Alan. b 38. Qu Coll Birm. **d** 79 **p** 80. Hon C Perry Beeches *Birm* 79-81; Hon C Kingstanding St Mark from 82. *43 Delhurst Road, Birmingham B44 9UT* 0121-360 7878

BARTLETT, Alan Bennett. b 58. G&C Coll Cam BA81 Birm Univ PhD87 St Jo Coll Dur BA90. Cranmer Hall Dur 88. **d** 91 **p** 92. C Newc H Cross *Newc* 91-94; C Newburn from 94. *St Mary's Parsonage, Throckley, Newcastle upon Tyne NE15 9AB*

BARTLETT, Alban Denys. b 26. St Jo Coll Ox BA50 MA55. St Mich Coll Llan and St D Coll Lamp 50. **d** 52 **p** 53. CF 57-81; Chapl R Hosp Chelsea 81-91; rtd 91. *17 Henley Close, Saxmundham, Suffolk IP17 1EY* Saxmundham (01728) 604418

BARTLETT, Anthony Martin. b 43. Cranmer Hall Dur 74. **d** 77 **p** 78. C Heworth St Mary *Dur* 77-80; V Cleadon 80-84; CF (TA) 81-90; Prec Dur Cathl *Dur* 85-87; V Harton 87-95; P-in-c Hendon from 95. *St Ignatius Rectory, Bramwell Road, Sunderland SR2 8BY* 0191-567 5575

BARTLETT, Basil Gordon. b 11. Selw Coll Cam BA34 MA38. Wells Th Coll 34. **d** 36 **p** 37. Chapl and Prin R Sch for the Blind Leatherhead 50-76; rtd 76; Perm to Offic *B & W* from 76; Perm to Offic *Ex* from 76. *Meadow Cottage, North Wootton, Shepton Mallet, Somerset BA4 4AQ* Pilton (01749) 890547

BARTLETT, Clifford William Tudor. b 15. ALCD38. **d** 38 **p** 39. V Ovingham *Newc* 60-80; rtd 80; Lic to Offic *Newc* from 85; Perm to Offic *Dur* from 81; Chapl Hunties Moor Hosp from 86. *69 Rectory Lane, Winlaton, Blaydon-on-Tyne, Tyne & Wear NE21 6PJ* 0191-414 4236

BARTLETT, Canon David Blandford. b 24. Cam Univ BA49 MA50. Sarum Th Coll. **d** 51 **p** 52. Tanganyika 54-64; Tanzania 64-90; Chan and Can Zanzibar 73-88; rtd 91; P-in-c Heptonstall *Wakef* 91-94; Perm to Offic *Nor* from 94. *25 Simpson Close, North Walsham, Norfolk NR28 0HZ* North Walsham (01692) 405304

BARTLETT, David John. b 36. Pemb Coll Ox BA61. Linc Th Coll 63. **d** 65 **p** 66. C Wollaton *S'well* 65-70; V Woodthorpe 70-83; P-in-c Kirklington w Hockerton from 83; Chapl Rodney Sch Kirklington from 83; V Farnsfield *S'well* from 83; RD S'well 83-93. *The Vicarage, Beck Lane, Farnsfield, Newark, Notts NG22 8ER* Mansfield (01623) 882247

BARTLETT, David William. b 59. Trin Coll Bris 89. **d** 91 **p** 92. C Frinton *Chelmsf* from 91. *28 St Mary's Road, Frinton-on-Sea, Essex CO13 9HS* Frinton-on-Sea (01255) 671974

BARTLETT, Canon Prof John Raymond. b 37. FSA88 BNC Ox BA59 MA62 BLitt62 TCD MA70 LittD. Linc Th Coll 61. **d** 63 **p** 64. C W Bridgford *S'well* 63-66; Lect Div TCD 66-86; Assoc Prof Bibl Studies 86-90; Prin CITC from 89; Prof Past Th from 90; Treas Ch Ch Cathl Dub *D & G* 86-88; Prec from 88. *CITC, Braemor Park, Rathgar, Dublin 14, Irish Republic* Dublin (1) 492-3506 or 492-3274 Fax 492-3082

BARTLETT, Kenneth Vincent John. b 36. OBE93. Or Coll Ox BA61 BTh63. Ripon Hall Ox. **d** 63 **p** 64. C Paddington St Jas *Lon* 63-67; Lic to Offic from 67. *13 Shaa Road, London W3 7LN* 0181-743 3989

BARTLETT, Canon Maurice Edward. b 33. G&C Coll Cam BA59 MA63. Wells Th Coll 59. **d** 60 **p** 61. C Batley All SS *Wakef* 60-64; Bp's Dom Chapl 64-66; Dir of Ords 64-66; Asst Chapl HM Pris Wakef 64-66; V Allerton *Liv* 66-81; V Lanc St Mary *Blackb* from 81; Sub-Chapl HM Pris Lanc from 81; Hon Can Blackb Cathl from 87. *The Vicarage, Priory Close, Lancaster LA1 1YZ* Lancaster (01524) 63200

BARTLETT, Michael Fredrick. b 52. Ex Univ BA74 Liv Univ BPhil75 Ox Univ BA79 MA. Ripon Coll Cuddesdon 76 Ven English Coll Rome 78. **d** 79 **p** 80. C Kirkby *Liv* 79-82; C Wordsley *Lich* 82-83; Chapl Wordsley Hosp 82-88; TV Wordsley *Lich* 83-88; TV Redditch, The Ridge *Worc* from 88. *St Peter's House, Littlewoods, Crabbs Cross, Redditch, Worcs B97 5LB* Redditch (01527) 545709

BARTLETT, Preb Michael George. b 35. S Dios Minl Tr Scheme 84. **d** 87 **p** 88. NSM Wimborne Minster and Holt *Sarum* 87-90; C Charlestown *Truro* 90-91; R St Endellion w Port Isaac and St Kew from 91; Preb St Endellion from 91. *The Rectory, St Endellion, Port Isaac, Cornwall PL29 3TP* Bodmin (01208) 880442

BARTLETT, Richard Charles. b 68. St Kath Coll Liv BA90. Westcott Ho Cam CTM94. **d** 94 **p** 95. C Wareham *Sarum* from 94. *110 Northmoor Way, Wareham, Dorset BH20 4ET* Wareham (01929) 552607

BARTLETT, Stephen Giles Howard. b 39. Bris Univ CertEd63. Lambeth STh86 Lich Th Coll 65. **d** 67 **p** 68. C Old Brumby *Linc* 67-70; C Cleobury Mortimer w Hopton Wafers *Heref* 70-72; C Caversham *Ox* 72-77; V Chalgrove w Berrick Salome 77-88; V W Brompton St Mary w St Pet *Lon* from 88. *24 Fawcett Street, London SW10 9EZ* 0171-351 4204 or 835 1440

40

BARTON, Canon Alfred Ernest. b 19. Man Univ BA52. Qu Coll Birm 50. d 52 p 53. V Benson Ox 67-92; RD Cuddesdon 73-85; Hon Can Ch Ch 85-92; RD Aston and Cuddesdon 85-88; rtd 92. *St Fergus Cottage, Cottisford, Brackley, Northants NN13 5SW* Brackley (01280) 847979

BARTON, Dr Andrew Edward. b 53. MRSC St Jo Coll Ox MA77 DPhil80. Ridley Hall Cam 87. d 90 p 91. C Ringwood *Win* 90-95; R Baughurst, Ramsdell, Wolverton w Ewhurst etc from 95. *The Rectory, Wolverton, Basingstoke, Hants RG26 5RU* Kingsclere (01635) 298008

BARTON, Canon Arthur Michael. b 33. CCC Cam BA57 MA61. Wycliffe Hall Ox 57. d 59 p 60. Min Can Bradf Cathl *Bradf* 59-61; C Maltby *Sheff* 61-63; V Silsden *Bradf* 63-70; V Moor Allerton *Ripon* 70-81; TR 81-82; V Wetherby from 82; Chapl HM Young Offender Inst Wetherby 82-89; RD Harrogate *Ripon* 88-95; Hon Can Ripon Cathl from 89. *The Vicarage, Parsons Green, Wetherby, W Yorkshire LS22 6RQ* Wetherby (01937) 582423

BARTON, Ven Charles John Greenwood. b 36. ALCD63. d 63 p 64. C Cant St Mary Bredin *Cant* 63-66; V Whitfield w W Langdon 66-75; V S Kensington St Luke *Lon* 75-83; AD Chelsea 80-83; Chief Broadcasting Officer for C of E 83-90; Lic to Offic *Lon* 84-90; Adn Aston and Can Res Birm Cathl *Birm* from 90. *26 George Road, Birmingham B15 1PJ* 0121-454 5525 Fax 455 6085

BARTON, Canon Cyril Albert. b 28. St Pet Hall Ox BA50 MA54. Ridley Hall Cam. d 52 p 53. C Maghull *Liv* 52-55; Min Can Bradf Cathl *Bradf* 55-58; V Oldham St Paul *Man* 58-68; V Norbury *Ches* 68-90; Hon Can Ches Cathl from 85; R Aldford and Bruera from 90. *The Rectory, Middle Lane, Aldford, Chester CH3 6JA* Chester (01244) 620281

BARTON, Dale. b 49. Selw Coll Cam BA71 MA76. Linc Th Coll 71. d 73 p 74. C Gosforth All SS *Newc* 73-77; Lesotho 77-81; Dep Warden CA Hostel Cam 82-83; C Shepton Mallet w Doulting *B & W* 83-88; TV Preston St Jo *Blackb* from 88. *St Stephen's Vicarage, 60 Broadgate, Preston PR1 8DU* Preston (01772) 555762

BARTON, David Gerald Story. b 38. Selw Coll Cam BA62 MA66. Cuddesdon Coll 63. d 65 p 66. C Cowley St Jas *Ox* 65-67; C Hambleden 67-70; Hon C Hammersmith St Jo *Lon* 72-77; Hon C Paddington St Jas 77-81; Hd Master Soho Par Sch 81-88; Hon C Westmr St Jas 81-92; RE Project Officer Lon Dioc Bd for Schs 88-92; Dioc Schs Adv *Ox* from 93; NSM Iffley from 93. *12 Parker Street, Oxford OX4 1TD* Oxford (01865) 240059

BARTON, Edward. b 23. d 75 p 76. C Budock *Truro* 75-79; P-in-c St Stithians w Perranarworthal 79-80; V St Stythians w Perranarworthal and Gwennap 80-82; rtd 88. *Riverside, 5 Riviera Terrace, Malpas, Truro TR1 1SR* Truro (01872) 71686

BARTON, Eric Alfred. b 13. Clifton Th Coll 38. d 40 p 41. V Buttershaw St Paul *Bradf* 61-70; V Nailsea Ch Ch *B & W* 70-82; rtd 82; Perm to Offic *Ex* from 82. *22 Woolbrook Rise, Sidmouth, Devon EX10 9UD* Sidmouth (01395) 514841

BARTON, Canon Geoffrey. b 27. Or Coll Ox BA48 MA52. Chich Th Coll 49. d 51 p 52. V Boroughbridge w Roecliffe *Ripon* 60-73; V Aldborough w Boroughbridge and Roecliffe 73; P-in-c Farnham w Scotton and Staveley and Copgrove 73-74; R 74-77; Chapl Roundway Hosp Devizes 77-92; Can and Preb Sarum Cathl *Sarum* 86-92; rtd 92. *4B Willow House, Downlands Road, Devizes, Wilts SN10 5EA* Devizes (01380) 725311

BARTON, Canon John. b 25. MBE91. Keble Coll Ox BA48 MA50. Ely Th Coll 48. d 50 p 51. Chapl Stanley Royd & Pinderfields Hosps Wakef 60-72; RD Wakef 68-72; Chapl Jo Radcliffe Hosp & Radcliffe Infirmary 72-90; Chapl Chu Hosp Ox 72-89; Hon Can Ch Ch *Ox* from 77; RD Cowley 89-94; rtd 90. *212 Headington Road, Oxford OX3 7PS* Oxford (01865) 63918

BARTON, Canon Dr John. b 48. Keble Coll Ox BA69 MA73 Mert Coll Ox DPhil74 St Cross Coll Ox DLitt88. d 73 p 73. Lect St Cross Coll Ox 74-89; Fell 74-91; Chapl 79-91; Reader in Bibl Studies 89-91; Prof and Fell Oriel Coll Ox from 91; Can Th Win Cathl *Win* from 91. *11 Withington Court, Abingdon, Oxon OX14 3QA* Abingdon (01235) 525925

BARTON, Canon John Christopher Peter. b 28. Trin Hall Cam BA51 MA56. Ridley Hall Cam 51. d 53 p 54. V Welling *Roch* 64-75; P-in-c Malmesbury w Westport *Bris* 75-84; P-in-c Charlton w Brokenborough and Hankerton 80-84; V Malmesbury w Westport and Brokenborough 84-94; Hon Can Kigezi from 92; rtd 94. *Orchard House, Orchard Road, Crewkerne, Somerset TA18 7AF* Crewkerne (01460) 72536

BARTON, Canon John Michael. b 40. TCD BA62 Div Test. d 63 p 64. C Coleraine *Conn* 63-68; C Portadown St Mark *Arm* 68-71; I Carnteel and Crilly 71-83; I Derryloran from 83; Preb Arm Cathl from 94. *Derryloran Rectory, 13 Loy Street, Cookstown, Co Tyrone BT80 8PZ* Cookstown (016487) 62261

BARTON, Dr Margaret Anne. b 54. St Anne's Coll Ox MA80 DPhil81 Selw Coll Cam BA89. Ridley Hall Cam 87. d 90 p 94. Par Dn Burley Ville *Win* 90-94; C 94; Chapl K Alfred Coll from 94. *King Alfred's College, Sparkford Road, Winchester, Hants SO22 4NR* Winchester (01962) 841515

BARTON, Samuel David. b 45. DipTh. d 84 p 85. C Ballywillan *Conn* 84-86; I Aghadowey w Kilrea *D & R* 86-92; Bp's C Fahan Lower and Upper from 92; Dio Educn Co-ord from 94. *Fahan Lower Rectory, Church Street, Buncrana, Co Donegal, Irish Republic* Buncrana (77) 61154

BARTON, Dr Stephen Christian. b 52. Macquarie Univ (NSW) BA75 DipEd75 Lanc Univ MA78 K Coll Lon PhD92. Cranmer Hall Dur 91. d 93 p 94. NSM Neville's Cross St Jo CD *Dur* from 93. *33 Nevilledale Terrace, Durham DH1 4QG* 0191-386 4983

BARTON, Stephen William. b 50. St Jo Coll Cam BA73 MA76 Leeds Univ MPhil81. Coll of Resurr Mirfield 75. d 77 p 78. C Horton *Bradf* 77-80; USPG 80-92; Bangladesh 81-92; TV Southn (City Cen) *Win* from 92. *St Matthew's Vicarage, 12-14 King's Park Road, Southampton SO15 2AT* Southampton (01703) 224588

BARTON, Canon Sydney Gerald. b 1900. St Jo Coll Dur LTh29 BA33. St Aid Birkenhead 26. d 30 p 31. R W Kirby St Bridget *Ches* 53-70; Hon Can Ches Cathl 61-70; rtd 70; Hon C Capenhurst *Ches* 71-78; Perm to Offic *Cant* 82-93. *The Old Rectory for the Elderly, Lanfranc Road, Harbledown, Canterbury, Kent CT2 8NN* Canterbury (01227) 768004

BARTON, Timothy Charles. b 47. Sarum & Wells Th Coll 73. d 76 p 77. C Upholland *Liv* 76-80; V Dalton from 80. *88 Lyndhurst Avenue, Skelmersdale, Lancs WN8 6UH* Skelmersdale (01695) 33148

BARTON, Trevor James. b 50. St Alb Minl Tr Scheme 79. d 87 p 88. NSM Hemel Hempstead *St Alb* from 87. *46 Crossfell Road, Hemel Hempstead, Herts HP3 8RQ* Hemel Hempstead (01442) 251537

BARWELL, Brian Bernard Beale. b 30. Preston Poly CertEd79. AKC59 St Boniface Warminster 59. d 60 p 61. V Farington *Blackb* 69-72; C-in-c Blackb St Luke w St Phil 72-75; C Standish 75-76; Lic to Offic 76-92; rtd 92; Perm to Offic *Blackb* from 92. *70 Claytongate, Coppull, Chorley, Lancs PR7 4PS* Coppull (01257) 794251

BARWOOD, Frederick James. b 05. Selw Coll Cam BA30 MA34. Ely Th Coll 33. d 34 p 35. V Hordle *Win* 61-74; rtd 74; Perm to Offic *Win* from 75. *94 Manor Road, New Milton, Hants BH25 5EJ* New Milton (01425) 616150

BARZEY, Ms Michele Alison Lesley. b 63. Trin Coll Bris BA94. d 94. C Gravelly Hill *Birm* from 94. *107 Mere Road, Birmingham B23 7LN* 0121-373 6702

BASFORD HOLBROOK, Colin Eric. b 42. St Steph Ho Ox 73. d 75 p 76. C Dovecot *Liv* 75-78; V Hollinfare 79-83; CMS 83-88; Cyprus 83-91; Chapl Athens, Kifissia, Patras, Thessaloniki etc *Eur* 91-93; Chapl Athens w Patras, Thessaloniki and Voula 93-94. *18 Shorwell Close, Great Sankey, Warrington WA5 3JZ*

BASHFORD, Richard Frederick. b 36. Lon Univ DipTh68. Clifton Th Coll. d 68 p 69. C Bedworth *Cov* 68-71; C Lower Homerton St Paul *Lon* 71-75; V Bordesley Green *Birm* 75-81; R Birm Bishop Latimer w All SS from 81. *The Vicarage, 28 Handsworth New Road, Birmingham B18 4PT* 0121-554 2221

BASHFORD, Robert Thomas. b 49. Ch Coll Cam BA70 CertEd72 MA74 Lon Univ BD84 MPhil89. Oak Hill Th Coll 86. d 88 p 89. C Frinton *Chelmsf* 88-91; C Galleywood Common from 91. *St Michael's House, 13 Roughtons, Galleywood, Chelmsford CM2 8PE* Chelmsford (01245) 474695

BASIL, Brother. See FARRANT, Jonathan

BASINGSTOKE, Archdeacon of. See KNIGHT, Ven Alexander Francis (Alec)

BASINGSTOKE, Suffragan Bishop of. See ROWELL, Rt Rev Douglas Geoffrey

BASKERVILLE, John. b 45. Open Univ BA78. Sarum & Wells Th Coll 92. d 93 p 94. C Wanstead St Mary w Ch Ch *Chelmsf* from 93. *2 Church Path, London E11 2SS* 0181-530 6875

BASKERVILLE, Philip Duncan. b 58. St Chad's Coll Dur BSc79 Or Coll Ox PGCE80. Trin Coll Bris BA87. d 88 p 89. C Roby *Liv* 88-93; Kenya from 93. *St Paul's Theological College, PO Box 18, Kapsabet, Kenya* Kenya (254) 326-2053 Fax 2451

BASON, Brian Vaudrey. b 27. Leeds Univ BA49 Lon Univ BD69. Coll of Resurr Mirfield 49. d 51 p 52. V Audenshaw St Hilda *Man* 56-89; Perm to Offic *Ches* from 89; Perm to Offic *Man* from 89; Audenshaw High Sch 89-92; rtd 92. *78 Windsor Road, Denton, Manchester M34 2HE* 0161-320 8455

BASS, Colin Graham. b 41. Liv Univ BSc62 Fitzw Ho Cam BA64 MA68. Ox NSM Course 84. d 87 p 88. Dir of Studies Leighton Park Sch Reading from 87; NSM Earley St Pet *Ox* 87-92; NSM Reading Deanery from 92. *9 Bramley Close, Reading RG6 7PL* Reading (01734) 663732

BASS, George Michael. b 39. Ely Th Coll 62. **d** 65 **p** 66. C Romaldkirk *Ripon* 65-68; C Kenton Ascension *Newc* 68-71; CF 71-94; Chapl N Tyneside Hosps from 94; Chapl Preston Hosp N Shields from 94. *North Tyneside General Hospital, Rake Lane, North Shields, Tyne & Wear NE29 8NH* 0191-259 6660

BASS, Mrs Rosemary Jane. b 38. Linc Th Coll 76. **dss** 79 **d** 87 **p** 94. Bedf All SS *St Alb* 79-84; Leavesden All SS 84-87; Par Dn 87-94; C 94-95; V Luton St Andr from 95. *St Andrew's Vicarage, 11 Blenheim Crescent, Luton LU3 1HA* Luton (01582) 32380

BASSETT, Abner Gerwyn. b 25. Univ of Wales (Lamp) BA48 LTh50. **d** 50 **p** 51. P-in-c Llanfair-ar-y-Bryn *St D* 58-73; V Llandysilio w Egremont and Llanglydwen etc 73-91; rtd 91. *1 Ger-y-Llan, The Parade, Carmarthen, Dyfed SA31 1LY* Carmarthen (01267) 235284

BASSETT, John Edmund. b 33. St Aid Birkenhead 63. **d** 66 **p** 67. C Guiseley *Bradf* 66-67; C Stechford *Birm* 67-71; C Ross *Heref* 71-72; P-in-c Brampton Abbotts 73-75; P-in-c Weston under Penyard 73-75; P-in-c Hope Mansell 73-75; TR Halesworth w Linstead and Chediston *St E* 75-78; P-in-c Irby on Humber *Linc* 78; R Laceby 78-83; V Sale St Paul *Ches* 83-88; P-in-c Southport All SS *Liv* 88-94; P-in-c Southport All So 88-94; V Southport All SS and All So from 94. *All Saints' Vicarage, 1 Park Avenue, Southport, Merseyside PR9 9LS* Southport (01704) 533336

BASTEN, Richard Henry. b 40. Codrington Coll Barbados 60. **d** 63 **p** 64. Barbados 68-72; C Hartlepool H Trin *Dur* 72-73; Chapl Bedstone Coll 73-88; C Clun w Chapel Lawn *Heref* 73-77; P-in-c Clungunford 77-78; R Clungunford w Clunbury and Clunton, Bedstone etc 78-88; R Rowde and Poulshot *Sarum* 88-95; rtd 95. *41 Bewley Way, Churchdown, Gloucester GL3 2DU* Gloucester (01452) 859738

BASTIDE, Derek. b 44. Dur Univ BA65 Reading Univ DipEd66 Sussex Univ MA77. Chich Th Coll 76. **d** 77 **p** 78. Hon C Lewes All SS, St Anne, St Mich and St Thos *Chich* 77-84; Prin Lect Brighton Poly 80-92; Prin Lect Brighton Univ from 92; P-in-c Hamsey *Chich* from 84. *The Rectory, Offham, Lewes, E Sussex BN7 3PX* Lewes (01273) 474356

BASTIN, Edward James. b 06. Lon Univ BSc28. Ridley Hall Cam 28. **d** 30 **p** 31. V Keresley and Coundon *Cov* 36-71; rtd 71. *7 Brownshill Court, Brownshill Green Road, Coventry CV6 2PE* Keresley (01203) 336698

BASTOCK, Kenneth William. b 22. Launde Abbey 75. **d** 76 **p** 77. C Glen Parva and S Wigston *Leic* 76-80; V Orton-on-the-Hill w Twycross etc 80-92; rtd 92. *18 Beech Road, Oadby, Leicester LE2 5QL* Leicester (0116) 271 0454

BASTON, Mrs Caroline. b 56. Birm Univ BSc78 CertEd79. Ripon Coll Cuddesdon 87. **d** 89 **p** 94. Par Dn Southn Thornhill St Chris *Win* 89-94; C 94-95; R Win All SS w Chilcomb and Chesil from 95; Dioc Communications Officer from 95. *All Saints' Rectory, 19 Petersfield Road, Winchester, Hants SO23 0JD* Winchester (01962) 853777

BATCHELOR, Alan Harold. b 30. Bris Univ BA54 Hull Univ MA63 DipPM68 LSE. Linc Th Coll 54. **d** 56 **p** 57. C Kingston upon Hull St Alb *York* 56-60; C Attercliffe w Carbrook *Sheff* 60-62; India 63-87; Ind Chapl *Ripon* from 87; C Kirkstall from 92. *23 Harrowby Road, Leeds LS16 5HX* Leeds (0113) 275 2709 or 242 4886

BATCHELOR, John Millar. b 35. CITC 76. **d** 78 **p** 79. C Belf All SS *Conn* 78-80; I Eglish w Killylea *Arm* from 80. *154 Killylea Road, Armagh BT60 4LN* Caledon (01861) 568320

BATCHELOR, Martin John. b 67. Plymouth Poly BSc91. St Jo Coll Nottm DTS94 MA95. **d** 95. C Brecon St Mary and Battle w Llanddew *S & B* from 95; Min Can Brecon Cathl from 95. *The Clergy House, Cathedral Close, Brecon, Powys LD3 9DP* Brecon (01874) 622972

BATE, Bernard Percival. b 12. Selw Coll Cam BA37 MA41. Wells Th Coll 37. **d** 38 **p** 39. R Lurgashall *Chich* 68-77; rtd 77; Perm to Offic *Bradf* 79-85. *4 Courtwood Close, Shady Bower, Salisbury SP1 2RX* Salisbury (01722) 328887

BATE, Dylan Griffin. b 48. Glam Poly HNC71. Mon Dioc Tr Scheme 91. **d** 94 **p** 95. NSM Fleur-de-Lis *Mon* from 94. *56 Apollo Way, Blackwood, Gwent NP2 1WB* Blackwood (01495) 222564

BATE, Lawrence Mark. b 40. Univ Coll Ox BA63. Coll of Resurr Mirfield 65. **d** 67 **p** 68. C Benwell St Jas *Newc* 67-69; C Monkseaton St Pet 69-72; TV Withycombe Raleigh *Ex* 72-84; RD Aylesbeare 81-84; R Alphington from 84. *The Rectory, Alphington, Exeter EX2 8XJ* Exeter (01392) 437662

BATE, Michael Keith. b 42. Lich Th Coll 67. **d** 69 **p** 70. C W Bromwich St Jas *Lich* 69-73; C Thornhill *Wakef* 73-76; V Wrenthorpe 76-82; V Upper Gornal *Lich* 82-93; V Upper Gornal *Worc* from 93; Chapl Burton Rd Hosp Dudley 82-94; Chapl Dudley Priority Health NHS Trust from 94. *St Peter's Vicarage, 35 Eve Lane, Upper Gornal, Dudley, W Midlands DY1 3TY* Sedgley (01902) 883467

BATEMAN, Alfred Neville. b 39. MIMI83. Oak Hill Th Coll 87. **d** 89 **p** 90. C Pendlebury St Jo *Man* 89-92; P-in-c Lt Hulton 92-93; TV Walkden Moor St Paul w Lt Hulton St Jo the Bapt from 93. *St John's Vicarage, Algernon Road, Worsley, Manchester M28 5RD* 0161-790 2338

BATEMAN, James Edward (Jim). b 44. Lon Univ BSc65 Bris Univ DipTh74. Trin Coll Bris 71. **d** 74 **p** 75. C Woodlands *Sheff* 74-77; C Rushden w Newton Bromswold *Pet* 77-84; R Vange *Chelmsf* 84-94; V Southminster from 94. *The Vicarage, Burnham Road, Southminster, Essex CM0 7ES* Maldon (01621) 772300

BATEMAN, Kenneth William. b 34. ACII58. N Ord Course 85. **d** 88 **p** 89. Hon C Pilling *Blackb* 88-91; Chapl Lanc Moor Hosp from 88; C Kirkby Lonsdale *Carl* from 91. *Croft House, Casterton, Kirkby Lonsdale, Carnforth, Cumbria LA6 2SA* Kirkby Lonsdale (015242) 72507

BATEMAN, Martyn Henry. b 31. Jes Coll Cam BA54 MA58. Clifton Th Coll 54. **d** 56 **p** 57. V Wickham Market *St E* 69-82; Hon Can St E Cathl 80-85; V Felixstowe SS Pet and Paul 82-85; TR Lydford, Brent Tor, Bridestowe and Sourton *Ex* 85-92; RD Tavistock 90-92; rtd 92. *Ardochy, Whitebridge, Inverness IV1 2UR* Gorthleck (01456) 486273

BATEMAN, Richard George. b 46. St Jo Coll Dur. **d** 82 **p** 83. C Wolviston *Dur* 82-85; C Greenside 85-87; V Newburn *Newc* from 87. *The Vicarage, Newburn, Newcastle upon Tyne NE15 8LQ* 0191-229 0522

BATEMAN, Richard William. b 36. AKC61. **d** 62 **p** 63. C Pennywell St Thos and Grindon St Oswald CD *Dur* 62-66; Trinidad and Tobago 66-70; R Etherley *Dur* 70-77; Ind Chapl *Roch* 77-83; Hon C Chatham St Steph 78-83; Chapl RN 79-83; V Kemsing w Woodlands *Roch* 83-90; P-in-c Petham and Waltham w Lower Hardres etc *Cant* from 90. *The Rectory, Curtis Lane, Stelling Minnis, Canterbury, Kent CT4 6BT* Stelling Minnis (0122787) 318

BATEMAN-CHAMPAIN, John Nicholas. b 30. Cam Univ BA53. S'wark Ord Course 85. **d** 85 **p** 86. C Harpenden St Jo *St Alb* 85-88; V Northaw from 88. *The Vicarage, 58 Hill Rise, Cuffley, Potters Bar, Herts EN6 4RG* Potters Bar (01707) 874126

BATES, David William. b 25. Cranmer Hall Dur 59. **d** 61 **p** 62. V Linc St Pet-at-Gowts and St Andr *Linc* 68-77; V Metheringham 77-81; V Metheringham w Blankney 81-91; rtd 91; Perm to Offic *Linc* from 91. *11 Neustadt Court, Danes Terrace, Lincoln LN2 1PG* Lincoln (01522) 545207

BATES, Derek Alvin. b 27. St Mich Coll Llan 57. **d** 59 **p** 60. V Shebbear *Ex* 67-71; R Buckland Filleigh 67-71; R Highampton w Sheepwash 71; R Coates *Ely* 72-80; R Clovelly *Ex* 80-92; V Woolfardisworthy and Buck Mills 80-92; rtd 92; Perm to Offic *Ex* from 92. *Jorejoder, 10 J H Taylor Drive, Laurel Park, Northam, Bideford, Devon EX39 1TU*

✠**BATES, Rt Rev Gordon.** b 34. Kelham Th Coll 54. **d** 58 **p** 59 **c** 83. C New Eltham All SS *S'wark* 58-62; Asst Youth Chapl *Glouc* 62-64; Youth Chapl *Liv* 65-69; Chapl Liv Cathl 65-69; V Huyton St Mich 69-73; Can Res and Prec Liv Cathl 73-83; Dir of Ords 73-83; Suff Bp Whitby *York* from 83. *Handyside, 60 West Green, Stokesley, Middlesbrough, Cleveland TS9 5BD* Stokesley (01642) 710390 Fax 710685

BATES, Harry. b 11. Sheff Univ BSc32. Trin Coll Bris 39. **d** 40 **p** 41. Australia 40-45 and from 54; R Barnwell *Pet* 46-54. *34 Pindari Avenue, Camden, NSW, Australia 2570* Campbelltown (46) 667920

BATES, James. b 46. Linc Th Coll 73. **d** 75 **p** 76. C Ewell *Guildf* 75-77; C Farncombe 77-80; V Pet St Mary *Pet* 80-92; V Kingston All SS w St Jo *S'wark* from 92. *All Saints' Vicarage, 15 Woodbine Avenue, Kingston upon Thames KT1 2AZ* 0181-546 2644

BATES, Michael. b 33. Dur Univ BSc57 Hull Univ ADME84. Clifton Th Coll 57. **d** 59 **p** 60. C Drypool St Columba w St Andr and St Pet *York* 59-62; C Cheadle *Ches* 62-67; V Newbottle *Dur* 67-75; Asst Master Bilton Grange High Sch Hull from 76; Hon C Kingston upon Hull H Trin *York* from 81. *68 Davenport Avenue, Hessle, N Humberside HU13 0RW* Hull (01482) 646392

BATES, Canon Paul Spencer. b 40. CCC Cam BA62 MA66. Linc Th Coll 63. **d** 65 **p** 66. C Bris St Andr Hartcliffe *Bris* 65-69; Chapl Win Coll 69-80; Dir of Tr *Win* 80-90; Hon Can Win Cathl 87-90; Can Westmr Abbey from 90; Steward Westmr Abbey from 90. *5 Little Cloister, Westminster Abbey, London SW1P 3PL* 0171-222 6939 Fax 233 2072

BATES, Miss Phyllis Edith. b 29. S'wark Ord Course 80. **dss** 83 **d** 87 **p** 94. Registrar S'wark Ord Course 83-89; Fulham St Dionis Parson's Green *Lon* 83-87; Hon Par Dn 87-94; rtd 89; NSM Hammersmith St Paul *Lon* from 94. *26 St Dionis Road, London SW6 4TT* 0171-731 6935

BATES, Mrs Rosemary Eileen Hamilton. b 45. Ripon Coll Cuddesdon 87. **d** 89 **p** 94. Par Dn Brackley St Pet w St Jas *Pet*

89-94; C 94-95; P-in-c N Hinksey and Wytham *Ox* from 95. *The Vicarage, 81 West Way, Oxford OX2 9JY* Oxford (01865) 242345

BATES, Stuart Geoffrey. b 61. Univ of Wales (Lamp) BA82. St Steph Ho Ox 83. **d** 85 **p** 86. C Bromley St Mark *Roch* 85-88; C Westmr St Matt *Lon* 88-89; C Gt Ilford St Mary *Chelmsf* 89-95; V Crofton Park St Hilda w St Cypr *S'wark* from 95. *St Hilda's Vicarage, 35 Buckthorne Road, London SE4 2DG* 0181-699 1277

BATES, Vincent. b 24. **d** 65 **p** 65. Kenya 65-66; Perm to Offic *Bris* 66-76; Perm to Offic *Ox* 68-72; C Yarlington *B & W* 72-76; Lic to Offic *Ox* from 76. *6 Nursery Gardens, Earl Shilton, Leicester LE9 7JE* Earl Shilton (01455) 841936

BATES, Wilfred Abel. b 11. AKC33. Bps' Coll Cheshunt 33. **d** 34 **p** 36. V Dudley St Jo *Worc* 63-73; V Offenham 73-79; P-in-c Bretforton 76-79; V Offenham and Bretforton 79-91; rtd 91. *29 Bramley Avenue, Worcester WR2 6DQ* Worcester (01905) 426996

BATES, William Frederic. b 49. St Jo Coll Dur BSc72 BA74. Cranmer Hall Dur DipTh75. **d** 75 **p** 76. C Knutsford St Jo and Toft *Ches* 75-78; C Ripley *Derby* 78-80; R Nether and Over Seale 81-93; V Lullington from 81; V Allestree St Nic from 93. *The Vicarage, 4 Lawn Avenue, Allestree, Derby DE22 2PE* Derby (01332) 550224

BATES, William Hugh. b 33. Keble Coll Ox BA56 MA59. Westcott Ho Cam 59. **d** 60 **p** 61. Tutor St Chad's Coll Dur 63-70; V Bishop Wilton *York* 70-76; RD Pocklington 74-76; V Pickering 76-82; Tutor NE Ord Course 79-94; P-in-c Crayke w Brandsby and Yearsley 82-94; P-in-c Stillington and Marton w Moxby 82-94; rtd 94; Perm to Offic *York* from 94. *Garden Cottage, Coxwold, York YO6 4AS* Coxwold (01347) 868758

BATESON, Canon Geoffrey Frederick. b 27. K Coll Lon BD51 AKC51. **d** 52 **p** 53. V Newc St Geo *Newc* 68-77; RD Newc 75-77; Chapl St Geo and Cottage Hosp Morpeth 77-89; R Morpeth *Newc* 77-89; Hon Can Newc Cathl 80-89; rtd 89. *1 Netherby Close, Sleights, Whitby, N Yorkshire YO22 5HD* Whitby (01947) 810997

BATESON, James Howard. b 36. CEng64 FIMM88 MSOSc88 Qu Mary Coll Lon BSc57. E Midl Min Tr Course 85. **d** 87 **p** 88. NSM W Bridgford *S'well* 87-88; NSM Wilford Hill from 88; Dioc Officer for NSMs from 94. *45 Stamford Road, Nottingham NG2 6GD* Nottingham (0115) 923 1820

BATEY, Canon Herbert Taylor. b 22. Qu Coll Ox BA46 MA48. Linc Th Coll 48. **d** 48 **p** 49. Chapl Culham Coll Abingdon 64-68; Prin Lect 68-75; P-in-c Culham *Ox* 68-75; Vice-Prin Coll of Ripon and York St Jo from 75; Hon Can Ripon Cathl *Ripon* 85-92; rtd 87. *29 College Road, Ripon, N Yorkshire HG4 2HE* Ripon (01765) 607096

BATEY, William Abbott. b 20. Cranmer Hall Dur 62. **d** 63 **p** 64. R Moresby *Carl* 66-77; P-in-c Arnside 77-85; V 85-90; rtd 90. *33 Greengate, Levens, Kendal, Cumbria LA8 8NF* Sedgwick (015395) 66791

BATH, David James William. b 43. Oak Hill NSM Course 87. **d** 89 **p** 90. NSM Henley *Ox* 89-90; Gen Manager Humberside Gd News Trust from 90. *Flat 1, 67 Wright Street, Hull HU2 8JD* Hull (01482) 28135 or 24040

BATH, Edward Nelson. b 16. Bps' Coll Cheshunt 55. **d** 57 **p** 58. V Charing Heath w Egerton *Cant* 67-82; P-in-c Pluckley w Pevington 78-82; rtd 82; Perm to Offic *Cant* from 82. *6 Lindens, Dental Street, Hythe, Kent CT21 5LH* Hythe (01303) 264896

BATH AND WELLS, Bishop of. See THOMPSON, Rt Rev James Lawton

BATH, Archdeacon of. See BURGESS, Ven John Edward

BATSLEER, Canon Albert. b 21. Selw Coll Cam BA46 MA54. Cuddesdon Coll 46. **d** 48 **p** 49. R Staveley *Derby* 65-72; V Riddings 72-81; RD Alfreton 76-81; V New Mills 81-85; RD Glossop 81-83; Hon Can Derby Cathl 81-85; rtd 85. *21 Dene Close, Skellingthorpe, Lincoln LN6 5SU* Lincoln (01522) 690901

BATSON, David Frederick Edward. b 38. K Coll Lon BD69. AKC61. **d** 62 **p** 63. C Southport H Trin *Liv* 62-64; Asst Chapl Hurstpierpoint Coll Hassocks 64-65; C Cleator Moor w Cleator *Carl* 65-66; Asst Master K Geo V Sch Southport 66-67; NSM Leigh w Bransford *Worc* 68-79; Lic to Offic 68-79; Hon Asst Chapl Convent of H Name Malvern Link 68-72; Lect and Tutor Langside Coll Glas from 95. *Connelcraig, Dalswinton, Dumfries DG2 0XY* Auldgirth (01387) 740589

BATSON, John Gordon Kemp. b 38. Kelham Th Coll 60 Bps' Coll Cheshunt 64. **d** 65 **p** 66. C Lamorbey H Redeemer *Roch* 65-69; Trinidad and Tobago 69-74; V Boro Green *Roch* 74-83; V Perry Street 83-92; V Yalding w Collier Street from 92. *The Vicarage, Vicarage Road, Yalding, Maidstone, Kent ME18 6DR* Maidstone (01622) 814182

BATSON, William Francis Robert. b 43. Nottm Univ DipTP69 St Jo Coll Dur BA72. **d** 73 **p** 74. C Eastwood *S'well* 73-77; R Long Marton w Dufton and w Milburn *Carl* 77-79; V Flimby

79-85; TR Raveningham *Nor* 85-91; R Kinver and Enville *Lich* from 91. *The Vicarage, Kinver, Stourbridge, W Midlands DY7 6HJ* Kinver (01384) 872556

BATT, Joseph William. b 39. Keele Univ BA62. Ripon Hall Ox 63. **d** 64 **p** 65. C Bushbury *Lich* 64-68; C Walsall 68-71; Nigeria 71-75; Area Sec (Dios Guildf and Chich) CMS 75-84; V Ottershaw *Guildf* from 84. *Christ Church Vicarage, Coach Road, Ottershaw, Chertsey, Surrey KT16 0PA* Ottershaw (01932) 873160

BATT, Kenneth Victor. b 41. Wycliffe Hall Ox 68. **d** 71 **p** 72. C Yateley *Win* 71-76; R The Candover Valley 76-82; R Durrington *Sarum* 82-89; V Kempshott *Win* from 89. *The Vicarage, 171 Kempshott Lane, Kempshott, Basingstoke, Hants RG22 5LF* Basingstoke (01256) 56400

BATTE, Mrs Kathleen (Kath). b 47. Homerton Coll Cam TCert68. NE Ord Course 91. **d** 94 **p** 95. NSM Newc St Gabr *Newc* from 94. *61 Cochrane Park Avenue, Newcastle upon Tyne NE7 7JU* 0191-266 6491

BATTELL, Canon Colin Frank. b 44. Keble Coll Ox BA66 MA71. St Steph Ho Ox 66. **d** 68 **p** 69. C Wellingborough St Mary *Pet* 68-71; Lic to Offic *Eur* 70-71; C Wanstead St Mary *Chelmsf* 71-76; USPG 76-94; Ethiopia 76-94; Hon Can All SS Cathl Cairo 86-94. *c/o 38 Rathmore Road, Cambridge CB1 4AD*

BATTEN, George William John. b 34. Bris & Glouc Tr Course 76. **d** 80 **p** 81. NSM Dean Forest St Paul *Glouc* from 80. *39 Bells Place, Coleford, Glos GL16 8BX* Dean (01594) 832291

BATTEN, Graham John. b 39. Open Univ BA81 Univ of Wales (Cardiff) DipTh65. St D Coll Lamp 65. **d** 66 **p** 67. C Llangynwyd w Maesteg *Llan* 66-70; C St Andrew's Major and Michaelston-le-Pit 70-72; Chapl RN 72-91; Asst Chapl Fleet 91-94; V Dover St Mary *Cant* from 94. *The Vicarage, Taswell Street, Dover, Kent CT16 1SE* Dover (01304) 206842

BATTEN, Thomas Cyril. b 10. St Jo Coll Dur BA37 DipTh38 MA40. **d** 38 **p** 39. V Mellor *Blackb* 59-70; rtd 70; Lic to Offic *Blackb* from 70. *40 Belgrave Avenue, Penwortham, Preston PR1 0BH* Preston (01772) 746473

BATTERSBY, David George Sellers. b 32. AKC57. St Boniface Warminster 57 Lambeth STh80. **d** 58 **p** 59. C Glas St Marg *Glas* 58-60; C Burnley St Pet *Blackb* 60-62; V Warton St Paul 62-71; Chapl K Wm's Coll Is of Man 71-91; C Ashchurch *Glouc* from 91. *The Old Stables, Back Lane, Beckford, Tewkesbury, Glos GL20 7AF* Evesham (01386) 881137

BATTERSBY, Harold. b 16. **d** 79 **p** 80. Hon C Werneth *Ches* 79-84; V 84-88; rtd 89. *3 Cote Green Lane, Marple Bridge, Stockport, Cheshire SK1 5DZ* 0161-427 1789

BATTERSBY, Paul Clifford. b 49. Bede Coll Dur TCert70 St Jo Coll Dur BA74. Cranmer Hall Dur DipTh75. **d** 75 **p** 76. C Sunderland St Chad *Dur* 75-78; Argentina 78-81; P-in-c Holme *Carl* 81-85; Dioc Youth Officer 81-85; Nat Officer for Youth Work Gen Syn Bd of Educn 85-92; TR Darwen St Pet w Hoddlesden *Blackb* 92-94; Soc Resp Officer from 95. *199 Pleckgate Road, Blackburn BB1 8QU* Blackburn (01254) 245181

BATTIN (nee WEBB), Mrs Frances Mary. b 52. W of England Minl Tr Course 92. **d** 95. NSM Inkberrow w Cookhill and Kington w Dormston *Worc* from 95. *Collitts Forge, Upper Moor, Pershore, Worcs WR10 2JR* Pershore (01386) 860467

BATTLE, Dean of. See CUMMINGS, Very Rev William Alexander Vickery

BATTMAN, John Brian. b 37. ALCD61. **d** 61 **p** 62. C Fulham Ch Ch *Lon* 61-64; Argentina 64-69; Paraguay 69-76; Adn Paraguay 70-76; Ext Sec SAMS 77-80; V Romford Gd Shep Collier Row *Chelmsf* 80-92; V Werrington *Pet* from 92. *The Vicarage, 51 The Green, Werrington, Peterborough PE4 6RT* Peterborough (01733) 571649

BATTY, John Ivan. b 35. Clifton Th Coll 59. **d** 62 **p** 63. C Clayton *Bradf* 62-67; V Toxteth Park St Clem *Liv* 67-73; R Darfield *Sheff* 73-90; Chapl Dusseldorf *Eur* from 90. *Rotterdamerstrasse 135, 40474 Dusseldorf, Germany* Dusseldorf (211) 452759

BATTY, Mark Alan. b 56. BSc. Ripon Coll Cuddesdon. **d** 82 **p** 83. C Bottesford w Ashby *Linc* 82-86; V Scunthorpe All SS from 86. *All Saints' Vicarage, 159 Warwick Road, Scunthorpe, S Humberside DN16 1HH* Scunthorpe (01724) 869081

BATTY, Stephen Roy. b 58. Chich Th Coll 88. **d** 90 **p** 91. C Wimborne Minster and Holt *Sarum* 90-94; P-in-c Yetminster w Ryme Intrinseca and High Stoy from 94. *The Rectory, Church Street, Yetminster, Sherborne, Dorset DT9 6LG* Yetminster (01935) 872237

BATTYE, Canon John Noel. b 42. TCD BA64 MA73. CITC 66. **d** 66 **p** 67. C Drumglass *Arm* 66-69; C Ballynafeigh St Jude *D & D* 70-73; Chapl Pemb Coll Cam 73-78; Bp's C Knocknagoney *D & D* 78-80; I Cregagh from 80; Preb Castleknock St Patr Cathl Dub from 94. *St Finnian's Rectory, 3 Upper Knockbreda Road, Belfast BT6 9QH* Belfast (01232) 793822

BATY, Dr Edward. b 30. ARICS59 Open Univ BA77 UEA PhD88. St Aid Birkenhead 60. **d** 62 **p** 63. V Becontree St Cedd *Chelmsf* 67-71; R Hope Bowdler w Eaton-under-Heywood *Heref* 71-79; R Rushbury 71-79; P-in-c Cardington 71-79; R Fincham *Ely* 79-82; OCF 79-94; R Long Stanton w St Mich *Ely* 82-94; P-in-c Lolworth 85-88; CF(V) 86-95; rtd 95. *25 Martindale Avenue, Camberley, Surrey GU15 1BB* Camberley (01276) 20315

BATY, Ernest John. b 20. Univ of Wales BA42. St Mich Coll Llan 42. **d** 44 **p** 45. V Lydiate *Liv* 62-67; Hon C Sefton 69-85; rtd 85. *7 Delph Park Avenue, Ormskirk, Lancs L39 5DE* Aughton Green (01695) 423711

BAUERSCHMIDT, John Crawford. b 59. Kenyon Coll Ohio BA81. Gen Th Sem (NY) MDiv84. **d** 84 **p** 85. USA 84-87; Lib Pusey Ho from 87; Lic to Offic *Ox* from 88. *Pusey House, Oxford OX1 3LZ* Oxford (01865) 278415

BAUGHEN, Andrew Jonathan. b 64. Lon Guildhall Univ BA87. Wycliffe Hall Ox BTh94. **d** 94 **p** 95. C Battersea Rise St Mark *S'wark* from 94. *24 Parma Crescent, London SW11 1LT* 0171-223 9341

✠**BAUGHEN, Rt Rev Michael Alfred.** b 30. Lon Univ BD55. Oak Hill Th Coll 51. **d** 56 **p** 57 **c** 82. C Hyson Green *S'well* 56-59; C Reigate St Mary *S'wark* 59-61; Ord Cand Sec CPAS 61-64; R Rusholme *Man* 64-70; TV St Marylebone All So w SS Pet and Jo *Lon* 70-75; R *Lon* 75-82; AD Westmr St Marylebone 78-82; Preb St Paul's Cathl 79-82; Bp Ches from 82. *Bishop's House, Abbey Square, Chester CH1 2JD* Chester (01244) 350864 Fax 314187

BAULCOMB, Geoffrey Gordon. b 46. K Coll Lon BD86 AKC68. **d** 69 **p** 70. C Crofton Park St Hilda w St Cypr *S'wark* 69-74; TV Padgate *Liv* 74-79; R Whitton and Thurleston w Akenham *St E* from 79. *The Rectory, Whitton Church Lane, Ipswich IP1 6LT* Ipswich (01473) 741389

✠**BAVIN, Rt Rev Timothy John.** b 35. Worc Coll Ox BA59 MA61. Cuddesdon Coll 59. **d** 61 **p** 62 **c** 74. S Africa 61-69 and 73-85; C Uckfield *Chich* 69-71; V Brighton Gd Shep Preston 71-73; Dean and Adn Johannesburg 73-74; Bp Johannesburg 74-85; Bp Portsm 85-95; OGS from 87. *Alton Abbey, Alton, Hants GU34 4AP* Alton (01420) 62145 or 63575

BAWTREE, Robert John. b 39. Oak Hill Th Coll 62. **d** 67 **p** 68. C Foord St Jo *Cant* 67-70; C Boscombe St Jo *Win* 70-73; C Kinson *Sarum* 73-75; TV Bramerton w Surlingham *Nor* 76-82; R Arborfield w Barkham *Ox* 82-91; V Hildenborough *Roch* from 91. *The Vicarage, 194 Tonbridge Road, Hildenborough, Tonbridge, Kent TN11 9HR* Hildenborough (01732) 833596

BAXANDALL, Peter. b 45. Tyndale Hall Bris 67. **d** 70 **p** 72. C Kidsgrove *Lich* 70-71; C St Helens St Mark *Liv* 71-75; C Ardsley *Sheff* 76-77; Rep Leprosy Miss E Anglia 77-86; P-in-c March St Wendreda *Ely* 86-87; R from 87; RD March from 93. *St Wendreda's Rectory, 21 Wimblington Road, March, Cambs PE15 9QW* March (01354) 53377

BAXENDALE, John Richard. b 48. Cranmer Hall Dur 89. **d** 91 **p** 92. C Carl St Jo *Carl* 91-94; C Dalston from 94. *2 Yetlands, Dalston, Carlisle CA5 7PB* Carlisle (01228) 710379

BAXENDALE, Rodney Douglas. b 45. Ex Univ BA66 Nottm Univ DipTh79. Linc Th Coll 78. **d** 80 **p** 81. C Maidstone All SS and St Phil w Tovil *Cant* 80-83; Chapl RN from 83. *Directorate Gen, RN Chapl Services, Room 203, Victory Building, HM Naval Base, Portsmouth PO1 3LS* Portsmouth (01705) 727903 Fax 727112

BAXTER, Brian Raymond. b 31. Tyndale Hall Bris. **d** 58 **p** 59. C Mile Cross *Nor* 74-76; C Farnborough *Guildf* 76-79; Ldr Southgate Chr Project Bury St Edmunds 79-84; Chapl W Suffolk Hosp 79-81; R Ringsfield w Redisham, Barsham, Shipmeadow etc *St E* 82-88; V Nor Heartsease St Fran *Nor* 88-91; rtd 91; Perm to Offic from 91. *50 Wensum Valley Close, Norwich NR6 5DJ* Norwich (01603) 483790

BAXTER, David Norman. b 39. Open Univ BA. Kelham Th Coll 59. **d** 64 **p** 65. C Tonge Moor *Man* 64-68; Chapl RN 68-84; P-in-c Becontree St Pet *Chelmsf* 84-85; TV Becontree W 85-86; TR 86-94; Spain from 94. *Cl Caral Vidal i Barraquer, 10, Escalera B, 1er, 2a, 08870 Sitges, Barcelona, Spain* Barcelona (3) 894-6151 Fax as telephone

BAXTER, Mrs Elizabeth Mary. b 49. Coll of Ripon & York St Jo CCouns91 Leeds Poly DipHE91 Leeds Metrop Univ BA93. N Ord Course 81. **dss** 84 **d** 87 **p** 94. Leeds St Marg *Ripon* 84-87; Chapl Abbey Grange Sch 85-93; Leeds All Hallows w Wrangthorn 85-87; Par Dn Leeds St Marg and All Hallows 87-93; Par Dn Topcliffe *York* 93-94; C from 94; Jt Dir N of England Chr Healing Trust from 93; Jt Dir Cen for Spirituality, Past Care and Healing from 95; Perm to Offic *Ripon* from 93; Perm to Offic *Dur* and *Newc* from 94; Perm to Offic *Bradf* from 95. *Holy Rood House, 10 Sowerby Road, Sowerby, Thirsk, N Yorkshire YO7 1HX* Thirsk (01845) 525591 or 522580

BAXTER, Harold Leslie. b 11. Roch Th Coll 62. **d** 64 **p** 65. C Corsham *Bris* 64-67; C Bath Lyncombe *B & W* 67-70; V Shapwick w Ashcott 70-88; P-in-c Burtle 75-88; V Shapwick w Ashcott and Burtle from 88. *The Vicarage, Vicarage Lane, Bridgwater, Somerset TA7 9LR* Ashcott (01458) 210260

BAXTER, Peter James. b 29. St Chad's Coll Dur BA53 DipTh55. **d** 55 **p** 56. R Eynesbury *Ely* 62-89; rtd 89. *15 Bromley College, London Road, Bromley BR1 1PE*

BAXTER, Canon Richard David. b 33. Kelham Th Coll 53. **d** 57 **p** 58. C Carl St Barn *Carl* 57-59; C Barrow St Matt 59-64; V Drighlington *Wakef* 64-73; V Penistone 73-80; V Carl St Aid and Ch Ch *Carl* 80-86; Can Res Wakef Cathl *Wakef* from 86; Prec from 86; Vice-Provost from 92. *4 The Cathedral Close, Margaret Street, Wakefield, W Yorkshire WF1 2DQ* Wakefield (01924) 361922

BAXTER, Stanley Robert. b 31. AMIWO69 Leeds Univ MA90. Chich Th Coll 79. **d** 80 **p** 81. C Far Headingley St Chad *Ripon* 80-82; P-in-c Leeds St Marg and All Hallows 82-87; P-in-c Leeds All Hallows w Wrangthorn 85-87; P-in-c Leeds St Marg and All Hallows 87-93; Dir Leeds Cen for Urban Th Studies 88-93; Assoc Chapl Leeds Univ 91-93; Perm to Offic from 93; P-in-c Topcliffe *York* 93-95; NSM from 95; Jt Dir N of England Chr Healing Trust from 93; Perm to Offic *Dur* and *Newc* from 94; Perm to Offic *Bradf* from 95; rtd 95. *Holy Rood House, 10 Sowerby Road, Sowerby, Thirsk, N Yorkshire YO7 1HX* Thirsk (01845) 525591 or 522580

BAXTER, Stuart. b 43. Liv Univ BA65 Nottm Univ PGCE66. Cuddesdon Coll 66. **d** 70 **p** 71. C Kirkby *Liv* 70-73; C Ainsdale 73-76; Sierra Leone 77-83; CMS 83-84; V Nelson in Lt Marsden *Blackb* 84-92; V Lostock Hall from 92. *St James's Vicarage, 76A BrowneDge Road, Lostock Hall, Preston PR5 5AD* Preston (01772) 35366

BAXTER, Terence Hugh (Terry). b 48. Leeds Poly BSc74. N Ord Course 89. **d** 92 **p** 93. NSM Guiseley w Esholt *Bradf* from 92. *2 Flatfield Cottage, Kelcliffe Lane, Guiseley, Leeds LS20 9DD* Guiseley (01943) 875170 Fax as telephone

BAYCOCK, Philip Louis. b 33. Wells Th Coll 64. **d** 66 **p** 67. C Kettering SS Pet and Paul *Pet* 66-68; C St Peter-in-Thanet *Cant* 68-72; V Bobbing w Iwade 72-73; Perm to Offic 73-76; V Thanington w Milton 77-84; R Chagford w Gidleigh and Throwleigh *Ex* from 84. *The Rectory, Chagford, Newton Abbot, Devon TQ13 8BW* Chagford (01647) 432265

BAYES, Frederick Alan. b 60. Imp Coll Lon BSc81. St Jo Coll Dur BA92 Cranmer Hall Dur DMinlStuds93. **d** 93 **p** 94. C Talbot Village *Sarum* from 93. *St Saviour's House, 18 Hillside Road, Poole, Dorset BH12 5DY* Poole (01202) 520251

BAYES, Paul. b 53. Birm Univ BA75 DipTh78. Qu Coll Birm 76. **d** 79 **p** 80. C Tynemouth Cullercoats St Paul *Newc* 79-82; Chapl Qu Eliz Coll *Lon* 82-87; Chapl Chelsea Coll 85-87; TV High Wycombe *Ox* 87-90; TR 90-94; TR Totton *Win* from 95. *Testwood Rectory, 92 Salisbury Road, Totton, Southampton SO4 3JA* Southampton (01703) 865103

BAYFORD, Mrs Daphne Jean. b 32. Lon Univ TCert53. Qu Coll Birm 84. **d** 87 **p** 94. NSM Brinklow *Cov* 87-95; NSM Harborough Magna 87-95; NSM Monks Kirby w Pailton and Stretton-under-Fosse 87-95; Perm to Offic from 95. *Warwick House, 36 Lutterworth Road, Pailton, Rugby, Warks CV23 0QE* Rugby (01788) 832797

BAYLEY, Albert William David. b 15. Lon Coll of Div 66. **d** 68 **p** 69. C St Giles-in-the-Fields *Lon* 71-78; rtd 78; Perm to Offic *St Alb* from 82. *25 Belper Road, Luton LU4 8RG* Luton (01582) 598196

BAYLEY, Dr Anne Christine. b 34. OBE86. MB, ChB58 FRCS66 FRCSEd86 Girton Coll Cam BA55. St Steph Ho Ox 90. **d** 91 **p** 94. NSM Wembley Park St Aug *Lon* from 91. *8 Winthrop Walk, Wembley, Middx HA9 7TT* 0181-904 6621

BAYLEY, Miss Barbara Alice. b 31. Cranmer Hall Dur. **d** 87 **p** 94. Par Dn Trowbridge H Trin *Sarum* 87-91; Par Dn Trowbridge St Jas 87-91; rtd 91. *52 Avenue Road, Trowbridge, Wilts BA14 0AQ* Trowbridge (01225) 764691

BAYLEY, Canon John Benson. b 39. K Coll Cam BA60 MA64. Qu Coll Birm 61. **d** 63 **p** 64. C Clee *Linc* 63-68; V Gainsborough H Trin 68-73; P-in-c Linc St Mich 73-75; P-in-c Linc St Pet in Eastgate w St Marg 73-75; P-in-c Linc St Mary Magd w St Paul 73-75; R Linc Minster Gp from 75; Can and Preb Linc Cathl from 75; Hon PV from 77. *St Peter's Vicarage, Lee Road, Lincoln LN2 4BH* Lincoln (01522) 525741

BAYLEY, Dr Michael John. b 36. CCC Cam BA60 MA64 Sheff Univ DSocStuds67 PhD73. Linc Th Coll 60. **d** 62 **p** 63. C Leeds Gipton Epiphany *Ripon* 62-66; NSM Sheff St Mark Broomhill *Sheff* 67-93; C Sheff St Mary w Highfield Trin 93-95; C Sheff St Mary Bramhall Lane from 95. *27 Meadowbank Avenue, Sheffield S7 1PB* Sheffield (0114) 258 5248

BAYLEY, Oliver James Drummond. b 49. Mansf Coll Ox MA PGCE. St Jo Coll Nottm 81. **d** 83 **p** 84. C Bath Weston St Jo w Kelston *B & W* 83-88; P-in-c Bathampton 88-93; P-in-c Claverton 92-93; R Bathampton w Claverton from 93. *Bathampton Vicarage, Bathampton Lane, Bath BA2 6SW* Bath (01225) 463570

BAYLEY, Dr Raymond. b 46. Keble Coll Ox BA68 MA72 Dur Univ DipTh69 Ex Univ PhD86. St Chad's Coll Dur 68. **d** 69 **p** 70. C Mold *St As* 69-74; C Llan w Capel Llanilltern *Llan* 74; PV Llan Cathl 74-77; V Cwmbach 77-80; Dir Past Studies St Mich Coll Llan 80-84; V Ynysddu *Mon* 84-86; V Griffithstown 86-92; V Rhosymedre *St As* from 92. *The Vicarage, Church Street, Rhosymedre, Wrexham, Clwyd LL14 3EA* Ruabon (01978) 810786

BAYLISS, Miss Joan Edith. b 34. RGN55. Qu Coll Birm 80. **dss** 83 **d** 87 **p** 94. Halesowen *Worc* 83-87; Hon Par Dn 87-89; Par Dn Bromsgrove St Jo 90-94; C 94; Chapl Bromsgrove and Redditch Distr Gen Hosp 90-94; C Upton Snodsbury and Broughton Hackett etc *Worc* 94; C Peopleton and White Ladies Aston w Churchill etc from 94. *4 Flax Piece, Upton Snodsbury, Worcester WR7 4PA* Worcester (01905) 381886

BAYLISS, Maurice Selwyn. b 13. Univ of Wales BA36. St Mich Coll Llan 36. **d** 37 **p** 38. V Bush Hill Park St Steph *Lon* 57-80; rtd 80; Perm to Offic *Lon* from 80; Perm to Offic *St Alb* from 85. *19 Canford Close, Enfield, Middx EN2 8QN* 0181-367 7436

BAYLOR, Nigel Peter. b 58. NUI BA80 TCD DipTh84 MPhil88. **d** 84 **p** 86. C Carrickfergus *Conn* 84-87; C Dundela *D & D* 87-89; I Galloon w Drummully *Clogh* 89-94; Adult Educn Adv 91-94; I Carnmoney *Conn* from 94. *Coole Glebe, 20 Glebe Road, Carnmoney, Newtownabbey, Co Antrim BT36 6UW* Glengormley (01232) 844981

BAYLY, Samuel Niall Maurice. b 36. TCD BA64 MA. CITC Div Test65. **d** 65 **p** 66. C Belf St Matt *Conn* 65-68; Miss to Seamen 68-69; C Belf St Pet *Conn* 69-74; I Belf Ch Ch from 74. *25 Beechlands, Malone Road, Belfast BT9 5HU* Belfast (01232) 668732

BAYNE, David William. b 52. St Andr Univ MA75. Edin Th Coll 88. **d** 90 **p** 91. C Dumfries *Glas* 90-92; P-in-c 92-93; R from 93. *The Rectory, 8 Newall Terrace, Dumfries DG1 1LW* Dumfries (01387) 54126

BAYNE, Mrs Felicity Meriel. b 47. W Midl Minl Tr Course 91. **d** 94. NSM Cheltenham Ch Ch *Glouc* from 94. *Hamfield House, Ham, Charlton Kings, Cheltenham, Glos GL52 6NG* Cheltenham (01242) 237074

BAYNES, Matthew Thomas Crispin. b 62. UEA BA83. Westcott Ho Cam BA86. **d** 87 **p** 88. C Southgate Ch Ch *Lon* 87-90; C Gt Berkhamsted *St Alb* 90-95; V Coseley Ch Ch *Worc* from 95. *The Vicarage, Church Road, Coseley, Bilston, W Midlands WV14 8YB* Bilston (01902) 353551

BAYNES, Simon Hamilton. b 33. New Coll Ox BA57 DipTh58 MA62. Wycliffe Hall Ox 57. **d** 59 **p** 60. C Rodbourne Cheney *Bris* 59-62; Japan 63-80; C Keynsham *B & W* 80-84; P-in-c Winkfield *Ox* 84-85; V Winkfield and Cranbourne from 85. *The Vicarage, Winkfield Street, Winkfield, Windsor, Berks SL4 4SW* Winkfield Row (01344) 882322

BAYNES, Timothy Francis de Brissac. b 29. Ely Th Coll 59. **d** 61 **p** 62. Ind Chapl *Man* 67-94; P-in-c Miles Platting St Jo 67-72; rtd 94. *5 Stainbank Green, Brigsteer Road, Kendal, Cumbria LA9 5RP* Kendal (01539) 740605

BAYNES, William Hendrie (Will). b 39. Adelaide Univ BA60. S'wark Ord Course 77. **d** 79 **p** 80. C Notting Hill All SS w St Columb *Lon* 79-85; Perm to Offic 86-88; C Paddington St Sav from 88. *39E Westbourne Gardens, London W2 5NR* 0171-727 9522 Fax as telephone

BAYNHAM, Canon George Thorp. b 19. TCD BA41. **d** 42 **p** 43. I Castlemacadam *D & G* 52-89; I Kilbride (Arklow) 64-73; Can Ch Ch Cathl Dub 71-89; I Castlemacadam w Ballinaclash, Aughrim etc 73-89; rtd 89. *2 St Peter's Place, Drogheda, Co Louth, Irish Republic* Drogheda (41) 36260

BAYNHAM, Matthew Fred. b 57. BA. Wycliffe Hall Ox 80. **d** 83 **p** 84. C Yardley St Edburgha *Birm* 83-87; TV Bath Twerton-on-Avon *B & W* 87-93; V Reddal Hill St Luke *Worc* from 93. *St Luke's Vicarage, Upper High Street, Cradley Heath, Warley, W Midlands B64 5HX* Cradley Heath (01384) 569940

BAYNHAM, William Benjamin. b 11. Fitzw Ho Cam BA34 MA37. Cuddesdon Coll 34. **d** 35 **p** 36. C Maidstone All SS *Cant* 35-37; CR from 44; rtd 81. *House of the Resurrection, Mirfield, W Yorkshire WF14 0BN* Mirfield (01924) 494318

BAZELY, William Francis (Bill). b 53. Sheff Univ BEng75. St Jo Coll Nottm DipTh79 DPS. **d** 81 **p** 82. C Huyton St Geo *Liv* 81-84; TV Netherthorpe *Sheff* 84-92; Chapl W Lambeth Community Care Trust from 92; Chapl Tooting Bec Hosp Lon from 92; Chapl SW Hosp Lon from 92. *4-5 Voss Court, London SW16 3BS, or 5 Glenhurst Rise, London SE19 3XN* 0181-771 9781 or 765 0699

BAZEN, David Peter. b 44. Birm Univ BPhil78 St Chad's Coll Dur BA65 DipTh69. **d** 69 **p** 71. C Acton Green St Pet *Lon* 69-70; Hon C Wylde Green *Birm* 70-78; Hon C Bordesley St Benedict 78-82; Hon C Bordesley SS Alb and Patr 82-94. *66 Station Road, Sutton Coldfield, W Midlands B73 5LA* 0121-354 5626 or 360 8345/1581

✠BAZLEY, Rt Rev Colin Frederick. b 35. St Chad's Coll Dur BA65 DipTh69. **d** 59 **p** 60 **c** 69. C Bootle St Leon *Liv* 59-62; SAMS from 62; Chile from 62; Asst Bp Cavtin and Malleco 69-75; Asst Bp Santiago 75-77; Bp Chile from 77; Primate CASA 77-83 and 89-95. *Iglesia Anglicana del Chile, Casilla 50675, Correo Central, Santiage, Chile* Santiago (2) 821-2478 or 383009

BAZLINTON, Stephen Cecil. b 46. MRCS Lon Univ BDS LDS. Ridley Hall Cam 78. **d** 85 **p** 86. NSM Stebbing w Lindsell *Chelmsf* from 85. *St Helens, High Street, Stebbing, Dunmow, Essex CM6 3SE* Stebbing (01371) 856495

BEACH, Jonathan Mark. b 67. Essex Univ BSc89. Trin Coll Bris BA94. **d** 94 **p** 95. C Oulton Broad *Nor* from 94. *3 Windward Way, Lowestoft, Suffolk NR33 9HF* Lowestoft (01502) 582083

BEACH, Mark Howard Francis. b 62. Kent Univ BA83. St Steph Ho Ox 85. **d** 87 **p** 88. C Beeston *S'well* 87-90; C Hucknall Torkard 90-93; R Gedling from 93. *The Rectory, Rectory Drive, Gedling, Nottingham NG4 4BG* Nottingham (0115) 961 3214

BEACH, Stephen John. b 58. Man Univ BA81 BD88 Didsbury Coll of Educn PGCE82. N Ord Course 92. **d** 93 **p** 94. NSM Harwood *Man* 93; C from 93. *School House, Stitch Mi Lane, Bolton BL2 4HR* Bolton (01204) 396864

BEACHAM, Ian William Henry. b 17. Dur Univ LTh41. ALCD41. **d** 41 **p** 42. R Kidlington *Ox* 58-70; R Hampton Poyle 58-70; V Banbury 70-77; TR 77-82; rtd 82. *11 West Lea Road, Weston, Bath BA1 3RL* Bath (01225) 421682

BEACHAM, Peter Martyn. b 44. Ex Coll Ox BA65 MA70 Lon Univ MPhil67. Sarum Th Coll. **d** 73 **p** 74. NSM Ex St Martin, St Steph, St Laur etc *Ex* 73-74; NSM Cen Ex 74-90. *Bellever, Barrack Road, Exeter EX2 6AB* Exeter (01392) 35074

BEACOM, Canon Thomas Ernest. b 12. TCD BA33 MA40 BD40. **d** 36 **p** 36. I Belf St Kath *Conn* 58-82; Can Belf Cathl 66-82; rtd 82. *4955-41 Avenue, Drayton Valley, Alberta, Canada, T7A 1V4*

BEACON, Canon Ralph Anthony. b 44. Univ of Wales (Ban) DipTh70. St Mich Coll Llan 70. **d** 71 **p** 72. C Neath w Llantwit *Llan* 71-74; TV Holyhead w Rhoscolyn *Ban* 74-78; R Llanenddwyn w Llanddwywe, Llanbedr w Llandanwg from 78; RD Ardudwy from 89; Hon Can Ban Cathl from 91. *The Rectory, Dyffryn Ardudwy, Gwynedd LL44 2EY* Dyffryn (01341) 247207

BEADLE, David Alexander. b 37. St And Dioc Tr Course. **d** 88 **p** 89. NSM St Andrews St Andr *St And* from 88. *48 Clayton Caravan Park, St Andrews, Fife KY16 9YB* St Andrews (01334) 870001

BEADLE, Ms Janet Mary. b 52. Philippa Fawcett Coll CertEd74. E Anglian Minl Tr Course 91. **d** 94 **p** 95. C Kingston upon Hull H Trin *York* from 94. *The Clergy House, 67 Adelaide Street, Hull HU3 2EZ* Hull (01482) 215665

✠BEAK, Rt Rev Robert Michael Cawthorn. b 25. OBE90. Lon Bible Coll DipTh51. **d** 53 **p** 54 **c** 84. C Tunbridge Wells St Jo *Roch* 53-55; BCMS 55-56 and 84-89; Kenya 56-69 and 84-89; R Heanton Punchardon *Ex* 70-84; Offg Chapl RAF 70-80; RD Barnstaple *Ex* 77-81; R Heanton Punchardon w Marwood 79-84; Preb Ex Cathl 82-84; Asst Bp Mt Kenya E 84-89; rtd 90; Asst Bp Derby from 91. *Hillcrest, Newton Road, Tibshelf, Alfreton, Derbyshire DE55 5PA* Ripley (01773) 872154

BEAK, Stephen Robert (Steve). b 64. City Univ BSc86 MBCO87. Wycliffe Hall Ox BTh94. **d** 94 **p** 95. C Lache cum Saltney *Ches* from 94. *69 Sandy Lane, Saltney, Chester CH4 8UB* Chester (01244) 683225

BEAKE, Christopher Martyn Grandfield. b 36. K Coll Lon BA60 AKC60. **d** 61 **p** 62. C Berwick H Trin *Newc* 61-66; V Tynemouth H Trin W Town 66-78; V Hanslope w Castlethorpe *Ox* from 78. *The Vicarage, Park Road, Hanslope, Milton Keynes MK19 7LT* Milton Keynes (01908) 510542

BEAKE, Kenneth George. b 37. Ripon Coll Cuddesdon 75. **d** 77 **p** 78. C Guisborough *York* 77-80; V Kingston upon Hull St Martin 80-84; V Hull St Martin w Transfiguration 84-88; P-in-c Gt Wishford *Sarum* 88-91; P-in-c S Newton 88-91; Dir of Ords 88-91; Dioc Dir of Ords *Nor* from 91; P-in-c Nor St Steph from 91; Hon Brigade Chapl to Norfolk Co Fire Service from 91. *12 The Crescent, Norwich NR2 1SA* Norwich (01603) 623045

BEAKE, Stuart Alexander. b 49. Em Coll Cam BA72 MA76. Cuddesdon Coll 72. **d** 74 **p** 75. C Hitchin St Mary *St Alb* 74-76; C Hitchin 77-79; TV Hemel Hempstead 79-85; Bp's Dom Chapl *S'well* 85-87; V Shottery St Andr *Cov* from 87; RD Fosse from 93. *The Vicarage, Church Lane, Stratford-upon-Avon, Warks CV37 9HQ* Stratford-upon-Avon (01789) 293381

BEAKEN, Robert William Frederick. b 62. SS Paul & Mary Coll Cheltenham BA83 Lambeth STh90. Ripon Coll Cuddesdon 85 Ven English Coll and Pontifical Gregorian Univ Rome 87.

d 88 **p** 89. C Forton *Portsm* 88-92; C Shepshed *Leic* 92-94; V Colchester St Barn *Chelmsf* from 94. *The Vicarage, 13 Abbot's Road, Colchester CO2 8BE* Colchester (01206) 797481

BEAL, David Michael. b 61. Nottm Univ BTh89. St Jo Coll Nottm 86. **d** 89 **p** 90. C Marton *Blackb* 89-92; C Darwen St Pet w Hoddlesden 92-93; TV from 93. *St Paul's Vicarage, Johnson New Road, Hoddlesden, Darwen, Lancs BB3 3NN* Darwen (01254) 702598

BEAL, Malcolm. b 31. Bris Univ BA52. Ridley Hall Cam 57. **d** 59 **p** 60. C Keynsham w Queen Charlton *B & W* 59-62; C Speke All SS *Liv* 62-65; Uganda 65-74; V Salford Priors *Cov* 74-83; R Jersey St Clem *Win* from 83. *St Clement's Rectory, Jersey, Channel Islands JE2 6RB* Jersey (01534) 851992

BEAL, Royston David. b 35. K Coll Lon BD60 AKC60. **d** 61 **p** 62. C Chesterfield All SS *Derby* 61-64; C Chiswick St Nic w St Mary *Lon* 64-70; V Kensal Green St Jo from 70. *St John's Vicarage, Kilburn Lane, London W10 4AA* 0181-969 2615

BEALE, Wilfred Henry Ellson. b 11. FCCA FCIS. **d** 69 **p** 71. Hon C Northwood H Trin *Lon* 69-82; Perm to Offic from 82. *23 Woodridge Way, Northwood, Middx HA6 2BE* Northwood (01923) 826301

BEALE, William Edgar. b 11. K Coll Lon 37. Bps' Coll Cheshunt 40. **d** 42 **p** 43. R Kedington *St E* 64-72; C Brighton St Paul *Chich* 72-73; C Bingley All SS *Bradf* 73-77; rtd 77. *Charterhouse, Charterhouse Square, London EC1M 6AN*

BEALES, Christopher Leader Day. b 51. St Jo Coll Dur BA72. Cranmer Hall Dur DipTh75. **d** 76 **p** 77. C Upper Armley *Ripon* 76-79; Ind Chapl 76-79; Ind Chapl *Dur* 79-84; Sen Chapl 82-84; Sec Ind Cttee of Gen Syn Bd for Soc Resp 85-91; Sec Inner Cities Relig Coun (DOE) 92-94; Dir NE Churches' Regional Comm *Dur* from 94. *12 Castle View, Chester le Street, Co Durham DH3 3XA* 0191-388 9941 Fax as telephone

BEALES, John David. b 55. SS Hild & Bede Coll Dur BA77 Univ of W Aus DipEd79 Nottm Univ DipTh82. St Jo Coll Nottm DPS83. **d** 83 **p** 84. Australia 83-89; Dir Educn and Tr Philo Trust 89-90; NSM Nottm St Nic *S'well* from 89. *17 Bramcote Drive, Beeston, Nottingham NG9 1AT* Nottingham (0115) 922 5031

BEALING, Andrew John. b 42. Sarum Th Coll 67. **d** 69 **p** 70. C Auckland St Andr and St Anne *Dur* 69-73; P-in-c Eastgate 73-76; P-in-c Rookhope 73-76; V Frosterley 76-85; V Rekendyke from 85; Chapl S Tyneside Distr Hosp from 90. *The Vicarage, St Jude's Terrace, South Shields, Tyne & Wear NE33 5PB* 0191-455 2338

BEALING, Mrs Patricia Ramsey. b 39. Lightfoot Ho Dur IDC63. **dss** 63 **d** 87 **p** 94. Rekendyke *Dur* 85-87; Par Dn 87-94; C from 94; Chapl S Tyneside Distr Hosp from 88. *The Vicarage, St Jude's Terrace, South Shields, Tyne & Wear NE33 5PB* 0191-455 2338

BEALL, John. b 19. Clare Coll Cam BA41 MA45. Westcott Ho Cam 41. **d** 42 **p** 43. V Oswaldtwistle Immanuel *Blackb* 61-82; rtd 82; Perm to Offic *Bris* 82-90; Perm to Offic *Glas* from 90. *12 Golf Crescent, Troon, Ayrshire KA10 6JZ* Troon (01292) 318055

BEAMENT, Owen John. b 41. Bps' Coll Cheshunt 61. **d** 64 **p** 65. C Deptford St Paul *S'wark* 64-68; C Peckham St Jo 69-73; C Vauxhall St Pet 73-74; V Hatcham Park All SS from 74. *All Saints Vicarage, 22 Erlanger Road, London SE14 5TG* 0171-639 3497

BEAMER, Neville David. b 40. Univ of Wales (Lamp) BA62 Jes Coll Ox BA65 MA70. Wycliffe Hall Ox 64. **d** 65 **p** 66. C Hornchurch St Andr *Chelmsf* 65-68; C Warw St Mary *Cov* 68-72; V Holton-le-Clay *Linc* 73-75; P-in-c Stoneleigh w Ashow *Cov* 75-79; P-in-c Baginton 77-79; V Fletchamstead 79-86; Warden Whatcombe Ho Blandford Forum 86-90; V Jersey Millbrook St Matt *Win* 90-95; R Jersey St Lawr 90-95; V Yateley from 95. *The Vicarage, 99 Reading Road, Yateley, Camberley, Surrey GU17 7LR* Yateley (01252) 873133

BEAMISH, Canon Frank Edwin. b 28. TCD BA49 MA. **d** 50 **p** 52. I Caledon w Brantry *Arm* 61-94; Preb Arm Cathl from 88; Treas Arm Cathl from 92; rtd 94. *214 Killylea Road, Caledon, Co Tyrone BT68 4TN* Caledon (01861) 568609

BEAN, Alan Evison. b 13. Ch Coll Cam BA35 MA39. Ely Th Coll 35. **d** 36 **p** 37. CF 42-45; SSJE from 47; Lic to Offic *Ox* from 55; rtd 83. *SSJE Priory, 228 Iffley Road, Oxford OX4 1SE* Oxford (01865) 248116

BEAN, Douglas Jeyes Lendrum. b 25. Worc Coll Ox BA50 MA53. Ely Th Coll 50. **d** 51 **p** 52. Min Can St Paul's Cathl *Lon* 68-72; Hon Min Can from 72; V St Pancras w St Jas and Ch Ch 72-93; PV Westmr Abbey 75-80; rtd 93. *26 Burnthwaite Road, London SW6 5BE* 0171-387 6460

BEAN, Canon John Victor. b 25. Down Coll Cam BA47 MA51. Sarum Th Coll 48. **d** 50 **p** 51. V Cowes St Mary *Portsm* 66-91; RD W Wight 68-72; Hon Can Portsm Cathl 70-91; P-in-c Cowes St Faith 77-80; C-in-c Gurnard All SS CD 78-91; Chapl to The Queen from 80; rtd 91. *Magnolia, 23 Seldon Avenue, Ryde, Isle of Wight PO33 1NS* Isle of Wight (01983) 812516

BEAN, Kevin Douglas. b 54. Edin Univ BD78. Edin Th Coll 75. **d** 81 **p** 82. USA 81-88 and from 89; C Edin St Marg *Edin* 88-89; C Edin Old St Paul 88-89. *1210 West 8th Street, Wilmington, Delaware 19801, USA*

BEANEY, John. b 47. Trin Coll Bris DipHE79. **d** 79 **p** 80. C Bromley Ch Ch *Roch* 79-84; V Broadheath *Ches* from 84; Chapl Altrincham Gen Hosp from 91. *The Vicarage, Lindsell Road, West Timperley, Altrincham, Cheshire WA14 5NX* 0161-928 4820

BEARCROFT, Bramwell Arthur. b 52. Homerton Coll Cam BEd82. E Anglian Minl Tr Course 87. **d** 90 **p** 91. Chapl and Hd Relig Studies Kimbolton Sch from 88; NSM Tilbrook *Ely* from 90; NSM Covington from 90; NSM Catworth Magna from 90; NSM Keyston and Bythorn from 90. *White House, High Street, Kimbolton, Huntingdon, Cambs PE18 0HB* Huntingdon (01480) 860469

BEARD, Christopher Robert (Chris). b 47. Chich Th Coll 81. **d** 83 **p** 84. C Chich St Paul and St Pet *Chich* 83-86; TV Ifield 86-91; V Haywards Heath St Rich from 91. *St Richard's Vicarage, Queen's Road, Haywards Heath, W Sussex RH16 1EB* Haywards Heath (01444) 413621

BEARD, Laurence Philip (Laurie). b 45. Lon Univ BA68. Trin Coll Bris 88. **d** 90 **p** 91. C Trentham *Lich* 90-94; V Wolv St Matt from 94. *St Matthew's Vicarage, 14 Sydenham Road, Wolverhampton WV1 2NY* Wolverhampton (01902) 453300

BEARD, Peter Harley. b 39. Coll of Resurr Mirfield 60. **d** 71 **p** 72. S Africa 71-75; Miss to Seamen 75-82; V St Osyth *Chelmsf* 81-86; P-in-c Wellington Ch Ch *Lich* 86-95; V Pelsall from 95. *The Vicarage, 39 Hall Lane, Pelsall, Walsall WS3 4JN* Pelsall (01922) 682098

BEARD, Robert John Hansley. b 61. St Andr Univ BD85. Ripon Coll Cuddesdon 86 Ch Div Sch of the Pacific (USA) 87. **d** 88 **p** 89. C Sheff Manor *Sheff* 88-91; C Rotherham 91-94; V Sheff Abbeydale St Pet from 94. *St Peter's Vicarage, Ashland Road, Sheffield S7 1RH* Sheffield (0114) 250 9716

BEARDALL, Raymond. b 32. St Jo Coll Nottm 70. **d** 72 **p** 73. C Ilkley All SS *Bradf* 72-74; C Seasalter *Cant* 74-79; V Farndon *S'well* 79-84; R Thorpe 79-84; V Blidworth from 84. *2 Kirk's Croft, Wain Street, Mansfield, Notts NG21 0QH* Mansfield (01623) 792306

BEARDMORE, John Keith. b 42. FCP85 Bris Univ BEd74 K Coll Lon MA90. **d** 77 **p** 78. NSM Newport Maindee St Jo Ev *Mon* from 77. *16 Hove Avenue, Newport, Gwent NP9 7QP* Newport (01633) 263272

BEARDSHAW, David. b 37. JP. DPS. Wells Th Coll 65. **d** 67 **p** 68. C Stoke *Cov* 70-73; V Whitley 73-77; Dioc Educn Officer 77-87; P-in-c Offchurch 87-93; Warden Offa Retreat Ho 87-93; rtd 93. *180 Ashington Grove, Coventry CV3 4DB*

BEARDSLEY, Christopher (Chris). b 51. Sussex Univ BA73. Westcott Ho Cam 76. **d** 78 **p** 79. C Portsea N End St Mark *Portsm* 78-85; V Catherington and Clanfield from 85. *The Vicarage, 330 Catherington Lane, Catherington, Waterlooville, Hants PO8 0TD* Horndean (01705) 593139

BEARDSLEY, Daniel Graham Richard. b 55. Liv Univ BA86. St Steph Ho Ox 90. **d** 92 **p** 93. C Stanley *Liv* 92-95; P-in-c Dovecot from 95. *Holy Spirit Vicarage, Dovecot Avenue, Liverpool L14 7QJ* 0151-220 6611

BEARDSMORE, Alan. b 45. Wycliffe Hall Ox 67. **d** 70 **p** 71. C Prittlewell St Mary *Chelmsf* 70-72; C Epsom St Martin *Guildf* 72-78; P-in-c Burbage and Savernake Ch Ch *Sarum* 78-79; P-in-c E Grafton, Tidcombe and Fosbury 78-79; TV Wexcombe 79-80; Chapl RN 80-83; TV Haverhill w Withersfield, the Wrattings etc *St E* 83-87; V Gt Barton 87-95; V Eaton *Nor* from 95. *The Vicarage, 210 Newmarket Road, Norwich NR4 7LA* Norwich (01603) 250915

BEARDSMORE, John. b 19. Kelham Th Coll 46. **d** 51 **p** 51. V Bromley H Trin *Roch* 69-70; V Buttershaw St Paul *Bradf* 70-88; rtd 88; Perm to Offic *Bradf* from 88. *41 Nab Wood Grove, Shipley, W Yorkshire BD18 4HR* Bradford (01274) 596197

BEARE, Canon William. b 33. TCD BA58 DipCSM77. **d** 59 **p** 60. C Waterford St Patr *C & O* 59-62; C Cork H Trin w Shandon St Mary *C, C & R* 62-64; I Rathcormac 64-68; I Marmullane w Monkstown 68-76; Dioc C 76-82; I Stradbally w Ballintubbert, Coraclone etc *C & O* from 82; Preb Ossory and Leighlin Cathls 88-90; Chan 90-92; Prec from 92. *The Rectory, Church Lane, Stradbally, Laois, Irish Republic* Portlaoise (502) 25173

BEARMAN, Leslie Raymond Livingstone. b 09. ALCD35. **d** 35 **p** 36. R Sherington w Chicheley *Ox* 61-74; R N Crawley and Astwood w Hardmead 74; rtd 74; Perm to Offic *Pet* from 75. *395A Kettering Road, Northampton NN3 1LW* Northampton (01604) 462326

BEARN, Hugh William. b 62. Man Univ BA84. Cranmer Hall Dur 86. **d** 89 **p** 90. C Heaton Ch Ch *Man* 89-92; Chapl RAF Coll Cranwell from 92. *Chaplaincy Services (RAF), HQ, Personnel and Training Command, RAF Innsworth, Gloucester GL3 1EZ* Gloucester (01452) 712612 Ext 5164 Fax 510828

BEARPARK, Canon John Michael. b 36. Ex Coll Ox BA59 MA63. Linc Th Coll 59. **d** 61 **p** 62. C Bingley H Trin *Bradf* 61-64; C Baildon 64-67; V Fairweather Green 67-77; Chapl Airedale Gen Hosp 77-94; Hon Can Bradf Cathl from 89; V Bentham St Marg from 94; RD Ewecross from 94. *St Margaret's Vicarage, 27 Station Road, High Bentham, Lancaster LA2 7LH* Bentham (015242) 61321

BEASLEY, Canon Arthur James. b 12. Hertf Coll Ox BA33 MA38. Ridley Hall Cam 34. **d** 36 **p** 37. V Heaton Ch Ch *Man* 48-81; Hon Can Man Cathl 72-81; rtd 81; Perm to Offic *Man* from 81. *40 Chorley New Road, Lostock, Bolton BL6 4AL* Bolton (01204) 494450

BEASLEY, Bernard Robinson. b 07. OBE56. Leeds Univ BA30 MA45. Coll of Resurr Mirfield 25. **d** 31 **p** 32. V Easebourne *Chich* 62-72; RD Midhurst 64-72; rtd 72. *Agra Cottage, Worton, Devizes, Wilts SN10 5SE* Devizes (01380) 723383

BEASLEY, Michael John. b 41. Dur Univ BA63. Sarum Th Coll 63. **d** 65 **p** 66. C Weston St Jo *B & W* 65-67; C Pinner *Lon* 67-69; C E Grinstead St Swithun *Chich* 69-72; Chapl St Mary's Hosp and Qu Hosp Croydon 72-77; Mayday Hosp Thornton Heath 72-77; TV Swanborough *Sarum* 77-82; V Stourbridge Norton St Mich *Worc* from 82. *St Michael's House, Westwood Avenue, Stourbridge, W Midlands DY8 3EN* Stourbridge (01384) 393647

BEASLEY, Canon Walter Sydney. b 33. Nottm Univ BA57. Linc Th Coll 57. **d** 59 **p** 60. C Harworth *S'well* 59-64; V Forest Town 64-70; R Bulwell St Mary from 70; Hon Can S'well Minster from 85. *The Rectory, Station Road, Bulwell, Nottingham NG6 9AA* Nottingham (0115) 927 8468

BEATER, David MacPherson. b 41. Chich Th Coll 66. **d** 69 **p** 70. C Withington St Crispin *Man* 69-72; C Lightbowne 72-74; V Prestwich St Hilda 74-81; V Northfleet *Roch* 81-85; C Bickley 86-90; TV Stanley *Dur* from 90. *St Thomas's Vicarage, Lowery Lane, Stanley, Co Durham DH9 6EN* Stanley (01207) 230316

BEATTIE, Margaret. b 43. S'wark Ord Course 90. **d** 93 **p** 94. NSM S'wark H Trin w St Matt *S'wark* from 93. *120 Merrow Street, London SE17 2NP* 0171-701 9262

BEATTIE, Noel Christopher. b 41. TCD BTh65 Cranfield Inst of Tech MSc86. **d** 68 **p** 69. C Belf H Trin *Conn* 68-70; C Belf St Bart 70-73; C Doncaster St Mary *Sheff* 73-77; TV Northn Em *Pet* 77-88; Ind Chapl 85-88; Ind Chapl *Linc* 88-92; Ind Chapl *Roch* from 92. *181 Maidstone Road, Chatham, Kent ME4 6JG* Medway (01634) 844867

BEATTY, Robert Harold. b 27. W Ontario Univ BA48 Keble Coll Ox BA55 MA58 McGill Univ Montreal PhD62. **d** 51 **p** 52. C W Byfleet *Guildf* 67-71; C Oseney Crescent St Luke w Camden Square St Paul *Lon* 71-72; R Cosgrove *Pet* 72-83; V Hebburn St Oswald *Dur* 83-93; rtd 93. *60 Briarwood Avenue, Gosforth, Newcastle-upon-Tyne NE3 5DB* 0191-285 2429

BEAUCHAMP, Anthony Hazlerigg Proctor. b 40. MICE68 Trin Coll Cam BA62 MA66. St Jo Coll Nottm 73. **d** 75 **p** 76. C New Humberstone *Leic* 75-77; C-in-c Polegate *Chich* 77-80; Chapl Bethany Sch Goudhurst 80-86; Chapl Luckley-Oakfield Sch Wokingham 86-88; Chapl Clayesmore Sch Blandford 89-93; R Kirby-le-Soken w Gt Holland *Chelmsf* from 93. *The Rectory, 18 Thorpe Road, Kirby Cross, Frinton-on-Sea, Essex CO13 0LT* Frinton-on-Sea (01255) 675997

BEAUCHAMP, Gerald Charles. b 55. Hull Univ BA78. Coll of Resurr Mirfield 78. **d** 80 **p** 81. C Hatcham St Cath *S'wark* 80-83; S Africa 83-86; C Ealing St Steph Castle Hill *Lon* 86-88; P-in-c Brondesbury St Anne w Kilburn H Trin 88-89; V 89-93; Chapl Kilburn Coll 88-93; C Chelsea St Luke and Ch Ch *Lon* from 93. *St Luke's Vicarage, 29 Burnsall Street, London SW3 3SR* 0171-352 5608 or 351 7365

BEAUCHAMP, John Nicholas. b 57. Wycliffe Hall Ox 92. **d** 94 **p** 95. C Ipswich St Jo *St E* from 94. *2A Norbury Road, Ipswich IP4 4RQ* Ipswich (01473) 710025

BEAUMONT, Arthur Ralph. b 37. Open Univ BA82 Salford Univ MSc86. Ely Th Coll 61. **d** 64 **p** 87. C Grimsby All SS *Linc* 64-65; Perm to Offic *S'well* 70-72; NSM Addingham, Edenhall, Langwathby and Culgaith *Carl* from 87. *Brookside, Melmerby, Penrith, Cumbria CA10 1HF* Langwathby (01768) 881270

BEAUMONT, Canon Brian Maxwell. b 34. Nottm Univ BA56. Wells Th Coll 58. **d** 59 **p** 60. C Clifton *S'well* 59-62; C E Stoke w Syerston 62; C Edgbaston St Geo *Birm* 62-65; V Smethwick St Alb 65-70; Asst Dir RE *Blackb* 70-73; V Blackb H Trin 70-77; Hon Can Blackb Cathl 73-77; Can Res 77-92; Dir RE 73-92; V Goosnargh w Whittingham from 92; Bp's Adv for Rural Areas from 92. *The Vicarage, Goosnargh Lane, Goosnargh, Preston PR3 2BN* Preston (01772) 865274

BEAUMONT, Canon John Philip. b 32. Leeds Univ BA55. Coll of Resurr Mirfield 55. **d** 57 **p** 58. C Leeds St Marg *Ripon* 57-60; C Wellingborough All Hallows *Pet* 60-64; Chapl HM Borstal Wellingborough 64-70; V Wellingborough St Andr *Pet* 64-70; V Finedon from 70; Can Pet Cathl from 80; RD Higham

83-87. *The Vicarage, Finedon, Wellingborough, Northants NN9 5NR* Wellingborough (01933) 680285

BEAUMONT, John William. b 19. MBE48. RMC 38. Qu Coll Birm 48. **d** 51 **p** 52. V S w N Hayling *Portsm* 59-74; R Droxford 74-86; R Meonstoke w Corhampton cum Exton 78-86; rtd 86; Perm to Offic *Portsm* from 86. *134 The Dale, Widley, Waterlooville, Hants PO7 5DF* Cosham (01705) 377492

BEAUMONT, Stephen Martin. b 51. K Coll Lon BD73 AKC74. St Aug Coll Cant 73. **d** 74 **p** 75. C Benwell St Jas *Newc* 74-77; Asst Chapl Marlborough Coll Wilts 77-81; R Ideford, Luton and Ashcombe *Ex* 81-84; Bp's Dom Chapl 81-84; Chapl Taunton Sch Somerset 85-91; Chapl Haileybury Coll Herts from 92. *Haileybury College, Hailgate, College Road, Hertford Heath, Hertford SG13 7PU* Hertford (01992) 462000

BEAUMONT, Terence Mayes. b 41. Lon Univ BA63 Nottm Univ DipTh69. Linc Th Coll 68. **d** 71 **p** 72. C Hitchin St Mary *St Alb* 71-74; C Harpenden St Nic 75-79; V Stevenage St Pet Broadwater 79-87; V St Alb St Mich from 87. *St Michael's Vicarage, St Michael's Street, St Albans, Herts AL3 4SL* St Albans (01727) 835037

BEAUMONT, Mrs Veronica Jean. b 38. Ox Min Course CBTS93. **d** 93 **p** 94. NSM High Wycombe *Ox* from 93. *Edgehill, Upper Stanley Road, High Wycombe, Bucks HP12 4DB* High Wycombe (01494) 523697

BEAUMONT of Whitley, Rev and Rt Hon Lord (Timothy Wentworth). b 28. Ch Ch Ox BA52 MA56. Westcott Ho Cam 54. **d** 55 **p** 56. Lic to Offic *Lon* 63-73; Hon C Balham Hill Ascension *S'wark* 85-86; P-in-c Richmond St Luke 86-87; P-in-c N Sheen St Phil and All SS 86-87; V Kew St Phil and All SS w St Luke 87-91; Perm to Offic from 91; rtd 93. *40 Elms Road, London SW4 9EX* 0171-498 8664

BEAVAN, Charles Kenneth. b 15. JP63. Lon Univ BA49. St Deiniol's Hawarden 66. **d** 67 **p** 68. Hd Master Meole Brace Sch 53-76; Hon C Meole Brace *Lich* 67-71; P-in-c Shrewsbury St Alkmund 71-89; Perm to Offic from 89. *School House, 5 Vicarage Road, Shrewsbury SY3 9EZ* Shrewsbury (01743) 344172

BEAVAN, Edward Hugh. b 43. Ex Coll Ox BA70 MA74. Cuddesdon Coll 69. **d** 71 **p** 72. C Ashford St Hilda *Lon* 71-74; C Newington St Mary *S'wark* 74-76; R Sandon *Chelmsf* 76-86; V Thorpe Bay from 86. *The Vicarage, 86 Tyrone Road, Southend-on-Sea, Essex SS1 3HB* Southend-on-Sea (01702) 587597

BEAVER, Christopher Martin. b 31. AKC56. **d** 60 **p** 61. V Normacot *Lich* 67-77; V Pheasey 77-83; V Dordon *Birm* 83-89; V Langley St Mich 89-94; rtd 94; Perm to Offic *Lich* from 94. *70 Filance Lane, Penkridge, Stafford ST19 5JT* Penkridge (01785) 715834

BEAVER, William Carpenter. b 45. Colorado Coll BA Wolfs Coll Ox DPhil. Ox NSM Course. **d** 82 **p** 83. NSM Kennington St Jo w St Jas *S'wark* from 82. *7 Shardcroft Avenue, London SE24 0DS* 0171-733 8616

BEAZLEY, Prof John Milner. b 32. DRCOG59 MRCOG62 FRCOG73 FACOG89 Man Univ MB, ChB57 MD64. St Deiniol's Hawarden 83. **d** 86 **p** 87. NSM W Kirby St Bridget *Ches* 86-92; NSM Newton 89-92; NSM Aspatria w Hayton Carl from 92. *High Rigg, Faugh, Heads Nook, Carlisle CA4 9EA* Hayton (01228) 70353

BEAZLEY, Miss Margaret Sheila Elizabeth Mary. b 32. Nor City Coll CertEd59. St Alb Minl Tr Scheme 86. **d** 89 **p** 94. NSM Ware St Mary *St Alb* from 89. *38 Fanshawe Crescent, Ware, Herts SG12 0AS* Ware (01920) 462349

BEBBINGTON, Myles. b 35. Kelham Th Coll 56. **d** 61 **p** 62. C Horbury *Wakef* 61-64; C Ardwick St Benedict *Man* 64-66; V Cudworth *Wakef* 66-73; P-in-c Kensington St Jo the Bapt *Lon* 73-78; P-in-c Walthamstow St Mich *Chelmsf* 78-80; V 80-89; V Sunderland Red Ho *Dur* from 89. *St Cuthbert's Vicarage, Rotherham Road, Sunderland SR5 5QS* 0191-549 1261

BECK, Alan. b 28. AKC50. **d** 53 **p** 54. V Puriton *B & W* 69-78; P-in-c Pawlett 74-78; V Puriton and Pawlett 78-79; P-in-c Staplegrove 79-84; R 84-88; rtd 88; Perm to Offic *B & W* from 88. *Redwing, Creech Heathfield, Taunton, Somerset TA3 5EG* Taunton (01823) 443030

BECK, Amanda Ruth. b 68. Liv Univ BA91 Birm Univ BD93. Qu Coll Birm 91. **d** 94 **p** 95. C W Derby Gd Shep *Liv* from 94. *345 Utting Avenue East, Liverpool L11 1DF* 0151-256 0510

BECK, Mrs Gillian Margaret. b 50. Sheff Univ CertEd71 Nottm Univ BTh78. Linc Th Coll 74. dss 78 **d** 87. Gt Grimsby St Mary and St Jas *Linc* 78-83; St Paul's Cathl *Lon* 84-87; Hon Par Dn St Botolph Aldgate w H Trin Minories 87-88; Par Dn Monkwearmouth St Andr *Dur* 88-94; C from 94. *St Andrew's Vicarage, Park Avenue, Sunderland SR6 9PU* 0191-548 6607

BECK, John Edward. b 28. ARCM52 FRCO59 St Jo Coll Ox BA56 MA59. Wells Th Coll 56. **d** 58 **p** 59. Rhodesia 65-70; C

Cheltenham Ch Ch *Glouc* 70-77; C Cirencester 77-93; rtd 93. *25 Bowling Green Road, Cirencester, Glos GL7 2HD* Cirencester (01285) 653778

BECK, Michael Leonard. b 50. K Coll Lon BD77 AKC77. Linc Th Coll 77. **d** 78 **p** 79. C Gt Grimsby St Mary and St Jas *Linc* 78-83; Min Can and Succ St Paul's Cathl *Lon* 83-88; V Monkwearmouth St Andr *Dur* from 88. *St Andrew's Vicarage, Park Avenue, Sunderland SR6 9PU* 0191-548 6607

BECK, Peter George Cornford. b 36. Dur Univ BA61. Ridley Hall Cam 61. **d** 63 **p** 64. C Slade Green *Roch* 63-65; C Aylesford 65-68; C-in-c Brampton St Mark CD *Derby* 68-70; V Brampton St Mark 71-75; P-in-c Alvaston 75-89. *Mixon Mines Farm, Onecote, Leek, Staffs ST13 7SH*

BECK, Ven Peter John. b 48. Mert Coll Ox BA69 MA75. Sarum Th Coll 69. **d** 72 **p** 73. C Banbury *Ox* 72-75; TV 75-78; Dioc Youth and Community Officer 75-78; P-in-c Linc St Mary-le-Wigford w St Benedict etc *Linc* 78-81; New Zealand from 81; Adn Waitemata from 87. *533 New North Road, Auckland 3, New Zealand* Auckland (9) 815-0400 or 379-0625

BECK, Preb Raymond Morris. b 13. Magd Coll Ox BA36 MA40. Cuddesdon Coll 37. **d** 38 **p** 39. V Taunton St Jo *B & W* 56-80; Preb Wells Cathl 78-80; C Hedworth *Dur* 80-82; rtd 82; Hon C Fairwarp *Chich* 82-87; Perm to Offic *Ex* from 87. *Shepherd's House, East Prawle, Kingsbridge, Devon TQ7 2BY* Chivelstone (015451) 247

BECK, Canon Stephen. b 16. St Pet Hall Ox BA44 MA45. Westcott Ho Cam 45. **d** 47 **p** 48. V Moseley St Agnes *Birm* 59-83; RD Moseley 71-81; Hon Can Birm Cathl 76-83; rtd 83. *Artro View, Llanbedr, Gwynedd LL45 2DQ* Llanbedr (0134123) 545

BECKERLEG, Barzillai. b 20. Selw Coll Cam BA43 MA46. Westcott Ho Cam 42. **d** 44 **p** 45. V Kippington *Roch* 64-75; R E Bergholt *St E* 75-79; Chapl St Mary's Sch Wantage 79-85; rtd 85; Perm to Offic *Roch* from 86. *3 April Close, Horsham, W Sussex RL12 2LL* Horsham (01403) 240867

BECKETT, George. b 26. Scawsby Coll of Educn CertEd76 Sheff Univ BEd77 Hull Univ MEd84. **d** 91 **p** 92. NSM Hatf *Sheff* from 91. *10 Norman Drive, Hatfield, Doncaster, S Yorkshire DN7 6AQ* Doncaster (01302) 841091

BECKETT, Michael Shaun. b 55. ACA79. Oak Hill Th Coll BA88. **d** 88 **p** 89. C Cam St Barn *Ely* 88-93; P-in-c Cam St Paul 93-94; V from 94. *St Paul's Vicarage, 15 St Paul's Road, Cambridge CB1 2EZ* Cambridge (01223) 354186

BECKETT, Canon Stanley. b 20. Linc Th Coll. **d** 64 **p** 65. C Barnston *Ches* 64-71; V Daresbury 71-87; Hon Can Ches Cathl 82-87; P-in-c Aston by Sutton 86-87; Hon C 87-90; rtd 87; Hon C Grappenhall *Ches* from 90. *13 Wilson Close, Thelwall, Warrington WA4 2ET* Warrington (01925) 663639

BECKHAM, John Francis. b 25. Bps' Coll Cheshunt 65. **d** 67 **p** 68. C Leytonstone St Jo *Chelmsf* 67-70; C Colchester St Mary V 70-73; R Lawford 73-80; V Gt w Lt Chesterford 80-90; rtd 90; Perm to Offic *St E* from 91. *Eastwood, Walberswick, Southwold, Suffolk IP18 6UN* Southwold (01502) 724919

BECKINSALE, Mrs Pamela Rachel. b 46. Man Univ BSc69. Cant Sch of Min 88. **d** 91 **p** 94. NSM Sittingbourne St Mich *Cant* from 91. *8 Glovers Crescent, Bell Road, Sittingbourne, Kent ME10 4DU* Sittingbourne (01795) 471631

BECKLEY, Peter William. b 52. Lon Univ BSc73 CertEd. Trin Coll Bris 76. **d** 79 **p** 80. C Plymouth St Jude *Ex* 79-83; C Ecclesall *Sheff* 83-88; V Greystones from 88. *The Vicarage, 1 Cliffe Farm Drive, Sheffield S11 7JW* Sheffield (0114) 266 7686

BECKLEY, Simon Richard. b 38. Lon Univ BA61. Oak Hill Th Coll 58. **d** 63 **p** 64. C Watford St Luke *St Alb* 63-67; C New Ferry *Ches* 67-70; C Chadderton Ch Ch *Man* 70-73; V Friarmere 73-80; V Tranmere St Cath *Ches* from 80. *St Catherine's Vicarage, 9 The Wiend, Birkenhead, Merseyside L42 6RY* 0151-645 4533

BECKWITH, Ian Stanley. b 36. Nottm Univ BA58. Linc Th Coll 78. **d** 79 **p** 80. NSM Linc Cathl *Linc* 79-85; Sen Lect Bp Grosseteste Coll Linc 80-86; NSM Wallingford w Crowmarsh Gifford etc *Ox* from 91. *10 St Leonard's Lane, Wallingford, Oxon OX10 0HA* Wallingford (01491) 836372

BECKWITH, Canon John Douglas. b 33. AKC57. **d** 58 **p** 65. C Streatham St Leon *S'wark* 58-59; Lic to Offic *Ripon* 59-60; Nigeria 60-62; C Bedale *Ripon* 62-63; C Mottingham St Andr *S'wark* 64-69; Chapl Gothenburg w Halmstad and Jonkoping *Eur* 69-70; Chapl to Suff Bp Edmonton 70-77; Lic to Offic *Lon* 70-77; Dir of Ords 70-77; V Brookfield St Anne, Highgate Rise 77-88; Can Gib Cathl *Eur* 84-88; Hon Can Gib Cathl from 88; P-in-c Bladon w Woodstock *Ox* 88-93; P-in-c Wootton by Woodstock 88; P-in-c Kiddington w Asterleigh 88; C Kidlington w Hampton Poyle 93-94; Lic to Offic *Lon* from 94. *1-16 Northwood Hall, Hornsey Lane, London N6 5PG* 0181-340 0626

BECKWITH, Dr Roger Thomas. b 29. St Edm Hall Ox BA52 MA56 BD85. Ripon Hall Ox 51 Tyndale Hall Bris 52 Cuddesdon Coll 54 Lambeth DD92. **d** 54 **p** 55. Lib Latimer

Ho *Ox* 63-73; Warden 73-94; Lect Wycliffe Hall Ox 71-94; Hon C Wytham *Ox* 88-90; Hon C N Hinksey and Wytham from 90; rtd 94. *Latimer House, 131 Banbury Road, Oxford OX2 7AJ* Oxford (01865) 513879

BEDDINGTON, Peter Jon. b 36. ACP68 DipEd81. NW Ord Course 71. **d** 74 **p** 75. C Bury St Pet *Man* 74-77; Hon C Bury Ch King 77-82; Hon C Elton All SS from 82. *18 Throstle Grove, Bury, Lancs BL8 1EB* 0161-764 3292

BEDDOES, Very Rev Ronald Alfred. b 12. St Chad's Coll Dur BA35 MA50. **d** 36 **p** 37. Provost Derby 53-80; V Derby All SS 53-80; rtd 80; P-in-c Beeley and Edensor *Derby* from 80. *The Vicarage, Edensor, Bakewell, Derbyshire DE45 1PH* Baslow (01246) 582130

BEDDOW, Arthur Josiah Comyns. b 13. Ch Coll Cam BA35 MA41. Linc Th Coll 38. **d** 40 **p** 41. R Bere Ferrers *Ex* 63-78; rtd 78; Perm to Offic *Sarum* from 79; Perm to Offic *B & W* from 84. *Flat 5, Hillside, South Street, Sherborne, Dorset DT9 3NH* Sherborne (01935) 815134

BEDDOW, Nicholas Mark Johnstone-Wallace. b 47. Birm Univ BA69. Qu Coll Birm 69. **d** 71 **p** 72. C Blackheath *Birm* 71-75; Zambia 75-80; V Escomb *Dur* from 80; V Witton Park from 80; Bp's Dom Chapl 80-85. *The Vicarage, Escomb, Bishop Auckland, Co Durham DL14 7ST* Bishop Auckland (01388) 602861

BEDELL, Anthony Charles. b 59. Worc Coll Ox BA81. Linc Th Coll 87. **d** 90 **p** 91. C Newbold and Dunston *Derby* 90-94; C Bedf Leigh *Man* from 94. *30 Carisbrook Road, Leigh, Lancs WN7 2XA* Leigh (01942) 607893

BEDFORD, Christopher John Charles. b 46. K Coll Lon BD69 AKC69. St Aug Coll Cant 69. **d** 70 **p** 71. C Doncaster Ch Ch *Sheff* 70-73; C St Pancras H Cross w St Jude and St Pet *Lon* 73-76; Selection Sec ACCM 76-81; P-in-c Old St Pancras w Bedf New Town St Matt *Lon* 76-81; P-in-c Bethnal Green St Matt 81-84; R Bethnal Green St Matt w St Jas the Gt from 84. *The Rectory, Hereford Street, London E2 6EX* 0171-739 7586 Fax 729 8163

BEDFORD, Colin Michael. b 35. ALCD60. **d** 61 **p** 62. C Woking St Mary *Guildf* 61-63; C Guildf St Sav 63-65; C Morden *S'wark* 65-69; V Toxteth Park St Philemon *Liv* 69-75; P-in-c Toxteth Park St Gabr 69-75; P-in-c Toxteth Park St Jas and St Matt 69-75; P-in-c Prince's Park St Paul 70-75; P-in-c Toxteth Park St Cleopas 73-78; TR Toxteth St Philemon w St Gabr 75-89; TR Toxteth St Philemon w St Gabr and St Cleopas 89-91; R Edgware *Lon* from 91. *The Rectory, Rectory Lane, Edgware, Middx HA8 7LG* 0181-952 1081

BEDFORD, Norman Stuart. b 28. Oak Hill Th Coll 66. **d** 68 **p** 69. C Iver *Ox* 68-71; V Warfield 71-75; V Southwold *St E* 75-83; V Dedham *Chelmsf* 83-93; rtd 93. *28 Hadleigh Road, Frinton-on-Sea, Essex CO13 9HU* Frinton-on-Sea (01255) 672752

BEDFORD, Richard Derek Warner. b 27. Clare Coll Cam BA52. ALCD54. **d** 54 **p** 55. V Epsom Common Ch Ch *Guildf* 66-81; R Walton-on-the-Hill 81-87; Asst Chapl Burrswood Home of Healing 87-92; rtd 92. *2 Lealands Close, Groombridge, Tunbridge Wells, Kent TN3 9ND* Tunbridge Wells (01892) 864550

BEDFORD, Archdeacon of. See LESITER, Ven Malcolm Leslie

BEDFORD, Suffragan Bishop of. See RICHARDSON, Rt Rev John Henry

BEDLOE, Horace Walter. b 11. Keble Coll Ox. Sarum Th Coll 37. **d** 37 **p** 38. Jamaica 49-56, 60-69 and 72-75; Can Res Bradf Cathl *Bradf* 70-71; P-in-c Brighton St Jo *Chich* 76-78; rtd 78; Chapl Malaga w Almunecar and Nerja *Eur* 81-83; Perm to Offic *S'wark* 83-94; Perm to Offic *Chich* from 83; Perm to Offic *Roch* from 84. *Manormead Residential Home, Tilford Road, Hindhead, Surrey GU26 6RA* Hindhead (01428) 607506

BEDWELL, Stanley Frederick. b 20. MPS42. Ox NSM Course 77. **d** 80 **p** 81. NSM Farnham Royal *Ox* 80-81; NSM Farnham Royal w Hedgerley from 81. *18 Ingleglen, Farnham Common, Slough SL2 3QA* Farnham Common (01753) 644522

BEEBY, Lawrence Clifford. b 28. S'wark Ord Course 70. **d** 73 **p** 74. C Notting Hill St Jo *Lon* 73-74; C Sunbury 74-76; C-in-c Hounslow Gd Shep Beavers Lane CD 76-80; Chapl Bedlays Park Hosp Chertsey 80-89; Hon Chapl from 89; rtd 89. *54 Bingley Road, Sunbury-on-Thames, Middx TW16 7RB* Sunbury-on-Thames (01932) 788922

BEECH, Miss Ailsa. b 44. N Co Coll Newc TDip65. Trin Coll Bris DipHE80. **dss** 80 **d** 87 **p** 94. Pudsey St Lawr *Bradf* 80-82; Pudsey St Lawr and St Paul 82-87; Par Dn 87-88; C Attleborough *Cov* 88-89; Par Dn Cumnor *Ox* 89-92; Asst Chapl Walsgrave Hosp Cov from 92. *48 Fulstaff Close, Nuneaton, Warks CV11 6FB* Nuneaton (01203) 532290 or 538950

BEECH, Frank Thomas. b 36. Tyndale Hall Bris 64. **d** 66 **p** 67. C Penn Fields *Lich* 66-70; C Attenborough w Chilwell *S'well* 70-74; P-in-c 74-75; P-in-c Attenborough 75-76; V 76-84; V Worksop St Anne from 84; Chapl Welbeck Coll from 84. *The Vicarage, 11 Poplar Close, Worksop, Notts S80 3BZ* Worksop (01909) 472069

BEECH, Canon Harold. b 17. Univ of Wales BA39. Chich Th Coll 39. **d** 41 **p** 42. Chapl Cell Barnes Hosp and Hill End Hosp St Alb 59-82; Hon Can St Alb 77-83; rtd 82; Perm to Offic *St Alb* from 83. *Milfraen House, 32 Campfield Road, St Albans, Herts AL1 5JA* St Albans (01727) 863608

BEECH, John. b 41. St Jo Coll Nottm. **d** 83 **p** 83. C York St Paul *York* 83-84; P-in-c Bubwith w Ellerton and Aughton 84-85; P-in-c Thorganby w Skipwith and N Duffield 84-85; V Bubwith w Skipwith 85-87; V Acomb H Redeemer from 87. *The Vicarage, 108 Boroughbridge Road, York YO2 6AB* York (01904) 798593

BEECH, John Thomas. b 38. St Aid Birkenhead 64. **d** 67 **p** 68. C Burton St Paul *Lich* 67-70; Chapl RN 70-85; V Ellingham and Harbridge and Ibsley *Win* 85-94; Chapl Whiteley Village *Guildf* from 94. *The Chaplaincy, Whiteley Village, Walton-on-Thames, Surrey KT12 4EJ* Walton-on-Thames (01932) 848260

BEECH, Peter John. b 34. Bps' Coll Cheshunt 58. **d** 61 **p** 62. C Fulham All SS *Lon* 61-64; S Africa 64-67; V S Hackney St Mich *Lon* 68-71; P-in-c Haggerston St Paul 68-71; V S Hackney St Mich w Haggerston St Paul 71-75; V Wanstead H Trin Hermon Hill *Chelmsf* 75-89; P-in-c St Mary-at-Latton 89-90; V from 90. *St Mary-at-Latton Vicarage, The Gowers, Harlow, Essex CM20 2JP* Harlow (01279) 424005

BEECHAM, Clarence Ralph. b 35. S'wark Ord Course. **d** 83 **p** 84. NSM Leigh-on-Sea St Jas *Chelmsf* from 83. *27 Scarborough Drive, Leigh-on-Sea, Essex SS9 3ED* Southend-on-Sea (01702) 574923

BEEDELL, Trevor Francis. b 31. ALCD65. **d** 65 **p** 66. C Walton *St E* 65-68; R Hartshorne *Derby* 68-79; RD Repton 74-79; V Doveridge 79-86; Chapl HM Det Cen Foston Hall 79-80; Dioc Dir of Chr Stewardship *Derby* from 79. *1 River View, Milford, Belper, Derbyshire DE56 0QR* Derby (01332) 842381

BEEDON, David Kirk. b 59. Birm Univ BA89 MPhil93. Qu Coll Birm 86. **d** 89 **p** 90. C Cannock *Lich* 89-92; V Wednesbury St Bart from 92. *The Vicarage, Little Hill, Wednesbury, W Midlands WS10 9DE* 0121-556 0378

BEEK, Canon Michael Peter. b 27. Em Coll Cam BA50 MA55. Linc Th Coll 50. **d** 52 **p** 53. R Gravesend St Geo *Roch* 66-74; R Gravesend St Jas 66-74; RD Gravesend 70-74; Hon Can Roch Cathl 73-92; RD Tunbridge Wells 74-83; R Speldhurst w Groombridge 74-77; P-in-c Ashurst 77; R Speldhurst w Groombridge and Ashurst 77-83; V Bromley SS Pet and Paul 83-92; rtd 92; Perm to Offic *Nor* from 92; RD Hartismere *St E* from 93. *18 Henry Ward Road, Harleston, Norfolk IP20 9EZ* Harleston (01379) 854003

BEER, Mrs Janet Margaret. b 43. Golds Coll Lon CertEd64. Oak Hill Th Coll 83. **dss** 86 **d** 87 **p** 94. C Colney St Pet *St Alb* 86-87; Hon C from 87; Chapl St Alb High Sch for Girls 87-89; Chapl Middx Univ *Lon* from 94. *The Vicarage, Riverside, London Colney, St Albans, Herts AL2 1QT* Bowmansgreen (01727) 822122

BEER, Canon John Stuart. b 44. Pemb Coll Ox BA65 MA70 Fitzw Coll Cam MA78. Westcott Ho Cam 69. **d** 71 **p** 72. C Knaresborough St Jo *Ripon* 71-74; Chapl Fitzw Coll and New Hall Cam 74-80; Fell Fitzw Coll 77-80; Lic to Offic *Ely* 74-80; P-in-c Toft w Caldecote and Childerley 80-83; R 83-87; P-in-c Hardwick 80-83; R 83-87; V Grantchester from 87; Dir of Ords, Post-Ord Tr and Student Readers from 88; Hon Can Ely Cathl from 89. *The Vicarage, 44 High Street, Grantchester, Cambridge CB3 9NF* Cambridge (01223) 840460

BEER, Michael Trevor. b 44. Chich Th Coll 66. **d** 69 **p** 70. C Leagrave *St Alb* 69-73; St Vincent 73-74; C Thorley w Bishop's Stortford H Trin *St Alb* 74-80; V Colney St Pet from 80. *The Vicarage, Riverside, London Colney, St Albans, Herts AL2 1QT* Bowmansgreen (01727) 822122

BEER, Nigel David. b 62. Portsm Poly BSc84. St Jo Coll Nottm DTS92 MA93. **d** 93 **p** 94. C Rastrick St Matt *Wakef* from 93. *2 Newbury Road, Brighouse, W Yorkshire HD6 3PG* Huddersfield (01484) 721066

BEER, William Barclay. b 43. ACT ThA68 St Steph Ho Ox. **d** 71 **p** 72. C St Marychurch *Ex* 71-76; V Pattishall w Cold Higham *Pet* 76-82; V Northn St Benedict 82-85; V Chislehurst Annunciation *Roch* from 85. *The Vicarage, 2 Foxhome Close, Chislehurst, Kent BR7 5JY* 0181-467 3606

BEESLEY, Michael Frederick. b 37. K Coll Cam BA59. Westcott Ho Cam 60. **d** 61 **p** 64. C Eastleigh *Win* 61-69. *42 Holland Road, Parkstone, Poole, Dorset BH14 0DX* Poole (01202) 730497

BEESLEY, Ramon John. b 27. Magd Coll Ox BA51 MA55. Wycliffe Hall Ox 51. **d** 53 **p** 56. C Gerrards Cross *Ox* 53-54; Asst Chapl Embley Park Sch Romsey 54-58; Perm to Offic *Guildf* 59-63; Perm to Offic *Win* from 63; Hd Master Bellemoor Sch Southn from 74. *Wayfarers, Burley, Ringwood, Hants BH24 4HW* Burley (01425) 402284

BEESLEY, Symon Richard. b 27. Bris Univ BA53. Tyndale Hall Bris 47. **d** 53 **p** 54. V Leic H Trin *Leic* 64-72; Dep Chapl HM Pris Leic 69-72; Jt Gen Sec CCCS 72-76; Lic to Offic *Lon*

73-76; P-in-c St Leonards St Leon *Chich* 76-77; R 77-82; Kenya 82-84; V Roby *Liv* 84-89; rtd 89. *8 Shales Road, Bitterne, Southampton SO2 5RN* Southampton (01703) 463671

BEESON, Christopher George. b 48. Man Univ BSc70. Qu Coll Birm 72. **d** 75 **p** 76. C Flixton St Mich *Man* 75-78; C Newton Heath All SS 78-80; R Gorton St Jas 80-90; Dioc Communications Officer *Blackb* 91-92; C Ribbleton 92-93; rtd 93; Perm to Offic *Blackb* from 93. *24 Arnold Close, Ribbleton, Preston PR2 6DX* Preston (01772) 702675

BEESON, Very Rev Trevor Randall. b 26. K Coll Lon MA76. **d** 51 **p** 52. C Leadgate *Dur* 51-54; C Norton St Mary 54-56; C-in-c Stockton St Chad CD 56-60; V Stockton St Chad 60-65; C St Martin-in-the-Fields *Lon* 65-71; V Ware St Mary *St Alb* 71-76; Can Westmr Abbey 76-87; Treas 78-82; R Westmr St Marg 82-87; Chapl to Speaker of Ho of Commons 82-87; Dean Win from 87; FKC from 87. *The Deanery, The Close, Winchester, Hants SO23 9LS* Winchester (01962) 853738

BEETHAM, Anthony (Tony). b 32. Lon Univ BSc53. Ox NSM Course. **d** 75 **p** 76. NSM Ox St Clem *Ox* from 75; Dir Chr Enquiry Agency from 88. *44 Rose Hill, Oxford OX4 4HS, or Inter-Church House, 31-35 Lower Marsh, London SE1 7RL* (01865) 770923 or 0171-620 4444 Fax 0171-928 0010

BEETON, David Ambrose Moore. b 39. Chich Th Coll 62. **d** 65 **p** 66. C Forest Gate St Edm *Chelmsf* 65-71; V Rush Green 71-81; V Coggeshall w Markshall from 81. *The Vicarage, 4 Church Green, Coggeshall, Colchester CO6 1UD* Coggeshall (01376) 561234

BEEVER, Miss Alison Rosemary. b 59. Man Univ BA80. Linc Th Coll 88. **d** 90 **p** 94. Par Dn Watford Ch Ch *St Alb* 90-94; C from 94. *77 Northfield Gardens, Watford WD2 4RF* Watford (01923) 225411

BEEVERS, Dr Colin Lionel. b 40. CEng70 MIEE70 MBIM73 K Coll Lon BSc62 PhD66 DMS72. Sarum & Wells Th Coll 87. **d** 89 **p** 90. C Ledbury w Eastnor *Heref* 89-93; C Lt Marcle 89-93; Asst Dir of Tr from 92; P-in-c Kimbolton w Hamnish and Middleton-on-the-Hill from 93; P-in-c Bockleton w Leysters from 93. *The Vicarage, Kimbolton, Leominster, Herefordshire HR6 0EJ* Leominster (01568) 615295

BEEVERS, Reginald (Reggie). b 22. Dur Univ BA48. Qu Coll Birm 48. **d** 50 **p** 51. Chapl Guy's Hosp Lon 65-70; Chapl Liv Coll 70-81; R Hatch Beauchamp w Beercrocombe, Curry Mallet etc *B & W* 81-88; rtd 88; P-in-c Oare w Culbone *B & W* 90-93. *18 Abbey Close, Curry Rivel, Langport, Somerset TA10 0EL* Langport (01458) 253676

BEEVOR, Michael Branthwayt. b 24. Sarum Th Coll 64. **d** 66 **p** 66. C Alton St Lawr *Win* 68-70; C Christchurch 70-73; C Bournemouth St Clem w St Mary 73-75; C S w N Hayling *Portsm* 75-77; rtd 79. *38 Hart Plain Avenue, Cowplain, Waterlooville, Hants PO8 8RX* Portsmouth (01705) 250264

BEGBIE, Jeremy Sutherland. b 57. ARCM LRAM MSSTh Edin Univ BA Aber Univ BD PhD. Ridley Hall Cam. **d** 82 **p** 83. C Egham *Guildf* 82-85; Chapl Ridley Hall Cam 85-87; Dir Studies 87-92; Vice-Prin from 92. *Ridley Hall, Cambridge CB3 9HG* Cambridge (01223) 60995 Fax 301287

BEGGS, Norman Lindell. b 32. CertFSW69 N Lon Poly CQSW77 DipSocWork77. S Dios Minl Tr Scheme 86. **d** 89 **p** 90. NSM Milborne St Andrew w Dewlish *Sarum* 89-92; C 92-95; C Piddletrenthide w Plush, Alton Pancras etc 92-95; C Puddletown and Tolpuddle 92-95; rtd 95. *Wallingford House, Dewlish, Dorchester, Dorset DT2 7LX* Milborne St Andrew (01258) 837320

BEGLEY, Frank William. b 18. Univ of Wales (Lamp) BA48. **d** 49 **p** 50. Guyana 66-70; C Roath St Marg *Llan* 70-74; V Cardiff St Dyfrig and St Samson 74-83; R Llanwenarth Ultra *Mon* 83-87; rtd 87; Perm to Offic *Llan* from 87. *24 St Teilo's Court, Church Terrace, Cardiff CF2 5AX* Cardiff (01222) 489375

BEGLEY, Mrs Helen. b 59. Kingston Poly BA81. N Ord Course 87. **d** 89 **p** 94. Par Dn Leeds H Trin *Ripon* 89-90; Chapl to the Deaf from 89; Par Dn Leeds City 91-94; C from 94. *34 Dale Park Avenue, Leeds LS16 7PU* Leeds (0113) 261 3009 or 243 8328

BEHENNA, Miss Gillian Eve. b 57. CertEd78. St Alb Minl Tr Scheme 82. **dss** 85 **d** 87 **p** 94. Chapl to the Deaf *Sarum* 85-90; Chapl to the Deaf *Ex* from 90. *16 Mayflower Avenue, Pennsylvania, Exeter EX4 5DS* Exeter (01392) 215174 or 427227 Fax 427227

BEHEYDT, Gregory S. b 47. **d** 74 **p** 75. In RC Ch 74-84; Chapl Tangier *Eur* from 93. *Edifice COFICOM, rue Mediterranée Apt 20, Tangier, Morocco* Tangier (9) 944709

BELBEN, Kenneth Frank. b 30. TD77. Cranmer Hall Dur 51. **d** 55 **p** 56. V Gt w Lt Maplestead *Chelmsf* 64-76; CF (TA) 65-95; P-in-c Gestingthorpe *Chelmsf* 75-76; V Gt and Lt

49

BELCHER

Maplestead w Gestingthorpe 76-95; ChStJ from 77; rtd 95. *69 Hunt Road, Earls Colne, Colchester CO6 2NY* Earls Colne (01787) 224094

BELCHER, David John. b 44. Ch Ch Ox BA65 MA69. Cuddesdon Coll 68. **d** 70 **p** 71. C Gateshead St Mary *Dur* 70-73; C Stockton St Pet 73-76; Lic to Offic *Lich* 76-81; P-in-c W Bromwich Ch Ch 81-85; P-in-c W Bromwich Gd Shep w St Jo 85-89; V 89-95; RD W Bromwich 90-94; P-in-c Edington and Imber, Erlestoke and E Coulston *Sarum* from 95. *The Vicarage, Upper Garston Lane, Bratton, Westbury, Wilts BA13 4SN* Bratton (01380) 830374

BELCHER, Derek George. b 50. MRSH73 MBIM82 DipDiet Lon Univ PGCE82 Univ of Wales MEd86. Chich Th Coll 74. **d** 77 **p** 78. C Newton Nottage *Llan* 77-81; V Llan w Capel Llanilltern 81; PV Llan Cathl 81-87; V Margam from 87. *The Vicarage, 59A Bertha Road, Margam, Port Talbot, W Glam SA13 2AP* Port Talbot (01639) 891067 or 891548

BELCHER, Frederick William (Fred). b 30. Kelham Th Coll 50 Chich Th Coll 53. **d** 54 **p** 55. V Eltham Park St Luke *S'wark* 62-64; Lic to Offic 65-81; NSM Charminster and Stinsford *Sarum* 88-94; Perm to Offic from 94; rtd 95. *Little Mead, North Street, Charminster, Dorchester, Dorset DT2 9QZ* Dorchester (01305) 260688

BELCHER, Nicholas Arthur John. b 59. Oak Hill Th Coll BA89. **d** 89 **p** 90. C Danbury *Chelmsf* 89-92; C Barnston *Ches* from 92. *8 Antons Road, Pensby, Wirral, Merseyside L61 9PT* 0151-648 1512

BELFAST, Dean of. *See* SHEARER, Very Rev John

BELHAM, John Edward. b 42. K Coll Lon BSc65 AKC65 PhD70. Oak Hill Th Coll 69. **d** 72 **p** 73. C Cheadle Hulme St Andr *Ches* 72-75; C Cheadle 75-83; R Gressenhall w Longham w Wendling etc *Nor* from 83. *The Rectory, Bittering Street, Gressenhall, Dereham, Norfolk NR20 4EB* Dereham (01362) 860211

BELHAM, Michael. b 23. Lon Univ BScEng50. **d** 67 **p** 68. C Hendon St Mary *Lon* 69-73; V Tottenham H Trin 73-78; V Hillingdon St Jo 78-85; P-in-c Broughton *Ox* 85; R Broughton w N Newington and Shutford 85-90; Chapl Horton Gen Hosp Banbury 85-90; rtd 90; Sec DBP *Ox* from 95. *6 Blackwood Place, Bodicote, Banbury, Oxon OX15 4BE* Banbury (01295) 253923

BELING, David Gibson. b 30. Fitzw Ho Cam BA54 MA58. **d** 56 **p** 57. R W Knighton w Broadmayne *Sarum* 61-73; V Paignton St Paul Preston *Ex* 73-91; rtd 91; Perm to Offic *Ex* from 91. *Broadview, 47 Dunstone Park Road, Paignton, Devon TQ3 3NF* Paignton (01803) 666125

BELITHER, John Roland. b 36. Oak Hill Th Coll 83. **d** 86 **p** 87. NSM Bushey Heath *St Alb* 86-91; V Marsh Farm from 91. *The Vicarage, 40 Purway Close, Marsh Farm, Luton LU3 3RT* Luton (01582) 575757

BELL, Adrian Christopher. b 48. AKC70. St Aug Coll Cant 70. **d** 71 **p** 72. C Sheff St Aid w St Luke *Sheff* 71-74; C Willesborough w Hinxhill *Cant* 74-78; P-in-c Wormshill 78; P-in-c Hollingbourne w Hucking 78-82; P-in-c Leeds w Broomfield 79-82; V Hollingbourne and Hucking w Leeds and Broomfield 82-84; V Herne Bay Ch Ch 84-91; R Washingborough w Heighington and Canwick *Linc* from 91. *The Rectory, Church Hill, Washingborough, Lincoln LN4 1EJ* Lincoln (01522) 794056

BELL, Alan. b 29. Handsworth Coll Birm 55 Linc Th Coll 64. **d** 65 **p** 65. R Ludford Magna w Ludford Parva *Linc* 67-76; V Burgh on Bain 68-76; V Kelstern, Calcethorpe and E Wykeham 68-76; Clerical Org Sec CECS 76-78; rtd 94. *116 The Birches, Crawley, W Sussex RH10 1RZ* Crawley (01293) 407195

BELL, Alan John. b 47. Liv Univ BA68. Ridley Hall Lam 69. **d** 72 **p** 73. C Speke St Aid *Liv* 72-77; P-in-c Halewood 77-81; R Wavertree St Mary 81-88; Chapl Mabel Fletcher Tech Coll Liv 81-88; Chapl Olive Mt Hosp 81-88; R Fakenham w Alethorpe *Nor* from 88; RD Burnham and Walsingham from 92. *The Rectory, Gladstone Road, Fakenham, Norfolk NR21 9BZ* Fakenham (01328) 862268

BELL, Allan McRae. b 49. Moray Ho Teacher Tr Coll Edin CertEd80 E Lon Poly BA90. S'wark Ord Course 86. **d** 91 **p** 95. NSM Bow H Trin and All Hallows *Lon* 91-93; NSM R Foundn of St Kath in Ratcliffe from 93. *83 Gore Road, London E9 7HW* 0181-986 8546 or 0171-790 3540

BELL, Andrew Thomas. b 58. Ripon Coll Cuddesdon 93. **d** 95. C Leighton Buzzard w Eggington, Hockliffe etc *St Alb* from 95. *138 Brooklands Drive, Leighton Buzzard, Beds LU7 8PG* Leighton Buzzard (01525) 850204

BELL, Anthony Lawson. b 47. AKC72. St Aug Coll Cant 71. **d** 72 **p** 73. C Peterlee *Dur* 72-77; C-in-c Stockton St Jas CD 82-89; P-in-c Byers Green from 89; Ind Chapl Teesside from 89. *St Peter's Rectory, Byers Green, Spennymoor, Co Durham DL16 7NW* Bishop Auckland (01388) 606659

BELL, Antony Fancourt. b 28. Magd Coll Ox BA51 MA58. Wells Th Coll 54. **d** 56 **p** 57. V Stanway *Chelmsf* 61-94; RD

Dedham and Tey 81-91; rtd 94. *Walsingham House, Ilchester Road, Charlton Mackrell, Somerton, Somerset TA11 6AN* Charlton Mackrell (01458) 223657

BELL, Arthur Francis. b 17. Leeds Univ BA39. Bps' Coll Cheshunt 40. **d** 41 **p** 42. R Charlcombe *B & W* 61-85; rtd 85; Perm to Offic *B & W* from 86. *31 New Road, Bradford-on-Avon, Wilts BA15 1AR* Bradford-on-Avon (01225) 867624

BELL, Arthur James. b 33. Ch Coll Cam BA55 MA60. Coll of Resurr Mirfield 57. **d** 59 **p** 60. C New Cleethorpes *Linc* 59-63; C Upperby St Jo *Carl* 63-66; Canada 67-72 and 77-83; Perm to Offic *Ely* 73-75; Lic to Offic *Carl* 75-76; Warden Retreat of the Visitation Rhandirmwyn from 83. *Nantymwyn, Retreat of the Visitation, Rhandirmwyn, Llandovery, Dyfed SA20 0NR* Rhandirmwyn (015506) 247

BELL, Bryan Bland. b 07. Wadh Coll Ox BA30. Tyndale Hall Bris 38. **d** 40 **p** 41. R Nedging w Naughton *St E* 68-72; rtd 72; P-in-c Chawleigh w Cheldon *Ex* 78-81; Perm to Offic from 81. *3 Cod Meadow, Hatherleigh, Okehampton, Devon EX20 3JB* Okehampton (01837) 810593

BELL, Miss Catherine Ann. b 63. Trin Coll Bris BA88. **d** 89 **p** 94. Par Dn Southsea St Jude *Portsm* 89-94; C from 94. *45 Great South Street, Southsea, Hants PO5 3BY* Portsmouth (01705) 863056

BELL, Charles William. b 43. TCD BA66 MA69. **d** 67 **p** 68. C Newtownards *D & D* 67-70; C Larne and Inver *Conn* 70-74; C Ballymena w Ballyclug 74-80; Bp's C Belf Ardoyne 80-88; RD M Belf 86-89; Bp's C Belf Ardoyne w H Redeemer 88-89; I Eglantine from 89; Dioc Info Officer from 89. *All Saints' Rectory, 16 Eglantine Road, Lisburn, Co Antrim BT27 5RQ* Lisburn (01846) 662634

BELL, Colin Ashworth. b 52. FCCA83. Westcott Ho Cam 89. **d** 91 **p** 92. C Lytham St Cuth *Blackb* 91-93; C Whittle-le-Woods from 93. *61 Cliff Drive, Whittle-le-Woods, Chorley, Lancs PR6 7HT* Chorley (01257) 268440

BELL, Cyril John. b 22. Hull Univ BA48. Wycliffe Hall Ox 52. **d** 53 **p** 54. C Monkwearmouth St Pet *Dur* 53-56; India 56-60; Hon C Westlands St Andr *Lich* 66-71; Lic to Offic *Ches* 71-82; Perm to Offic 82-90; Perm to Offic *Lich* from 90. *32 Summerhill Gardens, Market Drayton, Shropshire TF9 1BQ* Market Drayton (01630) 654196

BELL, David Owain. b 49. Dur Univ BA69 Nottm Univ DipTh70 Fitzw Coll Cam BA72 MA80. Westcott Ho Cam 70. **d** 72 **p** 73. C Houghton le Spring *Dur* 72-76; C Norton St Mary 76-78; P-in-c Worc St Clem *Worc* 78-84; R 84-85; R Old Swinford Stourbridge from 85; RD Stourbridge from 90. *The Rectory, Oldswinford, Stourbridge, W Midlands DY8 2HA* Stourbridge (01384) 395410

BELL, David James. b 62. QUB BSc84 BTh. **d** 91 **p** 92. C Ballyholme *D & D* 91-94; C Coleraine *Conn* from 94. *19 Adelaide Avenue, Coleraine, Co Londonderry BT52 1LT* Coleraine (01265) 43474

BELL, Derek Arthur. b 35. K Coll Lon BD61 AKC61. St Boniface Warminster 61. **d** 62 **p** 63. NSM S Shore H Trin *Blackb* from 66; Asst Master Arnold Sch Blackpool 66-92; rtd 94. *4 Mersey Road, Blackpool FY4 1EN*

BELL, Donald John. b 50. Sarum & Wells Th Coll 73. **d** 76 **p** 77. C Jarrow St Paul *Dur* 76-77; C Jarrow 77-80; C Darlington St Cuth w St Hilda 80-83; V Wingate Grange 83-89; V Sherburn w Pittington from 89; RD Dur from 93; R Shadforth from 94. *The Vicarage, 89 Front Street, Sherburn, Durham DH6 1HD* 0191-372 0374

BELL, Edwin Lucius Wyndham. b 19. Worc Coll Ox BA41 MA45. Westcott Ho Cam 41. **d** 43 **p** 44. V Maidstone St Paul *Cant* 63-78; P-in-c Nonington w Barfreystone 78-85; P-in-c Womenswold 78-85; rtd 85; Perm to Offic *Cant* from 85. *2 Boarley Court, Sandling Lane, Maidstone, Kent ME14 2NL* Maidstone (01622) 756924

BELL, Edwin Ray. b 23. Clifton Th Coll 60. **d** 62 **p** 63. V Rashcliffe *Wakef* 65-76; V Holmebridge 76-89; rtd 89. *10 Hill Walk, Leyland, Preston PR5 1NY* Preston (01772) 432774

BELL, Canon Francis William Albert. b 28. TCD BA52 MA57 BD57. **d** 53 **p** 54. P-in-c Ballyhalbert *D & D* 63-71; P-in-c Ardkeen 67-71; I Ballyhalbert w Ardkeen 71-95; Miss to Seamen 71-95; RD Ards *D & D* 73-95; Can Belf Cathl 89-95; rtd 95. *18 Kilmore Road, Crossgar, Downpatrick, Co Down BT30 9HJ* Crossgar (01396) 831665

BELL, Godfrey Bryan. b 44. Oak Hill Th Coll 72. **d** 75 **p** 76. C Penn Fields *Lich* 75-79; R Dolton *Ex* 79-89; R Iddesleigh w Dowland 79-89; R Monkokehampton 79-89; R Tollard Royal w Farnham, Gussage St Michael etc *Sarum* from 89. *The Rectory, Farnham, Blandford Forum, Dorset DT11 8DE* Tollard Royal (01725) 516221

BELL, Graham Dennis Robert. b 42. ALCM K Coll Lon BSc63 AKC63 Nottm Univ MTh73. Tyndale Hall Bris 65. **d** 68 **p** 69. C Stapleford *S'well* 68-71; C Barton Seagrave *Pet* 71-73; C Barton Seagrave w Warkton 73-76; Perm to Offic *Nor* 76-82; V Wickham Market *St E* 82-86; V Wickham Market w Pettistree and Easton from 86. *The Vicarage, Crown Lane, Wickham*

50

Market, Woodbridge, Suffolk IP13 0SA   Wickham Market (01728) 746314

BELL, Canon Jack Gorman. b 23. Lon Univ BSc48. Oak Hill Th Coll 51. **d** 53 **p** 54. V Mosley Common *Man* 69-89; Hon Can Man Cathl 87-89; rtd 89; Perm to Offic *Carl* from 89. *36 Sandgate, Kendal, Cumbria LA9 6HT*   Kendal (01539) 725807

BELL, James Harold. b 50. St Jo Coll Dur BA72 St Pet Hall Ox BA74 MA78. Wycliffe Hall Ox 72. **d** 75 **p** 76. Hon C Ox St Mich w St Martin and All SS *Ox* 75-76; Chapl and Lect BNC Ox 76-82; Lic to Offic 76-82; R Northolt St Mary *Lon* 82-93; AD Ealing 91-93; Adv for Min Willesden from 93. *71 Gayton Road, Harrow, Middx HA1 2LY*   0181-863 1530

BELL, James Samuel. b 40. MBE71. St Chad's Coll Dur BA69. Coll of Resurr Mirfield 71. **d** 72 **p** 73. C Lambeth St Phil *S'wark* 72-74; P-in-c St Ninian Invergordon 74-77; C N Lambeth 74; P-in-c Dornoch *Mor* 74-77; P-in-c Brora 74-77; V Pet H Spirit Bretton *Pet* 77-83; P-in-c Marholm 82-83; Chapl Tonbridge Sch Kent from 83. *High Trees, 8 Bourne Lane, Tonbridge, Kent TN9 1LG*   Tonbridge (01732) 352802

BELL, Jeffrey William. b 37. Sarum Th Coll 60. **d** 63 **p** 64. C Northn St Matt *Pet* 63-66; C Portishead *B & W* 66-68; C Digswell *St Alb* 68-72; V Pet St Jude *Pet* 72-79; V Buckm *Ox* 79-93; RD Buckm 84-88 and 89-90; V Portsea N End St Mark *Portsm* from 93. *The Vicarage, 3A Wharf Road, Portsmouth PO2 9ED*   Portsmouth (01705) 662500

BELL, Jeremy Aidan. b 46. DipHE. Oak Hill Th Coll 80. **d** 82. C St Paul's Cray St Barn *Roch* 82-83; Perm to Offic *Ex* from 83. *Address temp unknown*

BELL, John Alfred Collingwood. b 23. Fitzw Coll Cam BA47 MA52 St Jo Coll Dur DipTh51 DipEd59. **d** 51 **p** 52. CF (TAVR) 56-84; Perm to Offic *Roch* 60-74; CF (TA) from 71; C Beverley Minster *York* 74-77; TV Thornaby on Tees 77-78; C Scalby w Ravenscar and Staintondale 78-79; C Luton All SS w St Pet *St Alb* 79-80; C Hykeham *Linc* 81-85; Chapl Sea Cadet Corps RNVR 83-85; R Castle Douglas *Glas* 85-88; rtd 88; Perm to Offic *Linc* 88-89; Perm to Offic *Ripon* 89-91; Perm to Offic *B & W* from 91. *Flat 6, The Judge's Lodgings, 19 New Street, Wells, Somerset BA5 2LD*   Wells (01749) 672053

BELL, Canon John Christopher. b 33. TCD BA56 MA66. TCD Div Sch Div Test. **d** 56 **p** 57. C Newtownards *D & D* 56-59; C Willowfield 59-62; I Carrowdore 62-70; I Drumbo from 70; Chapl Young Offender Cen Belf from 79; RD Hillsborough *D & D* from 81; Can Down Cathl from 87; Treas from 91. *The Rectory, 5 Pinehill Road, Drumbo, Ballylesson, Belfast BT8 8LA*   Belfast (01232) 826225

BELL, John Edward. b 34. Cranmer Hall Dur. **d** 67 **p** 68. C Harraby *Carl* 67-70; C Dalton-in-Furness 70-72; V Pennington 72-75; V Carl St Herbert w St Steph 75-84; V Wreay 84-85. *189 Brampton Road, Carlisle CA3 9AX*   Carlisle (01228) 22746

BELL, John Holmes. b 50. Sheff City Coll of Educn CertEd71. Oak Hill Th Coll DipHE79 BA80. **d** 80 **p** 81. C Leic St Phil *Leic* 80-83; C Portswood Ch Ch *Win* 83-86; TV S Molton w Nymet St George, High Bray etc *Ex* from 86. *The Rectory, Kings Nympton, Umberleigh, Devon EX37 9ST*   Chulmleigh (01769) 80457

BELL, Joseph William. b 30. Pemb Coll Cam BA53 MA57. Wycliffe Hall Ox 53. **d** 55 **p** 56. C Blundellsands St Nic *Liv* 55-58; CF 58-68; V Roby *Liv* 68-70; CF 70-86; P-in-c Fovant, Sutton Mandeville and Teffont Evias etc *Sarum* 86-89; Perm to Offic from 89. *61 St Ann's Place, Salisbury SP1 2SU*   Salisbury (01722) 322576

BELL, Judith Margaret. See GRIEVE, Mrs Judith Margaret

BELL, Karl Edwin. b 33. Minnesota Univ BA56. Seabury-Western Th Sem MDiv61. **d** 61 **p** 62. USA 61-71 and 76-92; Venezuela 71-76; Chapl Wiesbaden *Eur* from 92. *c/o St Augustine of Canterbury, Frankfurterstrasse 3, 65189 Wiesbaden, Germany*   Wiesbaden (611) 306674 Fax 372270

BELL, Kenneth Murray. b 30. Sarum & Wells Th Coll 75. **d** 74 **p** 76. Perm to Offic *Guildf* 74-76; C Hartley Wintney and Elvetham *Win* 76-77; C Hartley Wintney, Elvetham, Winchfield etc 77-80; V Fair Oak from 80. *The Vicarage, Fair Oak Court, Fair Oak, Eastleigh, Hants SO5 7BG*   Southampton (01703) 692238

BELL, Kevin David. b 58. Newc Univ MA93. Selly Oak Coll CPS87 Aston Tr Scheme 78 Sarum & Wells Th Coll 80. **d** 83 **p** 84. C Weoley Castle *Birm* 83-87; C Acocks Green 87-89; CF from 89. *c/o MOD (Army), Bagshot Park, Bagshot, Surrey GU19 5PL*   Bagshot (01276) 471717 Fax 412834

BELL, Nicholas Philip Johnson. b 46. St Jo Coll Dur BSc69 Nottm Univ DipTh72. St Jo Coll Nottm 70. **d** 73 **p** 74. C Chadderton Ch Ch *Man* 73-77; C Frogmore H Trin *St Alb* 77-81; V Bricket Wood 81-91; RD Aldenham 87-91; V Luton St Mary from 91. *The Vicarage, 48 Crawley Green Road, Luton LU2 0QX*   Luton (01582) 28925 or 21867

BELL, Paul Joseph. b 35. Dur Univ BA56 DipEd57. Trin Coll Bris 77. **d** 77 **p** 78. CMS 77-82; C Highbury Ch Ch w St Jo and St Sav Lon 82-85; V Middleton w E Winch *Nor* from 85. *The Vicarage, 12 Hall Orchards, Middleton, King's Lynn, Norfolk PE32 1RY*   King's Lynn (01553) 840252

BELL, Philip Harold. b 19. Leeds Univ BA45. Coll of Resurr Mirfield 38. **d** 44 **p** 45. R Crawley w Littleton *Win* 61-72; V Holdenhurst 72-78; P-in-c Hilperton w Whaddon *Sarum* 78-84; P-in-c Staverton 78-84; R Hilperton w Whaddon and Staverton etc 85-86; rtd 86. *31 Duxford Close, Larksfield, Bowerhill, Melksham, Wilts SN12 6XN*   Melksham (01225) 709732

BELL, Reginald Leslie (Reg). b 13. Trin Coll Bris 72. **d** 74 **p** 75. NSM Stoke Bishop *Bris* 74-75 and 78-94; NSM Horfield H Trin 75-77; Perm to Offic from 94. *September Cottage, 14 Pitch and Pay Lane, Bristol BS9 1NH*   Bristol (0117) 968 1510

BELL, Dr Richard Herbert. b 54. Univ Coll Lon BSc75 PhD79 Tubingen Univ DrTheol91. Wycliffe Hall Ox BA82 MA87. **d** 83 **p** 84. C Edgware *Lon* 83-86; W Germany 86-90; Lect in Th Nottm Univ from 90. *14 Anderson Crescent, Beeston, Nottingham NG9 2PT*   Nottingham (0115) 922 2036

BELL, Robert Clarke. b 30. Roch Th Coll 63. **d** 65 **p** 66. R Newark St Leon *S'well* 69-71; V Gosberton Clough *Linc* 71-74; P-in-c Quadring 73-74; Chapl to the Deaf 74-85; V Harmston 85-94; V Coleby 85-94; RD Graffoe 92-94; rtd 94. *33 Mill Lane, Bolton le Sands, Carnforth, Lancs LA5 8EZ*

BELL, Robert Mason. b 35. Lon Coll of Div 66. **d** 68 **p** 69. C Burgess Hill St Andr *Chich* 68-78; R Lewes St Jo sub Castro from 78. *St John's Rectory, 1 The Avenue, Lewes, E Sussex BN7 1BA*   Lewes (01273) 473080

BELL, Ross. b 64. Bradf and Ilkley Coll BA87. Aston Tr Scheme 89 Westcott Ho Cam 91. **d** 94 **p** 95. C W Bromwich All SS *Lich* from 94. *50 Wilford Road, West Bromwich, W Midlands B71 1QN*   0121-588 3440

BELL, Simon Barnaby. b 48. Bris Univ CertEd70. Sarum & Wells Th Coll 87. **d** 89 **p** 90. C Ewyas Harold w Dulas *Heref* 89-90; C Ewyas Harold w Dulas, Kenderchurch etc 90-93; P-in-c Clungunford w Clunbury and Clunton, Bedstone etc from 93. *The Rectory, Clungunford, Craven Arms, Shropshire SY7 0PN*   Little Brampton (01588) 660342

BELL, Stuart Rodney. b 46. Ex Univ BA67. Tyndale Hall Bris 69. **d** 71 **p** 72. C Henfynyw w Aberaeron and Llanddewi Aberarth *St D* 71-74; V 81-88; V Llangeler 74-80; R Abth from 88. *The Rectory, Laura Place, Aberystwyth, Dyfed SA23 2AU*   Aberystwyth (01970) 617184 Fax as telephone

BELL-RICHARDS, Douglas Maurice. b 23. St Steph Ho Ox 59. **d** 61 **p** 62. V Dymock w Donnington *Glouc* 67-75; V Fairford 75-91; rtd 91. *5 Palace Yard, Hereford HR4 9BJ*   Hereford (01432) 341070

BELLAIRS-COX, Miss Diana Geraldine. b 27. LTCL CertEd47. S Dios Minl Tr Scheme 87. **d** 90 **p** 94. NSM Oakdale St Geo *Sarum* from 90. *24 Chalbury Close, Poole, Dorset BH17 8BS*   Poole (01202) 600219

BELLAMY, Charles Gordon. b 15. St Chad's Coll Dur BA42. St Deiniol's Hawarden 36. **d** 42 **p** 43. V Overton *Blackb* 67-80; rtd 80; Hon C Monkseaton St Mary *Newc* from 80. *60 Davison Avenue, Whitley Bay, Tyne & Wear NE26 1SH*   0191-251 3355

BELLAMY, David Quentin. b 62. Univ of Wales (Cardiff) BMus84. Ripon Coll Cuddesdon 87 Ch Div Sch of the Pacific (USA). **d** 90 **p** 91. C Rhyl w St Ann *St As* 90-94; V Llay from 94. *The Vicarage, First Avenue, Llay, Wrexham, Clwyd LL12 0TN*   Gresford (01978) 832262

BELLAMY, Mrs Dorothy Kathleen. b 33. Gilmore Course 74. **dss** 82 **d** 87 **p** 94. Feltham *Lon* 82-84; Twickenham St Mary 84; Hampton St Mary 84-85; Hampton Wick 85-87; Par Dn 87-88; Par Dn Teddington St Mark and Hampton Wick St Jo 88-90; Par Dn Westbury *Sarum* 90-94; C from 94. *11 Laverton Green, Westbury, Wilts BA13 3RP*   Westbury (01373) 858866

BELLAMY, John Stephen. b 55. Jes Coll Ox BA77 MA81 DipTh82 DPS84. St Jo Coll Nottm. **d** 84 **p** 85. C Allerton *Liv* 84-87; C Southport Ch Ch 87-89; Bp's Dom Chapl 89-91; V Birkdale St Jas from 91. *St James's Vicarage, 25 Lulworth Road, Southport, Merseyside PR8 2BQ*   Southport (01704) 66255

BELLAMY, Mervyn Roger Hunter. b 47. Sussex Univ CertEd. St Mich Coll Llan DipTh81. **d** 81 **p** 82. C Frecheville and Hackenthorpe *Sheff* 81-85; V Shiregreen St Hilda 85-94; RD Ecclesfield 93-94; R Rawmarsh w Parkgate from 94. *The Rectory, High Street, Rawmarsh, Rotherham, S Yorkshire S62 6NE*   Rotherham (01709) 527160

BELLAMY, Peter Charles William. b 38. Birm Univ MA70 PhD79 AKC61. **d** 62 **p** 63. C Allestree *Derby* 62-65; Chapl All SS Hosp Birm 65-73; Chapl St Pet Coll Saltley 73-78; Lic to Offic *Birm* 78-90; Chapl Qu Eliz Hosp Birm 78-90; Manager HIV Services Birm Cen HA from 90; Perm to Offic *Birm* from 90. *51 St Denis Road, Selly Oak, Birmingham B29 4JY*   0121-475 6363 or 627 2052

BELLENES, Peter Charles. b 49. Pontifical Univ Salamanca DipPhil68 Thurrock Coll Essex CQSW72 DipSocWork72. Linc Th Coll 79. **d** 81 **p** 90. C Penistone *Wakef* 81-82; Hon C Liskeard, St Keyne, St Pinnock, Morval etc *Truro* 89-92; Hon C Menheniot from 92. *Fernlea, Beneathway, Dobwalls, Liskeard, Cornwall PL14 6JN* Liskeard (01579) 20031

BELLINGER, Canon Denys Gordon. b 29. Sheff Univ BA49. Westcott Ho Cam 51. **d** 53 **p** 54. V Scotforth *Blackb* 68-93; RD Lanc 82-89; Hon Can Blackb Cathl 86-93; rtd 93. *40 Yewlands Drive, Garstang, Preston PR3 1JP*

BELLINGER, Richard George. b 47. Univ of Wales (Abth) BSc(Econ)69. S Dios Minl Tr Scheme 91. **d** 94. SSF from 94; NSM Guernsey St Steph *Win* from 94. *La Maison des Vinaires, Rues des Vinaires, St Peter's, Guernsey, Channel Islands GY7 9EZ* Guernsey (01481) 63203

BELOE, Archibald John Martin. b 15. Qu Coll Cam BA37 MA41. Man Egerton Hall 37. **d** 39 **p** 40. R Hilgay *Ely* 61-79; V Fordham St Mary 71-79; rtd 79. *132 Newmarket Road, Norwich NR4 6SB* Norwich (01603) 502610

BELOE, Robert Francis. b 39. Sarum Th Coll. **d** 65 **p** 71. C Nor Heartsease St Fran *Nor* 65-66; C Edmonton St Mary w St Jo *Lon* 68-70; C St Marylebone Ch Ch w St Paul 70-74; P-in-c Wicken *Ely* 74-76; V from 76. *The Vicarage, Wicken, Ely, Cambs CB7 5XT* Ely (01353) 720243

BEMAN, Donald Oliver. b 37. Southn Univ BA58. Coll of Resurr Mirfield 58. **d** 60 **p** 65. C Forton *Portsm* 60-61; Hon C Hound *Win* 64-68; Lic to Offic 69-82. *8 Avon Court, Netley Abbey, Southampton SO3 5BU* Southampton (01703) 453239

BEMENT, Peter James. b 43. Univ of Wales (Cardiff) BA64 PhD69. Wycliffe Hall Ox 92. **d** 94 **p** 95. C Hubbertson *St D* from 94. *30 Silverstream Drive, Hakin, Milford Haven, Dyfed SA73 3NL* Milford Haven (01646) 697362

BENBOW, Susan Catherine. *See* TURNER, Mrs Susan Catherine

BENCE, Canon Graham Edwin. b 16. Lon Univ BA54. Sarum Th Coll 64. **d** 65 **p** 66. R Barlborough *Derby* 68-86; RD Bolsover 70-73; RD Bolsover and Staveley 73-78; Hon Can Derby Cathl 78-86; rtd 86; Perm to Offic *Lich* from 87. *Flat 3, 4 Quarry Place, Shrewsbury SY1 1JN* Shrewsbury (01743) 233533

BENCE, Norman Murray. b 34. Ripon Hall Ox 63. **d** 63 **p** 64. C Eling *Win* 63-66; Australia 66 and 75; Lic to Offic *Win* 67-74 and 75-81; NSM Iford from 81. *22 Corhampton Road, Bournemouth BH6 5PB* Bournemouth (01202) 421992

BENCE, Roy. b 21. Chich Th Coll 55. **d** 57 **p** 58. V Bethnal Green St Jas the Gt w St Jude *Lon* 69-72; V Bush Hill Park St Mark 72-79; V Highgate St Aug 79-86; rtd 87. *5 St James's Close, Bishop Street, London N1 8PH* 0171-359 0885

BENDELL, David James. b 38. S'wark Ord Course. **d** 87 **p** 88. NSM Surbiton Hill Ch Ch *S'wark* from 87. *3 Pine Walk, Surbiton, Surrey KT5 8NJ* 0181-399 7143

BENDING, Richard Clement. b 47. Southn Univ BSc68. Ridley Hall Cam 87. **d** 89 **p** 90. Par Dn St Neots *Ely* 89-92; V Buckden from 92. *The Vicarage, Buckden, St Neots, Huntingdon, Cambs PE18 9TL* Huntingdon (01480) 810371

BENEDICT, Brother. *See* WINSPER, Arthur William

BENFIELD, Gordon. b 29. OBE95. Lon Univ BD60 STh79 Birm Univ MA81 LGSM Leeds Univ 60. **d** 80 **p** 81. NSM Warw *Cov* 80-85; Prin Westhill Coll of HE Birm 85-90; Perm to Offic *Birm* 85-90; Chmn Ch Educn Movement from 86; R Barford w Wasperton and Sherbourne *Cov* from 90. *The Rectory, Barford, Warwick CV35 8ES* Barford (01926) 624238

BENFIELD, Paul John. b 56. Barrister-at-Law (Lincoln's Inn) 78 Newc Univ LLB77 Southn Univ BTh89. Chich Th Coll 86. **d** 89 **p** 90. C Shiremoor *Newc* 89-92; C Hexham 92-93; TV Lewes All SS, St Anne, St Mich and St Thos *Chich* from 93. *St Michael's Rectory, St Andrew's Lane, Lewes, E Sussex BN7 1UW* Lewes (01273) 474723

BENFORD, Brian. b 47. Sheff Univ BA Hull Univ MEd PhD88. N Ord Course 82. **d** 85 **p** 86. NSM Stocksbridge *Sheff* 85-90; NSM Gawber *Wakef* from 90. *9 Midhope Way, Pogmoor, Barnsley, S Yorkshire S75 2LS* Barnsley (01226) 291407

BENGE, Charles David. b 40. Cranmer Hall Dur 63. **d** 68 **p** 69. C Millfield St Mark *Dur* 68-72; C Hensingham *Carl* 72-74; TV Maghull *Liv* 75-82; V Bootle St Leon from 82. *St Leonard's Vicarage, 60 Peel Road, Bootle, Merseyside L20 4RW* 0151-922 1434

BENIAMS, Alec Charles. b 28. AKC52. **d** 53 **p** 54. V Willington *Newc* 67-71; CF (TA - R of O) from 67; V Haydon Bridge *Newc* 71-85; R Yardley Hastings, Denton and Grendon etc *Pet* 85-90; rtd 90. *12 Dickson Drive, Highford Park, Hexham, Northd NE46 2RB* Hexham (01434) 600226

BENIANS, Martin Ackland. b 19. St Jo Coll Cam BA41 MA45. Ridley Hall Cam 59. **d** 59 **p** 60. R Rackheath *Nor* 62-89; V Salhouse 62-89; rtd 89. *26 Victoria Street, Sheringham, Norfolk NR26 8JZ* Sheringham (01263) 822563

BENISON, Brian. b 41. K Coll Lon 61. Bps' Coll Cheshunt 63. **d** 66 **p** 67. C Tynemouth Ch Ch *Newc* 66-70; C Gosforth All SS 70-72; TV Cullercoats St Geo 73-81; V Denton 81-93; V Blyth St Mary from 93; Chapl Blyth Community Hosp Northd from 93. *St Mary's Vicarage, 51 Marine Terrace, Blyth, Northd NE24 2JP* Blyth (01670) 353417

BENJAMIN, Adrian Victor. b 42. Wadh Coll Ox BA66 MA68. Cuddesdon Coll 66. **d** 68 **p** 69. C Gosforth All SS *Newc* 68-71; C Stepney St Dunstan and All SS *Lon* 71-75; V Friern Barnet All SS from 75; Relig Ed ITV Oracle from 83. *14 Oakleigh Park South, London N20 9JU* 0181-445 4645 or 445 6831

BENN, Wallace Parke. b 47. UCD BA69 Lon Univ DipTh71. Trin Coll Bris 69. **d** 72 **p** 73. C New Ferry *Ches* 72-76; C Cheadle 76-82; V Audley *Lich* 82-87; V Harold Wood *Chelmsf* from 87; Chapl Harold Wood Hosp Chelmsf from 87. *The Vicarage, 15 Athelstan Road, Harold Wood, Romford RM3 0QB* Ingrebourne (01708) 342080

BENNELL, Canon Richard. b 25. Leeds Univ BA45 DipEd45. Coll of Resurr Mirfield 46. **d** 48 **p** 49. V Knowle St Martin *Bris* 68-73; TR Knowle 73-80; RD Brislington 73-79; Hon Can Bris Cathl 76-91; Chapl St Monica Home Bris 80-91; rtd 91. *1B Cooper Road, Bristol BS9 3QZ* Bristol (0117) 962 2364

BENNET, Gordon Duncan Affleck. b 31. Lon Univ BSc(Econ)55. Clifton Th Coll 55. **d** 57 **p** 58. C Carl St Jo *Carl* 57-60; C W Kilburn St Luke w St Simon and St Jude *Lon* 60-63; C-in-c Dallam CD *Liv* 63-69; Lic to Offic *Man* 69-75; NW Area Sec CPAS 69-75; R Edgware *Lon* 75-91; V Walton le Soken *Chelmsf* from 91. *The Vicarage, Martello Road, Walton on the Naze, Essex CO14 8TA* Frinton-on-Sea (01255) 675452

BENNETT, Alan Robert. b 31. Roch Th Coll 62. **d** 64 **p** 65. C Asterby w Goulceby *Linc* 64-67; C St Alb St Pet *St Alb* 67-70; R Banham *Nor* 70-72; CF 72-77; P-in-c Colchester St Mary Magd *Chelmsf* 77; TV Colchester St Leon, St Mary Magd and St Steph 77-81; R Colne Engaine 81-88; P-in-c Stoke Ferry w Wretton *Ely* 88-89; V from 89; V Whittington from 88. *The Vicarage, Low Road, Wretton, King's Lynn, Norfolk PE33 9QN* Stoke Ferry (01366) 501075

BENNETT, Alan William. b 42. Sarum Th Coll 65. **d** 68 **p** 69. C Fareham H Trin *Portsm* 68-71; C Brighton St Matthias *Chich* 71-73; C Stanmer w Falmer and Moulsecoomb 73-75; C Moulsecoomb 76; V Lower Sandown St Jo *Portsm* 76-80; V Soberton w Newtown 80-87; R Aston Clinton w Buckland and Drayton Beauchamp *Ox* from 87; RD Wendover from 94. *The Rectory, New Road, Aston Clinton, Aylesbury, Bucks HP22 5JD* Aylesbury (01296) 631626

BENNETT, Alexander Steven Frederick. b 69. Hull Univ BA91. Westcott Ho Cam CTM95. **d** 95. C Whitton and Thurleston w Akenham *St E* from 95. *530 Norwich Road, Ipswich IP1 6JR* Ipswich (01473) 463676

BENNETT, Anthony. b 31. Qu Coll Birm 72. **d** 74 **p** 74. C Hobs Moat *Birm* 74-76; C Hill 76-79; R Grendon 79-82; R Upwell Ch Ch *Ely* 82-86; R Welney 82-86; P-in-c Coates 86-88; R 88-93; rtd 93. *77 Snoots Road, Whittlesey, Peterborough PE7 1NN* Peterborough (01733) 208214

BENNETT, Arnold Ernest. b 29. K Coll Lon BD59 AKC53. **d** 54 **p** 55. C S w N Hayling *Portsm* 54-59; C Stevenage *St Alb* 59-64; R N w S Wootton *Nor* 64-74; V Hykeham *Linc* 74-85; V Heckfield w Mattingley and Rotherwick *Win* from 85. *The Vicarage, Mattingley, Basingstoke, Hants RG27 8LF* Heckfield (01734) 326385

BENNETT, Arthur Harling. b 22. Ripon Hall Ox 70. **d** 71 **p** 72. C Standish *Blackb* 71-74; TV Darwen St Pet w Hoddlesden 75-79; V Whitechapel 79-89; V Whitechapel w Admarsh-in-Bleasdale 89-90; rtd 90; Perm to Offic *Blackb* from 90. *1 Eden Gardens, Mersey Street, Longridge, Preston PR3 3WF* Longridge (01772) 784924

BENNETT, Bernard Michael. b 27. Leeds Univ CertEd52 DipPE54. St Aid Birkenhead 55. **d** 58 **p** 59. V Birkenhead St Bede w All SS *Ches* 62-71; V Latchford St Jas 71-75; Chapl HM Pris Appleton Thorn 75-82; V Appleton Thorn and Antrobus *Ches* 75-86; Chapl HM Rem Cen Risley 81-84; rtd 86. *7 Montpelier Avenue, Blackpool FY2 9AE* Blackpool (01253) 51139

BENNETT, Bryan James. b 39. Tyndale Hall Bris 64. **d** 67 **p** 68. C Consett *Dur* 67-70; CF 70-84; R Leadenham *Linc* 84-91; V Welbourn 84-91; R Castle Bytham w Creeton from 91. *The Rectory, Holywell Road, Castle Bytham, Grantham, Lincs NG33 4SL* Stamford (01780) 410166

BENNETT, Clifford Orford. b 32. St Mich Coll Llan 73. **d** 75 **p** 76. C Holywell *St As* 75-79; V Pontblyddyn from 79. *The Vicarage, Pontblyddyn, Mold, Clwyd CH7 4HG* Pontybodkin (01352) 771489

BENNETT, David Edward. b 35. Fitzw Ho Cam BA56 MA60 Lon Univ PGCE. Wells Th Coll 58. **d** 60 **p** 61. C Lightcliffe *Wakef* 60-62; NE Area Sec Chr Educn Movement 62-68; Lic to Offic *S'well* 68-71; Gen Insp RE Nottm Co Coun from 68; Hon C Holme Pierrepont w Adbolton 71-85; NSM Radcliffe-on-Trent and Shelford etc from 85. *The Old Farmhouse, Main Street, Gunthorpe, Nottingham NG14 7EY* Nottingham (0115) 966 3451

BENNETT, David Lawrence. b 38. Liv Univ BA61. Ripon Hall Ox 61. **d** 63 **p** 64. C Harlington *Lon* 63-66; Zambia from 67. *clo University of Zambia, PO Box 2379, Lusaka, Zambia*

BENNETT, David Satterly. b 37. Lanc Univ BA79 Linc Coll Ox CertEd80. English Coll Valladolid 57. **d** 62 **p** 63. In RC Ch 63-72; RAChD 72-75; RE 77-84; NSM Alresford *Chelmsf* 83-84; C Chandler's Ford *Win* 84-89; C Bitterne Park 89-94; C W End from 94. *8 Bassett Close, Southampton SO2 3FP* Southampton (01703) 769404

BENNETT, Dennis Stanley. b 13. Chich Th Coll 37. **d** 39 **p** 40. R Frampton Cotterell *Bris* 65-72; C Wrington w Butcombe *B & W* 73-78; rtd 78; Perm to Offic *B & W* 78-94. *Ashcombe, West Hay Road, Wrington, Bristol BS18 7NN* Wrington (01934) 862529

BENNETT, Donovan Harry (Don). b 27. Qu Mary Coll Lon BScEng52 FGS61 AMICE61 CEng61 FICE72. Moray Ord Course 88. **d** 92 **p** 93. Hon C Dingwall *Mor* 92-93; Hon C Strathpeffer 92-93; Hon C Inverness St Mich from 93. *39 Firthview Avenue, Scorguie, Inverness IV3 6NT* Inverness (01463) 232574

BENNETT, Edwin James. b 23. St Barn Coll Adelaide ThL47 STh52. **d** 47 **p** 48. Australia 47-74; V Oldham St Barn *Man* 74-78; V Alderney *Win* 78-84; V Hatherden w Tangley, Weyhill and Penton Mewsey 84-89; rtd 89. *35 Charlton Village, Andover, Hants SP10 4AP* Andover (01264) 356358

BENNETT, Garry Raymond. b 46. K Coll Lon 66. **d** 70 **p** 71. C Mitcham St Mark *S'wark* 70-73; C Mortlake w E Sheen 73-75; TV 76-78; V Herne Hill St Paul 78-88; P-in-c Ruskin Park St Sav and St Matt 82-88; V Herne Hill 89; Sen Dioc Stewardship Adv *Chelmsf* 89-94; TR Southend from 94. *The Rectory, Burdett Avenue, Westcliff-on-Sea, Essex SS0 7JW* Southend-on-Sea (01702) 342687

BENNETT, Geoffrey Kenneth. b 56. Oak Hill Th Coll. **d** 89 **p** 90. C Ipswich St Matt *St E* 89-92; R St Ruan w St Grade and Landewednack *Truro* from 92. *The Rectory, Church Cove, The Lizard, Helston, Cornwall TR12 7PQ* The Lizard (01326) 290713

BENNETT, George Darley. b 21. ACIS47. **d** 66 **p** 67. Zambia 66-76; R Hulland, Atlow and Bradley *Derby* 76-78; P-in-c Hulland, Atlow, Bradley and Hognaston 76-78; R 78-86; RD Ashbourne 81-86; rtd 87; Perm to Offic *Derby* from 87. *11 Freemantle Road, Mickleover, Derby DE3 5HW* Derby (01332) 510212

BENNETT, George Edward. b 51. Univ of Wales (Abth) BA72. St Steph Ho Ox 73. **d** 76 **p** 77. C Clifton All SS w Tyndalls Park *Bris* 76-78; C Clifton All SS w St Jo 78-82; Chapl Newbury and Sandleford Hosps 82-93; TV Newbury *Ox* 82-93; V Llwynderw *S & B* from 93. *Llwynderw Vicarage, Fairwood Road, West Cross, Swansea SA3 5JP* Swansea (01792) 401903

BENNETT, Graham Eric Thomas. b 53. Sarum & Wells Th Coll 88. **d** 90 **p** 91. C Baswich (or Berkswich) *Lich* 90-94; C Codsall from 94. *Church House, Bilbrook Road, Bilbrook, Wolverhampton WV8 1EU* Wolverhampton (01902) 842912

BENNETT, Guy. b 33. St Edm Hall Ox BA56. Wells Th Coll 56. **d** 58 **p** 59. C Norbury St Phil *Cant* 58-61; C Minehead *B & W* 61-63; Chapl Butlin's Clacton-on-Sea 63; C Raynes Park St Sav *S'wark* 63-66; C Motspur Park H Cross CD 66-72; R Oxted from 72. *The Rectory, 29 Chichele Road, Oxted, Surrey RH8 0AE* Oxted (01883) 712955

BENNETT, Handel Henry Cecil. b 33. Cant Sch of Min 79. **d** 82 **p** 83. NSM St Margaret's-at-Cliffe w Westcliffe etc *Cant* 82-85; Dir Holy Land Chr Tours 85-94; Holy Land Consultant F T Tours from 95; Perm to Offic *St Alb* from 85. *23 The Marsh, Carlton, Bedford MK43 7JU* Bedford (01234) 720745 Fax as telephone

BENNETT, Harold Archibald Timson. b 11. Keble Coll Ox BA33 MA45. St Steph Ho Ox 34. **d** 35 **p** 36. V Kennington *Ox* 65-79; rtd 79; C Ox St Mary Magd *Ox* 79-87; Perm to Offic from 87. *St John's Home, St Mary's Road, Oxford OX4 1QE* Oxford (01865) 246937

BENNETT, Canon Ian Frederick. b 30. Ch Coll Cam BA54 MA62. Westcott Ho Cam 61. **d** 63 **p** 64. C Hemel Hempstead *St Alb* 63-68; Asst Chapl Man Univ *Man* 69-73; Sen Chapl 73-79; C Chorlton upon Medlock 69-73; P-in-c 73-79; TR Man Whitworth 79; Dioc Tr Officer *Birm* 79-88; Hon Can Birm Cathl 86-88; Can Res Newc Cathl *Newc* 88-90; Dioc Dir of Min and Tr from 90. *21 Otterburn Avenue, Gosforth, Newcastle upon Tyne NE3 4RR* 0191-285 1967 or 226 0622

BENNETT, James Kenneth Bretherton. b 11. St Jo Coll Ox BA33 DipTh34 MA37. Wycliffe Hall Ox 33. **d** 35 **p** 36. Asst Master Loretto Sch Musselburgh 67-73; Chapl Caldicott Sch Farnham Royal 73-76; rtd 76. *2 Elmfields Gate, Winslow, Buckingham MK18 3JG* Winslow (01296) 712725

BENNETT, John David. b 58. Ox Univ BA79 MA83. Westcott Ho Cam 81. **d** 83 **p** 84. C Taunton St Andr *B & W* 83-86; Chapl

Trowbridge Coll *Sarum* 86-90; AP Studley 86-90; V Yeovil H Trin *B & W* from 90. *Holy Trinity Vicarage, 24 Turners Barn Lane, Yeovil, Somerset BA20 2LM* Yeovil (01935) 23774

BENNETT, John Walker. b 09. Hatf Coll Dur BA39 LTh39 MA41. St Aug Coll Cant 35. **d** 39 **p** 40. R Bradfield St Clare *St E* 64-77; R Bradfield St Geo w Rushbrooke 64-77; rtd 77; Perm to Offic *St E* from 77. *5 Orchard Way, Barrow, Bury St Edmunds, Suffolk IP29 5BX* Bury St Edmunds (01284) 810617

BENNETT, Dr Joyce Mary. b 23. OBE79. Westf Coll Lon BA44 DipEd45 K Coll Lon DipTh61 Hon DSocSc84. **d** 62 **p** 71. Hong Kong 62-83; NSM St Martin-in-the-Fields *Lon* 84-87; Perm to Offic *Ox* from 87. *88 Wrights Lane, Prestwood, Great Missenden, Bucks HP16 0LG* Great Missenden (01494) 862647

BENNETT, Kenneth Leigh. b 18. Jes Coll Ox BA42 MA46. **d** 44 **p** 45. V Sneinton St Matthias *S'well* 55-90; rtd 90; Perm to Offic *S'well* from 90. *1 Grafton Avenue, Nottingham NG5 4GD* Nottingham (0115) 926 5469

BENNETT, Mark Ian. b 61. K Coll Cam BA83 MA86. Trin Coll Bris BA94. **d** 94 **p** 95. C Selly Park St Steph and St Wulstan *Birm* from 94. *98 Bournbrook Road, Birmingham B29 7BU* 0121-414 0089

BENNETT, Michael Edgar. b 32. Keble Coll Ox BA53 MA58 DipEd. Wells Th Coll 59. **d** 61 **p** 62. C Calne and Blackland *Sarum* 61-64; C Tewkesbury w Walton Cardiff *Glouc* 64-69; R Swindon w Uckington and Elmstone Hardwicke 69-92; Ed Glouc Dioc Gazette from 73; Chapl Sue Ryder Home Cheltenham 80-92; R Toddington, Stanton, Didbrook w Hailes etc from 92. *The Rectory, Church Lane, Toddington, Cheltenham, Glos GL52 5DQ* Cheltenham (01242) 620126

BENNETT, Michael John. b 43. AKC66. St Boniface Warminster. **d** 67 **p** 68. C Ches le Street *Dur* 67-71; C Portland All SS w St Pet *Sarum* 71-74; Chapl Portland Hosp Weymouth 74-85; V Portland St Jo *Sarum* 74-85; R Alveley and Quatt *Heref* 85-92; Dep Chapl HM Young Offender Inst Glen Parva 93-95; TV Wrexham *St As* from 95. *St Mark's Vicarage, Menai Road, Queens Park, Wrexham, Clwyd LL13 9LB* Wrexham (01978) 356647

BENNETT, Nigel John. b 47. Lon Univ DipTh69. Oak Hill Th Coll 66. **d** 71 **p** 72. C Tonbridge St Steph *Roch* 71-75; C Heatherlands St Jo *Sarum* 75-79; P-in-c Kingham w Churchill, Daylesford and Sarsden *Ox* 79; R 80-85; Chapl Blue Coat Sch Reading from 85. *13 Wilmington Close, Woodley, Reading RG5 4LR* Reading (01734) 699223

BENNETT, Osmond Shirley. b 36. Or Coll Ox BA67. Ripon Hall Ox 64. **d** 68 **p** 69. C Stocking Farm *Leic* 68-71; C Thurcaston 71-72; V Leic St Marg 72-82; V Leic St Marg and All SS 83-89; R Houghton-on-the-Hill, Keyham and Hungarton from 89. *The Rectory, 16 Main Street, Houghton-on-the-Hill, Leicester LE7 9GD* Leicester (0116) 241 2226

BENNETT, Paul John. b 47. Univ of Wales (Cardiff) DPS89. St Mich Coll Llan 88 Llan Dioc Tr Scheme 79. **d** 85 **p** 86. NSM Ystrad Rhondda w Ynyscynon *Llan* 85-89; C Tylorstown w Ynyshir 89-93; V Llanwynno from 93. *The Vicarage, 40 Hoel-y-Plwyf, Ynysybwl, Pontypridd, M Glam CF37 3HU* Ynysybwl (01443) 790340

BENNETT, Paul Jonathan. b 61. Ex Univ BA85. Ripon Coll Cuddesdon 85. **d** 87 **p** 88. C Henleaze *Bris* 87-91; P-in-c Swindon All SS 91-94; V Swindon All SS w St Barn from 94. *All Saints' Vicarage, Southbrook Street, Swindon SN2 1HF* Swindon (01793) 523572

BENNETT, Paul William. b 61. DCR92. Linc Th Coll CMinlStuds95. **d** 95. C Thornton-le-Fylde *Blackb* from 95. *6 Waring Drive, Thornton-Cleveleys, Blackpool FY5 2SP* Blackpool (01253) 855103

BENNETT, Peter Hugh. b 22. K Coll Lon 46. **d** 50 **p** 51. V Hillmorton *Cov* 64-76; R Beaudesert w Henley-in-Arden 76-81; P-in-c Ullenhall cum Aspley 76-81; R Beaudesert and Henley-in-Arden w Ullenhall 81-87; rtd 87; Perm to Offic *Cov* from 87. *20 Avon Crescent, Stratford-upon-Avon, Warks CV37 7EY* Stratford-upon-Avon (01789) 296278

BENNETT, Reginald George. b 11. K Coll Lon 32. **d** 35 **p** 36. V Kirtlington *Ox* 61-83; P-in-c Weston on the Green 76-83; rtd 83; Perm to Offic *Ox* from 83. *13 Kennett Road, Headington, Oxford OX3 7BH* Oxford (01865) 750826

BENNETT, Richard Edward Stuart. b 24. St Jo Coll Ox BA49 MA55. Wells Th Coll 50. **d** 51 **p** 52. R Camerton *B & W* 63-80; R Dunkerton 63-80; R Camerton w Dunkerton, Foxcote and Shoscombe 80-88; RD Midsomer Norton 86-88; rtd 88; Perm to Offic *B & W* 88-94. *Xlendi, 21 Kings Oak Meadow, Clutton, Bristol BS18 4SU* Temple Cloud (01761) 453586

BENNETT, Roger Sherwood. b 35. Nottm Univ BA56. Wells Th Coll 58. **d** 59 **p** 60. C Mansf Woodhouse *S'well* 59-60; C Spalding *Linc* 60-63; V Gedney 63-69; Chapl RNR 65-68; Chapl RN 69-90; V Amport, Grateley, Monxton and Quarley *Win* from 90. *The Vicarage, Amport, Andover, Hants SP11 8BE* Andover (01264) 772950

BENNETT, Roy Donald. b 40. St Jo Coll Nottm 78. **d** 80 **p** 81. C Fletchamstead *Cov* 80-83; C Bedworth 83-87; P-in-c Studley 87-93; Chapl Univ Hosp Nottm from 93; Chapl Qu Medical Cen Nottm from 94. *Queen's Medical Centre, Nottingham NG7 2UH* Nottingham (0115) 924 9924

BENNETT, William Leslie. b 52. TCD Div Sch DipTh90. **d** 90 **p** 91. C Carrickfergus *Conn* 90-93; I Lisnaskea *Clogh* from 93. *The Rectory, Castlebalfour Road, Lisnaskea, Enniskillen, Co Fermanagh BT92 0GJ* Lisnaskea (013657) 21237

✠**BENNETTS, Rt Rev Colin James.** b 40. Jes Coll Cam BA63 MA67. Ridley Hall Cam 63. **d** 65 **p** 66 **c** 94. C Tonbridge St Steph *Roch* 65-69; Chapl Ox Pastorate 69-79; C Ox St Aldate w H Trin *Ox* 69-73; Lic to Offic 73-78; Asst Chapl Jes Coll Ox 73-75; Chapl 75-78; P-in-c Ox St Andr *Ox* 79; V 80-90; RD Ox 84-89; Can Res Ches Cathl and Dioc Dir of ords *Ches* 90-94; Area Bp Buckm *Ox* from 94. *Sheridan, Grimms Hill, Great Missenden, Bucks HP16 9BD* Great Missenden (01494) 862173 Fax 890508

BENNETTS, Gordon Vivian. b 15. TD62. Open Univ BA78. **d** 77 **p** 78. NSM Phillack w Gwithian and Gwinear *Truro* 77-79; NSM Redruth 79-80; NSM Redruth w Lanner 80-82; Chapl Tehidy Hosp Camborne 82-87; Lic to Offic *Truro* from 82; Chapl Duchy Hosp Truro from 87. *66 Tregolls Road, Truro, Cornwall TR1 1LD* Truro (01872) 41857

BENNETTS, John Barrington. b 32. Local NSM Course 85. **d** 92 **p** 93. NSM Falmouth K Chas *Truro* from 92. *39 Budock Terrace, Falmouth, Cornwall TR11 3NE* Falmouth (01326) 314961 or 312111

BENNIE, Stanley James Gordon. b 43. Edin Univ MA65. Coll of Resurr Mirfield 66. **d** 68 **p** 69. C Inverness *Newc* 68-70; Prec St Andr Cathl Inverness *Mor* 70-74; Itinerant Priest 74-81; R Portsoy *Ab* 81-84; R Buckie 81-84; R Stornoway *Arg* from 84; R Eorrapaidh from 84; Miss to Seamen from 84. *St Peter's House, 10 Springfield Road, Stornoway, Isle of Lewis PA87 2PT* Stornoway (01851) 703609

BENNISON, Philip Owen. b 42. Dur Univ BA64. Coll of Resurr Mirfield. **d** 66 **p** 67. C Guisborough *York* 66-67; C S Bank 67-71; C Thornaby on Tees St Paul 71-72; TV Thornaby on Tees 72-74; R Skelton in Cleveland 74-78; R Upleatham 75-78; Chapl Freeman Hosp Newc 78-84; V Ashington *Newc* 84-93; Chapl N Tees Health NHS Trust Stockton-on-Tees from 93. *North Tees General Hospital, Hardwick Road, Stockton-on-Tees, Cleveland TS19 8PE* Stockton-on-Tees (01642) 617617

BENSON, Christopher Hugh. b 53. Bath Academy of Art BA75 Keble Coll Ox BA78 MA87. Chich Th Coll 78. **d** 80 **p** 81. C Heavitree w Ex St Paul *Ex* 80-83; P-in-c Broadclyst 83-85; TV Pinhoe and Broadclyst 85-90; V Kingsteignton from 90; Chapl Plymouth Univ from 92. *The Vicarage, 8 Vicarage Hill, Kingsteignton, Newton Abbot, Devon TQ12 3BA* Newton Abbot (01626) 54915

BENSON, Donald. b 26. NW Ord Course 75. **d** 78 **p** 79. NSM Edge Hill St Dunstan *Liv* 78-84; NSM Liv St Paul Stoneycroft from 84. *114 Claremont Road, Liverpool L13 3HL* 0151-733 8706

BENSON, Douglas Arthur Terrell. b 08. St Jo Coll Dur BA36. Lon Coll of Div 32. **d** 36 **p** 37. V Clapham *St Alb* 48-76; rtd 76; Perm to Offic *Ox* 76-91. *2 Beech Court, Tower Street, Taunton, Somerset TA1 4BH* Taunton (01823) 337963

BENSON, Gareth Neil. b 47. HNC71 Jordan Hill Coll Glas FETC80. St And NSM Tr Scheme 77. **d** 81 **p** 82. NSM Glenrothes *St And* 81-88; NSM Kinghorn from 88; NSM Kirkcaldy from 88. *129 Waverley Drive, Glenrothes, Fife KY6 2LZ* Glenrothes (01592) 759278

BENSON, George Patrick (Paddy). b 49. Ch Ch Ox BA70 Lon Univ BD77. All Nations Chr Coll 78 St Jo Coll Nottm 89. **d** 91 **p** 92. C Upton (or Overchurch) *Ches* 91-95; V Barnston from 95. *The Vicarage, Barnston, Wirral, Merseyside L61 1BW* 0151-648 1776

BENSON, Mrs Hilary Christine. b 51. Man Univ BA72 St Hugh's Coll Ox PGCE73. Trin Coll Bris DipHE83. **dss** 84 **d** 87 **p** 94. Starbeck *Ripon* 84-86; Birm St Martin w Bordesley St Andr *Birm* 86-87; NSM 87-91; NSM Brandwood from 91; Chapl Birm Univ from 92. *77 Doversley Road, Birmingham B14 6NN* 0121-624 0217

BENSON, James Christopher Reginald. b 14. TCD BA35 MA60. **d** 37 **p** 38. I Mullaghdun *Clogh* 57-61; rtd 61. *4 Morston Avenue, Bangor, Co Down BT20 3ES* Bangor (01247) 461049

BENSON, John David. b 36. Lon Univ Dip Th61 Hull Univ DipTh82. St Aid Birkenhead 58. **d** 61 **p** 62. C Kingston upon Hull St Martin *York* 61-65; C Marfleet 65-68; V Ingleby Greenhow 68-72; P-in-c Kildale 68-72; Asst Youth Chapl 68-72; Youth Chapl *Sheff* 72-78; V Thorne 78-91; V Totley from 91. *All Saints' Vicarage, 37 Sunnyvale Road, Sheffield S17 4FA* Sheffield (0114) 236 2322

BENSON, John Patrick. b 51. Univ of Wales (Ban) BSc72. Trin Coll Bris 83. **d** 85 **p** 86. C Stoke Damerel *Ex* 85-88; P-in-c Petrockstowe, Petersmarland, Merton and Huish 88; TV Shebbear, Buckland Filleigh, Sheepwash etc 89-94; RD

Torrington 93-94; P-in-c Newport, Bishops Tawton and Tawstock from 94. *The Vicarage, 40 Chichester Road, Newport, Barnstaple, Devon EX32 9EH* Barnstaple (01271) 72733

BENSON, John Patrick. b 52. Ch Coll Cam BA73 MA76 PhD76. Trin Coll Bris 78. **d** 81 **p** 82. C Walmley *Birm* 81-84; C Chadkirk *Ches* 84-86; Singapore from 87. *St George's Church, Minden Road, Singapore 1024*

BENSON, Nicholas Henry. b 53. Trin Coll Bris. **d** 84 **p** 85. C Starbeck *Ripon* 84-86; C Birm St Martin w Bordesley St Andr *Birm* 86-91; Chapl to the Markets 86-91; V Brandwood from 91. *The Vicarage, 77 Doversley Road, Birmingham B14 6NN* 0121-444 4631

BENSON, Peter Leslie. b 60. Leeds Univ BA81. Westcott Ho Cam 81. **d** 85 **p** 86. C Kippax w Allerton Bywater *Ripon* 85-88; C Potternewton 88-91; Asst Chapl St Jas Univ Hosp Leeds 91-94; Chapl Dewsbury Distr Hosp from 94. *Dewsbury & District Hospital, Healds Road, Dewsbury, W Yorkshire WF13 4HS* Dewsbury (01924) 465105

BENSON, Philip Steven. b 59. ACertCM79 LLCM80 Ulster Univ BSc81. S Dios Minl Tr Scheme 88. **d** 92 **p** 93. Producer Relig Broadcasting Dept BBC 91-94; NSM W Ealing St Jo w St Jas *Lon* 92-94; Lic to Offic *Ches* from 94; Relig Progr Producer BBC Man from 94. *4 Cranford Avenue, Knutsford, Cheshire WA16 0EB* Knutsford (01565) 652513

BENSON, Mrs Rachel Candia. b 43. JP76. TCD MA66 Lon Univ PGCE67 DipRS87. S'wark Ord Course 84. **d** 87 **p** 94. NSM Putney St Marg *S'wark* from 87. *34 St John's Avenue, London SW15 6AN* 0181-788 3828

BENSON, Richard Edmund Miller. b 12. TCD BA35 MA50. **d** 36 **p** 37. I Sixmilecross w Termonmaguirke *Arm* 69-76; rtd 76. *14 Dellmount Park, Bangor, Co Down BT20 4UA* Bangor (01247) 455175

BENSON, Richard John. b 55. Birm Coll of Educn CertEd78. Ripon Coll Cuddesdon DipMin94. **d** 94 **p** 95. C Alford w Rigsby *Linc* from 94. *Bilsby Vicarage, Alford Road, Bilsby, Alford, Lincs LN13 9PY* Alford (01507) 462770

BENSON, Preb Riou George. b 14. QGM79. Linc Th Coll 38. **d** 39 **p** 40. V Clun w Chapel Lawn *Heref* 61-79; V Bettws-y-Crwyn w Newc 63-79; P-in-c Clungunford 63-79; Preb Heref Cathl 65-91; P-in-c Bedstone w Hopton Castle 65-79; P-in-c Llanfair Waterdine w Stowe 73-79; P-in-c Clunbury 75-79; V Clun w Chapel Lawn, Bettws-y-Crwyn and Newc 79; rtd 79. *Maiden Hill Wood, All Stretton, Church Stretton, Shropshire SY6 6LA* Church Stretton (01694) 723610

BENSON, Terence Edward Benjamin. b 17. TCD BA37. **d** 41 **p** 42. I Brinny *C, C & R* 52-56; Perm to Offic *Clogh* from 56; rtd 79. *30 Willoughby Place, Enniskillen, Co Fermanagh BT74 7EX* Enniskillen (01365) 322817

BENSON, William George. b 26. Lon Univ BA51 CertEd52 Ex Univ BA56. Sarum & Wells Th Coll 76. **d** 79 **p** 80. Hon C Heanton Punchardon w Marwood *Ex* 79-88; TR Newport, Bishops Tawton and Tawstock 88-94; rtd 94. *7 Brynsworthy Park, Roundswell, Barnstaple, Devon EX31 3RB* Barnstaple (01271) 23547

BENSON, Canon William John Robinson. b 02. QUB BA25 DipHE40. **d** 26 **p** 27. I Coleraine *Conn* 62-76; Preb St Patr Cathl Dub 63-76; rtd 76. *16 Ratheane Avenue, Mountsandel Road, Coleraine, Co Londonderry BT52 1JH* Coleraine (01265) 51922

BENT, James. b 31. St Deiniol's Hawarden 79. **d** 81 **p** 82. C Prenton *Ches* 81-84; V W Derby St Jas *Liv* 84-88; NSM Newchurch and Glazebury 93-94; NSM Glazebury in Hollinfare from 94. *133 Bright Street, Leigh, Lancs WN7 5QN* Leigh (01942) 601065

BENT, Canon Michael Charles. b 31. Kelham Th Coll 51. **d** 55 **p** 56. C Wellingborough St Mary *Pet* 55-60; New Zealand 60-85 and from 89; Adn Taranaki 76-85; Dean H Trin Cathl Suva Fiji 85-89; Can St Pet Cathl Hamilton from 90. *The Vicarage, PO Box 38, Te Awamutu, New Zealand* Te Awamutu (7) 871-4627

BENTALL, Mrs Jill Margaret. b 44. MCSP66. S Dios Minl Tr Scheme 91. **d** 94 **p** 95. NSM W Andover *Win* 94-95; NSM Knights Enham from 95. *Old Farm Cottage, 102 Charlton, Andover, Hants SP10 4AN* Andover (01264) 365643

BENTHAM, John William. b 58. Loughb Univ BSc80 Nottm Univ LTh. St Jo Coll Nottm 82. **d** 85 **p** 86. C Burmantofts St Steph and St Agnes *Ripon* 85-88; C Horsforth 88-90; P-in-c Nottm St Sav *S'well* 90-92; V from 92. *St Saviour's Vicarage, Arkwright Walk, The Meadow, Nottingham NG2 2JU* Nottingham (0115) 986 4046

BENTINCK, Richard. b 13. Madras Univ BA35. **d** 43 **p** 44. V Kirkby-in-Cleveland *York* 67-75; V Middlesb St Martin 75-85; rtd 85; P-in-c Clifford *York* 86-89. *21 Beech Avenue, Bishopthorpe, York YO2 1RL* York (01904) 708486

✠**BENTLEY, Rt Rev David Edward.** b 35. Leeds Univ BA56. Westcott Ho Cam 58. **d** 60 **p** 61 **c** 86. C Bris St Ambrose

Whitehall *Bris* 60-62; C Guildf H Trin w St Mary *Guildf* 62-66; R Headley All SS 66-73; R Esher 73-86; RD Emly 77-82; Hon Can Guildf Cathl 80-86; Chmn Dioc Coun Soc Resp 80-86; Suff Bp Lynn *Nor* 86-93; Chmn Cand Cttee ACCM 87-91; ABM 91-93; Bp Glouc from 93. *Bishopscourt, Pitt Street, Gloucester GL1 2BQ* Gloucester (01452) 524598 Fax 310025

BENTLEY, Edward John. b 35. Bris Univ BA61. Tyndale Hall Bris 58. **d** 63 **p** 64. C Wolv St Luke *Lich* 63-66; BCMS 66-72; C Cheltenham St Mark *Glouc* 72-78; V Wallasey St Nic *Ches* from 78. *St Nicholas' Vicarage, 22 Groveland Road, Wallasey, Merseyside L45 8JY* 0151-639 3589

BENTLEY, Frank Richard. b 41. K Coll Lon BD67 AKC67. **d** 68 **p** 69. C Feltham *Lon* 68-72; P-in-c Bethnal Green St Bart 72-77; R Bow w Bromley St Leon 77-88; P-in-c Mile End Old Town H Trin 77-88; P-in-c Bromley All Hallows 77-88; AD Tower Hamlets 83-88; TR E Ham w Upton Park St Alb *Chelmsf* from 88. *The Rectory, Navarre Road, London E6 3AQ* 0181-470 0011

BENTLEY, Ven Frank William Henry. b 34. AKC57. **d** 58 **p** 59. C Shepton Mallet *B & W* 58-62; R Kingsdon w Podymore-Milton 62-66; P-in-c Yeovilton 62-66; P-in-c Babcary 64-66; V Wiveliscombe 66-76; RD Tone 73-76; V St Jo in Bedwardine *Worc* 76-84; RD Martley and Worc W 80-84; Hon Can Worc Cathl 81-84; P-in-c Worc St Mich 82-84; Adn Worc and Can Res Worc Cathl from 84; Chapl to The Queen from 94. *The Archdeacon's House, 56 Battenhall Road, Worcester WR5 2BQ* Worcester (01905) 764446 Fax 612302

BENTLEY, Canon Geoffrey Bryan. b 09. K Coll Cam BA32 MA35. Cuddesdon Coll 32. **d** 33 **p** 34. Can Windsor 57-82; Hon Can from 82; rtd 82. *5 The Cloisters, Windsor Castle, Windsor, Berks SL4 1NJ* Windsor (01753) 863001

BENTLEY, Graham John. b 29. S'wark Ord Course 77. **d** 80 **p** 81. NSM Mert St Mary *S'wark* 80-83; C Balham St Mary 83-84; C Wimbledon 85-86; V Raynes Park St Sav from 86. *St Saviour's Vicarage, Church Walk, London SW20 9DW* 0181-542 2787

BENTLEY, Ian Robert. b 55. Sheff Univ BA76 Sheff City Poly PGCE78. St Jo Coll Dur CTMin95. **d** 95. C Mattishall w Mattishall Burgh, Welborne etc *Nor* from 95. *1 Robert Key Drive, Mattishall, Dereham, Norfolk NR20 3RW* Dereham (01362) 858071

BENTLEY, Ian Ronald. b 51. BA79. Oak Hill Th Coll 76. **d** 79 **p** 80. C Northwood Em *Lon* 79-85; C St Marylebone All So w SS Pet and Jo 85-88; C Langham Place All So 88-91; V Eynsham and Cassington *Ox* from 91. *The Vicarage, 45 Acre End Street, Eynsham, Witney, Oxon OX8 1PF* Oxford (01865) 881323

BENTLEY, James. b 37. TD. Mert Coll Ox BA59 BTh61 MA63 BD75 Sussex Univ DPhil80. St Steph Ho Ox 59. **d** 62 **p** 63. C Elton St Steph *Man* 62-64; C Swinton St Pet 64-66; CF (TA) 65-82; R Stretford All SS *Man* 66-73; V Oldham St Mary w St Pet 73-77; Sen Chapl Eton Coll 79-82. *6 Arborfield Close, Slough, Berks SL1 2JW* Slough (01753) 573522

BENTLEY, Mrs Lesley. b 55. RMN80 Univ of Wales (Lamp) BA76 Nottm Univ MTh82. St Jo Coll Nottm DPS83. **dss** 82 **d** 87 **p** 94. Mickleover St Jo *Derby* 82-84; Thornton *Liv* 84-87; Par Dn 87-89; Dir Diaconal Mins 89-92; Par Dn Farnworth 92-94; C 94-95; V Westbrook St Phil from 95. *St Philip's Vicarage, 89 Westbrook Crescent, Warrington WA5 5TE* Warrington (01925) 574932

BENTLEY, Paul. b 48. Sarum & Wells Th Coll DipTh93. **d** 93 **p** 94. C Ex St Dav *Ex* from 93. *44 Wreford's Close, Exeter EX4 5AY* Exeter (01392) 211482

BENTLEY, William. Univ Coll Dur BA39 DipTh40 MA42. St Andr Whittlesford 40. **d** 41 **p** 42. R Hartlepool St Hilda *Dur* 59-82; rtd 82. *4 Lindisfarne, High Shincliffe, Durham DH1 2PH* 0191-384 9876

BENTON, John Anthony. b 27. Ex Coll Ox BA48 MA52. Sarum Th Coll 49. **d** 50 **p** 51. R Moretonhampstead *Ex* 68-74; RD Moreton 73-74; R Holsworthy w Cookbury and Hollacombe 74-80; TR Withycombe Raleigh 80-92; RD Aylesbeare 84-89; rtd 92; Perm to Offic *Ex* from 92. *38 Wreford's Close, Exeter EX4 5AY* Exeter (01392) 211428

BENTON, Canon Michael John. b 38. MSOSc Lon Univ BSc60. Sarum & Wells Th Coll 72. **d** 74 **p** 74. Hon C Weeke *Win* 74-76; Sen Lect K Alfred Coll Win 74-76; C Bursledon 76-78; R Over Wallop w Nether Wallop 78-83; Dir of Educn from 79; R Win St Lawr and St Maurice w St Swithun 83-90; Hon Can Win Cathl from 89. *28 Denham Close, Winchester SO23 7BL* Winchester (01962) 855964 or 844644 Fax 841815

BENWELL, John Desmond. Jes Coll Cam BA54 MA58 Sheff Univ DSocStuds58 Lon Univ CASS59. St Jo Coll Nottm CertCS88. **d** 89 **p** 89. Somalia 89-90; Chapl Fontainebleau *Eur* 91-93; Hon C Portswood Ch Ch *Win* from 93. *14 Furzedown Road, Southampton SO2 1PN* Southampton (01703) 557622

BENWELL, Dr Michael Patrick. b 55. Jes Coll Cam BA77 Glas Univ PhD80. Sarum & Wells Th Coll BTh92. **d** 92 **p** 93. C

Eastleigh *Win* from 92. *St Francis House, Nightingale Avenue, Eastleigh, Hants SO5 3JB* Southampton (01703) 619949

+**BENZIES, Rt Rev Keith John.** b 38. OBE93. Glas Univ MA60. Sarum Th Coll 60. **d** 62 **p** 63 **c** 82. C Kingston upon Hull St Nic *York* 62-66; Madagascar from 66; Prin Ambatoharanana Th Coll 66-79; Bp Antsiranana from 82. *Misiona Anglikana, BP 278, 201 Antsiranana, Madagascar* Diego Suarez (8) 22650

BERDINNER, Clifford. b 24. SS Mark & Jo Coll Plymouth BA88. **d** 64 **p** 65. R Heather *Leic* 67-72; NSM Totnes and Berry Pomeroy *Ex* 86-91; NSM Totnes, Bridgetown & Berry Pomeroy & Dartington 91-94; rtd 89. *Hilltop Cottage, Ashprington, Totnes, Devon TQ9 7UW* Harbertonford (01803) 732518

BERESFORD, Charles Edward. b 45. St Jo Coll Nottm. **d** 86 **p** 87. C Bushbury *Lich* 86-90; TV Glascote and Stonydelph from 90. *The New Vicarage, Bamford Street, Tamworth, Staffs B77 2AS* Tamworth (01827) 62612

BERESFORD, Eric Brian. b 57. Liv Univ BSc78 Ox Univ BA82 MA86. Wycliffe Hall Ox. **d** 82 **p** 83. C Upton (or Overchurch) *Ches* 82-85; Canada from 85; Asst Prof Ethics McGill Univ Montreal from 88. *4414 Beaconsfield, Montreal, Quebec, Canada, H4A 2H6*

BERESFORD, Mrs Florence. b 33. Cranmer Hall Dur 75. **dss** 78 **d** 87 **p** 94. Eighton Banks *Dur* 78-86; Lobley Hill 86-87; Par Dn 87-90; Par Dn Ches le Street 90-91; rtd 91. *Gilead, 39 Picktree Lodge, Chester-le-Street, Co Durham DH3 4DH* 0191-388 7425

BERESFORD, Peter Marcus de la Poer. b 49. Cranmer Hall Dur 74. **d** 77 **p** 78. C Walney Is *Carl* 77-80; C Netherton 80-83; TV Wednesfield *Lich* 83-88; TV Rugby St Andr *Cov* from 88. *The Vicarage, St Johns Avenue, Hillmorton, Rugby, Warks CV22 5HR* Rugby (01788) 577331

BERESFORD-DAVIES, Thomas. b 14. Univ of Wales (Lamp) BD67. **d** 42 **p** 43. V Twigworth w Down Hatherley *Glouc* 63-85; rtd 85; P-in-c Glouc St Mark *Glouc* 86-87. *Islwyn, Tewkesbury Road, Twigworth, Gloucester GL2 9PQ* Gloucester (01452) 730362

BERESFORD-PEIRSE, Mark de la Poer. b 45. Qu Coll Birm 73. **d** 76 **p** 77. C Garforth *Ripon* 76-79; C Beeston 79-83; V Barton and Manfield w Cleasby 83-90; V Pannal w Beckwithshaw from 90; Dioc Chapl MU from 91. *The Vicarage, 21 Crimple Meadows, Pannal, Harrogate, N Yorkshire HG3 1EL* Harrogate (01423) 870202

BERG, John Russell. b 36. MBE78. Sarum Th Coll 57. **d** 60 **p** 61. C Ipswich St Aug *St E* 60-64; C Whitton and Thurleston w Akenham 64-65; Miss to Seamen from 65; Hong Kong 65-72; Japan from 72. *Port PO Box 139, Naka-ku, Yokohama 231-91, Japan* Yokohama (45) 662-1871 Fax 641-5772

BERG, Canon Paul Michael. b 31. Lon Univ BA53. Oak Hill Th Coll 54. **d** 56 **p** 57. C Woodford Wells *Chelmsf* 56-60; V Tittensor *Lich* 60-65; V Rainham *Chelmsf* 65-74; R Wennington 65-74; V Clifton Ch Ch w Em *Bris* from 74; Hon Can Bris Cathl from 82; RD Clifton 87-93. *Christ Church Vicarage, 16 Mortimer Road, Bristol BS8 4EY* Bristol (0117) 973 6524

BERGER, Otto. b 19. CEng FIMechE. Oak Hill Th Coll. **d** 83 **p** 84. NSM Dovercourt and Parkeston *Chelmsf* 83-93; Perm to Offic from 93. *35 Gordon Road, Dovercourt, Harwich, Essex CO12 3TL* Harwich (01255) 502806

BERGQUIST, Dr Anders Karim. b 58. Peterho Cam BA79 MA83 PhD90. St Steph Ho Ox BA85 MA90. **d** 86 **p** 87. C Abbots Langley *St Alb* 86-89; C Cam St Mary Less *Ely* 89; Hon C from 89; Tutor Westcott Ho Cam from 89. *8 Park Street, Cambridge CB5 8AS* Cambridge (01223) 351587

BERKSHIRE, Archdeacon of. See HILL, Ven Michael Arthur

BERNARD, Brother. See APPS, Canon Michael John

BERNARDI, Frederick John. b 33. JP75 KCT89. Chich Th Coll 55. **d** 58 **p** 59. Barbados 67-71; V Sparkbrook St Agatha *Birm* 71-77; P-in-c Sparkbrook Ch Ch 73-75; V Haywards Heath St Wilfrid *Chich* 77-80; TR 80-87; Chapl Madrid *Eur* 87-90; NSM Tooting All SS *S'wark* 90-91; V Hanger Hill Ascension and W Twyford St Mary *Lon* 91-95; rtd 95. *13 Kingmere, South Terrace, Littlehampton, W Sussex BN17 5LD* Littlehampton (01903) 713543

BERNERS-WILSON (or SILLETT), Mrs Angela Veronica Isabel. b 54. St Andr Univ MTh76 St Jo Coll Dur DipTh78. **dss** 79 **d** 87 **p** 94. Southgate Ch Ch *Lon* 79-82; St Marylebone Ch Ch 82-84; Ind Chapl 82-84; Chapl Thames Poly *S'wark* 84-91; Chapl Bris Univ *Bris* from 91; C Bris St Mich and St Paul from 94. *67 Waverley Road, Bristol BS6 6ET* Bristol (0117) 924 4261 or 946 6142

BERNERS-WILSON, Daniel Downing. b 10. ALCD37. **d** 36 **p** 37. R Frant *Chich* 53-72; rtd 72. *Hamstede, Parkham Hill, Rotherfield, Crowborough, E Sussex TN6 3HR*

BERRETT, Paul Graham. b 49. St Chad's Coll Dur BA70. St Steph Ho Ox 71. **d** 74 **p** 75. C Hockerill *St Alb* 74-77; C

Leighton Buzzard 77-81; C Leighton Buzzard w Eggington, Hockliffe etc 81-83; V Bournemouth St Fran *Win* from 83. *St Francis's Clergy House, Charminster Road, Bournemouth BH8 9SH* Bournemouth (01202) 529336

BERRIDGE, Grahame Richard. b 38. S'wark Ord Course 71. **d** 72 **p** 73. NSM Beddington *S'wark* 72-75; NSM Mert St Jas 75-81; Perm to Offic from 81. *11 Cedar Walk, Kingswood, Tadworth, Surrey KT20 6HW* Burgh Heath (01737) 358882

BERRIMAN, Gavin Anthony. b 60. S'wark Ord Course 87. **d** 90 **p** 91. C Greenwich St Alfege w St Pet and St Paul *S'wark* 90-94; V Lee St Aug from 94. *St Augustine's Vicarage, 336 Baring Road, London SE12 0DU* 0181-857 4941

BERROW, Philip Rees. b 36. St D Coll Lamp 58. **d** 62 **p** 63. C Neath w Llantwit *Llan* 62-66; CF 67-87; R Welford w Weston and Clifford Chambers *Glouc* 87-94; P-in-c Badminton w Lt Badminton, Acton Turville etc from 94. *The Vicarage, Badminton, Avon GL9 1ET* Chipping Sodbury (01454) 218427

BERRY, Adrian Charles. b 50. Mert Coll Ox BA71 MA. Cuddesdon Coll 72. **d** 75 **p** 76. C Prestbury *Glouc* 75-79; C Cirencester 79-83; V Cam w Stinchcombe 83-88; Dioc Ecum Officer 83-95; P-in-c Twyning 88-95; R Leckhampton St Pet from 95. *The Rectory, Leckhampton, Cheltenham, Glos GL51 5XX* Cheltenham (01242) 513647

BERRY, Alan Peter. b 36. NW Ord Course 74. **d** 77 **p** 78. NSM Headingley *Ripon* 77-78; NSM Chapel Allerton 78-91; Perm to Offic from 91. *17 High Street, Spofforth, Harrogate, N Yorkshire HG3 1BQ* Wetherby (01937) 590503

BERRY, Anthony Nigel. b 53. Lon Bible Coll BA80 Sarum & Wells Th Coll 84. **d** 87 **p** 88. NSM Howell Hill *Guildf* 87-90; C 90; C Farnham 90-93; R Abinger cum Coldharbour from 93. *The Rectory, Abinger Common, Dorking, Surrey RH5 6HZ* Dorking (01306) 730746

BERRY, David Llewellyn Edward. b 39. St Jo Coll Cam BA61 MA65. Wells Th Coll 64. **d** 66 **p** 67. C Poplar All SS w St Frideswide *Lon* 66-69; C Ellesmere Port *Ches* 69-73; V Brafferton w Pilmoor and Myton on Swale *York* 73-79; P-in-c Thormanby 78-79; R Skelton in Cleveland 79; R Skelton w Upleatham 79-87; V Barrow St Aid *Carl* from 87. *The Vicarage, 31 Middle Hill, Barrow-in-Furness, Cumbria LA13 9HD* Barrow-in-Furness (01229) 830445

BERRY, Geoffrey Wilbur Ronald. b 22. Ridley Hall Cam 54. **d** 56 **p** 57. V Poplar St Matthias *Lon* 59-70; V Westacre *Nor* 70-79; R Gayton Thorpe w E Walton 71-79; P-in-c Maresfield *Chich* 79; R 79-87; P-in-c Nutley 79; V 79-87; rtd 87; Perm to Offic *Bris* from 87. *13 Manor Park, Great Somerford, Chippenham, Wilts SN15 5EQ* Chippenham (01249) 720530

BERRY, Graham Renwick (Silvanus). b 24. Univ of NZ BA54. Coll of Resurr Mirfield 55. **d** 57 **p** 58. C Earl's Court St Cuth w St Matthias *Lon* 57-61; Lic to Offic *Wakef* from 63; CR from 64; Prior 75-87; Superior from 87; Lic to Offic *Ripon* 68-75; rtd 94. *House of the Resurrection, Mirfield, W Yorkshire WF14 0BN* Mirfield (01924) 494318 Fax 492738

BERRY, John. b 41. Dur Univ BA62. Oak Hill Th Coll 63. **d** 65 **p** 66. C Burnage St Marg *Man* 65-68; C Middleton 68-70; Travelling Sec IVF 70-73; V Derby St Pet *Derby* 73-76; P-in-c Derby Ch Ch and H Trin 73-76; V Derby St Pet and Ch Ch w H Trin 76-81; Bp's Officer for Evang *Carl* 81-86; P-in-c Bampton and Mardale 81-86; TR N Wingfield, Pilsley and Tupton *Derby* 86-89; Evang Sec Evang Alliance 89-92; V Guernsey H Trin *Win* from 92. *Holy Trinity Vicarage, Brock Road, St Peter Port, Guernsey, Channel Islands GY1 1RS* Guernsey (01481) 724382

BERRY, Michael. b 22. Ex Coll Ox BA49 DipEd53 MA54. Westcott Ho Cam 69. **d** 71 **p** 72. C Didcot *Ox* 71-75; R Farthinghoe w Hinton-in-the-Hedges w Steane *Pet* from 75. *The Rectory, Farthinghoe, Brackley, Northants NN13 5NY* Banbury (01295) 710946

BERRY, Paul Edward. b 56. N Ord Course 91. **d** 94 **p** 95. C Halliwell St Luke *Man* from 94. *7 Russell Close, Bolton BL1 4BL* Bolton (01204) 27319

BERRY, Very Rev Peter Austin. b 35. Keble Coll Ox BA59 BTh61 MA63. St Steph Ho Ox 59. **d** 62 **p** 63. C Cov St Mark *Cov* 62-66; Dioc Community Relns Officer 64-70; C Cov Cathl 66-73; Can Res Cov Cathl 73-86; Bp's Adv for Community Relns 77-86; Vice-Provost Cov Cathl 77-86; Provost Birm from 86. *The Provost's House, 16 Pebble Mill Road, Birmingham B5 7SA* 0121-472 0709 or 236 4333 Fax 212 0868

BERRY, Miss Susan Patricia (Sue). b 49. Bris Univ BA70 CertEd72. Qu Coll Birm 77. **dss** 86 **d** 87 **p** 94. Chapl Barn Fellowship Whatcombe Ho 86-89; Chapl Lee Abbey 89-91; Lic to Offic *Ex* 89-91; Perm to Offic *Ox* 93; NSM Thatcham 93-95; Community of St Fran from 95. *Compton Durville Manor House, South Petherton, Somerset TA13 5ES* South Petherton (01460) 40473

BERRY, Timothy Hugh. b 50. Reading Univ BA72. Oak Hill NSM Course 81. **d** 84 **p** 85. NSM Swanley St Paul *Roch* 84-88;

Perm to Offic *S'wark* 86-88; C Gorleston St Andr *Nor* 88-93; V Grain w Stoke *Roch* 93-95; rtd 95. *39 Claremont Road, Swanley, Kent BR8 7RF* Swanley (01332) 662716

BERRY, William James. b 25. Bps' Coll Cheshunt 62. **d** 63 **p** 64. V Lidlington *St Alb* 67-72; R Dunton w Wrestlingworth and Eyeworth 72-83; V Earby *Bradf* 83-89; rtd 89. *34 Severn Way, Cressage, Shrewsbury SY5 6DS* Cressage (01952) 510462

BERRYMAN, William Arthur David. b 47. Lon Univ BD69 St Pet Coll Ox CertEd71. Sarum & Wells Th Coll 75. **d** 76 **p** 77. Asst Master Preston Sch Yeovil 76-80; Hon C Yeovil St Mich *B & W* 76-80; C Ex St Dav *Ex* 80-83; Chapl Ex Coll 80-83; Chapl RN 83-89; V Highertown and Baldhu *Truro* 89-95; TR Cov E *Cov* from 95. *St Peter's Rectory, Charles Street, Coventry CV1 5NP* Coventry (01203) 225907

BERSON, Alan Charles. b 31. Michigan Univ BA52 MA53 Lon Univ PhD62. St Steph Ho Ox 63. **d** 65 **p** 66. C Leeds St Pet *Ripon* 65-68; C St Giles-in-the-Fields *Lon* 68; Lic to Offic 69-80; Perm to Offic 80-88. *74 Ridgmount Gardens, London WC1E 7AX* 0171-636 1990

BERSWEDEN, Judith Anne. b 63. St Jo Coll Dur BA84. Ripon Coll Cuddesdon BA92. **d** 92 **p** 94. Par Dn Mirfield *Wakef* 92-94; NSM Roberttown from 94. *The Vicarage, Church Road, Liversedge, W Yorkshire WF15 7PF* Heckmondwike (01924) 404743

BERSWEDEN, Nils Herry Stephen. b 57. Newc Univ BSc78. Ripon Coll Cuddesdon 88. **d** 90 **p** 91. C Mirfield *Wakef* 90-93; P-in-c Purlwell 93-94; P-in-c Roberttown from 94. *The Vicarage, Church Road, Liversedge, W Yorkshire WF15 7PF* Heckmondwike (01924) 404743

BERTRAM, Preb Richard Henry. b 27. TCD BA50 MA64. CITC 50. **d** 53 **p** 54. C Sligo Cathl *K, E & A* 53-56; C Dub Booterstown *D & G* 56-58; I Stranorlar w Meenglas and Kilteevogue *D & R* 58-65; I Dub St Cath w St Jas *D & G* 65-73; I Dub Irishtown 73-74; I Dub Irishtown w Donnybrook from 74; Can Ch Ch Cathl Dub 86-92; Preb from 92; Treas from 95. *4 Ailesbury Grove, Dublin 4, Irish Republic* Dublin (1) 269-2090

BESS, Canon Cyril Henry George. b 20. AKC50. **d** 50 **p** 51. V E Grinstead St Mary *Chich* 60-75; RD E Grinstead 70-75; V Eastbourne St Mary 75-88; RD Eastbourne 75-88; Can and Preb Chich Cathl 75-87; C-in-c Hydneye CD 82-84; rtd 88. *43 Desmond Road, Eastbourne, E Sussex BN22 7LE* Eastbourne (01323) 738545

BESSANT, Brian Keith. b 32. Roch Th Coll 65. **d** 67 **p** 68. C Chatham St Wm *Roch* 67-70; C Cove St Jo *Guildf* 71-74; V Frimley Green from 74. *The Vicarage, 37 Sturt Road, Frimley Green, Camberley, Surrey GU16 6HY* Deepcut (01252) 835179

BESSANT, Idwal Brian. b 39. Cardiff Coll of Art NDD61 ATD62 Univ of Wales DipTh68. St Mich Coll Llan 65. **d** 68 **p** 69. C Llantwit Major and St Donat's *Llan* 68-73; C Llangammarch w Garth, Llanlleonfel etc *S & B* 73-77; C Crickhowell 77-78; CMS Miss 78-83; Cyprus 80-83; V Crickhowell w Cwmdu and Tretower *S & B* 83-91; RD Crickhowell 86-91; V Llanwrtyd w Llanddulas in Tir Abad etc from 91. *The Vicarage, Llanwrtyd Wells, Powys LD5 4SA* Llanwrtyd Wells (015913) 231

BESSANT, Simon David. b 56. Sheff Univ BMus77. St Jo Coll Nottm DipTh79. **d** 81 **p** 82. C Litherland St Jo and St Jas *Liv* 81-84; C Holloway Em w Hornsey Road St Barn *Lon* 84-86; C Holloway St Mark w Em 86-91; V Blackb Redeemer *Blackb* from 91. *The Redeemer Vicarage, 200 Old Bank Lane, Blackburn BB1 2HU* Blackburn (01254) 52782

BESSENT, Stephen Lyn. b 53. Bris Univ BA75. Wycliffe Hall Ox 75. **d** 77 **p** 78. C Patchway *Bris* 77-80; TV Swindon St Jo and St Andr 80-83; TV Eston w Normanby *York* 83-90; V Cogges *Ox* 90-94; P-in-c S Leigh 90-94; V Cogges and S Leigh from 94. *Cogges Priory, Church Lane, Witney, Oxon OX8 6LA* Witney (01993) 702155

BEST, Frank Milner. b 21. Linc Coll Ox BA49 MA49. Bps' Coll Cheshunt 49. **d** 50 **p** 51. R Sibson *Leic* 63-75; P-in-c Quendon w Rickling *Chelmsf* 75-78; R Quendon w Rickling and Wicken Bonhunt 78-86; rtd 86; Perm to Offic *Heref* from 87. *Besley House, Bishops Frome, Worcester WR6 5AP* Kyre (01885) 490675

BEST, Miss Karen Belinda. b 62. Qu Coll Birm 92. **d** 94 **p** 95. C Southall Green St Jo *Lon* from 94. *9 Derley Road, Southall, Middx UB2 5EJ* 0181-574 5016

BEST, Raymond. b 42. Sarum & Wells Th Coll 71. **d** 74 **p** 75. C Whorlton *Newc* 74-78; C Seaton Hirst 78-83; C Benwell St Jas 83-85; TV Benwell Team 85-89; V Walker from 89. *Walker Vicarage, Middle Street, Newcastle upon Tyne NE6 4BX* 0191-262 3666

BESTELINK, William Meindert Croft. b 48. Hull Univ BA70. Cuddesdon Coll 71. **d** 73 **p** 74. C Holt *Nor* 73-74; C E Dereham w Hoe 74-76; C Nor St Andr 76-80; R Colby w Banningham and Tuttington 80-90; R Felmingham 80-90; R Suffield 80-90; P-in-c Roydon St Remigius from 90. *The Rectory, High Road, Roydon, Diss, Norfolk IP22 3RD* Diss (01379) 642180

BESTLEY, Peter Mark. b 60. Qu Coll Cam MA Univ of Wales (Cardiff) MPhil92. St Mich Coll Llan 89. **d** 92 **p** 93. C Hampton All SS *Lon* 92-95; Chapl W Middx Univ Hosp Isleworth from 95. *The Chaplain's Office, West Middlesex University Hospital, Twickenham Road, Isleworth, Middx TW7 6AF* 0181-560 2121

BESWETHERICK, Andrew Michael. b 55. SS Mark & Jo Coll Plymouth BEd80. S'wark Ord Course 87. **d** 90 **p** 91. Dep Hd Maze Hill Sch Greenwich from 88; NSM Blackheath St Jo *S'wark* from 90. *112 Charlton Road, London SE7 7EY* 0181-853 0853

BESWICK, Canon Colin Edward. b 28. Leeds Univ BA51 Ex Univ MA75. Sarum Th Coll 58. **d** 60 **p** 61. Min Can Worc Cathl *Worc* 63-73; R Bredon w Bredon's Norton 73-79; RD Pershore 76-79; Hon Can Worc Cathl 78-84; Dir of Min 79-84; P-in-c Overbury w Alstone, Teddington and Lt Washbourne 81-84; Can Res Nor Cathl *Nor* 84-93; P-in-c Nor St Mary in the Marsh 84-87; rtd 93. *8 Mill Road, Rye, E Sussex TN31 7NN* Rye (01797) 223078

BESWICK, Canon Gary Lancelot. b 38. ALCD63. **d** 63 **p** 64. C Walthamstow St Mary *Chelmsf* 63-67; C Laisterdyke *Bradf* 67-70; V Idle H Trin 70-78; Area Sec (NW England) 78-92; Area Sec (N Thames) from 92; Lic to Offic *Man* 78-92; Lic to Offic *St Alb* from 92; Hon Can N Argentina from 87. *10 Valeside, Hertford SG14 2AR* Hertford (01992) 553274

BESWICK, Jonathan Warwick. b 67. Westcott Ho Cam. **d** 95. C Dudley St Fran *Worc* from 95. *273 The Broadway, Dudley, W Midlands DY1 3DP* Dudley (01384) 236249

BESWICK, Dr Joseph Hubert. b 25. Birm Univ MB, ChB48 Lon Univ DipTh58. **d** 59 **p** 60. Lic to Offic *S'well* from 59. *38 Hallams Lane, Beeston, Nottingham NG9 5FH* Nottingham (0115) 925 6719

BESWICK, Canon Walter. b 13. St Aid Birkenhead 46. **d** 48 **p** 49. R Dalby w Whenby *York* 64-85; V Terrington 64-85; RD Malton 75-80; Can and Preb York Minster 79-95; rtd 85. *23 Princess Court, Princess Road, Malton, N Yorkshire YO17 0HL* Malton (01653) 696128

BETSON, Stephen. b 53. Sarum & Wells Th Coll 89. **d** 91 **p** 92. C Sittingbourne St Mich *Cant* 91-95; V Fairweather Green *Bradf* from 95. *St Saviour's Vicarage, Ings Way, Bradford, W Yorkshire BD8 0LU* Bradford (01274) 544807

BETTELEY, John Richard. b 46. Sarum & Wells Th Coll 81. **d** 83 **p** 84. C Auchterarder *St And* 83-85; C Dunblane 83-85; Chapl RAF 85-89; R Callander *St And* 89-94; P-in-c Aberfoyle 89-94; P-in-c Doune 89-94; R Ballachulish *Arg* from 94; R Glencoe from 94; R Onich from 94. *The Rectory, Glencoe, Argyll PA39 4HP* Ballachulish (01855) 811335

BETTIS, Miss Margaret Jean. b 42. Gilmore Ho 72. **dss** 77 **d** 87 **p** 94. Kenya 77-79; Tutor Crowther Hall CMS Tr Coll Selly Oak 79-82; Hodge Hill *Birm* 82-87; Par Dn 87; Par Dn Flitwick *St Alb* 87-93; P-in-c Westoning w Tingrith 93-94; V from 94. *The Vicarage, Church Road, Westoning, Bedford MK45 5JW* Flitwick (01525) 713703

BETTRIDGE, Canon Graham Winston. b 39. Kelham Th Coll 60. **d** 65 **p** 66. C Burley in Wharfedale *Bradf* 65-67; C Baildon 67-70; V Harden and Wilsden 70-81; TR Kirkby Lonsdale *Carl* from 81; Hon Can Carl Cathl from 89. *The Rectory, Vicarage Lane, Kirkby Lonsdale, Carnforth, Lancs LA6 2BA* Kirkby Lonsdale (015242) 71320

BETTS, Alan John. b 55. Portsm Poly BSc77 St Martin's Coll Lanc PGCE81. St Jo Coll Nottm DTS93. **d** 93 **p** 94. C Cannock *Lich* from 93. *18 Queen Street, Cannock, Staffs WS11 1AE* Cannock (01543) 256036

BETTS, Anthony Clive (Tony). b 40. Wells Th Coll 63. **d** 65 **p** 66. C Leeds All Hallows w St Simon *Ripon* 65-67; C Wetherby 67-70; C Adel 70-73; V Leeds All SS 73-79; V Leeds Richmond Hill 79-84; R Knaresborough from 84; Chapl Knaresborough Hosp from 84; RD Harrogate *Ripon* from 95. *The Rectory, High Bond End, Knaresborough, N Yorkshire HG5 9BT* Harrogate (01423) 865273

BETTS, Canon Anthony Percy. b 26. Lon Univ BD52. ALCD52. **d** 52 **p** 53. V Derby Slg Way *Derby* 59-74; RD Derby 71-74; V Bracebridge *Linc* 74-83; P-in-c Fenny Bentley, Thorpe and Tissington *Derby* 83; P-in-c Kniveton w Hognaston 83; R Fenny Bentley, Kniveton, Thorpe and Tissington 83-91; RD Ashbourne 86-91; Hon Can Derby Cathl 87-91; rtd 91. *Otterbourne House, Windley, Belper, Derbyshire DE56 2LP* Cowers Lane (01773) 550677

BETTS, David John. b 38. Lon Univ BSc61. Oak Hill Th Coll 63. **d** 65 **p** 66. C Slough *Ox* 65-70; C Welling *Roch* 70-75; V Swanley St Paul 75-93; R Nottm St Nic *S'well* from 93. *18 Lenton Road, The Park, Nottingham NG7 1DU* Nottingham (0115) 941 1383

BETTS, Edmund John. b 51. St Chad's Coll Dur BA72 Lanc Univ MA81. Qu Coll Birm DipTh75 DPS76. **d** 76 **p** 77. C

Leagrave *St Alb* 76-79; Asst Chapl R Albert Hosp Lanc 79-81; Chapl Lea Castle Hosp and Kidderminster Gen Hosp 81-86; Prov Officer Educn for Min Ch in Wales 86-88; Exec Sec for Min 88-90; TR Haverhill w Withersfield, the Wrattings etc *St E* from 90; RD Clare from 91. *The Rectory, Great Thurlow, Haverhill, Suffolk CB9 7LF* Thurlow (0144083) 372

BETTS, George William John. b 23. Ex Univ BA51. Westcott Ho Cam 51. **d** 53 **p** 54. C Sherborne w Castleton and Lillington *Sarum* 68-69; C Brookfield St Anne, Highgate Rise *Lon* 69; rtd 88. *Flat 2, 13A Cranley Gardens, London SW7 3BB* 0171-373 8351

BETTS, Ivan Ringland. b 38. TCD BA61 MA67. **d** 62 **p** 63. C Ballyholme *D & D* 62-65; C Dundela 65-69; Miss to Seamen 69-73; Sudan 69-71; Trinidad and Tobago 71-73; C Drumglass *Arm* 73-81; I Augher w Newtownsaville and Eskrahoole *Clogh* 81-86; Bp's C Ballymacarrett St Martin *D & D* from 86. *7 Greenwood Park, Belfast BT4 3NJ* Belfast (01232) 658659

BETTS, Mrs Patricia Joyce (Pat). b 43. St Kath Coll Lon CertEd64. S Dios Minl Tr Scheme 90. **d** 94. NSM Bath Widcombe *B & W* from 94. *Hunters Lodge, North Road, Bath BA2 6HP* Bath (01225) 464918

BETTS, Paul Robert. b 31. Lon Univ BSc51. Oak Hill Th Coll 53. **d** 56 **p** 57. C Plymouth St Jude *Ex* 56-59; C Cheltenham St Mark *Glouc* 59-63; V Finchley St Paul Long Lane *Lon* 63-76; Warden St Columba Cen Cam 76-79; R Datchworth w Tewin *St Alb* from 79. *The Rectory, Brookbridge Lane, Datchworth, Knebworth, Herts SG3 6SU* Stevenage (01438) 813067

BETTS, Richard Alan. b 56. ACA83 UEA BA77. Sarum & Wells Th Coll DCTM93. **d** 93 **p** 94. C Mile Cross *Nor* from 93. *140 Mile Cross Road, Norwich NR3 2LD* Norwich (01603) 425493

✠**BETTS, Rt Rev Stanley Woodley.** b 12. CBE67. Jes Coll Cam MA37. Ridley Hall Cam 33. **d** 35 **p** 36 **c** 56. C Cheltenham St Paul *Glouc* 35-38; Chapl RAF 38-47; Chapl Clare Coll Cam 47-49; V Cam H Trin *Ely* 49-57; Suff Bp Maidstone *Cant* 56-66; Abp's Rep w HM Forces 57-66; Dean Roch 66-77; rtd 77. *2 Kings Houses, Pevensey, E Sussex BN24 5JR* Eastbourne (01323) 762421

BETTS, Steven James. b 64. York Univ BSc86. Ripon Coll Cuddesdon 87. **d** 90 **p** 91. C Bearsted w Thurnham *Cant* 90-94; Bp's Chapl *Nor* from 94. *The Vicarage, St Martin at Palace Plain, Norwich NR3 1RW* Norwich (01603) 614172 Fax 761613

BEUKES, Douglas. b 22. Oak Hill Th Coll 45. **d** 51 **p** 52. Utrecht w Arnhem, Zwolle, Amersfoort etc *Eur* 59-90; rtd 90. *Vogelzanglaan 6, 3571 ZM Utrecht, The Netherlands*

BEVAN, Alan John. b 29. Bris Univ BA54. Oak Hill Th Coll 54. **d** 56 **p** 59. C Darfield *Sheff* 68-71; C Drypool St Columba w St Andr and St Pet *York* 71-79; Chapl HM Pris Wandsworth 79-83; Chapl HM Pris Kirkham 83-86; rtd 86; Perm to Offic *Ex* from 86. *41 Bellever Close, Princetown, Yelverton, Devon PL20 6RT* Princetown (01822) 890625

BEVAN, Bryan David. Lon Univ BD60 MA70 CertEd65 DipEd66 MPhil84. Lambeth STh62 St Aug Coll Cant 62. **d** 64 **p** 66. C E Dereham w Hoe *Nor* 64-65; C Hove All SS *Chich* 65-67; Lect St Mich Coll Salisbury 67-70; The Coll Bedf from 70. *4A De Parys Lodge, De Parys Avenue, Bedford MK40 2TZ* Bedford (01234) 343622

BEVAN, Canon Charles Joseph Godfrey. b 22. TCD BA44 MA52. **d** 45 **p** 46. C Dub St Geo *D & G* 45-49; I Rathvilly *C & O* 49-59; I Carbury *M & K* 59-64; I Drogheda St Pet w Ballymakenny, Beaulieu etc *Arm* 64-90; I Drogheda w Ardee, Collon and Termonfeckin from 90; Miss to Seamen from 64; Can Arm Cathl *Arm* from 83; Chan 88-92; Prec from 92; RD Creggan and Louth from 90. *St Peter's Rectory, Drogheda, Co Louth, Irish Republic* Drogheda (41) 38441

BEVAN, David Graham. b 34. Univ of Wales (Lamp) BA54 LTh56. Gen Th Sem (NY) MDiv57. **d** 57 **p** 58. C Llanelli *St D* 57-60; CF 60-76. *148 Bromley Heath Road, Downend, Bristol BS16 6JJ* Bristol (0117) 956 0946

BEVAN, Dennis Butler. b 24. Bris Univ BA51. St Mich Coll Llan 53. **d** 54 **p** 55. V Cymmer and Porth *Llan* 67-79; V St Brides Major 79-89; rtd 89; Perm to Offic *Llan* from 89. *Glenside, 50 Allen Street, Mountain Ash, M Glam CF45 4BB* Mountain Ash (01443) 477585

BEVAN, Gordon Richard. b 26. NW Ord Course. **d** 75 **p** 76. C Spondon *Derby* 75-80; R Upper Langwith w Langwith Bassett etc 80-87; P-in-c Scarcliffe 82-87; R Upper Langwith w Langwith Bassett etc 87-94; TV E Scarsdale from 94. *Langwith Bassett Rectory, Upper Langwith, Mansfield, Notts NG20 9RE* Mansfield (01623) 742413

BEVAN, Herbert Richard. b 28. Birm Univ DipTh56 MA67. **d** 57 **p** 58. R Abberley *Worc* 62-92; RD Mitton 72-74; P-in-c Pensax 80-84; rtd 92. *Redlake Reach, Bridgend Lane, Bucknell, Shropshire SY7 0AL* Bucknell (015474) 427

BEVAN, Hubert Basil Henry. b 24. Univ of Wales (Lamp) BA52 LTh54 MTh77 PhD78. **d** 54 **p** 55. V Gilfach Goch w Llandyfodwg *Llan* 66-73; R Cregina *S & B* 73-78; V Bettws

57

Disserth w Llansantffraed in Elwell 73-78; V Glascwm and Rhulen 76-78; R Llanferres, Nercwys and Eryrys *St As* 78-80; Tutor St Deiniol's Lib Hawarden 79-89; V Treuddyn and Nercwys and Eryrys *St As* 80-85; R Llanfynydd 85-89; rtd 89. *Creiglys, Bangor Road, Caernarfon, Gwynedd LL55 1LR* Caernarfon (01286) 672874

BEVAN, John Vernon. b 16. Univ of Wales BA38. St Mich Coll Llan 38. **d** 39 **p** 40. R Enmore w Goathurst *B & W* 57-71; V Carhampton 71-81; rtd 82; Perm to Offic *B & W* 84-91. *12 Spring Gardens, Alcombe, Minehead, Somerset TA24 6BH* Minehead (01643) 702897

BEVAN, Noel Haden. b 34. St Aid Birkenhead 61. **d** 63 **p** 64. C Girlington *Bradf* 63-66; C Worksop St Jo *S'well* 66-68; V Everton w Mattersey 68-70; R Everton and Mattersey w Clayworth 70-77; TV Barton Mills *St E* 77-80; TV Barton Mills, Beck Row w Kenny Hill etc 80-85; TV Mildenhall 85-86; P-in-c Sternfield w Benhall and Snape 86-89; R from 89. *The Rectory, Benhall Green, Benhall, Saxmundham, Suffolk IP17 1HT* Saxmundham (01728) 603825

BEVAN, Paul John. b 49. Bris Sch of Min 84. **d** 87 **p** 88. NSM Bishopsworth *Bris* from 87. *10 Brookdale Road, Headley Park, Bristol BS13 7PZ* Bristol (0117) 964 6330

BEVAN, Peter John. b 54. K Coll Lon BA76 AKC76 MA86. St Steph Ho Ox BA79. **d** 80 **p** 81. C Brighouse *Wakef* 80-83; C Chapelthorpe 83-86; V Scholes 86-95; V Potters Bar *St Alb* from 95. *The Vicarage, 15 The Walk, Potters Bar, Herts EN6 1QN* Potters Bar (01707) 644539 or 645080

BEVAN, Philip Frank. b 41. Chich Th Coll 65. **d** 67 **p** 68. C Walton St Mary *Liv* 67-71; Bahamas from 71. *c/o N-963, Nassau, Bahamas*

BEVAN, Canon Richard Justin William. b 22. LTh42 St Chad's Coll Dur BA45 DTh72 PhD80. St Aug Coll Cant 39. **d** 45 **p** 46. Chapl Dur Univ *Dur* 61-74; V Dur St Oswald 64-74; R Dur St Mary le Bow w St Mary the Less 74-74; R Grasmere *Carl* 74-82; Can Res, Lib and Treas Carl Cathl 82-89; Vice-Dean Carl 86-89; Chapl to The Queen 86-93; rtd 89; Perm to Offic *Carl* from 89. *Beck Cottage, West End, Burgh-by-Sands, Carlisle CA5 6BT* Burgh-by-Sands (01228) 576781

BEVER, Canon Michael Charles Stephen. b 44. Selw Coll Cam BA66 MA70. Cuddesdon Coll. **d** 69 **p** 70. C Steeton *Bradf* 69-72; C Northn St Mary *Pet* 72-74; Niger 75-79; P-in-c Elmstead *Chelmsf* 80-83; V 83-85; Hon Can Awka from 83; V Bocking St Pet *Chelmsf* from 85. *The Vicarage, 6 St Peter's in the Fields, Bocking, Braintree, Essex CM7 9AR* Braintree (01376) 322698

BEVERIDGE, Mrs Freda Joy. b 38. Qu Mary Coll Lon BA59 Lon Inst of Educn PGCE60. Ripon Coll Cuddesdon 83. **dss** 85 **d** 87 **p** 94. Ox St Giles and SS Phil and Jas w St Marg *Ox* 85-87; Par Dn 87-88; Par Dn Woughton 88-94; C 94-95; TR from 95. *The Rectory, 10 Forest Rise, Milton Keynes MK6 5EU* Milton Keynes (01908) 670070

BEVERIDGE, Simon Alexander Ronald. b 61. Nottm Univ BA84. Chich Th Coll 84. **d** 87 **p** 88. C Braunton *Ex* 87-90; TV N Creedy 90-93; Chapl RN from 93. *Directorate Gen, RN Chapl Services, Room 203, Victory Building, HM Naval Base, Portsmouth PO1 3LS* Portsmouth (01705) 727903 Fax 727112

BEVERIDGE, Wilbert Esler. b 16. AFBpSS TCD BA38 Div Test40 BLitt52 MLitt60 Lon Univ MA64. **d** 40 **p** 41. Lic to Offic *Lon* 61-81; Prin Lect Middx Poly 69-81; rtd 81; Perm to Offic *Win* from 83. *33 Harewood Avenue, Boscombe, Bournemouth BH7 6NJ* Bournemouth (01202) 420463

BEVERLEY, Canon Arthur Leslie. b 14. Dur Univ BA37. Ely Th Coll 37. **d** 39 **p** 40. V Dorrington *Linc* 59-78; R Ruskington 59-78; Can and Preb Linc Cathl 72-79; RD Lafford 73-78; C Linc St Nic w St Jo Newport 78-79; rtd 79; Perm to Offic *Linc* from 79. *3 Middleton's Field, Lincoln LN2 1QP* Lincoln (01522) 523637

BEVERLEY, David John. b 46. Univ of Wales (Lamp) BA68. Linc Th Coll 71. **d** 73 **p** 74. C Cov E *Cov* 73-76; C Immingham *Linc* 76-84; V Bracebridge Heath 84-86; Ind Chapl from 86. *161 Ashby Road, Scunthorpe, S Humberside DN16 2AQ* Scunthorpe (01724) 844606

BEVERLEY, Suffragan Bishop of (Provincial Episcopal Visitor). *See* GAISFORD, Rt Rev John Scott

BEVINGTON, Canon Colin Reginald. b 36. ALCD63. Lon Coll of Div 63. **d** 63 **p** 64. C Devonport St Budeaux *Ex* 63-65; C Attenborough w Chilwell *S'well* 65-68; R Benhall w Sternfield *St E* 68-74; P-in-c Snape w Friston 73-74; V Selly Hill St Steph *Birm* 74-81; P-in-c Selly Oak St Wulstan 80-81; V Selly Park St Steph and St Wulstan 81-88; Dioc Ecum Officer and Adv on Miss *St E* from 88; Hon Can St E Cathl from 93; Bp's Dom Chapl from 95. *48 Thorney Road, Capel St Mary, Ipswich IP9 2UY* Great Wenham (01473) 311358

BEVINGTON, David John. b 51. Ch Coll Cam BA72 MA76. Trin Coll Bris 73. **d** 76 **p** 77. C Tulse Hill H Trin *S'wark* 76-79; C Galleywood Common *Chelmsf* 79-82; TV Hanley H Ev *Lich* 82-90; TV Hemel Hempstead *St Alb* from 90. *6 Arkley Road,*

Woodhall Farm, Hemel Hempstead, Herts HP2 7JT Hemel Hempstead (01442) 248008

BEVIS, Anthony Richard (Tony). b 34. Chich Th Coll 87. **d** 87 **p** 89. NSM Hamble le Rice *Win* 87-94; Chapl Moorgreen Hosp W End Southn from 90; NSM Woolston *Win* from 94. *Lynwood, High Street, Hamble, Southampton SO3 5HA* Southampton (01703) 453102

BEVIS, Derek Harold. FCIS. **d** 90 **p** 91. NSM Guildf Ch Ch *Guildf* from 90. *94 Wodeland Avenue, Guildford, Surrey GU2 5LD* Guildford (01483) 61968

BEWES, Emmanuel John. b 21. Edin Th Coll 49. **d** 52 **p** 53. V Hesket in the Forest *Carl* 60-76; V Hesket-in-the-Forest and Armathwaite 76-87; rtd 87; Perm to Offic *Carl* from 87. *1 Jennet Croft, Wetheral, Carlisle CA4 8JJ* Wetheral (01228) 561534

BEWES, Preb Richard Thomas. b 34. Em Coll Cam BA58 MA61. Ridley Hall Cam 57. **d** 59 **p** 60. C Beckenham Ch Ch *Roch* 59-65; V Harold Wood *Chelmsf* 65-74; V Northwood Em *Lon* 74-83; R St Marylebone All So w SS Pet and Jo 83-88; P-in-c Portman Square St Paul 87-88; R Langham Place All So from 88; Preb St Paul's Cathl from 88. *12 Weymouth Street, London W1N 3FB* 0171-580 6029 or 580 4357 Fax 436 3019

BEWLEY, Albert Latham. b 38. Leeds Univ BA61. Ely Th Coll 61. **d** 63 **p** 64. C Wigan St Mich *Liv* 63-65; C Caister *Nor* 65-69; R W Lynn 69-76; V Lakenham St Jo from 76. *Old Lakenham Vicarage, Harwood Road, Norwich NR1 2NG* Norwich (01603) 625678

BEXON, Miss Mavis Adelaide. b 31. St Mich Ho Ox. **d** 87 **p** 94. Bestwood St Matt *S'well* 77-86; Chaddesden St Mary *Derby* 86-87; Par Dn 87-91; rtd 91; Perm to Offic *S'well* from 91. *1 Dover Street, Southwell, Notts NG5 0EZ* Southwell (01636) 815976

BEYNON, Malcolm. b 36. Univ of Wales (Lamp) BA56 Univ of Wales (Swansea) DipSocSc59 Univ of Wales (Cardiff) PGCE71. St Mich Coll Llan 56. **d** 59 **p** 60. C Aberavon *Llan* 59-62; C Whitchurch 63-68; V Llanwynno 68-73; Chapl Old Hall Sch Wellington Shropshire 74-75; Perm to Offic *Leic* 75-82; Chapl Nevill Holt Sch Market Harborough 75-82; Chapl Denstone Coll Prep Sch 82-93; V Dale and St Brides w Marloes *St D* from 93. *The Vicarage, Dale, Haverfordwest, Dyfed SA62 3RN* Dale (01646) 636255

BEYNON, Nigel David. b 68. Collingwood Coll Dur BSc90. Ridley Hall Cam BA94. **d** 95. C Fulham St Matt *Lon* from 95. *2A Clancarthy Road, London SW6 3AB* 0171-736 4421

BEYNON, Sidney James. b 09. St D Coll Lamp BA34. **d** 35 **p** 36. V Newport St Andr *Mon* 65-76; rtd 76; Perm to Offic *Mon* from 76. *3 Eddystone Court, Hindhead Road, Churt, Surrey GU10 2NU* Headley Down (01428) 712896

BEYNON, Vincent Wyn. b 54. CertEd76 Univ of Wales DipTh81. St Mich Coll Llan 78. **d** 81 **p** 82. C Llantrisant *Llan* 81-83; C Caerphilly 84-85; R Gelligaer 85-88; TV Gtr Corsham *Bris* from 88. *The Vicarage, Wadswick Lane, Neston, Corsham, Wilts SN13 9TA* Hawthorn (01225) 810572

BIANCHI, Mrs Margaret Ruth. b 56. St Mary's Coll Dur BA77. Cranmer Hall Dur 78. **dss** 80 **d** 91 **p** 94. Ches le Street *Dur* 80-83; W Pelton 83-91; NSM 91-95; Perm to Offic from 95. *The Vicarage, West Pelton, Stanley, Co Durham DH9 6RT* 0191-370 2146

BIANCHI, Robert Frederick (Rob). b 56. St Jo Coll Dur BA77. Cranmer Hall Dur 78. **d** 80 **p** 81. C Ches le Street *Dur* 80-83; C W Pelton 83-86; P-in-c from 86. *The Vicarage, West Pelton, Stanley, Co Durham DH9 6RT* 0191-370 2146

BIBBY, Frank. b 37. ACP60 K Coll Lon BD64 AKC64. **d** 65 **p** 66. C Upholland *Liv* 65-67; Lect Birm Coll of Educn 67-72; V Prestwich St Gabr *Man* 72-76; Dir of Ords 72-76; V Hope St Jas 76-86; AD Salford 82-86; R Prestwich St Mary from 86. *The Rectory, Church Lane, Prestwich, Manchester M25 5AN* 0161-773 2912

BIBBY, Paul Benington. b 27. Magd Coll Cam BA51 MA56. Westcott Ho Cam 55. **d** 57 **p** 58. Hd of Cam Ho Camberwell 69-76; R Shepton Mallet *B & W* 76-81; P-in-c Doulting w E and W Cranmore and Downhead 78-81; R Shepton Mallet w Doulting 81-82; Sen Chapl Eton Coll 82-87; R Hambleden Valley *Ox* 87-93; rtd 93; Perm to Offic *Nor* from 94. *Vine Cottage, Cross Lane, Stanhoe, King's Lynn, Norfolk PE31 8PS* Docking (01485) 518291

BICK, David Jim. b 33. ALCD59 LTh74. **d** 59 **p** 60. C Glouc St Cath *Glouc* 59-61; C Coleford w Staunton 61-63; R Blaisdon w Flaxley 63-72; V Coaley 72-83; P-in-c Arlingham 80-83; P-in-c Frampton on Severn 80-83; Hon C Saul w Fretherne and Framilode 83-84; Perm to Offic from 84. *St Joseph's, Prinknash Park, Cranham, Glos GL4 8EX* Painswick (01452) 812973

BICKERDYKE, James Clifford. b 17. St Jo Coll Dur BA42 MA45. Oak Hill Th Coll LTh41. **d** 42 **p** 43. C Stockport St Geo *Ches* 42-43; C Cannock *Lich* 43-45; Normanton Sch Buxton

58

45-48; Chadderton Gr Sch 48-51; CF 51-67; Launceston Coll 67-75; Grove Sch Hindhead 75-81. *Lonningarth, Hawkshead, Ambleside, Cumbria LA22 0PU* Hawkshead (015394) 36100

BICKERSTETH, Anthony Cyril. b 33. K Coll Lon 54. Bps' Coll Cheshunt 55. **d** 58 **p** 59. V Stoke Newington Common St Mich *Lon* 68-74; V Nayland w Wiston *St E* 74-82; R Tolleshunt Knights w Tiptree *Chelmsf* 82-87; R Tolleshunt Knights w Tiptree and Gt Braxted 87; rtd 87; Perm to Offic *Chelmsf* from 87. *Lanreath, 125 Woodland Avenue, Hove, E Sussex BN3 6BJ* Brighton (01273) 564663

BICKERSTETH, David Craufurd. b 50. Wycliffe Hall Ox 71. **d** 75 **p** 76. C Beverley Minster *York* 75-79; C Farnborough *Guildf* 79-81; P-in-c Dearham *Carl* 81-85; V 85-86; R Gosforth w Nether Wasdale and Wasdale Head 86-93; P-in-c Harraby from 93. *St Elizabeth's Vicarage, Arnside Road, Carlisle CA1 3QA* Carlisle (01228) 596429

BICKERSTETH, Edward Piers. b 56. ARICS80. Wycliffe Hall Ox 89. **d** 91 **p** 92. NSM Bebington *Ches* 91-92; C 92-94; Perm to Offic *Lon* from 94. *The Proclamation Trust, St Peter's Church, Cornhill, London EC3V 3PD* 0171-626 6989

✠**BICKERSTETH, Rt Rev John Monier.** b 21. KCVO89. Ch Ch Ox BA49 MA53. Wells Th Coll 48. **d** 50 **p** 51. C Moorfields *Bris* 50-54; C-in-c Hurst Green CD *S'wark* 54-62; V Chatham St Steph *Roch* 62-70; Hon Can Roch Cathl 68-70; Suff Bp Warrington *Liv* 70-75; Bp B&W 75-87; Clerk of the Closet 79-89; rtd 87. *Beckfords, Newtown, Tisbury, Salisbury SP3 6NY* Tisbury (01747) 870479

BICKLEY, John. b 12. Magd Coll Ox BA34 MA38. Sarum Th Coll 35. **d** 36 **p** 37. R Huntingfield w Cookley *St E* 70-77; rtd 77; Perm to Offic *St E* from 77. *Breckland Cottage, Santon Downham, Brandon, Suffolk IP27 0TQ* Thetford (01842) 810497

BICKNELL (nee RIDING), Mrs Pauline Alison. b 61. SEN82. Oak Hill Th Coll BA90. **d** 90. Par Dn Moor Allerton *Ripon* 90-93; Par Dn Leeds St Aid 93-94; C from 94. *712 Foundry Lane, Leeds LS14 6BL* Leeds (0113) 260 2069

BIDDELL, Canon Christopher David. b 27. Ch Coll Cam BA48 MA52. Ridley Hall Cam 51. **d** 51 **p** 52. R Bishops Waltham *Portsm* 62-75; RD Bishops Waltham 69-74; V Stockport St Geo *Ches* 75-86; Hon Can Ches Cathl 81-86; Can Res 86-93; RD Stockport 85-86; Vice-Dean Ches 91-93; rtd 93; P-in-c Tillington *Chich* from 95. *3 Park Terrace, Tillington, Petworth, W Sussex GU28 9AE* Petworth (01798) 42008

BIDDELL, John Herman. b 15. Worc Coll Ox BA38 MA45. Wells Th Coll 38. **d** 47 **p** 48. V Milverton B&W 65-80; R Fitzhead 77-80; rtd 80; Perm to Offic B&W from 81. *Snape Cottage, Wiltown, Curry Rivel, Langport, Somerset TA10 0JF* Langport (01458) 251435

BIDDER, John. b 19. Cuddesdon Coll. **d** 62 **p** 63. R Croft *Leic* 65-71; R Witcham w Mepal *Ely* 71-80; R Coates 80-85; rtd 85; Perm to Offic *Blackb* from 86. *Carinya, 83 Main Street, Nether Kellett, Carnforth, Lancs LA6 1EF* Carnforth (01524) 734993

BIDDINGTON, Dr Terence Eric. b 56. MCollP83 Hull Univ BA77 Trin & All SS Coll Leeds PGCE78 Leeds Univ PhD86 Nottm Univ BTh88. Linc Th Coll 85. **d** 88 **p** 89. C Harpenden St Jo *St Alb* 88-90; Chapl Keele Univ *Lich* 90-93; Freelance Th Educator and Asst Lect Keele Univ from 94; NSM Betley and Keele from 90. *22 Water Street, Bollington, Macclesfield, Cheshire SK10 5PB* Macclesfield (01625) 576886

BIDDLE, Rodney William Dennis. b 44. St Jo Coll Nottm. **d** 85 **p** 86. C Penn *Lich* 85-89; P-in-c Shrewsbury St Geo 89-90; V from 90; P-in-c Montford w Shrawardine and Fitz 89; Chapl HM Pris Shrewsbury from 90; RD Shrewsbury Lich from 91. *The Vicarage, St George's Street, Shrewsbury SY3 8QA* Shrewsbury (01743) 235461 Fax 356926

BIDDLE, Miss Rosemary. b 44. CertEd67. St Jo Coll Dur 76. **dss** 79 **d** 87 **p** 94. Sheldon *Birm* 79-83; Burntwood *Lich* 83-87; Par Dn 87-89; Par Dn Gt Wyrley 89-94; C from 94. *131 High Street, Cheslyn Hay, Walsall WS6 7HT* Cheslyn Hay (01922) 419032

BIDDLECOMBE, Francis William. b 30. St Mich Coll Llan 57. **d** 59 **p** 60. V Llanddewi Rhondda w Bryn Eirw *Llan* 65-71; V Berse and Southsea *St As* 71-79; P-in-c Teme Valley S *Worc* 79-85; rtd 92. *Four Winds, New Road, Highley, Bridgnorth, Shropshire WV16 6NN* Highley (01746) 861746

BIDDLESTONE, Joseph. b 15. Wycliffe Hall Ox 67. **d** 68 **p** 68. C Woodley St Jo the Ev *Ox* 68-71; P-in-c Dunsden 71-77; P-in-c Kiddington w Asterleigh 77-85; P-in-c Wootton by Woodstock 77-85; rtd 85; Perm to Offic *Ox* from 85. *6 Dunsdale Rise, Duns Tew, Oxford OX6 4JQ* Steeple Aston (01869) 40350

BIDE, Mrs Mary Elizabeth. b 53. St Anne's Coll Ox BA74 MA76. S Dios Minl Tr Scheme 91. **d** 94 **p** 95. NSM Gt Bookham *Guildf* from 94. *19 The Lorne, Great Bookham, Surrey KT23 4JY* Leatherhead (01372) 453729

BIDE, Peter William. b 12. St Cath Soc Ox BA39 MA45. Wells Th Coll 38. **d** 49 **p** 50. Chapl LMH Ox 68-80; rtd 80; Prec Ch

Ch *Ox* 80-82; Perm to Offic *Portsm* from 84. *Meadow Corner, The Street, Boxgrove, Chichester, W Sussex PO18 0DY* Chichester (01243) 774134

BIDEN, Neville Douglas. b 31. Lon Univ DipRS80. S'wark Ord Course 76. **d** 79 **p** 80. C Ash *Guildf* 79-82; NSM Surbiton St Andr and St Mark *S'wark* 87-91; Chapl Asst Long Grove Hosp Epsom 90-91; Perm to Offic *Guildf* 90-91; C Coulsdon St Jo *S'wark* from 91; Perm to Offic *Heref* from 95. *8 Waddington Avenue, Coulsdon, Surrey CR5 1QE* Downland (01737) 556043

BIDGOOD, Kevin Patrick. b 46. Chich Th Coll 78. **d** 80 **p** 81. C Leigh Park *Portsm* 80-83; C Southsea H Spirit 83-86; V Portsea All SS 86-91; V Hamble le Rice *Win* 91-94. *35 Kingsmead Avenue, Stubbington, Fareham, Hants PO14 2NN*

BIENFAIT, Alexander (Alex). b 61. Hatf Poly BSc86. Sarum & Wells Th Coll BTh94. **d** 94 **p** 95. C Battersea St Luke *S'wark* from 94. *30 Canford Road, London SW11 6NZ* 0171-228 7431

BIERLEY, George Leslie. b 11. Worc Ord Coll 58. **d** 60 **p** 61. R Gt Coates *Linc* 63-71; R N Thoresby 71-82; R Grainsby 71-82; V Waithe 71-82; rtd 82; Perm to Offic *Linc* from 82. *57 Brackenborough Road, Louth, Lincs LN11 0AD* Louth (01507) 602516

BIGBY, Preb John Harman. b 16. Sarum Th Coll 46. **d** 48 **p** 49. V Ettingshall *Lich* 59-79; R Moreton Say 79-86; P-in-c Tilstock 83-84; Preb Lich Cathl 81-86; RD Hodnet 82-86; P-in-c Tilstock 83-84; rtd 86. *75 Glan y Mor Road, Penrhyn Bay, Gwynedd LL30 3PF* Colwyn Bay (01492) 544722

BIGG, Howard Clive. b 40. Jes Coll Cam BA68 MA72. Ridley Hall Cam 73. **d** 74 **p** 75. C Worksop St Jo *S'well* 74-76; Min Can St Alb 76-77; Perm to Offic *Ches* 78-82; Perm to Offic *Ely* from 82; Vice-Prin Romsey Ho Cam 86-89. *55 Hemingford Road, Cambridge CB1 3BY* Cambridge (01223) 410810

BIGGAR, Dr Nigel John. b 55. Worc Coll Ox BA76 MA88 Chicago Univ PhD86 AM81. **d** 90 **p** 91. Lib Latimer Ho Ox from 85; Asst Lect in Chr Ethics Wycliffe Hall Ox from 87; Chapl Or Coll Ox from 90. *The Chaplain's Office, Oriel College, Oxford OX1 4EW* Oxford (01865) 276580

BIGGIN, Ronald. b 20. NW Ord Course 70. **d** 73 **p** 74. C Thelwall *Ches* 73-79; V 79-87; rtd 87; NSM Lt Leigh and Lower Whitley *Ches* from 90. *44 Richmond Avenue, Grappenhall, Warrington, Cheshire WA4 2ND* Warrington (01925) 261531

BIGGS, David James. b 55. St Jo Coll Auckland LTh82. **d** 81 **p** 82. New Zealand 81-86; C Stevenage St Andr and St Geo *St Alb* 86-89; TV Moulsecoomb *Chich* from 89. *Barn Lodge, Norwich Drive, Brighton BN2 4LA* Brighton (01273) 602325

BIGGS, George Ramsay. b 45. Liv Univ BA67 Qu Coll Cam BA73. Westcott Ho Cam 72. **d** 74 **p** 75. C Lee St Aug *S'wark* 74-78; TV Eling, Testwood and Marchwood *Win* 78; TV Totton 78-93; V Wellow from 93. *Wellow Vicarage, 1 The Beeches, Slab Lane, West Wellow, Romsey, Hants SO51 6RN* West Wellow (01794) 32356

BIGGS, Canon Ivan Richard. b 22. Edgehill Th Coll Belf 49. **d** 73 **p** 73. Bp's C Killea C&O 73-82; I Kiltoghart w Drumshambo, Annaduff and Kilronan K,E&A 82-91; Preb Elphin Cathl 84-91; Dioc Sec (Elphin and Ardagh) from 87; Glebes Sec and Dioc Info Officer 87-91; rtd 91. *Carrowkeel Lodge, Castlebaldwin, Co Sligo, Irish Republic* Castlebaldwin (79) 66015 Fax as telephone

BIGGS, Laurence John. b 60. Leeds Univ BSc81. Trin Coll Bris DipHE94. **d** 94 **p** 95. C St Alb St Paul *St Alb* from 94. *46 Brampton Road, St Albans, Herts AL1 4PT* St Albans (01727) 841245

BIGGS, Philip John. b 51. Ripon Hall Ox 74 Ripon Coll Cuddesdon 75. **d** 77 **p** 78. C Maidstone All SS w St Phil and H Trin *Cant* 77-80; Dioc Youth Officer *Truro* 80-84; Australia from 84; Hon Chapl Miss to Seamen from 84. *118 Waddell Road, Bicton, W Australia 6157* Perth (9) 330-4938

BIGMORE, Graeme Paul. b 57. St Mich Coll Llan DipTh92. **d** 92 **p** 93. C Cardiff St Jo *Llan* from 92; Cardiff City Cen Chapl from 94. *17 Brithdir Street, Cardiff CF2 4LE* Cardiff (01222) 390703

BIGNELL, Alan Guy. b 39. Lon Univ BA64. Ox NSM Course. **d** 81 **p** 82. NSM Upton cum Chalvey *Ox* 81-90; NSM Burnham Deanery from 90. *2 Wheatlands Road, Slough SL3 7PD* Slough (01753) 523005

BIGNELL, David Charles. b 41. E Midl Min Tr Course 76. **d** 79 **p** 80. C Porchester *S'well* 79-82; V Awsworth w Cossall 82-86; Bp's Ecum Officer from 84; V Edwalton from 86. *The Vicarage, Edwalton, Notts NG12 4AB* Nottingham (0115) 923 2034

BILES, David George. b 35. Open Univ BA75 AKC58. **d** 59 **p** 60. C Cockerton *Dur* 59-62; C Winlaton 62-67; P-in-c Dipton 67-74; R Wolviston 74-89; P-in-c Thirkleby w Kilburn and Bagby *York* 89-90; V from 90; RD Thirsk 90-91; RD Mowbray from 91. *The Vicarage, Kilburn, York YO6 4AH* Coxwold (01347) 868234

59

BILES, Canon Timothy Mark Frowde. b 35. Univ of Wales DipTh64. St Mich Coll Llan 60. **d** 64 **p** 66. C Middleton St Cross *Ripon* 64-66; Chapl St Fran Sch Hooke 66-72; P-in-c Toller Porcorum w Hooke *Sarum* 72-73; P-in-c Melplash w Mapperton 74-79; P-in-c Beaminster 77-79; TR Beaminster Area from 79; Can and Preb Sarum Cathl from 83; RD Beaminster 84-89. *The Rectory, Barnes Lane, Beaminster, Dorset DT8 3BU* Beaminster (01308) 862150 Fax 863662

BILL, Alan. b 29. K Coll Lon BD66 AKC66. **d** 67 **p** 68. C Gt Burstead *Chelmsf* 67-70; TV Thornaby on Tees *York* 71-76; R E Gilling 76-81; V Ormesby 81-91; rtd 91. *13 Wilmington Close, Tudor Grange, Newcastle upon Tyne NE3 2SF* 0191-271 3556

BILL, Denis Aubrey. b 20. Coll of Resurr Mirfield 48. **d** 50 **p** 51. V Holy Is *Newc* 64-89; rtd 89. *The Annexe, Etal Manor, Berwick-upon-Tweed TD15 2PU* Crookham (01890) 820378

BILL, Herbert Sydney. b 12. Keble Coll Ox BA34 DipTh35. Wells Th Coll 35. **d** 36 **p** 37. Dioc Missr *Worc* 54-82; R Feckenham w Bradley 60-82; rtd 82; Perm to Offic *Worc* from 82. *31 Tredington Close, Woodrow, Redditch, Worcs B98 7UR*

BILL, Thomas Andrew Graham. b 47. Dur Univ BA76 DipTh78. Cranmer Hall Dur 78. **d** 77 **p** 78. C Penwortham St Mary *Blackb* 77-80; C Torrisholme 80-82; P-in-c Accrington St Pet 82-89; P-in-c Haslingden St Jo Stonefold 82-89; V Skerton St Chad from 89. *St Chad's Vicarage, 1 St Chad's Drive, Lancaster LA1 2SE* Lancaster (01524) 63816

BILLETT, Anthony Charles. b 56. Bris Univ BEd. Wycliffe Hall Ox 82. **d** 85 **p** 86. C Waltham Abbey *Chelmsf* 85-88; C Nor St Pet Mancroft w St Jo Maddermarket *Nor* 88-91; V Stalham and E Ruston w Brunstead from 91. *The Vicarage, Stalham, Norwich NR12 9DT* Stalham (01692) 580250

BILLINGHAM, Canon Peter Charles Geoffrey. b 34. Leeds Univ BA56. Westcott Ho Cam 61. **d** 62 **p** 63. C Halesowen *Worc* 62-66; R Addingham *Bradf* 66-70; R Droitwich St Nic w St Pet *Worc* 70-72; TR Droitwich 72-83; P-in-c Salwarpe 76-80; RD Droitwich 78-83; P-in-c Gt Malvern H Trin 83; P-in-c W Malvern 83; V Malvern H Trin and St Jas from 84; RD Malvern from 92; Hon Can Worc Cathl from 93. *The Vicarage, 2 North Malvern Road, Malvern, Worcs WR14 4LR* Malvern (01684) 574380

BILLINGHURST, Peter John. b 30. St Deiniol's Hawarden 77. **d** 79 **p** 80. C Hawarden *St As* 79-89; P-in-c from 89. *Kemendene, 14 Dinghouse Wood, Buckley, Clwyd CH7 3DH* Buckley (01244) 550023

BILLINGHURST, Richard George. b 48. FIA76 St Jo Coll Cam BA70 MA74. Ridley Hall Cam 76. **d** 79 **p** 80. C Caverswall *Lich* 79-81; C Cullompton *Ex* 81-84; R Redgrave cum Botesdale w Rickinghall *St E* 84-92; R Skellingthorpe w Doddington *Linc* from 92; RD Graffoe from 94. *The Rectory, 50 Lincoln Road, Skellingthorpe, Lincoln LN6 5UY* Lincoln (01522) 682520

BILLINGS, Dr Alan Roy. b 42. Em Coll Cam BA65 MA69 Bris Univ PGCE66 Leic Univ MEd75. NY Th Sem DMin87 Linc Th Coll 66. **d** 68 **p** 69. C Knighton St Mary Magd *Leic* 68-72; P-in-c Sheff Gillcar St Silas *Sheff* 72-76; V Beighton 76-77; Head RE Broadway Sch Barnsley 77-81; Perm to Offic 77-81; V Walkley 81-86; Perm to Offic *Ox* 86-92; Dir Ox Inst for Ch and Soc 86-92; Vice-Prin Ripon Coll Cuddesdon 88-92; Prin W Midl Minl Tr Course 92-94; V Kendal St Geo *Carl* from 94. *St George's Vicarage, 3 Firbank, Sedbergh Road, Kendal, Cumbria LA9 6BE* Kendal (01539) 723039

BILLINGS, Derek Donald. b 30. Fitzw Ho Cam BA54 MA59. Tyndale Hall Bris 55. **d** 56 **p** 57. C Attenborough w Bramcote and Chilwell *S'well* 56-58; R Ashley w Silverley *Ely* 59-66; V Bottisham 66-80; R Houghton w Wyton from 80. *The Rectory, 3 Rectory Lane, Wyton, Huntingdon, Cambs PE17 2AQ* St Ives (01480) 462499

BILLINGS, Roger Key. b 41. AIB. Oak Hill Th Coll BA80. **d** 80 **p** 81. C Tunbridge Wells St Jas *Roch* 80-84; V Chatham St Paul w All SS 84-95; V Carterton *Ox* from 95. *St John's Vicarage, Burford Road, Carterton, Oxon OX8 3AA* Carterton (01993) 842429

BILLINGSLEY, Raymond Philip. b 48. FCMA80. Qu Coll Birm 87. **d** 89 **p** 90. C Yardley St Edburgha *Birm* 89-92; V Ward End from 92. *The Vicarage, St Margaret's Avenue, Birmingham B8 2BH* 0121-327 0555

BILLINGTON, Charles Alfred. b 30. Leeds Univ BA55. Coll of Resurr Mirfield 53. **d** 55 **p** 56. V Gt Crosby St Faith *Liv* 66-72; R Harrold and Carlton w Chellington *St Alb* 72-80; R Tintinhull w Chilthorne Domer, Yeovil Marsh etc *B & W* 80-81; Chapl Leybourne Grange Hosp W Malling 81-85; Lic to Offic *Roch* 81-85; V Walsden *Wakef* 85-88; R Llanfair Talhaearn and Llansannan etc *St As* from 88; rtd 94. *The Rectory, Llanfairtalhaiarn, Abergele, Clwyd LL22 8ST* Llanfairtalhaiarn (0174584) 273

BILLINGTON, George. b 45. St Jo Coll Nottm DipThMin94. **d** 94 **p** 95. C Accrington St Jo w Huncoat *Blackb* from 94.

167 Manor Street, Accrington, Lancs BB5 6DZ Accrington (01254) 301297

BILLINGTON, John Keith. b 16. **d** 61 **p** 62. C-in-c Seacroft CD *Ripon* 68-73; rtd 73; Perm to Offic *Bradf* from 86. *9 The Lawns, Skipton Road, Ilkley, W Yorkshire LS29 9EW* Ilkley (01943) 602732

BILLOWES, David. b 20. Chich Th Coll. **d** 76 **p** 77. NSM Cowes St Mary *Portsm* 76-91; Chapl St Mary's Hosp Newport 82-91; rtd 91; Perm to Offic *Portsm* from 91. *45 Solent View Road, Gurnard, Cowes, Isle of Wight PO31 8JZ* Isle of Wight (01983) 297366

BILLS, Reginald. b 18. TCert47. Lich Th Coll 68 Wm Temple Coll Rugby DipTh68. **d** 70 **p** 71. C Wednesfield St Thos *Lich* 70-73; C Wolv St Pet 73-79; Chapl St Pet Colleg Sch 73-79; C Wolv St Andr 79-81; P-in-c Brockmoor 81-87; rtd 87. *43 Kewstoke Road, Willenhall, W Midlands WV12 5DY* Bloxwich (01922) 405049

BILNEY, Kenneth Henry. b 25. FBCS. St Deiniol's Hawarden 75. **d** 75 **p** 76. Hon C Knighton St Mary Magd *Leic* 75-78; C Leic St Jas 78-80; R Leire w Ashby Parva and Dunton Bassett 80-90; rtd 90. *20 Ferndale Road, Leicester LE2 6GN* Leicester (0116) 257 0436

BILTON, Paul Michael. b 52. AKC74. St Aug Coll Cant 74. **d** 75 **p** 76. C Skipton Ch Ch *Bradf* 75-79; Ind Chapl *Worc* 79-81; V Greetland and W Vale *Wakef* 81-88; R Mablethorpe w Trusthorpe *Linc* 88-91; V Bradf St Wilfrid Lidget Green *Bradf* from 91. *St Wilfrid's Vicarage, Lidget Green, Bradford, W Yorkshire BD7 2LU* Bradford (01274) 572504

BINDOFF, Stanley. b 54. Sarum & Wells Th Coll 79. **d** 82 **p** 83. C Thirsk *York* 82-86; Chapl HM Young Offender Inst Northallerton 85-89; P-in-c Rounton w Welbury *York* 86-89; Chapl HM Pris Gartree 89-92; Chapl HM Pris Frankland from 92. *The Chaplain's Office, HM Prison Frankland, Finchdale Avenue, Durham DH1 5YD* 0191-384 5544 Fax 384 9203

BINDON, David Charles. b 33. Lon Univ BSc58. Sarum & Wells Th Coll 77. **d** 79 **p** 80. C Yeovil *B & W* 79-83; R Kilmersdon w Babington 83-89; R Radstock w Writhlington 83-89; Chapl St Swithun's Sch Win from 89. *Pond View Cottage, 16 The Soke, Alresford, Hants SO24 9DB* Alresford (01962) 735334

BING, Alan Charles. b 56. St Edm Hall Ox BA78 DipInstM83. Oak Hill Th Coll DipHE91. **d** 91 **p** 92. C Fremington *Ex* 91-94; C-in-c Roundswell CD from 94. *16 Mulberry Way, Roundswell, Barnstaple, Devon EX31 3QZ* Barnstaple (01271) 75877

BINGHAM, Mrs Marie Joyce Phyllis. b 27. Glouc Sch of Min 80. **dss** 84 **d** 87 **p** 94. Glouc St Mary de Crypt w St Jo and Ch Ch *Glouc* 84-85; Glouc St Mary de Lode and St Nic 85-87; Hon C 87-95; Hon C Glouc St Mary de Crypt w St Jo and Ch Ch 94-95; Hon C Glouc St Mary de Crypt w St Jo, Ch Ch etc from 95. *Hazel Cottage, Sandhurst, Gloucester GL2 9NP* Gloucester (01452) 730285

BINGHAM, Norman James Frederick. b 26. Lon Univ BSc51. Tyndale Hall Bris 61. **d** 63 **p** 64. C Macclesfield St Mich *Ches* 67-71; P-in-c Macclesfield St Pet 71-73; V Leyton St Mary w St Edw *Chelmsf* 73-91; RD Waltham Forest 81-86; P-in-c Leyton St Luke 82-91; rtd 91. *97 Monks Walk, Buntingford, Herts SG9 9DP* Royston (01763) 272275

BINKS, Canon Edmund Vardy. b 36. FRSA89 K Coll Lon BD61 AKC61. **d** 62 **p** 63. C Selby Abbey *York* 62-65; Asst Chapl Univ Coll of Ripon & York St Jo 65-83; Prin St Kath Coll Liv 83-87; Prin Ches Coll *Ches* from 87; Hon Can Ches Cathl from 95. *Chester College, Cheyney Road, Chester CH1 4BJ* Chester (01244) 375444 Fax 373379

BINLEY, Miss Teresa Mary. b 37. Dalton Ho Bris 61. **d** 87 **p** 94. Par dn Ashton on Mersey St Mary *Ches* 87-92; Bp's Officer for Women in Min 87-92; C Chaddesden St Mary *Derby* from 92. *24 Ordish Avenue, Chaddesden, Derby DE21 6QF* Derby (01332) 662420

BINNEY, Mark James Gurney. b 58. K Coll Lon BD80. Qu Coll Birm 84. **d** 86 **p** 87. C Hornchurch St Andr *Chelmsf* 86-89; C Hutton 89-91; V Pheasey *Lich* from 91. *St Chad's Vicarage, Hillingford Avenue, Pheasey, Birmingham B43 7HN* 0121-360 7556

BINNIAN, Mrs Jennifer Ann. b 34. Qu Coll Birm 81. **dss** 84 **d** 87 **p** 94. Chaddesley Corbett and Stone *Worc* 84-85; Bewdley Far Forest 85-87; Chapl Home Care Hospice from 87; Chapl Asst Kidderminster Gen Hosp from 87. *Bodenham Farm, Wolverley, Kidderminster, Worcs DY11 5SY* Kidderminster (01562) 850382

BINNIE, Alexander David. b 22. Ripon Hall Ox 67. **d** 68 **p** 69. C Sutton Coldfield H Trin *Birm* 68-72; V Dosthill 72-88; C-in-c Wood End St Mich CD 72-83; rtd 88; Perm to Offic *Lich* from 88; Perm to Offic *Birm* from 88. *3 Walkers Croft, Lichfield, Staffs WS13 6TR* Lichfield (01543) 254250

BINNS, Dr John Richard. b 51. Cam Univ MA76 Lon Univ PhD89. Coll of Resurr Mirfield 74. **d** 76 **p** 77. C Clapham H Trin *S'wark* 76-78; C Clapham Old Town 78-80; TV Mortlake w E Sheen 80-87; V Upper Tooting H Trin 87-94; V Cam Gt St Mary w St Mich *Ely* from 94. *Great St Mary's Vicarage, 39 Madingley Road, Cambridge CB3 0EL*   Cambridge (01223) 355285

BINNS, Peter Rodney. b 44. St Andr Univ MA66. Ox NSM Course 72. **d** 75 **p** 76. NSM Amersham on the Hill *Ox* 75-90; NSM Wingrave w Rowsham, Aston Abbotts and Cublington from 90; NSM Hawridge w Cholesbury and St Leonard from 90. *16 Turnfurlong Row, Turnfurlong Lane, Aylesbury, Bucks HP21 7FF* Aylesbury (01296) 22705

BINNY, John Wallace. b 46. Univ of Wales (Lamp) BA70. St Mich Coll Llan 69. **d** 71 **p** 72. C Llantrisant *Llan* 71-77; V Troedrhiwgarth 77-82; R Eglwysbrewis w St Athan, Flemingston, Gileston 82-95; R Eglwysbrewis w St Athan w Gileston from 95. *The Rectory, Rectory Drive, St Athan, Barry, S Glam CF62 4PD* St Athan (01446) 750540

BIRBECK, Anthony Leng (Tony). b 33. MBE90. Linc Coll Ox BA59 MA61. Linc Th Coll 58. **d** 60 **p** 61. C Redcar *York* 60-74; Chapl Teesside Ind Miss 62-74; Can Res and Treas Wells Cathl *B & W* 74-78; NSM Wells St Thos w Horrington from 78. *4 Mount Pleasant Avenue, Wells, Somerset BA5 2JQ* Wells (01749) 673246 Fax 679485

BIRBECK, John Trevor. b 49. AIB77. St Jo Coll Nottm 86. **d** 88 **p** 89. C Eccleshill *Bradf* 88-92; V Hurst Green and Mitton from 92. *The Vicarage, Hurst Green, Clitheroe, Lancs BB7 9QR* Stonyhurst (01254) 826686

BIRCH, Arthur James Fleet. b 14. Univ Coll Dur BA36 MA39. **d** 37 **p** 38. R Lymm *Ches* 70-79; rtd 79; Perm to Offic *Ches* from 79. *21 Arran Drive, Frodsham, Warrington WA6 6AL* Frodsham (01928) 733709

BIRCH, Arthur Kenneth. b 15. Qu Coll Birm 46. **d** 48 **p** 49. Uganda 71-75; V Fence in Pendle *Blackb* 75-76; C Bollington St Jo *Ches* 77-79; R Church Lawton 79-81; rtd 81; Perm to Offic *Sarum* 81-95. *26 Smugglers Lane, Reepham, Norfolk NR10 4QT* Norwich (01603) 871405

BIRCH, Derek. b 31. Univ of Wales (Lamp) BA58. Coll of Resurr Mirfield 58. **d** 60 **p** 61. C S Elmsall *Wakef* 60-62; C Penistone w Midhope 62-66; V Silkstone 66-89; Chapl Stainborough 76-89; P-in-c Hoyland Swaine 85-89; V Hoylandswaine and Silkstone w Stainborough from 89. *The Vicarage, 12 High Street, Silkstone, Barnsley, S Yorkshire S75 4JN* Barnsley (01226) 790232

BIRCH, Henry Arthur. b 24. St Jo Coll Dur BA48. Tyndale Hall Bris 48. **d** 49 **p** 50. Australia 69-81 and from 84; S Africa 81-84; rtd 90. *9/87 Yathong Road, Caringbah, NSW, Australia 2229* Sydney (2) 525-1763

BIRCH, Janet Ann. St Alb Minl Tr Scheme 77. **dss** 80 **d** 87 **p** 94. Luton St Mary *St Alb* 80-87; Par Dn Streatley 87-91; rtd 91; NSM Aldeburgh w Hazlewood *St E* from 91. *3 Market Cross House, Wentworth Road, Aldeburgh, Suffolk IP15 5BJ* Aldeburgh (01728) 453371

BIRCH, Shirley Anne. b 34. E Midl Min Tr Course 88. **d** 91 **p** 94. Hon Par Dn Melton Gt Framland *Leic* 91-93; Hon C Melton Mowbray from 93. *16 Weaver Green, Melton Mowbray, Leics LE13 0UH* Melton Mowbray (01664) 69883

BIRCHALL, Maurice Molyneux. b 11. Dur Univ LTh41 BA45. Edin Th Coll 36. **d** 39 **p** 40. Clerical Org Sec CECS 65-73; C Habergham Eaves H Trin *Blackb* 73-77; rtd 77. *33 South Avenue, Morecambe, Lancs LA4 5RJ* Morecambe (01524) 414136

BIRCHALL, Robert Gary. b 59. Sheff Univ BA81. St Jo Coll Nottm 85. **d** 88 **p** 89. C Manston *Ripon* 88-91; C Leic Martyrs *Leic* 91-94; C New Humberstone from 94. *St Barnabas Vicarage, 32 St Barnabas Road, Leicester LE5 4DB* Leicester (0116) 276 6054

BIRCHARD, Canon Thaddeus Jude. b 45. Louisiana State Univ BA66 Nottm Univ DipTh68. Kelham Th Coll 66. **d** 70 **p** 71. C Devonport St Mark Ford *Ex* 70-73; C Southend St Jo w St Mark, All SS w St Fran etc *Chelmsf* 73-76; TV Poplar *Lon* 76-80; V Paddington St Jo w St Mich from 80; Hon Can Louisiana from 90. *18 Somers Crescent, London W2 2PN* 0171-262 1732

BIRCHBY, Martin Cecil. b 17. Worc Ord Coll 66. **d** 68 **p** 69. C Bromyard *Heref* 68-70; P-in-c Bredenbury and Wacton w Grendon Bishop 70-75; P-in-c Edwyn Ralph and Collington w Thornbury 71-75; P-in-c Pembridge 75-80; P-in-c Shobdon 79-80; R Pembridge w Moor Court and Shobdon 80-83; P-in-c Staunton-on-Arrow w Byton 81-83; R Pembridge w Moorcourt, Shobdon, Staunton etc 83-85; rtd 85; Perm to Offic *Heref* from 85. *Cornerways, 9 Bearcroft, Weobley, Hereford HR4 8TA* Weobley (01544) 318185

BIRCHMORE, Brian Leonard. b 35. ALCD59. **d** 59 **p** 60. C Rusthall *Roch* 59-62; C Rainham 62-64; C Belvedere All SS 64-66; V Meopham 66-74; R Chatham St Mary w St Jo 74-75; Perm to Offic *Chelmsf* 81-95; Ind Chapl Harlow from 83; P-in-c Bush End 83-89; P-in-c Hatf Broad Oak 83-89; P-in-c

Greenstead juxta Colchester from 89. *The Rectory, 74 Howe Close, Greenstead, Colchester CO4 3XD* Colchester (01206) 865762

BIRCHNALL, Canon Simeon Robert. b 18. St Jo Coll Dur BA42 MA45 DipTh43. **d** 43 **p** 44. C Pitsmoor w Wicker *Sheff* 43-46; C Conisbrough 46-47; C Clifton St Jas 47-50; C Chingford SS Pet and Paul *Chelmsf* 50-53; C-in-c Chingford St Anne 53-55; V 56-64; R Woodford St Mary 64-71; R Woodford St Mary w St Phil and St Jas from 71; Hon Can Chelmsf Cathl from 76; RD Redbridge 77-90; P-in-c Barkingside St Cedd 83-90. *8 Chelmsford Road, London E18 2PL* 0181-504 3472

BIRD, Alfred. b 10. Keble Coll Ox BA32 MA39. Melbourne Coll of Div MTh75 Bps' Coll Cheshunt 33. **d** 34 **p** 35. Chapl Eastbourne Coll 48-51; Australia from 51; rtd 76. *Unit 19, Pittwater Village, Brinawa Street, Mona Vale, NSW, Australia 2103* Sydney (2) 998-0119

BIRD (nee BAKER), Mrs Anne-Marie Clare. b 56. Wye Coll Lon BSc78 Glas Univ MSc80. St Jo Coll Nottm 88. **d** 90 **p** 94. Par Dn Levenshulme St Pet *Man* 90-94; C 94-95; P-in-c Crumpsall from 95. *St Matthew's Rectory, 30 Cleveland Road, Manchester M8 6QU* 0161-795 4376

BIRD, Dr Anthony Peter. b 31. St Jo Coll Ox BA54 BTh55 MA57 Birm Univ MB, ChB70. Cuddesdon Coll 55. **d** 57 **p** 58. C Stafford St Mary *Lich* 57-60; Chapl Cuddesdon Coll 60-61; Vice-Prin 61-64; C Selly Oak St Wulstan *Birm* 64-68; Lic to Offic 68-79; Prin Qu Coll Birm 74-79; Perm to Offic *Birm* from 85. *93 Bournbrook Road, Birmingham B29 7BX*

BIRD, Archibald Brian. b 02. AKC28. **d** 28 **p** 31. V Edwardstone w Groton *St E* 46-71; rtd 71; Perm to Offic *St E* from 72. *38 Maidenburgh Street, Colchester CO1 1UB* Colchester (01206) 44757

BIRD, Ven Colin Richard Bateman. b 33. Selw Coll Cam BA56 MA61. Cuddesdon Coll 56. **d** 58 **p** 59. S Africa 58-70; C Limpsfield and Titsey *S'wark* 70-75; V Hatcham St Cath 75-88; RD Deptford 80-85; Hon Can S'wark Cathl 82-88; Adn Lambeth from 88; P-in-c Brixton Hill St Sav 91-94. *7 Hoadly Road, London SW16 1AE* 0181-769 4384 or 780 2308

BIRD, David John. b 46. Univ of Wales (Lamp) BA70 Pittsburgh Univ PhD87. Gen Th Sem (NY) STM74. **d** 70 **p** 71. C Kidderminster St Geo *Worc* 70-72; USA from 72. *Grace Church, 1041 Wisconsin Avenue, Northwest, Georgetown, Washington DC 20007, USA* Washington DC (202) 333-7100

BIRD, David Ronald. b 55. York Univ BA76. St Jo Coll Nottm 83. **d** 86 **p** 87. C Kinson *Sarum* 86-90; R Thrapston *Pet* from 90; P-in-c Islip from 94; RD Higham from 94. *The Rectory, Thrapston, Kettering, Northants NN14 4PD* Thrapston (01832) 732393

BIRD, Donald Wilfred Ray. b 27. Dur Univ BA52. Linc Th Coll 61. **d** 63 **p** 64. Rhodesia 66-80; R Scotter w E Ferry *Linc* 80-92; rtd 92; Zimbabwe 94. *Bryn Hyfryd, 25 Mersey Street, Borth y Gest, Porthmadog, Gwynedd LL49 9UB* Porthmadog (01766) 514265

BIRD, Douglas Norman. b 38. Local NSM Course 89. **d** 92 **p** 93. NSM New Bury *Man* from 92. *14 Tudor Avenue, Farnworth, Bolton BL4 9RH* Bolton (01204) 861167

BIRD, Canon Frederick Hinton. b 38. St Edm Hall Ox BA62 MA66 Univ of Wales MEd81 PhD86. St D Coll Lamp BD65. **d** 65 **p** 66. C Mynyddislwyn *Mon* 65-67; Min Can St Woolos Cathl 67-70; Chapl Anglo-American Coll Farringdon 70-71; Perm to Offic *Ox* 70-78; Perm to Offic *Cant* 72-78; Perm to Offic *Mon* 76-82; V Rushen *S & M* from 82; Can St German's Cathl from 93. *Kirk Rushen Vicarage, Port St Mary, Isle of Man IM9 5LP* Port St Mary (01624) 832275

BIRD, Canon Geoffrey Neville. b 22. AKC48. St Boniface Warminster 48. **d** 49 **p** 50. R Edge w Pitchcombe *Glouc* 56-82; P-in-c Brookthorpe w Whaddon and Harescombe 76-82; R The Edge, Pitchcombe, Harescombe and Brookthorpe 82-90; Hon Can Glouc Cathl 83-90; RD Bisley 84-90; rtd 90. *Ivy Croft, Winstone, Cirencester, Glos GL7 7JZ* Cirencester (01285) 821664

BIRD, Henry John Joseph. b 37. ARCO58 Qu Coll Cam BA59 MA63. Linc Th Coll 62. **d** 64 **p** 65. C Harbledown *Cant* 64-68; C Skipton H Trin *Bradf* 68-70; V Oakworth 70-81; Chapl Abingdon Sch 81-82; P-in-c Doncaster St Geo *Sheff* 82-85; V from 85. *The Vicarage, 98 Thorne Road, Doncaster, S Yorkshire DN2 5BJ* Doncaster (01302) 368796 or 323748

BIRD, Dr Hugh Claud Handley. b 24. FRCGP SS Coll Cam MA MB BCh. Ridley Hall Cam. **d** 86 **p** 86. NSM Coxheath w E Farleigh, Hunton and Linton *Roch* from 86. *Heath House, Linton, Maidstone, Kent ME17 4PF* Maidstone (01622) 743438

BIRD, Jeffrey David. b 54. Nottm Univ BCombStuds85. Linc Th Coll 82. **d** 85 **p** 86. C Frome St Jo *B & W* 85-88; Asst Chapl HM Pris Pentonville 88-89; Chapl HM Pris Dartmoor from 89; Lic to Offic *Ex* from 89. *HM Prison Dartmoor, Princetown, Yelverton, Devon PL20 6RR* Princetown (01822) 890261 Fax 890679

BIRD, Jeremy Paul. b 56. Ex Univ BSc77 DipTh78 Hull Univ MA88. Sarum Th Coll 78. **d** 80 **p** 81. C Tavistock and Gulworthy *Ex* 80-83; Chapl Teesside Poly *York* 83-88; R Chipstable w Huish Champflower and Clatworthy *B & W* 88-93; Rural Affairs Officer 88-93; V Uffculme *Ex* from 93. *The Vicarage, Uffculme, Cullompton, Devon EX15 3AX* Craddock (01884) 841001

BIRD, Maurice Pidding. b 19. Linc Coll Ox BA40 MA44. Cuddesdon Coll 40. **d** 42 **p** 43. R Winterton w E Somerton *Nor* 59-71; V Heigham St Barn 71-75; V Heigham St Barn w St Bart 75-82; P-in-c Edington and Imber *Sarum* 82-83; P-in-c Erlestoke and Gt Cheverell 82-83; P-in-c Edington and Imber, Erlestoke and E Coulston 83-88; rtd 88. *61 Beechwood, Woodlesford, Leeds LS26 8PQ* Leeds (0113) 282 0865

BIRD, Norman David. b 32. CQSW73. Coll of Resurr Mirfield 87. **d** 89 **p** 90. NSM Willesden Green St Andr and St Fran of Assisi *Lon* 89-92; NSM Preston Ascension from 93. *5 Oldfield Road, London NW10 9UD* 0181-451 4160 or 459 2670

BIRD, Peter Andrew. b 40. Wadh Coll Ox BA62 MA68. Ridley Hall Cam 63. **d** 65 **p** 66. C Keynsham w Queen Charlton *B & W* 65-68; C Strood St Nic *Roch* 68-72; TV Strood 72-79; V S Gillingham 79-89; V Westerham from 89. *The Vicarage, Borde Hill, Vicarage Hill, Westerham, Kent TN16 1TL* Westerham (01959) 563127

BIRD, Rex Alan. b 30. Trin Coll Bris 54. **d** 57 **p** 58. C Wellington Ch Ch *Lich* 57-59; C St Alb St Paul *St Alb* 59-61; V Rainham *Chelmsf* 61-65; R Wennington 61-65; R Lavenham *St E* 65-75; CF (TA) from 65; RD Lavenham *St E* 72-75; Dean Battle *Chich* 75-84; V Battle 75-84; V Castle Hedingham *Chelmsf* 84-91; R Monks Eleigh w Chelsworth and Brent Eleigh etc *St E* from 91; P-in-c Kettlebaston from 94. *The Rectory, Monks Eleigh, Ipswich IP7 7AU* Bildeston (01449) 740244

BIRD, Canon Roger Alfred. b 49. AKC72. St Aug Coll Cant 72. **d** 73 **p** 74. C Prestatyn *St As* 73-78; R Llandysilio and Penrhos and Llandrinio etc 78-92; Dioc RE Adv from 84; Dioc Dir of Educn from 89; R Guilsfield from 92; Hon Can St As Cathl from 93. *The Vicarage, Guilsfield, Welshpool, Powys SY21 9NF* Welshpool (01938) 554245

BIRDSEYE, Miss Jacqueline Ann. b 55. Sussex Univ BEd78 Southn Univ BTh88. Sarum & Wells Th Coll 85. **d** 88 **p** 94. C Egham Hythe *Guildf* 88-91; C Fleet 91-92; C Shottermill 92-95; C Leavesden All SS *St Alb* from 95. *49 Ross Crescent, Garston, Watford WD2 6DA* Watford (01923) 673129

BIRDWOOD, William Halhed. b 51. St Jo Coll Dur BA73. Sarum & Wells Th Coll 76. **d** 78 **p** 79. C Royston *St Alb* 78-82; C Thorley w Bishop's Stortford H Trin 82-89; Chapl HM Pris Ex from 89; Lic to Offic *Ex* from 89. *HM Prison Exeter, New North Road, Exeter EX4 4EX* Exeter (01392) 78321 Fax 422647

BIRKENHEAD, Suffragan Bishop of. *See* LANGRISH, Rt Rev Michael Laurence

BIRKET, Cyril. b 28. ACIS70. NW Ord Course 71. **d** 74 **p** 75. C Broughton *Blackb* 74-79; V Wesham 79-86; V Overton from 86. *St Helen's Vicarage, Chapel Lane, Overton, Morecambe, Lancs LA3 3HU* Overton (01524) 858234

BIRKETT, Mrs Joyce. b 38. W Midl Minl Tr Course 84. **d** 87 **p** 94. Par Dn Hill *Birm* 87-91; Asst Chapl Highcroft Hosp Birm 87-91; Par Dn Rowley Regis *Birm* 91-94; C from 94. *194 Hanover Road, Rowley Regis, Warley, W Midlands B65 9EQ* 0121-559 3830

BIRKETT, Neil Warren. b 45. Lanc Univ BEd74 Southn Univ MA84. Kelham Th Coll 65. **d** 72 **p** 73. C Gt Ilford St Mary *Chelmsf* 72-75; C Upminster 75-78; Adn's Youth Chapl 77-80; Dioc Youth Officer 80-86; Chapl Stansted Airport from 86; P-in-c Manuden w Berden from 86; RD Newport and Stansted from 89. *24 Mallows Green Road, Manuden, Bishop's Stortford, Herts CM23 1DG* Bishop's Stortford (01279) 812228

BIRKETT, Peter. b 13. Univ Coll Dur BA35 MA39. **d** 36 **p** 37. R Holford w Dodington *B & W* 69-77; rtd 78; Perm to Offic *B & W* 82-87. *14 Long Street, Williton, Taunton, Somerset TA4 4NQ* Williton (01984) 632220

BIRLEY, John Lindsay. b 19. Kelham Th Coll 37. **d** 43 **p** 44. Asst Chapl St Jo Sch Leatherhead 54-64; Perm to Offic *Ox* 64-76; rtd 76. *Abtei Himmerod, D 54534 Grosslittgen, Germany* Grosslittgen (6575) 4110

BIRMINGHAM, Archdeacon of. *See* DUNCAN, Ven John Finch

BIRMINGHAM, Bishop of. *See* SANTER, Rt Rev Mark

BIRMINGHAM, Provost of. *See* BERRY, Very Rev Peter Austin

BIRT, David Edward. b 26. St Steph Ho Ox 86. **d** 86 **p** 87. NSM Ealing Ch the Sav *Lon* from 86. *10 Manor Court Road, London W7 3EL* 0181-579 4871

BIRT, Malcolm Douglas. b 33. Trin Coll Cam BA56 MA60. Ridley Hall Cam 56. **d** 58 **p** 59. C Barrow St Mark *Carl* 58-60; C Tunbridge Wells St Jo *Roch* 60-63; V Constable Lee *Man* 63-72; V Anslow *Lich* from 72; R Rolleston from 72. *The Rectory, Rolleston, Burton-on-Trent, Staffs DE13 9BE*

BIRT, Patrick. b 34. Glouc Th Course 71. **d** 75 **p** 75. NSM Bisley *Glouc* 75-76; NSM Whiteshill 76-81; C Stroud H Trin 81; R Ruardean 81-86; V Newbridge-on-Wye and Llanfihangel Brynpabuan *S & B* 86-88; TV Gillingham *Sarum* from 88. *The Vicarage, Stour Provost, Gillingham, Dorset SP8 5RU* East Stour (01747) 838216

BIRT, Richard Arthur. b 43. Ch Ch Ox BA66 MA69. Cuddesdon Coll 67. **d** 69 **p** 70. C Sutton St Mich *Yore* 69-71; C Wollaton S'well 71-75; R Kirkby in Ashfield 75-80; P-in-c Duxford *Ely* 80-87; R 87-88; P-in-c Hinxton 80-87; V 87-88; P-in-c Ickleton 80-87; V 87-88; V Weobley w Sarnesfield and Norton Canon *Heref* from 88; P-in-c Letton w Staunton, Byford, Mansel Gamage etc from 88. *The Vicarage, Church Road, Weobley, Hereford HR4 8SD* Weobley (01544) 318415

BIRT, Ven William Raymond. b 11. Ely Th Coll 55. **d** 56 **p** 57. P-in-c Enbourne w Hampstead Marshall *Ox* 68-70; RD Newbury 70-73; R W Woodhay 71-81; Adn Berks 73-77; Hon Can Ch Ch 79-82; rtd 81; C W Woodhay w Enborne, Hampstead Marshall etc *Ox* 81-91. *1 The Old Bakery, George Street, Kingsclere, Newbury, Berks RG15 8NQ* Newbury (01635) 297426

BIRTWISTLE, Canon James. b 33. FCA66. Ely Th Coll 57. **d** 59 **p** 60. C Southport St Luke *Liv* 59-63; V Cleator Moor w Cleator *Carl* 63-70; R Letchworth *St Alb* 70-73; P-in-c Wareside 73-80; Dep Dir of Educn 77-80; Dioc Dir of Educn from 80; Hon Can St Alb from 85; P-in-c Hertingfordbury from 88. *St Mary's Rectory, Hertingfordbury, Herts SG14 2LE* Hertford (01992) 554450 Fax Welwyn Garden (01707) 373089

BISCOE, Clive. b 45. St Deiniol's Hawarden 85. **d** 86 **p** 87. C Llansamlet *S & B* 86-90; V Landore 90-91. *6 Hazelwood Row, Cwmavon, Port Talbot, W Glam SA12 9DP*

BISH, Donald. b 26. Ripon Hall Ox. **d** 75 **p** 75. C S Gillingham *Roch* 75-79; R Wateringbury w Teston and W Farleigh 79-92; rtd 92; Perm to Offic *Cant* from 92. *5 Eynesford Road, Allington, Maidstone, Kent ME16 0TD* Maidstone (01622) 661847

BISHOP (nee WILKINSON), Mrs Alice Margaret Marion. b 67. Newnham Coll Cam BA89 MA93. Lon Univ MTh92. St Steph Ho Ox 92. **d** 94. C Stepney St Dunstan and All SS *Lon* from 94. *St Faith's House, Shandy Street, London E1 4ST* 0171-790 9961

BISHOP, Anthony John (Tony). b 43. G&C Coll Cam BA66 MA69 Lon Univ MTh69. ALCD67. **d** 69 **p** 70. C Eccleston St Luke *Liv* 69-73; C Gt Baddow *Chelmsf* 73-77; Nigeria 77-84; Lect Lon Bible Coll 84-85; TV Chigwell *Chelmsf* 85-93; P-in-c Walthamstow St Jo from 93. *60 Derby Road, London E18 2PS* 0181-504 9896

BISHOP, Anthony Peter. b 46. FRSA87. St Jo Coll Nottm LTh74 MPhil84 ALCD71. **d** 71 **p** 72. C Beckenham St Geo *Roch* 71-75; Chapl RAF 75-91; Asst Chapl-in-Chief RAF from 91. *Chaplaincy Services (RAF), HQ, Personnel and Training Command, RAF Innsworth, Gloucester GL3 1EZ* Gloucester (01452) 712612 Ext 5164 Fax 510828

BISHOP, Arthur Jack. b 07. St Jo Coll Dur BA28 MA31. **d** 30 **p** 31. R Scotter w E Ferry *Linc* 66-72; R Lympsham *B & W* 72-75; rtd 75; Australia from 76. *58 Tucker Drive, Laurence Park, Lara, Victoria, Australia 3212* Victoria (052) 824352

BISHOP, Miss Cecil Marie. b 18. Lon Univ DipTh48. St Chris Coll Blackheath 46 Gilmore Ho 56. **dss** 57 **d** 87. Jamaica 57-74; Gambia 74-76; Lic to Offic *Ex* 76-87; rtd 78; Hon Par Dn Paignton St Jo *Ex* 87-94. *Flat 5, Lancaster House, Belle Vue Road, Paignton, Devon TQ4 6HD* Paignton (01803) 523522

BISHOP, Christopher (Chris). b 48. K Coll Lon. St Aug Coll Cant 71. **d** 72 **p** 73. C Gt Ilford St Mary *Chelmsf* 72-75; C Upminster 75-78; Adn's Youth Chapl 77-80; Dioc Youth Officer 80-86; Chapl Stansted Airport from 86; P-in-c Manuden w Berden from 86; RD Newport and Stansted from 89. *24 Mallows Green Road, Manuden, Bishop's Stortford, Herts CM23 1DG* Bishop's Stortford (01279) 812228

BISHOP, Canon David Harold. b 28. ARIBA53 FRSA75 DipArch. Westcott Ho Cam 55. **d** 57 **p** 58. V All Hallows Lon Wall *Lon* 67-80; Architectural Adv CCC 67-80; Can Res Nor Cathl *Nor* 80-92; Vice-Dean from 84; rtd 92. *Coneycote, 6 Coneygar Park, Bridport, Dorset DT6 3BA* Bridport (01308) 424673

BISHOP, David Henry Ryder. b 27. R Agric Coll Cirencester MRAC50. Tyndale Hall Bris DipTh57. **d** 57 **p** 58. R Ox St Clem *Ox* 69-91; Zimbabwe 91-93; rtd 93. *38 Sandfield Road, Headington, Oxford OX3 7RT* Oxford (01865) 60099

BISHOP, Donald. b 22. Lon Univ BSc48. Qu Coll Birm 56. **d** 57 **p** 58. V Bodicote *Ox* 60-87; P-in-c Broughton 71-85; rtd 87; Perm to Offic *Cov* from 87. *66 Hanson Avenue, Shipston-on-Stour, Warks CV36 4HS* Shipston-on-Stour (01608) 663431

BISHOP, Huw Daniel. b 49. Univ of Wales (Lamp) BA71 DipTh73. Bp Burgess Hall Lamp CPS73. **d** 73 **p** 74. C Carmarthen St Pet *St D* 73-77; Prov Youth Chapl Wales 77-79; V Llanybydder and Llanwenog w Llanwnnen 79-80; Youth and Community Officer 80-81; Hd of Relig Studies Carre's Gr Sch Sleaford 81-85; Hd of Relig Studies K Sch Pet 85-92; Lic to Offic *Linc* from 83; CF (TA) from 85; Perm to Offic *Pet* 86-92; Perm to Offic *Lich* from 92. *5 Shaw Hall Lane, Coven Heath, Wolverhampton WV10 7EH*

BISHOP, Ian Gregory. b 62. ARICS87 Portsm Poly BSc84. Oak Hill Th Coll BA91. **d** 91 **p** 92. C Purley Ch Ch *S'wark* 91-95; P-in-c Saxlingham Nethergate and Shotesham *Nor* from 95. *The Rectory, Church Hill, Tasburgh, Norwich NR15 1NB* Swainsthorpe (01508) 470656

BISHOP, Jeremy Simon. b 54. Nottm Univ BSc75 Yonsei Univ S Korea 84. All Nations Chr Coll 82 Wycliffe Hall Ox 89. **d** 91 **p** 92. C Macclesfield Team Par *Ches* from 91. *7 Brocklehurst Way, Macclesfield, Cheshire SK10 2HY* Macclesfield (01625) 617680

BISHOP, John Baylis. b 32. Selw Coll Cam BA54 MA58. Cuddesdon Coll 54. **d** 56 **p** 57. C Middlesb St Oswald *York* 56-59; C Romsey *Win* 59-62; Chapl RN 62-66; P-in-c Linc St Mary-le-Wigford w St Martin *Linc* 66-67; V Linc St Faith 66-68; V Linc St Faith and St Martin w St Pet 69-71; Lic to Offic *Bris* 72-84; C Henbury 84-87; TV Bris St Agnes and St Simon w St Werburgh 87; TV Bris St Paul's 87-92; P-in-c Barrow Gurney *B & W* from 92; P-in-c Flax Bourton from 92; Asst Resources Adv from 92. *The Rectory, Main Road, Flax Bourton, Bristol BS19 3QJ* Flax Bourton (01275) 462582

BISHOP, John Charles Simeon. b 46. Chich Th Coll 77. **d** 79 **p** 79. SSF 66-86; P-in-c Edin St Dav *Edin* 82-86; Chapl to the Deaf *Birm* from 86. *135 Wellman Croft, Birmingham B29 6NS* 0121-471 3314 or 455 0601

BISHOP, John David. b 36. Liv Univ BEng MIMechE. E Midl Min Tr Course. **d** 85 **p** 86. NSM Ockbrook *Derby* from 85. *143 Victoria Avenue, Borrowash, Derby DE7 3HF* Derby (01332) 663828

BISHOP, John Harold. b 09. Univ Coll Dur BA31 MA45. Cuddesdon Coll 34. **d** 35 **p** 36. R Singleton *Chich* 60-79; V E Dean 60-79; V W Dean 75-79; RD Westbourne 73-78; rtd 80; Perm to Offic *Chich* from 80. *6 Tregarth Road, Chichester, W Sussex PO19 4QU* Chichester (01243) 527612

BISHOP, Malcolm Geoffrey. b 33. Leeds Univ BA59. Coll of Resurr Mirfield 59. **d** 61 **p** 62. C Kingswinford St Mary *Lich* 61-67; V Birches Head 67-72; P-in-c Oakamoor w Cotton 72-78; TV Billingham St Aid *Dur* 78-85; R Burnmoor from 85. *The Rectory, Burnmoor, Houghton le Spring, Tyne & Wear DH4 6EX* 091-385 2695

BISHOP, Mark Wreford. b 20. Ex Coll Ox BA42 MA45. Wycliffe Hall Ox 42. **d** 43 **p** 44. Lic to Offic *Bradf* 67-71; V Helme *Wakef* 71-77; Dioc Ecum Officer 71-77; P-in-c Graveley w Papworth St Agnes w Yelling etc *Ely* 77-78; R 78-85; rtd 85; Perm to Offic *Bradf* from 85. *5 Rowantree Avenue, Baildon, Shipley, W Yorkshire BD17 5LQ* Bradford (01274) 596006

BISHOP, Michael George. b 27. Wycliffe Hall Ox 63. **d** 65 **p** 66. P-in-c Edale *Derby* 68-71; V Doveridge 71-79; Chapl HM Det Cen Foston Hall 73-79; V Cotmanhay *Derby* 79-81; Chapl Ilkeston Gen Hosp 79-81; USA 81-89; Perm to Offic *Chich* from 89; rtd 92. *Kingsley, 50 Filsham Road, St Leonards-on-Sea, E Sussex TN38 0PA* Hastings (01424) 423539

BISHOP, Philip Michael. b 47. Lon Univ BD69 AKC69. St Aug Coll Cant 70. **d** 71 **p** 72. C Mansf Woodhouse *S'well* 71-76; C Liscard St Mary w St Columba *Ches* 76-78; V Thornton le Moors w Ince and Elton 78-90; V Sutton w Carlton and Normanton upon Trent etc *S'well* from 90. *The Vicarage, Old North Road, Sutton-on-Trent, Newark, Notts NG23 6PL* Newark (01636) 821797

BISHOP, Phillip Leslie. b 44. K Coll Lon BD66 AKC66. **d** 67 **p** 68. C Albrighton *Lich* 67-70; C St Geo-in-the-East St Mary *Lon* 70-71; C Middlesb Ascension *York* 71-73; P-in-c Witherwick 73-77; Ind Chapl 73-82; V Gt Ayton w Easby and Newton in Cleveland 82-89; RD Stokesley 85-89; R Guisborough from 89. *The Rectory, Guisborough, Cleveland TS14 6BS* Guisborough (01287) 632588

BISHOP, Stephen John. b 62. Hull Univ BA84 PGCE86. Ripon Coll Cuddesdon 90 Ch Div Sch of the Pacific (USA) 90. **d** 92 **p** 93. C Syston *Leic* 92-93; C Syston TM 93-95; C Market Harborough from 95. *The Vicarage, 49 Burnmill Road, Market Harborough, Leics LE16 7JF* Market Harborough (01858) 463441

BISHOP, Thomas Harold. b 21. Ridley Hall Cam 60. **d** 61 **p** 62. V Rainford *Liv* 69-87; rtd 87. *14 Keswick Road, Liverpool L18 9UH* 0151-724 6647

BISHOP, Thomas Harveyson. b 25. Coll of Resurr Mirfield 54. **d** 56 **p** 57. S Africa 56-79 and from 87; Lic to Offic *Lon* 79-87; Lon Sec USPG 79-87; rtd 91. *3 Grey Court, Sir George Grey Street, Oranjezicht, Cape Town, 8001 South Africa* Cape Town (21) 461-4858

BISHOP, Miss Waveney Joyce. b 38. Westf Coll Lon BSc60. Cranmer Hall Dur DipTh72. **dss** 82 **d** 87 **p** 94. Leyton St Mary w St Edw *Chelmsf* 82-84; Bishopsworth *Bris* 84-87; Hon Par Dn 87-94; Hon C from 94. *2 Bishop's Cove, Bishopsworth, Bristol BS13 8HH* Bristol (0117) 964 2588

BISHTON, Gerald Arthur (Gerry). b 32. MRSH76 Ruskin Coll Ox DipEcon56 St Pet Hall Ox BA59 MA63. Qu Coll Birm 60. **d** 61 **p** 62. C Forest Gate St Edm *Chelmsf* 61-64; Asst Chapl Lon Univ *Lon* 64-67; Chapl NE Lon Poly 68-73; Sen Lect

73-80; Chapl St Mary's Hosp Gt Ilford 68-80; Ind Chapl *Chelmsf* from 80; P-in-c Shopland 80-89; P-in-c Sutton 80-89; P-in-c Sutton w Shopland from 89. *The Rectory, Sutton Road, Rochford, Essex SS4 1LQ* Southend-on-Sea (01702) 544587

BISSET, Canon Robert McBain. b 05. Glas Univ MA30. Edin Th Coll 30. **d** 32 **p** 33. R Bearsden *Glas* 47-73; R Milngavie 56-73; Can St Mary's Cathl 62-73; rtd 73; Hon Can St Mary's Cathl *Glas* from 77. *Rannoch Lodge, Rannoch Drive, Cumbernauld, Glasgow G67 4EP* Cumbernauld (01236) 729273

BISSEX, Mrs Janet Christine Margaret. b 50. Westhill Coll Birm CertEd72. Trin Coll Bris 76. **dss** 86 **d** 87 **p** 94. Toxteth Park St Bede *Liv* 86-87; Par Dn 87-93; D-in-c Kirkdale St Mary and St Athanasius 93-94; P-in-c from 94. *St Mary's Vicarage, 54 Fonthill Road, Liverpool L4 1OQ* 0151-933 6860

BLACK, Canon Alexander Stevenson. b 28. Glas Univ MA53. Edin Th Coll 53. **d** 55 **p** 56. R Edin St Columba *Edin* 69-79; TV Edin St Jo 79-83; R Haddington 83-93; R Dunbar 83-93; Can St Mary's Cathl from 88; rtd 93. *3 Bass Rock View, Canty Bay, North Berwick, East Lothian EH39 5PJ* Canty Bay (01620) 894771

BLACK, Douglas John. b 58. **d** 91 **p** 92. C Wrexham *St As* from 91. *16 Foster Road, Wrexham, Clwyd LL11 2LT* Wrexham (01978) 365841

BLACK, Mrs Elizabeth Anne. b 47. Qu Coll Birm 80 Cranmer Hall Dur 81. **dss** 82 **d** 87. Cleadon *Dur* 82-85; S Westoe 85-88; Par Dn 87-88; Par Dn Ches le Street 88-92; Emmaus Chr Healing Trust from 93; Perm to Offic *Dur* from 95. *King's House Christian Healing Resource Centre, 29 Keppel Street, Dunston, Gateshead, Tyne & Wear NE11 9AR* 0191-460 7404

BLACK, Henry (Harry). b 40. Edin Th Coll 64. **d** 67 **p** 68. C Cleadon Park *Dur* 69-73; C Winlaton 73-78; R S Ockendon *Chelmsf* 78-93; rtd 93. *73 Derby Avenue, Upminster, Essex RM14 2NS*

BLACK, Ian Christopher. b 62. Kent Univ BA85 Nottm Univ MDiv93. Linc Th Coll 91. **d** 93 **p** 94. C Maidstone All SS and St Phil w Tovil *Cant* from 93. *85 Loose Road, Maidstone, Kent ME15 7DA* Maidstone (01622) 678679

BLACK, Ian Forbes. b 29. St Aid Birkenhead 55. **d** 58 **p** 59. R Edin Ch Ch-St Jas *Edin* 68-71; Asst Chapl HM Pris Liv 71-72; Chapl HM Pris Haverigg 72-73; P-in-c Whicham w Whitbeck 73-75; R Bootle, Corney, Whicham and Whitbeck 75-86; P-in-c Orton St Giles 86-89; R 89-94; P-in-c Aikton 86-89; R 89-94; rtd 94. *Solwayside, Fort Carlisle, Carlisle CA5 5BU* Wigton (016973) 51964

BLACK, Canon Leonard Albert (Len). b 49. Edin Th Coll 69. **d** 72 **p** 73. C Aber St Marg *Ab* 72-75; Chapl St Paul's Cathl Dundee *Bre* 75-77; P-in-c Aber St Ninian *Ab* 77-80; Miss to Seamen from 80; R Inverness St Mich *Mor* from 80; P-in-c Balloch New Town Distr 80-87; R Inverness St Jo 80-87; Relig Progr Producer Moray Firth Radio from 87; Syn Clerk *Mor* from 92; Can St Andr Cathl Inverness from 92. *St Michael's Rectory, 28 Abban Street, Inverness IV3 6HH* Inverness (01463) 233797 or 224433

BLACK, Canon Neville. b 36. DMS85. Oak Hill Th Coll 61. **d** 64 **p** 65. C Everton St Ambrose w St Tim *Liv* 64-69; P-in-c Everton St Geo 69-71; V 71-81; P-in-c Everton St Benedict 70-72; P-in-c Everton St Chad w Ch Ch 70-72; P-in-c Edge Hill St Nath 81; TR St Luke in the City from 81; Chapl Liv Women's Hosp from 82; Dioc Adv Urban Leadership *Liv* from 84; Hon Can Liv Cathl from 87; N Ord Course from 88. *445 Aigburth Road, Liverpool L19 3PA* 0151-427 9803

BLACK, Robert John Edward Francis Butler. b 41. TCD BA65 HDipEd70 DipG&C80 MA85. CITC 66. **d** 66 **p** 67. C Jordanstown *Conn* 66-68; C Dub St Steph and St Ann *D & G* 68-73; C Stillorgan w Blackrock 73-85; Hd Master Dundalk Gr Sch *Arm* from 85; Lic to Offic from 85. *Headmaster's Residence, The Grammar School, Dundalk, Co Louth, Irish Republic* Dundalk (42) 34459 Fax 39100

BLACK, Samuel James. b 38. CITC. **d** 68 **p** 69. C Cloughfern *Conn* 68-72; C Lisburn St Paul 72-78; I Rasharkin w Finvoy 78-82; I Belf Upper Malone (Epiphany) 82-95; I Ballymore *Arm* from 95. *The Rectory, Glebe Hill Road, Tandragee, Craigavon, Co Armagh BT62 2EP* Tandragee (01762) 840234

BLACK, William H.d 88 **p** 89. NSM Malahide w Balgriffin *D & G* 88-89; NSM Dub St Ann and St Steph 89-94; C from 94; Asst Hon Chapl Miss to Seamen from 89. *27 Greendale Avenue, Dublin 5, Irish Republic* Dublin (1) 832-3141

BLACKALL, Mrs Margaret Ivy. b 38. St Kath Coll Lon CertEd58. E Anglian Minl Tr Course 82. **dss** 86 **d** 87 **p** 94. NSM Wickham Market w Pettistree and Easton *St E* 86-88; Par Dn Leiston 88-92; Par Dn Gt and Lt Glemham, Blaxhall etc 92-94; P-in-c from 94. *The Rectory, Low Road, Stratford St Andrew, Saxmundham, Suffolk IP17 1LJ* Saxmundham (01728) 603180

BLACKALL, Robin Jeremy McRae. b 35. Ridley Hall Cam 67. **d** 69 **p** 70. C Stowmarket *St E* 69-72; R Stanstead w Shimplingthorne and Alpheton 72-77; R Bradwell on Sea

Chelmsf 77-79; R St Lawrence 77-79; Warden Bede Ho Staplehurst 79-81; Chapl HM Det Cen Blantyre Ho 81-82; R Edith Weston w N Luffenham and Lyndon w Manton *Pet* from 86. *The Rectory, 8 Church Lane, Edith Weston, Oakham, Leics LE15 8EY* Stamford (01780) 720931

BLACKBURN, David James. b 45. Hull Univ BA67. Trin Coll Bris DipHE87. **d** 87 **p** 88. C Bromsgrove St Jo *Worc* 87-90; V Cradley from 90. *34 Beecher Road, Halesowen, W Midlands B63 2DJ* Cradley Heath (01384) 566928

BLACKBURN, Canon Donald. b 02. OBE. St Jo Coll Dur BA30 MA33. Wycliffe Hall Ox 30. **d** 31 **p** 32. P-in-c Steventon *Ox* 68-71; rtd 71. *Maes y Llan, Llanfechain, Powys SY22 6UU*

BLACKBURN, Frederick John Barrie. b 28. TD73. Lich Th Coll 52. **d** 55 **p** 56. CF (TA) 61-87; V Eighton Banks *Dur* 64-75; R Stella 75-87; TV Bellingham/Otterburn Gp *Newc* 87-89; rtd 89. *47 Coldstream Road, Newcastle upon Tyne NE15 7BY* 0191-274 7851

BLACKBURN, John. b 47. Univ of Wales (Cardiff) DipTh69 DPS71 Open Univ BA88. St Mich Coll Llan 66. **d** 71 **p** 72. C Risca *Mon* 71-76; CF (TA) 73-76; CF from 76. *c/o MOD (Army), Bagshot Park, Bagshot, Surrey GU19 5PL* Bagshot (01276) 471717 Fax 412834

BLACKBURN, Keith Christopher. b 39. K Coll Lon BD63 AKC63. St Boniface Warminster 63. **d** 64 **p** 65. C Surbiton St Andr *S'wark* 64-66; C Battersea St Mary 67-70; Teacher Sir Walter St Jo Sch Battersea 67-70; Hon C Eltham H Trin 70-76; Hd of Ho Crown Woods Sch Eltham 70-76; Dep Hd Master Altwood C of E Sch 76-82; Lic to Offic *Ox* 76-82; Chapl and Hd Master St Geo Sch Gravesend 83-93; Hon C Fawkham and Hartley *Roch* 83-93; V Seal St Pet from 93. *The Vicarage, Church Street, Seal, Sevenoaks, Kent TN15 0AR* Sevenoaks (01732) 762955

BLACKBURN, Peter James Whittaker. b 47. Sydney Univ BA69. Coll of Resurr Mirfield DipTh71. **d** 72 **p** 73. C Felixstowe St Jo *St E* 72-76; C Bournemouth St Pet w St Swithun, St Steph etc *Win* 76-79; R Burythorpe, Acklam and Leavening w Westow *York* 79-85; Chapl Naples Ch Ch *Eur* 85-91; Chapl Algarve from 91. *Casa Sao Vicente, Apartado 135, Boliqueime, 8100 Loule, Algarve, Portugal* Loule (89) 366720

BLACKBURN, Richard Finn. b 52. St Jo Coll Dur BA74. Westcott Ho Cam 81. **d** 83 **p** 84. C Stepney St Dunstan and All SS *Lon* 83-87; P-in-c Isleworth St Jo 87-92; V Mosborough *Sheff* from 92. *The Vicarage, Duke Street, Mosborough, Sheffield S19 5DG* Sheffield (0114) 248 6518

BLACKBURN, Archdeacon of. *See* ROBINSON, Ven William David

BLACKBURN, Bishop of. *See* CHESTERS, Rt Rev Alan David

BLACKBURN, Provost of. *See* FRAYNE, Very Rev David

✠**BLACKBURNE, Rt Rev Hugh Charles.** b 12. Clare Coll Cam BA34 MA39. Westcott Ho Cam 36. **d** 37 **p** 38 **c** 77. C Almondbury *Wakef* 37-39; CF (R of O) 39-77; Chapl Clare Coll Cam 39-46; Chapl RMC 46-47; R Milton *Win* 47-53; Chapl to The Queen 61-77; R Hilborough w Bodney *Nor* 61-72; RD Swaffham 64-69; Hon Can Nor Cathl 65-80; Bp's Chapl Norfolk Broads 77-80; Suff Bp Thetford 77-80; rtd 80; Perm to Offic *Nor* from 80; Perm to Offic *St E* from 81. *4 Goodrick Place, Swaffham, Norfolk PE37 7RP* Swaffham (01760) 723230

BLACKER, Herbert John. b 36. Bris Univ BSc59. Cranmer Hall Dur DipTh61. **d** 61 **p** 62. C Wednesbury St Bart *Lich* 61-63; C Chasetown 63-65; C Chigwell *Chelmsf* 65-69; TV Barnham Broom w Kimberley, Bixton etc *Nor* 69-76; R Burgh Parva w Briston 76-92; P-in-c Melton Constable w Swanton Novers 86-92; R Briston w Burgh Parva and Melton Constable from 92. *The Vicarage, Grange Close, Briston, Melton Constable, Norfolk NR24 2LY* Melton Constable (01263) 860280

BLACKETT, James Gilbert. b 27. Tyndale Hall Bris 52. **d** 55 **p** 56. V Ledsham *York* 67-74; V Burton All SS *Lich* 74-82; V Burton All SS w Ch Ch 82-92; rtd 92. *103 Milford Avenue, Stony Stratford, Milton Keynes MK11 1EZ* Milton Keynes (01908) 265149

BLACKETT, Robert Peter. b 63. Dur Univ BSc85. Ripon Coll Cuddesdon BTh95. **d** 95. C Wigton *Carl* from 95. *8B Longthwaite Crescent, Wigton, Cumbria CA7 9JN* Wigton (016973) 45937

BLACKFORD, David Walker. b 25. Univ of Wales DipTh69. **d** 70 **p** 71. C Holyhead w Rhoscolyn w Llanfair-yn-Neubwll *Ban* 70-72; Lic to Offic *Blackb* 72-80; Hon C Bassaleg *Mon* 80-85; V Treuddyn and Nercwys and Eryrys *St As* 85-90; rtd 90. *11 White Chapel Walk, Magor, Gwent NP6 3NS* Magor (01633) 880507

BLACKIE, Richard Footner (Brother Edmund). b 37. St Cath Coll Cam BA59 MA63 Worc Coll Ox BA59 BSc61. Ely Th Coll 60. **d** 62 **p** 63. C Saffron Walden *Chelmsf* 62-65; SSF from 66. *St Francis House, 75 Deerpark House, Belfast BT14 7PW* Belfast (01232) 351480

BLACKLEDGE, David John. b 51. Oak Hill Th Coll 89. **d** 92 **p** 93. NSM Woodford Wells *Chelmsf* from 92. *Hornbeam, 143 Monkhams Lane, Woodford Green, Essex IG8 0NW* 0181-505 3554

BLACKMAN, Brian David Eric. b 38. Ox NSM Course 82. **d** 85 **p** 86. NSM Reading St Luke *Ox* 85-86; NSM Reading St Luke w St Bart from 86. *138 St Saviour's Road, Reading RG1 6ET* Reading (01734) 572232

BLACKMAN, Clive John. b 51. Hull Univ BSc73 MSc74 Birm Univ DipTh77. Qu Coll Birm 75. **d** 78 **p** 79. C Folkestone St Sav *Cant* 78-81; Chapl Birm Univ *Birm* 81-86; V Thorpe St Matt *Nor* 86-94; R Cringleford w Colney and Bawburgh from 94. *The Vicarage, Cringleford, Norwich NR4 6VE* Norwich (01603) 54424

BLACKMAN, James Bentley. b 57. SS Hild & Bede Coll Dur BEd80 Nottm Univ BTh88. Linc Th Coll 85. **d** 88 **p** 89. C Nether Hoyland St Pet *Sheff* 88-91; C Harrogate St Wilfrid and St Luke *Ripon* 91-94; V Leyburn w Bellerby from 94. *The Vicarage, Bellerby Road, Leyburn, N Yorkshire DL8 5JF* Wensleydale (01969) 22251

BLACKMAN, John Franklyn. b 34. LRAM70 DipRS75. S'wark Ord Course 72. **d** 75 **p** 76. NSM Cov H Trin *Cov* 75-81; Succ Cov Cathl 81-95; TV Cov E 88-95. *86A St George's Terrace, Jesmond, Newcastle-upon-Tyne NE2 2DL* 0191-281 5267

BLACKMAN, Michael Orville. b 46. Univ of W Ontario BMin80 Univ of W Indies LTh70. Codrington Coll Barbados 67. **d** 71 **p** 71. Antigua 71-73; Barbados 73-78 and 80-86 and from 91; Canada 78-80; TV E Ham w Upton Park St Alb *Chelmsf* 86-91. *The Rectory, St Peter's Church, Barbados* Barbados (1809) 422-2181

BLACKMAN, Peter Richard. b 28. Sarum Th Coll 52. **d** 55 **p** 56. V Ratby w Groby *Leic* 60-84; TR 84-93; rtd 93. *25 Turnbull Road, Chichester, W Sussex PO19 4LY* Chichester (01243) 787299

BLACKMORE, Cuthbert. b 17. Qu Coll Birm 57. **d** 59 **p** 60. V Seamer w E Ayton *York* 66-83; rtd 84. *85 West Garth, Cayton, Scarborough, N Yorkshire YO11 3SD* Scarborough (01723) 585156

BLACKMORE, Frank Ellis. b 43. Univ of Wales (Lamp) BA66. Wells Th Coll 65. **d** 67 **p** 68. C S'wark St Geo *S'wark* 67-70; Hon C Camberwell St Giles 70-79; NSM Paddington St Sav *Lon* from 79. *65 Sutherland Avenue, London W9 2HF* 0171-289 3020

BLACKMORE, Robert Ivor. b 37. Univ of Wales (Lamp) 59 Open Univ BA78. **d** 62 **p** 63. C Llangynwyd w Maesteg *Llan* 62-65; C Dowlais 65-67; C Neath w Llantwit 67-71; V Pontlottyn 71-73; V Troedrhiwgarth 73-80; V Seven Sisters from 80. *The Vicarage, Seven Sisters, Neath, W Glam SA10 9DT* Seven Sisters (01639) 700286

BLACKMORE, Vernon John. b 50. Southn Univ BSc Man Univ MSc Lon Univ DipTh K Coll Lon MTh. Oak Hill Th Coll DipHE. **d** 82 **p** 83. C Ecclesall *Sheff* 82-87; Bp's Adv on Youth 85-87; Ed Lion Publishing 87-90; Dir Par Resources CPAS from 90; Perm to Offic *Cov* from 90. *CPAS, Athena Drive, Tachbrook Park, Warwick CV34 6NG* Warwick (01926) 334242 Fax 337613

BLACKSHAW, Alfred. b 14. St Jo Coll Dur BA39 DipTh40 MA42. **d** 40 **p** 41. V Chesham Ch Ch *Ox* 66-72; V Copp *Blackb* 72-79; rtd 79; Perm to Offic *Blackb* from 79. *10 Denebank, All Hallows Road, Bispham, Blackpool FY2 0AS* Blackpool (01253) 595760

BLACKSHAW, Brian Martin. b 43. Lanc Univ MA74. Ox NSM Course 87. **d** 90 **p** 91. NSM Amersham *Ox* 90-93; C Hatch End St Anselm *Lon* 93-95. *542 Uxbridge Road, Pinner, Middx HA5 3QA* 0181-868 7011

BLACKSHAW, Trevor Roland. b 36. GIMechE59. Lon Coll of Div 67. **d** 69 **p** 70. C New Catton St Luke *Nor* 69-73; C Luton Lewsey St Hugh *St Alb* 73-78; V Llandinam w Trefeglwys w Penstrowed *Ban* 78-85; Youth Chapl 82-83; Dioc Dir of Adult Educn 84-85; Consultant Dir Wholeness Through Ch Min 85-92; Perm to Offic *Lich* 85-92; Midl Regional Co-ord BCMS 92-93; Crosslinks from 93; Perm to Offic *Linc* from 92; Perm to Offic *Birm* from 92; Perm to Offic *Leic* from 92; Perm to Offic *Nor* from 93. *4 Hervey Woods Road, Whitwick, Leicester LE67 5JR* Coalville (01530) 810802

BLACKTOP, Graham Leonard. b 33. St Alb Minl Tr Scheme. **d** 85 **p** 86. NSM Rickmansworth *St Alb* 85-92; Perm to Offic *Sarum* from 92. *Dairy House, Wolfeton, Dorchester, Dorset DT2 9QN* Dorchester (01305) 262184

BLACKWALL, David D'Arcy Russell. b 35. Southn Univ BSc60 Imp Coll Lon DIC62. Wycliffe Hall Ox 63. **d** 65 **p** 66. C Sutton Thornhill St Chris *Win* 66-68; V Long Sutton 69-72; Chapl Ld Wandsworth Coll Long Sutton 69-74; Hon C Odiham w S Warnborough *Win* 72-75; Chapl St Lawr Coll Ramsgate from 75. *Kerrison Cottage, Felderland Lane, Worth, Deal, Kent CT14 0BN* Sandwich (01304) 617708

BLACKWELL, Geoffrey Albert. b 27. Lon Coll of Div 62. **d** 65 **p** 66. Chapl RN 69-73; Warden St Mich Home of Healing

Cleadon 73-75; V S Hetton *Dur* 75-82; rtd 82; CSWG from 89; NSM Burpham *Chich* from 95. *The Vicarage, Burpham, Arundel, W Sussex BN18 9RJ* Arundel (01903) 882948

BLACKWELL, Geoffrey David. b 34. Jes Coll Ox BA57 MA61. Chich Th Coll 57. **d** 59 **p** 60. Chapl Westcott Ho Cam 68-73; V Forest Gate St Edm *Chelmsf* 73-81; Pilsdon Community from 83; Perm to Offic *Sarum* 83-93; rtd 94. *Pilsdon Manor, Pilsdon, Bridport, Dorset DT6 5NZ* Bridport (01308) 868308

BLACKWELL, Nicholas Alfred John. b 54. St Jo Coll Nottm BTh85. **d** 85 **p** 86. C Birkenhead Priory *Ches* 85-88; C Stratford-on-Avon w Bishopton *Cov* 88-91; TV Cov E from 91. *St Anne's Vicarage, 129A London Road, Coventry CV1 2JQ* Coventry (01203) 223381

BLACKWELL-SMYTH, Dr Charles Peter Bernard. b 42. TCD BA64 MA71 MB73. Gen Th Sem (NY) MDiv65. **d** 65 **p** 66. C Ban Abbey *D & D* 65-67; C Dub Ch Ch Leeson Park *D & G* 67-69; P-in-c Carbury *M & K* 73-75; Hon C St Stephen in Brannel *Truro* 87-94; Perm to Offic from 94. *Parcgwyn, Rectory Road, St Stephen, St Austell, Cornwall PL26 7RL* St Austell (01726) 822465

BLACOE, Canon Brian Thomas. b 36. Open Univ DipEH BA. Oak Hill Th Coll 63. **d** 66 **p** 67. C Dundonald *D & D* 66-69; C Drumcree *Arm* 69-74; I Ardtrea w Desertcreat 74-78; I Annalong *D & D* 78-95; Can Dromore Cathl from 93; I Knocknamuckley from 95. *30 Mossbank Road, Ballynagarrick, Portadown, Co Armagh BT63 5SL* Gilford (01762) 831227

BLADE, Brian Alan. b 24. ACCS55 ASCA66. Roch Th Coll 67. **d** 69 **p** 70. C Barnehurst *Roch* 69-71; C Crayford 71-76; V Buttershaw St Aid *Bradf* 76-80; R Etton w Helpston *Pet* 80-86; V Hardingstone and Horton and Piddington 86-90; rtd 90. *25 Dan Drive, The Chestnuts, Faversham, Kent ME13 7SW* Faversham (01795) 531842

BLADES, Canon Joseph Henry. b 13. St Chad's Coll Dur BA34 DipTh35 MA37. **d** 36 **p** 37. Hon Can Derby Cathl *Derby* 67-82; V Darley Abbey 68-82; rtd 82; Perm to Offic *Derby* from 82. *3 Aspen Court, Aspen Drive, Spondon, Derby DE21 7SG* Spondon (01332) 678243

BLADON, Ernest Albert. b 19. Ex Univ DipEd58. Glouc Sch of Min 75. **d** 78 **p** 78. Hon C Cinderford St Jo *Glouc* 78-89; rtd 89; Perm to Offic *Glouc* 89-94. *Valista, Grange Road, Littledean, Cinderford, Glos GL14 3NJ* Dean (01594) 822702

BLAGDON-GAMLEN, Peter Eugene. b 20. KLJ. SSC. AKC48 St Boniface Warminster 48. **d** 49 **p** 50. CF (R of O) 59-75; R & V Eastchurch *Cant* 68-71; R & V Eastchurch w Leysdown and Harty 71-87; CF (TA) 78-85; rtd 87; Perm to Offic *Ex* 87-93; Perm to Offic *Pet* from 93. *Blagdon House, 110 Neale Avenue, Kettering, Northants NN16 9HD* Kettering (01536) 84885

BLAGG, Colin. b 31. Leeds Univ BA57. Coll of Resurr Mirfield 57. **d** 59 **p** 60. C Edin Old St Paul *Edin* 59-63; R Gourock *Glas* 63-68; Chapl to the Deaf RADD Lon 68-74; Hon C Stoke Newington St Olave *Lon* 73-74; Chapl to the Deaf *Chich* 74-80; V Shoreham Beach from 80. *The Vicarage, West Beach, Shoreham-by-Sea, W Sussex BN43 5LF* Shoreham-by-Sea (01273) 453768

BLAIR, John Wallace. b 48. Lon Univ BSc70. Qu Coll Birm 79. **d** 81 **p** 82. C Chorlton-cum-Hardy St Werburgh *Man* 81-83; CF from 83. *c/o MOD (Army), Bagshot Park, Bagshot, Surrey GU19 5PL* Bagshot (01276) 471717 Fax 412834

BLAIR, Very Rev Patrick Allen. b 31. Trin Coll Cam BA54 MA58. Ridley Hall Cam 54. **d** 56 **p** 57. C Harwell *Ox* 56-59; Chapl Oundle Sch Pet 59-64; Jerusalem 64-66; Sudan 67-71; Provost Khartoum 67-71; R Ches le Street *Dur* 71-77; TR Barking St Marg w St Patr *Chelmsf* 77-87; Chapl Barking Hosp 77-87; Tunisia 87-91; Cyprus from 91; Provost Nicosia from 91. *PO Box 2014, Nicosia, Cyprus* Nicosia (2) 467897

BLAIR, Philip Hugh. b 39. St Edm Hall Ox BA62 MA67. Ridley Hall Cam 62. **d** 64 **p** 65. C Camborne *Truro* 64-68; C Kenwyn 68-70; Sudan 70-73 and from 78; P-in-c St Enoder *Truro* 73-76; Tutor Ex Univ *Ex* 76-77. *PO Box 322, Khartoum, Sudan*

BLAIR-BROWN, Dennis. b 17. LTh. Em Coll Saskatoon 52. **d** 56 **p** 56. C Lymington *Win* 63-70; V Wellow 70-93; rtd 93. *135 The Close, Salisbury SP1 2EY* Salisbury (01722) 334008

BLAIR-FISH, Canon John Christopher. b 20. Linc Coll Ox BA46 MA47. Cuddesdon Coll 48. **d** 49 **p** 50. V Surbiton St Mark *S'wark* 55-72; R Chipstead 73-89; Hon Can S'wark Cathl 79-88; rtd 89. *39 Beehive Lane, Ferring, Worthing, W Sussex BN12 5NR* Worthing (01903) 241480

BLAKE, Colin David. b 52. CertEd BEd BD. Trin Coll Bris 81. **d** 84 **p** 85. C Hucclecote *Glouc* 84-88; C Patchway *Bris* from 88. *106 Cooks Close, Bradley Stoke, Bristol BS12 0BB* Almondsbury (01454) 617569

BLAKE, Derek Gordon. b 10. St Jo Coll Dur 32. **d** 36 **p** 37. V Holme Cultram St Cuth *Carl* 69-88; P-in-c Allonby 77-81; rtd

89; Perm to Offic *Carl* from 89. *The Mount, Moor Road, Great Broughton, Cockermouth, Cumbria CA13 0YT* Cockermouth (01900) 827483

BLAKE, Ian Martyn. b 57. BA79. Oak Hill Th Coll 76. **d** 80 **p** 81. C Widford *Chelmsf* 80-84; C Barton Seagrave w Warkton *Pet* 84-90; V Sneinton St Chris w St Phil *S'well* from 90. *St Christopher's Vicarage, 180 Sneinton Boulevard, Nottingham NG2 4GL* Nottingham (0115) 950 5303

BLAKE, Preb Patrick John. b 30. Univ of Wales BA51 St Edm Hall Ox BA54 MA58. St Mich Coll Llan 54. **d** 55 **p** 56. V Cleeve *B & W* 63-71; R Bruton w Lamyatt, Wyke and Redlynch 71-83; Dioc Ecum Officer 79-84; Preb Wells Cathl 79-95; TR Yeovil 83-88; R Yeovil w Kingston Pitney 88; P-in-c Backwell 88-89; R 89-92; R Backwell w Chelvey and Brockley 92-95; RD Portishead 92-95; rtd 95. *The Firs, 47 Lower Street, Merriott, Somerset TA16 5NN* Crewkerne (01460) 78932

BLAKE, Peta Ruth. b 44. Lambeth STh89 Episc Div Sch Cam Mass MA89 DMin90 Trin Coll Bris 82. **dss** 83 **d** 87. New Swindon St Barn Gorse Hill *Bris* 83-87; Par Dn 87-88; Perm to Offic from 88. *10 Elmer Close, Malmesbury, Wilts SN16 9UE* Malmesbury (01666) 823722

BLAKE, Canon Peter Douglas Stuart. b 27. BNC Ox BA52 MA57. Westcott Ho Cam 52. **d** 54 **p** 55. V Leek St Edw *Lich* 70-76; P-in-c Hartfield *Chich* 76-78; R Hartfield w Coleman's Hatch 78-87; rtd 87; P-in-c Breamore *Win* 89-90; Perm to Offic *Glas* from 91. *Holmhouse Cottage, Tynron, Thornhill, Dumfriesshire DG3 4LE* Moniaive (018482) 417

BLAKE, Philip Charles. b 29. FAIW88 MACC88 Lon Univ DipTh57 Mitchell Coll (USA) BA80 Macquarie Univ (NSW) MA86 PhD91. Melbourne Coll of Div DipRE76 DPS80 Oak Hill Th Coll 54. **d** 57 **p** 58. V Branston *Lich* 62-69; Australia from 69; rtd 91. *Shalom, Bridgenorth Road, Bridgenorth, Tasmania, Australia 7277* Melbourne (3) 301663

BLAKE, Canon Roy Harold David. b 25. Chich Th Coll 54. **d** 57 **p** 58. V Bris St Agnes w St Simon *Bris* 65-72; TR Bris St Agnes and St Simon w St Werburgh 72-74; RD Bris City 73-74; V Purton 74-93; RD Cricklade 76-82; Hon Can Bris Cathl 77-93; rtd 93. *10 Elmer Close, Malmesbury, Wilts SN16 9UE* Malmesbury (01666) 823722

BLAKE, William Cornford. b 18. Ripon Hall Ox. **d** 67 **p** 68. C Putney St Mary *S'wark* 67-73; C Diss *Nor* 73-76; C Roydon St Remigius 73-76; P-in-c 76-79; R 79-85; rtd 85; Perm to Offic *Derby* from 85. *4 Farnway, Darley Abbey, Derby DE22 2BN* Derby (01332) 550431

BLAKELEY, Julian Graham. b 60. Oak Hill Th Coll BA88. **d** 88 **p** 89. C Bedworth *Cov* 88-91; C Harlow St Mary and St Hugh w St Jo the Bapt *Chelmsf* from 91. *134 East Park, Harlow, Essex CM17 0SR* Harlow (01279) 427357

BLAKELEY, Robert Daniel. b 29. Saskatchewan Univ BA63 St Pet Coll Ox BA66 MA70. Em Coll Saskatchewan LTh56. **d** 56 **p** 57. C High Wycombe *Ox* 68-71; USA 71-75; C St Marylebone St Mary *Lon* 75-82; Chapl Hill Ho Sch Knightsbridge 75-82; P-in-c Tasburgh *Nor* 82-85; P-in-c Tharston 82-85; P-in-c Forncett St Mary w St Pet 82-85; P-in-c Flordon 82-85; Hd Master & Chapl Corona Ravenscourt Sch Lon 85-92; rtd 92. *1 Summerfield Avenue, London NW6 6JT* 0181-930 1775

BLAKELY, Miss Denise Irene. b 69. QUB BD91 PGCE92. CITC DPS95. **d** 95. C Holywood *D & D* from 95. *51 Princess Gardens, Holywood, Co Down BT18 0PN* Holywood (01232) 424554

BLAKEMAN, Mrs Janet Mary. b 36. Man Univ BA57 CertEd58. Carl Dioc Tr Course 87. **d** 90. NSM Wetheral w Warw *Carl* from 90. *Langstrath, Greenfield Lane, Brampton, Cumbria CA8 1AU* Brampton (016977) 2008

BLAKEMAN, Walter John. b 37. Qu Coll Birm 74. **d** 76 **p** 77. C Gnosall *Lich* 76-83; C Cheadle 83-86; Res Min Hednesford 86-90; Min Roundshaw LEP *S'wark* 90-94; C Pleasley *Derby* 94; TV E Scarsdale from 94. *The Rectory, 57 Newboundmill Lane, Pleasley, Mansfield, Notts NG19 7PT* Mansfield (01623) 810775

BLAKESLEY, Ms Christine Marilyn. b 50. St Hugh's Coll Ox BA73 MA75 PGCE74. NE Ord Course 93. **d** 95. C Darlington H Trin *Dur* from 95. *12 Vane Terrace, Darlington, Co Durham DL3 7AT* Darlington (01325) 353326

BLAKESLEY, John. b 50. Keble Coll Ox BA72 MA76. St Steph Ho Ox 72. **d** 74 **p** 75. C Egremont *Carl* 74-77; C Doncaster Ch Ch *Sheff* 77-79; V Auckland St Helen *Dur* 79-94; Lect Th Dur Univ 91-94. *46 Northumberland Avenue, Bishop Auckland, Co Durham DL14 6NP* Bishop Auckland (01388) 605227

BLAKEWAY-PHILLIPS, Richard John. b 19. St Chad's Coll Dur BA43. **d** 43 **p** 44. V Arrington *Ely* 69-77; R Orwell 69-77; R Wimpole 69-77; P-in-c Gt w Lt Abington 77-86; P-in-c Hildersham 77-86; rtd 86; Perm to Offic *Heref* from 86. *Church Cottage, Clun, Craven Arms, Shropshire SY7 8JW* Clun (01588) 640494

BLAKEY

BLAKEY, Cedric Lambert. b 54. Fitzw Coll Cam BA76 MA80. St Jo Coll Nottm 77. **d** 79 **p** 80. C Cotmanhay *Derby* 79-83; C-in-c Blagreaves St Andr CD 83-89; P-in-c Sinfin Moor 84-89; V Heanor from 89; RD Heanor from 94. *The Vicarage, 1A Mundy Street, Heanor, Derbyshire DE75 7EB* Langley Mill (01773) 719800

BLAKEY, William George. b 51. Southn Univ BSc72 PGCE73. Oak Hill Th Coll BA82. **d** 82 **p** 83. C Cheltenham St Mark *Glouc* 82-85; P-in-c Parkham, Alwington, Buckland Brewer etc *Ex* 85-86; R 86-94; TR from 94; RD Hartland from 89; P-in-c Lundy Is from 92. *The Rectory, Parkham, Bideford, Devon EX39 5PL* Horns Cross (01237) 451204

BLAKISTON, Patrick. b 14. Magd Coll Cam BA36 MA42. Linc Th Coll 36. **d** 39 **p** 40. V Whittingham *Newc* 68-79; rtd 80. *1A Butt Lane, Milton, Cambridge CB4 6DQ* Cambridge (01223) 863204

BLAMIRE-BROWN, Charles Richard. b 21. St Cath Soc Ox BA49 MA53. Cuddesdon Coll 49. **d** 51 **p** 52. R Tewin *St Alb* 67-75; RD Hatf 71-75; V Chipperfield St Paul 75-86; rtd 86; Perm to Offic *Cov* from 87. *7 Willoughby Avenue, Kenilworth, Warks CV8 1DG* Kenilworth (01926) 50808

BLANCH, Paul Frederick. b 52. Chich Th Coll. **d** 86 **p** 87. C Chaddesden St Phil *Derby* 86-88; C Auckland St Andr and St Anne *Dur* 88-91; P-in-c Hunwick 91-94. *The House Manager's Apartment, Homedown House, High St, Gosforth, Newcastle upon Tyne NE3 1HN*

BLANCHARD, Christopher John. b 46. Univ of Wales (Lamp) BA70. St Mich Coll Llan 86. **d** 79 **p** 80. NSM Chepstow *Mon* 79-81; NSM Itton and St Arvans w Penterry and Kilgwrrwg etc 81-86; C Ebbw Vale 87-88; R 88-89; V Llangenni and Llanbedr Ystrad Yw w Patricio *S & B* from 89. *The Rectory, Llangenni, Crickhowell, Powys NP8 1HD* Crickhowell (01873) 810348

BLANCHARD, Ernest Desmond. b 26. St Jo Coll Dur BA55 DipTh56. **d** 56 **p** 57. V Ashton Ch Ch *Man* 66-83; RD Ashton-under-Lyne 74-83; Hon Can Man Cathl 78-83; V Kettlewell w Conistone and Hubberholme *Bradf* 83-84; P-in-c Arncliffe w Halton Gill 83-84; V Kettlewell w Conistone, Hubberholme etc 84-91; rtd 91. *15 Castle Street, Morpeth, Northd NE61 1UM* Morpeth (01670) 503550

BLANCHARD, Frank Hugh. b 30. St Jo Coll Dur BA54 DipTh55 MA62. **d** 55 **p** 56. V Kirby Grindalythe *York* 67-71; V N Grimston w Wharram Percy and Wharram-le-Street 67-71; P-in-c Thorpe Bassett 67-71; V Scarborough St Jas 71-79; P-in-c Scarborough H Trin 78-79; V Scarborough St Jas and H Trin 79-86; R Stockton-on-the-Forest w Holtby and Warthill 87-94; rtd 94. *8 Auchnacloich Road, Rothesay, Isle of Bute, Scotland PA20 0EB*

BLANCHARD, Mrs Jean Ann. b 43. St Alb Minl Tr Scheme 79. **dss** 85 **d** 87 **p** 94. Mill End and Heronsgate w W Hyde *St Alb* 85-87; Hon Par Dn 87-92; Par Dn Luton All SS w St Pet 92-94; C 94-95. *The Old Police House, Pit Lane, Gedney Drove End, Spalding, Lincs PE12 9PG*

BLANCHARD, Canon Lawrence Gordon. b 36. Edin Univ MA60. Linc Th Coll 63. **d** 65 **p** 66. C Woodhouse *Wakef* 65-67; C Cannock *Lich* 67-70; Swaziland 70-76; TV Raveningham *Nor* 76-80; V Ancaster *Linc* 80-87; Dir LNSM Linc 80-87; Hon Can Linc Cathl 85-88; Dir of Tr CA 88-93; V Roxton w Gt Barford *St Alb* from 93. *The Vicarage, High Street, Great Barford, Bedford MK44 3JJ* Bedford (01234) 870363

BLAND, Albert Edward. b 14. St Mich Coll Llan. **d** 62 **p** 63. V Feniscowles *Blackb* 67-84; rtd 85; Perm to Offic *Blackb* from 85. *22 Park Farm Road, Feniscowles, Blackburn BB2 3HN* Blackburn (01254) 201321

BLAND, Miss Jean Elspeth. b 42. K Coll Lon BA63. Glouc Sch of Min 87. **d** 90 **p** 94. Par Dn Cen Telford *Lich* 90-94; C 94; Asst Chapl HM Pris Shrewsbury 92-94; Asst Chapl HM Pris Doncaster from 94. *HM Prison Doncaster, Marshgate, Doncaster, S Yorkshire DN5 8UX* Doncaster (01032) 760870

BLAND, Thomas. b 12. Clifton Th Coll 39. **d** 42 **p** 43. R Stratford-on-Avon w Bishopton *Cov* 63-69; rtd 77. *1 Costard Avenue, Shipston-on-Stour, Warks CV36 4HW* Shipston-on-Stour (01608) 663284

BLANDFORD-BAKER, Neil James. b 64. Dundee Univ BSc86 Nottm Univ BTh92. St Jo Coll Nottm DipMM93. **d** 93 **p** 94. C The Quinton *Birm* from 93. *84 Highfield Lane, Birmingham B32 1QX* 0121-422 3596

BLANEY, Laurence (Laurie). b 41. Lon Univ DipTh69 Open Univ BA85 Essex Univ MA88. Oak Hill Th Coll 66. **d** 69 **p** 70. C Leyton St Mary w St Edw *Chelms* 69-73; P-in-c Wimbish w Thunderley 73-77; P-in-c Steeple 77-82; P-in-c Mayland 77-82; R Pitsea 82-95; R Pitsea w Nevendon from 95. *The Rectory, Rectory Road, Basildon, Essex SS13 2AA* Basildon (01268) 553240

BLANKENSHIP, Charles Everett. b 42. Santa Clara Univ BA64. Cuddesdon Coll 71. **d** 74 **p** 75. C Catford (Southend) and Downham *S'wark* 74-78; P-in-c Battersea St Phil w St Bart

78-83; V 83-85; TV Wimbledon 85-91; P-in-c Welling 91-92; V from 92. *St Mary's Vicarage, Sandringham Drive, Welling, Kent DA16 3QU* 0181-856 0684

BLANKLEY, Roger Henry. b 32. ARICS60. Clifton Th Coll 62. **d** 66 **p** 67. C Peckham St Mary Magd *S'wark* 66-69; SAMS 70-74; Brazil 74-80; R Gillingham w Geldeston, Stockton, Ellingham etc *Nor* 80-91; P-in-c Charmouth and Catherston Leweston *Sarum* from 91. *The Rectory, Willowmead, Meadow Way, Charmouth, Bridport, Dorset DT6 6NS* Charmouth (01297) 560409

BLANT, Edgar. b 18. St Chad's Coll Dur BA47 DipTh48. **d** 48 **p** 49. Antigua 55-85; St Kitts-Nevis 60-85; Adn St Kitts 78-85; rtd 86; Perm to Offic *Lich* from 86. *326 Sandon Road, Stoke-on-Trent ST3 7EB* Blythe Bridge (01782) 398300

BLATCHLEY, Owen Ronald Maxwell. b 30. Bps' Coll Cheshunt 62. **d** 64 **p** 65. C Boxmoor St Jo *St Alb* 64-67; C Boreham Wood All SS 67-69; C Frimley *Guildf* 69-77; V Manaccan w St Anthony-in-Meneage *Truro* 77-82; R Binfield *Ox* from 82. *The Rectory, Terrace Road North, Bracknell, Berks RG12 5JG* Bracknell (01344) 54406

BLATHWAYT, Canon Linley Dennys. b 16. Qu Coll Cam BA38 MA44. Wells Th Coll 38. **d** 40 **p** 41. R Gussage St Michael and Gussage All Saints *Sarum* 69-71; R Corscombe 71-75; P-in-c Frome St Quintin w Evershot and Melbury Bubb 71-75; R Evershot, Frome St Quinton, Melbury Bubb etc 75-79; RD Beaminster 75-81; Can and Preb Sarum Cathl 79-81; Preb Melbury 79-81; rtd 81. *50 Wentworth Park, Allendale, Hexham, Northd NE47 9DR* Hexham (01434) 683448

BLATHWAYT, Canon Wynter. b 18. St Pet Hall Ox BA40 MA44. Ripon Hall Ox 40. **d** 41 **p** 42. V Horning *Nor* 66-85; P-in-c Beeston St Laurence w Ashmanhaugh 78-85; Hon Can Nor Cathl 81-85; rtd 85; Perm to Offic *Nor* from 85. *155 Sir William Close, Aylsham, Norwich NR11 6AY* Aylsham (01263) 734502

BLAY, Ian. b 65. Man Univ BA88. Westcott Ho Cam 89. **d** 91 **p** 92. C Withington St Paul *Man* 91-94; C Elton All SS from 94. *171 Brandlesholme Road, Bury, Lancs BL8 1AZ* 0161-764 5231

BLEAKLEY, Melvyn Thomas. b 43. K Coll Lon BD66 AKC66. **d** 67 **p** 68. C Cross Heath *Lich* 67-70; TV High Wycombe *Ox* 70-77; Perm to Offic from 77. *294 Hughenden Road, High Wycombe, Bucks HP13 5PE* High Wycombe (01494) 529315

BLEASE, John Thomas. b 19. Edin Th Coll 41. **d** 43 **p** 44. Chapl RN 47-74; rtd 74. *180 Manor Road North, Thames Ditton, Surrey KT7 0BQ* 0181-398 5117

BLEE, Peter Michael. b 64. St Jo Coll Cam BA86. St Steph Ho Ox BTh94. **d** 94 **p** 95. C Guildf St Nic *Guildf* from 94. *St Catherine's House, 72 Wodeland Avenue, Guildford GU2 5LA* Guildford (01483) 67633

BLENCOE, Charles Dennis. b 17. Lon Univ BA38. Bps' Coll Cheshunt 38. **d** 41 **p** 42. C Sutton in Ashfield St Mary *S'well* 41-43; Chapl RAF 43-61; Canada from 61. *526 Bay View Place, Duncan, British Columbia, Canada, V9L 1M3*

BLENKIN, Hugh Linton. b 16. Trin Coll Cam BA39 MA43. Lambeth STh56 Westcott Ho Cam 39. **d** 40 **p** 41. Lect Sarum & Wells Th Coll 66-78; rtd 81. *31 Abbey Mews, Amesbury, Salisbury SP4 7EX* Amesbury (01980) 624813

BLENNERHASSETT, Canon Richard Noel Rowland. b 09. TCD BA33 MA52. **d** 33 **p** 34. I Timoleague *C, C & R* 69-73; rtd 72. *The Moorings, Fenit, Tralee, Co Kerry, Irish Republic* Tralee (66) 36198

BLENNERHASSETT, Canon Thomas Francis. b 15. TCD BA37 BD43 HDipEd56 MA68. **d** 39 **p** 40. I Howth *D & G* 58-90; Can Ch Ch Cathl Dub from 79; rtd 90; C Dalkey St Patr *D & G* from 90. *25 Bayside Square West, Sutton, Dublin 13, Irish Republic* Dublin (1) 832-3720

BLEWETT, Roy. b 32. K Coll Lon BSc54 MPhil74 Leeds Inst of Educn 66 Newc Univ DipRS81. Edin Th Coll 81. **d** 82 **p** 83. C Newc St Fran *Newc* 82-85; P-in-c Cornhill w Carham 85-91; P-in-c Branxton 85-91; rtd 92. *Bryn Mawr, Lower Broad Lane, Redruth, Cornwall TR15 3HT* Redruth (01209) 313152

BLEWETT, Timothy John (Tim). b 67. Surrey Univ BA88. Westcott Ho Cam 89. **d** 92 **p** 93. C Knaresborough *Ripon* 92-95; V Hanmer, Bronington, Bettisfield, Tallarn Green *St As* from 95. *The Vicarage, Hanmer, Whitchurch, Shropshire SY13 3DE* Hanmer (01948) 830468

BLIGH, Peter Alan. b 27. NE Ord Course 78. **d** 81 **p** 82. NSM Thornaby on Tees *York* 81; NSM Stockton *Dur* 87-95; Perm to Offic from 95. *52 Cambridge Road, Thornaby, Stockton-on-Tees, Cleveland TS17 6LR* Stockton-on-Tees (01642) 612700

BLIGH, Philip Hamilton. b 36. MInstP75 Lon Univ BSc57 PhD61 MEd79 St Cath Coll Ox BA63. S'wark Ord Course 86. **d** 88 **p** 89. C Abington *Pet* 88-90; V Bozeat w Easton Maudit from 90. *The Vicarage, Hensmans Lane, Bozeat, Wellingborough, Northants NN9 7NY* Wellingborough (01933) 663216

BLISS, Allan Ernest Newport. b 29. K Coll Lon AKC50. St Boniface Warminster 54. **d** 54 **p** 57. C Sundon w Streatley

66

St Alb 68-73; P-in-c Caldecote All SS 74-78; V 78-91; V Old Warden 81-91; Perm to Offic from 91; rtd 94. *6 Jubilee Gardens, Biggleswade, Beds SG18 0JW* Biggleswade (01767) 313797

BLISS, David Charles. b 52. Aston Univ BSc75 Cranfield Inst of Tech MSc82. St Jo Coll Nottm 87. **d** 89 **p** 90. C Burntwood *Lich* 89-93; P-in-c Todwick *Sheff* 93; TV Aston cum Aughton w Swallownest, Todwick & Ulley from 93. *The Vicarage, 15 Rectory Gardens, Todwick, Sheffield S31 0JU* Worksop (01909) 770283

BLISS, John Derek Clegg. b 40. Sarum Th Coll. **d** 68 **p** 69. C Wymondham *Nor* 68-73; V Easton 73-80; R Colton 73-80; USA from 80. *6395 Marguerite Drive, Newark, California 94560, USA*

BLISS, Neil Humberstone. b 29. TCD BA54 MA59. Coll of Resurr Mirfield 55. **d** 57 **p** 58. Swaziland 68-80; P-in-c Osmington w Poxwell *Sarum* 80-81; TV Preston w Sutton Poyntz and Osmington w Poxwell 81-84; V Ernesettle *Ex* 84-88; R S Tawton and Belstone 88-93; rtd 94. *Jordan House, Jordan, Lyme Regis, Dorset DT7 3AQ* Lyme Regis (01279) 445189

BLISS, Rupert Geoffrey. b 05. MIMechE27 K Coll Cam BA31 MA45. Ridley Hall Cam 32. **d** 50 **p** 50. P-in-c Melbury Abbas *Sarum* 66-73; rtd 73; Perm to Offic *Sarum* 73-81; Perm to Offic *S'wark* 81-82; Perm to Offic *Lon* 82-86; Perm to Offic *Glouc* 86-92. *32 York Road, Broadstone, Dorset BH18 8ET* Broadstone (01202) 692673

BLISSARD-BARNES, Christopher John. b 36. ARCO55 Linc Coll Ox BA61 MA64. Ridley Hall Cam 61. **d** 63 **p** 64. C Woking St Paul *Guildf* 63-67; C Orpington Ch Ch *Roch* 67-71; P-in-c Heref St Jas *Heref* 71-78; Chapl Heref Gen Hosp 71-78; R Hampreston *Sarum* 78-88; TR 88-89; RD Wimborne 80-85; P-in-c Hambledon *Guildf* 89-94; R Newdigate from 94. *The Rectory, Church Road, Newdigate, Dorking, Surrey RH5 5DL* Newdigate (01306) 631469

BLOCK, Robert Allen. b 62. Univ of Wales (Lamp) BA84. Coll of Resurr Mirfield 86. **d** 88 **p** 89. C Hampton *Worc* 88-91; C Notting Hill St Mich and Ch Ch *Lon* from 91. *St Francis House, Dalgarno Way, London W10 5EL* 0181-969 3813

BLOFELD, Thomas Guest. *See* GUEST-BLOFELD, Thomas

BLOGG, Kevin Derek. b 55. Ch Ch Coll Cant BSc82 PGCE87. Franciscan Ho of Studies. **d** 84 **p** 85. NSM Eythorne and Elvington w Waldershare etc *Cant* 89-92; Orchard Sch Cant 89-90; Harbour Sch Dover 92-93; NSM Colkirk w Oxwick w Pattesley, Whissonsett etc *Nor* from 95; Sidestrand Hall Sch Nor from 94. *Meadow House, School Road, Brisley, Dereham, Norfolk NR20 5LH* Dereham (01362) 668689

BLOOD, David John. b 36. G&C Coll Cam BA60 MA64. Westcott Ho Cam 64. **d** 62 **p** 63. C Rushmere *St E* 62-66; C Harringay St Paul *Lon* 66-71; Lic to Offic 71-81. *33 Rosebery Gardens, London N8 8SH* 0181-340 3312

BLOOD, Michael William. b 44. AKC67. **d** 69 **p** 70. C Moseley St Agnes *Birm* 69-75; V Cotteridge from 75; Relig Progr Producer BBC Radio W Midl from 76. *118 Northfield Road, Birmingham B30 1DX* 0121-458 2815

BLOOD, Stephen John. b 28. Keble Coll Ox BA53 MA58. Coll of Resurr Mirfield 53. **d** 55 **p** 56. C Greenford H Cross *Lon* 55-58; C Forest Gate St Edm *Chelmsf* 58-61; C-in-c Ashford St Hilda CD *Lon* 61-73; V Ashford St Hilda from 73. *The Vicarage, 8 Station Crescent, Ashford, Middx TW15 3HH* Ashford (01784) 254237

BLOOMFIELD, Mrs Gillian. b 38. Leeds Univ BA59. W Midl Minl Tr Course 84. **d** 87 **p** 94. Par Dn Highters Heath *Birm* 87-89; TD Chelmsley Wood 89-94; TV 94-95; Chapl Chelmsley Hosp Birm 89-95; Chapl Marston Green Hosp Birm 89-95; P-in-c Pattingham w Patshull *Lich* from 95. *20 Dartmouth Avenue, Pattingham, Wolverhampton WV6 7DP*

BLOOMFIELD, Harry. b 29. Chich Th Coll 57. **d** 60 **p** 61. C Brighton St Mich *Chich* 60-64; C Wantage *Ox* 64-84; V Kennington from 84. *The Vicarage, Kennington, Oxford OX1 5PG* Oxford (01865) 735135

BLOOMFIELD, John Michael. b 35. Univ of Wales (Lamp) BA57. Sarum Th Coll 59. **d** 61 **p** 62. C Fordington *Sarum* 61-64; C Branksome St Aldhelm 64-66; Youth Chapl *Win* 66-69; R Win All SS w Chilcomb and Chesil 71-79; P-in-c Corsley *Sarum* 79-81; C Swanage and Studland 83-86; Chapl HM Pris Dorchester 87-89; C Dorchester *Sarum* 87-89; Chapl HM Pris The Verne from 89. *The Chaplain's Office, HM Prison, The Verne, Portland, Dorset DT5 1EG* Portland (01305) 820124 Fax 823724

BLOOMFIELD, John Stephen. b 56. Southn Univ. Chich Th Coll 83. **d** 86 **p** 87. C Chich St Paul and St Pet *Chich* 86-89; TV Littlehampton and Wick from 89. *St James's Vicarage, 76 Arundel Road, Littlehampton, W Sussex BN17 7DF* Littlehampton (01903) 724311

BLOOMFIELD, Canon Peter Grayson. b 19. ACIS50 K Coll Lon BD60 AKC61. **d** 61 **p** 61. S Rhodesia 61-65; Rhodesia 65-78; Can Matabeleland 75-78; P-in-c Chideock *Sarum*

78-83; P-in-c Symondsbury 78-83; P-in-c Winterbourne Came w Whitcombe etc 83; Perm to Offic from 84; rtd 85. *Pilgrim's Rest, 62A Jestys Avenue, Weymouth, Dorset DT3 5NN* Upwey (01305) 813330

BLORE, John Francis. b 49. Jes Coll Ox BA72 MA76. Wycliffe Hall Ox 73. **d** 75 **p** 76. C Waltham Abbey *Chelmsf* 75-78; C E Ham St Geo 78-81; R Colchester St Mich Myland from 81; Chapl Oxley Parker Sch Colchester from 81. *Myland Rectory, Rectory Close, Colchester, Essex CO4 5DN* Colchester (01206) 853076

BLORE, Robert William. b 12. AKC39. **d** 39 **p** 40. V Thorpe Bay *Chelmsf* 56-79; rtd 79. *10 Victoria Close, Wivenhoe, Colchester CO7 9PL* Wivenhoe (01206) 824550

BLOUNT, Robin George. b 38. Lon Univ DipTh68. Lon Coll of Div 61 Wycliffe Hall Ox 67. **d** 68 **p** 69. C Bletchley *Ox* 68-71; C Washington *Dur* 71-74; TV Chelmsley Wood *Birm* 74-76; Ind Chapl *Worc* 76-89; AP Dudley St Jo 76-89; AP Dudley St Thos and St Luke 88-89; Ind Chapl (Eurotunnel Development) *Cant* from 89. *Rivendell, School Lane, Newington, Folkestone, Kent CT18 8AY* Folkestone (01303) 279222 Fax 273595

BLOWERS, Canon Ralph Barrie. b 28. Fitzw Ho Cam BA50 MA61. Ridley Hall Cam 51. **d** 53 **p** 54. V Normanton *Derby* 69-93; RD Derby 74-79; RD Derby S 79-89; Hon Can Derby Cathl 85-93; rtd 93. *8 Portland Close, Mickleover, Derby DE3 5BQ* Derby (01332) 517114

BLOWS, Canon Derek Reeve. b 26. MSAnPsych75 Linc Coll Ox BA50 MA52. Cuddesdon Coll 50. **d** 52 **p** 53. Hon Can S'wark Cathl *S'wark* 72; V Purley St Mark Woodcote 65-70; Dir Past Care and Counselling 70-80; Dir Westmr Past Foundn 80-91; Perm to Offic *Roch* from 80; rtd 91. *2 Blackmoor House, Four Elms, Edenbridge, Kent TM8 6PG* Four Elms (01732) 700770

BLOXAM-ROSE, Canon Simon Franklyn. b 61. Southn Univ BTh MA Hon FLCM88. Chich Th Coll 85. **d** 88 **p** 89. C Bassaleg *Mon* 88-89; Chapl Aldenham Sch Herts 89-94; Perm to Offic *Ex* from 90; Chapl (Sen) Millfield Sch Somerset from 94; Can St Jo Pro-Cathl Katakwa from 95. *Orchard Leigh, Millfield, Street, Somerset BA16 0DA* Street (01458) 841125 or 42291 Fax 47276

BLOXHAM, Oliver. b 27. Ely Th Coll 60. **d** 62 **p** 63. V Dudley *Newc* 69-79; P-in-c Balkwell 79-81; V 81-92; rtd 92. *23 Lambley Avenue, North Shields, Tyne & Wear NE30 3SL* 0191-926 1785

BLOY, Philip Penrose. b 19. Ox Univ MA49 Lanc Univ MA71. Wells Th Coll 49. **d** 51 **p** 53. N Rhodesia 60-64; Zambia 64-70; C-in-c Bris St Geo *Bris* 72-73; Chapl Gatwick Airport *Chich* 73-88; Can and Preb Chich Cathl 86-88; rtd 89. *Old Orchard, Blackford Road, Charlton Horethorne, Sherborne, Dorset DT9 4NS* Corton Denham (01963) 220418

BLUNDELL, Canon Derek George. b 32. Tyndale Hall Bris 58. **d** 61 **p** 62. C Fazakerley Em *Liv* 61-64; C-in-c Bath Odd Down *B & W* 64-69; V 69-74; V Tulse Hill H Trin *S'wark* 74-81; Org and Admin African Pastor Fund from 81; Perm to Offic *Cov* from 81; Hon Can Mityana from 90. *12 Ibex Close, Coventry CV3 2FB* Coventry (01203) 448068 Fax as telephone

BLUNDELL, Peter Grahame. b 61. Ealing Coll of Educn BA83. Oak Hill NSM Course 91. **d** 94 **p** 95. NSM Kensington St Barn *Lon* from 94. *13 Holmesdale Avenue, London SW14 7BQ* 0181-392 2135 or 0171-371 1451 Fax 0171-603 5861

BLUNDEN, Jacqueline Ann. *See* MILLER, Jacqueline Ann

BLUNSUM, Charles Michael. b 28. ACIB51 MBIM86. **d** 74 **p** 75. C Stoke Bishop *Bris* 74-79; Chapl Brunel Manor Chr Cen Torquay from 79. *5 Merrivale Close, Torquay TQ2 8PZ* Torquay (01803) 326089 or 329333

BLUNT, Paul David. b 44. Lon Univ BSc65 Leeds Univ DipTh70. Coll of Resurr Mirfield 67. **d** 70 **p** 71. C Norbury St Steph *Cant* 70-73; Canada from 73. *1234 Prestone Drive, Orleans, Ontario, Canada, K1E 3X6*

BLYDE, Ian Hay. b 52. Liv Univ BSc74 Edin Univ BD80. Edin Th Coll 77. **d** 80 **p** 81. C Ainsdale *Liv* 80-83; Chapl Birkenhead Sch Merseyside 83-90; Perm to Offic *Ches* 83-90; V Over St Chad 90-93; Chapl Ex Sch from 93; Chapl St Marg Sch Ex from 93. *2 Hulham Road, Exmouth, Devon EX8 3HR* Exmouth (01395) 264339

BLYTH, Bryan Edward Perceval. b 22. Linc Coll Ox BA49 MA52. Wells Th Coll 48. **d** 50 **p** 51. Teacher Westwood Co Jun Sch 68-72; Dep Hd 72-87; Hon C Thundersley *Chelmsf* 80-84; rtd 87. *Church Cottage, Chettle, Blandford Forum, Dorset DT11 8DB* Blandford (01258) 830396

BLYTH, Canon Drummond Gwyn. b 26. K Coll Lon 53. **d** 54 **p** 55. R Carlton Colville *Nor* 62-70; V Stalham w Brunstead 70-77; P-in-c E Ruston 76-77; RD Waxham 77-89; V Stalham and E Ruston w Brunstead 77-91; Hon Can Nor Cathl 87-91; rtd 91; Perm to Offic *Nor* from 91. *Pegg's Close, 6 St Nicholas Close, Sheringham, Norfolk NR26 8LE* Sheringham (01263) 822611

BLYTH, Mrs Geraldine Anne. b 50. Llan Dioc Tr Scheme 90. **d** 94. NSM Llantrisant *Llan* from 94. *1 Heol-y-Fro, Upper Church Village, Pontypridd, M Glam CF38 1UD* Newtown Llantwit (01443) 201761

BLYTH, John Reddie. b 25. Wadh Coll Ox BA48 MA50. Ridley Hall Cam 48. **d** 50 **p** 51. E Midl Area Sec CPAS 63-70; V Parkstone St Luke *Sarum* 70-90; Chapl Uplands Sch Parkstone 70-73; rtd 90. *5 Powell Road, Newick, E Sussex BN8 4LS* Newick (01825) 722011

BLYTH, John Stuart. b 36. Lon Univ BD64 DipTh. Lich Th Coll 63. **d** 65 **p** 66. C Knowle St Barn *Bris* 65-68; C Whitchurch *B & W* 68-70; P-in-c Sutton St Nicholas w Sutton St Michael *Heref* 70-73; Dioc RE Adv 70-73; Chapl RAF 73-77; P-in-c Launton *Ox* 77-79; TV Bicester w Bucknell, Caversfield and Launton 79-84; P-in-c Hanborough 84-86; R Hanborough and Freeland 86-89; Perm to Offic from 90. *12 Green Ridges, Oxford OX3 9PL* Oxford (01865) 62691

BLYTH, Kenneth Henry. b 35. Lon Univ DipTh60. Oak Hill Th Coll 58. **d** 61 **p** 62. C St Alb St Paul *St Alb* 61-65; P-in-c Aspenden and Layston w Buntingford 65-66; R 66-72; R Washfield, Stoodleigh, Withleigh etc *Ex* 72-82; P-in-c Cruwys Morchard 72-74; RD Tiverton 76-82; V Eastbourne H Trin *Chich* from 82. *Holy Trinity Vicarage, Trinity Trees, Eastbourne, E Sussex BN21 3BE* Eastbourne (01323) 729046

BLYTH, Dr Michael Graham. b 53. Jes Coll Ox BA75 MA78 Dur Univ PhD79. Qu Coll Birm 82. **d** 84 **p** 85. C Nantwich *Ches* 84-86; C Coppenhall 86-88; TV Southend *Chelmsf* from 88. *The Vicarage, 39 St John's Road, Westcliff-on-Sea, Essex SS0 7JY* Southend-on-Sea (01702) 433327

BOADEN, John Edward. b 15. Down Coll Cam BA41 MA45. Ridley Hall Cam 41. **d** 43 **p** 44. R Blackley St Andr *Man* 67-77; P-in-c Parkfield in Middleton 77-81; rtd 81; Hon C Constable Lee *Man* 81-83; Perm to Offic from 83. *11 Horncliffe Close, Rawtenstall, Rossendale, Lancs BB4 6EE* Rossendale (01706) 223696

BOAG, David. b 46. Edin Th Coll 69. **d** 72 **p** 73. C Edin Old St Paul *Edin* 72-75; P-in-c Edin St Andr and St Aid 75-88; Lic to Offic from 88. *26 Noble Place, Edinburgh EH6 8AX* 0131-554 7876

BOAK, Canon Donald Kenneth. b 30. MBAOT53. S'wark Ord Course DipRS85. **d** 85 **p** 86. C Tulse Hill H Trin and St Matthias *S'wark* 85-88; C Surbiton St Matt 88-91; Intercon Ch Soc, SAMS and Miss to Seamen 91-95; Peru 91-95; Dean Lima 93-95; rtd 95; Hon Can Peru from 95. *c/o 4 Bedford Road, London E18 2AQ* 0181-491 7842

BOAKE, Canon Henry Vaux. b 16. TCD BA38 MA52. CITC 38. **d** 39 **p** 40. I Crosspatrick Gp *C & O* 46-79; Chan Ferns Cathl 71-79; rtd 79. *Little Orton, Rutland, Palatine, Carlow, Irish Republic* Carlow (503) 43065

BOAKES, Norman. b 50. Univ of Wales (Swansea) BA71 Univ of Wales (Lamp) LTh73. Bp Burgess Hall Lamp 71. **d** 73 **p** 74. C Swansea St Mary w H Trin *S & B* 73-78; Chapl Univ of Wales (Swansea) 76-78; Chapl K Alfred Coll *Win* 78-82; V Colbury 82-91; Chapl Ashurst Hosp 82-91; Chapl Mental Handicap Services Unit 82-91; V Southn Maybush St Pet *Win* from 91. *Maybush Vicarage, Sedbergh Road, Southampton SO1 9HJ* Southampton (01703) 771996

BOAR, Alan Bennett. b 23. Sarum Th Coll 56. **d** 58 **p** 59. R Beeston St Laurence w Ashmanhaugh and Hoveton *Nor* 67-78; P-in-c Tunstead w Sco' Ruston 67-78; P-in-c Marsham 78-89; P-in-c Burgh 78-89; rtd 89; Perm to Offic *Nor* from 89. *20 Emelson Close, Dereham, Norfolk NR19 2ES* Dereham (01362) 698944

BOARDMAN, Dr Frederick Henry. b 25. Liv Univ BSc46 St Cath Soc Ox BA49 MA54 Birm Univ MEd71 PhD77. Wycliffe Hall Ox 47. **d** 50 **p** 51. V Stechford *Birm* 57-63; Lic to Offic *Liv* from 71; Hon C Sutton 76-89; Hon C Burtonwood from 89; rtd 90. *Woodside, Burtonwood Road, Great Sankey, Warrington WA5 3AN* Warrington (01925) 635079

BOARDMAN, John Frederick. b 37. Bolton Coll of Art NDD57 Leeds Univ ATD58 AKC64. **d** 65 **p** 66. C Harrogate St Wilfrid *Ripon* 65-68; C Fleetwood *Blackb* 68-71; C Cen Torquay *Ex* 71-77; Chapl S Devon Tech Coll Torbay 71-77; P-in-c Ellacombe *Ex* 76-77; V Milber from 77. *St Luke's Vicarage, Milber, Newton Abbot, Devon TQ12 4LQ* Newton Abbot (01626) 65837

BOARDMAN, Jonathan. b 63. Magd Coll Cam BA89 Magd Coll Ox MA90. Westcott Ho Cam 87. **d** 90 **p** 91. C W Derby St Mary *Liv* 90-93; Prec St Alb Abbey *St Alb* from 93. *Flat 1, The Deanery, Sumpter Yard, St Albans, Herts AL1 1BY* St Albans (01727) 855321

BOARDMAN, Ms Philippa Jane. b 63. Jes Coll Cam BA85 MA89. Ridley Hall Cam 87. **d** 90 **p** 94. Par Dn Walthamstow St Mary w St Steph *Chelmsf* 90-93; C Hackney Wick St Mary of Eton w St Aug *Lon* from 93; Dean of Women's Min Stepney Area from 94. *9 Oldbury Court, Mabley Street, London E9 5RY* 0181-533 2457   Fax as telephone

BOARDMAN, William (Bill). b 21. AKC52. **d** 53 **p** 54. V Barton Portsm 67-86; RD W Wight 78-82; rtd 86; Perm to Offic Portsm from 86. *41 Culver Way, Sandown, Isle of Wight PO36 8QJ* Isle of Wight (01983) 404552

BOASE, David John. b 49. St Jo Coll Dur BA71 Trin Coll Ox PGCE73. Cuddesdon Coll 71. **d** 73 **p** 74. C Penrith *Carl* 73-76; Tutor Greystoke Coll Carl 76-78; Prec Gib Cathl *Eur* 78-80; Miss to Seamen 78-80; Chapl Gothenburg w Halmstad and Jonkoping *Eur* 80-82; TV Thornaby on Tees *York* 82-88; V Kirkby-in-Cleveland from 88; Resp for Clergy In-Service Tr Cleveland W from 88. *3 Holmemead, The Holme, Great Broughton, Middlesbrough TS9 7HQ* Middlesbrough (01642) 710005

BOCKING (Essex), Dean of. *See* HAIG, Very Rev Alistair Matthew

BOCKING (Suffolk), Dean of. *Vacant*

BODDINGTON, Canon Alan Charles Peter. b 37. Lon Univ DipTh65. Oak Hill Th Coll 63. **d** 66 **p** 67. C Bedworth *Cov* 66-69; Bp's Officer for Min 69-75; Bp's Chapl for Miss 69-73; P-in-c Wroxall 72-75; P-in-c Honiley 72-75; V Westwood 75-85; Asst Chapl Warw Univ 78-85; R Farnborough *Guildf* from 85; RD Aldershot 88-93; Hon Can Guildf Cathl from 92. *The Rectory, 66 Church Avenue, Farnborough, Hants GU14 7AP* Farnborough (01252) 544754

BODDINGTON, Clive Frederick Malcolm. b 35. Qu Coll Cam BA59 MA63. Ridley Hall Cam 59. **d** 61 **p** 62. Kenya 67-94; rtd 95. *Coopers Bridge Farm, Bramshott, Liphook, Hants GU30 7RF* Liphook (01428) 722007

BODDINGTON, John Slater. b 17. Wells Th Coll 63. **d** 64 **p** 65. C Roxbourne St Andr *Lon* 68-71; V Acton St Martin 71-85; rtd 85; Perm to Offic *Ban* from 85; Perm to Offic *St As* from 85. *Lane End, Aber Place, Llandudno, Gwynedd LL30 3AR* Llandudno (01492) 547080

BODDY, Alan Richard. b 47. Ripon Coll Cuddesdon. **d** 84 **p** 85. C Eastcote St Lawr *Lon* 84-87; C Kensington St Mary Abbots w St Geo 87-90; Chapl HM Pris Brixton 90-91; Chapl HM Pris Send and Downview 91-92; Chapl HM Pris Highdown from 92. *HM Prison Highdown, Sutton Lane, Sutton, Surrey SM2 5PJ* 0181-643 0063

BODDY, David. b 57. SSF. Linc Th Coll CMinlStuds92. **d** 92 **p** 93. C Peterlee *Dur* 92-95; C Penshaw from 95; C Shiney Row from 95; C Herrington from 95. *St Oswald's Vicarage, Shiney Row, Houghton le Spring, Tyne & Wear DH4 4JV* 0191-385 7271

BODDY, Canon William Kenneth. b 16. TD63. St Jo Coll Dur BA39 DipTh40. Westcott Ho Cam 40. **d** 40 **p** 41. V Wylam *Newc* 65-82; RD Corbridge 71-82; Hon Can Newc Cathl 74-82; rtd 82. *21 Dukes Road, Hexham, Northd NE46 3AW* Hexham (01434) 602807

BODKIN, Thomas Patrick Joseph (Tom). b 45. Richmond Fellowship Coll DipHRel78 Open Univ BA77 BA90. St Hyacinth's Coll and RC Sem Mass 64 Franciscan Ho of Studies DipPhil67 DipTh70. **d** 80 **p** 80. In RC Ch 80-86; NSM Littlehampton and Wick *Chich* 91-93; Visiting Tutor Moral Th Chich Th Coll from 92; TV Aldrington from 93. *St Leonard's Vicarage, 18 Amesbury Crescent, Hove, E Sussex BN3 5RD* Brighton (01273) 328973   Fax as telephone

BODMIN, Archdeacon of. *See* WHITEMAN, Ven Rodney David Carter

BODY, Andrew. b 46. Pemb Coll Cam BA68 MA71. Ridley Hall Cam 68. **d** 70 **p** 71. C New Bury *Man* 70-73; TV Droylsden St Mary 73-78; V Low Harrogate St Mary *Ripon* 78-92; Trustee FLAME from 90; TR Redhorn *Sarum* from 92. *The Rectory, Urchfont, Devizes, Wilts SN10 4QP* Devizes (01380) 840672

BODY, Richard Sidney. b 25. CEng FIEE55 FIHospE72 BSc46 CertRS88. S'wark Ord Course 86. **d** 88 **p** 89. Hon C Chelsfield *Roch* from 88. *Beechwood, 96 Goddington Lane, Orpington, Kent BR6 9DY* Orpington (01689) 829990

BODYCOMBE, Stephen John. b 58. Lanchester Poly BA. St Mich Coll Llan DipTh83. **d** 83 **p** 84. C Cardiff St Jo *Llan* 83-86; V Dinas and Penygraig w Williamstown from 86. *The Vicarage, 1 Llanfair Road, Penygraig, Tonypandy, M Glam CF40 1TA* Tonypandy (01443) 422677

BOFF, Charles Roy. b 31. Pemb Coll Ox BA57 MA60. Clifton Th Coll 55. **d** 57 **p** 58. V Felbridge *S'wark* 68-79; V Steyning *Chich* 79-84; R Ashurst 79-84; RD Storrington 81-84; R Romaldkirk w Laithkirk *Ripon* 84-94; RD Richmond 90-93; rtd 94. *Laithkirk, Aikton, Wigton, Cumbria CA7 0HY* Wigton (016973) 45563

BOFFEY, Ian. b 40. Glas Univ MA63. Glas NSM Course 75. **d** 75 **p** 78. Hon C Dalry *Glas* 75-78; P-in-c from 78. *2 Kinloch Avenue, Stewarton, Kilmarnock, Ayrshire KA3 3HF* Stewarton (01560) 82586

BOGGIS, Miss Christine Louise. b 38. R Holloway Coll Lon BA60 Cam Univ CertEd61 Hull Univ BTh94. E Midl Min Tr Course DTPS94. **d** 94 **p** 95. NSM Scartho *Linc* from 94. *90 Waltham Road, Grimsby, S Humberside DN33 2NA* Grimsby (01472) 822108

BOGGUST, Mrs Patricia Anne. Portsm Dioc Tr Course. **d** 90. NSM Hook w Warsash *Portsm* 90-94; NSM Locks Heath from 94. *21 Beverley Close, Park Gate, Southampton SO3 6QU* Locks Heath (01489) 573586

BOGLE, James Main Lindam Linton. b 33. Peterho Cam BA56 MA60. Wells Th Coll 59. **d** 61 **p** 62. Chapl York Univ *York* 65-72; V Brayton 72-76; V Forest Hill St Aug *S'wark* 76-83; C Hatcham St Cath 83-85; NSM from 91; C Herne Hill St Paul 86-87; rtd 87. *8 Waller Road, London SE14 5LA* 0171-732 9420

BOHUN, Roger Alexander. b 32. Lon Univ BSc58. Cuddesdon Coll 65. **d** 68 **p** 69. C Rugby St Andr *Cov* 68-74; SSF from 74; Perm to Offic *Sarum* 74-76; Perm to Offic *Newc* 76-78; Tanzania 78-86; Zimbabwe 86-88. *The Friary, Hilfield, Dorchester, Dorset DT2 7BE* Cerne Abbas (01300) 341345

BOIT, Mervyn Hays. b 38. Univ of Wales (Lamp) BA59. St Mich Coll Llan 59. **d** 61 **p** 62. C Roath St German *Llan* 61-63; C Skewen 63-69; V Pontycymmer and Blaengarw from 69. *The Vicarage, St Davids Street, Pontycymmer, Bridgend, M Glam CF32 8LT* Bridgend (01656) 870280

BOLAND, Geoffrey. b 56. DipHE89. Oak Hill Th Coll 87. **d** 89 **p** 90. C Ormskirk *Liv* 89-94; C Woodside Park St Barn *Lon* from 94. *13 Chislehurst Avenue, London N12 0HU* 0181-346 0777

BOLD, Dr Peter Edward. b 64. Sheff Univ BEng86 PhD90. Cranmer Hall Dur BA94 DMS95. **d** 95. C Grenoside *Sheff* from 95. *49 Denistone Road, Grenoside, Sheffield S30 3QH* Sheffield (0114) 246 4436

BOLE, Malcolm Dennis. b 30. Oak Hill Th Coll 65. **d** 67 **p** 68. C Bridlington Priory *York* 67-70; Rwanda 71-73; P-in-c Combe Hay *B & W* 74-81; V Bath Odd Down 74-81; P-in-c Taunton St Jas 81-84; V 84-90; R Bicknoller w Crowcombe and Sampford Brett from 90. *The Rectory, 11 Trendle Lane, Bicknoller, Taunton, Somerset TA4 4EG* Stogumber (01984) 56262

BOLLARD, Canon Richard George. b 39. Fitzw Ho Cam BA61 MA65 K Coll Lon BD63 AKC63. **d** 64 **p** 65. C Southn Maybush St Pet *Win* 64-68; Chapl Aston Univ *Birm* 68-74; TR Chelmsley Wood 74-82; V Coleshill from 82; V Maxstoke from 82; RD Coleshill 82-92; Hon Can Birm Cathl from 85. *The Vicarage, High Street, Coleshill, Birmingham B46 3BP* Coleshill (01675) 462188

BOLLEN, Bryan Hayward. b 26. **d** 77 **p** 78. NSM Chippenham St Pet *Bris* 77-94; Perm to Offic from 94. *27 The Tinings, Chippenham, Wilts SN15 3LY* Chippenham (01249) 652515

BOLLEY, Michael Francis. b 55. St Cath Coll Ox BA76 MSc77. Ripon Coll Cuddesdon MA92. **d** 92 **p** 93. C Pinner *Lon* from 92. *16 Barrow Point Avenue, Pinner, Middx HA5 3HF* 0181-866 9006

BOLLOM, Canon David. b 23. Lambeth MA88 Wycliffe Hall Ox 72. **d** 74 **p** 75. C Norbiton *S'wark* 74-77; Dioc Sec 77-88; Hon Can S'wark Cathl 78-88; AP Upper Mole Valley Gp 88-90; rtd 91. *Karanga, North Street, South Petherton, Somerset TA13 5DA* South Petherton (01460) 42427

BOLSIN, Canon Cyril Edward. b 10. AKC41. **d** 41 **p** 42. R Colchester St Mich Myland *Chelmsf* 62-80; Hon Can Chelmsf Cathl 76-80; rtd 80. *130 Cranmere Court, Exeter Drive, Colchester CO1 2RX* Colchester (01206) 861989

BOLSTER, David Richard. b 50. BA. St Jo Coll Nottm. **d** 84 **p** 85. C Luton Lewsey St Hugh *St Alb* 84-87; V Woodside w E Hyde from 87. *The Vicarage, Church Road, Slip End, Luton LU1 4BJ* Luton (01582) 424363

BOLT, David Dingley. b 18. St Jo Coll Cam LLB58 LLM85. Westcott Ho Cam 66. **d** 68 **p** 69. Malawi 68-70; C Chesterton Gd Shep *Ely* 70-71; P-in-c Gt Wilbraham 71-74; V 74-86; P-in-c Lt Wilbraham 71-74; R 74-86; RD Quy 75-81; rtd 86; Perm to Offic *Ely* from 86. *24 Warwick Road, Cambridge CB4 3HN* Cambridge (01223) 66361

BOLT, George Henry. b 34. MInstP75 CPhys75 Lon Univ BSc60 Bath Univ MSc75. S Dios Minl Tr Scheme 85. **d** 88 **p** 89. NSM Oldbury *Sarum* 88-89; Chapl Chippenham Tech Coll 89-90; C Kington *Bris* 90-92; P-in-c Aldenham *St Alb* from 92. *The Vicarage, Aldenham, Watford WD2 8BE* Watford (01923) 855905

BOLT, Mrs Mary Veronica. b 36. S Dios Minl Tr Scheme 90. **d** 93 **p** 94. NSM Aldenham *St Alb* from 93; Sub-Chapl HM Pris The Mount from 93. *The Vicarage, Aldenham, Watford WD2 8BE* Watford (01923) 855905

BOLT, Philip John Mitchell. b 15. Bps' Coll Cheshunt 49. **d** 52 **p** 53. R Nunney *B & W* 65-74; P-in-c Wanstrow w Cloford 72-74; R Nunney w Wanstrow and Cloford 74-80; V Rotherham Ferham Park *Sheff* 80-84; rtd 84; Perm to Offic *B & W* from 85; C Stoke Lacy, Moreton Jeffries w Much Cowarne etc *Heref* 87-90. *192 Berrow Road, Burnham-on-Sea, Somerset TA8 2JF* Burnham-on-Sea (01278) 793094

BOLTON, Christopher Leonard. b 60. St Mich Coll Llan DipTh83. **d** 83 **p** 84. C Lamp St D 83-86; P-in-c Llanarth and Capel Cynon w Talgarreg etc 86-87; V from 87. *The Vicarage, Llanarth, Dyfed SA47 0NJ* Llanarth (01545) 580745

BOLTON, John. b 43. SS Paul & Mary Coll Cheltenham DipEd64. Trin Coll Bris 83. **d** 85 **p** 86. C Minehead *B & W* 85-89; R Winford w Felton Common Hill from 89. *The Rectory, 4 Parsonage Lane, Winford, Bristol BS18 8DG* Lulsgate (01275) 474636

BOLTON, Peter Richard Shawcross. b 58. Warw Univ BA79. Sarum & Wells Th Coll 80. **d** 83 **p** 84. C Beckenham St Jas *Roch* 83-86; C Bedf Leigh *Man* 86-88; V Royton St Paul 88-94; AD Tandle 93-94; NSM Salford St Paul w Ch Ch from 95. *1 Lamorna Close, Salford M7 3GT*

BOLTON, Richard David Edward. b 52. MA. St Steph Ho Ox 79. **d** 81 **p** 82. C Rawmarsh w Parkgate *Sheff* 81-84; Chapl Wellingborough Sch 85-92; Lic to Offic *Pet* 85-92; Chapl Merchant Taylors' Sch Northwood from 91. *19 Askew Road, Sandy Lodge, Northwood, Middx HA6 2JE* Northwood (01923) 821136 or 820644

BOLTON, Sidney Robert. b 15. Dur Univ LTh45. Edin Th Coll 42. **d** 44 **p** 45. V Bloxham and Milcombe *Ox* 59-81; V Bloxham w Milcombe and S Newington 81-84; rtd 84; Perm to Offic *Ox* from 84. *Finches, 1 Brookside, Hook Norton, Banbury, Oxon OX15 5NS* Hook Norton (01608) 737153

BOLTON, William. b 05. Tyndale Hall Bris 31. **d** 33 **p** 34. V Douglas St Ninian *S & M* 65-74; rtd 74; Perm to Offic *S & M* 74-91. *Carolyn Residential Home, Beefold Lane, Atherton, Manchester M29 0DF* Atherton (01942) 876585

BOLTON, Archdeacon of. *See* DAVIES, Ven Lorys Martin

BOLTON, Suffragan Bishop of. *See* BONSER, Rt Rev David

BOMFORD, Canon Rodney William George. b 43. BNC Ox BA64 DipTh66 MA68. Coll of Resurr Mirfield 67 Union Th Sem (NY) STM69. **d** 69 **p** 70. C Deptford St Paul *S'wark* 69-77; V Camberwell St Giles w St Matt from 77; RD Camberwell from 87; Hon Can S'wark Cathl from 93. *St Giles's Vicarage, Benhill Road, London SE5 8RB* 0171-703 4504

BOMYER, Julian Richard Nicholas Jeffrey. b 55. AKC78 Sarum & Wells Th Coll 78. **d** 79 **p** 80. C Rugby St Andr *Cov* 79-84; TV 85-88; P-in-c Clifton upon Dunsmore w Brownsover 84-85; Prec Ch Ch Ox 88-93; V Hampton Worc from 93; Chapl Evesham Coll from 93. *St Andrew's Vicarage, Pershore Road, Evesham, Worcs WR11 6PQ* Evesham (01386) 446381

BOND, Alan Richard. b 49. MBIM75 AFIMA75 MIIM79 Lon Univ BSc71 Imp Coll Lon ARCS71 Portsm Poly DMS74. S Dios Minl Tr Scheme 80. **d** 83 **p** 84. NSM Westbourne *Chich* 83-86. *14 Fraser Gardens, Southbourne, Emsworth, Hants PO10 8PY* Emsworth (01243) 378478

BOND, Arthur Edward Stephen. b 44. St Steph Ho Ox 66. **d** 69 **p** 69. S Africa 69-70; OGS 70-73; C Hendon St Alphage *Lon* 70-73; OSB 74-95; Asst Sec ACS 75-95; Hon C Sparkbrook St Agatha w Balsall Heath St Barn *Birm* 86-92; Hon C Washwood Heath 92-95. *58 rue Albert Vincon, Certe, 44570 Trignac, Loire Atlantique, France* France (33) 40 45 92 17 Fax 40 45 92 18

✝**BOND, Rt Rev Charles Derek.** b 27. AKC51. **d** 52 **p** 53 **c** 76. C Friern Barnet St Jas *Lon* 52-56; Lic to Offic *Birm* 56-58; Midl Sch Sec SCM 56-58; V Harringay St Paul *Lon* 58-62; V Harrow Weald All SS 62-72; P-in-c Pebmarsh *Chelmsf* 72-73; Adn Colchester 72-76; Suff Bp Bradwell 76-84; Area Bp Bradwell 84-92; rtd 92; Asst Bp Worc from 92. *Ambleside, 14 Worcester Road, Evesham, Worcs WR11 4JU* Evesham (01386) 446156

BOND, Charles Robert. b 25. Trin Coll Bris DipHE80. **d** 80 **p** 81. C Wythenshawe Wm Temple Ch *Man* 80-82; TV Cwmbran *Mon* 82-88; Chapl Corfu *Eur* 88-91; Chapl Playa de Las Americas Tenerife 91-93; rtd 93. *Urbanizacion Club Miraverde, Apartment 1, Edifico Iris, 38660 Playa de Las Americas, Tenerife, Canary Islands* Tenerife (22) 791082

BOND, Clifford Frank. b 24. St Aid Birkenhead 60. **d** 62 **p** 63. C Kirkham *Blackb* 62-64; C Wallingford St Mary w All Hallows and St Leon *Ox* 64-69; PM Reading St Barn CD 69-73; R Reading St Barn from 73. *St Barnabas' Rectory, 14 Elm Road, Reading RG6 5TS* Reading (01734) 871718

BOND, David. b 36. Oak Hill Th Coll 72. **d** 74 **p** 75. C Leyton St Mary w St Edw *Chelmsf* 74-78; C Slough *Ox* 78-80; V Selby St Jas *York* 80-93; P-in-c Wistow 89-93; RD Selby 89-93; P-in-c Northiam *Chich* 93-94; R from 94. *The Rectory, 17 Monks Way, Northiam, Rye, E Sussex TN31 6QQ* Northiam (01797) 253118

BOND, David Matthew. b 38. Leic Univ BA59 Nottm Univ MA85. Sarum Th Coll 59. **d** 61 **p** 62. C Leic St Anne *Leic* 61-64; Hon C Nor St Pet Mancroft *Nor* 64-67; E England Sec SCM from 64; Sen Lect Pet Regional Coll from 67; Hon C Stamford All SS w St Pet *Linc* 74-81; Hon C Stamford All SS w St Jo from 81; Perm to Offic *Pet* from 85. *2 The Courtyard, Cotterstock, Peterborough PE8 5HB* Cotterstock (018326) 255

BOND, David Warner. b 32. BSc. Cant Sch of Min. **d** 82 **p** 83. NSM Otham w Langley *Cant* from 82. *229 Willington Street, Maidstone, Kent ME15 8EW* Maidstone (01622) 761257

BOND, Douglas Gregory. b 39. Edin Th Coll 74. **d** 76 **p** 77. NSM Edin St Paul and St Geo *Edin* 76-83; P-in-c Abthorpe w Slapton *Pet* 83-84; P-in-c Silverstone and Abthorpe w Slapton 84; R 84-89; V Pet St Jude from 89. *St Jude's Vicarage, 49 Atherstone Avenue, Peterborough PE3 6TZ* Peterboro' (0733) 264169 or 268816

BOND, Gordon. b 44. Chich Th Coll 68. **d** 71 **p** 72. C Wisbech St Aug *Ely* 71-74; C Wembley Park St Aug *Lon* 74-77; C York Town St Mich *Guildf* 77-80; C Haywards Heath St Wilfrid *Chich* 80; TV 80-82; V Lower Beeding 82-86; V E Grinstead St Mary from 86. *The Vicarage, Windmill Lane, East Grinstead, W Sussex RH19 2DS* East Grinstead (01342) 323439

BOND, Canon John Albert. b 35. St Cath Soc Ox BA61 MA65 MPhil77 LRAM55 GGSM56. Wycliffe Hall Ox 58 Seabury-Western Th Sem BD62. **d** 62 **p** 63. C Chelmsf Cathl *Chelmsf* 62-63; Succ Chelmsf Cathl 63-64; Prec 64-66; Lect St Osyth Coll Clacton-on-Sea 66-69; Lic to Offic 66-69; Lect Ch Ch Coll Cant 69-73; Hon Min Can Cant Cathl *Cant* 70-85; Hon Can from 85; Sen Lect Ch Ch Coll Cant 73-85; Prin Lect and Hd Relig Studies from 85. *St Lawrence Priory, 136 Old Dover Road, Canterbury, Kent CT1 3NX* Canterbury (01227) 765575

BOND, John Frederick Augustus. b 45. Open Univ BA75. CITC 64. **d** 67 **p** 69. C Lisburn St Paul *Conn* 67-70; C Finaghy 70-77; I Ballynure and Ballyeaston from 77. *The Rectory, 11 Church Road, Ballynure, Ballyclare, Co Antrim BT39 9UF* Ballyclare (01960) 322350

BOND, Miss Kim Mary. b 58. SRN79. Trin Coll Bris BA87. **d** 87 **p** 94. Par Dn Cullompton *Ex* 87-91; Asst Chapl N Staffs R Infirmary Stoke-on-Trent 91-95. *6 Quarry Cottages, Nantwich Road, Audley, Stoke-on-Trent ST7 8DW* Stoke-on-Trent (01782) 722961

BOND, Lawrence (Laurie). b 53. ACIB77. Sarum & Wells Th Coll CMinlStuds92. **d** 92 **p** 93. C Saffron Walden w Wendens Ambo and Littlebury *Chelmsf* from 92. *17 Saxon Way, Saffron Walden, Essex CB11 4EQ* Saffron Walden (01799) 524808

BOND, Mark Francis Wilson. b 53. Sarum & Wells Th Coll 89. **d** 91 **p** 92. C Taunton Lyngford *B & W* 91-95; V Highbridge from 95. *The Vicarage, 81A Church Street, Highbridge, Somerset TA9 3HS* Burnham-on-Sea (01278) 783671

BOND, Norman. b 23. Wycliffe Hall Ox. **d** 70 **p** 71. C Warrington St Ann *Liv* 70-73; P-in-c 73-77; P-in-c Warrington St Pet 73-77; V Wigan St Cath 77-88; rtd 88. *Bridge House, Old Hutton, Kendal, Cumbria LA8 0NH* Kendal (01539) 722293

BOND, Paul Maxwell. b 36. TD73. ACIB56. Oak Hill Th Coll 76. **d** 79 **p** 80. Hon C Wisley w Pyrford *Guildf* 79-91; Deputation Appeals Org Children's Soc 88-91; C Egham *Guildf* 91-93; V Rockfield and St Maughen's w Llangattock etc *Mon* from 94. *The Vicarage, Rockfield, Monmouth, Gwent NP5 3QB* Monmouth (01600) 712003

BOND, Richard Jack. b 16. Lich Th Coll 38. **d** 41 **p** 42. V Balkwell *Newc* 68-78; R Allendale 78-79; R Allendale w Whitfield 79-83; rtd 83. *82 Brantwood Avenue, Whitley Bay, Tyne & Wear NE25 8NL* 0191-252 9798

BOND, Ven Thomas James. b 18. TCD BA41 MA68. CITC 41. **d** 42 **p** 43. I Bailieborough *K, E & A* 55-60; I Templemichael w Clongish, Clooncumber etc 60-91; Preb Elphin Cathl 77-91; Adn Elphin and Ardagh 78-91; rtd 91. *Halstow, Drumelis, Cavan, Co Cavan, Irish Republic* Cavan (49) 61812

BOND-THOMAS, David Harradence. b 23. Ch Coll Cam BA44 MA51. **d** 59 **p** 60. C Earley St Pet *Ox* 62-71; P-in-c Middleton Stoney 71-77; P-in-c Bucknell 71-76; P-in-c Weston on the Green 72-76; P-in-c Chesterton w Wendlebury 76-77; V Chesterton w Middleton Stoney and Wendlebury 77-89; rtd 89. *35 Greet Road, Winchcombe, Cheltenham, Glos GL54 5JT* Cheltenham (01242) 603150

✠**BONE, Rt Rev John Frank Ewan.** b 30. St Pet Coll Ox BA54 MA59 Whitelands Coll Lon PGCE71. Ely Th Coll 54. **d** 56 **p** 57 **c** 89. C Pimlico St Gabr *Lon* 56-60; C Henley *Ox* 60-63; V Datchet 63-76; RD Burnham 74-77; R Upton cum Chalvey 76-78; Adn Buckm 77-89; Area Bp Reading from 89. *Greenbanks, 25 Old Bath Road, Sonning, Reading RG4 0SY* Reading (01734) 692187 Fax 448482

BONE, Michael Thomas. b 33. ACMA62 Open Univ BA82. Brechin NSM Ord Course 79. **d** 83 **p** 84. Chapl Dundee Inst of Tech 83-93; Hon C Broughty Ferry *Bre* 83-84; Hon C Arbroath 84-87; Hon C Auchmithie 84-87; Hon C Dundee St Mary Magd from 87. *5 Roxburgh Terrace, Dundee DD2 1NZ* Dundee (01382) 66897

BONE, Noel Francis. b 18. TD64. Clifton Th Coll. **d** 59 **p** 60. Lic to Offic *Lon* 69-71; V Boxmoor St Jo *St Alb* 71-72; V Aston w Benington 72-83; C St Giles-in-the-Fields *Lon* 83; rtd 83; Perm to Offic *St Alb* 84-94; Perm to Offic *Nor* 87-95. *24 Livingstone Court, Christchurch Lane, Barnet, Herts EN5 4PL* 0181-441 6744

BONE, Canon Trevor Hubert. b 25. Ch Ch Ox BA49 MA50. Qu Coll Birm. **d** 51 **p** 52. V Barnsley St Edw *Wakef* 69-85; Hon Can Wakef Cathl 82-85; rtd 85; Perm to Offic *Wakef* 85-94. *The College of St Barnabas, Blackberry Lane, Lingfield, Surrey RH7 6NJ* Dormans Park (01342) 870185

BONHAM, Frederick Thomas (Fred). b 37. St Deiniol's Hawarden 70. **d** 72 **p** 73. C Northwood Hills St Edm *Lon* 72-75; C Clewer St Andr *Ox* 75-90; V Reading H Trin 90-93; TV Newbury from 93. *Saint Mary's Vicarage, 14 Strawberry Hill, Newbury, Berks RG13 1XJ* Newbury (01635) 40889

BONHAM-CARTER, Gerard Edmund David. b 31. Lon Univ BSc53 DCAe55. S'wark Ord Course. **d** 87 **p** 88. NSM Wandsworth St Paul *S'wark* from 87; Perm to Offic *St E* from 87; Chapl R Hosp and Home Putney from 92. *85 Victoria Drive, London SW19 6HW* 0181-788 1230

BONIFACE, Lionel Ernest George. b 36. Lon Coll of Div ALCD63 BD64. **d** 64 **p** 65. C Attenborough w Chilwell *S'well* 64-69; C Farndon 69-71; C Thorpe 69-71; P-in-c Mansf St Aug 71-77; V Oughtibridge *Sheff* 77-92; Ind Chapl 79-81; P-in-c Treeton 92-93; TV Brinsworth w Catcliffe and Treeton from 93. *The Rectory, Church Lane, Treeton, Rotherham, S Yorkshire S60 5QZ* Sheffield (0114) 269 6542

BONIWELL, Timothy Richard. b 51. AKC73. St Aug Coll Cant 74. **d** 75 **p** 76. C Walthamstow St Mich *Chelmsf* 75-78; C Wigmore Abbey *Heref* 78-83; C Studley *Sarum* 83-86; Chapl Trowbridge Coll 83-86; V Bath St Barn w Englishcombe *B & W* from 86. *The Vicarage, Mount View, Bath BA2 1JX* Bath (01225) 421838

BONNER, David Robert. b 28. ASCA66 FCIS72 FCIB74 Lon Univ DipRS78. S'wark Ord Course 74. **d** 77 **p** 78. NSM Hampton All SS *Lon* 77-84; P-in-c Twickenham All SS 84-91; rtd 91. *17 St James's Road, Hampton Hill, Hampton, Middx TW12 1DH* 0181-979 1565

BONNER, Frederick Charles. b 10. Worc Ord Coll 63. **d** 65 **p** 66. R W Ilsley w Farnborough *Ox* 69-75; P-in-c E Ilsley 70-74; rtd 75. *4 Ham View, Upton-upon-Severn, Worcester WR8 0QE* Upton-upon-Severn (01684) 592087

BONNER, James Maxwell Campbell. Sydney Univ BSc48 DipEd49 Lon Univ BD59. Oak Hill Th Coll. **d** 60 **p** 61. C Morden S'wark 63-65; Australia from 65; rtd 94. *13 Waratah Street, Croydon Park, NSW, Australia 2133* Sydney (2) 744-9832

BONNET, Tom. b 51. Univ of Wales (Ban) DipTh89 Univ of Wales (Cardiff) BTh90. St Mich Coll Llan 90. **d** 90 **p** 91. C Criccieth w Treflys *Ban* 90-91; C Denio w Aber-erch 91-93; R Llanfachraeth 93-94; P-in-c Valley w Llanfachraeth 94; R from 94. *The Rectory, London Road, Valley, Holyhead, Gwynedd LL65 3DP* Valley (01407) 741242

BONNEY, Mark Philip John. b 57. St Cath Coll Cam BA78 MA82. St Steph Ho Ox BA84 MA89. **d** 85 **p** 86. C Stockton St Pet *Dur* 85-88; Chapl St Alb Abbey *St Alb* 88-90; Prec 90-92; V Eaton Bray w Edlesborough from 92. *The Vicarage, Eaton Bray, Dunstable, Beds LU6 2DN* Eaton Bray (01525) 220261

BONNEY, Stuart Campbell. b 51. Edin Univ BD83. Edin Th Coll 81. **d** 83 **p** 84. C Edin St Luke *Edin* 83-86; C Edin St Martin 83-86; P-in-c Auchterarder *St And* 86-90; P-in-c Muthill 86-90; Dep Chapl HM Pris Leeds 90-91; Chapl HM Pris Moorland from 91. *HM Prison Moorland, Bowtry Road, Hatfield Woodhouse, Doncaster, S Yorkshire DN7 6EE* Doncaster (01302) 351500

BONNEYWELL, Miss Christine Mary. b 57. Univ of Wales (Lamp) BA78 LTh80. Sarum & Wells Th Coll 80. **d** 81 **p** 94. C Swansea St Pet *S & B* 81-84; C Llangyfelach 84-86; Chapl Univ of Wales (Lamp) *St D* 86-90; Educn Officer Wells Cathl *B & W* from 90. *14 Vicar's Close, Wells, Somerset BA5 2UJ* Wells (01749) 674483

BONSALL, Charles Henry Brash. b 42. Ex Univ BA66. Ridley Hall Cam 66. **d** 68 **p** 69. C Cheltenham St Mary *Glouc* 68-72; Sudan 72-77 and 79-83; Perm to Offic *Nor* 78; Development and Miss Sec Intercon Ch Soc 83-93; Perm to Offic *Birm* from 91; rtd 93. *3 Pakenham Road, Birmingham B15 2NE* 0121-440 6143

✠**BONSER, Rt Rev David.** b 34. Man Univ MA75 AKC61. **d** 62 **p** 63 **c** 91. C Heckmondwike *Wakef* 62-65; C Sheff St Geo *Sheff* 65-68; R Chorlton-cum-Hardy St Clem *Man* 68-82; Bp's Ecum Adv 73-81; Hon Can Man Cathl 81-82; AD Hulme 81-82; Adn Rochdale 82-91; TR Rochdale 82-91; Suff Bp Bolton from 91. *4 Sandfield Drive, Lostock, Bolton BL6 4DU* Bolton (01204) 843400 Fax 849652

BONSEY, Hugh Richmond Lowry. b 49. Sarum & Wells Th Coll 74. **d** 76 **p** 77. C Bris St Mary Redcliffe w Temple etc *Bris* 76-80; TV Sutton *Liv* 80-88; P-in-c Yatton Keynell *Bris* 88-89; P-in-c Biddestone w Slaughterford 88-89; P-in-c Castle Combe 88-89; P-in-c W Kington 88-89; P-in-c Nettleton w Littleton

Drew 88-89; C Westbury-on-Trym H Trin 89-90; V Peasedown St John w Wellow *B & W* from 90. *The Vicarage, 18 Church Road, Peasedown St John, Bath BA2 8AA* Mendip (01761) 432293

BONSEY, Thory Richmond. b 18. St Chad's Coll Dur 37. Cuddesdon Coll 46. **d** 47 **p** 48. R Ecton *Pet* 67-73; V Ketton 73-77; Australia from 77; rtd 83. *21/167 La Perouse Street, Red Hill, ACT, Australia 2603* Canberra (6) 295-2316

BOOCOCK, John Walter. b 31. Wells Th Coll 63. **d** 65 **p** 66. C Guisborough *York* 65-67; C Bottesford *Linc* 67-73; TV Bottesford w Ashby 73-74; V Riddlesden *Bradf* 74-83; V Darlington H Trin *Dur* 83-91; P-in-c Denton and Ingleton from 91; Dioc Par Development Officer 91-95. *The Vicarage, Ingleton, Darlington, Co Durham DL2 3HS* Darlington (01325) 730928

BOOKER, Gerald Dennis. b 30. St Pet Coll Ox BA52 MA56. Ridley Hall Cam 53 Oak Hill Th Coll 80. **d** 81 **p** 82. Hon C Hertf All SS *St Alb* 81-83; R Bramfield w Stapleford and Waterford from 83; Chapl Herts Univ from 90. *St Mary's Rectory, Stapleford, Hertford SG14 3NB* Hertford (01992) 581169

BOOKER, James Howard (Jim). b 57. CD (US Air)83. Edin Th Coll 88. **d** 90 **p** 91. C Peterhead *Ab* 90-92; C Old Deer 90-92; C Longside 90-92; C Strichen 90-92; Bp's Chapl Peterhead 92-93; Miss to Seamen from 92; R Peterhead *Ab* from 93. *19 York Street, Peterhead, Aberdeenshire AB42 6SN* Peterhead (01779) 472217 or 478626

BOOKER, Mrs Margaret Katharine. b 20. MCSP42. Westcott Ho Cam 82. **dss** 83 **d** 87 **p** 94. Stansted Mountfitchet *Chelmsf* 83-95; Par Dn 87-90; NSM 90-95; rtd 90; Perm to Offic *Ely* from 95. *49 Home Farm Road, Houghton, Huntingdon, Cambs PE17 2BN* Huntingdon (01480) 469167

BOOKER, Michael Charles. b 36. LLCM57 ARCO58. Lon Coll of Div LTh63. **d** 63 **p** 64. C Royston *St Alb* 63-66; C Mildenhall *St E* 66-68; Min Can St E Cathl 68-83; Prec St E Cathl 70-83; Chapl Framlingham Coll Suffolk from 84. *29 The Mowbrays, Framlingham, Woodbridge, Suffolk IP13 9DL* Framlingham (01728) 723122

BOOKER, Michael Paul Montague. b 57. Jes Coll Ox BA79 Bris Univ CertEd80. Trin Coll Bris 84. **d** 87 **p** 88. C Cant St Mary Bredin *Cant* 87-91; V Leamington Priors St Mary *Cov* from 91. *The Vicarage, 28 St Mary's Road, Leamington Spa, Warks CV31 1JP* Leamington Spa (01926) 425927

BOOKLESS, Andrew Pitcairn. b 63. Sheff Univ BA85. St Jo Coll Nottm DipMM92. **d** 92 **p** 93. C Llantrisant *Llan* from 92. *17 Parkdale View, Llantrisant, Pontyclun, M Glam CF7 8DT* Llantrisant (01443) 225704

BOOKLESS, David John Charles. b 62. Jes Coll Cam MA83 PGCE. Trin Coll Bris DipHE90 MA91. **d** 91 **p** 92. C Southall Green St Jo *Lon* from 91. *St George's Vicarage, 1 Lancaster Road, Southall, Middx UB1 1NP* 0181-574 1876

BOOKLESS, John Guy. b 19. Clare Coll Cam BA40 MA46 Serampore Univ MTh72. Ridley Hall Cam 47. **d** 49 **p** 50. India 53-72; C St Alb St Mich *St Alb* 73-76; C Harlow New Town w Lt Parndon *Chelmsf* 76-78; TV 78-79; P-in-c Widmerpool *S'well* 79-85; V Willoughby-on-the-Wolds w Wysall 79-85; V Willoughby-on-the-Wolds w Wysall and Widmerpool 85; rtd 85; Perm to Offic *S'well* from 85; Perm to Offic *Leic* from 85. *84 Kirkstone Drive, Loughborough, Leics LE11 3RW* Loughborough (01509) 263650

BOOKLESS, Mrs Rosemary. b 26. Westf Coll Lon BA47 DipEd49 Serampore Univ BD72. St Mich Ho Ox 56. **dss** 80 **d** 91 **p** 94. Willoughby-on-the-Wolds w Wysall and Widmerpool *S'well* 80-85; rtd 85; Perm to Offic *Leic* 85-89; Loughb Em 89-91; NSM from 91. *84 Kirkstone Drive, Loughborough, Leics LE11 3RW* Loughborough (01509) 263650

BOON, Nigel Francis. b 39. St Jo Coll Nottm. **d** 83 **p** 84. C St Helens St Helen *Liv* 83-86; V Kirkdale St Lawr 86-92; V Huyton Quarry from 92. *St Gabriel's Vicarage, 2 St Agnes Road, Huyton, Liverpool L36 5TA* 0151-489 2688

BOON, William John. b 54. Glouc Sch of Min 84. **d** 88 **p** 89. Hon C Matson *Glouc* 88-91; NSM St Witcombe 91; C from 91; C Brockworth from 91. *54 Abbotswood Road, Gloucester GL3 4NJ* Gloucester (01452) 862075

BOOTES, Michael Charles Edward. b 35. ACP70. Sarum Th Coll 58. **d** 61 **p** 62. C Winchmore Hill St Paul *Lon* 61-64; Switzerland 64-67; C St Marylebone All SS *Lon* 67-68; OGS from 68; Chapl Kingsley St Mich Sch W Sussex 69-75; V Brandon *Dur* 75-78; Chapl Shoreham Gr Sch 78-79; C Clayton w Keymer *Chich* 80-84; TV Ovingdean w Rottingdean and Woodingdean 84-85; TR Ovingdean 85-88; V Lundwood *Wakef* 88-92; C Pontefract St Giles from 92. *17 Hartley Park View, Pontefract, W Yorkshire WF8 4AP* Pontefract (01977) 600857 Fax as telephone

BOOTH, Charles Robert. b 48. Leeds Univ CertEd75. N Ord Course 79. **d** 82 **p** 83. C Eccleshill *Bradf* 82-84; C Jersey St Brelade *Win* 84-88; Australia 88-90; V Blurton *Lich* 90-93. *The*

Vicarage, School Lane, Stoke-on-Trent ST3 3DU Stoke-on-Trent (01782) 312163

BOOTH, David. b 44. Coll of Resurr Mirfield 72. **d** 74 **p** 75. C Osmondthorpe St Phil *Ripon* 74-77; C St Bart Armley w St Mary New Wortley 77-79; V Leeds St Wilfrid from 79. *St Wilfrid's Vicarage, Chatsworth Road, Leeds LS8 3RS* Leeds (0113) 249 7724

BOOTH, Derek. b 36. LTCL ALCM AKC61. **d** 62 **p** 63. C Woodchurch *Ches* 62-65; C Penrith St Andr *Carl* 65-67; C Tranmere St Paul *Ches* 67-70; C Wilmslow 70-72; V Micklehurst from 73. *All Saints' Vicarage, Mossley, Ashton-under-Lyne, Lancs OL5 9HY* Mossley (01457) 832393

BOOTH, Eric James. b 43. Open Univ BA84. N Ord Course 86. **d** 89 **p** 90. NSM Nelson St Phil *Blackb* 89-93; NSM Fence and Newchurch-in-Pendle from 93. *5 Round Hill Place, Park Road, Cliviger, Burnley BB10 4UA* Burnley (01282) 450708

BOOTH, Ewart Charles. b 67. LTCL85 K Coll Lon LLB88. Sarum & Wells Th Coll BTh93. **d** 93 **p** 95. NSM Tadley St Pet *Win* 93-95; C Highcliffe w Hinton Admiral from 95. *14 Lakewood Road, Christchurch, Dorset BH23 5NX* Highcliffe (01425) 273456

BOOTH, George Kenneth. b 12. Pemb Coll Ox BA37 MA40. Wells Th Coll 37. **d** 39 **p** 50. Lic to Offic *Ex* 59-78; Chapl St Luke's Coll Ex 59-78; rtd 78. *Furcroft, Rock, Wadebridge, Cornwall PL27 6LD* Bodmin (01208) 2476

BOOTH, Graham Richard. b 55. Birm Univ BSocSc75. St Jo Coll Nottm 89. **d** 91 **p** 92. C Woodthorpe *S'well* from 91. *22 Barden Road, Nottingham NG3 5QD* Nottingham (0115) 926 4731

BOOTH, Ian George. b 64. Chich Th Coll 85 Linc Th Coll 87. **d** 88 **p** 89. C Pet St Mary *Pet* 88-90; C Hawley H Trin *Guildf* 90-94; V Willesden St Mary *Lon* from 94. *Willesden Vicarage, 18 Neasden Lane, London NW10 2TT* 0181-459 2167

BOOTH, James Roger. b 46. Keble Coll Ox BA71 MA74 BTh77. Wycliffe Hall Ox 75. **d** 78 **p** 79. C Bridlington Priory *York* 78-83; V Nafferton w Wansford from 83. *The Vicarage, Nafferton, Driffield, N Humberside YO25 0JS* Driffield (01377) 44372

BOOTH, Jon Alfred. b 42. Nottm Univ BA64 Lon Univ MPhil72. Coll of Resurr Mirfield 78. **d** 80 **p** 81. C Elland *Wakef* 80-84; C Royston from 84. *The Vicarage, Church Street, Royston, Barnsley, S Yorkshire S71 4QZ* Barnsley (01226) 722410

BOOTH (nee YOUNG), Mrs Katharine Jane (Katie). b 65. Westmr Coll Ox BA87. Sarum & Wells Th Coll 89. **d** 91 **p** 94. Par Dn Basingstoke *Win* 91-94; C 94-95; Chapl Southn Inst of HE from 95. *1 The Glebe, St Michael's, Church Square, Basingstoke, Hants RG21 1QW* Basingstoke (01256) 466694

BOOTH, Leonard William. b 46. K Coll Lon BD70 AKC70. **d** 71 **p** 72. C Cockerton *Dur* 72-75; C Hove St Barn *Chich* 75-77; TV Brighton Resurr 77-78; C E Grinstead St Mary 78-81; USA from 81. *254 St Joseph Avenue, Long Beach, California 90803, USA* Long Beach (213) 433-6531

BOOTH, Michael Kevin. b 47. Louvain Univ Belgium BA. St Jo Coll Nottm 88 Oscott Coll (RC) 65. **d** 71 **p** 72. In RC Ch 71-87; C N Reddish *Man* 88-89; R Heaton Norris Ch w All SS from 89. *6 Glenfield Road, Stockport, Cheshire SK4 2QP* 0161-432 6838

BOOTH, Paul Harris. b 49. St Jo Coll Nottm LTh79. **d** 79 **p** 80. C Thorpe Edge *Bradf* 79-82; P-in-c Frizinghall 82-83; TV Shipley St Paul and Frizinghall from 83. *St Margaret's Vicarage, 213 Bradford Road, Frizinghall, Shipley, W Yorkshire BD18 3AA* Bradford (01274) 581470

BOOTH, Wallace. b 14. **d** 62 **p** 63. V Woodnesborough *Cant* 66-79; P-in-c Staple 77-79; rtd 79; Perm to Offic *Chich* from 87. *3 St Augustine's Close, Bexhill-on-Sea, E Sussex TN39 3AZ* Bexhill-on-Sea (01424) 214524

BOOTH, William James. b 39. TCD BA60 MA75. **d** 62 **p** 63. C Belf St Luke *Conn* 62-64; Chapl Cranleigh Sch Surrey 65-74; Chapl Westmr Sch 74-91; Lic to Offic *Lon* 74-93; P in O 76-93; PV Westmr Abbey 87-93; Sub Dean HM Chpls Royal and Dep Clerk of the Closet from 91; Sub Almoner and Dom Chapl to The Queen from 91. *Marlborough Gate, St James's Palace, London SW1A 1BG* 0171-930 6609

✠**BOOTH-CLIBBORN, Rt Rev Stanley Eric Francis.** b 24. Or Coll Ox BA51 MA56. Westcott Ho Cam 50. **d** 52 **p** 53 **c** 79. C Heeley *Sheff* 52-54; C Attercliffe w Carbrook 54-56; Kenya 56-67; P-in-c Linc St Mary-le-Wigford w St Martin *Linc* 67-70; P-in-c Linc St Mark 67-70; V Cam St St Mary w St Mich *Ely* 70-79; Hon Can Ely Cathl 76-79; Bp Man 79-92; rtd 92. *9 Kirkhill Drive, Edinburgh EH16 5DN* 0131-662 0443

BOOTHBY, Frank. b 29. St D Coll Lamp 56. **d** 58 **p** 59. C N Meols *Liv* 61-64; Miss to Seamen 64; rtd 94. *7 Belsfield Drive, Hesketh Bank, Preston PR4 6YB*

BOOTHMAN, Ms Olive. b 31. TCD BA. **d** 94 **p** 95. NSM Clondalkin w Rathcoole *D & G* from 94. *Miley Hall, Blessington, Co Wicklow, Irish Republic* Wicklow (45) 865119

BOOTHMAN, Canon Samuel. b 09. TCD BA34 Div Test35 MA37. **d** 35 **p** 35. R Farley Chamberlayne w Braishfield *Win* 46-81; RD Romsey 71-79; Hon Can Win Cathl 73-81; R Michelmersh, Timsbury, Farley Chamberlayne etc 81; rtd 81; Perm to Offic *Win* from 81. *Boldbrook Lodge, Pound Lane, Ampfield, Romsey, Hants SO51 9BP* Braishfield (01794) 68143

BOOTS, Claude Donald Roy. b 26. Roch Th Coll 67. **d** 69 **p** 70. C Midsomer Norton *B & W* 69-73; V Westf 73-80; P-in-c Hambridge w Earnshill and Isle Brewers 80; R Ilton w Hambridge, Earnshill, Isle Brewers etc 80-91; rtd 91. *41 Furlong Close, Midsomer Norton, Bath BA3 2PR* Midsomer Norton (01761) 419263

BOOTY, John Robert. b 04. AKC31. **d** 31 **p** 32. V Colney St Pet *St Alb* 49-79; rtd 79. *18 Larch Avenue, Bricket Wood, St Albans, Herts AL2 3SN* Garston (01923) 661602

BOREHAM, Harold Leslie (Harry). b 37. S'wark Ord Course. **d** 72 **p** 73. C Whitton and Thurleston w Akenham *St E* 72-77; R Saxmundham 77-85; V Felixstowe SS Pet and Paul from 85; Chapl Felixstowe Hosp from 85; Chapl Bartlet Hosp Felixstowe from 91. *The Vicarage, 14 Picketts Road, Felixstowe, Suffolk IP11 7JT* Felixstowe (01394) 284135

BORRETT, Ven Charles Walter. b 16. Em Coll Cam BA39 MA43. Ridley Hall Cam 39. **d** 41 **p** 43. V Tettenhall Regis *Lich* 49-70; RD Trysull 58-70; Preb Lich Cathl 64-71; Hon Can 71-82; Adn Stoke 70-82; P-in-c Sandon 76-82; Chapl to The Queen 80-86; rtd 82; Perm to Offic *St E* from 82. *34 Queensway, Mildenhall, Bury St Edmunds, Suffolk IP28 7JL* Mildenhall (01638) 712718

BORRILL, John. b 19. Lon Univ BD41 AKC41. Westcott Ho Cam 41. **d** 42 **p** 43. V St Pancras w St Jas and Ch Ch *Lon* 59-71; V Hendon St Mary 71-82; Chapl Puerto de la Cruz Tenerife *Eur* 82-84; rtd 84; Hon C Tenerife *Eur* 84-87. *Loganberry Cottage, Strand Hill, Winchelsea, E Sussex TN36 4JT* Rye (01797) 226489

BORROWDALE, Geoffrey Nigel. b 61. Southn Univ BSc83. Chich Th Coll 87. **d** 90. C Tilehurst St Mich *Ox* 90-91; Perm to Offic *Chich* from 93. *Ruskins, 2 High Street, Chichester, W Sussex PO20 6DD* Chichester (01243) 789269

BORSEBY, Alan. b 38. Linc Th Coll 71. **d** 73 **p** 73. C Bardsley *Man* 73-75; C Elton All SS 75-78; V Bury St Paul from 78. *St Paul's Vicarage, Parsonage Street, Bury, Lancs BL9 6BG* 0161-761 6991

BORTHWICK, Alexander Heywood (Sandy). b 36. MBPsS90 Open Univ BA80 Surrey Univ MSc89. Lich Th Coll 57. **d** 60 **p** 61. C Glas Ch Ch *Glas* 60-62; C Lanador *S & B* 62-64; C Swansea St Thos and Kilvey 64-65; Br Guiana 65-66; Guyana 66-70; C Oystermouth *S & B* 70-71; Lic to Offic *Man* 71-76; Area Sec (Dios Man and Liv) USPG 71-76; Area Sec (Dios Blackb and S & M) 73-76; Sch and Children's Work Sec 76-83; Chapl Tooting Bec Hosp Lon 83-91; Chapl Charing Cross Hosp Lon from 92. *The Chaplain's Office, Charing Cross Hospital, Fulham Palace Road, London W6 8RF* 0181-846 1040 or 846 1234

BOSHER, Philip Ross. b 61. Sarum & Wells Th Coll 84. **d** 87 **p** 88. C Warminster St Denys *Sarum* 87-90; P-in-c Farley w Pitton and W Dean w E Grimstead 90-91; TV Alderbury Team from 91. *The Rectory, West Dean, Salisbury SP5 1JL* Lockerley (01794) 340271

BOSSOM, Peter Emery. b 28. St D Dioc Tr Course. **d** 82 **p** 83. NSM Llandysilio w Egremont and Llanglydwen etc *St D* 82-86; rtd 86; Lic to Offic *St D* 86-90. *Glyn-y-Fran, Crymych, Dyfed SA41 3SN* Crymych (01239) 831347

BOSTOCK, Canon Geoffrey Kentigern. b 30. OGS. Sarum Th Coll 66. **d** 68 **p** 69. SSF 50-60; C Shrewsbury St Chad *Lich* 68-72; C Hanley w Hope 72-74; P-in-c Wednesbury St Jo 74-79; V Dudley Holly Hall St Aug *Worc* 79-80; V Sheff Parson Cross St Cecilia *Sheff* 80-92; V Bilham from 92. *Bilham Vicarage, Churchfield Road, Clayton, Doncaster, S Yorkshire DN5 7DH* Pontefract (01977) 643756

BOSTOCK, Peter Anthony. b 64. Nottm Univ BA85 Fitzw Coll Cam BA89. Westcott Ho Cam 87. **d** 90 **p** 91. C Brighton St Matthias *Chich* 90-94; C Leytonstone St Marg w St Columba *Chelmsf* from 94. *The Presbytery, 16 Terling Close, London E11 3NP* 0181-519 9252

BOSTOCK, Canon Peter Geoffrey. b 11. Qu Coll Ox BA33 MA37. Wycliffe Hall Ox 33. **d** 35 **p** 37. Asst Sec Miss and Ecum Coun of Ch Assembly 67-70; Dep Sec Bd Miss and Unity Gen Syn 71-73; Clergy Appts Adv 74-76; rtd 77; Perm to Offic *Ox* from 77. *6 Moreton Road, Oxford OX2 7AX* Oxford (01865) 515460

BOSTON, Jonathan Bertram. b 40. Ely Th Coll 61. **d** 64 **p** 65. C Eaton *Nor* 64-70; Sen Chapl ACF Norfolk from 70; V Horsham St Faith w Newton St Faith 70-90; V Horsford 71-90; V Horsford and Horsham w Newton St Faith from 90. *The Vicarage, Horsford, Norwich NR10 3DB* Norwich (01603) 898246

BOSWELL, Colin John Luke. b 47. Sarum & Wells Th Coll 72. **d** 74 **p** 75. C Upper Tooting H Trin *S'wark* 74-78; C Sydenham St Phil 78-79; C St Helier 80-83; P-in-c Caterham 83-95; P-in-c Chaldon 85-95; RD Caterham 85-95; V Croydon St Jo from 95. *Croydon Vicarage, 22 Bramley Hill, Croydon CR2 6LT* 0181-688 1387

BOTHAM, Cecil Norman. b 29. MRTS84 Nottm Univ MPhil80 Lon Univ CertEd55 DBRS66. S'wark Ord Course 63. **d** 66 **p** 67. Sen Lect Shoreditch Coll Egham 65-74; C Bagshot *Guildf* 69-73; C-in-c Bath H Trin *B & W* 74; Asst Dir RE 74; Sen Lect Doncaster Inst of HE 74-82; Public Preacher *S'well* 75; Perm to Offic *Sheff* 75; Hon AP Bawtry w Austerfield and Misson 75-85; Offg Chapl RAF 85-94; rtd 94. *Rufford, Mattersey Road, Ranskill, Retford, Notts DN22 8NF* Retford (01777) 818234

BOTT, Dr Theodore Reginald. b 27. CEng58 FIChemE68 Birm Univ BSc52 PhD68 DSc84. W Midl Minl Tr Course 85. **d** 86 **p** 87. NSM Harborne St Faith and St Laur *Birm* from 86. *17 Springavon Croft, Harborne, Birmingham B17 9BJ* 0121-427 4209

BOTTERILL, David Darrell. b 45. Open Univ BA. Sarum & Wells Th Coll 82. **d** 83 **p** 84. C Blandford Forum and Langton Long etc *Sarum* 83-86; TV Shaston from 86; Chapl HM Young Offender Inst Guys Marsh 89-91. *St James's Vicarage, 34 Tanyard Lane, Shaftesbury, Dorset SP7 8HW* Shaftesbury (01747) 852193

BOTTING, Canon Michael Hugh. b 25. K Coll Lon BSc51 AKC K Coll Lon PGCE52. Ridley Hall Cam 54. **d** 56 **p** 57. V Fulham St Matt *Lon* 61-72; V Leeds St Geo *Ripon* 72-84; RD Headingley 81-84; Hon Can Ripon Cathl 82-84; R Aldford and Bruera *Ches* 84-90; rtd 90; Jt Dir Lay Tr *Ches* from 90. *25 Woodfield Grove, Hoole, Chester CH2 3NY* Chester (01244) 321133

BOTTING, Paul Lloyd. b 43. St Mich Coll Llan 69. **d** 71 **p** 72. C Hucknall Torkard *S'well* 71-74; C Cen Torquay *Ex* 74-76; P-in-c Sutton in Ashfield St Mich *S'well* 76; V 77-88; Chapl King's Mill Hosp Sutton-in-Ashfield from 85; Perm to Offic *Leic* from 95; NSM Vale of Belvoir Gp from 95. *9 Orchard Close, Radcliffe-on-Trent, Nottingham NG12 2BN* Nottingham (0115) 933 2591

BOTTOMLEY, George Edward. b 06. St Jo Coll Dur LTh34. Bible Churchmen's Coll 30. **d** 35 **p** 36. V Cheltenham St Mark *Glouc* 61-76; rtd 76; Hon C Camborne *Truro* from 77. *Salem, Reskadinnick Road, Camborne, Cornwall TR14 7LR* Camborne (01209) 713028

BOTTOMLEY, Gordon. b 31. Oak Hill Th Coll 51. **d** 55 **p** 56. C Kinson *Sarum* 55-58; Lic to Offic *Man* 58-63; N Area Sec BCMS 58-63; V Hemswell w Harpswell *Linc* 63-72; V Glentworth 63-72; Chapl RAF 63-71; R Bucknall and Bagnall *Lich* 72-80; TR 80-82; P-in-c Worthing H Trin *Chich* 82-88; V Camelsdale from 88. *The Vicarage, School Road, Camelsdale, Haslemere, Surrey GU27 3RN* Haslemere (01428) 642983

BOTTOMLEY, Philip. b 45. Cranmer Hall Dur BA67 DipTh69. **d** 70 **p** 71. C Harlow New Town w Lt Parndon *Chelmsf* 70-74; C W Kilburn St Luke w St Simon and St Jude *Lon* 74-78; Midl Sec CMJ 78-84; Hon C Selly Park St Steph and St Wulstan *Birm* 81-84; USA from 84. *78 Main Street, Ambridge, Pennsylvania 15003, USA*

BOTWRIGHT, Adrian Paul. b 55. St Jo Coll Ox MA PGCE. Westcott Ho Cam 80. **d** 82 **p** 83. C Chapel Allerton *Ripon* 82-85; Chapl Chapel Allerton Hosp 82-85; C Bourne *Guildf* 85-88; V Weston 88-94; R Skipton H Trin *Bradf* from 94. *The Rectory, Rectory Lane, Skipton, N Yorkshire BD23 1ER* Skipton (01756) 793622

BOUCHER, Brian Albert. b 39. Univ of Wales (Lamp) BA61. Chich Th Coll 61. **d** 63 **p** 64. C Hoxton H Trin w St Mary *Lon* 63-67; Chapl RN 67-68; Lic to Offic *Lon* 68-86; Asst Chapl Harrow Sch Middx 68-73; Chapl 73-86; P-in-c Clerkenwell H Redeemer w St Phil *Lon* 86-91; P-in-c Myddleton Square St Mark 86-91; Chapl Hurstpierpoint Coll Hassocks from 92. *Hurstpierpoint College, Hassocks, W Sussex RH6 9JS* Hurstpierpoint (01273) 833636

BOUGHEY, Richard Keith. b 26. Man Univ MEd71. Qu Coll Birm 77. **d** 80 **p** 82. NSM Upper Tean *Lich* 80-81; NSM Stoke-upon-Trent 80-81; NSM Uttoxeter w Bramshall 82-88; rtd 88; Perm to Offic *Lich* from 88. *Kontokali, The Old Lane, Checkley, Stoke-on-Trent ST6 8TG* Tean (01538) 722013

BOUGHTON, Mrs Elisabeth Mary Victoria. b 66. St Anne's Coll Ox BA87. Ridley Hall Cam 89. **d** 91 **p** 94. C Guildf Ch Ch *Guildf* from 91; Chapl St Cath Sch Bramley from 92. *Curate's Flat, 23A Waterden Road, Guildford, Surrey GU1 2AZ* Guildford (01483) 502902

BOUGHTON, Michael John. b 37. Kelham Th Coll 57. **d** 62 **p** 63. C Grantham St Wulfram *Linc* 62-66; C Kingsthorpe *Pet* 66-68; C Linc St Nic w St Jo Newport *Linc* 68-72; V Scunthorpe All SS 72-79; V Crowle 79-89; R Epworth 80-89;

TR Bottesford w Ashby from 89. *St Paul's Rectory, Ashby, Scunthorpe, S Humberside DN16 3DL* Scunthorpe (01724) 856863

BOUGHTON, Paul Henry. b 55. ACA80 Imp Coll Lon BScEng77 ARSM77. Ridley Hall Cam 89. d 91 p 92. C Guildf Ch Ch *Guildf* from 91. *Curate's Flat, 23A Waterden Road, Guildford, Surrey GU1 2AZ* Guildford (01483) 502902

BOULCOTT, Thomas William. b 16. Bps' Coll Cheshunt 47. d 49 p 50. V N Evington *Leic* 61-73; Chapl Leic Gen Hosp 62-73; V Loppington w Newtown *Lich* 73-85; RD Wem and Whitchurch 83-85; rtd 85; Perm to Offic *Lich* from 85. *Silver Birch, Tilley Road, Wem, Shrewsbury SY4 5HA* Wem (01939) 233602

BOULD, Preb Arthur Roger. b 32. Selw Coll Cam BA54 MA58 Wadh Coll Ox BA55 DipTh56 DipEd57 MA58. St Steph Ho Ox 54. d 57 p 58. C Wednesfield St Thos *Lich* 57-64; V Wellington Ch Ch 64-71; R Cheadle 71-88; P-in-c Freehay 84-88; R Cheadle w Freehay 88-91; Chapl Cheadle Hosp 71-91; Chapl HM Pris Moorcourt 72-82; RD Cheadle 72-91; Preb Lich Cathl from 83; Asst to Bp Wolv from 91. *10 Paradise Lane, Pelsall, Walsall, W Midlands WS3 4NH* Pelsall (01922) 694299   Fax 694301

BOULD, Stephen Frederick. b 49. K Coll Lon BD78 AKC78. Sarum & Wells Th Coll 78. d 79 p 80. C Cantril Farm *Liv* 79-82; AV Hindley St Pet 82-85; C Wigan All SS 85; Hon C Leic H Spirit *Leic* 85-88; Chapl Leic Univ SS-88; V Leic St Pet 88; P-in-c Leic St Sav 88; V Leic Ch Sav from 88; P-in-c New Humberstone from 94. *St Saviour's Vicarage, Wood Hill, Leicester LE5 3JB* Leicester (0116) 251 3396   Fax 262 3240

BOULLIER, Kenneth John (Ken). b 51. Lon Bible Coll 79 Trin Coll Bris DipHE84. d 84 p 85. C Heref St Pet w St Owen and St Jas *Heref* 84-87; V Nutley *Chich* 88-93; R Maresfield 88-93; New Zealand from 93. *The Vicarage, 47 Church Road, Kaitaia, Northland, New Zealand* Auckland (9) 408-0528

BOULSOVER, Philip John. b 16. ACT ThL55 Kelham Th Coll 34. d 40 p 41. C Bexhill St Pet *Chich* 43-51; Australia from 51; rtd 81. *21 Chillagoe Street, Fisher, Canberra, Australia 2611* Canberra (6) 288-7589

BOULT, Audrey. Qu Coll Birm. dss 85 d 87 p 94. Sheldon *Birm* 85-87; NSM from 87. *17 Fulford Grove, Sheldon, Birmingham B26 3XX* 0121-743 9993

BOULT, Geoffrey Michael. b 56. Southn Univ BTh88 Bris Univ DPhil90. Sarum & Wells Th Coll 77. d 80 p 81. C Newark w Hawton, Cotham and Shelton *S'well* 80-83; TV Melksham *Sarum* 83-90; P-in-c Charminster and Stinsford from 90. *The Vicarage, Mill Lane, Charminster, Dorchester, Dorset DT2 8XJ* Dorchester (01305) 262477

BOULTBEE, John Michael Godolphin. b 22. Oak Hill Th Coll 66. d 68 p 69. C Hawkwell *Chelmsf* 68-71; C St Keverne *Truro* 71-73; V Constantine 74-79; P-in-c St Merryn 79-81; V 81-87; rtd 87; Perm to Offic *Ex* from 87. *8 Williams Close, Dawlish, Devon EX7 9SP* Dawlish (01626) 865761

BOULTER, Michael Geoffrey. b 32. Lon Univ BD56. Tyndale Hall Bris 53. d 57 p 58. C Tranmere St Cath *Ches* 57-60; R Cheetham Hill *Man* 60-65; R Tollard Royal w Farnham *Sarum* 65-66; Chapl Alderney Hosp Poole from 66; V Branksome St Clem *Sarum* from 66. *The Vicarage, 7 Parkstone Heights, Branksome, Poole, Dorset BH14 0QE* Parkstone (01202) 748058

BOULTER, Robert George. b 49. Man Univ BA90. St Aug Coll Cant 72. d 75 p 76. C Langley All SS and Martyrs *Man* 75-80; V Lower Kersal 80-84; Oman 84-86; Slough Community Chapl *Ox* 86-87; R Whalley Range St Marg *Man* from 87. *St Margaret's Rectory, Rufford Road, Whalley Range, Manchester M16 8AE* 0161-226 1289

BOULTON, Christopher David. b 50. Keble Coll Ox BA71 MA80. Cuddesdon Coll 71. d 74 p 75. C Harlow St Mary and St Hugh w St Jo the Bapt *Chelmsf* 74-77; C Shrub End 77-80; P-in-c Gt Bentley 80-83; V 83-89; V Cherry Hinton St Andr *Ely* from 89; P-in-c Teversham from 90. *Cherry Hinton Vicarage, Fulbourn Old Drift, Cambridge CB1 4LR* Cambridge (01223) 247740

BOULTON, Canon Peter Henry. b 25. St Chad's Coll Dur BA49. Ely Th Coll 49. d 50 p 51. Chapl Victoria Hosp Worksop 67-87; V Worksop Priory *S'well* 67-87; Hon Can S'well Minster 75-92; Dir of Educn 87-92; Chapl to The Queen from 91; rtd 92. *3 Grasmere Drive, Holmes Chapel, Crewe CW4 7JT*

BOULTON, Preb Thomas Oswald. b 10. Keble Coll Ox BA35 MA39. Wycliffe Hall Ox 35. d 36 p 37. RD Oswestry *Lich* 60-76; V Oswestry St Oswald 60-76; Preb Lich Cathl 67-76; rtd 76. *21 Rayleigh Road, Harrogate, N Yorkshire HG2 8QR* Harrogate (01423) 871753

BOULTON, Wallace Dawson. b 31. Lon Coll of Div 65. d 67 p 68. C Bramcote *S'well* 67-71; Dioc Public Relns Officer 69-71; Hon C St Bride Fleet Street w Bridewell etc *Lon* 71-86; Publicity Sec CMS 71-79; Media Sec 79-86; Lic to Offic *Chich* from 84; Guild Chapl from 86; Ed C of E Newspaper 86-88.

44 Winterbourne Close, Hastings, E Sussex TN34 1XQ Hastings (01424) 713743

BOULTON-LEA, Peter John. b 46. St Jo Coll Dur BA68. Westcott Ho Cam 69. d 71 p 72. C Farlington *Portsm* 72-75; C Darlington St Jo *Dur* 75-77; R E and W Horndon w Lt Warley *Chelmsf* 77-82; V Hersham *Guildf* 82-91; R Kirk Sandall and Edenthorpe *Sheff* from 91; RD Doncaster from 95. *The Rectory, 31 Doncaster Road, Kirk Sandall, Doncaster, S Yorkshire DN3 1HP* Doncaster (01302) 882861

BOUNDS, John Henry. b 11. Clifton Th Coll 36. d 40 p 41. V Leigh *Roch* 57-80; rtd 80; Perm to Offic *Chich* 80-81 and 84-93; Hon C Uckfield 81-84. *10 Curve Acre, Braunton, Devon EX33 2HR* Braunton (01271) 814794

BOUNDY, David. b 34. Kelham Th Coll 55. d 59 p 60. Chapl E Birm Hosp 64-74; V Bordesley St Oswald *Birm* 64-70; V S Yardley St Mich 70-74; R Bideford *Ex* 74-82; RD Hartland 80-82; R Northfield *Birm* 82-88; P-in-c Penzance St Mary w St Paul *Truro* 88-90; V 90-94; rtd 94; Chapl Convent of St Mary at the Cross Edgware from 94. *St John's House, 27 High View Avenue, Edgware, Middx HA8 9TX* 0181-958 8980

BOUNDY, Gerald Neville. b 36. BA. Linc Th Coll. d 65 p 66. C Bris St Mary Redcliffe w Temple etc *Bris* 65-70; P-in-c Southmead 70-72; V 72-81; V Cotham St Sav w St Mary from 81. *182 St Michael's Hill, Cotham, Bristol BS2 8DE* Bristol (0117) 974 3198 or 733395

BOURDEAUX, Canon Michael Alan. b 34. St Edm Hall Ox BA57 MA61 BD68. Wycliffe Hall Ox 57. d 60 p 61. C Enfield St Andr *Lon* 60-64; C Old Charlton *S'wark* 65-66; Lic to Offic *Roch* 66-70; Gen Dir Keston Coll Kent from 70; Hon Can Roch Cathl *Roch* from 90. *Keston Research, PO Box 276, Oxford OX2 6BQ* Oxford (01865) 311022   Fax 311280

BOURKE, Very Rev Francis Robert. b 16. TCD BA40 BD46 PhD61. CITC 41. d 42 p 42. Dean Kilfenora *L & K* 72-86; Dean Killaloe 72-86; I Killaloe 72-76; Can Killaloe Cathl 72-86; I Killaloe w Abington, Kiltinanlea etc 76-86; rtd 86. *Tinnaview, Inchanore, Ballina, Killaloe, Co Clare, Irish Republic* Killaloe (61) 76461

✠**BOURKE, Rt Rev Michael Gay.** b 41. CCC Cam BA63 MA67. Cuddesdon Coll 65. d 67 p 68 c 93. C Gt Grimsby St Jas *Linc* 67-71; C Digswell *St Alb* 71-73; C-in-c Panshanger CD 73-78; Course Dir St Alb Minl Tr Scheme 75-87; V Southill 78-86; Adn Bedf 86-93; Area Bp Wolv *Lich* from 93; Hon Can Lich Cathl from 93. *61 Richmond Road, Wolverhampton WV3 9JH* Wolverhampton (01902) 23008   Fax 25443

BOURKE, Ronald Samuel James. b 50. MA HDipEd. d 79 p 80. C Portadown St Mark *Arm* 79-83; I Carnteel and Crilly 83-90; I Mountmellick w Coolbanagher, Rosenallis etc *M & K* from 90. *The Rectory, Mountmellick, Co Laois, Irish Republic* Mountmellick (502) 24143

BOURKE, Stanley Gordon. b 48. CITC 78. d 78 p 79. C Dundonald *D & D* 78-80; C Lurgan Ch Ch 81-82; I Dungiven w Bovevagh *D & R* 82-89; I Lurgan St Jo *D & D* from 89. *St John's Rectory, Sloan Street, Lurgan, Craigavon, Co Armagh BT66 8NT* Lurgan (01762) 322770

BOURNE, David George. b 67. Coll of Ripon & York St Jo BA91. Coll of Resurr Mirfield BA93. d 94 p 95. C Portsea St Mary *Portsm* from 94. *1 Glebe Flats, Nutfield Place, Portsmouth PO1 4JF* Portsmouth (01705) 830154

BOURNE, David James. b 54. Reading Univ BA76. Trin Coll Bris 77. d 79 p 80. C W Bromwich Gd Shep w St Jo *Lich* 79-84; V Riseley w Bletsoe *St Alb* from 84. *The Vicarage, Church Lane, Riseley, Bedford MK44 1ER* Bedford (01234) 708234

BOURNE, Canon Dennis John. b 32. Loughb Coll of Educn DLC55. Ridley Hall Cam 58. d 60 p 61. C Gorleston St Andr *Nor* 60-64; Min Gorleston St Mary CD 64-79; V Costessey 79-86; R Hingham w Wood Rising w Scoulton from 86; RD Hingham and Mitford from 90; Hon Can Nor Cathl from 93. *The Rectory, Hingham, Norwich NR9 4HP* Attleborough (01953) 850211

BOURNE, Mrs Diana Mary. b 46. St Jo Coll York BEd68. S Dios Minl Tr Scheme 92. d 95. C Pinner Lon from 95. *58 Cannonbury Avenue, Pinner, Middx HA5 1JS* 0181-866 5604

BOURNE, Henry. b 34. Spurgeon's Coll 55. d 64 p 65. Chapl RAF 67-85; Asst Chapl-in-Chief RAF 85-87; P-in-c Bourn *Ely* 87-88; V 88-89; P-in-c Kingston 87-88; R 88-89; V Caxton 88-89; R Bourn and Kingston w Caxton and Longstowe 89-91; rtd 91. *Newlyn Cottage, The Coombe, Newlyn, Penzance, Cornwall TR18 5HS*

BOURNE, John Mark. b 49. Cant Sch of Min 88. d 91 p 92. C Allington and Maidstone St Pet *Cant* 91-94; V Marden from 94; Chapl HM Pris Blantyre Ho from 94. *The Vicarage, Haffenden Close, Marden, Tonbridge, Kent TN12 9DR* Maidstone (01622) 831379

BOURNE, Michael. b 30. AKC58. d 59 p 60. V Wroxall *Portsm* 67-73; TR Poplar Lon 73-89; Sec and Dir Tr Gen Syn Hosp Chapl Coun 89-94; rtd 95. *306B Amhurst Road, London N16 7UE* 0171-923 0485

BOURNE, Nigel Irvine. b 60. St Jo Coll Ox BA82 MA86. Trin Coll Bris BA92. **d** 92 **p** 93. C Bedhampton *Portsm* 92-94; C Newport St Jo from 94. *7 College Road, Newport, Isle of Wight PO30 1HB* Isle of Wight (01983) 825030

BOURNE, Philip John. b 61. Sussex Univ BEd83 Aber Univ MLitt86. Cranmer Hall Dur 85. **d** 87 **p** 88. C Gildersome *Wakef* 87-89; Chapl Ex Univ *Ex* 89-94; Lic to Offic 89-94; Assoc Chapl The Hague and Voorschoten *Eur* 94-95; Chapl Voorschoten from 95. *Chopinlaan 17, 2253 BS Voorschoten, The Netherlands* Leiden (71) 612762

BOURNER, Paul. b 48. CA Tr Coll. **d** 90 **p** 91. CA from 79; C Ipswich St Mary at Stoke w St Pet, Stoke Park *St E* 90-93; R Ufford w Bredfield and Hasketon from 93. *The Rectory, School Lane, Ufford, Woodbridge, Suffolk IP13 6DX* Eyke (01394) 460935

BOURNON, Dennis Harry. b 20. St Cuth Soc Dur LTh48 BA49. Oak Hill Th Coll 46. **d** 49 **p** 50. R Eastrop *Win* 65-80; R Nursling and Rownhams 80-85; rtd 85. *17 Wessex Avenue, New Milton, Hants BH25 6NG* New Milton (01425) 614016

BOURNON, Canon John Raymond. b 18. St Cath Soc Ox BA48 MA52. Oak Hill Th Coll 48. **d** 50 **p** 51. V Ware Ch Ch *St Alb* 60-85; RD Hertf 71-77; Hon Can St Alb 80-85; rtd 85; Perm to Offic *Linc* from 86; Perm to Offic *Pet* from 87. *Hawkesbury, 14 Cambridge Road, Stamford, Lincs PE9 1BN* Stamford (01780) 54394

BOUTLE, David Francis. b 44. Leeds Univ BSc67 Lon Univ DipTh72. Cuddesdon Coll 69. **d** 72 **p** 73. C Boston *Linc* 72-77; C Waltham 77-80; P-in-c Morton 80-81; V 81-94; Chapl Jo Coupland Hosp Gainsborough from 80; Local Mental Health Chapl from 88; P-in-c Heckington *Linc* from 94. *The Vicarage, Heckington, Sleaford, Lincs NG34 9RW* Sleaford (01529) 60302

BOVEY, Denis Philip. b 29. Ely Th Coll 50. **d** 53 **p** 54. R Aber St Jas *Ab* 66-74; R Old Deer 74-89; R Longside 74-89; R Strichen 74-89; Can St Andr Cathl 75-88; Syn Clerk 78-83; Dean Ab 83-88; R Alford 89-94; R Auchindoir 89-94; R Inverurie 89-94; P-in-c Dufftown 89-94; P-in-c Kemnay 89-94; rtd 94. *15 Loskin Drive, Glasgow GL22 7QV* 0141-772 2825

BOVILL, Francis William. b 34. Lon Univ DipTh58. St Aid Birkenhead 55. **d** 58 **p** 59. C Bispham *Blackb* 58-61; C Crosthwaite Keswick *Carl* 61-64; V Radcliffe St Andr *Man* 64-68; P-in-c Woodside St Steph *Glouc* 68; V 69-73; V Scotby *Carl* from 73; P-in-c Cotehill and Cumwhinton from 94. *The Vicarage, Lambley Bank, Scotby, Carlisle CA4 8BX* Scotby (01228) 513205

BOWDEN, Frank James. b 12. Lon Univ BA35. **d** 38 **p** 40. Lic to Offic *Nor* from 38. *52 Heigham Road, Norwich NR2 3AU* Norwich (01603) 624481

BOWDEN, John Stephen. b 35. CCC Ox BA59 MA62 Edin Univ Hon DD81. Linc Th Coll 59. **d** 61 **p** 62. C Nottm St Mary *S'well* 61-64; Lect Nottm Univ 64-66; Ed and Managing Dir SCM Press from 66; Hon C Highgate All SS *Lon* from 66; Hon C Brentford St Faith 80-87; Hon C Brentford from 87. *20 Southwood Avenue, London N6 5RZ or, 26 Tottenham Road, London N1 4BZ* 0181-340 7548 or 249 7262 Fax 249 3776

BOWDEN, John-Henry David. b 47. MIL78 Magd Coll Cam BA69 MA73 Man Poly DMS77. S Dios Minl Tr Scheme 81. **d** 84 **p** 85. NSM Redlynch and Morgan's Vale *Sarum* 84-88; NSM Cuckfield *Chich* 88-92; Perm to Offic from 92; NSM St Mary le Bow w St Pancras Soper Lane etc *Lon* from 92. *Dene House, South Chailey, Lewes, E Sussex BN8 4AB* Lewes (01273) 401076

BOWDEN, Canon Robert Andrew. b 38. Worc Coll Ox BA62 DipTh63 MA67 BDQ68. Cuddesdon Coll 63. **d** 65 **p** 66. C Wolv St Geo *Lich* 65-69; C Duston *Pet* 69-72; R Byfield 72-79; Chapl R Agric Coll Cirencester 79-93; R Coates, Rodmarton and Sapperton *Glouc* from 79; Bp's Adv on Rural Soc 81-93; Hon Can Glouc Cathl from 90; Chapl to The Queen from 92; Local Min Officer *Glouc* from 93. *Coates Rectory, Cirencester, Glos GL7 6NR* Cirencester (01285) 770235

BOWDER, Reginald William Maxwell (Bill). b 46. TCD BA68 MA81 Kent Univ DipSocWork71. S'wark Ord Course 78. **d** 80 **p** 81. C Bush Hill Park St Steph *Lon* 81-84; I Fiddown w Clonegam, Guilcagh and Kilmeaden *C & O* 84-87; I Lismore w Cappoquin, Kilwatermoy, Dungarvan etc 87-89; Dean Lismore 87-89; Chapl Kent Univ and KIAD *Cant* from 90. *The Chaplaincy, University of Kent, Canterbury, Kent CT2 7NX* Canterbury (01227) 764000 or 463097 Fax 475742

BOWDLER, Ernest Roy. b 10. Lich Th Coll 32. **d** 34 **p** 36. V Wolv Ch Ch *Lich* 57-71; Chapl CGA 71-73; C Langley Marish *Ox* 73-76; rtd 75; Hon C Worc St Martin w St Pet *Worc* 76-85; Hon C Walsall Pleck and Bescot *Lich* 85-87; Perm to Offic 87-94. *47 Melton Road, Wymondham, Norfolk NR28 0DE*

BOWEN, Colin Wynford. b 48. St D Coll Lamp DipTh71. **d** 71 **p** 72. C Hubberston w Herbrandston and Hasguard etc *St D* 71-75; R Cosheston w Nash and Upton 75-77; V Carew and

Cosheston w Nash and Upton 77-85; V Pemb St Mary and St Mich from 85. *The Vicarage, 18 Grove Hill, Pembroke, Dyfed SA71 5PT* Pembroke (01646) 682710

BOWEN, Daniel Austin. b 11. St D Coll Lamp BA33 St Steph Ho Ox 33. **d** 35 **p** 36. V Monkton *St D* 67-78; rtd 78; Perm to Offic *Chich* 78-95. *30 Old School Close, Stokenchurch, High Wycombe, Bucks HP14 3RB* High Wycombe (01494) 483871

BOWEN, David Gregory. b 47. Lanchester Poly BSc69. Cuddesdon Coll 70. **d** 74 **p** 75. C Rugby St Andr *Cov* 74-77; C Charlton St Luke w H Trin *S'wark* 78-80; TV Stantonbury *Ox* 80-82; Perm to Offic *B & W* from 89. *17 Chapel Hill, Clevedon, Avon BS21 7NL* Clevedon (01275) 878962

BOWEN, David John. b 46. Glouc Th Course 83. **d** 86 **p** 88. NSM Ross w Brampton Abbotts, Bridstow and Peterstow *Heref* 86-88; C Kingstone w Clehonger, Eaton Bishop etc 88-93; P-in-c Lugwardine w Bartestree and Weston Beggard 93-94; V Lugwardine w Bartestree, Weston Beggard etc from 94. *The Vicarage, Lugwardine, Hereford HR1 4AE* Hereford (01432) 850244

BOWEN, Mrs Delyth. b 54. St D Coll Lamp BA. St Mich Coll Llan. **d** 91. C Llandybie *St D* 91-95; P-in-c Llanllwni from 95. *The Vicarage, Llanllwni, Pencader, Dyfed SA39 9DR* Maesycrugiau (01559) 395413

BOWEN, Gwyn Humphrey. b 21. Univ of Wales (Lamp) BA54. **d** 56 **p** 57. V Cwmaman *Llan* 65-91; rtd 91; Perm to Offic *Llan* from 91. *18 St Luke's Avenue, Penarth, S Glam CF64 3PS*

BOWEN, Miss Jennifer Ethel. b 46. Liv Univ BSc68 CertEd69. N Ord Course 80. **dss** 83 **d** 87 **p** 94. Blundellsands St Nic *Liv* 83-86; W Derby St Mary 86-87; Par Dn 87-94; C from 94. *4 The Armoury, West Derby, Liverpool L12 5EL* 0151-256 6600

BOWEN, John. b 39. Univ of Wales DipTh63 Aus Nat Univ BA88. St Mich Coll Llan 60. **d** 68 **p** 69. C Aberavon *Llan* 68-73; Australia from 73. *c/o Radford College, College Street, Bruce, ACT, Australia 2617* Bruce (6) 251-4488 or 251-1810

BOWEN, John Roger. b 34. St Jo Coll Ox BA59 MA62. Tyndale Hall Bris 59. **d** 61 **p** 62. C Cam St Paul *Ely* 61-65; Tanzania 65-76; Kenya 76-80; Lic to Offic *S'well* from 80; Dir Past Studies St Jo Coll Nottm 80-85; Tutor from 85. *St John's College, Bramcote, Nottingham NG9 3DS* Nottingham (0115) 922 4086 or 251114 Fax 220134 or 436438

BOWEN, Lionel James. b 16. S'wark Ord Course 63. **d** 64 **p** 65. C Sanderstead All SS *S'wark* 67-74; V Pill *B & W* 74-79; Perm to Offic *Chich* from 79; rtd 81. *43 Sussex Court, Eaton Road, Hove, E Sussex BN3 3AS* Brighton (01273) 775945

BOWEN, Philip Jackson. b 10. St D Coll Lamp BA33 St Steph Ho Ox 33. **d** 35 **p** 36. V Llandeilo Fawr w Llandyfeisant *St D* 70-72; rtd 72. *3 Ger-y-Llan, The Parade, Carmarthen, Dyfed SA31 1LY* Carmarthen (01267) 233731

BOWEN, Roger William. b 47. Magd Coll Cam BA69 MA73. St Jo Coll Nottm 69. **d** 72 **p** 73. C Rusholme *Man* 72-75; Rwanda Miss 75-84; Burundi 77-84; Tutor and Lect All Nations Chr Coll Ware from 85; Lic to Offic *St Alb* from 86. *8 Elder Road, Ware, Herts SG12 7JF, or All Nations Christian College, Easneye, Ware, Herts SG12 8LX* Ware (01920) 469470 or 461243

BOWEN, Stephen Allan. b 51. Leic Univ BA72. Glouc Sch of Min 88. **d** 91 **p** 92. NSM Bream *Glouc* 91-92; NSM Tidenham w Beachley and Lancaut 91-94; C Glouc St Jas and All SS from 94. *16 Derby Road, Gloucester GL1 4AE* Gloucester (01452) 308951

BOWEN, Stephen Guy. b 47. Qu Coll Cam BA68 MA72 Bris Univ MA72. Clifton Th Coll 69. **d** 71 **p** 72. C Chelsea St Jo *Lon* 71-73; C Chelsea St Jo w St Andr 73; C Guildf St Sav *Guildf* 73-76; C Guildf St Sav w Stoke-next-Guildf 76-77; C Wallington H Trin *S'wark* 77-79; V Felbridge from 79. *The Vicarage, The Glebe, Felbridge, East Grinstead, W Sussex RH19 2QT* East Grinstead (01342) 321524

BOWEN, Thomas Raymond. b 20. Univ of Wales (Lamp) BA42. **d** 48 **p** 49. Chapl RAF 53-75; Chapl Gresham's Sch Holt 75-83; rtd 83; Perm to Offic *St D* from 83. *35 Gail Rise, Llangwm, Haverfordwest SA62 4HJ* Johnston (01437) 891179

BOWEN, Vincent Paul. b 26. Qu Coll Cam BA50 MA55. Ely Th Coll 51. **d** 53 **p** 54. R Cranham *Chelmsf* 61-71; R Wanstead St Mary 71-91; rtd 91. *44 Nunnery Fields, Canterbury, Kent CT1 3JT* Canterbury (01227) 472036

BOWER, Brian Mark. b 60. QUB BA DipTh. **d** 85 **p** 86. C Orangefield w Moneyreagh *D & D* 85-87; I Inver w Mountcharles, Killaghtee and Killybegs *D & R* 87-93; Miss to Seamen from 87; I Augher w Newtownsaville and Eskrahoole *Clogh* from 93. *16 Knockmay Road, Augher, Co Tyrone BT77 0DF* Clogher (016625) 48008 Fax as telephone

BOWER, James Hugh Marsh. b 17. St Chad's Coll Dur BA39 DipTh40 MA43. **d** 40 **p** 41. W Wolv St Andr *Lich* 58-74; R Cavendish *St E* 74-83; P-in-c Stansfield 78-83; RD Clare 82-83; rtd 83; Perm to Offic *St E* from 83. *142 Melford Road, Sudbury, Suffolk CO10 6JZ* Sudbury (01787) 372683

BOWERING, John Anthony (Tony). b 34. SS Coll Cam BA57 MA. Wycliffe Hall Ox 57. **d** 59 **p** 60. C Hornchurch St Andr *Chelmsf* 59-62; Succ Chelmsf Cathl 62; Prec 63; V Brampton Bierlow *Sheff* 64-70; V Norton Woodseats St Paul 70-80; V Tickhill w Stainton from 80; RD W Doncaster 87-92. *The Vicarage, 2 Sunderland Street, Tickhill, Doncaster, S Yorkshire DN11 9QJ* Doncaster (01302) 742224

BOWERING, Ven Michael Ernest. b 35. Kelham Th Coll 55. **d** 59 **p** 60. C Middlesb St Oswald *York* 59-62; C Huntington 62-64; V Brayton 64-72; RD Selby 71-72; V Saltburn-by-the-Sea 72-81; Can Res York Minster 81-87; Sec for Miss and Evang 81-87; Adn Lindisfarne *Newc* from 87. *12 Rectory Park, Morpeth, Northd NE61 2SZ* Morpeth (01670) 513207

BOWERS, David. b 55. Man Univ BA79. Wycliffe Hall Ox 82. **d** 84 **p** 85. C Lawton Moor *Man* 84-87; C Walmsley 87-93; V Milnrow from 93. *The Vicarage, 40 Eafield Avenue, Milnrow, Rochdale, Lancs OL16 3UN* Rochdale (01706) 42988

BOWERS, Francis Malcolm. b 44. Chan Sch Truro 79. **d** 82 **p** 83. NSM Penzance St Mary w St Paul *Truro* 82-83; C 86-88; NSM Madron 83-86; TV Redruth w Lanner and Treleigh 88-91; V St Blazey from 91. *The Vicarage, St Blazey, Par, Cornwall PL24 2NG* Par (01726) 812113

BOWERS, Canon John Edward. b 23. TD68. AKC50. **d** 51 **p** 52. V Ashby-de-la-Zouch St Helen w Coleorton *Leic* 63-88; CF (R of O) 67-78; RD Akeley W (Ashby) *Leic* 76-88; Hon Can Leic Cathl 78-88; rtd 88; Perm to Offic *Derby* 88-94; Perm to Offic *Leic* 88-94; Chapl High Sheriff of Derbyshire 89-90. *13 Bathurst, Orton Goldhay, Peterborough PE2 5QH* Peterborough (01733) 361834

BOWERS, Canon John Edward William. b 32. St Aid Birkenhead 60. **d** 63 **p** 64. C Bromborough *Ches* 63-68; Ind Chapl 68-74; P-in-c Crewe St Pet 69-71; V Crewe St Mich 71-74; TR Ellesmere Port 74-79; V Hattersley 79-91; Hon Can Ches Cathl from 80; RD Mottram 88-91; V Bunbury and Tilstone Fearnall from 91. *The Vicarage, Bunbury, Tarporley, Cheshire CW6 9PE* Bunbury (01829) 260283

BOWERS, Julian Michael. b 48. Edin Th Coll 69. **d** 72 **p** 73. C Chippenham St Andr w Tytherton Lucas *Bris* 72-74; C Henbury 74-77; Sri Lanka 77-82; P-in-c Evercreech w Chesterblade and Milton Clevedon *B & W* 82-83; V 83-89; V Enfield St Jas *Lon* from 89. *St James's Vicarage, 144 Hertford Road, Enfield, Middx EN3 5AY* 0181-804 1966

BOWERS, Michael Charles. b 52. Sarum & Wells Th Coll 89. **d** 91 **p** 92. C St Peter-in-Thanet *Cant* from 91. *64 High Street, St Peter's, Broadstairs, Kent CT10 2TD* Thanet (01843) 865229

BOWERS, Peter. b 47. Linc Th Coll 72. **d** 76 **p** 77. C Mackworth St Fran *Derby* 76-78; C Maidstone St Martin *Cant* 78-83; V Elmton *Derby* 83-89; V Swimbridge and W Buckland *Ex* from 89. *The Rectory, Barnstaple Hill, Swimbridge, Barnstaple, Devon EX32 0PH* Swimbridge (01271) 830257

BOWERS, Peter William Albert. b 36. K Coll Lon BD61 AKC61. **d** 62 **p** 63. C Chorley St Pet *Blackb* 62-64; C New Sleaford *Linc* 64-67; C Folkestone H Trin w Ch Ch *Cant* 67-72; V Deal St Geo 72-80; Dir Galilee Community 80-85; R River from 86; RD Dover from 93. *The Vicarage, 23 Lewisham Road, Dover, Kent CT17 0QG* Dover (01304) 822037

BOWERS, Raymond Franklin. b 26. Lon Univ BD40. ALCD40. **d** 40 **p** 41. V Bath St Steph *B & W* 66-76; P-in-c Gosforth *Carl* 76-78; P-in-c Wasdale Head and Nether Wasdale 76-78; R Gosforth w Nether Wasdale and Wasdale Head 78-80; rtd 81; Perm to Offic *Carl* from 81. *Brow House, Blackbeck, Egremont, Cumbria CA22 2NY* Beckermet (01946) 841345

BOWERS, Stanley Percival. b 20. Lon Univ BD45. Wartley Victoria Coll 40 Wells Th Coll 66. **d** 66 **p** 66. In Meth Ch 45-66; V Two Mile Hill St Mich *Bris* 69-91; rtd 91; Perm to Offic *Bris* from 91; Perm to Offic *B & W* from 91. *1 Windsor Road, Longwell Green, Bristol BS15 6AF* Bristol (0117) 932 4051

BOWES, Mrs Beryl Sylvia. b 48. SRN70 RSCN71 Hull Univ BTh89. NE Ord Course 89. **d** 91 **p** 94. NSM Kirk Ella *York* from 91; Chapl R Hull Hosps NHS Trust from 93. *236 West Ella Road, West Ella, Hull HU10 7SF* Hull (01482) 656392, 328541 or 674427

BOWES, Ernest Ward. b 04. Trin Coll Cam BA27 MA30. Ridley Hall Cam 27. **d** 29 **p** 30. V Weston-super-Mare Em *B & W* 52-70; rtd 70; Perm to Offic *Chich* 70-93. *6 Capel Court, The Burgage, Prestbury, Cheltenham, Glos GL52 3EL* Cheltenham (01242) 235637

BOWES, John Anthony Hugh. b 39. Ch Ch Ox BA62 DipTh63 MA65. Westcott Ho Cam 63. **d** 65 **p** 66. C Langley All SS and Martyrs *Man* 65-68; Asst Chapl Bris Univ *Bris* 68-73; TV Cramlington *Newc* 73-76; P-in-c Oldland *Bris* 76-80; TR 80-84; V Westbury-on-Trym St Alb from 84. *St Alban's Vicarage, 21 Canowie Road, Bristol BS6 7HR* Bristol (0117) 973 5844

BOWETT, Richard Julnes. b 45. E Anglian Minl Tr Course 86. **d** 89 **p** 90. C Hunstanton St Mary w Ringstead Parva, Holme etc *Nor* 89-93; C King's Lynn St Marg w St Nic 93-95; V Watton w Carbrooke and Ovington from 95. *The Vicarage, Norwich Road, Watton, Thetford, Norfolk IP25 6DB* Watton (01953) 881439

BOWIE, Dr Michael Nicholas Roderick. b 59. Sydney Univ BA78 CCC Ox DPhil90. St Steph Ho Ox MA90. **d** 91 **p** 92. C Swanley St Mary *Roch* 91-93; C Penarth w Lavernock *Llan* from 93. *Church House, 153 Windsor Road, Penarth, S Glam CF6 1JF* Cardiff (01222) 701144

BOWKER, Archibald Edward. b 18. Univ of Manitoba BA52. St Jo Coll Winnipeg LTh51. **d** 51 **p** 52. V Blackhill *Dur* 61-79; rtd 80. *19 Greenside, Greatham, Hartlepool, Cleveland TS25 2HS* Hartlepool (01429) 871973

BOWKER, Prof John Westerdale. b 35. Worc Coll Ox BA58. Ripon Hall Ox. **d** 61 **p** 62. Fell Lect and Dir of Studies CCC Cam 62-74; Lect Div Cam Univ 70-74; Prof of Relig Studies Lanc Univ 74-86; Hon Can Cant Cathl *Cant* from 85; Dean of Chpl Trin Coll Cam 86-91; rtd 91. *14 Bowers Croft, Cambridge CB1 4RP*

BOWKETT, Canon Cyril Edward Vivian. b 11. St Jo Coll Dur LTh38 BA39 MA68. Clifton Th Coll 35. **d** 39 **p** 40. R S'wark St Geo *S'wark* 64-82; Hon Can S'wark Cathl 66-82; P-in-c S'wark St Jude 75-82; rtd 82; Perm to Offic *B & W* from 82. *The Lookout, Warren Road, Brean, Burnham-on-Sea, Somerset TA8 2RP* Brean Down (01278) 751517

✠**BOWLBY, Rt Rev Ronald Oliver.** b 26. Trin Coll Ox BA50 MA54. Westcott Ho Cam 50. **d** 52 **p** 53 **c** 73. C Pallion *Dur* 52-56; C Billingham St Cuth 56-57; C-in-c Billingham St Aid CD 57-60; V Billingham St Aid 60-66; V Croydon *Cant* 66-73; Hon Can Cant Cathl 70-73; Bp Newc 73-80; Bp S'wark 80-91; rtd 91; Asst Bp Lich from 91. *4 Uppington Avenue, Shrewsbury SY3 7JL* Shrewsbury (01743) 244192

BOWLER, Christopher William. See JAGE-BOWLER, Christopher William

BOWLER, David Henderson. b 54. Kent Univ BA75. St Jo Coll Nottm 75. **d** 78 **p** 79. C Bramcote *S'well* 78-82; TV Kirby Muxloe *Leic* 82-88; V Quorndon from 88. *Quorn Vicarage, 6 Loughborough Road, Quorn, Loughborough, Leics LE12 8DX* Quorn (01509) 412593

BOWLER, Denis Charles Stanley. b 16. **d** 66 **p** 67. C Coleford w Staunton *Glouc* 69-72; V Coney Hill 72-77; V Lydbrook 77-82; rtd 82; Perm to Offic *Glouc* from 82. *22 Harpfield Road, Bishops Cleeve, Cheltenham, Glos GL52 4EB* Cheltenham (01242) 674307

BOWLER, Frederick Wallace. b 11. MBE46. AKC34. **d** 34 **p** 35. V Alcombe *B & W* 66-71; rtd 72. *The Manor Nursing Home, Bishop's Hull, Taunton, Somerset TA1 5EB* Taunton (01823) 336633

BOWLER, Preb Kenneth Neville. b 37. K Coll Lon 57. **d** 61 **p** 62. C Buxton *Derby* 61-67; R Sandiacre 67-75; V E Bedfont *Lon* 75-87; AD Hounslow 82-87; Preb St Paul's Cathl from 85; V Fulham All SS from 87. *All Saints' Vicarage, 70 Fulham High Street, London SW6 3LG* 0171-736 6301

BOWLER, Roy Harold. b 27. Wadh Coll Ox BA48 MA57. Wells Th Coll 52. **d** 53 **p** 54. C Clerkenwell H Redeemer w St Phil *Lon* 53-55; C Tottenham All Hallows 55-57; Lic to Offic *Cant* 57-61; S Rhodesia 61-65; Rhodesia 65-80; Zimbabwe from 80. *Box 537, Mutare, Zimbabwe*

✠**BOWLES, Rt Rev Cyril William Johnston.** b 16. Em Coll Cam Jes Coll Cam BA38 MA41. Ridley Hall Cam 37. **d** 39 **p** 40 **c** 69. C Barking St Marg *Chelmsf* 39-41; Chapl Ridley Hall Cam 42-44; Vice-Prin 44-51; Prin 51-63; Hon Can Ely Cathl *Ely* 59-63; Adn Swindon *Bris* 63-69; Hon Can Bris Cathl 63-69; Bp Derby 69-87; rtd 87. *Rose Lodge, Tewkesbury Road, Stow on the Wold, Cheltenham, Glos GL54 1EN* Cotswold (01451) 831965

BOWLES, David Anthony. b 44. Kelham Th Coll 63. **d** 68 **p** 69. C Bilborough w Strelley *S'well* 68-72; C Beeston 72-75; Ascension Is 75-77; V Wellingborough St Mark *Pet* 77-83; P-in-c Wilby 78-83; R Burton Latimer 83-90; V Sheff St Oswald *Sheff* 90-91; Perm to Offic *Derby* from 94. *64 Church Street, Matlock, Derbyshire DE4 3BY* Matlock (01629) 580529

BOWLES, John. b 32. N Ord Course. **d** 89 **p** 90. NSM Stockport St Mary Ches from 89. *13 Tragan Drive, Offerton, Stockport, Cheshire SK2 5QX* 0161-483 9566

BOWLES, Preb Michael Hubert Venn. b 36. Selw Coll Cam BA59 MA63. Ridley Hall Cam 59. **d** 61 **p** 62. C Woodside Park St Barn *Lon* 61-64; C Swanage *Sarum* 64-67; Asst St Mich Coll Llan 67-72; Chapl 67-70; Lib 70-72; Lect Th Univ of Wales (Cardiff) 67-72; Lic to Offic *Llan* 71-72; R Gt Stanmore *Lon* from 72; Preb St Paul's Cathl from 85. *The Rectory, Rectory Lane, Stanmore, Middx HA7 4AQ* 0181-954 0276

BOWLES, Peter John. b 39. Lon Univ BA60. Linc Th Coll 71. **d** 73 **p** 74. C Clay Cross *Derby* 73-76; C Boulton 76-79; R Brailsford w Shirley 79-85; P-in-c Osmaston w Edlaston 81-85; R Brailsford w Shirley and Osmaston w Edlaston 85-89; TR Old Brampton and Loundsley Green from 89. *The Rectory, 25 Oldridge Close, Chesterfield, Derbyshire S40 4UF* Chesterfield (01246) 236663

BOWLES, Ronald Leonard. b 24. K Coll Lon BD52 AKC52. **d** 53 **p** 54. V Woolston *Win* 66-75; V Moordown 75-89; rtd 89. *25 Cherry Tree Avenue, Cowplain, Waterlooville, Hants PO8 8BA* Portsmouth (01705) 267376

BOWLEY, John Richard Lyon. b 46. MRTPI76 Dur Univ BA68 QUB MSc72. CITC. **d** 79 **p** 80. C Knock *D & D* 79-81; Bp's C Knocknagoney 81-90; I Ballywalter w Inishargie from 90; RD Ards from 95. *The Vicarage, 2 Whitechurch Road, Ballywalter, Newtownards, Co Down BT22 2JY* Ballywalter (01247) 758416

BOWLZER, Ronald. b 41. CEng69 MIMechE69. **d** 84 **p** 84. NSM Rosyth *St And* 84-85; NSM Lochgelly 84-85; NSM Inverkeithing 84-85; NSM Dunfermline 85-89; C Whitehaven *Carl* 89-91; P-in-c Netherton from 91. *The Vicarage, Church Terrace, Netherton, Maryport, Cumbria CA15 7PS* Maryport (01900) 812200

BOWMAN, Miss Alison Valentine. b 57. St Andr Univ MA79. St Steph Ho Ox 86. **d** 89 **p** 94. Par Dn Peacehaven *Chich* 89-94; C from 94; Chapl to Area Bp Lewes from 93. *24 Woodlands Close, Peacehaven, E Sussex BN10 7SF* Brighton (01273) 581356

BOWMAN, Clifford William. b 57. St Jo Coll Dur BA78. Ridley Hall Cam. **d** 82 **p** 83. C Sawley *Derby* 82-85; C Hucknall Torkard *S'well* 85-89; R Warsop from 89. *The Rectory, Church Road, Warsop, Mansfield, Notts NG20 0SL* Mansfield (01623) 843290

BOWMAN-EADIE, Russell Ian. b 45. ACP68 K Coll Lon BD71 AKC71. St Aug Coll Cant 71. **d** 72 **p** 73. C Hammersmith St Pet *Lon* 72-74; V Leic St Nic *Leic* 74-81; Chapl Leic Univ 74-81; Adult Educn Adv *Dur* 81-84; Dir of Tr *B & W* from 84; Preb Wells Cathl from 90. *2 The Liberty, Wells, Somerset BA5 2SU* Wells (01749) 674702

BOWN, Francis Adrian Charles Simon. b 48. Jes Coll Cam BA72 MA74 Jes Coll Ox BA75 MA78 Hull Univ MA88. Linc Th Coll 76. **d** 77 **p** 78. C Howden *York* 77-79; C Howden TM 80; P-in-c Hull Sculcoates St Steph 80-85; V from 85. *St Stephen's Presbytery, 29 Westbourne Avenue, Hull HU5 3HN* Hull (01482) 46075

BOWN, Canon John Frederick Olney. b 13. TD. MA. **d** 37 **p** 38. QHC 67-70; R Fordingbridge w Ibsley *Win* 70-79; RD Christchurch 74-78; rtd 79; P-in-c Longstock w Leckford *Win* 79-87. *Dawlish House, 7 Trafalgar Way, Stockbridge, Hants SO20 6ET* Andover (01264) 810672

BOWNESS, William. b 48. Warw Univ BSc69. Ripon Coll Cuddesdon 80. **d** 82 **p** 83. C Lanc St Mary *Blackb* 82-86; V Lostock Hall 86-91; V Whittington w Arkholme and Gressingham from 91; RD Tunstall from 93. *The Vicarage, Arkholme, Carnforth, Lancs LA6 1AX* Hornby (015242) 21359

BOWRING, Stephen John. b 55. R Holloway Coll Lon BMus77 St Mary's Coll Twickenham PGCE78. E Midl Min Tr Course 89. **d** 92 **p** 93. C Thurmaston *Leic* 92-95; V Shepshed from 95. *The Vicarage, 36 Church Street, Shepshed, Loughborough, Leics LE12 9RH* Shepshed (01509) 502255

BOWSER, Alan. b 35. Univ of Wales (Lamp) BA60 DipTh63. **d** 63 **p** 64. C Gateshead St Chad *Bensham Dur* 63-67; C Owton Manor CD 67-72; V Horden from 72. *The Vicarage, Horden, Peterlee, Co Durham SR8 4JF* 0191-586 4423

BOWSHER, Andrew Peter (Andii). b 59. Reading Univ BA81 Nottm Univ DipTh84. St Jo Coll Nottm DPS86. **d** 86 **p** 87. C Grenoside *Sheff* 86-89; C Darfield 89-91; P-in-c Halifax All So *Wakef* from 91. *All Souls' Vicarage, 13 Booth Town Road, Halifax, W Yorkshire HX3 6EU* Halifax (01422) 321731

BOWSKILL, Robert Preston (Bob). b 48. S Dios Minl Tr Scheme 88. **d** 91 **p** 92. NSM Eastrop *Win* 91-94; NSM Winklebury from 94. *Old Sarum, 1 Camfield Close, Basingstoke, Hants RG21 3AQ* Basingstoke (01256) 27301

BOWTELL, Paul William. b 47. Lon Univ BSc68. St Jo Coll Nottm. **d** 82 **p** 83. C Gorleston St Andr *Nor* 82-85; TV Forest Gate St Sav w W Ham St Matt *Chelmsf* 85-91; R Spitalfields Ch Ch w All SS *Lon* from 91. *The Rectory, 2 Fournier Street, London E1 6QE* 0171-247 7202

BOWYER, Frank. b 28. Man Univ BA49 BD56. Oak Hill Th Coll 53. **d** 55 **p** 56. R Burnage St Marg *Man* 63-81; R Gosforth w Nether Wasdale and Wasdale Head *Carl* 81-85; R Holcombe *Man* 85-93; rtd 93. *43 New Church Road, Bolton BL1 5QQ* Bolton (01204) 844547

BOWYER, Geoffrey Charles. b 54. ACA79 ATII82 Lanc Univ BA76. St Jo Coll Nottm 85. **d** 87 **p** 88. C Walton *St E* 87-89; C

Macclesfield Team Par *Ches* 89-91; V Cinderford St Steph w Littledean *Glouc* from 91. *The Vicarage, St Annal's Road, Cinderford, Glos GL14 2AS* Dean (01594) 822286

BOWYER, Dr Richard Astley. b 55. Jes Coll Ox MA Ex Univ PhD. Chich Th Coll 82. **d** 84 **p** 85. C Ex St Jas *Ex* 84-87; TV Ex St Thos and Em from 87. *St Andrew's Vicarage, 78 Queens Road, Exeter EX2 9EW* Exeter (01392) 433656

BOX, David Norman. b 28. K Coll Lon BD48 AKC48. **d** 51 **p** 52. V Allerton *Bradf* 69-75; R Exford w Exmoor *B & W* 75-80; V Castle Cary w Ansford 80-90; P-in-c Childe Okeford, Manston, Hammoon and Hanford *Sarum* 90-91; R Childe Okeford, Okeford Fitzpaine, Manston etc 91-94; rtd 94. *Granary House, 1 Castle Street, Hilton, Appleby-in-Westmorland, Cumbria CA16 6LX* Appleby (017683) 52689

BOX, Reginald Gilbert (Brother Reginald). b 20. Lon Univ BD41 AKC41 Em Coll Cam BA52 MA57. Westcott Ho Cam 41. **d** 43 **p** 44. SSF from 51; New Zealand, Australia and Melanesia 69-84; Perm to Offic *Sarum* from 84; Perm to Offic *Ely* from 85; rtd 90; Chapl Chich Th Coll 90-92. *The Friary, Hilfield, Dorchester, Dorset DT2 7BE* Cerne Abbas (01300) 341345 Fax 341293

BOXALL, David John. b 41. Dur Univ BA63 DipTh65. Sarum Th Coll 65. **d** 66 **p** 67. C Ipswich St Aug *St E* 66-69; C Bourne *Linc* 69-71; C Woodside Park St Barn *Lon* 71-72; C Thundersley *Chelmsf* 72-76; P-in-c Farcet *Ely* 76-77; TV Stanground and Farcet 77-85; V Guyhirn w Ring's End 85-90; V Southea w Murrow and Parson Drove 85-90; P-in-c Fletton 90-94. *Address temp unknown*

BOXALL, Keith Michael. b 37. Trin Coll Bris. **d** 82 **p** 83. C Staines St Pet *Lon* 82-83; C Staines St Mary and St Pet 83-85; V Lydiard Millicent w Lydiard Tregoz *Bris* 85-86; TV The Lydiards 86-93; V Mangotsfield from 93. *The Vicarage, St James Place, Mangotsfield, Bristol BS17 3JA* Bristol (0117) 956 0510

BOXALL, Canon Martin Alleyne. b 37. Wells Th Coll 65. **d** 67 **p** 68. C Crowthorne *Ox* 67-70; C Tilehurst St Mich 70-76; V Tilehurst St Cath 76-78; V Padstow *Truro* from 78; Miss to Seamen from 78; RD Pydar *Truro* 93; Hon Can Truro Cathl from 93. *The Vicarage, 46 Treverbyn Road, Padstow, Cornwall PL28 8DN* Padstow (01841) 532224

BOXALL, Simon Roger. b 55. St Jo Coll Cam BA76. Ridley Hall Cam 77. **d** 79 **p** 80. C Eaton *Nor* 79-82; SAMS from 82; Brazil from 82. *Igreja Episcopal do Brasil, Caixa Postal 380, 96 400 970 Bage, RS Brasil*

BOXLEY, Christopher. b 45. K Coll Lon BD68 AKC68 Southn Univ CertEd73 Reading Univ MA84. **d** 69 **p** 70. C Bitterne Park *Win* 69-73; Perm to Offic *Chich* 73-78; Hd of Relig Studies Midhurst Gr Sch from 73; Dir Midhurst and Petworth Relig Studies Cen from 78; P-in-c Heyshott from 78. *The Rectory, Heyshott, Midhurst, W Sussex GU29 0DH* Midhurst (01730) 814405

BOYCE, Canon Brian David Michael. b 32. Fitzw Ho Cam BA55 MA62. Wells Th Coll 55. **d** 57 **p** 58. C Tavistock and Gulworthy *Ex* 57-60; C Paignton St Jo 60-62; S Africa from 62. *PO Box 131, South Broom, 4277 South Africa* South Broom (3931) 30828

BOYCE, Christopher Allan. b 44. ARIBA69 Brighton Coll of Art DipArch66. S Dios Minl Tr Scheme 84. **d** 87 **p** 88. NSM Eastbourne All SS *Chich* 87-93; C Upton (or Overchurch) *Ches* from 93. *65 Devonshire Road, Upton, Wirral, Merseyside L49 6NN* 0151-606 9995

BOYCE, John Frederick. b 33. ALCD57. **d** 57 **p** 58. C Earlsfield St Andr *S'wark* 57-60; C Westerham *Roch* 60-63; C Farnborough 63-66; V Sutton at Hone 66-73; P-in-c Chiddingstone 73-74; R Chiddingstone w Chiddingstone Causeway 74-84; V Brenchley from 84. *The Vicarage, 8 Broadoak, Brenchley, Tonbridge, Kent TN12 7NN* Brenchley (01892) 722140

BOYCE, Kenneth. b 21. St Aid Birkenhead 59. **d** 60 **p** 61. R N Reddish *Man* 66-86; rtd 86. *150 Overdale Road, Romiley, Stockport, Cheshire SK6 3EN* 0161-494 0934

BOYCE, Kenneth Albert (Ken). b 51. St Edm Hall Ox BA72 MA76 Selw Coll Cam BA75 MA79. Westcott Ho Cam 73. **d** 75 **p** 76. C Evington *Leic* 75-78; P-in-c Gt Bowden w Welham 78-81; Dioc Stewardship Adv 78-81; Chapl Leic Poly 81-86; TV Leic H Spirit 82-86; Chapl to the Deaf *Worc* 86-93; P-in-c Astwood Bank 86-93; R Fladbury, Wyre Piddle and Moor from 93; P-in-c Cropthorne w Charlton from 94. *The Rectory, Fladbury, Pershore, Worcs WR10 2QW* Evesham (01386) 860356

BOYCE, Robert Albert Wright. b 19. BA. St Alb Minl Tr Scheme. **d** 82 **p** 83. NSM Hatf *St Alb* 82-89; Perm to Offic from 89; rtd 90. *92 Park Meadow, Hatfield, Herts AL9 5HE* Hatfield (01707) 267531

BOYD, Alan McLean. b 50. St Jo Coll Nottm BTh79. **d** 79 **p** 80. C Bishops Waltham *Portsm* 79-83; Chapl Reading Univ *Ox*

83-88; Chapl E Birm Hosp 88-94; Chapl Solihull Distr Hosp from 94. *Solihull Hospital, Lode Lane, Solihull, W Midlands B91 2JL* 0121-711 4455

BOYD, Alexander Jamieson. b 46. MIBiol FSAScot St Chad's Coll Dur BSc68 Nottm Univ PGCE69. Coll of Resurr Mirfield 69. **d** 79 **p** 80. NSM Musselburgh *Edin* 79-83; CF from 83. *c/o MOD (Army), Bagshot Park, Bagshot, Surrey GU19 5PL* Bagshot (01276) 471717   Fax 412834

BOYD, Allan Gray. b 41. St Jo Coll Nottm 84. **d** 87 **p** 88. Hon Chapl Miss to Seamen from 87; NSM Glas St Gabr *Glas* 87-93; NSM Greenock from 93. *47 Holms Crescent, Erskine, Renfrewshire PA8 6DJ* 0141-812 2754

BOYD, Allan Newby. b 31. MInstM73 Ball Coll Ox MA. St Alb Minl Tr Scheme 81. **d** 84 **p** 85. NSM Watford St Luke *St Alb* 84-88; C Ardsley *Sheff* 88-91; V Barrow St Jo *Carl* 91-94; rtd 94. *Bishop Fold, Thoralby, Leyburn, N Yorkshire DL8 3SH* Leyburn (0969) 663474

BOYD, David Anthony. b 42. Sarum & Wells Th Coll 72. **d** 75 **p** 76. C Ches H Trin *Ches* 75-79; R 85-93; V Congleton St Jas 79-85; V Farndon and Coddington from 93. *The Vicarage, Farndon, Chester CH3 6QD* Farndon (01829) 270270

BOYD, Michael Victor. b 33. St Chad's Coll Dur BA57 DipAdEd69 MEd77 PhD81. Coll of Resurr Mirfield 57. **d** 59 **p** 60. C Warsop *S'well* 59-61; Chapl St Geo Coll Quilmes Argent 62-63; Chapl Wolsingham Sch 63-67; Lect St Hild Coll Dur 67-75; Lect SS Hild & Bede Dur 75-79; Lect Dur Univ 79-84. *4 Aykley Green, Whitesmocks, Durham DH1 4LN* 0191-384 9473

BOYD, Robert Henry. b 36. **d** 66 **p** 67. C Drumcree *Arm* 66-69; I Annaghmore 69-83; Bp's C Lissan 83-90; I from 90. *The Rectory, 150 Moneymore Road, Cookstown, Co Tyrone BT80 8PY* Cookstown (016487) 66112

BOYD, Samuel Robert Thomas. b 62. **d** 90 **p** 91. NSM Derryloran *Arm* 90-95; C from 95. *51 Oldtown Street, Cookstown, Co Tyrone BT80 8EE* Cookstown (016487) 66046

BOYD, Canon William John Peter. b 28. Lon Univ BA48 BD53 PhD77 Birm Univ MA60. **d** 57 **p** 58. Adult Educn Chapl *Truro* 64-85; Dioc Ecum Officer 65-83; R St Ewe 68-73; Preb St Endellion 73-85; V St Kew 73-77; R Falmouth K Chas 77-85; RD Carnmarth S 84-85; Dir of Tr 85-93; Prin SW Minl Tr Course 85-93; Can Res and Chan Truro Cathl *Truro* 85-93; rtd 93. *7 Chapel Crescent, Zelah, Truro, Cornwall TR4 9HN*

BOYD, William Thomas. b 15. TCD BA38 MA43. **d** 39 **p** 40. R W Parley *Sarum* 70-76; rtd 76. *Turlough, 4 Heath Farm Close, Ferndown, Dorset BH22 8JP* Ferndown (01202) 892055

BOYD-WILLIAMS, Anthony Robert. b 46. Univ of Wales (Cardiff) DPS88. St Mich Coll Llan 86. **d** 88 **p** 89. C Tonyrefail w Gilfach Goch *Llan* 88-91; V Treharris w Bedlinog from 91. *The Vicarage, 13 The Oaks, Quakers Yard, Treharris, M Glam CF46 5LA* Tonyrefail (01443) 410280

BOYDEN, Peter Frederick. b 41. Lon Univ BSc62 AKC62 Em Coll Cam BA64 MA68 MLitt69. Ridley Hall Cam 63. **d** 66 **p** 67. C Chesterton St Andr *Ely* 66-68; C Wimbledon *S'wark* 68-72; Chapl K Sch Cant 72-89; Chapl Radley Coll Abingdon from 89. *Radley College, Abingdon, Oxon OX13 2HR* Abingdon (01235) 530750

BOYES, Canon David Arthur Stiles. b 30. Lon Coll of Div 62. **d** 63 **p** 64. C Islington St Mary *Lon* 63-71; V Canonbury St Steph 71-75; V St Paul's Cray St Barn *Roch* 75-85; P-in-c Earl Soham w Cretingham and Ashfield cum Thorpe *St E* from 85; Dioc Development Officer 86-92; RD Loes from 91; Hon Can St E Cathl from 95. *The Rectory, Church Lane, Earl Soham, Woodbridge, Suffolk IP13 7SD* Earl Soham (01728) 685778

BOYES, Michael Charles. b 27. Lon Univ BA53 BD58. Wells Th Coll 53. **d** 55 **p** 56. V Broadclyst *Ex* 68-83; RD Aylesbeare 77-81; TR Sampford Peverell, Uplowman, Holcombe Rogus etc 83-85; TR Sampford Peverell, Uplowman, Holcombe Rogus etc 85-92; rtd 92; Perm to Offic *Ex* from 92. *Southdown, Burlescombe, Tiverton, Devon EX16 7LB* Craddock (01884) 840492

BOYLAND, David Henry. b 58. TCD BA79 BAI79. **d** 91 **p** 92. C Seapatrick *D & D* 91-94; I Celbridge w Straffan and Newcastle-Lyons *D & G* from 94. *The Rectory, Maynooth Road, Celbridge, Co Kildare, Irish Republic* Dublin (1) 628-8231

BOYLAND, Henry Hubert. b 23. DipMan. CITC. **d** 84 **p** 85. NSM Dunboyne w Kilcock, Maynooth, Moyglare etc *M & K* 84-87; Bp's C Carrickmacross w Magheracloone *Clogh* 87-90; I 90-93; rtd 93. *18 The Nurseries, Forest Road, Swords, Co Dublin, Irish Republic* Dublin (1) 840-8810

BOYLE, Andrew McKenzie. b 45. Down Coll Cam BA67 MA71 CEng72 MICE72. W Midl Minl Tr Course 82. **d** 85 **p** 86. NSM Woodthorpe *S'well* 85-87; Perm to Offic *Roch* 88-90; from 91; Hon C Sevenoaks St Luke CD 90-91. *31 Lambarde Drive, Sevenoaks, Kent TN13 3HX* Sevenoaks (01732) 456546

BOYLE, Christopher John. b 51. AKC75. St Aug Coll Cant 75. **d** 76 **p** 77. C Wylde Green *Birm* 76-80; Bp's Dom Chapl 80-83; R Castle Bromwich SS Mary and Marg from 83; RD Coleshill from 92. *The Rectory, Rectory Lane, Birmingham B36 9DH* 0121-747 2281

BOYLE, Canon Richard Henry. b 08. TCD BA30 LLB37 MA47. **d** 45 **p** 46. I Banagher *M & K* 60-82; Can Meath 69-82; rtd 82. *Shannon Cottage, West End, Banagher, Birr, Co Offaly, Irish Republic* Banagher (509) 51134

BOYLES, Peter John. b 59. Univ of Wales (Lamp) BA84. Sarum & Wells Th Coll 86. **d** 88 **p** 89. C Ches St Mary *Ches* 88-91; C Neston 91-95; R Lavendon w Cold Brayfield, Clifton Reynes etc *Ox* from 95. *The New Rectory, 7A Northampton Road, Lavendon, Olney, Bucks MK46 4EY* Bedford (01234) 712647

BOYLING, Canon Denis Hudson. b 16. Keble Coll Ox BA38 DipTh39 MA42. Cuddesdon Coll 39. **d** 40 **p** 41. V Almondbury *Wakef* 68-75; Can Res Wakef Cathl 75-82; rtd 82; Perm to Offic *Heref* from 82. *Brendon, Berrington Road, Tenbury Wells, Worcs WR15 8EN* Tenbury Wells (01584) 810360

BOYLING, Canon Mark Christopher. b 52. Keble Coll Ox BA74 BA76 MA78. Cuddesdon Coll 74. **d** 77 **p** 78. C Kirkby *Liv* 77-79; P-in-c 79-80; TV 80-85; Bp's Dom Chapl 85-89; V Formby St Pet 89-94; Can Res and Prec Liv Cathl from 94. *3 Cathedral Close, Liverpool L1 7BR* 0151-708 0934

BOYNS, Martin Laurence Harley. b 26. St Jo Coll Cam BA49 MA51. Ridley Hall Cam 50. **d** 52 **p** 53. V Duffield *Derby* 58-71; V Rawdon *Bradf* 71-76; Chapl Woodlands Hosp Rawdon 71-76; R Melton *St E* 76-85; R Gerrans w St Antony in Roseland *Truro* 85-92; Miss to Seamen 85-92; rtd 92. *Bojunda, Boscaswell Village, Pendeen, Penzance, Cornwall TR19 7EP* Penzance (01736) 788390

BOYNS, Timothy Martin Harley. b 58. Warw Univ BA80 Nottm Univ BCombStuds84. Linc Th Coll 81. **d** 84 **p** 85. C Oxhey St Matt *St Alb* 84-87; TV Solihull *Birm* 87-94; V Lillington *Cov* from 94. *The Vicarage, Lillington, Leamington Spa, Warks CV32 7RH* Leamington Spa (01926) 424674

BOYS, Mrs Margaret Ann. b 34. Lon Univ TCert56 Liv Univ DipPE59. Oak Hill Th Coll 91. **d** 94 **p** 95. NSM Hadleigh St Barn *Chelmsf* from 94. *10 Seymour Road, Westcliff-on-Sea, Essex SS0 8NJ* Southend-on-Sea (01702) 75997

BOYSE, Felix Vivian Allan. b 17. LVO78. CCC Cam BA39 MA42. Cuddesdon Coll 39. **d** 40 **p** 41. Chapl Chpl Royal Hampton Court Palace 65-82; Preacher Lincoln's Inn from 82; rtd 83. *Rose Cottage, Rookwood Road, West Wittering, Chichester, W Sussex PO20 8LT* Birdham (01243) 514320

BOZON, David Hamish. b 28. Fitzw Ho Cam BA52 MA56. Linc Th Coll 53. **d** 55 **p** 56. Info Officer RADD 68-84; Lic to Offic *Chelmsf* 74-84; R Sundridge w Ide Hill *Roch* 84-92; rtd 92. *22 Birch Close, Liss, Hants GU33 7HS* Liss (01730) 895525

BRACE, Dr Alistair Andrew. b 53. Newc Univ MB, BS76 DRCOG77. W Midl Minl Tr Course 90. **d** 94. NSM Broseley w Benthall, Jackfield, Linley etc *Heref* from 94. *Easthope Coppice Farm, Broseley, Shropshire TF12 5QR* Broseley (01952) 884031

BRACE, Stuart. b 49. Bp Burgess Hall Lamp DipTh74. **d** 74 **p** 75. C Llanelli Ch Ch *St D* 74-76; C Tenby w Gumfreston 76-77; V Ystradmeurig and Strata Florida 77-79; CF 79-86; Chapl HM Youth Cust Cen Everthorpe 86-88; Chapl HM Pris Stafford 88-93; Chapl HM Pris Long Lartin from 93. *HM Prison Long Lartin, South Littleton, Evesham, Worcs WR11 5TZ* Evesham (01386) 830101   Fax 832834

BRACEGIRDLE, Christopher Andrew. b 56. Dur Univ BEd79 St Edm Ho Cam BA84 MA89. Ridley Hall Cam 82. **d** 85 **p** 86. C Livesey *Blackb* 85-88; TV E Farnworth and Kearsley *Man* 88-92; V Astley from 92. *St Stephen's Vicarage, 7 Holbeck, Astley, Tyldesley, Manchester M29 7DU* Atherton (01942) 883313

BRACEGIRDLE, Mrs Cynthia Wendy Mary. b 52. LMH Ox BA73 MA77 Liv Univ DipAE82. N Ord Course. **d** 87 **p** 94. Chapl Asst Man R Infirmary 85-88; Dir Dioc Local Ord Min Scheme *Man* from 89. *The Rectory, Parsonage Close, Salford M5 3GT* 0161-872 0800

BRACEGIRDLE, Robert Kevin Stewart. b 47. Univ Coll Ox BA69 MA73. St Steph Ho Ox 70. **d** 73 **p** 74. C Dorchester *Sarum* 73-75; C Woodchurch *Ches* 75-78; V Bidston 78-82; P-in-c Salford St Ignatius *Man* 82-86; R Salford St Ignatius and Stowell Memorial from 86. *The Rectory, Parsonage Close, Salford M5 3GT* 0161-872 0800

BRACEWELL, David John. b 44. Leeds Univ BA66 Man Univ MA82. Tyndale Hall Bris 67. **d** 69 **p** 70. C Tonbridge St Steph *Roch* 69-72; C Shipley St Pet *Bradf* 72-75; V Halliwell St Paul *Man* 75-84; R Guildf St Sav *Guildf* from 84. *St Saviour's Rectory, Wharf Road, Guildford, Surrey GU1 4RP* Guildford (01483) 577811

BRACEWELL, Howard Waring. b 35. FRGS73. Tyndale Hall Bris. **d** 63 **p** 63. Canada 63-72; Travel Missr World Radio Miss

Fellowship 72-77; P-in-c Ashill Nor 72-74; Hon C Bris St Phil and St Jacob w Em *Bris* 77-84; Perm to Offic *St Alb* 84-86; R Odell 86-88; V Pavenham 86-88; rtd 88. *13 Ashbee Street, Asterley Bridge, Bolton, Manchester BL1 6NT* Bolton (01204) 591576

BRACEY, David Harold. b 36. AKC63. **d** 64 **p** 65. C Westleigh St Pet *Man* 64-67; C Dunstable *St Alb* 67-70; V Benchill *Man* 70-76; V Elton St Steph 76-87; V Howe Bridge from 87. *The Vicarage, Leigh Road, Atherton, Manchester M29 0PH* Atherton (01942) 883359

BRACHER, Paul Martin. b 59. Solicitor 84 Ex Univ LLB80. Trin Coll Bris BA90. **d** 90 **p** 91. C Sparkhill St Jo *Birm* 90; C Sparkhill w Greet and Sparkbrook 90-93; Chapl Birm Women's Hosp from 92; P-in-c Lea Hall *Birm* from 93. *St Richard's Vicarage, Hallmoor Road, Birmingham B33 9QY* 0121-783 2319

BRACK, Edward James (Ted). b 37. Sarum Th Coll 67. **d** 69 **p** 70. C Gravesend St Aid *Roch* 69-73; C Woodside Park St Barn *Lon* 73-77; C Wood Green St Mich 77-80; V Whitton SS Phil and Jas 80-83; TV Bethnal Green St Jo w St Bart 83-86; TV St Jo on Bethnal Green 87-94; C W Hackney St Barn from 94. *Basement Flat, 306 Amhurst Road, London N16 7UE* 0171-241 1474

BRACKENBURY, Ven Michael Palmer. b 30. Linc Th Coll 64. **d** 66 **p** 67. C S Ormsby w Ketsby, Calceby and Driby *Linc* 66-69; V Scothern w Sudbrooke 69-77; RD Lawres 73-78; Bp's Personal Asst 77-88; Dioc Dir of Ords 77-87; Can and Preb Linc Cathl from 79; Dioc Lay Min Adv 86-87; Adn Linc from 88. *2 Ashfield Road, Sleaford, Lincs NG34 7DZ* Sleaford (01529) 307149

BRACKLEY, Ian James. b 47. Keble Coll Ox BA69 MA73. Cuddesdon Coll 69. **d** 71 **p** 72. C Bris Lockleaze St Mary Magd w St Fran *Bris* 71-74; Asst Chapl Bryanston Sch Blandford 74-77; Chapl 77-80; V E Preston w Kingston *Chich* 80-88; RD Arundel and Bognor 82-87; TR Haywards Heath St Wilfrid from 88; RD Cuckfield from 89. *The Rectory, St Wilfrid's Way, Haywards Heath, W Sussex RH16 3QH* Haywards Heath (01444) 413300

BRACKLEY, Mark Ozanne. b 53. Boro Road Teacher Tr Coll CertEd75. S'wark Ord Course 90. **d** 93 **p** 94. NSM Hampstead St Steph w All Hallows *Lon* from 93. *12 Duncombe Road, London N19 3DP* 0171-263 8363

BRADBERRY, John. b 20. Clifton Th Coll 46. **d** 47 **p** 48. V Siddal *Wakef* 61-72; R Bentham St Jo *Bradf* 72-85; rtd 85; Perm to Offic *Wakef* from 85; Perm to Offic *Bradf* from 86. *18 Moor Bottom Road, Halifax, W Yorkshire HX2 9SR* Halifax (01422) 244944

BRADBERRY, John Stephen. b 47. Hull Univ BSc70 Leeds Univ CertEd71 MEd86. NW Ord Course 76. **d** 79 **p** 80. NSM Warley *Wakef* from 79. *129 Paddock Lane, Halifax, W Yorkshire HX2 0NT* Halifax (01422) 358282

BRADBROOK, Mrs Averyl. b 46. Girton Coll Cam BA67 MA88 Man Univ PGCE69. N Ord Course 90. **d** 93 **p** 94. C Heaton Ch Ch *Man* from 93. *4 Carlton Road, Bolton BL1 5HU* Bolton (01204) 842615

BRADBROOK, Peter David. b 33. Kelham Th Coll 54. **d** 60 **p** 61. C Ches St Oswald St Thos *Ches* 60-63; C Fulham St Etheldreda *Lon* 64-65; V Congleton St Jas *Ches* 65-79; V Wheelock 79-92; V Crewe All SS and St Paul from 92. *All Saints' Vicarage, 79 Stewart Street, Crewe CW2 8LX* Crewe (01270) 60310

BRADBURY, George Graham. b 35. AKC58. **d** 59 **p** 60. C Portsea St Mary *Portsm* 59-62; C Melksham *Sarum* 62-64; V Winfrith Newburgh w Chaldon Herring 64-68; CF 68-71. *16 Bread Street, Warminster, Wilts BA12 8DF* Warminster (01985) 213179

BRADBURY, Canon Herbert Cedric. b 30. FPS Man Univ PhC53. Linc Th Coll 64. **d** 66 **p** 67. C Blackpool St Steph *Blackb* 66-71; TV Hempnall *Nor* 71-75; TR 75-81; R Fritton w Morningthorpe w Shelton and Hardwick 74-77; RD Depwade 77-81; V Wroxham w Hoveton 81; P-in-c Belaugh 81; R Wroxham w Hoveton and Belaugh 81-92; RD Tunstead 83-91; Hon Can Nor Cathl from 90; R Gt and Lt Massingham and Harpley from 92; P-in-c South Raynham, E w W Raynham, Helhoughton, etc from 94. *The Rectory, Station Road, Great Massingham, King's Lynn, Norfolk PE32 2HW* Great Massingham (01485) 520211

BRADBURY, Julian Nicholas Anstey. b 49. BNC Ox BA71 MA75 Birm Univ MA84. Cuddesdon Coll 71. **d** 73 **p** 74. C S'wark H Trin *S'wark* 73-76; USA 76-79; V Tottenham H Trin *Lon* 79-85; Dir Past Th Sarum & Wells Th Coll 85-90; P-in-c Yatton Keynell *Bris* from 90; P-in-c Biddestone w Slaughterford from 90; P-in-c Castle Combe from 90; P-in-c W Kington from 90; P-in-c Nettleton w Littleton Drew from 90. *The Rectory, Yatton Keynell, Chippenham, Wilts SN14 7BA* Castle Combe (01249) 782663

BRADBURY, Kenneth James Frank. b 23. Qu Coll Birm 72. **d** 75 **p** 76. NSM Cen Telford *Lich* 75-77; C 77-80; V Chirbury *Heref* 80-88; V Marton 80-88; V Trelystan 80-88; rtd 88. *The Glebe, Rodington, Shrewsbury SY4 4QX* Telford (01952) 770312

BRADBURY, Norman Lunn. b 15. K Coll Lon BA36 AKC36. N Ord Course 76. **d** 77 **p** 78. NSM Paddock *Wakef* 77-81; NSM Rashcliffe and Lockwood 81-84; Perm to Offic from 84. *23 Springwood Hall Gardens, Huddersfield HD1 4HA* Huddersfield (01484) 427548

BRADBURY, Robert Douglas. b 50. Ripon Coll Cuddesdon 75. **d** 76 **p** 77. C Harlescott *Lich* 76-81; V Ruyton 81-88; P-in-c Gt w Lt Ness 84-88; V Ruyton XI Towns w Gt and Lt Ness from 88. *The Vicarage, The Village, Ruyton Eleven Towns, Shrewsbury SY4 1LQ* Baschurch (01939) 260254

BRADBURY, Roy Albert. b 30. Chich Th Coll 72. **d** 74 **p** 75. C Earlsdon *Cov* 74-76; C Cov Caludon 76-78; P-in-c Calow *Derby* 78-82; V Pensnett *Lich* 82-90; V Pattingham w Patshull 90-94; V Ocker Hill from 94. *St Mark's Vicarage, Ocker Hill Road, Tipton, W Midlands DY4 0XE* 0121-556 0678

BRADDICK-SOUTHGATE, Charles Anthony Michael. b 70. Univ Coll Lon BD92. Chich Th Coll MTh95. **d** 94 **p** 95. C Catford St Laur *S'wark* from 94. *33 Bromley Road, London SE6 2TS* 0181-461 5542

BRADDOCK, Arthur Derek. b 25. Bolton Inst of Educn BA90. Lich Th Coll 56. **d** 59 **p** 60. V Kearsley Moor *Man* 65-79; C Ellesmere Port *Ches* 79-85; rtd 85; Perm to Offic *Man* from 85. *1 Corrie Drive, Kearsley, Bolton BL4 8RG* 0161-794 8953

BRADFORD, John. b 34. FRSA FRGS Lon Univ BA60 Birm Univ MEd81 Ox Univ ACertEd70. Oak Hill Th Coll 55. **d** 60 **p** 61. C Walcot *B & W* 60-64; Ass Master Wendover C of E Primary Sch 64-65; Hd RE Dr Challoner's High Sch Lt Chalfont 65-69; Perm to Offic *Ox* 66-70; Lect St Pet Coll of Educn Saltley 70-77; Perm to Offic *Birm* 70-71; Lic to Offic from 71; Perm to Offic *Cov* from 77; Nat Chapl-Missr CECS from 77; Gen Perm to Offic Ch in Wales from 89. *27 Marsh Lane, Solihull, W Midlands B91 2PG* 0121-704 9895 or 0171-837 4299

BRADFORD, Peter. b 38. Sarum Th Coll 69. **d** 70 **p** 71. C Holdenhurst *Win* 70-73; C Stanmore 73-77; P-in-c Eling, Testwood and Marchwood 77-78; R Marchwood 78-86; C Christchurch 86-90; C Andover w Foxcott 90-92; V E and W Worldham, Hartley Mauditt w Kingsley etc from 92. *The Vicarage, East Worldham, Alton, Hants GU34 3AS* Alton (01420) 82392

BRADFORD, Archdeacon of. See SHREEVE, Ven David Herbert

BRADFORD, Bishop of. See SMITH, Rt Rev David James

BRADFORD, Provost of. See RICHARDSON, Very Rev John Stephen

BRADLEY, Andrew Robert. b 65. Clare Coll Cam BA88. St Jo Coll Nottm DTS93 MA94. **d** 94 **p** 95. C Burnage St Marg *Man* from 94. *29 Bournlea Avenue, Manchester M19 1AE* 0161-431 7272

BRADLEY, Anthony David. b 56. Wye Coll Lon BSc76. St Jo Coll Nottm DPS88. **d** 88 **p** 89. C Southchurch Ch Ch *Chelmsf* 88-91; C Cov H Trin *Cov* from 91; Dioc Lay Tr Adv from 93. *466 Tile Hill Lane, Coventry CV4 9DY* Coventry (01203) 471047

BRADLEY, Brian Hugh Granville. b 32. Lon Coll of Div 58. **d** 62 **p** 63. C E Twickenham St Steph *Lon* 62-65; C Herne Bay Ch Ch *Cant* 65-69; Miss to Seamen Teesside 69-71; Ceylon 71-72; Sri Lanka 72-74; Chapl Amsterdam w Haarlem and Den Helder *Eur* 75-79; Chapl Lyon w Grenoble and Aix-les-Bains 79-85; TV Bucknall and Bagnall *Lich* 87-93; Chapl N Staffs HA 87-93; Assoc Chapl Dubai, Sharjah and N Emirates from 93. *PO Box 7451, Dubai, UAE*

BRADLEY, Canon Cecil Robert Jones. b 23. TCD BA47 MA50. CITC 48. **d** 48 **p** 49. C Clooney *D & R* 48-50; C Derry Cathl 50-67; Dean's V St Patr Cathl Dub from 67; Preb Maynooth St Patr Cathl Dub from 81. *The Vicarage, St Patrick's Close, Dublin 8, Irish Republic* Dublin (1) 475-4817 Fax 454-6374

BRADLEY, Clifford David. b 36. Lon Univ BA60. St Aid Birkenhead 60. **d** 62 **p** 63. C Stoneycroft All SS *Liv* 62-65; C Chipping Sodbury and Old Sodbury *Glouc* 65-68; Br Honduras 68-70; C Leckhampton SS Phil and Jas *Glouc* 70-71; V Badgeworth w Shurdington 71-79; Dioc Missr *S & M* 79-84; V Santan 79-84; V Braddan 79-84; Bp's Dom Chapl 81-84; V Stroud and Uplands w Slad *Glouc* 84-89; C Shepshed *Leic* 90-92; R Leire w Ashby Parva and Dunton Bassett from 92. *The Rectory, Dunton Road, Leire, Lutterworth, Leics LE17 5HD* Leire (01455) 209421

BRADLEY, Canon Colin John. b 46. Edin Univ MA69 Hertf Coll Ox 71. Sarum & Wells Th Coll 72. **d** 75 **p** 76. C Easthampstead *Ox* 75-79; V Shawbury *Lich* 79-90; R Moreton Corbet 80-90; P-in-c Stanton on Hine Heath 81-90; Can Res Portsm Cathl *Portsm* from 90; Dir of Ords from 90. *61 St Thomas Street, Portsmouth PO1 2EZ* Portsmouth (01705) 824621

BRADLEY, Connla John Osman. b 08. Bible Churchmen's Coll. **d** 47 **p** 47. V Havering-atte-Bower *Chelmsf* 68-76; rtd 76; Perm to Offic *Chich* 76-88. *57 Davis Court, Marlborough Road, St Albans, Herts AL1 3XU* St Albans (01727) 846795

BRADLEY, Canon Donald John Walter. b 19. Em Coll Cam BA40 MA44. Westcott Ho Cam 40. **d** 42 **p** 43. Lic to Offic *Birm* 63-70; Hon Can Birm Cathl 70-84; V Edgbaston St Geo 71-84; RD Edgbaston 77-84; rtd 84. *32 St Mark's Road, Salisbury SP1 3AZ* Salisbury (01722) 334653

BRADLEY (nee DRAPER), Mrs Elizabeth Ann. b 38. Nottm Univ BTh75 Birm Univ DipTh77. Linc Th Coll 71. **dss** 84 **d** 87 **p** 94. Ind Chapl *Linc* 84-91; Bracebridge 84-87; Hon C 87-90; Chapl to GFS in Lon Ind Chapl *Lon* from 91. *26 Dewpond Road, Flitwick, Bedford MK45 1RT* Flitwick (01525) 712369

BRADLEY, Gary Scott. b 53. Lon Univ LLB75. Ripon Coll Cuddesdon 75. **d** 78 **p** 79. C St Jo Wood *Lon* 78-83; V Paddington St Sav from 83. *St Saviour's Vicarage, 24 Formosa Street, London W9 2QA* 0171-286 4962

BRADLEY, Miss Hazel. b 61. N Lon Poly BA85 Loughb Univ MSc87. Ripon Coll Cuddesdon 89. **d** 92 **p** 94. Par Dn Thurnby Lodge *Leic* 92-94; C 94-95; C Aylestone St Andr w St Jas from 95. *St James's Vicarage, 30 Park Hill Drive, Leicester LE2 8HR* Leicester (0116) 283 2458

BRADLEY, John Owen. b 30. Jes Coll Ox BA55 MA56. St Mich Coll Llan 52. **d** 56 **p** 57. C Cardiff St Mary *Llan* 56-59; Lect St Mich Coll Llan 59-61; C Caerau w Ely *Llan* 60; C Newton Nottage 61-64; V Aberavon H Trin 65-69; Lic to Offic *Cov* 70-76; C W Kirby St Bridget *Ches* 76-79; TV Knowle *Bris* 79-80; TR 80-91; RD Brislington 83-89; Chapl St Monica Home Bris from 91. *St Augustine, Cote Lane, Bristol BS9 3UL* Bristol (0117) 949 4019 or 949 4020

BRADLEY, Ms Joy Elizabeth. b 63. Sheff Univ BA85 Fitzw Coll Cam BA91. Ridley Hall Cam CTM92. **d** 92 **p** 94. Par Dn Wadsley *Sheff* 92-94; C from 94. *3 Overton Road, Sheffield S6 1WG* Sheffield (0114) 234 4697

BRADLEY, Kenneth Sutton. b 08. ALCD39. **d** 38 **p** 39. R Dogmersfield w Winchfield *Win* 53-72; rtd 73. *12 Mildway Court, Odiham, Basingstoke, Hants RG25 1AX* Basingstoke (01256) 704897

BRADLEY, Michael Frederick John. b 44. Qu Coll Birm 76. **d** 77 **p** 78. C Sheff St Cuth *Sheff* 77-78; C Alford w Rigsby *Linc* 78-83; V Bracebridge 83-90; V Flitwick *St Alb* from 90. *The Vicarage, 26 Dew Pond Road, Flitwick, Bedford MK45 1RT* Flitwick (01525) 712369

BRADLEY, Peter David Douglas. b 49. Nottm Univ BTh79. Linc Th Coll 75. **d** 79 **p** 80. C Upholland *Liv* 79-83; V Dovecot 83-94; Dir Continuing Minl Educn from 89; TR Upholland from 94. *The Rectory, 1A College Road, Upholland, Skelmersdale, Lancs WN8 0PY* Up Holland (01695) 622936

BRADLEY, Peter Edward. b 64. Trin Hall Cam BA86 Trin Coll Cam MA90. Ripon Coll Cuddesdon 86. **d** 88 **p** 89. C Northn St Mich w St Edm *Pet* 88-91; Chapl G&C Coll Cam 91-95. *The Vicarage, Farringdon Road, Abingdon, Oxon OX14 1BG* Abingdon (01235) 520297

BRADLEY, Ronald Percival. b 25. ACP51 FRSA52 TCert49. Ex & Turoa NSM Scheme 80. **d** 83 **p** 84. C Honiton, Gittisham, Combe Raleigh, Monkton etc *Ex* 83-86; P-in-c Halberton 86-87; rtd 90. *32 Homepalms House, Brunswick Square, Torquay TQ1 4UT* Torquay (01803) 212921

BRADNUM, Canon Ella Margaret. b 41. CertEd64 St Hugh's Coll Ox MA65. **dss** 69 **d** 87 **p** 94. Illingworth *Wakef* 69-72; Batley All SS 72-73; Lay Tr Officer 77-82; Min Tr Officer 82-88; Warden of Readers from 88; Sec Dioc Bd of Min from 88; Co-ord Lay Tr from 88; Hon Can Wakef Cathl from 94. *The Vicarage, 1 Sunnybank Road, Mixenden, Halifax, W Yorkshire HX2 8RX* Halifax (01422) 244761 or 240669

BRADNUM, Richard James (Dick). b 39. Pemb Coll Ox BA62 MA67. Ridley Hall Cam 62. **d** 64 **p** 65. C Birm St Martin *Birm* 64-68; C Sutton St Jas *York* 68-69; Perm to Offic *Wakef* 71-72; C Batley All SS 72-74; V Gawthorpe and Chickenley Heath 74-86; V Mixenden from 86. *The Vicarage, 1 Sunny Bank Road, Mixenden, Halifax, W Yorkshire HX2 8RX* Halifax (01422) 244761

BRADSHAW, Charles Anthony. b 44. Birm Univ MA76. Qu Coll Birm DipTh74. **d** 75 **p** 76. C Whickham *Dur* 75-78; C Bilton *Cov* 78-81; TV Cov Caludon 81-89; V Birstall and Wanlip *Leic* from 89. *The Rectory, 251 Birstall Road, Birstall, Leicester LE4 4DJ* Leicester (0116) 267 4517

BRADSHAW, Denis Matthew. b 52. Chich Th Coll 77. **d** 80 **p** 81. C Ruislip St Martin *Lon* 80-84; C Northolt Park St Barn 84-86; V Northolt W End St Jos from 86; C-in-c Hayes St Nic CD from 94. *St Joseph's Vicarage, 430 Yeading Lane, Northolt, Middx UB5 6JS* 0181-845 6161

BRADSHAW, George Henry. b 28. Wycliffe Hall Ox. **d** 62 **p** 63. Chapl RAF 65-84; R Wittering w Thornhaugh and Wansford *Pet* 65-84; Ascension Is 84-85; V The Suttons w Tydd *Linc* 85-87; rtd 87; Perm to Offic *Linc* from 87. *42 Welland Mews, Stamford, Lincs PE9 2LW* Stamford (01780) 56070

BRADSHAW, Gordon George. b 31. St Pet Coll Ox BA56 MA59. Wycliffe Hall Ox 56. **d** 58 **p** 59. V W Derby St Jas *Liv* 68-75; TR Keynsham *B & W* 75-83; rtd 83. *9-10 Priory Road, Keynsham, Bristol BS18 2BX*

BRADSHAW, Graham. b 58. Edin Univ BD86. Edin Th Coll 83. **d** 86 **p** 87. C Thornton-le-Fylde *Blackb* 86-89; C Kirkby Lonsdale *Carl* 89-91; V Langford *St Alb* from 91. *The Vicarage, 65 Church Street, Langford, Biggleswade, Beds SG18 9QT* Hitchin (01462) 700248

BRADSHAW, Miss Jennie McNeille. b 47. UEA BA69. Cranmer Hall Dur 85. **d** 90 **p** 94. Par Dn Herne *Cant* 90-94; C 94-95; P-in-c Claybrooke cum Wibtoft and Frolesworth *Leic* from 95. *The Rectory, Lutterworth Road, Bitteswell, Lutterworth, Leics LE17 4RX* Leire (01455) 556367

BRADSHAW, Jolyon Anthony. b 51. St Jo Coll Dur BA73. Trin Coll Bris 73. **d** 76 **p** 77. C Normanton *Wakef* 76-82; TV Wreningham *Nor* 82-89; P-in-c Bermondsey St Mary w St Olave, St Jo etc *S'wark* from 89. *The Rectory, 193 Bermondsey Street, London SE1 3UW* 0171-407 5273

BRADSHAW, Kenneth Allan. b 23. Roch Th Coll 60. **d** 62 **p** 63. C Preston *Chich* 67-71; C Haywards Heath St Wilfrid 71-82; C Sidley 82-88; rtd 88; Lic to Offic *Llan* from 88. *The Cottage, 115A Splott Road, Cardiff CF2 2BY* Cardiff (01222) 465998

BRADSHAW, Malcolm McNeille. b 45. Lon Univ DipTh69. Kelham Th Coll 65. **d** 70 **p** 71. C New Addington *Cant* 70-76; Chapl Milan w Cadenabbia, Varese and Lugano *Eur* 77-82; V Boxley w Detling *Cant* from 82. *The Vicarage, Boxley, Maidstone, Kent ME14 3DX* Maidstone (01622) 758606

BRADSHAW, Canon Prof Paul Frederick. b 45. Clare Coll Cam BA66 MA70 K Coll Lon PhD71. Westcott Ho Cam 67. **d** 69 **p** 70. C W Wickham St Jo *Cant* 69-71; C Cant St Martin and St Paul 71-73; Tutor Chich Th Coll 73-78; V Flamstead *St Alb* 78-82; Dir of Minl Tr Scheme 78-82; Vice-Prin Ripon Coll Cuddesdon 83-85; USA from 85; Prof Th Notre Dame Univ from 85; Hon Can N Indiana from 90. *17695 Fall Creek Drive, Granger, Indiana 46530, USA*

BRADSHAW, Philip Hugh. b 39. Qu Coll Ox BA64 MA67 Lon Univ DipRS91. S'wark Ord Course 88. **d** 91 **p** 92. NSM Bletchingley *S'wark* from 91; Ldr Community of Celebration from 91. *Community of Celebration, Berry House, 58 High Street, Bletchingley, Redhill RH1 4PA* Godstone (01883) 743911

BRADSHAW, Roy John. b 49. Sarum & Wells Th Coll 85. **d** 87 **p** 88. FSJ from 84; C Gainsborough All SS *Linc* 87-90; V New Waltham 90-94; R Killamarsh *Derby* from 94. *The Rectory, Sheepcote Road, Killamarsh, Sheffield S31 8BN* Sheffield (0114) 248 2769

BRADSHAW, Dr Timothy (Tim). b 50. PhD Keble Coll Ox BA72 MA78. St Jo Coll Nottm BA75. **d** 76 **p** 77. C Clapton Park All So *Lon* 76-79; Lect Trin Coll Bris 80-91; Hon C Sea Mills *Bris* 83-91; Tutor Regent's Park Coll Ox from 91; NSM Ox St Aldate w St Matt *Ox* 91-94; NSM Ox St Aldate from 95. *54 St Giles, Oxford OX1 3LU* Oxford (01865) 515951

BRADSHAW (nee STUART-BLACK), Mrs Veronica. b 52. St Jo Coll Dur BA75. Cranmer Hall Dur. **dss** 82 **d** 87. Borehamwood *St Alb* 82-84; Watford Ch Ch 84-85; Stevenage St Mary Shephall 85-87; Par Dn Stevenage St Mary Sheppall w Aston 87-88. *31 Harefield, Shephall, Stevenage, Herts SG2 9NG* Stevenage (01438) 365714

BRADWELL, Area Bishop of. *See* GREEN, Rt Rev Laurence Alexander (Laurie)

BRADY, Canon Ernest William. b 17. Dur Univ LTh42. Edin Th Coll 39. **d** 42 **p** 43. R Edin All SS *Edin* 57-71; R Edin St Mich and All SS 65-71; Can St Mary's Cathl 67-83; Syn Clerk 69-76; Dioc Supernumerary 71-74 and 82-90; P-in-c S Queensferry 74-82; Dean Edin 76-82 and 85-86; rtd 82; Hon Can St Mary's Cathl *Edin* 83-85 and from 86. *44 Glendevon Place, Edinburgh EH12 5UJ* 0131-337 9528

BRADY, Mrs Madalaine Margaret. b 45. Univ of Wales (Ban) BD88 CertEd91 MA92. **d** 89. Asst Chapl Univ of Wales (Ban) *Ban* from 89; Dioc Comm Officer from 94. *4 Salem Place, Llanllechid, Bangor, Gwynedd LL57 3ES* Bangor (01248) 600567

BRAGGER, Martin James. CEng72 MICE72 Sheff Univ BEng68. Ridley Coll Melbourne ThL90. **d** 90 **p** 90. Australia from 90. *16 Mustang Avenue, Fountain Gate, Melbourne, Victoria, Australia 3805* Melbourne (3) 704-6718

BRAILSFORD, Matthew Charles. b 64. Newc Univ BSc86. Cranmer Hall Dur BA95. **d** 95. C Hull Newland St Jo *York* from 95. *St Faith's House, Dunswell Lane, Dunswell, Hull HU6 0AG* Hull (01482) 854526

BRAIN, George. b 19. St Chad's Coll Dur BA41 DipTh43 MA44. **d** 43 **p** 44. V Leic St Leon *Leic* 54-81; Perm to Offic from 81; rtd 84. *1 Steyning Crescent, Glenfield, Leicester LE3 8PL* Leicester (0116) 287 8451

BRAIN, Michael Charles. b 39. ACP65 Culham Coll Ox 59 Ox Univ Inst of Educn TCert61. Lich Th Coll 68. **d** 70 **p** 71. C Stone St Mich *Lich* 70-73; C Harlescott 73-76; C Longton St

Jas 76-77; P-in-c Dudley St Edm *Worc* 77-79; V from 79; Chapl Dudley Coll of Tech from 77. *St Edmund's Vicarage, 9 Ednam Road, Dudley, W Midlands DY1 1JX* Dudley (01384) 252532

BRAIN, Vernon Roy. b 15. St D Coll Lamp BA38 Ripon Hall Ox 41. **d** 42 **p** 43. V Seaham w Seaham Harbour *Dur* 61-80; rtd 80. *61 Vicarage Close, Silksworth, Sunderland SR3 1JF* 0191-521 0847

BRAITHWAITE, Albert Alfred. b 24. Clifton Th Coll. **d** 59 **p** 60. Chapl RN 62-81; QHC from 77; C Southsea St Jude *Portsm* 82-90; Lic to Offic from 90; rtd 90. *3 Lorne Road, Southsea, Hants PO5 1RR* Portsmouth (01705) 738753

BRAITHWAITE, Canon Michael Royce. b 34. Linc Th Coll 71. **d** 73 **p** 74. C Barrow St Geo w St Luke *Carl* 73-77; V Kells 77-88; RD Calder 84-88; V Lorton and Loweswater w Buttermere from 88; Ldr Rural Life and Agric Team from 93; RD Derwent from 94; Hon Can Carl Cathl from 94. *The Vicarage, Loweswater, Cockermouth, Cumbria CA13 0RU* Lorton (01900) 85237

BRAITHWAITE, Canon Roy. b 34. Dur Univ BA56. Ridley Hall Cam 58. **d** 60 **p** 61. C Blackb St Gabr *Blackb* 60-63; C Burnley St Pet 63-66; V Accrington St Andr 66-74; V Blackb St Jas 74-95; RD Blackb 86-91; Hon Can Blackb Cathl from 93; V Garstang St Helen Churchtown from 95; Dioc Ecum Officer from 95. *St Helen's Vicarage, 6 Vicarage Lane, Churchtown, Preston PR3 0HW* Garstang (01995) 602294

BRAITHWAITE, Wilfrid. b 14. St Chad's Coll Dur BA41 MA44. **d** 42 **p** 43. V Lanercost w Kirkcambeck *Carl* 62-79; P-in-c Walton 78-79; rtd 79; Perm to Offic *Carl* from 82. *Brougham Lodge, Eamont Bridge, Penrith, Cumbria CA10 2BZ* Penrith (01768) 62939

BRALESFORD, Nicholas Robert. b 53. St Jo Coll Nottm LTh79 BTh79. **d** 79 **p** 80. C Leic St Chris *Leic* 79-82; C Heeley *Sheff* 82-85; TV Kings Norton *Birm* 85-90; V Chapel-en-le-Frith *Derby* from 90. *The Vicarage, 71 Manchester Road, Chapel-en-le-Frith, Stockport, Cheshire SK12 6TH* Chapel-en-le-Frith (01298) 812134

BRALEY, Robert James. b 57. Ch Ch Ox BA82 Down Coll Cam BA83 MA87. Ridley Hall Cam 81. **d** 84 **p** 85. C Thames Ditton *Guildf* 84-87; C Gravesend St Geo *Roch* 87-91; Perm to Offic *Blackb* 92-95; Perm to Offic *S'wark* from 95. *1 Glebe House, Waynflete Street, London SW18 3QG* 0181-946 0616

BRAMELD, Peter John. b 40. AKC62. **d** 63 **p** 64. C Hucknall Torkard *S'well* 63-66; C Ordsall 66-70; C Carlton 70-74; C Colwick 70-74; P-in-c Overton w Fyfield and E Kennett *Sarum* 74-75; TV Upper Kennett 75-80; R Hickling w Kinoulton and Broughton Sulney *S'well* 80-94; RD Bingham S 86-91. *108 Westgate, Southwell, Notts NG25 0LT* Southwell (01636) 816226

BRAMHALL, Eric. b 39. St Cath Coll Cam BA61 MA65. Tyndale Hall Bris 61. **d** 63 **p** 64. C Eccleston St Luke *Liv* 63-66; C Bolton Em *Man* 66-69; Perm to Offic *Ches* 70-74; Chapl Ormskirk Hosp Liv from 75; V Aughton Ch Ch *Liv* 75-92; V Childwall All SS from 92. *9 Abbey View, Childwall, Liverpool L16 5EZ* 0151-737 2169

BRAMMER, Charles Harold. b 08. Ripon Hall Ox 54. **d** 54 **p** 55. V St Cleer *Truro* 65-75; rtd 75; Perm to Offic *Liv* 75-85; Perm to Offic *Man* 85-90. *20 The Windrush, Rochdale, Lancs OL12 6DY* Rochdale (01706) 342818

BRAMPTON, Ms Fiona Elizabeth Gordon. b 56. St Jo Coll Dur BA78. Cranmer Hall Dur BA83. **dss** 84 **d** 87 **p** 94. Bris St Andr Hartcliffe *Bris* 84-87; Par Dn 87-90; C Orton Waterville *Ely* from 90; C-in-c Orton Goldhay CD from 90. *5 Riseholme, Orton Goldhay, Peterborough PE2 5SP* Peterborough (01733) 238591

BRANCHE, Brian Maurice. b 37. Chich Th Coll 73. **d** 75 **p** 76. C Brighton Resurr *Chich* 75-78; C Upper Norwood St Jo *Cant* 78-81; P-in-c Croydon St Martin 81-84; V Croydon St Martin *S'wark* 85-88; V St Helier 88-93; V New Eltham All SS from 93. *All Saints' Vicarage, 22 Bercta Road, London SE9 3TZ* 0181-850 9894

BRAND, Frank Ronald Walter. b 25. Lon Coll of Div ALCD56 LTh74. **d** 56 **p** 57. V N Greenford All Hallows *Lon* 67-91; rtd 91; Perm to Offic *B & W* from 91. *23 Hawthorn Grove, Combe Down, Bath BA2 5QA* Bath (01225) 834572

BRAND, Peter John. b 32. Lon Univ BSc54. Edin Dioc NSM Course 75. **d** 83 **p** 84. NSM Edin St Jo *Edin* from 83. *24 Drum Brae Park, Edinburgh EH12 8TF* 0131-339 4406

BRAND, Richard Harold Guthrie. b 65. Dur Univ BA87. Ripon Coll Cuddesdon 87. **d** 89 **p** 90. C N Lynn w St Marg and St Nic *Nor* 89-92; C King's Lynn St Marg w St Nic 92-93; C Croydon St Jo *S'wark* from 93. *8 The Ridgeway, Croydon CR0 4AB* 0181-686 3706

BRAND, Stuart William. b 30. Leeds Univ BSc53. Coll of Resurr Mirfield 53. **d** 55 **p** 56. V Widley w Wymering *Portsm* 67-72; Chapl Fieldhead Hosp Wakef 72-80; Chapl Pinderfields & Stanley Royd Hosps Wakef 72-80; Chapl Brook Gen Hosp

Lon 80-95; Chapl Greenwich Distr Hosp Lon 80-95; rtd 95. *4A Queen's Road, London SE15 2PT* 0171-635 9550

BRANDES, Simon Frank. b 62. Univ of Wales (Ban) BA83. Edin Th Coll 83. **d** 85 **p** 86. C Barton w Peel Green *Man* 85-88; Asst Dioc Youth Officer from 88; C Longsight St Jo w St Cypr 88-90; R 90-94; V Lt Lever from 94. *The Vicarage, Market Street, Little Lever, Bolton BL3 1HH* Farnworth (01204) 700936

BRANDIE, Canon Beaumont Lauder (Beau). b 40. K Coll Lon AKC64 BD66. **d** 65 **p** 66. C Whitton St Aug *Lon* 65-71; C Portsea St Mary *Portsm* 71-77; TR Brighton Resurr *Chich* from 77; Can and Preb Chich Cathl from 87. *St Martin's Rectory, Upper Wellington Road, Brighton BN2 3AN* Brighton (01273) 604687

BRANDON, Dennis Ralph. b 24. Leeds Univ BA50. Linc Th Coll 53. **d** 55 **p** 56. C Pickering *York* 68-71; P-in-c Newton-on-Rawcliffe 71-74; Hon C Newton Kyme 74-80; P-in-c 80-83; rtd 83. *21 The Coppice, Bishopthorpe, York YO2 1QP* York (01904) 707486

BRANDON, Canon Ernest Arthur. b 19. TCD BA42 MA45. CITC 43. **d** 43 **p** 44. I Taghmon w Horetown and Bannow *C & O* 63-94; Preb Ferns Cathl 81-85; Chan 85-91; Prec 91-94; Dioc Info Officer (Ferns) 92-94; rtd 95. *Forge House, Rosegarland, Wellingtonbridge, Co Wexford, Irish Republic* Wexford (51) 61363

BRANDON, Owen Rupert. b 08. Bris Univ MA51 Dur Univ MLitt62. ALCD34. **d** 34 **p** 35. R Fordwich *Cant* 66-73; rtd 73. *Halliwells Nursing Home, Kingswood Road, Tunbridge Wells, Kent TN2 4UN* Tunbridge Wells (01892) 525909

BRANDON, Miss Vera Eileen. b 12. Univ of Wales (Abth) CertEd35 BSc40 Lon Univ DipEd42 BD53. St Mich Ho Ox 51. **dss** 60 **d** 87. Tutor CA Wilson Carlile Coll of Evang 64-74; Community of the Word of God from 75; Lower Homerton St Paul *Lon* 75-80; Clapton Park All So 75-80; Tottenham St Ann 80-83; rtd 83; Tunbridge Wells St Pet *Roch* 83-87; Hon Par Dn 87-89; Perm to Offic from 89. *Florence Balls House, Trinity Close, Tunbridge Wells, Kent TN2 3PP* Tunbridge Wells (01892) 522430

BRANDWOOD, Herbert. b 05. Wadh Coll Ox BA27 BA29 Lon Univ DipEd50. St Aid Birkenhead 38. **d** 39 **p** 40. R Croxton Kerrial and Knipton w Harston etc *Leic* 63-73; rtd 73; Lic to Offic *Nor* 73-75; P-in-c Bodham 75-79; P-in-c E w W Beckham 75-78; Perm to Offic from 83. *Melrose, Morley Road North, Sheringham, Norfolk NR26 8JR* Sheringham (01263) 822281

BRANNAGAN, Alan McKenzie. b 34. Chich Th Coll 66. **d** 68 **p** 69. C N Hull St Mich *York* 68-70; C Dunstable *St Alb* 70-75; R E w W Rudham *Nor* 75-81; V Houghton 75-81; TV Wolv *Lich* 81-87; R W Felton from 87. *St Michael's Rectory, West Felton, Oswestry, Shropshire SY11 4LE* Queens Head (0169188) 228

BRANSCOMBE, Michael Peter. b 65. Cranmer Hall Dur BA95. **d** 95. C Ogley Hay *Lich* from 95. *50 Lichfield Road, Brownhills, Walsall WS8 6HT* Brownhills (01543) 378542

BRANSON, Canon Charles Stanley. b 07. St Aug Coll Cant 34. **d** 37 **p** 38. V Brampton SS Pet and Paul *Derby* 69-76; TR Old Brampton and Loundsley Green 76-78; Hon Can Derby Cathl 74-78; rtd 78; Perm to Offic *Derby* from 78. *5 Westbourne Grove, Chesterfield, Derbyshire S40 3QD* Chesterfield (01246) 569321

BRANSON, Robert David. b 46. Linc Th Coll 74. **d** 77 **p** 78. C Kempston Transfiguration *St Alb* 77-80; C Goldington 80-82; V Marsh Farm 82-91; V Aylsham *Nor* from 91. *The Vicarage, 64 Holman Road, Aylsham, Norwich NR11 6BZ* Aylsham (01263) 733871

BRANT, Anthony Richard. b 44. S Dios Minl Tr Scheme. **d** 82 **p** 83. NSM Felpham w Middleton *Chich* 82-84; C Clymping 84-85; NSM 85-87; Perm to Offic from 88. *23 Somerstown, Chichester, W Sussex PO19 4AG* Chichester (01243) 780550

BRANT, Anthony William. b 31. TD67. Linc Th Coll 73. **d** 75 **p** 76. C Cove St Jo *Guildf* 75-79; P-in-c Puttenham and Wanborough 79-83; V Lightwater 83-93; rtd 93. *1 Phoenix House, Ferring Grange Gardens, Ferring, Worthing, W Sussex BN12 5HU* Worthing (01903) 244772

BRANT, Leslie Harold. b 11. **d** 71 **p** 72. C Lower Sandown St Jo *Portsm* 71-74; P-in-c Newchurch 75-80; rtd 80; Perm to Offic *Portsm* from 82. *Seaspray, 22 The Esplanade, Ryde, Isle of Wight PO33 2DZ* Isle of Wight (01983) 564054

BRANWELL, Edward Bruce. b 20. St Cath Coll Cam BA42 MA46. Linc Th Coll 42. **d** 44 **p** 45. Chapl Aldenham Sch Herts 64-70; Asst Master Burlington Sch Lon 70-77; Perm to Offic *St Alb* 81-84; Perm to Offic *Ches* from 84; rtd 85. *16 King's Crescent West, Chester CH3 5HQ* Chester (01244) 313641

BRASIER, Ralph Henry (Jim). b 30. Cant Sch of Min 82. **d** 85 **p** 86. C S Ashford Ch Ch *Cant* 85-89; V Pembury *Roch* from 89. *The Vicarage, 4 Hastings Road, Pembury, Tunbridge Wells, Kent TN2 4PD* Pembury (01892) 824761

BRASNETT, Canon Leslie Stanley. b 97. Ch Ch Ox BA21 MA24. Cuddesdon Coll 21. d 21 p 22. V Runcorn All SS *Ches* 47-55; rtd 62. *clo Mrs D A Cooke, Barclays Trust Co, PO Box 27, Gadbrook Park, Northwich, Cheshire CW9 7RE* Northwich (01606) 40123

BRASSELL, Canon Kenneth William. b 23. Kelham Th Coll 46. d 50 p 51. V Beckenham St Jas *Roch* 63-88; P-in-c Beckenham St Aug 66-77; P-in-c Beckenham St Mich 77-78; P-in-c Beckenham St Mich w St Aug 77-78; Hon Can Roch Cathl 82-88; rtd 88. *20 College Green, Gloucester GL1 2LR* Gloucester (01452) 309080

BRASSER, Martin James. b 47. MICE72 CEng72 Sheff Univ BEng69. Ridley Coll Melbourne ThL90 BTh93. d 90 p 90. Australia from 90. *PO Box 185, Ferntree Gully, Victoria, Australia 3156* Melbourne (3) 758-1068

BRATLEY, David Frederick. b 42. Linc Th Coll 80. d 82 p 83. C Holbeach *Linc* 82-85; R Fleet w Gedney from 85. *The Rectory, Fleet, Spalding, Lincs PE12 8NQ* Holbeach (01406) 23795

BRATTON, Mark Quinn. b 62. Barrister 87 Lon Univ BA84 City Univ DipLaw85. Wycliffe Hall Ox BA94 DipMin94. d 94. C W Ealing St Jo w St Jas *Lon* from 94. *41 Leighton Road, London W13 9EL* 0181-566 2512

BRAUN, Dr Thom. b 53. St Jo Coll Ox BA76 MA76 Univ Coll Lon PhD80. S'wark Ord Course 89. d 92 p 93. Hon C Surbiton St Andr and St Mark *S'wark* from 92. *8 Kings Drive, Surbiton, Surrey KT5 8NG* 0181-399 6898

BRAUND, George Basil. b 26. SS Coll Cam BA50 MA54. Ely Th Coll 51. d 53 p 54. OGS from 52; Superior OGS 69-75; Travel Missr USPG 68-73; Overseas Sec USPG 73-79; Lic to Offic *Ox* 69-88; Assoc Sec Miss & Ecum Affairs ACC 79-88; Co Sec Angl Reformed Internat Commn 80-86; TV Wallingford w Crowmarsh Gifford etc *Ox* 88-93; rtd 93. *40 Warmans Close, Wantage, Oxon OX12 9XT* Wantage (01235) 767761

BRAVINER, William Edward (**Bill**). b 66. Leic Poly BSc88 ACA91. Cranmer Hall Dur BA94 DMS95. d 95. C Royton St Anne *Man* from 95. *387 Middleton Road, Royton, Oldham OL2 5EH* 0161-626 5986

BRAY, Anthony Markham. b 16. Magd Coll Cam BA37 MA43. Cuddesdon Coll 38. d 39 p 40. V Posbury Chap Ex 53-75; P-in-c Otterton *Ex* 76-80; rtd 81. Lic to Offic *Ex* from 81. *Quince, King Street, Colyton, Devon EX13 6LA* Colyton (01297) 553149

BRAY, Christopher Laurence. b 53. Leeds Univ BSc74 Qu Univ Kingston Ontario MSc76. St Jo Coll Nottm DipTh79 DPS81. d 81 p 82. C Aughton Ch Ch *Liv* 81-84; Hon C Scarborough St Mary w Ch Ch and H Apostles *York* 84-88; Chapl Scarborough Coll 84-88; V St Helens St Matt Thatto Heath *Liv* from 88. *The Vicarage, St Matthew's Grove, St Helens, Merseyside WA10 3SE* St Helens (01744) 24644

BRAY, Gerald Lewis. b 48. McGill Univ Montreal BA69. Ridley Hall Cam 76. d 78 p 79. C Canning Town St Cedd *Chelmsf* 78-80; Tutor Oak Hill NSM Course 80-92; Lic to Offic *Lon* 81-92; Ed Churchman from 93. *Church Society, Dean Wace House, 16 Rosslyn Road, Watford WD1 7EY* Watford (01923) 235111 Fax as telephone

BRAY, Jeremy Baptist. b 40. Man Univ BA62. Wells Th Coll 62. d 64 p 65. C Bris St Andr w St Bart *Bris* 64-67; C Bris H Cross Inns Court 67-71; C-in-c Stockwood CD 71-73; V Bris Ch the Servant Stockwood 73-83; RD Brislington 79-83; P-in-c Chippenham St Pet 83-88; V 88-93; V Fishponds St Jo from 93. *St John's Vicarage, Mayfield Park, Bristol BS16 3NW* Bristol (0117) 965 4130

BRAY, Joyce. b 32. CA Tr Coll. dss 80 d 87 p 94. Bloxworth *Lich* 80-84; Derringham Bank *York* 84-87; Par Dn 87-94; NSM from 94; rtd 94. *413 Willerby Road, Hull HU5 5JD* Hull (01482) 502193

BRAY, Kenneth John. b 31. St Mich Coll Llan 65. d 67 p 72. C S Harrow St Paul *Lon* 71-73; C Hillingdon St Jo 73-76; C Chipping Sodbury and Old Sodbury *Glouc* 76-79; C Worle *B & W* 79-80; Lic to Offic *Ches* 80-83; TV Wrexham *St As* 83-85; V Llay 85-94; rtd 94. *21 Glenthorn Road, Bexhill-on-Sea, E Sussex TN39 3QH* Bexhill-on-Sea (01424) 213965

BRAY, Richard. b 29. Linc Th Coll 55. d 57 p 58. R Tye Green w Netteswell *Chelmsf* 62-93; rtd 93. *14 The Wayback, Saffron Walden, Essex CB10 2AX* Saffron Walden (01799) 526901

BRAY, Thomas Chadwick. b 08. Qu Coll Birm 46. d 48 p 49. V Bolam *Newc* 69-74; rtd 74. *33 Heron Way, Newport, Shropshire TF10 8QF* Newport (01952) 825872

BRAYBROOKE, Marcus Christopher Rossi. b 38. Magd Coll Cam BA62 MA65 Lon Univ MPhil68. Wells Th Coll 63. d 64 p 65. C Frindsbury w Upnor *Roch* 67-72; TV Strood St Fran 72-73; P-in-c Swainswick w Langridge and Woolley *B & W* 73-76; Dir of Tr 79-84; Inter C Bath Ch Ch Prop Chpl 84-91; Exec Dir Coun of Chrs and Jews 84-87; rtd 88; Perm to Offic *Bris* 88-93; Preb Wells Cathl *B & W* from 90; Chapl Bath St Mary Magd Holloway 92-93; Perm to Offic 93; NSM Dorchester *Ox* from 93. *The Rectory, Marsh Baldon, Oxford OX44 9LS* Oxford (0865) 343215 Fax 343575

BRAZELL, Denis Illtyd Anthony. b 42. Trin Coll Cam BA64 MA68. Wycliffe Hall Ox 78. d 80 p 81. C Cheltenham Ch Ch *Glouc* 80-84; V Reading St Agnes w St Paul *Ox* from 84. *The Vicarage, 290 Northumberland Avenue, Reading RG2 8DE* Reading (01734) 874448

BRAZELL, Mrs Elizabeth Jane. b 44. LRAM64 ARCM65 GGSM65 AGSM65. Wycliffe Hall Ox 85. dss 86 d 87 p 94. Reading St Agnes w St Paul *Ox* 86-87; Par Dn 87-94; C from 94. *The Vicarage, 290 Northumberland Avenue, Reading RG2 8DE* Reading (01734) 874448

BRAZIER, Eric James Arthur. b 37. Qu Coll Birm 84. d 86 p 87. C Lighthorne *Cov* 86-89; P-in-c 89-92; P-in-c Chesterton 89-92; P-in-c Newbold Pacey w Moreton Morrell 89-92; R Astbury and Smallwood *Ches* from 92. *The Rectory, Astbury, Congleton, Cheshire CW12 4RQ* Congleton (01260) 272625

BRAZIER, Canon Raymond Venner (**Ray**). b 40. Wells Th Coll 68. d 71 p 72. C Horfield St Greg *Bris* 71-75; P-in-c Bris St Nath w St Kath 75-79; V 79-84; P-in-c Kingsdown 80-84; V Bris St Matt and St Nath from 84; RD Horfield 85-91; P-in-c Bishopston from 93; Hon Can Bris Cathl from 94. *The Vicarage, 11 Glentworth Road, Bristol BS6 7EG* Bristol (0117) 942 4186

BRAZINGTON, David Albert. b 36. Open Univ BA86. Glouc Th Course 75. d 78 p 79. Hon C Wotton St Mary *Glouc* 78-82; P-in-c Huntley 82-83; P-in-c Longhope 82-83; R Huntley and Longhope 83-89; R Glouc St Mary de Crypt w St Jo and Ch Ch 89-95; P-in-c Glouc St Mary de Lode and St Nic 92-95; R Glouc St Mary de Crypt w St Jo, Ch Ch etc from 95; Chapl Glouc Coll of Art and Tech 89-94. *The Rectory, 38 St Mary's Square, Gloucester GL1 2QY* Gloucester (01452) 412679

BREADEN, Very Rev Robert William. b 37. Edin Th Coll 58. d 61 p 62. C Broughty Ferry *Bre* 61-65; R from 72; R Carnoustie 65-72; Can St Paul's Cathl Dundee from 77; Dean Bre from 84. *46 Seafield Road, Broughty Ferry, Dundee DD5 3AN* Dundee (01382) 77477

BREADMORE, Martin Christopher. b 67. Lon Univ LLB89. Wycliffe Hall Ox BTh93. d 93 p 94. C Herne Bay Ch Ch *Cant* from 93. *19 Central Avenue, Herne Bay, Kent CT6 8RX* Herne Bay (01227) 360902

BREAR, Alvin Douglas. d 87 p 88. NSM Leic H Spirit *Leic* 87-88; NSM Leic St Pet 88; NSM Leic Ch Sav from 88. *84 Parkland Drive, Oadby, Leicester LE2 4DG* Leicester (0116) 271 4137

BREARLEY, Mrs Janet Mary. b 48. Cranmer Hall Dur 88. d 90 p 94. C Prudhoe *Newc* 90-91; C Fenham St Jas and St Basil from 91. *32 Auburn Gardens, Fenham, Newcastle upon Tyne NE4 9XP* 0191-274 0022

BREAY, John. b 19. Selw Coll Cam BA41 MA45 St Chad's Coll Dur DipTh42. d 42 p 43. V Shepreth *Ely* 59-77; V Barrington 77; V Gt w Lt Chesterford *Chelmsf* 77-79; rtd 79; Perm to Offic *Ely* from 79. *Flat 18, Havenfield, Arbury Road, Cambridge CB4 2JY* Cambridge (01223) 62226

BREBNER, Martin James. b 47. ARCS68 Imp Coll Lon BSc68. St Alb Minl Tr Scheme 87. d 90 p 91. Hon C Letchworth St Paul w Willian *St Alb* 90-94; Perm to Offic from 95. *42 Farthing Drive, Letchworth, Herts SG6 2TR* Letchworth (01462) 679129

BRECHIN, Mrs Valerie Becky Allan (**Val**). b 43. Ridley Hall Cam CTMin93. d 93 p 94. C Ipswich All Hallows *St E* from 93. *9 Melplash Road, Ipswich IP3 8QL* Ipswich (01473) 272725

BRECHIN, Bishop of. See HALLIDAY, Rt Rev Robert Taylor

BRECHIN, Dean of. See BREADEN, Very Rev Robert William

BRECKLES, Robert Wynford. b 48. St Edm Hall Ox BA72 MA74 CertEd. St Jo Coll Dur DipTh79. d 79 p 80. C Bulwell St Mary *S'well* 79-84; P-in-c Lady Bay 84; V from 84. *The Vicarage, 121 Holme Road, Nottingham NG2 5AG* Nottingham (0115) 981 3565

BRECKNELL, David Jackson. b 32. Keble Coll Ox BA53 MA57. St Steph Ho Ox 56. d 58 p 59. C Streatham St Pet *S'wark* 58-62; C Sneinton St Steph w St Alb *S'well* 62-64; C Solihull *Birm* 64-68; V Streatham St Paul *S'wark* 68-75; R Rumboldswyke *Chich* 75-81; P-in-c Portfield 79-81; R Whyke w Rumboldswhyke and Portfield 81-95; rtd 95. *8 Priory Close, Boxgrove, Chichester, W Sussex PO18 0EA* Chichester (01243) 782535

BRECKWOLDT, Peter Hans. b 57. Man Poly BA79. Oak Hill Th Coll BA88. d 88 p 89. C Knutsford St Jo and Toft *Ches* 88-92; V Moulton *Pet* from 92. *The Vicarage, 30 Cross Street, Moulton, Northampton NN3 1RZ* Northampton (01604) 491060

BRECON, Archdeacon of. See JAMES, Ven David Brian

BRECON, Dean of. See HARRIS, Very Rev John

BREED, Kenneth Wilfred. b 11. Leeds Univ BA33. Coll of Resurr Mirfield 33. d 35 p 36. V Shirley *Birm* 51-77; rtd 77; Hon C St Andr Holborn *Lon* 77-79; Perm to Offic *B & W* 86-91. *4 Yard Court, East Street, Warminster, Wilts BA12 9NY* Warminster (01985) 213230

BREEDS, Christopher Roger. b 51. LGSM83 ACertCM87 Lon Univ CertEd73. Chich Th Coll 84. d 87 p 88. C E Grinstead St

Swithun *Chich* 87-90; TV Aldrington 90-92; P-in-c Hove St Andr Old Ch 92-93; TV Hove from 93. *The Vicarage, 17 Vallance Gardens, Hove, E Sussex BN3 2DB* Brighton (01273) 734859

BREEN, Michael James. b 58. Oak Hill Th Coll BA79 MA85 LTh Cranmer Hall Dur 81. **d** 83 **p** 84. C Cam St Martin *Ely* 83-87; V Clapham Park All SS *S'wark* 87-92; USA 92-94; TR Crookes St Thos *Sheff* from 94. *The Rectory, 18A Hallam Gate Road, Sheffield S10 5BT* Sheffield (0114) 268 6362

BREENE, Timothy Patrick Brownell. b 59. Kent Univ BA81 CCC Cam BA89. Ridley Hall Cam 87. **d** 90 **p** 93. C Hadleigh w Layham and Shelley *St E* 90-95; C Martlesham w Brightwell from 95. *4 Sadlers Place, Martlesham Heath, Ipswich IP5 7SS* Ipswich (01473) 625433

BREFFITT, Geoffrey Michael. b 46. CChem MRIC72 Trent Poly CertEd77 DipPSE82. Qu Coll Birm 87. **d** 89 **p** 90. C Prenton *Ches* 89-92; V Frankby w Greasby from 92. *The Vicarage, 14 Arrowe Road, Greasby, South Wirral L49 1RA* 0151-678 6155

BRENCHLEY, Miss Joy Pamela. b 40. **d** 91. NSM Ramsgate St Luke *Cant* from 91. *66 Upper Dumpton Park Road, Ramsgate, Kent CT11 7PG* Thanet (01843) 587124

BRENDON-COOK, John Lyndon. b 37. FRICS. SW Minl Tr Course. **d** 81 **p** 82. NSM Bodmin *Truro* 81-82; NSM St Breoke and Egloshayle 82-90; NSM Helland 90-94; P-in-c from 94; NSM Cardynham 90-94. *Treworder Byre, 119 Egloshayle Road, Wadebridge, Cornwall PL27 6AG* Wadebridge (01208) 812488

BRENNAN, Dr John Lester. b 20. MRCP51 FRCPath77 Barrister-at-Law (Middle Temple) 71 Lon Univ MB, BS44 DipTh47 MD52 LLM86. St Aug Coll Cant 54. **d** 55 **p** 56. India 55-65; Hon C Woodside Park St Barn *Lon* 65-69; Lic to Offic *Lich* 69-88; P-in-c Chrishall *Chelmsf* 88-89; Hon C 89-91; Hon C Heydon, Gt and Lt Chishill, Chrishall etc 91-93; Perm to Offic *St Alb* from 93. *16 Butterfield Road, Wheathampstead, Herts AL4 8PU* Wheathampstead (01582) 832230

BRENNAN, Samuel James. b 16. St Aid Birkenhead. **d** 57 **p** 58. I Aghalee *D & D* 69-84; RD Shankill 77-84; rtd 84. *71 Bangor Road, Newtownards, Co Down BT23 3BZ* Newtownards (01247) 819139

BRENNEN, Canon Dr Colin. b 15. Lon Univ BA47 BD56 Dur Univ PhD88. Lon Coll Div 46. **d** 48 **p** 49. V Whitworth w Spennymoor *Dur* 58-78; RD Auckland 74-82; Hon Can Dur Cathl 78-93; V Hamsterley 78-82; rtd 82. *13 Springwell Road, Durham DH1 4LR* 0191-386 9386

BRENTNALL, David John. b 53. UEA BA75 MPhil82. Ridley Hall Cam 84. **d** 86 **p** 87. C Eaton *Nor* 86-90; V Stevenage St Pet Broadwater *St Alb* from 90. *St Peter's House, 1 The Willows, Stevenage, Herts SG2 8AN* Stevenage (01438) 352447

BRENTON, Basil. b 28. Sarum Th Coll. **d** 55 **p** 56. V Cowfold *Chich* 68-94; rtd 94. *74 Silver Lane, Billingshurst, W Sussex RH14 9QB* Billingshurst (01403) 783604

BRETEL, Keith Michael. b 51. St Mich Coll Llan 79. **d** 81 **p** 82. C Thundersley *Chelmsf* 81-84; CF from 84. *c/o MOD (Army), Bagshot Park, Bagshot, Surrey GU19 5PL* Bagshot (01276) 471717 Fax 412834

BRETHERTON, Donald John. b 18. Lon Univ BD57. Handsworth Coll Birm 38 Headingley Coll Leeds 38 St Aug Coll Cant 59. **d** 60 **p** 61. In Meth Ch 42-59; V Thornton Heath St Jude *Cant* 62-70; V Herne 70-82; RD Reculver 74-80; rtd 82; Perm to Offic *Cant* 84-92. *11 Mortonhall Park Way, Edinburgh EH17 8BW* 0131-664 6537

BRETHERTON, Canon William Alan. b 22. St Cath Coll Cam BA43 MA47. Lon Coll of Div BD49 ALCD49. **d** 49 **p** 50. V Ince Ch Ch *Liv* 65-72; V Kirkdale St Mary 72-73; V Kirkdale St Mary and St Athanasius 73-87; RD Liv 81-87; Hon Can Liv Cathl 81-87; rtd 87. *3 Bradville Road, Liverpool L9 9BH* 0151-525 0866

BRETHERTON-HAWKSHEAD-TALBOT, Richard Dolben. b 11. Trin Coll Cam BA32 MA56. Ely Th Coll 32. **d** 34 **p** 35. R Eccleston *Blackb* 58-78; rtd 78; Lic to Offic *Blackb* from 79. *The Delph, 71 Marsh Lane, Longton, Preston PR4 5ZL* Preston (01772) 600705

BRETT, Dennis Roy Anthony. b 46. Sarum & Wells Th Coll 86. **d** 88 **p** 89. C Bradford-on-Avon *Sarum* 88-92; P-in-c Bishopstrow and Boreham from 92; Chapl Warminster Hosp from 92. *The Rectory, 8 Rock Lane, Warminster, Wilts BA12 9JZ* Warminster (01985) 213000

BRETT, Canon Paul Gadsby. b 41. St Edm Hall Ox BA62 MA66. Wycliffe Hall Ox 64. **d** 65 **p** 66. C Bury St Pet *Man* 65-68; Asst Ind Chapl 68-72; Ind Chapl *Worc* 72-76; Asst Sec Ind Cttee of Gen Syn Bd for Soc Resp 76-84; Dir Soc Resp *Chelmsf* 85-94; Can Res Chelmsf Cathl 85-94; R Shenfield from 94. *The Rectory, 41 Worrin Road, Shenfield, Brentwood, Essex CM15 8DH* Brentwood (01277) 220360

BRETT, Canon Peter Graham Cecil. b 35. Em Coll Cam BA59 MA63. Cuddesdon Coll 59. **d** 61 **p** 62. C Tewkesbury w Walton Cardiff *Glouc* 61-64; C Bournemouth St Pet *Win*

64-66; Chapl Dur Univ *Dur* 66-72; R Houghton le Spring 72-83; RD Houghton 80-83; Can Res Cant Cathl *Cant* from 83. *22 The Precincts, Canterbury, Kent CT1 2EP* Canterbury (01227) 459757

BRETTELL, Robert Michael. b 20. St Cath Soc Ox BA49 MA54. Lon Coll of Div 46 Wycliffe Hall Ox 47. **d** 49 **p** 50. V Clifton Ch Ch w Em *Bris* 62-73; V Eastbourne H Trin *Chich* 73-82; V Bexhill St Steph 82-86; rtd 86; Perm to Offic *Chich* from 86. *229 Little Ridge Avenue, St Leonards-on-Sea, E Sussex TN37 7HN* Hastings (01424) 752035

BREUKELMAN, Stephen Peter. b 55. Keble Coll Ox BA77 DPhil79. Trin Coll Bris 83. **d** 86 **p** 87. C Gt Horton *Bradf* 86-90; V Sunnyside w Bourne End *St Alb* from 90. *St Michael's Vicarage, Berkhamsted, Herts HP4 2PP* Berkhamsted (01442) 865100

BREW, William Kevin Maddock. b 49. BA MSc. **d** 78 **p** 79. C Raheny w Coolock *D & G* 78-80; Bp's C Dub Finglas 80-83; I Mountmellick w Coolbanagher, Rosenallis etc *M & K* 83-89; I Ahoghill w Portglenone *Conn* from 89. *42 Church Street, Ahoghill, Ballymena, Co Antrim BT42 2PA* Ahoghill (01266) 871240

BREW, William Philip. b 43. FCollP84 Derby Coll of Educn CertEd64 Liv Univ DSpEd72. N Ord Course 84. **d** 87 **p** 88. In Independent Meth Min 70-83; Hd Master Birtenshaw Sch 78-90; NSM Holcombe *Man* 87-90; TV Horwich 91-93; TV Horwich and Rivington from 93. *St Elizabeth's Vicarage, Cedar Avenue, Horwich, Bolton BL6 6HT* Horwich (01204) 669120

BREWER, Barry James. b 44. Oak Hill Th Coll 72. **d** 75 **p** 76. C Hove Bp Hannington Memorial Ch *Chich* 75-78; C Church Stretton *Heref* 78-81; TV Bishopsnympton, Rose Ash, Mariansleigh etc *Ex* 81-87; R Swynnerton and Tittensor *Lich* from 87. *3 Rectory Gardens, Swynnerton, Stone, Staffs ST15 0RT* Swynnerton (0178135) 564

BREWER, Canon John Herbert. b 13. DDEd. St Steph Ho Ox 37. **d** 39 **p** 40. V Isleworth St Fran *Lon* 66-78; rtd 78; Lic to Offic *Nor* 78-86; Perm to Offic from 86. *36 Cleaves Drive, Walsingham, Norfolk NR22 6EQ* Walsingham (01328) 820579

BREWIN, Dr David Frederick. b 39. Leic Poly BSc PhD. Lich Th Coll 63. **d** 66 **p** 67. C Shrewsbury H Cross *Lich* 66-69; C Birstall *Leic* 69-73; V Eyres Monsell 73-79; V E Goscote 79-82; V E Goscote w Ratcliffe and Rearsby 82-90; R Thurcaston 90-91; R Thurcaston w Cropston from 92. *The Rectory, 74 Anstey Lane, Thurcaston, Leicester LE7 7JA* Leicester (0116) 236 2525

BREWIN, Donald Stewart (Don). b 41. Ch Coll Cam BA62 MA66. Ridley Hall Cam 68. **d** 71 **p** 72. C Ecclesall *Sheff* 71-75; V Anston 75-81; V Walton H Trin *Ox* 81-89; TR 89-94; RD Aylesbury 90-94; Nat Dir SOMA from 94. *Wickham Cottage, Gaddesden Turn, Billington, Leighton Buzzard, Beds LU7 9BW* Leighton Buzzard (01525) 373644 Fax 853787

BREWIN, Canon Eric Walter. b 16. Hertf Coll Ox BA42 MA42. Ripon Hall Ox 38. **d** 40 **p** 41. RD Forest S *Glouc* 57-81; Hon Can Glouc Cathl 65-81; R Leckhampton St Pet 70-81; rtd 81; Perm to Offic *Glouc* from 82. *The Pleck, Llangrove, Ross-on-Wye, Herefordshire HR9 6EU* Llangarron (01989) 770487

BREWIN, Karan Rosemary. b 42. CA Tr Coll 77 Glas NSM Course 80. **dss** 84 **d** 85. Clarkston *Glas* 84-89; Hon C 86-89 and from 91; OHP from 89. *85 Mearns Road, Clarkston, Glasgow G76 7LF* 0141-620 3203

BREWIN, Wilfred Michael. b 45. Nottm Univ BA69. Cuddesdon Coll 69. **d** 70 **p** 71. C Walker *Newc* 70-73; C Alnwick St Paul 73-74; C Alnwick w Edlingham and Bolton Chpl 74-77; Fell Sheff Univ 77-79; C Greenhill *Sheff* 79; P-in-c Eggleston *Dur* 79-81; V Norton St Mich 81-87; V Headington *Ox* from 87. *The Vicarage, 33 St Andrew's Road, Oxford OX3 9DL* Oxford (01865) 61094

BREWSTER, David Pearson. b 30. Clare Coll Cam BA54 MA58 Lon Univ BA65 Or Coll Ox MA66 DPhil76. Ridley Hall Cam. **d** 58 **p** 59. Lect Lady Spencer-Churchill Coll Ox 68-71; New Zealand 71-78; V Brockenhurst *Win* 78-95; rtd 95. *4 Saxonford Road, Christchurch, Dorset BH23 4ES* Christchurch (01425) 277860

BREWSTER, Jonathan David. b 67. **d** 94 **p** 95. C Gt Horton *Bradf* from 94. *18 Windermere Road, Great Horton, Bradford BD7 4RQ* Bradford (01274) 573261

BREWSTER, Lester Arnold. b 27. Fitzw Ho Cam BA51 MA55. Wycliffe Hall Ox 51. **d** 53 **p** 54. Org Sec Ox Miss to Calcutta 60-67; Lic to Offic *S'wark* from 67; rtd 93. *155 Demesne Road, Wallington, Surrey SM6 8EW* 0181-647 4174

BREWSTER, Noel Theodore. b 16. CCC Cam BA38 MA42. Qu Coll Birm 38. **d** 39 **p** 40. R Chilcomb w Win All SS and Chesil *Win* 69-70; V Grantchester *Ely* 71-86; rtd 86; Perm to Offic *Ely* 86-90; Chapl St Cross *Win* 86-90. *5 Carthagena, Sutton Scotney, Winchester, Hants SO21 3LJ* Winchester (01962) 760667

BREWSTER, William Taylor. b 26. Bps' Coll Cheshunt 58. **d** 59 **p** 60. R Woolfardisworthy w Kennerleigh *Ex* 61-71; R Washford Pyne w Puddington 61-71; P-in-c Cruwys Morchard 68-71; RD Cadbury 68-71; P-in-c Poughill w Stockleigh English 71; Asst Chapl HM Pris Man 71; Chapl HM Pris Maidstone 72-77; Chapl HM Pris Blundeston 77-84; Chapl HM Pris Featherstone 84-89; rtd 89; Perm to Offic *Lich* from 89. *4 Pinfold Road, Lichfield, Staffs WS13 7BX* Lichfield (01543) 254983

BRIAN, Stephen Frederick. b 54. Brighton Coll of Educn CertEd76 Sussex Univ BEd77 Birm Univ DipTh84 Open Univ MA90. Qu Coll Birm 82. **d** 85 **p** 86. C Scotforth *Blackb* 85-88; V Freckleton from 88. *Holy Trinity Vicarage, 3 Sunnyside Close, Freckleton, Preston PR4 1YJ* Freckleton (01772) 632209

BRIAN EDWARD, Brother. *See* STATHAM, Brian Edward

BRICE, Christopher John. b 48. St Edm Ho Cam MA80. Wycliffe Hall Ox 82. **d** 82 **p** 83. C N Hinksey *Ox* 82-86; Chapl Nuff Coll Ox 84-86; V S Hackney St Mich w Haggerston St Paul *Lon* 86-93; Dir Dioc Bd for Soc Resp from 93. *141 Culford Road, London N1 4HX* 0171-249 6290

BRICE, Jonathan Andrew William. b 61. **d** 92 **p** 93. C Buckhurst Hill *Chelmsf* from 92. *Glebe House, High Road, Buckhurst Hill, Essex IG9 5RX* 0181-504 6652

BRICE, Neil Alan. b 59. Man Univ BA81 Hughes Hall Cam CertEd87. Westcott Ho Cam 82. **d** 84 **p** 85. C Longton *Lich* 84-86; Hd of Relig Studies Coleridge Community Coll Cam 87-89; NSM Cherry Hinton St Andr *Ely* 88-89; C Fulbourn 89-92; C Gt Wilbraham 89-92; C Lt Wilbraham 89-92; V Arrington from 92; R Orwell from 92; R Wimpole from 92; R Croydon w Clopton from 92. *The Rectory, Fishers Lane, Orwell, Royston, Herts SG8 5QX* Cambridge (01223) 208653

BRICE, Paul Earl Philip. b 54. Bath Univ BSc77. Wycliffe Hall Ox 83. **d** 86 **p** 87. C Gt Baddow *Chelmsf* 86-89; Chapl Imp Coll *Lon* 89-95; St Mary's Hosp Med Sch 89-95; Chapl RCA 90-95; Sec HE/Chapl Gen Syn Bd of Educn from 95; Hon C Upper Chelsea H Trin w St Jude *Lon* from 95. *18 Collingham Road, London SW5 0LX* 0171-259 2301

BRIDCUT, William John. b 38. CITC 67. **d** 70 **p** 71. C Lisburn Ch Ch Cathl *Conn* 71-74; Dub Irish Ch Miss *D & G* from 74; Chapl Arbour Hill Pris from 88. *Irish Church Missions, 28 Bachelor's Walk, Dublin 1, Irish Republic* Dublin (1) 873-0829 or 821-2165 Fax 872-2669

BRIDGE, Very Rev Antony Cyprian. b 14. FSA. Linc Th Coll 53. **d** 55 **p** 56. Dean Guildf 68-86; rtd 86. *34 London Road, Deal, Kent CT14 9TE* Deal (01304) 366792

BRIDGE, Miss Helen Cecily. b 25. SRN47 SCM49 Open Univ BA80. Lambeth STh78 Dalton Ho Bris 70 Trin Coll Bris 70. **dss** 74 **d** 87 **p** 94. Tonbridge St Steph *Roch* 74-75; Countess of Ches Hosp 75-84; Plemstall w Guilden Sutton *Ches* 85-87; Hon Par Dn 87-88; NSM Stockport St Mary from 88. *25 Rectory Fields, Stockport, Cheshire SK1 4BX* 0161-477 2154

BRIDGE, Martin. b 45. Lon Univ BA66 Linacre Coll Ox BA71 MA73. St Steph Ho Ox 69. **d** 72 **p** 73. C St Peter-in-Thanet *Cant* 72-77; New Zealand from 77. *5 Landscape Road, Papatoetoe, PO Box 23-073, New Zealand* Auckland (9) 278-0656

BRIDGE-COLLYNS, Douglas Herbert. b 26. Nottm Univ BSc48 MPhil71. St Steph Ho Ox 51. **d** 53 **p** 54. C Leic St Pet *Leic* 53-57; S Rhodesia 58-65; C Nottm St Pet and St Jas *S'well* 65-68; Lic to Offic *Derby* 68-85; Perm to Offic *S'well* 76-84; Chapl Abbots Bromley Sch 84-87; V Whatton w Aslockton, Hawksworth, Scarrington etc *S'well* from 87. *The Vicarage, Main Street, Aslockton, Nottingham NG13 9AL* Whatton (01949) 51040

BRIDGEN, John William. b 40. K Coll Cam BA62 MA66. Ripon Hall Ox 66. **d** 70 **p** 72. C Headstone St Geo *Lon* 70-71; C Hanwell St Mary 71-75; C Tolladine *Worc* 75; TV Worc St Barn w Ch Ch 76; R Barrow *St E* 76-83; V Stadhampton St Mary 76-83; Perm to Offic *Ely* 84-88 and from 91; rtd 88; Perm to Offic *Glas* 89-91. *57 St Philip's Road, Cambridge CB1 3DA* Cambridge (01223) 248096

BRIDGEN, Mark Stephen. b 63. K Coll Lon BD85. Cranmer Hall Dur 86. **d** 88 **p** 89. C Kidderminster St Jo *Worc* 88-90; C Kidderminster St Jo and H Innocents 90-92; C Nor St Pet Mancroft w St Jo Maddermarket *Nor* 92-94; V Longbridge *Birm* from 94. *St John's Vicarage, 220 Longbridge Lane, Birmingham B31 4JT* 0121-475 3484

BRIDGER, Dr Francis William. b 51. Pemb Coll Ox BA73 MA78 Bris Univ DipTh75 PhD80. Trin Coll Bris 74. **d** 78 **p** 79. C Islington St Jude Mildmay Park *Lon* 80-82; C Mildmay Grove St Jude and St Paul 82; Lect St Jo Coll Nottm 82-90; Dir of Courses 88-89; Dir of Studies 89-90; Lic to Offic *S'well* 82-90; V Woodthorpe from 90. *St Mark's Vicarage, 37A Melbury Road, Nottingham NG5 4PG* Nottingham (0115) 926 7859

BRIDGER, Canon Gordon Frederick. b 32. Selw Coll Cam BA53 MA. Ridley Hall Cam 54. **d** 56 **p** 57. C Islington St Mary *Lon* 56-60; C Cam St Sepulchre *Ely* 60-62; V Fulham St Mary N End *Lon* 62-69; C Edin St Thos *Edin* 69-76; R Heigham H Trin *Nor* 76-87; RD Nor S 79-86; Hon Can Nor Cathl 84-87; Prin Oak Hill Th Coll from 87. *10 Farm Lane, London N14 4PP* 0181-441 7091 or 449 0467 Fax 441 5996

BRIDGER, Malcolm John. b 36. AKC62. **d** 63 **p** 64. C Sheff St Cuth *Sheff* 63-66; C Wythenshawe Wm Temple Ch CD *Man* 66-67; C-in-c Lower Kersal CD 67-72; V Lower Kersal 72-74; C Ifield *Chich* 75-78; TV 78-84; P-in-c Brentford St Paul w St Lawr and St Geo *Lon* 84-87; P-in-c Gunnersbury St Jas 85-87; TR Brentford 87-94; R Tidworth, Ludgershall and Faberstown *Sarum* from 94; RD Avon from 95. *The Rectory, 10 St James' Street, Ludgershall, Andover, Hants SP11 9QF* Andover (01264) 790393

BRIDGER, Nigel Egerton. b 23. Dartmouth RN Coll 40. Wells Th Coll 59. **d** 61 **p** 62. C Neston *Ches* 61-64; S Africa from 64. *PO Box 119, Queenstown, 5320 South Africa* Queenstown (451) 4377

BRIDGER, Mrs Renee Winifred. b 45. Lon Univ BD76. Trin Coll Bris. **dss** 80 **d** 87 **p** 94. Islington St Jude Mildmay Park *Lon* 80-82; Mildmay Grove St Jude and St Paul 82; St Jo Coll Nottm from 87; Hon Par Dn Chilwell *S'well* 87-88; C Woodthorpe 90-95; NSM from 95. *St Mark's Vicarage, 37A Melbury Road, Nottingham NG5 4PG* Nottingham (0115) 926 7859

✠BRIDGES, Rt Rev Dewi Morris. b 33. Univ of Wales (Lamp) BA54 CCC Cam BA56 MA60. Westcott Ho Cam 57. **d** 57 **p** 58 **c** 88. C Rhymney *Mon* 57-60; C Chepstow 60-63; V Tredegar St Jas 63-65; Lic to Offic *Worc* 65-69; V Kempsey 69-79; RD Upton 74-79; R Tenby and Gumfreston *St D* 79-85; RD Narberth 80-82; Adn St D 82-88; R Tenby 85-88; Bp S & B from 88. *Ely Tower, Brecon, Powys LD3 9DE* Brecon (01874) 622008

BRIDGES, Mrs Gillian Mary (Gill). b 43. E Anglian Minl Tr Course 85. **d** 88 **p** 94. Hon C Hellesdon *Nor* from 88. *2 Vera Road, Norwich NR6 5HU* Norwich (01603) 789634

BRIDGES, Ven Peter Sydney Godfrey. b 25. ARIBA51 Birm Univ DipL&A67. Linc Th Coll 56. **d** 58 **p** 59. Perm to Offic *Birm* 65-72; Lect Aston Univ 68-72; Dir Dioc Research and Development Unit 72-77; Adn Southend *Chelmsf* 72-77; P-in-c Southend St Jo w St Mark, All SS w St Fran etc 72-77; Adn Cov 77-83; Can Th Cov Cathl 77-90; Adn Warw 83-90; rtd 90; Dioc Adv for Chr Spirituality 90-93. *25 Rivermead Close, Romsey, Hants SO51 8HQ* Romsey (01794) 512889

BRIDGEWATER, Guy Stevenson. b 60. Ch Ch Ox BA83. Trin Coll Bris BA87. **d** 87 **p** 88. C Radipole and Melcombe Regis *Sarum* 87-90; Chapl Lee Abbey 90-93; Lic to Offic *Ex* 90-93; V Cranbrook *Cant* from 93. *The Vicarage, Waterloo Road, Cranbrook, Kent TN17 3JQ* Cranbrook (01580) 712150

BRIDGLAND, Cyril John Edwin. b 21. Trin Coll Bris 42. **d** 45 **p** 46. V Redhill H Trin *S'wark* 58-87; rtd 87. *3 Barned Court, Barming, Maidstone, Kent ME16 9EL* Maidstone (01622) 728451

BRIDGMAN, Canon Gerald Bernard. b 22. St Cath Coll Cam BA50 MA55. Wycliffe Hall Ox 50. **d** 51 **p** 52. V Kingston upon Hull H Trin *York* 67-87; Area Dean Cen and N Hull 81-86; Can and Preb York Minster 83-87; rtd 87; Perm to Offic *Chich* from 87. *129 The Welkin, Lindfield, Haywards Heath, W Sussex RH16 2PL* Lindfield (01444) 484563

BRIDGWATER, Edward Roden Gresham. b 98. Union Th Sem (NY) MDiv28 K Coll (NS) BA22 MA23. **d** 24 **p** 25. V Chilworth *Win* 62-72; rtd 72. *Flat 5, Capel Court, The Burgage, Prestbury, Cheltenham, Glos. GL52 3EL* Cheltenham (01242) 571812

BRIDGWATER, Philip Dudley. b 31. St Alb Minl Tr Scheme 88. **d** 91 **p** 92. NSM Buxton w Burbage and King Sterndale *Derby* 91-94; NSM Fairfield from 94. *Millstone, 9 College Road, Buxton, Derbyshire SK17 9DZ* Buxton (01298) 72876

BRIDLE, Geoffrey Peter. b 52. CITC 87. **d** 87 **p** 88. C Lurgan Ch the Redeemer *D & D* 87-91; I Carnteel and Crilly *Arm* from 91. *St James' Rectory, 22 Carnteel Road, Aughnacloy, Co Tyrone BT69 6DU* Aughnacloy (0166252) 682

BRIDLE, Reginald. b 05. Lon Univ BA30 BD50. Ripon Hall Ox 34. **d** 34 **p** 35. Chile 55-66; Nigeria 67-73; rtd 71; Perm to Offic *Win* from 73. *65 Barlows Lane, Andover, Hants SP10 2HB* Andover (01264) 352666

BRIDSON, Raymond Stephen. b 58. Southn Univ BTh82. Chich Th Coll. **d** 82 **p** 83. C St Luke in the City *Liv* 82-86; TV Ditton St Mich from 86. *All Saints' Vicarage, Hough Green Road, Widnes, Cheshire WA8 9SZ* 0151-420 4963

BRIDSTRUP, Juergen Walter. b 44. St Alb Minl Tr Scheme 84. **d** 87 **p** 88. C Leagrave *St Alb* 87-90; V Goff's Oak St Jas from 90. *St James's Vicarage, St James' Road, Goffs Oak, Herts EN7 6TP* Cuffley (01707) 872328

BRIERLEY, Charles Ian. b 46. MIMI69 Plymouth Coll of Tech C&G65 C&G67. S Dios Minl Tr Scheme CECM93. **d** 93 **p** 94. NSM Wellington and Distr *B & W* from 93. *46 Oakfield Park, Wellington, Somerset TA21 8EY* Wellington (01823) 666101

BRIERLEY, David James. b 53. Bris Univ BA75. Oak Hill Th Coll 75. **d** 77 **p** 78. C Balderstone *Man* 77-80; P-in-c Eccles St Andr 80-81; Bp's Ecum Adv 81-88; TV Eccles 81-85; V Harwood from 85; Sec Bd Miss and Unity from 88; AD Walmsley from 95. *The Vicarage, Stitch-mi-Lane, Bolton BL2 4HU* Bolton (01204) 25196

BRIERLEY, Eric. b 21. St Aid Birkenhead 47. **d** 50 **p** 51. V Horwich St Cath *Man* 66-74; V Irlam 74-81; V Farndon and Coddington *Ches* 81-86; rtd 86; Perm to Offic *Blackb* from 86. *6 Derbyshire Avenue, Garstang, Preston PR3 1DX* Garstang (01995) 602047

BRIERLEY, John Michael. b 32. Lon Univ BD71. Lich Th Coll 57. **d** 60 **p** 61. V Worc St Mich *Worc* 69-71; R Eastham w Rochford 71-79; P-in-c Knighton-on-Teme 76-79; P-in-c Reddal Hill St Luke 79-81; V 81-92; rtd 92. *4 Coppice Close, Malvern, Worcs WR14 1LE* Leigh Sinton (01886) 832759

BRIERLEY, Philip. b 49. CChem80 MRSC80 Salford Univ BSc74. Local NSM Course 89. **d** 92 **p** 93. NSM Stalybridge *Man* from 92. *Burnside, 30 Cranworth Street, Stalybridge, Cheshire SK15 2NW* 0161-303 0809

BRIERLEY, Dr William David. b 64. Kent Univ BA87 New Coll Ox DPhil93. Ripon Coll Cuddesdon DipMin93. **d** 93 **p** 94. C Amersham *Ox* from 93. *31 Piggott's End, Amersham, Bucks HP7 0JF* Amersham (01494) 726089

BRIERLEY, William Peter. b 13. Dur Univ BSc38. Cranmer Hall Dur 65. **d** 66 **p** 67. C Otterburn w Elsdon and Horsley w Byrness *Newc* 69-75; V Greenhead 75-78; P-in-c Lambley w Knaresdale 77-78; rtd 78; Perm to Offic *Carl* 79-87. *7 Hitcombe Bottom Cottage, Horningsham, Warminster, Wilts BA12 7LA* Warminster (01985) 844720

BRIERLY, Henry Barnard Lancelot. b 30. Or Coll Ox BA55 MA63. Clifton Th Coll 55. **d** 58 **p** 59. C Normanton *Derby* 58-61; C St Helens St Helen *Liv* 61-63; V Tebay *Carl* 63-69; R Ashwellthorpe w Wreningham *Nor* 69-74; P-in-c Fundenhall 70-74; P-in-c Tacolneston 70-74; TR Wreningham 74-86; R Tetsworth, Adwell w S Weston, Lewknor etc *Ox* from 86. *The Rectory, 46 High Street, Tetsworth, Thame, Oxon OX9 7AS* Tetsworth (01844) 281267

BRIGGS, Ven Archie. b 17. Dur Univ BA39 DipTh40 MA42. **d** 41 **p** 42. Brunei 59-60; Br N Borneo 61-63; Malaysia 63-74; Dean Kota Kinabalu 70-74; Taiwan 75-85; rtd 85. *46 Kell Crescent, Sherburn Hill, Durham DH6 1PP* 0191-372 2013

BRIGGS, Christopher Ronald (Chris). b 58. K Coll Lon BD79 AKC79 PGCE80. Sarum & Wells Th Coll 87. **d** 89 **p** 90. C Horsell *Guildf* 89-93; Hong Kong from 93. *19 Country Apartments, 19 Stanley Village Road, Stanley, Hong Kong* Hong Kong (852) 813-1047

BRIGGS, Derek. b 26. Lon Univ DipTh55. St Aid Birkenhead 52. **d** 55 **p** 56. V Farsley *Bradf* 67-90; rtd 90. *6 College Court, Bradley, Keighley, W Yorkshire BD20 9EA* Keighley (01535) 630585

✠**BRIGGS, Rt Rev George Cardell.** b 10. CMG80. SS Coll Cam BA33 MA37. Cuddesdon Coll 33. **d** 34 **p** 35 **c** 73. C Stockport St Alb Hall Street *Ches* 34-37; Tanzania 37-73; OGS from 39; Adn Newala 54-64; Can Zanzibar 64-65; Can Dar-es-Salaam 65-69; Can Masasi 69-73; Bp Seychelles 73-79; Asst Bp Derby 79-80; C Matlock and Tansley 79-80; rtd 80; Asst Bp Worc from 91. *1 Lygon Lodge, Beauchamp Community, The Quadrangle, Newland, Malvern, Worcester WR13 5AX* Malvern (01684) 572941

BRIGGS, John. b 39. Edin Univ MA61. Ridley Hall Cam 61. **d** 63 **p** 64. C Jesmond Clayton Memorial *Newc* 63-66; Schs Sec Scripture Union 66-79; Tutor St Jo Coll Dur 67-74; Lic to Offic *Dur* 67-74; Lic to Offic *Edin* 74-79; V Chadkirk *Ches* 79-88; RD Chadkirk 85-88; TR Macclesfield Team Par from 88; Chapl W Park Hosp Macclesfield from 90. *The Rectory, 85 Beech Lane, Macclesfield, Cheshire SK10 2DY* Macclesfield (01625) 426110

BRIGGS, Canon John Arthur. b 12. St Jo Coll Dur BA34 MA38 Lon Univ BD43. Wycliffe Hall Ox 34. **d** 35 **p** 36. V Formby H Trin *Liv* 62-78; Hon Can Liv Cathl 69-78; rtd 78; Perm to Offic *Liv* from 78. *3 Clifden Court, Formby, Liverpool L37 3QE* Formby (01704) 877739

BRIGGS, Michael Weston. b 40. Edin Th Coll 61. **d** 64 **p** 65. C Sneinton St Steph w St Alb *S'well* 64-67; C Beeston 67-70; P-in-c Kirkby Woodhouse 70-74; V Harworth 74-81; R Harby w Thorney and N and S Clifton 81-94; R N Wheatley, W Burton, Bole, Saundby, Sturton etc from 94. *The Rectory, Middlefield Road, North Wheatley, Retford, Notts DN22 9DA* Gainsborough (01427) 880293

BRIGGS, Roger Edward. b 36. ALCD61. **d** 61 **p** 61. Canada 61-71 and from 72; C Upper Armley *Ripon* 71-72. *3191 Riverside Drive, Ottawa, Ontario, Canada, K1V 8N8*

BRIGHAM, John Keith. b 48. FSAScot Man Univ CertEd70. St Steph Ho Ox 71. **d** 74 **p** 75. C Ches H Trin *Ches* 74-77; C Ealing Ch the Sav *Lon* 77-85; P-in-c Fulwell St Mich and St Geo 85-88; P-in-c Upper Teddington SS Pet and Paul 85-88; V Southport St Luke *Liv* 88-94; Dioc Chapl to the Deaf 88-94; V Lund *Blackb* from 94. *Lund Vicarage, Church Lane, Clifton, Preston PR4 0ZE* Kirkham (01772) 683617

BRIGHOUSE, George Alexander (Alex). b 46. N Ord Course 87. **d** 90 **p** 91. NSM Ingrow cum Hainworth *Bradf* 90-92; NSM Bradf St Wilfrid Lidget Green from 92. *4 Crestville close, Clayton, Bradford, W Yorkshire BD14 6DZ* Bradford (01274) 816547

BRIGHT, George Frank. b 50. Peterho Cam BA71 MA75 Leeds Univ DipTh73 LSE MSc83. Coll of Resurr Mirfield 71. **d** 74 **p** 75. C Notting Hill *Lon* 74-77; Perm to Offic 77-84; P-in-c Kentish Town St Benet and All SS 84-89; P-in-c Kensington St Jo the Bapt 89-93; V from 93. *The Vicarage, 176 Holland Road, London W14 8AH* 0171-602 4655

BRIGHT, Patrick John Michael. b 36. Keble Coll Ox BA59 MA64. Chich Th Coll 59. **d** 61 **p** 62. C Bracknell *Ox* 61-68; V Hitchin H Sav *St Alb* 68-76; V Royston 76-90; RD Buntingford from 88; R Ashwell 90-91; R Ashwell w Hinxworth and Newnham from 91. *The Rectory, Ashwell, Baldock, Herts SG7 6QG* Ashwell (01462) 742277

BRIGHT, Reginald. b 26. Tyndale Hall Bris 57. **d** 60 **p** 61. R Orton St Giles *Carl* 65-72; V Holme 72-79; P-in-c W Newton 79-81; V Bromfield w Waverton 79-81; R Bowness 81-93; rtd 93. *Spinney House, Cannonfield, Roadhead, Carlisle CA6 6NB* Roadhead (016978) 645

BRIGHTMAN, Peter Arthur. b 30. Lon Coll of Div ALCD61 LTh74. **d** 64 **p** 65. C Lydd *Cant* 67-70; C Lt Coates *Linc* 70; C Heaton Ch Ch *Man* 71-72; V Bolton SS Simon and Jude 72-77; R Bath St Sav *B & W* 77-85; R Farmborough, Marksbury and Stanton Prior 85-90; C Coney Hill *Glouc* 90-93; C Hardwicke, Quedgeley and Elmore w Longney 93-95; rtd 95; Perm to Offic *B & W* from 95. *2 Westmead Cottages, Dean Hill Lane, Weston, Bath BA1 4DT* Bath (01225) 315076

BRIGHTON, Herbert Ernest. b 96. Bris Univ BA22. St Aid Birkenhead 23. **d** 24 **p** 25. R Burnsall *Bradf* 47-57; rtd 57. *46 Greensey, Appleshaw, Andover, Hants SP11 9HY* Andover (01264) 359248

BRIGHTON, Terrence William. b 43. SW Minl Tr Course 85. **d** 88 **p** 89. C Dawlish *Ex* 88-92; P-in-c Newton Poppleford w Harpford 92-94; V Newton Poppleford, Harpford and Colaton Raleigh from 94. *The Vicarage, Newton Poppleford, Sidmouth, Devon EX10 0HB* Colaton Raleigh (01395) 568390

BRIGNALL, Simon Francis Lyon. b 54. St Jo Coll Dur BA78. Wycliffe Hall Ox 80. **d** 83 **p** 84. C Colne St Bart *Blackb* 83-86; SAMS from 86; Peru from 86. *Iglesia Christiana Episcopal, Apartado 1424, Arequipa, Peru*

BRIMICOMBE, Mark. b 44. Nottm Univ BA66 CertEd. SW Minl Tr Course 83. **d** 85 **p** 86. NSM Plympton St Mary *Ex* from 85. *4 David Close, Stoggy Lane, Plympton, Plymouth PL7 3BQ* Plymouth (01752) 338454

BRINDLE, John Harold. b 21. St Jo Coll Dur LTh42 BA43 MA46. St Aid Birkenhead 39. **d** 44 **p** 44. V Grimsargh *Blackb* 51-88; rtd 88. *8 Sussex Drive, Garstang, Preston PR3 1ET* Garstang (01995) 606588

BRINDLE, Peter John. b 47. MIStructE72. N Ord Course 78. **d** 81 **p** 82. NSM Bingley All SS *Bradf* 84; NSM Bingley H Trin 84-86; V Keighley All SS 86-91; V Kirkstall *Ripon* from 91. *Kirkstall Vicarage, Vicarage View, Leeds LS5 3HF* Leeds (0113) 278 1007

BRINDLEY, Canon David Charles. b 53. K Coll Lon BD75 AKC75 MTh76 MPhil81. St Aug Coll Cant 75. **d** 76 **p** 77. C Epping St Jo *Chelmsf* 76-79; Lect Coll of SS Mary and Paul Cheltenham 79-82; Lic to Offic *Glouc* 79-82; Dioc Dir of Tr *Leic* 82-86; V Quorndon 82-86; Prin Glouc Sch for Min *Glouc* 87-92; Prin W of England Minl Tr Course 92-94; Dir of Minl Tr 87-94; Dioc Officer for NSM 88-94; Hon Can Glouc Cathl 92-94; TR Warw *Cov* from 94. *St Mary's Vicarage, The Butts, Warwick CV34 4SS* Warwick (01926) 492909

BRINDLEY, Canon Stuart Geoffrey Noel. b 30. St Jo Coll Dur BA53 DipTh55. **d** 55 **p** 56. C Newc St Anne *Newc* 55-58; C Tynemouth Cullercoats St Paul 58-60; C Killingworth 60-63; V Newsham 63-69; W Germany 69-76; Asst Master Wyvern Sch Weston-super-Mare 76-80; V Stocksbridge *Sheff* 80-88; RD Tankersley 85-88; V Rotherham from 88; Hon Can Sheff Cathl from 95. *Rotherham Vicarage, 2 Heather Close, Rotherham, S Yorkshire S60 2TQ* Rotherham (01709) 364341

BRINKWORTH, Christopher Michael Gibbs. b 41. Lanc Univ BA70. Kelham Th Coll 62. **d** 67 **p** 68. C Lanc St Mary *Blackb* 67-70; C Milton *Portsm* 70-74; V Ault Hucknall *Derby* 74-84; V Derby St Anne and St Jo from 84. *The Vicarage, 25 Highfield Road, Derby DE22 1GX* Derby (01332) 32681

BRINSON, David Wayne Evans. b 32. Univ of Wales (Lamp) BA53 LTh55. **d** 55 **p** 56. P-in-c Swansea St John-juxta-Swansea *S & B* 63-82; V Llanrhidian w Llanmadoc and Cheriton 82-90; rtd 90. *Rosenberg, 157 Terrace Road, Mount Pleasant, Swansea SA1 6HU* Swansea (01792) 474069

BRION, Martin Philip. b 33. Ex Univ BA55. Ridley Hall Cam 57. **d** 59 **p** 60. V Low Elswick *Newc* 66-73; P-in-c Giggleswick *Bradf* 73-77; V 77-80; V Camerton H Trin W Seaton *Carl* 80-86; V Dearham 86-95; rtd 95. *7 Falcon Place, Moresby Parks, Whitehaven, Cumbria CA15 6BX* Whitehaven (01946) 691912

BRISCOE, Allen. b 42. Liv Univ BSc64 CertEd65. Coll of Resurr Mirfield 90. **d** 92 **p** 93. C Shiremoor *Newc* from 92. *31 Horsley Avenue, Shiremoor, Newcastle upon Tyne NE27 0UF* 0191-251 3067

BRISCOE, Canon Frances Amelia. b 35. Univ of Wales CertEd55 Leeds Univ DipRE62 Man Univ BA71 MA74. Gilmore Course 74. **dss** 77 **d** 87 **p** 94. Gt Crosby St Luke *Liv* 77-81; Dioc Lay Min Adv 81-87; Chapl Liv Cathl 81-89; Dir Diaconal Mins 87-89; Lect St Deiniol's Minl Tr Scheme from 88; Hon Can Liv Cathl *Liv* from 88; AD Sefton from 89; Dir of Reader Studies from 89; D-in-c Hightown 92-94; P-in-c from 94. *St Stephen's Vicarage, St Stephen's Road, Liverpool L38 0BL* 0151-926 2469

BRISCOE, Gordon Michael. b 24. Leeds Univ CertEd50. Ely Th Coll 51. **d** 53 **p** 54. Hon C Brookfield St Anne, Highgate Rise *Lon* 67-77; Hon C Paddington St Steph w St Luke 77-80; Hon C St Marylebone Annunciation Bryanston Street 80-83; Chapl Bedf Modern Sch 83-84; Hon Chapl 84-94; R Dunton w Wrestlingworth and Eyeworth *St Alb* 84-94; rtd 94. *59 Furland Road, Crewkerne, Somerset TA18 8DD* Crewkerne (01460) 78812

BRISCOE, Henry Ellis. b 15. QUB BA44 TCD MA49. CITC 46. **d** 46 **p** 47. V Sneyd *Lich* 62-77; V Llanyblodwel 77-82; rtd 82; P-in-c Clyro w Bettws *S & B* 82-85; Perm to Offic *St As* from 85; Perm to Offic *Lich* from 85. *Gwynfa, Llansilin, Oswestry, Shropshire SY10 7QB* Llansilin (0169170) 265

BRISON, Ven William Stanly (Bill). b 29. Alfred Univ NY BSc51 Connecticut Univ MDiv57 STM71. Berkeley Div Sch. **d** 57 **p** 57. USA 57-72; V Davyhulme Ch Ch *Man* 72-81; R Newton Heath All SS 81-85; AD N Man 81-85; Hon Can Man Cathl 82-85; Adn Bolton 85-92; TV E Farnworth and Kearsley 85-89; C Bolton St Thos 89-92; CMS 92-94; Nigeria 92-94; P-in-c Pendleton St Thos w Charlestown *Man* from 94. *Pendleton Rectory, 14 Eccles Old Road, Salford M6 7AF* 0161-737 2107

BRISTOL, Archdeacon of. See BANFIELD, Ven David John

BRISTOL, Bishop of. See ROGERSON, Rt Rev Barry

BRISTOL, Dean of. See CARR, Very Rev Arthur Wesley

BRISTOW, Arthur George Raymond. b 09. Lich Th Coll 32. **d** 35 **p** 36. V Willenhall St Steph *Lich* 57-75; rtd 75; C Emscote *Cov* from 75; Perm to Offic *Lich* from 85. *41 Badgers Way, Heath Hayes, Cannock, Staffs WS12 5XQ* Heath Hayes (01543) 275530

BRISTOW, Keith Raymond Martin. b 56. Ex Univ BA78. Chich Th Coll 87. **d** 89 **p** 90. C Kirkby *Liv* 89-93; C Portsea St Mary *Portsm* from 93. *166 Shearer Road, Portsmouth PO1 5LS*

BRISTOW, Peter. b 49. Pontificium Institutum Internationale Angelicum Rome JCL77 St Jos Coll Upholland 67. **d** 72 **p** 73. In RC Church 72-87; C Poplar *Lon* 89-92; Lay Tr Officer 89-90; TV Droitwich Spa *Worc* 92-94; TR from 94. *The Rectory, 29 Old Coach Road, Droitwich, Worcs WR9 8BB* Worcester (01905) 772841

BRISTOW, Roger. b 60. Aston Tr Scheme 81 Ridley Hall Cam 83. **d** 86 **p** 87. C Leyton St Mary w St Edw *Chelmsf* 86-90; TV Kings Norton *Birm* from 90. *Immanuel Vicarage, 53 Wychall Park Grove, Birmingham B38 8AG* 0121-458 1836 or 458 3289 Fax 486 2825

BRITT, Eric Stanley. b 47. St Jo Coll Nottm LTh74 BTh75. **d** 74 **p** 75. C Chorleywood Ch Ch *St Alb* 74-78; C Frimley *Guildf* 78-80; P-in-c Alresford *Chelmsf* 80-88; R Takeley w Lt Canfield 88-93; Asst Chapl R Free Hosp Lon from 93. *The Chaplain's Office, Royal Free Hospital, Pond Street, London NW3 2QG* 0171-794 0500

BRITTAIN, John. b 23. St Aug Coll Cant 59. **d** 60 **p** 61. V Highley *Heref* 62-88; rtd 88. *1 Mead Close, Leckhampton, Cheltenham, Glos GL53 7DX* Cheltenham (01242) 525987

BRITTON, Basil. b 29. Bris Univ BA50. S'wark Ord Course 66. **d** 69 **p** 70. C Roehampton H Trin *S'wark* 69-73; Hon C Hedsor and Bourne End *Ox* from 73. *5 Coach Ride, Marlow, Bucks SL7 3BN* Marlow (01628) 484339

BRITTON, John Timothy Hugh. b 50. Dundee Univ BSc73. Trin Coll Bris 73. **d** 76 **p** 77. C Cromer *Nor* 76-79; P-in-c Freethorpe w Wickhampton 79-82; P-in-c Beighton and Moulton 79-82; P-in-c Halvergate w Tunstall 79-82; CMS 82-89; Uganda 83-89; R Allesley *Cov* from 89. *The Rectory, Allesley, Coventry CV5 9EQ* Coventry (01203) 402006

BRITTON, John Anthony. b 39. Dur Univ BA60. Wycliffe Hall Ox 61. **d** 63 **p** 64. C Sheff St Swithun *Sheff* 63-64; C Sheff St Aid w St Luke 64-66; C Doncaster St Geo 66-68; C Grantham St Wulfram *Linc* 68-72; V Surfleet 72-76; V Bolsover *Derby* 76-86; V Harworth *S'well* from 86. *The Vicarage, Tickhill Road, Harworth, Doncaster, S Yorkshire DN11 8PD* Doncaster (01302) 744157

BRITTON, Canon Paul Anthony. b 29. SS Coll Cam BA52 MA57. Linc Th Coll 52. **d** 54 **p** 55. V Stanmore *Win* 61-70; V Bitterne Park 70-80; Can Res Win Cathl 80-94; Lib 81-85; Treas 85-94; rtd 94. *Pemberton, High Street, Hindon, Salisbury SP3 6DR* Hindon (01747) 820406

BRITTON, Robert. b 40. Univ of Wales DipTh64. St Mich Coll Llan 61. **d** 64 **p** 65. C Aberdare St Jo *Llan* 64-67; C Coity w Nolton 67-71; V Abercynon 71-75; V Tycoch *S & B* from 75. *The Vicarage, 26 Hendrefoilan Road, Swansea SA2 9LS* Swansea (01792) 204476

BRITTON, Robert (Bob). b 37. Oak Hill Th Coll 78. **d** 79 **p** 80. C St Helens St Helen *Liv* 79-83; V Lowton St Mary from 83; AD Winwick from 89. *The Vicarage, 1 Barford Drive, St Mary's Park, Lowton, Warrington WA3 1DD* Leigh (01942) 607705

BRITTON, Ronald George Adrian Michael (Robert). b 24. Oklahoma City SW Coll BA76 Elysion Coll California BA76 Univ of the State of NY BSc78 Clayton Univ St Louis PhD82 Nova Coll Edmonton EdD83 Hon LittLD84 Univ de la Romande Basle JD86. St Deiniol's Hawarden 85 St D Coll Lamp 63 Bapt Coll Louisiana MA79 Lambeth STh82 St Tim Sem Oklahoma Hon DD82 Cen Sch of Religion Indiana MA92. **d** 82 **p** 82. Arabia 82-85; Chapl Alassio *Eur* 85-90 and 92-93; Chapl San Remo 86; Hon C Southbourne St Kath *Win* 90-92; rtd 95. *2 Cherry Tree Road, Bristol BS16 4EY* Bristol (0117) 965 5734

BRIXWORTH, Suffragan Bishop of. See BARBER, Rt Rev Paul Everard

BROAD, David. b 59. Man Univ BA. Edin Th Coll. **d** 87 **p** 88. C Fulham All SS *Lon* 87-90; TV Clare w Poslingford, Cavendish etc *St E* 90-93; TV Totton *Win* from 93. *Eling Vicarage, Eling Hill, Totton, Southampton SO4 4HF* Southampton (01703) 866426

BROAD, Hugh Duncan. b 37. Lich Th Coll 64. **d** 67 **p** 68. C Heref H Trin *Heref* 67-72; Asst Master Bp's Sch Heref 72-73; C Fareham SS Pet and Paul *Portsm* 74-76; V Heref All SS *Heref* 76-90; R Matson *Glouc* from 90. *The Rectory, Matson Lane, Gloucester GL4 9DX* Gloucester (01452) 522698

BROAD, Hugh Robert. b 49. St Mich Coll Llan 67. **d** 72 **p** 73. C Tenby w Gumfreston *St D* 72-75; C Caerau w Ely *Llan* 75-79; V Llanharan w Peterston-super-Montem 79-89; RD Bridgend 88-89; Ex-Paroch Officer 90; V Whatborough Gp of Par *Leic* from 90. *The Vicarage, Oakham Road, Tilton on the Hill, Leicester LE7 9LB* Leicester (0116) 259 7244

BROAD, William Ernest Lionel. b 40. Ridley Hall Cam 64. **d** 66 **p** 67. C Ecclesfield *Sheff* 66-69; Chapl HM Pris Wormwood Scrubs 69; Chapl HM Pris Albany 70-74; Chapl HM Rem Cen Risley 74-76; V Ditton St Mich *Liv* 76-81; TR 82-83; P-in-c Mayland *Chelmsf* 83-91; P-in-c Steeple 83-91; V Blackhall *Dur* from 91. *The Vicarage, Blackhall, Hartlepool, Cleveland TS27 4LE* 0191-586 4202

BROADBENT, Mrs Doreen. b 36. Local Minl Tr Course 91. **d** 94 **p** 95. NSM Stalybridge *Man* from 94. *Lynford Cottage, Chamberlain Road, Heyrod, Stalybridge, Cheshire SK15 3BS* 0161-303 0501

BROADBENT, Edward Ronald. b 23. Man Univ BSc44. Westcott Ho Cam 53. **d** 55 **p** 56. SPCK Staff 63-87; Hon C Wilton w Netherhampton and Fugglestone *Sarum* 78-80; P-in-c S Newton 80-83; Hon C Chalke Valley W 84-91; rtd 88; Perm to Offic *Sarum* from 92. *2 Marlborough Road, Salisbury SP1 3TH* Salisbury (01722) 326809

BROADBENT, Hugh Patrick Colin. b 53. Selw Coll Cam BA75 MA. Wycliffe Hall Ox DipTh78. **d** 78 **p** 79. C Chatham St Steph *Roch* 78-82; C Shortlands 82-84; C Edenbridge 84-87; C Crockham Hill H Trin 84-87; V Bromley H Trin from 87; Chapl St Olave's Gr Sch Orpington from 95. *Holy Trinity Vicarage, Church Lane, Bromley BR2 8LB* 0181-462 1280

BROADBENT, Neil Seton. b 53. Qu Coll Birm DipTh80. **d** 81 **p** 82. C Knaresborough *Ripon* 81-84; C Leeds Gipton Epiphany 84-87; Lic to Offic 87-89; Chapl Minstead Community *Derby* 89; Perm to Offic from 89; Dir Sozein from 93. *The Old Vicarage, Church Lane, Horsley Woodhouse, Ilkeston, Derbyshire DE7 6BB* Derby (01332) 780598

BROADBENT, Paul John. b 41. Oak Hill Th Coll DipTh83. **d** 85 **p** 86. C Duston *Pet* 85-88; TV Ross w Brampton Abbotts, Bridstow and Peterstow *Heref* 88-91; R Pattishall w Cold Higham and Gayton w Tiffield *Pet* from 91. *The Vicarage, Pattishall, Towcester, Northants NN12 8NB* Pattishall (01327) 830043

BROADBENT, Ven Peter Alan (Pete). b 52. Jes Coll Cam BA74 MA78. St Jo Coll Nottm DipTh75. **d** 77 **p** 78. C Dur St Nic *Dur* 77-80; C Holloway Em w Hornsey Road St Barn *Lon* 80-83;

Chapl N Lon Poly 83-89; Hon C Islington St Mary 83-89; V Trin St Mich, Harrow 89-94; AD Harrow 94; Adn Northolt from 95. *247 Kenton Road, Harrow, Middx HA3 0HQ* 0181-907 5941 Fax 909 2368

BROADBENT, Ralph Andrew. b 55. K Coll Lon BD76 AKC76. Chich Th Coll 77. **d** 78 **p** 79. C Prestwich St Mary *Man* 78-82; R Man Miles Platting 82-84; CF 84-87; TV Wordsley *Lich* 88-93; Chapl Wordsley and Ridge Hill Hosps 88-93; V Wollescote *Worc* from 93. *The Vicarage, Oakfield Road, Stourbridge, W Midlands DY9 9DG* Stourbridge (01384) 422695

BROADBENT, Thomas William. b 45. Chu Coll Cam BA66 MA70 PhD70. Ridley Hall Cam 75. **d** 78 **p** 79. C Allington and Maidstone St Pet *Cant* 78-82; Chapl Mid Kent Coll of H&FE 80-82; C Kings Heath *Birm* 82-84; Hon C Pendleton St Thos *Man* 84-89; TV Pendleton St Thos w Charlestown 89-92; Chapl Salford Univ 84-92; Chmn Man Coun of Chr and Jews 89-92; R Claydon and Barham *St E* from 92; Chapl Suffolk Coll of HE from 92. *The Rectory, 7 Back Lane, Claydon, Ipswich IP6 0EB* Ipswich (01473) 830362

BROADBERRY, Canon Richard St Lawrence. b 31. TCD BA53 BD59 MLitt66. **d** 54 **p** 55. C Dub St Thos *D & G* 54-56; C Dub Grangegorman 56-62; Min Can St Patr Cathl Dub 58-62; Hon CV Ch Ch Cathl Dub *D & G* 62-64; C Dub Clontarf 62-64; C Thornton Heath St Jude *Cant* 64-66; V Norwood All SS 66-82; RD Croydon N 81-84; Hon Can Cant Cathl 82-84; V Upper Norwood All SS w St Marg 82-84; Hon Can S'wark Cathl *S'wark* from 85; RD Croydon N 85; V Mert St Mary 85-92; V Riddlesdown from 92. *St James's Vicarage, 1B St James's Road, Purley, Surrey CR8 2DL* 0181-660 5436

BROADHEAD, Dr Alan John. b 38. Lon Univ MD62. Cuddesdon Coll 65. **d** 66 **p** 67. C Willenhall H Trin *Lich* 66-68; USA from 71. *Address temp unknown*

BROADHURST, John Charles. b 42. AKC65. Lambeth STh82. **d** 66 **p** 67. C Southgate St Mich *Lon* 66-70; C Wembley Park St Aug 70-73; P-in-c 73-75; V 75-85; AD Brent 82-85; TR Wood Green St Mich w Bounds Green St Gabr etc from 85; AD E Haringey 85-91. *St Michael's Rectory, 39 Bounds Green Road, London N22 4HE* 0181-888 1968 or 881 0202

BROADHURST, John James. b 08. Birm Univ BA31. **d** 32 **p** 33. R S Hill w Callington *Truro* 59-73; rtd 73. *18 Monmouth Gardens, Beaminster, Dorset DT8 3BT* Beaminster (01308) 862509

BROADHURST, Jonathan Robin. b 58. Univ Coll Ox BA81 MA86. Wycliffe Hall Ox 85. **d** 88 **p** 89. C Hull Newland St Jo *York* 88-91; P-in-c Burton Fleming w Fordon, Grindale etc 91-92; V from 92. *The Vicarage, Back Street, Burton Fleming, Driffield, N Humberside YO25 0RD* Wing (01262) 470668

BROADHURST, Kenneth. b 33. Lon Coll of Div 56. **d** 59 **p** 60. R Clitheroe St Jas *Blackb* 67-82; V Leyland St Andr 82-88; rtd 89. *Paris House, 12 Ramsgreave Road, Ramsgreave, Blackburn BB1 9BH* Blackburn (01254) 240924

BROCK, Michael John. b 52. Birm Univ BSc74 Nottm Univ BA77. St Jo Coll Nottm 75. **d** 78 **p** 79. C Stapleford *S'well* 78-82; C Bestwood St Matt 82-86; TV Bestwood 86-90; R Epperstone from 90; R Gonalston from 90; V Oxton from 90; RD S'well from 93. *The Rectory, Main Street, Epperstone, Notts NG14 6AG* Nottingham (0115) 966 4220

BROCK, Preb Patrick Laurence. b 18. MBE45. Trin Coll Ox BA46 MA48. Ripon Hall Ox 55. **d** 57 **p** 58. V Belsize Park *Lon* 62-72; R Finchley St Mary 72-89; Preb St Paul's Cathl 80-89; AD Cen Barnet 80-85; rtd 89. *10 Albert Street, London NW1 7NZ* 0171-383 0198

BROCKBANK, Arthur Ross. b 51. Wigan Coll of Tech BTEC ND85. N Ord Course 87. **d** 90 **p** 91. C Haughton St Mary *Man* 90-93; V Bircle from 93; Chapl Fairfield Gen Hosp Bury from 93. *The Vicarage, 33 Castle Hill Road, Bury, Lancs BL9 7RW* 0161-764 3853

BROCKBANK, Donald Philip. b 56. Univ of Wales (Ban) BD78. Sarum & Wells Th Coll 79. **d** 81 **p** 82. C Prenton *Ches* 81-85; TV Birkenhead Priory 85-91; V Altrincham St Jo from 91; Urban Officer from 91. *St John's Vicarage, 52 Ashley Road, Altrincham, Cheshire WA14 2LY* 0161-928 3236 Fax as telephone

BROCKBANK, John Keith. b 44. Dur Univ BA65. Wells Th Coll 66. **d** 68 **p** 69. C Preston St Matt *Blackb* 68-71; C Lanc St Mary 71-73; V Habergham All SS 73-83; P-in-c Gannow 81-83; V W Burnley 83-86; Dioc Stewardship Adv from 86; P-in-c Shiresbead 86-92; V Kirkham from 92. *The Vicarage, Kirkham, Preston PR4 2SE* Kirkham (01772) 683644

BROCKBANK, Leslie David. b 35. St Aid Birkenhead 60. **d** 63 **p** 64. C Corby SS Pet and Andr *Pet* 63-66; C Darley w S Darley *Derby* 66-72; New Zealand from 72. *12 Mahana Road, Hamilton, New Zealand* Hamilton (7) 849-5104 or 849-5715

BROCKHOUSE, Grant Lindley. b 47. Adelaide Univ BA71 Ex Univ MA81. St Barn Coll Adelaide 70 ACT ThL72. **d** 73 **p** 74. Australia 73-78; C Ex St Jas *Ex* 78-80; Asst Chapl Ex Univ

80-83; Dep PV Ex Cathl from 81; V Marldon from 83. *The Vicarage, Marldon, Paignton, Devon TQ3 1NH* Paignton (01803) 557294

BROCKIE, William James Thomson. b 36. Pemb Coll Ox BA58 MA62. Linc Th Coll 58. **d** 60 **p** 61. C Lin St Jo Bapt CD *Linc* 60-63; V Gt Staughton *Ely* 63-68; Chapl HM Youth Cust Cen Gaynes Hall 63-68; TV Edin St Jo *Edin* 68-76; Chapl Edin Univ 71-76; USA 76; R Edin St Martin *Edin* from 76; P-in-c Edin St Luke 79-90. *15 Ardmillan Terrace, Edinburgh EH11 2JW* 0131-337 5493 or 337 9714

BROCKLEBANK, John. b 32. N Ord Course 83. **d** 86 **p** 87. NSM Warrington St Barn *Liv* 86-93; NSM Orford St Marg from 93. *55 St Mary's Road, Penketh, Warrington WA5 2DT* Penketh (01925) 722398

BROCKLEHURST, John Richard. b 51. Univ Coll Ox BA72 Lon Univ CertEd74. Oak Hill Th Coll BA81. **d** 81 **p** 82. C Harwood *Man* 81-85; V Hopwood from 85. *St John's Vicarage, Manchester Road, Heywood, Lancs OL10 2EQ* Heywood (01706) 369324

BROCKLEHURST, Simon. b 63. Cranmer Hall Dur 86. **d** 89 **p** 90. C Clifton *S'well* 89-93; TV from 93. *St Francis Vicarage, Southchurch Drive, Nottingham NG11 8AQ* Nottingham (0115) 921 2446

BRODDLE, Christopher Stephen Thomas. b 57. **d** 87 **p** 88. C Lisburn St Paul *Conn* 87-90; CF from 90. *c/o MOD (Army), Bagshot Park, Bagshot, Surrey GU19 5PL* Bagshot (01276) 471717 Fax 412834

BRODIE, Frederick. b 40. Leic Teacher Tr Coll TCert61. St Jo Coll Nottm DCM92. **d** 92 **p** 93. C Lutterworth w Cotesbach *Leic* 92-95; P-in-c Mountsorrel Ch Ch and St Pet from 95. *Christ Church Vicarage, 2 Rothley Road, Mountsorrel, Loughborough, Leics LE12 7JU* Leicester (0116) 230 2235

BRODY, Paul. b 40. N Ord Course 85. **d** 88 **p** 89. C Leigh St Mary *Man* 88-90; C Peel 90-91; V from 91. *The Rectory, 122 Peel Lane, Worsley, Manchester M28 6FL* 0161-790 4202

BROGGIO, Canon Bernice Muriel Croager. b 35. Bedf Coll Lon BA57 K Coll Lon BD66 IDC66 Glas Univ DSocStuds71 DASS72. K Coll Lon 63. **dss** 84 **d** 87 **p** 94. Bris St Paul w St Barn *Bris* 84-87; Hon Par Dn Bris St Paul's 87-88; C Charlton St Luke w H Trin *S'wark* 88-95; Hon Can S'wark Cathl from 95; V Upper Tooting H Trin from 95. *Holy Trinity Vicarage, 14 Upper Tooting Park, London SW17 7SW* 0181-672 4790

BROMAGE, Kenneth Charles. b 51. E Anglian Minl Tr Course. **d** 90 **p** 91. NSM Woolpit w Drinkstone *St E* 90-92; Chapl RN from 92. *Directorate Gen, RN Chapl Services, Room 203, Victory Building, HM Naval Base, Portsmouth PO1 3LS* Portsmouth (01705) 727903 Fax 727112

BROMFIELD, Michael. b 32. Kelham Th Coll 54 Lich Th Coll 59. **d** 62 **p** 63. C Sedgley All SS *Lich* 62-64; C Tunstall Ch Ch 64-67; P-in-c Grindon 67-70; R 70-80; P-in-c Butterton 67-70; V 70-80; R Hope Bowdler w Eaton-under-Heywood *Heref* from 80; R Rushbury from 80; V Cardington from 80. *The Rectory, Hope Bowdler, Church Stretton, Shropshire SY6 7DD* Church Stretton (01694) 722918

BROMFIELD, Richard Allan. b 47. Chich Th Coll 86. **d** 88 **p** 89. C Durrington *Chich* from 88. *8 Greenland Walk, Worthing, W Sussex BN13 2NS* Worthing (01903) 263304

BROMIDGE, Robert Harold. b 28. K Coll Lon BD52 AKC52. **d** 53 **p** 54. Min Arbourthorne CD *Sheff* 61-70; Lic to Offic from 71; rtd 88. *4 Barnfield Close, Sheffield S10 5TF* Sheffield (0114) 230 7889

BROMILEY, Paul Nigel. b 49. Univ of Wales (Cardiff) BSc71. Oak Hill Th Coll 88. **d** 90 **p** 91. C Gee Cross *Ches* 90-94; P-in-c Millbrook from 94. *St James's Vicarage, 28 Buckton Vale Road, Stalybridge, Cheshire SK15 3LW* Mossley (01457) 833295

BROMLEY, Mrs Janet Catherine Gay. b 45. Surrey Univ BSc68 Bradf Univ MSc72 Brunel Tech Coll Bris FETC86. S Dios Minl Tr Scheme 91. **d** 94. C Westbury-on-Trym H Trin *Bris* from 94. *4 Charlton Road, Westbury-on-Trym, Bristol BS10 6NG* Bristol (0117) 950 2983

BROMLEY, William James. b 44. Edin Univ BD74. Edin Th Coll 70. **d** 74 **p** 75. C Glas St Mary *Glas* 74-77; Bangladesh 77-80; R Glas H Cross *Glas* 80-89; R Stottesdon w Farlow, Cleeton and Silvington *Heref* from 89. *The Rectory, Stottesdon, Kidderminster, Worcs DY14 8UE* Stottesdon (0174632) 297

BROMLEY, Archdeacon of. See NORMAN, Ven Garth

BROMWICH, Edmund Eustace. b 15. Bris Univ BA35 St Cath Soc Ox BA39 MA43 TCD MA50. Ripon Hall Ox 37. **d** 40 **p** 41. R Wanstrow w Cloford *B & W* 49-57; Lic to Offic *Ches* from 68; rtd 80. *5B London Road, Alderley Edge, Cheshire SK9 7JT* Alderley Edge (01625) 585366

BRONNERT, Preb David Llewellyn Edward. b 36. Ch Coll Cam BA57 MA61 PhD61 Lon Univ BD62. Tyndale Hall Bris 60.

d 63 **p** 64. C Cheadle Hulme St Andr *Ches* 63-67; C Islington St Mary *Lon* 67-69; Chapl N Lon Poly 69-75; V Southall Green St Jo from 75; Preb St Paul's Cathl from 89; P-in-c Southall St Geo from 92; AD Ealing W 84-90. *St John's Vicarage, Church Avenue, Southall, Middx UB2 4DH* 0181-574 2055

BRONNERT, John. b 33. FCA57 Lon Univ DipTh68 Man Univ MA(Theol)84. Tyndale Hall Bris 65. **d** 68 **p** 69. C Hoole *Ches* 68-71; P-in-c Parr *Liv* 71-73; TV 73-85; V Runcorn St Jo Weston *Ches* from 85. *The Vicarage, 225 Heath Road South, Weston, Runcorn, Cheshire WA7 4LY* Runcorn (01928) 573798

BROOK, Kathleen Marjorie. b 23. IDC. Lightfoot Ho Dur 57. **dss** 66 **d** 87 **p** 94. Linthorpe *York* 66-75; Ormesby 75-83; rtd 83. *6 Station Square, Saltburn-by-the-Sea, Cleveland TS12 1AG* Guisborough (01287) 624006

BROOK, Peter Geoffrey (Brother Simon). b 47. N Ord Course 91. **d** 94 **p** 95. CGA from 94; NSM Heywood and Middleton Deanery from 94. *38 Burnside Crescent, Middleton, Manchester M24 3NN* 0161-643 5775

BROOK, Stephen Edward. b 44. Univ of Wales (Abth) BSc65. Wycliffe Hall Ox 71. **d** 74 **p** 75. C Heworth *York* 74-77; C Linthorpe 77-80; TV Deane *Man* 80-85; BCMS 87-93; Crosslinks from 93; Portugal from 87. *Bairro do Padre Nabeto, Lote 82-U, Aires, 2950 Palmela, Portugal* Lisbon (1) 235-3192

BROOK, William Neville. b 31. S'wark Ord Course 66. **d** 69 **p** 70. C Maidstone St Martin *Cant* 69-75; V Hartlip w Stockbury 75-80; R Willesborough w Hinxhill 80-86; R Willesborough 87-89; V Gt Staughton *Ely* from 89; V Hail Weston from 89. *St Andrew's Vicarage, The Causeway, Great Staughton, Huntingdon, Cambs PE19 4BA* Huntingdon (01480) 861554

BROOKE, Miss Bridget Cecilia. b 31. DBO51. Coll of Resurr Mirfield 88. **d** 89 **p** 94. Hon Par Dn Ranmoor *Sheff* 89-94; Hon C from 94; Bp's Officer for NSMs from 94. *166 Tom Lane, Sheffield S10 3PG* Sheffield (0114) 230 2147

BROOKE, Michael Zachery. b 21. G&C Coll Cam BA43 MA46. Cuddesdon Coll 46. **d** 48 **p** 49. R Old Trafford St Cuth *Man* 57-63; rtd 86. *21 Barnfield, Urmston, Manchester M31 1EW* 0161-746 8140

BROOKE, Robert. b 44. Birm Univ DPS77. Qu Coll Birm 70. **d** 73 **p** 74. C Man Resurr *Man* 73-76; C Bournville *Birm* 76-77; Chapl Qu Eliz Coll *Lon* 77-82; C Bramley *Ripon* 82-85; TV 85-86; V Hunslet Moor St Pet and St Cuth 86-93; Community Chapl for Mental Handicap 86-93; C Seacroft from 93; Chapl People w Learning Disabilities from 93. *51 St James's Approach, Leeds LS14 6JJ* Leeds (0113) 273 1396

BROOKE, Rosemary Jane. b 53. Cam Univ BEd75 Open Univ BA83. N Ord Course 86. **d** 89 **p** 94. NSM Poynton *Ches* from 89. *45 Brookfield Avenue, Poynton, Stockport, Cheshire SK12 1JE* Poynton (01625) 872822

BROOKE, Timothy Cyril. b 38. Jes Coll Cam BA60 MA70 Middx Poly CQSW76. Ripon Coll Cuddesdon 84. **d** 86 **p** 87. C Hillmorton *Cov* 86-90; V Earlsdon from 90. *St Barbara's Vicarage, 24 Rochester Road, Coventry CV5 6AG* Coventry (01203) 674057

BROOKE, Vernon. b 41. St Aid Birkenhead 62. **d** 65 **p** 66. C Crofton Park St Hilda w St Cypr *S'wark* 65-68; C Eccleshill *Bradf* 68-70; Ind Chapl *Linc* 70-84; Ind Chapl *Derby* from 84. *10 Oldridge Close, Chesterfield, Derbyshire S40 4UF* Chesterfield (01246) 270197

BROOKE, Canon William Edward. b 13. Birm Univ BA34 MA35. Westcott Ho Cam 35. **d** 37 **p** 38. R Castle Bromwich SS Mary and Marg *Birm* 60-78; Hon Can Birm Cathl 61-78; rtd 78; Perm to Offic *Heref* from 78. *Ivy Cottage, Tarrington, Hereford HR1 4HZ* Tarrington (01432) 890357

BROOKER, David George. b 34. Ely Th Coll 56. **d** 58 **p** 59. C Ealing St Pet Mt Park *Lon* 58-60; C Holborn St Alb w Saffron Hill St Pet 60-66; C W Wycombe *Ox* 67-68; C Winchmore Hill St Paul *Lon* 68; V Somers Town St Mary 68-79; V Bush Hill Park St Mark from 79. *St Mark's Vicarage, Bush Hill Park, Enfield, Middx EN1 1BE* 0181-363 2780

BROOKER, Mrs Wendy Ann. b 41. St Alb Minl Tr Scheme 82. **dss** 85 **d** 87 **p** 94. Pinner *Lon* 85-87; Greenhill St Jo 87; Par Dn 87-88; Ind Chapl 89-94; NSM Hayes St Edm 94; C from 95. *19 Wimborne Avenue, Hayes, Middx UB4 0HG* 0181-561 6933

BROOKES, Arthur George. b 21. ACIB52. Worc Ord Coll 64. **d** 66 **p** 67. C Fladbury w Throckmorton, Wyre Piddle and Moor *Worc* 67-70; C Abberton w Bishampton 67-70; R 70-73; V Cradley 73-78; P-in-c Castle Morton 78-79; P-in-c Holly Bush w Birtsmorton 78-79; P-in-c Castlemorton, Hollybush and Birtsmorton 79-80; P-in-c Norton w Whittington 80-81; TV Worc St Martin w St Pet, St Mark etc 81-86; rtd 86; Perm to Offic *Worc* from 86. *9 Bredon Lodge, Main Road, Bredon, Tewkesbury, Glos GL20 7LT* Bredon (01684) 772338

BROOKES, David Charles. b 45. St Mich Coll Llan 84. **d** 86 **p** 87. C Llanishen and Lisvane *Llan* 86-88; TV Brighouse St Martin *Wakef* 89-92; TV Brighouse and Clifton 92-94; V

Hollingbourne and Hucking w Leeds and Broomfield *Cant* from 94. *The Vicarage, Hollingbourne, Maidstone, Kent ME17 1UJ* Maidstone (01622) 880243

BROOKES, Derrick Meridyth. b 17. Trin Hall Cam BA38 MA42. Westcott Ho Cam 39. **d** 40 **p** 41. C Macclesfield St Mich *Ches* 40-44; Chapl RAFVR 44-46; C Wilmslow *Ches* 47-49; V Chipping Sodbury and Old Sodbury *Glouc* 49-53; Youth Chapl 51-53; Chapl RAF 53-71. *Woodpeckers, Pilcorn Street, Wedmore, Somerset BS28 4AW* Wedmore (01934) 712352

BROOKES, Geoffrey John Denis. b 24. CMS Tr Coll Crowther Hall 78 Ridley Hall Cam 84. **d** 85 **p** 86. Bahrain 85-88; Project Officer Ch Action w the Unemployed 88-91; Hon C Hastings All So *Chich* 88-91; Asst Chapl Milan w Genoa and Varese *Eur* 91-94; Canada from 94. *clo Bertling, 226 Jane Street, PO Box 390, Rodney, Ontario, Canada, N0L 2C0*

BROOKES, Keith Roy. b 37. St Aid Birkenhead 64. **d** 80 **p** 81. Hon C Stockport St Thos *Ches* 80-86; Hon C Stockport St Thos w St Pet 86-91; C from 91. *42 Derby Road, Stockport, Cheshire SK4 4NE* 0161-442 0307

BROOKES, Robin Keenan. b 47. Trin Coll Bris 72. **d** 75 **p** 76. C Livesey *Blackb* 75-78; C Burnley St Pet 78-80; P-in-c Bawdeswell w Foxley *Nor* 80-83; I Donagh w Tyholland and Errigal Truagh *Clogh* 83-91; RD Monaghan 86-91; Dioc Info Officer 90-91; I Dub Drumcondra w N Strand *D & G* from 91. *74 Grace Park Road, Drumcondra, Dublin 9, Irish Republic* Dublin (1) 837-2505   Fax 837-0204

BROOKES, Steven David. b 60. Lanc Univ BA81. Ripon Coll Cuddesdon 82. **d** 85 **p** 86. C Stanley *Liv* 85-88; C W Derby St Mary 88-90; Chapl RN 90-94; R Weybridge *Guildf* from 94. *The Rectory, 3 Churchfields Avenue, Weybridge, Surrey KT13 9YA* Weybridge (01932) 842566

BROOKFIELD, Patricia Anne. b 50. St Mary's Coll Dur BA72. Cranmer Hall Dur DipTh73 MA74. **dss** 84 **d** 87 **p** 94. Kingston upon Hull St Nic *York* 84-86; Acomb St Steph 86-87; Par Dn 87-94; C from 94. *12 Askham Lane, Acomb, York YO2 3HA* York (01904) 791511

BROOKHOUSE, Leslie. b 28. Ridley Hall Cam 69 St Aid Birkenhead 68. **d** 70 **p** 71. C Tonge *Man* 70-72; C Didsbury Ch Ch 72-74; V Newall Green 74-80; V High Crompton 80-86; R Ashwater, Halwill, Beaworthy, Clawton etc *Ex* from 86; RD Holsworthy from 94. *The Rectory, Ashwater, Beaworthy, Devon EX21 5EZ* Ashwater (01409) 211205

BROOKS, Andrew Richard. b 44. Leeds Univ BA Birm Poly PGCE DipInstAM. Qu Coll Birm 83. **d** 86 **p** 87. C Olton *Birm* 86-87; C Sheldon 87-89; V Erdington St Chad from 89. *St Chad's Vicarage, 10 Shepherd's Green Road, Birmingham B24 8EX* 0121-373 3915 or 373 9894

BROOKS, Mrs Christine Ellen. b 43. Sheff Univ BA65 Lon Univ BD81. Lambeth STh81 E Anglian Minl Tr Course 86. **d** 88 **p** 94. NSM Palgrave w Wortham and Burgate *St E* 88-89; Par Dn Thorndon w Rishangles, Stoke Ash, Thwaite etc 89-94; P-in-c Aldringham w Thorpe, Knodishall w Buxlow etc from 94. *The Rectory, Friston, Saxmundham, Suffolk IP17 1NP* Snape (01728) 688972

BROOKS, Edward Charles. b 18. Leeds Univ PhD71. Coll of Resurr Mirfield 42. **d** 44 **p** 45. P-in-c Herringfleet *Nor* 69-83; R Somerleyton w Ashby 69-83; rtd 83; Perm to Offic *St E* from 83. *Wheelwrights, Thorpe Morieux, Bury St Edmunds, Suffolk IP30 0NR* Bury St Edmunds (01284) 828353

BROOKS, Canon Francis Leslie. b 35. Kelham Th Coll 55. **d** 59 **p** 60. C Woodlands *Sheff* 59-61; Ind Missr S Yorkshire Coalfields 61-66; V Moorends 66-72; Chapl HM Borstal Hatf 67-72; Chapl HM Pris Acklington 72-75; Chapl HM Borstal Wellingborough 75-79; Chapl HM Pris Wakef 79-83; Area Sec (Dios Wakef and Bradf) USPG 83-88; V Carleton *Wakef* from 88; V E Hardwick from 88; Can Mara (Tanzania) from 88. *The Vicarage, 10 East Close, Pontefract, W Yorkshire WF8 3NS* Pontefract (01977) 702478

BROOKS, Henry Craven. b 12. CITC 62. **d** 64 **p** 65. I Dunlavin w Ballymore Eustace and Hollywood *D & G* 67-85; rtd 85; Lic to Offic *D & G* from 85. *9 Orwell Court, Braemor Road, Churchtown, Dublin 14, Irish Republic* Dublin (1) 298-5659

BROOKS, Ian George. b 47. Selw Coll Cam BA68 MA72. Chich Th Coll 68. **d** 70 **p** 71. C Stoke Newington St Mary *Lon* 70-74; C Hoxton St Anne w St Sav and St Andr 74-75; C Hoxton St Anne w St Columba 75-80; P-in-c Croxteth St Paul CD *Liv* 80-81; V Croxteth from 81. *St Paul's Vicarage, Delabole Road, Liverpool L11 6LG* 0151-548 9009

BROOKS, John Cowell. b 09. St Jo Coll Cam BA31 MA35. Coll of Resurr Mirfield 46. **d** 47 **p** 48. N Rhodesia 61-64; Zambia 64-71; Lic to Offic *Cant* 71-74; Chapl Dover Coll Kent 71-74; R Northbourne, Tilmanstone w Betteshanger and Ham *Cant* 74-86; rtd 86; Perm to Offic *Cant* from 86. *3 Mill Road, Deal, Kent CT14 9AB* Deal (01304) 367961

BROOKS, Jonathan Thorburn. b 53. Solicitor 76 G&C Coll Cam BA75 DipHE. Trin Coll Bris 84. **d** 86 **p** 87. C Dagenham

Chelmsf 86-88. *12 Hyde Avenue, Thornbury, Bristol BS12 1JA* Thornbury (01454) 411853

BROOKS, Canon Joseph (Joe). b 27. Univ Coll Dur BA53. St Aid Birkenhead 52. **d** 54 **p** 55. V Ipswich St Fran *St E* 65-75; R Freston w Woolverstone 75-76; P-in-c Holbrook and Stutton 75-76; R Holbrook w Freston and Woolverstone 76-82; R Horringer cum Ickworth 82-88; Chapl Ipswich Hosp 88-92; Hon Can St E Cathl *St E* 90-92; rtd 92. *289 Henley Road, Ipswich IP1 6TB* Ipswich (01473) 748245

BROOKS, Malcolm David. b 45. Univ of Wales (Lamp) DipTh71. **d** 71 **p** 72. C Pontllottyn w Fochriw *Llan* 71-72; C Caerphilly 72-78; V Ferndale w Maerdy 78-81; C Port Talbot St Theodore 82-84; V Ystrad Mynach 84-85; V Ystrad Mynach w Llanbradach from 85. *The Vicarage, Ystrad Mynach, Hengoed, M Glam CF8 7EG* Hengoed (01443) 813246

BROOKS, Neville Charles Wood. b 16. Bps' Coll Cheshunt 50. **d** 53 **p** 54. R Gilmorton w Peatling Parva *Leic* 66-86; R Gilmorton w Peatling Parva and Kimcote etc 86; rtd 86. *1 Cherry Tree Walk, Southam, Leamington Spa, Warks CV33 0EF*

BROOKS, Patrick John. b 27. Man Univ BA49 DipEd. Oak Hill Th Coll 78. **d** 77 **p** 79. Burundi 77-80; Perm to Offic *Ex* 80-83; P-in-c Phillack w Gwithian and Gwinear *Truro* 83-88; R 88-93; rtd 93. *Abbots, Claigmar Road, Rustington, Littlehampton, W Sussex BN16 2NL*

BROOKS, Paul John. b 59. Loughb Univ BSc81 DTS89 DPS90. St Jo Coll Nottm 87. **d** 90 **p** 91. C Long Eaton St Jo *Derby* 90-94; Min Jersey St Paul Prop Chpl *Win* from 94. *5 Claremont Avenue, St Saviour, Jersey, Channel Islands JE2 7SF* Jersey (01534) 880393

BROOKS, Peter Joseph. b 54. **d** 83 **p** 84. C Portslade St Nic and St Andr *Chich* 83-86; C Kingstanding St Luke *Birm* 86-91; V Nork *Guildf* from 91. *The Vicarage, Warren Road, Banstead, Surrey SM7 1LG* Burgh Heath (01737) 353849

BROOKS, Philip David. b 52. MA Cam Univ MTh. St Jo Coll Nottm 80. **d** 83 **p** 84. C Ipsley *Worc* 83-87; V Fulford w Hilderstone *Lich* from 87; Chapl Stallington Hosp from 87. *20 Tudor Hollow, Fulford, Stoke-on-Trent ST11 9NP* Blythe Bridge (01782) 397073

BROOKS, Raymond Samuel. b 11. ARIBA39. Clifton Th Coll 63. **d** 65 **p** 66. V Hastings Em and St Mary in the Castle *Chich* 71-82; rtd 82. *Brighnorton, Eight Acre Lane, Three Oaks, Hastings, E Sussex TN25 4NL* Hastings (01424) 754432

BROOKS, Mrs Susan Vera. b 51. N Ord Course 87. **d** 90 **p** 94. Par Dn Carleton *Wakef* 90-93; Par Dn E Hardwick 90-94; C from 94; TD Almondbury w Farnley Tyas 93-94; TV from 94. *150 Fleminghouse Lane, Huddersfield HD5 8UD* Huddersfield (01484) 545085

BROOKS, Mrs Vivien June. b 47. Univ of Wales (Ban) BA68 Southn Univ MA70. Ridley Hall Cam 87. **d** 89 **p** 95. C Exning St Martin w Landwade *St E* 89-92; Par Dn Hermitage and Hampstead Norreys, Cold Ash etc *Ox* 92-94; C 94-95; P-in-c Cox Green from 95. *The Vicarage, Warwick Close, Maidenhead, Berks SL6 3AL* Maidenhead (01628) 22139

BROOKS, Vivienne Christine. *See* ARMSTRONG-MacDONNELL, Mrs Vivienne Christine

BROOKSBANK, Alan Watson. b 43. Univ of Wales (Lamp) BA64 Edin Univ MEd76. Edin Th Coll 64. **d** 66 **p** 67. C Cleator Moor w Cleator *Carl* 66-70; V Dalston 70-80; P-in-c Greystoke, Matterdale and Mungrisdale 80-81; R 81-83; R Watermillock 81-83; R Hagley *Worc* 83-95; Bp's Officer for NSM 88-95; V Claines St Jo from 95. *The Vicarage, Claines Lane, Worcester WR3 7RN* Worcester (01905) 51251

BROOKSTEIN, Canon Royston. b 29. Qu Coll Birm 60. **d** 62 **p** 63. V Cotteridge *Birm* 66-75; V Hall Green St Pet 75-94; Hon Can Birm Cathl 84-94; rtd 94. *257 Wake Green Road, Birmingham B13 9XH* 0121-777 7989

BROOM, Andrew Clifford. b 65. Keele Univ BSocSc86. Trin Coll Bris BA92. **d** 92 **p** 93. C Wellington, All SS w Eyton *Lich* from 92. *1 Stile Rise, Shawbirch, Telford, Shropshire TF5 0LR* Telford (01952) 641229

BROOM, Bernard William. b 21. Roch Th Coll 64. **d** 66 **p** 67. R Alderford w Attlebridge and Swannington *Nor* 69-75; RD Sparham 73-75; R Drayton 75-80; P-in-c Felthorpe w Haveringland 77-80; R Drayton w Felthorpe 80-81; TV Eckington w Handley and Ridgeway *Derby* 84-88; rtd 88; Perm to Offic *Nor* from 88. *119A High Street, Blakeney, Holt, Norfolk NR25 7NU* Cley (01263) 740001

BROOM, Donald Rees. b 14. St Cath Soc Ox BA38 MA42. St D Coll Lamp BA36 BD45 Wycliffe Hall Ox 36. **d** 38 **p** 39. V Middleton Tyas and Barton *Ripon* 62-75; V Barton and Manfield w Cleasby 75-82; rtd 82. *47 Linden Avenue, Darlington, Co Durham DL3 8PS* Darlington (01325) 284216

BROOME, David Curtis. b 36. Leeds Univ BA63. Coll of Resurr Mirfield. **d** 65 **p** 66. C Winshill *Derby* 65-69; C Leigh-on-Sea St Marg *Chelmsf* 69-74; V Leeds St Marg *Ripon* 74-81; V Stoke H Cross w Dunston *Nor* 81-93; P-in-c Caistor w Markshall

92-93; P-in-c Arminghall 92-93; R Stoke H Cross w Dunston, Arminghall etc from 93. *The Vicarage, Stoke Holy Cross, Norwich NR14 8AB* Framingham Earl (01508) 492305

BROOME, Gordon Alty. b 13. Ripon Hall Ox 65. **d** 65 **p** 66. C Portchester *Portsm* 65-72; R Brighstone 72-79; R Brighstone and Brooke w Mottistone 79-80; rtd 80; Perm to Offic *Portsm* from 81. *St Saviour's Vicarage, Queens Road, Shanklin, Isle of Wight PO37 6AN* Isle of Wight (01983) 862786

BROOME, William Harold. b 09. Man Egerton Hall 32. **d** 34 **p** 35. R Nairn *Mor* 64-73; Can St Andr Cathl Inverness 66-73; R Selkirk *Edin* 73-75; rtd 75; Lic to Offic *Newc* 75-77; Hon C Morpeth 77-80; Hon C St Andrews St Andr *St And* 80-87. *122 North Street, St Andrews, Fife KY16 9AF* St Andrews (01334) 73204

BROOMFIELD, David John. b 37. Reading Univ BA59. Oak Hill Th Coll 64. **d** 66 **p** 67. C Gresley *Derby* 66-71; C Rainham *Chelmsf* 71-77; R High Ongar w Norton Mandeville 77-88; RD Ongar 83-88; P-in-c Stanford Rivers 84-86; P-in-c Loughton St Mary and St Mich 88-95; P-in-c Loughton St Mary from 95. *St Mary's Rectory, High Road, Loughton, Essex IG10 1BB* 0181-508 3643

BROOMFIELD, Iain Jonathan. b 57. Univ Coll Ox MA. Wycliffe Hall Ox 80. **d** 83 **p** 84. C Beckenham Ch Ch *Roch* 83-87; Schs Worker Scripture Union Independent Schs from 87; Perm to Offic *Ox* 87-89. *91 Walton Street, Oxford OX2 6EB* (01865) 59006 or 0171-782 0013 Fax 0171-782 0014

BROSNAN, Mark. b 61. St Martin's Coll Lanc BA83 RMN88 Otley Agric Coll. E Anglian Minl Tr Course 92. **d** 95. C Rushmere *St E* from 95. *5 The Limes, Rushmere, Ipswich IP5 7EA* Ipswich (01473) 713690

BROSTER, Godfrey David. b 52. Ealing Tech Coll BA75. Ripon Coll Cuddesdon 78. **d** 81 **p** 82. C Crayford *Roch* 81-82; C Brighton Resurr *Chich* 82-86; C-in-c Hydneye CD 86-91; R Plumpton w E Chiltington 91-93; R Plumpton w E Chiltington cum Novington from 93. *The Rectory, Station Road, Plumpton, Lewes, E Sussex BN7 3BU* Plumpton (01273) 890570

BROTHERSTON, Miss Isabel Mary. b 42. Cranmer Hall Dur 81. **dss** 83 **d** 87 **p** 94. Coleshill *Birm* 83-87; Par Dn Duddeston w Nechells 87-92; Par Dn Harlescott *Lich* 92-94; C from 94. *14 Maple Drive, Harlescott, Shrewsbury SY1 3SE* Shrewsbury (01743) 350907

BROTHERTON, Ven John Michael. b 35. St Jo Coll Cam BA59 MA63. Cuddesdon Coll 59. **d** 61 **p** 62. C Chiswick St Nic w St Mary *Lon* 61-65; Trinidad and Tobago 65-75; V Cowley St Jo *Ox* 76-81; Chapl St Hilda's Coll Ox 76-81; RD Cowley *Ox* 78-81; V Portsea St Mary *Portsm* 81-91; Hon Can Kobe Japan from 86; Adn Chich from 91. *4 Canon Lane, Chichester, W Sussex PO19 1PX* Chichester (01243) 779134 Fax 536452

BROTHERTON, Leslie Charles. b 22. OStJ FSCA MInstAM. St Steph Ho Ox 68. **d** 68 **p** 69. C Fenny Stratford *Ox* 68-70; C Solihull *Birm* 71-76; C 91-92; V Moseley St Anne 76-91; rtd 93; Perm to Offic *Birm* from 93. *3 St Alphege Close, Solihull, W Midlands B91 3RQ* 0121-705 7038

BROTHERTON, Michael. b 56. MBE93. Univ of Wales (Abth) BD80. Wycliffe Hall Ox 80. **d** 81 **p** 82. Hon Chapl Miss to Seamen 81-84; C Pemb Dock *St D* 81-84; Chapl RN from 84. *Directorate Gen, RN Chapl Services, Room 203, Victory Building, HM Naval Base, Portsmouth PO1 3LS* Portsmouth (01705) 727903 Fax 727112

BROTHERWOOD, Nicholas Peter. b 50. Oak Hill Th Coll BA83. **d** 83 **p** 84. C Nottm St Nic *S'well* 83-86; Canada from 86. *3498 Harvard Avenue, Montreal, Quebec, Canada, H4A 2W3* Montreal (514) 489-4158

BROTHWELL, Canon Paul David. b 37. Lich Th Coll 62. **d** 65 **p** 66. C Honley *Wakef* 65-68; Min Can Wakef Cathl 68-71; V Whittington St Giles *Lich* 71-83; P-in-c Weeford 78-83; V Whittington w Weeford 83-92; Chapl Kidderminster Gen Hosp from 92; Chapl Lea Castle Hosp Kidderminster from 94. *Kidderminster General Hospital, Bewdley Road, Kidderminster, Worcs DY11 6RJ* Kidderminster (01562) 823424/861951 Fax 67412

BROTHWOOD, Ian Sidney. b 56. K Coll Lon BD84. Linc Th Coll 87. **d** 89 **p** 90. C Selsdon St Jo w St Fran *S'wark* 89-93; P-in-c S Norwood St Alb from 93. *The Vicarage, 6 Dagmar Road, London SE25 6HZ* 0181-653 6092

BROTHWOOD, Dr John. b 31. Peterho Cam MA55 MB, ChB55. S'wark Ord Course 89. **d** 91 **p** 92. NSM Dulwich St Barn *S'wark* from 91. *81 Calton Avenue, London SE21 7DF* 0181-693 8273

BROUGH, Gerald William. b 32. Trin Coll Cam BA55 MA59. Ridley Hall Cam 55. **d** 57 **p** 58. V Mancetter *Cov* 62-73; P-in-c Bourton w Frankton and Stretton on Dunsmore etc 73-74; R 74-93; rtd 93. *17 Brookhurst Court, Beverley Road, Leamington Spa, Warks CV32 6PB* Leamington Spa (01926) 632805

BROUGHTON, Canon Harry. b 09. Dur Univ LTh32. Lich Th Coll 29. d 32 p 33. V Coxwold *York* 56-69; Can and Preb York Minster 66-94; rtd 70; RD Helmsley *York* 74-75. *Charters Garth, Hutton-le-Hole, York YO6 6UD* Lastingham (017515) 288

BROUGHTON, James Roger. b 48. Leeds Univ BA71 Nottm Univ CertEd72. Wycliffe Hall Ox 87. d 89 p 90. C Stoneycroft All SS *Liv* 89-92; P-in-c Carr Mill from 92. *St David's Vicarage, 27 Erkdale Avenue, Carr Mill, St Helens, Merseyside WA11 7EN* St Helens (01744) 32330

BROUGHTON, Stuart Roger. b 36. Univ of Wales DipTh65. St Mich Coll Llan 61. d 64 p 65. C Bromley Ch Ch *Roch* 64-67; SAMS from 67; V Stoke sub Hamdon *B & W* 79-83; V Blackb Ch Ch w St Matt *Blackb* 83-86; Portugal 86-92; Brazil from 92. *Christ Church, Rua Real Grandeze 99, Botafogo, Rio de Janeiro, 22 281 030, RJ Brazil* Rio de Janeiro (21) 226-2878 or 9488

BROUN, Canon Claud Michael. b 30. BNC Ox BA55. Edin Th Coll 56. d 58 p 59. Chapl St Mary's Cathl *Edin* 58-62; P-in-c Cambuslang *Glas* 62-70; R 70-75; R Hamilton 75-88; Can St Mary's Cathl from 84; R Gatehouse of Fleet from 88; R Kircudbright from 88. *Greyfriars Rectory, 54 High Street, Kirkcudbright DG6 4JX* Kirkcudbright (01557) 330580

BROWN, Canon Alan. b 37. Tyndale Hall Bris 59. d 63 p 64. C Braintree *Chelmsf* 63-66; C Tooting Graveney St Nic *S'wark* 66-68; C Chesham St Mary *Ox* 68-70; V Hornsey Rise St Mary *Lon* 70-75; V Sidcup Ch Ch *Roch* 75-88; V Newport St Jo *Portsm* from 88; RD W Wight from 91; Hon Can Portsm Cathl from 95. *St John's Vicarage, 3 Cypress Road, Newport, Isle of Wight PO30 1EY* Isle of Wight (01983) 522148

BROWN, Alan George. b 51. Bradf Univ BSc84 Leeds Univ CertEd92 MBA92 SRN72 RMN75 RNT81. N Ord Course 92. d 95. NSM Ilkley St Marg *Bradf* from 95. *Waverley, Wheatley Road, Ilkley, W Yorkshire LS29 8TS* Ilkley (01943) 601115 Fax as telephone

BROWN, Alan Michael Ernest. b 52. St Chad's Coll Dur BA74. St Jo Coll Nottm 81. d 83 p 84. C Bridlington Priory *York* 83-86; V Morton St Luke *Bradf* from 86. *The Vicarage, Morton, Keighley, W Yorkshire BD20 5RS* Bradford (01274) 563829

BROWN, Albert Harry Alfred Victor. b 12. d 81 p 83. Hon C Kennington Park St Agnes *S'wark* 81-92; Perm to Offic from 92. *61 Brittany Point, Lollard Street, London SE11 6PX* 0171-274 5982

BROWN, Alec Charles. b 33. AKC58. d 59 p 60. C S Mimms St Mary and Potters Bar *Lon* 59-63; C S Ashford Ch Ch *Cant* 63-66; New Zealand from 66. *24 Examiner Street, Nelson, New Zealand* Christchurch (3) 548-3644

BROWN, Alec George. b 53. Univ of Zimbabwe DipSocWork80 Univ of Wales (Cardiff) MSc(Econ)87. St Deiniol's Hawarden 88 N Ord Course 90. d 93 p 94. C Stockton Heath *Ches* from 93. *St Mary Magdalen House, 8 St Monica's Close, Appleton, Warrington WA4 3AW* Warrington (01925) 860484

BROWN, Alexander Peter-Aidan (Alex). b 48. Sarum & Wells Th Coll. d 82 p 83. C Ifield *Chich* 82-86; TV 86-91; V St Leonards SS Pet and Paul from 91. *The Vicarage, 10 Bloomfield Road, St Leonards-on-Sea, E Sussex TN37 6HH* Hastings (01424) 445606

BROWN, Alexander Thomas. b 21. Glas NSM Course 73. d 79 p 80. NSM Irvine St Andr *Glas* 79-83; NSM Ardrossan 79-83; rtd 83. *44 Ravenscroft, Irvine, Ayrshire KA12 9DE* Irvine (01294) 74354

BROWN, Allan James. b 47. K Coll Lon BD69 AKC69 MTh70. St Aug Coll Cant 69. d 73 p 74. Jerusalem 73-75; C Clifton *S'well* 75-77; CF from 77. *c/o MOD (Army), Bagshot Park, Bagshot, Surrey GU19 5PL* Bagshot (01276) 471717 Fax 412834

BROWN, Andrew. b 55. St Pet Hall Ox BA80 MA82. Ridley Hall Cam 79. d 80 p 81. C Burnley St Pet *Blackb* 80-82; C Elton All SS *Man* 82-86; P-in-c Ashton St Pet 86-93; V from 94. *The Vicarage, Chester Square, Ashton-under-Lyne, Lancs OL7 0LB* 0161-330 4285

BROWN, Andrew. b 65. Local NSM Course 92. d 95. NSM Heywood St Marg *Man* from 95. *24 Honiton Close, Heywood, Lancs OL20 3PF* Heywood (01706) 623091

BROWN, Anthony Paul. b 55. ARICS87 Reading Univ BSc75. Qu Coll Birm 77. d 80 p 81. C Pelsall *Lich* 80-83; C Leighton Buzzard w Eggington, Hockliffe etc *St Alb* 83-87; TV Langley Marish *Ox* 87-93; V Pet St Mary *Pet* from 93. *St Mary's Vicarage, 214 Eastfield Road, Peterborough PE1 4BD* Peterborough (01733) 343418

BROWN, Anthony Frank Palmer (Tony). b 31. Fitzw Ho Cam BA56 Fitzw Coll Cam MA84. Cuddesdon Coll 56. d 58 p 59. C Aldershot St Mich *Guildf* 58-61; C Chiswick St Nic w St Mary *Lon* 61-66; Asst Chapl Lon Univ 65-70; Lic to Offic 70-72; C-in-c Hammersmith SS Mich and Geo White City Estate CD

72-74; P-in-c Upper Sunbury St Sav 74-80; V from 80. *St Saviour's Vicarage, 205 Vicarage Road, Sunbury-on-Thames, Middx TW16 7TP* Sunbury-on-Thames (01932) 782800

BROWN, Antony William Keith. b 26. RN Coll Dartmouth 43. Trin Coll Bris 86. d 87 p 88. NSM Lawrence Weston *Bris* 87-89; Chapl Casablanca *Eur* 89-93; Asst Chapl Paris St Mich from 94. *25 Hameau de Bois Fountaine, 78170 La Celle St Cloud, France* France (33) 30 78 01 58 Fax as telephone

BROWN, Arthur Basil Etheredge. b 17. Reading Univ BA39. Wycliffe Hall Ox 46. d 47 p 48. R Camborne *Truro* 66-82; rtd 82. *14 Tregenna Fields, Camborne, Cornwall TR14 7QS* Camborne (01209) 711196

BROWN, Canon Arthur Henry. b 18. St Pet Hall Ox BA39 MA43. Wycliffe Hall Ox 39. d 41 p 42. V Worksop St Anne *S'well* 56-83; P-in-c Scofton w Osberton 66-83; RD Worksop 72-83; Hon Can S'well Minster 77-83; rtd 83; Perm to Offic *S'well* 83-87; Perm to Offic *Ex* from 87. *Gentians, Plymouth Road, Chudleigh Knighton, Newton Abbot, Devon TQ13 0HE* Chudleigh (01626) 853786

BROWN, Arthur William Neville. b 08. Kelham Th Coll 30. d 36 p 38. Hon CF from 44; V Ellington *Ely* 66-74; R Grafham 66-74; rtd 74. *85 Pirehill Lane, Stone, Staffs ST15 0AS* Stone (01785) 812538

BROWN, Arthur William Stawell. b 26. St Jo Coll Ox BA50 MA51. Cuddesdon Coll 63. d 65 p 66. C Petersfield w Sheet *Portsm* 67-75; V Portsea St Alb 75-79; R Smithfield St Bart Gt *Lon* 79-91; R St Sepulchre w Ch Ch Greyfriars etc 81-91; Chapl Madeira *Eur* 90-93; rtd 91. *9 Little Silver, Exeter EX4 4HU* Exeter (01392) 217630

BROWN, Canon Bernard Herbert Vincent. b 26. Mert Coll Ox BA50 MA52. Westcott Ho Cam 50. d 52 p 53. Ind Chapl *Roch* 62-73; Bp's Dom Chapl 66-73; R Crawley *Chich* 73-79; TR 79-83; Ind Chapl *Bris* 83-92; Bp's Soc and Ind Adv 84-92; Hon Can Bris Cathl 85-92; RD Bris City 85-91; rtd 92. *33 B London Road, Dorchester, Dorset DT1 1NF* Dorchester (01305) 260806

BROWN, Bernard Maurice Newall. b 26. Oak Hill Th Coll 47. d 51 p 52. V Stapenhill w Cauldwell *Derby* 68-72; C Weston-super-Mare Ch Ch *B & W* 72-74; R Spaxton w Charlynch 74-80; rtd 80. *12 Ewart Road, Weston-super-Mare, Avon BS22 8NU* Weston-super-Mare (01934) 412170

BROWN, Bill. b 64. Linc Th Coll 87. d 89 p 90. C Moulsham St Luke *Chelmsf* 89-91; C Prittlewell St Luke 91; C Prittlewell 91-94. *Address temp unknown*

BROWN, Brian Ernest. b 36. ALA64. Oak Hill NSM Course 82. d 85 p 86. NSM Wallington H Trin *S'wark* 85-91; C from 91. *St Patrick's House, 47 Park Hill Road, Wallington, Surrey SM6 0RU* 0181-647 5882

BROWN, Charles Hubert. b 21. S'wark Ord Course 82. d 84 p 85. NSM Shortlands *Roch* 84-86; P-in-c Seal St Lawr 86-90; P-in-c Underriver 86-90; rtd 90. *Barton Croft, 11 St Mary's Close, Sevenoaks, Kent TN15 8NH* Sevenoaks (01732) 882893

BROWN, Christopher. b 38. AKC62. d 63 p 64. C Crofton Park St Hilda w St Cypr *S'wark* 63-64; C S Beddington St Mich 64-67; C Herne Hill St Paul 67-68; Lic to Offic 68-72; Lic to Offic *Lich* 72-76; Lic to Offic *Worc* 77-79; Lic to Offic *Ox* 79-86; Lic to Offic *Chelmsf* from 86; Dir NSPCC from 89. *7 Baronia Croft, Highwoods, Colchester CO4 4EE* Colchester (01206) 844705

BROWN, Christopher. b 43. Linc Th Coll 79. d 81 p 82. C Stafford St Jo *Lich* 81-85; C Stafford St Jo and Tixall w Ingestre 85; V Alton w Bradley-le-Moors and Oakamoor w Cotton 85-94; Asst Chapl Nottm City Hosp from 94. *The Chaplain's Office, Nottingham City Hospital, Hucknall Road, Nottingham NG5 1BP* Nottingham (0115) 969 1169 or 962 7616

BROWN, Christopher Charles. b 58. Solicitor 82 Univ of Wales (Cardiff) LLB79. Westcott Ho Cam 87. d 90 p 91. C Taunton St Mary *B & W* 90-94; R Timsbury and Priston from 94. *The Rectory, Timsbury, Bath BA3 1HY* Timsbury (01761) 470153

BROWN, Christopher David. b 49. Birm Univ CertEd71 BEd72 Univ of Wales (Cardiff) DipPTh94. St Mich Coll Llan 93. d 94 p 95. C Swansea St Thos and Kilvey *S & B* from 94. *55 Ysgol Street, Port Tennant, Swansea SA1 8LG* Swansea (01792) 470521

BROWN, Christopher Edgar Newall. b 31. Oak Hill Th Coll 51. d 55 p 56. C Surbiton Hill Ch Ch *S'wark* 55-57; C Gipsy Hill Ch Ch 57-61; V Plumstead All SS 61-70; V Sissinghurst *Cant* 70-73; P-in-c Frittenden 72-73; V Sissinghurst w Frittenden 73-76; Perm to Offic *S & M* 84-91; Bp's Dom Chapl from 91. *21 College Green, Castletown, Isle of Man IM9 1BE* Castletown (01624) 822364 or 622108

BROWN, Christopher Francis. b 44. Sarum Th Coll 68. d 71 p 72. C High Wycombe *Ox* 71-74; C Sherborne w Castleton and Lillington *Sarum* 74-77; P-in-c Wylye, Fisherton Delamere and the Langfords 77-79; R Yarnbury 79-82; R Portland All SS w St Pet 82-88; RD Weymouth 85-89; R Trowbridge St Jas from 88; Chapl Trowbridge & Distr Hosp from 88; RD Bradf from 94. *The Rectory, Union Street, Trowbridge, Wilts BA14 8RU* Trowbridge (01225) 755121

BROWN, Christopher James (Chris). b 50. Open Univ BA92. Trin Coll Bris DipHE93. **d** 93 **p** 94. C Skelmersdale St Paul *Liv* from 93. *6 Wilcove, Skelmersdale, Lancs WN8 8NF* Skelmersdale (01695) 26491

BROWN, Clive Lindsey. b 33. Southn Univ BA55. Oak Hill Th Coll 57. **d** 59 **p** 60. C Becontree St Mary *Chelmsf* 59-62; Australia from 62. *30 William Street, Roseville, NSW, Australia 2069* Sydney (2) 407-2377

BROWN, Prof Colin. b 32. Liv Univ BA53 Lon Univ BD58 Nottm Univ MA61 Bris Univ PhD70. Tyndale Hall Bris 55. **d** 58 **p** 59. C Chilwell *S'well* 58-61; Lect Tyndale Hall Bris 61-78; Vice Prin 67-70; Dean Studies 70-71; USA from 78; Prof Systematic Th Fuller Th Sem California from 78; Assoc Dean Adv Th Studies from 88. *1024 Beverly Way, Altadena, California 91001, USA* Pasadena (818) 584-5239

BROWN, Cyril James. b 04. OBE56. Keble Coll Ox BA26 MA39. St Steph Ho Ox 26. **d** 27 **p** 28. R Warbleton *Chich* 70-77; R Warbleton and Bodle Street Green 77; rtd 77; Perm to Offic *Chich* from 78. *The Royal Alfred Home for Seamen, 5-11 Hartington Place, Eastbourne, E Sussex BN21 3BS* Eastbourne (01323) 721828

BROWN, David Charles Girdlestone. b 42. Solicitor 67. S'wark Ord Course 87. **d** 90 **p** 91. NSM Milford *Guildf* 90-92; Hon C Haslemere from 92. *Boundary House, Highercombe Road, Haslemere, Surrey GU27 2LQ* Haslemere (01428) 651889

BROWN, David Frederick. b 38. Illinois Univ BA60. Seabury-Western Th Sem MDiv67. **d** 67 **p** 67. USA 67-78; Hon C Battersea Ch Ch and St Steph *S'wark* 78-83; Chapl R Marsden Hosp Lon and Surrey from 83. *Royal Marsden Hospital, Fulham Road, London SW3 6JJ* 0171-352 8171 or 351 6082

BROWN, David Lloyd. b 44. DipTh80 TCD BTh90. **d** 86 **p** 87. C Cregagh *D & D* 86-91; Bp's C Knocknagoney from 91. *19 Old Holywood Road, Belfast BT4 2HJ* Belfast (01232) 763343

BROWN, David Victor Arthur. b 44. Em Coll Cam BA66 MA70 CertEd. Linc Th Coll 72. **d** 74 **p** 75. C Bourne *Linc* 74-77; Chapl St Steph Coll Broadstairs 77-79; TV Grantham *Linc* 79-81; Chapl Asst N Gen Hosp Sheff 81-84; C Sheff St Cuth *Sheff* 81-84; Chapl Ridge Lea Hosp Lanc from 84; Chapl Lanc Moor Hosp from 84; Chapl Lanc R Infirmary from 87. *Chaplain's Office, Royal Lancaster Infirmary, Ashton Road, Lancaster LA1 4PR* Lancaster (01524) 586436 or 65994

BROWN, Prof David William. b 48. Edin Univ MA70 Or Coll Ox BA72 Clare Coll Cam PhD76. Westcott Ho Cam 75. **d** 76 **p** 77. Chapl, Fell and Tutor Or Coll Ox 76-90; Van Mildert Prof Div Dur Univ from 90. *14 The College, Durham DH1 3EQ* 0191-386 4657

BROWN, Dennis Cockburn. b 27. Hatf Coll Dur BSc48 K Coll Dur PhD54. W Midl Minl Tr Course 79. **d** 82 **p** 83. C Bilton *Cov* 82-84; V Wolford w Burmington from 84; R Cherington w Stourton from 84; R Barcheston from 84. *The Vicarage, Great Wolford, Shipston-on-Stour, Warks CV36 5NQ* Barton-on-the-Heath (01608) 674361

BROWN, Canon Derek Frederick. b 27. St Fran Coll Brisbane ThL52. **d** 52 **p** 54. Australia 52-58; C Merstham and Gatton *S'wark* 59-61; R Deptford St Paul 61-69; Chapl RNR from 62; R Havant *Portsm* from 69. *St Faith's Rectory, Emsworth Road, Havant, Hants PO9 2FR* Havant (01705) 483485

BROWN, Derek Henry Pridgeon. b 46. Cam Coll of Art and Tech BA67 Leeds Univ PGCE71. St Steph Ho Ox 90. **d** 92 **p** 93. C Finchley St Mary *Lon* from 92. *45 Oakdene Park, London N3 1EU* 0181-343 4154

BROWN, Donald Evans. b 10. Ch Coll Cam BA34 MA38. Lon Coll of Div 34. **d** 37 **p** 38. V Hemingford Grey *Ely* 55-77; rtd 77. *21 Manor Drive, Fenstanton, Huntingdon, Cambs PE18 9QZ* St Ives (01480) 467073

BROWN, Canon Donald Fryer. b 31. St Jo Coll Dur BA56 DipTh61. Cranmer Hall Dur 60. **d** 61 **p** 62. Min Can Bradf Cathl *Bradf* 61-64; C Bingley All SS 64-66; V Low Moor H Trin from 66; Hon Can Bradf Cathl from 85; RD Bowling and Horton 87-95. *Holy Trinity Vicarage, Park House Road, Low Moor, Bradford, W Yorkshire BD12 0HR* Bradford (01274) 678859

BROWN, Mrs Doreen Marion. b 39. Cam Univ CertEd67 DCouns85. N Ord Course 85. **d** 88 **p** 94. Par Dn Axminster, Chardstock, Combe Pyne and Rousdon *Ex* 88-92; Ind Chapl *Linc* from 92. *23 Montaigne Crescent, Glebe Park, Lincoln LN2 4QN*

BROWN, Douglas Adrian Spencer. Univ of W Aus BA50. St Mich Th Coll Crafers ThL50. **d** 53 **p** 54. SSM from 54; Australia 53-60 and 67-90; Lic to Offic *S'wark* 60-67; Tutor and Chapl Kelham Th Coll 60-67; Chapl Bucharest w Sofia *Eur* 90-91; Dir Angl Cen Rome from 91. *Centro Anglicano, Palazzo Doria, Via del Corso 303, 00186 Rome, Italy* Rome (6) 678-0302

BROWN, Miss Elizabeth Charlotte (Beth). b 54. Bris Univ BSc76 PGCE77. Trin Coll Bris DipHE95. **d** 95. C Taunton Lyngford *B & W* from 95. *1 Kirke Grove, Taunton, Somerset TA2 8FB* Taunton (01823) 321801

BROWN, Eric. b 28. NW Ord Course 73. **d** 76 **p** 77. NSM S Kirkby *Wakef* 76-83; NSM Knottingley 83-94; NSM Kellington w Whitley 89-94; Sub Chapl HM Pris Lindholme 90-94; Perm to Offic from 94. *Wynberg, Barnsley Road, South Kirby, Pontefract, W Yorkshire WF9 3BG* Pontefract (01977) 643683

BROWN, Canon Ernest George. b 23. Em Coll Cam BA51 MA56. Oak Hill Th Coll 52. **d** 53 **p** 54. V Thurnby w Stoughton *Leic* 67-90; RD Gartree II (Wigston) 78-90; Hon Can Leic Cathl 82-90; rtd 90. *16 Holbeck Drive, Broughton Astley, Leics LE9 6UR* Sutton Elms (01455) 285458

BROWN, Ernest Harry. b 32. St Mich Coll Llan. **d** 59 **p** 60. C Swansea St Pet *S & B* 59-62; CF (TA) 62-68; C Gowerton w Waunarlwydd *S & B* 62-68; Chapl to the Deaf from 68. *Montreaux, 30 Lon Cedwyn, Sketty, Swansea SA2 0TH* Swansea (01792) 207628

BROWN, Frank Seymour. b 10. S'wark Ord Course 62 St Aug Coll Cant 65. **d** 65 **p** 66. C Bexleyheath Ch Ch *Roch* 65-70; R Cratfield w Heveningham and Ubbeston *St E* 70-76; rtd 76; Perm to Offic *St E* 76-86; P-in-c Ixworth and Ixworth Thorpe 78; P-in-c Euston w Barnham and Fakenham 80; Perm to Offic *St Alb* from 86. *3 Windsor Gardens, Kimbolton Road, Bedford MK40 3BU* Bedford (01234) 210999

BROWN, Geoffrey Gilbert. b 38. FBIS Dur Univ BA64 DipEd63 Fitzw Coll Cam BA69 MA73. Westcott Ho Cam 67. **d** 70 **p** 71. C Gosforth All SS *Newc* 70-73; Chapl Dauntsey's Sch Devizes 73-76; New Zealand 76-78 and 86-90; V Barrow St Aid *Carl* 79-86; C Digswell and Panshanger *St Alb* 91-93; NSM from 93; Chapl E Herts Hospice Care from 94. *Isabel Wing, Douglas Tilbe House, Hall Grove, Welwyn Garden City, Herts AL7 4PH* Welwyn Garden (01707) 330686 Fax 393132

BROWN, Canon Geoffrey Harold. b 30. Trin Hall Cam BA54 MA58. Cuddesdon Coll 54. **d** 56 **p** 57. R Birm St Geo *Birm* 63-73; TR Gt Grimsby St Mary and St Jas *Linc* 73-85; Can and Preb Linc Cathl 79-85; V St Martin-in-the-Fields 85-95; rtd 95. *32 Church Street, Hagley, Stourbridge, W Midlands DY9 0NA* Hagley (01562) 883609

BROWN, Ven Gerald Arthur Charles. b 35. CCC Cam BA56 MA60 CCM Ox BA58 DipTh59. St Steph Ho Ox 58. **d** 60 **p** 61. C Wolv St Pet *Lich* 60-66; V Trent Vale 66-74; V Wolv St Andr 74-82; Chapl Milan w Cadenabbia and Varese *Eur* 82-90; Adn Scandinavia from 90; Can Brussels Cathl from 90; Chapl Oslo w Bergen, Trondheim, Stavanger etc 90-92; Chapl Stockholm w Gavle and Vasteras from 92; Chapl Riga, Latvia from 94. *Styrmansgatan 1, 11454 Stockholm, Sweden* Stockholm (8) 663-8248 Fax 663-8911

BROWN, Graham Stanley. b 51. Sarum & Wells Th Coll 82. **d** 84 **p** 85. C Crediton and Shobrooke *Ex* 84-87; Chapl RAF 87-93; R Elgin w Lossiemouth *Mor* from 93. *The Rectory, 8 Gordon Street, Elgin, Morayshire IV30 1JQ* Elgin (01343) 547505

BROWN, Harold. b 53. SEN74 SRN77 RMN82 RCN CCT84. Edin Th Coll 86. **d** 88 **p** 89. C Upperby St Jo *Carl* 88-90; C Carl H Trin and St Barn 90-91; C Workington St Mich 91-93; TV from 93. *64 Curwendale, Workington, Cumbria CA14 4UT* Workington (01900) 61169

BROWN, Mrs Harriet Nina. b 37. Open Univ BA77 Lon Univ CertEd. Gilmore Course 80. **dss** 83 **d** 87 **p** 94. Greenstead juxta Colchester *Chelmsf* 83-87; Par Dn 87-90; Asst Chapl R Hosp Sch Holbrook 90-93; Perm to Offic *Chelmsf* from 93; Perm to Offic Samford Deanery *St E* from 93. *21 Royal Hospital School, Holbrook, Ipswich IP9 2RT* Holbrook (01473) 327310

BROWN, Henry. b 27. Lon Univ BSc51 BSc52. NW Ord Course 72. **d** 75 **p** 76. NSM Padiham *Blackb* 75-80; V Warton St Paul 80-90; rtd 90. *18 Windsor Gardens, Garstang, Preston PR3 1EG* Garstang (01995) 606592

BROWN, Ian. b 48. N Ord Course 89. **d** 91 **p** 92. C Burnage St Marg *Man* 91-94; P-in-c Halliwell St Paul from 94; Chapl Bolton Gen Hosp from 94. *St Paul's Vicarage, Halliwell Road, Bolton BL1 8BP* Bolton (01204) 495038

BROWN, Ian Barry. b 53. Ruskin Coll Ox 75 St Cuth Soc Dur BA80 PGCE81. Westmr Past Foundn CCouns90 Sarum & Wells Th Coll 84. **d** 86 **p** 87. C Winchmore Hill St Paul *Lon* 86-89; Hon Chapl Chase Farm Hosp Enfield 86-88; Hon Chapl Harley Street Area Hosps 88-90; Hon Chapl RAM 89; C St Marylebone w H Trin 89-94; rtd 94. *139 Whitfield Street, London W1P 5RY* 0171-916 2834

BROWN, Ian David. b 53. UEA BA76. Wycliffe Hall Ox BA80. **d** 81 **p** 82. C Southsea St Jude *Portsm* 81-84; Chapl Coll of SS Mary and Paul Cheltenham 84-89; V Lt Heath *St Alb* from 89. *The Vicarage, Thornton Road, Potters Bar, Herts EN6 1JJ* Potters Bar (01707) 654414

BROWN, Ivan James. b 24. Cant Sch of Min 84. **d** 86 **p** 87. NSM St Nicholas at Wade w Sarre and Chislet w Hoath *Cant* 86-94; rtd 94; Perm to offic Thanet Deanery from 94. *Hurst Cottage, Millbank, Hoath, Canterbury, Kent CT3 4LP* Chislet (01227) 860210

BROWN, Jack Robin. b 44. Linc Th Coll 67. **d** 69 **p** 70. C Canning Town St Cedd *Chelmsf* 69-72; C Dunstable *St Alb* 72-78; V Luton St Andr 78-85; V Kempston Transfiguration from 85; RD Bedf from 92. *The Transfiguration Vicarage, Cleveland Street, Kempston, Bedford MK42 8DW* Bedford (01234) 854788

BROWN, Canon James Philip. b 30. Ex Coll Ox BA54 MA55. Westcott Ho Cam 54. **d** 56 **p** 57. V Hellesdon *Nor* 63-71; P-in-c Kirkley w Lowestoft St Jo 71-79; TV Lowestoft St Marg 76-78; TV Lowestoft and Kirkley 79-81; P-in-c Northleach w Hampnett and Farmington *Glouc* 81-95; RD Northleach 83-92; P-in-c Cold Aston w Notgrove and Turkdean 86-95; Hon Can Glouc Cathl 91-95; rtd 95. *The Priest's House, 1 St Scholactica's Abbey, Teignmouth, Devon TQ14 8FF* Teignmouth (01626) 773623

BROWN, Ven James Russell. b 19. Qu Coll Ox BA52 MA56 Nashotah Ho Wisconsin DD70 Winnipeg Univ LLD77 LTh DD. Kelham Th Coll 37. **d** 43 **p** 44. C Bris St Jude w St Matthias *Bris* 43-45; C Portishead *B & W* 47-49; USA 52-55; C Brighton Gd Shep Preston *Chich* 55-47; C Abbots Langley *St Alb* 55-56; Canada from 56; Prof Nashotah Ho Wisconsin 61-70; Warden and Vice-Chan St Jo Coll Winnipeg 70-80; Can St Jo Cathl Winnipeg 70-80; Hon Can from 80; Lect Manitoba Univ from 80. *96 Kingsway Avenue, Winnipeg, Manitoba, Canada, R3M 0G9*

BROWN, Mrs Joan Leslie. b 31. SS Hild & Bede Coll Dur CertEd55. Oak Hill Th Coll BA85. **dss** 85 **d** 87 **p** 94. Fulwood *Sheff* 85-87; Par Dn 87-88; TD Netherthorpe 88-93; rtd 93; NSM Ellesmere St Pet *Sheff* from 93. *2 Kingston Street, Sheffield S4 7SU* Sheffield (0114) 243 3534

BROWN, John. b 21. **d** 50 **p** 51. I Clabby *Clogh* 62-75; V Dunham w Darlton and Ragnall *S'well* 75-87; R Fledborough 76-87; rtd 87. *The Groton, Norbury, Bishops Castle, Shropshire SY9 5DX* Linley (0158861) 272

BROWN, John. b 64. Kent Univ BA86. Westcott Ho Cam 87. **d** 90 **p** 91. C Lt Ilford St Mich *Chelmsf* 90-94; C E Ham w Upton Park St Alb 94; TV from 94. *147 Katherine Road, London E6 1ES* 0181-472 1067

BROWN, Canon John Roger. b 37. AKC60. **d** 61 **p** 62. C New Eltham All SS *S'wark* 61-64; C Bexhill St Pet *Chich* 64-68; V Eastbourne St Elisabeth 68-75; V E Grinstead St Swithun from 75; Chapl Qu Victoria's Hosp E Grinstead from 75; RD E Grinstead *Chich* 82-93; Can and Preb Chich Cathl from 89. *St Swithun's Vicarage, Church Lane, East Grinstead, W Sussex RH19 3BB* East Grinstead (01342) 323307

BROWN, John Bruce. b 42. Nottm Univ BA64 MA68. Cuddesdon Coll 64. **d** 66 **p** 67. C Warw St Nic *Cov* 66-71; C Hatf *St Alb* 71-78; V Watford St Mich from 78; RD Watford from 94. *St Michael's Vicarage, 5 Mildred Avenue, Watford WD1 7DY* Watford (01923) 232460

BROWN, Canon John Derek. b 41. Linc Th Coll 71. **d** 73 **p** 74. C Rotherham *Sheff* 73-76; P-in-c W Pinchbeck *Linc* 76-78; V Surfleet 76-82; R Boultham 83-94; RD Christianity 85-92; Hon Can Linc Cathl from 88; P-in-c Epworth and Wroot from 94. *St Andrew's Rectory, Belton Road, Epworth, Doncaster, S Yorkshire DN9 1JL* Epworth (01427) 872471

BROWN, John Dixon. b 28. Pemb Coll Cam BA52. Oak Hill Th Coll 52. **d** 54 **p** 55. V W Hampnett *Chich* 63-91; rtd 91. *3 Manor Way, Elmer Sands, Bognor Regis, W Sussex PO22 6LA* Bognor Regis (01243) 583449

BROWN, Canon John Duncan. b 43. St Pet Coll Ox BA64 BA66 MA68 Lon Univ BSc. Wycliffe Hall Ox 65. **d** 67 **p** 68. C Kingston upon Hull H Trin *York* 67-69; C St Leonards St Leon *Chich* 69-72; Hon C Norbiton *S'wark* 72-75; C Kirkcaldy *St And* 75-78; Prec and Chapl Chelmsf Cathl *Chelmsf* 78-86; P-in-c Kelvedon Hatch 86-92; P-in-c Navestock 86-92; P-in-c Fryerning w Margaretting from 92; Bp's ACORA Officer from 92; Hon Can Chelmsf Cathl from 93. *The Vicarage, Pennys Lane, Margaretting, Ingatestone, Essex CM4 0HA* Ingatestone (01277) 355692

✚**BROWN, Rt Rev John Edward.** b 30. Lon Univ BD68. Kelham Th Coll 50. **d** 55 **p** 56 **c** 87. Jerusalem 55-57; C Reading St Mary V *Ox* 57-60; Sudan 60-64; V Stewkley *Ox* 64-69; V Maidenhead St Luke 69-73; V Bracknell 73-77; RD Sonning 74-77; Adn Berks 78-87; Warden Ascot Priory 80-87; Bp Cyprus and the Gulf from 87. *2 Grigori Afxentiou, PO Box 2075, Nicosia 118, Cyprus* Nicosia (2) 451220 or 498013 Fax 466553

BROWN, John William Etheridge. b 13. St Pet Hall Ox BA35 MA39. Wycliffe Hall Ox 35. **d** 37 **p** 38. V Leusden *Ex* 61-79; V Widecombe in the Moor 61-79; P-in-c Holne 70-74; P-in-c Princetown 74-79; RD Moreton 74-80; Asst Chapl HM Pris Dartmoor 75-82; V Widecombe, Leusden and Princetown etc

Ex 79-82; rtd 82; Lic to Offic *Ex* from 82. *8 Emmetts Park, Ashburton, Newton Abbot, Devon TQ13 7DB* Ashburton (01364) 653072

BROWN, Jonathan. b 60. Univ Coll Dur BA83 MA85 Ex Univ CertEd86. Ripon Coll Cuddesdon 86 Ch Div Sch of the Pacific (USA) 88. **d** 89 **p** 90. C Esher *Guildf* from 89. *Hazel Cottage, Hillbrow Road, Esher, Surrey KT10 9UD* Esher (01372) 466865

BROWN, Kenneth Arthur Charles. b 27. ACP65. Local NSM Course 85. **d** 84 **p** 85. NSM Ingoldsby *Linc* from 84. *11 Ingoldsby Road, Lenton, Grantham, Lincs NG33 4HB* Ingoldsby (0147685) 763

BROWN, Canon Kenneth Edward. b 22. Qu Coll Cam BA43 MA47. Ridley Hall Cam 46. **d** 47 **p** 48. V Southbroom *Sarum* 69-83; RD Devizes 77-83; Can and Preb Sarum Cathl 77-87; TV Tisbury 83-87; rtd 87. *24 Broadleas Road, Devizes, Wilts SN10 5DG* Devizes (01380) 728254

BROWN, Kenneth Roger. b 48. Dur Univ BA69 St Chad's Coll Dur DipTh72. Liturg Inst Trier DipLit73. **d** 73 **p** 74. C Patchway *Bris* 73-77; C Fishponds St Jo 77-79; C Fishponds All SS 77-79; Chapl RAF 79-95; Chapl HM Pris Pentonville from 95. *HM Prison Pentonville, Caledonian Road, London N7 8TT* 0171-607 5353 Fax 700 0244

BROWN, Dr Leslie Maurice. b 04. Bris Univ BSc24 MSc25 St Andr Univ PhD38 FRSE47. Edin Th Coll 74. **d** 74 **p** 74. Hon C Edin St Jo *Edin* 74-89; rtd 89. *26 Falcon Court, Edinburgh EH10 4AE* 0131-447 5387

✚**BROWN, Rt Rev Leslie Wilfrid.** b 12. CBE65. Lon Univ BD36 MTh44 DD57 Cam Univ Hon MA53. Trin Coll Toronto Hon DD63 ALCD35. **d** 35 **p** 36 **c** 53. V Aldham *Portsm* 35-38; India 38-43 and 44-50; Chapl Down Coll Cam 43-44; C Cam H Trin *Ely* 43-44; Chapl Jes Coll Cam 50-51; Bp Uganda 53-60; Abp Uganda, Rwanda and Burundi 60-65; Bp Namirembe 60-65; Bp St E 66-78; ChStJ from 68; rtd 78. *47 New Square, Cambridge CB1 1EZ* Cambridge (01223) 352465

BROWN, Miss Louise Margaret. b 53. Trin Coll Bris DipHE82. **dss** 83 **d** 87 **p** 94. Woodley St Jo the Ev *Ox* 84-87; Par Dn Woodley 87-92; Asst Chapl Reading Hosps 92-94; C Shinfield 93-94; P-in-c Dedworth from 94. *The Vicarage, 3 Pierson Road, Windsor, Berks SL4 5RJ* Windsor (01753) 864591

BROWN, Malcolm Arthur. b 54. Or Coll Ox BA76 MA82. Westcott Ho Cam 77. **d** 79 **p** 80. C Riverhead w Dunton Green *Roch* 79-83; TV Southn (City Cen) *Win* 83-91; Lic to Offic *Man* from 91; Assoc Dir Wm Temple Foundn from 91. *c/o William Temple Foundation, Manchester Business School, Manchester M15 6PB* 0161-275 6533 Fax 273 7732

BROWN (nee PATTERSON), Mrs Marjorie Jean. b 54. Wooster Coll USA BA76 St Andr Univ 77. S Dios Minl Tr Scheme 92. **d** 95. C Poplar *Lon* from 95. *St Michael's Vicarage, St Leonard's Road, London E14 6PW* 0171-987 1795

BROWN, Mark Edward. b 61. Southn Univ BSc83 Cam Univ PGCE84. Trin Coll Bris DipHE87 BA88. **d** 88 **p** 89. C Egham *Guildf* 88-92; C Northwood Em *Lon* from 92. *14 Greenheys Close, Northwood, Middx HA6 2FR* Northwood (01923) 825505

BROWN, Martin Easdale. b 27. Ely Th Coll 53. **d** 55 **p** 66. V France Lynch *Glouc* 62-75; P-in-c Aysgarth *Ripon* 75-77; V 77-80; P-in-c Bolton w Redmire 78-80; V Aysgarth and Bolton cum Redmire 80-91; rtd 91; St Helena 94-95. *Rose Bank Cottage, Ampleforth, York YO6 4DX* Ampleforth (01439) 788711

BROWN, Ven Michael Rene Warneford. b 15. St Pet Coll Ox BA37 MA41. St Steph Ho Ox 38. **d** 41 **p** 42. Adn Nottm *S'well* 60-77; Perm to Offic *Cant* from 77; rtd 80; Hon OCF R Marines Sch of Music Deal from 85. *Faygate, 72 Liverpool Road, Deal, Kent CT14 7LR* Deal (01304) 361326

BROWN, Nicholas Francis Palgrave. b 23. Fitzw Ho Cam BA51 MA54. **d** 53 **p** 54. Gen Sec Ind Chr Fellowship 66-76; V St Kath Cree *Lon* 66-71; Chapl and Dir of Studies Holland Ho Cropthorne 76-80; P-in-c Cropthorne w Charlton *Worc* 76-88; Adult Educn Officer 80-85; rtd 88. *Bredon View, Rear of 40 Bridge Street, Pershore, Worcs WR10 1AT* Pershore (01386) 556816

BROWN, Canon Norman Charles Harry. b 27. Univ of Wales BSc46. St Mich Coll Llan 48. **d** 50 **p** 51. C Canton St Jo *Llan* 50-57; C Llanishen and Lisvane 58-63; V Miskin from 63; RD Aberdare from 82; Can Llan Cathl from 86. *The Vicarage, Miskin, Mountain Ash, M Glam CF45 3NE* Mountain Ash (01443) 473247

BROWN, Norman John. b 34. Thames Poly MA90. Ripon Hall Ox 72. **d** 74 **p** 75. C High Wycombe *Ox* 74-78; V Tilehurst St Cath 78-82; V Boyne Hill from 82; Chapl Windsor and Maidenhead Coll 87-89. *All Saints' Vicarage, Westmorland Road, Maidenhead, Berks SL6 4HB* Maidenhead (01628) 26921

BROWN, Paul David Christopher. b 50. Lon Univ LLB71. E Midl Min Tr Course 81. **d** 84 **p** 85. NSM Wollaton *S'well*

from 84. *32 Benington Drive, Wollaton, Nottingham NG8 2TF* Nottingham (0115) 928 4493

BROWN, Peter. b 38. Leeds Univ BSc62 PhD65. Nashotah Ho 85. **d** 87 **p** 88. USA 87-89; C Sprowston *Nor* 89-90; C Sprowston w Beeston 90-92; P-in-c W Winch 92; P-in-c W Winch w Setchey and N Runcton from 92. *The Rectory, West Winch, King's Lynn, Norfolk PE33 0NR* King's Lynn (01553) 840835

BROWN, Peter. b 47. RMN69. Kelham Th Coll 69. **d** 74 **p** 75. C Hendon *Dur* 74-80; C Byker St Ant *Newc* 80-90; C Brandon *Dur* from 90. *The Clergy House, Sawmill Lane, Brandon, Durham DH7 8NS* 0191-378 0845

BROWN, Peter. b 53. St Chad's Coll Dur BA75. Sarum & Wells Th Coll 75. **d** 77 **p** 78. C Tunstall Ch Ch *Lich* 77-79; C Tunstall 79-80; C Willenhall H Trin 80-83; V Weston Rhyn 83-88; Australia 88-90; R Hubbertson *St D* from 90. *Hubbertson Rectory, 35 Westaway Drive, Hubbertson, Milford Haven, Dyfed SA73 3EQ* Milford Haven (01646) 692251

BROWN, Canon Peter Kimpton. b 34. ALCD58. **d** 60 **p** 61. C Folkestone H Trin w Ch Ch *Cant* 60-63; C Swanage *Sarum* 63-67; Australia from 67. *43 Hamersely Drive, Bunbury, W Australia 6230*

BROWN, Peter Russell. b 43. Oak Hill Th Coll. **d** 71 **p** 72. C Gt Faringdon w Lt Coxwell *Ox* 71-73; C Reading Greyfriars 73-74; V Forty Hill Jes Ch *Lon* 74-81; V Laleham from 81. *The Vicarage, Laleham, Staines, Middx TW18 1SB* Staines (01784) 457330

BROWN, Philip Roy. b 41. St Steph Ho Ox 78. **d** 80 **p** 81. C Highters Heath *Birm* 80-83; P-in-c Washwood Heath 83-87; V Tysoe w Oxhill and Whatcote *Cov* 87-93; R Harbury and Ladbroke from 93; RD Southam from 95. *The Rectory, 2 Vicarage Lane, Harbury, Leamington Spa, Warks CV33 9HA* Harbury (01926) 612377

BROWN, Philip Anthony. b 54. Oak Hill Th Coll BA91. **d** 91 **p** 92. C Rock Ferry *Ches* 91-95; V Hattersley from 95. *St Barnabas's Vicarage, Hattersley Road East, Hyde, Cheshire SK14 3EQ* 0161-368 2795

BROWN, Phillip Murray. b 59. Keele Univ BSc80. Trin Coll Bris DipTh86 ADPS87. **d** 87 **p** 88. C Greasbrough *Sheff* 87-91; Ind Chapl from 87; V Thorne from 91. *The Vicarage, 2 Brooke Street, Thorne, Doncaster, S Yorkshire DN8 4AZ* Thorne (01405) 814055

BROWN, Raymond Isaac Harry. b 14. Kelham Th Coll 36. **d** 42 **p** 43. V Tintinhull *B & W* 66-74; RD Martock 70-75; Lesotho from 76; rtd 79. *Community of the Holy Name, PO Box 43, Leribe 300, Lesotho, South Africa* Lesotho (266) 400249

BROWN, Raymond John. b 49. Ox Univ BEd71. Wycliffe Hall Ox 72. **d** 75 **p** 76. C Barking St Marg w St Patr *Chelmsf* 75-78; C Walton H Trin *Ox* 78-82; V Enfield St Mich *Lon* 82-91; Chapl St Mich Hosp Enfield 82-91; R Springfield All SS *Chelmsf* from 91. *The Rectory, 9 Mulberry Way, Chelmsford CM1 5SN* Chelmsford (01245) 356720

BROWN, Richard George. b 38. Dur Univ BSc63. Wells Th Coll 63. **d** 65 **p** 66. C Norton St Mary *Dur* 65-69; C N Gosforth *Newc* 69-71; Chapl Wells Cathl Sch 71-81; P-in-c Dulverton and Brushford *B & W* 81-83; R 83-86; Chapl Millfield Jun Sch Somerset 86-89; Chapl Brighton Coll 89-92; Chapl Benenden Sch Kent 92-94; Perm to Offic *Chich* from 94. *26A Eaton Place, Brighton BN2 1EG* Brighton (01273) 621840

BROWN, Richard Lessey. b 27. Keble Coll Ox BA51 MA55. Qu Coll Birm 51. **d** 53 **p** 54. V York St Luke *York* 61-75; V Barlby 75-92; rtd 92. *1 Kings Court, King Street, Cottingham, N Humberside HU16 5RW* Hull (01482) 845299

BROWN, Ven Robert Saville. b 14. Selw Coll Cam BA39 MA43. Linc Th Coll 39. **d** 40 **p** 41. Hon Can St Alb 65-74; V Bedf St Paul 69-74; Adn Bedf 74-79; P-in-c Old Warden 74-79; rtd 79; Perm to Offic *Ox* 79-87. *The Rowans, 29 The Rise, Amersham, Bucks HP7 9AG* Amersham (01494) 728376

BROWN, Robin. b 38. Leeds Univ BA60 MPhil69. Qu Coll Birm 89. **d** 91 **p** 92. C Far Headingley St Chad *Ripon* 91-94; V Hawksworth Wood from 94. *St Mary's Vicarage, Cragside Walk, Leeds LS5 3QE* Leeds (0113) 258 2923

BROWN, Roger Lee. b 42. Univ of Wales (Lamp) BA63 Univ Coll Lon MA73. Wycliffe Hall Ox 66. **d** 68 **p** 69. C Dinas w Penygraig *Llan* 68-70; C Bargoed and Deri w Brithdir 70-72; TV Glyncorrwg w Afan Vale and Cymmer Afan 72-74; R 74-79; V Tongwynlais 79-93; R Welshpool w Castle Caereinion *St As* from 93. *The Vicarage, Church Street, Welshpool, Powys SY21 7DP* Welshpool (01938) 553164

✠**BROWN, Rt Rev Ronald.** b 26. St Jo Coll Dur BA50 DipTh52. **d** 52 **p** 53 **c** 74. C Chorley St Laur *Blackb* 52-56; V Whittle-le-Woods 56-61; V Halliwell St Thos *Man* 61-69; R Ashton St Mich 69-74; RD Ashton-under-Lyne 69-74; Suff Bp Birkenhead *Ches* 74-92; rtd 92. *Hurst Cottage, Moss Lane, Burscough, Ormskirk, Lancs L40 4BA* Burscough (01704) 897314

BROWN, Ronald Glyn. b 34. Lich Th Coll 70. **d** 73 **p** 74. C Weymouth St Paul *Sarum* 73-78; C Swanage 78-79; P-in-c

Bromham 79-80; P-in-c Chittoe 79-80; R Bromham, Chittoe and Sandy Lane from 80. *The Rectory, Bromham, Chippenham, Wilts SN15 2HA* Bromham (01380) 850322

BROWN, Ms Shelagh Margaret. b 30. Gilmore Course 78. **dss** 80 **d** 87 **p** 94. Reigate St Mark *S'wark* 80-81; St Marylebone Ch Ch *Lon* 81-82; Caterham Valley *S'wark* 82-86; Dir Abp Coggan's Tr Services Cen 86-89; Par Dn Reigate St Mary 89-91; rtd 91; NSM Reigate St Mary *S'wark* from 91; Commissioning Ed Bible Reading Fellowship from 91. *1 The Clears, Reigate, Surrey RH2 9JL* Reigate (01737) 245223

BROWN, Simon John. b 66. Birm Univ BSc87 PGCE88 Nottm Univ MA93. St Jo Coll Nottm DTS92. **d** 93 **p** 94. C Holbrooks *Cov* from 93. *85 Wheelwright Lane, Coventry CV6 4HN* Coventry (01203) 364874

BROWN, Canon Simon Nicolas Danton. b 37. Clare Coll Cam BA61 MA65. S'wark Ord Course 61 Linc Th Coll 63. **d** 64 **p** 65. C Lambeth St Mary the Less *S'wark* 64-66; Chapl and Warden LMH Settlement 66-72; P-in-c Southn St Mary w H Trin *Win* 72-73; TV Southn (City Cen) 73-79; R Gt Brickhill w Bow Brickhill and Lt Brickhill *Ox* 79-84; TR Burnham w Dropmore, Hitcham and Taplow from 84; RD Burnham from 87; Hon Can Ch Ch from 94. *The Rectory, The Precincts, Burnham, Slough SL1 7HU* Burnham (01628) 604173

BROWN, Stanley George. b 19. Bps' Coll Cheshunt 66. **d** 67 **p** 68. C Shrub End *Chelmsf* 67-71; R Dengie w Asheldham 71-89; V Tillingham 71-89; RD Maldon and Dengie 82-89; rtd 89. *134 Lynn Road, Ely, Cambs CB6 1DE* Ely (01353) 662888

BROWN, Stephen Charles. b 60. Leeds Univ BA83 BA89 Reading Univ PGCE89. Coll of Resurr Mirfield 87. **d** 90 **p** 91. C Whitkirk *Ripon* 90-93; Asst Youth Chapl 92-95; C Chapel Allerton 93-95; R Stanningley St Thos from 95. *The Rectory, Stanningley Road, Stanningley, Pudsey, W Yorkshire LS28 6NB* Leeds (0113) 257 3460 or 255 3830

BROWN, Stephen James. b 44. Bradf Univ BSc69. Westcott Ho Cam 71. **d** 72 **p** 73. C Seaton Hirst *Newc* 72-75; C Marton-in-Cleveland *York* 75-77; Dioc Youth Adv *Dur* 77-82; V Thorner *Ripon* 82-92; Dioc Officer for Local Min from 90; P-in-c Ripley from 92; Chapl Leeds Coll of Building from 92. *The Rectory, Ripley, Harrogate, N Yorkshire HG3 3AY* Harrogate (01423) 770147

BROWN, Mrs Verity Joy. b 68. Qu Mary Coll Lon BA89. Ripon Coll Cuddesdon BTh93. **d** 93 **p** 94. C Barnard Castle w Whorlton *Dur* from 93. *Glebe House, Newgate, Barnard Castle, Co Durham DL12 8NW* Staindrop (01833) 690435

BROWN, Victor Charles. b 31. S'wark Ord Course 67. **d** 71 **p** 72. C Pinhoe *Ex* 71-73; C Egg Buckland 73-74; C Oakdale St Geo *Sarum* 74-77; R Old Trafford St Hilda *Man* 77-83; R Chigwell Row *Chelmsf* 83-92; R Fenny Bentley, Kniveton, Thorpe and Tissington *Derby* from 92. *The Vicarage, Parwich, Ashbourne, Derbyshire DE6 1QD* Parwich (01335) 390226

BROWN, Wallace. b 44. Oak Hill Th Coll 77. **d** 79 **p** 80. C Oadby *Leic* 79-85; V Quinton Road W St Boniface *Birm* from 85. *St Boniface Vicarage, Quinton Road West, Birmingham B32 2QD* 0121-427 1939

BROWN, Walter Bertram John. b 09. K Coll Lon 43. **d** 43 **p** 44. Ex and Devon Miss to Adult Deaf & Dumb 53-73; Chapl to the Deaf *Chich* 73-75; rtd 75; Perm to Offic *Chich* 80-91. *7 Cowslip Meadow, Woodmancote, Cheltenham, Glos GL52 4TT* Cheltenham (01242) 673648

BROWN, William Martyn. b 14. Pemb Coll Cam BA36 MA47. Nor Ord Course 76. **d** 76 **p** 77. NSM Thornage w Brinton w Hunworth and Stody *Nor* 76-77; NSM Field Dalling w Saxlingham 77-84; RD Holt 84-88; NSM Gunthorpe w Bale w Field Dalling, Saxlingham etc 84-88; Perm to Offic from 88. *Lodge Cottage, Field Dalling, Holt, Norfolk NR25 7AS* Binham (01328) 830403

BROWNBRIDGE, Bernard Alan. b 19. NW Ord Course 74. **d** 77 **p** 78. NSM Huntington *York* 77-80; V Sand Hutton 80-86; rtd 87; Hon C Birdsall w Langton *York* 87-92. *127 Langton Road, Norton, Malton, N Yorkshire YO17 9AE* Malton (01653) 697626

BROWNBRIDGE, Peter John. b 31. BD. **d** 81 **p** 82. NSM Wingham w Elmstone and Preston w Stourmouth *Cant* 81-87; V from 87. *St Mary's House, 5 St Mary's Meadow, Wingham, Canterbury, Kent CT3 1DF* Canterbury (01227) 721530

BROWNE, Anthony Douglas. b 40. BD69 Aston Univ MSc74. Oak Hill NSM Course 88. **d** 91 **p** 92. NSM Woodford St Mary w St Phil and St Jas *Chelmsf* 91-93; Perm to Offic from 93. *1 Broadfield Way, Buckhurst Hill, Essex IG9 5AG* 0181-504 9540

BROWNE, Dr Arnold Samuel. b 52. MBPsS92 St Jo Coll Ox BA73 MA77 SS Coll Cam PhD87 Surrey Univ MSc89. Westcott Ho Cam 76. **d** 78 **p** 79. C Esher *Guildf* 78-81; C Worplesdon 81-86; Chapl R Holloway and Bedf New Coll 86-92; Fell and Dean of Chpl Trin Coll Cam from 92. *Trinity College, Cambridge CB2 1TQ* Cambridge (01223) 338400 Fax 338564

BROWNE, Arthur Donal. b 11. MC44. St Edm Hall Ox BA34 MA54. Wycliffe Hall Ox DipTh35. **d** 35 **p** 36. V S Kensington St Jude *Lon* 62-78; rtd 78; P-in-c Lydgate w Ousden and Cowlinge *St E* 80-82; P-in-c Glenurquhart *Mor* 84-89; Perm to Offic from 89. *Ham Farm, Dunnet, Thurso, Caithness KW14 8XP* Barrock (018478s) 232

BROWNE, Aubrey Robert Caulfeild. b 31. Moore Th Coll Sydney 54. **d** 55 **p** 56. Australia 55-71; Producer of Relig Radio Progr USPG 72-84; Hon C S Kensington St Steph *Lon* 78-88; Hd of Area Sec Dept USPG 84-87; P-in-c Nunhead St Antony *S'wark* 88-90; V Nunhead St Antony w St Silas from 90. *St Anthony's Vicarage, 2A Carden Road, London SE15 3UD* 0171-639 4261

BROWNE, Miss Christine Mary. b 53. Nottm Univ BEd75. E Midl Min Tr Course 87. **d** 90 **p** 94. Par Dn Bulwell St Mary *S'well* 90-94; C 94-95; Asst Chapl Nottm City Hosp from 94; TV Hucknall Torkard *S'well* from 95. *The Vicarage, Ruff's Drive, Hucknall, Nottingham NG15 6JG* Nottingham (0115) 963 3640

BROWNE, Cyril Theodore Martin. b 12. Tyndale Hall Bris 30. **d** 35 **p** 36. V Greenwich H Trin and St Paul *S'wark* 62-74; R Tilston and Shocklach *Ches* 74-78; rtd 78; C-in-c Reading St Mary Castle Street Prop Chpl *Ox* 78-84; Perm to Offic *Roch* from 85. *14 St Philip's Court, Sandhurst Road, Tunbridge Wells, Kent TN2 3SW* Tunbridge Wells (01892) 546356

BROWNE, Herman Beseah. b 65. K Coll Lon BD90 AKC90. Cuttington Univ Coll BA86. **d** 87. Liberia 87-90; C N Lambeth *S'wark* 90-91; Lect Simon of Cyrene Th Inst 90-91. *4 Cownington, Somerset Road, Kingston upon Thames, Surrey KT1 3EN* 0181-541 5163

BROWNE, Ian Cameron. b 51. St Cath Coll Ox BA74 MA78 Fitzw Coll Cam BA76 MA80. Ridley Hall Cam 74. **d** 77 **p** 78. C Cheltenham Ch Ch *Glouc* 77-80; Hon C Shrewsbury St Chad *Lich* 80-83; Asst Chapl Shrewsbury Sch 80-83; Chapl Bedf Sch from 83. *32 The Grove, Bedford MK40 3JW* Bedford (01234) 356004

BROWNE, John Burnell. b 15. MC45. Qu Coll Cam BA36 MA40. Westcott Ho Cam 46. **d** 47 **p** 48. V Barnard Castle *Dur* 59-71; RD Barnard Castle 59-71; V Billingham St Cuth 71-80; rtd 80; Perm to Offic *Wakef* 80-86. *40 Slack Top, Heptonstall, Hebden Bridge, W Yorkshire HX7 7HA* Hebden Bridge (01422) 843099

BROWNE, Leonard Joseph. b 58. St Cath Coll Cam BA81 MA84. Trin Coll Bris 87. **d** 89 **p** 90. C Reading Greyfriars *Ox* 89-92; V Cam St Barn *Ely* from 92. *The Vicarage, St Barnabas Road, Cambridge CB1 2BX* Cambridge (01223) 352924 or 316228

BROWNE, Norman Desmond. b 21. TCD BA42 BD46 MA61. CITC 43. **d** 44 **p** 45. R Hedgerley *Ox* 61-80; rtd 80. *8 Brett House Close, West Hill, London SW15 3JD* 0181-788 1365

BROWNE, Peter Clifford. b 59. SRN82 Bris Univ BA80. Ripon Coll Cuddesdon 88. **d** 90 **p** 91. C Southgate Ch Ch *Lon* 90-92; NSM Kemp Town St Mary *Chich* from 93. *37 Washington Street, Brighton BN2 2SR* Brighton (01273) 605706

BROWNING, Canon Denys James. b 07. Keble Coll Ox BA29 MA59. Coll of Resurr Mirfield 38. **d** 40 **p** 41. C Oxley *Lich* 40-42; CF (EC) 42-47; C Leeds St Aid *Ripon* 48-50; CF (TA) 49-50; Australia 50-55; Area Sec (Dios Ox and Cov) USPG 55-59; Papua New Guinea 59-81; Hon Prov Can Papua from 81; New Zealand from 81. *RD9, Hamilton, New Zealand* Hamilton (71) 495262

BROWNING, Edward Barrington Lee (Barry). b 42. St Pet Coll Saltley TCert65. Ripon Coll Cuddesdon 90. **d** 92 **p** 93. C Falmouth K Chas *Truro* from 92. *21 Avenue Road, Falmouth, Cornwall TR11 4AZ* Falmouth (01326) 212329

BROWNING, Canon John William. b 36. Keele Univ BA61. Ripon Hall Ox 61. **d** 63 **p** 64. C Baswich (or Berkswich) *Lich* 63-66; Chapl Monyhull Hosp Birm 67-71; Chapl Wharncliffe Hosp Sheff 71-78; Chapl Middlewood Hosp Sheff 71-94; Hon Can Sheff Cathl *Sheff* from 84; Chapl Sheff Mental Health Unit from 85. *131 Low Road, Stannington, Sheffield S6 5FZ* Sheffield (0114) 271 6518/271 6310

BROWNING, Julian. b 51. St Jo Coll Cam BA72 MA76. Ripon Coll Cuddesdon 77. **d** 80 **p** 81. C Notting Hill *Lon* 80-81; C W Brompton St Mary w St Pet 81-84; Perm to Offic 84-91. *82 Ashworth Mansions, Grantully Road, London W9 1LN* 0171-286 6034

BROWNING, Canon Richard Geoffrey Claude. b 25. Selw Coll Cam BA50 MA55. Lon Coll of Div BD53 ALCD53. **d** 53 **p** 54. V Old Hill H Trin *Worc* 65-91; Hon Can Worc Cathl 77-91; rtd 91. *Llwyn Rhug, Ffordd Dewi Sant, Nefyn, Pwllheli, Gwynedd LL53 6EG* Nefyn (01758) 720834

BROWNING, Robert Frank. b 11. K Coll Lon 56. **d** 57 **p** 58. V Lightwater *Guildf* 63-76; rtd 76; Perm to Offic *Guildf* from 76. *Braeholme, Rectory Lane, Windlesham, Surrey GU20 6BW* Bagshot (01276) 474813

BROWNING, Thomas Clive (Tom). b 35. Lon Univ DipTh65 BD67. Wycliffe Hall Ox 63. **d** 67 **p** 68. C Ipswich St Jo *St E*

67-69; Chapl Scargill Ho 69-70; C Downend *Bris* 70-73; C Hagley *Worc* 73-76; Asst Master Bay Ho Sch Gosport from 77; Perm to Offic *Portsm* from 82. *81 Oval Gardens, Gosport, Hants PO12 2RD* Gosport (01705) 584738

BROWNING, Canon Wilfrid Robert Francis. b 18. Ch Ch Ox BA40 MA44 BD49. Cuddesdon Coll 40. **d** 41 **p** 42. Lect Cuddesdon Coll 65-70; Can Res Ch Ch *Ox* 65-87; Hon Can 87-89; Dir of Post-Ord Tr 65-85; Dir of Ords 65-85; Lect Wycliffe Hall Ox 67-69; Dir Ox NSM Course 72-89; rtd 87. *42 Alexandra Road, Oxford OX2 0DB* Oxford (01865) 723464

BROWNLESS, Brian Paish. b 25. TD72. Keble Coll Ox BA50 MA50. Wells Th Coll 50. **d** 52 **p** 53. Area Sec (Dio Lich) USPG 66-77; Lic to Offic *Lich* 66-77; CF (TA - R of O) 66-72; R Yoxall *Lich* 77-82; V S Ramsey *S & M* 82-87; rtd 87; Perm to Offic *Heref* from 87. *10 Caple Avenue, Kings Caple, Hereford HR1 4TX* Carey (01432) 840246

BROWNLESS, Philip Paul Stanley. b 19. Selw Coll Cam BA41 MA45. Ridley Hall Cam 46. **d** 47 **p** 48. Chapl & Hd Master Lambrook Sch Bracknell 54-71; V Heckfield cum Mattingley *Win* 71-74; V Heckfield w Mattingley and Rotherwick 74-84; RD Odiham 83-84; rtd 85; Perm to Offic *Chich* from 85. *The Hornpipe, Oakmeadow, Birdham, Chichester, W Sussex PO20 7BH* Birdham (01243) 512177

BROWNLIE, Miss Caroline Heddon. b 47. Suffolk Poly CQSW75. St Jo Coll Nottm DPS80 Qu Coll Birm IDC81. **d** 87 **p** 94. Asst Chapl Fairfield Hosp Hitchin 87-91; NSM Ashwell w Hinxworth and Newnham *St Alb* from 92. *16 Kingland Way, Ashwell, Baldock, Herts SG7 5PZ* Ashwell (01462) 743296

BROWNRIDGE, Allan John Michael. b 32. Chan Sch Truro 80. **d** 82 **p** 83. C St Keverne *Truro* 82-86; P-in-c Werrington, St Giles in the Heath and Virginstow 86-92; R Boyton, N Tamerton, Werrington etc from 92; RD Trigg Major from 94. *The Rectory, Werrington, Launceston, Cornwall PL15 8TP* Launceston (01566) 773932

BROWNRIGG, Canon Ronald Allen. b 19. Em Coll Cam BA47 MA50. Westcott Ho Cam 47. **d** 49 **p** 50. R Bletchingley *S'wark* 60-74; V Petersham 74-85; Hon Can S'wark Cathl 78-85; Consultant Inter-Ch Travel from 83; rtd 85. *6 Stoneleigh Lodge, Branston Road, Kew, Richmond, Surrey TW9 3LD* 0181-940 3506

BROWNSELL, Preb John Kenneth. b 48. Hertf Coll Ox BA69 BA72 MA89. Cuddesdon Coll 70. **d** 73 **p** 74. C Notting Hill All SS w St Columb *Lon* 73-74; C Notting Hill 74-76; TV 76-82; V Notting Hill All SS w St Columb from 82; AD Kensington 84-92; Preb St Paul's Cathl from 92. *All Saints' Vicarage, Powis Gardens, London W11 1JG* 0171-727 5919

BRUCE, David Ian. b 47. Univ of Wales (Cardiff) DipTh73. St Mich Coll Llan 70. **d** 73 **p** 74. C Bordesley St Benedict *Birm* 73-74; C Llanishen and Lisvane *Llan* 74-81; V Canley *Cov* 81-90; V Longford from 90. *St Thomas's Vicarage, Hurst Road, Coventry CV6 6EL* Coventry (01203) 364078

BRUCE, Francis Bernard. b 30. Trin Coll Ox BA52 MA56. Westcott Ho Cam 52. **d** 54 **p** 55. R Croston *Blackb* 61-86; V Bibury w Winson and Barnsley *Glouc* 86-95; rtd 95. *6 Gloucester Street, Cirencester, Glos GL7 2DJ* Cirencester (01285) 641954

BRUCE, James Hamilton. b 57. Newc Univ MSc79 Dur Univ BSc78. Trin Coll Bris DipTh84. **d** 84 **p** 85. C Walmley *Birm* 84-86; Perm to Offic *Carl* 87-95; W Cumbria Sch Worker N Schs Chr Union 87-93; Nat Development Officer Wales Scripture Union 93; Kenya from 95. *St Andrew's School Turi, Private Bag, Molo, Kenya*

BRUCE, John. b 26. **d** 50 **p** 51. V Carl St Herbert w St Steph *Carl* 66-74; P-in-c Kendal St Geo 74-76; V 76-83; V Coundon *Dur* 83-86; rtd 86; Perm to Offic *Carl* from 86. *9 Penton Close, Carlisle CA3 0PX*

BRUCE, Dr Leslie Barton. b 23. Liv Univ MB, ChB48. **d** 71 **p** 72. NSM Wavertree H Trin *Liv* from 71. *3 Childwall Park Avenue, Liverpool L16 0JE* 0151-722 7664

BRUCE, Lewis Stewart. b 07. Sarum Th Coll 34. **d** 37 **p** 38. V Brockworth *Glouc* 54-75; rtd 76; P-in-c Bourton on the Hill *Glouc* 76-78; Hon C Hardwicke, Quedgeley and Elmore w Longney 78-87. *Sarum House, 1 Ryelands, Gloucester GL4 0QA* Gloucester (01452) 414292

BRUMPTON, Canon John Charles Kenyon. b 16. Selw Coll Cam BA38 MA42. Linc Th Coll 38. **d** 40 **p** 41. Chapl Asst Barnsley Gen Hosp 65-88; RD Barnsley *Wakef* 65-88; R Barnsley St Mary 66-88; Hon Can Wakef Cathl 67-88; rtd 88; Perm to Offic *Linc* from 88. *Greenside, 199 Legsby Avenue, Grimsby, S Humberside DN32 0AD* Grimsby (01472) 753258

BRUMWELL, Francis John Thomas. b 33. Lich Th Coll 57. **d** 61 **p** 62. V Calderbrook *Man* 65-73; V Bradley St Martin *Lich* 73-89; P-in-c Bilston St Mary 75-78; R Gorton St Phil *Man* 89-95; rtd 95. *53 Audmore Road, Gnosall, Stafford ST20 0HE* Stafford (01785) 822808

BRUNDLE, Michael Roy. b 52. Qu Coll Birm. **d** 84 **p** 85. C Swindon New Town *Bris* 84-88; TV Halifax *Wakef* 88-92; Chapl HM Young Offender Inst Feltham 92-94; C Notting Dale St Clem w St Mark and St Jas *Lon* 94-95; V Swanley St Mary *Roch* from 95. *St Mary's Vicarage, London Road, Swanley, Kent BR8 7AQ* Swanley (01322) 662201

BRUNDRITT, Cyril. b 97. AKC34. **d** 34 **p** 35. V Grateley cum Quarley *Win* 59-66; rtd 66; Perm to Offic *Win* from 67. *The Old Malt House, Middle Wallop, Stockbridge, Hants SO20 6ET* Andover (01264) 781353

BRUNING, Arthur Frederick. b 17. ALCD54. **d** 54 **p** 55. V Deptford St Luke *S'wark* 66-72; V Sporle w Gt and Lt Palgrave *Nor* 72-81; rtd 81; Perm to Offic *Nor* from 81. *3 Adams Road, Norwich NR7 8QT* Norwich (01603) 400457

BRUNNING, Canon David George. b 32. Univ of Wales (Lamp) BA53. St Mich Coll Llan 53. **d** 55 **p** 56. C Llantwit Major and St Donat's *Llan* 55-59; C Usk and Monkswood w Glascoed Chpl and Gwehelog *Mon* 59-62; V Abercarn 62-71; V Pontnewydd 71-89; RD Pontypool from 89; R Panteg from 90; Can St Woolos Cathl from 94. *Panteg Rectory, The Highway, New Inn, Pontypool, Gwent NP4 0PH* Pontypool (01495) 763724

BRUNNING, Neil. b 29. NW Ord Course 73. **d** 76 **p** 77. C Cheadle Hulme All SS *Ches* 76-79; V 79-88; V Glentworth *Linc* 88-93; P-in-c Hemswell w Harpswell 88-93; V Glentworth Gp 93-94; rtd 94. *11 Drovers Court, Lea Road, Gainsborough, Lincs DN21 1AN* Gainsborough (01427) 617938

BRUNNING, Sidney John George. b 13. Ely Th Coll 46. **d** 49 **p** 50. R Sunningwell *Ox* 55-81; rtd 81; Perm to Offic *Nor* 81-95. *c/o 47 Church Lane, Little Abington, Cambridge CB1 6BQ* Cambridge (01223) 891960

BRUNO, Allan David. b 34. AKC59. **d** 60 **p** 61. C Darlington H Trin *Dur* 60-64; S Africa 64-65 and 76-80; Rhodesia 65-70; Overseas Chapl Scottish Episc Ch 70-75; C Edin Old St Paul *Edin* 75-76; Namibia 80-86; Dean Windhoek 81-86; R Falkirk *Edin* from 86. *The Rectory, Kerse Lane, Falkirk FK1 1RX* Falkirk (01324) 623709

BRUNSDON, Canon Thomas Kenneth. b 08. Univ of Wales BA33. St Mich Coll Llan 33. **d** 34 **p** 35. V Newton St Pet *S & B* 61-76; rtd 76. *121 Homegower House, St Helen's Road, Swansea SA1 4DW* Swansea (01792) 463473

BRUNSKILL, Mrs Sheila Kathryn. See BANYARD, Sheila Kathryn

BRUNSWICK, Canon Robert John. b 38. TD86. St Aid Birkenhead 60. **d** 63 **p** 64. C Neston *Ches* 63-66; CF (TA - R of O) from 65; C Warrington St Paul *Liv* 66-68; V Liv St Paul Stoneycroft 68-78; V Southport St Luke 78-87; R Croston *Blackb* from 87; Chapl Bp Rawstorne Sch Croston Preston from 88; Hon Can Koforidua from 94. *St Michael's Rectory, 19 Westhead Road, Croston, Preston PR5 7RQ* Croston (01772) 600877

BRUNYEE, Miss Hilary. b 46. Linc Th Coll 76. **dss** 81 **d** 87 **p** 94. Longsight St Jo w St Cypr *Man* 81-87; Par Dn Peel 87-94; TV from 94. *7 Trent Drive, Worsley, Manchester M28 5TF* 0161-790 7761

BRUSH, Sally. b 47. Lon Univ BD. Trin Coll Bris 73. **dss** 76 **d** 80. Flint *St As* 76-80; C 80-83; C Cefn 83-87; Chapl St As Cathl 83-87; C St As and Tremeirchion 83-87; D-in-c Cerrigydrudion w Llanfihangel etc from 87. *The Rectory, Cerrigydrudion, Corwen, Clwyd LL21 0RU* Cerrigydrudion (0149082) 313

BRUSSELS, Dean of. See SCRIVEN, Rt Rev Henry William

BRUTON, Keith Leslie. b 39. S Dios Minl Tr Scheme 91. **d** 94. NSM Camelot Par *B & W* from 94. *Castle View House, Sparkford, Yeovil, Somerset BA22 7LH* Yeovil (01935) 440859 Fax as telephone

BRUTTON, Robert Springett. b 14. Trin Coll Cam BA34 MA55. Cuddesdon Coll 54. **d** 55 **p** 56. V Sonning *Ox* 65-74; rtd 79; Perm to Offic *Sarum* from 80. *7 North Street, Langton Matravers, Swanage, Dorset BH19 3HL* Swanage (01929) 425681

BRYAN, Cecil William. b 43. TCD BA66 MA73. CITC 66. **d** 68 **p** 69. C Dub Zion Ch *D & G* 68-72; Chapl RAF 72-75; Dioc Info Officer *D & G* 75-90; I Castleknock w Mulhuddart, Clonsilla etc 75-89; Chapl K Hosp Sch Palmerstown Dub from 89. *The King's Hospital, Palmerstown, Dublin 20, Irish Republic* Dublin (1) 626-5933 or 626-5959

BRYAN, Charles Rigney. b 10. TCD BA47 MA50 Leeds Univ MA60. Bps' Coll Cheshunt 36. **d** 37 **p** 38. V Sheff St Nath *Sheff* 65-77; rtd 78. *Ormond Nursing Home, Elm Lane, Lane Top, Sheffield S5 7TW* Sheffield (0114) 245 6026

BRYAN, Dr David John. b 56. Liv Univ BSc77 Hull Univ BTh85 Qu Coll Ox DPhil89. Ox Min Course 89. **d** 90 **p** 91. C Abingdon *Ox* 90-93; Tutor Qu Coll Birm from 93; Lic to Offic *Birm* from 93. *The Queen's College, Somerset Road, Birmingham B15 2QH* 0121-454 7506 or 454 8189

BRYAN, Dr Judith Claire. b 57. Aston Univ BSc79 PhD82 Trent Poly PGCE83. St Jo Coll Nottm BTh94 LTh95. **d** 95. C Wolv

St Matt *Lich* from 95. *29 Denmore Gardens, Wolverhampton WV1 2BN* Wolverhampton (01902) 453031

BRYAN, Leslie Harold. b 48. Div Hostel Dub 70. **d** 73 **p** 74. C Cork St Fin Barre's Cathl *C, C & R* 73-75; I Templebreedy w Tracton and Nohoval 75-79; CF from 79. *c/o MOD (Army), Bagshot Park, Bagshot, Surrey GU19 5PL* Bagshot (01276) 471717 Fax 412834

BRYAN, Michael John Christopher. b 35. MSBiblLit MCBiblAA Wadh Coll Ox BA58 BTh59 MA63 Ex Univ PhD83. Ripon Hall Ox 59. **d** 60 **p** 61. C Reigate St Mark *S'wark* 60-64; Tutor Sarum & Wells Th Coll 64-69; Vice-Prin 69-71; USA 71-74 and from 83; Sen Officer Educn and Community Dept *Lon* 74-79; Chapl Ex Univ *Ex* 79-83. *University of the South, Sewanee, TN 37375, USA*

BRYAN, Nigel Arthur. b 39. Univ of Wales (Lamp) BA61. Burgess Hall Lamp 61. **d** 63 **p** 64. C Llanstadwel *St D* 63-69; Chapl RAF 69-94; R Gt w Lt Milton and Gt Haseley *Ox* from 94. *The Rectory, Great Milton, Oxford OX44 7PN* Great Milton (01844) 279498

BRYAN, Patrick Joseph. b 41. St Jo Coll Cam BA63 MA67. St Steph Ho Ox 73. **d** 75 **p** 76. C Rushall *Lich* 75-78; C Brierley Hill 78-80; P-in-c Walsall St Mary and All SS Palfrey 80-87. *49 Hawthorn Road, Shelfield, Walsall WS5 4NB* Walsall (01922) 963234

BRYAN, Canon Percival John Milward. b 19. St Pet Coll Ox BA40 MA46 BTh47. Wycliffe Hall Ox 46. **d** 48 **p** 49. R Kings Cliffe *Pet* 56-85; Can Pet Cathl 73-86; rtd 86; Perm to Offic *Pet* from 86; Perm to Offic *Linc* from 91. *3 Saxon Road, Barnack, Stamford, Lincs PE9 3EQ* Stamford (01780) 740906

BRYAN, Canon Philip Richard. b 40. Dur Univ BA61. Wycliffe Hall Ox 72. **d** 74 **p** 75. C Macclesfield St Mich *Ches* 74-77; V St Bees *Carl* from 77; Chapl St Bees Sch Cumbria from 77; RD Calder *Carl* from 88; Hon Can Carl Cathl from 91. *The Priory, St Bees, Cumbria CA27 0DR* Egremont (01946) 822279

BRYAN, Mrs Sherry Lee. b 49. W Midl Minl Tr Course 88. **d** 91 **p** 94. Par Dn St Columb Minor and St Colan *Truro* 91-94; C from 94. *46 Willow Close, Quintrell Downs, Newquay, Cornwall TR8 4NG* Newquay (01637) 851936

BRYAN, Timothy James Bryan. b 23. Chich Th Coll 53. **d** 54 **p** 55. C Weybridge *Guildf* 54-57; Lebanon from 65. *PO Box 4008, Beirut, Lebanon*

BRYAN, William Terence. b 38. Chich Th Coll 73. **d** 75 **p** 76. C Shrewsbury St Giles *Lich* 75-79; V Churchstoke w Hyssington and Sarn *Heref* from 79. *The Vicarage, Church Stoke, Montgomery, Powys SY15 6AF* Church Stoke (01588) 620228

BRYANS, Joseph. b 15. TCD BA39 MA43. CITC 40. **d** 42 **p** 43. I Tamlaghtard w Aghanloo *D & R* 60-90; rtd 90. *1 Eventide Gardens, Limavady, Co Londonderry BT49 0AX* Limavady (015047) 62768

BRYANT, Andrew Watts. b 57. MA. Qu Coll Birm. **d** 83 **p** 84. C Pelsall *Lich* 83-87; NSM from 92; Perm to Offic 87-92. *Kaleidoscope Theatre, 19 Mellish Road, Walsall WS4 2DQ* Walsall (01922) 642751

BRYANT, Canon Christopher. b 32. AKC60. **d** 61 **p** 62. C Fareham H Trin *Portsm* 61-65; C Yatton Keynell *Bris* 65-71; V Chirton, Marden and Patney *Sarum* 71-76; V Chirton, Marden, Patney, Charlton and Wilsford 76-78; P-in-c Devizes St Jo w St Mary 78-79; R from 79; RD Devizes 83-92; Can and Preb Sarum Cathl from 87. *The Rectory, 39 Long Street, Devizes, Wilts SN10 1NS* Devizes (01380) 723705

BRYANT, Christopher John. b 62. Mansf Coll Ox BA83 MA87. Ripon Coll Cuddesdon 83. **d** 86 **p** 87. C High Wycombe *Ox* 86-89; Youth Chapl *Pet* 89-91; Perm to Offic *Lon* from 92. *1st Floor Flat, The Blockmakers Arms, 133 Shepherdess Walk, London N1 7QA* 0171-253 6301

BRYANT, David Charles. b 48. St Andr Univ BSc71. St Mich Coll Llan 71. **d** 74 **p** 75. C Llanilid w Pencoed *Llan* 74-78; C Caerphilly 78-79; V Crynant 79-84; V Llanegryn and Llanfihangel-y-Pennant etc *Ban* 84-93; V Llanwnda and Llandwrog from 93. *The Vicarage, Groeslon, Caernarfon, Gwynedd LL57 7DL* Llanwnda (01286) 831103

BRYANT, David Henderson. b 37. K Coll Lon BD60 AKC60. **d** 61 **p** 62. C Trowbridge H Trin *Sarum* 61-63; C Ewell *Guildf* 63-67; V Leiston *St E* 67-73; Chapl RN 73; C Northam *Ex* 74-75; P-in-c Clavering w Langley *Chelmsf* 76-77; Teacher Mountview High Sch Harrow 77-85; P-in-c Boosbeck w Moorsholm *York* 85-89; V 89-90; V Sowerby 90-95; P-in-c Sessay 90-95; V Lastingham w Appleton-le-Moors, Rosedale etc from 95. *The Vicarage, Lastingham, York YO6 6TN* Lastingham (01751) 417344

✠**BRYANT, Rt Rev Denis William.** b 18. DFC42. Qu Coll Birm 56. **d** 58 **p** 59 **c** 67. C Bourne *Guildf* 58-60; C Cuddington 60-61; Australia from 61; Adn Goldfields 66-67; Bp Kalgoorlie 67-72; Adn Northam 72-75; Asst Bp Perth 74-75; rtd 85. *1D Continental Court, 25 Victoria Avenue, Claremont, W Australia 6010* Perth (9) 384-1178

BRYANT, Donald Thomas. b 29. FSS59 SE Essex Coll BSc56 Birkb Coll Lon BSc58. S'wark Ord Course 85. **d** 88 **p** 89. NSM

Redhill St Matt *S'wark* from 88. *21 Windermere Way, Reigate, Surrey RH2 0LW* Redhill (01737) 762382

BRYANT, Canon Douglas William. b 17. St Boniface Warminster. **d** 41 **p** 42. V Burpham *Guildf* 57-70; V Egham Hythe 70-75; Hon Can Guildf Cathl 70-83; R Fetcham 75-83; rtd 83; Perm to Offic *Guildf* from 83. *4 Clandon Road, Guildford GU1 2DR* Guildford (01483) 572682

BRYANT, Edgar James. b 28. Univ of Wales (Swansea) BA49. St Mich Coll Llan 49. **d** 51 **p** 52. C Brynmawr *S & B* 51-55; C Llandrindod w Cefnllys 55-59; V Bettws Disserth w Llansantffraed in Elwell 59-69; V Disserth 59-69; V Llanelwedd w Llanfaredd w Llansantffraed etc 69-72; C Aymestrey and Leinthall Earles w Wigmore etc *Heref* 72-86 and 86-92; NSM Fownhope w Mordiford, Brockhampton etc 93-94; C Stoke Lacy, Moreton Jeffries w Much Cowarne etc from 95. *20 Bridgeford Close, Kings Acre, Hereford HR4 0QX* Hereford (01432) 265021

BRYANT, Edward Francis Paterson. b 43. S'wark Ord Course 75. **d** 78 **p** 79. NSM Hadlow *Roch* 78-84; C Dartford St Alb 84-87; R Hollington St Leon *Chich* 87-93; V Bexhill St Aug from 93. *St Augustine's Vicarage, St Augustine's Close, Bexhill-on-Sea, E Sussex TN39 3AZ* Bexhill-on-Sea (01424) 210785 Fax as telephone

BRYANT, Graham Trevor. b 41. Keble Coll Ox BA63 DipTh64 MA67. Chich Th Coll 64. **d** 66 **p** 67. C Leeds St Wilfrid *Ripon* 66-69; C Haywards Heath St Wilfrid *Chich* 69-74; V Crawley Down All SS 74-79; V Bexhill St Aug 79-85; V Charlton Kings St Mary *Glouc* from 85. *St Mary's Vicarage, 63 Church Street, Charlton Kings, Cheltenham, Glos GL53 8AT* Cheltenham (01242) 253402

BRYANT, Canon Mark Watts. b 49. St Jo Coll Dur BA72. Cuddesdon Coll 72. **d** 75 **p** 76. C Addlestone *Guildf* 75-79; C Studley *Sarum* 79-83; V 83-88; Chapl Trowbridge Coll 79-83; Voc Development Adv *Cov* from 88; Dioc Dir of Ords from 88; Hon Can Cov Cathl from 93. *35 Wood Lane, Shilton, Coventry CV7 9LA* Coventry (01203) 617512 or 674328

BRYANT, Max Gordon. b 09. Univ of NZ BA30 MA31 Lon Univ BD34. **d** 32 **p** 33. V Northaw *St Alb* 51-78; rtd 78; Perm to Offic *St D* from 78. *Llanina, Aberporth, Cardigan, Dyfed SA43 2EY* Aberporth (01239) 810124

BRYANT, Patricia Ann. b 46. Lon Univ BA. **d** 91. NSM Llanbadoc *Mon* 91-93; NSM Llangybi and Coedypaen w Llanbadoc from 93; Chapl Furthur Educn from 95. *Island House, Pontypool Road, Usk, Gwent NP5 1SY* Usk (01291) 672082

BRYANT, Richard Kirk. b 47. Ch Coll Cam BA68 MA72 Nottm Univ DipTh70. Cuddesdon Coll 70. **d** 72 **p** 73. C Newc St Gabr *Newc* 72-75; C Morpeth 75-78; C Benwell St Jas 78-82; V Earsdon and Backworth 82-93; V Wylam from 93. *The Vicarage, Wylam, Northd NE41 8AT* Wylam (01661) 853254

BRYANT, Richard Maurice. b 46. MAAIS80. W of England Minl Tr Course 90. **d** 93 **p** 94. NSM The Stanleys *Glouc* from 93. *6 Church Street, Kings Stanley, Stonehouse, Glos GL10 3HW* Stonehouse (01453) 823172

BRYANT, Royston George. b 09. St Aid Birkenhead 54. **d** 56 **p** 57. V Fishponds All SS *Bris* 69-76; rtd 76; Perm to Offic *Bris* 76-93. *c/o M G Bryant Esq, 18 Beechwood Drive, Scawby, Brigg, S Humberside DN20 9AR*

BRYANT, Sidney John. b 29. Linc Coll Ox BA52 MA56. St Steph Ho Ox 52. **d** 54 **p** 55. V New Southgate St Paul *Lon* 60-71; R Gt Leighs *Chelmsf* 71-92; P-in-c Lt Leighs 71-92; rtd 92. *16 Rydal Avenue, Felixstowe, Suffolk IP11 9SE* Felixstowe (01394) 275822

BRYANT, William George. b 22. Selw Coll Cam MA48. St Alb Minl Tr Scheme 78. **d** 81 **p** 82. NSM Welwyn w Ayot St Peter *St Alb* 81-82; NSM Balsall Heath St Paul *Birm* 82-85; P-in-c Teme Valley S *Worc* 85-89; rtd 89. *28 De Havilland Way, Christchurch, Dorset BH23 3JE* Christchurch (01202) 499231

BRYARS, Peter John. b 54. BA MEd PhD. St Jo Coll Nottm. **d** 84 **p** 85. C Kingston upon Hull St Martin *York* 84; C Hull St Martin w Transfiguration 84-87; TV Drypool 87-90; TV Glendale Gp *Newc* 90-94; P-in-c Heddon-on-the-Wall from 94; Adult Educn Adv from 94. *St Andrew's Vicarage, Towne Gate, Heddon-on-the-Wall, Newcastle upon Tyne NE15 0DT* Wylam (01661) 853142

BRYCE, Michael Adrian Gilpin. b 47. TCD BA. CITC 74. **d** 77 **p** 78. C Dub Ch Ch Cathl Gp *D & G* 77-79; Chapl Univ Coll Dub 79-82; I Ardamine w Kiltennel, Glascarrig etc *C & O* 82-84; CF from 84. *c/o MOD (Army), Bagshot Park, Bagshot, Surrey GU19 5PL* Bagshot (01276) 471717 Fax 412834

BRYER, Anthony Colin (Tony). b 51. Lon Univ BSc72 Bris Univ DipTh75. Trin Coll Bris 72. **d** 75 **p** 76. C Preston St Cuth *Blackb* 75-78; C Becontree St Mary *Chelmsf* 78-81; TV Loughton St Mary and St Mich 81-88; C Clifton St Paul *Bris* 88-91; P-in-c 91-94; R Bris St Mich and St Paul from 94. *St Paul's Rectory, 9 Leigh Road, Bristol BS8 2DA* Bristol (0117) 973 7427

BRYER, Paul Donald. b 58. Sussex Univ BEd80. St Jo Coll Nottm DipTh90. **d** 90 **p** 91. C Tonbridge St Steph *Roch* 90-94; TV Camberley St Paul *Guildf* from 94. *St Mary's House, 37 Park Road, Camberley, Surrey GU15 2SP* Camberley (01276) 22085

BUBBERS, David Bramwell. b 23. Lambeth MA84 Oak Hill Th Coll 51. **d** 54 **p** 55. V Northwood Em *Lon* 65-74; Perm to Offic *St Alb* from 74; Lic to Offic *Lon* 74-88; Gen Sec CPAS 74-88; rtd 88. *2 Earlsmead Court, 15 Granville Road, Eastbourne, E Sussex BN20 7HE* Eastbourne (01323) 737077

BUBBINGS, Charles Gardam. b 26. Qu Coll Birm 68. **d** 69 **p** 70. C Scarborough St Mary w Ch Ch, St Paul and St Thos *York* 69-72; C Fulford 72-74; V Middlesb St Oswald 74-81; V Ringley *Man* 81-88; rtd 88; Perm to Offic *Man* from 88. *4 Hilton Grove, Little Hulton, Manchester M38 0RY* 0161-702 9402

BUCHAN, Ven Eric Ancrum. b 07. St Chad's Coll Dur BA32. **d** 33 **p** 34. Adn Cov 65-77; rtd 77; Perm to Offic *Glouc* from 78. *6B Millers Green, Gloucester GL1 2BN* Gloucester (01452) 415944

BUCHAN, Geoffrey Herbert. b 38. CEng MIMechE. Nor Ord Course 91. **d** 94 **p** 95. NSM Barnton *Ches* from 94. *12 Hough Lane, Anderton, Northwich, Cheshire CW9 6AB* Northwich (01606) 74512

✠**BUCHANAN, Rt Rev Colin Ogilvie.** b 34. Linc Coll Ox MA. Lambeth Hon DD93 Tyndale Hall Bris 59. **d** 61 **p** 62 **c** 85. C Cheadle *Ches* 61-64; Tutor St Jo Coll Nottm 64-85; Lib 64-69; Registrar 69-74; Dir of Studies 74-75; Vice-Prin 75-78; Prin 79-85; Hon Can S'well Minster *S'well* 81-85; Suff Bp Aston *Birm* 85-89; Asst Bp Roch from 89; V Gillingham St Mark from 91; Asst Bp S'wark 90-91. *St Mark's Vicarage, 173 Canterbury Street, Gillingham, Kent ME7 5UA* Medway (01634) 851818 or 855252 Fax 573549

BUCHANAN, Canon Eric. b 32. Leeds Univ BA54. Coll of Resurr Mirfield 54. **d** 56 **p** 57. C Cov St Mark *Cov* 56-59; Asst Chapl Lon Univ *Lon* 59-64; C Bloomsbury St Geo w St Jo 59-64; V Duston *Pet* 64-79; RD Wootton 75-79; Can Pet Cathl from 77; V Wellingborough All Hallows 79-90; V Higham Ferrers w Chelveston from 90; Chapl to The Queen from 92. *The Vicarage, Wood Street, Higham Ferrers, Wellingborough, Northants NN9 8DL* Rushden (01933) 312433

BUCHANAN, George Rowland. b 15. St Aug Coll Cant. **d** 59 **p** 60. R Gt Wishford *Sarum* 67-73; R Lt Langford 67-73; RD Wylye and Wilton 69-73; Org Sec (Dios Ex and B & W) CECS 73-77; Perm to Offic *Sarum* from 77; rtd 80. *Cobblers, Greenhill, Sherborne, Dorset DT9 4EP* Sherborne (01935) 812263

BUCHANAN, John Fraser Walter. b 32. Em Coll Cam BA55. Local NSM Course 91. **d** 93 **p** 94. NSM Wainford *St E* from 93. *The Hermitage, Bridge Street, Beccles, Suffolk NR34 9BA* Beccles (01502) 712154

BUCK, Eric Joseph. b 14. Lon Univ BA35 DipEd54. Ridley Hall Cam 60. **d** 61 **p** 62. V Wicklewood and Crownthorpe *Nor* 62-79; P-in-c Deopham w Hackford 75-79; rtd 79; Perm to Offic *Nor* 80-95. *10 Robins Close, Great Bentley, Colchester CO7 8QH* Great Bentley (01206) 250623

BUCK, Nicholas John. b 57. BScEng Ridley Hall Cam 81. **d** 84 **p** 85. C Oakwood St Thos *Lon* 84-87; C Attercliffe *Sheff* 87-90; C Darnall H Trin 87-90; V Kimberworth from 90. *The Vicarage, 331 Kimberworth Road, Kimberworth, S Yorkshire S61 1HD* Rotherham (01709) 554441

BUCK, Canon Richard Peter Holdron. b 37. AKC64. Lambeth Hon MA93. **d** 65 **p** 66. C Mill Hill Jo Keble Ch *Lon* 65-68; C St Marylebone All SS 68-74; Can Res and Treas Truro Cathl *Truro* 74-76; V Primrose Hill St Mary w Avenue Road St Paul *Lon* 76-84; Bp's Ecum Adv S'wark 84-91; P-in-c Dulwich Common St Pet 84-86; Hon Can S'wark Cathl from 90; C Rotherhithe St Kath w St Barn 91-92; C Bermondsey St Kath w St Bart 92-94; C Greenwich St Alfege w St Pet and St Paul from 94. *88 Ashburnham Grove, London SE16 2LR* 0181-691 9916

BUCK, William Ashley. b 61. Man Univ BA82 Ox Univ BA86. Ripon Coll Cuddesdon 84. **d** 87 **p** 88. C Addington *S'wark* 87-91; C Pimlico St Pet w Westmr Ch Ch *Lon* 91-94; TV Wenlock *Heref* from 94. *The Vicarage, Harley Road, Cressage, Shrewsbury SY5 6DF* Cressage (01952) 510355

BUCKBY, Gary. b 69. Leeds Univ BA90. Coll of Resurr Mirfield 93. **d** 95. C Wolv St Steph *Lich* from 95. *St Stephen's Vicarage, Hilton Street, Wolverhampton WV10 0LF* Wolverhampton (01902) 454662

BUCKETT, Canon James Frederick. b 27. ACP. Roch Th Coll 60. **d** 62 **p** 63. V St Helens *Portsm* 66-72; CF (TA) 72-95; V Newport St Thos *Portsm* 72-95; Hon Can Portsm Cathl 81-95; rtd 95. *The Coach House, 140A Staplers Road, Newport, Isle of Wight PO30 2DJ* Isle of Wight (01983) 521847

BUCKINGHAM, Ven Hugh Fletcher. b 32. Hertf Coll Ox BA57 MA60. Westcott Ho Cam 55. **d** 57 **p** 58. C Halliwell St Thos *Man* 57-60; C Sheff Gillcar St Silas *Sheff* 60-65; V

Hindolveston *Nor* 65-70; V Guestwick 65-70; R Fakenham w Alethorpe 70-88; Chmn Dioc Bd Soc Resp 81-88; RD Burnham and Walsingham 81-87; Hon Can Nor Cathl 85-88; Adn E Riding *York* from 88. *Brimley Lodge, 27 Molescroft Road, Beverley, N Humberside HU17 7DX* Hull (01482) 881659

BUCKINGHAM, Richard Arthur John. b 49. Univ of Wales (Cardiff) BA71 PGCE72. Chich Th Coll 73. **d** 76 **p** 77. C Llantwit Major *Llan* 76-80; C Leigh-on-Sea St Marg *Chelmsf* 80-84; C Westmr St Matt *Lon* 84-87; R Stock Harvard *Chelmsf* from 87. *The Rectory, 61 High Street, Stock, Ingatestone, Essex CM4 9BN* Stock (01277) 840453

BUCKINGHAM, Archdeacon of. *See* MORRISON, Ven John Anthony

BUCKINGHAM, Area Bishop of. *See* BENNETTS, Rt Rev Colin James

BUCKLE, Graham Martin. b 62. Southn Univ BTh89. Sarum & Wells Th Coll 85. **d** 89 **p** 90. C Paddington St Jas *Lon* 89-94; P-in-c Paddington St Pet from 94. *St Peter's Vicarage, 59 Elgin Avenue, London W9 2DB* 0171-289 2011

BUCKLER, George Anthony (Tony). b 35. Open Univ BA74. Lich Th Coll 58. **d** 61 **p** 62. C Old Swinford *Worc* 61-65; C Droitwich St Nic w St Pet 65-67; C Droitwich St Andr w St Mary 65-67; Chapl Claybury Hosp Woodford Bridge 67-78; Chapl St Geo and Co Hosps Linc 78-87; Chapl Lawn Hosp Linc 78-81; Chapl Wexham Park Hosp Slough 87-90; Chapl Mapperley Hosp Nottm 90-94; Chapl Nottm Mental Illness & Psychiatric Unit from 90; Chapl Wells Rd Cen Nottm from 94; Chapl Qu Medical Cen Nottm from 94; Chapl Highbury Hosp Nottm from 94. *The Wells Road Centre, Wells Road, Nottingham NG3 3AA* Nottingham (0115) 969 1300

BUCKLER, Guy Ernest Warr. b 46. ACA69 FCA79. Linc Th Coll 71. **d** 74 **p** 75. C Dunstable *St Alb* 74-77; C Houghton Regis 77-86; TV Willington Team *Newc* 86-88; TR 88-95; Chapl N Tyneside Coll of FE 88-95; R Bedf St Pet w St Cuth *St Alb* from 95. *St Peter's Rectory, 36 De Parys Avenue, Bedford MK40 2TP* Bedford (01234) 354543

BUCKLER, Canon Peter. b 17. OBE79. Lon Univ BSc38. Linc Th Coll. **d** 66 **p** 67. R Grendon *Birm* 68-71; C-in-c Burton Dassett *Cov* 71-74; Hon Can Cov Cathl 76-83; P-in-c Baxterley w Hurley and Wood End and Merevale etc *Birm* 80-83; rtd 83; Perm to Offic *Cov* from 83; Perm to Offic *Birm* from 83. *9 St Michael's Close, Atherstone, Warks CV9 1LU* Atherstone (01827) 720133

BUCKLER, Philip John Warr. b 49. St Pet Coll Ox BA70 MA74. Cuddesdon Coll 70. **d** 72 **p** 73. C Bushey Heath *St Alb* 72-75; Chapl Trin Coll Cam 75-81; Min Can and Sacr St Paul's Cathl *Lon* 81-87; V Hampstead St Jo from 87; AD N Camden (Hampstead) from 93. *The Vicarage, 14 Church Row, London NW3 6UU* 0171-435 0553 or 794 5808

BUCKLEY, Alan. b 40. Tyndale Hall Bris. **d** 67 **p** 68. C Owlerton *Sheff* 67-70; C Mansf St Pet S'well 70-73; C Charlesworth *Derby* 73-75; P-in-c Whitfield 76-84; V Moldgreen *Wakef* 84-90; V Hadfield *Derby* from 90. *St Andrew's Vicarage, 122 Hadfield Road, Hadfield, Hyde, Cheshire SK14 8DR* Glossop (01457) 852431

BUCKLEY, Alexander Christopher. b 67. **d** 91 **p** 94. C Llandudno *Ban* 91-92; C Ynyscynhaearn w Penmorfa and Porthmadog 92-93 and from 94. *The Curate's House, Lletger Llan, Porthmadog, Gwynedd LL49 9PA* Porthmadog (01766) 514327

BUCKLEY, Basil Foster. b 11. Dorchester Miss Coll. **d** 38 **p** 39. R Salford St Ignatius *Man* 42-81; rtd 82; Hon C Salford St Paul w Ch Ch *Man* from 82. *Beech House, Radcliffe Park Crescent, Salford M6 7WQ* 0161-743 1420

BUCKLEY, Christopher Ivor. b 48. Chich Th Coll. **d** 86 **p** 87. C Felpham w Middleton *Chich* 86-89; C Jersey St Brelade *Win* 89-93; Chapl HM Pris Jersey from 90; V Jersey St Mark *Win* from 93. *St Mark's Vicarage, Springfield Road, St Helier, Jersey, Channel Islands JE2 4LE* Jersey (01534) 20595

BUCKLEY, David Rex. b 47. Ripon Coll Cuddesdon 75. **d** 77 **p** 78. C Witton *Ches* 77-81; V Backford 81-85; Youth Chapl from 81; V Barnton 85-93; P-in-c Harthill and Burwardsley from 93; P-in-c Bickerton w Bickley from 93. *The Vicarage, Harthill Road, Tattenhall, Chester CH3 9NU* Tattenhall (01829) 70067

BUCKLEY, Canon Derek Haslam. b 17. Bps' Coll Cheshunt 52. **d** 54 **p** 55. V Scropton *Derby* 67-73; R Boylestone 67-73; HM Det Cen Foston Hall 67-73; RD Longford *Derby* 71-81; P-in-c Ch Broughton w Boylestone & Sutton on the Hill 73-76; V 76-83; P-in-c Dalbury, Long Lane and Trusley 77-83; Hon Can Derby Cathl 79-83; rtd 83; Perm to Offic *Derby* from 83. *St Oswald's House, Belle Vue Road, Ashbourne, Derbyshire DE6 1AT* Ashbourne (01335) 345155

BUCKLEY, Ernest Fairbank. b 25. Jes Coll Cam BA49 MA50 Jes Coll Ox BLitt53. Westcott Ho Cam 55. **d** 55 **p** 56. V Baguley *Man* 64-79; V Clun w Chapel Lawn, Bettws-y-Crwyn and Newc *Heref* 79-87; RD Clun Forest 82-87; rtd 88.

Hawthorn Bank, Clunton, Craven Arms, Shropshire SY7 0HP Little Brampton (015887) 281

BUCKLEY, Michael. b 49. St Jo Coll Dur Cranmer Hall Dur 77. **d** 79 **p** 80. C Birkdale St Jo *Liv* 79-82; TV Maghull 82-88; V Earlestown from 88. *The Vicarage, 63 Market Street, Newton-le-Willows, Merseyside WA12 9BS* Newton-le-Willows (01925) 224771

BUCKLEY, Canon Michael Richard. b 20. Lon Univ BD42 AKC42. Cuddesdon Coll 42. **d** 43 **p** 44. R Weybridge *Guildf* 67-85; Hon Can Guildf Cathl 76-85; rtd 85; Perm to Offic *Chelmsf* from 85; Perm to Offic *Ely* from 86. *Bourn Cottage, High Street, Great Chesterford, Saffron Walden, Essex CB10 1PL* Saffron Walden (01799) 530398

BUCKLEY, Richard Francis. b 44. Ripon Hall Ox 69. **d** 72 **p** 73. C Portsea St Cuth *Portsm* 72-75; C Portsea All SS w St Jo Rudmore 75-79; Chapl RN from 79. *Directorate Gen, RN Chapl Services, Room 203, Victory Building, HM Naval Base, Portsmouth PO1 3LS* Portsmouth (01705) 727903 Fax 727112

BUCKLEY, Dr Richard John. b 43. Hull Univ BSc64 PhD87 Strathclyde Univ MSc69. Sarum Th Coll 64. **d** 66 **p** 67. C Huddersfield St Jo *Wakef* 66-68; C Sutton St Jas *York* 69-71; TV Sutton St Jas and Wawne 71-75; V Handsworth Woodhouse *Sheff* 75-85; R Adwick-le-Street 85-91; V Wentworth from 91. *The Vicarage, Church Drive, Wentworth, Rotherham, S Yorkshire S62 7TW* Barnsley (01226) 742274

BUCKLEY, Robert William. b 50. Grey Coll Dur BSc70 PhD73 MInstP75 CPhys75 MInstE92 FCollP93. N Ord Course 85. **d** 87 **p** 88. NSM N Greenford All Hallows *Lon* 87-94; P-in-c 91-94; NSM W Acton St Martin 94-95; NSM Ealing All SS from 94. *All Saints Vicarage, Elm Grove Road, London W5 3JH* 0181-567 8166

BUCKLEY, Stephen Richard. b 45. Cranmer Hall Dur 82. **d** 84 **p** 85. C Iffley *Ox* 84-88; TV Halesowen *Worc* from 88. *St Margaret's Vicarage, 55 Quarry Lane, Halesowen, W Midlands B63 4PD* 0121-550 8744

BUCKLEY, Timothy Denys. b 57. BA. St Jo Coll Nottm DipTh. **d** 83 **p** 84. C S Westoe *Dur* 83-85; C Paddington Em Harrow Road *Lon* 85-88; C Binley *Cov* from 88; Min Binley Woods LEP from 88. *20 Daneswood Road, Coventry CV3 2BJ* Coventry (01203) 543003

BUCKLEY, Wyndham Awdry. b 13. St Boniface Warminster 32. **d** 37 **p** 38. V Langham *Pet* 67-79; Chapl HM Pris Ashwell 67-79; rtd 79; Perm to Offic *Pet* from 85. *8 Uppingham Road, Oakham, Leics LE15 6JP* Oakham (01572) 756844

BUCKMAN, Rossly David. b 36. TCD BA64 MA67 St Pet Coll Ox BA65. Moore Th Coll Sydney ACT ThL59. **d** 59 **p** 60. Australia 59-61 and 76-80 and from 89; C Dub Harold's Cross *D & G* 61-64; C Ox St Mich *Ox* 64-65; Lect Th Bris Univ 65-69; Lic to Offic *Bris* 65-69; CF 69-76; P-in-c Mid Marsh Gp *Linc* 81-82; R 82-89. *St Martin's Rectory, 9 Centre Street, Blakehurst, Sydney, NSW, Australia 2221* Sydney (2) 546-6523

BUCKMASTER, Charles. b 20. St Jo Coll Dur BA50. Wells Th Coll 50. **d** 51 **p** 52. Prin St Pet Coll Birm 68-78; Cyprus 78-82; P-in-c Viney Hill *Glouc* 82-89; rtd 89. *Hazledene, Johnsons Way, Yorkley, Lydney, Glos GL15 4RZ* Dean (01594) 564167

BUCKNALL, Allan. b 35. ALCD62. Lon Coll of Div 62. **d** 62 **p** 63. C Harlow New Town w Lt Parndon *Chelmsf* 62-69; Chapl W Somerset Miss to Deaf 69-71; Perm to Offic *Bris* 71-77; P-in-c Wisborough Green *Chich* 77-79; R Tillington 78-86; R Duncton 82-86; R Up Waltham 82-86; C Henfield w Shermanbury and Woodmancote 86-89; Asst Chapl Princess Marg Hosp Swindon from 89. *Princesss Margaret Hospital, Okus Road, Swindon SN1 4JU, or, 5 The Willows, Swindon SN6 7PG* Swindon (01793) 426263 or 762721

BUCKNALL, Miss Ann Gordon. b 32. K Coll Lon BSc53 Hughes Hall Cam DipEd54. Qu Coll Birm 80. **dss** 81 **d** 87 **p** 94. Birm St Aid Small Heath *Birm* 81-85; Balsall Heath St Paul 85-87; Par Dn 87-92; C Handsworth St Jas from 92. *51 Westbourne Road, Handsworth, Birmingham B21 8AU* 0121-523 3439

BUCKNALL, William John. b 44. Lon Univ DipTh67. Kelham Th Coll 63. **d** 68 **p** 69. C Carl H Trin *Carl* 68-71; C Baswich (or Berkswich) *Lich* 71-73; P-in-c Ilam w Blore Ray and Okeover 73-76; V Wednesbury St Paul Wood Green 76-84; RD Wednesbury 78-84; TR Wordsley 84-90. *198 The Broadway, Dudley, W Midlands DY1 3DR* Dudley (01384) 214047

BUCKS, Ven Michael William. b 40. K Coll Lon BD63 AKC63. **d** 64 **p** 65. C Workington St Mich *Carl* 64-69; Chapl RN 69-93; Chapl of the Fleet and Adn for the RN from 93; Dir Gen Naval Chapl Services from 93; QHC from 93. *Directorate Gen, RN Chapl Services, Room 203, Victory Building, HM Naval Base, Portsmouth PO1 3LS* Portsmouth (01705) 727903 Fax 727112

BUDD, John Christopher. b 51. DLIS QUB BA73 TCD DipTh82. **d** 82 **p** 83. C Ballymena *Conn* 82-85; C Jordanstown w Monkstown 85-88; I Craigs w Dunaghy and Killagan from

88; RD Ballymena from 89; Dioc Info Officer from 89; Bp's Dom Chapl from 94. *Craigs Rectory, 95 Hillmount Road, Cullybackey, Ballymena, Co Antrim BT42 1NZ* Cullybackey (01266) 880248

BUDD, John Victor. b 31. CCC Ox BA55 MA58. Bps' Coll Cheshunt 57. **d** 59 **p** 60. C Friern Barnet St Jas *Lon* 59-64; C Harrow Weald All SS 64-70; Lic to Offic *St Alb* 70-73; V Lt Amwell from 73; RD Hertf 83-88. *The Vicarage, 17 Barclay Close, Hertford Heath, Hertford SG13 7RW* Hertford (01992) 589140

BUDD, Philip John. b 40. Bris Univ PhD78. Cranmer Hall Dur BA63 DipTh65 MLitt71. **d** 66 **p** 67. C Attenborough w Chilwell *S'well* 66-69; Lect Clifton Th Coll 69-71; Lect Trin Coll Bris 72-80; Tutor Ripon Coll Cuddesdon 80-88; Tutor Westmr Coll Ox from 80; Lect from 88. *Westminster College, Oxford OX2 9AT* Oxford (01865) 242788

BUDDEN, Clive John. b 39. Chich Th Coll. **d** 84 **p** 86. C Gaywood, Bawsey and Mintlyn *Nor* 84-87; TV Brixham w Churston Ferrers and Kingswear *Ex* 87-90; R Exton and Winsford and Cutcombe w Luxborough *B & W* from 90. *The Rectory, Winsford, Minehead, Somerset TA24 7JE* Winsford (0164385) 301

BUDGE, Leonard Percival. b 11. Dur Univ LTh40. St Aug Coll Cant 37. **d** 40 **p** 41. V Frithelstock *Ex* 64-76; V Monkleigh 64-76; V Littleham 70-76; rtd 76; Perm to Offic *Ex* from 76. *2 Chestnut Close, Braunton, Devon EX33 2EH* Braunton (01271) 814313

BUDGELL, Peter Charles. b 50. Lon Univ BD. **d** 83 **p** 84. C Goodmayes All SS *Chelmsf* 83-86; C Chipping Barnet w Arkley *St Alb* 86-88; V Luton St Anne from 88. *The Vicarage, 7 Blaydon Road, Luton LU2 0RP* Luton (01582) 20052

BUDGELL, Rosemary Anne. b 51. Lon Bible Coll BD73 CertEd76. **dss** 83 **d** 87 **p** 94. Goodmayes All SS *Chelmsf* 83-86; Chipping Barnet w Arkley *St Alb* 86-88; Hon Par Dn 87-88; Hon Par Dn Luton St Anne 88-94; Hon C from 94. *The Vicarage, 7 Blaydon Road, Luton LU2 0RP* Luton (01582) 20052

BUDGETT, Preb Anthony Thomas. b 26. TD60. Or Coll Ox BA50 MA57. Wells Th Coll 57. **d** 59 **p** 60. V Somerton *B & W* 68-80; RD Ilchester 72-81; P-in-c Compton Dundon 76-80; R Somerton w Compton Dundon 80-81; R Somerton w Compton Dundon, the Charltons etc 81-84; Preb Wells Cathl 83-90; P-in-c Bruton w Lamyatt, Wyke and Redlynch 84-85; P-in-c Batcombe w Upton Noble 84-85; P-in-c S w N Brewham 84-85; TR Bruton and Distr 85-90; rtd 90; Perm to Offic *Ex* from 90; Preb Emer Wells Cathl *B & W* from 94. *Cornerways, White Ball, Wellington, Somerset TA21 0LS* Wellington (01823) 672321

BUDGETT, Robert Brackenbury. b 08. Ch Coll Cam BA30 MA34 DIC31. Ridley Hall Cam 34. **d** 36 **p** 37. R Overstrand *Nor* 61-73; rtd 73; P-in-c Salle *Nor* 74-78; Perm to Offic from 79. *c/o C M Brown Esq, 24 Cromer Road, Aylsham, Norwich NR11 6HE* Aylsham (01263) 734214

BUFFEE, Canon Leslie John. b 30. AKC53 Open Univ BA88. **d** 54 **p** 55. V Becontree St Pet *Chelmsf* 67-72; Min Parkeston CD 72-83; TV Dovercourt and Parkeston 83-89; Miss to Seamen 83-89; C Southend St Sav Westcliff *Chelmsf* 89-95; rtd 95. *46 Stonebridge Way, Faversham, Kent ME13 7SB* Faversham (01795) 535970

BUFFETT, Frederick. b 11. Keble Coll Ox BA34 MA39. St Steph Ho Ox 34. **d** 35 **p** 36. V Ipplepen w Torbryan *Ex* 64-82; rtd 82; Perm to Offic *Ex* from 82. *Bramble Down Nursing Home, Woodland Road, Denbury, Newton Abbot, Devon TQ12 6DY* Ipplepen (01803) 812844

BUFFREY, Canon Samuel John Thomas. b 28. Keble Coll Ox BA52 MA57. Cuddesdon Coll 52. **d** 54 **p** 55. V Amesbury *Sarum* 69-80; RD Avon 77-80; P-in-c Broadstone 80-82; V 82-93; Can and Preb Sarum Cathl 87-93; rtd 93. *34 Woolslope Road, West Moors, Ferndown, Dorset BH22 0PD* Ferndown (01202) 875522

BUGBY, Timothy. b 53. AKC75. Chich Th Coll 76. **d** 77 **p** 78. C Hockerill *St Alb* 77-81; C Pimlico St Mary Graham Terrace *Lon* 81-87; V Highgate St Aug from 87. *St Augustine's Vicarage, Langdon Park Road, London N6 5BH* 0181-340 3567

BUGDEN, Ernest William. b 16. Lich Th Coll 56. **d** 58 **p** 59. C Esher *Guildf* 58-68; Hon C 68-81; rtd 81. *32 French's Road, Cambridge CB4 3LA* Cambridge (01223) 311306

BUGG, Canon Peter Richard. b 33. Univ of BC BA62. Wells Th Coll 63. **d** 64 **p** 64. C Whitley Ch Ch *Ox* 64-67; C Ludlow *Heref* 67-69; Zambia 69-72; P-in-c Brill w Boarstall *Ox* 72-78; P-in-c Chilton w Dorton 77-78; V Brill, Boarstall, Chilton and Dorton from 78; Hon Can Ch Ch from 92. *The Vicarage, Brill, Aylesbury, Bucks HP18 9ST* Brill (01844) 238325

BUIK, Allan David. b 39. St Andr Univ BSc61. Coll of Resurr Mirfield 66. **d** 68 **p** 69. Perm to Offic *Win* 68-69; C Eastleigh 69-72; C Brighton St Bart *Chich* 72-74; C Lavender Hill Ascension *S'wark* 74-78; V Kingstanding St Mark *Birm* 78-86;

Guyana 86-91; V Tunstall *Lich* from 91. *Christchurch Vicarage, 26 Stanley Street, Tunstall, Stoke-on-Trent ST6 6BW* Stoke-on-Trent (01782) 838288

BUIKE, Desmond Mainwaring. b 32. Ex Coll Ox BA55 MA69 Leeds Univ CertEd72. Qu Coll Birm DipTh57. **d** 57 **p** 58. V Queensbury *Bradf* 63-71; Perm to Offic 71-85; V Glaisdale *York* 85-93; rtd 93. *Wayside, 3 White Bridge Road, Whitby, N Yorkshire YO21 1BJ* Whitby (01947) 821440

BULL, Mrs Christine. b 45. Bedf Coll Lon BA67. N Ord Course 91. **d** 94 **p** 95. NSM High Lane *Ches* from 94. *Walk Mill Cottage, Hayfield, Stockport SK12 5ER* New Mills (01663) 744606

BULL, Christopher Bertram. b 45. Lon Bible Coll BA87. Wycliffe Hall Ox 88. **d** 90 **p** 91. C Leominster *Heref* 90-95; P-in-c Westbury from 95; P-in-c Yockleton from 95; P-in-c Gt Wollaston from 95. *The Rectory, Westbury, Shrewsbury SY5 9QX* Shrewsbury (01743) 884216

BULL, Christopher David (Chris). b 59. St Jo Coll Nottm 89. **d** 91 **p** 92. C Bowbrook S *Worc* 91-95; P-in-c Flackwell Heath *Ox* from 95. *The Vicarage, 9 Chapel Road, Flackwell Heath, High Wycombe, Bucks HP10 9AA* Bourne End (01628) 522795

BULL, Canon Frank Spencer. b 19. Lon Univ BD43. ALCD43. **d** 43 **p** 44. V Kenilworth St Nic *Cov* 66-85; RD Kenilworth 73-83; Hon Can Cov Cathl 74-85; rtd 85; Perm to Offic *Cant* 85-93. *74 Riverside Close, Bridge, Canterbury, Kent CT4 5TN* Canterbury (01227) 830440

BULL, Malcolm George. b 35. Portsm Dioc Tr Course 87. **d** 87. NSM Farlington *Portsm* 87-90; NSM Widley w Wymering 92-93; NSM S w N Hayling from 93. *20 Charleston Close, Hayling Island, Hants PO11 0JY* Hayling Island (01705) 462025

BULL, Malcolm Harold. b 44. BDS. St Alb Minl Tr Scheme. **d** 83 **p** 84. NSM Bedf St Paul *St Alb* from 83. *27 Cardington Road, Bedford MK42 0BN* Bedford (01234) 368163

BULL, Martin Wells. b 37. Worc Coll Ox BA61 MA68. Ripon Hall Ox 61. **d** 63 **p** 64. C Blackley St Andr *Man* 63-67; C Horton *Bradf* 67-68; V Ingrow cum Hainworth 68-78; RD S Craven 74-77; V Bingley All SS 78-80; TR 80-92; P-in-c Gargrave from 92. *The Vicarage, Gargrave, Skipton, N Yorkshire BD23 3NQ* Gargrave (01756) 749392

BULL, Michael John. b 35. Roch Th Coll 65. **d** 67 **p** 68. C N Wingfield *Derby* 67-69; C Skegness *Linc* 69-72; R Ingoldmells w Addlethorpe 72-79; Area Sec (Dio S'wark) USPG 79-85; Area Org RNLI (Lon) 86-88; C Croydon St Jo *S'wark* 89-93; P-in-c Mitcham Ch Ch from 93. *Christ Church Vicarage, Christchurch Road, London SW19 2NY* 0181-542 5125

BULL, Dr Norman John. b 16. Trin Coll Ox BTh38 BA39 MA48 Reading Univ PhD67. Linc Th Coll 38. **d** 39 **p** 40. C Colchester St Botolph w H Trin and St Giles *Chelmsf* 39-41; C Loughton St Mary 41-43; P-in-c Petersfield w Sheet *Portsm* 44-45; C Croydon *Cant* 45-46; Dioc Youth Chapl 46-48; Chapl St Luke's Coll *Ex* 49-60; Lect 49-75. *21 Wonford Road, Exeter EX4 2LH* Exeter (01392) 55806

BULL, Robert David. b 51. Man Univ DSPT86. Ripon Coll Cuddesdon 74. **d** 77 **p** 78. C Worsley *Man* 77-80; C Peel 80-81; TV 81-86; P-in-c Wisbech St Aug *Ely* 86-88; V from 88; RD Wisbech from 92. *St Augustine's Vicarage, Lynn Road, Wisbech, Cambs PE13 3DL* Wisbech (01945) 583724

BULL, Robert Humphrey. b 06. FIMarE73 CEng73. Ox Ord Course 72. **d** 74 **p** 74. Hon C Reading St Jo *Ox* 74-88; Perm to Offic 88-92; Perm to Offic *York* from 92. *25 Linden Grove, Middlesbrough, Cleveland TS5 5NF* Middlesbrough (01642) 826535

BULL, Stephen Andrew (Steve). b 58. St Jo Coll Nottm DCM93. **d** 93 **p** 94. C Wroughton *Bris* from 93. *21 Anthony Road, Wroughton, Swindon SN4 9HN* Swindon (01793) 813929

BULL, William George. b 28. Sarum Th Coll 65. **d** 66 **p** 67. V Swallowcliffe w Ansty *Sarum* 69-75; Dioc Youth Officer 69-71; P-in-c Laverstock 75-81; V 81-93; rtd 94. *Bungalow 1, Boreham Field, Warminster, Wilts BA12 9EB* Warminster (01985) 847830

BULLAMORE, John Richard. b 41. Linc Coll Ox BA64 MA. Wycliffe Hall Ox 74. **d** 95 **p** 95. Hon C Eorrapaidh *Arg* from 95. *White Rose House, 26 Sheshader, Isle of Lewis HS2 0EW* Garrabost (01851) 870743

BULLEN, Richard David Guy. b 43. Brasted Place Coll 71. Ripon Hall Ox 73. **d** 75 **p** 76. C Pocklington w Yapham-cum-Meltonby, Owsthorpe etc *York* 75-78; TV Thornaby on Tees 78-84; V New Marske 84-90; P-in-c Wilton 84-90; Ind Chapl 90-95. *26 Chestnut Close, Saltburn-by-the-Sea, Cleveland TS12 1PE* Guisborough (01287) 623287

BULLEY, Roger Charles. b 12. Lon Univ BCom34 BA37. Wells Th Coll 38. **d** 40 **p** 41. Chapl Community St Jo Bapt Clewer 71-79; rtd 78; Chapl Convent of Sisters of Charity Knowle 79-88. *Lindsay House, Lindsey Street, Epping, Essex CM16 6RB* Epping (01992) 578518

BULLEY, William Joseph. b 28. Chich Th Coll 65. **d** 67 **p** 68. C Littleham w Exmouth *Ex* 67-72; V Harberton w

Harbertonford 72-77; R Chagford 77-79; R Chagford w Gidleigh and Throwleigh 79-84; V Widecombe, Leusden and Princetown etc 84-85; TR Widecombe-in-the-Moor, Leusdon, Princetown etc 85-88; P-in-c Inverness St Jo *Mor* 88-93; Chapl Raigmore Hosp Inverness 88-93; rtd 93. *Dalcharn, Barevan, Cawdor, Nairn IV12 5XU* Croy (01667) 493215

BULLIVANT, Canon Ronald. b 13. Nashdom Abbey. **d** 43 **p** 43. V Brighton Annunciation *Chich* 53-89; Can and Preb Chich Cathl 78-89; rtd 89. *9 Farm Close, Castle Park, Whitby, N Yorkshire YO21 3LS* Whitby (01947) 601495

BULLIVANT, Ronald. b 32. CertEd DCouns. St Mich Coll Llan. **d** 59 **p** 60. V Horbury *Wakef* 66-69; Lic to Offic *Ripon* 70-78; Perm to Offic *Nor* 78-81; Lic to Offic from 81; rtd 94. *22 Cleaves Drive, Walsingham, Norfolk NR22 6EQ* Fakenham (01328) 820526

BULLOCK, Andrew Timothy. b 56. Southn Univ BTh91. Sarum & Wells Th Coll 89. **d** 91 **p** 92. C Erdington St Barn *Birm* 91-94; TV Solihull from 94. *St Francis House, Redlands Close, Solihull, W Midlands B91 1LZ* 0121-705 3234

BULLOCK, Canon John Raymond. b 16. Ch Ch Ox BA37 MA46. Westcott Ho Cam 46. **d** 48 **p** 49. RD Hartlepool *Dur* 62-78; V Hartlepool St Paul 62-86; P-in-c Hartlepool Ch Ch 65-73; Hon Can Dur Cathl 71-86; rtd 86. *4 The Green, Greatham, Hartlepool, Cleveland TS25 2HG* Hartlepool (01429) 870600

BULLOCK, Kenneth Poyser. b 27. Down Coll Cam BA50 MA55. Ridley Hall Cam 50. **d** 52 **p** 53. V Ainsworth *Man* 63-91; rtd 91. *26 Plas Penrhyn, Penrhyn Bay, Llandudno, Gwynedd LL30 3EU* Llandudno (01492) 543343

BULLOCK, Michael. b 49. Hatf Coll Dur BA71 Leeds Univ DipTh74. Coll of Resurr Mirfield 72. **d** 75 **p** 76. C Pet St Jo *Pet* 75-79; Zambia 79-86; V Longthorpe *Pet* 86-91; Chapl Naples w Sorrento, Largo Patria and Bari *Eur* 91-93; Chapl Naples w Sorrento, Capri and Bari from 93. *via S Pasquala a Chiaia 15B, 80121 Naples, Italy* Naples (81) 411842

BULLOCK, Miss Rosemary Joy. b 59. Portsm Poly BA81 Southn Univ BTh94. Sarum & Wells Th Coll 89. **d** 91 **p** 94. Par Dn Warblington and Emsworth *Portsm* 91-94; C 94-95; C Gt Parndon *Chelmsf* from 95. *29 Woodhill, Harlow, Essex CM18 7JS* Harlow (01279) 417644

BULLOCK (nee WHEALE), Mrs Sarah Ruth. b 64. Surrey Univ BA86 St Jo Coll Dur BA93. Cranmer Hall Dur 90. **d** 93 **p** 94. C Kersal Moor *Man* from 93. *6 Woodward Road, Prestwich, Manchester M25 8TU* 0161-773 1109

BULLOCK, Dr Stephanie Clair. b 46. St Mary's Hosp Medical Sch Lon MB, BS70. Ripon Coll Cuddesdon 90. **d** 92 **p** 94. Par Dn Cuddesdon *Ox* 92-94; Tutor Ripon Coll Cuddesdon 92-94; Asst Chapl Chu Hosp Ox from 94. *10 St Andrew's Road, Oxford OX3 9DL, or The Churchill, Old Road, Oxford OX3 7LJ* Oxford (01865) 63226 or 741841

BULLOCK, Father Victor James Allen. b 67. Southn Univ BTh90 St Mary's Coll Twickenham PGCE91. St Steph Ho Ox DipMin94. **d** 94 **p** 95. C Cowley St Jas *Ox* 94-95; C Reading St Giles from 95. *St Saviour's House, 31 Holybrook Road, Reading RG1 6DG* Reading (01734) 595280

BULLOCK-FLINT, Peter. b 22. Kelham Th Coll 39. **d** 45 **p** 46. C-in-c Tilehurst St Mary CD *Ox* 56-72; V Hughenden 72-83; V Ivinghoe w Pitstone and Slapton 83-91; RD Mursley 86-91; rtd 91. *1 Wellow Cottage, Salisbury Road, Pimperne, Blandford Forum, Dorset DT11 8UW* Blandford (01258) 450142

BULLOUGH, Canon Walter Herbert. b 15. AKC39. **d** 39 **p** 40. R Halsall *Liv* 59-91; RD Ormskirk 69-78; Hon Can Liv Cathl 71-91; rtd 91. *49 Moss Lane, Southport, Merseyside PR9 7QS*

BULMAN, Mrs Madeline Judith. b 61. K Coll Lon BD AKC. dss 86 **d** 87 **p** 94. Shepperton Lon 86-87; Par Dn 87-88; Par Dn Brentford 88-94; C from 94. *34 Brook Road South, Brentford, Middx TW8 0NN* 0181-568 6518

BULMAN, Michael Thomas Andrew. b 34. Jes Coll Cam BA59 MA61. Ridley Hall Cam 58. **d** 60 **p** 61. C Blackpool St Mark *Blackb* 60-63; C Branksome St Clem *Sarum* 63-67; V York St Barn *York* 67-84; CMJ 84-93; Israel 85-93; Can Jerusalem 87-93; R Maresfield *Chich* from 94; V Nutley from 94. *The Vicarage, Nutley, Uckfield, E Sussex TN22 2NH* Uckfield (01825) 712692

BULMAN, William Mark. b 61. K Coll Lon BD84. Sarum & Wells Th Coll 84. **d** 86 **p** 87. C Shepperton *Lon* 86-87; NSM Wootton w Glympton and Kiddington *Ox* 91-93; C Carterton 93-94; TV Halesworth w Linstead, Chediston, Holton etc *St E* from 94. *The Vicarage, Holton St Peter, Halesworth, Suffolk IP19 8NG* Halesworth (01986) 874548

BUNCE, Very Rev Dr Michael John. b 49. FRSA FSA St Andr Univ MTh79 PhD91. Westcott Ho Cam DipTh80. **d** 80 **p** 81. C Grantham *Linc* 80-83; TV 83-85; R Tarfside *Bre* 85-92; R Bre 85-92; R Auchmithie 91-92; Provost St Paul's Cathl Dundee from 92; R Dundee St Paul from 92. *The Cathedral Rectory, 4 Richmond Terrace, Dundee DD2 1BQ* Dundee (01382) 68548 or 24486

BUNCE, Raymond Frederick. b 28. Lon Univ DipSocSc53. Ely Th Coll 54. **d** 57 **p** 58. V Ealing All SS *Lon* 67-89; rtd 89; Chapl Ascot Priory 89-90; Perm to Offic *Portsm* from 91. *Dwarf Croft, Steephill Road, Ventnor, Isle of Wight PO38 1UF* Isle of Wight (01983) 855145

BUNCH, Andrew William Havard. b 53. Selw Coll Cam BA74 MA78 PhD79. Ox NSM Course 84. **d** 87 **p** 88. NSM Wantage *Ox* 87-91; C New Windsor 91-93; TV from 93. *The Vicarage, Hermitage Lane, Windsor, Berks SL4 4AZ* Windsor (01753) 858720

BUNDAY, Canon Paul. b 30. Wadh Coll Ox BA54 MA58. ALCD56. **d** 56 **p** 57. R Landford w Plaitford *Sarum* 66-77; RD Alderbury 73-77; TR Radipole and Melcombe Regis 77-86; RD Weymouth 82-85; Can and Preb Sarum Cathl 83-95; TV Whitton 86-91; TR 91-95; Chapl Duchess of Somerset Hosp Froxfield 86-94; rtd 95. *16 St John's Close, Tisbury, Salisbury SP3 6PN* Tisbury (01747) 871530

BUNDOCK, Anthony Francis. b 49. Qu Coll Birm 81. **d** 83 **p** 84. C Stansted Mountfitchet *Chelmsf* 83-86; TV Borehamwood *St Alb* 86-94; TR Seacroft *Ripon* from 94. *The Rectory, 47 St James Approach, Leeds LS14 6JJ* Leeds (0113) 273 2390

BUNDOCK, Dr Edward Leigh. b 52. Keble Coll Ox BA73 Open Univ PhD94. St Steph Ho Ox 74. **d** 76 **p** 77. C Malvern Link w Cowleigh *Worc* 76-80; C-in-c Portslade Gd Shep Mile Oak CD *Chich* 80-88; V Wisborough Green 88-94. *Oak Cottage, Kirdford, Billingshurst, W Sussex RH14 0LX* Kirdford (01403) 820481

BUNDOCK, John Nicholas Edward. b 45. Wells Th Coll 66. **d** 70 **p** 71. C Chingford SS Pet and Paul *Chelmsf* 70-74; P-in-c Gt Grimsby St Matt Fairfield CD *Linc* 74-81; V Hindhead *Guildf* from 81; RD Farnham from 91. *The Vicarage, Wood Road, Hindhead, Surrey GU26 6PX* Hindhead (01428) 605305

BUNDOCK, Ronald Michael (Ron). b 44. Leeds Univ BSc65. Ox NSM Course 87. **d** 90 **p** 91. NSM Buckm *Ox* 90-93; NSM Buckm w Radclive cum Chackmore from 93. *1 Holton Road, Buckingham MK18 1PQ* Buckingham (01280) 813887

BUNKER, Harry. b 28. Oak Hill Th Coll. **d** 59 **p** 60. C Longfleet *Sarum* 59-63; R Blisworth *Pet* from 63. *The Rectory, Blisworth, Northampton NN7 3BZ* Blisworth (01604) 858412

BUNKER, John Herbert George. b 31. AKC56. **d** 57 **p** 58. V Byker St Mich *Newc* 65-74; V Ashington 74-84; V Halifax St Aug *Wakef* 84-93; rtd 93. *1 Hebble Dean, Hebble Lane, Halifax, W Yorkshire HX3 5JL*

BUNKER, Very Rev Michael. b 37. Oak Hill Th Coll 59. **d** 63 **p** 64. C Alperton *Lon* 63-66; C St Helens St Helen *Liv* 66-70; V Muswell Hill St Matt *Lon* 70-79; V Muswell Hill St Jas 78-79; V Muswell Hill St Jas w St Matt 79-92; AD W Haringey 85-90; Preb St Paul's Cathl 90-92; Dean Pet from 92. *The Deanery, Minster Precincts, Peterborough PE1 1XS* Peterborough (01733) 62780 Fax 897874

BUNKER, Neil John. b 59. K Coll Lon BD77 AKC77. Ripon Coll Cuddesdon 82. **d** 83 **p** 84. C Bromley St Andr *Roch* 83-87; Chapl Farnborough Psychiatric Unit 85-87; Chapl Farnborough Hosp Orpington from 87; Chapl Orpington Hosp from 87; Distr Chapl Bromley HA from 89. *Farnborough Hospital, Orpington, Kent BR6 8ND, or 6 Ruskin Road, Belvedere, Kent DA17 5BB* Orpington (01689) 814000

BUNNELL, Adrian. b 49. Univ of Wales (Abth) BSc72. St Mich Coll Llan 74. **d** 75 **p** 76. C Wrexham *St As* 75-78; C Rhyl w St Ann 78-79; CF 79-95; R Aberfoyle *St And* from 95; R Callander from 95. *St Mary's Rectory, Aberfoyle, Stirling FK8 3UJ* Aberfoyle (01877) 382887

BUNT, Brian William. b 34. Bris Univ BA63 Lon Univ BD67. Tyndale Hall Bris. **d** 68 **p** 69. C Chich St Pancras and St Jo *Chich* 68-72; C Camborne *Truro* 72-75; P-in-c Kenwyn St Jo 75-93; P-in-c Penzance St Jo 93-94; rtd 94. *28 Trewidden Close, Truro, Cornwall TR1 1LN* Truro (01872) 77753

BUNTING, Canon Ian David. b 33. Ex Coll Ox BA58 MA61. Tyndale Hall Bris 57 Princeton Tn Sem ThM60. **d** 60 **p** 61. C Bootle St Leon *Liv* 60-63; V Waterloo St Jo 64-71; Dir Past Studies St Jo Coll Dur 71-78; R Ches le Street *Dur* 78-87; RD Ches le Street 79-84; Kingham Hill Fellow 87-89; Dioc Dir of Ords *S'well* from 90; C Lenton from 90; Hon Can S'well Minster from 93. *13 Rolleston Drive, Lenton, Nottingham NG7 1JS* Nottingham (0115) 947 2777

BUNTING, Jeremy John. b 34. St Cath Coll Cam BA56 MA60 Worc Coll Ox BA58 MA60. St Steph Ho Ox 57. **d** 59 **p** 60. C Bickley *Roch* 59-62; C Cam St Mary Less *Ely* 62-66; USA 66-68; R Stock Harvard *Chelmsf* 68-87; RD Wickford 73-79; V Hampstead Garden Suburb *Lon* 87-94. *Fairview, 82 New Road, Haslingfield, Cambridge CB3 7LP* Cambridge (01223) 871602

BUNYAN, Richard Charles. b 43. Oak Hill Th Coll 63 Ridley Hall Cam 69. **d** 71 **p** 72. C Luton Ch Ch *Roch* 71-74; C Bexleyheath Ch Ch 74-76; C Bexley St Jo 76-79; TV Northn Em *Pet* 79-81; V Erith St Jo *Roch* 81-86; V S Woodham Ferrers *Chelmsf* 86-89; Chapl Scargill Ho 89-91; Sub-Chapl HM Pris Swaleside 91-94; Dep Chapl HM Pris Belmarsh from

94. *HM Prison Belmarsh, Western Way, London SE28 0EB* 0181-317 2426 Fax 317 2421

BURBERY, Ian Edward. b 37. Univ of Wales (Lamp) BA59. Coll of Resurr Mirfield 59. **d** 61 **p** 62. C Penarth w Lavernock *Llan* 61-68; V Porth 68-77; V Cainscross w Selsley *Glouc* 77-89; P-in-c Cheltenham Em from 89. *Emmanuel Vicarage, 115 Old Bath Road, Cheltenham, Glos GL53 7DE* Cheltenham (01242) 525059

BURBIDGE, Canon Edward Humphrey. b 07. Qu Coll Cam BA30 MA34. St Aug Coll Cant 30. **d** 31 **p** 32. C Castleford All SS *Wakef* 31-34; Australia from 34; rtd 70. *48 Ullapool Road, Mount Pleasant, W Australia 6153* Perth (9) 364-1019

BURBRIDGE, Very Rev John Paul. b 32. FSA89 K Coll Cam BA54 MA58 New Coll Ox BA54 MA58. Wells Th Coll 58. **d** 59 **p** 60. Can Res and Prec York Minster 66-76; Adn Richmond *Ripon* 76-83; Can Res Ripon Cathl 76-83; Dean Nor 83-95; rtd 95. *The School House, High Fremington, Richmond, N Yorkshire DL11 6AS*

BURBRIDGE, Richard James. b 47. Univ of Wales (Ban) BSc68. Oak Hill Th Coll 68. **d** 72 **p** 73. C Rodbourne Cheney *Bris* 72-75; C Downend 75-78; P-in-c Bris H Cross Inns Court 78-83; P-in-c Fishponds All SS 83-86; V from 86; RD Stapleton from 89. *All Saints' Vicarage, Grove Road, Fishponds, Bristol BS16 2BW* Bristol (0117) 965 4143

BURCH, Cyril John. b 18. AKC49. **d** 49 **p** 50. V Stoke Mandeville *Ox* 63-86; rtd 86. *4 Gange Mews, Middle Row, Faversham, Kent ME13 7ED* Faversham (01795) 538166

BURCH, Canon John Christopher (Chris). b 50. Trin Coll Cam BA71 MA74 Leeds Univ MPhil95. St Jo Coll Nottm 73. **d** 76 **p** 77. C Sheff St Jo *Sheff* 76-79; C Holbeck *Ripon* 79-82; V Burmantofts St Steph and St Agnes 82-95; Prec Cov Cathl from 95. *35 Asthill Grove, Coventry CV3 6HN* Coventry (01203) 505426

BURCH, Canon Peter John. b 36. ACA60 FCA71. Ripon Hall Ox 62. **d** 64 **p** 65. C Brixton St Matt *S'wark* 64-67; Sierra Leone 67-72; P-in-c Chich St Pet *Chich* 72-76; V Broadwater Down 76-85; V Steyning 85-94; R Ashurst 85-94; Hon Can Bauchi from 93; V Broadway *Worc* from 94. *The Vicarage, 4 Lifford Gardens, Broadway, Worcs WR12 7DA* Broadway (01386) 852352

BURCH, Stephen Roy. b 59. St Jo Coll Nottm LTh82. **d** 85 **p** 86. C Ipswich St Aug *St E* 85-89; P-in-c Kinwarton w Gt Alne and Haselor *Cov* from 89; Youth Chapl from 89. *The Rectory, Great Alne, Alcester, Warks B49 6HY* Great Alne (01789) 488344

BURCH, Victor Ernest Charles. b 18. Nor Ord Course 73. **d** 76 **p** 77. NSM Heigham St Barn w St Bart *Nor* 76-80; NSM Lakenham St Jo 80-88; Perm to Offic from 88. *35 Oaklands, Framingham Earl, Norwich NR14 7QS* Framingham Earl (01508) 492790

BURCHILL, Dr Jane. b 31. Dalhousie Univ Canada BSc54 Aber Univ PhD81. Moray Ho Edin CertEd56 St Jo Coll Nottm 85. **d** 88 **p** 94. NSM Inverurie *Ab* from 88; NSM Auchindoir from 88; NSM Alford from 88; NSM Kemnay from 88. *5 Hopetoun Avenue, Bucksburn, Aberdeen AB2 9QU* Aberdeen (01224) 712931

BURDEN, Miss Anne Margaret. b 47. Ex Univ BSc69 LSE DSA70 CQSW72. Linc Th Coll 89. **d** 91 **p** 94. Par Dn Mill Hill Jo Keble Ch *Lon* 91-94; C 94; TV Basingstoke *Win* from 94. *219 Paddock Road, Basingstoke, Hants RG22 6QP* Basingstoke (01256) 464393

BURDEN, Arthur Theodore. b 11. St Pet Hall Ox BA35 MA42. Wycliffe Hall Ox 35. **d** 37 **p** 38. V Dorking St Paul *Guildf* 63-73; V Defford w Besford *Worc* 73-78; V Eckington 73-78; rtd 78; Perm to Offic *Glouc* from 78; Perm to Offic *Worc* from 78; P-in-c Ripple, Earls Croome w Hill Croome and Strensham 87. *Wellspring, 7 Golden Valley, Castlemorton, Malvern, Worcs WR13 6AA* Birtsmorton (01684) 833341

BURDEN, Derek. b 29. St Edm Hall Ox BA52 MA56. Wells Th Coll 56. **d** 58 **p** 59. V N Bradley *Sarum* 69-79; V Steeple Ashton w Semington 79-84; V Keevil 79-84; V Steeple Ashton w Semington and Keevil 84-89; rtd 89. *9 Farleigh Avenue, Trowbridge, Wilts BA14 9DS* Trowbridge (01225) 754759

BURDEN, Derek Ronald. b 37. Sarum Th Coll 59. **d** 62 **p** 63. C Cuddington *Guildf* 62-64; C Leamington Priors All SS *Cov* 64-66; C Stamford All SS w St Pet *Linc* 66-74; C-in-c Stamford Ch Ch CD 71-74; P-in-c Ashbury w Compton Beauchamp *Ox* 74-77; V 77-81; V Ashbury, Compton Beauchamp and Longcot w Fernham 81-84; V Wokingham St Sebastian from 84. *St Sebastian's Vicarage, Nine Mile Ride, Wokingham, Berks RG11 3AT* Crowthorne (01344) 761050

BURDEN, Michael Henry. b 36. Selw Coll Cam BA59 MA63 Hull Univ MEd81. Ridley Hall Cam 60. **d** 62 **p** 63. C Ashton on Mersey St Mary *Ches* 62-65; Chapl St Pet Sch York 65-70; Asst Master Beverley Gr Sch 70-74; R Walkington *York* 74-77; Chapl Asst Berwick R Infirmary 82-94; P-in-c Berwick H Trin *Newc* 82-87; V 87-89; P-in-c Berwick St Mary 82-87; V Berwick H Trin and St Mary 89-94; P-in-c Skirwith, Ousby

and Melmerby w Kirkland *Carl* from 94; Sec Guild of St Raphael from 94. *The Vicarage, Skirwith, Penrith, Cumbria CA10 1RQ* Culgaith (01768) 88663

BURDEN, Paul. b 62. AMIMechE87 Rob Coll Cam BA84 MA88. Wycliffe Hall Ox BA91. **d** 92 **p** 93. C Clevedon St Andr and Ch Ch *B & W* from 92. *23 Turner Way, Clevedon, Avon BS21 7YN* Clevedon (01275) 872134

BURDETT, John Fergusson. b 25. Pemb Coll Cam BA47 MA79. **d** 79 **p** 80. C Edin St Jo *Edin* 79-87 and from 90; Cyprus 87-90. *80/1 Barton Park View, Edinburgh EH4 6HJ* 0131-339 7226

BURDETT, Stephen Martin. b 49. AKC72. St Aug Coll Cant 73. **d** 74 **p** 75. C Walworth St Pet *S'wark* 74-75; C Walworth 75-77; C Benhilton 77-80; P-in-c Earlsfield St Jo 80-83; V 83-89; V N Dulwich St Faith from 89. *St Faith's Vicarage, Red Post Hill, London SE24 9JQ* 0171-274 1338 or 274 3924

BURDITT, Jeffrey Edward (Jeff). b 46. Ex Univ BA67 CertEd68 Lon Univ MPhil79. Westcott Ho Cam 86. **d** 88 **p** 89. C Saffron Walden w Wendens Ambo and Littlebury *Chelmsf* 88-92; V Hatf Peverel w Ulting 92-95. *26 Mill Road, Burnham-on-Crouch, Essex CM0 8PZ* Burnham-on-Crouch (01621) 786154

BURDON, Anthony James (Tony). b 46. Ex Univ LLB67 Lon Univ BD73. Oak Hill Th Coll 71. **d** 73 **p** 74. C Ox St Ebbe w St Pet *Ox* 73-76; C Church Stretton *Heref* 76-78; Cand Sec CPAS 78-81; Hon C Bromley Ch Ch *Roch* 78-81; V Filkins w Broadwell, Broughton, Kelmscot etc *Ox* 81-84; R Broughton Poggs w Filkins, Broadwell etc 84-85; V Reading St Jo from 85. *St John's Vicarage, 50 London Road, Reading RG1 5AS* Reading (01734) 872366

BURDON, Christopher John. b 48. Jes Coll Cam BA70 MA74 Leeds Univ DipTh73. Coll of Resurr Mirfield 71. **d** 74 **p** 75. C Chelmsf All SS *Chelmsf* 74-78; TV High Wycombe *Ox* 78-84; P-in-c Olney w Emberton 84-90; R 90-92; Lic to Offic *Glas* 92-94; Lay Tr Officer *Chelmsf* from 94. *9 Boswells Drive, Chelmsford CM2 6LD* Chelmsford (01245) 283235

BURDON, Edward Arthur. b 11. Linc Th Coll 44. **d** 46 **p** 47. V Gosfield *Chelmsf* 54-72; V Coggeshall w Markshall 72-80; rtd 80; Perm to Offic *St E* from 81. *The Nutshell, 20 Naverne Meadows, Woodbridge, Suffolk IP12 1HU* Woodbridge (01394) 384787

BURDON, Mrs Pamela Muriel (Pam). b 46. Ex Univ BA68 Reading Univ DipEd69. Wycliffe Hall Ox 88. **d** 90 **p** 94. Par Dn Reading St Jo *Ox* 90-94; C from 94. *St John's Vicarage, 50 London Road, Reading RG1 5AS* Reading (01734) 872366

BURDON, William. b 23. Leeds Univ BA51. Coll of Resurr Mirfield 51. **d** 53 **p** 54. V Skirwith *Carl* 64-73; V Skirwith w Ousby and Melmerby 73-84; R Maidwell w Draughton, Scaldwell, Lamport etc *Pet* 84-88; rtd 88. *The Rectory, Church Park, Tenby, Dyfed SA70 7EE* Tenby (01834) 842068

BURFITT, Edward Ronald (Eddy). b 42. MIMA64 Liv Univ CSocSc67 Newc Univ DASS68. Cranmer Hall Dur CTMin93. **d** 93 **p** 94. C Monkseaton St Mary *Newc* from 93. *89 Queen's Road, Whitley Bay, Tyne & Wear NE26 3AS* 0191-252 7769

BURGER, David Joseph Cave. b 31. Selw Coll Cam BA58 MA62 Leic Univ 68. Coll of Resurr Mirfield 58. **d** 60 **p** 61. Teacher Ysgol y Gader Dolgellau Gwynedd 68-85; Resettlement Officer Ches Aid to the Homeless 86-92; rtd 92. *Pwllygele Mawr, Llanfachreth, Dolgellau, Gwynedd LL40 2DP*

BURGESS, Alan James. b 51. Ridley Hall Cam 87. **d** 89 **p** 90. C Glenfield *Leic* 89-92; V Donisthorpe and Moira w Stretton-en-le-Field from 92. *St John's Vicarage, Donisthorpe, Swadlincote, Derbyshire DE12 7PX* Measham (01530) 271456

BURGESS, Alfred George. b 18. Univ of Wales BA39. St Mich Coll Llan 39. **d** 41 **p** 42. V Alveston *Cov* 58-81; R Ilmington w Stretton on Fosse and Ditchford 81-84; rtd 84; Perm to Offic *Cov* from 84. *139 Evesham Road, Stratford-upon-Avon, Warks CV37 9BP* Stratford-upon-Avon (01789) 293321

BURGESS, Preb Colin. b 38. St Aid Birkenhead 63. **d** 65 **p** 66. C Blackb St Steph *Blackb* 65-68; Trinidad and Tobago 68-71; Miss to Seamen 71-73 and 76-84; Tanzania 73-76; Prov Sec and Sen Chapl Ch in Wales 79-84; Asst Chapl HM Pris Pentonville 85; Chapl HM Youth Cust Cen E Sutton Park 85-88; Chapl HM Pris Maidstone 85-88; Chapl HM Pris Holloway from 88; Preb St Paul's Cathl *Lon* from 92. *The Chaplain's Office, HM Prison, Parkhurst Road, London N7 0NU* 0171-607 6747 Fax 700 0296

BURGESS, David James. b 58. **d** 89 **p** 90. C S Mimms Ch Ch *Lon* 89-93; C Hanwell St Mary w St Chris from 93. *The Vicarage, Bordars Road, London W7 1AG* 0181-578 2796

BURGESS, David John. b 39. Trin Hall Cam BA62 MA66 Univ Coll Ox MA66. Cuddesdon Coll 62. **d** 65 **p** 66. C Maidstone All SS w St Phil *Cant* 65; Asst Chapl Univ Coll Ox 66-70; Chapl 70-78; Can and Treas Windsor 78-87; Chapl to The Queen from 87; V St Lawr Jewry *Lon* from 87. *St Lawrence Jewry Vicarage, Next Guildhall, London EC2V 5AA* 0171-600 9478

BURGESS, Derek Mark. b 31. Brasted Place Coll 61. St Mich Coll Llan 61. **d** 89 **p** 90. Australia 89-92; P-in-c Knowbury *Heref* from 93; P-in-c Coreley w Doddington from 93. *Knowbury Vicarage, Clee Hill, Ludlow, Shropshire SY8 3JG* Ludlow (01584) 890129

BURGESS, Edwin Michael. b 47. Ch Coll Cam BA69 MA73. Coll of Resurr Mirfield 70. **d** 72 **p** 73. C Beamish *Dur* 72-77; C Par *Truro* 77-80; P-in-c Duloe w Herodsfoot 80-83; R 83-86; Jt Dir SW Min Tr Course *Ex* 80-86; Subwarden St Deiniol's Lib Hawarden 86-91; R Oughtrington *Ches* from 91; P-in-c Warburton from 93. *The Rectory, Oughtrington, Lymm, Cheshire WA13 9JB* Lymm (01925) 752388

BURGESS, Canon Henry James. b 08. Lon Univ BA31 MA49 PhD54. Wycliffe Hall Ox 35. **d** 36 **p** 37. Can Res Sheff Cathl *Sheff* 70-75; Dioc Dir of Educn 70-75; rtd 75; Perm to Offic *Truro* 75-85; Perm to Offic *Roch* from 85. *Flat 21, Bromley College, London Road, Bromley BR1 1PE* 0181-290 1362

BURGESS, Canon Henry Percival. b 21. Leeds Univ BA48. Coll of Resurr Mirfield 48. **d** 50 **p** 51. V Wylde Green *Birm* 62-89; Hon Can Birm Cathl 75-90; RD Sutton Coldfield 76-88; rtd 90. *39 Chestnut Drive, Birmingham B36 9BH* 0121-747 9926

BURGESS, James Graham. b 30. Lon Univ BA51 St Cath Coll Ox DipTh55. Ripon Hall Ox 53. **d** 55 **p** 56. C Northn St Jas *Pet* 55-58; C Mortlake w E Sheen *S'wark* 58-61; R Morley *Nor* 61-63; Perm to Offic *Derby* from 71; Hd Relig Studies Coalville Gr Sch 63-71; St Elphin's Sch Darley Dale 71-88; Hd Hist from 88. *Appletrees, 7 Church Road, Darley Dale, Matlock, Derbyshire DE4 2GG* Matlock (01629) 734379

BURGESS, Ven John Edward. b 30. Lon Univ BD57. ALCD56. **d** 57 **p** 58. C Bermondsey St Mary w St Olave and St Jo *S'wark* 57-60; C Southn St Mary w H Trin *Win* 60-62; V Dunston w Coppenhall *Lich* 62-67; Chapl Stafford Coll of Tech 63-67; V Keynsham w Queen Charlton *B & W* 67-75; R Burnett 67-75; RD Keynsham 72-75; Adn Bath and Preb Wells Cathl from 75. *Birnfels, 56 Grange Road, Saltford, Bristol BS18 3AG* Saltford (01225) 873609 Fax 874110

BURGESS, John Henry William. b 35. Westhill Coll Birm CYCW72. Wells Th Coll 65. **d** 67 **p** 68. C Teddington St Alb *Lon* 67-72; C Northolt W End St Jos 72-74; Perm to Offic *B & W* from 93. *10 Pendragon Park, Glastonbury, Somerset BA6 9PQ* Glastonbury (01458) 833287

BURGESS, John Michael. b 36. ALCD61. **d** 61 **p** 62. C Eccleston St Luke *Liv* 61-64; S Rhodesia 64-65; Rhodesia 65-74; V Nottm St Andr *S'well* 74-79; Bp's Adv on Community Relns 77-79; V Earlestown *Liv* 79-87; RD Warrington 82-87; TR Halewood 87-94; V Southport St Phil and St Paul from 94; AD N Meols from 95. *St Philip's Vicarage, Scarisbrick New Road, Southport, Merseyside PR8 6QF* Southport (01704) 532886

BURGESS, John Mulholland. b 32. Cranmer Hall Dur 58. **d** 61 **p** 62. C Frimley *Guildf* 61-67; C Cheltenham St Luke and St Jo *Glouc* 67-69; P-in-c Withington w Compton Abdale 69-74; R Woolstone w Gotherington and Oxenton 74-75; Chapl Rotterdam w Schiedam etc *Eur* 75-78; Sliema 78-80; C Nottm All SS *S'well* 80; C Rolleston w Morton 80-83; C Rolleston w Fiskerton, Morton and Upton 83-84; V Mansf St Aug from 84; Asst RD Mansf 88-92; RD Mansf from 92. *St Augustine's Vicarage, 46 Abbott Road, Mansfield, Notts NG19 6DD* Mansfield (01623) 21247

BURGESS, Michael Anglin. b 34. St Deiniol's Hawarden 81. **d** 83 **p** 84. C Habergham Eaves St Matt *Blackb* 83-85; C Burnley (Habergham Eaves) St Matt w H Trin 85-86; V Preston St Matt 86-93; V Nelson St Bede from 93. *St Bede's Vicarage, Railway Street, Nelson, Lancs BB9 0LT* Nelson (01282) 614197

BURGESS, Michael James. b 42. Coll of Resurr Mirfield 74. **d** 76 **p** 77. C Leigh-on-Sea St Marg *Chelmsf* 76-79; C St Peter-in-Thanet *Cant* 79-82; Canada from 82. *66 Spencer Avenue, Toronto, Ontario, Canada, M6K 2J6* Toronto (416) 531-4037

BURGESS, Michael Walter. Bps' Coll Cheshunt 66. **d** 68 **p** 70. C Hammersmith St Matt *Lon* 68-70; C Boreham Wood All SS *St Alb* 70-73; V Flamstead 74-77; V St Marylebone Annunciation Bryanston Street *Lon* from 77. *4 Wyndham Place, London W1H 1AP* 0171-262 4329

BURGESS, Neil. b 53. Univ of Wales (Lamp) BA75 Nottm Univ MTh87. St Mich Coll Llan 75. **d** 77 **p** 78. C Cheadle *Lich* 77-79; C Longton 79-82; TV Hanley H Ev 82-86; C Uttoxeter w Bramshall 86-87; Lect Linc Th Coll 87-95; Dioc Dir of Tr *S'well* from 95. *23 Drury Lane, Lincoln LN1 3BP* Lincoln (01522) 539408

BURGESS, Sister Patricia Jean. b 16. Edin Univ BSc38. dss 69 **d** 86. NSM Roslin (Rosslyn Chpl) *Edin* 69-73; Community of the Transfiguration Midlothian from 72. *House of the Transfiguration, 70E Clerk Street, Loanhead, Midlothian EH20 9RG*

BURGESS, Paul Christopher James. b 41. Qu Coll Cam BA63 MA67. Lon Coll of Div 66. **d** 68 **p** 69. C Islington St Mary *Lon* 68-72; C Church Stretton *Heref* 73-74; Pakistan 74-83; Warden Carberry Tower (Ch of Scotland) 84-86; Progr Co-

ord 86-88; TV Livingston LEP *Edin* from 88. *124 Mowbray Rise, Livingston, West Lothian EH54 6JP* Livingston (01506) 417158

BURGESS, Roy. b 32. S Dios Minl Tr Scheme 80. **d** 83 **p** 84. NSM Bentworth and Shalden and Lasham *Win* 83-89; R Ingoldsby *Linc* from 89; RD Beltisloe from 93. *The Rectory, Back Lane, Ingoldsby, Grantham, Lincs NG33 4EW* Ingoldsby (01476) 585746

BURGESS, Roy Graham. b 47. Birm Univ CertCYW72 Bulmershe Coll of HE DMS81. Ox Min Course CBTS94. **d** 94. C Easthampstead *Ox* from 94. *St Michael's House, Crowthorne Road, Bracknell, Berkshire RG12 4ER* Bracknell (01344) 429397

BURGHALL, Kenneth Miles. b 34. Selw Coll Cam BA57 MA61. Qu Coll Birm 57. **d** 59 **p** 60. C Macclesfield St Mich *Ches* 59-63; CF 63-66; P-in-c Birkenhead Priory *Ches* 67-71; V Macclesfield St Paul 71-87; V Nether Peover from 87; P-in-c Over Peover from 92. *The Vicarage, Lower Peover, Knutsford, Cheshire WA16 9PZ* Lower Peover (01565) 722304

BURGIN, Henry Kenneth. b 36. S'wark Ord Course 70. **d** 71 **p** 72. C Caterham Valley *S'wark* 71-73; C Benhilton 73-77; V Cheam Common St Phil 77-82; P-in-c Blackheath All SS 82-89; V from 89. *All Saints' Vicarage, 10 Duke Humphrey Road, London SE3 0TY* 0181-852 4280

BURGON, Canon George Irvine. b 41. Edin Th Coll. **d** 65 **p** 66. C Dundee St Mary Magd *Bre* 65-68; C Wellingborough All Hallows *Pet* 68-71; P-in-c Norton 71-73; TV Daventry w Norton 73-75; V Northn St Mary from 75; Can Pet Cathl from 95. *St Mary's Vicarage, Towcester Road, Northampton NN4 9EZ* Northampton (01604) 761104

BURGOYNE, Edward Geoffrey. b 27. Univ of Wales (Abth) BA49. St Mich Coll Llan 49. **d** 51 **p** 52. V Bockleton w Leysters *Heref* 63-70; Lic to Offic 70-91; rtd 91. *Lawnswood, Tupsley, Hereford HR1 1UT* Hereford (01432) 268860

BURGOYNE, Percy John (Jack). b 19. OBE74. Univ of Wales (Cardiff) BSc41. St Mich Coll Llan. **d** 43 **p** 44. Chapl RN 52-78; QHC 72-75; P-in-c Kelsale w Carlton *St E* 78-85; R Kelsale-cum-Carlton, Middleton-cum-Fordley etc 85-90; rtd 90; Perm to Offic *St E* from 90. *St Dyfrig, Woods Lane, Melton, Woodbridge, Suffolk IP12 1JF* Woodbridge (01394) 384884

BURGOYNE-JOHNSON, Philip Simon (Brother Thaddeus). b 51. S'wark Ord Course 81. **d** 84 **p** 85. SSF from 71; Lic to Offic *Heref* from 84. *Holy Trinity House, Orsett Terrace, London W2 6AH* 0171-723 9735

BURKE, Charles Michael. b 28. Keble Coll Ox BA51 MA54 Ox Univ DipEd52. Glouc Th Course. **d** 84 **p** 85. C Colwall w Upper Colwall and Coddington *Heref* 84-88; V Canon Pyon w Kings Pyon and Birley from 88. *The Vicarage, Brookside, Canon Pyon, Hereford HR4 8NY* Canon Pyon (01432) 830802

BURKE, Christopher Mark (Chris). b 65. Cov Poly LLB87. Ripon Coll Cuddesdon 89. **d** 92 **p** 93. C Nunthorpe *York* from 92. *15 Ripon Road, Nunthorpe, Middlesbrough, Cleveland TS7 0HX* Middlesbrough (01642) 310834

BURKE, Colin Douglas. b 41. Bp Otter Coll CertEd64 Local NSM Course. **d** 92 **p** 93. NSM Fressingfield, Mendham, Metfield, Weybread etc *St E* from 92. *St Andrews, Weybread, Diss, Norfolk IP21 5TU* Harleston (01379) 852063

BURKE, Eric John. b 44. Llan Dioc Tr Scheme 81. **d** 85 **p** 86. NSM Cardiff St Jo *Llan* from 85. *81 Ty Mawr Road, Rumney, Cardiff CF3 8BS* Cardiff (01222) 798147

BURKE, Jonathan. b 53. Lon Univ BEd. Westcott Ho Cam 79. **d** 82 **p** 83. C Weymouth H Trin *Sarum* 82-85; R Bere Regis and Affpuddle w Turnerspuddle 85-92. *Address temp unknown*

BURKE, Michael Robert. b 61. Leeds Univ BA83. Trin Coll Bris BA89. **d** 89 **p** 90. C Anston *Sheff* 89-92; V Crosspool from 92. *The Vicarage, 1 Barnfield Road, Sheffield S10 5TD* Sheffield (0114) 230 2531

BURKE, William Spencer Dwerryhouse. b 46. Ripon Coll Cuddesdon 90. **d** 92 **p** 93. C Watford St Mich *St Alb* from 92. *57 Whippendell Road, Watford WD1 7LY* Watford (01923) 248739

BURKETT, Christopher Paul. b 52. Warw Univ BA75 Birm Univ DipTh77 Westmr Coll Ox DipApTh92 Ox Univ MTh93. Qu Coll Birm 75. **d** 78 **p** 79. C Streetly *Lich* 78-81; C Harlescott 81-83; TV Leek and Meerbrook 83-89; Chapl Leek Moorlands Hosp 83-89; Area Sec (Dio Ches) USPG 89-92; Lic to Offic *Ches* 89-92; V Whitegate w Lt Budworth from 92. *The New Vicarage, Cinder Hill, Whitegate, Northwich, Cheshire CW8 2BH* Sandiway (01606) 882151

BURKILL, Mark Edward. b 56. MA PhD. Trin Coll Bris. **d** 84 **p** 85. C Cheadle *Ches* 84-88; C Harold Wood *Chelmsf* 88-91; V Leyton Ch Ch from 91. *The Vicarage, 52 Elm Road, London E11 4DN* 0181-539 4980

BURKITT, Paul Adrian. b 49. RMN75 SRN77 Coll of Ripon & York St Jo CCouns89. St Steph Ho Ox 84. **d** 86 **p** 87. C Whitby *York* 86-90; V Egton w Grosmont 90-93; V Newington w

Dairycoates from 93. *St John's Vicarage, 203 St George's Road, Hull HU3 3SP* Hull (01482) 214551

BURKITT, Richard Francis. b 49. Leeds Univ BA71 CertEd72. Sarum & Wells Th Coll 82. **d** 90 **p** 90. R Fraserburgh w New Pitsligo *Ab* 90-95; R Fortrose *Mor* from 95; R Cromarty from 95; R Arpafeelie from 95. *St Andrew's Rectory, 1 Deans Road, Fortrose, Ross-shire IV10 8TJ* Fortrose (01381) 620255

BURLAND, Clive Beresford. b 37. Sarum & Wells Th Coll 81. **d** 85 **p** 86. C Warblington and Emsworth *Portsm* 85-87; C Cowes St Mary 87-92; R Gurnard from 92; R Northwood from 93. *The Rectory, Chawton Lane, Cowes, Isle of Wight PO31 8PR* Isle of Wight (01983) 292050

BURLEIGH, David John. b 42. FCII69. St Deiniol's Hawarden 84. **d** 87 **p** 88. NSM Lache cum Saltney *Ches* 87-88; NSM Eastham 89-92; C Birkenhead Priory from 92. *St Mark's Vicarage, 7 Slatey Road, Birkenhead L43 1TA* 0151-652 5768

BURLEIGH, Walter Coleridge. b 41. W Midl Minl Tr Course 89. **d** 89 **p** 90. NSM N Evington *Leic* from 90. *90 Farrier Lane, Leicester LE4 0WA* Leicester (0116) 235 9663

BURLES, Robert John. b 54. Bris Univ BSc75. St Jo Coll Nottm LTh86. **d** 88 **p** 89. C Mansf St Pet *S'well* 88-91; C The Lydiards *Bris* 91-92; TV from 92. *1 Brandon Close, Swindon SN5 6AA* Swindon (01793) 870244

BURLEY, Canon John Anderson. b 11. Selw Coll Cam BA33 MA37. Ely Th Coll 33. **d** 34 **p** 35. V Clacton St Jas *Chelmsf* 59-70; Hon Can Utrecht Old Cathl Ch *Eur* from 69; R Gt and Lt Braxted *Chelmsf* 70-83; rtd 83. *Braxted, Church Road, Lyminge, Kent CT18 8JA* Lyminge (01303) 862610

BURLEY, John Roland James. b 46. St Jo Coll Cam BA67 MA70 Ball Coll Ox DipGeochem68. Trin Episc Sch for Min Ambridge Penn MDiv88. **d** 81 **p** 82. SAMS 81-90; Chile 81-90; TV Southgate *Chich* from 90. *Holy Trinity Vicarage, Titmus Drive, Crawley, W Sussex RH10 5EU* Crawley (01293) 525809

BURLEY, Michael. b 58. Ridley Hall Cam 86. **d** 89 **p** 90. C Scarborough St Mary w Ch Ch and H Apostles *York* 89-92; C Drypool 93; TV from 93. *St Andrew's House, 2 Harcourt Drive, Hull HU9 2AR* Hull (01482) 23840

BURLTON, Aelred Harry. b 49. Sarum & Wells Th Coll 75. **d** 78 **p** 79. C Feltham *Lon* 78-82; Chapl Heathrow Airport 83-94; P-in-c Harmondsworth 92-94; R St Buryan, St Levan and Sennen *Truro* from 94. *The Rectory, St Buryan, Penzance, Cornwall TR19 6BB* St Buryan (01736) 810216

BURLTON, Robert Michael. b 18. Ely Th Coll 40 Chich Th Coll 41. **d** 42 **p** 43. R Lound *Nor* 65-76; P-in-c Fritton St Edm 65-83; R Blundeston w Flixton and Lound 76-83; rtd 83. *Heatherley, 3 Furze Park, Trelights, Port Isaac, Cornwall PL29 3TG*

BURLTON, William Frank. b 12. K Coll Lon. **d** 43 **p** 44. R Cromhall *Glouc* 51-78; HM Pris Leyhill 54-89; R Cromhall w Tortworth *Glouc* 78-82; rtd 82; Perm to Offic *Glouc* from 82; Perm to Offic *Truro* from 89. *24 Godolphin Terrace, Marazion, Penzance, Cornwall TR17 0EX* Penzance (01736) 710699

BURMAN, Philip Harvey. b 47. Kelham Th Coll 66. **d** 70 **p** 71. C Huyton St Mich *Liv* 70-75; C Farnworth 75-77; TV Kirkby 77-83; V Hindley All SS 83-93; V Middlesb St Martin *York* from 93. *St Martin's Vicarage, Whinney Banks, Middlesbrough, Cleveland TS5 4LA* Middlesbrough (01642) 819634

BURMAN, Thomas George (Tom). b 41. S'wark Ord Course 86. **d** 89 **p** 90. Hon C Forest Hill *S'wark* from 89. *131 Como Road, London SE23 2JN* 0181-699 8929

BURMAN, William Guest. b 26. St Cath Coll Cam MA55 Worc Coll Ox MA63. St Steph Ho Ox 81. **d** 83 **p** 84. C Weymouth H Trin *Sarum* 83-86; R Exton and Winsford and Cutcombe w Luxborough *B & W* 86-89; TV Langport Area *Chs* 89-91; rtd 91; Bath St Mary Magd Holloway *B & W* from 94. *38 Belgrave Crescent, Bath BA1 5JU* Bath (01225) 312140

BURN, Canon Alan Edward. b 24. St Chad's Coll Dur BA49 DipTh51. **d** 51 **p** 52. V Binley *Cov* 67-73; R Allesley 73-89; RD Cov E 71-73; RD Cov N 79-87; Hon Can Cov Cathl 87-89; rtd 89. *3 Church Farm, South Kilvington, Thirsk, N Yorkshire YO7 2NL* Thirsk (01845) 524184

BURN, Ms Kathleen Doreen. b 48. Bp Grosseteste Coll CertEd69. NY Th Sem MDiv82. **d** 82 **p** 83. USA 82-93; TV Dunstable *St Alb* from 94. *St Augustine's Vicarage, 83 Half Moon Lane, Dunstable, Beds LU5 4AE* Dunstable (01582) 668019

BURN, Leonard Louis. b 44. K Coll Lon BD67 AKC67. **d** 68 **p** 69. C Kingswinford St Mary *Lich* 68-70; C S Ascot *Ox* 70-72; C Caversham 72-76; Chapl Selly Oak Hosp Birm 76-81; Bris City Hosp 81-82; P-in-c Bris St Mich *Bris* 81-83; R Peopleton and White Ladies Aston etc *Worc* 83-88; V Bengeworth from 88; Chapl St Rich Hospice Worc from 88; Chapl Evesham Coll from 90. *The Vicarage, Broadway Road, Bengeworth, Evesham, Worcs WR11 6BB* Evesham (01386) 446164

BURN, Richard James Southerden. b 34. Pemb Coll Cam BA56. Wells Th Coll 56. **d** 58 **p** 59. C Cheshunt *St Alb* 58-62; C Leighton Buzzard 65-66; C Glastonbury St Jo *B & W* 66-68;

P-in-c Prestonpans *Edin* 68-71; P-in-c Stokesay *Heref* 71-75; P-in-c Dorrington 75-81; P-in-c Stapleton 75-81; P-in-c Leebotwood w Longnor 75-81; P-in-c Smethcott w Woolstaston 81; TR Melbury *Sarum* 81-87; P-in-c Quendon w Rickling and Wicken Bonhunt *Chelmsf* 87-92; R Quendon w Rickling & Wicken Bonhunt & Widdington from 92. *St Francis Vicarage, 865 Great West Road, Isleworth, Middx TW7 5PD* 0181-568 9098

BURN, Dr Robert Pemberton. b 34. Peterho Cam BA56 MA60 Lon Univ PhD68. CMS Tr Coll Chislehurst 60. **d** 63 **p** 81. India 63-71; Perm to Offic *Ely* 71-81; P-in-c Foxton 81-88; Perm to Offic *Ex* from 89. *Flat 4, 9 Lansdowne Terrace, Exeter EX2 4JJ* Exeter (01392) 430028

BURN-MURDOCH, Aidan Michael. b 35. Trin Coll Cam BA60 MA63. Ridley Hall Cam. **d** 61 **p** 62. C Bishopwearmouth St Gabr *Dur* 61-63; Tutor Ridley Hall Cam 63-67; CMS Miss 67-70; India 68-70; R Hawick *Edin* 70-77; Bp's Co-ord of Evang *S & B* 77-81; R Reynoldston w Penrice and Llangennith 77-83; V Port Eynon w Rhosili and Llanddewi and Knelston 83-89; R Uddingston *Glas* from 89; R Cambuslang from 89. *5 Brownside Road, Cambuslang, Glasgow G72 8NL* 0141-641 1173

BURNE, Christopher John Sambrooke. b 16. DSO45. Linc Th Coll 58. **d** 59 **p** 60. V N Leigh *Ox* 63-81; rtd 81; Perm to Offic Win from 81. *Beam Ends, Middle Road, Tiptoe, Lymington, Hants SO41 6FX* Lymington (01590) 682898

BURNE, Canon Wilfrid Durnford Elvis. b 07. OBE65. Keble Coll Ox BA29 MA57. Bps' Coll Cheshunt 30. **d** 31 **p** 32. V Manea *Ely* 67-72; rtd 72. *1 Waterloo Road, Salisbury SP1 2JR* Salisbury (01722) 324396

BURNET, Norman Andrew Gray. b 32. Aber Univ BEd77. Edin Th Coll 53. **d** 55 **p** 56. C Ayr *Glas* 55-58; S Africa 58-69; R Leven *St And* 69-72; Perm to Offic *Ab* 73-81; Perm to Offic *Bre* 73-81; Perm to Offic *Ely* 73-81; P-in-c Brinkley, Burrough Green and Carlton 82-83; P-in-c Westley Waterless 82-83; Australia 83-84; R Fraserburgh w New Pitsligo *Ab* 85-89; P-in-c Bicker Linc 89; V Bicker and Wigtoft from 89. *St Swithin's Vicarage, 14 Old Main Road, Bicker, Boston, Lincs PE20 3EF* Spalding (01775) 820574

BURNETT, Canon John Capenhurst. b 19. AKC49. **d** 49 **p** 50. R Wroughton *Bris* 56-76; RD Cricklade 70-76; Hon Can Bris Cathl 74-85; V Bris St Andr w St Bart 76-85; rtd 85; Perm to Offic *Bris* from 85. *7 Queen Victoria Road, Bristol BS6 7PD* Bristol (0117) 973 8856

BURNETT, Susan Mary. b 50. Lon Univ BEd73 St Jo Coll Dur DipTh76. **dss** 78 **d** 87 **p** 94. Welling *S'wark* 78-83; E Greenwich Ch Ch w St Andr and St Mich 83-91; Par Dn 87-91; Par Dn Sydenham All SS 91-94; C from 94; Par Dn Lower Sydenham St Mich 91-94; C from 94. *St Michael's Vicarage, Champion Crescent, London SE26 4HH* 0181-778 7196

BURNETT-HALL, Mrs Karen. b 46. Bp Grosseteste Coll CertEd68 Lon Univ BD82. Oak Hill Th Coll 86. **d** 89 **p** 94. NSM Norbury *Ches* 89-90; Par Dn 90-92; NSM York St Paul *York* from 93. *12 Kyme Street, York YO1 1HG* York (01904) 638935

BURNHAM, Andrew. b 48. ARCO New Coll Ox BA69 BA71 Westmr Coll Ox CertEd72. St Steph Ho Ox 81. **d** 83 **p** 84. Hon C Clifton *S'well* 83-85; C Beeston 85-87; V Carrington 87-94; Vice-Prin St Steph Ho Ox from 95. *St Stephen's House, 16 Marston Street, Oxford OX4 1JX* Oxford (01865) 247874

BURNHAM, Cecil Champneys. b 14. AKC39. **d** 39 **p** 40. V Westham *Chich* 66-74; R Harting 74-79; rtd 79; Perm to Offic *Chich* from 82. *25 Sovereign Court, Campbell Road, Bognor Regis, W Sussex PO21 1AH* Bognor Regis (01243) 822119

BURNHAM, Frank Leslie. b 23. Edin Th Coll 52. **d** 55 **p** 56. V Marfleet *York* 62-72; TR 72-74; V Acomb St Steph 74-85; C Fulford 85-88; rtd 88. *Dulverton Hall, St Martin's Square, Scarborough, N Yorkshire YO11 2DB* Scarborough (01723) 373082

BURNINGHAM, Frederick George. b 34. ALCD60. **d** 60 **p** 61. C New Beckenham St Paul *Roch* 60-63; Canada 63-67 and from 89; C Wisley w Pyrford *Guildf* 68-69; P-in-c Sydenham H Trin *S'wark* 69-71; C Broadwater St Mary *Chich* 72-77; R Sotterley, Willingham, Shadingfield, Ellough etc *St E* 77-82; R Ipswich St Clem w H Trin 82-89. *Box 64, 135 McDougal Road, Fort Smith, NWT, Canada, X0E 0P0*

BURNISTON, Aubrey John. b 53. St Jo Coll Dur BA. Cranmer Hall Dur. **d** 83 **p** 84. C Owton Manor *Dur* 83-86; TV Rugby St Andr *Cov* 86-93; V Heaton St Martin *Bradf* from 93. *St Martin's Vicarage, Haworth Road, Bradford, W Yorkshire BD9 6LL* Bradford (01274) 543004

BURNLEY, William Francis Edward. b 06. Lon Univ BD40. Sarum Th Coll 32. **d** 35 **p** 36. Hon CF from 45; V Westwood *Sarum* 68-74; rtd 74. *Sunnyhill, 2A Perry's Lane, Seend, Melksham, Wilts SN12 6QA* Devizes (01380) 828510

BURNLEY, Suffragan Bishop of. See JARRETT, Rt Rev Martyn William

BURNS, Dane. b 51. DipTh. **d** 85 **p** 86. C Enniskillen *Clogh* 85-87; I Augher w Newtownsaville and Eskrahoole 87-92; Dioc Info Officer 91-92; I Camus-juxta-Bann *D & R* from 92. *19 Dunderg Road, Macosquin, Coleraine, Co Londonderry BT51 4PN* Coleraine (01265) 43918

BURNS, Douglas Thomas.d 85 **p** 86. NSM Dub Crumlin *D & G* 85-91; NSM Dub Crumlin w Chapelizod 91; NSM Leighlin w Grange Sylvae, Shankill etc *C & O* from 91; Vice-Pres Nat Bible Soc of Ireland from 93. *St Laserian's Deanery, Old Leighlin, Co Carlow, or 100 Cherryfield Road, Dublin 12, Irish Republic* Carlow (503) 21411 or Dublin (1) 490-5337 Fax Dublin (1) 490-3531

BURNS, Canon Edward Joseph. b 38. Liv Univ BSc58 St Cath Soc Ox BA61 MA64. Wycliffe Hall Ox 58. **d** 61 **p** 62. C Leyland St Andr *Blackb* 61-64; C Burnley St Pet 64-67; V Chorley St Jas 67-75; V Fulwood Ch Ch from 75; RD Preston 79-86; Chapl Sharoe Green Hosp Preston from 81; Hon Can Blackb Cathl *Blackb* from 86; Bp's Adv on Hosp Chapls from 89. *Christ Church Vicarage, 19 Vicarage Close, Fulwood, Preston PR2 8EG* Preston (01772) 719210

BURNS, James Denis. b 43. Lich Th Coll 69. **d** 72 **p** 73. C Gt Wyrley *Lich* 72-75; C Atherton *Man* 75-76; Asst Chapl Sheff Ind Miss *Sheff* 76-79; C-in-c Masborough St Paul w St Jo 76-78; C-in-c Northfield St Mich 76-78; V Rotherham Ferham Park 78-79; V Lanc Ch Ch *Blackb* 79-81; V Lanc Ch Ch w St Jo and St Anne 81-86; V Chorley St Pet from 86. *St Peter's Vicarage, Harpers Lane, Chorley, Lancs PR6 0HT* Chorley (01257) 263423

BURNS, Michael John. b 53. AKC76. Chich Th Coll 76. **d** 77 **p** 78. C Broseley w Benthall *Heref* 77-81; C Stevenage All SS Pin Green *St Alb* 81-84; V Tattenham Corner and Burgh Heath *Guildf* 84-92; Chapl Milton Keynes *Ox* from 92. *2 Symington Court, Shenley Lodge, Milton Keynes MK5 7AN* Milton Keynes (01908) 235265 or 237777

BURNS, Robert Joseph. b 34. Wycliffe Hall Ox 67. **d** 71 **p** 72. C Portswood Ch Ch *Win* 71-73; C Woking St Jo *Guildf* 73-77; C Glas St Mary *Glas* 77; Bp's Dom Chapl 77-78; R Glas Gd Shep and Ascension 78-92; rtd 92. *85/8 Lancefield Quay, Glasgow G3 8HA*

BURNS, Brother Stuart Maitland. b 46. Leeds Univ BA67. Coll of Resurr Mirfield 67. **d** 69 **p** 70. C Wyther Ven Bede *Ripon* 69-73; Asst Chapl Leeds Univ 73-77; Asst Chapl Leeds Poly 73-77; P-in-c Thornthwaite w Thruscross and Darley 77-84; V Leeds Gipton Epiphany 84-89; Prior of Our Lady Burford from 89; Lic to Offic *Ox* from 89. *Burford Priory, Priory Lane, Burford, Oxford OX18 4SQ* Burford (01993) 823605

BURR, Mrs Ann Pamela. b 39. S Dios Minl Tr Scheme 83. **dss** 86 **d** 87 **p** 94. Fareham H Trin *Portsm* 86-87; Hon C from 87; Chapl Portsm Hosps from 92. *3 Bruce Close, Fareham, Hants PO16 7QJ* Fareham (01329) 281375

BURR, Brian Gilbert. b 23. AKC49. St Boniface Warminster 50. **d** 50 **p** 51. V Churston Ferrers w Goodrington *Ex* 63-76; RD Ipplepen 69-77; V Brixham 76-77; V Brixham w Churston Ferrers 77; R Cen Torquay 77-81; TR Torre 81-87; rtd 87; Perm to Offic *Ex* 89-91; Chapl Beauchamp Community from 91. *The Chaplain's House, Beauchamp Community, The Quadrangle, Newland, Malvern, Worcs WR13 5AX* Malvern (01684) 893243

BURR, Raymond Leslie. b 43. NE Ord Course 82 Edin Th Coll 84. **d** 85 **p** 86. C Hartlepool St Paul *Dur* 85-87; C Sherburn w Pittington 87-89; R Lyons from 89. *The Rectory, High Street, Easington Lane, Houghton le Spring, Tyne & Wear DH5 0JN* 0191-526 5505

BURRELL, David Philip. b 56. Southn Univ BTh90. Sarum & Wells Th Coll 85. **d** 88 **p** 89. C Ixworth and Bardwell *St E* 88-91; P-in-c Haughley w Wetherden from 91. *The Vicarage, Haughley, Stowmarket, Suffolk IP14 3NS* Stowmarket (01449) 673467

BURRELL, Godfrey John. b 49. Reading Univ BSc70 Qu Coll Ox CertEd71. Wycliffe Hall Ox 84. **d** 86 **p** 87. C Didcot All SS *Ox* 86-89; S Africa from 90. *St Alban's College, Private Bag 1, Alkantrant, Pretoria, 0005 South Africa* Pretoria (12) 476147 or 475451

BURRELL, Martin John. b 51. ARCM71. Trin Coll Bris BA95. **d** 95. C Cant St Mary Bredin *Cant* from 95. *38 Nunnery Road, Canterbury, Kent CT1 3LS* Canterbury (01227) 455723

BURRELL, Canon Maurice Claude. b 30. Bris Univ BA54 MA63 Lanc Univ PhD78. Tyndale Hall Bris. **d** 55 **p** 56. C Wandsworth St Steph *S'wark* 55-57; C Whitehall Park St Andr Hornsey Lane *Lon* 57-59; R Kirby Cane Nor 59-63; R Ellingham 61-63; Chapl K Sch Gutersloh, W Germany 63-67; R Widford *Chelmsf* 67-71; Chapl and Lect St Mary's Coll Cheltenham 71-75; Dir of Educn Nor 75-86; Hon Can Nor Cathl from 77; Dioc Dir of Tr from 87. *37 Ireton Close, Thorpe St Andrew, Norwich NR7 0TW* Norwich (01603) 702510 or 611196 Fax 766476

BURRIDGE, Richard Alan. b 55. Univ Coll Ox BA77 MA81 Nottm Univ CertEd78 DipTh83 PhD89. St Jo Coll Nottm 82. **d** 85 **p** 86. C Bromley SS Pet and Paul *Roch* 85-87; Chapl Ex Univ *Ex* 87-94; Dean K Coll Lon from 94. *King's College, Strand, London WC2R 2LS* 0171-837 2333

BURRIDGE-BUTLER, Paul David. b 67. Sheff Univ BA88. Linc Th Coll CMM92. **d** 92 **p** 93. C Handsworth Woodhouse *Sheff* from 92. *19 Hail Mary Drive, Sheffield S13 9XW* Sheffield (0114) 269 4964

✠**BURROUGH, Rt Rev John Paul.** b 16. MBE46. St Edm Hall Ox BA37 DipTh38 MA45. Ely Th Coll 45. **d** 46 **p** 47 **c** 68. C Aldershot St Mich *Guildf* 46-51; Korea 51-59; Chapl to Overseas Peoples *Birm* 59-67; Hon Can Birm Cathl 65-67; Can Res 67-68; Bp Mashonaland 68-81; R Empingham *Pet* 81-85; Asst Bp Pet 81-85; RD Rutland 82-85; rtd 85; Perm to Offic *Ox* from 85. *6 Mill Green Close, Bampton, Oxon OX8 2HF* Bampton Castle (01993) 850952

BURROUGHS, Edward Graham. b 36. K Coll Lon BD AKC. **d** 60 **p** 61. C Walton St Mary *Liv* 60-63; S Rhodesia 63-65; Rhodesia 65-80; Zimbabwe from 80. *Box 8045, Belmont, Bulawayo, Zimbabwe* Bulawayo (9) 78711

BURROW, Miss Alison Sarah. b 59. Homerton Coll Cam BEd82. Westcott Ho Cam 84. **d** 87. Par Dn Hebden Bridge *Wakef* 87-88; Par Dn Prestwood and Gt Hampden *Ox* 88-90; Par Dn Olney w Emberton 90-92; rtd 92. *56 Christian Court, Willen, Milton Keynes MK15 9HY*

BURROW, Ronald. b 31. Univ Coll Dur BA55. St Steph Ho Ox 83. **d** 85 **p** 86. C Dawlish *Ex* 85-87; TV Ottery St Mary, Alfington, W Hill, Tipton etc 87-91; P-in-c Pyworthy, Pancrasweek and Bridgerule from 91. *The Rectory, Pyworthy, Holsworthy, Devon EX22 6SU* Holsworthy (01409) 254062

BURROWES, Thomas Cecil. b 13. TCD BA36 MA43. TCD Div Sch Div Test36. **d** 37 **p** 38. I Killinchy *D & D* 50-78; RD Killinchy 71-78; rtd 78. *1 Kilmood Church Road, Kilmood, Killinchy, Newtownards, Co Down BT23 6SA* Killinchy (01238) 541942

BURROWS, Canon Brian Albert. b 34. Lon Univ DipTh59. St Aid Birkenhead. **d** 59 **p** 60. C Sutton St Geo *Ches* 59-62; Canada 62-69 and from 74; V Stratton St Margaret *Bris* 70-74; Hon Can Frobisher Bay 82-88. *705 Main Street East, Hamilton, Ontario, Canada, L8M 1K8*

BURROWS, Prof Clifford Robert. b 37. MIMechE68 Univ of Wales BSc62 Lon Univ PhD69. Chich Th Coll 75. **d** 76 **p** 77. NSM Brighton St Pet *Chich* 76-78; NSM Brighton St Pet w Chpl Royal 78-80; NSM Brighton St Pet w Chpl Royal and St Jo 80-82; Perm to Offic *Glas* 82-85 and 86-89; NSM Clarkston 85-86; NSM Bath Ch Ch Prop Chpl *B & W* from 90. *Stonecroft, Entry Hill Drive, Bath BA2 5NL* Bath (01225) 334743

BURROWS, David. b 62. Leeds Univ BA85. Linc Th Coll 86. **d** 88 **p** 89. C Kippax w Allerton Bywater *Ripon* 88-91; C Manston 91-95; V Halifax St Anne Southowram *Wakef* from 95. *St Anne's Vicarage, Church Lane, Southowram, Halifax, W Yorkshire HX3 9TD* Halifax (01422) 365229

BURROWS, David MacPherson. b 43. N Ord Course. **d** 82 **p** 83. NSM Newburgh *Liv* 82-93; NSM Ch Ch Newburgh w St Jas Westhead from 93. *34 Woodrow Drive, Newburgh, Wigan, Lancs WN8 7LB* Parbold (01257) 462948

BURROWS, Canon George Henry Jerram. b 10. TCD BA31 MA37. TCD Div Sch 31. **d** 33 **p** 38. P-in-c Dub St Luke *D & G* 71-78; rtd 78; CV Ch Ch Cathl Dub *D & G* 81-90. *22 Longwood Avenue, Dublin 8, Irish Republic* Dublin (1) 454-3629

BURROWS, Graham Charles. b 47. Leeds Univ CertEd69 Open Univ BA81. N Ord Course 87. **d** 90 **p** 91. C Chorlton-cum-Hardy St Clem *Man* 90-93; TV Horwich 93; TV Horwich and Rivington 93-94. *101 Bramhall Avenue, Bolton BL2 4EX6* Bolton (01204) 525188

BURROWS, Miss Jean. b 54. CertEd75. Trin Coll Bris 89. **d** 91 **p** 94. C Allesley *Cov* from 91. *42 Lincroft Crescent, Coventry CV5 8GU* Coventry (01203) 679015

BURROWS, John Edward. b 36. Leeds Univ BA60 PGCE63. Coll of Resurr Mirfield. **d** 63 **p** 65. C Much Hadham *St Alb* 63-65; Hon C Haggerston St Mary w St Chad *Lon* 65-73; P-in-c Finsbury St Clem w St Barn and St Matt 73-76; Chapl Woodbridge Sch Suffolk 76-83; Lic to Offic *St E* 76-83; V Ipswich St Bart from 83. *St Bartholomew's Vicarage, Newton Road, Ipswich IP3 8HQ* Ipswich (01473) 727441

BURROWS, Joseph Atkinson. b 32. St Aid Birkenhead 57. **d** 61 **p** 62. C Hoole *Ches* 61-67; Jamaica 67-68; C Ayr *Glas* 68-74; R Prestwick 74-78; Australia from 78. *60 Memorial Avenue, St Ives, NSW, Australia 2075* Sydney (2) 488-9393

BURROWS, Leonard Ernest. b 14. Roch Th Coll. **d** 62 **p** 63. V Thurmaston *Leic* 70-79; V Leic St Eliz Nether Hall 79-81; rtd 81; Lic to Offic *Ely* from 81. *44 Humberley Close, Eynesbury, St Neots, Huntingdon, Cambs PE19 2SE* Huntingdon (01480) 213524

BURROWS, Michael Andrew James. b 61. TCD BA82 MA85 MLitt86 DipTh87. **d** 87 **p** 88. C Douglas Union w Frankfield *C, C & R* 87-91; Dean of Residence TCD 91-94; Lic to Offic *D & G* 91-94; Min Can St Patr Cathl Dub from 91; I Bandon Union *C, C & R* from 94. *The Rectory, Bandon, Co Cork, Irish Republic* Bandon (23) 41259 Fax as telephone

BURROWS, Paul Anthony. b 55. Nottm Univ BA77. Gen Th Sem (NY) STM88 St Steph Ho Ox 77. **d** 79 **p** 80. C Camberwell St Giles *S'wark* 79-81; C St Helier 81-83; C Fareham SS Pet and Paul *Portsm* 83-85; USA from 85. *Address temp unknown*

BURROWS, Peter. b 55. BTh. Sarum & Wells Th Coll 80. **d** 83 **p** 84. C Baildon *Bradf* 83-87; R Broughton Astley *Leic* from 87; RD Guthlaxton I (Blaby) from 94. *St Mary's Rectory, St Mary's Close, Broughton Astley, Leicester LE9 6PF* Sutton Elms (01455) 282261

BURROWS, Philip Geoffrey. b 59. Birm Univ BSc80. Oak Hill Th Coll DipHE92. **d** 92 **p** 93. C Poynton *Ches* from 92. *11 Deva Close, Poynton, Stockport, Cheshire SK12 1HH* Poynton (01625) 871958

BURROWS, Samuel Reginald (Sam). b 30. AKC57. **d** 58 **p** 59. C-in-c Leam Lane CD *Dur* 67-72; C-in-c Bishopwearmouth St Mary V w St Pet CD 72-77; R Bewcastle and Stapleton *Carl* 77-82; R Harrington 82-90; P-in-c Millom 90; V 90-95; rtd 95. *30 Springfield Close, Lincoln LN1 3ET* Lincoln (01522) 542085

✠**BURROWS, Rt Rev Simon Hedley.** b 28. K Coll Cam BA52 MA56. Westcott Ho Cam 52. **d** 54 **p** 55 **c** 74. C St Jo Wood *Lon* 54-57; Chapl Jes Coll Cam 57-60; V Wyken *Cov* 60-67; V Fareham H Trin *Portsm* 67-71; TR 71-74; Suff Bp Buckm *Ox* 74-87; Area Bp Buckm 87-94; rtd 94. *8 Quarry Road, Winchester, Hants SO23 0JF* Winchester (01962) 853332

BURSELL, Chan Rupert David Hingston. b 42. QC. Ex Univ LLB63 St Edm Hall Ox BA67 MA72 DPhil72. St Steph Ho Ox 67. **d** 68 **p** 69. NSM St Marylebone w H Trin *Lon* 68-69; NSM Almondsbury *Bris* 69-71; NSM Bedminster St Fran 71-75; NSM Bedminster 75-82; NSM Bris Ch Ch w St Ewen and All SS 83-88; NSM City of Bris 83-88; Lic to Offic from 88; Lic to Offic *B & W* 72-92; Chan from 92; NSM Cheddar from 93. *Brookside, 74 Church Road, Winscombe, Avon BS25 1BP*

BURSLEM, Christopher David Jeremy Grant. b 35. AKC85. **d** 59 **p** 60. C Bocking St Mary *Chelmsf* 59-63; C Glouc All SS *Glouc* 64-67; R Amberley 67-87; P-in-c Withington and Compton Abdale w Haselton from 87. *The Rectory, Withington, Cheltenham, Glos GL54 4BG* Cheltenham (01242) 890242

BURSON-THOMAS, Michael Edwin. b 52. Sarum & Wells Th Coll 84. **d** 86 **p** 87. C Bitterne Park *Win* 86-89; V Lockerley and E Dean w E and W Tytherley from 89. *The Vicarage, The Street, Lockerley, Romsey, Hants SO51 0JF* Lockerley (01794) 340635

BURSTON, Richard John. b 46. ARICS70 MRTPI73. S Dios Minl Tr Scheme 89. **d** 93 **p** 94. Hon C Stratton St Margaret w S Marston etc *Bris* from 93. *17 Crawley Avenue, Swindon SN3 4LB* Swindon (01793) 822403

BURSTON, Robert Benjamin Stuart. b 45. St Chad's Coll Dur BA68 DipTh70. **d** 70 **p** 71. C Whorlton *Newc* 70-77; V Alwinton w Holystone and Alnham 77-83; TR Glendale Gp from 83. *The Rectory, 5 Fenton Drive, Wooler, Northd NE71 6DT* Wooler (01668) 281551

BURT, Leslie Reginald. b 22. ACIS49. St Aug Coll Cant 65. **d** 66 **p** 67. C Petersfield w Sheet *Portsm* 66-70; Perm to Offic from 82. *44B Victoria Road South, Southsea, Hants PO5 2BT* Portsmouth (01705) 730989

BURT, Noel Bryce. b 21. Clare Coll Cam BA49 MA53. Cuddesdon Coll 49. **d** 51 **p** 52. R Invergowrie *Bre* 67-76; R Glencarse 71-76; V Denton and Ingleton *Dur* 76-88; rtd 88. *49 Balmer Hill, Gainford, Darlington, Co Durham DL2 3EL* Darlington (01325) 730075

BURT, Paul Andrew. b 52. Leeds Univ BA74. Ridley Hall Cam 82. **d** 84 **p** 85. C Edin St Thos *Edin* 84-88; CMS 88-90; Bahrain 88-90; R Melrose *Edin* from 91. *The Rectory, 20 High Cross Avenue, Melrose, Roxburghshire TD6 9SU* Melrose (01896) 822626

BURT, Robert. b 08. Lich Th Coll 31. **d** 34 **p** 35. V Darlington St Matt *Dur* 61-77; rtd 77. *Dulverton Hall, St Martin's Square, Scarborough YO11 2DB* Scarborough (01723) 373082

BURT, Roger Malcolm. b 45. St Jo Coll Auckland LTh74 SSC. **d** 73 **p** 74. New Zealand 73-80; P-in-c Colton *Nor* 80; P-in-c Easton 80; V Easton w Colton and Marlingford 80-88; CF from 88. *c/o MOD (Army), Bagshot Park, Bagshot, Surrey GU19 5PL* Bagshot (01276) 471717 Fax 412834

BURTON, Andrew John. b 52. Kath Coll Liv BA84 CertDiv84. Cranmer Hall Dur 86. **d** 88 **p** 89. C Harlescott *Lich* 88-91; C Ches H Trin *Ches* 91-94; P-in-c Congleton St Jas from 94. *St James's Vicarage, 116 Holmes Chapel Road, Congleton, Cheshire CW12 4NX* Congleton (01260) 273722

BURTON, Antony William James. b 29. Ch Coll Cam BA52 MA56. Cuddesdon Coll 52. **d** 54 **p** 55. V Winterton *Linc* 62-82; V Roxby w Risby 70-82; RD Manlake 76-82; V Nettleham 82-94; rtd 94. *28 Eastfield Road, Messingham, Scunthorpe, S Humberside DN17 3PG* Scunthorpe (01724) 763916

BURTON, Cecil John. b 17. Tyndale Hall Bris 39. **d** 43 **p** 44. V Muswell Hill St Matt *Lon* 63-70; Perm to Offic *S'wark* from 70; Perm to Offic *Ches* 71-78; rtd 82. *6 Lawman Court, 262 Kew Road, Richmond, Surrey TW9 3EF* 0181-940 1578

BURTON, Christopher Paul (Chris). b 38. FCA75. Clifton Th Coll 67. **d** 69 **p** 70. C Wandsworth All SS *S'wark* 69-72; C York St Paul *York* 72-75; V Castle Vale *Birm* 75-82; R Gt Parndon *Chelmsf* from 82. *Great Parndon Rectory, Perry Road, Harlow, Essex CM18 7NP* Harlow (01279) 432626

BURTON, Daniel John Ashworth. b 63. Regent's Park Coll Ox BA88 MA93 Heythrop Coll Lon MTh93. St Mich Coll Llan 93. **d** 94 **p** 95. C Mountain Ash *Llan* from 94. *The Church House, Tancoch Terrace, Cefn Pennar, Mountain Ash, M Glam CF45 4DY* Mountain Ash (01443) 479470

BURTON, David Alan. b 53. St Jo Coll Dur BA. Westcott Ho Cam 81. **d** 84 **p** 85. C Bedf St Andr *St Alb* 84-87; C Leighton Buzzard w Eggington, Hockliffe etc 87-91; V Kingsbury Episcopi w E Lambrook *B & W* 91-94; V Kingsbury Episcopi w E Lambrook, Hambridge etc from 94. *The Vicarage, Folly Road, Kingsbury Episcopi, Martock, Somerset TA12 6BH* Martock (01935) 824605

BURTON, Desmond Jack. b 49. Sarum & Wells Th Coll 70. **d** 73 **p** 74. C Lakenham St Jo *Nor* 73-77; C Gt Yarmouth 77-80; R Tidworth *Sarum* 80-83; Chapl HM Pris Pentonville 83-84; Chapl HM Pris Standford Hill 84-88; Chapl HM Pris Swaleside 88-93; Chapl HM Pris Roch from 93. *HM Prison, 1 Fort Road, Rochester, Kent ME1 3QS* Medway (01634) 830300 Fax 826712

BURTON, Edward Arthur. b 15. Tyndale Hall Bris 39. **d** 42 **p** 43. V Beckford w Ashton under Hill *Glouc* 63-78; rtd 78; Perm to Offic *Chich* from 83. *B5 Hatfield Court, Salisbury Road, Hove, E Sussex BN3 3AA* Brighton (01273) 727560

BURTON, Edward Arthur. b 40. AKC63. **d** 64 **p** 65. C Upper Teddington SS Pet and Paul *Lon* 64-69; C-in-c Hammersmith SS Mich and Geo White City Estate CD 69-71; C Addlestone *Guildf* 71-74; V Harlesden All So *Lon* 75-89; V Notting Dale St Clem w St Mark and St Jas 89-94. *38 Great College Street, Brighton, E Sussex BN2 1HL* Brighton (01273) 602598

BURTON, Frank Victor. b 10. Linc Th Coll 76. **d** 76 **p** 77. Hon C Folkingham w Laughton *Linc* 76-77; Hon C S Lafford 77-79; Hon C Helpringham 79; Hon C New Sleaford 79-80; Perm to Offic from 80. *27 Gardenfield, Skellingthorpe, Lincoln LN6 5SP* Lincoln (01522) 688697

BURTON, Geoffrey Robert William. b 20. Ridley Hall Cam. **d** 63 **p** 64. R Scarning w Wendling *Nor* 67-71; V Bacton w Edingthorpe 71-80; P-in-c Witton w Ridlington 75-80; V Bacton w Edingthorpe w Witton and Ridlington 80-87; rtd 87; Perm to Offic *Nor* from 87; Hon C Duns *Edin* from 87. *Harelaw Brae, Grantshouse, Duns, Berwickshire TD11 3RP*

BURTON, Graham John. b 45. Bris Univ BA69. Tyndale Hall Bris 69. **d** 71 **p** 72. C Leic St Chris *Leic* 71-75; C Southall Green St Jo *Lon* 75-79; CMS 80-92; Pakistan 80-92; P-in-c Basford w Hyson Green *S'well* from 92. *18 Russell Road, Nottingham NG7 6HB* Nottingham (0115) 978 7473

BURTON, Harold Alban. b 10. Worc Ord Coll. **d** 53 **p** 54. C Worthing St Paul *Chich* 69-74; rtd 74; Hon C Leek and Meerbrook *Lich* 83-90. *Fosbrooke House, 8 Clifton Drive, Lytham, Lytham St Annes, Lancs FY8 5RE* Lytham (01253) 731125

BURTON, Hugh Anthony. b 56. Edin Univ BD79. Cranmer Hall Dur 81. **d** 83 **p** 84. C Coalville and Bardon Hill *Leic* 83-87; P-in-c Packington w Normanton-le-Heath 87-92; V from 92. *The Vicarage, Mill Street, Packington, Ashby-de-la-Zouch, Leics LE6 5WL* Ashby-de-la-Zouch (01530) 412215

BURTON, John Richard. b 22. Em Coll Cam BA47 MA51. Wycliffe Hall Ox 49. **d** 50 **p** 51. V Ellacombe *Ex* 59-74; TV Cen Torquay 74-76; Warden Maillard Ho of Healing 76-87; Hon C Torre 76-82; rtd 87; Perm to Offic *Ex* 87-94. *6 Princess Cottages, Coffinswell, Newton Abbot, Devon TQ12 4SR* Kingskerswell (01803) 873758

BURTON, Leslie Samuel Bertram. b 23. **d** 91 **p** 92. NSM St Cleer *Truro* 91-93; Perm to Offic from 93. *41 Park View, Liskeard, Cornwall PL14 3EF* Liskeard (01579) 344891

BURTON, Michael John. b 55. Leeds Univ BSc76 Leeds Poly BSc80. St Jo Coll Nottm LTh88. **d** 88 **p** 89. C Charles w St Matthias Plymouth *Ex* 88-92; V Paignton St Paul Preston from 92. *St Paul's Vicarage, Locarno Avenue, Preston, Paignton, Devon TQ3 2DH* Paignton (01803) 522872

BURTON, Nicholas John. b 52. St Steph Ho Ox 77. **d** 80 **p** 81. C Leic St Matt and St Geo *Leic* 80-82; C Leic Resurr 82-83; TV 83-88; C Narborough and Huncote 88-90; R from 90. *All Saints' Rectory, 15 Church View, Narborough, Leicester LE9 5GY* Leicester (0116) 275 0388

103

BURTON, Norman George. b 30. N Ord Course. **d** 83 **p** 84. C Rothwell w Lofthouse *Ripon* 83-86; C Rothwell 86-87; V Lofthouse from 87. *The Vicarage, 8 Church Farm Close, Lofthouse, Wakefield, W Yorkshire WF3 3SA* Wakefield (01924) 823286

BURTON, Richard Peter. b 56. Nottm Univ BA80. Cranmer Hall Dur 80. **d** 82 **p** 83. C Linthorpe *York* 82-85; R Bishop Burton w Walkington 85-91; V Tadcaster w Newton Kyme from 91. *The Vicarage, 78 Station Road, Tadcaster, N Yorkshire LS24 9JR* Tadcaster (01937) 833394

BURTON EVANS, David. *See* EVANS, David Burton

BURTON-JONES, Simon David. b 62. Em Coll Cam BA84 MA88 Nottm Univ BTh92 MA93. St Jo Coll Nottm 90. **d** 93 **p** 94. C Darwen St Pet w Hoddlesden *Blackb* from 93. *2 Prince Lee Meadows, Darwen, Lancs BB3 2BQ* Darwen (01254) 703796

BURTT, Andrew Keith. b 50. Massey Univ (NZ) BA72 MA74 DipEd76. St Jo Coll (NZ) LTh82. **d** 81 **p** 82. New Zealand 81-83; CF 84-92; Sen Chapl Brighton Coll from 93. *Brighton College, Eastern Road, Brighton BN2 2AL, or 8 Walpole Road, Brighton BN2 2EA* Brighton (01273) 606524

BURTWELL, Stanley Peter. b 32. Leeds Univ BA55. Coll of Resurr Mirfield 55. **d** 57 **p** 58. C Leeds St Hilda *Ripon* 57-61; S Africa 61-72; P-in-c Gt Hanwood *Heref* 72-78; R 78-83; RD Pontesbury 80-83; V Upper Norwood St Jo *Cant* 83-84; V Upper Norwood St Jo *S'wark* 85-90; RD Croydon N 85-90; TR Bourne Valley *Sarum* from 90. *The Rectory, Newton Toney Road, Allington, Salisbury SP4 0BZ* Idmiston (01980) 610663

BURY, Herbert John Malcolm. b 28. Linc Coll Ox BA52 MA56. Roch Th Coll 68. **d** 69 **p** 70. C Bexleyheath Ch Ch *Roch* 69-72; V Ryarsh w Birling 72-83; P-in-c Addington w Trottiscliffe 76-83; R Knockholt w Halstead 83-93; rtd 93. *Star Cottage, High Street, Burwash, Etchingham, E Sussex TN19 7HA* Burwash (01435) 882326

BURY, Canon Nicholas Ayles Stillingfleet (Nick). b 43. Qu Coll Cam BA65 MA69 Ch Ch Ox MA71. Cuddesdon Coll. **d** 68 **p** 69. C Liv Our Lady and St Nic *Liv* 68-71; Chapl Ch Ch *Ox* 71-75; V Stevenage St Mary Shephall *St Alb* 75-84; V St Peter-in-Thanet *Cant* from 84; RD Thanet from 93; Hon Can Cant Cathl from 94. *The Vicarage, 14 Vicarage Street, St Peters, Broadstairs, Kent CT10 2SG* Thanet (01843) 869169 or 866061

BUSBY, Ian Frederick Newman. b 32. Roch Th Coll 61. **d** 64 **p** 65. C Stevenage St Geo *St Alb* 67-71; V Stevenage St Mary Shephall 71-75; V Kildwick *Bradf* 75-92; rtd 93. *65 Main Street, Farnhill, Keighley, W Yorkshire BD20 9BJ* Cross Hills (01535) 633001

BUSBY, Jack Wright. b 12. Leeds Univ BA35. Coll of Resurr Mirfield 35. **d** 37 **p** 38. R Barkestone cum Plungar and Redmile *Leic* 70-77; rtd 77. *43 Chestnut Avenue, Waltham, Grimsby, S Humberside DN37 0DF* Grimsby (01472) 823208

BUSBY, John. b 38. CEng St Cath Coll Cam MA60. Local Minl Tr Course. **d** 93 **p** 94. NSM Worplesdon *Guildf* from 93. *Iona, Fox Corner, Worplesdon, Guildford, Surrey GU3 3PP* Worplesdon (01483) 234562

BUSH, Alfred Edward Leonard. b 09. ALCD39. **d** 39 **p** 40. V Oakwood St Thos *Lon* 58-75; rtd 75; Perm to Offic *Chich* 75-78; Perm to Offic *St E* 78-86; Perm to Offic *Ox* from 86. *11 Pitford Road, Woodley, Reading RG5 4QF* Reading (01734) 698115

BUSH, Mrs Ann Kathleen. b 47. MATCA65. Marlow Past Foundn DCouns90 Ox Min Course 90. **d** 93 **p** 94. NSM Warfield *Ox* from 93. *Trinity House, 9 Sylverns Court, Bracknell, Berks RG12 6SL* Ascot (01344) 411105

BUSH, David. b 25. FRIBA47 Liv Univ BArch47. S'wark Ord Course 73. **d** 77 **p** 77. C Douglas St Geo and St Barn *S & M* 77-80; Chapl Ballamona Hosp and Cronk Grianagh 80-86; V Marown 80-87; R The Rissingtons *Glouc* 87-92; rtd 92. *The Retreat, Victoria Street, Bourton-on-the-Water, Cheltenham, Glos GL54 2BX* Cotswold (01451) 810882

BUSH, George Raymond. b 57. St Jo Coll Cam BA81 MA84. Ripon Coll Cuddesdon BA88 MA88. **d** 85 **p** 86. C Leeds St Aid *Ripon* 85-89; Chapl St Jo Coll Cam 89-94; V Hoxton St Anne w St Columba *Lon* from 94. *St Anne's Vicarage, 37 Hemsworth Street, London N1 5LF* 0171-729 1243

BUSH, Mrs Glenda. b 41. **d** 95. NSM Bolton St Phil *Man* from 95. *46 Mary Street West, Horwich, Bolton BL6 7JU* Bolton (01204) 691539

BUSH, Roger Charles. b 56. K Coll Lon BA78 Leeds Univ BA85. Coll of Resurr Mirfield 83. **d** 86 **p** 87. C Newbold and Dunston *Derby* 86-90; TV Leic Resurr *Leic* 90-94; TR Redruth w Lanner and Treleigh *Truro* from 94. *The Rectory, 53 Clinton Road, Redruth, Cornwall TR15 2LP* Redruth (01209) 215258

BUSHAU, Reginald Francis. b 49. St Steph Ho Ox BA73. **d** 74 **p** 75. C Deptford St Paul *S'wark* 74-77; C Willesden St Andr *Lon* 77; C Gladstone Park St Fran 77-82; P-in-c Brondesbury

St Anne w Kilburn H Trin 83-88; V Paddington St Mary Magd from 88; AD Westmr Paddington from 92. *St Mary Magdalene Vicarage, Rowington Close, London W2 5TF* 0171-289 1818

BUSHELL, Roy. b 32. NW Ord Course 75. **d** 79 **p** 80. NSM Croft w Southworth *Liv* 79-87; C Netherton 87-89; R Newton in Makerfield Em from 89. *The Rectory, Wargrave Road, Newton-le-Willows, Merseyside WA12 8RR* Newton-le-Willows (01925) 224920

BUSHELL, Stephen Lionel. b 60. K Coll Lon BA84. Ripon Coll Cuddesdon 92. **d** 94 **p** 95. C Exhall *Cov* from 94. *222 Coventry Road, Exhall, Coventry CV7 9BH* Coventry (01203) 313975

BUSK, David Westly. b 60. Magd Coll Cam BA. Cranmer Hall Dur. **d** 89 **p** 90. C Old Swinford Stourbridge *Worc* 89-93; USPG from 93. *8 Bedcote Place, Stourbridge, W Midlands DY8 1LD* Stourbridge (01384) 390367

BUSK, Horace. b 34. Clifton Th Coll 56. **d** 60 **p** 61. C Burton All SS *Lich* 60-63; Paraguay 63-66; C Silverhill St Matt *Chich* 66-67; Lic to Offic *Sarum* 67-69; C W Kilburn St Luke w St Simon and St Jude *Lon* 69-74; TV Ashwellthorpe w Wreningham *Nor* 74-81; TV Wreningham 81; P-in-c Meysey Hampton w Marston Meysey and Castle Eaton *Glouc* 81-82; R from 82. *The Rectory, Church Street, Meysey Hampton, Cirencester, Glos GL7 5JX* Poulton (01285) 851249

BUSS, Gerald Vere Austen. b 36. CCC Cam PhD87. St Steph Ho Ox 59. **d** 63 **p** 64. C Petersham *S'wark* 63-66; C Brompton H Trin *Lon* 66-69; Asst Chapl Hurstpierpoint Coll Hassocks 70-73; Chapl 74-90; Ho Master from 90. *Hurstpierpoint College, Hassocks, W Sussex BN6 9JS* Hurstpierpoint (01273) 833636

BUSS, Philip Hodnett. b 37. Ch Coll Cam BA59 MA63. Tyndale Hall Bris 61. **d** 63 **p** 64. Tutor Lon Coll of Div 62-66; Chapl 66-69; Hon C Northwood Em *Lon* 63-70; V Handsworth Woodhouse *Sheff* 70-74; V Fulham Ch Ch *Lon* 74-82; V Woking St Pet *Guildf* 82-88; Hon C Ham St Rich *S'wark* from 94. *80 Woodville Road, Ham, Richmond, Surrey TW10 7QN* 0181-940 3703

BUSSELL, Ronald William. b 34. CA Tr Coll 57 St Deiniol's Hawarden 81. **d** 83 **p** 84. C Claughton cum Grange *Ches* 83-85; P-in-c Preston St Oswald *Blackb* 85-87; V Fleetwood St Nic 87-93; Dioc Chapl MU from 91; R Tarleton from 93. *The Rectory, Blackgate Lane, Tarleton, Preston PR4 6UT* Hesketh Bank (01772) 812614

BUSSEY, Norman. b 22. Clifton Th Coll 63. **d** 65 **p** 66. V Bradley *Wakef* 69-88; rtd 88. *43 Crispin Road, Winchcombe, Cheltenham, Glos GL54 5JX* Cheltenham (01242) 602754

BUSTARD, Guy Nicholas. b 51. K Coll Lon BD77 AKC77. St Steph Ho Ox 77. **d** 78 **p** 79. C Hythe *Cant* 78-81; Chapl RN 81-85; V Haddenham *Ely* 85-89; V Wilburton 85-89; Chapl Qu Eliz Hosp Welwyn Garden City from 89. *The Chaplain's Office, Queen Elizabeth II Hospital, Welwyn Garden City, Herts AL7 4HQ* Welwyn Garden (01707) 328111

BUSTIN, Canon Peter Ernest. b 32. Qu Coll Cam BA56 MA60. Tyndale Hall Bris 56. **d** 57 **p** 58. C Welling *Roch* 57-60; C Farnborough *Guildf* 60-62; V Hornsey Rise St Mary *Lon* 62-70; R Barnwell *Pet* 70-78; RD Oundle 76-84; P-in-c Luddington w Hemington and Thurning 77-78; R Barnwell w Thurning and Luddington 78-84; V Southwold *St E* from 84; RD Halesworth from 90; Hon Can St E Cathl from 91. *The Vicarage, Gardner Road, Southwold, Suffolk IP18 6HJ* Southwold (01502) 722397

BUSTIN, Peter Laurence. b 54. St Steph Ho Ox. **d** 83 **p** 84. C Northolt St Mary *Lon* 83-86; C Pimlico St Pet w Westmr Ch Ch 86-88; C Heston 88-91; P-in-c Twickenham All SS from 91. *All Saints' Vicarage, 18 Belmont Road, Twickenham TW2 2DA* 0181-894 3580

BUTCHER, Andrew John. b 43. Trin Coll Cam BA66 MA69. Cuddesdon Coll 66. **d** 68 **p** 69. C Sheff St Mark Broomhall *Sheff* 68-70; P-in-c Louth H Trin *Linc* 70-72; Chapl RAF 72-87; Lic to Offic *Ox* 85-87; TR Cove St Jo *Guildf* 87-91; V Egham Hythe from 91. *St Paul's Vicarage, 214 Wendover Road, Staines, Middx TW18 3DF* Staines (01784) 453625

BUTCHER, Canon Douglas Claude. b 08. Ch Coll Cam BA29 MA44. Oak Hill Th Coll 50. **d** 51 **p** 52. Egypt 60-72; C Swanage *Sarum* 72-78; rtd 78. *7 Brookside, Shreen Way, Gillingham, Dorset SP8 4HR* Gillingham (01747) 823865

BUTCHER, Edwin William. b 39. Portsm Dioc Tr Course 91. **d** 92. NSM Ryde All SS *Portsm* from 92. *23 Quarry Road, Ryde, Isle of Wight PO33 2TX* Isle of Wight (01983) 616889

BUTCHER, Francis Walter Lowndes. b 17. Bps' Coll Cheshunt 49. **d** 52 **p** 53. V Malden St Jas *S'wark* 63-80; rtd 82; Perm to Offic *S'wark* from 82; Perm to Offic *Guildf* from 86. *12 Glenavon Close, Claygate, Esher, Surrey KT10 0HP* Esher (01372) 464597

BUTCHER, Dr Hubert Maxwell. b 24. Ch Coll Cam BA48 MA53. Trin Coll Toronto BD68 San Francisco Th Sem DMin78 Wycliffe Hall Ox 49. **d** 51 **p** 52. P-in-c Bradf St Jo

Bradf 58-62; Canada from 63; rtd 88. *Box 129, Sorrento, British Columbia, Canada, V0E 2 W0* Sorrento (604) 675 2783

BUTCHER, Ivan. b 50. Oak Hill Th Coll DipHE92. **d** 92 **p** 93. C Gtr Corsham *Bris* from 92. *76 Lypiatt Road, Corsham, Wilts SN13 9JB* Corsham (01249) 712619

BUTCHER, Philip Warren. b 46. Trin Coll Cam BA68 MA70. Cuddesdon Coll 68. **d** 70 **p** 71. C Bris St Mary Redcliffe w Temple etc *Bris* 70-73; Hon C W Wickham St Fran *Cant* 73-78; Chapl Abingdon Sch 78-85; Chapl K Edw VI Sch Nor from 85. *17 Welsford Road, Eaton Rise, Norwich NR4 6QA* Norwich (01603) 664042

BUTCHER, Richard Peter. b 50. St Chad's Coll Dur BA71. Chich Th Coll 73. **d** 74 **p** 75. C Yeovil St Mich *B & W* 74-77; Chapl Wellingborough Sch 77-83; R Gt w Lt Billing *Pet* 83-88; Chapl Bp Stopford Sch Kettering 88-90; Perm to Offic *Pet* from 90. *55 Field Street, Kettering, Northants NN16 8LN*

BUTCHERS, Mark Andrew. b 59. Trin Coll Cam BA81 Southn Univ BTh87 K Coll Lon MTh90. Chich Th Coll 84. **d** 87 **p** 88. C Chelsea St Luke *Lon* 87; C Chelsea St Luke and Ch Ch 87-90; C Mitcham SS Pet and Paul *S'wark* 90-93; R N Tawton, Bondleigh, Sampford Courtenay etc *Ex* from 93. *The Rectory, Essington, North Tawton, Devon EX20 2EX* North Tawton (01837) 82645

BUTLAND, Cameron James. b 58. BA. Ripon Coll Cuddesdon 81. **d** 84 **p** 85. C Tettenhall Regis *Lich* 84-88; V Bodicote *Ox* from 88. *The Vicarage, Wykham Lane, Bodicote, Banbury, Oxon OX15 4BN* Banbury (01295) 270174

BUTLAND, Godfrey John. b 51. Grey Coll Dur BA72. Wycliffe Hall Ox 73. **d** 75 **p** 76. C Much Woolton *Liv* 75-78; Bp's Dom Chapl 78-81; V Everton St Geo 81-94; AD Liv N from 89; V Allerton from 94. *Allerton Vicarage, Harthill Road, Liverpool L18 3HU* 0151-724 1561

BUTLAND, William Edwin. b 09. Lon Coll of Div 49. **d** 51 **p** 52. V Colney Heath St Mark *St Alb* 59-80; rtd 80; Perm to Offic *St Alb* from 80. *9 Studley Road, Wootton, Bedford MK43 9DL* Bedford (01234) 767620

BUTLER, Alan. b 53. Carl Dioc Tr Inst 89. **d** 89 **p** 90. NSM Flookburgh *Carl* 89-93; C Maryport from 93; C Flimby from 93. *The Vicarage, Church Road, Flimby, Maryport, Cumbria CA15 8TJ* Maryport (01900) 812386 Fax as telephone

BUTLER, Alan. b 57. Leic Univ BA78. Coll of Resurr Mirfield 80. **d** 83 **p** 84. C Skerton St Luke *Blackb* 83-87; C Birch w Fallowfield *Man* 87-90; V Claremont H Angels from 90; Chapl Pendleton Coll from 95. *The Vicarage, Moorfield Road, Salford M6 7EY* 0161-736 3064

BUTLER, Canon Alan John. b 30. Kelham Th Coll 51. **d** 56 **p** 57. S Africa 79-95; Botswana 66-79; V Fletchamstead *Cov* 71-79; Adn Griqualand W 79-85; Adn Kuruman 79-85; Dir Moffat Miss, Kuruman 81-95; TV Hanley H Ev *Lich* 95; rtd 95. *4 Osborne Road, Wimborne, Dorset BH21 1BL* Wimborne (01202) 848859

BUTLER, Mrs Angela Elizabeth. b 31. Studley Coll DipHort53. Gilmore Ho 60 DipTh64 Lambeth STh64. **dss** 81 **d** 87 **p** 94. Cookham *Ox* 81-86; Wheatley w Forest Hill and Stanton St John 86-87; Hon Par Dn 87-89; NSM from 93; rtd 91. *10 River Gardens, Purley-on-Thames, Reading RG8 8BX* Reading (01734) 422055

BUTLER, Angela Madeline. b 47. Oak Hill NSM Course 87. **d** 90 **p** 94. Hon Par Dn Chipperfield St Paul *St Alb* 90-93; D-in-c 93-94; P-in-c from 94; Staff Oak Hill Th Coll from 93. *The Vicarage, Chipperfield, Kings Langley, Herts WD4 9BJ* Kings Langley (01923) 263054 Fax 0181-441 5996

BUTLER, Christopher John. b 25. Leeds Univ BA50. Chich Th Coll 50. **d** 52 **p** 53. V Blackmoor *Portsm* 60-70; V Wellingborough St Andr *Pet* 70-79; P-in-c Garsington *Ox* 79-83; R Garsington and Horspath 83-95; rtd 95. *33 Oak Tree Road, Whitehill, Bordon, Hants GU35 9DF*

BUTLER, Colin Sydney. b 59. Bradf Univ BSc81. Wycliffe Hall Ox 81. **d** 84 **p** 85. C Farsley *Bradf* 84-87; C Bradf St Aug Undercliffe 87-89; P-in-c Darlaston All SS *Lich* 89-95; Ind Missr 89-95; TR Chell from 95. *The Rectory, 203 St Michael's Road, Stoke-on-Trent ST6 6JT* Stoke-on-Trent (01782) 838708

BUTLER, Ven Cuthbert Hilary. b 13. St Jo Coll Cam BA35 MA39. Westcott Ho Cam. **d** 40 **p** 41. Canada 58-84; Adn Colombia 77-78; rtd 78; Perm to Offic *Ex* from 85. *Four Chimneys, Bratton Clovelly, Okehampton, Devon EX20 4JS* Bratton Clovelly (0183787) 409

BUTLER, David Edwin. b 56. ACA83 Jes Coll Ox BA79 BA86. St Steph Ho Ox MA87. **d** 87 **p** 88. C Hulme Ascension *Man* 87-90; V Patricroft 90-94. *77A Mountside Crescent, Prestwich, Manchester M25 3JH*

BUTLER, Derek John. b 53. Aston Univ BSc74 St Jo Coll York PGCE75. St Jo Coll Dur 79. **d** 82 **p** 83. C Bramcote *S'well* 82-86; Perm to Offic *Roch* 86-92; Perm to Offic *Portsm* 86-92; Lon and SE Co-ord CPAS 86-88; NSM Bromley Ch Ch *Roch* 88-91; NSM Chesham Bois *Ox* from 92. *121 Woodside Road, Amersham, Bucks HP6 6AL* Amersham (01494) 724577

BUTLER, Donald Arthur. b 31. **d** 79 **p** 80. Hon C Apsley End *St Alb* 79-80; Hon C Chambersbury (Hemel Hempstead) from 80. *143 Belswains Lane, Hemel Hempstead, Herts HP3 9UZ*

BUTLER, Edward Daniel. b 42. Rhodes Univ BA65 MA70. Qu Coll Birm. **d** 68 **p** 69. C Edgbaston St Bart *Birm* 68-72; Perm to Offic 72-73; Perm to Offic *Chich* from 74. *43 Princes Terrace, Brighton BN2 5JS*

BUTLER, Frederick Walter (Fred). b 28. Chich Th Coll 67. **d** 69 **p** 70. C Seaford w Sutton *Chich* 69-73; V Peacehaven 73-75; P-in-c Copthorne 75-81; V 81-83; TR Moulsecoomb 83-86; R Etchingham 86-94; V Hurst Green 86-94; rtd 94; Perm to Offic *Chich* from 94. *5 Robin Close, Eastbourne, E Sussex BN23 7RJ* Eastbourne (01323) 765717

BUTLER, George James. b 53. AKC74. St Aug Coll Cant 75. **d** 76 **p** 77. C Ellesmere Port *Ches* 76-79; C Eastham 79-81; Chapl RAF 81-83; C W Kirby St Bridget *Ches* 83-84; V Newton 84-86; CF 86-91; V Folkestone St Sav *Cant* from 91. *St Saviour's Vicarage, 134 Canterbury Road, Folkestone, Kent CT19 5PH* Folkestone (01303) 254686

BUTLER, George William. DipTh. **d** 90 **p** 91. C Drung w Castleterra, Larah and Lavey etc *K, E & A* 90-93; I 93-95; I Castlemacadam w Ballinaclash, Aughrim etc *D & G* from 95. *The Vicarage, Castlemacadam, Avoca, Co Wicklow, Irish Republic* Avoca (402) 35127

BUTLER, Henry. b 25. Ridley Hall Cam 73. **d** 75 **p** 76. C Cam St Paul *Ely* 75-77; P-in-c Stilton w Denton and Caldecote 77-83; P-in-c Folksworth w Morborne 77-83; V Histon 83-90; P-in-c Impington 84-90; rtd 90. *85 High Street, Cherry Hinton, Cambridge CB1 4LU*

BUTLER, Huw. b 63. Univ of Wales (Ban) BSc84. St Mich Coll Llan DipTh94 BTh95. **d** 95. C Llantwit Fadre *Llan* from 95. *63 St Anne's Drive, Llantwit Fardre, Pontypridd, M Glam CF38 2PB* Pontypridd (01443) 206857

BUTLER, Ian Malcolm. b 39. Bris Univ BA67 BA69. Clifton Th Coll 67. **d** 69 **p** 70. C Clapham Common St Barn *S'wark* 69-73; C Reigate St Mary 73-78; V Sissinghurst w Frittenden *Cant* 78-91; rtd 92. *High Cedars, Theobalds, Hawkhurst, Cranbrook, Kent TN18 4AJ* Cranbrook (01580) 752366

BUTLER, Ivor John. b 36. Dur Univ BA58. Ely Th Coll 58. **d** 60 **p** 60. C W Bromwich All SS *Lich* 60-64; V Upper Gornal 64-72; V Tividale 72-79; Hon Chapl RN from 79; V Dartmouth *Ex* 79-95; RD Totnes 90-95; P-in-c Mullion *Truro* from 95. *The Vicarage, Nansmellyon Road, Mullion, Helston, Cornwall TR12 7DH* Mullion (01326) 240325

BUTLER, John. b 38. Univ of Wales DipTh67 DPS68 Gwent Coll Newport CertEd77. St Mich Coll Llan. **d** 68 **p** 69. C Ebbw Vale *Mon* 68-70; TV 70-75; Perm to Offic 76-77 and 79-88; P-in-c Crumlin 77-78; R Gt and Lt Casterton w Pickworth and Tickencote *Pet* 88-91; R Woolstone w Gotherington and Oxenton etc *Glouc* from 91. *The Rectory, Malleson Road, Woolstone, Cheltenham, Glos GL52 4EX* Cheltenham (01242) 672921

BUTLER, John Philip. b 47. Leeds Univ BA70. Coll of Resurr Mirfield 70. **d** 72 **p** 73. C Elton All SS *Man* 72-75; C Bolton St Pet 75-78; Chapl Bolton Colls of FE 75-78; Hon C Clifton St Paul *Bris* 78-81; Asst Chapl Bris Univ 78-81; V Llansawel w Briton Ferry *Llan* 81-84; Warden Bp Mascall Cen *Heref* 84-85; Vice-Prin Glouc Sch for Min 85-88; Chapl Univ of Wales (Ban) *Ban* from 88. *Anglican Chaplaincy Centre, Prince's Road, Bangor, Gwynedd LL57 2BD* Bangor (01248) 370566 Fax 354472

BUTLER, Linda Jane. b 56. SRN77. St Jo Coll Nottm 85. **d** 88 **p** 94. Par Dn Burbage w Aston Flamville *Leic* 88-90; Chapl Asst Leic R Infirmary 91-93; Chapl Asst Leics Mental Health Service Unit from 92; Chapl Asst Towers Hosp Humberstone from 93. *Mental Health Services Unit, Towers Hospital, Gypsy Lane, Leicester LE5 0TD* Leicester (0116) 246 0460

BUTLER, Malcolm. b 40. Linc Th Coll 76. **d** 78 **p** 79. C Whickham *Dur* 78-82; V Leam Lane 82-87; R Penshaw 87-90; rtd 90. *2 Lapwing Court, Barcus Close Lane, Burnopfield, Newcastle upon Tyne NE16 4DZ* Burnopfield (01207) 71559

BUTLER, Michael. b 41. Univ of Wales (Ban) DipTh62. St Mich Coll Llan 62 St Deiniol's Hawarden 63. **d** 64 **p** 65. C Welshpool *St As* 64; C Welshpool w Castle Caereinion 65-73; TV Abth *St D* 73-80; Chapl Univ of Wales (Abth) 73-80; V St Issell's and Amroth from 80; RD Narberth from 94. *St Issell's Vicarage, Saundersfoot, Dyfed SA69 9BD* Saundersfoot (01834) 812375

BUTLER, Canon Michael John. b 32. Keble Coll Ox BA58 MSW. Coll of Resurr Mirfield. **d** 59 **p** 60. C Poplar All SS w St Frideswide *Lon* 59-68; Hon C St Steph Walbrook and St Swithun etc 68-73; C Godalming *Guildf* 73-76; P-in-c Brighton St Anne *Chich* 77-79; Dioc Communications Officer & Dir Soc Resp 77-83; Dioc Dir of Soc Resp from 83; Can and Preb Chich Cathl from 85. *30 Bigwood Avenue, Hove, E Sussex BN3 6FD* Brighton (01273) 725811

BUTLER, Michael Weeden. b 38. Clare Coll Cam BA60 MA65. Westcott Ho Cam 63. **d** 65 **p** 66. C Bermondsey St Mary w St

Olave, St Jo etc *S'wark* 65-68; Ind Chapl 68-72; Sierra Leone 73-77; Ind Chapl *Cant* 77-86; R Gt Chart 77-86; RD E Charing 81-86; V Glouc St Jas and All SS *Glouc* from 86; RD Glouc City from 94. *The Vicarage, 1 The Conifers, Upton Street, Gloucester GL1 4LP* Gloucester (01452) 422349

BUTLER, Ms Pamela. b 53. Nottm Univ BTh86. Linc Th Coll 83. **dss** 86 **d** 87 **p** 94. Rotherhithe H Trin *S'wark* 86-87; Par Dn 87-88; Par Dn Old Trafford St Jo *Man* 88-89; Par Dn Claremont H Angels 90-94; C from 94. *The Vicarage, Moorfield Road, Salford M6 7EY* 0161-736 3064

BUTLER, Paul Roger. b 55. Nottm Univ BA77 St Mary's Coll Dur BD91. Wycliffe Hall Ox BA82. **d** 83 **p** 84. C Wandsworth All SS *S'wark* 83-87; Inner Lon Ev Scripture Union 87-92; Dep Hd of Miss 92-94; NSM E Ham St Paul *Chelmsf* 87-94; P-in-c Walthamstow St Mary w St Steph from 94; P-in-c Walthamstow St Luke from 94. *St Mary's Rectory, 117 Church Hill, London E17 3BD* 0181-520 4281 Fax as telephone

BUTLER, Perry Andrew. b 49. FRHistS York Univ BA70 Jes Coll Ox DPhil78 Nottm Univ DipTh79. Linc Th Coll 78. **d** 80 **p** 81. C Chiswick St Nic w St Mary *Lon* 80-83; C S Kensington St Steph 83-87; V Bedf Park from 87; Angl Adv Lon Weekend TV from 87. *St Michael's Vicarage, Priory Gardens, London W4 1TT* 0181-994 1380

BUTLER, Richard Charles Burr. b 34. St Pet Hall Ox BA59 MA62. Linc Th Coll 58. **d** 60 **p** 61. C St Jo Wood *Lon* 60-63; V Kingstanding St Luke *Birm* 63-75; R Lee St Marg *S'wark* from 75. *St Margaret's Rectory, Brandram Road, London SE13 5EA* 0181-852 0633

BUTLER, Robert Clifford. b 25. AKC54. **d** 55 **p** 56. V Stanbridge w Tilsworth *St Alb* 63-73; R Maulden 73-80; R Oldbury *Sarum* 80-93; rtd 93. *3 Mithras Close, Dorchester, Dorset DT1 2RF* Dorchester (01305) 264817

BUTLER, Canon Robert Edwin (Bob). b 37. Ely Th Coll 60. **d** 62 **p** 63. C Lewisham St Jo Southend *S'wark* 62-65; C Eastbourne St Elisabeth *Chich* 65-69; V Langney from 69; Can and Preb Chich Cathl from 94. *St Richard's Rectory, 7 Priory Road, Eastbourne, E Sussex BN23 7AX* Eastbourne (01323) 761158

BUTLER (nee McVEIGH), Mrs Sandra (Sandie). b 58. Reading Univ BA80. Cranmer Hall Dur CTMin95. **d** 95. C Stranton *Dur* from 95. *41 Arncliffe Gardens, Hartlepool, Cleveland TS26 9JG* Hartlepool (01429) 277591

BUTLER, Sidney. b 07. Dur Univ LTh35. St Aid Birkenhead 33. **d** 35 **p** 36. R Bilsthorpe *S'well* 69-73; R Eakring 71-73; rtd 73; Perm to Offic *S'well* 73-88. *25 Westmoore Court, Nottingham NG3 6EE* Nottingham (0115) 962 5228

BUTLER, Simon. b 64. UEA BSc86 RN Coll Greenwich. St Jo Coll Nottm DTS91 MA92. **d** 92 **p** 93. C Chandler's Ford *Win* 92-94; C Northolt W End St Jos *Lon* from 94. *8 Wells Close, Northolt, Middx UB5 6JD* 0181-845 5338

✠**BUTLER, Rt Rev Thomas Frederick.** b 40. Leeds Univ BSc61 MSc62 PhD72. Coll of Resurr Mirfield 62. **d** 64 **p** 65 **c** 85. C Wisbech St Aug *Ely* 64-66; C Folkestone St Sav *Cant* 66-67; Zambia 68-73; Chapl Kent Univ *Cant* 73-80; Six Preacher Cant Cathl 79-84; Adn Northolt *Lon* 80-85; Area Bp Willesden 85-91; Bp Leic from 91. *Bishop's Lodge, 10 Springfield Road, Leicester LE2 3BD* Leicester (0116) 270 8985 Fax 270 3288

BUTLER, Canon William Hamilton Arthur. b 14. **d** 40 **p** 47. V Kensington St Mary Abbots w St Geo *Lon* 69-72; Gen Sec Rwanda Miss 72-77; V Laleham *Lon* 77-80; rtd 80; Perm to Offic *Chich* from 85. *Venn House, 17 Boyne Park, Tunbridge Wells, Kent TN4 8EL* Tunbridge Wells (01892) 518185

BUTLER-SMITH, Basil George (Bob). b 30. Bps' Coll Cheshunt 66. **d** 67 **p** 68. C Bray and Braywood *Ox* 67-71; R Norton *St E* 71-74; P-in-c Tostock 71-74; R Rotherfield Peppard *Ox* from 76; P-in-c Rotherfield Greys 79-80; R from 80. *The Rectory, Rotherfield Peppard, Henley-on-Thames, Oxon RG9 5JN* Rotherfield Greys (01491) 628603

BUTLIN, David Francis Grenville. b 55. Bris Univ BA77 Ox Univ CertEd78. Sarum & Wells Th Coll 85. **d** 87 **p** 88. C Bedf St Andr *St Alb* 87-90; C Milton *Portsm* 90-92; V Hurst Green *S'wark* from 92. *The Vicarage, 14 Oast Road, Oxted, Surrey RH8 9DU* Oxted (01883) 712674

BUTLIN, Timothy Greer. b 53. St Jo Coll Dur BA75 Ox Univ CertEd76. Wycliffe Hall Ox 85. **d** 87 **p** 88. C Eynsham and Cassington *Ox* 87-91; V Loudwater from 91. *The Vicarage, Loudwater, High Wycombe, Bucks HP10 9QL* Bourne End (01628) 526087

BUTT, Adrian. b 37. **d** 71 **p** 72. S Africa 71-76; C Ilkeston St Mary *Derby* 76-79; P-in-c Sturton w Littleborough *S'well* 79-84; P-in-c Bole w Saundby 79-84; R N and S Wheatley w W Burton 79-84; R N Wheatley, W Burton, Bole, Saundby, Sturton etc 84-85; R Kirkby in Ashfield from 85. *The Rectory, 12 Church Street, Kirkby-in-Ashfield, Nottingham NG17 8LE* Mansfield (01623) 753790

BUTT, Christopher Martin. b 52. St Pet Coll Ox BA74 Fitzw Coll Cam BA77. Ridley Hall Cam 75. **d** 79 **p** 80. C Cam St Barn *Ely*

79-82; Hong Kong 82-89; P-in-c Windermere *Carl* from 89. *The Rectory, Longlands, Windermere, Cumbria LA23 3AS* Windermere (015394) 43063

BUTT, Edward. b 46. Huddersfield Poly DipSocWork80 CQSW80. Trin Coll Bris DipHE88. **d** 88 **p** 89. C Erith St Paul *Roch* 88-92; C Shirley *Win* from 92. *16 Radway Road, Southampton SO1 2PW* Southampton (01703) 779605

BUTT, Martin James. b 52. Sheff Univ LLB75. Trin Coll Bris 75. **d** 78 **p** 79. C Aldridge *Lich* 78-84; C Walsall 84-87; TV 87-94; P-in-c Farewell from 94; P-in-c Gentleshaw from 94. *The Vicarage, Budds Road, Rugeley, Staffs WS15 4NB* Burntwood (01543) 684329

BUTT, William Arthur. b 44. Kelham Th Coll 70 Linc Th Coll 71. **d** 71 **p** 72. C Mackworth St Fran *Derby* 71-75; C Aston cum Aughton *Sheff* 76-79; V Dalton 79-88; TR Staveley and Barrow Hill *Derby* from 88. *The Rectory, Staveley, Chesterfield, Derbyshire S43 3XZ* Chesterfield (01246) 472270

BUTTANSHAW, Graham Charles. b 59. TCD BA(Econ)80 BA85. St Jo Coll Nottm 88. **d** 91 **p** 92. C Toxteth St Cypr w Ch Ch *Liv* 91-94; CMS from 94; Uganda from 95. *c/o The Rt Rev Seme Solomona, Diocese of Yei, PO Box 370, Arua, Uganda*

BUTTERFIELD, David John. b 52. Lon Univ BMus73. St Jo Coll Nottm DipTh75. **d** 77 **p** 78. C Southport Ch Ch *Liv* 77-81; Min Aldridge St Thos CD *Lich* 81-91; V Lilleshall and Sheriffhales from 91. *The Vicarage, 25 Church Road, Lilleshall, Newport, Shropshire TF10 9HE* Telford (01952) 604281 Fax as telephone

BUTTERFIELD, John Kenneth. b 52. Nottm Univ BCombStuds. Linc Th Coll 79. **d** 82 **p** 83. C Cantley *Sheff* 82-84; C Doncaster St Leon and St Jude 84-86; TV Ilfracombe, Lee, Woolacombe, Bittadon etc *Ex* 86-88; V Thurcroft *Sheff* from 88. *The Vicarage, 122 Green Arbour Road, Thurcroft, Rotherham, S Yorkshire S66 9ED* Rotherham (01709) 542261

BUTTERWORTH, Antony James. b 51. Hull Univ BSc73 Bris Univ DipTh76. Trin Coll Bris 73. **d** 76 **p** 77. C Halliwell St Pet *Man* 76-81; V Werneth 81-90; V Tonge Fold from 90. *St Chad's Vicarage, Tonge Fold Road, Bolton BL2 6AW* Bolton (01204) 25809

BUTTERWORTH, Derek. b 27. Wells Th Coll 63. **d** 65 **p** 65. C Bottesford *Linc* 65-73; TV Bottesford w Ashby 73-83; Chapl St Hilda's Sch Whitby 83-85; V Derringham Bank *York* 85-90; rtd 90. *17 Gale Garth, Alne, York YO6 2LQ*

BUTTERWORTH, Elsie. b 27. Linc Th Coll 81. **dss** 83 **d** 87 **p** 94. OHP 83-85; Derringham Bank *York* 85-87; Par Dn 87-88; Par Dn Filey 88-94; C from 94; rtd 93. *3 Brooklands Close, Filey, N Yorkshire YO14 9BJ* Scarborough (01723) 515781

BUTTERWORTH, Dr George Michael. b 41. Man Univ BSc63 Lon Univ BD67 PhD89 Nottm Univ MPhil71. Tyndale Hall Bris. **d** 67 **p** 68. C S Normanton *Derby* 67-71; India 72-79; Lect Oak Hill Th Coll from 80; Perm to Offic *St Alb* from 80. *6 Farm Lane, Oak Hill College, London N14 4PP* 0181-441 5889 or 449 0467 Fax 441 5996

BUTTERWORTH, George John. b 58. Liv Univ BA85. Chich Th Coll CMT92. **d** 92 **p** 93. C Mayfield *Chich* 92-93; C Hastings St Clem and All SS from 93. *6 Arundel Court, Edwin Road, Hastings, E Sussex TN35 5JX* Hastings (01424) 714743

BUTTERWORTH, Ian Eric. b 44. Aber Univ MA67 MTh79. Edin Th Coll 67. **d** 69 **p** 70. C Langley All SS and Martyrs *Man* 69-71; Prec St Andr Cathl *Ab* 71-75; V Bolton St Matt w St Barn *Man* 75-85; C-in-c Lostock CD 85-92. *32 Kilworth Drive, Lostock, Bolton BL6 4RL* Bolton (01204) 843559

BUTTERWORTH, Canon James Frederick. b 49. St Chad's Coll Dur BA70. Cuddesdon Coll 70. **d** 72 **p** 73. C Kidderminster St Mary *Worc* 72-76; P-in-c Dudley St Barn 76-79; V 79-82; Prec and Min Can Worc Cathl 82-88; TR Bridgnorth, Tasley, Astley Abbotts, Oldbury etc *Heref* 88-94; Can Res and Treas Heref Cathl from 94. *7 College Cloisters, Cathedral Close, Hereford HR1 2NG* Hereford (01432) 341432

BUTTERWORTH, James Kent. b 49. Southn Univ BTh79. Chich Th Coll 75. **d** 79 **p** 80. C Heckmondwike *Wakef* 79-83; V Wrenthorpe from 83. *121 Wrenthorpe Road, Wrenthorpe, Wakefield, W Yorkshire WF2 0JS* Wakefield (01924) 373758

BUTTERWORTH, John Walton. b 49. St Jo Coll Dur BSc70 DipTh73. **d** 74 **p** 75. C Todmorden *Wakef* 74-77; Chapl Wakef Cathl 77-78; C Wakef Cathl 77-78; V Outwood from 78. *Outwood Vicarage, 424 Leeds Road, Wakefield, W Yorkshire WF1 2JB* Wakefield (01924) 823150

BUTTERWORTH, Ms Julia Kay. b 42. Edin Univ MA64 Bris Univ CertEd66 Nottm Univ DipTh75. Linc Th Coll 73. **dss** 77 **d** 87 **p** 94. Cov E *Cov* 77-79; Cant Cathl *Cant* 79-88; Dioc Adv in Women's Min from 82; Faversham 84-87; Par Dn 87-92; TD Whitstable 92-94; TV from 94. *St Andrew's Vicarage, Saddleton Road, Whitstable, Kent CT5 4JH* Whitstable (01227) 263152

BUTTERWORTH, Keith. b 45. St Paul's Cheltenham CertEd66. Linc Th Coll 69. **d** 72 **p** 73. C Hollinwood *Man* 72-75; C Failsworth H Family CD 75-76; R Man Clayton St Cross w St Paul 76-87; V Lawton Moor from 87. *140 Wythenshaw Road, Manchester M23 0PD* 0161-998 2461

BUTTERWORTH, Roy. b 31. Selw Coll Cam BA55 MA59. Wells Th Coll 55. **d** 57 **p** 58. V Dearnley *Man* 63-81; V Tyldesley w Shakerley 81-83; V Healey 83-94; rtd 94. *102 Greenbank Road, Rochdale, Lancs OL12 0EN* Rochdale (01706) 350808

BUTTERY, Graeme. b 62. York Univ BA84. St Steph Ho Ox 85. **d** 88 **p** 89. C Peterlee *Dur* 88-91; C Sunderland 91-92; TV 92-94; V Horsley Hill S Shields from 94. *St Lawrence House, 84 Centenary Avenue, South Shields, Tyne & Wear NE34 6SF* 0191-456 1747

BUTTIMORE, Canon John Charles. b 27. St Mich Coll Llan 55. **d** 57 **p** 58. C Treherbert *Llan* 57-60; C Aberdare St Fagan 60-64; V Williamstown 64-71; Chapl Ely Hosp Cardiff from 71; V Caerau w Ely *Llan* from 71; RD Cardiff 83-89; Can Llan Cathl from 87. *The Vicarage, Cowbridge Road West, Cardiff CF5 5BQ* Cardiff (01222) 563254

BUTTLE, Leslie Albert. b 32. Open Univ BA89. Edin Th Coll 61. **d** 64 **p** 65. C Sowerby Bridge w Norland *Wakef* 64-66; C Plymstock *Ex* 66-69; C Ilfracombe H Trin 69-71; V Woolfardisworthy and Buck Mills 71-76; C Sticklepath 76-77; Asst Chapl HM Pris Leeds 77-80; Lic to Offic *Ripon* 77-80; Chapl HM Youth Cust Cen Hindley 80-84; Perm to Offic *Ex* 86-93; Hon C Braunton from 93. *Church House, Saunton, Braunton, Devon EX33 1LG* Braunton (01271) 817022

BUTTLE, Leslie Ronald Frank. b 07. Lon Univ BA28. **d** 34 **p** 35. R Lowick w Sudborough and Slipton *Pet* 67-73; rtd 73. *5 Castle Street, Launceston, Cornwall PL15 8BA* Launceston (01566) 772052

BUTTON, David Frederick. b 27. St Chad's Coll Dur BA53 DipTh54. **d** 54 **p** 55. V Surfleet *Linc* 54-71; R Belton SS Pet and Paul 71-78; V Barkston w Syston 72-78; V Honington 73-78; R Gunhouse w Burringham 78-82; P-in-c Gt w Lt Hockham w Wretham w Illington *Nor* 82-84; P-in-c Shropham w Larling and Snetterton 82-84; V Hockham w Shropham Gp of Par 84-91; rtd 91; Perm to Offic *Nor* from 91. *6 Vallibus Close, Oulton, Lowestoft, Suffolk NR32 3DS* Lowestoft (01502) 585670

BUXTON, Canon Derek Major. b 31. Lon Univ BD63. Ripon Hall Ox 58. **d** 60 **p** 61. C Leic St Nic *Leic* 60-64; Chapl Leic Univ 60-64; Chapl Leic Coll of Art and Tech 61-65; Min Can Leic Cathl 64-69; Prec 67-69; R Ibstock 69-76; R Ibstock w Heather 76-87; Chapl ATC from 78; OCF and Cen and E Regional Chapl from 87; RD Akeley S (Coalville) *Leic* 84-87; P-in-c Woodhouse Eaves 87-91; V Woodhouse and Woodhouse Eaves from 91; Chapl Roecliffe Manor Cheshire Home from 87; Chapl Coun OStJ from 87; Hon Can Leic Cathl *Leic* from 88. *The Vicarage, 32 Church Hill, Woodhouse Eaves, Loughborough, Leics LE12 8RI* Woodhouse Eaves (01509) 890226

BUXTON, Canon Digby Hugh. b 16. Trin Coll Cam BA38 MA41. Wycliffe Hall Ox 39. **d** 41 **p** 42. Canada 50-77; C Gt Burstead *Chelmsf* 77-78; C Sandhurst *Ox* 78-81; rtd 81; Hon C Barkway, Reed and Buckland w Barley *St Alb* 81-87. *Rosemary Holt, Edward Road, St Cross, Winchester, Hants SO23 9RB* Winchester (01962) 860877

BUXTON, Preb Edmund Digby. b 08. Trin Coll Cam BA29 MA33. Ridley Hall Cam 29. **d** 33 **p** 34. V Milborne Port w Goathill *B & W* 54-74; rtd 74; Perm to Offic *Win* 74-75 and from 78; Tristan da Cunha 75-78. *10 Pound Hill, Alresford, Hants SO24 9BW* Alresford (01962) 732353

BUXTON, Edmund Francis. b 42. Trin Coll Cam BA65 MA68 DPS74. Linc Th Coll 65. **d** 67 **p** 68. C Wanstead St Mary *Chelmsf* 67-70; C Cam Gt St Mary w St Mich *Ely* 70-73; C Barking St Marg w St Patr *Chelmsf* 74-75; India 75-79; Chapl Bath Univ *B & W* 79-89; TR Willenhall H Trin *Lich* from 89. *The Rectory, Short Heath, Willenhall, W Midlands WV12 5PT* Bloxwich (01922) 476416

BUXTON, Edward Brian. b 41. AKC65 BEd79. **d** 66 **p** 67. C Laindon w Basildon *Chelmsf* 66-73; P-in-c Grays All SS 73-76; Perm to Offic from 76. *Address temp unknown*

BUXTON, Graham. b 45. BA MSc. St Jo Coll Nottm 83. **d** 83 **p** 84. C Ealing Dean St Jo *Lon* 83-84; C W Ealing St Jo w St Jas 84-86; C S Harrow St Paul 86-89; P-in-c 89-91; Australia from 91. *Tabor College, 7 Lynton Avenue, South Plympton, S Australia 5038*

BUXTON, Dr Richard Fowler. b 40. Lon Univ BSc62 Linacre Coll Ox BA67 MA71 Ex Univ PhD73. St Steph Ho Ox 65. **d** 68 **p** 69. C Whitley Ch Ch *Ox* 68-70; C Pinhoe *Ex* 70-71; Asst Chapl Ex Univ 71-73; Tutor Sarum & Wells Th Coll 73-77; Vice-Prin 77; Perm to Offic *Ches* 77-94; Lect Liturgy Man

Univ 80-94; Perm to Offic *Man* 81-94; Subwarden St Deiniol's Lib Hawarden from 94; Lic to Offic *St As* from 94. *St Deiniol's Library, Hawarden, Deeside, Clwyd CH5 3DF* Hawarden (01244) 532350 or 520647 Fax 520643

BUXTON, Trevor George. b 57. Ex Univ BEd78. Chich Th Coll 81. **d** 83 **p** 84. C Hove All SS *Chich* 83-87; C Burgess Hill St Jo 87-91; V Brighton St Aug and St Sav from 91. *St Anne's House, 24 Stanford Avenue, Brighton BN1 6EA* Brighton (01273) 561755

BUXTON, William Arnold Greaves (Paddy). b 33. FBIM78 FInstD78 FInstM79. Sarum & Wells Th Coll 80. **d** 82 **p** 83. C Durrington *Chich* 82-85; R Kingston Buci 85-89; TR Rye 89-94; rtd 94. *The Old House, 45 The Mint, Rye, E Sussex TN31 7EN* Rye (01797) 223191

BYE, Dennis Robert. b 20. **d** 86 **p** 87. NSM Bishop's Cleeve *Glouc* 86-90; rtd 90; Perm to Offic *Glouc* from 90. *The Old Coach House, Lye Lane, Cleeve Hill, Cheltenham, Glos GL52 3QD* Cheltenham (01242) 673587

BYE, Peter John. b 39. Lon Univ BD65. Clifton Th Coll 62. **d** 67 **p** 68. C Hyson Green *S'well* 67-70; C Dur St Nic *Dur* 70-73; V Lowestoft Ch Ch *Nor* 73-80; V Carl St Jo *Carl* from 80; Chapl Carl Gen Hosp from 80. *St John's Vicarage, London Road, Carlisle CA1 2QQ* Carlisle (01228) 21601 or 595792

BYERS, Christopher Martin. b 33. Jes Coll Ox BA59 MA62. Wycliffe Hall Ox 59. **d** 60 **p** 61. C Bermondsey St Mary w St Olave, St Jo etc *S'wark* 60-66; R Mottingham St Andr 66-86; TR Thamesmead from 86. *Thamesmead Rectory, 22 Manor Close, London SE28 8EY* 0181-311 7278 or 310 6814

BYFORD, Canon David Charles. b 30. Bps' Coll Cheshunt 58. **d** 61 **p** 62. C Short Heath *Birm* 61-63; C Londonderry 63-65; Chapl Selly Oak Hosp Birm 65-70; V Rowley Regis *Birm* 70-78; V Polesworth from 78; RD Polesworth 84-91; Hon Can Birm Cathl from 87. *Polesworth Vicarage, Tamworth, Staffs B78 1DU* Tamworth (01827) 892340

BYLES, Canon Raymond Vincent. b 30. Univ of Wales (Lamp) BA52. St Mich Coll Llan 52. **d** 54 **p** 55. C Llanfairisgaer *Ban* 54-57; C Llandudno 57-59; V Carno 59-64; V Trefeglwys 63; V Newmarket and Gwaenysgor *St As* 64-72; R Llysfaen 72-80; V Bodelwyddan and St George 80-85; V Bodelywddan from 85; Hon Can St As Cathl from 89. *The Vicarage, Bodelwyddan, Rhyl, Clwyd LL18 5UR* St Asaph (01745) 583034

BYLLAM-BARNES, Paul William Marshall. b 38. Birm Univ BCom Lon Univ MSc. Sarum & Wells Th Coll. **d** 84 **p** 85. C Gt Bookham *Guildf* 84-87; R Cusop w Clifford, Hardwicke, Bredwardine etc *Heref* from 87. *The Vicarage, Cusop, Hay-on-Wye, Hereford HR3 5RF* Hay-on-Wye (01497) 820634

BYNON, William. b 43. St Aid Birkenhead 63. **d** 66 **p** 67. C Huyton St Mich *Liv* 66-69; C Maghull 69-72; TV 72-75; V Highfield 75-82; V Southport All SS 82-88; P-in-c Southport All So 86-88; V Newton in Makerfield St Pet 88-94; V Caerhun w Llangelynnin w Llanbedr-y-Cennin *Ban* from 94. *Caerhun Vicarage, Tyn-y-Groes, Conwy, Gwynedd LL32 8UG* Tynygroes (01492) 650250

BYRNE, David Patrick. b 48. St Jo Coll Nottm 74. **d** 77 **p** 78. C Bordesley Green *Birm* 77-79; C Weoley Castle 79-82; TV Kings Norton 82-92; Perm to Offic 92; TV Hodge Hill 92-94. *46 Orchard Road, Birmingham B24 9JA* 0121-766 6611

BYRNE, David Rodney. b 47. St Jo Coll Cam BA70 MA73. Cranmer Hall Dur 71. **d** 73 **p** 74. C Maidstone St Luke *Cant* 73-77; C Patcham *Chich* 77-83; TV Stantonbury *Ox* 83-87; TV Stantonbury and Willen 87-92; TV Woodley from 92. *Airfield Church Centre, 171 Hurricane Way, Woodley, Reading RG5 4UH* Reading (01734) 692981

BYRNE, John Victor. b 47. FCA. St Jo Coll Nottm LTh73. **d** 73 **p** 74. C Gillingham St Mark *Roch* 73-76; C Cranham Park *Chelmsf* 76-80; V Balderstone *Man* 80-87; V Southsea St Jude *Portsm* from 87. *St Jude's Vicarage, 7 Hereford Road, Southsea, Hants PO5 2DH* Portsmouth (01705) 821071

BYRNE, Very Rev Matthew. b 27. Man Univ MA69 TCD HDipEd81. Tyndale Hall Bris 47. **d** 51 **p** 52. R Whalley Range St Marg *Man* 62-80; P-in-c Chapelizod *D & G* 80-83; Chapl K Hosp Sch Palmerstown Dub 83-89; Dean Kildare *M & K* 89-93; I Kildare w Kilmeague and Curragh 89-93; Producer Relig Dept RTE 83-92; Chapl Defence Forces 89-92; rtd 92. *5 Fairfield Park, Greystones, Co Wicklow, Irish Republic* Dublin (1) 287-3622 Fax as telephone

BYRNE, Miriam Alexandra Frances. b 46. Westcott Ho Cam. **d** 87 **p** 94. Par Dn Beoley *Worc* 87-90; C Ayr *Glas* 92; P-in-c 92-94 and from 94. *45 St Andrew's Crescent, Dumbarton G82 3ES* Dumbarton (01389) 64590

BYRNE, Robert James Matthew (Bob). b 64. Oak Hill Th Coll BA95. **d** 95. C Tonbridge St Steph *Roch* from 95. *20 Woodfield Road, Tonbridge, Kent TN9 2LQ* Tonbridge (01732) 770944

BYRNE, Rodney Edmund. b 18. **d** 84 **p** 84. Hon C Leckhampton SS Phil and Jas w Cheltenham St Jas *Glouc* 84-88; rtd 88; Perm to Offic *Glouc* from 88. *39 Collum End Rise, Cheltenham, Glos GL53 0PA* Cheltenham (01242) 526428

BYRNE, Ronald Brendan Anthony (Bryn). b 31. Reading Univ BA72. Westcott Ho Cam 86. **d** 64 **p** 65. Chapl Cov Cathl *Cov* 87-91; Chapl Lanchester Poly 87-91; Lic to Offic 91-94; Chapl Limerick Univ *L & K* from 94; Lic to Offic from 94. *Villiers Square, Church Street, Limerick, Republic of Ireland* Limerick (61) 400346

BYROM, Canon John Kenneth. b 20. Selw Coll Cam BA41 MA45. Westcott Ho Cam 41. **d** 43 **p** 44. Warden Brasted Place Coll Westerham 64-74; V Swaffham Prior *Ely* 74-88; Dir of Ords 75-87; Dir of Post-Ord Tr 75-87; Hon Can Ely Cathl 78-88; RD Fordham 78-83; rtd 88. *62 Cambridge Road, Great Shelford, Cambridge CB2 5JS* Cambridge (01223) 844015

BYROM, Canon Malcolm Senior. b 37. Edin Th Coll 65. **d** 67 **p** 68. C Allerton *Bradf* 67-69; C Padstow *Truro* 69-72; V Hessenford 72-77; P-in-c St Martin by Looe 72-77; V Kenwyn 77-91; R Kenwyn w St Allen from 91; Sub-Warden Community of the Epiphany Truro from 85; RD Powder *Truro* 88-90; Hon Can Truro Cathl from 92. *The Vicarage, Kenwyn Close, Truro, Cornwall TR1 3DX* Truro (01872) 72664

BYRON, Frederick. b 14. Dur Univ BA38. St Jo Coll Dur 38. **d** 39 **p** 40. V Out Rawcliffe *Blackb* 68-78; C Standish 78-79; rtd 79. *18 Scott Avenue, Hindley, Wigan, Lancs WN2 4DG* Wigan (01942) 53807

BYRON, Frederick Thomas Christopher. b 16. Mert Coll Ox BA39 MA43. St Steph Ho Ox 39. **d** 40 **p** 41. V Ruislip St Martin *Lon* 62-70; V Kensington St Jas Norlands 70-83; rtd 83. *63 Belvedere Court, 372/4 Upper Richmond Road, London SW15 6HZ* 0181-785-7567

BYRON, Terence Sherwood. b 26. Keble Coll Ox BA50 MA54. Linc Th Coll 50. **d** 52 **p** 53. India 60-76; C-in-c Beaumont Leys (Ex-paroch Distr) *Leic* 76-85; V Beaumont Leys 85-86; RD Christianity (Leic) N 86-92; P-in-c Leic St Phil 86-88; V 88-92; rtd 93. *84 Flax Road, Leicester LE4 6QD* Leicester (0116) 266 1922

BYRON-DAVIES, Peter. b 49. K Coll Lon BD75 AKC75 Nottm Univ MTh85. St Aug Coll Cant 75. **d** 76 **p** 77. C Wootton Bassett *Sarum* 76-79; Chapl Charterhouse Godalming 79-80; R Bassingham *Linc* 80-85; V Aubourn w Haddington 80-85; V Carlton-le-Moorland w Stapleford 80-85; R Thurlby w Norton Disney 80-85; Canada 85-88; R Chalke Valley E *Sarum* from 88. *The Rectory, Bishopstone, Salisbury SP5 4AN* Salisbury (01722) 77330

BYSOUTH, Paul Graham. b 55. Oak Hill Th Coll. **d** 84 **p** 85. C Gorleston St Andr *Nor* 84-87; C Ripley *Derby* 87-91; TV N Wingfield, Clay Cross and Pilsley from 91. *Pilsley Vicarage, Chesterfield, Derbyshire S45 8EF* Ripley (01773) 590529

BYWATER, Hector William Robinson. b 10. ALCD32. **d** 33 **p** 34. V Derby St Alkmund *Derby* 40-84; rtd 84; Perm to Offic *Derby* from 84. *15 Bath Road, Mickleover, Derby DE3 5BW* Derby (01332) 513281

BYWORTH, Christopher Henry Briault (Chris). b 39. Or Coll Ox BA61 MA65 Bris Univ BA63. Lon Coll of Div 64. **d** 65 **p** 66. C Low Leyton *Chelmsf* 65-68; C Rusholme *Man* 68-70; Lic to Offic *Lon* 71-75; TR Thetford *Nor* 75-79; Warden Cranmer Hall Dur 79-83; TR Fazakerley Em *Liv* 83-90; P-in-c St Helens St Helen 90-94; TR from 94; AD St Helens from 90. *The Vicarage, 51A Rainford Road, St Helens, Merseyside WA10 6BZ* St Helens (01744) 22067

BYWORTH, Mrs Ruth Angela. b 49. Cranmer Hall Dur BA82. dss 83 **d** 92 **p** 94. Kirkby *Liv* 83-89; Aintree St Pet 89-92; D-in-c 92-94; P-in-c from 94. *The Vicarage, 51A Rainford Road, St Helens, Merseyside WA10 6BZ* St Helens (01744) 22067

C

CABLE, Patrick John. b 50. AKC72. **d** 74 **p** 75. C Herne *Cant* 74-78; CF from 78. *c/o MOD (Army), Bagshot Park, Bagshot, Surrey GU19 5PL* Bagshot (01276) 471717 Fax 412834

CADDELL, Richard Allen. b 54. Auburn Univ Alabama BIE77. Trin Coll Bris BA88. **d** 88 **p** 89. C Uphill *B & W* 88-94; Perm to Offic from 94. *31 Severn Avenue, Weston-super-Mare, Avon BS23 4DG* Weston-super-Mare (01934) 636349

CADDEN, Brian Stuart. b 58. BSc BTh TCD. **d** 89 **p** 90. C Lecale Gp *D & D* 89-92; C Killowen *D & R* 92-95; I Muckamore *Conn* from 95. *The Rectory, 5 Ballycraigy Road, Muckamore, Antrim BT41 1QP* Antrim (01849) 462073

CADDEN, Terence John. b 60. TCD BTh89. CITC 86. **d** 89 **p** 90. C Coleraine *Conn* 89-92; C Lurgan Ch the Redeemer *D & D* from 92. *14 Sandhill Park, Lurgan, Craigavon, Co Armagh BT66 7AX* Lurgan (01762) 326040

CADDICK, Jeremy Lloyd. b 60. St Jo Coll Cam BA82 MA86 K Coll Lon MA93. Ripon Coll Cuddesdon BA86 MA91. **d** 87 **p** 88. C Kennington St Jo w St Jas *S'wark* 87-90; Chapl Lon Univ *Lon* 90-94; Chapl R Free Medical Sch 90-94; Chapl R Veterinary Coll 90-94; PV Westmr Abbey 92-94; Dean Em Coll Cam from 94. *Emmanuel College, Cambridge CB2 3AP* Cambridge (01223) 334264 Fax 334426

CADDICK, Canon Dr Lloyd Reginald. b 31. Bris Univ BA56 St Cath Coll Ox BA58 MA62 Nottm Univ MPhil73 K Coll Lon PhD78 Open Univ Hon MA79. St Steph Ho Ox 56. **d** 59 **p** 59. C N Lynn w St Marg and St Nic *Nor* 59-62; Chapl Oakham Sch Leics 62-66; P-in-c Bulwick, Harringworth w Blatherwycke and Laxton *Pet* 66-67; R Bulwick, Blatherwycke w Harringworth and Laxton 67-77; V Oundle from 77; Can Pet Cathl from 94. *The Vicarage, 12 New Street, Oundle, Peterborough PE8 4EA* Oundle (01832) 273595

CADDY, Dennis Gordon James. b 27. Bps' Coll Cheshunt 62. **d** 64 **p** 65. C-in-c Harlington Ch Ch CD *Lon* 69-72; V N Harrow St Alb 72-83; R Corsley *Sarum* 83-92; rtd 92. *2 Ivy Cottage, Marcombelake, Bridport, Dorset DT6 6EE* Lyme Regis (01297) 489120

CADDY, Michael George Bruce Courtenay. b 45. K Coll Lon. **d** 71 **p** 72. C Walton St Mary *Liv* 71-76; C Solihull *Birm* 76-79; TV 79-81; V Shard End 81-87; TV Shirley 87; TR from 87. *The Vicarage, 2 Bishopton Close, Shirley, Solihull, W Midlands B90 4AH* 0121-744 3123

CADE, Simon Peter Vincent. b 69. Univ of Wales BA90. Westcott Ho Cam CTM94. **d** 94 **p** 95. C Calne and Blackland *Sarum* from 94. *5 Tyning Park, Calne, Wilts SN11 0QE* Calne (01249) 814860

CADMAN, Kenneth Claude. b 14. St Jo Coll Dur BA40. **d** 40 **p** 41. R Guernsey St Pierre du Bois *Win* 69-81; R Guernsey St Philippe de Torteval 80-81; Vice Dean Guernsey 70-81; rtd 81; Perm to Offic *Win* from 82. *Marske, Rue de St Apolline, St Saviour's, Guernsey, Channel Islands GU7 9QJ* Guernsey (01481) 63720

CADMAN, Robert Hugh. b 49. Nottm Univ DipTh76. St Jo Coll Nottm 77. **d** 78 **p** 79. C Ecclesall *Sheff* 78-82; C Worting *Win* 82-84; C-in-c Winklebury CD 84-87; R Widford *Chelmsf* 87-94; Chapl Anglia Poly Univ from 94. *The Rectory, 6 Acres End, Chelmsford CM1 2XR* Chelmsford (01245) 359743

CADMORE, Albert Thomas. b 47. Open Univ BA81 NE Lon Poly Nor City Coll DMS84 SS Mark & Jo Coll Plymouth Lon Inst of Educn CertEd68. E Anglian Minl Tr Course 85. **d** 88 **p** 89. NSM Gorleston St Andr *Nor* from 88; NSM Winterton w E and W Somerton and Horsey from 94. *10 Upper Cliff Road, Gorleston, Great Yarmouth, Norfolk NR31 6AL* Great Yarmouth (01493) 668762

CADOGAN, Paul Anthony Cleveland. b 47. AKC74. **d** 75 **p** 76. C Fishponds St Jo *Bris* 75-79; C Swindon New Town 79-81; P-in-c Swindon All SS 81-82; V 82-90; R Lower Windrush *Ox* 90-94. *2 Malthouse Close, Ashbury, Oxon SN6 8PB* Swindon (01793) 710488

CAESAR, Canon Anthony Douglass. b 24. LVO87 CVO91. FRCO47 Magd Coll Cam BA47 MusB47 MA49. St Steph Ho Ox 59. **d** 61 **p** 62. Chapl RSCM Addington 65-70; ACCM 65-70; P-in-O 68-70; C Bournemouth St Pet *Win* 70-73; Prec and Sacr Win Cathl 74-79; Hon Can 75-76 and 79-91; Can Res 76-79; Dom Chapl to The Queen 79-91; Extra Chapl to The Queen from 91; Sub Almoner and Dep Clerk of the Closet 79-91; Sub Dean of HM Chpls Royal 79-91; rtd 91; Chapl St Cross Hosp Win 91-93. *Flat 2, Old Kiln, Brading, Sandown, Isle of Wight PO36 0BP* Isle of Wight (01983) 406435

CAFFYN, Douglas John Morris. b 36. ACIS77 Peterho Cam MA60 Nairobi Univ MSc69 Westmr Coll Ox DipEd61. S Dios Minl Tr Scheme 87. **d** 90 **p** 91. NSM Hampden Park *Chich* 90-94; Chapl amongst the Deaf from 94. *255 King's Drive, Eastbourne, E Sussex BN21 2UR* Eastbourne (01323) 500977

CAHILL, Nigel. b 59. St Mich Coll Llan DipTh80 DPS82. **d** 82 **p** 83. C Whitchurch *Llan* 82-86; V Tonypandy w Clydach Vale from 86; RD Rhondda from 93. *The Vicarage, St Andrew's Church Grounds, Tonypandy, M Glam CF40 2LD* Tonypandy (01443) 437759

CAIGER, Canon Douglas George Colley. b 23. Kelham Th Coll 39. **d** 46 **p** 48. R Lowestoft St Marg *Nor* 69-78; Hon Can Nor Cathl 73-78; TR Shaston *Sarum* 78-86; rtd 86; Perm to Offic *Portsm* from 86; Perm to Offic *Chich* from 86. *11 Record Road, Emsworth, Hants PO10 7NS* Emsworth (01243) 376058

CAIN, Andrew David. b 63. Aber Univ BSc86. Ripon Coll Cuddesdon BA89. **d** 90 **p** 91. C Walworth St Jo *S'wark* 90-94; Bp's Dom Chapl *Ox* from 94. *55 Marsh Lane, Marston, Oxford OX3 0NQ* Oxford (01865) 67946

CAIN, Frank Robert. b 56. Oak Hill Th Coll BA88. **d** 88 **p** 89. C Aughton Ch Ch *Liv* 88-91; P-in-c Toxteth Park St Clem from

91. *The Vicarage, 76 Beaumont Street, Liverpool L8 0XA*
0151-709 9880

CAIN, Michael John. b 62. Chich Th Coll 88. **d** 91 **p** 92. C Cainscross w Selsley *Glouc* 91-94; C Mackworth St Fran *Derby* from 94. *St Francis House, 76A Collingham Gardens, Derby DE22 4FQ* Derby (01332) 383288

CAINE (nee BALDWIN), Mrs Joyce Gertrude. b 21. Nottm Univ BA42 Cam Univ CertEd43 Lon Univ BD58. **d** 87. NSM Redland *Bris* from 87. *164 Bishop Road, Bristol BS7 8NB* Bristol (0117) 942 7113

CAINK, Richard David Somerville. b 37. Lich Th Coll 68. **d** 71 **p** 72. C Prittlewell St Mary *Chelmsf* 71-74; C Gt Yarmouth *Nor* 74-76; P-in-c Blickling w Ingworth 76-80; P-in-c Saxthorpe and Corpusty 76-80; P-in-c Oulton SS Pet and Paul 76-80; R Cheddington w Mentmore and Marsworth *Ox* 80-87; P-in-c Wooburn 87-90; V from 90. *Wooburn Vicarage, Windsor Hill, Wooburn Green, High Wycombe, Bucks HP10 0EH* Bourne End (01628) 520030

✠**CAIRD, Most Rev Donald Arthur Richard.** b 25. TCD BA49 MA55 BD55 HDipEd59 Hon DD88 Hon LLD93. TCD Div Sch 49. **d** 50 **p** 51 **c** 70. C Dundela *D & D* 50-53; Chapl and Asst Master Portora R Sch Enniskillen 53-57; Lect St D Coll Lamp 57-60; I Rathmichael *D & G* 60-69; Asst Master St Columba's Coll Dub 60-62; Lect TCD 62-64; Lect in Philosophy of Relig Div Hostel Dub 64-69; Dean Ossory *C & O* 69-70; Preb Leighlin Cathl 69-70; I Kilkenny 69-70; Bp Limerick, Ardfert and Aghadoe *L & K* 70-76; Bp M & K 76-85; Abp Dub *D & G* from 85; Prec Cualaun St Patr Cathl Dub from 85. *The See House, 17 Temple Road, Milltown, Dublin 6, Irish Republic* Dublin (1) 497-7849 Fax 497-6355

CAIRNS, Henry Alfred. Melbourne Univ BA49 Ridley Coll Melbourne. ACT ThL43. **d** 42 **p** 43. Australia 42-81; Can Gippsland 59-60; Perm to Offic *Cant* 81-83; Perm to Offic *St Alb* 81-83 and from 85; Hon C Radlett 83-85. *47 Westminster Court, St Stephen's Hill, St Albans, Herts AL1 2DX* St Albans (01727) 850949

CAIRNS, Robert Hill. b 21. Aber Univ MA50. St Deiniol's Hawarden. **d** 83 **p** 83. Lic to Offic *Ab* 83-86; Portsoy 86-88. *Flat 3, South College House, Elgin, Morayshire IV30 1EP* Elgin (01343) 541190

CALAMINUS, Peter Andrew Franz. b 14. Lon Univ BA44. Cuddesdon Coll 69. **d** 71 **p** 71. C Westbury *Sarum* 71-73; P-in-c Pitcombe w Shepton Montague and Bratton St Maur *B & W* 73-76; V 76-78; rtd 79. *9 St Matthew's Cottages, Macalister Street, Rockhampton, Queensland, Australia 4701* Rockhampton (79) 225386

CALCOTT-JAMES, Colin Wilfrid. b 25. Bris Univ BSc48. S'wark Ord Course 77. **d** 80 **p** 81. NSM Barnes H Trin *S'wark* 80-85; C Hykeham *Linc* 85-88; R Barrowby 88-92; rtd 92; Perm to Offic *Lon* from 93. *23 Gwendolen Avenue, London SW15 6ET* 0181-788 6591

CALDER, Ian Fraser. b 47. York Univ BA68 CertEd69. Glouc Sch of Min 84. **d** 87 **p** 88. NSM Lydney w Aylburton *Glouc* 87-91; C Cirencester 91-95; V Coney Hill from 95. *St Oswald's Vicarage, Coney Hill, Gloucester GL4 7LX* Gloucester (01452) 523618

CALDER, Roger Paul. b 53. Hatf Coll Dur BA75. Chich Th Coll 76. **d** 79 **p** 80. C Addlestone *Guildf* 79-82; C Grangetown *Dur* 82-84; TV Brighton Resurr *Chich* 84-87; CF 87-92; P-in-c Cocking, Bepton and W Lavington *Chich* 92-95; P-in-c Bognor from 95. *The Vicarage, 17 Victoria Drive, Bognor Regis, W Sussex PO21 2RH* Bognor Regis (01243) 821965

CALDERBANK, Geoffrey Randall. b 59. Man Poly BA81 Man Univ MA89. Ripon Coll Cuddesdon. **d** 86 **p** 87. C Flixton St Mich *Man* 86-89; P-in-c Dixon Green 89-91; Ecum Chapl Glam Univ *Llan* 91-95; V Tregaron w Ystrad Meurig and Strata Florida *St D* from 95. *The Vicarage, Tregaron, Dyfed SY25 6HL* Tregaron (01974) 298280

CALDICOTT, Anthony. b 31. ARCO52 FRCO62 ADCM66 St Jo Coll Dur BA53. Ripon Hall Ox 55. **d** 57 **p** 58. C Finham *Cov* 57-61; C Bedf St Andr *St Alb* 61-64; Chapl Lindisfarne Coll 64-67; C W Bromwich All SS *Lich* 67-69; Lic to Offic *Cov* 69-75; Hon C Twickenham St Mary *Lon* 75-89; Perm to Offic from 91. *38 Lyndhurst Avenue, Twickenham TW2 6BX* 0181-894 6859

CALDICOTT, Canon John Michael Parlane. b 46. Selw Coll Cam BA69. St Steph Ho Ox 69. **d** 71 **p** 72. C Mayfield *Chich* 71-74; Hon C Deptford St Paul *S'wark* 74-76; P-in-c Sydenham St Phil 76-83; P-in-c Forest Hill Ch Ch 83-91; P-in-c Forest Hill St Paul 84-91; RD W Lewisham 87; V Hove All SS *Chich* 91-93; P-in-c Hove St Jo 91-93; TR Hove from 93; Chapl Catisfield Hosp from 91; RD Hove *Chich* from 92; Can and Preb Chich Cathl from 92. *The Vicarage, Wilbury Road, Hove, E Sussex BN3 3PB* Brighton (01273) 733331

CALDWELL, Alan. b 29. Oak Hill Th Coll 65. **d** 67 **p** 68. C New Malden and Coombe *S'wark* 69-73; C Edgware St Andr CD *Lon* 73-78; P-in-c Pettaugh and Winston *St E* 78; R Helmingham w Framsden and Pettaugh w Winston 78-87; R

Cowden w Hammerwood *Chich* 87-94; rtd 94. *Ael-y-Bryn, Druid Road, Menai Bridge, Gwynedd LL59 5BY* Menai Bridge (01248) 713550

CALDWELL, David Denzil. b 24. TD70. Bps' Coll Cheshunt 53. **d** 55 **p** 56. I Kilwaughter w Cairncastle *Conn* 61-90; CF (TAVR) 67-90; RD Carrickfergus *Conn* 70-90; CF (R of O) 70-80; Asst ChStJ from 80; rtd 90. *Clogher Croft, 193 Straid Road, Bushmills, Co Antrim BT57 8XW* Bushmills (012657) 32336

CALDWELL, Ian Charles Reynolds. b 43. St Mich Coll Llan 68. **d** 70 **p** 71. C Oakham w Hambleton and Egleton *Pet* 70-74; C Swindon New Town *Bris* 74-78; P-in-c Honicknowle *Ex* 78-80; V 80-88; V Norton St Mich *Dur* 88-94. *Address excluded by request*

CALDWELL, Mrs Jill. b 47. Lon Univ BPharm69 MRPharmS70. S Dios Minl Tr Scheme 89. **d** 92 **p** 94. NSM Yiewsley *Lon* from 92. *20 Old Slade Lane, Iver, Bucks SL0 9DR* Iver (01753) 651913

CALDWELL, Canon John Donaldson. b 19. TCD BA41. **d** 42 **p** 43. I Kilmegan w Maghera *D & D* 55-89; RD Kilmegan 62-89; Can Dromore Cathl 85-89; rtd 89; Lic to Offic *D & D* from 90. *66 Castlewellan Road, Newcastle, Co Down BT33 0JP* Newcastle (013967) 24874

CALDWELL, Robert McKinley. b 20. Pittsburgh Univ BSc42. Nashotah Ho MDiv64. **d** 64 **p** 64. USA 64-85; P-in-c Kenmare w Sneem, Waterville etc *L & K* from 87. *St Patrick's Rectory, Kenmare, Killarney, Co Kerry, Irish Republic* Killarney (64) 41121 Fax as telephone

CALDWELL, Roger Fripp. b 31. Cranmer Hall Dur. **d** 64 **p** 65. C Sugley *Newc* 67-74; R Helmdon w Stuchbury and Radstone *Pet* 74-91; R Greatworth 74-91; rtd 91. *Quiet Waters, Station Road, Heyford, Oxford OX5 3PD*

CALE, Clifford Roy Fenton. b 38. St Mich Coll Llan 65. **d** 67 **p** 68. C Griffithstown *Mon* 67-72; V Cwm 72-73; V Abersychan 73-79; V Abersychen and Garndiffaith 79-82; R Goetre w Llanover and Llanfair Kilgeddin 82-85; R Goetre w Llanover from 85; RD Raglan-Usk from 90. *The Rectory, Nantyderry, Abergavenny, Gwent NP7 9DW* Nantyderry (01873) 880378

CALE, Nicholas. b 66. St Mich Coll Llan DipTh92. **d** 92 **p** 93. C Tenby *St D* from 92. *St Mary's House, 55 Upper Hill Park, Tenby, Dyfed SA70 8JF* Tenby (01834) 844330

CALEY, Charles Joseph. b 16. AKC47. Bp Wilson Coll 35. **d** 39 **p** 40. V E Farleigh and Coxheath *Roch* 62-82; rtd 82; Perm to Offic *Roch* from 82; Perm to Offic *Cant* from 83. *1 Bakery Cottages, Oakvale, Chatham Road, Sandling, Maidstone, Kent ME14 3BE* Maidstone (01622) 673397

CALLAGHAN, Canon Harry. b 34. AKC59 Open Univ BA83. **d** 60 **p** 61. C Sheff Parson Cross St Cecilia *Sheff* 60-63; Br Guiana 63-66; Guyana 66-70; Barbados 70-74; Lic to Offic *Man* 74-84; Miss to Seamen 74-76; Area Sec (Dios Blackb, Man and S & M) USPG 76-84; P-in-c Wythenshawe St Martin *Man* 84-85; V 85-91; V Bolton St Jo from 91; Hon Can Mass from 92. *St John's Vicarage, 7 Alford Close, Bolton BL2 6NR* Bolton (01204) 418233 or 520863

CALLAGHAN, Martin Peter. b 57. Edin Th Coll 91. **d** 93 **p** 94. C Ayr *Glas* from 93. *6 Hillpark Drive, Kilmarnock, Ayrshire KA3 1HR* Kilmarnock (01563) 20107

CALLAGHAN, Robert Paul. b 59. K Coll Lon BD81. Linc Th Coll 81. **d** 83 **p** 85. C Winchmore Hill St Paul *Lon* 83-85; C Paddington St Jo w St Mich 85-91; V Dartford St Edm *Roch* from 91. *The Vicarage, St Edmund's Road, Temple Hill, Dartford DA1 5ND* Dartford (01322) 225335

CALLAN, Canon Terence Frederick. b 26. CITC 55. **d** 57 **p** 58. P-in-c Ballymacash *Conn* 67-70; I Belf St Aid 70-79; I Agherton 79-94; Can Conn Cathl from 86; Treas from 90; rtd 94. *18 Central Avenue, Portstewart, Co Londonderry BT55 7BS* Portstewart (01265) 832704

CALLAN-TRAVIS, Anthony. b 46. N Ord Course 90. **d** 93 **p** 94. C Tong *Bradf* from 93. *St Christopher's Vicarage, 207 Broadstone Way, Bradford, W Yorkshire BD4 9BT* Bradford (01274) 685256

CALLARD, Canon David Kingsley. b 37. St Pet Coll Ox BA61 MA65. Westcott Ho Cam 61. **d** 63 **p** 64. C Leamington Priors H Trin *Cov* 63-66; C Wyken 66-68; C Hatf *St Alb* 68-73; R Bilton *Cov* 73-83; TR Swanage and Studland *Sarum* 83-93; TR Oakdale St Geo from 93; Hon Can Sarum Cathl from 95. *The Rectory, 99 Darby's Lane, Poole, Dorset BH15 3EU* Poole (01202) 675419

CALLENDER, Thomas Henry. b 13. SS Coll Cam BA35 MA39. Sarum Th Coll 35. **d** 37 **p** 38. V Carbrooke *Nor* 66-76; R Ovington 66-76; V Carbrooke w Ovington, Woodrising and Scoulton 76-78; rtd 78; Perm to Offic *Nor* from 78. *4 Bickley Close, Mill Lane, Attleborough, Norfolk NR17 2NT* Attleborough (01953) 454727

CALLER, Laurence Edward Harrison. b 19. Lon Univ BMus77 MA82. Lich Th Coll 39. **d** 42 **p** 43. V Harlescott *Lich* 63-67; rtd 84. *103 Fronks Road, Dovercourt, Harwich, Essex CO12 4EG* Harwich (01255) 504501

CALLON, Andrew McMillan. b 56. Chich Th Coll 77. **d** 80 **p** 81. C Wigan All SS *Liv* 80-85; V Abram 85-90; V Bickershaw 89-90; Chapl RN from 90. *Directorate Gen, RN Chapl Services, Room 203, Victory Building, HM Naval Base, Portsmouth PO1 3LS* Portsmouth (01705) 727903 Fax 727112

CALTHROP-OWEN, William Gordon. b 35. Chich Th Coll 62. **d** 63 **p** 64. C Egremont St Jo *Ches* 63-68; C Bawtry w Austerfield *S'well* 68-69; P-in-c Radford All So w Ch Ch 69-73; P-in-c Radford St Mich 69-73; R Bilsthorpe 73-90; R Eakring 73-90; P-in-c Winkburn 77-90; P-in-c Maplebeck 77-90; V Woodborough from 90; Chapl HM Young Offender Inst Lowdham Grange 90-91. *The Vicarage, Lingwood Lane, Woodborough, Nottingham NG14 6DX* Nottingham (0115) 965 2250

CALVER, Mrs Gillian Margaret. b 47. Qu Eliz Coll Lon BSc68. Cant Sch of Min 89. **d** 92 **p** 94. NSM Folkestone H Trin w Ch Ch *Cant* from 92. *21 Chichester Road, Sandgate, Folkestone, Kent CT20 3BN* Folkestone (01303) 248725

CALVER, Nicholas James. b 58. Nottm Univ BTh83 Dur Univ MA90. Cranmer Hall Dur 86. **d** 88 **p** 89. C Forest Hill Ch Ch *S'wark* 88-91; C Forest Hill 91-92; P-in-c Mottingham St Edw from 92; Voc Adv Lewisham Adnry from 94. *St Edward's Vicarage, St Keverne Road, London SE9 4AQ* 0181-857 6278

CALVER, Sydney Bertram. b 10. Keble Coll Ox BA33. Chich Th Coll 33. **d** 35 **p** 36. R Stonesfield *Ox* 56-75; rtd 75; Perm to Offic *Ox* 75-77; Perm to Offic *B & W* 77-93. *8 Parkfield Drive, Taunton, Somerset TA1 5BT* Taunton (01823) 272535

CALVERT, Dr Geoffrey Richard. b 58. Edin Univ BSc79 PhD84 Leeds Univ BA86. Coll of Resurr Mirfield 84. **d** 87 **p** 88. C Curdworth w Castle Vale *Birm* 87-90; C Barnsley St Mary *Wakef* 90-92; TV Halifax 92-94; V Halifax H Trin from 95. *Holy Trinity Vicarage, 9 Love Lane, Halifax, W Yorkshire HX1 2BQ* Halifax (01422) 352446

CALVERT, Canon Jean. b 34. Lightfoot Ho Dur IDC. **dss** 78 **d** 87 **p** 94. S Bank *York* 78-84; Chapl Asst Rampton Hosp Retford from 84; D-in-c Dunham w Darlton and Ragnall *S'well* 88-89; D-in-c E Drayton w Stokeham 88-89; D-in-c Fledborough 88-89; D-in-c Dunham-on-Trent w Darlton, Ragnall etc 89-94; R from 94; Hon Can S'well Minster from 93; *The Vicarage, Dunham-on-Trent, Newark, Notts NG22 0UL* Dunham-on-Trent (01777) 228707

CALVERT, John Raymond. b 42. Lon Coll of Div 64. **d** 67 **p** 68. C Kennington St Mark *S'wark* 67-70; C Southborough St Pet *Roch* 70-72; C Barton Seagrave *Pet* 72-75; Asst Master Shaftesbury High Sch 78-79; Dioc Children's Officer *Glouc* 79-87; P-in-c S Cerney w Cerney Wick and Down Ampney 87-89; V from 89. *The Vicarage, Silver Street, South Cerney, Cirencester, Glos GL7 5TP* Cirencester (01285) 860221

CALVERT, John Stephen. b 27. Lon Univ BSc53. Wycliffe Coll Toronto BTh61. **d** 61 **p** 62. C Preston St Jo *Blackb* 63-70; rtd 92. *17 Leyster Street, Morecambe, Lancs LA4 5NE* Morecambe (01524) 424491

CALVERT, Canon Peter Noel. b 41. Ch Coll Cam BA63 MA67. Cuddesdon Coll 64. **d** 66 **p** 67. C Brighouse *Wakef* 66-71; V Heptonstall 71-82; V Todmorden from 82; P-in-c Cross Stone 83-93; RD Calder Valley from 84; Hon Can Wakef Cathl from 92. *The Vicarage, Todmorden, Lancs OL14 7BS* Todmorden (01706) 813180

CALVIN-THOMAS, David Nigel. b 43. Univ of Wales (Cardiff) BSc64 Lon Univ BD77 Leeds Univ DipC&G88. St Mich Coll Llan 77. **d** 78 **p** 79. C Pontypridd St Cath *Llan* 78-80; Malawi 81-84; V Rastrick St Matt *Wakef* 84-88; V Birchencliffe 88-93; Chapl Huddersfield R Infirmary 88-93; R Aber St Pet *Ab* from 93; P-in-c Cove Bay from 93. *123 Walker Road, Aberdeen AB1 3DH* Aberdeen (01224) 248193

CALWAY, Geoffrey. b 45. Bris Sch of Min. **d** 87 **p** 88. NSM Cotham St Sav w St Mary *Bris* 87-94; NSM Horfield H Trin from 94. *1 Oakley Road, Bristol BS7 0HR* Bristol (0117) 969 8715

CAM, Julian Howard. b 48. York Univ BA69 Birm Univ DipTh74. Qu Coll Birm 73. **d** 75 **p** 76. C St Ives *Truro* 75-80; C Lelant 78-80; V Flookburgh *Carl* 80-82; V St Stephen by Saltash *Truro* 82-83; V Low Marple *Ches* from 83. *St Martin's Vicarage, 15 Brabyns Brow, Marple Bridge, Stockport, Cheshire SK6 5DT* 0161-427 2736

CAMENISCH, Richard Frank. b 12. Univ Coll Dur BA34. Wells Th Coll 34. **d** 35 **p** 36. V Bicker *Linc* 68-77; rtd 77; Perm to Offic *S'well* from 77; Perm to Offic *Sheff* from 86. *The Whipping Post, Norwell Lane, Newark, Notts NG23 6JE* Newark (01636) 821423

✠**CAMERON, Rt Rev Andrew Bruce.** b 41. New Coll Edin CPS72. Sheff Urban Th Unit 82 Edin Th Coll 61. **d** 64 **p** 65 **c** 92. C Helensburgh *Glas* 64-67; C Edin H Cross *Edin* 67-71; Prov and Dioc Youth Chapl 69-75; Chapl St Mary's Cathl 71-75; R Dalmahoy 75-82; Chapl Heriot-Watt Univ 75-82; TV Livingston LEP 82-88; R Perth St Jo *St And* 88-92; Convener Prov Miss Bd 88-92; Bp Ab from 92. *Bishop's House, Ashley House, Ashley Gardens, Aberdeen AB1 6RQ* Aberdeen (01224) 208142 or 636653 Fax 636186

CAMERON, David Alan. b 59. Glas Univ MA81 DipEd82 PGCE82. Ripon Coll Cuddesdon 88. **d** 91 **p** 92. C Farncombe *Guildf* 91-93; C Guildf H Trin w St Mary from 93. *102 The Street, Shalford, Guildford, Surrey GU4 8BN* Guildford (01483) 61633

CAMERON, David Alexander. b 42. MRTPI Reading Univ BA63 Leeds Art Coll DipTP69. St And Dioc Tr Course 80. **d** 90 **p** 93. NSM Blairgowrie *St And* from 90; NSM Coupar Angus from 90; NSM Alyth from 90. *Firgrove, Golf Course Road, Blairgowrie, Perthshire PH10 6LF* Blairgowrie (01250) 3272

CAMERON, Donald Eric Nelson. b 29. St Jo Coll Dur 68. **d** 70 **p** 71. C Kingston upon Hull H Trin *York* 70-73; V Eston 73-82; R Balerno *Edin* 82-87; rtd 94. *The Granary, Crauchie, East Linton, East Lothian EH40 3EB* East Linton (01620) 860067

✠**CAMERON, Rt Rev Douglas MacLean.** b 35. Univ of S Tennessee 61. Edin Th Coll 59. **d** 62 **p** 63 **c** 93. C Falkirk *Edin* 62-65; Papua New Guinea 66-74; Adn New Guinea Mainland 72-74; P-in-c Edin St Fillan *Edin* 74-78; R 78-88; R Edin St Hilda 77-88; R Dalkeith 88-92; R Lasswade 88-92; Can St Mary's Cathl 90-91; Syn Clerk 90-91; Dean Edin 91-92; Bp Arg from 93. *Bishop's Office, The Pines, Ardconnel Road, Oban, Argyll PA34 5DR* Oban (01631) 66912 Fax as telephone

CAMERON, Gregory Kenneth. b 59. Linc Coll Ox BA80 MA84 Down Coll Cam BA82 MA85 Univ of Wales (Cardiff) DPS83 MPhil92. St Mich Coll Llan 82. **d** 83 **p** 84. C Newport St Paul *Mon* 83-86; Tutor St Mich Coll Llan 86-89; C Llanmartin *Mon* 86-87; TV 87-88; Chapl Wycliffe Coll Stonehouse Glos 88-94; Dir Bloxham Project from 94. *St Thomas's House, 12 St Thomas's Square, Monmouth, Gwent NP5 3ES* Monmouth (01600) 716912 Fax as telephone

CAMERON, Mrs Margaret Mary. b 48. Qu Mary Coll Lon BA69 Liv Univ DAA70 Ex Univ MA95. SW Minl Tr Course 87. **d** 90 **p** 94. NSM Budleigh Salterton *Ex* 90-95; C Whipton from 95. *Holy Trinity House, Arena Park, Exeter EX4 8RD* Exeter (01392) 465427

CAMERON, Michael John. b 41. Sheff Tech Coll HNC63 DipM66 Nottm Univ CTPS90. Linc Th Coll 91. **d** 92 **p** 93. C Dinnington *Sheff* from 92. *32 Shakespeare Drive, Dinnington, Sheffield S31 7RP* Dinnington (01909) 563682

CAMERON, Peter Samuel Griswold. b 30. TD76. New Coll Ox BA53 MA56. Wells Th Coll 53. **d** 55 **p** 56. C Westbury-on-Trym St Alb *Bris* 55-58; C Henbury 58-60; CF (TA) 59-70, 72-78 and 80-87; Perm to Offic *Ely* 60-63; Chapl K Coll Cam 60-63; C-in-c Davyhulme CD *Man* 63-69; V Davyhulme Ch Ch 69-72; V Worsley 72-79; V Waterbeach *Ely* 79-83; R Landbeach 79-83; RD Quy 81-83; V Chesterton Gd Shep 83-93; P-in-c Fenstanton 93-94; V from 94; P-in-c Hilton 93-94; V from 94. *The Vicarage, 16 Church Street, Fenstanton, Huntingdon, Cambs PE18 9JL* St Ives (01480) 463334

CAMERON, William Hugh Macpherson. b 59. Edin Univ LLB82 BD86. Edin Th Coll 83. **d** 86 **p** 87. C Cheadle Hulme All SS *Ches* 86-89; Asst Chapl and Hd Relig Studies Wellington Coll 89-93; Chapl K Sch Bruton from 93. *King's School, Bruton, Somerset BA10 0ED* Bruton (01749) 813326

CAMERON, William James. b 35. St Aid Birkenhead 60. **d** 64 **p** 65. C Halewood *Liv* 64-66; C-in-c Halewood St Mary CD 66-68; Asst Chapl Leeds Univ *Ripon* 68-71; Ind Chapl *Liv* 71-77; Tr Officer Gen Syn Bd of Educn 77-84; V Hickling and Waxham w Sea Palling *Nor* 89-95; RD Waxham from 93; P-in-c Ludham w Potter Heigham 94-95; V Ludham, Potter Heigham and Hickling from 95. *The Vicarage, Norwich Road, Ludham, Great Yarmouth, Norfolk NR29 5QA* St Benets (01692) 678282

CAMIER, Canon James. b 12. TCD BA33 MA67 Div Test. **d** 35 **p** 36. I Borrisokane w Ardcroney, Aglishcloghane etc *L & K* 61-86; RD Ely O'Carroll 62-86; Can Killaloe Cathl from 65; Prec 72-86; rtd 86. *Ferndale, Shillelagh, Co Wicklow, Irish Republic* Shillelagh (55) 29227

CAMM, Howard Arthur. b 56. Newc Univ BEd79 Lon Univ BD82 DipTh82. St Jo Coll Dur MA91. **d** 91 **p** 92. C S Westoe *Dur* 91-92; C Seaham w Seaham Harbour 92-95; TV Brighton Resurr *Chich* from 95. *St Luke's Vicarage, Queen's Park Terrace, Brighton BN2 2YA* Brighton (01273) 603946

CAMM, Joseph Arnold. b 12. Worc Ord Coll 68 Ridley Hall Cam 69. **d** 69 **p** 70. C Gt and Lt Driffield *York* 69-72; V Stillingfleet w Naburn 72-78; rtd 78. *Rectory Farm, Walkington, Beverley, N Humberside HU17 8RY* Hull (01482) 862928

CAMMELL, William John. b 36. Glouc Sch of Min 89. **d** 92 **p** 93. NSM Ruardean *Glouc* from 92. *The Beeches, High Beech, The Pludds, Ruardean, Glos GL17 9UD* Dean (01594) 860603

CAMP, Brian Arthur Leslie. b 50. St Jo Coll Nottm. **d** 83 **p** 84. C Blackheath *Birm* 83-86; TV Halesowen *Worc* from 86. *St Peter's Vicarage, 15 Cricklewood Drive, Halesowen, W Midlands B62 8SN* 0121-550 5458

CAMP, Frederick Walter. b 19. Sarum Th Coll 47. **d** 49 **p** 50. V Brigham *Carl* 58-80; V Whittingham *Newc* 80-84; V Whittingham and Edlingham w Bolton Chapel 84-85; rtd 85; Perm to Offic *Carl* from 85. *10 Meadow Close, Maryport, Cumbria CA15 7AS* Maryport (01900) 817936

CAMP, John Edward. b 44. Barrister 69 Jes Coll Ox MA68 Brunel Univ MTech69. Ripon Coll Cuddesdon DipTh88. **d** 88 **p** 89. NSM High Wycombe *Ox* 88-89; Chapl St Andr Hosp Northn from 89; Chapl Three Shires Hosp Northn from 89; Lic to Offic *Pet* from 89. *St Andrew's Hospital, Billing Road, Northampton NN1 5DG, or 4 Elwes Way, Great Billing, Northampton NN3 9EA* Northampton (01604) 785130 or 29696 Fax 232325

CAMP, Michael Maurice. b 52. BTh CertEd. Sarum & Wells Th Coll 78. **d** 81 **p** 82. C Loughton St Jo *Chelmsf* 81-84; C Chingford SS Pet and Paul 84-87; V Northfleet *Roch* 87-94; V Hadlow from 94. *The Vicarage, Maidstone Road, Hadlow, Tonbridge, Kent TN11 0DJ* Sevenoaks (01732) 850238

CAMPBELL, Allan. b 14. Selw Coll Cam BA36 MA40. Westcott Ho Cam 36. **d** 38 **p** 39. R Amersham *Ox* 63-86; Chapl Amersham Gen Hosp 63-86; rtd 86; Perm to Offic *Carl* from 86. *Bridge House, Cockermouth, Cumbria CA13 0HF* Cockermouth (01900) 826748

CAMPBELL, Andrew Victor. b 20. St Chad's Coll Dur 39. Linc Th Coll 46. **d** 49 **p** 50. S Africa 52-72; Adn N Transvaal 67-72; V Hunstanton St Edm *Nor* 72-74; Chapl Coll of the Ascension Selly Oak 74-75; TV Devonport St Aubyn *Ex* 75-76; P-in-c Whitleigh 76-80; V 80-83; RD Plymouth 79-82; P-in-c Harberton w Harbertonford 83-85; rtd 85; Perm to Offic *Ex* 85-92. *Little Clevedale, 24 Christchurch Road, Winchester, Hants SO23 9SS* Winchester (01962) 864317

CAMPBELL, Miss Brenda. b 47. St Jo Coll Nottm DipTh94. **d** 94 **p** 95. C Rothley *Leic* from 94. *105 Balmoral Road, Mountsorrel, Loughborough, Leics LE12 7EL* Leicester (0116) 230 3199

CAMPBELL, David. b 70. St Andr Univ MTheol92 New Coll Edin MTh94. Edin Th Coll CECM94. **d** 94 **p** 95. C Perth St Jo *St And* from 94. *30 Glengarry Road, Perth PH2 0QA* Perth (01738) 633847

CAMPBELL, Frederick David Gordon. b 15. Ex Coll Ox BA39. Wells Th Coll 39. **d** 40 **p** 41. V Isleworth St Mary *Lon* 51-54; SSJE from 57; Superior Gen SSJE 76-91; Lic to Offic *Lon* from 69; rtd 85. *St Edward's House, 22 Great College Street, London SW1P 3QA* 0171-222 9234

CAMPBELL, George St Clair. b 32. Lon Univ BSc53. Clifton Th Coll 58. **d** 60 **p** 61. V Tunbridge Wells St Pet *Roch* 60-64; C Clitheroe St Jas *Blackb* 64-70; V Tibshelf *Derby* 70-86; V W Bromwich H Trin *Lich* from 86; Chapl Heath Lane Hosp from 87. *The Vicarage, 1 Burlington Road, West Bromwich, W Midlands B70 6LF* 0121-525 3595

CAMPBELL, Canon Ian David. b 33. AKC57. **d** 58 **p** 59. C Liv Our Lady and St Nic w St Anne *Liv* 58-62; V Edge Hill St Dunstan 62-70; R Loughb Em *Leic* 70-80; V Leamington Priors All SS *Cov* 80-91; Hon Can Cov Cathl 87-91; RD Warw and Leamington 87-91; TR Brixham w Churston Ferrers and Kingswear *Ex* from 91. *The Rectory, 6 Durleigh Road, Brixham, Devon TQ5 9JJ* Brixham (01803) 854924

CAMPBELL, James Duncan. b 55. Qu Eliz Coll Lon BSc77. St Jo Coll Dur 85. **d** 87 **p** 88. C Hendon St Paul Mill Hill *Lon* 87-92; V Stevenage SS Hugh and Jo Chells *St Alb* from 92. *St Hugh's House, 4 Mobbsbury Way, Chells, Stevenage, Herts SG2 0HL* Stevenage (01438) 354307

CAMPBELL, James Larry. b 46. Indiana Univ BSc69 E Kentucky Univ MA73 Hull Univ MA91. Linc Th Coll 86. **d** 88 **p** 89. C N Hull St Mich *York* 88-92; C Hessle from 92. *The Clergy House, 167 First Lane, Hessle, N Humberside HU13 9EY* Hull (01482) 642169

CAMPBELL, James Malcolm. b 55. ARICS81 R Agric Coll Cirencester DipREM77. Wycliffe Hall Ox 89. **d** 91 **p** 92. C Scole, Brockdish, Billingford, Thorpe Abbots etc *Nor* 91-95; R Bentley and Binsted *Win* from 95. *Holy Cross Vicarage, Binsted, Alton, Hants GU34 4NX* Bentley (01420) 22174

CAMPBELL, James Norman Thompson. b 49. BTh. **d** 86 **p** 87. C Arm St Mark w Aghavilly *Arm* 86-89; I Belf H Trin and Ardoyne *Conn* 89-95; I Dundela *D & D* from 95. *St Mark's Rectory, 4 Sydenham Avenue, Belfast BT4 2DR* Belfast (01323) 659047

CAMPBELL, John Frederick Stuart. b 25. Open Univ BA80. ACT ThL50 Oak Hill Th Coll 51. **d** 52 **p** 53. Australia 65-74; V Bath Weston St Jo *B & W* 74-80; R Bath Weston St Jo w Kelston 81-90; rtd 90; Chapl Shepton Mallet Hosps from 91. *3 Lewmond Avenue, Wells, Somerset BA5 2TS* Wells (01749) 675016

CAMPBELL, Canon John Norman. b 16. Ch Coll Cam BA38 MA42. Ridley Hall Cam 38. **d** 40 **p** 41. Uganda 49-70; R Stapleton *Bris* 70-85; rtd 85; Perm to Offic *Bris* from 85. *71 Gloucester Road, Malmesbury, Wilts SN16 0AJ* Malmesbury (01666) 822730

CAMPBELL, Kenneth Scott. b 47. BA82. Oak Hill Th Coll. **d** 82 **p** 83. C Aughton St Mich *Liv* 82-85; V Brough w Stainmore *Carl* 85-90; R Brough w Stainmore, Musgrave and Warcop 90-92; rtd 92. *4 Quarry Close, Kirkby Stephen, Cumbria CA17 4SS* Kirkby Stephen (017683) 72390

CAMPBELL, Lawrence Henry. b 41. TCD BA63 MA66. **d** 63 **p** 65. C Larne and Inver *Conn* 63-66; C Finaghy 66-67; Chapl RN 67-83; R Brancaster w Burnham Deepdale and Titchwell *Nor* 83-95; P-in-c Hunstanton St Mary w Ringstead Parva, Holme etc 94-95; R Hunstanton St Mary w Ringstead Parva etc from 95. *St Mary's Rectory, Hunstanton, Norfolk PE36 6JS* Hunstanton (01485) 532169

CAMPBELL, Nelson James. b 10. AKC33. **d** 33 **p** 34. V Whitton SS Phil and Jas *Lon* 68-79; rtd 79; Perm to Offic *St E* 79-84; Perm to Offic *Lon* 84-90; Perm to Offic *Portsm* from 90; Perm to Offic *Win* from 90. *Karen House, Hilbrow, Liss, Hants GU33 7PB* Liss (01730) 893640

CAMPBELL, Patrick Alistair. b 36. Qu Coll Birm 64. **d** 67 **p** 68. C Paston *Pet* 67-71; C Stockton Heath *Ches* 71-73; V Egremont St Jo 73-78; V Bredbury St Mark 78-85; R Astbury and Smallwood 85-91; V Wybunbury w Doddington from 91. *The Vicarage, Main Road, Wybunbury, Nantwich, Cheshire CW5 7LS* Nantwich (01270) 841178

CAMPBELL, Robin William. b 41. TCD BA63 MA67. Ridley Hall Cam 63. **d** 65 **p** 66. C Netherton *Liv* 65-68; C Liv Our Lady and St Nic w St Anne 68-70; V Hooton *Ches* from 70. *Hooton Vicarage, Chester Road, Wirral, Merseyside L66 1QH* 0151-339 2020

CAMPBELL, Roger Stewart. b 40. Birm Univ BSc61 PhD65 St Jo Coll Dur BA71. Cranmer Hall Dur 68. **d** 71 **p** 72. C Jesmond Clayton Memorial *Newc* 71-77; Singapore 78-85; C Nottm St Nic *S'well* 86-90; V Holloway St Mark w Em *Lon* 90-92; TR Tollington from 92. *St Mark's Vicarage, 1 Moray Road, London N4 3LD* 0171-272 5376

CAMPBELL, Stephen James. b 60. **d** 91 **p** 92. C Lisburn Ch Ch *Conn* 91-95; I Kilcronaghan w Draperstown and Sixtowns *D & R* from 95. *The Rectory, 10 Rectory Road, Tobermore, Magherafelt, Co Londonderry BT45 5QP* Draperstown (01648) 28823

CAMPBELL-SMITH, Canon Robert Campbell (Bob). b 38. CCC Cam BA61 MA66 Ibadan Univ Nigeria 62. Linc Th Coll 61. **d** 63 **p** 64. C Norbury St Steph *Cant* 63-66; C W Wickham St Mary 66-71; V Croydon St Aug 71-81; V Goudhurst 81-87; RD W Charing 82-89; P-in-c Kilndown 83-87; V Goudhurst w Kilndown from 87; Hon Can Cant Cathl from 94. *The Vicarage, Goudhurst, Cranbrook, Kent TN17 1AN* Goudhurst (01580) 211332

CAMPBELL-TAYLOR, William Goodacre. b 65. **d** 94 **p** 95. C Chingford SS Pet and Paul *Chelmsf* from 94. *2 Sunnyside Drive, London E4 7DZ*

CAMPBELL-WILSON, Allan. b 43. Dur Univ BEd74. NE Ord Course 79. **d** 82 **p** 83. NSM Boosbeck w Moorsholm *York* 82-85; R Easington w Skeffling, Kilnsea and Holmpton 85-87; P-in-c Middlesb St Jo the Ev 89-95; V from 95. *St John's Vicarage, 45 Lothian Road, Middlesbrough, Cleveland TS4 2HS* Middlesbrough (01642) 242926

CAMPEN, William Geoffrey. b 50. Liv Univ CertEd71 Southn Univ BTh81. Sarum & Wells Th Coll 76. **d** 79 **p** 80. C Peckham St Jo w St Andr *S'wark* 79-83; P-in-c Mottingham St Edw 83-92; R Charlwood from 92; R Sidlow Bridge from 92. *The Rectory, Charlwood, Horley, Surrey RH6 0EE* Norwood Hill (01293) 862343

CAMPION, Keith Donald. b 52. S Dios Minl Tr Scheme. **d** 84 **p** 87. NSM Scilly Is *Truro* from 84. *20 Launceston Close, St Mary's, Isles of Scilly TR21 0LN* Scillonia (01720) 22606

CAMPION, Peter Robert. b 64. Bp's Univ Canada BA87 TCD BTh90. **d** 90 **p** 91. C Belf H Trin and Ardoyne *Conn* 90-93; Canada 93-94; C Taney *D & G* from 94. *Church Cottage, 21 Taney Road, Dundrum, Dublin 14, Irish Republic* Dublin (1) 296-0736 or 298-5491

CAMPLING, Very Rev Christopher Russell. b 25. St Edm Hall Ox BA50 MA54. Cuddesdon Coll 50. **d** 51 **p** 52. P-in-c Birlingham w Nafford *Worc* 68-75; V Pershore w Wick 68-75; RD Pershore 70-76; Hon Can Worc Cathl 74-84; V Pershore w Pinvin, Wick and Birlingham 75-76; Dioc Dir of Educn 76-84; Adn Dudley 76-84; P-in-c Dodderhill 76-84; Dean Ripon 84-95; Chmn CCC 88-94; rtd 95. *Pebble Ridge, Aglaia Road, Worthing, W Sussex BN11 5SW* Worthing (01903) 246598

CAMPLING, Michael. b 27. Trin Coll Cam BA50 MA61. Wells Th Coll 51. **d** 53 **p** 54. V Crowthorne *Ox* 61-75; P-in-c Foleshill St Laur *Cov* 75-81; V 81-83; R Old Alresford and Bighton *Win* 83-92; rtd 92; Chapl St Marg Convent E Grinstead from 92.

The Chaplain's Cottage, St Margaret's Convent, East Grinstead, W Sussex RH19 3LE East Grinstead (01342) 323497

CANDLER, David Cecil. b 24. Cape Town Univ BSc47 Keble Coll Ox BA50 MA55. St Paul's Grahamstown 56. **d** 56 **p** 57. S Rhodesia 57-65; Rhodesia 65-80; Zimbabwe 80-85; R Barningham w Matlaske w Baconsthorpe etc *Nor* 85-94; Perm to Offic from 94; rtd 94. *Millstone, Mill Lane, Aldborough, Norwich NR11 7NS* Matlaske (01263) 577420

CANE, Anthony William Nicholas Strephon. b 61. Cape Town Univ BA81 Birm Univ MPhil93. Westcott Ho Cam 87. **d** 90 **p** 91. C Kings Heath *Birm* 90-93; Chapl Brighton Univ *Chich* from 93. *3 Great Wilkins, Brighton BN1 9QW* Brighton (0h273) 643592

CANEY, Canon Robert Swinbank. b 37. St Jo Coll Cam 57. Lich Th Coll 58. **d** 61 **p** 62. C Kingswinford H Trin *Lich* 61-64; C Castle Church 64-67; V Bradwell *Derby* 67-73; V Fairfield 73-84; RD Buxton 78-84; P-in-c Peak Forest and Wormhill 79-83; R Wirksworth w Alderwasley, Carsington etc 84-92; TR Wirksworth from 92; Hon Can Derby Cathl from 93. *The Rectory, Wirksworth, Matlock, Derbyshire DE4 4FB* Wirksworth (01629) 824707

CANHAM, John Graham. b 33. Univ of Wales (Lamp) BA55. Chich Th Coll 55. **d** 57 **p** 58. C Hawarden *St As* 57-64; Asst Chapl Ellesmere Coll Shropshire 64-66; Chapl Ches Cathl Choir Sch 66-73; Chapl Choral Ches Cathl *Ches* 66-73; Asst Chapl Rossall Sch Fleetwood 73-76 and 83-93; Chapl 76-83; V Minera *St As* from 93. *The Vicarage, Church Road, Minera, Wrexham, Clwyd LL11 3DA* Wrexham (01978) 755679

CANHAM, Philip Edward. b 15. St Aid Birkenhead 46. **d** 46 **p** 47. V Dalston *Carl* 65-70; V Irthington 70-76; P-in-c Addingham 76-79; P-in-c Edenhall w Langwathby and Culgaith 76-79; P-in-c Greenhead *Newc* 79-80; P-in-c Lambley w Knaresdale 79-80; rtd 80. *6 Eden Park Crescent, Carlisle CA1 2UF* Carlisle (01228) 47236

CANHAM, Robert Edwin Francis. b 24. FRCO59 ARCM. **d** 74 **p** 75. NSM Newlyn St Pet *Truro* 74-75; C Phillack w Gwithian 75-79; P-in-c Phillack w Gwithian and Gwinear 79-83; V Greenham *Ox* 83-93; rtd 93. *Cross Way, 1A Torton Hill Road, Arundel, W Sussex BN18 9HF* Aundel (01903) 883614

CANHAM, William Alexander. b 26. Clare Coll Cam BA47 MA56. Roch Th Coll 65. **d** 67 **p** 68. C Orpington St Andr *Roch* 67-70; C Guernsey St Steph *Win* 70-75; Chapl Eliz Coll Guernsey 72-75; R Tadley St Pet 75-83; V Bournemouth St Luke 83-91; R Guernsey St Marguerite de la Foret from 91. *The Rectory, Le Bourg, Foret, Guernsey, Channel Islands GY8 0BR* Guernsey (01481) 38392

CANN, Christopher James. b 64. St Andr Univ BA MA. St Steph Ho Ox. **d** 91 **p** 92. C Newport St Julian *Mon* 91-93; Chapl Smallwood Manor Sch Uttoxeter from 93. *Smallwood Manor School, Uttoxeter, Staffs ST14 8NS* Uttoxeter (01889) 562083

CANN, Stanley George. b 16. St Boniface Warminster 40 Linc Th Coll. **d** 43 **p** 44. V Sidley *Chich* 66-84; P-in-c 84; RD Battle and Bexhill 77-84 and 85-86; rtd 84; Perm to Offic *Chich* from 86. *45 First Avenue, Bexhill-on-Sea, E Sussex TN40 2PL* Bexhill-on-Sea (01424) 211867

CANNER, Canon Peter George. b 24. St Chad's Coll Dur BA49 DipTh51 MA55. **d** 51 **p** 52. V Tynemouth Ch Ch *Newc* 63-77; V Ponteland 77-89; Hon Can Newc Cathl 80-89; rtd 89. *The Rigg, 4 Back Croft, Rothbury, Morpeth, Northd NE65 7YB* Rothbury (01669) 21319

CANNING, Canon Arthur James. b 45. St Jo Coll Dur BA66 Linacre Coll Ox BA70 MA74 Lambeth STh90. Ripon Hall Ox 67. **d** 71 **p** 72. C Coleshill *Birm* 71-74; C Frome St Jo *B & W* 75-76; V Frizington and Arlecdon *Carl* 76-80; P-in-c Foleshill St Paul *Cov* 80-81; V from 81. *St Paul's Vicarage, 13 St Paul's Road, Coventry CV6 5DE* Coventry (01203) 688283

CANNING, Arthur Brian. b 12. St Jo Coll Dur BA37 MA40. **d** 37 **p** 38. V New Romney w Hope and St Mary's Bay etc *Cant* 66-71; V Boughton Monchelsea 71-79; rtd 79; Perm to Offic *Heref* from 81. *Harp Cottage, Old Radnor, Presteigne, Powys LD8 2RH* New Radnor (0154421) 312

CANNING, Graham Gordon Blakeman. b 33. S'wark Ord Course 73. **d** 76 **p** 77. NSM Mill Hill Jo Keble Ch *Lon* 76-78; TV Dorchester *Ox* 78-85; V Shipton-under-Wychwood w Milton-under-Wychwood from 85. *The Vicarage, Shipton-under-Wychwood, Chipping Norton, Oxon OX7 6BP* Shipton-under-W'wood (0993) 830257

CANNING, John Graham. b 21. Edin Th Coll 47. **d** 49 **p** 50. V Hammersmith St Jo *Lon* 62-90; rtd 90; Perm to Offic *B & W* from 90. *11 Circus Field Road, Glastonbury, Somerset BA6 9PE* Glastonbury (01458) 833708

CANNING, Peter Christopher. b 52. Birm Poly DipSocWork78 CQSW. St Jo Coll Nottm 87. **d** 89 **p** 90. C Cov St Mary *Cov* 89-93; V Hartshill from 93. *The Vicarage, Church Road, Hartshill, Nuneaton, Warks CV10 0LY* Chapel End (01203) 392266

CANNING, Canon Richard Dandridge. b 16. St Chad's Coll Dur BA41 DipTh42 MA44. **d** 42 **p** 43. Hon Can Antigua from 64; St Kitts-Nevis 68-75; Grenada 76-81; rtd 81. *Manormead Nursing Home, Tilford Road, Hindhead, Surrey GU26 6RA* Hindhead (01428) 604780

CANNON, Alan George. b 35. FRSA MBIM Lon Univ BA57 MA63 PhD71 AKC. Sarum & Wells Th Coll 76. **d** 80 **p** 81. Hon C Whipton *Ex* 80-89; Perm to Offic from 89. *6 Devonshire Place, Exeter EX4 6JA* Exeter (01392) 55944

CANNON, Mark Harrison. b 60. Keble Coll Ox BA82. Cranmer Hall Dur 83. **d** 85 **p** 86. C Skipton Ch Ch *Bradf* 85-88; Dioc Youth Officer 88-92; C Baildon 88-92; P-in-c Church Coniston *Carl* from 92; P-in-c Torver from 92. *St Andrew's Vicarage, Yewdale Road, Coniston, Cumbria LA21 8DB* Coniston (015394) 41262

CANSDALE, George Graham. b 38. Mert Coll Ox BA60 MA64 DipEd61. Clifton Th Coll 62. **d** 64 **p** 65. C Heatherlands St Jo *Sarum* 64-67; Kenya 68-76; P-in-c Clapham *St Alb* 76-80; V 80-89; Bedf Sch 89-93; Lic to Offic *St Alb* from 93. *40 Bridle Drive, Clapham, Bedford MK41 6BE* Bedford (01234) 328184

CANSDALE, Simon James Lee. b 68. Keble Coll Ox BA90. Wycliffe Hall Ox 93. **d** 95. C Bletchley *Ox* from 95. *65 Bushey Close, Bletchley, Milton Keynes MK3 6PX* Milyon Keynes (01908) 643902

CANT, Christopher Somerset Travers. b 51. Keble Coll Ox BA72 MA76 Ex Univ PGCE77. All Nations Chr Coll 80 Wycliffe Hall Ox 93. **d** 87 **p** 90. Pakistan 87-92; Lic to Offic *Cov* 92-93; Warden St Clem Family Cen Ox 93-95. *49 St Andrew's Road, Ilford, Essex IG1 3PE* 0181-554 7423

CANT, David Edward. b 49. Sheff Univ LLB70. Oak Hill Th Coll DipTh89. **d** 89 **p** 90. C Newburn *Newc* 89-92; C N Shields 92-93; TV from 93; Chapl Tynemouth Coll from 94. *The Vicarage, 51 Drummond Terrace, North Shields, Tyne & Wear NE30 2AW* 0191-258 3083

CANTERBURY, Archbishop of. See CAREY, Most Rev and Rt Hon George Leonard

CANTERBURY, Archdeacon of. See TILL, Ven Michael Stanley

CANTERBURY, Dean of. See SIMPSON, Very Rev John Arthur

CANTI, Mrs Christine. b 24. St Alb Minl Tr Scheme 82. **dss** 85 **d** 87 **p** 94. Radlett *St Alb* 85-86; Hon C Pitminster w Corfe *B & W* 87-90; Perm to Offic from 90. *Brook Farm House, Corfe, Taunton, Somerset TA3 7BU* Blagdon Hill (01823) 421623

CANTRELL, David Grindon. b 59. Bris Univ BSc80 Nottm Univ PhD83 Pemb Coll Cam BA88. Ridley Hall Cam 86. **d** 89 **p** 90. C Low Harrogate St Mary *Ripon* 89-90; C Horsforth 90-94; Chapl Nottm Trent Univ *S'well* from 94. *2 College Drive, Clifton, Nottingham NG11 8NS* Nottingham (0115) 921 4560

CAPEL-EDWARDS, Dr Maureen. b 36. Southn Univ BSc60 Reading Univ PhD69. St Alb Minl Tr Scheme 84. **d** 87 **p** 94. NSM Ware St Mary *St Alb* 87-90; Chapl Ware Coll 87-90; NSM Hertf All SS 90-94; NSM Aspenden and Layston w Buntingford 94-95; NSM Aspenden, Buntingford and Westmill from 95. *5 Pearman Drive, Dane End, Ware, Herts SG12 0LW* Dane End (01920) 438365

CAPENER, Herbert Francis. b 30. Jes Coll Ox BA53 MA58. Cuddesdon Coll 53. **d** 55 **p** 56. V Shirley St Geo *Cant* 63-70; V Folkestone St Pet 70-89; rtd 90. *1 Baldric Road, Folkestone, Kent CT20 2NR* Folkestone (01303) 254579

CAPERON, John Philip. b 44. Bris Univ BA66 Open Univ MPhil80 Ox Univ MSc83. Ox NSM Course 80. **d** 83 **p** 84. NSM Hook Norton w Gt Rollright, Swerford etc *Ox* 83-86; NSM Knaresborough *Ripon* 86-93; Dep Hd St Aid Sch Harrogate 86-93; Chapl Bennett Memorial Sch Tunbridge Wells from 93. *Bennett Memorial School, Culverden Down, Tunbridge Wells, Kent TN4 9SH* Tunbridge Wells (01892) 521595 Fax 514424

CAPES, Arthur Geoffrey. b 33. Bps' Coll Cheshunt 58. **d** 61 **p** 62. C Seacroft *Ripon* 61-66; Guyana 66-80; V Claremont H Angels *Man* 80-85; V Blyton w Pilham *Linc* 85-90; V E Stockwith 86-90; V Laughton w Wildsworth 86-90; R Broad Town, Clyffe Pypard and Tockenham *Sarum* 90-94; R Broad Town, Clyffe Pypard, Hilmarton etc from 94. *The Rectory, Wood Lane, Clyffe Pypard, Swindon SN4 7PY* Swindon (01793) 731623

CAPES, Dennis Robert. b 34. Linc Th Coll 65 Handsworth Coll Birm DipTh58. **d** 64 **p** 65. In Meth Ch (Sarawak) 59-63; C Lt Coates *Linc* 64-66; Malaysia 66-69; V Gosberton Clough *Linc* 69-71; V Kirton in Holland 71-80; Area Sec (Dios Cov, Heref and Worc) USPG 80-87; Chapl Copenhagen w Aarhus *Eur* 87-93; TV Liv Our Lady and St Nic w St Anne *Liv* from 93. *29 Moel Famau View, Priory Park, Riverside Drive, Liverpool L17 5AX* 0151-727 0576 or 236 5287

CAPIE, Fergus Bernard. b 47. Auckland Univ BA68 MA71. Wycliffe Hall Ox BA77. **d** 77 **p** 78. C Ox St Mich w St Martin and All SS *Ox* 77-80; Chapl Summer Fields Sch Ox 80-91;

Hon C Wolvercote w Summertown *Ox* 87-91; Perm to Offic *St E*91; TV E Ham w Upton Park St Alb *Chelmsf*91-95; P-in-c Brondesbury St Anne w Kilburn H Trin *Lon* from 95; Chapl NW Lon Coll from 95. *49 Keslake Road, London NW6 6DH* 0181-968 3898

CAPLE, Stephen Malcolm. b 55. Chich Th Coll 86. **d** 88 **p** 89. C Newington St Mary *S'wark* 88-92; V Eltham St Sav from 92. *St Saviour's Vicarage, 98 Middle Park Avenue, London SE9 5JH* 0181-850 6829

CAPON, Canon Anthony Charles. b 26. Trin Coll Cam BA51 MA55. Wycliffe Coll Toronto BD65 DD82 Oak Hill Th Coll 51. **d** 53 **p** 54. C Portman Square St Paul *Lon* 53-56; Canada from 56; Hon Can Montreal from 78; Prin Montreal Dioc Th Coll 78-91. *5 Loradean Crescent, Kingston, Ontario, Canada, K7K 6X9*

CAPON, Canon Martin Gedge. b 09. Magd Coll Cam BA31 MA36. Wycliffe Hall Ox 34. **d** 35 **p** 36. V Breage w Germoe *Truro* 70-74; rtd 74; Perm to Offic *Ex* from 74. *Flat 2, 26 Alexandra Terrace, Exmouth, Devon EX8 1BB* Exmouth (01395) 265128

✠**CAPPER, Rt Rev Edmund Michael Hubert.** b 08. OBE61. Dur Univ LTh32. St Aug Coll Cant 28. **d** 32 **p** 33 **c** 67. C Strood St Mary *Roch* 32-36; Tanganyika 36-62; Adn Lindi 48-54; Adn Dar-es-Salaam 54-57; Provost 57-62; Chapl Palma *Eur* 62-67; Bp St Helena 67-73; Aux Bp Eur from 73; Chapl Malaga 73-76; Asst Bp S'wark from 81; rtd 86. *Flat 8, Morden College, London SE3 0PW* 0181-858 9169

CAPPER, Mrs Elizabeth Margaret. b 31. St Chris Coll Blackheath 52. **dss** 79 **d** 87 **p** 94. The Dorothy Kerin Trust Burrswood 79-91; Whitstable *Cant* 80-87; Hon Par Dn 87-91; rtd 91; Perm to Offic *Cant* from 91. *26 Swalecliffe Road, Whitstable, Kent CT5 2PR* Whitstable (01227) 272800

CAPPER, Canon James Frank. b 18. Qu Coll Ox BA40 MA44. Westcott Ho Cam 48. **d** 48 **p** 49. V Erdington St Barn *Birm* 64-75; V Coleshill 75-82; V Maxstoke 75-82; RD Coleshill 77-82; Perm to Offic *Ex* from 82; rtd 83. *Martlets, Harpford, Sidmouth, Devon EX10 0NQ* Colaton Raleigh (01395) 68198

CAPPER, John Raymond. b 29. Liv Univ BA53. Coll of Resurr Mirfield 53. **d** 55 **p** 56. C Birm St Aid Small Heath *Birm* 55-58; C Widley w Wymering *Portsm* 60-63; C Portsea St Sav 63-68; V Gosport H Trin from 68. *Holy Trinity Vicarage, Trinity Green, Gosport, Hants PO12 1HL* Gosport (01705) 580173

CAPPER, Richard. b 49. Leeds Univ BSc70 Fitzw Coll Cam BA72 MA79. Westcott Ho Cam 70. **d** 73 **p** 74. C Wavertree H Trin *Liv* 73-76; P-in-c Ince St Mary 76-79; V 79-83; V Crosby St Faith from 83; AD Bootle from 89. *St Faith's Vicarage, Crosby Road North, Liverpool L22 4RE* 0151-928 3342

CAPPER, Robert Melville (Bob). b 52. Chu Coll Cam BA74 MA. Wycliffe Hall Ox 74. **d** 77 **p** 78. C Newport Maindee St Jo Ev *Mon* 77-81; Chapl Univ of Wales (Abth) *St D* 81-87; TV Abth 81-87; V Malpas *Mon* from 87. *The Vicarage, Malpas, Newport, Gwent NP9 6GQ* Newport (01633) 852047

CAPPER, William Alan. QUB BTh. **d** 88 **p** 89. C Dundonald *D & D* 88-91; C Lisburn Ch Ch *Conn* 91-94; I Tamlaght O'Crilly Upper w Lower *D & R* from 94. *The Rectory, 16 Hervey Hill Road, Kilrea, Co Londonderry BT51 5TT* Kilrea (012665) 40296

CAPRON, David Cooper. b 45. Open Univ BA80. Sarum & Wells Th Coll 71. **d** 75 **p** 76. C Cov St Mary *Cov* 75-79; V Shottery St Andr 79-86; TV Stratford-on-Avon w Bishopton 79-86; V Shottery St Andr 86; V Newton Aycliffe *Dur* 86-89; TR 89-90; P-in-c Alcester and Arrow w Oversley and Weethley *Cov* 90-95; R from 95; Chapl Warks Fire and Rescue Service from 93. *St Nicholas' Rectory, Old Rectory Garden, Alcester, Warks B49 5DB* Alcester (01789) 764261 Fax as telephone Mobile (0585) 308414

CAPRON, Ronald Beresford. b 35. Clifton Th Coll. **d** 62 **p** 63. R Gaddesby w S Croxton *Leic* 67-71; R Beeby 67-71; Chapl RAF 71-83; rtd 95. *12 Mountbatten Road, Oakham, Leics LE15 6LS* Oakham (01572) 756219

CAPSTICK, John Nowell. b 30. AKC54. **d** 55 **p** 56. C Skipton Ch Ch *Bradf* 55-57; C Buxton *Derby* 57-61; V Codnor and Loscoe 61-63; C-in-c Rawthorpe CD *Wakef* 63-64; V Rawthorpe 64-70; V Netherthong 70-89; TV Upper Holme Valley from 89. *The Vicarage, Netherthong, Holmfirth, Huddersfield HD7 2UQ* Holmfirth (01484) 682430

CAPSTICK, William Richard Dacre. b 32. Pemb Coll Ox. Chich Th Coll 61. **d** 64 **p** 65. C Hunslet St Mary and Stourton St Andr *Ripon* 64-67; C Knaresborough H Trin 67-71; V Stratfield Mortimer *Ox* 71-76; P-in-c St Marylebone Ch Ch w St Paul *Lon* 76-78; TV St Marylebone Ch Ch 78-79; TR Newbury *Ox* 79-89; TV Brighton St Pet and St Nic w Chpl Royal *Chich* from 89. *13 Ditchling Road, Brighton BN1 4SB* Brighton (01273) 609144

CARBERRY, Leon Carter. b 54. Pennsylvania Univ BSc76. St Steph Ho Ox 81. **d** 84 **p** 85. C Peterlee *Dur* 84-87; C Newton Aycliffe 87-89; VC York Minster *York* 89-94; Chapl St Pet Sch York from 94. *2A Sycamore Terrace, York YO3 7DN* York (01904) 646727

CARBUTT, George Maurice. b 06. **d** 44 **p** 45. OSP 25-69; rtd 69; Perm to Offic *Wakef* from 71. *52 Fieldhead Crescent, Birstall, Batley, W Yorkshire WF17 9BP*

CARBY, Stuart Graeme. b 51. CBiol77 MIBiol77 LRSC78 Man Univ BSc73 Leeds Univ PGCE74. St Jo Coll Nottm DTS92. **d** 92 **p** 93. C Magor w Redwick and Undy *Mon* from 92. *3 The Meadows, Magor, Newport, Gwent NP6 3LA* Magor (01633) 881714

CARD, Terence Leslie. b 37. K Coll Lon BD68 AKC68 Heythrop Coll Lon MTh84. **d** 69 **p** 70. C Thundersley *Chelmsf* 69-72; Lic to Offic *Bradf* 72-75; V Chingford St Anne *Chelmsf* 75-81; RD Waltham Forest 78-81; R Springfield All SS 81-83; C Becontree St Jo 85-87; rtd 87. *39 Kings Chase, Brentwood, Essex CM14 4LD*

CARD, Thomas Ian. b 36. RD76. Master Mariner 61. Portsm Dioc Tr Course 88. **d** 89. NSM Binstead *Portsm* from 89; Miss to Seamen from 89; NSM Swanmore St Mich w Havenstreet *Portsm* 89-92; NSM Havenstreet St Pet from 92. *Dolphins, 49 Mayfield Road, Ryde, Isle of Wight PO33 3PR* Isle of Wight (01983) 564749

CARDALE, Charles Anthony. b 21. St D Coll Lamp BA47 Lich Th Coll 55. **d** 56 **p** 57. V Staverton w Landscove *Ex* 69-87; R Broadhempston, Woodland, Staverton etc 88-89; Perm to Offic from 89; rtd 90. *Keyberry, 13 Woodland Close, Staverton, Totnes, Devon TQ9 6PQ* Staverton (0180426) 277

CARDALE, Edward Charles. b 50. CCC Ox BA72. Cuddesdon Coll 72 Union Th Sem (NY) STM74. **d** 74 **p** 75. C E Dulwich St Jo *S'wark* 74-77; USA 77-80; V Ponders End St Matt *Lon* 80-84; V Lytchett Minster *Sarum* from 84. *The Vicarage, Lytchett Minster, Poole, Dorset BH16 6JQ* Wimborne (01202) 622253

CARDELL-OLIVER, John Anthony. b 43. Em Coll Cam BA67 MA72 Univ of W Aus BEd75 MEd85. Westcott Ho Cam 86. **d** 86 **p** 88. Australia 86-88; Perm to Offic *Ely* 88-89; C Stansted Mountfitchet *Chelmsf* 89-92; R Boxted w Langham from 92. *The Rectory, Wick Road, Langham, Colchester CO4 5PG* Colchester (01206) 230666

CARDEN, Edwin William. b 54. Cranmer Hall Dur 85. **d** 87 **p** 88. C Thundersley *Chelmsf* 87-91; CUF 91-93; NSM Poplar *Lon* 91-93; Chapl Springfield Hosp *Lon* from 93; Chapl Wandsworth Mental Health Unit from 93. *The Chaplaincy, Springfield Hospital, 61 Glenburnie Road, London SW17 7DJ* 0181-672 9911

CARDEN, John Brumfitt. b 24. Lon Coll of Div 48. **d** 52 **p** 53. Asia Sec CMS 70-76; Hon C Croydon St Sav *Cant* 75-76; C-in-c Bath St Steph *B & W* 76-82; V 82-84; CMS 84-89; Jerusalem 84-87; Exec Asst WCC Geneva 87-89; rtd 89; Miss Partner CMS from 89. *81 The Village, Haxby, York YO3 3JE* York (01904) 750035

CARDIGAN, Archdeacon of. See JONES, Ven Benjamin Jenkin Hywel

CARDINAL, Ian Ralph. b 57. Qu Coll Birm 81. **d** 84 **p** 85. C Whitkirk *Ripon* 84-87; C Knaresborough 87-89; P-in-c Wilsford *Linc* 89; P-in-c Ancaster 89; R Ancaster Wilsford Gp 89-94; P-in-c Wigginton *Lich* from 94. *The Vicarage, Wigginton, Tamworth, Staffs B79 9DN* Tamworth (01827) 64537

CARDWELL, Edward Anthony Colin. b 42. Trin Coll Cam BA63 MA68. St Jo Coll Nottm 73. **d** 75 **p** 76. C Stapenhill w Cauldwell *Derby* 75-78; C Bramcote *S'well* 78-81; V S'well H Trin 81-92; R Eastwood from 92. *The Rectory, 5A Woodland Way, Eastwood, Nottingham NG16 3BU* Langley Mill (01773) 712395

CARDWELL, Joseph Robin. b 47. Qu Coll Cam BA68 MA77. Trin Coll Bris 73. **d** 76 **p** 77. C Bromley Ch Ch *Roch* 76-79; C Shirley *Win* 79-82; V Somborne w Ashley 82-90; V Derry Hill *Sarum* 90-94; V Derry Hill w Bremhill and Foxham from 94; Community Affairs Chapl from 90. *The Vicarage, Derry Hill, Calne, Wilts SN11 9NN* Calne (01249) 812172

CARE, Canon Charles Richard. b 21. Univ of Wales (Lamp) BA42. St Mich Coll Llan 42. **d** 44 **p** 45. R St Brides Minor *Llan* 57-88; RD Bridgend 75-88; Can Llan Cathl 83-88; Prec 87-88; rtd 88; Perm to Offic *Llan* from 88. *31 Laburnam Drive, Danygraig, Porthcawl, M Glam CF36 5UA* Porthcawl (01656) 715446

CAREW, Bryan Andrew. b 38. AIB63 ACIB87. St D Coll Lamp DipTh69. **d** 67 **p** 68. C Pemb Dock *St D* 67-70; CF 70-74; P-in-c Gt and Lt Henny w Middleton *Chelmsf* 74-76; P-in-c Wickham St Paul w Twinstead 75-76; R Gt and Lt Henny w Middleton, Wickham St Paul etc from 76. *The Rectory, Great Henny, Sudbury, Suffolk CO10 7NW* Twinstead (01787) 269336

CAREY, Alan Lawrence. b 29. K Coll Lon AKC53. **d** 54 **p** 55. C-in-c Cippenham CD *Ox* 65-77; rtd 94. *12 Ormsby Street, Reading RG1 7YR* Reading (01734) 612309

CAREY, Charles John. b 29. K Coll Lon BD53 AKC53. St Aug Coll Cant 71. **d** 72 **p** 73. C Spring Park *Cant* 72-74; C Ifield *Chich* 74-78; C Burgess Hill St Jo 78-80; Chapl Rush Green Hosp Romford 80-94; Chapl Oldchurch Hosp Romford 80-94; rtd 94. *Address excluded by request*

CAREY, Christopher Lawrence John (Chris). b 38. St Andr Univ BSc61 Lon Univ BD64. Clifton Th Coll 61. **d** 64 **p** 65. C Battersea Park St Sav *S'wark* 64-67; Kenya 68-79; Overseas Regional Sec for E Africa CMS from 79; Perm to Offic *Roch* from 81. *5 Downs Avenue, Chislehurst, Kent BR7 6HG* 0181-467 4417 or 0171-928 8681 Fax 0171-401 3215

✠**CAREY, Most Rev and Rt Hon George Leonard.** b 35. PC91. Lon Univ BD66 MTh65 PhD71 Dur Univ Hon DD93 Open Univ Hon DD95. ALCD61. **d** 62 **p** 63 **c** 87. C Islington St Mary *Lon* 62-66; Lect Oak Hill Th Coll 66-70; Lect St Jo Coll Nottm 70-75; V Dur St Nic *Dur* 75-82; Chapl HM Rem Cen Low Newton 77-81; Prin Trin Coll Bris 82-87; Hon Can Bris Cathl *Bris* 84-87; Bp B & W 87-91; Abp Cant from 91; FKC from 93. *Lambeth Palace, London SE1 7JU, or The Old Palace, Canterbury, Kent CT1 2EE* 0171-928 8282 or Canterbury (01227) 459401 Fax 0171-261 9836

CAREY, Graham Charles. b 33. Kelham Th Coll 53. **d** 57 **p** 58. C Millfield St Mary *Dur* 57-66; V Northfield St Mich *Sheff* 66-76; P-in-c Jarrow St Mark *Dur* 76-77; TV Jarrow 77-84; P-in-c Southwick St Pet *Chich* from 84; Miss to Seamen from 84. *St Peter's Vicarage, Gardner Road, Southwick, Brighton BN41 1PN* Brighton (01273) 592474

CAREY, Very Rev James Maurice George. b 26. TCD BA49 MA52 BD52. CITC 51. **d** 52 **p** 53. C Larne and Inver *Conn* 52-55; USA 55-56; C Dub St Ann *D & G* 57-58; Hon CV Ch Ch Cathl Dub 58; Dean of Residences QUB 58-64; I Dub St Bart *D & G* 64-71; Dean Cork *C, C & R* 71-93; I Cork St Fin Barre's Cathl 71-87; I Cork St Fin Barre's Union 87-93; I Cork St Nic w H Trin 71-75; Radio Officer (Cork) 90-93; P-in-c Dub Sandymount *D & G* from 93. *91 Klonkeen Road, Blackrock, Co Dublin, Irish Republic* Dublin (1) 289-5121

CAREY, Mark Jonathan. b 65. St Jo Coll Nottm BTh94. **d** 94 **p** 95. C S Ossett *Wakef* from 94. *40 Broomcroft Road, Ossett, W Yorkshire WF5 8LH* Wakefield (01924) 263320

CAREY, Canon Ronald Clive Adrian. b 21. K Coll Cam BA46 MA48. Chich Th Coll 47. **d** 48 **p** 49. V Claygate *Guildf* 68-78; RD Emly 72-77; Hon Can Guildf Cathl 78-86; R Guildf H Trin w St Mary 78-86; RD Guildf 84-86; rtd 86; Perm to Offic *Roch* from 86. *4 Chart View, Kemsing, Sevenoaks, Kent TN15 6PP* Sevenoaks (01732) 762629

CAREY, Mrs Wendy Marion. b 45. Bris Univ BA66 Lon Inst of Educn CertEd67. W Midl Minl Tr Course 90. **d** 93 **p** 94. NSM Milton Keynes *Ox* from 93; Sub-Chapl HM Pris Woodhill from 93. *46 Parklands, Great Linford, Milton Keynes MK14 5DZ* Milton Keynes (01908) 605997

CARHART, John Richards. b 29. Bris Univ BA50 Salford Univ MSc77. St Deiniol's Hawarden 63. **d** 65 **p** 66. C Ches St Oswald w Lt St Jo *Ches* 65-72; Lect Ches Coll of HE 65-72; Prin Lect from 72; Dean Academic Studies from 88; C Ches 72; Lic to Offic 73-85; Hon C Ches St Mary from 85. *29 Abbot's Grange, Chester CH2 1AJ* Chester (01244) 380923

CARLESS, Canon Frank. b 22. Lon Univ BD56. St Aid Birkenhead 53. **d** 56 **p** 57. V Warley *Wakef* 64-87; RD Halifax 82-86; Hon Can Wakef Cathl 86-87; rtd 87. *130 Savile Park Road, Halifax, W Yorkshire HX1 2EX* Halifax (01422) 348379

CARLILE, Edward Wilson. b 15. ACA39 FCA59 K Coll Lon AKC43 BD46. **d** 43 **p** 44. V Leic St Pet *Leic* 60-73; R Swithland 73-76; P-in-c Belgrave St Mich 76-81; rtd 81; Perm to Offic *Leic* from 81. *120A Mount View Road, Sheffield S8 8PL* Sheffield (0114) 258 1098

CARLILL, Adam Jonathan. b 66. Keble Coll Ox BA88. Linc Th Coll 88. **d** 90 **p** 91. C Romford St Edw *Chelmsf* 90-94; C Uckfield *Chich* from 94. *School House, Belmont Road, Uckfield, E Sussex TN22 1BP* Uckfield (01825) 761373

CARLILL, Richard Edward. b 38. Westcott Ho Cam 77. **d** 79 **p** 80. C Prittlewell *Chelmsf* 79-83; TV Saffron Walden w Wendens Ambo and Littlebury 83-89; V Langtoft w Foxholes, Butterwick, Cottam etc *York* 89-94; V Gt and Lt Driffield from 94. *The Vicarage, Downe Street, Driffield, N Humberside YO25 7DX* Driffield (01377) 253394

CARLIN, William Patrick Bruce. b 53. St Steph Ho Ox 75. **d** 78 **p** 79. C Penistone *Wakef* 78-81; C Barnsley St Mary 81-83; V Stockton St Chad *Dur* 83-93; V Hedworth from 93. *St Nicholas Vicarage, Hedworth Lane, Boldon Colliery, Tyne & Wear NE35 9JA* 0191-536 7552

CARLING, Mrs Bronwen Noel. b 43. SRN65 SCM73. Linc Th Coll 89. **d** 91 **p** 94. C Blakeney w Cley, Wiveton, Glandford and

Nor 91-94; C Trunch from 94. *The Rectory, Clipped Hedge Lane, Southrepps, Norwich NR11 8NS* Southrepps (01263) 833404

CARLISLE, Christopher John. b 39. Sheff Univ BEng62. NW Ord Course 72. **d** 75 **p** 76. C Bury St Paul *Man* 75-80; C Walkden Moor 80-82; V Lytham St Jo *Blackb* from 82. *The Vicarage, East Beach, Lytham, Lytham St Annes, Lancs FY8 5EX* Lytham (01253) 734396

CARLISLE, John Patrick. b 66. St Andr Univ MTh89 Hughes Hall Cam PGCE90. St Steph Ho Ox 93. **d** 95. C Grahame Park St Aug CD *Lon* from 95. *18 Montrose Avenue, Edgware, Middx HA8 0DQ* 0181-952 1635

CARLISLE, Archdeacon of. See TURNBULL, Ven David Charles

CARLISLE, Bishop of. See HARLAND, Rt Rev Ian

CARLISLE, Dean of. See STAPLETON, Very Rev Henry Edward Champneys

CARLOS, Francis John. b 29. Jes Coll Cam BA54 MA57. Wells Th Coll 52. **d** 55 **p** 56. R Wentnor and Ratlinghope w Myndtown and Norbury *Heref* 65-89; P-in-c More w Lydham 82-89; P-in-c Snead 85-89; R Wentnor w Ratlinghope, Myndtown, Norbury etc 89-94; rtd 94. *16 Springfield Park, Clee Hill, Ludlow, Shropshire SY8 3QY* Ludlow (01584) 891253

CARLSSON, Miss Siw. b 43. **d** 92 **p** 94. Par Dn Barnes St Mary *S'wark* 92-93; C Mitcham SS Pet and Paul from 93. *32 Lewis Road, Mitcham, Surrey CR4 3DE* 0181-646 2268

CARLTON, Roger John. b 51. **d** 80 **p** 81. NSM Downend *Bris* 80-83; NSM Heavitree w Ex St Paul *Ex* 83-87; Chapl St Marg Sch Ex 83-87; Chapl Ex Sch 83-87; TV Bickleigh (Plymouth) *Ex* 87-91; TR 91-93; TR Bickleigh (Roborough) and Shaugh Prior from 94; RD Ivybridge from 93. *The Vicarage, 2 Blackeven Close, Roborough, Plymouth PL6 7AX* Plymouth (01752) 702119

CARLYON (nee ENGLAND), Mrs Jessie Marguerite Tarie. b 44. Westf Coll Lon BA66 K Coll Lon PGCE67. W Midl Minl Tr Course 92. **d** 95. C Pontypool *Mon* from 95. *St Matthew's House, Victoria Road, Pontypool, Gwent NP4 5JU*

CARMARTHEN, Archdeacon of. See JOHN, Ven Islwyn David

CARMICHAEL, Peter Iain. b 28. Chich Th Coll 75. **d** 75 **p** 76. C Rye w Rye Harbour and Playden *Chich* 75-79; C Rye, Rye Harbour and Playden and Iden 79-80; R Earnley and E Wittering 80-94; rtd 94. *20 East Street, Selsey, Chichester, W Sussex PO20 0BJ* Selsey (01243) 606197

CARMODY, Preb Dermot Patrick Roy. b 41. CITC 77. **d** 77 **p** 78. C Dub Zion Ch *D & G* 77-79; I Dunganstown w Redcross 79-84; TV Dub Ch Ch Cathl Gp 84-93; Can Ch Ch Cathl Dub 84-92; Preb Ch Ch Cathl Dub 92-93; I Mullingar, Portnashangan, Moyliscar, Kilbixy etc *M & K* from 93. *All Saints' Rectory, Mullingar, Co Westmeath, Irish Republic* Mullingar (44) 48376

CARMYLLIE, Robert Jonathan. b 63. Cov Poly BSc85. St Jo Coll Dur 85. **d** 88 **p** 89. C Horwich *Man* 88-92; P-in-c Edgeside from 92. *St Anne's Vicarage, Ashworth Road, Waterfoot, Rossendale, Lancs BB4 9JE* Rossendale (01706) 215090

CARNE, Canon Brian George. b 29. FSA Liv Univ BCom50. Qu Coll Birm 53. **d** 55 **p** 56. V Bris St Andr Hartcliffe *Bris* 68-74; V Almondsbury 74-91; RD Westbury and Severnside 80-86; Hon Can Bris Cathl 82-91; P-in-c Littleton on Severn w Elberton 83-91; P-in-c Olveston 83-91; rtd 91. *Whitehouse Farm, English Bicknor, Coleford, Glos GL16 9PA* Dean (01594) 860200

CARNE, Norman David John. b 27. Roch Th Coll 59. **d** 62 **p** 63. R Westcote Barton and Steeple Barton *Ox* 68-74; P-in-c Enstone and Heythrop 74-82; V 82-92; rtd 92. *45 Beckingthorpe Drive, Bottesford, Notts NG13 0DN*

CARNE-ROSS, Stewart Pattison. b 24. Wycliffe Hall Ox 58. **d** 59 **p** 60. V Champion Hill St Sav *S'wark* 64-70; P-in-c Stanton Lacy *Heref* 70-72; V 72-77; V Bromfield 70-77; R Culmington w Onibury 70-77; V Hambledon *Portsm* 77-79; Chapl HM Pris Kingston (Portsm) 79-90; C Portsea St Mary *Portsm* 86-90; rtd 90. *7 Hanover Court, Highbury Street, Portsmouth PO1 2BN* Portsmouth (01705) 752698

CARNELL, Canon Geoffrey Gordon. b 18. St Jo Coll Cam BA40 MA44. Cuddesdon Coll 40. **d** 42 **p** 43. R Isham *Pet* 53-71; V Gt w Lt Harrowden 53-71; Dir of Ords 62-85; Can Pet Cathl 65-85; R Boughton 71-85; Chapl to The Queen 81-88; rtd 85; Perm to Offic *Pet* from 86. *52 Walsingham Avenue, Kettering, Northants NN15 5ER* Kettering (01536) 511415

CARNELLEY, Ven Desmond. b 29. Open Univ BA77 Leeds Univ CertEd Ex Univ CertRE. Ripon Hall Ox 59. **d** 60 **p** 61. V Balby w Hexthorpe *Sheff* 67-73; P-in-c Mosborough 73-74; V 74-85; RD Attercliffe 79-84; Adn Doncaster 85-94; Dioc Dir of Educn 91-94; rtd 94. *7 Errwood Avenue, Buxton, Derbyshire SK17 9BD* Buxton (01298) 71460

CARNELLEY, Ms Elizabeth Amy. b 64. St Aid Coll Dur BA85 Selw Coll Cam MPhil87. Ripon Coll Cuddesdon 88. **d** 90 **p** 94. Par Dn Sheff Sharrow *Sheff* 90-93; Par Dn Is of Dogs Ch Ch and St Jo w St Luke *Lon* 93-94; C from 94. *Flat 2, St Mildred's House, Roserton Street, London E14 3PG*   0171-515 7975

CARNEY, David Anthony. b 42. Salford Univ BSc77. Linc Th Coll 77. **d** 79 **p** 80. C Wythenshawe St Martin *Man* 79-81; CF 81-84; Canada 84-91; P-in-c Whaplode *Linc* from 91. P-in-c Holbeach Fen from 91. *St Mary's Vicarage, Whaplode, Spalding, Lincs PE12 6TD*   Holbeach (01406) 370318

CARNEY, Mrs Mary Patricia. b 42. Univ of Wales (Ban) BSc62 DipEd63. Wycliffe Hall Ox. **d** 90 **p** 94. Par Dn Carterton *Ox* 90-93; Par Dn Harwell w Chilton 93-94; C from 94. *31 Crafts End, Chilton, Didcot, Oxon OX11 0SA*   Didcot (01235) 532366

CARNEY, Richard Wayne. b 52. Lon Teachers Coll Ontario TCert73 Toronto Univ BA79. Trin Coll Toronto MDiv84. **d** 84 **p** 85. Canada 84-95; Bp's C Clonfert Gp of Par *L & K* from 95. *The Rectory, Banagher, Birr, Co Offaly, Irish Republic*   Birr (509) 51269   Fax as telephone

CARNLEY, Ronald Birch. b 18. Pemb Coll Ox BA47 MA47. Cuddesdon Coll 47. **d** 49 **p** 50. V Matfield *Roch* 59-78; Perm to Offic *Chich* from 79; Perm to Offic *Roch* from 79; rtd 83. *5 Cleeve Avenue, Hawkenbury, Tunbridge Wells, Kent TN2 4TY*   Tunbridge Wells (01892) 530045

CARPENTER, Bruce Leonard Henry. b 32. Lon Univ BA54 St Chad's Coll Dur DipTh59. **d** 59 **p** 60. C Portsea N End St Mark *Portsm* 59-63; C Fareham SS Pet and Paul 63-67; V Locks Heath 67-74; TR Fareham H Trin 74-84; RD Alverstoke 71-76; Hon Can Portsm Cathl 79-84; V Richmond St Mary w St Matthias and St Jo *S'wark* 84-91; Chapl Ch Ch Sch Ashford Kent 91-93; P-in-c S Ashford Ch Ch *Cant* from 94. *2 Jemmett Road, Ashford, Kent TN23 2QD*   Ashford (01233) 626284

CARPENTER, David James. b 52. St Steph Ho Ox 74. **d** 76 **p** 77. C Newport St Julian *Mon* 76-77; C Pontypool 77-79; C Ebbw Vale 79-81; TV 81-85; V Pontnewynydd 85-88; V Bedwellty from 88. *The Rectory, Bedwellty, Blackwood, Gwent NP2 0BE*   Bargoed (01443) 831078

CARPENTER, Derek George Edwin. b 40. K Coll Lon BD62 AKC62. **d** 63 **p** 64. C Friern Barnet All SS *Lon* 63-66; C Chingford SS Pet and Paul *Chelmsf* 66-70; V Dartford St Alb *Roch* 70-79; R Crayford 79-90; RD Erith 82-90; R Beckenham St Geo from 90. *The Rectory, 14 The Knoll, Beckenham, Kent BR3 2JW*   0181-650 0983

CARPENTER, Donald Arthur. b 35. Roch Th Coll 65. **d** 67 **p** 68. C Thornton Heath St Jude *Cant* 67-73; V Earby *Bradf* 73-78; V Skipton Ch Ch 78-88; V Baildon 88-91; P-in-c Perivale *Lon* from 91. *The Rectory, Federal Road, Greenford, Middx UB6 7AP*   0181-997 1948

CARPENTER, Very Rev Dr Edward Frederick. b 10. K Coll Lon BA32 MA34 BD35 AKC35 PhD43. Lambeth DD79. **d** 35 **p** 36. Can Westmr Abbey 51-74; Treas 59-74; Adn Westmr 63-74; Dean Westmr 74-85; rtd 85. *6 Selwyn Avenue, Richmond, Surrey TW9 2HA*   0181-940 3896

CARPENTER, Ven Frederick Charles. b 20. SS Coll Cam BA47 MA49 St Cath Soc Ox DipTh48 Ex Univ MPhil93. Wycliffe Hall Ox 47. **d** 49 **p** 50. Can Res Portsm Cathl *Portsm* 68-77; Dir RE 68-75; Adn Is of Wight 77-86; P-in-c Binstead 77-86; rtd 86; Perm to Offic *Portsm* from 86; Perm to Offic *Sarum* from 86; Chapl Godolphin Sch Salisbury from 89. *Gilston, Mount Pleasant, Stoford, Salisbury SP2 0PP*   Salisbury (01722) 790335

CARPENTER, Gilbert Lant. b 10. Down Coll Cam BA34 MA38. Ely Th Coll 34. **d** 35 **p** 36. V Willesden St Andr *Lon* 57-76; rtd 76. *2 Rushbury Court, Station Road, Hampton, Middx TW12 2DD*   0181-941 1449

CARPENTER, Mrs Judith Margaret. b 47. Bris Univ BA68 CertEd69. Trin Coll Bris BA95. **d** 95. C Warmley, Syston and Bitton *Bris* from 95. *Beaufort House, 52 Park Road, Bristol BS16 1AU*   Bristol (0117) 965 4191

CARPENTER, Leonard Richard. b 32. E Midl Min Tr Course. **d** 85 **p** 86. NSM Leic H Apostles *Leic* 85-90; P-in-c Barlestone from 90. *The New Vicarage, 22 Bosworth Road, Barlestone, Nuneaton, Warks CV13 0EL*   Market Bosworth (01455) 290249

CARPENTER, William Brodie (Bill). b 35. St Alb Minl Tr Scheme 76. **d** 79 **p** 80. NSM Hemel Hempstead *St Alb* 79-85; C Hatf 85-88; C Caversham and Mapledurham *Ox* 88-89; R Caversham St Andr from 89. *St Andrew's Vicarage, Harrogate Road, Reading RG4 7PW*   Reading (01734) 472788

CARR, Alan Cotban. b 49. Nottm Univ BTh88. Linc Th Coll 85. **d** 88 **p** 89. C Rustington *Chich* 88-92; V Highbrook and W Hoathly from 92. *The Vicarage, West Hoathly, East Grinstead, W Sussex RH19 4QF*   Sharpthorne (01342) 810494

CARR, Anthony Howard. b 62. Ex Univ BA. **d** 92 **p** 93. C Taverham w Ringland *Nor* from 92. *232 Taverham Road, Taverham, Norwich NR8 6SX*   Norwich (01603) 861076

CARR, Very Rev Arthur Wesley. b 41. Jes Coll Ox BA64 MA67 Jes Coll Cam BA66 MA70 Sheff Univ PhD75. Ridley Hall Cam 65. **d** 67 **p** 68. C Luton w E Hyde *St Alb* 67-71; Tutor Ridley Hall Cam 70-71; Chapl 71-72; Hon C Ranmoor *Sheff*

72-74; Chapl Chelmsf Cathl *Chelmsf* 74-78; Can Res Chelmsf Cathl 78-87; Dep Dir Cathl Cen for Research and Tr 74-82; Dioc Dir of Tr 76-84; Dean Bris from 87. *The Deanery, 20 Charlotte Street, Bristol BS1 5PZ*   Bristol (0117) 926 4879 or 926 2443   Fax 925 3678

CARR, Douglas Nicholson. b 20. Jes Coll Cam BA47 MA50. Cranmer Hall Dur. **d** 65 **p** 66. Home Dir OMF 69-85; Lic to Offic *S'wark* 77-86; rtd 85. *Willow Cottage, 435 Paiswick Road, Gloucester GL4 9BY*   Gloucester (01452) 507455

CARR, Miss Eveline. b 45. St Jo Coll Dur 91. **d** 93 **p** 94. NSM Eighton Banks *Dur* from 93. *10 Lanchester Avenue, Gateshead, Tyne & Wear NE9 7AJ*   0191-482 1157

CARR, Geoffrey. b 09. Ch Coll Cam BA33. Ridley Hall Cam 34. **d** 35 **p** 36. R Arborfield *Ox* 63-76; rtd 76; Chapl St Luke's Hosp Guildf 77-78; Hon Chapl from 78. *9 Deneyhurst Court, York Road, Guildford, Surrey GU1 4EA*   Guildford (01483) 502923

CARR, Preb James Arthur. b 28. St Aid Birkenhead 62. **d** 64 **p** 65. V Edensor *Lich* 68-72; V Caverswall 72-85; P-in-c Dilhorne 83-85; P-in-c St Martin's 85-86; V 86-94; RD Oswestry 87-92; Preb Lich Cathl 89-94; rtd 94. *7 Mickleby Way, Meir Park, Stoke-on-Trent, Staffs ST3 7RU*   Stoke-on-Trent (01782) 399547

CARR, John Robert. b 40. ACII62. Oak Hill Th Coll 63. **d** 66 **p** 67. C Tonbridge St Steph *Roch* 66-70; C Cheadle Hulme St Andr *Ches* 70-79; R Widford *Chelmsf* 79-87; TV Becontree W 87-93; V Basildon St Andr w H Cross from 93. *St Andrew's Vicarage, 3 The Fremnells, Basildon, Essex SS14 2QX*   Basildon (01268) 520516

CARR, Miss Joy Vera. b 32. DipEd52. Dalton Ho Bris 56. **dss** 80 **d** 87 **p** 94. Scarborough St Jas and H Trin *York* 80-82; Kingston upon Hull St Matt w St Barn 82-87; Par Dn 87-89; Par Dn Elloughton and Brough w Brantingham 89-92; rtd 92. *15 Sea View Gardens, Scarborough, N Yorkshire YO11 3JD*   Scarborough (01723) 376986

CARRE, Canon John Trenchard. b 23. Lich Th Coll 42 Linc Th Coll 45. **d** 46 **p** 47. V Steeple Morden *Ely* 60-74; V Guilden Morden 60-74; RD Shingay 67-74; V Wendy w Shingay 69-74; R Croydon w Clopton 69-74; R Hatley 69-74; V Litlington w Abington Pigotts 69-74; V Tadlow w E Hatley 69-74; V Chesterton St Andr 74-88; Hon Can Ely Cathl 79-88; rtd 88. *North Barn, 17 Cromwell Road, Ely, Cambs CB6 1AS*   Ely (01353) 662471

CARRICK, Canon Ian Ross. b 13. Clare Coll Cam BA35 MA39. Chich Th Coll 35. **d** 37 **p** 38. C Sculcoates St Paul *York* 37-39; C Staveley *Derby* 39-43; Min St Barn CD Northolt 43-54; V Northolt Park St Barn *Lon* 54-58; S Africa from 58. *65 First Crescent, Fish Hoek, 7975 South Africa*   Cape Town (21) 825586

CARRINGTON, Mrs Elizabeth Ashby (Liz). b 46. E Midl Min Tr Course 86. **d** 90 **p** 94. NSM Nottm St Ann w Em *S'well* 90-91; C Basford w Hyson Green from 92. *The Vicarage, 152 Perry Road, Nottingham NG5 1GL*   Nottingham (0115) 960 5602

CARRINGTON, Philip John. b 48. MIEE MBIM Leeds Poly CEng. Chich Th Coll 83. **d** 85 **p** 86. C W Acklam *York* 85-88; V Middlesb St Agnes 88-92; Chapl Middlesb Gen Hosp 92-93; Chapl S Cleveland Hosp from 93. *South Cleveland Hospital, Marton Road, Middlesbrough, Cleveland TS4 3BW*   Middlesbrough (01642) 850850/854802

CARRIVICK, Derek Roy. b 45. Birm Univ BSc66. Ripon Hall Ox 71. **d** 74 **p** 75. C Enfield St Jas *Lon* 74-78; C-in-c Woodgate Valley CD *Birm* 78-83; TR Chelmsley Wood 83-92; Dioc Ecum Officer from 86; R Baxterley w Hurley and Wood End and Merevale etc from 92. *The Rectory, 7 Easthouse Drive, Hurley, Atherstone, Warks CV9 2HB*   Tamworth (01827) 874252

CARROLL, Ven Charles William Desmond. b 19. TCD BA43 MA46. St Chad's Coll Dur. **d** 48 **p** 49. Dir RE *Blackb* 59-73; Can Res Blackb Cathl 64-75; Adn Blackb 73-86; V Balderstone 73-86; rtd 86; Lic to Offic *Blackb* from 86. *11 Assheton Road, Blackburn BB2 6SF*   Blackburn (01254) 251915

CARROLL, Frederick Albert. b 16. Worc Coll Ox BA51 MA55. Ripon Hall Ox 46. **d** 51 **p** 52. V Castle Vale *Birm* 68-74; V Coughton *Cov* 74-87; R Spernall, Morton Bagot and Oldberrow 74-87; RD Alcester 84-87; rtd 87. *8 Gracey Court, Woodland Road, Broadclyst, Exeter EX5 3LP*   Exeter (01392) 460788

CARROLL, James Thomas. b 41. Pittsburgh Univ MA85. St Deiniol's Hawarden 89 Oblate Fathers Sem Dub 59. **d** 63 **p** 64. C Dub St Patr Cathl Gp *D & G* 89-92; Min Can St Patr Cathl Dub from 90; I Raheny w Coolock *D & G* from 92. *403 Howth Road, Raheny, Dublin 5, Irish Republic*   Dublin (1) 831-3929

CARROLL, John Hugh. b 31. Bris Univ BA57. Tyndale Hall Bris 54. **d** 58 **p** 59. V S Lambeth St Steph *S'wark* 61-72; V Norwood 72-81; P-in-c Purley Ch Ch 81-85; V 85-93; rtd 93; Perm to Offic *S'wark* from 93. *75 Court Avenue, Coulsdon, Surrey CR5 1HJ*   Downland (01737) 552464

CARROLL, Miss Joy Ann. b 59. SS Mark & Jo Coll Plymouth BEd82. Cranmer Hall Dur 85. **d** 88 **p** 94. Par Dn Hatcham St Jas *S'wark* 88-93; Par Dn Streatham Immanuel and St Andr 93-94; C from 94. *98 Ellison Road, London SW16 5DD* 0181-679 4301

CARRUTHERS, Alan. b 15. **d** 60 **p** 61. V Wigan St Jas *Liv* 65-70; P-in-c Wigan St Thos 65-70; V Wigan St Jas w St Thos 70-87; rtd 87. *Low Meadow, Cat Tree Road, Grange-over-Sands, Cumbria LA11 7ED* Grange-over-Sands (015395) 33037

CARRUTHERS, Arthur Christopher (Kester). b 35. Lon Coll of Div ALCD60 LTh73. **d** 60 **p** 61. C Addiscombe St Mary *Cant* 60-62; Prec Bradf Cathl *Bradf* 62-64; CF 64-92; R W Tanfield and Well w Snape and N Stainley *Ripon* from 92. *The Rectory, Main Street, West Tanfield, Ripon, N Yorkshire HG4 5JJ* Bedale (01677) 470321

CARRY, Canon Edward Austin. b 18. TCD BA41 MA47. **d** 42 **p** 43. I Killiney H Trin *D & G* 56-86; Preb St Patr Cathl Dub 83-86; rtd 86. *2 Roxboro Close, Ballinclea Road, Killiney, Co Dublin, Irish Republic* Dublin (1) 285-8847

CARSON, Christopher John. b 69. QUB BA91 TCD BTh94. **d** 94 **p** 95. C Ban St Comgall *D & D* from 94. *17 Grange Road, Bangor, Co Down BT20 3QQ* Bangor (01247) 456683

CARSON, Ernest. b 17. S'wark Ord Course 68. **d** 71 **p** 72. C Baldock w Bygrave and Clothall *St Alb* 71-75; R Hertingfordbury 75-86; rtd 86; Perm to Offic *Worc* from 86. *16 Woodward Close, Pershore, Worcs WR10 1LP* Pershore (01386) 553511

CARSON, Gerald James Alexander. b 24. TCD BA49 MA52. **d** 49 **p** 50. RD Kilmacrenan W *D & R* 60-85; Can Raphoe Cathl 67-81; I Urney w Sion Mills 68-85; Can Derry Cathl 81-85; I Clonallon w Warrenpoint *D & D* 85-90; rtd 90. *84 Avonbrook Gardens, Mountsandel, Coleraine, Co Derry BT52 1SS* Coleraine (01265) 56047

CARSON, Herbert Moore. b 22. TCD BA43 BD45. **d** 45 **p** 46. V Cam St Paul *Ely* 58-65; rtd 87. *19 Hillcrest Road, Leicester LE2 6HG* Leicester (0116) 288 2720

CARSON, James Irvine. b 59. TCD BA DipTh84 MTh. **d** 84 **p** 85. C Willowfield *D & D* 84-87; C Lecale Gp 87-89; I Devenish w Boho *Clogh* 89-95; Dioc Youth Adv 91-95; Dioc Info Officer 93-95; I Belf Upper Malone (Epiphany) *Conn* from 95. *The Rectory, 74 Locksley Park, Upper Lisburn Road, Belfast BT10 0AS* Belfast (01232) 601588

CARSON-FEATHAM, Lawrence William. b 53. AKC DipTh74. **d** 78 **p** 79. SSM from 77; C Walton St Mary *Liv* 78-82; Chapl Bolton Colls of FE 82-87; C Bolton St Pet *Man* 82-87; TV Oldham 87-92; V Ashton St Jas 92-95. *The Vicarage, Union Street, Ashton-under-Lyne, Lancs OL6 9NQ* 0161-330 2771

CARTER, Andrew Graham. b 65. UEA BSc86. St Jo Coll Nottm DTS90 DPS91. **d** 91 **p** 92. C Biggleswade *St Alb* 91-95; C Leavesden All SS from 95. *24 Kimpton Place, Garston, Watford WD2 6RD* Watford (01923) 670318

CARTER, Anthony James. b 24. Sarum Th Coll 54. **d** 56 **p** 57. V Walton-on-Thames *Guildf* 68-78; P-in-c Lytchett Minster *Sarum* 78-81; V 81-83; V Teddington St Mark *Lon* 83-88; V Teddington St Mark and Hampton Wick St Jo 88-89; rtd 89. *3 Westport Cottages, West Street, Wareham, Dorset BH20 4LF* Wareham (01929) 554255

CARTER, Barry Graham. b 54. K Coll Lon BD76 AKC76. St Steph Ho Ox 76. **d** 77 **p** 78. C Evesham *Worc* 77-81; C Amblecote 81-84; TV Ovingdean w Rottingdean and Woodingdean *Chich* 84-85; TR Woodingdean 85-95; V Lancing St Mich from 95. *The Vicarage, 117 Penhill Road, Lancing, W Sussex BN15 8HD* Lancing (01903) 753653

CARTER, Celia. b 38. JP74. Glouc Sch of Min 86. **d** 89 **p** 94. NSM Avening w Cherington *Glouc* from 89; Asst Chapl Stoud Gen Hosp from 89. *Avening Park, Avening, Tetbury, Glos GL8 8NE* Stroud (01453) 832716

CARTER, Canon Charles Trevelyan Aubrey. b 14. TCD BA36 MA46. TCD Div Sch Div Test37. **d** 37 **p** 38. I Dub Sandford *D & G* 67-85; Can Ch Ch Cathl Dub 71-85; I Dub Sandford w Milltown 82-85; rtd 85. *7 South Hill, Dartry, Dublin 6, Irish Republic* Dublin (1) 497-1171

CARTER (nee SMITH), Mrs Christine Lydia. b 43. Lon Hosp SRN64 Bristol Hosp SCM67 Bris Poly DipNursing76 Wolv Poly CertFE84. Trin Coll Bris DipHE91. **d** 91 **p** 94. Par Dn Penkridge Team *Lich* 91-94; C from 94. *31 Saxon Road, Penkridge, Staffs ST19 5EP* Penkridge (01785) 713489

CARTER, Christopher Franklin. b 37. Wadh Coll Ox BA59 MA63. Wycliffe Hall Ox 60. **d** 64 **p** 65. C Clifton St Jas *Sheff* 64-67; C Handsworth 67-70; C Clun w Chapel Lawn *Heref* 70-74; Lic to Offic 74-76; P-in-c Ironbridge 76-78; C Coalbrookdale, Iron-Bridge and Lt Wenlock 78-80; V Llansilin w Llangadwaladr and Llangedwyn *St As* from 80; RD Llanfyllin from 88. *The Vicarage, Llansilin, Oswestry, Shropshire SY10 7PX* Llansilin (0169170) 209

CARTER, Dr Colin John. b 56. FRCS86 Fitzw Coll Cam BA77 MA81 Cam Univ MB80 BChir80. Trin Coll Bris BA93. **d** 93

p 94. C Ripley *Derby* from 93. *15 Lime Avenue, Ripley, Derbyshire DE5 3HD* Ripley (01773) 743799

CARTER, David John. b 37. Chich Th Coll 64. **d** 67 **p** 68. C Plaistow St Andr *Chelmsf* 67-70; C Wickford 70-73; Chapl Asst Runwell Hosp Essex 71-73; Chapl Basingstoke Distr Hosp 73-80; R E Woodhay and Woolton Hill *Win* from 80. *The Rectory, The Mount, Woolton Hill, Newbury, Berks RG15 9QZ* Highclere (01635) 253323

CARTER, Dudley Herbert. b 25. Peterho Cam BA49 MA51. Ridley Hall Cam 49. **d** 51 **p** 52. Chapl Colston's Sch Bris 65-67; Lic to Offic *B & W* 67-85; Perm to Offic from 85; rtd 90. *24 Caernarvon Way, Burnham-on-Sea, Somerset TA8 2DQ* Burnham-on-Sea (01278) 789572

CARTER, Duncan Robert Bruton. b 58. Univ of Wales (Cardiff) BA79 Cam Univ BA83 MA89. Ridley Hall Cam 81. **d** 84 **p** 85. C Harold Wood *Chelmsf* 84-88; C S Kensington St Luke *Lon* 88-90; V Rotherfield Greys H Trin *Ox* from 90. *Holy Trinity Vicarage, Church Street, Henley-on-Thames, Oxon RG9 1SE* Henley-on-Thames (01491) 574822

CARTER, Eric. b 17. **d** 58 **p** 59. V Adlington *Blackb* 69-75; V Garstang St Thos 75-84; rtd 84. *1 Arncliffe Road, Harrogate, N Yorkshire HG2 8NQ* Harrogate (01423) 884867

CARTER, Frank Howard James. b 23. Chich Th Coll 58. **d** 59 **p** 60. V Haggerston All SS *Lon* 65-75; V Alexandra Park St Andr 75-88; rtd 88. *53 Naylor Road, London N20 0HE* 0181-445 0982

CARTER, Dr Grayson Leigh. b 53. Univ of S California BSc70 Ch Ch Ox DPhil90. Fuller Th Sem California MA84 Wycliffe Hall Ox 89. **d** 90 **p** 91. C Bungay H Trin w St Mary *St E* 90-92; Chapl, Tutor and Lect BNC Ox from 92; Lic to Offic *Ox* from 92; Hon C Ox St Mary V w St Cross and St Pet from 93. *Brasenose College, Oxford OX1 4AJ* Oxford (01865) 277869 or 793575 Fax 277514

CARTER, Hazel June. b 48. Doncaster Coll of Educn CertEd72. Carl Dioc Tr Inst 89. **d** 92 **p** 94. NSM Dalston *Carl* from 92; NSM Raughton Head w Gatesgill from 92; NSM Wreay from 92. *The Vicarage, Wreay, Carlisle CA4 0RL* Southwaite (016974) 73463

CARTER, Hector Thomas. b 26. St Paul's Grahamstown LTh51. **d** 52 **p** 54. C Ludford *Heref* 67-70; S Africa 71-83; V Barrow St Jas *Carl* 83; Perm to Offic *Heref* from 84; rtd 87. *13 Millmead, Mayfield Avenue, Craven Arms, Shropshire SY7 9PL*

CARTER, Ian Sutherland. b 51. Trin Coll Ox BA73 MA77 DPhil77 Leeds Univ BA80. Coll of Resurr Mirfield 78. **d** 81 **p** 82. C Shildon *Dur* 81-84; C Darlington H Trin 84-87; Chapl Liv Univ *Liv* 87-93; V Hindley St Pet from 93. *St Peter's Vicarage, Wigan Road, Hindley, Wigan, Lancs WN2 3DF* Wigan (01942) 55505

CARTER (nee O'NEILL), Mrs Irene. b 44. Worc Coll of Educn CertEd65. E Midl Min Tr Course CTPS92. **d** 93. Hon C N and S Leverton *S'well* from 93. *25 Mill Close, North Leverton, Retford, Notts DN22 0AT* Gainsborough (01427) 880451

CARTER, John Henry. b 24. Oak Hill Th Coll 66. **d** 68 **p** 69. C Halliwell St Paul *Man* 68-71; V Bolton St Phil 71-76; Chapl to the Deaf (Dios Man and Blackb) 76-82; V Childs Ercall *Lich* 82-87; R Stoke upon Tern 82-87; rtd 87. *3 Chestnut Drive, Hemingbrough, Selby, N Yorkshire YO8 7UE* Selby (01757) 638197

CARTER, John Howard Gregory. b 55. York Univ BA76. St Jo Coll Nottm LTh87. **d** 87 **p** 88. C Nailsea H Trin *B & W* 87-91; TV Camberley St Paul *Guildf* from 91; Chapl Elmhurst Ballet Sch Camberley from 91. *61 Goldney Road, Camberley, Surrey GU15 1DW* Camberley (01276) 20897

✠**CARTER, Rt Rev John Stanley.** b 21. Lon Univ BA47. Oak Hill Th Coll 46 Wycliffe Hall Ox 48. **d** 49 **p** 50 **c** 68. C Walthamstow St Mary *Chelmsf* 49-52; C Streatham Immanuel w St Anselm *S'wark* 52-53; S Africa from 53; Suff Bp Johannesburg 68-77. *The Rectory, 43 Pypies Plein, Devil's Peak, Cape Town, 8001 South Africa* Cape Town (21) 461-5350

CARTER, Leslie Alfred Arthur. b 27. K Coll Lon 50 St Boniface Warminster 53. **d** 54 **p** 55. Chapl Quainton Hall Sch Harrow 68-77; TV Brighton Resurr *Chich* 77-81; TV Southend St Jo w St Mark, All SS w St Fran etc *Chelmsf* 81-82; TV Southend 82-88; V Gt Waltham w Ford End 88-93; rtd 94. *52 Masefield Road, Warminster, Wilts BA12 8HY* Warminster (01985) 215268

CARTER, Ms Marian. b 40. Whitelands Coll Lon TCert61 Lon Univ DipTh62 BD67 Reading Univ DASE73 Nottm Univ MPhil79. Nor Bapt Coll MA84. **d** 92 **p** 94. Par Dn Kempshott *Win* 92-93; Tutor SW Minl Tr Course from 92; Tutor Coll of SS Mark and Jo Plymouth from 93; Lic to Offic *Ex* from 94. *Shalom, 20 St Mark's Road, Plymouth PL6 8BS* Plymouth (01752) 709321

CARTER, Michael John. b 32. St Alb Minl Tr Scheme 81. **d** 84 **p** 85. NSM Radlett *St Alb* 84-88; Chapl SW Herts HA from

88; Chapl Watford Gen Hosp from 88. *Watford General Hospital, Vicarage Road, Watford WD1 8HB* Radlett (01923) 244366 or 856009

CARTER, Nicholas Adrian. b 47. Ripon Hall Ox 71. **d** 74 **p** 75. C Sowerby *Wakef* 74-79; V Hanging Heaton 79-83; CF 83-86; V Elton All SS *Man* 86-90; C Milton *Win* 90-94; P-in-c Boscombe St Andr 94; V from 94. *St Andrew's Vicarage, 3 Wilfred Road, Bournemouth BH5 1NB* Bournemouth (01202) 394575

CARTER, Nigel John. b 53. N Staffs Poly C&G80 Bolton Inst of Educn CertEd89. Sarum & Wells Th Coll DCM93. **d** 93 **p** 94. C Burntwood *Lich* from 93. *9 Derwent Grove, Burntwood, Walsall WS7 9JN* Burntwood (01543) 674324

CARTER, Noel William. b 53. Birm Univ BSc75 Bris Univ CertEd76 Nottm Univ BSc83. Linc Th Coll. **d** 83 **p** 84. C Penrith w Newton Reigny and Plumpton Wall *Carl* 83-86; TR from 91; C Barrow St Matt 86-87; V Netherton 87-91. *The Rectory, Carlton Road, Penrith, Cumbria CA11 8LT* Penrith (01768) 63000 or 62867

CARTER, Canon Norman. b 23. Leeds Univ BSc48. Coll of Resurr Mirfield 48. **d** 50 **p** 51. V Orford St Marg *Liv* 56-71; V Knotty Ash H Spirit 71-74; V Dovecot 74-83; RD W Derby 78-83; Hon Can Liv Cathl 82-88; V Formby St Pet 83-88; rtd 88. *34 Granby Close, Southport, Merseyside PR9 9QG* Southport (01704) 32283

CARTER, Canon Paul Brian. b 22. AKC49. **d** 50 **p** 51. R Ainderby Steeple and Scruton *Ripon* 60-79; P-in-c Danby Wiske w Yafforth and Hutton Bonville 76-79; R Ainderby Steeple w Yafforth and Scruton 79-87; Hon Can Ripon Cathl 86-87; rtd 87. *Cliffe Cottage, West Tanfield, Ripon, N Yorkshire HG4 5JR* Bedale (01677) 470203

CARTER, Paul Joseph. b 67. St Chad's Coll Dur BA88. St Steph Ho Ox 89. **d** 91 **p** 92. C Ipswich All Hallows *St E* 91; C Newmarket St Mary w Exning St Agnes 91-94; V Thorpe-le-Soken *Chelmsf* from 94. *The Vicarage, Mill Lane, Thorpe-le-Soken, Clacton-on-Sea, Essex CO16 0ED* Clacton-on-Sea (01255) 861234

CARTER, Paul Mark. b 56. BA78 MA90. Ridley Hall Cam 79. **d** 81 **p** 82. C Kidsgrove *Lich* 81-84; CF from 84. *c/o MOD (Army), Bagshot Park, Bagshot, Surrey GU19 5PL* Bagshot (01276) 471717 Fax 412834

CARTER, Paul Rowley. b 45. Lon Bible Coll BD69 Southn Univ PGCE70. Trin Coll Bris. **d** 91 **p** 92. C Penkridge Team *Lich* from 91. *31 Saxon Road, Penkridge, Staffs ST19 5EP* Penkridge (01785) 713489

CARTER, Raymond Timothy. b 27. Qu Coll Birm 57. **d** 59 **p** 60. V Harrow Weald St Mich *Lon* 67-79; V Teddington St Mary w St Alb 79-92; rtd 92. *21 Manor Road, Teddington, Middx TW11 8AA* 0181-943 9489

CARTER, Robert Desmond (Bob). b 35. Cranmer Hall Dur 62. **d** 65 **p** 66. C Otley *Bradf* 65-69; C Keighley 69-73; V Cowling from 73. *The Vicarage, Gill Lane, Cowling, Keighley, W Yorkshire BD22 0DD* Cross Hills (01535) 632050

CARTER, Robert Edward. b 44. Univ of Wales (Ban) BSc66. St Jo Coll Nottm 79. **d** 81 **p** 82. C Caverswall *Lich* 81-86; V Biddulph 86-94; V Wolv St Jude from 94. *St Jude's Vicarage, St Jude's Road, Wolverhampton WV6 0EB* Wolverhampton (01902) 753360

CARTER, Robin. b 46. Chich Th Coll 71. **d** 74 **p** 75. C Wortley de Leeds *Ripon* 74-76; C Hutton *Chelmsf* 76-78; C Wickford 78-81; TV Wickford and Runwell 81-83; Chapl HM Pris Leeds 83-85; Chapl HM Pris Reading 85-89; Chapl HM Young Offender Inst Huntercombe and Finnamore 85-89; Chapl HM Young Offender Inst Finnamore Wood Camp 86-89; Lic to Offic *Ox* 85-89; Gov HM Pris Channings Wood from 89; Perm to Offic *Ex* from 90. *HM Prison Channings Wood, Denbury, Newton Abbot, Devon TQ12 6DW* Ipplepen (01803) 812361 Fax 813175

CARTER, Ronald George. b 31. Leeds Univ BA58. Coll of Resurr Mirfield 58. **d** 60 **p** 61. V Woodhall *Bradf* 66-77; Chapl Qu Marg Sch Escrick Park 77-83; Min Can, Prec and Sacr Pet Cathl 83-88; R Upper St Leonards St Jo *Chich* 88-94; rtd 94. *5 Greenwich Close, York YO3 6WN* York (01904) 610237

CARTER, Ronald William. b 01. ATCL25 ALCD31. **d** 31 **p** 32. V Staines St Pet *Lon* 41-78; rtd 78; Perm to Offic *Win* from 78. *24 Vespasian Way, Eastleigh, Hants SO5 2DF* Chandler's Ford (01703) 269520

CARTER, Russell James Wigney. b 29. Chich Th Coll 80. **d** 82 **p** 83. C Aldwick *Chich* 82-86; R Buxted and Hadlow Down 86-90; rtd 90. *6 Lucerne Court, Aldwick, Bognor Regis, W Sussex PO21 4XL* Bognor Regis (01243) 862858

CARTER, Samuel. b 49. St Jo Coll Dur BA71 DipTh72. Cranmer Hall Dur 73. **d** 74 **p** 75. C Kingswinford St Mary *Lich* 74-77; C Shrewsbury H Cross 77-84; V Normacot 84-94. *Address excluded by request*

CARTER, Stanley Reginald. b 24. St Jo Coll Dur BA49 DipTh50. **d** 50 **p** 51. V Sneinton St Chris w St Phil *S'well* 69-89;

rtd 89; Perm to Offic *S'well* from 89. *31 Pateley Road, Nottingham NG3 5QF* Nottingham (0115) 926 4054

CARTER, Stephen. b 56. Univ of Wales (Lamp) BA77 Southn Univ BTh81. Sarum & Wells Th Coll 78. **d** 81 **p** 82. C Halstead St Andr w H Trin and Greenstead Green *Chelmsf* 81-84; C Loughton St Jo 84-89; V N Shoebury from 89. *The Vicarage, 2 Weare Gifford, Shoeburyness, Southend-on-Sea SS3 8AB* Southend-on-Sea (01702) 584053

CARTER, Stephen Howard. b 47. City Univ BSc72. St Jo Coll Nottm LTh85. **d** 85 **p** 86. C Hellesdon *Nor* 85-88; Chapl Asst Birm Children's Hosp 88-91; Chapl Asst Birm Maternity Hosp 88-91; Lic to Offic *Birm* 88-91; TV Tettenhall Wood *Lich* from 91; Chapl Compton Hall Hospice Wolv from 91. *The Vicarage, 12 Windmill Lane, Wolverhampton WV3 8HJ* Wolverhampton (01902) 761170

CARTER, Stuart Conway. b 58. Lon Bible Coll DipRS83 St Jo Coll Nottm DipMM92. **d** 92 **p** 93. C Birm St Luke *Birm* from 92. *63 Princess Road, Birmingham B5 7PZ* 0121-440 6794

CARTER, Terence John (Terry). b 31. K Coll Lon BD57 AKC57 Lon Univ BA68 PGCE69. **d** 58 **p** 59. R Ockham w Hatchford *Guildf* 63-69; Lic to Offic *S'wark* 69-78; Lic to Offic *Portsm* 78-82; Perm to Offic from 82; rtd 91. *15 Balliol Road, Portsmouth PO2 7PP* Portsmouth (01705) 699167

CARTLEDGE, Mark John. b 62. Lon Bible Coll BA85. Oak Hill Th Coll MPhil89. **d** 88 **p** 89. C Formby H Trin *Liv* 88-91; Miss Partner CMS 91-93; Nigeria 91-93; Chapl Liv Univ *Liv* from 93. *The Beeches, 71 Woodlands Road, Liverpool L17 0AL* 0151-727 6291

CARTMAN, James. b 10. OBE55. Man Univ BA37 MA50 Lon Univ BD44 MTh48. Westcott Ho Cam 51. **d** 51 **p** 51. Prin Lect Relig Studies Heref Coll of Educn 69-78; Lic to Offic *Heref* 69-78; rtd 78; Perm to Offic *Win* from 78; Perm to Offic *Guildf* 79-92. *9 Handcroft Close, Crondall, Farnham, Surrey GU10 5RY* Aldershot (01252) 850234

CARTMELL, Richard Peter. b 43. Cranmer Hall Dur 77. **d** 79 **p** 80. C Whittle-le-Woods *Blackb* 79-85; V Lower Darwen St Jas from 85; RD Darwen from 91. *The Vicarage, Stopes Brow, Lower Darwen, Darwen, Lancs BB3 0QP* Blackburn (01254) 253898

CARTMILL, Ralph Arthur. b 40. St Jo Coll Dur BA62 Em Coll Cam MA64. Ridley Hall Cam 63. **d** 65 **p** 66. C Dukinfield St Jo *Ches* 65-68; C Wilmslow 68-69; Warden Walton Youth Cen Liv 69-70; Asst Master Aylesbury Gr Sch 70-74; Perm to Offic *Ox* 72-74; V Terriers 74-85; P-in-c Chinnor w Emmington and Sydenham 85-86; R Chinnor w Emmington and Sydenham etc from 86. *The Rectory, Chinnor, Oxon OX9 4DH* Kingston Blount (01844) 351309

CARTWRIGHT, Cyril Hicks. b 13. Selw Coll Cam BA35 MA44. Linc Th Coll 36. **d** 38 **p** 39. C Forest Row *Chich* 62-70; V Whitehawk 70-75; C Hove All SS 76-80; rtd 80; Perm to Offic *Chich* from 80. *Flat 17, Harewood Court, Wilbury Road, Hove, E Sussex BN3 3GL* Brighton (01273) 737814

✠CARTWRIGHT, Rt Rev Edward David. b 20. Selw Coll Cam BA41 MA45. Westcott Ho Cam 41. **d** 43 **p** 44 **c** 84. C Boston *Linc* 43-48; V Bris St Leon Redfield *Bris* 48-52; V Olveston 52-60; V Bishopston 60-73; Hon Can Bris Cathl 70-73; Adn Win 73-84; Hon Can Win Cathl 73-88; V Sparsholt w Lainston 73-84; Suff Bp Southn 84-88; rtd 88. *Bargate House, 25 Newport, Warminster, Wilts BA12 8RH* Warminster (01985) 216298

CARTWRIGHT, Preb Hugh Bent. b 07. St Steph Ho Ox 30. **d** 32 **p** 33. V Alexandra Park St Andr *Lon* 46-73; rtd 73; Perm to Offic *Heref* from 73. *21 Queens Court, Ledbury, Herefordshire HR8 2AL* Ledbury (01531) 633123

CARTWRIGHT, John Walter Deryk. b 25. Lon Univ BSc. On NSM Course. **d** 82 **p** 83. NSM Welford w Wickham and Gt Shefford *Ox* 82-85; TV Newbury 85-93; rtd 93. *St Mary's Vicarage, 14 Strawberry Hill, Newbury, Berks RG13 1XJ* Newbury (01635) 40889

CARTWRIGHT, Michael John. b 42. Birm Univ DipL&A70. Qu Coll Birm 67. **d** 70 **p** 71. C Astwood Bank w Crabbs Cross *Worc* 70-75; P-in-c Worc St Mich 75-77; V Stockton St Paul *Dur* 77-87; V Market Rasen *Linc* from 87; V Legsby from 87; R Linwood from 87; RD W Wold from 89. *The Vicarage, 13 Lady Frances Drive, Market Rasen, Lincs LN8 3JJ* Market Rasen (01673) 843424

✠CARTWRIGHT, Rt Rev Richard Fox. b 13. Pemb Coll Cam BA35 MA39 Univ of the South (USA) Hon DD69. Cuddesdon Coll 35. **d** 36 **p** 37 **c** 72. C Kennington Cross St Anselm *S'wark* 36-40; C Kingswood 40-45; V Surbiton St Andr 45-52; V Bris St Mary Redcliffe w Temple etc *Bris* 52-72; Hon Can Bris Cathl 60-72; Suff Bp Plymouth *Ex* 72-81; rtd 82; Asst Bp Truro from 82; Asst Bp Ex from 88. *5 Old Vicarage Close, Ide, Exeter EX2 9RT* Exeter (01392) 211270

CARTWRIGHT, Roy Arthur. b 29. CCC Cam BA52 MA56. Wycliffe Hall Ox. **d** 54 **p** 55. V Prittlewell St Steph *Chelmsf* 69-72; rtd 72; Hon C S Shoebury *Chelmsf* 77-94. *21 Winfield, Newent, Glos GL18 1QB* Newent (01531) 821335

CARTWRIGHT, Samuel. b 27. Cuddesdon Coll 71. **d** 72 **p** 72. C Rochdale *Man* 72-76; V Roundthorn 76-83; V Ashton Ch Ch 83-93; rtd 93. *8 Wentworth Avenue, Walton, Chesterfield, Derbyshire S40 3JB* Chesterfield (01246) 232252

CARTWRIGHT, Sidney Victor. b 22. Launde Abbey 73. **d** 74 **p** 75. C Braunstone *Leic* 74-78; P-in-c Arnesby w Shearsby 78-86; R Arnesby w Shearsby and Bruntingthorpe 86-87; rtd 87; Perm to Offic *Leic* from 87; Perm to Offic *Pet* from 87. *32 Northleigh Grove, Market Harborough, Leics LE16 9QX* Market Harborough (01858) 463915

CARTWRIGHT, William Michael. b 44. Birm Univ CertEd67. Coll of Resurr Mirfield 83. **d** 83 **p** 84. Hd Master Chacombe Sch 83-85; Hon C Middleton Cheney w Chacombe *Pet* 83-85; Hd Master Chacombe Sch Banbury 83-85; C Kettering SS Pet and Paul *Pet* 85-86; Perm to Offic 86-88; Chapl Northaw Prep Sch Win 89-92; P-in-c Altarnon w Bolventor, Laneast and St Clether *Truro* from 92. *The Vicarage, Altarnon, Launceston, Cornwall PL15 7SG* Pipers Pool (01566) 86108

CARTY, Very Rev Hilton Manasseh. b 21. OBE85. Dur Univ BA45 LTh45. Codrington Coll Barbados. **d** 45 **p** 45. C Cowley St Jas *Ox* 65-73; V Earley St Bart 73-77; Dean Antigua 77-86; rtd 86. *Carnival Gardens, PO Box 1447, St Johns, Antigua* Antigua (1809) 461-1440

CARUANA, Mrs Rosemary Anne. b 38. St Alb Minl Tr Scheme 81. **dss** 84 **d** 87 **p** 94. Hertf St Andr *St Alb* 84-87; Par Dn Hertingfordbury 87-94; C 94; C from 94. *36 Holly Croft, Sele Farm Estate, Hertford SG14 2DR* Hertford (01992) 587625

CARVER, Arthur Tregarthen. b 15. Tyndale Hall Bris 37. **d** 41 **p** 42. R Uphill *B & W* 69-80; rtd 80; Perm to Offic *Ches* from 80. *Copinsay, 20 Hayton Street, Knutsford, Cheshire WA16 0DR* Knutsford (01565) 651622

CARVOSSO, John Charles. b 45. ACA71 FCA79. Oak Hill Th Coll 75. **d** 78 **p** 79. C Chelsea St Jo w St Andr *Lon* 78-81; Chapl RAF 81-84; P-in-c Tawstock *Ex* 84-85; TV Newport, Bishops Tawton and Tawstock from 85. *The Rectory, Tawstock, Barnstaple, Devon EX31 3HZ* Barnstaple (01271) 74963

CASE, Mrs Catherine Margaret. b 44. Ripon Coll Cuddesdon 86. **d** 88 **p** 94. C Blurton *Lich* 88-92; Min to Hanley Care Agencies from 92; TD Hanley H Ev 92-94; P-in-c Wrockwardine Wood from 95. *The Rectory, Church Road, Wrockwardine, Telford, Shropshire TF2 7AH* Telford (01952) 613865

CASE, Philip Thomas Charles. b 17. Lon Univ BSc(Econ)51. Sarum Th Coll 51. **d** 53 **p** 54. V Witley *Guildf* 66-84; RD Godalming 79-84; rtd 84; Perm to Offic *Ex* from 85. *The Old Malthouse, Vine Street, Winkleigh, Devon EX19 8HN* Winkleigh (01837) 83283

CASEBOW, Ronald Philip. b 31. Roch Th Coll 59. **d** 61 **p** 62. C Oseney Crescent St Luke w Camden Square St Paul *Lon* 64-70; Warden St Paul's Ho Student Hostel 64-70; V Colchester St Steph *Chelmsf* 70-74; V Burnham 74-89; rtd 89. *The Priory, Priory Road, Palgrave, Diss, Norfolk IP22 1AJ* Diss (01379) 651804 Fax as telephone

CASEY, Ernest George. b 14. St Chad's Coll Dur BA36 DipTh. **d** 37 **p** 38. V Dur St Giles *Dur* 59-79; rtd 79. *7 Hampshire Road, Belmont, Durham DH1 2DJ* 0191-384 9228

CASHEL, Dean of. *See* KNOWLES, Very Rev Philip John

CASHEL, WATERFORD AND LISMORE, Archdeacon of. *See* MURRAY, Ven John Grainger

CASHEL, WATERFORD, LISMORE, OSSORY, FERNS AND LEIGHLIN, Bishop of. *See* WILLOUGHBY, Rt Rev Noel Vincent

CASHMORE, Cyril. b 01. St Aug Coll Cant 20. **d** 25 **p** 32. V Bilsby w Farlesthorpe *Linc* 68-71; R Hannah cum Hagnaby w Markby 68-71; rtd 71. *Connaught Court, St Oswald's Road, Fulford, York YO1 4QA* York (01904) 656046

CASIOT, David John. b 39. St Pet Coll Ox BA63 MA67. Clifton Th Coll 63. **d** 65 **p** 66. C Drypool St Columba w St Andr and St Pet *York* 65-67; C Barking St Marg *Chelmsf* 67-71; R Whalley Range St Edm *Man* 71-84; V Wandsworth St Mich *S'wark* from 84. *St Michael's Vicarage, 73 Wimbledon Park Road, London SW18 5TT* 0181-874 7682

CASON, Preb Ronald Arthur. b 28. Kelham Th Coll 48. **d** 53 **p** 54. R Blakenall Heath *Lich* 67-74; R Stoke upon Trent 74-80; Preb Lich Cathl 75-93; RD Stoke 78-88; TR Stoke-upon-Trent 80-91; Lect Tettenhall Par 91-93; rtd 93. *130 Main Road, Brereton, Rugeley, Staffs WS15 1EB* Rugeley (01889) 582267

CASSAM, Victor Reginald. b 33. Chich Th Coll 59. **d** 62 **p** 63. C Portsea St Jo Rudmore *Portsm* 62-64; C W Leigh CD 64-66; C Torquay St Martin Barton *Ex* 66-69; C Stanmer w Falmer and Moulsecoomb *Chich* 69-73; P-in-c Catsfield 73-76; R Catsfield and Crowhurst 76-81; R Selsey from 81. *The Rectory, St Peter's Crescent, Selsey, Chichester, W Sussex PO20 0NA* Selsey (01243) 602363

CASSELTON, John Charles. b 43. Oak Hill Th Coll DipTh67. **d** 68 **p** 69. C Upton *Ex* 68-73; C Braintree *Chelmsf* 73-80; V

Ipswich St Jo *St E* 80-92; RD Ipswich 86-92; Chapl St Clem Hosp and St Eliz Hospice Ipswich from 92. *331 Woodbridge Road, Ipswich IP4 4AX, or St Clement's Hospital, Foxhall Rod, Ipswich IP3 8LS* Ipswich (01473) 273665 or 715111

CASSIDY, Brian Ross. b 31. Cape Town Univ. St Bede's Coll Umtata 88. **d** 89 **p** 91. S Africa 89-92; C Lymington *Win* 92-93; P-in-c Hyde Common from 93. *The Vicarage, Hyde, Fordingbridge, Hants SP6 2QJ* Fordingbridge (01425) 653216

CASSIDY, Ven George Henry. b 42. QUB BSc65 Lon Univ MPhil67. Oak Hill Th Coll 70. **d** 72 **p** 73. C Clifton Ch Ch w Em *Bris* 72-75; V Sea Mills 75-82; V Portman Square St Paul *Lon* 82-87; Adn Lon and Can Res St Paul's Cathl from 87; P-in-c St Ethelburga Bishopgate 89-91. *2 Amen Court, Warwick Lane, London EC4M 7BU* 0171-248 3312 Fax 489 8579

CASSIDY, Very Rev Herbert. b 35. TCD BA57 MA65. CITC 58. **d** 58 **p** 59. C Belf H Trin *Conn* 58-60; C Londonderry Ch Ch *D & R* 60-62; I Aghavilly w Derrynoose *Arm* 62-65; Hon VC Arm Cathl 63-85; C Portadown St Columba 65-67; I 67-85; Dean Kilmore *K, E & A* 85-89; I Kilmore w Ballintemple 85-86; I Kilmore w Ballintemple, Kildallon etc 86-89; Dir of Ords 89; Dean Arm and Keeper of Public Lib *Arm* from 89; I Arm St Patr from 89; Hon Sec Gen Syn from 90. *The Library, Abbey Street, Armagh BT61 7DY* Armagh (01861) 523142 Fax 524177

CASSIDY, Patrick Nigel. b 40. TCD BA63 MA66. Sarum Th Coll 64. **d** 66 **p** 67. C Heaton St Barn *Bradf* 66-68; Asst Chapl Brussels *Eur* 68-70; Chapl SW France 70-72; V Oseney Crescent St Luke w Camden Square St Paul *Lon* 72-83; Chapl Strasbourg w Stuttgart and Heidelberg *Eur* 83-84; Perm to Offic *Chich* 86-90; Chapl Marseille w Aix-en-Provence *Eur* from 90; Hon Chapl Miss to Seamen from 90. *399 rue Paradis, 13008 Marseille, France* France (33) 91 22 01 78 Fax as telephone

CASSIDY, Ronald. b 43. Lon Univ BD66 Man Univ MPhil85. Tyndale Hall Bris 63. **d** 68 **p** 69. C Kirkdale St Lawr *Liv* 68-70; C Bolton Em *Man* 70-74; V Roughtown 74-89; R Denton St Lawr from 89. *St Lawrence's Rectory, 131 Town Lane, Denton, Manchester M34 2DJ* 0161-320 4895

CASSON, David Christopher. b 41. Qu Coll Cam BA64 MA68. Ridley Hall Cam 65. **d** 67 **p** 68. C Birm St Martin *Birm* 67-72; C Luton St Mary *St Alb* 72-77; P-in-c 77; V Luton St Fran 77-84; V Richmond H Trin and Ch Ch *S'wark* from 84. *Holy Trinity Vicarage, Sheen Park, Richmond, Surrey TW9 1UP* 0181-940 3995

CASSON, Canon James Stuart. b 32. Liv Univ BA54 Nottm Univ MPhil70. Ridley Hall Cam. **d** 61 **p** 62. C Eccleston Ch Ch *Liv* 61-64; C Littleover *Derby* 64-67; V Dearham *Carl* 67-76; V Holme Eden from 76; RD Brampton from 91; Hon Can Carl Cathl from 93; P-in-c Croglin from 93. *St Paul's Vicarage, Warwick Bridge, Carlisle CA4 8RF* Wetheral (01228) 560332

CASSWELL, David Oriel. b 52. Loughb Coll of Educn CertEd74 Leeds Univ CQSW79. Oak Hill Th Coll DipHE87. **d** 87 **p** 88. C Acomb St Steph *York* 87-91; Dep Chapl HM Pris Leeds 91-92; Chapl HM Pris Everthorpe 92; Chapl HM Wolds Rem Cen from 92. *The Chaplain's Office, HM Wolds Remand Centre, Everthorpe, Brough, N Humberside HU15 7JZ* Howden (01430) 421588 Fax 421589

CASSWELL, Canon Peter Joyce. b 22. Trin Coll Cam BA48 MA50. Ridley Hall Cam 48. **d** 50 **p** 51. Chapl Forest Gate Hosp Lon 64-78; R Buckhurst Hill *Chelmsf* 64-78; Hon Can Chelmsf Cathl 75-78; R Lutterworth w Cotesbach *Leic* 78-90; RD Guthlaxton II (Lutterworth) 89-90; rtd 90. *74 Coventry Road, Broughton Astley, Leics LE9 6QA* Sutton Elms (01455) 282630

CASTERTON, Michael John. b 39. Univ of Wales (Lamp) BA62. St Mich Coll Llan 63. **d** 65 **p** 66. C Sidcup St Jo *Roch* 65-67; C Brighouse *Wakef* 67-73; Chapl Choral Ches Cathl *Ches* 73-75; V Roberttown *Wakef* 75-87; V Birkenshaw w Hunsworth 87-93; R Addingham *Bradf* from 93. *The Rectory, Low Mill Lane, Addingham, Ilkley, W Yorkshire LS29 0QP* Addingham (01943) 830276

CASTLE, Dr Brian Colin. b 49. Lon Univ BA72 Ox Univ BA77 MA80 Birm Univ PhD89. Cuddesdon Coll 74. **d** 77 **p** 78. C Sutton St Nic *S'wark* 77; C Limpsfield and Titsey 77-81; USPG 81-84; Zambia 81-84; Lect Ecum Inst WCC Geneva 84-85; V N Petherton w Northmoor Green *B & W* 85-92; Dir of Studies & Vice-Prin Ripon Coll Cuddesdon from 92; Lic to Offic *Ox* from 92. *3 College Fields, Cuddesdon, Oxford OX44 9HL* Oxford (01865) 874974

CASTLE, Brian Stanley. b 47. Oak Hill Th Coll 70. **d** 73 **p** 74. C Barnsbury St Andr w St Thos and St Matthias *Lon* 73-76; C Lower Homerton St Paul 76-79; P-in-c Bethnal Green St Jas Less from 79. *St James the Less Vicarage, St James's Avenue, London E2 9JD* 0181-980 1612

CASTLE, Charles. b 01. AKC35. Bps' Coll Cheshunt 35. **d** 35 **p** 36. V Thurnham w Detling *Cant* 66-71; rtd 71. *16 Pannal Ash*

Crescent, Harrogate, N Yorkshire HG2 0HT Harrogate (01423) 567731

CASTLE, Daphne Susan (Dee). b 39. Lon Inst of Educn TCert60 Open Univ BA88. Ox Min Course CBTS93. **d** 93 **p** 94. NSM Newbury *Ox* from 93; Chapl Clere Sch Newbury from 93. *20 Falkland Garth, Newbury, Berks RG14 6PB*

CASTLE, John Arthur. b 61. G&C Coll Cam BA83 S Bank Univ DMS88. Aston Tr Scheme 90 Cranmer Hall Dur BA95. **d** 95. C Southborough St Pet w Ch Ch and St Matt *Roch* from 95. *54 Holden Park Road, Southborough, Tunbridge Wells, Kent TN4 0EP* Tunbridge Wells (01892) 529153

CASTLE, Michael David. b 38. Wells Th Coll 69. **d** 71 **p** 72. C Acocks Green *Birm* 71-75; C Weoley Castle 76-78; V from 78. *St Gabriel's Vicarage, 83 Marston Road, Birmingham B29 5LS* 0121-475 1194

CASTLE, Roger James. b 39. St Jo Coll Cam BA62 MA66. Clifton Th Coll 63. **d** 65 **p** 66. C Rushden w Newton Bromswold *Pet* 65-68; C Stapenhill w Cauldwell *Derby* 68-72; V Hayfield 72-89; R Coxheath w E Farleigh, Hunton and Linton *Roch* from 89. *The Rectory, 19 Westerhill Road, Coxheath, Maidstone, Kent ME17 4DQ* Maidstone (01622) 747570

CASTLE, Vincent Clifton. b 15. ALCD37 St Jo Coll Dur LTh38 BA39. **d** 39 **p** 40. Miss to Seamen 63-71; V Creeksea w Althorne *Chelmsf* 71-79; RD Dengie 74-82; V Creeksea w Althorne, Latchingdon and N Fambridge 80-82; rtd 82; Perm to Offic *Chelmsf* from 82. *49 Winstree Road, Burnham-on-Crouch, Essex CM0 8ET* Maldon (01621) 782807

CASTLE, Wilfrid Thomas Froggatt. b 11. Qu Coll Cam BA33 MA37. Wycliffe Hall Ox 33. **d** 35 **p** 36. V Bocking St Pet *Chelmsf* 65-72; R Paisley St Barn *Glas* 72-77; P-in-c 77-79; rtd 77. *5 Freemen's Court, Water Lane, Clifton, York YO3 6PR* York (01904) 640185

CASTLETON, David Miles. b 39. Oak Hill Th Coll 69. **d** 72 **p** 73. C Canonbury St Steph *Lon* 72-76; C Stoke next Guildf St Jo *Guildf* 76; C Guildf St Sav w Stoke-next-Guildf 76-89. *26 Keswick Road, Great Bookham, Leatherhead, Surrey KT23 4BH* Bookham (01372) 454990

CASWELL, Roger John. b 47. St Chad's Coll Dur BA70. St Steph Ho Ox 75. **d** 77 **p** 78. C Brighton Resurr *Chich* 77-83; TV Crawley 83-90; TR Littlehampton and Wick from 90; Chapl Littlehampton Hosp from 90. *34 Fitzalan Road, Littlehampton, W Sussex BN17 5ET* Littlehampton (01903) 724410

CASWELL, Thomas Hubert (Tom). b 55. Aston Tr Scheme 90 Coll of Resurr Mirfield 92. **d** 94 **p** 95. C Sheff Norwood St Leon *Sheff* from 94. *29 Piper Road, Sheffield S5 7HZ* Sheffield (0114) 242 6875

CATCHPOLE, Geoffrey Alan (Geoff). b 53. AKC. Westcott Ho Cam 76. **d** 77 **p** 78. C Camberwell St Luke *S'wark* 77-80; C Dulwich St Barn 80-82; TV Canvey Is *Chelmsf* 82-87; Ind Chapl from 83; P-in-c Bradwell on Sea 87-92; V Holland-on-Sea from 92. *The Vicarage, 297 Frinton Road, Clacton-on-Sea, Essex CO15 5SP* Clacton-on-Sea (01255) 812420

CATCHPOLE, Guy St George. b 30. **d** 82 **p** 83. Kenya 82-89; C Woodford Wells *Chelmsf* 89-95; rtd 95. *The Vicarage, Bull Lane, Bethersden, Ashford, Kent TN26 3HA* Bethersden (01233) 820266

CATCHPOLE, Canon Keith William. b 30. AKC56. St Boniface Warminster 54. **d** 57 **p** 58. C Woodchurch *Ches* 57-61; C W Kirby St Bridget 61-64; C-in-c Upton Priory CD 64-72; R Lavant *Chich* 72-82; RD Chich from 80; Can and Preb Chich Cathl from 82; V Chich St Paul and St Pet from 82; P-in-c W Hampnett from 91. *The Vicarage, Tower Close, Chichester, W Sussex PO19 1QN* Chichester (01243) 531624

CATCHPOLE, Richard James Swinburne. b 65. St Steph Ho Ox 92. **d** 95. C Eastbourne St Andr *Chich* from 95. *75 Churchdale Road, Eastbourne, E Sussex BN22 8RX* Eastbourne (01323) 736312

CATCHPOLE, Roy. b 46. St Jo Coll Nottm LTh74 MMin MTheol. **d** 74 **p** 75. C Rainham *Chelmsf* 74-76; C Hyson Green *S'well* 76-79; V Broxtowe 79-86; V Calverton 86-94. *Society of St Francis, The Friary, Hilfield, Dorchester, Dorset DT2 7BE* Hilfield (01300) 341181

CATCHPOOL, Terence David Housden (Terry). b 34. MIBiol Hatf Coll Dur BSc56. Trin Coll Bris 85. **d** 86 **p** 87. NSM Bath Odd Down w Combe Hay *B & W* from 86. *119 Rush Hill, Bath BA2 2QT* Bath (01225) 424828

CATER, Henry Derek. b 17. Clutton Th Coll 49. **d** 51 **p** 52. rtd 69; Lic to Offic *Eur* 69-84. *5 Furniss Court, Cranleigh, Surrey GU6 8TN* Cranleigh (01483) 275941

CATER, Lois May. b 37. S Dios Minl Tr Scheme 81. **dss** 84 **d** 87 **p** 94. Calne and Blackland *Sarum* 84-89; Hon Par Dn 87-89; Hon Par Dn Devizes St Jo w St Mary 89-94; Hon C from 94. *Pear Cottage, 28 Pans Lane, Devizes, Wilts SN10 5AF* Devizes (01380) 723034

CATERER, James Albert Leslie Blower. b 44. New Coll Ox BA67 MA81. Sarum & Wells Th Coll 79. **d** 81 **p** 82. C Cheltenham St Luke and St Jo *Glouc* 81-85; V Standish w

---

Haresfield and Moreton Valence etc from 85. *The Vicarage, Church Lane, Moreton Valence, Gloucester GL2 7NB* Gloucester (01452) 720258

CATES, Canon Geoffrey Charles. b 18. Leeds Univ BA42. Coll of Resurr Mirfield 42. **d** 44 **p** 45. Br Guiana 61-66; Guyana 66-71; Dean Georgetown 61-71; R Salford Sacred Trin *Man* 71-82; RD Salford 71-82; Hon Can Man Cathl 80-82; Soc Resp Adv *St E* 82-88; Hon Can St E Cathl 85-88; rtd 88. *55 Berners Street, Ipswich IP1 3LN* Ipswich (01473) 216629

CATHCART, Adrian James. b 51. N Ord Course. **d** 87 **p** 88. C Blackley St Andr *Man* 87-90. *54 Tweedhill Road, Manchester M9 3LG* 0161-740 6774

CATHERALL, Mark Leslie. b 64. Chich Th Coll BTh93. **d** 93 **p** 94. C Lancing w Coombes *Chich* from 93. *30 Greenoaks, Lancing, W Sussex BN15 0HE* Lancing (01903) 767077

CATHIE, Sean Bewley. b 43. Dur Univ BA67. Cuddesdon Coll 67. **d** 69 **p** 70. C Kensal Rise St Martin *Lon* 69-73; C Paddington H Trin w St Paul 73-75; P-in-c Bridstow w Peterstow *Heref* 76-79; Hon C Westmr St Jas *Lon* from 85. *23 Brookfield Mansions, Highgate West Hill, London N6 6AS* 0181-340 6603

CATLEY, John Howard. b 37. AKC60. **d** 61 **p** 62. C Sowerby Bridge w Norland *Wakef* 61-64; C Almondbury 64-67; V Earlsheaton 67-75; V Brownhill 75-86; V Morley St Pet w Churwell 86-92; V St Annes St Marg *Blackb* from 92; RD Kirkham from 94. *St Margaret's Vicarage, 13 Rowsley Road, Lytham St Annes, Lancs FY8 2NS* St Annes (01253) 722648

CATLING, Michael David. b 56. Golds Coll Lon CertEd77 DipEd84 Whitelands Coll Lon DipC&S88. Cranmer Hall Dur 88. **d** 90 **p** 91. C Cullercoats St Geo *Newc* 90-94; TV Glendale Gp from 94. *Eglingham Vicarage, Alnwick, Northd NE66 2TX* Powburn (0166578) 250

CATLING, Canon Robert Mason. b 19. St Jo Coll Ox BA41 MA44. St Steph Ho Ox 41. **d** 43 **p** 44. V Beckenham St Barn *Roch* 64-72; V Devoran *Truro* 72-87; Hon Can Truro Cathl 77-87; rtd 87; Perm to Offic *Ex* and *Truro* from 87. *Ground Floor Flat, 31 Cranford Avenue, Exmouth, Devon EX8 2QA* Exmouth (01395) 267896

CATO, Percy William Frederick. b 06. OBE51. AKC35. **d** 35 **p** 36. R Cottesmore *Pet* 64-75; rtd 75. *20 Torkington Gardens, Stamford, Lincs PE9 2EW* Stamford (01780) 62460

CATO (formerly LEGGETT), Ms Vanessa Gisela. b 51. St Osyth Coll of Educn TCert75. Westcott Ho Cam CTMin93. **d** 93. C Southchurch H Trin *Chelmsf* from 93. *254 Woodgrange Drive, Southend-on-Sea SS1 2SH* Southend-on-Sea (01702) 616192

CATON, David Arthur. b 25. Trin Coll Ox BA50 MA50. St Steph Ho Ox 49. **d** 51 **p** 52. V Hurst *Man* 59-75; V Hanwell St Thos *Lon* 75-84; AD Ealing W 82-84; V Staincross *Wakef* 84-95; rtd 95. *Priest's Lodge, 48 Greenside, Barnsley, S Yorkshire S75 6AY* Barnsley (01226) 382261

CATON, Philip Cooper. b 47. Oak Hill Th Coll 79. **d** 81 **p** 82. C Much Woolton *Liv* 81-85; TV Parr from 85. *St Paul's Vicarage, 75 Chain Lane, St Helens, Merseyside WA11 9QF* St Helens (01744) 34335

CATT, Albert Henry. b 08. St Steph Ho Ox 34. **d** 37 **p** 38. V Hornsey St Geo *Lon* 49-74; rtd 74; Perm to Offic *Ely* from 75. *48 Green Park, Chatteris, Cambs PE16 6DL* Chatteris (01354) 693102

CATT, Douglas Gordon. b 23. MCSP49 SRP67. Roch Th Coll 61. **d** 63 **p** 64. R Croughton *Pet* 66-75; R Hinton in the Hedges w Steane 66-75; V Evenley 72-75; Chapl St Andr Hosp Northn 75-89; Lic to Offic *Pet* from 75; rtd 88. *195 Billing Road, Northampton NN1 5RS* Northampton (01604) 27710

CATTANACH, Alexander Hamilton Avery. b 16. Univ of Wales BA37. St Mich Coll Llan 38. **d** 39 **p** 40. V Lt Thornton *Blackb* 61-81; rtd 81; Lic to Offic *Blackb* from 81. *4 Dawson Road, St Annes, Lytham St Annes, Lancs FY8 3AJ* St Annes (01253) 727099

CATTELL, Ven Jack. b 15. Univ Coll Dur BA37 DipTh38 MA40 Lon Univ BD53. Sarum & Wells Th Coll 38. **d** 39 **p** 40. C Royston *Wakef* 39-41; Perm to Offic *Sarum* 41-42; CF (EC) 42-46; Lic to Offic *Ripon* 46-49; Chapl R Wanstead Sch 49-53; Bermuda 53-82; Adn Bermuda 61-82; Perm to Offic *Mon* from 82. *39A Risca Road, Newport, Gwent NP9 4HX* Newport (01633) 54529

CATTELL, John Eugene Brownlow. b 11. TD62. Selw Coll Cam BA34 MA44. Wells Th Coll 35. **d** 36 **p** 37. V Piddletrenthide w Alton Pancras and Plush *Sarum* 65-74; R Piddlehinton 73-74; P-in-c Kington Magna and Buckhorn Weston 74-77; rtd 77. *Tredinnock, Bishops Hill Road, New Polzeath, Wadebridge, Cornwall PL27 6UF* Trebetherick (01208) 862348

CATTERALL, Canon David Arnold. b 53. ARCS Lon Univ BSc74. Cranmer Hall Dur DipTh78. **d** 78 **p** 79. C Swinton St Pet *Man* 78-81; C Wythenshawe St Martin 81-83; R Heaton Norris Ch w All SS 83-88; I Fanlobbus Union *C, C & R* 88-95; RD Mid W Cork from 90; Can Cork and Ross Cathls from 93;

Warden Ch's Min of Healing in Ireland from 95. *38 Springfield Road, Templeogue, Dublin 6, Irish Republic*   Dublin (1) 490-6765 or 872-7876

CATTERALL, Mrs Janet Margaret. b 53. Univ of Wales (Ban) BA74. Cranmer Hall Dur DipTh77. **dss** 81 **d** 87 **p** 90. Wythenshawe St Martin *Man* 81-83; Heaton Norris Ch w All SS 83-87; Par Dn 87-88; C Bandon Union *C, C & R* 88-89; Dioc Youth Adv (Cork) 89-94; Dio Youth Chapl from 94. *38 Springfield Road, Templeogue, Dublin 6, Irish Republic* Dublin (1) 490-6765

CATTERICK, Matthew John. b 68. W Sussex Inst of HE BA92. St Steph Ho Ox BTh95. **d** 95. C Colchester St Jas, All SS, St Nic and St Runwald *Chelmsf* from 95. *Benson House, 13 Roman Road, Colchester CO1 1UR*   Colchester (01206) 573038

CATTLE, Richard John. b 40. W Midl Minl Tr Course 88. **d** 90 **p** 91. NSM Brixworth Deanery *Pet* 90-91; NSM Welford w Sibbertoft and Marston Trussell 91-92; V from 92. *The Vicarage, 35 The Leys, Welford, Northampton NN6 7HS* Welford (01858) 575252

CATTLEY, Richard Melville. b 49. Trin Coll Bris DipTh73. **d** 73 **p** 74. C Kendal St Thos *Carl* 73-77; Nat Sec Pathfinders CPAS 77-82; Exec Sec 82-85; V Dalton-in-Furness *Carl* 85-90; V Dulwich St Barn *S'wark* from 90; Chapl Alleyn's Foundn Dulwich from 90. *St Barnabas's Vicarage, 38 Calton Avenue, London SE21 7DG*   0181-693 2936

CATTON, Canon Cedric Trevor. b 36. JP. DipRJ. Lambeth STh94 Wells Th Coll 70. **d** 72 **p** 73. C Solihull *Birm* 72-74; R Whepstead w Brockley *St E* 74-75; R Hawstead and Newton w Stanningfield etc 74-79; Dioc Stewardship Adv 77-83; R Cockfield 79-83; V Exning St Martin w Landwade from 83; Chapl Newmarket Gen Hosp from 85; Hon Can St E Cathl *St E* from 90; Chapl Dio Mothers Union from 94. *The Vicarage, New River Green, Exning, Newmarket, Suffolk CB8 7HS* Exning (01638) 577413

CAVAGAN, Dr Raymond. b 35. Hull Univ MA86 PhD87. Oak Hill Th Coll DipTh62. **d** 63 **p** 64. C Upper Holloway St Pet *Lon* 63-66; C Hurworth *Dur* 66-68; V New Shildon 68-76; P-in-c Toxteth Park St Andr Aigburth Road *Liv* 76-77; V Toxteth Park St Mich 76-77; V Toxteth Park St Mich w St Andr 78-88; V Stamfordham w Matfen *Newc* from 88; Hon CF from 90. *The Vicarage, Stamfordham, Newcastle upon Tyne NE18 0QQ* Stamfordham (01661) 886456   Fax as telephone

CAVAGHAN, Dennis Edgar. b 45. St Jo Coll Nottm BTh72. **d** 72 **p** 73. C Hartford *Ches* 72-76; C Plymouth St Andr w St Paul and St Geo *Ex* 76-80; V Cofton w Starcross 80-88; P-in-c W Exe 88-93; Perm to Offic *B & W* from 93. *The Manor House, Thurloxton, Taunton, Somerset TA2 8RH*   Taunton (01823) 413777

CAVAN, Lawrence Noel. b 38. Trin Coll Bris 72. **d** 75 **p** 76. C Lurgan Ch Ch *D & D* 75-78; C Chorleywood Ch Ch *St Alb* 78-82; I Durrus *C, C & R* 82-85; I Portarlington w Cloneyhurke and Lea *M & K* 85-90; TV Eston w Normanby *York* from 90. *The Vicarage, 73A High Street, Eston, Middlesbrough, Cleveland TS6 9EH*   Eston Grange (01642) 456755

CAVANAGH, Capt Kenneth Joseph. b 41. CA Tr Coll 60. **d** 77 **p** 77. CA from 64; Paraguay 70-83; P-in-c Gt w Lt Snoring *Nor* 83-85; R Gt w Lt Snoring w Kettlestone and Pensthorpe 85-88; R Glencarse *Bre* 88-94; CA Co-ord (Scotland/Ireland) & Regional Voc Adv from 90. *2 Westfield Crescent, Forfar, Angus DD8 1EG* Forfar (01307) 464630

CAVANAGH, Michael Richard. b 49. MIDPM78. N Ord Course 89. **d** 92 **p** 93. NSM Stalybridge H Trin and Ch Ch *Ches* from 92. *139 Mottram Road, Stalybridge, Cheshire SK15 2QU* 0161-303 1314   Fax 304 9997

CAVANAGH, Peter Bernard. b 49. Sarum & Wells Th Coll 71. **d** 73 **p** 74. C Gt Crosby St Faith *Liv* 73-76; C Stanley 76-79; V Anfield St Columba from 79. *St Columba's Vicarage, Pinehurst Avenue, Liverpool L4 2TZ*   0151-474 7231

CAVE, Canon Alan John. b 17. IPFA52 Lon Univ DipTh65. Cuddesdon Coll 64. **d** 65 **p** 66. C Ribbleton *Blackb* 68-72; V Burnley St Cath 72-78; P-in-c Burnley St Alb w St Paul 77-78; R Ribchester w Stidd 78-85; Hon Can Blackb Cathl 81-85; rtd 85; Perm to Offic *Guildf* from 86. *Mellstock, 23 Portmore Park Road, Weybridge, Surrey KT13 8ET*   Weybridge (01932) 851635

CAVE, Anthony Sidney. b 32. E Midl Min Tr Course. **d** 84 **p** 85. C Immingham *Linc* 84-88; V Keelby 88-89; V Riby 88-89; V Keelby w Riby and Aylesby from 89. *The Vicarage, Keelby, Grimsby, S Humberside DN37 8EH* Roxton (01469) 560251

CAVE, Brian Malcolm. b 37. St Cath Soc Ox BA60 MA64. Oak Hill Th Coll. **d** 63 **p** 64. C Tunbridge Wells St Jas *Roch* 68-71; V Bootle St Leon *Liv* 71-75; Min St Mary w St John Bootle 73-75; Area Sec Leprosy Miss 75-81; V Hurst Green *Bradf* 81-82; P-in-c Mitton 81-82; V Hurst Green and Mitton 82-91; rtd 91. *63 Westway, Nailsea, Avon BS19 1EF* Nailsea (01275) 654892

CAVE, Cyril Hayward. b 20. Nottm Univ MA60 BD63. AKC49. **d** 50 **p** 51. Lic to Offic *Ex* from 65; Lect Th Ex Univ 65-80; Sen Lect 80-85; rtd 85. *Berry House, Cheriton Fitzpaine, Crediton, Devon EX17 4HZ* Cheriton Fitzpaine (01363) 866548

CAVE, Douglas Lionel. b 26. Lon Bible Coll 50 Lon Coll of Div 64. **d** 66 **p** 67. C Barking St Marg *Chelmsf* 69-73; V Blackb St Barn *Blackb* 73-81; Ind Chapl *Lon* 81-91; rtd 91. *8 Wood Rise, Pinner, Middx HA5 2JD* Uxbridge (01895) 677426

CAVE, Ven Guy Newell. b 19. TCD BA41 MA58. CITC 41. **d** 42 **p** 43. P-in-c Kildrumferton w Ballymachugh *K, E & A* 45-73; Preb St Patr Cathl Dub 65-72; Adn Kilmore *K, E & A* 72-87; P-in-c Ballymachugh w Kildrumferton and Ballyjamesduff 73-87; rtd 87. *5 Yew Point, Hodson's Bay, Athlone, Co Westmeath, Irish Republic* Athlone (902) 92718

CAVE, John Edwin Dawson. b 43. Cranmer Hall Dur 71. **d** 74 **p** 75. C Gt Ayton w Easby and Newton in Cleveland *York* 74-77; C Redcar w Kirkleatham 77-78; C Redcar 78-80; P-in-c Aislaby and Ruswarp 80-81; V 81-87; V Dormanstown from 87. *All Saints' Vicarage, South Avenue, Redcar, Cleveland TS10 5LL* Redcar (01642) 478334

CAVE, Robert Philip. b 23. Roch Th Coll 64. **d** 67 **p** 68. C York Town St Mich *Guildf* 67-71; C Yaxley *Ely* 71-75; R Cottenham 75-88; rtd 88; Perm to Offic *Pet* from 89. *14 St Mary's Way, Roade, Northampton NN7 2PQ* Roade (01604) 864420

CAVE BERGQUIST, Julie Anastasia. b 59. St Jo Coll Dur BA80 Franciscan Univ Rome STL87. St Steph Ho Ox 85. **d** 87. Par Dn Kennington *Cant* 87-89; Chapl Trin Coll Cam 89-94; Chapl Westcott Ho Cam from 94. *Westcott House, Jesus Lane, Cambridge CB5 8BP* Cambridge (01223) 350074   Fax 301512

CAVE-BROWNE-CAVE, Bernard James William. b 54. Trin Hall Cam BA76 MA80 Bradf Univ MA90. Westcott Ho Cam 77. **d** 79 **p** 80. C Chesterton Gd Shep *Ely* 79-83; Chapl Lanc Univ *Blackb* 83-95; HM Pris Service Chapl from 95. *HM Prison Service Chaplaincy, Abell House, John Islip Street, London SW1P 4LH* 0171-217 5683

✠**CAVELL, Rt Rev John Kingsmill.** b 16. Qu Coll Cam BA39 MA44. Wycliffe Hall Ox 39. **d** 40 **p** 41 **c** 72. C Folkestone H Trin *Cant* 40; C Addington 40-44; Lic to Offic *Ox* 45-52; Area Sec (Dio Ox) CMS 44-52; Dio Pet 44-49; Tr Officer 49-52; V Cheltenham Ch Ch *Glouc* 52-62; V Plymouth St Andr *Ex* 62-72; RD Plymouth 67-72; Preb Ex Cathl 67-72; V E Stonehouse 68-72; Suff Bp Southn *Win* 72-84; Hon Can Win Cathl 72-84; rtd 84; Perm to Offic *Win* from 84; Asst Bp Sarum from 88; Can and Preb Sarum Cathl from 88. *5 Constable Way, West Harnham, Salisbury SP2 8LN* Salisbury (01722) 334782   Fax 413112

CAVELL-NORTHAM, Canon Cavell Herbert James. b 32. St Steph Ho Ox 53. **d** 56 **p** 57. C W Wycombe *Ox* 56-61; CF (TA) 60-63; V Lane End *Ox* 61-68; V Stony Stratford from 68; P-in-c Calverton 69-72; R from 72; Hon Can Ch Ch from 91. *The Vicarage, London Road, Stony Stratford, Milton Keynes MK11 1JA* Milton Keynes (01908) 562148

CAW, Alison Mary. b 40. Natal Univ BA62 Ox Univ PGCE64. Ox Min Course CBTS93. **d** 93 **p** 94. NSM Beaconsfield *Ox* from 93. *1 Westway, Beaconsfield, Bucks HP9 1DQ* Beaconsfield (01494) 674524

CAW, Miss Hannah Mary. b 69. Birm Univ BMus91. St Jo Coll Nottm DTS94 MA95 LTh95. **d** 95. C Northn St Giles *Pet* from 95. *18 The Avenue, Cliftonville, Northampton NN1 5BT* Northampton (01604) 24797

CAWDELL, Mrs Sarah Helen Louise. b 65. St Hugh's Coll Ox MA91 Trin Coll Cam BA94. Ridley Hall Cam BA94 CTM95. **d** 95. C Belmont *S'wark* from 95. *75 Brinkley Road, Worcester Park, Surrey KT4 8JE* 0181-330 7210

CAWDELL, Simon Howard. b 65. Univ Coll Dur BA86. Ridley Hall Cam CTM94. **d** 94 **p** 95. C Cheam Common St Phil *S'wark* from 94. *75 Brinkley Road, Worcester Park, Surrey KT4 8JE* 0181-330 7210

CAWLEY, David Lewis. b 44. FSA81. AKC71 St Aug Coll Cant 71. **d** 72 **p** 73. C Sprowston *Nor* 72-75; Chapl HM Pris Nor 74-75; C Wymondham *Nor* 75-77; C Buckland in Dover w Buckland Valley *Cant* 77-83; V Eastville St Anne w St Mark and St Thos *Bris* 83-95; V Leic St Mary *Leic* from 95. *The Vicarage, 15 Castle Street, Leicester LE1 5WN*   Leicester (0116) 262 8727

CAWLEY, Stephen. b 42. RMCM GRSM63. St Deiniol's Hawarden 81. **d** 84 **p** 85. C Tranmere St Paul w St Luke *Ches* 84-88; TV Hawarden *St As* 88-93; V Gwernaffield and Llanferres from 93. *The Vicarage, Cilcain Road, Gwernaffield, Mold, Clwyd CH7 5DQ* Mold (01352) 740205

CAWRSE, Christopher William. b 60. Univ of Wales (Cardiff) DipTh. Westcott Ho Cam. **d** 84 **p** 85. C Stoke Newington St Mary *Lon* 84-86; Chapl St Mark's Hosp Lon 86-90; C Islington St Jas w St Phil *Lon* 86-87; C Islington St Jas w St Pet 87-90; Chapl Asst Charing Cross Hosp Lon 90-93; rtd 93; C Isleworth All SS *Lon* 93. *179 Grange Hill Road, London SE9 1SR*

CAWTE, Canon David John. b 30. St Mich Coll Llan. **d** 65 **p** 66. C Boyne Hill *Ox* 67-74; C-in-c Cox Green CD 75-78; V Cox Green 78-94; Hon Can Ch Ch 88-94; rtd 94. *6 Broadfields Close, Milford on Sea, Lymington, Hants SO41 0SE* Lymington (01590) 642793

CAWTHORNE, Jack. b 22. ATD50 Lon Univ DipTh71. Cuddesdon Coll 69. **d** 71 **p** 72. NSM Newchurch *Man* 71-86; NSM Garforth *Ripon* 87-88; Perm to Offic from 88. *15 Arran Drive, Garforth, Leeds LS25 2BU* Leeds (0113) 286 9527

CAYTON, John. b 32. Bps' Coll Cheshunt 54. **d** 57 **p** 58. C Hindley All SS *Liv* 57-59; C Littleham w Exmouth *Ex* 59-63; V Burnley St Cath *Blackb* 63-72; V Marton 72-87; V Fleetwood from 87; Miss to Seamen from 87. *St Peter's Vicarage, 39 Mount Road, Fleetwood, Lancs FY7 6EX* Fleetwood (01253) 771642

CECIL, Kevin Vincent. b 54. BA PGCE. St Mich Coll Llan DipTh82. **d** 82 **p** 83. C Llanilid w Pencoed *Llan* 82-85; C Coity w Nolton 85-88; Area Sec (Dios St D, Llan, Mon and S & B) CMS from 88. *Gronw House, Llanharri, Pontyclun, M Glam CF7 9LH* Llantrisant (01443) 225035 Fax 0171-401 3215

CHADD, Jeremy Denis. b 55. Jes Coll Cam BA77 MA81. Coll of Resurr Mirfield 78. **d** 81 **p** 82. C Seaton History *Newc* 81-84; C N Gosforth 84-88; V Sunderland St Chad *Dur* from 88. *St Chad's Vicarage, Charter Drive, Sunderland SR3 3PG* 0191-528 2397

CHADD, Canon Leslie Frank. b 19. Leeds Univ BSc41. Coll of Resurr Mirfield 41. **d** 43 **p** 44. V Fareham SS Pet and Paul *Portsm* 65-92; Relig Adv STV 72-81; Hon Can Portsm Cathl 81-92; rtd 92. *Tree Tops, Hoads Hill, Wickham, Fareham, Hants PO17 5BX* Wickham (01329) 834397

CHADWICK, Charles John Peter. b 59. Birm Univ BA81 Slough Coll DMS84 Southn Univ BTh90. Sarum & Wells Th Coll 85. **d** 88 **p** 89. C Chalfont St Peter *Ox* 88-91; C Gt Marlow 91-93; TV Gt Marlow w Marlow Bottom, Lt Marlow and Bisham 93-95; P-in-c Stokenchurch and Ibstone from 95; Asst Dir Chiltern Ch Tr Course from 95. *The Vicarage, Wycombe Road, Stokenchurch, High Wycombe, Bucks HP14 3RG* High Wycombe (01494) 483384

CHADWICK, David Guy Evelyn St Just. b 36. Bps' Coll Cheshunt 61. **d** 68 **p** 69. C Edmonton All SS *Lon* 68-71; C Edmonton St Mary w St Jo 71-72; C Greenhill St Jo 72-74; Bp's Dom Chapl *Truro* 74-79; Chapl Community of the Epiphany Truro 77-78; P-in-c Crantock *Truro* 79-83; R Clydebank *Glas* 83-87; R Renfrew 87-94; rtd 94. *La Verna, 1 Nithsdale Crescent, Bearsden, Glasgow G61 4DF*

CHADWICK, Francis Arnold Edwin. b 30. AKC54. **d** 55 **p** 56. V Kingshurst *Birm* 67-73; V York Town St Mich *Guildf* 73-83; P-in-c Long Sutton w Long Load *B & W* 83-87; R Stockbridge and Longstock and Leckford *Win* 87-93; rtd 93; Chapl Helsinki w Tallin *Eur* from 95. *Mannerheimintie 19 A7, 00250 Helsinki, Finland* Helsinki (0) 490424 Fax 447987

CHADWICK, Canon George Bancroft. b 12. Linc Th Coll 40. **d** 42 **p** 43. V Cullercoats St Geo *Newc* 55-70; RD Tynemouth 67-70; V Corbridge w Halton 70-81; Hon Can Newc Cathl 74-82; P-in-c Newton Hall 79-81; V Corbridge w Halton and Newton Hall 82; rtd 82. *14 Alexandra Terrace, Hexham, Northd NE46 3JH* Hexham (01434) 602092

✠**CHADWICK, Rt Rev Graham Charles.** b 23. Keble Coll Ox BA49 MA53. St Mich Coll Llan 49. **d** 50 **p** 51 **c** 76. C Oystermouth *S & B* 50-53; Basutoland 53-63; Chapl Univ of Wales (Swansea) *S & B* 63-68; Sen Bursar Qu Coll Birm 68-69; Lic to Offic *S'wark* 69-70; Lesotho 70-76; S Africa 76-82; Bp Kimberley and Kuruman 76-82; Dioc Adv on Spirituality *St As* 83-90; Chapl St As Cathl 83-90; rtd 90; Asst Bp Liv from 90. *423 Eaton Road, West Derby, Liverpool L12 2AJ* 0151-228 2891

CHADWICK, Helen Jane. *See* MARSHALL, Mrs Helen Jane

CHADWICK, Canon Prof Henry. b 20. KBE89 OM(Ger)93. FBA60 MRIA Magd Coll Cam BA41 MusBac41 MA45 DD57 Glas Univ Hon DD57 Uppsala Univ Hon DD67 Yale Univ Hon DD70 Man Univ Hon DD75 Leeds Univ Hon DD80. Ridley Hall Cam 42. **d** 43 **p** 44. C S Croydon Em *Cant* 43-45; Asst Chapl Wellington Coll Berks 45-46; Chapl Qu Coll Cam 46-50; Dean 50-55; Can Ch Ch *Ox* 59-69; Regius Prof Div Ox 59-69; Vice-Pres Br Academy 68-69; Dean Ch Ch *Ox* 69-79; Regius Prof Div Cam Univ 79-82; Hon Can Ely Cathl *Ely* 79-83; Lic to Offic from 83; Master Peterho Cam 87-93. *46 St John Street, Oxford OX1 2LH* Oxford (01865) 512814

CHADWICK, Canon Martin James. b 27. Trin Hall Cam BA51 MA54. Cuddesdon Coll 52. **d** 54 **p** 55. C Earl's Court St Cuth w St Matthias *Lon* 54-58; Chapl Trin Hall Cam 58-63; Chapl Ch Ch Ox 63-67; V Market Lavington and Easterton *Sarum* 67-79; V Charlbury w Shorthampton *Ox* from 79; RD Chipping Norton from 79; Hon Can Ch Ch from 91. *The Vicarage, Charlbury, Chipping Norton, Oxon OX7 3PX* Charlbury (01608) 810286

CHADWICK, Peter MacKenzie. b 21. Lich Th Coll 63. **d** 65 **p** 66. Jt Hd Master Forres Sch Swanage 56-81; Chapl 66-85; NSM

Kingston, Langton Matravers and Worth Matravers *Sarum* 85-92; rtd 89; Perm to Offic *Sarum* from 92. *Cull's, Langton Matravers, Swanage, Dorset BH19 3HJ* Swanage (01929) 422258

CHADWICK, Roger Vernon. b 39. Dur Univ BA60. Cranmer Hall Dur DipTh62. **d** 62 **p** 63. C Swinton St Pet *Man* 62-65; C Heworth St Mary *Dur* 65-68; Hon C 68-74; V Hartlepool St Aid 75-84; R Egglescliffe from 84. *The Rectory, 10 Butts Lane, Egglescliffe, Stockton-on-Tees, Co Durham TS16 9BT* Eaglescliffe (01642) 780185

CHADWICK, Prof William Owen. b 16. KBE82. FBA62 St Jo Coll Cam BA39 MA42 BD51 DD55 St Andr Univ Hon DD60 Ox Univ Hon DD73. Cuddesdon Coll 39. **d** 40 **p** 41. C Huddersfield St Jo *Wakef* 40-42; Chapl Wellington Coll Berks 42-46; Lic to Offic *Ely* from 47; Fell Trin Hall Cam 47-56; Dean 49-56; Master Selw Coll Cam 56-83; Dixie Prof Ecclesiastical Hist 58-68; Regius Prof Modern Hist 68-83; Pres Br Academy 81-85; Chan UEA from 85. *67 Grantchester Street, Cambridge CB7 9HZ* Cambridge (01223) 314000

CHADWIN, James William. b 01. Glas Univ MA23 Lon Univ BA39. Edin Dioc NSM Course 75. **d** 76 **p** 77. NSM Edin H Cross *Edin* 76-83; rtd 83. *Braeburn, 35 Inverleith Terrace, Edinburgh EH3 5NU* 0131-332 1481

CHAFFEY, Jane Frances. b 59. Somerville Coll Ox BA80 MA84 St Jo Coll Dur BA86. Cranmer Hall Dur 84. **d** 88 **p** 94. Par Dn Roby *Liv* 88-90; NSM Finningley w Auckley *S'well* from 90. *10 Ash Grove, Finningley, Doncaster, S Yorkshire DN9 3LN* Doncaster (01302) 770046

CHAFFEY, Jonathan Paul Michael. b 62. St Chad's Coll Dur BA83. Cranmer Hall Dur 84. **d** 87 **p** 88. C Gateacre *Liv* 87-90; Chapl RAF from 90. *Chaplaincy Services (RAF), HQ, Personnel and Training Command, RAF Innsworth, Gloucester GL3 1EZ* Gloucester (01452) 712612 Ext 5164 Fax 510828

CHAFFEY, Michael Prosser. b 30. Lon Univ BA51. St Steph Ho Ox 53. **d** 55 **p** 56. C Victoria Docks Ascension *Chelmsf* 55-59; C Leytonstone H Trin Harrow Green 59-62; V Walthamstow St Mich 62-69; R Cov St Jo *Cov* 69-85; P-in-c Cov St Thos 69-75; Hon C Bideford *Ex* 85; P-in-c Charlestown *Man* 85-88; V Sutton St Mich *York* from 88. *St Michael's Vicarage, 751 Marfleet Lane, Hull HU9 4TJ* Hull (01482) 74509

CHALCRAFT, Christopher Warine Terrell (Kit). b 37. Oak Hill Th Coll. **d** 67 **p** 68. C Egham *Guildf* 67-70; P-in-c Slough *Ox* 70-73; TV Bramerton w Surlingham *Nor* 73-87; P-in-c Cockley Cley w Gooderstone 87-95; P-in-c Gt and Lt Cressingham w Threxton 87-95; P-in-c Didlington 87-95; P-in-c Hilborough w Bodney 87-95; P-in-c Oxborough w Foulden and Caldecote 87-95. *Address temp unknown*

CHALK, Francis Harold. b 25. Lich Th Coll 61. **d** 62 **p** 63. R Gt Gonerby *Linc* 69-89; rtd 89. *Chalkleigh, 3 Church Street, St Just, Penzance, Cornwall TR19 7HA* Penzance (01736) 787925

CHALK, John Edward. b 33. St D Coll Lamp BA57. **d** 58 **p** 59. C Connah's Quay *St As* 58-61; C Abergele 61-65; R Merthyr Tydfil and Cyfarthfa *Llan* 65-72; V Pyle w Kenfig 72-77; Lect in FE 84-92; NSM Mansf Woodhouse *S'well* 92; Perm to Offic *Lich* from 92; NSM Salt and Sandon w Burston from 94. *The Vicarage, Salt, Stafford ST18 0BW* Sandon (01889) 508341 Fax as telephone

CHALK, Norman Albert. b 25. S'wark Ord Course 69. **d** 71 **p** 72. C Northwood Hills St Edm *Lon* 71-76; R Cowley 76-90; rtd 91. *23 Rushmoor Avenue, Hazelmere, High Wycombe, Bucks HP15 7NT* High Wycombe (01494) 813438

CHALK, Miss Susan Christine (Sue). b 50. Warw Univ BSc71 Man Univ CertEdD72. S Dios Minl Tr Scheme 90. **d** 93 **p** 94. NSM Radipole Peverell, Stratton, Frampton etc *Sarum* from 93. *2 Dorchester Road, Stratton, Dorchester, Dorset DT2 9RT* Dorchester (01305) 268464

CHALKLEY, Henry Roy. b 23. St Aid Birkenhead 58. **d** 59 **p** 60. Miss to Seamen 85-87; rtd 88. *32 Spriteshall Lane, Felixstowe, Suffolk IP11 9QY* Felixstowe (01394) 277600

CHALLEN, Canon Peter Bernard. b 31. Clare Coll Cam BA56 MA60. Westcott Ho Cam 56. **d** 58 **p** 59. C Goole *Sheff* 58-61; V Dalton 61-67; Sen Ind Chapl *S'wark* from 67; R S'wark Ch Ch from 67; Hon Can S'wark Cathl from 74. *Christ Church Rectory, 49 Colombo Street, London SE1 8DP* 0171-928 4707 or 928 3970 Fax 401 9101

CHALLEN, Victor Stanley. b 14. Bede Coll Dur BSc39. **d** 41 **p** 43. V Bedf St Martin *St Alb* 52-83; rtd 83; Perm to Offic *St Alb* 83-93; Perm to Offic *Nor* from 93. *57 Hunstanton Road, Dersingham, King's Lynn, Norfolk PE31 6ND* Dersingham (01485) 540964

CHALLENGER, Canon Clifford. b 32. CITC 67. **d** 67 **p** 68. C Belf St Luke *Conn* 67-70; C Kilkenny w Aghour and Odagh *C & O* 70-71; Bp's V and Lib Kilkenny Cathl 70-71; Dioc Registrar (Ossory, Ferns and Leighlin) 70-71; I Fenagh w Myshall and Kiltennel 71-76; I Fenagh w Myshall, Aghade and Ardoyne 76-79; I Crosspatrick Gp from 79; Preb Ferns Cathl 85-88; Dioc Glebes Sec (Ferns) 86-91; Treas Ferns Cathl 88-91; Chan from 91; RD Wexford from 89. *The Rectory,*

Tinahely, Arklow, Co Wicklow, Irish Republic Arklow (402) 38178 Fax 38497

CHALLENGER, Peter Nelson. b 33. St Jo Coll Cam BA57 MA61. Ripon Hall Ox 57. **d** 59 **p** 60. C Bushbury *Lich* 59-62; V Horsley Woodhouse *Derby* 62-67; V Derby St Barn 67-75; Brazil 75-80; TV New Windsor *Ox* 80-89; V Wootton (Boars Hill) from 89. *Wootton Vicarage, Boars Hill, Oxford OX1 5JL* Oxford (01865) 735661

CHALLENGER, Miss Susanne Christine. b 41. Bp Grosseteste Coll TCert64 Leeds Poly DipSocSc68 Teesside Poly DMS86. NE Ord Course 88. **d** 91 **p** 94. NSM Middlesb St Cuth *York* from 91. *Hundlebrook, 11 Garbutts Lane, Hutton Rudby, Yarm, Cleveland TS15 0UN* Stokesley (01642) 700391

CHALLICE, John Richard. b 34. ACP65. Sarum & Wells Th Coll 73. **d** 75 **p** 76. C Warminster St Denys *Sarum* 75-78; R Longfield *Roch* from 78. *The Rectory, 67 Main Road, Longfield, Kent DA3 7PQ* Longfield (01474) 702201

CHALLIS, Ian. b 46. St Jo Coll Nottm 82. **d** 84 **p** 85. C Heatherlands St Jo *Sarum* 84-86; C Lytchett Minster 86-88; Perm to Offic from 88; NSM Canford Magna from 95. *9 Haven Road, Corfe Mullen, Wimborne, Dorset BH21 3SY* Wimborne (01202) 691300

CHALLIS, Preb James Dobb. b 16. St Jo Coll Cam BA38 MA42. Ridley Hall Cam 39. **d** 40 **p** 41. V Penn Fields *Lich* 67-81; Preb Lich Cathl 80-81; rtd 81. *21 Seymour Avenue, Louth, Lincs LN11 9EW* Louth (01507) 602637

CHALLIS, Terence Peter. b 40. St Aid Birkenhead 65. **d** 68 **p** 69. C Billericay St Mary *Chelmsf* 68-71; Kenya 72-75; P-in-c Sparkbrook Ch Ch *Birm* 76-80; V Enfield St Jas *Lon* 80-89; V Astley Bridge *Man* from 89. *St Paul's Vicarage, Sweetloves Lane, Bolton BL1 7ET* Bolton (01204) 304119

CHALLIS, William George. b 52. Keble Coll Ox BA73 K Coll Lon MTh75. Oak Hill Th Coll 73. **d** 75 **p** 76. C Islington St Mary *Lon* 75-79; Lect Trin Coll Bris 79-81; C Stoke Bishop *Bris* 79-81; Lect Oak Hill Th Coll 82; Burundi 82-85; P-in-c Bishopston *Bris* 86-89; TR 89-92; Vice-Prin Wycliffe Hall Ox from 93. *Wycliffe Hall, 54 Banbury Road, Oxford OX2 6PW* Oxford (01865) 274200/5 Fax 274215

CHALMERS, Brian. b 42. Or Coll Ox BA64 MA68 DPhil70 BA71. Wycliffe Hall Ox 71. **d** 72 **p** 73. C Luton St Mary *St Alb* 72-76; Chapl Cranfield Inst of Tech 76-81; Chapl Kent Univ *Cant* 81-89; Six Preacher Cant Cathl from 85; V Charing w Charing Heath and Lt Chart from 89. *The Vicarage, Pett Lane, Charing, Ashford, Kent TN27 0DL* Charing (01233) 712598

CHALMERS, Robert Alan. b 66. LLCM QUB LLB88 TCD BTh91. **d** 91 **p** 92. C Lurgan etc w Ballymachugh, Kildrumferton etc *K, E & A* 91-94; Dioc Registrar (Kilmore) 92-94; I Lurgan etc w Ballymachugh, Kildrumferton etc from 94. *Kildrumferton Rectory, Corsserlough PO, Ceanannus Mor, Co Meath, Irish Republic* Cavan (49) 36211

CHALONER, Stephen Mason. b 34. Dur Univ BA57. Ridley Hall Cam 57. **d** 59 **p** 60. C Aspley *S'well* 59-62; Chapl RNR from 61; P-in-c Eakring *S'well* 62-65; R 65-69; R Bilsthorpe 62-69; Chapl Saxondale Hosp Radcliffe-on-Trent 69-73; P-in-c Holme Pierrepont w Adbolton *S'well* 69-73; V Shelford 69-73; V Radcliffe-on-Trent 69-73; C Rowner *Portsm* 73-74; Hon C 74-81; Miss to Seamen 81-86; P-in-c Binstead *Portsm* 86-92; R from 92; P-in-c Swanmore St Mich w Havenstreet 86-92; V Havenstreet St Pet from 92; RD E Wight 88-94. *The Rectory, Pitts Lane, Ryde, Isle of Wight PO33 3SU* Isle of Wight (01983) 562890

CHAMBERLAIN, David (Bernard). b 28. Fitzw Ho Cam BA51. Linc Th Coll 52. **d** 54 **p** 55. CR 63-85; S Africa 68-70; Bp's Adv on Community Relns *Wakef* 71-85; Bp's Adv Community Relns & Inter-Faith Dialogue *Bris* 86-93; V Easton All Hallows 86-93; rtd 93; Perm to Offic *B & W* from 94. *43 Bath Road, Wells, Somerset BA5 3HR* Wells (01749) 679369

CHAMBERLAIN, David Murray. b 22. Cuddesdon Coll 55. **d** 57 **p** 58. Japan 60-71 and 76-81; V Edgbaston St Germain *Birm* 71-76; Miss to Seamen N Australia 81-88; rtd 88. *42 Tresawls Road, Truro, Cornwall TR1 3LE* Truro (01872) 72270

CHAMBERLAIN, Eric Edward. b 34. Lon Univ DipTh64. Tyndale Hall Bris 62. **d** 65 **p** 66. C Chell *Lich* 65-73; P-in-c Preston St Mary *Blackb* 73-76; V 76-89; P-in-c Preston St Luke 81-83; R S Normanton *Derby* from 89. *The Rectory, Church Street, South Normanton, Alfreton, Derbyshire DE55 2BT* Ripley (01773) 811273

CHAMBERLAIN, Frederick George. b 19. Univ of Wales (Lamp) BA50. Chich Th Coll 50. **d** 52 **p** 53. R Tilshead, Orcheston and Chitterne *Sarum* 71-80; P-in-c Handley w Gussage St Andrew and Pentridge 81. R 82-84; rtd 84. *Mill Cottage, Codford St Mary, Warminster, Wilts BA12 0ND* Warminster (01985) 50519

CHAMBERLAIN, Canon Neville. b 39. Nottm Univ BA61 MA73 CQSW73. Ripon Hall Ox 61. **d** 63 **p** 64. C Balsall Heath St Paul *Birm* 63-64; C Hall Green Ascension 64-66; C-in-c Gospel Lane CD 66-69; V Gospel Lane St Mich 69-72; Lic to

Offic *Linc* 73-74; Soc Resp Sec 74-82; Can and Preb Linc Cathl from 79; R Edin St Jo *Edin* from 82. *1 Ainslie Place, Edinburgh EH3 6AR* 0131-225 5004 or 229 7565

CHAMBERLAIN, Dr Nicholas Alan. b 63. St Chad's Coll Dur BA85 PhD91 New Coll Edin BD91. **d** 91 **p** 92. C Cockerton *Dur* 91-94; C Newton Aycliffe from 94. *St Francis Vicarage,, Burnhope, Newton Aycliffe, Co Durham DL5 7ER* Darlington (01325) 321533

CHAMBERLAIN, Roger Edward. b 53. BEd76 BA87. Trin Coll Bris 84. **d** 87 **p** 88. C Plymouth Em w Efford *Ex* 87-90; C Selly Park St Steph and St Wulstan *Birm* 90-94; V Yardley St Cypr Hay Mill from 94. *The Vicarage, 7 The Fordrough, Birmingham B25 8DL* 0121-773 1278

CHAMBERLAIN, Russell Charles. b 51. Oak Hill Th Coll 75. **d** 78 **p** 79. C Harold Hill St Geo *Chelmsf* 78-80; C Uckfield *Chich* 80-83; R Balcombe 83-90; V Okehampton w Inwardleigh *Ex* 90-94; TR Okehampton w Inwardleigh, Bratton Clovelly etc from 94; RD Okehampton from 93. *The Vicarage, 1 Church Path, Okehampton, Devon EX20 1LW* Okehampton (01837) 52731

CHAMBERLAIN, David John. b 56. St Jo Coll Nottm DipThMin94. **d** 94 **p** 95. C Chatham St Phil and St Jas *Roch* from 94. *3A Kit Hill, Chatham, Kent ME5 9ET* Medway (01634) 864348

CHAMBERLAIN, John Malcolm. b 38. Carl Dioc Tr Course 84. **d** 87 **p** 88. NSM Cockermouth w Embleton and Wythop *Carl* from 87. *45 Dale View, Cockermouth, Cumbria CA13 9EW* Cockermouth (01900) 822849

CHAMBERS, Anthony Frederick John. b 40. Sarum Th Coll 69. **d** 71 **p** 72. C Hall Green St Pet *Birm* 71-74; C Holdenhurst *Win* 74-77; P-in-c Ropley w W Tisted 77-79; P-in-c Bishop's Sutton 79; R Bishop's Sutton and Ropley and W Tisted 79-83; V Pokesdown St Jas from 83. *St James's Vicarage, 12 Harewood Avenue, Bournemouth BH7 6NQ* Bournemouth (01202) 425918

CHAMBERS, Mrs Barbara Mary Sinnott. b 43. SRN65 RM67 Birm Poly HVCert75 TCert77. W Midl Minl Tr Course 87. **d** 93 **p** 94. Par Dn Blurton *Lich* 93-94; C from 94. *St Alban's House, 51 Ripon Road, Stoke-on-Trent ST3 3BS* Stoke-on-Trent (01782) 315029

CHAMBERS, Canon George William. b 24. TCD BA46 MA57. CITC 47. **d** 47 **p** 48. C Conwall *D & R* 47-50; Chapl Portora R Sch Enniskillen 50-51; I Tullyaughnish w Milford *D & R* 51-61; I Adare *L & K* 61-81; Dioc Registrar (Limerick etc) 62-81; Adn Limerick 69-81; Dean Limerick 81-86; I Killeshin w Cloydagh and Killabban *C & O* from 86; Preb Ossory and Leighlin Cathls 90-92; Treas Ossory and Leighlin Cathls from 92. *The Rectory, Ballickmoyler, Carlow, Irish Republic* Athy (507) 25321

CHAMBERS, Canon Peter Lewis. b 43. Imp Coll Lon BScEng64. St Steph Ho Ox 64. **d** 66 **p** 67. C Llan w Capel Llanilltern *Llan* 66-70; Chapl Ch in Wales Youth Coun 70-73; Youth Chapl *Bris* 73-78; V Bedminster St Mich 78-84; RD Bedminster 81-84; Adv Ho of Bps Marriage Educn Panel Gen Syn 84-88; Dir Dioc Coun for Soc Resp *Guildf* 88-94; Hon Can Guildf Cathl 89-94; Dir Tr *Sheff* from 95. *27 Common Road, Thorpe Salvin, Worksop, Notts S80 3JJ* Worksop (01909) 770260

CHAMP, Darren David. b 60. Kent Univ BA93. Linc Th Coll DipMM94. **d** 95. C Ashford *Cant* from 95. *19 The Weald, Ashford, Kent TN24 8RA* Ashford (01233) 629819

CHAMPION, Canon John Oswald Cecil. b 27. St Chad's Coll Dur BA49 DipTh51. **d** 51 **p** 52. V Redditch St Steph *Worc* 68-75; R Fladbury, Wyre Piddle and Moor 75-93; RD Pershore 79-85; Hon Can Worc Cathl 81-93; rtd 93. *Black Horse Cottage, 3 Church Row, Pershore, Worcs WR10 1BL* Pershore (01386) 552403

CHAMPNEYS, Michael Harold. b 46. LRAM66 GRSM67 ARCO67. Linc Th Coll 69. **d** 72 **p** 73. C Poplar *Lon* 72-73; C Bow w Bromley St Leon 73-75; P-in-c Bethnal Green St Barn 75-76; C Tewkesbury w Walton Cardiff *Glouc* 76-78; V Bedf Park *Lon* 78-83; V Shepshed *Leic* 84-87; Community Educn Tutor Bolsover 88-93; Perm to Offic *Derby* 90-92; NSM Bolsover 92-93; V Potterspury, Furtho, Yardley Gobion and Cosgrove *Pet* from 93; RD Towcester from 94. *The Vicarage, 11 Church Lane, Potterspury, Towcester, Northants NN12 7PU* Yardley Gobion (01908) 542428

CHANCE, David Newton. b 44. Univ of Wales (Lamp) BA68. St Steph Ho Ox 68. **d** 70 **p** 71. C Selsdon St Jo w St Fran *Cant* 70-73; C Plymstock *Ex* 73-77; P-in-c Northam 77-79; TR Northam w Westward Ho! and Appledore 79-93; V Banstead *Guildf* from 93. *The Vicarage, Court Road, Banstead, Surrey SM7 2NQ* Burgh Heath (01737) 351134

CHAND, Wazir. b 29. Punjab Univ BA56 BT59. Ox NSM Course. **d** 90 **p** 91. NSM Cowley St Jas *Ox* from 90. *7 Frederick Road, Oxford OX4 3HL* Oxford (01865) 714160

CHANDA, Daniel Khazan. b 28. Punjab Univ BA57 MA62 Saharanputh Coll. **d** 70 **p** 70. Hon C Handsworth St Jas *Birm*

70-83; Hon C Perry Barr 83-89; C Small Heath St Greg 89-92; C Small Heath St Aid w St Greg and St Oswald from 92. *22 Tennyson Road, Birmingham B10 0HB* 0121-766 5659

CHANDLER, Derek Edward. b 67. Southn Univ BTh91 Nottm Univ MDiv93. Linc Th Coll 91. **d** 93 **p** 94. C Bitterne Park *Win* from 93. *24 Lacon Close, Southampton SO2 4JA* Southampton (01703) 584640

CHANDLER, Ian Nigel. b 65. K Coll Lon BD89 AKC89. Chich Th Coll CMT92. **d** 92 **p** 93. C Hove All SS *Chich* 92-93; C Hove from 93. *Flat 1, 28 Tisbury Road, Hove, E Sussex BN3 3BA* Brighton (01273) 720342

CHANDLER, John Charles. b 46. Solicitor. Oak Hill Th Coll 91. **d** 94 **p** 95. C Tonbridge St Steph *Roch* from 94. *35 Waterloo Road, Tonbridge, Kent TN9 2SW* Tonbridge (01732) 351906

CHANDLER, John Edmond Owen. b 18. St Cath Soc Ox BA48 MA48. Cuddesdon Coll 68. **d** 68 **p** 69. Hon C Quarndon *Derby* 68-72; Lic to Offic *S'well* 73-78; P-in-c Oxton 79-85; R Epperstone 79-85; R Gonalston 79-85; rtd 85; Perm to Offic *S'well* from 85. *18 Thoresby Dale, Hucknall, Nottingham NG15 7UG* Nottingham (0115) 963 5945

CHANDLER, Canon Michael John. b 45. Lon Univ DipTh75 K Coll Lon PhD87. Lambeth STh80 Linc Th Coll 70. **d** 72 **p** 73. C Cant St Dunstan w H Cross *Cant* 72-75; C Margate St Jo 75-78; V Newington w Bobbing and Iwade 78-83; P-in-c Hartlip w Stockbury 80-83; V Newington w Hartlip and Stockbury 83-88; RD Sittingbourne 84-88; R Hackington 88-95; RD Cant 94-95; Can Res Cant Cathl from 95. *15 The Precincts, Canterbury, Kent CT1 2EL*

CHANDLER, Quentin David. b 62. Aston Tr Scheme 87 Trin Coll Bris DipHE91 BA92. **d** 92 **p** 93. C Goldington *St Alb* from 92. *1 Atholl Walk, Bedford MK41 0BG* Bedford (01234) 212973

CHANNER, Christopher Kendall. b 42. K Coll Lon BD64 AKC64. **d** 65 **p** 66. C Norbury St Steph *Cant* 65-68; C S Elmsall *Wakef* 68-70; V Dartford St Edm *Roch* 70-75; Chapl Joyce Green Hosp Dartford 73-75; V Bromley St Andr *Roch* 75-81; V Langton Green 81-94; Chapl Holmewood Ho Sch Tunbridge Wells from 94. *The Little House, Holmewood House Sch, Langton Green, Tunbridge Wells, Kent TN3 0EB* Langton (01892) 861285

CHANT, Edwin John. b 14. Lon Univ BA62. Clifton Th Coll 46. **d** 47 **p** 48. V Gentleshaw *Lich* 56-80; V Farewell 56-80; rtd 80; Perm to Offic *Lich* from 80. *31 Huntsmans Gate, Burntwood, Staffs WS7 9LL*

CHANT, Harry. b 40. Oak Hill Th Coll DipHE78. **d** 78 **p** 79. C Heatherlands St Jo *Sarum* 78-81; P-in-c Bramshaw 81-83; P-in-c Landford w Plaitford 81-83; R Bramshaw and Landford w Plaitford 83-87; V Fareham St Jo *Portsm* from 87. *St John's Vicarage, 3A St Michael's Grove, Fareham, Hants PO14 1DN* Fareham (01329) 280762

CHANT, Kenneth William. b 37. St Deiniol's Hawarden 67. **d** 70 **p** 71. C Ynyshir *Llan* 70-74; C Bargoed and Deri w Brithdir 74; P-in-c Aberpergwm and Blaengwrach 74-77; V 77-81; V Cwmavon from 81. *The Vicarage, Coed Parc, Cwmavon, Port Talbot, W Glam SA12 9BL* Port Talbot (01639) 896254

CHANT, Maurice Ronald. b 26. Chich Th Coll 51. **d** 54 **p** 55. Chapl Miss to Seamen Sydney 67-71; Gt Yarmouth 71-77; Australia 77-84 and from 85; Singapore 84-85; rtd 91. *47 Regent Street, Wynnum North, Queensland, Australia 4178* Brisbane (7) 893-1251

CHANTER, Canon Anthony Roy. b 37. ACP60 Open Univ BA72 Lon Univ MA75. Sarum Th Coll 64. **d** 66 **p** 67. C W Tarring *Chich* 66-69; Chapl St Andr Sch Worthing 69-70; Hd Master Bp K Sch Linc 70-73; Hon PV Linc Cathl *Linc* 70-73; Hd Master Grey Court Comp Sch Richmond 73-76; Hon C Kingston All SS *S'wark* 73-76; Hd Master Bp Reindorp Sch Guildf 77-84; Hon Can Guildf Cathl *Guildf* from 84; Dir of Educn from 84. *Grasshoppers, Woodland Avenue, Cranleigh, Surrey GU6 7HU* Cranleigh (01483) 273833 or 571826

CHANTREY, Dr David Frank. b 48. K Coll Cam BA70 PhD73 MA74. Westcott Ho Cam 83. **d** 86 **p** 87. C Wordsley *Lich* 86-89; C Beckbury 89-90; P-in-c 90-93; C Badger 89-90; P-in-c 90-93; C Kemberton, Sutton Maddock and Stockton 89-90; P-in-c 90-93; C Ryton 89-90; P-in-c 90-93; R Beckbury, Badger, Kemberton, Ryton, Stockton etc from 93. *The Rectory, Beckbury, Shifnal, Shropshire TF11 9DG* Ryton (0195287) 474

CHANTRY, Ms Helen Fiona. b 59. Bradf Univ BSc82 Leeds Univ CertEd83. Trin Coll Bris BA89. **d** 89 **p** 94. NSM Hyde St Geo *Ches* 89-92; Dioc Youth Officer from 92; NSM Barrow from 94. *The Rectory, Mill Lane, Great Barrow, Chester CH3 7JF* Tarvin (01829) 740263

CHANTRY, Peter Thomas. b 62. Bradf Univ BSc83. Trin Coll Bris BA89. **d** 89 **p** 90. C Hyde St Geo *Ches* 89-92; Dioc Youth Officer 91-94; P-in-c Barrow from 94. *The Rectory, Mill Lane, Great Barrow, Chester CH3 7JF* Tarvin (01829) 740263

CHANTRY, Richard Michael. b 31. Hertf Coll Ox BA55 MA57. Ridley Hall Cam 55. **d** 57 **p** 57. C Boulton *Derby* 57-59; C Ox St

Aldate w H Trin *Ox* 59-68; P-in-c 74-75; Chapl Hertf Coll Ox from 61; Chapl Ox United Football Club from 65; Chapl Somerville Coll from 95. *11 Talbot Road, Oxford OX2 8LL* Oxford (01865) 58286 or 279400

CHANTRY, Mrs Sandra Mary. b 41. Cam Inst of Educn CertEd63. E Midl Min Tr Course 83. **dss** 86 **d** 87 **p** 94. Loughb Gd Shep *Leic* 86-87; Par Dn 87-89; Par Dn Belton and Osgathorpe 89-90; Par Dn Hathern, Long Whatton and Diseworth w Belton etc 90-94; C from 94. *The Rectory, Presents Lane, Belton, Loughborough, Leics LE12 9UN* Coalville (01530) 222554

CHAPLIN, Colin. b 33. Edin Dioc NSM Course 74. **d** 76 **p** 77. NSM Penicuik *Edin* 76-91; P-in-c Peebles 89-90; NSM Bathgate from 91. *26 Broomhill Road, Penicuik, Midlothian EH26 9EE* Penicuik (01968) 672050

CHAPLIN, Douglas Archibald. b 59. Em Coll Cam BA81. St Jo Coll Nottm DipTh84. **d** 86 **p** 87. C Glouc St Geo w Whaddon *Glouc* 86-89; C Lydney w Aylburton 89-93; R Worc St Clem Worc from 93. *St Clement's Rectory, 124 Laugherne Road, Worcester WR2 5LT* Worcester (01905) 422675

CHAPLIN, Frederick David. b 20. CCC Ox BA49 MA54. Cuddesdon Coll 49. **d** 51 **p** 52. Trinidad and Tobago 61-72; Asst to Gen Sec ACC 72-78; Sec C of E Partnership for World Miss 79-85; Perm to Offic *Ox* from 83; rtd 86. *19 Granville Court, Cheney Lane, Oxford OX3 0HS* Oxford (01865) 240489

CHAPLIN, Paul. b 57. Hull Univ BA80 CertEd81 K Coll Lon MA89. St Steph Ho Ox 85. **d** 87 **p** 88. C Ex St Jas *Ex* 87-90; C Wokingham St Paul *Ox* from 90. *St Nicholas House, 13 Brook Close, Wokingham, Berks RG11 1ND* Wokingham (01734) 780034

CHAPMAN, Canon Albert Aidan. b 09. TD. Em Coll Cam BA35 MA39. Lon Coll of Div. **d** 37 **p** 38. Hon Can Roch Cathl *Roch* 64-76; V Westerham 64-76; rtd 76; Perm to Offic *St E* from 76. *41 Honeymeade Close, Stanton, Bury St Edmunds, Suffolk IP31 2EF* Stanton (01359) 50518

CHAPMAN, Ms Ann Beatrice. b 53. Hull Coll of Educn BEd77 Leeds Univ BA87. St Jo Coll Nottm MA95. **d** 95. C Burley *Ripon* from 95. *33 Stanmore Crescent, Leeds LS4 2RY* Leeds (0113) 274 4073

CHAPMAN, Barry Frank. b 48. Trin Coll Bris. **d** 82 **p** 83. NSM Bradford-on-Avon Ch Ch *Sarum* from 82; Assoc Chapl Bath Univ from 83. *16 Church Acre, Bradford-on-Avon, Wilts BA15 1RL* Bradford-on-Avon (01225) 866861

CHAPMAN, Mrs Celia. b 32. Whitelands Coll Lon TCert53 Open Univ BA82. W Midl Minl Tr Course 84. **d** 87 **p** 94. NSM Bilston *Lich* 87-93; Ind Chapl Black Country Urban Ind Miss from 93; Chapl St Pet Colleg Sch Wolv from 93. *St Leonard's Vicarage, Dover Street, Bilston, W Midlands WV14 6AW* Bilston (01902) 491560

CHAPMAN, Christopher Robin. b 37. Nottm Univ DipAdEd71 Cam Univ DipRK74. Ripon Hall Ox 72. **d** 73 **p** 74. C Kidbrooke St Jas *S'wark* 73-77; V Corton Nor 77-80; V Hopton 77-80; RD Lothingland 80-86; V Hopton w Corton 80-92; P-in-c Loddon w Sisland 92-93; P-in-c Loddon, Sisland w Hales and Heckingham from 93; RD Loddon from 95. *The Vicarage, 4 Market Place, Loddon, Norwich NR14 6EY* Loddon (01508) 20251

CHAPMAN, Colin. b 38. St Andr Univ MA60 Lon Univ BD62. Ridley Hall Cam. **d** 64 **p** 65. C Edin St Jas *Edin* 64-67; Egypt 68-74; Perm to Offic *Birm* 74-77; Lebanon 77-83; Lect Trin Coll Bris 83-90; Prin Crowther Hall CMS Tr Coll Selly Oak from 90. *Crowther Hall, Weoley Park Road, Birmingham B29 6QT* 0121-472 4228 or 0171-928 8681 Fax 0171-401 3215

CHAPMAN, David John. b 28. Jes Coll Ox BA52 MA56. Wells Th Coll 52. **d** 54 **p** 55. R Sawley *Derby* 69-79; P-in-c Holkham w Egmere and Waterden *Nor* 79-83; P-in-c Warham w Wighton 79-83; R Wells next the Sea 79-83; R Holkham w Egmere w Warham, Wells and Wighton 83; V Feltham *Lon* 83-93; rtd 93. *12 Little Penny Rope, Pershore, Worcestershire WR10 1QN* Pershore (01386) 561558

CHAPMAN, Canon Derek. b 22. Westcott Ho Cam 52. **d** 53 **p** 54. V E Malling *Roch* 58-79; R Hever w Mark Beech 79-89; P-in-c Four Elms 80-89; Hon Can Roch Cathl 84-89; rtd 89; Perm to Offic *Roch* from 89; Perm to Offic *Chich* from 89. *1 Moat Lane, Sedlescombe, Battle, E Sussex TN33 0RZ* Hastings (01424) 754455

CHAPMAN, Mrs Dorothy. b 38. Nottm Univ CTPS. E Midl Min Tr Course. **d** 89 **p** 94. Par Dn Bingham *S'well* 89-92; Sub-Chapl HM Pris Whatton 89-92; C Lenton from 92. *86 Kenrick Road, Nottingham NG3 6FB* Nottingham (0115) 950 3088

CHAPMAN, Drummond John. b 36. Cant Sch of Min 80. **d** 83 **p** 86. C Kington w Huntington, Old Radnor, Kinnerton etc *Heref* 83-84; C Llanidloes w Llangurig *Ban* 86-90; V Llanwnnog and Caersws w Carno from 90. *The Vicarage, Llanwnnog, Caersws, Powys SY17 5JG* Caersws (01686) 688318

CHAPMAN, Edwin Thomas. b 32. Man Univ BA60. St Mich Coll Llan 62. **d** 63 **p** 64. C Cleveleys *Blackb* 63-65; C Ox St Mary V w St Cross and St Pet *Ox* 65-67; Chapl LMH Ox 67-68; Asst Dir of Educn *York* 68-75; R E Gilling 68-76; P-in-c Hockley *Chelmsf* 76-77; V 77-82; P-in-c Gosberton Clough and Quadring *Linc* 82-83; Chapl St Cath Sch Bramley 83-86; R Bulmer w Dalby, Terrington and Welburn *York* from 86; RD Bulmer and Malton from 91. *The Rectory, Terrington, York YO6 4PU* Coneysthorpe (01653) 648226

CHAPMAN, Canon Eric Ronald. b 19. Man Univ BA41 BD59. Bps' Coll Cheshunt 41. **d** 43 **p** 44. RD Whitehaven *Carl* 66-70; R Egremont 66-81; Hon Can Carl Cathl 79-85; TR Egremont and Haile 81-85; rtd 85; Perm to Offic *Carl* from 86. *Bernaville, Highfield Road, Grange-over-Sands, Cumbria LA11 7JA* Grange-over-Sands (015395) 34351

CHAPMAN, Gorran. b 55. Dur Univ BA. Westcott Ho Cam 78. **d** 80 **p** 81. C Par *Truro* 80-82; C Kenwyn 82-84; P-in-c Penwerris 84-89; V 89-92; V Torquay St Martin Barton *Ex* from 92. *St Martin's Vicarage, Beechfield Avenue, Barton, Torquay TQ2 8HU* Torquay (01803) 327223

CHAPMAN, Canon Guy Godfrey. b 33. Southn Univ BSc57. Clifton Th Coll 60. **d** 62 **p** 63. C Chadderton Ch Ch *Man* 62-67; V Edgeside 67-70; P-in-c Shipton Bellinger *Win* 70-72; V 72-83; RD Andover 75-85; Hon Can Win Cathl 79-91; R Over Wallop w Nether Wallop 83-91; V Ambrosden w Mert and Piddington *Ox* from 91; RD Bicester and Islip from 95. *The Vicarage, Ambrosden, Bicester, Oxon OX6 0UJ* Bicester (01869) 247813

CHAPMAN, Henry Davison (Harry). b 31. Bris Univ BA55. Tyndale Hall Bris 52. **d** 56 **p** 57. SW Area Sec CPAS 68-72; V Eccleston St Luke *Liv* 72-78; P-in-c Ringshall w Battisford, Barking w Darmsden etc *St E* 78-80; R 80-93; RD Bosmere 87-91; rtd 93. *Daracombe, The Clays, Market Lavington, Devizes, Wilts SN10 4AY* Devizes (01380) 813774

CHAPMAN, Ian Martin. b 47. Oak Hill Th Coll BA94. **d** 94 **p** 95. C S Mimms Ch Ch *Lon* from 94. *8 Wentworth Road, Barnet, Herts EN5 4NT* 0181-441 0645

CHAPMAN (nee CRAVEN), Mrs Janet Elizabeth. b 58. St Jo Coll Dur BSc80 Dur Univ MA92. Cranmer Hall Dur 84. **d** 87 **p** 95. Par Dn Darlington St Cuth *Dur* 87-92; NSM Edin Gd Shep *Edin* from 93. *26 Cameron March, Lady Road, Edinburgh EH16 5XG* 0131-662 1513

CHAPMAN, John. b 24. St Cuth Soc Dur BA51 St Chad's Coll Dur DipTh53. **d** 53 **p** 54. V Annfield Plain *Dur* 63-78; V Bolton All So w St Jas *Man* 78-85; V Baddesley Ensor w Grendon *Birm* 85-91; rtd 91; Perm to Offic *Birm* from 91. *The Angelus, 49 Alfriston Road, Coventry CV3 6FG* Coventry (01203) 413758

CHAPMAN (nee WHITFIELD), Mrs Joy Verity. b 46. SRN67 SCM71 MTD80. Trin Coll Bris BA88. **d** 88 **p** 94. C Littleover *Derby* 88-92; Par Dn Bucknall and Bagnall *Lich* 92-94; C 94; TV from 94. *St Mary's Vicarage, 12 Tansey Close, Stoke-on-Trent ST2 9QX* Stoke-on-Trent (01782) 503696

CHAPMAN, Dr Mark David. b 60. Trin Coll Ox MA83 DipTh84 DPhil89. Ox Min Course 93. **d** 94. Lect Ripon Coll Cuddesdon from 92; NSM Dorchester *Ox* from 94. *Ripon College, Cuddesdon, Oxford OX44 9EX* Oxford (01865) 874310

CHAPMAN, Mary Elizabeth. NE Ord Course. dss 84 **d** 87 **p** 94. Newc St Gabr *Newc* 84-87; Hon C 87-95. *9 Sefton Avenue, Newcastle upon Tyne NE6 5QR* 0191-265 9931

CHAPMAN, Ven Michael Robin. b 39. Leeds Univ BA61. Coll of Resurr Mirfield 61. **d** 63 **p** 64. C Southwick St Columba *Dur* 63-68; Chapl RN 68-84; V Hale *Guildf* 84-91; RD Farnham 88-91; Adn Northn *Pet* from 91. *Westbrook, 11 The Drive, Northampton NN1 4RZ* Northampton (01604) 714015 Fax 792016

CHAPMAN, Miss Patricia Ann. b 42. dss 84 **d** 87 **p** 94. Rainworth *S'well* 84-87; Par Dn 87-94; C from 94. *8 Hartington Court, Oak Tree Lane Estate, Mansfield, Notts NG18 3QJ* Mansfield (01623) 645030

CHAPMAN, Canon Percy Frank. b 06. Bris Univ BSc27 MA31. **d** 36 **p** 37. V Aldbourne and Baydon *Sarum* 65-72; R Whitton 65-72; V Coombe Bissett w Homington 72-81; P-in-c Bishopstone w Stratford Tony 80-81; R Chalke Valley E 81-88; Can and Preb Sarum Cathl 83-88; rtd 88; Perm to Offic *Chich* from 92. *College of St Barnabas, Blackberry Lane, Lingfield, Surrey RH7 6NJ* Dormans Park (01342) 870762

CHAPMAN, Peter Harold White. b 40. AKC64. **d** 65 **p** 66. C Havant *Portsm* 65-69; C Stanmer w Falmer and Moulsecoomb *Chich* 69-73; Chapl RN 73-86; Chapl Chigwell Sch Essex 86-90; P-in-c Stapleford Tawney w Theydon Mt *Chelmsf* from 87. *The Rectory, Theydon Mount, Epping, Essex CM16 7PW* Epping (01992) 578723

CHAPMAN, Peter John. b 33. Dur Univ BA56. Cranmer Hall Dur DipTh59. **d** 59 **p** 60. C Boulton *Derby* 59-62; Uganda 63-70; P-in-c Southn St Matt *Win* 71-73; TV Southn (City Cen) 73-78; V Bilston St Leon *Lich* 78-79; P-in-c Bilston St

Mary 78-79; TR Bilston from 80; RD Wolv from 89. *St Leonard's Vicarage, Dover Street, Bilston, W Midlands WV14 6AW* Bilston (01902) 491560

CHAPMAN, Raymond. b 24. FRSA90 Jes Coll Ox BA45 MA59 Lon Univ MA47 BD75 PhD78. S'wark Ord Course 72. **d** 74 **p** 75. NSM St Mary-le-Strand w St Clem Danes *Lon* 74-82; NSM Barnes St Mary *S'wark* 82-94; Perm to Offic from 94; Perm to Offic *Lon* 82-91. *6 Kitson Road, London SW13 9HJ* 0181-748 9901

CHAPMAN, Raymond. b 41. Linc Th Coll 68. **d** 71 **p** 72. C Dronfield *Derby* 71-74; C Delaval *Newc* 75-76; TV Whorlton 76-79; V Newc St Hilda 79-83; V Blyth St Cuth 83-89. *5 Dukes Gardens, Blyth, Northd NE24 5HD* Blyth (01670) 352226

CHAPMAN, Canon Rex Anthony. b 38. Univ Coll Lon BA62 St Edm Hall Ox BA64 MA68 Birm Univ DPS67. Wells Th Coll 64. **d** 65 **p** 66. C Stourbridge St Thos *Worc* 65-68; Chapl Aber Univ *Ab* 68-78; Can St Andr Cathl 76-78; Bp's Adv for Educn *Carl* 78-85; Dir of Educn from 85; Can Res Carl Cathl from 78. *1 The Abbey, Carlisle CA3 8TZ* Carlisle (01228) 597614 or 38086 Fax 48769

CHAPMAN, Rodney Andrew. b 53. AKC75. St Aug Coll Cant 75. **d** 76 **p** 77. C Hartlepool St Aid *Dur* 76-81; Lic to Offic 81-83; C Owton Manor 83-87; P-in-c Kelloe 87-92; V Sharlston *Wakef* from 92. *St Luke's Vicarage, 45 West Lane, Sharlston Common, Wakefield, W Yorkshire WF4 1EP* Wakefield (01924) 862414

CHAPMAN, Roger John. b 34. AKC58. **d** 59 **p** 60. C Guildf Ch Ch *Guildf* 59-61; Kenya 61-67; R S Milford *York* 68-77; RD Selby 72-77; V Beverley St Mary 77-88; RD Beverley 85-88; V Desborough *Pet* from 88; R Brampton Ash w Dingley and Braybrooke from 88. *St Giles' Vicarage, Desborough, Kettering, Northants NN14 2NP* Kettering (01536) 760324

CHAPMAN, Mrs Sally Anne. b 55. Lanchester Poly BSc76 Univ of Wales (Swansea) PGCE77. W Midl Minl Tr Course 87. **d** 90 **p** 94. Par Dn Stoneydelph St Martin CD *Lich* 90; Par Dn Glascote and Stonydelph 90-93; Par Dn Willenhall H Trin 93-94; C from 94. *18 Heather Grove, Willenhall, W Midlands WV12 4BT* Willenhall (01902) 631498

CHAPMAN, Mrs Sarah Jean. b 55. Lon Univ DipCOT77. Sarum & Wells Th Coll 86. **d** 89 **p** 94. NSM Rogate w Terwick and Trotton w Chithurst *Chich* 89-94; NSM Easebourne from 94. *Church House, Rogate, Petersfield, Hants GU31 5EA* Rogate (01730) 821784

CHAPMAN, Sydney William. b 12. Didsbury Meth Coll 32 Sarum Th Coll 55. **d** 56 **p** 57. In Meth Ch 32-55; V Walberton w Binsted *Chich* 60-81; rtd 81; Perm to Offic *Win* 82-91. *16 Walberton Park, Walberton, Arundel, W Sussex BN18 0PJ* Bognor Regis (01243) 551777

CHAPMAN, Thomas Graham (Tom). b 33. Trin Coll Bris 73. **d** 75 **p** 76. C Branksome St Clem *Sarum* 75-81; V Quarry Bank *Lich* 81-93; V Quarry Bank *Worc* from 93. *The Vicarage, Maughan Street, Brierley Hill, W Midlands DY5 2DN* Cradley Heath (01384) 565480

CHAPMAN, William Henry Stanley (Peter). b 08. OBE58. St Chad's Coll Dur BA31. **d** 32 **p** 33. W Dean *Chich* 63-73; rtd 73; Perm to Offic *Chich* from 73. *Moons, Green Lane, Crowborough, E Sussex TN6 2DE* Crowborough (01892) 661568

CHAPMAN, William Howard Dale. b 11. Edin Th Coll 33. **d** 38 **p** 39. R Brookthorpe w Whaddon and Harescombe *Glouc* 71-76; rtd 76; Perm to Offic *Glouc* 85-91. *35A Winchester Road, Eastleigh, Hants SO5 2GF* Chandler's Ford (01703) 268907

CHAPPELL, Allan. b 27. Selw Coll Cam BA51 MA56. Coll of Resurr Mirfield 51. **d** 53 **p** 54. C-in-c Broxtowe CD *S'well* 67-73; P-in-c Flintham 73-82; R Car Colston w Screveton 73-82; V Mansf St Lawr 82-92; rtd 93; Perm to Offic *S'well* from 93. *43 Hillsway Crescent, Mansfield, Notts NG18 5DR* Mansfield (01623) 654155

CHAPPELL, Edward Michael. b 32. Glouc Sch of Min 84. **d** 87 **p** 88. NSM Wotton-under-Edge w Ozleworth and N Nibley *Glouc* from 87. *20 Old Town, Wotton-under-Edge, Glos GL12 7DH* Dursley (01453) 844250

CHAPPELL, Eric Richardson. b 08. Keble Coll Ox BA30 MA34. Cuddesdon Coll 30. **d** 31 **p** 32. V Goodnestone H Cross w Chillenden and Knowlton *Cant* 64-78; P-in-c Adisham 75-78; rtd 78; Perm to Offic *Cant* from 78. *33 Sandgate Hill, Folkestone, Kent CT20 3AX* Folkestone (01303) 248141

CHAPPELL, Frank Arnold. b 37. Dur Univ BA58. Bps' Coll Cheshunt 58. **d** 60 **p** 61. C Headingley *Ripon* 60-65; V Beeston Hill St Luke 65-73; R Garforth 73-91; V Dacre w Hartwith and Darley w Thornthwaite from 91. *The Vicarage, Dacre Banks, Harrogate, N Yorkshire HG3 4ED* Harrogate (01423) 780262

CHAPPELL, Preb George Thomas. b 04. St Jo Coll Dur LTh28 BA29 MA32. Lon Coll of Div 24. **d** 28 **p** 29. V Paddington St Jas *Lon* 43-71; Preb St Paul's Cathl 63-71; rtd 71; C S

Kensington H Trin w All SS *Lon* 71-74; P-in-c 74-75; Perm to Offic 75-85. *Flat 3, 19 Burton Road, Poole, Dorset BH13 6DT* Poole (01202) 764665

CHAPPELL, Henry Pegg. b 09. DSC42. St Cath Coll Cam BA31 MA35. Wells Th Coll 33. **d** 34 **p** 35. P-in-c How Caple w Sollers Hope *Heref* 71-76; rtd 76; Perm to Offic *Heref* 76-95. *c/o R Otto Esq, Kidsons Impey, Chartered Accountants, Bank House, 8 Cherry Street, Birmingham B2 5AD* 0121-631 2631

CHAPPELL, Michael Paul. b 35. Selw Coll Cam BA57 MA61 ACertCM65. Cuddesdon Coll 60. **d** 62 **p** 63. C Pershore w Pinvin, Wick and Birlingham *Worc* 62-65; Malaysia 65-67; VC and Chapl Heref Cathl *Heref* 67-71; Min Can Dur Cathl *Dur* 71-76; Prec 72-76; Chapl H Trin Sch Stockton 76-87; C-in-c Stockton Green Vale H Trin CD *Dur* 82-87; V Scarborough St Luke *York* from 87; Chapl Scarborough Gen Hosp from 87. *The Vicarage, 37 Woodland Ravine, Scarborough, N Yorkshire YO12 6TA* Scarborough (01723) 372831

CHARD, Canon Francis Eric. b 24. Dur Univ BA53 MLitt81. St Jo Coll Dur DipTh55. **d** 55 **p** 56. V Ewood *Blackb* 60-72; V Downham 72-88; RD Whalley 83-89; Hon Can Blackb Cathl 86-93; Co Ecum Officer 88-93; rtd 93. *21 Moorland Crescent, Clitheroe, Lancs BB7 4PY* Clitheroe (01200) 27480

CHARD, Reginald Jeffrey. b 40. Univ of Wales (Lamp) BA62 Birm Poly CQSW75. Coll of Resurr Mirfield 62. **d** 64 **p** 65. C Ystrad Mynach *Llan* 64-67; C Aberdare St Fagan 67-71; V Hirwaun 71-74; Hon C Stretford *Birm* 74-78; TV Banbury *Ox* 78-86; Ind Chapl from 86; P-in-c Claydon w Mollington from 86. *18 Bignold's Close, Claydon, Banbury, Oxon OX17 1ER* Banbury (01295) 690315

CHARE, Frederic Keith. b 16. Hatf Coll Dur LTh38 BA39. Edin Th Coll 35. **d** 39 **p** 40. V Barming Heath *Cant* 69-73; V Upchurch 74-75; V Upchurch w Lower Halstow 75-82; rtd 82; Perm to Offic *Cant* from 82. *71 Douglas Road, Maidstone, Kent ME16 8ER* Maidstone (01622) 761370

CHARING CROSS, Archdeacon of. *See* KLYBERG, Rt Rev Charles John

CHARKHAM, Rupert Anthony. b 59. Ex Univ BA81. Wycliffe Hall Ox 83. **d** 89 **p** 89. C Ox St Aldate w St Matt *Ox* 89-92; P-in-c Fisherton Anger *Sarum* from 92. *St Paul's Rectory, Salisbury SP2 7QW* Salisbury (01722) 334005

CHARLES, John Hugo Audley. b 04. Worc Coll Ox BA25 MA46. Cuddesdon Coll 27. **d** 29 **p** 30. V Lyme Regis *Sarum* 62-74; rtd 74. *Badgworth Court, Axbridge, Somerset BS26 6QZ* Axbridge (01934) 732843

CHARLES, Canon Jonathan. b 42. Ripon Coll Cuddesdon 78. **d** 79 **p** 80. C Leagrave *St Alb* 79-82; Chapl Denstone Coll Uttoxeter 82-86; Chapl Malvern Girls' Coll Worcs 86-89; Chapl K Sch Worc from 89; Min Can Worc Cathl *Worc* from 89. *12A College Green, Worcester WR1 2LH*

CHARLES, Martin. b 40. **d** 90 **p** 91. C Market Harborough *Leic* 90-91; P-in-c Higham-on-the-Hill w Fenny Drayton and Witherley from 91. *The Rectory, Old Forge Road, Fenny Drayton, Nuneaton, Warks CV13 6BD* Atherstone (01827) 715460

CHARLES, Meedperdas Edward. b 28. Fitzw Ho Cam BA60 MA64. Bangalore Th Coll BD54. **d** 54 **p** 55. V Gravelly Hill *Birm* 66-78; V Endcliffe *Sheff* 79-90; rtd 91. *60 Ringinglow Road, Sheffield S11 7PQ* Sheffield (0114) 266 4980

CHARLES, Robert Sidney James. b 40. Lon Univ CertEd77 Open Univ BA79. St Mich Coll Llan DipTh65. **d** 65 **p** 66. C Merthyr Tydfil *Llan* 65-68; C Shotton *St As* 68-70; R Stock and Lydlinch *Sarum* 70-74; R Hubberston *St D* 74-76; Perm to Offic *Chelmsf* 81-83; V Crossens *Liv* from 83. *The Vicarage, Rufford Road, Southport, Merseyside PR9 8JH* Southport (01704) 27662

CHARLES, Robin. b 50. N Staffs Poly HND72. Sarum & Wells Th Coll. **d** 86 **p** 87. C Chesterton *Lich* 86-89; C Rugeley 89-90; TV from 90. *The Vicarage, 14 Peakes Road, Etching Hill, Rugeley, Staffs WS15 2LY* Rugeley (01889) 582809

CHARLES, Theodore Arthur Barker. b 24. K Coll Cam BA45 MA48 Lon Univ DipRS71. S'wark Ord Course 68. **d** 71 **p** 72. C Cuckfield *Chich* 71-77; V Rudgwick 77-89; rtd 89; Perm to Offic *Ox* from 89. *1 Herringcote, Dorchester-on-Thames, Wallingford, Oxon OX10 7RD* Oxford (01865) 341321

CHARLES-EDWARDS, David Mervyn. b 38. Trin Coll Cam BA61. Linc Th Coll 62. **d** 64 **p** 65. C Putney St Mary *S'wark* 64-65; Chief Exec Officer Br Assn for Counselling 82-87; Gen Manager Lon Lighthouse AIDS Project 87-88; Consultant and Counsellor on Human Development from 88; NSM Rugby St Andr *Cov* from 89. *236 Hillmorton Road, Rugby, Warks CV22 5BG* Rugby (01788) 569212

CHARLESWORTH, Eric Charlesworth. b 29. Kelham Th Coll 49. **d** 54 **p** 56. C Woodbridge St Mary *St E* 54-57; Asst Chapl Oslo St Edm *Eur* 57-59; Canada 60-66; R Huntingfield w Cookley *St E* 66-70; R Slimbridge *Glouc* from 70. *The Rectory, Slimbridge, Gloucester GL2 7BJ* Dursley (01453) 890233

CHARLESWORTH, Ian Peter. b 65. Lanc Univ BA87. St Mich Coll Llan DipTh93. **d** 93 **p** 94. C Caereithin *S & B* 93-95; C Oystermouth from 95. *66 Queen's Road, Mumbles, Swansea SA3 4AN* Swansea (01792) 360438

CHARLEY, Canon Julian Whittard. b 30. New Coll Ox BA55 MA58. Ridley Hall Cam 55. **d** 57 **p** 58. C St Marylebone All So w SS Pet and Jo *Lon* 57-64; Lect Lon Coll of Div 64-70; Vice-Prin St Jo Coll Nottm 70-74; Warden Shrewsbury Ho 74-87; TR Everton St Pet *Liv* 74-87; P-in-c Gt Malvern St Mary *Worc* from 87; Hon Can Worc Cathl from 91. *Priory Vicarage, Clarence Road, Malvern, Worcs WR14 3EN* Malvern (01684) 563707

CHARLTON, Canon Arthur David. b 23. Open Univ BA73 BPhil83. Chich Th Coll. **d** 66 **p** 67. C Rotherfield *Chich* 66-70; C Uckfield 70-72; C Isfield 70-72; C Lt Horsted 70-72; R Cocking w Bepton 72-79; P-in-c W Lavington 78-79; R Cocking, Bepton and W Lavington 79-90; Can and Preb Chich Cathl 88-90; rtd 90. *33 High Cross Field, Crowborough, E Sussex TN6 2SN* Crowborough (01892) 661351

CHARLTON, Colin. b 32. Em Coll Cam BA56 MA60. Oak Hill Th Coll 56. **d** 58 **p** 59. Area Sec (Dios Chelmsf and St Alb) CMS 66-72; P-in-c Becontree St Eliz *Chelmsf* 72-78; P-in-c Bentley Common 78-93; rtd 93. *11 Elliot Close, South Woodham Ferrers, Chelmsford CM3 5YN*

CHARMAN, Jane Ellen Elizabeth. b 60. St Jo Coll Dur BA81 Selw Coll Cam BA84 MA88. Westcott Ho Cam 82. **d** 87 **p** 94. Glouc St Geo w Whaddon *Glouc* 85-87; C 87-90; Chapl and Fell Clare Coll Cam from 90. *69 Alpha Road, Cambridge CB4 3DQ* Cambridge (01223) 66266 or 333229

CHARNOCK, Deryck Ian. b 47. Oak Hill Th Coll 78. **d** 80 **p** 81. C Rowner *Portsm* 80-84; TV Southgate *Chich* 84-90; V Penge St Paul *Roch* from 90. *St Paul's Vicarage, Hamlet Road, London SE19 2AW* 0181-653 0978

CHARNOCK, Ernest Burrell. b 14. ACIS42 AACCA50 Lon Univ DipTh60. **d** 61 **p** 62. V Buglawton *Ches* 64-70; R Tattenhall 70-77; P-in-c Handley 72-77; R Tattenhall and Handley 77-80; rtd 80; Perm to Offic *Ches* 85-87; Perm to Offic *Glouc* from 87. *26 Pegasus Court, St Stephen's Road, Cheltenham, Glos GL51 5AB* Cheltenham (01242) 578651

CHARRETT, Geoffrey Barton. b 36. ALCM Nottm Univ BSc57. Ridley Hall Cam 65. **d** 67 **p** 68. C Clifton *York* 67-68; Lic to Offic *Blackb* 69-80; C Walthamstow St Mary w St Steph *Chelmsf* 81-82; TV 82-87; Chapl Gordon's Sch Woking 87-94; P-in-c Hambledon *Guildf* from 94. *The Rectory, Hambledon Road, Hambledon, Godalming, Surrey GU8 4DR* Wormley (01428) 682753

CHARRINGTON, Nicholas John. b 36. MA. Cuddesdon Coll 60. **d** 62 **p** 63. C Shrewsbury St Chad *Lich* 62-65; C Gt Grimsby St Mary and St Jas *Linc* 65-72; P-in-c Wellington Ch Ch *Lich* 72-78; R Edgmond 78-89; R Edgmond w Kynnersley and Preston Wealdmoors 89-91; C Plymstock *Ex* 91-94; Chapl St Luke's Hospice Plymouth 91-94; P-in-c Longden and Annscroft w Pulverbatch *Heref* from 94. *The Rectory, Longden, Shrewsbury SY5 8ET* Shrewsbury (01743) 861003

CHARTERIS, Hugo Arundale. b 64. Witwatersrand Univ BA88. Cranmer Hall Dur 90. **d** 93 **p** 94. C Byker St Mark and Walkergate St Oswald *Newc* from 93. *258 Westbourne Avenue, Newcastle-upon-Tyne NE6 4XU* 0191-262 4875

CHARTERS, Alan Charles. b 35. Trin Hall Cam BA60 MA63. Linc Th Coll 60. **d** 62 **p** 63. C Gt Grimsby St Mary and St Jas *Linc* 62-65; Chapl Eliz Coll Guernsey 65-70; Dep Hd Master Park Sch Swindon 70-74; Chapl St Jo Sch Leatherhead 74-77; Dep Hd Master 77-83; Master K Sch Ely 83-92; V Aberedw w Llandeilo Graban and Llanbadarn etc *S & B* from 92. *Aberedw Rectory, Builth Wells, Powys LD2 3UW* Builth Wells (01982) 560359

CHARTERS, John Nicholson. b 27. Trin Hall Cam BA51 MA55. Westcott Ho Cam 51. **d** 53 **p** 54. Hon C Beeford w Lissett *York* 68-77; Hon C Beeford w Frodingham and Foston 77-89; R 90-93; rtd 93. *2 Alton Park, Beeford, Driffield, N Humberside YO25 8BZ* Beeford (01262) 488485

✠**CHARTRES, Rt Rev Richard John Carew.** b 47. Trin Coll Cam BA68 MA73 BD83. Cuddesdon Coll 69 Linc Th Coll 72. **d** 73 **p** 74 **c** 92. C Bedf St Andr *St Alb* 73-75; Bp's Dom Chapl 75-80; Abp's Chapl *Cant* 80-84; P-in-c Westmr St Steph w St Jo *Lon* 84-85; V 86-92; Dir of Ords 85-92; Prof Div Gresham Coll 86-92; Six Preacher Cant Cathl *Cant* from 91; Area Bp Stepney *Lon* from 92. *63 Coborn Road, London E3 2DB* 0181-981 2323 Fax 981 8015

CHASE, Canon Frank Selby Mason. b 15. Univ Coll Dur BSc37 DipTh39. St Aug Coll Cant 39. **d** 39 **p** 40. V S Westoe *Dur* 60-78; Hon Can Dur Cathl from 71; RD Jarrow 75-77; V Lanchester 78-82; rtd 82. *21 Broadoak Drive, Lanchester, Durham DH7 0PN* Lanchester (01207) 520393

CHASE, Lt-Col Frederick Jack. b 14. Westcott Ho Cam 61. **d** 62 **p** 63. Rhodesia 69-70; V St Columb Minor *Truro* 71-73; V St Columb Minor and St Colan 73-76; P-in-c Arreton *Portsm* 76-82; rtd 82; Perm to Offic *Cant* 82-93. *60 Stade Street, Hythe, Kent CT21 6BD* Hythe (01303) 265663

CHATER, John Leathley. b 29. Qu Coll Cam BA54 MA58. Ridley Hall Cam 54. **d** 56 **p** 57. C Bath Abbey w St Jas *B & W* 56-60; V Bermondsey St Anne *S'wark* 60-64; Ind Chapl 60-64; V Heslington *York* 64-69; Chapl York Univ 64-69; V Lawrence Weston *Bris* 69-73; Perm to Offic 74-80; P-in-c Wraxall *B & W* 80-82; R 82-84; V Battle *Chich* 84-90; Dean Battle 84-90; RD Battle and Bexhill 86-90; R St Marylebone w H Trin *Lon* from 90. *21 Beaumont Street, London W1N 1FF* 0171-935 8965

CHATFIELD, Adrian Francis. b 49. Leeds Univ BA71 MA72 MPhil89. Coll of Resurr Mirfield 71. **d** 72 **p** 73. Trinidad and Tobago 72-83; TV Barnstaple, Goodleigh and Landkey *Ex* 83-84; TV Barnstaple 85; TR 85-88; Lect St Jo Coll Nottm from 88. *5 Peatfield Road, Stapleford, Nottingham NG9 8GN* Nottingham (0115) 939 1287 or 251114 Fax 220134 or 436438

CHATFIELD, Preb Frederick Roy. b 06. **d** 32 **p** 33. V Cockington *Ex* 47-72; Preb Ex Cathl 71-82; rtd 72; Lic to Offic *Ex* 82-95. *c/o Miss J C Chatfield, La Croute Havilland, St Peter Port, Guernsey, Channel Islands GY1 1ET*

CHATFIELD, Mrs Gillian (Jill). b 50. Leeds Univ BA71 PGCE72. St Jo Coll Nottm MA94. **d** 94 **p** 95. C Greasley *S'well* from 94. *2 Grantham Close, Giltbrook, Nottingham NG16 2WB* Nottingham (0115) 938 4960

CHATFIELD, Canon Norman. b 37. Fitzw Ho Cam BA59 MA68. Ripon Hall Ox 60. **d** 62 **p** 63. C Burgess Hill St Jo *Chich* 62-65; C Uckfield 65-69; V Lower Sandown St Jo *Portsm* 69-76; V Locks Heath 76-83; Bp's Chapl for Post Ord Tr 78-85; R Alverstoke 83-91; Chapl HM Pris Haslar 83-90; Chapl Gosport War Memorial Hosp 83-91; Hon Can Portsm Cathl *Portsm* 85-91; Can Res Glouc Cathl *Glouc* from 91. *6 College Green, Gloucester GL1 2LX* Gloucester (01452) 521954

CHATFIELD, Thomas William. b 19. Lon Univ. Chich Th Coll 44. **d** 46 **p** 47. P-in-c Hastings St Mary Magd *Chich* 68-71; R 71-78; P-in-c Bishopstone 78-84; rtd 84; Perm to Offic *Chich* from 84. *5 Leeds Close, Victoria Avenue, Ore Village, Hastings, E Sussex TN35 5BX* Hastings (01424) 437413

CHATFIELD-JUDE, Jonathan Charles Henry. b 09. OBE76. AKC32. **d** 32 **p** 33. Chapl Lisbon *Eur* 66-76; rtd 76; Perm to Offic *Win* 76-94. *Flat 1, Manormead, Tilford Road, Hindhead, Surrey GU26 6RA* Hindhead (01428) 605843

CHATHAM, Richard Henry. b 28. Launde Abbey 71. **d** 71 **p** 72. C Aylestone *Leic* 71-76; R Hoby cum Rotherby 76-77; P-in-c Brooksby 76-77; R Hoby cum Rotherby w Brooksby, Ragdale & Thru'ton 77-85; R Overstrand *Nor* 85-93; rtd 93; Perm to Offic *Nor* from 93. *Sandyside, Sandy Lane, Cromer, Norfolk NR27 9JT* Cromer (01263) 513456

CHATTERJI DE MASSEY, Robert Arthur Sovan Lal. b 15. Chich Th Coll 54. **d** 56 **p** 57. R Abberton w Langenhoe *Chelmsf* 60-90; rtd 90. *Clare House, 82 Main Street, Witchford, Ely, Cambs CB6 2HQ*

CHATWIN, Barbara. b 07. MCSP33. Selly Oak Coll 62. **dss** 65 **d** 87. Birm St Dav *Birm* 63-67; Londonderry 69-87; Pershore w Pinvin, Wick and Birlingham *Worc* 69-87; Hon C from 87; Perm to Offic from 90. *Myrtle Cottage, Broad Street, Pershore, Worcs WR10 1BB* Pershore (01386) 552080

CHATWIN, Ronald Ernest. b 34. St Aid Birkenhead 58. **d** 60 **p** 61. C Selsdon St Jo *Cant* 60-64; C Crawley *Chich* 64-68; V Coldwaltham 68-74; TV Ovingdean w Rottingdean and Woodingdean 74-83; V Saltdean 83-91; V Hellingly and Upper Dicker from 91. *The Vicarage, Hellingly, Hailsham, E Sussex BN27 4EY* Hailsham (01323) 843346

CHAVE, Brian Philip. b 51. Open Univ BA. Trin Coll Bris. **d** 84 **p** 85. C Cullompton *Ex* 84-87; TV Bishopsnympton, Rose Ash, Mariansleigh etc 87-93; Chapl for Agric *Heref* from 93. *Church Gate, Almeley, Hereford HR3 6LB* Kington (01544) 328497

CHAVE-COX, Guy. b 56. St Andr Univ BSc79. Wycliffe Hall Ox 83. **d** 86 **p** 87. C Wigmore Abbey *Heref* 86-88; C Bideford *Ex* 88-91; TV Barnstaple from 91. *St Paul's Vicarage, Old Sticklepath Hill, Barnstaple, Devon EX31 2BG* Barnstaple (01271) 44400

CHAVNER, Robert. b 59. ALCM82 AGSM85 Guildhall Sch of Music and Drama PdipEM86. Linc Th Coll 90. **d** 92 **p** 93. C Beckenham St Geo *Roch* from 92. *37 Rectory Road, Beckenham, Kent BR3 1HL* 0181-658 7005

CHEADLE, Preb Robert. b 24. MBE71 TD66. Leeds Univ BA49. Coll of Resurr Mirfield 49. **d** 51 **p** 52. V Bloxwich *Lich* 60-72; V Penkridge w Stretton 72-89; Preb Lich Cathl 79-89; P-in-c Dunston w Coppenhall 79-82; V 82-89; P-in-c Acton Trussell w Bednall 80-82; V 82-89; rtd 89. *26 Audley Place,*

Newcastle, Staffs ST5 3RS Newcastle-under-Lyme (01782) 618685

CHEAL, Kenneth Herbert. b 12. Sarum Th Coll 46. **d** 48 **p** 49. R Rodborough *Glouc* 61-77; rtd 78; Perm to Offic *Glouc* 78-94; Perm to Offic *Bris* from 79. *6 The Ferns, Tetbury, Glos GL8 8JE* Tetbury (01666) 503100

CHEALL, Henry Frederick Knowles. b 34. Ex Coll Ox BA56 MA60. Ripon Hall Ox 58. **d** 60 **p** 61. C Sutton *Liv* 60-63; C Blundellsands St Mich 63-66; Nigeria 66-68; R Crumpsall St Matt *Man* 68-76; R Crumpsall 76-84; V Chipping and Whitewell *Blackb* from 84. *The Vicarage, Garstang Road, Chipping, Preston PR3 2QH* Chipping (01995) 61252

CHEATLE, Adele Patricia. b 46. York Univ BA73. Trin Coll Bris 76. **d** 87. Par Dn Harborne Heath *Birm* 87; NSM 92-93. *The Mews House, Mordiford, Hereford HR1 4LN* Hereford (01432) 870440

CHEATLE, Christopher Robert David. b 41. Leeds Univ BA63. Coll of Resurr Mirfield. **d** 65 **p** 66. C Hangleton *Chich* 65-66; C Corringham *Chelmsf* 66-70; Bp's Adv on Child Protection from 95. *28 Park Road, Leigh-on-Sea, Essex SS9 2PE* Leigh-on-Sea (01702) 79043

CHEDZEY, Derek Christopher. b 67. Trin Coll Bris BA93. **d** 93 **p** 94. C Bedgrove *Ox* from 93. *16 Patrick Way, Aylesbury, Bucks HP21 7XH* Aylesbury (01296) 434529

CHEEK, Richard Alexander. b 35. Lon Univ LDS60. Ox NSM Course 72. **d** 75 **p** 76. NSM Maidenhead St Luke *Ox* 75-94; Asst Chapl Heatherwood Hosp E Berks from 94; Asst Chapl Wexham Park Hosp Slough from 94. *Windrush, Sheephouse Road, Maidenhead, Berks SL6 8EX* Maidenhead (01628) 28484

CHEESEMAN, Colin Henry. b 47. Reading Univ BA. Sarum & Wells Th Coll 82. **d** 84 **p** 85. C Cranleigh *Guildf* 84-87; C Godalming 87-89; V Cuddington from 89. *The Vicarage, St Mary's Road, Worcester Park, Surrey KT4 7JL* 0181-337 4026

CHEESEMAN, John Anthony. b 50. Or Coll Ox BA73 MA75. Trin Coll Bris DipTh76. **d** 76 **p** 77. C Sevenoaks St Nic *Roch* 76-79; C Egham *Guildf* 79-82; V Leyton Ch Ch *Chelmsf* 82-90; V Westgate St Jas *Cant* from 90. *St James's Vicarage, Orchard Gardens, Westgate-on-Sea, Kent CT9 5JT* Thanet (01843) 832073

CHEESEMAN, Kenneth Raymond (Ken). b 29. Roch Th Coll 63. **d** 66 **p** 67. C Beckenham St Jas *Roch* 69-75; V Belvedere St Aug 75-83; V Thorley *Portsm* 83-94; R Yarmouth 83-94. *10 St Catherine's View, Godshill, Ventnor, Isle of Wight PO38 3JJ* Isle of Wight (01983) 840700

CHEESMAN, Ashley Frederick Bruce. b 53. Oak Hill Th Coll. **d** 83 **p** 84. C Tranmere St Cath *Ches* 83-88; R Gaulby *Leic* from 88. *The Rectory, Gaulby, Leicester LE7 9BB* Leicester (0116) 259 6228

CHEESMAN, Peter. b 43. ACA65 FCA76 MBIM. Ridley Hall Cam 66. **d** 69 **p** 70. C Herne Bay Ch Ch *Cant* 69-74; TV Lowestoft St Marg *Nor* 75-78; TV Lowestoft and Kirkley 79-81; Ind Chapl *Glouc* 81-84; P-in-c Saul w Fretherne and Framilode 84-85; V Frampton on Severn, Arlingham, Saul etc from 85. *The Vicarage, The Street, Frampton on Severn, Gloucester GL2 7ED* Gloucester (01452) 740966

CHEETHAM, Eric. b 34. Trin Hall Cam BA57 MA61. Coll of Resurr Mirfield 57. **d** 59 **p** 60. C S Kirkby *Wakef* 59-62; C-in-c Mixenden CD 62-65; Bahamas 65-69; V Grimethorpe *Wakef* 69-81; V Featherstone 81-90; V Leeds Belle Is St Jo and St Barn *Ripon* 90-94. *22 Rosedale, Rothwell, Leeds LS26 0HR* Leeds (0113) 282 5602

CHEETHAM, Richard Ian. b 55. CCC Ox BA77 CertEd78 MA82. Ripon Coll Cuddesdon 85. **d** 87 **p** 88. C Newc H Cross *Newc* 87-90; V Luton St Aug Limbury *St Alb* from 90; RD Luton from 94. *The Vicarage, 215 Icknield Way, Luton LU3 2JR* Luton (01582) 572415

CHEEVERS, George Alexander. b 42. CITC 70. **d** 73 **p** 74. C Carrickfergus *Conn* 73-81; C Kilroot 78-81; I Kilmakee 82-91; I Magheragall from 91. *Magheragall Rectory, 70 Ballinderry Road, Lisburn, Co Antrim BT28 2QS* Maze (01846) 621273

CHELMSFORD, Bishop of. See WAINE, Rt Rev John

CHELMSFORD, Provost of. See MOSES, Very Rev Dr John Henry

CHELTENHAM, Archdeacon of. See LEWIS, Ven John Arthur

CHENNELL, Capt Arthur John. b 28. St Deiniol's Hawarden 77. **d** 77 **p** 78. CA from 58; C Prenton *Ches* 77-79; V Liscard St Thos 79-82; V Lt Thornton *Blackb* 82-94; rtd 94. *79 Cobham Road, Moreton, Wirral, Merseyside L46 0RA* 0151-678 5708

CHERRILL, John Oliver. b 33. Bath Univ MArch75 DipArch61. Sarum & Wells Th Coll 76. **d** 79 **p** 80. NSM Blackmoor *Portsm* 79-83; NSM Headley All SS *Guildf* 83-85; C 86-90. *7 Oaktree Road, Whitehill, Bordon, Hants GU35 9DF* Bordon (01420) 473193

CHERRIMAN, Colin Wilfred (Brother Colin Wilfred). b 37. Leeds Univ BA63. Coll of Resurr Mirfield 63. **d** 65 **p** 66. C Bournemouth St Fran *Win* 65-69; SSF from 69; Lic to Offic *Chelmsf* 73-75; Lic to Offic *Cant* 75-77; Lic to Offic *Edin* 77-79; Lic to Offic *Sarum* 79-82; Lic to Offic *Newc* 82-88; Perm to Offic *Lon* 88-91; Adv HIV/AIDS Unit 91-92; HIV Support Worker Aldgate St Botolph Lon from 92. *St Botolph's Church, Aldgate, London EC3N 1AB* 0171-283 1670

CHERRY, David. b 30. Roch Th Coll 59. **d** 61 **p** 62. R Bamford *Derby* 67-75; Chapl Malaga w Almunecar and Nerja *Eur* 83-91; rtd 91. *El Penon, La Molineta 12, Frigiliana, 29788 Malaga, Spain* Malaga (52) 533084

CHERRY, David Warwick. b 61. Cape Town Univ BMus86 Leeds Univ BA91. Coll of Resurr Mirfield CPT92. **d** 92 **p** 93. C Hammersmith SS Mich and Geo White City Estate CD *Lon* from 92. *St Luke's Vicarage, 450 Uxbridge Road, London W12 0NS* 0181-749 7523

CHERRY, Malcolm Stephen. b 28. Open Univ BA81. Sarum Th Coll 51. **d** 54 **p** 55. V Horndon on the Hill *Chelmsf* 68-79; Ind Chapl 69-79; Voc Officer Southend Adnry 74-79; R Lochgilphead *Arg* 79-82; V Mill End and Heronsgate w Hyde *St Alb* 82-90; TV Chipping Barnet w Arkley 90-94; rtd 94. *Nether Hankleys, Barrow Road, Higham, Bury St Edmunds, Suffolk IP28 6NN* Bury St Edmunds (01284) 810269

CHERRY, Stephen Arthur. b 58. St Chad's Coll Dur BSc79 Fitzw Coll Cam BA85. Westcott Ho Cam 83. **d** 86 **p** 87. C Baguley *Man* 86-89; Chapl K Coll Cam 89-94; R Loughb All SS and H Trin *Leic* from 94. *The Rectory, Steeple Row, Loughborough, Leics LE11 1UX* Loughborough (01509) 212780

CHESHAM, William Gerald. b 23. MIMechE55 Birm Univ DPS66. Wells Th Coll 61. **d** 63 **p** 64. V Smethwick *Birm* 68-72; Lic to Offic *Heref* 72-78; TV Glendale Gp *Newc* 78-84; rtd 84; Hon Asst Chapl Algarve *Eur* from 84. *Casita de Paz, Pedreiras, 8375 Sao Bartolomeu de Messines, Algarve, Portugal* Portimao (82) 330659

CHESSUN, Christopher Thomas James. b 56. Univ Coll Ox BA78 MA82 Trin Hall Cam BA82. Westcott Ho Cam. **d** 83 **p** 84. C Sandhurst *Ox* 83-87; C Portsea St Mary *Portsm* 87-89; Min Can and Chapl St Paul's Cathl *Lon* 89-93; Voc Adv from 90; R Stepney St Dunstan and All SS from 93. *The Rectory, Rectory Square, London E1 3NG* 0171-791 3545

CHESTER, Mark. b 55. Lanc Univ BA79. Wycliffe Hall Ox 86. **d** 88 **p** 89. C Plymouth St Andr w St Paul and St Geo *Ex* 88-94; V Burney Lane *Birm* from 94. *Christ Church Vicarage, Burney Lane, Birmingham B8 2AS* 0121-783 7455

CHESTER, Philip Anthony Edwin. b 55. Birm Univ LLB76. St Jo Coll Dur DipTh80. **d** 80 **p** 81. C Shrewsbury St Chad *Lich* 80-85; C St Martin-in-the-Fields *Lon* 85-88; Chapl K Coll Lon 88-95; PV Westmr Abbey from 90; P-in-c Westmr St Matt *Lon* from 95. *St Matthew Clergy House, 20 Great Peter Street, London SW1P 2BU* 0171-222 3704

CHESTER, Archdeacon of. See HEWETSON, Canon Christopher

CHESTER, Bishop of. See BAUGHEN, Rt Rev Michael Alfred

CHESTER, Dean of. See SMALLEY, Very Rev Stephen Stewart

CHESTERFIELD, Archdeacon of. See PHIZACKERLEY, Ven Gerald Robert

CHESTERMAN, Canon Dr George Anthony (Tony). b 38. Man Univ BSc62 DipAdEd Nottm Univ PhD89. Coll of Resurr Mirfield 62. **d** 64 **p** 65. C Newbold and Dunston *Derby* 64-68; C Derby St Thos 68-70; Adult Educn Officer 70-79; R Mugginton and Kedleston 70-89; Vice-Prin E Midl Min Tr Course from 79; Can Res Derby Cathl *Derby* from 89; Dioc Clergy In-Service Tr Adv from 89. *13 Newbridge Road, Ambergate, Belper, Derbyshire DE56 2GR* Ambergate (01773) 852236

CHESTERMAN, Lawrence James. b 16. AKC91. K Coll Lon 48 St Boniface Warminster. **d** 49 **p** 50. V Idmiston *Sarum* 69-73; TR Bourne Valley 73-81; rtd 81; Perm to Offic *Sarum* from 81. *2 Beacon Close, Amesbury, Salisbury SP4 7EG* Amesbury (01980) 622205

✠**CHESTERS, Rt Rev Alan David.** b 37. St Chad's Coll Dur BA59 St Cath Soc Ox BA61 MA65. St Steph Ho Ox 59. **d** 62 **p** 63 **c** 89. C Wandsworth St Anne *S'wark* 62-66; Hon C 66-68; Chapl Tiffin Sch Kingston-upon-Thames 66-72; Hon C Ham St Rich *S'wark* 68-72; Dioc Dir of Educn *Dur* 72-85; R Brancepeth 72-85; Hon Can Dur Cathl 75-85; Adn Halifax *Wakef* 85-89; Bp Blackb from 89. *Bishop's House, Ribchester Road, Blackburn BB1 9EF* Blackburn (01254) 248234 Fax 246668

CHESTERS, Peter Durrant. b 17. ACII52. K Coll Lon 54. **d** 56 **p** 57. R Ludgershall and Faberstown *Sarum* 66-82; rtd 82; Perm to Offic *Heref* 82-93; Perm to Offic *Ex* from 95. *18 Gracey Court, Woodland Road, Broadclyst, Exeter EX5 3LP* Exeter (01392) 462574

CHESTERS, Simon. b 66. Rob Coll Cam BA87 MA91. Wycliffe Hall Ox BA94 DipMin95. **d** 95. C Bidston *Ches* from 95. *55 Bridle Close, Birkenhead, Merseyside L43 9UU* 0151-677 8700

CHESTERTON, Robert Eric. b 31. St Aid Birkenhead 63. **d** 65 **p** 66. Canada 75-78; V Southminster *Chelmsf* 69-75; V Wythenshawe Wm Temple Ch *Man* 78-82; TV Marfleet *York* 82-85; V Marshchapel *Linc* 85-88; R N Coates 85-88; V Grainthorpe w Conisholme 85-88; V Langtoft Gp 88-91; V Kingsbury *Birm* 91-94; rtd 94. *46 Tyne Road, Oakham, Leics LE15 6SJ* Oakham (01572) 757262

CHETWOOD, Noah. b 14. St Jo Coll Dur BA38 DipTh39 MA41 Nottm Univ MEd58. **d** 39 **p** 40. C Ludlow *Heref* 39-45; Lic to Offic *Derby* 45-54; Lic to Offic *Ox* from 54. *Evergreens, 10 Longfield Drive, Amersham, Bucks HP6 5HD* Amersham (01494) 725259

CHETWYND, Edward Ivor. b 45. Leeds Univ DipTh68. Coll of Resurr Mirfield 68. **d** 70 **p** 71. C Westgate Common *Wakef* 70-74; C Penistone w Midhope 74-75; V Smawthorpe St Mich from 75. *St Michael's Vicarage, St Michael's Close, Castleford, W Yorkshire WF10 4ER* Castleford (01977) 557079

CHEVALIER, Harry Ensor Estienne. b 23. Mert Coll Ox BA49 MA56. Ely Th Coll 49. **d** 51 **p** 52. V Bradninch *Ex* 66-71; Perm to Offic 71-74; Hon C Christchurch *Win* 74-75; rtd 75; Perm to Offic *Win* from 75. *c/o S A Chevalier Esq, 44A Elder Road, Bere Regis, Wareham, Dorset BH20 7NB* Bere Regis (01929) 471096

CHEVERTON, Miss Jill. b 48. RGN71 RHV77 Leeds Poly DSocStuds73. Cranmer Hall Dur CTMin93. **d** 93 **p** 94. Par Dn Bilton *Ripon* 93-94; C from 94. *13 Albany Road, Harrogate, N Yorkshire HG1 4NS* Harrogate (01423) 566983

CHICHESTER, Archdeacon of. See BROTHERTON, Ven John Michael

CHICHESTER, Bishop of. See KEMP, Rt Rev Eric Waldram

CHICHESTER, Dean of. See TREADGOLD, Very Rev John David

CHICKEN, Peter Lindsay. b 46. St Andr Univ BSc71. Chich Th Coll 77. **d** 79 **p** 80. C High Wycombe *Ox* 79-83; V The Stanleys *Glouc* from 83; Bp's Adv for Continued Minl Educn from 92. *The Vicarage, Leonard Stanley, Stonehouse, Glos GL10 3NP* Stonehouse (01453) 823161

CHIDLAW, Richard Paul. b 49. St Cath Coll Cam BA71 MA. Ripon Hall Ox 72. **d** 74 **p** 81. C Ribbesford w Bewdley and Dowles *Worc* 74-76; NSM Coaley *Glouc* 81-83; NSM Frampton on Severn 81-83; NSM Arlingham 81-83; NSM Saul w Fretherne and Framilode 83-84; NSM Cam w Stinchcombe 85-90; Perm to Offic 90-91; NSM Berkeley w Wick, Breadstone and Newport from 91. *38 May Lane, Dursley, Glos GL11 4HU* Dursley (01453) 547838

CHIDWICK, Alan Robert. b 49. MIL MA. Oak Hill NSM Course. **d** 84 **p** 85. NSM Pimlico St Pet w Westmr Ch Ch *Lon* from 84. *119 Eaton Square, London SW1W 9AL* 0171-235 4242

CHILCOTT, Dr Mark David. b 62. Ch Coll Cam BA83 MA87 PhD88. Ripon Coll Cuddesdon BA92. **d** 93 **p** 94. C Warrington St Elphin *Liv* from 93. *Church House, 133 Church Street, Warrington WA1 2TL* Warrington (01925) 633940

CHILD, Margaret Mary. See MASLEN, Mrs Margaret Mary

CHILD, Canon Rupert Henry. b 29. St Jo Coll Dur 50 K Coll Lon DipTh56 St Boniface Warminster 57. **d** 58 **p** 59. V Luton St Chris Round Green *St Alb* 65-74; V Sawbridgeworth 74-95; Hon Can St Alb 86-95; rtd 95. *6 Lakes Close, Langford, Biggleswade, Beds SG18 9SJ* Hitchin (01462) 700303

CHILD, Theodore Hilary. b 09. MA. **d** 33 **p** 34. V Southwold *St E* 59-74; rtd 74; P-in-c Starston *Nor* 75-87; Perm to Offic from 87; Perm to Offic *St E* from 87. *41 Deans Mill Court, The Causeway, Canterbury, Kent CT1 2BF* Canterbury (01227) 785920

CHILDS, Ernest Edmund. b 23. Lich Th Coll 63. **d** 65 **p** 66. Clerical Org Sec CECS (Dios Pet, Leic and Ely) 69-72; V Staverton w Helidon and Catesby *Pet* 72-76; rtd 77; Perm to Offic *Nor* 77-91; Hon C W Lynn *Ely* 92-94; P-in-c 94-95; Perm to Offic from 95. *4 Fieldview Court, The Paddocks, Fakenham, Norfolk NR21 8PB* Fakenham (01328) 856595

CHILDS, Leonard Neil. b 44. Leeds Univ BA65. Wells Th Coll 66. **d** 68 **p** 69. C Matlock and Tansley *Derby* 68-72; C Chesterfield All SS 72-74; P-in-c Stonebroom 74-81; P-in-c Morton 78-81; R Morton and Stonebroom 81-84; TV Buxton w Burbage and King Sterndale 84-92; V Derby St Mark from 92. *St Mark's Vicarage, 119 Francis Street, Derby DE21 6DE* Derby (01332) 340183

CHILDS, Theodore John. b 12. St Edm Hall Ox BA34 MA47 BLitt47. Ripon Hall Ox 37. **d** 40 **p** 41. R Chelvey w Brockley

B & W 61-70; R Ballaugh *S & M* 70-77; rtd 77; Perm to Offic *S & M* from 77. *9 Ballagorry Drive, Glen Mona, Ramsey, Isle of Man IM7 1HE* Ramsey (01624) 861993

CHILLINGWORTH, Very Rev David Robert. b 51. TCD BA73 Or Coll Ox BA75 MA81. Ripon Coll Cuddesdon 75. **d** 76 **p** 77. C Belf H Trin *Conn* 76-79; Ch of Ireland Youth Officer 79-83; C Ban Abbey *D & D* 83-86; I Seagoe from 86; Dean Dromore from 95. *8 Upper Church Lane, Portadown, Craigavon, Co Armagh BT63 5JE* Portadown (01762) 332538 or 350583

CHILLMAN, David James. b 59. Southn Univ BA82. Trin Coll Bris ADMT95. **d** 95. C Yateley *Win* from 95. *37 Walnut Close, Yateley, Camberley, Surrey GU17 7DA* Yateley (01252) 875798

CHILTON, Kenneth Chapman. b 20. St Cuth Soc Dur BA49 DipTh51. **d** 51 **p** 52. V Thorpe St Matt *Nor* 57-85; rtd 85; Perm to Offic *Nor* from 85. *3 Hillcrest Road, Norwich NR7 0JZ* Norwich (01603) 36948

CHIN, Michael Shoon Chion. b 41. Lon Univ BD71 Melbourne Univ BA76 DipEd79. Moore Th Coll Sydney 60 Trin Th Coll Singapore BTh64 Ridley Coll Melbourne 68 Melbourne Coll of Div DipRE74. **d** 64 **p** 65. Malaysia 64-68; Australia 69-80 and 87-91; Miss to Seamen from 72; USA 81-82; Perm to Offic *Win* from 93; Gen Sec Internat Chr Maritime Assn from 93. *International Christian Maritime Ass, 213 Orchard Place, Southampton SO14 3BR* Southampton (01703) 336111 Fax 333567

CHING, Derek. b 37. MA. Qu Coll Birm. **d** 83 **p** 84. C Finham *Cov* 83-87; V Butlers Marston and the Pillertons w Ettington from 87. *The Vicarage, Ettington, Stratford-upon-Avon, Warks CV37 7SH* Stratford-upon-Avon (01789) 740225

CHIPLIN, Christopher Gerald. b 53. Lon Univ BSc75. St Steph Ho Ox BA77 MA81. **d** 78 **p** 79. C Chesterfield All SS *Derby* 78-80; C Thorpe *Nor* 80-84; V Highbridge *B & W* 84-94; V Midsomer Norton w Clandown from 94. *The Vicarage, 42 Priory Close, Midsomer Norton, Bath BA3 2HZ* Midsomer Norton (01761) 412118

CHIPLIN, Gareth Huw. b 50. Worc Coll Ox BA71 MA. Edin Th Coll 71. **d** 73 **p** 74. C Friern Barnet St Jas *Lon* 73-75; C Eastcote St Lawr 76-79; C Notting Hill St Mich and Ch Ch 79-84; V Hammersmith St Matt from 84. *St Matthew's Vicarage, 1 Fielding Road, London W14 0LL* 0171-603 9769

CHIPLIN, Howard Alan. b 43. Sarum & Wells Th Coll 84. **d** 86 **p** 87. C Caerleon *Mon* 86-89; V Ferndale w Maerdy *Llan* 89-91; V Ysbyty Cynfyn w Llantrisant and Eglwys Newydd *St D* 91-95; R Narberth w Mounton w Robeston Wathen and Crinow from 95. *The Rectory, Adams Drive, Narberth, Dyfed SA67 7AE* Narberth (01834) 860370

CHIPLIN, Malcolm Leonard. b 42. Llan Dioc Tr Scheme 86. **d** 88 **p** 89. C Newton Nottage *Llan* 88-91; V Pwllgwaun w Llanddewi Rhondda from 91. *The Vicarage, Lanelay Crescent, Maesycoed, Pontypridd, M Glam CF37 1JB* Pontypridd (01443) 402417

CHIPPENDALE, Peter David. b 34. Dur Univ BA55. Linc Th Coll 57. **d** 59 **p** 60. C Claines St Jo *Worc* 59-63; V Defford w Besford 63-73; P-in-c Eckington 66-69; V 69-73; V Kidderminster St Geo 73-76; V The Lickey *Birm* from 76. *The Vicarage, 30 Lickey Square, Rednal, Birmingham B45 8HB* 0121-445 1425

CHISHOLM, David Whitridge. b 23. Keble Coll Ox BA48 MA48. Linc Th Coll 48. **d** 50 **p** 51. V N Harrow St Alb *Lon* 66-72; V Paddington St Jas 72-78; RD Westmr Paddington 74-79; C Paddington St Jas 78-79; V Hurley *Ox* 79-90; rtd 90. *32 Herons Place, Marlow, Bucks SL7 3HP* Marlow (01628) 483243

CHISHOLM, Ian Keith. b 36. AKC62. **d** 63 **p** 64. C Lich St Chad *Lich* 63-66; C Sedgley All SS 66-69; V Rough Hills 69-77; V Harrow Weald All SS *Lon* 77-88; V W Moors *Sarum* from 88. *The Vicarage, 57 Glenwood Road, West Moors, Wimborne, Dorset BH22 0EN* Ferndown (01202) 893197

CHISHOLM, Ian Stuart. b 37. ALCD63. **d** 63 **p** 64. C Worksop St Jo *S'well* 63-66; Succ Sheff Cathl *Sheff* 66-68; Bp's Chapl for Soc Resp 68-72; C Ox St Andr *Ox* 72-76; Tutor Wycliffe Hall Ox 72-76; V Conisbrough *Sheff* 76-94; Chapl Conisbrough Hosp 76-94; RD W Doncaster 82-87 and 93-94; V Chilwell *S'well* from 94. *Christ Church Vicarage, 8 College Road, Beeston, Nottingham NG9 4AS* Nottingham (0115) 922 2809

CHISHOLM, Canon Reginald Joseph. b 13. TCD BA40 MA51. CITC 42. **d** 42 **p** 43. I Newtownards *D & D* 51-82; Treas Down Cathl 80-82; rtd 82. *20 Glendun Park, Bangor, Co Down BT20 4UX* Bangor (01247) 450100

CHISHOLM, Samuel James. b 20. Edin Th Coll 74 St Jo Coll Nottm 86. **d** 86 **p** 87. NSM Eastriggs *Glas* 87-92; NSM Gretna 90-91; rtd 92; Perm to Offic *Chich* from 95. *1 Elm Tree House, 5 Hastings Road, Bexhill-on-Sea, E Sussex TN40 2HJ* Bexhill-on-Sea (01424) 219294

CHITHAM, Ernest John. b 57. LSE BSc79 PGCE80 Dur Univ MA84. **d** 91 **p** 92. C Swanborough *Sarum* 91-94; Lebanon

from 95. *All Saints Church, PO Box 11-2211, Beirut, Lebanon* Grand Beirut (1) 803630

CHITTENDEN, John Bertram d'Encer. b 24. ASCA. Lon Coll of Div 56. **d** 58 **p** 59. R Acrise *Cant* 64-82; R Hawkinge 64-82; R Hawkinge w Acrise and Swingfield 82-90; rtd 91. *19 Hasborough Road, Folkestone, Kent CT19 6BQ* Folkestone (01303) 241773

CHITTENDEN, Nils Philip d'Encer. b 69. St Chad's Coll Dur BA91. Westcott Ho Cam CTM95. **d** 95. C Benfieldside *Dur* from 95. *36 Barley Mill Crescent, Consett, Co Durham DH8 3JX* Consett (01207) 590650

CHITTLEBOROUGH, Canon Gordon Arthur. b 16. Adelaide Univ 38 K Coll Lon BD62. Moore Th Coll Sydney 37. **d** 63 **p** 63. Tanganyika 63-64; Can Tanganyika 63-66; Tanzania 64-78; Kenya 78-84; Perm to Offic *S'wark* from 94. *2 Brooklands Park, London SE3 9BL* 0181-852 0205

CHITTY, Philip Crofts. b 27. Roch Th Coll 61. **d** 63 **p** 64. V Long Itchington *Cov* 68-77; R Ufton 69-77; P-in-c Cov St Marg 77-84; rtd 84. *17 Rotherham Road, Coventry CV6 4FF* Coventry (01203) 685398

✠**CHIU, Rt Rev Joshua Ban It.** b 18. Barrister-at-Law (Inner Temple) 41 K Coll Lon AKC43 LLB41. Westcott Ho Cam 43. **d** 45 **p** 46 **c** 66. C Bournville *Birm* 45-47; Malaya 47-50; Singapore 50-59 and 66-82; Hon Can St Andr Cathl Singapore 56-59; Australia 59-62; Service Laymen Abroad WCC Geneva 62-65; Fell St Aug Coll Cant 65-66; Bp Singapore and Malaya 66-70; Bp Singapore 70-82; Member Cen Cttee WCC 68-75; Member ACC 75-79; rtd 82; Perm to Offic *Sarum* from 82. *12 Dewlands Road, Verwood, Dorset BH31 6PL* Verwood (01202) 822307

CHIVERS, Ernest Alfred John. b 34. Bris & Glouc Tr Course. **d** 83 **p** 84. NSM Bedminster *Bris* 83-87; NSM Whitchurch from 87. *40 Calcott Road, Bristol BS4 2HD* Bristol (0117) 977 7867

CHIVERS, Ronald. b 27. Dur Univ BA52. Oak Hill Th Coll 52. **d** 53 **p** 54. N Sec CCCS 61-71; Lic to Offic *Blackb* 66-71; V Woodside *Ripon* 71-91; rtd 91; Perm to Offic *York* from 91. *18 Spen Road, West Park, Leeds LS16 5BT* Leeds (0113) 274 7709

CHIVERS, Royston George (Roy). b 34. Glouc Th Course. **d** 83 **p** 84. NSM Gorsley w Cliffords Mesne *Glouc* 83-85; NSM Newent and Gorsley w Cliffords Mesne from 85. *Mayfield, Gorsley, Ross-on-Wye, Herefordshire HR9 7SJ* Gorsley (01989) 720492

CHIVERS, Canon William Herbert. b 20. Univ of Wales (Cardiff) BA42. Coll of Resurr Mirfield 42. **d** 44 **p** 45. R Bushey *St Alb* 60-81; Australia 81-83; R Llandogo and Tintern *Mon* 83-86; rtd 86; Asst Chapl Athens w Kifissia, Patras, Thessaloniki & Voula *Eur* 86-91. *3 Downing Court, Grenville Street, London WC1N 1LX* 0171-713 7847

CHIVERTON, Dennis Lionel Dunbar. b 26. St D Coll Lamp BA51. **d** 53 **p** 54. R Llanfabon *Llan* 67-91; rtd 91; Perm to Offic *Llan* from 91. *3 Park Terrace, Trelewis, Treharris, M Glam CF46 6BT* Treharris (01443) 411237

CHORLTON, John Samuel Woodard. b 45. Newc Univ BSc67. Wycliffe Hall Ox 89. **d** 89 **p** 91. Jerusalem 82-92; C Ox St Aldate w St Matt *Ox* 92-94; C Ox St Aldate from 95. *2 Shirelake Close, Oxford OX1 1SN* Oxford (01865) 721150

CHOULES, Edward Frank. b 16. St Steph Ho Ox 75. **d** 78 **p** 79. NSM Boyne Hill *Ox* 78-84; Lic to Offic from 84. *Chantry House, 6 Benyon Mews, Bath Road, Reading RG1 6HX*

CHOW, Ting Suie Roy. b 46. Brasted Th Coll 68 Sarum & Wells Th Coll 70. **d** 72 **p** 73. C Weaste *Man* 72-74; C Swinton St Pet 74-78; R Blackley St Paul 78-85; Sec SPCK (Dio Man) from 80; R Burnage St Nic *Man* 85-95; P-in-c Man Gd Shep from 95. *All Soul's Rectory, Every Street, Ancoats, Manchester M4 7DQ* 0161-273 6582

CHOWN, Ernest John Richard. b 17. St Steph Ho Ox 48. **d** 51 **p** 52. C Ox St Paul *Ox* 51-53; C Brighton St Paul *Chich* 53-65; V Swanley St Mary *Roch* 65-72; V Worthing St Andr *Chich* from 72. *St Andrew's Vicarage, 21 Victoria Road, Worthing, W Sussex BN11 1XB* Worthing (01903) 233442

CHOWN, William Richard Bartlett. b 27. AKC54. **d** 55 **p** 56. R Romford St Andr *Chelmsf* 61-78; R Newton Longville w Stoke Hammond, Whaddon etc *Ox* 78-83; P-in-c Kidmore End 83-85; V 85-90; rtd 90; NSM Harpsden w Bolney *Ox* 93-94; Perm to Offic from 94. *26 Lovell Close, Henley-on-Thames, Oxon RG9 1PX* Henley-on-Thames (01491) 575735

CHRISTENSEN, Canon Norman Peter. b 37. St D Coll Lamp BA63. Ridley Hall Cam 63. **d** 65 **p** 66. C Barnston *Ches* 65-70; V Over St Jo 70-77; R Bromborough 77-92; RD Wirral S 86-92; Hon Can Ches Cathl from 90; Chapl Arrowe Park Hosp Birkenhead from 92. *Arrowe Park Hospital, Arrowe Park Road, Upton, Wirral, Merseyside L49 5PE* 0151-608 5461 or 678 5111

CHRISTIAN, Mrs Alison Jean. b 51. Cen Sch Speech & Drama DipAct72. S Dios Minl Tr Scheme 88. **d** 91 **p** 94. Par Dn Uxbridge *Lon* 91-94; C from 94; Chapl Uxbridge Coll 91-95.

St Laurence Rectory, Church Road, Uxbridge, Middx UB8 3NB Uxbridge (01895) 232728

CHRISTIAN, Anthony Clive Hammond. b 46. Kent Univ BA74. K Coll Lon 74. St Aug Coll Cant 74. **d** 76 **p** 77. C Faversham *Cant* 76-79; C St Laurence in the Isle of Thanet 79-81; P-in-c 81-84; R Gt Mongeham w Ripple and Sutton by Dover 84-88; V Pevensey *Chich* 88-94; P-in-c from 94. *Marsh Hall, Church Lane, Pevensey, E Sussex BN24 5LD* Eastbourne (01323) 762247

CHRISTIAN, Brother. See PEARSON, Christian David John

CHRISTIAN, Gerald. b 29. MBIM SSC FCP. Qu Coll Birm 74. **d** 77 **p** 77. NSM Stirchley *Birm* 77-82; S Africa from 82. *PO Box 905-1397, Garsfontein, Pretoria, 0042 South Africa* Pretoria (12) 348-9094

CHRISTIAN, Mark Robert. b 58. Linc Th Coll CMinlStuds95. **d** 95. C Stockport South West *Ches* from 95. *40 Beechfield Road, Stockport, Cheshire SK3 8SF* 0161-483 3350

CHRISTIAN, Paul. b 49. Cant Sch of Min 84. **d** 87 **p** 88. C Folkestone St Sav *Cant* 87-91; R Temple Ewell w Lydden from 91. *The Rectory, Green Lane, Temple Ewell, Dover, Kent CT16 3AS* Dover (01304) 822865

CHRISTIAN, Richard. b 37. Nottm Univ DipEd74 Ox Univ MA81. AKC62. **d** 63 **p** 65. C Camberwell St Mich w All So w Em *S'wark* 63-66; C Woolwich St Mary w H Trin 66-70; Chapl and Lect Bp Lonsdale Coll Derby 70-74; Keble Coll Ox 74-76; P-in-c Hurley *Ox* 76-79; Chapl Lancing Coll W Sussex 79-81; Chapl Harrow Sch Middx 82-89; Lic to Offic *Lon* 82-91; Chapl R W Sussex Hosp Chich 89-91; P-in-c Cowley *Lon* from 91; Chapl Hillingdon Hosp Uxbridge from 91. *The Rectory, Church Road, Cowley, Uxbridge, Middx UB8 3NB* Uxbridge (01895) 232728

CHRISTIAN, Canon Ronald George. b 20. AKC48. **d** 49 **p** 50. V Bramford *St E* 62-91; Dioc Exam Officer 66-88; Hon Can St E Cathl 75-91; Bruges Link Dioc Co-ord from 88; rtd 91; Perm to Offic *St E* from 91. *54 Pine View Road, Ipswich IP1 4HR* Ipswich (01473) 463031

CHRISTIAN-EDWARDS, Canon Michael Thomas. b 36. Down Coll Cam BA60 MA64. Clifton Th Coll 60. **d** 62 **p** 63. C Ex St Leon w H Trin *Ex* 62-67; V Trowbridge St Thos *Sarum* 67-75; R Wingfield w Rowley 67-75; P-in-c Fisherton Anger 75-81; R 81-92; Ind Chapl 85-92; RD Salisbury 85-90; Can and Preb Sarum Cathl 87-92; V Crofton *Portsm* from 92. *The Vicarage, Vicarage Lane, Stubbington, Fareham, Hants PO14 2JX* Stubbington (01329) 661154

CHRISTIANSON, Rodney John (Bill). b 47. St Paul's Grahamstown DipTh72. **d** 72 **p** 73. S Africa 72-76; 82-91; Miss to Seamen from 76; Min Sec from 93; Hon C Milton next Gravesend Ch Ch *Roch* 78-82; Chapl Hull Miss to Seamen 91-93; Hon Can Bloemfontein Cathl from 93; Lic to Offic *Lon* from 94. *Missions to Seamen, St Michael Paternoster Royal, College Hill, London EC4R 2RL* 0171-248 5202 Fax 248 4761

CHRISTIE, Alexander Robert (Sandy). b 58. Qu Coll Cam BA79 LLM80. Oak Hill Th Coll DipHE94. **d** 94 **p** 95. C W Norwood, St Luke *S'wark* from 94. *12 Chestnut Road, London SE27 9LF* 0181-670 2400

CHRISTIE, David James. b 58. York Univ BA80 MA83 PGCE81 Leeds Univ MPhil88. Cranmer Hall Dur 89. **d** 91 **p** 92. C Drypool *York* 91-95; V Patrick Brompton and Hunton *Ripon* from 95. *The Vicarage, Patrick Brompton, Bedale, N Yorkshire DL8 1JN* Bedale (01677) 450439

CHRISTIE, Canon Graham. b 08. Leeds Univ BA31. Coll of Resurr Mirfield 31. **d** 33 **p** 34. Tutor Hull Univ 55-80; V Millington w Gt Givendale *York* 60-81; V Pocklington w Yapham-cum-Meltonby, Owsthorpe etc 60-81; RD Pocklington 60-75; Can and Preb York Minster 62-91; rtd 81; Perm to Offic *York* from 91. *Pax Intranti, 66 Wold Road, Pocklington, York YO4 2QG* Pocklington (01759) 304200

CHRISTIE, Canon Thomas Richard. b 31. CCC Cam BA53 MA57. Linc Th Coll 55. **d** 57 **p** 58. C Portsea N End St Mark *Portsm* 57-60; C Cherry Hinton St Andr *Ely* 60-62; C-in-c Cherry Hinton St Jas CD 62-66; V Wisbech St Aug *Ely* 63-75; V Whitstable All SS *Cant* 73-75; V Whitstable All SS w St Pet 75-80; Can Res and Treas Pet Cathl *Pet* from 80; RD Pet from 87. *Prebendal House, Minster Precincts, Peterborough PE1 1XX* Peterborough (01733) 69441

CHRISTOU, Sotirios. b 51. Avery Hill Coll DipHE80. St Jo Coll Nottm 84. **d** 88 **p** 92. C Berechurch St Marg w St Mich *Chelmsf* 88-89; C Goodmayes All SS 89-90; NSM Harston w Hauxton *Ely* from 92. *13 Clover Court, Cherry Hinton, Cambridge CB1 4YN* Cambridge (01223) 411033

CHUBB, John Nicholas. b 33. St Cath Soc Ox BA55 MA58. Qu Coll Birm 57. **d** 59 **p** 60. V Brixworth *Pet* 69-74; P-in-c Holcot 73-74; V Brixworth w Holcot 74-81; V Hampton Hill *Lon* 81-88; Chapl Pet Distr Hosp from 88; Chapl Edith Cavell Hosp from 88; Perm to Offic *Linc* from 88; Perm to Offic *Nor* 88-94; rtd 94. *40 Bathurst, Orton Goldhay, Peterborough PE2 5QH* Peterborough (01733) 234089

CHUBB, Richard Henry. b 45. Univ of Wales (Cardiff) BMus67. Linc Th Coll 67. **d** 70 **p** 71. C Chippenham St Andr w Tytherton Lucas *Bris* 71-72; C-in-c Stockwood CD 72-73; C Bris Ch the Servant Stockwood 73-76; Perm to Offic 76-79; Min Can and Succ Bris Cathl from 79; Chapl to the Deaf from 83; Chapl Qu Eliz Hosp Sch Bris from 87. *55 Pembroke Road, Bristol BS8 3BE* Bristol (0117) 973 7658

CHUDLEY, Cyril Raymond. b 29. Lon Univ BA53 DipEd. Wells Th Coll 70. **d** 72 **p** 73. C Newark St Mary *S'well* 72-75; C Egg Buckland *Ex* 75-77; P-in-c Plymouth St Aug 77-80; V 80-83; V Milton Abbot, Dunterton, Lamerton etc 83-91; TV Wickford and Runwell *Chelmsf* 91-95; rtd 95. *Ten Acres, Cox Park, Gunnislake, Cornwall PL18 9AZ* Gunnislake (01822) 832345

CHURCH, Mrs Linda Ann. b 51. MCSP73. E Midl Min Tr Course 88. **d** 91 **p** 94. NSM Kirkby in Ashfield St Thos *S'well* 91-95; NSM Skegby from 95. *246 Diamond Avenue, Kirkby-in-Ashfield, Notts NG17 7NA* Mansfield (01623) 758966

CHURCHILL, Canon Aubrey Gilbert Roy. b 12. Southn Univ 36. Sarum Th Coll 37. **d** 39 **p** 40. R Wilmcote w Billesley *Cov* 55-76; Hon Can Cov Cathl 72-76; rtd 76; Perm to Offic *Cov* from 76. *9 Farley Avenue, Harbury, Leamington Spa, Warks CV33 9LX* Harbury (01926) 613309

CHURCHMAN, David Ernest Donald (Don). b 21. Clifton Th Coll 45. **d** 48 **p** 49. V Southsea St Jude *Portsm* 59-74; V Enfield Ch Ch Trent Park *Lon* 74-86; RD Enfield 75-82; rtd 86. *Heronsbrook, 158 Havant Road, Hayling Island, Hants PO11 0LJ* Hayling Island (01705) 463216

CHURCHUS, Eric Richard Ivor. b 28. Lon Univ BSc MSc56. **d** 78 **p** 79. Hon C Withington w Westhide *Heref* 78-82; C Heref St Martin 82-85; P-in-c Woolhope 85-93; rtd 93. *27 Aconbury Avenue, Hereford HR2 6HR* Hereford (01432) 267022

CHYNCHEN, John Howard. b 38. FRICS72. Sarum & Wells Th Coll 88. **d** 89 **p** 90. Bp's Dom Chapl *Sarum* from 89; Hong Kong from 90. *18 The Circus, Bath BA1 2ET, or B2, On Lee, 2 Mount Davis Road, Hong Kong* Bath (01225) 316269 or Hong Kong (852) 28550005 Fax 28550420

CIANCHI, Dalbert Peter. b 28. Lon Univ BSc57. Westcott Ho Cam 69. **d** 70 **p** 71. C Harpenden St Nic *St Alb* 70-74; TV Woughton *Ox* 74-80; P-in-c Wavendon w Walton 74-80; P-in-c Lavendon w Cold Brayfield 80-84; R Lavendon w Cold Brayfield, Clifton Reynes etc 84-94; rtd 94. *20 Springfield Drive, Bromham, Bedford MK43 8LE*

CIECHANOWICZ, Edward Leigh Bundock. See BUNDOCK, Dr Edward Leigh

CIRCUS, Robert William. b 19. Lon Univ BSc(Econ)90. Wycliffe Hall Ox 52. **d** 54 **p** 55. V Werrington *Pet* 60-70; R The Quinton *Birm* 70-76; P-in-c Wolverley *Worc* 76-82; V Wolverley and Cookley 82-84; rtd 84; Perm to Offic *Worc* from 84. *5 Berrow Hill Road, Franche, Kidderminster, Worcs DY11 5LH* Kidderminster (01562) 753067

CLABON, Harold William George. b 31. **d** 85 **p** 86. NSM Newport St Julian *Mon* 85-91; rtd 91. *38 St Julian's Avenue, Newport, Gwent NP9 7JU* Newport (01633) 215419

CLACEY, Derek Phillip. b 48. LTh. St Jo Coll Nottm 76. **d** 79 **p** 80. C Gt Parndon *Chelmsf* 79-82; C Walton H Trin *Ox* 82-88; R Bramshaw and Landford w Plaitford *Sarum* from 88. *The Rectory, Wych Green, Bramshaw, Lyndhurst, Hants SO4 7JF* Romsey (01794) 390256

CLACK, Robert John Edmund. b 63. Lanc Univ BA85. Coll of Resurr Mirfield 89. **d** 92 **p** 93. C Bury St Pet *Man* from 92. *424 Manchester Road, Bury, Lancs BL9 9NS* 0161-761 7605

CLACKER, Martin. b 56. Trin Coll Bris DipHE95. **d** 95. C Yate New Town *Bris* from 95. *67 Mountbatten Close, Yate, Bristol BS17 5TE* Chipping Sodbury (01454) 316920

CLANCEY, Ms Blanche Elizabeth Fisher. b 28. SRN50 Lon Univ CertEd71. Gilmore Ho 64. **dss** 78 **d** 87 **p** 94. Bromley Common St Aug *Roch* 78-83; Hanley H Ev *Lich* 83-87; D-in-c 87-89; rtd 89; NSM Gamston and Bridgford *S'well* from 91. *5 Sloane Court, Nottingham NG2 7SY* Nottingham (0115) 921 6997

CLANCY, Michael. b 24. Kensington Univ (USA) BA82. Glas NSM Course 76. **d** 79 **p** 80. Hon C Glas St Silas *Glas* from 79. *33 Highfield Drive, Clarkston, Glasgow G76 7SW* 0141-638 4469

CLAPHAM, John. b 47. Open Univ BA76. Sarum & Wells Th Coll 77. **d** 80 **p** 81. Dep PV Ex Cathl *Ex* from 80; C Lympstone 85-87; P-in-c from 87. *The Rectory, Lympstone, Exmouth, Devon EX8 5HP* Exmouth (01395) 273343

CLAPHAM, Kenneth. b 47. Trin Coll Bris 76. **d** 78 **p** 79. C Pemberton St Mark Newtown *Liv* 78-81; C Darfield *Sheff* 81-83; P-in-c Over Kellet *Blackb* 83-88; V from 88. *The Vicarage, 3 Kirklands Road, Over Kellet, Carnforth, Lancs LA6 1DJ* Carnforth (01524) 734189

CLAPP, Andrew Gerald Drummond (Gerry). b 58. Coll of Resurr Mirfield 87. **d** 90 **p** 91. C Tilbury Docks *Chelmsf* 90-93; C Walthamstow St Sav from 93. *212 Markhouse Road, London E17 8EP* 0181-556 4912

CLAPP, Nicholas Michel Edward. b 48. Univ of Wales (Cardiff) DipTh74. St Mich Coll Llan 71. **d** 74 **p** 75. C Walsall St Gabr Fulbrook *Lich* 74-77; C Burnley St Cath *Blackb* 77-80; R Blackley H Trin *Man* 80-87; V Carl St Aid and Ch Ch *Carl* from 87. *St Aidan's Vicarage, 6 Lismore Place, Carlisle CA1 1LX* Carlisle (01228) 22942

CLAPSON, Clive Henry. b 55. Leeds Univ BA76. Trin Coll Toronto MDiv79. **d** 79 **p** 80. Canada 79-83; USA 83-88; C Hawley H Trin *Guildf* 88-90; Miss to Seamen from 90; I Invergordon St Ninian *Mor* from 90; Vice Prin Ord and Lay Tr Course from 90. *St Ninian's Rectory, 132 High Street, Invergordon, Ross-shire IV18 0AE* Invergordon (01349) 852392

CLARE, Christopher. b 52. Sheff Univ BSc73 Nottm Univ PGCE74. Ox Min Course 89. **d** 92 **p** 93. NSM Chesham Bois *Ox* from 92. *3 The Gowers, Chestnut Lane, Amersham, Bucks HP6 5ER* Amersham (01494) 722748

CLARE, Lionel Philip. b 19. St Aid Birkenhead 46. **d** 49 **p** 50. V Sunnyside w Bourne End *St Alb* 66-74; V Kirkbymoorside w Gillamoor, Farndale & Bransdale *York* 74-84; rtd 84; Perm to Offic *Bradf* from 84. *Flat 1, Regent Court, 20 Regent Road, Ilkley, W Yorkshire LS29 9EA* Ilkley (01943) 609330

CLARE, Sister. See LOCKHART, Clare Patricia Anne

CLARIDGE, Antony Arthur John. b 37. LRAM Hull Univ MA. Bris & Glouc Tr Course. **d** 84 **p** 85. NSM Keynsham *B & W* from 84; Bp's Officer for NSMs from 90. *62 Cranwells Park, Weston, Bath BA1 2YE* Bath (01225) 427462

CLARIDGE, Michael John. b 61. MIEH Matt Bourton Tech Coll Birm DipEH82. Qu Coll Birm 89 Bossey Ecum Inst Geneva CES92. **d** 92 **p** 93. C Harlescott *Lich* 92-95; P-in-c Wellington Ch Ch from 95. *Christ Church Vicarage, 1 Church Walk, Wellington, Telford, Shropshire TF1 1RW* Telford (01952) 223185

CLARINGBULL, Canon Denis Leslie. b 33. MIPM85 K Coll Lon BD57 AKC57. **d** 58 **p** 59. C Croydon St Aug *Cant* 58-62; Ind Chapl to Bp Croydon 62-71; Ind Chapl *Cov* 71-75; Chapl Cov Cathl 71-75; Succ 72-75; V Norbury St Phil *Cant* 75-80; Sen Ind Chapl *Birm* from 80; P-in-c Birm St Paul 85-88; V from 88; Hon Can Birm Cathl from 87. *197 Russell Road, Birmingham B13 8RR* 0121-449 1435 or 449 1435

CLARINGBULL (nee DAVID), Mrs Faith Caroline. b 55. St Aid Coll Dur BA77 Univ of Wales (Abth) DipLib80. Ripon Coll Cuddesdon 87. **d** 89 **p** 94. Par Dn Is of Dogs Ch Ch and St Jo w St Luke *Lon* 89-93; Chapl Asst R Lon Hosp (Whitechapel) from 93. *Royal London Hospital, Whitechapel, London E1 1BB, or 138D Brooke Road, London N16 7RR* 0171-377 7385 or 0181-806 1337

CLARK, Albert Percival (Peter). b 17. Hatf Coll Dur LTh39 BA39. St Boniface Warminster 36. **d** 40 **p** 41. R The Quinton *Birm* 61-70; V Werrington *Pet* 70-77; S Africa 77-80; R Chipping Warden w Edgcote and Aston le Walls *Pet* 80-83; rtd 83; Perm to Offic *S'wark* from 83; Perm to Offic *Guildf* from 86. *3 Falconhurst, The Crescent, Surbiton, Surrey KT6 4BP* 0181-399 2032

CLARK, Alexander Rees. b 19. Univ of Wales (Lamp) BA48 Hull Univ CertEd50. St D Coll Lamp 50. **d** 51 **p** 52. V Eglwysnewydd *St D* 84-90; V Pontyates 61-74; V Ysbyty Cynfyn w Llantrisant 74-90; rtd 90. *Llety'r Dryw, 1 Lon Tyllwyd, Llanfarian, Aberystwyth, Dyfed SY23 4UH* Aberystwyth (01970) 612736

CLARK, Andrew James. b 50. ACIB72 ACIS76. E Midl Min Tr Course DipPhThS94. **d** 94 **p** 95. NSM Allestree *Derby* from 94. *44 Crabtree Close, Allestree, Derby DE22 2SW* Derby (01332) 552492

CLARK, Andrew Mark. b 62. W Midl Coll of Educn BEd85. Coll of Resurr Mirfield 87. **d** 90 **p** 91. C Cov St Fran N Radford *Cov* 90-94; Chapl HM Young Offender Inst Hollesley Bay Colony from 94. *HM Young Offender Institute, Hollesley, Woodbridge, Suffolk IP12 3JS* Shottisham (01394) 411741 Fax 411071

CLARK, Antony. b 61. York Univ BA83. Wycliffe Hall Ox 84. **d** 88 **p** 89. C Ashton on Mersey St Mary *Ches* 88-92; Chapl Lee Abbey 92-95; Lic to Offic *Ex* 92-95; Chapl Univ Westmr *Lon* from 95. *4A Locksborough Street, London W1M 3LG*

CLARK, Arthur. b 30. MIBiol FRSC Sheff Univ BSc MCB. St D Dioc Tr Course. **d** 88 **p** 89. NSM Haverfordwest St Mary and St Thos w Haroldston *St D* 88-91; C 91-92; V Llawhaden w Bletherston and Llanycefn from 92. *The Vicarage, Llawhaden, Narberth, Dyfed SA67 8DS* Llawhaden (01437) 541225

CLARK, Arthur Towers. b 08. OBE45. AKC36. **d** 36 **p** 37. V Roberttown *Wakef* 56-58; Perm to Offic from 73; rtd 86. *32 Broomcroft Road, Ossett, W Yorkshire WF5 8LH* Wakefield (01924) 261139

CLARK, Bernard Charles. b 34. Open Univ BA81. S'wark Ord Course 65. **d** 68 **p** 69. C Pemberton St Jo *Liv* 68-71; C Winwick 71-73; P-in-c Warrington St Barn 74-76; V 76-78; V Hindley All SS 78-83; Perm to Offic 86-94; P-in-c Hollinfare 94; R Newchurch and Glazebury 94; R Glazebury w Hollinfare

from 94. *The Vicarage, 11 Meadow Bank Gardens, Glazebury, Warrington WA3 5LX* Warrington (01925) 767946

CLARK, Charles Gordon Froggatt. b 07. Em Coll Cam BA29 MA33. Wycliffe Hall Ox 29. **d** 31 **p** 32. V Crowborough *Chich* 48-67; Chapl Crowborough Hosp 59-67; rtd 67; Chapl Kent and Sussex Hosp Tunbridge Wells 68-80; Hon C Tunbridge Wells H Trin w Ch Ch *Roch* 68-80; Hon C Penshurst and Fordcombe 80-84; Asst Chapl Dorothy Kerin Trust 80-87; Perm to Offic *Roch* from 84; Perm to Offic *Pet* from 89. *4 Village Farm Close, Castor, Peterborough PE5 7BX* Peterborough (01733) 380527

CLARK, David. b 30. Nottm Univ BSc51 Lon Univ DipTh57. St Aid Birkenhead 55. **d** 57 **p** 58. V Ashton St Jas *Man* 60-64; rtd 93. *Roz an Avalou, 22340 Mael-Carhaix, France* France (33) 96 24 65 04

CLARK, Canon David George Neville. b 25. Linc Coll Ox BA49 MA59. Wells Th Coll 49. **d** 51 **p** 52. V Sutton New Town St Barn *S'wark* 59-72; R Charlwood 72-90; P-in-c Sidlow Bridge 76-77; R 77-90; P-in-c Buckland 85-87; P-in-c Leigh 87-90; Hon Can S'wark Cathl 88-90; rtd 90. *12 Marlborough Road, Coventry CV2 4EP* Coventry (01203) 442400

CLARK, David Gordon. b 29. Clare Coll Cam BA52 MA57. Ridley Hall Cam 52. **d** 54 **p** 55. R Stansted *Roch* 69-82; R Stansted w Fairseat and Vigo 82-94; rtd 94. *1 Coastguard Cottages, Wareham, Dorset BH20 5PF* Wareham (01929) 480753

CLARK, David Humphrey. b 39. G&C Coll Cam BA60. Wells Th Coll 62. **d** 64 **p** 65. C Leigh St Mary *Man* 64-68; Min Can and Prec Man Cathl 68-70; Ind Chapl *Nor* 70-85; P-in-c Nor St Clem and St Geo 70-76; P-in-c Nor St Sav w St Paul 70-76; V Nor-over-the-Water Colegate St Geo 76-79; Hon AP Nor St Pet Mancroft 79-85; R Oadby *Leic* from 85. *St Peter's Rectory, 1 Leicester Road, Oadby, Leicester LE2 5BD* Leicester (0116) 271 2135

CLARK, David John. b 40. CEng MIStructE Surrey Univ MPhil75. Ridley Hall Cam 81. **d** 83 **p** 84. C Combe Down w Monkton Combe and S Stoke *B & W* 83-89; Voc Adv Bath Adnry from 89; R Freshford, Limpley Stoke and Hinton Charterhouse from 89. *The Rectory, Crowe Lane, Freshford, Bath BA3 6EB* Bath (01225) 723135

CLARK, Dennis Henry Graham. b 26. St Steph Ho Ox 52. **d** 55 **p** 56. Chapl RAF 61-78; Asst Chapl-in-Chief RAF 78-82; Chapl St Clem Danes (RAF Ch) 79-82; V Godmanchester *Ely* 82-91; rtd 91. *8 Arran Way, St Ives, Huntingdon, Cambs PE17 6DT* St Ives (01480) 301951

CLARK, Edward Robert. b 39. Ex Coll Ox BA61 MA65 Bris Univ DSA68 CASS69. St Steph Ho Ox 61. **d** 63 **p** 64. C Solihull *Birm* 63-67; Perm to Offic *Bris* 67-69; Perm to Offic *Leic* 69-71; Perm to Offic *Ox* 71-80; Perm to Offic *St Alb* 80-84; Perm to Offic *Cant* from 84. *41 The Street, Kingston, Canterbury, Kent CT4 6JQ* Canterbury (01227) 830074

CLARK, Ellen Jane. See CLARK-KING, Mrs Ellen Jane

CLARK, Eric Douglas Colbatch. b 08. OBE66 MBE62. St Jo Coll Ox BA29. Wycliffe Hall Ox 39. **d** 40 **p** 41. Dir Overseas Studies Commendation Cen Lon 70-71; Warden Student Res Cen Wimbledon 72-77; rtd 77; Perm to Offic *S'wark* from 82. *11 Rosemary Cottages, The Drive, London SW20 8TQ* 0181-879 0344

CLARK, Frederick Albert George. b 15. MBE68. ACP66. **d** 67 **p** 68. Hon C Stroud *Glouc* 67-84; Hon C Stroud and Uplands w Slad 84-85; Perm to Offic from 85. *2 Terrace Cottages, Thrupp, Stroud, Glos GL5 2BN* Brimscombe (01453) 882060

CLARK, Henry. b 23. AKC52. **d** 53 **p** 54. V Middlesb St Chad *York* 63-91; rtd 91. *Broadview, Ferry Road, Fingringhoe, Colchester CO5 7BY* Colchester (01206) 729248

CLARK, Hugh Lockhart. b 44. Oak Hill Th Coll 69. **d** 72 **p** 73. C Islington St Jude Mildmay Park *Lon* 72-75; C N Walsham w Antingham *Nor* 75-78; TV S Molton, Nymet St George, High Bray etc *Ex* 78-81; CF 81-83; V Gisburn *Bradf* 83-89; R Clitheroe St Jas *Blackb* 89-92. *Address temp unknown*

CLARK, Ian. b 31. Lich Th Coll 63. **d** 65 **p** 66. C Droylsden St Mary *Man* 65-68; C Bedf Leigh 68-70; V Broughton Moor *Carl* 70-80; R Kirton *S'well* 80-94; V Walesby 80-94; P-in-c Egmanton 80-81; V 81-94. *27 Barripper Road, Camborne, Cornwall TR14 7QW* Camborne (01209) 716084

CLARK, Dr Ian Duncan Lindsay. b 35. K Coll Cam BA59 MA63 PhD64 Ox Univ DipTh63. Ripon Hall Ox 62. **d** 64 **p** 65. C Willington *Newc* 64-66; India 66-76; Chapl St Cath Coll Cam 76; Tutor 78-85; Dean of Chpl 80-85. *4 Yewtree Lane, Yetholm, Kelso, Roxburghshire TD5 8RZ* Yetholm (01573) 420323

CLARK, Miss Janet Elizabeth. b 44. Derby Coll of Educn CertEd65 Open Univ BA75. All Nations Chr Coll CertRS84 Oak Hill Th Coll DipHE91 BA92. **d** 92 **p** 94. Par Dn Edmonton All SS w St Mich *Lon* 92-94; C from 94. *60 Tillotson Road, London N9 9AH* 0181-803 1590

CLARK, Mrs Jean Robinson. b 32. K Coll Lon AKC BD79. St Chris Coll Blackheath CertRK53. **dss** 85 **d** 87 **p** 94. Cov E *Cov*

85-87; C 87-88; NSM Upper Mole Valley Gp *S'wark* 89-90; Hon Par Dn Charlwood 89-90; Lic to Offic *Cov* from 90; rtd 92. *12 Marlborough Road, Coventry CV2 4EP* Coventry (01203) 442400

CLARK, John Ronald Lyons. b 47. TCD BA69 MA72. Div Hostel Dub 67. **d** 70 **p** 71. C Dundela *D & D* 70-72; CF 72-75; C Belf St Aid *Conn* 75-76; I Stranorlar w Meenglas and Kilteevogue *D & R* 76-81; Chapl Wythenshawe Hosp Man 81-95; I Kilgariffe Union *C, C & R* from 95. *The Rectory, Gallanes, Clonakilty, Co Cork, Irish Republic* Clonakilty (23) 33357

CLARK, John David Stanley. b 36. Dur Univ BA64. Ridley Hall Cam 64. **d** 66 **p** 67. C Benchill *Man* 66-69; C Beverley Minster *York* 69-74; Perm to Offic *S'well* 74-76; Lic to Offic 76-77; Lic to Offic *Chelmsf* 77-80; Miss to Seamen 77-80; Perm to Offic *York* 80-83; V Egton w Grosmont 83-89; R Thornton Dale and Ellerburne w Wilton from 89. *Thornton Dale Rectory, Pickering, N Yorkshire YO18 7QH* Pickering (01751) 474244

CLARK, John Edward Goodband. b 49. Chich Th Coll 70. **d** 73 **p** 74. C Thorpe *Nor* 73-76; C Earlham St Anne 76-78; Chapl RN 78-82; P-in-c Tittleshall w Godwick, Wellingham and Weasenham *Nor* 82-85; R South Raynham, E w W Raynham, Helhoughton, etc 85-90; R Taverham w Ringland from 90. *The Rectory, Taverham, Norwich NR8 6TE* Norwich (01603) 868217

CLARK, John Michael. b 35. DSMS63 DipYW65 Leic Poly DCEd80. E Midl Min Tr Course 87. **d** 90 **p** 91. Chapl to the Deaf *Linc* from 86; NSM Bracebridge Heath from 90. *3 Hawthorn Road, Cherry Willingham, Lincoln LN3 4JU* Lincoln (01522) 751759

CLARK, Dr John Patrick Hedley. b 37. St Cath Coll Cam BA61 MA65 Worc Coll Ox BA63 MA72 BD74 Lambeth Hon DD89. St Steph Ho Ox 61. **d** 64 **p** 65. C Highters Heath *Birm* 64-67; C Eglingham *Newc* 67-72; P-in-c Newc St Anne 72-77; V Longframlington w Brinkburn 77-95; V Chevington from 95. *The Vicarage, 98 The Farnes, South Broomhill, Morpeth, Northd NE65 9SE* Morpeth (01670) 760273

CLARK, Jonathan Dunnett. b 61. Ex Univ BA83 DipHE86 Bris Univ MLitt90. Trin Coll Bris 84. **d** 88 **p** 89. C Stanwix *Carl* 88-92; Chapl Bris Univ *Bris* 92-93; S Dios Minl Tr Scheme from 94. *19 The Close, Salisbury SP1 2EE* Salisbury (01722) 412996 Fax 338508

CLARK, Jonathan Jackson. b 57. Linc Coll Ox 79 Down Coll Cam 83. Ridley Hall Cam 81. **d** 84 **p** 85. C W Derby St Luke *Liv* 84-87; C Gt Clacton *Chelmsf* 87-93; V Hammersmith St Simon *Lon* from 93. *153 Blyth Road, London W14 0HL* 0171-602 1043 or 603 4879

CLARK, Kathleen Christine. *See* LEFROY, Mrs Kathleen Christine

CLARK, Ven Kenneth James. b 22. DSC44. St Cath Soc Ox BA48 MA52. Cuddesdon Coll 52. **d** 52 **p** 53. V Westbury-on-Trym H Trin *Bris* 61-72; V Bris St Mary Redcliffe w Temple etc 72-82; P-in-c Bedminster St Mich 73-78; RD Bedminster 73-79; Hon Can Bris Cathl from 74; Adn Swindon 82-92; rtd 92. *6 Saxon Road, Harnham, Salisbury SP2 8JZ* Salisbury (01722) 421410

CLARK, Lance Edgar Dennis. b 52. MBE93. Linc Th Coll 74. **d** 77 **p** 78. C Arnold *S'well* 77-82; V Brinsley w Underwood 82-87; Chapl RAF from 87. *Chaplaincy Services (RAF), HQ, Personnel and Training Command, RAF Innsworth, Gloucester GL3 1EZ* Gloucester (01452) 712612 Ext 5164 Fax 510828

CLARK, Canon Malcolm Aiken. b 05. Lich Th Coll 32. **d** 34 **p** 35. R Edin Gd Shep *Edin* 56-77; rtd 77; Chapl Edin St Vin *Edin* from 77; Dean Edin 82-85; Can St Mary's Cathl 82-85; Hon Can St Mary's Cathl from 85. *12 St Vincent Street, Edinburgh EH3 6SH* 0131-557 3662

CLARK, Martin Hudson. b 46. K Coll Lon BD68 AKC68. **d** 71 **p** 72. C S'wark H Trin *S'wark* 71-74; C Parkstone St Pet w Branksea and St Osmund *Sarum* 74-77; V E Wickham *S'wark* 77-86; V Wandsworth St Anne from 86; RD Wandsworth 90-95. *St Anne's Vicarage, 182 St Ann's Hill, London SW18 2RS* 0181-874 2809

CLARK, Michael Arthur. b 46. S Dios Minl Tr Scheme. **d** 83 **p** 84. NSM Monkton Farleigh, S Wraxall and Winsley *Sarum* from 83. *62 Tyning Road, Winsley, Bradford-on-Avon, Wilts BA15 2JW* Bradford-on-Avon (01225) 866652

CLARK, Michael David. b 45. Ox Univ MA68. Trin Coll Bris DipTh72. **d** 72 **p** 73. C Cheadle *Ches* 72-76; Brazil 77-86; Bolivia 86-88; C Wilton *B & W* 89-90; TV from 90. *St Michael's House, 1 Comeytrowe Lane, Taunton, Somerset TA1 5PA* Taunton (01823) 337458

CLARK, Michael Wilford. b 23. OBE91 JP75. Loughb Univ TCert49. **d** 87 **p** 88. In Meth Ch 57-87; Chapl Asst Nightingale MacMillan Hospice Derby 87-89; Hon C Marston on Dove w Scropton *Derby* 87-89; P-in-c Longford, Long Lane, Dalbury and Radbourne 89-95; rtd 95. *Ashcroft, Etwall Road, Mickleover, Derby DE3 5DN* Derby (01332) 516968

CLARK, Miss Patricia Mary (Pat). b 36. Liv Univ BSc. **d** 88 **p** 94. Par Dn Leasowe *Ches* 88-92; Bp's Officer for Women in Min from 89; Par Dn Davenham 92-94; C from 94. *9 Granville Road, Leftwich, Northwich, Cheshire CW9 8HE* Northwich (01606) 350458

CLARK, Peter. b 39. Ch Coll Cam BA61 MA65. Chich Th Coll 61. **d** 63 **p** 64. C Huddersfield SS Pet and Paul *Wakef* 63-67; C Notting Hill St Jo *Lon* 67-74; Grenada 75-79; C Hove All SS *Chich* 79; P-in-c Hove St Patr 79-82; V Hove St Patr w Ch Ch and St Andr 82-83; V Battersea Ch Ch and St Steph *S'wark* from 83; RD Battersea from 90. *Christ Church Vicarage, Candahar Road, London SW11 2PU* 0171-228 1225

CLARK, Peter. b 45. Sarum & Wells Th Coll 87. **d** 89 **p** 90. C Portsea St Cuth *Portsm* 89-92; TV Rye *Chich* from 92. *Camber Vicarage, Lydd Road, Rye, E Sussex TN31 7RN* Rye (01797) 225386

CLARK, Peter Norman. b 53. Qu Coll Cam BA79. Westcott Ho Cam 78. **d** 80 **p** 81. C Bris St Mary Redcliffe w Temple etc *Bris* 80-83; C Potternewton *Ripon* 83-86; R Longsight St Luke *Man* from 86. *St Luke's Rectory, Stockport Road, Longsight, Manchester M13 9AB* 0161-273 6662

CLARK, Mrs Prudence Anne. b 44. Man Coll of Educn CertEd78. N Ord Course 89. **d** 92 **p** 94. NSM Royton St Anne *Man* 92-94; Hon C from 94. *1 Hereford Way, Stalybridge, Cheshire SK15 2TD* 0161-338 5275

CLARK, Reginald Isaac. b 16. AKC47. **d** 47 **p** 48. Chapl Shenley Hosp Radlett Herts 65-84; rtd 84. *1 Monks Walk, Spalding, Lincs PE11 3LG* Spalding (01775) 768304

CLARK, Richard Martin. b 60. Ch Coll Cam MA81. Trin Coll Bris BA86. **d** 86 **p** 87. C Orpington Ch Ch *Roch* 86-89; C Marple All SS *Ches* 89-92; V Nottm St Andr *S'well* from 92. *St Andrew's Vicarage, Chestnut Grove, Nottingham NG3 5AD* Nottingham (0115) 960 4961

CLARK, Robert Henry. b 32. Oak Hill Th Coll 61. **d** 64 **p** 65. C Tranmere St Cath *Ches* 67-75; V Platt Bridge *Liv* 75-84; V Litherland St Paul Hatton Hill 84-94; rtd 94. *9 Lime Vale, Spring Gardens, Wigan, Lancs WN3 4PE* Wigan (01942) 861751

CLARK, Canon Robert James Vodden. b 07. Edin Th Coll 40. **d** 41 **p** 42. R Lasswade *Edin* 69-79; Can St Mary's Cathl 72-76; Hon Can St Mary's Cathl from 76; rtd 79. *15 North Street, St Andrews, Fife KY16 9PW* St Andrews (01334) 76237

CLARK, Canon Robin. b 27. Lon Univ BA79 BD69 MPhil77 St Jo Coll Dur DipTh54. **d** 54 **p** 55. R Brant Broughton w Stragglethorpe *Linc* 61-90; RD Loveden 72-93; Can and Preb Linc Cathl from 84; R Brant Broughton and Beckingham 90-93; rtd 93. *Ravenshurst Cottage, 23 The Green, Ingham, Lincoln LN1 2XT*

CLARK, Preb Roland Mark Allison. b 21. St Cath Coll Cam BA48 MA53. Wells Th Coll 48. **d** 50 **p** 51. V Wilton *B & W* 56-79; Preb Wells Cathl from 63; R Backwell 79-88; RD Portishead 82-86; rtd 88. *12 West Croft, Clevedon, Avon BS21 7TZ* Bristol (0117) 987 6395

CLARK, Roy. b 21. MBE64. Roch Th Coll 65. **d** 67 **p** 68. C New Sleaford *Linc* 67-70; R Stickney 70-72; rtd 87. *35 Princess Anne Road, Boston, Lincs PE21 9AP* Boston (01205) 361017

CLARK, Russell John. b 15. LSE BSc(Econ)38. Local NSM Course. **d** 93 **p** 93. NSM Hoxne w Denham, Syleham and Wingfield *St E* from 93. *Old School, Wingfield, Diss, Norfolk IP21 5RG* Stradbroke (01379) 384537

CLARK, Stephen Kenneth. b 52. Bris Univ BEd74. Wycliffe Hall Ox 80. **d** 83 **p** 84. C Pitsea *Chelmsf* 83-86; Chapl Scargill Ho 86-89; R Elmley Castle w Bricklehampton and Combertons *Worc* from 89. *The Rectory, 22 Parkwood, Elmley Castle, Pershore, Worcs WR10 3HT* Elmley Castle (01386) 710394

CLARK, Trevor Bartholomew. b 44. Qu Coll Birm 68. **d** 71 **p** 72. C Maltby *Sheff* 71-75; V New Rossington 75-80; V Campsall from 80. *The Vicarage, High Street, Campsall, Doncaster, S Yorkshire DN6 9AD* Doncaster (01302) 700286

CLARK-KING (nee CLARK), Mrs Ellen Jane. b 62. Newnham Coll Cam BA85 MA89 Reading Univ PCVG86. Ripon Coll Cuddesdon 89. **d** 92 **p** 94. C Colwall w Upper Colwall and Coddington *Heref* from 92. *21 Biddulph Way, Ledbury, Herefordshire HR8 2HP* Ledbury (01531) 631939

CLARK-KING (formerly KING), Jeremy Norman. b 66. K Coll Lon BD88 AKC88. Ripon Coll Cuddesdon 88. **d** 90 **p** 91. C Ashby-de-la-Zouch St Helen w Coleorton *Leic* 90-93; C Ledbury w Eastnor *Heref* from 93. *21 Biddulph Way, Ledbury, Herefordshire HR8 2HP* Ledbury (01531) 631939

CLARKE, Alan John. b 55. St Jo Coll Dur BA77 MA85. Westcott Ho Cam 78. **d** 80 **p** 81. C Heworth St Mary *Dur* 80-83; C Darlington St Jo 83-87; Asst Chapl Bryanston Sch Blandford 87-91; Chapl St Pet High Sch Ex from 91. *41 Stuart Road, Exeter EX1 2SZ* Exeter (01392) 213596 or 74383

CLARKE, Alan Keith. b 38. Leic Coll of Educn DipYL64 Newc Univ DipAdEdStud73 MA89. SW Minl Tr Course. **d** 87 **p** 88.

NSM Wolborough w Newton Abbot *Ex* from 87. *School House, 20 Coach Place, Newton Abbot, Devon TQ12 1ES* Newton Abbot (01626) 63515

CLARKE, Alfred Charles Reginald. b 19. ACII. Qu Coll Birm 71. **d** 74 **p** 74. Hon C Yardley St Cypr Hay Mill *Birm* 74-80; Hon C Packwood w Hockley Heath 80-89; rtd 89; Lic to Offic *Birm* from 89. *15 Newton Road, Knowle, Solihull, W Midlands B93 9HL* Knowle (01564) 773861

CLARKE, Miss Alison Clare. b 33. MCST54 Open Univ BA85. E Anglian Minl Tr Course 90. **d** 93. NSM Lt Ilford St Mich *Chelmsf* from 93. *29 Glengall Road, Woodford Green, Essex IG8 0DN* 0181-504 5106

CLARKE, Andrew John. b 58. New Coll Edin BD82 Graduate Soc Dur PGCE89. Linc Th Coll 84. **d** 86 **p** 87. C High Harrogate Ch Ch *Ripon* 86-88; RE Teacher Royds Hall High Sch Huddersfield 89-91; C Thornbury *Bradf* 91-93; P-in-c Bingley H Trin from 93. *Holy Trinity Vicarage, Oak Avenue, Bingley, W Yorkshire BD16 1ES* Bradford (01274) 563909

CLARKE, Arthur. b 34. Lon Univ BD66 Nottm Univ MPhil75 DipEd. Sarum & Wells Th Coll 75. **d** 76 **p** 77. C Wollaton *S'well* 76-79; P-in-c Normanton on Soar 79-91; R Sutton Bonington 79-91; R Sutton Bonington w Normanton-on-Soar 91-93; P-in-c Arnold 93-94; V from 94. *St Mary's Vicarage, Church Lane, Arnold, Nottingham NG5 8HJ* Nottingham (0115) 926 2946

CLARKE, Miss Audrey May. b 35. Gilmore Ho 65. **dss** 75 **d** 87 **p** 94. Crofton Park St Hilda w St Cypr *S'wark* 75-79; Chapl Asst Middx Hosp Lon 80-84; Mottingham St Andr *S'wark* 84-87; Par Dn 87-89; C Westborough *Guildf* 89-95; rtd 95; Hon C St Mary's Bay w St Mary-in-the-Marsh etc *Cant* from 95. *The Vicarage, Jefferstone Lane, St Mary's Bay, Romney Marsh, Kent TN29 0SW* Romney Marsh (01303) 874188

CLARKE, Benjamin Blanchard. b 08. Birm Univ BSc31 MSc34 St Cath Soc Ox BA33 MA37. Ripon Hall Ox 31. **d** 33 **p** 34. V Padstow *Truro* 53-73; rtd 73. *4 Athelstan Park, Bodmin, Cornwall PL31 1DS* Bodmin (01208) 73989

CLARKE, Bernard Ronald. b 53. FRGS. Ridley Hall Cam 74. **d** 77 **p** 78. C Leigh Park *Portsm* 77-78; C Petersfield w Sheet 78-81; Chapl RN from 81; Dir of Ords RN from 93. *Directorate Gen, RN Chapl Services, Room 205, Victory Building, HM Naval Base, Portsmouth PO1 3LS* Portsmouth (01705) 727900 Fax 727112

CLARKE, Charles David. b 37. LCP77 Univ of Wales BA76 DPS90 Cam Univ DipEd77. St Mich Coll Llan 88. **d** 90 **p** 91. C Whitchurch *Llan* 90-93; V Graig from 93; P-in-c Cilfynydd from 93. *St John's Vicarage, Llantrisant Road, Graig, Pontypridd, M Glam CF37 1LW* Pontypridd (01443) 402436

CLARKE, Miss Christine Vera. b 45. Lon Univ CertEd66. Qu Coll Birm 79. **dss** 81 **d** 87 **p** 94. Bris St Mary Redcliffe w Temple etc *Bris* 81-86; Ind Chapl from 86; NSM Westbury-on-Trym St Alb from 94. *St Leonard's Vicarage, Parkfield Avenue, Bristol BS5 8DP* Bristol (0117) 955 6286

CLARKE, Christopher George (Chris). b 43. Sarum Th Coll 67. **d** 68 **p** 69. C Sprowston *Nor* 68-72; V Hemsby 72-77; V Sutton Courtenay w Appleford *Ox* 77-84; TR Bracknell from 84; RD Bracknell from 90. *The Rectory, 26 Park Road, Bracknell, Berks RG12 2LU* Bracknell (01344) 423869

CLARKE, Colin David Emrys. b 42. Leeds Univ DipAdEd82 MEd84. Wells Th Coll 67. **d** 68 **p** 69. C Plumstead St Nic *S'wark* 68-71; C N Lynn w St Marg and St Nic *Nor* 71-75; Miss to Seamen 71-75; Asst Chapl HM Pris Wakef 75-77; V Birkenshaw w Hunsworth *Wakef* 77-87; V Illingworth 87-92; R Burnsall w Rylstone *Bradf* from 92. *The Rectory, Burnsall, Skipton, N Yorkshire BD23 6BP* Burnsall (01756) 720331

CLARKE, Daniel (Dan). b 17. TCD BA39 MA44 BD66. **d** 41 **p** 42. C Dub St Bart *D & G* 41-44; Dioc C Killaloe *L & K* 44-46; Chapl Roscrea Hosp Inst 46-48; C-in-c Corbally 46-48; I Borrisokane 48-55; RD Upper Ormond 55-57; RD Lower Ormond 58-59; Asst Master Robert Bloomfield Sch Shefford 59-62; Hd Relig Studies Reigate Gr Sch 62-82; Chapl 75-84; Chapl Reigate St Mary's Sch from 85. *4 Orchard Way, Reigate, Surrey RH2 8DT* Reigate (01737) 246169

CLARKE, Canon David George Alexander. b 23. TCD BA47 MA51 BD55 PhD57. **d** 48 **p** 49. I Kilrossanty *C & O* 61-73; Preb Newc St Patr Cathl Dub 65-89; Prec Waterford and Lismore *C & O* 67-73; Dean Cashel 73-83; I Cashel St Jo 73-83; I Ballymascanlan w Creggan, Forkhill etc *Arm* 83-89; rtd 89; Lic to Offic *Arm* from 90; Lic to Offic *D & D* from 90. *2 Ashley Court, Warrenpoint, Newry, Co Down BT34 3RN* Warrenpoint (016937) 72416

CLARKE, Dr David James. b 55. Univ of Wales (Abth) BSc(Econ)77 Keele Univ MA78 PhD83. Trin Coll Bris DipTh84. **d** 84 **p** 85. C Cardigan and Mwnt and Y Ferwig *St D* 84-87; P-in-c Llansantffraed and Llanbadarn Trefeglwys etc 87-88; V 88-91; Chapl Coll of St Mark and St Jo Plymouth *Ex* from 91; Lic to Offic from 91. *Staff House 2, College of St Mark and St John, Derriford Road, Plymouth PL6 8BH* Plymouth (01752) 770809 or 777188

CLARKE, Denis John. b 23. Local NSM Course. **d** 87 **p** 88. NSM Brothertoft Gp *Linc* from 87. *49 Punchbowl Lane, Boston, Lincs PE21 8HU* Boston (01205) 363512

CLARKE, Douglas Charles. b 33. Bps' Coll Cheshunt 65. **d** 66 **p** 67. C Chingford SS Pet and Paul *Chelmsf* 66-72; V Romford Ascension Collier Row 72-79; V Bembridge *Portsm* 79-83; V Bournemouth St Mary *Win* 83-87; R High Wych and Gilston w Eastwick *St Alb* from 87. *The Rectory, High Wych, Sawbridgeworth, Herts CM21 0HX* Bishop's Stortford (01279) 723346

CLARKE, Dudley Barrington. b 22. OBE. Em Coll Cam BA46 MA48 PhD. Ridley Hall Cam 46. **d** 48 **p** 49. Chapl Monkton Combe Sch Bath 50-58; Australia from 59; rtd 87. *11 Proctors Road, Hobart, Tasmania, Australia 7005* Hobart (2) 348658

CLARKE, Duncan James Edward. b 54. Wycliffe Hall Ox 75. **d** 78 **p** 79. C Newport St Andr *Mon* 78-80; C Griffithstown 80-82; Trinidad and Tobago 82-84; NSM Fleckney and Kilby *Leic* 92-95; USPG from 95; Trinidad and Tobago from 95. *USPG, Partnership House, 157 Waterloo House, London SE1 8XA* 0171-928 8681 Fax 928 2371

CLARKE, Edward. b 02. Dur Univ LTh28 St Jo Coll Dur BA30 MA32. St Aid Birkenhead 25. **d** 29 **p** 30. V Kirkburton *Wakef* 64-70; rtd 70; Perm to Offic *Wakef* from 70. *Timinetes, Northgate Road, Honley, Huddersfield HD7 2QL*

CLARKE, Edwin Joseph Alfred. b 18. Ripon Hall Ox 64. **d** 66 **p** 67. C Yardley St Edburgha *Birm* 66-70; R Nether Whitacre 70-88; rtd 89. *114 Main Street, Clifton Campville, Tamworth, Staffs B79 0AP* Clifton Campville (0182786) 587

CLARKE, Eric Samuel. b 26. Nottm Univ BSc51 St Cath Coll Ox BA69 MA69. Wycliffe Hall Ox 51. **d** 54 **p** 55. C Gedling *S'well* 54-57; C Nottm St Pet and St Jas 57-69; Perm to Offic *Derby* from 63. *16 Menin Road, Allestree, Derby DE22 2NL*

CLARKE, Frank. b 21. St Jo Coll Nottm. **d** 85 **p** 87. NSM Farnsfield *S'well* from 85. *Belvedere, Tippings Lane, Farnsfield, Newark, Notts NG22 8EP* Mansfield (01623) 882528

CLARKE, Canon Harold George. b 29. St D Coll Lamp 58. **d** 61 **p** 62. C Ebbw Vale Ch Ch *Mon* 61-64; C Roath St German *Llan* 64-73; Chapl Wales Poly 73-74; V Glyntaff 73-84; V Roath St Martin from 84; RD Cardiff from 89; Can Llan Cathl from 91. *St Martin's Vicarage, Strathnairn Street, Roath, Cardiff CF2 3JL* Cardiff (01222) 482295

CLARKE, Harold Godfrey Coddrington. b 26. S'wark Ord Course 71. **d** 74 **p** 75. C Redhill St Jo *S'wark* 74-79; P-in-c Blindley Heath from 79. *The Vicarage, Blindley Heath, Lingfield, Surrey RH7 6JR* Lingfield (01342) 832337

CLARKE, Ven Herbert Lewis. b 20. Jes Coll Ox BA43 MA46. Union Th Sem (NY) STM50 Linc Th Coll 44. **d** 45 **p** 46. R Caerphilly *Llan* 67-77; Can Llan Cathl 75-77; Adn Llan 77-88; R St Fagans w Michaelston-super-Ely 77-90; rtd 90; Perm to Offic *Llan* from 90. *First Floor Flat, St Andrew, High Street, Llandaff, Cardiff CF5 2DX* Cardiff (01222) 578581

CLARKE, Canon Hilary James. b 41. JP. Univ of Wales (Lamp) BA64 Ox Univ DipEd65. St Steph Ho Ox 64. **d** 66 **p** 67. C Kibworth Beauchamp *Leic* 66-68; Chapl to the Deaf 68-71; Prin Officer Ch Miss for Deaf Walsall 71-73; Prin Officer and Sec Leic & Co Miss for the Deaf 73-89; TV Leic H Spirit *Leic* 82-89; Hon Can Leic Cathl from 88; Sec Gen Syn Coun for the Deaf from 88; Bp's Press Relns and Dio Communications Officer *Leic* from 95. *158 Westcotes Drive, Leicester LE3 0SP* Leicester (0116) 255 7283 Fax 233 0839

CLARKE, Jason Scott. b 65. Leeds Univ BA87. Coll of Resurr Mirfield 89. **d** 91 **p** 92. C Hendon St Mary *Lon* from 91. *Christchurch House, 76 Brent Street, London NW4 2EF* 0181-202 8123

CLARKE, Canon John Cecil. b 32. St Jo Coll Dur BA70 DipTh71. Cranmer Hall Dur. **d** 75 **p** 76. Dioc Ecum Officer and Adv in Miss 75-87; Hon C Ches St Mary *Ches* 75-78; R Barrow 78-87; V Thornton Hough from 87; Dioc Projects Officer 87-92; Hon Can Ches Cathl from 91; RD Wirral S from 92. *All Saints' Vicarage, Thornton Hough, Wirral, Merseyside L63 1JP* 0151-336 3429

CLARKE, John Charles. b 31. St Jo Coll Nottm 91. **d** 92 **p** 93. NSM Winshill *Derby* 92-95; P-in-c Stanley from 95. *The Vicarage, Station Road, Stanley, Derby DE7 6FB* Nottingham (0115) 932 2942

CLARKE, John David Maurice. b 60. **d** 89 **p** 90. C Dub Whitechurch *D & G* 89-92; Asst Chapl St Vin Hosp Donnybrook 89-92; I Navan w Kentstown, Tara, Slane, Painestown etc *M & K* from 92. *The Rectory, Boyne Road, Navan, Co Meath, Irish Republic* Navan (46) 21172

CLARKE, John Martin. b 52. Hertf Coll Ox BA89 MA89 Edin Univ BD76. Edin Th Coll 73. **d** 76 **p** 77. C Kenton Ascension *Newc* 76-79; Prec St Ninian's Cathl Perth *St And* 79-82; Info Officer to Scottish Episc Gen Syn 82-87; Greece 87-88; V Battersea St Mary *S'wark* from 89. *St Mary's Vicarage, 32 Vicarage Crescent, London SW11 3LD* 0171-228 9648

CLARKE, John Patrick Hatherley. b 46. Pemb Coll Ox BA68 Man Univ MBA73. St Jo Coll Nottm DipTh83. **d** 83 **p** 84. C Leic H Trin w St Jo *Leic* 83-87; C Selly Park St Steph and St Wulstan *Birm* 87-92; Hon C Woking St Mary *Guildf* 92-94; V Greenham *Ox* from 94. *The Vicarage, New Road, Greenham, Newbury, Berks RG14 7RZ* Newbury (01635) 41075

CLARKE, John Percival. b 44. TCD BA67. **d** 69 **p** 70. C Belf St Simon *Conn* 69-72; C Monkstown *D & G* 72-76; Asst Chapl TCD 76-78; I Durrus *C, C & R* 79-82; I Carrigrohane Union 82-89; Tanzania 89-92; I Wicklow w Killiskey *D & G* from 92; Abp's Dom Chapl from 95. *The Rectory, Wicklow, Irish Republic* Wicklow (404) 67132

CLARKE, John Philip. b 31. Trin Hall Cam BA54 MA62. Linc Th Coll. **d** 57 **p** 58. C Walworth Lady Marg w St Mary *S'wark* 57-59; C Warlingham w Chelsham and Farleigh 59-62; C Mottingham St Andr 62-67; C Eltham Park St Luke 67-72; Chapl Leeds Gen Infirmary 72-91; C Far Headingley St Chad *Ripon* from 91; Bp's Adv on Chr Healing from 91. *75 Weetwood Lane, Leeds LS16 5NU* Leeds (0113) 275 9526 or 274 4322

CLARKE, Miss Joyce Nancy. b 32. CertEd58. N Ord Course 82. **dss** 85 **d** 87 **p** 94. Prestbury *Ches* 85-87; Par Dn 87-94; C from 94. *2 Peterborough Close, Macclesfield, Cheshire SK10 3DT* Macclesfield (01625) 611809

CLARKE, Mrs Joyce Willoughby Price. b 36. Gilmore Course 78. **dss** 81 **d** 87 **p** 94. Heston *Lon* 81-87; Par Dn 87-89; Deanery Youth Chapl *Sarum* from 90. *Ankadown, 22 Sherford Close, Wareham, Dorset BH20 4JL* Wareham (01929) 554115

CLARKE, Kenneth Herbert (Ken). b 49. TCD BA71. **d** 72 **p** 73. C Magherafelt *D & D* 72-75; C Dundonald 75-78; Chile 78-82; I Crinken *D & G* 82-86; I Coleraine *Conn* from 86; Chmn SAMS (Ireland) from 94. *St Patrick's Rectory, Mountsandel Road, Coleraine, Co Londonderry BT52 1JE* Coleraine (01265) 43429 or 44213

CLARKE, Canon Malcolm Methuen. b 08. K Coll Cam BA36 MA40. Cuddesdon Coll 37. **d** 38 **p** 39. V Wellingborough All Hallows *Pet* 49-78; rtd 78; Hon C Northn St Matt *Pet* from 78. *11A Kingsley Road, Northampton NN2 7BN* Northampton (01604) 713695

CLARKE, Canon Margaret Geraldine. b 33. Dalton Ho Bris 62. **dss** 68 **d** 87 **p** 94. Wells St Thos w Horrington *B & W* 68-74; Easthampstead *Ox* 74-87; Par Dn 87-94; C 94; Hon Can Ch Ch 90-94; rtd 94. *Hermon, London Road, Bracknell, Berks RG12 2XH* Bracknell (01344) 427451

CLARKE, Martin Geoffrey. b 45. Dur Univ BA66. Wells Th Coll 67. **d** 69 **p** 70. C Atherstone *Cov* 69-72; C Keresley and Coundon 72-75; R Scorborough w Leconfield *York* 75-79; P-in-c Lockington w Lund 78-79; R Lockington and Lund and Scorborough w Leconfield 79-81; R Romsley *Worc* from 81; Chapl Halesowen Coll from 81. *The Rectory, St Kenelm's Road, Romsley, Halesowen, W Midlands B62 0PH* Romsley (01562) 710216

CLARKE, Martin Howard. b 47. AKC70. St Aug Coll Cant 70. **d** 71 **p** 72. C Saffron Walden w Wendens Ambo *Chelmsf* 71-74; C Ely 74-78; V Messing w Inworth *Chelmsf* 78-90; V Layer-de-la-Haye from 90. *45 Malting Green Road, Layer-de-la-Haye, Colchester CO2 0JJ* Layer-de-la-Haye (01206) 734243

CLARKE, Ms Mary Margaret. b 65. K Coll Lon BD86 AKC86. Linc Th Coll CMM89. **d** 89 **p** 94. Par Dn Northn St Jas *Pet* 89-93; Chapl Nene Coll of HE Northn 92-93; TD Cov Caludon *Cov* 93-94; TV from 94. *St Catherine's House, 7 St Catherine's Close, Coventry CV3 1EH* Coventry (01203) 635737

CLARKE, Maurice Fulford Lovell. b 12. Clare Coll Cam BA34 MA38. Wells Th Coll 35. **d** 36 **p** 37. R Ashley *Lich* 65-77; rtd 77; Perm to Offic *Heref* from 77. *8 St Mary's Mews, Ludlow, Shropshire SY8 1DZ* Ludlow (01584) 874111

CLARKE, Maurice Gordon. b 29. Lon Univ BSc52 MSc79. Westcott Ho Cam 52. **d** 54 **p** 55. Dir Past Counselling and Public Preacher *S'wark* 64-69; rtd 91. *Bancroft Cottage, Mill Green, Burston, Diss, Norfolk IP22 3TJ* Diss (01379) 741296

CLARKE, Maurice Harold. b 30. K Alfred's Coll Win CertEd56 Sussex Univ MA79 LCP69. Cuddesdon Coll 65. **d** 67 **p** 68. Hd Master Co Sec Sch Cowplain (Lower Sch) 67-72; Hon C Waterlooville *Portsm* 67-70; Hon C Fareham SS Pet and Paul 70-72; Hon C Higham and Merston *Roch* 72-83; Dep Hd Master Thameswiew High Sch 72-80; Hd Master Eltham Green Comp Sch 80-83; V Hamble le Rice *Win* 83-90; rtd 91; Perm to Offic *Chich* from 92. *10 Worcester Road, Chichester, W Sussex PO19 4DJ* Chichester (01243) 775646

CLARKE, Michael. b 39. Ely Th Coll 60. **d** 62 **p** 63. C S Stoneham *Win* 62-64; C Greenford H Cross *Lon* 64-69; Hon C Milton *Portsm* 69-74; Chapl St Jas Hosp Portsm 69-91; Chapl Hurstpierpoint Coll Hassocks 91-92; R Highnam, Lassington, Rudford, Tibberton etc *Glouc* from 92. *The*

Rectory, 13 Maidenhall, Highnam, Gloucester GL2 8DJ Gloucester (01452) 525567

CLARKE, Neil Malcolm. b 53. Solicitor 79 MLawSoc80. W Midl Minl Tr Course 89. **d** 92 **p** 93. NSM Desborough *Pet* from 92; NSM Brampton Ash w Dingley and Braybrooke from 92. *53 Breakleys Road, Desborough, Kettering, Northants NN14 2PT* Kettering (01536) 760667

CLARKE, Norman. b 28. Keble Coll Ox BA52 MA58. St Steph Ho Ox 52. **d** 54 **p** 55. Lic to Offic *Leic* 63-74; C Knighton St Mary Magd 74-81; Dioc Communications Officer 81-88; P-in-c Sproughton w Burstall *St E* 81-88; P-in-c Dunsford and Doddiscombsleigh *Ex* 88-95; P-in-c Cheriton Bishop 88-95; rtd 95. *78 Malden Road, Sidmouth, Devon EX10 9NA* Sidmouth (01395) 515849

CLARKE, Oswald Reeman. b 12. Liv Univ BA35 St Cath Soc Ox BA37 MA40. Ripon Hall Ox 34. **d** 36 **p** 37. V Upper Chelsea St Simon *Lon* 58-85; rtd 85; Perm to Offic *Lon* 85-90; P-in-c St Mary Abchurch from 90. *13 Down Quadrangle, Morden College, 19 St Germans Place, London SE3 0PW* 0181-293 1181

CLARKE, Canon Peter. b 25. Lon Univ BSc49 St Chad's Coll Dur DipTh51. **d** 51 **p** 52. V Bardney *Linc* 68-75; V Apley w Stainfield 68-75; V Linc St Nic w St Jo Newport 75-88; RD Christianity 78-85; Can and Preb Linc Cathl from 79; rtd 88. *46 Swallow Avenue, Skellingthorpe, Lincoln LN6 5XW* Lincoln (01522) 684261

CLARKE, Peter Gerald. b 38. Cuddesdon Coll 74. **d** 76 **p** 77. Hon C Marston Magna w Rimpton *B & W* 76-79; Hon C Queen Camel, Marston Magna, W Camel, Rimpton etc 79-87; Hon C Chilton Cantelo, Ashington, Mudford, Rimpton etc 87-88; R Tintinhull w Chilthorne Domer, Yeovil Marsh etc 88-94; TV Weston-super-Mare Cen Par from 94. *The Vicarage, 46 Manor Road, Weston-super-Mare, Avon BA23 2SU* Weston-super-Mare (01934) 623230

CLARKE, Philip John. b 44. Bris Univ BA65 Univ of Wales (Abth) DipEd66. N Ord Course 84. **d** 87 **p** 88. NSM Crewe Ch Ch and St Pet *Ches* 87-88; NSM Coppenhall 88-90; Lic to Offic 90-91; C Altrincham St Geo 91-95; C Odd Rode from 95. *53 Heath Avenue, Rode Heath, Stoke-on-Trent ST7 3RY* Alsager (01270) 877762

CLARKE, Richard Leon. b 37. Sarum Th Coll 62. **d** 65 **p** 66. C Fordington *Sarum* 65-68; C Haywards Heath St Rich *Chich* 68-72; C Goring-by-Sea 72-76; P-in-c Portslade St Andr 76-77; P-in-c Southwick St Pet 76-77; V Portslade St Pet and St Andr 77-79; R Clayton w Keymer from 79; RD Hurst from 90. *The Rectory, Keymer, Hassocks, W Sussex BN6 8RB* Hassocks (01273) 843570

CLARKE, Very Rev Richard Lionel. b 49. TCD BA71 MA79 PhD90 K Coll Lon BD75 AKC75. **d** 75 **p** 76. C Holywood *D & D* 75-77; C Dub St Bart w Ch Ch Leeson Park *D & G* 77-79; Dean of Residence TCD 79-84; I Bandon Union *C, C & R* 84-93; Dir of Ords 85-93; Cen Dir of Ords 82-93; Can Cork and Ross Cathls 91-93; Dean Cork from 93; I Cork St Fin Barre's Union from 93. *The Deanery, 9 Dean Street, Cork, Irish Republic* Cork (21) 964742 Fax as telephone

CLARKE, Dr Robert George. b 36. Natal Univ PhD83. Cranmer Hall Dur BA65 DipTh67. **d** 67 **p** 68. C Basingstoke *Win* 67-70; S Africa from 71. *26 Somerset Street, Grahamstown, 6140 South Africa* Grahamstown (461) 27803 or 311100

CLARKE, Robert Graham (Bob). b 28. S Dios Minl Tr Scheme 78. **d** 81 **p** 82. NSM Woolston *Win* 81-89; NSM Portswood St Denys 89-93; Chapl Torrevieja *Eur* 93-95; Perm to Offic *Win* from 95; Perm to Offic *Eur* from 95. *10 River Green, Hamble, Southampton SO31 4JA* Southampton (01703) 454230

CLARKE, Robert James. b 22. ACP58 DTh. CITC 67. **d** 69 **p** 70. C Belf St Mary *Conn* 69-70; C and Min Can Limerick Cathl *L & K* 70-72; Asst Chapl Wilson's Hosp Sch Multyfarnham 72-85; Chapl 85-87; Lic to Offic *M & K* from 87. *clo Mrs T Coleborn, 9 Punchestown Gate, Naas, Co Kildare, Irish Republic* Naas (45) 74416

CLARKE, Robert Michael (Bob). b 45. Oak Hill Th Coll BD71 Sarum & Wells Th Coll 78. **d** 78 **p** 79. Hon C Glastonbury St Jo w Godney *B & W* 78-81; Asst Hd Master Edington Sch 78-81; Chapl Felsted Sch Essex 81-84; Asst Chapl and Ho Master 85-92; Lic to Offic *Chelmsf* 85-92; Hd Master Brocksford Hall from 92; Lic to Offic *Derby* from 92. *Brocksford Hall, Doveridge, Ashbourne, Derbyshire DE6 5PA* Uttoxeter (01889) 562809 Fax 567972

CLARKE, Robert Sydney. b 35. AKC64. **d** 65 **p** 66. C Hendon St Mary *Lon* 65-69; C Langley Marish *Ox* 69-70; Chapl New Cross Hosp Wolv 70-74; Chapl Herrison Hosp Dorchester 74-80; Chapl Westmr Hosp Lon 80-85; Chapl R Hants Co Hosp Win from 85; Sen Chapl Win HA from 88; Chapl to The Queen from 87; Sec and Dir Tr Gen Syn Hosp Chapl Coun from 94; Perm to Offic *S'wark* from 95. *Royal Hants County Hospital, Romsey Road, Winchester, Hants SO22 5DG* Winchester (01962) 824906

CLARKE, Robert William. b 56. TCD DipTh83. d 83 p 84. C Cloughfern *Conn* 83-85; C Drumragh w Mountfield *D & R* 85-87; I Edenderry w Clanabogan from 87. *Edenderry Rectory, 91 Crevenagh Road, Omagh, Co Tyrone BT79 0EZ* Omagh (01662) 245525

CLARKE, Roger David. b 58. Man Univ BA Ox Univ MA. Ripon Coll Cuddesdon 80. d 83 p 84. C Frodsham *Ches* 83-86; C Wilmslow 86-88; V High Lane 88-93; V Heald Green St Cath from 93. *The Vicarage, 217 Outwood Road, Cheadle, Cheshire SK8 3JS* 0161-437 4614

CLARKE, Ronald George (Ron). b 31. Oak Hill Th Coll. d 64 p 65. V Bestwood St Matt *S'well* 68-76; V Barnsbury St Andr w St Thos and St Matthias *Lon* 76-77; V Barnsbury St Andr 77-78; V Barnsbury St Andr w H Trin 79-80; P-in-c Battle Bridge All SS w Pentonville St Jas 79-81; V Barnsbury St Andr and H Trin w All SS 81-86; TR Bath Twerton-on-Avon *B & W* 86-94; rtd 94; P-in-c Churchstanton, Buckland St Mary and Otterford *B & W* from 94. *The Rectory, Churchstanton, Taunton, Somerset TA3 7QE* Churchstanton (01823) 601570

CLARKE, Royston James. b 33. ALCD58. d 58 p 59. R Stockton *Cov* 65-72; P-in-c Leamington Priors St Mary 72-75; V 75-91; R Gunton St Pet *Nor* 91-94; rtd 94. *1 Water Lane, South Godstone, Godstone, Surrey RH9 8JX* South Godstone (01342) 892655

CLARKE, Thomas Percival. b 15. Univ of Wales BA39. Lich Th Coll 39. d 41 p 42. V Blackheath All SS *S'wark* 59-73; Chapl Charing Cross Hosp Lon 73-81; rtd 80. *1 Trenos Gardens, Llanharan, Pontyclun, M Glam CF7 9SZ* Llantrisant (01443) 227662

CLARKE, Ms Valerie. b 45. Nor Ord Course 91. d 94. NSM Ulverston St Mary w H Trin *Carl* from 94. *18 Church Walk, Ulverston, Cumbria LA12 7EN* Ulverston (01229) 586133

CLARKE, Valerie Diane. b 45. N Ord Course. d 95. NSM Sherburn and W and E Heslerton w Yedingham *York* from 95; C Sherburn in Elmet w Saxton from 95. *23 A Springfield Road, Sherburn in Elmet, Leeds LS25 6BU* Leeds (0113) 253 1789

CLARKE, Vernon Douglas. b 18. Jes Coll Cam BA48 MA50. Bps' Coll Cheshunt 47. d 49 p 50. V Millom H Trin *Carl* 63-71; V Cockermouth All SS w Ch Ch 71-74; P-in-c Kirkland 75-83; P-in-c Gt Salkeld 79-80; C Gt Salkeld w Lazonby 80-83; rtd 83; Perm to Offic *Carl* from 84. *Birchfield, Great Salkeld, Penrith, Cumbria CA11 9LW* Lazonby (01768) 898380

CLARKE, Mrs Yvonne Veronica. b 58. CA Tr Coll. dss 86 d 87 p 94. Nunhead St Silas *S'wark* 86-87; Par Dn 87-90; Par Dn Nunhead St Antony w St Silas 90-91; Par Dn Mottingham St Andr 91-94; C from 94. *St Alban's Parsonage, 132 William Barefoot Drive, London SE9 3BP* 0181-857 7702

CLARKSON, Ven Alan Geoffrey. b 34. Ch Coll Cam BA57 MA61. Wycliffe Hall Ox 57. d 59 p 60. C Penn *Lich* 59-60; C Oswestry St Oswald 60-63; C Wrington *B & W* 63-65; V Chewton Mendip w Emborough 65-74; Dioc Ecum Officer 65-75; V Glastonbury St Jo w Godney 74-84; P-in-c W Pennard 80-84; P-in-c Meare 81-84; P-in-c Glastonbury St Benedict 82-84; V Glastonbury w Meare, W Pennard and Godney 84; Hon Can Win Cathl *Win* from 84; Adn Win from 84; V Burley Ville from 84. *The Vicarage, Church Corner, Burley, Ringwood, Hants BH24 4AP* Burley (01425) 402303 Fax 403753

CLARKSON, David James. b 42. St Andr Univ BSc66. N Ord Course 85. d 88 p 89. NSM Slaithwaite w E Scammonden *Wakef* 88-89; C Morley St Pet w Churwell 89-91; R Cumberworth w Denby Dale 91-93; P-in-c Denby 91-93; R Cumberworth, Denby and Denby Dale from 93. *The Rectory, 43 Hollybank Avenue, Upper Cumberworth, Huddersfield HD8 8NY* Huddersfield (01484) 606225

CLARKSON, Eric George. b 22. St Jo Coll Dur BA48 DipTh50. d 50 p 51. V Blackb St Mich *Blackb* 66-75; V Blackb St Mich w St Jo 75; V Chapeltown *Sheff* 75-86; C Ranmoor 86-87; V Crosspool 87-92; rtd 92. *2 Harewood Drive, Filey, N Yorkshire YO14 0DE* Scarborough (01723) 513957

CLARKSON, Geoffrey. b 35. AKC61. d 62 p 63. C Shildon *Dur* 62-65; Asst Chapl HM Pris Liv 65-66; Chapl HM Borstal Feltham 66-71; Hon C Hampton St Mary *Lon* 71-90; Chapl HM Rem Cen Ashford 88-90; Chapl HM Pris Coldingley from 90; Chapl HM Pris Send from 92. *HM Prison Coldingley, Bisley, Woking, Surrey GU24 9EX* Brookwood (01483) 476721 Fax 488586

CLARKSON, John Thomas. b 30. AKC54. St Boniface Warminster 54. d 54 p 55. C Luton St Sav *St Alb* 54-59; Australia 59-73 and from 77; V Dallington *Pet* 73-77. *88 Adelaide Street, Blayney, NSW, Australia 2799* Orange (63) 682065

CLARKSON, Michael Livingston. b 48. California Univ BA70 Loyola Univ JD73. Wycliffe Hall Ox 87. d 89 p 90. C Kensington St Barn *Lon* 89-93; Min Oaktree Angl Fellowship from 93. *17 Devonport Road, London W12 8NZ* 0181-743 2784

CLARKSON, Richard. b 33. Man Univ BSc54 Ball Coll Ox DPhil57. Oak Hill Th Coll 89. d 91 p 92. NSM Sunnyside w Bourne End *St Alb* from 91. *Kingsmead, Gravel Path, Berkhamsted, Herts HP4 2PH* Berkhamsted (01442) 873014

CLARKSON, Richard Michael. b 38. St Jo Coll Dur BA60 Lanc Univ PGCE68. Cranmer Hall Dur DipTh62. d 62 p 63. Asst Master Kirkham Gr Sch 68-90; Lic to Offic *Blackb* 69-90; Asst Master Hurstpierpoint Coll 90-91; Asst Master St Mary's Hall Brighton from 92; rtd 93. *West Lowe, Malthouse Lane, Hurstpierpoint, Hassocks, W Sussex BN6 9JY* Brighton (01273) 835094

CLARKSON, Robert Christopher. b 32. Dur Univ BA53 DipEd54. S Dios Minl Tr Scheme 85. d 87 p 88. NSM Wonston and Stoke Charity w Hunton *Win* from 87. *27 Wrights Way, South Wonston, Winchester, Hants SO21 3HE* Winchester (01962) 881692

CLARRIDGE, Donald Michael. b 41. DipOT86. Oak Hill Th Coll 63. d 66 p 67. C Newc St Barn and St Jude *Newc* 66-70; C Pennycross *Ex* 70-76; R Clayhanger 76-83; R Petton 76-83; R Huntsham 76-83; V Bampton 76-83. *5 Surrey Close, Tunbridge Wells, Kent TN2 5RF* Tunbridge Wells (01892) 533796

CLASBY, Michael Francis Theodore. b 37. Lon Univ BA59. Chich Th Coll 59. d 61 p 62. C Leigh-on-Sea St Marg *Chelmsf* 61-64; C Forest Gate St Edm 64-69; V Walthamstow St Mich 69-70; Chapl Community of Sisters of the Love of God 87-89; Perm to Offic *St Alb* 87-89; NSM Hemel Hempstead 90-93; Perm to Offic from 93. *47 Wrensfield, Hemel Hempstead, Herts HP1 1RP* Hemel Hempstead (01442) 254400

CLASPER, John. b 42. AKC67. d 68 p 69. C Leeds All Hallows w St Simon *Ripon* 68-71; C Hawksworth Wood 72-74; Ind Chapl *Dur* from 74; TV Jarrow St Paul 75-77; TV Jarrow 77-91; Dioc Urban Development Officer 90-91; TR E Darlington from 91. *East Darlington House, 30 Smithfield Road, Darlington, Co Durham DL1 4DD* Darlington (01325) 369523

CLASSON, Michael Campbell. b 32. TCD BA52 HDipEd54 MA55. CITC 87. d 89 p 91. NSM Conwal Union w Gartan *D & R* 89-90; NSM Ardara w Glencolumbkille, Inniskeel etc from 90. *Summy, Portnoo, Co Donegal, Irish Republic* Portnoo (75) 45242

CLATWORTHY, Jonathan Richard. b 48. Univ of Wales BA70. Sarum & Wells Th Coll 71. d 76 p 77. C Man Resurr *Man* 76-78; C Bolton St Pet 78-81; V Ashton St Pet 81-85; Chapl Sheff Univ *Sheff* 85-91; V Denstone w Ellastone and Stanton Lich from 91. *The Vicarage, Denstone, Uttoxeter, Staffs ST14 5HF* Rocester (01889) 590263

CLAUSEN, John Frederick. b 37. Sarum Th Coll 65. d 68 p 69. C Kentish Town St Jo *Lon* 68-71; C Rainham *Roch* 71-77; R Stone 77-89; Lic to Dartford RD from 89. *14 Watling Street, Dartford DA1 1RF* Dartford (01322) 279570

CLAWSON, Derek George. b 35. AMCST62. Qu Coll Birm 63. d 66 p 67. C Ditton St Mich *Liv* 66-70; C Speke All SS 70-72; V Hindley Green 72-85; V Wigan St Mich from 85. *St Michael's Vicarage, Duke Street, Wigan, Lancs WN1 2DN* Wigan (01942) 42381

CLAXTON, Leslie Edward Mitchell. b 20. MC46. ARCM61 Peterho Cam BA33 MA48. Cuddesdon Coll 34. d 35 p 36. R St Olave Hart Street w All Hallows Staining etc *Lon* 68-85; rtd 85. *Flat 5, 83 St George's Drive, London SW1V 4DB* 0171-834 9407

CLAY, Colin Peter. b 32. Ch Coll Cam BA55 MA59. Em Coll Saskatoon Hon DD91 Wells Th Coll 55. d 57 p 58. C Malden St Jas *S'wark* 57-59; Canada from 59; Asst Prof Relig Studies Laurentian Univ 69-72. *College of Emmanuel and St Chad, 1337 College Drive, Saskatoon, Saskatchewan, Canada, S7N 0W6* Saskatoon (306) 966-8500

CLAY, Elizabeth Jane. b 50. Ridley Hall Cam. dss 86 d 87 p 94. Birstall *Wakef* 86-87; Hon Par Dn Lupset 87-90; Par Dn 90-94; C from 94. *The Vicarage, Broadway, Lupset, Wakefield, W Yorkshire WF2 8AA* Wakefield (01924) 373088

CLAY, Geoffrey. b 51. CertEd. Ridley Hall Cam. d 86 p 87. C Birstall *Wakef* 86-90; V Lupset from 90. *The Vicarage, Broadway, Lupset, Wakefield, W Yorkshire WF2 8AA* Wakefield (01924) 373088

CLAY, Peter Herbert. b 31. Lich Th Coll 62. d 64 p 65. C Ross *Heref* 64-67; C Leamington Priors All SS *Cov* 67-70; P-in-c Temple Grafton w Binton 70-73; V 73-75; P-in-c Exhall w Wixford 70-73; V 73-75; TV Cen Telford *Lich* 75-86; USPG 86-90; V Loughb Gd Shep *Leic* from 90. *Good Shepherd Vicarage, 2 Howe Road, Loughborough, Leics LE11 2JJ* Loughborough (01509) 211005

CLAY, Timothy Francis (Tim). b 61. St Mark & St Jo Coll Lon BA85 Ealing Coll of Educn 89. Linc Th Coll CMinlStuds95.

d 95. C Wickford and Runwell *Chelmsf* from 95. *8 Honington Close, Wickford, Essex SS11 8XB* Wickford (01268) 561044

CLAYDEN, David Edward. b 42. Oak Hill Th Coll 74. **d** 76 **p** 77. C Worksop St Jo *S'well* 76-79; V Clarborough w Hayton 79-84; C Bloxwich *Lich* 87-90; TV 90-93; TV Tollington *Lon* from 93. *Emmanuel Vicarage, 145 Hornsey Road, London N7 6DU* 0171-700 7110

CLAYDON, Preb Graham Leonard. b 43. K Coll Lon BA65. Clifton Th Coll 66. **d** 68 **p** 69. C Walthamstow St Mary w St Steph *Chelmsf* 68-73; Hon C St Marylebone All So w SS Pet and Jo *Lon* 73-81; V Islington St Mary from 81; Preb St Paul's Cathl from 92. *St Mary's Vicarage, Upper Street, London N1 2TX* 0171-226 3400 or 354 3427

CLAYDON, John Richard. b 38. St Jo Coll Cam BA61 MA65. Trin Coll Bris DipTh72. **d** 73 **p** 74. C Finchley Ch Ch *Lon* 73-76; Asst Chapl K Edw Sch Witley 76-77; C Macclesfield St Mich *Ches* 77-81; V Marple All SS 81-91; CMJ from 91; Israel from 91. *Immanuel House, PO Box 2773, Tel Aviv 61027, Israel* Tel Aviv (3) 821459

CLAYPOLE WHITE, Douglas Eric. b 29. FCA ATII. St Alb Minl Tr Scheme 77. **d** 80 **p** 81. NSM Sharnbrook and Knotting w Souldrop *St Alb* 80-82; NSM Felmersham 82-87; P-in-c from 87. *Homelands, High Street, Turvey, Bedford MK43 8DB* Turvey (01234) 881661

CLAYTON, Canon Anthony Edwin Hay. b 36. Sarum Th Coll 61. **d** 63 **p** 64. C Tooting All SS *S'wark* 63-68; Perm to Offic *Leic* 69-74; Perm to Offic *S'well* 73-80; Hon C Lockington w Hemington *Leic* 74-80; P-in-c Eastwell 80-83; P-in-c Eaton 80-83; P-in-c Croxton Kerrial, Knipton, Harston, Branston etc 83-84; R 84-93; R High Framland Par from 93; Chapl Belvoir Castle from 85; RD Framland (Melton) 90-94; Hon Can Leic Cathl from 92. *High Framland Rectory, Harston, Grantham, Lincs NG32 1PP* Grantham (01476) 870329

CLAYTON, Geoffrey Buckroyd. b 26. Newc Univ BA67. Roch Th Coll 62. **d** 64 **p** 65. C Newc St Geo *Newc* 64-67; C Byker St Ant 67-68; C Cheddleton *Lich* 69-72; V Arbory *S & M* from 72; RD Castletown from 82; V Santan from 88. *Arbory Vicarage, Ballabeg, Castletown, Isle of Man IM9 4LG* Castletown (01624) 823595

CLAYTON, George Hamilton. b 42. Strathclyde Univ BSc65. S'wark Ord Course 90. **d** 93 **p** 94. NSM Send *Guildf* from 93. *137 Knightswood, Woking, Surrey GU21 3PX* Woking (01483) 720698

CLAYTON, Canon Giles. b 21. Keble Coll Ox BA42 MA47. St Steph Ho Ox 42. **d** 44 **p** 45. R Durrington *Sarum* 52-70; RD Avon 67-70; R Salisbury St Martin 70-86; RD Salisbury 72-77; Can and Preb Sarum Cathl 73-92; rtd 86; Master St Nic Hosp Salisbury from 86. *9 Fisherton Island, Salisbury SP2 7TG* Salisbury (01722) 320177

CLAYTON, Canon John. b 11. Leeds Univ BA33 MA43. Wells Th Coll 34. **d** 35 **p** 36. V Otley *Bradf* 65-76; rtd 76; Perm to Offic *Bradf* from 76; Perm to Offic *Ripon* from 76. *10 Sandy Walk, Bramhope, Leeds LS16 9DW* Leeds (0113) 261 1388

CLAYTON, Dr Melanie Yvonne. b 62. St Aid Coll Dur BA84 Victoria Univ (BC) MA85 Hertf Coll Ox DPhil89. W Midl Minl Tr Course 91. **d** 94 **p** 95. C Penn *Lich* from 94. *105 Brenton Road, Penn, Wolverhampton WV4 5NS* Wolverhampton (01902) 335439

CLAYTON, Michael John. b 32. Ox NSM Course. **d** 79 **p** 80. NSM Wokingham St Paul *Ox* 79-81; C 82-84; C Christchurch *Win* 84-95; rtd 95. *37 Ridgefield Gardens, Christchurch, Dorset BH23 4QG* Highcliffe (01425) 276267

CLAYTON, Norman James. b 24. AKC52. **d** 53 **p** 54. S Africa 60-78; Dioc Communications Officer *Derby* 78-88; P-in-c Risley 78-87; R 87-89; rtd 89; Perm to Offic *Derby* from 89. *6 Allendale Avenue, Beeston, Nottingham NG9 6AN* Nottingham (0115) 925 0060

CLAYTON, Sydney Cecil Leigh. b 38. Pemb Coll Ox BA62 MA65 Lon Univ BD65. Linc Th Coll. **d** 65 **p** 66. C Birch St Jas *Man* 65-68; Lect Bolton Par Ch 68-77; V Denshaw from 77. *The Vicarage, Huddersfield Road, Denshaw, Oldham OL3 5SB* Saddleworth (01457) 874575

CLAYTON, Wilfred. b 10. Worc Ord Coll 57. **d** 59 **p** 60. R Whitwell *Derby* 68-73; P-in-c Calow 74-77; rtd 77; Perm to Offic *Derby* from 77. *The Haven, Hodthorpe, Worksop, Notts S80 4UZ* Worksop (01909) 720006

CLAYTON, William Alan. b 32. Liv Univ BSc54 Lon Univ BD60. **d** 63 **p** 64. C Wallasey St Hilary *Ches* 63-67; R Burton Agnes w Harpham *York* 67-69; V Batley St Thos *Wakef* 69-72; Lic to Offic *Ripon* 73-85; Hon C Grinton 75-85; R Barningham w Hutton Magna and Wycliffe from 85. *The Rectory, Barningham, Richmond, N Yorkshire DL11 7DW* Teesdale (01833) 621217

CLAYTON-JONES, Roger Francis. b 39. AKC64. **d** 66 **p** 67. C Oxton *Ches* 66-69; Asst Chapl R Hosp Sch Ipswich 69-71; Jamaica 71-73; CF 73-93; Chapl St Mary's Sch Wantage from 93. *Alma House, 35 Newbury Street, Wantage, Oxon OX12 8DJ* Wantage (01235) 763617

CLEAR, Peter Basil. b 13. New Coll Ox BA35 MA40. Chich Th Coll 35. **d** 36 **p** 37. R Pen Selwood *B & W* 52-68; rtd 69. *21 Portland Court, Lyme Regis, Dorset DT7 3ND* Lyme Regis (01297) 442273

CLEASBY, Very Rev Thomas Wood Ingram. b 20. Magd Coll Ox BA47 MA47. Cuddesdon Coll 47. **d** 49 **p** 50. V Chesterfield All SS *Derby* 63-70; Hon Can Derby Cathl 63-78; Adn Chesterfield 63-78; R Morton 70-78; Dean Ches 78-86; rtd 86; Perm to Offic *Carl* from 86; Perm to Offic *Bradf* from 87. *Low Barth, Dent, Sedbergh, Cumbria LA10 5SZ* Dent (015396) 25476

CLEATON, John. S Dios Minl Tr Scheme. **d** 92 **p** 93. NSM Wareham *Sarum* from 92. *1 Avon Drive, Wareham, Dorset BH20 4EL* Wareham (01929) 553149

CLEAVER, Gerald. b 20. Lon Univ BSc52. St Jo Coll Nottm 85. **d** 86 **p** 87. NSM W Bridgford *S'well* from 86. *62 South Road, Nottingham NG2 7AH* Nottingham (0115) 981 0196

CLEAVER, Gordon Philip. b 29. SW Minl Tr Course. **d** 78 **p** 79. NSM St Ruan w St Grade *Truro* 78-86; Perm to Offic from 86. *Bryn-Mor, Cadgwith, Ruan Minor, Helston, Cornwall TR12 7JZ* The Lizard (01326) 290328

CLEAVER, John Martin. b 42. K Coll Lon BD64 AKC64. St Boniface Warminster 61. **d** 65 **p** 66. C Bexley St Mary *Roch* 65-69; C Ealing St Steph Castle Hill *Lon* 69-71; P-in-c Bostall Heath *Roch* 71-76; V Green Street Green 76-85; Primary Adv Lon Dioc Bd for Schs *Lon* 85-92; V Teddington St Mary w St Alb from 92. *The Vicarage, 11 Twickenham Road, Teddington, Middx TW11 8AQ* 0181-977 2767

CLEAVER, Stuart Douglas. b 46. ACIS. Oak Hill Th Coll. **d** 83 **p** 84. C Portsdown *Portsm* 83-86; C Blendworth w Chalton w Idsworth etc 86-88; P-in-c Whippingham w E Cowes from 88. *The Rectory, 73 Cambridge Road, East Cowes, Isle of Wight PO32 6AH* Isle of Wight (01983) 292130

CLEEVE, Admire William. b 43. ACIS78 MBIM81 CPPS83. Sierra Leone Th Hall 78. **d** 82 **p** 83. Sierra Leone 82-86; NSM Douglas St Geo and St Barn *S & M* 87-91; TV Langley Marish *Ox* from 91. *Christ the Worker Vicarage, Parlaunt Road, Slough SL3 8BB* Slough (01753) 545167

CLEEVE, Martin. b 43. ACP67 Open Univ BA80. Bp Otter Coll TCert65 Oak Hill Th Coll 69. **d** 72 **p** 73. C Margate H Trin *Cant* 72-76; V Southminster *Chelmsf* 76-86; Perm to Offic from 86; Teacher Castle View Sch Canvey Is 86-91; Hd RE Bromfords Sch Wickford from 91. *44 Ditton Court Road, Westcliffe-on-Sea, Essex SS0 7HF*

CLEEVES, David John. b 56. Univ of Wales (Lamp) BA Fitzw Coll Cam MA85. Westcott Ho Cam. **d** 82 **p** 83. C Cuddington *Guildf* 82-85; C Dorking w Ranmore 85-87; V Sandal St Fran 87-94; P-in-c Rotherfield w Mark Cross *Chich* from 94. *The Rectory, Rotherfield, Crowborough, E Sussex TN6 3LU* Rotherfield (01892885) 2536

CLEGG, David Kneeshaw. b 46. N Ord Course 77. **d** 80 **p** 81. C Briercliffe *Blackb* 80-83; Chapl Lancs (Preston) Poly 83-89; rtd 89. *Field House, Albert Street, Durham DH1 4RL* 0191-386 5806

CLEGG, Herbert. b 24. Fitzw Ho Cam BA59 MA63 Bris Univ MA65. Sarum Th Coll 52. **d** 54 **p** 55. P-in-c Aldsworth *Glouc* 70-75; P-in-c Sherborne w Windrush 70-75; V Marcham w Garford *Ox* 75-83; R Chipping Warden w Edgcote and Aston le Walls *Pet* 83-89; rtd 89; C Ox St Giles and SS Phil and Jas w St Marg *Ox* 90-94. *6 Floreys Close, Hailey, Witney, Oxford OX8 5UG* Witney (01993) 700281

CLEGG, Jeffrey Thomas. b 50. Padgate Coll of Educn BEd79 DAES85. N Ord Course 87. **d** 90 **p** 91. C Gateacre *Liv* 90-93; V W Derby Gd Shep 93-94; V Wigan St Cath from 94. *St Catharine's Vicarage, St Catharine Terrace, Wigan, Lancs WN1 3JW* Wigan (01942) 820668

CLEGG, John Anthony Holroyd. b 44. Kelham Th Coll 65. **d** 70 **p** 71. C St Annes *Blackb* 70-74; C Lanc St Mary 74-76; V Lower Darwen St Jas 76-80; TV Shaston *Sarum* 80-86; Chapl HM Youth Cust Cen Guys Marsh 80-86; R Poulton-le-Sands w Morecambe St Laur *Blackb* from 86; RD Lanc 89-94. *The Rectory, Church Walk, Morecambe, Lancs LA4 5PR* Morecambe (01524) 410941

CLEGG, John Lovell. b 48. Qu Coll Ox BA70 MA74. Trin Coll Bris DipTh75. **d** 75 **p** 76. C Barrow St Mark *Carl* 75-79; R S Levenshulme *Man* from 79. *St Andrew's Rectory, 27 Errwood Road, Levenshulme, Manchester M19 2PN* 0161-224 5877

CLEGG, Peter Douglas. b 49. Sarum & Wells Th Coll 83. **d** 85 **p** 86. C Hangleton *Chich* 85-88; C-in-c Portslade Gd Shep CD 88-94; V Portslade Gd Shep from 94. *35 Stanley Avenue, Portslade, Brighton, E Sussex BN41 2WH* Brighton (01273) 419518

CLEGG, Roger Alan. b 46. St Jo Coll Dur BA68 Nottm Univ DipTh76. St Jo Coll Nottm 75. **d** 78 **p** 79. C Harwood *Man* 78-81; TV Sutton St Jas and Wawne *York* 81-87; V Kirk Fenton w Kirkby Wharfe and Ulleskelfe from 87; OCF from 87. *The Vicarage, Church Street, Church Fenton, Tadcaster, N Yorkshire LS24 9RD* Tadcaster (01937) 557387

CLELAND, Richard. b 26. MPS47. St Aid Birkenhead 58. **d** 60 **p** 61. C Lisburn Ch Ch *Conn* 60-63; C Ballynafeigh St Jude *D & D* 63-66; C Portman Square St Paul *Lon* 66-67; V Ilkley All SS *Bradf* 67-83; Master Wyggeston's Hosp Leic from 83. *The Master's House, Wyggeston's Hospital, Hinkley Road, Leicester LE3 0UX* Leicester (0116) 254 8682 or 254 1803

CLEMAS, Nigel Antony. b 53. Wycliffe Hall Ox. **d** 83 **p** 84. C Bootle St Mary w St Paul *Liv* 83-87; V Kirkdale St Mary and St Athanasius 87-91; TV Netherthorpe *Sheff* 91-93; V Netherthorpe St Steph from 93. *The Rectory, 115 Upperthorpe Road, Sheffield S6 3EA* Sheffield (0114) 276 7130

CLEMENCE, Paul Robert Fraser. b 50. MRTPI82 Man Univ DipTP74 St Edm Hall Ox MA90. Wycliffe Hall Ox 88. **d** 90 **p** 91. C Lanc St Mary *Blackb* 90-94; Chapl HM Pris Lanc 90-94; V Lt Thornton *Blackb* from 94. *St John's Vicarage, 35 Station Road, Thornton-Cleveleys, Blackpool FY5 5HY* Cleveleys (01253) 825107

CLEMENT, Miss Barbara Winifred. b 20. Gilmore Ho 49. **dss** 56 **d** 87. Hd Dss *Guildf* 66-74; Dioc Adv Lay Min 74-82; Frimley 74-82; Frimley Hosp 74-87; rtd 82; Perm to Offic *Guildf* from 82. *9 Merlin Court, The Cloisters, Frimley, Camberley, Surrey GU16 5JN* Camberley (01276) 22527

CLEMENT, Peter James. b 64. UMIST BSc88. Qu Coll Birm 89. **d** 92 **p** 93. C Grange St Andr *Ches* 92-95; C Man Apostles w Miles Platting *Man* from 95. *116A Victoria Square, Manchester M4 5EA* 0161-237 1955

CLEMENT, Thomas Gwyn. b 51. Lon Univ BMus73 Golds Coll Lon PGCE74. St Steph Ho Ox DipMin93. **d** 93 **p** 94. C Friern Barnet St Jas *Lon* from 94. *2 Hatley Close, London N11 3LN* 0181-361 9228

CLEMENT, Timothy Gordon (Tim). b 54. Usk Coll of Agric NCA75 OND76. Trin Coll Bris 92. **d** 94 **p** 95. C Chepstow *Mon* from 94. *St Christopher's House, Bulwark Road, Bulwark, Chepstow, Gwent NP6 5JW* Chepstow (01291) 625054

CLEMENTS, Alan Austin. b 39. ACIB66 Newc Univ MA93. Linc Th Coll 74. **d** 76 **p** 77. C Woodley St Jo the Ev *Ox* 76-79; C Wokingham All SS 79-83; V Felton *Newc* 83-95; P-in-c Wallsend St Pet from 95. *St Peter's Rectory, Wallsend, Tyne & Wear NE28 6PY* 0191-262 3852

CLEMENTS, Andrew. b 48. K Coll Lon BD72 AKC72. St Aug Coll Cant 72. **d** 73 **p** 74. C Langley All SS and Martyrs *Man* 73-76; C Westhoughton 76-81; R Thornton Dale and Ellerburne w Wilton *York* 81-89; Prec Leic Cathl *Leic* 89-91; V Market Weighton *York* from 91; R Goodmanham from 91. *The Vicarage, 38 Cliffe Road, Market Weighton, York YO4 3BN* Market Weighton (01430) 873230

CLEMENTS, Doris Thomasina Sara. b 46. TCD BA MA. **d** 95. NSM Killala w Dunfeeny, Crossmolina, Kilmoremoy etc *T, K & A* from 95. *Doobeg House, Bunnadadden, Ballymote, Co Sligo, Irish Republic*

CLEMENTS, Edwin George. b 41. Chich Th Coll 77. **d** 79 **p** 80. C Didcot St Pet *Ox* 79-83; C Brixham w Churston Ferrers *Ex* 83; TV 84-86; TV Brixham w Churston Ferrers and Kingswear 86-88; P-in-c Hagbourne *Ox* 88; V 88-90; P-in-c Blewbury 89-90; P-in-c Upton 89-90; R Blewbury, Hagbourne and Upton from 90. *The Rectory, Blewbury, Didcot, Oxon OX11 9QH* Blewbury (01235) 850267 Fax 850267

CLEMENTS, John Derek Howard. b 65. Man Univ BA88. St Steph Ho Ox 88. **d** 90 **p** 91. C Ex St Jas *Ex* 90-93; TV Withycombe Raleigh from 93. *All Saints Vicarage, Church Road, Exmouth, Devon EX8 1RZ* Exmouth (01395) 263572

CLEMENTS, Miss Mary Holmes. b 43. Bedf Coll Lon BA64 Lon Bible Coll DipTh66 Lon Univ CertEd69. Ox Min Course DipMin94. **d** 94. NSM High Wycombe *Ox* from 94. *2 Firs Close, Hazlemere, High Wycombe, Bucks HP15 7TF* Penn (01494) 814707

CLEMENTS, Philip Christian. b 38. K Coll Lon BD64 AKC64. **d** 65 **p** 66. C S Norwood St Mark *Cant* 65-68; Chapl R Russell Sch Croydon 68-75; Asst Chapl Denstone Coll Uttoxeter 75-76; Chapl 76-81; Chapl Lancing Coll W Sussex 82-90; R Ninfield *Chich* from 90; V Hooe from 90. *The Rectory, Church Lane, Ninfield, Battle, E Sussex TN33 9JW* Ninfield (01424) 892308

CLEMENTS, Philip John Charles. b 42. Nottm Univ CertEd64. Ridley Hall Cam. **d** 85 **p** 86. C Aylestone St Andr w St Jas *Leic* 85-87; P-in-c Swinford w Catthorpe, Shawell and Stanford 87-91; V from 91; RD Guthlaxton II (Lutterworth) from 94. *The Vicarage, Kilworth Road, Swinford, Lutterworth, Leics LE17 6BQ* Rugby (01788) 860221

CLEMENTS, Canon Roy Adrian. b 44. Dur Univ BA68 DipTh69 MA. St Chad's Coll Dur 65. **d** 69 **p** 70. C Royston *Wakef* 69-73; V Clifton 73-77; V Rastrick St Matt 77-84; V Horbury Junction 84-92; Dioc Communications Officer from 84; Bp's Chapl from 92; Hon Can Wakef Cathl from 94. *Bishop's Lodge, Woodthorpe Lane, Wakefield, W Yorkshire WF2 6JJ* Wakefield (01924) 255349 Fax 250202

CLEMETSON, Thomas Henry. b 22. **d** 62 **p** 63. V Hurdsfield *Ches* 65-76; V Stockport St Sav 76-88; rtd 88. *23 Old Field*

Crescent, Lache Lane, Chester CH4 7PD Chester (01244) 676492

CLEMETT, Peter Thomas. b 33. Univ of Wales (Lamp) BA60. Sarum Th Coll 59. **d** 61 **p** 62. CF 66-88; Chapl R Memorial Chpl Sandhurst 84-88; rtd 88. *clo MOD (Army), Bagshot Park, Bagshot, Surrey GU19 5PL* Bagshot (01276) 471717 Fax 412834

CLENCH, Brian Henry Ross. b 31. Ripon Coll Cuddesdon. **d** 82 **p** 83. C Fulham All SS *Lon* 82-85; Ind Chapl *Truro* 85-92; P-in-c St Mewan 85-92; rtd 92. *The Old Post Office, Stoke Abbot, Beaminster, Dorset DT8 3JT*

CLENDON, David Arthur. b 33. Em Coll Cam BA56 MA61. Wells Th Coll 56. **d** 58 **p** 59. P-in-c Luton Ch Ch *St Alb* 71-76; V Caddington 65-71; P-in-c Pirton 75-85; V 85-91; P-in-c Offley w Lilley 85-88; rtd 91. *1 Docklands, Pirton, Hitchin, Herts SG5 3QF* Hitchin (01462) 712741

CLEVELAND, Michael Robin. b 52. Warw Univ BA73. St Jo Coll Nottm 86 Serampore Th Coll BD88. **d** 88 **p** 89. C Bushbury *Lich* 88-92; V Foleshill St Laur *Cov* from 92. *St Laurence's Vicarage, 142 Old Church Road, Coventry CV6 7ED* Coventry (01203) 688271

CLEVELAND, Archdeacon of. See HAWTHORN, Ven Christopher John

CLEVERLEY, Michael Frank. b 36. Man Univ BScTech57. Wells Th Coll 61. **d** 63 **p** 64. C Halifax St Aug *Wakef* 63; C Huddersfield St Jo 63-66; C Brighouse 66-69; V Gomersal 69-83; P-in-c Clayton W w High Hoyland 83-89; P-in-c Scissett St Aug 83-89; R High Hoyland, Scissett and Clayton W from 89. *The Rectory, Church Lane, Clayton West, Huddersfield HD8 9LY* Huddersfield (01484) 862321

CLEVERLY, Charles St George (Charlie). b 51. Ox Univ MA. Trin Coll Bris. **d** 82 **p** 83. C Cranham Park *Chelmsf* 82-89; V 89-92; BCMS 92-93; Crosslinks from 93. *clo Crosslinks, 251 Lewisham Way, London SE4 1XF* 0181-691 6111 Fax 694 8023

CLEWS, Nicholas. b 57. CIPFA85 SS Coll Cam BA80 MA84 Leeds Univ BA87. Coll of Resurr Mirfield 85. **d** 88 **p** 89. C S Elmsall *Wakef* 88-91; V Featherstone from 91. *All Saints' Vicarage, Featherstone, Pontefract, W Yorkshire WF7 6AH* Pontefract (01977) 792280

CLIFF, Frank Graham. b 38. Lon Univ DipTh66. Clifton Th Coll. **d** 66 **p** 67. C Park Estate St Chris CD *Leic* 66-69; C Whitton and Thurleston w Akenham *St E* 69-71; USA from 71. *210 Spring Hill Road, Honesdale, Pennsylvania 18431, USA*

CLIFF, Philip Basil. b 15. Lon Univ BSc61 Birm Univ PhD. Independent Coll Bradf. **d** 77 **p** 77. Hon C Northfield *Birm* 77-91; Perm to Offic from 91. *4 Fox Hill Close, Birmingham B29 4AH* 0121-472 1556

CLIFFORD, Douglas Newson. b 16. St And Dioc Tr Course 81. **d** 83 **p** 84. NSM Strontian *Arg* from 83; NSM Fort William from 83; NSM Kinlochmoidart from 83; Bp's Dom Chapl from 83. *Bellsgrove Lodge, Strontian, Acharacle, Argyll PH36 4JB* Strontian (01967) 2152

CLIFFORD, Raymond Augustine. b 45. Birkb Coll Lon CertRS91. Coll of Resurr Mirfield 91. **d** 93 **p** 94. C Saltdean *Chich* from 93. *129 Rodmell Avenue, Saltdean, Brighton BN2 8PH* Brighton (01273) 309546

CLIFT, Norman Charles. b 21. Kelham Th Coll 40. **d** 45 **p** 46. V Leytonstone St Marg w St Columba *Chelmsf* 61-75; V Gt and Lt Bardfield 75-91; rtd 91. *Squirrels, High Street, Great Chesterford, Saffron Walden, Essex CB10 1TL* Saffron Walden (01799) 531319

CLIFTON, Robert Walter. b 39. Solicitor. Westcott Ho Cam 82. **d** 84 **p** 85. C Bury St Edmunds St Geo *St E* 84-87; P-in-c Culford, W Stow and Wordwell 87-88; R Culford, W Stow and Wordwell w Flempton etc from 88; RD Thingoe from 93; P-in-c Fornham All SS and St Martin w Timworth from 93. *The Rectory, West Stow, Bury St Edmunds, Suffolk IP28 6ET* Culford (01284) 728556

CLIFTON, Canon Roger Gerald. b 45. ACA70 FCA. Sarum & Wells Th Coll 70. **d** 73 **p** 74. C Winterbourne *Bris* 73-76; P-in-c Brislington St Cuth 76-83; P-in-c Colerne w N Wraxall 83-95; RD Chippenham 88-94; Hon Can Bris Cathl from 94; TR Gtr Corsham from 95. *The Rectory, Newlands Road, Corsham, Wilts SN13 0BS* Corsham (01249) 713232

CLIFTON-SMITH, Gregory James. b 52. GGSM73 Lon Univ TCert74 Golds Coll Lon BMus82. Sarum & Wells Th Coll 87. **d** 89 **p** 90. C Welling *S'wark* 89-93; V Tattenham Corner and Burgh Heath *Guildf* from 93. *St Mark's Vicarage, St Mark's Road, Epsom, Surrey KT18 5RD* Burgh Heath (01737) 353011

CLINCH, Christopher James. b 60. Nottm Univ BEd82 BTh89. Linc Th Coll 86. **d** 89 **p** 90. C Newc St Geo *Newc* 89-92; C Seaton Hirst 92-94; TV Ch the King in the Dio of Newc from 94. *The Vicarage, 2 East Acres, Dinnington, Newcastle upon Tyne NE13 7NA* Dinnington (01661) 871377

CLINCH, Kenneth Wilfred. b 22. Bps' Coll Cheshunt 62. **d** 64 **p** 65. C Lancing St Mich *Chich* 67-73; R Upper St Leonards St Jo 73-88; rtd 88. *Brae Cottage, 193 Hastings Road, Battle, E Sussex TN33 0TP* Battle (01424) 774130

CLITHEROW, Andrew. b 50. St Chad's Coll Dur BA72 Ex Univ MPhil87. Sarum & Wells Th Coll 78. **d** 79 **p** 80. Hon C Bedf Ch Ch *St Alb* 79-84; Asst Chapl Bedf Sch 79-84; Chapl Caldicott Sch Farnham Royal 84-85; C Penkridge w Stretton *Lich* 85-88; Min Acton Trussell w Bednall 85-88; Chapl Rossall Sch Fleetwood 89-94; V Scotforth *Blackb* from 94. *St Paul's Vicarage, 24 Scotforth Road, Lancaster LA1 4ST* Lancaster (01524) 32106

CLOCKSIN (nee HOYLE), Mrs Pamela Margaret. b 61. Nottm Univ BA82. St Jo Coll Nottm 84. **d** 87 **p** 94. Par Dn Bulwell St Jo *S'well* 87-91; Cam Pastorate Chapl 91-95; Par Dn Cam H Trin w St Andr Gt *Ely* 91-92; C Cam H Trin 92-95. *78 Windsor Road, Cambridge CB4 3JN* Cambridge (01223) 464922

CLOCKSIN, Dr William Frederick. b 55. BA76 St Cross Coll Ox MA81 Trin Hall Cam MA87 PhD93. E Anglian Minl Tr Course 91. **d** 94 **p** 95. Asst Chapl Trin Hall Cam from 94. *Trinity Hall, Cambridge CB2 1TJ* Cambridge (01223) 332543 Fax 334678

CLODE, Arthur Raymond Thomas. b 35. Roch Th Coll 67. **d** 69 **p** 70. C Blackheath *Birm* 69-72; V Londonderry 73-75; R Bride *S & M* 75-79; UAE 80-83; Min Stewartly LEP 86-90; C Wootton *St Alb* 86-90; C St Alb St Paul 90-94; rtd 94. *Little Waggoners, The Spinney, Grayshott, Hindhead, Surrey GU26 6DY* Hindhead (01428) 605219

CLOETE, Richard James. b 47. AKC71. St Aug Coll Cant 72. **d** 72 **p** 73. C Redhill St Matt *S'wark* 72-76; V Streatham St Paul 76-84; P-in-c W Coker *B & W* 84-88; P-in-c Hardington Mandeville w E Chinnock and Pendomer 84-88; R W Coker w Hardington Mandeville, E Chinnock etc 88; R Wincanton from 88; R Pen Selwood from 88; Sec and Treas Dioc Hosp Chapl Fellowship from 91. *The Rectory, Bayford Hill, Wincanton, Somerset BA9 9LQ* Wincanton (01963) 33367

CLOGHER, Archdeacon of. *See* PRINGLE, Ven Cecil Thomas

CLOGHER, Bishop of. *See* HANNON, Rt Rev Brian Desmond Anthony

CLOGHER, Dean of. *See* MOORE, Very Rev Thomas Robert

CLONMACNOISE, Dean of. *See* BARRETT, Very Rev John Alan Gardiner

CLOSE, Brian Eric. b 49. St Chad's Coll Dur BA74 MA76. Ridley Hall Cam 74. **d** 76 **p** 77. C Far Headingley St Chad *Ripon* 76-79; C Harrogate St Wilfrid 79-80; C Harrogate St Wilfrid and St Luke 80-82; P-in-c Alconbury w Alconbury Weston *Ely* 82-83; V 83-86; P-in-c Buckworth 82-83; R 83-86; P-in-c Upton and Copmanford 82-83; Chapl Reed's Sch Cobham from 86. *Clover, Sandy Lane, Cobham, Surrey KT11 2EL* Cobham (01932) 564057 or 864975

CLOSS-PARRY, Ven Selwyn. b 25. Univ of Wales (Lamp) BA50. St Mich Coll Llan 50. **d** 52 **p** 53. R Llangystennin *St As* 66-71; V Holywell 71-77; Can St As Cathl 76-82; Prec 82-84; Preb 82-90; V Colwyn 77-84; Adn St As 84-90; R Trefnant 84-90; rtd 91. *3 Llys Brompton, Brompton Avenue, Rhos-on-Sea, Clwyd LL28 4ZB* Colwyn Bay (01492) 545801

CLOTHIER, Gerald Harry. b 34. Oak Hill Th Coll 75. **d** 78 **p** 79. Hon C Highwood *Chelmsf* 78-79; Hon C Writtle w Highwood 79-83; P-in-c Westhall w Brampton and Stoven *St E* 83-86; TV Beccles St Mich 86-93; R Rougham, Beyton w Hessett and Rushbrooke from 93. *The Rectory, Rougham, Bury St Edmunds, Suffolk IP30 9JJ* Beyton (01359) 70250

CLOUGH, Harry. b 11. AKC39. **d** 39 **p** 40. V Upper Hopton *Wakef* 68-76; rtd 76; Perm to Offic *Wakef* from 76. *2 Kirkgate Lane, South Hiendley, Barnsley, S Yorkshire S72 9DS* Barnsley (01226) 711470

CLOVER, Brendan David. b 58. LTCL74 G&C Coll Cam BA79 MA83. Ripon Coll Cuddesdon 79. **d** 82 **p** 83. C Friern Barnet St Jas *Lon* 82-85; C W Hampstead St Jas 85-87; Chapl Em Coll Cam 87-92; Dean Em Coll Cam 92-94; P-in-c St Pancras w St Jas and Ch Ch *Lon* from 94. *St Pancras' Vicarage, 3 Wren Street, London WC1X 0HA* 0171-837 2146 or 387 8250

CLOWES, John. b 45. AKC67. **d** 68 **p** 69. C Corby St Columba *Pet* 68-71; R Itchenstoke w Ovington and Abbotstone *Win* 71-74; V Acton w Gt and Lt Waldingfield *St E* 74-80; Asst Dioc Chr Stewardship Adv 75-80; TV Southend St Jo w St Mark, All SS w St Fran etc *Chelmsf* 80-82; TV Southend 82-85; Ind Chapl 80-85; R Ashwick w Oakhill and Binegar *B & W* 85-91; P-in-c Brompton Regis w Upton and Skilgate from 91. *The Vicarage, Brompton Regis, Dulverton, Somerset TA22 9NN* Brompton Regis (013987) 239

CLOYNE, Dean of. *See* HILLIARD, Very Rev George Percival St John

CLUCAS, Robert David (Bob). b 55. Cranmer Hall Dur. **d** 82 **p** 83. C Gateacre *Liv* 82-86; P-in-c Bishop's Itchington *Cov* 86-93; CPAS Staff from 93. *c/o CPAS, Athena Drive, Tachbrook Park, Warwick CV34 6NG* Warwick (01926) 334242 Fax 337613

CLUER, Donald Gordon. b 21. S'wark Ord Course 61. **d** 64 **p** 65. C Bexhill St Pet *Chich* 68-73; V Shoreham Beach 73-77;

V Heathfield St Rich 77-86; C Eastbourne St Mary 86-90; rtd 90; Perm to Offic *Ox* from 90. *10 Windsor Street, Oxford OX3 7AP* Oxford (01865) 67270

CLUES, David Charles. b 66. K Coll Lon BD87. St Steph Ho Ox 88. **d** 90 **p** 91. C Notting Hill All SS w St Columb *Lon* 90-94; NSM from 94. *28 Barlby Road, London W10 6AR*

CLUETT, Michael Charles. b 53. Kingston Poly BSc78. St Steph Ho Ox 84. **d** 86 **p** 87. C Pontesbury I and II *Heref* 86-90; TV Wenlock from 90. *14 Stretton Road, Much Wenlock, Shropshire TF13 6AS* Much Wenlock (01952) 728211

CLULEE, Miss Elsie Ethel. b 18. St Andr Ho Portsm 46. **dss** 56 **d** 87. Stirchley *Birm* 66-87; Hon Par Dn 87-90; Perm to Offic from 90. *42 Woodbrooke Road, Birmingham B30 1UD* 0121-472 2662

CLUNIE, Grace. b 60. Ulster Univ BA82 MA91 QUB DipLib85. CITC BTh95. **d** 95. C Newtownards *D & D* from 95. *10 Londonderry Road, Newtownards, Co Down BT23 3AY* Newtownards (01247) 814750

CLUTTERBUCK, Herbert Ivan. b 16. Ch Coll Cam BA38 MA42. Chich Th Coll 38. **d** 39 **p** 40. Org Sec Ch Union 66-74; Chapl Qu Marg Sch Escrick Park 74-76; Chapl Roedean Sch Brighton 76-81; rtd 82; Master St Jo Hosp Lich 82-91. *7 Springfield Road, St Martin Field, East Looe, Cornwall PL13 1HB* Looe (01503) 263509

CLUTTERBUCK, Miss Marion Isobel. b 56. All Nations Chr Coll DipRS87 Oak Hill Th Coll BA91. **d** 92 **p** 94. C Lindfield *Chich* from 92. *32 Noah's Ark Lane, Lindfield, Haywards Heath, W Sussex RH16 2LT* Haywards Heath (01444) 482989

CLYDE, John. b 39. CITC BTh70. **d** 71 **p** 72. C Belf St Aid *Conn* 71-74; I Belf St Barn 74-80; I Belf H Trin 80-89; Bp's C Acton w Drumbanagher *Arm* 89-94; I Desertlyn w Ballyeglish from 94. *24 Cookstown Road, Moneymore, Magherafelt, Co Londonderry BT45 7QF* Moneymore (016487) 48200

CLYNES, William. b 33. Sarum & Wells Th Coll 78. **d** 79 **p** 80. C Winterbourne *Bris* 79-83; TV Swindon St Jo and St Andr 83-91; rtd 91. *185A Claverham Road, Claverham, Bristol BS19 4LE*

COATES, Alan Thomas. b 55. St Jo Coll Nottm 87. **d** 89 **p** 90. C Heeley *Sheff* 89-90; C Bramley and Ravenfield 90-92; V Askern from 92. *The Vicarage, Askern, Doncaster, S Yorkshire DN6 0PH* Doncaster (01302) 700404

COATES, Christopher Ian. b 59. Qu Coll Birm 81. **d** 84 **p** 85. C Cottingham *York* 84-87; TV Howden TM 87-91; V Sherburn in Elmet 91-94; V Sherburn in Elmet w Saxton from 94. *The Vicarage, 2 Sir John's Lane, Sherburn-in-Elmet, Leeds LS25 6BJ* South Milford (01977) 682122

COATES, Canon Francis Gustav. b 10. OBE63. G&C Coll Cam BA32 MA36. Ridley Hall Cam 32. **d** 52 **p** 54. R Heydon w Irmingland *Nor* 68-82; rtd 82; Perm to Offic *Nor* from 82. *13 Stuart Court, Recorder Road, Norwich NR1 1NP* Norwich (01603) 664910

COATES, John David Spencer. b 41. Dur Univ BA64 DipTh66. Cranmer Hall Dur 64. **d** 66 **p** 67. C Chipping Campden *Glouc* 66-69; CF from 69. *c/o MOD (Army), Bagshot Park, Bagshot, Surrey GU19 5PL* Bagshot (01276) 471717 Fax 412834

COATES, Canon Kenneth Will. b 17. St Jo Coll Dur LTh45 BA46. Tyndale Hall Bris 39. **d** 42 **p** 43. TR St Helens St Helen *Liv* 60-88; Hon Can Liv Cathl 71-88; rtd 88. *122 Broadway, Eccleston, St Helens WA10 5DH* St Helens (01744) 29629

COATES, Maxwell Gordon (Max). b 49. Lon Univ CertEd70 Open Univ BA83 ADEd87 UEA MA86. Trin Coll Bris DipTh77. **d** 77 **p** 78. C Blackheath Park St Mich *S'wark* 77-79; Chapl Greenwich Distr Hosp Lon 77-79; Asst Teacher Saintbridge Sch Glouc 79-81; Teacher Gaywood Park High Sch King's Lynn 81-85; NSM Lynn St Jo *Nor* 81-85; Dep Hd Teacher Winton Comp Sch Bournemouth 85-90; Hd Teacher St Mark's Comp Sch Bath from 90; NSM Canford Magna *Sarum* 85-86; NSM Stoke Gifford *Bris* from 93. *127 North Road, Stoke Gifford, Bristol BS12 6PE* Bristol (0117) 983 0351

COATES, Nigel John. b 51. Reading Univ BSc MA. Trin Coll Bris. **d** 83 **p** 84. C Epsom St Martin *Guildf* 83-87; C Portswood Ch Ch *Win* 86-88; Chapl Southn Univ from 89; Chapl Southn Inst of HE 89-95. *Chaplain's Lodge, South Stoneham, Wessex Lane, Southampton SO2 2JS* Southampton (01703) 558126 or 593511

COATES, Peter Frederick. b 50. K Coll Lon BD79 AKC79. St Steph Ho Ox 79. **d** 80 **p** 81. C Woodford St Barn *Chelmsf* 80-83; C E and W Keal *Linc* 83-86; R The Wainfleets and Croft 86-94; R The Wainfleet Gp from 94; RD Calcewaithe and Candleshoe from 92. *The Rectory, Vicarage Lane, Wainfleet St Mary, Skegness, Lincs PE24 4JJ* Skegness (01754) 880401

COATES, Raymond Frederick William. b 14. AKC39. Bps' Coll Cheshunt 39. **d** 39 **p** 40. R Kings Somborne w Lt Somborne, Up Somborne etc *Win* 69-76; V Kings Somborne w Ashley 76-81; rtd 81; Perm to Offic *St E* 82-85. *Jameson, 26 St Matthew's Road, Winchester, Hants SO22 9BU* Winchester (01962) 861467

COATES, Robert. b 63. Aston Tr Scheme 87 St Steph Ho Ox 89. **d** 92 **p** 93. C Heavitree w Ex St Paul *Ex* 92-95; Chapl RN from 95. *Directorate Gen, RN Chapl Services, Room 203, Victory Building, HM Naval Base, Portsmouth PO1 3LS* Portsmouth (01705) 727903 Fax 727112

COATES, Robert Charles (Bob). b 44. Open Univ BA76. Cant Sch of Min 83. **d** 86 **p** 87. C Deal St Leon and St Rich and Sholden *Cant* 86-89; V Loose from 89. *The Vicarage, 17 Linton Road, Loose, Maidstone, Kent ME15 0AG* Maidstone (01622) 743513

COATES, Robert James. b 16. Lon Coll of Div 57. **d** 59 **p** 60. Chapl St Geo Hosp Stafford 67-81; rtd 81; Perm to Offic *Lich* 81-89; Perm to Offic *Ex* from 89. *The Dales, 19/20 Howell Road, Exeter EX4 4LG* Exeter (01392) 221266

COATES, Stuart Murray. b 49. Lon Univ BA70 Edin Univ MTh91. Wycliffe Hall Ox 72. **d** 75 **p** 76. C Rainford *Liv* 75-78; C Orrell 78-79; V 79-86; Chapl Strathcarron Hospice Falkirk from 86; Hon C Stirling *Edin* 86-90; NSM Doune *St And* from 89. *Westwood Smithy, Chalmerston Road, Stirling FK9 4AG* Gargunnock (01786) 860531

COATHAM, Canon Sydney. b 16. Leeds Univ BA40. Coll of Resurr Mirfield 40. **d** 42 **p** 43. V Lindley *Wakef* 63-81; rtd 82; Perm to Offic *Wakef* 82-95; Perm to Offic *Leic* 82-95. *c/o Prickley Green Farm, Martley, Worcester WR6 6QQ*

COATSWORTH, Nigel George. b 39. Trin Hall Cam BA61 MA. Cuddesdon Coll 61. **d** 63 **p** 64. C Hellesdon *Nor* 63-66; Ewell Monastery 66-80; TV Folkestone H Trin and St Geo w Ch Ch *Cant* 83-85; C Milton next Sittingbourne 85-86; P-in-c Selattyn *Lich* 86-91; P-in-c Weston Rhyn 88-91; R Weston Rhyn and Selattyn from 91. *The Rectory, Selattyn, Oswestry, Shropshire SY10 7DH* Oswestry (01691) 659755

COBB, Douglas Arthur. b 25. Kelham Th Coll 49. **d** 54 **p** 55. V Kentish Town St Silas *Lon* 63-87; P-in-c Kentish Town St Martin w St Andr 81-85; Chapl Convent of St Mary at the Cross Edgware 87-92; rtd 92. *Padre Pio House, 10 Buckingham Gardens, Edgware, Middx HA8 6NB* 0181-951 1231

COBB, George Reginald. b 50. Oak Hill Th Coll BA81. **d** 81 **p** 82. C Ware Ch Ch *St Alb* 81-84; C Uphill *B & W* 84-89; R Alresford *Chelmsf* from 89. *The Rectory, St Andrew's Close, Alresford, Colchester CO7 8BL* Colchester (01206) 822088

COBB, Jeremy William Levi. b 62. Southn Univ BA84. Coll of Resurr Mirfield 84. **d** 86 **p** 87. C Greenhill *Sheff* 86-91; TV Redruth w Lanner and Treleigh *Truro* 91-94. *Kings Lodge, Bridewell Street, Walsingham, Norfolk NR22 6BJ* Walsingham (01328) 821001

COBB, John Philip Andrew. b 43. Man Univ BSc65 New Coll Ox BA67 MA71. Wycliffe Hall Ox 66. **d** 68 **p** 69. Par Dn Reading St Jo *Ox* 68-71; Par Dn Romford Gd Shep Collier Row *Chelmsf* 71-73; SAMS from 74; Chile from 74. *Iglesia Anglicana del Chile, Casilla 50675, Correo Central, Santiago, Chile* Santiago (2) 227-5713

COBB, Miss Marjorie Alice. b 24. St Chris Coll Blackheath IDC52. **dss** 61 **d** 87. CSA 56-85; rtd 85; Perm to Offic *Cant* from 87; Chapl Jes Hosp Cant from 90. *2 John Boys Wing, Jesus Hospital, Sturry Road, Canterbury, Kent CT1 1BS* Canterbury (01227) 472615

COBB, Mark Robert. b 64. Lanc Univ BSc86. Ripon Coll Cuddesdon 88. **d** 91 **p** 92. C Hampstead St Jo *Lon* 91-94; Asst Chapl Derbyshire R Infirmary from 94. *Derbyshire Royal Infirmary, London Road, Derby DE1 2QY* Derby (01332) 347141

COBB, Michael Hewett. b 28. K Coll Lon 53. **d** 54 **p** 56. Quest Community 70-83; Perm to Offic *Birm* 71-83; V Gravelly Hill 83-90; rtd 90. *27 Mount Pleasant Avenue, Exmouth, Devon EX8 4QH*

COBB, Canon Peter George. b 37. Ch Ch Ox BA59 MA63. St Steph Ho Ox 64. **d** 65 **p** 66. C Solihull *Birm* 65-69; Lib Pusey Ho 69-71; Sen Tutor St Steph Ho Ox 71-76; Cust Lib Pusey Ho 76-78; V Clandown *B & W* 78-83; V Midsomer Norton 78-83; V Midsomer Norton w Clandown 83-84; RD Midsomer Norton 83-84; V Clifton All SS w St Jo *Bris* from 84; Hon Can Bris Cathl from 92. *All Saints' Vicarage, 68 Pembroke Road, Bristol BS8 3ED* Bristol (0117) 974 1355

COBB, Peter Graham. b 27. St Jo Coll Cam BA48 MA52. Ridley Hall Cam 66. **d** 68 **p** 69. C Porthkerry *Llan* 68-71; P-in-c Penmark 71-72; V Penmark w Porthkerry 72-81; V Magor w Redwick and Undy *Mon* 82-95; rtd 95. *2 Talycoed Court, Talycoed, Monmouth, Gwent NP5 4HR* Llantilio (01600) 780309

COBERN, Canon Charles John Julian. b 14. Keble Coll Ox BA36 MA62. Cuddesdon Coll 36. **d** 37 **p** 38. V Woburn Sands *St Alb* 68-79; rtd 79; Perm to Offic *Chich* from 89. *Miles Court, Hereford Street, Brighton BN2 1JT* Kemptown (01273) 696017

COCHLIN, Maurice Reginald. b 19. ACP60 FFChM Sussex Univ CertEd70. Cen Sch of Religion MA Lambeth STh74 Chich Th Coll 70. **d** 70 **p** 71. C Rowlands Castle *Portsm* 70-72; Chapl Paulsgrove Sch Cosham 71; C Warblington and Emsworth *Portsm* 72-75; C S w N Bersted *Chich* 76-78; Hd

Littlemead Upper Sch Chich 78-79; C Saltdean *Chich* 79-83; V Kirdford 83-88; rtd 88. *56 Farnhurst Road, Barnham, Bognor Regis, W Sussex PO22 0JW* Yapton (01243) 553584

COCHRANE, Alan George. b 28. S'wark Ord Course. **d** 82 **p** 83. NSM Clapham Old Town *S'wark* 82-85; C Spalding St Jo w Deeping St Nicholas *Linc* 85-87; R Southery *Ely* from 87; V Fordham St Mary 87-91; R Hilgay from 87. *The Rectory, Hilgay, Downham Market, Norfolk PE38 0JL* Downham Market (01366) 384418

COCHRANE, Canon Kenneth Wilbur. b 27. TCD BA58 MA61 Trin Coll Newburgh PhD88. **d** 58 **p** 59. C Belf St Aid *Conn* 58-61; C Belf St Nic 61-62; C Lisburn Ch Ch 62-63; P-in-c Lisburn St Paul 63-65; I from 65; Can Belf Cathl from 86; Preb Clonmethan St Patr Cathl Dub from 90. *St Paul's Rectory, 3 Ballinderry Road, Lisburn, Co Antrim BT28 1UD* Lisburn (01846) 663520

COCHRANE, Norman John Michael Antony Ferguson. b 24. QUB BA46. Linc Th Coll 49. **d** 51 **p** 52. C Horsham *Chich* 56-76; V Aldwick 76-90; rtd 90. *41 Grindstone Crescent, Knaphill, Woking, Surrey GU21 2RZ* Brookwood (01483) 487981

COCHRANE, Canon Roy Alan. b 25. AKC53. **d** 54 **p** 55. V Glanford Bridge *Linc* 69-89; Chapl Glanford Hosp 69-89; RD Yarborough 76-81; Can and Preb Linc Cathl from 77; Chapl and Warden St Anne's Bedehouses 89-93; rtd 90. *5 Chippendale Close, Lincoln LN6 3PR* Lincoln (01522) 689221

COCKAYNE, Gordon. b 34. RMN73. **d** 92 **p** 93. NSM Owlerton *Sheff* from 92. *6 Austin Close, Loxley, Sheffield S6 6QD* Sheffield (0114) 233 3057

COCKAYNE, Mark Gary. b 61. UEA LLB82. St Jo Coll Nottm BTh92 MA93. **d** 93 **p** 94. C Armthorpe *Sheff* from 93. *55 Fernbank Drive, Armthorpe, Doncaster, S Yorkshire DN3 2HB* Doncaster (01302) 832815

COCKBILL, Douglas John. b 53. Chicago Univ BA75. Gen Th Sem (NY) MDiv78. **d** 78 **p** 79. Virgin Is 79-80; Bahamas 80-83; USA 84-90; P-in-c Roxbourne St Andr *Lon* 90-92; V from 92. *St Andrew's Vicarage, Malvern Avenue, Harrow, Middx HA2 9ER* 0181-422 3633

COCKBURN, Sidney. b 14. Leeds Univ BA36. Coll of Resurr Mirfield 36. **d** 38 **p** 40. V Long Eaton St Jo *Derby* 51-85; rtd 85; Perm to Offic *Derby* from 85. *10 Poplar Road, Breaston, Derby DE7 3BH* Draycott (01332) 872363

COCKCROFT, Basil Stanley. b 26. CEng MICE Leeds Univ BSc49. Wells Th Coll 64. **d** 66 **p** 67. C Norton St Mary *Dur* 69-71; P-in-c Eldon 71-75; NSM Elland *Wakef* from 75; rtd 91. *9 Dene Close, South Parade, Elland, W Yorkshire HX5 0NS* Elland (01422) 374465

COCKE, James Edmund. b 26. Wadh Coll Ox BA50 MA55. Wells Th Coll 50. **d** 52 **p** 53. C Christchurch *Win* 52-57; V Highfield *Ox* from 57; Chapl Wingfield-Morris Hosp Ox 57-90; Chapl Nuff Orthopaedic Cen Ox from 90. *All Saints' Vicarage, 85 Old Road, Oxford OX3 7LB* Oxford (01865) 62536

COCKELL, Ms Helen Francis. b 69. Trin Hall Cam BA90 MA94. Qu Coll Birm BD94. **d** 95. C Bracknell *Ox* from 95. *15 Oakwood Road, Bracknell, Berks RG12 2SP* Bracknell (01344) 51952

COCKELL, Timothy David (Tim). b 66. Qu Coll Birm BTh95. **d** 95. C Bracknell *Ox* from 95. *15 Oakwood Road, Bracknell, Berks RG12 2SP* Bracknell (01344) 51952

COCKERELL, David John. b 47. Univ of Wales (Cardiff) BA71 Univ of Wales (Swansea) MA74 Qu Coll Cam BA75. Westcott Ho Cam 73. **d** 76 **p** 77. C Chapel Allerton *Ripon* 76-79; C Farnley 79-81; TV Hitchin *St Alb* 81-89; TV Dorchester *Ox* 89-92; Adult Educn and Tr Officer *Ely* from 92. *1 Granta Close, Witchford, Ely, Cambs CB6 2HR* Ely (01353) 669460

COCKERTON, Canon John Clifford Penn. b 27. Liv Univ BA48 St Cath Soc Ox BA54 MA58. Wycliffe Hall Ox 51. **d** 54 **p** 55. Warden Cranmer Hall Dur 68-70; Vice-Prin St Jo Coll Dur 63-70; Prin 70-78; R Wheldrake *York* 78-84; R Wheldrake w Thorganby 84-92; Can and Preb York Minster 87-92; rtd 92. *50 Allerton Drive, Nether Poppleton, York YO2 6NW* York (01904) 789287

COCKERTON, Thomas Charles (Tom). b 24. **d** 88 **p** 90. NSM Bermondsey St Mary w St Olave, St Jo etc *S'wark* 88-94; Perm to Offic from 94. *30 Carrick Court, Kennington Park Road, London SE11 4EE* 0171-735 6966

COCKETT, Elwin Wesley. b 59. Aston Tr Scheme 86 Oak Hill Th Coll DipHE90 BA91. **d** 91 **p** 92. C Chadwell Heath *Chelmsf* 91-94; Chapl W Ham United Football Club from 92; C Harold Hill St Paul 94-95; P-in-c from 95. *St Paul's Vicarage, Redcar Road, Romford RM3 9PT* Ingrebourne (01708) 341225

✠**COCKIN, Rt Rev George Eyles Irwin.** b 08. Leeds Univ BA31. Linc Th Coll 52. **d** 53 **p** 54 **c** 59. C Kimberworth *Sheff* 53-55; Nigeria 55-69; Bp Owerri 59-69; Asst Bp York from 69; V Bainton 69-78; RD Harthill 73-78; rtd 79. *42 Carr Lane, Willerby, Hull HU10 6JW* Hull (01482) 653086

COCKING, Kermode Neil. b 48. TD. St Pet Coll Birm CertEd69. Sarum & Wells Th Coll 71. **d** 74 **p** 75. C Shirley *Birm* 74-76; CF (TA) 75-89; C Ealing Ch the Sav *Lon* 76-78; Hon C Streatham Ch Ch *S'wark* 78-81; Hon C Deptford St Paul 81-84; Lic to Offic *Lon* from 84; Hon C S Kensington St Steph from 90; Hd Master Melcombe Primary Sch *Lon* from 90. *51 Melrose Avenue, London SW19 8BU*   0181-947 7042

COCKING, Martyn Royston. b 53. Trin Coll Bris 83. **d** 85 **p** 86. C Weston-super-Mare Cen Par *B & W* 85-88; C Kingswood *Bris* 88-89; TV 89-93; V Pill w Easton in Gordano and Portbury *B & W* from 93. *The Vicarage, 1 Station Road, Pill, Bristol BS20 0AB*   Pill (01275) 372230

COCKMAN, David Willis. b 32. Ex & Truro NSM Scheme. **d** 82 **p** 83. Warden Mercer Ho from 82; NSM Exwick *Ex* 82-86; Lic to Offic from 86. *Mercer House, Exwick Road, Exeter EX4 2AT*   Exeter (01392) 219609

✠**COCKS, Rt Rev. Francis William.** b 13. CB59. St Cath Coll Cam BA35 MA43. Westcott Ho Cam 35. **d** 37 **p** 37 **c** 70. C Portswood Ch Ch *Win* 37-39; Chapl RAFVR 39-45; Chapl RAF 45-50; Asst Chapl-in-Chief RAF 50-59; Chapl-in-Chief RAF 59-65; QHC 59-65; Can and Preb Linc Cathl *Linc* 59-65; R Wolv St Pet *Lich* 65-70; RD Wolv 65-70; P-in-c Wolv All SS 66-70; P-in-c Wolv St Geo 67-70; Preb Lich Cathl 68-70; Hon Can Lich Cathl from 70; Suff Bp Shrewsbury 70-80; rtd 80; Perm to Offic *St E* from 80. *41 Beatrice Avenue, Felixstowe, Suffolk IP11 9HB*   Felixstowe (01394) 283574

COCKS, Howard Alan Stewart. b 46. St Barn Coll Adelaide 78 ACT ThD. **d** 80 **p** 81. Australia 80-82; C Prestbury *Glouc* 82-87; P-in-c Stratton w Baunton 87-94; P-in-c N Cerney w Bagendon 91-94; R Stratton, N Cerney, Baunton and Bagendon from 95. *The Rectory, 94 Gloucester Road, Cirencester, Glos GL7 2LJ*   Cirencester (01285) 653359

COCKS, Canon John Cramer. b 14. Lon BD50. ALCD50. **d** 50 **p** 51. V Rothwell w Orton *Pet* 62-83; rtd 83; Perm to Offic *Pet* from 85. *30 Playford Close, Rothwell, Kettering, Northants NN14 6TU*   Kettering (01536) 418319

COCKS, Michael Dearden Somers. b 28. Univ of NZ MA50 St Cath Coll Ox BA53 MA57. **d** 53 **p** 54. New Zealand 53-93; Chapl Gothenburg w Halmstad, Jonkoping etc *Eur* from 93. *Norra Liden 15, 411-18 Gothenburg, Sweden*   Gothenburg (31) 711-1915

COCKSEDGE, Hugh Francis. b 26. Magd Coll Cam BA50 MA52. **d** 88 **p** 89. NSM Alton All SS *Win* 88-89; Lic to Offic 89-91; Chapl Ankara *Eur* from 91. *Sehit Ersan, Caddesi 32/12, Cankaya, Ankara, Turkey*   Ankara (312) 467-8276 or 468-6238

COCKSWORTH, Dr Christopher John. b 59. Man Univ BA80 PGCE81 PhD89. St Jo Coll Nottm 84. **d** 88 **p** 89. C Epsom Common Ch Ch *Guildf* 88-92; Chapl R Holloway and Bedf New Coll from 92. *10 Willow Walk, Engelfied Green, Egham, Surrey TW20 0DQ*   Egham (01784) 432025 or 443070

CODLING, Timothy Michael (Tim). b 62. Trin Coll Ox BA84 MA91. St Steph Ho Ox 89. **d** 91 **p** 92. C N Shoebury *Chelmsf* from 91. *7 Sandpipers Close, Shoeburyness, Southend-on-Sea SS3 9YJ*   Southend-on-Sea (01702) 298069

CODRINGTON, Canon George Herbert. b 13. ALCD34 St Jo Coll Dur BA36 LTh36 MA39. **d** 36 **p** 37. V Melton Mowbray w Thorpe Arnold *Leic* 65-80; rtd 81; C Welsh Newton w Llanrothal *Heref* 81-85; C St Weonards w Orcop, Garway, Tretire etc 85-87. *Glebe Cottage, Staunton-on-Arrow, Leominster, Herefordshire HR6 9HR*   Pembridge (015447) 378

COE, Andrew Derek John. b 58. Nottm Univ BTh86. St Jo Coll Nottm 83. **d** 86 **p** 87. C Pype Hayes *Birm* 86-88; C Erdington St Barn 88-91; C Birm St Martin w Bordesley St Andr from 91. *175 St Andrew's Road, Bordesley Gardens, Birmingham B9 4NB*   0121-771 0237

COE, David. b 45. **d** 69 **p** 70. C Belf St Matt *Conn* 69-72; C Belf St Donard *D & D* 72-75; I Tullylish 75-81; I Lurgan St Jo 81-89; I Ballymacarrett St Patr from 89. *St Patrick's Vicarage, 155 Upper Newtownards Road, Belfast BT4 3HX*   Belfast (01232) 657180

COE, John Norris. b 31. Oak Hill Th Coll 57. **d** 59 **p** 60. C Stoughton *Guildf* 59-61; C Guernsey St Michel du Valle *Win* 61-63; C Norbiton *S'wark* 63-67; V Bath Widcombe *B & W* 67-84; R Publow w Pensford, Compton Dando and Chelwood from 84. *The Rectory, Compton Dando, Bristol BS18 4LA*   Compton Dando (01761) 490221

COE, Stephen David. b 49. Ch Coll Cam MA72. Ox Min Course CBTS93. **d** 93 **p** 94. NSM Abingdon *Ox* from 93. *9 Apppleford Drive, Abingdon, Oxon OX14 2DB*   Abingdon (01235) 523228

COEKIN, Richard John. b 61. Solicitor 86 Jes Coll Cam BA83 MA87. Wycliffe Hall Ox 89. **d** 91 **p** 92. C Cheadle *Ches* 91-95; Hon C Wimbledon Em Ridgway Prop Chpl *S'wark* from 95. *107 Merton Hall Road, London SW19 3PY*   0181-542 8739

COFFEY, Hubert William (Bill). b 15. MBE46. TCD BA37 MA40. TCD Div Sch Div Test38. **d** 38 **p** 39. I Milltown *Arm* 47-52; Australia from 53; rtd 80. *23 Hawthorn Avenue, Caulfield North, Victoria, Australia 3161*   Melbourne (3) 527-7875

COFFIN, Stephen. b 52. Pemb Coll Ox BA74 MA79. Trin Coll Bris 74. **d** 77 **p** 78. C Illogan *Truro* 77-80; C Liskeard w St Keyne and St Pinnock 80-82; C Liskeard w St Keyne, St Pinnock and Morval 82; CMS 82-86; Burundi 82-86; V St Germans *Truro* from 86. *The Vicarage, Quay Road, St Germans, Saltash, Cornwall PL12 5LY*   St Germans (01503) 30275

✠**COGGAN of Canterbury and Sissinghurst, Most Rev and Rt Hon Lord (Frederick Donald).** b 09. PC61. St Jo Coll Cam BA31 MA35 Leeds Univ Hon DD58 Cam Univ Hon DD62 Aber Univ Hon DD63 Tokyo Univ Hon DD63 Lanc Univ Hon DLitt67 Liv Univ Hon LLD72 Man Univ Hon DD72 Kent Univ Hon DCL75 York Univ DUniv75. Wycliffe Coll Toronto BD41 Hon DD44 Lambeth DD57 Gen Th Sem (NY) Hon STD67 Wycliffe Hall Ox 34. **d** 34 **p** 35 **c** 56. C Islington St Mary *Lon* 34-37; Canada 37-44; Prin Lon Coll of Div 44-56; Bp Bradf 56-61; Abp York 61-74; Abp Cant 74-80; FKC from 75; rtd 80; Asst Bp Cant 80-88. *28 Lions Hall, St Swithun Street, Winchester SO23 9HW*   Winchester (01962) 864289

COGGINS, Edwin Stanley Claude. b 14. Bris Univ BSc36 DipEd37. Leic Dioc Th Course 63. **d** 64 **p** 65. Hon C Knighton St Mary Magd *Leic* 64-72; V Barlestone 72-77; P-in-c E w W Beckham *Nor* 78-84; rtd 84; Perm to Offic *Nor* from 84. *21 Caxton Park, Beeston Regis, Sheringham, Norfolk NR26 8ST*   Sheringham (01263) 824119

COGGINS, Glenn. b 60. Warw Univ BA81. St Jo Coll Dur CTM93. **d** 95. C Warminster St Denys, Upton Scudamore etc *Sarum* from 95. *39 Manor Gardens, Warminster, Wilts BA12 8PN*   Warminster (01985) 214953

COGGINS, Richard James. b 29. Ex Coll Ox BA50 MA54 DipTh53 BD75. St Steph Ho Ox 52. **d** 54 **p** 55. Lic to Offic *Lon* 64-94; Sub-Warden K Coll Lon 62-67; Lect 62-81; Sen Lect 81-94; rtd 94. *3 de Mowbray Way, Lymington, Hants SO41 3PD*   Lymington (01590) 673626

COGHLAN, Patrick John. b 47. Down Coll Cam BA(Econ)69 Nottm Univ MA73. St Jo Coll Nottm LTh72. **d** 73 **p** 74. C Crookes St Thos *Sheff* 73-78; Brazil 78-92; V Anston *Sheff* from 92. *The Vicarage, 17 Rackford Road, Anston, Sheffield S31 7DE*   Dinnington (01909) 563447

COGMAN, Canon Frederick Walter. b 13. Lon Univ BD38 AKC38. **d** 38 **p** 39. R Guernsey St Martin *Win* 48-76; Dean Win 67-78; Dean Guernsey 67-78; R Guernsey St Peter Port 76-78; rtd 78; Perm to Offic *Win* from 78. *Oriana Lodge, rue des Fontenelles, Forest, Guernsey, Channel Islands*   Guernsey (01481) 64940

COHEN, Canon Clive Ronald Franklin. b 46. ACIB71. Sarum & Wells Th Coll 79. **d** 81 **p** 82. C Esher *Guildf* 81-85; R Winterslow *Sarum* from 85; RD Alderbury 89-93; Can and Preb Sarum Cathl from 92. *The Rectory, Winterslow, Salisbury SP5 1RE*   Winterslow (01980) 862231

COHEN, David Mervyn Stuart. b 42. Sydney Univ BA63 MA78. **d** 67 **p** 68. Mauritius 67-69; New Zealand 70-72; Regional Sec (Africa) Bible Soc 73-75; Australia 75-85; Gen Dir Scripture Union (England and Wales) 86-93; Perm to Offic *Lon* 92-94. *75 The Heights, London SE7 8JQ*   0181-853 2257

COHEN, Ian Geoffrey Holland. b 51. Nottm Univ BA74. Ripon Coll Cuddesdon 77. **d** 79 **p** 80. C Sprowston *Nor* 79-83; TV Wallingford w Crowmarsh Gifford etc *Ox* 83-88; V Chalgrove w Berrick Salome from 88. *The Vicarage, 58 Brinkinfield Road, Chalgrove, Oxford OX44 7QX*   Stadhampton (01865) 890392

COHEN, John Arthur. b 47. Bede Coll Dur BA68 CertEd69. E Anglian Minl Tr Course 84. **d** 87 **p** 88. C Raydon St E 87-93; C Holton St Mary w Gt Wenham 87-93; C Stratford St Mary 87-93; C Higham 87-93; P-in-c Bildeston w Wattisham from 93; P-in-c Kersey w Lindsey from 93. *The Rectory, 176 High Street, Bildeston, Ipswich IP7 7EF*   Bildeston (01449) 740530

COHEN, Malcolm Arthur. b 38. Canberra Coll of Min DipTh79. **d** 78 **p** 79. Australia 79-84; Chapl Asst Thurrock Hosp 84-86; Hon Chapl ATC from 86; R Stifford *Chelmsf* 84-92; P-in-c Mayland from 92; P-in-c Steeple from 92. *The Vicarage, 31 Imperial Avenue, Mayland, Essex CM3 6AH*   Maldon (01621) 740943

COKE, William Robert Francis. b 46. St Edm Hall Ox BA68 MA79 Lon Univ BD78. Trin Coll Bris 75. **d** 79 **p** 80. C Blackb Sav *Blackb* 79-83; V Fence in Pendle 83-84; P-in-c Newchurch-in-Pendle 83-84; V Fence and Newchurch-in-Pendle 84-89; Switzerland from 89. *Aiglon College, Villars, Switzerland*

COKER, Dr Alexander Bryan (Alex). b 48. MCollP84 K Coll Lon BD75 AKC76 MTh76 ThD81 MA84 MEd87. St Aug Coll Cant 75. **d** 86 **p** 87. Overstone Coll Northn 82-87; NSM Belsize Park *Lon* 86-90; Thames Educn Inst 87-90; C Croydon Woodside *S'wark* 90-93; C Cheam Common St Phil 93-94. *32 Waterer Rise, Wallington, Surrey SM6 9DN*   0181-773 2842

COKER, Barry Charles Ellis. b 46. K Coll Lon BD69 AKC69. **d** 70 **p** 71. C Newton Aycliffe *Dur* 70-74; Trinidad and Tobago

74-78; R Matson *Glouc* 78-90; V Stroud and Uplands w Slad from 90; RD Bisley from 94. *The Vicarage, Church Street, Stroud, Glos GL5 1JL* Stroud (01453) 764555
COLBOURN, John Martin Claris. b 30. Selw Coll Cam BA52 MA56. Ridley Hall Cam 52. **d** 54 **p** 55. V Fareham St Jo *Portsm* 65-87; V Crich *Derby* 87-95; RD Alfreton 88-95; rtd 95. *Stanton View Cottage, Dale Road North, Darley Dale, Matlock, Derbyshire DE4 2HX* Matlock (01629) 733284
COLBY, David Allan. b 33. Ox NSM Course 78. **d** 81 **p** 82. NSM Gt Faringdon w Lt Coxwell *Ox* 81-83; TV Ewyas Harold w Dulas, Kenderchurch etc *Heref* 83-84; TV Ewyas Harold w Dulas, Kenderchurch etc 84-91; V Westbury-on-Severn w Flaxley and Blaisdon *Glouc* from 91. *The Vicarage, Westbury-on-Severn, Glos GL14 1LW* Gloucester (01452) 760592
COLBY, Preb Robert James. b 31. Roch Th Coll 62. **d** 64 **p** 65. C Luton Ch Ch *St Alb* 64-68; C Chirbury *Heref* 68-70; P-in-c 70-78; V 78-79; P-in-c Trelystan 70-78; V 78-79; P-in-c Marton 70-78; V 78-79; P-in-c Whitbourne 79-82; P-in-c Tedstone Delamere and Edvin Loach etc 80-82; P-in-c Upper Sapey w Wolferlow 80-82; R Edvin Loach w Tedstone Delamere etc from 82; Preb Heref Cathl from 94. *The Rectory, Whitbourne, Worcester WR6 5RP* Knightwick (01886) 21285
COLCHESTER, Archdeacon of. *See* STROUD, Ven Ernest Charles Frederick
COLCHESTER, Area Bishop of. *See* HOLLAND, Rt Rev Edward
COLCLOUGH, Ven Michael John. b 44. Leeds Univ BA69. Cuddesdon Coll 69. **d** 71 **p** 72. C Burslem St Werburgh *Lich* 71-75; C Ruislip St Mary *Lon* 75-79; P-in-c Hayes St Anselm 79-85; V 85-86; AD Hillingdon 85-92; P-in-c Uxbridge St Marg 86-88; P-in-c Uxbridge St Andr w St Jo 86-88; TR Uxbridge 88-92; Adn Northolt 92-94; P-in-c St Vedast w St Mich-le-Querne etc from 94; Bp's Dom Chapl from 94; Dep P in O from 95. *St Vedast's Rectory, 4 Foster Lane, London EC2V 6HH* 0171-606 3998
COLDERWOOD, Alfred Victor. b 26. Bps' Coll Cheshunt 58. **d** 60 **p** 61. V Edmonton St Aldhelm *Lon* 66-91; rtd 91. *11 Mill Row, Birchington, Kent CT7 9TT* Thanet (01843) 41544
COLDHAM, Miss Geraldine Elizabeth. b 35. FLA66 Trevelyan Coll Dur BA80. Cranmer Hall Dur 82. dss 83 **d** 87 **p** 94. S Normanton *Derby* 83-87; Par Dn 87; Par Dn Barking St Marg w St Patr *Chelmsf* 87-90; Par Dn Stifford 90-94; C from 94. *22 Prince Philip Avenue, Stifford, Grays, Essex RM16 2BT* Grays Thurrock (01375) 379830
COLDWELLS, Canon Alan Alfred. b 30. Univ Coll Ox BA55 MA57. Wells Th Coll 53. **d** 55 **p** 56. C Rugby St Andr *Cov* 55-62; V Sprowston *Nor* 62-73; R Beeston St Andr 62-73; RD Nor N 70-72; R Rugby St Andr *Cov* 73-82; TR 83-87; RD Rugby 73-78; Hon Can Cov Cathl 83-87; Can and Treas Windsor from 87. *6 The Cloisters, Windsor Castle, Windsor, Berks SL4 1NJ* Windsor (01753) 866313
COLE, Adrian Peter. *See* ROBBINS-COLE, Adrian Peter
COLE, Alan John. b 35. Cam Univ CCouns90. Bps' Coll Cheshunt 63. **d** 66 **p** 67. C Boreham Wood All SS *St Alb* 66-69; C St Alb St Mich 69-72; V Redbourn 72-80; R Thorley w Bishop's Stortford H Trin 80-87; Chapl St Edw K and Martyr Cam *Ely* 87-94; Chapl Arthur Rank Hospice Cam 87-94; SSF from 88; P-in-c Gamlingay w Hatley St Geo and E Hatley *Ely* from 94. *The Rectory, Stocks Lane, Gamlingay, Sandy, Beds SG19 3JP* Gamlingay (01767) 651204
COLE, Brian Robert Arthur. b 35. Nottm Univ BA57. Ridley Hall Cam 59. **d** 61 **p** 62. C Tye Green w Netteswell *Chelmsf* 61-64; C Keighley *Bradf* 64-67; Chapl Halifax Gen Hosp 67-73; V Copley *Wakef* 67-73; R Gt w Lt Dunham *Nor* 73-82; R Gt w Lt Fransham 74-82; P-in-c Sporle w Gt and Lt Palgrave 81-82; R Gt and Lt Dunham w Gt and Lt Fransham and Sporle from 83; RD Brisley and Elmham from 93. *The Rectory, Great Dunham, King's Lynn, Norfolk PE32 2LQ* Fakenham (01328) 701466
COLE, Charles Vincent. b 26. Kelham Th Coll 47. **d** 51 **p** 52. V Blackhall *Dur* 56-91; rtd 91. *66 Scott Green Crescent, Gildersome, Leeds LS27 7DF* Leeds (0113) 253 0021
COLE, David. b 40. Qu Coll Birm 66. **d** 66 **p** 67. C Kensington St Helen w H Trin *Lon* 66-69; C Altham w Clayton le Moors *Blackb* 69-72; P-in-c Preston St Luke 72-75; V Inskip 75-80; C-in-c Chelmsley Wood St Aug CD *Birm* 80-87; C Cannock *Lich* 87-93; I Kinneigh Union *C, C & R* from 93. *The Rectory, Ballineen, Co Cork, Irish Republic* Clonakilty (23) 47047
COLE, David Henry. b 30. San Francisco Th Sem DMin87 ALCD56. **d** 56 **p** 57. C Ashtead *Guildf* 56-59; C Farnham 59-60; Canada from 60. *10922 79A Avenue, Delta, British Columbia, Canada, V4C 1T4* New Westminster (604) 596-4987 Fax Toronto (416) 340-9755
COLE, Canon Donald Robertson. b 24. Edin Th Coll 57. **d** 59 **p** 60. R Edin St Cuth *Edin* 69-94; Hon Can St Mary's Cathl from 91; rtd 94. *92 Spottiswoode Street, Edinburgh EH9 1DJ* 0131-447 9230

COLE, Guy Spenser. b 63. Univ of Wales (Ban) BA84 Jes Coll Cam BA88. Westcott Ho Cam 85. **d** 88 **p** 89. C Eastville St Anne w St Mark and St Thos *Bris* 88-92; P-in-c Penhill 92-95; V from 95. *The Vicarage, Bremhill Close, Penhill, Swindon SN2 5LJ* Swindon (01793) 721921
COLE, Henry Frederick Charles. b 23. ALCD52. **d** 52 **p** 53. Ind Chapl *Sheff* 67-72; V Wadsley 72-88; RD Hallam 83-87; rtd 88. *Julians, 217 Tullibardine Road, Sheffield S11 7GQ* Sheffield (0114) 268 4719
COLE, John Charles. b 22. CQSW70. E Midl Min Tr Course CPTS82. **d** 82 **p** 83. NSM Skirbeck H Trin *Linc* from 82. *27 Blackthorn Lane, Boston, Lincs PE21 9BG* Boston (01205) 366255
COLE, John Gordon. b 43. Magd Coll Cam BA65 MA69. Cuddesdon Coll 66. **d** 68 **p** 69. C Leeds St Pet *Ripon* 68-71; C Moor Allerton 71-75; P-in-c Pendleton *Blackb* 75-86; Dioc Communications Officer 75-86; Dioc Missr *Linc* from 86. *Pelham House, Little Lane, Wrawby, Brigg, S Humberside DN20 8RW* Brigg (01652) 657484
COLE, John Spensley. b 39. FCA65 Clare Coll Cam BA62 MA66 Nottm Univ DipTh79. Linc Th Coll 78. **d** 80 **p** 81. C Cowes St Mary *Portsm* 80-83; C Portchester 83-87; V Modbury *Ex* from 87; R Aveton Gifford from 87. *The Vicarage, Modbury, Ivybridge, Devon PL21 0QN* Modbury (01548) 830260
COLE, John Wilfrid. b 06. Keble Coll Ox BA30 DipTh31 MA34 DipPsych48 BSc51. Wycliffe Hall Ox 30. **d** 32 **p** 33. R Lyford w Charney *Ox* 47-71; rtd 71. *36 Plantation Road, Oxford OX2 6HE* Oxford (01865) 57927
COLE, Lawrence Howard. b 09. ALCD39 Dur Univ BA47. **d** 39 **p** 40. V Cogges *Ox* 60-77; rtd 77; Perm to Offic *Worc* from 77. *Perrins House, Moorlands Road, Malvern, Worcs WR14 2TZ* Malvern (01684) 563732
COLE, Melvin George Merriman. b 05. Fourah Bay Coll Freetown. **d** 48 **p** 53. Sierra Leone 69-76; rtd 74; Perm to Offic *S'wark* from 76. *101 Pendle Road, London SW16 6RX* 0181-769 2704
COLE, Michael Berkeley. b 44. **d** 72 **p** 73. C Shepshed *Leic* 72-76; V Leic St Chad 76-79; NSM Painswick w Sheepscombe *Glouc* from 94. *The Barn, Well Farm, Wick Street, Painswick, Glos GL6 7QR* Painswick (01452) 812824
COLE, Dr Michael George. b 35. CD75. Wesley Th Sem Washington DMin88 Kelham Th Coll 56 Lich Th Coll 57. **d** 60 **p** 61. C Doncaster Ch Ch *Sheff* 60-63; Chapl RAF 63-68; Canada 68-82; USA from 82. *484 Mountain Road, Halifax, Virginia 24558-2171, USA* Norfolk (804) 476-6473
COLE, Canon Michael John. b 34. St Pet Hall Ox BA56 MA60. Ridley Hall Cam 56. **d** 58 **p** 59. C Finchley Ch Ch *Lon* 58-61; C Leeds St Geo *Ripon* 58-61; Travelling Sec IVF 61-64; V Crookes St Thos *Sheff* 64-71; R Rusholme *Man* 71-75; V Woodford Wells *Chelmsf* from 75; Chapl Leytonstone Ho Hosp from 85; Hon Can Chelmsf Cathl *Chelmsf* from 89. *All Saints' Vicarage, 4 Inmans Row, Woodford Green, Essex IG8 0NH* 0181-504 0266
COLE, Norman George. b 05. St Jo Coll Dur BA27 DipTh28 MA30. **d** 28 **p** 29. V Stainland *Wakef* 60-63; rtd 70. *2 Corondale Road, Beacon Park, Plymouth PL2 2RF* Plymouth (01752) 559348
COLE, Canon Peter George Lamont. b 27. Pemb Coll Cam BA49 MA52. Cuddesdon Coll 50. **d** 52 **p** 53. V Bromley St Andr *Roch* 65-72; V Folkestone St Mary and St Eanswythe *Cant* 72-87; Hon Can Cant Cathl 80-87; V E and W Worldham, Hartley Mauditt w Kingsley etc *Win* 87-92; RD Alton 89-92; rtd 92; RD Petworth *Chich* 94-95; Perm to Offic from 95. *Marula Cottage, Lower Street, Fittleworth, Pulborough, W Sussex RH20 1JE* Fittleworth (01798) 865540
COLE, Richard Leslie. b 08. Ball Coll Ox BA31 MA35. St Steph Ho Ox DipTh32. **d** 32 **p** 33. Br Guiana 61-66; Guyana 66-84; rtd 84; Perm to Offic *Llan* 84-93. *Ellesborough Manor, Butlers Cross, Aylesbury, Bucks HP17 0XF* Wendover (01296) 696817
COLE, Canon Robert Alan. b 23. TCD BA44 MA46 PhD48 Lon Univ BD49 MTh51. Oak Hill Th Coll 46. **d** 50 **p** 51. Australia 69-88 and from 94; Hon Can Sydney from 79; Singapore 88-94; rtd 94. *1/20 Musgrave Street, Mosman, NSW, Australia 2088* Sydney (2) 960-3161
COLE, Ven Ronald Berkeley. b 13. Bps' Coll Cheshunt 40. **d** 42 **p** 43. Adn Leic 63-80; Can Res Leic Cathl 78-80; rtd 80; RD Repps *Nor* 83-86; Perm to Offic from 86. *Harland Rise, 70 Cromer Road, Sheringham, Norfolk NR26 8RT* Sheringham (01263) 824955
COLE, Timothy Alexander Robertson. b 60. Aber Univ MA83 Edin Univ BD86. Edin Th Coll 83. **d** 86 **p** 87. C Dunfermline *St And* 86-89; Vice-Provost St Andr Cathl Inverness *Mor* 89-90; R Inverness St Andr 89-90; R Edin St Mich and All SS *Edin* 90-95; CF from 95. *c/o MOD (Army), Bagshot Park, Bagshot, Surrey GU19 5PL* Bagshot (01276) 471717 Fax 412834

COLE, Walter John Henden. b 04. Bps' Coll Cheshunt 25. d 27 p 28. V W Hampstead St Jas *Lon* 55-76; rtd 76. *87 College Road, Isleworth, Middx TW7 5DP* 0181-568 2708

COLE, William Pritchard. b 09. OBE51. St D Coll Lamp BA32. d 33 p 35. Chapl Upper Chine Sch Shanklin 65-76; rtd 76. *27 Burton Road, Bridport, Dorset DT6 4JD* Bridport (01308) 56289

COLE-KING, Dr Susan Mary. b 34. Lon Univ MB, BS62 DTPH71. Gen Th Sem (NY) 84. d 86 p 87. USA 86-88; Par Dn Dorchester *Ox* 89-92; D-in-c Drayton St Pet (Berks) 92-94; P-in-c from 94. *The Vicarage, 8 Gravel Lane, Drayton, Abingdon, Oxon OX14 4HY* Abingdon (01235) 531374

COLEBROOK, Christopher John. b 36. Qu Mary Coll Lon BA60 BD69. St D Coll Lamp DipTh62. d 62 p 63. C Llandeilo Tal-y-bont *S & B* 62-66; C Llansamlet 66-71; V Nantmel w St Harmon's and Llanwrthwl 71-76; V Glantawe 76-85; V Gowerton from 85; RD Llwchwr from 93. *The Vicarage, Church Street, Gowerton, Swansea SA4 3EA* Swansea (01792) 872266

COLEBROOK, Peter Acland. b 29. Coates Hall Edin 52. d 55 p 56. C Bideford *Ex* 62-66; rtd 89. *Vale Cottage, Ham Lane, Marnhull, Sturminster Newton, Dorset DT10 1JN* Marnhull (01258) 820246

COLEBROOKE, Andrew. b 50. Imp Coll Lon BSc71 MSc72 PhD75. Ridley Hall Cam 92. d 94 p 95. C Shrub End *Chelmsf* from 94. *St Cedd's House, Eldred Avenue, Colchester CO2 9AR* Colchester (01206) 572017

COLEBY, Andrew Mark. b 59. FRHistS88 Linc Coll Ox MA85 DPhil85 Dur Univ BA90. Cranmer Hall Dur 88. d 91 p 92. C Heeley *Sheff* 91-94; TV Gleadless from 94. *St Peter's Vicarage, 51 White Lane, Sheffield S12 3GD* Sheffield (0114) 239 6132

COLEMAN, Mrs Ann Valerie. b 51. K Coll Lon BD72. St Aug Coll Cant. dss 80 d 87 p 94. Hampstead Garden Suburb *Lon* 80-84; Golders Green 85-87; Selection Sec and Voc Adv ACCM 87-91; ABM 91; Teacher Bp Stoppard Sch 92-93; Perm to Offic *Lon* 92-93; C Eastcote St Lawr from 93; Chapl Bp Ramsey Sch from 93. *St Lawrence's Vicarage, 2 Bridle Road, Pinner, Middx HA5 2SJ* 0181-866 1263

COLEMAN, Beverley Warren. b 20. Leeds Univ BA41. Coll of Resurr Mirfield 41. d 43 p 44. CF (TA) 52-87; V Albrighton *Lich* 64-71; R Jersey St Sav *Win* 71-84; rtd 87. *44 Walnut Crescent, Fruit Lands, Malvern Wells, Worcs WR14 4AX* Malvern (01684) 563535

COLEMAN, Brian James. b 36. K Coll Cam BA58 MA61. Ripon Hall Ox 58. d 60 p 61. C Allestree *Derby* 60-65; V Allestree St Nic 65-69; Chapl and Lect St Mich Coll Sarum 69-77; P-in-c Matlock Bank 77-86; R Frimley *Guildf* 86-92; V Guildf All SS from 92. *All Saints' Vicarage, 18 Vicarage Gate, Guildford, Surrey GU2 5QJ* Guildford (01483) 572006

COLEMAN, Charles Romaine Boldero. b 10. Clifton Th Coll 46. d 39 p 40. R Sampford Brett *B & W* 61-77; rtd 78; Perm to Offic *Nor* from 81. *1 The Firs, Redgate Hill, Hunstanton, Norfolk TE36 6LQ* Hunstanton (01485) 532946

COLEMAN, David. b 49. K Coll Lon BD72 AKC72. St Aug Coll Cant 72. d 73 p 74. C Is of Dogs Ch Ch and St Jo w St Luke *Lon* 73-77; C Greenford H Cross 77-80; V Cricklewood St Pet 80-85; V Golders Green 85-90; V Eastcote St Lawr from 90. *St Lawrence's Vicarage, 2 Bridle Road, Pinner, Middx HA5 2SJ* 0181-866 1263

COLEMAN, Dr Frank. b 58. Hull Univ BA Ox Univ BA83 MA87 PhD88. St Steph Ho Ox 80. d 83 p 84. C Brandon *Dur* 83-85; C Newton Aycliffe 85-88; V Denford w Ringstead *Pet* from 88; P-in-c Islip from 95. *The Vicarage, 11 Mountbatten Drive, Ringstead, Kettering, Northants NN14 4TX* Wellingborough (01933) 624627

COLEMAN, Frederick Philip. b 11. Lon Univ BSc(Econ)33. St Steph Ho Ox 38. d 40 p 41. R St Andr-by-the-Wardrobe w St Ann, Blackfriars *Lon* 71-84; Warden Community of St Jo Bapt Clewer 68-79; P-in-c St Nic Cole Abbey 78-82; AD The City 79-82; rtd 84; Hon C St Botolph Aldgate w H Trin Minories *Lon* from 85. *Charterhouse, Charterhouse Square, London EC1M 6AN* 0171-608 1077

COLEMAN, John Edward Noel. b 15. St Chad's Coll Dur BA37 DipTh39 MA49. d 39 p 40. V Silverdale *Blackb* 55-82; rtd 82; Perm to Offic *Blackb* from 82; Perm to Offic *Carl* from 83. *25 Coach Road, Warton, Carnforth, Lancs LA5 9PR* Carnforth (01524) 732368

COLEMAN, John Harold. b 38. Cant Sch of Min 83. d 86 p 87. NSM Dover St Martin *Cant* 86-92; V St Mary's Bay w St Mary-in-the-Marsh etc from 92; P-in-c New Romney w Old Romney and Midley from 95. *The Vicarage, North Street, New Romney, Kent TN28 8DC* New Romney (01679) 362308

COLEMAN, John Wycliffe. d 77 p 78. CMS 84-91; Egypt 84-91. *25 Southborough Road, London E9 7EF* 0181-985 7525

COLEMAN, Miss Mary Eileen. b 30. dss 84 d 87 p 94. Harlesden All So *Lon* 84-87; Par Dn 87-89; Par Dn Brondesbury St Anne

w Kilburn H Trin 89-90; rtd 90; NSM Langley Marish *Ox* from 94. *37 Willoughby Road, Langley, Slough SL3 8JH* Slough (01753) 581940

✠COLEMAN, Rt Rev Peter Everard. b 28. Barrister 65 Lon Univ LLB53 AKC53 Bris Univ MLitt76. Westcott Ho Cam 53. d 55 p 56 c 84. C Bedminster St Fran *Bris* 55-58; C St Helen Bishopsgate w St Martin Outwich *Lon* 58-60; Asst Sec SCM 58-60; Chapl and Lect K Coll Lon 60-66; V Clifton St Paul *Bris* 66-71; Chapl Bris Univ 66-71; Can Res Bris Cathl 71-81; Dir Ord Tr 71-81; Dir Bris & Glouc Tr Course 77-81; Adn Worc and Can Res Worc Cathl *Worc* 81-84; Suff Bp Crediton *Ex* from 84. *10 The Close, Exeter EX1 1EZ* Exeter (01392) 73509 Fax 431266

COLEMAN, Peter Nicholas. b 42. St Mich Coll Llan 83. d 85 p 86. C Skewen *Llan* 85-88; V Ystradyfodwg from 88. *The Vicarage, St David's Close, Pentre, M Glam CF41 7AX* Tonypandy (01443) 434201

COLEMAN, Robert William Alfred. b 16. Ch Coll Cam BA39 MA42. Bible Churchmen's Coll 39. d 40 p 41. Chapl Seaford Coll Sussex 60-81; rtd 81; Perm to Offic *Chich* from 83. *Villa Florence, 24 West Drive, Bognor Regis, W Sussex PO22 7TS* Middleton-on-Sea (01243) 583410

COLEMAN, Sybil Jean. b 30. St Deiniol's Hawarden 83. d 85. NSM Manselton *S & B* 85-90; C Swansea St Mark and St Jo 90-94; P-in-c from 94. *The Parsonage, 27 Bowen Road, Swansea SA1 2NA* Swansea (01792) 465074

COLEMAN, Terence Norman. b 37. St Mich Coll Llan 83. d 85 p 86. C Machen *Mon* 85-87; C Penmaen and Crumlin 87-89; V 89-93; V Newbridge from 93. *St Paul's Vicarage, High Street, Newbridge, Gwent NP1 4FW* Newbridge (01495) 243975

COLEMAN, Timothy (Tim). b 57. CEng86 MIChemE86 Southn Univ BSc79. Ridley Hall Cam 87. d 89 p 90. C Bisley and W End *Guildf* 89-93; C Hollington St Jo *Chich* from 93. *227 Hillside Road, Hastings, E Sussex TN34 2QY* Hastings (01424) 752065

COLES, Francis Herbert. b 35. Selw Coll Cam BA59 MA63. Coll of Resurr Mirfield 59. d 61 p 62. C Wolvercote *Ox* 61-65; C Farnham Royal 65-69; V Lynton and Brendon *Ex* 69-73; V Countisbury 70-73; TR Lynton, Brendon, Countisbury, Lynmouth etc 73-76; P-in-c Iffley *Ox* 76-88; V Ivybridge w Harford *Ex* from 88. *The Vicarage, Blachford Road, Ivybridge, Devon PL21 0AD* Plymouth (01752) 690193

COLES, Geoffrey Herbert. b 38. Nottm Univ CertEd59 TCert62 Loughb Coll of Educn DLC60. N Ord Course 77. d 80 p 81. NSM Shelf *Bradf* 80-85; C Manningham 85-86; TV 86-92; P-in-c Wyke from 92. *St Mary's Vicarage, 6 Vicarage Close, Wyke, Bradford, W Yorkshire BD12 8QW* Bradford (01274) 678216

COLES, John Spencer Halstaff. b 50. Hertf Coll Ox BA72 MA76. Wycliffe Hall Ox 72. d 75 p 76. C Reading Greyfriars *Ox* 75-79; C Clifton Ch Ch w Em *Bris* 79-82; V Woodside Park St Barn *Lon* from 82. *St Barnabas' Vicarage, 98 Westbury Road, London N12 7PD* 0181-445 3598 or 446 7506

COLES, Robert Charles. b 41. Bps' Coll Cheshunt 66. d 68 p 69. C Northn St Alb *Pet* 68-72; C Durrington *Chich* 72-74; C Portslade St Nic 74-78; C Horsham 78-82; C-in-c Parklands St Wilfrid CD 82-87; V Eastbourne St Phil from 87. *The Vicarage, 1 St Philip's Avenue, Eastbourne, E Sussex BN22 8LU* Eastbourne (01323) 732381

COLES, Robert Reginald (Bob). b 47. Surrey Univ BSc69. Cant Sch of Min 82. d 85 p 86. NSM Sittingbourne St Mich *Cant* 85-87; C St Laurence in the Isle of Thanet 87-93; P-in-c St Nicholas at Wade w Sarre and Chislet w Hoath from 93. *The Vicarage, The Length, St Nicholas-at-Wade, Birchington, Kent CT7 0PW* Thanet (01843) 47200

COLES, Stephen Richard. b 49. Univ Coll Ox BA70 MA74 Leeds Univ BA80. Coll of Resurr Mirfield 78. d 81 p 82. C Stoke Newington St Mary *Lon* 81-84; Chapl K Coll Cam 84-89; V Finsbury Park St Thos *Lon* from 89. *25 Romilly Road, London N4 2QY* 0171-359 5741

COLESHILL, Archdeacon of. Vacant

COLEY, Frederick Albert. b 13. Lich Th Coll 65. d 66 p 67. C Tardebigge *Worc* 68-72; P-in-c Stoke Bliss w Kyre Wyard 72-73; P-in-c Hanley William w Hanley Child 72-73; P-in-c Stoke Bliss w Kyre Wyard, Hanley William etc 73-78; rtd 78; Perm to Offic *Worc* from 78. *Greenfields, Kyre Wood, Tenbury Wells, Worcs WR15 8SQ* Tenbury Wells (01584) 810961

COLEY, Peter Leonard. b 45. CEng MIMechE Bath Univ BSc67 City Univ MSc84. Oak Hill Th Coll 85. d 87 p 88. C Mile Cross *Nor* 87-92; R Stratton St Mary w Stratton St Michael etc from 92. *The Rectory, Flowerpot Lane, Long Stratton, Norwich NR15 2TS* Long Stratton (01508) 30238

✠COLIN, Rt Rev Gerald Fitzmaurice. b 13. TCD BA34 MA46. CITC 36. d 36 p 37 c 66. C Ballywillan *Conn* 36-38; C Dub St Geo *D & G* 38-47; Chan V St Patr Cathl Dub 38-47; Chapl RAFVR 39-47; V Frodingham *Linc* 47-66; Can and

Preb Linc Cathl 60-79; RD Manlake 60-66; Suff Bp Grimsby 66-78; rtd 79; Asst Bp Linc 79-94. *11 Upton Close, Norwich NR4 7PD* Norwich (01603) 51612

COLIN WILFRED, Brother. *See* CHERRIMAN, Colin Wilfred

COLLARD, Fred. b 25. Lon Bible Coll 51 Wycliffe Hall Ox 61. **d** 61 **p** 63. OMF 61-81; Malaysia 63-75; Perm to Offic *Ox* 71-81; TV Cheltenham St Mary, St Matt, St Paul and H Trin *Glouc* 81-92; rtd 92. *17 Dubrae Close, St Albans, Herts AL3 4JT* St Albans (01727) 869138

COLLARD, Canon Harold. b 27. Wycliffe Hall Ox 51. **d** 53 **p** 54. R Chesterfield H Trin *Derby* 68-77; P-in-c Matlock Bath 77-83; V 83-92; Hon Can Derby Cathl 87-92; RD Wirksworth 88-92; rtd 92. *10 Kirkby Avenue, Ripon, N Yorkshire HG4 2DR* Ripon (01765) 606306

COLLARD, John Cedric. b 30. Pemb Coll Cam BA53 MA76. St Alb Minl Tr Scheme 77. **d** 80 **p** 81. NSM Roxton w Gt Barford *St Alb* 80-84; C Liskeard w St Keyne, St Pinnock and Morval *Truro* 84-87; TV Liskeard, St Keyne, St Pinnock, Morval etc 87-93; rtd 93. *Curlew Cottage, Bohetherick, Saltash, Cornwall PL12 6SZ* Liskeard (01579) 50560

COLLARD, Norton Harvey. b 22. Open Univ BA80. Roch Th Coll 63. **d** 65 **p** 66. C Dartford H Trin *Roch* 67-70; V Grantham St Anne *Linc* 70-87; rtd 87. *1 Kenwick Drive, Grantham, Lincs NG31 9DP* Grantham (01476) 77345

COLLAS, Canon Victor John. b 23. Pemb Coll Ox BA44 MA48. Wycliffe Hall Ox 49. **d** 51 **p** 52. R Guernsey St Andr *Win* 58-81; Perm to Offic from 81; rtd 88. *Paradis, La Rue du Paradis, Vale, Guernsey, Channel Islands GY3 5BL* Guernsey (01481) 44450

COLLEDGE, Christopher Richard (Chris). b 58. Chich Th Coll. **d** 82 **p** 83. C Deal St Leon *Cant* 82-83; C Deal St Leon and St Rich and Sholden 83-85; Bermuda 85-88; TV Wickford and Runwell *Chelmsf* 88-90; Chapl Runwell Hosp Essex 88-90; Chapl RAD from 90. *St Saviour's Centre, 1 Armstrong Road, London W3 7JL* 0181-743 2209

COLLESS, Mrs Salma. b 55. SRN77 RM80. E Anglian Minl Tr Course 89. **d** 92. NSM Chesterton St Andr *Ely* 92-93; Australia from 93. *3 Cooba Place, Rivett, ACT, Australia 2611* Canberra (6) 288-7835

COLLETT, Albert Ernest Jack. b 15. S'wark Ord Course 62. **d** 65 **p** 66. C Lewisham St Jo Southend *S'wark* 65-73; C-in-c Reigate St Phil CD 73-82; rtd 83; Perm to Offic *S'wark* from 83. *42 Wimborne Avenue, Redhill RH1 5AG* Redhill (01737) 763218

COLLETT, Maurice John. b 28. S'wark Ord Course 76. **d** 79 **p** 80. NSM Feltham *Lon* from 79. *58 Shakespeare Avenue, Feltham, Middx TW14 9HX* 0181-751 4144

COLLETT-WHITE, Thomas Charles. b 36. Trin Coll Cam BA61 MA86. Ridley Hall Cam 60. **d** 62 **p** 63. C Gillingham St Mark *Roch* 62-66; V 79-90; C Normanton *Wakef* 66-69; V Highbury New Park St Aug *Lon* 69-76; Canada 76-79; Chapl Medway Hosp Gillingham 79-85; P-in-c Clerkenwell St Jas and St Jo w St Pet *Lon* from 90. *4 Owens Row, London EC1V 4NP* 0171-833 8947

COLLIE, Dr Bertie Harold Guy. b 28. Glas Univ MB, ChB56. Glas Univ Course 75. **d** 76 **p** 77. NSM Ayr *Glas* 76-84; NSM Maybole 76-84; NSM Girvan from 76; NSM Pinmore from 76. *Hillside, Cargill Road, Maybole, Ayrshire KA19 8AF* Maybole (01655) 883564

COLLIE, Canon John Norman. b 25. Em Coll Cam BA51 MA56. Ridley Hall Cam 52. **d** 54 **p** 55. V Ecclesall *Sheff* 68-90; Hon Can Sheff Cathl 83-90; RD Ecclesall 85-89; rtd 90. *46 Sunnyvale Road, Totley, Sheffield S17 4FB* Sheffield (0114) 235 2249

COLLIER, Anthony Charles. b 45. Peterho Cam BA68 MA72 Or Coll Ox DipTh70 Whitelands Coll Lon CertEd76. Cuddesdon Coll 68. **d** 71 **p** 72. C N Holmwood *Guildf* 71-75; Perm to Offic *S'wark* 75-79; Chapl Colfe's Sch Lon 80-84; Hon C Shirley St Jo *Cant* 80-84; Hon C Shirley St Jo *S'wark* from 85. *56 Bennetts Way, Shirley, Croydon CR0 8AB* 0181-777 5719

COLLIER, Michael Francis. b 29. Wycliffe Hall Ox 71. **d** 73 **p** 74. C Hamstead St Paul *Birm* 73-75; P-in-c Castleton *Derby* 75-80; P-in-c Hope 78-80; V Hope and Castleton from 80; RD Bakewell and Eyam from 90. *The Vicarage, Hope, Sheffield S30 2RN* Hope Valley (01433) 620534

COLLIER, Paul Clive. b 53. Trin Coll Bris 80. **d** 82 **p** 83. C Hazlemere *Ox* 82-90; V from 90. *The New Vicarage, 260 Amersham Road, High Wycombe, Bucks HP15 7PZ* High Wycombe (01494) 439404

COLLIER, Paul Edward (Edge). b 63. Solicitor 93 Mert Coll Ox BA85 Lon Univ PGCE87. S'wark Ord Course 91. **d** 94. C E Dulwich St Jo *S'wark* from 94. *11 Hinckley Road, London SE15 4HZ* 0171-732 8983

COLLIER, Richard John Millard. b 45. E Anglian Minl Tr Course 78. **d** 81 **p** 82. NSM Nor St Pet Mancroft *Nor* 81-82;

NSM Nor St Pet Mancroft w St Jo Maddermarket from 82. *11 The Close, Norwich NR1 4DH* Norwich (01603) 624204

COLLIER, Stephen John. b 46. St Pet Coll Ox MA68 Univ of Wales (Cardiff) DipSocWork74. Qu Coll Birm DipTh94. **d** 94 **p** 95. C Thorpe *Nor* from 94. *24 Naseby Way, Norwich NR7 0TP* Norwich (01603) 31868

COLLIN, Anthony Garth. b 27. Roch Th Coll 64. **d** 66 **p** 67. C Hove 69-72; R Rumboldswyke *Chich* 72-75; Chapl R W Sussex and Graylingwell Hosps Chich 75-88; rtd 88; Lic to Offic *Sheff* from 88. *6 Muirfield Avenue, Doncaster, S Yorkshire DN4 6UP* Doncaster (01302) 538512

COLLIN, Terry. b 39. St Aid Birkenhead 65. **d** 67 **p** 68. C Bolton St Jas w St Chrys *Bradf* 67-71; C Keighley 71-74; V Greengates from 74. *The Vicarage, 138 New Line, Greengates, Bradford, W Yorkshire BD10 0BX* Bradford (01274) 613111

COLLING, Canon James Oliver (Joc). b 30. MBE95. Man Univ BA50. Cuddesdon Coll 52. **d** 54 **p** 55. C Wigan All SS *Liv* 54-59; V Padgate Ch Ch 59-71; R Padgate 71-73; RD Warrington 70-82 and 87-89; AD from 89; R Warrington St Elphin from 73; Hon Can Liv Cathl from 76; Chapl to The Queen from 90. *The Rectory, Warrington WA1 2TL* Warrington (01925) 635020

COLLING, Terence John. b 47. Linc Th Coll 84. **d** 86 **p** 87. C Wood End *Cov* 86-90; V Willenhall from 90. *The Vicarage, Robin Hood Road, Coventry CV3 3AY* Coventry (01203) 303266

COLLINGS, Neil. b 46. K Coll Lon BD69 AKC69. **d** 70 **p** 71. C Littleham w Exmouth *Ex* 70-72; TV 72-74; Chapl Westmr Abbey 74-79; Preb Heref Cathl *Heref* 79-86; Dir of Ords and Post Ord Tr 79-86; R Heref St Nic 79-86; Bp's Dom Chapl 82-86; R Harpenden St Nic *St Alb* from 86. *The Rectory, 9 Rothamsted Avenue, Harpenden, Herts AL5 2DD* Harpenden (01582) 712202

COLLINGS, Robert Frank. b 26. Lon Univ BD53. ALCD52. **d** 52 **p** 53. C Bayswater *Lon* 52-55; Australia from 55; rtd 87. *Lot 6, Maguire Place, Dardanup, W Australia 6236* Dardanup (97) 281264

COLLINGWOOD, Christopher Paul. b 54. MA BMus. Ripon Coll Cuddesdon. **d** 83 **p** 84. C Tupsley *Heref* 83-86; Prec St Alb Abbey *St Alb* 86-90; V Bedf St Paul from 90. *St Paul's Vicarage, 12 The Embankment, Bedford MK40 3PD* Bedford (01234) 352314 or 340163

COLLINGWOOD, Deryck Laurence. b 50. St Jo Coll Cam BA72. Edin Th Coll BD85. **d** 85 **p** 85. Chapl Napier Poly *Edin* 85-92; Chapl Napier Univ from 92; C Edin Ch Ch 85-88; TV from 88; Tutor Edin Th Coll from 89; NSM Edin St Hilda *Edin* from 94; NSM Edin St Fillan from 94. *St Hilda's House, 114 Oxgangs Road, Edinburgh EH13 9JA* 0131-441 1235

COLLINGWOOD, Graham Lewis. b 63. Open Univ BA92. St Steph Ho Ox DipMin95. **d** 95. C Heavitree w Ex St Paul *Ex* from 95. *2 Sherwood Close, Exeter EX1 5DX* Exeter (01392) 78591

COLLINGWOOD, John Jeremy Raynham. b 37. Barrister 62 CCC Cam BA60 MA68 Lon Univ BD78. Trin Coll Bris 75. **d** 78 **p** 79. C Henleaze *Bris* 78-80; P-in-c Clifton H Trin, St Andr and St Pet 80-81; V 81-91; RD Clifton 84-87; Bp's Officer for Miss and Evang 87-91; V Guildf Ch Ch *Guildf* from 91. *Christ Church Vicarage, 25 Waterden Road, Guildford, Surrey GU1 2AZ* Guildford (01483) 68886

COLLINS, Adelbert Andrew. b 15. Lich Th Coll. **d** 61 **p** 62. C Sedgley All SS *Lich* 61-77; P-in-c Enville 77-81 and 86-88; R 81-86; C Kinver and Enville 88-90; rtd 90. *West Cottage, Bridgnorth Road, Enville, Stourbridge, W Midlands DY7 5JA* Kinver (01384) 873733

COLLINS, Barry Douglas. b 47. Kelham Th Coll 66. **d** 70 **p** 71. C Peel Green *Man* 70-73; C Salford St Phil w St Steph 73-75; R Blackley H Trin 75-79; Perm to Offic *Ripon* 80-83; Perm to Offic *Pet* 83-85; Perm to Offic *Cov* from 85. *c/o 10 Onley Park, Willoughby, Rugby, Warks CV23 8AN* Rugby (01788) 817579

COLLINS, Bruce Churton. b 47. BSc. Oak Hill Th Coll. **d** 83 **p** 84. C Notting Hill St Jo *Lon* 83-87; C Notting Hill St Jo and St Pet 87-90; V Roxeth Ch Ch and Harrow St Pet 90-93; P-in-c S Harrow St Paul 91-93; TR Roxeth from 93. *Christ Church Rectory, Roxeth Hill, Harrow, Middx HA2 0JN* 0181-422 3241

COLLINS, Ms Cheryl Anne. b 62. MCA90 Rob Coll Cam BA85 MA89. Ripon Coll Cuddesdon 91. **d** 93 **p** 94. C Sheff Sharrow *Sheff* from 93. *18 Raven Road, Sheffield S7 1NA* Sheffield (0114) 258 0926

COLLINS, Christopher. b 46. K Coll Lon BSc67 AKC67 Pemb Coll Ox BA70. St Steph Ho Ox 68. **d** 71 **p** 72. C Pennywell St Thos and Grindon St Oswald CD *Dur* 71-74; C Pallion 74-76; C Millfield St Mary 74-76; C Bishopwearmouth Gd Shep 74-76; C Harton Colliery 76-78; TV Winlaton 78-85; V Grangetown from 85. *St Aidan's Vicarage, Grangetown, Sunderland SR2 9RS* 0191-514 3485

COLLINS, Christopher David. b 43. Sheff Univ BA(Econ)64. Tyndale Hall Bris 65. **d** 68 **p** 69. C Rusholme *Man* 68-71; C

Bushbury *Lich* 71-74; V Fairfield *Liv* 74-81; V Tunbridge Wells St Jo *Roch* 81-92; R Luton Ch Ch from 92; RD Roch from 94. *Luton Rectory, Capstone Road, Chatham, Kent ME5 7PN* Medway (01634) 843780

COLLINS, Donard Michael. b 55. TCD BA. Oak Hill Th Coll. **d** 83 **p** 84. C Lurgan Ch the Redeemer *D & D* 83-87; I Ardmore w Craigavon from 87. *Ardmore Rectory, Derryadd, Lurgan, Craigavon, Co Armagh BT66 6QR* Derryadd (01762) 340357

COLLINS, Frank. b 56. Oak Hill Th Coll BA92. **d** 92 **p** 93. C Heref St Pet w St Owen and St Jas *Heref* 92-95; CF from 95. *clo MOD (Army), Bagshot Park, Bagshot, Surrey GU19 5PL* Bagshot (01276) 471717 Fax 412834

COLLINS, Canon Frederick Spencer. b 36. FACCA Birm Univ DipTh67. Ripon Hall Ox. **d** 67 **p** 68. C Evington *Leic* 67-71; C Hall Green Ascension *Birm* 71-73; V Burney Lane 73-79; Dioc Stewardship Adv 79-84; V Yardley St Edburgha from 84; RD Yardley 86-92; Hon Can Birm Cathl from 89. *The Vicarage, Yardley, Birmingham B33 8PH* 0121-628 9548

COLLINS, George Martyn. b 36. Bris Univ BA58. Coll of Resurr Mirfield. **d** 62 **p** 63. C Widley w Wymering *Portsm* 62-64; C Kingstanding St Mark CD *Birm* 64-69; V Weoley Castle 69-78; R Curdworth 78-83; TR Curdworth w Castle Vale 83-88; V Westbury-on-Trym H Trin *Bris* from 88. *Holy Trinity Vicarage, 44 Eastfield Road, Westbury-on-Trym, Bristol BS9 4AG* Bristol (0117) 962 1536 or 950 8644

COLLINS, Canon Ian Geoffrey. b 37. Hull Univ BA60 CertEd. Sarum Th Coll 60. **d** 62 **p** 63. C Gainsborough All SS *Linc* 62-65; Min Can Windsor 65-81; Succ Windsor 67-81; R Kirkby in Ashfield *S'well* 81-85; Can Res S'well Minster from 85; P-in-c Edingley w Halam from 91. *5 Vicar's Court, Southwell, Notts NG25 0HP* Southwell (01636) 815056

COLLINS, James Frederick. b 10. St Jo Coll Cam BA34 MA38. Westcott Ho Cam 34. **d** 35 **p** 36. Dir of Ords *Sarum* 68-73; Hon C Devizes St Jo w St Mary 68-75; rtd 75; Perm to Offic *St Alb* from 81. *3 Parkinson Close, Marford Road, Wheathampstead, St Albans, Herts AL4 5DP* Wheathampstead (01582) 833944

COLLINS, Miss Janet May. b 55. Qu Mary Coll Lon BA78 St Jo Coll Dur BA84. Cranmer Hall Dur 82. **dss** 85 **d** 87 **p** 94. Willington Team *Newc* 85-87; C 87-88; Par Dn Stevenage St Hugh Chells *St Alb* 88-90; Par Dn Goldington 90-93; TD Witney *Ox* 93-94; TV from 94. *The Vicarage, 292 Thorney Leys, Witney, Oxon OX8 7YW* Witney (01993) 773821

COLLINS, John Gilbert. b 32. S'wark Ord Course 67. **d** 71 **p** 72. C Coulsdon St Jo *S'wark* 71-75; Chapl St Fran Hosp Haywards Heath 75-84; Chapl Hurstwood Park Hosp Haywards Heath 75-84; R Stedham w Iping, Elsted and Treyford-cum-Didling *Chich* 84-92; rtd 92; Perm to Offic *Chich* from 94. *12 Exeter Road, Broyle, Chichester, W Sussex PO19 4EF* Chichester (01243) 536861

COLLINS, Preb John Theodore Cameron Bucke. b 25. Clare Coll Cam BA49 MA52. Ridley Hall Cam 49. **d** 51 **p** 52. V Gillingham St Mark *Roch* 57-71; Chapl Medway Hosp Gillingham 70-71; V Canford Magna *Sarum* 71-80; RD Wimborne 79-80; V Brompton H Trin w Onslow Square St Paul *Lon* 80-85; C 85-89; AD Chelsea 84-88; Preb St Paul's Cathl 85-89; rtd 89; Perm to Offic *Lon* 89-90; Perm to Offic *Win* from 89. *7 Solent Court, Cornwallis Road, Milford on Sea, Lymington, Hants SO41 0NH* Lymington (01590) 645961

COLLINS, Ms Kathryne Broncy. b 51. Portland State Univ BSc75 Lon Univ MSc76. Linc Th Coll 92. **d** 94 **p** 95. C Bishop's Castle w Mainstone *Heref* from 94. *7 Lavender Bank, Bishops Castle, Shropshire SY9 5BD* Bishops Castle (01588) 638024

COLLINS, Maurice Arthur Reily. b 19. Clare Coll Cam BA41 MA45. Westcott Ho Cam 45. **d** 47 **p** 48. R Ockley *Guildf* 53-82; R Ockley, Okewood and Forest Green 82-85; rtd 85; Perm to Offic *Portsm* from 86. *Old Wheatsheaf, Privett, Alton, Hants GU34 3NX* Privett (0173088) 287

COLLINS, Canon Norman Hilary. b 33. Mert Coll Ox BA55 MA58. Wells Th Coll 58. **d** 60 **p** 61. C Ystrad Mynach *Llan* 60-62; C Gelligaer 62-67; V Maerdy 67-77; R Penarth w Lavernock from 77; RD Penarth and Barry from 87; Can Llan Cathl from 92. *The Rectory, 13 Hickman Road, Penarth, S Glam CF62 2AJ* Penarth (01222) 709463

COLLINS, Paul David Arthur. b 50. Lanc Univ MSc91. K Coll Lon BD72 AKC72 St Aug Coll Cant 73. **d** 73 **p** 74. C Rotherhithe St Mary w All SS *S'wark* 73-76; C Stocking Farm *Leic* 76-78; V 78-83; R Husbands Bosworth w Mowsley and Knaptoft etc 83-87; Soc Resp Officer *Blackb* 87-94; R Worc City St Paul and Old St Martin etc *Worc* from 94; Chapl Worcs Tech Coll from 94; Min Can Worc Cathl *Worc* from 95. *The Rectory, 7 Aldersey Close, Worcester WR5 3EH* Worcester (01905) 767912

COLLINS, Paul Myring. b 53. St Jo Coll Dur BA75. St Steph Ho Ox BA78 MA83. **d** 79 **p** 80. C Meir *Lich* 79-82; C Fenton 82-83; TV Leek and Meerbrook 83-87; Tutor in Th and

Liturgy Chich Th Coll 87-94; Dir of Studies 90-94; V Brighton Gd Shep Preston *Chich* from 94. *The Good Shepherd Vicarage, 272 Dyke Road, Brighton BN1 5AE* Brighton (01273) 882987

COLLINS, Canon Peter Churton. b 13. Lon Univ BD35. Ely Th Coll 35. **d** 36 **p** 37. R Crayford *Roch* 60-78; V Dartford St Alb 42-60; Hon Can Roch Cathl 63-79; RD Erith 65-79; rtd 79; Chapl Huggens Coll Northfleet 79-87. *College of St Barnabas, Blackberry Lane, Lingfield, Surrey RH7 6NJ* Dormans Park (01342) 870260

COLLINS, Peter John. b 33. Open Univ BA. Oak Hill Th Coll 64. **d** 66 **p** 67. C Low Leyton *Chelmsf* 66-69; C Portsdown *Portsm* 69-72; V Gatten St Paul 72-79; C-in-c Ingrave St Steph CD *Chelmsf* 79-85; V Roydon from 85. *St Peter's Vicarage, Church Mead, Roydon, Harlow, Essex CM19 5EY* Roydon (01279) 792103

COLLINS, Philip Howard Norton. b 50. AKC73. St Aug Coll Cant 73. **d** 74 **p** 75. C Stamford Hill St Thos *Lon* 74-78; C Upwood w Gt and Lt Raveley *Ely* 78-81; C Ramsey 78-81; R Leverington 81-92; P-in-c Wisbech St Mary 89-92; RD Wisbech 90-92; TR Whittlesey and Pondersbridge from 92. *8 The Grove, Whittlesey, Peterborough PE7 2RF* Peterborough (01733) 202563

COLLINS, Richard Andrew. b 65. K Coll Lon BD92 AKC92. St Steph Ho Ox 92. **d** 94 **p** 95. C Whickham *Dur* from 94. *St Mary's House, 7A Coalway Drive, Whickham, Newcastle upon Tyne NE16 4BT* 0191-488 3015 Fax as telephone

COLLINS, Rodney Harry. b 20. SSC Open Univ BA74. S'wark Ord Course 75. **d** 78 **p** 79. NSM Swanley St Mary *Roch* 78-94. *16 Stanhope Road, Sidcup, Kent DA15 7AA* 0181-302 0867

COLLINS, Roger Richardson. b 48. Birm Univ BPhil88. W Midl Minl Tr Course 78. **d** 81 **p** 82. NSM Cotteridge *Birm* from 81. *6 Chesterfield Court, Middleton Hall Road, Birmingham B30 1AF* 0121-459 4009

COLLINS, Ross Nicoll Ferguson. b 64. Ripon Coll Cuddesdon. **d** 92 **p** 93. C Goring w S Stoke *Ox* from 92. *11 Westway, Goring, Reading RG8 0BX* Goring-on-Thames (01491) 873890

COLLINS, Canon Stella Vivian. b 32. Sarum Th Coll 74. **dss** 77 **d** 87 **p** 94. Harnham *Sarum* 77-88; Hon Par Dn 87-88; Dioc Lay Min Adv from 82; Hon Par Dn Wilton w Netherhampton and Fugglestone 88-94; Hon C from 94; RD Wylye and Wilton 89-94; Hon Can Sarum Cathl from 93. *Shawmeare, Coombe Road, Salisbury SP2 8BT* Salisbury (01722) 336420

COLLINS, William Arthur Donovan. b 21. AKC49. **d** 50 **p** 51. S Africa 66-80; Adn Cape Town 75-80; V Birchington w Acol and Minnis Bay *Cant* 80-85; Warden Coll of St Barn Lingfield 85-88; rtd 88. *Cedar Cottage, Parmoor, Frieth, Henley-on-Thames, Oxon RG9 6NN* High Wycombe (01494) 881446

COLLINS, William Carpenter. b 35. BA55 MA57 MDiv65. Ch Div Sch of the Pacific (USA) 63. **d** 66 **p** 67. USA 66-71; Hon C Newlyn St Pet *Truro* 82-93; Perm to Offic from 93. *Cape House, Cape Cornwall, St Just, Penzance, Cornwall TR19 7NN* Penzance (01736) 787112

COLLINS, William Francis Martin. b 43. St Cath Coll Cam BA66 MA70. Cuddesdon Coll 68. **d** 70 **p** 71. C Man Victoria Park *Man* 70-73; P-in-c Ancoats 73-78; Chapl Abraham Moss Cen 78-91; Hon C Cheetham Hill 81-84; Chs' FE Officer for Gtr Man 84-91; V Norbury *Ches* from 91. *Norbury Vicarage, 75 Chester Road, Hazel Grove, Stockport, Cheshire SK7 5PE* 0161-483 8640

COLLINS, Winfield St Clair. b 41. Univ of W Indies BA83 Man Univ BA88 MEd91. Codrington Coll Barbados LTh77. **d** 76 **p** 76. Asst Chapl HM Pris Wakef 76; Barbados 76-84; Asst Chapl HM Pris Wandsworth 85; Chapl HM Young Offender Inst Thorn Cross 85-91; Chapl HM Pris Pentonville from 91. *HM Prison Pentonville, Caledonian Road, London N7 8TT* 0171-607 5353 Fax 700 0244

COLLINSON, Ernest John. b 12. ALCD36. **d** 36 **p** 37. V Tiverton St Geo *Ex* 66-73; Perm to Offic from 74; rtd 77. *Flat 4, Lion House, 2 Carlton Hill, Exmouth, Devon EX8 2ST* Exmouth (01395) 265202

COLLINSON, Canon Joan Irene. b 31. ALA55 Westf Coll Lon BA52. **dss** 63 **d** 87 **p** 94. Westmr St Steph w St Jo *Lon* 65-68; R Foundn of St Kath 68-73; Qu Mary Coll 68-73; Notting Hill St Jo 73-74; Kent Univ *Cant* 74-82; Dean of Women's Min *S'wark* 82-89; Hon Can S'wark Cathl 88-89; TD Newc Epiphany *Newc* 89-94; TV from 94; Hon Can Newc Cathl from 89; Adv for Accredited Lay Min 89-94; Asst Dio Dir of Ords from 94. *St Hugh's Vicarage, Wansbeck Road, Gosforth, Newcastle upon Tyne NE3 2LR* 0191-285 8792

COLLINSON, Leslie Roland (Les). b 47. St Jo Coll Nottm DCM92. **d** 92 **p** 93. C Gorleston St Andr *Nor* from 92. *2 Elmgrove Road, Gorleston, Great Yarmouth, Norfolk NR31 7PP* Great Yarmouth (01493) 659410

COLLIS, Michael Alan. b 35. K Coll Lon BD60 AKC60. **d** 61 **p** 62. C Worc St Martin *Worc* 61-63; C Dudley St Thos 63-66; C St Peter-in-Thanet *Cant* 66-70; V Croydon H Trin 70-77; P-in-c Norbury St Steph 77-81; V 81-82; V Sutton Valence w E

Sutton and Chart Sutton 82-89; R New Fishbourne *Chich* from 89; P-in-c Appledram from 89. *The Rectory, 12 Fishbourne Road, Chichester, W Sussex PO19 3HX* Chichester (01243) 783364

COLLIS, Stephen Thomas. b 47. Cranmer Hall Dur 80. **d** 82 **p** 83. C Crewe All SS and St Paul *Ches* 82-84; C Wilmslow 84-86; Chapl RAF from 86. *Chaplaincy Services (RAF), HQ, Personnel and Training Command, RAF Innsworth, Gloucester GL3 1EZ* Gloucester (01452) 712612 Ext 5164 Fax 510828

COLLIS SMITH, Charles Philip. b 39. St Cath Coll Cam BA61. Lich Th Coll 61. **d** 63 **p** 64. C Hednesford *Lich* 66-71; V High Offley 71-80; R Myddle 80-92; V Broughton 80-92; rtd 92. *Trenance, 19 Wellgate, Wem, Shrewsbury SY4 5ES* Wem (01939) 235013

COLLISHAW, Arthur Beecroft. b 13. Qu Coll Cam BA35 MA48. Chich Th Coll 38. **d** 40 **p** 41. Ghana 69-78; rtd 78; Perm to Offic *Lon* 85-90. *15 Up The Quadrangle, Morden College, St German's Place, London SE3 0PW* 0181-293 5486

COLLISON, Christopher John. b 48. Oak Hill Th Coll 68. **d** 72 **p** 73. C Cromer *Nor* 72-75; C Costessey 76-78; V 87-95; C Heckmondwike *Wakef* 78-79; P-in-c Shepley 79-83; Dioc Communications Officer 79-83; Chapl Flushing Miss to Seamen *Eur* 83-85; Asst Min Sec Miss to Seamen 85-87; C St Mich Paternoster Royal *Lon* 85-87; P-in-c Swainsthorpe w Newton Flotman *Nor* from 95; Dioc Evang Officer from 95. *The Rectory, Church Road, Newton Flotman, Norwich NR15 1QB* Swainsthorpe (01508) 470762

COLLISON, Ms Elizabeth. b 38. Man Univ CertEd58. N Ord Course 85. **d** 88 **p** 94. C Huyton St Mich *Liv* 88-94; C Rainhill from 94. *26 Calder Drive, Prescot, Merseyside L35 0NW* 0151-426 3853

COLLYER, Canon David John. b 38. JP. Keble Coll Ox BA61 Ox Univ MA86. Westcott Ho Cam 61. **d** 63 **p** 64. C Perry Beeches *Birm* 63-65; Bp's Chapl for Special Youth Work 65-70; P-in-c Deritend 66-70; Bp's Youth Chapl and Dioc Youth Officer 70-73; R Northfield 73-78; Hon Chapl Birm Cathl 78-81; Hon C Birm St Geo 81-86; V Handsworth St Andr from 86; Hon Can Birm Cathl from 95. *St Andrew's Vicarage, Laurel Road, Birmingham B21 9PB* 0121-551 2097

COLLYER, John Gordon Llewellyn. b 15. Lon Univ BA. Sarum Th Coll 69. **d** 70 **p** 71. C Portchester *Portsm* 70-74; C Portsea All SS w St Jo Rudmore 74-75; TV Boscastle w Davidstow *Truro* 75-77; rtd 80; P-in-c Copdock w Washbrook and Belstead *St E* 80-83; Perm to Offic *Glouc* 83-86; Perm to Offic *Truro* 86-91. *Stonecote, 12 The Street, Ovington, Thetford, Norfolk IP25 6RT* Watton (01953) 881569

COLMAN, Cyril Vickers. b 14. ALCD40. **d** 40 **p** 41. R Orlestone w Ruckinge *Cant* 58-70; V Lower Halstow 70-72; V Guernsey St Matt *Win* 72-84; rtd 84; Perm to Offic *Win* from 84. *Les Mouettes Cottage, rue de la Lande, Castel, Guernsey, Channel Islands* Guernsey (01481) 55060

COLMAN, Geoffrey Hugh. b 29. Univ Coll Ox BA53 MA68. Wells Th Coll 67. **d** 68 **p** 69. C Wanstead St Mary *Chelmsf* 68-72; V Barking St Erkenwald 72-77; Youth Chapl 78-81; C Maidstone All SS and St Phil w Tovil *Cant* 85-88; P-in-c Norton 88-93; R from 93; P-in-c Teynham 88-93; P-in-c Lynsted w Kingsdown 88-93; V Teynham w Lynsted and Kingsdown from 93. *The Vicarage, 76 Station Road, Teynham, Sittingbourne, Kent ME9 9ES* Teynham (01795) 522510

COLMER, Malcolm John. b 45. Sussex Univ MSc67 Nottm Univ BA73. St Jo Coll Nottm 71. **d** 73 **p** 74. C Egham *Guildf* 73-76; C Chadwell *Chelmsf* 76-79; V S Malling *Chich* 79-85; V Hornsey Rise St Mary w St Steph *Lon* 85-87; TR Hornsey Rise Whitehall Park Team from 87; AD Islington 90-94. *St Mary's Vicarage, 3 Highcroft Road, London N19 3AQ* 0171-272 9084 or 272 1783

COLQUHOUN, Canon Frank. b 09. Univ Coll Dur LTh32 BA33 MA37. Bible Churchmen's Coll 29. **d** 33 **p** 34. Can Res S'wark Cathl *S'wark* 61-73; Chan 66-73; Prin S'wark Ord Course 66-71; Can Res Nor Cathl *Nor* 73-78; rtd 78; Perm to Offic *Chich* from 80. *21 Buckholt Avenue, Bexhill-on-Sea, E Sussex TN40 2RS* Bexhill-on-Sea (01424) 221138

COLSON, Major Alexander Francis Lionel. b 21. MBE45. St Jo Coll Cam BA43 MA61. Tyndale Hall Bris 60. **d** 62 **p** 63. R Elmswell *St E* 65-73; V W Kilburn St Luke w St Simon and St Jude *Lon* 73-82; R Thrandeston, Stuston and Brome w Oakley *St E* 82-86; rtd 86; Perm to Offic *Nor* from 86. *10 Soanes Court, Lyng, Norwich NR9 5RE* Norwich (01603) 872812

COLSON, Ian Richard. b 65. Wolv Poly BSc86 Nottm Univ BTh89. Linc Th Coll 86. **d** 89 **p** 90. C Nunthorpe *York* 89-92; C Thornaby on Tees 92-93; Chapl RAF from 93. *Chaplaincy Services (RAF), HQ, Personnel and Training Command, RAF Innsworth, Gloucester GL3 1EZ* Gloucester (01452) 712612 Ext 5164 Fax 510828

COLSON, John Edward. b 43. Open Univ BA91 Leeds Univ MA94. Lich Th Coll 65. **d** 68 **p** 69. C Bromsgrove All SS *Worc* 68-71; C Tettenhall Wood *Lich* 71-74; V Alrewas 74-88; V

Wychnor 74-88; R Ainderby Steeple w Yafforth and Kirby Wiske etc *Ripon* 88-95; Warden of Readers from 90; V High Harrogate Ch Ch from 95. *Christ Church Vicarage, 11 St Hilda's Road, Harrogate, N Yorkshire HG2 8JX* Harrogate (01423) 883390

COLTHURST, Ven Reginald William Richard. b 22. TCD BA44. CITC 45. **d** 45 **p** 46. I Richhill *Arm* 66-94; RD Kilmore 79-94; Adn Arm 85-92; rtd 94. *14 Cabin Hill Gardens, Belfast BT75 7AP* Belfast (01232) 472288

COLTON, Leonard Henry. b 35. All Nations Chr Coll 59 Bris & Glouc Tr Course 81. **d** 84 **p** 85. NSM Swindon Ch Ch *Bris* 84-90; NSM Lyddington w Wanborough 90-91; NSM Bishopstone w Hinton Parva 90-91; C Shepton Mallet w Doulting *B & W* 91-94; Chapl HM Pris Shepton Mallet 92-94; TV Wellington and Distr *B & W* from 94. *The Vicarage, Ashbrittle, Wellington, Somerset TA21 0LF* Wellington (01823) 672495

COLTON, William Paul. b 60. NUI BCL81 TCD DipTh84 MPhil87. **d** 84 **p** 85. C Lisburn St Paul *Conn* 84-87; Bp's Dom Chapl 85-90; VC Belf Cathl 87-90; Min Can Belf Cathl 89-90; PV, Registrar and Chapter Clerk Ch Ch Cathl Dub *D & G* 90-95; I Castleknock and Mulhuddart, w Clonsilla from 90; Co-ord Protestant Relig Progr RTE from 93; RD St Mary from 94; Hon Chapl Actors' Ch Union from 94. *12 Hawthorn Lawn, Castleknock, Dublin 15, Irish Republic* Dublin (1) 821-3083 Fax as telephone

COLVEN, Canon Christopher George. b 45. Leeds Univ BA66. Coll of Resurr Mirfield 66. **d** 68 **p** 69. C Tottenham St Paul *Lon* 68-74; C Notting Hill St Mich and Ch Ch 74-76; V W Hampstead St Jas 76-81; P-in-c Hampstead All So 78-81; Admin of Shrine of Our Lady Walsingham 81-86; P-in-c E w N and W Barsham *Nor* 81-84; Hon Can Nor Cathl 86-87; V S Kensington St Steph *Lon* from 87; AD Kensington 92-94; Perm to Offic *Nor* from 91; Master of Guardians Shrine Our Lady Walsingham from 93. *9 Eldon Road, London W8 5PU* 0171-937 5083

COLVER, Canon John Lawrence. b 14. Keble Coll Ox BA36 MA40. Cuddesdon Coll 36. **d** 37 **p** 38. V Bembridge *Portsm* 65-79; rtd 79; Perm to Offic *Portsm* from 81. *Lynton, 10 Yelfs Road, Ryde, Isle of Wight PO33 2LY* Isle of Wight (01983) 566498

COLVILLE, Gary Stanley. b 59. QPFF83. Sarum & Wells Th Coll 90. **d** 92 **p** 93. C Plaistow St Mary *Roch* 92-94; P-in-c Foots Cray from 94. *The Rectory, Rectory Lane, Footscray, Kent DA14 5BP*

COLWILL, James Patrick (Jay). b 68. Man Poly BA91. St Jo Coll Nottm BTh93 MA94. **d** 94 **p** 95. C Reading St Agnes w St Paul *Ox* from 94. *St Paul's House, 3 Whitley Wood Lane, Reading RG2 8PN* Reading (01734) 862513

COLWILL, Raymond William (Ray). b 06. Ripon Hall Ox. **d** 71 **p** 71. Hon C Wilton *B & W* from 71. *Hamara, Comeytrowe Lane, Taunton, Somerset TA1 5JB* Taunton (01823) 331833

COMBE, Edward Charles. b 40. N Ord Course. **d** 89 **p** 90. NSM Broadheath *Ches* 89-94; USA from 94. *Address temp unknown*

COMBE, Very Rev John Charles. b 33. TCD BA53 MA56 BD57 MLitt65 PhD70. **d** 56 **p** 57. C Cork St Luke w St Ann *C, C & R* 56-58; C Ballynafeigh St Jude *D & D* 58-61; I Crinken *D & G* 61-66; Hon CV Ch Ch Cathl Dub 63-66; C Belf St Bart *Conn* 66-70; I Belf St Barn 70-74; I Portadown St Mark *Arm* 74-84; I Arm St Mark w Aghavilly 84-90; Can Arm Cathl 85-90; Dean Kilmore *K, E & A* from 90; I Kilmore w Ballintemple, Kildallon etc from 90. *The Deanery, Danesfort, Kilmore, Cavan, Irish Republic* Cavan (49) 31918

COMBER, Mrs Alison. Local NSM Course. **d** 94 **p** 95. C New Bury *Man* from 94. *12 Seymour Grove, Farnworth, Bolton BL4 0HF* Bolton (01204) 397745

COMBER, Ven Anthony James. b 27. Leeds Univ BSc49 MSc52. St Chad's Coll Dur 53. **d** 56 **p** 57. V Hunslet St Mary *Ripon* 69-77; RD Armley 72-75 and 79-81; R Farnley 77-82; Hon Can Ripon Cathl 80-92; Adn Leeds 82-92; rtd 92. *25 Chelwood Drive, Bradford, W Yorkshire BD15 7YD* Bradford (01274) 818232

COMBER, Keith Charles. b 15. Wycliffe Hall Ox 71. **d** 73 **p** 74. C Walmley *Birm* 73-76; V Barston 76-79; rtd 80; Perm to Offic *Ely* 80-86; Perm to Offic *Nor* 86-79; Lic to Offic *Chich* 86-88; Perm to Offic from 88. *2 Boscobel Court, 42 West Hill Road, St Leonards-on-Sea, E Sussex TN38 0ND* Hastings (01424) 720334

COMBER, Michael. b 35. **d** 72 **p** 72. CA 59-72; C Carl H Trin and St Barn *Carl* 72-73; C Upperby St Jo 73-76; V Dearham 76-81; V Harraby 81-84; R Orton and Tebay w Ravenstonedale etc 84-90; I Clonfert Gp of Par *L & K* 90-94; I Convoy w Monellan and Donaghmore *D & R* from 94. *Convoy Rectory, Convoy, Lifford, Co Donegal, Irish Republic* Convoy (74) 47164

COMBES, Roger Matthew. b 47. K Coll Lon LLB69. Ridley Hall Cam 72. **d** 74 **p** 75. C Onslow Square St Paul *Lon* 74-77; C Brompton H Trin 76-77; C Cam H Sepulchre w All SS *Ely*

77-86; R Silverhill St Matt *Chich* from 86. *The Rectory, St Matthew's Road, St Leonards-on-Sea, E Sussex TN38 0TN* Hastings (01424) 423790

COMER, Michael John. b 30. St Mich Coll Llan 79. **d** 81 **p** 82. C Bistre *St As* 81-84; R Llanfyllin and Bwlchycibau 84-91; C Hattersley *Ches* 91; V 91-94; rtd 94. *134 Sycamore Drive, Newtown, Powys SY16 2QE* Newtown (01686) 624557

COMFORT, Alan. b 64. Ridley Hall Cam CTM94. **d** 94 **p** 95. C Chadwell Heath *Chelmsf* from 94. *3 St Chad's Road, Chadwell Heath, Romford RM6 6JB* 0181-597 2811

COMLEY, Thomas Hedges. b 36. Leeds Univ BA62 Birm Univ DipSocWork78. Coll of Resurr Mirfield 62. **d** 64 **p** 65. C Leadgate *Dur* 64-67; C Shirley *Birm* 67-71; V Smethwick St Alb 71-76; Perm to Offic 76-82; V N Wembley St Cuth *Lon* 82-92; V Taddington, Chelmorton and Flagg, and Monyash *Derby* from 92. *The Vicarage, Monyash, Bakewell, Derbyshire DE45 1JH* Bakewell (01629) 812234

COMMANDER, Reginald Arthur. b 20. RGN Aston Univ DHSA BA. Qu Coll Birm 75. **d** 78 **p** 79. NSM Wolv *Lich* from 78. *15 Coulter Grove, Perton, Wolverhampton WV6 7UA* Wolverhampton (01902) 744276

COMPTON, Barry Charles Chittenden. b 33. Linc Th Coll 60. **d** 62 **p** 63. Hon C Limpsfield and Titsey *S'wark* 62-69; R Ridley *Roch* 69-70; R Ash 69-70; Perm to Offic *S'wark* from 70; rtd 94. *14 Hallsland Way, Oxted, Surrey RH8 9AL* Oxted (01883) 714896 Fax 722842

COMPTON, Frank Edward. b 12. St Jo Coll Dur BSc34 St Cath Soc Ox BA36 MA40. Ripon Hall Ox 34. **d** 36 **p** 37. V Caynham *Heref* 60-77; rtd 77; Perm to Offic *Heref* 79-95. *2 Boyne House, Broad Street, Ludlow, Shropshire SY8 1NL* Ludlow (10584) 876994

COMYNS, Clifford John. b 28. TCD BA50 HDipEd53 MA53 BD67. **d** 51 **p** 52. C Chapelizod *D & G* 51-55; CF 55-75; Asst Master Eastbourne Coll from 75; Asst Chapl from 85. *Eastbourne College, Eastbourne, E Sussex BN21 4JY* Eastbourne (01323) 737411

CONANT, Fane Charles. b 44. Oak Hill Th Coll 83. **d** 85 **p** 86. C Hoole *Ches* 85-89; V Kelsall from 89. *St Philip's Vicarage, Chester Road, Kelsall, Tarporley, Cheshire CW6 0SA* Kelsall (01829) 51472

CONAWAY, Barry Raymond. b 41. CertEd69 Nottm Univ BEd70. Sarum & Wells Th Coll 86. **d** 88 **p** 89. C Ross w Brampton Abbotts, Bridstow and Peterstow *Heref* 88-91; R Bishop's Frome w Castle Frome and Fromes Hill from 91; P-in-c Acton Beauchamp and Evesbatch w Stanford Bishop from 91. *The Vicarage, Bishop's Frome, Worcester WR6 5AR* Munderfield (01885) 490204

CONDELL, Canon Joseph Alfred Ambrose. b 48. CITC 70. **d** 73 **p** 74. C Donaghcloney *D & D* 73-76; I Achonry w Tubbercurry and Killoran *T, K & A* 76-79; I Roscrea w Kyle, Bourney and Corbally *L & K* from 79; Can Killaloe Cathl 83-89; RD Killaloe and Roscrea 89-95; Prec Limerick and Killaloe Cathls from 89; Sec Dioc Bd of Educn from 91. *St Conan's Rectory, Roscrea, Co Tipperary, Irish Republic* Roscrea (505) 21725 Fax 21993

CONDER, Paul Collingwood Nelson. b 33. St Jo Coll Cam BA56 MA60. Ridley Hall Cam 56. **d** 58 **p** 59. C Grassendale *Liv* 58-61; Tutor St Jo Coll Dur 61-67; R Sutton *Liv* 67-74; TR 74-75; V Thames Ditton *Guildf* 75-86; RD Emly 82-86; V Blundellsands St Mich *Liv* from 86. *St Michael's Vicarage, 41 Dowhills Road, Liverpool L23 8SJ* 0151-924 3424

CONDRY, Edward Francis. b 53. UEA BA74 Ex Coll Ox DipSocAnth75 BLitt77 DPhil80 Nottm Univ DipTh81. Linc Th Coll 80. **d** 82 **p** 83. C Weston Favell *Pet* 82-85; V Bloxham w Milcombe and S Newington *Ox* 85-93; TR Rugby St Andr *Cov* from 93. *The Rectory, Church Street, Rugby, Warks CV21 3QH* Rugby (01788) 565609

CONEY, Joanna Margery. b 39. Culham Coll of Educn CertEd75 Open Univ BA83. Ox Min Course CBTS93. **d** 93 **p** 94. Par Dn Wolvercote w Summertown *Ox* 93-94; C from 94. *13 Sparsey Place, Oxford OX2 8NL* Oxford (01865) 511187

CONEY, Miss Mary Margaret. b 37. K Coll Lon BD58 CertEd59 DipAdEd78 Ex Univ MA87. **d** 87 **p** 94. NSM Penzance St Mary w St Paul *Truro* 87-90; Public Preacher from 90. *The Old Chapel, Lady Downs, Newmill, Penzance, Cornwall TR20 8UZ* Penzance (01736) 797164

CONEY, Preb Peter Norman Harvey. b 28. Keble Coll Ox BA51 MA55. Cuddesdon Coll 51. **d** 53 **p** 54. Chapl K Coll Taunton 65-70; V Martock *B & W* 70-72; V Martock w Ash 72-92; RD Martock 80-90; Dioc Press Officer 83-88; Preb Wells Cathl 85-92; rtd 93. *Les Aubepines, La Cawsse, 46500 Mayrinhac-Lentour, France* France (33) 65 38 22 19

CONEYS, Stephen John. b 61. Sheff Univ LLB82. St Jo Coll Nottm 87. **d** 90 **p** 91. C Plymouth Em w Efford *Ex* 90-92; C Plymouth Em, Efford and Laira 93-94; TV Whitstable *Cant* from 94. *11 Kimberley Grove, Seasalter, Whitstable, Kent CT5 4AY* Whitstable (01227) 276795

CONGDON, John Jameson. b 30. St Edm Hall Ox BA53 MA57. Wycliffe Hall Ox 53. **d** 55 **p** 56. V Spring Grove St Mary *Lon* 70-84; V Woodley St Jo the Ev *Ox* 84-89; Chapl W Middx Univ Hosp Isleworth 89-95; rtd 95. *95 Harewood Road, Isleworth, Middlesex TW7 5HN* 0181-568 6504

CONLEY, James Alan. b 29. Dur Univ BSc51. St Jo Coll Nottm. **d** 87 **p** 88. NSM Cropwell Bishop w Colston Bassett, Granby etc *S'well* from 87. *8 Willow Lane, Langar, Nottingham NG13 9HL* Harby (01949) 60820

CONLON, Shaun. b 69. Birm Univ BA90. Ripon Coll Cuddesdon DipMin93. **d** 93 **p** 94. C Castle Bromwich SS Mary and Marg *Birm* from 93. *4 Wasperton Close, Birmingham B36 9DZ* 0121-747 7467

CONN, Alistair Aberdein. b 37. Down Coll Cam BA60 MA64. Linc Th Coll 60. **d** 62 **p** 63. C W Hartlepool St Paul *Dur* 62-65; Uganda 65-66; Chapl Shrewsbury Sch 66-73; R Coupar Angus *St And* 73-78; V Ravenshead *S'well* 78-93; RD Newstead 90-93; R Collingham w S Scarle and Besthorpe and Girton from 93. *The Rectory, 1 Vicarage Close, Collingham, Newark, Notts NG23 7PQ* Newark (01636) 892317

CONN, Robert Edwin. b 14. TCD BA38 MA44. **d** 39 **p** 40. I Killyleagh *D & D* 65-88; rtd 88. *9 Drumkeen Court, Belfast BT8 4FY* Belfast (01232) 644305

CONNELL, Miss Heather Josephine. b 38. SRN60 SCM61 Open Univ BA86. S'wark Ord Course 77. **dss** 79 **d** 87 **p** 94. Heston *Lon* 79-84; Gillingham St Barn *Roch* 84-87; Par Dn 87-90; NSM from 91; Chapl Medway Hosp Gillingham from 91. *44 Seaview Road, Gillingham, Kent, ME7 4HN, or Medway Hospital, Gillingham, Kent ME7 5NY* Medway (01634) 576343 or 830000

CONNELL, John Richard. b 63. K Coll Lon BD84. St Mich Coll Llan DPT94. **d** 94. C Caldicot *Mon* from 94. *7 The Grove, Church Road, Caldicot, Newport, Gwent NP6 4GY*

CONNER, Mrs Cathryn. b 42. Birm Univ BSc64. NE Ord Course 91. **d** 94. NSM Bainton w N Dalton, Middleton-on-the-Wolds etc *York* from 94. *Centre House, North Dalton, Driffield, N Humberside YO25 9XA* Driffield (01377) 217265

CONNER, Charles Borthwick. b 20. Keble Coll Ox BA43 MA49. St Steph Ho Ox 48. **d** 50 **p** 51. C Saltburn-by-the-Sea *York* 50-52; Chapl Ely Th Coll 52-53; CF 53-70; Perm to Offic *Sarum* from 80. *Angel Cottage, West Knighton, Dorchester, Dorset DT2 8PE* Warmwell (01305) 852465

✠**CONNER, Rt Rev David John.** b 47. Ex Coll Ox BA69 MA77. St Steph Ho Ox 69. **d** 71 **p** 72 **c** 94. Hon C Summertown *Ox* 71-76; Asst Chapl St Edw Sch Ox 71-73; Chapl 73-80; TV Wolvercote w Summertown *Ox* 76-80; Chapl Win Coll 80-87; V Cam Gt St Mary w St Mich *Ely* 87-94; RD Cam 89-94; Suff Bp Lynn *Nor* from 94. *The Old Vicarage, Castle Acre, King's Lynn, Norfolk PE32 2AA* Swaffham (01760) 755553 Fax 755085

CONNOCK, Gilbert Ronald. b 14. St Cath Soc Ox BA49 MA53. St Steph Ho Ox. **d** 49 **p** 50. R Hayes St Mary *Lon* 68-77; R The Sampfords *Chelmsf* 77-84; rtd 84; Perm to Offic *Bris* from 85. *16 Hengrove Road, Bristol BS4 2PS* Bristol (0117) 972 1630

CONNOLL, Miss Helen Dorothy. b 45. Oak Hill Th Coll BA86. **dss** 86 **d** 87 **p** 94. Leytonstone St Jo *Chelmsf* 86-87; Par Dn 87-90; Asst Chapl Grimsby Distr Gen Hosp 90-93; Chapl Kent and Cant Hosp from 93; Chapl Nunnery Fields Hosp Cant from 94. *Kent and Canterbury Hospital, Ethelbert Road, Canterbury, Kent CT1 3NG* Canterbury (01227) 766877

CONNOLLY, Daniel (Dan). b 51. BEng. St Jo Coll Nottm DPS84. **d** 84 **p** 85. C Bedgrove *Ox* 84-87; C-in-c Crookhorn Ch Cen CD *Portsm* 87-88; V Crookhorn from 88. *The Vicarage, 87 Perseus Place, Waterlooville, Hants PO7 8AW* Portsmouth (01705) 267647

CONNOLLY, Miss Lynne. b 53. Aston Tr Scheme 88 Linc Th Coll CMinlStuds92. **d** 92 **p** 94. Par Dn Hurst *Man* 92-94; C from 94. *239 Whiteacre Road, Ashton-under-Lyne, Lancs OL6 9QB* 0161-330 6537

CONNOLLY, Sydney Herbert. b 40. Leeds Univ BA66. Coll of Resurr Mirfield 66. **d** 68 **p** 69. C W Derby St Mary *Liv* 68-71; C Prescot 71-74; V Burtonwood 74-80; V Walker *Newc* 80-89; TR Whorlton from 89. *The Vicarage, 8 Frenton Close, Newcastle upon Tyne NE5 1EH* 0191-267 4069

CONNOR, Dennis George Austin. b 16. K Coll Lon BD40 AKC40. **d** 40 **p** 41. V Harefield *Lon* 52-94; Chapl Harefield Hosp Middx 52-94; RD Hillingdon *Lon* 70-75; rtd 94. *2 Springwell Lane, Harefield, Middx UB9 6PG* Harefield (01895) 824915

CONNOR, Ellis Jones. b 16. Univ of Wales BA38. St Mich Coll Llan 38. **d** 39 **p** 41. R Desford *Leic* 55-73; R N Hill *Truro* 73-75; R Llanddewi Skirrid w Llanvetherine etc *Mon* 75-78; C Spalding St Jo *Linc* 79-82; rtd 82; Perm to Offic *Leic* from 82. *35 Sycamore Street, Blaby, Leicester LE8 4FL* Leicester (0116) 277 7725

CONNOR, Geoffrey. b 46. K Coll Lon BD73 AKC73. St Aug Coll Cant. **d** 74 **p** 75. C Cockerton *Dur* 74-79; Dioc Recruitment Officer 79-87; Chapl St Chad's Coll Dur 84-87;

Vice-Provost St Mary's Cathl *Edin* 87-90; R Edin St Mary 87-90; Dioc Dir of Ords (Dios Edin and Arg) 87-90; V Whitechapel w Admarsh-in-Bleasdale *Blackb* from 90; Dir of Ords from 90. *The Vicarage, Church Lane, Whitechapel, Preston PR3 2EP* Brock (01995) 640282

CONNOR, Patrick Francis Latham. b 25. Ex Coll Ox BA47 MA52. Gen Th Sem (NY) STB53. **d** 53 **p** 53. R Sparkford w Weston Bampfylde *B & W* 64-85; P-in-c Sutton Montis 70-85; R Mawnan *Truro* 85-89; rtd 89; Perm to Offic *Truro* from 89. *Trelatham, Boyton, Launceston, Cornwall PL15 9RJ* Launceston (01566) 776078

CONNOR, Stephen John. b 58. MA. Ridley Hall Cam. **d** 84 **p** 85. C Beamish *Dur* 84-86; C Wordsley *Lich* 86-90; TV Langport Area Chs *B & W* from 90. *The Vicarage, 2 Mill Road, High Ham, Langport, Somerset TA10 9DJ* Langport (01458) 253038

CONNOR, Archdeacon of. See ROLSTON, Ven John Ormsby

CONNOR, Bishop of. See MOORE, Rt Rev James Edward

CONNOR, Dean of. See FAIR, Very Rev James Alexander (Lex)

CONRAD, Paul Derick. b 54. Worc Coll Ox BA76 MA82. St Steph Ho Ox 78. **d** 80 **p** 81. C Wanstead St Mary *Chelmsf* 80-83; C Somers Town St Mary *Lon* 83-85; P-in-c Kentish Town St Martin w St Andr 85-91; V 91-95; P-in-c Hampstead Ch Ch from 95. *Christ Church Vicarage, 10 Cannon Place, London NW3 1EJ* 0171-435 6784

CONSTABLE, Douglas Brian. b 40. Lon Univ BA62. Linc Th Coll 63. **d** 65 **p** 66. C Stockwood CD *Bris* 65-70; Hon C Clifton St Paul 70-72; Asst Chapl Bris Univ 70-72; Chapl Lee Abbey 72-77; V Derby St Thos *Derby* 77-85; TV Southn (City Cen) *Win* 85-92; rtd 92. *9 Ordnance Road, Southampton SO15 2AZ* Southampton (01703) 228953

CONSTANT, Arden. b 09. K Coll Cam BA32 MA36. Cuddesdon Coll. **d** 34 **p** 35. V Kirkby Malham *Bradf* 66-73; rtd 72. *38 Bushwood Road, Kew, Richmond, Surrey TW9 3BQ* 0181-940 3156

CONSTANTINE, Miss Elaine Muriel. b 50. Univ of Wales (Swansea) BSc72 CertEd73 DipEd75 Lon Univ MEd78. St Alb Minl Tr Scheme. **dss** 86 **d** 87 **p** 94. Bedf St Martin *St Alb* 86-87; Par Dn 87-88; Par Dn Leighton Buzzard w Eggington, Hockliffe etc 88-94; C from 94. *Emmaus House, 63 Jupiter Drive, Leighton Buzzard, Beds LU7 8XA* Leighton Buzzard (01525) 373167

CONSTANTINE, Leonard. b 30. AKC57. **d** 58 **p** 59. C W Hartlepool St Aid *Dur* 58-61; C Sheff St Geo and St Steph *Sheff* 61-62; Nyasaland 62-64; Malawi 64-69; V W Pelton *Dur* 69-73; V Shotton 73-78; V Stillington 78-80; V Grindon and Stillington 80-82; V Corbridge w Halton and Newton Hall *Newc* from 82; Chapl Charlotte Straker Hosp from 82. *St Andrew's Vicarage, Corbridge, Northd NE45 5DW* Hexham (01434) 632128

CONVERY, Arthur Malcolm. b 42. Sheff Univ BSc63 DipEd64. N Ord Course 79. **d** 82 **p** 83. NSM Parr *Liv* 82-87; V Marown *S & M* from 87. *The Vicarage, Marown, Crosby, Isle of Man IM4 4BH* Marown (01624) 851378

CONWAY, Alfred Sydney. b 22. Kelham Th Coll 40. **d** 45 **p** 46. V Croxley Green All SS *St Alb* 63-81; V Walton St Jo *Liv* 81-89; rtd 89; Perm to Offic *Ex* from 89. *14 Mount Close, Honiton, Devon EX14 8QZ* Honiton (01404) 46052

CONWAY, Glyn Haydn. b 38. St Mich Coll Llan DipTh65. **d** 65 **p** 66. C Wrexham *St As* 65-71; TV 71-77; V Holywell 77-83; V Upton Ascension Ches from 83. *The Vicarage, Demage Lane, Chester CH2 1EL* Chester (01244) 383518

CONWAY, Canon Owen Arnott. b 35. Dur Univ BA58. St Steph Ho Ox 58. **d** 60 **p** 61. C Manston *Ripon* 60-64; V Osmondthorpe St Phil 64-70; Warden Dioc Ho Barrowby 70-73; V St Bart Armley w St Mary New Wortley 73-81; V Headingley 81-91; RD Headingley 87-91; Hon Can Ripon Cathl 87-91; Can Res Ches Cathl *Ches* from 91. *9 Abbey Street, Chester CH1 2JF* Chester (01244) 316144

CONWAY, Philip James. b 66. Liv Inst of Educn BA91. St Steph Ho Ox DipMin95. **d** 95. C High Harrogate Ch Ch *Ripon* from 95. *7 Kingsway Drive, Harrogate, N Yorkshire HG1 5NJ* Harrogate (01423) 526846

CONWAY, Reginald Henry. b 02. St Aid Birkenhead 29. **d** 33 **p** 34. R Conington *Ely* 64-69; rtd 69. *42 Cloverfields, Sandpit Lane, Thurston, Bury St Edmunds, Suffolk IP31 3TJ* Pakenham (01359) 31301

CONWAY, Mrs Sandra Coralie (Sandy). b 45. Bris Univ BA66. S'wark Ord Course DipRS92. **d** 92. Hon C Kenley *S'wark* from 92. *28 Russell Hill, Purley, Surrey CR8 2JA* 0181-668 2890

CONWAY, Stephen David. b 57. Keble Coll Ox BA80 MA84 CertEd81 Selw Coll Cam BA85. Westcott Ho Cam 83. **d** 86 **p** 87. C Heworth St Mary *Dur* 86-89; C Bishopwearmouth St Mich w St Hilda 89-90; Hon C Dur St Marg 90-94; Dir of Ords

90-94; P-in-c Cockerton from 94. *St Mary's Vicarage, Cockerton, Darlington, Co Durham DL3 9EX* Darlington (01325) 463705

CONWAY, Thomas Robertson. b 36. DipTh. **d** 86 **p** 87. C Ban Abbey *D & D* 86-89; I Dungiven w Bovevagh *D & R* from 89. *14 Main Street, Dungiven, Londonderry BT47 4LB* Dungiven (015047) 41226

CONWAY-LEE, Stanley. b 17. Linc Th Coll 68. **d** 70 **p** 71. C Dedham *Chelmsf* 70-72; C Lt Ilford St Mich 72-74; V Tollesbury 74-75; V Tollesbury w Salcot Virley 75-79; V Bocking St Pet 79-85; rtd 85; Perm to Offic *Chelmsf* from 85. *10 Northumberland Close, Braintree, Essex CM7 6NLL* Braintree (01376) 550117

COOGAN, Ven Robert Arthur William. b 29. Univ of Tasmania BA51 St Jo Coll Dur DipTh53. **d** 53 **p** 54. V N Woolwich *Chelmsf* 62-73; P-in-c W Silvertown St Barn 62-73; V Hampstead St Steph *Lon* 73-77; P-in-c N St Pancras All Hallows 74-77; RD S Camden (Holborn and St Pancras) 75-81; P-in-c Old St Pancras w Bedf New Town St Matt 76-80; V Hampstead St Steph w All Hallows 77-85; P-in-c Kentish Town St Martin w St Andr 78-81; AD N Camden (Hampstead) 78-83; Preb St Paul's Cathl 82-85; Adn Hampstead 85-94; rtd 94. *30 Marchwood Gate, Marchwood, Chichester, W Sussex PO19 4HA* Chichester (01243) 528828

COOK, Alan. b 27. St Deiniol's Hawarden 79. **d** 80 **p** 81. Hon C Gatley *Ches* 80-83; Chapl Man R Eye Hosp 83-86; Chapl Asst Man R Infirmary 80-83 and 86-88; V Congleton St Jas *Ches* 89-93; rtd 93. *15 Buttermere Road, Gatley, Cheadle, Cheshire SK8 4RQ* 0161-428 4350

COOK, Brian Edwin. b 36. Sarum & Wells Th Coll 78. **d** 80 **p** 81. C E Wickham *S'wark* 80-83; C Petersfield w Sheet *Portsm* 83-86; R Liss from 86; RD Petersfield from 91. *The Rectory, Station Road, Liss, Hants GU33 7AQ* Liss (01730) 893175

COOK, Brian Robert. b 43. Chich Th Coll 83. **d** 85 **p** 86. C Whyke w Rumboldswhyke and Portfield *Chich* 85-87; C Worth 87-90; TV 90-94; P-in-c Chidham from 94. *The Vicarage, Chidham, Chichester, W Sussex PO18 8TA* Bosham (01243) 573147

COOK, Canon Charles Peter. b 32. St Jo Coll Dur BA54 DipTh58. **d** 58 **p** 59. C Kingston upon Hull H Trin *York* 58-64; V High Elswick St Paul *Newc* 64-74; V Cheadle Hulme St Andr *Ches* from 74; Hon Can Ches Cathl from 91. *St Andrew's Priory, Cheadle Road, Cheadle Hulme, Cheadle, Cheshire SK8 5EU* 0161-485 1112 or 485 2648

COOK, Christopher. b 44. Qu Coll Birm 68. **d** 69 **p** 70. C Gt Ilford St Mary *Chelmsf* 69-72; C Corringham 72-77; R E Donyland 77-84; R Pentlow, Foxearth, Liston and Borley 84-88; Chapl RAD Essex Area 88-89; rtd 89; Perm to Offic *Chelmsf* from 89. *Oak Mill, Field View Lane, Little Totham, Maldon, Essex CM9 8ND* Maldon (01621) 893280

COOK, Ven Christopher Arthur. Edin Th Coll 53. **d** 56 **p** 58. C Motherwell *Glas* 56-59; S Africa 61-64 and from 70; Adn Grahamstown from 80; USPG 65-70. *PO St Matthews 5680, 5680 South Africa* St Matthews (12) 40242

COOK, David. b 46. Hertf Coll Ox BA MA72. Wycliffe Hall Ox 69. **d** 73 **p** 74. C Hartlepool All SS Stranton *Dur* 74-75; Lect Qu Coll Birm 75-81; Chapl Cranbrook Sch Kent from 81. *33 Oatfield Drive, Cranbrook, Kent TN17 3LA* Cranbrook (01580) 713310

COOK, David Arthur. b 50. St Jo Coll Dur BA74. St Steph Ho Ox 86. **d** 88 **p** 89. C S Bank *York* 88-91; C Up Hatherley *Glouc* 91-93; P-in-c Cumbernauld *Glas* from 93. *The Parsonage, Fleming Road, Cumbernauld, Glasgow G67 1LJ* Cumbernauld (01236) 721599

COOK, David Charles Murray. b 41. MA. Wycliffe Hall Ox 65. **d** 67 **p** 68. C Chatham St Phil and St Jas *Roch* 67-71; S Africa 71-89; TR Newbury *Ox* from 89. *The Rectory, 64 North Croft Lane, Newbury, Berks RG13 1BN* Newbury (01635) 40203

COOK, Canon David Reginald Edmund. b 25. Wells Th Coll 65. **d** 67 **p** 68. C Gt Ilford St Clem *Chelmsf* 67-71; P-in-c Langdon Hills 71-75; R 75-79; RD Basildon 76-79; P-in-c W Bergholt 79-80; R 80-90; Hon Can Chelmsf Cathl 86-90; rtd 90. *177 Straight Road, Lexden, Colchester CO3 5DG* Colchester (01206) 573231

COOK, David Smith. b 47. Hull Univ BTh88 MA93. Lich Th Coll 68. **d** 71 **p** 72. C Tudhoe Grange *Dur* 71-75; C Bishopwearmouth St Mary V w St Pet CD 75-77; V Copley *Wakef* 77-80; V Birstall 80-83; V Holme-on-Spalding Moor *York* from 83. *The Vicarage, Holme-on-Spalding Moor, York YO4 4AG* Market Weighton (01430) 860248

COOK, Canon Derek Edward. b 23. AKC51. **d** 52 **p** 53. V Luton St Paul *St Alb* 64-78; P-in-c Stanbridge w Tilsworth 78-80; V Totternhoe, Stanbridge and Tilsworth 80-88; Hon Can St Alb 85-88; rtd 88. *8 Ridgeway, Eynesbury, St Neots, Huntingdon, Cambs PE19 2QY* Huntingdon (01480) 475141

COOK, Canon Edward Rouse. b 28. Linc Coll Ox BA51 MA55. Linc Th Coll 51. **d** 53 **p** 54. V Saxilby *Linc* 67-90; R Broxholme 69-90; P-in-c Burton by Linc 78-94; Can and Preb Linc Cathl 79-94; Chmn Dioc Readers 86-94; RD Corringham 87-93; R

Saxilby w Ingleby and Broxholme 90-94; rtd 94. *80 Lincoln Road, Dunholme, Lincoln LN2 3QY* Lincoln (01673) 861534

COOK, Dr Elspeth Jean. b 34. Edin Univ BSc56 PhD66. S Dios Minl Tr Scheme 85. **d** 88 **p** 94. C Yateley *Win* 88-91; Assoc Chapl Ld Mayor Treloar Hosp Alton 91-93; NSM Dunfermline *St And* from 93. *12 River View, Dalgety Bay, Dunfermline, Fife KY11 5YE* Dalgety Bay (01383) 825222

COOK, George Basil Frederick. b 21. K Coll Lon BA42 St Cath Soc Ox BA48 MA52. Ripon Hall Ox 46. **d** 49 **p** 50. V Mitcham St Barn *S'wark* 55-91; rtd 91; Perm to Offic *S'wark* from 91. *6 Cranmer Road, Mitcham, Surrey CR4 4LD* 0181-648 1980

COOK, Ian Bell. b 38. NW Ord Course 70. **d** 73 **p** 74. C Oldham St Paul *Man* 73-75; Ind Chapl 76-79; P-in-c Newton Heath St Wilfrid and St Anne 76-79; V Middleton Junction from 79. *The Vicarage, Greenhill Road, Middleton Junction, Manchester M24 2BD* 0161-643 5064

COOK, Preb Ian Brian. b 38. MBIM73 Aston Univ MSc72 Birm Univ MA76. Kelham Th Coll 58. **d** 63 **p** 64. C Langley Marish *Ox* 63-66; C Stokenchurch and Cadmore End 66-68; V Lane End 68-72; P-in-c Ibstone w Fingest 68-72; Tutor W Bromwich Coll of Comm & Tech 72-74; Sen Tutor 74-80; Perm to Offic *Lich* 75-77; NSM W Bromwich St Pet 77-80; P-in-c Wednesbury St Jo 80; P-in-c Wednesbury St Jas and St Jo 80; R from 80; Dir St Jas Tr Inst from 81; RD Wednesbury from 88; Preb Lich Cathl from 94. *The Rectory, 1 Hollies Drive, Wednesbury, W Midlands WS10 9EQ* 0121-505 1188 or 505 1568

COOK, James Christopher Donald. b 49. Ch Ch Ox BA70 MA74. St Steph Ho Ox 79. **d** 80 **p** 81. C Witney *Ox* 80-83; CF from 83. *clo MOD (Army), Bagshot Park, Bagshot, Surrey GU19 5PL* Bagshot (01276) 471717 Fax 412834

COOK, Mrs Joan Lindsay. b 46. SRN70. St Jo Coll Dur 86. **d** 88 **p** 94. Par Dn Hartlepool St Hilda *Dur* 88-93; D-in-c 93-94; P-in-c from 94. *The Rectory, Church Close, Hartlepool, Cleveland TS24 0PW* Hartlepool (01429) 267030

COOK, John. b 32. Linc Th Coll 87. **d** 89 **p** 90. C Bourne *Linc* 89-92; R Colsterworth Gp from 92. *The Rectory, Church Street, Skillington, Grantham, Lincs NG33 5HQ* Grantham (01476) 861443

COOK, John Edward. b 35. AKC61. **d** 62 **p** 63. C York Town St Mich *Guildf* 62-67; Singapore 67-77; P-in-c Beoley *Worc* 78-83; V 83-89; V Bromsgrove All SS from 89. *All Saints' Vicarage, 20 Burcot Lane, Bromsgrove, Worcs B60 1AE* Bromsgrove (01527) 579849 Fax as telephone

COOK, John Henry. b 11. Mert Coll Ox BA34 BSc35 MA39 MSc81. Clifton Th Coll 36. **d** 38 **p** 39. R Witney *Ox* 68-78; rtd 79; Hon C Witney *Ox* from 79. *9 Church View Road, Witney, Oxon OX8 7HT* Witney (01993) 704609

COOK, John Michael. b 48. Coll of Resurr Mirfield 72. **d** 74 **p** 75. C Weymouth H Trin *Sarum* 74-76; C Felixstowe St Jo *St E* 76-79; P-in-c Gt and Lt Whelnetham 79-84; P-in-c Cockfield 84-85; P-in-c Bradfield St George w Bradfield St Clare etc 84-85; R Cockfield w Bradfield St Clare, Felsham etc 85-87; V Workington St Jo *Carl* from 87. *St John's Vicarage, 59 Thorncroft Gardens, Workington, Cumbria CA14 4DP* Workington (01900) 602383

COOK, John Richard Millward. b 61. St Jo Coll Dur BA. Wycliffe Hall Ox 83. **d** 85 **p** 86. C Brampton St Thos *Derby* 85-89; C Farnborough *Guildf* 89-92; C Langham Place All So *Lon* from 92. *12 De Walden Street, London W1M 7PH* 0171-935 9811 or 580 3522 Fax 436 3019

COOK, Kenneth George Thomas. b 36. ACA59 AHA69 FCA70 Man Univ DSA65. Coll of Resurr Mirfield 86. **d** 88 **p** 89. C Stocking Farm *Leic* 88-91; Chapl Leics Hospice from 91. *44 Glenfield Frith Drive, Glenfield, Leicester LE3 8PQ* Leicester (0116) 287 8912/231 3771

COOK, Canon Kenneth Hugh. b 30. ALAM. AKC55. **d** 56 **p** 57. C Netherfield *S'well* 56-59; C Newark w Coddington 59-61; V Basford St Aid 61-67; V Gargrave *Bradf* 67-77; Dir of Ords 77-89; Can Res Bradf Cathl from 77. *3 Cathedral Close, Bradford, W Yorkshire BD1 4EG* Bradford (01274) 727720

COOK, Kenneth Robert. b 42. Huddersfield Poly BA86. Chich Th Coll 66. **d** 68 **p** 69. C Upton *Ox* 68-72; C Duston *Pet* 72-76; V Halifax St Hilda *Wakef* 76-79; Chapl Huddersfield Poly 79-90; V Linc St Mary-le-Wigford w St Benedict etc *Linc* from 90. *220 Boultham Park Road, Lincoln LN6 7SU* Lincoln (01522) 540549

COOK, Marcus John Wyeth. b 41. Chich Th Coll 67. **d** 70 **p** 71. C Friern Barnet St Jas *Lon* 70-73; Hon C St Geo-in-the-East w St Paul from 73. *St George-in-the-East Church, Cannon Street Road, London E1 0BH* 0171-481 1345

COOK, Nicholas Leonard. b 59. Nottm Univ BCombStuds84. Linc Th Coll 81. **d** 84 **p** 85. C Leic St Pet *Leic* 84-85; C Knighton St Mich 85-86; Chapl Asst Towers Hosp Humberstone 86-90; Chapl 90-91; Chapl Leics Mental Health Service Unit 89-91; CF (TA) 88-91; Chapl Quainton Hall Sch

Harrow 91-94; CF from 94. *clo MOD (Army), Bagshot Park, Bagshot, Surrey GU19 5PL* Bagshot (01276) 471414 Fax 412834

COOK, Peter John. b 57. Ridley Hall Cam CTM95. **d** 95. C Romford Gd Shep Collier Row *Chelmsf* from 95. *244 Mersey Road, Colchester CO2 8OX* Colchester (01206) 44682

COOK, Peter John Arthur. b 42. Reading Univ BA64 Brandeis Univ (USA) MA65 QUB PhD81. Tyndale Hall Bris 68. **d** 71 **p** 72. C Everton St Chrys *Liv* 71-74; Chapl Stranmillis Coll of Educn Belf 74-87; Hon C Belf All SS *Conn* 81-87; USA from 87. *123 West Sale Road, Lake Charles, Louisiana 70605, USA*

COOK, Richard John Noel. b 49. Univ Coll Ox BA70 MA74 PGCE72. Wycliffe Hall Ox MA77. **d** 78 **p** 79. C Fulwood *Sheff* 78-80; C Bolton St Paul w Em *Man* 81-86; TV 86-93; V Goldsworth Park *Guildf* from 93. *St Andrew's Vicarage, 8 Cardingham, Woking, Surrey GU21 3LN* Woking (01483) 764523

COOK, Canon Robert Bond. b 28. Dur Univ BSc54. Ripon Hall Ox 54. **d** 56 **p** 57. V Denton *Newc* 64-75; V Haltwhistle 75-88; P-in-c Greenhead 84-88; V Haltwhistle and Greenhead 88-93; RD Hexham 88-93; Hon Can Newc Cathl 92-93; rtd 93. *Ashcroft, Heath Road, Woolpit, Bury St Edmunds, Suffolk IP30 9RN* Elmswell (01359) 240670

COOK, Ronald Thomas (Ron). b 50. St Steph Ho Ox BA79 MA83. **d** 80 **p** 81. C Willesden St Andr *Lon* 80-83; USA 83-87; C Northolt Park St Barn *Lon* 87-90; Chapl HM Pris Blundeston from 90. *The Chaplain's Office, HM Prison Blundeston, Lowestoft, Suffolk NR32 5BG* Lowestoft (01502) 730591 Fax 730138

COOK, Stephen. b 62. Brunel Univ BSc(Econ)84 Birkb Coll Lon CertRS91 DipRS92. S'wark Ord Course 89. **d** 92 **p** 93. Hon C Forest Hill St Aug *S'wark* from 92. *20 Goodrich Road, London SE22 9EQ* 0181-693 7703

COOK, Stephen William. b 57. BA DipHE. Lambeth STh87 Trin Coll Bris. **d** 85 **p** 86. C Heref St Pet w St Owen and St Jas *Heref* 85-89; TV Keynsham *B & W* 89-95; V Hanham *Bris* from 95. *Christchurch Vicarage, Church Road, Bristol BS15 3AF* Bristol (0117) 967 3580

COOK, Timothy John. b 62. Cranmer Hall Dur CTMin95. **d** 95. C Dorchester *Sarum* from 95. *10 Treves Road, Dorchester, Dorset DT1 2HD* Dorchester (01305) 260552

COOK, Trevor Vivian. b 43. Sarum Th Coll 67. **d** 69 **p** 70. C Lambeth St Phil *S'wark* 69-73; C St Buryan, St Levan and Sennen *Truro* 73-75; V The Ilketshalls *St E* 75-79; P-in-c Rumburgh w S Elmham 75-79; R Rumburgh w S Elmham w the Ilketshalls 79-84; TR Langport Area Chs *B & W* from 84. *The Rectory, Huish Episcopi, Langport, Somerset TA10 9QR* Langport (01458) 250480

COOK, Canon William George. b 14. St Jo Coll Dur LTh36 BA37. St Aid Birkenhead 33. **d** 37 **p** 38. V Allestree *Derby* 68-79; Hon Can Derby Cathl 78-79; rtd 79; Perm to Offic *St E* from 79; Perm to Offic *Pet* from 85; P-in-c Starston *Nor* 85. *1 Orchard Grove, Diss, Norfolk IP22 3LX* Diss (01379) 642058

COOKE, Alan. b 50. Nottm Univ BTh74 Lanc Univ PGCE75. Kelham Th Coll 69. **d** 75 **p** 76. C Tyldesley w Shakerley *Man* 75-78; C Salford Ordsall St Clem 78-80; C Langley All SS and Martyrs 80-82; TV Langley and Parkfield 82-83; P-in-c Chadderton St Mark 83-85; V from 85. *St Mark's Vicarage, Milne Street, Chadderton, Oldham OL9 0HR* 0161-624 2005

COOKE, Angela Elizabeth. b 42. SRN65 SCM67 MTD72. St Jo Coll Nottm 85. **d** 87 **p** 94. Par Dn Walton H Trin *Ox* 87-92; Par Dn Bexleyheath Ch Ch *Roch* 92-94; C from 94. *69 Garden Avenue, Bexleyheath, Kent DA7 4LE* 0181-303 9509

COOKE, Arthur Lewis. b 16. Keble Coll Ox BA38 MA43 Univ of Wales BD48. St Mich Coll Llan 39. **d** 39 **p** 41. R Hope *St As* 59-82; rtd 82. *144 Gresford Road, Llay, Wrexham, Clwyd LL12 0NW* Gresford (01978) 853644

COOKE, Mrs Beatrice Lilian. b 21. Gilmore Ho 67 Linc Th Coll. dss 77 **d** 87. Northaw *St Alb* 77-87; Hon Par Dn from 87. *30 St Michael's Gardens, South Petherton, Somerset TA13 5BD* South Petherton (01460) 241195

COOKE, Christopher Stephen. b 54. Lon Univ BA76 MA77 Ox Univ BA81 MA88. Ripon Coll Cuddesdon 79. **d** 82 **p** 83. C Cen Telford *Lich* 82-86; R Uffington, Upton Magna and Withington from 86; RD Wrockwardine from 92. *The Rectory, Upton Magna, Shrewsbury SY4 4TZ* Upton Magna (01743) 709283

COOKE, David John. b 31. Linc Th Coll 60. **d** 62 **p** 63. C Brighton Gd Shep Preston *Chich* 62-65; C Clayton w Keymer 65-70; R Stone w Hartwell w Bishopstone *Ox* 70-77; R Stone w Dinton and Hartwell from 77. *The Rectory, Stone, Aylesbury, Bucks HP17 8RZ* Aylesbury (01296) 748215

COOKE, Edward Alan. b 18. St D Coll Lamp BA41. **d** 46 **p** 47. CF 50-73; R Ightfield w Calverhall *Lich* 73-83; P-in-c Ash 78-83; rtd 83. *Guadalest, Hollins Lane, Tilstock, Whitchurch, Shropshire SY13 3NT* Whixall (01948) 880421

COOKE, Frederic Ronald. b 35. Selw Coll Cam BA58 MA61. Ridley Hall Cam 59. **d** 61 **p** 62. C Flixton St Mich *Man* 61-64; C-in-c Flixton St Jo CD 64-67; V Flixton St Jo 68-74; R Ashton St Mich 74-77; Jerusalem 77-80; V Walmsley *Man* 80-85; AD Walmsley 81-85; Malaysia 85-90; Prin Ho of Epiphany Th Coll Borneo 85-90; P-in-c Accrington *Blackb* 90-91; TR from 91. *St Paul's Vicarage, Barnfield Street, Accrington, Lancs BB5 2AQ* Accrington (01254) 399322

COOKE, Geoffrey. b 38. Sarum Th Coll 61. **d** 64 **p** 65. C Eastover *B & W* 64-67; Chapl RAF 67-71; C Bridgwater St Jo *B & W* 71-76; R N Newton w St Michaelchurch and Thurloxton 76-78; R N Newton w St Michaelchurch, Thurloxton etc 78-83; TV Yeovil 83-88; V Yeovil H Trin 88-89; R Staple Fitzpaine, Orchard Portman, Thurlbear etc from 89. *The Rectory, Thurlbear, Taunton, Somerset TA3 5BW* Taunton (01823) 443581

COOKE (married name SHEARD), Ms Gillian Freda. b 39. Lon Univ DipTh70 BD73 Leeds Univ MA87. Linc Th Coll IDC75. **dss** 78 **d** 87 **p** 94. Cricklewood St Pet CD *Lon* 78-80; Chapl Middx Poly 78-80; Chapl Leeds Poly *Ripon* 80-87; N Humberside Ind Chapl *York* 87-90; Asst Chapl HM Pris Hull 90-94; Chapl Keele Univ *Lich* from 94; C Betley and Keele from 94. *Berachah House, 51 Quarry Bank Road, Keele, Newcastle, Staffs ST5 5AG* Newcastle-under-Lyme (01782) 627385

COOKE, Harry Burford. b 18. **d** 64 **p** 65. C Slad *Glouc* 64-68; Chapl Marling Sch Stroud 68-78; Hon C Bisley, Oakridge, Miserden and Edgeworth *Glouc* 83-88; Perm to Offic from 88. *Norman Cottage, Miserden, Stroud, Glos GL6 7JA* Cirencester (01285) 821672

COOKE, Hereward Roger Gresham. b 39. ACA64 K Coll Lon BD69 AKC70. **d** 70 **p** 71. C Rugby St Andr *Cov* 70-76; P-in-c St Kath Cree *Lon* 76-82; P-in-c St Botolph without Aldersgate 82-89; AD The City 82-85; P-in-c St Edm the King and St Mary Woolnoth etc 82-89; TV Nor St Pet Parmentergate w St Jo *Nor* 89-93; Ind Miss 89-93; Sen Ind Chapl from 93; RD Nor E from 93; Hon C Nor St Pet Mancroft w St Jo Maddermarket from 93. *St John's Vicarage, 31 Bracondale, Norwich NR1 2AT* Norwich (01603) 624827

COOKE, Ian Kirk Hamel. b 17. Birm Univ BA39. Chich Th Coll 39. **d** 41 **p** 42. V Addlestone *Guildf* 63-75; R Tittleshall w Godwick and Wellingham *Nor* 75-76; R Tittleshall w Godwick, Wellingham and Weasenham 76-82; rtd 82; Perm to Offic *Nor* from 82. *Crugmeer, Croft Yard, Wells-next-the-Sea, Norfolk NR23 1JS* Fakenham (01328) 710358

COOKE, James Percy. b 13. St D Coll Lamp BA51. **d** 52 **p** 54. R Derwen and Llanelidan *St As* 57-83; rtd 83. *28 Maes Cantaba, Ruthin, Clwyd LL15 1YP* Ruthin (01824) 704905

COOKE, John Stephen. b 35. K Coll Lon BD58 AKC58. **d** 59 **p** 60. C W Bromwich St Fran *Lich* 59-62; C Chalfont St Peter *Ox* 62-66; V Cross Heath *Lich* 66-72; R Haughton 72-86; P-in-c Ellenhall w Ranton 72-80; V Eccleshall from 86; Sub-Chapl HM Pris Drake Hall from 86. *The Vicarage, Church Street, Eccleshall, Stafford ST21 6BY* Eccleshall (01785) 850351

COOKE, Canon Kenneth John. b 29. Linc Coll Ox BA53 MA57. Ely Th Coll 53. **d** 55 **p** 56. V Meriden *Cov* 66-76; V Cov St Geo 76-84; V Leamington Spa and Old Milverton 84-94; Hon Can Cov Cathl 92-94; rtd 94. *47 Brook End Drive, Henley-in-Arden, Solihull, W Midlands B95 5JD* Henley-in-Arden (01564) 792281

COOKE, Dr Michael David. b 46. New Coll Ox BA68 MA71 DPhil71. Ox NSM Course 75. **d** 78 **p** 79. NSM Newport Pagnell *Ox* 78-85; NSM Newport Pagnell w Lathbury and Moulsoe 85-88; NSM Beckenham Ch Ch *Roch* from 90. *70 Kingswood Avenue, Bromley BR2 0NP* 0181-460 8748

COOKE, Michael John. b 39. Ab Dioc Tr Course 78. **d** 80 **p** 81. NSM St Andr Cathl *Ab* 80-81; Chapl Miss to Seamen 81-88; Hon C Immingham *Linc* 81-88; Miss to Seamen Tilbury 88-91; Ind Chapl Teesside *Dur* from 91. *8 Beckston Close, Naisberry Park, Hartlepool, Cleveland TS26 0PA* Hartlepool (01429) 221448

COOKE, Miss Priscilla Garland Hamel. b 24. Gilmore Ho 69. **dss** 80 **d** 87 **p** 94. Bromsgrove St Jo *Worc* 80-82; Lee Abbey 82-85; Torquay St Matthias, St Mark and H Trin *Ex* 86-87; NSM 87-92 and from 94; Perm to Offic 92-94. *St Nicholas, Woodend Road, Torquay, Devon TQ1 2PZ* Torquay (01803) 297366

COOKE, Raymond. b 34. Liv Univ BSc56. Wells Th Coll 58. **d** 60 **p** 61. C Newton Heath All SS *Man* 60-64; C-in-c Failsworth H Family CD 64-75; R Failsworth H Family 75-83; P-in-c Man Gd Shep 83-88; V Westleigh St Pet from 88. *St Peter's Vicarage, 6 Malham Close, Leigh, Lancs WN7 4SD* Leigh (01942) 673626

COOKE, Richard James. b 60. Pemb Coll Ox BA82 MA88. Trin Coll Bris 85. **d** 88 **p** 89. C Rugby St Matt *Cov* 88-92; V Fletchamstead from 92. *St James's Vicarage, 395 Tile Hill Lane, Coventry CV4 9DP* Coventry (01203) 466262

COOKE, Samuel. b 17. Tyndale Hall Bris. **d** 49 **p** 50. V Scarborough H Trin *York* 62-77; rtd 82. *4 33179 Nelson Avenue, Abbotsford, British Columbia, Canada V25 2L6* Vancouver (604) 850-1043

COOKMAN, Alan George. b 26. Keble Coll Ox BA50 MA56. St Steph Ho Ox 50. **d** 52 **p** 53. V Lavender Hill Ascension *S'wark* 65-72; R Lympstone *Ex* 72-81; V Laira 81-88; Chapl Convent of Sisters of Charity Knowle 88-91; rtd 91. *Little Orchard, Priestlands, Sherborne, Dorset DT9 4HW* Sherborne (01935) 813467

COOKSON, Miss Diane Veronica. b 51. N Ord Course 81. **dss** 84 **d** 87 **p** 94. Gt Sutton *Ches* 84-86; Neston 86-87; Par Dn 87-94; C from 94. *Alphega House, 26 Stratford Road, Little Neston, South Wirral L64 0SH* 0151-336 3059

COOKSON, Graham Leslie. b 37. Sarum Th Coll 64. **d** 67 **p** 68. C Upton Ascension *Ches* 67-69; C Timperley 69-75; V Godley cum Newton Green 75-83; R Tarporley from 83. *The Rectory, Tarporley, Cheshire CW6 0AG* Tarporley (01829) 732491

COOLING, Derrick William. b 35. AKC58 Heref Coll of Educn TCert68 Lon Univ BD69 DipEd71 Univ of Wales (Cardiff) MEd81. St Boniface Warminster 58. **d** 59 **p** 60. C Haydock St Jas *Liv* 59-61; C Hove St Barn *Chich* 61-63; V Llangattock-vibon-Avel w St Maughan's etc *Mon* 63-68; R Blaina 68-70; Perm to Offic *Sarum* 70-74; Chapl Windsor Girls' Sch Hamm 74-75; Asst Master Croesyceiliog Sch Cwmbran 75-81; Perm to Offic *Mon* 79-81; Chapl Epsom Coll Surrey 81-84; V Bettws *Mon* 84-95; P-in-c Purleigh, Cold Norton and Stow Maries *Chelmsf* from 95. *All Saints Rectory, The Street, Purleigh, Chelmsford CM3 6QH* Maldon (01621) 828743   Fax as telephone

COOLING, Mrs Margaret Dorothy. b 37. K Coll Lon BA59 AKC Lon Univ BD69 DipEd71 Univ of Wales MEd81. St Deiniol's Hawarden. **d** 90 **p** 95. NSM Bettws *Mon* 90-95; NSM Purleigh, Cold Norton and Stow Maries *Chelmsf* from 95. *All Saints Rectory, The Street, Purleigh, Chelmsford CM3 6QH* Maldon (01621) 828743   Fax as telephone

COOMBE, James Anthony. b 31. Em Coll Cam BA53 MA57 Lon Univ BD60. Tyndale Hall Bris 57. **d** 60 **p** 61. C Chadderton Ch Ch *Man* 60-63; C Worthing St Geo *Chich* 63-65; V Wandsworth St Mich *S'wark* 65-74; P-in-c Warboys *Ely* 74-76; R 76-87; RD St Ives 83-87; P-in-c Broughton 84-87; P-in-c Wistow 84-87; V Alconbury w Alconbury Weston from 87; R Buckworth from 87. *The Vicarage, Alconbury, Huntingdon, Cambs PE17 5DX* Huntingdon (01480) 890284

COOMBE, John Morrell (Brother Martin). b 25. Chich Th Coll 56. **d** 57 **p** 58. SSF from 49; Chapl Ranby Ho Sch Retford 69-71; V Cam St Benedict *Ely* 71-85; Perm to Offic Jerusalem 85-86; Lic to Offic *Linc* from 86; Prov Sec SSF from 86; rtd 95. *St Francis House, Normanby Road, Scunthorpe, S Humberside DN15 6AR* Scunthorpe (01724) 853899

COOMBE, Kenneth Harry Southcott. b 24. Clifton Th Coll 61. **d** 63 **p** 64. C Cullompton *Ex* 63-66; C-in-c Elburton CD 66-73; V Elburton from 73. *St Matthew's Vicarage, 3 Sherford Road, Plymouth PL9 8DQ* Plymouth (01752) 402771

COOMBE, Michael Thomas. b 31. Lon Univ BA64. Ox NSM Course 73. **d** 75 **p** 76. Chapl St Piran's Sch Maidenhead 75-81; Hon C Furze Platt *Ox* 76-81; C 86-88; Asst Chapl Oslo St Edm *Eur* 81-84; Chapl Belgrade w Zagreb 84-86; Chapl Marseille 86-89; C Old Windsor *Ox* 91-92; P-in-c Clewer St Andr 92-93; C New Windsor 93; C Reading St Mark from 93; C Reading H Trin 93-95; Prec Gib Cathl and Port Chapl *Eur* from 95. *Port Chaplain's Flat, Flying Angel Club, North Mole, Gibraltar* Gibraltar (350) 41799

COOMBER, Ian Gladstone. b 47. Ch Ch Coll Cant CertEd68 Southn Univ BTh79. Sarum & Wells Th Coll 73. **d** 76 **p** 77. C Weeke *Win* 76-79; TV Saffron Walden w Wendens Ambo and Littlebury *Chelmsf* 79-82; V Weston *Win* 82-90; R Bedhampton *Portsm* from 90. *The Rectory, Bidbury Lane, Bedhampton, Havant, Hants PO9 3JG* Havant (01705) 483013

COOMBES, Derek Fennessey. b 42. Edin Th Coll 61. **d** 65 **p** 66. Prec St Andr Cathl Inverness *Mor* 65-68; Bp's Chapl 65-68; Perm to Offic *Nor* 76-79; V Happisburgh w Walcot 79-83; C Tewkesbury Abbey 84-85; Ind Chapl *S'wark* 85-89; R Asterby Gp *Linc* 89-95; Mental Health Chapl Louth 91-95; Chapl SS Mary and Anne's Sch Abbots Bromley from 95; Perm to Offic *Lich* from 95. *St Mary's Lodge, High Street, Abbots Bromley, Rugely, Staffs WS15 3BW* Burton-on-Trent (01283) 840225

COOMBES, Edward David. b 39. Dur Univ BA61. Qu Coll Birm DipTh63. **d** 63 **p** 64. C Claines St Jo *Worc* 63-65; C Halesowen 65-69; V Beoley 69-77; V Edgbaston St Bart *Birm* from 77; Chapl Birm Univ from 77. *Edgbaston Vicarage, 1B Arthur Road, Birmingham B15 2UW* 0121-454 0070

COOMBES, Frederick Brian John. b 34. FRTPI63 Nottm Univ BA56 Univ Coll Lon DipTP63 Plymouth Poly MPhil73. SW Minl Tr Course 83. **d** 88 **p** 93. NSM Bodmin w Lanhydrock and Lanivet *Truro* from 88. *5 Valley View, Bodmin, Cornwall PL31 1BE* Bodmin (01208) 73036

COOMBS, Edward Neve. b 66. Bris Univ BSc88. Cranmer Hall Dur BA93 DMS94. **d** 94. C Edin St Thos *Edin* from 94. *81 Glasgow Road, Edinburgh EH12 8LJ* 0131-334 4434

COOMBS, John Allen. b 46. Portsm Poly BSc70. Oak Hill Th Coll DipHE88 Sarum & Wells Th Coll 89. **d** 89 **p** 90. C Leverington *Ely* from 89; C Wisbech St Mary 89-93; P-in-c Emneth from 93. *The Vicarage, Church Road, Emneth, Wisbech, Cambs PE14 8AF* Wisbech (01945) 583089

COOMBS, John Kendall. b 47. Culham Coll Ox BEd73. Sarum & Wells Th Coll 75. **d** 77 **p** 78. C Fareham H Trin *Portsm* 77-80; C Petersfield w Sheet 80-83; TV Beaminster Area *Sarum* 83-87; TR Preston w Sutton Poyntz and Osmington w Poxwell from 87. *The Rectory, Sutton Road, Preston, Weymouth, Dorset DT3 6BX* Preston (01305) 833142

COOMBS, Patrick Michael Joseph. b 65. St Steph Ho Ox BTh94. **d** 94. C Torquay St Martin Barton *Ex* from 94. *141 Barton Hill Road, Barton, Torquay TQ2 8HM* Torquay (01803) 312596

COOMBS, Ven Peter Bertram. b 28. Bris Univ BA58 MA61. Clifton Th Coll 55. **d** 60 **p** 61. C Beckenham Ch Ch *Roch* 60-63; R Nottm St Nic *S'well* 63-68; V New Malden and Coombe *S'wark* 68-75; RD Kingston 71-75; Adn Wandsworth 75-88; Adn Reigate 88-95; rtd 95. *89 Nutfield Road, Redhill RH1 3HD* Redhill (01737) 642375

COOMBS, Richard Murray. b 63. St Chad's Coll Dur BSc85 Rob Coll Cam BA88. Ridley Hall Cam 87. **d** 90. C Enfield Ch Ch Trent Park *Lon* 90-94; C St Helen Bishopsgate w St Andr Undershaft etc from 94. *12 Merrick Square, London SE1 4JB* 0171-378 0229

COOMBS, Stephen John. b 54. Open Univ BA86. Trin Coll Bris 85. **d** 87 **p** 88. C Norton Canes *Lich* 87-90; Chapl Trowbridge Coll *Sarum* 90-94; C Studley 90-94. *48 Whitstone Rise, Shepton Mallet, Somerset BA4 5QB* Shepton Mallet (01749) 343750

COOMBS, Canon Walter James Martin. b 33. Keble Coll Ox BA57 MA61. Cuddesdon Coll 59. **d** 61 **p** 62. C Kennington St Jo *S'wark* 61-64; Chapl Em Coll Cam 64-68; Bp's Dom Chapl *S'wark* 68-70; V E Dulwich St Jo 70-77; V Pershore w Pinvin, Wick and Birlingham *Worc* 77-92; Hon Can Worc Cathl from 84; RD Pershore 85-91; TV Dorchester *Ox* from 92. *The Vicarage, The Green North, Warborough, Oxford OX10 7DW* Warborough (0186732) 8381

COON, Clayton Hollis. b 37. California Univ BA60. Episc Th Sch Cam Mass BD66. **d** 66 **p** 67. USA 66-71; C Hove St Jo *Chich* 71-74; C Brighton St Paul 74-79; V Linthwaite *Wakef* from 79. *The Vicarage, Church Lane, Linthwaite, Huddersfield HD7 5TA* Huddersfield (01484) 842591

COONEY, Michael Patrick. b 55. City of Lon Poly BA77. Ripon Coll Cuddesdon 77. **d** 80 **p** 81. C Cov E *Cov* 80-83; C Old Brumby *Linc* 83-85; V Linc St Jo 85-90; V Frodingham from 90. *The Vicarage, Vicarage Gardens, Scunthorpe, S Humberside DN15 7AZ* Scunthorpe (01724) 842726

COONEY, William Barry. b 47. K Coll Lon 69. **d** 70 **p** 71. C W Bromwich All SS *Lich* 70-73; C Wolv St Pet 73-75; C Rugeley 75-78; V Sneyd Green 78-87; R Sandiacre *Derby* from 87. *St Giles's Rectory, Church Drive, Sandiacre, Nottingham NG10 5EE* Nottingham (0115) 939 7163

COOPER, Alfred Philip. b 50. Bris Univ BA71. All Nations Chr Coll 72. **d** 77 **p** 78. Chile from 75; SAMS from 77. *Inglesia Anglicana del Chile, Casilla 50675, Correo Central, Santiago, Chile* Santiago (2) 226-8794

COOPER, Andrew John. b 62. W Sussex Inst of HE BA87. St Steph Ho Ox 88. **d** 91 **p** 92. C Rawmarsh w Parkgate *Sheff* 91-93; C Mosborough 93-95; P-in-c Donnington Wood *Lich* from 95. *The Vicarage, St George's Road, Donnington Wood, Telford, Shropshire TF2 7NJ* Telford (01952) 604239

COOPER, Andrew John Gearing. b 48. Sir John Cass Coll Lon BSc70. Ripon Coll Cuddesdon 73. **d** 76 **p** 77. C Potternewton *Ripon* 76-79; Antigua 79-81; Anguilla 81-87; V W Bromwich St Andr w Ch Ch *Lich* 88-92. *50 Hunter Avenue, Burntwood, Walsall, W Midlands WS7 9AQ* Burntwood (01543) 677817

COOPER, Mrs Annette Joy. b 53. Open Univ BA80 Lon Univ CQSW87 DipSocWork84. S'wark Ord Course DipRS88. **d** 88 **p** 94. NSM Pembury *Roch* 88; Chapl Tunbridge Wells Hosps 88-91; Chapl Kent and Sussex Hosp Tunbridge Wells 88-91; Chapl Leybourne Grange Hosp W Malling 88-91; Chapl Bassetlaw Distr Gen 91-92; Chapl Bassetlaw Hosp & Community Services NHS Trust from 92. *51 Blyth Road, Worksop, Notts, S81 0JJ, or Bassetlaw Hospital, Kilton Road, Worksop, Notts S81 0BD* Worksop (01909) 472925 or 500990

COOPER, Barrie Keith. b 56. Oak Hill Th Coll. **d** 85 **p** 86. C Partington and Carrington *Ches* 85-89; V Stockport St Mark 89-93; Chapl HM Young Offender Inst Stoke Heath from 93. *HM Young Offender Institution, Stoke Heath, Market Drayton, Shropshire TF9 2LJ* Market Drayton (01630) 654231 Fax 838875

COOPER, Barry Jack. Sarum Th Coll 59. **d** 61 **p** 62. C Norbury St Oswald *Cant* 61-64; C Crook *Dur* 64-68; R Cheriton *Cant* 68-84; V Cant All SS from 84. *All Saints' Vicarage, Military Road, Canterbury, Kent CT1 1PA* Canterbury (01227) 463505

COOPER, Canon Bede Robert. b 42. Ex Univ BA69. Coll of Resurr Mirfield 69. **d** 71 **p** 72. C Weymouth H Trin *Sarum* 71-74; P-in-c Broad Town 74-79; V Wootton Bassett 74-86; R Wilton w Netherhampton and Fugglestone from 86; Can and Preb Sarum Cathl from 88. *The Rectory, 27A West Street, Wilton, Salisbury SP2 0DL* Salisbury (01722) 743159

COOPER, Brian Hamilton. b 35. Keble Coll Ox BA58 MA67. Ripon Hall Ox 58. **d** 60 **p** 61. C Woolwich St Mary w H Trin *S'wark* 60-64; Canada 64-66; Vice-Prin Westcott Ho Cam 66-71; R Downham Market w Bexwell *Ely* 71-82; RD Fincham 80-82; V Chesterfield All SS *Derby* 82-91; V Herringthorpe *Sheff* from 91; RD Rotherham from 93. *493 Herringthorpe Valley Road, Rotherham, S Yorkshire S60 4LB* Rotherham (01709) 836052

COOPER, Carl Norman. b 60. Univ of Wales (Lamp) BA82. Wycliffe Hall Ox 82. **d** 85 **p** 86. C Llanelli *St D* 85-87; P-in-c Llanerch Aeron w Ciliau Aeron and Dihewyd etc 87-88; R 88-93; R Dolgellau w Llanfachreth and Brithdir etc *Ban* from 93. *The Rectory, Dollgellau, Gwynedd LL40 3YW* Dolgellau (01341) 422225

COOPER, Cecil Clive. b 26. TD75. AKC52. **d** 53 **p** 54. CF (TA) 63-75; R Woodmansterne *S'wark* 65-91; RD Sutton 80-90; rtd 91; Perm to Offic *Pet* from 91; Perm to Offic *Cov* from 91. *10 Mill Close, Braunston, Daventry, Northants NN11 7HY* Rugby (01788) 890596

COOPER, Chan Cecil William Marcus. b 32. TCD BA58 MA66. CITC 57. **d** 59 **p** 60. C Cork St Fin Barre and St Nic *C, C & R* 59-62; Bp's V, Lib and Registrar Kilkenny Cathl *C & O* 62-64; C Knockbreda *D & D* 65-67; Asst Ed Ch of Ireland Gazette 66-82; Ed from 82; I Magheradroll 67-82; Dioc Registrar 81-90; I Drumbeg from 82; Can Down Cathl from 86; Prec Down Cathl 90-91; Chan Down Cathl from 91. *The Rectory, Drumbeg Road, Dunmurry, Belfast BT17 9LE* Belfast (01232) 613265 Fax Lisburn (01846) 675743

COOPER, Christopher. b 09. Worc Coll Ox BA31 MA35. St Jo Hall Highbury 33. **d** 34 **p** 35. C Hampstead Ch Ch *Lon* 73-79; rtd 79; Perm to Offic *Lon* 79-90; Australia from 90. *6 Dauncey Street, Kingscote, Kangaroo Island, S Australia 5223* Adelaide (8) 482-3097

COOPER, Clive Anthony Charles. b 38. Lon Univ BEd74. ALCD62. **d** 62 **p** 63. C Morden *S'wark* 62-65; Argentina 65-71; Hon C Cranleigh *Guildf* 78-79; Hon C Ewhurst 80-82; Hon Chapl Duke of Kent Sch 83-92; Chapl Felixstowe Coll 92-93; Perm to Offic *Ex* 94-95; Chapl Puerto Pollensa *Eur* from 95. *Lista de Correos Apt 78, Pollensa, Mallorca, Spain*

COOPER, Colin. b 55. Open Univ BA. St Jo Coll Nottm 83. **d** 86 **p** 87. C Cheadle Hulme St Andr *Ches* 86-89; C Tunbridge Wells St Jo *Roch* 89-93; V Whitfield *Derby* from 93. *The Vicarage, 116 Charlestown Road, Glossop, Derbyshire SK13 8LB* Glossop (01457) 864938

COOPER, Colin Charles. b 40. Oak Hill Th Coll 62. **d** 66 **p** 67. C Islington St Andr w St Thos and St Matthias *Lon* 66-69; Bermuda 69-76; V Gorleston St Andr *Nor* 77-94; USA from 94. *Address temp unknown*

COOPER, David. b 44. AKC69. **d** 69 **p** 70. C Wortley de Leeds *Ripon* 69-73; CF 73-83; Lic to Offic *Ox* from 84; Chapl Eton Coll Windsor from 85. *Eton College, Windsor, Berks SL4 6DW* Windsor (01753) 864587

COOPER, David Jonathan. b 44. Sarum & Wells Th Coll 70. **d** 74 **p** 75. C Charlton-in-Dover *Cant* 74-79; TV Wednesfield *Lich* 79-83; SSF 83-85; V Grimsby St Aug *Linc* 85-89; TV Trowbridge H Trin *Sarum* from 89. *The Team Vicarage, 1 Chepston Place, Trowbridge, Wilts BA14 9TA* Trowbridge (01225) 751275

COOPER, David Philip. b 65. York Univ BA86. Qu Coll Birm BTh94. **d** 94 **p** 95. C Burslem *Lich* from 94. *3 Ullswater Avenue, Burslem, Stoke-on-Trent ST6 4JW* Stoke-on-Trent (01782) 827715

COOPER, Dennis Bradley. b 29. New Coll Ox BA52 MA57. Cuddesdon Coll 52. **d** 54 **p** 55. V Middlesb St Martin *York* 67-74; V Norton 74-92; RD Buckrose 85-90; rtd 93. *156 Long Street, Easingwold, York YO6 3JA* Easingwold (01347) 822953

COOPER, Derek Edward. b 30. Bps' Coll Cheshunt 61. **d** 62 **p** 63. C Bishop's Stortford St Mich *St Alb* 62-66; V Westcliff St Cedd *Chelmsf* 66-89; R Camerton w Dunkerton, Foxcote and Shoscombe *B & W* from 89. *The Rectory, Camerton, Bath BA3 1PU* Timsbury (01761) 470249

COOPER, Donald Martin. b 12. K Coll Lon BD35 AKC35 MTh40 PhD44. **d** 35 **p** 36. Chapl Tooting Bec Hosp Lon 51-77; rtd 77; Perm to Offic *Guildf* 82-91. *17 Killaser Court, Station Approach, Tadworth, Surrey KT20 5AN* Tadworth (01737) 812954

COOPER, Eric John. b 22. Cam Univ MA47. Chich Th Coll 52. **d** 53 **p** 54. V Bedminster Down *Bris* 66-72; rtd 87. *6 Deveron Grove, Keynsham, Bristol BS18 1UJ* Bristol (0117) 986 7339

COOPER, Frederick. b 30. Cranmer Hall Dur 68. **d** 70 **p** 71. C Preston All SS *Blackb* 70-72; C Preston St Jo 72-76; TV 76-78; V Higher Walton 78-91; P-in-c Preston All SS from 91. *31 Churchfields, Fulwood, Preston PR2 8GT* Preston (01772) 713808

COOPER, George Frank. b 19. St Aid Birkenhead 41. **d** 45 **p** 46. V Countesthorpe w Foston *Leic* 61-74; R Thurlaston 74-76; R Thurlaston and Peckleton w Kirkby Mallory 76-82; R Croft and Stoney Stanton 82-84; rtd 84; Perm to Offic *Leic* from 84; Perm to Offic *Linc* from 84. *Breezy Mere, 30 Signal Road, Grantham, Lincs NG31 9BL* Grantham (01476) 60689

COOPER, Ms Gillian Anne. b 55. LMH Ox BA76 CertEd77 MA80. St Jo Coll Nottm 84. **dss** 86 **d** 87 **p** 94. Tutor E Midl Min Tr Course from 86; Beeston S'well 86-87; Lect St Jo Coll Nottm from 87. *24 Chapel Street, Beeston, Nottingham NG9 3HB* Nottingham (0115) 925 3573 or 251114 Fax 220134 or 436438

COOPER, Graham Denbigh. b 48. Nottm Univ BTh75. St Jo Coll Nottm LTh75. **d** 75 **p** 76. C Collyhurst *Man* 75-78; C Stambermill *Worc* 78-80; V The Lye and Stambermill 80-90; P-in-c Frome H Trin *B & W* 90; V 91-95; Appeals Organiser Children's Soc from 95. *Flat 3, 3 St Leonard's Road, Surbiton, Surrey KT6 4DE* 0181-390 9763

COOPER, Herbert William (Bert). b 29. Chich Th Coll 77. **d** 79 **p** 80. C Leigh Park *Portsm* 79-82; C-in-c Hayling St Pet CD 82-85; V Whitwell 85-94; R St Lawrence 85-94; P-in-c Niton 89-94; rtd 94. *10 Henley Orchards, Ludlow, Shropshire SY8 1TN* Ludlow (01584) 874985

COOPER, Ian Clive. b 48. FCA Ex Univ BA76 K Coll Lon MTh94. Linc Th Coll 76. **d** 78 **p** 79. C Sunbury *Lon* 78-81; P-in-c Astwood Bank *Worc* 81-85; P-in-c Feckenham w Bradley 82-85; TV Hemel Hempstead *St Alb* 85-95; R Bushey from 95. *The Rectory, High Street, Bushey, Watford WD2 1BD* 0181-950 6408 or 950 1546

COOPER, Jack. b 44. St Jo Coll Nottm 76. **d** 78 **p** 79. C Roundhay St Edm *Ripon* 78-80; C Ripley *Derby* 81-82; V Willington 82-88; V Findern 82-88; P-in-c Parwich w Alsop en le Dale 88-94. *16 Keeper's Court, Crescent Avenue, Whitby, N Yorkshire YO21 3DP, or Rock Mount, Shaw Lane, Parwich, Ashbourne, Derbyshire DE6 1QJ* Whitby (01947) 604213

COOPER, James Peter. b 61. Westf Coll Lon BSc82. Sarum & Wells Th Coll 82. **d** 85 **p** 86. C Durrington *Chich* 85-88; C Clayton w Keymer from 88. *11 The Spinney, Hassocks, W Sussex BN6 8EJ* Hassocks (01273) 842599

COOPER, Jeremy John. b 45. Kelham Th Coll 65 Linc Th Coll 71. **d** 71 **p** 72. C Derby St Luke *Derby* 71-76; TV Malvern Link w Cowleigh *Worc* 76-79; P-in-c Claypole *Linc* 79-80; P-in-c Westborough w Dry Doddington and Stubton 79-80; C Eye w Braiseworth and Yaxley *St E* 80-82; P-in-c Hundon w Barnardiston 82-85; R from 85. *The Vicarage, 5 Armstrong Close, Hundon, Sudbury, Suffolk CO10 8HD* Hundon (0144086) 617

COOPER, John. b 34. BEd. N Ord Course. **d** 83 **p** 84. C Tong *Bradf* 83-87; V Bingley H Trin 87-92; V Silsden from 92. *The Vicarage, Briggate, Silsden, Keighley, W Yorkshire BD20 9JS* Steeton (01535) 652670

COOPER, John. b 47. Sarum & Wells Th Coll 71. **d** 74 **p** 75. C Spring Grove St Mary *Lon* 74-77; C Shepherd's Bush St Steph w St Thos 77-82; V Paddington St Pet 82-89; V Darwen St Cuth w Tockholes St Steph *Blackb* from 89. *St Cuthbert's Vicarage, Earnsdale Road, Darwen, Lancs BB3 1JA* Darwen (01254) 775039

COOPER, John Edward. b 40. K Coll Lon BD63 AKC63. **d** 64 **p** 65. C Prittlewell St Mary *Chelmsf* 64-67; C Up Hatherley *Glouc* 67-69; C-in-c Dorridge CD *Birm* 69-71; P-in-c Alkmonton w Yeaveley *Derby* 71-76; V Longford 71-76; TV Canvey Is *Chelmsf* 76-82; R Spixworth w Crostwick *Nor* 82-91; R Frettenham w Stanninghall 82-91; V Gt w Lt Harrowden and Orlingbury *Pet* from 91. *The Vicarage, 18 Kings Lane, Little Harrowden, Wellingborough, Northants NN9 5BL* Wellingborough (01933) 678225

COOPER, Canon John Leslie. b 33. Lon Univ BD65 MPhil78. Chich Th Coll 59. **d** 62 **p** 63. C Kings Heath *Birm* 62-65; Asst Chapl HM Pris Wandsworth 65-66; Chapl HM Borstal Portland 66-68; Chapl HM Pris Bris 68-72; P-in-c Balsall Heath St Paul *Birm* 73-81; V 81-82; Adn Aston and Can Res Birm Cathl 82-90; Adn Coleshill 90-93; C Sutton Coldfield H Trin from 93; Hon Can Birm Cathl from 93. *1 Trinity Hill, Sutton Coldfield, W Midlands B72 1SH* 0121-355 3352

COOPER, John Northcott. b 44. MIIM81. Ox Min Course DipRS92. **d** 92 **p** 93. NSM Burghfield *Ox* from 92. *Westmore, Palmers Lane, Burghfield Common, Reading RG7 3DU* Reading (01734) 832754

COOPER, Jonathan Mark Eric. b 62. Man Univ BSc83 Edin Univ BD88. Edin Th Coll 85. **d** 88 **p** 89. C Stainton-in-Cleveland *York* 88-91; C W Bromwich All SS *Lich* 91-93; C-in-c Ingleby Barwick CD *York* from 93. *4 Barwick Close,*

Ingleby Barwick, Stockton-on-Tees, Cleveland TS17 0SY Stockton-on-Tees (01642) 766033

COOPER, Joseph Trevor. b 32. Linc Th Coll 65. **d** 67 **p** 68. Ind Chapl *Cov* 69-90; rtd 92. *16 Trevor Close, Tile Hill, Coventry CV4 9HP* Coventry (01203) 462341 or 27597

COOPER, Kenneth Cantlay. b 17. Qu Coll Cam BA39 MA43. Ridley Hall Cam 39. **d** 41 **p** 42. R Fisherton Anger *Sarum* 65-74; P-in-c Fovant w Compton Chamberlayne etc 74-79; R Fovant, Sutton Mandeville and Teffont Evias etc 79-82; rtd 82; Perm to Offic *B & W* from 83. *8 Helena Road, East Coker, Yeovil, Somerset BA20 2HQ* West Coker (01935) 862291

COOPER, Leslie Martin. b 17. Jes Coll Cam BA39 MA43. Con Coll of Div 39. **d** 40 **p** 41. Chapl Wrekin Coll Shropshire 71-79; Perm to Offic *Glouc* from 79; rtd 82. *87 Corinium Gate, Cirencester, Glos GL7 2PX* Cirencester (01285) 654094

COOPER, Ms Louise Helena. b 68. Leeds Univ BA90. Qu Coll Birm DipTh93. **d** 93 **p** 94. Par Dn Dovecot *Liv* 93-94; C from 94. *8B Grant Road, Liverpool L14 0LQ* 0151-489 2163

COOPER, Malcolm Tydeman. b 37. Pemb Coll Ox BA61 MA64. Linc Th Coll 63. **d** 63 **p** 64. C Spennithorne *Ripon* 63-66; C Caversham *Ox* 66-71; Hon C Blackbird Leys CD 71-75; Lic to Offic *Sarum* 75-78; Lic to Offic *B & W* 78-82; NSM Sutton *Ely* from 82; NSM Witcham w Mepal from 82. *91 The Row, Sutton, Ely, Cambs CB6 2PB* Ely (01353) 777310

COOPER, Marc Ashley. b 62. Leeds Univ BA85. Linc Th Coll CMM92. **d** 92 **p** 93. C Bolton St Jas w St Chrys *Bradf* from 92. *1128 Bolton Road, Bradford, W Yorkshire BD2 4HS* Bradford (01274) 634711

COOPER, Sister Margery. b 26. Cam Inst of Educn CertRK52. CA Tr Coll 49. **dss** 79 **d** 87 **p** 94. Evang Family Miss (Dios Dur, Newc and York) 79-86; rtd 86; Perm to Offic *York* 86-91; NSM Fulford from 91. *7 Grange Street, Fulford Road, York YO1 4BH* York (01904) 633990

COOPER, Maxwell Edgar. b 11. CD63. Jes Coll Cam BA37 MA41. Wycliffe Hall Ox 37. **d** 39 **p** 40. C Meole Brace *Lich* 39-41; CF (EC) 41-46; CF 46-54; Canada 55-91. *16 Solsbury Way, Fairfield Park, Bath BA1 6HH* Bath (01225) 311949

COOPER, Canon Michael Leonard. b 30. St Jo Coll Cam BA53 MA58. Cuddesdon Coll 53. **d** 55 **p** 56. C Croydon *Cant* 55-61; V Spring Park 61-71; V Boxley 71-82; RD Sutton 74-80; Hon Can Cant Cathl from 76; V Cranbrook 82-92; Hon Chapl to Suff Bp Dover from 93; Asst Chapl Kent and Cant Hosp from 94; Asst Chapl Nunnery Fields Hosp Cant from 94. *1 Hunter's Way, Sheldwich Lees, Faversham, Kent ME13 0NB* Faversham (01795) 534094

COOPER, Michael Sydney. b 41. Univ of Wales (Lamp) BA63. Westcott Ho Cam 63. **d** 65 **p** 66. C Farlington *Portsm* 65-69; Pakistan 70-71; Mauritius 71-73; C-in-c Hayling St Pet CD *Portsm* 74-81; V Carisbrooke St Mary 81-92; V Carisbrooke St Nic 81-92; P-in-c Gatcombe 85-86; V Hartplain from 92. *The Vicarage, 61 Hartplain Avenue, Waterlooville, Hants PO8 8RG* Waterlooville (01705) 264551

COOPER, Nigel Scott. b 53. CBiol MIBiol Ox Univ MA Cam Univ MA PGCE. Ripon Coll Cuddesdon. **d** 83 **p** 84. C Moulsham St Jo *Chelmsf* 83-88; R Rivenhall from 88. *The Rectory, 40 Church Road, Rivenhall, Witham, Essex CM8 3PQ* Witham (01376) 511161

COOPER, Noel. b 49. Oak Hill Th Coll. **d** 88 **p** 89. C Plymouth St Jude *Ex* 88-92; V Clapham Park All SS *S'wark* from 92. *All Saints' Vicarage, 250 Lyham Road, London SW2 5NP* 0181-678 6020 or 674 4994

COOPER, Peter David. b 48. Sarum & Wells Th Coll 70. **d** 73 **p** 74. C Yateley *Win* 73-78; C Christchurch 78-81; P-in-c Southn St Mark 81-83; V from 83. *St Mark's Vicarage, 54 Archers Road, Southampton SO1 2LU* Southampton (01703) 636425

COOPER, Richard Thomas. b 46. Leeds Univ BA69. Coll of Resurr Mirfield 69. **d** 71 **p** 72. C Rothwell *Ripon* 71-75; C Adel 75-78; C Knaresborough 78-81; P-in-c Croft 81-90; P-in-c Eryholme 81-90; P-in-c Middleton Tyas and Melsonby 81-90; RD Richmond 86-90; V Aldborough w Boroughbridge and Roecliffe from 90; RD Ripon from 93. *The Vicarage, Church Lane, Boroughbridge, York YO5 9BA* Boroughbridge (01423) 322433

COOPER, Robert Gerard (Bob). b 68. Univ of Wales (Abth) BD91. Linc Th Coll CMM93. **d** 93 **p** 94. C Whitkirk *Ripon* from 93. *6 Hollyshaw Crescent, Leeds LS15 7AN* Leeds (0113) 260 6355

COOPER, Robert James. b 52. Bris Univ BA75. Ridley Hall Cam 76. **d** 78 **p** 79. C Street w Walton *B & W* 78-82; C Batheaston w St Cath 82-86; Asst Chapl to Arts and Recreation from 86; P-in-c Sadberge *Dur* from 86. *The Rectory, Middleton Road, Sadberge, Darlington, Co Durham DL2 1RP* Dinsdale (01325) 333771

COOPER, Roger Charles. b 48. GRSM ARMCM69 PGCE70. Coll of Resurr Mirfield 79. **d** 81 **p** 82. C Monkseaton St Mary *Newc* 81-83; C Morpeth 83-87; Min Can and Prec Man Cathl

Man 87-90; V Blackrod from 90. *St Katharine's Vicarage, Blackhorse Street, Blackrod, Bolton BL6 5EN* Horwich (01204) 68150

COOPER, Stephen. b 54. Bernard Gilpin Soc Dur 73 Chich Th Coll 74. **d** 77 **p** 78. C Horbury *Wakef* 77-78; C Horbury w Horbury Bridge 78-81; C Barnsley St Mary 81-84; TV Elland 84-91; Hon C Huddersfield St Thos 93-94; P-in-c Middlesb St Columba w St Paul *York* from 94; Chapl Middlesb Gen Hosp from 94. *St Columba's Vicarage, 115 Cambridge Road, Middlesbrough, Cleveland TS5 5HF* Middlesbrough (01642) 824779

COOPER, Stephen Paul Crossley (Steve). b 58. Aston Tr Scheme 89 Trin Coll Bris DipTh93. **d** 93 **p** 94. C Blackb Redeemer *Blackb* 93-95; C Altham w Clayton le Moors from 95. *1 Oakfield Avenue, Clayton le Moors, Accrington, Lancs BB5 5XG* Blackburn (01254) 231227

COOPER, Susan Mira. See RAMSARAN, Dr Susan Mira

COOPER, Sydney Bernard Nikon. b 27. K Coll Lon BD49 AKC49. **d** 51 **p** 52. V Stoke Newington St Olave *Lon* 66-76; R Chigwell Row *Chelmsf* 76-83; P-in-c Easton on the Hill, Collyweston w Duddington etc *Pet* 83; R 84-88; rtd 88. *Chase View, Church Road, Walpole St Peter, Wisbech, Cambs PE14 7NU* Wisbech (01945) 780473

COOPER, Thomas. b 20. Man Univ BA42. Edin Th Coll 42. **d** 44 **p** 45. V Bolton le Sands *Blackb* 63-85; rtd 85; Perm to Offic *Blackb* from 85. *Hillcrest, 21 Hazelmount Drive, Warton, Carnforth, Lancs LA5 9HR* Carnforth (01524) 732507

COOPER, Dr Thomas Joseph Gerard Strickland. b 46. Lanc Univ PhD85. Ven English Coll and Pontifical Gregorian Univ Rome PhL67 STL71. **d** 70 **p** 70. In RC Ch 70-92; Chapl St Woolos Cathl *Mon* from 93. *10 Clifton Road, Newport, Gwent NP9 6EW* Newport (01633) 264805

COOPER, Trevor John. b 51. Wycliffe Hall Ox 75. **d** 79. C Southsea St Pet *Portsm* 79-80; NSM Heavitree w Ex St Paul Ex 93-95; Perm to Offic from 92. *73 Wonford Street, Exeter EX2 5DF* Exeter (01392) 213056

COOPER, Wallace Peter. b 24. Kelham Th Coll 47. **d** 51 **p** 52. C New Brompton St Luke *Roch* 54-56; Perm to Offic *Ox* 62-81; Hon C Earley St Pet 81-83; Hon C Earley St Nic from 83; rtd 90. *10 Morton Court, Christchurch Road, Reading RG2 7BB* Reading (01734) 860528

COOPER, William Douglas. b 42. Dur Univ CertEd69 Open Univ BA83 Nottm Univ DipMM94 ARCST65 LIMA86. St Jo Coll Nottm CTPS92 Qu Coll Birm 93. **d** 94 **p** 95. NSM Melbourne *Derby* from 94. *The Post Office, 3 Derby Road, Melbourne, Derby DE73 1FE* Melbourne (01332) 862501

COOPER, Very Rev William Hugh Alan. b 09. Ch Coll Cam BA31 MA35. Lon Coll of Div 31. **d** 32 **p** 33. Provost Bradf 62-77; rtd 77; P-in-c Chrishall *Chelmsf* 81-88. *4 Eastgate Gardens, Guildford, Surrey GU1 4AZ* Guildford (01483) 67128

COOPER-SMITH, Alfred Riddington. b 13. TD63. St Deiniol's Hawarden 74. **d** 74 **p** 75. Hon C Smeeton Westerby w Saddington *Leic* 74-80; Perm to Offic from 80; Perm to Offic *Pet* from 80. *63 Stockerston Crescent, Uppingham, Oakham, Leics LE15 9UA* Uppingham (01572) 822412

COOTE, Bernard Albert Ernest. b 28. Lon Univ BD53. Chich Th Coll 54. **d** 55 **p** 56. Chapl HM Borstal E Sutton Park 63-74; V Sutton Valence w E Sutton *Cant* 63-76; P-in-c Chart next Sutton Valence 71-76; Chapl and Dir R Sch for the Blind Leatherhead 76-91; rtd 91. *6 Coxham Lane, Steyning, W Sussex BN44 3LZ* Steyning (01903) 813762

✠**COOTE, Rt Rev Roderic Norman.** b 15. TCD BA37 MA41 DD54. TCD Div Sch. **d** 38 **p** 39 **c** 51. C Dub St Bart *D & G* 38-41; Gambia 41-57; Bp Gambia and Rio Pongas 51-57; Suff Bp Fulham *Lon* 57-66; Suff Bp Colchester *Chelmsf* 66-84; Area Bp Colchester 84-87; Adn Colchester 69-72; rtd 87. *Friday Woods, Stoke Road, Cobham, Surrey KT11 3AS* Cobham (01932) 867306

COPE, James Brian Andrew. b 58. Chich Th Coll 80. **d** 83 **p** 84. C Poulton-le-Fylde *Blackb* 83-86; C Fleetwood 86-87; V Fleetwood St Dav 87-94; P-in-c Somercotes *Derby* from 94. *The Vicarage, Nottingham Road, Somercotes, Alfreton, Derbyshire DE55 4LY* Leabrooks (01773) 602840

COPE, Mrs Melia Lambrianos. b 53. Cape Town Univ BSocSc73 Worc Coll of Tech CertMS84. St Jo Coll Nottm 80 W Midl Minl Tr Course 83. **dss** 86 **d** 93 **p** 94. W Bromwich All SS *Lich* 86-93; NSM 93-94; NSM W Bromwich St Mary Magd CD 93-94; Ecum Youth Chapl from 94. *Church House, 50 Deepdale, Hollinswood, Telford, Shropshire TF3 2EJ* Telford (01952) 200546

COPE, Miss Olive Rosemary. b 29. Birm Univ DPS73. Gilmore Ho 63. **dss** 69 **d** 87 **p** 94. Kentish Town St Martin w St Andr *Lon* 69-72; Enfield St Andr 73-87; Par Dn 87-89; Hon Par Dn 89-94; Hon C from 94; rtd 89. *7 Calder Close, Enfield, Middx EN1 3TS* 0181-363 8221

COPE, Dr Peter John. b 42. Mert Coll Ox BA64 MA68 Lon Univ MSc74 Man Univ PhD91. Cuddesdon Coll 64. **d** 66 **p** 67.

C Chapel Allerton *Ripon* 66-69; Ind Chapl *Lon* 69-76; Min Can Worc Cathl *Worc* 76-85; Ind Chapl 76-85; P-in-c Worc St Mark 76-81; Min W Bromwich St Mary Magd CD *Lich* 85-94; Ind Chapl 85-94; Chapl Ecum Youth Chapl from 94. *Church House, 50 Deepdale, Hollinswood, Telford, Shropshire TF3 2EJ* Telford (01952) 200546

COPE, Stephen Victor. b 60. St Jo Coll Ox BA81 DipTh84 MA87. Chich Th Coll 86. **d** 89 **p** 90. C Newmarket St Mary w Exning St Agnes *St E* 89-92; C Northn St Matt *Pet* 92-94; V Rudston w Boynton and Kilham *York* from 94. *The Vicarage, Rudston, Driffield, N Humberside YO25 0XA* Kilham (01262) 420474

COPELAND, Christopher Paul. b 38. AKC64. **d** 65 **p** 66. C Luton St Andr *St Alb* 65-67; C Droitwich St Nic w St Pet *Worc* 67-71; C Kings Norton *Birm* 71-72; TV 73-78; V Tyseley 78-88; P-in-c Grimley w Holt *Worc* from 88; Dioc Stewardship Missr from 88. *Holt Vicarage, Holt Heath, Worcester WR6 6NJ* Worcester (01905) 620646

COPELAND, Derek Norman. b 38. Worc Coll Ox BA62 MA68. Westcott Ho Cam 63. **d** 64 **p** 65. C Portsea St Mary *Portsm* 64-71; P-in-c Avonmouth St Andr *Bris* 71-77; P-in-c Chippenham St Paul w Langley Burrell 78-79; Ind Chapl from 78; TR Chippenham St Paul w Hardenhuish etc 79-89; V Kington 79-89; Perm to Offic *B & W* from 90. *51B Lowden, Chippenham, Wilts SN15 2BG* Chippenham (01249) 443879

COPESTAKE, Leslie. b 13. ALCD39. **d** 39 **p** 40. V Beckermet St Jo *Carl* 61-71; V Egton w Newland 71-78; rtd 78; Perm to Offic *Carl* from 78. *Fosbrooke House, 8 Clifton Drive, Lytham, Lytham St Annes, Lancs FY8 5RE* Lytham (01253) 738998

COPINGER, Stephen Hubert Augustine (Brother Hubert). b 18. Lon Univ BA48. Ely Th Coll 60. **d** 62 **p** 63. SSF from 61; P-in-c Hillfield and Hermitage *Sarum* 68-76; Lic to Offic *Conn* 76-83; Lic to Offic *M & K* 78-80; Chapl R Victoria Hosp Belf 83-86; rtd 86. *The Society of St Francis, The Friary, Hilfield, Dorchester, Dorset DT2 7BE* Cerne Abbas (01300) 341345

COPLAND, Carole Jean. b 37. Man Univ BA60. Wm Temple Coll Rugby DipRK67. **d** 87 **p** 94. NSM Northallerton w Kirby Sigston *York* 87-90; Dioc Adv in Children's Work 81-90; Par Dn Dunnington 90-94; Faith in the City Link Officer from 90; C Dunnington from 94. *30 Curlew Glebe, Dunnington, York YO1 5PQ* York (01904) 488755

COPLAND, Canon Charles McAlester. b 10. CCC Cam BA33 MA36. Cuddesdon Coll 33. **d** 34 **p** 35. R Oban St Jo *Arg* 59-79; Provost St Jo Cathl Oban 59-79; Dean Arg 77-79; rtd 79; Hon Can St Jo Cathl Oban *Arg* from 79. *Fir Cottage, South Crieff Road, Comrie, Crieff, Perthshire PH6 2HF* Comrie (01764) 70185

COPLEY, Dr Colin. b 30. FRSA85 Nor City Coll HNC49. Kelham Th Coll 51. **d** 55 **p** 56. Chapl HM Pris Liv 66-70; Chapl HM Pris Styal 70-73; N Regional Chapl HM Pris and Borstals 70-73; Midl Region 73-75; Chapl HM Pris Drake Hall 73-75; Asst Chapl Gen of Pris (Midl) 75-90; Chapl HM Open Pris Sudbury 90-95; Chapl HM Open Pris Foston Hall 90-95; rtd 95. *67 Porlock Avenue, Stafford ST17 0HT* Stafford (01785) 663162

COPLEY, David Judd. b 15. Linc Coll Ox BA48 MA53. Wycliffe Hall Ox 48. **d** 50 **p** 51. V Tardebigge *Worc* 67-81; rtd 81; Perm to Offic *Worc* from 82. *220 Bromsgrove Road, Hunnington, Halesowen, W Midlands B62 0JS* Romsley (01562) 710247

COPLEY, Edmund Miles. b 27. Lon Univ BScEng50 Birm Univ DipTh57. Qu Coll Birm 55. **d** 57 **p** 58. R Uggeshall w Sotherton, Wangford and Henham *St E* 65-94; rtd 94. *Bullions, Uggeshall, Beccles, Suffolk NR34 8BB* Wangford (0150278) 235

COPPEN, Colin William. b 53. BCombStuds85. Linc Th Coll. **d** 85 **p** 86. C Tokyngton St Mich *Lon* 85-88; C Somers Town St Mary 88-90; P-in-c Edmonton St Alphege 90-92; V from 92. *St Alphege's Vicarage, Rossdale Drive, London N9 7LG* 0181-245 3588 Fax as telephone

COPPEN, Martin Alan. b 48. Ex Univ BA69 Nottm Univ DipTh84. St Jo Coll Nottm 83. **d** 85 **p** 86. C Bitterne *Win* 85-88; V St Mary Bourne and Woodcott from 88. *The Vicarage, St Mary Bourne, Andover, Hants SP11 6AY* St Mary Bourne (01264) 738308

COPPEN, Peter Euan. b 39. Ripon Coll Cuddesdon 79. **d** 81 **p** 82. C New Sleaford *Linc* 81-86; V Scawby and Redbourne 86-89; V Scawby, Redbourne and Hibaldstow from 89. *The Vicarage, Scawby, Brigg, S Humberside DN20 9LX* Brigg (01652) 654251

COPPEN, Robert George. b 39. Cape Town Univ BA66. St Jo Coll Dur 79. **d** 81 **p** 82. C Douglas St Geo and St Barn *S & M* 81-84; TV Kidlington w Hampton Poyle *Ox* from 84; Chapl HM Young Offender Inst Campsfield Ho 84-91. *St John's Vicarage, The Broadway, Kidlington, Oxon OX5 1EF* Kidlington (01865) 375611

COPPIN, Canon Ronald Leonard. b 30. Birm Univ BA52. Ridley Hall Cam 54. **d** 56 **p** 57. C Harrow Weald All SS *Lon* 56-59; Bp's Dom Chapl *Man* 59-63; Chapl St Aid Birkenhead 63-65;

Vice-Prin 65-68; Selection Sec ACCM 68-71; Selection Sec and Sec Cttee for Th Educn ACCM 71-74; Lib Dur Cathl from 74; Dir of Clergy Tr *Dur* from 74; Can Res Dur Cathl from 74; Warden NE Ord Course 76-84; Dir Post-Ord Tr from 86. *3 The College, Durham DH1 3EQ* 0191-384 2415

COPPING, John Frank Walter Victor. b 34. K Coll Lon BD58 AKC58. **d** 59 **p** 60. C Hampstead St Jo *Lon* 59-62; C Bray and Braywood *Ox* 62-65; V Langley Mill *Derby* 65-71; V Cookham Dean *Ox* from 71; RD Maidenhead 87-94. *The Vicarage, Cookham Dean, Maidenhead, Berks SL6 9PN* Marlow (01628) 483342

COPPING, Raymond. b 36. Wycliffe Hall Ox 72. **d** 74 **p** 75. C High Wycombe *Ox* 74-77; TV 77-87; TV Digswell and Panshanger *St Alb* 87-95; P-in-c Charlton Kings H Apostles *Glouc* from 95. *The Vicarage, Langton Grove Road, Charlton Kings, Cheltenham, Glos GL52 6JA* Cheltenham (01242) 512254

COPSEY, Canon Harry Charles Frederick. b 05. Linc Th Coll 31. **d** 34 **p** 35. V E Grinstead St Swithun *Chich* 54-75; Chapl Qu Victoria's Hosp E Grinstead 55-75; Chapl Sackville Coll E Grinstead 56-75; Can and Preb Chich Cathl *Chich* 70-85; rtd 75. *Flat 22, Old Parsonage Court, Otterbourne, Winchester, Hants PO21 2EP* Twyford (01962) 715425

COPSEY, Nigel John. b 52. K Coll Lon BD75 AKC75 Surrey Univ MSc. St Aug Coll Cant 72. **d** 76 **p** 77. C Barkingside St Fran *Chelmsf* 76-78; C Canning Town St Cedd 78-80; P-in-c Victoria Docks Ascension 80-87; Chapl Cane Hill Hosp Coulsdon 87-90; Chapl Netherne Hosp Coulsdon 87-90; Chapl E Surrey Mental Health Unit from 90; Chapl R Earlswood Hosp Redhill from 94. *Chaplain's Office, Royal Earlswood, Brighton Road, Redhill RH1 6JL* Redhill (01737) 763591

COPUS, Brian George. b 36. AKC59. **d** 60 **p** 61. C Croydon St Mich *Cant* 60-63; C Swindon New Town *Bris* 63-69; V Colebrooke *Ex* 69-73; P-in-c Hittisleigh 69-73; R Perivale *Lon* 73-82; V Ruislip St Mary from 82. *St Mary's Vicarage, 9 The Fairway, South Ruislip, Middx HA4 0SP* 0181-845 3485

COPUS, James Lambert. b 19. Edin Th Coll 47. **d** 50 **p** 51. V S Lambeth All SS and St Barn *S'wark* 58-77; TV Eling, Testwood and Marchwood *Win* 77-78; TV Totton 78-79; rtd 80. *94 Moorfield, Harlow, Essex CM18 7QG* Harlow (01279) 417666

COPUS, John Cecil. b 38. TCert64 Maria Grey Coll Lon DipEd71 Open Univ BA78. Cant Sch of Min. **d** 83 **p** 84. Hon C Folkestone H Trin and St Geo w Ch Ch *Cant* 83-85; Hon C Midsomer Norton w Clandown *B & W* 85-91; Dioc Adv for Children's Work *Ex* from 91. *106 Clyst Valley Road, Clyst St Mary, Exeter EX5 1DE* Topsham (01392) 875017

COPUS, Jonathan Hugh Lambert. b 44. LGSM66 BNC Ox BA66 MA71. S'wark Ord Course 68. **d** 71 **p** 72. C Horsell *Guildf* 71-73; Producer Relig Progr BBC Radio Solent 73-87; Lic to Offic from 74. *55 Lower Ashley Road, New Milton, Hants BH25 5QF* New Milton (01425) 619400

CORBET-MILWARD, Canon Richard George Corbet. b 12. K Coll Cam BA36 MA40. Cuddesdon Coll 37. **d** 38 **p** 39. V Portsea St Alb *Portsm* 48-74; RD Portsm 65-70; V Ryde H Trin 74-79; RD E Wight 75-78; rtd 80; Perm to Offic *Portsm* 82-93. *The College of Saint Barnabas, Blackberry Lane, Lingfield, Surrey RH7 6NJ* Lingfield (01342) 870717

CORBETT, Canon Charles Eric. b 17. Jes Coll Ox BA39 MA43. Wycliffe Hall Ox 39. **d** 40 **p** 41. V Farnworth *Liv* 61-71; adn Liv 71-79; Can Res Liv Cathl 71-79; Can Res and Treas Liv Cathl 79-83; rtd 83; Perm to Offic *Ches* from 85. *80 Latham Avenue, Helsby, Cheshire WA6 0EB* Helsby (01928) 724184

CORBETT, George. b 18. Bible Churchmen's Coll 47. **d** 50 **p** 51. V Hatherleigh *Ex* 63-78; P-in-c Ringmore and Kingston 78-84; R Bigbury, Ringmore and Kingston 84-86; rtd 86; Perm to Offic *Heref* from 87. *2 Quantock Close, Hereford HR4 0TD* Hereford (01432) 269211

CORBETT, Henry. b 53. CCC Cam BA75. Wycliffe Hall Ox DipTh78. **d** 78 **p** 79. C Everton St Pet *Liv* 78-84; TV 84-87; TR from 87. *Shrewsbury House, Langrove Street, Liverpool L5 3LT* 0151-207 1948

CORBETT, Canon Ian Deighton. b 42. St Cath Coll Cam BA64 MA68 Salford Univ MSc83. Westcott Ho Cam 67. **d** 69 **p** 70. C New Bury *Man* 69-72; C Bolton St Pet 72-75; Chapl Bolton Colls of FE 72-75; Dioc FE Officer 74-83; R Man Victoria Park *Man* 75-80; Chapl Salford Univ 80-83; Hon Can Man Cathl 83-87; P-in-c Salford Sacred Trin 83-87; Dir of In-Service Tr 83-87; Lesotho from 87. *Lelapa la Jesu Seminary, Roma 180, Lesotho*

CORBETT, John David. b 32. Or Coll Ox BA55 MA59. St Steph Ho Ox 55. **d** 57 **p** 58. C Plymouth St Pet *Ex* 57-64; V Mankind 64-74; TV Bournemouth St Pet w St Swithun, St Steph etc *Win* 74-83; V Beckenham St Barn *Roch* 83-88; V King's Sutton and Newbottle and Charlton *Pet* from 88. *The Vicarage, Church*

Avenue, Kings Sutton, Banbury, Oxon OX17 3RJ Banbury (01295) 811364

CORBETT, Miss Phyllis. b 34. Cranmer Hall Dur 76. **dss** 80 **d** 87 **p** 94. Walsall Wood *Lich* 80-87; Par Dn Baswich (or Berkswich) 87-94; C 94-95; rtd 95. *9 Redhill Gorse, Crab Lane, Trinity Fields, Stafford ST16 1SW*

CORBETT, Stephen Paul. b 57. BA80. St Jo Coll Nottm 83. **d** 85 **p** 86. C Tollington Park St Mark w St Anne *Lon* 85-86; C Holloway St Mark w Em 86-91; V Chitts Hill St Cuth 91-93; V Springfield *Birm* from 93. *The Vicarage, 172 Woodlands Road, Birmingham B11 4ET* 0121-777 4908

CORBIN, Frederick Athelston. b 42. S Dios Minl Tr Scheme 80. **d** 83 **p** 85. NSM Basingstoke *Win* 83-84; C Hulme Ascension *Man* 84-86; Lic to Hulme Deanery 86-87; C E Crompton 87-89; V Oldham St Barn from 89. *St Barnabas's Vicarage, 1 Arundel Street, Oldham OL4 1NL* 0161-624 7708

CORBYN, John. b 58. Man Univ BA79 Ven English Coll and Pontifical Gregorian Univ. Wycliffe Hall Ox BA83 MA87. **d** 84 **p** 85. C Deane *Man* 84-87; C Lanc St Mary *Blackb* 87-90; Chapl HM Pris Lanc 89-90; V Blackb St Gabr *Blackb* from 90. *St Gabriel's Vicarage, 284 Pleckgate Road, Blackburn BB1 8QU* Blackburn (01254) 248430

CORBYN, John Robert. b 54. Qu Coll Birm. **d** 82 **p** 83. C Northolt W End St Jos *Lon* 82-86; Urban Miss Priest *York* 86-88; C Sutton St Mich 86-88; V Dalton *Sheff* from 88. *The Vicarage, 2 Vicarage Close, Dalton, Rotherham, S Yorkshire S65 3QL* Rotherham (01709) 850377

CORDELL, Derek Harold. b 34. Chich Th Coll 57. **d** 60 **p** 61. C Whitstable All SS *Cant* 60-63; C Moulsecoomb *Chich* 63-69; Chapl Bucharest *Eur* 69-71; V Brighton St Wilfrid *Chich* 71-74; Chapl HM Borstal Roch 74-80; Asst Chapl HM Pris Man 80-81; Chapl HM Pris The Verne 81-89; Chapl HM Pris Channings Wood 89-90; Chapl Milan w Genoa and Varese *Eur* 90-91; Chapl Mojacar 91-94. *9 Elwell Street, Weymouth, Dorset DT3 5QF*

CORDINER, Alan Dobson. b 61. W Cumbria Coll of Science and Tech HTC83 Westmr Coll Ox BA87. **d** 92 **p** 93. C Upperby St Jo *Carl* from 92. *49 Carliol Drive, Harraby, Carlisle CA1 2RF* Carlisle (01228) 34457

CORDINGLEY, Canon Brian Lambert. b 30. St Aid Birkenhead 55. **d** 57 **p** 58. Ind Chapl *Man* 63-92; R Old Trafford St Cuth 63-81; V Hamer 81-92; Hon Can Man Cathl 87-92; rtd 92. *Wellsprings, 27 Fernthorpe Avenue, Uppermill, Oldham OL3 6EA* Oldham (01457) 820130

CORDY, Gordon Donald. b 30. Nor Th Coll 61. **d** 63 **p** 64. C Badgeworth w Shurdington *Glouc* 68-71; V Coleford w Staunton 71-73; C Digswell *St Alb* 73-75; TV Litlington w Abington Pigotts *Ely* 75-78; R March St Jo 78-83; Perm to Offic *Nor* 84-87; P-in-c Smallburgh w Dilham w Honing and Crostwight 87-94; rtd 95. *6 Leopold Close, Norwich NR4 7PR* Norwich (01603) 51198

CORE, Edward. b 54. BTh. Sarum & Wells Th Coll. **d** 82 **p** 83. C Newbold and Dunston *Derby* 82-86; Chapl RAF from 86. *Chaplaincy Services (RAF), HQ, Personnel and Training Command, RAF Innsworth, Gloucester GL3 1EZ* Gloucester (01452) 712612 Ext 5164 Fax 510828

CORFE, David Robert. b 35. Pemb Coll Cam BA58 MA62. Lambeth DipTh70 Cuddesdon Coll 58. **d** 60 **p** 61. C Wigan All SS *Liv* 60-63; India 63-68 and 70-75; C Northwood Em *Lon* 75; V Westwell *Cant* 75-80; R Eastwell w Boughton Aluph 75-80; V Hildenborough *Roch* 80-91; Lic Preacher Stretford St Bride *Man* from 91; Miss Partner CMS from 91. *6 Darley Road, Old Trafford, Manchester M16 0DQ* 0161-232 9388 or 860 4224

CORFIELD, John Bernard. b 24. Jes Coll Cam BA49 MA51. Ridley Hall Cam 64. **d** 66 **p** 67. P-in-c Bledlow Ridge *Ox* 69-75; P-in-c Bradenham 71-75; R Sherington w Chicheley, N Crawley, Astwood etc 75-82; V Terrington St Clement *Ely* 82-90; rtd 90; Perm to Offic *Ox* from 90. *13 Sturt Road, Charlbury, Chipping Norton, Oxon OX7 3SX* Charlbury (01608) 811464

CORK, Ronald Edward. b 43. Plymouth Poly CQSW72. N Ord Course 89. **d** 92 **p** 93. Hon C Altrincham St Geo *Ches* from 92. *5 Hunters Mews, Oakfield, Sale, Cheshire M33 6WA* 0161-969 7797

CORK, CLOYNE AND ROSS, Archdeacon of. See WHITE, Ven Robin Edward Bantry

CORK, CLOYNE AND ROSS, Bishop of. See WARKE, Rt Rev Robert Alexander

CORK, Dean of. See CLARKE, Very Rev Richard Lionel

CORKE, Bryan Raymond. b 49. Westmr Coll Lon 81 FBIST77 BAPO95. Local NSM Course 92. **d** 95. NSM Flixton St Jo *Man* from 95. *40 Daresbury Avenue, Manchester M41 8GL* 0161-748 1827

CORKE, Colin John. b 59. St Pet Coll Ox BA81. Cranmer Hall Dur 83. **d** 85 **p** 86. C Chapel Allerton *Ripon* 85-88; C

Burmantofts St Steph and St Agnes 88-91; P-in-c Tatsfield S'wark from 91; Reigate Adnry Ecum Officer from 92. *The Rectory, Ricketts Hill Road, Tatsfield, Westerham, Kent TN16 2NA* Tatsfield (01959) 577289

CORKE, John Harry. b 29. AKC55. **d** 56 **p** 57. V Hartshill *Cov* 60-80; R Hampton Lucy w Charlecote and Loxley 80-94; rtd 94. *18 Haven Close, Fleet, Spalding, Lincs PE12 8NS* Holbeach (01406) 426038

CORKE, Roderick Geoffrey (Rod). b 58. UEA BEd79. St Jo Coll Nottm DTS92. **d** 92 **p** 93. C Trimley *St E* 92-95; C Walton from 95. *1 Parsonage Close, Felixstowe, Suffolk IP11 8QR* Felixstowe (01394) 284803

CORKER, John Anthony. b 37. ACIB75 AKC63. **d** 64 **p** 65. C Lindley *Wakef* 64-68; V Brotherton 68-72; Perm to Offic 72-82; Hon C Askham Bryan *York* 82-91; TV York All SS Pavement w St Crux and St Martin etc from 95. *12 Muncastergate, York YO3 9LA* York (01904) 430428

CORKER, Canon Ronald. b 30. Ely Th Coll 51. **d** 54 **p** 55. R Willington *Dur* 68-75; P-in-c Sunnybrow 73-75; R Willington and Sunnybrow 75-80; V Billingham St Cuth 80-85; RD Stockton 83-85; TR Jarrow 85-95; Hon Can Dur Cathl from 90; rtd 95. *195 Beaconsides, Cleadon Manor, South Shields, Tyne & Wear NE34 7PT* 0191-454 2987

CORKETT, Canon Cecil Harry. b 10. Dur Univ LTh41. Sarum Th Coll 32. **d** 35 **p** 36. V Whitechapel *Wakef* 43-80; rtd 80; Perm to Offic *Wakef* 80-92. *4 Woodland View, Southwell, Notts NG25 0AG*

CORLESS, Canon Keith Ronald. b 37. Edin Th Coll 58. **d** 61 **p** 62. C Cheltenham All SS *Glouc* 61-64; C Leckhampton SS Phil and Jas 66-69; R Ashchurch from 69; Hon Can Glouc Cathl from 95. *The Rectory, Ashchurch, Tewkesbury, Glos GL20 8JZ* Tewkesbury (01684) 293729

CORLETT, Ewan Christian Brew. b 23. OBE85. FEng74 FRSA FIMarE FRIN FRINA Qu Coll Ox MA47 K Coll Dur PhD50. Is of Man Tr Inst 88. **d** 91 **p** 92. NSM Maughold *S & M* from 91. *Cottimans, Port-e-Vullen, Ramsey, Isle of Man IM7 1AP* Ramsey (01624) 814009

CORNE, Ronald Andrew. b 51. Sarum & Wells Th Coll 87. **d** 89 **p** 90. Par Dn Bitterne Park *Win* 89-92; C 92-93; R King's Worthy from 93. *The Rectory, Campion Way, King's Worthy, Winchester, Hants SO23 7QP* Winchester (01962) 882166

CORNECK, Canon Warrington Graham. b 35. FCA62 ACA60. Clifton Th Coll. **d** 65 **p** 66. C Islington St Jude Mildmay Park *Lon* 65-67; C Southgate *Chich* 67-73; P-in-c Deptford St Nic w Ch Ch *S'wark* 73-76; P-in-c Deptford St Luke 73-76; V Deptford St Nic and St Luke from 76; RD Deptford from 85; Hon Can S'wark Cathl from 91. *St Nicholas' Vicarage, 41 Creek Road, London SE8 3BU* 0181-692 2749

CORNELIUS, Donald Eric. b 31. K Coll Lon BD AKC. **d** 84 **p** 85. Hon C Crowle *Linc* from 84; Hon C Flixborough w Burton upon Stather from 91. *4 Mulberry Drive, Crowle, Scunthorpe, S Humberside DN17 4JF* Scunthorpe (01724) 710279

CORNELL, Miss Jean Cranston. b 36. Man Univ CertEd59 BA64 York Univ BPhil71. Ripon Coll Cuddesdon 87. **d** 89 **p** 94. C Matson *Glouc* 89-92; C Bishop's Cleeve from 92. *1 Apple Tree Close, Woodmancote, Cheltenham, Glos GL52 4UA* Cheltenham (01242) 673721

CORNELL, John Lister. b 12. St Pet Hall Ox BA34 MA39. Wycliffe Hall Ox 35. **d** 35 **p** 36. R Mickleham *Guildf* 53-78; rtd 78. *Staddles, Windmill Hill, Ashill, Ilminster, Somerset TA19 9NT* Hatch Beauchamp (01823) 480012

CORNELL, Michael Neil. b 45. Ripon Coll Cuddesdon 79. **d** 81 **p** 82. C Gt Bookham *Guildf* 81-84; C York Town St Mich 84-93; V Camberley St Martin Old Dean from 93. *St Martin's Vicarage, Hampshire Road, Camberley, Surrey GU15 4DW* Camberley (01276) 23958

CORNES, Andrew Charles Julian. b 49. CCC Ox BA70 MA73 St Jo Coll Dur DipTh73. Wycliffe Hall Ox 70 Cranmer Hall Dur 72. **d** 73 **p** 74. C York St Mich-le-Belfrey *York* 73-76; C St Marylebone All So w SS Pet and Jo *Lon* 76-85; USA 85-88; V Crowborough *Chich* from 89. *All Saints' Vicarage, Chapel Green, Crowborough, E Sussex TN6 1ED* Crowborough (01892) 667384

CORNISH, Anthony. b 30. Roch Th Coll 64. **d** 67 **p** 68. C Goodmayes All SS *Chelmsf* 67-71; C Buckhurst Hill 71-73; V Westcliff St Andr 73-83; R Rawreth w Rettendon from 83. *The Rectory, Church Road, Rawreth, Wickford, Essex SS11 8SH* Wickford (01268) 766766

CORNISH, Dennis Henry Ronald. b 31. FCIB72 FCIS81. S'wark Ord Course 83. **d** 86 **p** 87. NSM Uxbridge *Lon* 86-89; R Lurgashall, Lodsworth and Selham *Chich* from 89. *The Rectory, Lodsworth, Petworth, W Sussex GU28 9DE* Lodsworth (01798) 861274

CORNISH, Canon Edward Maurice John. b 14. TD51. Qu Coll Birm 48. **d** 48 **p** 49. V Chorley St Geo *Blackb* 56-70; Bp's Dom Chapl 70-78; R Ribchester w Stidd 70-78; Hon Can Blackb Cathl 74-81; C Fairhaven 78-87; rtd 79; Perm to Offic *Blackb* from 87. *16 Ripon Road, Ansdell, Lytham St Annes, Lancs FY8 4DS* Lytham (01253) 739845

CORNISH, Francis John. b 14. Hertf Coll Ox BA36 MA42. Wycliffe Hall Ox 37. **d** 38 **p** 39. R Poynings *Chich* 57-79; R Edburton 57-79; rtd 79. *Four Winds, The Street, Clapham, Worthing, W Sussex BN13 3UU* Patching (0190674) 359

CORNISH, Graham Peter. b 42. Dur Univ BA67. NE Ord Course 82. **d** 84 **p** 85. NSM Harrogate St Wilfrid and St Luke *Ripon* from 84. *33 Mayfield Grove, Harrogate, N Yorkshire HG1 5HD* Harrogate (01423) 562747

CORNISH, Ivor. b 40. Reading Univ BSc61 DipEd62 ADipR79. Ox Min Course 86. **d** 89 **p** 90. NSM Aston Clinton w Buckland and Drayton Beauchamp *Ox* from 89. *79 Weston Road, Aston Clinton, Aylesbury, Bucks HP22 5EP* Aylesbury (01296) 630345

CORNISH, John Douglas. b 42. Lich Th Coll 67. **d** 70 **p** 71. C Lt Stanmore St Lawr *Lon* 70-73; C Harefield from 73. *23 High Street, Harefield, Middx UB9 6BX* Harefield (01895) 822510

CORNISH, Peter Andrew. b 55. Ch Ch Ox BA77 MA80 Ex Univ CertEd78. St Jo Coll Nottm 84. **d** 87 **p** 88. C Sanderstead All SS *S'wark* 87-92; TV Cen Telford *Lich* from 92. *20 Burlington Close, Dawley, Telford, Shropshire TF4 3TD* Telford (01952) 595915

CORNISH, Philip Gordon Pym. b 01. K Coll Lon AKC25 BD28. **d** 26 **p** 27. R Lt Waltham *Chelmsf* 59-67; rtd 67. *Penn Haven, 13 Penn Hill Avenue, Poole, Dorset BH14 9LU* Parkstone (01202) 747085

CORNWALL, Canon John Whitmore. b 1900. Cuddesdon Coll 29. **d** 31 **p** 32. UMCA (Masasi) 33-54; R Minchinhampton *Glouc* 59-72; rtd 72; Perm to Offic *Glouc* from 77. *6 Southgate Crescent, Rodborough, Stroud, Glos GL5 3TS* Stroud (01453) 764816

CORNWALL-JONES, Canon Guy Rupert. b 30. Jes Coll Cam BA54 MA59. Westcott Ho Cam 55. **d** 57 **p** 58. C Longton St Jas *Lich* 57-60; C Wood End *Cov* 60-64; R Caldecote 64-84; R Weddington 64-84; RD Nuneaton 79-84; Hon Can Cov Cathl from 80; R Bilton 84-91; P-in-c Leek Wootton from 91. *The Vicarage, Leek Wootton, Warwick CV35 7QL* Kenilworth (01926) 54832

CORNWALL, Archdeacon of. *See* RAVENSCROFT, Ven Raymond Lockwood

CORNWELL, Christopher Richard. b 43. Dur Univ BA67. Cuddesdon Coll 67. **d** 69 **p** 70. C Cannock *Lich* 69-75; P-in-c Hadley 75-80; V 80-81; Bp's Dom Chapl 81-86; Subchanter Lich Cathl 81-86; V Ellesmere 86-89; V Welsh Frankton 86-89; V Ellesmere and Welsh Frankton 89-92; TV Leeds City *Ripon* from 92; RD Allerton from 94. *St Peter's Vicarage, 15 Parkside Green, Leeds LS6 4NY* Leeds (0113) 278 7449

CORNWELL, Gertrude Florence. b 21. CertEd48 Nottm Univ DipEd72. Gilmore Ho 56 Lambeth STh60. **dss** 62 **d** 87. Sen Lect Bp Grosseteste Coll Linc 64-81; rtd 81. *Flat 2A, 14 Minster Yard, Lincoln LN2 1PW* Lincoln (01522) 527249

CORRADINE, John. b 29. St Aid Birkenhead. **d** 58 **p** 59. C Tarporley *Ches* 58-61; C Wilmslow 61-64; V Moulton from 64. *The Vicarage, Moulton, Northwich, Cheshire CW9 8NR* Winsford (01606) 593355

CORRAN, Dr Henry Stanley. b 15. Trin Coll Cam BA36 PhD41. CITC 76. **d** 77 **p** 78. NSM Bray Ch Ch *D & G* 77-85; rtd 85. *71 Alderley Road, Hoylake, Wirral, Merseyside L47 2AU* 0151-632 2750

CORREY, William Henry. b 14. Liv Univ BA37. ALCD49. **d** 49 **p** 50. V Bishopwearmouth St Gabr *Dur* 68-73; R Gt Parndon *Chelmsf* 73-80; RD Harlow 80-83; V Hatf Broad Oak 80-83; rtd 83; Perm to Offic *Chich* from 83. *Highgrove House, 32 Winchester Road, Worthing, W Sussex BN11 4DH*

CORRIE, John. b 48. Imp Coll Lon BScEng69 MSc70 DIC70 PhD73 Lon Univ DipTh77 Nottm Univ MTh86. Trin Coll Bris 74. **d** 77 **p** 78. C Kendal St Thos *Carl* 77-80; C Attenborough *S'well* 80-86; Chapl Intercon Ch Soc 86-91; Peru 86-91; Tutor and Lect All Nations Chr Coll Ware from 91. *10 Peters Wood Hill, Ware, Herts SG12 9NR* Ware (01920) 462676

CORRIE, Paul Allen. b 43. St Jo Coll Nottm 77. **d** 79 **p** 80. C Beverley Minster *York* 79-82; V Derby St Werburgh *Derby* 82-84; V Derby St Alkmund and St Werburgh from 84. *4 Spindle Mill, Skipton, N Yorkshire BD23 1NY*

CORRIGAN, Ven Thomas George. b 28. TCD BTh91. CITC 56. **d** 58 **p** 59. C Cavan and Drung *K, E & A* 58-60; I Drung 60-67; I Belf St Mich *Conn* 67-70; I Kingscourt w Drumconrath, Syddan and Moybologue *M & K* from 70; Adn Meath from 81; Dioc Registrar (Meath) 87-90. *St Ernan's Rectory, Kingscourt, Co Cavan, Irish Republic* Dundalk (42) 67255 Fax 67949

CORSIE, Andrew Russell. b 57. Trin Coll Bris DipHE93. **d** 93 **p** 94. C Northolt Park St Barn *Lon* from 93. *3 Vernon Rise, Greenford, Middx UB6 0EQ* 0181-422 6989

CORSTORPHINE, Miss Margaret. b 34. SRN57 SCM59. Cranmer Hall Dur 70. **dss** 84 **d** 87 **p** 94. Colchester St Jo *Chelmsf* 84-87; Par Dn 87-94; C 94; rtd 94. *12 Oakmeadow Close, Emsworth, Hants PO10 7RL*

CORTEEN, Robert. b 18. ACII. Coll of Resurr Mirfield 77. **d** 79 **p** 80. NSM Chorlton-cum-Hardy St Clem *Man* 79-88; Perm to Offic from 88. *23 Meadow Bank, Manchester M21 2EF* 0161-881 1118

CORY, Ms Valerie Ann (Val). b 44. CertEd65 Nottm Univ BEd85. E Midl Min Tr Course 85. **d** 88 **p** 94. Area Sec (Dios Linc and Pet) CMS 87-91; NSM Grantham *Linc* 88-91; Par Dn Ealing St Mary *Lon* 91-94; Chapl NW Lon Poly 91-92; Chapl Thames Valley Univ from 92; C Ealing St Mary from 94. *16 Gerrards Court, South Ealing Road, London W5 4QB* 0181-579 1591 or 579 5000

COSBY, Ingrid St Clair. b 34. ALCM LLCM DipEd Lon Univ DipTh. **dss** 71 **d** 86. Cumbernauld *Glas* 71-73; Asst CF 73-78; Stromness *Ab* from 83. *Quarrybrae, Hillside Road, Stromness, Orkney KW16 3HR* Stromness (01856) 850832

COSENS, William Edward Hyde (Ted). b 38. Lich Th Coll 61. **d** 64 **p** 65. C W Drayton *Lon* 64-68; C Roehampton H Trin *S'wark* 68-70; ILEA Youth Ldr 69-70; Miss to Seamen from 70; Chapl Rotterdam Miss to Seamen *Eur* 70-72; Tilbury 72-76; Australia 76-81; New Zealand 81-89; Chapl Immingham Seafarers' Cen from 89; Hon C Immingham *Linc* from 89. *342 Pelham Road, Immingham, Grimsby, S Humberside DN40 1PU* Immingham (01469) 572818 or 574195

COSH, Roderick John. b 56. Lon Univ BSc78. St Steph Ho Ox 78. **d** 81 **p** 82. C Swindon New Town *Bris* 81-86; Chapl Asst R Marsden Hosp Lon and Surrey 86-91; V Whitton St Aug *Lon* from 91. *St Augustine's Vicarage, Hospital Bridge Road, Whitton, Middx TW2 6DE* 0181-894 3764 Fax 894 4543

COSLETT, Anthony Allan. b 49. Cuddesdon Coll. **d** 84 **p** 85. C Notting Hill St Clem and St Mark *Lon* 84-85; C Brentford 85-87; C-in-c Hounslow Gd Shep Beavers Lane CD 87-90; V Hounslow W Gd Shep 90-92; CF from 92. *clo MOD (Army), Bagshot Park, Bagshot, Surrey GU19 5PL* Bagshot (01276) 471717 Fax 412834

COSSAR, David Vyvyan. b 34. Lon Univ BA63. Chich Th Coll 63. **d** 65 **p** 66. C Upper Clapton St Matt *Lon* 65-68; C Withycombe Raleigh *Ex* 68-72; V Honicknowle 72-78; V Brixham w Churston Ferrers 78-86; P-in-c Kingswear 85-86; TR Brixham w Churston Ferrers and Kingswear 86-90; V Lamorbey H Trin *Roch* from 90. *Holy Trinity Vicarage, 1 Hurst Road, Sidcup, Kent DA15 9AE* 0181-300 8231

COSSAR, Miss Heather Jillian Mackenzie. b 27. **dss** 83 **d** 91 **p** 94. Miss Partner CMS 83-90; Kenya 83-90; Slindon, Eartham and Madehurst *Chich* 90-91; NSM from 91. *31 Madehurst, Arundel, W Sussex BN18 0NJ* Slindon (01243) 814291

COSSAR, John Robert Mackenzie. b 26. Oak Hill Th Coll 53. **d** 56 **p** 57. V Madehurst *Chich* 62-81; Dioc Youth Chapl 61-78; P-in-c Slindon w Eartham 81; R Slindon, Eartham and Madehurst 81-93; rtd 93. *16 Long Mead, Walberton, Arundel, W Sussex BN18 0QG* Eastergate (01243) 543353

COSSINS, John Charles. b 43. Hull Univ BSc65. Oak Hill Th Coll 65. **d** 67 **p** 68. C Kenilworth St Jo *Cov* 67-70; C Huyton St Geo *Liv* 70-73; TV Maghull 73-79; Chapl Oakwood Hosp Maidstone 79-85; Maidstone Hosp 85-88; Chapl Park Lane Hosp Liv from 88; Chapl Moss Side Hosp Liv from 88; Chapl Ashworth Hosp from 88. *9 Longton Drive, Liverpool L37 7ET, or Ashworth Hospital, Parkbourn, Maghull, Liverpool L31 1HW* Formby (01704) 833136/0151-471 2608

COSSINS, Roger Stanton. b 40. K Coll Lon BD67 AKC67. **d** 68 **p** 69. C Bramley *Ripon* 68-71; C W End *Win* 71-76; V Bramley 76-91; P-in-c Bournemouth H Epiphany 91-94; V from 94. *The Vicarage, 81 Castle Lane West, Bournemouth BH9 3LH* Bournemouth (01202) 512481

COSSLETT, Ronald James. b 38. St D Coll Lamp DipTh70. **d** 70 **p** 71. C Newport St Teilo *Mon* 70-74; C Epsom St Barn *Guildf* 74-78; C Shrewsbury St Mary w All SS and St Mich *Lich* 78-80; V Smallthorne 80-91; V Landore *S & B* from 91. *The Vicarage, 16 Trewyddfa Terrace, Plasmarl, Swansea SA6 8BP* Swansea (01792) 773680

COSTERTON, Alan Stewart. b 40. Bris Univ BA67. Clifton Th Coll 67. **d** 69 **p** 70. C Peckham St Mary Magd *S'wark* 69-73; C Forest Gate St Sav w W Ham St Matt *Chelmsf* 73-76; TV 76-79; V Thornton cum Bagworth *Leic* 79-85; V Thornton, Bagworth and Stanton 85-95; TR Sileby, Cossington and Seagrave from 95. *The Rectory, 11 Mountsorrel Lane, Sileby, Loughborough, Leics LE12 7NE* Sileby (01509) 813455

COTGROVE, Alan Edward. b 26. AKC51. **d** 52 **p** 53. C Earl's Court St Cuth w St Matthias *Lon* 52-55; Perm to Offic *Ox* 56-58; Lic to Offic 58-62 and 65-76; SSJE from 58; India 62-65; Lic to Offic *Lon* from 76. *St Edward's House, 22 Great College Street, London SW1P 3QA* 0171-222 9234

COTGROVE, Canon Edwin John. b 23. Kelham Th Coll 42. **d** 47 **p** 48. V Hampton All SS *Lon* 64-72; RD Hampton 72-82; R

Bartlow *Ely* 82-91; V Linton 82-91; P-in-c Shudy Camps 85-91; P-in-c Castle Camps 85-91; RD Linton 88-93; Hon Can Ely Cathl from 89; rtd 91. *96 The High Street, Great Abington, Cambridge CB1 6AE* Cambridge (01223) 893735

COTGROVE, Norman James. b 24. CCC Cam BA53 MA57. Kelham Th Coll 46. **d** 50 **p** 51. R Ashingdon w S Fambridge *Chelmsf* 60-80; P-in-c Gt w Lt Tey 80-81; P-in-c Wakes Colne w Chappel 80-81; R Gt Tey and Wakes Colne w Chappel 81-90; rtd 90. *42 Manchester Drive, Leigh-on-Sea, Essex SS9 3HR* Southend-on-Sea (01702) 711046

COTMAN, John Sell Granville (Jan). b 44. St Jo Coll Dur BA69 Bris Univ DSA72. Wells Th Coll 70. **d** 73 **p** 74. C Leigh St Mary *Man* 73-76; P-in-c Coldhurst 76-78; TV Oldham 78-82; TV E Ham w Upton Park St Alb *Chelmsf* 82-85; C Hove All SS *Chich* 88-93; TV Hove from 93. *Church House Flat, Wilbury Road, Hove, E Sussex BN3 3PB* Brighton (01273) 736643

COTTAM, Kenneth Michael David. b 46. FTC70 Leic Univ NDA70 Brooksby Agric Coll NDFOM70. St Mich Coll Llan DMinlStuds93. **d** 93 **p** 94. Lic to Offic Llangadog and Llandeilo Deanery *St D* from 93. *The Vicarage, Llangadog, Dyfed SA19 9AE* Llangadog (01550) 777604

COTTEE, Christopher Paul. b 54. Newc Univ BSc75. Wycliffe Hall Ox 77. **d** 80 **p** 81. C Much Woolton *Liv* 80-84; C Prescot 84-88; NSM Parr 89-91; V Watford St Pet *St Alb* from 91. *St Peter's Vicarage, 61 Westfield Avenue, Watford WD2 4HT* Watford (01923) 226717

COTTEE, Mary Jane. b 43. CertEd64 Open Univ BA81. Oak Hill Th Coll 87. **d** 90 **p** 94. NSM Gt Baddow *Chelmsf* 90-95; NSM Woodham Ferrers and Bicknacre from 95. *19 Avenue Road, Great Baddow, Chelmsford CM2 9TY* Chelmsford (01245) 266225

COTTER, Graham Michael. b 50. Univ of Wales (Ban) BA72. Ridley Hall Cam 75. **d** 78 **p** 79. C Headley All SS *Guildf* 78-81; C Plymouth St Andr w St Paul and St Geo *Ex* 81-84; V Buckland Monachorum from 84; RD Tavistock from 93. *The Vicarage, Buckland Monachorum, Yelverton, Devon PL20 7LQ* Yelverton (01822) 852227

COTTER, James England. b 42. G&C Coll Cam BA64 MA67. Linc Th Coll 65. **d** 67 **p** 68. C Stretford St Matt *Man* 67-70; Lect Linc Th Coll 70-73; Lic to Offic *Lon* 73-74; Chapl G&C Coll Cam 74-77; C Leavesden All SS *St Alb* 77-83; Asst Prin St Alb Minl Tr Scheme 77-83; Course Dir 83-86; Perm to Offic *Ex* 86-88; Perm to Offic *Sheff* 88-89; Lic to Offic from 89. *47 Firth Park Avenue, Sheffield S5 6HF* Sheffield (0114) 243 1182

COTTER, Canon John Beresford Dolmage. b 20. TCD BA47 BD55. **d** 47 **p** 48. Bahrain 69-75; V Towednack *Truro* 76-89; V Zennor 76-89; Past Tr Chapl 82-89; rtd 89. *Thimble Cottage, 64 Mount Road, Bath BA2 1LH* Bath (01225) 337414

COTTERELL, Michael Clifford. b 54. Oak Hill Th Coll 81. **d** 84 **p** 85. C Lutterworth w Cotesbach *Leic* 84-87; C Belper Derby 87-91; V Locking *B & W* from 91. *The Vicarage, The Green, Locking, Weston-super-Mare, Avon BS24 8DA* Banwell (01934) 823556

COTTERILL, Joseph Charles (Joe). b 17. AMCT38 Lon Univ DipTh BD California Coll Peking MA46. Ox Min Course 92. **d** 93 **p** 94. NSM Marcham w Garford *Ox* from 93. *8 Draycott Road, Southmoor, Abingdon, Oxon OX13 5BY* Longworth (01865) 820436

COTTINGHAM, Peter John Garnet. b 24. Wadh Coll Ox BA48 MA50. Ridley Hall Cam 48. **d** 50 **p** 51. V S Mimms Ch Ch *Lon* 68-81; V Derby St Pet and Ch w H Trin *Derby* 81-89; rtd 89. *5 Broadway, Rhos-on-Sea, Colwyn Bay, Clwyd LL28 4AR* Colwyn Bay (01492) 548840

COTTON, Charles Anthony. b 50. Linc Coll Ox BA72 MA77 PGCE73. Ridley Hall Cam 89. **d** 91 **p** 92. C Hendon St Paul Mill Hill *Lon* from 91. *46 Shakespeare Road, London NW7 4BE* 0181-959 8461

COTTON, Canon John Alan. b 24. Qu Coll Ox BA48 MA52. Chich Th Coll 50. **d** 51 **p** 52. V Fairwarp *Chich* 69-82; Dir of Educn 72-78; Can and Preb Chich Cathl 72-89; Bp's Adv on Min 79-89; Dir of Ords 79-89; rtd 89. *1 Westhaven, Thursby, Carlisle CA5 6PH* Carlisle (01228) 711506

COTTON, John Horace Brazel. b 28. MIMechE St Jo Coll Cam BA50 MA76. St Alb Minl Tr Scheme 78. **d** 81 **p** 82. NSM Lt Berkhamsted and Bayford, Essendon etc *St Alb* 81-87; P-in-c from 87. *49 Sherrardspark Road, Welwyn Garden City, Herts AL8 7LD* Welwyn Garden (01707) 321815

COTTON, John Kenneth. b 25. Westcott Ho Cam 57. **d** 58 **p** 59. Canada 68-71; TV Sandringham w W Newton *Nor* 71-76; P-in-c Assington *St E* 80-86; P-in-c Lt Cornard 80-86; P-in-c Newton 80-86; P-in-c Eyke w Bromeswell, Rendlesham, Tunstall etc 86-89; P-in-c Alderton w Ramsholt and Bawdsey 89-92; rtd 92. *8 Chillesford Lodge Bungalows, Sudbourne, Woodbridge, Suffolk IP12 2AN* Orford (01394) 450740

COTTON, John Wallis. b 31. Wells Th Coll 57. **d** 59 **p** 60. C Stepney St Dunstan and All SS *Lon* 59-64; C Hanworth All SS 64-67; V Hammersmith St Sav 67-74; R Lancing w Coombes

Chich 75-86; RD Worthing 83-85; R Bexhill St Pet 86-90; TR from 90; RD Battle and Bexhill from 92. *The Rectory, Old Town, Bexhill-on-Sea, E Sussex TN40 2HE* Bexhill-on-Sea (01424) 211115

COTTON, John William. b 53. Basford Coll Nottm DipInstBM74. Oak Hill Th Coll DipHE86. **d** 86 **p** 87. C New Clee *Linc* 86-89; Chapl St Andr Hospice Grimsby 88-89; R Middle Rasen Gp 89-95; P-in-c Broughton from 95. *The Rectory, 22 Scawby Road, Broughton, Brigg, S Humberside DN20 0AF* Brigg (01652) 652506

COTTON, Mrs Margaret Elizabeth. b 30. JP79. Newnham Coll Cam BA53 MA66. St Alb Minl Tr Scheme 78. **dss** 82 **d** 87 **p** 94. Lt Berkhamsted and Bayford, Essendon etc *St Alb* 82-87; Hon Par Dn 87-94; Hon C from 94. *49 Sherrardspark Road, Welwyn Garden City, Herts AL8 7LD* Welwyn Garden (01707) 321815

COTTON, Norman Joseph. b 39. Kelham Th Coll 59. **d** 64 **p** 65. C Auckland St Helen *Dur* 64-67; C Withington *Man* 67-68; C Hucknall Torkard *S'well* 69-71; TV 71-73; TV Fenny Stratford *Ox* 73-75; TV Fenny Stratford and Water Eaton 75-82; P-in-c Broughton and Milton Keynes 82; P-in-c Wavendon w Walton 82; R Walton 82-90; TR Walton Milton Keynes 90-92; V Stewkley w Soulbury and Drayton Parslow from 92; RD Mursley from 94. *The Vicarage, Stewkley, Leighton Buzzard, Beds LU7 0OH* Leighton Buzzard (01525) 240287

COTTON, Miss Patricia Constance. b 32. Gilmore Ho 54. **dss** 60 **d** 87 **p** 94. Basildon St Martin w H Cross and Laindon *Chelmsf* 65-79; Gt Burstead 79-87; Par Dn Maldon All SS w St Pet 87-91; rtd 92; NSM Holland-on-Sea *Chelmsf* from 94. *21 Stallards Crescent, Kirby Cross, Frinton-on-Sea, Essex CO13 0TN* Frinton-on-Sea (01255) 672711

COTTON, Patrick Arthur William. b 46. Essex Univ BA67 Cam Univ MA73. Linc Th Coll 68. **d** 71 **p** 72. C Earlham St Anne *Nor* 71-73; Chapl Down Coll Cam 73-78; V Eaton Socon *St Alb* 78-84; TR Newc Epiphany *Newc* 84-90; V Tunstall w Melling and Leck *Blackb* from 90. *The New Vicarage, Church Lane, Tunstall, Carnforth, Lancs LA6 2QN* Tunstall (01524) 274376

COTTON, Peter John. b 45. BNC Ox BA66 Bris Univ CQSW76. Cuddesdon Coll 67. **d** 69 **p** 70. C Salford St Phil w St Steph *Man* 69-73; Asst Educn Officer *St Alb* 73-75; C Bris St Geo *Bris* 75-76; C-in-c Portsea St Geo CD *Portsm* 76-80; Soc Resp Adv 78-88; Can Res Portsm Cathl 84-88; V St Laurence in the Isle of Thanet *Cant* 88-93; TR from 93. *St Laurence Vicarage, 2 Newington Road, Ramsgate, Kent CT11 0QT* Thanet (01843) 592478

COTTON, Richard William (Dick). b 35. Hertf Coll Ox BA58 MA62. Clifton Th Coll 58. **d** 60 **p** 61. C Harold Wood *Chelmsf* 60-64; C Higher Openshaw *Man* 64-67; Lic to Offic 67-71; Ch Youth Fellowships Assn & Pathfinders 67-71; Nat Sec Pathfinders CPAS 71-76; Lic to Offic *St Alb* 73-76; V Chislehurst Ch Ch *Roch* 76-92; V Herne Bay Ch Ch *Cant* from 92; RD Reculver from 93. *Christ Church Vicarage, 38 Beltinge Road, Herne Bay, Kent CT6 5BP* Herne Bay (01227) 374906 or 366640

COTTON, Robert Lloyd. b 58. Mert Coll Ox MA79 Louvain Univ Belgium DipTh81. Westcott Ho Cam 81. **d** 83 **p** 84. C Plaistow St Mary *Roch* 83-86; C Bisley and W End *Guildf* 87-89; P-in-c E Molesey St Paul from 89; Dir of Reader Tr from 90. *St Paul's Vicarage, 101 Palace Road, West Molesey, Surrey KT8 9DU* 0181-979 1580

COTTON, Roy William. b 29. Jes Coll Ox BA53 MA61. Chich Th Coll 66. **d** 66 **p** 67. C Eastney *Portsm* 66-71; R Harting *Chich* 71-74; P-in-c Eastbourne St Andr 74-76; V 76-84; R Brede w Udimore from 84. *The Rectory, Brede, Rye, E Sussex TN31 6DX* Brede (01424) 882457

COTTRELL, Bertram Lionel. b 23. Lich Th Coll 51. **d** 54 **p** 56. V Isleworth St Jo *Lon* 63-83; rtd 83; Perm to Offic *Lon* from 83. *13 Sutton Square, Heston, Middx TW5 0JB* 0181-572 5034

COTTRELL, Stephen Geoffrey. b 58. Cen Lon Poly BA79. St Steph Ho Ox 81. **d** 84 **p** 85. C Forest Hill Ch Ch *S'wark* 84-88; C-in-c Parklands St Wilfrid CD *Chich* 88-93; Asst Dir of Past Studies Chich Th Coll 88-93; Dioc Missr *Wakef* from 93; Bp's Chapl for Evang from 93. *68 Glenholt Road, Huddersfield HD1 4HD* Huddersfield (01484) 542163

COTTRILL, Derek John. b 43. MA. Qu Coll Birm. **d** 82 **p** 83. C Southn Maybush St Pet *Win* 82-85; V Barton Stacey and Bullington etc 85-92; R Bishopstoke from 92. *The Rectory, 10 Stoke Park Road, Eastleigh, Hants SO50 6DA* Eastleigh (01703) 612712

COUCH, Andrew Nigel. b 48. K Coll Lon BD70 AKC70 Ex Coll Ox PGCE72. St Aug Coll Cant 70. **d** 71 **p** 72. C St Ives *Truro* 71-74; C St Martin-in-the-Fields *Lon* 74-78; USPG 78-91; Uruguay 79-84; Argentina 85-91; Chapl Qu Mary Coll Lon 91-94; V St Ives *Truro* from 94. *The Parsonage, St Andrew's Street, St Ives, Cornwall TR26 1AH* Penzance (01736) 796404

COUCHMAN, Anthony Denis. b 37. Sarum Th Coll 66. **d** 69 **p** 70. C Barkingside St Fran *Chelmsf* 69-71; C Chingford SS Pet and Paul 71-76; P-in-c Walthamstow St Barn and St Jas Gt 76-80; V from 80. *St Barnabas' Vicarage, St Barnabas Road, London E17 8JZ* 0181-520 5323

COUGHTREY, Miss Sheila Frances. b 48. RSCN73 SRN73 S Bank Poly BSc79. Qu Coll Birm 79. **dss** 81 **d** 87 **p** 94. Sydenham St Bart *S'wark* 81-85; Roehampton H Trin 85-87; Par Dn 87-91; Par Dn Brixton Hill St Sav 91-94; Min K Acre LEP from 91; C Brixton Hill St Sav 94; P-in-c from 94. *6 Blenheim Gardens, London SW2 5ET* 0181-674 6914

COULDRIDGE, Janice Evelyn. *See* FOX, Mrs Janice Evelyn

COULING, Albert James. b 10. Linc Th Coll 43. **d** 44 **p** 45. R Bleadon *B & W* 59-78; rtd 78; Perm to Offic *B & W* from 79. *Flat 3, Clarence House, 17 Clarence Road North, Weston-super-Mare, Avon BS23 4AS* Weston-super-Mare (01934) 415171

COULING, David Charles. b 36. Open Univ BA89. Qu Coll Birm 61. **d** 63 **p** 64. C Harborne St Faith and St Laur *Birm* 63-66; C E Grinstead St Mary *Chich* 66-70; V Copthorne 70-75; V Eastbourne St Mich 75-82; V Brighton St Matthias 82-83; C-in-c Harton St Lawr CD *Dur* 84-90; V Horsley Hill S Shields 91-94; P-in-c Greatham from 94; Master Greatham Hosp from 94. *Greatham Hall, Greatham, Hartlepool, Cleveland TS25 2HS* Hartlepool (01429) 871148

COULSON, Robert Gustavus. b 99. Wycliffe Hall Ox 45. **d** 45 **p** 45. R Stansted *Roch* 50-61; rtd 68. *The Old Vicarage, Moulsford, Wallingford, Oxon OX10 9JB* Cholsey (01491) 651368

COULSON, Stephen Hugh. b 60. St Edm Hall Ox BA82 MA88 Lon Univ CertEd83. Wycliffe Hall Ox 85. **d** 88 **p** 89. C Summerfield *Birm* 88-91; Perm to Offic 91-92; CMS from 92; Uganda from 92. *PO Box 5627, Kampala, Uganda*

COULSON, Canon Thomas Stanley. b 32. TCD BA54 MA68. TCD Div Sch 55. **d** 55 **p** 56. C Maghera *D & R* 55-62; I Aghalurcher and Tattykeeran *Clogh* 62-63; I Woodschapel w Gracefield *Arm* from 63; Preb Arm Cathl from 88; RD Tullyhogue from 90; Treas Arm Cathl from 94. *140 Ballyronan Road, Magherafelt, Co Derry BT45 6HU* Ballyronan (01648) 87230

COULSON, Tony Erik Frank. b 32. St Edm Hall Ox BA55 DipTh56 MA59. Wycliffe Hall Ox 55. **d** 57 **p** 58. C Walthamstow St Mary *Chelmsf* 57-60; C Reading St Jo *Ox* 60-63; V Iver 63-86; R White Waltham w Shottesbrooke from 86. *The Vicarage, White Waltham, Maidenhead, Berks SL6 3JD* Littlewick Green (01628) 822000

COULTER, Edmond James. b 60. QUB BSc82 TCD DipTh87. **d** 87 **p** 88. C Ballymena w Ballyclug *Conn* 87-90; C Knockbreda *D & D* 90-92; I Belf Upper Falls *Conn* from 92. *Upper Falls Rectory, 38 Upper Green, Dunmurry, Belfast BT17 0EL* Belfast (01232) 610755

COULTER, Richard Samuel Scott. b 09. Dur Univ LTh39. Clifton Th Coll 35. **d** 38 **p** 39. Hon CF from 46; V Upton Snodsbury w Broughton Hackett etc *Worc* 61-77; rtd 77. *29 Greenheart Way, Southmoor, Abingdon, Oxon OX13 5DF* Longworth (01865) 820912

COULTHARD, Miss Nina Marion. b 50. CertEd71 Bp Lonsdale Coll BEd72. Trin Coll Bris DipHE91. **d** 91 **p** 94. Par Dn Cant St Mary Bredin *Cant* 91-94; C 94-95; C Bath Abbey w St Jas *B & W* from 95. *7 Holloway, Bath BA2 4PS* Bath (01225) 484469

COULTHURST, Jeffrey Evans. b 38. Man Univ BA. Local NSM Course 85. **d** 84 **p** 85. NSM Ancaster *Linc* 84-89; NSM Ancaster Wilsford Gp from 89. *5 North Drive, Ancaster, Grantham, Lincs NG32 3RB* Loveden (01400) 30280

COULTON, David Stephen. b 41. Sarum Th Coll 64. **d** 67 **p** 68. C Guildf H Trin w St Mary *Guildf* 67-70; Asst Chapl Radley Coll Abingdon 70-83; Chapl from 83. *Radley College, Abingdon, Oxon OX14 2HR* Abingdon (01235) 534651

COULTON, Very Rev Nicholas Guy. b 40. Lon Univ BD72. Cuddesdon Coll 65. **d** 67 **p** 68. C Pershore w Wick *Worc* 67-70; Bp's Dom Chapl *St Alb* 71-75; P-in-c Bedf St Paul 75-79; V 79-90; Hon Can St Alb 89-90; Provost Newc from 90. *The Cathedral Vicarage, 26 Mitchell Avenue, Jesmond, Newcastle upon Tyne NE2 3LA* 0191-281 6554 or 232 1939

COULTON, Philip Ernest. b 31. St Cath Coll Cam BA54 MA58 TCD BD68 Open Univ BA84. Ely Th Coll 55. **d** 57 **p** 58. C Newark w Coddington *S'well* 57-61; Min Can and Sacr Cant Cathl *Cant* 61-63; Min Can Ripon Cathl *Ripon* 63-68; Hd of RE Ashton-under-Lyne Gr Sch 69-84; Perm to Offic *Ches* 70-71; Lic to Offic 71-84; V Ulceby Gp *Linc* 85-89; P-in-c Ingatestone w Buttsbury *Chelmsf* from 89; P-in-c Fryerning w Margaretting 89-92. *1 Rectory Close, Ingatestone, Essex CM4 0DB* Ingatestone (01277) 353768

COUNSELL, Edwin Charles Robert. b 63. Univ of Wales (Cardiff) BA84. St Steph Ho Ox 85. **d** 88 **p** 89. C Cardiff St Mary and St Steph w St Dyfrig etc *Llan* 88-94; Sub-Chapl HM Pris Cardiff 90-94; V Pendoylan and Welsh St Donats from 94.

The Vicarage, 9 Heol St Cattwg, Pendoylan, Cowbridge, S Glam CF7 7UJ Peterston-super-Ely (01446) 760210

COUNSELL, Michael John Radford. b 35. Pemb Coll Cam BA59 MA63. Ripon Hall Ox 59. **d** 61 **p** 62. C Handsworth St Mary *Birm* 61-63; Singapore 64-68; Vietnam and Cambodia 68-71; Seychelles 72-76; Dean Mahe 73-76; V Harborne St Pet *Birm* 76-89; Relig Consultant to Inter-Ch Travel Ltd 89-90; V Forest Hill St Aug *S'wark* from 90. *St Augustine's Vicarage, 8 Hengrave Road, London SE23 3NW* 0181-699 1535

COUPAR, Thomas. b 50. BA71. Edin Dioc NSM Course 77. **d** 80 **p** 81. NSM Dunbar *Edin* 80-86; NSM Haddington 80-86; Hd Master Pencaitland Primary Sch E Lothian 80-81; Hd Master K Meadow Sch E Lothian 81-87; Asst Dioc Supernumerary *Edin* from 87; Primary Educn Adv Fife from 88; Dioc Supernumerary Chapl from 90. *8A Garscube Terrace, Edinburgh EH12 6BQ* 0131-337 2988

COUPER, Jeanette Emily (Jean). b 40. S'wark Ord Course 85. **d** 88. Par Dn Mitcham SS Pet and Paul *S'wark* 88-93; Perm to Offic from 93; Chapl Asst Guy's Hosp Lon 93-94. *Ivy Lodge, Morden Hall Road, Morden, Surrey SM4 5JD* 0181-640 8137

COUPER, Jonathan George. b 51. St Jo Coll Dur BA73. Wycliffe Hall Ox 73. **d** 75 **p** 76. C Clifton *York* 75-78; C Darfield *Sheff* 78-81; V Bridlington Quay Ch Ch *York* from 81. *21 Kingston Road, Bridlington, N Humberside YO15 3NF* Bridlington (01262) 673538

COUPLAND, Simon Charles. b 59. St Jo Coll Cam BA82 PGCE83 MA85 PhD87. Ridley Hall Cam 88. **d** 91 **p** 92. C Bath St Luke *B & W* from 91. *59 Longfellow Avenue, Bath BA2 4SH* Bath (01225) 480189

COURAGE, Roy Kenneth. b 25. ACCS63 ACIS70. St D Coll Lamp 67. **d** 69 **p** 70. C Blaenavon w Capel Newydd *Mon* 69-71; R Blaina 71-78; V Blackwood 78-89; rtd 89. *Ysgubor Wen, Tylsaf Farm, Llechryd, Rhymney, Gwent NP22 5QU* Rhymney (01685) 841260

COURT, David Eric. b 58. Southn Univ BSc80 PhD83 PGCE84. Oak Hill Th Coll BA91. **d** 91 **p** 92. C Barton Seagrave w Warkton *Pet* 91-94; C Kinson *Sarum* from 94. *4 Home Road, Bournemouth BH11 9BN* Bournemouth (01202) 578355

COURT, Canon Kenneth Reginald. b 36. AKC60. **d** 61 **p** 62. C Garforth *Ripon* 61-63; C Harrogate St Wilfrid 63-65; V Thornbury *Bradf* 65-73; Prec Leic Cathl *Leic* 73-76; V Douglas St Matt *S & M* 76-84; V Syston *Leic* 84-93; TR Syston TM from 93; RD Goscote from 90; Hon Can Leic Cathl from 92. *The Vicarage, Upper Church Street, Syston, Leicester LE7 1HR* Leicester (0116) 260 8276

COURT, Martin Jeremy. b 61. GRNCM84 Nottm Univ BTh89. Linc Th Coll 86. **d** 89 **p** 90. C Thurmaston *Leic* 89-92; C Leic St Jas 92-93; TV Leic Resurr from 93. *St Gabriel's House, 20 Kerrysdale Avenue, Leicester LE4 7GH* Leicester (0116) 266 1452

COURT, Nicholas James Keble. b 56. Chich Th Coll 86. **d** 88 **p** 89. C Golders Green *Lon* 88-91; C Westbury-on-Trym H Trin *Bris* 91-94; PV Llan Cathl *Llan* from 94. *1 White House, The Cathedral Green, Llandaff, Cardiff CF5 2EB* Cardiff (01222) 569521

COURTAULD, Augustine Christopher Caradoc. b 34. Trin Coll Cam BA58. Westcott Ho Cam 58. **d** 60 **p** 61. C Oldham St Mary *Man* 60-63; Chapl Trin Coll Cam 63-68; Chapl The Lon Hosp (Whitechapel) 68-78; V Wilton Place St Paul *Lon* from 78; AD Westmr St Marg from 92. *St Paul's Vicarage, 32 Wilton Place, London SW1X 8SH* 0171-235 1810 or 235 3460

COURTIE, Dr John Malcolm. b 42. BNC Ox BA65 DPhil72 St Jo Coll Dur BA76 DipTh77. Cranmer Hall Dur 74. **d** 77 **p** 78. C Mossley Hill St Matt and St Jas *Liv* 77-80; V Litherland St Paul Hatton Hill 80-84; Wellingborough Sch 84-89; Hon C Wollaston and Strixton *Pet* 84-89; V Woodford Halse w Eydon from 89. *The New Vicarage, Parsons Street, Woodford Halse, Daventry, Northants NN11 3RE* Byfield (01327) 261477 Fax as telephone Mobile (0589) 319801

COURTNEY, Canon Brian Joseph. b 44. BD92. CITC 70. **d** 73 **p** 74. C Willowfield *D & D* 73-78; I Aghavea *Clogh* 78-83; I Carrickfergus *Conn* 83-95; I Enniskillen *Clogh* from 95; Prec Clogh Cathl from 95. *St Macartin's Rectory, 13 Church Street, Enniskillen, Co Fermanagh BT74 7DW* Enniskillen (01365) 322465 or 322917

COURTNEY, Michael Monlas. b 19. Coll of Resurr Mirfield 58. **d** 60 **p** 61. V N Keyham *Ex* 68-73; TV Sidmouth, Woolbrook and Salcombe Regis 73-79; TV Sidmouth, Woolbrook, Salcombe Regis etc 79-84; rtd 84; Perm to Offic *Ex* from 86. *Furzehill Farm House, Sidbury, Sidmouth, Devon EX10 0RE* Sidbury (01395) 597440

COUSINS, Christopher William. b 44. Oak Hill Th Coll DipHE87. **d** 87 **p** 88. C Wallasey St Hilary *Ches* 87-90; R Rollesby w Burgh w Billockby w Ashby w Oby etc *Nor* 90-94; P-in-c Ormesby w Scratby 92-94; V Ormesby St Marg w Scratby, Ormesby St Mich etc from 94; RD Gt Yarmouth from 94. *The Vicarage, Ormesby, Great Yarmouth, Norfolk NR29 3PZ* Great Yarmouth (01493) 730234

COUSINS, Graham John. b 55. Oak Hill Th Coll BA91. **d** 91 **p** 92. C Birkenhead St Jas w St Bede *Ches* 91-95; C Bebington from 95. *48 Acreville Road, Bebington, Wirral, Merseyside L63 2HY* 0151-645 9584

COUSINS, Herbert Ralph. b 13. Bps' Coll Cheshunt 52. **d** 54 **p** 55. R Clophill *St Alb* 71-78; rtd 78. *Evensong, Sand Road, Weston-super-Mare, Avon BS22 9UF* Weston-super-Mare (01934) 413260

COUSINS, Philip John. b 35. K Coll Cam BA58 MA62. Cuddesdon Coll 59. **d** 61 **p** 62. C Marton *Blackb* 61-63; PV Truro Cathl *Truro* 63-67; Ethiopia 67-75; V Henleaze *Bris* 75-84; RD Clifton 79-84; Provost All SS Cathl Cairo 84-89; Chan Malta Cathl *Eur* 89-95; Valletta w Gozo 89-95; R Llandudno *Ban* from 95. *The Rectory, Church Walk, Llandudno, Gwynedd LL30 2HL* Llandudno (01492) 876624

COUSLAND, Andrew Oliver. b 41. Golds Coll Lon MA92. Edin Th Coll 62. **d** 65 **p** 66. C Broughty Ferry *Bre* 65-68; C Ayr *Glas* 68-70; R Renfrew 70-73; Perm to Offic *St E* 75-79; CF (TAVR) 76-82; Perm to Offic *Bre* 79-84; Perm to Offic *S'wark* 89-94; R Aber St Pet *Ab* from 94. *St Peter's Rectory, 6 Crimond Court, Fraserburgh AB43 5QW* Fraserburgh (01346) 518158

COUSSENS, Mervyn Haigh Wingfield. b 47. St Jo Coll Nottm BTh74. **d** 74 **p** 75. C Clifton Ch Ch w Em *Bris* 74-77; C Morden *S'wark* 77-83; V Patchway *Bris* 83-91; R Lutterworth w Cotesbach *Leic* from 91; P-in-c Bitteswell from 95. *The Rectory, Coventry Road, Lutterworth, Leics LE17 4SH* Lutterworth (01455) 552669

COUSSMAKER, Canon Colin Richard Chad. b 34. Worc Coll Ox BA57 BSc58 MA63 MSc85. Chich Th Coll 59. **d** 60 **p** 61. C Newtown St Luke *Win* 60-64; C Whitley Ch Ch *Ox* 64-67; Chapl Istanbul *Eur* 67-72; Chapl Sliema 72-77; Chapl Antwerp St Boniface 77-93; Can Brussels Cathl from 81; Chapl Moscow from 93. *c/o The British Embassy, Moscow 72, Sofiiskaya, Neberezhnaya 14, Russia* Moscow (095) 245-3837 or 266-0907 Fax 956-7480

COUTTS, Ian Alexander. b 56. Warw Univ BA77 Jes Coll Ox MSc80 CQSW80. St Jo Coll Nottm DipTh89. **d** 89 **p** 90. C Hamstead St Bernard *Birm* 89-92; C Warlingham w Chelsham and Farleigh *S'wark* from 92. *St Christopher's Vicarage, Chelsham Road, Warlingham, Surrey CR6 9EQ* Upper Warlingham (01883) 624494

COUTTS, James Allan. b 58. Fitzw Coll Cam MA. St Jo Coll Nottm MTh84. **d** 84 **p** 85. C Dishley and Thorpe Acre *Leic* 84-88; TV Kirby Muxloe from 88. *106 Hinckley Road, Leicester Forest East, Leicester LE3 3JS* Leicester (0116) 238 6344/238 6811

COUTTS, Canon James Walter Cargill. b 35. Univ of Wales (Lamp) BA57 CCC Cam BA59. St Mich Coll Llan 59. **d** 60 **p** 61. C Cardiff St Mary *Llan* 60-63; C Greenford H Cross *Lon* 63-67; C Swansea St Gabr *S & B* 67-71; V Llanwrtyd w Llanddulas in Tir Abad etc 71-78; V Brecon St Dav 78-80; V Brecon St David w Llanspyddid and Llanilltyd 80-84; V Mon from 84; Can St Woolos Cathl from 94. *The Vicarage, The Parade, Monmouth, Gwent NP5 3PA* Monmouth (01600) 713141

COUTTS, Robin Iain Philip. b 52. Sarum & Wells Th Coll. **d** 83 **p** 84. C Alverstoke *Portsm* 83-86; Min Leigh Park St Clare CD 86-89; V Warren Park St Clare 89-91; V Purbrook from 91. *The Vicarage, Purbrook, Waterlooville, Hants PO7 5RS* Waterlooville (01705) 262307

COVE, Kenneth John. b 34. Lich Th Coll 58. **d** 60 **p** 61. C Crosland Moor *Wakef* 60-63; C Halifax St Jo Bapt 63-65; V Wakef St Jo 65-73; V Appleby *Carl* 73-78; RD Appleby 74-78; V Ambleside w Brathay 78-87; V Thames Ditton *Guildf* 87-94; P-in-c Morland, Thrimby and Gt Strickland *Carl* from 94. *The Vicarage, Morland, Penrith, Cumbria CA10 3AX* Morland (01931) 714620

COVE, Tom Griffiths William. b 10. **d** 64 **p** 65. OSB from 59; Lic to Offic *Ox* 65-84; Australia from 84. *St Mark's Priory, PO Box 111, Camperdown, Victoria 3260, Australia* Camperdown (55) 932848

COVENTRY, Archdeacon of. *See* RUSSELL, Ven Harold Ian Lyle

COVENTRY, Bishop of. *See* BARRINGTON-WARD, Rt Rev Simon

COVENTRY, Provost of. *See* PETTY, Very Rev John Fitzmaurice

COVINGTON, Canon Michael William Rock. b 38. Open Univ BA78. Sarum Th Coll 60. **d** 63 **p** 64. C Daventry *Pet* 63-66; C Woolwich St Mary w H Trin *S'wark* 66-68; C Northn All SS w St Kath *Pet* 68-71; V Longthorpe 71-86; Hon Min Can Pet Cathl 75-86; Can Pet Cathl from 86; V Warmington, Tansor, Cotterstock and Fotheringhay 86-95; Warden Dioc Assn of Readers from 87; RD Oundle from 89; V Oakham,

Hambleton, Egleton, Braunston and Brooke from 95. *The Vicarage, Oakham, Leics LE15 6EG* Oakham (01572) 722108

COWARD, Colin Charles Malcolm. b 45. Westcott Ho Cam 75. **d** 78 **p** 79. C Camberwell St Geo *S'wark* 78-82; P-in-c Wandsworth St Faith 82-90; V from 90. *St Faith's Vicarage, 2 Alma Road, London SW18 1AB* 0181-874 8567

COWARD, Raymond. b 41. NW Ord Course 79. **d** 82 **p** 83. C Turton *Man* 82-84; C Heaton Ch Ch 84-86; V Rochdale St Geo w St Alb 86-92; V Daisy Hill from 92. *The Vicarage, Lower Leigh Road, Daisy Hill, Westhoughton, Bolton BL5 2EH* Westhoughton (01942) 813155

COWBURN, John Charles. b 48. Sarum & Wells Th Coll 88. **d** 90 **p** 91. C Andover w Foxcott *Win* 90-94; C Christchurch from 94. *St George's House, Jumpers Road, Christchurch, Dorset BH23 2JR* Christchurch (01202) 486248

COWDREY, Herbert Edward John. b 26. Trin Coll Ox BA49 MA51. St Steph Ho Ox 50. **d** 52 **p** 53. Lic to Offic *Ox* from 52; Fell St Edm Hall Ox from 56; Chapl 56-78; rtd 91. *30 Oxford Road, Old Marston, Oxford OX3 0PQ* Oxford (01865) 279015

COWDRY, Gilbert. b 26. Wells Th Coll 70. **d** 72 **p** 73. C Bath Twerton-on-Avon *B & W* 72-76; V Long Sutton w Long Load 76-82; TV S Molton w Nymet St George, High Bray etc *Ex* from 82; RD S Molton 87-93. *Springfield, East Street, North Molton, South Molton, Devon EX36 3HX* North Molton (01598) 740325

COWELL, Arthur John. b 10. Wycliffe Hall Ox 40. **d** 41 **p** 42. V Prittlewell St Pet *Chelmsf* 60-80; Chapl Southend Gen Hosp 68-80; rtd 80; Perm to Offic *Chelmsf* from 80. *Nazareth House, London Road, Southend-on-Sea SS1 1PP* Southend-on-Sea (01702) 345627

COWELL, Mrs Irene Christine. b 58. RGN80. Ridley Hall Cam CTM94. **d** 94 **p** 95. C Litherland St Phil *Liv* from 94. *3 Harrington Road, Litherland, Liverpool L21 7NA* 0151-928 7879

COWELL, Peter James. b 58. Peterho Cam BA80 MA84. Coll of Resurr Mirfield 80. **d** 82 **p** 83. C Folkestone St Sav *Cant* 82-86; Chapl Asst St Thos Hosp Lon 86-90; Chapl R Lon Hosp (Mile End) from 90; Chapl R Lon Hosp (Whitechapel) from 90; PV Westmr Abbey from 94. *The Chaplain's Office, The Royal London Hospital, London E1 1BB* 0171-377 7000 or 377 7385

COWEN, Brian. b 45. Nottm Univ BTh77. Linc Th Coll 73. **d** 77 **p** 78. C Hexham *Newc* 77-80; C Eastnor *Heref* 80-81; C Ledbury 80-81; C Ledbury w Eastnor 81; TV Glendale Gp *Newc* 81-90; V Lesbury w Alnmouth from 90; RD Alnwick from 93. *The Vicarage, Lesbury, Alnwick, Northd NE66 3AU* Alnwick (01665) 830281

COWEN, Richard James. b 48. St Jo Coll Nottm. **d** 83 **p** 84. C Kenilworth St Jo *Cov* 83-87; TV Becontree W *Chelmsf* from 87. *St Cedd's Vicarage, 185 Lodge Avenue, Dagenham, Essex RM8 2HQ* 0181-592 5900

COWGILL, Michael. b 48. Linc Th Coll 84. **d** 86 **p** 87. C Bolton St Jas w St Chrys *Bradf* 86-89; V Buttershaw St Paul 89-93; P-in-c Cullingworth from 93; Dir Dioc Foundn Course from 93. *The Vicarage, Halifax Road, Cullingworth, Bradford, W Yorkshire BD13 5DE* Cullingworth (01535) 272434

COWHAM, Hugh Nicholas Gerard. b 26. MACE81 Selw Coll Cam BA51 MA78 Aber Univ CertEd73. Local NSM Course 75. **d** 78 **p** 79. Hon C Elgin w Lossiemouth *Mor* 78-81; Asst Chapl Gordonstoun Sch 78-81; Australia from 81. *25 Equinox Court, Mudgeeraba, Queensland, Australia 4123* Gold Coast (75) 302378

COWIE, Derek Edward. b 33. S'wark Ord Course 70. **d** 73 **p** 74. C Maldon All SS w St Pet *Chelmsf* 73-76; R Bowers Gifford w N Benfleet 76-79; V Chelmsf Ascension 79-84; V Shrub End from 84. *All Saints' Vicarage, 270 Shrub End Road, Colchester CO3 4RL* Colchester (01206) 574178

COWIE, Leonard Wallace. b 19. Pemb Coll Ox BA41 DipTh43 MA46 Lon Univ PhD54. Ripon Hall Ox 42. **d** 43 **p** 44. C High Wycombe All SS *Ox* 43-45; Tutor Coll SS Mark and Jo Chelsea 45-68; Chapl 45-47; Tutor Whitelands Coll Putney 68-82; Lic to Offic *S'wark* from 68. *38 Stratton Road, London SW19 3JG* 0181-542 5036

COWLAN, William Thomas. b 12. OBE. Leeds Univ BD. **d** 79 **p** 79. NSM Kenton w Mamhead and Powderham *Ex* 79-82; Perm to Offic from 82. *4 Court Hall, Kenton, Exeter EX6 8NA* Starcross (01626) 890210

COWLES, Richard Martin. b 53. Birm Univ BSc74 DipTh76. Ripon Coll Cuddesdon DipMin93. **d** 93 **p** 94. C Iffley *Ox* from 93. *Church House, The Oval, Oxford OX4 4SE* Oxford (01865) 718600

COWLEY, Charles Frederick. See HOWARD-COWLEY, Joseph Charles

COWLEY, Mrs Elizabeth Mary (Liz). b 47. Bris Univ PQCSW84. W Midl Minl Tr Course 89. **d** 92 **p** 94. NSM Wolston and Church Lawford *Cov* from 92. *14 Sycamore*

Grove, Rugby, Warks CV21 2QY Rugby (01788) 576723

COWLEY, Geoffrey Willis. b 17. FICE50 FRTPI54. St Alb Minl Tr Scheme 77. **d** 80 **p** 81. NSM Stevington *St Alb* 80-87; rtd 87; Lic to Offic *St Alb* from 87. *The Cottage, 30 High Street, Carlton, Bedford MK43 7LA* Bedford (01234) 720451

COWLEY, Herbert Kenneth. b 20. Glouc Sch of Min 75. **d** 79 **p** 80. Hon C Lydney w Aylburton *Glouc* 79-89; rtd 89. *19 Beechwood Road, Nailsea, Bristol BS19 2AF* Nailsea (01275) 856198

COWLEY, Ian Michael. b 51. Natal Univ BCom72 BA75 Sheff Univ MA83. Wycliffe Hall Ox 75. **d** 78 **p** 79. S Africa 78-81 and 83-94; C Norton Woodseats St Chad *Sheff* 81-83; R Milton Ely from 94. *The Rectory, Church Lane, Milton, Cambridge CB4 4AB* Cambridge (01223) 861511

COWLEY, Leslie. b 22. St Jo Coll Nottm 70. **d** 71 **p** 72. C Worksop St Jo *S'well* 71-73; P-in-c Awsworth w Cossall 74-77; V Basford St Leodegarius 77-88; rtd 88; Perm to Offic *Linc* from 88. *12 Ridgeway, Nettleham, Lincoln LN2 2TL* Lincoln (01522) 752447

COWLEY, Samuel Henry (Sam). b 44. St Jo Coll Nottm 85. **d** 87 **p** 88. C Hadleigh w Layham and Shelley *St E* 87-91; P-in-c Ipswich St Mich from 91. *22 Tuddenham Road, Ipswich IP4 2SG* Ipswich (01473) 252939

COWLING, Canon Douglas Anderson. b 19. Leeds Univ BA40. Coll of Resurr Mirfield 40. **d** 42 **p** 43. V Spalding St Paul *Linc* 61-84; Can and Preb Linc Cathl 77-93; rtd 84. *24 Campbell's Close, Spalding, Lincs PE11 2UH* Spalding (01775) 767044

COWLING, John Francis. b 32. K Coll Cam BA56. Linc Th Coll 56. **d** 58 **p** 59. C Leigh St Mary *Man* 58-61; Sec SCM in Schs Liv and Ches 61-65; V Bolton St Matt 65-71; V Bolton St Matt w St Barn 71-75; V Southport H Trin *Liv* 75-91; R St Olave Hart Street w All Hallows Staining etc *Lon* from 91; Dir of Ords from 92. *St Olave's Rectory, 8 Hart Street, London EC3R 7NB* 0171-488 4318 Fax 702 0811

COWLING, Simon Charles. b 59. G&C Coll Cam BA80 MA88 K Coll Lon PGCE82. Linc Th Coll BTh91. **d** 91 **p** 92. C Potternewton *Ripon* 91-94; C Far Headingley St Chad from 94. *64 Becketts Park Crescent, Leeds LS6 3PF* Leeds (0113) 274 3636 or 274 4322

COWLING, Wilfred Edmund. b 14. Dur Univ BA38 MA42. St Aid Birkenhead 38. **d** 40 **p** 41. V Kirkburn *York* 57-83; V Garton on the Wolds 57-83; RD Harthill 63-73 and 78-80; rtd 83. *14 Ashleigh Drive, Beeford, Driffield, N Humberside YO25 8AU* Beeford (01262) 488277

COWMEADOW, Derek Lowe. b 28. Wells Th Coll 68. **d** 70 **p** 71. C Ledbury *Heref* 70-72; C Llanrhos *St As* 72-74; V Bringhurst w Gt Easton *Leic* 74-77; P-in-c Coln St Aldwyn w Hatherop and Quenington *Glouc* 77-82; V Coln St Aldwyns, Hatherop, Quenington etc 82-93; rtd 93. *2 Hampton Grove, Meysey Hampton, Cirencester, Glos GL7 5JN* Cirencester (01285) 851645

COWPER, Christopher Herbert. b 44. AKC67 Open Univ BA76. **d** 68 **p** 69. C Pitsmoor *Sheff* 68-71; C Ulverston St Mary w H Trin *Carl* 71-74; R Kirklinton w Hethersgill and Scaleby 74-83; V Bridekirk 83-94; Chapl Dovenby Hall Hosp Cockermouth 83-94; P-in-c Wetheral w Warw *Carl* from 94. *The Rectory, Plains Road, Wetheral, Carlisle CA4 8LE* Wetheral (01228) 560216

COWPER, Peter James. b 67. Wadh Coll Ox BA89. Edin Th Coll BD94. **d** 94 **p** 95. C Kippax w Allerton Bywater *Ripon* from 94. *32 Ebor Mount, Kippax, Leeds LS25 7PA* Leeds (0113) 286 1111

COX, Alan John. b 34. Lon Coll of Div ALCD65 LTh. **d** 65 **p** 66. C Keynsham w Queen Charlton *B & W* 67-71; R Chipstable w Huish Champflower and Clatworthy 71-76; TV Strood *Roch* 76-80; V Strood St Fran 80-83; R Keston 83-95; rtd 95. *12 Beech Court, 46 Copers Cope Road, Beckenham, Kent BR3 1LD*

COX, Alexander James. b 12. Pemb Coll Ox BA34 MA43. Westcott Ho Cam 34. **d** 36 **p** 37. CR from 63; Barbados 64-75; rtd 82. *House of the Resurrection, Mirfield, W Yorkshire WF14 0BN* Mirfield (01924) 494318

COX, Canon Anthony James Stuart (Tony). b 46. BNC Ox BA68 MA74. Qu Coll Birm DipTh70 DPS71. **d** 71 **p** 72. C Smethwick St Matt w St Chad *Birm* 71-74; Chapl Liv Univ *Liv* 74; Malawi 75-87; Hon Can S Malawi from 80; Chapl Loughb Gr Sch from 87. *Loughborough Grammar School, Denton House, 7 Burton Walks, Loughborough, Leics LE11 2DU* Loughborough (01509) 267225

COX, Brian Leslie. b 49. S Dios Minl Tr Scheme 91. **d** 94 **p** 95. C Southn Maybush St Pet *Win* from 94. *St Peter's House, Lockersley Crescent, Southampton SO16 4BP* Southampton (01703) 775014

COX, Bryan Leslie. b 41. Qu Coll Birm 77. **d** 79 **p** 80. C Stantonbury *Ox* 79-82; TV Fenny Stratford and Water Eaton 82-89; P-in-c Elford *Lich* from 89; Dioc Past Counsellor from 89. *The Vicarage, Church Road, Elford, Tamworth, Staffs B79 9DA* Harlaston (01827) 383212

COX, Canon Christopher George Stuart. b 17. St Jo Coll Dur BA38 DipTh39 MA41. **d** 40 **p** 41. V Knighton St Jo *Leic* 69-77; R Appleby 77-81; R Appleby Magna and Swepstone w Snarestone 81-83; rtd 83; Perm to Offic *Leic* from 83. *Fairhaven, South Street, Ashby-de-la-Zouch, Leics LE65 1BR* Ashby-de-la-Zouch (01530) 414198

COX, David. b 20. SS Coll Cam BA46 MA48 BD57. Qu Coll Birm 47. **d** 48 **p** 49. V Chatham All SS *Roch* 55-75; V Southborough St Thos 75-87; rtd 87. *9 Hollicondane Road, Ramsgate, Kent CT11 7JP* Thanet (01843) 585775

COX, David John. b 51. S Bank Poly HNC76. Qu Coll Birm 76. **d** 79 **p** 80. C Brampton Bierlow *Sheff* 79-82; Miss Partner CMS 82-88; Malaysia 83-88; V Friarmere *Man* from 88. *The Vicarage, 1 Cobler's Hill, Delph, Oldham OL3 5HT* Saddleworth (01457) 874209

COX, Canon Eric William. b 30. Dur Univ BA54. Wells Th Coll 54. **d** 56 **p** 57. C Sutton in Ashfield St Mary *S'well* 56-59; Asst Chapl Brussels *Eur* 59-62; V Winnington *Ches* 62-71; V Middlewich 71-76; Chapl Leighton Hosp Crewe from 73; P-in-c Biley *Ches* 73-76; V Middlewich w Byley from 76; RD Middlewich 80-94; Hon Can Ches Cathl from 84. *St Michael's Vicarage, 37 Queen Street, Middlewich, Cheshire CW10 9AR* Middlewich (01606) 833124 Fax Crewe (01270) 587696

COX, Geoffrey Sidney Randel. b 33. Mert Coll Ox BA56 MA60. Tyndale Hall Bris. **d** 58 **p** 59. C St Paul's Cray St Barn CD *Roch* 58-61; C Bromley Ch Ch 61-64; V Gorsley w Cliffords Mesne *Glouc* 64-79; V Hucclecote 79-89; V Wollaston and Strixton *Pet* from 89. *The Vicarage, 81 Irchester Road, Wollaston, Wellingborough, Northants NN9 7RW* Wellingborough (01933) 664256

COX, George William. b 25. St Steph Ho Ox 83. **d** 86 **p** 87. NSM Abingdon *Ox* from 86; rtd 92. *103 Bath Street, Abingdon, Oxon OX14 1EG* Abingdon (01235) 521375

COX, James David Robert. b 65. Lanc Univ BA88. Qu Coll Birm BD92. **d** 93 **p** 94. C Harborne St Pet *Birm* from 93. *21 Vicarage Road, Birmingham B17 0SN* 0121-426 1318

COX, James Edward Thomas. b 20. Sheff Univ BA47. Cuddesdon Coll 47. **d** 49 **p** 50. Chapl Abbey Sch Malvern 64-79; V Lt Malvern *Worc* 65-85; P-in-c 85-90; rtd 85. *4 Lucerne Avenue, Malvern, Worcs WR14 3QA* Malvern (01684) 564392

COX, John Anthony. b 45. Hull Univ BA67 Birm Univ DipTh72. Qu Coll Birm 71. **d** 73 **p** 74. C Buckm *Ox* 73-76; C Whitley Ch Ch 76-81; V Reading St Agnes w St Paul 81-83; V Chaddesley Corbett and Stone *Worc* from 83. *The Vicarage, Butts Lane, Stone, Kidderminster, Worcs DY10 4BH* Kidderminster (01562) 69438

COX, John Edgar. b 26. CEng MIEE56 Lon Univ BSc50 MSc69. Bps' Coll Cheshunt 67. **d** 68 **p** 69. NSM Harlow St Mary Magd *Chelmsf* 68-76; C S Petherwin w Trewen *Truro* 77-79; P-in-c 79-82; P-in-c Lawhitton 81-82; P-in-c Lezant 81-82; R Lezant w Lawhitton and S Petherwin w Trewen 82-83; V Breage w Germoe 83-91; rtd 91. *Manderley, 8 Trewartha Road, Praa Sands, Penzance, Cornwall TR20 9ST* Penzance (01736) 762582

COX, John Hamilton. b 23. Univ of Wales (Cardiff) BA48. St Mich Coll Llan 49. **d** 51 **p** 52. V Tylorstown *Llan* 61-85; V Llansawel w Briton Ferry 85-89; rtd 89; Perm to Offic *Llan* from 89. *59 Cwrt Sart, Briton Ferry, Neath, W Glam SA11 2SR* Briton Ferry (01639) 820515

COX, Ven John Stuart. b 40. Fitzw Ho Cam BA62 MA66 Linacre Coll Ox BA67 Birm Univ DPS68. Wycliffe Hall Ox 64. **d** 68 **p** 69. C Prescot *Liv* 68-71; C Birm St Geo *Birm* 71-73; R 73-78; Selection Sec ACCM 78-83; Hon C Orpington All SS *Roch* 78-83; Dioc Dir of Ords *S'wark* 83-91; Can Res and Treas S'wark Cathl 83-91; V Roehampton H Trin 91-95; Adn Sudbury *St E* from 95. *Archdeacon's House, 84 Southgate Street, Bury St Edmunds, Suffolk IP33 2BJ* Bury St Edmunds (01284) 766796 Fax 768655

COX, Leonard James William. b 27. Sarum & Wells Th Coll 79. **d** 81 **p** 82. C Hythe *Cant* 81-84; V Thanington 84-92; rtd 92; Perm to Offic *Cant* from 92. *3 Nursery Walk, Forty Acres Road, Canterbury, Kent CT2 7TF*

COX, Martin Lloyd. b 57. Wilson Carlile Coll and Sarum & Wells Th Coll. **d** 88 **p** 89. C Risca *Mon* 88-91; TV Pontypool from 91. *St Luke's Vicarage, Pontnewynydd, Pontypool, Gwent NP4 8LW* Pontypool (01495) 763019

COX, Paul Graham. b 40. Keele Univ BA62 DipEd62 Ibadan Univ Nigeria 63. Westcott Ho Cam 77. **d** 78 **p** 79. NSM Kemsing w Woodlands *Roch* 78-80; Hd Master and Chapl St Mich Sch Otford 81-90; C Petham and Waltham w Lower Hardres etc *Cant* from 90; C Elmsted w Hastingleigh from 90;

Bp's Officer for NSM from 91. *The Vicarage, Pilgrims Lane, Hastingleigh, Ashford, Kent TN25 5HP* Elmsted (01233) 750414

COX, Peter Allard. b 55. Univ of Wales (Lamp) BA76. Wycliffe Hall Ox 77. **d** 79 **p** 80. C Penarth All SS *Llan* 79-82; V Aberpergwm and Blaengwrach 82-86; V Bargoed and Deri w Brithdir from 86. *The Vicarage, Moorland Road, Bargoed, M Glam CF8 8UH* Bargoed (01443) 831069

COX, Mrs Sheila Stuart. b 41. Robert Gordon Inst of Tech Aber TDDSc62 Aber Coll of Educn CertEd63. Edin Dioc NSM Course 85. **d** 88 **p** 94. NSM Livingston LEP *Edin* 88-93; Asst Chapl St Jo and Bangour Hosps W Lothian 89-93; NSM Edin St Mark from 93. *St Aidan's House, 188 Duddingston Park South, Edinburgh EH15 3EH* 0131-657 5814

COX, Dr Simon John. b 53. MIBiol79 CBiol79 Qu Mary Coll Lon BSc74 Liv Univ PhD81 Selw Coll Cam BA81 MA85 Lanc Univ MA87. Ridley Hall Cam 79. **d** 82 **p** 83. C Livesey *Blackb* 82-85; C Cheadle Hulme St Andr *Ches* 85-89; V Disley 89-94; R Bispham *Blackb* from 94. *The Rectory, All Hallows Road, Blackpool FY2 0AY* Blackpool (01253) 51886

COX, Stephen. b 38. Open Univ BA80. Bps' Coll Cheshunt 65. **d** 68 **p** 69. C Gaywood, Bawsey and Mintlyn *Nor* 68-72; Youth Chapl 72-82; C N Lynn w St Marg and St Nic 73-82; Chapl Guildf Coll of Tech 82-87; Chapl Surrey Univ *Guildf* 82-91; Jas Paget Hosp Gorleston from 91. *James Paget Hospital, Gorleston, Great Yarmouth, Norfolk NR31 6LA* Great Yarmouth (01493) 600611

COX, Stephen John Wormleighton. b 54. New Coll Ox MA79 Fitzw Coll Cam BA79. Ridley Hall Cam 77. **d** 80 **p** 81. C Clapton Park All So *Lon* 80-85; TV Hackney Marsh 85-87; V Holloway St Mary w St Jas 87-88; P-in-c Barnsbury St Dav w St Clem 87-88; V Holloway St Mary Magd from 88; AD Islington from 95. *St Mary Magdalene Vicarage, 28 Witherington Road, London N5 1PP* 0171-607 3919

COX, Canon William Arthur Moncrieff. b 13. TCD BA35 MA50. **d** 37 **p** 38. I Bunclody *C & O* 68-83; Treas Ferns Cathl 81-83; rtd 83. *Kilgolan House, Kilcormac, Birr, Co Offaly, Irish Republic*

COX, William John Francis. b 24. SW Minl Tr Course. **d** 77 **p** 78. NSM Liskeard w St Keyne and St Pinnock *Truro* 77-82; NSM Liskeard w St Keyne, St Pinnock and Morval 82-86; NSM N Hill w Altarnon, Bolventor and Lewannick 86-87; TV Bolventor 87-92; P-in-c North Hill and Lewannick 92-94; rtd 94. *9 Trelawney Rise, Callington, Cornwall PL17 7PT* Callington (01579) 384347

COXHEAD, Mrs Margaret. b 40. S Dios Minl Tr Scheme 91. **d** 94 **p** 95. NSM High Hurstwood *Chich* from 94. *Rock Hall, Chillies Lane, High Hurstwood, Uckfield, E Sussex TN22 4AD* Buxted (01825) 733833

COYLE, Matthew Ernest. b 11. Lon Coll of Div 31. **d** 34 **p** 35. R Weare Giffard w Landcross *Ex* 62-69; rtd 69. *c/o Miss M Coyle, Ground Floor Flat, 3 The Avenue, Taunton, Somerset TA1 1EA* Taunton (01823) 276489

COYNE, John Edward. b 55. Oak Hill Th Coll BA79. **d** 79 **p** 80. C Cheadle Hulme St Andr *Ches* 79-81; C Macclesfield St Mich 81-83; V Stalybridge H Trin and Ch Ch 83-88; Chapl RAF from 88. *Chaplaincy Services (RAF), HQ, Personnel and Training Command, RAF Innsworth, Gloucester GL3 1EZ* Gloucester (01452) 712612 Ext 5164 Fax 510828

COYNE, Terence Roland Harry. b 39. Chich Th Coll 64. **d** 66 **p** 67. C Meir *Lich* 66-69; C Horninglow 69-72; V Walsall St Gabr Fulbrook from 72. *St Gabriel's Vicarage, Walstead Road, Walsall WS5 4LZ* Walsall (01922) 22583

COZENS, Mrs Audrey Lilian. b 35. St Hugh's Coll Ox BA56 MA84. Gilmore Course 79. **dss** 82 **d** 87 **p** 94. Shenfield *Chelmsf* 82-87; Par Dn 87-89; Par Dn Westcliff St Andr 89-94; C 94-95; P-in-c Chelmsf St Andr from 95; P-in-c The Chignals w Mashbury from 95. *The Vicarage, 88 Chignal Road, Chelmsford CM1 2JB* Chelmsford (01245) 496722

COZENS, Daniel Harry. b 44. Oak Hill Th Coll DipTh70. **d** 71 **p** 72. C St Paul's Cray St Barn *Roch* 71-74; C Deptford St Nic w Ch Ch *S'wark* 74-76; C Deptford St Nic and St Luke 76-78; Dioc Missr *Ely* from 78; Six Preacher Cant Cathl *Cant* from 94. *The Rectory, 73 High Street, Coton, Cambridge CB3 7PL* Madingley (01954) 210239

COZENS, Michael Graeme. b 59. Chich Th Coll 91. **d** 93 **p** 94. C Emscote *Cov* from 93. *1 All Saints' Road, Warwick CV34 5NL* Warwick (01926) 491450

✝**CRABB, Most Rev Frederick Hugh Wright.** b 15. Lon Univ BD39. Wycliffe Coll Toronto Hon DD60 St Andr Coll Saskatoon Hon DD67 Coll of Em and St Chad Hon DD77 ALCD39. **d** 39 **p** 40 **c** 75. C W Teignmouth *Ex* 39-41; C Plymouth St Andr 41-42; CMS 42-51; Sudan 42-51; Prin Bp Gwynne Coll 42-51; Vice-Prin Lon Coll of Div 51-57; Canada from 57; Prin Em Coll Saskatoon 57-67; Bp Athabasca 75-83; Abp Rupertsland 77-83. *3483 Chippendale Drive, Calgary, Alberta, Canada, T2L 0W7*

CRABB, Paul Anthony. b 58. St Chad's Coll Dur BSc79 Leeds Univ PGCE80. Qu Coll Birm 90. **d** 91 **p** 92. C Gomersal *Wakef* 91-95; V Drighlington from 95. *The Vicarage, Drighlington, Bradford, W Yorkshire BD11 1LS* Leeds (0113) 285 2402

CRABTREE, Derek. b 32. Leic Univ BSc(Econ)53. Cant Sch of Min 91. **d** 94. C Hackington *Cant* from 94; Asst Chapl Kent Univ from 94. *53 Hackington Road, Tyler Hill, Canterbury, Kent CT2 9HE* Canterbury (01227) 471503

CRABTREE, Stephen. *See* JONES-CRABTREE, Stephen

CRABTREE, Victor. b 18. Kelham Th Coll 36. **d** 43 **p** 44. R Shirland *Derby* 66-84; P-in-c Brackenfield w Wessington 77-79; rtd 84. *31 Pinelands, Briergate, Haxby, York YO3 3YT* York (01904) 761941

CRACE, John Allan. b 21. DSC43. Master Mariner 62. Wells Th Coll 62. **d** 64 **p** 65. V Milton Lilbourne w Easton Royal *Sarum* 67-86; R Wootton Rivers 71-86; RD Pewsey 79-84; rtd 86. Perm to Offic *Portsm* from 86; Perm to Offic *Win* from 86. *Venables, Steep Marsh, Petersfield, Hants GU32 2BP* Petersfield (01730) 263553

CRADDOCK, Brian Arthur. b 40. Chich Th Coll 67. **d** 70 **p** 71. C Stoke-upon-Trent *Lich* 70-74; Bermuda 75-89; P-in-c Bury and Houghton *Chich* 89-95; Chapl St Mich Sch Burton Park 89-95; Chapl Mojacar *Eur* from 95. *Apartment 617, Mojacar Playa, Almeria 04638, Spain* Almeria (50) 478066

CRADDOCK, Jeremy Graham. b 37. Lon Univ BSc64 Nottm Univ MPhil72. E Anglian Minl Tr Course 93. **d** 94 **p** 95. NSM Godmanchester *Ely* from 94. *8 Hall Close, Hartford, Huntingdon, Cambs PE18 7XJ* Huntingdon (01480) 458011

CRADDUCK, Martin Charles. b 50. Hull Univ BSc71. St Jo Coll Nottm DipTh77. **d** 79 **p** 80. C W Kilburn St Luke w St Simon and St Jude *Lon* 79-83; C Oxhey All SS *St Alb* 83-86; Asst Chapl HM Pris Man 86-87; Dep Chapl HM Young Offender Inst Glen Parva 87-89; Chapl HM Pris Stocken from 89. *The Chaplain's Office, HM Prison Stocken, Stretton, Oakham, Leics LE15 7RD* Stamford (01780) 410771 Fax 410767

CRAFT, William Newham. b 46. MIPM70 Lon Univ BSc68. Oak Hill Th Coll 87. **d** 89 **p** 90. C Werrington *Pet* 90-93; C-in-c Norfolk Park St Leonard CD *Sheff* from 93. *19 Norfolk Park Avenue, Sheffield S2 2RA* Sheffield (0114) 272 7423

✠**CRAGG, Rt Rev Albert Kenneth.** b 13. Jes Coll Ox BA34 MA38 DPhil50 Huron Coll Hon DD63 Leeds Univ Hon DD93. Virginia Th Sem Hon DD85 Tyndale Hall Bris 34. **d** 36 **p** 37 **c** 70. C Tranmere St Cath *Ches* 36-39; Lebanon 39-47; R Longworth *Ox* 47-51; USA 51-56; Can Res Jerusalem 56-59; St Aug Coll Cant 59-60; Sub-Warden 60-61; Warden 61-67; Hon Can Cant Cathl *Cant* 61-80; Hon Can Jerusalem 65-73; Asst Bp Jerusalem 70-73; Bye-Fellow G&C Coll Cam 69-70; Asst Bp Chich 73-78; Asst Bp Wakef 78-81; V Helme 78-81; rtd 81; Asst Bp Ox from 82. *3 Goring Lodge, White House Road, Oxford OX1 4QE* Oxford (01865) 249895

CRAGG, Canon Leonard Albert. b 28. TCD BA53 MA56. Cuddesdon Coll 54. **d** 55 **p** 56. V Padiham *Blackb* 69-80; V Lytham St Cuth 80-93; Hon Can Blackb Cathl 84-93; RD Fylde 85-88; rtd 93; Perm to Offic *Blackb* from 93. *18 Old Well Hall, Dournham, Clitheroe, Lancs BB7 4BW* Clitheroe (01200) 441804

CRAGGS, Colin Frederick. b 41. Open Univ BA80. Sarum & Wells Th Coll 85. **d** 88 **p** 89. NSM Wilton *B & W* 88-90; NSM Taunton St Andr from 90. *18 Manor Road, Taunton, Somerset TA1 5BD* Taunton (01823) 271989

CRAGGS, Michael Alfred. b 43. Open Univ BA79. St Mich Coll Llan 66. **d** 69 **p** 70. C Clee *Linc* 69-72; C Old Brumby 72-76; TV Kingsthorpe w St Dav Northn *Pet* 76-83; P-in-c Gt w Lt Addington 83-89; RD Higham 88-89; TR Corby SS Pet and Andr w Gt and Lt Oakley from 89; RD Corby from 90. *The Rectory, 40 Beanfield Avenue, Corby, Northants NN18 0EH* Corby (01536) 267620 or 402442

CRAGO, Geoffrey Norman. b 44. Linc Th Coll 67. **d** 70 **p** 71. C Matson *Glouc* 70-75; V Dean Forest H Trin 75-80; Relig Progr Producer Radio Severn Sound 80-85; P-in-c Huntley 80-82; Perm to Offic 82-90; Dioc Communications Officer 84; Gen Syn Broadcasting Dept 85-88; Hon C Highnam, Lassington, Rudford, Tibberton etc from 90. *Milestones, 2 Two Mile Lane, Highnam, Gloucester GL2 8DW* Gloucester (01452) 750575

CRAIG, Canon Alan Stuart. b 38. Leeds Univ BA59. Cranmer Hall Dur DipTh61. **d** 61 **p** 62. C Newc w Butterton *Lich* 61-65; C Scarborough St Mary w Ch Ch, St Paul and St Thos *York* 65-67; V Werrington *Lich* 67-72; Asst Chapl HM Pris Man 72-73; Chapl HM Borstal Hindley 73-78; Chapl HM Pris Acklington 78-84; V Longhirst *Newc* 84-90; RD Morpeth from 84; R Morpeth from 90; Chapl St Geo and Cottage Hosp Morpeth from 90; Hon Can Newc Cathl *Newc* from 90. *The Rectory, Cottingwood Lane, Morpeth, Northd NE61 1ED* Morpeth (01670) 513517

CRAIG, David Paul. b 46. Hon DD94. Aus Coll of Th ThDip. **d** 84 **p** 85. Australia 84-89; Canada 89-94; Miss to Seamen 89-94; Chapl Immingham Seafarers' Cen from 94. *The*

Seafarers' Centre, Lockside Road, Immingham, Grimsby, S Humberside DN40 2NN Grimsby (01469) 574195 Fax 574740

CRAIG, Eric. b 39. Birm Univ BA62 DipTh63. Qu Coll Birm 62. **d** 64 **p** 65. C Todmorden *Wakef* 64-68; C Hurstpierpoint *Chich* 68-70; C Cobham *Guildf* 70-73; V Dawley St Jerome *Lon* 73-76; V Stainland *Wakef* 76-87; R Yarnton w Begbroke and Shipton on Cherwell *Ox* from 87. *The Rectory, 26 Church Lane, Yarnton, Kidlington, Oxon OX5 1PY* Kidlington (01865) 375749

CRAIG, Gillean Weston. b 49. York Univ BA72 Qu Coll Cam BA76 MA80. Westcott Ho Cam 76. **d** 77 **p** 78. C St Marylebone Ch Ch *Lon* 77-82; C Ealing St Barn 82-88; P-in-c St Geo-in-the-East w St Paul 88-89; R from 89. *St George's Rectory Flat, Cannon Street Road, London E1 0BH* 0171-481 1345

CRAIG, Canon John Newcome. b 39. Selw Coll Cam BA63 MA67. Linc Th Coll 63. **d** 65 **p** 66. C Cannock *Lich* 65-71; V Gt Wyrley 71-79; TR Wednesfield 79-91; Prec Leic Cathl *Leic* from 91; Hon Can Leic Cathl from 93. *154 Barclay Street, Leicester LE3 0JB* Leicester (0116) 255 7327

CRAIG, Julie Elizabeth. *See* LEAVES, Julie Elizabeth

CRAIG, Julie Elizabeth. *See* EATON, Julie Elizabeth

CRAIG, Patrick Thomas (Paddy). b 36. BA. St D Coll Lamp 59 Bps' Coll Cheshunt 59. **d** 61 **p** 62. C Belf St Mary *Conn* 61-65; C Belf St Pet 65-69; CF 69-88; R Hartfield w Coleman's Hatch *Chich* from 88. *The Rectory, Hartfield, E Sussex TN7 4AG* Hartfield (01892) 770850

CRAIG, Richard Harvey. b 31. Em Coll Cam BA58. Linc Th Coll. **d** 60 **p** 61. C Bottesford *Linc* 60-65; Bp's Ind Chapl 65-69; Dioc Adv on Laity Tr *Bris* 69-74; V Whitchurch 74-86; TV N Lambeth *S'wark* from 86; Bp's Ecum Adv from 88; Ecum Officer from 90. *Lambeth Mission, 1-5 Lambeth Road, London SE1 7DQ or, 10 Wincott Street, London SE11 4NT* 0171-735 2926 or 207 4868

CRAIG, Robert Joseph. b 43. TCD BA65 Div Test66 Birm Univ CertEd70. **d** 66 **p** 67. C Carrickfergus *Conn* 66-69; Chapl Ld Wandsworth Coll Long Sutton 75-85; Chapl K Sch Macclesfield from 85; Lic to Offic *Ches* from 85. *5 Lincoln Close, Rainow, Macclesfield, Cheshire SK10 5UH* Macclesf'd (0625) 573720 or 422505

CRAIG-WILD, Ms Dorothy Elsie. b 54. Birm Univ BA77. Qu Coll Birm 79. **dss** 81 **d** 87 **p** 94. Middleton St Mary *Ripon* 81-87; Par Dn Chapeltown *Sheff* 88-94; C from 94. *The Vicarage, 23 Housley Park, Chapeltown, Sheffield S30 4UE* Sheffield (0114) 257 0966

CRAIG-WILD, Peter John. b 55. Leeds Univ BA77. Qu Coll Birm 77. **d** 80 **p** 81. C Rothwell w Lofthouse *Ripon* 80-83; C Beeston 83-87; V Chapeltown *Sheff* from 87; RD Tankersley from 93. *The Vicarage, 23 Housley Park, Chapeltown, Sheffield S30 4UE* Sheffield (0114) 257 0966

CRAMERI, Mrs Mary Barbara. b 44. K Coll Lon BD65 AKC91 Lon Inst of Educn PGCE66. S Dios Minl Tr Scheme 86. **d** 88 **p** 94. C Whitton SS Phil and Jas *Lon* 88-91; Staff Member S Dios Minl Tr Scheme from 91; Vice-Prin Sarum & Wells Th Coll from 93; Par Dn Bemerton *Sarum* 91-92. *2 Richard's Way, Harnham, Salisbury SP2 8NT* Salisbury (01722) 338673

CRAMPTON, Canon John Leslie. b 41. CITC 64. **d** 67 **p** 68. C Lurgan Ch Ch *D & D* 67-71; C Dundela 71-73; Rhodesia 73-80; Zimbabwe 80-82; I Killanne w Killegney, Rossdroit and Templeshanbo *C & O* 82-88; Preb Ferns Cathl 85-88; Chapl Wilson's Hosp Sch Multyfarnham *M & K* 88-91; C Mullingar, Portnashangan, Moyliscar, Kilbixy etc 89-91; I Athy w Kilberry, Fontstown and Kilkea *D & G* from 91; Can Ch Ch Cathl Dub from 95. *The Rectory, Church Road, Athy, Co Kildare, Irish Republic* Athy (507) 31446

CRAN, Preb Alexander Strachan. b 09. St Jo Coll Dur BA31 MA43. St Aid Birkenhead 31. **d** 32 **p** 33. V Congresbury *B & W* 48-73; Preb Wells Cathl from 61; P-in-c Puxton w Hewish St Ann and Wick St Lawrence 71-73; rtd 73. *Rowan Wick, Wolvershill Road, Banwell, Weston-super-Mare, Avon BS24 6DR* Banwell (01934) 823209

CRANCH, Peter Kenneth. b 47. St Chad's Coll Dur BA70 DipTh71 PGCE72. **d** 73 **p** 74. C Tavistock and Gulworthy *Ex* 73-78; TV Cen Torquay 78-80; C Heavitree w Ex St Paul 80-84; TV Withycombe Raleigh 84-93; C Ex St Sidwell and St Matt from 93. *10 Victoria Park Road, Exeter EX2 4NT* Exeter (01392) 77685

CRANE, Bryant Frederick Francis. b 13. Qu Coll Cam BA35 MA39. Ridley Hall Cam 35. **d** 37 **p** 38. R Astbury and Smallwood *Ches* 64-78; rtd 78; Perm to Offic *Ches* from 78; Perm to Offic *Lich* from 78. *6 Ridgefields, Biddulph Moor, Stoke-on-Trent ST8 7JE* Stoke-on-Trent (01782) 513752

CRANE, John Walter. b 32. Chich Th Coll. **d** 58 **p** 59. Min Can and Chapl Windsor 67-79; Chapl St Geo Sch Ascot 67-79; Warden Dioc Retreat Ho (Holland Ho) Cropthorne *Worc* 79-83; P-in-c Harvington, Norton and Lenchwick 84-87; rtd

159

87. *16 Allesborough Drive, Pershore, Worcs WR10 1JH*
Pershore (01386) 556444

CRANE, Robert Bartlett. b 14. Clare Coll Cam BA36 MA40. Qu
Coll Birm 37. **d** 39 **p** 40. Area Sec (Dio S'wark) USPG 70-79;
rtd 79; Hon C Bellingham St Dunstan *S'wark* from 79.
8 Bromley College, London Road, Bromley BR1 1PE 0181-
460 4578

CRANE, Ronald Edward. b 48. Wilson Carlile Coll 73 St Steph
Ho Ox 83. **d** 85 **p** 86. C Bicester w Bucknell, Caversfield and
Launton *Ox* 85-88; P-in-c Washwood Heath *Birm* 88-92; V
from 92. *St Mark's Vicarage, 266 Washwood Heath Road,
Birmingham B8 2XS* 0121-327 1461

CRANE, Vincent James. b 10. St Aid Birkenhead 62. **d** 64 **p** 65. C
Penn *Lich* 64-70; R Himley 70-78; V Swindon 70-78; rtd 78.
*14 Holcroft Road, Wall Heath, Kingswinford, W Midlands
DY6 0HP* Kingswinford (01384) 292208

CRANFIELD, Dr Nicholas William Stewart. b 56. Mert Coll Ox
BA77 MA81 DPhil88 Leeds Univ BA81 Cam Univ MA95
PhD95. Coll of Resurr Mirfield 79 Union Th Sem (NY)
STM84. **d** 86 **p** 87. C Ascot Heath *Ox* 86-89; Prin Berks Chr Tr
Scheme 89-92; Hon C Reading St Mary w St Laur 89-92;
Chapl and Fell Selw Coll Cam from 92; Dean Chapel from 94;
Chapl Newnham Coll Cam from 92. *Selwyn College,
Cambridge CB3 9DQ* Cambridge (01223) 335875 Fax
335837

CRANIDGE, Mrs Wendy Ann. b 31. Sheff Univ CertEd52. Cant
Sch of Min 81. **dss** 84 **d** 87 **p** 94. Roch 84-87; Hon Par Dn
87-88; Soc Resp Adv (Dios Cant and Roch) 86-88; Hon C
Washingborough w Heighington and Canwick *Linc* 88-92;
Perm to Offic 92-93; Perm to Offic *Roch* 93-94; C
Farnborough from 94. *Church House, Leamington Avenue,
Orpington, Kent BR6 9BQ* Orpington (01689) 852843

CRANKSHAW, Ronald. b 41. Coll of Resurr Mirfield 74. **d** 76
p 77. C Orford St Andr *Liv* 76; C N Meols 76-79; V Abram
79-85; V Wigan St Anne from 85; AD Wigan W from 94. *St
Anne's Vicarage, 154 Beech Hill Avenue, Wigan, Lancs
WN6 7TA* Wigan (01942) 41930

CRANSTON, Robert William. b 23. Bris Univ BSc47. Oak Hill
Th Coll 76. **d** 79 **p** 80. Hon C Heanton Punchardon w
Marwood *Ex* 79-94; Perm to Offic from 94. *Broom Cottage,
Middle Marwood, Barnstaple, Devon EX31 4EG* Barnstaple
(01271) 72426

CRANWELL, Brian Robert. b 32. Sheff Poly MSc. Cranmer
Hall Dur. **d** 84 **p** 85. C Ecclesfield *Sheff* 84-86; V Handsworth
Woodhouse from 86. *St James's Vicarage, Tithe Barn Lane,
Woodhouse, Sheffield S13 7LL* Sheffield (0114) 269 4146

CRAPNELL, Graham Nicholas (Nick). b 31. Lon Univ BSc55.
St Alb Minl Tr Scheme 89. **d** 92 **p** 93. NSM Woodside w E
Hyde *St Alb* from 92. *25 Wardown Crescent, Luton LU2 7JS*
Luton (01582) 21840

CRASKE, Leslie Gordon Hamilton. b 29. AKC54. Lambeth
STh80. **d** 55 **p** 56. C Malden St Jo *S'wark* 55-58; C Streatham
St Leon 58-60; S Rhodesia 60-65; Rhodesia 65-66; V Upper
Norwood St Jo *Cant* 67-83; R Guernsey St Sav *Win* from 83.
*St Saviour's Rectory, Neuf Chemin Road, Guernsey, Channel
Islands GY7 9FQ* Guernsey (01481) 63045

CRASTON (nee FULLALOVE), Mrs Brenda Hurst. b 33. Open
Univ BA75 Man Univ MPhil86. St Mich Ho Ox 58. **dss** 80 **d** 87
p 94. Bolton St Paul w Em *Man* 80-87; Par Dn 87-93; rtd 93;
Hon C Horwich and Rivington *Man* from 94. *12 Lever Park
Avenue, Horwich, Bolton BL6 7LE* Horwich (01204) 699972

CRASTON, Canon Richard Colin. b 22. Bris Univ BA49 Lon
Univ BD51. Tyndale Hall Bris 46. **d** 51 **p** 52. V Bolton St Paul
Man 54-76; V Bolton Em 66-76; Hon Can Man Cathl 68-93;
RD Bolton 72-93; V Bolton St Paul w Em 77-86; TR 86-93;
Chapl to The Queen 85-93; rtd 93. *12 Lever Park Avenue,
Horwich, Bolton BL6 7LE1* Bolton (01204) 842303

CRATE, Canon George Frederick Jackson. b 28. Lon Univ
BD56. ALCD55. **d** 56 **p** 57. V Mountsorrel Ch Ch *Leic* 64-83;
RD Akeley E (Loughb) 75-92; Hon Can Leic Cathl 80-94; V
Mountsorrel Ch Ch and St Pet 83-94; rtd 94. *115 Nanpantan
Road, Loughborough, Leics LE11 3YB* Loughborough
(01509) 269505

CRAVEN, Alan. b 32. N Ord Course. **d** 87. NSM Hessle *York*
87-91; NSM Newington w Dairycoates from 91. *28 Weelsby
Way, Booterferry Road, Hessle, N Humberside HU13 0JW*
Hull (01482) 643214

CRAVEN, Canon Allan. b 35. LTCL77 Univ of Wales (Lamp)
BA57 Lon Univ BD72. Chich Th Coll 57. **d** 59 **p** 60. C Blaenau
Ffestiniog *Ban* 59-61; C Milford Haven *St D* 61-65; V
Llwynhendy 65-68; R Nolton w Roch from 68; RD Roose
from 85; Can St D Cathl from 91. *The Rectory, Nolton,
Haverfordwest, Dyfed SA62 3NW* Haverfordwest (01437)
710213

CRAVEN, Colin Peter. b 48. Dartmouth RN Coll. St Steph Ho
Ox 83. **d** 85 **p** 86. C Holbeach *Linc* 85-88; Chapl Fleet Hosp

from 86; TV Grantham *Linc* from 88; OCF from 88. *St Anne's
Vicarage, Harrowby Road, New Somerby, Grantham, Lincs
NG31 9ED* Grantham (01476) 62822

CRAVEN, Gordon Forster. b 26. Qu Coll Cam BA50 MA55.
Wells Th Coll 51. **d** 53 **p** 54. V King Sterndale *Derby* 57-72; V
Fairfield 57-72; Perm to Offic *B & W* from 81; rtd 91.
Kingfisher Cottage, 41 Southover, Wells, Somerset BA5 1UH
Wells (01749) 672282

CRAVEN, Janet Elizabeth. *See* CHAPMAN, Mrs Janet
Elizabeth

CRAVEN, Archdeacon of. *See* GRUNDY, Ven Malcolm Leslie

CRAWFORD, Albert Edward. b 13. TCD BA37 MA43. **d** 37
p 38. I Camlough *Arm* 65-78; rtd 78. *Shalom, 54 Edenvale
Avenue, Banbridge, Co Down BT32 3RH* Banbridge (018206)
22924

CRAWFORD, Canon Arthur Edward. b 14. TCD BA39 MA51.
TCD Div Sch Div Test39. **d** 40 **p** 41. I Clara *M & K* 66-85; Can
Meath 84-85; rtd 85. *Klosters, Crookedwood, Mullingar, Co
Westmeath, Irish Republic* Mullingar (44) 72272

CRAWFORD, Duncan Alexander. b 59. Newc Univ BA81
MA83 K Coll Lon CertEd83. St Jo Coll Nottm 86. **d** 89 **p** 90. C
Hatcham St Jas *S'wark* 89-92; Perm to Offic from 93.
26 Millmark Grove, London SE14 6QR 0181-692 4645

CRAWFORD, Miss Ivy Elizabeth. b 50. Trin Coll Bris DipTh85.
dss 85 **d** 87 **p** 94. Collier Row St Jas *Chelmsf* 85; Collier Row St
Jas and Havering-atte-Bower 86-87; Par Dn 87-89; Par Dn
Harlow New Town w Lt Parndon 89-94; C Harlow Town
Centre w Lt Parndon 94-95; V Blackmore and Stondon
Massey from 95. *The Vicarage, Church Street, Blackmore,
Ingatestone, Essex CM4 0RN* Ingatestone (01277) 821464

CRAWFORD, John. b 22. TCD BA50. **d** 51 **p** 53. C Lt Marlow
Ox 67-83; rtd 83. *33 Wenlock Edge, Charvil, Reading
RG10 9QG* Reading (01734) 341848

CRAWFORD, Canon John William Rowland. b 53. AKC75
Open Univ BA81. CITC 75. **d** 76 **p** 77. C Dundela *D & D*
76-79; C Taney Ch Ch *D & G* 79-84; TV Dub St Patr Cathl Gp
from 84; Preb Tipperkevin St Patr Cathl Dub from 84.
*248 South Circular Road, Dolphin's Barn, Dublin 8, Irish
Republic* Dublin (1) 454-2274

CRAWFORD, Peter. b 22. Trin Coll Cam BA49 MA54.
Wycliffe Hall Ox 49. **d** 51 **p** 52. V Masham *Ripon* 60-75; RD
Ripon 70-75; V Masham and Healey 75-79; R E Bergholt *St E*
79-87; RD Samford 82-86; rtd 87; Perm to Offic *St E* from 87.
*3 Burl's Yard, Crown Street, Needham Market, Ipswich
IP6 8AJ* Needham Market (01449) 722343

CRAWFORD, Philip Hugh Southern. b 16. Lon Univ BA40.
Chich Th Coll 41. **d** 42 **p** 43. V Healaugh w Wighill and
Bilbrough *York* 60-78; P-in-c Slingsby 78-86; P-in-c
Hovingham 78-86; V 86; RD Bulmer and Malton 80-85; rtd
86; C Hovingham *York* 86-88. *44 Bootham Crescent, York
YO3 7AH* York (01904) 630386

CRAWFORD, Robin. b 33. Pemb Coll Cam BA57 MA61. **d** 67
p 80. Ghana 67-69; Dep Sec Chrs Abroad 69-73; Nigeria
77-78; Perm to Offic *Win* 78-80; Dep Sec Buttle Trust 78-86;
Sec 86-90; Dir from 90; Hon C Win H Trin *Win* 80-82; Hon C
Notting Hill All SS w St Columb *Lon* 82-87; Hon C Westmr St
Matt 87-94. *20 Great Peter Street, London SW1P 2BU* 0171-
222 4532 or 931 8013

CRAWLEY, David. b 47. St Steph Ho Ox 75. **d** 78 **p** 79. C
Solihull *Birm* 78-81; TV Newbury *Ox* 81-84; Lic to Offic from
84; Chapl Stoke Mandeville Hosp Aylesbury from 84; Distr
Chapl from 88. *Stoke Mandeville Hospital, Mandeville Road,
Aylesbury, Bucks HP20 8AL* Aylesbury (01296) 316677 or
315000

CRAWLEY, John Lloyd Rochfort. b 22. Selw Coll Cam BA47
MA52. Cuddesdon Coll 47. **d** 49 **p** 50. Chapl Newc Univ *Newc*
69-74; C-in-c Newc St Thos Prop Chpl 69-74; P-in-c
Cockermouth All SS w Ch Ch *Carl* 74-77; TR Cockermouth w
Embleton and Wythop 77-86; Perm to Offic *Arg* from 86; rtd
87. *Cove, Campbeltown Road, Tarbert, Argyll PA29 6SX*
Tarbert (01880) 820842

CRAWLEY, Leonard Frank. b 38. ARCA63. NW Ord Course
74. **d** 77 **p** 78. NSM Bradf St Wilfrid Lidget Green *Bradf* 77-92;
NSM Manningham from 92. *185 Highgate, Bradford, W
Yorkshire BD9 5PU* Bradford (01274) 487249

CRAWLEY, Nicholas Simon (Nick). b 58. ACIB82 AIIM85
Southn Univ BSc79. Wycliffe Hall Ox 85. **d** 88 **p** 89. C E
Twickenham St Steph *Lon* 88-93; Zimbabwe from 93.
*Avondale Anglican Church, 2 Church Road, Avondale, Harare,
Zimbabwe* Harare (4) 39697

CRAWLEY, Simon Ewen. b 31. Em Coll Cam BA57 MA60.
Ridley Hall Cam 56. **d** 58 **p** 59. C Denton Holme *Carl* 58-61;
P-in-c Cinderford St Steph w Littledean *Glouc* 61-67; V
Margate H Trin *Cant* 67-74; V Folkestone H Trin w Ch Ch
74-81; R Patterdale *Carl* 81-87; RD Penrith 83-86; R Culworth
w Sulgrave and Thorpe Mandeville etc *Pet* from 87; RD
Brackley from 89. *The Rectory, Culworth, Banbury, Oxon
OX17 2AT* Sulgrave (01295) 760383 Fax as telephone

CRAWLEY-BOEVEY, Robert Arthur. b 12. Hertf Coll Ox BA34 MA38. Cuddesdon Coll 35. **d** 37 **p** 38. V Seer Green *Ox* 59-78; rtd 78. *3 St Michael's Close, Urchfont, Devizes, Wilts SN10 4QJ* Devizes (01380) 840635

CRAWSHAW, Charles Barritt. b 14. Leeds Univ BA36. Coll of Resurr Mirfield 36. **d** 38 **p** 39. V Smethwick H Trin 54-60; Lect Ashton Coll of FE 60-63; Hd of Humanities Brunel Coll of Tech 63-80; rtd 79; Lic to Offic *B & W* from 80. *Crow Wood, 30 Hillcrest Road, Portishead, Bristol BS20 8HP* Bristol (0117) 984 2659

CRAWSHAW, Henry Michael Aitken. b 15. Em Coll Cam BA37 MA43. Westcott Ho Cam 39. **d** 40 **p** 41. R Barnham Broom w Kimberley, Bixton etc *Nor* 64-70; R Brandon Parva 64-70; P-in-c Wramplingham w Barford 64-70; P-in-c Coston w Runhall 64-70; P-in-c Hardingham 64-70; P-in-c Garveston w Thuxton 64-70; R Brancaster 70-80; R Burnham Deepdale 71-80; R Brancaster w Burnham Deepdale and Titchwell 80-83; rtd 83; Perm to Offic *Nor* 83-92. *Furze Hill Lodge, Furze Hill, Kingswood, Surrey KT20 6ET*

CRAY, Graham Alan. b 47. Leeds Univ BA68. St Jo Coll Nottm 69. **d** 71 **p** 72. C Gillingham St Mark *Roch* 71-75; N Area Co-ord CPAS Youth Dept 75-78; C York St Mich-le-Belfrey *York* 78-82; V 82-92; Prin Ridley Hall Cam from 92. *Ridley Hall, Cambridge CB3 9HG* Cambridge (01223) 353040 Fax 301287

CREAN, Patrick John Eugene. b 38. TCD BA81 MA84. Edin Th Coll 82. **d** 84 **p** 85. C Perth St Jo *St And* 84-86; P-in-c Liv St Phil w St Dav *Liv* 86-87; V 87-90; R Cupar *St And* 90-92; R Ladybank 90-92; P-in-c Sefton *Liv* from 92; Dioc Children's Officer from 92. *The Rectory, Glebe End, Liverpool L29 6YB* 0151-531 7021

CREASER, Canon David Edward. b 35. St Cath Coll Cam BA58 MA62. Clifton Th Coll 59. **d** 61 **p** 62. C Cheadle *Ches* 61-67; V Weston *Bradf* 67-69; P-in-c Denton 67-69; V Weston w Denton 69-74 and from 82; Dir Educn from 73; V Frizinghall 74-82; Hon Can Bradf Cathl from 80. *The Vicarage, Askwith, Otley, W Yorkshire LS21 2HX* Otley (01943) 461139

CREASEY, Graham. b 51. Trent Poly BA. Cranmer Hall Dur 80. **d** 83 **p** 84. C Birstall and Wanlip *Leic* 83-87; C-in-c Wheatley Park St Paul CD *Sheff* 87-92; V Wheatley Park St Paul from 92. *The Vicarage, 278 Thorne Road, Doncaster, S Yorkshire DN2 5AJ* Doncaster (01302) 326041

CREBER, Arthur Frederick. b 45. Lon Univ DipTh67. N Ord Course 84. **d** 87 **p** 88. C Rickerscote *Lich* 87-91; V Gt Wyrley from 91; RD Rugeley from 94. *St Mark's Vicarage, 1 Cleves Crescent, Cheslyn Hay, Walsall WS6 7LR* Cheslyn Hay (01922) 414309

CREDITON, Suffragan Bishop of. See COLEMAN, Rt Rev Peter Everard

CREE, John Richard. b 44. Open Univ BA74. Coll of Resurr Mirfield. **d** 83 **p** 84. C Blackb St Jas *Blackb* 83-86; V Feniscowles from 86; Chapl Blackb Coll from 86. *The Vicarage, 732 Preston Old Road, Feniscowles, Blackburn BB2 5EN* Blackburn (01254) 201236

CREER, Irene. See SHAW, Mrs Irene

CREERY-HILL, Anthony Thomas. b 23. BNC Ox BA49 MA54. Ridley Hall Cam 49. **d** 51 **p** 52. Chapl Dean Close Sch Cheltenham 59-74; Dep Hd Master Larchfield Sch Helensburgh 75-77; Kenya 77-83; Chapl Chantilly *Eur* 83-86; rtd 87; Perm to Offic *Heref* from 87. *Under Down, Ledbury, Herefordshire HR8 2JU* Ledbury (01531) 635608

CREES, Geoffrey William. b 35. ONC Open Univ BA85. Cranmer Hall Dur 65. **d** 67 **p** 68. C Hoddesdon *St Alb* 67-70; C Harwell *Ox* 70-73; C Chilton All SS 70-73; V Greenham 73-82; AD E Hull Deanery 82-88; TR Marfleet *York* 82-88; TR Rodbourne Cheney *Bris* from 88. *St Mary's Rectory, 298 Cheney Manor Road, Swindon SN2 2PF* Swindon (01793) 522379

CREIGHTON, Frederick David. b 50. ACII74 TCD BTh88. **d** 88 **p** 89. C Lisburn Ch Ch *Conn* 88-91; I Drumclamph w Lower and Upper Langfield *D & R* from 91. *The Rectory, 70 Greenville Road, Castlederg, Co Tyrone BT81 7NU* Castlederg (016626) 71433

CREIGHTON, Mrs Judith. b 36. Reading Univ BSc57. Trin Coll Bris 80 Edin Th Coll 81. **dss** 83 **d** 87 **p** 94. Greenock *Glas* 83-85; Lawrence Weston *Bris* 85-87; Par Dn Kingswood 87-90; Chapl Stoke Park and Purdown Hosps Stapleton 90-93; Hon C Marshfield w Cold Ashton and Tormarton etc *Bris* from 93. *Home Farm Cottage, West Littleton, Marshfield, Chippenham, Wilts SN14 8JE* Bath (01225) 891021

CREIGHTON, Ms Rachel Margaret Maxwell. b 64. Br Is Nazarene Coll BTh86 BD87. Cranmer Hall Dur DMinlStuds94 Lon Bible Coll MA89. **d** 94 **p** 95. C Basford w Hyson Green *S'well* from 94. *8 Austen Avenue, Nottingham NG7 6PE* Nottingham (0115) 978 5541

CRELLIN, Howard Joseph. b 30. Magd Coll Cam BA52 MA56 Magd Coll Ox BA54 DipTh55 MA56. Wycliffe Hall Ox 53. **d** 55 **p** 56. R Theydon Garnon *Chelmsf* 58-70; Select Preacher

Ox Univ 68; Perm to Offic *Ox* 70-82; Hon C High Wycombe 72-77; Master K Chas I Sch Kidderminster 74-80; rtd 77; Perm to Offic *Chelmsf* from 82; Master Caldicott Sch Farnham 80-82; Fryerns Sch Basildon 82-88; St Anselm's Sch Basildon 88-91; P-in-c Whatfield w Semer, Nedging and Naughton *St E* from 91. *The Rectory, Whatfield, Ipswich IP7 6QU* Ipswich (01473) 822100

CRESSALL, Paul Richard. b 51. UEA BA74. Ripon Coll Cuddesdon 86. **d** 88 **p** 89. C Stevenage H Trin *St Alb* 88-91; V Caldecote All SS from 91; V Old Warden from 91. *The Vicarage, 2A Biggleswade Road, Biggleswade, Beds SG18 9BL* Biggleswade (01767) 315578

CRESSEY, Roger Wilson. b 35. Chich Th Coll 72. **d** 74 **p** 75. C Pontefract St Giles *Wakef* 74-77; Hon C Dewsbury All SS 77-80; Chapl Pinderfields Gen Hosp Wakef from 80; Chapl Carr Gate Hosp Wakef from 80; Chapl Fieldhead Hosp Wakef from 80. *Pinderfields General Hospital, Aberford Road, Wakefield, W Yorkshire WF1 4DG* Wakefield (01924) 201688

CRESSWELL, Howard Rex. b 31. Ely Th Coll 56. **d** 59 **p** 60. V Victoria Docks Ascension *Chelmsf* 64-71; R E w W Harling *Nor* 71-72; TV Quidenham w Eccles and Snetterton 72-75; V Arminghall 75-82; R Caistor w Markshall 75-82; V Trowse 75-82; V Heigham St Barn w St Bart 82-91; Perm to Offic from 91; rtd 91. *3 Cranleigh Rise, Eaton, Norwich NR4 6PQ* Norwich (01603) 454389

CRESSWELL, Canon Jack Joseph. b 11. Qu Coll Cam BA39 MA43. Wycliffe Hall Ox 39. **d** 40 **p** 41. R Busbridge *Guildf* 70-78; Perm to Offic *Glouc* from 75; rtd 78; C Broughton Poggs w Filkins, Broadwell etc *Ox* 88-93. *12 Eastleach, Cirencester, Glos GL7 3NQ* Southrop (0136785) 261

CRESSWELL, Jeremy Peter. b 49. St Jo Coll Ox BA72 MA78. Ridley Hall Cam 73. **d** 75 **p** 76. C Wisley w Pyrford *Guildf* 75-78; C Weybridge 78-82; P-in-c E Clandon 82-83; P-in-c W Clandon 82-83; R E and W Clandon 83-90; V Oxshott from 90. *The Vicarage, Steel's Lane, Oxshott, Leatherhead, Surrey KT22 0QH* Oxshott (01372) 842071

CRESSWELL, Preb Kenneth Benjamin. b 17. St D Coll Lamp BA50. **d** 51 **p** 52. V Horninglow *Lich* 67-81; Preb Lich Cathl 80-83; TV Stoke-upon-Trent 81-83; rtd 83; Perm to Offic *Lich* from 83. *1 Chartwell Close, Woodsetton, Dudley, W Midlands DY1 4LY* Sedgley (01902) 663354

CRETNEY, Mrs Antonia Lois. b 48. York Univ BA69 Bris Univ BA87 PGCE89. S Dios Minl Tr Scheme 92. **d** 94 **p** 95. NSM Bedminster *Bris* from 94. *15 Canynge Square, Bristol BS8 3LA* Bristol (0117) 973 2983

CRIBB, Robert John. b 22. Spurgeon's Coll 45. **d** 85 **p** 86. NSM Curry Rivel w Fivehead and Swell *B & W* 85-89; rtd 89; Perm to Offic *B & W* 89-94. *4 Heale Lane, Curry Rivel, Langport, Somerset TA10 0PG* Langport (01458) 252333

CRICHTON, James Kenneth. b 35. Glouc Sch of Min 78. **d** 80 **p** 80. NSM Minchinhampton *Glouc* 80-83; NSM Nailsworth 83-86; Dep Chapl HM Pris Pentonville 86-87; Chapl HM Pris The Mount from 87. *The Chaplain's Office, HM Prison, The Mount, Molyneaux Avenue, Hemel Hempstead, Herts HP3 0NZ* Hemel Hempstead (01442) 834363 Fax 834321

CRICK, Canon Peter. b 39. Lon Univ BD68 NY Univ DMin84. Wells Th Coll 66. **d** 67 **p** 68. C Horsham *Chich* 67-71; Asst Dioc Youth Officer *Ox* 71-75; R Denham 75-88; Bp's Adv for Continuing Minl Educn *Dur* from 88; P-in-c Coniscliffe from 88; Hon Can Dur Cathl from 93. *76 Merrybent Village, Darlington, Co Durham DL2 2LE* Darlington (01325) 374510

CRICK, Philip Benjamin Denton (Ben). b 33. Bris Univ BA63. Clifton Th Coll 60. **d** 64 **p** 65. C Clerkenwell St Jas and St Jo w St Pet *Lon* 64-67; CF 67-72; C Southall Green St Jo *Lon* 72-75; P-in-c Southall H Trin 75-83; P-in-c Kidbrooke St Jas *S'wark* 83-85; TV 85-92; C E Acton St Dunstan w St Thos *Lon* from 92; Sub-Chapl HM Pris Wormwood Scrubs from 92. *5 Godolphin Place, Vyner Road, London W3 7NB* 0181-749 6744 Fax 749 5655

CRINGLE, William Edward James. b 15. Lon Univ BD40. **d** 41 **p** 41. V Lezayre St Olave Ramsey *S & M* 61-80; rtd 80; Perm to Offic *S & M* from 80. *3 Queens Drive West, Ramsey, Isle of Man IM8 2JB* Ramsey (01624) 814608

CRINKS, Kevin David. b 63. Aston Tr Scheme 86 Sarum & Wells Th Coll BTh91. **d** 93 **p** 94. C Aylesford *Roch* from 93. *59 Greenway, Chatham, Kent ME5 9UX* Maidstone (01622) 791214

CRIPPS, Harold Ernest. b 04. AKC47. **d** 47 **p** 48. V Burtonwood *Liv* 59-74; rtd 74; Perm to Offic *Chich* 77-92. *15 Hillyard Court, Mill Lane, Wareham, Dorset BN20 4QX* Wareham (01929) 550926

CRIPPS, Keith Richard John. b 21. Trin Coll Cam BA43 MA47 Newc Univ PhD80. Ridley Hall Cam 43. **d** 45 **p** 47. Lic to Offic *Newc* 65-84; Lic to Offic *Ely* 84-86; Lect Newc Poly 74-79; Chapl Jes Coll Cam 84; rtd 86. *8 Pentlands Court, Pentlands Close, Cambridge CB4 1JN* Cambridge (01223) 354216

CRIPPS, Martyn Cyril Rowland. b 46. Solicitor 71 Birm Univ LLB68. Wycliffe Hall Ox 80. **d** 82 **p** 83. C Canford Magna

Sarum 82-86; V Preston St Cuth *Blackb* 87-94; Guernsey St Andr *Win* 94; Warden Les Cotils from 94. *Les Cotils, St Peter Port, Guernsey GY1 1UU* Guernsey (01481) 727793

CRIPPS, Michael Frank Douglas. b 28. Ch Ch Ox BA50 MA53. Ridley Hall Cam 58. **d** 59 **p** 60. C-in-c Swindon Covingham CD *Bris* 66-72; V Swindon St Paul 72-73; P-in-c Aldbourne and Baydon *Sarum* 73; TV Whitton 73-81; C Marlborough 81-94; rtd 94; Chapl Pau *Eur* from 94. *43 rue Montpensier, 64000 Pau, France* France (33) 59 62 56 45 or 59 83 82 06

CRIPPS, Thomas Royle. b 12. St Jo Coll Lusaka 64. **d** 68 **p** 68. S Africa 68-88; rtd 88; Perm to Offic *S'wark* 88-91. *College of St Barnabas, Blackberry Lane, Lingfield, Surrey RH7 6NJ* Dormans Park (01342) 870760

CRISALL, Christopher James Philip. b 34. St Deiniol's Hawarden 87. **d** 89 **p** 90. NSM Low Marple *Ches* 89-90; C Woodchurch 90-92; V Latchford Ch Ch from 92. *Christchurch Vicarage, Wash Lane, Warrington WA4 1HT* Warrington (01925) 630846

CRITCHLEY, Colin. b 41. Dur Univ BA63 Liv Univ MA69. NW Ord Course 75. **d** 78 **p** 79. NSM Halewood *Liv* from 78. *53 Elwyn Drive, Halewood, Liverpool L26 0UX* 0151-487 5710

CRITCHLEY, Ronald John. b 15. Kelham Th Coll 31. **d** 38 **p** 39. V Fylingdales *York* 63-80; V Hawsker 63-80; rtd 80. *4A North Promenade, Whitby, N Yorkshire YO21 3JX* Whitby (01947) 600238

CRITCHLOW, Trevor Francis. b 61. Lanc Univ BA83. Westcott Ho Cam 88. **d** 90 **p** 91. C Croydon St Jo *S'wark* 90-92; C Lewisham St Mary 92-94; Perm to Offic *Ely* from 94. *97 Riverside, Cambridge CB4 8HN* Cambridge (01223) 501010 Fax as telephone

CRITTALL, Richard Simon. b 47. Sussex Univ BA69 Linacre Coll Ox BA71. St Steph Ho Ox 69. **d** 72 **p** 73. C Oswestry H Trin *Lich* 72-75; C E Grinstead St Mary *Chich* 75-78; TV Brighton Resurr 78-83; R E Blatchington from 83. *The Rectory, 25 Blatchington Hill, Seaford, E Sussex BN25 2AJ* Seaford (01323) 892964

CROAD, Arthur Robert. b 35. Down Coll Cam BA58 MA61. Clifton Th Coll 58. **d** 61 **p** 62. C Sneinton St Chris w St Phil *S'well* 61-64; C Kinson *Sarum* 64-72; R Sherfield English *Win* 72-74; R Awbridge w Sherfield English 74-92; P-in-c Hinton Ampner w Bramdean and Kilmeston from 92. *The Rectory, Bramdean, Alresford, Hants SO24 0JN* Bramdean (01962) 771223

CROAD, David Richard. b 31. Reading Univ BSc55. Clifton Th Coll. **d** 57 **p** 58. V Loudwater *Ox* 63-72; SW Area Sec CPAS 72-78; V Bovingdon *St Alb* 78-91; Min Hampstead St Jo Downshire Hill Prop Chpl *Lon* 91-94; rtd 94. *The Old Parsonage, Bentley, Farnham, Surrey GU10 5JN* Bentley (01420) 23227

CROCKER, Keith Gwilliam. b 49. Lanchester Poly BSc70 DipPTh78. Oak Hill Th Coll 74. **d** 77 **p** 78. C Whitnash *Cov* 77-80; C Gt Horton *Bradf* 80-83; C Grays SS Pet and Paul, S Stifford and W Thurrock *Chelmsf* 83-84; TV Grays Thurrock 84-88; TR Wreningham *Nor* 88-95; P-in-c New Catton Ch Ch from 95. *Christ Church Vicarage, 65 Elm Grove Lane, Norwich NR3 3LF* Norwich (01603) 408332

CROCKER, Richard Campbell. b 54. BSc Nottm Univ MA. Wycliffe Hall Ox. **d** 82 **p** 83. C Summerfield *Birm* 82-84; Chapl K Edw Sch Birm 84-91; USA from 91. *821 Ironwood Court, Council Bluffs, Iowa 51503, USA*

CROCKETT, Peter James Sinclair. b 44. Sarum & Wells Th Coll 74. **d** 77 **p** 78. C Heavitree *Ex* 77; C Heavitree w Ex St Paul 78-80; TV Ex St Thos and Em 80-87; V Wear St Luke from 87. *The Vicarage, 375 Topsham Road, Exeter EX2 6HB* Topsham (01392) 873263

CROCKETT, Phillip Anthony. b 45. K Coll Lon BA67 BD70 AKC70. St Mich Coll Llan DPS71. **d** 71 **p** 72. C Aberdare St Jo *Llan* 71-74; C Whitchurch 74-78; V Llanfihangel-y-Creuddyn, Llanafan w Llanwnnws *St D* 78-86; Sec Prov Selection Panel 83-87; V Ysbyty Ystwyth 84-86; R Dowlais *Llan* 86-91; Exec Sec for Min from 91. *3 Cosmeston Drive, Penarth, S Glam CF6 2FA or, 39 Cathedral Close, Cardiff CF1 9XF* Cardiff (01222) 705015 or 231638

CROFT, Bernard Theodore. b 10. Kelham Th Coll 30. **d** 35 **p** 36. V Reighton w Speeton *York* 68-75; rtd 75; Perm to Offic *York* from 75. *4 Freeman's Court, Water Lane, York YO3 6PR* York (01904) 656611

CROFT, James Stuart. b 57. K Coll Lon BD80. Ripon Coll Cuddesdon 83. **d** 85 **p** 86. C Friern Barnet St Jas *Lon* 85-88; R Lea *Linc* 88-93; V Knaith 88-93; V Upton 88-93; R Gate Burton 88-93; Chapl N Lincs Coll 90-93; R Lea Gp *Linc* from 93. *The Rectory, 18 Gainsborough Road, Lea, Gainsborough, Lincs DN21 5HZ* Gainsborough (01427) 613188

CROFT, John Armentieres. b 15. MC44. Sarum Th Coll 56. **d** 57 **p** 58. V Gwinear *Truro* 60-70; rtd 70; Perm to Offic *Truro* from 70; Perm to Offic *Sarum* from 70; Perm to Offic *B & W* from 70. *Vine House, Common Road, Wincanton, Somerset BA9 9RB* Wincanton (01963) 32253

CROFT, Michael Peter. b 60. GradIPM. Trin Coll Bris BA88. **d** 88 **p** 89. C Drypool *York* 88-91; P-in-c Sandal St Cath *Wakef* from 91; Chapl Manygates Maternity Hosp Wakef from 91. *The Vicarage, 157 Agbrigg Road, Wakefield, W Yorkshire WF1 5AU* Wakefield (01924) 254176

CROFT, Canon Peter Gardom. b 25. St Jo Coll Cam BA48 MA50. Wells Th Coll 50. **d** 52 **p** 53. R Washington *Dur* 65-78; Dioc Info Officer *Sheff* 78-83; Can Res and Sub-Dean Guildf Cathl *Guildf* 83-94; rtd 94. *45 Gough Way, Cambridge CB3 9LN* Cambridge (01223) 355026

CROFT, Ronald. b 37. St Aid Birkenhead 61. **d** 63 **p** 64. C Lawton Moor *Man* 63-65; C Withington St Crispin 65-66; R 74-86; C Prestwich St Marg 66-67; V Oldham St Ambrose 67-71; P-in-c Oldham St Jas 67-68; V 68-71; V Prestwich St Hilda 71-74; R Heaton Norris St Thos from 86. *St Thomas's Rectory, 6 Heaton Moor Road, Stockport, Cheshire SK4 4NS* 0161-432 1912

CROFT, Simon. b 51. St Steph Ho Ox 75. **d** 78 **p** 79. C Heavitree w Ex St Paul *Ex* 78-83; V Seaton 83-93; P-in-c Ex St Mark from 93. *St Mark's Vicarage, 8 Lamacraft Drive, Exeter EX4 8QS* Exeter (01392) 421050

CROFT, Stephen John Lindsey. b 57. MA PhD. Cranmer Hall Dur 80. **d** 83 **p** 84. C Enfield St Andr *Lon* 83-87; V Ovenden *Wakef* from 87; Dio Miss Consultant from 94. *St George's Vicarage, Bracewell Drive, Wheatley, Halifax, W Yorkshire HX3 5BT* Halifax (01422) 354153

CROFT, William Alan. b 15. Lich Th Coll 55. **d** 57 **p** 58. V Cornworthy *Ex* 59-73; TR Cheriton Fitzpaine, Woolfardisworthy etc 74-76; TR N Creedy 76-80; rtd 80. *31 Holyoake road, Headington, Oxford OX3 8AF* Oxford (01865) 69908

CROFT, William Stuart (Bill). b 53. Trin Hall Cam BA76 MA79 MTh88. Ripon Coll Cuddesdon BA80. **d** 80 **p** 81. C Friern Barnet St Jas *Lon* 80-83; Tutor Chich Th Coll 83-92; Vice-Prin 88-92; V Fernhurst *Chich* from 92. *The Vicarage, Fernhurst, Haslemere, Surrey GU27 3EA* Haslemere (01428) 652229

CROFTON, Edwin Alan. b 46. Univ Coll Ox BA68 MA72. Cranmer Hall Dur DipTh72. **d** 73 **p** 74. C Hull Newland St Jo *York* 73-77; C Worksop St Jo *S'well* 77-81; Chapl Kilton Hosp Worksop 80-81; V Scarborough St Mary w Ch Ch and H Apostles *York* 81-91; Miss to Seamen 81-91; Chapl St Mary's Hosp Scarborough 82-91; V Cheltenham Ch Ch *Glouc* from 91. *Christ Church Vicarage, Malvern Road, Cheltenham, Glos GL50 2NU* Cheltenham (01242) 515983

CROFTS, Charles Arthur. b 14. Ball Coll Ox BA38 MA48. Lich Th Coll 38. **d** 39 **p** 40. V Hexton *St Alb* 69-77; Hon Can St Alb 69-71; C Merstham and Gatton *S'wark* 77-80; Dir RE and Chapl St Bede's Sch Redhill 77-80; rtd 80. *5 Manaton Close, Haywards Heath, W Sussex RH16 3HS* Haywards Heath (01444) 457190

CROFTS, Ian Hamilton. b 55. BSc. St Jo Coll Nottm 79. **d** 82 **p** 83. C Leamington Priors St Paul *Cov* 82-86; C Oadby *Leic* 86; TV 86-91; V Maidstone St Faith *Cant* from 91. *St Faith's Vicarage, Moncktons Lane, Maidstone, Kent ME14 2PY* Maidstone (01622) 751079

CROMBIE, William Ian. b 52. Ex Coll Ox BA76 MA79. Ripon Coll Cuddesdon 76. **d** 78 **p** 79. C Broadstone *Sarum* 78; C Warminster St Denys 78-81; C Fleetwood *Blackb* 81-85; Tanzania from 85. *PO Box 2184, Dar-es-Salaam, Tanzania*

CROMPTON, Roger Martyn Francis. b 47. Sheff Univ BA69 PGCE73. St Jo Coll Dur Cranmer Hall Dur BA84. **d** 85 **p** 86. C Woodford Wells *Chelmsf* 85-89; V Golcar *Wakef* from 89. *The Vicarage, Church Street, Golcar, Huddersfield HD7 4PX* Huddersfield (01484) 654647

CRONK, Simon Nicholas. b 59. CQSW85 Wales Poly BA82. Wycliffe Hall Ox 89. **d** 92 **p** 93. C Cheltenham Ch Ch *Glouc* from 92. *1 Kensington Avenue, Cheltenham, Glos GL50 2NQ* Cheltenham (01242) 515915

CROOK, Colin. b 44. JP. Brighton Poly ALA67 DMS81 Lon Univ BSc(Econ)74. S'wark Ord Course 87. **d** 90 **p** 91. NSM Dartford Ch Ch *Roch* from 90. *Walliscote, 4 Swaisland Road, Dartford DA1 3DA* Dartford (01322) 272957

CROOK, David Creighton. b 37. Trin Coll Cam BA61 MA68. Cuddesdon Coll 61. **d** 63 **p** 64. C Workington St Mich *Carl* 63-66; C Penrith St Andr 66-70; V Barrow St Jas 70-78; V Maryport 78-81; TV Greystoke, Matterdale and Mungrisdale 81-87; TV Watermillock 84-87; V Hesket-in-the-Forest and Armathwaite from 87. *The Vicarage, High Hesket, Carlisle CA4 0HU* Southwaite (016974) 73320

CROOK, Canon Dennis Eric. b 40. AKC65. **d** 66 **p** 67. C Penwortham St Mary *Blackb* 66-69; C Kirkham 69-71; V Accrington St Jo 72-89; RD Accrington 82-90; P-in-c Huncoat 86-89; Hon Can Blackb Cathl from 89; V Accrington St Jo w Huncoat from 89. *St John's Vicarage, 11 Queen's Road, Accrington, Lancs BB5 6AR* Accrington (01254) 234587

CROOK, Frederick Herbert. b 17. Oak Hill Th Coll. **d** 52 **p** 53. C Bournemouth St Jo *Win* 52-55; V Margate H Trin *Cant* 55-66; Gen Sec Commonwealth and Continental Ch Soc 66-71;

Canada 71-89; Perm to Offic *Ches* from 89. *4 Heathfield Road, Bebington, Wirral, Merseyside L63 3BS*   0151-645 2664

CROOK, George Brian. b 56. Univ of Ottawa BAdmin78. Wycliffe Hall Ox. **d** 86 **p** 87. C Chaddesden St Mary *Derby* 86-89; Chapl Asst Gt Ormond Street Hosp for Sick Children Lon 89-91; Perm to Offic *Roch* 89-91; Perm to Offic Edmonton Episc Area *Lon* 89-91; Asst Chapl Vevey w Chateau d'Oex and Villars *Eur* 91-94; Hong Kong from 94. *Jian Hua Foundation, PO Box 71675, Kowloon CPO, Hong Kong* Hong Kong (852) 336-5312 Fax 337-2965

CROOK, Graham Leslie. b 49. Chich Th Coll 74. **d** 76 **p** 77. Chapl Southend Hosp from 92; C Withington St Crispin *Man* 76-79; C Prestwich St Marg 79-82; V Nelson St Bede *Blackb* 82-92; Chapl Southend Health Care NHS Trust from 92. *Southend Hospital, Prittlewell Chase, Westcliff-on-Sea, Essex SS0 0RY* Southend-on-Sea (01702) 435555

CROOK, Malcolm Geoffrey. b 53. St Steph Ho Ox 88. **d** 90 **p** 91. C Pet St Jude *Pet* 90-93; C Barrow St Matt *Carl* from 93. *St Francis House, 158 Schneider Road, Barrow-in-Furness, Cumbria LA14 5ER* Barrow-in-Furness (01229) 823155

CROOK, Rowland William. b 39. Lon Univ DipTh63. Tyndale Hall Bris 61. **d** 64 **p** 65. C Penn Fields *Lich* 64-68; C Lower Broughton St Clem w St Matthias *Man* 68-70; C Bucknall and Bagnall *Lich* 70-76; V New Shildon *Dur* 76-86; V Northwich St Luke and H Trin *Ches* from 86. *St Luke's Vicarage, Dyar Terrace, Northwich, Cheshire CW8 4DL* Northwich (01606) 74632

CROOKS, Christopher John (Kip). b 53. St Bede's Coll Dur CertEd75. Trin Coll Bris BA90. **d** 90 **p** 91. C The Quinton *Birm* 90-93; V Ince Ch Ch *Liv* from 93. *The Vicarage, 70 Belle Green Lane, Ince, Wigan, Lancs WN2 2EP* Wigan (01942) 495831

CROOKS, Canon David William Talbot. b 52. TCD BA75 MA78 BD83. **d** 77 **p** 78. C Glendermott *D & R* 77-81; C Edin Old St Paul *Edin* 81-84; I Taughboyne, Craigadooish, Newtowncunningham etc *D & R* from 84; Bp's Dom Chapl from 88; Can Raphoe Cathl from 91. *Taughboyne Rectory, Churchtown, Carrigans, Lifford, Co Donegal, Irish Republic* Letterkenny (74) 40135

CROOKS, Eric. b 34. Oak Hill Th Coll 68. **d** 70 **p** 71. C Chadderton Ch Ch *Man* 70-73; C Bolton St Paul 73-75; C Lurgan Ch Ch *D & D* 75-77; I Aghaderg w Donaghmore 77-80; I Dundonald from 80. *St Elizabeth's Rectory, 26A Ballyregan Road, Dundonald, Belfast BT16 0HY* Belfast (01232) 483153

CROOKS, Frederick Walter (Mike). b 18. TCD BA41 MA45. TCD Div Sch Div Test41. **d** 41 **p** 42. V Epsom St Martin *Guildf* 69-74; Hon Can Guildf Cathl 69-74; V Shalfleet *Portsm* 74-80; V Thorley 75-80; Perm to Offic from 80; rtd 83. *Flat 23, Carlton Court, 24/25 South Parade, Southsea, Hants PO5 2JF* Portsmouth (01705) 870470

CROOKS, Henry Cecil. b 15. Edin Th Coll 71. **d** 72 **p** 72. P-in-c Kinross *St And* 72-75; R 75-81; P-in-c Dollar 76-81; rtd 81; Perm to Offic *Bris* 81-86; Perm to Offic *Chich* from 87. *Terry's Cross, Bungalow 8, Brighton Road, Henfield, W Sussex BN5 9SX* Henfield (01273) 493802

CROOKS, Kenneth Robert. b 36. CEng FBIM FIEE. S'wark Ord Course 80. **d** 83 **p** 84. NSM Wisley w Pyrford *Guildf* from 83. *Combley Wood, Hurst Way, Woking, Surrey GU22 8PH* Byfleet (01932) 336600

CROOKS, Peter James. b 50. St Jo Coll Cam BA72. Cranmer Hall Dur DipTh76. **d** 76 **p** 77. C Onslow Square St Paul *Lon* 76-77; C Brompton H Trin w Onslow Square St Paul 77-79; C Wembley St Jo 79-82; CMS 82-92; Lebanon 83-89; Syria 85-89; Dean Jerusalem 89-92; P-in-c Hunningham *Cov* from 92; P-in-c Wappenbury w Weston under Wetherley from 92. *The Vicarage, Hunningham, Leamington Spa, Warks CV33 9DS* Marton (01926) 632739

CROOKSHANK, Stephen Graham. b 08. Lon Univ BA37. Westcott Ho Cam 39. **d** 40 **p** 41. V Seal St Pet *Roch* 66-73; rtd 73; Lic to Offic *Cant* 73-76; Lic to Offic *S'wark* 73-76; Lic to Offic *Roch* 73-76; Perm to Offic from 76. *Manormead Residential Home, Tilford Road, Hindhead, Surrey GU26 6RA* Hindhead (01428) 604780

CROSBY, Bernard Edward. b 47. Oak Hill Th Coll 86. **d** 88 **p** 89. C Springfield H Trin *Chelmsf* 88-91; C Penn Fields *Lich* 91-94; V St Leonards St Ethelburga *Chich* from 94. *St Ethelburga's Vicarage, 4 Gretham Way, St Leonards-on-Sea, E Sussex TN38 0UE* Hastings (01424) 421488

CROSFIELD, Canon George Philip Chorley. b 24. OBE90. Selw Coll Cam BA50 MA55. Edin Th Coll 46. **d** 51 **p** 52. Can St Mary's Cathl *Edin* 68-91; Vice-Provost 68-70; Provost 70-90; R Edin St Mary 70-90; rtd 90; Hon Can St Mary's Cathl *Edin* from 91. *21 Biggar Road, Silverburn, Penicuik, Midlothian EH26 9LQ* Penicuik (01968) 676607

CROSS, Alan. b 43. Chich Th Coll 68. **d** 70 **p** 71. C Bordesley St Oswald *Birm* 70; C S Yardley St Mich 70-73; C Colchester St

Jas, All SS, St Nic and St Runwald *Chelmsf* 73-77; V Leigh-on-Sea St Jas 77-89; V Woodford St Barn from 89. *127 Snakes Lane East, Woodford Green, Essex IG8 7HX* 0181-504 4687

CROSS, Preb Elizabeth Mary (Liz). b 46. Leeds Univ BA69 CertEd70. Sarum Th Coll 80. **dss** 83 **d** 87 **p** 94. Wootton Bassett *Sarum* 83-86; Westbury 86-87; Par Dn 87-89; C Glastonbury w Meare, W Pennard and Godney *B & W* from 89; Asst Dir of Ords from 89; Preb Wells Cathl from 93. *St Nicholas Cottage, Newtown Lane, West Pennard, Glastonbury, Somerset BA6 8NL* Glastonbury (01458) 832317

CROSS, Greville Shelly. b 49. Birm Univ DPS80. Sarum & Wells Th Coll 73. **d** 76 **p** 77. C Kidderminster St Mary *Worc* 76-80; P-in-c Worc St Mark 80-81; TV Worc St Martin w St Pet, St Mark etc 81-85; R Inkberrow w Cookhill and Kington w Dormston from 85; RD Evesham from 93. *The Vicarage, High Street, Inkberrow, Worcester WR7 4DU* Inkberrow (01386) 792222

CROSS, James Stuart (Jim). b 36. Magd Coll Ox BA65 MA71. Ripon Hall Ox 62. **d** 65 **p** 66. C Leckhampton SS Phil and Jas *Glouc* 65-66; CF 66-92; QHC 89-92; R Stretford St Pet *Man* from 92. *The Rectory, 24 Canute Road, Stretford, Manchester M32 0RJ* 0161-865 1802

CROSS, Jeremy Burkitt. b 45. St Pet Coll Ox BA68 MA71. Wycliffe Hall Ox 67. **d** 69 **p** 70. C Mildenhall *St E* 69-72; C Lindfield *Chich* 72-77; V Framfield 77-89; R St Leonards St Leon from 89. *81A Filsham Road, St Leonards-on-Sea, E Sussex TN38 0PE* Hastings (01424) 422199

CROSS, John Henry Laidlaw. b 30. Peterho Cam BA53 MA57. Ridley Hall Cam 53. **d** 55 **p** 56. C Ealing Dean St Jo *Lon* 55-58; C Gt Baddow *Chelmsf* 58-60; V Maidenhead St Andr and St Mary Magd *Ox* 60-68; News Ed C of E Newspaper 68-71; Dir Chr Weekly Newpapers Ltd 71-79; Assoc Ed 71-72; Ed 72-75; Hon C St Pet Cornhill *Lon* 68-87; P-in-c from 87; Hon C Chelsea All SS 76-87. *4 Coombe Hill Glade, Beverley Lane, Kingston-upon-Thames, Surrey KT2 7EF* 0181-942 7563

CROSS, Michael Anthony. b 45. Leeds Univ BA67 BA69. Coll of Resurr Mirfield 68. **d** 70 **p** 71. S Africa 70-73; C Adel *Ripon* 74-76; Chapl Birm Univ *Birm* 76-81; V Chapel Allerton *Ripon* 81-92; V Headingley from 92. *Headingley Vicarage, 16 Shire Oak Road, Leeds LS6 2DE* Leeds (0113) 275 1526

CROSS, Canon Michael Harry. b 28. Liv Univ BVSc50. Cuddesdon Coll 74. **d** 76 **p** 77. C Ledbury *Heref* 76-79; P-in-c Bosbury 79-82; P-in-c Coddington 79-82; P-in-c Wellington Heath 79-82; V Bosbury w Wellington Heath etc 82-83; V Bishop's Castle w Mainstone 83-84; P-in-c Snead 83-84; V Morland, Thrimby and Gt Strickland *Carl* 84-93; RD Appleby 91-93; Hon Can Carl Cathl from 92; rtd 93. *Hollin Knowle, Kilmidyke Road, Grange-over-Sands, Cumbria LA11 7AQ* Grange-over-Sands (015395) 35908

CROSSE, Canon Michael Selby. b 09. Linc Th Coll 29. **d** 33 **p** 34. V Hazelwood *Derby* 68-74; rtd 74. *Astell, Overton Park Road, Cheltenham, Glos GL50 3BT* Cheltenham (01242) 517823

CROSSEY, Nigel Nicholas. b 59. Cam Univ BA TCD DipTh84. **d** 84 **p** 85. C Drumglass w Moygashel *Arm* 84-87; I Magheraculmoney *Clogh* 87-93; CF from 93. *c/o MOD (Army), Bagshot Park, Bagshot, Surrey GU19 5PL* Bagshot (01276) 471717 Fax 412834

CROSSLAND, Felix Parnell. b 20. CEng MIMechE57 Univ of Wales (Swansea) BSc49. St Deiniol's Hawarden 73. **d** 75 **p** 76. Hon C Skewen *Llan* 75-78; Hon C Neath w Llantwit 78-85; rtd 85; Perm to Offic *Llan* from 85. *21 Cimla Road, Neath, W Glam SA11 3PR* Neath (01639) 643560

CROSSLAND, Sister Joyce. b 19. Gilmore Ho IDC48. **dss** 54 **d** 87. CSA 49-78; St Etheldreda's Children's Home Bedf 62-90; Hon Par Dn Bedf St Paul *St Alb* 87-91; rtd 91; Perm to Offic *St Alb* 91-94; Perm to Offic *Ox* from 94. *6 Linford Lane, Willen, Milton Keynes MK15 9AB* Milton Keynes (01908) 661554

CROSSLAND, Richard Henry. b 49. Ex Univ BA72. S'wark Ord Course 91. **d** 94. NSM Surbiton St Andr and St Mark *S'wark* from 94. *8 Foxwarren, Claygate, Esher, Surrey KT10 0LB* Esher (01372) 465971

CROSSLEY, David. b 50. FISMM94. Coll of Resurr Mirfield 80. **d** 82 **p** 83. C Barton w Peel Green *Man* 82-85; TV Swinton St Pet 85-87; Perm to Offic from 89. *106 Buckstones Road, Shaw, Oldham OL2 8DN* Shaw (01706) 882171

CROSSLEY, Dennis Thomas. b 23. AKC52 St Boniface Warminster. **d** 53 **p** 54. C Crofton Park St Hilda *S'wark* 53-56; C Beddington 56-59; C Talbot Village *Sarum* 59-62; R Finchampstead *Ox* from 62. *The Rectory, Finchampstead, Wokingham, Berks RG11 3SE* Eversley (01734) 732102

CROSSLEY, George Alan. b 34. Dur Univ BA56. Cranmer Hall Dur DipTh60. **d** 60 **p** 61. C Blackb St Steph *Blackb* 60-63; C Ashton-on-Ribble St Andr 63-65; V Oswaldtwistle St Paul 65-72; R Dufton *Carl* 72-73; P-in-c Milburn w Newbiggin 72-73; R Long Marton w Dufton and w Milburn 73-76; P-in-c Beckermet St Jo 76-78; V Beckermet St Jo and St Bridget w Ponsonby 78-84; Chapl Furness Gen Hosp 84-89; TV

Newbarns w Hawcoat *Carl* 84-89; Chapl Princess R Hosp Telford from 89. *Princess Royal Hospital, Apley Castle, Telford, Shropshire TF6 6TF* Telford (01952) 253802 or 641222

CROSSLEY, Dr George John. b 57. Bradf Univ BA81 PhD84. N Ord Course 91. **d** 94 **p** 95. C Balderstone *Man* from 94. *2 Buersil Avenue, Rochdale, Lancs OL16 4TP* Rochdale (01706) 357633

CROSSLEY, Hugh Vaughan. b 20. AKC42. Bps' Coll Cheshunt. **d** 47 **p** 48. S Africa 60-73; Adn Mafeking 66-70; R Orsett *Chelmsf* 73-85; P-in-c Bulphan 77-85; rtd 85; Perm to Offic *Nor* from 86. *15 Knyvett Green, Ashwellthorpe, Norwich NR16 1HA* Fundenhall (0150841) 489

CROSSLEY, James Salter Baron. b 39. Linc Th Coll 70. **d** 72 **p** 74. C Chesterfield All SS *Derby* 72-75; Chapl Chendale R Infirmary 75-92; Chapl Doncaster R Infirmary & Montague Hosp NHS Trust 92-95; Chapl Asst Tickhill Road and St Cath Hosps 75-92; Hon C Doncaster Intake *Sheff* 78-95; rtd 95. *143 Thorne Road, Doncaster, S Yorkshire DN2 5BH* Doncaster (01302) 326306

CROSSLEY, John Eric. b 51. St Martin's Coll Lanc BA92. Carl Dioc Tr Inst 92. **d** 94. C Westf St Mary *Carl* from 94. *34 Ashfield Road, Workington, Cumbria CA14 3JT* Workington (01900) 603158

CROSSLEY, Canon Dr Robert Scott. b 36. Lon Univ BSc61 BD68 PhD75. ALCD64. **d** 64 **p** 65. C Beckenham St Jo *Roch* 64-68; C Morden *S'wark* 68-72; Chapl Ridley Hall Cam 72-75; V Camberley St Paul *Guildf* 75-83; TR from 83; RD Surrey Heath 81-84; Hon Can Guildf Cathl from 89. *St Paul's Rectory, Crawley Ridge, Camberley, Surrey GU15 2AD* Camberley (01276) 22773

CROSSLEY, William Jeremy Hugh. b 55. St Jo Coll Dur BA76. Cranmer Hall Dur 81. **d** 84 **p** 85. C Gillingham St Mark *Roch* 84-87; C Ches Square St Mich w St Phil *Lon* 87-94; V Westminster St Jas the Less from 94. *13 Churton Place, London SW1V 2LN* 0171-630 6282

CROSSMAN, Mrs Charmian Jeanette. b 27. Lon Univ BA48 Lanc Univ MA81 Edin Univ DipMin84. **d** 91 **p** 94. NSM Carl St Jo *Carl* 91-94; RD Carl 94-95; P-in-c Thursby from 95. *The Vicarage, Church Lane, Thursby, Carlisle CA5 6PF* Dalston (01228) 710303

CROSSMAN, Miss Sharon Margaret Joan. b 65. St Loyes Sch of Occupational Therapy DipCOT87. Linc Th Coll BTh93. **d** 93 **p** 94. Par Dn Chippenham St Andr w Tytherton Lucas *Bris* 93-94; C from 94. *18 Downham Mead, Chippenham, Wilts SN15 3LN* Chippenham (01249) 653932

CROSTHWAITE, George Roger. b 38. Dur Univ BSc62. Ridley Hall Cam 62 Fuller Th Sem California DMin83. **d** 65 **p** 66. C Bradf Cathl Par *Bradf* 65-67; C Ox St Aldate w H Trin *Ox* 67-70; Youth Adv CMS 70-73; P-in-c Derby St Werburgh *Derby* 73-78; V 78-82; USA 77-78; V Anston *Sheff* 82-83; C St Giles-in-the-Fields *Lon* 83-86; V Barnes St Mich *S'wark* 86-88; Perm to Offic *Guildf* 88-93; Dir Cen Essential Psychology from 92. *11 Pangbourne Avenue, London W10 6DJ* 0181-969 8932 or (01903) 217186

CROUCH, Keith Matheson. b 45. AKC70 Whitelands Coll Lon CertEd71. **d** 72 **p** 73. C Hill *Birm* 72-75; P-in-c Woodgate Valley CD 75-77; V Bishop's Castle w Mainstone *Heref* from 91. *The Vicarage, Church Lane, Bishops Castle, Shropshire SY9 5AF* Bishops Castle (01588) 638445

CROUCH, Raymond. b 21. Cuddesdon Coll 66. **d** 68 **p** 69. C Bracknell *Ox* 68-71; P-in-c Littlemore 71-78; C Boxgrove *Chich* 78-81; C Tangmere 78-81; P-in-c Oving w Merston 78-81; V Winkfield *Ox* 81-84; P-in-c Cranbourne 81-84; C Thame w Towersey 84-86; rtd 86; Perm to Offic *Ox* from 86. *9 Orchard Close, Chalgrove, Oxford OX44 7RA* Stadhampton (01865) 890653

CROUCHMAN, Eric Richard. b 30. Bps' Coll Cheshunt 64. **d** 66 **p** 67. C Ipswich H Trin *St E* 66-69; C Ipswich All Hallows 69-72; R Crowfield w Stonham Aspal and Mickfield 72-81; R Combs 81-90; RD Stowmarket 84-90; P-in-c Lydgate w Ousden and Cowlinge 90-95; R Wickhambrook w Lydgate, Ousden and Cowlinge from 95. *The Rectory, Lidgate, Newmarket, Suffolk CB8 9PP* Ouden (0638) 500437

CROW, Arthur. b 26. St Chad's Coll Dur BA51 DipTh52. **d** 52 **p** 53. V Flockton cum Denby Grange *Wakef* 63-91; rtd 91. *2 Thatchers Croft, Copmanthorpe, York YO2 3YD* York (01904) 709861

CROW, Michael John. b 35. AKC63. **d** 64 **p** 65. C Welwyn Garden City *St Alb* 64-67; C Sawbridgeworth 67-69; C Biscot 69-71; V Luton St Aug Limbury 71-79; TR Borehamwood 79-87; V Markyate Street from 87. *The Vicarage, High Street, Markyate, St Albans, Herts AL3 8PD* Luton (01582) 841701

CROWDER, Ven Norman Harry. b 26. St Jo Coll Cam BA48 MA52. Westcott Ho Cam 50. **d** 52 **p** 53. Chapl Canford Sch Wimborne 64-72; V Oakfield St Jo *Portsm* 72-75; Can Res

Portsm Cathl 75-85; Dir RE 75-85; Adn Portsm 85-93; rtd 93. *37 Rectory Road, Salisbury SP2 7SD* Salisbury (01722) 320052

CROWE, Anthony Murray. b 34. St Edm Hall Ox BA58 MA61. Westcott Ho Cam 57. **d** 59 **p** 60. V Clapham St Jo *S'wark* 66-73; R Charlton St Luke w H Trin 73-94; rtd 94. *9 Park Avenue, Whitstable, Kent CT5 2DD* Whitstable (01227) 273046

CROWE, Eric Anthony. b 29. St Jo Coll Dur BA53. Cuddesdon Coll 53. **d** 55 **p** 56. V Battyeford *Wakef* 68-74; P-in-c Pitminster w Corfe *B & W* 75-76; V 76-90; rtd 90. *70 Woolbrook Road, Sidmouth, Devon EX10 9XB* Sidmouth (01395) 579085

CROWE, Canon John Yeomans. b 39. Keble Coll Ox BA62 MA66. Linc Th Coll 62. **d** 64 **p** 65. C Tettenhall Regis *Lich* 64-67; C Caversham *Ox* 67-71; V Hampton *Worc* 72-76; P-in-c Leek St Edw *Lich* 76-79; TR Leek 79-83; TR Leek and Meerbrook 83-87; RD Leek 82-87; TR Dorchester *Ox* from 87; RD Aston and Cuddesdon from 93; Hon Can Ch Ch from 94. *The Rectory, Dorchester-on-Thames, Wallingford, Oxon OX10 7HZ* Oxford (01865) 340007

CROWE, Leonard Charles (Len). b 25. S Dios Minl Tr Scheme 80. **d** 82 **p** 83. NSM Buxted and Hadlow Down *Chich* 82-84; NSM Fairlight 84-86; P-in-c 86-89; V 89-92; rtd 92; RD Rye *Chich* 93-95. *Deforal, Sea Road, Fairlight, Hastings, E Sussex TN55 4AX*

CROWE, Canon Norman Charles. b 23. ADipR62. Ridley Abbey. **d** 63 **p** 64. V Leic St Chad *Leic* 68-73; V Market Harborough 73-88; RD Gartree I (Harborough) 76-81; Hon Can Leic Cathl 80-88; rtd 88; Perm to Offic *Leic* from 88; Perm to Offic *Pet* from 88. *8 Wilton Close, Desborough, Kettering, Northants NN14 2QJ* Kettering (01536) 760820

CROWE, Canon Philip Anthony. b 36. Selw Coll Cam BA60 MA64. Ridley Hall Cam 60. **d** 62 **p** 63. Tutor Oak Hill Th Coll 62-67; C Enfield Ch Ch Trent Park *Lon* 62-65; Ed C of E Newspaper 67-71; Lect Birm St Martin 71-76; R Breadsall *Derby* 77-88; Prin and Tutor Sarum & Wells Th Coll 88-95; Can and Preb Sarum Cathl *Sarum* 91-95; R Overton and Erbistock and Penley *St As* from 95. *The Rectory, 4 Sundorne, Overton, Wrexham, Clwyd LL13 0EB* Wrexham (01978) 73229

CROWE, Canon Sydney Ralph. b 32. Edin Th Coll 61. **d** 63 **p** 64. C Bingley H Trin *Bradf* 63-66; C Bierley 66-69; V Manningham St Chad from 69; Hon Can Bradf Cathl from 85; RD Airedale from 95. *The Vicarage, St Chad's Road, Toller Lane, Bradford, W Yorkshire BD8 9DE* Bradford (01274) 543957

CROWHURST, David Brian. b 40. Qu Coll Birm 77. **d** 80 **p** 81. NSM Ribbesford w Bewdley and Dowles *Worc* 80-82; Hon Chapl Birm Cathl *Birm* 81-82; C Kidderminster St Jo *Worc* 82-83; C-in-c Wribbenhall 83-84; P-in-c 84-87; V Oswestry St Oswald *Lich* 87-94; P-in-c Oswestry H Trin 93-94; V Oswestry from 94; P-in-c Rhydycroesau 90-91; R from 91. *The Vicarage, Penylan Lane, Oswestrey, Shropshire SY11 2AN* Oswestry (01691) 653467 or 652861

CROWIE, Hermon John. b 41. Kelham Th Coll 61. **d** 69 **p** 73. C Sneinton St Cypr *S'well* 69; C Balderton 72-75; V Basford St Aid 75-78; R Everton and Mattersey w Clayworth 78-84; St Helena 84-89; Chapl HM Pris Nor 89-91; Chapl HM Pris Cant from 91. *The Chaplain's Office, HM Prison, 46 Longport, Canterbury, Kent CT1 1PJ* Canterbury (01227) 762244 Fax 450203

CROWLEY, Brian Golland. b 01. Keble Coll Ox BA23 MA28. Westcott Ho Cam 26. **d** 27 **p** 28. V Clifton Hampden *Ox* 54-69; rtd 69. *2 Woodlands Paddock, Penn Road, Wolverhampton WV4 4DY* Wolverhampton (01902) 330544

CROWLEY, Michael Patrick Sainsbury. b 51. Newc Univ BA74 PGCE75. Lon Bible Coll BA78 MA84. **d** 87 **p** 87. Chile from 87. *Casilla 87, Valdivia, Chile, or Casilla 50675, Santiago, Chile* Santiago (2) 683009 Fax 639-4581

CROWSON, Richard Charles Marriott. b 39. Down Coll Cam BA62 MA66. Lich Th Coll 62. **d** 64 **p** 65. C Smethwick *Birm* 64-67; V Nottm St Andr *S'well* 67-74; Chapl Community Relns *Pet* 74-80; Asst Sec for Race and Community Relns Gen Syn from 93; Public Preacher *Lon* from 93. *11 Ellington Road, London N7 8PP* 0171-609 1984 or 222 9011 Fax 799 2714

✠CROWTHER, Rt Rev Clarence Edward. b 29. Leeds Univ BA50 LLB52 LLM53 California Univ PhD75. Cuddesdon Coll 55. **d** 56 **p** 57 **c** 65. C Ox SS Phil and Jas *Ox* 56-59; USA 59-64 and from 67; S Africa 64-67; Bp Kimberley and Kuruman 65-67; Asst Bp California from 73. *210 San Ysidro Road, Santa Barbara, California 93108, USA*

CROWTHER, Donald James. b 23. Oak Hill NSM Course. **d** 82 **p** 83. NSM Seal St Lawr *Roch* 82-85; NSM Sevenoaks St Nic 85-87; P-in-c Sevenoaks Weald 87-90; Perm to Offic from 90. *Midhope, Pilgrims Way, Kemsing, Sevenoaks, Kent TN15 6LS* Sevenoaks (01732) 761035

CROWTHER, Frank. b 28. Qu Coll Birm 68. **d** 69 **p** 70. C Bulwell St Mary *S'well* 69-72; TV Clifton 72-77; R Kirkby in

Ashfield St Thos 77-85; rtd 86; Perm to Offic *S'well* from 86. *30 Bramley Court, Sutton-in-Ashfield, Notts NG17 4AT* Mansfield (01623) 443251

CROWTHER, Ronald. b 22. Sarum Th Coll. **d** 53 **p** 54. V Tooting All SS *S'wark* 67-73; R Brinkley, Burrough Green and Carlton *Ely* 73-80; P-in-c Westley Waterless 78-80; R Brandon and Santon Downham *St E* 80-87; rtd 87. *21 Pinewood Drive, Brandon, Suffolk IP27 0HF* Thetford (01842) 811258

CROWTHER, Stephen Alfred. b 59. TCD DipTh87. **d** 87 **p** 88. C Willowfield *D & D* 87-89; I Belf St Chris 89-92; I Kiltegan w Hacketstown, Clonmore and Moyne *C & O* from 93. *The Rectory, Kiltegan, Baltinglass, Co Wicklow, Irish Republic* Kiltegan (508) 73368   Fax 73414

CROWTHER-ALWYN, Benedict Mark. b 53. Kent Univ BA74. Qu Coll Birm 74. **d** 77 **p** 78. C Fenny Stratford and Water Eaton *Ox* 77-80; C Moulsecoomb *Chich* 80-81; TV 81-83; R Glas St Serf *Glas* 83-87; R Baillieston 83-87; R Bassingham *Linc* 87-90; V Aubourn w Haddington 87-90; V Carlton-le-Moorland w Stapleford 87-90; R Thurlby w Norton Disney 87-90; V Elmton *Derby* from 90. *The Vicarage, Creswell, Worksop, Notts S80 4HD* Worksop (01909) 721264

CROWTHER-GREEN, Canon John Patrick Victor. b 18. Hatf Coll Dur LTh41 BA42. St Boniface Warminster 39. **d** 42 **p** 44. V Leic St Sav *Leic* 58-73; V Blaby 73-87; RD Guthlaxton I (Blaby) 81-87; Hon Can Leic Cathl 82-87; rtd 87. *40 Craighill Road, Knighton, Leicester LE2 3FB* Leicester (0116) 270 7615

CROWTHER-GREEN, Michael Leonard. b 36. K Coll Lon 56. **d** 60 **p** 61. Chr Aid Area Sec (Berks, Oxon and Bucks) 69-78; Lic to Offic *Ox* 78-83; Dioc Stewardship Adv 83-92; rtd 92. *8 Egerton Road, Reading RG2 8HQ* Reading (01734) 872502

CROYDON, Archdeacon of. *See* DAVIES, Ven Vincent Anthony

CROYDON, Area Bishop of. *See* WOOD, Rt Rev Dr Wilfred Denniston

CRUICKSHANK, Jonathan Graham. b 52. K Coll Lon BD74 AKC74 Ox Univ PGCE75. St Aug Coll Cant 75. **d** 76 **p** 77. C Stantonbury *Ox* 76-79; C Burnham 79-82; Chapl RNR 80-83; C Burnham w Dropmore, Hitcham and Taplow *Ox* 82-83; Chapl RN 83-89; TV New Windsor *Ox* from 89. *Holy Trinity Rectory, 73 Alma Road, Windsor, Berks SL4 3HD* Windsor (01753) 853585

CRUISE, Brian John Alexander. Bris Univ BA TCD BTh. **d** 88 **p** 89. C Lurgan Ch the Redeemer *D & D* 88-92; I Kildress w Altedesert *Arm* from 92. *Kildress Rectory, 6 Rectory Road, Cookstown, Co Tyrone BT80 9RX* Cookstown (016487) 51215

CRUMP, John. b 27. AKC54. **d** 55 **p** 56. V Highams Park All SS *Chelmsf* 65-78; RD Waltham Forest 75-78; R Lambourne w Abridge and Stapleford Abbotts 78-83; V Walton le Soken 83-90; rtd 90. *14 Kenilworth Road, Holland-on-Sea, Clacton-on-Sea, Essex CO15 5NX* Clacton-on-Sea (01255) 814511

CRUMPTON, Colin. b 38. AKC61. **d** 64 **p** 65. C Billingham St Cuth *Dur* 64-66; C Shirley *Birm* 66-69; V Mossley *Ches* 69-75; Miss to Seamen 75-77; V Burslem St Paul *Lich* 77-82; V Edensor from 82. *The Vicarage, 131 Longton Hall Road, Stoke-on-Trent ST3 2EL* Stoke-on-Trent (01782) 319210

CRUMPTON, Michael Reginald. b 33. Chich Th Coll 66. **d** 69 **p** 70. C Longton St Mary and St Chad *Lich* 69-72; C Rugeley 72-76; C Kingswinford St Mary 76-87; V Moxley 87-91; Chapl Moxley Hosp Lich 88-91; rtd 91. *115 Field Lane, Burton-on-Trent, Staffs DE13 0NJ* Burton-on-Trent (01283) 542049

CRUSE, Jack. b 35. ARIBA67. Sarum & Wells Th Coll 76. **d** 79 **p** 80. NSM W Teignmouth *Ex* 79-85; NSM Ideford, Luton and Ashcombe 85-87; C 87-89; NSM Bishopsteignton 85-87; C 87-89; C Teignmouth, Ideford w Luton, Ashcombe etc 90; R Broadhempston, Woodland, Staverton etc from 90; RD Totnes from 94. *The Rectory, Broadhempston, Totnes, Devon TQ9 6AU* Ipplepen (01803) 813646

CRUSE, John Jeremy. b 58. Univ of Wales (Lamp) BA79 Hughes Hall Cam CertEd87. Sarum & Wells Th Coll 81. **d** 82 **p** 83. C Newton St Pet *S & B* 82-84; P-in-c Newbridge-on-Wye and Llanfihangel Brynpabuan 84-86; Perm to Offic *Heref* 88-89; C Waltham H Cross *Chelmsf* 89-91; TV Yatton Moor *B & W* from 91. *The Vicarage, North End Road, Yatton, Bristol BS19 4AS* Yatton (01934) 832776

CRUST, John Allen. b 40. Linc Th Coll. **d** 68 **p** 69. C Spalding *Linc* 68-73; C Cullercoats St Geo *Newc* 73-75; V Scotswood 75-82; V Old Leake w Wrangle *Linc* 82-87; R Crowland from 87. *The Abbey Rectory, East Street, Crowland, Peterborough PE6 0EN* Peterborough (01733) 210499

CRUTTENDEN, Leslie Roy. b 39. Cant Sch of Min. **d** 84 **p** 85. NSM Maidstone St Luke *Cant* 84-86; NSM Charlton-in-Dover 86-90; NSM River from 90. *6 Citadel Heights, Dover, Kent CT17 9DS* Dover (01304) 205281

CRYER, Gordon David. b 34. St D Coll Lamp BA63 DipTh64. **d** 64 **p** 65. C Mortlake w E Sheen *S'wark* 64-67; C Godstone 67-70; R Stoke Damerel *Ex* from 71; Chapl St Dunstan's

CRYER, Neville Barker. b 24. Hertf Coll Ox BA48 MA52. Ridley Hall Cam. **d** 50 **p** 51. Sec Conf Br Miss Socs 67-70; Gen Sec BFBS 70-86; rtd 86. *14 Carmires Road, Haxby, York YO3 3NN* York (01904) 763371

CRYER, Percival. b 11. AKC39. **d** 39 **p** 40. Chapl Princess Chr Hosp Hildenborough Kent 62-82; Leybourne Grange Hosp W Malling 62-82; rtd 82; Perm to Offic *Chich* from 86. *19 Ascot Close, St John's Road, Eastbourne, E Sussex BN20 7HL* Eastbourne (01323) 735211

CUFF, Gregor John. b 61. Keele Univ BSc82. Ridley Hall Cam 93. **d** 95. C Stanley *Liv* from 95. *Vicarage Flat, 8 Derwent Square, Liverpool L13 6QT* 0151-252 1522

CUFF, Mrs Pamela (Pam). b 47. MCSP68. S Dios Minl Tr Scheme 89. **d** 92 **p** 94. NSM Nether Stowey w Over Stowey *B & W* 92-93; NSM Quantoxhead from 93; Asst Chapl Taunton Hosps 93-94. *Millands, Kilve, Bridgwater, Somerset TA5 1EA* Holford (01278) 741229

CULBERTSON, Eric Malcolm. b 54. Ch Ch Ox BA76 MA80 K Coll Lon PhD91. Edin Th Coll 78. **d** 80 **p** 81. C Edin St Thos *Edin* 80-83; C Ealing St Mary *Lon* 83-87; R Clarkston *Glas* 87-89; Area Sec BCMS 89-93; Area Sec Crosslinks 93-94; Hon C Halliwell St Luke *Man* 90-94; I Tullaniskin w Clonoe *Arm* from 94. *215 Brackaville Road, Newmills, Dungannon, Co Tyrone BT71 4EJ* Coalisland (01868) 747154

CULL, Ernest Geoffrey. b 20. Coll of Resurr Mirfield 57. **d** 57 **p** 58. V Barrowhill *Derby* 61-70; V Derby St Paul 71-80; V Mackworth St Fran 80-90; rtd 90. *15 Lodge Lane, Spondon, Derby DE21 7GD* Derby (01332) 674562

CULL, Canon Francis Cyril Duncan. b 15. Natal Univ BA63 York Univ PhD73 Univ of S Africa DLitt79. Clifton Th Coll 35. **d** 38 **p** 39. C Waltham Abbey *Chelmsf* 38-40; C Streatham St Paul *S'wark* 40-42; C Newington St Mary 42-45; Min St Mary's CD Welling 46-52; V Battersea St Steph 52-57; S Africa from 58; Lect Rhodes Univ 65-73; Lect Witwatersrand Univ 74-78; Prov Can from 88. *Bishopscourt, Bishopscourt Drive, Claremont, South Africa* Cape Town (21) 797-6451

CULL, John. b 31. Oak Hill Th Coll 56. **d** 59 **p** 60. Chapl Mariners' Ch Glouc 66-70; R Woodchester *Glouc* 70-90; RD Stonehouse 85-89; V Walton *St E* 90-94; rtd 94. *Hillgrove Stables, Bear Hill, Woodchester, Stroud, Glos GL5 5DH* Stroud (01453) 872145

CULLEN, Dr John Austin. b 43. FRSA89 Auckland Univ BA67 Otago Univ BD76 Keble Coll Ox DPhil86 St Jo Coll Auckland 66. **d** 69 **p** 70. New Zealand 69-78; Asst Chapl Keble Coll Ox 79-82; Perm to Offic *Lon* 82-84; Chapl and Lect Worc Coll Ox 84-86; C St Botolph Aldgate w H Trin Minories *Lon* 86-87; Hon C St Marylebone All SS 87-91; Dir Inst of Chr Studies 87-91; Dir of Tr *Win* from 91. *Church House, 9 The Close, Winchester SO23 9LS* Winchester (01962) 844644 Fax 841815

CULLIFORD, Michael. b 26. Qu Coll Birm 56. **d** 58 **p** 59. V Heald Green St Cath *Ches* 62-80; Perm to Offic *Man* from 89; rtd 91. *23 Field Vale Drive, Stockport, Cheshire SK5 6XZ* 0161-432 1706 or 442 0493

CULLING, Elizabeth Ann. b 58. St Mary's Coll Dur BA79 St Jo Coll Dur PhD87 Rob Coll Cam BA88. Ridley Hall Cam 86. **d** 89 **p** 94. Par Dn S Cave and Ellerker w Broomfleet *York* 89-92; Tutor Cranmer Hall Dur 92-95; P-in-c Cherry Burton *York* from 95; Abp's Sen Adv on Rural Affairs from 95; Chapl Bp Burton Coll York from 95. *The Rectory, Cherry Burton, Beverley, N Humberside HU17 7RF* Hornsea (01964) 550293

CULLINGWORTH, Anthony Robert. b 42. BSc. Ox NSM Course. **d** 83 **p** 84. NSM Slough *Ox* from 83. *375 Goodman Park, Slough SL2 5NW* Slough (01753) 536274

CULLIS, Andrew Stanley Weldon. b 48. Hertf Coll Ox BA69 LTh. St Jo Coll Nottm 70. **d** 73 **p** 74. C Reigate St Mary *S'wark* 73-78; C Yateley *Win* 78-82; V Dorking St Paul *Guildf* from 82; RD Dorking from 94. *St Paul's Vicarage, South Terrace, Dorking, Surrey RH4 2AB* Dorking (01306) 883023

CULLWICK, Christopher John. b 53. Hull Univ BA75 Reading Univ Ox Univ BA80 MA85. Wycliffe Hall Ox 78. **d** 81 **p** 82. C Nottm St Jude *S'well* 81-84; C York St Mich-le-Belfrey *York* 84-87; TV Huntington from 87. *The Vicarage, 64 Strensall Road, Huntington, York YO3 9SH* York (01904) 764608

CULLY, Miss Elizabeth Faith. b 46. SRN67 SCM69 RGN72. Trin Coll Bris BA88. **d** 88 **p** 94. Par Dn Filton *Bris* 88-92; Par Dn Fishponds St Jo 92-94; C from 94. *The Vicarage, 102A Church Lane, Brinsley, Notts NG16 5AB* Langley Mill (01773) 713978

CULPIN, Albert. b 16. Open Univ BA75. St Deiniol's Hawarden 76. **d** 77 **p** 78. NSM Bidston *Ches* 77-87; Perm to Offic from 87. *27 Derwent Road, Meols, Wirral, Merseyside L47 8XY* 0151-632 3542

CULROSS, James Fred. b 17. Lon Univ BD51. Bps' Coll Cheshunt 47. **d** 50 **p** 51. Chapl R Wanstead Sch 67-71; Chapl Sir Roger Manwood's Sch Sandwich 71-79; R Barrowden and Wakerley w S Luffenham *Pet* 79-82; rtd 82; Perm to Offic *B & W* from 82. *34 Heritage Court, Magdalene Street, Glastonbury, Somerset BA6 9ER* Glastonbury (01458) 834179

CULVERWELL, Martin Phillip. b 48. Sarum & Wells Th Coll 72. **d** 75 **p** 76. C Ashford St Hilda *Lon* 75-78; C Chelsea St Luke 78-80; Chapl RN 80-83; TV Yeovil *B & W* 83-87; P-in-c Sarratt *St Alb* 87-90; NSM Bradf w Oake, Hillfarrance and Heathfield *B & W* 90-92; R Rode Major from 92. *The Rectory, Church Lane, Rode, Bath BA3 6PN* Frome (01373) 831234

CUMBERLAND, Very Rev Barry John. b 44. Birm Univ BA67 Worc Coll Ox DipEd68 Trin Coll Singapore MDiv88. **d** 88 **p** 89. NSM Westmr St Matt *Lon* 88-90; Perm to Offic from 90; The Philippines from 90; Dean Manila from 92. *Makati Central PO Box 1245, 1252 Makati, Metro Manila, The Philippines* Manila (2) 817-9440 or 817-8350 Fax 817-8350

CUMBERLAND, Leslie Hodgson. b 15. Leeds Univ BA37. Coll of Resurr Mirfield 37. **d** 39 **p** 40. V Bradf St Columba *Bradf* 55-64; Lic to Offic 64-85; rtd 80; Perm to Offic *Bradf* from 85. *29 Union Road, Low Moor, Bradford, W Yorkshire BD12 0DW* Bradford (01274) 676138

CUMBERLEGE, Francis Richard. b 41. AKC65. **d** 66 **p** 67. C Leigh Park St Fran CD *Portsm* 66-71; Papua New Guinea 71-81; Adn N Papua 74-81; C Portsea St Mary *Portsm* 81; R Hastings St Clem and All SS *Chich* 81-86; V Broadwater Down 86-91; V Tunbridge Wells St Mark *Roch* from 91. *The Vicarage, 1 St Mark's Road, Tunbridge Wells, Kent TN2 5LT* Tunbridge Wells (01892) 526069

CUMBERLIDGE, Anthony Wynne. b 49. ACIB75. Sarum & Wells Th Coll 79. **d** 82 **p** 83. C Llanrhos *St As* 82-85; R Llanfair Talhaearn and Llansannan etc 85-87; CF from 87. *c/o MOD (Army), Bagshot Park, Bagshot, Surrey GU19 5PL* Bagshot (01276) 471717 Fax 412834

CUMBRAE, Provost of. *Vacant*

CUMING, Mark Alexander. b 53. AKC75. Westcott Ho Cam 76. **d** 77 **p** 78. C Newc H Cross *Newc* 77-80; Perm to Offic *Birm* 87-93; R Blanchland w Hunstanworth and Edmundbyers etc *Newc* from 95. *The Vicarage, Blanchland, Consett, Co Durham DH8 9ST* Hexham (01434) 675207

CUMINGS, Llewellyn Frank Beadnell. b 29. Natal Univ BA50 St Cath Coll Cam CertEd53. Ridley Hall Cam 65. **d** 67 **p** 68. C Leamington Priors St Mary *Cov* 67-70; V Lobley Hill *Dur* 70-74; R Denver *Ely* 74-82; V Ryston w Roxham 74-82; R St Leonards St Leon *Chich* 82-88; V Billinghay *Linc* 88-93; rtd 93. *Y Bwthyn, Coedllan, Llanfyllin, Powys SY22 5BP* Llanfyllin (01691) 648013

CUMMING, Nigel Patrick. b 42. St Jo Coll Nottm 73. **d** 75 **p** 76. C Castle Hall *Ches* 75-77; C Stalybridge H Trin and Ch Ch 77-78; C Tadley St Pet *Win* 78-82; R Overton w Laverstoke and Freefolk from 82; RD Whitchurch from 89. *The Rectory, 54 Lordsfield Gardens, Overton, Basingstoke, Hants RG25 3EW* Basingstoke (01256) 770207

CUMMING, Ms Susan Margaret. b 47. Man Univ BSc68 Makerere Univ Kampala DipEd69. E Midl Min Tr Course CTPS82. **dss** 82 **d** 87 **p** 95. Cinderhill *S'well* 82-85; Dioc Adv in Adult Educn 85-92; Lect St Mary's Coll Nottm from 93; Par Dn Nottm St Mary and St Cath 93-95; C from 95. *11 Clumber Crescent North, The Park, Nottingham NG7 1EY* Nottingham (0115) 941 7156

CUMMINGS, Elizabeth. b 45. St Jo Coll Dur BA84. NE Ord Course. **d** 87 **p** 94. NSM Dur St Giles *Dur* 87-89; Chapl HM Pris Dur 89-90; Chapl HM Rem Cen Low Newton from 90. *The Chaplain's Office, HM Remand Centre Low Newton, Durham DH1 5SD* 0191-386 1141 or 386 8469 Fax 386 2620

CUMMINGS, George Osmond. b 21. St Chad's Coll Dur BA43 MA48 DipTh45. **d** 45 **p** 46. P-in-c New Cantley CD *Sheff* 67-72; V Campsall 72-80; V Arksey 80-86; RD Adwick 82-84; rtd 86; Lic to Offic *Sheff* from 87. *7 Lidget Close, Doncaster, S Yorkshire DN4 6EE* Doncaster (01302) 536999

CUMMINGS, Richard Vivian Payn. b 21. Lon Univ BSc41. Chich Th Coll 51. **d** 53 **p** 54. V Wellingborough St Barn *Pet* 69-73; RD Wellingborough 70-73; P-in-c Milton Malsor 73-80; R Collingtree w Courteenhall 73-80; R Collingtree w Courteenhall and Milton Malsor 80-90; rtd 90. *55 Watersmeet, Northampton NN1 5SQ* Northampton (01604) 37027

CUMMINGS, Very Rev William Stuart Margaret Vickery. b 38. Ch Ch Ox BA62 MA64. Wycliffe Hall Ox 61. **d** 64 **p** 65. C Leytonstone St Jo *Chelmsf* 64-67; C Writtle 67-71; R Stratton St Mary w Stratton St Michael *Nor* 71-73; R Wacton Magna w Parva 71-73; R Stratton St Mary w Stratton St Michael etc 73-91; RD Depwade 81-91; Hon Can Nor Cathl 90-91; V Battle *Chich* from 91; Dean Battle from 91. *The Deanery, Mount Street, Battle, E Sussex TN33 0JY* Battle (01424) 772693

CUMMINS, Ashley Wighton. b 56. St Andr Univ BD83. Coates Hall Edin DipMin84. **d** 84 **p** 85. C Broughty Ferry *Bre* 84-87; P-in-c Dundee St Ninian 87-92; P-in-c Invergowrie from 92; Chapl Angl Students Dundee Univ from 92. *27 Errol Road, Invergowrie, Dundee DD2 5AG* Dundee (01382) 562525

CUMMINS, James Ernest. b 32. Westcott Ho Cam 57. **d** 60 **p** 61. C Baswich (or Berkswich) *Lich* 60-64; V Hales w Heckingham *Nor* 64-70; V Raveningham 70-76; Perm to Offic *Heref* from 76. *Skyborry, Knighton, Powys LD7 1TW* Knighton (01547) 528369

CUMMINS, Canon Nicholas Marshall. b 36. CITC. **d** 67 **p** 68. C Ballymena *Conn* 67-70; C Belf St Nic 70-73; I Buttevant Union *C, C & R* 73-78; I Mallow Union 78-83; I Kilmoe Union from 83; Preb Cork Cathl from 90; Treas Cork Cathl from 95; Preb Tymothan St Patr Cathl Dub from 95. *Altar Rectory, Toormore, Goleen, Co Cork, Irish Republic* Skibbereen (28) 28249

CUMMINS, William Frederick. b 17. St Pet Hall Ox BA39 DipTh40 MA44. Wycliffe Hall Ox 39. **d** 41 **p** 42. Chapl R Gr Sch Worc 67-75; P-in-c Peopleton *Worc* 70-75; R 75-78; P-in-c White Ladies Aston w Spetchley and Churchill 76-78; R Peopleton and White Ladies Aston etc 78-83; rtd 83; Perm to Offic *Birm* from 84; Perm to Offic *Cov* from 86. *27 The Birches, Bulkington, Nuneaton, Warks CV12 9PW* Nuneaton (01203) 317830

CUMPSTY, Prof John Sutherland. b 31. Barrister-at-Law (Middle Temple) K Coll Dur BSc53 PhD56 St Jo Coll Dur DipTh60 Carnegie-Mellon Univ MSc58. Cranmer Hall Dur 58. **d** 60 **p** 61. C Normanton *Wakef* 60-62; Tutor St Jo Coll Dur 62-66; Lect Glas Univ 66-69; S Africa from 70; Prof Relig Studies Cape Town Univ from 70. *Department of Religious Studies, University of Cape Town, Rondebosch, 7700 South Africa* Cape Town (21) 650-3455

CUNDIFF, Mrs Margaret Joan. b 32. Man Univ DMS60. St Mich Ho Ox 51. **dss** 77 **d** 87 **p** 94. Broadcasting Officer *York* from 75; Angl Adv Yorkshire TV 79-90; Selby St Jas *York* 77-87; Par Dn from 87; NSM Wistow from 87. *32 Oaklands, Camblesforth, Selby, N Yorkshire YO8 8HH* Selby (01757) 618148

✠**CUNDY, Rt Rev Ian Patrick Martyn.** b 45. Trin Coll Cam BA67 MA71. Tyndale Hall Bris 67. **d** 69 **p** 70 **c** 92. C New Malden and Coombe *S'wark* 69-73; Lect Oak Hill Th Coll 73-77; TR Mortlake w E Sheen *S'wark* 78-83; Warden Cranmer Hall Dur 83-92; Area Bp Lewes *Chich* from 92. *Beacon House, Berwick, Polegate, E Sussex BN26 6ST* Alfriston (01323) 870387 Fax 870967

CUNLIFFE, Christopher John. b 55. Ch Ch Ox BA77 MA81 DPhil81 Trin Coll Cam BA82 MA86. Westcott Ho Cam 80. **d** 83 **p** 84. C Chesterfield All SS *Derby* 83-85; Chapl Linc Coll Ox 85-89; Chapl Guildhall Sch of Music & Drama 89-91; Chapl City Univ *Lon* 89-91; Voc Officer and Selection Sec ABM from 91; Perm to Offic *S'wark* from 91. *St Paul's Vicarage, Rectory Grove, London SW4 0DX* 0171-627 3315 or 222 9011 Fax 799 2714

CUNLIFFE, Gerald Thomas. b 35. Linc Th Coll 74. **d** 76 **p** 77. C Sidcup St Jo *Roch* 76-80; C Pembury 80-82; V Lamorbey H Redeemer 82-89; V Riverhead w Dunton Green from 89. *The Vicarage, Riverhead, Sevenoaks, Kent TN13 3BS* Sevenoaks (01732) 455736

CUNLIFFE, Harold. b 28. St Aid Birkenhead 57. **d** 60 **p** 61. R Golborne *Liv* 70-93; rtd 93. *51 Greenfields Crescent, Ashton-in-Makerfield, Wigan, Lancs WN4 8QY* Ashton-in-Makerfield (01942) 274021

CUNLIFFE, Ms Helen Margaret. b 54. St Hilda's Coll Ox BA77 MA78. Westcott Ho Cam 81. **dss** 83 **d** 87 **p** 94. Chesterfield All SS *Derby* 83-85; Ox St Mary V w St Cross and St Pet *Ox* 86-87; Par Dn 87-89; Chapl Nuff Coll Ox 86-89; TV Clapham TM *S'wark* from 89. *St Paul's Vicarage, Rectory Grove, London SW4 0DX* 0171-622 2128

CUNLIFFE, Peter Henry. b 54. SRN77 RSCN79 RCN83 Univ of Wales MA93 Lon Univ DN84. Trin Coll Bris DipHE94. **d** 94 **p** 95. C Carshalton Beeches *S'wark* from 94. *91 Stanley Park Road, Carshalton, Surrey SM5 3HX* 0181-401 6327

CUNNINGHAM, Arthur. b 48. Lon Bible Coll MA89. Inst of Chr Tr Dallas DipMin79 Oak Hill Th Coll DipHE87 BA88 N Ord Course 92. **d** 93 **p** 94. C Walkden Moor *Man* 93; C Walkden Moor St Paul w Lt Hulton St Jo the Bapt from 93; Chapl Salford Coll from 93. *37 Park Road, Worsley, Manchester M28 5DU* 0161-799 1412

CUNNINGHAM, Brian James. b 65. York Univ BA88. Ripon Coll Cuddesdon BA91. **d** 92 **p** 93. C Merrow *Guildf* from 92. *2 Spring Cottage, Merrow Street, Guildford, Surrey GU4 7AW* Guildford (01483) 34365

CUNNINGHAM, Philip John. b 52. St Jo Coll Dur BA74 PGCE75 MA85. N Ord Course 93. **d** 95. NSM York St Luke *York* from 95. *9 Upper Newborough Street, York YO3 7AN* York (01904) 647657

CUNNINGHAM, Canon Robert Stewart. b 16. d 59 p 60. I Portglenone *Conn* 63-74; I Belf Whiterock 74-83; I Sallaghy *Clogh* 83-86; I Monaghan w Tydavnet and Kilmore 86-91; Can Clogh Cathl 88-89; Preb Clogh Cathl from 89; rtd 91. *Flat 3, 16 Cathedral Close, Armagh BT61 7EE*   Armagh (01861) 527868

CUNNINGTON, Andrew Thomas. b 56. Southn Univ BTh86. Sarum & Wells Th Coll 82. d 85 p 86. C Ifield *Chich* 85-89; TV Haywards Heath St Wilfrid 89-94; V Midhurst from 94; R Woolbeding from 94. *The Vicarage, June Lane, Midhurst, W Sussex GU29 9EW*   Midhurst (01730) 813339

CUNNINGTON, Miss Avril. b 41. St Mary's Cheltenham CertEd61 Man Univ BA68 MEd73. N Ord Course 93. d 95. NSM Milnrow *Man* from 95. *Alston Londes, 629 Huddersfield Road, Lees, Oldham OL4 3PY*   0161-624 9614

CUNNINGTON, Edgar Alan. b 37. Oak Hill Th Coll 68. d 70 p 71. C Highbury Ch Ch *Lon* 70-73; P-in-c W Holl St Dav 73-76; V Martham *Nor* 76-83; V W Somerton 76-83; V Martham w Repps w Bastwick 83-84; RD Flegg (Gt Yarmouth) 84-87; TV Trunch from 89. *The Rectory, Knapton Road, Trunch, North Walsham, Norfolk NR28 0QE*   Mundesley (01263) 720420

CUNNINGTON, Howard James. b 56. Southn Univ BA77 St Jo Coll Dur PGCE78. Trin Coll Bris ADMT92. d 92 p 93. C Ex St Leon w H Trin *Ex* from 92. *27 Barnardo Road, Exeter EX2 4ND*   Exeter (01392) 77540

CUPITT, Don. b 34. Trin Hall Cam BA55 MA59. Westcott Ho Cam 57. d 59 p 60. C Salford St Phil w St Steph *Man* 59-62; Vice-Prin Westcott Ho Cam 62-66; Lic to Offic *Ely* 63-94; Dean Em Coll Cam 66-91; Asst Lect Div Cam Univ 68-73; Lect from 73. *Emmanuel College, Cambridge CB2 3AP* Cambridge (01223) 334200

CURD, Christine Veronica Letsom. b 51. Bris Univ BA. Oak Hill Th Coll 84 W Midl Min Tr Course 88. d 89 p 94. NSM Widecombe-in-the-Moor, Leusdon, Princetown etc *Ex* 89-93; Asst Chapl HM Pris Channings Wood from 92; NSM Bovey Tracey SS Pet, Paul and Thos w Hennock *Ex* from 94. *The Vicarage, Ilsington, Newton Abbot, Devon TQ13 9RW* Haytor (01364) 661245   Fax Ipplepen (01803) 813175

CURD, Clifford John Letsom. b 45. RNT Qu Eliz Coll Lon SRN. Oak Hill Th Coll 84. d 86 p 87. C Stone Ch Ch *Lich* 86-89; C Stone Ch Ch and Oulton 89; TV Widecombe-in-the-Moor, Leusdon, Princetown etc *Ex* 89-93; P-in-c Ilsington from 93. *The Vicarage, Ilsington, Newton Abbot, Devon TQ13 9RW* Haytor (01364) 661245

CURGENVEN, Peter. b 10. MBE45. CCC Cam BA33 MA36. Cuddesdon Coll 48. d 49 p 50. R Rotherfield *Chich* 70-79; RD E Grinstead 75-77; rtd 79; Perm to Offic *B & W* 91-93. *Tretawn, 2 Church Hill, Marnhull, Sturminster Newton, Dorset DT10 1PU*   Marnhull (01258) 820802

CURL, Roger William. b 50. BA BD DPhil. Oak Hill Th Coll. d 82 p 83. C Cromer *Nor* 82-86; C Sevenoaks St Nic *Roch* 86-88; V Fulham St Mary N End *Lon* from 88. *St Mary's Vicarage, 2 Edith Road, London W14 9BA*   0171-602 1996

CURNEW, Dr Brian Leslie. b 48. Qu Coll Ox BA69 DPhil77 MA77 DipTh78. Ripon Coll Cuddesdon 77. d 79 p 80. C Sandhurst *Ox* 79-82; Tutor St Steph Ho Ox 82-87; V Fishponds St Mary *Bris* 87-94; TR Ludlow, Ludford, Ashford Carbonell etc *Heref* from 94. *The Rectory, 4 College Street, Ludlow, Shropshire SY8 1AN*   Ludlow (01584) 874988

CURNOW, Terence Peter. b 37. Univ of Wales (Lamp) BA62 DipTh63. d 63 p 64. C Llanishen and Lisvane *Llan* 63-71; Youth Chapl 67-71; Asst Chapl K Coll Taunton 71-74; Chapl Taunton Sch Somerset 74-84; Ho Master from 84. *Fairwater, Taunton School, Taunton, Somerset TA2 6AD*   Taunton (01823) 275988

CURRAH, Michael Ewart. b 31. Down Coll Cam BA54 MA58. Sarum Th Coll 54. d 56 p 57. C Calne *Sarum* 56-60; V Southbroom 60-69; Perm to Offic 70-88; Hd Relig Studies Woodroffe Sch Lyme Regis 70-85; Perm to Offic *B & W* from 88. *123 South Road, Taunton, Somerset TA1 3ED*   Taunton (01823) 284057

CURRAN, Patrick Martin Stanley. b 56. Southn Univ BTh84. K Coll (NS) BA80 Chich Th Coll 80. d 84 p 85. C Heavitree w Ex St Paul *Ex* 84-87; Bp's Chapl to Students *Bradf* 87-93; Chapl Bonn w Cologne *Eur* from 93. *c/o The British Embassy, Friedrich-Ebert Allee 77, 53113 Bonn, Germany*   Bonn (228) 234061 or 384925

CURRELL, Miss Linda Anne. b 62. K Alfred's Coll Win BEd84. Trin Coll Bris BA92. d 92 p 94. Par Dn Tunbridge Wells St Mark *Roch* 92-94; C from 94. *18 Hargate Close, Tunbridge Wells, Kent TN2 5PA*   Tunbridge Wells (01892) 511015

CURRIE, Piers William Edward. b 13. MC44. BNC Ox BA35 MA62. E Anglian Minl Tr Course 79. d 80 p 81. Hon C Holt *Nor* 80-82; P-in-c Baconsthorpe and Hempstead 84-85; Perm to Offic 85-86; Hon C Blakeney w Cley, Wiveton, Glandford

etc 86-89; Hon C Nor St Mary in the Marsh from 90; Hon PV Nor Cathl from 94. *48 The Close, Norwich NR1 4EG* Norwich (01603) 764247

CURRIE, Stuart William. b 53. Hertf Coll Ox MA79 Fitzw Coll Cam BA85 CertEd. Westcott Ho Cam 82. d 85 p 86. C Whitley Ch Ch *Ox* 85-89; TV Banbury 89-94; V Barbourne *Worc* from 94. *St Stephen's Vicarage, 1 Beech Avenue, Worcester WR3 8PZ*   Worcester (01905) 452169

CURRIE, William George. b 08. Clifton Th Coll 38. d 41 p 42. V Lt Bedwyn *Sarum* 65-81; V Gt Bedwyn 65-81; V Savernake Forest 65-81; rtd 81. *The Old School House, Savernake, Marlborough, Wilts SN8 3BG*   Marlborough (01672) 870267

CURRIN, John. b 56. Keele Univ CertEd78 Birm Poly DipMathEd87. St Jo Coll Nottm DTS92 MA93. d 93 p 94. C Eastwood *S'well* from 93. *26 Coppice Drive, Eastwood, Nottingham NG16 3PL*   Langley Mill (01773) 712395

CURRY, Anthony Bruce. b 31. ARCO49 St Edm Hall Ox BA53 MA56. Wells Th Coll 53. d 55 p 56. R Penshurst *Roch* 61-75; Dir Music Kelly Coll Tavistock 75-85; Hon C Calstock *Truro* 75-85; R Brasted *Roch* 85-93; rtd 93. *L'Ecurie, Montceau-Echarnant, 21360 Bligny-Sur-Ouche, France*   France (33) 80 20 25 12

CURRY, Bruce. b 39. Dur Univ BA61. Wells Th Coll 61. d 63 p 64. C Shepton Mallet *B & W* 63-67; C Cheam *S'wark* 67-71; R W Walton *Ely* 71-78; V St Neots 78-94; RD St Neots from 90; P-in-c Everton w Tetworth from 94; P-in-c Abbotsley from 94; P-in-c Waresley from 94. *The Vicarage, Everton, Sandy, Beds SG19 3JY*   Sandy (01767) 691827

CURRY, David John. b 24. St Cath Coll Cam BA48 MA58 DipTh. Oak Hill Th Coll 73. d 74 p 75. C Watford *St Alb* 74-77; V Whitehall Park St Andr Hornsey Lane *Lon* 77-82; P-in-c Heydon w Lt Chishall *Chelmsf* 82; R Heydon w Gt and Lt Chishill 82-88; rtd 89. *3 St Mary's Cottages, Rectory Lane, Pulborough, W Sussex RH20 2AD*   Pulborough (01798) 873409

CURRY, Canon George Christopher. b 14. TCD BA42 MA55 Div Test. d 44 p 45. I Edenderry w Clanabogan *D & R* 64-86; Can Derry Cathl 79-86; rtd 86. *8 Rutherglen Park, Bangor, Co Down BT19 1DX*   Bangor (01247) 455970

CURRY, George Robert. b 51. JP90. Bede Coll Dur BA72. Cranmer Hall Dur DipTh74 Oak Hill Th Coll DPS76. d 76 p 77. C Denton Holme *Carl* 76-81; V Low Elswick *Newc* from 81. *St Stephen's Vicarage, Clumber Street, Newcastle upon Tyne NE4 7ST*   0191-273 4680

CURRY, James Sebastian. b 63. Hatf Coll Dur BA84. Ripon Coll Cuddesdon BTh93. d 93 p 94. C Four Oaks *Birm* from 93. *12 Clarence Gardens, Sutton Coldfield, W Midlands B74 4AP* 0121-308 6279

CURRY, Thomas Christopher (Tom). b 47. Sarum & Wells Th Coll 71. d 74 p 75. C Bradford-on-Avon *Sarum* 74-78; Asst Chapl Hurstpierpoint Coll Hassocks 78-82; P-in-c The Donheads *Sarum* from 82; RD Chalke 87-92. *The Rectory, Donhead St Andrew, Shaftesbury, Dorset SP7 9DZ*   Donhead (01747) 828370

CURSON, James Desmond. b 30. Keble Coll Ox BA54 MA60. St Steph Ho Ox 54. d 56 p 57. V Hockley *Chelmsf* 67-75; Chapl HM Borstal Bullwood Hall 68-75; V Treverbyn *Truro* 75-79; P-in-c Marazion 79-85; P-in-c St Hilary w Perranuthnoe 81-83; R 83-93; Perm to Offic *Nor* from 93; rtd 93. *Roslyn, 3 Kenwyn Close, Holt, Norfolk NR25 6RS*   Holt (01263) 712976

CURTIS, Bert. b 20. Lon Univ BCom42 BA46. Ripon Hall Ox. d 46 p 47. Perm to Offic *Carl* from 74. *Greystones, Embleton, Cockermouth, Cumbria CA13 9YP*   Bassenthwaite Lake (017687) 76503

CURTIS, Clement Ernest. b 09. Ch Coll Cam BA32 MA36. Ely Th Coll 32. d 33 p 35. V Gateshead St Chad Bensham *Dur* 61-74; rtd 74. *Park View Cottage, King's Arms Lane, Alston, Cumbria CA9 3JF*   Alston (01434) 381693

CURTIS, Colin. b 47. ALA69 Open Univ BA80. Local NSM Course 80 St Jo Coll Nottm CertCS91. d 93 p 94. Hon C Clarkston *Glas* from 93. *78 Auldhouse Road, Glasgow G43 1UR*   0141-632 8486

✠**CURTIS, Most Rev Ernest Edwin.** b 06. CBE76. ARCS27 Lon Univ BSc27. Wells Th Coll 32. d 33 p 34 c 66. C Waltham Cross *St Alb* 33-36; Mauritius 37-44; C Portsea St Mary *Portsm* 44-47; V Portsea All SS 47-55; Chapl Portsm R Hosp 47-55; C-in-c Portsea St Agatha 54-55; V Locks Heath *Portsm* 55-66; RD Alverstoke 64-66; Bp Mauritius 66-76; Abp Indian Ocean 72-76; rtd 76; Asst Bp Portsm from 76. *5 Elizabeth Gardens, Havenstreet, Ryde, Isle of Wight PO33 4DU*   Isle of Wight (01983) 883049

CURTIS, Frederick John. b 36. SS Coll Cam MA64. Ridley Hall Cam 77. d 79 p 80. C Chilvers Coton w Astley *Cov* 79-82; V Claverdon w Preston Bagot 82-87; V Allesley Park and Whoberley from 87. *St Christopher's Vicarage, 99 Buckingham Rise, Coventry CV5 9HF*   Coventry (01203) 672879

CURTIS

CURTIS, Canon Geoffrey John. b 35. Dur Univ BA57. Ripon Hall Ox 59. **d** 61 **p** 62. C Gosport Ch Ch *Portsm* 61-65; C Bedhampton 65-68; Producer Schs Broadcasting Dept BBC Lon 68-75; Dioc Communications Adv *Guildf* from 75; P-in-c Grayswood 75-91; Dir Grayswood Studio from 84; Hon Can Guildf Cathl from 87. *The Vicarage, Clammer Hill Road, Grayswood, Haslemere, Surrey GU27 2DZ* Haslemere (01428) 644208

CURTIS, Gerald Arthur. b 46. Lon Univ BA69. Sarum & Wells Th Coll 85. **d** 87 **p** 88. C Allington and Maidstone St Pet *Cant* 87-90; TV Gt Grimsby St Mary and St Jas *Linc* from 90. *4 Freshney Drive, Grimsby, S Humberside DN31 1TP* Grimsby (01472) 359332

CURTIS, Miss Jacqueline Elaine. b 60. Sarum & Wells Th Coll 87. **d** 90 **p** 94. Par Dn Bridport *Sarum* 90-94; C 94-95; TV Melbury from 95. *The Vicarage, Maiden Newton, Dorchester, Dorset DT2 0AT* Maiden Newton (01300) 320284

CURTIS, Mrs Jane Darwent. b 64. Leic Univ BA86. Linc Th Coll BTh93. **d** 93 **p** 94. Par Dn Oadby *Leic* 93-94; C from 94. *41 Cairnsford Road, Leicester LE2 6GG* Leicester (0116) 288 6097

CURTIS, John Durston. b 43. Lich Th Coll 65. **d** 68 **p** 69. C Coseley Ch Ch *Lich* 68-71; C Sedgley All SS 71-74; CF 74-79; P-in-c Newton Valence *Win* 79-82; P-in-c Selborne 79-82; R Newton Valence, Selborne and E Tisted w Colemore 82-87; R Marchwood from 87. *St John's Vicarage, Vicarage Road, Marchwood, Southampton SO4 4UZ* Southampton (01703) 861496

CURTIS, Layton Richard. b 61. Leic Univ BSc84 PGCE85. Linc Th Coll BTh93. **d** 93 **p** 94. C Knighton St Mary Magd *Leic* from 93. *41 Cairnsford Road, Leicester LE2 6GG* Leicester (0116) 288 6097

CURTIS, Peter Bernard. b 35. St Pet Hall Ox BA60 MA64. Westcott Ho Cam 60. **d** 62 **p** 63. C Warsop *S'well* 62-65; Chapl Dur Univ *Dur* 65-69; V Worle *B & W* 69-78; R Crewkerne w Wayford from 78. *The Rectory, Gouldsbrook Terrace, Crewkerne, Somerset TA18 7JA* Crewkerne (01460) 72047

CURTIS, Thomas John (Tom). b 32. Pemb Coll Ox BA55 MA59 Lon Univ BD58. Clifton Th Coll 55. **d** 58 **p** 59. Chile 61-71; R Saxmundham *St E* 71-77; V Cheltenham St Mark *Glouc* 77-84; TR 84-86; V Chipping Norton *Ox* 86-95; rtd 95. *Touchwood Cottage, Chapel Road, Saxstead, Woodbridge, Suffolk IP13 9QZ* Woodbridge (01728) 685719

CURTIS, Very Rev Wilfred Frank. b 23. AKC51. **d** 52 **p** 53. Lic to Offic *Ex* 55-74; Home Sec CMS 65-74; Provost Sheff 74-88; Hon Can N Maseno from 82; rtd 88; Perm to Offic *Ex* from 88; RD Okehampton 89-92. *Ashplant's Fingle Cottage, Church Gate, Drewsteignton, Exeter EX6 6QX* Drewsteignton (01647) 281253

CURTIS, Wilfrid Fitz-Harold. b 23. St Aug Coll Cant 47 Linc Th Coll 49. **d** 51 **p** 52. CF (TA) 58-90; V Filey *York* 67-90; rtd 90; P-in-c Hackness w Harwood Dale *York* from 91; Chapl St Cath Hospice Scarborough from 91. *23 Scholes Park Road, Scarborough, N Yorkshire YO12 6RE* Scarborough (01723) 366410

CURWEN, David. b 38. St Cath Coll Cam BA62. Cuddesdon Coll 62. **d** 64 **p** 65. C Orford St Andr *Liv* 64-67; Ind Chapl *Cant* 67-77 and 83-84; C S'wark Ch Ch *S'wark* 78-83; Ind Chapl 78-83 and 85-88; Dioc Soc Resp Adv *St E* 88-93; Dioc Adv for Continuing Minl Educn from 93. *41 Cuckfield Avenue, Ipswich IP3 8SA* Ipswich (01473) 727632

CURZEN, Prof Peter. b 31. MRCOG62 FRCOG70 Lon Univ BSc52 MB, BS55 MD66. Sarum & Wells Th Coll 93. **d** 94 **p** 95. NSM Bemerton *Sarum* from 94. *2 Bishop's Drive, Harnham Wood, Salisbury SP2 8NZ* Salisbury (01722) 412713

CUTCLIFFE, Neil Robert. b 50. NUU BA72 TCD BA72. **d** 75 **p** 76. C Belf St Mary *Conn* 75-78; C Lurgan Ch the Redeemer *D & D* 78-80; I Garrison w Slavin and Belleek *Clogh* 80-86; I Mossley *Conn* from 86. *558 Doagh Road, Mossley, Newtownabbey, Co Antrim BT36 6TA* Glengormley (01232) 832726

CUTHBERT, Frederick Norton. b 07. Worc Ord Coll 67. **d** 68 **p** 69. C Cov St Marg *Cov* 68-73; C Cov Caludon 73-79; rtd 79; Perm to Offic *Cov* from 79. *2 Harefield Road, Coventry CV2 4DF* Coventry (01203) 452248

CUTHBERT, Dr John. b 52. Edin Univ BSc76 PhD80. Coates Hall Edin BD92. **d** 92 **p** 93. Chapl St Mary's Cathl *Edin* from 92; C Edin St Mary from 92. *33 Manor Place, Edinburgh EH3 7EB* 0131-226 3389

CUTHBERT, John Hamilton. b 34. Univ of Wales (Lamp) BA59. Coll of Resurr Mirfield 59. **d** 61 **p** 62. C Cov St Pet *Cov* 61-64; Australia 64-69; C Willesden St Andr *Lon* 69-72; C Sheff Parson Cross St Cecilia *Sheff* 72-74; V Lavender Hill Ascension *S'wark* from 74. *The Ascension Clergy House, Pountney Road, London SW11 5TU* 0181-228 5584

CUTHBERTSON, Christopher Martin (Chris). b 48. K Coll Lon BD74 AKC74 CertEd75 MTh80. St Aug Coll Cant 75. **d** 76

p 77. C Whitstable All SS w St Pet *Cant* 76-79; Chapl Princess Marg R Free Sch Windsor 79-84; Perm to Offic *Win* from 84; Chapl Bp Wordsworth Sch Salisbury from 84. *14 Stephen Martin Gardens, Parsonage Park, Fordingbridge, Hants SP6 1RF* Fordingbridge (01425) 655865

CUTHBERTSON, John Dickon. b 19. Lon Univ BSc49. Oak Hill Th Coll 51. **d** 53 **p** 54. V Upper Holloway St Jo *Lon* 69-77; R Stanstead w Shimplingthorne and Alpheton *St E* 77-84; P-in-c Lawshall 80-84; rtd 84; Perm to Offic *Ox* from 84. *86 Evans Road, Eynsham, Witney, Oxon OX8 1QS* Oxford (01865) 880904

CUTHBERTSON, Raymond. b 52. AKC75. Coll of Resurr Mirfield 76. **d** 77 **p** 78. C Darlington St Mark w St Paul *Dur* 77-81; C Usworth 81-83; C Darlington St Cuth 83-86; V Shildon w Eldon from 86; RD Auckland from 94. *St John's Vicarage, Central Parade, Shildon, Co Durham DL4 1DW* Bishop Auckland (01388) 772122

CUTLER, Francis Bert. b 15. Kelham Th Coll 32. **d** 38 **p** 39. R Crowland *Linc* 64-80; rtd 80. *10 Waterford Court, Moorend Park Road, Cheltenham, Glos GL53 0LA* Cheltenham (01242) 255706

CUTLER, Nicholas (Nick). b 59. St Jo Coll Cam MA84. St Jo Coll Nottm DTS94. **d** 94 **p** 95. C Cam St Phil *Ely* from 94. *99 Brooks Road, Cambridge CB1 3HP* Cambridge (01233) 412749

CUTLER, Robert Francis. b 37. Lon Univ BSc57. Clifton Th Coll 62. **d** 64 **p** 65. C Peckham St Mary Magd *S'wark* 64-68; C Redhill H Trin 68-70; Travel Sec Inter-Coll Chr Fellowship of IVF 70-74; Hon C Selly Hill St Steph *Birm* 70-74; Partner Interserve Internat 74-93; Bangladesh 74-93; Internat Fellowship Evangelical Students 74-85; Bible Students Fellowship of Bangladesh 85-93; V Rochdale Deeplish St Luke *Man* from 94. *St Luke's Vicarage, 9 Deeplish Road, Rochdale, Lancs OL11 1NY* Rochdale (01706) 354628

CUTLER, Roger Charles. b 49. MInstPkg76. Coll of Resurr Mirfield 86. **d** 88 **p** 89. C Walney Is *Carl* 88-91; Chapl RN from 91; Perm to Offic *Glas* from 91; Hon C Challoch w Newton Stewart from 95. *Directorate Gen, RN Chapl Services, Room 203, Victory Building, HM Naval Base, Portsmouth PO1 3LS* Portsmouth (01705) 727903 Fax 727112

CUTT, Canon Samuel Robert. b 25. Selw Coll Cam BA50 MA54. Cuddesdon Coll 51. **d** 53 **p** 54. Tutor Chich Th Coll 65-71; PV Chich Cathl *Chich* 66-71; Min Can St Paul's Cathl *Lon* 71-79; Lect K Coll Lon 71-79; P in O 75-79; Can Res Wells Cathl *B & W* 79-93; Chan 79-85; Treas 85-93; Dir of Ords 79-86; Warden Community of St Denys Warminster 87-93; rtd 93. *9 Eastfield Grove, Peterborough PE1 4BB* Peterborough (01733) 345197

CUTTELL, Jeffrey Charles. b 59. Birm Univ BSc80 PhD83 Sheff Univ MA92. Trin Coll Bris DipHE86. **d** 87 **p** 88. C Normanton *Wakef* 87-91; V 91-95. *Address temp unknown*

CUTTER, John Douglas. b 31. Lon Univ BD61. Chich Th Coll 56. **d** 59 **p** 60. V Rocester *Lich* 65-73; V Shrewsbury St Giles 73-83; R Yoxall 83-91; Dean's V Lich Cathl 83-91; rtd 91. *Little Wykeham, 111 Teg Down Meads, Winchester SO22 5NN* Winchester (01962) 852203

CUTTING, Alastair Murray. b 60. Westhill Coll Birm BEd83. St Jo Coll Nottm LTh86 DPS87. **d** 87 **p** 88. C Woodlands *Sheff* 87-88; C Wadsley 89-91; C Uxbridge *Lon* from 91; Chapl to the Nave and Uxbridge Town Cen from 91. *84 Harefield Road, Uxbridge, Middx UB8 1PN* Uxbridge (01895) 254121 or 812193 Fax 812194

CUTTS, David. b 52. Van Mildert Coll Dur BSc73 Nottm Univ BA79. St Jo Coll Nottm BA77. **d** 80 **p** 81. C Ipswich St Matt *St E* 80-82; Bp's Dom Chapl 82-85; R Coddenham w Gosbeck and Hemingstone w Henley 85-94; RD Bosmere 92-94; V Ipswich St Marg from 94. *St Margaret's Vicarage, 32 Constable Road, Ipswich IP4 2UW* Ipswich (01473) 253906

CUTTS, Elizabeth Joan Gabrielle. See STRICKLAND, Mrs Elizabeth Joan Gabrielle

CUTTS, Nigel Leonard. b 57. Sheff Univ BA86 BTh. Linc Th Coll 83. **d** 87 **p** 88. C Old Brampton and Loundsley Green *Derby* 87-89; C Chesterfield All SS 89-91; V Morecambe St Barn *Blackb* from 91. *St Barnabas' Vicarage, 101 Regent Road, Morecambe, Lancs LA3 1AG* Morecambe (01524) 411283

✠**CUTTS, Rt Rev Richard Stanley.** b 19. AKC47. Coll of Resurr Mirfield 47. **d** 51 **p** 52 **c** 75. C Godalming *Guildf* 51-56; S Africa 56-71; Adn Kuruman 69-71; Rhodesia 71-75; Dean Salisbury 71-75; Bp Argentina and Uruguay 75-89; rtd 90; Asst Bp Linc from 90; NSM S Lafford from 90. *37 King Street, West Deeping, Peterborough PE6 9HP* Market Deeping (01778) 342831

CYSTER, Canon Raymond Frederick. b 13. CCC Ox BA35 MA40. Wycliffe Hall Ox 40. **d** 42 **p** 43. R Fenny Compton and Wormleighton *Cov* 64-76; Hon Can Cov Cathl 74-80; P-in-c Hampton Lucy w Charlecote 76-79; R Hampton Lucy w

168

Charlecote and Loxley 79-80; rtd 80; Perm to Offic *Cov* from 80. *47 Cherry Orchard, Stratford-upon-Avon, Warks CV37 9AP* Stratford-upon-Avon (01789) 295012

CZERNIAWSKA EDGECUMBE, Mrs Irena Christine. b 59. Trin Coll Ox BA82. Oak Hill Th Coll 93. **d** 95. NSM De Beauvoir Town St Pet *Lon* from 95. *24 Calabria Road, London N5 1JA* 0171-359 7526

D

DABBS, Roger Stevens. b 09. Bp Wilson Coll 29. **d** 32 **p** 33. R Jersey Grouville *Win* 53-74; rtd 74; Perm to Offic *Ex* from 74. *Flat 21, Bedford Park, Pearn Road, Plymouth PL3 5JF* Plymouth (01752) 774677

DABORN, Robert Francis. b 53. Keble Coll Ox BA74 MA78 Fitzw Coll Cam BA77. Ridley Hall Cam 75. **d** 78 **p** 79. C Mortlake w E Sheen *S'wark* 78-81; Chapl Collingwood and Grey Coll Dur 82-86; V Lapley w Wheaton Aston *Lich* 86-91; P-in-c Blymhill w Weston-under-Lizard 89-91; P-in-c Tibberton w Bolas Magna and Waters Upton from 91; Shropshire Local Min Adv from 91; P-in-c Childs Ercall 92-95; P-in-c Stoke upon Tern 92-95. *The Rectory, Tibberton, Newport, Shropshire TF10 8NN* Sambrook (01952) 550409

DACK, Miss Margaret Patricia. b 39. Offley Teacher Tr Coll TCert61. All Nations Chr Coll CDRS82 Oak Hill NSM Course 91. **d** 93 **p** 94. NSM Letchworth St Paul w Willian *St Alb* from 93. *91 Penn Way, Letchworth, Herts SG6 2SH* Letchworth (01462) 685168

DACK, Paul Marven. K Coll Lon AKC51 BD51. St Boniface Warminster. **d** 52 **p** 53. R Quedgeley *Glouc* 61-82; P-in-c Hasfield w Tirley and Ashleworth 82-90; rtd 90. *19 Arle Gardens, Cheltenham, Glos GL51 8HP* Cheltenham (01242) 261627

DACRE, Roy Aubrey. b 17. AKC41 Lon Univ BD41. Linc Th Coll 41. **d** 41 **p** 42. Lic to Offic *Sheff* 66-74; rtd 82; Perm to Offic *Chich* from 83. *27 The Lawns, Sompting, Lancing, W Sussex BN15 0DT* Lancing (01903) 754840

DADD, Alan Edward. b 50. St Jo Coll Nottm 77. **d** 78 **p** 79. C Bishopsworth *Bris* 78-81; V Springfield *Birm* 81-85; Chapl Poly Cen Lon 85-86; V Tottenham St Ann 86-93; rtd 93. *11 Eaton Close, Bristol BS16 3XL*

DADD, Canon Peter Wallace. b 38. Sheff Univ BA59. Qu Coll Birm 59. **d** 61 **p** 62. C Grays Thurrock *Chelmsf* 61-65; C Grantham St Wulfram *Linc* 65-70; C Grantham w Manthorpe 70-72; TV 72-73; V Haxey 73-90; RD Is of Axholme 82-90; V Gainsborough All SS from 90; Can and Preb Linc Cathl from 91. *All Saints' Vicarage, 32 Morton Terrace, Gainsborough, Lincs DN21 2RQ* Gainsborough (01427) 612965

DADSON, Lawrence Michael (Mike). b 29. G&C Coll Cam MA56 Lon Univ BSc(Econ)64. St Deiniol's Hawarden 80. **d** 92 **p** 92. NSM Bramhall *Ches* from 92. *14 Yew Tree Park Road, Cheadle Hulme, Cheadle, Cheshire SK8 7EP* 0161-485 2482

DADSON, Stephen Michael. b 57. BA. Cuddesdon Coll. **d** 84 **p** 85. C Wednesfield *Lich* 84-87; Lic to Offic *Ox* 88-91; Chapl Asst John Radcliffe Hosp Ox 88-91; Chapl Asst Radcliffe Infirmary Ox 88-91. *Laurel Cottage, Wareham, Dorset BH20 7AB* Wareham (01929) 556786

DADSWELL, David Ian. b 58. New Coll Ox BA80 MA83. Westcott Ho Cam 80. **d** 83 **p** 84. C W Derby St Mary *Liv* 83-87; Chapl Brunel Univ *Lon* from 87. *26 Church Road, Cowley, Uxbridge, Middx UB8 3NA* Uxbridge (01895) 238815 or 203308

DAFFERN, Adrian Mark. b 68. St Jo Coll Dur BA89. St Steph Ho Ox 90. **d** 92 **p** 93. C Lich St Chad *Lich* from 92. *38 St Chad's Road, Lichfield, Staffs WS13 7ND* Lichfield (01543) 251009

DAFFURN, Lionel William. b 19. DFC43. AKC49. **d** 50 **p** 51. R Brampton St Thos *Derby* 57-74; P-in-c Hindon w Chicklade w Pertwood *Sarum* 74-76; R E Knoyle, Hindon w Chicklade and Pertwood 76-84; rtd 84; Perm to Offic *Cov* from 84. *Bankside, Quineys Road, Stratford-upon-Avon, Warks CV37 9BW* Stratford-upon-Avon (01789) 292703

DAGGER, John Henry Kynaston. b 07. Selw Coll Cam BA31 MA35. Cuddesdon Coll. **d** 32 **p** 34. R Sutton w Bignor *Chich* 61-77; R Barlavington 62-77; rtd 77; Perm to Offic *Win* from 78. *Greenways, Copthorne Lane, Fawley, Southampton SO4 1DP* Fawley (01703) 891582

DAGGER, Kenneth (Ken). b 46. Bernard Gilpin Soc Dur 72 Cranmer Hall Dur 73. **d** 76 **p** 77. C Blackb St Jas *Blackb* 76-79; C Colne St Bart 79-81; R Hesketh w Becconsall 81-85;

Deputation Appeals Org Children's Soc 85-89; C Lowton St Mary *Liv* 89-91; C Rainhill 91-94; TV Maghull from 94. *St James Vicarage, 23 Green Link, Maghull, Liverpool L31 8DW* 0151-526 6626

DAGGETT, Michael Wayne. b 47. Portland State Univ BSc72. Ridley Hall Cam 84. **d** 86 **p** 87. C Tyldesley w Shakerley *Man* 86-90; V Swinton H Rood from 90. *Holy Rood Vicarage, 33 Moorside Road, Swinton, Manchester M27 3EL* 0161-794 2464

DAGLEISH, John. b 38. ACIB74 MBAC85 Lon Univ DipRS78. S'wark Ord Course 75. **d** 78 **p** 79. NSM Riddlesdown *S'wark* from 78; NSM All Hallows by the Tower etc *Lon* 79-89; Chapl Asst Guy's Hosp Lon 87-89. *42 Brancaster Lane, Purley, Surrey CR8 1HF* 0181-660 6060

DAGLISH, John Davis. b 44. RMCS BSc70. Cranmer Hall Dur 76. **d** 77 **p** 78. C Ormesby *York* 77-79; C Kirk Ella 79-82; V Hull St Cuth from 82. *St Cuthbert's Vicarage, 112 Marlborough Avenue, Hull HU5 3JX* Hull (01482) 42848

DAGNALL, Bernard. b 44. CChem MRSC K Coll Lon BSc65 AKC65 Ox Univ BA75 MA78. St Steph Ho Ox 72. **d** 75 **p** 76. C Stanningley St Thos *Ripon* 75-76; C Lightbowne *Man* 76-78; P-in-c Grahame Park St Aug CD *Lon* 78-84; V Earley St Nic *Ox* 84-91; Ind Chapl 85-91; TR N Huddersfield *Wakef* 91-93; TV Newbury *Ox* from 93. *The Vicarage, 1 Chesterfield Road, Newbury, Berks RG14 7QA* Newbury (01635) 40387

DAILEY, Arthur John Hugh. b 25. Lon Univ BScEng45. Clifton Th Coll 63. **d** 65 **p** 66. C Wandsworth All SS *S'wark* 65-70; V Frogmore H Trin *St Alb* 70-81; RD Aldenham 75-79; C St Alb St Paul 82-90; Perm to Offic *St Alb* from 90. *24 Clifton Street, St Albans, Herts AL1 3RY* St Albans (01727) 850639

DAILEY, Douglas Grant. b 56. Nottm Univ BTh88. Linc Th Coll 85. **d** 88 **p** 89. C Leominster *Heref* 88-91; USA from 91. *Address temp unknown*

DAIMOND, John Ellerbeck. b 39. Dur Univ BA61. Ripon Hall Ox 61. **d** 63 **p** 64. C Caverswall *Lich* 63-66; Chapl RAF 66-85; Asst Chapl-in-Chief RAF 85-91; QHC 89-91; V Shawbury *Lich* from 91; V Stanton on Hine Heath from 91; R Moreton Corbet from 91. *The Vicarage, Shawbury, Shrewsbury, Shropshire SY4 4NH* Shawbury (01939) 250419

✠**DAIN, Rt Rev Arthur John.** b 12. OBE79. Ridley Hall Cam 59. **d** 59 **p** 59 **c** 65. Australia 59-82; Asst Bp Sydney 65-82; rtd 82; Perm to Offic *Chich* 87-90. *14 Kipling Court, Winnals Park, Haywards Heath, W Sussex RH16 1EX* Haywards Heath (01444) 453091

DAIN, Frederick Ronald. OBE80. Jes Coll Ox BA31 MA43. St Aug Coll Cant 61. **d** 62 **p** 64. Kenya 62-80; Perm to Offic *St Alb* from 80. *2 Eastbury Court, Lemsford Road, St Albans, Herts AL1 3PS* St Albans (01727) 863923

DAINTREE, Geoffrey Thomas. b 54. Bris Univ BSc77. Trin Coll Bris 78. **d** 81 **p** 82. C Old Hill H Trin *Worc* 81-85; C Tunbridge Wells St Jo *Roch* 85-89; V Framfield *Chich* from 89. *The Vicarage, Framfield, Uckfield, E Sussex TN22 5NH* Framfield (01825) 890365

DAINTY, James Ernest (Jim). b 46. Open Univ BA86 Lon Bible Coll DipTh68 ALBC68. Cranmer Hall Dur 71. **d** 73 **p** 74. C Normanton *Wakef* 73-76; C Gillingham St Mark *Roch* 76-78; V Barnsley St Geo *Wakef* 78-88; Chapl Barnsley Distr Gen Hosp 78-88; Chapl Seacroft Hosp Leeds 88-94; Chapl Killingbeck and Meanwood Park Hosps Leeds 88-94; P-in-c Turnham Green Ch Ch *Lon* from 94. *The Vicarage, 2 Wellesey Road, London W4 4BL* 0181-994 1617

DAKIN (nee HOLLETT), Mrs Catherine Elaine (Cathy). b 53. Qu Eliz Coll Lon BSc74 DipTh90. St Jo Coll Nottm 88. **d** 90. Par Dn Horley *S'wark* 90-93; NSM Heydon, Gt and Lt Chishill, Chrishall etc *Chelmsf* from 93. *The Vicarage, Bury Lane, Elmdon, Saffron Walden, Essex CB11 4NQ* Royston (01763) 838893

DAKIN, Canon John Edward Clifford. b 10. AKC40. **d** 40 **p** 41. R Thrapston *Pet* 57-78; Can Pet Cathl 71-78; rtd 78; Lic to Offic *Pet* 78-85; Perm to Offic from 85. *8 Derling Drive, Raunds, Wellingborough, Northants NN9 6LF* Wellingborough (01933) 623069

DAKIN, Peter David. b 57. Wye Coll Lon BSc79. St Jo Coll Nottm DTS91. **d** 91 **p** 92. NSM Southgate *Chich* 91-93; C Heydon, Gt and Lt Chishill, Chrishall etc *Chelmsf* from 93. *The Vicarage, Bury Lane, Elmdon, Saffron Walden, Essex CB11 4NQ* Roydon (01763) 838893

DAKIN, Reginald James Blanchard. b 25. S'wark Ord Course 66. **d** 70 **p** 71. C Preston Ascension *Lon* 70-74; C Greenhill St Jo 74-76; P-in-c Littleton 76-80; R 80-95; CF (ACF) 78-95; Warden for Readers (Kensington Episc Area) 88-95; rtd 95. *22 Heywood Avenue, Diss, Norfolk IP22 3DN* Diss (01379) 641167

DAKIN, Canon Stanley Frederick. b 30. Roch Th Coll 63. **d** 65 **p** 66. C Meole Brace *Lich* 65-68; V 68-72; R Sutton 68-72; Kenya 72-75; P-in-c Nettlebed *Ox* 75-81; V Bix w Pishill 77-81; P-in-c Highmore 78-81; R Nettlebed w Bix and Highmore 81; V Ealing Dean St Jo *Lon* 81-84; P-in-c Ealing St

Jas 81-84; V W Ealing St Jo w St Jas 84-92; Hon Can Mombasa from 89; CA from 92. *c/o Church Army, Independents Road, London SE3 9LG* 0181-318 1226

DALAIS, Duncan John. b 56. St Paul's Grahamstown. **d** 83 **p** 84. S Africa 83-87; C Chingford SS Pet and Paul *Chelmsf* 87-92; V Aldersbrook from 92. *St Gabriel's Vicarage, 12 Aldersbrook Road, London E12 5HH* 0181-989 0315

DALBY, John. b 43. Cuddesdon Coll 72. **d** 74 **p** 75. C Baildon *Bradf* 74-78; P-in-c Austwick 78-85; P-in-c Clapham 84-85; V Clapham-with-Keasden and Austwick from 85. *The Vicarage, Austwick, Lancaster LA2 8BE* Clapham (015242) 51313

DALBY, Ven Dr John Mark Meredith. b 38. Ex Coll Ox BA61 MA65 Nottm Univ PhD77. Ripon Hall Ox 61. **d** 63 **p** 64. C Hambleden *Ox* 63-68; C Medmenham 66-68; V Birm St Pet *Birm* 68-75; RD Birm City 73-75; Hon C Tottenham All Hallows *Lon* 75-80; Selection Sec and Sec Cttee for Th Educn ACCM 75-80; V Worsley *Man* 80-84; TR 84-91; AD Eccles 87-91; Adn Rochdale from 91. *21 Belmont Way, Rochdale, Lancs OL12 6HR* Rochdale (01706) 48640 Fax as telephone

DALE, Miss Barbara. b 48. Cranmer Hall Dur 78. **dss** 81 **d** 87 **p** 94. N Wingfield, Pilsley and Tupton *Derby* 81-87; Par Dn 87-90; Par Dn N Wingfield, Clay Cross and Pilsley 90-94; TD 94; TV from 94. *The Vicarage, Ankerbold Road, Tupton, Chesterfield, Derbyshire S42 6BX* Chesterfield (01246) 864524

DALE, Ms Christine. b 62. Ox Poly DipCart82. Trin Coll Bris BA94. **d** 94 **p** 95. C Thatcham *Ox* from 94. *28 Masefield Road, Newbury, Berks RG13 4AS* Newbury (01635) 872004

DALE, David William. b 35. Open Univ BA74 MPhil87 Heref Coll of FE CertEd78. Wells Th Coll 61. **d** 63 **p** 64. C Weybridge *Guildf* 63-66; C Farnham 67-69; P-in-c Downton w Burrington and Aston and Elton *Heref* 69-76; P-in-c Brampton Bryan w Lingen 69-76; V Leintwardine 69-76; P-in-c Wigmore w Leinthall Starkes 72-76; V Heref H Trin 76-81; Chapl Shiplake Coll Henley 81-91; Lic to Offic *Ox* 85-92; Chapl Reading Sch 91-92; P-in-c Ryde All SS *Portsm* from 92. *3 Coniston Drive, Ryde, Isle of Wight PO33 3AE* Isle of Wight (01983) 611749

DALE, Eric Stephen. b 24. Roch Th Coll 63. **d** 65 **p** 66. V Askham Bryan *York* 69-70; V Askham Richard 69-70; V Askham Bryan w Askham Richard 70-78; Chapl HM Pris Askham Grange 69-78; Chapl HM Pris Wakef 78-79; Chapl HM Pris Gartree 79-82; Chapl HM Pris Leeds 82-89; rtd 89. *31 Kirkwood Lane, Leeds LS16 7EN* Leeds (0113) 230 0766

DALE, Miss Olive Sylvia. b 44. Stockwell Coll of Educn TCert66. Faculte de Theologie Evangelique Vaux-sur-Seine France MScRel76 W of England Minl Tr Course 91. **d** 94. C Highley *Heref* from 94. *43 Yew Tree Grove, Highley, Bridgnorth, Shropshire WV16 6DG* Bridgnorth (01746) 861218

DALES, Douglas John. b 52. FRHistS90 Ch Ch Ox BA74 MA78 BD89. Cuddesdon Coll 74. **d** 77 **p** 78. C Shepperton *Lon* 77-81; C Ely 81-83; Chapl Marlborough Coll Wilts from 84; Hd of RE from 84. *Hillside, Bath Road, Marlborough, Wilts SN8 1NN* Marlborough (01672) 514557 or 515511

DALEY, David Michael. b 50. Oak Hill Th Coll BA90. **d** 92 **p** 92. C Enfield Ch Ch Trent Park *Lon* 92-94; V Chitts Hill St Cuth from 94. *St Cuthbert's Vicarage, 85 Wolves Lane, London N22 5JD* 0181-888 6178

DALEY, Victor Leonard. b 38. Chich Th Coll 76. **d** 78 **p** 79. C Durrington *Chich* 78-81; C Somerton w Compton Dundon, the Charltons etc *B & W* 81-87; P-in-c Cheddar 87-88; V from 88; RD Axbridge from 91. *The Vicarage, Church Street, Cheddar, Somerset BS27 3RF* Cheddar (01934) 742535

DALL, Kathleen Ria Agnes. b 32. St Andr Univ MA54 Edin Univ DipEd57 HDipRE57. **dss** 82 **d** 86 **p** 94. NSM Dundee St Paul *Bre* 82-89; D-in-c Muchalls 89-94; P-in-c from 94. *St Ternan's Rectory, Muchalls, Stonehaven, Kincardineshire AB3 2PP* Stonehaven (01569) 730625

DALLAWAY, Philip Alan. b 48. Chich Th Coll 80. **d** 81 **p** 82. C Newbury *Ox* 81-83; C Newport Pagnell w Lathbury 83-85; C Newport Pagnell w Lathbury and Moulsoe 85; V Stewkley w Soulbury and Drayton Parslow 85-92; P-in-c Didcot All SS from 92. *The Rectory, 140 Lydalls Road, Didcot, Oxon OX11 7EA* Didcot (01235) 813244

DALLING, Antony Fraser. b 26. Magd Coll Cam MA50. Westcott Ho Cam 64. **d** 65 **p** 66. C Ipswich St Mary le Tower *St E* 65-67; C Hemel Hempstead *St Alb* 67-70; Ind Chapl 70-76; Hon C Bexley St Jo *Roch* from 76; Ind Chapl from 76. *30 Maiden Erlegh Avenue, Bexley, Kent DA5 3PD* Crayford (01322) 529776

DALLING, Roger Charles. b 26. Lon Univ BSc53 DChemEng55. S Dios Minl Tr Scheme 79. **d** 83 **p** 84. NSM Lewes St Jo sub Castro *Chich* 83-84; NSM Uckfield from 84; NSM Isfield from 84; NSM Lt Horsted from 84. *The Parsonage, Isfield, Uckfield, E Sussex TN22 5TX* Isfield (01825) 750439

DALLISTON, Christopher Charles. b 56. Ox Univ BA Cam Univ MA. St Steph Ho Ox 81. **d** 84 **p** 85. C Halstead St Andr w H Trin and Greenstead Green *Chelmsf* 84-87; Bp's Dom Chapl 87-91; V Forest Gate St Edm from 91. *St Edmund's House, 264 Plashet Grove, London E6 1DQ* 0181-552 1444

DALLY, Keith Richard. b 47. FCCA77. St Jo Coll Nottm 80. **d** 82 **p** 83. C Southend St Sav Westcliff *Chelmsf* 82-85; Ind Chapl 85-93; C Southend 85-86; TV 86-92; C Harold Hill St Geo 92-93. *Address temp unknown*

DALRIADA, Archdeacon of. *See* DUNCAN, Ven William Albert

DALTON, Anthony Isaac. b 57. Em Coll Cam BA78 MA82 Leeds Univ BA82. Coll of Resurr Mirfield. **d** 82 **p** 83. C Carl St Aid and Ch Ch *Carl* 82-86; C Caversham and Mapledurham *Ox* 86-88; P-in-c Accrington St Mary *Blackb* 88-91; V 91-92; Chapl Victoria Hosp Accrington 88-92; V Sheff Parson Cross St Cecilia *Sheff* from 92. *St Cecilia's Priory, 98 Chaucer Close, Sheffield S5 9QE* Sheffield (0114) 232 1084

DALTON, Canon Arthur Benjamin. b 07. Univ Coll Lon BA27 Ox Univ BA30 MA35. Ripon Hall Ox 27. **d** 30 **p** 31. V Forest Hill St Aug *S'wark* 49-75; Hon Can S'wark Cathl 71-75; rtd 75. *c/o Bickley Court, 36 Chislehurst Road, Bromley BR1 2NW* 0181-467 3918

DALTON, Bertram Jeremy (Tod). b 32. AIB64. Sarum & Wells Th Coll 81. **d** 83 **p** 84. C Ringwood *Win* 83-86; R Norton sub Hamdon, W Chinnock, Chiselborough etc *B & W* from 86. *The Rectory, Cat Street, Chiselborough, Stoke-sub-Hamdon, Somerset TA14 6TT* Chiselborough (01935) 881202

DALTON, Derek. b 40. N Ord Course. **d** 84 **p** 85. NSM Pool w Arthington *Ripon* 84-87; P-in-c Thornton Watlass w Thornton Steward 87-90; C Bedale 87-90; R Wensley 90-95; V W Witton 90-95; R Romaldkirk w Laithkirk from 95. *The Rectory, Romaldkirk, Barnard Castle, Co Durham DL12 9EE* Teesdale (01833) 650202

DALTON, Kevin. b 32. TCD BA65. Ch Div Sch of the Pacific (USA) BD67 CITC 66. **d** 66 **p** 67. C Stillorgan *D & G* 66-72; I Dub Drumcondra w N Strand 72-79; I Monkstown from 79. *62 Monkstown Road, Monkstown, Blackrock, Co Dublin, Irish Republic* Dublin (1) 280-6596

DALTON, Lawrence Richard. b 18. Qu Coll Birm 57. **d** 58 **p** 59. Chapl Antwerp Seafarers' Cen *Eur* 68-71; V Birstall *Wakef* 71-79; V Darrington w Wentbridge 79-84; rtd 84; Perm to Offic *Wakef* from 84. *31 Barnsley Road, Cawthorne, Barnsley, S Yorkshire S75 4HW* Barnsley (01226) 790696

DALTON, Ronald. b 20. St Deiniol's Hawarden 60. **d** 61 **p** 62. V Rillington *York* 64-73; V Scampston 64-73; rtd 73. *15 Ambrey Close, Hunmanby, Filey, N Yorkshire YO14 0LZ* Scarborough (01723) 890037

DALTRY, Paul Richard. b 56. Tottenham Coll of Tech DipEH79. St Jo Coll Nottm DCM92. **d** 92 **p** 93. C Ipswich St Matt *St E* from 92. *70 Orford Street, Ipswich IP1 3PE* Ipswich (01473) 210539

DALY, Jeffrey. b 50. Bris Univ BA73 Jes Coll Cam PGCE74 Fitzw Coll Cam BA82 MA86. Ridley Hall Cam 80. **d** 83 **p** 84. C Tilehurst St Mich *Ox* 83-89; P-in-c Steventon w Milton 89-92; Asst Chapl Sherborne Sch Dorset from 92. *Wharton, 30 Acreman Street, Sherborne, Dorset DT9 3NX* Sherborne (01935) 813039

DAMIAN, Brother. *See* KIRKPATRICK, Roger James

DAMMERS, Very Rev Alfred Hounsell. b 21. Pemb Coll Cam BA45 MA47. Westcott Ho Cam 46. **d** 48 **p** 49. Can Res Cov Cathl *Cov* 65-73; Dean Bris 73-87; rtd 87; Perm to Offic *Bris* from 87. *4 Bradley Avenue, Bristol BS11 9SL* Bristol (0117) 982 9121

DAMPIER, Robert Cecil Walter. b 19. Pemb Coll Cam BA40 MA47. Ely Th Coll 46. **d** 48 **p** 49. V Tettenhall Wood *Lich* 67-82; V Coven 82-90; rtd 90; Hon C Lapley w Wheaton Aston *Lich* from 90; Hon C Blymhill w Weston-under-Lizard from 90. *Blymhill Rectory, Shifnal, Shropshire TF11 8LL* Weston-under-Lizard (0195276) 273

DANA, Canon Edmund Francis Kinnaird (Eddie). b 15. ALCD40. **d** 40 **p** 41. R Northwood *Portsm* 63-80; Hon Can Portsm Cathl 77-80; V W Cowes H Trin 78-80; rtd 80; Perm to Offic *Portsm* from 82. *15 Littlestairs Road, Shanklin, Isle of Wight PO37 6HR* Isle of Wight (01983) 864153

DANCE, Peter Patrick. b 31. Em Coll Saskatoon 66. **d** 69 **p** 69. Canada 69-71; C Hednesford *Lich* 71-75; P-in-c Westcote Barton and Steeple Barton *Ox* 76-77; P-in-c Sandford St Martin 76-77; R Westcote Barton w Steeple Barton, Duns Tew etc 77-89; R Castle Douglas *Glas* from 89. *St Ninian's Rectory, 68 St Andrews Street, Castle Douglas, Kirkcudbrightshire DG7 1EN* Castle Douglas (01556) 3818

DAND, Robert William Scrymgour. b 17. Pemb Coll Ox BA MA45. Cuddesdon Coll. **d** 47 **p** 48. V Bracknell *Ox* 68-72; C Upton cum Chalvey 73-82; rtd 82; Perm to Offic *Cov* from 82. *11 Foxes Way, Warwick CV34 6AX* Warwick (01926) 490864

DANDO, Stephen. b 49. Golds Coll Lon TCert70. Coll of Resurr Mirfield 81. **d** 83 **p** 84. C Wandsworth St Anne *S'wark* 83-87; V Stainland *Wakef* from 87. *The Vicarage, 295 Stainland Road, Holywell Green, Halifax, W Yorkshire HX4 9EH*   Halifax (01422) 374767

DANES, Charles William. b 28. Chich Th Coll 54. **d** 56 **p** 57. V Hanworth All SS *Lon* 68-76; P-in-c Wick *Chich* 76-78; V Littlehampton St Jas 76-78; P-in-c Littlehampton St Mary 76-78; V W Worthing St Jo 78-87; Chapl Monte Carlo *Eur* 87-93; rtd 93. *31 Oakley Road, Braintree, Essex CM7 5QS*   Braintree (01376) 324586

DANGERFIELD, Andrew Keith. b 63. Univ of Wales (Ban) BD87. St Steph Ho Ox 87. **d** 89 **p** 90. C St Marychurch *Ex* 89-93; C-in-c Grahame Park St Aug CD *Lon* from 93. *St Augustine's House, Great Field, London NW9 5SY*   0181-205 1979

DANIEL, Alan Noel. b 09. AKC35. Ripon Hall Ox 35. **d** 36 **p** 37. V Dormansland *S'wark* 58-76; rtd 76; Perm to Offic *Chich* from 76. *31 Large Acres, Selsey, Chichester, W Sussex PO20 9BA*   Selsey (01243) 604566

DANIEL, Arthur Guy St John. b 12. K Coll Cam BA33 MA37. Cuddesdon Coll 34. **d** 35 **p** 36. V Colnbrook *Ox* 46-78; TV Riverside 78-80; rtd 80; Perm to Offic *Ox* 80-87. *2 Gervis Court, Penwerris Avenue, Osterley, Middx TW7 4QU*   0181-572 1848

DANIEL, Herrick Haynes. b 38. Open Univ BA81. Trin Coll Bris 73. **d** 75 **p** 76. C Harlesden St Mark *Lon* 75-78; C Livesey *Blackb* 78-81; V Blackb St Barn from 81. *St Barnabas' Vicarage, 20 Buncer Lane, Blackburn BB2 6SE*   Blackburn (01254) 56587

DANIEL, Isaac Thomas. b 11. Univ of Wales BA34. St D Coll Lamp 35. **d** 36 **p** 37. V Wolv St Chad *Lich* 55-76; rtd 76. *113 Brynian Road, West Shore, Llandudno, Gwynedd LL30 2DZ*   Llandudno (01492) 870487

DANIEL, Mrs Joy. b 44. Gilmore Course 81 Oak Hill Th Coll 82. **dss** 84 **d** 87 **p** 94. Luton St Fran *St Alb* 84-87; Par Dn 87-94; C from 94. *22 Rowelfield, Luton LU2 9HN*   Luton (01582) 35237

DANIEL, Michael George. b 23. Magd Coll Cam BA49 MA52 Lon Univ BSc64 MPhil67. Linc Th Coll 49. **d** 51 **p** 52. C Ches Square St Mich w St Phil *Lon* 61-64; Adv R Foundn of St Kath Stepney 64-66; rtd 66. *84 North Lane, Rustington, Littlehampton, W Sussex BN16 3PW*   Rustington (01903) 773837

DANIEL, Philip Sharman. b 62. Man Univ BA83 Rob Coll Cam CertEd84. Wycliffe Hall Ox 84. **d** 86 **p** 87. C Macclesfield Team Par *Ches* 86-89; C Cheadle 89-94; V Disley from 94. *Disley Vicarage, Red Lane, Disley, Stockport, Cheshire SK12 2NP*   Disley (01663) 762068

DANIEL, Rajinder Kumar. b 34. St Steph Coll Delhi 55 Westcott Ho Cam 61. **d** 63 **p** 64. C Purley St Barn *S'wark* 63-66; C Battersea St Pet 66-67; C N Harrow St Alb *Lon* 67-72; TV Beaconsfield *Ox* 72-75; V Smethwick St Matt w St Chad *Birm* 75-87; Dioc Adv on Black Min 87-92; Chapl Birm Gen Hosp 91-92; TR Braunstone *Leic* from 92. *The Rectory, Braunstone, Leicester LE3 3AL*   Leicester (0116) 289 3377

DANIELL, Robert. b 37. **d** 87 **p** 88. C Camberwell St Giles w St Matt *S'wark* 90-92; V Lewisham St Swithun from 92. *St Swithun's Vicarage, 191 Hither Green Lane, London SE13 6QE*   0181-852 5088

DANIELS, Alan Henry. b 14. Keble Coll Ox BA35 BSc39 MA39. Wycliffe Hall Ox 63. **d** 64 **p** 65. R Yarmouth *Portsm* 67-82; rtd 82; Perm to Offic *Portsm* from 82. *11 Queens Close, Freshwater, Isle of Wight PO40 9EU*   Isle of Wight (01983) 752681

DANIELS, Geoffrey Gregory. b 23. St Pet Coll Ox BA48 MA53. Lambeth STh60 Linc Th Coll 73. **d** 73 **p** 75. NSM Diss *Nor* 73-74; NSM Bexhill St Pet *Chich* 74-83; C Eastbourne St Andr 83-84; V Horam 84-88; rtd 88; Chapl Convent of Dudwell St Mary from 88; NSM Bexhill St Andr CD *Chich* from 90. *The Parsonage, 18 Woodville Road, Bexhill-on-Sea, E Sussex TN39 3EU*   Bexhill-on-Sea (01424) 215460

DANIELS, Hubert Frederick. b 05. Hon CF46 TD50. Richmond Th Coll 28 Qu Coll Birm 51. **d** 52 **p** 53. In Meth Ch 28-51; V Alfriston and Lullington *Chich* 66-85; rtd 85. *45 Clementine Avenue, Seaford, E Sussex BN25 2UU*   Seaford (01323) 898619

DANIELS, Dr John Wyn. b 60. Southn Univ BSc82 PhD87 Bris Univ MA92. Trin Coll Bris DipHE91. **d** 92 **p** 93. C Roundhay St Edm *Ripon* from 92. *1 Gledhow Grange View, Leeds LS8 1PH*   Leeds (0113) 266 8212

DANIELS, Kenneth Percival Thomas. b 17. AKC50. St Boniface Warminster 50. **d** 51 **p** 52. V Lamorbey H Redeemer *Roch* 58-75; V Kemsing w Woodlands 75-82; rtd 82; Perm to Offic *Roch* from 83. *Shepherd's Hey, 21 Priestley Drive, Tonbridge, Kent TN10 4RS*   Tonbridge (01732) 352677

DANIELS, Norman. b 38. Leeds Univ BA60. St Mich Coll Llan 71. **d** 73 **p** 74. C Pontnewynydd *Mon* 73-76; W Germany 76-82; Chapl Giggleswick Sch 82-93; P-in-c Keighley All SS *Bradf* from 93. *All Saints Vicarage, 21 View Road, Keighley, W Yorkshire BD20 6JN*   Keighley (01535) 607002

DANKS, Alan Adam. b 41. Edin Th Coll 61. **d** 64 **p** 65. C Dumfries *Glas* 64-67; C Earl's Court St Cuth w St Matthias *Lon* 68-71; C St Steph Walbrook and St Swithun etc 71-74; C Brookfield St Mary 75-76; C Hendon St Mary 76-85. *33 Park Road, London W4 3EY*   0181-994 3131

DANSIE, Bruce John. b 40. CEng72 Woolwich Poly BSc67 Univ Coll Lon MSc71. Linc Th Coll CMinlStuds92. **d** 92 **p** 93. C Ivybridge w Harford *Ex* from 92. *12 Buddle Close, Ivybridge, Devon PL21 0JU*   Plymouth (01752) 690797

DANSKIN, William Campbell. b 35. Edin Th Coll 78. **d** 80 **p** 81. C Largs *Glas* 80-81; C Gourock 80-81; P-in-c 81-84; P-in-c Pinmore 84-87; R Girvan 84-87; R Maybole 84-87; R Challoch w Newton Stewart 87-95. *Address temp unknown*

DANSON, Mrs Mary Agatha. MPS48 Strathclyde Univ PhC48. St Jo Coll Nottm 82. **d** 88 **p** 94. NSM Uddingston *Glas* from 88; NSM Cambuslang from 88. *3 Golf Road, Rutherglen, Glasgow G73 4JW*   0141-634 4330

DAPLYN, Timothy James (Tim). b 52. Ripon Coll Cuddesdon DipMin94. **d** 94 **p** 95. C Southmead *Bris* from 94. *79 Ullswater Road, Bristol BS10 6DP*   Bristol (0117) 959 3105

DARBY, Anthony Ernest. b 26. Linc Th Coll 74. **d** 76 **p** 77. C Chilvers Coton w Astley *Cov* 76-79; P-in-c Longford 79-81; V 81-84; V Cov St Mary 84-91; RD Cov S 88-91; rtd 91; Chapl Cov Cathl *Cov* from 91. *53 Ivybridge Road, Styvechale, Coventry CV3 5PF*   Coventry (01203) 414174

DARBY, Michael Barwick. b 34. St D Coll Lamp BA61 Tyndale Hall Bris 61. **d** 63 **p** 64. C Islington St Andr w St Thos and St Matthias *Lon* 63-66; C Ealing Dean St Jo 66-68; V Broomfleet *York* 68-73; Area Sec (Dios York and Sheff) CCCS 68-73; V Paddington Em Harrow Road *Lon* 73-78; Iran 78-79; Brazil 80-83; Perm to Offic *Cant* 80-84; V Maidstone St Faith 84-90; UAE 90-92; V Platt Bridge *Liv* from 93. *The Vicarage, Ridyard Street, Platt Bridge, Wigan, Lancs WN2 3TD*   Wigan (01942) 866269

DARBY, Nicholas Peter. b 50. Kent Univ BA82. Sarum & Wells Th Coll 71. **d** 74 **p** 75. C Walton-on-Thames *Guildf* 74-78; C Horsell 78-80; USA 82-84; Chapl Lon Univ *Lon* 84-89; Chapl R Lon Hosp (Whitechapel) 90-91; Perm to Offic *S'wark* 90-91; Perm to Offic *Lon* 90-91; V Kew St Phil and All SS w St Luke *S'wark* from 91. *St Philip's Vicarage, 70 Marksbury Avenue, Richmond, Surrey TW9 4JF*   0181-392 1425

DARBY, Philip William. b 44. Bede Coll Dur TCert66. Qu Coll Birm DipTh70. **d** 70 **p** 71. C Kidderminster St Geo *Worc* 70-74; P-in-c Dudley St Jo 74-79; V 79-80; P-in-c Catshill 80-82; V Catshill and Dodford 82-88; V Ipplepen w Torbryan *Ex* from 88; RD Ipplepen from 93. *The Vicarage, Paternoster Lane, Ipplepen, Newton Abbot, Devon TQ12 5RY*   Ipplepen (01803) 812215

DARBYSHIRE, Brian. b 48. Kent Univ DipTh81 BA83. Oak Hill Th Coll. **d** 83 **p** 84. C Enfield St Jas *Lon* 83-86; R Slaidburn *Bradf* 86-92; V Gt Harwood St Jo *Blackb* from 92. *St John's Vicarage, 42 Russell Place, Great Harwood, Blackburn BB6 7JP*   Great Harwood (01254) 886309

DARCH, John Henry. b 52. Univ of Wales (Lamp) BA73 Lon Univ CertEd74 MA77 DipHE82. Trin Coll Bris 80. **d** 82 **p** 83. C Meole Brace *Lich* 82-85; C Hoole *Ches* 85-88; V Hyde St Geo from 88; P-in-c Godley cum Newton Green 89-93; RD Mottram from 91. *The Vicarage, 85 Edna Street, Hyde, Cheshire SK14 1DR*   0161-367 8787

DARE, Charles Gilbert Francis. b 22. Dur Univ BA48. St Jo Coll Dur 46. **d** 48 **p** 49. V S Harrow St Paul *Lon* 60-74; V Ealing St Pet Mt Park 74-81; V Wisborough Green *Chich* 81-87; rtd 87; Perm to Offic *Chich* from 87. *39 Langdale Avenue, Oving, Chichester, W Sussex PO19 2JQ*   Chichester (01243) 782798

DARK, Ronald Henry Richard (Ron). b 31. Oak Hill Th Coll. **d** 85 **p** 86. NSM Fyfield *Chelmsf* 85-89; NSM Fyfield and Moreton w Bobbingworth 90-93; NSM Fyfield, Moreton w Bobbingworth & Willingale etc from 93. *74 Warescot Road, Brentwood, Essex CM15 9HE*   Brentwood (01277) 214797

DARLEY, Canon Shaun Arthur Neilson. b 36. Dur Univ BA61 DipTh63 Reading Univ MSc75. Cranmer Hall Dur 61. **d** 63 **p** 64. C Luton w E Hyde *St Alb* 63-67; Chapl Bris Tech Coll 67-69; Chapl Bris Poly *Bris* 69-92; Chapl Univ of the W of England, Bris from 92; Lect 69-75; Sen Lect from 75; Lic to Offic 67-69; Bp's Cathl Chapl from 69; Hon Can Bris Cathl from 89. *24 Downs Park East, Bristol BS6 7QD, or The Octagon, UWE, Coldharbour Lane, Bristol BS16 1QY*   Bristol (0117) 962 9219 or 965 6261   Fax 976 3964

✠**DARLING, Rt Rev Edward Flewett.** b 33. TCD BA55 MA58. **d** 56 **p** 57 **c** 85. C Belf St Luke *Conn* 56-59; C Orangefield *D & D* 59-62; C-in-c Carnalea 62-72; Chapl Ban Hosp 63-72; I Belf

Malone St Jo *Conn* 72-85; Min Can Belf Cathl 78-85; Chapl Ulster Independent Clinic 81-85; Bp L & K from 85. *Bishop's House, North Circular Road, Limerick, Irish Republic* Limerick (61) 451532   Fax as telephone

DARLING, John. b 47. CMBHI. Sarum & Wells Th Coll 76. **d** 79 **p** 80. NSM Trowbridge St Thos *Sarum* 79-82; NSM Trowbridge St Thos and W Ashton from 82. *24 Eastbourne Road, Trowbridge, Wilts BA14 7HN*   Trowbridge (01225) 762864

DARLINGTON, Preb David John. b 14. Oak Hill Th Coll 33. **d** 37 **p** 38. V Tollington Park St Mark w St Anne *Lon* 65-81; Preb St Paul's Cathl 79-81; rtd 81; Perm to Offic *St Alb* from 81; Perm to Offic *Lon* 84-91. *39 Grasmere Road, Luton LU3 2DT*   Luton (01582) 591547

DARLISON, Geoffrey Stuart. b 49. MRTPI80 Liv Poly DipTP74. St Jo Coll Nottm DCM91. **d** 91 **p** 92. C Horncastle w Low Toynton *Linc* 91-95; P-in-c Welton and Dunholme w Scothern from 95. *The Vicarage, Holmes Lane, Dunholme, Lincoln LN2 3QT*   Welton (01673) 860132

DARMODY, Richard Arthur (Aidan). b 52. Lon Univ DipTh77 BD90. Linc Th Coll MDiv94. **d** 94 **p** 95. C Cherry Hinton St Jo *Ely* from 94. *46 Holbrook Road, Cambridge CB1 4ST* Cambridge (01223) 246469

DARRALL, Charles Geoffrey. b 32. Nottm Univ BA55 MA57. Qu Coll Birm 56. **d** 57 **p** 58. C Cockermouth All SS w Ch Ch *Carl* 57-63; Chapl Dioc Youth Cen from 63; V St Johns-in-the-Vale w Wythburn from 63; P-in-c Threlkeld from 85. *The Vicarage, St Johns-in-the-Vale, Naddle, Keswick, Cumbria CA12 4TF*   Keswick (017687) 72542

DARRALL, John Norman. b 34. Nottm Univ BA57. Ripon Hall Ox 57. **d** 60 **p** 61. C Nottm St Mary *S'well* 60-65; Chapl Nottm Children's Hosp 64-65; V Bole w Saundby *S'well* 65-66; V Sturton w Littleborough 65-66; Chapl Oakham Sch Leics from 84; Lic to Offic *Pet* from 84. *Choir Close, 3 Church Passage, Oakham, Leics LE15 6DR*   Oakham (01572) 723136

DARROCH, Ronald Humphrey. b 45. Trin Coll Cam BA67 MA71 Ch Ch Ox BA67 MA71. Ripon Hall Ox 67. **d** 70 **p** 71. C Kingston upon Hull St Nic *York* 70-73; Hon C 73-74; Hon C Perth St Jo *St And* from 74; Chapl Stancliffe Hall Derby 84-87; Perm to Offic *Worc* from 87; Chapl Old Swinford Hosp Sch Worc from 89. *17 Viewlands Terrace, Perth, PH1 1BN, or Old Swinford Hospital, Stourbridge, W Midlands DY8 1QX* Perth (01738) 28880 or Stourbridge (01384) 396541

DART, John Peter. b 40. St Jo Coll Ox BA63. Cuddesdon Coll 62. **d** 64 **p** 65. C W Hartlepool St Aid *Dur* 64-67; C Alverthorpe *Wakef* 67-70; Lic to Offic 70-84. *3 Springhill Avenue, Crofton, Wakefield, W Yorkshire WF4 1HA*   Wakefield (01924) 863782

DARVILL, Christopher Mark. b 61. Ox Univ BA83. St Steph Ho Ox 84. **d** 86 **p** 87. C Tottenham St Paul *Lon* 86-88; C Oystermouth *S & B* 88-90; Chapl Univ of Wales (Swansea) 90-94; Asst Dioc Warden of Ords from 92; V Llansamlet from 94. *The Vicarage, 61 Church Road, Llansamlet, Swansea SA7 9RL*   Swansea (01792) 771420

DARVILL, Geoffrey. b 43. Aston Univ DipHE81. Oak Hill Th Coll 79. **d** 81 **p** 82. C Barking St Marg w St Patr *Chelmsf* 81-84; C Widford 84-86; P-in-c Ramsden Crays w Ramsden Bellhouse 86-90; Dep Chapl HM Pris Pentonville 90-91; Chapl HM Young Offender Inst Onley from 91. *HM Young Offender Institution, Onley, Willoughby, Rugby, Warks CV23 8AP* Rugby (01788) 522022   Fax 522260

DARVILL, Canon George Collins. b 36. Kelham Th Coll 56. **d** 61 **p** 62. C Middlesb St Chad *York* 61-64; C Manston *Ripon* 64-66; V Kippax 66-79; V Catterick 79-88; RD Richmond 80-86; P-in-c Adel 88-89; R from 89; RD Headingley from 91; Hon Can Ripon Cathl from 91. *The Rectory, 25 Church Lane, Adel, Leeds LS16 8DQ*   Leeds (0113) 267 3676

✠**DARWENT, Rt Rev Frederick Charles.** b 27. JP87. ACIB. Wells Th Coll 61. **d** 63 **p** 64 **c** 78. C Pemberton St Jo *Liv* 63-65; R Strichen *Ab* 65-71; R New Pitsligo 65-71; R Fraserburgh w New Pitsligo 71-78; Can St Andr Cathl 71-78; Dean Ab 73-78; Bp Ab 78-92; rtd 92. *107 Osborne Place, Aberdeen AB2 4DD* Aberdeen (01224) 646497

DASH, Mrs Janet Eleanor Gillian (Jan). b 47. SRN69. Cant Sch of Min 89. **d** 93 **p** 94. Par Dn Morden *S'wark* 93-94; C from 94. *192 Central Road, Morden, Surrey SM4 5RQ*   0181-646 0334

DATSON, Sheila Mary. CertEd62. S'wark Ord Course 76. **dss** 78 **d** 87 **p** 94. Bexleyheath Ch Ch *Roch* 78-87; Hon Par Dn 87-94; NSM Stourport-on-Severn and Wilden *Worc* from 94. *17 Moorhall Lane, Stourport-on-Severn, Worcs DY13 8RB* Stourport (01299) 823044

DAUBNEY, Howard. b 49. Woolwich Poly BA70. S'wark Ord Course 86. **d** 89 **p** 90. NSM Roch from 89. *Trehaun, 20 City Way, Rochester, Kent ME1 2AB*   Medway (01634) 401691

DAUBUZ, Michael Claude. b 19. Trin Coll Cam BA40 MA53. Wells Th Coll 40. **d** 42 **p** 43. C Twyford *Win* 64-70; V Colden 70-84; rtd 84. *31 St Osmund Close, Yetminster, Sherborne, Dorset DT9 6LU*   Yetminster (01935) 872584

DAULMAN, John Henry. b 33. Lich Th Coll 60. **d** 62 **p** 63. C Monkseaton St Mary *Newc* 62-65; Min Can Newc Cathl 65-67; Chapl Crumpsall & Springfield Hosp 67-73; V Tyldesley w Shakerley *Man* 73-81; V Turton from 81. *St Anne's Vicarage, High Street, Turton, Bolton BL7 0EH* Turton (01204) 852222

DAUNTON-FEAR, Andrew. b 45. Univ of Tasmania BSc64 Qu Coll Cam BA67 MA72 Lon Univ DipLib74 St Andr Univ BPhil76. Ridley Hall Cam 67 ACT ThL68. **d** 68 **p** 70. Australia 68-71; P-in-c Islington H Trin Cloudesley Square *Lon* 71-75; Hon C Islington St Mary 71-75; C Stoke Bishop *Bris* 76-79; R Thrapston *Pet* 79-89; R Barming *Roch* from 89. *The Rectory, Church Lane, Barming, Maidstone, Kent ME16 9HA* Maidstone (01622) 726263

DAVAGE, William Ernest Peter. b 50. BA80 PGCE81 MPhil. St Steph Ho Ox 89. **d** 91 **p** 92. C Eyres Monsell *Leic* 91-94; Priest Lib Pusey House Ox from 94. *Pusey House, Oxford OX1 3LZ* Oxford (01865) 278415

DAVENPORT (nee HILL), Ms Elizabeth Jayne Louise. b 55. St Hugh's Coll Ox BA77 MA81. Fuller Th Sem California ThM89 N Ord Course 79. **dss** 82 **d** 87 **p** 91. Halliwell St Pet *Man* 82-83; Paris St Mich *Eur* 83-85; Lic to Offic *St Alb* 85-87; Hon Par Dn Chorleywood St Andr 87-89; USA from 89. *University of Southern California, Student Union 202, Los Angeles, California 90089-0890, USA*

DAVENPORT, Ian Arthan. b 54. Linc Th Coll 85. **d** 87 **p** 88. C Ches H Trin *Ches* 87-91; V Newton from 91. *St Michael's House, Queensbury Road, Newton, Wirral, Merseyside L48 6EP*   0151-625 8517

DAVENPORT, Michael Arthur. b 38. Kelham Th Coll 58 Lich Th Coll 60. **d** 62 **p** 63. C Bilborough w Strelley *S'well* 62-66; C Kettering St Mary *Pet* 66-69; V Tottenham St Benet Fink *Lon* from 69. *St Benet's Vicarage, Walpole Road, London N17 6BH* 0181-888 4541

DAVENPORT, Miss Sybil Ann. b 36. Nottm Univ DipTh88. E Midl Min Tr Course 85. **d** 89 **p** 94. NSM Thurgarton w Hoveringham and Bleasby etc *S'well* 89-94; NSM Collingham w S Scarle and Besthorpe and Girton from 94. *Holmedale, North Muskham, Newark, Notts NG23 6HQ*   Newark (01636) 701552

DAVEY, Andrew John. b 53. Univ of Wales (Cardiff) DPS77. St Mich Coll Llan DipTh76. **d** 77 **p** 78. C Gt Stanmore *Lon* 77-79; C Potters Bar *St Alb* 92-95; P-in-c Clenchwarton *Ely* from 95; P-in-c W Lynn from 95. *The Rectory, Clenchwarton, King's Lynn, Norfolk PE34 4DT*   King's Lynn (01552) 772089

DAVEY, Andrew John. b 57. Magd Coll Ox BA78 MA83. Wycliffe Hall Ox 80. **d** 83 **p** 84. C Bermondsey St Jas w Ch Ch *S'wark* 83-87; Chapl Trin Coll Cam 87-92. *Pilsdon Manor, Pilsdon, Bridport, Dorset DT6 5NZ*

DAVEY, Andrew Paul. b 61. Southn Univ BA82. Westcott Ho Cam 85. **d** 87 **p** 88. C S'wark H Trin w St Matt *S'wark* 87-91; V Camberwell St Luke from 91. *St Luke's Vicarage, 123 Farnborough Way, London SE15 6HL*   0171-703 5587

DAVEY, Christopher Mark. b 64. EN(G)84 RGN89. St Steph Ho Ox DipMin95. **d** 95. C Leeds Belle Is St Jo and St Barn *Ripon* from 95. *St Barnabas House, Low Grange View, Leeds LS10 3DR*   Leeds (0113) 271 1457

DAVEY, Canon Clive Herbert George. b 09. St Jo Coll Dur BA31 MA34. Wycliffe Hall Ox 31. **d** 32 **p** 33. V Guildf Ch Ch *Guildf* 63-78; RD Guildf 73-78; Hon Can Guildf Cathl 76-78; rtd 78; Perm to Offic *B & W* from 78. *24 Prewater Road, Wookey, Wells, Somerset BA5 1LE*   Wells (01749) 677865

DAVEY, Dr Colin Hugh Lancaster. b 34. Em Coll Cam BA56 MA60 PhD89. Cuddesdon Coll 59. **d** 61 **p** 62. C Moseley St Agnes *Birm* 61-64; Lic to Offic *Eur* 64-65; Sub Warden St Boniface Coll Warminster 66-69; C Bath Weston St Jo *B & W* 69-70; Asst Gen Sec C of E Coun on Foreign Relns 70-74; Hon C St Dunstan in the West *Lon* 71-73; Hon C Kennington St Jo *S'wark* 73-74; V S Harrow St Paul *Lon* 74-80; V Paddington St Jas 80-83; Lic to Offic *Eur* 81-83; Asst Gen Sec BCC 83-90; Ch Life Sec CCBI from 90. *30 Westwick Gardens, London W14 0BU*   0171-602 6860 or 620 4444

DAVEY, Eric Victor. b 28. Wycliffe Hall Ox 53 Ridley Hall Cam. **d** 56 **p** 57. V Pontefract St Giles *Wakef* 68-83; V Wakef St Jo 83-93; rtd 93. *15B St John's Croft, Wakefield, W Yorkshire WF1 2RQ*

DAVEY, Canon Frederick Hutley David. b 14. Cranmer Hall Dur 58. **d** 60 **p** 62. E Pakistan 69-71; Bangladesh 71-76; Chapl De Beer Miss to Seamen *Eur* 77-82; rtd 82; Perm to Offic *B & W* from 82. *126 Ashtree Road, Frome, Somerset BA11 2SF* Frome (01373) 467545

DAVEY, James Garland. b 21. **d** 75 **p** 76. C Liskeard w St Keyne and St Pinnock *Truro* 75-77; Perm to Offic *B & W* 77-80; TV S Molton w Nymet St George, High Bray etc *Ex* 80-86; rtd 86; Perm to Offic *B & W* from 86. *Keeper's Cottage, Ham Lane, Compton Dundon, Somerton, Somerset TA11 6PQ*   Somerton (01458) 45991

DAVEY, Dr John. b 35. FRSH89 CPsychol92 AFBPsS92 Birkb Coll Lon BSc84 MPhil87 PhD91. Chich Th Coll 67. **d** 69 **p** 70.

C Eastbourne St Elisabeth *Chich* 69-72; C Eastbourne St Mary 72-74; V W Wittering 74-77; Min Can and Chapl Windsor 77-81; R The Rissingtons *Glouc* 81-85; R Alfriston w Lullington, Litlington and W Dean *Chich* 85-92; Chapl Bramshill Police Coll *Win* from 92. *11 Reading Road North, The Police Staff College, Bramshill, Basingstoke, Hants RG27 0JW* Hartley Wintney (01252) 842931 Fax 843204

DAVEY, John Michael. b 31. St Chad's Coll Dur BA54 DipTh56. **d** 56 **p** 61. C Southwick H Trin *Dur* 56-57; C Harton 60-64; C Bawtry w Austerfield *S'well* 64-67; V Stillington *Dur* 67-70; Lic to Offic 70-78; Perm to Offic *Sheff* from 78. *254 Albert Road, Sheffield S8 9QU* Sheffield (0114) 258 8734

DAVEY, Julian Metherall. b 40. Jes Coll Ox BA62 MA65. Wells Th Coll 62. **d** 64 **p** 65. C Weston-super-Mare St Jo *B & W* 64-66; Perm to Offic *St Alb* 66-68; Chapl St Alb Sch 68-73; Chapl Merchant Taylors' Sch Crosby 73-82; Perm to Offic *Truro* 82-83; P-in-c Meavy w Sheepstor *Ex* 83-85; P-in-c Walkhampton 83-85; R Meavy, Sheepstor and Walkhampton 85; Chapl Warw Sch 86-89; P-in-c The Winterbournes and Compton Valence *Sarum* 89-94. *18 Pondfield Road, Latchbrook, Saltash, Cornwall PL12 4UA* Saltash (01752) 840086

DAVEY, Dr Julian Warwick. b 45. LRCPI DCH DRCOG. Qu Coll Birm 78. **d** 81 **p** 82. NSM Ipsley *Worc* from 81. *2 Meeting Lane, Alcester, Warks B49 5QT* Alcester (01789) 764640

DAVEY, Kenneth William. b 41. Lanc Coll HNC. Qu Coll Birm 84. **d** 86 **p** 87. C Baswich (or Berkswich) *Lich* 86-90; V Lostock Gralam *Ches* from 90. *The Vicarage, Lostock Gralam, Northwich, Cheshire CW9 7PS* Northwich (01606) 43806

DAVEY, Preb Norman John. b 23. Bps' Coll Cheshunt 51. **d** 53 **p** 54. C Ex St Martin, St Steph, St Laur etc *Ex* 67-70; R Ex St Mary Arches 70-73; TR Cen Ex 74-77; P-in-c Ide 75-77; Dioc Dir of Educn 77-88; Preb Ex Cathl from 77; V Holcombe Burnell 77-88; rtd 88. *2 The Poplars, Park Lane, Pinhoe, Exeter EX6 9HH*

DAVEY, Peter Francis. b 40. Trin Coll Cam BA63 MA68. Cuddesdon Coll 63. **d** 65 **p** 66. C Atherton *Man* 65-69; C Leesfield 69-72; V High Crompton 72-79; V Blackrod 79-89; P-in-c Ringley 89-91; V Ringley St Sav w H Trin Prestolee from 91. *The Vicarage, Stoneleigh Drive, Radcliffe, Manchester M26 9FZ* Farnworth (01204) 73742

DAVEY, Peter William. b 44. Culham Coll of Educn TCert65. Linc Th Coll CMinlStuds93. **d** 93 **p** 94. C Cheadle w Freehay *Lich* from 93. *3 Byron Close, Cheadle, Stoke-on-Trent ST10 1XB* Cheadle (01538) 756166

DAVEY, Piers Damer. b 57. Dur Univ BSc. Coll of Resurr Mirfield 80. **d** 83 **p** 84. C Heworth St Mary *Dur* 83-86; C Barnard Castle w Whorlton 86-89; V Aycliffe from 89. *The Vicarage, Aycliffe, Newton Aycliffe, Co Durham DL5 6JT* Aycliffe (01325) 313395

DAVEY, Richard Henry. b 66. Man Univ BA88. Linc Th Coll BTh93. **d** 93 **p** 94. C Parkstone St Pet w Branksea and St Osmund *Sarum* from 93. *79 Church Road, Poole, Dorset BH14 0NS* Parkstone (01202) 743016

DAVEY, William Edwin. b 15. TCD BA39 MA42. TCD Div Sch. **d** 41 **p** 42. V Gt Harwood St Jo *Blackb* 67-72; R Mamble w Bayton *Worc* 72-80; rtd 80. *Flat 26, Pembroke Court, West Street, Wilton, Salisbury SP2 0DG* Salisbury (01722) 744939

DAVID, Brother. See JARDINE, David John

DAVID, Evan David Owen Jenkin. b 10. St D Coll Lamp BA34. **d** 34 **p** 35. R Llandyrnog and Llangwyfan *St As* 67-77; rtd 77; Perm to Offic *Ches* from 90. *Flat 29, Cromer Court, 81 Alderley Road, Hoylake, Wirral, Merseyside L47 2AU* 0151-632 6474

DAVID, Faith Caroline. See CLARINGBULL, Mrs Faith Caroline

DAVID, Canon Kenith Andrew. b 39. Natal Univ BA(Theol)64. Coll of Resurr Mirfield 64. **d** 66 **p** 67. C Harpenden St Nic *St Alb* 66-69; S Africa 69-71; P-in-c Southwick *Chich* 71-72; Th Educn Sec Chr Aid 72-75; Project Officer India and Bangladesh 76-81; Hon C Kingston All SS *S'wark* 72-76; Hon C Kingston All SS w St Jo 76-81; Botswana 81-83; Hon C Geneva *Eur* 83-95; Co-ord Urban Rural Miss WCC 83-94; Can Dio Lundi Zimbabwe from 93; V Hessle *York* from 95. *The Vicarage, 4 Chestnut Avenue, Hessle, N Humberside HU13 0RH* Hull (01482) 648555 Fax as telephone

DAVID, Michael Anthony Louis. b 29. AKC58. **d** 59 **p** 60. V Gravesend St Mary *Roch* 63-78; V Foremark *Derby* 78-81; V Repton 78-81; TV Buxton w Burbage and King Sterndale 81-85; R Warlingham w Chelsham and Farleigh *S'wark* 85-90; rtd 90. *95 Lulworth Avenue, Hamworthy, Poole, Dorset BH15 4DH* Poole (01202) 684475

DAVID, Philip Evan Nicholl. b 31. Jes Coll Ox BA53 MA57 Univ of Wales BA61 Nottm Univ MPhil86 Leic Univ MEd88. St Mich Coll Llan 56. **d** 57 **p** 58. C Llanblethian w Cowbridge *Llan* 57-60; C Cardiff St Jo 60-64; Chapl Ch Coll Brecon 64-75; P-in-c Aberyscir and Llanfihangel Nantbran *S & B* 70-75; Chapl Loretto Sch Musselburgh 75-82; Lic to Offic *Derby* 80-91; Chapl Trent Coll Nottm 83-91; R Llanfyllin and

---

Bwlchycibau *St As* from 91; P-in-c Llangynog from 95. *The Rectory, Llanfyllin, Powys SY22 5BW* Llanfyllin (01691) 648306

DAVID COLUMBA, Brother. See HARE, David

DAVID STEPHEN, Brother. See STEVENS, Canon David Johnson

DAVIDSON, Canon Charles Hilary. b 29. St Edm Hall Ox BA52 MA56 Leic Univ MPhil89. Lich Th Coll 52. **d** 54 **p** 55. P-in-c Lamport w Faxton *Pet* 66-76; R Maidwell w Draughton and Scaldwell 67-76; R Maidwell w Draughton, Scaldwell, Lamport etc 77-80; RD Brixworth 77-79; Can Pet Cathl 79-94; V Roade 80-87; V Roade and Ashton w Hartwell 87-94; RD Towcester 91-94; rtd 94. *Croftside, Butlins Lane, Roade, Northampton NN7 2PU* Roade (01604) 863016

DAVIDSON, Christopher John. b 45. E Anglian Minl Tr Course. **d** 91 **p** 92. NSM Taverham w Ringland *Nor* 91-93; Dir of Educn 91-93; V Whixley w Green Hammerton *Ripon* from 93; RE Adv from 93. *The Vicarage, Whixley, York YO5 8AR* Boroughbridge (01423) 330269

DAVIDSON, Ian George. b 32. Lon Univ BSc53. Linc Th Coll 55. **d** 58 **p** 59. C Waltham Cross *St Alb* 58-60; C St Alb Abbey 61-63; Hon PV S'wark Cathl *S'wark* 63-67; V Gt Cornard *St E* 67-72; R Lt Cornard 67-70; Lic to Offic 72-79; Student Counsellor Suffolk Coll 72-79; P-in-c Witnesham w Swilland and Ashbocking 79-83; Warden Scargill Ho 83-88; Chapl Chr Fellowship of Healing (Scotland) from 88. *28 Fox Spring Crescent, Edinburgh EH10 6NQ* 0131-445 3381

DAVIDSON, John. b 34. Edin Th Coll. **d** 66 **p** 67. C Helensburgh *Glas* 66-69; C Kirkby *Liv* 69-70; TV 70-74. *Flat 19, 153-155 Seymour Place, London W1H 5TQ* 0171-723 4262

DAVIDSON, John Lindsay. b 27. LRCP51 St Cath Soc Ox DipTh57. St Steph Ho Ox. **d** 58 **p** 59. V Lewisham St Steph *S'wark* 67-70; V Croydon St Mich *Cant* 70-80; V Croydon St Mich w St Jas 80-81; TR N Creedy *Ex* 81-92; RD Cadbury 86-90; rtd 92; Perm to Offic *Ex* from 92. *12 Highfield, Lapford, Crediton, Devon EX17 6PY* Lapford (01363) 83764

DAVIDSON, Canon John Noble. b 15. Edin Th Coll 52. **d** 54 **p** 55. V Southport H Trin *Liv* 69-75; V Blackford w Scaleby *Carl* 75-78; V Rockcliffe 75-78; rtd 78; Perm to Offic *Carl* from 78; Hon Can Malta Cathl *Eur* 81-84. *6 Netherend Road, Penrith, Cumbria CA11 8PF* Penrith (01768) 63274

DAVIDSON, Norman Martin. b 24. BSc. W Midl Minl Tr Course. **d** 85 **p** 86. NSM Allesley *Cov* 85-90; rtd 90; Perm to Offic *Cov* from 90. *77 Four Pounds Avenue, Coventry CV5 8DH* Coventry (01203) 673682

DAVIDSON, Air Vice-Marshal Sinclair Melville. b 22. CBE68. CEng FRAeS FIEE. Chich Th Coll 79. **d** 81 **p** 81. Hon C High Hurstwood *Chich* 81-82; P-in-c 83-88; Perm to Offic from 88. *Trinity Cottage, Chilles Lane, High Hurstwood, Uckfield, E Sussex TN22 4AA* Buxted (01825) 732151

DAVIDSON, Trevor John. b 49. CertEd DipHE. Oak Hill Th Coll 80. **d** 85 **p** 86. C Drypool *York* 85-88; V Bessingby from 88; V Carnaby from 88; Chapl Bridlington and Distr Gen Hosp from 88. *The Vicarage, Kent Road, Bessingby, Bridlington, N Humberside YO16 4RU* Bridlington (01262) 670399

DAVIDSON, William Watkins. b 20. Wadh Coll Ox BA48 MA53. Westcott Ho Cam 49. **d** 50 **p** 51. V Westmr St Steph w St Jo *Lon* 65-83; rtd 85. *32 Hamilton Avenue, Woking, Surrey GU22 8RS* Weybridge (01932) 342711

DAVIE (nee JONES), Mrs Alyson Elizabeth. b 58. Ex Univ BA86. Wycliffe Hall Ox 86. **d** 88 **p** 94. Par Dn Ipswich St Fran *St E* 88-92; Perm to Offic *Ox* 92-93; Perm to Offic *St Alb* 93-94; NSM E Barnet from 94; Asst Chapl Oak Hill Th Coll from 94. *13 Farm Lane, London N14 4PP* 0181-440 1363

DAVIE, Peter Edward Sidney. b 36. Lon Univ BSc57 MPhil78 Birm Univ MA73 Kent Univ PhD91. Coll of Resurr Mirfield 57. **d** 60 **p** 61. C De Beauvoir Town St Pet *Lon* 60-63; C-in-c Godshill CD *Portsm* 63-67; R Upton St Leonards *Glouc* 67-73; Sen Lect Ch Ch Coll Cant from 73. *8 Brockenhurst Close, Canterbury, Kent CT2 7RX* Canterbury (01227) 451572

DAVIE, Stephen Peter (Steve). b 52. MRTPI77 S Bank Poly BA75 Cam Univ DipRS90. Oak Hill Th Coll BA93. **d** 93 **p** 94. C Luton Ch Ch *Roch* from 93. *11 Fallowfield, Chatham, Kent ME5 0DU* Medway (01634) 408246

DAVIES, Adrian Paul. b 43. K Coll Lon. **d** 69 **p** 70. C Nottm St Mary *S'well* 69-74; C w Lt Billing *Pet* 74-75; P-in-c Marholm 75-82; R Castor 75; R Castor w Sutton and Upton 76-82; V Byker St Mich w St Lawr *Newc* 82-94; rtd 95. *9 Arrow Lane, Halton, Lancaster LA2 6QS*

DAVIES, Alan Arthur. b 35. Sarum & Wells Th Coll 83. **d** 85 **p** 86. C Eastleigh *Win* 85-88; C Portsea N End St Mark *Portsm* 88-90; V Lydiate *Liv* from 90. *The Vicarage, Lydiate, Liverpool L31 4HL* 0151-526 0512

DAVIES, Alastair John. b 56. Nottm Univ BA MTh. Westcott Ho Cam. **d** 84 **p** 85. C Eltham St Jo *S'wark* 84-87; C Dulwich St Barn 87-89; Chapl RAF from 89. *Chaplaincy Services (RAF), HQ, Personnel and Training Command, RAF Innsworth,*

Gloucester GL3 1EZ   Gloucester (01452) 712612 Ext 5032
Fax 712612 5987

DAVIES, Alcwyn Ivor. b 09. Univ of Wales BA32 DipEd33. St D
Coll Lamp 36. **d** 38 **p** 39. R Fowlmere *Ely* 53-76; V Thriplow
53-76; rtd 76. *17 Station Road, Lode, Cambridge CB5 9HB*
Cambridge (01223) 811867

DAVIES, Aldwyn Ivan. b 09. St D Coll Lamp BA31. St Mich
Coll Llan. **d** 32 **p** 33. Miss to Seamen 39-43, 46-54, 56-57 and
69-78; V Port Eynon w Rhosili and Llanddewi and Knelston
S & B 69-74; V Llangennith 75-77; rtd 77. *Sea Beach Nursing
Home, Horton, Swansea SA3 1LB*   Gower (01792) 390252

DAVIES, Alexander Richard. b 12. St Deiniol's Hawarden 63.
d 64 **p** 65. V Llanfihangel Crucorney w Oldcastle etc *Mon*
69-77; rtd 77; Perm to Offic *St As* from 77; Perm to Offic *Ches*
83-89; Perm to Offic *Ban* from 90. *2 Gorphwysfa, Glyn Ceiriog,
Llangollen, Clwyd LL20 7EB*   Glyn Ceiriog (01691) 718999

DAVIES, Canon Alfred Joseph. b 23. St D Coll Lamp BA49. **d** 50
p 51. V Llangeler *St D* 54-74; RD Emlyn 70-73; Chapl
Cardigan Hosp 74-88; V Cardigan and Mwnt and Y Ferwig
St D 74-88; Can St D Cathl 79-88; rtd 88; Hon Can St D Cathl
St D from 88. *19 Penbryn Avenue, Carmarthen, Dyfed
SA31 3DH*   Carmarthen (01267) 234045

DAVIES, Alun Edwards. b 13. Univ of Wales BA40. St D Coll
Lamp 45. **d** 46 **p** 47. R Lower Crumpsall *Man* 72-84; rtd 84;
Perm to Offic *Man* from 84. *48 Ashtree Road, Crumpsall,
Manchester M8 6AT*   0161-720 8345

DAVIES, Very Rev Alun Radcliffe. b 23. Univ of Wales BA45
Keble Coll Ox BA47 MA51. St Mich Coll Llan 47. **d** 48 **p** 49.
Warden of Ords *Llan* 50-71; V Ystrad Mynach 59-75; Chan
Llan Cathl 69-71; Adn Llan 71-77; Can Res Llan Cathl 75-77;
Dean Llan 77-93; V Llan w Capel Llanilltern 77-93; rtd 93.
*15 Sinclair Drive, Colchester Avenue, Penylan, Cardiff
CF3 7AH*   Cardiff (01222) 456149

DAVIES, Anthony William (Tony). b 29. St Jo Coll Ox BA52
MA58 Man Univ MEd73. S Dios Minl Tr Scheme 84. **d** 87
p 88. C Burnham *B & W* 87-89; R Westcote Barton w Steeple
Barton, Duns Tew etc *Ox* from 89; RD Woodstock from 92.
*The Rectory, 29 Enstone Road, Middle Barton, Chipping
Norton, Oxon OX7 7AA*   Steeple Aston (01869) 340510

DAVIES, Arthur Lloyd. b 31. Univ of Wales BA55. Cuddesdon
Coll 55. **d** 57 **p** 58. C Tonypandy w Clydach Vale *Llan* 57-59; C
Merthyr Dyfan 59-62; C Amersham *Ox* 62-65; V Tilehurst St
Geo 65-73; R Wokingham St Paul 73-84; R Nuthurst *Chich*
84-90; I Fiddown w Clonegam, Guilcagh and Kilmeaden
C & O from 90. *Piltown Rectory, Piltown, Co Kilkenny, Irish
Republic*   Waterford (51) 43275

DAVIES, Canon Arthur Cadwaladr. b 19. Univ of Wales BA41.
Wells Th Coll 41. **d** 43 **p** 44. V Stockton Heath *Ches* 64-85; RD
Gt Budworth 81-85; rtd 85; Perm to Offic *Ban* from 85.
*Highfield, Treforris Road, Penmaenmawr, Gwynedd
LL34 6RH*   Penmaenmawr (01492) 623739

DAVIES, Arthur Cecil Francis. b 11. Keble Coll Ox BA34
MA42. Bps' Coll Cheshunt 35. **d** 37 **p** 38. V Horncastle w Low
Toynton *Linc* 59-80; rtd 80; Perm to Offic *Pet* from 80; Perm to
Offic *Linc* from 87. *30 Church Lane, Greetham, Oakham, Leics
LE15 7NF*   Oakham (01572) 812600

DAVIES, Arthur Gerald Miles. b 29. Univ of Wales (Ban) BA51.
St Mich Coll Llan. **d** 53 **p** 54. V Llansilin w Llangadwaladr and
Llangedwyn *St As* 68-71; V Llanfair Caereinion w Llanllugan
71-75; TV Wrexham 75-83; V Hanmer, Bronington,
Bettisfield, Tallarn Green 83-94; rtd 94. *Elland, School Lane,
Bronington, Whitchurch, Shropshire SY13 3HN*   Whitchurch
(01948) 73296

DAVIES, Basil Tudor. b 18. Keble Coll Ox BA40 MA48.
Westcott Ho Cam 40. **d** 42 **p** 43. V Wigston Magna *Leic* 57-73;
R Upwell St Pet *Ely* 73-77; P-in-c Nordelph 75-77; Chapl
Community of St Mary V Wantage 77-88; Lic to Offic *Ox*
77-88 and from 89; rtd 88; P-in-c Steventon w Milton *Ox*
88-89. *St Katharine's House, Garden Flat B, Ormond Road,
Wantage, Oxon OX12 8EA*   Wantage (01235) 760883

DAVIES, Benjamin John. b 27. Glouc Sch of Min 80 Trin Coll
Bris 87. **d** 88 **p** 89. NSM Cinderford St Steph w Littledean
Glouc from 88. *Mannings Well, The Ruffit, Littledean,
Cinderford, Glos GL14 3LA*   Dean (01594) 822352

DAVIES, Bernard. b 24. St D Coll Lamp BA49. **d** 51 **p** 52. V
Stand Lane St Jo *Man* 63-66; rtd 84. *7 Maritoba Close,
Lakeside, Cardiff CF2 6HD*

DAVIES, Canon Bernard. b 34. Lon Univ BD63. Oak Hill Th
Coll 59. **d** 63 **p** 64. C Rawtenstall St Mary *Man* 63-69; Sec
Rwanda Miss 69-71; R Widford *Chelmsf* 71-78; V Braintree
from 78; RD Braintree 87-95; Hon Can Chelmsf Cathl from
92. *St Michael's Vicarage, 10A Marshalls Road, Braintree,
Essex CM7 7LL*   Braintree (01376) 322840

DAVIES, Bruce Edmund. b 22. Univ of Wales BA44. St Mich
Coll Llan 44. **d** 46 **p** 47. Chapl Univ of Wales (Cardiff) *Llan*
56-78; R Peterston-super-Ely w St Brides-super-Ely 78-87; rtd
87; Perm to Offic *Llan* from 87. *7 St Paul's Court, Heol Fair,
Llandaff, Cardiff CF5 2ES*   Cardiff (01222) 553144

DAVIES, Cadoc Trevor. b 28. Keble Coll Ox BA52 MA57.
Cuddesdon Coll 57. **d** 57 **p** 58. V Water Orton *Birm* 64-83; R
Kislingbury w Rothersthorpe *Pet* 83-92; rtd 92; C Ridgeway
Ox 92-94. *15 Union Street, Oxford OX4 1JP*   Oxford (01865)
727823

DAVIES, Catharine Mary. *See* FURLONG, Mrs Catharine
Mary

DAVIES, Charles William Keith. b 48. MIOT71. Linc Th Coll.
d 83 **p** 84. C Hythe *Cant* 83-86; Chapl RAF from 86; Perm to
Offic *Linc* from 93. *Chaplaincy Services (RAF), HQ,
Personnel and Training Command, RAF Innsworth, Gloucester
GL3 1EZ*   Gloucester (01452) 712612 Ext 5164   Fax 510828

DAVIES, Christopher John. b 55. St Mich Tr Scheme 83. **d** 86
p 87. C Tooting All SS *S'wark* 86-90; V Malden St Jas from 90;
RD Kingston from 92. *St James's Vicarage, 7 Bodley Road,
New Malden, Surrey KT3 5QD*   0181-942 1860 or 942 5070

DAVIES, Clifford Morgan. b 19. Univ of Wales BA41. St Mich
Coll Llan 41. **d** 43 **p** 44. Chapl Duke of York's R Mil Sch
Dover 61-77; rtd 84. *37 Applegarth Avenue, Guildford, Surrey
GU2 6LX*   Guildford (01483) 579415

DAVIES, Clifford O'Connor. b 17. Lon Univ BCom37. St Aug
Coll Cant 42. **d** 44 **p** 45. C Lamorbey H Trin *Roch* 44-46;
S Africa from 46. *64 Schuller Street, Forest Hill, 2091 South
Africa*   Johannesburg (11) 683-3680

DAVIES, Clifford Thomas. b 41. Glouc Th Course. **d** 83 **p** 84.
NSM Dean Forest H Trin *Glouc* 83-87; C Huntley and
Longhope 87; R Ruardean from 87. *The Rectory, High Street,
Ruardean, Glos GL17 9US*   Dean (01594) 542214

DAVIES, David Anthony (Tony). b 57. ARICS84 Thames Poly
BSc81. Coll of Resurr Mirfield 85. **d** 88 **p** 89. C Stalybridge
Man 88-91; C Swinton and Pendlebury 91-92; TV from 92. *All
Saint's Vicarage, 4 Banbury Mews, Wardley, Swinton,
Manchester M27 3QZ*   0161-794 5934

DAVIES, David Arthur Guy Hampton. b 27. St Jo Coll Ox BA50
DipTh51 MA55. Ely Th Coll 51. **d** 53 **p** 54. R Stamford St
Mary and St Mich *Linc* 62-90; rtd 90. *8 Holywell Terrace,
Shrewsbury SY2 5DF*   Shrewsbury (01743) 245086

DAVIES, David Barry Grenville. b 38. St Jo Coll Dur BA60
MA77. Sarum Th Coll 61. **d** 63 **p** 64. C Abth St Mich *St D*
63-66; Min Can St D Cathl 66-72; R Stackpole Elidor w St
Petrox 72-83; V Laugharne w Llansadwrnen and Llandawke
from 83. *The Vicarage, King Street, Laugharne, Dyfed
SA33 4QE*   Laugharne (01994) 427218

DAVIES, David Christopher (Chris). b 52. Lon Univ BSc73
Leeds Univ DipTh75. Coll of Resurr Mirfield 73. **d** 76 **p** 77. C
Bethnal Green St Jo w St Simon *Lon* 76-78; C Bethnal Green
St Jo w St Bart 78-80; C-in-c Portsea St Geo CD *Portsm* 80-81;
Relig Affairs Producer Radio Victory 81-86; V Portsea St Geo
81-87; Chapl Ham Green Hosp Bris from 87; Chapl
Southmead Hosp Bris from 87. *Southmead Hospital,
Westbury-on-Trym, Bristol BS10 5NB, or 28 Hortham Lane,
Almondsbury, Bristol BS12 4JL*   Bristol (0117) 950 5050 or
959 5447

DAVIES, David Geoffrey George. b 24. Univ of Wales (Ban)
BA49 Lon Univ BD55 Chorley Coll of Educn PGCE75. St
Mich Coll Llan 49. **d** 51 **p** 52. Warden of Ords *St As* 62-70; V
Ruabon 63-70; Hon Can St As Cathl 66-69; Cursal Can 69-70;
NSM W Derby (or Tuebrook) St Jo *Liv* 70-81; Chapl to Welsh
Speaking Angl in Liv 74-81; TV Bourne Valley *Sarum* 81-87;
TR 87-89; Bp's Chapl to Schs 83-89; RD Alderbury 86-89; rtd
89; Hon Chapl Liv Cathl *Liv* from 89; Sub-Chapl HM Prison
Risley from 90. *55 Hattons Lane, Liverpool L16 7QR*   0151-
722 1415

DAVIES, Chan David Hywel. b 13. Univ of Wales BA40. St Mich
Coll Llan 41. **d** 42 **p** 43. V Carmarthen St Pet *St D* 67-83; Can
St D Cathl 72-82; Chan 82-83; rtd 83. *The Vicarage,
Llanfihangel Abercywyn, St Clears, Dyfed SA33 4ND*   St
Clears (01994) 231019

DAVIES, Canon David Ioan Gwyn. b 19. Univ of Wales BA41
MA54. Lich Th Coll 41. **d** 43 **p** 44. V Blackpool St Paul *Blackb*
59-86; RD Blackpool 73-84; Hon Can Blackb Cathl 77-86; rtd
86. *37 Oakfield Street, Pontardulais, Swansea SA4 1LN*
Swansea (01792) 883947

DAVIES, David Islwyn. b 42. St Deiniol's Hawarden 83. **d** 85
p 86. C Llangiwg *S & B* 85-87; C Swansea St Pet 87-89; Miss to
Seamen 89-94; Chapl Schiedam Miss to Seamen *Eur* 89-92;
Chapl Milford Haven Miss to Seamen 92-94; V Pontyates and
Llangyndeyrn *St D* from 94. *The Vicarage, 1 Heol Mansant,
Pontiets, Llanelli, Dyfed SA15 5SB*   Pontiets (01269) 860451

DAVIES, Canon David Jeremy Christopher. b 46. CCC Cam
BA68 MA72. Westcott Ho Cam 68. **d** 71 **p** 72. C Stepney St
Dunstan and All SS *Lon* 71-74; Chapl Qu Mary Coll 74-78;
Chapl Univ of Wales (Cardiff) *Llan* 78-85; Can Res Sarum
Cathl *Sarum* from 85. *Hungerford Chantry, 54 The Close,
Salisbury SP1 2EL*   Salisbury (01722) 330914

DAVIES, David John. b 36. St Cath Soc Ox BA58 MA62. St D
Coll Lamp 58. **d** 60 **p** 61. C Rhosddu *St As* 60-68; Chr Aid

Area Sec (Glos, Herefordshire and Worcs) 68-85; Midl Regional Co-ord 78-85; Area Co-ord (Devon and Cornwall) from 86; Perm to Offic *Ex* from 94. *Poldhu, 8 Carne Road, Newlyn, Penzance, Cornwall TR18 5QA* Penzance (01736) 60401

DAVIES, David Leslie Augustus. b 25. St D Coll Lamp BA50. d 51 p 52. Chapl May Day, Qu and St Mary's Hosps Croydon 65-71; V Penrhyn-coch and Elerch *St D* 71-74; Chapl R Berks and Reading Distr Hosps 74-89; rtd 90; Perm to Offic *Win* from 90. *Basset Down, 31 Three Acre Drive, New Milton, Hants BH25 7LG* New Milton (01425) 610376

DAVIES, David Michael Cole. b 44. St D Coll Lamp DipTh69. d 68 p 69. C Carmarthen St Pet *St D* 68-72; R Dinas 72-77; V Ty-Croes w Saron 77-80; V Llanedi w Tycroes and Saron 80-90; RD Dyffryn Aman 85-90; V Dafen and Llwynhendy 90-94. *Address temp unknown*

DAVIES, Prof David Protheroe. b 39. CCC Cam BA62 MA66 CCC Ox MA69 BD69. Ripon Hall Ox 62. d 64 p 65. C Swansea St Mary w H Trin *S & B* 64-67; Lect Th Univ of Wales (Lamp) 67-75; Sen Lect 75-86; Dean Faculty of Th 75-77 and from 81; Hd Th and Relig Studies from 84; Prof Th Univ of Wales (Lamp) from 86; Bp's Chapl for Th Educn *S & B* from 79. *St David's College, Lampeter, Dyfed SA48 7ED* Lampeter (01570) 422351

DAVIES, David Vernon. b 14. AFBPsS68 Univ of Wales (Swansea) BA35 BD38 St Cath Coll Ox MA40 K Coll Lon PhD56. St D Coll Lamp 41. d 41 p 42. Lic to Offic *Llan* 68-94; Prin Lect Llan Coll of Educn 68-77; Sen Lect Univ of Wales (Cardiff) 77-79; rtd 79. *41 Cefn Coed Avenue, Cyncoed, Cardiff CF2 6HF* Cardiff (01222) 757635

DAVIES, David William. b 64. d 90 p 91. C Newton St Pet *S & B* 90-93; V Llywel and Traean-glas w Llanulid from 93. *Llywel Vicarage, Trecastle, Brecin, Powys LD3 8UW* Sennybridge (0187482) 481

DAVIES, Dennis William. b 24. Leeds Univ BA46 K Coll Lon AKC54 BD65. d 54 p 55. C Aylesbury *Ox* 54-58; Lic to Offic from 60; rtd 90. *45 Green End Street, Aston Clinton, Aylesbury, Bucks HP22 5JE* Aylesbury (01296) 630989

DAVIES, Dewi Caradog. b 14. St D Coll Lamp BA35. d 38 p 39. R Canton St Jo *Llan* 66-79; rtd 79. *10 Insole Gardens, Llandaff, Cardiff CF5 2HW* Cardiff (01222) 563743

DAVIES, Canon Dillwyn. b 30. St Mich Coll Llan 52. d 54 p 55. R Winthorpe *S'well* 62-71; V Langford w Holme 62-71; V Mansf Woodhouse 71-85; R Gedling 85-92; RD Gedling 85-90; Hon Can S'well Minster 90-92; rtd 92. *7 Norbury Drive, Mansfield, Notts NG18 4HT*

DAVIES, Canon Dilwyn Morgan. b 10. Univ of Wales BA32 DipEd33. St Mich Coll Llan 32. d 34 p 35. Hon Can Cov Cathl *Cov* 65-80; P-in-c Ilmington w Stretton on Fosse and Ditchford 72-76; R 77-80; rtd 80; Perm to Offic *Cov* from 80. *6 Manor Barns, Ilmington, Shipston-on-Stour, Warks CV36 4LS* Ilmington (01608) 682568

DAVIES, Dorrien Paul. b 34. Univ of Wales (Ban) DipTh86. Llan Dioc Tr Scheme. d 88 p 89. C Llanelli *St D* 88-91; V Llanfihangel Ystrad and Cilcennin w Trefilan etc from 91. *Ystrad Vicarage, Felinfach, Lampeter, Dyfed SA48 8AE* Aeron (01570) 471073

DAVIES, Prof Douglas James. b 47. St Jo Coll Dur BA69 St Pet Coll Ox MLitt72 Nottm Univ PhD80. Cranmer Hall Dur 71. d 75 p 76. Lect Nottm Univ from 75; Sen Lect from 90; Hon C Wollaton *S'well* 75-83; Hon C Attenborough 83-85; Hon C E Leake 85-91; Hon C Daybrook from 91; Prof Relig Studies Nottm Univ from 93. *The Warden, Derby Hall, University Park, Nottingham NG7 2QT* Nottingham (0115) 951 4374 Fax 951 4386

DAVIES, Canon Douglas Tudor. b 20. Univ of Wales (Ban) BA44. Coll of Resurr Mirfield 44. d 46 p 47. V Treboeth *S & B* 65-90; RD Penderi 78-90; Hon Can Brecon Cathl 82-83; Can from 83; rtd 90. *245A Swansea Road, Waunarlwydd, Swansea SA5 4SN* Swansea (01792) 879587

DAVIES, Edward Trevor. b 37. LRSC62 MInstE74 CEng78. N Ord Course 92. d 95. NSM Waverton *Ches* from 95; Asst Chapl Chester Hospitals from 95. *Athergreen, 5 Allansford Avenue, Waverton, Chester CH3 7QH* Chester (01244) 332106 Fax as telephone

DAVIES, Edward Earl. b 40. Llan Dioc Tr Scheme 88. d 90 p 91. C Pontypridd St Cath w St Matt *Llan* 90-93; V Ferndale w Maerdy from 93. *The Vicarage, Woodville Place, Maerdy, Ferndale, M Glam CF43 4LS* Ferndale (01443) 756322

DAVIES, Edward William Llewellyn. b 51. Nottm Univ BTh77. St Jo Coll Nottm 73. d 78 p 79. C Southsea St Jude *Portsm* 78-81; C Alverstoke 81-84; R Abbas and Templecombe w Horsington *B & W* 84-89; Perm to Offic *Ches* from 89. *2 Cranford Avenue, Macclesfield, Cheshire SK10 7DJ* Macclesfield (01625) 500544

DAVIES, Dr Elizabeth Jean. b 39. MRCS LRCP65 Lon Univ MB, BS63. S Dios Minl Tr Scheme 86 Chich Th Coll 86. d 89 p 95. Par Dn Southwick *Chich* 89-91; Par Dn Littlehampton

and Wick 91-95; C Seaford w Sutton from 95. *51 Chyngton Gardens, Seaford, E Sussex BN25 3RS* Seaford (01323) 893876

DAVIES, Eric Brian. b 36. St Jo Coll Nottm. d 87 p 89. NSM Castle Donington and Lockington cum Hemington *Leic* 87-88; Hon C Hathern, Long Whatton and Diseworth 89-90; Hon C Hathern, Long Whatton and Diseworth w Belton etc 90-93; C Minster in Sheppey *Cant* from 93. *St Peter's House, Halfway, Sheerness, Kent ME12 3DD* Sheerness (01795) 662399

DAVIES, Evan Wallis. b 08. Bps' Coll Cheshunt. d 42 p 43. V Pirton *St Alb* 48-52; rtd 71. *7 Treetops, Swiss Valley Park, Llanelli, Dyfed SA14 8DW* Llanelli (01554) 752316

DAVIES, Ven Francis James Saunders. b 37. Univ of Wales (Ban) BA60 Selw Coll Cam BA62 MA66 Bonn Univ 63. St Mich Coll Llan 62. d 63 p 64. C Holyhead w Rhoscolyn *Ban* 63-67; Chapl Ban Cathl 67-69; R Llanllyfni 69-75; Can Missr Ban Cathl 75-78; V Gorseinon *S & B* 78-86; RD Llwchwr 83-86; V Cardiff Dewi Sant *Llan* 86-93; Adn Meirionnydd *Ban* from 93; R Criccieth w Treflys from 93. *The Rectory, Criccieth, Gwynedd LL52 0AG* Criccieth (01766) 523222

DAVIES, Frank Ernest. b 13. Dur Univ LTh43. Clifton Th Coll 39. d 43 p 44. R Bigbury *Ex* 60-84; rtd 84; Perm to Offic *Ches* from 84. *93 Heywood Boulevard, Thingwall, Wirral, Merseyside L61 3XE* 0151-648 3561

DAVIES, Gareth Rhys. b 51. DipHE. Oak Hill Th Coll. d 83 p 84. C Gt Warley Ch Ch *Chelmsf* 83-86; C Oxhey All SS *St Alb* 86-90; C Aldridge *Lich* from 90. *227 Walsall Road, Aldridge, Walsall WS9 0QA* Aldridge (01922) 57732

DAVIES, Gary. b 37. AKC62. d 63 p 64. C Dovercourt *Chelmsf* 63-65; C Lambeth St Phil *S'wark* 65-68; P-in-c 68-70; V W Brompton St Mary *Lon* 70-72; V W Brompton St Mary w St Pet 73-83; RD Chelsea 76-80; Dir Post-Ord Tr 78-81; Perm to Offic from 83. *21 Margravine Gardens, London W6 8RL* 0181-741 9315

DAVIES, Canon Geoffrey Lovat. b 30. St Aid Birkenhead. d 62 p 63. C Davenham *Ches* 62-65; C Higher Bebington 65-67; V Witton 67-80; R Lymm from 80; Dioc Clergy Widows and Retirement Officer 87-91; Hon Can Ches Cathl from 88; RD Gt Budworth from 91. *The Rectory, Rectory Lane, Lymm, Cheshire WA13 0AL* Lymm (01925) 752164

DAVIES, Geoffrey Michael. b 43. St D Coll Lamp DipTh70. d 70 p 71. C Brynmawr *S & B* 70-73; Coll of the Ascension Selly Oak 73-74; S Africa 74-91; C Roath St Marg *Llan* 91-95; V Llanishen w Trellech Grange and Llanfihangel etc *Mon* from 95. *The Vicarage, Llanishen, Chepstow, Gwent NP6 6QL* Trelleck (01600) 860845

DAVIES, George Vivian. b 21. CCC Cam BA47 MA49. Ely Th Coll. d 49 p 50. R Warehorne w Kenardington *Cant* 59-74; R Rounton w Welbury *York* 74-86; Perm to Offic *Derby* from 86. *12 Rectory Drive, Wingerworth, Chesterfield, Derbyshire S42 6RT* Chesterfield (01246) 279222

DAVIES, George William. b 51. MITD MIMgt MBTI Open Univ BA74 MPhil89 Liv Univ DMS76. Sarum & Wells Th Coll 83. d 85 p 86. C Mansf St Pet *S'well* 85-89; Chapl Cen Notts HA 86-89; P-in-c Fobbing *Chelmsf* from 89; Ind Chapl from 89; Chapl ATC from 92; Chapl Thurrock Lakeside Shopping Cen *Chelmsf* from 93. *The Rectory, High Road, Fobbing, Stanford-le-Hope, Essex SS17 9JH* Stanford-le-Hope (01375) 672002 or Rainham (01708) 869933 Fax Rainham (01708) 865870

DAVIES, Glanmor Adrian. b 51. St D Coll Lamp DipTh73. d 73 p 75. C Llanstadwel *St D* 73-78; R Dinas w Llanllawer and Pontfaen w Morfil etc 78-84; V Lamphey w Hodgeston 84-85; V Lamphey w Hodgeston and Carew from 85. *The Vicarage, Lamphey, Pembroke, Dyfed SA71 5NR* Lamphey (01646) 672407

DAVIES, Glyn Richards. b 28. Solicitor 52. d 79 p 80. NSM Michaelston-y-Fedw and Rudry *Mon* 79-88; NSM St Mellons and Michaelston-y-Fedw from 88. *Ty Golau, 8 Tyr Winch Road, St Mellons, Cardiff CF3 9UX* Cardiff (01222) 792813

DAVIES, Glyndwr George. b 36. Glouc Sch of Min 88. d 91 p 92. NSM Clodock and Longtown w Craswall, Llanveynoe etc *Heref* from 91. *White House Farm, Llanfihangel Crucorney, Abergavenny, Gwent NP7 8HW* Crucorney (01873) 890251

DAVIES, Canon Graham James. b 35. Univ of Wales BD72 St D Coll Lamp BA56. St Mich Coll Llan 56 Episc Th Sch Cam Mass 58. d 59 p 60. C Johnston w Steynton *St D* 59-62; C Llangathen w Llanfihangel Cilfargen 62-64; Min Can St D Cathl 64-66; R Burton 66-71; R Hubberston 71-74; Hon C Lenham w Boughton Malherbe *Cant* 74-80; V Cwmddauddwr w St Harmon's and Llanwrthwl *S & B* 80-86; V Cydweli and Llandyfaelog *St D* from 86; Can St D Cathl from 92. *The Vicarage, Cydweli, Dyfed SA17 4SY* Cydweli (01554) 890295

DAVIES, Harry Bertram. b 11. Chich Th Coll 70. d 70 p 71. C Fareham H Trin *Portsm* 70-74; R Lowick w Sudborough and Slipton *Pet* 74-81; P-in-c Islip 78-81; rtd 81; Perm to Offic *Lich* from 81. *22 Beachwood Avenue, Wall Heath, Kingswinford, W Midlands DY6 0HL* Kingswinford (01384) 292000

DAVIES, Hedleigh Llewelyn. b 17. Worc Coll Ox BA40 MA44. Westcott Ho Cam 40. **d** 41 **p** 42. Sacr Nor Cathl *Nor* 66-71; V Nor St Andr 66-72; P-in-c Nor St Mich at Plea and St Pet Hungate 66-72; V Nor St Mary in the Marsh 67-72; R Brooke w Kirstead 72-82; Hon Min Can Nor Cathl from 78; rtd 82; Perm to Offic Nor from 91. *April Rise, Rectory Road, East Carleton, Norwich NR14 8HT* Mulbarton (01508) 70420

DAVIES, Henry Joseph. b 38. Univ of Wales (Cardiff) BSc61. St Mich Coll Llan 75. **d** 76 **p** 77. C Griffithstown *Mon* 76-79; TV Cwmbran 79-85; V Newport St Andr from 85. *The Vicarage, 1 Brookfield Close, Liswerry, Newport, Gwent NP9 0LA* Newport (01633) 271904

DAVIES, Canon Henry Lewis. b 20. St Jo Coll Dur BA42 DipTh43 MA45. **d** 43 **p** 44. R Old Swinford *Worc* 65-78; R Old Swinford Stourbridge 78-85; rtd 85; Perm to Offic *Worc* from 87. *15 Bramley Road, Bewdley, Worcs DY12 2BU* Bewdley (01299) 402713

DAVIES, Herbert John. b 30. Glouc Sch of Min 84. **d** 87 **p** 88. NSM Cheltenham St Mark *Glouc* from 87. *45 Farmington Road, Benhall, Cheltenham, Glos GL51 6AG* Cheltenham (01242) 515996

DAVIES, Herbert Lewis Owen. b 08. CBE. Ox Univ BA31 MA36. St Steph Ho Ox 31. **d** 32 **p** 33. R Bourton on the Hill *Glouc* 68-75; rtd 75. *Conway, Croft Drive West, Caldy, Wirral, Merseyside L48 2JQ* 0151-625 1860

✠**DAVIES, Rt Rev Howell Haydn.** b 27. ARIBA55 DipArch54. Tyndale Hall Bris 56. **d** 59 **p** 60. C Heref St Pet w St Owen *Heref* 59-61; Kenya 61-79; Adn N Maseno 71-74; Provost Nairobi 74-79; V Woking St Pet *Guildf* 79-81; Uganda 81-87; Bp Karamoja 81-87; V Wolv St Jude *Lich* 87-93; rtd 93. *3 Gilberts Wood, Ewyas Harold, Hereford HR2 0JL* Golden Valley (01981) 240984

DAVIES, Hugh Middlecott. b 19. Worc Ord Coll 58. **d** 59 **p** 60. R Ightfield w Calverhall *Lich* 66-72; Chapl HM Borstal Stoke Heath 70-72; R Catfield *Nor* 72-74; Chapl Nor Hosp 74-75; Asst Chapl HM Pris Nor 74-77; R Bunwell w Carleton Rode 75-77; Master Charterhouse Hull 77-80; rtd 80; Chapl Addenbrooke's Hosp Cam 80-81; Perm to Offic *Nor* 81-94. *1 The Beeches, Station Road, Holt, Norfolk NR25 6BS* Holt (01263) 711898

DAVIES, Ian. b 45. Man Coll of Educn TCert74 Open Univ BA79. Carl Dioc Tr Inst 88. **d** 91 **p** 92. NSM Harraby *Carl* from 91. *4 St Andrew's Close, Carlisle CA1 2SG* Carlisle (01228) 32804

DAVIES, Ian Charles. b 51. Sarum & Wells Th Coll 78. **d** 81 **p** 82. C E Bedfont *Lon* 81-84; C Cheam *S'wark* 84-87; V Mert St Jas from 87; RD Merton from 91. *St James's Vicarage, Beaford Grove, London SW20 9LB* 0181-540 3122

DAVIES, Ian Elliott. b 64. Univ of Wales (Ban) BD85. Ridley Hall Cam 86. **d** 88 **p** 89. C Baglan *Llan* 88-90; C Skewen from 90. *Manod, 21 Drummau Road, Neath Abbey, W Glam SA10 6NT* Swansea (01792) 321324

DAVIES, Ieuan. b 39. Lon Univ BSc60 K Coll Cam 60 New Coll Ox 63. St Steph Ho Ox 63. **d** 65 **p** 66. C Pimlico St Gabr *Lon* 65-68; USA from 68. *Address temp unknown*

DAVIES, Canon Ivor Llewellyn. b 35. Univ of Wales BA56 St Cath Soc Ox BA58 MA63. Wycliffe Hall Ox 56. **d** 62 **p** 63. C Wrexham *St As* 62-64; India 65-71; V Connah's Quay *St As* 71-79; P-in-c Gorsley w Cliffords Mesne *Glouc* 79-84; P-in-c Hempsted 84-90; Dir of Ords 84-90; Hon Can Glouc Cathl from 89; V Dean Forest St Paul from 90. *The Vicarage, Parkend, Lydney, Glos GL15 4HL* Dean (01594) 562284

DAVIES, Canon Ivor Llewelyn. b 23. Univ of Wales (Swansea) BA49 St Cath Soc Ox DipTh52 Fitzw Coll Cam BA56 MA60. Wycliffe Hall Ox 49. **d** 51 **p** 52. R Llanfeugan w Llanddetty and Glyncollwg *S & B* 59-70; P-in-c Llansantffraed-juxta-Usk 67-70; V Hay 70-72; RD Hay 73-82; V Hay w Llanigon and Capel-y-Ffin 72-87; Hon Can Brecon Cathl 76-79; Can Brecon Cathl 79-89; RD Hay 85-87; V Knighton and Norton 87-89; Treas Brecon Cathl 88-89; rtd 89. *Holly Cottage, 5 The Cwm, Knighton, Powys LD7 1HF* Knighton (01547) 520253

DAVIES, James Alan. b 38. St Jo Coll Nottm Lambeth STh95. **d** 83 **p** 84. C Fletchamstead *Cov* 83-87; P-in-c Hartshill 87-89; V 89-93; Asst RD Nuneaton from 90; V E Green from 93. *St Andrew's Vicarage, Church Lane, Eastern Green, Coventry CV5 7BX* Coventry (01203) 466215

DAVIES, James Owen. b 26. St Aid Birkenhead 60. **d** 61 **p** 62. C Drayton in Hales *Lich* 61-65; V Tipton St Jo 65-69; P-in-c Lt Drayton 70-73; V from 73. *The Vicarage, Little Drayton, Market Drayton, Shropshire TF9 1DY* Market Drayton (01630) 652801

DAVIES, Canon James Trevor Eiddig. b 17. St D Coll Lamp BA39 AKC41. **d** 41 **p** 42. V Llantarnam *Mon* 68-71; R Cwmbran 71-86; Hon Can St Woolos Cathl 83-86; rtd 86. *34 Rockfield Road, Monmouth, Gwent NP5 3BA* Monmouth (01600) 716649

DAVIES, James William. b 51. Trin Hall Cam BA72 MA76 St Jo Coll Dur BA79. **d** 80 **p** 81. C Croydon Ch Ch Broad Green *Cant* 80-83; CMS 83-86; Chapl Bethany Sch Goudhurst 86-90; P-in-c Parkstone St Luke *Sarum* from 90. *The Vicarage, 2 Birchwood Road, Parkstone, Poole, Dorset BH14 9NP* Parkstone (01202) 741030

DAVIES, Jeremy Michael Widdrington. b 60. LRAM84. Chich Th Coll BTh92. **d** 92 **p** 93. C Wood Green St Mich w Bounds Green St Gabr etc *Lon* from 92. *44 Cornwall Avenue, London N22 4DA* 0181-889 4006

DAVIES, Sister Joan Margaret. b 06. Bedf Coll Lon BA28 Maria Grey Coll Lon DipEd29. **dss** 37 **d** 87. CSA from 34; Notting Hill St Clem *Lon* 37-43; Paddington St Steph w St Luke 48-69; Shadwell St Paul w Ratcliffe St Jas 69-73; R Foundn of St Kath in Ratcliffe 69-73; Abbey Ho Malmesbury 76-79; Lic to Offic *Bris* 76-79. *St Andrew's House, 2 Tavistock Road, London W11 1BA* 0171-229 2662

DAVIES, John Atcherley. b 27. St Jo Coll Dur BA55. Wycliffe Hall Ox 55. **d** 57 **p** 58. Chapl RN 61-82; V Hyde Common *Win* 82-92; rtd 92. *6 Durlston Crescent, St Catherine's Hill, Christchurch, Dorset BH23 2ST* Christchurch (01202) 484398

DAVIES, John Barden. b 47. Univ of Wales (Ban) DipTh70. St D Coll Lamp 70. **d** 71 **p** 72. C Rhosllannerchrugog *St As* 71-75; R Llanbedr-y-Cennin *Ban* 75-86; Adult Educn Officer 86-93; V Betws-y-Coed and Capel Curig w Penmachno etc 86-93; R Llanfwrog and Clocaenog and Gyffylliog *St As* from 93. *The Rectory, Mwrog Street, Ruthin, Clwyd LL15 1LE* Ruthin (01824) 24866

DAVIES, Preb John Conway de la Tour. b 16. Jes Coll Cam BA38 MA42. Ripon Hall Ox 39. **d** 40 **p** 41. V Peterchurch *Heref* 57-83; V Vowchurch and Turnastone 57-83; P-in-c Bredwardine w Brobury 77-83; R Peterchurch w Vowchurch, Turnastone and Dorstone 83-92; RD Abbeydore 78-84; Preb Heref Cathl from 79; rtd 92. *The Palace, Peterchurch, Hereford HR2 0RY* Peterchurch (01981) 550445

DAVIES, John David Edward. b 53. Southn Univ LLB74 Univ of Wales (Cardiff) DipTh84. St Mich Coll Llan 82. **d** 84 **p** 85. C Chepstow *Mon* 84-86; C Michaelston-y-Fedw and Rudry 86-89; R Bedwas and Rudry 89-95; V Newport Maindee St Jo Ev from 95. *St John's Vicarage, 25 St John's Road, Maindee, Newport, Gwent NP9 8GR* Newport (01633) 277009

✠**DAVIES, Rt Rev John Dudley.** b 27. Trin Coll Cam BA51 MA63. Linc Th Coll 52. **d** 53 **p** 54 **c** 87. C Leeds Halton St Wilfrid *Ripon* 53-56; S Africa 57-71; Sec Chapls in HE Gen Syn Bd of Educn 71-74; P-in-c Keele *Lich* 74-76; Chapl Keele Univ 74-76; Lic to Offic *Birm* 76-81; Prin USPG Coll of the Ascension Selly Oak 76-81; Preb Lich Cathl *Lich* 76-87; Can Res, Preb and Sacr St As Cathl *St As* 82-85; Dioc Missr 82-87; V Llanrhaeadr-ym-Mochnant, Llanarmon, Pennant etc 85-87; Suff Bp Shrewsbury *Lich* 87-92; Area Bp Shrewsbury 92-94; Hon Can Lich Cathl 87-92; rtd 94. *Angorfa, 3 Canal Terrace, Canalside, Froncysyllte, Llangollen, Clwyd LL20 7RB*

DAVIES, John Edwards Gurnos. b 18. Ch Coll Cam BA41 MA45. Westcott Ho Cam 40. **d** 42 **p** 43. CF 46-73; R Monk Sherborne and Pamber *Win* 73-76; P-in-c Sherborne 76; R The Sherbornes w Pamber 76-83; rtd 83. *3 Parsonage Lane, Edington, Westbury, Wilts BA13 4QS* Devizes (01380) 830479

DAVIES, John Gwylim. b 27. Ripon Hall Ox 67. **d** 70 **p** 71. C Ox St Mich *Ox* 70-71; C Ox St Mich w St Martin and All SS 71-72; TV New Windsor 73-77; R Hagley *Worc* 77-83; TV Littleham w Exmouth *Ex* 83-92; Asst Dioc Stewardship Adv 83-92; rtd 92; Perm to Offic *Ex* from 92. *5 The Retreat, The Retreat Drive, Topsham, Exeter EX3 0LS* Topsham (01392) 876995

DAVIES, John Gwyn. b 12. St Cath Coll Cam BA36 MA40. Ely Th Coll 36. **d** 37 **p** 38. V Rowington *Cov* 54-77; rtd 78; Perm to Offic *Cov* from 78. *Lapwater, Pinley, Claverdon, Warwick CV35 8NA* Claverdon (01926) 842597

DAVIES, John Harverd. b 57. Keble Coll Ox BA80 MA84 CCC Cam MPhil82. Westcott Ho Cam 82. **d** 84 **p** 85. C Liv Our Lady and St Nic w St Anne *Liv* 84-87; C Pet St Jo Pet 87-90; Min Can Pet Cathl 88-90; V Anfield St Marg *Liv* 90-94; Chapl Fell and Lect Keble Coll Ox from 94. *Keble College, Oxford OX1 3PG* Oxford (01865) 272787 or 272727

DAVIES, Canon John Howard. b 29. St Jo Coll Cam BA50 MA54 Nottm Univ BD62. Westcott Ho Cam 54. **d** 55 **p** 56. Lect Th Southn Univ 63-81; Lic to Offic *Win* 63-81; Sen Lect 74-81; Dir Th and Relig Studies Southn Univ 81-94; Can Th Win Cathl *Win* 81-91; Hon C Southn St Alb 88-91; Hon C Swaythling 91-94; rtd 94. *13 Glen Eyre Road, Southampton SO2 3GA* Southampton (01703) 679359

DAVIES, Canon John Howard. b 35. Ely Th Coll 62. **d** 64 **p** 65. C Bromsgrove All SS *Worc* 64-67; C Astwood Bank w Crabbs Cross 67-70; R Worc St Martin 70-74; P-in-c Worc St Pet 72-74; R Worc St Martin w St Pet 74-79; RD Worc E 77-79; TR Malvern Link w Cowleigh 79-93; Hon Can Worc Cathl from 81; RD Malvern 83-92; V Bromsgrove St Jo from 93. *The Vicarage, 12 Kidderminster Road, Bromsgrove, Worcs B61 7JW* Bromsgrove (01527) 876517

DAVIES, John Hugh Conwy. b 42. CEng MICE72 Bris Univ BSc64 PhD67. Linc Th Coll 84. **d** 86 **p** 87. C Gt Limber w Brocklesby *Linc* 86-89; R Wickenby Gp 89-94; R Denbigh and Nantglyn *St As* from 94. *The Rectory, St David's Lane, Denbigh, Clwyd LL16 3EP* Denbigh (01745) 812970

DAVIES, John Hywel Morgan. b 45. St D Coll Lamp BA71 LTh73. **d** 73 **p** 74. C Milford Haven *St D* 73-77; V from 89; R Castlemartin w Warren and Angle etc 77-82; R Walton W w Talbenny and Haroldston W 82-89. *St Katharine's Vicarage, 1 Sandhurst Road, Milford Haven, Dyfed SA73 3JU* Milford Haven (01646) 693314

DAVIES, John Ifor. b 20. ACP DipEd. **d** 80 **p** 81. Hon C Allerton *Liv* 80-84; Hon C Ffynnongroyw *St As* 84-87; Hon C Whitford 87-88. *Hafan Deg, Ffordd-y-Graig, Lixwm, Holywell, Clwyd CH8 8LY* Halkyn (01352) 781151

DAVIES, John Keith. b 33. St Mich Coll Llan 80. **d** 82 **p** 83. C Llanbadarn Fawr w Capel Bangor and Goginan *St D* 82-84; V Llandygwydd and Cenarth w Cilrhedyn etc 84-89; V Abergwili w Llanfihangel-uwch-Gwili etc from 89; RD Carmarthen from 93. *The Vicarage, Wellfield Road, Abergwili, Carmarthen, Dyfed SA31 2JQ* Carmarthen (01267) 234189

DAVIES, John Melvyn George. b 37. Wycliffe Hall Ox 68. **d** 71 **p** 72. C Norbury *Ches* 71-75; C Heswall 76-78; V Claughton cum Grange 78-83; R Waverton from 83; RD Malpas from 90. *The Vicarage, Waverton, Chester CH3 7QN* Chester (01244) 335581

DAVIES, John Neville Milwyn. b 15. MBE45. Univ of Wales BA37. St Steph Ho Ox 37. **d** 38 **p** 39. CF 42-73; QHC 69-73; V Clapham H Spirit *S'wark* 73-80; rtd 80; Perm to Offic *B & W* 91-94. *Brooklands, Durcott Lane, Camerton, Bath BA3 1QE* Bath (01225) 471361

DAVIES, Canon John Oswell. b 27. St D Coll Lamp 74. **d** 75 **p** 76. C Henfynyw w Aberaeron and Llanddewi Aberarth *St D* 75-76; P-in-c Eglwyswenydd w Ysbyty Ystwyth 76-77; V 77-83; R Maenordeifi and Capel Colman w Llanfihangel etc 83-93; RD Cemais and Sub-Aeron 87-93; Hon Can St D Cathl 92-93; rtd 93. *Hafod, Carregwen, Llechryd, Cardigan, Dyfed SA43 2PJ* Llechryd (01239) 682568

DAVIES, John Rees. b 07. St D Coll Lamp BA38. **d** 41 **p** 42. V Resolven *Llan* 67-77; rtd 77; Perm to Offic *Llan* from 78. *24 Broniestyn Terrace, Trecynon, Aberdare, M Glam CF44 8EG* Aberdare (01685) 875049

DAVIES, Ven John Stewart. b 43. MSOTS Univ of Wales BA72 Qu Coll Cam MLitt74. Westcott Ho Cam 72. **d** 74 **p** 75. C Hawarden *St As* 74-78; Tutor St Deiniol's Lib Hawarden 76-83; V Rhosymedre *St As* 78-87; Dir Dioc Minl Tr Course from 83; Warden of Ords 83-91; Hon Can St As Cathl from 86; V Mold 87-92; Adn St As from 91; R Llandyrnog and Llangwyfan from 92. *The Rectory, Ffordd Las, Llandyrnog, Denbigh, Clwyd LL16 4LT* Llandyrnog (01824) 790777

DAVIES, Canon John Treharne. b 14. St D Coll Lamp BA36. **d** 38 **p** 39. V Potterne *Sarum* 59-73; V Worton 67-73; Can and Preb Sarum Cathl 72-82; P-in-c Ramsbury 73-74; R Whitton 74-76; TR Whitton 76-81; rtd 81; Perm to Offic *Heref* from 82. *16 Lambourne Close, Ledbury, Herefordshire HR8 2HW* Ledbury (01531) 634629

DAVIES, John Vernon. b 16. Or Coll Ox BA40 MA43. Cuddesdon Coll 40. **d** 41 **p** 42. R Radyr *Llan* 69-83; rtd 83; Perm to Offic *Llan* from 83. *8 Insole Gardens, Llandaff, Cardiff CF5 2HW* Cardiff (01222) 562130

DAVIES, John Vernon. b 20. Clifton Th Coll 66. **d** 68 **p** 69. C Surbiton Hill Ch Ch *S'wark* 68-70; C Heatherlands St Jo *Sarum* 70-75; V Wandsworth St Mich *S'wark* 75-83; rtd 83. *11 Pearson Avenue, Parkstone, Poole, Dorset BH14 0DT* Poole (01202) 731591

DAVIES, Johnston ap Llynfi (Ion). b 28. St D Coll Lamp BA51 St Mich Coll Llan 51. **d** 53 **p** 54. Perm to Offic *Ox* 67-72; Perm to Offic *York* 72-86; V Creeksea w Althorne, Latchingdon and N Fambridge *Chelmsf* 86-88; rtd 88; Asst Chapl Costa Blanca *Eur* 89-92; Chapl Costa Blanca 92-93; Lic to Offic from 93. *Pasionaria, 10B Las Adelfas, Calpe 03710, Alicante, Spain* Alicante (65) 583-4165

DAVIES, Joseph Henry. b 17. St D Coll Lamp BA40 St Mich Coll Llan 40. **d** 41 **p** 42. V Barlaston *Lich* 66-78; R Mucklestone 78-82; rtd 82; Perm to Offic *St As* from 82. *5 Dinas Road, Llandudno, Gwynedd LL30 2JD* Llandudno (01492) 878526

DAVIES, Joseph Thomas. b 32. **d** 71 **p** 72. C St Geo-in-the-East w St Paul *Lon* 71-79; R Roos and Garton in Holderness w Tunstall etc *York* 79-89; R Pentlow, Foxearth, Liston and Borley *Chelmsf* from 89. *The Rectory, The Street, Foxearth, Sudbury, Suffolk CO10 7JG* Sudbury (01787) 313132

DAVIES, Dr Julian Edward. b 60. Jes Coll Ox BA82 MA86 DPhil87 Selw Coll Cam BA92. Ridley Hall Cam 90. **d** 94 **p** 95. C Hucknall Torkard *S'well* from 94. *The Knoll, 149 Beardall Street, Hucknall, Nottingham NG15 7HA* Nottingham (0115) 964 1088

DAVIES, Kenneth John. b 42. Ripon Coll Cuddesdon 79. **d** 80 **p** 81. C Buckm *Ox* 80-83; V Birstall *Wakef* 83-91; TV Crookes St Thos *Sheff* 91-94; TR Huntington *York* from 94. *The Rectory, New Lane, Huntington, York YO3 9NU* York (01904) 768160

DAVIES, Kevin Godfrey (Kev). b 62. Univ Coll Ox BA84 MA87. Trin Coll Bris BA93. **d** 93 **p** 94. C Otley *Bradf* from 93. *73 St Clair Road, Otley, W Yorkshire LS21 1DE*

DAVIES, Laurence Gordon. b 28. Down Coll Cam BA52 MA56. Linc Th Coll 52. **d** 54 **p** 55. R Gt w Lt Billing *Pet* 69-83; V Welton w Ashby St Ledgers 83-88; rtd 88; Perm to Offic *Ox* from 89. *Cherry Pie, 56 Couching Street, Watlington, Oxon OX9 5PU* Watlington (01491) 612446

DAVIES, Lawrence. b 14. Univ of Wales (Lamp) BA36. Chich Th Coll 36. **d** 38 **p** 39. V Longdon *Worc* 54-78; V Queenhill w Holdfast 54-78; V Longdon, Bushley and Queenhill w Holdfast 78-86; RD Upton 80-86; rtd 86; Perm to Offic *Worc* from 86. *Theocsbury, Bushley, Tewkesbury, Glos GL20 6HX* Tewkesbury (01684) 294220

DAVIES, Lawrence. b 20. BEM45. Tyndale Hall Bris 46. **d** 49 **p** 50. V Preston All SS *Blackb* 61-73; V St Michaels on Wyre 73-85; rtd 85; Perm to Offic *Blackb* from 85; Perm to Offic *Carl* from 85. *23 Inglemere Gardens, Arnside, Carnforth, Lancs LA5 0BX* Carnforth (01524) 762141

DAVIES, Lawrence Vercoe. b 40. Lich Th Coll 67. **d** 70 **p** 71. C Glan Ely *Llan* 70-77; V Grangetown from 77. *St Paul's Vicarage, Llanmaes Street, Cardiff CF1 7LR* Cardiff (01222) 228707

DAVIES, Ven Lorys Martin. b 36. JP. ALCM52 Univ of Wales (Lamp) BA57. Wells Th Coll 57. **d** 59 **p** 60. C Tenby w Gumfreston *St D* 59-62; Brentwood Sch Essex 62-66; Chapl Solihull Sch Warks 66-68; V Moseley St Mary *Birm* 68-81; Can Res Birm Cathl 81-92; Dioc Dir of Ords 82-90; Adn Bolton *Man* from 92; Bp's Adv Hosp Chaplaincies from 92; Warden of Readers from 92. *45 Rudgwick Drive, Brandlesholme, Bury, Lancs BL8 1YA* 0161-761 6117 Fax as telephone

DAVIES, Malcolm. b 35. St Mich Coll Llan 82. **d** 84 **p** 85. C Roath St Marg *Llan* 84-88; C Pentre 88-94; V Llancarfan w Llantrithyd from 94. *The Vicarage, Llancarfan, Barry, S Glam CF62 3AD* St Athan (01446) 750241

DAVIES, Malcolm Thomas. b 36. Open Univ BA81. St Mich Coll Llan 71. **d** 73 **p** 74. C Betws St Dav w Ammanford *St D* 73-76; V Cilycwm and Ystrad-ffin w Rhandir-mwyn etc 76-80; V Llangyfelach *S & B* 80-85; V Lougher 85-94; V Llanelli St Paul *St D* from 94. *St Peter's Vicarage, St Peter's Close, Paddock Street, Llanelli, Dyfed SA15 2RU* Llanelli (01554) 773865

DAVIES, Mark. b 62. BA85. Coll of Resurr Mirfield 86. **d** 89 **p** 90. C Barnsley St Mary *Wakef* 89-95; R Hemsworth from 95. *The Rectory, 3 Church Close, Hemsworth, Pontefract, W Yorkshire WF9 4SJ* Hemsworth (01977) 610507

DAVIES, Martyn John. b 60. Chich Th Coll 82. **d** 85 **p** 86. C Llantrisant *Llan* 85-87; C Whitchurch 87-90; V Porth w Trealaw from 90. *St Paul's Vicarage, Birchgrove Street, Porth, M Glam CF39 9UU* Porth (01443) 682401

DAVIES, Canon Mervyn Morgan. b 25. Univ of Wales BA49. Coll of Resurr Mirfield 49. **d** 51 **p** 52. C Penarth w Lavernock *Llan* 51-58; Lic to Offic *Wakef* 58-60; C Port Talbot St Theodore *Llan* 60-63; V Pontycymmer and Blaengarw 63-69; V Fairwater from 69; RD Llan from 81; Ed Welsh Churchman from 82; Can Llan Cathl 84-89; Prec from 89. *The Vicarage, 21 St Fagan's Road, Fairwater, Cardiff CF5 3DW* Cardiff (01222) 562551 or 708234

DAVIES, Meurig Ceredig. b 21. Univ of Wales (Abth) BA43. St Mich Coll Llan 43. **d** 45 **p** 46. Perm to Offic *Pet* 64-74; V St Dogmael's w Moylgrove and Monington *St D* 74-86; rtd 86. *Geinfe, Gelliwen, Llechryd, Cardigan, Dyfed SA43 2PQ* Llechryd (01239) 682550

DAVIES, Miss Moira Kathleen. b 41. Cant Sch of Min. **d** 88 **p** 94. Par Dn Walmer *Cant* 88-94; C from 94. *9 Roselands, Deal, Kent CT14 7QE* Deal (01304) 368656

DAVIES, Canon Mostyn David. b 37. AKC64. **d** 65 **p** 66. C Corby St Columba *Pet* 65-69; Ind Chapl from 69; P-in-c Pet St Barn from 80; Can Pet Cathl from 95. *16 Swanspool, Peterborough PE3 7LS* Peterborough (01733) 262034

DAVIES, Myles Cooper. b 50. Sarum & Wells Th Coll 71. **d** 74 **p** 75. C W Derby St Mary *Liv* 74-77; C Seaforth 77-80; V 80-84; Chapl Rathbone Hosp *Liv* from 84; V Stanley *Liv* from 84; Dir of Ords from 94. *St Anne's Vicarage, 8 Derwent Square, Liverpool L13 6QT* 0151-228 5252

DAVIES, Neil Anthony Bowen. b 52. Ex Univ BSc74. Westcott Ho Cam 75. **d** 78 **p** 79. C Llanblethian w Cowbridge and Llandough etc *Llan* 78-80; C Aberdare St Jo 80-82; V Troedyrhiw w Merthyr Vale 82-88; Min Lower Earley LEP *Ox* 88-92; V Earley Trinity 92-95; P-in-c Reading St Luke w St Bart from 95. *St Luke's Vicarage, 14 Erleigh Road, Reading RG1 5LH* Reading (01734) 262372

DAVIES, Nigel Lawrence. b 55. Lanc Univ BEd77. Sarum & Wells Th Coll 84. **d** 87 **p** 88. C Heywood St Luke w All So *Man* 87-91; V Burneside *Carl* from 91. *St Oswald's Vicarage, Burneside, Kendal, Cumbria LA9 6QJ* Kendal (01539) 722015

DAVIES, Noel Paul. b 47. Chich Th Coll 83. **d** 85 **p** 86. C Milford Haven *St D* 85-89; R Jeffreyston w Reynoldston and E Williamston etc from 89. *The Rectory, Jeffreyston, Kilgetty, Dyfed SA68 0SG* Carew (01646) 651269

DAVIES, Norman Edward. b 37. Worc Coll Ox BA62. Cuddesdon Coll 62. **d** 64 **p** 65. C Mottingham St Andr *S'wark* 64-67; Hon C 67-75 and 83-87; Hd Master W Hatch Sch Chigwell 76-82; Hd Master Sedghill Sch Lon 82-87; Hon C Eltham H Trin *S'wark* 77-82; V Plumstead St Mark and St Marg from 87. *St Mark's Vicarage, 11 Old Mill Road, London SE18 1QE* 0181-854 2973

DAVIES, Miss Patricia Elizabeth. b 36. Westf Coll Lon BA58 Hughes Hall Cam CertEd59 Leeds Univ MA74. NE Ord Course 83. **dss** 86 **d** 87 **p** 94. Killingworth *Newc* 86-87; Hon C 87-90; Hon C Newc H Cross from 91. *27 Crossway, Jesmond, Newcastle upon Tyne NE2 3QH* 0191-281 3520

DAVIES, Paul Lloyd. b 46. Solicitor 71 Bris Univ LLB68 Trin Coll Carmarthen 84. **d** 87 **p** 88. NSM Newport w Cilgwyn and Dinas w Llanllawer *St D* from 87. *Priors Wood, The Paddock, Fishguard, Dyfed SA65 9NU* Fishguard (01348) 873306

DAVIES, Paul Martin. b 35. Lon Univ BD75. Sarum & Wells Th Coll 75. **d** 75 **p** 76. C Walthamstow St Mary w St Steph *Chelmsf* 75-79; Kenya 79-86; R Leven w Catwick *York* 86-95; RD N Holderness 90-95; rtd 95. *54 The Meadows, Cherry Burton, Beverley, N Humberside HU17 7SD* Beverley (01964) 551739

DAVIES, Paul Scott. b 59. Cranmer Hall Dur 85. **d** 88 **p** 89. C New Addington *S'wark* 88-91; C Croydon H Sav 91-94; P-in-c Norton in the Moors *Lich* from 94. *The New Rectory, Norton Lane, Stoke-on-Trent ST6 8BY* Stoke-on-Trent (01782) 534622

DAVIES, Percy Sharples. b 10. Univ of Wales BA32. St Steph Ho Ox 32. **d** 34 **p** 35. V Plumstead St Mark and St Marg *S'wark* 68-77; rtd 77. Perm to Offic *Cant* from 77. *The Rectory, Eythorne, Dover, Kent CT15 4AN* Shepherdswell (01304) 830241

DAVIES, Peter Huw. b 57. Crewe & Alsager Coll BEd79. Wycliffe Hall Ox 87. **d** 89 **p** 90. C Moreton *Ches* 89-93; V Weston-super-Mare St Paul *B & W* from 93. *St Paul's Vicarage, 33 Clarence Road North, Weston-super-Mare, Avon BS23 4AW* Weston-super-Mare (01934) 412687

DAVIES, Peter Richard. b 32. St Jo Coll Ox BA55 MA58. Westcott Ho Cam 56. **d** 58 **p** 59. Kenya 63-76; Chapl Bedf Sch 76-85; V Dale and St Brides w Marloes *St D* 85-92; rtd 92. *Canthill Cottage, Dale, Haverfordwest, Dyfed SA62 3QJ* Dale (01646) 636535

DAVIES, Peter Timothy William. b 50. Leeds Univ BSc74. Oak Hill Th Coll 75. **d** 78 **p** 79. C Kingston Hill St Paul *S'wark* 78-81; C Hove Bp Hannington Memorial Ch *Chich* 81-88; V Audley *Lich* from 88. *The Vicarage, Wilbraham Walk,
Audley, Stoke-on-Trent ST7 8HL* Stoke-on-Trent (01782) 720392

DAVIES, Ven Philip Bertram. b 33. Cuddesdon Coll 61. **d** 63 **p** 64. C Atherton *Man* 63-66; V Winton 66-71; R Salford St Phil w St Steph 71-76; V Radlett *St Alb* 76-87; RD Aldenham 79-87; Adn St Alb from 87. *6 Sopwell Lane, St Albans, Herts AL1 1RR* St Albans (01727) 857973

DAVIES, Philip James. b 58. UEA BA79 Keswick Hall Coll PGCE80. Ridley Hall Cam 86. **d** 89 **p** 90. C Rainham *Roch* 89-90; C Gravesend St Geo 90-95; V Rosherville from 95. *St Mark's Vicarage, 123 London Road, Gravesend, Kent DA11 9NH* Gravesend (01474) 534430

DAVIES, Raymond Emlyn Peter. b 25. St Mich Coll Llan 51. **d** 53 **p** 54. V Penrhiwceiber w Matthewstown and Ynysboeth *Llan* 68-72; C Whitchurch 72-73; V Childs Ercall *Lich* 73-81; R Stoke upon Tern 73-81; P-in-c Hamstall Ridware w Pipe Ridware 81-82; P-in-c Kings Bromley 81-82; P-in-c Mavesyn Ridware 81-82; R The Ridwares and Kings Bromley 83-90; rtd 90; Perm to Offic *B & W* from 95. *22 Drake Road, Wells, Somerset BA5 3JX* Wells (01749) 679155

DAVIES, Reginald Charles. b 33. Tyndale Hall Bris 58. **d** 64 **p** 65. C Heywood St Jas *Man* 64-66; C Drypool St Columba w St Andr and St Pet *York* 66-69; V Denaby Main *Sheff* from 69. *The Vicarage, Church Road, Denaby Main, Doncaster, S Yorkshire DN12 4AD* Rotherham (01709) 862297

DAVIES, Rendle Leslie. b 29. St Chad's Coll Dur BA52 DipTh54. **d** 54 **p** 55. C Mon 54-58; V Llangwm Uchaf w Llangwm Isaf w Gwernesney etc 58-63; V Usk and Monkswood w Glascoed Chpl and Gwehelog from 63; Chapl HM Young Offender Inst Usk and Prescoed from 63. *The Vicarage, Castle Parade, Usk, Gwent NP5 1AA* Usk (01291) 672653 Fax 673800

DAVIES, Richard Henry. b 44. Mansf Coll Ox BA72 MA78. St Steph Ho Ox 68. **d** 72 **p** 73. C Higham Ferrers w Chelveston *Pet* 72-80; C Cantley *Sheff* 80-82; V Leic St Aid *Leic* 82-85; C Tonge Moor *Man* 85-94. *46 Ashford Road, Withington, Manchester M20 3EH* 0161-445 2987

DAVIES, Richard James. b 42. Peterho Cam BA64 MA68. St Steph Ho Ox 67. **d** 69 **p** 70. Rhodesia 69-72 and 75-80; Zimbabwe from 80; C Southwick *Chich* 72-74; P-in-c Malmesbury w Westport *Bris* 75. *James's Mission, PO Box 23, Nyamandlovu, Zimbabwe*

DAVIES, Richard Paul. b 48. Wycliffe Hall Ox 72. **d** 75 **p** 76. C Everton St Sav w St Cuth *Liv* 75-78; Chapl Asst Basingstoke Distr Hosp 78-80; TV Basingstoke *Win* 80-85; V Southn Thornhill St Chris 85-94; V Eastleigh from 94. *The Vicarage, 1 Cedar Road, Eastleigh, Hants SO5 5DB* Eastleigh (01703) 612073

DAVIES, Robert Emlyn. b 56. N Staffs Poly BA79. Coll of Resurr Mirfield 83. **d** 86 **p** 87. C Cardiff St Jo *Llan* 86-90; V Cwmparc from 90. *St George's Vicarage, Cwmparc, Treorchy, M Glam CF42 6NA* Treorchy (01443) 773303

DAVIES, Canon Ronald. b 14. Univ of Wales BA36. St Steph Ho Ox 36. **d** 39 **p** 40. V Abergavenny H Trin *Mon* 60-84; Can St Woolos Cathl 76-84; rtd 84; Lic to Offic *Mon* from 84. *The Bungalow, 11 Ysgubarwen, Abergavenny, Gwent NP7 6EE* Abergavenny (01873) 854401

DAVIES, Ross Owen. b 55. Melbourne Univ BA77 LLB79. ACT ThL81. **d** 81 **p** 82. Australia 81-91; P-in-c Mundford w Lynford *Nor* 91-94; P-in-c Ickburgh w Langford 91-94; P-in-c Cranwich 91-94; C Somerton w Compton Dundon, the Charltons etc *B & W* from 94. *The Parsonage, Charlton Adam, Somerton, Somerset TA11 7AS* Charlton Mackrell (01458) 223061

DAVIES, Preb Roy Basil. b 34. Bris Univ BA55. Westcott Ho Cam 57. **d** 59 **p** 60. C Ipswich St Mary le Tower *St E* 59-63; C Clun w Chapel Lawn *Heref* 63-70; V Bishop's Castle w Mainstone 70-83; RD Clun Forest 72-83; Preb Heref Cathl from 82; P-in-c Billingsley w Sidbury 83-86; P-in-c Chelmarsh 83-86; P-in-c Chetton w Deuxhill and Glazeley 83-86; P-in-c Middleton Scriven 83-86; R Billingsley w Sidbury, Middleton Scriven etc 86-89; RD Bridgnorth 87-89; TR Wenlock from 89. *The Rectory, Much Wenlock, Shropshire TF13 6BN* Much Wenlock (01952) 727396

DAVIES, Roy Gabe. b 38. Univ of Wales DipTh64. St Mich Coll Llan 61. **d** 64 **p** 65. C St Issells *St D* 64-65; C Milford Haven 65-67; C Codsall *Lich* 67-70; V Wolv St Steph 70-79; V Newport St Julian *Mon* 79-89; V Lakenheath *St E* 89-94; R Llanllwchaearn and Llanina *St D* from 94. *The Rectory, Llandysul Road, New Quay, Dyfed SA45 9RF* New Quay (01545) 560059

✠**DAVIES, Rt Rev Roy Thomas.** b 34. St D Coll Lamp BA55 Jes Coll Ox DipTh58 BLitt59. St Steph Ho Ox 57. **d** 59 **p** 60 **c** 85. C Llanelli St Paul *St D* 59-64; V Llanafan y Trawscoed and Llanwnnws 64-67; Chapl Univ of Wales (Abth) 67-73; C Abth 67-69; TV 70-73; Sec Ch in Wales Prov Coun for Miss and Unity 73-79; V Carmarthen St Dav *St D* 79-83; Adn Carmarthen 82-85; V Llanegwad w Llanfynydd 83-85; Bp Llan from 85. *Llys Esgob, The Cathedral Green, Llandaff, Cardiff CF5 2YE* Cardiff (01222) 562400

DAVIES, Miss Sally Jane. b 63. Linc Coll Ox BA86. Trin Coll Bris BA92. **d** 92 **p** 94. C E Molesey St Paul *Guildf* from 92. *11 Adecroft Way, West Molesey, Surrey KT8 1PH* 0181-979 9977

DAVIES, Sarah Isabella. b 39. Llan Dioc Tr Scheme 87. **d** 91. NSM Pontypridd St Cath w St Matt *Llan* 91-93; NSM Ferndale w Maerdy from 93. *The Vicarage, Woodville Place, Maerdy, Ferndale, M Glam CF43 4LS* Ferndale (01443) 756322

DAVIES, Sidney. b 16. St D Coll Lamp BA40. **d** 41 **p** 42. R Llanerch Aeron w Ciliau Aeron and Dihewyd *St D* 69-82; rtd 82. *12 Pontfaen, Porthyrhyd, Carmarthen, Dyfed SA32 8PE* Llanddarog (01267) 275525

DAVIES, Stanley James. b 18. MBE54. St Chad's Coll Dur BA40 DipTh41 MA44. **d** 41 **p** 42. CF 45-68; Asst Chapl Gen Lon 68-70; BAOR 70-73; QHC from 72; R Uley w Owlpen and Nympsfield *Glouc* 73-84; rtd 84; Perm to Offic *Ex* from 86. *Peverell Cottage, Doddiscombsleigh, Exeter EX6 7PR* Christow (01647) 52616

DAVIES, Stephen Walter. b 26. AKC54. **d** 55 **p** 56. Chapl RAF 61-77; R Feltwell *Ely* 78-84; R N Newton w St Michaelchurch, Thurloxton etc *B & W* 84-91; rtd 91. *5 Manchester Road, Exmouth, Devon EX8 1DE*

DAVIES, Stuart Simeon. b 13. St Chad's Coll Dur BA41 DipTh42 MA44. Knutsford Test Sch 37. **d** 42 **p** 43. R Fifield w Idbury *Ox* 65-74; rtd 74. *Wing 3, Home of St Monica, Cote Lane, Bristol BS9 3UN* Bristol (0117) 962 9281

DAVIES, Preb Thomas Derwent. b 16. St D Coll Lamp BA38 St Mich Coll Llan 39. **d** 39 **p** 41. Preb Ex Cathl *Ex* from 69;

V Cadbury 74-81; V Thorverton 74-81; rtd 82. *12 Blagdon Rise, Crediton, Devon EX17 1EN* Crediton (01363) 773856

DAVIES, Thomas Stanley. b 10. Nashdom Abbey 33. **d** 37 **p** 38. V Stansted Mountfitchet *Chelmsf* 71-78; rtd 78; Perm to Offic *Chelmsf* from 78. *54 Newbiggen Street, Thaxted, Essex CM6 2QT* Thaxted (01371) 830110

DAVIES, Thomas Neville James. b 27. St Mich Coll Llan 54. **d** 56 **p** 57. C Wrexham *St As* 56-62; V Bronnington and Bettisfield 62-65; CF 65-83. *Address temp unknown*

DAVIES, Canon Thomas Philip. b 27. Univ of Wales (Ban) BEd73. St Mich Coll Llan 55. **d** 56 **p** 57. V Holt and Isycoed *St As* 69-77; Dioc Dir of Educn 76-92; Dioc RE Adv 76-92; RD Wrexham 76-77; R Hawarden 77-92; Can St As Cathl 79-92; rtd 93. *11 Rosewood Grove, Buckley, Clwyd CH7 3JT*

DAVIES, Timothy Robert (Tim). b 64. Bradf Univ BSc87. Wycliffe Hall Ox BTh93. **d** 93 **p** 94. C Eynsham and Cassington *Ox* from 93. *44 Shakespeare Road, Eynsham, Witney, Oxon OX8 1PY* Oxford (01865) 881669

DAVIES, Tommy. b 16. St D Coll Lamp. **d** 39 **p** 40. V Llanfihangel y Pennant and Talyllin *Ban* 54-63; rtd 63. *Gwynfro, Ciliau Aeron, Lampeter, Dyfed SA48 8BX* Cardigan (01239) 614018

DAVIES, Canon Trevor Gwesyn. b 28. Univ of Wales (Ban) BEd73. St Mich Coll Llan 55. **d** 56 **p** 57. C Holywell *St As* 56-63; V Cwm 63-74; V Colwyn Bay from 74; Can St As Cathl from 79. *The Vicarage, Woodland Road East, Colwyn Bay, Clwyd LL29 7DT* Colwyn Bay (01492) 532403

DAVIES, Ven Vincent Anthony (Tony). b 46. Brasted Th Coll 69 St Mich Coll Llan 71. **d** 73 **p** 74. C Owton Manor CD *Dur* 73-76; C Wandsworth St Faith *S'wark* 76-78; P-in-c 78-81; V Walworth St Jo 81-94; RD S'wark and Newington 88-93; Adn Croydon from 94. *246 Pampisford Road, South Croydon, Surrey CR2 6DD* 0181-688 2943

DAVIES, Walter Hugh. b 28. St Deiniol's Hawarden 64. **d** 66 **p** 67. P-in-c Rhosybol and Llandyfrydog *Ban* 70; TV Amlwch, Rhosybol and Llandyfrydog 71-74; R Llanfaethlu w Llanfwrog and Llanrhuddlad etc 74-93; RD Llifon and Talybolion 85-93; rtd 93. *14 Y Fron, Cemaes Bay, Gwynedd LL60 0HU* Cemaes Bay (01407) 710333

DAVIES, Ven Walter Merlin. b 10. St D Coll Lamp BA36 Westcott Ho Cam 37. **d** 38 **p** 39. C Bris St Mich *Bris* 38-40; New Zealand 40-44; Dir of Educn *Bris* 45-49; V Baswich (or Berkswich) *Lich* 49-59; New Zealand from 59; Adn Akaroa and Ashburton 59-69; Adn Sumner 69-73; Hon Can H Trin Cathl Auckland 74-76. *St Hilda's Retreat House, 20 Queen Street, Auckland 9, New Zealand* Auckland (9) 480-7225

DAVIES, William Martin. b 56. Univ of Wales (Cardiff) BSc78. Wycliffe Hall Ox 78. **d** 81 **p** 82. C Gabalfa *Llan* 81-84; P-in-c Beguildy and Heyope *S & B* 84-85; V 85-87; V Swansea St Thos and Kilvey 87-93; Asst Chapl Miss to Seamen from 89; V Belmont *Lon* from 93. *St Anselm's Vicarage, Ventnor Avenue, Stanmore, Middx HA7 2HU* 0181-907 3186

DAVIES, Canon William David. b 19. Bris Univ BA41. St Mich Coll Llan 48. **d** 43 **p** 44. R Porthkerry *Llan* 68-72; R Barry All SS 72-85; RD Penarth and Barry 75-85; Can Llan Cathl 82-85; rtd 85; Perm to Offic *Llan* from 85. *3 Brookfield Park Road, Cowbridge, S Glam CF7 7HS* Cowbridge (01446) 775259

DAVIES, Canon William John Morgan. b 10. St D Coll Lamp BA32. **d** 36 **p** 37. V Defynnog w Rhydybriw and Llandeilo'r Fan *S & B* 54-84; RD Brecon II 76-80; Can Brecon Cathl 78-84; rtd 84. *Bronwysg, Sennybridge, Brecon, Powys LD3 8PG* Sennybridge (01874) 636226

DAVIES, William Morris. b 19. LCP56 Univ of Wales (Lamp) BA41 Jes Coll Ox BA43 MA47 Man Univ DipEd61 Liv Univ MEd68. St Mich Coll Llan 43. **d** 44 **p** 45. Lect Div Crewe Coll Educn 65-68; Sen Lect 68-71; Hd Div Dept 71-75; Tutor Th & Educn Crewe & Alsager Coll of HE 75-79; Tutor Open Univ 78-81; V Norley *Ches* 79-85; Tutor St Deiniol's Lib Hawarden 83-85; rtd 85; Sub-Chapl HM Young Offender Inst Thorn Cross 85-89; Lic to Offic *Ches* from 85. *Eastwood, Willington, Tarporley, Cheshire CW6 0NE* Kelsall (01829) 52181

DAVIES, William Morris. b 23. St Mich Coll Llan 66. **d** 68 **p** 68. C Llangiwg *S & B* 68-72; V Bryngwyn and Newchurch and Llanbedr etc 72-77; R Bedwas *Mon* 77-88; rtd 88. *31 Landore Avenue, Killay, Swansea SA2 7BP* Swansea (01792) 206704

DAVIES-COLE, Charles Sylester. b 38. New Coll Dur BA 80. Edin Th Coll 66. **d** 66. Hon C Edin Old St Paul *Edin* from 66. *121 Mayburn Avenue, Loanhead, Midlothian EH20 9ER* 0131-440 4190

DAVILL, Robin William. b 51. CertEd73 SS Paul & Mary Coll Cheltenham BEd74 Leic Univ MA79. Westcott Ho Cam 86. **d** 88 **p** 89. C Broughton *Blackb* 88-91; C Howden TM *York* 91-93; NSM Crayke w Brandsby and Yearsley from 93. *Leyland House, 44 Uppleby, Easingwold, York YO6 3BB* Easingwold (01347) 823472

DAVIS, Alan. b 34. Birm Univ BSc56. Ox NSM Course. **d** 75 **p** 76. NSM Chesham St Mary *Ox* 75-80; NSM Gt Chesham from 80. *18 Cheyne Walk, Chesham, Bucks HP5 1AY* Chesham (01494) 782124

DAVIS, Alan John. b 33. St Alb Minl Tr Scheme 77. **d** 80 **p** 81. NSM Goldington *St Alb* 80-84; C Benchill *Man* 84-86; R Gt Chart *Cant* from 86. *The Rectory, Great Chart, Ashford, Kent TN23 3AY* Ashford (01233) 620371

DAVIS, Alan Norman. b 38. Open Univ BA75. Lich Th Coll 63. **d** 65 **p** 66. C Kingstanding St Luke *Birm* 65-68; C-in-c Ecclesfield St Paul CD *Sheff* 68-73; V Sheff St Paul Wordsworth Avenue 73-75; V Shiregreen St Jas and St Chris 75-80; R Maltby 80-81; TR 81-89; Abp's Officer for UPA 90-92; Lic to Offic *St Alb* 90-92; P-in-c Carl St Cuth w St Mary Carl from 92; Dioc Communications Officer from 92. *St Cuthbert's Vicarage, West Walls, Carlisle CA3 8UF* Carlisle (01228) 21982 or 22573 Fax 48769

DAVIS, Allan. b 15. ALCD54. **d** 54 **p** 55. V Colchester St Jo *Chelmsf* 67-80; rtd 80; Perm to Offic *St Alb* from 80. *5 Pipit Close, Flitwick, Beds MK45 1NJ* Flitwick (01525) 713854

DAVIS, Andrew Fisher. b 46. St Chad's Coll Dur BA67. St Steph Ho Ox 68. **d** 70 **p** 71. C Beckenham St Jas *Roch* 70-74; C Kensington St Mary Abbots w St Geo *Lon* 74-80; V Sudbury St Andr 80-90; AD Brent 85-90; V Ealing Ch the Sav from 90. *The Clergy House, The Grove, London W5 5DX* 0181-567 1288

DAVIS, Andrew George (Andy). b 63. Bath Univ BSc Edin Univ BD. Edin Th Coll. **d** 89 **p** 90. C Alverstoke *Portsm* 89-92; C Portsea N End St Mark from 92. *St Francis House, 186 Northern Parade, Portsmouth PO2 9LU* Portsmouth (01705) 662467

DAVIS, Arthur Vivian. b 24. Clifton Th Coll 60. **d** 62 **p** 63. V Cam St Andr Less *Ely* 68-75; V Kirtling 75-86; V Wood Ditton w Saxon Street 75-86; P-in-c Cheveley 83-86; P-in-c Ashley w Silverley 83-86; rtd 86. *408 Studland Park, Newmarket, Suffolk CB8 7BB* Newmarket (01638) 661709

DAVIS, Canon Bernard Rex. b 33. FRSA87 Sydney Univ BA55 Newc Univ MA67. Gen Th Sem (NY) MDiv60 Coll of Resurr Mirfield. **d** 57 **p** 58. C Guildf St Nic *Guildf* 57-59; USA 59-61; Australia 62-68; Exec Sec Unit 3 WCC Geneva 68-77; Warden Edw K Ho from 77; Can Res and Sub Dean Linc Cathl *Linc* from 77; Treas from 85. *The Subdeanery, 18 Minster Yard, Lincoln LN2 1PX* Lincoln (01522) 521932

DAVIS, Canon Brian. b 40. AKC69 BD69. St Aug Coll Cant 69. **d** 70 **p** 71. C Humberstone *Leic* 70-73; C Kirby Muxloe 73-74; V Countesthorpe w Foston 74-91; RD Guthlaxton I (Blaby) 90-91; V Hinckley St Mary from 91; RD Sparkenhoe W (Hinkley and Bosworth) from 92; Hon Can Leic Cathl from 94. *St Mary's Vicarage, Hinckley, Leics LE10 1EQ* Hinckley (01455) 234241

DAVIS, Christopher Eliot. b 28. Pemb Coll Cam BA50 MA55. Wells Th Coll 52. **d** 54 **p** 55. Perm to Offic *Lich* from 62; Chapl Magd Coll Ox 71-74; rtd 93. *28 Newbridge Crescent, Wolverhampton WV6 0LH* Wolverhampton (01902) 759220

DAVIS, Christopher James. b 63. Worc Coll Ox BA85. Cranmer Hall Dur 88. **d** 91 **p** 92. C Margate H Trin *Cant* 91-94; C Cam H Sepulchre *Ely* from 94. *9 Victoria Street, Cambridge CB1 1JP* Cambridge (01223) 359314

DAVIS, Clinton Ernest Newman. b 46. Solicitor 71. Wycliffe Hall Ox 78. **d** 80 **p** 81. C Margate H Trin *Cant* 80-84; C St Laurence in the Isle of Thanet 84-87; V Sandgate St Paul 87-92; P-in-c Folkestone St Geo 92; R Sandgate St Paul w Folkestone St Geo from 92. *St George's Vicarage, 133 Shorncliffe Road, Folkestone, Kent CT20 3PB* Folkestone (01303) 255907

DAVIS, Donald Richard. b 59. Oak Hill Th Coll DipHE94. **d** 94 **p** 95. C Plymouth St Jude *Ex* from 94. *120 Salisbury Road, Plymouth PL4 8TB* Plymouth (01752) 224877

DAVIS, Edwin John Charles. b 36. Dur Univ BA60 St Cath Soc Ox BA62 MA66. Ripon Hall Ox 60. **d** 62 **p** 63. C Kington w Huntington *Heref* 62-65; Lect Lich Th Coll 65-66; Chapl Edin Th Coll 66-70; Hon Chapl St Mary's Cathl *Edin* 66-70; P-in-c Hope w Shelve *Heref* 70-78; R 78-81; P-in-c Middleton 70-78; V 78-81; P-in-c Worthen 75-78; R 78-81; V S Hinksey *Ox* from 81; Dep Dir Tr Scheme for NSM from 84. *New Hinksey Vicarage, Vicarage Road, Oxford OX1 4RD* Oxford (01865) 245879

DAVIS, Mrs Elizabeth Jane. b 42. S'wark Ord Course 91. **d** 94. NSM Plaistow St Mary *Roch* from 94. *3 Kinnaird Avenue, Bromley BR1 4HG* 0181-460 4672

DAVIS, Canon Herbert Roger. b 36. Kelham Th Coll 60. **d** 65 **p** 66. C Barkingside St Fran *Chelmsf* 65-69; C Harpenden St Nic *St Alb* 69-73; P-in-c Eaton Bray 73-75; V Eaton Bray w Edlesborough 75-81; RD Dunstable 77-81; R Gt Berkhamsted from 81; Hon Can St Alb from 93. *The Rectory, Berkhamsted, Herts HP4 2DH* Berkhamsted (01442) 864194

DAVIS, Ian Andrew. b 58. MIBiol85 CBiol85 Sheff Univ BSc79 PGCE80. St Jo Coll Nottm LTh89 DPS90. **d** 90 **p** 91. C Hatf *Sheff* 90-92; C Beighton 92-95; R Thurnscoe St Helen from 95. *The Rectory, 4 High Street, Thurnscoe, Rotherham, S Yorkshire S63 0SU* Rotherham (01709) 893186

DAVIS, Ivor Leslie. b 23. TCD BA48 MA53. **d** 48 **p** 49. V Eccleston Park *Liv* 61-70; R Maghull 70-72; TR 72-88; rtd 88. *3 Oxford Gardens, Oxford Road, Southport, Merseyside PR8 2LL* Southport (01704) 69480

DAVIS, Jack. b 35. LRSC63 CChem80 MRSC80 Sheff City Poly HNC59 Sheff Univ MSc88. Oak Hill Th Coll DipHE88. **d** 88 **p** 89. C Owlerton *Sheff* 88-91; V Manea *Ely* 91-93; R Wimblington 91-93; P-in-c Walsoken 93-94; R from 94. *The Rectory, Walsoken, Wisbech, Cambs PE13 3RA* Wisbech (01945) 583740

DAVIS, James Raymond. b 17. Mert Coll Ox BA40 MA44. Wells Th Coll 40. **d** 41 **p** 42. V Borden *Cant* 64-84; rtd 84; Perm to Offic *Llan* from 85. *277 Albany Road, Cardiff CF2 3NX* Cardiff (01222) 495860

DAVIS, John Basil. b 20. Lon Univ BA69. Bps' Coll Cheshunt 46. **d** 49 **p** 50. V Bacton w Edingthorpe *Nor* 61-66; Perm to Offic *S'well* 71-86; rtd 85; Hon C Bingham *S'well* from 86. *1 Banks Crescent, Bingham, Nottingham NG13 8BP* Bingham (01949) 837721

DAVIS, John Brian. b 33. Linc Th Coll 72. **d** 75 **p** 76. Hon C Bungay H Trin w St Mary *St E* 75-84; P-in-c Barrow 84-85; P-in-c Denham St Mary 84-85; R Barrow w Denham St Mary and Higham Green from 85. *The Rectory, Barrow, Bury St Edmunds, Suffolk IP29 5AA* Bury St Edmunds (01284) 810279

DAVIS, John Harold. b 54. St Jo Coll Dur BSc76 DipTh78 MA86. Cranmer Hall Dur 76. **d** 79 **p** 80. C Marske in Cleveland *York* 79-82; C Pocklington w Yapham-cum-Meltonby, Owsthorpe etc 82-83; TV Pocklington Team 84-86; V Carlton and Drax 86-95; Ind Chapl from 88; V Sowerby from 95; P-in-c Sessay from 95. *The Vicarage, The Close, Sowerby, Thirsk, N Yorkshire YO7 1JA* Thirsk (01845) 523546

DAVIS, John Stephen. b 51. N Staffs Poly BSc75. Wycliffe Hall Ox 75. **d** 78 **p** 79. C Meole Brace *Lich* 78-81; C Bloxwich 81-85; V Walsall St Paul from 85. *St Paul's Vicarage, 57 Mellish Road, Walsall WS4 2DG* Walsall (01922) 24963

DAVIS, Kenneth Gordon. b 18. Selw Coll Cam BA40 MA43. Qu Coll Birm 40. **d** 42 **p** 43. V Exbury *Win* 63-77; V Beaulieu and Exbury 77-83; rtd 83; Perm to Offic *Win* from 83; Hon C Highcliffe w Hinton Admiral from 85. *2 Chatsworth Way, New Milton, Hants BH25 5UL* New Milton (01425) 618520

DAVIS, Preb Kenneth William (Ken). b 25. Ripon Hall Ox 60. **d** 62 **p** 63. R Axbridge *B & W* 65-72; V Wells St Cuth 72-73; V Wells St Cuth w Wookey Hole 73-92; RD Shepton Mallet 79-86; Preb Wells Cathl 83-92; rtd 92. *Ramel, Green Lane, Street, Somerset BA16 0QL* Street (01458) 841673

DAVIS, Martyn Kevin. b 59. Chich Th Coll 84. **d** 87 **p** 88. C Hove All SS *Chich* 87-91; Youth Officer *Pet* 92-95. *5 Kestrel Close, Weston Favell, Northampton NN3 3JG* Northampton (01604) 414801

DAVIS, Michael James Burrows. b 36. ED JP87. St Deiniol's Hawarden Ridley Hall Cam. **d** 72 **p** 72. Bermuda from 72. *PO Box SN 74, Southampton SN BX, Bermuda* Bermuda (1-809) 238-0236 Fax 238-3767

DAVIS, Nicholas Anthony Wylie. b 56. BA. Chich Th Coll. **d** 84 **p** 85. C N Lambeth *S'wark* 84-88; TV Catford (Southend) and Downham 88-94; V Camberwell St Phil and St Mark from 94. *St Philip's Vicarage, Avondale Square, London SE1 5PD* 0171-237 3239

DAVIS, Norman. b 38. FCII66. Oak Hill Th Coll 77. **d** 79 **p** 80. C Walton *St E* 79-82; P-in-c Bredfield w Boulge 86-91; P-in-c Grundisburgh w Burgh 82-91; RD Woodbridge from 90; R Boulge w Burgh and Grundisburgh from 91. *The Rectory, Grundisburgh, Woodbridge, Suffolk IP13 6UF* Grundisburgh (01473) 735749

DAVIS, Norman John. b 41. Oak Hill Th Coll 63. **d** 66 **p** 67. C Wellington w Eyton *Lich* 66-70; C Higher Openshaw *Man* 70-72; R S Levenshulme 72-79; P-in-c Berrow w Pendock and Eldersfield *Worc* 79-81; R 81-87; R Churchill-in-Halfshire w Blakedown and Broome from 87. *The Rectory, 5 Mill Lane, Blakedown, Kidderminster, Worcs DY10 3ND* Kidderminster (01562) 700293

DAVIS, Paul Montague. b 29. St Jo Coll Dur BA52. Ely Th Coll 52. **d** 54 **p** 55. Hon C Colchester St Jas, All SS, St Nic and St Runwald *Chelmsf* 72-81; C Hockley 67-70; V Lt Horkesley 81-85; R The Bromleys 85-94; rtd 94. *5 Coltsfoot Court, Colchester CO4 5UD* Colchester (01206) 852474

DAVIS, Ronald Geoffrey. b 47. St Jo Coll Nottm 79. **d** 81 **p** 81. C Maidstone St Luke *Cant* 81-84; P-in-c Lostwithiel *Truro* 84-86; P-in-c Lanhydrock 84-86; Asst Dioc Youth Officer 84-86; P-in-c Boughton Monchelsea *Cant* 86-88; V from 88; Six Preacher Cant Cathl from 94; C Maidstone St Martin from 95. *The Vicarage, Church Hill, Boughton Monchelsea, Maidstone, Kent ME17 4BU* Maidstone (01622) 743321

DAVIS, Ronald Frank. b 26. Oak Hill Th Coll 62. **d** 64 **p** 65. V N and S Otterington *York* 67-77; C Rainham *Chelmsf* 77-82; V Hainault 82-88; rtd 88. *Home View, Westview Grove, Keighley, W Yorkshire BD20 6JJ* Keighley (01535) 681294

DAVIS, Royston Grandfield. b 33. Sarum & Wells Th Coll 86. **d** 88 **p** 89. C Cainscross w Selsley *Glouc* 88-90; TV Hugglescote w Donington, Ellistown and Snibston *Leic* 90-93; P-in-c Gilmorton w Peatling Parva and Kimcote etc 93-95; R Ogwell and Denbury *Ex* from 95. *The Rectory, 1 St Bartholomew Way, Ogwell, Newton Abbot, Devon TQ12 6YW* Newton Abbot (01626) 54330

DAVIS, Sidney Charles. b 31. DMA61 ACIS61 FCIS73. S Dios Minl Tr Scheme 80. **d** 83 **p** 84. NSM Amesbury *Sarum* 83-93; Nat Chapl Ex-Prisoners of War Assn from 90. *4 Stonehenge Road, Amesbury, Salisbury SP4 7BA* Amesbury (01980) 623248

DAVIS, Simon Charles. b 63. Plymouth Poly BSc86. Trin Coll Bris BA92. **d** 92 **p** 93. C Bollington St Jo *Ches* from 92. *5 Sandy Close, Bollington, Macclesfield, Cheshire SK10 5DT* Bollington (01625) 572856

DAVIS, Stephen Charles. b 19. AKC48 St Cath Soc Ox BA50 MA54. Wycliffe Hall Ox 48. **d** 50 **p** 51. R Dur St Marg *Dur* 64-87; rtd 87. *6 Juniper Way, Malvern, Worcs WR14 4XG* Malvern (01684) 561039

DAVIS, Thomas Edward. b 20. **d** 83 **p** 84. NSM Cen Telford *Lich* from 83. *14 Bembridge, Telford, Shropshire TF3 1NA* Telford (01952) 592352

DAVIS, Timothy Charles (Tim). b 59. Reading Univ BA81 Homerton Coll Cam PGCE82. Trin Coll Bris DipHE91. **d** 91 **p** 92. C Normanton *Wakef* from 91. *8 Prospect Avenue, Ashgap Lane, Normanton, Wakefield, W Yorkshire WF6 2DS* Wakefield (01924) 892773

DAVIS, Trevor Lorenzo. b 45. Simon of Cyrene Th Inst 92. **d** 94. NSM Upper Norwood St Jo *S'wark* from 94. *31B Thornlaw Road, London SE27 0SH* 0181-766 6238

DAVIS, William Henry (Bill). b 17. Open Univ BA84. Bps' Coll Cheshunt. **d** 67 **p** 68. C Sudbury St Andr *Lon* 67-70; V Wickhambrook *St E* 70-72; V Wickhambrook w Stradishall and Denston 72-91; V Wickhambrook 91-95; P-in-c Stansfield 76-78; rtd 95. *Folly Barn, 10 Bellevue Road, Weymouth, Dorset DT4 8RX* Weymouth (01305) 784853

DAVIS-JONES, Noel Jenkin. b 10. St D Coll Lamp BA32. **d** 33 **p** 34. R Amcotts w Luddington and Garthorpe *Linc* 65-76; RD Is of Axholme 69-76; P-in-c Althorpe 70-76; rtd 76; P-in-c Llanddewi Ystradenni and Abbey Cwmhir *S & B* 76-84; P-in-c Llanddewi Ystradenni 84-94; P-in-c Llanbister and Llanbadarn Fynydd w Llananno 84-87. *Llandewi Vicarage, Llandrindod Wells, Powys LD1 6SE* Penybont (01597) 851424

DAVISON, Miss Beryl. b 37. Lightfoot Ho Dur 62. **d** 87 **p** 94. Par Dn Consett *Dur* 87-92; D-in-c Holmside 92-94; P-in-c from 94. *Holmside Vicarage, Burnhope, Durham DH7 0DP* Lanchester (01207) 529274

DAVISON, George Thomas William. b 65. St Andr Univ BD88. Oak Hill Th Coll 88 CITC BTh92. **d** 92 **p** 93. C Portadown St Mark *Arm* 92-95; I Kinawley w Drumany and Crom *K, E & A* from 95. *Kinawley Rectory, Derrylin, Enniskillen, Co Fermanagh BT92 9LA* Derrylin (0136574) 284

DAVISON, Ralph Guild. b 13. Ely Th Coll 33. **d** 36 **p** 37. R Bagborough *B & W* 63-78; Hd Chapl Franciscans Posbury from 78; Lic to Offic *Ex* from 78. *St Mary of the Angels, Posbury, Crediton, Devon EX17 3QF* Crediton (01363) 773280

DAVISON, Richard Ireland. b 42. St Chad's Coll Dur BSc63. Linc Th Coll 64. **d** 66 **p** 67. C Cockerton *Dur* 66-70; C Houghton le Spring 70-73; V Heworth St Alb 73-80; Ascension Is 80-82; V Dunston *Dur* 82-85; V Bishopwearmouth Ch Ch from 85; RD Wearmouth from 94. *Christ Church Vicarage, 7 St Bede's Park, Sunderland SR2 7DZ* 0191-565 8077

DAVISON, Richard John. b 32. St Andr Univ MA56. Linc Th Coll 56. **d** 58 **p** 59. C S Shields St Hilda *Dur* 58-61; C Dur St Cuth 61-63; R Wyberton *Linc* 63-86; RD Holland W 84-86; TR Swan *Ox* 86-91; V Streatley w Moulsford from 91. *The Vicarage, Streatley, Reading RG8 9HX* Goring-on-Thames (01491) 872191

DAVISON, Canon Roger William. b 20. Kelham Th Coll 46. **d** 51 **p** 52. V Higham Ferrers w Chelveston *Pet* 65-88; rtd 88; Perm to Offic *Roch* from 88. *17 Hermitage Road, Higham, Rochester, Kent ME3 7DB* Shorne (01474) 823824

DAVISON, Thomas Alfred. b 28. St Aug Coll Cant 48 St Chad's Coll Dur 52. **d** 60 **p** 61. R Coates *Glouc* 65-76; R Coates, Rodmarton and Sapperton etc 76-78; Chapl R Agric Coll Cirencester 67-78; P-in-c Bleadon *B & W* 78-81; Chapl HM Pris Leeds 81-84; Chapl HM Pris Channings Wood 84-89; P-in-c Pyworthy, Pancrasweek and Bridgerule *Ex* 89-91; P-in-c Otterton and Colaton Raleigh 91-94; rtd 94. *6 Grosvenor Terrace, Ferndale Road, Teignmouth, Devon TQ14 8NE* Teignmouth (01626) 779202

DAVISON, William. b 18. St D Coll Lamp 58. **d** 60 **p** 61. R Mareham le Fen *Linc* 66-76; Lic to Offic 77-78; P-in-c Barkestone cum Plungar and Redmile *Leic* 78; R 78-81; rtd 82. *28 Stoney Way, Tetney, Grimsby, S Humberside DN36 5PG* Grimsby (01472) 814252

DAVOLL, Ivan John (Snowy). b 33. DipYW67. Local NSM Course 87. **d** 88 **p** 90. NSM Bermondsey St Jas w Ch Ch *S'wark* 88-93; C from 93. *2 Thurland Road, London SE16 4AA* 0171-237 8741

DAVY, Peter Geoffrey. b 31. **d** 94. NSM St Columb Minor and St Colan *Truro* from 94. *9 Tredour Road, Newquay, Cornwall TR7 2EY* Newquay (01637) 872241

DAW, Geoffrey Martin (Geoff). b 57. Oak Hill Th Coll 81. **d** 84 **p** 85. C Hollington St Leon *Chich* 84-87; C Seaford w Sutton 87-90; V Iford w Kingston and Rodmell from 90. *The Rectory, 14 Lockitt Way, Kingston, Lewes, E Sussex BN7 3LG* Lewes (01273) 473665

DAWE, David Fife Purchas. b 20. Keble Coll Ox BA41 MA45. Wells Th Coll 41. **d** 43 **p** 44. V Criftins *Lich* 61-77; V Dudleston 63-77; P-in-c Alkmonton w Yeaveley *Derby* 77-81; P-in-c Cubley w Marston Montgomery 77-81; V Alkmonton, Cubley, Marston, Montgomery etc 81-85; rtd 85; Perm to Offic *Derby* 85-94; Perm to Offic *Lich* 85-94. *11 Coaching Walk, Northampton NN3 3EU* Northampton (01604) 414083

DAWES, Dori Katherine. b 37. ARCM. Oak Hill NSM Course 85. **d** 88 **p** 94. Par Dn Watford St Luke *St Alb* 88-90; Par Dn Watford 90-94; C from 94. *135 Abbots Road, Abbots Langley, Herts WD5 0BJ* Kings Langley (01923) 262516

DAWES, Hugh William. b 48. Univ Coll Ox BA71 MA76. Cuddesdon Coll 71. **d** 74 **p** 75. C Purley St Mark Woodcote *S'wark* 74-77; Chapl G&C Coll Cam 77-82; Lic to Offic *Ely* 78-87; Chapl Em Coll Cam 82-87; V Cam St Jas *Ely* from 87. *St James's Vicarage, 110 Wulfstan Way, Cambridge CB1 4QJ* Cambridge (01223) 246419

DAWES, Julian Edward. b 27. RAF Coll Cranwell 49. Bps' Coll Cheshunt 58. **d** 59 **p** 60. V Overbury w Alstone, Teddington and Lt Washbourne *Worc* 65-70; V Cropthorne w Charlton 70-76; Chapl Dioc Conf Cen 70-76; Chapl Exe Vale Hosp Gp 76-84; Chapl Bromsgrove and Redditch Distr Gen Hosp 84-86; rtd 91. *41 Thornton Hill, Exeter EX4 4NR* Exeter (01392) 77928

DAWES, Peter Martin. b 24. Westmr Coll Cam 52. **d** 81 **p** 81. C Dunscroft Ch Ch *Sheff* 81-83; V 83-89; rtd 89. *2 Holway Cottages, The Mall, Swindon SN1 4JB* Swindon (01793) 615878

✠**DAWES, Rt Rev Peter Spencer.** b 28. Hatf Coll Dur BA52. Tyndale Hall Bris 53. **d** 54 **p** 55 **c** 88. C Whitehall Park St Andr Hornsey Lane *Lon* 54-57; C Ox St Ebbe *Ox* 57-60; Tutor Clifton Th Coll 60-65; V Romford Gd Shep Collier Row *Chelmsf* 65-80; Hon Can Chelmsf Cathl 78-80; Adn W Ham 80-88; Dioc Dir of Ords 80-86; Bp Derby 88-95; rtd 95. *45 Arundell, Ely, Cambs CB6 1BQ* Ely (01353) 661241

DAWES, Victor. b 18. Wycliffe Hall Ox 63. **d** 64 **p** 65. V Andreas St Jude *S & M* 67-73; V Jurby 67-73; Warden Baycliff Healing Cen 73-83; Perm to Offic from 85; rtd 89. *48 Ballakane Close, Port Erin, Isle of Man IM9 6EH* Port Erin (01624) 832921

DAWKES, Peter. b 31. Roch Th Coll 64. **d** 66 **p** 67. C Buxton *Derby* 69-72; V Somercotes 72-93; rtd 93; Hon C Kenton, Mamhead, Powderham, Cofton and Starcross *Ex* from 93. *All Saints House, Kenton, Exeter EX6 8NG* Starcross (01626) 890214

DAWKIN, Peter William. b 60. Nottm Univ BTh88 Open Univ BA91. St Jo Coll Nottm 85. **d** 88 **p** 89. C Birkdale St Jo *Liv* 88-91; C Netherton 91-93; V Liv Ch Ch Norris Green from 93. *Christ Church Vicarage, Sedgemoor Road, Liverpool L11 3BR* 0151-226 1774

DAWKINS, Canon Alan Arthur Windsor. b 26. Lon Univ DipTh54. St Aid Birkenhead 53. **d** 55 **p** 56. V Westgate St Jas *Cant* 66-74; V Herne Bay Ch Ch 74-83; Hon Can Cant Cathl 79-91; P-in-c Chilham 83-85; Adv for Miss and Unity 85-91; rtd 91. *5 Randolph Close, Canterbury, Kent CT1 3AZ* Canterbury (01227) 452009

DAWKINS, Anthony Norman. b 32. HNC55. NW Ord Course 70. **d** 73 **p** 74. C Man Clayton St Cross w St Paul *Man* 73-74; C Chorlton-cum-Hardy St Werburgh 74-77; C Scarborough St Martin *York* 77-78; P-in-c Kexby w Wilberfoss 78-84; R Dodleston *Ches* 84-88; V Felkirk w Brierley *Wakef* from 88. *The Vicarage, George Street, Brierley, Barnsley, S Yorkshire S72 9BX* Barnsley (01226) 715315

DAWKINS, Canon Cuthbert Howard. b 10. Peterho Cam BA32 MA47. St Andr Coll Pampisford 47. **d** 47 **p** 48. Kenya from 56; rtd 75. *Trinity Fellowship, PO Box 376, Kisumu, Kenya* Kisumu (35) 2948

DAWKINS, Michael Howard. b 44. BTh. Tyndale Hall Bris 67. **d** 69 **p** 69. C Drypool St Columba w St Andr and St Pet *York* 69-73; CF 74-80; P-in-c Bulford *Sarum* 80-81; P-in-c Figheldean w Milston 80-81; R Meriden *Cov* from 85. *The Rectory, The Green, Meriden, Coventry CV7 7LN* Meriden (01676) 22719

DAWSON, Alan. b 28. St Jo Coll Dur BA54 Liv Univ MA67. Clifton Th Coll 54. **d** 56 **p** 57. V Birkdale St Pet *Liv* 69-91; rtd 91. *8 Dunbar Avenue, Kirkcudbright DG6 4HD* Kirkcudbright (01557) 30017

DAWSON, Arthur Roger. b 38. Sarum Th Coll 64. **d** 66 **p** 66. C Addiscombe St Mildred *Cant* 66-67; C Cove St Jo *Guildf* 67-69; C-in-c Newton-in-Makerfield Em CD *Liv* 75-77; R Newton in Makerfield Em 77-83; BCC 83-87; Hon C Dulwich St Barn *S'wark* 84-92; R Hockering, Honingham, E and N Tuddenham *Nor* from 92. *The Rectory, Hockering, Dereham, Norfolk NR20 3HP* Norwich (01603) 880121

DAWSON, Barry. b 38. Lon Univ DipTh65. Oak Hill Th Coll 63. **d** 66 **p** 67. C Fulham St Mary N End *Lon* 66-69; C St Marylebone All So w SS Pet and Jo 69-73; Bp's Chapl *Nor* 73-76; Gen Sec CEMS 76-81; V Rye Park St Cuth *St Alb* 81-89; V Attenborough *S'well* from 89. *The Vicarage, 6 St Mary's Close, Attenborough, Notts NG9 6AT* Nottingham (0115) 925 9602

DAWSON, Canon Brian. b 33. Leeds Univ BA54 Lon Univ DipTh57 Man Univ MA84. Coll of Resurr Mirfield 56. **d** 58 **p** 59. C Hollinwood *Man* 58-62; C Rawmarsh w Parkgate *Sheff* 62-63; V Royton St Anne *Man* 63-75; V Urswick *Carl* 75-86; V Bardsea 75-86; R Skelton and Hutton-in-the-Forest w Ivegill from 86; RD Penrith from 91; Hon Can Carl Cathl from 94. *The Rectory, Skelton, Penrith, Cumbria CA11 9SE* Skelton (017684) 84295

DAWSON, Christopher John Rowland. b 26. OBE QPM. Lon Univ DipTh86. S'wark Ord Course 82. **d** 86 **p** 87. NSM Sevenoaks St Jo *Roch* from 86. *Craggan House, 58 Oak Hill Road, Sevenoaks, Kent TN13 1NT* Sevenoaks (01732) 458037

DAWSON, Clifford Mildmay Asquith. b 22. Wycliffe Hall Ox. **d** 58 **p** 59. R Bradfield *Sheff* 68-77; V Brodsworth 77; V Brodsworth w Hooton Pagnell, Frickley etc 77-80; V Wentworth 80-87; rtd 87; Perm to Offic *Linc* from 87. *2A Trinity Lane, Louth, Lincs LN11 8DL* Louth (01507) 603167

DAWSON, Canon Cyril. b 34. St Chad's Coll Dur BA58 DipTh59. **d** 59 **p** 60. C Honicknowle *Ex* 59-63; C Paignton St Jo 63-66; V Heptonstall *Wakef* 66-71; V Todmorden 71-82; RD Calder Valley 75-82; Can Res Wakef Cathl 82-92; Vice-Provost 86-92; Hon Can from 92; V Darrington w Wentbridge from 92. *The Vicarage, Darrington, Pontefract, W Yorkshire WF8 3AB* Pontefract (01977) 704744

DAWSON, Edward. **d** 81 **p** 83. Hon C Newington St Paul *S'wark* 81-85; Hon C Walworth St Jo from 85; Chapl Asst Maudsley Hosp Lon from 87. *3 Ethel Street, London SE17 1NH* 0171-701 8923

DAWSON, Francis Andrew Oliver Duff. b 48. Keble Coll Ox BA70 MA74. St Jo Coll Nottm 74. **d** 76 **p** 77. C Billericay St Mary *Chelmsf* 76-77; C Billericay and Lt Burstead 77-80; C Childwall All SS *Liv* 80-84; Chapl St Kath Coll 80-84; V Shevington *Blackb* from 84. *St Anne's Vicarage, Gathurst Lane, Shevington, Wigan, Lancs WN6 8HW* Appley Bridge (01257) 252136

DAWSON, Frederick William (Fred). b 44. St Chad's Coll Dur BA66 Nottm Univ MTh74. Linc Th Coll 67. **d** 69 **p** 70. C Caversham *Ox* 69-72; C Ranmoor *Sheff* 72-79; R Kibworth Beauchamp *Leic* 79-82; R Kibworth and Smeeton Westerby and Saddington 82-94; R Tilehurst St Mich *Ox* from 94. *Tilehurst Rectory, Routh Lane, Reading RG3 4JY* Reading (01734) 411127 or 427331

DAWSON, George Cuming. b 17. Ch Ch Ox BA38 TCD BA56. TCD Div Sch. **d** 58 **p** 59. Hon CV Ch Ch Cathl Dub *D & G* 68-92; P-in-c Dub St Werburgh 74-79; C Dub Ch Ch Cathl Gp 79-84; rtd 84. *Kilronan, Cloghran, Co Dublin, Irish Republic* Dublin (1) 840-1224

DAWSON, Ian Douglas. b 52. Liv Univ BSc73. N Ord Course 83. **d** 86 **p** 87. NSM Southport SS Simon and Jude *Liv* 86-93; NSM Birkdale St Jas from 93. *15 Melling Road, Southport, Merseyside PR9 9DY* Southport (01704) 533172

DAWSON, John Thomas Merrilees. b 22. Newc Univ CertBS63. NE Ord Course 61 Wycliffe Hall Ox 81. **d** 82 **p** 83. C Kingston upon Hull H Trin *York* 82-86; P-in-c Settrington w N Grimston and Wharram 86-95; rtd 95. *Earlwood, 131 Welham Road, Norton, Malton, N Yorkshire YO17 9DU* Malton (01653) 692192

DAWSON, John William Arthur. b 43. E Midl Min Tr Course DipTh95. **d** 95. NSM Breedon cum Isley Walton and Worthington *Leic* from 95. *Orchard House, Manor Drive, Worthington, Ashby-de-la-Zouch, Leics LE65 1RN* Ashby-de-la-Zouch (01530) 222673

DAWSON, Miss Mary. b 51. Loughb Coll of Educn ALA73. E Midl Min Tr Course 85. **d** 90 **p** 94. Par Dn Braunstone *Leic*

DAWSON

90-92; Par Dn Shrewsbury H Cross *Lich* 92-94; C 94-95; P-in-c Glentworth Gp *Linc* from 95. *The Vicarage, 1 Stone Lane, Glentworth, Gainsborough, Lincs DN21 5DF*   Hemswell (01427) 668203

DAWSON, Neil. b 49. Ripon Hall Ox 71. **d** 74 **p** 75. C Putney St Mary *S'wark* 74-78; C Camberwell St Giles 78-80; TV N Lambeth 84-86; V E Dulwich St Clem 86; V Dulwich St Clem w St Pet 86-89; NSM Wilton Place St Paul *Lon* from 92. *5 Clitheroe Road, London SW9 9DY*   0171-326 4682

DAWSON, Nicholas Anthony. b 52. St Jo Coll Nottm 88. **d** 90 **p** 91. C Mortomley St Sav High Green *Sheff* from 90. *45 Oaklodge Road, High Green, Sheffield S30 4QA*   Sheffield (0114) 284 5049

DAWSON, Norman William. b 41. K Coll Lon BD63 AKC63. **d** 65 **p** 66. C Salford St Phil w St Steph *Man* 65-68; C Heaton Ch Ch 68-70; R Longsight St Jo 70-75; R Longsight St Jo w St Cypr 75-82; R Withington St Paul from 82; AD Withington from 91. *The Rectory, 491 Wilmslow Road, Manchester M20 4AW*   0161-445 3781

DAWSON, Paul Christopher Owen. b 61. Leeds Univ BA82. Ripon Coll Cuddesdon 83. **d** 85 **p** 86. C Dovecot *Liv* 85-89; V Westbrook St Phil 89-94; Bp's Dom Chapl from 94. *48 Babbacombe Road, Liverpool L16 9JW*   0151-722 7543 or 709 9722

DAWSON, Ven Peter. b 29. Keble Coll Ox BA52 MA56. Ridley Hall Cam 52. **d** 54 **p** 55. R Morden *S'wark* 68-77; RD Merton 75-77; Adn Norfolk *Nor* 77-93; rtd 93; Perm to Offic *Nor* from 93. *Elm Cottage, The Drift, Church Road, Tostock, Bury St Edmunds, Suffolk IP30 9PD*   Beyton (01359) 70005

DAWSON, Peter. b 34. E Midl Min Tr Course 73. **d** 76 **p** 77. NSM Blyton w Pilham *Linc* 76-80; NSM Laughton w Wildsworth 76-80; C E Stockwith 77-80; C Blyth St Mary *Newc* 80-84; P-in-c Lowick and Kyloe w Ancroft 84-89; P-in-c Ford 87-89; P-in-c Sleekburn from 89. *St John's Vicarage, North View, Bedlington, Northd NE22 7ED*   Bedlington (01670) 822309

DAWSON, Ronald Eric John. b 27. St Mark & St Jo Coll Lon TCert54 Lon Univ BD64. Bps' Coll Cheshunt 62. **d** 62 **p** 63. C Fulham St Etheldreda *Lon* 66-74; V Brentford St Faith 74-80; rtd 92. *13 Birkbeck Road, London W5 4ES*   0181-560 3564

DAWSON, Thomas Douglas. b 52. Newc Univ BA. St Steph Ho Ox. **d** 80 **p** 82. C N Gosforth *Newc* 80-81; C Leic St Chad *Leic* 82-85; TV Catford (Southend) and Downham *S'wark* 85-88; V Chevington *Newc* 88-94; V Cowgate from 94. *St Peter's Vicarage, Druridge Drive, Newcastle upon Tyne NE5 3LP*   0191-286 9913

DAWSON, William James Andrew. MA. CITC 88. **d** 88 **p** 89. NSM Killyman *Arm* 88-91; NSM Pomeroy from 91. *Tamlaght, Coagh, Cookstown, Co Tyrone BT80 0AB*   Coagh (016487) 37151

DAWSON, William John. b 26. ACP68 TEng74 MIEE74. CITC 77. **d** 80 **p** 81. NSM Lisburn St Paul *Conn* 80-85; Dioc C from 85. *55 Thornleigh Drive, Lisburn, Co Antrim BT28 2DA*   Lisburn (01846) 670252

DAWSWELL, Jonathan Andrew. b 65. Jes Coll Cam BA86. Wycliffe Hall Ox BA91. **d** 92 **p** 93. C Childwall All SS *Liv* from 92. *80 Green Lane North, Liverpool L16 8NL*   0151-737 2214

DAWTRY, Dr Anne Frances. b 57. Westf Coll Lon BA79 PhD85. Ripon Coll Cuddesdon DipMin93. **d** 93 **p** 94. C Corfe Mullen *Sarum* from 93. *8 Diprose Road, Corfe Mullen, Wimborne, Dorset BH21 3QY*   Wimborne (01202) 699147

DAXTER, Gregory. b 42. Lon Univ DipTh66. Oak Hill Th Coll 64. **d** 68 **p** 69. C Paignton St Paul Preston *Ex* 68-72; C Woodford Wells *Chelmsf* 72-75; Hon C Harold Hill St Paul 75-77; Hon C Wilmington *Roch* 77-87; Chapl Ex Cathl Sch from 87; PV Ex Cathl *Ex* from 87. *6A The Close, Exeter EX1 1EZ*   Exeter (01392) 58892

DAY, Sister Audrey. b 30. CA Tr Coll IDC57. **d** 88 **p** 94. CA 57-91; Norton Canes *Lich* 64-70; Knotty Ash St Jo *Liv* 70-75; Chapl Alder Hey Hosp Liv 70-75; Par Dn Mildenhall *St E* 88-91; Dioc Officer for the Care of the Elderly 91-95; NSM Blackbourne from 94; rtd 95. *Peace Haven, Duke Street, Stanton, Bury St Edmunds, Suffolk IP33 2AB*   Stanton (01359) 250742

DAY, Charles George. b 28. Keble Coll Ox BA51 MA63. Cuddesdon Coll 51. **d** 53 **p** 54. V Brenchley *Roch* 65-75; rtd 93. *Sparks Hall, Forsham Lane, Sutton Valence, Maidstone, Kent ME17 3EW*   Maidstone (01622) 843248   Fax 844298

DAY, Charles Ian. b 48. Univ of Wales (Ban) BA72. St Mich Coll Llan 73. **d** 75 **p** 76. C Llanrhos *St As* 75-79; V Mochdre 79-83; CF 83; V Minera *St As* 83-92; Dioc Soc Resp Officer from 89; V Mold from 92. *The Vicarage, Church Lane, Mold, Clwyd CH7 1BW*   Mold (01352) 752090

DAY, Canon Colin Michael. b 40. Lon Univ BSc62 AKC62 Em Coll Cam BA66 MA71. Ridley Hall Cam 65. **d** 67 **p** 68. C Heworth w Peasholme St Cuth *York* 67-70; C Ox St Clem *Ox* 70-76; V Kidsgrove *Lich* 76-86; Exec Officer Angl Evang Assembly & C of E Coun 86-90; Adv on Miss and Evang

Sarum from 90; Hon Can Sarum Cathl from 94. *Bowmoor House, Anvil Road, Blandford Forum, Dorset DT11 8UQ*   Blandford (01258) 480606

DAY, David John. b 44. CEng72 MICE72. Trin Coll Bris DipHE. **d** 90 **p** 91. C Stratton St Margaret w S Marston etc *Bris* 90-94. *56 Beechcroft Road, Swindon SN2 6PX*   Swindon (01793) 725721

DAY, David William. b 37. St Andr Univ MA58 BD61 CertEd73. St And Dioc Tr Course 74. **d** 76 **p** 77. C St Andrews All SS *St And* 76-77; P-in-c Dundee St Ninian *Bre* 77-84; Itinerant Priest *Arg* from 84; R Duror from 91; P-in-c Gruline from 91; P-in-c Kentallen from 91; P-in-c Kinlochleven from 91; P-in-c Kinlochmoidart from 91; P-in-c Lochbuie from 91; P-in-c Portnacrois from 91; P-in-c Strontian from 91. *St Adamnan's Rectory, Duror of Appin, Argyll PA38 4BS*   Duror (0163174) 218

DAY, Fergus William. b 09. TCD BA40 MA45. **d** 41 **p** 41. Dean Waterford *C & O* 67-79; I Waterford w Killea, Drumcannon and Dunhill 67-79; rtd 79. *10 Brabazon House, Gilford Road, Sandymount, Dublin 4, Irish Republic*   Dublin (1) 283-7898

DAY, Frank Henry. b 18. Clifton Th Coll 40. **d** 43 **p** 44. R Stanton St Quintin w Grittleton etc *Bris* 68-76; R Stanton St Quintin, Hullavington, Grittleton etc 76-81; rtd 81; Perm to Offic *Bris* from 81. *17 Avon Mead, Chippenham, Wilts SN15 3PP*

DAY, George Chester. b 45. Ex Univ BA66 Lon Univ BD70. Clifton Th Coll 67. **d** 71 **p** 72. C Reading St Jo *Ox* 71-75; C Morden *S'wark* 75-81; Sec for Voc and Min CPAS 81-86; Hon C Bromley Ch Ch *Roch* 83-86; V St Paul's Cray St Barn from 86. *The Vicarage, Rushet Road, Orpington, Kent BR5 2PU*   Orpington (01689) 821353

DAY, Hilary Paul Wilfrid. b 13. Qu Coll Birm 47. **d** 48 **p** 49. V Slade Green *Roch* 62-71; R Milton next Gravesend w Denton 71-87; rtd 87. *1 Killick Road, Hoo St Werburgh, Rochester, Kent ME3 9EP*   Medway (01634) 252960

DAY, Canon James Alfred. b 23. DFC44. AKC49. **d** 50 **p** 51. V Tattershall *Linc* 66-80; R Coningsby 66-80; RD Horncastle 73-80; Can and Preb Linc Cathl from 77; V Heckington 80-89; rtd 89. *22 Ancaster Drive, Sleaford, Lincs NG34 7LY*   Sleaford (01529) 305318

DAY, Miss Jennifer Ann. b 67. Aber Univ BSc89. Wycliffe Hall Ox BTh95. **d** 95. C Whitburn *Dur* from 95. *9 Cedar Grove, Whitburn, Sunderland SR6 7BD*   0191-529 3572

DAY, John. b 44. Oak Hill NSM Course 87. **d** 90 **p** 91. NSM Bexleyheath St Pet *Roch* 90-93; C Erith Ch Ch 93-95; C Erith St Jo from 93; P-in-c from 95. *St John's Church House, 100 Park Crescent, Erith, Kent DA8 3DZ*   Erith (01322) 332555

DAY, Canon John Alfred. b 25. TCD BA51. **d** 51 **p** 52. I Maguiresbridge w Derrybrusk *Clogh* 67-91; Can Clogh Cathl from 78; rtd 91. *Killeenifinane Cottage, 40 Ballylucas Road, Tamlaght, Enniskillen, Co Fermanagh BT74 4HD*   Enniskillen (01365) 387835

DAY, John Cuthbert. b 36. Sarum Th Coll 66. **d** 68 **p** 69. C Bedhampton *Portsm* 68-72; V Froxfield 72-73; V Froxfield w Privett 73-77; V Warminster Ch Ch *Sarum* 77-81; R Pewsey 81-90; Chapl Pewsey Hosp Wilts 81-90; P-in-c Sturminster Newton and Hinton St Mary *Sarum* from 90; P-in-c Stock and Lydlinch from 90. *The Vicarage, Sturminster Newton, Dorset DT10 1DB*   Sturminster Newton (01258) 472531

DAY, John Kenneth. b 58. Hull Univ BA85. Cranmer Hall Dur 85. **d** 87 **p** 88. C Thornbury *Bradf* 87-90; V from 90. *The Vicarage, Upper Rushton Road, Thornbury, Bradford, W Yorkshire BD3 7HX*   Bradford (01274) 664702

DAY, John Nathaniel. b 36. Kelham Th Coll 59. **d** 64 **p** 65. C Mansf St Mark *S'well* 64-69; C W Wycombe *Ox* 69-75; TV High Wycombe 75-77; C-in-c Britwell St Geo CD 77-78; TV W Slough 78-87; TV Langley Marish from 87. *St Francis Vicarage, 21 Lynwood Avenue, Slough SL3 7BJ*   Slough (01753) 527903

DAY, Miss Mary Elizabeth. b 57. Leic Poly BEd79. St Jo Coll Nottm DTS93. **d** 93 **p** 94. C Newbarns w Hawcoat *Carl* from 93. *50 Furness Park Road, Barrow-in-Furness, Cumbria LA14 5PS*   Barrow-in-Furness (01229) 836953

DAY, Michael. b 37. AKC61 RCA(Lon) MA75. **d** 62 **p** 63. C Hulme St Phil *Man* 62-65; Asst Chapl Newc Univ *Newc* 65-70; Chapl Chelsea Coll *Lon* 70-85; Chapl R Coll of Art 70-90; Chapl Cen, Chelsea and St Martin's Schs of Art *Lon* 85-90; P-in-c Bloomsbury St Geo w Woburn Square Ch Ch from 91. *6 Gower Street, London WC1 6DP, or 7 Little Russell Street, London WC1A 2HR*   0171-580 4010 or 405 3044

DAY, Paul Geoffrey. b 51. Dur Univ BEd75. Trin Coll Bris 76. **d** 78 **p** 79. C Roxeth Ch Ch *Lon* 78-82; C Roxeth Ch Ch and Harrow St Pet 82; TV Barking St Marg w St Patr *Chelmsf* 82-87; V Barrow St Mark *Carl* from 87. *St Mark's Vicarage, Rawlinson Street, Barrow-in-Furness LA14 1BX*   Barrow-in-Furness (01229) 820405

DAY, Paul Geoffrey. b 56. St Pet Coll Ox BA77. St Jo Coll Nottm 87. **d** 89 **p** 90. C Mildmay Grove St Jude and St Paul

182

Lon 89-92; C Loughb Em *Leic* from 92. *134 Valley Road, Loughborough, Leics LE11 3QA*   Loughborough (01509) 234472

DAY, Peter. b 50. BPharm71. Coll of Resurr Mirfield 85. **d** 87 **p** 88. C Eastcote St Lawr *Lon* 87-91; C Wembley Park St Aug 91-94; V Glen Parva and S Wigston *Leic* from 94. *The Vicarage, 1 St Thomas's Road, Wigston, Leics LE18 4TA* Leicester (0116) 278 2830

DAY, Canon Philip Maurice. b 45. TCD BA69 MA78. **d** 70 **p** 71. C Crumlin *Conn* 70-73; Asst Chapl K Hosp Sch Dub 73-76; I Mountmellick *M & K* 76-83; Can Kildare Cathl 82-83; Warden Wilson's Hosp 83-85; I Maryborough w Dysart Enos and Ballyfin *C & O* from 85; Preb Stagonil St Patr Cathl Dub from 87. *The Rectory, Portlaoise, Co Laoise, Irish Republic* Portlaoise (502) 21154

DAY, Robert Clifford. b 08. **d** 70 **p** 71. C Lt Stanmore St Lawr *Lon* 70-75; Perm to Offic *Worc* from 75. *10 Forge Lane, Blakedown, Kidderminster, Worcs DY10 3JF* Kidderminster (01562) 700205

DAY, Roy Frederick. b 24. S'wark Ord Course 63. **d** 67 **p** 68. C Newington St Paul *S'wark* 67-70; C Radlett *St Alb* 70-72; P-in-c Ponsbourne 72-76; R Campton 76-82; V Shefford 76-82; R Shenley 82-89; rtd 89. *11 Hill End Lane, St Albans, Herts AL4 0TX* St Albans (01727) 845782

DAY, Canon Samuel Richard. b 14. Reading Univ BSc36 Ch Ch Ox BA48 MA52 DPhil56. St D Coll Lamp 37. **d** 38 **p** 39. V Gt Marlow *Ox* 66-89; RD Wycombe 68-74; Hon Can Ch Ch 70-89; rtd 89. *3 Leighton House, Glade Road, Marlow, Bucks SL7 1EA*   Marlow (01628) 484922

DAY, Terence Patrick. b 30. Lon Univ BD60 K Coll Lon MTh63 PhD66. Lon Coll of Div ALCD59. **d** 60 **p** 61. India 63-71; CMS 66-71; Kenya 71-73; Canada from 73; Prof Religions Univ of Manitoba 74-95; rtd 95. *7 Hazel Park Drive, Winnipeg, Manitoba, Canada, R3T 5H5*

DAY, William Charles (Bill). b 47. Portsm Poly BEd86. Ripon Coll Cuddesdon 88. **d** 90 **p** 91. C Bishops Waltham *Portsm* 90-93; P-in-c Greatham w Empshott and Hawkley w Prior's Dean 93-95; R from 95. *The Vicarage, Hawkley, Liss, Hants GU33 6NF*   Hawkley (01730) 827459

DAYKIN, Timothy Elwin (Tim). b 54. Lon Univ BSc75 Dur Univ DipTh77 MA81 K Coll Lon MPhil93. Cranmer Hall Dur 75. **d** 78 **p** 79. C Bourne *Guildf* 78-81; Chapl K Alfred Coll *Win* 82-87; C-in-c Valley Park CD 87-91; V Valley Park 91-92; P-in-c Fordingbridge from 92; P-in-c Hale w S Charford from 94. *The Vicarage, Church Street, Fordingbridge, Hants SP6 1BB*   Fordingbridge (01425) 653163

DAYNES, Andrew John. b 47. Jes Coll Cam BA69 MA73. Westcott Ho Cam 69. **d** 72 **p** 73. C Radlett *St Alb* 72-76; Chapl St Alb Abbey 76-80; Chapl Bryanston Sch Blandford from 80. *Bryanston School, Blandford Forum, Dorset DT11 0PX* Blandford (01258) 456863 or 452411

DAZELEY, Mrs Lorna. b 31. CertEd53 New Hall Cam BA82 MA86. E Anglian Minl Tr Course 82. **dss** 84 **d** 87 **p** 94. Chesterton St Andr *Ely* 84-87; C from 87. *Chesterton House, Church Street, Chesterton, Cambridge CB4 1DT*   Cambridge (01223) 356243

de BERRY, Andrew Piers. b 44. St Jo Coll Dur BA66. Ripon Hall Ox 70. **d** 74 **p** 75. C Aylesbury *Ox* 74-77; USA 78; TV Clyst St George, Aylesbeare, Clyst Honiton etc *Ex* 78-80; Asst Chapl HM Pris Wormwood Scrubs 80-82; Chapl HM Pris Sudbury 82-84; V Blackwell *Derby* 84-91; V Thurgarton w Hoveringham and Bleasby etc *S'well* from 91. *The Vicarage, 208 Southwell Road, Thurgarton, Nottingham NG14 7QP* Newark (01636) 830234

de BERRY, Robert Delatour. b 42. Qu Coll Cam BA64 MA68. Ridley Hall Cam 65. **d** 67 **p** 68. Min Can Bradf Cathl *Bradf* 67-70; Uganda 71-75; V Attercliffe *Sheff* 75-83; V W Kilburn St Luke w St Simon and St Jude *Lon* from 83; Chapl City of Westmr Coll from 84. *The Vicarage, 19 Macroom Road, London W9 3HY*   0181-969 0876

de BOWEN, Alfred William. b 24. KStJ KLJ. Leeds Univ DipHort. St Paul's Grahamstown 76. **d** 78 **p** 86. S Africa 78-86; NSM Cilycwm and Ystrad-ffin w Rhandir-mwyn etc *St D* 86-88; Lic to Offic *Ex* 88-92; rtd 90. *Sunhaven, 11 Sea Way, Middleton-on-Sea, Bognor Regis, W Sussex PO22 7RZ* Middleton-on-Sea (01243) 587352

de BRETT, Rodney John Harry. b 13. Open Univ BA89. Wells Th Coll 63. **d** 64 **p** 65. V Stoke St Gregory *B & W* 66-75; V Stoke St Gregory w Burrowbridge 75-78; V Stoke St Gregory w Burrowbridge and Lyng 78-81; RD Taunton N 80-81; rtd 81; Perm to Offic *Ex* 81-95. *106 Whipton Lane, Exeter EX1 3DJ*   Exeter (01392) 55940

de BURGH-THOMAS, George Albert. b 30. Univ of Wales (Ban) BA50. St Mich Coll Llan 51. **d** 53 **p** 54. C Hawarden *St As* 53-56 and 60-63; C Roath St Martin *Llan* 56-58; C Llangeinor 58-60; V Bampton and Mardale *Carl* 63-70; V Fritwell *Ox* 70-83; R Souldern 70-83; R Fritwell w Souldern and Ardley w Fewcott 83-87; R Hawridge w Cholesbury and

St Leonard from 87; V Lee from 87. *The Vicarage, The Lee, Great Missenden, Bucks HP16 9LZ* High Wycombe (01494) 442200

de CHAZAL, John Robert. b 16. Bris Univ. Wycliffe Hall Ox 53. **d** 55 **p** 56. R Caldecote *Cov* 64-71; R Bradf Peverell w Stratton *Sarum* 72-77; P-in-c Sydling St Nic 77; P-in-c Frampton 77; R Bradf Peverell, Stratton, Frampton etc 77-80; rtd 81. *Lavender Cottage, East Street, Sydling St Nicholas, Dorchester, Dorset DT2 9NX* Cerne Abbas (01300) 341693

de CHAZAL, Mrs Nancy Elizabeth. b 28. Bedf Coll Lon BA52 Lambeth STh90. Sarum & Wells Th Coll 81. **dss** 84 **d** 87 **p** 94. NSM Melbury *Sarum* from 84. *Lavender Cottage, East Street, Sydling St Nicholas, Dorchester, Dorset DT2 9NX* Cerne Abbas (01300) 341693

de GARIS, Jean Helier Thomson. b 60. K Alfred's Coll Win BA82 PGCE83. Sarum & Wells Th Coll BTh93. **d** 93 **p** 94. C Chandler's Ford *Win* from 93. *St Martin's House, 50 Randall Road, Eastleigh, Hants SO53 1AL* Chandler's Ford (01703) 254469

de GREY-WARTER, Philip. b 67. Leeds Univ BEng89. Ridley Hall Cam BA94 CTM94. **d** 94 **p** 95. C Bromley Ch Ch *Roch* from 94. *4 Meadow Road, Bromley BR2 0DX*   0181-464 1898 Fax 464 5846

DE GRUYTHER, Albert Alfred. b 14. Magd Coll Ox BA48 MA60. Ridley Hall Cam. **d** 50 **p** 51. R Ulverston St Mary w H Trin *Carl* 67-73; R Gt Salkeld 73-79; rtd 79; Perm to Offic *Carl* from 82. *Lynburn, Lindale, Grange-over-Sands, Cumbria LA11 6LF*   Grange-over-Sands (015395) 32968

DE HOOP, Thomas Anthony (Brother Thomas Anthony). b 38. Bp's Univ Lennox BA63 LTh63. **d** 68 **p** 69. Canada 68-79; SSF from 79; P-in-c Cam St Benedict *Ely* 85-88; V 88-92. *St Francis House, 15 Botolph Lane, Cambridge CB2 3RD*   Cambridge (01223) 353903

DE KEYSER, Nicholas David Llewellyn (Nick). b 49. Nottm Univ BTh75 MTh86. St Jo Coll Nottm 71. **d** 75 **p** 76. C Portswood Ch Ch *Win* 75-77; C Yateley 77-81; TV Grantham *Linc* 81-86; V Heyside *Man* 86-91; R Charlton-in-Dover *Cant* from 91. *The Rectory, St Alphege Road, Dover, Kent CT17 2PU*   Dover (01304) 201143

de la BAT SMIT, Reynaud. b 53. St Edm Hall Ox BA80 MA86 Dur Univ PhD94 FRSA94. Ripon Coll Cuddesdon. **d** 82 **p** 83. C Headington *Ox* 82-85; Chapl St Hild and St Bede Coll Dur from 85. *College of St Hilda and St Bede, University of Durham, Durham DH1 1SZ*   0191-374 3069

de la HOYDE, Canon Denys Ralph Hart. b 33. G&C Coll Cam BA57 MA61. Westcott Ho Cam 57. **d** 59 **p** 60. C Moss Side Ch Ch *Man* 59-60; Chapl G&C Coll Cam 60-64; India 64-68; C Eltham H Trin *S'wark* 68-69; Chapl Bromsgrove Sch Worcs 69-71; Lic to Offic *Ripon* 71-78; V Pool w Arthington from 86; Dioc Dir of Ords from 86; Hon Can Ripon Cathl from 92. *The Vicarage, Old Pool Bank, Pool in Wharfedale, Otley, W Yorkshire LS21 1LH*   Leeds (0113) 284 3706

de la MARE, Benedick James Hobart. b 38. Trin Coll Ox BA63 MA67. Cuddesdon Coll 63. **d** 65 **p** 66. C Gosforth All SS *Newc* 65-68; Chapl Trin Coll Cam 68-73; V Newc St Gabr *Newc* 73-81; V Dur St Oswald *Dur* from 81; Chapl Collingwood Coll from 95. *St Oswald's Vicarage, Church Street, Durham DH1 3DG*   0191-386 4313

de la MOUETTE, Norman Harry. b 39. Southn Univ BEd73. Sarum & Wells Th Coll 76. **d** 79 **p** 80. NSM Win St Lawr and St Maurice w St Swithun *Win* from 79; Deputation Appeals Org (Win and Portsm) CECS from 83. *146 Greenhill Road, Winchester, Hants SO22 5DR*   Winchester (01962) 853191

DE LACEY, Thomas. b 46. HNC68. Carl Dioc Tr Inst 88. **d** 91 **p** 92. NSM Ingol *Blackb* 91-93; NSM Ribbleton from 93. *5 Fulwood Hall Lane, Fulwood, Preston PR2 8DA*   Preston (01772) 700923

DE MEL, Basil William. b 18. Keble Coll Ox BA41 MA47 BLitt47. Westcott Ho Cam 41. **d** 43 **p** 44. Chapl Manor Hosp Epsom 53-83; rtd 83; Perm to Offic *Guildf* from 85. *83 Manor Green Road, Epsom, Surrey KT19 8LW*   Epsom (01372) 722134

de MELLO, Gualter Rose. b 34. Ridley Hall Cam 63. **d** 64 **p** 65. C S Hackney St Jo w Ch Ch *Lon* 64-66; Toc H Chapl (Hackney) 66-72; Dir Friends Anonymous Service from 73; Hon C All Hallows by the Tower etc *Lon* from 73; Dir Community of Reconciliation & Fellowship from 88. *Prideaux House, 10 Church Crescent, London E9 7DL*   0181-986 2233

DE MURALT, Dr Robert Willem Gaston. b 25. Utrecht Univ LLM48 DLSc54. Chich Th Coll 90. **d** 90 **p** 91. Hon Asst Chapl The Hague *Eur* from 90. *Zuidwerflaan 5, 2594 CW The Hague, The Netherlands*   The Hague (70) 383-8520

✠**de PINA CABRAL, Rt Rev Daniel Pereira dos Santos.** b 24. Lisbon Univ LLB47. Lon Coll of Div. **d** 47 **p** 49 **c** 67. Portugal 47-67; Portuguese E Africa 67-75; Mozambique 75-76; Asst Bp Lebombo 67-68; Bp Lebombo 68-76; Aux Bp Eur from 76; Hon Can Gib Cathl 79-87; Adn Gib 87-93; rtd 89. *Rua Henrique Lopes de Mendonça 253-42, 4150 Oporto, Portugal* Oporto (2) 617-7772

de POMERAI, Dr David Ian Morcamp. b 50. Edin Univ BSc72 Univ Coll Lon PhD75. E Midl Min Tr Course 90. **d** 93 **p** 94. NSM Sutton in Ashfield St Mary *S'well* from 93. *Grosvenor House, Grosvenor Avenue, Sutton-in-Ashfield, Notts NG17 1FG* Mansfield (01623) 552572

de POMERAI, Mrs Lesley Anne. b 60. AIPM82. St Jo Coll Nottm BTh90. **d** 92 **p** 94. Par Dn Sutton in Ashfield St Mary *S'well* 92-94; C from 94. *Grosvenor House, Grosvenor Avenue, Sutton-in-Ashfield, Notts NG17 1FG* Mansfield (01623) 552572

DE PURY, Andrew Robert. b 28. K Coll Lon BD57 AKC57. **d** 58 **p** 59. V Harold Hill St Geo *Chelmsf* 65-72; Missr Swan Par Gp *Ox* 72-76; TR Swan 76-85; R Worminghall w Ickford, Oakley and Shabbington 85-95; rtd 95. *8 Russell Pope Avenue, Chard, Somerset TA20 2JN* Chard (01460) 66714

DE SAUSMAREZ, Canon John Havilland Russell. b 26. Lambeth MA81 Wells Th Coll 54. **d** 56 **p** 57. V St Peter-in-Thanet *Cant* 68-81; RD Thanet 74-81; Hon Can Cant Cathl 78-81; Can Res Cant Cathl 81-94; rtd 94. *9 St Peter's Court, Broadstairs, Kent CT10 2UU* Thanet (01843) 867050

DE SILVA, David Ebenezer Sunil. b 48. Sri Lanka Nat Sem DipTh. **d** 72 **p** 73. Sri Lanka 72-84; C Elm Park St Nic Hornchurch *Chelmsf* 84-87; R Mistley w Manningtree and Bradfield 87-90; TR Stanground and Farcet *Ely* from 90. *The Rectory, 9 Mace Road, Stanground, Peterborough PE2 8RQ* Peterborough (01733) 890552

DE SMET, Andrew Charles. b 58. Ex Univ BSc79 Southn Univ BTh88. Sarum & Wells Th Coll 85. **d** 88 **p** 89. C Portsea St Mary *Portsm* 88-93; R Shipston-on-Stour w Honington and Idlicote *Cov* from 93. *Shipston Rectory, 8 Glen Close, Shipston-on-Stour, Warks CV36 4ED* Shipston-on-Stour (01608) 662661

de VERNY, David Dietrich. b 55. Trier Univ MTh81 DTh89. **d** 83 **p** 83. Asst Chapl Bonn *Eur* 83; C Henfield w Shermanbury and Woodmancote *Chich* 84-86; C Westmr St Sav and St Jas Less *Lon* 86-88; P-in-c Cheddington w Mentmore and Marsworth *Ox* 88-90; Gen Sec Fellowship of St Alb and St Sergius 90-92. *147 Friern Barnet Lane, London N20 0NP* 0181-445 7844

de VIAL, Raymond Michael. b 39. Oak Hill Th Coll 77. **d** 80 **p** 81. NSM Beckenham St Jo *Roch* 80-84; C Morden *S'wark* 84-88; TV 88-94; V Kingston Hill St Paul from 94. *The Vicarage, 33 Queen's Road, Kingston upon Thames, Surrey KT2 7SF* 0181-549 8597

de VOIL, Paul Walter. b 29. FTII64 Solicitor 67 Hertf Coll Ox BA50 MA87. Local NSM Course. **d** 92 **p** 93. NSM Denston w Stradishall and Stansfield *St E* from 92. *Water Lane Barn, Denston, Newmarket, Suffolk CB8 8PP* Wickhambrook (01440) 820181 Fax as telephone

✠de WAAL, Rt Rev Hugo Ferdinand. b 35. Pemb Coll Cam BA58 MA63. Ridley Hall Cam 59. **d** 60 **p** 61 **c** 92. C Birm St Martin *Birm* 60-64; Chapl Pemb Coll Cam 64-68; P-in-c Dry Drayton *Ely* 64-68; R 68-74; Min Bar Hill LEP 68-74; V Blackpool St Jo *Blackb* 74-78; Prin Ridley Hall Cam 78-92; Lic to Offic *Ely* 78-86; Hon Can Ely Cathl 86-92; Suff Bp Thetford *Nor* from 92. *Rectory Meadow, Bramerton, Norwich NR14 7OW* Surlingham (01508) 538251 Fax 538371

de WAAL, Dr Victor Alexander. b 29. Pemb Coll Cam BA49 MA53 Nottm Univ Hon DD83. Ely Th Coll 50. **d** 52 **p** 53. Can Res and Chan Linc Cathl *Linc* 69-76; Dean Cant 76-86; Perm to Offic *Heref* from 88; rtd 90; Chapl Soc of Sacred Cross Tymawr from 90; Lic to Offic *Mon* from 90. *Cwm Cottage, Rowlestone, Hereford HR2 0DP* Golden Valley (01981) 240391

DE WIT, John. b 47. Or Coll Ox BA69 MA73 Clare Coll Cam BA78 MA84. Westcott Ho Cam 75. **d** 78 **p** 79. C The Quinton *Birm* 78-81; TV Solihull 81-85; V Kings Heath 85-94; RD Moseley 91-94; V Hampton in Arden from 94. *The Vicarage, Hampton in Arden, Solihull, W Midlands B92 0AE* Hampton-in-Arden (01675) 442604

DEACON, Charles Edward. b 57. Westf Coll Lon BSc78. Ridley Hall Cam CTM94. **d** 94 **p** 95. C Ex St Jas *Ex* from 94. *103 Old Tiverton Road, Exeter EX4 6LD* Exeter (01392) 412575

DEACON, Donald (Brother Angelo). Chich Th Coll 66. **d** 68 **p** 69. SSF from 63; Lic to Offic *Man* 69-70; USA 70-72; C Kennington St Jo *S'wark* 72-73; C Wilton Place St Paul *Lon* 74-75; Angl-Franciscan Rep Ecum Cen Assisi *Eur* 75; Franciscanum Sem 76-78; Perm to Offic *Sarum* 78-82; Lic to Offic *Chelmsf* 82-90; Lic to Offic *Birm* 90-93; Lic to Offic *Linc* from 94. *St Francis House, Normanby Road, Scunthorpe, S Humberside DN15 6AR* Scunthorpe (01724) 953899

DEACON, Edwin William Frederick. b 18. Oak Hill Th Coll 46. **d** 48 **p** 49. R Lustleigh *Ex* 69-85; Perm to Offic from 85; rtd 86. *Dunoon, 17A Highweek Village, Newton Abbot, Devon TQ12 1QA* Newton Abbot (01626) 65433

DEACON, Frederick George Raymond. b 15. Tyndale Hall Bris 63. **d** 65 **p** 66. C Leckhampton SS Phil and Jas *Glouc* 69-71; V Longcot *Ox* 71-72; V Longcot w Fernham and Bourton 72-77;

Zambia 77-80; P-in-c Cressage w Sheinton *Heref* 80-81; P-in-c Harley w Kenley 80-81; TV Wenlock 81-85; rtd 85; Perm to Offic *Heref* 85-90. *29 Robinson Meadow, Ledbury, Herefordshire HR8 1SU* Ledbury (01531) 634500

DEACON, John. b 37. Arm Aux Min Course 87. **d** 90 **p** 91. NSM Enniscorthy w Clone, Clonmore, Monart etc *C & O* from 90. *The Rectory, Creagh, Gorey, Co Wexford, Irish Republic* Gorey (55) 20354

DEACON, Canon Peter Olford. b 26. MBIM84 MInstAM84. K Coll Lon 48. **d** 52 **p** 53. Chapl RN 68-85; V Gen to Bp Eur 85-92; Can Gib Cathl 86-92; rtd 92. *46 Valiant House, Vicarage Crescent, London SW11 3LU* 0171-2233 6559

DEACON, Timothy Randall. b 55. Ex Univ BA78. Chich Th Coll 79. **d** 80 **p** 81. C Whiteleigh *Ex* 80-83; P-in-c Devonport St Aubyn 83-88; P-in-c Newton Ferrers w Revelstoke 88-94; R from 94; P-in-c Holbeton from 93. *The Rectory, Court Road, Newton Ferrers, Plymouth PL8 1DL* Plymouth (01752) 872530

DEADMAN, Richard George Spencer. b 63. Ex Univ BA85. Coll of Resurr Mirfield 86. **d** 88 **p** 89. C Grangetown *York* 88-91; P-in-c 91-93; V from 93. *The Vicarage, Clynes Road, Grangetown, Middlesbrough, Cleveland TS6 7LY* Eston Grange (01642) 453704

DEAKIN, Preb John Hartley. b 27. K Coll Cam BA50 MA63. Cranmer Hall Dur DipTh65. **d** 65 **p** 66. C Newc St Geo *Lich* 65-70; V Cotes Heath 70-84; RD Eccleshall 82-92; R Standon and Cotes Heath from 84; Preb Lich Cathl from 88; Sub-Chapl HM Pris Drake Hall from 89. *The Vicarage, Cotes Heath, Stafford ST21 6RX* Standon Rock (01782) 791268

DEAN, Ven Alan. b 38. Hull Univ BA61. Qu Coll Birm DipTh63. **d** 63 **p** 64. C Clitheroe St Mary *Blackb* 63-67; C Burnley St Pet 67-68; CF 68-93; Dep Chapl Gen from 93; Adn for the Army from 93; QHC from 93. *c/o MOD (Army), Bagshot Park, Bagshot, Surrey GU19 5PL* Bagshot (01276) 471717 Fax 412834

DEAN, Andrew Duncan. b 40. Sarum Th Coll 62. **d** 64 **p** 65. C Stockton Heath *Ches* 64-68; C Mottram in Longdendale w Woodhead 68-71; P-in-c Over Tabley 71-73; V Over Tabley and High Legh 73-79; R Astbury and Smallwood 79-85; R Woodchurch from 85. *The Rectory, Church Lane, Upton, Wirral, Merseyside L49 7LS* 0151-677 5352

DEAN, Andrew James. b 40. FCII ACIArb. W of England Minl Tr Course 92. **d** 95. NSM Rodbourne Cheney *Bris* from 95. *Koinonia, 2 Wicks Close, Haydon Wick, Swindon SN2 3QH* Swindon (01793) 725526

DEAN, Archibald Charles. b 13. Wycliffe Hall Ox 52. **d** 54 **p** 55. R Odcombe *B & W* 61-91; R Brympton 61-91; R Lufton 61-91; P-in-c Montacute 78-86; rtd 91; Perm to Offic *B & W* from 91. *3 Chur Lane, West Coker, Yeovil, Somerset BA22 9BH* West Coker (01935) 862224

DEAN, Arthur. b 32. CQSW80. S Dios Minl Tr Scheme 89. **d** 90 **p** 90. NSM Eastney *Portsm* from 90. *9 Kingsley Road, Southsea, Hants PO4 8HJ* Portsmouth (01705) 735773

DEAN, Canon Desmond Keable. b 06. ALCD30 St Jo Coll Dur LTh30 BA31 MA37 BD41. **d** 30 **p** 31. R Tooting Graveney St Nic *S'wark* 51-76; Hon Can S'wark Cathl 63-76; rtd 76; Perm to Offic *Chich* from 76. *68 Milland Road, Harmers Hay, Hailsham, E Sussex BN27 1TY* Hailsham (01323) 843910

DEAN, Francis John Michael. b 15. Univ Coll Ox BA38 MA42. Cuddesdon Coll 38. **d** 39 **p** 40. V Regent's Park St Mark *Lon* 64-81; rtd 81. *74 Temple Fortune Lane, London NW11 7TT* 0181-455 6309

DEAN, John Milner. b 27. S'wark Ord Course 69. **d** 72 **p** 73. C Lewisham St Mary *S'wark* 72-75; C Mert St Mary 75-77; V S Beddington St Mich from 77. *St Michael's Vicarage, Milton Road, Wallington, Surrey SM6 9RP* 0181-647 1201

DEAN, Malcolm. b 34. Tyndale Hall Bris 67. **d** 69 **p** 70. C Daubhill *Man* 69-73; P-in-c Constable Lee 73-74; V 74-79; P-in-c Everton St Sav w St Cuth *Liv* 79-86; P-in-c Anfield SS Simon and Jude 81-86; V Walton Breck Ch Ch 86-89; rtd 89. *6 Sunny Lea Street, Rawtenstall, Rossendale, Lancs BB4 8JE* Rossendale (01706) 215953

DEAN, Canon Maurice. b 12. Birm Univ BA37. Ripon Hall Ox 37. **d** 38 **p** 39. V Bromsgrove St Jo *Worc* 68-77; RD Bromsgrove 73-77; Hon Can Worc Cathl 76-77; rtd 77. *9 Farley Road, Malvern, Worcs WR14 1NF* Malvern (01684) 566741

DEAN, Preb Raymond Charles. b 27. Bris Univ BA51. Wycliffe Hall Ox 51. **d** 53 **p** 54. V Lyngford *B & W* 59-70; V Burnham 70-93; Preb Wells Cathl 73-93; RD Burnham 82-91; RD Axbridge 87-91; rtd 93. *258 Berrow Road, Berrow, Burnham-on-Sea, Somerset TA8 2JH* Burnham-on-Sea (01278) 780979

DEAN, Simon Timothy Michael Rex. b 62. Liv Univ BEng83. Ridley Hall Cam 86. **d** 89 **p** 90. C St German's Cathl *S & M* 89-92; V Castletown from 92. *The Vicarage, Arbory Road, Castletown, Isle of Man IM9 1ND* Castletown (01624) 823509

DEANE, Gilbert Ernest. b 06. Lon Univ BD38. Lon Coll of Div 34. **d** 38 **p** 39. Teacher Forest Sch Horsham 64-74; rtd 74.

1 Barnfield Close, Lower Park Road, Braunton, Devon EX33 2HL Braunton (01271) 812949

DEANE, Nicholas Talbot Bryan. b 46. Bris Univ BA69. Clifton Th Coll 70. **d** 72 **p** 73. C Accrington Ch Ch *Blackb* 72-75; OMF 75-89; Korea 75-89; P-in-c Newburgh *Liv* 90-93; P-in-c Westhead 90-93; V Ch Ch Newburgh w St Jas Westhead from 93. *The Vicarage, Back Lane, Newburgh, Wigan, Lancs WN8 7XB* Parbold (01257) 463267

DEANE, Robert William. b 52. DipTh85. CITC 85. **d** 85 **p** 86. C Raheny w Coolock *D & G* 85-88; I Clonsast w Rathangan, Thomastown etc *M & K* from 88; Dioc Youth Officer (Kildare) from 90. *The Rectory, Edenderry, Co Offaly, Irish Republic* Edenderry (405) 31585

DEANE, Stuart William. b 45. Sarum & Wells Th Coll 86. **d** 88 **p** 89. C Bromyard *Heref* 88-92; V Astley, Clive, Grinshill and Hadnall *Lich* from 92. *The Vicarage, Hadnall, Shrewsbury SY4 4AQ* Hadnall (01939) 210241

DEANE-HALL, Henry Michael. b 21. Leeds Univ BA46. Coll of Resurr Mirfield 47. **d** 49 **p** 50. R Duloe w Herodsfoot *Truro* 71-79; V Morval 71-79; P-in-c Donhead St Mary *Sarum* 79-80; R The Donheads 80-82; rtd 82; Perm to Offic *Ex* 82-95. *Flat A, Warden's Lodge, Newland, Malvern, Worcs WR13 5AX* Malvern (01684) 577546

DEAR, Graham Frederick. b 44. St Luke's Coll Ex CertEd66. Wycliffe Hall Ox 67. **d** 70 **p** 71. C Chigwell *Chelmsf* 70-73; C Chingford SS Pet and Paul 73-75; V Southchurch Ch Ch 75-82; CF 82-89; P-in-c The Cowtons *Ripon* 89-94; RE Adv from 89; P-in-c Startforth and Bowes and Rokeby w Brignall 94-95; V from 95. *The Vicarage, High Startforth, Barnard Castle, Co Durham DL12 9AF* Teesdale (01833) 637371

DEAR, Neil Douglas Gauntlett. b 35. Linc Th Coll 87. **d** 89 **p** 90. C Framlingham w Saxtead *St E* 89-92; P-in-c Eyke w Bromeswell, Rendlesham, Tunstall etc from 92. *The Rectory, Eyke, Woodbridge, Suffolk IP12 2QW* Eyke (01394) 460289

DEARDEN, James Varley. b 22. Wycliffe Hall Ox 61. **d** 62 **p** 63. V Newington Transfiguration *York* 66-75; V Huddersfield H Trin *Wakef* 75-87; rtd 87. *26 Sycamore Avenue, Meltham, Huddersfield HD7 3EE* Huddersfield (01484) 852519

DEARDEN, Philip Harold. b 43. AKC65. **d** 66 **p** 67. C Haslingden w Haslingden Grane *Blackb* 66-69; C Burnley St Pet 69-71; V Langho Billington 71-78; TR Darwen St Pet w Hoddlesden 78-91; RD Darwen 86-91; V Altham w Clayton le Moors from 91; RD Accrington from 95. *The Vicarage, Church Street, Clayton le Moors, Accrington, Lancs BB5 5HT* Accrington (01254) 384321

DEARING, Henry Ernest. b 26. Lon Univ BD53. St Deiniol's Hawarden 55. **d** 55 **p** 56. V Huncoat *Blackb* 57-60; rtd 95. *7 Troon Way, Abergele, Clwyd LL22 7TT* Abergele (01745) 826714

DEARING, Trevor. b 33. Lon Univ BD58. Qu Coll Birm MA63. **d** 61 **p** 62. C Harlow New Town w Lt Parndon *Chelmsf* 68-70; V Hainault 70-75; Dir Healing Miss 75-79; Hon C Gt Ilford St Andr 75-79; Perm to Offic *Linc* 80-81; USA 81-83; rtd 83. *4 Rock House Gardens, Radcliffe Road, Stamford, Lincs PE9 1AS* Stamford (01780) 51680

DEARNLEY, Mark Christopher. b 59. Cranmer Hall Dur 84. **d** 87 **p** 88. C Purley Ch Ch *S'wark* 87-91; C Addiscombe St Mary 91-93; C Addiscombe St Mary Magd w St Martin 93-94; V Hook from 94. *The Vicarage, 278 Hook Road, Chessington, Surrey KT9 1PF* 0181-397 3521

DEARNLEY, Preb Patrick Walter. b 34. Nottm Univ BA55 LTh75. ALCD64. **d** 64 **p** 65. C New Malden and Coombe *S'wark* 64-68; C Portswood Ch Ch *Win* 68-71; C Leeds St Geo *Ripon* 71-74; Hon C Nottm St Nic *S'well* 74-77; P-in-c Holloway Em w Hornsey Road St Barn *Lon* 77-85; AD Islington 80-85; Abp's Officer for UPA 85-90; Preb St Paul's Cathl *Lon* 86-91; P-in-c Waterloo St Jo *Liv* from 91. *St John's Vicarage, 16 Adelaide Terrace, Waterloo, Liverpool L22 8QD* 0151-928 3793

DEAS, Canon Leonard Stephen. b 52. New Coll Ox BA75 CertEd76 MA78. St Mich Coll Llan 81. **d** 82 **p** 83. C Dowlais *Llan* 82-84; Chapl St Mich Coll Llan 84-85; Chapl Univ of Wales (Cardiff) *Llan* 85-86; V Newbridge *Mon* 86-93; Can Res St Woolos Cathl from 93. *16 Stow Park Crescent, Newport, Gwent NP9 4HD* Newport (01633) 264919

DEAVE, Mrs Gillian Mary. b 31. E Midl Min Tr Course 79. **dss** 82 **d** 87 **p** 94. Nottm St Pet and St Jas *S'well* 82-87; Par Dn 87-91; rtd 91; Perm to Offic *S'well* from 91; Perm to Offic *Leic* from 91. *Greensmith Cottage, Stathern, Melton Mowbray, Leics LE14 4HE* Harby (01949) 60340

DEBENHAM, Mrs Joan Winifred. b 26. LRAM57 Lon Univ BA47 Cam Univ DipEd48. SW Minl Tr Course. **dss** 82 **d** 87 **p** 94. Plymouth St Jas Ham *Ex* 82-86; Asst Chapl Coll of SS Mark and Jo Plymouth 87-89; Par Dn Teignmouth, Ideford w Luton, Ashcombe etc *Ex* from 89. *Radway Lodge, Radway Street, Bishopsteignton, Teignmouth, Devon TQ14 9SS* Teignmouth (01626) 775540

DEBNEY, Canon Wilfred Murray. b 26. ACA48 FCA60. Wycliffe Hall Ox 58. **d** 60 **p** 61. TV Wendy w Shingay *Ely* 69-75; R Brampton 75-94; Offg Chapl RAF 75-94; RD Huntingdon *Ely* 81-94; Hon Can Ely Cathl 85-94; rtd 94. *3 Hoo Close, Buckden, St Neots, Huntingdon, Cambs PE18 9TX* Huntingdon (01480) 810652

DEBOO, Alan John. b 45. Qu Coll Cam BA73 MA77. Westcott Ho Cam 72. **d** 74 **p** 75. C Brackley St Pet w St Jas *Pet* 74-77; Perm to Offic *Sarum* 85-94; NSM Wexcombe from 94. *Mayzells Cottage, Collingbourne Kingston, Marlborough, Wilts SN8 3SD* Collingbourne Ducis (01264) 850683

DEBOYS, David Gordon. b 54. QUB BD76 Wolfs Coll Ox MLitt. Ridley Hall Cam 90. **d** 92 **p** 93. C Ipswich St Aug *St E* 92-93; C Whitton and Thurleston w Akenham 93-95; R Hardwick *Ely* from 95; R Toft w Caldecote and Childerley from 95. *The Rectory, 50 Main Street, Hardwick, Cambridge CB3 7QS* Madingley (01954) 210695

DEDMAN, Roger James. b 45. Oak Hill Th Coll 68. **d** 71 **p** 72. C Gresley *Derby* 71-74; C Ipswich St Fran *St E* 74-79; P-in-c Bildeston w Wattisham 79-92; P-in-c Bramford from 92; P-in-c Somersham w Flowton and Offton w Willisham from 94. *The Vicarage, Vicarage Lane, Bramford, Ipswich IP8 4AE* Ipswich (01473) 741105

DEE, Clive Hayden. b 61. Ripon Coll Cuddesdon 86. **d** 89 **p** 90. C Bridgnorth, Tasley, Astley Abbotts, Oldbury etc *Heref* 89-93; P-in-c Wellington w Pipe-cum-Lyde and Moreton-on-Lugg from 93. *The Rectory, 5 Nursery Drive, Moreton-on-Lugg, Hereford HR4 8DJ* Canon Pyon (01432) 760758

DEEDES, Canon Arthur Colin Bouverie. b 27. Bede Coll Dur BA51. Wells Th Coll 51. **d** 53 **p** 54. V Fleet *Guildf* 66-73; RD Aldershot 69-73; TR Bournemouth St Pet w St Swithun, St Steph etc *Win* 73-80; RD Bournemouth 74-80; Hon Can Win Cathl 78-92; Master Win St Cross w St Faith 80-92; rtd 92. *Dolphins, 17 Chesil Street, Winchester, Hants SO23 0HU* Winchester (01962) 861617

DEEGAN, Arthur Charles. b 49. CertEd71 Birm Univ BEd86. Qu Coll Birm 86. **d** 88 **p** 89. C Leic St Jas *Leic* 88-91; C Melton Gt Framland 91-92; TV 92-93; TV Melton Mowbray from 93. *26 Firwood Road, Melton Mowbray, Leicester LE13 1SA* Melton Mowbray (01664) 61066

DEEMING, Paul Leyland. b 44. CA Tr Coll 65 CMS Tr Coll Selly Oak 70. **d** 80 **p** 80. CMS 71-82; Pakistan 71-82; R E and W Horndon w Lt Warley *Chelmsf* 83-89; V Gt Ilford St Andr from 89. *The Vicarage, St Andrew's Road, Ilford, Essex IG1 3PE* 0181-554 3858

DEETH, William Stanley. b 38. St Pet Coll Ox BA59 MA62. St Steph Ho Ox 66. **d** 68 **p** 69. C Eastbourne St Mary *Chich* 68-71; C Benwell St Jas *Newc* 71-75; C-in-c Byker St Martin CD 75-76; P-in-c Byker St Martin 76; V 76-89; P-in-c Bothal 89-91; R Bothal and Pegswood w Longhirst 91-94; rtd 94. *17 Osborne Gardens, North Sunderland, Seahouses, Northd NE68 7UF* Seahouses (01665) 720067

DEFTY, Henry Gordon. b 14. St Chad's Coll Dur BA38 MA41 DipTh41. **d** 39 **p** 40. V Hartlepool St Aid *Dur* 68-73; Can Res Ches Cathl *Ches* 73-74; V Gainford *Dur* 74-80; R Winston 76-80; rtd 80. *39 Crossgate, Durham DH1 4PS* 0191-384 4334

DEGG, Ralph William. b 26. Lon Univ BSc57. Wells Th Coll 61. **d** 63 **p** 64. C The Lickey *Birm* 66-71; R Grendon 71-78; V Tanworth St Patr Salter Street 78-86; rtd 89; Perm to Offic *Birm* from 89. *23 Wayfield Road, Shirley, Solihull, W Midlands B90 3HF* 0121-744 3564

DeGROOSE, Leslie John. b 28. Oak Hill Th Coll 62. **d** 64 **p** 65. Chapl RN 67-83; P-in-c Gt Oakley *Chelmsf* 83-85; R Gt Oakley w Wix 85-92; rtd 92. *1 Queensberry Mews, Newmarket, Suffolk CB8 9AE* Newmarket (01638) 660599

✠**DEHQANI-TAFTI, Rt Rev Hassan Barnaba.** b 20. Tehran Univ BA43. Virginia Th Sem DD81 Ridley Hall Cam 47. **d** 49 **p** 50 **c** 61. Iran 49-61; Bp Iran 61-90; Pres Bp Episc Ch Jerusalem and Middle E 76-86; Asst Bp Win from 82; rtd 90. *Sohrab House, 1 Camberry Close, Basingstoke, Hants RG21 3AG* Basingstoke (01256) 27457

DEIGHTON, Ian Armstrong. b 19. Glas Univ MA40. Edin Th Coll 40. **d** 43 **p** 44. R Musselburgh *Edin* 57-84; P-in-c Prestonpans 76-84; rtd 84. *6 Duddingston Park South, Edinburgh EH15 3PA* 0131-669 5108

DEIGHTON, William John. b 44. K Coll Lon AKC68 Plymouth Poly CQSW74. St Boniface Warminster 68. **d** 69 **p** 70. C Kenwyn *Truro* 69-72; Hon C Winterbourne *Bris* from 90. *22 Salem Road, Winterbourne, Bristol BS17 1QF* Winterbourne (01454) 778847

DEIMEL, Mrs Margaret Mary. b 49. Notre Dame Coll Liv CertEd71. W Midl Minl Tr Course 91. **d** 94 **p** 95. NSM Bidford-on-Avon *Cov* from 94. *3 Manor Mews, Manor Road, Studley, Warks B80 7NA* Redditch (01527) 852830

DEIMEL, Richard Witold. b 49. Lon Univ BA84. Cranmer Hall Dur 86. **d** 88 **p** 89. C Bilton *Cov* 88-93; P-in-c Studley from 93. *3 Manor Mews, Manor Road, Studley, Warks B80 7NA* Studley (01527) 852830

DELACOUR, Arthur Winter. b 14. Lon Univ BSc52. Sarum & Wells Th Coll 79. **d** 80 **p** 81. NSM Gtr Corsham *Bris* 80-83; Perm to Offic *Win* 83-86; Chapl St Jo Win Charity 86-89; Perm to Offic *Cov* from 89. *3 Margetts Close, Kenilworth, Warks CV8 1EN* Kenilworth (01926) 55667

DELAMERE, Allen Stephen.BTh. **d** 90 **p** 91. C Ban Abbey *D & D* 90-93; I Saintfield from 93. *The Vicarage, 11 Lisburn Road, Saintfield, Ballynahinch, Co Down BT24 7AZ* Ballynahinch (01238) 510286

DELANEY, Anthony. b 65. Man Poly HNC91. St Jo Coll Bramcote BTh95. **d** 95. C Cullompton *Ex* from 95. *27 Forcefield Road, Cullompton, Devon EX15 1QB* Cullompton (01884) 32509

DELANEY, Canon Peter Anthony. b 37. AKC65. **d** 66 **p** 67. C St Marylebone w H Trin *Lon* 66-70; Chapl Nat Heart Hosp Lon 66-70; Res Chapl Univ Ch Ch the K 70-73; Can Res and Prec S'wark Cathl *S'wark* 73-77; V All Hallows by the Tower etc *Lon* from 77; Can Cyprus and the Gulf from 88; Preb St Paul's Cathl *Lon* from 95. *All Hallows by the Tower, Byward Street, London EC3R 5BJ* 0171-481 2928 or 488 4772 Fax 488 3333

DELANY, Michael Edward. b 34. Lon Univ BSc55 PhD58. S'wark Ord Course 80. **d** 83 **p** 84. NSM Hampton St Mary *Lon* 83-87; R Copythorne and Minstead *Win* 87-94; rtd 94. *Littlecott, Tytherley Road, Winterslow, Salisbury SP5 1PZ* Winterslow (01980) 862183

DELFGOU, John. b 35. Oak Hill Th Coll 81. **d** 84 **p** 85. NSM Loughton St Mary and St Mich *Chelmsf* 84-90; NSM Loughton St Jo 90-93; C 93-94; TV from 94. *20 Carroll Hill, Loughton, Essex IG10 1NN* 0181-508 6333

DELFGOU, Jonathan Hawke. b 63. Aston Tr Scheme 89 Linc Th Coll BTh94. **d** 94 **p** 95. C Greenstead juxta Colchester *Chelmsf* from 94. *1 Stour Walk, Colchester CO4 3UX* Colchester (01206) 871757

DELIGHT, Ven John David. b 25. Liv Univ CSocSc48 Open Univ BA75. Oak Hill Th Coll 49. **d** 52 **p** 53. R Aldridge *Lich* 69-82; Preb Lich Cathl 80-90; RD Walsall 81-82; Adn Stoke 82-90; rtd 90. *42 Little Tixall Lane, Great Haywood, Stafford ST18 0SE* Little Haywood (01889) 881684

DELIGHT, Paul Charles. b 31. Loughb Coll of Educn DipEd54 Newc Univ ADEd71. Oak Hill Th Coll 59. **d** 62 **p** 63. C Macclesfield Ch Ch *Ches* 62-65; Ho Master Mobberley Sch Knutsford 65-68; Perm to Offic 68-71; Asst Master Mile Oak Sch Portslade 68-70; Dep Prin Thortoun Sch Kilmarnock 70-74; Perm to Offic *Glas* 71-75; R Snodland All SS w Ch Ch *Roch* 74-81; V Guernsey H Trin *Win* 81-92; Chapl HM Pris Guernsey 81-92; R The Stodden Churches *St Alb* from 92. *Stodden Rectory, High Street, Upper Dean, Huntingdon, Cambs PE18 0ND* Bedford (01234) 708531

DELL, Dr Murray John. b 31. Cape Town Univ BA51 BSc54 Edin Univ MB, ChB59. Westcott Ho Cam 63. **d** 65 **p** 65. S Africa 65-70; Dean Windhoek 71-80; V Lyme Regis *Sarum* from 80; Chapl Lyme Regis Hosp from 80. *The Vicarage, West Hill Road, Lyme Regis, Dorset DT7 3LW* Lyme Regis (01297) 443134

DELL, Ven Robert Sydney. b 22. Em Coll Cam BA46 MA50. Ridley Hall Cam 46. **d** 48 **p** 49. V Chesterton St Andr *Ely* 66-73; Adn Derby 73-92; Hon Can Derby Cathl 73-81; Can Res 81-92; rtd 92. *7 Moss Drive, Haslingfield, Cambridge CB3 7JB* Cambridge (01223) 872195

DELVE, Albert William John. b 15. Leeds Univ BA38. Coll of Resurr Mirfield 38. **d** 40 **p** 41. R Thurlestone *Ex* 69-83; R Thurlestone w S Milton 83-85; rtd 85; Perm to Offic *Ex* from 85. *Jalmar, Littlemead Lane, Exmouth, Devon EX8 3BU* Exmouth (01395) 278373

DELVE, Eric David. b 42. Trin Coll Bris. **d** 89 **p** 90. NSM Bris St Matt and St Nath *Bris* 89-92; P-in-c Kirkdale St Lawr *Liv* from 93. *St Lawrence's Vicarage, 21 Westminster Close, Liverpool L4 1XB* 0151-922 5794

DELVES, Anthony James. b 47. Birm Univ BSocSc70 Hull Univ PhD94. St Steph Ho Ox 83. **d** 85 **p** 86. C Cantley *Sheff* 85-90; V Goldthorpe w Hickleton from 90. *Goldthorpe Presbytery, Lockwood Road, Goldthorpe, Rotherham, S Yorkshire S63 9JY* Rotherham (01709) 898426

DELVES-BROUGHTON, Simon Brian Hugo. b 33. Ex Coll Ox BA56 MA64. Kelham Th Coll 56. **d** 59 **p** 60. E Pakistan 67-71; Bangladesh 71-74; V Northn Ch Ch *Pet* 74-95; Chapl Northn Gen Hosp 77-87; rtd 95. *71A Observatory Street, Oxford OX2 6EP* Oxford (01865) 515463

DENBY, Canon Paul. b 47. NW Ord Course 73. **d** 76 **p** 77. C Stretford All SS *Man* 76-80; V Stalybridge 80-87; Chapl Tameside Distr Gen Hosp Ashton-under-Lyne 82-87; Dir of Ords *Man* from 87; Hon Can Man Cathl from 92. *9 Bettwood Drive, Manchester M8 6JY* 0161-740 5711 or 792 2096 Fax 792 6826

DENCH, Christopher David. b 62. RGN83. Aston Tr Scheme 86 Sarum & Wells Th Coll 88. **d** 91 **p** 92. C Crayford *Roch* 91-94; P-in-c Leybourne from 94. *The Rectory, 73 Rectory Lane, Leybourne, Maidstone, Kent ME19 5HD* West Malling (01732) 842187

DENERLEY, John Keith Christopher. b 34. Qu Coll Ox BA58 MA61. St Steph Ho Ox 58. **d** 61 **p** 62. C Airedale w Fryston *Wakef* 61-64; Chapl Sarum Th Coll 64-68; Min Can Cov Cathl *Cov* 68-76; Chapl Lanchester Poly 70-76; Chapl The Dorothy Kerin Trust Burrswood 76-85; V Trelleck and Cwmcarvan *Mon* 85-87; V Penallt 85-87; V Penallt and Trellech from 87; Chapl Ty Mawr Convent (Wales) from 85; RD Mon from 93. *The Vicarage, Penallt, Monmouth, Gwent NP5 4SE* Monmouth (01600) 716622

DENFORD, Keith Wilkie. b 35. AKC62. **d** 63 **p** 64. C Gunnersbury St Jas *Lon* 63-66; C Brighton St Pet *Chich* 66-71; Min Can Cant Cathl *Cant* 71-75; R W Tarring *Chich* 75-85; C Burgess Hill St Jo 85-90; R Pulborough from 90. *The Rectory, 2 London Road, Pulborough, W Sussex RH20 1AP* Pulborough (01798) 875773

DENGATE, Richard Henry (Dick). b 39. Cant Sch of Min 82. **d** 85 **p** 86. NSM Wittersham w Stone-in-Oxney and Ebony *Cant* 85; R Sandhurst w Newenden from 90. *The Rectory, Bodium Road, Sandhurst, Hawkhurst, Kent TN18 5LE* Sandhurst (01580) 850213

DENHAM, Anthony Christopher (Chris). b 43. Keble Coll Ox BA65 MA70. Oak Hill Th Coll DipHE93. **d** 93 **p** 94. C Hythe *Cant* from 93. *2 Palmarsh Avenue, Hythe, Kent CT21 6NT* Hythe (01303) 261699

DENHAM, Nicholas Philip. b 50. Salford Univ BSc72 Birm Univ CertEd74. Wycliffe Hall Ox 87. **d** 89 **p** 90. C Bishopwearmouth St Gabr *Dur* 89-90; C Ches le Street 90-92; TV Rushden w Newton Bromswold *Pet* from 92. *45 Pytchley Road, Rushden, Northants NN10 9XB* Rushden (01933) 56398

DENHAM, Thomas William. b 17. Wycliffe Hall Ox 58. **d** 59 **p** 60. Area Sec CMS 62-82; Perm to Offic *Liv* 62-73; P-in-c Bishopwearmouth St Gabr *Dur* 73-82; rtd 82. *Forresters Cottage, Nether Ervie, Parton, Castle Douglas, Kirkcudbrightshire DG7 3NG* Parton (016447) 215

DENHOLM, Edward Godfrey Denholm. b 08. AKC34. **d** 35 **p** 36. Chapl St Kath Convent Parmoor 68-73; rtd 73. *Round Lodge, Godstone, Surrey RH9 8DB*

DENHOLM, Canon Robert Jack. b 31. Edin Th Coll 53. **d** 56 **p** 57. R N Berwick *Edin* 69-80; R Gullane 76-80; R Edin St Mark 80-90; Can St Mary's Cathl from 88; rtd 90. *39 South Street, St Andrews, Fife KY16 9QR* St Andrews (01334) 75971

DENING, John Cranmer. b 21. Clare Coll Cam BA48 MA52. Qu Coll Birm 50. **d** 52 **p** 53. C Moulsham St Jo *Chelmsf* 69-70; C W Teignmouth *Ex* 70-73; C N Stoneham *Win* 73-80; C Sholing 80-85; rtd 86. *27 The Paddocks, Brandon, Suffolk IP27 0DX*

DENISON, Canon Keith Malcolm. b 45. Down Coll Cam BA67 MA71 PhD70. Westcott Ho Cam 70. **d** 71 **p** 72. C Chepstow *Mon* 71-72; C Bassaleg 72-75; Post-Ord Tr Officer 75-85; V Mathern and Mounton 75-80; V Mathern and Mounton w St Pierre 80-85; RD Chepstow 82-85; V Risca 85-91; V Goldcliffe and Whiston and Nash from 91; Hon Can St Woolos Cathl 91-94; Can from 94; Dir of Adult Educn from 91. *The Vicarage, Whitson, Newport, Gwent NP6 2PG* Newport (01633) 278106

DENISON, Philip. b 55. York Univ BA77 CertEd. St Jo Coll Nottm 83. **d** 86 **p** 87. C Barnoldswick w Bracewell *Bradf* 86-88; P-in-c Basford St Leodegarius *S'well* 88-91; C Basford w Hyson Green 91-94; V Nether Stowey w Over Stowey *B & W* from 94. *St Mary's Vicarage, 25 St Mary Street, Nether Stowey, Bridgwater, Somerset TA5 1LJ* Nether Stowey (01278) 732247

DENMAN, Frederick George. b 46. Chich Th Coll 67. **d** 70 **p** 71. C Stafford St Mary *Lich* 70-72; C Ascot Heath *Ox* 72-75; P-in-c Culham 75-77; P-in-c Sutton Courtenay w Appleford 75-77; P-in-c Clifton Hampden 77; TV Dorchester 78-81; C Ox St Mich w St Martin and All SS 80; Chapl Henley Memorial Hosp 81-82; P-in-c W Hill *Ex* 82; TV Ottery St Mary, Alfington and W Hill 82-87; V Sparkwell from 87; V Shaugh Prior 87-93. *The Vicarage, Sparkwell, Plymouth PL7 5DB* Cornwood (01752) 837218

DENMAN, Preb Ronald. b 19. St Chad's Coll Dur LTh44 BA46. St Aug Coll Cant 40. **d** 44 **p** 45. V Cheddar *B & W* 57-86; Preb Wells Cathl 77-86; rtd 86; Perm to Offic *B & W* from 86. *3 Gardenhurst Close, Burnham-on-Sea, Somerset TA8 2EQ* Burnham-on-Sea (01278) 781386

DENNEN, Lyle. b 42. Harvard Univ LLB67 Trin Coll Cam BA70 MA75. Cuddesdon Coll 72. **d** 72 **p** 73. C S Lambeth St Ann *S'wark* 72-75; C Richmond St Mary 75-78; P-in-c Kennington St Jo 78-79; V Kennington St Jo w St Jas from 79; P-in-c Brixton Rd Ch Ch 81-89; RD Brixton from 90. *The Vicarage, 92 Vassall Road, London SW9 6IA* 0171-735 9340

DENNESS, Mrs Linda Christine. b 51. Portsm Dioc Tr Course. **d** 89. NSM Milton *Portsm* 89-93; NSM Portsea St Mary from

93. *88 Mayles Road, Portsmouth PO4 8NS* Portsmouth (01705) 738353

DENNETT, John Edward. b 36. Tyndale Hall Bris 66. **d** 68 **p** 69. C Chell *Lich* 68-71; C Bispham *Blackb* 71-73; C Cheltenham Ch Ch *Glouc* 73-75; V Coppull *Blackb* 75-79; P-in-c Parkham, Alwington and Buckland Brewer *Ex* 79-80; R 80-84; V Blackpool St Thos *Blackb* 84-92; rtd 92. *37 Village Way, Bispham, Blackpool FY2 0AH* Blackpool (01253) 58039

✠**DENNIS, Rt Rev John.** b 31. St Cath Coll Cam BA54 MA59. Cuddesdon Coll 54. **d** 56 **p** 57 **c** 79. C Armley St Bart *Ripon* 56-60; C Kettering SS Pet and Paul *Pet* 60-62; V Is of Dogs Ch Ch and St Jo w St Luke *Lon* 62-71; V Mill Hill Jo Keble Ch 71-79; RD W Barnet 73-79; Preb St Paul's Cathl 77-79; Suff Bp Knaresborough *Ripon* 79-86; Dioc Dir of Ords 80-86; Bp St E from 86. *Bishop's House, 4 Park Road, Ipswich IP1 3ST* Ipswich (01473) 252829 Fax 232552

DENNIS, Canon John Daniel. b 20. LLCM. St D Coll Lamp BA41 LTh43. **d** 43 **p** 44. R Worthenbury w Tallarn Green *St As* 62-71; V Chirk 71-86; RD Llangollen 74-86; Hon Can St As Cathl 83-86; rtd 86; Perm to Offic *St As* from 86. *Mount Cottage, Chirk, Wrexham, Clwyd LL14 5HD* Chirk (01691) 773382

DENNIS, John William. b 13. St Pet Hall Ox BA38 MA45. Linc Th Coll 38. **d** 39 **p** 40. V Linc St Swithin *Linc* 60-82; rtd 83; Perm to Offic *Linc* from 83. *17 Eastbrook Road, Swallowbeck, Lincoln LN6 7ER* Lincoln (01522) 680373

DENNIS, Keith Aubrey Lawrence. b 55. City of Lon Poly BA79. Cranmer Hall Dur 88. **d** 90 **p** 91. C Bushbury *Lich* 90-94; P-in-c Newc St Geo from 94. *St George's Vicarage, 28 Hempstalls Lane, Newcastle, Staffs ST5 0SS* Newcastle-under-Lyme (01782) 710056

DENNIS, Patrick John. b 44. Linc Th Coll 67. **d** 70 **p** 71. C Eccleshill *Bradf* 70-72; C Ponteland *Newc* 73-75; Chr Aid Org Leic and Linc 75-78; TV Cullercoats St Geo *Newc* 78-82; Dioc Ecum Officer 79-82; R Bradfield *Sheff* 82-91; Dioc Ecum Adv 82-93; Sec & Ecum Officer S Yorkshire Ecum Coun 91-93; R Braithwell w Bramley 91-93. *Address excluded by request*

DENNIS, Canon Dr Trevor John. b 45. St Jo Coll Cam BA68 MA71 PhD74. Westcott Ho Cam 71. **d** 72 **p** 73. C Newport Pagnell *Ox* 72-74; Chapl Eton Coll Windsor 75-82; Tutor Sarum & Wells Th Coll 82-94; Vice-Prin and Admissions Tutor 89-94; Can Res Ches Cathl *Ches* from 94. *13 Abbey Street, Chester CH1 2JF* Chester (01244) 314408 Fax 313155

DENNISON, Philip Ian. b 52. Nottm Univ BTh81. St Jo Coll Nottm 77. **d** 81 **p** 82. C Stalybridge H Trin and Ch Ch *Ches* 81-84; C Heswall 84-91; TV Bushbury *Lich* from 91. *131 Taunton Avenue, Wolverhampton WV10 6PN* Wolverhampton (01902) 781944

DENNISTON, James Keith Stuart. b 49. Barrister-at-Law 70 Down Coll Cam MA70. Oak Hill Th Coll DipEd92. **d** 93 **p** 94. C Harborne Heath *Birm* from 93. *55 Albert Road, Harborne, Birmingham B17 0AP* 0121-426 2548

DENNISTON, Robin Alastair. b 26. Ch Ox MA48. **d** 78 **p** 79. NSM Clifton upon Teme *Worc* 78-81; NSM Clifton-on-Teme, Lower Sapey and the Shelsleys 81-85; NSM S Hinksey *Ox* 85-87; NSM Gt w Lt Tew 87-90; NSM Aberdour *St And* 90-94; NSM W Fife Team Min 90-94; Hon C St Marylebone St Mark Hamilton Terrace *Lon* from 94. *112 Randolph Avenue, London W9 1PQ* 0171-286 0880

DENNO, Basil. b 52. Dundee Univ BSc74. Oak Hill Th Coll BA81. **d** 81 **p** 83. C Chaddesden St Mary *Derby* 81-83; Hon C 83-84. *21 Parkside Road, Chaddesden, Derby DE21 6QR* Derby (01332) 672687

DENNY, John Peter Sekeford. b 43. RIBA69 Portsm Sch of Architecture DipArch67. Chich Th Coll 90. **d** 91 **p** 92. C Aylmerton w Runton *Nor* 91-95; P-in-c Barney, Fulmodeston w Croxton, Hindringham etc from 95. *The Vicarage, Hindringham, Fakenham, Norfolk NR21 0AA* Thursford (01328) 878338

DENNY, Laurence Eric. b 29. Oak Hill Th Coll 54. **d** 57 **p** 58. V Leyton St Mary w St Edw *Chelmsf* 64-72; V Pennycross *Ex* 73-93; rtd 93; Perm to Offic *Ex* from 94. *5 Treloweth Close, Manadon, Plymouth PL2 3SL* Plymouth (01752) 781405

DENNY, Michael Thomas. b 47. Kelham Th Coll 67. **d** 73 **p** 74. C Gospel Lane St Mich *Birm* 73-77; P-in-c Frankley 77-82; R from 82. *The Rectory, Frankley Green, Birmingham B32 4AS* 0121-475 3724

DENNY, Peter Bond. b 17. Lon Univ BA41. Bps' Coll Cheshunt 41. **d** 43 **p** 44. V Newlyn St Newlyn *Truro* 56-83; RD Pydar 74-81; rtd 83. *Tralee, The Crescent, Truro, Cornwall TR1 3ES* Truro (01872) 74492

DENT, Christopher Mattinson. b 46. K Coll Lon BA68 AKC68 MTh69 Jes Coll Cam BA72 MA76 New Coll Ox MA76 DPhil80. Westcott Ho Cam 70. **d** 72 **p** 73. C Chelsea St Luke *Lon* 72-76; Asst Chapl New Coll Ox 76-79; Dean of Div 79-84; V Hollingbourne and Hucking w Leeds and Broomfield *Cant*

84-93; V Bedf St Andr *St Alb* from 93. *St Andrew's Vicarage, 1 St Edmond Road, Bedford MK40 2NQ* Bedford (01234) 354234

DENT, Michael Leslie. b 54. Leeds Univ BEd76. St Steph Ho Ox DipMin95. **d** 95. C Cockerton *Dur* from 95. *213 Brinkburn Road, Darlington, Co Durham DL3 9LE* Darlington (01352) 603944

DENT, Nigel Clive. b 56. K Coll Lon BD77 Keble Coll Ox DPhil85. St Steph Ho Ox 83. **d** 85 **p** 86. C High Wycombe *Ox* 85-89; Asst Chapl HM Pris Wormwood Scrubs 89-90; Chapl HM Young Offender Inst Wellingborough from 90. *HM Prison Wellingborough, Millers Park, Doddington Road, Wellingborough, Northants NN8 2NH* Wellingborough (01933) 224151 Fax 273903

DENT, Raymond William. b 47. Birm Coll of Educn CertEd68 Open Univ BA84. Ridley Hall Cam 70. **d** 73 **p** 74. C Hyde St Geo *Ches* 73-76; C Eastham 76-79; TV E Runcorn w Halton 79-80; V Hallwood 80-83; V New Brighton Em 83-94; V Willaston from 94. *The Vicarage, 13 Hooton Road, Willaston, South Wirral L64 1SE* 0151-327 4737

DENT, Richard William. b 32. Down Coll Cam BA56 MA LLB59. Bris Sch of Min 73. **d** 77 **p** 78. NSM Southmead *Bris* 77-81; NSM Henleaze 81-85; V Highworth w Sevenhampton and Inglesham etc 85-88; TV Oldland 88-91; V Longwell Green 91-93; C Bedminster St Mich 93-94; C from 94; Chapl Frenchay Hosp Bris from 94. *1 Addison Road, Bristol BS3 4QH* Bristol (0117) 966 0278

DENTON, Kenneth Percival. b 14. Clifton Th Coll 54. **d** 55 **p** 56. V Middlesb St Thos *York* 69-73; C Rufforth w Moor Monkton and Hessay 73-76; P-in-c Escrick 76-80; rtd 80; Perm to Offic *B & W* from 81. *46 Pedlars Grove, Packsaddle Way, Frome, Somerset BA11 2SX* Frome (01373) 463875

DENTON, Peter Brian. b 37. Kelham Th Coll 57. **d** 62 **p** 63. C Ellesmere Port *Ches* 62-66; Chapl HM Borstal Hollesley 66-69; CF 69-90; Warden Bridge Cen from 90; C Hounslow H Trin w St Paul *Lon* 90-92; V Northolt Park St Barn from 92. *The Vicarage, Raglan Way, Northolt, Middx UB5 4SX* 0181-422 3775

DENTON, Peter Charles. St Jo Coll Dur BA52. Oak Hill Th Coll 49. **d** 52 **p** 53. Lect City of Newc Coll of Educn 67-75; Sen Lect Newc Poly 75-90; rtd 90. *10 Whitesmocks Avenue, Durham DH1 4HP* 0191-384 3247

DENYER, Alan Frederick. b 31. Wycliffe Hall Ox 80. **d** 82 **p** 83. C Rodbourne Cheney *Bris* 82-84; P-in-c Garsdon w Lea and Cleverton 84-87; R Garsdon, Lea and Cleverton and Charlton 87-91; R Lydbury N w Hopesay and Edgton *Heref* from 91. *The Vicarage, Lydbury North, Shropshire SY7 8AU* Lydbury North (015888) 609

DENYER, Paul Hugh. b 46. Lon Univ BA68. Ripon Coll Cuddesdon 74. **d** 77 **p** 78. C Horfield H Trin *Bris* 77-82; TV Yate New Town 82-88; V Bris Lockleaze St Mary Magd w St Fran from 88. *The Parsonage, Copley Gardens, Bristol BS7 9YE* Bristol (0117) 951 2516 Fax 951 8300

DENZIL, Sister. See ONSLOW, Sister Denzil Octavia

DERBRIDGE, Roger. b 39. Clifton Th Coll 63. **d** 66 **p** 69. C Surbiton Hill Ch Ch *S'wark* 66-67; C Richmond Ch Ch 67-70; C Toxteth Park St Philemon *Liv* 70-75; TV Toxteth St Philemon w St Gabr 75-84; V Woking St Mary *Guildf* from 84. *St Mary of Bethany Vicarage, West Hill Road, Woking, Surrey GU22 7UJ* Woking (01483) 761269

DERBY, Archdeacon of. See GATFORD, Ven Ian

DERBY, Bishop of. See BAILEY, Rt Rev Jonathan Sansbury

DERBY, Provost of. See LEWERS, Very Rev Benjamin Hugh (Ben)

DERBYSHIRE, Alan George. b 16. Lon Univ BA41. Linc Th Coll 41. **d** 43 **p** 44. R Merrow *Guildf* 67-81; rtd 81; Perm to Offic *Heref* 81-94. *2A Abbey Cottages, Abbey Precinct, Tewkesbury, Glos GL20 5SR* Tewkesbury (01684) 295743

DERBYSHIRE, Mrs Anne Margaret. b 31. Lon Univ CertEd75 Open Univ BA87. SW Minl Tr Course. **dss** 84 **d** 87. NSM Tiverton St Pet *Ex* 87-90; Perm to Offic from 90. *38 Greenway Gardens, King Street, Tiverton, Devon EX16 5JL* Tiverton (01884) 255966

DERBYSHIRE, Douglas James. b 26. **d** 81 **p** 82. Hon C Heald Green St Cath *Ches* 81-86; Hon C Stockport St Geo 86-89; C 89-91; rtd 91; Perm to Offic *Man* from 92. *91 East Avenue, Heald Green, Cheadle, Cheshire SK8 3BR* 0161-437 3748

DERBYSHIRE, Philip Damien. b 50. Sarum & Wells Th Coll 80. **d** 82 **p** 83. C Chatham St Wm *Roch* 82-86; Zimbabwe 86-88; TV Burnham w Dropmore, Hitcham and Taplow *Ox* 88-92; Chapl HM Pris Reading from 92. *The Chaplain's Office, HM Prison Reading, Forbury Road, Reading RG1 3HY* Reading (01734) 587031 Fax 591058

DERHAM, Miss Hilary Kathryn. b 50. MRPharmS Nottm Univ BPharm71. Chich Th Coll 89. **d** 91 **p** 95. Par Dn Stevenage H Trin *St Alb* 91-94; C from 94. *413 Scarborough Avenue, Stevenage, Herts SG1 2QA* Stevenage (01438) 361179

DERISLEY, Canon Albert Donald. b 20. Ely Th Coll 60. **d** 62 **p** 63. V Gt w Lt Plumstead *Nor* 66-72; V N Elmham w Billingford 72-85; RD Brisley and Elmham 77-85; Hon Can Nor Cathl 78-85; rtd 85; Perm to Offic *Nor* from 85. *22 Stuart Road, Aylsham, Norwich NR11 6HN* Aylsham (01263) 734579

DERMOTT, David John. b 34. Hull Univ BA60. Cuddesdon Coll 67. **d** 68 **p** 69. C Howden *York* 68-71; C W Acklam 71-74; TV Thornaby on Tees 74-79; R Hinderwell w Roxby from 79. *The Rectory, Hinderwell, Saltburn, Cleveland TS13 5JH* Whitby (01947) 840249

DEROY-JONES, Philip Antony (Tony). b 49. St Mich Coll Llan DMinlStuds92. **d** 92 **p** 93. C Neath w Llantwit *Llan* 92-95; V Caerau St Cynfelin from 95. *The Vicarage, Cymmer Road, Caerau, Maesteg, W Glam CF34 0YR* Maesteg (01656) 734223

DERRETT, Canon Leslie John. b 14. St Jo Coll Dur BA41 MA45. **d** 41 **p** 42. TR Witham *Chelmsf* 68-76; Hon Can Chelmsf Cathl 76-80; V Thorpe-le-Soken 76-80; rtd 80. *27 Bromley College, London Road, Bromley BR1 1PE* 0181-460 0291

DERRICK, David John. b 46. S'wark Ord Course. **d** 84 **p** 85. NSM Angell Town St Jo *S'wark* from 84; NSM St Mary-le-Strand w St Clem Danes *Lon* 86-93. *Weavers Cottage, 8 Bellvue Place, London E1 4UG* 0171-791 2943

DERRICK, Mrs Dorothy Margaret. b 41. St Mary's Cheltenham CertEd63 RTC63. Ox Min Course CBTS92. **d** 92 **p** 94. NSM Gt Missenden w Ballinger and Lt Hampden *Ox* from 92. *Pinecroft, Copes Road, Great Kingshill, High Wycombe, Bucks HP15 6JE* High Wycombe (01494) 714571

DERRIMAN, Graham Scott. b 39. Bps' Coll Cheshunt 63. **d** 66 **p** 67. C Wandsworth St Mich *S'wark* 66-70; C Mert St Mary 70-74; P-in-c Earlsfield St Andr 75-81; V Camberwell St Luke 81-90; V Croydon St Aug from 90; Voc Adv Croydon Adnry from 93; RD Croydon Cen from 95. *The Vicarage, 23A St Augustine's Avenue, Croydon CR2 6JN* 0181-688 2663

DERRY, Eric Leonard Stobart. b 15. Worc Ord Coll 62. **d** 64 **p** 65. V Luddenden *Wakef* 68-73; V Dodworth 73-83; rtd 84; Perm to Offic *Wakef* from 84. *29 Barnsley Road, Cawthorne, Barnsley, S Yorkshire S75 4HW* Barnsley (01226) 790697

DERRY, Hugh Graham. b 10. Or Coll Ox BA35 MA50. Ely Th Coll 46. **d** 48 **p** 49. S Africa 58-72; rtd 72; Perm to Offic *Ex* from 74. *Beech Tree Cottage, Cheriton Fitzpaine, Crediton, Devon EX17 4JJ* Cheriton Fitzpaine (01363) 866438

DERRY AND RAPHOE, Bishop of. *See* MEHAFFEY, Rt Rev Dr James

DERRY, Archdeacon of. *See* SIMPSON, Ven Samuel

DERRY, Dean of. *See* ORR, Very Rev David Cecil

DESBRULAIS, Mrs Patricia Mary. b 27. Qu Coll Birm 77. **dss** 79 **d** 87. Gt Bowden w Welham *Leic* 79-83; Market Harborough 83-87; Hon Par Dn 87-89; rtd 89; Perm to Offic *Leic* from 89. *78 Rainsborough Gardens, Market Harborough, Leics LE16 9LW* Market Harborough (01858) 466766

DESERT, Thomas Denis. b 31. Bps' Coll Cheshunt 54. **d** 56 **p** 57. C Goldington *St Alb* 56-60; C-in-c Luton St Hugh Lewsey CD 60-63; C St Alb St Sav 63-65; C Cheshunt 65-68; V Bedf All SS 68-89; R Northill w Moggerhanger from 89. *The Rectory, 3 Bedford Road, Northill, Biggleswade, Beds SG18 9AH* Northill (01767) 627262

DESHPANDE, Miss Lakshmi Anant. b 64. Liv Univ BSc86 Ex Univ PGCE87. Wycliffe Hall Ox BTh94. **d** 94 **p** 95. C Long Eaton St Jo *Derby* from 94. *66 Curzon Street, Long Eaton, Nottingham NG10 4FT* Nottingham (0115) 946 0557

DESMOND, Mrs Elspeth Margaret. b 49. Trin Coll Bris CPS90 S Dios Minl Tr Scheme 90. **d** 93 **p** 95. NSM Filton *Bris* from 93. *14 Kenmore Crescent, Bristol BS7 0TH* Bristol (0117) 976 3390

DESON, Rolston Claudius. b 39. Qu Coll Birm 85. **d** 84 **p** 85. NSM Saltley *Birm* 84-86; C Edgbaston SS Mary and Ambrose 86-90; V W Bromwich St Phil *Lich* from 90. *The Vicarage, 33 Reform Street, West Bromwich, W Midlands B70 7PF* 0121-525 1985

DESPARD, Canon Eric Herbert. b 17. TCD BA40 BD48. CITC 41. **d** 41 **p** 42. RD Rathdrum *D & G* 63-77; I Lucan w Leixlip 65-92; Can Ch Cath Cathl Dub 73-92; RD Ballymore 77-85; RD Omorthy 86-92; rtd 92. *59 Sweetmount Park, Dundrum, Dublin 14, Irish Republic* Dublin (1) 298-2489

DESROSIERS, Jacques Thomas Maurice. b 55. Qu Univ Kingston Ontario BCom77. S'wark Ord Course 91. **d** 94. NSM Benenden *Cant* from 94. *2 Twysden Cottage, Bodiam Road, Sandhurst, Kent TN18 5LF* Sandhurst (01580) 850592

DETTMER, Douglas James. b 64. Univ of Kansas BA86 Yale Univ MDiv90. Berkeley Div Sch 90. **d** 90 **p** 91. C Ilfracombe, Lee, Woolacombe, Bittadon etc *Ex* 90-94; Bp's Dom Chapl from 94. *2 Palace Cottages, Palace Gate, Exeter EX1 1HY* Exeter (01392) 211360

DEUCHAR, Andrew Gilchrist. b 55. Southn Univ BTh86. Sarum & Wells Th Coll 81. **d** 84 **p** 85. C Alnwick St Mich and St Paul *Newc* 84-88; TV Heref St Martin w St Fran (S Wye TM) *Heref* 88-90; Adv to Coun for Soc Resp (Dios Cant and Roch) *Cant* 90-94; Sec for Angl Communion Affairs from 94. *73 St Luke's Road, Maidstone, Kent ME14 5AS* Maidstone (01622) 765010

DEUCHAR, John. b 24. Or Coll Ox BA49 MA50. Westcott Ho Cam 49. **d** 51 **p** 52. R Woolwich St Mary w H Trin *S'wark* 68-72; V Whitley Ch Ch *Ox* 72-84; Chapl and Tutor Whittington Coll Felbridge 84-89; rtd 89; Perm to Offic *Sarum* from 89; Perm to Offic *Win* from 89. *2 The Leys, 63 Church Street, Fordingbridge, Hants SP6 1BB* Fordingbridge (01425) 655407

DEVAMANIKKAM, Trevor. b 47. Ripon Hall Ox 74. **d** 76 **p** 77. C Manston *Ripon* 76-79; P-in-c Moor Allerton 79-81; P-in-c Harrogate St Wilfrid and St Luke 81-84; V Buttershaw St Aid *Bradf* 84-85; Succ St D Cathl *St D* 85-87; V Llanwnda, Goodwick, w Manorowen and Llanstinan 87-90; Chapl RN 90-94; Chapl Fuengirola St Andr *Eur* from 94. *Edificio Alessandra 208, Torre Blanc Del Sol, 29640 Fuengirola, Spain* Malaga (52) 581192

DEVENNEY, Raymond Robert Wilmont. b 47. TCD BA69 MA73. CITC 70. **d** 70 **p** 71. C Ballymena *Conn* 70-75; C Ballyholme *D & D* 75-81; I Killinchy w Kilmood and Tullynakill from 81. *The Rectory, 11 Whiterock Road, Killinchy, Newtownards, Co Down BT23 6PR* Killinchy (01238) 541249

✠**DEVENPORT, Rt Rev Eric Nash.** b 26. Open Univ BA74. Kelham Th Coll 46. **d** 51 **p** 52 **c** 80. C Leic St Mark *Leic* 51-54; C Barrow St Matt *Carl* 54-56; Succ Leic Cathl *Leic* 56-59; V Shepshed 59-64; R Oadby 64-73; Hon Can Leic Cathl 73-80; Dioc Missr 73-80; Suff Bp Dunwich *St E* 80-92; rtd 92; Adn Italy *Eur* from 92; Chapl Florence w Siena from 92; Aux Bp Eur from 93. *16/18 via Maggio, 50125 Florence, Italy* Florence (55) 294764

DEVERELL, William Robert Henry. b 61. CITC 88 St Jo Coll Nottm CertCS92. **d** 92 **p** 93. C Agherton *Conn* 92-95; I Sixmilecross w Termonmaguirke *Arm* from 95. *104 Cooley Road, Sixmilecross, Co Tyrone BT79 9DH* Beragh (016627) 58218

DEVEREUX, Canon John Swinnerton. b 32. Lon Univ BSc53. Wells Th Coll. **d** 58 **p** 59. C Wigan St Mich *Liv* 58-60; C Goring-by-Sea *Chich* 60-69; Ind Chapl from 69; Can and Preb Chich Cathl from 90. *4 The Driveway, Shoreham-by-Sea, W Sussex BN43 5GG* Shoreham-by-Sea (01273) 454093

DEVONSHIRE, Roger George. b 40. AKC62. **d** 63 **p** 64. C Rotherhithe St Mary w All SS *S'wark* 63-67; C Kingston Hill St Paul 67-71; Chapl RN 71-95; R Pitlochry *St And* from 95; R Kilmaveonaig from 95. *The Parsonage, Pitlochry, Perthshire PH16 5DJ* Pitlochry (01796) 472176

DEW, Lindsay Charles. b 52. Cranmer Hall Dur 85. **d** 86 **p** 86. C Knottingley *Wakef* 86-89; V Batley St Thos from 89. *The Vicarage, 16 Stockwell Drive, Batley, W Yorkshire WF17 5PA* Batley (01924) 473901

DEW, Robert David John (Bob). b 42. St Pet Coll Ox BA63. St Steph Ho Ox 63. **d** 65 **p** 66. C Abington *Pet* 65-69; Chapl Tiffield Sch Northants 69-71; Ind Chapl *Pet* 71-79; Ind Chapl *Liv* 79-87; Sen Ind Missr 88-91; R Skelsmergh w Selside and Longsleddale *Carl* from 91; Bp's Research Officer from 91. *The Vicarage, Skelsmergh, Kendal, Cumbria LA9 6NU* Kendal (01539) 724498

DEWAR, Francis John Lindsay. b 33. Keble Coll Ox BA56 MA59. Cuddesdon Coll 58. **d** 60 **p** 61. C Hessle *York* 60-63; V Stockton St Chad *Dur* 63-66; V Sunderland St Chad 66-81; Org Journey Inward, Journey Outward Project from 82. *35 Glebe Rise, Kings Sutton, Banbury, Oxon OX17 3PH* Banbury (01295) 810285

DEWAR, Ian John James. b 61. Kingston Poly BA83. Cranmer Hall Dur 89. **d** 92 **p** 93. C Blackb St Gabr *Blackb* 92-95; C Darwen St Cuth w Tockholes St Steph from 95. *Old School House, Rock Lane, Tockholes, Darwen, Lancs BB3 0LX* Blackburn (01254) 702676

DEWAR, John. b 32. Chich Th Coll 58. **d** 61 **p** 62. C Leeds St Hilda *Ripon* 61-65; C Cullercoats St Geo *Newc* 65-69; V Newsham 69-76; V Kenton Ascension 76-86; R Wallsend St Pet 86-92; V Longhorsley and Hebron from 92. *The Vicarage, Longhorsley, Morpeth, Northd NE65 8UU* Longhorsley (0167088) 218

DEWAR, Canon Michael Willoughby. b 21. Em Coll Cam BA47 MA49 Lon Univ DipTh57 QUB PhD60. St Aid Birkenhead 47. **d** 49 **p** 50. C-in-c Magherally w Annaclone *D & D* 64-73; I Helen's Bay 73-86; Preb Castleknock St Patr Cathl Dub 83-86; rtd 86; Perm to Offic *Glouc* from 86. *4 St Kenelms, Shurdington Road, Cheltenham, Glos GL53 0JH* Cheltenham (01242) 523030

DEWES, Ms Deborah Mary. b 59. **d** 92 **p** 94. C Stockton St Pet *Dur* from 92. *55 Kensington Road, Stockton-on-Tees, Cleveland TS18 4DQ* Stockton-on-Tees (01642) 678400

DEWEY, David Malcolm. b 43. Lon Univ BA72 LSE MSc(Econ)87 Fitzw Coll Cam MPhil94. Westcott Ho Cam 76. **d** 78 **p** 79. Sen Lect Middx Poly 72-92; Sen Lect Middx Univ from 92; Hon C Enfield St Mich *Lon* 78-79; Hon C Bush Hill Park St Steph 79-84; Hon C Palmers Green St Jo 84-90; Perm to Offic from 90; Perm to Offic *St Alb* from 95. *44 The Elms, Hertford SG13 7UX* Hertford (01992) 501214

DEWEY, Peter Lewis. b 38. Wycliffe Hall Ox 69. **d** 71 **p** 72. C Hammersmith St Sav *Lon* 71-73; Chapl to Bp Kensington 73-75; C Isleworth All SS 75-81; TV Dorchester *Ox* 81-91; CF (TA) 86-91; Chapl Gordonstoun Sch from 92. *Ogstoun House, Gordonstoun School, Elgin, Morayshire IV30 2RF* Hopeman (01343) 835804

DEWEY, Sanford Dayton. b 44. Syracuse Univ AB67 MA72. Gen Th Sem (NY) MDiv79. **d** 79 **p** 80. USA 79-87; C St Mary le Bow w St Pancras Soper Lane etc *Lon* 87-92; C Hampstead St Steph w All Hallows 92-94; NSM from 94. *43 Shirlock Road, London NW3 2HR* 0171-482 1527

DEWHURST, George. b 34. TD76. AKC58. **d** 59 **p** 60. C Chorley St Pet *Blackb* 59-61; C-in-c Oswaldtwistle All SS CD 61-65; CF (TA) 63-67; V Shevington *Blackb* 65-83; CF (TAVR) 67-83; CF (TA - R of O) 83-88; V Horsley and Newington Bagpath w Kingscote *Glouc* from 83. *The Vicarage, Horsley, Stroud, Glos GL6 0PR* Stroud (01453) 833814

DEWHURST, George Gabriel. b 30. **d** 59 **p** 60. In RC Ch 60-69; C Darlington St Jo *Dur* 70; C Bishopwearmouth St Nic 71-73; C-in-c Stockton St Mark CD 73-81; V Harton 81-86; R Castle Eden w Monkhesleden from 86. *The Rectory, Castle Eden, Hartlepool, Cleveland TS27 4SL* Wellfield (01429) 836846

DEWIS, Harry Kenneth. b 19. NW Ord Course 75. **d** 78 **p** 79. NSM Bedale *Ripon* 78-89; Perm to Offic from 89. *11 Masham Road, Bedale, N Yorkshire DL8 2AF* Bedale (01677) 423588

DEXTER, Canon Frank Robert. b 40. Cuddesdon Coll 66. **d** 68 **p** 69. C Newc H Cross *Newc* 68-71; C Whorlton 71-73; V Pet Ch Carpenter *Pet* 73-80; V High Elswick St Phil *Newc* 80-85; RD Newc W 81-85; P-in-c Newc St Aug 85; V Newc St Geo from 85; Hon Can Newc Cathl from 94; P-in-c Newc St Hilda from 95. *St George's Vicarage, St George's Close, Jesmond, Newcastle upon Tyne NE2 2TF* 0191-281 1628

DEY, Charles Gordon Norman. b 46. Lon Coll of Div DipTh70. **d** 71 **p** 72. C Almondbury *Wakef* 71-76; V Mixenden 76-85; TR Tong *Bradf* from 85. *The Rectory, Holmewood Road, Tong, Bradford, W Yorkshire BD4 9EJ* Bradford (01274) 682100

DEY, John Alfred. b 33. ALCD57 ALCM57. **d** 57 **p** 58. C Man Albert Memorial Ch *Man* 57-60; C Pennington 60-62; V Mosley Common 62-69; V Chadderton Em 69-79; V Flixton St Jo from 79. *St John's Vicarage, Irlam Road, Flixton, Manchester M41 6AP* 0161-748 6754

DI CASTIGLIONE, Nigel Austin. b 57. St Jo Coll Dur BA78. St Jo Coll Nottm MA94. **d** 94 **p** 95. C Tamworth *Lich* from 94. *19 Perrycrofts Crescent, Tamworth, Staffs B79 8UA* Tamworth (01827) 69021

DIAMOND, Gordon Ernest. b 08. ALCD37. **d** 36 **p** 37. R Newick *Chich* 56-73; RD Uckfield 64-73; rtd 73; Hon C Battle *Chich* 74-83. *203 The Welkin, Lindfield, Haywards Heath, W Sussex RH16 2PW* Lindfield (01444) 484201

DIAMOND, Michael Lawrence. b 37. St Jo Coll Dur BA60 MA74. Sussex Univ DPhil84. Lon Coll of Div ALCD62 LTh74. **d** 62 **p** 63. C Wandsworth St Mich *S'wark* 62-64; C Patcham *Chich* 64-69; R Hamsey 70-75; P-in-c Cam St Andr Less *Ely* 75-86; V from 86. *The Vicarage, Parsonage Street, Cambridge CB5 8DN* Cambridge (01223) 353794

DIAMOND, Capt Richard Geoffrey Colin. b 49. CA Tr Coll DipEvang89. **d** 93 **p** 93. Miss to Seamen from 90; Kenya from 90. *The Missions to Seamen, PO Box 80424, Mombasa, Kenya* Mombasa (11) 312817 or 316502 Fax 316391

DIAPER, James Robert (Bob). b 30. Portsm Dioc Tr Course 84. **d** 85. NSM Portsea St Sav *Portsm* 85-89 and 91-95; NSM Milton 89-91; rtd 95. *48 Wallington Road, Portsmouth PO2 0HB* Portsmouth (01705) 691372

DIAPER, Trevor Charles. b 51. ALA79. Coll of Resurr Mirfield 88. **d** 90 **p** 91. C N Walsham w Antingham *Nor* 90-94; P-in-c Ardleigh *Chelmsf* from 94; P-in-c The Bromleys from 94. *The Rectory, Hall Road, Great Bromley, Colchester CO7 7TS* Colchester (01206) 230344

DIBB SMITH, John. b 29. Ex & Truro NSM Scheme 78. **d** 81 **p** 82. NSM Carbis Bay *Truro* 81-82; NSM Carbis Bay w Lelant 82-84; Warden Trelowarren Fellowship Helston 84-91; Chapl 89-91; NSM Halsetown *Truro* from 91. *St John in the Fields Vicarage, St Ives, Cornwall TR26 2HG* Penzance (01736) 796035

DIBBENS, Hugh Richard. b 39. Lon Univ BA63 MTh67 St Pet Coll Ox BA65 MA74. Oak Hill Th Coll 60. **d** 67 **p** 68. C Holborn St Geo w H Trin and St Bart *Lon* 67-72; CMS 73-74; Japan 74-77; TR Chigwell *Chelmsf* 78-92; V Hornchurch St Andr from 92. *222 High Street, Hornchurch, Essex RM12 6QP* Hornchurch (01708) 441571

DIBBS, Canon Geoffrey. b 24. Man Univ BA51 ThD69. Wycliffe Hall Ox 51. **d** 53 **p** 54. R Burton Agnes w Harpham *York* 59-66; Canada from 66; rtd 88. *13414 Desert Glen Drive, Sun City West, Az 85375, USA*

DIBDEN, Alan Cyril. b 49. Hull Univ LLB70 Fitzw Coll Cam BA72 MA76. Westcott Ho Cam 70. **d** 73 **p** 74. C Camberwell St Luke *S'wark* 73-77; TV Walworth 77-79; TV Langley Marish *Ox* 79-84; C Chalfont St Peter 84-90; TV Burnham w Dropmore, Hitcham and Taplow from 90. *Taplow Rectory, Maidenhead, Berks SL6 0ET* Maidenhead (01628) 661182

DIBDIN, Ronald Frank. b 20. Glouc Sch of Min 84 Trin Coll Bris 84. **d** 84 **p** 84. NSM Newent *Glouc* 84-85; NSM Newent and Gorsley w Cliffords Mesne 85-90; rtd 90; Perm to Offic *Glouc* from 90. *The Retreat, High Street, Newent, Glos GL18 1AS* Newent (01531) 822090

DICK, Alexander Walter Henry. b 20. Lon Univ BSc49 BSc(Econ)56. Sarum & Wells Th Coll 73. **d** 74 **p** 75. C Totnes *Ex* 74-77; Min Estover LEP 77-80; V Estover 80-81; P-in-c Broadwoodwidger 81-83; V 83-86; P-in-c Kelly w Bradstone 81-83; R 83-86; P-in-c Lifton 81-83; R 83-86; rtd 86; Perm to Offic *Ex* 86-95; Perm to Offic *Lon* 86-94. *Flat 1, Fairfield, Huxtable Hill, Torquay TQ2 6RN, or 25 Freegrove Road, London N7 9RG* Torquay (01803) 605126 or 0171-607 7799

DICK, Mrs Caroline Ann. b 61. Nottm Univ BTh88. Linc Th Coll 85. **d** 88 **p** 94. Par Dn Houghton le Spring *Dur* 88-93; Par Dn Hetton-le-Hole 93-94; C from 94; Chapl Sunderland Univ from 94. *The Rectory, Houghton Road, Hetton-le-Hole, Houghton le Spring, Tyne & Wear DH5 9PH* 0191-526 3198

DICK, Cecil Bates. b 42. Selw Coll Cam BA68 MA72. E Midl Min Tr Course 73. **d** 76 **p** 78. NSM Cinderhill *S'well* 76-79; Chapl Dame Allan's Schs Newc 79-85; C Gosforth All SS *Newc* 85-87; Chapl HM Pris Dur 88-89; Chapl HM Pris Hull from 89. *The Chaplain's Office, HM Prison Hull, Hedon Road, Hull HU9 5LS* Hull (01482) 20673 Fax 229018

DICK, Norman MacDonald. b 32. ACIB. Ox NSM Course 87. **d** 90 **p** 91. NSM Bedgrove *Ox* 90-95; NSM Ellesborough, The Kimbles and Stoke Mandeville from 95. *21 Camborne Avenue, Aylesbury, Bucks HP21 7UH* Aylesbury (01296) 85530

DICK, Raymond Owen. b 53. Edin Univ BD77. Edin Th Coll 73. **d** 77 **p** 78. C Glas St Mary *Glas* 77-84; Perm to Offic *St Alb* 84-85; P-in-c Edin St Paul and St Geo *Edin* 85; P-in-c Edin SS Phil and Jas 85-86; P-in-c Edin St Marg 85-87; TV Edin Old St Paul 87-88; R Hetton-le-Hole *Dur* from 88. *The Rectory, Houghton Road, Hetton-le-Hole, Houghton le Spring, Tyne & Wear DH5 9PH* 0191-526 3198

DICKEN, Dr Eric William Trueman. b 19. Ex Coll Ox BA39 MA46 DD64. Cuddesdon Coll 49. **d** 49 **p** 50. Warden Lenton Hall Nottm Univ 65-80; R Maidwell w Draughton, Scaldwell, Lamport etc *Pet* 80-84; rtd 84. *Monks Barn, Maughersbury, Cheltenham, Glos GL54 1HP* Cotswold (01451) 830562

DICKENS, Adam Paul. b 65. Man Univ BA89 Nottm Univ MDiv93. Linc Th Coll 91. **d** 93 **p** 94. C Pershore w Pinvin, Wick and Birlingham *Worc* from 93. *10 Redlands, Pershore, Worcs WR10 1EJ* Pershore (01386) 553294

DICKENS, Philip Henry Charles. b 28. S'wark Ord Course 76. **d** 79 **p** 80. NSM Headley All SS *Guildf* 79-81; C 81-84; V Wrecclesham from 84. *The Vicarage, 2 Kings Lane, Wrecclesham, Farnham, Surrey GU10 4QB* Farnham (01252) 716431

DICKENS, Timothy Richard John. b 45. Leeds Univ BSc68. Westcott Ho Cam 68. **d** 71 **p** 72. C Meole Brace *Lich* 71-74; C-in-c Stamford Ch Ch CD *Linc* 74-80; V Anlaby St Pet *York* 80-91; V Egg Buckland *Ex* from 91. *The Vicarage, 100 Church Hill, Plymouth PL6 5RD* Plymouth (01752) 701399

DICKENSON, Charles Gordon. b 29. Bps' Coll Cheshunt 53. **d** 56 **p** 57. V Latchford Ch Ch *Ches* 68-74; P-in-c Hargrave 74-79; V Birkenhead St Jas w St Bede 79-83; R Tilston and Shocklach 83-94; rtd 94. *58 Kingsway, Crewe CW2 7ND* Crewe (01270) 60722

DICKENSON, Geoffrey. b 20. Kelham Th Coll 38. **d** 44 **p** 45. V Frecheville *Derby* 67-70; RD Staveley 68-70; V Scarcliffe 70-75; R Walton on Trent w Croxall 75-83; Perm to Offic *Heref* from 83; rtd 85. *26 Churchill Road, Church Stretton, Shropshire SY6 6EP* Church Stretton (01694) 723015

DICKER, David. b 31. St Pet Hall Ox BA57 MA58. Linc Th Coll 55. **d** 57 **p** 58. C Wootton Bassett *Sarum* 57-60; C Broad Town 57-60; C Weymouth H Trin 60-63; Antigua 63-64; R Tisbury *Sarum* 64-71; Argentina 71-77; Miss to Seamen 77-81; Chapl Dunkerque w Lille Arras etc Miss to Seamen *Eur* 81-86; TR Shaston *Sarum* from 86; RD Blackmore Vale from 90. *The Rectory, Bleke Street, Shaftesbury, Dorset SP7 8AH* Shaftesbury (01747) 852547

DICKER, Ms Jane Elizabeth. b 64. Whitelands Coll Lon BA87. Linc Th Coll 87. **d** 89 **p** 94. Par Dn Mert St Jas *S'wark* 89-93; C Littleham w Exmouth *Ex* from 93; Chapl Plymouth Univ from 93. *The Vicarage, 96 Littleham Road, Littleham, Exmouth, Devon EX8 2QX* Exmouth (01395) 272061

DICKER, Miss Mary Elizabeth. b 45. Girton Coll Cam BA66 MA70 Sheff Univ MSc78. Cranmer Hall Dur 83. **dss** 85 **d** 87 **p** 94. Mortlake w E Sheen *S'wark* 85-87; Par Dn 87-88; Par Dn Irlam *Man* 88-92; Par Dn Ashton Ch Ch 92-94; C from 94. *33 Taunton Road, Ashton-under-Lyne, Lancs OL7 9DP* 0161-339 6128

DICKIE, James Graham Wallace. b 50. Worc Coll Ox BA72 MA BLitt77. Westcott Ho Cam 78. **d** 81 **p** 82. C Bracknell *Ox* 81-84; Lic to Offic *Ely* 84-89; Chapl Trin Coll Cam 84-89; Chapl Clifton Coll Bris from 89. *6 College Fields, Clifton, Bristol BS8 3HP* Bristol (0117) 973 2580

DICKINSON, Anthony William (Tony). b 48. New Coll Ox BA71 MA74 Nottm Univ DipHE82. Linc Th Coll 80. **d** 82 **p** 83. C Leavesden All SS *St Alb* 82-86; TV Upton cum Chalvey *Ox* 86-94; P-in-c Terriers from 94. *St Francis's Vicarage, Terriers, High Wycombe, Bucks HP13 5AB* High Wycombe (01494) 520676

DICKINSON, Very Rev the Hon Hugh Geoffrey. b 29. Trin Coll Ox BA53 DipTh54 MA56. Cuddesdon Coll 54. **d** 56 **p** 57. C Melksham *Sarum* 56-58; Chapl Trin Coll Cam 58-63; Chapl Win Coll 63-69; P-in-c Milverton *Cov* 69-77; V St Alb St Mich *St Alb* 77-86; Dean Sarum from 86. *The Deanery, 7 The Close, Salisbury SP1 2EF* Salisbury (01722) 322457

DICKINSON, John Frederick. b 48. Hull Univ BA CertEd. Qu Coll Birm 84. **d** 86 **p** 87. C Gt Parndon *Chelmsf* 86-89; C Harrogate St Wilfrid and St Luke *Ripon* 89-93; V Beeston from 93. *Beeston Vicarage, 16 Town Street, Leeds LS11 8AN* Leeds (0113) 270 5529 or 277 1494

DICKINSON, Matthew Lewis. b 22. SRN51 MRIPHH54. Launde Abbey 77. **d** 79 **p** 80. C Leic St Anne *Leic* 79-81; C Leic St Eliz Nether Hall 81-87; OStJ from 80; rtd 87; Perm to Offic *Leic* from 87; Perm to Offic *Pet* from 88. *32 Glebe Way, Oakham, Leicester LE15 6XL* Oakham (01572) 722680

DICKINSON, Robert Edward. b 47. Nottm Univ BTh74. St Jo Coll Nottm 70. **d** 74 **p** 75. C Birm St Martin *Birm* 74-78; P-in-c Liv St Bride w St Sav *Liv* 78-81; TV St Luke in the City 81-86; Chapl Liv Poly 86-92; Chapl Liv Jo Moores Univ from 92. *45 Queen's Drive, Liverpool L18 2DT* 0151-722 1625 or 231 2121

DICKINSON, Stephen Paul. b 54. SRN75. N Ord Course 85. **d** 88 **p** 89. Hon C Purston cum S Featherstone *Wakef* 88-91; C Goldthorpe w Hickleton *Sheff* 91-94; V New Bentley from 94. *The Vicarage, Victoria Road, Bentley, Doncaster, S Yorkshire DN5 0EZ* Doncaster (01302) 875266

DICKINSON, Victor Tester. b 48. Univ of Wales (Cardiff) BSc70. St Steph Ho Ox 70. **d** 73 **p** 74. C Neath w Llantwit *Llan* 73-76; Asst Chapl Univ of Wales (Cardiff) 76-79; TV Willington Team *Newc* 79-86; V Kenton Ascension from 86. *The Vicarage, Creighton Avenue, Newcastle upon Tyne NE3 4UN* 0191-285 7803

DICKINSON, Wilfrid Edgar. b 21. AKC42 Lon Univ BD42. Linc Th Coll. **d** 44 **p** 45. V Chigwell *Chelmsf* 54-74; TR 74-78; V Hatf Heath 78-86; rtd 86; Perm to Offic *Heref* from 86. *4 Bearcroft, Weobley, Hereford HR4 8TA* Weobley (01544) 318641

DICKSON, Anthony Edward. b 59. Nottm Univ BTh88. Linc Th Coll 85. **d** 88 **p** 89. C Portsea St Alb *Portsm* 88-91; C Cleobury Mortimer w Hopton Wafers *Heref* 91-94; R Fownhope w Mordiford, Brockhampton etc from 94. *The Vicarage, Fownhope, Hereford HR1 4PS* Fownhope (01432) 860365

DICKSON, Brian John. b 19. Reading Univ BSc41 Birm Univ DipTh51. Qu Coll Birm 49. **d** 51 **p** 52. Lic to Offic *Bris* 67-74; Chapl Colston's Sch Bris 67-74; V Bishopston *Bris* 74-85; RD Horfield 80-85; rtd 85; Perm to Offic *Worc* from 85. *One Acre Cottage, Abberley, Worcester WR6 6BS* Great Witley (01299) 896442

DICKSON, Richard Arthur. b 67. LSE BSc(Econ)88. Ripon Coll Cuddesdon BA92. **d** 93 **p** 94. C Sale St Anne *Ches* from 93. *3 Windermere Avenue, Sale, Cheshire M33 3FP* 0161-962 9608 Fax as telephone

DICKSON, Canon Samuel Mervyn James. b 41. CITC. **d** 66 **p** 67. C Ballyholme *D & D* 66-70; C Knockbreda 70-75; I Clonallon w Warrenpoint 75-84; RD Kilbroney from 82; I Down H Trin w Hollymount from 84; RD Lecale from 85; Can Down Cathl from 91. *50 St Patrick's Avenue, Downpatrick, Co Down BT30 6DW* Downpatrick (01396) 612286

DILL, Peter Winston. b 41. ACP66 K Coll Lon BD72 AKC72. **d** 73 **p** 74. C Warsop *S'well* 73-75; C Rhyl w St Ann *St As* 75-77; C Oxton *Ches* 77-78; V Newton in Mottram 78-82; P-in-c Oxon and Shelton *Lich* 82-84; V 84-87; Chapl Clifton Coll Bris from 87. *85 Pembroke Road, Clifton, Bristol BS8 3EB* Bristol (0117) 973 9769

DILNOT, Canon John William. b 36. Selw Coll Cam BA60 MA64. Cuddesdon Coll 60. **d** 62 **p** 63. C Stafford St Mary *Lich* 62-66; C Stoke upon Trent 66-67; V Leek All SS 67-74; V Leeds w Broomfield *Cant* 74-79; P-in-c Aldington 79-81; P-in-c Bonnington w Bilsington 79-81; P-in-c Fawkenhurst 79-81; R Aldington w Bonnington and Bilsington 81-87; RD

N Lympne 82-87; Hon Can Cant Cathl from 85; V Folkestone St Mary and St Eanswythe from 87. *The Vicarage, Priory Gardens, Folkestone, Kent CT20 1SW* Folkestone (01303) 252947

DILWORTH, Anthony. b 41. St Deiniol's Hawarden 87. **d** 90 **p** 91. NSM Gt Saughall *Ches* 90-93; P-in-c Cwmcarn *Mon* 93-95; V from 95. *The Vicarage, Park Street, Cwmcarn, Cross Keys, Newport, Gwent NP1 7EL* Cross Keys (01495) 270479

DIMMER, Harry James. b 12. Chich Th Coll 73. **d** 73 **p** 73. NSM Fareham H Trin *Portsm* 73-82; rtd 82; Perm to Offic *Portsm* 82-90. *9 Bradley Road, Fareham, Hants PO15 5BW* Titchfield (01329) 847131

DIMOLINE, Keith Frederick. b 22. Clifton Th Coll 48. **d** 51 **p** 52. V Coalpit Heath *Bris* 65-74; V Hanham 74-83; C Cudworth w Chillington *B & W* 83-84; P-in-c Dowlishwake w Chaffcombe, Knowle St Giles etc 83-84; R Dowlishwake w Chaffcombe, Knowle St Giles etc 84-88; rtd 88; Perm to Offic *B & W* from 88. *16 Exeter Road, Weston-super-Mare, Avon BS23 4DB* Weston-super-Mare (01934) 635006

DINES, Anthony Bernard. b 25. Clifton Th Coll 57. **d** 60 **p** 61. R Glas St Silas *Glas* 67-78; R Gunton St Pet *Nor* 78-90; rtd 90; NSM Flixton w Homersfield and S Elmham *St E* 90-92; NSM S Elmham and Ilketshall 92-93. *215 Prestbury Road, Cheltenham, Glos GL52 3ES* Cheltenham (01242) 525840

DINES, Philip Joseph (Griff). b 59. BSc PhD MA. Westcott Ho Cam 83. **d** 86 **p** 87. C Northolt St Mary *Lon* 86-89; C Withington St Paul *Man* 89-91; V Wythenshawe St Martin from 91; P-in-c Newall Green from 95. *St Martin's Vicarage, 2 Blackcarr Road, Manchester M23 1LX* 0161-998 3408

DINGLE, John Rodger. b 14. Keble Coll Ox BA37 MA41. Westcott Ho Cam 38. **d** 39 **p** 40. C Billingham St Cuth *Dur* 39-42; Lic to Offic *Worc* 42-43; C Hartlepool H Trin *Dur* 43-44; C Shadforth 44-46; C Worc St Martin-in-the-Cornmarket *Worc* 76-80; C Worc City St Paul and Old St Martin etc 80-82; Perm to Offic from 83. *34 Beech Avenue, Worcester WR3 8PY* Worcester (01905) 53053

DINNEN, Canon John Frederick. b 42. TCD BA65 BD72 QUB MTh91. **d** 66 **p** 67. C Belf All SS *Conn* 66-68; ICM Dub 69-71; C Carnmoney 71-73; Asst Dean of Residences QUB 73-74; Dean 74-84; I Hillsborough *D & D* from 84; Preb Down Cathl from 93. *17 Dromore Road, Hillsborough, Co Down BT26 6HS* Hillsborough (01846) 682366

DINSMORE, Stephen Ralph. b 56. Wye Coll Lon BSc78. Cranmer Hall Dur 82. **d** 85 **p** 86. C Haughton le Skerne *Dur* 85-88; C Edgware *Lon* 88-93; V Plymouth St Jude *Ex* from 93. *St Jude's Vicarage, Knighton Road, Plymouth PL4 9BU* Plymouth (01752) 661232

DISNEY, Peter James. b 13. Univ of BC BA36. BC Th Coll LTh37. **d** 37 **p** 38. V Halstead H Trin *Chelmsf* 69-78; rtd 78; Perm to Offic *St E* from 78. *16 Lower Byfield, Monks Eleigh, Ipswich IP7 7JJ* Bildeston (01449) 740994

DISS, Canon Ronald George. b 31. Sarum Th Coll 58. **d** 61 **p** 62. C Greenwich St Alfege w St Pet *S'wark* 61-65; Lic to Offic 65-80; Lic to Offic *Lon* 68-77; Chapl Lon Univ 68-71; Bp's Dom Chapl *Win* 78-80; V South Maybush St Pet 80-91; Hon Can Win Cathl from 85; R Freemantle from 91. *The Rectory, 129 Paynes Road, Southampton SO1 3BW* Southampton (01703) 221804

DITCH, David John. b 45. St Cath Coll Cam BA67 MA70 Leeds Univ PGCE68. W Midl Minl Tr Course 88. **d** 91 **p** 92. C Biddulph *Lich* 91-94; V Hednesford from 94. *The Vicarage, Church Hill, Hednesford, Cannock, Staffs WS12 5BD* Hednesford (01543) 422635

DITCHBURN, Canon Hazel. b 44. NE Ord Course 82. **dss** 84 **d** 87 **p** 94. Scotswood *Newc* 84-86; Ind Chapl *Dur* from 86; RD Gateshead from 92; Hon Can Dur Cathl from 94. *2 Woburn Way, Westerhope, Newcastle upon Tyne NE5 5JD* 0191-283 0553

DITCHFIELD, Timothy Frederick. b 61. CCC Cam BA83. Cranmer Hall Dur 85. **d** 88 **p** 89. C Accrington St Jo *Blackb* 88-89; C Accrington St Jo w Huncoat 89-91; C Whittle-le-Woods 91-95; Chapl K Coll Lon from 95. *19 Maunsel Street, London SW1P 2QN, or King's College, Strand, London WC2R 2LS* 0171-828 1772 or 873 2373 Fax 873 2344

DITTMER, Canon Michael William. b 17. St Edm Hall Ox BA39 MA43. Sarum Th Coll 40. **d** 41 **p** 42. V Yatton Keynell *Bris* 52-88; R Biddestone w Slaughterford 53-88; R Castle Combe 53-88; RD Chippenham 66-76; R W Kington 75-88; Hon Can Bris Cathl 84-88; P-in-c Nettleton w Littleton Drew 85-88; rtd 88; Perm to Offic *B & W* from 88. *Greenacres, Summerhedge Lane, Othery, Bridgwater, Somerset TA7 0JD* Burrowbridge (01823) 698288

DIVALL, David Robert. b 40. New Coll Ox BA64 Sussex Univ DPhil74. Sarum & Wells Th Coll 75. **d** 77 **p** 78. Hon C Catherington and Clanfield *Portsm* 77-92; Hon C Rowlands Castle 92-93. *17 Pipers Mead, Clanfield, Waterlooville, Hants PO8 0ST* Horndean (01705) 594845

DIXON, Miss Anne Nicholson. b 28. Lightfoot Ho Dur 54. **dss** 60 **d** 87 **p** 94. Dioc RE Adv *Dur* 62-83; RE Consultant Gateshead 83-89; rtd 89. *12 Wellbank Road, Washington, Tyne & Wear NE37 1NH*   0191-416 1130

DIXON, Bruce Richard. b 42. Lon Univ BScEng63. Sarum Th Coll 66. **d** 68 **p** 69. C Walton St Mary *Liv* 68-70; C Harnham *Sarum* 70-73; C Streatham St Leon *S'wark* 73-77; R Thurcaston *Leic* 77-83; R Cranborne w Boveridge, Edmondsham etc *Sarum* from 83. *The Rectory, Grugs Lane, Cranborne, Wimborne, Dorset BH21 5PX*   Cranborne (01725) 517232

DIXON, Bryan Stanley. b 61. St Jo Coll Nottm BTh93. **d** 93 **p** 94. C Beverley Minster *York* from 93. *16 The Leases, Beverley, N Humberside HU17 8LG*   Hull (01482) 881324

DIXON, Charles William. b 41. NW Ord Course 78. **d** 81 **p** 82. C Almondbury *Wakef* 81-82; C Almondbury w Farnley Tyas 82-84; P-in-c Shepley 84-88; P-in-c Shelley 84-88; V Shelley and Shepley 88-89; V Ripponden 89-94; V Barkisland w W Scammonden 89-94; P-in-c Thornes St Jas w Ch Ch from 94. *The Vicarage, St James Court, Park Avenue, Wakefield, W Yorkshire WF2 8DW*   Wakefield (01924) 290501

DIXON, Canon David. b 19. Lich Th Coll 57. **d** 58 **p** 59. Warden Rydall Hall 68-84; P-in-c Rydal *Carl* 78-84; rtd 84; Hon Can Carl Cathl *Carl* 84-85. *Rheda, The Green, Millom, Cumbria LA18 5JA*   Millom (01229) 774300

DIXON, David Hugh. b 40. Chich Th Coll 90. **d** 92 **p** 93. C Launceston *Truro* 92-95; TV Probus, Ladock and Grampound w Creed and St Erme from 95. *The Rectory, Ladock, Truro, Cornwall TR2 4PL*   St Austell (01726) 882554

DIXON, Edward Ashby. b 15. AKC40 BD45. **d** 40 **p** 41. V Frampton on Severn *Glouc* 66-75; V Frampton on Severn w Whitminster 75-80; P-in-c Arlingham 66-80; RD Glouc S 67-79; rtd 80; Perm to Offic *Glouc* from 80. *3 Grange Close, Minchinhampton, Stroud, Glos GL6 9DF*   Brimscombe (01453) 882560

DIXON, Edward Michael (Mike). b 42. St Chad's Coll Dur BA64 DipTh66. **d** 66 **p** 67. C Hartlepool H Trin *Dur* 66-70; C Howden *York* 70-73; Chapl HM Pris Liv 73; Chapl HM Pris Onley 74-82; Chapl HM Pris Frankland 82-87; Chapl HM Pris Dur from 87. *HM Prison, Old Elvet, Durham DH1 3HU*   0191-386 2621   Fax 386 2524

DIXON, Eric. b 31. MPS. E Midl Min Tr Course 78. **d** 81 **p** 82. NSM Kirk Langley *Derby* from 81; NSM Mackworth All SS from 81. *Silverdale, Lower Road, Mackworth, Derby DE22 4NG*   Kirk Langley (01332) 824543

DIXON, Mrs Francesca Dorothy. b 52. Cam Univ MA73 Birm Univ DipTh83. **dss** 84 **d** 87 **p** 94. W Bromwich All SS *Lich* 84-87; Par Dn 87-94; C 94; Chapl Burrswood Chr Cen *Roch* from 95. *Burrswood, Groombridge, Tunbridge Wells, Kent TN3 3PY*   Tunbridge Wells (01892) 863637   Fax 862597

DIXON, Canon Guy Kenneth. b 08. Hertf Coll Ox BA30 MA34. Cuddesdon Coll 30. **d** 31 **p** 32. R Thrybergh *Sheff* 45-73; Asst RD Rotherham 47-73; Hon Can Sheff Cathl 64-73; rtd 73; Perm to Offic *Chich* from 74. *20 Alderton Court, West Parade, Bexhill-on-Sea, E Sussex TN39 3HF*   Bexhill-on-Sea (01424) 218834

DIXON, John Kenneth (Ken). b 40. Linc Th Coll 79. **d** 81 **p** 82. C Goldington *St Alb* 81-85; V Cardington 85-94; RD Elstow from 89; R Clifton from 94; P-in-c Southill from 94. *The Rectory, 8 Rectory Close, Clifton, Shefford, Beds SG17 5EL*   Hitchin (01462) 812295

DIXON, John Martin. b 42. Kelham Th Coll Lich Th Coll. **d** 72 **p** 73. C Ellesmere Port *Ches* 72-74; C Bredbury St Mark 74-75; P-in-c Greenlands *Blackb* 75-78; Chapl Victoria Hosp Blackpool 75-78; Chapl RAF 78-81; Asst Chapl HM Pris Featherstone 81-85; Dep Chapl HM Pris Wormwood Scrubs 85-87; Chapl HM Pris Rudgate and Thorp Arch 87-89; Chapl HM Pris Leeds from 89. *HM Prison, Armley, Leeds LS12 2TJ*   Leeds (0113) 263 6411   Fax 790151

DIXON, Canon John Wickham. b 18. St Jo Coll Dur BA43 MA46. St Aid Birkenhead LTh41. **d** 43 **p** 44. V Blackb St Steph *Blackb* 54-85; Can Res Blackb Cathl 65-73; Hon Can 74-85; rtd 86; Perm to Offic *Blackb* from 86. *11A Sunnyside Avenue, Wilpshire, Blackburn BB1 9LW*   Blackburn (01254) 246145

DIXON, Nicholas Scarth. b 30. G&C Coll Cam BA54 MA63. Westcott Ho Cam 54. **d** 56 **p** 57. V Whitehaven Ch Ch w H Trin *Carl* 62-70; R Blofield w Hemblington *Nor* 70-77; P-in-c Bowness *Carl* 77-79; R 79-81; V Frizington and Arlecdon 81-87; V Barton, Pooley Bridge and Martindale 87-95; rtd 95. *7 Mayburgh Avenue, Penrith, Cumbria CA11 8PA*   Penrith (01768) 892864

DIXON, Dr Peter. b 36. Qu Coll Ox BA58 MA62. Qu Coll Birm DipTh60 BD65 PhD75. **d** 60 **p** 61. C Mountain Ash *Llan* 60-63; C Penrhiwceiber w Matthewstown and Ynysboeth 63-68; P-in-c 68-70; V Bronllys and Llanfilo w Llandefaelog Tre'graig *S & B* from 70; Bp's Chapl for Readers from 80;

Bp's Chapl for Th Educn from 83; RD Hay from 90. *The Vicarage, Bronllys, Brecon, Powys LD3 0HS*   Talgarth (01874) 711200

DIXON, Peter David. b 48. Edin Univ BSc71. **d** 79 **p** 80. NSM Prestonpans *Edin* 79-91; NSM Musselburgh 79-91; P-in-c Edin St Barn from 91. *8 Oswald Terrace, Prestonpans, East Lothian EH32 9EG*   Prestonpans (01875) 812985

DIXON, Philip. b 48. Leeds Univ BSc69. St Jo Coll Nottm 77. **d** 80 **p** 81. C Soundwell *Bris* 80-82; C Stoke Bishop 82-84; TV Hemel Hempstead *St Alb* 84-85; Chapl Westonbirt Sch from 85; Perm to Offic *Bris* from 86. *East Lodge, Westonbirt School, Tetbury, Glos GL8 8QG*   Tetbury (01666) 880333

DIXON, Philip Roger. b 54. CCC Ox BA77 MA80. Oak Hill Th Coll BA80. **d** 80 **p** 81. C Droylsden St Mary *Man* 80-84; TV Rochdale 84-91; V Audenshaw St Steph from 91. *St Stephen's Vicarage, 176 Stamford Road, Audenshaw, Manchester M34 5WW*   0161-370 1863

DIXON, Richard Russell. b 32. Dur Univ BA60. Chich Th Coll 60. **d** 62 **p** 70. C Thirsk w S Kilvington *York* 69-73; P-in-c Swine 73-81; Youth Officer 73-78; V Beverley St Nic 81-91; rtd 91. *7 Mallard Avenue, Leven, Hull HU17 5NA*   Patching (01903) 544989

DIXON, Robert. b 50. Univ of Wales (Lamp) BA80. Chich Th Coll 80. **d** 81 **p** 82. C Maidstone St Martin *Cant* 81-84; Chapl HM Youth Cust Cen Dover 84-88; C All Hallows by the Tower etc *Lon* 88-90; P-in-c Southwick H Trin *Dur* from 90. *The Rectory, Church Bank, Southwick, Sunderland SR5 2DU*   0191-548 1349

DIXON, Roger John. b 33. Magd Coll Cam BA58 MA61. E Anglian Minl Tr Course 78. **d** 79 **p** 80. NSM Fakenham w Alethorpe *Nor* 79-82; C Brandeston w Kettleburgh *St E* 82-84; P-in-c from 84; Asst Chapl Framlingham Coll Suffolk from 82. *The Rectory, Kettleburgh, Woodbridge, Suffolk IP13 7JP*   Framlingham (01728) 723080

DIXON, Ms Sheila. b 46. Open Univ BA78 Trent Poly CertEd79. St Jo Coll Nottm DTS93. **d** 93 **p** 94. Par Dn Ordsall *S'well* 93-94; C from 94. *Croft Cottage, Church Lane, Retford, Notts DN22 7TU*   Retford (01777) 700733

D'MORIAS, Sydney James. b 07. Madras Univ BA29 Serampore Coll BD32. Bp's Coll Calcutta 30. **d** 32 **p** 33. V Finsbury Park St Thos *Lon* 68-78; rtd 78; Hon C Wood Green St Mich w Bounds Green St Gabr etc *Lon* 83-86; Perm to Offic from 89. *Ground Floor Flat, 21 Albert Road, London N22 4AA*   0181-888 6427

DOBB, Canon Arthur Joseph. b 31. ARIBA54 Man Coll of Art DA52 ACertCM80. Oak Hill Th Coll 56. **d** 58 **p** 59. C Bolton St Paul *Man* 58-60; C Rawtenstall St Mary 60-62; V Bircle 62-72; V Harwood 72-84; Hon Can Man Cathl from 81; V Wingates from 84. *Wingates Vicarage, 91 Chorley Road, Westhoughton, Bolton BL5 3PG*   Westhoughton (01942) 812119

DOBB, Christopher. b 46. Dur Univ BA68. Cuddesdon Coll 68. **d** 70 **p** 71. C Portsea St Mary *Portsm* 70-73; Lic to Offic *S'wark* 73-77; Perm to Offic *Bris* 77-79; Lic to Offic 79-81; V Swindon St Aug from 81. *St Augustine's Vicarage, Morris Street, Swindon SN2 2HT*   Swindon (01793) 522741   Fax 611998

DOBBIE, Gary. b 51. FSA St Andr Univ MA75 BD77 Magd Coll Cam CertEd80. **d** 83 **p** 83. C Kimbolton Sch Cambs 83-84; Hon C Kimbolton *Ely* 83-84; Chapl Ch Hosp Horsham from 84. *Whites, Christ's Hospital, Horsham, W Sussex RH13 7LP*   Horsham (01403) 266305

DOBBIN, Canon Charles Philip. b 51. Jes Coll Cam BA73 MA77 Or Coll Ox BA75 MA88. St Steph Ho Ox 74. **d** 76 **p** 77. C New Addington *Cant* 76-79; C Melton Mowbray w Thorpe Arnold *Leic* 79-83; V Loughb Gd Shep 83-89; V Ashby-de-la-Zouch St Helen w Coleorton from 89; RD Akeley W (Ashby) from 93; Hon Can Leic Cathl from 94. *The Rectory, Prior Park, Ashby-de-la-Zouch, Leics LE65 1BH*   Ashby-de-la-Zouch (01530) 412180

DOBBIN, Harold John. b 47. Liv Univ BSc69. St Steph Ho Ox 70. **d** 73 **p** 74. C Newbold and Dunston *Derby* 73-77; C Leckhampton SS Phil and Jas w Cheltenham St Jas *Glouc* 77-80; V Hebburn St Cuth *Dur* 80-86; R Barlborough *Derby* from 86. *The Rectory, Barlborough, Chesterfield, Derbyshire S43 4EP*   Chesterfield (01246) 810401

DOBBS, George Christopher. b 43. Linc Th Coll 66. **d** 68 **p** 69. C Hykeham *Linc* 68-71; Asst Master Heneage Sch Grimsby 71-78; Perm to Offic *S'well* 78-80; TV Chelmsley Wood *Birm* 80-84; TV Rochdale *Man* from 84. *St Aidan's Vicarage, 498 Manchester Road, Rochdale, Lancs OL11 3HE*   Rochdale (01706) 31812

DOBBS, John Hedley. b 03. Magd Coll Cam BA26 MA32. Ridley Hall Cam 26. **d** 27 **p** 28. V Durnford *Sarum* 59-74; RD Avon 70-74; rtd 74; Perm to Offic *Win* 74-84; Perm to Offic *Guildf* from 85. *25 Stanton Close, Cranleigh, Surrey GU6 8UH*   Cranleigh (01483) 275991

DOBBS, Michael John. b 48. Linc Th Coll 74. **d** 77 **p** 78. C Warsop *S'well* 77-82; V Worksop St Paul 82-89; P-in-c Mansf

St Mark from 89. *St Mark's Vicarage, Nottingham Road, Mansfield, Notts NG18 1BP* Mansfield (01623) 655548

DOBBYN, Dr Michael Newham. b 27. St Edm Hall Ox BA50 MA52 Columbia Univ EdD62. Cuddesdon Coll 50. **d** 52 **p** 53. Asst Chapl Eliz Coll Guernsey 55-57; rtd 92. *Mathurst Barn, Goudhurst Road, Staplehurst, Tonbridge, Kent TN12 0HQ*

DOBLE, Mrs Maureen Mary Thompson. b 44. RGN65. S Dios Minl Tr Scheme CECM93. **d** 93 **p** 94. NSM Kingston St Mary w Broomfield etc *B & W* from 93. *Davestones, Mill Cross, Kingston St Mary, Taunton, Somerset TA2 8HH* Taunton (01823) 451209

DOBLE, Dr Peter. b 29. Univ of Wales (Cardiff) BA51 Fitzw Coll Cam BA54 MA58 St Edm Hall Ox MA68 Leeds Univ PhD92. Wesley Ho Cam 52. **d** 55 **p** 58. In Ch of S India 55-60; In Meth Ch 60-64; Hd of RE Qu Mary Sch Lytham St Annes *Blackb* 64-67; Lect Relig Studies Culham Coll Abingdon *Ox* 67-69; Sen Lect 69-74; Prin Lect and Hd Relig Studies 74-80; Perm to Offic *York* from 80; Dir York RE Cen from 80. *The York Religious Education Centre, College of Ripon and York St John, Lord Mayor's Walk, York YO3 7EX* York (01904) 656771   Fax 612512

DOBSON, Christopher John. b 62. Univ of Wales (Abth) BA84 Ox Univ BA88. Wycliffe Hall Ox 86. **d** 89 **p** 90. C Biggin Hill *Roch* 89-92; C Tunbridge Wells St Jas w St Phil from 92. *3 Andrew's Close, Tunbridge Wells, Kent TN2 3PA* Tunbridge Wells (01892) 531297

DOBSON, Geoffrey Norman. b 46. ACP70 MCCEd71 Leeds Univ CertEd68 BA77 Open Univ BA73. Sarum & Wells Th Coll 72. **d** 74 **p** 75. C S Woodford H Trin CD *Chelmsf* 74-76; Colchester Adnry Youth Chapl 76-78; C Halstead St Andr w H Trin and Greenstead Green 76-78; Asst Dir Youth Educn *Carl* 78-82; P-in-c Kirkandrews-on-Eden w Beaumont and Grinsdale 78-82; V Illingworth *Wakef* 82-86; V Roxton w Gt Barford *St Alb* 86-93; P-in-c Newton Heath St Wilfrid and St Anne *Man* from 93; Chapl N Man Gen Hosp from 93. *St Wilfrid's Rectory, 929 Oldham Road, Manchester M10 6EF* 0161-205 1235

DOBSON, Canon John Francis Alban. b 12. **d** 38 **p** 45. V New Groombridge *Chich* 57-58; Canada from 58. *10 Kensington Road, Suite 1509, Bramalea, Ontario, Canada, L6T 3V4*

DOBSON, John Haselden. b 29. Mert Coll Ox BA52 MA55 Lon Univ BD58. Oak Hill Th Coll 54. **d** 56 **p** 57. Uganda 60-72; C Gorleston St Andr *Nor* 73-77; R Saxlingham Nethergate w Saxlingham Thorpe 77-90; V Shotesham 77-90; R Saxlingham Nethergate and Shotesham 90-93; rtd 94; Perm to Offic *Nor* from 94. *Karanga, The Street, Hardwick, Norwich NR15 2AB* Long Stratton (01508) 30611

DOBSON, John Richard. b 64. Van Mildert Coll Dur BA87. Ripon Coll Cuddesdon 87. **d** 89 **p** 90. C Benfieldside *Dur* 89-92; C Darlington St Cuth from 92. *65 Carmel Road South, Darlington, Co Durham DL3 8DS* Darlington (01325) 354503

DOBSON, Kenneth Shuard. b 26. Oak Hill Th Coll 53. **d** 56 **p** 57. P-in-c Deopham w Hackford *Nor* 68-74; Chapl Eccles Hall Sch Quidenham 74-78; R Elvedon *St E* 78-84; R Eriswell 78-84; R Icklingham 78-84; RD Mildenhall 80-81; rtd 84; Lic to Offic *Nor* from 84. *57 Hargham Road, Attleborough, Norfolk NR17 2HG*

DOBSON, Philip Albert. b 52. Lanc Univ BA73 CertEd74. Trin Coll Bris DipHE89. **d** 89 **p** 90. C Grenoside *Sheff* 89-92; C Cove St Jo *Guildf* 92-93; TV from 93. *Southwood Vicarage, 15 The Copse, Southwood, Farnborough, Hants GU14 0QD* Farnborough (01252) 513422

DOBSON, Robert William. b 19. Univ of Wales BA41. Coll of Resurr Mirfield 41. **d** 43 **p** 44. Chapl St Mary's Coll Ban 62-77; V Holt and Isycoed *St As* 77-83; V Holt 83-84; rtd 84. *Martin's Rise, Ellesmere Road, Tetchill, Ellesmere, Shropshire SY12 9AP*

DOBSON, Stuart Joseph. b 51. Westmr Coll Ox BA85. Chich Th Coll 86. **d** 88 **p** 89. C Costessey *Nor* 88-90; C Chaddesden St Phil *Derby* 90-92; C Friern Barnet St Jas *Lon* 92-93; TV Plymouth Em, Efford and Laira *Ex* from 93. *St Mary's Vicarage, Federation Road, Plymouth PL3 6BR* Plymouth (01752) 257284

✠**DOCKER, Rt Rev Ivor Colin.** b 25. Birm Univ BA46 St Cath Soc Ox BA49 MA52. Wycliffe Hall Ox 46. **d** 49 **p** 50 **c** 75. C Normanton *Wakef* 49-52; C Halifax St Jo Bapt 52-54; Area Sec (Dios Derby Linc and S'well) CMS 54-58; Metrop Sec (S) 58-59; V Midhurst *Chich* 59-64; RD Midhurst 61-64; R Woolbeding 61-64; V Seaford w Sutton 64-71; RD Seaford 64-71; Can and Preb Chich Cathl 66-91; V Eastbourne St Mary 71-75; RD Eastbourne 71-75; Suff Bp Horsham 75-84; Area Bp Horsham 84-91; rtd 91; Asst Bp Ex from 91. *Braemar, Bradley Road, Bovey Tracey, Newton Abbot, Devon TQ13 9EU* Newton Abbot (01626) 832468

DOCKRELL, George Thomas. b 29. TCD BA50 Div Test51 MA66. **d** 51 **p** 53. V Jersey St Andr *Win* 68-80; Asst Chapl HM Pris Pentonville 80-81; Chapl HM Pris Coldingley 81-84; Chapl HM Pris Wayland 84-93; rtd 93; Perm to Offic *Nor* from 93. *37 Priory Road, Watton, Thetford, Norfolk IP25 6PQ* Watton (01953) 882107

DODD, Alan Henry. b 42. Man Univ BA70 MA79. Chich Th Coll 82. **d** 82 **p** 83. C Fareham H Trin *Portsm* 82-84; TV 84-89; V Osmotherley w Harlsey and Ingleby Arncliffe *York* from 89. *The Vicarage, Osmotherley, Northallerton, N Yorkshire DL6 3BB* Osmotherley (01609) 883282

DODD, Charles Nathanael. b 30. Westcott Ho Cam. **d** 57 **p** 58. C Milton *Portsm* 57-62; Australia 62-91; P-in-c Bretby w Newton Solney *Derby* from 91; Bp's Ind Adv from 91. *The Vicarage, St Mary's Close, Newton Solney, Burton-on-Trent DE15 0SE* Burton-on-Trent (01283) 701235

DODD, Cyril. b 20. SS Hild & Bede Coll Dur MA48 DipEd. Coll of Resurr Mirfield 80. **d** 81 **p** 82. Hon C Guiseley *Bradf* 81-83; Hon C Guiseley w Esholt 83-90; rtd 90; Perm to Offic *Bradf* from 90. *Brierley, 37 Croft Park, Menston, Ilkley, W Yorkshire LS29 6LY* Menston (01943) 872132

DODD, Ian Neville. b 16. ACA39 FCA52. LTh. **d** 67 **p** 68. Canada 67-74; C Kingstanding St Mark *Birm* 74-75; P-in-c Smallburgh w Barton Turf w Dinham *Nor* 75-76; P-in-c Smallburgh w Dilham 77-80; P-in-c Smallburgh w Dilham w Honing and Crostwight 80-81; rtd 81; Perm to Offic *Chich* from 81. *Flat 2, High Trees, Carew Road, Eastbourne, E Sussex BN21 2JB* Eastbourne (01323) 644809

DODD, James Henry Birchenough. b 25. CPsychol AFBPsS Ox Univ MA. Westcott Ho Cam 85. **d** 85 **p** 86. NSM Epping Upland *Chelmsf* 85-95; NSM Epping Distr from 95. *The Chequers, Epping, Essex CM16 6PH* Epping (01992) 572561

DODD, John Dudley. b 15. Liv Univ BA36 Lon Univ BD51 DipEd54. Westcott Ho Cam 54. **d** 54 **p** 55. C Jersey St Helier *Win* 54-78; rtd 78; P-in-c Jersey Gouray St Martin *Win* 78-93; NSM Jersey St Luke from 94. *10 Clos de Gouray, Gorey Village, Jersey, Channel Islands JE3 9EN* Jersey (01534) 854713

DODD, John Stanley. b 24. Huron Coll Ontario 46. **d** 50 **p** 51. V Meanwood *Ripon* 65-89; rtd 89. *3 Shawdene, Burton Crescent, Leeds LS6 4DN* Leeds (0113) 278 9069

DODD, Lawrence Walter. b 04. Wells Th Coll 45. **d** 47 **p** 47. V Stratton Truro 55-69; rtd 69. *Sligon Field, Trebetherick, Wadebridge, Cornwall PL27 6SB* Trebetherick (01208) 862341

DODD, Malcolm Ogilvie. b 46. Dur Univ BSc67 Loughb Univ MSc90. Edin Th Coll 67. **d** 70 **p** 71. C Hove All SS *Chich* 70-73; C Crawley 73-78; P-in-c Rusper 79-83; Chapl Brighton Coll Jun Sch 83; Perm to Offic *Derby* from 84; Chapl Stancliffe Hall Sch from 84. *40 Jackson Road, Matlock, Derbyshire DE4 3JQ* Matlock (01629) 582800

DODD, Michael Christopher. b 33. Ch Coll Cam BA55 MA59. Ridley Hall Cam 57. **d** 59 **p** 60. V Quinton Road W St Boniface *Birm* 62-72; TV Paston *Pet* 72-77; TR Hodge Hill *Birm* 77-89; rtd 90. *39 Regency Gardens, Birmingham B14 4JS* 0121-474 6945

DODD, Canon Peter Curwen. b 33. St Jo Coll Cam BA57. Linc Th Coll 58 Wm Temple Coll Rugby 59. **d** 60 **p** 61. C Eastwood *Sheff* 60-63; Ind Chapl 63-67; Ind Chapl *Newc* from 67; RD Newc E 78-83 and from 92; Hon Can Newc Cathl from 82. *Glenesk, 28 The Oval, Benton, Newcastle upon Tyne NE12 9PP* 0191-266 1293

DODD, Peter Lawrence. b 38. MBE. Leeds Univ BA61. Qu Coll Birm DipThol. **d** 63 **p** 64. C Marske in Cleveland *York* 63-67; Malaysia 67-69; CF 70-89; V Selby Abbey *York* 90-93; Chapl Castle Hill Hosp from 93. *Castle Hill Hospital, Castle Road, Cottingham, N Humberside HU16 5JQ* Hull (01482) 875875

DODD, Walter Herbert. b 96. Qu Coll Birm 33. **d** 35 **p** 36. V Weston upon Trent *Lich* 40-63; rtd 63. *Flat 1, Brunswick House, 112 Graham Road, Great Malvern, Worcs WR14 2HX*

DODD, William Samuel (Bill). b 31. RMN80. Oak Hill Th Coll 64. **d** 66 **p** 67. C Stratford St Jo and Ch Ch w Forest Gate St Jas *Chelmsf* 67-70; C Woodford Wells 70-72; V E Ham St Paul 72-77; Perm to Offic 77-82; V Harwich 82-89; Chapl Jes Hosp Bray 89-90; Perm to Offic *Ox* from 90; rtd 91. *37 Brunel Road, Maidenhead, Berks SL6 2RP* Maidenhead (01628) 76876

DODDS, Canon Arthur Whitfield. b 20. FRMetS Qu Coll Ox BA48 MA53. Wells Th Coll 49. **d** 50 **p** 51. V Chedworth w Yanworth and Stowell *Glouc* 64-75; RD Northleach 73-83; V Chedworth, Yanworth and Stowell, Coln Rogers etc 75-85; Hon Can Glouc Cathl 78-90; rtd 86. *Church Lane Cottage, Harnhill, Cirencester, Glos GL7 5PT* Cirencester (01285) 851288

DODDS, Brian Martin. b 37. AKC62. **d** 63 **p** 64. C Morpeth *Newc* 63-67; Guyana 67-71; V Willington *Newc* 71-74; TV Brayton *York* 75-79; V Gravelly Hill *Birm* 79-83; V Winterton *Linc* 83-85; V Winterton Gp 85-90; V Gainsborough St Jo 90; V Morton from 95. *St John's Vicarage, 97A Sandsfield Lane, Gainsborough, Lincs DN21 1DA* Gainsborough (01427) 612847

DODDS, Graham Michael. b 58. GTCL80. Trin Coll Bris. **d** 84 **p** 85. C Reigate St Mary *S'wark* 84-91; P-in-c Bath Walcot *B & W* 91-93; R from 93. *The Rectory, 6 Rivers Street, Bath BA1 2PZ* Bath (01225) 425570

DODDS, Canon Neil Sutherland. b 35. ARCO59 Keble Coll Ox BA59 DipTh61 MA63. Linc Th Coll 60. **d** 62 **p** 63. C Handsworth St Jas *Birm* 62-65; V Highters Heath 65-75; V Olton from 75; RD Solihull 79-89; Hon Can Birm Cathl from 82. *St Margaret's Vicarage, 5 Old Warwick Road, Solihull, W Midlands B92 7JU* 0121-706 2318

DODDS, Norman Barry. b 43. Open Univ BA. CITC 73. **d** 76 **p** 77. C Ballynafeigh St Jude *D & D* 76-80; I Belf St Mich *Conn* from 80; Chapl HM Pris Belf from 84; RD M Belf *Conn* from 93. *5 Sunningdale Park, Belfast BT14 6RU* Belfast (01232) 715463

DODDS, Peter. b 35. W Midl Minl Tr Course 88 Qu Coll Birm 88. **d** 91 **p** 92. NSM Hartshill *Cov* from 91. *Wem House, 51 Magyar Crescent, Nuneaton, Warks CV11 4SQ* Nuneaton (01203) 384061

DODGSON, Ronald. b 27. Sarum & Wells Th Coll 72. **d** 74 **p** 75. Sub Warden Barn Fellowship Blandford Forum 74-85; Hon C Canford Magna *Sarum* 78-85; C Hartley Wintney, Elvetham, Winchfield etc *Win* 85-92; rtd 92. *84 Tavistock Road, Fleet, Aldershot, Hants GU13 8EZ* Fleet (01252) 624991

DODHIA, Hitesh Kishorilal. b 57. Cranmer Hall Dur 85. **d** 88 **p** 89. C Leamington Priors All SS *Cov* 88-91; Chapl HM Young Offender Inst Glen Parva 91-92; Chapl from 94; Chapl HM Pris Roch 92-94. *HM Young Offender Institution, Glen Parva, Tiger's Road, Wigston, Leics LE18 2TN* Leicester (0116) 277 2022 Fax 247 7679

DODSON, Canon Gordon. b 31. Barrister 56 Em Coll Cam BA54 LLB55 MA58. Ridley Hall Cam 57. **d** 59 **p** 60. V Snettisham *Nor* 69-81; RD Heacham and Rising 76-81; P-in-c Reepham and Hackford w Whitwell and Kerdiston 81-83; P-in-c Salle 81-83; P-in-c Thurning w Wood Dalling 81-83; R Reepham, Hackford w Whitwell, Kerdiston etc 83-94; Hon Can Nor Cathl 85-94; rtd 94; Perm to Offic *Nor* from 94. *Poppygate, 2 The Loke, Cromer, Norfolk NR27 9DH* Cromer (01263) 511811

DODSON, James Peter. b 32. DipMin88. Lich Th Coll 58. **d** 61 **p** 62. V Halifax St Hilda *Wakef* 68-76; V Upperthong 76-85; TV York All SS Pavement w St Crux and St Martin etc *York* 85-90; rtd 92. *5B Mawson Lane, Ripon, N Yorkshire HG4 1PW* Ripon (01756) 602030

DODSWORTH, George Brian Knowles. b 34. Univ of Wales DipTh62 Birm Univ DPS66 Open Univ AdvDipCrim92. St Mich Coll Llan 59. **d** 62 **p** 63. C Kidderminster St Mary *Worc* 62-67; Asst Chapl HM Pris Man 67-68; Chapl HM Pris Eastchurch 68-70; Chapl HM Pris Wakef 70-74; Chapl HM Pris Wormwood Scrubs 74-83; Asst Chapl Gen of Pris (SE) 83-90; Asst Chapl Gen of Pris (HQ) 90-94; Chapl HM Pris Brixton from 94; Lic to Offic *Lon* 83-94. *HM Prison Brixton, PO Box 369, Jebb Avenue, London SW2 5XF* 0181-674 9811 Fax 674 6128

DOE, Canon Francis Harold. b 22. S'wark Ord Course 68. **d** 71 **p** 72. C Sompting *Chich* 71-74; C Stopham 74-78; C Hardham 74-78; P-in-c Sutton w Bignor 79-81; P-in-c Barlavington 79-81; V Warnham 81-87; R Stopham and Fittleworth 87-92; RD Petworth 88-92; Can and Preb Chich Cathl 89-92; rtd 92; Hon C Stansted *Chich* 92-94; Perm to Offic from 94. *30 School Hill, Warnham, Horsham, W Sussex RH12 3QN* Horsham (01403) 218291

DOE, Martin Charles. b 54. Lon Univ BSc(Econ)75 PGCE87. St Steph Ho Ox 89. **d** 91 **p** 92. C Portsea St Mary *Portsm* 91-94; Chapl Abbey Grange High Sch Leeds from 94. *5 Derwentwater Grove, Leeds LS6 3EN, or St Andrew's House, Butcher Hill, Leeds LS16 5BG* Leeds (0113) 278 4560 or 275 7877

✠**DOE, Rt Rev Michael David.** b 47. St Jo Coll Dur BA69. Ripon Hall Ox 69. **d** 72 **p** 73 **c** 94. C St Helier *S'wark* 72-76; Youth Sec BCC 76-81; C-in-c Blackbird Leys CD *Ox* 81-88; V Blackbird Leys 88-89; RD Cowley 86-89; Soc Resp Adv *Portsm* 89-94; Can Res Portsm Cathl 89-94; Suff Bp Swindon *Bris* from 94. *Mark House, Field Rise, Old Town, Swindon SN1 4HP* Swindon (01793) 538654 Fax as telephone

DOHERTY, Deana Rosina Mercy. b 21. St Aid Coll Dur BA55. **dss** 82 **d** 87 **p** 94. Sutton St Jas and Wawne *York* 82-87; Par Dn 87-94; C 94-95. *Sutton-on-Hull Rectory, Hull HU7 4TL* Hull (01482) 782154

DOHERTY, Terence William. b 30. Shoreditch Coll Lon TCert St Jo Coll Dur BA56. Ripon Hall Ox 56. **d** 58 **p** 59. C Church Stretton *Heref* 58-60; C Halesowen *Worc* 60-62; Lic to Offic 62-64 and 69-78; R Hagley 64-69; Warden Dioc Conf Cen *Ches* 69-78; Lic to Offic *B & W* 70-78; TR Sutton St Jas and Wawne *York* from 78. *Sutton-on-Hull Rectory, Hull HU7 4TL* Hull (01482) 782154

DOHERTY, Thomas Alexander. b 48. Chich Th Coll 73. **d** 76 **p** 77. VC Derry Cathl *D & R* 76-79; C Llan w Capel Llanilltern

Llan 79-80; PV Llan Cathl 80-84; V Penmark w Porthkerry 84-90; R Merthyr Dyfan from 90. *Merthyr Dyfan Rectory, 10 Buttrills Road, Barry, S Glam CF62 8EF* Barry (01446) 735943

DOIDGE, Dr Charles William. b 44. RIBA ARCUK Univ Coll Lon BSc65 MSc67 PhD72. E Midl Min Tr Course CTPS93. **d** 93 **p** 94. NSM Blaby *Leic* from 93. *32 Peveril Road, Ashby Magna, Lutterworth, Leics LE17 5NQ* Leire (01455) 209800

DOIG, Dr Allan George. b 51. Univ of BC BA69 K Coll Cam BA73 MA80 PhD82. Ripon Coll Cuddesdon 86. **d** 88 **p** 89. C Abingdon *Ox* 88-91; Chapl LMH Ox from 91. *Liddell Building, 60 Iffley Road, Oxford OX4 1EQ or, Lady Margaret Hall, Oxford OX2 6QA* Oxford (01865) 242715 or 274386 Fax 511069

DOLL, Dr Peter Michael. b 62. Yale Univ BA84 Ch Ch Ox DPhil89. Cuddesdon Coll BA94 DipMin95. **d** 95. C Cowley St Jo *Ox* from 95. *129 Magdalen Road, Oxford OX4 1RJ* Oxford (01865) 241804

DOLMAN, Derek Alfred George Gerrit. b 40. ALCD64. **d** 64 **p** 65. C St Alb St Paul *St Alb* 65-68; C Bishopwearmouth St Gabr *Dur* 68-72; R Jarrow Grange 72-80; V New Catton St Luke *Nor* from 80. *St Luke's Vicarage, Aylsham Road, Norwich NR3 2HF* Norwich (01603) 425959

DOMINIC MARK, Brother. *See* IND, Dominic Mark

DOMINY, Canon Peter John. b 36. Qu Coll Ox BA60 MA64 Aber Univ MLitt83. Oak Hill Th Coll 60. **d** 62 **p** 63. C Bedworth *Cov* 62-66; Nigeria 67-84; R Broadwater St Mary *Chich* 84-92; TR from 92; Can and Preb Chich Cathl from 93. *Broadwater Rectory, 8 Sompting Avenue, Worthing, W Sussex BN14 8HT* Worthing (01903) 823916

DOMMETT, Canon Richard Radmore. b 19. St Jo Coll Ox BA41 MA45. Wells Th Coll 41. **d** 43 **p** 44. R Caister *Nor* 60-81; Hon Can Nor Cathl 77-85; P-in-c Saxthorpe and Corpusty 81-85; P-in-c Oulton SS Pet and Paul 81-85; P-in-c Blickling w Ingworth 81-85; P-in-c Heydon w Irmingland 82-85; rtd 85; Perm to Offic *St E* from 85; Perm to Offic *Nor* from 85. *14 Norwich Road, Halesworth, Suffolk IP19 8HN* Halesworth (01986) 873778

DONALD, Andrew William. b 19. St Jo Coll Morpeth 47 ACT ThL50. **d** 49 **p** 50. Chapl Halmstad *Eur* 65-68; Australia from 68; rtd 84. *18A Cobham Way, Westfield Park, Kelmscott, W Australia 6112* Perth (9) 390-8425

DONALD, Brother. *See* GREEN, Donald Pentney

DONALD, Dennis Curzon. b 38. Oak Hill Th Coll 68. **d** 70 **p** 71. C Carl St Jo *Carl* 70-73; Lic to Offic 73-77; Warden Blaithwaite Ho Chr Conf Cen Wigton from 73; Perm to Offic *Carl* from 77; Chapl Eden Valley Hospice Carl from 92. *Windyfell, Raughton Head, Carlisle CA5 7DG* Raughton Head (016974) 76246

DONALD, Robert Francis. b 49. St Jo Coll Nottm BTh75 LTh. **d** 75 **p** 76. C New Barnet St Jas *St Alb* 75-79; C St Alb St Paul 79-86; C St Alb St Mary Marshalswick 86-87; Lic to Offic from 87; Dir Chr Alliance Housing Assn Ltd from 87. *85A Abbots Park, St Albans, Herts AL1 1TN, or Exton Street, London SE1 8UE* St Albans (01727) 841647 or 0171-620 1455

DONALD, Steven. b 55. CertEd76. Oak Hill Th Coll BA88. **d** 88 **p** 89. C Cheadle All Hallows *Ches* 88-91; C Ardsley *Sheff* 91; V Kendray from 92. *St Andrew's Vicarage, 82 Hinningley Lane, Barnsley, S Yorkshire S70 3DT* Barnsley (01226) 203906

DONALD, William. b 30. Lon Univ DipTh61. Tyndale Hall Bris 58. **d** 61 **p** 62. Lic to Offic *Bris* 66-70; C Cheltenham St Mark *Glouc* 70-77; C Glouc St Jas 77-82; Lic to Offic from 82; rtd 95. *82 Forest View Road, Gloucester GL4 0BY* Gloucester (01452) 506993

DONALDSON, Christopher William. b 17. Lon Univ BD49. Kelham Th Coll. **d** 42 **p** 43. R Cant St Martin and St Paul *Cant* 63-76; Six Preacher Cant Cathl 72-78; rtd 82; Perm to Offic *B & W* 82-94. *The Cottage, 13 Beadon Lane, Merriott, Crewkerne, Somerset TA16 5QT* Crewkerne (01460) 72593

DONALDSON, Miss Elizabeth Anne. b 55. Univ of Wales (Ban) BSc76 Surrey Univ MSc80 Nottm Univ BA82. St Jo Coll Nottm DPS83. **dss** 83 **d** 87 **p** 94. Guildf Ch Ch *Guildf* 83-86; Cuddington 86-87; C 87-90; C Keresley and Coundon *Cov* from 90. *32 Parkfield Road, Keresley, Coventry CV7 8LR* Keresley (01203) 333694

DONALDSON, John Colvin. b 22. TCD BA49 MA57. **d** 50 **p** 51. V Ilsington *Ex* 59-73; RD Moreton 69-73; V Cockington 73-87; RD Ipplepen 78-82; rtd 87; Perm to Offic *Ex* from 87. *42 Bidwell Brook Drive, Paignton, Devon TQ4 7NF* Churston (01803) 845154

DONALDSON, Malcolm Alexander. b 48. Cranmer Hall Dur 84. **d** 86 **p** 87. C Heworth *York* 86-89; Chapl York Distr Hosp 86-89; C Marfleet *York* 89-90; TV from 90. *St Hilda's House, 256 Annandale Road, Greatfield Estate, Hull HU9 4JY* Hull (01482) 799100

DONALDSON, Maurice Coburne. b 19. Univ of Wales BA40 Lon Univ BD47. St Mich Coll Llan 41. **d** 42 **p** 43. V Ruabon *St As* 70-77; V Abergele 77-84; rtd 84; Perm to Offic *St As*

from 84; Perm to Offic *Ban* from 84. *7 Llys Mair, Bryn Eithinog, Bangor, Gwynedd LL57 2LA*

DONALDSON, Roger Francis. b 50. Jes Coll Ox BA71 MA75. Westcott Ho Cam 72. **d** 74 **p** 75. C Mold *St As* 74-78; V Denio w Aber-erch *Ban* 78-95; R Llanbeblig w Caernarfon and Betws Garmon etc from 95. *The Rectory, 4 Ffordd Menai, Caernarfon, Gwynedd LL55 1LF* Caernarfon (01286) 673750

DONALDSON, William Richard. b 56. St Cath Coll Cam BA78 MA81. Ridley Hall Cam 79. **d** 82 **p** 83. C Everton St Sav w St Cuth *Liv* 82-85; C Reigate St Mary *S'work* 85-89; V Easton H Trin w St Gabr and St Lawr and St Jude *Bris* from 89. *The Vicarage, 69 Stapleton Road, Easton in Gordano, Bristol BS5 0PQ* Bristol (0117) 955 4255

DONCASTER, Reginald Arthur. b 23. Leeds Univ BA48. Coll of Resurr Mirfield. **d** 50 **p** 51. R Pleasley *Derby* 54-73; V Ardleigh *Chelmsf* 73-91; rtd 91. *Manormead, Tilford Road, Hindhead, Surrey GU26 6RA* Hindhead (01428) 604780

DONCASTER, Archdeacon of. See HOLDRIDGE, Bernard Lee

DONCASTER, Suffragan Bishop of. See GEAR, Rt Rev Michael Frederick

DONE, Mrs Margaret. b 43. Local NSM Course 84 Linc Th Coll 91. **d** 92 **p** 94. NSM Coningsby w Tattershall *Linc* from 92. *43 Park Lane, Coningsby, Lincoln LN4 4SW* Coningsby (01526) 343013

DONELLA, Mother. See MATHIE, Patricia Jean

DONKIN, Robert. b 50. Univ of Wales (Cardiff) DipTh74. St Mich Coll Llan 71. **d** 74 **p** 75. C Mountain Ash *Llan* 74-77; C Coity w Nolton 77-79; V Oakwood 79-84; V Aberaman and Abercwmboi 84-91; V Aberaman and Abercwmboi w Cwmaman from 91. *St Margaret's Vicarage, Aberaman, Aberdare, M Glam CF44 6RT* Aberdare (01685) 872871

DONOHOE, Olive. d 95. C Bandon Union *C, C & R* from 95. *3 The Pines, Kilbrittain Road, Bandon, Co Cork, Republic of Ireland*

DONSON, Miss Helen Cripps. b 32. Somerville Coll Ox DipEd55 MA58. Dalton Ho Bris 58 Gilmore Ho 69. **dss** 79 **d** 87. Staines St Pet *Lon* 80-83; Staines St Mary and St Pet 83-90; Par Dn 87-90; Par Dn Herne Bay Ch Ch *Cant* 90-92; rtd 93; Hon Par Dn Bexhill St Aug *Chich* 93-94. *2 St Augustine's Close, Cooden Drive, Bexhill-on-Sea, E Sussex TN39 3AZ* Bexhill-on-Sea (01424) 734640

DOOLAN, Leonard Wallace. b 57. St Andr Univ MA79 Ox Univ BA82 MA88. Ripon Coll Cuddesdon 80. **d** 83 **p** 84. C High Wycombe *Ox* 83-85; C Bladon w Woodstock 85-88; C Wootton by Woodstock 85-88; P-in-c 88-90; C Kiddington w Asterleigh 85-88; P-in-c 88-90; P-in-c Glympton 88-90; R Wootton w Glympton and Kiddington 90-91; TR Halesworth w Linstead, Chediston, Holton etc *St E* from 91. *The Rectory, Highfield Road, Halesworth, Suffolk IP19 8LP* Halesworth (01986) 872602

DOORES, Peter George Herbert. b 46. DipYESTB71 Hull Univ BSc67 Birm Univ PGCE68. Linc Th Coll CMinlStuds92. **d** 92 **p** 93. C N Stoneham *Win* from 92. *All Saints Lodge, Pointout Road, Southampton SO1 7DL* Southampton (01703) 791090

DORAN, Edward Roy. b 47. St Jo Coll Nottm. **d** 85 **p** 86. C Roby *Liv* 85-88; V Ravenhead from 88. *St John's Vicarage, Crossley Road, Ravenhead, St Helens, Merseyside WA10 3ND* St Helens (01744) 23601

DORAN, Sidney William. b 12. AKC40. **d** 40 **p** 41. V Bray and Braywood *Ox* 61-77; RD Maidenhead 74-77; rtd 77; Hon C Boscastle w Davidstow *Truro* from 85. *St Michael's, Combe Lane, Widemouth Bay, Bude, Cornwall EX23 0AA* Widemouth Bay (01288) 361386

DORBER, Adrian John. b 52. St Jo Coll Dur BA74. Westcott Ho Cam 76. **d** 79 **p** 80. C Easthampstead *Ox* 79-85; C Caversham and Mapledurham 85-88; Chapl Portsm Poly *Portsm* 88-92; Chapl Portsm Univ from 92. *40 Worthing Road, Southsea, Hants PO5 2RN* Portsmouth (01705) 839029 or 843161

DORCHESTER, Area Bishop of. See RUSSELL, Rt Rev Anthony John

DORE, Eric George. b 47. S Dios Minl Tr Scheme 87. **d** 90 **p** 91. NSM Hove Bp Hannington Memorial Ch *Chich* 90-92; C Burgess Hill St Andr 92-95; R Frant w Eridge from 95. *The Rectory, Frant, Tunbridge Wells, Kent TN3 9DX* Frant (01892) 750638

DORE, Robert Edward Frederick. b 28. Birm Univ BCom51. Wycliffe Hall Ox. **d** 58 **p** 59. R Billingsley w Sidbury *Heref* 67-82; R Chetton w Deuxhill and Glazeley 67-82; R Middleton Scriven 67-82; RD Bridgnorth 71-78; Preb Heref Cathl 75-82; P-in-c Chelmarsh 80-82; V 82; P-in-c Carhampton *B & W* 82-84; P-in-c Dunster 82-84; R Dunster, Carhampton and Withycombe w Rodhuish 84-93; rtd 93. *26 Church Hill Meadow, Ledbury, Herefordshire HR8 2DG*

DOREY, Trevor Eric. b 30. ACIS53. S Dios Minl Tr Scheme 87. **d** 90 **p** 91. NSM E Woodhay and Woolton Hill *Win* from 90. *Little Oxleas, Woolton Hill, Newbury, Berks RG15 9XQ* Newbury (01635) 253391

DORGU, Dr Woyin Karowei. b 58. MB, BS85. Lon Bible Coll BA93 Oak Hill Th Coll DipHE95. **d** 95. C Tollington *Lon* from 95. *St Mark's Church, 68 Tollington park, London N4 3RA* 0171-263 5384

DORKING, Archdeacon of. See HERBERT, Ven Christopher William (Chris)

DORKING, Suffragan Bishop of. *Vacant*

DORMAN, John Richard. b 16. Keble Coll Ox BA38 MA55. Ely Th Coll 38. **d** 39 **p** 40. R Threlkeld *Carl* 46-57; Br Guiana 57-66; Guyana from 66; rtd 85. *St Francis de Sales Parish, Kamarang, Upper Mazaruni River, Guyana*

DORMANDY, Richard Paul. b 59. Univ Coll Lon BA81 St Edm Ho Cam BA88. Ridley Hall Cam 86. **d** 89 **p** 90. C Sydenham H Trin *S'work* 89-93; V from 93. *Holy Trinity Vicarage, 1 Sydenham Park Road, London SE26 4DY* 0181-699 5303

DORMER, Canon Christopher Robert. b 39. Bris Univ BA61. Lich Th Coll 61. **d** 63 **p** 64. C Sheff Parson Cross St Cecilia *Sheff* 63-67; C Greenford H Cross *Lon* 67-69; Australia 69-74; Sec (Ireland) USPG 74-75; R Catton *York* 75-78; R Stamford Bridge Gp of Par 78-81; RD Pocklington 80-81; Itinerant Priest *Mor* from 81; R Lochalsh from 81; R Poolewe from 81; R Ullapool from 81; Miss to Seamen from 81; Hon Can St Andr Cathl Inverness *Mor* from 94. *The Parsonage, 25 Market Street, Ullapool, Ross-shire IV26 2XE* Ullapool (01854) 612143

DORMOR, Duncan James. b 67. Magd Coll Ox BA88 Lon Univ MSc89. Ripon Coll Cuddesdon BA94 DipMin95. **d** 95. C Tettenhall Regis *Lich* from 95. *11 Harwin Close, Tettenhall, Wolverhampton WV6 9LF* Wolverhampton (01902) 755292

DORMOR, Duncan Stephen. b 36. St Edm Hall Ox BA60. Cuddesdon Coll 60. **d** 62 **p** 63. C Headington *Ox* 62-66; USA 66-72; R Hertf St Andr *St Alb* 72-88; RD Hertf 77-83; R Burford I *Heref* from 88; TR Tenbury from 88; R Burford II w Greete and Hope Bagot from 88; R Burford III w Lt Heref from 88; V Tenbury St Mich from 94. *The Vicarage, Tenbury Wells, Worcs WR15 8BP* Tenbury Wells (01584) 810702

DORRINGTON, Brian Goodwin. b 32. Leeds Univ CertEd55. St Deiniol's Hawarden 65. **d** 66 **p** 67. C Poynton *Ches* 66-71; Perm to Offic *Truro* 71-78; Hd Master Veryan Sch Truro 71-84; Hon C Veryan *Truro* 78-84; C N Petherwin 84-87; C Boyton w N Tamerton 84-87; TV Bolventor 87-90; R Kilkhampton w Morwenstow from 90; RD Stratton from 92. *The Rectory, East Road, Kilkhampton, Bude, Cornwall EX23 9QS* Kilkhampton (01288) 321314

DORRINGTON, Richard Bryan. b 48. Linc Th Coll 79. **d** 81 **p** 82. C Streetly *Lich* 81-84; C Badger 84-85; R 85-88; C Ryton 84-85; R 85-88; C Beckbury 84-85; R 85-88; V Geddington w Weekley *Pet* from 88. *The Vicarage, West Street, Geddington, Kettering, Northants NN14 1BD* Kettering (01536) 742200

DORSET, Archdeacon of. See WALTON, Ven Geoffrey Elmer

DORSETT, Dr Mark Richard. b 63. Univ of Wales (Lamp) BA84 MTh86 Birm Univ PhD90. Ripon Coll Cuddesdon 91. **d** 93 **p** 94. C Yardley St Edburgha *Birm* from 93. *422 Church Road, Birmingham B33 8PB* 0121-783 7318

DOSSETOR, Robert Francis. b 14. St Pet Hall Ox BA37 MA62 Lon Univ BA63 MA67. Ripon Hall Ox 37. **d** 37 **p** 38. V Lower Streatham St Andr *S'work* 61-80; rtd 80; P-in-c Tilshead, Orcheston and Chitterne *Sarum* 80-85. *42 Fowlers Road, Salisbury SP1 2PU* Salisbury (01722) 320725

DOSSOR, John Haley. b 41. Leeds Univ BA62. E Anglian Minl Tr Course 87. **d** 90 **p** 91. NSM Hadleigh w Layham and Shelley *St E* from 90. *Butterfly Hall, Hadleigh, Ipswich IP7 5JZ* Ipswich (01473) 823338

DOTCHIN, Mrs Joan Marie. b 47. NE Ord Course 84. **d** 87 **p** 94. C Newc St Gabr *Newc* 87-92; TD Willington Team 92-94; TV from 94. *St Mary's Vicarage, Churchill Street, Wallsend, Tyne & Wear NE28 7TE* 0191-262 8208

DOTY, Joseph Bonn. b 27. Woodstock Coll PhL51 STL58 Fordham Univ MA63. **d** 57 **p** 57. In RC Ch 57-70; USA 57-85; Prec St Ninian's Cathl Perth *St And* 85-88; V Church Brampton, Chapel Brampton, Harleston etc *Pet* 88-93; rtd 93. *Sun Cottage, Broad Chalke, Salisbury SP5 5EN* Salisbury (01722) 780008

DOUBLE, Richard Sydney (Brother Samuel). b 47. K Coll Lon BD69 AKC69. St Aug Coll Cant 69. **d** 70 **p** 71. C Walton St Mary *Liv* 70-74; SSF from 75; Lic to Offic *Liv* from 88. *St Francis House, 68 Laurel Road, Liverpool L7 0LW* 0151-263 8581

DOUBTFIRE, Miss Barbara. b 39. LMH Ox BA61 MA65. **d** 91 **p** 94. Par Development Officer *Ox* from 88; NSM Kidlington w Hampton Poyle from 91. *6 Meadow Walk, Woodstock, Oxon OX20 1NR* Woodstock (01993) 812095

DOUBTFIRE, Samuel. b 33. Edin Th Coll 63. **d** 66 **p** 66. V Ripponden *Wakef* 68-76; V Crosthwaite Keswick *Carl* 76-81; V Barrow St Matt 81-87; R N Reddish *Man* 87-92; rtd 92. *Greenacre, Station Road, Threshfield, Skipton, N Yorkshire BD23 5EP* Gressington (01756) 752260

DOUGALL, David Brian. b 23. CBE. Oak Hill Th Coll. d 81 p 82. C Sandringham w W Newton *Nor* 81-83; P-in-c Fritton St Edm 83-84; R Somerleyton w Ashby 83-84; R Somerleyton w Ashby, Fritton and Herringfleet 84-92; rtd 92. *Plot 2, The Green, Dauntsey, Chippenham, Wilts SN15 4HY* Malmesbury (01666) 510759

DOUGHTY, Andrew William. b 56. K Coll Lon BD AKC. Westcott Ho Cam. d 82 p 83. C Alton St Lawr *Win* 82-85; TV Basingstoke 85-91; V Chilworth w N Baddesley 91-95; Bermuda from 95. *PO Box WK 530, Warwick WK BX, Bermuda* Bermuda (1-809) 236-5744 Fax 236-3667

DOUGLAS, Canon Alexander Joseph. b 18. TCD BA45 MA61. CITC 45. d 45 p 46. I Orangefield w Moneyreagh *D & D* 63-86; rtd 86. *6 Rannoch Road, Holywood, Co Down BT18 0NA* Belfast (01232) 423661

DOUGLAS, Ann Patricia. b 49. Lon Univ CertEd71. Oak Hill NSM Course 85. d 88 p 94. Par Dn Chorleywood Ch Ch *St Alb* 88-94; V Oxhey All SS from 94. *All Saints' Vicarage, Gosforth Lane, Watford WD1 6AX* 0181-428 3696

DOUGLAS, Anthony Victor. b 51. St Jo Coll Nottm 74. d 76 p 77. C Gt Crosby St Luke *Liv* 76-79; TV Fazakerley Em 79-84; TR Speke St Aid 84-90; TR Gt and Lt Coates w Bradley *Linc* from 90. *St Michael's Rectory, 28 Great Coates Road, Grimsby, S Humberside DN34 4NE* Grimsby (01472) 844570

DOUGLAS, Canon Archibald Sholto. b 14. TD50. Selw Coll Cam BA37 MA46. Wells Th Coll 38. d 47 p 48. V Capesthorne w Siddington and Marton *Ches* 69-82; Hon Can Ches Cathl 78-82; rtd 82; Perm to Offic *Ches* from 82. *Monks Heath Hall Farm, Chelford, Macclesfield, Cheshire SK10 4SY* Chelford (01625) 861154

DOUGLAS, Charles David. b 29. Leeds Univ BSc50. Linc Th Coll 68. d 70 p 71. C Royton St Anne *Man* 70-73; V Edenfield 73-83; V Spotland 83-88; P-in-c Calderbrook 88-95; P-in-c Shore 92-95; rtd 95. *11 Harrison Crescent, Blackrod, Bolton BL6 5EX* Bolton (01204) 667595

DOUGLAS, George Gawain. b 35. Qu Coll Birm 59. d 61 p 62. C Workington St Jo *Carl* 61-64; C Upperby St Jo 64-67; C-in-c Carl St Luke Morton CD 67-68; V Carl St Luke Morton 68-72; V Aspatria w Hayton 72-92; P-in-c Leven Valley from 92. *The Vicarage, Haverthwaite, Ulverston, Cumbria LA12 8AJ* Newby Bridge (015395) 31476

DOUGLAS, Ian Alexander. b 11. St Aug Coll Cant 71. d 71 p 72. C Palmers Green St Jo *Lon* 71-81; rtd 81; Perm to Offic *Lon* from 82. *105 The Chine, London N21 2EG* 0181-360 3472

DOUGLAS, Miss Janet Elizabeth. b 60. SS Paul & Mary Coll Cheltenham BEd83. Cranmer Hall Dur 88. d 90 p 94. Par Dn Yardley St Edburgha *Birm* 90-93; Par Dn Hamstead St Paul 93-94; C from 94. *14 Yateley Avenue, Birmingham B42 1JN* 0121-358 0351

DOUGLAS, John Beresford. b 36. Sarum & Wells Th Coll 78. d 81 p 82. NSM Bath Bathwick *B & W* 81-94. *241 Bailbrook Lane, Bath BA1 7AA* Bath (01225) 858936

DOUGLAS, John Howard Barclay. b 23. St Jo Coll Dur BA48. Bps' Coll Cheshunt 48. d 50 p 51. V Thirkleby w Kilburn and Bagby *York* 60-88; rtd 88. *6 St Giles Close, York Road, Thirsk, N Yorkshire YO7 3BU* Thirsk (01845) 524573

DOUGLAS, Martyn Graham. b 59. St Steph Ho Ox 85. d 88 p 89. C Stanmore *Win* 88-91; TV Basingstoke 91-94; USA from 94. *2509 Reabok Circle, Huntsville, Alabama 35803, USA* Mobile (205) 881-7041 or 534-7733 Fax 534-7733

DOUGLAS (nee MAGGS), Mrs Pamela Jean. b 47. Girton Coll Cam MA76 K Coll Lon BD79 AKC79. Qu Coll Birm 79. dss 80 d 87. Tottenham H Trin *Lon* 80-84; Asst Chapl Bryanston Sch Blandford 84-87; Perm to Offic *Chich* 87-94. *40 Maidenhead Lane, Borrowdale, Harare, Zimbabwe*

DOUGLAS, Robert Vernon. b 24. Pemb Coll Cam BA48 MA53. Wells Th Coll 48. d 50 p 51. R N Cray w Ruxley *Roch* 66-80; V Platt 80-92; rtd 92. *Foxleigh, Symondsbury, Bridport, Dorset DT6 6HF* Bridport (01308) 424026

DOUGLAS-JONES, Ian Elliott. b 14. Trin Hall Cam BA35 MA39. Wycliffe Hall Ox 35. d 37 p 38. V Mayfield *Lich* 68-79; rtd 79; Perm to Offic *Worc* 79-92. *48 Webbs Close, Wolvercote, Oxford OX2 8PX* Oxford (01865) 52444

DOUGLAS LANE, Charles Simon Pellew. b 47. BNC Ox MA70 MIPM74. Oak Hill Th Coll. d 94 p 95. NSM Whitton St Aug *Lon* from 94. *The Little Cottage, 12 Church Street, Hampton, Middx TW12 2EG* 0181-979 2480

DOUGLASS, Philip. b 48. Open Univ BA88. St Steph Ho Ox 87. d 89 p 90. C Peterlee *Dur* 89-92; V Crowan w Godolphin *Truro* from 92. *Crowan Vicarage, 37 Trethannas Gardens, Praze, Camborne, Cornwall TR14 9NB* Praze (01209) 831009

DOULL, Iain Sinclair. b 43. Univ of Wales (Cardiff) DPS88. d 88 p 89. C Malpas *Mon* 88-91; P-in-c Newport All SS from 91. *The Vicarage, Brynglas Road, Newport, Gwent NP9 5QY* Newport (01633) 854657

DOULTON, Dick (Dic). b 32. St Cath Coll Cam BA60 MA64. Ridley Hall Cam 61. d 63 p 64. C Gedling *S'well* 63-65; C Danbury *Chelmsf* 65; Lic to Offic *Ox* 85-90; Lic to Offic *L & K*

from 90. *Ballygriffin, Kenmare, Killarney, Co Kerry, Irish Republic* Killarney (64) 41743

DOULTON, Roderick John (Rod). b 55. Oak Hill Th Coll DipHE93. d 93 p 94. C Hoddesdon *St Alb* from 93. *St Catherine's House, Paul's Lane, Hoddesdon, Herts EN11 8TS* Hoddesdon (01992) 443724

DOVE, Canon Reginald George James Thomas. b 16. Leeds Univ BA38. Coll of Resurr Mirfield 38. d 40 p 41. C Blyth St Mary *Newc* 40-43; S Africa from 43; rtd 88. *PO Box 2263, Edenvale, 1610 South Africa* Johannesburg (11) 609-4257

DOVER, Canon Oswald Leslie Simpson. b 18. Edin Th Coll 46. d 47 p 48. R Melrose *Edin* 59-85; Hon Can St Mary's Cathl from 77; rtd 85; Hon C Galashiels *Edin* from 88. *12 Shielswood Court, Tweedbank, Galashiels, Selkirkshire TD1 3RH* Galashiels (01896) 56946

DOVER, Suffragan Bishop of. See LLEWELLIN, Rt Rev John Richard Allan

DOW, Andrew John Morrison. b 46. Univ Coll Ox BA67 MA71. Oak Hill Th Coll 69. d 71 p 72. C Watford St Luke *St Alb* 71-74; C Chadderton Ch Ch *Man* 75-78; V Leamington Priors St Paul *Cov* 78-85; V Knowle *Birm* from 88; RD Solihull from 95. *The Vicarage, 1811 Warwick Road, Knowle, Solihull, W Midlands B93 0DS* Knowle (01564) 773666

✠DOW, Rt Rev Geoffrey Graham. b 42. Qu Coll Ox BA63 BSc65 MA68 Birm Univ DipTh74 Ox Univ MSc Nottm Univ MPhil82. Clifton Th Coll 66. d 67 p 68 c 92. C Tonbridge SS Pet and Paul *Roch* 67-72; Chapl St Jo Coll Ox 72-75; Lect St Jo Coll Nottm 75-81; V Cov H Trin *Cov* 81-92; Can Th Cov Cathl 88-92; Area Bp Willesden *Lon* from 92. *173 Willesden Lane, London NW6 7YN* 0181-451 0189 Fax 451 4606

DOWD, Garfield George. b 60. QUB BSc TCD DipTh83. d 86 p 87. C Monkstown *D & G* 86-90; I Carlow w Urglin and Staplestown *C & O* from 90. *The Rectory, Green Road, Carlow, Irish Republic* Carlow (503) 32565

DOWDEN, Gordon Frederick. b 25. Selw Coll Cam BA51 MA55. Chich Th Coll 51. d 53 p 54. R Hulme St Phil *Man* 58-70; R Hulme Ascension 70-78; RD Hulme 73-78; P-in-c Holybourne cum Neatham *Win* 78-82; RD Alton 79-82; C Man Resurr *Man* 82; AD Ardwick 82-90; C Man Gd Shep 82-91; Chapl Ancoats Hosp Man 85-90; rtd 91. *41 Rozel Square, Manchester M3 4FQ* 0161-832 5592

DOWDING, Edward Brinley. b 47. St Mich Coll Llan 70 St D Coll Lamp BA71. d 72 p 73. C Canton St Cath *Llan* 72-75; C Aberdare St Jo 75-78; V Aberavon H Trin 78-85; R Sully from 85. *The Rectory, 26 South Road, Sully, Penarth, S Glam CF64 5TG* Cardiff (01222) 530221

DOWDING, Jeremy Charles. b 51. RMN72. St Steph Ho Ox 89. d 91 p 92. C Newport St Steph and H Trin *Mon* 91-94; C Risca from 94. *18 Commercial Street, Risca, Newport, Gwent NP1 6AY* Newport (01633) 250160

DOWDING, Stanley Frederick. b 10. ALCD32 St Jo Coll Dur BA33 LTh33. d 34 p 35. V Nelson in Lt Marsden *Blackb* 55-75; rtd 75; Lic to Offic *Blackb* from 76. *4 Hillside Avenue, Reedley, Burnley, Lancs BB10 2NF* Nelson (01282) 693030

DOWDLE, Miss Cynthia. b 48. Cranmer Hall Dur 88. d 90 p 94. C Allerton *Liv* 90-94; TR Halewood from 94. *22 Kenton Road, Halewood, Liverpool L26 9LA* 0151-486 3180

DOWELL, Graham Moffat. b 26. Magd Coll Cam BA48 MA53. Ely Th Coll 51. d 53 p 54. Zambia 68-70; Chapl LSE *Lon* 70-74; V Hampstead St Jo 74-86; Perm to Offic *Heref* from 87; rtd 91. *8 Bridge Street, Clun, Craven Arms, Shropshire SY7 8JP* Clun (01588) 640521

DOWIE, Miss Winifred Brenda McIntosh. b 57. Callendar Park Coll of Educn Falkirk DipEd78. Trin Coll Bris BA91. d 92 p 94. Par Dn Downend *Bris* 92-94; C from 94. *5 Queensholm Close, Bristol BS16 6LD* Bristol (0117) 956 2081

DOWLAND, Martin John. b 48. Lon Univ BD70 Southn Univ PGCE71. Wycliffe Hall Ox 75. d 77 p 78. C Jesmond Clayton Memorial *Newc* 77-80; C Chadderton Ch Ch *Man* 80-85; R Haughton St Mary from 85. *Haughton Green Rectory, Meadow Lane, Denton, Manchester M34 1GD* 0161-336 4529

DOWLEN, Edward Mark. b 25. DLC47 Cranfield Inst of Tech MSc49. St Jo Coll Dur 79. d 79 p 80. C Rhyl w St Ann *St As* 79-82; C Warton St Paul *Blackb* 83-90; rtd 90; Lic to Offic *Sarum* from 90; Lic to Offic *Mor* from 93. *33 Hythe Road, Poole, Dorset BH15 3NN* Parkstone (01202) 737699 or 770636

DOWLER, Robert Edward Mackenzie. b 67. Ch Ch Ox BA89 Selw Coll Cam BA93. Westcott Ho Cam 91. d 94 p 95. C Southgate Ch Ch *Lon* from 94. *7 The Green, London N14 7EG* 0181-886 2389

DOWLING, Donald Edward. b 43. St Jo Coll Dur DipTh74 St Andr Univ MA66. d 74 p 75. C Thame w Towersey *Ox* 74-77; C Norton *St Alb* 77-80; V Wilbury from 81. *Church House, 103 Bedford Road, Letchworth, Herts SG6 4DU* Letchworth (01462) 679236

DOWLING, Paul Martin. b 55. ACA G&C Coll Cam MA79. Cranmer Hall Dur 88. d 90 p 91. C Redhill St Jo *S'wark* 90-94;

V Wakef St Jo *Wakef* from 94. *St John's Vicarage, 65 Bradford Road, Wakefield, W Yorkshire WF1 2AA* Wakefield (01924) 371029

DOWMAN, John Frederick. b 26. AKC52. **d** 53 **p** 54. V Legbourne w Lt Cawthorpe *Linc* 64-81; R Muckton w Burwell and Walmsgate 64-81; P-in-c Withcall 79-81; P-in-c Tathwell w Haugham 79-81; V Legbourne 81-92; R Raithby 81-92; rtd 92; Perm to Offic *Linc* from 92. *Parklands, Park Lane, Manby, Louth, Lincs LN11 8HH* Louth (01507) 602535

DOWMAN, Peter Robert. b 52. City Univ BSc. Wycliffe Hall Ox 82. **d** 84 **p** 85. C Cheltenham Ch Ch *Glouc* 84-87; C Danbury *Chelmsf* 87-90; R Woodham Ferrers and Bicknacre from 90. *Church House, Main Road, Bicknacre, Chelmsford CM3 4HA* Danbury (01245) 224895

DOWN, Martin John. b 40. Jes Coll Cam BA62 MA68. Westcott Ho Cam 63. **d** 65 **p** 66. C Bury St Mary *Man* 65-68; C Leigh St Mary 68-70; R Fiskerton *Linc* 70-75; V Irnham w Corby 75-79; RD Beltisloe 76-84; P-in-c Creeton w Swinstead 78-79; P-in-c Swayfield 78-79; V Corby Glen 79-84; Good News Trust 84-88; Perm to Offic 84-88; Perm to Offic *Pet* 86-88; P-in-c Ashill w Saham Toney *Nor* 88-94; R from 94. *The Rectory, Ashill, Thetford, Norfolk IP25 7BT* Holme Hale (01760) 440247

DOWN, Peter Michael. b 54. K Coll Lon BD78 AKC. Coll of Resurr Mirfield 78. **d** 79 **p** 80. C Swindon Ch Ch *Bris* 79-82; C Southmead 82-84; TV Cannock *Lich* 84-92; V Coleford w Holcombe *B & W* from 92. *The Vicarage, Church Street, Coleford, Bath BA3 5NG* Mells (01373) 813382

DOWN, Philip Roy. b 53. R Melbourne Inst of Tech DipApSc76 Hull Univ MA93. Melbourne Coll of Div BTh82 MTh88. **d** 89 **p** 89. C Gt Grimsby St Mary and St Jas *Linc* 89-91; TV from 91. *62A Brighowgate, Grimsby, S Humberside DN32 0QW* Grimsby (01472) 250877 or 358610

DOWN, Canon Wilfred Samuel. b 26. Keble Coll Ox BA50 MA54. Linc Th Coll 50. **d** 51 **p** 52. R Monkton Farleigh w S Wraxall *Sarum* 69-76; TR Marlborough 76-91; Can and Preb Sarum Cathl 83-91; RD Marlborough 86-90; rtd 91. *14 Eyres Drive, Alderbury, Salisbury SP5 3TD* Marlborough (01672) 512357

✠**DOWN, Rt Rev William John Denbigh.** b 34. St Jo Coll Cam BA57 MA61. Ridley Hall Cam 57. **d** 59 **p** 60 **c** 90. C Fisherton Anger *Sarum* 59-63; Miss to Seamen 63-90; Australia 71-74; Dep Gen Sec Miss to Seamen 75; Gen Sec 76-90; Hon C Gt Stanmore *Lon* 75-90; Chapl St Mich Paternoster Royal 76-90; Perm to Offic *St Alb* 78-90; Hon Can Gib Cathl *Eur* 85-90; Hon Can Kobe Japan from 87; Bp Bermuda 90-95; Asst Bp Leic from 95; P-in-c Humberstone from 95. *St Mary's Vicarage, 56 Vicarage Lane, Humberstone, Leicester LE5 1EE* Leicester (0116) 276 7281

DOWN AND DROMORE, Bishop of. See McMULLAN, Rt Rev Gordon

DOWN, Archdeacon of. *Vacant*

DOWN, Dean of. See LECKEY, Very Rev Hamilton

DOWNER, Cuthbert John. b 18. S'wark Ord Course 60. **d** 74 **p** 75. Hon C Kirdford *Chich* 74-76; C Halesworth w Linstead and Chediston *St E* 76-79; P-in-c Knodishall w Buxlow 79-80; P-in-c Friston 79-80; R Bacton w Wyverstone 80-83; P-in-c Cotton and Wickham Skeith 80-83; R Bacton w Wyverstone and Cotton 83-84; rtd 84; Perm to Offic *St E* 84-87; Perm to Offic *B & W* from 88. *3 Stable Cottages, Skepton Road, Oakhill, Bath BA3 5HT*

DOWNES, Richard John. b 63. Cranmer Hall Dur CTM94. **d** 94. C Bishopwearmouth St Gabr *Dur* from 94. *112 Cleveland Road, Sunderland SR4 7JT* 0191-528 5470

DOWNEY, John Stewart. b 38. QUB CertEd60 Open Univ BA76. Oak Hill Th Coll 63. **d** 66 **p** 67. C Londonderry St Aug *D & R* 66-71; I Dungiven w Bovevagh 71-82; Bp's Dom Chapl 75-82; V Bishopwearmouth St Gabr *Dur* 82-91; V New Malden and Coombe *S'wark* from 91. *The Vicarage, 93 Coombe Road, New Malden, Surrey KT3 4RE* 0181-942 0915

DOWNHAM, Canon Peter Norwell. b 31. Man Univ BA52. Ridley Hall Cam 54. **d** 56 **p** 57. V Denton Holme *Carl* 68-79; V Reading Greyfriars *Ox* 79-95; Hon Can Ch Ch 90-95; rtd 95; NSM Cotehill and Cumwhinton *Carl* from 95. *The Vicarage, Cotehill, Carlisle CA4 0DY* Carlisle (01228) 60323

DOWNHAM, Simon Garrod. b 61. Solicitor 87 K Coll Lon LLB84. Wycliffe Hall Ox BA93 DipMin94. **d** 94 **p** 95. C Brompton H Trin w Onslow Square St Paul *Lon* from 94. *3 Holy Trinity Church House, Brompton Road, London SW7 2RW* 0171-589 3589 Fax 589 3390

DOWNIE, James Hubert. b 23. DL. Barrister 58 FRSA70. **d** 92 **p** 93. NSM Stornoway *Arg* from 92. *Dunarin, Strond, Leverburgh, Isle of Harris PA83 3UD* Leverburgh (01859) 520247

DOWNING, Francis Gerald. b 35. Qu Coll Ox BA56 MA60. Linc Th Coll. **d** 58 **p** 59. C Filwood Park CD *Bris* 58-60; Tutor Linc Th Coll 60-64; V Unsworth *Man* 64-80; Tutor N Ord

Course 80-82; Vice-Prin 82-90; Lic to Offic *Man* 80-90; V Bolton SS Simon and Jude from 90. *The Vicarage, 15 Lowick Avenue, Bolton BL3 2DS* Bolton (01204) 23919

DOWNS, Miss Geinor. b 47. UEA BA72 Southn Univ BTh89. Chich Th Coll 85. **d** 87 **p** 94. Par Dn Wellingborough All SS *Pet* 87-89; Development Officer Chich Th Coll 89-92; C Durrington *Chich* 92-95; Chapl City Hosp NHS Trust from 95. *Chaplaincy Department, City Hospital NHS Trust, Dudley Road, Birmingham B18 7QH* 0121-554 3801 Fax 523 0951

DOWNS, Ivan Frederick. b 26. Chich Th Coll 63. **d** 66 **p** 67. C Corbridge w Halton *Newc* 66-70; C Tynemouth Ch Ch 70-74; V Walker 74-79; V Dudley 79-89; V Weetslade 90-91; rtd 91. *East Cottage, Stannersburn, Hexham, Northd NE48 1DD* Bellingham (01434) 240471

DOWNS, John Alfred. b 58. MIBiol80 CBiol80 Leic Univ BSc79 PGCE80. E Midl Min Tr Course 90. **d** 93 **p** 94. NSM Barlestone *Leic* from 93. *29 Meadow Road, Barlestone, Nuneaton, Warks CV13 0JG* Market Bosworth (01455) 290195

DOWSE, Edgar. b 10. Dur Univ LTh35 Lon Univ BD37 Fitzw Coll Cam BA74 Lon Univ MPhil90. Clifton Th Coll 32. **d** 35 **p** 36. St Dunstan-in-the-Wall *Lon* 70-71; V Acton Green St Alb *Lon* 72-75; rtd 75. *87 College Road, Isleworth, Middx TW7 5DP* 0181-568 2548

DOWSE, Ivor Roy. b 35. ARHistS MRSL. St Deiniol's Hawarden 66. **d** 68 **p** 70. C Sudbury St Andr *Lon* 69-71; C Weeke *Win* 71-73; Min Can Ban Cathl *Ban* 73-78; V Hollym w Welwick and Holmpton *York* 78-81; R Bearwood *Ox* 81-82; P-in-c Rothesay *Arg* 83-86; C Boxmoor St Jo *St Alb* 86-92; rtd 92; Hon C Cowes H Trin and St Mary *Portsm* from 92. *14 Charles Road, Cowes, Isle of Wight PO31 8HG* Isle of Wight (01983) 294782

DOWSETT, Alan Charles. b 27. Selw Coll Cam BA51 MA55 Bris Poly CQSW76. Cuddesdon Coll 51. **d** 53 **p** 54. C Stoke Bishop *Bris* 65-68; Lic to Offic from 69; rtd 89. *23 Upper Cranbrook Road, Bristol BS6 7UW* Bristol (0117) 924 3227

DOWSETT, Marian Ivy Rose. b 40. **d** 88. NSM Rumney *Mon* 88-94; C St Mellons and Michaelston-y-Fedw from 94. *114 Ridgeway Road, Cardiff CF3 9AB* Cardiff (01222) 792635

DOWSON, Roger Christopher. b 32. Clifton Th Coll 60. **d** 63 **p** 64. V Thorpe Edge *Bradf* 68-80; V Wyke 80-91; rtd 91; Hon C Coley *Wakef* from 91. *1 Windsor Villas, Norwood Green, Halifax, W Yorkshire HX3 8QS* Bradford (01274) 674557

DOXSEY, Roy Desmond. b 41. St D Coll Lamp 64. **d** 67 **p** 68. C Pemb St Mary and St Mich *St D* 67-70; C Milford Haven 70-73; C Loughton *Ox* 73-75; Chapl Llandovery Coll 75-81 and from 92; Zambia 81-86; Chapl Epsom Coll Surrey 86-92. *Llandovery College, Queensway, Llandovery, Dyfed SA20 0EE* Llandovery (01550) 20315

DOYE, Andrew Peter Charles. b 64. BNC Ox BA85. Trin Coll Bris BA93. **d** 93 **p** 94. C Surbiton St Matt *S'wark* from 93. *15 Tolworth Road, Surbiton, Surrey KT6 7TA* 0181-397 7806

DOYLE, Canon Alan Holland. b 22. JP. Lon Univ BD55 Birm Univ MA86 Buckm Univ DPhil93. Wycliffe Hall Ox 52. **d** 52 **p** 53. R Salwarpe *Worc* 67-74; RD Droitwich 69-78; P-in-c Himbleton w Huddington 74-78; Hon Can Worc Cathl 74-87; P-in-c Ombersley w Doverdale 78-83; R 83-87; rtd 87. *3 Graham Court, Graham Road, Malvern, Worcs WR14 2HX* Malvern (01684) 892133

DOYLE, Andrew Michael. b 63. K Coll Lon BD85 AKC85. Ripon Coll Cuddesdon 86. **d** 88 **p** 89. C Lytchett Minster *Sarum* 88-92; TV Kirkby *Liv* from 92. *The Vicarage, 9 Redwood Way, Tower Hill, Liverpool L32 4DU* 0151-548 7969

DOYLE, Brian William. b 31. RMN61. Sarum Th Coll 87. **d** 87 **p** 88. NSM Heene *Chich* 87-91; Chapl Qu Alexandra's Hosp Worthing 89-91; C W Tarring *Chich* 91-93; C Hangleton from 93. *58 Nevill Avenue, Hove, E Sussex BN3 7NA* Brighton (01273) 208458

DOYLE, Edward Michael. b 70. Univ of Wales (Cardiff) DipTh91. St Mich Coll Llan BTh93. **d** 94 **p** 95. C Sketty *S & B* from 94. *10 Sketty Park Close, Sketty, Swansea SA2 8LR* Swansea (01792) 204086

DOYLE, Graham Thomas. b 48. Worc Coll Ox BA85 MA90. St Barn Coll Adelaide ThL73 ThSchol77. **d** 73 **p** 74. Australia 73-83; Perm to Offic *Ox* 83-85; C Cobbold Road St Sav w St Mary *Lon* 86; P-in-c Bradf St Oswald Chapel Green *Bradf* 86-91; Chapl Belgrade w Zagreb *Eur* 91-93; Chapl Belgrade from 93. *Chaplain's Flat, 1 Branks Djonovica, 11000 Belgrade, Serbia* Belgrade (11) 660456 Fax 659651

DOYLE, Robin Alfred. b 43. Dur Univ BA65. Westcott Ho Cam 66. **d** 68 **p** 69. C Edgbaston St Geo *Birm* 68-70; C Erdington St Barn 70-73; P-in-c Oldbury 73-81; V Maker w Rame *Truro* from 81. *The Vicarage, Fore Street, Torpoint, Cornwall PL10 1NB* Plymouth (01752) 822302

DRACKLEY, John Oldham. b 36. Em Coll Cam BA57 MA61. Wells Th Coll 57. **d** 59 **p** 60. C Matlock and Tansley *Derby*

67-77; P-in-c Radbourne 77-82; P-in-c Dalbury, Long Lane and Trusley 77-82; P-in-c Longford 77-82; Sec Dioc Cttee for Care of Chs from 82; rtd 95. *26 Highfield Drive, Matlock, Derbyshire DE4 3FZ* Matlock (01629) 55902

DRAFFAN, Prof Ian William. b 42. FBCS77 CEng88 Aston Univ BSc65 MSc66. N Ord Course 83. **d** 86 **p** 87. NSM Millhouses H Trin *Sheff* from 86. *8 Silverdale Crescent, Sheffield S11 9JH* Sheffield (0114) 236 4523

DRAIN, Walter. b 39. ACP66 Open Univ BA76. NW Ord Course 76. **d** 79 **p** 80. NSM Cheadle *Ches* 79-81; C 81-84; V Chatburn *Blackb* from 84; Asst Chapl HM Pris Preston from 94. *The Vicarage, Chatburn, Clitheroe, Lancs BB7 4AA* Clitheroe (01200) 441317

DRAKE, Miss Frances. b 43. Brentwood Coll of Educn TCert67 Sussex Univ BEd74. S'wark Ord Course 90. **d** 93 **p** 94. NSM Fryerning w Margaretting *Chelmsf* from 93. *Little Pump House, Ongar Road, Kelvedon Hatch, Brentwood, Essex CM15 0LA* Ongar (01277) 364383

DRAKE, Graham. b 46. Linc Th Coll 81. **d** 83 **p** 85. C Alford w Rigsby *Linc* 83-84; Perm to Offic *Wakef* 84-85; Hon C Purston cum S Featherstone 85-89; NSM Castleford All SS 89-92; C Cudworth 92-95. *Flat 3, Woodland House, 5 Mill Hill, Pontefract, W Yorkshire WF8 4HR* Pontefract (01977) 708713

DRAKE, Graham Rae. b 45. Fitzw Coll Cam BA68 MA72. Qu Coll Birm 70. **d** 73 **p** 74. C New Windsor *Ox* 73-77; TV 77-78; P-in-c Bath Ascension *B & W* 78-81; TV Bath Twerton-on-Avon 81-86; P-in-c Buxton w Oxnead *Nor* 86-90; P-in-c Lammas w Lt Hautbois 86-90; RD Ingworth 88-94; R Buxton w Oxnead, Lammas and Brampton from 90. *The Vicarage, Back Lane, Buxton, Norwich NR10 5HD* Buxton (01603) 279394

DRAKE, John Paul. b 19. Qu Coll Ox BA41 MA44. Cuddesdon Coll 46. **d** 47 **p** 48. V Stewkley *Ox* 69-75; V Stewkley w Soulbury and Drayton Parslow 75-85; RD Mursley 77-83; rtd 85; Perm to Offic *St Alb* from 85. *3 The Cloisters, Welwyn Garden City, Herts AL8 6DU* Welwyn Garden (01707) 325379

DRAKE, Leslie Sargent. b 47. Boston Univ BA69 MTh72 Hull Univ BPhil74. Coll of Resurr Mirfield 78. **d** 78 **p** 79. C Oldham *Man* 78-81; TV Rochdale 81-83; V Palmers Green St Jo *Lon* 83-89; St Mary's Sch Cheshunt from 89. *29 Arundel Gardens, London N21 3AG* 0181-886 9104

DRAKE-BROCKMAN, Archibald David. b 12. Magd Coll Cam BA34 MA37. Ely Th Coll 35. **d** 36 **p** 37. C-St Mary V *Ox* 36; Lic to Offic 36-39; Chapl Bradfield Coll Berks 38-41; Asst Master 41-48; V Framfield *Chich* 48-49; Chapl Bedf Sch 49-65; Lic to Offic *St E* 70-79; Perm to Offic from 79. *Rosemary Cottage, Grundisburgh, Woodbridge, Suffolk IP13 6RA* Grundisburgh (01473) 735449

DRAKELEY, Stephen Richard Francis. b 51. Aston Univ BSc73. Chich Th Coll 76. **d** 76 **p** 77. C Yardley Wood *Birm* 76-79; V Rednal 79-89; TV Bodmin w Lanhydrock and Lanivet *Truro* from 89. *The Vicarage, Rectory Road, Lanivet, Bodmin, Cornwall PL30 5HG* Bodmin (01208) 831743

DRAPER, Ven Alfred James. b 23. Natal Univ BA50. St Aug Coll Cant DipTh59 St Paul's Grahamstown LTh54. **d** 54 **p** 54. S Africa 75-87; V Tile Cross *Birm* 63-75; V Olton 72-75; Adn Durban 79-87; R S Ferriby *Linc* 87-93; V Horkstow 87-93; R Saxby All Saints 87-93; rtd 93. *4 Rugby Close, Macclesfield, Cheshire SK10 2HW* Macclesfield (01625) 619033

DRAPER, Charles. b 59. Dur Univ BSc80 Cam Univ BA86. Ridley Hall Cam 84. **d** 87 **p** 88. C Wareham *Sarum* 87-90; C Maltby *Sheff* 90-93; R The Claydons *Ox* from 93. *The Rectory, Queen Catherine Road, Steeple Claydon, Buckingham MK18 2PY* Aylesbury (01296) 738055

DRAPER, Derek Vincent. b 38. Linc Th Coll 65. **d** 68 **p** 69. C Orpington All SS *Roch* 68-72; C Bramley *Guildf* 72-74; P-in-c Kempston St Alb 74-76; Min Kempston Transfiguration CD 77-79; V Kempston Transfiguration 79-84; RD Bedf 79-84; V Bromham w Oakley 84-88; P-in-c Stagsden 84-88; V Bromham w Oakley and Stagsden from 88; Chapl Bromham Hosp from 84. *The Vicarage, 47 Stagsden Road, Bromham, Bedford MK43 8PY* Oakley (01234) 823268

DRAPER, Elizabeth Ann. *See* BRADLEY, Mrs Elizabeth Ann

DRAPER, Dr Ivan Thomas. b 32. FRCP FRCPGlas Aber Univ MB, ChB56. St Jo Coll Nottm 87. **d** 90 **p** 91. NSM Glas St Bride *Glas* from 90. *13/1 Whistlefield Court, 2 Canniesburn Road, Bearsden, Glasgow G61 1PX* 0141-943 0954

DRAPER, Jack William. b 18. Oak Hill Th Coll 51. **d** 53 **p** 54. R Bramerton w Surlingham *Nor* 62-75; R Ashby w Thurton, Claxton and Carleton 70-75; R Rockland St Mary w Hellington 70-75; R Framingham Pigot 70-75; R Bergh Apton w Yelverton 70-75; RD Loddon 71-75; P-in-c Hoxne w Denham St Jo *St E* 75-79; P-in-c Hoxne w Denham St Jo and Syleham 79-80; V 80-84; rtd 84; Lic to Offic *St E* 84-85 and from 92; Hon C Yoxford 85-91; Hon C Yoxford and Peasenhall w Sibton 91-92; Lic to Offic *Nor* from 92. *7 Church*

Close, Green Street, Hoxne, Eye, Suffolk IP21 5AZ Eye (01379) 668517

DRAPER, Jean Margaret. b 31. **d** 80. NSM Pontnewydd *Mon* 80-83; BRF from 82; NSM Llantillio Pertholey w Bettws Chpl etc *Mon* from 83. *Govilon House, Govilon, Abergavenny, Gwent NP7 9BA* Abergavenny (01873) 830380

DRAPER, John William. b 54. Aston Tr Scheme 86 Qu Coll Birm 88. **d** 90 **p** 91. C Stepney St Dunstan and All SS *Lon* 90-94; C Leigh Park *Portsm* from 94. *Saint Francis House, Riders Lane, Havant, Hants PO9 4QT* Havant (01705) 475276 Fax as telephone

DRAPER, Dr Jonathan Lee. b 52. Gordon Coll Mass BA76 St Jo Coll Dur BA78 PhD84. Ripon Coll Cuddesdon 83. **d** 83 **p** 84. C Baguley *Man* 83-85; Dir Academic Studies Ripon Coll Cuddesdon 85-92; V Putney St Mary *S'wark* from 92. *The Vicarage, 45 St John's Avenue, London SW15 6AL* 0181-788 4575

DRAPER, Ven Martin Paul. b 50. Birm Univ BA72 Southn Univ BTh79. Chich Th Coll 72. **d** 75 **p** 76. C Primrose Hill St Mary w Avenue Road St Paul *Lon* 75-78; C Westmr St Matt 79-84; Chapl Paris St Geo *Eur* from 84; Adn France from 94; Can Gib Cathl from 94. *7 rue Auguste-Vacquerie, 75116 Paris, France* Paris (331) 47 20 22 51

DRAPER, Patrick Hugh. b 43. S Dios Minl Tr Scheme 91. **d** 94 **p** 95. NSM Boscombe St Jo *Win* from 94. *82 Tuckton Road, Bournemouth BH6 3HT* Bournemouth (01202) 424100

DRAPER, Paul Richard. b 64. Glas Univ MA87 TCD BTh90. **d** 90 **p** 91. C Drumragh w Mountfield *D & R* 90-94; I Ballydehob w Aghadown *C, C & R* from 94. *The Rectory, Ballydehob, Co Cork, Irish Republic* Bantry (28) 37117

DRAPER, Raymond James. b 48. Ex Coll Ox BA70 MA75 Em Coll Cam BA73 MA78. Ridley Hall Cam 71. **d** 74 **p** 75. C Sheff Manor *Sheff* 74-78; Ind Chapl 78-82; R Wickersley from 82. *The Rectory, Church Lane, Wickersley, Rotherham, S Yorkshire S66 0ES* Rotherham (01709) 543111

DRAPER, Mrs Sylvia Edith. b 39. ARCM60. N Ord Course 86. **d** 89 **p** 94. C Aughton St Mich *Liv* 89-92; Par Dn Wigan St Jas w St Thos 92-94; Asst Chapl Billinge Hosp Wigan from 92; C Wigan St Jas w St Thos *Liv* from 94. *16 Mervyn Place, Wigan WN3 5JS* Wigan (01942) 496922

DRAX, Miss Elizabeth Margaret (Liz). b 57. St Jo Coll Nottm DipMin93. **d** 94. C Kimberworth *Sheff* from 94. *32 Hill View Road, Rotherham, S Yorkshire S67 2AJ* Rotherham (01709) 559010

DRAY, John. b 66. St Chad's Coll Dur BSc87. St Steph Ho Ox BTh95. **d** 95. C Byker St Ant *Newc* from 95. *87 St Anthony's House, Caldbeck Avenue, Newcastle upon Tyne NE6 3SH* 0191-265 4101

DRAYCOTT, John. b 53. Sheff Univ BA84 DCEd82. Br Isles Nazarene Coll DipTh77 Linc Th Coll 85. **d** 85 **p** 86. In Wesleyan Reform Union 77-82; C Wombwell *Sheff* 85-87; V W Bessacarr 87-92; V Erith Ch Ch *Roch* from 92; P-in-c Erith St Jo 92-95. *Christ Church Vicarage, Victoria Road, Erith, Kent DA8 3AN* Erith (01322) 334729

DRAYCOTT, Philip John. b 27. Sarum & Wells Th Coll. **d** 83 **p** 84. C Bishop's Cleeve *Glouc* 83-86; V Chedworth, Yanworth and Stowell, Coln Rogers etc 86-93; rtd 94. *April Cottage, Newton Road, North Petherton, Bridgwater, Somerset TA6 6NA* Bridgwater (01278) 662487

DRAYSON, Nicholas James Quested. b 53. Keble Coll Ox BA75 MA83. Wycliffe Hall Ox DipTh83. **d** 79 **p** 79. SAMS from 79; Argentina 79-82 and from 93; Spain 83-92; Adn Andalucia 88-90; C Kirkheaton *Wakef* 85. *Iglesia Anglicana, Casilla 30, 4560 Tartagal, Salta, Argentina* Salta (87) 311718

DRAYTON, James Edward. b 30. St Deiniol's Hawarden 81. **d** 84 **p** 86. Hon C Heald Green St Cath *Ches* 84-88; C Bollington St Jo 88-92; P-in-c Lt Leigh and Lower Whitley from 92; P-in-c Aston by Sutton from 92; P-in-c Antrobus from 92. *The Vicarage, Street Lane, Lower Whitely, Warrington WA4 4EN* Norcott Brook (01925) 730850

DREDGE, David John. b 32. Cranmer Hall Dur 69. **d** 71 **p** 72. C Goole *Sheff* 71-74; P-in-c Eastoft 74-77; V Whitgift w Adlingfleet 74-77; V Whitgift w Adlingfleet and Eastoft 77-78; V Walkley 78-81; TV Bicester w Bucknell, Caversfield and Launton *Ox* 81-86; V N Brickhill and Putnoe *St Alb* 86-90; P-in-c Sarratt 90-95; rtd 95. *19 Waterdale, Wombourne, Wolverhampton WV5 0DH* Wolverhampton (01902) 897467

DREDGE, David Julian. b 36. ALA74 Sheff Univ BA59. Cranmer Hall Dur 61 Ban Ord Course 85. **d** 87 **p** 88. NSM Dwygyfylchi (or Penmaenmawr) *Ban* 87-92; R Llanllechid from 92. *The Rectory, Llanllechid, Bangor, Gwynedd LL57 3SD* Bangor (01248) 602779

DREW, Gerald Arthur. b 36. Bps' Coll Cheshunt 59. **d** 61 **p** 62. C Lyonsdown H Trin *St Alb* 61-67; C Tring 67-71; R Bramfield w Stapleford and Waterford 71-78; V Langleybury St Paul 78-90; P-in-c Hormead, Wyddial, Anstey, Brent Pelham etc from 90. *The Vicarage, Great Hormead, Buntingford, Herts SG9 0NT* Great Hormead (01763) 289258

DREW, John Whatley. b 24. CCC Cam BA54 MA58. Kelham Th Coll 46. **d** 51 **p** 52. V Thorington w Wenhaston *St E* 60-76; V Wenhaston w Thorington and Bramfield w Walpole 76; V Leiston 76-82; Chapl St Audry's Hosp Melton 82-89; P-in-c Ufford *St E* 82-91; P-in-c Bredfield w Boulge 86-91; P-in-c Hasketon 89-91; R Ufford w Bredfield and Hasketon 91-92; rtd 92; Perm to Offic *Nor* 92-94. *Kingside, 1 Roundhead Court, Norwich NR7 0TD* Norwich (01603) 702074

DREW, Joseph Harold. b 09. St D Coll Lamp BA30. St Mich Coll Llan 30. **d** 32 **p** 33. Chapl and Sec Pris Chapl Coun 64-74; Asst Chapl Gen of Pris 64-74; rtd 74; Perm to Offic *S'wark* from 82. *50 Kingsley Court, Pincott Road, Bexleyheath, Kent DA6 7LA* 0181-298 1216

DREW, Michael Edgar Cecil. b 31. Or Coll Ox BA55 MA59. St Steph Ho Ox 55. **d** 57 **p** 58. C Plymouth St Pet *Ex* 57-63; Missr Pemb Coll Cam Miss Walworth 63-67; Asst Chapl All Hallows Sch Rousdon 67-75; Chapl 80-81; Lic to Offic *Ex* 76-83; Chapl Ex Sch 81-83; V Hungarton *Leic* 83-87; V Scraptoft from 83; P-in-c Leic St Eliz Nether Hall from 87. *The Vicarage, Scraptoft, Leicester LE7 9ST* Leicester (0116) 241 2318

DREW, Mrs Rosemary. b 43. SRN64. E Anglian Minl Tr Course 90. **d** 93. NSM Gt Dunmow *Chelmsf* from 93. *Stocks Farm, Rayne, Braintree, Essex CM7 8SY* Braintree (01376) 343257

DREWERY, Dr Graeme Robert. b 66. FRCO89 St Jo Coll Cam BA88 MA92 PhD94. Linc Th Coll MDiv94. **d** 94 **p** 95. C Paston *Pet* from 94. *13 Holmes Way, Peterborough PE4 6XZ* Peterborough (01733) 236873

DREWETT, Canon Mervyn Henry. b 27. Wadh Coll Ox BA50 MA53. Linc Th Coll 52. **d** 54 **p** 55. V Henbury *Bris* 67-80; RD Westbury and Severnside 79-80; Hon Can Bris Cathl 80-94; TR Gtr Corsham 80-94; RD Chippenham 82-88; rtd 94. *14 The Beeches, Shaw, Melksham, Wilts SN12 8EP* Melksham (01225) 702726

DREWETT, Robert John. b 40. Ripon Hall Ox 64. **d** 66 **p** 67. C Fishponds St Jo *Bris* 66-70; C Oldland 70-74; P-in-c Coalpit Heath 74-76; TV Cannock *Lich* from 90; Chapl Chase Hosp Cannock from 90. *St Chad's Vicarage, Cannock Road, Chadsmoor, Cannock, Staffs WS11 2TH* Cannock (01543) 579381

DREYER, Ven Rodney Granville. b 55. **d** 81 **p** 82. NSM Northolt St Mary *Lon* 86-87; C Portsea St Mary *Portsm* 87-90; V Sudbury St Andr *Lon* 90-94; S Africa from 94; Adn W and S Free State, S Africa from 94. *5 Anjon Street, Bayswater, Bloemfontein, South Africa 9301*

DRINKWATER, Frank. b 10. K Coll Lon BSc32 AKC34. **d** 34 **p** 35. C Earley St Pet *Ox* 69-72; V Coley *Wakef* 72-77; rtd 77; Perm to Offic *Glouc* 78-94. *The Springs, Lower Power Street, Duddenhoe End, Saffron Walden, Essex CB11 4UP* Saffron Walden (01763) 838425

DRISCOLL, David. b 42. Lon Univ BSc64 Nottm Univ DipTh69. Linc Th Coll 68. **d** 71 **p** 72. C Walthamstow St Jo *Chelmsf* 71-76; Chapl NE Lon Poly 71-79; C-in-c Plaistow St Mary 76-79; P-in-c Stratford St Jo and Ch Ch w Forest Gate St Jas 79-89; V Theydon Bois from 89; RD Epping Forest from 92. *The Vicarage, 2 Piercing Hill, Theydon Bois, Epping, Essex CM16 7JN* Theydon Bois (01992) 814725

DRISCOLL, Edward Llewellyn. b 09. Kelham Th Coll 33. **d** 38 **p** 39. V Fairhaven *Blackb* 67-74; rtd 75; Lic to Offic *Blackb* from 75. *32 Ashley Road, Lytham St Annes, Lancs FY8 3AS* St Annes (01253) 727026

DRIVER, Anthony. b 28. Chich Th Coll 76. **d** 76 **p** 77. Prec Gib Cathl *Eur* 76-78; C Harton *Dur* 78-82; V Tow Law 82-91; rtd 91. *34 Minster Avenue, Beverley, N Humberside HU17 0NL* Hull (01482) 864448

DRIVER, Arthur John Roberts. b 44. FCIPA73 SS Coll Cam MA70 Nottm Univ DipTh75. Linc Th Coll 73. **d** 76 **p** 77. C S'wark H Trin w St Matt *S'wark* 76-80; TV N Lambeth 80-85; CMS 85-92; Sri Lanka 86-92; V Putney St Marg *S'wark* from 92. *St Margaret's Vicarage, 46 Luttrell Avenue, London SW15 6PE* 0181-788 5522

DRIVER, Bruce Leslie. b 42. Lon Univ LLB73 Nottm Univ DipTh77. Linc Th Coll 76. **d** 78 **p** 79. C Dunstable *St Alb* 78-81; TV 81-86; V Rickmansworth from 86; RD Rickmansworth from 91. *The Vicarage, Bury Lane, Rickmansworth, Herts WD3 1ED* Rickmansworth (01923) 772627

DRIVER, Geoffrey. b 41. Chich Th Coll 86. **d** 88 **p** 89. C Pontefract St Giles *Wakef* 88-91; V Glasshoughton from 91. *The Vicarage, Churchfield Lane, Glasshoughton, Castleford, W Yorkshire WF10 4BP* Castleford (01977) 551031

DRIVER, Geoffrey Lester. b 59. Liv Poly BA83. Chich Th Coll 86. **d** 89 **p** 90. C Walton St Mary *Liv* 89-92; C Walton-on-the-Hill 92; C Selsey *Chich* 92-95; V Cowfold from 95. *The Vicarage, Cowfold, Horsham, W Sussex RH13 8AH* Cowfold (01403) 864296

DRIVER (nee FRENCH), Janet Mary. b 43. Leeds Univ BA65 PGDE66. Linc Th Coll 73. **dss** 78 **d** 92 **p** 94. St Paul's Cathl *Lon*

79-80; Miss Partner CMS 86-92; Sri Lanka 86-92; NSM Putney St Marg *S'wark* from 92. *St Margaret's Vicarage, 46 Luttrell Avenue, London SW15 6PE* 0181-788 5522

DRIVER, Miss Penelope May. b 52. N Ord Course. **d** 87 **p** 94. Dioc Youth Adv *Newc* 86-88; C Cullercoats St Geo 87-88; Youth Chapl *Ripon* from 88; Dioc Adv Women's Min from 91. *7 Loxley Grove, Wetherby, W Yorkshire LS22 7YG* Wetherby (01937) 585440

DRIVER, Roger John. b 64. Trin Coll Bris BA88. **d** 90 **p** 91. C Much Woolton *Liv* 90-93; C Fazakerley Em 93-94; TV from 94. *St Paul's Vicarage, Formosa Drive, Liverpool L10 7LB* 0151-521 3344

DRIVER, Canon Stuart Clare. b 15. Ch Coll Cam BA37 MA41. Ridley Hall Cam 37. **d** 38 **p** 39. V Werneth *Man* 45-80; Hon Can Man Cathl 76-80; RD Oldham 76-80; rtd 80; Perm to Offic *Ches* from 80; Perm to Offic *Man* from 80. *9 Brookside Lane, High Lane, Stockport, Cheshire SK6 8HL* Disley (01663) 762263

DROMORE, Archdeacon of. See NEILL, Ven William Barnet

DROMORE, Dean of. See CHILLINGWORTH, Very Rev David Robert

DROWLEY, Arthur. b 28. Oak Hill Th Coll 54. **d** 56 **p** 57. V Taunton St Jas *B & W* 62-73; RD Taunton N 72-73; V Rodbourne Cheney *Bris* 73-87; R Bigbury, Ringmore and Kingston *Ex* 87-94; rtd 94; NSM Bigbury, Ringmore and Kingston *Ex* from 94. *The Rectory, Ringmore, Kingsbridge, Devon TQ7 4HR* Bigbury-on-Sea (01548) 810565

DROWN, Richard. b 19. BNC Ox BA41 MA43. Wycliffe Hall Ox 41. **d** 42 **p** 43. Kenya 65-73; Hd Master Edin Ho Sch New Milton 73-84; rtd 84; Hon C Brockenhurst *Win* from 85. *3 Waters Green Court, Brockenhurst, Hants SO42 7QR* Lymington (01590) 624038

DRUCE, Brian Lemuel. b 31. ARICS55. Bps' Coll Cheshunt 58. **d** 60 **p** 61. R Birch St Agnes *Man* 66-70; V Overbury w Alstone, Teddington and Lt Washbourne *Worc* 70-81; Ind Chapl 81-91; rtd 91. *Park Cottage, Elmley Castle, Pershore, Worcs WR10 3HU* Elmley Castle (01386) 710577

DRUCE, John Perry. b 34. ALCM86 Em Coll Cam BA57 MA61. Wycliffe Hall Ox 57. **d** 59 **p** 60. C Wednesbury St Bart *Lich* 59-62; C Bushbury 62-64; V Walsall Wood 64-74; R Farnborough *Roch* 74-87; R E Bergholt *St E* from 87. *The Rectory, White Horse Road, Colchester CO7 6TR* Colchester (01206) 298076

DRUMMOND, Canon Christopher John Vaughan. b 26. Magd Coll Ox MA51 Magd Coll Cam MA56. Ridley Hall Cam 51. **d** 53 **p** 54. V Walthamstow St Jo *Chelmsf* 69-74; P-in-c Stantonbury *Ox* 74-75; R 75-84; P-in-c Ducklington 84-88; Dioc Ecum Officer 84-88; Can Ibadan from 87; Home Sec Gen Syn Bd for Miss and Unity 88-91; rtd 91; P-in-c Colton *Lich* 91-94. *Church Cottage, Slitting Mill, Rugeley, Staffs WS15 2TG* Rugeley (01889) 570172

DRUMMOND, John Malcolm. b 44. Nottm Univ CertEd65. Edin Th Coll 68. **d** 71 **p** 72. C Kirkholt *Man* 71-74; C Westleigh St Pet 74-76; Hd of RE Leigh High Sch from 76; Lic to Offic from 76; Hon C Leigh St Jo 84-90. *14 Bull's Head Cottages, Turton, Bolton BL7 0HS* Bolton (01204) 852232

DRUMMOND, Josceline Maurice Vaughan (Jos). b 29. Lon Univ DipTh59 BD70. Wycliffe Hall Ox 55. **d** 58 **p** 59. V Leyton St Cath *Chelmsf* 71-85; Gen Dir CMJ 85-94; Public Preacher *St Alb* 88-94; rtd 94. *3 Fryth Mead, St Albans, Herts AL3 4TN* St Albans (01727) 857620

DRURY, Esmond Peter. b 24. Sheff Univ BSc43 Newc Univ DipEd64. Coll of Resurr Mirfield 47. **d** 49 **p** 50. Min Hackenthorpe Ch Ch CD *Derby* 57-60; rtd 89. *74 Beach Road, North Shields, Tyne & Wear NE30 2QW* 0191-257 4350

DRURY, Very Rev John Henry. b 36. Trin Hall Cam MA66. Westcott Ho Cam 61. **d** 63 **p** 64. C St Jo Wood *Lon* 63-66; Chapl Down Coll Cam 66-69; Chapl Ex Coll Ox 69-73; Can Res Nor Cathl *Nor* 73-79; Vice-Dean 78-79; Lect Sussex Univ 79-81; Dean and Chapl K Coll Cam 81-91; Dean Ch Ch *Ox* from 91. *The Deanery, Christ Church, Oxford OX1 1DP* Oxford (01865) 276162

DRURY, Michael Dru. b 31. Trin Coll Ox BA55 MA59. Wycliffe Hall Ox DipTh57. **d** 58 **p** 59. C Fulham St Mary N End *Lon* 58-62; C Blackheath St Jo *S'wark* 62-64; Chapl and Asst Master Canford Sch Wimborne 64-80; Chapl and Teacher Fernhill Manor Sch New Milton 80-81; P-in-c Stowe *Ox* 82-92; Asst Master Stowe Sch Bucks 82-92; R Rampton w Laneham, Treswell, Cottam and Stokeham *S'well* from 92. *The Rectory, Main Street, Rampton, Retford, Notts DN22 0HR* Rampton (01777) 248143

DRURY, Valerie Doreen. b 40. MBATOD80 Univ of Wales (Cardiff) BA62 K Coll Lon PGCE63 Lon Inst of Educn ADEDC80. Oak Hill Th Coll 85. **d** 87 **p** 94. NSM Becontree St Alb *Chelmsf* 87-89; NSM Becontree S from 89. *63 Tilney Road, Dagenham, Essex RM9 6HL* 0181-592 7285

DRURY, William. b 30. Qu Coll Cam BA53 MA56. Trin Coll Toronto STB61. **d** 61 **p** 61. Canada 61-66; C Ashford *Cant* 66-70; V Milton next Sittingbourne from 70. *The Vicarage, Vicarage Road, Milton Regis, Sittingbourne, Kent ME10 2BL* Sittingbourne (01795) 472016

DRYDEN, Canon Leonard. b 29. MIEE59 MIMechE59 Lon Univ BD64 Bath Univ MSc73. Ridley Hall Cam. **d** 61 **p** 62. C-in-c Bedminster *Bris* 65-74; Bp's Soc and Ind Adv 65-74; Chapl Bris Cathl 66-70; Hon Can Bris Cathl 70-74; Dir CORAT 74-76; Sec from 76; Team Ldr and Convener Lon Ind Chapl *Lon* 77-85; V Frindsbury w Upnor *Roch* 85-91; rtd 91; P-in-c Sevenoaks Weald *Roch* from 91. *The Vicarage, Weald, Sevenoaks, Kent TN14 6LT* Sevenoaks (01732) 463291

DRYE, Douglas John. b 37. Man Univ BSc61. Clifton Th Coll. **d** 63 **p** 64. V Worsbrough Common *Sheff* 68-86; R Armthorpe 86-92; rtd 92. *25 Willow Crescent, Oakham, Leics LE15 6EQ* Oakham (01572) 770429

du HEAUME, Cecil Cabot. b 04. Keble Coll Ox BA29 MA40. Wycliffe Hall Ox 27. **d** 31 **p** 32. Sec Leprosy Miss (Ireland) 56-74; P-in-c Glympton *Ox* 74-80; rtd 80; Perm to Offic *Mon* from 80. *Hillgrove, Rockfield, Monmouth, Gwent NP5 4EZ* Monmouth (01600) 713806

DUBLIN (Christ Church), Dean of. *See* PATERSON, Very Rev John Thomas Farquhar

DUBLIN (St Patrick's), Dean of. *See* STEWART, Very Rev Maurice Evan

DUBLIN and Bishop of Glendalough, Archbishop of. *See* CAIRD, Most Rev Donald Arthur Richard

DUBLIN, Archdeacon of. *See* LINNEY, Ven Gordon Charles Scott

DUCE, Alan Richard. b 41. St Pet Coll Ox BA65 MA68. Cuddesdon Coll 65. **d** 67 **p** 68. C Boston *Linc* 67-71; Chapl St Geo Hosp Lon 71-75; Chapl HM Pris Pentonville 75-76; Chapl HM Pris The Verne 76-81; Chapl HM Pris Linc from 81. *The Chaplain's Office, HM Prison, Greetwell Road, Lincoln LN2 4BD* Lincoln (01522) 533633 Fax 532116

DUCKER, Vere Townshend. b 04. Wadh Coll Ox BA26 MA30. Wycliffe Hall Ox 27. **d** 28 **p** 29. R Hanborough *Ox* 61-66; Perm to Offic *Guildf* 66-92; rtd 69; Perm to Offic *Chich* from 69. *Paddock Corner, Farnham Lane, Haslemere, Surrey GU27 1HB* Haslemere (01428) 642827

DUCKETT, Brian John. b 45. ALCD70. **d** 70 **p** 71. C S Lambeth St Steph *S'wark* 70-73; C Norwood 73-75; C Bushbury *Lich* 75-77; TV 77-79; V Dover St Martin *Cant* 79-92; TR Swindon Dorcan *Bris* from 92. *The Vicarage, St Paul's Drive, Swindon SN3 5BY* Swindon (01793) 525130

DUCKETT, Edward. b 36. Keble Coll Ox BA59 MA61 Portsm Poly CQSW72. Cuddesdon Coll 59. **d** 61 **p** 62. C Portsea St Cuth *Portsm* 61-65; C Rotherham *Sheff* 65-68; Lic to Offic *Portsm* 68-69; Hon Chapl Portsm Cathl 69-75; Perm to Offic *Ely* 75-82; R Rampton 82-89; R Willingham 82-89; RD N Stowe 83-89; P-in-c Ramsey 89-90; P-in-c Upwood w Gt and Lt Raveley 89-90; TR The Ramseys and Upwood 90-92; RD St Ives 89-92; P-in-c Bassingbourn 93-95; V from 95; P-in-c Whaddon 93-95; V from 95. *The Vicarage, 21 North End, Bassingbourn, Royston, Herts SG8 5NZ* Royston (01763) 843119

DUCKETT, John Dollings. b 41. Nottm Univ BA62 BTh81. Linc Th Coll 79. **d** 81 **p** 82. C Boston *Linc* 81-84; V Baston 84-86; V Langtoft Gp 86-88; V Sutterton and Wigtoft 88-89; R Sutterton w Fosdyke and Algarkirk 89-92; P-in-c Chapel St Leonards w Hogsthorpe from 92. *The Vicarage, Church Lane, Chapel St Leonards, Skegness, Lincs PE24 5UJ* Skegness (01754) 872666

DUCKWORTH, Capt Brian George. b 47. CA79. Edin Th Coll 85. **d** 87 **p** 88. C Sutton in Ashfield St Mary *S'well* 87-95; C Sutton in Ashfield St Mich 89-95; P-in-c from 95. *The Vicarage, Northern View, Sutton-in-Ashfield, Notts NG17 2AQ* Mansfield (01623) 555031

DUCKWORTH, Derek. b 29. Fitzw Ho Cam BA52 MA58 Lon Univ PGCE66 Lanc Univ PhD72. Oak Hill Th Coll 52. **d** 54 **p** 55. C Whalley *Blackb* 64-73; Hon C Newbury *Ox* 73-80; Perm to Offic 80-81; Perm to Offic *Cant* 81-84 and 85-86; P-in-c Dymchurch w Burmarsh and Newchurch 84-85; Chapl Leybourne Grange Hosp W Malling 85-86; P-in-c Rampton w Laneham, Treswell, Cottam and Stokeham *S'well* 86-89; R 89-91; rtd 91. *Glebe Cottage, Church Walk, Headcorn, Kent TN27 9ND* Headcorn (01622) 890143

DUDDING, Edward Leslie (Father Gregory). b 30. Auckland Univ MSc52 St Jo Coll Auckland LTh56. **d** 57 **p** 57. New Zealand 57-60; Lic to Offic *Chich* from 62; CSWG from 62; Father Superior from 73. *Monastery of The Holy Trinity, Crawley Down, Crawley, W Sussex RH10 4LH* Copthorne (01342) 712074

DUDLEY, Harold George. b 14. St Mich Coll Llan 68. **d** 70 **p** 70. C Fleur-de-Lis *Mon* 70-73; V Goldcliffe and Whiston and Nash 73-83; rtd 83; Lic to Offic *Mon* from 83. *3 St John's Court, Oakfield Road, Newport, Gwent NP6 4LNJ* Newport (01633) 253610

DUDLEY, Mrs Janet Carr. b 36. E Midl Min Tr Course 86. **d** 89 **p** 94. Hon C Countesthorpe w Foston *Leic* 89-94; Hon C Arnesby w Shearsby and Bruntingthorpe from 94. *The Vicarage, Fenny Lane, Shearsby, Lutterworth, Leics LE17 6PL* Leicester (0116) 247 8371

DUDLEY, John Rea. b 31. Pemb Coll Cam BA54 MA58. St Steph Ho Ox. **d** 57 **p** 58. C Kennington St Jo *S'wark* 57-61; C Merstham and Gatton 61-68; V N Gosforth *Newc* 68-79; RD Newc Cen 77-82; V Newc St Jo 79-91; V Sunbury *Lon* from 91. *The Vicarage, Thames Street, Sunbury-on-Thames, Middx TW16 6AA* Sunbury-on-Thames (01932) 785448

DUDLEY, Dr Martin Raymond. b 53. K Coll Lon BD77 AKC77 MTh78 PhD94 DPS79 FRHistS95. St Mich Coll Llan 78. **d** 79 **p** 80. C Whitchurch *Llan* 79-83; V Weston *St Alb* 83-88; P-in-c Ardeley 87-88; V Owlsmoor *Ox* 88-95; Lect Simon of Cyrene Th Inst from 92; R Smithfield St Bart Gt *Lon* from 95. *Church House, Cloth Fair, London EC1A 7JQ* 0171-606 5171 or 248 3110 Fax 600 6909

DUDLEY, Miss Wendy Elizabeth. b 46. City of Sheff Coll CertEd68. Cranmer Hall Dur 79. **dss** 81 **d** 87 **p** 94. Cumnor *Ox* 81-87; Par Dn 87-89; Par Dn Hodge Hill *Birm* 89-94; C 94-95; TV from 95. *95 Hodge Hill Road, Birmingham B34 6DX* 0121-783 0140

✠**DUDLEY-SMITH, Rt Rev Timothy.** b 26. Pemb Coll Cam BA47 MA51. Lambeth MLitt91 Ridley Hall Cam 48. **d** 50 **p** 51 **c** 81. C Erith St Paul *Roch* 50-53; Lic to Offic *S'wark* 53-62; Hd of Cam Univ Miss Bermondsey 53-55; Chapl 55-60; Ed Sec Evang Alliance and Ed Crusade 55-59; Asst Sec CPAS 59-65; Gen Sec 65-73; Adn Nor 73-81; Suff Bp Thetford 81-91; rtd 92. *9 Ashlands, Ford, Salisbury SP4 6DY* Salisbury (01722) 326417

DUDLEY, Archdeacon of. *See* GATHERCOLE, Ven John Robert

DUDLEY, Area Bishop of. *See* HOARE, Rt Rev Rupert William Noel

DUERDEN, Martin James. b 55. Liv Poly BA77. Oak Hill Th Coll 86. **d** 88 **p** 89. C Tunbridge Wells St Jas *Roch* 88-92; V Southport SS Simon and Jude *Liv* from 92. *The Vicarage, 128 Roe Lane, Southport, Merseyside PR9 7PJ* Southport (01704) 27095

DUFF, Adam Alexander Howard. b 16. Linc Coll Ox BA38 DipH43 MA46. Wycliffe Hall Ox 42. **d** 43 **p** 44. V Paddington H Trin w St Paul *Lon* 62-79; C Kilburn St Aug w St Jo 79-81; rtd 81. *Cedar Cottage, Water Eaton Road, Oxford OX2 7QQ* Oxford (01865) 58621

DUFF, Mrs Alison. b 59. SEN79. Sarum & Wells Th Coll CMinlStuds92. **d** 92 **p** 94. Par Dn Banbury *Ox* 92-94; C 94-95. *10 Hardwick Road, Banbury, Oxon OX16 7YD* Banbury (01295) 255022

DUFF, Andrew John. b 57. MIOT. Sarum & Wells Th Coll CMinlStuds92. **d** 92 **p** 93. C Banbury *Ox* 92-95; C Bracknell from 95. *St Andrew's Vicarage, Stoney Road, Bracknell, Berks RG12 1XY* Bracknell (01344) 425529

DUFF, Garden Ian. b 34. ACGI56 Imp Coll Lon BScEng56. Sarum & Wells Th Coll 92. **d** 93 **p** 94. NSM Ashton Gifford *Sarum* from 93. *West Farm, Knook, Warminster, Wilts BA12 0JF* Warminster (01985) 850291

DUFF, Canon Harold Patterson. b 23. Edin Th Coll 48. **d** 51 **p** 52. P-in-c Dundee St Martin *Bre* 62-74; R Dundee St Salvador 69-91; Can St Paul's Cathl Dundee 76-91; rtd 91; Hon C Broughty Ferry *Bre* from 91. *13 Sherbrook Street, Dundee DD3 8NA* Dundee (01382) 88514

DUFF, John Alexander. b 57. York Univ BA78. E Midl Min Tr Course DTPS94. **d** 94 **p** 95. NSM Linc St Geo Swallowbeck *Linc* from 94. *34 Swallowbeck Avenue, Lincoln LN6 7HA* Lincoln (01522) 683475

DUFF, Timothy Cameron. b 40. Solicitor 65 G&C Coll Cam BA62 LLM63 MA66. NE Ord Course 90. **d** 93 **p** 94. NSM Tynemouth Priory *Newc* from 93. *26 The Drive, North Shields, Tyne & Wear NE30 4JW* 0191-257 1463 Fax 296 1904

DUFFETT, Canon Paul Stanton. b 33. Keble Coll Ox BA55 MA59. Ripon Hall Ox DipTh58. **d** 59 **p** 60. C Portsea St Cuth *Portsm* 59-63; S Africa 63-80; P-in-c Greatham w Empshott *Portsm* 80-85; R 85-88; Hon Can Zululand from 87; R Papworth Everard *Ely* from 88; Chapl Papworth Hosps from 88. *The Rectory, Papworth Everard, Cambridge CB3 8QJ* Huntingdon (01480) 830061

DUFFIELD, Dr Ian Keith. b 47. K Coll Lon BD71 AKC71 MTh73. NY Th Sem DMin84. **d** 73 **p** 74. C Broxbourne *St Alb* 73-77; C Harpenden St Nic 77-81; TV Sheff Manor *Sheff* 81-87; V Walkley from 87. *St Mary's Vicarage, 150 Walkley Road, Sheffield S6 2XQ* Sheffield (0114) 234 5029

DUFFIELD, John Ernest. b 55. BA86. Oak Hill Th Coll 83. **d** 86 **p** 87. C Walton Breck Ch Ch *Liv* 86-89; TV Fazakerley Em

DUFFIELD

from 89. *St George's Vicarage, 72 Stopgate Lane, Liverpool L9 6AR* 0151-523 1536

DUFFIELD, Ronald Bertram Charles (Ron). b 26. Hull Univ Coll BA49 TCert50. Sarum & Wells Th Coll 91. **d** 92 **p** 93. NSM E Knoyle, Semley and Sedgehill *Sarum* from 92. *The Rectory, Semley, Shaftesbury, Dorset SP7 9AU* Shaftesbury (01747) 830362

DUFTON, Francis Trevor. b 29. Trin Coll Cam BA51 MA55. Ridley Hall Cam 51. **d** 53 **p** 54. R Elmdon and Wendon Lofts *Chelmsf* 67-80; R Strethall 67-80; P-in-c Bottisham *Ely* 80-85; rtd 85; Perm to Offic *Ely* 85-91. *23 Hyde Road, Eastbourne, E Sussex BN21 4SX* Eastbourne (01323) 416659

DUGDALE, Canon Dennis. b 19. OBE78. Worc Ord Coll 65. **d** 68 **p** 69. C Shalford *Guildf* 68-70; V Sandon and Wallington w Rushden *St Alb* 71-74; Chapl Ghent w Ypres *Eur* 74-84; Hon Can Brussels Cathl 82-84; rtd 84; Perm to Offic *Chich* from 85. *21 Stuart Court, High Street, Kibworth, Leicester LE8 0LE* Leicester (0116) 279 6345

✠**DUGGAN, Rt Rev John Coote.** b 18. TCD BA40 BD47. CITC 41. **d** 41 **p** 42 **c** 70. C Cork St Luke *C, C & R* 41-43; C Taney Ch Ch *D & G* 43-48; R Portarlington *M & K* 48-55; I Glenageary *D & G* 55-69; I Aughaval *T, K & A* 69-70; Adn Tuam 69-70; Bp T, K & A 70-85; rtd 85; Chapl Malaga *Eur* 93-94. *22 Pennington Park, Cairnshill Road, Belfast BT8 4GJ*

DUGUID, Reginald Erskine. b 29. S'wark Ord Course. **d** 88 **p** 89. NSM Notting Hill All SS w St Columb *Lon* from 88. *53 Sandbourne, Dartmouth Close, London W11 1DA* 0171-221 4436

DUKE, Alan Arthur. b 38. Tyndale Hall Bris 59. **d** 64 **p** 65. C Whalley Range St Mary *Man* 64-67; C Folkestone H Trin w Ch Ch *Cant* 67-71; V Queenborough 71-76; V Bearsted w Thurnham 76-86; P-in-c Thurnham w Detling 77-82; P-in-c Torquay St Luke *Ex* 86-91; R Barham w Bishopsbourne and Kingston *Cant* from 91; Dioc Communications Officer from 91. *The Rectory, The Street, Barham, Canterbury, Kent CT4 6PA* Canterbury (01227) 831340 Fax as telephone

DUKE, Brian Peter. b 33. Pemb Coll Cam BA55 MA59. Ely Th Coll 55. **d** 57 **p** 58. C Blyth St Mary *Newc* 57-61; C Newc St Andr 61-63; Perm to Offic *Guildf* from 64. *24 Regent Close, Fleet, Aldershot, Hants GU13 9NS* Fleet (01252) 614548

DULFER, John Guidi. b 37. Lich Th Coll 62. **d** 64 **p** 65. C Fenny Stratford and Water Eaton *Ox* 64-67; C Cheshunt *St Alb* 67-68; C Kennington Cross St Anselm *S'wark* 68-74; C N Lambeth 74-76; P-in-c Kensington St Phil Earl's Court *Lon* 76-79; V 79-84; Chapl Odstock Hosp Salisbury 84; USA from 84. *162 Harrison Avenue, Jersey City, New Jersey 07304, USA*

DULLEY, Arthur John Franklyn. b 32. Mert Coll Ox BA54 MA57. St Jo Coll Nottm 69. **d** 71 **p** 72. Lect St Jo Coll Nottm from 71; Hon C Attenborough w Chilwell *S'well* 71-73; C Penn Fields *Lich* 73-74; Chapl Aldenham Sch Herts 74-79; Chapl HM Pris Ashwell 79-87; V Langham *Pet* from 79. *The Vicarage, Langham, Oakham, Leics LE15 7JE* Oakham (01572) 722969

DUMAT, Mrs Jennifer (Jenny). b 42. ARCM62. Qu Coll Birm 80 E Midl Min Tr Course 82. **dss** 83 **d** 87 **p** 94. Chapl Asst Pilgrim Hosp Boston 83-94; P-in-c Friskney *Linc* from 94. *The Vicarage, Yawling Road, Friskney, Boston, Lincs PE22 8NA* Boston (01754) 820418

✠**DUMPER, Rt Rev Anthony Charles (Tony).** b 23. Ch Coll Cam BA45 MA48. Westcott Ho Cam. **d** 47 **p** 48 **c** 77. C E Greenwich Ch Ch w St Andr and St Mich *S'wark* 47-49; Malaya 49-63; Malaysia 63-64; Dean Singapore 64-70; V Stockton St Pet *Dur* 70-77; P-in-c Stockton H Trin 76-77; RD Stockton 70-77; Suff Bp Dudley *Worc* 77-93; rtd 93; Asst Bp Birm from 93. *117 Burberry Close, Birmingham B30 1TB* 0121-458 3011

DUNBAR, George Alban Charles. b 08. AKC40. **d** 40 **p** 41. V Whetstone St Jo *Lon* 56-81; rtd 81; Perm to Offic *Linc* from 82. *63 Harrowby Road, Grantham, Lincs NG31 9ED* Grantham (01476) 62935

DUNBAR, Peter Lamb. b 46. Bede Coll Dur DipEd68. Lambeth STh77 N Ord Course 78. **d** 81 **p** 82. NSM Knaresborough *Ripon* 81-82; C Knaresborough 82-84; R Farnham w Scotton, Staveley, Copgrove etc 84-92; V Upper Nidderdale from 92; Chapl St Aid Sch Harrogate 86-94. *The Vicarage, Pateley Bridge, Harrogate, N Yorkshire HG3 5LQ* Harrogate (01423) 711414

DUNCAN, Canon Anthony Douglas. b 30. Chich Th Coll 60. **d** 62 **p** 63. R Highnam w Lassington and Rudford *Glouc* 69-73; V Newc St Jo *Newc* 73-79; V Warkworth and Acklington 79-87; Hon Can Newc Cathl 84-95; V Whitley 87-95; Chapl Hexham Gen and War Memorial Hosps 87-95; rtd 95. *7 Aydon Drive, Corbridge, Northd NE45 5DE* Corbridge (01434) 633149

DUNCAN, Canon Bruce. b 38. MBE93. FRSA Leeds Univ BA60. Cuddesdon Coll 65. **d** 67 **p** 68. C Armley St Bart *Ripon* 67-69; Lic to Offic *Ely* 69-70; Chapl Vienna w Budapest and Prague *Eur* 71-75; V Crediton *Ex* 75-82; R Crediton and Shobrooke 82-86; RD Cadbury 76-81 and 84-86; Can Res Man Cathl *Man* from 86. *1 Barnhill Road, Prestwich,*

Manchester M25 8WH 0161-773 3171 or 833 2220 Fax 773 3171 or 839 6226

DUNCAN, Charles Patrick Maxwell. b 37. Ch Ch Ox MA62. St Jo Coll Dur 78. **d** 81 **p** 82. C York St Mich-le-Belfrey *York* 81-84; Perm to Offic 84-86; Asst Chapl Ch Hosp Horsham from 86. *Christ's Hospital, Horsham, W Sussex RH13 7LS* Horsham (01403) 258195

DUNCAN, Christopher Robin (Chris). b 41. AKC71. **d** 72 **p** 73. C Allington *Cant* 72-77; P-in-c Wittersham 77-82; R Wittersham w Stone-in-Oxney and Ebony 82-85; P-in-c Chilham 85-86; V 86-92; P-in-c Challock w Molash 87-92; RD W Bridge from 92; V Chilham w Challock and Molash from 92. *The Vicarage, 3 Hambrook Close, Chilham, Canterbury, Kent CT4 8EJ* Canterbury (01227) 730235

DUNCAN, Colin Richard. b 34. SS Coll Cam BA58 MA60. Ripon Coll Cuddesdon 83. **d** 85 **p** 86. C Stafford *Lich* 85-89; C Wednesfield 89-90; TV from 90. *St Alban's House, Griffiths Drive, Wolverhampton WV11 2LJ* Wolverhampton (01902) 732317

DUNCAN, George Ballie. b 12. Edin Univ MA32. Clifton Th Coll 35. **d** 37 **p** 38. I Cockfosters Ch Ch CD *Lon* 51-58; rtd 77; Perm to Offic *Chich* 80-91. *41 Merchiston Crescent, Edinburgh EH10 5AJ* 0131-229 2071

DUNCAN, Dr Gregor Duthie. b 50. Glas Univ MA72 Clare Coll Cam PhD77 Or Coll Ox BA83. Ripon Coll Cuddesdon 81. **d** 83 **p** 84. C Oakham, Hambleton, Egleton, Braunston and Brooke *Pet* 83-86; Edin Th Coll 87-89; R Largs *Glas* from 89. *St Columba's Rectory, Aubery Crescent, Largs, Ayrshire KA30 8PR* Largs (01475) 673143

DUNCAN, Harold Norton. b 03. Bible Churchmen's Coll 28. **d** 29 **p** 37. R Easton w Letheringham *St E* 66-72; C-in-c Dub St Thos *D & G* 72-75; Lic to Offic *Cant* 75-79; rtd 82; Perm to Offic *Chich* 82-91. *Manormead Nursing Home, Tilford Road, Hindhead, Surrey GU26 6RA* Hindhead (01428) 604780

DUNCAN, James Montgomerie. b 29. Edin Th Coll 53. **d** 56 **p** 57. C Edin St Pet *Edin* 56-59; C Edin Old St Paul 59-60; S Africa 60-65; Prov Youth Org Scotland 65-69; R Edin St Salvador *Edin* 69-86; Chapl HM Pris Saughton 69-86; R Aberlour *Mor* from 86; R Fochabers from 86. *Gordon Chapel House, Castle Street, Fochabers, Morayshire IV32 7DW* Fochabers (01343) 820337

DUNCAN, John. b 22. Open Univ BA. Roch Th Coll 64. **d** 66 **p** 67. C Boultham *Linc* 68-71; V W Pinchbeck 72-76; Canada 76-81; R Ridgewell w Ashen, Birdbrook and Sturmer *Chelmsf* 81-88; rtd 88. *20 Westcott Way, Northampton NN3 3BE* Northampton (01604) 30797

DUNCAN, Ven John Finch. b 33. Univ Coll Ox BA57 MA63. Cuddesdon Coll 57. **d** 59 **p** 60. C S Bank *York* 59-61; SSF 61-62; C Birm St Pet *Birm* 62-65; Chapl Birm Univ 65-76; V Kings Heath 76-85; Hon Can Birm Cathl 83-85; Adn Birm from 85. *122 Westfield Road, Birmingham B15 3JQ* 0121-454 3402 Fax 455 6178

DUNCAN, Peter Harold Furlong. b 25. AKC52 Lon Univ BA68 Golds Coll Lon BA71 MPhil79. **d** 53 **p** 54. Hon C All Hallows by the Tower etc *Lon* 67-73; Ind Chapl Lon Docks 67-73; Sen Lect in Sociology City of Lon Poly 73-87; Hon C Gt Ilford St Andr *Chelmsf* 73-80; P-in-c Gt Canfield 80-87; P-in-c N Woolwich w Silvertown 87-93; rtd 93; Perm to Offic *York* from 93. *179 Windsor Drive, Haxby, York YO3 3YD* York (01904) 769888

DUNCAN, Mrs Virginia Elinor. b 39. DNEd. W Midl Minl Tr Course 86 Qu Coll Birm 86. **d** 89 **p** 94. Par Dn Wednesfield *Lich* 89-94; C from 94. *St Alban's House, Griffiths Drive, Wolverhampton WV11 2LJ* Wolverhampton (01902) 732317

DUNCAN, Ven William Albert. b 30. TCD BA53 MA61 BD66. CITC 54. **d** 54 **p** 55. C Ban Abbey *D & D* 54-57; C Larne and Inver *Conn* 57-61; Hd of Trin Coll Miss Belf 61-66; I Rasharkin w Finvoy 66-78; I Ramoan w Ballycastle and Culfeightrin from 78; Adn Dalriada from 93. *12 Novally Road, Ballycastle, Co Antrim BT54 6HB* Ballycastle (012657) 62461

DUNCAN-JONES, Andrew Roby. b 14. St Edm Hall Ox BA38 MA41. Linc Th Coll 39. **d** 40 **p** 41. Head St Chad's Cathl Sch Lich 57-70; R Lochgilphead *Arg* 70-79; rtd 79; Perm to Offic *Arg* from 79. *Barrachourin, Kilmartin, Lochgilphead, Argyll PA31 8QP* Kilmartin (015465) 204

DUNCANSON, Derek James. b 47. TD93. AKC69 Open Univ BA80 Lon Univ MA(Ed)93 FCollP94. St Aug Coll Cant 69. **d** 70 **p** 71. C Norbury St Oswald *Cant* 70-72; CF (TAVR) from 71; C Woodham *Guildf* 72-76; CF 76-79; V Burneside *Carl* 79-84; R Coppull St Jo *Blackb* 84-86; Chapl Bloxham Sch Oxon from 86. *Courtington House, Courtington Lane, Bloxham, Banbury, Oxon OX15 4PQ* Banbury (01295) 720626

DUNDAS, Edward Paul. b 67. NUU BSc88. TCD Div Sch BTh91. **d** 91 **p** 92. C Portadown St Mark *Arm* 91-95; I Ardtrea w Desertcreat from 95. *Tullyhogue Rectory, 50 Lower Grange Road, Cookstown, Co Tyrone BT80 8SL* Cookstown (016487) 61163

DUNDAS, Edward Thompson. b 36. TCD BA63. **d** 64 **p** 65. C Conwall *D & R* 64-67; I Kilbarron 67-78; I Donagheady 78-84; I Kilmore St Aid w St Sav *Arm* from 84. *38 Vicarage Road, Portadown, Craigavon, Co Armagh BT62 4HF* Portadown (01762) 332664

DUNDEE, Provost of. *See* BUNCE, Very Rev Dr Michael John

DUNFORD, Evelyn Cecil Braley. b 11. Jes Coll Cam BA34 MA39. Wells Th Coll 36. **d** 37 **p** 38. R Marhamchurch *Truro* 62-76; rtd 76; Perm to Offic *Truro* from 76; Perm to Offic *Chich* from 92. *College of St Barnabas, Blackberry Lane, Lingfield, Surrey RH7 6NJ* Lingfield (01342) 87522

DUNFORD, Malcolm. b 34. FCA74. E Midl Min Tr Course 73. **d** 76 **p** 77. NSM Frodingham *Linc* from 76. *57 Rowland Road, Scunthorpe, S Humberside DN16 1SP* Scunthorpe (01724) 840879

DUNFORD, Reginald John. b 15. Worc Ord Coll. **d** 60 **p** 61. V Lenton *S'well* 68-80; rtd 80; Perm to Offic *S'well* from 80. *Mosley, 33 Cow Lane, Bramcote, Nottingham NG9 3DJ* Nottingham (0115) 925 6841

DUNHILL, Robin Arnold. b 15. BNC Ox BA38 MA46. Cuddesdon Coll. **d** 46 **p** 47. V Hampstead Garden Suburb *Lon* 63-73; RD W Barnet 70-73; Perm to Offic *Pet* from 74; rtd 80; Perm to Offic *Linc* from 91. *Manor Cottage, Newton, Geddington, Kettering, Northants NN14 1BW* Great Oakley (01536) 460659

DUNK, Michael Robin. b 43. Oak Hill Th Coll BA82. **d** 82 **p** 83. C Northn All SS w St Kath *Pet* 82-86; Ind Chapl *Birm* from 86. *68 Oakfield Road, Birmingham B29 7EG* 0121-427 5141 or 472 0034

DUNK, Peter Norman. b 43. Sarum Th Coll 67. **d** 69 **p** 70. C Sheff St Mary w St Simon w St Matthias *Sheff* 69-71; C Margate St Jo *Cant* 71-74; Dioc Youth Officer *Birm* 74-78; R Hulme Ascension *Man* 78-83; V E Farleigh and Coxheath *Roch* 83; P-in-c Linton w Hunton 83; R Coxheath w E Farleigh, Hunton and Linton 83-88; Australia from 88. *105 Shenton Road, Swanbourne, W Australia 6010* Perth (9) 384-2958

DUNKERLEY, James Hobson. b 39. Seabury-Western Th Sem BD69 STh70. **d** 64 **p** 65. C Stirchley *Birm* 64-66; C Perry Barr 66-70; USA from 70. *621 Belmont Avenue, Chicago, Illinois 60657, USA*

DUNKLEY, Christopher. b 52. Edin Univ MA74 Ox Univ BA77 MA81. St Steph Ho Ox 75. **d** 78 **p** 79. C Newbold and Dunston *Derby* 78-82; C Chesterfield All SS 82; Chapl Leic Univ *Leic* 82-85; P-in-c Leic St Aid 85; TV Leic Ascension 85-92; V Leic St Aid from 92. *St Aidan's Vicarage, St Oswald's Road, Leicester LE3 6RJ* Leicester (0116) 287 2342

DUNKLEY, Reginald Alfred Lorenz. b 13. Clifton Th Coll 56. **d** 58 **p** 59. R Longfield *Roch* 64-78; rtd 78. *33 Sheriff Drive, Chatham, Kent ME5 9PU* Medway (01634) 862143

DUNLOP, Canon Arthur John. b 27. AKC52. **d** 53 **p** 54. R Laindon w Basildon *Chelmsf* 65-72; RD Basildon 65-72; V Maldon All SS w St Pet 72-92; RD Maldon 73-82; Hon Can Chelmsf Cathl 80-92; RD Maldon and Dengie 89-92; rtd 92. *Maeldune, 64 Highfield Road, Sudbury, Suffolk CO10 6QJ* Sudbury (01787) 881699

DUNLOP, Canon Ian Geoffrey David. b 25. FSA New Coll Ox BA48 MA56. Linc Th Coll 54. **d** 56 **p** 57. C Bures *St E* 62-72; Can Res and Chan Sarum Cathl *Sarum* 72-92; Dir Post-Ord Tr 72-92; Dir of Ords 73-92; Lect Sarum & Wells Th Coll 76-92; rtd 92. *Gowanbrae, The Glebe, Selkirk TD7 5AB* Selkirk (01750) 20706

DUNLOP, Peter John. b 44. TCD BA68 MA72 Dur Univ DipTh70 CertEd71. Cranmer Hall Dur. **d** 71 **p** 72. C Barking St Marg w St Patr *Chelmsf* 71-75; C Gt Malvern Ch Ch *Worc* 75-78; Chapl K Sch Tynemouth 78-89; V Monkseaton St Pet *Newc* from 90. *St Peter's Vicarage, 6 Elmwood Road, Whitley Bay, Tyne & Wear NE25 8EX* 0191-252 1991

DUNN, Alastair Matthew Crusoe. b 40. Lon Univ LLB64 AKC64. Wycliffe Hall Ox 78. **d** 80 **p** 81. C Yardley St Edburgha *Birm* 80-83; R Bishop's Sutton and Ropley and W Tisted *Win* 83-90; V Milford from 90. *The Vicarage, Lymington Road, Milford on Sea, Lymington, Hants SO41 0QN* Lymington (01590) 643289

DUNN, Mrs Barbara Anne. b 42. Man Univ BA72 Sheff Univ CQSW76. N Ord Course 92. **d** 95. NSM Stretford St Matt *Man* from 95. *71 Manley Road, Whalley Range, Manchester M16 8WF* 0161-881 6929

DUNN, Brian. b 40. St Aid Birkenhead 66. **d** 69 **p** 70. C Over Darwen H Trin *Blackb* 69-71; C Burnley St Pet 71-74; V Darwen St Barn 74-84; V S Shore H Trin from 84; Chapl Arnold Sch Blackpool from 84. *Holy Trinity Vicarage, 1 Windermere Road, Blackpool FY4 2BX* Blackpool (01253) 42362

DUNN, Christopher George Hunter. b 28. Pemb Coll Cam BA49 MA53. Oak Hill Th Coll 51. **d** 53 **p** 54. C Tunbridge Wells H Trin *Roch* 53-54; C Broadwater St Mary *Chich* 54-58; R Garsdon w Lea and Cleverton *Bris* 58-74; V Tiverton St Geo *Ex* from 74; Chapl Marie Curie Foundn (Tidcombe Hall) from 74; RD Tiverton *Ex* 84-91. *St George's Vicarage, St Andrew Street, Tiverton, Devon EX16 6PH* Tiverton (01884) 252184 or 243281

DUNN, David. b 42. Univ of Wales DipTh65. St Mich Coll Llan 62. **d** 66 **p** 67. C Brighton St Wilfrid *Chich* 66-69; C Tunbridge Wells St Barn *Roch* 69-74; TV Brighton Resurr *Chich* 74-77; V Southsea H Spirit *Portsm* 77-88; P-in-c Bournemouth St Mary *Win* 88-95. *St Mary's Vicarage, 49 Thistlebarrow Road, Bournemouth BH7 7AL* Bournemouth (01202) 398376

DUNN, David James. b 47. CertEd79 BA82 DipHE90. Trin Coll Bris 88. **d** 90 **p** 91. C Magor w Redwick and Undy *Mon* 90-92; C St Mellons and Michaelston-y-Fedw 92-93; V Pontnewydd from 93. *The Vicarage, 44 Church Road, Pontnewydd, Cwmbran, Gwent NP44 1AT* Cwmbran (01633) 482300

DUNN, David Michael. b 47. AKC70. St Aug Coll Cant 70. **d** 71 **p** 72. C Padgate *Liv* 71-74; C Halliwell St Marg *Man* 74-76; V Lever Bridge 76-84; V Bradshaw from 84. *The New Vicarage, Bolton Road, Bolton BL2 3EU* Bolton (01204) 304240

DUNN, David Whitelaw Thomas. b 34. Trin Coll Carmarthen CertEd54. St Mich Coll Llan 87 St Deiniol's Hawarden 83. **d** 83 **p** 85. NSM Brecon St Mary and Battle w Llanddew *S & B* 83-87; Min Can Brecon Cathl 87-88; V Llanfihangel Crucorney w Oldcastle etc *Mon* from 88. *The Vicarage, Llanfihangel Crucorney, Abergavenny, Gwent NP7 8DH* Crucorney (01873) 890349

DUNN, Derek William Robert. b 48. AMusTCL74 LTCL75 Stranmillis Coll CertEd70 Open Univ BA81 QUB DASE86. **d** 85 **p** 87. NSM Carnalea *D & D* 85-91; Lic to Offic from 91. *13 Wandsworth Park, Carnalea, Bangor, Co Down BT19 1BD* Bangor (01247) 456898

DUNN, John Frederick. b 44. Trin Coll Bris 71. **d** 74 **p** 75. C Carl St Jo *Carl* 74-77; C Tooting Graveney St Nic *S'wark* 77-82; V Attleborough *Cov* 85; Perm to Offic *Cant* from 86. *73 St Luke's Avenue, Ramsgate, Kent CT11 7JY* Thanet (01843) 581632

DUNN, John Samuel. b 39. CEng MIM HNC. Llan Dioc Tr Scheme. **d** 88 **p** 89. NSM Aberavon H Trin *Llan* 88-94; NSM Port Talbot St Theodore from 94. *46 Vivian Terrace, Port Talbot, W Glam SA12 6ET* Port Talbot (01639) 886786

DUNN, Kevin Lancelot. b 62. Newc Univ BSc83. St Steph Ho Ox 89. **d** 92 **p** 93. C Tynemouth Cullercoats St Paul *Newc* 92-95; C Newc St Matt w St Mary from 95. *St Matthews Vicarage, 10 Winchester Terrace, Newcastle upon Tyne NE4 6EY* 0191-232 2866

DUNN, Michael Henry James. b 34. Em Coll Cam BA56 MA62. Cuddesdon Coll 57 and 62. **d** 62 **p** 63. C Chatham St Steph *Roch* 62-66; C Bromley SS Pet and Paul 66-70; V Roch St Justus 70-83; P-in-c Malvern Wells and Wyche *Worc* 83-85; P-in-c Lt Malvern, Malvern Wells and Wyche from 85. *1 The Moorlands, Malvern Wells, Malvern, Worcs WR14 4PS* Malvern (01684) 575123

DUNN, Paul James Hugh. b 55. Dur Univ PhD93. Ripon Coll Cuddesdon. **d** 83 **p** 84. C Wandsworth St Paul *S'wark* 83-87; C Richmond St Mary w St Matthias and St Jo 88-92; TV Wimbledon from 92. *St Matthews House, 61 Melbury Gardens, London SW20 0DL* 0181-946 0092

DUNN, Reginald Hallan. b 31. Oak Hill NSM Course. **d** 82 **p** 83. NSM Enfield St Andr *Lon* 82-93; NSM Enfield Chase St Mary from 93. *3 Conway Gardens, Enfield, Middx EN2 9AD* 0181-366 3982

DUNN, Struan Huthwaite. b 43. Ch Coll Hobart 66 Moore Th Coll Sydney ThL68 Clifton Th Coll 68. **d** 70 **p** 71. C Orpington Ch Ch *Roch* 70-74; C Cheltenham St Mary *Glouc* 74-76; C Cheltenham St Mary, St Matt, St Paul and H Trin 76; C Welling *Roch* 76-79; Chapl Barcelona w Casteldefels *Eur* 79-83; R Addington w Trottiscliffe *Roch* 83-89; P-in-c Ryarsh w Birling 83-89; P-in-c S Gillingham 89-90; TR from 90; RD Gillingham from 91. *The Rectory, 4 Drewery Drive, Wigmore, Gillingham, Kent ME8 0NX* Medway (01634) 231071

DUNNE, Kevin Headley. b 43. Cranmer Hall Dur 85. **d** 87 **p** 88. C Ches le Street *Dur* 87-90; V S Hetton w Haswell 90-94; P-in-c Oxclose from 94. *37 Brancepeth Road, Washington, Tyne & Wear NE38 0LA* 0191-416 2561

DUNNE, Nigel Kenneth. b 57. TCD. **d** 90 **p** 91. C Dub St Bart w Ch Ch Leeson Park *D & G* 90-93; C Taney 93-95; I Blessington w Kilbride, Ballymore Eustace etc from 95. *The Rectory, Blessington, Co Wicklow, Irish Republic* Naas (45) 865178

DUNNETT, John Frederick. b 58. CQSW82 SS Coll Cam MA84 Worc Coll Ox MSc83. Trin Coll Bris BA87. **d** 88 **p** 89. C Kirkheaton *Wakef* 88-93; V Cranham Park *Chelmsf* from 93. *St Luke's Vicarage, 201 Front Lane, Upminster, Essex RM14 1LD* Upminster (01708) 225262

DUNNETT, Robert Curtis. b 31. SS Coll Cam BA54 MA58. Oak Hill Th Coll 56. **d** 58 **p** 59. C Markfield *Leic* 58-60; C Bucknall and Bagnall *Lich* 60-73; Perm to Offic *Birm* from 72; Chapl and Tutor Birm Bible Inst from 72; Vice-Prin from 84. *7 Pakenham Road, Birmingham B15 2NN* 0121-440 3105

DUNNILL

DUNNILL, Dr John David Stewart. b 50. UEA BA72 Birm Univ DipTh82 PhD88. Ripon Coll Cuddesdon 86. **d** 88 **p** 89. C Tupsley *Heref* 88-92; Australia from 92. *Anglican Institute of Theology, Mount Claremont, Perth, W Australia 6010*

DUNNING, David John. b 52. Liv Univ BA Ox Univ CertEd. Ripon Coll Cuddesdon 79. **d** 82 **p** 84. C N Gosforth *Newc* 82-83; C Willington Team 83-85; C Bellingham/Otterburn Gp 85-86; Chapl Magd Coll Sch Ox from 86. *Magdalen College School, Oxford OX4 1DZ* Oxford (01865) 242191

DUNNING, George Henry John. b 27. Sarum Th Coll 57. **d** 59 **p** 60. V Auckland St Pet *Dur* 64-75; V Clay Cross *Derby* 75-83; V S Norwood St Alb *Cant* 83-85; V S Norwood St Alb *S'wark* 85-92; rtd 92. *8 Otley Close, Worcester WR4 0BJ* Worcester (01905) 616049

DUNNING, John Stanley. b 19. Lon Univ BSc41. E Midl Min Tr Course 78. **d** 81 **p** 82. NSM Nottm St Pet and St Jas *S'well* 81-85; rtd 85; Perm to Offic *S'well* from 85. *12 Brookhill Drive, Wollaton, Nottingham NG8 2PS* Nottingham (0115) 928 3357

DUNNING, Martyn Philip. b 51. MRTPI77 Reading Univ MSc79 Dur Univ MA95. St Jo Coll Dur 89. **d** 92 **p** 93. C Beverley Minster *York* from 92. *38 Highgate, Beverley, N Humberside HU17 0DN* Hull (01482) 862656

DUNNINGS, Reuben Edward. b 36. Clifton Th Coll 62. **d** 66 **p** 67. C Longfleet *Sarum* 66-70; C Melksham 70-73; TV 73-78; R Broughton Gifford w Gt Chalfield 78-84; V Holt St Kath 78-84; R Broughton Gifford, Gt Chalfield and Holt 85-86; V Salisbury St Fran from 86. *The Vicarage, 52 Park Lane, Salisbury SP1 3NP* Salisbury (01722) 333762

DUNSETH, George William. b 52. Multnomah Sch of the Bible Oregon BRE79. Oak Hill Th Coll BA85. **d** 85 **p** 86. C Cheadle All Hallows *Ches* 85-88; C New Boro and Leigh *Sarum* 88-91; V Thurnby w Stoughton *Leic* from 91. *The Vicarage, Thurnby, Leicester LE7 9PN* Leicester (0116) 241 2263

DUNSTAN, Canon Alan Leonard. b 28. Wadh Coll Ox BA49 MA52. Ripon Hall Ox 50. **d** 52 **p** 53. Vice-Prin 66-70; Hon C Ox St Mary V w St Cross and St Pet *Ox* 70-78; Chapl Keble Coll Ox 70-71; Vice-Prin Ripon Hall Ox 71-74; Acting Prin 74-75; Vice-Prin Ripon Coll Cuddesdon 75-78; Can Res Glouc Cathl *Glouc* 78-93; rtd 93. *7 The Crescent, Truro, Cornwall TR1 3ES* Truro (01872) 79604

DUNSTAN, Prof Gordon Reginald. b 17. CBE89. Hon MRCP87 Leeds Univ BA38 MA39 Ex Univ Hon DD73 Leic Univ Hon LLD86. Coll of Resurr Mirfield 39. **d** 41 **p** 42. Hon Can Leic Cathl *Leic* 66-82; Prof Moral and Soc Th K Coll Lon 67-82; Chapl to The Queen 76-87; rtd 82; Perm to Offic *Ex* from 82. *9 Maryfield Avenue, Exeter EX4 6JN* Exeter (01392) 214691

DUNSTAN, Gregory John Orchard. b 50. Cam Univ MA75 TCD BTh90. **d** 90 **p** 91. C Ballymena w Ballyclug *Conn* 90-93; I Belf St Matt from 93. *Shankill Rectory, 51 Ballygomartin Road, Belfast BT13 3LA* Belfast (01232) 714325

DUNSTAN, Kenneth Ian (Ken). b 40. ACP Golds Coll Lon BEd71. Oak Hill NSM Course 86. **d** 88 **p** 89. NSM Creeksea w Althorne, Latchingdon and N Fambridge *Chelmsf* 88-94; P-in-c Woodham Mortimer w Hazeleigh from 94. *35 Ely Close, Southminster, Essex CM0 7AQ* Maldon (01621) 772199

DUNSTAN-MEADOWS, Victor Richard. b 63. Chich Th Coll BTh90. **d** 90 **p** 91. C Clacton St Jas *Chelmsf* 90-93; C Stansted Mountfitchet 93-95; CF from 95. *clo MOD (Army), Bagshot Park, Bagshot, Surrey GU19 5PL* Bagshot (01276) 471717 Fax 412834

DUNTHORNE, Paul. b 63. K Coll Lon LLB85 Paris Sorbonne 85 St Jo Coll Dur BA90. Cranmer Hall Dur 88. **d** 91 **p** 92. C Heacham and Sedgeford *Nor* 91-95; C Heacham 95; C Eastbourne H Trin *Chich* from 95. *33 Hyde Road, Eastbourne, E Sussex BN21 4SX* Eastbourne (01323) 737743

DUNWICH, Suffragan Bishop of. *See* STEVENS, Rt Rev Timothy John

DUNWOODY, Canon Thomas Herbert Williamson. b 35. TCD BA58 MA64. TCD Div Sch Div Test59. **d** 59 **p** 60. C Newc *D & D* 59-61; C Ballymacarrett St Martin 61-63; C Lurgan Ch Ch 63-66; I Ardglass w Dunsford 66-74; V Urmston *Man* 74-85; Miss to Seamen from 85; I Wexford w Ardcolm and Killurin *C & O* 85-93; Can Ferns Cathl 88-93; RD Wexford 92-93; I Newry St Mary and St Patr *D & D* from 93. *The Glebe, Windsor Avenue, Newry, Co Down BT34 1EG* Newry (01693) 62621

DUPLOCK, Canon Peter Montgomery. b 16. OBE76. Qu Coll Cam BA38 MA42. Ridley Hall Cam 38. **d** 40 **p** 41. Chapl Brussels w Charleroi, Liege and Waterloo *Eur* 71-81; Chan Brussels Cathl 81; Adn NW Eur 81; rtd 81; Hon Can Brussels Cathl *Eur* 81-84; V Breamore *Win* 81-86; Perm to Offic from 86. *14 Broomfield Drive, Alderholt, Fordingbridge, Hants SP6 3HY* Fordingbridge (01425) 656000

DUPREE, Hugh Douglas. b 50. Univ of the South (USA) BA72 Ch Ch Ox MA86 Ball Coll Ox DPhil88. Virginia Th Sem MDiv75. **d** 75 **p** 76. USA 75-80; Hon C Ox St Mich w St Martin and All SS *Ox* 80-87; Asst Chapl Ball Coll Ox 84-87;

Chapl from 87; Chapl HM Pris Ox from 88. *Balliol College, Oxford OX1 3BJ* Oxford (01865) 277777 or 721261 Fax 723453

DURAND, Noel Douglas. b 33. Jes Coll Cam BA57 MA61 BD76. Westcott Ho Cam 72. **d** 74 **p** 75. C Eaton *Nor* 74-78; V Cumnor *Ox* from 78. *The Vicarage, 1 Abingdon Road, Cumnor, Oxford OX2 9QN* Oxford (01865) 862198

DURANT, Robert-Ashton. b 23. OSB Univ of Wales (Lamp) BA47. Bp Burgess Hall Lamp. **d** 48 **p** 49. V Slapton *Ex* 69-81; V Strete 69-81; R E Allington, Slapton and Strete 81-92; rtd 92; Perm to Offic *Ex* from 92. *18 Grosvenor Avenue, Torquay TQ2 7LA* Torquay (01803) 613710

DURANT, Stanton Vincent. b 42. S'wark Ord Course 69. **d** 72 **p** 73. C Ickenham *Lon* 72-76; C Paddington Em Harrow Road 76-78; V 78-87; AD Westmr Paddington 84-87; TR Hackney Marsh 87-91; Adn Liv 91-93; V Stoneycroft All SS 91-93; Hon Can Liv Cathl 91-93. *Address temp unknown*

DURANT, William John Nicholls. b 55. K Coll Lon BA76 DipTh DPS. St Jo Coll Nottm 77. **d** 80 **p** 81. C Norwood *S'wark* 80-83; C Morden 83-88; TV 88-92; V Frindsbury w Upnor *Roch* from 92. *All Saints' Vicarage, 4 Parsonage Lane, Frindsbury, Rochester, Kent ME2 4UR* Medway (01634) 717580

DURBIN, Roger. b 41. Bris Sch of Min 83. **d** 85 **p** 86. NSM Bedminster *Bris* 85-91; NSM Henbury 91-94; NSM Clifton All SS w St Jo from 94. *13 Charbury Walk, Bristol BS11 9UU* Bristol (0117) 982 7858

DURELL, Miss Jane Vavasor. b 32. Bedf Coll Lon BSc55. Gilmore Ho 61 Lambeth STh64. **dss** 86 **d** 87 **p** 94. Banbury *Ox* 86-87; Par Dn 87-92; rtd 92; Perm to Offic *Nor* from 92. *51 Branford Road, Norwich NR3 4QD2* Norwich (01603) 486084

DURHAM, Archdeacon of. *See* HODGSON, Ven John Derek

DURHAM, Bishop of. *See* TURNBULL, Rt Rev Anthony Michael Arnold

DURHAM, Dean of. *See* ARNOLD, Very Rev John Robert

DURKIN, Anthony Michael (Tony). b 45. Sarum & Wells Th Coll 87. **d** 89 **p** 90. C Faversham *Cant* 89-92; V St Margarets-at-Cliffe w Westcliffe etc from 92. *The Vicarage, Sea Street, St Margarets-at-Cliffe, Dover, Kent CT15 6AR* Dover (01304) 852179

DURNDELL, Miss Irene Frances. b 43. Nottm Univ DipRE78. Trin Coll Bris DipHE86. **dss** 86 **d** 87 **p** 94. Erith Ch Ch *Roch* 86-87; Par Dn 87-93; Par Dn Erith St Paul 93-94; C from 94; Asst Dir of Tr from 93. *113 Belmont Road, Erith, Kent DA8 1LF* Dartford (01322) 334762

DURNELL, John. b 32. St Aid Birkenhead 64. **d** 66 **p** 67. C Newport w Longford *Lich* 66-69; P-in-c Church Aston 69-72; R 72-77; V Weston Rhyn 77-82; P-in-c Petton w Cockshutt and Weston Lullingfield etc 82-83; R Petton w Cockshutt, Welshampton and Lyneal etc from 83. *The Rectory, Cockshutt, Ellesmere, Shropshire SY12 0JQ* Cockshutt (01939) 270211

DURNFORD, Miss Catherine Margaret. b 36. St Mary's Coll Dur BA57 DipEd58. Gilmore Course 78 NW Ord Course 77. **d** 87 **p** 94. Area Sec (Dios York and Ripon) USPG 82-89; Par Dn Whitby 89-92; Par Dn Redcar 92-94; C 94; C Selby Abbey from 94. *57 Woodville Terrace, Selby, N Yorkshire YO8 8AJ* Selby (01757) 705419

DURNFORD, John Edward. b 30. CCC Cam BA53 MA61. Linc Th Coll 53. **d** 55 **p** 56. Rhodesia 65-76; V Hebden Bridge *Wakef* 76-84; RD Calder Valley 82-84; P-in-c Blanchland w Hunstanworth *Newc* 84-90; P-in-c Edmundbyers w Muggleswick *Dur* 84-90; RD Corbridge *Newc* 88-93; R Blanchland w Hunstanworth and Edmundbyers etc 90-94; rtd 94. *7 Islestone Drive, Seahouses, Nothd NE68 7XB* Seahouses (01665) 721032

DURNFORD, Comdr Peter Jeffrey. b 20. Bps' Coll Cheshunt 63. **d** 65 **p** 66. R St Just in Roseland *Truro* 70-82; P-in-c Ruan Lanihorne w Philleigh 70-82; P-in-c St Mewan 82-85; Chapl Mount Edgcumbe Hospice 82-88; rtd 85. *8 Tredenham Road, St Mawes, Truro, Cornwall TR2 5AN* St Mawes (01326) 270793

DURRAN, Ms Margaret (Maggie). b 47. Lady Spencer Chu Coll of Educn CertEd70. S'wark Ord Course 88. **d** 91 **p** 94. Par Dn Brixton St Matt *S'wark* 91-94; C 94; C Streatham St Leon 94-95; V Walworth St Chris from 95. *76 Tatum Street, London SE17 1QR* 0171-701 4162

DURRANS, Canon Anthony. b 37. Leeds Univ BA59. Linc Th Coll 60. **d** 62 **p** 63. C Stanningley St Thos *Ripon* 62-64; C Chorlton upon Medlock *Man* 64-69; SCM Field Sec Man 64-66; NW Sec 66-68; Asst Gen Sec 68-69; R Old Trafford St Jo *Man* 69-80; V Langley All SS and Martyrs 80-82; TR Langley and Parkfield 82-85; R Man Miles Platting 85-87; P-in-c Man Apostles 85-87; R Man Apostles w Miles Platting from 87; Hon Can Man Cathl from 86; AD Ardwick from 91. *The Rectory, Ridgway Street, Manchester M10 7FY* 0161-205 1742

DURRANT, Reginald Patrick Bickersteth. b 37. AKC64. **d** 65 **p** 66. C Ascot Heath *Ox* 68-71; C Heene *Chich* 71-76; R Burwash 76-94; rtd 94. *17 Glebeland Close, West Stafford, Dorchester, Dorset DT2 8AE*

DURSTON, Canon David Michael Karl. b 36. Em Coll Cam BA60 MA64. Clifton Th Coll 61. **d** 63 **p** 64. C Wednesfield Heath *Lich* 63-66; Project Officer Grubb Inst 67-78; Ind Chapl *Lich* 78-84; P-in-c W Bromwich St Paul Golds Hill 78-82; V 82-84; Adult Educn Officer 84-92; Preb Lich Cathl 89-92; Can Res and Chan Sarum Cathl *Sarum* from 92. *24 The Close, Salisbury SP1 2EH* Salisbury (01722) 336809

DUST, Simon Philip. b 63. Oak Hill Th Coll BA95. **d** 95. C Chesham Bois *Ox* from 95. *67A Woodley Hill, Chesham, Bucks HP5 1SP* Chesham (01494) 774868

DUTFIELD, Canon Alan. b 20. Linc Th Coll 54. **d** 55 **p** 56. V New Rossington *Sheff* 60-71; R Old Brumby *Linc* 71-77; TR 77-86; Can and Preb Linc Cathl 81-86; RD Manlake 82-86; rtd 86; Perm to Offic *Linc* 86-94. *30 Barnes Green, Scotter, Gainsborough, Lincs DN21 3RW* Scunthorpe (01724) 764220

DUTHIE, Elliot Malcolm. b 31. Clifton Th Coll 63. **d** 66 **p** 67. Malaysia 70-75; P-in-c Bootle St Leon *Liv* 76-78; V 78-81; V Charlton Kings H Apostles *Glouc* 81-94; rtd 94. *71 North Upton Lane, Barnwood, Gloucester GL4 7XW*

DUTTON, Leonard Arthur. b 35. Bps' Coll Cheshunt 63. **d** 66 **p** 67. C Knighton St Jo *Leic* 66-70; C Chilvers Coton w Astley *Cov* 70-73; R Hathern *Leic* 73-79; V Ashby-de-la-Zouch H Trin from 79. *Holy Trinity Vicarage, 1 Trinity Close, Ashby-de-la-Zouch, Leics LE65 2GQ* Ashby-de-la-Zouch (01530) 412339

DUVAL, Canon David. b 14. Ch Ch Ox BA36 MA41. Wells Th Coll 36. **d** 38 **p** 39. Hon Can St E Cathl *St E* 62-83; R Withersfield 73-79; P-in-c 79-82; rtd 79; TV Haverhill w Withersfield, the Wrattings etc *St E* 82-83; Perm to Offic from 83. *Fornham House, Fornham St Martin, Bury St Edmunds, Suffolk IP31 1SR*

DUVAL, Canon Philip Ernest. b 18. MBE45. Mert Coll Ox BA45 MA45. Westcott Ho Cam 47. **d** 47 **p** 48. R Merstham and Gatton *S'wark* 66-86; Hon Can S'wark Cathl 78-86; rtd 86. *2 The Holt, Frogs Hill, Newenden, Hawkhurst, Kent TN18 5PX* Northiam (01797) 252578

DUVALL, Michael James. b 31. **d** 79 **p** 80. Hon C Kings Langley *St Alb* 79-89; Hon C Selworthy and Timberscombe and Wootton Courtenay *B & W* 89-95; Hon C Luccombe 89-95; Hon C Selworthy, Timberscombe, Wootton Courtenay etc from 95. *The Parsonage, Luccombe, Minehead, Somerset TA24 8TE* Minehead (01643) 862834

DUXBURY, Clive Robert. b 49. St Jo Coll Nottm DCM92. **d** 92 **p** 93. C Horwich *Man* 92-93; C Horwich and Rivington from 93. *St Catherine's House, Richmond Street, Horwich, Bolton BL6 5QT* Bolton (01204) 699162

DUXBURY, James Campbell. b 33. Tyndale Hall Bris 58. **d** 61 **p** 62. C Southport SS Simon and Jude *Liv* 61-65; V Tittensor *Lich* 65-70; V W Bromwich Gd Shep w St Jo 70-75; P-in-c Wellington w Eyton 75-80; V 80-85; V Padiham *Blackb* from 85. *The Vicarage, 1 Arbory Drive, Padiham, Burnley, Lancs BB12 8JS* Padiham (01282) 772442

DUXBURY, Miss Margaret Joan. b 30. JP81. DipEd52. St Jo Coll Nottm 83. dss 84 **d** 87 **p** 94. Thornthwaite w Thruscross and Darley *Ripon* 83-86; Middleton St Cross 86-87; C 87-90; Par Dn Dacre w Hartwith and Darley w Thornthwaite 90-94; C from 94. *Scot Beck House, Darley, Harrogate, N Yorkshire HG3 2QN* Harrogate (01423) 780451

DYALL, Henry. b 19. ARICS51 Lon Univ BSc51 LLB58. S'wark Ord Course 81. **d** 82 **p** 83. Hon C St Mary Cray and St Paul's Cray *Roch* 82-84; Perm to Offic 84-86; Hon C Sidcup Ch Ch from 86. *8 Saxville Road, Orpington, Kent BR5 3AW* Orpington (01689) 872598

DYAS, Stuart Edwin. b 46. Lon Univ BSc67. Ridley Hall Cam 78. **d** 80 **p** 81. C Bath Weston St Jo *B & W* 80; C Bath Weston St Jo w Kelston 81-83; C Tunbridge Wells St Jas *Roch* 83-90; V Nottm St Jude *S'well* from 90; AD Nottm Cen from 93. *St Jude's Vicarage, Woodborough Road, Mapperley, Nottingham NG3 5HE* Nottingham (0115) 960 4102

DYER, Mrs Anne Catherine. b 57. St Anne's Coll Ox MA80 Lon Univ MTh89. Wycliffe Hall Ox 84. **d** 87 **p** 94. NSM Beckenham St Jo *Roch* 87-88; NSM Beckenham St Geo 88-89; Hon Par Dn Luton Ch Ch 89-94; Chapl for Evang from 93; NSM Istead Rise from 94. *The Vicarage, Upper Avenue, Gravesend, Kent DA13 9DA* Southfleet (01474) 832403

DYER, Ms Catherine Jane. b 46. Westf Coll Lon BA68. Ox NSM Course 85. **d** 88 **p** 94. Hon C Wokingham All SS *Ox* 88-90; C 90-95; TV W Slough from 95. *Saint Andrew's House, Washington Drive, Slough SL1 5RE* Burnham (01628) 661994

DYER, Mrs Christine Anne. b 53. Nottm Univ BEd75. E Midl Min Tr Course 81. dss 84 **d** 87 **p** 94. Mickleover St Jo *Derby* 85-87; Par Dn 87-90; Dioc Voc Adv 86-90; Par Educn Adv from 90. *4 Chain Lane, Mickleover, Derby DE3 5AJ* Derby (01332) 514390

DYER, Mrs Gillian Marie. b 50. Sheff Univ BA71 Leic Univ CertEd72. S Dios Minl Tr Scheme 81. dss 84 **d** 87 **p** 94. Witney *Ox* 84-85; Carl St Cuth w St Mary *Carl* 86-87; Par Dn 87-89; Dioc Communications Officer 86-89; Par Dn Kirkbride w Newton Arlosh 89-91; Par Dn Carl H Trin and St Barn 91-94; TV from 94. *Holy Trinity Vicarage, 25 Wigton Road, Carlisle CA2 7BB* Carlisle (01228) 26284

DYER, Canon James Henry. b 14. ALCD39. **d** 39 **p** 40. C S Hackney St Jo w Ch Ch *Lon* 39-43; C New Malden and Coombe *S'wark* 43-50; New Zealand from 50; Hon Can Nelson Cathl from 85. *41 Oxford Street, Richmond, Nelson, New Zealand* Christchurch (3) 544-7440

DYER, Janet. b 35. Local NSM Course 77. dss 85 **d** 86 **p** 94. Balerno *Edin* 85-86; NSM 86-93; Chapl Edin R Infirmary 88-93; D-in-c Roslin (Rosslyn Chpl) *Edin* 93-94; P-in-c from 94. *499 Lanark Road West, Balerno, Midlothian EH14 7AL* 0131-449 3767

DYER, John Alan. b 31. Linc Coll Ox BA53 MA57 BD58. Tyndale Hall Bris 53. **d** 56 **p** 57. C Weston-super-Mare Ch Ch *B & W* 56-60; V Battersea St Geo w St Andr *S'wark* 60-69; Australia from 69. *The Rectory, 9 Janice Place, Narreweena, NSW, Australia 2099* Sydney (2) 972-1082

DYER, Stephen Roger. b 57. Brunel Univ BSc. Wycliffe Hall Ox 83. **d** 86 **p** 87. C Beckenham St Jo *Roch* 86-89; C Luton Ch Ch 89-94; V Istead Rise from 94. *The Vicarage, Upper Avenue, Gravesend, Kent DA13 9DA* Southfleet (01474) 832403

DYER, Sydney Charles George. b 03. ALCD33 St Jo Coll Dur LTh33 BA34 MA38. **d** 34 **p** 35. V Redhill St Jo *S'wark* 55-69; rtd 69; Hon C Tenerife *Eur* 72-75. *85 Old Fort Road, Shoreham-by-Sea, W Sussex BN43 5HA* Shoreham-by-Sea (01273) 454422

DYER, Terence Neville. b 50. Sheff Univ BEng71 Leic Univ PGCE72. Carl Dioc Tr Course 86. **d** 89 **p** 90. NSM Kirkbride w Newton Arlosh *Carl* 89-91; NSM Carl H Trin and St Barn from 91. *Holy Trinity Vicarage, 25 Wigton Road, Carlisle CA2 7BB* Carlisle (01228) 26284

DYKE, Mrs Elizabeth Muriel. b 55. St Mary's Coll Dur BSc77 St Martin's Coll Lanc PGCE78. Oak Hill Th Coll 92. **d** 94 **p** 95. C High Wycombe *Ox* 94-95; C W Wycombe w Bledlow Ridge, Bradenham and Radnage from 95. *283 Deeds Grove, High Wycombe, Bucks HP12 3PF* High Wycombe (01494) 533622

DYKE, George Edward. b 22. TCD BA65 BCom65 MA80. CITC. **d** 79 **p** 80. NSM Dub St Geo *D & G* 79-82; NSM Tallaght 83-89; NSM Killiney Ballybrack 89-90; Bp's C Dub St Geo and St Thos, Finglas and Free Ch from 90; Chapl Mountjoy Pris from 90. *45 Thornhill Road, Mount Merrion, Co Dublin, Irish Republic* Dublin (1) 288-9376

DYKE, Kenneth Aubrey. b 30. Sarum Th Coll 61. **d** 63 **p** 64. Chapl RAF 66-82; R Bottesford and Muston *Leic* 82-92; rtd 92. *18 Nursery Road, Bingham, Nottingham NG13 8EH* Bingham (01949) 837052

DYKES, John Edward. b 33. DipHE84. Trin Coll Bris 82. **d** 84 **p** 85. C Rushden w Newton Bromswold Per 84-87; R Heanton Punchardon w Marwood *Ex* from 87. *The Rectory, Heanton, Barnstaple, Devon EX31 4DG* Braunton (01271) 812249

DYKES, Michael David Allan. b 42. Chich Th Coll 68. **d** 71 **p** 72. C Pocklington w Yapham-cum-Meltonby, Owsthorpe etc *York* 72-75; C Howden 75-77; V Eskdaleside w Ugglebarnby and Sneaton 77-85; R Stokesley from 85; P-in-c Hilton in Cleveland from 85; P-in-c Seamer in Cleveland from 85. *The Rectory, Leven Close, Stokesley, Middlesbrough, Cleveland TS9 5AP* Stokesley (01642) 710405

DYKES, Philip John. b 61. Loughb Univ BSc83 DIS83. Trin Coll Bris DTS90 ADPS91. **d** 91 **p** 92. C Morden *S'wark* 91-95; C St Helier from 95. *Bishop Andrews House, Wigmore Road, Carshalton, Surrey SM4 1RG* 0181-644 9203

DYMOCK, Michael James Paul. b 45. AKC69. St Aug Coll Cant 70. **d** 70 **p** 71. C Benhilton *S'wark* 70-73; V Clapham St Jo 73-77; P-in-c Clapham Ch Ch 76-77; V Clapham Ch Ch and St Jo 77-80; V Hackbridge and N Beddington 80-84; V Plumstead St Nic 84-91; Sub-Dean Woolwich 87-91; Sub-Dean Greenwich 91-92; V Elham w Denton and Wootton Cant 92-95. *Downs Cottage, Mutton Hall Hill, Heathfield, E Sussex TN21 8NB* Heathfield (01435) 868276

DYSON, Prof Anthony Oakley. b 35. Em Coll Cam BA59 MA63 Ex Coll Ox BD64 DPhil68. Ripon Hall Ox. **d** 61 **p** 62. C Putney St Mary *S'wark* 61-63; Chapl Ripon Hall Ox 63-68; Prin 69-74; Can Windsor 74-77; Lect Kent Univ 77-80; Perm to Offic *Man* from 80; Prof of Soc and Past Th Man Univ from 80. *33 Danesmoor Road, Manchester M20 9JT* 0161-434 5410

DYSON, Frank. b 28. Open Univ BA. Oak Hill Th Coll 60. **d** 62 **p** 63. V Newchapel *Lich* 65-77; R Bunwell w Carleton Rode *Nor* 77-79; P-in-c Tibenham 78-80; R Bunwell w Carleton Rode and Tibenham 80-81; R Pakefield 81-93; Perm to Offic from 93; rtd 93. *12 Viburnum Green, Lowestoft, Suffolk NR32 2SN* Lowestoft (01502) 574898

DYSON, Peter Whiteley. b 51. Man Univ BA73 LLB75. Qu Coll Birm DipTh80. **d** 81 **p** 82. C Swindon Ch Ch *Bris* 81-84; P-in-c

DYSON

Brislington St Luke 84-91; V Bourne *Guildf* 91-92. *28 Wellesley Avenue, Iver, Bucks SL0 9BN*   Iver (01753) 653980

DYSON, Philip. b 45. AKC67. **d** 68 **p** 69. C Kennington St Jo *S'wark* 68-71; C Petersham 71-74; C Ham St Rich 71-74; V Ponders End St Matt *Lon* 74-80; P-in-c Old St Pancras w Bedf New Town St Matt 80-87; V from 87; V Somers Town St Mary from 80; P-in-c Oseney Crescent St Luke w Camden Square St Paul 84-87; P-in-c Oseney Crescent St Luke 87-89; AD S Camden (Holborn and St Pancras) 86-91; V Camden Square St Paul from 87; P-in-c Kentish Town St Silas 88-89. *St Mary's Church House, Eversholt Street, London NW1 1BN*   0171-387 7301

DYSON, Ven Thomas. b 17. OBE91. Man Univ BA38 Lon Univ BD44 St Edm Hall Ox DipEd47 BA50 MA53. Ely Th Coll 38. **d** 40 **p** 41. V Colne Ch Ch *Blackb* 55-57; Bermuda from 57; Miss to Seamen from 57; Hon Can Bermuda Cathl from 73; Adn Bermuda from 82; rtd 94. *The Rectory, 15 Longford Road, PO Box 248 WK, Warwick WK 06, Bermuda*   Bermuda (1-809) 236-5744

E

EADE, John Christopher. b 45. Ch Coll Cam BA68 MA72. Linc Th Coll 68. **d** 70 **p** 71. C Portsea N End St Mark *Portsm* 70-73; C Henleaze *Bris* 73-77; V Slad *Glouc* 77-82; V N Bradley, Southwick and Heywood *Sarum* 82-91; R Fovant, Sutton Mandeville and Teffont Evias etc from 91. *The Rectory, Brookwood House, Fovant, Salisbury SP3 5JA*   Salisbury (01722) 714826

EADE, Stephen David. b 29. Wells Th Coll 67. **d** 69 **p** 70. C Soundwell *Bris* 69-72; C Chippenham St Paul w Langley Burrell 72-75; P-in-c Pilning 76-80; C Bath Twerton-on-Avon *B & W* 80-81; TV Bath Twerton-on-Avon 81-91; Perm to Offic from 91; rtd 94. *41A Stafford Road, Weston-super-Mare, Avon BS23 3BP*   Weston-super-Mare (01934) 612252

EADES, Jonathan Peter. b 51. Dundee Univ MA74 Edin Univ BD77. Coates Hall Edin 74. **d** 77 **p** 78. Chapl St Paul's Cathl Dundee *Bre* 77-88; Chapl Dundee Univ 79-88; TV Leek and Meerbrook *Lich* from 88; RD Leek from 93. *All Saints' Vicarage, Compton, Leek, Staffs ST13 5PT*   Leek (01538) 382588

EADY, David Robert. b 43. Salford Univ BSc Birm Univ DSocStuds. Glouc Th Course 82. **d** 85 **p** 86. NSM Highnam, Lassington, Rudford, Tibberton etc *Glouc* 85-95; NSM Stratton, N Cerney, Baunton and Bagendon from 95. *Little Gables, Hayes Lane, Woodmancote, Cirencester, Glos GL7 7EE*   Cirencester (01285) 813725

EADY, Timothy William (Tim). b 57. Open Univ BA. Cranmer Hall Dur 82. **d** 85 **p** 86. C Boulton *Derby* 85-88; C Portchester *Portsm* 88-92; Relig Progr Adv Ocean Sound Radio from 88; R Brighstone and Brooke w Mottistone *Portsm* from 92. *The Rectory, Brighstone, Newport, Isle of Wight PO30 4AQ*   Isle of Wight (01983) 740267

EAGER, Ms Rosemary Anne McDowall. b 65. St Andr Univ MA87 Strathclyde Univ 88. Ridley Hall Cam CTM95. **d** 95. C Walthamstow St Mary w St Steph *Chelmsf* from 95. *9 Church End, London E17 9RJ*   0181-509 3746   Fax 520 4281

EAGGER, Mrs Christine Mary. b 32. **d** 94 **p** 95. NSM Arlesey w Astwick *St Alb* from 94; NSM Upper w Lower Gravenhurst from 94. *43 Cainhoe Road, Clophill, Bedford MK43 4AQ*   Silsoe (01525) 860973

EAGLE, John Frederick Laurence. b 16. St Chad's Coll Dur BA39 DipTh40 MA42. **d** 41 **p** 41. R Stanwick *Pet* 58-72; P-in-c Hargrave 59-72; R Stanwick w Hargrave 72-87; rtd 87; Perm to Offic *Pet* from 87. *Mandell House, Minster Precincts, Peterborough PE1 1XX*   Peterborough (01733) 61807

EAGLE, Canon Julian Charles. b 32. Qu Coll Cam BA56 MA60. Westcott Ho Cam. **d** 58 **p** 59. C Billingham St Aid *Dur* 58-61; C Eastleigh *Win* 61-65; Ind Chapl from 65; Hon Can Win Cathl from 83. *24 Butterfield Road, Southampton SO1 7EE*   Southampton (01703) 791097

EAGLES, Anthony Arthur. b 39. S'wark Ord Course 81. **d** 84 **p** 85. NSM Hillingdon All SS *Lon* 84-87; C Uxbridge 87-90; C Gt Marlow *Ox* 91-93; TV Gt Marlow w Marlow Bottom, Lt Marlow and Bisham from 93. *165 Marlow Bottom Road, Marlow, Bucks SL7 3PL*   Marlow (01628) 472816

EAGLES, Peter Andrew. b 58. K Coll Lon BA82 AKC82 Ox Univ BA88. St Steph Ho Ox 86. **d** 89 **p** 90. C Ruislip St Martin *Lon* 89-92; CF from 92. *c/o MOD (Army), Bagshot Park, Bagshot, Surrey GU19 5PL*   Bagshot (01276) 471717   Fax 412834

EALES, Howard Bernard. b 46. Sarum & Wells Th Coll 73. **d** 76 **p** 77. C Timperley *Ches* 76-78; C Stockport St Thos 78-82; V Wythenshawe Wm Temple Ch *Man* from 82. *William Temple Vicarage, Robinswood Road, Manchester M22 0BU*   0161-437 3194

EALES WHITE, Donald James. b 16. MC45. St Jo Coll Ox BA44 MA44. St Deiniol's Hawarden 60. **d** 61 **p** 62. Lic to Offic *Arg* 69-71; V Mendham *St E* 71-72; P-in-c Metfield w Withersdale 71-72; Perm to Offic 73-74; P-in-c Eorrapaidh *Arg* 74-77 and 79-81; R Dalbeattie *Glas* 77-79; P-in-c Dornoch *Mor* 81-82; P-in-c Brora 81-82; rtd 82; Perm to Offic *Arg* from 82. *Dell Cottage, South Dell, Isle of Lewis PA86 0SP*   Port-of-Ness (0185181) 726

EAMAN, Michael Leslie. b 47. Ridley Hall Cam 87. **d** 89 **p** 90. C Wharton *Ches* 89-93; V Buglawton from 93. *St John's Vicarage, Buxton Road, Congleton, Cheshire CW12 2DT*   Congleton (01260) 273294

✠**EAMES, Most Rev Robert Henry Alexander.** b 37. QUB LLB60 PhD63 Hon LLD89 TCD Hon LLD92 Cam Univ Hon DD94 Lanc Univ Hon LLD94. TCD Div Sch Div Test60. **d** 63 **p** 64 **c** 75. C Ban St Comgall *D & D* 63-66; I Gilnahirk 66-74; Bp's Dom Chapl 70-72; I Dundela 74-75; Bp D & R 75-80; Bp D & D 80-86; Abp Arm from 86. *The See House, Cathedral Close, Armagh BT61 7EE*   Armagh (01861) 522851 or 527144   Fax 527823

EARDLEY, John. b 38. Ch Coll Cam BA61. Ridley Hall Cam 60. **d** 62 **p** 63. C Barnston *Ches* 62-65; C Wilmslow 65-67; V Hollingworth 67-75; V Leasowe 75-91; RD Wallasey 86-91; V Church Hulme from 91; Chapl Cranage Hall Hosp from 91. *The Vicarage, Holmes Chapel, Crewe CW4 7BD*   Holmes Chapel (01477) 533124

EARDLEY, Canon John Barry. b 35. MEd87. AKC62. **d** 63 **p** 64. C Mert St Jas *S'wark* 63-66; C St Helier 66-69; C Bilton *Cov* 69-70; C Canley CD 70-74; P-in-c Church Lawford w Newnham Regis 74-80; P-in-c Leamington Hastings and Birdingbury 82-88; Dioc Educn Officer from 82; Hon Can Cov Cathl from 87. *The Rectory, Bubbenhall, Coventry CV8 3BD*   Coventry (01203) 302345 or 674328

EARDLEY, Paul Wycliffe. b 19. ALCD42. **d** 42 **p** 43. R Ripe w Chalvington *Chich* 62-71; V Kemp Town St Mark and St Matt 71-84; rtd 84; Perm to Offic *Chich* from 84. *Saxons, 2 Falmer Road, Rottingdean, Brighton BN2 7DA*   Brighton (01273) 302255

EARDLEY, Robert Bradford. b 44. St Alb Minl Tr Scheme 90. **d** 93 **p** 94. NSM Digswell and Panshanger *St Alb* from 93. *16 Coneydale, Welwyn Garden City, Herts AL8 7RZ*   Welwyn Garden (01707) 332609

EAREY, Mark Robert. b 65. Loughb Univ BSc87. Cranmer Hall Dur BA91. **d** 91 **p** 92. C Glen Parva and S Wigston *Leic* 91-94; C Luton Ch Ch *Roch* from 94. *6 Thrush Close, Chatham, Kent ME5 7TG*   Medway (01634) 685828

EARIS, Stanley Derek. b 50. Univ Coll Dur BA71 BCL80. Ripon Hall Ox BA73 MA80. **d** 74 **p** 75. C Sutton St Jas and Wawne *York* 74-77; C Acomb St Steph 77-81; V Skelmanthorpe *Wakef* 81-87; R Market Deeping *Linc* from 87. *The Rectory, Church Street, Market Deeping, Peterborough PE6 8DA*   Market Deeping (01778) 342237

EARL, David Arthur. b 34. Hartley Victoria Coll 63 Coll of Resurr Mirfield. **d** 83 **p** 83. In Meth Ch 67-83; P-in-c Paddock *Wakef* 83-84; C Huddersfield St Pet and All SS from 84. *All Saints Vicarage, 17 Cross Church Street, Huddersfield HD1 4SN*   Huddersfield (01484) 530814

EARL, Very Rev David Kaye Lee. b 28. TCD BA54. **d** 55 **p** 56. I Killarney *L & K* 65-79; RD Tralee 71-77; Prec Limerick Cathl 77-79; Dean Ferns *C & O* 79-94; I Ferns w Kilbride, Toombe, Kilcormack etc 79-94; rtd 94. *Random, Seafield, Tramore, Co Waterford, Irish Republic*   Waterford (51) 390503

EARL, Stephen Geoffrey Franklyn. b 53. Univ Coll Lon BA76 Golds Coll Lon PGCE77. Ridley Hall Cam 91. **d** 93 **p** 94. C Sawston *Ely* from 93. *23 Teversham Way, Sawston, Cambridge CB2 4DF*   Cambridge (01223) 832955

EARL, Victor Charles. b 22. Bede Coll Dur BA49. ALCD54. **d** 51 **p** 52. Lic to Offic *Man* 67-82; R Gorton St Phil 82-88; Perm to Offic *Derby* from 88. *4 Burdekin Close, Chapel-en-le-Frith, Stockport, Cheshire SK12 6QA*   Chapel-en-le-Frith (01298) 815312

EARLE, Charles Walter. b 08. Keble Coll Ox BA31 MA35. Linc Th Coll 31. **d** 32 **p** 33. R Newent *Glouc* 69-76; rtd 76. *39 Kingsfield Road, Dane End, Ware, Herts SG12 0LZ*   Ware (01920) 438514

EARLE, Canon George Halden. b 14. St Chad's Coll Dur LTh39 BA40 MA44. Qu Coll Newfoundland 35. **d** 38 **p** 39. Canada from 57; V Choppington *Newc* 52-57; Can St Jo Cathl Newfoundland from 72; rtd 79. *5 Howlett Avenue, St John's, Newfoundland, Canada, A1B 1K8*

204

EARLE, John Nicholas Francis. b 26. Trin Coll Cam BA47 MA52. Westcott Ho Cam 50. **d** 52 **p** 53. Asst Master Dulwich Coll Lon 61-71; Hd Master Bromsgrove Sch Worcs 71-85; Asst Teacher Jas Allen's Girls Sch Lon from 87; rtd 91. *1 Red Post Hill, London SE21 7BX* 0181-693 5829

EARLEY, Stephen John. b 48. Trin Coll Bris DipHE93. **d** 93 **p** 94. C Stroud H Trin *Glouc* from 93. *Waldringfield, London Road, Stroud, Glos GL5 2AJ* Stroud (01453) 758618

EARNEY, Graham Howard. b 45. AKC67. **d** 68 **p** 69. C Auckland St Helen *Dur* 68-72; C Corsenside *Newc* 72-76; P-in-c 76-79; TV Willington Team 79-83; TR 83-87; Dioc Soc Resp Officer *B & W* 87-95; Warden Bp Mascall Cen *Heref* from 95; NSM Ludlow, Ludford, Ashford Carbonell etc from 95. *The Director's House, The Bishop Mascall Centre, Ludlow, Shropshire SY8 1RX* Ludlow (01584) 876318

EARNSHAW, Alan Mark. b 36. CQSW81. Lon Coll of Div LTh60. **d** 60 **p** 61. C Fazakerley Em *Liv* 60-65; V Ovenden *Wakef* 65-79; NSM Halifax St Jude 79-90; V Coley from 90. *The Vicarage, 41 Ing Head Terrace, Shelf, Halifax, W Yorkshire HX3 7LB* Halifax (01422) 202292

EARNSHAW, Robert Richard (Rob). b 42. N Ord Course 78. **d** 81 **p** 82. NW Area Sec Bible Soc 78-85; NSM Liv All So Springwood *Liv* 81-85; R Hinton Ampner w Bramdean and Kilmeston *Win* 85-87; Chapl HM Young Offender Inst Huntercombe and Finnamore 87-92; Chapl HM Young Offender Inst Finnamore Wood Camp 87-92; R Spaxton w Goathurst, Enmore and Charlynch *B & W* from 92; P-in-c Aisholt from 92. *The Rectory, Church Road, Spaxton, Bridgwater, Somerset TA5 1DA* Spaxton (01278) 671265

EARP, John William. b 19. Jes Coll Cam BA42 MA45. Ridley Hall Cam 42. **d** 43 **p** 44. V Hartley Wintney and Elvetham *Win* 62-77; RD Odiham 76-83; V Hartley Wintney, Elvetham, Winchfield etc 77-88; rtd 88; Perm to Offic *Nor* from 89. *3 The Driftway, Sheringham, Norfolk NR26 8LD* Sheringham (01263) 825487

EARWAKER, John Clifford. b 36. Keble Coll Ox BA59 MA63 Man Univ MEd71. Linc Th Coll 59. **d** 61 **p** 62. C Ecclesall *Sheff* 61-64; Succ St Mary's Cathl *Edin* 64-65; Lic to Offic *Man* 65-69; Lic to Offic *Sheff* from 69; Chapl and Lect Sheff Poly 81-92; Chapl and Lect Sheff Hallam Univ from 92. *24 Newbould Lane, Sheffield S10 2PL* Sheffield (0114) 266 5745/266 5274

EASON, Canon Cyril Edward. b 21. Leeds Univ BA43 MA67. Coll of Resurr Mirfield 43. **d** 45 **p** 46. Area Sec (Dio B & W) USPG 65-86; Area Sec (Dios Ex and Truro) USPG 75-86; Perm to Offic *Truro* 75-86; Hon Can Mufulira from 85; rtd 86; P-in-c Tilshead, Orcheston and Chitterne *Sarum* 86-92. *11 Bishop's Court, Williamson Drive, Ripon, N Yorkshire HG4 1AY* Ripon (01765) 608300

EAST, Bryan Victor. b 46. Oak Hill Th Coll DipHE93. **d** 93 **p** 94. C Waltham Cross *St Alb* from 93. *103 Northfield Road, Waltham Cross, Herts NE8 7RD* Waltham Cross (01992) 627246

EAST, Mark Richard. b 57. Trin Coll Bris BA89. **d** 89 **p** 90. C Dalton-in-Furness *Carl* 89-93; TV Bucknall and Bagnall *Lich* from 93. *St John's Parsonage, 28 Greasley Road, Stoke-on-Trent ST2 8JE* Stoke-on-Trent (01782) 542861

EAST, Peter Alan. b 62. ACIB89 Southn Univ LLB82. Cranmer Hall Dur 90. **d** 93 **p** 94. C Combe Down w Monkton Combe and S Stoke *B & W* from 93. *13A Foxhill, Combe Down, Bath BA2 5QL* Bath (01225) 836092

EAST, Reginald Walter. b 16. St Jo Coll Dur BA49 DipTh50. **d** 50 **p** 51. V W Mersea *Chelmsf* 57-71; R E Mersea 57-71; C Winterborne Whitechurch w Clenston *Sarum* 71-75; Warden Barn Fellowship Whatcombe Ho 75-80; Lic to Offic 80-85; rtd 85. *Shepherds Cottage, Winterborne Whitechurch, Blandford Forum, Dorset DT11 0NZ* Milton Abbas (01258) 880190

EAST, Richard Kenneth. b 47. Oak Hill Th Coll 86. **d** 88 **p** 89. C Necton w Holme Hale *Nor* 88-92; R Garsdon, Lea and Cleverton and Charlton *Bris* from 92; RD Malmesbury from 93. *The Rectory, Lea, Malmesbury, Wilts SN16 9PG* Malmesbury (01666) 823861

EAST, Stuart Michael. b 50. Chich Th Coll 86. **d** 88 **p** 89. C Middlesb St Martin *York* 88-92; R Upper Ryedale from 92. *The Rectory, Old Byland, York YO6 5LG* Bilsdale (01439) 798355

EAST RIDING, Archdeacon of. See BUCKINGHAM, Ven Hugh Fletcher

EASTELL, Dr John Kevin. b 42. Liv Univ DSocStuds77 DipAdEd80 MedEd Open Univ BA83 Lon Univ PhD92. Lambeth STh82 Kelham Th Coll 61 Wells Th Coll 64. **d** 66 **p** 67. C Horbury *Wakef* 66-69; C Armley St Bart *Ripon* 69-72; V Toxteth St Marg *Liv* 72-76; V Formby St Pet 76-82; V Royton St Paul *Man* 82-88; Dir Professional Min *Lon* from 88. *23A Culmington Road, London W13 9NJ* 0181-579 8083

EASTER, Sister Ann Rosemarie. SRN68 DipRS78. Qu Coll Birm. **dss** 80 **d** 87 **p** 94. Chapl Asst Newham Gen Hosp 80-89; Stratford St Jo and Ch Ch w Forest Gate St Jas *Chelmsf* 80-87; Par Dn 87-89; NSM Forest Gate Em w Upton Cross from 89. *St Luke's House, 36 Stratford Street, London E14 8LT* 0171-538 9316

EASTER, Dr Brian James Bert. b 33. Lon Univ DipTh55 Birm Univ DPS75 PhD83. Tyndale Hall Bris 53 St Aug Coll Cant 56. **d** 57 **p** 58. C Tipton St Martin *Lich* 57-59; Midl Area Sec BCMS 59-64; V Barston *Birm* 64-72; Chapl Mentally Handicapped S Birm HA from 72; Chapl Monyhull Hosp Birm from 72; Lect Birm Univ from 86. *995 Yardley Wood Road, Birmingham B14 4BS* 0121-474 2622 or 627 1627

EASTER, Stephen Talbot. b 22. St Cath Coll Cam BA47 MA53. Ely Th Coll. **d** 50 **p** 51. V St Margarets-at-Cliffe w Westcliffe etc *Cant* 61-85; rtd 85; Perm to Offic *Cant* from 85. *9/11 Blenheim Road, Deal, Kent CT14 7AJ* Deal (01304) 368021

EASTGATE, Canon John. b 30. Kelham Th Coll 47. **d** 54 **p** 55. V Glen Parva and S Wigston *Leic* 69-74; V Woodley St Jo the Ev *Ox* 74-83; V Hughenden 83-94; RD Wycombe 87-90; Hon Can Ch Ch 90-94; rtd 94. *11 Orchard Park, Holmer Green, High Wycombe, Bucks HP15 6QY* High Wycombe (01494) 713761

EASTOE, Robin Howard Spenser. b 53. Lon Univ BD75 AKC75. Coll of Resurr Mirfield 77. **d** 78 **p** 79. C Gt Ilford St Mary *Chelmsf* 78-81; C Walthamstow St Sav 81-84; V Barkingside St Fran 84-92; V Leigh-on-Sea St Marg from 92. *St Margaret's Vicarage, 1465 London Road, Leigh-on-Sea, Essex SS9 2SB* Southend-on-Sea (01702) 471773

EASTON, Christopher Richard Alexander. b 60. TCD BA DipTh. **d** 84 **p** 85. C Belf St Donard *D & D* 84-89; I Inishmacsaint *Clogh* 89-95; I Magheralin w Dollingstown *D & D* from 95. *The Rectory, 12 New Forge Road, Magheralin, Craigavon, Co Armagh BT67 0QJ* Moira (01848) 611273 Fax 619569

EASTON, Dr Donald Fyfe. b 48. St Edm Hall Ox BA69 MA85 Nottm Univ CertEd70 Univ Coll Lon MA76 PhD90 Clare Hall Cam MA85. Westcott Ho Cam 89. **d** 90 **p** 91. NSM Fulham St Andr Fulham Fields *Lon* 90-94; Perm to Offic from 94. *12 Weltje Road, London W6 9TG* 0181-741 0233

EASTON, John. b 34. St Cath Soc Ox BA59 MA63. Chich Th Coll 59. **d** 61 **p** 62. C Rugeley *Lich* 61-64; TR 72-87; C Shrewsbury All SS 64-66; Ind Chapl *Sheff* 66-72; V Bolsover *Derby* from 87; RD Bolsover and Staveley from 93. *The Vicarage, Bolsover, Chesterfield, Derbyshire S44 6BG* Chesterfield (01246) 824888

EASTON, Richard Huntingford. b 26. Or Coll Ox BA51 MA51. Westcott Ho Cam 53. **d** 54 **p** 55. C Bris St Ambrose Whitehall *Bris* 54-57; New Zealand from 57. *Muriwai Road, RD1 Waimauku, Auckland, New Zealand* Auckland (9) 411-8320

EASTWOOD, Arthur Christopher John. b 5. St Edm Hall Ox BA45 MA45. Westcott Ho Cam 45. **d** 47 **p** 48. V Cowplain *Portsm* 62-86; rtd 86; Perm to Offic *Bris* from 87. *40 Templar Road, Yate, Bristol BS17 5TG* Chipping Sodbury (01454) 322405

EASTWOOD, Colin Foster. b 34. Leeds Univ BA56 MA66. Linc Th Coll 65. **d** 67 **p** 68. C Cottingham *York* 67-70; C Darlington St Cuth *Dur* 70-75; V Eighton Banks 75-81; V Sutton St Jas *Ches* from 81. *St James's Vicarage, Sutton, Macclesfield, Cheshire SK11 0DS* Sutton (01260) 252228

EASTWOOD, Harry. b 26. Man Univ BSc48. Ridley Hall Cam 81. **d** 82 **p** 83. NSM Barton Seagrave w Warkton *Pet* from 82. *22 Poplars Farm Road, Kettering, Northants NN15 5AF* Kettering (01536) 513271

EASTWOOD, Irvine Thomas. b 17. Sheff Univ BSc38. CITC 88. **d** 90 **p** 91. NSM Wexford w Ardcolm and Killurin *C & O* from 90. *Dubross, Trinity Street, Wexford, Irish Republic* Wexford (53) 23604

EASTWOOD, Miss Janet. b 54. Wycliffe Hall Ox 83. **dss** 86 **d** 87 **p** 94. Ainsdale *Liv* 86-87; Par Dn 87-90; TD Kirkby Lonsdale *Carl* 90-94; TV 94-95; Dioc Youth Officer 90-94; R Wavertree H Trin *Liv* from 95. *Wavertree Rectory, Hunters Lane, Liverpool L15 8HL* 0151-733 2172

EATOCK, John. b 45. Lanc Univ MA82. Lich Th Coll 67. **d** 70 **p** 71. C Crumpsall St Mary *Man* 70-73; C Atherton 73-74; C Ribbleton *Blackb* 74-77; V Ingol 77-83; V Laneside 83-92; RD Accrington 90-92; Perm to Offic from 92. *57 Heys Avenue, Haslingden, Rossendale, Lancs BB4 5DU* Rossendale (01706) 222531

EATON, David Andrew. b 58. ACA83 Man Univ BSc79. Trin Coll Bris BA89. **d** 89 **p** 90. C Barking St Marg w St Patr *Chelmsf* 89-92; C Billericay and Lt Burstead 92-95; P-in-c Vange from 95. *Vange Rectory, 782 Clay Hill Road, Vange, Basildon, Essex SS16 4NG* Basildon (01268) 581574

EATON, David John. b 45. Nottm Univ LTh BTh74. St Jo Coll Nottm 70. **d** 74 **p** 75. C Headley All SS *Guildf* 74-77; Ind Chapl *Worc* 77-82; TV Halesowen 80-82; V Rowledge *Guildf* 82-89;

EATON

V Leatherhead from 89; RD Leatherhead from 93. *The Vicarage, 2 St Mary's Road, Leatherhead, Surrey KT22 8EZ* Leatherhead (01372) 372313

✠EATON, Rt Rev Derek Lionel. b 41. QSM85. DMSchM68 Neuchatel Univ Switz Cert Français 69 Internat Inst Chr Communication Nairobi 74 Univ of Tunis CertFAI70 Univ of Missouri MA78. Trin Coll Bris DipTh66 WEC Miss Tr Coll DipTh66. d 71 p 71 c 90. C Brislington St Luke *Bris* 71-72; Chapl Br Emb Tunisia 72-78; Provost All SS Cathl Cairo and Chapl Br Emb 78-83; Hon Can from 85; New Zealand from 84; Bp Nelson from 90. *PO Box 100, 218 Trafalgar Street, Nelson, New Zealand* Christchurch (3) 548-8991 or 3124

EATON (nee CRAIG), Julie Elizabeth. b 57. SEN81. Trin Coll Bris DipHE89. d 89 p 94. Par Dn Gt Ilford St Andr *Chelmsf* 89-92; NSM Billericay and Lt Burstead 92-95; C Billericay and Lt Burstead from 95. *Vange Rectory, 782 Clay Hill Road, Vange, Basildon, Essex SS16 4NG* Basildon (01268) 581574

EATON, Mrs Margaret Anne. b 44. Ab Dioc Tr Course 82. dss 84 d 86 p 94. NSM Ellon *Ab* 84-95; NSM Cruden Bay 84-95; NSM Bridge of Don from 95. *55 Eilean Rise, Ellon, Aberdeenshire AB41 9NF* Ellon (01358) 721806

EATON, Oscar Benjamin (Ben). b 37. Puerto Rico Th Coll STB66. d 66 p 67. Ecuador 66-69; C Wandsworth St Anne *S'wark* 69-71; C Aldrington *Chich* 71-73; TV Littleham w Exmouth *Ex* 74-79; R Alphington 79-84; Chapl Barcelona w Casteldefels *Eur* 84-88; Chapl Maisons-Laffitte from 88. *15 Avenue Carnot, 78600 Maisons-Laffitte, France* Paris (331) 39 62 34 97

EATON, Canon Peter David. b 58. K Coll Lon BA82 AKC82 Qu Coll Cam BA85 MA89 Magd Coll Ox MA90. Westcott Ho Cam 83. d 86 p 87. C Maidstone All SS and St Phil w Tovil *Cant* 86-89; Fells' Chapl Magd Coll Ox 89-91; Lic to Offic *Ox* from 89; USA from 91; Can Th Dio Utah from 91. *119 N Duke Street, Lancaster, Pennsylvania 17602, USA* (717) 397-4858 Fax 397-7548

EATON, Miss Phyllis Mary. b 42. SRD Qu Eliz Coll Lon BSc63 Univ of S Africa BA79. W Midl Minl Tr Course 87. d 90 p 94. NSM Washwood Heath *Birm* 90-91; NSM Edgbaston SS Mary and Ambrose from 91. *Flat 14, Mark House, 14 Wake Green Road, Birmingham B13 9HA* 0121-449 2431

EAVES, Alan Charles. b 37. Lon Univ DipTh64. Tyndale Hall Bris 62. d 65 p 66. C Southport SS Simon and Jude *Liv* 65-66; C Eccleston Ch Ch 66-70; V Earlestown 70-79; V Orpington Ch Ch *Roch* from 79. *Christ Church Vicarage, 165 Charterhouse Road, Orpington, Kent BR6 9EP* Orpington (01689) 870923

EAVES, Brian Maxwell. b 40. Tyndale Hall Bris 66. d 69 p 70. C Wolv St Jude *Lich* 69-72; C Fazeley 72-75; TV Ipsley *Worc* 75-79; Chapl Amsterdam *Eur* 79-86; Chapl Bordeaux w Riberac, Cahors, Duras etc 86-91; Monaco 91-93; TV Buckhurst Hill *Chelmsf* from 93. *The Vicarage, 10 Albert Road, Buckhurst Hill, Essex IG9 6EH* 0181-504 6698

EBBITT, Francis Simon (Frank). b 20. TCD BA42 MA49 BD56. TCD Div Sch 40. d 43 p 44. V Rainhill *Liv* 65-74; V Stanford in the Vale w Goosey and Hatford *Ox* 74-80; RD Vale of White Horse 75-80; V Furze Platt 80-87; Chapl St Mark's and Clarefield Hosps Ox 80-87; rtd 87; Asst Chapl Malaga *Eur* 87-90. *229A Courthouse Road, Maidenhead, Berks SL6 6HF* Maidenhead (01628) 22418

EBBITT, Robert David. b 22. TCD BA44 MA56. TCD Div Sch 44. d 45 p 46. C Belf St Nic *Conn* 45-47; CF 47-65; Dep Asst Chapl Gen 65-72; Asst Chapl Gen 72-78; Perm to Offic *D & D* from 94. *13 The Meadow, Groomsport, Co Down BT19 6JH* Bangor (01247) 464443

EBBSFLEET, Suffragan Bishop of (Provincial Episcopal Visitor). See RICHARDS, Rt Rev John

EBELING, Mrs Barbara. b 44. d 94 p 95. C Stevenage SS Hugh and Jo Chells *St Alb* from 94. *7 Wicklands Road, Hunsdon, Ware, Herts SG12 8PD* Much Hadham (01279) 842086

ECCLES, Ernest Pattison. b 23. Kelham Th Coll 46. d 50 p 51. R Braithwell w Bramley *Sheff* 56-88; P-in-c Hooton Roberts w Ravenfield 62-75; rtd 88. *Stonegates, Back Lane, Maltby, Rotherham, S Yorkshire S66 7HA* Rotherham (01709) 867910

ECCLES, James Henry. b 30. DLC64 Lon Univ CertPsych70 DipEd. Wycliffe Hall Ox 86. d 87 p 88. NSM Llandudno *Ban* 87-91; rtd 91; NSM Llanrhos *St As* from 94. *Lowlands, 7 St Seiriol's Road, Llandudno, Gwynedd LL30 2YY* Llandudno (01492) 878524

ECCLES, Mrs Vivien Madeline. Local NSM Course. d 92 p 94. NSM Stretford St Bride *Man* from 92. *49 Barton Road, Stretford, Manchester M32 9TA* 0161-748 9795

ECKERSLEY, Mrs Nancy Elizabeth. b 50. York Univ BA72 Leeds Univ CertEd73. NE Ord Course 86. d 89 p 94. NSM Clifton *York* from 89; Chapl York Distr Hosp 90-93; Lay Tr Officer *York* from 93. *30 Howard Drive, Rawcliffe, York YO3 6XB* York (01904) 658905

ECKERSLEY, Canon Richard Hugh. b 25. Trin Coll Cam BA48 MA50. Chich Th Coll 49. d 51 p 52. V Paulsgrove *Portsm*

62-73; V Brighton St Nic *Chich* 73-84; Can Res Portsm Cathl *Portsm* 84-92; rtd 92. *136 Kensington Road, Portsmouth PO2 0QY* Portsmouth (01705) 653512

EDDERSHAW, Lionel Francis Trevor. b 34. Down Coll Cam BA58 MA62. Linc Th Coll 58. d 60 p 61. C Wallsend St Luke *Newc* 60-63; C Balkwell CD 63-68; R Falstone 68-75; R St Jo Lee 75-84; R Rothbury from 84; Chapl Coquetdale Cottage Hosp from 84. *The Rectory, Rothbury, Morpeth, Northd NE65 7TL* Rothbury (01669) 20482

EDDISON, Frederick Donald Buchanan. b 19. Trin Coll Cam BA41 MA46. Ridley Hall Cam 47. d 48 p 49. V Tunbridge Wells St Jo *Roch* 65-80; rtd 80; Perm to Offic *Roch* from 81. *43 East Cliff Road, Tunbridge Wells, Kent TN4 9AG* Tunbridge Wells (01892) 520991

EDDISON, Robert John Buchanan. b 16. Trin Coll Cam BA38 MA42. Ridley Hall Cam 38. d 39 p 40. Travelling Sec Scripture Union 42-80; rtd 81; Perm to Offic *Chich* from 81. *Durham Lodge, Crowborough, E Sussex TN6 1EW* Crowborough (01892) 652606

EDE, Albert Alfred. b 11. Dur Univ LTh44 BA45. Clifton Th Coll 36. d 39 p 40. R Fulletby w Greetham and Ashby Puerorum *Linc* 46-87; V High Toynton 52-87; V Mareham on the Hill 57-87; R Hameringham w Scrafield and Winceby 63-87; rtd 87; Perm to Offic *Linc* from 90. *The Chantry, Greetham, Horncastle, Lincs LN9 6NT* Winceby (01507) 588211

EDE, Ven Dennis. b 31. Nottm Univ BA55 Birm Univ MSocSc73. Ripon Hall Ox 55. d 57 p 58. C Sheldon *Birm* 57-60; C Castle Bromwich SS Mary and Marg 60-64; Chapl E Birm Hosp 60-76; C-in-c Hodge Hill CD *Birm* 64-70; V Hodge Hill 70-72; TR 72-76; Chapl Sandwell Distr Gen Hosp 76-90; V W Bromwich All SS *Lich* 76-90; P-in-c W Bromwich Ch Ch 76-79; RD W Bromwich 76-90; Preb Lich Cathl 83-90; Adn Stoke from 90; Hon Can Lich Cathl from 90. *39 The Brackens, Clayton, Newcastle, Staffs ST5 4JL* Newcastle-under-Lyme (01782) 663066 Fax 711165

EDE, Preb Oswald George. b 16. Lich Th Coll 37. d 39 p 40. V Marchington w Marchington Woodlands *Lich* 46-82; rtd 82; Perm to Offic *Lich* from 82. *19 St Mary's Crescent, Uttoxeter, Staffs ST14 7BH* Uttoxeter (01889) 566106

EDEN, Henry. b 36. G&C Coll Cam BA59 MA64. Ox NSM Course. d 87 p 88. NSM Abingdon w Shippon *Ox* 87-88; Chapl Brentwood Sch Essex 88-95; TV Beaconsfield *Ox* from 95. *St Michael's Parsonage, St Michael's Green, Beaconsfield, Bucks HP9 2BN* Beaconsfield (01494) 673464

EDEN, Leslie Thomas Ernest. b 19. ACII55. S'wark Ord Course. d 69 p 70. NSM Kidbrooke St Jas *S'wark* 69-94; rtd 94; Perm to Offic *S'wark* from 94. *47 Begbie Road, London SE3 8DA* 0181-856 3088

EDEN, Michael William. b 57. Nottm Univ BTh86. Linc Th Coll 83. d 86 p 87. C Daventry *Pet* 86-89; TV Northn Em 89-92; V Corby St Columba from 92. *St Columba's Vicarage, 157 Studfall Avenue, Corby, Northants NN17 1LG* Corby (01536) 204158 or 261436

EDGAR, David. b 59. Newc Univ BA81. Linc Th Coll BTh86. d 86 p 87. C Wednesbury St Paul Wood Green *Lich* 86-91; V Winterton Gp *Linc* from 91. *The Vicarage, High Street, Winterton, Scunthorpe, S Humberside DN15 9PU* Scunthorpe (01724) 732262

EDGAR, Canon Granville George. b 25. St Pet Hall Ox BA46 MA50. St Mich Coll Llan 46. d 48 p 49. V Llantilio Crossenny and Llanfihangel Ystern etc *Mon* 69-73; Dioc Dir RE 73-86; R Llangybi 73-91; Can St Woolos Cathl 75-91; rtd 91. *28 Manor Court, Baron Street, Usk, Gwent NP5 1DQ* Usk (01291) 673451

EDGAR, Timothy Roy. b 56. K Coll Lon BD78 AKC78. Coll of Resurr Mirfield 79. d 80 p 81. C Hampstead Garden Suburb *Lon* 80-82; C Cantley *Sheff* 82-86; V Sheff St Cath Richmond Road 86-90; Dir Past Studies Coll of the Resurr Mirfield 90-94. *20 Barnet Way, London NW7 3BH* 0181-906 0271

EDGE, Canon John Francis. b 32. Ex Coll Ox BA54 MA56. St Steph Ho Ox 54. d 58 p 59. C Oswestry H Trin *Lich* 58-62; V 64-79; Tutor Lich Th Coll 62-64; Malaysia 79-87; Hon Can Kuching from 88; TV Wolv *Lich* 88-91; Chapl R Hosp Wolv 88-91; Subwarden St Deiniol's Lib Hawarden 91-93; C Briercliffe *Blackb* from 93. *31 Sutcliffe Street, Briercliffe, Burnley, Lancs BB10 2JW* Burnley (01282) 456541

EDGE, Michael MacLeod. b 45. St Andr Univ BSc68 Qu Coll Cam BA70 MA74. Westcott Ho Cam 68. d 72 p 73. C Allerton *Liv* 72-76; R Bretherton *Blackb* 76-82; P-in-c Kilpeck *Heref* 82-84; P-in-c St Devereux w Wormbridge 82-84; TR Ewyas Harold w Dulas, Kenderchurch etc 82-93; RD Abbeydore 84-90; V Enfield St Andr *Lon* from 93. *The Vicarage, Silver Street, Enfield, Middx EN1 3EG* 0181-363 8676

EDGE, Philip John. b 54. Ripon Coll Cuddesdon 77. d 80 p 81. C N Harrow St Alb *Lon* 80-83; C St Giles Cripplegate w St Bart Moor Lane etc 83-86; P-in-c Belmont 86-88; V 88-92; V Ellesmere and Welsh Frankton *Lich* from 92. *The Vicarage,*

Church Hill, Ellesmere, Shropshire SY12 0HB Ellesmere (01691) 622571

EDGE, Miss Renate Erika. b 50. Bonn Chamber of Commerce TransDip75 DIL77. Cranmer Hall Dur 86. **d** 88. Par Dn Leic H Spirit *Leic* 88-89; Asst Chapl Leic and Co Miss for the Deaf 88-89; Par Dn Leic H Apostles *Leic* 89-94. *Address temp unknown*

EDGE, Timothy Peter. b 55. CEng85 MIEE85 FRAS80 Brighton Poly BSc80. Westcott Ho Cam 85. **d** 88 **p** 89. C Norton *Ches* 88-91; C Bedworth *Cov* from 91. *38 Gallagher Road, Bedworth, Nuneaton, Warks CV12 8SD* Bedworth (01203) 491767

EDGECUMBE, Irena Christine. See CZERNIAWSKA EDGECUMBE, Mrs Irena Christine

EDGELL, Hugh Anthony Richard. b 31. ARHistS84. AKC57. **d** 58 **p** 59. C N Lynn w St Marg and St Nic *Nor* 58-64; R S Walsham 64-74; V Upton w Fishley 64-74; R Hingham 74-81; R Hingham w Woodrising w Scoulton 81-85; OStJ 79-88; SBStJ from 88; V Horning *Nor* 85-89; P-in-c Beeston St Laurence w Ashmanhaugh 85-89; R Horning w Beeston St Laurence and Ashmanhaugh from 89; Prior St Benet's Abbey Horning from 87. *The Vicarage, Horning, Norwich NR12 8PZ* Horning (01692) 630216

EDGELL, William John Raymond. b 15. St Aid Birkenhead 63. **d** 65 **p** 66. V Bury St Paul *Man* 68-77; rtd 80. *Dunromin, 18 Greenbrock Close, Bury, Lancs BL9 6NS* 0161-797 1513

EDGERTON, Ms Hilary Ann. b 66. R Holloway and Bedf New Coll Lon BSc88. Wycliffe Hall Ox BTh93. **d** 93 **p** 94. Par Dn S Cave and Ellerker w Broomfleet *York* 93-94; C from 94. *11 St Katherine's Road, South Cave, Brough, N Humberside HU15 2JB* Howden (01430) 421014

EDINBOROUGH, David. b 36. BA MEd. E Midl Min Tr Course. **d** 82 **p** 83. NSM Bramcote *S'well* from 82; Dioc Officer for NSMs from 89. *105A Derby Road, Beeston, Nottingham NG9 3GZ* Nottingham (0115) 925 1066

EDINBURGH, Bishop of. See HOLLOWAY, Most Rev Richard Frederick

EDINBURGH, Dean of. See MORRIS, Very Rev Timothy David

EDINBURGH, Provost of. See FORBES, Very Rev Graham John Thompson

EDIS, John Oram. b 26. ACIS50 ACP52 FCP89 CDipAF78 Open Univ BA81. Ox NSM Course 85. **d** 88 **p** 89. Hon Warden and Chapl E Ivor Hughes Educn Foundn from 88; NSM Gt Chesham *Ox* from 88. *21 Greenway, Chesham, Bucks HP5 2BW* Chesham (01494) 785815

EDMEADS, Andrew. b 53. Linc Th Coll 84. **d** 86 **p** 87. C Sholing *Win* 86-89; R Knights Enham from 89. *The Rectory, 1 Ryon Close, Knights Enham, Andover, Hants SP10 4DG* Andover (01264) 357032

EDMONDS, Bernard Bruce. b 10. Ch Coll Cam BA32 MA36. St Steph Ho Ox 36. **d** 37 **p** 38. V Caxton *Ely* 61-72; rtd 73; Perm to Offic *St Alb* from 74. *26 Bosmere Court, The Causeway, Needham Market, Ipswich IP6 8BQ* Needham Market (01449) 720238

EDMONDS (nee HARRIS), Mrs Catherine Elizabeth. b 52. Leic Coll of Educn CertEd73 ACP79 K Alfred's Coll Win 86 Basingstoke Coll of Tech 87. S Dios Minl Tr Scheme 91. **d** 95. NSM Basing *Win* from 95. *Woodside, Elms Road, Hook, Hants RG27 9DP* Hook (01256) 764486

EDMONDS, Clive. b 42. ACII. S'wark Ord Course 78. **d** 81 **p** 82. C Horsell *Guildf* 81-85; R Bisley and W End 85-92; RD Surrey Heath 90-92; R Haslemere from 92. *The Rectory, 7 Derby Road, Haslemere, Surrey GU27 2PA* Haslemere (01428) 644578

EDMONDS, Canon John Herbert. b 16. BNC Ox BA38 MA41. Cuddesdon Coll 39. **d** 40 **p** 41. C Northolt St Mary *Lon* 40-44; Chapl Woodbridge Sch Suffolk 44-47; Perm to Offic *Cant* 47-49 and 56-74 and from 80; Chapl K Sch Cant 47-56; Min Can Cant Cathl *Cant* 49-56; Hd Master K Jun Sch Cant 56-78; Hon Can Cant Cathl *Cant* 74-80. *15 Burgate, Canterbury, Kent CT1 2HG* Canterbury (01227) 455840

EDMONDS, Canon Joseph William. b 12. Bps' Coll Cheshunt 46. **d** 49 **p** 50. R Dickleburgh w Thelveton and Frenze *Nor* 69-80; RD Redenhall 73-88; R Dickleburgh w Thelveton w Frenze and Shimpling 80-81; rtd 81; Perm to Offic *Nor* 81-84; Hon Can Nor Cathl 84-89. *Rookery Nook, Plot 4, Sunnyside, Diss, Norfolk IP22 3DS* Diss (01379) 643369

EDMONDS, Richard Henry. b 11. Em Coll Cam BA34 MA39. Chich Th Coll 35. **d** 36 **p** 37. V Torquay St Jo *Ex* 67-74; R Cen Torquay 74-77; rtd 77; Lic to Offic *Ex* from 77. *Larksborough, Rectory Road, Newton Abbot, Devon TQ12 6AH* Newton Abbot (01626) 62857

EDMONDS, Sidney. b 20. Oak Hill Th Coll. **d** 58 **p** 59. Chapl HM Pris Liv 61-63; Dur 63-69; Parkhurst 69-74; Chapl HM Pris Reading 74-85; V Aldworth and Ashampstead *Ox* 74-85; rtd 85. *22 Sandlea Park, Wirral, Merseyside L48 0QF* 0151-625 6147

EDMONDS-SEAL, Dr John. b 34. FFARCS63 Lon Univ MB, BS58. Ox NSM Course DipTh90. **d** 90 **p** 91. NSM Ox St Aldate w St Matt *Ox* 90-94; NSM Ox St Aldate from 95. *Otway, Woodperry Road, Oxford OX3 9UY* Stanton St John (01865) 351582

EDMONDSON, Christopher Paul (Chris). b 50. Dur Univ BA71 MA81 St Jo Coll Dur DipTh72. **d** 73 **p** 74. C Kirkheaton *Wakef* 73-79; V Ovenden 79-86; Bp's Adv on Evang 81-86; P-in-c Bampton w Mardale *Carl* 86-92; Dioc Officer for Evang 86-92; V Shipley St Pet *Bradf* from 92. *The Vicarage, 2 Glenhurst Road, Shipley, W Yorkshire BD18 4DZ* Bradford (01274) 584488 or 583381

EDMONDSON, John James William. b 55. St Jo Coll Dur BA83 MA91. Cranmer Hall Dur 80. **d** 83 **p** 84. C Gee Cross *Ches* 83-86; C Camberley St Paul *Guildf* 86-88; TV 88-90; V Foxton w Gumley and Laughton and Lubenham *Leic* 90-94; R Bexhill St Mark *Chich* from 94. *St Mark's Rectory, 11 Coverdale Avenue, Bexhill-on-Sea, E Sussex TN39 4TY* Bexhill-on-Sea (01424) 843733

EDMONDSON, Canon Norman Ross. b 16. St Jo Coll Dur BA39. **d** 39 **p** 40. R Crook *Dur* 55-72; RD Stanhope 61-72; Hon Can Dur Cathl 66-91; R Sedgefield 72-84; RD Sedgefield 78-84; rtd 84. *2 Spring Lane, Sedgefield, Stockton-on-Tees, Cleveland TS21 2DG* Sedgefield (01740) 20629

EDMONTON, Area Bishop of. See MASTERS, Rt Rev Brian John

EDMUND, Brother. See BLACKIE, Richard Footner

EDMUNDS, Andrew Charles. b 57. Whitelands Coll Lon BEd80 Croydon Coll DASS83 CQSW83. Oak Hill NSM Course 87. **d** 89 **p** 90. NSM Hawkwell *Chelmsf* 89-95; C Torquay St Matthias, St Mark and H Trin *Ex* from 95. *St Martin, 9 Lower Warberry Road, Torquay, Devon TQ1 1QP* Torquay (01803) 212872

EDMUNDS, Eric John. b 39. Univ of Wales TCert60. W Midl Minl Tr Course 87. **d** 90 **p** 91. NSM Brewood *Lich* 90-93; Chapl R Wolv Sch 91-92; R Llanerch Aeron w Ciliau Aeron and Dihewyd etc *St D* from 93. *The Rectory, Ciliau Aeron, Lampeter, Dyfed SA48 7SG* Aeron (01570) 470901

EDMUNDS, Gerald. b 12. ACIB. Glouc Th Course 72. **d** 72 **p** 73. NSM Tewkesbury w Walton Cardiff *Glouc* 72-82; Perm to Offic from 82. *29 Manor Park, Tewkesbury, Glos GL20 8BQ* Tewkesbury (01684) 294150

EDMUNDSON, Thomas. b 09. Oak Hill Th Coll 58. **d** 59 **p** 60. V Halliwell St Paul *Man* 61-75; rtd 75; Lic to Offic *Blackb* from 76. *10 The Hayels, Blackburn BB1 9HZ* Blackburn (01254) 246408

EDNEY, William Henry. b 13. Birm Univ BA34. Qu Coll Birm 77. **d** 78 **p** 79. Hon C Cov St Geo *Cov* 78-85; Perm to Offic from 85. *20 Loudon Avenue, Coventry CV6 1JH* Coventry (01203) 592168

EDSON, Ven Michael (Mike). b 42. Birm Univ BSc64 Leeds Univ BA71. Coll of Resurr Mirfield 69. **d** 72 **p** 73. C Barnstaple St Pet w H Trin *Ex* 72-77; TV Barnstaple and Goodleigh 77-79; TV Barnstaple, Goodleigh and Landkey 79-82; V Roxbourne St Andr *Lon* 82-89; AD Harrow 85-89; P-in-c S Harrow St Paul 86-89; Warden Lee Abbey 89-94; Lic to Offic *Ex* 89-94; Adn Leic from 94. *13 Stoneygate Avenue, Leicester LE2 3HE* Leicester (0116) 270 4441 Fax 270 1091

EDWARD, Brother. See LEES-SMITH, Christopher John

EDWARDS, Preb Albert. b 20. Univ of Wales (Lamp) BA48. St Mich Coll Llan 48. **d** 50 **p** 51. V Tamworth *Lich* 65-86; RD Tamworth 69-81; Preb Lich Cathl 73-86; rtd 86; Perm to Offic *Lich* from 86. *Broom Cottage, Mount Street, Welshpool, Powys SY21 7LW* Welshpool (01938) 4008

EDWARDS, Aled. b 55. Univ of Wales (Lamp) BA77. Trin Coll Bris 77. **d** 79 **p** 80. C Glanogwen *Ban* 79-82; V Llandinorwig w Penisa'r-waen 82-85; R Mellteyrn w Botwnnog and Llandygwnnin etc 85-93; V Cardiff Dewi Sant *Llan* from 93. *Hafod-Ion, 51 Heath Park Avenue, Cardiff CF4 3RF* Cardiff (01222) 751418

EDWARDS, Andrew Jonathan Hugo. b 56. Ex Univ BA78. Sarum & Wells Th Coll BTh93. **d** 93 **p** 94. C Honiton, Gittisham, Combe Raleigh, Monkton etc *Ex* from 93. *55 Church Hill, Honiton, Devon EX14 8DB* Honiton (01404) 44371

EDWARDS, Andrew Colin. b 55. ACA81 Pemb Coll Cam BA77 MA80. St Mich Coll Llan BD89. **d** 89 **p** 90. C Newport St Paul *Mon* 89-91; C Newport St Woolos 91-93; Min Can St Woolos Cathl 91-93; P-in-c Ynysddu 93-95; TV Mynyddislwyn from 95. *The Vicarage, Commercial Road, Cwmfelinfach, Newport, Gwent NP1 7HW* Blackwood (01495) 200257

EDWARDS, Andrew David. b 42. Tyndale Hall Bris 67. **d** 70 **p** 71. C Blackpool Ch Ch *Blackb* 70-73; C W Teignmouth *Ex* 73-76; P-in-c Ilfracombe SS Phil and Jas 76-85; C-in-c Lundy Is 79-89; V Ilfracombe SS Phil and Jas w W Down 85-89; TV Canford Magna *Sarum* from 89. *The Vicarage, 11 Plantagenet Crescent, Bournemouth BH11 9PL* Bournemouth (01202) 573872

EDWARDS, Andrew James. b 54. York Univ BA76. Wycliffe Hall Ox 77. **d** 80 **p** 81. C Beckenham St Jo *Roch* 80-83; C Luton Ch Ch 83-87; V Skelmersdale Ch at Cen *Liv* 87-95; V Netherton from 95. *The Vicarage, 183 St Oswald's Lane, Bootle, Merseyside L30 5SR* 0151-525 1882

EDWARDS, Canon Arthur John. b 42. Qu Mary Coll Lon BA64 MPhil66. St Mich Coll Llan 66. **d** 68 **p** 69. C Newport St Woolos *Mon* 68-71; V Llantarnam 71-74; Chapl The Bp of Llan High Sch 74-78; V Griffithstown *Mon* 78-86; Dioc Dir RE from 86; R Cwmbran 86-95; Hon Can St Woolos Cathl 88-91; Can from 91; V Caerleon from 95. *The Vicarage, Caerleon, Newport, Gwent NP6 1AZ* Caerleon (01633) 420248

EDWARDS, Canon Carol Rosemary. b 46. Lon Univ DipTh76. Trin Coll Bris 74. **dss** 81 **d** 87 **p** 94. Hengrove *Bris* 81-82; Filton 82-85; Brislington St Chris 85-87; D-in-c 87-94; P-in-c from 94; Hon Can Bris Cathl from 93. *The Vicarage, 24 Hampstead Road, Bristol BS4 3HJ* Bristol (0117) 977 3670

EDWARDS, Charles Grayson. b 37. Macalester Coll (USA) BSc59. Ripon Hall Ox 64. **d** 66 **p** 67. C Bletchley *Ox* 66-68; C Ware St Mary *St Alb* 68-73; TV Basingstoke *Win* 73-80; P-in-c Sandford w Upton Hellions *Ex* 80-82; R 82-94; Perm to Offic from 95. *The Peak, Crediton, Devon EX17 2EU* Crediton (01363) 772530

EDWARDS, Cyril Arthur. b 28. St Jo Coll York TCert47. Ripon Hall Ox 54. **d** 56 **p** 57. Lic to Offic *Bris* from 61; Chapl & Hd of RE St Mary Redcliffe & Temple Sch 65-86; Sen Master 65-86; rtd 92. *1A Colston Parade, Bristol BS1 6RA* Bristol (0117) 926 2770

EDWARDS, David Arthur. b 26. Wadh Coll Ox BA50 MA51. Wycliffe Hall Ox 50. **d** 52 **p** 53. V Yardley St Edburgha *Birm* 65-73; Org Sec (Dios Blackb, Carl and Man) CECS 73-78; R Man Resurr *Man* 78-81; V Lorton and Loweswater w Buttermere *Carl* 81-87; USPG 87-92; Malaysia 87-92; rtd 92. *Glentarkie, Lochmaben, Lockerbie, Dumfriesshire DG11 1SB* Parkgate (0138786) 231

EDWARDS, David Henry Oswald. b 16. St D Coll Lamp BA38. **d** 41 **p** 42. C Fishguard w Llanychar *St D* 71-81; rtd 81. *Walmer House, West Street, Fishguard, Dyfed SA65 9DF* Fishguard (01348) 873329

EDWARDS, Very Rev David Lawrence. b 29. OBE95. Magd Coll Ox BA52 MA56 Lambeth Hon DD90. Westcott Ho Cam 53. **d** 54 **p** 55. Dean K Coll Cam 66-70; Six Preacher Cant Cathl *Cant* 69-76; Can Westmr Abbey 70-78; R Westmr St Marg 70-78; Chapl to Speaker of Ho of Commons 72-78; Sub-Dean Westmr 74-78; Chmn Chr Aid 71-78; Dean Nor 78-83; Provost S'wark 83-94; rtd 94. *19 Crispstead Lane, Winchester SO23 9SF* Winchester (01962) 862597

EDWARDS, Ms Diana Clare. b 56. SRN77 RSCN81 Nottm Univ BTh86. Linc Th Coll 83. **dss** 86 **d** 87 **p** 94. S Wimbledon H Trin and St Pet *S'wark* 86-87; Par Dn 87-90; Par Dn Lingfield and Crowhurst 90-94; C from 94; Chapl St Pier's Hosp Sch Lingfield from 90. *Old Star Flat, Church Road, Lingfield, Surrey RH7 6AH* Lingfield (01342) 835589

EDWARDS, Dudley James Milne. b 15. AKC38. **d** 38 **p** 39. V Mackworth St Fran *Derby* 68-75; R Ashwick w Oakhill and Binegar *B & W* 75-80; rtd 80; Perm to Offic *B & W* from 81. *Trefechan, The Street, Draycott, Cheddar, Somerset BS27 3TH* Cheddar (01934) 743573

EDWARDS, Canon Emrys Llewelyn. b 14. St D Coll Lamp BA37. **d** 39 **p** 41. V Llanelli Ch Ch *St D* 60-72; R Llanbadarn Fawr 72-79; Can St D Cathl 72-79; rtd 79. *Llys-y-Coed, New Road, New Quay, Dyfed SA45 9SB* New Quay (01545) 560143

EDWARDS, Frances Mary. b 39. RSCN61 SRN64. St Mich Ho Ox CertRK68 Cranmer Hall Dur IDC71. **d** 92 **p** 94. NSM Skerton St Chad *Blackb* from 92; Asst Chapl R Albert Hosp Lanc from 92. *17 Church Brow, Bolton le Sands, Carnforth, Lancs LA5 8DY* Hest Bank (01524) 822229

EDWARDS, Canon Geoffrey Lewis. b 14. Lon Univ BD39 AKC39. **d** 39 **p** 40. V Mill End *St Alb* 47-72; V W Hyde St Thos 47-72; RD Watford 68-70; RD Rickmansworth 70-72; V Hockerill 72-84; RD Bishop's Stortford 74-84; Hon Can St Alb 76-84; rtd 84; Perm to Offic *Heref* 84-94. *91 Early Road, Witney, Oxon OX8 6ET* Witney (01993) 704342

EDWARDS, Geraint Wyn. b 47. St D Coll Lamp DipTh70. **d** 71 **p** 72. C Llandudno *Ban* 71-73; C Ban St Mary 73-74; V Penisarwaen and Llanddeiniolen 74-77; V Llandinorwig w Penisarwaun and Llanddeiniolen 77-78; R Llanfechell w Bodewryd w Rhosbeirio etc from 78; RD Twrcelyn from 94. *The Rectory, Llanfechell, Amlwch, Gwynedd LL68 0RE* Cemaes Bay (01407) 710356

EDWARDS, Canon Gerald Lalande. b 30. Bris Univ MEd72. Glouc Th Course 75. **d** 76 **p** 76. NSM Cheltenham All SS *Glouc* 76-79; NSM Cheltenham St Mich from 79; Hon Can Glouc Cathl from 91. *26 Monica Drive, Cheltenham, Glos GL50 4NQ* Cheltenham (01242) 516863

EDWARDS, Gordon Henry. b 33. FRICS60 FCILA67 FCIArb72 Reading Univ PhD87. Ripon Coll Cuddesdon 89. **d** 90 **p** 91. Hon C Sherston Magna, Easton Grey, Luckington etc *Bris* 90-92; Hon C Yatton Keynell from 92. *The Old Vicarage, Sherston, Malmesbury, Wilts SN16 0LR* Malmesbury (01666) 840405

EDWARDS, Canon Graham Arthur. b 32. St D Coll Lamp 56. **d** 61 **p** 62. R Castlemartin w Warren and Angle etc *St D* 69-77; V St Clears w Llangynin and Llanddowror 77-83; CF (TAVR) 78-94; V St Clears w Llangynin and Llanddowror etc *St D* 83-94; Can St D Cathl 90-94; rtd 94. *Caswell, Station Road, St Clears, Carmarthen, Dyfed SA33 4BX* St Clears (01994) 230342

EDWARDS, Graham Charles. b 40. Qu Coll Birm 80. **d** 82 **p** 83. C Baswich (or Berkswich) *Lich* 82-86; C Tamworth 86-88; R Hertf St Andr *St Alb* from 88. *St Andrew's Rectory, 43 North Road, Hertford SG14 1LZ* Hertford (01992) 582726

EDWARDS, Harold James. b 50. Lon Univ CertEd72. Ridley Hall Cam 84 Qu Coll Birm 78. **d** 81 **p** 82. NSM The Quinton *Birm* 81-84; C Highters Heath 84-85; V Llanwddyn and Llanfihangel and Llwydiarth *St As* 85-88; V Ford *Heref* from 88; V Alberbury w Cardeston from 88. *The Vicarage, Ford, Shrewsbury SY5 9LZ* Shrewsbury (01743) 850254 Fax as telephone

EDWARDS, Harry Steadman. b 37. St Aid Birkenhead 64. **d** 66 **p** 67. Hon C Handsworth St Jas *Birm* 66-83; Hon C Curdworth w Castle Vale 83-85; P-in-c Small Heath St Greg 85-88; V High Crompton *Man* from 88. *St Mary's Vicarage, 18 Rushcroft Road, Shaw, Oldham OL2 7AA* Shaw (01706) 847455

EDWARDS, Helen Glynne. See WEBB, Mrs Helen Glynne

EDWARDS, Very Rev Henry St John. b 30. Southn Univ DipEd. Ripon Hall Ox. **d** 59 **p** 60. Australia from 62; Dean Grafton 69-79; rtd 95. *PO Box 416, Dorrigo, NSW, Australia 2453*

EDWARDS, Henry Victor (Harry). b 48. AKC71 Open Univ BA85. St Aug Coll Cant 72. **d** 73 **p** 74. C W Leigh CD *Portsm* 73-77; V Cosham 77-84; V Reydon *St E* 84-92; P-in-c Walberswick w Blythburgh 86-92; Chapl St Felix Sch Southwold from 86; Chapl Blythburgh Hosp from 86; V Blythburgh w Reydon *St E* from 92. *The Vicarage, Wangford Road, Reydon, Southwold, Suffolk IP18 6PZ* Southwold (01502) 722192

EDWARDS, Herbert Joseph. b 29. Nottm Univ BA51. Wells Th Coll 54. **d** 56 **p** 57. C Leic St Pet *Leic* 56-61; C-in-c Broom Leys CD 61-65; V Broom Leys 65-68; Lect Lich Th Coll 68-71; Rhodesia 71-79; Botswana 74-75; V Bloxwich *Lich* 80-84; R Asfordby *Leic* 84-92; R N w S Kilworth and Misterton from 92. *The Rectory, Dag Lane, North Kilworth, Lutterworth, Leics LE17 6HA* Market Harborough (01858) 880436

EDWARDS, Canon James Frederick. b 36. ALCD62. **d** 62 **p** 63. C Kenwyn *Truro* 62-68; V Tuckingmill 68-76; V St Columb Minor and St Colan from 76; RD Pydar 84-93; Hon Can Truro Cathl from 92. *The Vicarage, Parkenbutts, St Columb Minor, Newquay, Cornwall TR7 3HE* Newquay (01637) 873496

EDWARDS, Mrs Jill Kathleen. b 48. Man Univ BA69 Golds Coll Lon CQSW72 Lon Univ DipRS85. S'wark Ord Course 90. **d** 93. NSM Grays Thurrock *Chelmsf* from 93. *53 Bradleigh Avenue, Grays, Essex RM17 5RJ* Grays Thurrock (01375) 372887

EDWARDS, John Gregory. b 29. Univ of Wales BA49 MA53. St Steph Ho Ox 64. **d** 66 **p** 67. C Ealing Ch the Sav *Lon* 66-70; C Greenford H Cross 70-75; P-in-c Poundstock *Truro* 75-82; R Week St Mary w Poundstock and Whitstone 82-94; rtd 94. *8 Vestry Drive, Exeter EX2 8FG* Exeter (01392) 432603

EDWARDS, Jonathan Guy. b 63. Bris Univ BA85. Ridley Hall Cam BA93. **d** 94 **p** 95. C Preston Plucknett *B & W* from 94. *5 Lime Kilns, Yeovil, Somerset BA21 3RW* Yeovil (01935) 22553

EDWARDS, Canon Jonathan Gilbert. b 19. Keble Coll Ox BA41 MA50. Linc Th Coll 41. **d** 43 **p** 44. R Gt Bookham *Guildf* 67-80; RD Leatherhead 77-80; Hon Can Guildf Cathl 78-85; V Bramley 80-81; V Grafham 80-81; RD Cranleigh 81-85; V Bramley and Grafham 81-85; rtd 85. *Cyprus Cottage, Bath Road, Sturminster Newton, Dorset DT10 1DU* Sturminster Newton (01258) 72933

EDWARDS, Kenneth Barnsley. b 19. Birm Univ BSc48. Wells Th Coll 70. **d** 72 **p** 73. C Furze Platt *Ox* 72-74; C Henley 74-77; P-in-c Hatch Beauchamp w Beercrocombe *B & W* 77-80; P-in-c W Hatch 77-80; P-in-c Curry Mallet 79-80; C Ex St Thos and Em *Ex* 81; Perm to Offic *B & W* 82-87; R Tollard Royal w Farnham, Gussage St Michael etc *Sarum* 87-89; rtd 89. *99 Periton Lane, Minehead, Somerset TA24 8EA* Minehead (01643) 704323

EDWARDS, Leigh Cameron. b 17. St Cath Soc Ox BA38 MA42. St Steph Ho Ox 38. **d** 40 **p** 41. C Roath St Marg *Llan* 40-43; P-in-c Llangeview *Mon* 43-46; P-in-c Gwernesney 43-46; C Bournemouth St Mary *Win* 46-49; V Southn St Jas 49-54; C Win St Jo cum Winnall 54-58; R Carshalton *S'wark* from 58. *The Rectory, 2 Talbot Road, Carshalton, Surrey SM5 3BS* 0181-647 2366

EDWARDS, Leslie. b 27. Univ of Wales (Ban) DipTh54. St D Coll Lamp 54. **d** 55 **p** 56. R Halkyn and Caerfallwch *St As* 66-92; P-in-c Rhesycae 74-92; rtd 92. *23 Troed-y-Fenlli, Llanbedr Dyffryn Clwyd, Ruthin, Clwyd LL15 1BQ* Ruthin (01824) 703922

EDWARDS, Malcolm Ralph. b 27. Man Univ 49. Cranmer Hall Dur 57. **d** 59 **p** 60. R Longsight St Jo *Man* 64-70; V Halliwell St Thos 70-81; V Milnrow 81-92; rtd 92. *20 Upper Lees Drive, Westhoughton, Bolton BL5 3UE* Westhoughton (01942) 813279

EDWARDS, Mark Anthony. b 61. Moorlands Bible Coll DipThMin86 St Jo Coll Dur CTMin95. **d** 95. C Ulverston St Mary w H Trin *Carl* from 95. *Church House, 18 Church Walk, Ulverston, Cumbria LA12 7EN* Ulverston (01229) 586133

EDWARDS, Michael Norman William. b 34. St Paul's Grahamstown 62. **d** 63 **p** 65. S Africa 63-81; Tristan da Cunha 81-83; R Aston-on-Trent and Weston-on-Trent *Derby* 84-87; V Derby St Thos 87-95; P-in-c Blackwell from 95. *St Werburgh's Vicarage, Church Hill, Blackwell, Alfreton, Derbyshire DE55 5HN* Ripley (01773) 863242

EDWARDS, Nicholas John. b 53. UEA BA75 Fitzw Coll Cam BA77 MA80. Westcott Ho Cam 75. **d** 78 **p** 79. C Kirkby *Liv* 78-81; V Cantril Farm 81-87; V Hale 87-94; R Chingford SS Pet and Paul *Chelmsf* from 94; Asst RD Waltham Forest from 94. *The Rectory, 2 The Green Walk, London E4 7ER* 0181-529 1291

EDWARDS, Mrs Nita Mary. b 50. Univ of Wales (Ban) BD72 Nottm Univ PGCE73. Cranmer Hall Dur DMinlStuds93. **d** 93 **p** 94. C Ormesby *York* from 93. *9 Lobelia Close, Middlesbrough, Cleveland TS7 9PJ* Middlesbrough (01642) 315850

EDWARDS, Mrs Patricia Anne. b 52. E Midl Min Tr Course 76. dss 79 **d** 87 **p** 94. Hon Par Dn Clifton *S'well* 87-91; NSM Edwalton from 91. *148 Wilford Road, Ruddington, Nottingham NG11 6FB* Nottingham (0115) 984 3402

EDWARDS, Peter Clive. b 50. Lon Univ BA72. St Steph Ho Ox 83. **d** 85 **p** 86. C Lee St Aug *S'wark* 85-90; V Salfords from 90. *The Vicarage, Honeycrock Lane, Redhill RH1 5DF* Redhill (01737) 762232

EDWARDS, Canon Peter John Smallman. b 48. Univ of Wales (Ban) BD72 MTh75. Linc Th Coll 72. **d** 73 **p** 74. C Llanelli *St D* 73-76; Prec St Andr Cathl Inverness *Mor* 76-77; R Walton W w Talbenny and Haroldston W *St D* 77-81; P-in-c Invergordon St Ninian *Mor* 81-86; I 86-89; Prin Moray Dioc Ord Course 81-86; Can St Andr Cathl Inverness 81-89; Hon Can St Andr Cathl Inverness from 90; Offg Chapl RAF 82-88; Syn Clerk *Mor* 85-89; V Caldicot *Mon* from 89. *The Vicarage, 39 Church Road, Caldicot, Newport, Gwent NP6 4HT* Caldicot (01291) 420221

EDWARDS, Canon Philip John. b 28. Lon Univ MRCS51 LRCP51. Chich Th Coll 58. **d** 60 **p** 61. C Mayfield *Chich* 67-71; V Haywards Heath St Rich 71-91; Can and Preb Chich Cathl 84-91; rtd 91. *21 Haywards Road, Haywards Heath, W Sussex RH16 4HX* Haywards Heath (01444) 457880

EDWARDS, Philip Osbert Clifford. b 11. St Jo Coll Ox BA33 MA47. Wycliffe Hall Ox 35. **d** 35 **p** 36. Chapl Algarve *Eur* 74-77; rtd 77; Perm to Offic *Heref* 86-92. *8 The Old Orchard, Nash Meadows, South Warnborough, Hants RG25 1RJ* Basingstoke (01256) 862960

EDWARDS, Phillip Gregory. b 52. MSOSc90 Lon Univ BSc73 Imp Coll Lon ARCS73. Qu Coll Birm DipTh80. **d** 81 **p** 82. C Lillington *Cov* 81-85; P-in-c Cov St Alb 85-86; TV Cov E from 86. *St Alban's Vicarage, Mercer Avenue, Coventry CV2 4PQ* Coventry (01203) 452493

EDWARDS, Raymond Lewis. Keble Coll Ox BA46 MA47. St Deiniol's Hawarden 69. **d** 70 **p** 71. Prin Educn Cen Penmaenmawr 56-81; Hon C Dwygyfylchi (or Penmaenmawr) *Ban* 70-81; P-in-c Llandwrog 81-82; V 82-90; Dioc Dir of Educn from 84; rtd 90. *Dulyn View, 23 Rhiwlas Road, Talysarn, Penygroes, Gwynedd LL54 6HU* Penygroes (01286) 881090

EDWARDS, Rhys Meurig. b 16. St D Coll Lamp BA37. **d** 39 **p** 41. V Kenley *S'wark* 55-74; V Kingston Vale St Jo 74-84; rtd 84; Perm to Offic *Chich* from 84. *5 Paddock Close, Fernhurst, Haslemere, Surrey GU27 3JZ* Haslemere (01428) 656695

EDWARDS, Roger Brian. b 41. Sarum & Wells Th Coll 87. **d** 89 **p** 90. C Wellington and Distr *B & W* 89-92; V Hursley and Ampfield *Win* from 92. *The Vicarage, Knapp Lane, Ampfield, Romsey, Hants SO5 9BT* Braishfield (01794) 368291

EDWARDS, Canon Ronald William. b 20. Kelham Th Coll 37. **d** 43 **p** 44. Australia from 62; Adn of the Coast 71-74; Dean Bathurst 74-77; Can Perth 79-88; rtd 88. *2/31 Park Street, Como, W Australia 6152* Perth (9) 450-6272

EDWARDS, Rowland Thomas. b 62. **d** 88 **p** 89. C Llangiwg *S & B* 88-90; C Morriston 90-91; V Llangorse, Cathedine, Llanfihangel Talyllyn etc from 91. *Llangorse Vicarage, Brecon, Powys LD3 7UG* Llangorse (0187484) 298

EDWARDS, Dr Ruth Blanche. b 39. Girton Coll Cam BA61 MA65 PhD68 Aber Coll of Educn CertEd75. Ab Dioc Tr Course 77. **d** 87 **p** 94. Lect Aber Univ *Ab* 77-90; Sen Lect from 90; NSM Aber St Jas 87-88; NSM Aber St Jo from 88. *39 Woodstock Road, Aberdeen AB2 4EX* Aberdeen (01224) 314734

EDWARDS, Stephen. b 44. S'wark Ord Course. **d** 82 **p** 83. C Benhilton *S'wark* 82-86; P-in-c Clapham Ch Ch and St Jo 86-87; TV Clapham TM 87-94; Chapl HM Pris Wormwood Scrubs from 94. *HM Prison Wormwood Scrubs, PO Box 757, Du Cane Road, London W12 0AE* 0181-743 0311 Fax 749 5655

EDWARDS, Stephen Zachary. b 04. Down Coll Cam BA30 MA33. **d** 31 **p** 32. R Siddington w Preston *Glouc* 65-69; rtd 70. *38 Richmond Road, Pelynt, Looe, Cornwall PL13 2NH* Lanreath (01503) 220788

EDWARDS, Dr Steven Charles. b 58. Sheff Poly HND80 Lanc Univ BSc82 PhD86. Linc Th Coll CMinlStuds94. **d** 94 **p** 95. C Bradshaw *Man* from 94. *5 Hilmarton Close, Bolton BL2 3HJ* Bolton (01204) 305442

EDWARDS, Stuart. b 46. Lon Univ DipTh70 Lanc Univ BA73. Kelham Th Coll 66. **d** 71 **p** 72. C Skerton St Luke *Blackb* 71-76; C Ribbleton 76-80; TV 80-82; V Blackb St Mich w St Jo and H Trin 82-91; V Blackpool H Cross from 91; RD Blackpool from 93. *Holy Cross Vicarage, Central Drive, Blackpool FY1 6LA* Blackpool (01253) 341263

EDWARDS, Mrs Susan. b 54. R Holloway Coll Lon BSc75 SS Hild & Bede Coll Dur PGCE76. Qu Coll Birm 78. dss 81 **d** 87 **p** 94. Lillington *Cov* 81-85; Cov E 85-87; C 87-91; Par Dn 91-94; C from 94. *St Alban's Vicarage, Mercer Avenue, Coventry CV2 4PQ* Coventry (01203) 452493

EDWARDS, Mrs Susan Diane. b 48. St Alb Minl Tr Scheme 86 Cranmer Hall Dur 91. **d** 92 **p** 94. Par Dn Borehamwood *St Alb* 92-94; C from 94. *16 Bullhead Road, Borehamwood, Herts WD6 1HS*

EDWARDS, Very Rev Thomas Erwyd Pryse. b 33. Univ of Wales (Lamp) BA56. St Mich Coll Llan 56. **d** 58 **p** 59. C Llanbeblig w Caernarfon *Ban* 58-63; Chapl Asst St Geo Hosp Lon 63-66; Lic to Offic *S'wark* 63-66; Chapl K Coll Hosp Lon 66-72; R Penmon and Llangoed w Llanfihangel Dinsylwy *Ban* 72-75; V Llandysilio and Llandegfan 75-81; V Glanadda 81-85; Chapl St D Hosp Ban 81-84; Chapl Gwynedd Hosp Ban 84-86; V Caerhun w Llangelynnin w Llanbedr-y-Cennin *Ban* 86-88; Dean Ban from 88; Hon Can Ban Cathl from 88; R Ban 88-93. *The Deanery, Cathedral Precinct, Bangor, Gwynedd LL57 1LH* Bangor (01248) 370693 or 353983 Fax 353882

EDWARDS, Thomas Harold David. b 16. Jes Coll Ox BA38 MA46. Westmr Coll Cam 38 St Aug Coll Cant 58. **d** 58 **p** 59. V Bledlow Ox 64-73; RD Aylesbury 72-77; R Bledlow w Saunderton and Horsenden 73-89; rtd 89; Perm to Offic *Heref* 89-95. *22 St Anne's Grove, Knowle, Solihull, W Midlands B93 9JB* Solihull (0564) 772593

EDWARDS, Thomas Victor. b 22. Univ of Wales (Lamp) BA52 LTh54 Birm Univ MA57. **d** 54 **p** 55. V Oxley *Lich* 65-71; R Kingsley 71-90; rtd 90. *14 Pastoral Close, Madeley, Crewe CW3 9PU* Stoke-on-Trent (01782) 751502

EDWARDS, Walter Harry. b 12. Launde Abbey 59. **d** 60 **p** 61. R Dunkeld *St And* 70-72; rtd 80. *Dail an t-Sagairt, Calvine, Pitlochry, Perthshire PH18 5UB*

EDWARDS, William Emrys. b 13. Univ of Wales BA35. St Mich Coll Llan 35. **d** 36 **p** 37. Asst Master Caernarvon Gr Sch 52-72; V Llandwrog *Ban* 72-78; rtd 78; Lic to Offic *Ban* from 78. *Menai, Campbell Road, Caernarfon, Gwynedd LL55 1BG* Caernarfon (01286) 673115

EDWARDSON, David Roger Hately. b 54. Stirling Univ BSc79 DipEd79 Edin Univ BD91. Edin Th Coll 88. **d** 91 **p** 92. C Edin St Jo *Edin* 91-93; P-in-c Kelso from 93. *The Rectory, Forestfield, Kelso, Roxburghshire TD5 7BX* Kelso (01573) 224163

EDWARDSON, Joseph Philip. b 28. Dur Univ BA52 Leeds Univ PGCE53. Wells Th Coll 61. **d** 63 **p** 64. V Egremont St Jo *Ches* 66-72; V Eastham 72-81; V Poulton 81-94; rtd 94. *Keppler, 38 Hazel Grove, Irby, Wirral, Merseyside L61 4UZ*

EDY, Robert James (Bob). b 48. Southn Univ BA70 CertEd71. Ox Min Course CBTS93. **d** 93 **p** 94. Dep Hd Master Henry Box Sch Witney from 90; NSM Ducklington *Ox* from 93. *4 Elm Close, Witney, Oxon OX8 5BT* Witney (01993) 705376

EDYE, Ian Murray. b 21. K Coll Lon BD AKC. S'wark Ord Course 66. **d** 69 **p** 70. NSM E Grinstead St Swithun *Chich* from 69. *Thrush Field, Coombe Hill Road, East Grinstead, W Sussex RH19 4LY* East Grinstead (01342) 323157

EFEMEY, Raymond Frederick. b 28. Ball Coll Ox BA51 MA64. Cuddesdon Coll 51. **d** 53 **p** 54. V Dudley St Thos and St Luke *Worc* 69-75; Hon C Stretford All SS *Man* 76-82; SSF from 81; P-in-c Weaste *Man* 82-87; W 87-93; rtd 93. *20 Groby Road, Chorlton-cum-Hardy, Manchester M21 1DD* 0161-860 5416

EGERTON, George. b 28. S'wark Ord Course 70. **d** 73 **p** 74. NSM Shere *Guildf* 73-94; Perm to Offic from 94. *6 Heathrow, Gomshall, Guildford, Surrey GU5 9QD* Shere (01483) 202549

EGERTON, Ronald. b 14. St D Coll Lamp BA37 St Mich Coll Llan 37. **d** 38 **p** 39. R Rhydycroesau *Lich* 63-77; R Selattyn 63-77; R Chewton Mendip w Ston Easton, Litton etc *B & W* 77-80; rtd 80; Perm to Offic *Lich* from 80. *10 Rosehill Close, Whittington, Oswestry, Shropshire SY11 4DY* Oswestry (01691) 662453

EGGERT, Max Alexander. b 43. AKC67 Birkb Coll Lon BSc74 Cen Lon Poly MA87 CPsychol90. **d** 67 **p** 68. C Whitton St Aug *Lon* 67-69; Hon C Hackney 72-74; Hon C Llantwit Major *Llan* 74-76; NSM Haywards Heath St Rich *Chich* 78-93; Lic to Offic from 93. *94 High Street, Lindfield, Haywards Heath, W Sussex RH16 2HP* Lindfield (01444) 483057

EGGINGTON, William Charles. b 10. Lon Univ BSc31. Coll of Resurr Mirfield 32. **d** 34 **p** 35. V Barnet Vale St Mark *St Alb* 60-80; rtd 80; Perm to Offic *St Alb* from 80. *The Rectory, Pirton Road, Holwell, Hitchin, Herts SG5 3SS* Hitchin (01462) 712307

EGLIN, Ian. b 55. St Jo Coll Dur BA76. Coll of Resurr Mirfield 77. **d** 79 **p** 80. C Cov St Mary *Cov* 79-83; TV Kingsthorpe w St Dav Northn *Pet* 83-87; Chapl RN from 87. *Directorate Gen, RN Chapl Services, Room 203, Victory Building, HM Naval Base, Portsmouth PO1 3LS* Portsmouth (01705) 727903 Fax 727112

EICHELMAN, Canon George Charles. b 14. Roch Univ NY BA37. **d** 40 **p** 40. USA 40-78; rtd 79; Hon C Costa Blanca *Eur* 83-86; Hon Can Gib Cathl 85-86. *6C Marisol Park, Calpe, Alicante, Spain*

EKE, Canon Robert Foord Stansfield. b 17. K Coll Lon BD39 AKC39. Ely Th Coll 40. **d** 40 **p** 41. St Kitts-Nevis 62-72; V Alton St Lawr *Win* 72-89; Bp's Ecum Officer 80-82; Hon Can Win Cathl 82-89; RD Alton 82-89; rtd 89; Perm to Offic *Chich* from 89. *77 Hangleton Way, Hove, E Sussex BN3 8AF* Brighton (01273) 421443

EKIN, Tom Croker. b 29. Linc Th Coll 59. **d** 60 **p** 61. R Ilmington w Stretton-on-Fosse *Cov* 63-72; S Africa 72-77; R Moreton-in-Marsh w Batsford *Glouc* 77-83; R Moreton-in-Marsh w Batsford, Todenham etc 83-94; rtd 95. *St Mark's House, Englefield, Reading RG7 5EN* Reading (01734) 302227

ELBOURNE, Keith Marshall. b 46. Nottm Univ BTh74 Lon Univ BD76. Westmr Past Foundn DAPC89 St Jo Coll Nottm 70. **d** 74 **p** 75. C Romford Gd Shep Collier Row *Chelmsf* 74-78; C Victoria Docks St Luke 78-81; P-in-c 81-92; V Walthamstow St Pet from 92. *121 Forest Rise, London E17 3PW* 0181-520 3854

ELBOURNE, Raymond Nigel Wilson. b 43. Dur Univ BA66. Linc Th Coll 67. **d** 69 **p** 70. C Liscard St Mary *Ches* 69-72; V Hattersley 72-77; R Odd Rode from 77. *Odd Rode Rectory, Church Lane, Scholar Green, Cheshire ST7 3QN* Alsager (01270) 882195

ELBOURNE, Timothy (Tim). b 60. Selw Coll Cam BA81 PGCE82 MA85. Westcott Ho Cam 84. **d** 86 **p** 87. C Tottenham H Trin *Lon* 86-88; Chapl York Univ *York* 88-94; P-in-c Thorp Arch w Walton from 94. *The Vicarage, Church Causeway, Thorp Arch, Wetherby, W Yorkshire LS23 7AE* Boston Spa (01937) 842430

ELCOAT, Canon George Alastair. b 22. Qu Coll Birm. **d** 51 **p** 52. V Chatton w Chillingham *Newc* 62-70; V Sugley 70-81; RD Newc W 77-81; Hon Can Newc Cathl 79-91; P-in-c Tweedmouth 81-87; V 87-91; RD Norham 82-91; Miss to Seamen 81-91; Chapl to The Queen 82-93; rtd 91. *42 Windsor Crescent, Berwick-upon-Tweed, Northd TD15 1NT* Berwick-upon-Tweed (01289) 331936

ELDER, Andrew John. b 49. Sunderland Poly BSc72 MSc76. NE Ord Course 91. **d** 94. NSM Wallsend St Luke *Newc* from 94. *51 Rowantree Road, Newcastle upon Tyne NE6 4TE* 0191-262 8795

ELDER, David. b 28. Brechin NSM Ord Course 75. **d** 79 **p** 80. NSM Dundee St Salvador *Bre* 79-93; rtd 93; P-in-c Dundee St Martin *Bre* from 93. *Thistlemount, 21 Law Road, Dundee DD3 6PZ* Dundee (01382) 827844

ELDER, Nicholas John. b 51. Hatf Poly BA73. Cuddesdon Coll 73. **d** 76 **p** 77. C Mill End *St Alb* 76-77; C Mill End and Heronsgate w W Hyde 77-79; TV Borehamwood 79-85; V Bedf St Mich 85-90; V Bedf All SS from 90. *All Saints' Vicarage, 1 Cutliffe Place, Bedford MK40 4DF* Bedford (01234) 266945

ELDRID, John Gisborne Charteris. b 25. AKC52. **d** 53 **p** 54. C St Steph Walbrook and St Swithun etc *Lon* 72-81; V Portsea All SS *Portsm* 64-71; P-in-c Portsea St Jo Rudmore 69-71; V Portsea All SS w St Jo Rudmore 71-72; Gen Consultant Lon Samaritans 72-74; Dir The Samaritans 74-87; Gen Consultant-Dir from 87; Lic to Offic *Lon* from 82; rtd 90. *46 Marshall Street, London W1V 1LR* 0171-439 1406

ELDRIDGE, John Frederick. b 48. Loughb Univ BSc70. Golden Gate Sem (USA) MDiv83 Oak Hill Th Coll 90. **d** 92 **p** 93. C Maidstone St Luke *Cant* from 92. *75 Snowdon Avenue, Maidstone, Kent ME14 5NT* Maidstone (01622) 755774

ELDRIDGE, John Kenneth Tristan. b 59. St Steph Ho Ox 90. **d** 92 **p** 93. C Brighton Resurr *Chich* from 92. *St Wilfrid's Vicarage, 107 Hartington Road, Brighton BN2 3PA* Brighton (01273) 673811

ELDRIDGE, Canon Richard Henry. b 21. Lon Univ BSc48 MSc50 BD61. Ridley Hall Cam 56. **d** 58 **p** 59. V Lt Heath *St Alb* 67-76; P-in-c Belper *Derby* 76-88; RD Duffield 81-87; Hon Can Derby Cathl 83-88; rtd 88; Perm to Offic *Pet* from 89. *16 Polwell Lane, Kettering, Northants NN15 6UA* Kettering (01536) 83138

ELDRIDGE, Stephen William. b 50. Chich Th Coll 87. **d** 89 **p** 90. C Stroud and Uplands w Slad *Glouc* 89-92; C Glouc St Mary de Crypt w St Jo and Ch Ch 92-95; Bp's Chapl 92-93; P-in-c Kingswood w Alderley and Hillesley from 95. *The Rectory, High Street, Kingswood, Wotton-under-Edge, Glos GL12 8RS* Dursley (01453) 843361

ELEY, John Edward. b 49. Sarum & Wells Th Coll 74. **d** 77 **p** 78. C Sherborne w Castleton and Lillington *Sarum* 77-80; Min Can Carl Cathl *Carl* 80-84; V Bromsgrove All SS *Worc* 84-88; Perm to Offic *St E* from 90. *Topos, Lackford, Bury St Edmunds IP28 6HR* Bury St Edmunds (01284) 728511

ELFORD, Keith Anthony. b 59. Em Coll Cam BA80 MA84. Wycliffe Hall Ox 87. **d** 90 **p** 91. C Chertsey *Guildf* 90-94; P-in-c Ockham w Hatchford from 94; Bp's Chapl from 94. *The Rectory, Ockham Lane, Ockham, Woking, Surrey GU23 6NP* Guildford (01483) 225358

ELFORD, Canon Robert John. b 39. Man Univ MA71 Ex Univ PhD74. Brasted Th Coll 64 Ridley Hall Cam 66. **d** 68 **p** 69. C Denton St Lawr *Man* 68-71; P-in-c Gwinear *Truro* 71-74; R Phillack w Gwithian and Gwinear 74-78; Lect Man Univ 78-87; Hon C Withington St Paul *Man* 79-83; Warden St Anselm Hall 82-87; Lic to Offic 84-87; Hd and Pro-R Liv Inst of HE from 88; Lic to Offic *Liv* from 88; Can Th Liv Cathl from 92. *St Katharine's College, Stand Park Road, PO Box 6, Liverpool L16 9JD* 0151-722 2361

ELFRED, Michael William. b 48. BA76 MPhil. Linc Th Coll 77. **d** 79 **p** 80. C Boultham *Linc* 79-82; C Croydon H Sav *Cant* 82-84; C Upper Norwood All SS w St Marg 84; C Upper Norwood All SS *S'wark* 85-88; V Sanderstead St Mary from 88. *The Vicarage, 85 Purley Oaks Road, South Croydon, Surrey CR2 0NY* 0181-657 1725

ELGAR, Frederick Stanton. b 20. AKC56. **d** 56 **p** 57. C-in-c Pound Hill CD *Chich* 60-80; rtd 85. *31 Byrefield Road, Guildford, Surrey GU2 6UB* Guildford (01483) 37587

ELGAR, Dr Richard John. b 50. MRCGP80 Charing Cross Hosp Medical Sch MB, BS73. St Jo Coll Nottm DTS92. **d** 92 **p** 93. NSM Derby St Alkmund and St Werburgh *Derby* from 92. *50 Kedleston Road, Derby DE22 1GW* Derby (01332) 291236

ELIOT, Ven Peter Charles. b 10. MBE TD. Magd Coll Cam BA31 MA35. Westcott Ho Cam 53. **d** 54 **p** 55. Adn Worc 61-75; Can Res Worc Cathl 65-75; Perm to Offic *Heref* from 72; rtd 75. *Old House, Kingsland, Leominster, Herefordshire HR6 9QS* Kingsland (01568) 708285

ELIOT, Whately Ian. b 12. **d** 39 **p** 40. R Ex St Paul *Ex* 64-77; rtd 77; Perm to Offic *Ex* from 77. *21 Rydon Lane, Exeter EX2 7AN* Topsham (01392) 873034

ELIZABETH, Sister. See WEBB, Marjorie Valentine

ELKINGTON, Mrs Audrey Anne. b 57. St Cath Coll Ox BA80 UEA PhD83 Nottm Univ DipTh86. St Jo Coll Nottm 85 E Anglian Minl Tr Course 86. **dss** 88 **d** 92 **p** 94. Monkseaton St Mary *Newc* 88-91; Ponteland 91-92; Par Dn 92-93; C Prudhoe from 93. *The Vicarage, 5 Kepwell Court, Prudhoe, Northd NE42 5PE* Prudhoe (01661) 836059

ELKINGTON, David John. b 51. Nottm Univ BTh76 Leic Univ MEd81. St Jo Coll Nottm 73. **d** 76 **p** 77. C Leic Martyrs *Leic* 76-78; C Kirby Muxloe 78-80; Asst Chapl Leic Univ 80-82; Hon C Leic H Spirit 82; Chapl UEA *Nor* 82-88; TV Newc Epiphany *Newc* 88-91; TR 91-93; P-in-c Prudhoe from 93. *The Vicarage, 5 Kepwell Court, Prudhoe, Northd NE42 5PE* Prudhoe (01661) 836059

ELKINS, Alan Bernard. b 47. Sarum & Wells Th Coll 70. **d** 73 **p** 74. C Wareham *Sarum* 73-77; P-in-c Codford, Upton Lovell and Stockton 77-79; P-in-c Boyton w Sherrington 77-79; C Ashton Gifford 79; R Bishopstrow and Boreham 79-92; R

Corfe Mullen from 92. *The Rectory, Wareham Road, Corfe Mullen, Wimborne, Dorset BH21 3LE* Broadstone (01202) 692129

ELKINS, Canon Patrick Charles. b 34. St Chad's Coll Dur BA57 DipTh60 DipEd. **d** 60 **p** 61. C Moordown *Win* 60-63; C Basingstoke 64-67; V Bransgore from 67; Hon Can Win Cathl from 89. *The Vicarage, Ringwood Road, Bransgore, Christchurch, Dorset BH23 8JH* Bransgore (01425) 672327 Fax 674190

ELKS, Roger Mark. b 60. ACGI83 Imp Coll Lon BSc83. Wycliffe Hall Ox 89. **d** 92 **p** 93. C St Austell *Truro* from 92. *10 Glenview, Truro Road, St Austell, Cornwall PL25 5JG* St Austell (01726) 63028

ELLA, David John. b 51. Trin Coll Bris DipTh83. **d** 85 **p** 86. C Canford Magna *Sarum* 85-89; TV Southend *Chelmsf* 89-93; Youth Development Officer from 89; TR Canvey Is from 93. *St Nicholas House, 210 Long Road, Canvey Island, Essex SS8 0JR* Canvey Island (01268) 511098

ELLAM, Stuart William. b 53. Westcott Ho Cam. **d** 85 **p** 86. C Ditton St Mich *Liv* 85-88; C Greenford H Cross *Lon* 88-91; Perm to Offic 91-94. *26 Church Road, Cowley, Uxbridge, Middx UB8 3NA* Uxbridge (01895) 238815

ELLEANOR, David John. b 48. Leic Univ LLB70 St Jo Coll Dur BA88. Cranmer Hall Dur 85. **d** 88 **p** 89. C Consett *Dur* 88-90. *c/o 2 Farm Cottages, Ellingham, Chathill, Northd NE67 5HD*

ELLEL, Thomas Fielding. b 20. Cranmer Hall Dur. **d** 63 **p** 64. V Huncoat *Blackb* 67-74; V Worsthorne 74-88; rtd 88. *20 Trevethan Court, Falmouth, Cornwall TR11 2UQ*

ELLEM, Peter Keith. b 58. CQSW. St Jo Coll Nottm BTh90. **d** 90 **p** 91. C Islington St Mary *Lon* 90-94; C Leeds St Geo *Ripon* from 94. *22 Hanover Square, Leeds LS3 1AP* Leeds (0113) 244 0604 or 243 8498

ELLENS (or STEWART ELLENS), Dr Gordon Frederick Stewart. b 26. FRAS Columbia Univ (NY) MPhil62 PhD68. K Coll Lon BD52 AKC52 St Boniface Warminster 52. **d** 53 **p** 54. Canada 57-60; USA 62-66 and from 88; Japan 70-88; Asst Prof Relig St Sophia Univ Tokyo 70-75; Rikkyo Women's Univ 75-84; Prof Humanities Ueno Gakueu 84-88; rtd 92. *PO Box 1578, Santa Monica, California 90406, USA* Santa Monica (310) 396-2062 Fax 396-5543

ELLERTON, Mrs Mary Diane. b 45. RGN67 RHV68 Huddersfield Poly CertHE89. N Ord Course 90. **d** 93 **p** 94. NSM Upper Holme Valley *Wakef* from 93. *16 Binns Lane, Holmfirth, Huddersfield HD7 1BL* Huddersfield (01484) 684207 Fax 545411

ELLERY, Arthur James Gabriel. b 28. St Jo Coll Dur BSc49. Linc Th Coll 51. **d** 53 **p** 54. V Tanfield *Dur* 62-70; Chapl St Olave's Sch York 70-78; V Gt Ayton w Easby and Newton in Cleveland *York* 78-81; Chapl Bancroft's Sch Woodford Green 81-86; V Chipperfield St Paul *St Alb* 86-93; rtd 93. *7 Church Drive, Orton Waterville, Peterborough PE2 5EX* Peterborough (01733) 231800

ELLERY, Ian Martyn William. b 56. K Coll Lon BD AKC. Chich Th Coll. **d** 82 **p** 83. C Hornsey St Mary w St Geo *Lon* 82-85; VC York Minster *York* 85-89; Subchanter York Minster 86-89; R Patrington w Hollym, Welwick and Winestead from 89. *The Rectory, Patrington, Hull HU12 0PB* Withernsea (01964) 630327

ELLERY, Robert Martin. b 53. Jes Coll Ox BA76. St Mich Coll Llan 74. **d** 77 **p** 80. C Earlsfield St Jo *S'wark* 77-80; C Clapham Ch Ch and St Jo 81-85; Perm to Offic 85-89. *Address temp unknown*

ELLINGTON, David John. b 39. Or Coll Ox BA63 MA. Cuddesdon Coll 63. **d** 65 **p** 66. C Timperley *Ches* 68-72; P-in-c Altrincham St Jo 72-74; V 74-80; P-in-c Ashley 82-86; rtd 86; Perm to Offic *Ches* from 87. *6 Hough Green, Ashley, Altrincham, Cheshire WR15 0QS* 0161-928 2173

ELLIOT, Hugh Riversdale. b 25. Bps' Coll Cheshunt. **d** 62 **p** 65. P-in-c Welborne *Nor* 68-72; P-in-c Yaxham 68-80; P-in-c N Tuddenham 72-80; R E w W Harling 80-90; R Bridgham and Roudham 81-90; R E w W Harling and Bridgham w Roudham 90-92; rtd 92; Perm to Offic *Nor* from 93. *Berryfields, 27 The Street, Alburgh, Harleston, Norfolk IP20 0DJ* Homersfield (0198686) 498

ELLIOT, William (Bill). b 33. Glouc Sch of Min 84. **d** 87 **p** 88. C Kington w Huntington, Old Radnor, Kinnerton etc *Heref* 87-90; C Heref H Trin 90-92; Chapl Corfu *Eur* from 92. *The Chaplaincy Flat, 21 L Mavili Street, Corfu, Greece 491 00* Corfu (661) 31467

ELLIOT, William Brunton. b 41. Edin Th Coll 90 Edin Dioc NSM Course 81. **d** 84 **p** 85. NSM Lasswade *Edin* 84-92; NSM Dalkeith 84-92; NSM Edin St Pet 92-94; R Selkirk from 94. *St John's Rectory, 23 Viewfield Park, Selkirk TD7 4LH* Selkirk (01750) 21364

ELLIOT-NEWMAN, Christopher Guy. b 43. Bede Coll Dur TCert67 Hull Univ BTh83 MEd87. Westcott Ho Cam 67. **d** 70 **p** 71. C Ditton St Mich *Liv* 70-73; C Hazlemere *Ox* 73-77; R Stockton-on-the-Forest w Holtby and Warthill *York* 77-87;

Dir of Educn *Cant* 87-94. *12 Priestlands Road, Hexham, Northd NE46 4AJ* Hexham (01434) 607853

ELLIOTT, Brian. b 49. Dur Univ BA73. Coll of Resurr Mirfield 73. **d** 75 **p** 76. C Nunthorpe *York* 75-77; CF from 77. *c/o MOD (Army), Bagshot Park, Bagshot, Surrey GU19 5PL* Bagshot (01276) 471717 Fax 412834

ELLIOTT, Charles. b 15. Lon Univ BA55. St Steph Ho Ox 51. **d** 53 **p** 54. V Lower Gornal *Lich* 61-80; rtd 80; Lic to Offic *Lich* from 80; Lic to Offic *Worc* 81-83; Perm to Offic from 83. *1 The Village, Kingswinford, W Midlands DY6 8AY* Kingswinford (01384) 279360

ELLIOTT, Preb Dr Charles Middleton. b 39. Linc Coll Ox BA60 Nuff Coll Ox DPhil62. Linc Th Coll 62. **d** 64 **p** 65. Lect Nottm Univ 63-65; C Wilford *S'well* 64-65; Zambia 65-69; Chapl Lusaka Cath 65-69; Asst Gen Sec Jt Cttee WCC 69-72; Asst Gen Sec Pontifical Commn Justice and Peace 69-72; Sen Lect UEA 72-77; Hon Min Can Nor Cathl *Nor* 73-77; Prof Development Studies Univ of Wales (Swansea) 77-82; Dir Chr Aid 82-84; Asst Gen Sec BCC 82-84; Prof Bris Univ 85-87; Australia 87-88; Visiting Prof K Coll Lon 88-89; Preb Lich Cathl *Lich* from 88; Dean Trin Hall Cam from 90. *Trinity Hall, Cambridge CB2 1TJ* Cambridge (01223) 332525 or 69233 Fax 332537

ELLIOTT, Christopher John. b 44. Sarum Th Coll 66. **d** 69 **p** 70. C Walthamstow St Pet *Chelmsf* 69-71; C Witham 71-74; P-in-c Gt and Lt Bentley 74-80; R Colchester Ch Ch w St Mary V 80-85; R Sible Hedingham 85-93; V Leigh-on-Sea St Aid from 93. *St Aidan's Vicarage, Moor Park Gardens, Leigh-on-Sea, Essex SS9 4PY* Southend-on-Sea (01702) 525338

ELLIOTT, Christopher John. b 67. Southn Univ 93. Chich Th Coll CMT94. **d** 94 **p** 95. C Alton St Lawr *Win* from 94. *13 Walnut Close, Alton, Hants GU34 2BA* Alton (01420) 88226

ELLIOTT, Canon Colin. b 23. St Pet Coll Ox BA48 DipTh49 MA52. Wycliffe Hall Ox 48. **d** 49 **p** 50. R Windermere St Martin *Carl* 59-88; RD Windermere 79-84; Hon Can Carl Cathl 81-88; rtd 88. *Fairbank View, Brow Lane, Staveley, Kendal, Cumbria LA8 9PJ* Staveley (01539) 821758

ELLIOTT, Colin David. b 32. AKC55. **d** 56 **p** 57. C W Wickham St Jo *Cant* 56-59; C Dover St Mary 59-64; V Linton 64-66; V Gillingham H Trin *Roch* 66-81; V Belvedere All SS 81-88; V Bromley St Jo from 88. *St John's Vicarage, 9 Orchard Road, Bromley BR1 2PR* 0181-460 1844

ELLIOTT, Very Rev David. b 31. Bps' Coll Cheshunt 60. **d** 63 **p** 64. C Chingford St Anne *Chelmsf* 63-64; C Woodford St Mary 64-66; Trucial States 67-69; Prec St Alb Abbey *St Alb* 69-72; Zambia 72-75; Dean Ndola 72-75; Can Ndola (Zambia) from 75; TR Borehamwood *St Alb* 75-79; Dean Jerusalem 79-86; OStJ 80-82; CStJ from 82; R Covent Garden St Paul *Lon* from 86. *21A Down Street, London W1Y 7DN* 0171-499 5290

ELLIOTT, David Reed. b 62. Lon Bible Coll BA91. Oak Hill Th Coll 91. **d** 93 **p** 94. C Luton Lewsey St Hugh *St Alb* from 93. *247 Leagrave High Street, Luton LU4 0NA*

ELLIOTT, Derek John. b 26. Pemb Coll Cam BA50 MA55. Oak Hill Th Coll 48. **d** 51 **p** 53. Chapl Bedf Modern Sch 68-83; V Potten End w Nettleden *St Alb* 83-91; rtd 91; Hon C Twickenham St Mary *Lon* from 91. *23 Bosner Road, Twickenham TW1 4RQ* 0181-744 2761

ELLIOTT, Miss Eveline Mary. b 39. ALA63 Bedf Coll Lon BA60. E Anglian Minl Tr Course 92. **d** 95. NSM Bury St Edmunds St Mary *St E* from 95. *4 St Michael's Close, Northgate Street, Bury St Edmunds, Suffolk IP33 1HT* Bury St Edmunds (01284) 753592

ELLIOTT, George Evan. b 17. Sarum Th Coll. **d** 58 **p** 59. V Kimblesworth *Dur* 64-71; V Sutton St James *Linc* 71-77; V Sutton St Edmund 73-77; P-in-c Bishop Norton 77-80; R Wadingham w Snitterby 77-80; R Bishop Norton, Wadingham and Snitterby 80-82; rtd 82; Perm to Offic *Nor* from 82. *10 Dugard Avenue, Norwich NR1 4NQ* Norwich (01603) 35806

ELLIOTT, Gordon. b 25. St Aid Birkenhead 63. **d** 65 **p** 66. C Bollington St Jo *Ches* 68-70; V Dukingfield St Mark 70-73; TV Tenbury *Heref* 74-78; V Bromfield 78-82; R Culmington w Onibury 78-82; V Stanton Lacy 78-82; P-in-c Withybrook w Copston Magna *Cov* 82-83; P-in-c Wolvey, Burton Hastings and Stretton Baskerville 82-83; V Wolvey w Burton Hastings, Copston Magna etc 83-90; rtd 90. *39 Beech Close, Ludlow, Shropshire SY8 2PD* Ludlow (01584) 875084

ELLIOTT, Ian David. b 40. Qu Coll Cam BA61 MA65. Tyndale Hall Bris 64. **d** 66 **p** 67. C Halewood *Liv* 66-71; C Gt Crosby St Luke 71-74; C-in-c Dallam CD 74-80; V Dallam 80-83; TV Fazakerley Em 83-92; V Warrington H Trin from 92. *Holy Trinity Vicarage, 6 Palmyra Square North, Warrington WA1 1JQ* Warrington (01925) 630057

ELLIOTT, John Philip. b 37. MIChemE61 MBIM Salford Univ CEng. Glouc Th Course 79. **d** 80 **p** 80. NSM Brimscombe *Glouc* 80-86; C Caverswall *Lich* 86-91; R Tredington and

Darlingscott w Newbold on Stour *Cov* from 91. *The Rectory, Tredington, Shipston-on-Stour, Warks CV36 4NG* Shipston-on-Stour (01608) 661264

ELLIOTT, John George. b 15. Qu Coll Ox BA37 MA46. Westcott Ho Cam 46. **d** 47 **p** 48. Chapl Loughb Gr Sch 61-80; rtd 80; Perm to Offic *Leic* from 80. *14 Victoria Street, Loughborough, Leics LE11 2EN* Loughborough (01509) 263365

ELLIOTT, Joseph William. b 37. Chich Th Coll. **d** 66 **p** 67. C Whickham *Dur* 66-72; V Lamesley 72-78; TR Usworth 78-93; P-in-c Belmont from 93. *The Vicarage, Broomside Lane, Durham DH1 2QW* 0191-386 1545

ELLIOTT, Keith Alcock. b 51. St Jo Coll Dur. **d** 95. C Chulmleigh *Ex* from 95; C Chawleigh w Cheldon from 95; C Wembworthy w Eggesford from 95. *The Rectory, Chawleigh, Chulmleigh, Devon EX18 7HJ* Chulmleigh (01769) 581163

ELLIOTT (nee JUTSUM), Mrs Linda Mary. b 56. St Pet Coll Birm CertEd77. W Midl Minl Tr Course 92. **d** 95. NSM Longthorpe *Pet* from 95. *68 Bradwell Road, Peterborough PE3 9PZ* Peterborough (01733) 262593

ELLIOTT, Maurice John. b 65. St Andr Univ MA87 TCD BTh92 MPhil93. CITC 89. **d** 93 **p** 94. C Coleraine *Conn* from 93. *42 Kenuarra Park, Coleraine, Co Londonderry BT52 1RT* Coleraine (01265) 57828

ELLIOTT, Michael James. b 58. LTh. St Jo Coll Nottm 80. **d** 83 **p** 84. C Pontypridd St Cath *Llan* 83-86; C Leamington Priors St Paul *Cov* 86-89; Chapl RAF from 89. *Chaplaincy Services (RAF), HQ, Personnel and Training Command, RAF Innsworth, Gloucester GL3 1EZ* Gloucester (01452) 712612 Ext 5164   Fax 510828

ELLIOTT, Nigel Harvey. b 55. St Jo Coll Nottm DCM92. **d** 92 **p** 93. C Radcliffe *Man* 92-95; V Kilnhurst *Sheff* from 95. *The Vicarage, Highthorne Road, Kilnhurst, Rotherham, S Yorkshire S62 5TX* Mexborough (01709) 589674

ELLIOTT, Ven Peter. b 41. Hertf Coll Ox BA63 MA68. Linc Th Coll 63. **d** 65 **p** 66. C Gosforth All SS *Newc* 65-68; C Balkwell 68-72; V High Elswick St Phil 72-80; V N Gosforth 80-87; V Embleton w Rennington and Rock 87-93; RD Alnwick 89-93; Hon Can Newc Cathl 90-93; Adn Northd and Can Res Newc Cathl from 93. *80 Moorside North, Newcastle upon Tyne NE4 9DU* 0191-273 8245

ELLIOTT, Peter Wolstenholme. b 31. CChem MRSC. NE Ord Course 78. **d** 81 **p** 82. NSM Yarm *York* from 81. *48 Butterfield Drive, Eaglescliffe, Stockton-on-Tees, Cleveland TS16 0EZ* Eaglescliffe (01642) 782788

ELLIOTT, Simon Richard James. b 66. Lon Univ BSc88. Cranmer Hall Dur BA95. **d** 95. C Hendon St Paul Mill Hill *Lon* from 95. *46 Shakespeare Road, London NW7 4BE* 0181-959 8461

ELLIOTT, Stanley Griffin. b 19. Lon Univ BA50. Ridley Hall Cam 50. **d** 52 **p** 53. R Ashton upon Mersey St Martin *Ches* 59-80; V Tile Hill *Cov* 80-85; rtd 85; Perm to Offic *Win* from 85. *Flat 3 Chartwell, 8 The Avenue, Branksome Park, Poole, Dorset BH13 6AG* Poole (01202) 766080

ELLIOTT, William (Bill). b 20. Lon Univ BA56. Ripon Hall Ox 60. **d** 61 **p** 62. C Kidderminster St Mary *Worc* 61-70; V Bewdley Far Forest 70-78; V Rock w Heightington w Far Forest 78-82; V Mamble w Bayton, Rock w Heightington etc 82-85; rtd 85; Perm to Offic *Heref* from 85; Perm to Offic *Worc* from 85. *8 Lea View, Cleobury Mortimer, Kidderminster DY14 8EE* Cleobury Mortimer (01299) 270993

ELLIOTT, William Henry Venn (Ben). b 34. K Coll Cam BA55 MA59. Wells Th Coll 59. **d** 61 **p** 62. C Almondbury *Wakef* 61-66; V Bramshaw *Sarum* 66-81; P-in-c Landford w Plaitford 77-81; V Mere w W Knoyle and Maiden Bradley from 81. *The Vicarage, Angel Lane, Mere, Warminster, Wilts BA12 6DH* Mere (01747) 860292

ELLIOTT, Dr William James. b 38. Jes Coll Cam BA62 MA66 Birm Univ MA69 PhD74. Qu Coll Birm 62. **d** 64 **p** 65. C Hendon St Paul Mill Hill *Lon* 64-67; C St Pancras w St Jas and Ch Ch 67-69; P-in-c Preston St Paul *Blackb* 69-74; R Elstree *St Alb* from 74. *The Rectory, St Nicholas' Close, Elstree, Borehamwood, Herts WD6 3EW* 0181-953 1411

ELLIOTT, William Norman. b 20. Kelham Th Coll 37. **d** 43 **p** 44. V S Crosland *Wakef* 64-85; rtd 85; Chapl Community of St Pet Horbury from 85. *18 Woodlands, Horbury, Wakefield, W Yorkshire WF4 5HH* Wakefield (01924) 265547

ELLIS, Anthony Colin. b 56. Keble Coll Ox BA77 Man Univ PhD80. Linc Th Coll 80. **d** 81 **p** 82. C Mill Hill Jo Keble Ch *Lon* 81-83; Staff Tutor in Relig Studies Man Univ from 83; C Stretford St Pet *Man* 83-87; NSM Shore 87-89; Lic to Offic from 89. *2 Crowther Terrace, Blackshaw, Hebden Bridge, W Yorkshire HX7 6DE* Hebden Bridge (01422) 844242

ELLIS, Canon Bryan Stuart. b 31. Qu Coll Cam BA54 MA58. Ridley Hall Cam 55. **d** 57 **p** 58. C Ramsgate St Luke *Cant* 57-59; C Herne Bay Ch Ch 59-62; V Burmantofts St Steph and St Agnes *Ripon* 62-81; RD Wakef from 81; V Wakef St Andr and St Mary from 81; Hon Can Wakef Cathl from 89.

2 Kilnsey Road, Wakefield, W Yorkshire WF1 4RW Wakefield (01924) 372105

ELLIS, Charles Harold. b 50. N Ord Course 78. **d** 81 **p** 82. C Davyhulme St Mary *Man* 81-85; V Tonge w Alkrington 85-91; P-in-c Radcliffe St Thos and St Jo 91; P-in-c Radcliffe St Mary 91; TR Radcliffe from 91. *The Vicarage, Vicarage Street, Radcliffe, Manchester M26 9TG* 0161-723 2123

ELLIS, Christopher Charles. b 55. Societas Oecumenica 90 Edin Univ BD78 Hull Univ MA80. Edin Th Coll 76 Irish Sch of Ecum 78. **d** 79 **p** 80. C Selby Abbey *York* 79-82; C Fulford 82-85; Dioc Ecum Officer from 81; Dioc Ecum Adv from 90; Lect Ecum Th Hull Univ from 84; P-in-c Kexby w Wilberfoss 85-90; Ecum Officer S Cleveland & N Yorkshire Ecum Coun from 88. *21 Sandstock Road, Pocklington, York YO4 2HN* Pocklington (01759) 305881

ELLIS, Canon David Craven. b 34. Man Univ BA56 MA57. St Aid Birkenhead 59. **d** 61 **p** 62. C Gt Crosby St Luke *Liv* 61-65; Hong Kong 65-69; P-in-c Sawrey *Carl* 69-74; Dioc Youth Officer 69-74; V Halifax St Aug *Wakef* 74-84; R Greystoke, Matterdale and Mungrisdale *Carl* 84-87; R Watermillock 84-87; TR Greystoke, Matterdale, Mungrisdale, etc 88-91; RD Penrith 87-91; TR Carl H Trin and St Barn from 91; Hon Can Carl Cathl from 91. *St Barnabas' Rectory, Brookside, Carlisle CA2 7JU* Carlisle (01228) 515274

ELLIS, Hugh William. b 54. Sussex Univ BSc76. Ridley Hall Cam 88. **d** 90 **p** 91. C Reading St Jo *Ox* 90-93; P-in-c Bradfield and Stanford Dingley from 93. *The Rectory, Southend Road, Bradfield, Reading RG7 6EU* Bradfield (01734) 744333

ELLIS, Dr Ian Morton. b 52. QUB BD75 MTh82 TCD PhD89. CITC. **d** 77 **p** 78. C Portadown St Columba *Arm* 77-79; C Arm St Mark 79-85; Chapl Arm R Sch 79-85; Hon VC Arm Cathl 82-93; I Mullavilly 85-93; Dom Chapl to Abp Arm 86-93; Tutor for Aux Min (Arm) 90-93; Dioc Adv on Ecum 92-93; I Newc *D & D* from 93. *The Rectory, 1 King Street, Newcastle, Co Down BT33 0HD* Newcastle (013967) 22439

ELLIS, Ian William. b 57. QUB BSc78 CertEd79 TCD BTh89. CITC 86. **d** 89 **p** 90. C Arm St Mark w Aghavilly *Arm* 89-91; I Loughgall w Grange from 91. *2 Main Street, Loughgall, Armagh BT61 8HZ* Loughgall (01762) 891587

ELLIS, Jean Miriam. b 55. NSM Llanelli *S & B* from 95. *Llanelly Rectory, Abergavenney Road, Gilwern, Abergavenney, Gwent NP7 0AD*

ELLIS, John. b 27. Glouc Th Course 83. **d** 85 **p** 86. NSM Dowdeswell and Andoversford w the Shiptons etc *Glouc* 85-94; rtd 94; Perm to Offic *Glouc* from 94. *18 Hunter's Way, Andoversford, Cheltenham, Glos GL54 4JW* Cheltenham (01242) 820746

ELLIS, John Anthony (Tony). b 47. Univ of Wales (Lamp) DipTh70 Open Univ BA80. Coll of Resurr Mirfield 70. **d** 72 **p** 73. C Sketty *S & B* 72-75; C Duston *Pet* 75-80; R Lichborough w Maidford and Farthingstone 80-85; V Stratfield Mortimer *Ox* from 85; P-in-c Mortimer W End w Padworth from 85. *St John's House, Loves Wood, Mortimer, Reading RG7 2JX* Mortimer (01734) 332401

ELLIS, John Beaumont. b 45. Univ of Wales (Lamp) BA67 LTh69. Bp Burgess Hall Lamp. **d** 69 **p** 70. C Abergavenny St Mary w Llanwenarth Citra *Mon* 69-72; C Swansea St Gabr *S & B* 72-75; V Llanbister and Llanbadarn Fynydd w Llananno 75-77; V Newport St Andr *Mon* 77-80; V Risca 80-84; V Cheadle Heath *Ches* 84-94. *12 Upper Hibbert Lane, Marple, Stockport, Cheshire SK6 7HX* 0161-427 1963

ELLIS, John Franklyn. b 34. Leeds Univ BA58. Linc Th Coll 58. **d** 60 **p** 61. C Ladybarn *Man* 60-63; C Stockport St Geo *Ches* 63-66; V High Lane 66-81; V Chelford w Lower Withington from 81. *The Vicarage, Chelford, Macclesfield, Cheshire SK11 9AH* Chelford (01625) 861231

ELLIS, John Frederick Alexander. b 23. Sarum Th Coll 50. **d** 52 **p** 53. V Harnham *Sarum* 65-80; RD Salisbury 77-80; Can and Preb Sarum Cathl 77-80; P-in-c Belstone *Ex* 80-81; P-in-c S Tawton 80-81; R S Tawton and Belstone 81-87; RD Okehampton 82-87; TR Yelverton, Meavy, Sheepstor and Walkhampton 87-89; rtd 89. *55 Church Street, Tisbury, Salisbury SP3 6NH* Tisbury (01747) 871447

ELLIS, John Roland. b 32. Wells Th Coll 67. **d** 69 **p** 70. C Kettering SS Pet and Paul *Pet* 69-71; C Kingsthorpe 71-73; TV 73-74; TV Ebbw Vale *Mon* 74-76; V Llanddewi Rhydderch w Llanvapley etc 76-83; Miss to Seamen from 79; V New Tredegar *Mon* 83-86; V Llanelli *S & B* from 86; RD Crickhowell from 91. *Llanelli Rectory, Abergavenny Road, Gilwern, Abergavenny, Gwent NP7 0AD* Gilwern (01873) 830280

ELLIS, John Wadsworth. b 42. TCD BA64. **d** 66 **p** 67. C Lisburn Ch Ch Cathl *Conn* 66-69; C Norbiton *S'wark* 69-72; C New Clee *Linc* 72-85; V from 85; RD Grimsby and Cleethorpes from 94. *120 Queen Mary Avenue, Cleethorpes, S Humberside DN35 7SZ* Cleethorpes (01472) 696521

ELLIS, Joseph Walter. b 08. St D Coll Lamp BA32. **d** 32 **p** 33. V Gt w Lt Chesterford *Chelmsf* 64-77; rtd 77. *5 Southfield, Back*

Lane, Ickleton, Saffron Walden, Essex CB10 1SJ Saffron Walden (01799) 530334

ELLIS, Malcolm Railton. b 35. LTCL71 Univ of Wales (Lamp) BA56. Sarum Th Coll 56. **d** 58 **p** 59. C Llangynwyd w Maesteg *Llan* 58-61; C Llantrisant 61-67; V Troedrhiwgarth 67-70; PV Truro Cathl *Truro* 70-73; V Egloshayle 73-81; V Margam *Llan* 81-87; V Cardiff St Jo from 87; Offic Chapl Priory for Wales OStJ from 87. *The Vicarage, 16 Queen Anne Square, Cathays Park, Cardiff CF1 3ED* Cardiff (01222) 220375

ELLIS, Preb Mark Durant. b 39. Ex Univ BA62. Cuddesdon Coll 62. **d** 64 **p** 65. C Lyngford *B & W* 64-67; V Weston-super-Mare St Andr Bournville 67-76; TV Yeovil 76-88; V Yeovil St Mich from 88; Preb Wells Cathl from 90; RD Merston from 94. *St Michael's Vicarage, Yeovil, Somerset BA21 4LH* Yeovil (01935) 75752

ELLIS, Paul. b 56. Man Poly HNC79. Aston Tr Scheme 88 Trin Coll Bris DipHE92. **d** 92 **p** 93. C Pennington *Man* from 92. *11 Ruby Grove, Pennington, Leigh, Lancs WN7 4JW* Leigh (01942) 681874

ELLIS, Peter Andrew. b 46. St D Coll Lamp 65. **d** 69 **p** 70. C Milford Haven *St D* 69-71; R Walwyn's Castle w Robeston W 71-74; Miss to Seamen from 74; Hong Kong 74-75 and from 92; Singapore 75-82; The Tees and Hartlepool 82-92. *The Mariner's Club, 11 Middle Road, Kowloon, Hong Kong* Hong Kong (852) 368-8261 Fax 366-0928

ELLIS, Robert Albert. b 48. K Coll Lon BD70 AKC70. St Aug Coll Cant 70. **d** 72 **p** 73. C Liv Our Lady and St Nic w St Anne *Liv* 72-76; P-in-c Meerbrook *Lich* 76-80; Producer Relig Progr BBC Radio Stoke 76-80; V Highgate All SS *Lon* 80-81; Dioc Communications Officer *Lich* from 81; P-in-c Longdon 81-87. *The Pump House, Jack's Lane, Marchington, Uttoxeter, Staffs ST14 8LW* Burton-on-Trent (01283) 820732

ELLIS, Ven Robin Gareth. b 35. Pemb Coll Ox BA57 BCL58 MA62. Chich Th Coll 58. **d** 60 **p** 61. C Swinton St Pet *Man* 60-63; Asst Chapl Worksop Coll Notts 63-66; V Swaffham Prior *Ely* 66-74; Asst Dir Educn 66-74; V Wisbech St Aug 74-82; V Yelverton *Ex* 82-86; Adn Plymouth from 82. *33 Leat Walk, Roborough, Plymouth PL6 7AT* Plymouth (01752) 793397 Fax as telephone

ELLIS, Roger Henry. b 40. Natal Univ BA61 Selw Coll Cam BA64 MA68 Linacre Coll Ox BLitt69. **d** 66 **p** 67. C Ox St Mich *Ox* 66-68; S Africa 68-76; P-in-c Wrentham *St E* 77; V Wheatley Hills *Sheff* 77-84; Chapl St Edm Sch Cant from 84. *1 The Close, Canterbury, Kent CT2 8HU* Canterbury (01227) 450218 or 454575

ELLIS, Miss Sheila. b 39. Lon Univ CertRK. St Mich Ho Ox 67 Dalton Ho Bris 68. **dss** 80 **d** 87 **p** 94. Kirkdale St Mary and St Athanasius *Liv* 81-87; Par Dn 87-91; C W Derby St Luke from 91. *66 Baycliff Road, Liverpool L12 6QX* 0151-228 5455

ELLIS, Timothy William. b 53. AKC75. St Aug Coll Cant 75. **d** 76 **p** 77. C Old Trafford St Jo *Man* 76-80; V Pendleton St Thos 80-87; Chapl Salford Coll of Tech 80-87; V Sheff Norwood St Leon *Sheff* from 87; P-in-c Shiregreen St Hilda from 94; RD Ecclesfield from 94. *St Leonard's Vicarage, Everingham Road, Sheffield S5 7LE* Sheffield (0114) 243 6689 Fax as telephone

ELLIS, Canon Vorley Michael Spencer. b 15. St Edm Hall Ox BA38 MA41. St Steph Ho Ox 37. **d** 39 **p** 40. V Keswick St Jo *Carl* 50-83; Hon Can Carl Cathl 78-83; P-in-c Threlkeld 80-83; rtd 83; Perm to Offic *Leic* from 83. *12 Brookfield Way, Kibworth, Leicester LE8 0SA* Leicester (0116) 279 3138

ELLIS JONES, Betty Mary. CertEd41. Bps' Coll Cheshunt. **dss** 62 **d** 87 **p** 94. Perm to Offic *St E* from 62. *St Martin's Cottage, 8 Old Kirton Road, Trimley, Ipswich IP10 0QH* Felixstowe (01394) 275233

✠ELLISON, Rt Rev John Alexander. b 40. ALCD67. **d** 67 **p** 68 **c** 88. C Woking St Paul *Guildf* 67-74; SAMS from 80; Argentina 80-83; R Aldridge *Lich* 83-88; Bp Paraguay from 88. *Iglesia Anglicana Paraguaya, Casilla 1124, Asuncion, Paraguay*

ELLISTON, John Ernest Nicholas. b 37. ALCD61. **d** 61 **p** 62. C Gipsy Hill Ch Ch *S'wark* 61-64; C Whitton and Thurleston w Akenham *St E* 64-68; P-in-c New Clee *Linc* 68-71; V Grimsby St Steph 71-75; V New Clee 75-76; P-in-c Mildenhall *St E* 77-79; P-in-c Barton Mills, Beck Row w Kenny Hill etc 80; V 80-84; RD Mildenhall 81-84; V Ipswich St Aug from 84. *St Augustine's Vicarage, 2 Bucklesham Road, Ipswich IP3 8TJ* Ipswich (01473) 728654

ELLMORE, Geoffrey Richard. b 36. CEng68 MIMechE68 Leic Coll of Art & Tech BScEng57. S'wark Ord Course 86. **d** 87 **p** 88. NSM Coxheath w E Farleigh, Hunton and Linton *Roch* from 87. *31 Parkway, Coxheath, Maidstone, Kent ME17 4HH* Maidstone (01622) 744737

ELLMORE, Peter Robert. b 44. Sarum & Wells Th Coll 84. **d** 86 **p** 87. C Bridgemary *Portsm* 86-89; C Portsea N End St Mark 89-91; Asst Chapl St Mary's Hosp Portsm 91-92; Chapl Qu Alexandra Hosp Portsm from 92; Chapl Portsm Hosps NHS Trust from 93. *40 Colville Road, Cosham, Portsmouth,*

PO2 2DY, or Queen Alexandra Hospital, Cosham, Portsmouth PO6 3LY Portsmouth (01705) 383203 or 379451

ELLOR, Michael Keith (Mick). b 52. St Jo Coll Nottm 92. **d** 94 **p** 95. C Stafford St Jo and Tixall w Ingestre *Lich* from 94. *42 Longhurst Drive, Kingston Hill, Stafford ST16 3RG* Stafford (01785) 214239

ELLSLEY, Howard. b 23. Roch Th Coll 65. **d** 67 **p** 68. C Glas St Marg *Glas* 67-71; R Dalbeattie 71-77; TV Melton Mowbray w Thorpe Arnold *Leic* 77-78; R Balcombe *Chich* 78-83; R Airdrie *Glas* 83-88; R Gartcosh 83-88; rtd 88. *Auchencraig, Lower Barcaple, Ringford, Castle Douglas, Kirkcudbrightshire DG7 2AP* Ringford (015572) 228

ELLSON, Montague Edward. b 33. Birm Univ BA56 Cam Univ ACertEd67. E Anglian Minl Tr Course 84. **d** 87 **p** 88. Hon C Freethorpe w Wickhampton, Halvergate etc *Nor* 87-90; C Gaywood, Bawsey and Mintlyn 90-92; Miss to Seamen from 90; R Pulham *Nor* 92-94; P-in-c Starston 93-94; Dioc NSM Officer from 94; R Pulham Market, Pulham St Mary and Starston from 94; RD Redenhall from 95. *The Rectory, Pulham Market, Diss, Norfolk IP21 4TE* Pulham Market (01379) 676256

ELLSWORTH, Dr Lida Elizabeth. b 48. Columbia Univ (NY) BA70 Girton Coll Cam PhD76. E Midl Min Tr Course. **d** 88 **p** 94. NSM Bakewell *Derby* from 88. *Apple Croft, Granby Gardens, Bakewell, Derbyshire DE45 1ET* Bakewell (01629) 814255

ELLWOOD, Keith Brian. b 36. AIGCM58 FRSA65 DipRIPH&H65 ACP66 FCollP83 Curwen Coll Lon BA58 MMus65 Bede Coll Dur CertEd59. Bps' Coll Cheshunt 64. **d** 64 **p** 65. Chapl R Wanstead Sch 64-66; C Wanstead St Mary *Chelmsf* 64-66; CF 66-70; OCF 70-71 and 76-79; Hong Kong 70-71; P-in-c Bicknoller *B & W* 71-73; Chapl Roedean Sch Brighton 73-76; Perm to Offic *B & W* 74-79; W Germany 76-79; Chapl Trin Coll Glenalmond 79-81; Hd Master St Chris Sch Burnham-on-Sea 82-86; Hon C Burnham *B & W* 82-86; R Staple Fitzpaine, Orchard Portman, Thurlbear etc 86-89; P-in-c Hugill *Carl* 89-93; Educn Adv 89-93; P-in-c Coldwaltham and Hardham *Chich* from 93. *The Vicarage, Coldwaltham, Pulborough, W Sussex RH20 1LF* Pulborough (01798) 872146

ELMORE, Graeme Martin. b 47. Sarum & Wells Th Coll 71. **d** 74 **p** 75. C Norbury St Oswald *Cant* 74-77; P-in-c St Allen *Truro* 77-79; P-in-c St Erme 77-79; V Newlyn St Pet 79-85; CF (TA) 80-86; R Redruth w Lanner *Truro* 85-86; Chapl RN from 86. *Directorate Gen, RN Chapl Services, Room 203, Victory Building, HM Naval Base, Portsmouth PO1 3LS* Portsmouth (01705) 727903 Fax 727112

ELPHICK, Robin Howard. b 37. ALCD63. **d** 64 **p** 65. C Clapham Common St Barn *S'wark* 64-67; C Woking St Pet *Guildf* 67-71; R Rollesby w Burgh w Billockby *Nor* 71-80; P-in-c Ashby w Oby, Thurne and Clippesby 79-80; R Rollesby w Burgh w Billockby w Ashby w Oby etc 80-84; R Frinton *Chelmsf* 84-94; P-in-c W w E Mersea from 94; P-in-c Peldon w Gt and Lt Wigborough from 94. *The Rectory, 93 Kingsland Road, West Mersea, Colchester CO5 8AG* West Mersea (01206) 385635

ELPHICK, Miss Vivien Margaret. b 53. Solicitor 77 Kent Univ BA74. Trin Coll Bris BA90. **d** 90 **p** 94. C Oulton Broad *Nor* 90-94; P-in-c Burlingham St Edmund w Lingwood, Strumpshaw etc from 94. *The Rectory, Barn Close, Lingwood, Norwich NR13 4TS* Norwich (01603) 713880

ELPHIN AND ARDAGH, Archdeacon of. See JACKSON, Ven Robert Stewart

ELPHIN AND ARDAGH, Dean of. See McGEE, Very Rev Stuart Irwin

ELSDON, Bernard Robert. b 29. Roch Th Coll 65. **d** 67 **p** 68. C Wallasey St Hilary *Ches* 67-71; C Liv Our Lady and St Nic w St Anne *Liv* 71-72; V Anfield St Marg 73-89; Dioc Exec Dir for Chr Resp 80-83; rtd 89. *31 Douglas Road, Hazel Grove, Stockport, Cheshire SK7 4JE* 0161-456 6824

ELSDON, Janice Margaret. b 49. **d** 95. NSM Cloughfern *Conn* from 95. *128 Station Road, Greenisland, Carrickfergus, Co Antrim BT38 8UW* Whiteabbey (01232) 869123

ELSEY, Cyril. b 08. Ridley Hall Cam 65. **d** 66 **p** 67. R Petton w Cockshutt *Lich* 69-75; rtd 75; Perm to Offic *Ex* from 82. *9 Raleigh Court, Raleigh Road, Budleigh Salterton, Devon EX9 6HR* Budleigh Salterton (01395) 445504

ELSMORE, Guy Charles. b 66. Edin Univ BSc88. Ridley Hall Cam CTMin93. **d** 93 **p** 94. C Huyton St Mich *Liv* from 93. *1 Derby Terrace, Liverpool L36 9XJ* 0151-449 3700

ELSON, Christopher John. b 52. K Coll Lon BD75 AKC75. St Aug Coll Cant. **d** 76 **p** 77. C New Haw *Guildf* 76-79; C Guildf H Trin w St Mary 79-82; C Hale 85-87; V Ripley from 87; Sub-Chapl HM Pris Send from 88. *The Vicarage, High Street, Ripley, Woking, Surrey GU23 6AE*

ELSON, John Frederick. Roch Th Coll 62. **d** 64 **p** 65. P-in-c Chart next Sutton Valence *Cant* 68-71; V Fletching *Chich* 71-93; Chapl Wivelsfield Green Hospice 91-93; rtd 93.

213

Fernbank, 36 Olive Meadow, Uckfield, E Sussex TN22 1QY Newick (01825) 760663

ELSTOB, Stephen William. b 57. Sarum & Wells Th Coll. d 86 p 87. C Sunderland Springwell w Thorney Close *Dur* 86-88; C Upholland *Liv* 88-89; TV from 89. *158 Birleywood, Skelmersdale, Lancs WN8 9BX* Skelmersdale (01695) 28091

ELSTON, Philip Herbert. b 35. RD80 and Bar 90 KCT95. Leeds Univ MA76. AKC63. d 64 p 65. C Thurnby Lodge *Leic* 64-66; Hon C 66-67; Chapl RNR 67-90; Malawi 68-75; Hon C Far Headingley St Chad *Ripon* 75-79; V Knowl Hill w Littlewick *Ox* 79-84; Chapl RN Sch Haslemere 85-89; C Felpham w Middleton *Chich* 89-90; Asst S Regional Dir Miss to Seamen 91-93; Dep S Regional Dir from 93; Perm to Offic *Win* from 93; Perm to Offic *Cant* from 94. *The Missions to Seamen, Flying Angel House, Littlehampton, W Sussex BN17 5BY* Littlehampton (01903) 726969 Fax 734455

ELTON, Clarence Edward. b 09. ALCD36. d 36 p 37. R Hambledon *Guildf* 57-74; rtd 74; Perm to Offic *Guildf* from 74; Perm to Offic *Chich* from 83. *76 Church Road, Milford, Godalming, Surrey GU8 5JD* Godalming (01483) 417959

ELTON, Derek Hurley. b 31. Lon Univ BSc52. Wycliffe Hall Ox 53. d 55 p 56. C Ashton-on-Ribble St Andr *Blackb* 55-58; India 58-71; R Wickmere w Lt Barningham and Itteringham *Nor* 71-79; R Lt w Gt Ellingham 79-83; P-in-c Rockland All SS and St Andr w St Pet 81-83; R Lt w Gt Ellingham w Rockland 83-88; Chapl Wayland Hosp Norfolk 86-88; CMS from 88; Miss to Seamen from 88; JMECA from 89; Algeria 89-92; Perm to Offic *Nor* from 92. *7 Roseberry Road, Cromer, Norfolk NR27 0BX*

ELTRINGHAM, Mrs Fiona Ann. b 48. CertEd69. NE Ord Course 86. d 89 p 94. Par Dn Willington Team *Newc* 89-92; Chapl HM Young Offender Inst Castington from 92. *HM Young Offender Institution, Castington, Morpeth, Northd NE55 9XF* Morpeth (01670) 760942 Fax 761484

ELVERSON, Ronald Peter Charles. b 50. St Edm Hall Ox BA73 MA86. St Jo Coll Nottm 84. d 86 p 87. C Whitnash *Cov* 86-90; V Dunchurch from 90. *The Vicarage, 11 Critchley Drive, Dunchurch, Rugby, Warks CV22 6PJ* Rugby (01788) 810274

ELVEY, Ms Charlotte Evanthia. b 44. St Anne's Coll Ox BA66 Bris Univ CertEd67 Open Univ DipReadDev86. S'wark Ord Course 91. d 94. NSM Sydenham St Bart *S'wark* from 94. *30 Overhill Road, London SE22 0PH* 0181-693 1735

ELVIN, Jonathan Paul Alistair. b 65. Bris Univ BSc90 Fitzw Coll Cam BA94. Ridley Hall Cam CTM95. d 95. C Gravesend St Geo *Roch* from 95. *71 Peacock Street, Gravesend, Kent DA12 1EG* Gravesend (01474) 320886

ELVIN, Keith Vernon. b 24. Bris Univ BSc52. d 65 p 65. C St Clement *Truro* 65-66 and 67-75 and 76-79; Chapl Truro Cathl 66-67; C St John w Millbrook *Truro* 75-76; Hon C Truro St Paul and St Clem 79-80; Vice-Prin Chan Sch and SW Minl Tr Sch Truro 80-82; Lic to Offic 80-84; Perm to Offic from 84. *26 Westfield House, Cote Lane, Bristol BS9 3UN* Bristol (0117) 962 8328

ELVY, Canon Peter David. b 38. Lon Univ BA62 Fitzw Ho Cam BA64 MA68. Ridley Hall Cam. d 65 p 66. C Herne *Cant* 65-66; C New Addington 66-68; C Addiscombe St Mildred 69-71; Youth Chapl *Chelmsf* 71-80; V Gt Burstead 75-92; Can Chelmsf Cathl 80-92; V Chelsea All SS *Lon* from 92. *4 Old Church Street, London SW3 5DQ* 0171-352 5627

ELWIN, Ernest John. b 31. Selw Coll Cam BA54 MA58. Ridley Hall Cam 54. d 56 p 57. C Wandsworth All SS *S'wark* 56-59; C Harlow New Town w Lt Parndon *Chelmsf* 59-61; Tidworth Down Sch Dorset 61-63; V Soundwell *Bris* 63-66; Perm to Offic *Sarum* from 66; Master Seldown Sch Dorset 66-68; Wareham Modern Sch 68-69; S Dorset Tech Coll Weymouth 70-85; Weymouth Coll 85-88. *4 Portesham Hill, Portesham, Weymouth, Dorset DT3 4EU* Weymouth (01305) 871358

ELWOOD, Alan Roy. b 54. Sarum & Wells Th Coll 90. d 92 p 93. C Street w Walton *B & W* from 92. *54 Green Lane Avenue, Street, Somerset BA16 0QU* Street (01458) 42430

ELY, Nigel Patrick. b 62. Thames Poly BA83 Southn Univ BTh92. Chich Th Coll 89. d 92 p 93. C Rustington *Chich* 92-93; C Bexhill St Pet from 93. *73A Dorset Road, Bexhill-on-Sea, E Sussex TN40 1SQ* Bexhill-on-Sea (01424) 212453

ELY, Archdeacon of. See WATSON, Ven Jeffrey John Seagrief (Jeff)

ELY, Bishop of. See SYKES, Rt Rev Stephen Whitefield

ELY, Dean of. See HIGGINS, Very Rev Michael John

EMBERTON, John Nicholas. b 45. FCA69. Oak Hill NSM Course 85. d 88 p 89. NSM Purley Ch Ch *S'wark* from 88. *49 Oakwood Avenue, Purley, Surrey CR8 1AR* 0181-668 2684

EMBLETON, Harold. b 21. Ch Coll Cam BA47 MA52. Qu Coll Birm 47. d 49 p 50. Chapl RN 53-76; QHC 74-76; V Bognor *Chich* 76-84; RD Arundel and Bognor 77-82; V Skirwith, Ousby and Melmerby w Kirkland *Carl* 84-87; rtd 87; Perm to Offic *Carl* 87-93. *Flat 5, 7 Chatsworth Gardens, Eastbourne, E Sussex BN20 7JP* Eastbourne (01323) 411426

EMBLIN, Richard John. b 48. BEd71 MA81. S Dios Minl Tr Scheme 83. d 86 p 87. C S w N Hayling *Portsm* 86-89; P-in-c Wootton 89-95; V Cowes H Trin and St Mary from 95. *The Vicarage, Church Road, Cowes, Isle of Wight PO31 8HA* Isle of Wight (01983) 292509

EMBRY, Miss Eileen Margaret. b 38. Westf Coll Lon BA60 Lon Univ BD71. dss 81 d 87 p 94. Lect Trin Coll Bris 81-83; Bishopsworth *Bris* 83-87; Par Dn 87-89; rtd 89; Perm to Offic *Bris* from 89; Tutor Trin Coll Bris from 92. *2 Bishop's Cove, Bristol BS13 8HH* Bristol (0117) 964 2588

EMERSON, Arthur Edward Richard. b 24. Lich Th Coll 69. d 72 p 73. C Barton upon Humber *Linc* 72-74; V Chapel St Leonards 75-88; P-in-c Hogsthorpe 77-88; V Chapel St Leonards w Hogsthorpe 88-91; rtd 91; Perm to Offic *Linc* from 91. *47 Highfields, Nettleham, Lincoln LN2 2SZ* Lincoln (01522) 754175

EMERSON, David. b 43. BNC Ox BA66 MA70 DPhil70. Edin Dioc NSM Course 83. d 86 p 87. NSM Edin St Hilda *Edin* from 86; NSM Edin St Fillan from 86. *25 Little Road, Edinburgh EH16 6SH* 0131-664 3035

EMERSON, Mrs Jan Vivien. b 44. S Dios Minl Tr Scheme 89. d 92 p 95. NSM Chich St Paul and St Pet *Chich* 92-94; NSM Bosham from 94. *23 Lavant Road, Chichester, W Sussex PO19 4RA* Chichester (01243) 527214

EMERTON, Canon John Adney. b 28. FBA79 CCC Ox BA50 MA54 CCC Cam BD60 DD73 Edin Univ Hon DD77. Wycliffe Hall Ox 50. d 52 p 53. C Birm Cathl *Birm* 52-53; Asst Lect Th Birm Univ 52-53; Lect Hebrew Dur Univ 53-55; Lect Div Cam Univ 55-62; Reader in Semitic Philology Ox Univ 62-68; Lic to Offic *Ely* from 68; Regius Prof Hebrew Cam Univ from 68; Fell St Jo Coll Cam from 70; Hon Can Jerusalem from 84. *34 Gough Way, Cambridge CB3 9LN* Cambridge (01223) 63219

EMERY, Frank. b 07. d 67 p 68. C Holyhead w Rhoscolyn *Ban* 67-71; C Holyhead w Rhoscolyn w Llanfair-yn-Neubwll 71-80; rtd 80. *Bodhyfryd, 16 Seabourne Road, Holyhead, Gwynedd LL65 1AL* Holyhead (01407) 762491

EMERY, Ms Karen Maureen. b 53. R Holloway Coll Lon BA74. St Alb Minl Tr Scheme 88. d 92 p 94. Par Dn Royston *St Alb* 92-94; C from 94. *12 Prince Andrew's Close, Royston, Herts SG8 9DZ* Royston (01763) 243265

EMES, Leonard Bingham. b 10. Wycliffe Hall Ox 69. d 70 p 70. C Thame *Ox* 70-73; P-in-c Tetsworth 73-77; P-in-c Adwell w S Weston 73-77; rtd 77; Perm to Offic *St E* 77-83; Perm to Offic *Cant* 83-93. *47 Summerlands Lodge, Wellbrook Road, Farnborough, Kent BR6 8ME* Farnborough (01689) 851076

EMM, Robert Kenneth. b 46. K Coll Lon BD68 AKC68. d 69 p 70. C Hammersmith SS Mich and Geo White City Estate CD *Lon* 69-72; C Keynsham *B & W* 72-75; C Yeovil 75-80; TV Gt Grimsby St Mary and St Jas *Linc* 80-85; R N Thoresby 85-94; R Grainsby 85-94; V Waithe 85-94; R The North-Chapel Parishes from 94. *The Rectory, North Thoresby, Grimsby, S Humberside DN36 5QG* Grimsby (01472) 840029

EMMEL, Canon Malcolm David. b 32. Qu Coll Birm DipTh58. d 58 p 59. C Hessle *York* 58-62; Canada 62-66; V Catterick *Ripon* 66-73; V Pateley Bridge and Greenhow Hill 73-77; P-in-c Middlesmoor w Ramsgill 76-77; V Upper Nidderdale 77-88; RD Ripon 79-86; Hon Can Ripon Cathl from 84; R Bedale from 88; P-in-c Leeming from 88. *The Rectory, Bedale, N Yorkshire DL8 1AB* Bedale (01677) 422103

EMMERSON, Peter Barrett. b 29. Fitzw Ho Cam BA54 MA58. Tyndale Hall Bris 50. d 54 p 57. Distr Sec BFBS (Northd and Dur) 64-70; Distr Sec BFBS (Warks, Staffs and Birm) 70-74; W Midl Regional Sec BFBS 72-74; Hon C Boldmere *Birm* 71-74; C-in-c Crown E CD *Worc* 74-77; P-in-c Crown E and Rushwick 77-81; R Stoke Prior, Wychbold and Upton Warren 81-93; rtd 93; Perm to Offic *Worc* from 93. *Fir Tree Cottage, Ivy Lane, Fernhill Heath, Worcester WR3 8RW* Worcester (01905) 456416

✠EMMERSON, Rt Rev Ralph. b 13. AKC38 Lon Univ BD38. Westcott Ho Cam 38. d 38 p 39 c 72. C Leeds St Geo *Ripon* 38-41; C-in-c Seacroft CD 41-48; C Methley 48-49; P-in-c 49-52; R 52-56; P-in-c Mickletown 49-52; R 52-56; V Headingley 56-66; Hon Can Ripon Cathl 64-66; Can Res Ripon Cathl 66-72; Suff Bp Knaresborough 72-79; rtd 79; Asst Bp Ripon from 86. *Flat 1, 15 High St Agnes Gate, Ripon, N Yorkshire HG4 1QR* Ripon (01765) 701626

EMMET, Herbert Gerald. b 18. Trin Coll Cam BA40. Linc Th Coll 40. d 42 p 43. V Harpenden St Jo *St Alb* 64-73; V Kings Langley 73-80; rtd 80; Perm to Offic *St Alb* from 80. *39 Linwood Grove, Leighton Buzzard, Beds LU7 8RP* Leighton Buzzard (01525) 377350

EMMETT, Kerry Charles. b 46. St Jo Coll Dur BA68. St Jo Coll Nottm 71. d 73 p 74. C Attenborough w Chilwell *S'well* 73-75; C Chilwell 75-76; C Wembley St Jo *Lon* 76-79; V Hanworth St Rich 79-89; R Ravenstone and Swannington *Leic* from 89. *The Rectory, 9 Orchard Close, The Limes, Ravenstone, Coalville, Leics LE67 2JW* Coalville (01530) 839802

EMMETT, Thomas. b 40. Chich Th Coll 67. **d** 70 **p** 71. C Shiremoor *Newc* 70-73; C Haltwhistle 73-75; V Newc Ch Ch 75-80; P-in-c Newc St Anne 77-80; V Newc Ch Ch w St Ann 81-87; V Bywell St Pet from 87. *St Peter's Vicarage, Meadowfield Road, Bywell, Stocksfield, Northd NE43 7PY* Stocksfield (01661) 842272

EMMOTT, David Eugene. b 41. St Chad's Coll Dur BA63 DipTh66. **d** 66 **p** 67. C Bingley H Trin *Bradf* 66-69; C Anfield St Marg *Liv* 69-70; C Kirkby 70-75; Chapl Newc Poly *Newc* 75-78; Hon C Toxteth Park St Marg *Liv* 78-80; TV Upholland 80-88; V Southfields St Barn *S'wark* from 88. *St Barnabas's Vicarage, 430 Merton Road, London SW18 5AE* 0181-874 7768

EMMOTT, Douglas Brenton. b 45. K Coll Lon BD78 AKC78. Linc Th Coll 79. **d** 80 **p** 81. C Kingston upon Hull St Alb *York* 80-83; V Scarborough St Sav w All SS 83-91; V York St Chad from 91. *St Chad's Vicarage, Campleshon Road, York YO2 1EY* York (01904) 654707

EMPEY, Canon Clement Adrian. b 42. TCD BA64 MA68 PhD71. CITC. **d** 74 **p** 75. Hon Chapl Miss to Seamen from 75; C Dub St Ann *D & G* 75-76; I Kells-Inistioge Gp *C & O* 76-84; Preb Tassagard St Patr Cathl Dub from 82; I Clane w Donadea and Coolcarrigan *M & K* 84-88; I Dub St Ann and St Steph *D & G* from 88; Treas St Patr Cathl Dub 89-91; Chan from 91. *St Ann's Vicarage, 88 Mount Anville Wood, Lower Kilmacud, Dublin 14, Irish Republic* Dublin (1) 288-0663

✠**EMPEY, Most Rev Walton Newcome Francis.** b 34. TCD BA57. K Coll (NS) BD68. **d** 58 **p** 59 **c** 81. C Glenageary *D & G* 58-60; Canada 60-66; I Stradbally *C & O* 66-71; I Limerick St Mich *L & K* 71-81; Dean Limerick 71-81; Preb Taney St Patr Cathl Dub 73-81; Bp L & K 81-85; Bp M & K from 85. *Bishop's House, Moyglare, Maynooth, Co Kildare, Irish Republic* Dublin (1) 628-9354 Fax 628-9696

EMSLEY, John Stobart. b 13. Qu Coll Birm 39. **d** 41 **p** 41. V Yeadon St Andr *Bradf* 71-79; rtd 79. *11 Bishop Garth, Pateley Bridge, Harrogate, N Yorkshire HG3 5LL* Harrogate (01423) 711835

EMSON, Stanley George. b 26. Glouc Sch of Min. **d** 89 **p** 90. NSM Cirencester *Glouc* 89-92; NSM Coates, Rodmarton and Sapperton etc from 92. *Flat 1, Rodmarton Manor, Rodmarton, Cirencester, Glos GL7 6PF* Cirencester (01285) 841362

EMTAGE, Miss Susan Raymond. b 34. St Mich Ho Ox 63. **dss** 79 **d** 87 **p** 94. SW Area Sec CPAS Women's Action 75-82; Leic St Chris *Leic* 82-86; Bramerton w Surlingham *Nor* 86-87; C 87-88; C Rockland St Mary w Hellington, Bramerton etc 88-89; Par Dn W Bromwich St Jas *Lich* 89-94; Par Dn W Bromwich St Paul Golds Hill 89-94; C W Bromwich St Jas 94; C W Bromwich St Paul Golds Hill 94; rtd 94. *55 Sheldrake Drive, Bristol BS16 1UE* Bristol (0117) 965 7188

ENDALL, Peter John. b 38. Linc Th Coll 83. **d** 85 **p** 86. C Burley in Wharfedale *Bradf* 85-88; V Thwaites Brow from 88. *The Vicarage, Spring Avenue, Thwaites Brow, Keighley, W Yorkshire BD21 4TA* Keighley (01535) 602830

ENDEAN, Michael George Devereux. b 33. Ox NSM Course. **d** 84 **p** 85. NSM Wantage Downs *Ox* from 84. *2 Mount Pleasant, East Hendred, Wantage, Oxon OX12 8LA* Abingdon (01235) 833497

ENEVER, Mrs Rosemary Alice Delande. b 45. Oak Hill Th Coll 86. **d** 88 **p** 94. NSM Gt Ilford St Jo *Chelmsf* 88-94; TV Waltham H Cross from 94. *St Lawrence House, 46 Mallion Court, Ninefields, Waltham Abbey, Essex EN9 3EQ* Lea Valley (01992) 767916

ENEVER, Mrs Susan Elizabeth. b 33. W Midl Minl Tr Course 87. **d** 92 **p** 94. NSM Rugby St Andr *Cov* from 92. *7 Rocheberie Way, Rugby, Warks CV22 6EG* Rugby (01788) 813135

ENEVER, Vivian John. b 61. Collingwood Coll Dur BA82 Cam Univ PGCE85. Westcott Ho Cam 88. **d** 91 **p** 92. C Gt Crosby St Faith *Liv* 91-95; C Cantril Farm from 95. *16 Nevitte Close, Liverpool L28 1RA* 0151-220 3066

ENGEL, Jeffrey Davis. b 38. Man Univ BA59 Liv Univ PGCE60 Keele Univ ADC69 Aston Univ MSc82 FCP83. St Deiniol's Hawarden 86. **d** 89 **p** 90. NSM Formby St Pet *Liv* 89-92; C Prescot 92-94; Dioc Adv For Pastoral Care & Counselling from 94; P-in-c Hale from 94. *The Vicarage, Hale, Liverpool L24 4AX* 0151-425 3195

ENGELSEN, Christopher James. b 57. Nottm Univ BTh86. Linc Th Coll 83. **d** 86 **p** 87. C Sprowston *Nor* 86-89; C High Harrogate Ch Ch *Ripon* 89-92; TV Seacroft 92-95; P-in-c Foulsham w Hindolveston and Guestwick *Nor* from 95. *The Rectory, Guist Road, Foulsham, Dereham, Norfolk NR20 5RZ* Foulsham (01362) 683275

ENGH, Timm Gray. b 38. Univ of the South (USA) 79 Arizona Univ BSc66 Michigan State Univ MSc69. **d** 81 **p** 82. USA 81-86; R Melrose *Edin* 86-90; R Edin St Mark from 90; R Edin St Andr and St Aid from 90. *27 Argyle Crescent, Edinburgh EH15 2QE* 0131-669 3452

ENGLAND, Jessie Margaret Tarie. See CARLYON, Mrs Jessie Marguerite Tarie

ENGLAND, Robert Gordon. b 39. TCD BA62 QUB MTh76. TCD Div Sch Div Test65. **d** 66 **p** 67. C Raheny w Coolock *D & G* 66-69; C Lisburn Ch Ch *Conn* 72-73; Lic to Offic *D & D* from 74; Hd RE Regent Ho Sch Newtownards from 74. *20 Loury Court, 27 Hampton Park, Belfast BT7 3JY*

ENGLER, Mrs Margaret Dorothy. b 44. Lon Univ TCert77. S'wark Ord Course 90. **d** 93 **p** 94. NSM Harlesden All So *Lon* from 93. *22A Langton Road, London NW2 6QA* 0181-450 2395

ENGLISH, Peter Gordon. b 31. Edin Univ MA55. Ripon Hall Ox 59. **d** 61 **p** 62. C Bingley All SS *Bradf* 61-64; V Cottingley 64-66; Uganda from 66. *PO Box 7062, Kampala, Uganda*

ENGLISH, Peter Redford. b 26. Ridley Hall Cam 70. **d** 72 **p** 73. C Tyldesley w Shakerley *Man* 72-74; C Worsley 74-76; R Levenshulme St Mark 76-81; R Heytesbury and Sutton Veny *Sarum* 81-91; rtd 91. *The Old Rectory, Bromsberrow, Ledbury, Herefordshire HT8 1RU* Ledbury (01531) 650362

ENNION, Peter. b 56. Aston Tr Scheme 85 Coll of Resurr Mirfield 87. **d** 89 **p** 90. C Middlewich w Byley *Ches* 89-91; C Aylestone St Andr w St Jas *Leic* 91-92; C Coppenhall *Ches* 92-94; P-in-c Newton in Mottram from 94. *St Mary's Vicarage, 39 Bradley Green Road, Hyde, Cheshire SK14 4NA* 0161-368 1489

ENNIS, Martin Michael. b 58. MCollP84 Man Univ BSc80. Sarum & Wells Th Coll 87. **d** 89 **p** 90. C Newquay *Truro* 89-92; C Tewkesbury w Walton Cardiff *Glouc* 92-95; P-in-c Brockworth from 95. *The Vicarage, 42 Court Road, Gloucester GL3 4ET* Gloucester (01452) 862725

ENOCH, David John. b 34. Univ of Wales (Ban) BA55 Univ of Wales (Abth) MA69. United Th Coll Abth 55 Glouc Sch of Min 89. **d** 91 **p** 92. NSM Much Birch w Lt Birch, Much Dewchurch etc *Heref* 91-94; P-in-c How Caple w Sollarshope, Sellack etc 94; P-in-c from 95. *The Rectory, Kings Caple, Hereford HR1 4TX* Hereford (01432) 840485

ENOCH, William Frederick Palmer. b 30. E Midl Min Tr Course 76. **d** 79 **p** 80. NSM Ilkeston St Mary *Derby* 79-85; P-in-c Ilkeston H Trin from 85. *9 Henley Way, West Hallam, Derbyshire DE7 6LU* Nottingham (0115) 944 3003

ENRIGHT, Canon James Leslie. b 06. **d** 66 **p** 66. I Dromod *L & K* 67-76; Can Limerick Cathl 72-76; Prec Limerick Cathl 72-76; rtd 76. *8 Seafield, Newtown Hill, Tramore, Co Waterford, Irish Republic* Tramore (51) 381855

ENSOR, David Alec. b 25. Cape Town Univ BA67. Cuddesdon Coll 48. **d** 50 **p** 51. V Quadring *Linc* 68-73; V Gt Grimsby St Andr and St Luke 73-74; V Grimsby St Aug 73-84; R Claypole 84-86; V Whaplode Drove 86-91; V Gedney Hill 86-91; rtd 91; Perm to Offic *Linc* from 91. *73 Monks Dyke Road, Louth, Lincs LN11 8QN* Louth (01507) 604341

ENSOR, Keith Victor. b 08. Dur Univ LTh32. Lon Coll of Div 27. **d** 31 **p** 32. C Holloway St Jas *Lon* 31-34; Org Sec (N Prov) BCMS 34-38; Algeria 38-39; Chapl RAFVR 39-47; V Wolvey, Burton Hastings and Stretton Baskerville *Cov* 47-50; Chapl RAF 50-63; R Horton and Lt Sodbury *Glouc* from 64. *The Rectory, Horton, Chipping Sodbury, Bristol BS17 6QP* Chipping Sodbury (01454) 313256

ENSOR, Paul George. b 56. Ripon Coll Cuddesdon. **d** 82 **p** 83. C Newington St Mary *S'wark* 82-87; TV Croydon St Jo 87-91; P-in-c Brandon and Santon Downham *St E* 91-92; R Brandon and Santon Downham w Elveden 92-95; V Mitcham St Olave *S'wark* from 95. *St Olave's Vicarage, 22 Church Walk, London SW16 5JH* 0181-764 2048

ENSOR, Stephen Herbert Paulett. b 07. ALCD31 St Jo Coll Dur LTh31 BA32. **d** 32 **p** 33. TR Bedworth *Cov* 70-81; rtd 81; Perm to Offic *B & W* from 82. *Hillside Cottage, South Street, Castle Cary, Somerset BA7 7ES* Castle Cary (01963) 51003

ENSOR, Terrence Bryon. b 45. K Coll Lon BD78 AKC78. Westcott Ho Cam 78. **d** 79 **p** 80. C S'wark St Sav w All Hallows *S'wark* 79-82; Seychelles 82-85; V Northn St Benedict *Pet* 85-90; Uruguay 90-93; USPG Fieldworker (Blackb, Bradf, Carl & Wakef) from 93. *c/o USPG, Partnership House, 157 Waterloo Road, London SE1 8XA* 0171-928 8681 Fax 928 2371

ENTWISLE, Canon George Barry. b 43. St Jo Coll Ox BA66 MA73. Linc Th Coll 73. **d** 75 **p** 76. C Rawmarsh w Parkgate *Sheff* 75-78; New Zealand from 78; Can St Paul's Cathl Dunedin from 87. *15 Trafford Street, Gore, New Zealand* Christchurch (3) 208-7366

ENTWISTLE, Alan. b 41. ACP69 Nottm Univ CertEd67 Open Univ BA80 Man Univ MEd85. NW Ord Course 72. **d** 75 **p** 76. C Bury H Trin *Man* 75-78; Hd Master Hazlehurst Sch Bury from 78; Lic to Offic *Man* from 78. *1 Alderwood Grove, Edenfield, Bury, Lancs BL0 0HQ* Ramsbottom (01706) 824221

ENTWISTLE, Christopher John. b 47. N Ord Course 79. **d** 82 **p** 83. NSM Colne H Trin *Blackb* 82-84; C Poulton-le-Fylde 84-87; V Blackpool St Paul from 87; RD Blackpool from 94. *St Paul's Vicarage, Edgerton Road, Blackpool FY1 2NP* Blackpool (01253) 25308

215

ENTWISTLE, Frank Roland. b 37. Dur Univ BA59 DipTh60. Cranmer Hall Dur 59. **d** 61 **p** 62. C Harborne Heath *Birm* 61-65; S Area Sec BCMS 65-66; Educn Sec 66-73; Hon C Wallington H Trin *S'wark* 68-73; UCCF from 73; Hon C Ware Ch Ch *St Alb* 73-76; Hon C Leic H Trin w St Jo *Leic* from 76. *157 Shanklin Drive, Leicester LE2 3QG* Leicester (0116) 270 0759/255 1700 Fax 255 5316

ENTWISTLE, Harry. b 40. St Chad's Coll Dur BSc61 DipTh63. **d** 63 **p** 64. C Fleetwood *Blackb* 63-69; P-in-c Aston Abbots w Cublington *Ox* 69-74; P-in-c Hardwick St Mary 69-74; Chapl HM Pris Aylesbury 69-74; Chapl HM Pris Lewes 74-77; Chapl HM Rem Cen Risley 77-81; Chapl HM Pris Wandsworth 81-88; Australia from 88. *32 Agincourt Drive, Willeton, W Australia 6155* Perth (9) 332-1639 or 325-4911

ENTWISTLE, Howard Rodney. b 36. Ball Coll Ox BA61. Linc Th Coll 61. **d** 63 **p** 64. C Langley St Aid CD *Man* 63-64; C Langley All SS and Martyrs 64-66; V Wythenshawe St Martin 66-73; R Stretford St Matt from 73. *St Matthew's Rectory, 39 Sandy Lane, Stretford, Manchester M32 9DB* 0161-865 2535

EPERSON, Canon Donald Birkby. b 04. Ch Ch Ox BA27 MA30. Ripon Hall Ox 30. **d** 30 **p** 31. Perm to Offic *Cant* from 64; rtd 71. *12 Puckle Lane, Canterbury, Kent CT1 3JX* Canterbury (01227) 766477

EPPINGSTONE, Preb Rudolph Oscar Herbert. b 19. Kelham Th Coll 47. **d** 51 **p** 52. R Clovelly *Ex* 59-78; RD Hartland 67-74; V Woolfardisworthy and Buck Mills 77-78; V Beer 78-86; Preb Ex Cathl from 82; Hon C Combe Martin and Berrynarbor from 86; rtd 87. *Parson's Pightle, Berrynarbor, Ilfracombe, Devon EX34 9TB* Combe Martin (01271) 882802

EPPS, Christopher Derek (Chris). b 54. ACII79. Linc Th Coll CMinlStuds95. **d** 95. C Clevedon St Jo *B & W* from 95. *53 Woodington Road, Clevedon, Avon BS21 5LB* Clevedon (01275) 879832

EPPS, Gerald Ralph. b 31. Open Univ BA79. Oak Hill Th Coll 52 K Coll Lon 54. **d** 57 **p** 58. V Freethorpe w Wickhampton *Nor* 60-70; V Halvergate w Tunstall 67-70; R Pulham St Mary Magd 70-80; P-in-c Alburgh 76-77; P-in-c Denton 76-77; P-in-c Pulham St Mary V 76-80; R Pulham 80-91; rtd 91; Perm to Offic *Nor* from 91. *10 Lime Close, Harleston, Norfolk IP20 9DG* Harleston (01379) 854532

EQUEALL, David Edward Royston. b 41. Open Univ BA. St Mich Coll Llan 68. **d** 71 **p** 72. C Mountain Ash *Llan* 71-74; C Gabalfa 74-77; Chapl Asst Univ Hosp of Wales Cardiff 74-77; Chapl 77-79; Chapl N Gen Hosp Sheff from 79. *Northern General Hospital, Herries Road, Sheffield S5 7AU, or 2 Longley Lane, Sheffield S5 7JD* Sheffield (0114) 271 5056 or 243 4343

ERRIDGE, David John. b 45. Lon Univ DipTh68. Tyndale Hall Bris 66. **d** 69 **p** 70. C Bootle St Matt *Liv* 69-72; C Horwich H Trin *Man* 72-77; R Blackley St Andr from 77; AD N Man 85-94. *The Vicarage, Churchdale Road, Higher Blackley, Manchester M9 3ND* 0161-740 2961

ERSKINE, Canon Samuel Thomas. b 19. TCD BA42 MA46. **d** 43 **p** 44. RD Canewdon and Southend *Chelmsf* 68-84; V Prittlewell St Mary 68-77; V Prittlewell 77-84; rtd 84; Perm to Offic *St E* from 85. *11 Kembold Close, Moreton Rise, Bury St Edmunds, Suffolk IP32 7EF* Bury St Edmunds (01284) 706337

ESAU, John Owen. b 39. St Mich Coll Llan DipPTh95. **d** 95. Min Can St D Cathl *St D* from 95. *Pembroke Cottage, Glasfryn Lane, St Davids, Haverfordwest, Dyfed SA62 6ST* St Davids (01437) 720252

ESCOLME, Miss Doreen. b 29. St Jo Coll Nottm 82. **dss** 83 **d** 87 **p** 94. Hunslet Moor St Pet and St Cuth *Ripon* 83-87; C 87-88; Par Dn Wyther Ven Bede 88-94; C 94; rtd 94; Perm to Offic *Ripon* from 94. *6 Heather Gardens, Leeds LS13 4LF* Leeds (0113) 257 9055

ESCRITT, Canon Margaret Ruth. b 37. Selly Oak Coll IDC62. **d** 87 **p** 94. Dioc Adv for Diaconal Mins *York* 85-91; Chapl HM Pris Full Sutton 92-94; Par Dn Kexby w Wilberfoss *York* 93-94; C 94; Chapl HM Pris Everthorpe from 95; Can York Minster *York* from 95. *HM Young Offender Institution, Everthorpe, Brough, N Humberside HU15 1RB* Howden (01430) 422471 Fax 421351

ESCRITT, Michael William. b 35. Birm Univ DipTh67. Qu Coll Birm 64. **d** 67 **p** 68. C Huntington *York* 67-69; Abp's Dom Chapl 69-72; V Bishopthorpe 72-83; V Acaster Malbis 73-83; V Selby Abbey 83-90; TR Haxby w Wigginton from 90. *The Rectory, 3 Westfield Close, Haxby, York YO3 3JG* York (01904) 760455

ESDAILE, Canon Adrian George Kennedy. b 35. Mert Coll Ox BA57 MA61. Wells Th Coll 59. **d** 61 **p** 62. C St Helier *S'wark* 61-64; C Wimbledon 64-68; V Hackbridge and N Beddington 68-80; RD Sutton 76-80; TR Chipping Barnet w Arkley *St Alb* from 80; RD Barnet 89-94; Hon Can St Alb from 94. *The Rectory, 38 Manor Road, Barnet, Herts EN5 2JJ* 0181-449 3894

ESPIN-BRADLEY, Richard John. b 61. Lanc Univ BSc84. Oak Hill Th Coll DipHE95. **d** 95. C Brundall w Braydeston and Postwick *Nor* from 95. *8 Greenacre Close, Brundall, Norwich NR13 5QF* Norwich (01603) 714570

ESSER, Lindsay Percy David. b 53. BA. Oak Hill Th Coll. **d** 84 **p** 85. C Barnsbury St Andr and H Trin w All SS *Lon* 84-87; Chapl Paris St Mich *Eur* 87-90; C Spring Grove St Mary *Lon* from 90. *16 Spencer Road, Isleworth, Middx TW7 6BH* 0181-560 7141

ESSERY, Canon Eric Albert. b 28. TD ED78. Univ of Wales (Lamp) BA53 Reading Univ CertEd76. St Mich Coll Llan 53. **d** 55 **p** 56. C Skewen *Llan* 55-57; C Oakwood 57-59; C Sunbury *Lon* 59-63; Ind Chapl *Chich* 63-64; P-in-c Crawley 63-64; V Hammersmith St Paul *Lon* 64-74; CF (TAVR) from 65; V Shinfield *Ox* 74-84; V Whitley Ch Ch from 84; RD Reading 85-95; Hon Can Ch Ch from 88. *Christ Church Vicarage, 4 Vicarage Road, Reading RG2 7AJ* Reading (01734) 871250

ESTDALE, Canon Francis Albert. b 26. ALCD53. **d** 53 **p** 54. V Stopsley *St Alb* 61-94; Hon Can St Alb Abbey 90-94; rtd 94. *4 Peacock Way, South Bretton, Peterborough PE3 9AA* Peterborough (01733) 261048

ETCHELLS, Peter. b 26. Kelham Th Coll 48. **d** 52 **p** 53. C Chesterton St Geo *Ely* 52-55; C Leic St Marg *Leic* 55-58; R Willoughby Waterleys, Peatling Magna etc from 58. *The Vicarage, Gilmorton Road, Ashby Magna, Lutterworth, Leics LE17 5NF* Leire (01455) 209406

ETCHES, Haigh David. b 45. St Jo Coll Dur BA71 DipTh72. **d** 73 **p** 74. C Whitnash *Cov* 73-77; C Wallingford *Ox* 77-79; C Wallingford w Crowmarsh Gifford etc 79-83; P-in-c Bearwood 83-86; R from 86. *The Rectory, 6 St Catherine's Close, Wokingham, Berks RG11 5BZ* Wokingham (01734) 794364

ETHERIDGE, Mrs Marjorie. b 18. Univ of Wales (Ban) BA38 Open Univ BA84. St Alb Minl Tr Scheme 80. **dss** 83 **d** 87 **p** 94. Hitchin *St Alb* 83-94; Hon Par Dn 87-94; Lic to Offic from 94. *23 Stormont Road, Hitchin, Herts SG5 1SH* Hitchin (01462) 450496

ETHERIDGE, Richard Thomas. b 32. Lon Univ BD62. ALCD61. **d** 62 **p** 63. C Wilmington *Roch* 62-65; C Rainham 65-69; V Langley St Jo *Birm* from 69; P-in-c Oldbury from 83; P-in-c Langley St Mich from 95. *The Vicarage, St John's Road, Oldbury, Warley, W Midlands B68 9RF* 0121-552 5005

ETHERIDGE, Terry. b 44. Wells Th Coll 68. **d** 70 **p** 71. C Barrow St Jo *Carl* 70-73; C Wilmslow *Ches* 73-76; V Knutsford St Cross 76-85; R Malpas and Threapwood from 85. *The Rectory, Malpas, Cheshire SY14 8PP* Malpas (01948) 860209

ETHERINGTON, Ernest Hugh. b 12. CCC Cam BA34 MA39. Linc Th Coll 34. **d** 35 **p** 36. Asst Master Horbury Sec Sch 61-77; Perm to Offic *Wakef* 72-94; rtd 77. *Fosbrooke House, Clifton Drive, Lytham, Lytham St Annes, Lancs FY8 5RE* Lytham (01253) 795399

ETHERINGTON, Mrs Ferial Mary Gould. b 44. FILEx83. St Alb Minl Tr Scheme 86. **d** 93 **p** 94. NSM Luton St Chris Round Green *St Alb* from 93. *St Christopher's Vicarage, 33 Felix Avenue, Luton LU2 7LE* Luton (01582) 24754 Fax 718581

ETHERINGTON, Robert Barry. b 37. Man Univ BA62. Linc Th Coll 62. **d** 64 **p** 65. C Linc St Jo *Linc* 64-67; C Frodingham 67-69; V Reepham 69-78; Ind Chapl 70-78; Ind Chapl *St Alb* 78-88; V Luton St Chris Round Green from 88. *St Christopher's Vicarage, 33 Felix Avenue, Luton LU2 7LE* Luton (01582) 24754 Fax 718581

ETTERLEY, Peter Anthony Gordon. b 39. Kelham Th Coll 63 Wells Th Coll 66. **d** 68 **p** 69. C Gillingham St Aug *Roch* 68-71; Papua New Guinea 71-80; V Cleeve w Chelvey and Brockley *B & W* 80-84; V Seaton Hirst *Newc* 84-86; TR from 86. *The Vicarage, Newbiggin Road, Ashington, Northd NE63 0TQ* Ashington (01670) 813218

ETTLINGER, Max Brian. b 28. Sarum & Wells Th Coll 70. **d** 72 **p** 73. C Mill Hill Jo Keble Ch *Lon* 72-74; Min Cricklewood St Pet CD 74-78; R Monken Hadley 78-88; Bp's Dom Chapl *St E* 88-91; Dioc Communications Officer 88-91; P-in-c Stratford St Mary 91-93; P-in-c Raydon 91-93; P-in-c Holton St Mary w Gt Wenham 91-93; P-in-c Higham 92-93; rtd 93. *11 Bowthorpe Close, Ipswich IP1 3PZ* Ipswich (01473) 214362

ETTRICK, Peter Alured. b 14. TD56 and Bars OBE67. Ch Coll Cam BA36 MA41. Qu Coll Birm 36. **d** 37 **p** 38. V Bisley *Glouc* 70-79; rtd 79; Perm to Offic *Glouc* from 80. *Meiktila, The Ridge, Bussage, Stroud, Glos GL6 8BB* Brimscombe (01453) 883272

EUROPE, Bishop of Gibraltar in. See HIND, Rt Rev John William

EUROPE, Suffragan Bishop in. See SCRIVEN, Rt Rev Henry William

EUSTICE, Peter Lafevre. b 32. AKC56. **d** 57 **p** 58. C Finsbury Park St Thos *Lon* 57-60; C Redruth *Truro* 60-63; V Treslothan 63-71; V Falmouth All SS 71-76; R St Stephen in Brannel from 76. *The Rectory, 70 Rectory Road, St Stephen, St Austell, Cornwall PL26 7RL* St Austell (01726) 822236

EVA, Canon Owen Vyvyan. b 17. MBE83. Selw Coll Cam BA39 MA43. Ridley Hall Cam 46. **d** 47 **p** 48. R Halewood *Liv* 62-83; TR 83-86; RD Farnworth 71-81; Hon Can Liv Cathl 74-86; rtd 86; Perm to Offic *Ches* from 87; Perm to Offic *Liv* from 87. *10 Saddlers Rise, Norton, Runcorn, Cheshire WA7 6PG* Runcorn (01928) 717119

EVANS, Alan David Carter. b 35. Clifton Th Coll 62. **d** 65 **p** 66. C Gt Baddow *Chelmsf* 65-68; C Walthamstow St Mary 68-72; V Forest Gate St Mark 72-77; V Chadwell Heath 77-86; V Squirrels Heath from 86; Chapl Havering Coll of F & HE 88-94. *The Vicarage, 36 Ardleigh Green Road, Hornchurch, Essex RM11 2LQ* Hornchurch (01708) 446571

EVANS, Alun Wyn. b 47. Down Coll Cam BA70 MA73. Cuddesdon Coll 70. **d** 72 **p** 73. C Bargoed w Brithdir *Llan* 72-74; C Bargoed and Deri w Brithdir 74-75; C Coity w Nolton 75-77; V Cwmavon 77-81; Warden of Ords 80-81; V Llangynwyd w Maesteg 81-86; Prov Officer for Soc Resp 86-93; V Llanishen Ch Ch from 93. *Christ Church Vicarage, 25 Mountbatten Close, Cardiff CF2 5QG* Cardiff (01222) 757190

EVANS, Andrew. b 57. Southn Univ BEd80. S Dios Minl Tr Scheme 88. **d** 91 **p** 92. NSM Cricklade w Latton *Bris* from 91. *35 Pittsfield, Cricklade, Wilts SN6 6AW* Swindon (01793) 751688

EVANS, Anthony Nigel. b 53. Nottm Univ BA74 Fitzw Coll Cam BA76. Westcott Ho Cam 74. **d** 77 **p** 78. C Sneinton St Cypr *S'well* 77-80; C Worksop Priory 80-83; V Nottm St Geo w St Jo 83-88; R Ordsall from 88. *St Mary's Vicarage, Church Avenue, Sutton-in-Ashfield, Notts NG17 2GR* Sutton-in-Ashfield (01623) 554509

EVANS, Benjamin John. b 13. JP. St Mich Coll Llan 75. **d** 76 **p** 77. NSM Barry All SS *Llan* 76-83; rtd 83. *167 Pontypridd Road, Barry, S Glam CF6 8LW* Barry (01446) 734742

EVANS, Brian. b 34. Univ of Wales (Cardiff) DipTh58 Open Univ BA86. St Deiniol's Hawarden 70. **d** 71 **p** 72. C Porthkerry *Llan* 71-72; C Barry All SS 72-75; V Abercynon 75-82; V Pendoylan and Welsh St Donats 82-87; R Maentwrog w Trawsfynydd *Ban* from 87. *The Rectory, Trawsfynydd, Blaenau Ffestiniog, Gwynedd LL41 4RY* Trawsfynydd (0176687) 482

EVANS, Caroline Mary. b 46. CertEd69. St Jo Coll Nottm DipTh86. **d** 86. C Llanbeblig w Caernarfon and Betws Garmon etc *Ban* 86-88; D-in-c Bodedern w Llechgynfarwy and Llechylched etc from 88. *The Vicarage, Bodedern, Holyhead, Gwynedd LL65 3SU* Valley (01407) 740340

EVANS, Charles Wyndham. b 28. Univ of Wales (Ban) BA49 St Cath Soc Ox BA51 MA55. St Steph Ho Ox 49. **d** 52 **p** 53. C Denbigh *St As* 52-56; Lic to Offic *St D* 56-79; Chapl Llandovery Coll 56-67; Chapl and Sen Lect Trin Coll Carmarthen 67-79; V Llanrhaeadr-yng-Nghinmeirch and Prion *St As* from 79; Dioc RE Adv from 82; Tutor St Deiniol's Lib Hawarden from 84; Chapl Ruthin Sch from 84; RD Denbigh *St As* from 84. *The Vicarage, Llanrhaeadr, Denbigh, Clwyd LL16 4NN* Llanynys (0174578) 250

EVANS, Prof Christopher Francis. b 09. CCC Cam BA32 MA38 Ox Univ MA48 Southn Univ Hon DLitt77. Linc Th Coll 33. **d** 34 **p** 35. Prof NT Studies K Coll Lon 62-77; rtd 77. *4 Church Close, Cuddesdon, Oxford OX44 9EX* Wheatley (01865) 874406

EVANS, Christopher Idris. b 51. Chich Th Coll 74. **d** 77 **p** 78. C Gelligaer *Llan* 77-80; C St Andrew's Major and Michaelston-le-Pit 80-81; V Llangeinor 81-87; V Watlington w Pyrton and Shirburn *Ox* from 87. *The Vicarage, Hill Road, Watlington, Oxon OX9 5AD* Watlington (01491) 612494

EVANS, Christopher Jonathan. b 43. AKC67 AKC88. **d** 68 **p** 69. C Wednesfield St Thos *Lich* 68-71; C Dorridge *Birm* 71-74; V Marston Green 74-81; V Acocks Green 81-86; RD Yardley 84-86; V Hill 86-88; Area Officer COPEC Housing Trust 88-91; V Harborne St Pet from 91. *The Vicarage, Old Church Road, Birmingham B17 0BB* 0121-427 1949

EVANS, Clive Roger. b 59. Worc Coll Ox BA80 MA84. St Jo Coll Nottm DTS94. **d** 94 **p** 95. C Barton Seagrave w Warkton *Pet* from 94. *Rectory Cottage, St Botolph's Road, Kettering, Northants NN15 6SR* Kettering (01536) 517760

EVANS, Canon Colin Rex. b 24. Keble Coll Ox BA49. Linc Th Coll. **d** 57 **p** 58. R Bassingham *Linc* 66-74; V Aubourn w Haddington 66-74; V Carlton-le-Moorland w Stapleford 66-74; R Skinnand 66-74; R Thurlby w Norton Disney 66-74; RD Graffoe 69-74; RD Elloe E 74-89; Can and Preb Linc Cathl 74-89; V Holbeach 74-89; rtd 90; Hon C Dawlish *Ex* from 90; RD Kenn from 95. *24 Sweetbriar Lane, Holcombe, Dawlish, Devon EX7 0JZ* Dawlish (01626) 862860

EVANS, Miss Daphne Gillian. b 41. Bible Tr Inst Glas 67 Trin Coll Bris IDC75. dss 83 **d** 87. Wenlock *Heref* 83-88; TD 87-88; rtd 88. *12 Greenmeadow Grove, Endon, Stoke-on-Trent ST9 9EU* Stoke-on-Trent (01782) 504686

EVANS, David. b 37. Keble Coll Ox BA60 MA65 Lon Univ BD64. Wells Th Coll 62. **d** 64 **p** 65. Min Can Brecon Cathl *S & B* 64-68; C Brecon w Battle 64-68; C Swansea St Mary and H Trin 68-71; Chapl Univ of Wales (Swansea) 68-71; Bp's Chapl for Samaritan and Soc Work *Birm* 71-75; Jt Gen Sec Samaritans 75-84; Gen Sec 84-89; Lic to Offic *Ox* 75-89; R Heyford w Stowe Nine Churches *Pet* from 89; Chapl Northants Police from 89. *The Rectory, Nether Heyford, Northampton NN7 3LQ* Weedon (01327) 40487

EVANS, David. b 37. Open Univ BA73. St Mich Coll Llan 65. **d** 67 **p** 68. C Swansea St Pet *S & B* 67-70; C St Austell *Truro* 70-75; R Purley *Ox* 75-90; RD Bradfield 85-90; R Bryanston Square St Mary w St Marylebone St Mark *Lon* from 90; P-in-c St Marylebone Ch Ch 90-91. *73 Gloucester Place, London W1H 3PF* 0171-935 2200

EVANS, David Alexander Noble. b 13. Pemb Coll Ox BA36 MA41. Wells Th Coll 38. **d** 40 **p** 41. V Sunningdale *Ox* 67-80; rtd 80; Perm to Offic *Ex* from 80. *High Bank, Chapel Lane, Manaton, Newton Abbot, Devon TQ13 9UA* Manaton (01647) 221336

EVANS, David Aylmer. b 28. Lon Univ CertEd62 Reading Univ DipC&G73. St D Coll Lamp BA49 LTh51. **d** 51 **p** 52. Perm to Offic *Ox* 65-73; Wokingham Gr Sch 65-72; Counsellor S Molton Sch and Community Coll 73-87; V Middlezoy and Othery and Moorlinch *B & W* 87-93; rtd 93; Perm to Offic *Ex* from 94. *2 Higher Mead, Hemyock, Cullompton, Devon EX15 3QH* Hemyock (01823) 680974

EVANS (or BURTON EVANS), David Burton. b 35. Open Univ BA87 Golds Coll Lon BMus93. K Coll Lon 58 Edin Th Coll 60. **d** 62 **p** 63. C Leeds St Hilda *Ripon* 62-63; C Cross Green St Sav and St Hilda 63-67; Min Can Dur Cathl *Dur* 67-71; Chapl Prebendal Sch Chich 71-74; PV Chich Cathl *Chich* 71-74; V Lynch w Iping Marsh 74-79; Chapl K Edw VII Hosp Midhurst 77-86; V Easebourne *Chich* 79-86; R St Mich Cornhill w St Pet le Poer etc *Lon* from 86. *St Michael's Rectory, St Michael's Alley, London EC3V 9DS* 0171-626 8841 Fax 283 3029

EVANS, Canon David Conrad. b 16. St D Coll Lamp BA40. **d** 42 **p** 43. V Llanfihangel Abercywyn *St D* 63-83; Hon Can St D Cathl 79-83; rtd 83. *17 Penbryn Avenue, Carmarthen, Dyfed SA31 3DH* Carmarthen (01267) 234333

EVANS, Ven David Eifion. b 11. Univ of Wales BA32 MA51. St Mich Coll Llan 33. **d** 34 **p** 35. Adn Cardigan *St D* 67-79; V Newc Emlyn 69-79; rtd 79. *31 Bryn Castell, Bow Street, Aberystwyth, Dyfed SY24 5DE* Aberystwyth (01970) 828747

EVANS, David Elwyn. b 43. St Mich Coll Llan 71. **d** 73 **p** 74. C Llandybie *St D* 73-75; C Llanelli 75-78; V Tre-lech a'r Betws w Abernant and Llanwinio from 78. *Tre-Lech Vicarage, Pen-y-Bont, Carmarthen, Dyfed SA33 6PJ* Madox (01994) 484335

EVANS, David Frederick Francis. b 35. Univ of Wales BSc59. Wells Th Coll 59. **d** 61 **p** 62. C Eltham St Jo *S'wark* 61-64; C Banbury *Ox* 64-69; V Brize Norton and Carterton 69-73; V Tilehurst St Geo 73-84; V Lydney w Aylburton *Glouc* 84-95; V Lydney from 95; RD Forest S from 90. *The Vicarage, Church Road, Lydney, Glos GL15 5EG* Dean (01594) 842321

EVANS, Canon David Geraint. b 24. Univ of Wales BA47. St D Coll Lamp 49. **d** 49 **p** 50. R Ystradgynlais *S & B* 68-91; Hon Can Brecon Cathl 86-91; rtd 91; Perm to Offic *St D* from 91. *Tan-ur-Allt, 117 Heol Cae Gurwen, Gwaun Cae Gurwen, Ammanford, Dyfed SA18 1PD* Amman Valley (01269) 842719

EVANS, David John. b 49. Univ of Wales (Ban) BSc72 Bath Univ CertEd73 Leeds Univ DipTh77. Coll of Resurr Mirfield 75. **d** 78 **p** 79. C Wandsworth St Anne *S'wark* 78-81; C Angell Town St Jo 81-82; TV Catford (Southend) and Downham 82-90; P-in-c Somersham w Pidley and Oldhurst *Ely* 90-91; P-in-c Broughton 90-91; R Somersham w Pidley and Oldhurst from 91. *The Rectory, Rectory Lane, Somersham, Huntingdon, Cambs PE17 3EL* Ramsey (01487) 840676

EVANS, Canon David Leslie Bowen. b 28. Univ of Wales (Lamp) BA52 LTh54. **d** 54 **p** 55. V Burry Port and Pwll *St D* 64-76; V Cardiff Dewi Sant *Llan* 76-86; Asst Chapl HM Pris Cardiff 76-86; V Llan-llwch w Llangain and Llangynog *St D* 86-95; Can St D Cathl from 89; rtd 95. *The Vicarage, Llanllwch, Carmarthen, Dyfed SA31 3RN* Carmarthen (01267) 236805

EVANS, David Richard. b 47. St Steph Ho Ox 68. **d** 72 **p** 73. C Cardiff St Jo *Llan* 72-76; PV Llan Cathl 76-80; V Cleeve Prior and The Littletons *Worc* from 80. *The Vicarage, South Littleton, Evesham, Worcs WR11 5TJ* Evesham (01386) 830397

+EVANS, Rt Rev David Richard John. b 38. G&C Coll Cam BA63 MA66. Clifton Th Coll 63. **d** 65 **p** 66 **c** 78. C Enfield Ch Ch Trent Park *Lon* 65-68; Argentina 69-77; Peru 77-88; Bp Peru 78-88; Bp Bolivia 82-88; Asst Bp Bradf 88-93; Gen Sec SAMS from 93; Asst Bp Roch from 95. *c/o SAMS, Allen Gardiner House, Pembury Road, Tunbridge Wells, Kent TN2 3QU, or The Rectory, Maresfield, Uckfield, E Sussex TN22 2HB* Tunbridge Wells (01892) 538647/8 or Uckfield (01825) 763817 Fax Tunbridge Wells (01892) 525797 or Uckfield as telephone

EVANS, David Russell. Liv Univ BA57. Ripon Hall Ox 59. **d** 61 **p** 62. C Netherton CD *Liv* 61-65; Asst Chapl Can Slade Sch Bolton from 65; Lic to Offic *Man* from 66; Perm to Offic *Liv* from 76. *2 Rushford Grove, Bolton BL1 8TD* Bolton (01204) 592981

EVANS, David Thomas Pugh. b 95. St Aid Birkenhead 41. **d** 44 **p** 45. C-in-c Birkenhead St Winifred's Welsh Ch *Ches* from 44; Chapl Birkenhead Gen Hosp 46-82; V Birkenhead H Trin 54-74; rtd 82. *33 Harcourt Street, Birkenhead, Merseyside L42 5LU* 0151-652 4617

EVANS, David Victor (formerly David John Parker Smith). b 47. S'wark Ord Course 83. **d** 86. SSF 71-94; Hon C Stepney St Dunstan and All SS *Lon* 86-89; Educn Development Officer 86-89; Guardian Hilfield Friary Dorchester 89-91; Novice Guardian Liv 91-93; Birm 93-94; Lic to Offic Sarum 89-91; Liv 91-93; Birm 93-94; NSM Southmead *Bris* from 94; Par Co-ord Southmead St Steph from 94. *The Garden Flat, 9 Cotham Gardens, Bristol BS6 6HD* Bristol (0117) 959 3290

EVANS, Derek. b 45. St D Coll Lamp DipTh68. **d** 68 **p** 69. C Pemb Dock *St D* 68-74; V Ambleston, St Dogwells, Walton E and Llysyfran 74-78; V Wiston w Ambleston, St Dogwells and Walton E 78-81; V Wiston w Ambleston, St Dogwells, Walton E etc 81-85; R Haverfordwest St Mary and St Thos w Haroldston from 85. *The Rectory, Scarrowscant Lane, Haverfordwest, Dyfed SA61 1EP* Haverfordwest (01437) 763170

EVANS, Preb Derek Courtenay. b 29. Down Coll Cam BA52 MA56. St Aid Birkenhead 55. **d** 57 **p** 58. V Trull *B & W* 61-77; RD Taunton S 72-77; P-in-c Walton 77; R Street 77; Preb Wells Cathl 77-94; R Street w Walton 78-94; RD Glastonbury 79-82; R Greinton 81-93; rtd 94; Perm to Offic *B & W* from 94. *41 Moorham Road, Winscombe, Avon BS25 1HS* Winscombe (01934) 843150

EVANS, Desmond. b 26. Univ of Wales (Lamp) BA48 St Cath Soc Ox BA50 MA54. St Steph Ho Ox 48. **d** 51 **p** 52. V Clydach *S & B* 82-87; Lic to Offic *Ban* 59-78; V Llanwrtyd w Llanddulas in Tir Abad etc *S & B* 78-82; RD Builth 79-82; V Abercraf and Callwen 87-95; rtd 95. *26 Palleg Road, Lower Cwmtwrch, Swansea SA9 2QE*

EVANS, Donald Henry. b 13. St D Coll Lamp BA35. **d** 36 **p** 37. V Seighford, Derrington and Cresswell *Lich* 64-78; rtd 78; Perm to Offic *Ches* from 80. *3 Highfield Avenue, Audlem, Crewe CW3 0HW* Audlem (01270) 811165

EVANS, Edward John. b 47. Univ of Wales (Cardiff) DipTh71. St Mich Coll Llan 67. **d** 71 **p** 72. C Llantwit Fadre *Llan* 71-77; R Eglwysilan 77-88; V Laleston w Tythegston and Merthyr Mawr from 88; RD Bridgend from 94. *The Vicarage, Rogers Lane, Laleston, Bridgend, M Glam CF32 0LB* Bridgend (01656) 654254

✠**EVANS, Rt Rev Edward Lewis.** b 04. Lon Univ BD34 MTh39. Bps' Coll Cheshunt 35. **d** 37 **p** 38 c 57. C Prittlewell *Chelmsf* 37-40; Jamaica 40-60; Suff Bp Kingston 57-60; Bp Barbados 60-71; rtd 71. *Terry's Cross, Brighton Road, Henfield, W Sussex BN5 9SX* Henfield (01273) 493334

EVANS, Elwyn David. b 36. Keble Coll Ox BA58 MA62. St Mich Coll Llan 60. **d** 61 **p** 62. C Abth H Trin *St D* 61-63; C Llanelli St Paul 63-66; C Roath St German *Llan* 66-69; V Crynant 69-78; R Llanilid w Pencoed from 79. *The Rectory, 60 Coychurch Road, Pencoed, Bridgend, M Glam CF35 5NA* Pencoed (01656) 860337

EVANS, Elwyn Thomas. b 12. Univ of Wales BA36. St D Coll Lamp 37. **d** 38 **p** 39. V Tyseley *Birm* 64-78; rtd 78. *8 Gipsy Lane, Balsall Common, Coventry CV7 7FW*

EVANS, Emrys. b 17. St D Coll Lamp BA41. **d** 42 **p** 43. V Twickenham All SS *Lon* 60-81; rtd 81; Perm to Offic *Chich* from 81. *5 Rowan Drive, Billingshurst, W Sussex RH14 9NE* Billingshurst (01403) 784312

EVANS, Ernest Maurice. b 28. MIMechE66. St As Minl Tr Course 84. **d** 86 **p** 87. NSM Hope *St As* 86-89; P-in-c Corwen and Llangar 89-90; R Corwen and Llangar w Gwyddelwern and Llawrybetws 90-95; rtd 95. *43 Cil-y-Graig, Llanfairpwll-gwyngyll, Gwynedd LL61 5NZ*

EVANS, Evan Walter. b 16. MBE65. St D Coll Lamp BA36. **d** 39 **p** 40. C Cellan w Llanfair Clydogau *St D* 39; C Narberth 39-40; C Cardigan 40-42; CF (EC) 42-47; C Llandysul *St D* 47; R Didmarton w Oldbury-on-the-Hill and Sopworth *Glouc* 47-52; CF 52-72; Chapl R Hosp Chelsea 72-81; Perm to Offic *St D* from 85. *3 Cilgwyn Row, Llandysul, Dyfed SA44 4BD* Llandysul (01559) 362275

EVANS, Frank Owen. b 23. Univ of Wales BA44. St D Coll Lamp44. **d** 46 **p** 63. C Llanelli *St D* 63-81; Hd Master Coleshill Secondary Sch Dyfed 74-82; Hon C Cydweli and Llandyfaelog *St D* 81-82; V Martletwy w Lawrenny and Minwear and Yerbeston 82-87; rtd 87. *35 Stradey Park Avenue, Llanelli, Dyfed SA15 3EG* Llanelli (01554) 777149

EVANS, Canon Frederick John Margam. b 31. Magd Coll Ox BA53 MA57. St Mich Coll Llan 53. **d** 54 **p** 55. C New Tredegar *Mon* 54-58; C Chepstow 58-60; Asst Chapl United Sheff

Hosps 60-62; Chapl Brookwood Hosp Woking 62-70; V Crookham *Guildf* from 70; RD Aldershot 78-83; Hon Can Guildf Cathl from 89. *14 Gally Hill Road, Church Crookham, Fleet, Hants GU13 0LH* Fleet (01252) 617130

EVANS, Frederick Albert (Fred). b 29. **d** 83 **p** 84. NSM Maisemore *Glouc* 83-94; NSM Glouc St Geo w Whaddon 86-94; Perm to Offic from 94. *10 Hillborough Road, Gloucester GL4 0JQ* Gloucester (01452) 526034

EVANS, Frederick James Stephens. b 21. Qu Coll Cam BA42 MA46. St D Coll Lamp LTh44. **d** 44 **p** 45. R Chalfont St Peter *Ox* 65-78; V Rustington *Chich* 78-86; rtd 86; Perm to Offic *Chich* from 86. *45 Falmer Avenue, Goring-by-Sea, Worthing, W Sussex BN12 4SY* Worthing (01903) 503905

EVANS, Gareth Milton. b 39. Bris Univ LLB60 St Cath Coll Ox BA62 MA66. Ripon Hall Ox 60. **d** 63 **p** 64. C Hengrove *Bris* 63-65; Min Can Bris Cathl 65-68; C Bishopston 68-71; C Notting Hill *Lon* 71-83; V Bayswater from 83. *St Matthew's Vicarage, 27 St Petersburgh Place, London W2 4LA* 0171-229 2192

EVANS, Ven Geoffrey Bainbridge. b 34. St Mich Coll Llan 56 Lambeth MA94. **d** 58 **p** 59. C Llan All SS CD *Llan* 58-60; C Llan N 60-67; Guyana 67-73; Chapl Izmir (Smyrna) w Bornova *Eur* 73-94; Adn Aegean 78-94; Chapl Ankara 85-91; Chapl Istanbul 87-89; Chapl Rome from 94. *All Saints, via del Babuino 153, 00187 Rome, Italy* Rome (6) 36002171 or 36001881

EVANS, Geoffrey David. b 44. Ex Univ PGCE74. K Coll Lon BD69 AKC69 St Aug Coll Cant 69. **d** 70 **p** 71. C Lawrence Weston *Bris* 70-73; Chapl and Head of RE Grenville Coll Bideford 74-79; Chapl and Head of RE Eastbourne Coll 79-82; Chapl Taunton and Somerset Hosp 83-91; Chapl Musgrove Park Hosp 83-91; Chapl Taunton Sch Somerset from 92. *Hele Manor, Bradford on Tone, Taunton, Somerset TA4 1AH* Taunton (01823) 461561

EVANS, Gerald Arthur. b 35. Univ of Wales (Swansea) BA57 Lon Univ DipRS77. S'wark Ord Course 74. **d** 77 **p** 78. NSM Balcombe *Chich* 77-81; NSM Cuckfield 81-87; R Tillington 87-93; R Duncton 87-93; R Up Waltham 87-93; R W Chiltington from 93; Dioc Ecum Officer from 93; RD Storrington from 93. *The Rectory, West Chiltington, Pulborough, W Sussex RH20 2JY* West Chiltington (01798) 813117

EVANS, Mrs Gillian (Jill). b 39. Imp Coll Lon BSc61 Univ of Wales (Cardiff) DPS88. Mon Dioc Tr Scheme 84. **d** 88 **p** 94. NSM Penallt and Trellech *Mon* 88-89; NSM Overmonnow w Wonastow and Michel Troy 89-92; C Ludlow *Heref* 92-93; C Ludlow, Ludford, Ashford Carbonell etc from 93; Dioc Ecum Officer from 92. *St Mary's House, Ashford Carbonell, Ludlow, Shropshire SY8 4DA* Richards Castle (01584) 74352

EVANS, Canon Glyn. b 10. Univ of Wales BA33. St Steph Ho Ox 33. **d** 34 **p** 35. V St Issells *St D* 55-80; RD Narberth 65-80; Treas St D Cathl 77-80; rtd 80. *3 Flemish Close, St Florence, Tenby, Dyfed SA70 8LT* Manorbier (01834) 871434

EVANS, Glyn. b 59. Nene Coll Northampton BA80 Leic Univ BA80 Ch Ch Coll Cant CertEd82 Kent Univ PGCE82 Birm Univ DipTh87. Qu Coll Birm 85. **d** 88 **p** 89. C Denton *Newc* 88-92; V Choppington from 92. *The Vicarage, Scotland Gate, Choppington, Northd NE62 5SX* Bedlington (01670) 822216

EVANS, Glyn Peter. b 54. Leeds Univ BA75. Ripon Coll Cuddesdon 76. **d** 77 **p** 78. C Binley *Cov* 77-80; C Clifton upon Dunsmore w Brownsover 80-84; P-in-c Lacock w Bowden Hill *Bris* 84-89; P-in-c Lt Compton w Chastleton, Cornwell etc *Ox* from 89; Agric Chapl from 89. *The Rectory, Little Compton, Moreton-in-Marsh, Glos GL56 0SE* Moreton-in-Marsh (01608) 674313

EVANS, Guy Maxwell Lyon. b 23. Univ of Wales (Cardiff) BA50 St D Coll Lamp 51. Llan Dioc Tr Scheme 81. **d** 82 **p** 83. NSM Cardiff Dewi Sant *Llan* 82-84; P-in-c Llanfihangel-ar-arth *St D* 84-85; V 85-91; rtd 91; Perm to Offic *Llan* from 91. *86 Redlands Road, Penarth, S Glam CF64 2WL* Penarth (01222) 701963

EVANS, Miss Gwyneth Mary. b 43. Gilmore Ho Linc Th Coll 69. dss 74 **d** 87 **p** 94. Stamford Hill St Thos *Lon* 72-79; Chapl Asst R Free Hosp Lon 79-89; Chapl Odstock Hosp Salisbury 89-94; Chapl Salisbury Hosps from 89. *Salisbury District Hospital, Salisbury SP2 8BJ* Salisbury (01722) 336262

EVANS, Canon Henry Thomas Platt. b 28. Selw Coll Cam BA51 MA55. Linc Th Coll 51. **d** 53 **p** 54. R Stretford St Matt *Man* 67-73; V Knighton St Mary Magd *Leic* 73-83; Hon Can Leic Cathl 76-93; RD Christianity (Leic) S 81-83; Warden Launde Abbey 83-93; P-in-c Loddington *Leic* 83-92; rtd 93. *16 Central Avenue, Leicester LE2 1TB* Leicester (0116) 270 2169

EVANS, Ven Hugh Arfon. b 13. St D Coll Lamp BA35 St Mich Coll Llan 35. **d** 36 **p** 37. V Llanfairisgaer *Ban* 52-73; RD Arfon 58-73; Can Treas 66-73; Adn Ban 73-83; rtd 83. *79 Chambers Lane, Mynydd Isa, Mold, Clwyd CH7 6UZ* Mold (01352) 759269

EVANS, Hywel Victor. b 14. Univ of Wales BA36. St Steph Ho Ox 36. **d** 38 **p** 39. V Bunny w Bradmore *S'well* 66-74; V

Walesby 74-79; R Kirton 74-79; P-in-c Egmanton 77-79; rtd 79. *2 The Retreat, King's Fee, Monmouth, Gwent NP5 3DU* Monmouth (01600) 712268

EVANS, Mrs Jennifer (Jennie). b 41. Sarum Th Coll. **d** 88. C Bramshott *Portsm* 88-91; C Bramshott and Liphook 91-92; Par Dn Whippingham w E Cowes 92-95. *7 Adelaide Grove, East Cowes, Isle of Wight PO32 6DB* Isle of Wight (01983) 297349

EVANS, Ven John Barrie. b 23. Univ of Wales (Lamp) BA47 St Edm Hall Ox BA49 MA54. St Mich Coll Llan 50. **d** 51 **p** 52. V Chepstow *Mon* 64-79; Can St Woolos Cathl 71-77; Adn Mon 77-86; R Llanmartin w Wilcrick and Langstone 79-83; R Llanmartin 83-86; Adn Newport 86-93; rtd 93. *Rockfield, Coleford Road, Tutshill, Chepstow, Gwent NP6 7BU* Chepstow (01291) 626147

EVANS, John David Vincent. b 41. CQSW78. Lich Th Coll 66. **d** 68 **p** 70. C Kingsthorpe *Pet* 68-69; C Corby Epiphany w St Jo 69-72; Bp's Adv in Children's Work 72-74; Perm to Offic 88-90; R Green's Norton w Bradden 90-91; R Greens Norton w Bradden and Lichborough from 91. *The Rectory, Greens Norton, Towcester, Northants NN12 8BL* Towcester (01327) 359508

EVANS, John Eric. b 14. St D Coll Lamp BA38. **d** 38 **p** 39. V Churchstoke w Hyssington *Heref* 64-77; V Churchstoke w Hyssington and Sarn 77-79; rtd 79. *52 Oaklands Road, Chirk Bank, Wrexham, Clwyd LL14 5DW* Chirk (01691) 772115

EVANS, John Griffiths. b 37. Glouc Th Course 76. **d** 77 **p** 77. Hd Master Corse Sch Glos from 70; C Hartpury w Corse and Staunton *Glouc* 77-79; P-in-c from 79. *Gadfield Elm House, Staunton, Gloucester GL19 3PA* Staunton Court (01452) 840302

EVANS, Canon John Hopkin. b 17. St D Coll Lamp BA41. **d** 42 **p** 44. R Llanfechain *St As* 60-82; Hon Can St As Cathl 76-82; rtd 82. *Church View, Llanfechain, Powys SY22 6UL* Llansantffraid (01691) 828446

EVANS, John Laurie. b 34. Pretoria Univ BSc54 Imp Coll Lon BSc55 Rhodes Univ BA59. Ripon Coll Cuddesdon 84. **d** 86 **p** 87. C Bruton and Distr *B & W* 86-89; P-in-c Ambrosden w Mert and Piddington *Ox* 89-91; C Pet St Mary *Pet* 91-93; V Michael *S & M* from 93; R Ballaugh from 93. *The Rectory, Ballaugh, Isle of Man IM7 5AQ* Sulby (01624) 897873 Fax as telephone

EVANS, Canon John Mascal. b 15. BNC Ox BA37 MA43. Wells Th Coll 37. **d** 38 **p** 39. Adn Surrey *Guildf* 68-80; rtd 80; C Ridgeway *Sarum* 80-84; Perm to Offic *Ex* from 94. *6 Gracey Court, Woodland Road, Broadclyst, Exeter EX5 3LP* Exeter (01392) 462445

EVANS, John Morgan. b 14. MBE87. St D Coll Lamp BA37. **d** 37 **p** 38. V Llangenny *S & B* 55-79; CF (EC) 46-48; CF (TA) 61-87; OCF from 55; rtd 79; Lic to Offic *S & B* from 79. *Milfraen, 17 St John's Road, Brecon, Powys LD3 9DS* Brecon (01874) 624054

EVANS, John Rhys. b 45. Hull Univ BSc66. Sarum & Wells Th Coll 77. **d** 79 **p** 80. C Alton St Lawr *Win* 79-82; C Tadley St Pet 82-85; V Colden 85-91; V Bitterne Park from 91. *Bitterne Park Vicarage, 7 Thorold Road, Southampton SO2 4HZ* Southampton (01703) 555814

EVANS, John Ronald. b 16. Univ of Wales BA40. St Mich Coll Llan 41. **d** 42 **p** 44. V Glyndyfrdwy *St As* 54-81; RD Edeyrnion 64-81; Dioc Sec SPCK 66-81; rtd 81. *21 Bryn Hyfryd, Johnstown, Wrexham, Clwyd LL14 1PR* Rhosllanerchrugog (01978) 842300

EVANS, John Thomas. b 43. Univ of Wales DipTh66 DPS67. St Mich Coll Llan 66. **d** 67 **p** 68. C Connah's Quay *St As* 67-71; C Llanrhos 71-74; Chapl Rainhill Hosp Liv 74-78; TV Wrexham *St As* 78-83; V Holywell from 83; RD Holywell from 95. *The Vicarage, Fron Park Road, Holywell, Clwyd CH8 7UT* Holywell (01352) 710010

EVANS, Very Rev John Wyn. b 46. FSA88 Univ of Wales (Cardiff) BA68 BD71. St Mich Coll Llan 68. **d** 71 **p** 72. C St D Cathl *St D* 71-72; Min Can St D Cathl 72-75; Perm to Offic *Ox* 75-76; Dioc Archivist *St D* 76-82; R Llanfallteg w Clunderwen and Castell Dwyran etc 77-82; Warden of Ords 78-83; Dioc Dir of Educn 82-94; Chapl Trin Coll Carmarthen 82-94; Dean of Chpl 90-94; Hon Can St D Cathl *St D* 88-90; Can St D Cathl 90-94; Dean St D from 94; V St D Cathl from 94. *The Deanery, St Davids, Haverfordwest, Dyfed SA62 6RH* St Davids (01437) 720202

EVANS, Jonathan Alan. b 53. Fitzw Coll Cam BA75 PGCE77 MA79. St Jo Coll Nottm MA95. **d** 95. C Drypool *York* from 95. *2 Pavilion Close, Chamberlain Road, Hull HU8 8EA* Hull (01482) 712597

EVANS, Joseph Henry Godfrey. b 31. Univ of Wales (Lamp) BA50 St Mary's Cheltenham CertEd75 Kingston Poly 89. Qu Coll Birm 53. **d** 55 **p** 56. V Cheltenham St Pet *Glouc* 65-74; R Willersey w Saintbury 74-77; Chapl Tiffin Sch Kingston-upon-Thames 77-94; rtd 95. *300 Raeburn Avenue, Surbiton, Surrey KT5 9EF* 0181-390 0936

EVANS, Keith. b 57. Trin Coll Carmarthen CertEd81 BEd82. St D Coll Lamp BA84 Sarum & Wells Th Coll 84. **d** 85 **p** 86. C Swansea St Thos and Kilvey *S & B* 85-87; C Gorseinon 87-89; V Oxwich w Penmaen and Nicholaston 89-94; Dir of Post-Ord Tr from 93; R Ystradgynlais from 94. *The Rectory, 2 Heol yr Eglwys, Ystradgynlais, Swansea SA9 1EY* Glantawe (01639) 843200

EVANS, Kenneth. b 50. Bp Burgess Hall Lamp DipTh74. **d** 74 **p** 75. C Llanaber w Caerdeon *Ban* 74-79; C Upper Clapton St Matt *Lon* 79-82; P-in-c Tottenham St Phil from 82. *St Philip's Vicarage, 226 Philip Lane, London N15 4HH* 0181-808 4235

✠**EVANS, Rt Rev Kenneth Dawson.** b 15. Clare Coll Cam BA37 MA41. Ripon Hall Ox 37. **d** 38 **p** 39 **c** 68. C Northn St Mary *Pet* 38-41; C Northn All SS w St Kath 41-45; R Ockley *Guildf* 45-49; V Ranmore 49-57; V Dorking 49-57; V Dorking w Ranmore 57-63; RD Dorking 57-63; Hon Can Guildf Cathl 55-63 and 79-85; Can Res Guildf Cathl 63-68; Adn Dorking 63-68; Suff Bp Dorking 68-85; rtd 85. *3 New Inn Lane, Guildford, Surrey GU4 7HN* Guildford (01483) 67978

EVANS, Kenneth Percy. b 16. OBE. Keble Coll Ox BA37 MA42. Wells Th Coll 38. **d** 39 **p** 40. QHC 68-72; V Bradninch *Ex* 72-83; RD Cullompton 77-81; rtd 83; Chapl Menton w San Remo *Eur* 83-87; Perm to Offic *St As* from 87. *Heulfron, Pant-y-Ffridd, Berriew, Welshpool, Powys SY21 8BH* Berriew (01686) 650426

EVANS, Kenneth Roy. b 47. Lon Univ BSc. Ridley Hall Cam 79. **d** 81 **p** 81. C Stratford-on-Avon w Bishopton *Cov* 81-82; C Trunch *Nor* 82-85; Chapl Nottm Mental Illness & Psychiatric Unit from 85; Chapl Mapperley Hosp Nottm 85-89; Lic to Offic *S'well* from 85. *31 Foxhill Road, Burton Joyce, Nottingham NG14 5DR* Nottingham (0115) 931 4081

EVANS, Kenwyn Harries Price. b 29. Univ of Wales (Lamp) BA52. St Mich Coll Llan 56. **d** 57 **p** 58. V Nantymoel w Wyndham *Llan* 65-71; V Pwllgwaun 71-75; V Pwllgwaun w Llanddewi Rhondda 75-88; R Llandough w Leckwith 88-94; Chapl Llandough Hosp 88-94; rtd 94. *15 Neyland Close, Tonteg, Pontypridd, M Glam CF38 1HH* Pontypridd (01443) 218673

EVANS, Kevin Stuart. b 56. Bris Poly CQSW80. Qu Coll Birm DipTh95. **d** 95. C Madeley *Heref* from 95. *7 Mellor Close, Madeley, Telford, Shropshire TF7 5SS* Telford (01952) 588332

EVANS, Lewys Thomas Gareth. b 29. St Mich Coll Llan. **d** 58 **p** 59. R Vaynor and Capel Taffechan *S & B* 65-80; V Defynnog w Rhydybriw, Llandeilo'r Fan etc 80-83; V Defynnog w Rhydybriw and Llandilo'r-fan 83-87; V Ystalyfera 87-95; rtd 95. *The Vicarage, Ystalyfera, Swansea SA9 2EP* Glantawe (01639) 842257

EVANS, Ms Linda Mary. b 49. Univ of Wales (Cardiff) BA71 K Coll Lon BD74 AKC74. Yale Div Sch STM76. **dss** 76 **d** 80. Llanishen and Lisvane *Llan* 76-78; Wrexham *St As* 78-80; C 80-82; Chapl Maudsley Hosp Lon 82-84; Bethlem R Hosp Beckenham 82-84; Chapl Lon Univ *Lon* 84-87. *2 Rhes Eldon, Allt Glanrafon, Bangor, Gwynedd LL57 2RA* Bangor (01248) 370561

EVANS, Miss Madeleine Thelma Bodenham. b 30. K Coll Lon BD76 AKC76. Gilmore Course 80. **dss** 85 **d** 87 **p** 94. Chapl Pipers Corner Sch 85-91; Par Dn Calne and Blackland *Sarum* 91-94; C from 94; Chapl St Mary's Sch Calne from 91. *62 Braemor Road, Calne, Wilts SN11 9DU* Calne (01249) 814245

EVANS, Ms Margaret Elizabeth. b 48. Leeds Univ BA69 Lon Inst of Educn CertEd70. Oak Hill Th Coll 91. **d** 94 **p** 95. NSM Canonbury St Steph *Lon* from 94. *5 Canonbury Place, London N1 2NQ* 0171-359 4343

EVANS, Martin Lonsdale. b 69. Man Univ BA91. Ripon Coll Cuddesdon DipMin95. **d** 95. C Morpeth *Newc* from 95. *42 Grange Road, Stobhill, Morpeth, Northd NE61 2UF* Morpeth (01670) 513413

EVANS, Michael. b 49. St Jo Coll Nottm 88. **d** 90 **p** 91. C Beeston *S'well* 90-93; P-in-c Kirkby in Ashfield St Thos from 93. *The Vicarage, 109 Diamond Avenue, Kirkby-in-Ashfield, Nottingham NG17 7LX* Mansfield (01623) 755131

EVANS, Neil Glynne. b 55. Lon Univ DipTh78 Leeds Univ BA81. Trin Coll Bris DPS82. **d** 82 **p** 83. C Llandybie *St D* 82-86; NSM 87-89; V Gwaun-cae-Gurwen 90-92; Tutor St Jo Coll Dur 92-94; Chapl from 94. *St John's College, South Bailey, Durham DH1 3RJ* 0191-374 3593

EVANS, Neil Robert. b 54. Lon Univ MA93. Coll of Resurr Mirfield. **d** 84 **p** 85. C Bethnal Green St Jo w St Bart *Lon* 84-86; C St Jo on Bethnal Green 87-88; P-in-c Stoke Newington Common St Mich from 88. *St Michael's Vicarage, 55 Fountayne Road, London N16 7ED* 0181-806 4225 Fax as telephone

EVANS, Nicholas Anthony Paul. b 60. Sheff Univ BA81 Liv Univ PGCE86. Qu Coll Birm 81. **d** 84 **p** 87. C Ludlow *Heref*

84-85; C Sunbury *Lon* 86-92; Head RE Guilford County Sch from 93; NSM Crookham *Guildf* from 94. *93 Cambridge Road, Aldershot, Hants GU11 3LD* Aldershot (01252) 343890

EVANS, Ven Patrick Alexander Sidney. b 43. Linc Th Coll 70. **d** 73 **p** 74. C Lyonsdown H Trin *St Alb* 73-76; C Royston 76-78; V Gt Gaddesden 78-82; V Tenterden St Mildred w Smallhythe *Cant* 82-89; Adn Maidstone from 89; Hon Can Cant Cathl from 89; Dir of Ords from 89. *The Archdeacon's House, Charing, Ashford, Kent TN27 0LU* Ashford (01233) 712294 Fax 713651

EVANS, Percy. b 12. St Mich Coll Llan St Deiniol's Hawarden BA33. **d** 35 **p** 36. R Manordeifi and Llangoedmor w Llechryd *St D* 43-84; rtd 84. *Ucheldir, Maenordeifi, Cardigan, Dyfed SA43 2PJ* Llechryd (01239) 682239

EVANS, Peter. b 35. St Aid Birkenhead 57. **d** 60 **p** 61. C Higher Bebington *Ches* 60-63; C W Kirby St Bridget 63-66; P-in-c Lower Tranmere 66-68; V Flimby *Carl* 68-74; V Kirkby Ireleth 74-79; P-in-c Kirkbride w Newton Arlosh 79-80; R 80-85; V Beckermet St Jo and St Bridget w Ponsonby from 85. *St John's Vicarage, 11 Lowrey Close, Beckermet, Cumbria CA21 2YX* Beckermet (01946) 841327

EVANS, Peter. b 40. S'wark Ord Course 75. **d** 75 **p** 76. C Welling S'wark 75-78; C Sutton New Town St Barn 78-81; C Kingston All SS w St Jo 81-87; V Croydon Woodside from 87. *St Luke's Vicarage, Portland Road, London SE25 4RB* 0181-654 1225

EVANS, Peter Anthony. b 36. Lon Univ BScEng Ox Univ DipTh59. St Steph Ho Ox 58. **d** 60 **p** 61. C Surbiton St Mark S'wark 60-63; Asst Chapl Lon Univ *Lon* 63-64; C S Kensington St Luke 64-68; C Surbiton St Andr and St Mark S'wark 68-69; C Loughton St Jo *Chelmsf* 69-74; P-in-c Becontree St Geo 74-82; NSM Romford St Alb 89-93; NSM Coopersale 93-95; NSM Epping Distr from 95. *6 Woodhall Crescent, Hornchurch, Essex RM11 3NN* Hornchurch (01708) 474995

EVANS, Peter Gerald. b 41. Man Univ BA71. AKC65. **d** 65 **p** 66. C Kidbrooke St Jas *S'wark* 65-68; C Fallowfield *Man* 68-71; C Brockley Hill St Sav *S'wark* 71-73; P-in-c Colchester St Botolph w H Trin and St Giles *Chelmsf* 74-79; V 79-92; Perm to Offic from 93. *97 Northgate Street, Colchester CO1 1EY* Colchester (01206) 43297

EVANS, Peter Kenneth Dunlop. b 38. Ch Coll Cam BA60. St D Coll Lamp 72. **d** 74 **p** 75. C Roath St Marg *Llan* 74-77; V Buttington and Pool Quay *St As* 77-87; V Llanfair Caereinion w Llanllugan from 87. *The Vicarage, Llanfair Caereinion, Welshpool, Powys SY21 0RR* Llanfair Caereinion (01938) 810146

EVANS, Philip Ronald. b 55. Qu Coll Cam BA77 MA81 Dur Univ CCouns90. Cranmer Hall Dur 88. **d** 90 **p** 91. C Devonport St Budeaux *Ex* 90-92; C Torquay St Matthias, St Mark and H Trin 92-94; Chapl St Jas Univ Hosp Leeds from 94. *The Chaplain's Office, St James's University Hospital, Leeds LS9 7TF* Leeds (0113) 243 3144

EVANS, Reginald Arthur. b 07. Bris Univ BA38. Sarum Th Coll 38 Wells Th Coll 39. **d** 40 **p** 41. V Batheaston w St Cath *B & W* 49-77; Preb Wells Cathl 73-77; rtd 77; Perm to Offic *Bris* from 81. *4 Heberden House, Bath Road, Cricklade, Wilts SN6 6AS* Swindon (01793) 750109

EVANS, Richard Edward Hughes. b 14. Univ of Wales BA44. St Mich Coll Llan. **d** 45 **p** 46. V Llanybydder and Llanwenog w Llanwnnen *St D* 64-72; V Llanychaiarn 72-79; rtd 79. *23 Gwarfelin, Llanilar, Aberystwyth, Dyfed SY23 4PE* Llanilar (01974) 241357

EVANS, Richard Edward Victor. b 21. Linc Th Coll 66. **d** 68 **p** 69. C Aston cum Aughton *Sheff* 68-71; C Prestwich St Mary *Man* 71-74; R Moston St Jo 74-83; R Failsworth H Family 83-91; rtd 91. *508 Edge Lane, Droylesden, Manchester M35 6JW* 0161-370 1947

EVANS, Richard Gregory. b 50. Univ of Wales (Cardiff) DipTh72. St Mich Coll Llan 69. **d** 73 **p** 74. C Oystermouth *S & B* 73-76; C Clydach 76-79; CF 78-81; V Llanddew and Talachddu *S & B* 79-83; Youth Chapl 79-83; Hon Min Can Brecon Cathl 79-83; New Zealand from 83. *97 Liverpool Street, Wanganui, New Zealand* Wanganui (64) 345-0587

EVANS, Richard Lee. b 47. Univ of Wales (Cardiff) BA71 LTh. St D Coll Lamp 71. **d** 73 **p** 74. C Llantwit Major *Llan* 73-74; C Roath St Sav 74-77; C Penarth w Lavernock 77-78; C-in-c Rhydyfelin 78-82; P-in-c Clydach Vale 78; V Rhydyfelin 82-84; Vice-Prin Chich Th Coll 84-88; V Southsea H Spirit *Portsm* 89-94; rtd 94. *20 Lombard Court, Lombard Street, Portsmouth PO1 2HU*

EVANS, Richard Neville. b 15. Qu Coll Cam BA36 MA44. Ripon Hall Ox 36. **d** 38 **p** 39. V Cam St Andr Gt *Ely* 60-72; V Waterbeach 72-74; Perm to Offic 75-86; rtd 84; Perm to Offic *Truro* from 86. *2 Hounster Drive, Millbrook, Torpoint, Cornwall PL10 1BZ* Plymouth (01752) 822811

EVANS, Richard Trevor. b 33. Jes Coll Ox MA58 DipEd58. St And Dioc Tr Course 73. **d** 76 **p** 76. NSM Leven *St And* from

76. *33 Huntingtower Park, Whinnyknowe, Glenrothes, Fife KY6 3QF* Glenrothes (01592) 741670

EVANS, Canon Robert Arthur. b 24. Univ of Wales (Cardiff) BA48. St Mich Coll Llan 48. **d** 50 **p** 51. Chapl Supt Mersey Miss to Seamen 62-74 and 79-89; Chapl RNR 67-89; V Rainhill *Liv* 74-79; Perm to Offic *Ches* 79-91; Hon Can Liv Cathl *Liv* 88-89; rtd 89. *1 Floral Wood, Riverside Gardens, Liverpool L17 7HR* 0151-727 3608

EVANS, Robert Charles. b 55. K Coll Lon BA77 AKC77 MA78 MTh89 Qu Coll Cam BA80 MA83 CertEd85. Westcott Ho Cam 79. **d** 81 **p** 87. C St Breoke *Truro* 81-83; C St Columb Minor and St Colan 83-84; Chapl Rob Coll Cam 87-92. *Address temp unknown*

EVANS, Robert George Roger. b 49. Cam Univ MA. Trin Coll Bris 74. **d** 77 **p** 78. C Bispham *Blackb* 77-80; C Chadwell *Chelmsf* 80-84; V Ardsley *Sheff* from 84. *The Vicarage, Doncaster Road, Barnsley, S Yorkshire S71 5EF* Barnsley (01226) 203784

EVANS, Robert Stanley. b 51. Univ of Wales (Lamp) BA72 Univ of Wales (Cardiff) PGCE73. St Mich Coll Llan DPS92. **d** 92 **p** 93. C Penarth All SS *Llan* from 92. *84 Coleridge Avenue, Penarth, S Glam CF64 2SR* Penarth (01222) 708044

EVANS, Ronald. b 47. Univ of Wales (Cardiff) DipTh87. St Mich Coll Llan 85. **d** 87 **p** 88. C Flint *St As* 87-91; V Wrexham from 91. *The Vicarage, 37 Acton Gate, Wrexham, Clwyd LL11 2PW* Wrexham (01978) 290143

EVANS, Simon. b 55. Newc Univ BA77. St Steph Ho Ox 78. **d** 80 **p** 81. C Pet St Jude *Pet* 80-84; C Wantage *Ox* 84-87; V W Leigh *Portsm* from 87. *St Alban's Vicarage, Martin Road, Havant, Hants PO9 5TE* Havant (01705) 451751

EVANS, Simon Andrew. b 59. Sarum & Wells Th Coll 81. **d** 84 **p** 85. C Norbury St Steph and Thornton Heath *Cant* 84; C Norbury St Steph and Thornton Heath *S'wark* 85-88; C Putney St Mary 88-92; P-in-c Telford Park St Thos 92-94; V from 94. *St Thomas's Vicarage, 39 Telford Avenue, London SW2 4XL* 0181-674 4343

EVANS, Stanley Munro. b 30. AKC53. **d** 54 **p** 55. C Norbury St Oswald *Cant* 54-57; C St Laurence in the Isle of Thanet 57-63; V Bredgar 63-71; V Bredgar w Bicknor and Huckinge 71-72; V Westgate-on-Sea St Sav from 72. *St Saviour's Vicarage, Thanet Road, Westgate-on-Sea, Kent CT8 8PB* Thanet (01843) 831869

EVANS, Stephen John. b 60. Dartmouth RN Coll 81 Ox Univ BA85 MA89. St Steph Ho Ox 83. **d** 86 **p** 87. Prec St Andr Cathl Inverness *Mor* 86-89; R Montrose *Bre* 89-91; P-in-c Inverbervie 89-91; Miss to Seamen 89-91; V North St Paul *Pet* from 91. *St Paul's Vicarage, 104 Semilong Road, Northampton NN2 6EX* Northampton (01604) 712688

EVANS, Ms Susan Mary. b 55. St Jo Coll Dur BA76 CertEd77 Nottm Univ BCombStuds84. Linc Th Coll 81. **dss** 84 **d** 87 **p** 94. Weaste *Man* 84-87; Par Dn 87-88; Par Dn Longsight St Luke 88-92; Par Dn Claydon and Barham *St E* 92-94; C from 94. *The Rectory, 7 Back Lane, Claydon, Ipswich IP6 0EB* Ipswich (01473) 830362

EVANS, Terence. b 35. St Mich Coll Llan 67. **d** 69 **p** 70. C Lougher *S & B* 69-73; C Gowerton w Waunarlwydd 73-77; V Llanbister and Llanbadarn Fynydd w Llananno 77-82; V Llanyrnewydd from 82. *The Vicarage, Crofty, Penclawdd, Swansea SA4 3RP* Penclawdd (01792) 850285

EVANS, Terence Robert (Terry). b 45. N Ord Course 82. **d** 85 **p** 86. C Warrington St Elphin *Liv* 85-88; V Cantril Farm 88-94; V Rainhill from 94. *St Ann's Vicarage, View Road, Prescot, Merseyside L35 0LE* 0151-426 4666

EVANS, Very Rev Thomas Eric. b 28. Univ of Wales (Lamp) BA50 St Cath Coll Ox BA53 MA57. St Steph Ho Ox. **d** 54 **p** 55. C Margate St Jo *Cant* 54-58; C Bournemouth St Pet *Win* 58-62; Hon Min Can Glouc Cathl *Glouc* 62-69; Dioc Can Res 69-88; Youth Chapl 62-69; Can Missr 69-75; Adn Cheltenham 75-88; Dean St Paul's *Lon* from 88; P-in-c St Martin Ludgate from 89. *The Deanery, 9 Amen Court, London EC4M 7BU* 0171-236 2827 Fax 332 0298

EVANS, Thomas Howell. b 13. St Cath Soc Ox BA37 MA40. Ripon Hall Ox 36. **d** 37 **p** 38. V Anstey *St Alb* 58-74; V Brent Pelham w Meesden 58-74; P-in-c Albury 74-79; V Braughing w Albury, Furneux Pelham etc 79; rtd 79; Perm to Offic *Chelmsf* from 79; Perm to Offic *St Alb* from 79. *Farm Cottage, 1 Coxford Abbey, Coxford, King's Lynn, Norfolk PE31 6TB* East Rudham (01485) 528042

EVANS, Canon Thomas Norman. b 30. K Coll Lon BA51 BD53 AKC56. **d** 56 **p** 57. C Handsworth *Sheff* 56-59; C Mexborough 59-61; V Denaby Main 61-65; V Wythenshawe Wm Temple Ch *Man* 65-78; RD Withington 72-78; R Prestwich St Mary 78-85; AD Radcliffe and Prestwich 78-85; Hon Can Man Cathl 79-85; R Skelton w Upleatham *York* from 87; RD Guisborough from 91. *The Rectory, North Terrace, Skelton-in-Cleveland, Cleveland TS12 2ES* Guisborough (01287) 650329

EVANS, Timothy Simon. b 57. York Univ BA79 Sussex Univ MA81 Fitzw Coll Cam BA85 MA88. Ridley Hall Cam 83. **d** 87 **p** 88. C Whitton St Aug *Lon* 87-90; C Ealing St Steph Castle Hill 90-93; P-in-c Shireshead *Blackb* from 93; Asst Chapl Lanc Univ from 93. *The Vicarage, Shireshead, Forton, Preston PR3 0AE* Forton (01524) 791355 or 67128

EVANS, Canon Trefor Rhys. b 06. Univ of Wales BA32. St Mich Coll Llan 33. **d** 33 **p** 34. V Lamp *St D* 56-74; rtd 74. *60 Penbryn, Lampeter, Dyfed SA48 7EU* Lampeter (01570) 422060

EVANS, Canon Trevor Owen. b 37. Univ of Wales BSc59. Coll of Resurr Mirfield 59. **d** 61 **p** 62. C Llanaber w Caerdeon *Ban* 61-64; C Llandudno 64-70; TV 70-75; V Llanidloes w Llangurig 75-89; RD Arwystli 75-89; Can and Preb Ban Cathl from 82; Dioc Adv on Spirituality from 84; R Trefdraeth 89-90; Dir of Min from 89; R Llanfairpwll w Penmynydd from 90. *The Rectory, Holyhead Road, Llanfairpwll, Gwynedd LL61 5SX* Llanfairpwll (01248) 716472

EVANS, Walter Tenniel. b 26. Lon NSM Course. **d** 84 **p** 85. NSM Beaconsfield *Ox* from 84. *Candlemas, Jordans, Beaconsfield, Bucks HP9 2ST* Chalfont St Giles (01494) 873165

EVANS, Walter James. b 29. Huron Coll Ontario LTh58. **d** 58 **p** 59. R Chilthorne Domer, Yeovil Marsh and Thorne Coffin *B & W* 65-70; V Chalford *Glouc* 70-91; rtd 91. *67 Mandara Grove, Gloucester GL4 9XT* Gloucester (01452) 385157

EVANS, Canon William Brewster. b 15. TCD BA37 MA43. CITC 37. **d** 38 **p** 39. I Castlerock Union *D & R* 60-82; Can Derry Cathl 72-82; rtd 82. *4 Bells Hill, Limavady, Co Londonderry BT49 0DQ* Limavady (015047) 64349

EVANS, William James Lynn. b 30. St D Coll Lamp 73. **d** 75 **p** 76. P-in-c Penbryn and Blaenporth *St D* 75-77; V Penbryn and Betws Ifan w Bryngwyn 77-79; V Penrhyn-coch and Elerch 79-83; V Cynwil Elfed and Newchurch 83-87; V Llandybie 87-95; rtd 95. *The Vicarage, 7 Kings Road, Llandybie, Ammanford, Dyfed SA18 2TL* Llandybie (01269) 850337

EVANS-PUGHE, Thomas Goronwy. b 29. TCD. Wycliffe Hall Ox 59. **d** 61 **p** 62. R Birchanger *Chelmsf* 69-94; rtd 94. *Bath Orchard, Blockley, Moreton-in-Marsh, Glos GL56 9HU* Blockley (01386) 701223

EVASON, Stuart Anthony. b 44. Salford Univ BSc. Chich Th Coll 79. **d** 81 **p** 82. C Heref St Martin *Heref* 81-85; TV Cleethorpes *Linc* 85-87; TV Howden TM *York* 87-92; V Heywood St Jas *Man* from 92. *St James's Vicarage, 46 Bury Old Road, Heywood, Lancs OL10 3JD* Heywood (01706) 369745

EVE, Cedric Robert Sutcliff. b 18. Lon Coll of Div 63. **d** 65 **p** 66. C Ipsley *Worc* 69-73; TV 73-78; P-in-c Norton and Lenchwick 78; P-in-c Harvington 78; P-in-c Norton and Lenchwick 78-84; rtd 84; Perm to Offic *Chich* from 85. *Flat 2, Woodfold, Fernhurst, Haslemere, Surrey GU27 3ET* Haslemere (01428) 654085

EVE, David Charles Leonard. b 45. AKC74 St Aug Coll Cant 74. **d** 75 **p** 76. C Hall Green Ascension *Birm* 75-79; TV Kings Norton 79-84; V Rowley Regis 84-93; Perm to Offic *Heref* from 94. *Cleanlyseat Farm, Neen Savage, Cleobury Mortimer, Kidderminster, Worcs DY14 8EN* Cleobury Mortimer (01299) 270510

EVE, Hilary Anne. b 57. Lon Univ BEd80. Ripon Coll Cuddesdon 89. **d** 91 **p** 94. Par Dn Coulsdon St Andr *S'wark* 91-94; C 94-95; Chapl Croydon 92-94; Chapl Harestone Marie Curie Cen Caterham from 94; Asst Chapl Mayday Univ Hosp Thornton Heath from 94. *23 Rickman Hill, Coulsdon, Surrey CR5 3DS* Downland (01737) 557732

EVELEIGH, Raymond. b 36. Univ of Wales (Cardiff) BSc58. NW Ord Course 73. **d** 76 **p** 77. NSM S Cave and Ellerker w Broomfleet *York* 76-79; P-in-c Kingston upon Hull St Mary 79-82; Chapl Hull Coll of FE from 79; V Anlaby Common St Mark *York* 82-94; V Langtoft w Foxholes, Butterwick, Cottam etc from 94. *The Vicarage, Langtoft, Driffield, N Humberside YO25 0TN* Driffield (01377) 87226

EVENS, Philip Alistair. b 36. Leic Univ BA61. Trin Coll Bris 84. **d** 86 **p** 87. C Aston SS Pet and Paul *Birm* 86-89; V Tyseley from 89. *St Edmund's Vicarage, 277 Reddings Lane, Tyseley, Birmingham B11 3DD* 0121-777 2433

EVENS, Robert John Scott (Bob). b 47. ACIB74 DipTh. Trin Coll Bris 74. **d** 77 **p** 78. C Southsea St Simon *Portsm* 77-79; C Portchester 79-83; V Locks Heath from 83; RD Fareham from 93. *The Vicarage, 125 Locks Heath Park Road, Locks Heath, Southampton SO3 6LY* Locks Heath (01489) 572497

EVEREST, Harold William. b 26. Lon Univ BD54. Tyndale Hall Bris 51. **d** 54 **p** 55. V Sheff St Jo *Sheff* 67-78; V Tinsley 78-91; Ind Chapl 78-91; rtd 91. *34 Oakdale Road, Bakersfield, Nottingham NG3 7EE* Nottingham (0115) 987 6155

EVEREST, Canon John Cleland. b 45. Sarum Th Coll 66. **d** 68 **p** 69. C Moulsecoomb *Chich* 68-71; C Easthampstead *Ox* 71-74; C Southwick *Chich* 74-77; Dioc Soc Services Adv *Worc* 77-84; Ind Chapl from 84; R Worc City St Paul and Old St Martin etc 84-93; RD Worc E 89-93; Hon Can Worc Cathl

from 90; TR Halesowen from 93; RD Dudley from 95. *The Rectory, Bundle Hill, Halesowen, W Midlands B63 4AR* 0121-550 1158

EVERETT, Alan Neil. b 57. St Cath Coll Ox BA79 SS Coll Cam BA84. Westcott Ho Cam 82. **d** 85 **p** 86. C Hindley All SS *Liv* 85-88; Chapl Qu Mary Coll *Lon* 88-91; V S Hackney St Mich w Haggerston St Paul from 94. *97 Lavender Grove, London E8 3LR* 0171-249 4440

EVERETT, Anthony William. b 60. S Bank Poly BA82. Oak Hill Th Coll BA89. **d** 89 **p** 90. C Hailsham *Chich* 89-92; C New Malden and Coombe *S'wark* from 92. *2 California Road, New Malden, Surrey KT3 3RU* 0181-942 0544

EVERETT, Bryan John. b 25. ALCD54. **d** 54 **p** 55. V Lullington *Derby* 69-80; R Nether and Over Seale 69-80; P-in-c Longstone 80-90; rtd 90. *2 Lime Grove, Ashbourne, Derbyshire DE6 1HP* Ashbourne (01335) 300303

EVERETT, Mrs Christine Mary. b 46. St Osyth Coll of Educn CertEd67. Westcott Ho Cam 90. **d** 92 **p** 94. Par Dn Ipswich St Fran *St E* 92-94; C from 94. *76 Holcombe Crescent, Ipswich IP2 9PW* Stowmarket (01449) 774551

EVERETT, Colin Gerald Grant. b 44. Open Univ BA77 Keswick Hall Coll CertEd. Ripon Coll Cuddesdon 79. **d** 81 **p** 82. C Aston cum Aughton *Sheff* 81-84; R Fornham All SS and St Martin w Timworth *St E* 84-92; P-in-c Old Newton w Stowupland 92-94; C Ipswich All Hallows 94-95; TV Ipswich St Fran from 95. *76 Holcombe Crescent, Ipswich IP2 9PW* Ipswich (01473) 688399

EVERETT, David Gordon. b 45. Pemb Coll Ox BA67 MA. Lon Coll of Div 68. **d** 70 **p** 71. C Hatcham St Jas *S'wark* 70-73; C Reading St Jo *Ox* 73-77; TV Fenny Stratford and Water Eaton 77-83; Hon C Bletchley 83-87; C Loughton 84-85; NSM Stantonbury and Willen 87-93; Chapl Ox Brookes Univ from 92; NSM Iffley from 93. *45 Freelands Road, Oxford OX4 4BS* Oxford (01865) 242411

EVERETT, Canon John Wilfred. b 37. Qu Coll Cam BA61 MA65. Cuddesdon Coll 64. **d** 66 **p** 67. C St Helier *S'wark* 66-69; C Yeovil St Jo w Preston Plucknett *B & W* 69-73; R Wincanton 73-82; R Pen Selwood 80-82; V Ashford *Cant* from 82; Hon Can Cant Cathl from 90; Chapl Ashford Hosp from 94. *The College, Church Yard, Ashford, Kent TN23 1QG* Ashford (01233) 620672

EVERETT, Robert Henry. b 60. Em Coll Cam BA82 BA85 MA86. St Steph Ho Ox 83. **d** 86 **p** 87. C Ex St Thos and Em *Ex* 86-88; C Plymstock 88-91; R St Dominic, Landulph and St Mellion w Pillaton *Truro* from 91. *The Rectory, St Mellion, Saltash, Cornwall PL12 6RN* Liskeard (01579) 50061

EVERETT, Robin Nigel. b 34. Dur Univ BA55 DipTh59. Cranmer Hall Dur 57. **d** 59 **p** 60. C New Humberstone *Leic* 59-62; C Humberstone 62-66; V Quorndon 66-74; V Castle Donington 74-82; P-in-c Lockington w Hemington 81-82; V Castle Donington and Lockington cum Hemington 82-86; Antigua 86-87; R Ibstock w Heather *Leic* from 87. *The Rectory, Ibstock, Leics LE67 6JQ* Ibstock (01530) 260246

EVERETT, Simon Francis. b 58. Oak Hill Th Coll BA89. **d** 89 **p** 90. C Wroughton *Bris* 89-93; TV Wexcombe *Sarum* from 93. *The Vicarage, Collingbourne Ducis, Marlborough, Wilts SN8 3EL* Collingbourne Ducis (01264) 850279

EVERETT-ALLEN, Clive. b 47. AKC70. St Aug Coll Cant 69. **d** 70 **p** 71. C Minera *St As* 70-72; C Hatcham St Cath *S'wark* 72-75; C Beaconsfield *Ox* 75; TV 75-83; R Southwick *Chich* from 83. *The Rectory, 22 Church Lane, Southwick, Brighton BN42 4GB* Brighton (01273) 592303

EVERITT, Mark. b 34. Linc Coll Ox BA58 MA62. Wells Th Coll. **d** 60 **p** 61. C Hangleton *Chich* 60-63; Chapl Mert Coll Ox from 63. *Merton College, Oxford OX1 4JD* Oxford (01865) 276365

EVERITT, Michael John. b 68. K Coll Lon BD90 AKC90. Qu Coll Birm 90 English Coll Rome 91. **d** 92 **p** 93. C Cleveleys *Blackb* 92-95; S Africa from 95. *Cathedral Church of St Andrew, PO Box 1523, Bloemfontein 9300, South Africa* Bloemfontein (51) 474266 Fax 483078

EVERITT, William Frank James. b 38. FCA63 Dur Univ BA68 DipTh69. Cranmer Hall Dur 65. **d** 69 **p** 70. C Leic St Phil *Leic* 69-73; P-in-c Prestwold w Hoton 73-77; R Settrington w N Grimston and Wharram *York* 77-84; RD Buckrose 80-84; V Cheltenham St Pet *Glouc* from 84. *St Peter's Vicarage, 375 Swindon Road, Cheltenham, Glos GL51 9LB* Cheltenham (01242) 524369

EVERS, Dr Timothy Michael. b 48. Birm Univ BA70 Witwatersrand Univ MA75 PhD89 UNISA BTh93. Local NSM Course 79. **d** 82 **p** 84. S Africa 82-88; Australia from 88. *8 Hall Road, Roleystone, W Australia 6111* Perth (9) 496-1283

EVERSON, Canon Owen Neville. b 32. St Jo Coll Cam BA56 MA61. Wycliffe Hall Ox 56. **d** 58 **p** 59. C Edgbaston St Aug *Birm* 58-63; Tutor Wycliffe Hall Ox 63-66; Chapl 66-67; V Lee Gd Shep w St Pet *S'wark* 67-85; Hon Can S'wark Cathl from 83; V W Wickham St Fran from 85. *St Francis's Vicarage, 2 The Grove, West Wickham, Kent BR4 9JS* 0181-777 6010

EVERSON, Simon Charles. b 58. Leeds Univ BA80. Ripon Coll Cuddesdon 80. **d** 83 **p** 84. C Rotherhithe St Mary w All SS *S'wark* 83-87; P-in-c Kennington Park St Agnes 87-94; V from 94. *The Vicarage, 37 St Agnes Place, London SE11 4BB* 0171-735 3860

EVERY, Canon Edward. b 09. Mert Coll Ox BA30 MA46. Linc Th Coll 36. **d** 36 **p** 37. Can Jerusalem 52-79; rtd 79; Perm to Offic *Lon* 82-88. *College of St Barnabas, Blackberry Lane, Lingfield, Surrey RH7 6NJ* Dormans Park (01342) 870260

EVES, Barry. b 51. Sunderland Poly DipHums86. Cranmer Hall Dur 86. **d** 88 **p** 89. C Tadcaster w Newton Kyme *York* 88-91; C York St Paul 91-93; V Bubwith w Skipwith from 93. *The Vicarage, North Duffield, Selby, N Yorkshire YO8 7RR* Selby (01757) 288079

EWBANK, Very Rev Robert Arthur Benson. b 22. Ox Univ MA48. Cuddesdon Coll 46. **d** 48 **p** 49. C Boston *Linc* 48-52; Chapl Uppingham Sch Pet 52-56; S Rhodesia 57-65; Rhodesia 65-80; Zimbabwe from 80; Dean Bulawayo 82-90. *45A Leander Avenue, Bulawayo, Zimbabwe*

EWBANK, Robin Alan. b 42. Ex Coll Ox BA64 MA88 Lon Univ BD68. Clifton Th Coll 66. **d** 69 **p** 70. C Woodford Wells *Chelmsf* 69-72; Warden Cam Univ Miss Bermondsey 72-76; TV Sutton St Jas and Wawne *York* 76-82; R Bramshott *Portsm* 82-91; R Bramshott and Liphook from 91; Chmn IDWAL (Dios Chich, Guildf and Portsm) from 90. *The Rectory, 6 Portsmouth Road, Bramshott, Liphook, Hants GU30 7AA* Liphook (01428) 723119

EWBANK, Ven Walter Frederick. b 18. Ball Coll Ox BA45 MA45 BD52. Bps' Coll Cheshunt. **d** 46 **p** 47. Hon Can Carl Cathl *Carl* 66-78 and 83-84; V Carl St Cuth 66-71; Adn Westmorland and Furness 71-77; V Winster 71-78; Adn Carl 78-84; Can Res Carl Cathl 78-82; rtd 84; Perm to Offic *Carl* from 84. *7 Castle Court, Castle Street, Carlisle CA3 8TP* Carlisle (01228) 810293

EWEN, Keith John McGregor. b 43. Sarum & Wells Th Coll 77. **d** 79 **p** 80. C Kington w Huntington *Heref* 79-82; C Kington w Huntington, Old Radnor, Kinnerton etc 82-83; P-in-c Culmington w Onibury 83-89; P-in-c Bromfield 83-89; P-in-c Stanton Lacy 83-89; R Culmington w Onibury, Bromfield etc from 90. *The Vicarage, Bromfield, Ludlow, Shropshire SY8 2JP* Ludlow (01584) 77234

EWER, Edward Sydney John (Jonathan). b 36. Univ of New England BA69. ACT ThL63. **d** 62 **p** 63. Australia 62-83; SSM from 68; Perm to Offic *Blackb* 83-84; Lic to Offic *Dur* from 84; Prior SSM Priory Dur from 85; Dir of Ords from 94. *St Antony's Priory, Claypath, Durham DH1 1QT* 0191-384 3747

EWINGTON, John. b 43. ARICS65. Chich Th Coll 74. **d** 78 **p** 79. C Walthamstow St Jo *Chelmsf* 78-81; Papua New Guinea 81-87; V Southend St Sav Westcliff *Chelmsf* from 87. *St Saviour's Vicarage, 33 King's Road, Southend-on-Sea SS0 8LL* Southend-on-Sea (01702) 342920

EXALL, John Aubrey. b 20. Univ Coll Lon BSc41. Cuddesdon Coll 46. **d** 48 **p** 49. V Southn St Barn *Win* 57-85; rtd 86; Perm to Offic *Win* from 86. *Delve Cottage, 36 Church Lane, Romsey, Hants SO51 8EP* Romsey (01794) 522928

EXCELL, Robin Stanley. b 41. AKC64. St Boniface Warminster 64. **d** 65 **p** 66. C Ipswich St Mary Stoke *St E* 65-68; C Melton Mowbray w Thorpe Arnold *Leic* 68-70; TV Gt and Lt Blakenham w Baylham *St E* 71-76; R Gt and Lt Blakenham w Baylham and Nettlestead 76-86; RD Bosmere 84-86; NSM Sproughton w Burstall 91-94; R Rattlesden w Thorpe Morieux and Brettenham from 94; P-in-c Hitcham w Lt Finborough from 95. *The Rectory, High Street, Rattlesden, Bury St Edmunds, Suffolk IP30 0RA* Rattlesden (01449) 737993

EXELL, Ernest William Carter. b 28. Qu Coll Cam BA52 MA53. Tyndale Hall Bris 49. **d** 52 **p** 53. Tanzania 66-70; R Abbess and Beauchamp Roding *Chelmsf* 70-71; P-in-c White Roding w Morrell Roding 70-71; R Abbess Roding, Beauchamp Roding and White Roding 71-94; RD Roding 75-79; rtd 94. *8 Ickworth Drive, Bury St Edmunds, Suffolk IP33 3PX* Bury St Edmunds (01284) 724726

EXELL, Michael Andrew John (Mike). b 45. MRIPHH67 MICA70. Sarum & Wells Th Coll 87. **d** 89 **p** 90. C Ryde H Trin *Portsm* 89-93; C Swanmore St Mich w Havenstreet 89-92; C Swanmore St Mich and All Angels 92-93; P-in-c Carisbrooke St Mary from 93. *The Vicarage, Clatterford Road, Newport, Isle of Wight PO30 1PA* Isle of Wight (01983) 522095

EXETER, Archdeacon of. *See* TREMLETT, Ven Anthony Frank (Tony)

EXETER, Bishop of. *See* THOMPSON, Rt Rev Geoffrey Hewlett

EXETER, Dean of. *See* EYRE, Very Rev Richard Montague Stephens

EXLEY, Malcolm. b 33. Cranmer Hall Dur. **d** 67 **p** 68. C Sutton St Jas *York* 67-73; V Mappleton w Goxhill 73-77; V Market Weighton 77-90; P-in-c Goodmanham 77-78; R 78-90; V Bridlington Em from 90. *Emmanuel Vicarage, 72 Cardigan Road, Bridlington, York YO15 3JT* Bridlington (01262) 604948

EYDEN, Christopher David. b 59. DipRSAMDA81. St Steph Ho Ox 88. **d** 91 **p** 92. C Tottenham St Paul *Lon* 91-93; C Ealing St Pet Mt Park from 93. *The Vicarage Flat, St Peter's Vicarage, Mount Park Road, London W5 2RU* 0181-998 7493

EYDEN, Canon Eric Westley. b 09. Lon Univ BA31 AKC33 BD34. **d** 33 **p** 34. Can Res and Prec Heref Cathl *Heref* 64-75; rtd 75; Perm to Offic *B & W* from 75. *Little Croft, 5 The Grange, Chilton Polden, Bridgwater, Somerset TA7 9DW* Chilton Polden (01278) 722622

EYLES, Anthony John. b 34. Bris Univ BSc57. Sarum Th Coll 61. **d** 63 **p** 64. C Wellington w W Buckland *B & W* 63-67; V Wilton 67-74; Ind Chapl *Dur* 74-85; Ind Chapl *Worc* 85-90; P-in-c Bickenhill w Elmdon *Birm* 90; P-in-c Bickenhill St Pet from 90; Chapl Birm Airport from 90. *The Vicarage, Barndale House, Church Lane, Solihull, W Midlands B92 0DT* Hampton-in-Arden (01675) 442215

EYLES, David William. b 45. Sarum & Wells Th Coll 75. **d** 77 **p** 78. C Knaresborough *Ripon* 77-80; C Chapel Allerton 80-82; P-in-c W Tanfield and Well w Snape and N Stainley 82-83; R 83-91; P-in-c Middleham w Coverdale and E Witton 93-94; R from 94; P-in-c Thornton Watlass w Thornton Steward from 94. *The Rectory, The Springs, Middleham, Leyburn, N Yorkshire DL8 4RB* Wensleydale (01969) 622276

EYRE, John Trevor. b 42. BA88. Oak Hill Th Coll 86. **d** 89 **p** 90. C Watton w Carbrooke and Ovington *Nor* 89-94; TV Lowestoft and Kirkley 94; R Kirkley St Pet and St Jo from 94. *3 Aldwyck Way, Lowestoft, Suffolk NR33 9JQ* Lowestoft (01502) 508289

EYRE, Very Rev Richard Montague Stephens. b 29. Or Coll Ox BA53 MA56. St Steph Ho Ox 53. **d** 56 **p** 57. C Portsea N End St Mark *Portsm* 56-59; Tutor Chich Th Coll 59-61; Chapl 61-62; Chapl Eastbourne Coll 62-65; V Arundel w Tortington and S Stoke *Chich* 65-73; V Brighton Gd Shep Preston 73-75; Dir of Ords 75-79; Adn Chich 75-81; Can Res and Treas Chich Cathl 78-81; Dean Ex from 81. *The Deanery, Exeter EX1 1HT* Exeter (01392) 52891 or 72697

EYRE, Richard Stuart. b 48. Nottm Univ MTh86 Bris Univ BEd81. Linc Th Coll 74. **d** 77 **p** 78. C Henbury *Bris* 77-81; C Bedminster 81-82; TV 82-84; Chapl Bp Grosseteste Coll Linc 84-95; Sen Tutor 89-95; Chapl Riseholme Coll of Agric 84-95; P-in-c Long Bennington w Foston *Linc* from 95. *Saxonwell Vicarage, Church Street, Long Bennington, Newark, Notts NG23 5ES* Long Bennington (01400) 282545

EYRE-WALKER, John Benson. b 15. St Pet Hall Ox BA40 DipTh41 MA44. Wycliffe Hall Ox. **d** 42 **p** 43. V Burton Ches 57-80; rtd 80; Perm to Offic *Carl* from 81. *Sunrise Cottage, Kilmidyke Road, Grange-over-Sands, Cumbria LA11 7AQ* Grange-over-Sands (015395) 32647

EYRES, Canon Leslie. b 10. AKC41. **d** 41 **p** 42. R Aughton St Mich *Liv* 65-78; rtd 78; Hon C N Meols *Liv* 78-93. *25 Montrose Drive, Southport, Merseyside PR9 7JA* Southport (01704) 27776

F

FACER, Miss Rosemary Jane. b 44. LTCL72 Hull Univ BA65 Reading Univ CertEd66. Trin Coll Bris DipHE80. **dss** 80 **d** 87. St Paul's Cray St Barn *Roch* 80-87; Par Dn 87-88; C Cheltenham St Mark *Glouc* from 88. *33 Campden Road, Cheltenham, Glos GL51 6AA* Cheltenham (01242) 239477

FACEY, Andrew John. b 57. Barrister 80 Trin Coll Cam MA83. Trin Coll Bris BA92. **d** 92 **p** 93. C Egham *Guildf* from 92. *33 Grange Road, Egham, Surrey TW20 9QP* Egham (01784) 434137

FAGAN, John Raymond. b 32. Lon Univ BD69. Ripon Hall Ox 71. **d** 72 **p** 73. C Stalybridge *Man* 72-74; C Madeley *Heref* 74-79; V Amington *Birm* 79-91; P-in-c Stonnall *Lich* from 91; Chapl HM Young Offender Inst Swinfen Hall from 91. *2 St Peter's Close, Stonnall, Walsall WS9 9EN* Brownhills (01543) 373088 Fax 480138

FAGAN, Thomas. b 27. NW Ord Course 78. **d** 81 **p** 82. NSM Rainhill *Liv* 81-89; NSM Prescot from 89. *4 Wensleydale Avenue, Prescot, Merseyside L35 4NR* 0151-426 4788

FAGERSON, Joseph Leonard Ladd. b 35. Harvard Univ BA57 Lon Univ DipTh62. Ridley Hall Cam 61. **d** 63 **p** 64. C Tonbridge SS Pet and Paul *Roch* 63-67; Afghanistan 67-74; P-in-c Marbury *Ches* 74-75; P-in-c Kinloch Rannoch *St And* from 75; Chapl Rannoch Sch Perthshire from 75. *The Chaplain's House, Rannoch School, Rannoch Station, Perthshire PH17 2QQ* Kinloch Rannoch (01882) 632235

FAGG, Alan Gordon. b 06. K Coll Lon 54. **d** 55 **p** 56. V Forest Row *Chich* 63-70; Perm to Offic from 70; rtd 78. *11 Davis Court, Marlborough Road, St Albans, Herts AL1 3XU* St Albans (01727) 847146

FAHIE, Mrs Stephanie Bridget. b 48. St Jo Coll Nottm 85. **d** 87 **p** 94. Par Dn Leic St Chris *Leic* 87-90; Chapl Scargill Ho from 90. *Swale Cottage, Kettlewell, Skipton, N Yorkshire BD23 5RW* Kettlewell (01756) 760332

FAINT, Paul Edward. b 38. Qu Coll Birm 85. **d** 87 **p** 88. C Cradley *Worc* 87-90; V Hanley Castle, Hanley Swan and Welland 90-94; V Northwood H Trin *Lon* from 94. *Holy Trinity Vicarage, Gateway Close, Northwood, Middx HA6 2RW* Northwood (01923) 825732

FAIR, Very Rev James Alexander (Lex).TCD BA48 MA59. CITC 49. **d** 49 **p** 50. C Monaghan w Tyholland *Clogh* 49-52; C Portadown St Mark *Arm* 52-56; I Woodschapel 56-60; C-in-c Rathcoole *Conn* 62-68; Dioc Chief Insp of Educn 63-81; Miss to Seamen from 68; I Larne and Inver *Conn* from 68; Preb Conn Cathl 82-84; Treas 84-86; Chan 86-90; Dean Conn from 90; Bp's C Glynn w Raloo from 90. *The Rectory, Lower Carncastle Road, Larne, Co Antrim BT40 1PQ* Larne (01574) 272788

FAIRALL, Michael John. b 45. SW Minl Tr Course 88. **d** 90 **p** 91. NSM Southway *Ex* from 90. *132 Lakeview Close, Tamerton Foliot, Plymouth PL5 4LX* Plymouth (01752) 707694

FAIRBAIRN, John Alan. b 46. Trin Coll Cam BA67 MA72. Wycliffe Hall Ox 84. **d** 86 **p** 87. C Boscombe St Jo *Win* 86-89; C Edgware *Lon* from 89. *St Peter's Parsonage, Stonegrove, Edgware, Middx HA8 8AB* 0181-958 5791

FAIRBAIRN, Stella Rosamund.d 87 **p** 94. NSM Banbury *Ox* from 87; Perm to Offic from 88. *Hillside, Overthorpe, Banbury, Oxon OX17 2AF* Banbury (01295) 710648

FAIRBANK, Brian Douglas Seeley. b 53. AKC75. St Steph Ho Ox 77. **d** 78 **p** 79. C Newton Aycliffe *Dur* 78-81; C Stocking Farm *Leic* 81-84; TV Ratby w Groby 84-91; Chapl RN from 91. *Directorate Gen, RN Chapl Services, Room 203, Victory Building, HM Naval Base, Portsmouth PO1 3LS* Portsmouth (01705) 727903 Fax 727112

FAIRBROTHER, Robin Harry. b 44. Univ of Wales DipTh68. Ho of Resurr Mirfield 64 Wells Th Coll 68. **d** 69 **p** 70. C Wrexham *St As* 69-74; C Welshpool w Castle Caereinion 74-77; V Bettws Cedewain and Tregynon 77-80; V Betws Cedewain and Tregynon and Llanwyddelan 80-92; TR Marshwood Vale TM *Sarum* from 92. *The Rectory, Whitchurch Canonicorum, Bridport, Dorset DT6 6RQ* Chideock (01297) 489223

FAIRBROTHER, Ronald Peter. b 20. St Steph Ho Ox 59. **d** 61 **p** 62. R Newton Ferrers w Revelstoke *Ex* 69-83; V Abbotskerswell 83-89; rtd 90. *3 Chestnut Court, Alphington, Exeter EX2 8XY*

FAIRBURN, Peter. b 16. Linc Th Coll 42. **d** 42 **p** 43. V Arkendale *Ripon* 54-82; R Goldsborough 54-82; rtd 82. *13 Woodpark Drive, Knaresborough, N Yorkshire HG5 9DN* Harrogate (01423) 864851

FAIRCLOUGH, John Frederick. b 40. DMS78 MBIM St Jo Coll Dur BA63 MA68. Coll of Resurr Mirfield 81. **d** 83 **p** 84. C Horninglow *Lich* 83-87; V Skerton St Luke *Blackb* 87-94; V Thornton-le-Fylde from 94. *The Vicarage, Meadows Avenue, Thornton Cleveleys, Lancs FY5 2TW* Cleveleys (01253) 855099

FAIRHURST, Canon Alan Marshall. b 30. Clare Coll Cam BA52 MA56 Lon Univ BD56. Tyndale Hall Bris 53 Hask's Th Academy Istanbul 54 Wycliffe Hall Ox 55. **d** 56 **p** 57. Tutor St Jo Coll Dur 56-60; C Stockport St Geo *Ches* 60-62; Ceylon 62-66; R Ashley w Silverley *Ely* 67-71; R Stockport St Mary *Ches* from 71; Chapl Stepping Hill Hosp Stockport from 76; Hon Can Ches Cathl *Ches* from 81; RD Stockport from 86. *St Mary's Rectory, Gorsey Mount Street, Stockport, Cheshire SK1 4DU* 0161-429 6564

FAIRHURST, John Graham. b 39. Linc Th Coll 86. **d** 88 **p** 89. C Whiston *Sheff* 88-91; V Elsecar from 91. *The Vicarage, Wath Road, Elsecar, Barnsley, S Yorkshire S74 8HJ* Barnsley (01226) 742149

FAIRHURST, Ms Rosemary Anne (Rosy). b 63. Newnham Coll Cam BA85 MA85 Lon Inst of Educn PGCE86. Wycliffe Hall Ox BA92. **d** 93 **p** 94. C Hackney Marsh *Lon* from 93. *84 Roding Road, London E5 0DS* 0181-533 4034

FAIRLAMB, Neil. b 49. Univ of Wales (Ban) BA71 Jes Coll Ox BPhil73 Pemb Coll Cam CertEd74. S'wark Ord Course 90. **d** 93 **p** 94. Hon C Dulwich St Barn S'wark 93-95; P-in-c Penrhyn-coch and Elerch *St D* from 95. *The Vicarage, Penrhyn-coch, Aberystwyth, Dyfed SA23 3EF* Aberystwyth (01970) 828746

FAIRWEATHER, David James. b 35. Keele Univ BEd79. Wycliffe Hall Ox 70. **d** 72 **p** 73. C Trentham *Lich* 72-76; C Cheddleton 76; C Hanley H Ev 77-79; C Rugeley 79-86; V Brown Edge from 86. *St Anne's Vicarage, Church Road, Brown Edge, Stoke-on-Trent ST6 8TD* Stoke-on-Trent (01782) 502134

FAIRWEATHER, John. b 39. K Coll Lon AKC66 BD72. **d** 67 **p** 68. C Plymouth St Jas Ham *Ex* 67-69; C Townstal w St Sav and St Petrox w St Barn 69-73; R Corringham w Springthorpe *Linc* 73-78; P-in-c Blyborough 76-78; P-in-c Heapham 76-78; P-in-c Willoughton 76-78; V Pinchbeck 78-82; V Exwick *Ex* from 82. *Exwick Vicarage, Exwick Road, Exeter EX4 2AT* Exeter (01392) 55500

FALCONER, Ian Geoffrey. b 40. BNC Ox BA62. Cuddesdon Coll 62. **d** 64 **p** 65. C Chiswick St Nic w St Mary *Lon* 64-68; C-in-c Hounslow Gd Shep Beavers Lane CD 68-76; P-in-c Hammersmith St Matt 76-84; P-in-c Byker St Silas *Newc* 84-93; V 93-95; P-in-c Newc St Phil and St Aug from 95; P-in-c Newc St Matt w St Mary from 95. *The Vicarage, St Philip's Close, Newcastle upon Tyne NE4 5JE* 0191-273 7407

FALCONER, John Geikie. b 13. Selw Coll Cam BA33 MA37. Lon Coll of Div 33. **d** 36 **p** 37. Deputation Sec Leprosy Miss 62-70; Perm to Offic Kensington Deanery *Lon* 71-82; Perm to Offic from 82; rtd 78. *10 Hounslow Avenue, Hounslow TW3 2DX* 0181-898 1122

FALKNER, Jonathan Michael Shepherd. b 47. Open Univ BA74 St Jo Coll Dur DipTh78. **d** 79 **p** 80. C Penrith *Carl* 79; C Penrith w Newton Reigny 79-81; C Penrith w Newton Reigny and Plumpton Wall 81-82; C Dalton-in-Furness 82-84; V Clifton 84-90; P-in-c Dean 85-89; R 89-90; P-in-c Rumburgh w S Elmham w the Ilketshalls *St E* 90-92; R S Elmham and Ilketshall from 92; RD Beccles and S Elmham from 94. *Church House, Ilkestall St Margaret, Bungay, Suffolk NR35 1QZ* Bungay (01986) 781345

FALL, Harry. b 17. Leeds Univ BA40 BD51 Dur Univ BA42 MA48. **d** 42 **p** 43. R Scrayingham *York* 57-71; R York H Trin w St Jo Micklegate and St Martin 71-84; rtd 84. *20 Weaponness Valley Road, Scarborough, N Yorkshire YO11 2JF* Scarborough (01723) 361822

FALL, John David McPherson. b 29. St Paul's Grahamstown LTh64. **d** 64 **p** 65. Rhodesia 65-80; Zimbabwe 80-82; P-in-c Dorrington *Heref* 82-92; P-in-c Leebotwood w Longnor 82-92; P-in-c Stapleton 82-92; P-in-c Smethcott w Woolstaston 82-92; rtd 92. *69 Raymead Close, West Mersea, Colchester CO5 8DN* West Mersea (01206) 385277

FALLONE, Christopher (Chris). b 55. Aston Tr Scheme 85 Oak Hill Th Coll 87. **d** 90 **p** 91. C Rochdale *Man* 90-93; P-in-c Thornham w Gravel Hole from 93. *St John's Vicarage, 1177 Manchester Road, Rochdale, Lancs OL11 2XZ* Rochdale (01706) 31825

FALLOWS, Stuart Adrian. b 50. Moray Ho Edin 75. **d** 78 **p** 79. Hon C Forres *Mor* 78-81; Hon C Elgin w Lossiemouth 81-86; C Brighton St Geo w St Anne and St Mark *Chich* 86-89; V Wivelsfield from 89. *New Vicarage, Church Lane, Wivelsfield, Haywards Heath, W Sussex RH17 7RD* Wivelsfield Green (01444) 471783

FALSHAW, Simon Meriadoc. b 60. Leeds Univ BSc82. Oak Hill Th Coll BA93. **d** 93 **p** 94. C Stapleford *S'well* from 93. *22 Shanklin Drive, Stapleford, Nottingham NG9 8EZ* Nottingham (0115) 939 2643

FANE, Clifford Charles. b 39. Kelham Th Coll 62. **d** 67 **p** 68. C Heston *Lon* 67-73; C Bedminster St Mich *Bris* 73-76; P-in-c 76-77; C Gaywood, Bawsey and Mintlyn *Nor* 77-81; V Bolton St Jo *Man* 81-90; rtd 90. *10 Booth Road, Little Lever, Bolton BL3 1JY* Farnworth (01204) 709420

FANTHORPE, Robert Lionel. b 35. FBIM81 FCP90 CertEd63 Open Univ BA80. Llan Dioc Tr Scheme. **d** 87 **p** 88. NSM Roath St German *Llan* from 87. *Riverdell, 48 Claude Road, Roath, Cardiff CF2 3QA* Cardiff (01222) 498368

FARADAY, John. b 49. Leeds Univ BSc71 MICE78. Oak Hill Th Coll 81. **d** 83 **p** 84. C Sutton *Liv* 83-86; C Rainhill 86-89; Chapl Whiston Hosp 86-89; V Over Darwen St Jas *Blackb* from 89. *St James's Vicarage, Winterton Road, Darwen, Lancs BB3 0ER* Darwen (01254) 702364

FARAH, Mones Anton. b 64. Trin Coll Bris BA88. **d** 88 **p** 89. C Abth *St D* 88-91; Chapl St D Coll Lamp from 91. *Gelli Aur, Bryn Road, Lampeter, Dyfed SA48 7EE* Lampeter (01570) 422894

FARAH, Ven Rafiq Amin. b 21. Beirut Univ BA45. Near E Sch of Th 45. **d** 46 **p** 48. Jerusalem 46-86; Adn and Can Res 74-86; Min to Arab Angl and Evang in Lon 86-92; Hon C Herne Hill S'Wark 86-92; Canada 92-95. *27 Fordington House, Sydenham Hill, London SE26 6TX* 0181-291 0696

FARBRIDGE, Nicholas Brisco. b 33. FCA. Sarum & Wells Th Coll 75. **d** 77 **p** 78. C Gt Bookham *Guildf* 77-80; C Ewell 80-83; V Addlestone 83-89; R Shere from 89. *The Rectory, Spinning Walk, Shere, Guildford, Surrey GU5 9HN* Shere (01483) 202394

FARDON, Jean Audrey May. b 24. Westf Coll Lon BA45 Lon Inst of Educn DipEd46. Gilmore Ho DipTh69. **dss** 79 **d** 87 **p** 94. St Alb St Pet *St Alb* 79-92; Hon Par Dn 87-92; NSM Powyke *Worc* 92-94; Perm to Offic from 94. *35 King's End Road, Powick, Worcester WR2 4RB* Worcester (01905) 830472

FARDON, Raymond George Warren. b 30. St Pet Hall Ox BA52 MA56. Ridley Hall Cam 54. **d** 59 **p** 60. C High Wycombe All

SS *Ox* 59-63; Chapl Bedf Secondary Modern Sch 63-68; Hd Master K Sch Grantham 72-82; Travelling Ev from 82; Hon C Longfleet *Sarum* 82-83; Perm to Offic from 83. *26 Kingland Road, Poole, Dorset BH15 1TP* Poole (01202) 675609

FAREY, David Mark. b 56. St Jo Coll Dur BA85. Cranmer Hall Dur 82. **d** 86 **p** 87. C Brackley St Pet w St Jas *Pet* 86-89; TV Kingsthorpe w St Dav Northn from 89. *St David's Vicarage, 88 Eastern Avenue, Northampton NN2 7QB* Northampton (01604) 714536

FARGUS, Gavin James Frederick. b 30. AKC54. **d** 55 **p** 57. R Nether Lochaber *Arg* 65-81; R Kinlochleven 65-81; rtd 81; Lic to Offic *Arg* from 82. *Benvheir Cottage, Ballachulish, Argyll PA39 4JX* Ballachulish (018552) 420

FARGUS, Maxwell Stuart. b 34. Linc Coll Ox BA57 MA61 Leeds Univ DipAdEd79. Cuddesdon Coll 57. **d** 59 **p** 60. Dioc Youth Officer *Ripon* 64-76; R Kirkby Wiske 64-76; Community Educn Officer Barnsley MBC 76-88; Perm to Offic *Sheff* 77-88; Perm to Offic *Wakef* 77-88; Perm to Offic *York* 77-88; V Rudston w Boynton and Kilham 88-93; rtd 93. *56 Fir Tree Drive, Filey, N Yorkshire YO14 9NR*

FARISH, Alan John. b 58. Lanc Univ BA. St Jo Coll Nottm LTh86 DPS86. **d** 86 **p** 87. C Bishopwearmouth St Gabr *Dur* 86-89; C Fatfield from 89. *17 Whittonstall, Washington, Tyne & Wear NE38 8PH* 0191-415 5424

FARLEY, David Stuart. b 53. Univ Coll Dur BA75 Nottm Univ DipTh82. St Jo Coll Nottm. **d** 84 **p** 85. C Bath Weston All SS w N Stoke *B & W* 84-87; Chapl Scargill Ho 87-90; Min Hedge End N CD *Win* 90-94; V Hedge End St Luke from 94. *16 Elliot Rise, Hedge End, Southampton SO3 4RU* Botley (01489) 786717

FARLEY, Edward Albert (Ted). b 36. Lon Univ BSc59 ARCS59 Em Coll Cam BA61. Ridley Hall Cam 60. **d** 62 **p** 63. C Bitterne *Win* 62-65; C Swindon Ch Ch *Bris* 65-68; V Dunston w Coppenhall *Lich* 68-71; V Blurton 71-82; V Cheddleton 82-92; Chapl St Edward's Hosp Cheddleton 82-92; RD Leek *Lich* 87-92; P-in-c Bourton-on-the-Water w Clapton *Glouc* from 92. *The Rectory, Bourton-on-the-Water, Cheltenham, Glos GL54 2AP* Cotswold (01451) 820386

FARLEY, Dr Ian David. b 56. Linc Coll Ox BA78 MA87 Dur Univ PhD88. Cranmer Hall Dur 84. **d** 87 **p** 88. C Dishley and Thorpe Acre *Leic* 87-92; V S Lambeth St Steph *S'wark* from 92. *The Vicarage, St Stephen's Terrace, London SW8 1DH* 0171-735 8461

FARLEY, James Trevor. b 37. IEng MIEE FRSA. E Midl Min Tr Course 80. **d** 82 **p** 83. NSM Grantham *Linc* from 82. *Highfield Cottage, Station Road, Bottesford, Nottingham NG13 0EN* Bottesford (01949) 43646

FARLEY, Lionel George Herbert. b 10. Chich Th Coll 32. **d** 35 **p** 36. V Marazion *Truro* 51-78; rtd 78. *Karenza, 22 Chestnut Way, Gillingham, Dorset SP8 4RT* Gillingham (01747) 823530

FARLEY, Ronald Alexander. b 30. Oak Hill NSM Course. **d** 79 **p** 80. NSM Stoke Newington St Faith, St Matthias and All SS *Lon* from 79. *20 Chaucer Court, Howard Road, London N16 8TS* 0171-249 4349

FARLIE, Canon Hugh. b 29. Lon Univ BSc53. Linc Th Coll 53. **d** 55 **p** 56. Chapl Bath Univ *B & W* 65-73; P-in-c Knowle St Barn *Bris* 73-85; V 85-94; Hon Can Bris Cathl 89-94; rtd 94. *16 Croft Road, Hastings, E Sussex TN34 3HJ*

FARMAN, Robert Joseph. b 54. Ridley Hall Cam 86. **d** 88 **p** 89. C Sutton St Nic *S'wark* 88-90; C Cheam Common St Phil 90-92; R Wootton w Glympton and Kiddington *Ox* from 92. *The Vicarage, Castle Road, Wooton, Oxon OX20 1EG* Woodstock (01993) 812543

FARMAN, Mrs Roberta. b 48. Aber Univ MA70 Cam Univ CertEd72. Qu Coll Birm 78. dss 82 **d** 87. Ovenden *Wakef* 80-82; Scargill Ho 83-84; Coulsdon St Jo *S'wark* 85-86; Hon Par Dn Cam St Mark *Ely* 86-88; Hon Par Dn Sutton St Nic *S'wark* 88-92; Hon Par Dn Wootton w Glympton and Kiddington *Ox* from 92. *The Vicarage, Castle Road, Wooton, Oxon OX20 1EG* Woodstock (01993) 812543

FARMBOROUGH, James Laird McLelland. b 22. MBE90. Magd Coll Cam BA49 MA54. Tyndale Hall Bris. **d** 52 **p** 53. Org Sec SAMS 65-70; V Marple All SS *Ches* 70-80; Chile 80-92; Miss to Seamen 80-92; rtd 88. *Pear Tree House, 7 High Street, Whitehaven, Cumbria CA28 7PZ* Whitehaven (01946) 693500

✠**FARMBROUGH, Rt Rev David John.** b 29. Linc Coll Ox BA51 MA53. Westcott Ho Cam 51. **d** 53 **p** 54 **c** 81. C Hatf *St Alb* 53-57; P-in-c 57-63; V Bishop's Stortford St Mich 63-74; RD Bishop's Stortford 73-74; Adn St Alb 74-81; Suff Bp Bedf 81-93; rtd 94. *St Michael Mead, 110 Village Road, Bromham, Bedford MK43 8HU* Oakley (01234) 825042

FARMER, George Wilson. b 37. Lich Th Coll 61. **d** 65 **p** 66. C Kingston All SS *S'wark* 65-69; C Heston *Lon* 69-74; C Southmead *Bris* 74-75; C Bedminster 75-80; TV Langley

Marish *Ox* 80-86; R Wexham from 86. *The Rectory, 7 Grangewood, Wexham, Slough SL3 6LP* Slough (01753) 523852

FARMER, Kenneth William. b 29. CPM. FBIM. Ripon Coll Cuddesdon 75 Launde Abbey 76. **d** 77 **p** 78. C Evington *Leic* 77-80; V Wymeswold and Prestwold w Hoton 80-85; P-in-c Barney w Thursford *Nor* 85-87; P-in-c Fulmodeston w Croxton 85-87; P-in-c Hindringham and Binham 85-87; R Barney, Fulmodeston w Croxton, Hindringham etc 87-93; RD Holt 88-93; rtd 93; Perm to Offic *Nor* from 93. *Mo Fan, 25 Deans Gate Drive, Houghton-on-the-Hill, Leicester LE7 9HA* Leicester (0116) 243 2452

FARMER, Robert John. b 62. Kent Univ BA84. St Steph Ho Ox 91. **d** 93. C Leigh St Clem *Chelmsf* from 93. *109 Oakleigh Park Drive, Leigh-on-Sea, Essex SS9 1RR* Southend-on-Sea (01702) 74352

FARMER, Simon John. b 60. Birm Univ BSc82. St Jo Coll Nottm. **d** 89 **p** 90. C Ulverston St Mary w H Trin *Carl* 89-92; CF from 92. *c/o MOD (Army), Bagshot Park, Bagshot, Surrey GU19 5PL* Bagshot (01276) 471717 Fax 412834

FARMER, Canon William John Cotton. b 19. St Jo Coll Dur LTh42 BA43. St Aid Birkenhead. **d** 43 **p** 44. V Packwood w Hockley Heath *Birm* 64-81; Hon Can Birm Cathl 80-81; rtd 84. *Flat 12, Bowling Green Court, Moreton-in-Marsh, Glos GL56 0BX* Moreton-in-Marsh (01608) 51082

FARMILOE, Trevor James. b 42. Sarum & Wells Th Coll. **d** 82. C S Petherton w the Seavingtons *B & W* 82-85; R Norton St Philip w Hemington, Hardington etc 85-93; Chapl Rural Affairs Wells Adnry 87-92; RD Frome 89-93; V Martock w Ash from 93. *The Vicarage, 10 Water Street, Martock, Somerset TA12 6JN* Martock (01935) 822579

FARNHAM, Douglas John (Doug) (Brother Anselm). b 30. SS Mark & Jo Coll Plymouth TCert52 Ex Univ ADEd66 MEd75. S Dios Minl Tr Scheme 80. **d** 83 **p** 84. Lect W Sussex Inst of HE 83-92; NSM Barnham and Eastergate *Chich* 83-85; NSM Aldingbourne, Barnham and Eastergate 85-92; R from 92. *The Rectory, 97 Barnham Road, Barnham, Bognor Regis, W Sussex PO22 0EQ* Yapton (01243) 554077

FARNWORTH, Michael Godfrey Frankland. b 18. Selw Coll Cam BA40 MA46. Westcott Ho Cam 40. **d** 42 **p** 43. CF 50-72; P-in-c Hindringham and Binham *Nor* 72-77; R 77-84; rtd 84; Perm to Offic *Nor* from 85. *15 Sheldrake Close, Fakenham, Norfolk NR21 8ND* Fakenham (01328) 855211

FARNWORTH, Russell. b 60. Lon Bible Coll BA82 Nottm Univ MTh85. St Jo Coll Nottm DPS84. **d** 84 **p** 85. C Blackpool St Jo *Blackb* 84-87; TV Darwen St Pet w Hoddlesden 87-91; V Kidsgrove *Lich* from 91. *St Thomas's Vicarage, The Avenue, Kidsgrove, Stoke-on-Trent ST7 1AG* Stoke-on-Trent (01782) 771367

FARQUHAR, Miss Patricia Ann. b 42. dss 78 **d** 87 **p** 94. S Hackney St Jo w Ch Ch *Lon* 80-87; Par Dn 87-94; C from 94. *19 Valentine Road, London E9 7AD* 0181-986 6273

FARQUHARSON, Hunter Buchanan. b 58. ALAM LLAM. Edin Th Coll 85. **d** 88 **p** 89. C Dunfermline *St And* 88-91; R Glenrothes from 91. *St Luke's Rectory, 60 Ninian Quadrant, Glenrothes KY7 4HP* Glenrothes (01592) 759764

FARQUHARSON-ROBERTS, Donald Arthur (Don). b 21. Bps' Coll Cheshunt 64. **d** 65 **p** 66. R Pimperne *Sarum* 68-89; P-in-c Stourpaine, Durweston and Bryanston 77-89; rtd 90. *30 East House Avenue, Fareham, Hants PO14 2RE* Fareham (01329) 667333

FARR, Arthur Ronald. b 24. JP77. Llan Dioc Tr Scheme 77. **d** 80 **p** 81. NSM Penarth All SS *Llan* 80-90; rtd 90; Perm to Offic *Llan* from 90. *3 Cymric Close, Ely, Cardiff CF5 4GR* Cardiff (01222) 561765

FARR, Mark Julian Richard. b 60. **d** 87 **p** 88. C Clapham TM *S'wark* 87-91; TV Wimbledon from 91. *55 Alwyne Road, London SW19 7AE* 0181-946 4175

FARR, Richard William. b 55. Ridley Hall Cam. **d** 83 **p** 84. C Enfield Ch Ch Trent Park *Lon* 83-87; C Eastbourne H Trin *Chich* 87-90; P-in-c Henham and Elsenham w Ugley *Chelmsf* from 90. *The Vicarage, Carters Lane, Henham, Bishop's Stortford, Herts CM22 6AQ* Bishop's Stortford (01279) 850281

FARRAN, Canon George Orman. b 35. Worc Coll Ox BA58 MA62. Wycliffe Hall Ox 58. **d** 60 **p** 61. C Tyldesley w Shakerley *Man* 60-62; Tutor Wycliffe Hall Ox 62-64; V Netherton *Liv* 64-73; R Sefton 69-73; R Credenhill w Brinsop, Mansel Lacey, Yazor etc *Heref* 73-83; RD Heref Rural 81-83; R Ditcheat w E Pennard and Pylle *B & W* 83-94; Dir of Ords 86-89; Can and Chan Wells Cathl from 85. *8 The Liberty, Wells, Somerset BA5 2SU* Wells (01749) 678763 or 674483

FARRANCE, William Kenneth. b 22. Univ of Wales (Ban) 46. Bps' Coll Cheshunt 49. **d** 52 **p** 53. V Heddon-on-the-Wall *Newc* 63-78; Chapl Tynemouth Hosps 79-82; AP Tynemouth Ch Ch 79-82; rtd 82; Perm to Offic *Newc* from 82. *5 Prestwick Terrace, Prestwick, Ponteland, Newcastle upon Tyne NE20 9BZ* Ponteland (01661) 825163

FARRANT, David Stuart. b 38. Ripon Coll Cuddesdon 82. **d** 84 **p** 85. C Woodford St Mary w St Phil and St Jas *Chelmsf* 84-87; P-in-c Clymping *Chich* 87; V Clymping and Yapton w Ford 87-92; Lic to Offic from 92; Dioc Schs Admin Officer from 92; Chapl Qu Alexandra's Hosp Home Worthing from 95. *101 Nutley Crescent, Goring-by-Sea, Worthing, W Sussex BN12 4LB* Worthing (01903) 507458

FARRANT, Canon John Frederick Ames. b 30. Aber Univ MA51 BD58 MTh80. Edin Th Coll 51. **d** 53 **p** 54. C Dundee St Mary Magd *Bre* 53-58; R Clydebank *Glas* 58-65; R Motherwell 65-70; Papua New Guinea 70-73 and 81-84; R Glas St Bride *Glas* 73-81; Can St Mary's Cathl 77-81; Provost Rabaul 81-84; R Penicuik *Edin* from 85; R W Linton from 85; Can St Mary's Cathl from 92. *The Rectory, 23 Broomhill Road, Penicuik, Midlothian EH26 9EE* Penicuik (01968) 72862

FARRANT, Jonathan (Brother Basil). b 44. St Mark's Dar-es-Salaam 72. **d** 73 **p** 74. Tanzania 73-78; SSF from 74; Lic to Offic *Heref* 78-80. *3 The Mount, Worcester Park, Surrey KT4 8UD* 0181-393 4003

FARRANT, Martyn John. b 38. AKC61. **d** 62 **p** 63. C Hampton St Mary *Lon* 62-65; C Shere *Guildf* 65-67; V Stoneleigh 67-75; V Addlestone 75-83; V Dorking w Ranmore from 83; RD Dorking 89-94. *St Martin's Vicarage, Westcott Road, Dorking, Surrey RH4 3DP* Dorking (01306) 882875

FARRAR, Canon James Albert. b 27. TCD BA55 MA57. CITC 56. **d** 56 **p** 57. I Ballinaclash *D & G* 61-72; I Dunganstown w Redcross 72-79; Warden Ch Min of Healing 79-95; Hon CV Ch Ch Cathl Dub 79-92; Can Ch Ch Cathl Dub from 92; rtd 95. *15 Hillside, Greystones, Co Wicklow, Irish Republic* Dublin (1) 287-2706

FARRELL, Peter Godfrey Paul. b 39. Sarum & Wells Th Coll 72. **d** 74 **p** 75. C St Just in Roseland *Truro* 74-77; C Kenwyn 77-80; V Knighton St Jo *Leic* 80-86; TR Clarendon Park St Jo w Knighton St Mich 86-89; V Woodham *Guildf* from 89. *The Vicarage, 25 Woodham Waye, Woodham, Woking, Surrey GU21 5SW* Woking (01483) 762857

FARRELL, Robert Edward. b 54. Univ of Wales (Abth) BA74 Jes Coll Ox BA77 MA81. Qu Coll Birm 85. **d** 86 **p** 87. C Llanrhos *St As* 86-88; C Prestwich St Marg *Man* 89-91; V Moulsham St Luke *Chelmsf* from 91. *St Luke's House, 26 Lewis Drive, Chelmsford CM2 9EF* Chelmsford (01245) 354479

FARRELL, Ronald Anthony. b 57. Edin Univ BD84 Birm Univ MA86. Qu Coll Birm 84. **d** 86 **p** 87. C Shard End *Birm* 86-87; C Shirley 87-89; Bp's Officer for Schs and Young People 89-93; V Kingstanding St Mark from 93. *St Mark's Clergy House, Bandywood Crescent, Birmingham B44 9JX* 0121-360 7288

FARRELL, Thomas Stanley. b 32. Lon Univ BD71. Ridley Hall Cam 69. **d** 71 **p** 72. C Much Woolton *Liv* 71-73; C Gt Sankey 73-74; Asst Chapl Dulwich Coll 74-76; Chapl 76-81; P-in-c Wonersh *Guildf* 81-86; V 86-90; RD Cranleigh 87-90; R St Marg Lothbury and St Steph Coleman Street etc *Lon* from 90; V St Botolph without Aldersgate from 90. *The Rectory, 1 St Olave's Court, London EC2V 8EX* 0171-600 2379 or 606 0684

FARRER, Miss Carol Elizabeth. b 47. Open Univ BA88. Cranmer Hall Dur 81. **dss** 83 **d** 87 **p** 94. Newbarns w Hawcoat *Carl* 83-86; Egremont and Haile 86-87; Par Dn 87-91; Dioc Lay Min Adv 87-88; Assoc Dir of Ords from 88; TD Penrith w Newton Reigny and Plumpton Wall 91-94; TV from 94. *4 Barco Terrace, Penrith, Cumbria CA11 8NB* Penrith (01768) 899540 or 62867

FARRER, Canon Michael Robert Wedlake. b 22. St Pet Hall Ox BA52 MA57. Tyndale Hall Bris 47. **d** 52 **p** 53. R Barton Seagrave *Pet* 65-73; R Barton Seagrave w Warkton 73-78; V Cam St Paul *Ely* 78-92; RD Cam 84-89; Hon Can Ely Cathl 88-92; rtd 92; Bp's Sen Chapl *Ely* from 92. *2 Houghton Gardens, Ely, Cambs CB7 4JN* Ely (01353) 665654

FARRER, Simon James Anthony. b 52. St Cath Coll Cam MA77 BD78. AKC78 Coll of Resurr Mirfield 78. **d** 79 **p** 80. C St Jo Wood *Lon* 79-84; C N Harrow St Alb 84-87; P-in-c Hammersmith St Luke 87-93; USPG from 93; Zambia from 94. *St George's Church, PO Box 90189, Luanshya, Zambia*

FARRINGTON, Canon Christine Marion. b 42. Birkb Coll Lon BA65 Nottm Univ DASS66 Middx Poly MA75. St Alb Minl Tr Scheme 79. **dss** 82 **d** 87 **p** 94. Redbourn *St Alb* 82-87; Dir Past Studies Linc Th Coll 86-87; HM Pris Linc 86-87; Dir Sarum Chr Cen 87-93; Dn Sarum Cathl *Sarum* 87-93; Hon Can Ely Cathl *Ely* from 93; Co-Dir Ords and Dir Women's Min from 93; C Cam Gt St Mary w St Mich from 93. *20 Barton Road, Ely, Cambs CB7 4DE* Ely (01353) 663632

FARROW, Edward. b 38. Sarum Th Coll 69. **d** 71 **p** 72. C Parkstone St Pet w Branksea *Sarum* 71-74; R Tidworth 74-79; P-in-c W and E Lulworth 79-80; P-in-c Winfrith Newburgh w Chaldon Herring 79-80; R The Lulworths, Winfrith Newburgh and Chaldon 80-83; V Ensbury Park from 83. *The Vicarage, 42 Coombe Avenue, Bournemouth BH10 5AE* Bournemouth (01202) 514286

FARROW, Elizabeth Maura. b 43. Edin Th Coll. **d** 91. NSM Knightswood H Cross Miss *Glas* from 91. *5 Campsie Road, Strathblane G63 9AB* Drymen (01360) 70936

FARROW, Ian Edmund Dennett. b 38. S'wark Ord Course 70. **d** 72 **p** 73. C Tunbridge Wells St Jo *Roch* 72-78; Chapl N Cambs Gen Hosp Gp 78-92; P-in-c Walsoken *Ely* 78-80; R 80-92; V Bisley, Oakridge, Miserden and Edgeworth *Glouc* from 92. *The Vicarage, Monor Street, Bisley, Stroud, Glos GL6 7BJ* Gloucester (01452) 770056

FARROW, Peter Maurice. b 44. St Chad's Coll Dur BSc65 DipTh68. **d** 68 **p** 69. C Gt Yarmouth *Nor* 68-71; C N Lynn w St Marg and St Nic 71-75; P-in-c Sculthorpe w Dunton and Doughton 75-77; Perm to Offic 78-89; TV Lowestoft and Kirkley 89-94; Ind Miss 89-94; Sen Ind Chapl from 94; Asst RD Lothingland 94-95; TV Gaywood St Faith, Kings Lynn from 95. *The Church Bungalow, Gayton Road, Gaywood, King's Lynn, Norfolk PE30 4DZ* King's Lynn (01553) 766552

FARTHING, Michael Thomas. b 28. St Cuth Soc Dur 48. Lambeth STh81 St Steph Ho Ox. **d** 58 **p** 59. C St Marylebone St Mark w St Luke *Lon* 58-63; C Newport Pagnell *Ox* 63-69; R Standlake 69-76; R Yelford 69-76; R Lower Windrush 76-82; V Wheatley w Forest Hill and Stanton St John from 82. *The Vicarage, 18 London Road, Wheatley, Oxford OX33 1YA* Wheatley (01865) 872224

FARTHING, Ronald Edward. b 27. Oak Hill Th Coll. **d** 58 **p** 59. R Langley *Cant* 67-72; V Bapchild w Tonge and Rodmersham 72-80; TV Widecombe, Leusden and Princetown etc *Ex* 80-84; P-in-c Riddlesworth w Gasthorpe and Knettishall *Nor* 84-87; P-in-c Garboldisham w Blo' Norton 84-87; P-in-c Brettenham w Rushford 84-87; R Garboldisham w Blo' Norton, Riddlesworth etc 88-92; rtd 92; Perm to Offic *Nor* from 92. *Fairways, New Street, Stradbroke, Eye, Suffolk IP21 5JJ* Stradbroke (01379) 388189

FASHOLE-LUKE, Edward William. b 34. Dur Univ BA63. Cranmer Hall Dur 61. **d** 62 **p** 63. C Dur St Cuth *Dur* 62-64; Sierra Leone from 64. *Fourah Bay College, Freetown, Sierra Leone*

FASS, Michael John. b 44. Trin Coll Cam MA75. Edin Dioc NSM Course 89. **d** 95. NSM Penicuik *Edin* from 95; NSM W Linton from 95. *20 Fountainhall Road, Edinburgh EH9 2NN* 0131-558 3338 Fax 556 8777

FATHERS, Canon Derek Esmond. b 27. Magd Coll Ox MA50 DipEd52. St Aid Birkenhead DipTh56. **d** 56 **p** 57. V Thornton Hough *Ches* 63-86; RD Wirral S 78-86; Hon Can Ches Cathl 82-92; C Woodchurch 86-89; Chapl Arrowe Park Hosp Birkenhead 86-92; rtd 92. *6 Ashton Drive, West Kirby, Wirral, Merseyside L48 0RQ* 0151-625 1181

FAULDS, John Parker. b 33. Edin Th Coll 55. **d** 57 **p** 58. C Edin St Dav *Edin* 57-58; C Edin St Jo 58-60; Chapl Dundee Hosps 60-63; Chapl Qu Coll Dundee 60-63; Dioc Supernumerary *Bre* 60-63; Lic to Offic *Birm* 65-66 and from 87; P-in-c Aston Brook 66-69; V Handsworth St Pet 69-87. *6 Little Heath Close, Audlem, Crewe CW3 0HX*

FAULKES, Edmund Marquis. b 62. Hatf Coll Dur BA. Ridley Hall Cam 87 Coates Hall Edin 90. **d** 91 **p** 92. C Broughty Ferry *Bre* 91-93; P-in-c Dundee St Ninian from 93. *St Ninian's Church House, Kingsway East, Dundee DD4 7RW* Dundee (01382) 459626

FAULKNER, Brian Thomas. b 48. S Dios Minl Tr Scheme. **d** 84 **p** 85. C W Leigh *Portsm* 84-88; R Foulsham w Hindolveston and Guestwick *Nor* 88-93; P-in-c Erpingham w Calthorpe, Ingworth, Aldborough etc 93-94; R from 94. *The Rectory, Erpingham, Norwich NR11 7QX* Cromer (01263) 768073

FAULKNER, David Ernest. b 43. Univ of Wales (Lamp) DipTh65. St Mich Coll Llan 65. **d** 66 **p** 67. C Abth St Mich *St D* 66-68; C Tenby and Gumfreston 68-69; C Burry Port and Pwll 69-73; R Jeffreyston w Reynalton and E Williamston 73-79; R Jeffreyston w Reynoldston and E Williamston etc 79-89; V Whitland and Kiffig 89-90; V Whitland w Cyffig and Henllan Amgoed and Llan-gan from 90. *The Vicarage, North Road, Whitland, Dyfed SA34 0DH* Whitland (01994) 240494

FAULKNER, Henry Odin. b 35. G&C Coll Cam BA56 MA60. St Jo Coll Nottm DipTh73. **d** 74 **p** 75. C Heigham H Trin *Nor* 74-76; C Heeley *Sheff* 76-80; TV Netherthorpe 80-84; Perm to Offic *St Alb* from 84. *69 Holywell Hill, St Albans, Herts AL1 1HF* St Albans (01727) 854177

FAULKNER, Peter Charles. b 46. Chich Th Coll 72. **d** 74 **p** 75. C St Bart Armley w St Mary New Wortley *Ripon* 74-76; C Tilehurst St Mich *Ox* 76-80; V Calcot 80-82; V Hagbourne 82-88; TV W Slough from 88. *St George's House, Long Furlong Drive, Slough SL2 2LX* Slough (01753) 525935

FAULKNER, Peter Graham. b 47. Lon Univ CertEd69. Oak Hill Th Coll BA87. **d** 82 **p** 83. C Crofton *Portsm* 87-89; R Mid Marsh Gp *Linc* from 89. *The Rectory, 37 Tinkle Street, Grimoldby, Louth, Lincs LN11 8SW* South Cockerington (01507) 327429

FAULKNER, Robert Henry. b 20. St Edm Hall Ox BA48 MA53. Wycliffe Hall Ox 48. **d** 50 **p** 51. V Thame w Towersey *Ox* 60-85;

R Aston Sandford 73-85; rtd 85; Perm to Offic *Ox* from 85. *5 Mavor Close, Old Woodstock, Oxon OX20 1YL* Woodstock (01993) 812059

FAULKNER, Canon Roger Kearton. b 36. AKC62. **d** 63 **p** 64. C Oxton *Ches* 63-67; C Ellesmere Port 67-69; V Runcorn H Trin 69-73; TV E Runcorn w Halton 73-76; V Altrincham St Geo 76-90; Chapl Altrincham Gen Hosp from 80; Hon Can Ches Cathl *Ches* from 88; V Higher Bebington from 90. *The Vicarage, Higher Bebington, Wirral, Merseyside L63 8LX* 0151-608 4429

FAULKS, David William. b 45. E Midl Min Tr Course 82. **d** 86 **p** 87. C Market Harborough *Leic* 86-88; C Wootton Bassett *Sarum* 88-90; R Clipston w Naseby and Haselbech w Kelmarsh *Pet* from 90. *The Rectory, 18 Church Lane, Clipston, Market Harborough, Leics LE16 9RW* Clipston (01858) 525342

FAULL, Very Rev Cecil Albert. b 30. TCD BA52. **d** 54 **p** 55. C Dub Zion Ch *D & G* 54-57; C Dub St Geo 57-59; Hon CV Ch Ch Cathl Dub 58-63; C Dun Laoghaire 59-63; I Portarlington w Cloneyhurke and Lea *M & K* 63-71; I Dub St Geo and St Thos *D & G* 71-80; I Clondalkin w Rathcoole 81-91; Can Ch Ch Cathl Dub 90-91; I Dunleckney w Nurney, Lorum and Kiltennel *C & O* from 91; Dean Leighlin from 91; P-in-c Leighlin w Grange Sylvae, Shankill etc from 91. *St Mary's Rectory, Dunleckney, Muine Bheag, Co Carlow, Irish Republic* Carlow (503) 21570

FAULL, Canon Vivienne Frances. b 55. St Hilda's Coll Ox BA77 MA82 Clare Coll Cam MA90. St Jo Coll Nottm BA81 DPS82. **dss** 82 **d** 87 **p** 94. Mossley Hill St Matt and St Jas *Liv* 82-85; Chapl Clare Coll Cam 85-90; Chapl Glouc Cathl *Glouc* 90-94; Can Res Cov Cathl *Cov* from 94. *35 Morningside, Coventry CV5 6PD* Coventry (01203) 675446

FAULL, William Baines. b 29. FRCVS Lon Univ BSc51. NW Ord Course 77. **d** 79 **p** 80. NSM Willaston *Ches* 79-80; NSM Neston 80-82; P-in-c Harthill and Burwardsley 82-86; Perm to Offic 87-91; Sen Fell Liv Univ from 89; V Ashton Hayes *Ches* from 91. *St John's Vicarage, Church Road, Ashton, Chester CH3 8AB* Kelsall (01829) 51265

FAUNCH, Canon Paul. b 13. FPhS46 FTSC65. Hong Kong DD72 St Jo Coll Dur 51. **d** 53 **p** 54. R E Donyland *Chelmsf* 65-75; OSJM from 72; rtd 78; Perm to Offic *Lon* from 78; Perm to Offic *Chich* from 78; Perm to Offic *S'wark* from 78; Hon Can St Ephraim Solna Sweden from 87. *78 St Andrew's Road, Portslade, Brighton BN41 1DE* Brighton (01273) 414204

FAVELL, Brian Jeffrey. b 23. Cuddesdon Coll 64. **d** 66 **p** 67. Lic to Offic *Birm* 70-76; V Cwmtillery *Mon* 76-86; P-in-c Six Bells 77-86; RD Blaenau Gwent 83-86; V Cwmcarn 86-88; rtd 88. *3 Church Street, Fladbury, Pershore, Worcs WR10 2QB* Pershore (01386) 860585

FAWCETT, Canon Frederick William. TCD BA49 MA52. CITC 50. **d** 50 **p** 51. C Belf St Aid *Conn* 50-52; C-in-c Draperstown *D & R* 52-59; I 59-60; I Cumber Upper w Learmount 60-87; Can Derry Cathl from 86; I Camus-juxta-Mourne from 87. *The Rectory, Newtown Street, Strabane, Co Tyrone BT82 8DW* Strabane (01504) 882314

FAWCETT, Canon Pamela Margaret. b 29. Univ Coll Lon BA52 DipEd75. E Anglian MinI Tr Course 83. **dss** 86 **d** 87 **p** 94. Stiffkey w Morston, Langham Episcopi etc *Nor* 86-87; Hon C Stiffkey and Cockthorpe w Morston, Langham etc 87-90; Hon Asst Min Repps Deanery 91-93; Hon C Trunch from 93; Asst Dioc Dir of Ords from 93; Bp's Consultant for Women's Min from 93; Hon Can Nor Cathl from 94. *Seekings, 47A High Street, Mundesley, Norwich NR11 8JL* Mundesley (01263) 721752

FAWCETT, Timothy John. b 44. K Coll Lon BD66 AKC67 PhD71. **d** 67 **p** 68. C Blackpool St Steph *Blackb* 67-70; Hon C St Marylebone All SS *Lon* 68-70; C Southgate St Mich 70-72; Sacr Dur Cathl *Dur* 72-75; V Wheatley Hill 75-79; V Torrisholme *Blackb* 79-84; V Thaxted *Chelmsf* 84-89; Perm to Offic *Nor* 89-94; NSM Holt Dnry from 94. *Dowitchers, 14 The Cornfield, Langham, Holt, Norfolk NR25 7DQ* Fakenham (01328) 830415

FAYERS, Robert Stanley. b 48. DipFD. St Steph Ho Ox 82. **d** 84 **p** 85. C Deptford St Paul *S'wark* 84-88; V Beckenham St Mich w St Aug *Roch* from 88. *St Michael's Vicarage, 120 Birkbeck Road, Beckenham, Kent BR3 4SS* 0181-778 6569

FAYLE, David Charles Wilfred. b 51. Sarum & Wells Th Coll. **d** 83 **p** 84. C Parkstone St Pet w Branksea and St Osmund *Sarum* 83-87; TV Dorchester from 87. *The Vicarage, 17A Edward Road, Dorchester, Dorset DT1 2HL* Dorchester (01305) 268434

FEAK, Christopher Martin (Chris). b 52. Keele Univ BA75 Trent Poly DCG76. Trin Coll Bris DipHE94. **d** 94 **p** 95. C Handsworth St Mary *Birm* from 94. *43 St Christophers, Birmingham B20 1BP* 0121-554 7749

FEARN, Anthony John. b 34. Lich Th Coll 58. **d** 61 **p** 62. C Redditch St Steph *Worc* 61-64; C Bladon w Woodstock *Ox* 64-66; V Ruscombe and Twyford 67-85; P-in-c Westmill w Gt

Munden *St Alb* 85-87; Asst Dioc Stewardship Adv 85-87; Chr Giving Adv *Heref* from 87. *Crozen Cottage, Felton, Hereford HR1 3PW* Hereford (01432) 820161 Fax as telephone

FEARN, Preb Hugh. b 18. Selw Coll Cam BA48 MA52 Sheff Univ MA52 Lon Univ PhD57 FRHistS60. **d** 58 **p** 59. V Northwood H Trin *Lon* 65-81; Preb St Paul's Cathl 77-88; R St Clem Eastcheap w St Martin Orgar 81-88; rtd 88. *c/o P W E Lea Esq, 17 Rowan Way, Forest Green, Nailsworth, Stroud, Glos GL6 0TE* Stroud (01453) 836160

FEARN, Michael Wilfrid (Mike). b 47. MBIM MIHT Plymouth Poly 70. Sarum & Wells Th Coll DipTh94. **d** 94 **p** 95. C Blandford Forum and Langton Long *Sarum* from 94. *50 East Leaze Road, Blandford Forum, Dorset DT11 7UN* Blandford (01258) 480445

FEARN, Robert Benjamin. b 27. Bps' Coll Cheshunt 62. **d** 64 **p** 65. V Basford St Aid *S'well* 68-74; V Beckingham w Walkeringham 74-83; V N and S Muskham 83-94; R Averham w Kelham 83-94; rtd 94. *Brentwood, Low Street, Elston, Newark, Notts NG23 5PA* Newark (01636) 525138

FEARNLEY, Jeffrey Malcolm. b 46. Newc Univ BSc69. St Jo Coll Nottm DCM92. **d** 92 **p** 93. C Bispham *Blackb* from 92. *Church Villa, All Hallows Road, Bispham, Blackpool FY2 0AY* Blackpool (01253) 53648

FEARON, Mrs Doris Ethel Elizabeth. b 26. Gilmore Ho 66. **dss** 72 **d** 87. Lingfield *S'wark* 68-75; Farnborough *Roch* 75-77; Bitterne *Win* 78-86; rtd 86; Bexhill St Pet *Chich* 86-87; Hon Par Dn 87-89; Perm to Offic from 89. *Delrosa, 32 Dalehurst Road, Bexhill-on-Sea, E Sussex TN39 4BN* Bexhill-on-Sea (01424) 221013

FEAST, Robert Butler. b 08. Trin Hall Cam BA30 MA36. Cuddesdon Coll 30. **d** 31 **p** 32. R Northlew w Ashbury *Ex* 69-73; rtd 73. *Rose Cottage, Boddington Lane, Northleigh, Witney, Oxon OX8 6PU* Freeland (01993) 881396

FEATHERSTONE, Andrew. b 53. St Chad's Coll Dur BA74. Sarum & Wells Th Coll 78. **d** 80 **p** 81. C Newc H Cross *Newc* 80-83; C Seaton Hirst 83-86; TV 86-87; R Crook *Dur* from 87; V Stanley from 87; RD Stanhope from 94. *The Rectory, 14 Hartside Close, Crook, Co Durham DL15 9NH* Bishop Auckland (01388) 764024

FEATHERSTONE, Gray. b 42. Stellenbosch Univ BA62 LLB64. Cuddesdon Coll. **d** 67 **p** 68. S Africa 67-70; Swaziland 70-72; Portuguese E Africa 73-75; Mozambique 75-76; Miss to Seamen 76-80; V Upper Clapton St Matt *Lon* 80-83; V Stamford Hill St Thos 80-89; Chr Aid Area Sec (NW Lon) from 89. *1 Oak Lane, London N2 8LP* 0181-349 1838 or 0171-620 4444 Fax 0171-620 0719

FEATHERSTONE, John. b 23. Kelham Th Coll 40. **d** 46 **p** 47. V Longford *Derby* 66-70; V Alkmonton w Yeaveley 66-70; V Chaddesden St Phil 70-72; V Denby 72-77; R Whitwell 77-84; RD Bolsover and Staveley 78-81; P-in-c Barlow 84-88; rtd 88; Perm to Offic *Derby* from 88. *16 Fern Close, Eckington, Sheffield S31 9HE* Eckington (01246) 432440

FEATHERSTONE, John. b 32. Man Univ BA53 St Cath Soc Ox BA59 Dur Univ DipEd66. Wycliffe Hall Ox 57. **d** 60 **p** 61. Hd RE Co Gr Sch Pet 66-70; Hd RE Qu Anne Gr Sch York 70-85; Chapl Tangier *Eur* 86-87 and 90-93; Chapl Pau w Biarritz 87-88; C Mexborough *Sheff* 88-90; rtd 93. *39 Cambridge Avenue, Marton-in-Cleveland, Middlesbrough, Cleveland TS7 8EH*

FEATHERSTONE, Robert Leslie. b 54. LLCM74 Lon Univ CertEd75. Chich Th Coll 84. **d** 86 **p** 87. C Crayford *Roch* 86-89; V Belvedere St Aug 89-94; V Withyham St Jo *Chich* from 94. *St John's Vicarage, St John's Road, Crowborough, E Sussex TN6 1RZ* Crowborough (01892) 654660

✠**FEAVER, Rt Rev Douglas Russell.** b 14. Keble Coll Ox BA35 MA39. Wells Th Coll 37. **d** 38 **p** 39 **c** 72. C St Alb Abbey *St Alb* 38-42; Chapl RAFVR 42-46; Can Res and Sub-Dean St Alb 46-58; V Nottm St Mary *S'well* 58-72; RD Nottm 58-72; Hon Can S'well Minster 58-72; Bp Pet 72-84; rtd 84; Perm to Offic *Ely* from 85; Perm to Offic *B & W* from 85. *6 Mill Lane, Bruton, Somerset BA10 0AT* Bruton (01749) 813485

FEDDEN, Canon Patrick Vincent. b 17. Ex Coll Ox BA40 MA43. Westcott Ho Cam 40. **d** 41 **p** 42. V Totteridge *St Alb* 59-72; RD Barnet 69-72; V Lower Mitton *Worc* 72-83; RD Stourport 75-80; Hon Can Worc Cathl 79-83; rtd 83; Perm to Offic *Glouc* from 83. *Church House, High Street, Newnham, Glos GL14 1AA* Dean (01594) 516259

FEENEY, Damian Prescott Anthony. b 62. ALCM81 Grey Coll Dur BA83 PGCE84. Chich Th Coll BTh94. **d** 94 **p** 95. C Harrogate St Wilfrid and St Luke *Ripon* from 94. *7 Lindrick Way, Harrogate, N Yorkshire HG1 2SU* Harrogate (01423) 508128

FEHRENBACH, Donald Joseph. b 17. Selw Coll Cam BA49 MA53. Qu Coll Birm 49. **d** 51 **p** 52. V Sandford-on-Thames *Ox* 65-84; rtd 84; Perm to Offic *Ox* from 84. *2 Walbury, Bracknell, Berks RG12 3JB* Bracknell (01344) 422759

FEIST, Johannes James. b 45. Solicitor 70. St Jo Coll Nottm LTh76. **d** 76 **p** 77. C Didsbury St Jas *Man* 76-80; TV Didsbury

St Jas and Em 80; V Friarmere 80-88; R Middleton from 88. *St Leonard's Rectory, Mellalieu Street, Middleton, Manchester M24 3DN* 0161-643 2693

FEIT, Michael John. b 24. FICE68 FIStructE68. S'wark Ord Course. **d** 69 **p** 71. C Feltham *Lon* 69-76; C Ashford St Matt 76-78; C Hykeham *Linc* 78-81; V Cranwell 81-85; R Leasingham 81-85; R Bishop Norton, Wadingham and Snitterby 85-90; rtd 90. *10229-149 Street, Suite 313, Surrey, British Columbia, Canada, V3R 4A1*

FELCE, Brian George. b 30. Jes Coll Ox BA54 MA57. Oak Hill Th Coll. **d** 58 **p** 59. R Bedingfield w Southolt *St E* 64-73; V Preston All SS *Blackb* 73-86; rtd 86. *11 St Barnabas Road, Sutton, Surrey SM1 4NL* 0181-642 7885

FELIX, David Rhys. b 55. Solicitor 81 Univ of Wales (Cardiff) LLB76. Ripon Coll Cuddesdon 83. **d** 86 **p** 87. C Bromborough *Ches* 86-89; V Grange St Andr from 89; Chapl Halton Gen Hosp from 95. *37 Lime Grove, Runcorn, Cheshire WA7 5JZ* Runcorn (01928) 574411

FELIX, Donald Cameron. b 24. St Aid Birkenhead 64. **d** 65 **p** 66. V Pype Hayes *Birm* 68-73; V Burslem St Paul *Lich* 73-76; V Bloxwich 76-79; P-in-c Seighford, Derrington and Cresswell 79-81; V 81-86; V Hanbury w Newborough 86-94; rtd 94; NSM Hanbury w Newborough *Lich* from 94. *The New Vicarage, Hanbury, Burton-on-Trent, Staffs DE13 8TF* Burton-on-Trent (01283) 813357

FELL, Alan William. b 46. Ball Coll Ox BA69 Leeds Univ DipTh70. Coll of Resurr Mirfield 68. **d** 71 **p** 72. C Woodchurch *Ches* 71-74; C Man Clayton St Cross w St Paul *Man* 74-75; C Prestwich St Marg 75-77; V Hyde St Thos *Ches* 77-80; R Tattenhall and Handley 80-86; V Sedbergh, Cautley and Garsdale *Bradf* from 86; Hon C Firbank, Howgill and Killington from 86. *The Vicarage, Sedbergh, Cumbria LA10 5SQ* Sedbergh (015396) 20283

FELL, Stephen. b 18. St Jo Coll Dur LTh41 BA42. Oak Hill Th Coll 38. **d** 42 **p** 43. R Castleford All SS *Wakef* 58-83; rtd 83. *255 Lower Mickletown, Methley, Leeds LS26 9AN* Castleford (01977) 515530

FELL, Willis Marshall. b 29. NW Ord Course 73. **d** 75 **p** 76. C Bolsover *Derby* 75-78; C Clay Cross 78-80; V Brampton St Mark 80-94; rtd 95. *The Willows, 12 Brandene Close, Calow, Chesterfield, Derbyshire S44 5TS* Chesterfield (01246) 270824

FELLINGHAM, John. b 25. RMC 44. Lon Coll of Div 52. **d** 55 **p** 56. R Coltishall w Gt Hautbois *Nor* 59-70; RD Ingworth 65-70; Chapl HM Pris Nor 69-73; P-in-c Nor St Helen *Nor* 70-73; Perm to Offic from 73; rtd 90; Asst Chapl HM Pris Wayland from 90. *Fielding Cottage, Anchor Corner, Attleborough, Norfolk NR17 1JX* Attleborough (01953) 455185 Fax 885775

FELLOWS, Grant. b 56. K Coll Lon BD77 AKC77. Coll of Resurr Mirfield 79. **d** 80 **p** 81. C Addington *Cant* 80-84; C S Gillingham *Roch* 84-86; V Heath and Reach *St Alb* 86-94; V Radlett from 94. *The Vicarage, Church Field, Christchurch Crescent, Radlett, Herts WD7 8EE* Radlett (01923) 856606

FELLOWS, John Lambert. b 35. LTCL67 SS Mark & Jo Coll Chelsea CertEd58. Portsm Dioc Tr Course 86. **d** 88. NSM Portsea St Cuth *Portsm* 88-94; NSM Farlington from 94. *7 Court Lane, Portsmouth PO6 2LG* Cosham (01705) 377270

FELLOWS, John Michael. b 46. Or Coll Ox MA77. Coll of Resurr Mirfield 74. **d** 77 **p** 78. C Kings Heath *Birm* 77-80; TV E Ham w Upton Park St Alb *Chelmsf* 80-85; P-in-c Worminsford 85-90; P-in-c Mt Bures 85-90; P-in-c Lt Horkesley 85-90; V Worminsford, Mt Bures and Lt Horkesley 90; R Compton w Shackleford and Peper Harow *Guildf* from 90. *The Rectory, The Street, Compton, Guildford, Surrey GU3 1ED* Guildford (01483) 810328

FELLOWS, Peter William. b 48. CertEd70 DipEd79. Chich Th Coll 86. **d** 88 **p** 89. C Westmr St Steph w St Jo *Lon* 88-93; R Deptford St Paul *S'wark* from 93. *St Paul's Rectory, 35 Albury Street, London SE8 3PT* 0181-692 0989

FELLOWS, Roy. b 30. Keble Coll Ox BA53 MA57. St Steph Ho Ox 53. **d** 56 **p** 57. R Withington St Crispin *Man* 63-74; V Southport St Luke *Liv* 74-78; V Bedf Leigh *Man* 78-81; Warden Co of Miss Priests 81-87; Lic to Offic *Wakef* 81-87; Admin of Shrine of Our Lady of Walsingham 87-93; Lic to Offic *Nor* 87-93; rtd 93. *Moor Rigg, Grisedale, Sedbergh, Cumbria LA10 5PS* Sedbergh (015396) 20690

FELTHAM, Keith. b 40. Lon Univ DipTh66. **d** 75 **p** 76. In Bapt Ch 66-75; C Plympton St Mary *Ex* 75-79; TV Northam w Westward Ho! and Appledore 79-82; TR Lynton, Brendon, Countisbury, Lynmouth etc 82-85; P-in-c Bickleigh (Plymouth) 85-86; TR 86-91; Chapl R Bournemouth Gen Hosp from 91. *Royal Bournemouth Hospital, Castle Lane East, Bournemouth BH7 7DW* Bournemouth (01202) 704221 or 303626

FENN, Norman Alexander. b 20. Kelham Th Coll 37. **d** 43 **p** 44. V Ellesmere *Lich* 61-85; V Welsh Frankton 62-85; RD Ellesmere 70-85; rtd 85; Perm to Offic *Lich* from 85. *1 Larkhill Road, Oswestry, Shropshire SY11 4AW* Oswestry (01691) 659411

FENN, Dr Roy William Dearnley. b 33. FRHistS70 FCP86 FSA88 Jes Coll Ox BA54 MA59 BD68. St Mich Coll Llan 54. **d** 56 **p** 57. C Swansea St Mary and H Trin *S & B* 57-59; C Cardiff St Jo *Llan* 59-60; C Coity w Nolton 60-63; V Glascombe w Rhulen and Gregrina *S & B* 63-68; V Glascwm and Rhulen 68-74; P-in-c Letton w Staunton, Byford, Mansel Gamage etc *Heref* 75-79; Perm to Offic *S & B* 80-85; Perm to Offic *Heref* from 85. *9 Victoria Road, Kington, Herefordshire HR5 3BX* Kington (01544) 230018

FENNELL, Canon Alfred Charles Dennis. b 15. Bp's Coll Calcutta 35. **d** 38 **p** 39. V Yardley St Cypr Hay Mill *Birm* 65-80; Hon Can Birm Cathl 78-80; rtd 80; Perm to Offic *Birm* from 80. *27 Madresfield Road, Malvern, Worcs WR14 2AS* Malvern (01684) 560613

FENNELL, Anthony Frederick Rivers. b 26. Pemb Coll Cam BA50 MA55 York Univ BPhil76. Ab Dioc Tr Course 90. **d** 90 **p** 91. NSM Braemar *Ab* from 90; NSM Ballater from 90; NSM Aboyne from 90. *19 Craigendarroch Circle, Ballater, Aberdeenshire AB35 5ZA* Ballater (013397) 55048

FENNEMORE, Nicholas Paul. b 53. Wycliffe Hall Ox 76. **d** 79 **p** 80. C N Mymms *St Alb* 79-82; C Chipping Barnet w Arkley 82-83; TV 83-84; TV Preston w Sutton Poyntz and Osmington w Poxwell *Sarum* 84-86; Chapl St Helier Hosp Carshalton 86-90; Chapl Jo Radcliffe Hosp Ox from 90. *John Radcliffe Hospital, Oxford OX3 9DU* Oxford (01865) 741166 or 221732

FENNING, John Edward. b 32. CITC 86. **d** 88 **p** 89. NSM Douglas Union w Frankfield *C, C & R* 88-89; Chapl Ashton Sch Cork from 88; NSM Moviddy Union *C, C & R* from 89. *Moviddy Rectory, Aherla, Co Cork, Irish Republic* Cork (21) 331511 or 966044 Fax 966321

FENSOME, Anthony David (Tony). b 49. DipYL74 Open Univ BA89. Sarum & Wells Th Coll 82. **d** 84 **p** 85. C Gtr Corsham *Bris* 84-88; P-in-c Lyddington w Wanborough 88-91; P-in-c Bishopstone w Hinton Parva 88-91; R Lyddington and Wanborough and Bishopstone etc 91-93; V Chippenham St Pet from 93; RD Chippenham from 94. *St Peter's Vicarage, Lords Mead, Chippenham, Wilts SN14 0LL* Chippenham (01249) 654835

FENTIMAN, David Frank. b 43. RIBA74 Cen Lon Poly DipArch72. S Dios Minl Tr Scheme 90. **d** 93 **p** 94. NSM Hastings St Clem and All SS *Chich* from 93. *4 Barnfield Close, Hastings, E Sussex TN34 1TS* Hastings (01424) 432854

FENTON, Barry Dominic. b 59. Leeds Univ BA85. Coll of Resurr Mirfield 85. **d** 87 **p** 88. C Leigh Park *Portsm* 87-90; Chapl and Prec Portsm Cathl 90-95; Prec Westmr Abbey from 95. *7 Little Cloister, Westminster Abbey, London SW1P 3PL* 0171-222 4023 or 222 6428 Fax 233 2072

FENTON, Christopher Miles Tempest. b 28. MInstPC75 Qu Coll Cam BA50 LLB51 MA55. Ridley Hall Cam 52. **d** 54 **p** 55. V Ramsgate Ch Ch *Cant* 65-71; Hd Dept of Gp Studies Westmr Past Foundn 71-83; P-in-c Mottingham St Andr *S'wark* 71-73; Sen Tutor Cambs Consultancy in Counselling 73-85; Perm to Offic *Ely* 73-85; Co-ord of Tr St Alb Past Foundn 80-88; Perm to Offic *St Alb* 80-88; Dir St Anne's Trust for Psychotherapy Ledbury from 85; Perm to Offic *Heref* from 85; rtd 93. *The Leys, Aston, Kingsland, Leominster, Herefordshire HR6 9PU* Kingsland (01568) 708632

FENTON, Heather. b 48. Trin Coll Bris CertEd78. **d** 87. C Corwen and Llangar *St As* 87-89; C Corwen & Llangar w Gwyddelwern and Llawrybetws from 89; Dioc Rural Min Co-ord from 87. *Coleg y Groes, The College, Corwen, Clwyd LL21 0AU* Corwen (01490) 412169

FENTON, Ian Christopher Stuart. b 40. AKC62. **d** 63 **p** 64. C Banstead *Guildf* 63-67; V N Holmwood 67-84; RD Dorking 80-84; V Witley from 84. *The Vicarage, Petworth Road, Witley, Godalming, Surrey GU8 5LT* Wormley (01428) 682886

FENTON, Canon John Charles. b 21. Qu Coll Ox BA43 MA47 BD53. Linc Th Coll 43. **d** 44 **p** 45. Prin St Chad's Coll Dur 65-78; Can Res Ch Ch *Ox* 78-91; rtd 91; Hon Can Ch Ch *Ox* 91-92. *8 Rowland Close, Oxford OX2 8PW* Oxford (01865) 54099

FENTON, Michael John. b 42. Linc Th Coll 67. **d** 69 **p** 70. C Guiseley *Bradf* 69-72; C Heswall *Ches* 72-75; TV Birkenhead Priory 75-81; V Alvanley 81-91; Chapl Crossley Hosp Cheshire 82-91; V Holbrook and Lt Eaton *Derby* from 91. *The Vicarage, 30 Moorside Lane, Holbrook, Belper, Derbyshire DE56 0TW* Derby (01332) 880254

FENTON, Canon Wallace. b 32. TCD. **d** 64 **p** 65. C Glenavy *Conn* 64-67; I Tullaniskin w Clonoe *Arm* 67-87; Bp's C Sallaghy *Clogh* from 87; Warden of Readers from 91; RD Clones from 93; Preb Clogh Cathl from 95. *Sallaghy Rectory, Lisnaskea, Enniskillen, Co Fermanagh BT92 5FG* Lisnaskea (013657) 21372

FENWICK, Edward Hartwig. b 05. Fitzw Coll Cam BA33 MA43. Westcott Ho Cam 32. **d** 33 **p** 34. R Baddesley Clinton *Birm* 60-76; R Lapworth 60-76; rtd 76; C Solihull *Birm* 76-90. *1 St Alphege Close, Church Hill Road, Solihull, W Midlands B91 3RQ* 0121-704 4736

FENWICK

FENWICK, Very Rev Jeffrey Robert. b 30. Pemb Coll Cam BA53 MA57. Linc Th Coll 53. **d** 55 **p** 56. C Upholland *Liv* 55-58; S Rhodesia 58-64; Rhodesia 65-78; Area Sec (Dio Ox) USPG 64-65; Adn Charter 73-75; Dean Bulawayo 75-78; Adn Bulawayo 75-78; Can Res Worc Cathl *Worc* 78-89; R Guernsey St Peter Port *Win* from 89; Dean Guernsey from 89; Hon Can Win Cathl from 89; Pres Guernsey Miss to Seamen from 89. *The Deanery, St Peter Port, Guernsey, Channel Islands GY1 1BZ* Guernsey (01481) 720036

FENWICK, Dr John Robert Kipling. b 51. Van Mildert Coll Dur BSc72 Nottm Univ BA74 MTh78 K Coll Lon PhD85. Lambeth STh84 St Jo Coll Nottm 72. **d** 77 **p** 78. C Dalton-in-Furness *Carl* 77-80; Lect Trin Coll Bris 80-88; Chapl 80-87; Lic to Offic *Bris* 81-88; Abp Cant's Asst Sec for Ecum Affairs 88-92; NSM Purley Ch Ch *S'wark* 88-92; Asst ChStJ from 89; R Chorley St Laur *Blackb* from 92. *The Rectory, Rectory Close, Chorley, Lancs PR7 1QW* Chorley (01257) 263114

FENWICK, Malcolm Frank. b 38. Cranmer Hall Dur 62. **d** 65 **p** 66. C Tynemouth Cullercoats St Paul *Newc* 65-68; C Bywell St Pet 68-73; V Alnmouth 73-75; CF(TAVR) 75-83; V Lesbury w Alnmouth *Newc* 75-80; V Delaval 80-91; RD Bedlington 83-88; V Riding Mill from 91; P-in-c Whittonstall from 91; Chapl Shepherd's Dene Retreat Ho from 91; RD Corbridge from 93. *The Vicarage, Oaklands, Riding Mill, Northd NE44 6AS* Riding Mill (01434) 682811

FENWICK, Canon Richard David. b 43. FLCM68 FTCL76 Univ of Wales (Lamp) BA66 MA86 TCD MusB79. Ridley Hall Cam 66. **d** 68 **p** 69. C Skewen *Llan* 68-72; C Penarth w Lavernock 72-74; PV, Succ and Sacr Roch Cathl *Roch* 74-78; Min Can St Paul's Cathl *Lon* 78-79; Min Can and Succ 79-83; Warden Coll Min Cans 81-83; PV Westmr Abbey 83-90; V Ruislip St Martin *Lon* 83-90; Can Res and Prec Guildf Cathl *Guildf* from 90. *3 Cathedral Close, Guildford, Surrey GU2 5TL* Guildford (01483) 69682

FEREDAY, Adrian Paul. b 57. Huddersfield Poly CQSW88 DipSocWork88. Coll of Resurr Mirfield 92. **d** 94 **p** 95. C Gleadless *Sheff* from 94. *238 Hollinsend Road, Sheffield S12 2EJ* Sheffield (0114) 264 5682

FEREDAY, Harold James Rodney (Rod). b 46. Sheff Univ CEIR76. St Jo Coll Nottm 87. **d** 89 **p** 90. C Rastrick St Matt *Wakef* 89-92; V Siddal from 92. *St Mark's Vicarage, 15 Whitegate Road, Siddal, Halifax, W Yorkshire HX3 9AD* Halifax (01422) 369558

FERGUSON, Aean Michael O'Shaun. **d** 90 **p** 91. NSM Kilmallock w Kilflynn, Kilfinane, Knockaney etc *L & K* 90-91; NSM Killaloe w Stradbally 91-94; NSM Adare w Kilpeacon and Croom from 94. *Moohane, Lough Gur, Bruff, Co Limerick, Irish Republic* Limerick (61) 385195

FERGUSON, Dr Alistair Stuart. b 45. MRCS69 LRCP69 Ball Coll Ox BA78 MA82 Lon Univ MB, BS69. St Steph Ho Ox. **d** 82 **p** 83. NSM Dengie w Asheldham *Chelmsf* 82-86; NSM Mayland 86-89; NSM Steeple 86-89; Perm to Offic 89-91; Zimbabwe from 91. *St Andrew's Rectory, PO Box 21, Mvurwi, Zimbabwe* Mvurwi (77) 2401

FERGUSON, Ian John. b 51. Aber Univ BD77. Trin Coll Bris 77. **d** 78 **p** 79. C Foord St Jo *Cant* 78-82; C Bieldside *Ab* 82-86; Dioc Youth Chapl 82-86; P-in-c Westhill from 86. *1 Westwood Drive, Westhill, Skeene, Aberdeenshire AB32 6WW* Aberdeen (01224) 740007

FERGUSON, James Paterson. b 07. Glas Univ MA29 Qu Coll Ox BA33. Wycliffe Hall Ox 33. **d** 33 **p** 34. Swaziland 70-71; rtd 72; Perm to Offic *S & M* from 72. *Creigneish, 27 Albany Road, Douglas, Isle of Man IM2 3NF* Douglas (01624) 673130

FERGUSON, John Duncan. b 31. Clare Coll Cam BA54 MA58. Kelham Th Coll 54. **d** 59 **p** 60. C Old Charlton *S'wark* 59-63; Ghana 63-75; Lic to Offic *Pet* 75-76; Lic to Offic *Ox* 75-77; Lic to Offic *Truro* 86-91; V Hessenford 77-84; Dioc Development Rep 80-86; Public Preacher from 94; RD Trigg Major from 91. *Hampton Manor, Stoke Climsland, Callington, Cornwall PL17 8LZ* Stoke Climsland (01579) 370494

FERGUSON, John Aitken. b 40. ARCST64 CEng MICE Glas Univ BSc64 Strathclyde Univ PhD74. Linc Th Coll 79. **d** 81 **p** 82. C Morpeth *Newc* 81-85; V Whittingham and Edlingham w Bolton Chapel from 85. *The Vicarage, Whittingham, Alnwick, Northd NE66 4UP* Whittingham (0166574) 224

FERGUSON, John Harold Preston. b 34. CITC 63. **d** 65 **p** 66. C Dundela *D & D* 65-70; I Annahilt 70-76; I Belf St Brendan 76-94; rtd 94. *49 Kinedale Park, Ballynahinch, Co Down BT24 8YS* Ballynahinch (01238) 562599

FERGUSON, Mrs Kathleen (Kathy). b 46. ALA76 LMH Ox BA68 MA72. **d** 88. NSM Llanidloes w Llangurig *Ban* from 88. *Oerle, Trefeglwys, Caersws, Powys SY17 5QX* Llanidloes (01686) 430626

FERGUSON, Michelle. Ottawa Univ BA. Cranmer Hall Dur. **d** 95. NSM Newton Aycliffe *Dur* from 95. *4 Highside Road, Heighington Village, Newton Aycliffe, Co Durham DL5 6PG* Aycliffe (01325) 320860

FERGUSON, Canon Paul John. b 55. FRCO75 New Coll Ox BA76 MA80 K Coll Cam BA84 MA88. Westcott Ho Cam 82. **d** 85 **p** 86. C Ches St Mary *Ches* 85-88; Sacr and Chapl Westmr Abbey 88-92; Prec 92-95; Can Res and Prec York Minster *York* from 95. *2 Minster Court, York YO1 2JJ* York (01904) 624965 or 642526   Fax 654604

FERGUSON, Richard Archie. b 39. Dur Univ BA62. Linc Th Coll 62. **d** 64 **p** 65. C Stretford St Matt *Man* 64-68; Bp's Dom Chapl *Dur* 68-69; C Newc St Geo *Newc* 69-71; V Glodwick *Man* 71-77; V Tynemouth Ch Ch *Newc* 77-82; P-in-c Tynemouth St Aug 82-87; V Tynemouth Ch Ch w H Trin 82-87; TR N Shields 87-90; TR Upton cum Chalvey *Ox* from 90. *The Rectory, 18 Albert Street, Slough SL1 2BU* Slough (01753) 529988

FERGUSON, Robert Garnett Allen. b 48. Leeds Univ LLB70 Clare Coll Cam. Cuddesdon Coll 71. **d** 73 **p** 74. C Wakef Cathl *Wakef* 73-76; V Lupset 76-83; Chapl Cheltenham Coll 83-87; Sen Chapl Win Coll from 87. *Winchester College, Winchester, Hants SO23 9NA* Winchester (01962) 884056

FERGUSON, Robin Sinclair. b 31. Worc Coll Ox BA53 MA57 Lon Univ CertEd63. ALCD55 Wycliffe Coll Toronto 55. **d** 57 **p** 58. C Brompton H Trin *Lon* 57-60; C Brixton St Matt *S'wark* 60-63; Hon C Framlingham w Saxtead *St E* 63-65; Hon C Haverhill 65-67; Chapl St Mary's Sch Richmond 67-75; C Richmond St Mary *S'wark* 76-87; P-in-c Shilling Okeford *Sarum* 76-87; Chapl Croft Ho Sch Shillingstone 76-87; R Milton Abbas, Hilton w Cheselbourne etc *Sarum* from 87. *The Rectory, Ansty, Dorchester, Dorset DT2 7PX* Milton Abbas (01258) 880372

FERGUSON, Ronald Leslie. b 36. Open Univ BA86 BA89 Newc Poly CertFT90. Chich Th Coll 65. **d** 68 **p** 69. C Toxteth Park St Marg *Liv* 68-72; C Oakham w Hambleton and Egleton *Pet* 72-74; Asst Chapl The Dorothy Kerin Trust Burrswood 74-76; V Castleside *Dur* from 76. *The Vicarage, Castleside, Consett, Co Durham DH8 9AP* Consett (01207) 508242

FERGUSON, Wallace Raymond. b 47. Qu Coll Birm BTh CITC 76. **d** 78 **p** 79. C Lurgan Ch Ch *D & D* 78-80; I Newtownards w Movilla Abbey 80-84; I Mullabrack w Markethill and Kilcluney *Arm* from 84; Hon VC Arm Cathl from 86; Dioc Chapl to Rtd Clergy from 92. *The Rectory, Mullurg Road, Mullabrack, Armagh BT60 1QN* Markethill (01861) 551092

FERGUSSON, Miss Catherine Margaret (Kate). b 28. MIPM Birm Univ CSocStuds50. Linc Th Coll 77. **dss** 79 **d** 87 **p** 94. Watford St Pet *St Alb* 79-82; Prestwood *Ox* 82-86; Gt Horwood 86-87; Par Dn 87-89; Dir Cottesloe Chr Tr Progr 86-89; rtd 89. *Checkmate, Middle Ground, Fovant, Salisbury SP3 5LP* Fovant (01722) 720314

FERLEY, Canon John Harold. b 07. Lon Coll of Div 25 ALCD29. **d** 30 **p** 31. V Hunstanton St Edm *Nor* 52-72; RD Heacham 66-70; RD Heacham and Rising 70-72; Hon Can Nor Cathl 70-85; rtd 72; P-in-c Nor St Geo Tombland *Nor* 72-85; Perm to Offic from 85. *10 Kingsley Road, Norwich NR1 3RB* Norwich (01603) 610268

FERMER, Michael Thorpe. b 30. Lon Univ BSc52 ARCS52 St Cath Soc Ox BA54. Wycliffe Hall Ox 52. **d** 54 **p** 55. Lic to Offic *Sheff* 66-73; V Holmesfield *Derby* 73-79; TR Old Brampton and Loundsley Green 79-83; V Brightside St Thos and St Marg *Sheff* 83; V Brightside w Wincobank 83-89; V Loscoe *Derby* 89-94; rtd 94. *123 Bacons Lane, Chesterfield, Derbyshire S40 2TN* Chesterfield (01246) 555793

FERN, John. b 36. Nottm Univ BA57 DipRE64 MA88. Coll of Resurr Mirfield 57. **d** 59 **p** 60. C Carlton *S'well* 59-61; C Hucknall Torkard 61-68; V Rainworth from 68. *The Vicarage, 27 St Peter's Drive, Rainworth, Mansfield, Notts NG21 0BE* Mansfield (01623) 792293

FERNANDO, Percy Sriyananda. b 49. Dundee Coll DCEd81. St And Dioc Tr Course 85. **d** 88 **p** 89. NSM Blairgowrie *St And* from 88; NSM Coupar Angus from 89; NSM Alyth from 89. *Gowrie Cottage, Perth Road, Blairgowrie, Perthshire PH10 6QB*

FERNANDO, Mrs Susan Joy. b 50. Nottm Univ CertEd77 BEd78. Linc Th Coll 83. **dss** 85 **d** 87. Kingsbury H Innocents *Lon* 85-88; Par Dn 87-88; Par Dn Harmondsworth 88-91; Perm to Offic *Guildf* 91-92 and 93-94; C Frimley 92-93; Chapl Grove Sch Hindhead 92-94. *Flat 2, Fircroft, School Road, Grayshott, Hindhead, Surrey GU26 6LR* Haslemere (01428) 606494

FERNS, Stephen Antony Dunbar. b 61. St Chad's Coll Dur BA84 Ox Univ BA87. Ripon Coll Cuddesdon 85. **d** 88 **p** 89. C Billingham St Cuth *Dur* 88-90; Chapl Dur Univ 91; Chapl Van Mildert and Trevelyan Coll Dur 91-95; P-in-c Norton St Mary from 95. *The Vicarage, Norton, Stockton-on-Tees, Cleveland TS20 3LE* Stockton-on-Tees (01642) 558888

FERNS, Archdeacon of. See WILKINSON, Ven Kenneth Samuel

FERNS, Dean of. See FORREST, Very Rev Leslie David Arthur

FERNSBY, Jack. b 08. St Chad's Coll Dur BA39 DipTh40 MA42. **d** 40 **p** 41. C Billingham St Cuth *Dur* 40-42; C

Kennington St Jo *S'wark* 42-46; C St Marylebone All SS *Lon* 46-47; C Upper Norwood St Jo *S'wark* 47-48; V Weoley Castle *Birm* 48-51; V Nether Stowey *B & W* 51-55; Perm to Offic *Lich* from 72. *15 Fairfield Close, Gobowen, Oswestry, Shropshire SY11 3JP* Oswestry (01691) 650473

FERNYHOUGH, Ven Bernard. b 32. St D Coll Lamp BA53. **d** 55 **p** 56. Trinidad and Tobago 55-61; R Stoke Bruerne w Grafton Regis and Alderton *Pet* 61-67; RD Preston 65-67; V E Haddon 67-69; V Ravensthorpe 67-69; R Holdenby 67-69; RD Haddon 68-71; V Ravensthorpe w E Haddon and Holdenby 69-77; RD Brixworth 71-77; Can Pet Cathl 74-77 and from 89; Can Res Pet Cathl 77-89; Adn Oakham from 77; P-in-c Empingham and Exton w Horn w Whitwell from 95. *The Rectory, 5 Nook Lane, Empingham, Oakham, Rutland LE15 8PT* Empingham (0178086) 215

FERNYHOUGH, Timothy John Edward. b 60. Leeds Univ BA81. Linc Th Coll 81. **d** 83 **p** 84. C Daventry *Pet* 83-86; Chapl Tonbridge Sch Kent 86-92; Chapl Dur Sch from 92. *7 Pimlico, Durham DH1 4QW* 0191-384 3664 or 384 7977

FERRIDAY, Donald Martin. b 30. Univ of Wales (Lamp) BA55. Qu Coll Birm 55. **d** 57 **p** 58. C Stockport St Sav *Ches* 57-59; C Heswall 59-64; V Cheadle Hulme All SS 64-72; V Ches 72-76; TR Ches Team 76-77; R W Kirby St Bridget from 77. *The Rectory, West Kirby, Wirral, Merseyside L48 7HL* 0151-625 5229

FERRIER, Malcolm. b 38. St Mich Coll Llan 67. **d** 69 **p** 70. C Solihull *Birm* 69-73; C E Grinstead St Swithun *Chich* 73-75; V Saltley *Birm* 75-82; V Waterlooville *Portsm* from 82. *The Vicarage, Stakes Hill Road, Waterlooville, Hants PO7 7LB* Waterlooville (01705) 262145

FERRY, David Henry John. b 53. TCD BTh88. **d** 88 **p** 89. C Enniskillen *Clogh* 88-90; I Leckpatrick w Dunnalong *D & R* from 90. *1 Lowertown Road, Ballymagorry, Strabane, Co Tyrone BT82 0LE* Strabane (01504) 883545

FESSEY, Mrs Annis Irene. b 40. SS Paul & Mary Coll Cheltenham CertEd60. Ripon Coll Cuddesdon 88. **d** 90 **p** 94. Par Dn Bris St Andr Hartcliffe *Bris* 90-94; C 94; C The Lydiards 94-95. *The Vicarage, 4 Church Street, Purton, Wilts SN5 9DS* Swindon (01793) 770210

FESSEY, Brian Alan. b 39. Bris Univ CertEd61 Leeds Univ DipEd71. Ripon Coll Cuddesdon 88. **d** 90 **p** 91. Hon C Bishopsworth *Bris* 90; C Withywood CD 91-94; V Purton from 94. *The Vicarage, 4 Church Street, Purton, Wilts SN5 9DS* Swindon (01793) 770210

FETHNEY, John Garside. b 27. Linc Coll Ox BA52 NE Lon Poly DCS72. Linc Th Coll 51. **d** 53 **p** 54. Area Sec (Dio York) USPG 68-70; (Dio Lon) 70-73; (Dios Chich and Guildf) 86-92; Deputation and Th Colls Sec 73-83; Adult and HE Officer 83-86; Hon C St Botolph without Bishopsgate *Lon* 73-86; rtd 92. *21 Proper Close, East Wittering, Chichester, W Sussex PO20 8PW* Bracklesham Bay (01243) 670145 or 670000

FEWKES, Jeffrey Preston. b 47. Wycliffe Hall Ox 72. **d** 75 **p** 76. C Ches le Street *Dur* 75-78; C Kennington St Mark *S'wark* 78-81; V Bulwell St Jo *S'well* from 81. *St John's Vicarage, Snape Wood Road, Bulwell, Nottingham NG6 7GH* Nottingham (0115) 927 8025

FIDDAMAN, Ernest Robert. b 13. **d** 78 **p** 78. Hon C Preston *Chich* 78-83; Chapl Wokingham Hosp from 83; Hon C Wokingham All SS *Ox* from 83. *2 Beckett Close, Wokingham, Berks RG11 1YZ* Wokingham (01734) 791451

FIDDYMENT, Alan John. b 40. Cant Sch of Min 91. **d** 94. NSM Chatham St Wm *Roch* from 94. *29 Tunbury Avenue, Chatham, Kent ME5 9EH* Medway (01634) 666155

FIDLER, John Harvey. b 49. Hatf Poly BSc72. St Alb Minl Tr Scheme 84. **d** 87 **p** 88. NSM Royston *St Alb* from 87. *8 Stamford Avenue, Royston, Herts SG8 7DD* Royston (01763) 241886

FIELD, David Hibberd. b 36. K Coll Cam BA58. Oak Hill Th Coll 58. **d** 60 **p** 61. C Aldershot H Trin *Guildf* 60-63; C Margate H Trin *Cant* 63-66; Sec Th Students Fellowship 66-68; Tutor Oak Hill Th Coll 68-93; Vice Prin 79-93; Dean Minl Tr Course 88-93; Dir Professional Min Div CPAS from 94; Patr Sec CPAS from 94. *CPAS, Athena Drive, Tachbrook Park, Warwick CV43 6NG* Warwick (01926) 334242 Fax 337613

FIELD, Donald Charles. b 21. Lon Univ BSc50. Glouc Th Course 65. **d** 66 **p** 67. C Tewkesbury w Walton Cardiff *Glouc* 69-72; V Standish w Hardwicke and Haresfield 72-74; V Standish w Haresfield and Moreton Valence 74-80; V Deerhurst, Apperley w Forthampton and Chaceley 80-86; rtd 86; Perm to Offic *St D* from 87. *20 Highfield Road, Ammanford, Dyfed SA18 1JL* Amman Valley (01269) 822716

FIELD, Geoffrey Alder. b 13. Ely Th Coll. **d** 47 **p** 48. V Whittlesey St Andr *Ely* 54-75; V Foxton 75-80; rtd 80. *14 Poplar Close, Great Shelford, Cambridge CB21 5LX* Cambridge (01223) 842099

FIELD, Gerald Gordon. b 54. K Coll Lon BD75 AKC75. Coll of Resurr Mirfield 76. **d** 77 **p** 78. C Broughton *Blackb* 77-79; C Blackpool St Steph 79-82; V Skerton St Luke 82-86; NSM

Westleigh St Pet *Man* 92-93; V Shap w Swindale and Bampton w Mardale *Carl* from 93. *The Vicarage, Shap, Penrith, Cumbria CA10 3LB* Shap (01931) 716232

FIELD, Leonard Frederick. b 34. Man Univ BSc56 Lon Univ CertEd57. E Midl Min Tr Course 85. **d** 88 **p** 89. NSM Holton-le-Clay *Linc* 88-94. *35 Bedford Road, Humberston, Grimsby, S Humberside DN35 0PZ* Grimsby (01472) 812489

FIELD, Martin Richard. b 55. Keswick Hall Coll CertEd76 Leic Univ MA87. St Jo Coll Nottm BTh82 LTh. **d** 82 **p** 83. C Gaywood, Bawsey and Mintlyn *Nor* 82-85; Perm to Offic *Leic* 85-87; Hon C S'well Minster *S'well* 87-88; Hon C Stand *Man* 88-89; Dioc Press and Communications Officer 88-91. *2 Hamilton Road, Prestwich, Manchester M25 8GG* 0161-773 5963

FIELD, Miss Olwen Joyce. b 53. St Jo Coll Nottm 86. **d** 88 **p** 94. Par Dn Kensal Rise St Mark and St Martin *Lon* 88-91; Par Dn Northwood H Trin 91-94; Chapl Mt Vernon Hosp Uxbridge from 91; C Northwood H Trin *Lon* from 94. *81 Myrtleside Close, Northwood, Middx HA6 2XQ* Northwood (01923) 823221

FIELD, Richard Colin (Dick). b 33. St Cath Soc Ox BA54 MA63. Clifton Th Coll 63. **d** 65 **p** 66. C Highbury Ch Ch *Lon* 65-70; V Tottenham St Ann 70-85; V Leytonstone St Jo *Chelmsf* from 85. *St John's Vicarage, 44 Hartley Road, London E11 3BL* 0181-989 5447

FIELD, Miss Susan Elizabeth (Sue). b 59. York Univ BA80 Birm Univ CertEd81. Qu Coll Birm 84. **d** 87 **p** 94. C Coleshill *Birm* 87-90; Chapl Loughb Univ *Leic* from 91; Dir Post Ord Tr from 95. *13 Spinney Hill Drive, Loughborough, Leics LE11 3LB* Loughborough (01509) 268203

FIELD, William Jenkin. b 25. St Deiniol's Hawarden. **d** 66 **p** 67. C Cardiff St Jo *Llan* 66-72; V Llancarfan w Llantrithyd 72-94; rtd 94. *20 Whitmore Park Drive, Barry, S Glam CF62 8JL* Barry (01446) 701027

FIELDEN, Hugh. b 66. BNC Ox BA88 Birm Univ PGCE90. Qu Coll Birm 91. **d** 93 **p** 94. C Sholing *Win* from 93. *93 Spring Road, Southampton SO2 7QH* Southampton (01703) 420371

FIELDEN, Robert. b 32. Linc Th Coll 65. **d** 67 **p** 68. C Bassingham *Linc* 67-72; R Anderby w Cumberworth 72-88; P-in-c Huttoft 72-88; P-in-c Mumby 77-88; R Fiskerton w Reepham 88-90; rtd 90; Perm to Offic *Linc* from 91. *Valley Howe, Allithwaite Road, Cartmel, Grange-over-Sands, Cumbria LA11 7SB* Cartmel (015395) 36159

FIELDER, Canon Arthur John. b 14. Lon Univ DipTh48. Bps' Coll Cheshunt 46. **d** 47 **p** 50. Hon Can Leic Cathl *Leic* 67-77; Dir of Educn 67-77; Master Wyggeston's Hosp Leic 68-78; rtd 78; Perm to Offic *St Alb* from 78; Perm to Offic *Chich* from 92. *3 Morley House, College of St Barnabas, Lingfield, Surrey RH7 6NJ* Dormans Park (01342) 870407

FIELDGATE, John William Sheridan. b 44. St Jo Coll Dur BA68. Ox NSM Course 75. **d** 79 **p** 80. NSM Haddenham w Cuddington, Kingsey etc *Ox* 79-90; C Northleach w Hampnett and Farmington *Glouc* 90-92; C Cold Aston w Notgrove and Turkdean 90-92; P-in-c Upper and Lower Slaughter w Eyford and Naunton from 92. *The Rectory, Copse Hill Road, Lower Slaughter, Cheltenham, Glos GL54 2HY* Cotswold (01451) 810812

FIELDING, John Joseph. b 29. TCD BA53 MA65. **d** 54 **p** 55. C Belf St Luke *Conn* 54-57; C Belf St Mary Magd 57-60; W Germany 61-69; Chapl St Edw Sch Ox 69-73; V Highgate St Mich *Lon* from 73. *The Vicarage, 10 The Grove, London N6 6LB* 0181-340 7279

FIELDING, Canon Ronald Jeffrey. b 17. Lon Univ BSc38. Qu Coll Birm 40. **d** 42 **p** 43. C Selly Oak St Mary *Birm* 42-46; S Africa from 46; Hon Can Grahamstown Cathl from 86. *40 Kennington Road, Nahoon, East London, 5241 South Africa* East London (431) 353735

FIELDING, Stephen Aubrey. b 67. Ulster Univ BSc89 TCD BTh93. CITC 90. **d** 93 **p** 94. C Ban Abbey *D & D* from 93. *13 Morston Park, Bangor, Co Down BT20 3ER* Bangor (01247) 473741

FIELDING, Canon William (Bill). b 35. St Jo Coll Dur BA60. Ridley Hall Cam. **d** 62 **p** 63. C Ashton-on-Ribble St Mich *Blackb* 62-64; C Broughton 64-67; V Knuzden 67-75; V Darwen St Cuth 75-85; RD Darwen 77-87; P-in-c Tockholes 79-83; V Darwen St Cuth w Tockholes St Steph 85-87; V St Annes from 87; RD Kirkham 91-94; Hon Can Blackb Cathl from 93. *St Thomas's Vicarage, Victoria Road, St Annes, Lytham St Annes, Lancs FY8 1LE* St Annes (01253) 723750

FIELDSEND, John Henry. b 31. Nottm Univ BSc54 Lon Univ BD61. ALCD59. **d** 61 **p** 62. C Pennington *Man* 61-64; C Didsbury Ch Ch 64-66; P-in-c Bayston Hill *Lich* 66-67; V 67-88; UK Dir CMJ from 89; Min at Large CMJ from 91. *27 Charmouth Road, St Albans, Herts AL1 4RS* St Albans (01727) 869537

FIELDSON, Robert Steven. b 56. Qu Coll Cam BA78 MA81 Wye Coll Lon MSc79 Nottm Univ BA86. St Jo Coll Nottm 84. **d** 87 **p** 88. C Walmley *Birm* 87-90; Oman 90-95; P-in-c Cofton

Hackett w Barnt Green *Birm* from 95. *The Vicarage, 8 Cofton Church Lane, Barnt Green, Birmingham B45 8PT* 0121-445 1269

FIENNES, Very Rev the Hon Oliver William. b 26. New Coll Ox BA54 MA55. Cuddesdon Coll 52. **d** 54 **p** 55. Can and Preb Linc Cathl *Linc* from 69; Dean Linc 69-89; rtd 89; Perm to Offic *Pet* from 89. *Home Farm House, Colsterworth, Grantham, Lincs NG33 5NE* Grantham (01476) 860811

FIFE, Miss Janet Heather. b 53. Sussex Univ BA77. Wycliffe Hall Ox 84. **d** 87 **p** 94. Chapl Bradf Cathl *Bradf* 87-89; Par Dn York St Mich-le-Belfrey *York* 89-92; Chapl Salford Univ *Man* from 92; Hon C Pendleton St Thos w Charlestown from 92. *2 Hilton Drive, Prestwich, Manchester M25 8NN* 0161-773 9408 or 745 5000

FIGG, Robin Arthur Rex. b 62. RN Eng Coll Plymouth BScEng84. Westcott Ho Cam CTM94. **d** 94 **p** 95. C Old Cleeve, Leighland and Treborough *B & W* from 94. *Willow Bank, Washford, Watchet, Somerset TA23 0PT* Watchet (01984) 40691

FILBERT-ULLMANN, Mrs Clair. b 51. Louvain Univ Belgium BTh94. Virginia Th Sem. **d** 94. USA 94-95; Asst Chapl Charleroi *Eur* from 95. *Avenue des Pelerins 16, B1380 Lasne, Belgium* Brussels (2) 633-5043

FILBY, John Michael (Jack). b 34. Oak Hill Th Coll 56. **d** 60 **p** 61. C Penge St Jo *Roch* 60-64; C Foord St Jo *Cant* 64-66; Dioc Ev (Dios Roch, Guildf and Chelmsf) 66-75; Perm to Offic *Roch* 66-68; Perm to Offic *Guildf* 68-71; Perm to Offic *Chelmsf* 71-75; V Broxted w Chickney and Tilty and Lt Easton 75-85; P-in-c Gt Easton 83-85; R Broxted w Chickney and Tilty etc from 85. *The Rectory, Park Road, Little Easton, Dunmow, Essex CM6 2JJ* Great Dunmow (01371) 872509

FILBY, Ven William Charles Leonard. b 33. Lon Univ BA58. Oak Hill Th Coll 53. **d** 59 **p** 60. C Eastbourne All SS *Chich* 59-62; C Woking St Jo *Guildf* 62-65; V Richmond H Trin *S'wark* 65-71; V Hove Bp Hannington Memorial Ch *Chich* 71-79; R Broadwater St Mary 79-83; RD Worthing 80-83; Can and Preb Chich Cathl 81-83; Adn Horsham from 83. *The Archdeaconry, Itchingfield, Horsham, W Sussex RH13 7NX* Slinfold (01403) 790315 Fax 791153

FILE, Canon Roy Stephen. b 23. Leeds Univ BA50. Coll of Resurr Mirfield 50. **d** 53 **p** 54. S Africa 66-80; V Ilkley St Marg *Bradf* 80-88; rtd 88; Perm to Offic *Bradf* from 88; Hon Can Cape Town from 90. *4 Bowling View, Skipton, N Yorkshire BD23 1SR* Skipton (01756) 795599

FILER, Victor John. b 43. Sarum Th Coll 66. **d** 69 **p** 70. C Mortlake w E Sheen *S'wark* 69-74; SSF 75-82; P-in-c Plaistow SS Phil and Jas w St Andr *Chelmsf* 80-83; Chapl Plaistow Hosp 81-83; TV Plaistow 83; TV Beaconsfield *Ox* 84-90; TR Maltby *Sheff* from 90. *The Rectory, 69 Blyth Road, Maltby, Rotherham, S Yorkshire S66 7LF* Rotherham (01709) 812684

FILES, Ian James. b 54. Loughb Univ BSc76. Chich Th Coll 85. **d** 87 **p** 88. C Prestwich St Mary *Man* 87-89; C Man Clayton St Cross w St Paul 89-91. *12 Freestone Close, Woodhill, Bury BL8 1US* 0161-763 3447

FILLERY, William Robert. b 42. Univ of Wales BA65. St D Coll Lamp CPS68 BD69. **d** 68 **p** 69. C Llangyfelach and Morriston *S & B* 68-71; C Morriston 71-72; Lic to Offic *Ox* 73-76; W Germany 76-81; Chapl Reed's Sch Cobham 81-86; V Oxshott *Guildf* 86-89; P-in-c Seale 89-91; P-in-c Puttenham and Wanborough 89-91; Hd of RE Streatham Hill & Clapham Sch for Girls from 91. *20 Moor Park Lane, Farnham, Surrey GU9 9JB* Farnham (01252) 734790

FINCH, Christopher. b 41. Lon Univ BA63 AKC63 BD69. Sarum Th Coll 63. **d** 65 **p** 66. C High Wycombe *Ox* 65-69; Prec Leic Cathl *Leic* 69-73; R Lt Bowden St Nic 73-81; V Evington from 81; P-in-c Leic St Phil from 95. *The Vicarage, Stoughton Lane, Evington, Leicester LE2 2FH* Leicester (0116) 271 2032

FINCH, David Walter. b 40. FIBMS69 Cam Univ MA74. Ridley Hall Cam. **d** 91 **p** 92. C Ixworth and Bardwell *St E* 91-92; C Blackbourne 92-94; P-in-c Stoke by Nayland w Leavenheath from 94; P-in-c Polstead from 95. *The Vicarage, Church Street, Stoke by Nayland, Colchester CO6 4QH* Nayland (01206) 262248

FINCH, Canon Edward Alfred. b 23. Lon Univ BSc50. Sarum Th Coll 50. **d** 52 **p** 53. V Walthamstow St Pet *Chelmsf* 59-70; Can Res Chelmsf Cathl 70-85; Dir Interface Assn 85-90; rtd 90; Perm to Offic *St E* from 91. *St Clare, The Street, Pakenham, Bury St Edmunds, Suffolk IP31 2LG* Pakenham (01359) 323885

FINCH, Frank. b 33. Qu Coll Birm 72. **d** 74 **p** 75. C Bilston St Leon *Lich* 74-78; R Sudbury and Somersal Herbert *Derby* 78-87; Chapl HM Pris Sudbury 78-87; HM Det Cen Foston Hall 80-87; V Lilleshall and Sheriffhales *Lich* 87-90; R The Ridwares and Kings Bromley from 90. *The Rectory, Alrewas Road, Kings Bromley, Burton-on-Trent, Staffs DE13 7HP* Yoxall (01543) 472932

FINCH, Frederick. b 22. Lon Coll of Div 59. **d** 60 **p** 61. Area Sec (W Midl) CPAS 68-71; V Blackpool Ch Ch *Blackb* 71-77;

Canada from 78; rtd 90. *5905 Veronique, Brossard, Quebec, Canada, J4W 1G6*

FINCH, Jeffrey Walter. b 45. Man Univ BA(Econ)66 Liv Univ DASE80. Linc Th Coll 82. **d** 84 **p** 85. C Briercliffe *Blackb* 84-87; P-in-c Brindle 87-93; Asst Dir of Educn 87-93; V Laneside from 93. *St Peter's Vicarage, Laneside, Haslingden, Rossendale, Lancs BB4 4BG* Rossendale (01706) 213838

FINCH, John. b 20. Bps' Coll Cheshunt 59. **d** 61 **p** 62. V Habergham Eaves St Matt *Blackb* 68-75; V Garstang St Helen Churchtown 75-86; rtd 86; Perm to Offic *Blackb* from 86. *55 Worcester Avenue, Garstang, Preston PR3 1FJ* Garstang (01995) 602386

FINCH, Paul William. b 50. Oak Hill Th Coll DipTh73 Lon Bible Coll. **d** 75 **p** 76. C Hoole *Ches* 75-78; C Charlesworth *Derby* 78-87; C Charlesworth and Dinting Vale 87-88; TV Radipole and Melcombe Regis *Sarum* from 88. *The Vicarage, 74 Field Barn Drive, Weymouth, Dorset DT4 0EF* Weymouth (01305) 778995

FINCH, Ronald. b 15. Qu Coll Birm 79. **d** 80 **p** 80. Hon C Welford w Weston and Clifford Chambers *Glouc* 80-85; Perm to Offic *Ches* from 85. *Cornerstone, 1 Penrhyd Road, Irby, Wirral L61 2XJ* 0151-648 1559

FINCH, Miss Rosemary Ann. b 39. Leeds Univ CertEd60. Local NSM Course 91. **d** 93 **p** 94. NSM S Elmham and Ilketshall *St E* from 93. *St John's Lodge Barn, Ilketshall St John, Beccles, Suffolk NR34 8JH* Ilketshall (01986) 781533

FINCH, Canon Stanley James. b 31. Mert Coll Ox BA55 MA58. Wells Th Coll 55. **d** 57 **p** 58. C Leic St Mary *Blackb* 57-61; C Leeds St Pet *Ripon* 61-65; V Habergham All SS *Blackb* 65-73; V S Shore H Trin 73-84; V Broughton from 84; RD Preston 86-92; Hon Can Blackb Cathl from 91. *The Vicarage, 410 Garstang Road, Broughton, Preston PR3 5JB* Broughton (01772) 862330

FINCH, Thomas. b 20. Lon Univ BD57. Edin Th Coll 48. **d** 51 **p** 51. V Wellingborough St Mary *Pet* 67-88; rtd 88. *18 Royal Avenue, Leyland, Preston PR5 1BQ* Leyland (01772) 433780

FINCHAM, Nicholas Charles. b 56. St Jo Coll Dur BA78 MA80. Westcott Ho Cam 80 Bossey Ecum Inst Geneva 81. **d** 82 **p** 83. C Seaham w Seaham Harbour *Dur* 82-85; C Lydney w Aylburton *Glouc* 85-87; C Isleworth All SS *Lon* 87-95; P-in-c Chiswick St Mich from 95. *St Michael's Vicarage, 59 Sutton Lane South, London W4 3JR* 0181-994 3173

FINDLAY, Brian James. b 42. Wellington Univ (NZ) BA62 MA63 BMus66 Magd Coll Ox MA75. Qu Coll Birm DipTh71. **d** 72 **p** 73. C Deptford St Paul *S'wark* 72-75; Chapl and Dean of Div Magd Coll Ox 75-84; V Tonge Moor *Man* from 84. *St Augustine's Vicarage, Ainsworth Lane, Bolton BL2 2QW* Bolton (01204) 23899

FINDLAYSON, Roy. b 44. Man Univ CQSW69 MA89. Sarum & Wells Th Coll 80. **d** 82 **p** 83. C Benwell St Jas *Newc* 82-83; Hon C 83-85; C Morpeth 85-88; C N Gosforth 88; TV Ch the King in the Dio of Newc 88-94; V Newc St Fran from 94. *St Francis's Vicarage, Cleveland Gardens, Newcastle upon Tyne NE7 7RE* 0191-266 1071

FINDLEY, Peter. b 55. Barrister-at-Law (Gray's Inn) 78 Trin Coll Ox MA77. Trin Coll Bris DipHE92. **d** 92 **p** 93. C Yateley *Win* from 92. *18 Hall Farm Crescent, Yateley, Camberley, Surrey GU17 7HT* Yateley (01252) 876416

FINDON, Dr John Charles. b 50. Keble Coll Ox BA71 MA75 DPhil79. Ripon Coll Cuddesdon DipTh76. **d** 77 **p** 78. C Middleton *Man* 77-80; Lect Bolton St Pet 80-83; V Astley 83-91; V Baguley from 91. *St John's Vicarage, 186 Brooklands Road, Sale, Cheshire M33 3PB* 0161-973 5947

FINKENSTAEDT, Harry Seymour. b 23. Yale Univ BA49 Mass Univ MA68. Episc Th Sch Cam Mass BD50. **d** 53 **p** 54. USA 53-71; C Hazlemere *Ox* 71-73; C Huntingdon St Mary w St Benedict *Ely* 73-75; R Castle Camps 75-84; R Shudy Camps 75-84; P-in-c W Wickham 79-84; P-in-c Horseheath 79-81; P-in-c Gt w Lt Stukeley 84-88; rtd 88. *4 The Fairway, Bar Hill, Cambridge CB3 8SR* Crafts Hill (01954) 782224

FINLAY, Hueston Edward. b 64. TCD BA85 BAI85 BTh89 MA92. CITC 86. **d** 89 **p** 90. C Kilkenny w Aghour and Kilmanagh *C & O* 89-92; Bp Ossory Dom Chapl 89-92; Lib and Registrar Kilkenny Cathl 89-92; Bp's V Ossory Cathl 90-92; Chapl Girton Coll Cam 92-95; C Cam Gt St Mary w St Mich *Ely* 92-95; Chapl Magd Coll from 95. *Magdalene College, Cambridge CB3 0AG* Cambridge (01223) 332129

FINLAY, Michael Stanley. b 45. N Ord Course 78. **d** 81 **p** 82. C Padgate *Liv* 81-85; V Newton-le-Willows 85-90; V Orford St Marg from 90. *St Margaret's Vicarage, St Margaret's Avenue, Orford, Warrington WA2 8DT* Warrington (01925) 631937

FINLAYSON, Duncan. b 24. Local NSM Course 73. **d** 76 **p** 76. NSM Bridge of Allan *St And* from 76; NSM Alloa from 77; NSM Dollar from 77; Hon AP Hillfoots Team 80-87. *29 Cawdor Road, Bridge of Allan, Stirling FK9 4JJ* Bridge of Allan (01786) 833074

FINLAYSON, Capt Grantley Adrian. b 55. Wilson Carlile Coll 74 Chich Th Coll 87. **d** 89 **p** 90. C Watford St Mich *St Alb*

89-92; TV W Slough *Ox* from 92. *St Michael's House, Whitby Road, Slough, Berks SL1 3DW* Slough (01753) 521785

FINLINSON, Paul. b 58. St Chad's Coll Dur BA79 St Martin's Coll Lanc PGCE81. Carl Dioc Tr Course 86. **d** 89 **p** 90. NSM Kirkby Lonsdale *Carl* from 89; Perm to Offic *Blackb* from 95. *6 Sandown Road, Lancaster LA1 4LN* Lancaster (01524) 69652

FINN, Gordon Frederick. b 33. Dur Univ BA60. Ely Th Coll 60. **d** 62 **p** 63. C Kingswinford St Mary *Lich* 62-65; C Northn St Mary *Pet* 65-67; Chapl Barnsley Hall Hosp Bromsgrove 67-71; Chapl Lea Hosp Bromsgrove 67-71; C Swanage *Sarum* 71-73; P-in-c Ford End *Chelmsf* 73-79; V S Shields St Oswin *Dur* from 79. *The Vicarage, St Oswin's Street, South Shields, Tyne & Wear NE33 4SE* 0191-455 3072

FINN, Ian Michael. b 58. AKC. Chich Th Coll 81. **d** 82 **p** 83. C Habergham All SS *Blackb* 82-83; C W Burnley 83-85; C Torrisholme 85-87; V Lanc Ch Ch w St Jo and St Anne 87-91; P-in-c Tillingham *Chelmsf* from 91; P-in-c Dengie w Asheldham from 91. *Tillingham Vicarage, 6 Bakery Close, Southminster, Essex CM0 7TW* Tillingham (01621) 778017

FINN, Miss Sheila. b 30. LMH Ox BA68 MA69. Gilmore Ho 68. **dss** 78 **d** 87 **p** 94. Tettenhall Wood *Lich* 78-86; Dioc Ecum Officer 86-95; The Ridwares and Kings Bromley 86-87; Par Dn 87-94; C from 94. *The Rectory, 56 Uttoxeter Road, Hill Ridware, Rugeley, Staffs WS15 3QU* Armitage (01543) 492023

FINNEMORE, Ernest Harold. b 28. Keble Coll Ox BA49 MA53. St Steph Ho Ox 51. **d** 53 **p** 54. V Hanford *Lich* 64-90; rtd 90. *24 Belgrave Road, Newcastle-under-Lyme, Staffs ST5 1LR* Newcastle-under-Lyme (01782) 638179

FINNEMORE, James Christopher. b 59. Pemb Coll Cam BA81 MA85. Coll of Resurr Mirfield. **d** 85 **p** 86. C Manston *Ripon* 85-88; C Hessle *York* 88-92; R Bishop Wilton w Full Sutton, Kirby Underdale etc from 92. *The Rectory, Bishop Wilton, York YO4 1RZ* Bishop Wilton (01759) 368230

FINNEY, David. b 41. St Mich Coll Llan 68. **d** 70 **p** 71. C Wythenshawe Wm Temple Ch *Man* 70-73; C Bedf Leigh 73-75; V Royton St Anne 75-81; V Dearnley 81-94; TV Rochdale from 94. *The Vicarage, Clement Royds Street, Rochdale, Lancs OL12 6PL* Rochdale (01706) 46272

FINNEY, Canon Fred. b 17. Bris Univ BA38 DipEd39. Wycliffe Hall Ox 61. **d** 62 **p** 63. V Ashton-in-Makerfield St Thos *Liv* 66-86; Hon Can Liv Cathl 83-86; rtd 86; Perm to Offic *Blackb* from 86; Perm to Offic *Liv* from 86. *1 Howard Drive, Tarleton, Preston PR4 6DA* Hesketh Bank (01772) 812598

FINNEY, Canon John Thomas. b 27. Sheff Univ BA51 DipEd52. Ripon Hall Ox 60. **d** 62 **p** 63. C Leigh St Mary *Man* 62-65; V from 83; V Peel 65-69; Chapl Hockerill Coll Bishop's Stortford 69-74; V Astley *Man* 74-83; AD Leigh 85-93; Hon Can Man Cathl from 87. *The Vicarage, Vicarage Square, Leigh, Lancs WN7 1YD* Leigh (01942) 673546

✠**FINNEY, Rt Rev John Thornley.** b 32. Hertf Coll Ox BA55. Wycliffe Hall Ox DipTh58. **d** 58 **p** 59 **c** 93. C Highfield *Ox* 58-61; C Weston Turville 61-65; R Tollerton *S'well* 65-71; V Aspley 71-80; Bp's Adv on Evang 80-89; Bp's Research Officer 88-89; Hon Can S'well Minster 84-89; Officer for Decade of Evang in C of E 90-93; Suff Bp Pontefract *Wakef* from 93. *181A Manygates Lane, Wakefield, W Yorkshire WF2 7DR* Wakefield (01924) 250781 Fax 240490

FINNEY, Ms Melva Kathleen. b 24. LTh76. St Jo Coll Auckland 47 Gilmore Ho 56. **dss** 57 **d** 78. Community of Sisters of the Love of God Ox 59-61; New Zealand from 61; rtd 86. *22 Gunns Crescent, Cashmere, Christchurch, New Zealand 8002* Christchurch (3) 332-7100

FINNIE, Robert. b 20. **d** 84 **p** 84. NSM Aber St Andr *Ab* from 84; NSM Aber St Ninian from 84. *10 Cairngorm Crescent, Aberdeen AB1 5BL* Aberdeen (01224) 874669

FINNIMORE, Keith Anthony. b 36. AKC59. **d** 60 **p** 61. C Wanstead H Trin Hermon Hill *Chelmsf* 60-63; C Kingswood *S'wark* 63-65; V Bolney *Chich* 65-67; V Elmstead *Chelmsf* 67-73; R Pentlow, Foxearth, Liston and Borley 73-77; NSM Cockfield w Bradfield St Clare, Felsham etc *St E* 89-91; R Hawstead and Nowton w Stanningfield etc from 91. *The Rectory, Hawstead, Bury St Edmunds, Suffolk IP29 5NT* Bury St Edmunds (01284) 386529

FIRMIN, Mrs Dorrie Eleanor Frances. b 19. Local NSM Course. **d** 88 **p** 94. NSM Ellon *Ab* from 88; NSM Cruden Bay from 88. *Minas Tirith, 7 Slains Avenue, Ellon, Aberdeenshire AB41 0ZA* Ellon (01358) 721623

FIRMIN, Paul Gregory. b 57. ACIB80. Trin Coll Bris BA87. **d** 87 **p** 88. C Swindon Ch Ch *Bris* 87-91; V Shrewsbury H Trin w St Julian *Lich* from 91. *Holy Trinity Vicarage, Greyfriars Road, Shrewsbury SY3 7EP* Shrewsbury (01743) 232158

FIRMSTONE, Ian Harry. b 44. Qu Coll Birm. **d** 82 **p** 83. C Warminster St Denys *Sarum* 82-84; C N Stoneham *Win* 84-88; R Freemantle 88-90; V Littleport *Ely* 90-91; TV Stanground and Farcet from 91. *The Vicarage, Main Street, Farcet, Peterborough PE7 3AX* Peterborough (01733) 240286

FIRTH, Barry. b 37. ACA60 FCA71. NW Ord Course 74. **d** 77 **p** 78. NSM Brighouse *Wakef* 77-81; P-in-c Batley St Thos 81-85; V 85-88; V Rastrick St Matt from 88; RD Brighouse and Elland from 92. *St Matthew's Vicarage, 1 Vicarage Gardens, Ogden Lane, Brighouse, W Yorkshire HD6 3HD* Brighouse (01484) 713386

FIRTH, Christopher John Kingsley. b 37. St Mich Coll Llan DipTh66. **d** 66 **p** 67. C Sutton in Ashfield St Mary *S'well* 66-70; V Langold 70-74; C Falmouth K Chas *Truro* 74-77; P-in-c Mabe 77-81; V 81-95; RD Carnmarth S 90-94. *White Sails, 2 The Lookout, High Street, Falmouth, Cornwall TR11 2AB* Falmouth (01326) 315735

FIRTH, Cyril Bruce. b 05. Fitzw Ho Cam BA28 MA32. Cheshunt Coll Cam 25. **d** 65 **p** 66. Asia Sec Conf of Miss Socs of GB & Ireland 65-74; Hon C Wellow *Win* 65-88; rtd 88. *Steplake Cottage, Sherfield English, Romsey, Hants SO51 6EP* West Wellow (01794) 22563

FIRTH, George Cuthbert. b 19. Keble Coll Ox BA41 MA45. Lich Th Coll 41. **d** 43 **p** 44. Chapl to the Deaf *Lich* 66-71; P-in-c Patshull 71-73; Lic to Offic *Ex* 74-84; Chapl to the Deaf 74-84; rtd 84. *18 Sydney Road, Exeter EX2 9AH* Exeter (01392) 75568

FIRTH, Graham Alfred. b 38. Man Univ BA60. Ripon Hall Ox. **d** 62 **p** 63. C Norton Woodseats St Paul *Sheff* 62-65; C-in-c Kimberworth Park CD 65-69; V Kimberworth Park 69-71; P-in-c Egmanton *S'well* 71-77; P-in-c Laxton 71-77; V Sibthorpe from 77; R Elston w Elston Chapelry from 77; R E Stoke w Syerston from 77; R Shelton from 91. *The Rectory, Top Street, Elston, Newark, Notts NG23 5PC* East Stoke (01636) 525383

✠**FIRTH, Rt Rev Peter James.** b 29. Em Coll Cam BA52 MA63. St Steph Ho Ox 53. **d** 55 **p** 56 **c** 83. C Barbourne *Worc* 55-58; C Malvern Link St Matthias 58-62; R Abbey Hey *Man* 62-66; Asst Network Relig Broadcasting BBC Man 66-67; Sen Producer/Org Relig Progr TV & Radio BBC Bris 67-83; Hon Can Bris Cathl *Bris* 74-83; Suff Bp Malmesbury 83-94; Angl Adv HTV W 84-94; rtd 94. *7 Ivywell Road, Bristol BS9 1NX* Bristol (0117) 968 5931

FIRTH, Ronald Mahlon. b 22. Linc Th Coll 60. **d** 61 **p** 62. V York St Thos w St Maurice *York* 66-73; V Marton-in-Cleveland 73-87; rtd 87. *24 Whenby Grove, Huntington, York YO3 9DS* York (01904) 634531

FISH, Winthrop. b 40. Dalhousie Univ Canada BA63 BEd Birm Univ BPhil76 MEd78. K Coll(NS) 62. **d** 64 **p** 65. Canada 64-74; Perm to Offic *Birm* 74-77; Asst Chapl Solihull Sch W Midl 77-79; Chapl Wroxall Abbey Sch 79-82; C Newquay *Truro* 82-84; V Highertown and Baldhu 84-89; P-in-c Newlyn St Newlyn from 89; Dioc Children's Adv from 89; Dioc Adv in RE from 95. *The Vicarage, Newlyn East, Newquay, Cornwall TR8 5LJ* Mitchell (01872) 510383

FISHER, Adrian Charles Proctor. b 24. TCD BA48 MA62. TCD Div Sch Div Test47. **d** 49 **p** 50. P-in-c N Stoke w Mongewell and Ipsden *Ox* 70-83; V 83-92; Chapl Oratory Prep Sch 73-80; rtd 92. *3 Aldermaston Soke, Silchester, Reading RG7 2PB* Silchester (01734) 700246

FISHER, Mrs Diana Margaret. b 44. E Midl Min Tr Course DipTh94. **d** 94 **p** 95. NSM E and W Leake, Stanford-on-Soar, Rempstone etc *S'well* from 94. *The Thatch, 6 Main Street, Rempstone, Loughborough, Leics LE12 6RH* Loughborough (01509) 881512

FISHER, Eric William. b 30. Birm Univ BA53. Coll of Resurr Mirfield 70. **d** 72 **p** 73. C Styvechale *Cov* 72-75; C Chesterfield All SS *Derby* 75-78; Chapl Buxton Hosps 78-84; TV Buxton w Burbage and King Sterndale *Derby* 78-84; R Shirland 84-89; V Sheff St Matt *Sheff* 89-95; rtd 95. *25 Robertville Road, Stoke-on-Trent ST2 9HD* Stoke-on-Trent (01782) 215571

FISHER, Ernest George Reginald. b 15. St Aid Birkenhead 66. **d** 68 **p** 69. C Brampton St Thos *Derby* 68-71; P-in-c Langley Mill 71-79; rtd 79; Perm to Offic *Newc* 79-86; Perm to Offic *Derby* from 86. *Flat 23, Harehill Court, Harehill Road, Chesterfield, Derbyshire S40 2NG* Chesterfield (01246) 559731

FISHER, George Arnold. b 54. Lon Univ BD75. N Ord Course 81. **d** 84 **p** 85. C Conisbrough *Sheff* 84-92; V Blackpool St Thos *Blackb* from 92. *St Thomas's Vicarage, 80 Devonshire Road, Blackpool FY3 8AE* Blackpool (01253) 392544

FISHER, Gordon. b 44. NW Ord Course 74. **d** 77 **p** 78. NSM Airedale w Fryston *Wakef* 77-81; C Barkisland w W Scammonden 81-84; C Ripponden 81-84; V Sutton St Mich *York* 84-87; V Marton-in-Cleveland from 87. *The Vicarage, Stokesley Road, Marton-in-Cleveland, Middlesbrough TS7 8JU* Middlesbrough (01642) 316201

FISHER, Henry John. b 25. Lich Th Coll 64. **d** 66 **p** 67. C Kings Norton *Birm* 66-70; C Weston-super-Mare St Jo *B & W* 70-75; C Weston-super-Mare H Trin 72-75; P-in-c Leigh upon Mendip 75-78; P-in-c Stoke St Michael 75-78; P-in-c Leigh upon Mendip w Stoke St Michael 78-80; C Wilton 80-88; C Street w Walton 88-90; rtd 90. *18 Hawker's Lane, Wells, Somerset BA5 3JL* Street (01458) 42044

FISHER, Humphrey John. b 33. **d** 91 **p** 92. NSM Bryngwyn and Newchurch and Llanbedr etc *S & B* from 91. *Rose Cottage, Newchurch, Kington, Hereford HR5 3QF* Kington (01544) 22632

FISHER, Dr Ian St John. b 59. Down Coll Cam BA80 MA84 Leic Univ PhD84. St Steph Ho Ox BA88. **d** 88 **p** 89. C Colwall w Upper Colwall and Coddington *Heref* 88-91; Chapl Surrey Univ *Guildf* from 92. *6 Cathedral Close, Guildford, Surrey GU2 5TL* Guildford (01483) 576380

FISHER, James Atherton. b 09. SS Coll Cam BA32 MA45. Cuddesdon Coll 32. **d** 33 **p** 34. Can and Treas Windsor 58-78; rtd 78. *32 High Lawn, Devizes, Wilts SN10 2BA* Devizes (01380) 724254

FISHER, John Andrew. b 63. Bath Univ BSc85. Wycliffe Hall Ox BA93 DipMin94. **d** 94 **p** 95. C Rayleigh *Chelmsf* from 94. *86 Lower Lambricks, Rayleigh, Essex SS6 8DB* Rayleigh (01268) 777430

FISHER, John Bertie. b 15. TCD BA36 BD44. CITC 39. **d** 39 **p** 40. I Kilternan *D & G* 51-83; rtd 83. *21 Rathdown Park, Greystones, Co Wicklow, Irish Republic* Dublin (1) 287-4904

FISHER, Canon John Douglas Close. b 09. SS Coll Cam BA31 MA47 BD66. Lich Th Coll 36. **d** 38 **p** 39. Can and Preb Chich Cathl *Chich* 66-84; V Cuckfield 67-77; rtd 77. P-in-c Hove St Jo *Chich* 77-81. *clo T G D Fisher Esq, 2 Tindal Close, Burgess Hill, W Sussex RH15 0LB* Burgess Hill (01444) 233364

FISHER, John Victor. b 33. Brasted Th Coll 64 Coll of Resurr Mirfield 66. **d** 68 **p** 69. C Stepney St Dunstan and All SS *Lon* 68-71; C E Ham w Upton Park *Chelmsf* 71-73; P-in-c Becontree St Pet 73-82; V Barkingside St Geo from 82. *St George's Vicarage, Woodford Avenue, Ilford, Essex IG2 6XQ* 0181-550 4149

FISHER, Kenneth Francis McConnell (Frank). b 36. K Coll Lon 57. **d** 61 **p** 62. C Sheff St Geo and St Steph *Sheff* 61-63; Chapl Sheff Univ 64-69; Chapl Lon Univ *Lon* 69-75; P-in-c Dean *Carl* 75-80; Soc Resp Officer 75-80; TR Melksham *Sarum* 80-90; P-in-c Stapleford *Ely* from 90; Dioc Ecum Officer from 90; RD Shelford from 94. *Stapleford Vicarage, Cambridge CB2 5BG* Cambridge (01223) 842150

FISHER, Canon Michael Harry. b 39. Ex Univ BA61. St Steph Ho Ox 61. **d** 63 **p** 64. C Wolv St Pet *Lich* 63-67; C Newquay *Truro* 67-70; V Newlyn St Pet 70-75; P-in-c Launceston St Steph w St Thos 75-82; V Carbis Bay w Lelant 82-95; Hon Can Truro Cathl from 85; RD Penwith from 88; V Newquay from 95. *The Vicarage, 41 Trebarwith Crescent, Newquay, Cornwall TR7 1DX* Newquay (01637) 872724

FISHER, Michael John. b 43. Leic Univ BA64 Keele Univ MA67. Qu Coll Birm 75. **d** 78 **p** 79. NSM Stafford St Mary and St Chad *Lich* 78-79; NSM Stafford from 79. *35 Newland Avenue, Stafford ST16 1NL* Stafford (01785) 45069

FISHER, Paul Vincent. b 43. ARCM73 Worc Coll Ox BA66 MA70. Qu Coll Birm DipTh68. **d** 70 **p** 71. C Redditch St Steph *Worc* 70-73; C Chorlton upon Medlock *Man* 73-79; Chapl Man Univ 73-79; Exec Sec Community Affairs Division BCC 79-81; Asst Dir of Tr and Dir of Lay Tr *Carl* 81-86; P-in-c Raughton Head w Gatesgill 81-85; Lay Tr Officer *S'wark* 86-90; Dir of Tr 90-94; V Kingswood from 94. *The Vicarage, Woodland Way, Tadworth, Surrey KT20 6NW* Mogador (01737) 832164

FISHER, Peter Francis Templar. b 36. CCC Cam BA60 MA. Wells Th Coll 62. **d** 63 **p** 64. C Gt Ilford St Mary *Chelmsf* 63-67; C Colchester St Mary V 67-70; C-in-c Basildon St Andr CD 70-72; P-in-c Edstaston *Lich* 83-87; P-in-c Whixall 83-87; P-in-c Tilstock 84-87; V Oxon and Shelton from 87. *The Vicarage, Shelton Gardens, Bicton, Shrewsbury SY3 8DJ* Shrewsbury (01743) 232774

FISHER, Peter Timothy. b 44. Dur Univ BA68 MA75. Cuddesdon Coll 68. **d** 70 **p** 71. C Bedf St Andr *St Alb* 70-74; Chapl Surrey Univ *Guildf* 74-78; Sub-Warden Linc Th Coll 78-83; R Houghton le Spring *Dur* 83-94; RD Houghton 87-92; Prin Qu Coll Birm from 94. *71 Farquhar Road, Birmingham B15 2QP, or, Queen's College, Somerset Road, Birmingham B15 2QH* 0121-455 7577 or 454 1527

✠**FISHER, Rt Rev Reginald Lindsay (Brother Michael).** b 18. Lambeth MA78 Westcott Ho Cam 51. **d** 53 **p** 54 **c** 79. SSF from 42; Lic to Offic *Ely* 53-62; Lic to Offic *Newc* 62-67; Lic to Offic *Sarum* 67-79; Suff Bp St Germans *Truro* 79-85; Bp HM Pris 85; Min Gen SSF 85-91; rtd 85; Asst Bp Ely from 85. *15 Botolph Lane, Cambridge CB2 3RD* Cambridge (01223) 353903

FISHER, Richard John. b 60. K Coll Lon BA82 AKC82 Selw Coll Cam BA87. Ridley Hall Cam 85. **d** 88 **p** 89. C Woodley St Jo the Ev *Ox* 88-91; C Acomb St Steph *York* from 91. *36 Fellbrook Avenue, Acomb, York YO2 5PS* York (01904) 793240

FISHER, Roy Percy. b 22. Lon Univ TCert49. Linc Th Coll 51. **d** 53 **p** 54. V Westgate-on-Sea St Sav *Cant* 66-71; R Staplegrove *B & W* 71-79; TR Eckington w Handley and Ridgeway *Derby* 79-87; rtd 87. *258 New Road, Porthcawl, M Glam CF36 5BA* Porthcawl (01656) 718682

FISHER, Stephen Newson. b 46. CEng82 MIEE82 Univ of Wales (Swansea) BSc67. Linc Th Coll 84. **d** 86 **p** 87. C Nunthorpe *York* 86-89; P-in-c Middlesb St Oswald 89-90; V 90-94; V Redcar from 94. *St Peter's Vicarage, 66 Aske Road, Redcar, Cleveland TS10 2BP* Redcar (01642) 490700

FISHER, Thomas Andrew (Tom). b 35. Sarum & Wells Th Coll 84. **d** 86 **p** 87. C Win Ch Ch *Win* 86-89; Chapl Salisbury Coll of Tech *Sarum* 89-94; Chapl Salisbury Coll of FE 89-94. *7 Empire Road, Salisbury SP2 9DE* Salisbury (01722) 335155

FISHER, Thomas Ruggles. b 20. Cranmer Hall Dur 58. **d** 60 **p** 61. R Husbands Bosworth *Leic* 63-74; R Husbands Bosworth w Mowsley and Knaptoft 74-79; R Husbands Bosworth w Mowsley and Knaptoft etc 79-82; Perm to Offic from 82; Perm to Offic *Pet* from 83; rtd 85. *12 The Dell, Oakham, Leics LE15 6JG* Oakham (01572) 757630

FISHWICK, Alan. b 48. Chich Th Coll 87. **d** 89 **p** 90. C Laneside *Blackb* 89-92; C Accrington 92-93; TV from 93. *St Andrew's Vicarage, 356 Blackburn Road, Accrington, Lancs BB5 1RZ* Accrington (01254) 386958

FISHWICK, Ian Norman. b 54. Lanc Univ BEd. St Jo Coll Nottm DipTh. **d** 82 **p** 83. C High Wycombe *Ox* 82-87; V Walshaw Ch Ch *Man* 87-93; Area Voc Adv 88-93; V W Ealing St Jo w St Jas *Lon* from 93; Dioc Dir Ords Willesden from 94. *St John's Vicarage, 23 Culmington Road, London W13 9NJ* 0181-566 3462 or 566 3507

FISK, Paul. b 35. St Jo Coll Cam BA60 MA64. Wells Th Coll 60. **d** 62 **p** 63. C Ipswich H Trin *St E* 62-65; C Wrentham w Benacre, Covehithe and Henstead 65-67; R Copdock w Washbrook and Belstead 67-73; R Brantham 73-75; RD Samford 73-75; TV Old Brumby *Linc* 85-88; W Germany 88-90; Germany from 90. *Selma-Lagerloef-Strasse 3, D-63454 Hanau, Germany*

FISKE, Paul Francis Brading. b 45. St Jo Coll Dur BA68 PhD72. Wycliffe Hall Ox DipTh72. **d** 73 **p** 74. C Sutton *Liv* 73-76; TV Cheltenham St Mary, St Matt, St Paul and H Trin *Glouc* 76-80; C-in-c Hartplain CD *Portsm* 80-84; Hd of Miss UK CMJ 84-86; Hon C Edgware *Lon* 84-86; R Broughton Gifford, Gt Chalfield and Holt *Sarum* 86-95; TV Bourne Valley from 95. *The Vicarage, Winterbourne Earls, Salisbury SP4 6HA* Idmiston (01980) 611350

FISON, Geoffrey Robert Martius. b 34. Dur Univ BA59. Ely Th Coll 59. **d** 61 **p** 62. C Heavitree *Ex* 61-64; Australia 64-69; BSB 64-69; C Southn Maybush St Pet *Win* 70-73; TV Strood *Roch* 73-79; TV Swindon Dorcan *Bris* 79-83; P-in-c Brislington St Cuth from 83. *St Cuthbert's Vicarage, 35 Wick Crescent, Bristol BS4 4HG* Bristol (0117) 977 6351

FITCH, Alan John. b 45. Open Univ BA82 Warw Univ MA84. Wilson Carlile Coll 64 Qu Coll Birm 92. **d** 92 **p** 93. CA from 66; C Glouc St Jas and All SS *Glouc* from 92; NSM Wotton St Mary from 93. *4 The Hedgerows, Gloucester GL2 9JE* Gloucester (01452) 503068

FITCH, Canon John Ambrose. b 22. CCC Cam BA44 MA48. Wells Th Coll 45. **d** 47 **p** 48. V Reydon *St E* 51-70; R Brandon and Santon Downham 70-80; Hon Can St E Cathl 75-87; RD Mildenhall 78-80; R Monks Eleigh w Chelsworth and Brent Eleigh etc 80-87; rtd 87; Perm to Offic *St E* from 87; Perm to Offic *Chelmsf* from 87. *The Oak House, High Street, Great Yeldham, Halstead, Essex CO9 4EX* Great Yeldham (01787) 237058

FITZ, Lionel Alfred. b 24. **d** 87 **p** 88. NSM Cheltenham St Mary, St Matt, St Paul and H Trin *Glouc* 87-94; Perm to Offic from 94. *9 Foxgrove Drive, Cheltenham, Glos GL52 6TQ* Cheltenham (01242) 243405

FITZGERALD, John Edward. b 44. Oak Hill Th Coll 74. **d** 76 **p** 77. C Rainham *Chelmsf* 76-79; C Cam St Andr Less *Ely* 79-86; V Holmesfield *Derby* 86-88; Chapl HM Pris Wakef 88-90; Chapl HM Pris Nottm from 90; Chapl HM Pris Whatton from 90. *The Chaplaincy Office, HM Prison Nottingham, Perry Road, Sherwood, Nottingham NG5 3AG* Nottingham (0115) 962 5022 Fax 603605

FITZGIBBON, Kevin Peter. b 49. St Jo Coll Nottm BTh81. **d** 81 **p** 82. C Corby St Columba *Pet* 81-85; V Newborough from 85. *The Vicarage, Newborough, Peterborough PE6 7QZ* Peterborough (01733) 810682

FITZHARRIS, Barry. b 47. Lon Univ BA69 W Ontario Univ MA70 K Coll Lon BD72 AKC72. St Aug Coll Cant 72. **d** 73 **p** 74. C Whitstable All SS *Cant* 73-75; C Whitstable All SS w St Pet 75-76; Hon C Clapham Old Town *S'wark* 77-79; Asst Chapl Abp Tenison Gr Sch Kennington 78-84; Hd of Relig Studies from 87; Hon C Streatham Ch Ch *S'wark* 80-84; R Radwinter w Hempstead *Chelmsf* 84-87. *The Chaplain's Office, Archbishop Tenison's School, London SE11 5SR* 0171-735 4070

FITZHARRIS, Robert Aidan. b 46. Sheff Univ BDS71. Linc Th Coll 87. **d** 89 **p** 90. C Dinnington *Sheff* 89-92; V Bentley from 92; RD Adwick from 95. *The Vicarage, 3A High Street, Bentley, Doncaster, S Yorkshire DN5 0AA* Doncaster (01302) 876272 Fax as telephone

FITZSIMONS, Mrs Kathryn Anne. b 57. Bedf Coll of Educn CertEd78. NE Ord Course 87. **d** 90 **p** 94. NSM Bilton *Ripon* from 90. *17 Strawberry Dale Avenue, Harrogate, N Yorkshire HG1 5EA* Harrogate (01423) 563074

FITZWILLIAMS, Canon Mark Morshead. b 36. Trin Coll Cam BA59 MA64. Westcott Ho Cam 59. **d** 61 **p** 62. C St Jo Wood *Lon* 61-64; C Hempnall *Nor* 64-70; R Lathbury *Ox* 70-78; R Newport Pagnell 70-78; RD Newport 73-78; TR Beaconsfield 78-94; RD Amersham 82-86; Hon Can Ch Ch from 88; P-in-c Hambleden Valley from 94. *The Rectory, Hambleden, Henley-on-Thames, Oxon RG9 6RP* Henley-on-Thames (01491) 571231

FLACH, Deborah Mary Rollins (Debbie). b 54. Trin Coll Bris DipHE81 Sarum & Wells Th Coll 88. **d** 94. C Chapl Chantilly *Eur* from 94. *63 rue des Boissy, 60340 St Leu d'Esserent, France* France (33) 44 56 76 08

FLACK, Ven John Robert. b 42. Leeds Univ BA64. Coll of Resurr Mirfield 64. **d** 66 **p** 67. C Armley St Bart *Ripon* 66-69; C Northn St Mary *Pet* 69-72; V Chapelthorpe *Wakef* 72-81; V Ripponden 81-85; V Barkisland w W Scammonden 81-85; V Brighouse 85-88; TR Brighouse St Martin 88-92; RD Brighouse and Elland 86-92; Hon Can Wakef Cathl 89-92; Adn Pontefract from 92. *10 Arden Court, Horbury, Wakefield, W Yorkshire WF4 5AH* Wakefield (01924) 276797 Fax 261095

FLAGG, David Michael. b 50. CCC Cam BA71 MA75. St Jo Coll Nottm BA76 DipPs77 DipPC94. **d** 77 **p** 78. C Hollington St Leon *Chich* 77-80; C Woodley St Jo the Ev *Ox* 80-86; Chapl The Dorothy Kerin Trust Burrswood 86-94; R Knockholt w Halstead *Roch* from 94. *The Rectory, Church Road, Halstead, Sevenoaks, Kent TN14 7HQ* Knockholt (01959) 532133

✠FLAGG, Rt Rev John William Hawkins (Bill). b 29. **d** 59 **p** 61 **c** 69. Paraguay 59-63; Argentina 64-73; Adn N Argentina 65-69; Bp Paraguay and N Argentina 69-73; Asst Bp Chile 73-77; Bp Peru 73-77; Asst Bp Liv 78-86; V Toxteth St Cypr w Ch Ch 78-85; P-in-c Litherland Ch Ch 85-86; Gen Sec SAMS 86-93; Asst Bp Roch 87-92; Asst Bp S'well from 92; Dioc Stewardship Adv from 93; Dioc Adv for Overseas Affairs from 94. *8 Ransome Close, Newark, Notts NG24 2LQ* Newark (01636) 74889

FLAHERTY, Alan Thomas. b 45. N Ord Course 85. **d** 88 **p** 89. NSM Howe Bridge *Man* 88-90; C 90-92; V Ainsworth from 92. *The Vicarage, Ainsworth Hall Road, Ainsworth, Bolton BL2 5RY* Bolton (01204) 398567

FLAHERTY, Jane Venitia. *See* ANDERSON, Mrs Jane Venitia

FLATHER, Peter George. b 29. Sarum Th Coll. **d** 59 **p** 60. R E w W Bradenham *Nor* 65-72; P-in-c Speke All SS *Liv* 72-73; P-in-c Sharrington *Nor* 73-87; R Gunthorpe w Bale 73-87; P-in-c Gt w Lt Snoring 77-83; R Gunthorpe w Bale w Field Dalling, Saxlingham etc 87-89; rtd 89. *29 Jannys Close, Aylsham, Norwich NR11 6DL* Aylsham (01263) 733548

FLATMAN, Martin Edward. b 46. Hull Univ BA68. Cuddesdon Coll 69. **d** 71 **p** 72. C Reading St Giles *Ox* 71-75; TV Newbury 75-82; V Cowley St Jo 82-94. *26 Fairfax Avenue, Marston, Oxford OX4 0RP* Oxford (01865) 243168

FLATT, Donald Clifford. b 15. Worc Ord Coll 63. **d** 65 **p** 66. V Wigginton *St Alb* 67-75; Chapl HM Pris Bedf 75-80; V Biddenham *St Alb* 75-82; rtd 83; P-in-c Oare w Culbone *B & W* 83-86; Perm to Offic from 86. *The Stables Cottage, Lamb Court, Dulverton, Somerset TA22 9AP* Dulverton (01398) 23088

FLATT, Roy Francis Ferguson. b 47. Edin Th Coll 78. **d** 80 **p** 81. C St Andrews St Andr *St And* 80-82; C Elie and Earlsferry 80-82; C Pittenweem 80-82; Dioc Supernumerary 82-83; R Kilmartin *Arg* from 83; R Lochgilphead from 83; Dioc Sec 83-87; Dioc Youth Chapl from 83; R Inveraray 83-90. *Bishopton, Bishopton Road, Lochgilphead, Argyll PA31 8PY* Lochgilphead (01546) 602315

FLATT, Stephen Joseph. b 57. Sarum & Wells Th Coll CMinlStuds92. **d** 92 **p** 93. C Limpsfield and Titsey *S'wark* from 92. *Berry House, High Street, Oxted, Surrey RH8 0DT* Oxted (01883) 713683

FLATTERS, Clive Andrew. b 56. Sarum & Wells Th Coll 83. **d** 86 **p** 88. C Weston Favell *Pet* 86-87; C Old Brumby *Linc* 88-91; C Syston *Leic* 91-93; TV Syston TM from 93. *The Vicarage, 20 Hoby Road, Thrussington, Leicester LE7 4TH* Rearsby (01664) 424962

FLAVELL, Paul William Deran. b 44. Univ of Wales (Ban) DipTh66. St Mich Coll Llan DPS68. **d** 68 **p** 69. Australia 68-71; C Blaenavon w Capel Newydd *Mon* 71-74; V Ynysddu 74-84; R Llanaber w Caerdeon *Ban* from 84. *The Rectory, Mynach Road, Barmouth, Gwynedd LL42 1RL* Barmouth (01341) 280516

FLEET, Daniel James Russell. b 60. Wye Coll Lon BSc84. St Jo Coll Nottm LTh88 DPS89. **d** 89 **p** 90. C Boldmere *Birm* 89-92; C Caverswall *Lich* 92; C Caverswall and Weston Coyney w Dilhorne 92. *30 Firbank Place, Park Hall, Weston Coyney, Stoke-on-Trent ST3 5RU* Stoke-on-Trent (01782) 334500

FLEETWOOD, John Arnold. b 10. K Coll Lon BD39 AKC39. **d** 39 **p** 40. V Canvey Is *Chelmsf* 57-73; R Kelvedon Hatch 73-78; V Navestock 73-78; rtd 78. *15 Orchard Piece, Blackmore, Ingatestone, Essex CM4 0RX* Blackmore (01277) 822683

FLEMING, Ven David. b 37. Kelham Th Coll 58. **d** 63 **p** 64. C Walton St Marg Belmont Road *Liv* 63-67; Chapl HM Borstal Gaynes Hall 68-76; V Gt Staughton *Ely* 68-76; RD St Neots 72-76; V Whittlesey 76-85; RD March 77-82; Hon Can Ely Cathl 82-93; P-in-c Ponds Bridge 83-85; Adn Wisbech 84-93; V Wisbech St Mary 85-89; Chapl Gen of Pris from 93. *123 Wisbech Road, Littleport, Ely, Cambs CB6 1JJ, or Cleland House, Page Street, London SW1P 4LN* Ely (01353) 862498 or 0171-217 6266 Fax 0171-217 6635

FLEMING, George. b 39. IDC. CITC. **d** 78 **p** 79. C Donaghcloney w Waringstown *D & D* 78-80; C Newtownards 80; I Movilla 80; C Heref St Pet w St Owen and St Jas *Heref* 80-85; V Holmer w Huntington from 85. *The Vicarage, Holmer, Hereford HR4 9RG* Hereford (01432) 273200

FLEMING, Mrs Penelope Rawling. b 43. Glas Univ MA63. Westcott Ho Cam 87. **d** 89 **p** 94. C Bourne *Guildf* 89-94; R Wotton and Holmbury St Mary from 94. *The Rectory, Holmbury St Mary, Dorking, Surrey RH5 6NL* Dorking (01306) 730285

FLEMING, Ronald Thorpe. b 29. Codrington Coll Barbados 52. **d** 56 **p** 57. V Ancroft w Scremerston *Newc* 69-81; V Longhirst 81-84; Lic to Offic from 84; Chapl Preston Hosp N Shields 84-94; Chapl N Tyneside Hosps 84-94; rtd 94. *18 Holly Avenue, Whitley Bay, Tyne & Wear NE26 1ED* 0191-252 7414

FLEMING, Canon William Edward Charlton. b 29. TCD BA51 MA65. CITC 52. **d** 52 **p** 53. C Dub Santry *D & G* 52-56; C Arm St Mark *Arm* 56-61; I Tartaraghan 61-80; Prov Registrar from 79; I Tartaraghan w Diamond from 80; Can Arm Cathl from 86; Treas Arm Cathl 88-92; Chan Arm Cathl from 92. *Tartaraghan Rectory, 5 Tarthlogue Road, Portadown, Co Armagh BT62 1RB* Annaghmore (01762) 851289

FLENLEY, Benjamin Robert Glanville (Ben). b 50. Sarum & Wells Th Coll 86. **d** 88 **p** 89. C Eastleigh *Win* 88-92; V Micheldever and E Stratton, Woodmancote etc from 92. *The Vicarage, Micheldever, Winchester, Hants SO21 3DA* Micheldever (01962) 774233

FLETCHER, Anthony Peter Reeves. b 46. Bede Coll Dur CertEd Nottm Univ BTh78. Kelham Th Coll 63 Ridley Hall Cam DPT. **d** 74 **p** 75. C Luton St Mary *St Alb* 74-78; Chapl RAF from 78. *Chaplaincy Services (RAF), HQ, Personnel and Training Command, RAF Innsworth, Gloucester GL3 1EZ* Gloucester (01452) 712612 Ext 5164 Fax 510828

FLETCHER, Arthur William George. b 24. Leeds Univ BA50. Coll of Resurr Mirfield 50. **d** 52 **p** 53. Chapl RAF 61-72; R Challoch w Newton Stewart *Glas* 73-75; R Kilmacolm 75-82; R Bridge of Weir 75-82; R Largs 82-89; rtd 89; Perm to Offic *Glas* from 89. *Westhaven, Main Road, Inverkip, Greenock, Renfrewshire PA16 0EA* Wemyss Bay (01475) 521611

FLETCHER, Dr Christopher Ian. b 43. BSc PhD. Glouc Sch of Min. **d** 89 **p** 90. C Tenbury *Heref* 89-93; R Bredenbury w Grendon Bishop and Wacton etc from 93. *The Rectory, Bredenbury, Bromyard, Herefordshire HR7 4TF* Bromyard (01885) 482236

FLETCHER, Colin John. b 46. Chich Th Coll. **d** 83 **p** 84. C Ilford St Mich *Chelmsf* 83-86; C Hockerill *St Alb* 86-89; V New Cantley *Sheff* from 89. *St Hugh's House, Levet Road, Cantley, Doncaster, S Yorkshire DN4 6JQ* Doncaster (01302) 535739

FLETCHER, Canon Colin William. b 50. Trin Coll Ox BA72 MA76. Wycliffe Hall Ox 72. **d** 75 **p** 76. C Shipley St Pet *Bradf* 75-79; Tutor Wycliffe Hall Ox 79-84; Hon C Ox St Andr *Ox* 79-84; V Margate H Trin *Cant* 84-93; RD Thanet 88-93; Abp's Chapl from 93; Hon Can Dallas from 93. *7 The Cottages, Lambeth Palace, London SE1 7JU* 0171-928 8282

FLETCHER, David Clare Molyneux. b 32. Worc Coll Ox BA55 MA59 DipTh56. Wycliffe Hall Ox 56. **d** 58 **p** 59. C Islington St Mary *Lon* 58-62; Hon C 62-83; Field Worker Scripture Union 62-86; Lic to Offic *St Alb* 83-86; R Ox St Ebbe w H Trin and St Pet *Ox* from 86. *St Ebbe's Rectory, 2 Roger Bacon Lane, Oxford OX1 1QE* Oxford (01865) 248154

FLETCHER, David Mark. b 56. Chich Th Coll 84. **d** 87 **p** 88. C Taunton St Andr *B & W* 87-91; P-in-c Chard Furnham w Chaffcombe, Knowle St Giles etc 91-95; P-in-c Tiverton St Andr *Ex* from 95. *St Andrew's Vicarage, Blackmore Road, Tiverton, Devon EX16 4AR* Tiverton (01884) 257865

FLETCHER, Douglas. b 40. Coll of Resurr Mirfield 67. **d** 68 **p** 69. C Notting Hill St Jo *Lon* 68-73; C Cam St Mary Less *Ely*

233

FLETCHER

73-74; C Fulham St Jo Walham Green *Lon* 74-76; C Walham Green St Jo w St Jas 76-84; P-in-c Kensal Town St Thos w St Andr and St Phil 84-92; V from 92. *St Thomas's Vicarage, 231 Kensal Road, London W10 5DB* 0181-960 3703

FLETCHER, Francis Cecil. b 12. Clifton Th Coll 33. **d** 36 **p** 38. V Weston upon Trent *Lich* 66-75; rtd 77. *243 Congleton Road, Biddulph, Stoke-on-Trent ST8 7RQ*

FLETCHER, George Henry Yorke. b 11. Wycliffe Hall Ox 58. **d** 59 **p** 60. V Hall Green St Pet *Birm* 67-75; V Clive w Grinshill *Lich* 75-80; rtd 80; Perm to Offic *Lich* from 80. *4 Croft Close, Bomere Heath, Shrewsbury SY4 3PZ* Bomere Heath (01939) 290337

FLETCHER, Gordon Wolfe. b 31. Edin Th Coll. **d** 62 **p** 63. C Eston *York* 62-65; C Harton Colliery *Dur* 65-68; V Pelton 68-81; V Ryhope from 81. *St Paul's Vicarage, Ryhope, Sunderland SR2 0HH* 0191-521 0238

FLETCHER, James Anthony. b 36. St Edm Hall Ox BA60 DipTh61 MA66. St Steph Ho Ox 60. **d** 62 **p** 63. C Streatham St Pet *S'wark* 62-65; C Hobs Moat CD *Birm* 65-68; C Cowley St Jo *Ox* 68-77; V Hanworth All SS *Lon* from 77; P-in-c Hanworth St Geo 89-91. *All Saints' Vicarage, Uxbridge Road, Feltham, Middx TW13 5EE* 0181-894 9330

FLETCHER, Jeremy James. b 60. Dur Univ BA81. St Jo Coll Nottm DipTh86. **d** 88 **p** 89. C Stranton *Dur* 88-91; C Nottm St Nic *S'well* 91-94; P-in-c Skegby from 94. *The Vicarage, Mansfield Road, Skegby, Sutton-in-Ashfield, Notts NG17 3ED* Mansfield (01623) 558800

FLETCHER, John Alan Alfred. b 33. Oak Hill Th Coll 58. **d** 61 **p** 62. C Erith St Paul *Roch* 61-64; C Rushden *Pet* 64-67; R Hollington St Leon *Chich* 67-86; V Chadwell Heath *Chelmsf* from 86; Chapl Chadwell Heath Hosp from 86; RD Barking and Dagenham *Chelmsf* from 91. *The Vicarage, 10 St Chad's Road, Romford RM6 6JB* 0181-590 2054

FLETCHER, Jonathan James Molyneux. b 42. Hertf Coll Ox BA66 MA68. Wycliffe Hall Ox 66. **d** 68 **p** 69. C Enfield Ch Ch Trent Park *Lon* 68-72; C Cam St Sepulchre *Ely* 72-76; C St Helen Bishopsgate w St Martin Outwich *Lon* 76-81; Min Wimbledon Em Ridgway Prop Chpl *S'wark* from 82. *Emmanuel Parsonage, 8 Sheep Walk Mews, London SW19 4QL* 0181-946 4728

FLETCHER, Keith. b 47. Man Univ DipTh72. Chich Th Coll 79. **d** 80 **p** 81. C Hartlepool St Paul *Dur* 80-82; V Eighton Banks 82-85; V Haydon Bridge *Newc* from 85; RD Hexham from 91; P-in-c Beltingham w Henshaw from 93. *The New Vicarage, Station Yard, Haydon Bridge, Hexham, Northd NE47 6LL* Haydon Bridge (01434) 684307

FLETCHER, Miss Linden Elisabeth. b 50. Lon Univ BEd73 MA80. St Jo Coll Nottm 87. **d** 89 **p** 94. C Fakenham w Alethorpe *Nor* 89-93; C Cumnor *Ox* from 93. *2 Ashcroft Close, Oxford OX2 9SE* Oxford (01865) 863224

FLETCHER, Paul Gordon MacGregor. b 61. St Andr Univ MTh84. Edin Th Coll 84. **d** 86 **p** 87. C Cumbernauld *Glas* 86-89; C-in-c Glas H Cross 89-93; C Milngavie from 93. *73 Finlay Rise, Milngavie, Glasgow G62 6QL* 0141-956 2363

FLETCHER, Ralph Henry Maurice. b 43. St Steph Ho Ox 71. **d** 74 **p** 75. C Chislehurst Annunciation *Roch* 74-77; Chapl Quainton Hall Sch Harrow 77-87 and from 94; Hon C Hillingdon All SS *Lon* 87-94. *8 Radnor Road, Harrow, Middx HA1 1RY* 0181-723 0548 or 427 1304

FLETCHER, Robert Alexander. b 52. Ridley Hall Cam. **d** 84 **p** 85. C Chalfont St Peter *Ox* 84-88; C Bushey *St Alb* 88-93; TV 93; TV Digswell and Panshanger from 93. *71 Haldens, Welwyn Garden City, Herts AL7 1DH* Welwyn Garden (01707) 335537

FLETCHER, Canon Robin Geoffrey. b 32. Nottm Univ BA57. Ridley Hall Cam 57. **d** 59 **p** 60. C S Mimms Ch Ch *Lon* 59-64; V Wollaton Park *S'well* 64-71; V Clifton *York* from 71; Chapl Clifton Hosp York 71-88; RD City of York from 86; Can and Preb York Minster from 89. *The Vicarage, Clifton, York YO3 6BH* York (01904) 655071

FLETCHER, Mrs Sheila Elizabeth. b 35. Nottm Univ BA57 CertEd58. NE Ord Course 84. **d** 87 **p** 94. NSM Dringhouses *York* 87-90; Par Dn 90-94; C from 94. *The Vicarage, Clifton, York YO3 6BH* York (01904) 655071

FLETCHER, Stanley Philip. b 27. St Jo Coll Dur BA52 MA73. **d** 54 **p** 55. V Bishopton w Gt Stainton *Dur* 66-76; V Cornforth 76-82; R Hartlepool St Hilda 82-92; RD Hartlepool 86-91; rtd 92. *8 Serpentine Gardens, Hartlepool, Cleveland TS26 0HQ* Hartlepool (01429) 223154

FLETCHER, Stephen. b 57. Man Univ BA79 MA84. St Jo Coll Nottm 82. **d** 84 **p** 85. C Didsbury St Jas and Em *Man* 84-88; R Kersal Moor from 88. *St Paul's Rectory, 1 Moorside Road, Kersal, Salford M7 3PJ* 0161-792 5362

FLETCHER, Stephen William. b 62. Wolv Poly BA84 Birm Univ DipTh87. Qu Coll Birm 85. **d** 88 **p** 89. C Rainham *Roch* 88-91; C Shottery St Andr *Cov* from 91; Min Bishopton St Pet from 91. *63 Baker Avenue, Bishopton, Stratford-upon-Avon, Warks CV37 9PN* Stratford-upon-Avon (01789) 415868

FLETCHER, Steven John Carylon. b 60. NCTJ83. Aston Tr Scheme 89 Ripon Coll Cuddesdon 89. **d** 92. C Newquay *Truro* 92-93. *10 Boswedden Terrace, St Just, Penzance, Cornwall TR19 7NF* Penzance (01736) 788994

FLETCHER, Timothy. b 27. Reading Univ BSc48. Linc Th Coll 50. **d** 52 **p** 53. R Binfield *Ox* 67-81; R Barcombe *Chich* 81-92; rtd 92. *15 Sadlers Way, Ringmer, Lewes, E Sussex BN8 5HG* Ringmer (01273) 812077

FLETCHER-CAMPBELL, Walter John Fletcher. b 12. Magd Coll Ox BA33 BSc38 MA44. Wells Th Coll 37. **d** 38 **p** 39. V Stanton Harcourt w Northmoor *Ox* 70-75; P-in-c Bampton Aston w Shifford 75-76; P-in-c Bampton Proper w Bampton Lew 75-76; rtd 77; RD Abingdon *Ox* 80-87; C Radley 89-90; C Radley and Sunningwell 90-93. *153 Upper Road, Kennington, Oxford OX1 5LR* Oxford (01865) 730467

FLEURY, Dr Phyllis Mary. LRCP Lon Univ MRCS49 Dur Univ MB, BS50. CITC 87. **d** 89 **p** 91. Hon Par Dn Ardara w Glencolumbkille, Inniskeel etc *D & R* 89-92; NSM Gweedore, Carrickfin and Templecrone 92-95; Lic to Offic from 95. *Inisfree House, Portnoo, Co Donegal, Irish Republic* Ardara (75) 45231

FLEWKER, David William. b 53. Birm Univ BA75. Wycliffe Hall Ox 76. **d** 78 **p** 79. C Netherton *Liv* 78-82; C Prescot 82-84; V Seaforth 84-88; TV Whitstable *Cant* from 88; Miss to Seamen from 88. *St Alphege's Vicarage, 28 West Cliff, Whitstable, Kent CT5 1DN* Whitstable (01227) 277904

FLIGHT, Michael John. b 41. Sarum Th Coll 68. **d** 71 **p** 72. C Wimborne Minster *Sarum* 71-75; R Tarrant Gunville, Tarrant Hinton etc 75-78; P-in-c Tarrant Rushton, Tarrant Rawston etc 77-78; R Tarrant Valley 78-80; V Westbury from 80; RD Heytesbury 83-87. *The Vicarage, Bitham Lane, Westbury, Wilts BA13 3JU* Westbury (01373) 822209

FLINDALL, Roy Philip. b 39. Lon Univ BD64 MPhil71 Keswick Hall Coll PGCE71. St Boniface Warminster 58 K Coll Lon AKC61. **d** 63 **p** 64. C Gt Yarmouth *Nor* 63-68; V Nor St Sav w St Paul 68-70; C-in-c Nor St Clem and St Geo 68-70; Lic to Offic *Ely* 90-92; Teacher Bluecoat Sch Lon from 92; Lic to Offic *S'wark* from 92. *53 Little Heath, London SE7 8EU* 0181-854 4446 or 858 8221

FLINN, Canon John Robert Patrick. b 30. **d** 65 **p** 66. I Baltinglass w Ballynure etc *C & O* 67-76; I Castlepollard and Oldcastle w Loughcrew etc *M & K* 76-84; rtd 84; Treas Ossory and Leighlin Caths *C & O* 90-92; Chan Ossory and Leighlin Caths from 92. *The Old School House, Kells, Kilkenny, Irish Republic* Kilkenny (56) 28297

FLINT, John Hedley. b 32. Edin Th Coll 55. **d** 57 **p** 58. C Glas Ch Ch *Glas* 57-60; C Motherwell 60-62; P-in-c Glas St Gabr 62-65; C-in-c Harlow Green CD *Dur* 65-73; V Gannow *Blackb* 74-76; Chapl RADD S Lon 76-79; P-in-c Idridgehay *Derby* 79-84; P-in-c Kirk Ireton 79-84; Chapl to the Deaf 84-87; C Derby St Luke from 87. *75 Otter Street, Derby DE1 3FD* Derby (01332) 345251

FLINT, Nicholas Angus. b 60. Chich Th Coll 84. **d** 87 **p** 88. C Aldwick *Chich* 87-91; Bp's Asst Chapl for the Homeless *Lon* 91-92; TV Ifield *Chich* from 92. *1 Francis Edwards Way, Bewbush, Crawley, W Sussex RH11 8GG* Crawley (01293) 851758

FLOATE, Herbert Frederick Giraud. b 25. Keble Coll Ox BA50 MA54. Qu Coll Birm 50. **d** 61 **p** 62. Australia 66-72; R Stroxton *Linc* 72-74; R Harlaxton w Wyville and Hungerton 72-74; Lect Shenston New Coll Worcs 74-78; P-in-c Redditch St Geo *Worc* 78-79; Lic to Offic 80-84; R Upton Snodsbury and Broughton Hackett etc 84-89; Chapl Mojacar *Eur* 89-91; rtd 91. *12 Fairways Avenue, Coleford, Glos GL16 8RJ* Dean (01594) 837178

FLOOD, Nicholas Roger. b 42. FCA. Ripon Hall Ox 71. **d** 92 **p** 93. NSM Romsey *Win* 92-95; Chapl R Hants Co Hosp Win from 95; Chapl St Paul's Hosp and The Mount Hosp Bishopstoke from 95. *Royal Hampshire County Hospital, Romsey Road, Winchester, Hants SO22 5DG* Winchester (01962) 824906 or 863535

FLORANCE, James Andrew Vernon. b 44. MCIOB. Linc Th Coll 84. **d** 86 **p** 87. C Lt Ilford St Mich *Chelmsf* 86-90; TV Becontree S 90-93; P-in-c Orsett and Bulphan 93; P-in-c Horndon on the Hill 93; R Orsett and Bulphan and Horndon on the Hill from 93. *The Rectory, Orsett, Grays, Essex RM16 3JT* Grays Thurrock (01375) 891254

FLORY, John Richard. b 35. Clare Coll Cam BA59 MA63. Westcott Ho Cam 69. **d** 71 **p** 72. C Shirehampton *Bris* 71-74; V Patchway 74-82; R Lydiard Millicent w Lydiard Tregoz 82-86; TR The Lydiards 86-93; R Box w Hazlebury and Ditteridge from 93. *The Vicarage, Church Lane, Box, Corsham, Wilts SN13 8NR* Bath (01225) 744458

FLOWER, Preb Roger Edward. b 45. AKC68. **d** 69 **p** 70. C Gt Stanmore *Lon* 69-72; C Wells St Cuth w Coxley and Wookey Hole *B & W* 72-77; V Tatworth 77-82; P-in-c Taunton St Andr

82-84; V from 84; RD Taunton from 90; Preb Wells Cathl from 92. *118 Kingston Road, Taunton, Somerset TA2 7SR* Taunton (01823) 332544

FLOWERDAY, Andrew Leslie. b 53. Imp Coll Lon BSc75. St Jo Coll Nottm DipTh. **d** 90 **p** 91. C Farnborough *Guildf* from 90. *St Peter's House, 22 Rectory Road, Farnborough, Hants GU14 7BY* Farnborough (01252) 517886

FLOWERDAY, Edward Arthur. b 04. Richmond Th Coll 28. **d** 43 **p** 43. V Acomb St Steph *York* 58-74; rtd 74; Perm to Offic *Carl* from 77. *14 Barton View, Penrith, Cumbria CA11 8AU* Penrith (01768) 64192

FLOWERDAY, Leslie Frank. b 26. DGA ADipR. **d** 87 **p** 88. NSM Gtr Corsham *Bris* from 87. *14 Station Road, Corsham, Wilts SN13 9EX* Corsham (01249) 712236

FLOWERDEW, George Douglas Hugh. b 10. MBE44. Wycliffe Hall Ox 66. **d** 67 **p** 68. C Chandler's Ford *Win* 67-70; R Baughurst w Ramsdale 70-80; rtd 80; Perm to Offic *Ox* from 83. *3 Lovelace Road, Oxford OX2 8LP* Oxford (01865) 513145

FLOWERDEW, Martin James. b 56. Herts Coll CertEd78 Pemb Coll Cam BEd79 UEA CertCS82. Sarum & Wells Th Coll 89. **d** 91 **p** 92. C Leagrave *St Alb* 91-95; C Radlett from 95. *43 Gills Hill Lane, Radlett, Herts WD7 8DG* Radlett (01923) 855921

FLOWERS, John Henry. b 33. Qu Coll Birm 63. **d** 65 **p** 66. C Llantrisant *Llan* 68-72; V Nantymoel w Wyndham 72-76; Asst Chapl HM Pris Wormwood Scrubs 76-78; Chapl HM Pris Birm 78-80; Chapl HM Pris Albany 80-93; rtd 93. *1 Ulster Crescent, Newport, Isle of Wight PO30 5RU* Isle of Wight (01983) 525493

FLUCK, Canon Peter Ernest. b 29. Linc Th Coll. **d** 61 **p** 62. R Uffington *Linc* 64-70; V Tallington 64-70; V Barholm w Stowe 66-70; V Linc St Nic w St Jo Newport 70-75; P-in-c Haugh 75-84; P-in-c Harrington w Brinkhill 75-84; P-in-c Oxcombe 75-84; P-in-c Ruckland w Farforth and Maidenwell 75-84; P-in-c Somersby w Bag Enderby 75-84; P-in-c Tetford and Salmonby 75-84; R S Ormsby w Ketsby, Calceby and Driby 75-84; V Boston 84-94; Miss to Seamen 84-94; Can and Preb Linc Cathl *Linc* 87-94; rtd 94. *Glebe House, Moorby, Revesby, Boston, Lincs PE22 7PL* Louth (01507) 568769

FLUX, Brian George. b 39. Oak Hill Th Coll 68. **d** 71 **p** 72. C Chadderton Ch Ch *Man* 71-74; C Preston All SS *Blackb* 74-76; Min Preston St Luke 76-81; CF (TA) from 78; R Higher Openshaw *Man* 81-88; Chapl HM Pris Haverigg 88-92; rtd 92. *Greenbank, Silecroft, Millom, Cumbria LA18 5LS* Millom (01229) 775224

FLYNN, Alexander Victor George. b 45. DTh. **d** 90 **p** 91. C Kilsaran w Drumcar, Dunleer and Dunany *Arm* 90-91; P-in-c 91-94; I from 94. *Dromena House, Dromiskin Road, Castlebellingham, Co Louth, Irish Republic* Castlebellingham (42) 72699

FLYNN, Peter Murray. b 35. Oak Hill Th Coll 76. **d** 79 **p** 80. Hon C Finchley St Mary *Lon* 79-83; Hon C Mill Hill Jo Keble Ch 84-86; C Mill End and Heronsgate w W Hyde *St Alb* 86-92; V Chessington *Guildf* from 92. *The Vicarage, Garrison Lane, Chessington, Surrey KT9 2LB* 0181-397 3016

FODEN, Eric. Local Minl Tr Course. **d** 93 **p** 94. NSM New Bury *Man* from 93. *66A St James Street, Farnworth, Bolton BL4 9SL* Farnworth (01204) 794880

FOGDEN, Canon Elizabeth Sally. b 40. MCSP61 DipRS77. Qu Coll Birm 76. **dss** 78 **d** 87 **p** 94. Chevington w Hargrave and Whepstead w Brockley *St E* 78-84; Honington w Sapiston and Troston 84-87; Par Dn 87-92; Par Dn Euston w Barnham, Elvedon and Fakenham Magna 90-92; TD Blackbourne 92-94; Chapl Center Parc Elvedon from 90; Dioc Adv Women's Min from 90; Hon Can St E Cathl from 92; TV Blackbourne from 94. *The Rectory, Honington, Bury St Edmunds, Suffolk IP31 1RG* Honington (01359) 269265

FOIZEY, Michael John. b 24. Trin Coll Cam BA45 MA65. Westcott Ho Cam 45. **d** 47 **p** 48. R Lon Docks St Pet w Wapping St Jo *Lon* 60-82; V Ealing Ch the Sav 82-89; Preb St Paul's Cathl 83-89; rtd 89. *157 Birmingham Road, Kidderminster, Worcs DY10 2SL* Kidderminster (01562) 823277

✠FOLEY, Rt Rev Ronald Graham Gregory. b 23. St Jo Coll Dur BA49 DipTh50. **d** 50 **p** 51 **c** 82. C S Shore H Trin *Blackb* 50-54; V Blackb St Luke 54-60; Dir RE *Dur* 60-71; R Brancepeth 60-71; Hon Can Dur Cathl 65-71; Hon Can Ripon Cathl *Ripon* 71-82; V Leeds St Pet 71-82; Chapl to The Queen 77-82; Suff Bp Reading *Ox* 82-87; Area Bp Reading 87-89; rtd 89. *3 Poplar Avenue, Kirkbymoorside, York YO6 6ES* Kirkbymoorside (01751) 303943

FOLKARD, Oliver Goring. b 41. Nottm Univ BA63. Lich Th Coll 64. **d** 66 **p** 67. C Carlton *S'well* 66-67; C Worksop Priory 67-68; C Brewood *Lich* 68-71; C Folkingham w Laughton *Linc* 72-75; P-in-c Gedney Hill 76-77; V 77-84; V Whaplode Drove 76-84; V Sutton St Mary 84-94; RD Elloe E 89-94;

P-in-c Scotter w E Ferry from 94. *The Rectory, Church Lane, Scotter, Gainsborough, Lincs DN21 3RZ* Scunthorpe (01724) 762662

FOLKS, Andrew John. b 42. St Jo Coll Dur BA65 DipTh69. **d** 69 **p** 70. C Stranton *Dur* 69-72; Chapl Sandbach Sch Cheshire 73-80; Lic to Offic *Carl* 80-85; Chapl Casterton Sch 80-85; Hd Master Fernhill Manor Sch New Milton from 85; Perm to Offic *Win* from 85. *Fernhill Manor School, New Milton, Hants BH25 5JL* New Milton (01425) 611090

FOLKS, Peter William John. b 30. FRCO56 ARCM. Launde Abbey 72. **d** 72 **p** 73. C Leic St Aid *Leic* 72-76; V Newfoundpool 76-84; V Whetstone 84-94; rtd 94. *214 Tudor Road, Leicester LE3 5HW* Leicester (0116) 242 5072

FOLLAND, Mark Wilkins. b 59. Univ of Wales (Cardiff) DipTh86 Southn Univ BTh88. Sarum & Wells Th Coll 86. **d** 88. C Kirkby *Liv* 88-91; Chapl Man R Infirmary from 91; Chapl C Man Healthcare Trust from 93; Lic Preacher *Man* from 91. *Chaplains Department, Manchester Royal Infirmary, Oxford Road, Manchester M13 9WL* 0161-276 4582 or 276 1234

FOLLAND, Ronald George. b 14. AKC48. St Boniface Warminster 48. **d** 49 **p** 50. V E Teignmouth *Ex* 66-79; rtd 79; Public Preacher *Ex* 80-89; Perm to Offic *Sarum* from 89. *1 Hollows Close, Salisbury SP2 8JU* Salisbury (01722) 338562

FOLLETT, Jeremy Mark. b 60. Jes Coll Cam BA82. St Jo Coll Nottm DTS90. **d** 91 **p** 92. C Newark-upon-Trent *S'well* 91-95; C Hellesdon *Nor* from 95. *50 Wensum Valley Close, Norwich NR6 5DJ* Norwich (01603) 483790

FOLLETT, Neil Robert Thomas. b 50. RMCS BSc75 Open Univ BA85. E Anglian Minl Tr Course 86. **d** 89 **p** 90. C Godmanchester *Ely* 89-92; V from 92. *The Vicarage, 59 Post Street, Godmanchester, Huntingdon, Cambs PE18 8AQ* Huntingdon (01480) 453354

FOLLIS, Raymond George Carlile. b 23. DFC45. Lich Th Coll 63. **d** 65 **p** 66. R New Fishbourne *Chich* 69-88; P-in-c Appledram 84-88; rtd 88. *8 Old Rectory Gardens, Felpham, Bognor Regis, W Sussex PO22 7EP* Bognor Regis (01243) 825388

FOOD, Frank Herbert. b 02. Wycliffe Hall Ox 37. **d** 38 **p** 39. R Markfield *Leic* 61-71; rtd 71; Chapl Torbay Hosp Torquay 71-77; Perm to Offic *Ex* from 77. *354A Torquay Road, Paignton, Devon TQ3 2BT* Paignton (01803) 552544

FOOKES, Roger Mortimer. b 24. VRD63 and Bars 73. Ch Ch Ox BA49 MA53. Wells Th Coll 48. **d** 50 **p** 51. Chapl RNR 58-74; V Midsomer Norton *B & W* 62-78; RD Midsomer Norton 72-78; P-in-c Stratton on the Fosse 74-78; P-in-c Clandown 75-78; V Wotton-under-Edge w Ozleworth and N Nibley *Glouc* 78-89; RD Dursley 85-89; rtd 89; Perm to Offic *Ex* from 90. *Feniton Cottage, Feniton, Honiton, Devon EX14 0BE* Honiton (01404) 850300

FOOKS, George Edwin. b 25. Trin Hall Cam BA49 MA52 Reading Univ ADEd70. Linc Th Coll 49. **d** 51 **p** 52. C Portsea St Cuth *Portsm* 51-53; C Fareham SS Pet and Paul 53-55; Chapl Earaseat Sch Carl 55-59; V Sheff St Cuth *Sheff* 59-64; Hd Careers Feinfox Gr Sch Bradf 64-66; Hd RE/Careers Battenshaw Comp Sch Bradf 66-70; Counsellor Ifield Sch Crawley 70-73; Hd Guidance Hengrove Sch Bris 73-78; Counsellor w Hearing Impaired Children (Avon) 78-89; Perm to Offic *Bris* from 83; Chapl Southmead Hosp Bris 89-90; Chapl Qu Eliz Hosp Bris from 90; Chapl Thornbury Hosp Bris from 90. *26 Rudgeway Park, Rudgeway, Bristol BS12 2RU* Almondsbury (01454) 614072

FOORD, Claude Victor. b 07. Worc Ord Coll. **d** 56 **p** 57. V Cleeve Prior *Worc* 64-72; rtd 72. *9 Lincoln Green, Worcester WR5 1QU* Worcester (01905) 359322

FOOT, Daniel Henry Paris. b 46. Peterho Cam BA67 MA74 Didsbury Coll of Educn CertEd68 Selw Coll Cam 76. Ridley Hall Cam 77. **d** 79 **p** 80. C Werrington *Pet* 79-82; P-in-c Cranford w Grafton Underwood 82; R Cranford w Grafton Underwood and Twywell from 83; P-in-c Lowick w Sudborough and Slipton from 94. *The Rectory, Cranford, Kettering, Northants NN14 4AH* Cranford (01536) 78231

FOOT, Leslie Frank. b 07. Dur Univ 30. St Boniface Warminster 27. **d** 32 **p** 33. R Eastergate *Chich* 63-75; rtd 75; Perm to Offic *Chich* from 75. *120 Little Breach, Chichester, W Sussex PO19 4TZ* Chichester (01243) 789640

FOOT, Leslie Robert James. b 33. Bris Univ BSc54. Wells Th Coll 67. **d** 69 **p** 70. Hon C Yeovil *B & W* 69-76; Lic to Offic from 76. *45 The Roman Way, Glastonbury, Somerset BA6 8AB* Glastonbury (01458) 832247

FOOT, Paul. b 41. Lon Univ BA64. Chich Th Coll 65. **d** 67 **p** 68. C Portsea N End St Mark *Portsm* 67-72; C Grimsbury *Ox* 72-74; V Cury w Gunwalloe *Truro* 74-80; P-in-c Port Isaac 80-83; P-in-c St Kew 80-83; V St Day 83-91; rtd 95. *3 High Street, Llandovery, Dyfed SA20 0PU* Llandovery (01550) 21428

FOOTE, Desmond. b 46. S Dios Minl Tr Scheme. **d** 82 **p** 83. NSM Furze Platt *Ox* 82-88; NSM Ruscombe and Twyford from 88. *52 Broadwater Road, Twyford, Reading RG10 0KU* Reading (01734) 342603

FOOTE, Dr John Bruce. b 18. FRCPath G&C Coll Cam BA39 MA43 MD51. St Jo Coll Nottm 78. **d** 79 **p** 80. NSM Crookes St Thos *Sheff* 79-88; Perm to Offic *Derby* from 79; rtd 88. *67 St Thomas Road, Sheffield S10 1UW* Sheffield (0114) 266 5021

FOOTITT, John Michael. b 35. Lon Univ DipTh62. St Aid Birkenhead 60. **d** 62 **p** 63. C Dudley St Barn *Worc* 62-69; V 69-76; Perm to Offic *Ripon* from 93. *6 Robert Street, Harrogate, N Yorkshire HG1 1HP* Harrogate (01423) 560497

FOOTITT, Ven Anthony Charles. b 35. K Coll Cam BA57 MA70. Cuddesdon Coll 59. **d** 61 **p** 62. C Wymondham *Nor* 61-64; C Blakeney w Lt Langham 64-67; P-in-c Hindringham w Binham and Cockthorpe 67-71; P-in-c Yarlington *B & W* 71-76; R N Cadbury 71-75; P-in-c S Cadbury w Sutton Montis 75-76; TR Camelot Par 76-81; RD Cary 79-81; Dioc Missr *Linc* 81-87; Hon Can Linc Cathl 86-87; Dioc Rural Officer *Nor* 87; Adn Lynn from 87; P-in-c Cockley Cley w Gooderstone from 95; P-in-c Gt and Lt Cressingham w Threxton from 95; P-in-c Didlington from 95; P-in-c Hilborough w Bodney from 95; P-in-c Oxborough w Foulden and Caldecote from 95. *Ivy House, Whitwell Street, Reepham, Norwich NR10 4RA* Norwich (01603) 870340 Fax as telephone

FOOTITT, John Guy. b 11. Jes Coll Cam BA34. Wycliffe Hall Ox 34. **d** 35 **p** 36. R Whatfield w Semer *St E* 51-77; P-in-c Nedging w Naughton 74-77; rtd 77. *Dane House, Kettlestone, Fakenham, Norfolk NR21 6AU* Fakenham (01328) 878455

FORAN, Andrew John. b 55. Aston Tr Scheme 84 Linc Th Coll 86. **d** 88 **p** 89. C Epping St Jo *Chelmsf* 88-92; TV Canvey Is from 92. *St Katherine's House, 17 The Ridings, Canvey Island, Essex SS8 9QZ* Canvey Island (01268) 682586

FORBES, Mrs Angela Laura. b 47. Ox Min Course 91. **d** 94. NSM Cowley St Jo *Ox* from 94. *80 Southfield Road, Oxford OX4 1PA* Oxford (01865) 242697

FORBES, Very Rev Graham John Thompson. b 51. Aber Univ MA73 Edin Univ BD76. Edin Th Coll 73. **d** 76 **p** 77. C Edin Old St Paul *Edin* 76-82; Can St Ninian's Cathl Perth *St And* 82-90; R Stanley 82-88; Provost St Ninian's Cathl Perth 82-90; R Perth St Ninian 82-90; Provost St Mary's Cathl *Edin* from 90; R Edin St Mary from 90. *8 Landsdowne Crescent, Edinburgh EH12 5EQ* 0131-225 2978 or 225 6293 Fax 225 3181

FORBES, Iain William. b 56. Ex Univ BA81. Chich Th Coll 83. **d** 85 **p** 86. C Upper Norwood St Jo *S'wark* 85-88; C Lewisham St Mary 88-90; Chapl St Martin's Coll of Educn *Blackb* 90-94; P-in-c Woodplumpton from 94; Dio Voc Adv from 94. *The Vicarage, Sandy Lane, Woodplumpton, Preston PR4 0RX* Catforth (01772) 690355

FORBES, James Paterson. b 32. Brechin NSM Ord Course 85. **d** 88 **p** 90. NSM Dundee St Jo *Bre* from 88. *6 Gillies Place, Broughty Ferry, Dundee DD5 3LE* Dundee (01382) 79655

FORBES, John Francis. b 29. CITC 85. **d** 88 **p** 90. C Ferns w Kilbride, Toombe, Kilcormack etc *C & O* 88-90; NSM Gorey w Kilnahue, Leskinfere and Ballycanew from 90. *Ballinabarna House, Enniscorthy, Co Wexford, Irish Republic* Enniscorthy (54) 33353

FORBES, Very Rev John Franey. b 33. AKC57. **d** 58 **p** 59. C Darlington H Trin *Dur* 58-62; S Africa from 62; Dean Pietermaritzburg from 76. *Deanery, PO Box 1639, Pietermaritzburg, 3200 South Africa* Pietermaritzburg (331) 425848

FORBES, Patrick. b 38. Lon Univ DipSoc74 Open Univ BA82. Linc Th Coll 64. **d** 66 **p** 67. C Yeovil *B & W* 66-69; C Plumstead Wm Temple Ch Abbey Wood CD *S'wark* 69-70; Thamesmead Ecum Gp 70-73; TV Thamesmead 73-78; Dioc Communications Officer *St Alb* 78-90; P-in-c Offley w Lilley 78-82; Lic to Offic 91-95; Info Officer Communications Dept Ch Ho Lon 91-95; Press Officer Miss to Seamen from 95. *Missions to Seamen, St Michael Paternoster Royal, College Hill, London EC4R 2RL* 0171-248 5202 Fax 248 4761

FORBES, Raymond John. b 34. ALCD58. **d** 58 **p** 59. C Wandsworth St Steph *S'wark* 58-61; C Kewstoke *B & W* 61-63; V Fordcombe *Roch* 63-73; R Ashurst 64-73; P-in-c Morden w Almer and Charborough *Sarum* 73-76; P-in-c Bloxworth 73-76; V Red Post 76-84; P-in-c Hamworthy 84-92; P-in-c Symondsbury and Chideock from 92. *The Rectory, Shutes Lane, Symondsbury, Bridport, Dorset DT6 6HF* Bridport (01308) 422145

FORBES, Stuart. b 33. Lon Univ BD59. Oak Hill Th Coll 56. **d** 61 **p** 62. C Halliwell St Pet *Man* 61-64; P-in-c Wicker w Neepsend *Sheff* 64-69; V Stainforth 69-77; V Salterhebble All SS *Wakef* 77-89; V Toxteth Park St Mich w St Andr *Liv* from 89. *St Michael's Vicarage, 6 St Michael's Church Road, Liverpool L17 7BD* 0151-727 2601

FORBES ADAM, Stephen Timothy Beilby. b 23. Ball Coll Ox. Chich Th Coll 59. **d** 61 **p** 62. R Barton in Fabis *S'well* 64-70; V Thrumpton 65-70; P-in-c S Stoke *B & W* 74-81; C Combe Down w Monkton Combe and S Stoke 81-83; Perm to Offic

83-86; Perm to Offic *Ox* 86-87; NSM Epwell w Sibford, Swalcliffe and Tadmarton from 87; rtd 88. *Woodhouse Farm, Escrick, York YO4 6HT* York (01904) 878827

FORCE-JONES, Graham Roland John. b 41. Sarum Th Coll 65. **d** 68 **p** 69. C Calne and Blackland *Sarum* 68-73; TV Oldbury 73-78; R 78-80; TR Upper Kennett 80-94; RD Marlborough 90-94; P-in-c Atworth w Shaw and Whitley from 94. *The Vicarage, Corsham Road, Shaw, Melksham, Wilts SN12 8EH* Shaw (01706) 703335

FORD, Adam. b 40. Lanc Univ MA72 K Coll Lon BD63 AKC63. **d** 65 **p** 65. C Cirencester *Glouc* 65-70; V Hebden Bridge *Wakef* 70-76; Chapl St Paul's Girls Sch Hammersmith from 77; P in O 84-91. *55 Bolingbroke Road, London W14 0AH* 0171-602 5902

FORD, Mrs Avril Celia. b 43. St Mary's Coll Dur BSc64 Chelsea Coll Lon PGCE65. Local NSM Course 85. **d** 92 **p** 94. NSM Horncastle w Low Toynton *Linc* from 92. *Frolic, Reindeer Close, Horncastle, Lincs LN9 5AA* Horncastle (01507) 526234

FORD, Dr Christopher Simon. b 51. AKC74 Leeds Univ MPhil86 PhD91. **d** 75 **p** 76. C Wythenshawe Wm Temple Ch *Man* 75-77; C New Bury 77-80; R Old Trafford St Jo 80-94; Bp's Adv on Archives from 93; R Moston St Jo from 94; AD N Man from 94. *St John's Rectory, Railton Terrace, Manchester M9 1WW* 0161-205 4967

FORD, Canon Colin David. b 28. MIMechE59. Oak Hill Th Coll 60. **d** 62 **p** 63. V Goodnestone St Bart and Graveney *Cant* 67-71; V Croydon Ch Ch Broad Green 71-84; V Croydon Ch Ch *S'wark* 85-93; Hon Can S'wark Cathl 93; rtd 93. *11 Boston Close, Eastbourne, E Sussex BN23 6RA* Eastbourne (01323) 470164

FORD, Canon David George. b 37. Lon Coll of Div ALCD61 LTh74. **d** 61 **p** 62. C Walthamstow St Barn and St Jas Gt *Chelmsf* 61-64; C Wisbech SS Pet and Paul *Ely* 64-66; C-in-c Cherry Hinton St Jas CD 66-73; V Cam St Jas 73-80; Can Res Ripon Cathl *Ripon* from 80. *St Peter's House, Minster Close, Ripon, N Yorkshire HG4 4QJ* Ripon (01765) 604108

FORD, David John. b 38. Lon Coll of Div BD68. **d** 69 **p** 70. C Blackheath St Jo *S'wark* 69-71; C Westlands St Andr *Lich* 71-75; V Sheff St Steph w St Phil and St Ann *Sheff* 75-77; R Netherthorpe 77-80; TR 80-84; R Thrybergh 82-84; R Thrybergh w Hooton Roberts 84-94; Ind Chapl 86-87; TV Parkham, Alwington, Buckland Brewer etc *Ex* from 94. *The Vicarage, Hartland, Bideford, North Devon EX39 6BP* Hartland (01237) 441240

FORD, Derek Ernest. b 32. St Mich Coll Llan 56. **d** 58 **p** 59. C Roath St Martin *Llan* 58-61; C Newton Nottage 61-67; V Abercanaid 67-70; Perm to Offic *Win* 70-80; SSF from 72; Lic to Offic *Sarum* 73-80; Lic to Offic *Newc* 75-80; USA from 80. *Little Portion Friary, PO Box 399, Mount Sinai, New York 11766, USA* Mount Sinai (516) 473-0553

FORD, Preb Douglas William Cleverley. b 14. Lon Univ BD36 MTh41. ALCD36. **d** 37 **p** 38. V S Kensington H Trin w All SS *Lon* 55-74; RD Westmr St Marg 67-74; Preb St Paul's Cathl 68-80; Prov Can of York from 69; Chapl to The Queen 73-84; Abp's Sen Chapl *Cant* 75-80; rtd 80; Six Preacher Cant Cathl *Cant* from 82; Perm to Offic *S'wark* 83-94. *Rostrevor, Lingfield, Surrey RH7 6BZ* Lingfield (01342) 832461

FORD, Eric Charles. b 31. Ely Th Coll 56. **d** 59 **p** 60. C Kettering St Mary *Pet* 59-65; R Bowers Gifford *Chelmsf* 65-69; V Walthamstow St Barn and St Jas Gt 69-76; V Chingford St Edm from 76. *St Edmund's Vicarage, Larkswood Road, London E4 9DS* 0181-529 5226

FORD, Eric Copeland. b 20. Linc Th Coll 68. **d** 70 **p** 71. C Lupset *Wakef* 70-73; V Cornholme 73-78; V Sharlston 78; V Wragby w Sharlston 78-85; P-in-c Hightown 85-87; V 87-88; V Hartshead and Hightown 88-90; rtd 90; P-in-c Halifax St Jo Cragg Vale *Wakef* 90-91; Chapl Las Palmas *Eur* from 91. *Calle Montevideo 2, 35007 Las Palmas, Canary Islands* Las Palmas (28) 267202

FORD, Canon Henry Malcolm. b 33. Em Coll Cam BA54 MA58. Ely Th Coll 58. **d** 59 **p** 69. C Ipswich St Matt *St E* 59-61; Hon C Bury St Edmunds St Jo 66-76; Hon C Hawstead and Nowton w Stanningfield etc 76-89; Hon Can St E Cathl from 86; NSM Cockfield w Bradfield St Clare, Felsham etc from 89. *Cross Green, Cockfield, Bury St Edmunds, Suffolk IP30 0LG* Cockfield Green (01284) 828479

FORD, Hubert. b 14. Kelham Th Coll 30. **d** 38 **p** 39. V Hurst Green *S'wark* 64-79; rtd 79; Perm to Offic *Chich* from 79. *88 Barrington Road, Worthing, W Sussex BN12 4RS* Worthing (01903) 244428

FORD, John. b 15. Linc Th Coll 38. **d** 40 **p** 41. R Aikton *Carl* 67-72; P-in-c Lambeth St Jo w All SS *S'wark* 72-76; rtd 76. *The Old House, Gornal Ground, Thwaites, Millom, Cumbria LA18 5JX* Broughton-in-Furness (01229) 716733

FORD, John. b 31. Sarum Th Coll 58. **d** 61 **p** 62. VC S'well Minster *S'well* 67-72; R N and S Wheatley w W Burton 72-78; P-in-c Sturton w Littleborough 72-78; P-in-c Bole w Saundby

72-78; V Edwinstowe w Carburton 78-95; rtd 95. *Sidings, 21 The Lawns, Collingham, Newark, Notts NG23 7NT* Newark (01636) 892588

FORD, Canon John Albert. b 13. TCD BA35 MA38. CITC 36. **d** 36 **p** 37. I Drumcree *Arm* 61-83; Can Arm Cathl 75-83; rtd 83. *84 Bleary Road, Portadown, Co Armagh BT63 5NF* Craigavon (01762) 345484

FORD, John Frank. b 52. Chich Th Coll 76. **d** 79 **p** 80. C Forest Hill Ch Ch *S'wark* 79-82; V Lee St Aug 82-91; V Lower Beeding *Chich* 91-94; Dom Chapl to Area Bp Horsham 91-94; Dioc Missr from 94. *27 Gatesmead, Haywards Heath, W Sussex RH16 1SN* Haywards Heath (01444) 414658 Fax as telephone

FORD, Jonathan Lawrence. *See* ALDERTON-FORD, Jonathan Laurence

FORD, Leslie Charles. b 08. S'wark Ord Course 65. **d** 68 **p** 69. C Norwood *S'wark* 68-76; rtd 76. *Capel Court, The Burgage, Prestbury, Cheltenham, Glos GL52 3EL* Cheltenham (01242) 579410

FORD, Lionel Peter. b 32. St Mich Coll Llan 57. **d** 60 **p** 61. C Ribbesford w Bewdley and Dowles *Worc* 60-63; C St Mary in the Marsh *Cant* 63-67; P-in-c 76-78; V Elmsted w Hastingleigh 67-71; V New Romney w Hope 71-78; RD S Lympne 75-81; V New Romney w Hope and St Mary's Bay etc 78-82; Hon Can Cant Cathl 82-94; V New Romney w Old Romney and Midley 82-94; Asst Chapl Oslo w Bergen, Trondheim, Stavanger etc *Eur* from 94. *Vallhallveien 9, 4043 Hafrsfjord, Norway* Hafrsfjord (51) 556712

FORD, Peter. b 46. ACP75 Bede Coll Dur TCert72. Linc Th Coll 76. **d** 78 **p** 79. OGS from 72; C Hartlepool H Trin *Dur* 78-81; Dioc Youth Officer *Wakef* 81-84; C Mirfield Eastthorpe St Paul 82-84; C Upper Hopton 82-84; V Dodworth 84-88; Chapl and Hd Relig Studies Rishworth Sch from 88; Ho Master from 94. *Oldham Road, Rishworth, Sowerby Bridge, W Yorkshire HX6 4QA* Halifax (01422) 823622 or 822217 Fax 823231

FORD, Peter Collins. b 23. Roch Th Coll 60. **d** 62 **p** 63. V Milton next Gravesend Ch Ch *Roch* 69-72; V Gosfield *Chelmsf* 72-84; RD Colne 79-81; RD Halstead and Coggeshall 81-84; rtd 88. *Little Winster, 12 Upper Fourth Avenue, Frinton-on-Sea, Essex CO13 9JS* Frinton-on-Sea (01255) 677151

FORD, Richard Graham. b 39. AKC65. **d** 66 **p** 67. C Morpeth *Newc* 66-71; C Fordingbridge w Ibsley *Win* 71-73; TV Whorlton *Newc* 73-80; V Choppington 80-92; V Tynemouth Priory from 92. *Holy Saviour Vicarage, 1 Crossway, North Shields, Tyne & Wear NE30 2LB* 0191-257 1636

FORD, Roger James. b 33. Sarum & Wells Th Coll 81. **d** 83 **p** 84. C Sidcup St Jo *Roch* 83-86; V Darenth from 86. *Darenth Vicarage, Lane End, Dartford DA2 7JR* Dartford (01322) 227153

FORD, Roger Lindsay. b 47. Ex Univ LLB68. Llan Dioc Tr Scheme 87. **d** 91 **p** 92. NSM Fairwater *Llan* from 91. *46 St Michael's Road, Llandaff, Cardiff CF5 2AP* Cardiff (01222) 565716

FORD, Mrs Shirley Elsworth. b 40. Open Univ BA88. Sarum & Wells Th Coll 89. **d** 91 **p** 94. C Farnham *Guildf* from 91. *6 High Park Road, Farnham, Surrey GU9 7JL* Farnham (01252) 726057

FORD, William John. b 50. Linc Th Coll 89. **d** 91 **p** 92. C Marton-in-Cleveland *York* 91-94; V Whorlton w Carlton and Faceby from 94. *The Vicarage, 18 Church Lane, Swainby, Northallerton, N Yorkshire DL6 3EA* Stokesley (01642) 700321

FORDE, Stephen Bernard. b 61. Edin Univ BSc TCD DipTh. **d** 86 **p** 87. C Belf St Mary *Conn* 86-89; Chapl QUB 89-95; Min Can Belf Cathl 89-91; Bp's Dom Chapl *Conn* 90-95; I Dub Booterstown *D & G* from 95; Dean of Residence Univ Coll Dub from 95. *The Rectory, Cross Avenue, Blackrock, Co Dublin, Irish Republic* Dublin (1) 288-7118

FORDER, Ven Charles Robert. b 07. Ch Coll Cam BA28 MA32. Ridley Hall Cam 28. **d** 30 **p** 31. Adn York 57-72; Can and Preb York Minster 57-76; rtd 72. *Dulverton Hall, St Martin's Square, Scarborough, N Yorkshire YO11 2DB* Scarborough (01723) 379534

FORDER, Harry Walter. b 15. AKC39. **d** 39 **p** 40. R W Horsley *Guildf* 53-87; rtd 87. *Grove Cottage, 10 Levylsdene, Guildford, Surrey GU1 2RS* Guildford (01483) 506102

FORDHAM, Mrs June Erica. b 28. DCR52. Oak Hill Th Coll 83. **dss** 86 **d** 87 **p** 94. Digswell and Panshanger *St Alb* 86-87; Par Dn 87-90; TD 91-93; rtd 93; NSM Lemsford *St Alb* from 93. *22 Crossway, Welwyn Garden City, Herts AL8 7EE* Welwyn Garden (01707) 326997

FORDHAM, Philip Arthur Sidney. b 51. Avery Hill Coll DipEd. St Steph Ho Ox. **d** 81 **p** 82. C Wanstead St Mary *Chelmsf* 81-82; C Romford St Edw 82-83; C Shrub End 83-86; TV Brighton St Pet and St Nic w Chpl Royal *Chich* 86-88; V Eastbourne Ch Ch from 88. *18 Addingham Road, Eastbourne, E Sussex BN22 7DY* Eastbourne (01323) 721952

FORDHAM, Richard George. b 34. AIMarE60 LicIM&C67 TEng71 FBIM74 SBStJ84 ONC62. **d** 91 **p** 92. NSM Cookham *Ox* 91-94; NSM Hedsor and Bourne End from 94.

Warrington, Hedsor Road, Bourne End, Bucks SL8 5DH Maidenhead (01628) 523134

FOREMAN, Joseph Arthur (Joe).d 86 **p** 87. NSM Win St Bart *Win* from 86. *4 Denham Close, Winchester, Hants SO23 7BL* Winchester (01962) 852138

FOREMAN, Patrick Brian. b 41. CertEd. St Jo Coll Nottm 77. **d** 79 **p** 80. C Gainsborough All SS *Linc* 79-83; V Thornton St Jas *Bradf* 83-91; R Hevingham w Hainford and Stratton Strawless *Nor* from 91; RD Ingworth from 94. *The Rectory, Westgate Green, Hevingham, Norfolk NR10 5NH* Hevingham (01603) 754643

FOREMAN, Roy Geoffrey Victor. b 31. Oak Hill Th Coll 62. **d** 64 **p** 65. C Chitts Hill St Cuth *Lon* 64-67; C Rodbourne Cheney *Bris* 67-70; C Walthamstow St Mary w St Steph *Chelmsf* 71-92; TV from 92. *41 Fraser Road, London E17 9DD* 0181-521 1361

FORGAN, Eleanor. b 44. St Andr Univ MA66 Aber Univ DipEd67. St And Dioc Tr Course. **d** 89 **p** 95. NSM Alloa *St And* from 89. *8 Crophill, Sauchie, Alloa, Clackmannanshire FK10 3EZ* Alloa (01259) 212836

FORMAN, Alastair Gordon. b 48. St Jo Coll Nottm 78. **d** 80 **p** 81. C Pennycross *Ex* 80-83; C Woking St Jo *Guildf* 83-88; V Luton Lewsey St Hugh *St Alb* from 88. *St Hugh's Vicarage, 367 Leagrave High Street, Luton LU4 0ND* Luton (01582) 664433

FORMAN, Diana Blanche Grant. b 19. DCR51. Edin Dioc NSM Course 79. **dss** 83 **d** 86 **p** 94. Edin St Jo *Edin* 83-86; NSM 86-91; rtd 91. *7/3 Myreside Court, Edinburgh EH10 5LX* 0131-447 1463

FORRER, Michael Dennett Cuthbert. b 34. St Pet Hall Ox BA59 MA63. Wycliffe Hall Ox 59. **d** 60 **p** 61. C Westwood *Cov* 60-63; Ind Chapl 63-69; C Cov Cathl 63-71; Sen Ind Chapl 69-71; Hon C All Hallows by the Tower etc *Lon* from 76. *117 London Road, Marlborough, Wilts SN8 1LH* Marlborough (01672) 55275

FORREST, John Sagar. b 15. Ridley Hall Cam 65. **d** 66 **p** 67. R Man St Pet Oldham Road w St Jas *Man* 69-75; R Man St Paul New Cross 72-75; Chapl Wythenshawe and Christie Hosps Man 75-80; rtd 80; Perm to Offic *Man* from 80. *8 Merton Street, Bury, Lancs BL8 1AW*

FORREST, Canon Kenneth Malcolm. b 38. Linc Coll Ox BA61 MA65. Wells Th Coll 60. **d** 62 **p** 63. C Walton St Mary *Liv* 62-65; Asst Chapl Liv Univ 65-67; Chapl Blue Coat Sch Liv 67-75; R Wavertree H Trin 67-75; R Wigan All SS from 75; Hon Can Liv Cathl from 87; AD Wigan E from 89. *The Hall, Wigan, Lancs WN1 1HN* Wigan (01942) 44459

FORREST, Very Rev Leslie David Arthur. b 46. TCD BA68 MA86. CITC 70. **d** 70 **p** 71. C Conwall *D & R* 70-73; I Tullyaughnish 73-80; I Athenry w Monivea *T, K & A* 80-82; I Galway w Kilcummin 80-95; RD Tuam 82-91; Dir of Ords 84-95; Can Tuam Cathl 86-95; Provost Tuam 91-95; Preb Tassagard St Patr Cathl Dub 91-95; Dean Ferns *C & O* from 95; I Ferns w Kilbride, Toombe, Kilcormack etc from 95. *The Deanery, Ferns, Co Wexford, Irish Republic* Wexford (54) 66124

FORREST, Michael Barry Eric. b 38. Lon Univ BA87 MA89. NZ Bd of Th Studies LTh62 Chich Th Coll 64. **d** 66 **p** 67. C Beckenham St Jas *Roch* 66-70; Papua New Guinea 70-76; C Altarnon and Bolventor *Truro* 76-78; TV N Hill w Altarnon, Bolventor and Lewannick 78-79; R St Martin w E and W Looe 79-84; V Kensington St Phil Earl's Court *Lon* from 84. *St Philip's Vicarage, 46 Pembroke Road, London W8 6NU* 0171-602 5025 or 373 4847

FORREST, Very Rev Robin Whyte. b 33. Edin Th Coll 58. **d** 61 **p** 62. C Glas St Mary *Glas* 61-66; R Renfrew 66-70; R Motherwell 70-79; R Wishaw 75-79; R Forres *Mor* from 79; R Nairn 79-92; Can St Andr Cathl Inverness from 88; Syn Clerk 91-92; Dean Mor from 92. *St John's Rectory, Victoria Road, Forres, Morayshire IV36 0BN* Forres (01309) 672856

FORRESTER, Edward. b 27. MIEH76 MIHE79 MIOSH80 R Tech Coll Salford DipEH51. St Aid Birkenhead 58. **d** 60 **p** 61. R Salford St Clem w St Cypr Ordsall *Man* 62-71; V Bury St Pet 71-73; rtd 93; Hon C Salford Ordsall St Clem *Man* from 93. *62 Affleck Avenue, Radcliffe, Manchester M26 9HN* Farnworth (01204) 78216

FORRESTER, Herbert Howarth. b 19. Liv Univ LLB46. Wycliffe Hall Ox 65. **d** 67 **p** 68. C Blundellsands St Nic *Liv* 67-70; V Liv St Phil 70-76; V Liv St Phil w St Dav 76-85; rtd 85; Perm to Offic *Liv* from 85. *5 Kenilworth Road, Liverpool L16 7PS* 0151-722 1365

FORRESTER, Ian Michael. b 56. Chich Th Coll. **d** 82 **p** 83. C Leigh-on-Sea St Marg *Chelmsf* 82-84; Min Can, Succ and Dean's V Windsor 84-86; Perm to Offic *Ox* 84-86; Chapl Distinguished Conduct Medal League 86-95; Chapl Gallantry Medallists' League from 95; Prec and Chapl Chelmsf Cathl *Chelmsf* 86-91; Perm to Offic from 91; Chapl Lancing Coll

W Sussex from 91. *Lancing College, Lancing, W Sussex BN15 0RW, or Ladywell House, Lancing, W Sussex BN15 0RN* Brighton (01273) 452213 or 454624

FORRESTER, James Oliphant. b 50. SS Coll Cam BA72 MA76. Wycliffe Hall Ox 73. **d** 76 **p** 77. C Hull Newland St Jo *York* 76-80; C Fulwood *Sheff* 80-87; V Lodge Moor St Luke 87-90; V Ecclesfield from 90. *The Vicarage, 230 The Wheel, Ecclesfield, Sheffield S30 3ZB* Sheffield (0114) 257 0002

FORRESTER, Mrs Joyce. b 33. Thornbridge Hall Coll of Educn TCert53 ACP84 Crewe & Alsager Coll MSc88. St Jo Coll Nottm 94. **d** 94 **p** 95. NSM Endon w Stanley *Lich* from 94. *Sprinks Farm, The Hollands, Biddulph Moor, Stoke-on-Trent ST8 7LE* Stoke-on-Trent (01782) 513626

FORRESTER, Kenneth Norman. b 22. Ely Th Coll 46. **d** 49 **p** 50. C Brighton St Bart *Chich* 68-71; Chapl Montreux *Eur* 71-79; Chapl Malaga w Almunecar and Nerja 79-81; Chapl Pau w Biarritz 81-86; rtd 87. *Residence Callebaste Cristal, 42 rue de Masure, 64100 Bayonne, France* France (33) 59 42 07 03

FORRESTER, Matthew Agnew. b 31. Univ of Wales (Cardiff) BA64 Lon Univ DipTh72. Trin Coll Bris 70. **d** 72 **p** 73. C Tonbridge SS Pet and Paul *Roch* 72-77; Chapl Elstree Sch Woolhampton 77-78; Chapl Duke of York's R Mil Sch Dover from 78. *The Chaplain's House, Duke of York's Royal Military School, Guston, Dover, Kent CT15 5EG* Dover (01304) 203012 or 210019

FORRYAN, Canon John Edward. b 31. Wells Th Coll 58. **d** 60 **p** 61. C Leckhampton SS Phil and Jas *Glouc* 60-63; C Cirencester 63-68; V Glouc St Paul 68-78; R Rodborough 78-91; P-in-c Deerhurst, Apperley w Forthampton and Chaceley from 91; Hon Can Glouc Cathl from 94. *The Vicarage, 1 The Green, Apperley, Gloucester GL19 4EB* Gloucester (01452) 780880

FORRYAN, Thomas Quested (Tom). b 64. Pemb Coll Cam BA85 DipTh86. Wycliffe Hall Ox 87. **d** 90 **p** 91. C Cheadle Hulme St Andr *Ches* 90-93; C Aberavon *Llan* 93-94. *Address temp unknown*

FORSE, Reginald Austin (Reg). b 43. Oak Hill Th Coll 77. **d** 79 **p** 80. C Crofton *Portsm* 79-84; NSM Gosport Ch Ch from 91. *40 Osprey Gardens, Lee-on-the-Solent, Hants PO13 8LJ* Portsmouth (01705) 553395

FORSHAW, David Oliver. b 27. Trin Coll Cam BA50 MA52. Qu Coll Birm. **d** 53 **p** 54. V Whitehaven St Nic *Carl* 66-76; P-in-c Whitehaven Ch Ch w H Trin 73-76; V Benchill *Man* 76-89; C Elton All SS 89-92; rtd 92. *Tynashee, Church Street, Broughton-in-Furness, Cumbria LA20 6HJ* Broughton-in-Furness (01229) 716068

FORSHAW, Canon Eric Paul. b 42. Lon Univ BSc63 Birm Univ MA78 Zurich Univ ThD90. Ridley Hall Cam 67 Gossner Inst Mainz 73. **d** 70 **p** 71. C Yardley St Edburgha *Birm* 70-72; Ind Chapl 72-78; Hon C Edgbaston St Geo 72-78; Bp's Adv on Ind Soc *S'well* 78-90; Perm to Offic 78-82; Assoc Min Nottm St Pet and St Jas 82-94; Hon Can S'well Minster from 85; Bp's Research Officer 90-92; Progr Dir Nottm Common Purpose 92-94; TR Clifton from 94. *11 Clumber Crescent North, Nottingham NG7 1EY* Nottingham (0115) 941 7156 Fax as telephone

FORSTER, Andrew James. b 67. QUB BA89. CITC BTh92. **d** 92 **p** 93. C Willowfield *D & D* 92-95; Dean of Residences QUB from 95. *20 Elmwood Avenue, Belfast BT9 6AY* Belfast (01232) 667754

FORSTER, Bennet Fermor. b 21. BNC Ox BA48 MA53. Cuddesdon Coll. **d** 51 **p** 52. Chapl Bedf Sch 65-72; C Bedf St Pet *St Alb* 72-73; Lic to Offic 73-78; P-in-c Froxfield w Privett *Portsm* 78-81; V 81-88; P-in-c Hawkley w Prior's Dean 78-81; V 81-88; rtd 88. *39 Parkview, Abbey Road, Malvern, Worcs WR14 3HG* Malvern (01684) 567915

FORSTER, Brian John. b 34. Chich Th Coll 64. **d** 68 **p** 69. C Orford St Andr *Liv* 68-71; C Knotty Ash H Spirit 71-74; TV Kirkby 74-79; V Liv St Paul Stoneycroft 79-94; rtd 94. *134 Ophir Road, Portsmouth PO2 9ET* Portsmouth (01705) 662231

FORSTER, Charles Clifford. b 34. AKC59. **d** 60 **p** 61. V Brafferton w Pilmoor and Myton on Swale *York* 65-72; V Derringham Bank 72-81; V Brompton w Snainton 81-83; V Brompton-by-Sawdon w Snainton, Ebberston etc 83-92; rtd 92. *33 Marshall Drive, Pickering, N Yorkshire YO18 7JT* Pickering (01751) 473655

FORSTER, Eric Lindsay. b 11. Worc Coll Ox BA33 MA38. Wycliffe Hall Ox 34. **d** 39 **p** 40. R Spaldwick w Barham and Woolley *Ely* 57-75; P-in-c Easton 58-75; rtd 75. *32 Tudor Road, Godmanchester, Huntingdon, Cambs PE18 8DP* Huntingdon (01480) 433183

FORSTER, Gregory Stuart. b 47. Worc Coll Ox BA69 MA73 DipSocAnth70. Wycliffe Hall Ox 69. **d** 72 **p** 73. C Bath Walcot *B & W* 72-74; C Bolton Em *Man* 74-76; C Bolton St Paul w Em 77-79; R Northenden from 79. *The Rectory, Ford Lane, Northenden, Manchester M22 4NQ* 0161-998 2615

FORSTER, Ian Robson. b 33. AKC59. **d** 60 **p** 61. C Leigh St Mary *Man* 60-62; C Chorlton-cum-Hardy St Werburgh 62-64; Grenada 64-66; St Lucia 66-69; P-in-c Alberbury w Cardeston *Heref* 69-76; V Ford 69-76; P-in-c Wolv St Chad *Lich* 76-78; TV Wolv 78-86; V Battersea St Phil w St Bart *S'wark* from 86. *St Philip's Vicarage, Queenstown Road, London SW8 3RT* 0171-622 1929

FORSTER, Dr Kenneth. b 27. St Jo Coll Cam BA50 MA52 Salford Univ MSc77 PhD80. NE Ord Course 83. **d** 86 **p** 87. NSM Hessle *York* 86-92; Chapl Humberside Poly 87-91; Chapl Humberside Univ 92; rtd 92; NSM Hull Sculcoates St Mary *York* from 92. *Birchwood, 12 Tower View, Anlaby, Hull HU10 7EG* Hull (01482) 657931

FORSTER, Dr Peter Robert. b 50. Mert Coll Ox MA73 Edin Univ BD77 PhD85. Edin Th Coll 78. **d** 80 **p** 81. C Mossley Hill St Matt and St Jas *Liv* 80-82; Sen Tutor St Jo Coll Dur 83-91; V Beverley Minster *York* from 91; C Routh from 91. *The Minster Vicarage, Highgate, Beverley, N Humberside HU17 0DN* Hull (01482) 881434

FORSTER, Ven Victor Henry. b 17. TCD BA45 MA49. **d** 45 **p** 46. I Aghalurcher w Tattykeeran, Cooneen etc *Clogh* 67-89; RD Clogh 73-89; Preb Clogh Cathl 80-83; Adn Clogh 83-89; rtd 89; Lic to Offic *D & D* from 90. *4 Ard-Na-Ree, Groomsport, Bangor, Co Down BT19 2JL* Bangor (01247) 464548

FORSTER, William (Bill). b 50. Liv Poly HNC71. N Ord Course 92. **d** 95. C Ashton-in-Makerfield St Thos *Liv* from 95. *79 Greenfields Crescent, Ashton-in-Makerfield, Wigan, Lancs WN4 8QY* Wigan (01942) 273611

FORSYTH, Jeanette Mary Shaw. b 48. Moray Ho Edin 67 St Jo Coll Nottm 85. **d** 89. NSM Old Deer *Ab* 89-92; NSM Longside 89-92; NSM Strichen 89-92; NSM Fraserburgh 92-94. *Mossside of Strichen, Bogensourie, Strichen, Fraserburgh, Aberdeenshire AB43 4TU* Strichen (01771) 637230

FORSYTH, William. b 10. Lich Th Coll 55. **d** 56 **p** 57. V Netherton *Carl* 65-70; V Levens 70-77; rtd 77; Perm to Offic *Carl* from 77. *2 Vicarage Road, Levens, Kendal, Cumbria LA8 8PY* Sedgwick (015395) 60926

FORSYTHE, Canon John Leslie. b 27. CITC. **d** 65 **p** 66. C Carnmoney *Conn* 67-71; I Mossley 71-80; I Antrim All SS 80-95; Preb Conn Cathl 94-95; rtd 95. *The Vicarage, 10 Vicarage Gardens, Station Road, Antrim BT41 4JP* Antrim (01849) 462186

FORTNUM, Brian Charles Henry. b 48. Hertf Coll Ox MA Imp Coll Lon MSc. Wycliffe Hall Ox 82. **d** 84 **p** 85. C Tonbridge St Steph *Roch* 84-87; V Shorne 87-94; R Speldhurst w Groombridge and Ashurst from 94. *The Rectory, Southfield Road, Speldhurst, Tunbridge Wells, Kent TN3 0PD* Langton (01892) 862821

FORTUNE-WOOD, Dr Janet. b 61. Selw Coll Cam BA82 MA88 CertEd83. Trin Coll Bris 86. **d** 88 **p** 94. Par Dn Rotherhithe H Trin *S'wark* 88-92; TD Swindon St Jo and St Andr *Bris* 92-94; TV from 94. *St Andrew's Church House, Raleigh Avenue, Walcot, Swindon SN3 3DZ* Swindon (01793) 480078

FORWARD, Eric Toby. b 50. Nottm Univ BEd72 Hull Univ MA93. Cuddesdon Coll 74. **d** 77 **p** 78. C Forest Hill Ch Ch *S'wark* 77-80; Chapl Golds Coll Lon 80-84; Chapl Westwood Ho Sch Pet 84-86; V Brighton St Aug and St Sav *Chich* 86-90; Perm to Offic *York* 90-95; V Kingston upon Hull St Alb from 95. *St Alban's Vicarage, 32 Hall Road, Hull HU6 8SA* Hull (01482) 446639 Fax as telephone

FORWARD, Canon Ronald George. b 25. Selw Coll Cam BA50 MA54. Ridley Hall Cam 50. **d** 52 **p** 53. V Kendal St Thos *Carl* 66-90; V Crook 78-90; Hon Can Carl Cathl 79-90; rtd 90. *51 Mayo Park, Cockermouth, Cumbria CA13 0BJ* Cockermouth (01900) 824359

FOSBUARY, David Frank. b 32. Leeds Univ BA63. Coll of Resurr Mirfield 63. **d** 65 **p** 66. C Fleetwood *Blackb* 65-68; Lesotho 69-76; C Dovercourt *Chelmsf* 76-78; TV 78-79; TV Basildon St Martin w H Cross and Laindon etc 79-82; R Colsterworth *Linc* 82-84; R Colsterworth Gp 84-90; RD Beltisloe 89-90; R Lawshall w Shimplingthorne and Alpheton *St E* from 90. *The Rectory, Harrow Green, Lawshall, Bury St Edmunds, Suffolk IP29 4PB* Bury St Edmunds (01284) 830184

FOSDIKE, Lewis Bertram. b 23. Keble Coll Ox BA52 MA56. Wells Th Coll 52. **d** 54 **p** 55. V Summertown *Ox* 64-76; TR Wolvercote w Summertown 76-89; rtd 89; Chapl St Hugh's Coll Ox from 89. *18 Osberton Road, Oxford OX2 7NU* Oxford (01865) 515817

FOSKETT, Eric William. b 29. Qu Coll Birm 75. **d** 78 **p** 79. NSM Billesley Common *Birm* 78-82; V Allens Cross 82-95; Chapl Hollymoor Hosp Birm 90-95; rtd 95; Perm to Offic *Birm* from 95. *1 Warmington Road, Hollywood, Birmingham B47 5PE* Knowle (01564) 526181

FOSKETT, Canon John Herbert. b 39. St Cath Coll Cam BA62. Chich Th Coll 62. **d** 64 **p** 65. C Malden St Jo *S'wark* 64-70; P-in-c Kingston St Jo 70-76; Chapl Maudsley Hosp Lon

76-94; Chapl Bethlem R Hosp Beckenham 76-94; Hon Can S'wark Cathl *S'wark* 88-94; rtd 94; Perm to Offic *B & W* from 95. *Cob Cottage, Duck Lane, Limington, Yeovil, Somerset BA22 8EL* Yeovil (01935) 840941

FOSS, **David Blair**. b 44. Bris Univ BA65 Dur Univ MA66 Fitzw Coll Cam BA68 MA72 K Coll Lon PhD86. St Chad's Coll Dur 68. **d** 69 **p** 70. C Barnard Castle *Dur* 69-72; Sierra Leone 72-74; Chapl St Jo Coll York 74-75; Chapl Ch Ch Coll Cant 75-80; Chapl Elmslie Girls' Sch Blackpool 80-83; Tutor Coll of Resurr Mirfield 83-88; V Battyeford *Wakef* from 88. *The Vicarage, 109 Stocksbank Road, Mirfield, W Yorkshire WF14 9QT* Mirfield (01924) 493277

FOSS, **William Cecil Winn**. b 40. Man Univ BA68 MA87 Lon Univ DipTh66 CertEd72 BD76. Ely Th Coll 64. **d** 68 **p** 69. C S'wark St Geo *S'wark* 68-73; Perm to Offic *Ches* 73-79; V Crewe Ch Ch 79-83; V Crewe Ch Ch and St Pet from 83. *Christ Church Vicarage, 3 Heathfield Avenue, Crewe CW1 3BA* Crewe (01270) 213148

FOSSETT, **Michael Charles Sinclair**. b 30. CEng MIMechE59 Dur Univ BSc54. NE Ord Course 82. **d** 90 **p** 91. Hon C Nether w Upper Poppleton *York* from 90. *20 Fairway Drive, Upper Poppleton, York YO2 6HE* York (01904) 794712

FOSTEKEW, **Dean James Benedict**. b 63. Bulmershe Coll of HE BEd86. Chich Th Coll 89. **d** 92 **p** 93. C Boyne Hill *Ox* 92-95; P-in-c Lockerbie *Glas* from 95; P-in-c Annan from 95. *All Saints Rectory, Ashgrove Terrace, Lockerbie, Dumfriesshire DG11 2BQ* Lockerbie (01576) 202484

FOSTER, **Antony John**. b 39. Down Coll Cam BA61 MA65. Ridley Hall Cam 65. **d** 66 **p** 67. Uganda 69-74; V Mt Pellon *Wakef* 74-92; rtd 92. *32 Savile Drive, Halifax, W Yorkshire HX1 2EU* Halifax (01422) 344152

FOSTER, **Canon Christopher Richard James**. b 53. Univ Coll Dur BA75 Man Univ MA77 Trin Hall Cam BA79 MA83 Wadh Coll Ox MA83. Westcott Ho Cam 78. **d** 80 **p** 81. C Tettenhall Regis *Lich* 80-82; Chapl Wadh Coll Ox 82-86; C Ox St Mary V w St Cross and St Pet *Ox* 82-86; V Southgate Ch Ch *Lon* 86-94; Continuing Minl Educn Officer 88-94; Can Res St Alb from 94. *The Old Rectory, Sumpter Yard, St Albans AL1 1BY*

FOSTER, **David Brereton**. b 55. Selw Coll Cam BA77 MA81 Ox Univ BA80. Wycliffe Hall Ox 78. **d** 81 **p** 82. C Luton St Mary *St Alb* 81-84; C Douglas St Geo and St Barn *S & M* 84-87; V S Ramsey 87-91; Dir Dioc Tr Inst 88-91; Asst Dir Buckm Adnry Chr Tr Scheme *Ox* 91-95; Dir Buckm Adnry Chr Tr Sch from 95; C W Wycombe w Bledlow Ridge, Bradenham and Radnage from 91. *175 Dashwood Avenue, High Wycombe, Bucks HP12 3DB* High Wycombe (01494) 474996

FOSTER, **Donald Wolfe**. b 24. St Cath Coll Cam BA48 MA50 TCD BD56. **d** 50 **p** 51. Asst Chapl Loughb Gr Sch 67-80; Chapl 80-87; Perm to Offic *Leic* from 81; rtd 87. *90 Brook Street, Wymeswold, Loughborough, Leics LE12 6TU* Loughborough (01509) 880029

FOSTER, **Edward James Graham**. b 12. St Jo Coll Cam BA34 MusBac35 MA38. Wells Th Coll 35. **d** 37 **p** 38. V Ashford w Sheldon *Derby* 67-78; rtd 78; Perm to Offic *Derby* from 78. *Montrose, Ashford Road, Bakewell, Derbyshire DE45 1GL* Bakewell (01629) 813718

FOSTER, **Edward Philip John**. b 49. Trin Hall Cam BA70 MA74. Wycliffe Hall Ox 78. **d** 79 **p** 80. C Finchley Ch Ch *Lon* 79-82; C Marple All SS *Ches* 82-86; P-in-c Cam St Matt *Ely* from 86. *St Matthew's Vicarage, 24 Geldart Street, Cambridge CB1 2LX* Cambridge (01223) 63545 Fax 512304

FOSTER, **Frances Elizabeth**. See TYLER, Mrs Frances Elizabeth

FOSTER, **Francis Desmond**. b 11. ALCD33. **d** 34 **p** 35. V Throwley *Cant* 48-75; V Throwley w Stalisfield and Otterden 75-77; rtd 77; Perm to Offic *Chich* from 78. *43 Milton Road, Eastbourne, E Sussex BN21 1SH* Eastbourne (01323) 639430

FOSTER, **Gareth Glynne**. b 44. Open Univ BA. Chich Th Coll 66. **d** 69 **p** 70. C Fairwater *Llan* 69-71; C Merthyr Tydfil 71-72; C Merthyr Tydfil and Cyfarthfa 72-76; TV 76-87; Dioc Soc Resp Officer from 87; P-in-c Abercanaid from 87. *19 The Walk, Merthyr Tydfil, M Glam CF47 8RU* Merthyr Tydfil (01685) 722375

FOSTER, **James**. b 29. Man Univ BA52 MA55 Lon Univ CertEd53 Leeds Univ MEd74. NE Ord Course 82. **d** 85 **p** 86. NSM Aldborough w Boroughbridge and Roecliffe *Ripon* 85-91; P-in-c Kirby-on-the-Moor, Cundall w Norton-le-Clay etc 91; P-in-c from 91. *Ford House, Farnham, Knaresborough, N Yorkshire HG5 9JD* Boroughbridge (01423) 340200

FOSTER, **John Francis**. b 13. Chich Th Coll 47. **d** 49 **p** 50. V S Ramsey *S & M* 64-79; rtd 79; P-in-c Leck *Blackb* 79-83; Perm

to Offic from 84; Perm to Offic *Carl* from 85; Perm to Offic *Bradf* from 87. *49 Fairgarth Drive, Kirkby Lonsdale, Carnforth, Lancs LA6 2DT* Kirkby Lonsdale (015242) 71753

FOSTER, **Very Rev John William**. b 21. BEM. St Aid Birkenhead 51. **d** 54 **p** 55. Hong Kong 57-73; Dean Hong Kong 64-73; Hon Can Hong Kong from 73; V Lythe *York* 73-78; Angl Adv Channel TV 78-88; Hon Can Win Cathl *Win* 78-88; R Guernsey St Peter Port 78-88; Dean Guernsey 78-88; rtd 88; Perm to Offic *York* from 88. *14 Lightfoots Avenue, Scarborough, N Yorkshire YO12 5NS* Scarborough (01723) 379012

FOSTER, **Jonathan Guy Vere**. b 56. Golds Coll Lon BA78. Wycliffe Hall Ox 83. **d** 86 **p** 87. C Hampreston *Sarum* 86-90; Chapl Chantilly *Eur* from 90. *7A Avenue du Bouteiller, 60500 Chantilly, France* France (33) 44 58 53 22

FOSTER, **Joseph James Frederick (Joe)**. b 22. SS Paul & Mary Coll Cheltenham CertEd42 Birm Univ DipEd59. **d** 88 **p** 88. NSM Elstead *Guildf* 88-94; Perm to Offic from 94. *Wodenscroft, Thursley Road, Elstead, Godalming, Surrey GU8 6DH* Elstead (01252) 703198

FOSTER, **Leslie (Les)**. b 49. Linc Th Coll 89. **d** 91 **p** 92. C Coseley Ch Ch *Lich* 91-93; C Coseley Ch Ch *Worc* 93-95; V Firbank, Howgill and Killington *Bradf* from 95. *5 Highfield Road, Sedbergh, Cumbria LA10 5DH* Sedbergh (015396) 20670

FOSTER, **Michael John**. b 52. St Steph Ho Ox 76. **d** 79 **p** 80. C Wood Green St Mich *Lon* 79-82; C Wood Green St Mich w Bounds Green St Gabr etc 82; TV Clifton *S'well* 82-85; P-in-c Aylesbury *Ox* 85-87; Dep Warden Durning Hall Chr Community Cen 87-89; V Lydbrook *Glouc* from 89. *The Vicarage, Church Hill, Lydbrook, Glos GL17 9SW* Dean (01594) 860225

FOSTER, **Neville Colin**. b 34. Aston Univ BSc67. W Midl Minl Tr Course 78. **d** 81 **p** 82. C Castle Bromwich St Clem *Birm* 81-84; V Tile Cross from 84. *The Vicarage, Haywood Road, Birmingham B33 0LH* 0121-779 2739

FOSTER, **Paul**. b 60. MAAT80. Oak Hill Th Coll DipHE93. **d** 93 **p** 94. C New Clee *Linc* from 93. *73 Carr Lane, Cleethorpes, S Humberside DN35 7SA* Grimsby (01472) 356416

FOSTER, **Phillip Deighton**. b 38. Lon Univ BD70. St Aid Birkenhead 62. **d** 66 **p** 67. C Castleton Moor *Man* 66-70; V Facit 70-76; R Salford St Phil w St Steph from 76; AD Salford from 94. *St Philip's Rectory, 6 Encombe Place, Salford M3 6FJ* 0161-834 2041

FOSTER, **Robin**. b 46. ACP70 Bede Coll Dur CertEd67 Nottm Univ BTh75 Lanc Univ MA87 Open Univ BA88. Linc Th Coll 71. **d** 75 **p** 76. C Briercliffe *Blackb* 75-77; Asst Dir RE 77-79; P-in-c Tockholes 77-79; Lic to Offic 80-83; Hon C Walmsley *Man* 83-88; Lic to Offic *Dur* 88-94; NSM Bolton le Sands *Blackb* from 94. *3 Tarnbrook Close, Crag Bank, Carnforth, Lancs LA5 9UL* Carnforth (01524) 734395

FOSTER, **Ronald George**. b 25. Bris Univ BSc51 AKC51. **d** 52 **p** 53. Chapl Bearwood Coll Wokingham 60-83; R Wantage Downs *Ox* 83-91; rtd 91; RD Wantage *Ox* 92-95. *Ascension Cottage, Horn Lane, East Hendred, Wantage, Oxon OX12 8LD* Abingdon (01235) 820790

FOSTER, **Simon Cuthbert**. b 63. Kent Univ BA88. Chich Th Coll 89. **d** 92 **p** 93. C Sunderland Pennywell St Thos *Dur* 92-94; C Consett from 94. *Church House, 1C Aynsley Terrace, Consett, Co Durham DH8 5LX* Consett (01207) 509998

FOSTER, **Simon John Darby**. b 57. Qu Mary Coll Lon BSc78. Wycliffe Hall Ox 85. **d** 88 **p** 89. C Bedgrove *Ox* 88-92; C Glyncorrwg w Afan Vale and Cymmer Afan *Llan* 92-94; R Breedon cum Isley Walton and Worthington *Leic* from 94. *The Rectory, Rectory Close, Breedon-on-the-Hill, Derby DE73 1AT* Melbourne (01332) 864056

FOSTER, **Stephen**. b 47. Leeds Univ CertEd69. NE Ord Course 83. **d** 86 **p** 87. NSM Kingston upon Hull St Nic *York* 86-89; NSM Aldbrough, Mappleton w Goxhill and Withernwick from 89. *1 Westbourne Road, Hornsea, N Humberside HU18 1PQ* Hornsea (01964) 533679

FOSTER, **Stephen Arthur**. b 54. Coll of Resurr Mirfield 75. **d** 78 **p** 79. C Ches H Trin *Ches* 78-82; C Tranmere St Paul w St Luke 82-83; V Grange St Andr 83-88; V Cheadle Hulme All SS 88-94; P-in-c Stockport St Matt from 94. *St Matthew's Vicarage, 99 Chatham Street, Stockport, Cheshire SK3 9EG* 0161-480 5515

FOSTER, **Steven**. b 52. Wadh Coll Ox BA75 MA80. Ridley Hall Cam 76. **d** 79 **p** 80. C Ipsley *Worc* 79-83; TV Woughton *Ox* 83-94; V Walshaw Ch Ch *Man* from 94. *Christ Church Vicarage, 37 Gisburn Drive, Walshaw, Bury, Lancs BL8 8DH* 0161-763 1193

FOSTER, **Steven Francis**. b 55. FRSA90 Lon Univ BD76 AKC76 Open Univ BA91. Coll of Resurr Mirfield 77. **d** 78 **p** 79. C Romford St Edw *Chelmsf* 78-80; C Leigh St Clem 80-83; Ed Mayhew McCrimmon Publishers 84-86; Lic to Offic 84; Hon C Southend 85-86; P-in-c Sandon 86-90; R 90-91; R Wanstead St Mary 91-93; R Wanstead St Mary w Ch Ch

FOSTER

from 93. *The Rectory, 37 Wanstead Place, London E11 2SW* 0181-989 9101

FOSTER, Stuart Jack. b 47. DipHE79 BA80. Lambeth STh86 Oak Hill Th Coll 77. **d** 80 **p** 81. C Worting *Win* 80-84; C-in-c Kempshott CD 84-88; R Hook from 88. *The Rectory, London Road, Hook, Basingstoke, Hants RG27 9EG* Hook (01256) 762268

FOSTER, Thomas Andrew Hayden. b 43. DipEcum. CITC 70. **d** 73 **p** 74. C Dub Clontarf *D & G* 73-78; I Drumcliffe w Clare Abbey and Kildysart *L & K* 78-80; P-in-c Polstead *St E* 78; I Kilscoran w Killinick and Mulrankin *C & O* 80-85; I Fanlobbus Union *C, C & R* 85-86; R Lasswade *Edin* 86-87; R Dalkeith 86-87; C Woodford St Mary w St Phil and St Jas *Chelmsf* 87-88; I New w Old Ross, Whitechurch, Fethard etc *C & O* 89-91; Dioc Info Officer (Ferns) 90-91. *Address temp unknown*

FOSTER, Thomas Arthur. b 23. Univ of Wales (Lamp) BA47. Cuddesdon Coll 47. **d** 49 **p** 50. R Llanfoist and Llanellen *Mon* 59-92; rtd 92. *The Bungalow, 5 The Bryn, Llangattock-juxta-Usk, Abergavenny, Gwent NP7 9AG* Gobion (01873) 840516

FOSTER, William Basil. b 23. Worc Ord Coll 65. **d** 67 **p** 68. C Folkingham w Laughton *Linc* 65-71; P-in-c Gedney Hill 71-75; V Whaplode Drove 71-75; R Heydour w Culverthorpe, Welby and Londonthorpe 75-77; P-in-c Ropsley 75-79; R 79-93; R Sapperton w Braceby 79-93; R Old Somerby 82-93; rtd 93. *31 Hedgefield Road, Barrowby, Grantham, Lincs NG32 1TA* Grantham (01476) 75925

FOTHERGILL, Anthony Page. b 36. Dur Univ BA60. Cranmer Hall Dur DipHE62. **d** 62 **p** 63. V Wellington St Luke *Lich* 69-77; TV Hanley H Ev 77-78; V Rocester 78-87; P-in-c Croxden 85-87; RD Uttoxeter 87; rtd 87. *Bowerleigh, 24 Purley Rise, Purley-on-Thames, Reading RG8 8AE* Reading (01734) 842984

FOTHERGILL, Guy Sherbrooke. Lon Coll of Div. **d** 47 **p** 48. V Drax *Sheff* 65-72; V Eldersfield *Worc* 72-77; rtd 77; Perm to Offic *Glouc* from 77. *96 Colesbourne Road, Cheltenham, Glos GL51 6DN* Cheltenham (01242) 527884

FOTHERGILL, Leslie Gurth. b 09. Tyndale Hall Bris 46. **d** 49 **p** 50. V Poughill *Truro* 65-74; rtd 74; Perm to Offic *Ex* from 74. *Magnolia Cottage, Kingscott, Torrington, Devon EX38 7JJ* Torrington (01805) 623554

FOULDS, John Stuart. b 64. Lanc Univ BA87 Southn Univ BTh91. Chich Th Coll 88. **d** 91 **p** 92. C Eastcote St Lawr *Lon* 91-95; C Wembley Park St Aug from 95. *194 Windermere Avenue, Wembley, Middx HA9 8QT* 0181-908 2252

FOULGER, Bernard Darwin. b 28. Cant Sch of Min 86. **d** 89 **p** 90. NSM Sittingbourne H Trin w Bobbing *Cant* from 89. *30 Frederick Street, Sittingbourne, Kent ME10 1AU* Sittingbourne (01795) 422724

FOULIS BROWN, Graham Douglas. b 50. JP. St Steph Ho Ox 80. **d** 82 **p** 83. C Hungerford and Denford *Ox* 82-84; C Bicester w Bucknell, Caversfield and Launton 84-85; TV 85-90; V Kidmore End from 90. *The Vicarage, Kidmore End, Reading RG4 9AY* Kidmore End (01734) 723987

FOULKES, Chan Meurig. b 21. St D Coll Lamp BA46. St Mich Coll Llan 46. **d** 47 **p** 48. RD Ardudwy *Ban* 64-76; R Llanaber w Caerdeon 66-76; Can Ban Cathl 71-89; Treas 74-83; Chan 83-89; R Llandegfan and Beaumaris w Llanfaes w Penmon etc 76-89; rtd 90. *Llanaber, 11 Gogarth Avenue, Penmaenmawr, Gwynedd LL34 6PY* Penmaenmawr (01492) 623011

FOULKES, Simon. b 58. Ox Poly BA81. Oak Hill Th Coll BA89. **d** 89 **p** 90. C St Austell *Truro* 89-92; C Boscombe St Jo *Win* 92-94; P-in-c Portswood St Denys from 94. *St Denys Vicarage, 54 Whitworth Crescent, Southampton SO2 4GD* Southampton (01703) 672108

FOUNTAIN, David Roy (Brother Malcolm). b 48. Qu Coll Birm 85. **d** 87 **p** 88. SSF from 72; NSM Handsworth St Mich *Birm* 87-92. *The Friary, Hilfield, Dorchester, Dorset DT2 7BE* Cerne Abbas (01300) 341345

FOUNTAIN, John Stephen. b 43. RAF Coll Cranwell 65 Solicitor 80. Local NSM Course 91. **d** 93 **p** 94. NSM Nacton and Levington w Bucklesham and Foxhall *St E* from 93. *High Trees, Bridge Road, Levington, Ipswich IP10 0LZ* Ipswich (01473) 659908

FOWELL, Graham Charles. b 48. Southn Univ BTh85. Chich Th Coll. **d** 82 **p** 83. C Clayton *Lich* 82-86; C Uttoxeter w Bramshall 86-90; V Oxley from 90. *The Vicarage, Lymer Road, Oxley, Wolverhampton WV10 6AA* Wolverhampton (01902) 783342

FOWKE, Lt-Comdr Thomas Randall. b 07. Master Mariner 33. Chich Th Coll 52. **d** 54 **p** 55. V Brighton St Aug *Chich* 63-76; rtd 76; Perm to Offic *Heref* from 76. *6 Lower Road, Pontesbury, Shrewsbury SY5 0YH* Shrewsbury (01743) 790450

FOWKE, Canon Walter Henry. b 06. Keble Coll Ox BA28 MA32. Cuddesdon Coll 30. **d** 30 **p** 31. V Chaddesley Corbett *Worc* 66-76; RD Kidderminster 72-76; Hon Can Worc Cathl 75-76; rtd 76. *3 Queens Terrace, Church Street, Wiveliscombe, Taunton, Somerset TA4 2LP* Wiveliscombe (01984) 23661

FOWLER, Anthony Lewis (Tony). b 57. Oak Hill Th Coll BA93. **d** 93 **p** 94. C Walton *St E* from 93. *27 Treetops, Felixstowe, Suffolk IP11 9ER* Felixstowe (01394) 282654

FOWLER, Colin. b 40. Linc Th Coll 80. **d** 82 **p** 83. C Barbourne *Worc* 82-85; TV Worc St Martin w St Pet, St Mark etc 85-86; TV Worc SE 86-92; P-in-c Moulton *Linc* 92-95; Chapl Puerto de la Cruz Tenerife *Eur* from 95. *Apartado 68, Taora Park, 38400 Puerto de la Cruz, Tenerife, Canary Islands* Tenerife (22) 384038

FOWLER, David Mallory. b 51. Lancs Coll of Agric OND72. Trin Coll Bris 75. **d** 78 **p** 79. C Rainhill *Liv* 78-81; C Houghton *Carl* 81-84; P-in-c Grayrigg 84-89; P-in-c Old Hutton w New Hutton 84-89; V Kirkoswald, Renwick and Ainstable from 89. *The Vicarage, Kirkoswald, Penrith, Cumbria CA10 1DQ* Lazonby (01768) 898176

FOWLER, Mrs Janice Karen Brenda (Jan). b 56. Oak Hill Th Coll DipHE93. **d** 93 **p** 94. NSM Walton *St E* from 93. *27 Treetops, Felixstowe, Suffolk IP11 9ER* Felixstowe (01394) 282654

FOWLER, John Douglass. b 22. Worc Ord Coll 61. **d** 63 **p** 64. P-in-c Huish Champflower w Clatworthy *B & W* 67-71; P-in-c Chipstable w Raddington 67-71; R Chelvey w Brockley 71-73; Asst Chapl Scilly Is *Truro* 73; TV 74-78; P-in-c Ashbrittle w Bathealton, Stawley and Kittisford *B & W* 78-81; TV Wellington and Distr 81-86; Perm to Offic *Ex* from 86; rtd 87. *Rosedene, 1 Venn Lane, Stoke Fleming, Dartmouth, Devon TQ6 0QH* Stoke Fleming (01803) 770362

FOWLER, John Ronald. b 30. Ely Th Coll 55. **d** 58 **p** 59. C Surbiton St Andr *S'wark* 58-61; Guyana 61-70 and 83-89; V Sydenham All SS *S'wark* 70-81; V Wood End *Cov* 81-83; Can St Geo Cathl 86-89; Adn Demerara 86-89; V Bedf St Mich *St Alb* from 90. *St Michael's Vicarage, Faldo Road, Bedford MK42 0EH* Bedford (01234) 266920

FOWLER, Canon John Sims. b 25. Trin Coll Cam BA46 MA50 Lon Univ BD52. Clifton Th Coll 48. **d** 52 **p** 53. Nigeria 61-72; Hon Can Ibadan from 71; Hon Can Lagos from 72; R Creiff *St And* 73-78; R Muthill 74-78; R Comrie 77-78; Warden Leasow Ho Selly Oak 78-84; V Fulham St Dionis Parson's Green *Lon* 84-90; rtd 90; Perm to Offic *Worc* from 90. *5 Mason Close, Malvern Link, Worcs WR14 2NF* Malvern (01684) 574463

FOWLER, Miss Morag Margaret. b 45. CertEd67 DipRE67 DipLib76 St Andr Univ MA66. St Jo Coll Nottm 84. dss 85 **d** 87 **p** 94. Skipton H Trin *Bradf* 85-87; Par Dn 87-89; Par Dn Market Bosworth, Cadeby w Sutton Cheney etc *Leic* 90-94; C 94; TV from 94. *4 Springfield Avenue, Market Bosworth, Nuneaton, Warks CV13 0NS* Market Bosworth (01455) 292157

FOWLES, Canon Christopher John. b 31. Lich Th Coll 54. **d** 58 **p** 59. V Chessington *Guildf* 69-77; V Horsell 77-95; RD Woking 92-94; Hon Can Guildf Cathl 94-95; rtd 95. *78 St Jude's Road, Egham, Surrey TW20 0DF* Egham (01784) 439457

FOWLES, Peter. b 30. St Deiniol's Hawarden 71. **d** 72 **p** 73. C Connah's Quay *St As* 72-76; V Towyn 76-83; V Esclusham 83-89; rtd 89. *Filiz Casan, Towyn Road, Abergele, Clwyd LL17 7PY* Abergele (01745) 826891

FOX, Albert. b 06. MBE. **d** 73 **p** 74. C Bris St Ambrose Whitehall *Bris* 73-75; Hon C E Bris 75-79; rtd 79. *20 New Brunswick Avenue, Bristol BS5 8PW* Bristol (0117) 967 2632

FOX, Canon Bernard John Gurney. b 07. Hertf Coll Ox BA28 MA35. Cuddesdon Coll 31. **d** 32 **p** 33. V Warkworth and Acklington *Newc* 68-73; rtd 74; Perm to Offic *Newc* 74-93; Hon Can Kuala Lumpur from 87. *59 West Avenue, Filey, N Yorkshire YO14 9AX* Scarborough (01723) 513289

FOX, Cecil George. b 15. TCD BA47 MA64. **d** 48 **p** 49. Chapl HM Pris Lewes 66-70; V Charsfield *St E* 70-77; R Monewden and Hoo 70-77; V Charsfield w Debach and Monewden w Hoo 77-82; rtd 82; Perm to Offic *St E* from 82. *1 Ivy Cottages, Walberswick, Southwold, Suffolk IP18 6UX* Southwold (01502) 724263

FOX, Canon Charles Alfred. b 08. St Aid Birkenhead 31. **d** 33 **p** 34. Hon Can Chelmsf Cathl *Chelmsf* 63-78; V Stratford St Jo and Ch Ch w Forest Gate St Jas 66-78; rtd 78; Perm to Offic *Lich* from 78. *5 Limewood Close, Blythe Bridge, Stafford ST11 9NZ* Blythe Bridge (01782) 395164

FOX, Charles Edward. b 36. Lich Th Coll 62. **d** 66 **p** 67. C S Bank *York* 66-69; C Stokesley 69-72; P-in-c Ugthorpe 72-82; V Egton w Grosmont 72-82; P-in-c Newbold Verdon *Leic* 82-93; R Newbold de Verdun and Kirkby Mallory from 84. *The Rectory, Main Street, Newbold Verdon, Leicester LE9 9NN* Hinckley (01455) 822528

FOX, Colin George. b 46. TD. Southn Univ DipTh75. Sarum & Wells Th Coll 73. **d** 75 **p** 76. C N Hammersmith St Kath *Lon* 75-79; CF (TA) 76-90; C Heston *Lon* 79-81; TV Marlborough

240

Sarum 81-90; P-in-c Pewsey 90-91; TR Pewsey TM from 91; Chapl Pewsey Hosp Wilts from 90. *The Rectory, Church Street, Pewsey, Wilts SN9 5DL* Marlborough (01672) 63203

FOX, Harvey Harold. b 27. Lich Th Coll 58. **d** 60 **p** 61. V Sparkbrook Em *Birm* 65-71; V Dordon 71-77; V Four Oaks 77-82; V Packwood w Hockley Heath 82-90; rtd 90. *3 St James' Close, Kissing Tree Lane, Alveston, Stratford-upon-Avon, Warks CV37 7RH* Stratford-upon-Avon (01789) 268263

FOX, Herbert Frederick. b 26. Leeds Univ BA50. Coll of Resurr Mirfield 50. **d** 52 **p** 53. V Turton *Man* 61-72; V Farnworth and Kearsley 72-78; RD Farnworth 77-84; TR E Farnworth and Kearsley 78-84; Hon Can Man Cathl 81-84; V Ashford Hill w Headley *Win* 84-91; rtd 91. *9 Highfield Road, Blackrod, Bolton BL6 5BP* Bolton (01204) 698368

FOX, Canon Ian James. b 44. Selw Coll Cam BA66 MA70. Linc Th Coll 66. **d** 68 **p** 69. C Salford St Phil w St Steph *Man* 68-71; C Kirkleatham *York* 71-73; TV Redcar w Kirkleatham 73-77; V Bury St Pet *Man* 77-85; V Northallerton w Kirby Sigston *York* from 85; RD Northallerton 85-91; Chapl Friarage and Distr Hosp Northallerton from 88; Can York Minster *York* from 95. *The Vicarage, Northallerton, N Yorkshire DL7 8DJ* Northallerton (01609) 780825

FOX, Miss Jacqueline Frederica. b 43. Ripon Coll of Educn CertEd66 Leeds Univ BEd74 MEd84 Hon RCM85. S Dios Minl Tr Scheme 83. **dss** 85 **d** 87 **p** 94. RCM *Lon* 85-86; Dioc FE Officer from 87; Hon C Acton St Mary from 87. *3 Roman Close, Avenue Gardens, London W3 8HE* 0181-993 5042

FOX, Mrs Jane. b 47. ALA70 Bp Otter Coll Chich CertEd75 Open Univ BA91. S Dios Minl Tr Scheme 92. **d** 95. NSM W Blatchington *Chich* from 95. *68 Poplar Avenue, Hove, E Sussex BN3 8PS* Hove (01273) 726955

FOX (nee COULDRIDGE), Mrs Janice Evelyn. b 49. Bognor Regis Coll of Educn CertEd71. Glouc Sch of Min 89. **d** 92 **p** 94. C Tupsley w Hampton Bishop *Heref* from 92. *2 Litley Close, Tupsley, Hereford HR1 1TN* Hereford (01432) 350805

FOX, Jeremy Robin. b 68. St Chad's Coll Dur BA89 MA92 Leeds Univ BA94. Coll of Resurr Mirfield 92. **d** 95. C S Shields All SS *Dur* from 95. *4 Mitford Road, South Shields, Tyne & Wear NE34 0EQ* 0191-456 1300

FOX, John Brian. b 38. **d** 94. NSM Phillack w Gwithian and Gwinear *Truro* from 94. *Abbeydale, 26 Tresdale Parc, Connor Downs, Hayle, Cornwall TR27 5DX* Hayle (01736) 753935

FOX, Jonathan Alexander. b 56. St Jo Coll Nottm LTh BTh81. **d** 81 **p** 82. C Chasetown *Lich* 81-85; TV Fazakerley Em *Liv* 85-89; Perm to Offic *Derby* from 89. *Charity Cottage, Turners Lane, The Delves, Swanwick, Alfreton, Derbyshire DE55 1AS* Leabrooks (01773) 540712

FOX, Canon Joseph Denis. b 06. St Edm Hall Ox BA28 MA33. Cuddesdon Coll 28. **d** 29 **p** 30. R Neatishead w Irstead *Nor* 62-76; Hon Can Nor Cathl 75-77; rtd 76. *Seaward, Verriotts Lane, Bridport, Dorset DT6 6DX* Chideock (01297) 397

FOX, Leonard (Len). b 41. AKC66. **d** 67 **p** 68. C Salford Stowell Memorial *Man* 67-68; C Hulme St Phil 68-72; C Portsea All SS w St Jo Rudmore *Portsm* 72-75; V Oakfield St Jo 75-92; V Portsea All SS from 92; All SS Urban Miss Cen from 92. *All Saints' Vicarage, 51 Staunton Street, Portsmouth PO1 2EJ* Portsmouth (01705) 872815

FOX, Mrs Lynn. b 51. E Midl Min Tr Course CTPS92. **d** 92 **p** 94. NSM Clifton *S'well* from 92. *St Mary's Rectory, 58 Village Road, Nottingham NG11 0NE* Nottingham (0115) 921 1856

FOX, Maurice Henry George. b 24. Lon Univ BD58. St Aid Birkenhead 47. **d** 49 **p** 50. V Sutton *Bradf* 62-79; V Grange-over-Sands *Carl* 79-88; rtd 89. *7 Manor Close, Topcliffe, Thirsk, N Yorkshire YO7 3RH* Thirsk (01845) 578322

FOX, Ven Michael John. b 49. Hull Univ BSc63. Coll of Resurr Mirfield 64. **d** 66 **p** 67. C Becontree St Eliz *Chelmsf* 66-70; C Wanstead H Trin Hermon Hill 70-72; V Victoria Docks Ascension 72-76; V Chelmsf All SS 76-88; P-in-c Chelmsf Ascension 85-88; RD Chelmsf 86-88; R Colchester St Jas, All SS, St Nic and St Runwald 88-93; Hon Can Chelmsf Cathl 91-93; Adn Harlow from 93. *The Archdeacon's Office, Church Lane, Sheering, Bishop's Stortford, Herts CM22 7NR* Bishop's Stortford (01279) 689524 Fax 734426

FOX, Michael John. b 41. Lon Univ BD68. Oak Hill Th Coll 64. **d** 69 **p** 70. C Reigate St Mary *S'wark* 69-73; Hon C from 76; C Guildf St Sav *Guildf* 73-76; C Guildf St Sav w Stoke-next-Guildf 76; Asst Chapl Reigate Gr Sch 76-81; Chapl from 81. *71 Blackborough Road, Reigate, Surrey RH2 7BU* Reigate (01737) 249017

FOX, Canon Michael Storrs. b 05. Em Coll Cam BA28 MA32. Bps' Coll Cheshunt 31. **d** 33 **p** 34. Can York Minster *York* 63-87; Preb York Minster (Dunnington) 63-90; R Barton le Street 64-77; V Salton 64-77; rtd 77. *Hawthorn Cottage, Coneysthorpe, York YO6 7DD* Coneysthorpe (0165384) 358

FOX, Nigel Stephen. b 35. Sarum Th Coll 59. **d** 62 **p** 63. C Rainbow Hill St Barn *Worc* 62-65; C Kidderminster St Geo 65-67; C-in-c Warndon CD 67-69; V Warndon 69-74; R S Hill

w Callington *Truro* 74-85; RD E Wivelshire 78-81; R St Martin w E and W Looe from 85. *St Martin's Rectory, Barbican Road, Looe, Cornwall PL13 1NX* Looe (01503) 263070

FOX, Norman Stanley. b 39. Univ of Wales DipTh64. St Mich Coll Llan 61. **d** 64 **p** 65. C Brierley Hill *Lich* 64-67; C Tettenhall Regis 67-70; V Cradley *Worc* 70-73; Asst Chapl HM Pris Wakef 73-74; Chapl HM Pris The Verne 74-76; R Clayton W w High Hoyland *Wakef* 76-81; R Cumberworth 81-84; C Tettenhall Wood *Lich* 85-89; TV 89-91; V Pensnett 91-93. *Address temp unknown*

FOX, Peter John. b 52. AKC74. St Aug Coll Cant 74. **d** 75 **p** 76. C Wymondham *Nor* 75-79; Papua New Guinea 79-85; P-in-c Tattersett *Nor* 85-88; P-in-c Houghton 85-88; P-in-c Syderstone w Barmer and Bagthorpe 85-88; P-in-c Tatterford 85-88; P-in-c E w W Rudham 85-88; R Coxford Gp 88-89; TR Lynton, Brendon, Countisbury, Lynmouth etc *Ex* 89-95; RD Shirwell 93-95; P-in-c Harpsden w Bolney *Ox* from 95; Gen Sec Melanesian Miss from 95. *The Rectory, 2 Harpsden Way, Henley-on-Thames, Oxon RG9 1NL* Henley-on-Thames (01491) 573401

FOX, Raymond. b 46. QUB BSc69. CITC 71. **d** 71 **p** 72. C Holywood *D & D* 71-75; C Min Can Down Cathl 75-78; I Killinchy w Kilmood and Tullynakill 78-81; I Belf St Mary *Conn* 81-88; I Killaney w Carryduff *D & D* from 88; RD Killinchy from 93. *700 Saintfield Road, Carryduff, Belfast BT8 8BU* Carryduff (01232) 812342

FOX, Robert. b 54. Man Univ BEd76. N Ord Course 89. **d** 91 **p** 92. NSM Stalybridge *Man* 91; NSM Ashton St Mich from 91. *36 Norman Road, Stalybridge, Cheshire SK15 1LY* 0161-338 8481

FOX, Dr Sidney. b 47. Nottm Univ BTh79 PhD93. Linc Th Coll 75. **d** 79 **p** 80. C Middlesb St Oswald *York* 79-81; P-in-c 81-86; V 86-87; V Newby 87-92; R Auchmithie *Bre* from 92; R Bre from 92; R Tarfside from 92. *39 Church Street, Brechin, Angus DD9 6HB* Brechin (01356) 622708

FOX, Timothy William Bertram. b 37. CCC Cam BA61. Qu Coll Birm 66. **d** 68 **p** 69. C Cannock *Lich* 68-72; C Bilston St Leon 72-75; V Essington 75-81; R Buildwas and Leighton w Eaton Constantine etc 81-92; RD Wrockwardine 88-92; P-in-c Moreton and Church Eaton 92; P-in-c Bradeley St Mary and All SS 92; R Bradeley, Church Eaton and Moreton from 92. *The Rectory, Church Eaton, Stafford ST20 0AG* Stafford (01785) 823091

FOX-WILSON, Francis James (Frank). b 46. Nottm Univ BTh73. Linc Th Coll 69. **d** 73 **p** 74. C Eastbourne St Elisabeth *Chich* 73-76; C Seaford w Sutton 76-78; P-in-c Hellingly 78-79; P-in-c Upper Dicker 78-79; V Hellingly and Upper Dicker 79-85; V Goring-by-Sea 85-93; R Alfriston w Lullington, Litlington and W Dean from 93. *The Rectory, Sloe Lane, Alfriston, Polegate, E Sussex BN26 5UY* Eastbourne (01323) 870376

FOXCROFT, James. b 05. St Andr Coll Pampisford 47. **d** 49 **p** 49. V Louth H Trin *Linc* 65-70; R Cattistock w Chilfrome *Sarum* 70-73; rtd 73; Perm to Offic *S'well* from 74. *Bradleys Cottage, 47 The Holme, Southwell, Notts NG25 0NF* Southwell (01636) 813910

FOXWELL, Rupert Edward Theodore. b 54. Solicitor 79 Magd Coll Cam BA76 MA80. Wycliffe Hall Ox 91. **d** 93 **p** 94. C Tonbridge SS Pet and Paul *Roch* from 93. *14 Salisbury Road, Tonbridge, Kent TN10 4PB* Tonbridge (01732) 355200

FOY, Malcolm Stuart. b 48. ACP80 FCollP FRSA Univ of Wales (Lamp) BA71 Magd Coll Cam CertEd72 K Coll Lon MA89. Ox NSM Course 84. **d** 87 **p** 88. NSM Tilehurst St Mich *Ox* 87-90; C Ireland Wood *Ripon* from 90; Adv RE Leeds Adnry from 90. *The Clergy House, 11 Bedford View, Leeds LS16 6DL* Leeds (0113) 267 2599

FRAIS, Jonathan Jeremy. b 65. Kingston Poly LLB87. Oak Hill Th Coll BA92. **d** 92 **p** 93. C Orpington Ch Ch *Roch* from 92. *43 Haileybury Road, Orpington, Kent BR6 9EZ* Orpington (01689) 823774

FRAMPTON, Miss Marcia Ellen. b 36. SRN65 SCM66. Ripon Coll Cuddesdon 86. **d** 88 **p** 95. Par Dn Paston *Pet* 88-89; Par Dn Burford w Fulbrook and Taynton *Ox* 90-92; Par Dn Witney 92-93; NSM Heref St Martin w St Fran (S Wye TM) *Heref* from 94. *27 Webb Tree Avenue, Hereford HR2 6HG* Hereford (01432) 269606

FRAMPTON-MORGAN, Anthony Paul George. b 57. Sarum & Wells Th Coll 89. **d** 91 **p** 92. C Plymstock *Ex* 91-95; P-in-c Wolborough w Newton Abbot from 95. *5 Coach Place, Newton Abbot, Devon TQ12 1ES* Newton Abbot (01626) 52088

FRANCE, Evan Norman Lougher. b 52. Jes Coll Cam BA74 MA78. Wycliffe Hall Ox 76. **d** 79 **p** 80. C Hall Green Ascension *Birm* 79-82; CMS 82-84; C Bexhill St Pet *Chich* 84-87; V Westf from 87. *The Vicarage, Westfield, Hastings, E Sussex TN35 4SD* Hastings (01424) 751029

FRANCE, Geoffrey. b 37. S Dios Minl Tr Scheme 87. **d** 90 **p** 91. NSM Uckfield *Chich* 90-92; C 92-94; R Warbleton and Bodle Street Green from 94. *Warbleton Rectory, Rushlake Green, Heathfield, E Sussex TN21 9QJ* Rushlake Green (01435) 830421

FRANCE, Canon Geoffrey Charles. b 23. Ripon Hall Ox 57. **d** 59 **p** 60. V Sneinton St Cypr *S'well* 68-90; Hon Can S'well Minster 87-90; rtd 90; Perm to Offic *Nor* from 90. *11 Elsden Close, Holt, Norfolk NR25 6JW* Holt (01263) 711210

FRANCE, Dr Malcolm Norris. b 28. Ch Ch Ox BA53 MA57 Essex Univ PhD75. Westcott Ho Cam 53. **d** 55 **p** 56. Chapl Essex Univ *Chelmsf* 64-73; Perm to Offic *Chich* 77-87; P-in-c Starston *Nor* 87-93; rtd 93. *The Old Rectory, Starston, Harleston, Norfolk IP20 9NG* Harleston (01379) 854326

FRANCE, Canon Dr Richard Thomas (Dick). b 38. Ball Coll Ox BA60 MA63 Lon Univ BD62 Bris Univ PhD67. Tyndale Hall Bris 60. **d** 66 **p** 67. C Cam St Matt *Ely* 66-69; Nigeria 69-73 and 76-77; Lib Tyndale Ho Cam 73-76; Warden 78-81; Vice-Prin Lon Bible Coll 81-88; Lic to Offic *St Alb* 83-95; Prin Wycliffe Hall Ox 89-95; Hon Can Th Ibadan, Nigeria from 94; R Wentnor w Ratlinghope, Myndtown, Norbury etc *Heref* from 95. *The Rectory, Wentnor, Bishops Castle, Shropshire SY9 5EE* Linley (01588) 650244

FRANCIS, Miss Annette. b 44. DCR66. Trin Coll Bris DipHE93. **d** 93 **p** 94. NSM Belmont *Lon* 93; C from 94. *116 Uppingham Avenue, Stanmore, Middx HA7 2JU* 0181-907 8573

FRANCIS, Claude Vernon Eastwood. b 15. Univ of Wales BA38. Ripon Hall Ox 38. **d** 40 **p** 41. R E Pennard w Pylle *B & W* 55-75; R Ditcheat w E Pennard and Pylle 75-81; rtd 81; Perm to Offic *B & W* from 81. *Millbank, Mill Lane, Alhampton, Shepton Mallet, Somerset BA4 6PX* Ditcheat (01749) 860225

FRANCIS, David Carpenter. b 45. Southn Univ BSc66 Loughb Univ MSc71 Sussex Univ MA83. Westcott Ho Cam 85. **d** 87 **p** 88. C Ealing St Mary *Lon* 87-90; Chapl Ealing Coll of HE 87-90; Chapl Claybonds Hosp Ealing 88-90; P-in-c Wembley St Jo *Lon* 90-93; Chapl Wembley Hosp 90-93; V Platt *Roch* from 93; Post Ord Tr Officer from 93. *The Vicarage, Comp Lane, Platt, Sevenoaks, Kent TN15 8NR* Borough Green (01732) 885482

FRANCIS, David Everton Baxter. b 45. St Deiniol's Hawarden 76. **d** 77 **p** 78. C Llangyfelach *S & B* 77-78; C Llansamlet 78-80; V Llanrhaeadr-ym-Mochnant, Llanarmon, Pennant etc *St As* 80-85; V Penrhyn-coch and Elerch *St D* 85-93; V Borth and Eglwys-fach w Llangynfelyn from 93. *The Vicarage, Swn y Mor, The Cliff, Borth, Dyfed SY24 5NG* Aberystwyth (01970) 817594

FRANCIS, Donald. b 31. Bris Univ BA52. St Mich Coll Llan 52. **d** 54 **p** 55. R Wolvesnewton w Kilgwrrwg and Devauden *Mon* 61-74; V Llantilio Pertholey w Bettws Chpl 74-83; V Llantillio Pertholey w Bettws Chpl etc 83-93; RD Abergavenny 87-93; rtd 93; Perm to Offic *Heref* from 93. *114 Park Street, Hereford HR1 2RE* Hereford (01432) 269674

FRANCIS, Ven Edward Reginald (Ted). b 29. Roch Th Coll 59. **d** 61 **p** 62. C-in-c Chatham St Wm CD *Roch* 64-71; V Chatham St Wm 71-73; RD Roch 73-78; V Roch 73-78; Hon Can Roch Cathl 79-94; Ind Chapl 79-89; Dir Continuing Minl Educn 89-94; Adn Bromley 79-94; rtd 94. *71 Ash Tree Drive, West Kingsdown, Sevenoaks, Kent TN15 6LW*

FRANCIS, Canon Ernest Walter. b 08. MBE45. Clifton Th Coll 29. **d** 36 **p** 37. S Area Sec BCMS 67-74; rtd 74; Perm to Offic *Cov* from 76; Hon Can Burma from 82. *7 Margetts Close, Kenilworth, Warks CV8 1EN* Kenilworth (01926) 52560

FRANCIS, Miss Gillian Cartwright. b 40. CertEd61. Dalton Ho Bris Trin Coll Bris DipTh71. dss 85 **d** 87 **p** 94. Blackheath *Birm* 86-87; Par Dn 87-94; C 94; P-in-c Stechford from 94. *The Vicarage, Albert Road, Birmingham B33 8UA* 0121-783 2463

FRANCIS, Graham John. b 45. Univ of Wales (Cardiff) DipTh70. St Mich Coll Llan 66. **d** 70 **p** 71. C Llanblethian w Cowbridge and Llandough etc *Llan* 70-76; V Penrhiwceiber w Matthewstown and Ynysboeth from 76. *The Vicarage, Penrhiwceiber, Mountain Ash, M Glam CF45 3YF* Mountain Ash (01443) 473716

FRANCIS, Hilton Barrington. b 23. Selw Coll Cam BA46 MA48. Ridley Hall Cam 61. **d** 62 **p** 63. Lect Nor City Coll 69-75; Tutor Adult Educn 75-81; P-in-c Gt w Lt Plumstead *Nor* 81-87; rtd 88. *190 Church End, Cherry Hinton, Cambridge CB1 3LB* Cambridge (01223) 212081

FRANCIS, James More MacLeod. b 44. Edin Univ MA65 BD68 PhD74. Yale Div Sch STM69. **d** 87 **p** 87. NSM Sunderland St Chad *Dur* from 87. *73 Hillcrest, Sunderland SR3 3NN* 0191-528 1326

FRANCIS, Canon James Woodcock. b 28. Wilberforce Univ Ohio AB57 Payne Th Sem Ohio BD58. Bexley Hall Div Sch Ohio 59. **d** 59 **p** 60. USA 59-84; Can Res Bermuda Cathl from 85. *PO Box HM 627, Hamilton HM CX, Bermuda* Bermuda (1-809) 295-1125 Fax 292-5421

FRANCIS, Jeffrey Merrick. b 46. Bris Univ BSc69. Qu Coll Birm 72. **d** 76 **p** 77. C Bris Ch the Servant Stockwood *Bris* 76-79; C Bishopston 79-82; V Bris St Andr Hartcliffe 82-93; TV Bris St Paul's from 93. *St Werburgh's Vicarage, 15 St Werburgh's Park, Bristol BS2 9XD* Bristol (0117) 955 8863

FRANCIS, Jeremy Montgomery. b 31. BNC Ox BA53 MA. Glouc Sch of Min 84. **d** 87 **p** 88. NSM Chedworth, Yanworth and Stowell, Coln Rogers etc *Glouc* 87-90; NSM Coates, Rodmarton and Sapperton etc from 90; NSM Daglingworth w the Duntisbournes and Winstone from 95. *Old Barnfield, Duntisbourne Leer, Cirencester, Glos GL7 7AS* Cirencester (01285) 821370

FRANCIS, John Sims. b 25. Fitzw Ho Cam BA54 MA58. St D Coll Lamp BA47 LTh49. **d** 49 **p** 50. R Willingham *Ely* 65-82; RD N Stowe 78-82; R Rampton 82; P-in-c Buckden 82-91; rtd 91; Perm to Offic *Linc* from 92. *3 The Brambles, Bourne, Lincs PE10 9TF* Bourne (01778) 426396

FRANCIS, Julian Montgomery. b 60. Selw Coll Cam MA83. S'wark Ord Course 88. **d** 91 **p** 92. C S Wimbledon H Trin and St Pet *S'wark* from 91. *50 Evelyn Road, London SW19 8NT* 0181-542 6229

FRANCIS, Kenneth. b 30. Em Coll Cam BA56 MA60. Coll of Resurr Mirfield. **d** 58 **p** 59. C De Beauvoir Town St Pet *Lon* 58-61; N Rhodesia 62-64; Zambia 64-70; V Harlow St Mary Magd *Chelmsf* 70-76; V Felixstowe St Jo *St E* from 76. *St John's Vicarage, Princes Road, Felixstowe, Suffolk IP11 7PL* Felixstowe (01394) 284226

FRANCIS, Kenneth Charles. b 22. Oak Hill Th Coll 46. **d** 50 **p** 51. V Summerstown *S'wark* 61-77; R Cratfield w Heveningham and Ubbeston etc *St E* 77-87; rtd 87. *Trenute Barns, Trebullett, Launceston, Cornwall PL15 9QB* Coads Green (01566) 82257

FRANCIS, Canon Kenneth Edgar. b 15. St D Coll Lamp BA38. **d** 39 **p** 40. R Aberdovey *Ban* 55-80; V Beddgelert 80-84; Hon Can Ban Cathl 81-84; rtd 84; Perm to Offic *Ban* from 84. *6 Edmund House, Y Maes, Criccieth, Gwynedd LL52 0AN* Criccieth (01766) 522678

FRANCIS (or ROOSE FRANCIS), Leslie. b 18. Magd Coll Ox BA48 MA52. Westcott Ho Cam 48. **d** 49 **p** 50. V Hilmarton and Highway *Sarum* 68-78; rtd 83. *2 Merton Cottages, Tregatta, Tintagel, Cornwall PL34 0DY* Camelford (01840) 770446

FRANCIS, Prof Leslie John. b 47. FBPsS88 FCP94 Pemb Coll Ox BA70 MA74 BD90 Qu Coll Cam PhD76 Nottm Univ MTh76 Lon Univ MSc77. Westcott Ho Cam 70. **d** 73 **p** 74. Hon C Haverhill *St E* 73-75; C 75-77; NSM Gt Bradley 78-82; NSM Gt w Lt Wratting 79-82; NSM N Cerney w Bagendon *Glouc* 82-85; Research Officer Culham Coll Inst 82-88; Perm to Offic from 85; Fell Trin Coll Carmarthen from 89; Prof Th Univ of Wales (Lamp) from 92. *Trinity College, Carmarthen, Dyfed SA31 3EP* Carmarthen (01267) 237971

FRANCIS, Martin Rufus. b 37. Pemb Coll Ox BA60 MA64. Linc Th Coll 60. **d** 63 **p** 64. C W Hartlepool St Paul *Dur* 63-67; C Yeovil St Jo w Preston Plucknett *B & W* 67-69; Chapl Tonbridge Sch Kent 69-83; Chapl and Dep Hd St Jo Sch Leatherhead 83-94; R Herstmonceux and Wartling *Chich* from 94. *The Rectory, Herstmonceux, Hailsham, E Sussex BN27 4NY* Herstmonceux (01323) 833124

FRANCIS, Noel Charles. b 14. St Andr Univ. St D Coll Lamp BA36. **d** 38 **p** 39. V Manningham St Paul and St Jude *Bradf* 69-81; I Aughaval w Burrishoole, Knappagh and Louisburgh *T, K & A* 81-85; rtd 85; Perm to Offic *York* from 87. *5 Foxcroft, Haxby, York YO3 3GY* York (01904) 769160

FRANCIS, Paul Edward. b 52. Southn Univ BTh84. Sarum & Wells Th Coll 78. **d** 81 **p** 82. C Biggin Hill *Roch* 81-85; R Fawkham and Hartley 85-90; V Aylesford from 90. *The Vicarage, Vicarage Close, Aylesford, Kent ME20 7BB* Maidstone (01622) 717434

FRANCIS, Very Rev Peter Brereton. b 53. St Andr Univ MTh77. Qu Coll Birm 77. **d** 78 **p** 79. C Hagley *Worc* 78-81; Chapl Qu Mary Coll *Lon* 81-87; R Ayr *Glas* 87-92; Miss to Seamen 87-92; Provost St Mary's Cathl *Glas* from 92; R Glas St Mary from 92. *45 Rowallan Gardens, Glasgow G11 7LH* 0141-339 4956 Fax 357 4544

FRANCIS, Peter Philip. b 48. St Jo Coll Dur BA73. Wycliffe Hall Ox 73. **d** 75 **p** 76. C Foord St Jo *Cant* 75-78; C Morden S'wark 78-83; P-in-c Barford St Martin, Dinton, Baverstock etc *Sarum* 83-88; P-in-c Fovant, Sutton Mandeville and Teffont Evias etc 83-86; R Newick *Chich* from 88. *The Rectory, Church Road, Newick, Lewes, E Sussex BN8 4JX* Newick (01825) 722692

FRANCIS, Philip Thomas. b 58. St D Coll Lamp BA81. Chich Th Coll 81. **d** 82 **p** 83. C Llanelli St Paul *St D* 82-84; C Barnsley St Mary *Wakef* 84-87; V Burton Dassett *Cov* from 87; V Gaydon w Chadshunt from 87. *Burton Dassett Vicarage, Northend, Leamington Spa, Warks CV33 0TH* Fenny Compton (01295) 770400

FRANCIS-DEHQANI, Lee Thomas. b 67. Nottm Univ BA89. Sarum & Wells Th Coll 92 Trin Coll Bris BA95. **d** 95. C Putney

St Mary *S'wark* from 95. *8 Deodar Road, London SW15 2NN*
0181-785 3821   Fax 788 4414

FRANK, Derek John. b 49. ACGI70 Imp Coll Lon BScEng70 Warw Univ MSc71. Cranmer Hall Dur 83. **d** 85 **p** 86. C Clay Cross *Derby* 85-87; C Crookes St Thos *Sheff* 87-90; TV 90-93; Chapl Vevey w Chateau d'Oex and Villars *Eur* from 93. *The Parsonage, Chemin de Champsavaux 1, 1807 Blonday, Switzerland* Lausanne (21) 943-2239

FRANK, Richard Patrick Harry. b 40. St Chad's Coll Dur BA66 DipTh68. **d** 68 **p** 69. C Darlington H Trin *Dur* 68-72; C Monkwearmouth St Andr 72-74; C-in-c Harlow Green CD 74-79; R Skelton and Hutton-in-the-Forest w Ivegill *Carl* 79-86; V Carl St Luke Morton 86-92; RD Carl 88-89; P-in-c Thursby 89-90; P-in-c Kirkbride w Newton Arlosh 89-92; TR Greystoke, Matterdale, Mungrisdale, etc from 92. *The Rectory, Greystoke, Penrith, Cumbria CA11 0TJ* Greystoke (017684) 83293

FRANKHAM, Very Rev Harold Edward. b 11. Lon Coll of Div 39. **d** 41 **p** 42. V Luton w E Hyde *St Alb* 61-70; R S'wark St Sav w All Hallows *S'wark* 70-82; Provost S'wark 70-82; rtd 83; Perm to Offic *B & W* 83-94. *Flat 3, Harnleigh Green, Harnham Road, Salisbury SP2 8JN* Salisbury (01722) 321846

FRANKLAND, John Ashlin. b 12. Hatf Coll Dur LTh36 BA37 MA47 Liv Univ DipEd52. Edin Th Coll 35. **d** 37 **p** 38. Sierra Leone 53-59; Perm to Offic *Ches* from 76; rtd 77; Perm to Offic *Man* from 77. *27 Warwick Road, Hale, Altrincham, Cheshire WA15 9NP* 0161-928 5178

FRANKLIN, Archibald William. b 01. Lon Univ BD32 AKC32. **d** 32 **p** 33. V Pool *Ripon* 66-74; V Pool w Arthington 74-77; rtd 77. *56 New Adel Lane, Leeds LS16 6AN* Leeds (0113) 261 0796

FRANKLIN, Arthur Harrington. b 03. MBE45 TD51. Linc Coll Ox BA26 MA29. Bps' Coll Cheshunt 34. **d** 34 **p** 35. R Gt Leighs *Chelmsf* 45-70; RD Roding 62-70; rtd 71. *Hea Corner, Mill Lane, Felsted, Dunmow, Essex CM6 3HQ* Great Dunmow (01371) 820519

FRANKLIN, Eric Edward Joseph. b 29. St Pet Hall Ox BA53 MA58. Qu Coll Birm DipTh55. **d** 55 **p** 56. Tutor St Chad's Coll Dur 66-72; Tutor Chich Th Coll 72-74; C Margate St Jo *Cant* 74-83; Vice-Prin St Steph Ho Ox 83-90; Dir of Studies St Steph Ho Ox 91-94; rtd 94; Perm to Offic *Cant* from 94. *St Stephen's House, 16 Marston Street, Oxford OX4 1JX* Oxford (01865) 247874 or 243427

FRANKLIN, Joan Mary. b 20. St Andr Ho Portsm 47. **dss** 61 **d** 87. Scunthorpe St Jo *Linc* 66-70; Gt Grimsby St Mary and St Jas 70-86; rtd 86. *56 Vicarage Gardens, Grimsby, S Humberside DN34 4PZ* Grimsby (01472) 242341

FRANKLIN, Kenneth Douglas. b 20. Worc Ord Coll 61. **d** 62 **p** 63. Singapore 69-72 and 78-80; V Southsea St Pet *Portsm* 72-77; C Portsea St Mary 81; Chapl Qu Alexandra Hosp Portsm 81-83; rtd 83; Perm to Offic *Chich* from 84. *56A Langdale Gardens, Hove, E Sussex BN3 4HH* Brighton (01273) 731187

FRANKLIN, Richard Charles Henry. b 48. Ch Ch Coll Cant CertEd70. Sarum & Wells Th Coll 75. **d** 78 **p** 79. C Pershore w Pinvin, Wick and Birlingham *Worc* 78-80; Educn Chapl 80-85; V Wollescote 85-92; V Fareham SS Pet and Paul *Portsm* from 92. *St Peter and St Paul's Vicarage, 22 Harrison Road, Fareham, Hants PO16 7EJ* Fareham (01329) 280256

FRANKLIN, Richard Heighway. b 54. Southn Univ BA75 MPhil83. Sarum & Wells Th Coll 75. **d** 78 **p** 79. C Thame w Towersey *Ox* 78-81; Asst Chapl Southn Univ *Win* 81-83; Dir of Studies Chich Th Coll 83-89; P-in-c Stalbridge *Sarum* 89-94; V Weymouth H Trin from 94. *Holy Trinity Vicarage, 7 Glebe Close, Weymouth, Dorset DT4 9RL* Weymouth (01305) 760354

FRANKLIN, Simon George. b 54. Bris Univ BA75. Ridley Hall Cam 77. **d** 79 **p** 80. C Woodmansterne *S'wark* 79-83; C St Peter-in-Thanet *Cant* 83-86; R Woodchurch from 86. *The Rectory, Woodchurch, Ashford, Kent TN26 3QJ* Woodchurch (01233) 860257

FRANKLIN, Stephen Alaric (Steve). b 58. Lon Univ BD87. Sarum & Wells Th Coll 87. **d** 89 **p** 90. C Chenies and Lt Chalfont, Latimer and Flaunden *Ox* 89-93; CF from 93. *c/o MOD (Army), Bagshot Park, Bagshot, Surrey GU19 5PL* Bagshot (01276) 471717   Fax 412834

✠**FRANKLIN, Rt Rev William Alfred.** b 16. OBE64. Kelham Th Coll 33. **d** 40 **p** 41 **c** 72. C Bethnal Green St Jo *Lon* 40-42; C Palmers Green St Jo 43-45; Argentina 45-58; Chile 58-65; Colombia 65-78; Adn 66-71; Bp 72-78; Asst Bp Pet 78-86; rtd 86; Asst Bp Cant 86-92; Perm to Offic from 93. *Flat C, 26 The Beach, Walmer, Deal, Kent CT14 7HJ* Deal (01304) 361807

FRANKLIN, William Henry. b 50. Macquarie Univ (NSW) BA78 Birkb Coll Lon MA82. Moore Th Coll Sydney 76 Melbourne Coll of Div 83 Chich Th Coll 85. **d** 86 **p** 87. C S Leamington St Jo *Cov* 86-89; Chapl RN from 89. *Directorate*

Gen, RN Chapl Services, Room 203, Victory Building, HM Naval Base, Portsmouth PO1 3LS Portsmouth (01705) 727903   Fax 727112

FRANKS, Dennis Leslie. b 24. BEM55. Bps' Coll Cheshunt 65. **d** 67 **p** 68. C Anlaby Common St Mark *York* 67-70; V Middlesb Ascension 71-75; P-in-c Whorlton 76-77; V Whorlton w Carlton and Faceby 77-82; V Saltburn-by-the-Sea 82-87; rtd 87. *41 Hunter's Way, Dringhouses, York YO2 2JL* York (01904) 709001

FRANKS, John Edward. b 29. **d** 61 **p** 62. V Upton Grey w Weston Patrick and Tunworth *Win* 66-77; V Upton Grey, Weston Patrick, Tunworth etc 77-79; P-in-c Wolverton cum Ewhurst and Hannington 79-80; R Baughurst, Ramsdell, Wolverton w Ewhurst etc 81-94; rtd 94. *Victoria, 26 Triq Santa Lucia, Naxxar, NXR 02, Malta*

FRANZ, Very Rev Kevin Gerhard. b 53. Edin Univ MA74 BD79. Edin Th Coll 76. **d** 79 **p** 80. C Edin St Martin *Edin* 79-83; R Selkirk 83-90; Provost St Ninian's Cathl Perth *St And* from 90; R Perth St Ninian from 90. *St Ninian's House, 40 Hay Street, Perth PH1 5HS* Perth (01738) 26874

FRASER, Alister Douglas. b 26. Qu Coll Cam BA49 MA55. Tyndale Hall Bris 50. **d** 68 **p** 69. C Weymouth St Jo *Sarum* 68-72; R Kingswood *Glouc* 72-80; V Woodside St Steph 80-84; RD Forest S 84-88; V Cinderford St Steph w Littledean 84-90; rtd 90; Perm to Offic *Ex* from 91. *4 Stevens Cross Close, Sidmouth, Devon EX10 9QJ* Sidmouth (01395) 579568

FRASER, Andrew Thomas. b 52. Newc Univ Aus BA81. St Jo Coll (NSW) ThL79. **d** 81 **p** 82. Australia 81-87; C Prestbury *Glouc* 87-91; C Wotton St Mary 91-92. *79 Victoria Street, Gloucester GL1 4AP* Gloucester (01452) 381884

FRASER, David Ian. b 32. Em Coll Cam BA54 MA58. Oak Hill Th Coll 56. **d** 58 **p** 59. V Preston St Luke *Blackb* 67-71; V Surbiton Hill Ch Ch *S'wark* 71-91; rtd 91. *31 Gosfield Road, Epsom, Surrey KT19 8HF* Epsom (01372) 725620

FRASER, Ernest William Emerson. b 04. AKC27. Westcott Ho Cam 28. **d** 28 **p** 29. V Downe *Roch* 51-57; Perm to Offic *Chich* from 57; rtd 69. *The Goodalls, Ellerslie Lane, Bexhill-on-Sea, E Sussex TN39 4LJ* Bexhill-on-Sea (01424) 211141

FRASER, Geoffrey Michael. b 29. Sarum Th Coll. **d** 59 **p** 60. C Dunsford and Doddiscombsleigh *Ex* 65-70; V Uffculme 70-92; rtd 92. *46 Priory Road, Great Malvern, Worcs WR14 3DB* Malvern (01684) 576302

FRASER, Giles. b 64. Ripon Coll Cuddesdon. **d** 93 **p** 94. C Streetly *Lich* from 93. *36 Foley Road East, Sutton Coldfield, W Midlands B74 3JL* 0121-352 0698

FRASER, Air Marshal Sir Henry Paterson. b 07. KBE61 CB53 AFC37. CEng FRAeS Pemb Coll Cam BA29 MA73. **d** 77 **p** 78. APM Ramsey Deanery *S & M* from 77; Perm to Offic from 94. *803 King's Court, Ramsey, Isle of Man IM8 1LP* Ramsey (01624) 813069

FRASER, Jane Alicia. b 44. Man Univ BA. Glouc Sch of Min. **d** 89 **p** 94. NSM Upton-upon-Severn *Worc* from 89. *Sunnybank House, Holly Green, Upton-on-Severn, Worcester WR8 0PG* Upton-on-Severn (01684) 594715

FRASER, Canon John Sheean. b 23. TCD BA47 MA52. **d** 47 **p** 50. C Dub St Geo *D & G* 47-48; C Dub St Steph 50-52; I Leney and Kilbixy *M & K* 52-59; I Killucan Union 59-65; I Limerick St Mary *L & K* 65-67; Can Res and Preb Limerick Cathl 67-76; Sub-Dean 74-76; Lic to Offic from 82. *5 Ashbrook, Ennis Road, Limerick, Irish Republic* Limerick (61) 453502

FRASER, Lesley. b 34. ALCD62. **d** 62 **p** 63. R Collyhurst St Oswald and St Cath *Man* 67-72; P-in-c Collyhurst St Jas 67-72; R Collyhurst 72-74; RNLI 75-92; rtd 95; Hon C Bispham *Blackb* from 95. *Ingol, 9 Hodgson Road, Blackpool FY1 2LZ* Blackpool (01253) 592538

FRASER, Ross Dominic. b 24. St Jo Coll Morpeth. **d** 47 **p** 48. V Ryhope *Dur* 70-74; P-in-c Elton 74-75; P-in-c Medomsley 75-76; V 76-84; rtd 84. *19 Laburnum Gardens, Low Fell, Gateshead, Tyne & Wear NE9 5TN*

FRASER-SMITH, Keith Montague. b 48. St Jo Coll Dur BA70. Trin Coll Bris DipTh72. **d** 73 **p** 74. C Bishopsworth *Bris* 73-75; CMS 76-84; Egypt 76-80; Jerusalem 80-84; Asst Chapl Marseille w St Raphael, Aix-en-Provence etc *Eur* 84-90; Media Dir Arab World Min 84-94; NSM Worthing Ch the King *Chich* 90-94; Cyprus from 94. *PO Box 7177, Lykavitos, 1642 Nicosia, Cyprus* Nicosia (2) 317092

FRAY, Roger William. b 43. Philippa Fawcett Coll TCert69 Reading Univ BEd76. St Jo Coll Nottm MA95. **d** 95. C Grove *Ox* from 95. *21 Albermarle Drive, Grove, Wantage, Oxon OX12 0NB* Wantage (01235) 769722

FRAY, Vernon Francis. b 41. Southn Coll of Tech HNC62 FCIOB79. S'wark Ord Course 91. **d** 94 **p** 95. NSM Heston *Lon* from 94. *75 Central Avenue, Hounslow, Middx TW3 2QW* 0181-984 5774

FRAY, Mrs Vivienne Jane. b 49. Liv Univ CertEd71 BEd72. W of England Minl Tr Course 91. **d** 94. NSM Glouc St Jas and

All SS *Glouc* from 94. *56 Stonechat Avenue, Abbeydale, Gloucester GL4 9XE* Gloucester (01452) 301075

FRAYLING, Canon Nicholas Arthur. b 44. Ex Univ BA69. Cuddesdon Coll 69. **d** 71 **p** 72. C Peckham St Jo *S'wark* 71-74; V Tooting All SS 74-83; Can Res and Prec Liv Cathl *Liv* 83-87; R Liv Our Lady and St Nic w St Anne 87-90; TR from 90; Hon Can Liv Cathl from 89. *25 Princes Park Mansions, Sefton Park Road, Liverpool L8 3SA* 0151-727 4692 or 236 5287

FRAYNE, Very Rev David. b 34. St Edm Hall Ox BA58 MA62 Birm Univ DipTh60. Qu Coll Birm 58. **d** 60 **p** 61. C E Wickham *S'wark* 60-63; C Lewisham St Jo Southend 63-67; V N Sheen St Phil and All SS 67-73; R Caterham 73-83; RD Caterham 80-83; Hon Can S'wark Cathl 82-83; V Bris St Mary Redcliffe w Temple etc *Bris* 83-92; RD Bedminster 86-92; Hon Can Bris Cathl 91-92; Provost Blackb from 92. *The Provost's House, Preston New Road, Blackburn BB2 6PS* Blackburn (01254) 252502

FRAYNE, Derek Arthur Vivian. b 30. Univ of Wales (Swansea) BA52. Wells Th Coll 52. **d** 54 **p** 55. V Llanharan w Peterston-super-Montem *Llan* 64-79; Chapl St Dav Hosp 79-95; R Canton St Jo 79-95; rtd 95. *31 Cae Syr Dafydd, Cardiff CF1 9QG1* Cardiff (01222) 235369

FRAZER, Ven Albert Henry Victor. b 14. TCD BA38 MA62. CITC 38. **d** 38 **p** 39. I Rathdrum w Glenealy, Derralossary and Laragh *D & G* 66-84; Adn Glendalough 70-84; rtd 83; Chapl Kingston Coll Co Cork from 84. *The Chaplaincy, 17 Kingston College, Michelstown, Co Cork, Irish Republic* Fermoy (25) 24429

FRAZER, David. b 60. QUB BSSc TCD DipTh84. TCD Div Sch. **d** 84 **p** 85. C Taney *D & G* 84-87; C Dub Ch Ch Cathl Gp 87-88; I Clane w Donadea and Coolcarrigan *M & K* from 88. *St Michael's Vicarage, Sallins, Naas, Co Kildare, Irish Republic* Kildare (45) 868276

FRAZER, Ian Martin. b 44. QUB DipTh MTh. **d** 91 **p** 93. Lic to Offic *D & D* from 91. *The Stacks, Deramore Park South, Belfast BT9 5JY* Belfast (01232) 667100

FRAZER, Chan James Stewart. b 27. TCD. **d** 57 **p** 58. I Milltown *Arm* 65-70; Australia 70-74; I Dromore *Clogh* 74-82; RD Kesh 78-82; Bp Dom Chapl 82; I Derryvullen S w Garvary 82-90; Can Clogh Cathl 83-85; Preb 85-94; RD Enniskillen 89-90; I Clogh w Errigal Portclare 90-94; Glebes Sec 91-94; Chan Clogh Cathl 93-94; rtd 94. *34 Clonlee Drive, Belfast BT4 3DA* Belfast (01232) 659593

FRAZER, Milburn Ronald. b 18. Worc Ord Coll 63. **d** 65 **p** 66. C Bexhill St Pet *Chich* 67-71; R Tillington 71-78; Chapl Upper Chine Sch Shanklin 78-84; rtd 85; Chapl Shoreham Coll 86-90; Perm to Offic *Chich* from 92. *34 Overmead, Shoreham-by-Sea, W Sussex BN43 5NS* Brighton (01273) 455023

FREAR, Philip Scott. b 45. Univ of Wales (Lamp) BA66. **d** 80 **p** 81. Hon C Purton *Bris* 80-81; C Rodbourne Cheney 81-85; V Hengrove from 85. *Christ Church Vicarage, 7 Petherton Road, Bristol BS14 9BP* Whitchurch (01275) 832346

FREARSON, Andrew Richard. b 57. BA. Wycliffe Hall Ox. **d** 83 **p** 84. C Acocks Green *Birm* 83-86; C Moseley St Mary 86-89; P-in-c Holme-in-Cliviger *Blackb* from 89. *St John's Vicarage, Burnley Road, Cliviger, Burnley, Lancs BB10 4SU* Burnley (01282) 22467

FREATHY, Nigel Howard. b 46. Lon Univ BA68 CertEd. Sarum & Wells Th Coll 79. **d** 81 **p** 82. C Crediton *Ex* 81-82; C Crediton and Shobrooke 82-84; TV Ex St Thos and Em 84-86; V Beer and Branscombe from 86. *The Vicarage, Mare Lane, Beer, Seaton, Devon EX12 3NB* Seaton (01297) 20996

FREDERICK, Dr John Bassett Moore. b 30. Princeton Univ BA51 Birm Univ PhD73. Gen Th Sem (NY) MDiv54. **d** 54 **p** 55. USA 61-71; R Bletchingley *S'wark* 74-95; Reigate Adnry Ecum Officer 90-95; RD Godstone 92-95; rtd 95. *32 Chestnut Street, Princeton, New Jersey 08542, USA* Princeton (609) 924 7590

FREDERICK, Warren Charles. b 47. Qu Coll Birm 86. **d** 88 **p** 89. C W Leigh *Portsm* 88-91; V N Holmwood *Guildf* from 91. *The Vicarage, Willow Green, North Holmwood, Dorking, Surrey RH5 4JB* Dorking (01306) 882135

FREDRIKSEN, Martin. b 47. St Chad's Coll Dur BA69 DipTh70. **d** 70 **p** 71. C Bideford *Ex* 70-73; C Guildf St Nic *Guildf* 73-76; R Cossington *B & W* 76-82; V Woolavington 76-82; Asst Chapl K Coll Taunton 82-84; C Hatf *St Alb* 84-94; P-in-c Broadstone *Sarum* 94; V from 94. *St John's Vicarage, Macaulay Road, Broadstone, Dorset BH18 8AR* Broadstone (01202) 694109

FREE, Canon James Michael. b 25. K Coll Lon BD50 AKC50. **d** 51 **p** 52. V Pilning *Bris* 67-75; P-in-c Lydiard Millicent w Lydiard Tregoz 75-82; Hon Can Bris Cathl 76-82; Can Res, Prec and Sacr Bris Cathl 82-83; Can Treas 83-90; Bp's Adv for Miss 82-87; Bp's Officer for Miss and Evang 87-89; rtd 90; Perm to Offic *Bris* from 90. *23 Manor Drive, Merriott, Somerset TA16 5PB* Crewkerne (01460) 76053

FREEBAIRN-SMITH, Mrs Jane. b 36. K Coll Lon DipTh59 DipPC86. St Chris Coll Blackheath IDC60. **d** 88 **p** 94. NSM

Uddingston *Glas* 88-91; NSM Cambuslang 88-91; Dioc Missr 88-92; Dioc Past Counsellor 92-95; NSM Baillieston 91-92; C St Mary's Cathl 92-95; TV Hykeham *Linc* from 95. *23 Baildon Crescent, North Hykeham, Lincoln LN6 8HS* Lincoln (01522) 690885

FREEBORN, John Charles Kingon. b 30. G&C Coll Cam BA52 MA56. Ridley Hall Cam 53. **d** 55 **p** 56. R Flixton St Mich *Man* 61-72; C Leic H Apostles *Leic* 72-73; Teacher Greenacres Sch Oldham 73-75; C E Crompton *Man* 73-74; Hon C Ashton St Mich 74-76; Teacher St Jo Sch Ellesmere 75-79; Perm to Offic 77-80; Hd Master H Trin Sch Halifax 80-88; Teacher St Chad's Sch Hove Edge Wakef 88-91; Lic to Offic *Wakef* 80-83; Hon C Sowerby 83-94; NSM Salterhebble All SS from 94; rtd 95. *27 Crossley Hill, Halifax, W Yorkshire HX3 0PL* Halifax (01422) 342489

FREEMAN, Canon Alan John Samuel. b 27. SS Coll Cam BA48 MA52. Sarum Th Coll 50. **d** 52 **p** 53. R Aspley Guise *St Alb* 60-75; RD Fleete 67-70; RD Ampthill 70-75; Hon Can St Alb 74-92; V Boxmoor St Jo 75-92; Chapl Hemel Hempstead Gen Hosp (W Herts Wing) 75-92; RD Berkhamsted *St Alb* 85-92; rtd 92. *3A Queen Street, Leighton Buzzard, Beds LU7 7BZ* Leighton Buzzard (01525) 384799

FREEMAN, Anthony John Curtis. b 46. Ex Coll Ox BA68 MA72. Cuddesdon Coll 70. **d** 72 **p** 73. C Worc St Martin *Worc* 72-74; C Worc St Martin w St Pet 74-75; Bp's Dom Chapl *Chich* 75-78; C-in-c Parklands St Wilfrid CD 78-82; V Durrington 82-89; P-in-c Staplefield Common 89-94; Bp's Adv Continuing Minl Educn 89-93; Asst Dir of Ords 89-93. *The Old Bakery, Somerton Road, North Aston, Bicester, Oxon OX6 4HX* Steeple Aston (01869) 340188 Fax 340198

FREEMAN, Canon Douglas Charles. b 29. Lon Univ BD54 AKC54. **d** 55 **p** 56. R Duloe w Herodsfoot *Truro* 63-70; V Morval 66-70; V St Ives 70-82; P-in-c Lelant 78-80; Hon Can Truro Cathl 80-82; V Forton *Portsm* 82-89; RD Alverstoke 86-89; V Widley w Wymering 89-94; rtd 94. *7 Cleveland Drive, Fareham, Hants PO14 1SW* Fareham (01329) 231322

FREEMAN, Douglas James. b 20. Ox NSM Course 80. **d** 83 **p** 84. NSM Ellesborough *Ox* 83-91; NSM Wendover Deanery from 87; NSM Ellesborough, The Kimbles and Stoke Mandeville from 91. *Chadley, Butlers Cross, Aylesbury, Bucks HP17 0TS* Wendover (01296) 623240

FREEMAN, Gordon Bertie. b 37. CITC BTh95. **d** 95. C Lecale Gp *D & D* from 95. *St Nicholas' Rectory, 48 High Street, Ardglass, Downpatrick, Co Down BT30 7TU* Ardglass (01396) 841311

FREEMAN, James Henry. b 14. **d** 79 **p** 80. Hon C Wandsworth St Steph *S'wark* from 79. *43 Oakhill Road, London SW15 2QJ* 0181-874 1501

FREEMAN, Karl Fredrick. b 57. St Luke's Coll Ex BEd80. **d** 90 **p** 91. C Plymouth St Andr w St Paul and St Geo *Ex* 90-95; C Plymouth St Andr and St Paul Stonehouse 95; TV from 95. *18 Glenhurst Road, Plymouth PL3 5LT* Plymouth (01752) 267025

FREEMAN, Malcolm Robin. b 48. St And NSM Tr Scheme 85. **d** 88 **p** 89. NSM Kirkcaldy *St And* from 88; NSM Kinghorn from 91. *Cherrybank Cottage, Main Street, Auchtertool, Fife KY2 5XW* Glenrothes (01592) 781439

FREEMAN (nee ADAMS), Mrs Margaret Anne. b 27. AKC48. Gilmore Ho. **dss** 82 **d** 87 **p** 94. Gt Yarmouth *Nor* 80-87; rtd 87; Hon Par Dn Malborough w S Huish, W Alvington and Churchstow *Ex* 87-94; Hon C from 94. *26 Weymouth Park, Hope Park, Kingsbridge, Devon TQ7 3HD* Kingsbridge (01548) 561274

FREEMAN, Michael Charles. b 36. Magd Coll Cam BA61 MA68 Lon Univ BD69. Clifton Th Coll 67. **d** 69 **p** 70. C Bedworth *Cov* 69-72; C Morden *S'wark* 72-77; P-in-c Westcombe Park St Geo 77-85; V Kingston Vale St Jo 85-94. *Flat 3, 2 Westbourne Park Road, Bournemouth NH4 8HG* Bournemouth (01202) 752113

FREEMAN, Michael Curtis. b 51. Lanc Univ BA72. Cuddesdon Coll 72. **d** 75 **p** 76. C Walton St Mary *Liv* 75-78; C Hednesford *Lich* 78-81; TV Solihull *Birm* 81-86; V Yardley Wood 86-90; V Farnworth *Liv* from 90. *The Vicarage, Coroners Lane, Farnworth, Widnes, Cheshire WA8 9HY* 0151-424 2735

FREEMAN, Michael Raymond. b 58. Chu Coll Cam BA80 MA84 Ox Univ BA87. St Steph Ho Ox 85. **d** 88 **p** 89. C Clifton All SS w St Jo *Bris* 88-92; TV Elland *Wakef* from 92. *All Saints Vicarage, Charles Street, Elland, W Yorkshire HX5 0JF* Elland (01422) 373184

FREEMAN, Mrs Pamela Mary. b 45. W Midl Minl Tr Course 83. **dss** 86 **d** 87 **p** 94. Cannock *Lich* 86-88; Par Dn 87-88; Min for Deaf (Salop Adnry) 88-95; Par Dn Oxon and Shelton 88-94; C 94-95; TV Stafford from 95. *The Vicarage, Victoria Terrace, Stafford ST16 3HA* Stafford (01785) 52523

FREEMAN, Philip Michael. b 25. Jes Coll Cam BA50 MA54. Qu Coll Birm 50. **d** 52 **p** 53. P-in-c Bottesford w Ashby *Linc* 66-73; TR 73-75; P-in-c Warw St Nic *Cov* 75-76; TV Warw

77-87; P-in-c Claverdon w Preston Bagot 87-90; rtd 90; Perm to Offic *Cov* from 90. *38 Cocksparrow Street, Warwick CV34 4ED* Warwick (01926) 411431

FREEMAN, Philip Martin. b 54. Westcott Ho Cam 76. **d** 79 **p** 80. C Stanley *Liv* 79-82; C Bromborough *Ches* 82-84; Chapl Halton Gen Hosp 84-91; V Runcorn H Trin *Ches* 84-91; R Ashton upon Mersey St Martin from 91. *St Martin's Rectory, 367 Glebelands Road, Sale, Cheshire M33 5GG* 0161-973 4204

FREEMAN, Richard Alan. b 52. Ripon Coll Cuddesdon. **d** 83 **p** 84. C Crayford *Roch* 83-86; V Slade Green 86-94; R Eynsford w Farningham and Lullingstone from 94. *The Rectory, Pollyhaugh, Eynsford, Dartford DA4 0HE* Farningham (01322) 863050

FREEMAN, Canon Robert John. b 52. St Jo Coll Dur BSc74 Fitzw Coll Cam BA76 MA. Ridley Hall Cam 74. **d** 77 **p** 78. C Blackpool St Jo *Blackb* 77-81; TV Chigwell *Chelmsf* 81-85; V Leic Martyrs *Leic* from 85; Hon Can Leic Cathl from 94. *The Vicarage, 17 Westcotes Drive, Leicester LE3 0QT* Leicester (0116) 254 6162

FREEMAN, Ronald Mercer. b 24. Trin Coll Cam BA45 MA50. Wycliffe Hall Ox 47. **d** 49 **p** 50. R Kersal Moor *Man* 67-78; V Walmersley 78-90; rtd 90. *3 High Avenue, Bolton BL2 5AZ* Bolton (01204) 385341

FREEMAN, Shirley Beckett. b 14. Ch Coll Cam BA36 MA40. Ridley Hall Cam 36. **d** 38 **p** 39. R Compton Valence *Sarum* 65-75; R Long Bredy w Lt Bredy and Kingston Russell 65-75; rtd 74. *Eckling Grange, Norwich Road, Dereham, Norfolk NR20 3BB* Dereham (01362) 691189

FREEMAN, Terence. b 40. Wells Th Coll 67. **d** 70 **p** 71. C Hanham *Bris* 70-75; C Cockington *Ex* 75-77; R Sampford Spiney w Horrabridge 77-89; V Wembury from 89; Hon Chapl RN from 89. *The Vicarage, 63 Church Road, Wembury, Plymouth PL9 0JJ* Plymouth (01752) 862319

FREER, Andrew Selwyn Bruce. b 26. Wells Th Coll 55. **d** 57 **p** 58. R Byfield *Pet* 62-71; V Brackley St Pet w St Jas 71-81; R Bincombe w Broadwey, Upwey and Buckland Ripers *Sarum* 81-91; rtd 91. *1 Grove Cottages, Mill Lane, Chetnole, Sherborne, Dorset DT9 6PB* Yeovil (01935) 873468

FREER, Bernard. b 22. St Aid Birkenhead 60. **d** 62 **p** 63. V Stanley *Derby* 65-73; P-in-c Scropton 73; P-in-c Marston on Dove 73; V Marston on Dove w Scropton 74-92; RD Longford 81-86; rtd 92. *95 Scropton Road, Hatton, Derby DE65 5GJ* Burton-on-Trent (01283) 812681

FREETH, Barry James. b 35. Birm Univ BA60. Tyndale Hall Bris 60. **d** 62 **p** 64. C Selly Hill St Steph *Birm* 62-63; C Birm St Jo Ladywood 63-71; Chapl RAF 71-75; P-in-c Crudwell w Ashley *Bris* 75-81; P-in-c Lanreath *Truro* 81-84; R 84-87; P-in-c Pelynt 81-84; V 84-87; R Harvington, Norton and Lenchwick *Worc* 87-93; V Ramsden, Finstock and Fawler, Leafield etc *Ox* from 93. *The Vicarage, Mount Skippett, Ramsden, Chipping Norton, Oxon OX7 3AP* Witney (01993) 868687

FREETH, Ven John Stanton. b 40. Selw Coll Cam BA62 MA66. Ridley Hall Cam 64. **d** 66 **p** 67. C Gillingham St Mark *Roch* 66-72; TV Heslington *York* 72-80; Chapl York Univ 72-80; S Africa from 80; Adn Athlone from 88. *Address temp unknown*

FREETH, Richard Hudson de Wear. b 13. Worc Ord Coll. **d** 64 **p** 65. V Mayland *Chelmsf* 67-76; V Steeple 67-76; rtd 76. *71 College Road, Epsom, Surrey KT17 4HQ* Epsom (01372) 726934

FRENCH, Basil Charles Elwell. b 19. Edin Th Coll LTh44. **d** 45 **p** 46. S Rhodesia 59-65; Rhodesia 65-80; Zimbabwe 80-85; rtd 85; Hon C Wrington w Butcombe *B & W* 85-88; Perm to Offic 88-92; Perm to Offic *Ex* from 92. *9 Elmbridge Gardens, Exeter EX4 4AE* Exeter (01392) 215933

FRENCH, Clive Anthony. b 43. AKC70. St Aug Coll Cant 70. **d** 71 **p** 72. C Monkseaton St Mary *Newc* 71-73; Dioc Youth Adv 73-76; Chapl RN from 76; Dir of Ords RN from 84. *Directorate Gen, RN Chapl Services, Room 203, Victory Building, HM Naval Base, Portsmouth PO1 3LS* Portsmouth (01705) 727903 Fax 727112

FRENCH, Canon Dendle Charles. b 29. Lon Univ BD56. ALCD55. **d** 56 **p** 57. V Sedgeford w Southmere *Nor* 66-71; R Gt Ringstead 66-71; TV Thetford 71-74; Chapl Hockerill Coll Bishop's Stortford 74-78; P-in-c St Paul's Walden *St Alb* 78-85; V 85-94; RD Hitchin 84-89; Hon Can St Alb 91-94; rtd 94; Chapl Glamis Castle from 94. *Woodfaulds, Glamis, Forfar, Angus DD8 1RW* Forfar (01307) 840485

FRENCH, Derek John. b 47. Ripon Coll Cuddesdon DipMin95. **d** 95. C Stand *Man* from 95. *67 Bury Old Road, Whitefield, Manchester M45 6TB* 0161-798 9261

FRENCH, George Leslie. b 47. AIFST NE Lon Poly BSc70. S'wark Ord Course 86. **d** 89 **p** 90. NSM Reading St Barn *Ox* from 89. *Hawthorne House, 2 Cutbush Close, Lower Earley, Reading RG6 4XA* Reading (01734) 861886

FRENCH, Janet Mary. *See* DRIVER, Janet Mary

FRENCH, Jonathan David Seabrook. b 60. Westcott Ho Cam 84. **d** 87 **p** 88. C Loughton St Jo *Chelmsf* 87-90; Chapl St Bede's Ch for the Deaf Clapham 90-92; C Richmond St Mary w St Matthias and St Jo *S'wark* from 92; Chapl amongst the Deaf from 92. *19 Old Deer Park Gardens, Richmond, Surrey TW9 2TN* 0181-940 8359

FRENCH, Ms Judith Karen. b 60. St D Coll Lamp BA89. St Steph Ho Ox 89. **d** 91 **p** 94. Par Dn Botley *Portsm* 91-94; C Bilton *Cov* from 94. *St Mark's House, 51 Falstaff Drive, Rugby, Warks CV22 6LJ* Rugby (01788) 810761

FRENCH, Michael Anders. b 61. Ch Coll Cam BA83 MA87. Ridley Hall Cam BA91. **d** 92 **p** 93. C Norbury *Ches* from 92. *27 Davenport Road, Hazel Grove, Stockport, Cheshire SK7 4HA* 0161-483 6922

FRENCH, Peter Robert. b 65. Man Univ BTh87. Qu Coll Birm 88. **d** 90 **p** 91. C Unsworth *Man* 90-93; C Bury Ch King w H Trin 93-95; V Bury Ch King from 95. *St Thomas's Vicarage, Pimhole Road, Bury, Lancs BL9 7EY* 0161-764 1157

FRENCH, Philip Colin. b 50. Sarum & Wells Th Coll 81. **d** 83 **p** 84. C Llansamlet *S & B* 83-86; P-in-c Waunarllwydd 86-87; V from 87. *St Barnabas' Vicarage, Waunarllwyd, Swansea SA5 4SY* Gowerton (01792) 872251

FRENCH, Richard John (Dick). b 34. Open Univ BA82. Tyndale Hall Bris 62. **d** 64 **p** 65. C Rustington *Chich* 64-68; C Walton H Trin *Ox* 68-72; V Grove from 72. *The Vicarage, Grove, Wantage, Oxon OX12 7LQ* Wantage (01235) 766484

FRENCH, Stephen Robert James. b 52. St Jo Coll Nottm. **d** 87 **p** 88. C Chell *Lich* 87-91; TV 91-94; V Wednesfield Heath from 94. *Holy Trinity Vicarage, Bushbury Road, Heath Town, Wolverhampton WV10 0LY* Wolverhampton (01902) 738313

FREND, Prof William Hugh Clifford. b 16. TD59. FSA52 FRHistS54 FRSE79 FBA83 Keble Coll Ox BA37 DPhil40 MA51 DD66 Cam Univ BD64 Edin Univ Hon DD74. **d** 82 **p** 83. Prof Ecclesiastical Hist Glas Univ 69-84; NSM Aberfoyle *St And* 82-84; P-in-c Barnwell w Thurning and Luddington *Pet* 84-90; rtd 90. *The Clerk's Cottage, Little Wilbraham, Cambridge CB1 5CB* Cambridge (01223) 811731

FRERE, Christopher Michael Hanbury. b 21. Worc Th Coll 65. **d** 67 **p** 68. C Spilsby w Hundleby *Linc* 67-71; V N Kelsey 71-76; V Cadney 71-76; P-in-c Aisthorpe w W Thorpe and Scampton 75-79; P-in-c Brattleby 75-79; R Fillingham 76-78; V Ingham w Cammeringham 76-78; RD Lawres 78-84; V Ingham w Cammeringham w Fillingham 79-86; R Aisthorpe w Scampton w Thorpe le Fallows etc 79-86; rtd 86. *164 Newark Road, North Hykeham, Lincoln LN6 8LZ* Lincoln (01522) 689145

FRESTON, John Samuel Kern. b 28. Lich Th Coll 70. **d** 72 **p** 73. C Walsall *Lich* 72-75; TV Trunch w Swafield *Nor* 75-77; TV Trunch 77-82; R W Winch 82-91; Chapl St Jas Hosp King's Lynn 82-85; Qu Eliz Hosp King's Lynn 85-90; rtd 91; Perm to Offic *Nor* from 91. *71 The Howdale, Downham Market, Norfolk PE38 9AH* Downham Market (01366) 385936

FRETWELL, Brian George. b 34. TD. CEng MIMechE. Chich Th Coll 79. **d** 81 **p** 82. C Bude Haven *Truro* 81-82; C Saltash 82-85; C Walthamstow St Sav *Chelmsf* 85-87; V Doncaster Intake *Sheff* from 87. *The Vicarage, Kingston Road, Intake, Doncaster, S Yorkshire DN2 6LS* Doncaster (01302) 323167

FRETWELL, Cynthia Mary. b 37. E Midl Min Tr Course 90. **d** 91 **p** 94. Chapl Asst Doncaster R Infirmary 91-92; Chapl Asst Doncaster R Infirmary & Montague Hosp NHS Trust 92-95; Chapl from 95; Chapl Asst Tickhill Road & St Cath Hosps from 91. *The Vicarage, Kingston Road, Intake, Doncaster, S Yorkshire DN2 6LS* Doncaster (01302) 323167 or 366666

FREWIN, William Charles. b 46. Trin Coll Bris 84. **d** 86 **p** 87. C Southchurch H Trin *Chelmsf* 86-89; C Shrub End 89-91; R W Bergholt from 91. *The Rectory, 1 Church Close, West Bergholt, Colchester CO6 3JZ* Colchester (01206) 240273

FREY, Christopher Ronald (Chris). b 44. AKC69 Uppsala Univ BD73 MTh77. St Aug Coll Cant 69. **d** 70 **p** 71. C Addington *Ox* 70-72; Lic to Offic *Eur* 73-78; Chapl Stockholm w Uppsala 78-85; Can Brussels Cathl 81-85; Lic to Offic *Carl* 85-89; Chapl Casterton Sch 85-89; Chapl Epsom Coll Surrey 89-91; Chapl Worksop Coll Notts from 91. *2 North Copse, Worksop College, Worksop, Notts S80 3AP* Worksop (01909) 479306 or 472286

FRIARS, Ian Malcolm George. b 50. Sarum & Wells Th Coll 83. **d** 85 **p** 86. C Norton *St Alb* 85-88; C Ramsey *Ely* 88-90; TV The Ramseys and Upwood 90-93; P-in-c Cottenham 93-94; R from 94. *The Rectory, 6 High Street, Cottenham, Cambridge CB4 4SA* Cottenham (01954) 50454

FRIARS, Robert John. b 32. Trin Coll Cam BA55 MA59. Wells Th Coll 55. **d** 57 **p** 58. C St Andr Holborn *Lon* 62-70; Sen Youth Chapl 65-70; TV Hackney 70-79; V Sompting *Chich* 79-91; rtd 92. *47 Cowslip Close, Cansbrook Green, Gosport, Hants PO13 0BQ* Worthing (01903) 234511

FRICKER, Canon David Duncan. b 27. Lon Univ BA53. Ridley Hall Cam 53. **d** 55 **p** 56. C Ecclesfield *Sheff* 55-58; C Luton St Mary *St Alb* 58-61; V Luton St Paul 61-64; R Bedf St Pet 64-75; RD Bedf 69-79; Hon Can St Alb 74-88; P-in-c Bedf St Paul 75-79; R Bedf St Pet w St Cuth 75-88; R Brightling, Dallington, Mountfield & Netherfield *Chich* from 88; RD Dallington from 88. *The Rectory, Brightling, Robertsbridge, E Sussex TN32 5HE* Brightling (0142482) 281

FRIEND, Frederick James. b 41. BA. Oak Hill NSM Course. **d** 82 **p** 83. NSM Hughenden *Ox* from 82. *The Chimes, Cryers Hill Road, High Wycombe, Bucks HP15 6JS* Naphill (01494) 563168

FRIEND, Graham Arthur. b 39. Bernard Gilpin Soc Dur 59 Chich Th Coll 60. **d** 63 **p** 64. C Syston *Leic* 63-65; V 82-83; C Barnstaple St Pet w H Trin *Ex* 65-67; C Clewer St Andr *Ox* 67-74; R E and W Hendred 74-78; R Wantage Downs 78-82; P-in-c Mears Ashby and Hardwick and Sywell etc *Pet* 92-94; R from 95. *The Vicarage, 46 Wellingborough Road, Mears Ashby, Northampton NN6 0DZ* Northampton (01604) 812907

FRIENDSHIP, Roger Geoffrey (Brother John-Francis). b 46. ACII72. W Midl Minl Tr Course 90. **d** 93 **p** 94. SSF from 76; NSM Harborne St Faith and St Laur *Birm* 93-94; Asst Novice Guardian Hilfield Friary from 94. *The Friary, Hilfield, Dorchester, Dorset DT2 7BE* Cerne Abbas (01300) 341345

FRIESS, Herbert Friedrich. b 09. Leipzig Univ BD. **d** 41 **p** 42. Dean Killala *T, K & A* 67-73; I Achill w Dugort, Castlebar and Turlough 73-79; rtd 79. *Mulrany, Westport, Co Mayo, Irish Republic* Westport (98) 36126

FRIGGENS, Canon Maurice Anthony. b 40. Sheff Univ BA65. Westcott Ho Cam 65. **d** 67 **p** 68. C Stocksbridge *Sheff* 67-70; C St Buryan, St Levan and Sennen *Truro* 70-72; R 72-84; RD Penwith 82-84; R St Columb Major w St Wenn 84-91; Hon Can Truro Cathl from 87; Dioc Dir of Ords from 87; V St Cleer from 91. *The Vicarage, St Cleer, Liskeard, Cornwall PL14 5DJ* Liskeard (01579) 343240

FRITH, Christopher John Cokayne. b 44. Ex Coll Ox BA65 MA69. Ridley Hall Cam 66. **d** 68 **p** 69. C Crookes St Thos *Sheff* 68-71; C Rusholme *Man* 71-74; R Haughton St Mary 74-85; R Brampton St Thos *Derby* from 85. *The Rectory, 481 Chatsworth Road, Chesterfield, Derbyshire S40 3AD* Chesterfield (01246) 232717

FRITH, David William. b 65. K Coll Lon BD87 PGCE88. Westcott Ho Cam 88 Lambeth STh90. **d** 90 **p** 91. C St Jo Wood *Lon* 90-93; C Maidstone All SS and St Phil w Tovil *Cant* from 93. *16 Greenside, Maidstone, Kent ME15 7SA* Maidstone (01622) 761476

FRITH, Ivy Florence. b 24. CertEd56. Lambeth DipTh93 St Chris Coll Blackheath 48. **dss** 79 **d** 87 **p** 94. St Alb Abbey *St Alb* 79-82; Truro St Paul and St Clem *Truro* 82-84; C Truro St Mary from 85; Asst Dioc Dir of Ords from 85; Dioc Lay Min Adv from 85; Hon Cathl Dn Truro Cathl from 87; MU Chapl from 91; NSM Feock from 94. *42 Tregolls Road, Truro, Cornwall TR1 1LA* Truro (01872) 79463

FRITH, Ven Richard Michael Cokayne. b 49. Fitzw Coll Cam BA72 MA76. St Jo Coll Nottm 72. **d** 74 **p** 75. C Mortlake w E Sheen *S'wark* 74-78; TV Thamesmead 78-83; TR Keynsham *B & W* 83-92; Preb Wells Cathl from 91; Adn Taunton from 92. *4 Westerkirk Gate, Staplegrove, Taunton, Somerset TA2 6BQ* Taunton (01823) 323838 Fax 325420

FRIZELLE, Canon Thomas Herbert. b 07. TCD BA36 MA40. **d** 38 **p** 39. I Dundonald *D & D* 51-80; Treas Down Cathl 74-80; rtd 80. *24 Killeaton Park, Derriaghy, Dunmurry, Belfast BT17 9HE* Belfast (01232) 621233

FROGGATT, Jeffrey. b 27. Ch Coll Cam BA48 MA52. Ridley Hall Cam 49. **d** 51 **p** 52. V Malin Bridge *Sheff* 62-73; Ind Chapl 73-79; V Wortley 73-79; R Todwick 79-85; V Dore 85-92; rtd 92. *20 Bocking Lane, Sheffield S8 7BH* Sheffield (0114) 262 0914

FROGGATT, Peter Michael. b 65. St Hild Coll Dur BA86 PGCE88. Wycliffe Hall Ox BTh95. **d** 95. C Bebington *Ches* from 95. *8 Rolleston Drive, Bebington, Wirral, Merseyside L63 3DB* 0151-645 6478

FROOM, Ian Leonard John. b 42. Sarum Th Coll 69. **d** 71 **p** 72. C Gillingham and Fifehead Magdalen *Sarum* 71-75; C Parkstone St Pet w Branksea and St Osmund 75-78; V Sedgley St Mary *Lich* 78-85; TV Weston-super-Mare Cen Par *B & W* 85-94. *25 Greenhill Close, Weston-super-Mare, Avon BS22 0PE* Weston-super-Mare (01934) 513133

FROST, Alan Sydney. b 26. K Coll Lon BD50 AKC50. **d** 51 **p** 52. Asst Chapl Mersey Miss to Seamen 63-66; rtd 91. *Address excluded by request*

FROST, David J. b 48. **d** 86 **p** 87. Hon C Upper Norwood All SS *S'wark* 86-89; C Battersea St Luke 90-94; V Shirley St Geo from 94. *St George's Vicarage, The Glade, Croydon CR0 7QJ* 0181-654 8747

FROST, David Richard. b 54. Ridley Hall Cam 84. **d** 86 **p** 87. C Burgess Hill St Andr *Chich* 86-90; TV Rye 90-94; V Bexhill St Steph from 94. *The Vicarage, 67 Woodsgate Park, Bexhill-on-Sea, E Sussex TN39 4DL* Bexhill-on-Sea (01424) 211186

FROST, Derek Charles. b 47. Lich Th Coll. **d** 71 **p** 72. C Woodley St Jo the Ev *Ox* 71-76; V Bampton w Clanfield 76-81; V Minster Lovell and Brize Norton 81-88; TV Upper Kennett *Sarum* 88-92; P-in-c Seend and Bulkington from 92. *The Vicarage, High Street, Seend, Melksham, Wilts SN12 6NR* Devizes (01380) 828615

FROST, Ven George. b 35. Dur Univ BA56 MA61. Linc Th Coll 57. **d** 60 **p** 61. C Barking St Marg *Chelmsf* 60-64; C-in-c Marks Gate CD 64-70; V Tipton St Matt *Lich* 70-77; V Penn 77-87; RD Trysull 84-87; Preb Lich Cathl 85-87; Hon Can Lich Cathl from 87; Adn Salop from 87; V Tong from 87. *Tong Vicarage, Shifnal, Shropshire TF11 8PW* Albrighton (01902) 372622 Fax 374021

FROST, James Michael. b 29. Liv Univ BA51 DipEd52 DUP54. NE Ord Course 81. **d** 84 **p** 85. NSM Huntington *York* 84-89; TV Heworth 89-95; rtd 95. *3 Elmpark Way, York YO3 0DY* York (01904) 414667

FROST, Jonathan Hugh. b 64. Aber Univ BD88. Ridley Hall Cam CTMin93. **d** 93 **p** 94. C W Bridgford *S'well* from 93; Police Chapl Trent Division from 94. *26 Stanley Road, Nottingham NG2 6DF* Nottingham (0115) 923 3592

FROST, Julian. b 36. Solicitor 57 Bris Univ BA61 MA65 Lon Univ CertEd70. Clifton Th Coll 64. **d** 65 **p** 66. C Welling *Roch* 65-69; Hon C 70-73; Dep Dir Schs Coun RE Project Lanc Univ 73-78; V New Beckenham St Paul from 78. *St Paul's Vicarage, Brackley Road, Beckenham, Kent BR3 1RB* 0181-650 3400

FROST, Michael John (Mike). b 42. Westmr Coll Ox TCert64. Local NSM Course 92. **d** 95. NSM Harwood *Man* from 95. *62 Appledore Drive, Bolton BL2 4HH* Bolton (01204) 535214

FROST, Ronald Andrew. b 48. Can Univ DipRS77 Univ of S Carolina BTh81. Ridley Hall Cam 86. **d** 87 **p** 88. C Gt Wilbraham *Ely* 87-89; P-in-c Stow Longa 89-91; V from 91; P-in-c Kimbolton 89-91; V from 91. *The Vicarage, Kimbolton, Huntingdon, Cambs PE18 0HB* Huntingdon (01480) 860279

FROST, Stanley. b 37. MIBiol FAEB Univ of Wales MSc Liv Univ PhD. N Ord Course 79. **d** 82 **p** 83. NSM Lower Kersal *Man* 82-87; NSM Patricroft 87-89; NSM Convenor (Dio Man) from 87; Perm to Offic from 89. *5 Moorside Road, Kersal, Salford M7 0PJ* 0161-792 3107

FROST, Thomas Laurence. b 20. Linc Th Coll 60. **d** 62 **p** 63. V Knaresborough H Trin *Ripon* 69-78; R Stoke Climsland *Truro* 78-79; Chapl Sliema *Eur* 79-81; R Kirriemuir *St And* 81-85; rtd 85. *Ramley House Nursing Home, Ramley Road, Pennington, Lymington, Hants S04 8LH* Lymington (01590) 677645

FROST, Preb William Selwyn. b 29. Wells Th Coll 61. **d** 62 **p** 63. C Cheddleton *Lich* 62-67; V Longdon-upon-Tern 67-81; R Rodington 67-81; RD Wrockwardine 77-84; Preb Lich Cathl from 81; R Longdon-upon-Tern, Rodington, Uppington etc 81-84; R Whittington St Jo 84-86; C Trysull 86-89; TV Wombourne w Trysull and Bobbington from 89. *The Vicarage, Trysull, Wolverhampton WV5 7HR* Wombourne (01902) 892647

FROSTICK, Alan Norman. b 25. Ripon Hall Ox 74. **d** 75 **p** 76. C Crewkerne w Wayford *B & W* 75-78; P-in-c Brompton Regis w Upton and Skilgate 78-80; V Buttershaw St Aid *Bradf* 80-83; V Aylesham *Cant* 83-85; P-in-c Adisham 84-85; R Aylesham w Adisham 85-90; rtd 90. *18 Hawthorn Close, St Marys Bay, Romney Marsh, Kent TN29 0SZ* Dymchurch (01303) 875158

FROSTICK, Canon John George. b 23. Wells Th Coll 52. **d** 54 **p** 55. V Frisby-on-the-Wreake w Kirby Bellars *Leic* 58-71; V Shepshed 71-83; Hon Can Leic Cathl 80-83; R Kirton w Falkenham *St E* 83-90; rtd 90. *68 Melton Road, Barrow-upon-Soar, Loughborough, Leics LE12 8NX* Quorn (01509) 620110

FROSTICK, Paul Andrew. b 52. CertEd. Ripon Hall Ox 74 Ripon Coll Cuddesdon 75. **d** 77 **p** 78. C Shepton Mallet *B & W* 77-80; TV Barton Mills, Beck Row w Kenny Hill etc *St E* 80-85; TV Mildenhall 85-86; TV Raveningham *Nor* 86-89; V Bottisham *Ely* 89-90; P-in-c Lode and Longmeadow 89-90; V Bottisham and Lode w Long Meadow 90-94. *Address temp unknown*

FROUD, Andrew William. b 65. Mansf Coll Ox BA87 St Cath Coll Cam MPhil92. Westcott Ho Cam 90. **d** 93 **p** 94. C Almondbury w Farnley Tyas *Wakef* from 93. *30 Benomley Road, Huddersfield HD5 8LS* Huddersfield (01484) 537773

FROUD, James George (Jimmy). b 23. MBE89. **d** 54 **p** 55. Hong Kong 54-58; C All Hallows by the Tower etc *Lon* 58-61; Chapl Durning Hall Chr Community Cen Forest Gate 61-82; P-in-c Forest Gate St Jas *Chelmsf* 61-66; Chapl Forest Gate Hosp Lon 61-69; Chapl Aston Charities Trust from 82; NSM Barking St Marg w St Patr *Chelmsf* from 91. *37 The Drive, Loughton, Essex IG10 1HB* 0181-508 6479

FROUDE (nee WOOLCOCK), Mrs Christine Ann. b 47. ACII73. S Dios Minl Tr Scheme 92. **d** 95. NSM Stoke Bishop *Bris* from 95. *2 Bramble Drive, Bristol BS9 1RE* Bristol (0117) 968 5449

FROWLEY, Peter Austin. b 32. CEng61 MIMechE61. W Midl Minl Tr Course 82. **d** 84 **p** 85. NSM Tardebigge *Worc* 84-87; P-in-c 87-88; NSM Redditch St Steph 84-87; Hong Kong 88-92; V St Minver *Truro* from 92. *The Vicarage, St Minver, Wadebridge, Cornwall PL27 6QH* Trebetherick (01208) 862398

FRY, Barry James. b 49. ACIB. Ripon Coll Cuddesdon 81. **d** 83 **p** 84. C Highcliffe w Hinton Admiral *Win* 83-87; V Southn St Barn from 87. *St Barnabas's Vicarage, 12 Rose Road, Southampton SO2 1AE* Southampton (01703) 223107

FRY, David John. b 36. Lon Univ BSc59. Wells Th Coll 61. **d** 62 **p** 63. C Radstock w Writhlington *B & W* 62-64; C Kettering SS Pet and Paul *Pet* 64-66; Hd Master Swinton Middle Sch Mexborough 73-78. *c/o Britannia Inn, Elterwater, Ambleside, Cumbria LA22 9HP* Langdale (015394) 37210

FRY, Mrs Florence Marion. b 24. W Midl Minl Tr Course 87. **d** 88 **p** 94. Chapl and Welfare Officer to the Deaf 70-94; Chapl Cov Cathl *Cov* 88-94; Chmn Cov Coun of Chs 88-91; rtd 94. *37 Grace Gardens, Bishop's Stortford, Herts CM23 3EU* Bishop's Stortford (01279) 652315

FRY, Canon James Reinhold. b 30. St Cuth Soc Dur BSc53 MA70. Oak Hill Th Coll 55. **d** 57 **p** 58. C Bromley St Jo *Roch* 57-60; V Deptford St Luke *S'wark* 60-66; V Chalk *Roch* from 66; RD Gravesend 81-91; Hon Can Roch Cathl from 87. *The Vicarage, 2A Vicarage Lane, Gravesend, Kent DA12 4TF* Gravesend (01474) 567906

FRY, Miss Joan Aileen. b 29. Bedf Coll Lon BA50. Qu Coll Birm 79. **dss** 82 **d** 87 **p** 94. Colindale St Matthias *Lon* 82-87; Hendon St Mary 84-87; Hon Par Dn Swanage and Studland *Sarum* 87-95; Hon C Bridport from 95. *21 St James's Park, Bridport, Dorset DT6 3UR* Bridport (01308) 458614

FRY, Michael John. b 59. Nottm Univ BA80 Sheff Univ CQSW83 Cam Univ BA85. Westcott Ho Cam 83. **d** 86 **p** 87. C Upholland *Liv* 86-89; C Dovecot 89-91; TV St Luke in the City from 91. *2 Minster Court, Crown Street, Liverpool L7 3QB* 0151-709 9665

FRY, Nigel Edward. b 57. E Warks Coll DipGD78. St Jo Coll Nottm DCM93. **d** 93 **p** 94. C Wellingborough All Hallows *Pet* from 93. *2 Troon Crescent, Wellingborough, Northants NN8 5WG* Wellingborough (01933) 679614

FRY, Roger Joseph Hamilton. b 29. Em Coll Cam BA52 MA56. Clifton Th Coll 52. **d** 54 **p** 55. V Bowling St Jo *Bradf* 61-87; V Ingleton w Chapel le Dale 87-95; rtd 95. *5 Margerison Crescent, Ilkley, W Yorkshire LS29 8QZ* Ilkley (01943) 608738

FRY, Roger Owen. b 30. Sarum Th Coll 58. **d** 60 **p** 61. P-in-c Weston-in-Gordano *B & W* 64-70; R Clapton-in-Gordano 64-70; R Portishead 64-80; V Weston Zoyland w Chedzoy 80-94; rtd 94; Perm to Offic *B & W* from 95. *Two Jays, 37A Wellow Lane, Peasedown St John, Bath BA2 8HY*

FRY, Stephen. b 57. St Steph Ho Ox 83. **d** 86 **p** 87. C Wood Green St Mich w Bounds Green St Gabr etc *Lon* 86-89; C Kentish Town St Jo 89-93; C Kentish Town 93. *318 Fellows Court, Weymouth Terrace, London E2 8LA* 0171-739 2662

FRYAR, John Davies. b 53. St Steph Ho Ox 77. **d** 80 **p** 81. C Bidston *Ches* 80-81; C Thame w Towersey *Ox* 81-84; C Dorchester 84-85; TV 85-88; TR Catford (Southend) and Downham *S'wark* from 88. *St John's Rectory, 353 Bromley Road, London SE6 2RP* 0181-698 3898

FRYDAY, Mrs Barbara Yvonne. b 47. Ch of Ireland Tr Coll TCert67. CITC 90. **d** 92 **p** 93. Bp's VC Cashel Cathl and Educn Officer from 92; NSM Cashel w Magorban, Tipperary, Clonbeg etc *C & O* from 93. *The Beeches, Kilpatrick, Dundrum, Co Tipperary, Irish Republic* Tipperary (62) 71332

FRYER, Anthony Charles. b 18. RMA. Wycliffe Hall Ox. **d** 60 **p** 60. C Furze Platt *Ox* 60-62; V Shinfield 62-73; Perm to Offic *Pet* 85-86 and from 91; P-in-c Charwelton w Fawsley and Preston Capes 86-91. *Byfield House, Byfield, Daventry, Northants NN11 6XN* Byfield (01327) 60244

FRYER, Dr Charles Eric John. b 14. Lon Univ BA54 PhD84. Linc Th Coll 62. **d** 63 **p** 64. C Finham *Cov* 63-66; Perm to Offic *S'well* 66-75; Lic to Offic 75-79; R Killin *St And* from 79; R Lochearnhead 79-89. *The Shieling, Crianlarich, Perthshire FK20 8RU* Crianlarich (018383) 237

FRYER, George. b 33. St Jo Coll Cam BA57 MA61. Ox NSM Course 73. **d** 76 **p** 77. NSM Wallingford *Ox* 76-79; C Wokingham St Paul 79-83; V Linc St Swithin *Linc* 83-88; P-in-c Walsden *Wakef* from 88. *The Vicarage, 6 Stoneley Drive, Todmorden, Lancs OL14 7UR* Todmorden (01706) 817776

FRYER, Mrs Jenifer Anne (Jeni). b 43. N Ord Course 89. **d** 92 **p** 94. Par Dn Ecclesfield *Sheff* 92-94; C 94-95; Chapl R Hallamshire Hosp Sheff from 92. *1 Nursery Drive, Ecclesfield, Sheffield S30 3XU* Sheffield (0114) 246 1027

FRYER, Kenneth Wesley. b 34. AKC59. **d** 60 **p** 61. V Tinsley *Sheff* 73-77; P-in-c Scarcliffe *Derby* 77-80; V Newhall 80-94; rtd 94. *3 Ael y Glynn, Nant Road, Harlech, Gwynedd LL46 2UE* Harlech (01766) 780174

FRYER, Michael Andrew. b 56. St Jo Coll Nottm 88. **d** 90 **p** 91. C Hull St Martin w Transfiguration *York* 90-95; V Kingston upon Hull Southcoates St Aid from 95. *St Aidan's Vicarage, 139 Southcoates Avenue, Hull HU9 3HF* Hull (01482) 374403

FRYER, Preb Peter Hugh. b 25. Linc Th Coll 58. **d** 60 **p** 61. R St Buryan *Truro* 64-72; R St Levan 66-72; R St Sennen 70-72; R Elgin w Lossiemouth *Mor* 72-76; Chapl RAF 72-76; P-in-c Lewannick *Truro* 76-78; P-in-c Altarnon and Bolventor 76-78; P-in-c N Hill 76-78; TR N Hill w Altarnon, Bolventor and Lewannick 78-84; P-in-c Laneast w St Clether and Tresmere 80-84; Preb St Endellion 84-90; R St Endellion w Port Isaac and St Kew 84-90; rtd 90. *Blythswood, Fore Street, Marazion, Cornwall TR17 0AS* Penzance (01736) 711857

FUDGE, Prof Erik Charles. b 33. Ch Coll Cam BA55 MA59 Southn Univ CertEd58 Cam Univ PhD68. Ox Min Course 91. **d** 93 **p** 94. NSM Wokingham St Sebastian *Ox* from 93. *4 South Close, Wokingham, Berks RG11 2DJ* Wokingham (01734) 786081

FUDGER, David John. b 53. Coll of Resurr Mirfield 76. **d** 77 **p** 78. C Sutton in Ashfield St Mary *S'well* 77-80; C Duston *Pet* 80-82; V Radford All So w Ch Ch and St Mich *S'well* 82-91; Min Bermondsey St Hugh CD *S'wark* from 91. *Charterhouse Mission, 40 Tabard Street, London SE1 4JU* 0171-407 1123

FUDGER, Michael Lloyd. b 55. K Coll Lon BD77 AKC77. Coll of Resurr Mirfield 77. **d** 78 **p** 79. C Weston Favell *Pet* 78-82; C Pet H Spirit Bretton 82-84; V Irchester 84-90; TV Darnall-cum-Attercliffe *Sheff* from 90; RD Attercliffe from 91. *The Vicarage, 66 Mather Road, Sheffield S9 4GQ* Sheffield (0114) 244 0167

FUGGLE, Francis Alfred. b 13. Selw Coll Cam BA34 MA38. Wells Th Coll 35. **d** 36 **p** 37. C Kingsbury St Andr *Lon* 36-38; S Africa from 38. *360A Florida Road, Durban, 4001 South Africa* Durban (31) 238923

FULFORD, Herbert Anthony. b 31. FRICS70. SW Minl Tr Course. **d** 85 **p** 86. NSM Topsham *Ex* from 85. *Coach House, Grove Hill, Topsham, Exeter EX3 0EG* Topsham (01392) 874296

FULHAM, Suffragan Bishop of. See KLYBERG, Rt Rev Charles John

FULLAGAR, Michael Nelson. b 35. SS Coll Cam BA57 MA61. Chich Th Coll 57. **d** 59 **p** 60. C Camberwell St Giles *S'wark* 59-61; C Northolt Park St Barn *Lon* 61-64; C Hythe *Cant* 64-66; Zambia 66-78; R Freemantle *Win* 78-87; P-in-c Westbury w Turweston, Shalstone and Biddlesden *Ox* 87-94; Chapl S Bucks NHS Trust from 94; Chapl Wycombe Gen Hosp from 94. *Wycombe General Hospital, Queen Alexandra Road, High Wycombe, Bucks HP11 2TT* High Wycombe (01494) 425072/526255

FULLALOVE, Brenda Hurst. See CRASTON, Mrs Brenda Hurst

FULLARTON, Mrs Heather Mary. b 42. Whitelands Coll Lon TCert63. Qu Coll Birm 90. **d** 92 **p** 94. Par Dn Colwich w Gt Haywood *Lich* 92-94; C from 94. *2 Penn Croft, Little Haywood, Stafford ST18 0UY* Little Haywood (01889) 882596

FULLER, Alison Jane. b 61. St Andr Univ MTheol84. Edin Th Coll 85. **d** 87 **p** 94. C Selkirk *Edin* 87-89; C Melrose 87-89; C Galashiels 87-89; C Edin H Cross 89-92; D-in-c Edin St Columba 92-94; R from 94. *2/2 Boswell's Court, 352 Castlehill, Edinburgh EH1 2NF* 0131-225 1634

FULLER, Alistair James. b 66. Univ of Wales (Lamp) BA87. Ripon Coll Cuddesdon 88. **d** 90 **p** 91. C Thornton-le-Fylde *Blackb* 90-95; V Skerton St Luke from 95. *St Luke's Vicarage, Slyne Road, Lancaster LA1 2HU* Lancaster (01524) 63249

FULLER, Christopher John. b 53. Chich Th Coll 85. **d** 87 **p** 88. C Swinton St Pet *Man* 87; C Swinton and Pendlebury 87-90; C Chiswick St Nic w St Mary *Lon* 90-92; V Hounslow W Gd Shep from 92. *Good Shepherd House, 360 Beavers Lane, Hounslow TW4 6HJ* 0181-570 4035

FULLER, Canon Frank William. b 22. Chich Th Coll 53. **d** 54 **p** 55. R Cockfield *St E* 61-72; RD Lavenham 64-72; Hon Can St E Cathl 67-87; V Bungay H Trin w St Mary 73-87; RD Beccles and S Elmham 76-83; rtd 87. *23 Middle Street, Puriton, Bridgwater, Somerset TA7 8AU* Bridgwater (01278) 684131

FULLER, Frederick Walter Tom. b 17. St Cath Coll Cam BA48 MA53 Bris Univ MLitt72 Ex Univ PhD74. Union Th Sem (NY) STM54 Cuddesdon Coll 49. **d** 51 **p** 52. Lect and Chapl St Luke's Coll Ex 59-78; Hon C Swindon New Town *Bris* 79-82; Perm to Offic *Bris* from 89. *29 Oxford Road, Swindon SN3 4HP* Swindon (01793) 824980

FULLER, Canon Graham Drowley. b 33. AKC58. **d** 59 **p** 60. C E Grinstead St Swithun *Chich* 59-62; C Coulsdon St Andr *S'wark* 62-64; Chapl RN 64-68; V Battersea St Luke *S'wark* 68-75; V S Stoneham *Win* 75-90; Bp's Ecum Officer 84-90; R Eversley from 90; Hon Can Win Cathl from 93. *The Rectory, Glaston Hill Road, Eversley, Basingstoke, Hants RG27 0LX* Eversley (01734) 733237

FULLER, Canon John James. b 38. SS Coll Cam BA63. Chich Th Coll 63 Union Th Sem (NY) STM64. **d** 65 **p** 66. C Westmr St Steph w St Jo *Lon* 65-71; Tutor Cuddesdon Coll 71-75; Tutor Ripon Coll Cuddesdon 75-77; Prin S Dios Minl Tr Scheme from 77; Can and Preb Sarum Cathl *Sarum* from 83. *The Theological College, 19 The Close, Salisbury SP1 2EE* Salisbury (01722) 412996   Fax 338508

FULLER, Michael George. b 46. Chich Th Coll 90. **d** 92 **p** 93. C Fulham All SS *Lon* 92-94; C Kensington St Mary Abbots w St Geo from 94; Dir Post-Ord Tr Kensington Area from 94. *25 Campden Hill Square, London W8 7JY*   0171-727 9486

FULLER, Dr Michael Jeremy. b 63. Worc Coll Ox BA85 MA89 DPhil89 Qu Coll Cam BA91. Westcott Ho Cam CTM92. **d** 92 **p** 93. C High Wycombe *Ox* from 92. *21 The Haystacks, High Wycombe, Bucks HP13 6PY* High Wycombe (01494) 451202

FULLER, Canon Reginald Horace. b 15. Cam Univ BA37 MA41. Qu Coll Birm 39. **d** 40 **p** 41. USA from 55; Lic to Offic *Derby* from 64; rtd 80. *5001 East Seminary Avenue, Richmond, Virginia 23227, USA*   Richmond (804) 277-6010

FULLER, Robert James. b 10. Lon Univ BD53. **d** 55 **p** 56. R Exford w Exmoor *B & W* 61-75; rtd 75. *Verna, Trefonen, Oswestry, Shropshire SY10 9DJ*   Oswestry (01691) 653505

FULLER, Robert Peter. b 49. Bernard Gilpin Soc Dur 71 Trin Coll Bris 72. **d** 75 **p** 76. C Tonbridge SS Pet and Paul *Roch* 75-79; C Welling 79-83; V Nottm St Sav *S'well* 83-89; V Ripley *Derby* from 89. *The Vicarage, 26 Mount Pleasant, Ripley, Derbyshire DE5 3DX*   Ripley (01773) 749641

FULLER, Canon Terence James. b 30. Bris Univ BA55. Clifton Th Coll. **d** 56 **p** 57. C Uphill *B & W* 56-60; V Islington St Jude Mildmay Park *Lon* 60-67; V Southgate *Chich* 67-80; R Stoke Climsland *Truro* from 80; RD Trigg Major 85-91; P-in-c Lezant w Lawhitton and S Petherwin w Trewen from 93; Hon Can Truro Cathl from 94. *The Rectory, Stoke Climsland, Callington, Cornwall PL17 8NZ*   Stoke Climsland (01579) 370501

FULLERTON, Hamish John Neville. b 45. Ball Coll Ox BA68 MA73. S'wark Ord Course 76. **d** 79 **p** 80. NSM Clapham Old Town *S'wark* 79-82; Abp Tennison's Sch Kennington 79-88; Perm to Offic 82-89; Hon C Brixton Rd Ch Ch 89-91; C Streatham Ch Ch from 91. *Flat 4, 21 Offerton Road, London SW4 0DJ*   0171-622 7890

FULLJAMES, Mrs Janet Kathleen Doris. b 43. Open Univ BA79. Qu Coll Birm 85. **d** 87 **p** 94. Par Dn Harborne St Pet *Birm* 87-93; Par Dn Smethwick SS Steph and Mich 93-94; C from 94. *99 Lewisham Road, Smethwick, Warley, W Midlands B66 2DD*   0121-558 3583

FULLJAMES, Michael William. b 36. OBE94. AKC60. **d** 61 **p** 62. C Armley St Bart *Ripon* 61-64; C E Wells *B & W* 64-67; R Stanningley St Thos *Ripon* 67-73; Chapl St Aug Hosp Cant 73-88; St Martin's Hosp 82-88; RD W Bridge *Cant* 87-88; Chapl Rotterdam *Eur* 88-94; Sen Chapl Rotterdam Miss to Seamen 88-94; Sen Chapl Burrswood Chr Cen *Roch* from 94. *The Chaplain's House, Burrswood, Groombridge, Tunbridge Wells, Kent TN3 9PY* Tunbridge Wells (01892) 864459   Fax 862597

FULLJAMES, Peter Godfrey. b 38. BNC Ox BA60 MA64. Qu Coll Birm DipTh62. **d** 62 **p** 63. C Mexborough *Sheff* 62-65; India 65-69; Lic to Offic *Lich* 70-79; Moorside High Sch Werrington 71-79; Kenya 80-85; Research Fell Qu Coll Birm 85-87; Perm to Offic *Birm* 85-90; Tutor W Midl Minl Tr Course 87-92; Lic to Offic *Birm* from 90; Tutor Crowther Hall CMS Tr Coll Selly Oak from 95. *99 Lewisham Road, Smethwick, Warley, W Midlands B66 2DD or Crowther Hall, Selly Oak, Birmingham B29 6QT*   0121-558 3583 or 472 4228

FULLWOOD, William. b 11. St Aid Birkenhead 45. **d** 48 **p** 49. V Laxton w Blacktoft *York* 68-74; V Rudston w Boynton 74-77; rtd 77. *11 Ambrey Close, Hunmanby, Filey, N Yorkshire YO14 0LZ* Scarborough (01723) 891027

FULTON, John William. b 49. Ex Coll Ox BA71 BPhil72 MA75 MPhil79. Wycliffe Hall Ox 72. **d** 76 **p** 77. C Bexleyheath Ch Ch *Roch* 76-79; C Ealing Dean St Jo *Lon* 79-83; V Aldborough Hatch *Chelmsf* 83-87; Chapl Chantilly *Eur* 87-90; R Hepworth, Hinderclay, Wattisfield and Thelnetham *St E* from 90. *The Rectory, Church Lane, Hepworth, Diss, Norfolk IP22 2PU*   Stanton (01359) 50285

FUNNELL, Norman Richard James. b 40. Univ of Wales (Lamp) BA64. Ripon Hall Ox 64. **d** 66 **p** 67. C Hackney *Lon* 66-70; Hon C 71-85; TV 85-93; R S Hackney St Jo w Ch Ch from 93. *The Rectory, Church Crescent, London E9 7DH* 0181-985 5145

FURBER, Peter. b 43. Ex Univ BA. Sarum & Wells Th Coll 83. **d** 85 **p** 86. C Stanmore *Win* 85-88; TV Basingstoke from 88. *15 Ashburn Garth, Hightown, Ringwood, Hants BH24 3DS*

FURLONG, Andrew William Ussher. b 47. TCD BA69 Jes Coll Cam BA71. Westcott Ho Cam 70 CITC 71. **d** 72 **p** 73. C Dundela *D & D* 72-76; C Dub St Ann w St Mark and St Steph *D & G* 76-83; Zimbabwe 83-94; Adn W Harare 88-89; Can Harare 89-94; Asst Chapl Leeds Gen Infirmary from 94.

Chaplaincy Department, Leeds General Infirmary, St George Street, Leeds LS1 3EX   Leeds (0113) 292 3527 or 243 2799

FURLONG (nee DAVIES), Mrs Catharine Mary. b 48. Philippa Fawcett Coll CertEd73. E Midl Min Tr Course 85. **d** 88 **p** 95. C Spalding *Linc* 88-92; Zimbabwe 92-94; C Gt w Lt Gidding and Steeple Gidding *Ely* 94-95; NSM from 95. *The Rectory, 6 Luddington Road, Great Gidding, Huntingdon, Cambs PE17 5PA*   Winwick (01832) 293587

FURLONGER, Maurice Frank. b 25. AKC50. **d** 51 **p** 52. V St Minver *Truro* 67-70; V St Gluvias 70-74; TV Seacroft *Ripon* 74-77; V Hunslet St Mary 77-81; USA 81-88; C Dalton le Dale *Dur* 88-90; rtd 90; Hon C Diptford, N Huish, Harberton and Harbertonford *Ex* 91-94. *31 Penoweth, Mylor Bridge, Falmouth, Cornwall TR11 5NQ* Falmouth (01326) 374047

FURNELL, Very Rev Raymond. b 35. Linc Th Coll 63. **d** 65 **p** 66. C Cannock *Lich* 65-69; V Clayton 69-75; RD Stoke N 75-81; R Shelton 75-77; TR Hanley H Ev 77-81; Provost St E 81-94; V St E Cathl Distr 81-94; Dean York from 94. *The Deanery, York YO1 2JD* York (01904) 623608

FURNESS, Colin. b 43. Lich Th Coll 65. **d** 68 **p** 69. C New Bentley *Sheff* 68; C Sheff Parson Cross St Cecilia 68-74; V Edlington 74-78; C Heavitree w Ex St Paul *Ex* 78-81; TV 81-89; R Sampford Spiney w Horrabridge from 89. *The Rectory, Tor View, Horrabridge, Yelverton, Devon PL20 7RE* Yelverton (01822) 855198

FURNESS, Dominic John. b 53. Bris Univ BA76. Ridley Hall Cam 82. **d** 84 **p** 85. C Downend *Bris* 84-88; V Stoke Hill *Guildf* from 88. *St Peter's House, 37 Hazel Avenue, Guildford, Surrey GU1 1NP* Guildford (01483) 572078

FURNESS, Edward Joseph. b 42. S'wark Ord Course 74. **d** 77 **p** 78. NSM S Lambeth St Steph *S'wark* 77-81; Min Mayflower Family Cen Canning Town *Chelmsf* from 82. *5 Cooper Street, London E16 1QU*   0171-476 1171

FURNESS, Edward Peter Alexander. b 29. St Edm Hall Ox BA52 MA56. St Aid Birkenhead 52. **d** 54 **p** 55. V Worsthorne *Blackb* 88-94; V Longridge 64-88; rtd 94. *26 Severn Street, Longridge, Preston PR3 3ND*   Longridge (01772) 784092

FURNESS, John Alfred. b 31. Chich Th Coll 60. **d** 62 **p** 63. C Leeds St Aid *Ripon* 62-66; C Rickmansworth *St Alb* 66-73; R Wymington 73-75; P-in-c Podington w Farndish 74-75; R Wymington w Podington 75-79; V Waltham Cross 79-89; RD Cheshunt 84-89; R Swyncombe w Britwell Salome *Ox* from 89. *The Rectory, Swyncombe, Henley-on-Thames, Oxon RG9 6EA* Nettlebed (01491) 641249

FURST, John William. b 41. Ripon Coll Cuddesdon. **d** 84 **p** 85. C Bris Ch the Servant Stockwood *Bris* 84-88; V Hanham 88-94. *32 Riversdale, Llandaff, Cardiff CF5 2QL* Cardiff (01222) 567212

FUSSELL, Preb Laurence Walkling. b 14. Keble Coll Ox BA35 MA39. Wells Th Coll 36. **d** 37 **p** 38. R Wraxall *B & W* 59-79; Preb Wells Cathl from 69; rtd 79; Perm to Offic *B & W* from 79. *2 South Meadows, Wrington, Bristol BS18 7PF* Wrington (01934) 862924

FUTCHER, Christopher David. b 58. Edin Univ BD80. Westcott Ho Cam 80. **d** 82 **p** 83. C Borehamwood *St Alb* 82-85; C Stevenage All SS Pin Green 85-88; V from 88. *All Saints' Vicarage, 100 Derby Way, Stevenage, Herts SG1 5TJ* Stevenage (01438) 318706

FUTERS, Michael Roger. b 58. Trin & All SS Coll Leeds BEd80. St Jo Coll Nottm 82. **d** 85 **p** 86. C Narborough and Huncote *Leic* 85-87; C Spondon *Derby* 87-90; P-in-c Derby St Jas from 90. *St James's Vicarage, 224 Osmaston Road, Derby DE23 8JX* Derby (01332) 343911

FUTTER, Ivan Herbert. b 31. Roch Th Coll 62. **d** 64 **p** 65. C Buckhurst Hill *Chelmsf* 64-66; Canada from 66. *RR1, 3610 Fo'csle Road, Pender Island, British Columbia, Canada, V0N 2M0*

FYFFE, Robert Clark. b 56. Edin Univ BD78 Bris Poly DAVM87. Edin Th Coll 74. **d** 79 **p** 80. C Edin St Jo 79-83; Youth Chapl *B & W* 83-87; Prov Youth Officer Scottish Episc Ch 87-92; Co-ord Internat Angl Youth Network from 88; R Perth St Jo *St And* from 93. *23 Comley Bank, Perth PH2 7HU* Perth (01738) 25394

FYFFE, Timothy Bruce. b 25. New Coll Ox MA54. Westcott Ho Cam 54. **d** 56 **p** 57. TV Lowestoft St Marg *Nor* 69-80; Chapl HM Pris Blundeston 70-78; TV Tettenhall Regis *Lich* 80-85; Chapl Compton Hall Hospice Wolv 85-87; NSM Wolv St Andr *Lich* 88-90; rtd 90. *21 Sandy Lane, Tettenhall, Wolverhampton WV6 9EB* Wolverhampton (01902) 752066

FYLES, Gordon. b 39. Trin Coll Bris 76. **d** 78 **p** 79. C Islington St Mary *Lon* 77-81; Ext Sec BCMS 81-93; Ext Sec Crosslinks from 93; Hon C Kingston Hill St Paul *S'wark* 82-88; C Wimbledon Em Ridgway Prop Chpl from 88. *25 Richmond Road, London SW20 0PG* 0181-946 9940 or 691 6111   Fax 694 8023

FYSH, Leslie David. b 35. Glouc Sch of Min 88. **d** 91 **p** 92. NSM Stonehouse *Glouc* 91-95; Asst Chapl Wycliffe Coll Stonehouse Glos 91-95; NSM W Walton *Ely* from 95. *Cornerways, 53 School Road, West Walton, Wisbech, Cambs PE14 7ES* Wisbech (01945) 584631

G

GABB-JONES, Adrian William Douglas. b 43. ARICS. Ripon Coll Cuddesdon 79. **d** 81 **p** 82. C Northolt Park St Barn *Lon* 81-84; C Ruislip St Martin 84-89; V Minster Lovell and Brize Norton *Ox* from 89. *The Vicarage, Burford Road, Minster Lovell, Oxford OX8 5RA* Witney (01993) 776492

GABE, Dr Eric Sigurd. b 15. Lon Univ BA52 PhD94. St Aid Birkenhead 54. **d** 55 **p** 55. V Cricklewood St Mich *Lon* 60-72; V Brondesbury St Anne w Kilburn H Trin 72-80; rtd 80; Perm to Offic *St Alb* from 80; Perm to Offic *Lon* from 81. *21 Cromer Road, Barnet, Herts EN5 5HT* 0181-449 6779

GABLE, Michael David. b 70. Wales Poly BEng92. St Mich Coll Llan DipTh94 BTh95. **d** 95. C Newton Nottage *Llan* from 95. *79 Meadow Lane, Porthcawl, M Glam CF36 5EY* Porthcawl (01656) 788176

GABRIEL, Michael Hunt. b 29. BA. **d** 57 **p** 58. C Hillingdon St Jo *Lon* 67-86; C Kingston Buci *Chich* 86-94; rtd 94. *Flat 1, 6 Dittons Road, Eastbourne, E Sussex BN21 1DN*

GADD, Dr Alan John. b 44. FRMetS67 Imp Coll Lon BSc65 PhD69. S'wark Ord Course 68. **d** 71 **p** 72. Asst Chapl Lon Univ *Lon* 71-72; Perm to Offic S'wark 73-91; NSM Battersea Park All SS 91-95; C 95; P-in-c from 95. *100 Prince of Wales Drive, London SW11 4BD* 0171-622 3809

GADD, Brian Hayward. b 33. Hatf Coll Dur BA54 DipEd55. Glouc Sch of Min 82. **d** 85 **p** 87. NSM Cleobury Mortimer w Hopton Wafers *Heref* 85-93; NSM Cleobury Mortimer w Hopton Wafers etc from 93. *34 Lower Street, Cleobury Mortimer, Kidderminster, Worcs DY14 8AB* Cleobury Mortimer (01299) 270758

GADD, Bryan Stephen Andrew. b 56. Dur Univ BA Ox Univ CertEd. Chich Th Coll. **d** 81 **p** 82. C Newlyn St Pet *Truro* 81-86; R St Mawgan w St Ervan and St Eval 86-90; Chapl Summer Fields Sch Ox from 90. *Little Cottage, Summer Fields School, Oxford OX2 7EN* Oxford (01865) 58729

GADD, Frederick Arthur. b 15. St Jo Coll Dur BA40 MA43. **d** 40 **p** 41. V Gillingham St Mark *Roch* 52-57; Canada from 57; rtd 80. *Address temp unknown*

GAGE, Robert Edward. b 47. Whitman Coll Washington BA69. Cuddesdon Coll BA75 MA81. **d** 76 **p** 77. C Cheshunt *St Alb* 76-79; C Harpenden St Nic 79-81; V S Mymms 81-82; P-in-c Ridge 81-82; V S Mymms and Ridge from 82. *The Vicarage, Blanche Lane, Potters Bar, Herts EN6 3PE* Potters Bar (01707) 642142

GAINER, Jeffrey. b 51. Jes Coll Ox BA73 MA77. Wycliffe Hall Ox 74. **d** 77 **p** 78. C Baglan *Llan* 77-81; V Cwmbach 81-85; V Tonyrefail w Gilfach Goch and Llandyfodwg 85-87; Dir NT Studies 87-92; Dir Past Studies St Mich Coll Llan 87-92; V Meidrim and Llanboidy and Merthyr *St D* from 92. *The Vicarage, Meidrim, Carmarthen, Dyfed SA33 5QF* St Clears (01994) 231247

GAIR, Andrew Kennon. b 62. Westcott Ho Cam 88. **d** 91 **p** 92. C Clare w Poslingford, Cavendish etc *St E* 91-95; R Debden and Wimbish w Thunderley *Chelmsf* from 95. *The Rectory, Debden, Saffron Walden, Essex CM11 3LB* Saffron Walden (01799) 540285

✠**GAISFORD, Rt Rev John Scott.** b 34. St Chad's Coll Dur BA59 DipTh60 MA76. **d** 60 **p** 61 **c** 94. C Audenshaw St Hilda *Man* 60-62; C Bramhall *Ches* 62-65; V Crewe St Andr 65-86; RD Nantwich 74-85; Hon Can Ches Cathl 80-86; Adn Macclesfield 86-94; Suff Bp Beverley (PEV) *York* from 94. *3 North Lane, Roundhay, Leeds LS8 2QJ* Leeds (0113) 273 2003/(0860) 289550 Fax 273 3002

GAIT, David James. b 48. BNC Ox BA71 BSc72 MA77 Ox Univ MSc83. Ridley Hall Cam 71. **d** 74 **p** 75. C Litherland St Paul Hatton Hill *Liv* 74-77; C Farnworth 77-80; V Widnes St Jo from 80; Chapl Widnes Maternity Hosp from 86. *St John's House, Greenway Road, Widnes, Cheshire WA8 6HA* 0151-424 3134

GAKURU, Griphus. Makerere Univ Kampala BSc81 PGDE83 Selw Coll Cam MPhil92. Bp Tucker Coll Mukono BD88. **d** 88 **p** 91. Uganda 89-91; Hon C Cam H Trin w St Andr Gt *Ely* 91-92; Hon C Cam H Trin from 92. *Selwyn College, Cambridge CB3 9DQ* Cambridge (01223) 464041

GALBRAITH, Alexander Peter James. b 65. Qu Coll Ox BA86 MA90. Wycliffe Hall Ox 87. **d** 90 **p** 91. C Southport Em *Liv* 90-94; C Mossley Hill St Matt and St Jas from 94. *120 Abbotshey Road, Liverpool L18 7TJ* 0151-724 1454

GALBRAITH, John Angus Frame. b 44. Sarum Th Coll 68. **d** 71 **p** 72. C Buckhurst Hill St Mary *S'wark* 71-74; Chapl W Lon Colls 74-79; V S'wark H Trin w St Matt 79-95; V New Addington from 95. *St Edward's Vicarage, Cleves Crescent, Croydon CR0 0DL* Lodge Hill (01689) 845588

GALBRAITH, John Watson Joseph Denham. b 19. Glas Univ MA41. Bps' Coll Cheshunt 47. **d** 48 **p** 49. Dep Asst Chapl Gen

GALBRAITH, Peter John. b 59. QUB BA MTh TCD DipTh. ·**d** 85 **p** 86. C Knockbreda *D & D* 85-88; C Ballynafeigh St Jude 88-91; I Broomhedge *Conn* from 91. *Broomhedge Rectory, 30 Lurganure Road, Broughmore, Lisburn, Co Antrim BT28 2TR* Maze (01846) 621229

GALE, Christopher. b 44. ALCD67. **d** 68 **p** 69. C Balderton *S'well* 68-72; C Bilborough St Jo 72-75; P-in-c Colwick 75-78; V Radford St Pet 78-84; V Sherwood from 84; AD Nottm N from 90. *St Martin's Vicarage, Trevose Gardens, Sherwood, Nottingham NG5 3FU* Nottingham (0115) 960 7547

GALE, Colin Edward. b 49. Lon Univ PGCE74. St Jo Coll Nottm LTh BTh73. **d** 79 **p** 80. C Hoole *Ches* 79-82; C Woodley St Jo the Ev *Ox* 82-87; V Clapham St Jas *S'wark* from 87. *St James's Vicarage, 1 Rodenhurst Road, London SW4 8AE* 0181-674 3973

GALE, Douglas Norman. b 32. Birkb Coll Lon BA72. Franciscan Ho of Studies E Bergholt 53. **d** 61 **p** 61. Asst Master Judd Sch Tonbridge 72-74; K Sch Ches 74-80; C Ches Team *Ches* 79-83; TV 83-87; rtd 87. *6 Allen Court, Hauxton Road, Trumpington, Cambridge CB2 2LU* Cambridge (01223) 841197

GALE, Edwin Donald. b 12. AKC40. **d** 40 **p** 41. V Hebburn St Oswald *Dur* 69-72; rtd 72. *6 The Peacheries, Bognor Road, Chichester, W Sussex PO19 2NP* Chichester (01243) 776129

GALE, John. b 34. Univ of Wales (Lamp) 67. **d** 69 **p** 70. C Aberdare St Jo *Llan* 69-71; C Merthyr Dyfan 71-74; S Africa from 74. *PO Box 67, Knysna, 6570 South Africa* Knysna (445) 21239

GALE, Keith George. b 44. St Jo Coll Lusaka 68 Sarum Th Coll 69. **d** 70 **p** 71. C Sheff St Cuth *Sheff* 70-77; P-in-c Brightside All SS 72-77; C Birm St Martin *Birm* 77-81; USPG 81-94; Malawi 81-94; Adn Lilongwe Lake Malawi 89-92; TV Sampford Peverell, Uplowman, Holcombe Rogus etc *Ex* from 94. *The Vicarage, Lower Town, Halberton, Tiverton, Devon EX16 7AU* Tiverton (01884) 821149

GALE, Ms Lucille Catherine. b 67. Sarum & Wells Th Coll 92. **d** 94 **p** 95. C Welling *S'wark* from 94. *21 Hill View Drive, Welling, Kent DA16 3RS* 0181-856 3500

GALE, Peter Simon. b 56. BD. St Mich Coll Llan. **d** 83 **p** 84. C Caerphilly *Llan* 83-89; Chapl RN 89-93; V Ystrad Rhondda w Ynyscynon *Llan* from 93. *St Stephen's Vicarage, Ystrad, Pentre, M Glam CF41 7RR* Tonypandy (01443) 434426

GALES, Alan. b 29. Sarum Th Coll 56. **d** 59 **p** 60. Ind Chapl *Dur* 60-70; V Marley Hill 63-94; Asst Chapl HM Pris Dur 74-81; rtd 94. *46 Coxsair, Whickham, Newcastle upon Tyne NE16 5YA* 0191-488 7352

GALES, Bernard Henry. b 27. Lon Univ BSc(Econ)51. Wells Th Coll 62. **d** 64 **p** 65. C Fordingbridge w Ibsley *Win* 67-71; C S Molton w Nymet St George *Ex* 71-73; C Thelbridge 73-77; P-in-c 77-78; P-in-c Creacombe 77-78; P-in-c W w E Worlington 77-78; P-in-c Meshaw 77-78; P-in-c Witheridge 77-78; C Witheridge, Thelbridge, Creacombe, Meshaw etc 79-80; R Bow w Broad Nymet 80-93; V Colebrooke 80-93; R Zeal Monachorum 80-93; RD Cadbury 90-93; rtd 93. *8 Old Rectory Gardens, Morchard Bishop, Crediton, Devon EX17 6PF* Morchard Bishop (01363) 877601

GALES, Simon Richard. b 59. CEng87 MICE87 Jes Coll Cam BA81 MA84. Wycliffe Hall Ox 91. **d** 93 **p** 94. C Houghton *Carl* from 93. *167 Kingstown Road, Carlisle CA3 0AX* Carlisle (01228) 591600 or 515972

GALILEE, George David Surtees. b 37. Or Coll Ox BA60 MA64. Westcott Ho Cam 61. **d** 62 **p** 63. C Knighton St Mary Magd *Leic* 62-67; V Stocking Farm 67-69; Tutor Westcott Ho Cam and Homerton Coll 69-71; V Sutton *Ely* 71-80; P-in-c Addiscombe St Mildred *Cant* 80-81; V 81-84; V Addiscombe St Mildred *S'wark* from 85. *St Mildred's Vicarage, Sefton Road, Croydon CR0 7HR* 0181-654 3569

GALLAGHER, Adrian Ian. b 43. TCD Div Sch 89. **d** 92 **p** 93. C Drumachose *D & R* from 92. *92 Main Street, Limavady, Co Londonderry BT49 0ET* Limavady (015047) 68692

GALLAGHER, Hubert. b 31. Linc Th Coll 78. **d** 80 **p** 81. C Lupset *Wakef* 80-82; C Badsworth 82-86; V Kinsley 86-88; V Kinsley w Wragby 88-91; rtd 91. *The Little House, Nostell Priory, Wakefield, W Yorkshire WF4 1QE* Wakefield (01924) 865498

GALLAGHER, Ian. BTh. **d** 90 **p** 91. C Annagh w Drumgoon, Ashfield etc *K, E & A* 90-93; I Drumcliffe w Lissadell and Munninane from 93. *The Rectory, Drumcliffe, Co Sligo, Irish Republic* Sligo (71) 63125

GALLAGHER, Michael Collins. b 48. Dur Univ BA. Sarum Th Coll. **d** 82 **p** 83. C Bridport *Sarum* 82-86; V Downton from 86; RD Alderbury from 93. *The Vicarage, Barford Lane, Downton, Salisbury SP5 3QA* Downton (01725) 510326

GALLAGHER, Neville Roy. b 45. Lon Univ CertEd66 AKC70 Lon Univ BD76. **d** 71 **p** 72. C Folkestone St Mary and St

Eanswythe *Cant* 71-74; Hon C Sutton Valence w E Sutton and Chart Sutton 74-76; TV Cen Telford *Lich* 76-78; P-in-c Gt Mongeham *Cant* 78-80; P-in-c Ripple 78-80; R Gt Mongeham w Ripple and Sutton by Dover 80-83; V Kennington 83-88; Chapl Bedgebury Sch Kent from 88. *3 Beech Drive, Bedgebury Park, Goudhurst, Kent TN17 2SJ* Goudhurst (01580) 211989 or 211221

GALLAGHER, Robert. b 43. St Chad's Coll Dur BSc65 DipTh67. **d** 67 **p** 68. C Crosland Moor *Wakef* 67-69; C Huddersfield SS Pet and Paul 69-71; Chapl Huddersfield Poly 72-79; Min Coulby Newham Ecum Project *York* 79-90; V Toxteth St Marg *Liv* from 90. *St Margaret's Vicarage, 3 Princes Road, Liverpool L8 1TG* 0151-709 1526

GALLAGHER, Stephen. b 58. Southn Univ BTh89. Chich Th Coll 86. **d** 89 **p** 90. C S Shields All SS *Dur* 89-92; C Hartlepool St Paul 92-94; Chapl Hartlepool Gen Hosp 92-94; R Loftus and Carlin How w Skinningrove *York* from 94. *The Rectory, Loftus, Saltburn-by-the-Sea, Cleveland TS13 4JY* Castleton (01287) 640738

GALLETLY, Thomas. b 23. St Chad's Coll Dur BA50 DipTh52. **d** 52 **p** 53. Chapl Chailey Heritage Hosp and Sch Lewes 57-88; Lic to Offic *Chich* from 59; rtd 88. *The Glen, Lewes Road, Scaynes Hill, Haywards Heath, W Sussex RH17 7PG* Haywards Heath (01444) 831510

GALLEY, Giles Christopher. b 32. Qu Coll Cam BA56 MA60. Linc Th Coll 56. **d** 58 **p** 59. C Gt Yarmouth *Nor* 58-62; C N Lynn w St Marg and St Nic 62-66; C Leeds St Pet *Ripon* 66-69; V N Hull St Mich *York* 69-79; V Strensall from 79; RD Easingwold from 82. *The Vicarage, 10 York Road, Strensall, York YO3 5UB* York (01904) 490683

GALLICHAN, Henry Ernest. b 45. Sarum Th Coll 70. **d** 72 **p** 73. C Kenton Ascension *Newc* 72-76; Tanzania 76-80; Lic to Offic *Truro* from 80. *Karibu, Trevelmond, Liskeard, Cornwall PL14 4LZ* Liskeard (01579) 20530

✠**GALLIFORD, Rt Rev David George.** b 25. Clare Coll Cam BA49 MA51. Westcott Ho Cam. **d** 51 **p** 52 **c** 75. C Newland St Jo *York* 51-54; C Eton w Boveney *Ox* 54-56; Min Can Windsor 54-56; V Middlesb St Oswald *York* 56-61; R Bolton Percy 61-71; Dioc Adult Tr Officer 61-71; Can and Preb York Minster 69-70; Can Res and Treas 70-75; Suff Bp Hulme *Man* 75-84; Suff Bp Bolton 84-91; rtd 91. *Bishopgarth, Maltongate, Thornton Dale, Pickering, N Yorkshire YO18 7SA* Pickering (01751) 74605

GALLON, Edward George. b 16. St Steph Ho Ox 64. **d** 66 **p** 67. C Hockley *Chelmsf* 69-74; R Takeley w Lt Canfield 74-83; rtd 83; Perm to Offic *S'wark* from 84. *42 Home Park, Oxted, Surrey RH8 0JU* Oxted (01883) 714091

GALLOWAY, Charles Bertram. b 41. Lon Univ BA62 Birm Univ DipTh64. Qu Coll Birm 64. **d** 64 **p** 65. C Darlington H Trin *Dur* 64-68; Ind Chapl Teesside 68-77; Sen Ind Chapl *Liv* 77-87; Team Ldr and Convener Lon Ind Chapl *Lon* 87-93; P-in-c Gosforth w Nether Wasdale and Wasdale Head *Carl* from 93; Part-time Chapl Sellafield from 94. *The Rectory, Gosforth, Seascale, Cumbria CA20 1AZ* Gosforth (019467) 25251

GALLOWAY, Michael Edward. b 41. Chich Th Coll 72. **d** 74 **p** 75. C Aldwick *Chich* 74-77; C Bournemouth St Clem w St Mary *Win* 78-82; V S Benfleet *Chelmsf* from 83. *St Mary's Vicarage, 105 Vicarage Hill, Benfleet, Essex SS7 1PD* South Benfleet (01268) 792294

GALLOWAY, Dr Peter John. b 54. JP89. FRSA88 Golds Coll Lon BA76 K Coll Lon PhD87. St Steph Ho Ox 80. **d** 83 **p** 84. C St Jo Wood *Lon* 83-86; C St Giles-in-the-Fields 86-90; Warden of Readers (Lon Episc Area) 87-92; P-in-c Hampstead Em W End from 90; OStJ 86-92; ChStJ from 92. *Emmanuel Vicarage, Lyncroft Gardens, London NW6 1JU* 0171-435 1911 Fax 431 5521

GALLUP, Peter Whitfield. b 06. Sarum Th Coll 51. **d** 53 **p** 54. R Buriton *Portsm* 61-74; rtd 74; Perm to Offic *Win* from 74. *16 St Swithun's Street, Winchester, Hants SO23 9JD* Winchester (01962) 854090

GALT, Ian Ross. b 34. Leeds Univ BSc56. **d** 76 **p** 77. NSM Newport St Julian *Mon* 76-87; NSM Newport St Teilo from 87. *47 Brynglas Avenue, Newport, Gwent NP9 5LR* Newport (01633) 857134

GAMBLE, David Lawrence. b 34. AKC61. **d** 62 **p** 63. C-in-c Shrub End All SS CD *Chelmsf* 62-65; C Colchester St Jas, All SS, St Nic and St Runwald 65-69; V Chelmsf St Andr 69-73; P-in-c Hatf Heath 69-73; C 74-77; TV Hemel Hempstead *St Alb* 77-82; P-in-c Renhold 82-90; Chapl HM Pris Bedf 82-90; P-in-c Petersham *S'wark* from 90; Chapl HM Pris Latchmere Ho from 90. *99 Barnfield Avenue, Kingston-upon-Thames, Surrey KT2 5RG* 0181-549 8296 Fax 332 1359

GAMBLE, Donald William. b 67. NUU BSc88. TCD Div Sch BTh91. **d** 91 **p** 92. C Belf St Mich *Conn* 91-95; I Dromore Clogh from 95. *The Rectory, 15 Galbally Road, Dromore, Omagh, Co Tyrone BT8 3EE* Dromore (01662) 898300

GAMBLE, Ian Robert. b 66. Ulster Univ BA90 TCD BTh93. CITC 90. **d** 93 **p** 94. C Ban St Comgall *D & D* from 93; C Ban Primacy from 93. *4 Glendowan Way, Gransha Green, Bangor, Co Down BT19 2SP* Bangor (01247) 457057

GAMBLE, Norman Edward Charles. b 50. TCD BA72 HDipEd73 PhD78. CITC 76. **d** 79 **p** 80. C Ban St Comgall *D & D* 79-83; I Dunleckney w Nurney, Lorum and Kiltennel *C & O* 83-90; Warden of Readers 84-90; RD Aghade 85-90; P-in-c Leighlin w Grange Sylvae, Shankill etc 89-90; Preb Leighlin Cathl 89-90; Preb Ossory Cathl 89-90; I Malahide w Balgriffin *D & G* from 90; Abp's Dom Chapl from 95. *The Rectory, Church Road, Malahide, Co Dublin, Irish Republic* Dublin (1) 845-4770

GAMBLE, Peter John. b 20. St Cath Soc Ox BA51 MA55 DipEd59. Ripon Hall Ox 48. **d** 52 **p** 53. Prin Anglo-American Coll Faringdon 67-71; Chapl and Tutor Harrow Sch Middx 72-82; rtd 82. *2 Lawn Road, Guildford, Surrey GU2 5DE* Guildford (01483) 576902

GAMBLE, Robin Philip. b 53. Oak Hill Th Coll 74. **d** 77 **p** 78. C Kildwick *Bradf* 77-78; C Laisterdyke 78-80; C York St Paul *York* 80-82; V Bradf St Aug Undercliffe *Bradf* 82-95; Dioc Adv in Evang from 93. *6 Glenhurst Road, Shipley, W Yorkshire BD18 4DZ* Bradford (01274) 586414

GAMBLES, Una Beryl. b 33. Man Univ BEd78. St Chris Coll Blackheath 59. **d** 87 **p** 94. NSM Upton Priory *Ches* from 87; Chapl Parkside Hosp Ches from 87. *23 Grangelands, Upton, Macclesfield, Cheshire SK10 4AB* Macclesfield (01625) 421691

GAMESTER, Sidney Peter. b 27. SS Coll Cam BA51 MA55. Oak Hill Th Coll 56. **d** 58 **p** 59. R Silverhill St Matt *Chich* 69-86; R Bexhill St Mark 86-93; rtd 93. *18 Crofton Park Avenue, Bexhill-on-Sea, E Sussex TN39 3SE* Hastings (01424) 842276

GAMMON, William Paul Lachlan (Bill). b 60. SS Hild & Bede Coll Dur BA82. St Steph Ho Ox 89. **d** 91 **p** 92. C Chalfont St Peter *Ox* 91-94; Lect Bolton St Pet *Man* from 94. *114 Bromwich Street, Bolton, Lancs BL2 1LL* Bolton (01204) 393615

GANDIYA, Leonard Farirayi (Lee). b 64. Colorado Coll 87 Boston Univ 90 MA92. Ridley Hall Cam 92. **d** 94. NSM Camberwell St Luke *S'wark* 94-95; C Lowestoft St Marg *Nor* from 95. *5 Magdalen Close, Lowestoft, Suffolk NR32 4TP* Lowestoft (01502) 517841

GANDON, Andrew James Robson. b 54. St Jo Coll Dur BA76. Ridley Hall Cam 76. **d** 78 **p** 79. C Aston SS Pet and Paul *Birm* 78-82; CMS 82-95; Zaire 82-88; Kenya 89-94; V Harefield *Lon* from 95. *9 Lewis Close, Harefield, Uxbridge, Middx UB9 6RD* Uxbridge (01895) 825960

GANDON, James Philip. b 31. ALCD56. **d** 56 **p** 57. C Westcliff St Mich *Chelmsf* 56-58; Canada from 58; rtd 92. *185 Jones Street, Goderich, Ontario, Canada, N7A 3B5* Goderich (519) 524-9718

GANDON, Percy James. b 22. ALCD53. **d** 53 **p** 54. V Hoddesdon *St Alb* 63-83; RD Cheshunt 81-83; Perm to Offic *Nor* 83-85 and from 86; P-in-c Lyng w Sparham 85-86; rtd 87. *The Old Bakery, Hindolveston, Dereham, Norfolk NR20 5DF* Melton Constable (01263) 861325

GANDY, Nicholas John. b 53. CBiol79 MIBiol Westf Coll Lon BSc75 Reading Univ MSc76 Ex Coll Ox CertEd78. St Steph Ho Ox 86. **d** 88 **p** 89. C Crowthorne *Ox* 88-93; C Tilehurst St Mary 89-93; P-in-c Didcot St Pet from 93. *St Peter's Vicarage, Didcot, Oxon OX11 8PN* Didcot (01235) 812114

GANE, Canon Christopher Paul. b 33. Qu Coll Cam BA57 MA61. Ridley Hall Cam 57. **d** 59 **p** 60. C Rainham *Chelmsf* 59-62; C Farnborough *Guildf* 62-64; V Erith St Paul *Roch* 64-71; V Ipswich St Marg *St E* 71-88; Hon Can St E Cathl from 82; R Hopton, Market Weston, Barningham etc from 88. *The Rectory, Nethergate Street, Hopton, Diss, Norfolk IP22 2QZ* Garboldisham (0195381) 8239

GANE, Nicholas. b 57. St Jo Coll Nottm DipThMin95. **d** 95. C Keynsham *B & W* from 95. *88 Chandag Road, Keynsham, Bristol BS18 1QE* Bristol (0117) 986 1056

GANGA, Jeremy Franklin. b 62. Cape Town Univ BSocSc86 Lon Bible Coll BA92. St Jo Coll Nottm MA93 Ridley Hall Cam CTM95. **d** 95. C St Peter-in-Thanet *Cant* from 95. *Lane Cottage, Tippledore Lane, Broadstairs, Kent CT10 2TG* Broadstairs (01843) 604502

GANJAVI, John Farhad. b 57. ACGI79 Imp Coll Lon BSc79. Ridley Hall Cam 79. **d** 82 **p** 83. C Yardley St Edburgha *Birm* 82-85; C Knowle 85-89; P-in-c Beaudesert and Henley-in-Arden w Ullenhall *Cov* 89-92; R from 92; RD Alcester from 92. *The Rectory, Beaudesert Lane, Henley-in-Arden, Solihull, W Midlands B95 5JY* Henley-in-Arden (01564) 792570

GANN, Canon Anthony Michael. b 37. TCD BA60 MA64 BD64. **d** 62 **p** 63. VC Derry Cathl *D & R* 62-66; Lesotho 66-74; Dioc Officer for Miss and Unity *Carl* 75-80; P-in-c Bampton and

Mardale 75-80; TV Cen Telford *Lich* 80-89; TR Wolvercote w Summertown *Ox* from 89; RD Ox from 95. *The Rectory, Lonsdale Road, Oxford OX2 7ES* Oxford (01865) 56079

GANN, John West. b 29. Ex Coll Ox BA55 MA59. Wells Th Coll 55. **d** 57 **p** 58. R Didcot *Ox* 62-70; R Newbury St Nic 70-78; TR Newbury 73-78; V Twickenham St Mary *Lon* 78-87; Dir of Ords 81-87; TR Bridport *Sarum* 87-94; RD Lyme Bay 89-92; rtd 94. *Three Gables, Charlton Road, Tetbury, Glos GL6 8DX* Tetbury (01666) 503965

GANT, Canon Brian Leonard. b 45. K Coll Lon 72. **d** 73 **p** 74. C Hillmorton *Cov* 73-75; C Cov St Geo 76; P-in-c Maldon St Mary *Chelmsf* 76-79; R Muthill *St And* 79-81; R Crieff 79-81; R Comrie 79-81; V Walsall St Paul *Lich* 81-84; Min Can Worc Cathl *Worc* 84-89; Chapl K Sch Worc 84-89; V Tunbridge Wells K Chas *Roch* 89-95; Hon Can Kumasi from 94; V Wymondham *Nor* from 95. *The Vicarage, 5 Vicar Street, Wymondham, Norfolk NR18 0PL* Wymondham (01953) 602269

GANT, Peter Robert. b 38. BNC Ox BA60 MA64 G&C Coll Cam BA62 MA67. Ridley Hall Cam 61. **d** 63 **p** 64. V Blackheath *Birm* 67-73; Asst Master Harold Malley Gr Sch Solihull 73-75; Perm to Offic 73-75; Perm to Offic *Guildf* from 75; rtd 93. *8 Sandon Close, Esher, Surrey KT10 8JE* 0181-398 5107

GANZ, Timothy Jon. b 36. ARCM63 Univ Coll Ox BA58 MA62. St Steph Ho Ox 58. **d** 61 **p** 62. C Shrewsbury H Cross *Lich* 61-65; Asst Chapl Hurstpierpoint Coll Hassocks 65-69; Chapl 69-73; Chapl Univ of Wales (Swansea) *S & B* 74-75; P-in-c Hanley All SS *Lich* 75-80; TV Stoke-upon-Trent 80-81; V Tutbury from 81. *The Vicarage, Tutbury, Burton-on-Trent, Staffs DE13 9JF* Burton-on-Trent (01283) 813127

GARBUTT, Gerald. b 41. St Aid Birkenhead 65. **d** 67 **p** 68. C Stretford All SS *Man* 67-70; Lic to Offic 70-72; R Salford St Bart 72-74; V Lower Kersal 74-79; V Bethnal Green St Jo w St Bart *Lon* 79-90; P-in-c Stepney St Pet w St Benet 85-87; Chapl Furness Gen Hosp from 90; Chapl S Cumbria HA from 90. *6 Dale Garth, Leece, Ulverston, Cumbria LA12 0QU* Dalton-in-Furness (01229) 823852

GARDEN, Robert Andrew (Robin). b 26. MInstP58 FIMA72 Edin Univ BSc49 Kent Univ MA95. Cant Sch of Min 87. **d** 90 **p** 91. NSM Sandwich *Cant* from 90. *Naini, 164 St George's Road, Sandwich, Kent CT13 9LD* Sandwich (01304) 612116

GARDINER, Anthony Reade. b 35. Univ of NZ BA59. Cuddesdon Coll 60. **d** 62 **p** 63. C Gosforth All SS *Newc* 62-65; New Zealand 65-93; C Highcliffe w Hinton Admiral *Win* 93-94; TV N Creedy *Ex* from 94. *The Vicarage, Down St Mary, Crediton, Devon EX17 6EF* Crediton (01363) 84835

GARDINER, Canon Arthur John. b 22. Ch Ch Ox BA46 MA50. Ely Th Coll 49. **d** 50 **p** 51. S Rhodesia 64-65; Rhodesia 65-80; R Rushton and Glendon w Thorpe Malsor *Pet* 81-86; P-in-c Loddington w Cransley 82-86; Chapl Soc of St Marg E Grinstead 86-91; rtd 88; Perm to Offic *Chich* from 92. *St Mary's Cottage, Windmill Road, East Grinstead RH19 2DS* East Grinstead (01342) 315897

GARDINER, James Carlisle. b 18. St Jo Coll Dur LTh48. Tyndale Hall Bris. **d** 49 **p** 50. R Ditton *Roch* 56-83; rtd 83; Perm to Offic *Roch* from 83. *5 Larch Crescent, Tonbridge, Kent TN10 3NN* Tonbridge (01732) 362323

GARDINER, John. b 15. Clifton Th Coll 67. **d** 68 **p** 69. C Halliwell St Pet *Man* 68-71; V Monton 71-80; V Hoghton *Blackb* 80-84; rtd 84; Perm to Offic *Blackb* from 84. *4 Chestnut Drive, Morecambe, Lancs LA4 6HN* Morecambe (01524) 425639

GARDINER, John Kingsmill. b 18. OBE51. Bps' Coll Cheshunt 53. **d** 55 **p** 56. R Hardenhuish *Bris* 62-68; Lic to Offic 69-89; Perm to Offic from 89; rtd 83. *Combe Head, Giddeahall, Chippenham, Wilts SN14 7ES* Castle Combe (01249) 782497

GARDINER, Canon Kenneth Ashton. b 27. S'wark Ord Course 60. **d** 63 **p** 64. C Macclesfield St Mich *Ches* 67-70; V Chatham St Phil and St Jas *Roch* 70-93; RD Roch from 88; Hon Can Roch Cathl 88-93; rtd 93. *44 Trevale Road, Rochester, Kent ME1 3PA* Medway (01634) 844524

GARDINER, Thomas Alfred (Tom). b 29. St Cuth Soc Dur BA52 MA56. Ridley Hall Cam 54. **d** 56 **p** 57. C Stockport St Geo *Ches* 56-60; Asst Chapl Brentwood Sch Essex 60-62; Chapl 62-88; R Greensted-juxta-Ongar w Stanford Rivers *Chelmsf* from 88. *The Rectory, Greensted, Ongar, Essex CM5 9LA* Ongar (01277) 364694

GARDINER, William Gerald Henry. b 46. Lon Univ BD72. Oak Hill Th Coll 68. **d** 72 **p** 73. C Beckenham St Jo *Roch* 72-75; C Cheadle *Ches* 75-81; P-in-c Swynnerton *Lich* 81-83; P-in-c Tittensor 81-83; R Swynnerton and Tittensor 83-86; V Westlands St Andr from 86. *St Andrew's Vicarage, 50 Kingsway West, Westlands, Newcastle, Staffs ST5 3PU* Newcastle-under-Lyme (01782) 619594

GARDNER, Canon Anthony Brian. b 32. Lon Coll of Div 62. **d** 64 **p** 65. C Stoke *Cov* 64-68; R Whitnash from 68; RD Leamington 78-79; RD Warw and Leamington 79-87; Hon Can Cov Cathl from 83. *St Margaret's Rectory, 2 Church Close, Whitnash, Leamington Spa, Warks CV31 2HJ* Leamington Spa (01926) 425070

GARDNER, Charles Graham. b 18. AKC49. **d** 50 **p** 51. C Clapham H Trin *S'wark* 50-54; S Africa from 54. *49 Dahlia Avenue, Virginia, 9430 South Africa* Virginia (1722) 28187

GARDNER, Canon Christopher John. b 23. Jes Coll Cam BA47 MA53. Ely Th Coll 48. **d** 50 **p** 51. R Orton Waterville *Ely* 63-89; RD Yaxley 79-82; Hon Can Ely Cathl 81-89; P-in-c Alwalton 83-89; P-in-c Chesterton w Haddon 83-89; rtd 89. *73 Five Arches, Orton Wistow, Peterborough PE2 6FQ* Peterborough (01733) 371349

GARDNER, Ven Clifton Gordon. b 15. Toronto Univ BA36 Lon Univ BD39 AKC39. **d** 39 **p** 40. C Maidenhead St Luke *Ox* 39-41 and 46-47; Chapl RNVR 41-46; V Furze Platt *Ox* 47-52; Canada 52-76; Can St Paul's Cathl Lon Ontario 64-74; Adn Middx Ontario 74-76; Perm to Offic *Chelmsf* from 77. *1 Shepherd's Way, Saffron Walden, Essex CB10 2AH* Saffron Walden (01799) 527890

GARDNER, David. b 57. Oak Hill Th Coll BA87. **d** 87 **p** 88. C Ogley Hay *Lich* 87-91; TV Mildenhall *St E* from 91. *The Vicarage, 2 Oak Drive, Beck Row, Bury St Edmunds, Suffolk IP28 8UA* Mildenhall (01638) 717331

GARDNER, David Edward. b 21. Oak Hill Th Coll 44. **d** 49 **p** 50. Chapl Dockland Settlement No 1 Canning Town *Chelmsf* 55-60; Nat Chapl and Evang to Boy's Covenanter Union from 60; rtd 90. *15 Churchmead Close, Barnet, Herts EN4 8UY* 0181-449 4213

GARDNER, Geoffrey Maurice. b 28. K Coll Lon BA51 Lon Inst of Educn PGCE52 Bris Univ DipEd74. Cranmer Hall Dur DipTh59. **d** 59 **p** 60. Nigeria 62-72; Hon C Bath St Luke *B & W* 72-73; Perm to Offic 73-90; NSM Bath Widcombe 90-94; rtd 94. *4 St Winifred's Drive, Bath BA2 7HR* Bath (01225) 832953

GARDNER, Ian Douglas. b 34. St Pet Hall Ox BA58 MA62. Oak Hill Th Coll 58. **d** 60 **p** 61. C Biddulph *Lich* 60-63; C Weston St Jo *B & W* 64; Nigeria 65-76; P-in-c Hurstbourne Tarrant and Faccombe *Win* 77-79; V Hurstbourne Tarrant, Faccombe, Vernham Dean etc 79-85; R Nursling and Rownhams from 85. *The Vicarage, 27 Horns Drove, Rownhams, Southampton SO1 8AH* Southampton (01703) 738293

GARDNER, Canon John Phillip Backhouse. b 21. St Aid Birkenhead 49. **d** 52 **p** 53. R Wisley w Pyrford *Guildf* 70-87; RD Woking 82-87; Hon Can Guildf Cathl 86-87; rtd 87; Perm to Offic *Pet* from 87. *82 Water Lane, Wootton, Northampton NN4 0HG* Northampton (01604) 760254

GARDNER, Leslie John Thomas. b 15. Wells Th Coll 68. **d** 69 **p** 70. C Tiverton St Pet *Ex* 69-70; C Thornton *Leic* 70-72; P-in-c Wilne and Draycott w Breaston *Derby* 72-74; C Fordingbridge w Ibsley *Win* 74-75; C Welwyn w Ayot St Peter *St Alb* 75-78; C Compton Gifford *Ex* 78-82; rtd 82; Perm to Offic *Ex* from 82. *Braelea, 44 Newland Park, Seaton, Devon EX12 2SF* Seaton (01297) 21520

GARDNER, Mark Douglas. b 58. TCD BA80 MA83 DipTh83. **d** 83 **p** 84. C Ballymacarrett St Patr *D & D* 83-87; C Belf St Steph w St Luke *Conn* 87-89; C Hendon and Sunderland *Dur* 89-90; TV Sunderland 90-95; I Santry *D & G* from 95. *The Rectory Cappagh Road, Finglas, Dublin 11, Irish Republic* Dublin (1) 834-1015

GARDNER, Mary Christine. b 42. SRN65 Liv Univ HVCert71. St Jo Coll Nottm 80. dss 82 **d** 87 **p** 94. Ches St Paul *Ches* 82-84; Macclesfield St Mich 84-85; Macclesfield Team Par 85-87; Par Dn 87; Chapl Asst Nottm City Hosp 87-93; Chapl St Chris Hospice Lon from 93. *The Chaplain's Office, St Christopher's Hospice, Lawrie Park Road, London SE26 6DZ* 0181-778 9252

GARDNER, Dr Paul Douglas. b 50. K Coll Lon BA72 AKC72 SS Coll Cam PhD89. Reformed Th Sem Mississippi MDiv79 Ridley Hall Cam 79. **d** 80 **p** 81. C Cam St Martin *Ely* 80-83; Lect Oak Hill Th Coll 83-90; V Hartford *Ches* from 90; RD Middlewich from 94. *St John's Vicarage, Hartford, Northwich, Cheshire CW8 1QA* Northwich (01606) 77557

GARDNER, Richard Beverley Twynam. b 11. Chich Th Coll 33. **d** 36 **p** 37. V Botleys and Lyne *Guildf* 54-71; V Long Cross 56-71; V Ewshott 71-76; rtd 76; Perm to Offic *Guildf* 81-93. *16 Palace Gate, High Street, Odiham, Basingstoke, Hants RG25 1JZ* Odiham (01256) 704563

GARDNER, Ronald Frederick. b 25. Dur Univ BA51 DipTh52 Birm Univ MA79. **d** 52 **p** 53. V Forsbrook *Lich* 69-83; V Mow Cop 83-89; rtd 89. *Rode Mill House, Church Lane, Scholar Green, Stoke-on-Trent ST7 3QR* Alsager (01270) 877245

GARDOM, Francis Douglas. b 34. Trin Coll Ox BA55 MA59. Wells Th Coll 58. **d** 60 **p** 61. C Greenwich St Alfege w St Pet *S'wark* 60-68; C Lewisham St Steph and St Mark 68-76; Hon C from 76. *79 Maze Hill, London SE10 8XQ* 0181-858 7052 or 825 1474 Fax 293 4407

GARDOM, James Theodore Douglas. b 61. St Anne's Coll Ox BA83 K Coll Lon PhD92. Ripon Coll Cuddesdon 87. **d** 90 **p** 91. C Witney *Ox* 90-92; USPG from 92; Zimbabwe from 92. *9 Thornburg Avenue, Mount Pleasant, Harare, Zimbabwe*

GARLAND, Christopher John. b 47. Ex Univ BA69 PhD72. Qu Coll Birm 78. **d** 80 **p** 81. C Beckenham St Jas *Roch* 80-82; C Roch 82-85; Papua New Guinea from 85. *Newton Theological College, PO Box 162, Popondetta, Papua New Guinea*

GARLAND, Michael. b 50. St D Coll Lamp DipTh72 Sarum & Wells Th Coll 2 **d** 73 **p** 74. C Swansea St Thos and Kilvey *S & B* 73-76; C Boldmere *Birm* 76-79; V Kingshurst 79-88; P-in-c Curdworth w Castle Vale 88-90; R Curdworth from 90. *The Rectory, Glebe Fields, Curdworth, Sutton Coldfield, W Midlands B76 9ES* Curdworth (01675) 470384

GARLAND, Peter Stephen John. b 52. ALA79 Univ Coll Lon BA73 Univ of W Ontario MA74 Dur Univ PGCE75. Ripon Coll Cuddesdon 88. **d** 90 **p** 91. C Crookham *Guildf* 90-94; V Tongham from 94; Chapl Farnborough Coll of Tech from 94. *The Vicarage, Poyle Road, Tongham, Farnham, Surrey GU10 1DU* Runfold (01252) 782224

GARLICK, Canon David. b 37. Nottm Univ BA62 Ox Univ DipPSA63. St Steph Ho Ox 62. **d** 64 **p** 65. C Kennington St Jo *S'wark* 64-66; Hon C Newington St Paul 66-68; P-in-c Vauxhall St Pet 68-79; V Lewisham St Mary from 79; RD E Lewisham from 92; Hon Can S'wark Cathl from 93. *Lewisham Vicarage, 48 Lewisham Park, London SE13 6QZ* 0181-690 2682 or 690 1585

GARLICK, Dennis. b 26. ACIS. Qu Coll Birm. **d** 84 **p** 85. NSM Dronfield *Derby* 84-88; C 88-89; C-in-c Holmesfield 89-90; TV Dronfield w Holmesfield 90-93; rtd 93. *51 Holmesdale Road, Dronfield, Sheffield S18 6FA* Dronfield (01246) 418792

GARLICK, Mrs Kathleen Beatrice. b 49. Leeds Univ BA71 Birm Univ CertEd72. Glouc Sch of Min 87. **d** 90 **p** 94. Hon C Much Birch w Lt Birch, Much Dewchurch etc *Heref* from 90. *Birch Lodge, Much Birch, Hereford HR2 8HT* Golden Valley (01981) 540666

GARLICK, Canon Peter. b 34. AKC57. **d** 58 **p** 59. V Heyside *Man* 66-73; R Stretford All SS 73-79; RD Wootton *Pet* 79-88; V Duston 79-91; TR Duston Team 91-94; Can Pet Cathl 85-94; rtd 94. *120 Worcester Close, Northampton NN3 9GD* Northampton (01604) 416511

GARMAN, Canon Bernard Wilfred. b 16. Edin Th Coll 47. **d** 49 **p** 50. V Bywell St Andr *Newc* 66-73; V Riding Mill 66-77; Chapl Dioc Retreat Ho 69-77; Asst Dioc Tr Officer from 77; rtd 77; Hon Can Newc Cathl *Newc* 77-88. *Thropton Hill, Physic Lane, Thropton, Morpeth, Northd NE65 7HU* Rothbury (01669) 20840

GARNER, Alistair Ross. b 58. Pemb Coll Ox BA81 MA86. St Jo Coll Nottm DTS92. **d** 92 **p** 93. C Ashton on Mersey St Mary *Ches* from 92. *109 Ascot Avenue, Sale, Cheshire M33 4QT* 0161-976 1693

GARNER, Canon Carl. b 42. Rhodes Univ BA62 Keble Coll Ox BA65 MA70. St Paul's Grahamstown 66. **d** 67 **p** 68. S Africa 67-84; Dioc Missr *St Alb* from 84; Can Res St Alb from 84. *Holywell Close, 43 Holywell Hill, St Albans, Herts AL1 1HE* St Albans (01727) 854832

GARNER, David Henry. b 40. Trin Coll Bris 70. **d** 73 **p** 74. C Tunstead *Man* 73-75; C Fazeley *Lich* 76-78; V Sparkhill St Jo *Birm* 78-85; V Blackheath from 85. *St Paul's Vicarage, 83 Vicarage Road, Halesowen, W Midlands B62 8HX* 0121-559 1000

GARNER, Geoffrey Walter. b 40. Ripon Hall Ox 69. **d** 71 **p** 72. C Stoke *Cov* 71-76; V Tile Hill 76-80; TV Hackney *Lon* 80-89; R Bow w Bromley St Leon from 89. *16 Tomlins Grove, London E3 4NX* 0181-981 6710

GARNER, Martin Wyatt. b 39. Lon Coll of Div 60 Tyndale Hall Bris 63 Sarum Th Coll 66. **d** 66 **p** 67. C Coleraine *Conn* 66-70; C Cam St Martin *Ely* 70-72; V Edge Hill St Nath *Liv* 72-80; P-in-c Burton in Kendal *Carl* 80-87; R Burghclere w Newtown and Ecchinswell w Sydmonton *Win* 87-93; R Ewelme, Brightwell Baldwin, Cuxham w Easington *Ox* from 93. *The Rectory, Ewelme, Oxford OX10 6HP* Wallingford (01491) 837823

GARNER, Peter. b 35. Lon Univ BSc56. Wycliffe Hall Ox 56. **d** 58 **p** 59. C Walthamstow St Jo *Chelmsf* 58-61; V Hainault 61-70; R Theydon Garnon 70-73; P-in-c Kirby le Soken 73-74; V 74-82; P-in-c Fountains *Ripon* 82-88; P-in-c Kirkby Malzeard w Grewelthorpe and Mickley etc 82-88; Par Development Adv from 88; P-in-c Birstwith 91-93; R Farnham w Scotton, Staveley, Copgrove etc from 93. *The Rectory, Staveley, Knaresborough, N Yorkshire HG5 9LD* Boroughbridge (01423) 340275

GARNER, Rodney George. b 48. MIPM75 Birm Univ DipTh77 Lon Univ BA87. Qu Coll Birm 75. **d** 78 **p** 79. C Tranmere St Paul w St Luke *Ches* 78-81; V Eccleston St Thos *Liv* 81-90; P-in-c Sculcoates St Paul w Ch Ch and St Silas *York* 90-95;

Lay Tr Officer (E Riding Adnry) 90-95; P-in-c Southport H Trin *Liv* from 95. *Holy Trinity Vicarage, 24 Roe Lane, Southport, Merseyside PR9 9DX* Southport (01704) 538560

GARNER, Thomas Richard. b 43. K Coll Lon. **d** 69 **p** 70. C Tynemouth Ch Ch *Newc* 69-73; C Fenham St Jas and St Basil 73-76; V Hamstead St Bernard *Birm* 76-80; New Zealand from 80. *120 Cambridge Street, Levin, New Zealand* Levin (6) 368-5955

GARNETT, David Christopher. b 45. Nottm Univ BA67 Fitzw Coll Cam BA69 MA73. Westcott Ho Cam 67. **d** 69 **p** 70. C Cottingham *York* 69-72; Chapl Selw Coll Cam 72-77; P-in-c Patterdale *Carl* 77-80; Dir of Ords 78-80; V Heald Green St Cath *Ches* 80-87; R Christleton 87-92; TR Ellesmere Port from 92. *The Rectory, Vale Road, Ellesmere Port, South Wirral L65 9AY* 0151-355 2516

GARNETT, James Arthur. b 42. N Ord Course 77. **d** 80 **p** 81. C Kirkby *Liv* 80-91; P-in-c Liv St Phil w St Dav from 91. *The Vicarage, 55 Sheil Road, Liverpool L6 3AD* 0151-263 6202

GARNETT, Joseph William. b 20. AKC48. Edin Th Coll 48. **d** 49 **p** 50. V Carl St Aid and Ch Ch *Carl* 69-73; R Nairn *Mor* 73-78; R Greenock *Glas* 78-80; R Castle Douglas 80-83; rtd 85; Perm to Offic *Glas* from 85. *Knockelly Cottage, Penpont, Thornhill, Dumfriesshire DG3 4NF* Marrburn (018486) 274

GARNETT, Peter. b 17. Bps' Coll Cheshunt 49. **d** 51 **p** 52. Rhodesia 69-71; C Wyken *Cov* 71-73; C Malden St Jo *S'wark* 73-77; C Headington Quarry *Ox* 77-82; rtd 82. *Dulverton Hall, St Martin's Square, Scarborough YO11 2DB* Scarborough (01723) 373082

GARNETT, Preb Ralph Henry. b 28. Cuddesdon Coll 58. **d** 60 **p** 61. RD Ludlow *Heref* 72-75; R Burford II w Greete and Hope Bagot 69-87; R Burford III w Lt Heref 69-87; P-in-c Burford I 72-74; R 74-87; V Tenbury 69-74; TR 74-87; Preb Heref Cathl 82-93; P-in-c Fownhope 87-93; P-in-c Brockhampton w Fawley 87-93; RD Heref Rural 92-93; rtd 93. *2 The Craft, Sutton St Nicholas, Hereford HR1 3BZ* Sutton St Nicholas (01432) 880697

GARNETT, Roger James. b 58. Dur Univ BA79. Wycliffe Hall Ox 89. **d** 91 **p** 92. C Forest Gate St Sav w W Ham St Matt *Chelmsf* 91-94; C Collier Row St Jas and Havering-atte-Bower from 94. *St John's House, 428 Havering Road, Romford RM1 4DF* Romford (01708) 43330

GARNSEY, George Christopher. b 36. Qu Coll Ox BA63. **d** 60 **p** 60. Lic to Offic *Wakef* 78-79; C Lupset 80; Australia from 80. *The Rectory, Gresford, NSW, Australia 2311*

GARRARD, Mrs Christine Ann. b 51. LCST75 Open Univ BA86. E Anglian Minl Tr Course 87. **d** 90 **p** 94. Par Dn Kesgrave *St E* 90-94; C from 94. *2 Wainwright Way, Kesgrave, Ipswich IP5 7XG* Ipswich (01473) 623840

GARRARD, Dr James Richard. b 65. Dur Univ BA88 Ox Univ DipPhil92. Westcott Ho Cam CTM94. **d** 94 **p** 95. C Elland *Wakef* from 94. *48 Grasmere Drive, Elland, W Yorkshire HX5 9PW* Elland (01422) 311706

GARRARD, Nicholas James Havelock. b 62. Leeds Univ BA83. Westcott Ho Cam 86. **d** 88 **p** 89. C Scotforth *Blackb* 88-91; C Eaton *Nor* 91-95; V Heigham St Thos from 95. *St Thomas's Vicarage, Edinburgh Road, Norwich NR2 3RL* Norwich (01603) 624390

✠**GARRARD, Rt Rev Richard.** b 37. K Coll Lon BD60 AKC60. **d** 61 **p** 62 **c** 94. C Woolwich St Mary w H Trin *S'wark* 61-66; C Cam St St Mary w St Mich *Ely* 66-68; Chapl Keswick Hall Coll Nor 68-74; Prin CA Wilson Carlile Coll of Evang 74-79; Can Res and Chan S'wark Cathl *S'wark* 79-87; Dir of Tr 79-87; Can Res St E Cathl *St E* 87-94; Dioc Adv for Continuing Minl Educn 87-91; Adn Sudbury 91-94; Suff Bp Penrith *Carl* from 94. *Holm Croft, 13 Castle Road, Kendal, Cumbria LA9 7AU* Kendal (01539) 727836 Fax 734380

GARRATT, Bernard John. b 43. Lon Univ BA65 Linacre Coll Ox BA67 MA71. St Steph Ho Ox 65. **d** 68 **p** 69. C Notting Hill St Jo 68-71; C Fareham SS Pet and Paul *Portsm* 71-73; Chapl City of Lon Poly *Lon* 73-79; R Trowbridge H Trin *Sarum* 79-81; TR 81-87; V Wootton Bassett from 87; RD Calne 88-90. *The Vicarage, Glebe Road, Wootton Bassett, Swindon SN4 7DU* Swindon (01793) 854302 or 853272

GARRATT, John William. b 11. **d** 78 **p** 78. Hon C Hounslow H Trin *Lon* 78-88; Hon C Hounslow H Trin w St Paul 88-94; Perm to Offic from 94. *Flat 25, Smoothfield, 130 Hibernia Road, Hounslow TW3 3RJ* 0181-570 6009

GARRATT, Peter James. b 37. ALCD64. **d** 64 **p** 65. C Bingham *S'well* 64-67; C Mansf St Pet 67-69; R Purlwell *Wakef* 69-73; R Kirk Sandall and Edenthorpe *Sheff* 73-82; R Whippingham w E Cowes *Portsm* 82-87; V Soberton w Newtown from 87. *The Vicarage, Soberton, Southampton SO3 1PF* Droxford (01489) 877400

GARRATT, Roger Charles. b 50. St Jo Coll Dur BA72 DipTh73. Cranmer Hall Dur 73. **d** 74 **p** 75. C Leamington Priors St Paul *Cov* 74-77; Chapl Emscote Lawn Sch Warw from 77. *8 Wasdale Close, Leamington Spa, Warks CV32 6NF* Leamington Spa (01926) 335495/491961

GARRETT, Christopher Hugh Ahlan. b 35. Sarum & Wells Th Coll 72. **d** 75 **p** 76. C Addiscombe St Mildred *Cant* 75-81; V Thornton Heath St Jude w St Aid *S'wark* from 81. *St Jude's Vicarage, 11 Dunheved Road North, Thornton Heath, Surrey CR7 6AH* 0181-684 1630

GARRETT, Edgar Ashton. b 20. S'wark Ord Course 62. **d** 65 **p** 66. C Horsell *Guildf* 65-70; V Send 70-79; Perm to Offic *Chich* from 79; rtd 85. *14 Crosbie Close, Chichester, W Sussex PO19 2RZ* Chichester (01243) 789770

GARRETT, Miss Elizabeth Clare. b 46. Trin Coll Bris. **d** 94 **p** 95. C Ewyas Harold w Dulas, Kenderchurch etc *Heref* from 94. *Brightwell, Olde Shoppe Lands, Ewyas Harold, Hereford HR2 0HR* Golden Valley (01981) 241017

GARRETT, Canon Frederick Henry. b 18. TCD BA43. **d** 43 **p** 44. I Mallow *C, C & R* 55-74; I Kilshannig 57-74; I Castlemagner 71-74; RD Midleton 65-75; I Glengarriff w Berehaven 74-87; Preb Ross Cathl 76-87; Preb Cork Cathl 76-87; rtd 87. *Meadow Cottage, Wood View, Mallow, Co Cork, Irish Republic* Mallow (22) 21748

GARRETT, Geoffrey David. b 57. Oak Hill Th Coll 83. **d** 86 **p** 87. C Trentham *Lich* 86-90; V Rhodes *Man* from 90. *The Vicarage, Rhodes, Middleton, Manchester M24 4PU* 0161-643 3224

GARRETT, Ian Lee. b 60. MCSP DipPh 81. Sarum & Wells Th Coll 86. **d** 89 **p** 90. C Maidstone St Martin *Cant* 89-95; P-in-c S Ashford St Fran from 95. *St Francis House, Cyrol Road, Ashford, Kent TN23 5AS* Ashford (01233) 625555

GARRETT, John Watkins. b 09. St Chad's Coll Dur BA35 LTh36. **d** 36 **p** 37. Chapl Carlton Hayes Psychiatric Hosp Narborough 54-90; R Narborough *Leic* 59-75; rtd 75; Lic to Offic *Leic* 75-81; Perm to Offic from 81. *4 Walcot Lane, Folkingham, Sleaford, Lincs NG34 0TP* Folkingham (01529) 497385

GARRETT, Kevin George. b 48. Oak Hill Th Coll BA86. **d** 86 **p** 87. C Hoddesdon *St Alb* 86-89; C Loughton St Mary and St Mich *Chelmsf* 89-90; TV 90-95; P-in-c Loughton St Mich from 95. *St Mary's House, Roding Road, Loughton, Essex IG10 3EJ* 0181-508-1489

GARROW, Alan John Philip. b 67. Lon Bible Coll BA90. Wycliffe Hall Ox MPhil94. **d** 93 **p** 94. C Waltham H Cross *Chelmsf* from 93. *Abbey Lodge, 5A Greenyard, Waltham Abbey, Essex EN9 1RD* Lea Valley (01992) 763186 Fax as telephone

GARRUD, Christopher Charles. b 54. Cranmer Hall Dur DipTh84. **d** 85 **p** 86. C Watford *St Alb* 85-89; C Ireland Wood *Ripon* from 89; Chapl Cookridge Hosp Leeds from 93. *6 Holt Park Gardens, Leeds LS16 7RB* Leeds (0113) 267 5417

GARSIDE, Canon Howard. b 24. Leeds Univ BA49. Coll of Resurr Mirfield 49. **d** 51 **p** 52. V Manston *Ripon* 64-70; RD Whitkirk 70-78; Hon Can Ripon Cathl 78-89; V Harrogate St Wilfrid 78-80; P-in-c Harrogate St Luke 78-80; V Harrogate St Wilfrid and St Luke 80-89; RD Harrogate 83-88; rtd 89. *73 Kirkby Road, Ripon, N Yorkshire HG4 2HH* Ripon (01765) 690625

GARSIDE, Melvin. b 42. N Ord Course 85. **d** 88 **p** 89. C Lindley *Wakef* 88-91; C Shelf *Bradf* 91-93; V Lundwood *Wakef* from 93. *The Vicarage, Littleworth Lane, Barnsley, S Yorkshire S71 5RG* Barnsley (01226) 203194

GARTLAND, Christopher Michael. b 49. Man Univ BA78. Coll of Resurr Mirfield 82. **d** 84 **p** 85. C Almondbury w Farnley Tyas *Wakef* 84-87; P-in-c Upperthong 87-89; TV Upper Holme Valley 89-91; Chapl Stanley Royd Hosp Wakef from 91; Chapl to Mental Health Services Wakef HA from 91. *c/o Stanley Royd Hospital, Aberford Road, Wakefield, W Yorkshire WF1 2DQ* Wakefield (01924) 814630

GARTON, Derek John. b 33. ALCD59. **d** 59 **p** 60. C Bromley Common St Aug *Roch* 59-62; C Gravesend St Aid 64-66; Hon C Gravesend St Geo 66-73; Perm to Offic *Ex* 77-83; Australia from 83. *The Manse, 31 Bekta Street, Mallacoota, Victoria, Australia 3889* Moe (51) 580394

GARTON, Canon John Henry. b 41. Worc Coll Ox BA66 MA DipTh67. Cuddesdon Coll 67. **d** 69 **p** 70. CF 69-73; Lect Linc Th Coll 73-78; TR Cov E *Cov* 78-86; C Vuddesdon *Ox* from 86; Prin Ripon Coll Cuddesdon from 86; Hon Can Worc Cathl *Worc* from 87. *The Old Vicarage, Cuddesdon, Oxford OX44 9HP* Wheatley (01865) 874427 or 874368

GARTSIDE, Philip. b 60. Pemb Coll Ox BA82 MA86 Leeds Univ BA92. Coll of Resurr Mirfield CPT93. **d** 93 **p** 94. C Walton-on-the-Hill *Liv* from 93. *10 Lochinver Street, Walton, Liverpool L9 1ER* 0151-523 6617

GARWELL, John Arthur. b 25. K Coll Lon 48. **d** 52 **p** 53. Chapl RN 60-76; C Guildf St Nic *Guildf* 76-77; Sec Sir Oswald Stoll Foundn Fulham 78-86; rtd 90. *75 Portsmouth Road, Guildford, Surrey GU2 5BS* Guildford (01483) 64255

GARWOOD, Albert Wells. b 14. Ripon Hall Ox. **d** 59 **p** 60. C Dartford H Trin *Roch* 59-60; Canada from 60. *Apartment 515, 1186 Queen Street, Halifax, Nova Scotia, Canada, B3H 4K9*

GARWOOD, David John Shirley (Damian). b 31. Leeds Univ BA59. Coll of Resurr Mirfield. **d** 61 **p** 62. C Meir *Lich* 61-66; Lic to Offic *Wakef* 67-71 and from 74; CR from 68; S Africa 71-74. *House of the Resurrection, Mirfield, W Yorkshire WF14 0BN* Mirfield (01924) 494318

GASCOIGNE, Peter Francis. b 36. Linc Th Coll 85. **d** 87 **p** 88. C Wath-upon-Dearne w Adwick-upon-Dearne *Sheff* 87-90; R Thurnscoe St Helen 90-94; V New Rossington from 94. *St Luke's Vicarage, The Circle, New Rossington, Doncaster, S Yorkshire DN11 0QP* Doncaster (01302) 868288

GASCOIGNE, Philip. b 27. Oak Hill Th Coll. **d** 62 **p** 63. C Blackpool Ch Ch *Blackb* 62-65; V Bootle St Leon *Liv* 65-71; Staff Evang CPAS 71-74; V St Helens St Mark *Liv* 74-77; V Blackpool Ch Ch *Blackb* 77-81; V Blackpool Ch Ch w All SS from 81. *The Vicarage, 23A North Park Drive, Blackpool FY3 8LR* Blackpool (01253) 391235

GASH, Christopher Alan Ronald. b 39. St Andr Univ 57 Nottm Univ CPTS. E Midl Min Tr Course 83. **d** 86 **p** 87. C Thurmaston *Leic* 86-89; P-in-c Stoke Golding w Dadlington from 89. *The Vicarage, High Street, Stoke Golding, Nuneaton, Warks CV13 6EJ* Hinckley (01455) 212317

GASH, Canon Wilfred John. b 31. Lon Univ DipTh62. St Aid Birkenhead 60. **d** 62 **p** 63. C St Mary Cray and St Paul's Cray *Roch* 62-65; C Bexley St Jo 65-67; R Levenshulme St Pet *Man* 67-72; V Clifton 72-94; AD Eccles 81-87; Hon Can Man Cathl from 86; P-in-c Pendlebury Ch Ch 86-87; P-in-c Pendlebury St Aug 86-87; Dioc Adv on Evang from 89; TR Bolton St Paul w Em from 94. *St Paul's Vicarage, 174 Chorley New Road, Bolton BL1 4PF* Bolton (01204) 842303

GASKELL, David. b 48. Lon Univ BD76. Trin Coll Bris 72. **d** 76 **p** 77. C Eccleston Ch Ch *Liv* 76-80; C Rainhill 80-83; V Over Darwen St Jas *Blackb* 83-88; V Livesey 88-95; V Preston St Cuth from 95. *St Cuthbert's Vicarage, 20 Black Bull Lane, Fulwood, Preston PR2 3PX* Preston (01772) 717346

GASKELL, Ian Michael. b 51. Nottm Univ BTh81. Linc Th Coll 77. **d** 81 **p** 82. C Wakef St Jo *Wakef* 81-83; Ind Chapl *Sheff* 83-86; V Cleckheaton St Luke and Whitechapel *Wakef* 86-93; V Birkenshaw w Hunsworth from 93. *St Paul's Vicarage, 6 Vicarage Gardens, Birkenshaw, Bradford, W Yorkshire BD11 2EF* Bradford (01274) 683776

GASKELL, Preb John Bernard. b 28. Jes Coll Ox BA52 MA58. Chich Th Coll 59. **d** 60 **p** 61. C-in-c Grosvenor Chpl *Lon* 68-79; Warden Liddon Ho Lon 68-79; V Holborn St Alb w Saffron Hill St Pet *Lon* 79-93; AD S Camden (Holborn and St Pancras) 81-86; Preb St Paul's Cathl 85-93; rtd 93. *The Point, Church Island, Staines, Middlesex TW18 4YE* Staines (01784) 469894

GASKELL, Mary. b 50. Nottm Univ BTh81 Bradf and Ilkley Coll CertEd89. Linc Th Coll 77. **dss** 81 **d** 89 **p** 94. NSM Cleckheaton St Luke and Whitechapel *Wakef* 89-93; NSM Birkenshaw w Hunsworth 93-95; Asst Chapl St Jas Univ Hosp Leeds from 95. *St James's University Hospital, Beckett Street, Leeds LS9 7TF* Leeds (0113) 243 3144

GASKILL, Ernest Raymond. b 17. St Chad's Coll Dur BA39 DipTh41 MA42. **d** 41 **p** 42. V Doncaster Ch Ch *Sheff* 66-82; rtd 82; Perm to Offic *Sheff* from 82. *37 Glamis Road, Doncaster, S Yorkshire DN2 6DP* Doncaster (01302) 320845

GATENBY, Canon Denis William. b 31. Ex Coll Ox BA54 DipTh55 MA58 Man Univ DSPT82. Wycliffe Hall Ox 54. **d** 56 **p** 57. C Deane *Man* 56-60; C Bradf Cathl *Bradf* 60-63; V Bootle St Matt *Liv* 63-72; V Horwich H Trin *Man* 72-84; TR Horwich 84-93; TR Horwich and Rivington from 93; AD Deane from 87; Hon Can Man Cathl from 91. *The Rectory, Chorley Old Road, Horwich, Bolton BL6 6AX* Horwich (01204) 68263

GATENBY, Paul Richard. b 32. Dur Univ BA56. Qu Coll Birm DipTh64. **d** 64 **p** 65. C Wellingborough St Barn *Pet* 64-68; V Braunston w Brooke 68-71; C Langley Marish *Ox* 71-72; TV Basildon St Martin w H Cross and Laindon *Chelmsf* 73-76; R Isham w Pytchley *Pet* from 77. *The Rectory, Kettering Road, Isham, Kettering, Northants NN14 1HQ* Burton Latimer (01536) 722371

GATENBY, Simon John Taylor. b 62. Nottm Univ BA83. St Jo Coll Nottm 84. **d** 87 **p** 88. C Haughton St Mary *Man* 87-90; C Newburn *Newc* 90-93; P-in-c Brunswick *Man* from 93. *The Rectory, Brunswick Street, Manchester M13 9TP* 0161-273 2470

GATES, John Michael. b 35. Dur Univ BA56 DipTh60. Cranmer Hall Dur 58. **d** 60 **p** 61. C Felixstowe St Jo *St E* 60-67; R Boyton w Capel St Andrew and Hollesley from 67; P-in-c Shottisham w Sutton 87-92. *The Rectory, Hollesley, Woodbridge, Suffolk IP12 3RE* Shottisham (01394) 411252

GATES, John Richard. b 47. Oak Hill Th Coll DipTh73. **d** 73 **p** 74. C Iver *Ox* 73-76; C Broadwater St Mary *Chich* 76-79; Dioc Youth Officer *Nor* 79-82; V Cosby *Leic* 82-86. *Address temp unknown*

GATES, Richard James. b 46. BA85. Oak Hill Th Coll 82. **d** 85 **p** 86. C Heald Green St Cath *Ches* 85-89; V Norton from 89.

The Vicarage, Windmill Hill, Runcorn, Cheshire WA7 6QE Runcorn (01928) 715225

GATES, Simon Philip. b 60. St Andr Univ MA82 BA86. Cranmer Hall Dur 84. **d** 87 **p** 88. C Southall Green St Jo *Lon* 87-91; Hong Kong from 91. *St Andrew's Church, 138 Nathan Road, Kowloon, Hong Kong* Hong Kong (852) 367-1478 Fax 367-6562

GATFORD, Ven Ian. b 40. AKC65. **d** 67 **p** 68. C Clifton w Glapton *S'well* 67-71; R 71-75; V Sherwood 75-84; Can Res Derby Cathl *Derby* 84-93; Adn Derby from 93. *72 Pastures Hill, Littleover, Derby DE23 7BB* Derby (01332) 512700 Fax 292969

GATHERCOLE, Ven John Robert. b 37. Fitzw Ho Cam BA59 MA63. Ridley Hall Cam 59. **d** 62 **p** 63. C Dur St Nic *Dur* 62-66; C Croxdale 66-69; Bp's Soc and Ind Adv 66-69; Ind Chapl *Worc* 69-87; RD Bromsgrove 77-85; Sen Chapl Worcs Ind Miss from 85; Hon Can Worc Cathl from 80; Adn Dudley from 87. *15 Worcester Road, Droitwich, Worcs WR9 8AA* Worcester (01905) 773301 Fax as telephone

GATLIFFE, David Spenser. b 45. Keble Coll Ox BA67 Fitzw Coll Cam BA69. Westcott Ho Cam 67. **d** 69 **p** 70. C Oxted *S'wark* 69-72; C Roehampton H Trin 72-75; C S Beddington St Mich 76-77; TV Clapham Old Town 78-87; P-in-c Clapham Ch Ch and St Jo 81-87; TV Clapham TM 87-89; V S Wimbledon H Trin and St Pet from 89. *The Vicarage, 234 The Broadway, London SW19 1SB* 0181-542 7098 or 542 1388

GATRILL, Adrian Colin. b 60. Southn Univ BTh82. Linc Th Coll 83. **d** 85 **p** 86. C W Bromwich St Andr *Lich* 85-88; C W Bromwich St Andr w Ch Ch 88-89; Chapl RAF from 89; Perm to Offic *St D* 90-95. *Chaplaincy Services (RAF), HQ, Personnel and Training Command, RAF Innsworth, Gloucester GL3 1EZ* Gloucester (01452) 712612 Ext 5164 Fax 510828

GAUGE, Canon Barrie Victor. b 41. St D Coll Lamp BA62 Selw Coll Cam BA64 MA74 Liv Univ CQSW81. Bp Burgess Hall Lamp DPS65. **d** 65 **p** 66. C Newtown w Llanllwchaiarn w Aberhafesp *St As* 65-68; C Prestatyn 68-73; R Bodfari 73-76; Dioc RE Adv 73-76; Perm to Offic *Ches* 76-84; V Birkenhead St Jas w St Bede 84-90; Dir of Resources from 90; Hon Can Ches Cathl from 94; C Lache cum Saltney from 95. *103 Five Ashes Road, Chester CH4 7QA* Chester (01244) 680804 or 379222

GAUNT, Arthur Raymond. b 15. St Aid Birkenhead 47. **d** 49 **p** 50. V Kexby w Wilberfoss *York* 66-71; V Scarborough St Columba 71-78; rtd 78; Perm to Offic *Bradf* from 80. *20 Grantley Drive, Harrogate, N Yorkshire HG3 2ST* Harrogate (01423) 504998

GAUNT, Eric Emmerson. b 33. Sarum Th Coll 65. **d** 67 **p** 68. C Hatch End St Anselm *Lon* 67-74; V Neasden cum Kingsbury St Cath 74-80; V Neasden St Cath w St Paul from 80. *The Vicarage, Tanfield Avenue, London NW2 7RX* 0181-452 7322

GAUNT, Roger Cecil. b 30. K Coll Cam BA52. Westcott Ho Cam 53. **d** 55 **p** 56. R Limpsfield and Titsey *S'wark* 68-77; Dioc Dir of Educn *St Alb* 77-79; Can Res St Alb 77-79; Perm to Offic *Truro* 79-84; Perm to Offic *S'wark* 79-88; Lic to Offic 88-91; Hon C Charlwood from 91; Perm to Offic *Guildf* 84-86; rtd 95. *Apple Hill, Old Road, Buckland, Betchworth, Surrey RH3 7DU* Betchworth (01737) 843393

GAUSDEN, Peter James. b 32. Qu Coll Birm 57. **d** 60 **p** 61. C Battersea St Pet *S'wark* 60-63; C St Peter-in-Thanet *Cant* 63-68; V Sturry 68-74; R Sturry w Fordwich and Westbere w Hersden from 74; Dioc Ecum Officer from 91. *The Rectory, 2 The Hamels, Church Lane, Sturry, Canterbury, Kent CT2 0BL* Canterbury (01227) 710320

GAVIN, David Guy. b 63. Birm Univ BA85 Dur Univ BA90. Cranmer Hall Dur 88. **d** 91 **p** 92. C Parr *Liv* from 91. *5 Epsom Street, St Helens, Lancs WA9 2DT* St Helens (01744) 31434

GAWITH, Canon Alan Ruthven. b 24. Man Univ SACert47. Lich Th Coll 54. **d** 56 **p** 57. V Kendal St Geo *Carl* 67-74; Soc Resp Officer *Man* 74-89; Hon Can Man Cathl 82-89; Bp's Adv on AIDS from 88; rtd 90. *7 Redwaters, Leigh, Lancs WN7 1JD* Leigh (01942) 676641

GAWNE-CAIN, John. b 38. CEng MICE G&C Coll Cam BA61 MA66. Cuddesdon Coll 74. **d** 76 **p** 77. C Cowley St Jas *Ox* 76-80; P-in-c Ox St Giles 80-85; V Ox St Giles and SS Phil and Jas w St Marg 85-92; P-in-c Uffington w Woolstone and Baulking 92-93; P-in-c Shellingford 92-93; R Uffington, Shellingford, Woolstone and Baulking from 93. *St Mary's Vicarage, Uffington, Faringdon, Oxon SN7 7RA* Faringdon (01367) 820633

GAWTHROP-DORAN, Mrs Sheila Mary. b 37. Birm Univ CertEd. Dalton Ho Bris 68. **dss** 79 **d** 87. Halliwell St Paul *Man* 79-82; New Bury 82-89; Par Dn 87-89; Par Dn Tonge w Alkrington 89-94; rtd 94. *8 The Vale, Skelton, York YO2 6YH* York (01904) 470218

GAY, Colin James. b 37. Univ of Wales (Lamp) BA63. Chich Th Coll 63. **d** 65 **p** 66. C W Hackney St Barn *Lon* 65-69; C Hitchin

St Alb 69-74; P-in-c Apsley End 74-80; TV Chambersbury (Hemel Hempstead) 80-85; V Barnet Vale St Mark from 85. *St Mark's Vicarage, 56 Potters Road, Barnet, Herts EN5 5HN* 0181-449 4265

GAY, David Charles. b 46. CCC Cam BA68 MA72 PhD71. Coll of Resurr Mirfield DipTh74. **d** 75 **p** 76. C Sheff St Mark Broomhall *Sheff* 75-78; Bp's Chapl for Graduates 78-80; Lib Pusey Ho 78-80; Lic to Offic *Sheff* 80-82; C Warmsworth 82-84; V Worsbrough St Thos and St Jas from 84. *The Vicarage, 13 Bank End Road, Worsbrough, Barnsley, S Yorkshire S70 4AF* Barnsley (01226) 203426

GAY, Dr John Dennis. b 43. St Pet Coll Ox BA64 DipTh65 MA68 DPhil69 MSc78. Ripon Coll Cuddesdon BA86. **d** 67 **p** 68. C Paddington St Jas *Lon* 67-71; P-in-c 71-72; Lic to Offic *Ox* from 72; Chapl Culham Coll Abingdon 72-79; Lect Ox Univ 78-80; Dir Culham Coll Inst from 80; Perm to Offic *Chich* 87-89. *Culham College Institute, 60 East St Helen Street, Abingdon, Oxon OX14 5EB* Abingdon (01235) 520458 or 532992

GAY, Canon Perran Russell. b 59. St Cath Coll Cam BA81 MA85 Ex Univ CertEd82. Ripon Coll Cuddesdon BA86. **d** 87 **p** 88. C Bodmin w Lanhydrock and Lanivet *Truro* 87-90; Bp's Dom Chapl 90-94; Dioc Officer for Unity 90-94; Can Res and Chan Truro Cathl from 94; Dir of Tr from 94. *52 Daniell Road, Truro, Cornwall TR1 2DA* Truro (01872) 76491 or 76782 Fax 77788

GAYLER, Roger Kenneth. b 44. Lich Th Coll 68. **d** 70 **p** 71. C Chingford St Anne *Chelmsf* 70-75; P-in-c Marks Gate 75-81; V from 81. *The Vicarage, 187 Rose Lane, Romford RM6 5NR* 0181-599 0415

GAZE, Canon Arthur Philip Atkinson. b 14. St Jo Coll Ox BA36 MA47 Otago Univ MLitt88. Linc Th Coll 39. **d** 41 **p** 42. C Romford St Edw *Chelmsf* 41-48; Master and Chapl Cumnor Sch 48-50; R Puttenham and Wanborough *Guildf* 50-57; Dioc Insp of Schs 55-62; V Horsell 57-62; New Zealand from 62; Hon Can St Paul's Cathl 75-80. *18 Drivers Road, Maori Hill, Dunedin, New Zealand* Christchurch (3) 467-5951

GAZE, George Henry. b 23. St Jo Coll Dur BA50 DipTh51 MA56. **d** 51 **p** 52. R Slaidburn *Bradf* 56-85; rtd 85; Perm to Offic *Bradf* 86-90. *6 The Croft, Woods Lane, Stapenhill, Burton-on-Trent, Staffs DE15 9ED* Burton-on-Trent (01283) 36513

GAZZARD, Canon Richard George Edward. b 40. Lich Th Coll. **d** 67 **p** 68. C Lewisham St Mary *S'wark* 67-71; C Milton next Gravesend Ch Ch *Roch* 71-74; R Gravesend H Family w Ifield 74-81; V S Ashford Ch Ch *Cant* 81-93; RD E Charing 86-92; Hon Can Cant Cathl 90-93. *9 Culloden Mews, Cravengate, Richmond, N Yorkshire DL10 4XL*

GEACH, Canon Michael Bernard. b 26. Qu Coll Cam BA51 MA56. Westcott Ho Cam 51. **d** 53 **p** 54. C Kenwyn *Truro* 53-56; C Bodmin 56-59; C Helland 56-59; R St Dominic 59-65; Chapl Cotehele Ho Chapl Cornwall 60-65; V Linkinhorne 65-84; R Veryan w Ruan Lanihorne from 84; Hon Can Truro Cathl from 92. *The Vicarage, Veryan, Truro, Cornwall TR2 5QA* Truro (01872) 501618

GEAKE, Peter Henry. b 17. Trin Hall Cam BA39 MA46. Cuddesdon Coll 45. **d** 47 **p** 48. PC Tattenham Corner and Burgh Heath 62-69 *Guildf*; V 69-72; R Fulbeck *Linc* 72-82; P-in-c Carlton Scroop w Normanton 72-82; rtd 82. *30 Swallowfield Park, Swallowfield, Reading RG7 1TG* Reading (01734) 885975

GEAR, John Arthur. b 37. St Aid Birkenhead 62. **d** 64 **p** 66. C Attleborough *Cov* 64-66; C Attercliffe *Sheff* 66-68; C Sheerness H Trin w St Paul *Cant* 68-73; Asst Youth Adv *S'wark* 73-78; Youth Chapl *Lich* 78-88; V Stafford St Jo and Tixall w Ingestre 88-92; Gen Sec NCEC from 92. *Greenside, Lime Kiln Bank, Telford, Shropshire TF2 9NU* Telford (01952) 613487 Fax Redhill (01737) 822116

✝**GEAR, Rt Rev Michael Frederick.** b 34. Dur Univ BA59 DipTh61. Cranmer Hall Dur 59. **d** 61 **p** 62 **c** 93. C Bexleyheath Ch Ch *Roch* 61-64; C Ox St Aldate w H Trin *Ox* 64-67; V Clubmoor *Liv* 67-71; Rhodesia 71-76; Tutor Wycliffe Hall Ox 76-80; V Macclesfield St Mich *Ches* 80-85; RD Macclesfield 84-88; TR Macclesfield Team Par 85-88; Hon Can Ches Cathl 86-88; Adn Ches 88-93; Suff Bp Doncaster *Sheff* from 93. *Bishop's Lodge, Hooton Roberts, Rotherham, S Yorkshire S65 4PF* Rotherham (01709) 853370 Fax 852310

GEARY, Sidney Thomas William. b 11. St Deiniol's Hawarden. **d** 80 **p** 81. NSM Syston *Leic* 80-82; NSM Hoby cum Rotherby w Brooksby, Ragdale & Thru'ton 82-93; NSM Upper Wreake from 93. *Cedarwood, Sixhills Road, Ragdale, Melton Mowbray, Leics LE14 3PP* Rotherby (01664) 434289

GEBAUER, George Gerhart. b 25. Sarum & Wells Th Coll 71. **d** 73 **p** 74. C Portsdown *Portsm* 73-78; V Purbrook 78-91; rtd 91. *52 St John's Road, Locks Heath, Southampton SO3 6NF* Locks Heath (01489) 575172

GEDDES, Gordon David. b 38. St Chad's Coll Dur BA59 DipTh60. **d** 61 **p** 62. C Bishopwearmouth St Mary V w St Pet

CD *Dur* 61-65; P-in-c Jarrow 65-68; Teacher Crewe Boys' Gr Sch 68-71; Hd of Relig Studies 71-78; Hd of RE Ruskin Sch Crewe 78-90; Lic to Offic *Ches* 68-90; P-in-c Church Minshull w Leighton and Minshull Vernon 90-91; V Leighton-cum-Minshull Vernon from 91. *The Vicarage, Minshull Vernon, Crewe CW1 4RD* Church Minshull (01270) 71213

GEDDES, Peter Henry. b 51. DipHE86. Trin Coll Bris 84. **d** 86 **p** 87. C Blackpool St Mark *Blackb* 86-88; C Barnston *Ches* 88-92; V Haslington w Crewe Green from 92. *The Vicarage, 163 Crewe Road, Haslington, Crewe CW1 1RL* Crewe (01270) 582388

GEDDES, Roderick Charles. b 47. Man Univ DipEd78 MPhil85. N Ord Course 88. **d** 91 **p** 93. C Alverthorpe *Wakef* 91-92; C S Ossett 92-94; V Jurby *S & M* from 94; R Andreas from 94; V Andreas St Jude from 94. *The Rectory, Village Road, Andreas, Ramsey, Isle of Man IM7 4HH* Ramsey (01624) 880419

GEDGE, Lloyd Victor. b 23. Cuddesdon Coll 54. **d** 57 **p** 58. Canada 66-82 and from 86; P-in-c N Creake *Nor* 82-83; P-in-c S Creake 82-83; R N and S Creake w Waterden 84-86; rtd 88. *PO Box 187, Holden, Alberta, Canada, T0B 2C0*

GEDGE, Simon John Francis. b 44. Keble Coll Ox BA67 MA73. Cuddesdon Coll 67. **d** 69 **p** 70. C Perry Barr *Birm* 69-73; C Handsworth St Andr 73-75; V Birm St Pet 75-81; Perm to Offic *Lon* 81-85; Hon C Croydon St Jo *S'wark* from 85. *121 Albany Road, London SE8 4EB* 0181-692 7328

GEDYE, Timothy Robin William (Tim). b 56. Newc Univ BSc77. Wycliffe Hall Ox 81. **d** 89 **p** 90. NSM Ox St Aldate w St Matt *Ox* 89-91; Chapl St Luke's Nursing Home Ox from 91. *42 Thorne Close, Kidlington, Oxon OX5 1SJ* Kidlington (01865) 378808

GEE, Mrs Dorothy Mary. b 33. St Jo Coll Nottm 88. **d** 89 **p** 94. Chapl Asst Univ Hosp Nottm 89-95; NSM Plumtree *S'well* from 95. *16 The Leys, Normanton-on-the-Wolds, Keyworth, Notts NG12 5NV* Nottingham (0115) 937 4927

GEE, Canon Edward. b 28. St Deiniol's Hawarden 59. **d** 61 **p** 62. V Brownhill *Wakef* 65-75; V Alverthorpe 75-84; R Castleford All SS 84-92; Hon Can Wakef Cathl 87-92; rtd 92. *1 Holme Ghyll, Colne Road, Glusburn, Keighley, W Yorkshire BD20 8RG* Cross Hills (01535) 630060

GEE, Michael Terence. b 29. Dur Univ BSc54. Tyndale Hall Bris 60. **d** 62 **p** 63. V Brimscombe *Glouc* 68-80; V Tidenham w Beachley and Lancaut 80-91; P-in-c Sherborne, Windrush, the Barringtons etc 91-94; rtd 94. *32 Homefield, Shortwood, Nailsworth, Stroud, Glos GL6 0SP* Stroud (01453) 832742

GEE, Norman. b 11. Lon Univ BA33 St Cath Soc Ox BA35 MA42. Wycliffe Hall Ox 33. **d** 35 **p** 36. V Bath St Bart *B & W* 58-73; V Curry Rivel 73-78; rtd 78; Perm to Offic *B & W* from 79. *5 Barn Close, Nether Stowey, Bridgwater, Somerset TA5 1PA* Nether Stowey (01278) 732317

GEEN, James William (Jim). b 50. Chich Th Coll 76. **d** 79 **p** 80. C Brandon *Dur* 79-84; C Sunderland Red Ho 84-86; P-in-c N Hylton St Marg Castletown 86-89; V 89-91; Dep Chapl HM Pris Dur 91-92; Chapl HM Young Offender Inst Lanc Farms from 92. *HM Young Offender Institution, Lancaster Farms, Stone Row Head, Quernmore Road, Lancaster LA1 3QZ* Lancaster (01524) 848745 Fax 848393

GEERING, Anthony Ernest. b 43. Lon Univ DipTh66 Columbia Pacific Univ BSc. Kelham Th Coll 62. **d** 68 **p** 69. C Cov St Mary *Cov* 68-71; New Zealand 71-75; P-in-c Brinklow *Cov* 75-77; R 77-81; V Monks Kirby w Pailton and Stretton-under-Fosse 77-81; R Harborough Magna 77-81; V Pilton w Ashford *Ex* 81-86; P-in-c Shirwell w Loxhore 83-86; R Crediton and Shobrooke from 86; RD Cadbury from 93. *The Vicarage, Crediton, Devon EX17 2AF* Crediton (01363) 772669 or 773226

GEESON, Brian Alfred. b 30. Qu Coll Ox BA51 Trin & All SS Coll Leeds PGCE76. Qu Coll Birm 54. **d** 55 **p** 56. R Broughton *Bradf* 64-71; TV Seacroft *Ripon* 71-77; Hon C Hanging Heaton *Wakef* 77-87; Hon C Purlwell 87-94; rtd 94. *30 Ullswater Avenue, Dewsbury, W Yorkshire WF12 7PL* Dewsbury (01924) 465621

GEILINGER, John Edward. b 27. Lon Univ BSc53 BD58 BA76 MPhil79. Tyndale Hall Bris. **d** 59 **p** 60. Nigeria 63-77; Perm to Offic *Portsm* from 79; rtd 92. *Emmaus House, Colwell Road, Freshwater, Isle of Wight PO40 9LY* Isle of Wight (01983) 753030

GELDARD, Mark Dundas. b 50. Liv Univ BA71 Bris Univ MA75. Trin Coll Bris 73. **d** 75 **p** 76. C Aughton Ch Ch *Liv* 75-78; Tutor Trin Coll Bris 78-84; V Fairfield *Liv* 84-88; Dir of Ords *Lich* from 88. *10 The Brambles, Boley Park, Lichfield, Staffs WS14 9SE* Lichfield (01543) 415318

GELL, Reginald Arthur Patrick. b 10. ALCD32. **d** 33 **p** 34. V Paignton Ch Ch *Ex* 63-90; rtd 90; Perm to Offic *Ex* from 90. *Town Orchard, Church Close, Abbotskerswell, Newton Abbot, Devon TQ12 5NY* Newton Abbot (01626) 61911

GELLI, Frank Julian. b 43. Birkb Coll Lon BA78 K Coll Lon MTh82. Ripon Coll Cuddesdon 84. **d** 86 **p** 87. C Chiswick St

Nic w St Mary *Lon* 86-89; Chapl Ankara *Eur* 89-91; C Kensington St Mary Abbots w St Geo *Lon* from 91. *1 Vicarage Cottage, Vicarage Gate, London W8 4HN* 0171-937 2364

GELLING, Canon John Drury. b 22. Pemb Coll Ox BA44 DipTh45 MA48. Wycliffe Hall Ox 44. **d** 54 **p** 55. V Rushen *S & M* 64-77; RD Castletown 71-77; R Ballaugh 77-92; P-in-c Michael 77-78; V 78-92; Can St German's Cathl 80-92; rtd 92; Perm to Offic *S & M* from 93. *Uplands, Ballavitchell Road, Crosby, Douglas, Isle of Man IM4 2DN* Douglas (01624) 851223

GELSTON, Dr Anthony. b 35. Keble Coll Ox BA57 MA60 DD85. Ridley Hall Cam 59. **d** 60 **p** 61. Lic to Offic *Dur* from 62; Lect Th Dur Univ 62-76; Sen Lect 76-88; Reader 89-95; Dean Div Faculty 77-79; rtd 95. *Lesbury, Hetton Road, Houghton le Spring, Tyne & Wear DH5 8JW* 0191-584 2256

GEMMELL, Ian William Young. b 52. ALAM. St Jo Coll Nottm LTh77. **d** 77 **p** 78. C Old Hill H Trin *Worc* 77-81; C Selly Hill St Steph *Birm* 81; C Selly Park St Steph and St Wulstan 81-83; V Leic St Chris *Leic* 83-93; RD Christianity (Leic) S 92-93; P-in-c Gt Bowden w Welham, Glooston and Cranoe from 93; P-in-c Church Langton w Tur Langton, Thorpe Langton etc from 93. *The Rectory, Dingley Road, Great Bowden, Market Harborough, Leics LE16 7ET* Market Harborough (01858) 462032

GENDERS, Nigel Mark. b 65. Oak Hill Th Coll BA92. **d** 92 **p** 93. C New Malden and Coombe *S'wark* from 92. *12 Rosebery Avenue, New Malden, Surrey KT3 4JS* 0181-942 2523

✠**GENDERS, Rt Rev Roger Alban Marson (Anselm).** b 19. BNC Ox BA47 MA47. Coll of Resurr Mirfield 48. **d** 52 **p** 52 **c** 77. Lic to Offic *Wakef* 52-55; CR from 52; Barbados 55-65; Rhodesia 66-75; Adn E Distr 70-75; Bp Bermuda 77-82; Asst Bp Wakef from 83; rtd 84. *House of the Resurrection, Mirfield, W Yorkshire WF14 0BN* Mirfield (01924) 494318

GENOWER, Arthur Herbert. b 98. Leeds Univ BA30. Ripon Hall Ox 33. **d** 33 **p** 34. R Wootton *Portsm* 40-68; rtd 68. *28 Manormead Nursing Home, Tilford Road, Hindhead, Surrey GU26 6RP* Hindhead (01428) 606823

GENT, Canon Comdr Anthony Leonard. b 20. CEng MIMechE. Sarum Th Coll 66. **d** 67 **p** 68. C Forrabury w Minster and Trevalga *Truro* 67-70; C Davidstow w Otterham 67-70; C Boscastle w Davidstow 67-70; V St Minver 70-91; RD Trigg Minor 73-84; P-in-c St Kew 77-78; Hon Can Truro Cathl 84-91; rtd 91. *15 Middleway, Taunton, Somerset TA1 3QH* Taunton (01823) 323426

GENT, Mrs Miriam. b 29. Leeds Univ BA51. SW Minl Tr Course 84. **d** 87 **p** 94. NSM Pinhoe and Broadclyst *Ex* from 87. *Mosshaye Cottage, West Clyst, Exeter EX1 3TR* Exeter (01392) 67288

GEOFFREY, Brother. *See* PEARSON, Harold

GEORGE, Canon Alec. b 29. Lich Th Coll 56. **d** 59 **p** 60. C Holbrooks *Cov* 59-65; R Lower Broughton Ascension *Man* 65-71; V Hollinwood from 71; Hon Can Man Cathl from 94. *St Margaret's Vicarage, Chapel Road, Oldham OL8 4QQ* 0161-681 4541

GEORGE, Alexander Robert. b 46. K Coll Lon BD69 AKC69. St Aug Coll Cant. **d** 70 **p** 71. C Newmarket St Mary w Exning St Agnes *St E* 70-74; C Swindon Ch Ch *Bris* 74-76; C Henbury 76-79; Lic to Offic 79-80; TV Oldland 80-88; C Ipswich St Aug *St E* 89; C Hadleigh w Layham and Shelley 89-90; P-in-c Assington 90-91; R Assington w Newton Green and Lt Cornard from 91; Dioc Moderator for Reader Tr from 95. *The Vicarage, Assington, Sudbury, Suffolk CO10 5LQ* Boxford (01787) 210249

GEORGE, Charles Roy. b 32. St Edm Hall Ox BA55 MA59. Cuddesdon Coll 55. **d** 57 **p** 58. C Chorley St Laur *Blackb* 57-60; C Norton *Derby* 60-64; V Eltham St Barn *S'wark* 64-74; V Milton *Portsm* 74-90; R Rowner from 90. *The Rectory, 174 Rowner Lane, Gosport, Hants PO13 9SU* Gosport (01705) 581834

GEORGE, Ven David Michael. b 45. Selw Coll Cam BA66 MA70. Chich Th Coll 70. **d** 73 **p** 74. C Chiswick St Nic w St Mary *Lon* 73-76; C Kensington St Mary Abbots w St Geo 76-78; C Northolt Park St Barn 78-81; Argentina from 81; Adn River Plate from 84. *San Lorenzo 2274, 1640 Martinez, Buenos Aires, Argentina* Buenos Aires (1) 798-0078

GEORGE, Mrs Elizabeth Ann. b 33. Westf Coll Lon BA56. S Dios Minl Tr Scheme. **d** 87 **p** 94. NSM Basingstoke *Win* from 87. *71 Camrose Way, Basingstoke, Hants RG21 3AW* Basingstoke (01256) 464763

GEORGE, Frederick. b 39. St Luke's Coll Ex CertEd61. Chich Th Coll 82. **d** 72 **p** 83. Australia 72-75; Brunei 75-80; Gambia 80-82 and 83-88; C Hellingly and Upper Dicker *Chich* 83; P-in-c Ringsfield w Redisham, Barsham, Shipmeadow etc *St E* 89-92; R Wainford from 92. *The Rectory, School Road, Ringsfield, Beccles, Suffolk NR34 8NZ* Beccles (01502) 717862

GEORGE, Preb John Thomas. b 17. St D Coll Lamp BA42 Selw Coll Cam BA44 MA47. Westcott Ho Cam 44. **d** 45 **p** 46. R

Backwell *B & W* 62-72; RD Portishead 68-72; V Wellington w W Buckland and Nynehead 72-76; R Wellington and Distr 76-82; Preb Wells Cathl 78-86; rtd 82; Hon C Diptford, N Huish, Harberton and Harbertonford *Ex* from 85. *12 Woolcombe Lane, Ivybridge, Devon PL21 0UA* Plymouth (01752) 698284

GEORGE, Martin Walter. b 31. TD85. Bris Univ BEd73. Sarum & Wells Th Coll. **d** 82 **p** 82. C Bruton w Lamyatt, Wyke and Redlynch *B & W* 82-85; V Middlezoy and Othery and Moorlinch 85-87; Perm to Offic from 87. *17 Lewis Crescent, Frome, Somerset BA11 2LF* Frome (01373) 462094

GEORGE, Nicholas Paul. b 58. St Steph Ho Ox 86. **d** 89 **p** 90. C Leeds St Aid *Ripon* 89-92; C Leeds Richmond Hill from 92; Chapl Agnes Stewart C of E High Sch Leeds from 93. *St Hilda's Clergy House, 70 Cross Green Lane, Leeds LS9 0DG* Leeds (0113) 248 1145

✠**GEORGE, Rt Rev Randolph Oswald.** b 24. Codrington Coll Barbados 46. **d** 50 **p** 51 **c** 76. Barbados 50-53; C Leigh *Lich* 53-55; C Ardwick St Benedict *Man* 55-57; C Bedf Park *Lon* 57-58; C Lavender Hill Ascension *S'wark* 58-60; Trinidad and Tobago 60-71; Hon Can Trinidad 68-71; Guyana from 71; Dean Georgetown 71-76; Suff Bp Stabroek 76-80; Bp Guyana 80-94; rtd 94. *Austin House, Kingston, Georgetown 1, Guyana*

GEORGE, William Havard. b 15. St D Coll Lamp BA37 St Mich Coll Llan 38. **d** 41 **p** 42. V Bassenthwaite *Carl* 57-74; P-in-c Isel w Setmurthy 72-74; V Bassenthwaite, Isel and Setmurthy 74-83; rtd 83. *Gwyntmor, West Green, Allonby, Maryport, Cumbria CA15 6PG* Allonby (01900) 881475

GEORGE-JONES, Canon Gwilym Ifor. b 26. K Coll (NS) 56. **d** 57 **p** 57. V Kirton in Lindsey *Linc* 61-71; R Grayingham 61-71; R Manton 61-71; V Alford w Rigsby 71-92; R Maltby 71-92; R Well 71-92; V Bilsby w Farlesthorpe 71-92; R Hannah cum Hagnaby w Markby 71-92; R Saleby w Beesby 71-92; RD Calcewaithe and Candleshoe 77-85 and 87-89; Can and Preb Linc Cathl from 81; rtd 92. *42 Kelstern Road, Doddington Park, Lincoln LN6 3NJ* Lincoln (01522) 691896

GERARD, John William. b 23. BNC Ox BA47 MA52. **d** 51 **p** 51. Canada 51-61; Perm to Offic *Chelmsf* from 74; rtd 81. *Oak Tree Cottage, 31 Wycke Lane, Tollesbury, Maldon, Essex CM9 8ST* Maldon (01621) 869318

GERD, Sister. *See* SWENSSON, Sister Gerd Inger

GERRANS, Nigel Henry. b 31. Cam Univ MA54. St Steph Ho Ox 78. **d** 81 **p** 81. C Bicester w Bucknell, Caversfield and Launton *Ox* 81-84; Chapl Qu Alexandra Hosp Portsm 84-92; rtd 92. *56 Bishopsgate Walk, Chichester, W Sussex PO19 4FQ* Chichester (01243) 539131

GERRARD, Brian James. b 38. Wycliffe Hall Ox 72. **d** 74 **p** 75. C Ditton St Mich *Liv* 74-78; V Lydiate 78-89; P-in-c N Meols 89-92; R from 92; P-in-c Banks 89-92; V from 92. *76 Beresford Drive, Southport, Merseyside PR9 7LQ* Southport (01704) 25436

GERRARD, Ven David Keith Robin. b 39. St Edm Hall Ox BA61. Linc Th Coll 61. **d** 63 **p** 64. C Stoke Newington St Olave *Lon* 63-66; C Primrose Hill St Mary w Avenue Road St Paul 66-69; V Newington St Paul *S'wark* 69-79; V Surbiton St Andr and St Mark 79-89; RD Kingston 84-88; Hon Can S'wark Cathl 85-89; Adn Wandsworth from 89. *68 North Side, London SW18 2QX* 0181-874 5766 Fax 789 3985

GERRARD, Dr George Ernest. b 16. TEM. FCIS60 DD94. Ridley Hall Cam 66. **d** 68 **p** 69. OStJ from 65; C Ramsey *Ely* 70-75; rtd 81; Perm to Offic *Nor* from 86. *1 Goodrick Place, Beech Close, Swaffham, Norfolk PE37 7RP* Swaffham (01760) 723311

GERRISH, David Victor. b 38. St Jo Coll Dur BSc61 MA65. Oak Hill Th Coll 61. **d** 64 **p** 65. C Fareham St Jo *Portsm* 64-66; Asst Chapl K Sch Roch 67-71; Asst Chapl Bryanston Sch Blandford *Ox* 71-73; Chapl 73-77; Chapl Mon Sch 77-86; Chapl Warminster Sch Wilts 86-89; R Portland All SS w St Pet *Sarum* from 89. *The Rectory, Straits, Easton, Portland, Dorset DT5 1HG* Portland (01305) 861285

GERRY, Brian John Rowland. b 38. Oak Hill Th Coll 69. **d** 71 **p** 72. C Hawkwell *Chelmsf* 71-74; C Battersea Park St Sav *S'wark* 74-77; C Battersea St Geo w St Andr 74-77; V Axmouth w Musbury *Ex* 77-86; R Upton from 86. *Upton Rectory, Furzehill Road, Torquay TQ1 3JG* Torquay (01803) 211572

GETHYN-JONES, Canon John Eric. b 09. MBE45 TD50. FSA61 Bris Univ MA66. Qu Coll Birm 32. **d** 34 **p** 35. V Berkeley *Glouc* 67-76; Hon Can Glouc Cathl 68-89; rtd 76. *Canonbury House, Canonbury Street, Berkeley, Gloucester GL13 9BG* Dursley (01453) 810296

GHEST, Richard William Iliffe. b 31. Em Coll Cam BA53 MA57 Lon Univ BA66. Wells Th Coll 53. **d** 55 **p** 56. C Weston-super-Mare St Jo *B & W* 55-57; India 58-63; C Holborn St Geo w H Trin and St Bart *Lon* 63-67; Ceylon 67-68; C Combe Down *B & W* 68-73; C Combe Down w Monkton Combe 73-74;

R Tickenham from 74. *The Rectory, 27 Clevedon Road, Tickenham, Clevedon, Avon BS21 6RA* Nailsea (01275) 853278

GHINN, Edward. b 45. Oak Hill Th Coll 71. **d** 74 **p** 75. C Purley Ch Ch *S'wark* 74-77; Chile 77-82; V Sevenoaks Weald *Roch* 82-86; Chapl HM Pris Hull 86-89; Chapl HM Pris Pentonville 89-91; Chapl HM Pris Maidstone from 91. *The Chaplain's Office, HM Prison, County Road, Maidstone, Kent ME14 1UZ* Maidstone (01622) 755611 Fax 688038

GHOSH, Dipen. b 43. St Jo Coll Nottm 71. **d** 74 **p** 75. C Bushbury *Lich* 74-77; Hon C 86-89; C Wednesfield Heath 89-91; TV Wolv from 91. *St Marks Vicarage, 20 Tettenhall Road, Wolverhampton WV1 4SW* Wolverhampton (01902) 771375

GIBB, David Richard Albert. b 68. Cov Univ MPhil95. Lon Bible Coll BA90 Wycliffe Hall Ox DipMin95. **d** 95. C Ox St Ebbe w H Trin and St Pet *Ox* from 95. *Paravel, 25 Norreys Avenue, Oxford OX1 4ST* Oxford (01865) 249828

GIBBARD, Roger. b 48. Southn Univ BA73. Cuddesdon Coll 73. **d** 75 **p** 76. C Portsea St Mary *Portsm* 75-79; P-in-c New Addington *Cant* 79-81; C Ditton St Mich *Liv* 81-82; TV 82-88; Asst Chapl HM Pris Liv 88-89; Chapl HM Young Offender Inst Hindley 89-92; Chapl HM Rem Cen Risley from 92. *HM Remand Centre, Warrington Road, Risley, Warrington WA3 6BP* Culcheth (01925) 763871 Fax 764103

GIBBARD, Sydney Mark. b 10. Selw Coll Cam BA32 MA37. Cuddesdon Coll 33. **d** 33 **p** 34. SSJE from 43; USA 70-71 and 75-76 and 80-81; Asst Chapl Ex Coll Ox 71-75; India 77-78; Australia 78-79; New Zealand 79-80; rtd 80. *St John's Home, St Mary's Road, Oxford OX4 1QE* Oxford (01865) 247725

GIBBINS, John Grenville. b 53. Aston Tr Scheme 89 Linc Th Coll 89. **d** 91 **p** 92. C Market Harborough *Leic* from 91. *5 Ashfield Road, Market Harborough, Leics LE16 7LX* Market Harborough (01858) 431977

GIBBON, Edward Herbert Morgan. b 15. St D Coll Lamp BA37 St Mich Coll Llan 38. **d** 40 **p** 41. V Sunninghill *Ox* 66-79; rtd 79; Perm to Offic *Guildf* from 82. *Starlings, Sandpit Hall Road, Chobham, Woking, Surrey GU24 8HA* Chobham (01276) 856863

GIBBON, Gordon Percy. b 17. Oak Hill Th Coll 63. **d** 64 **p** 65. V Walthamstow St Gabr *Chelmsf* 68-82; rtd 82; Perm to Offic *Chich* from 82. *20 Black Path, Polegate, E Sussex BN26 5AP* Polegate (01323) 486751

GIBBONS, David Austen. b 63. York Univ BSc84. Berkeley Div Sch 93 Ripon Coll Cuddesdon BA94. **d** 94 **p** 95. C Ryde H Trin *Portsm* from 94. *38 Trinity Street, Ryde, Isle of Wight PO33 2BU* Isle of Wight (01983) 811963

GIBBONS, David Robin Christian. b 36. Chich Th Coll 82. **d** 84 **p** 85. C Seaford w Sutton *Chich* 84-87; R Harting 87-93; R Harting w Elsted and Treyford cum Didling from 93. *The Rectory, South Harting, Petersfield, Hants GU31 5QB* Harting (01730) 825234

GIBBONS, Eric. b 47. Sarum & Wells Th Coll 69. **d** 72 **p** 73. C New Haw *Guildf* 72-76; C Hawley H Trin 76-79; P-in-c Blackheath and Chilworth 79-90; V from 90. *The Vicarage, Blackheath, Guildford, Surrey GU4 8QT* Guildford (01483) 893129

GIBBONS, John. b 31. K Coll Lon 52. Oak Hill Th Coll 55. **d** 57 **p** 58. C Islington St Steph w St Bart and St Matt *Lon* 57-60; C Rolleston *Lich* 60-63; C Anslow 60-63; V Bobbington 63-83; V N Axholme Gp *Linc* from 83; RD Is of Axholme from 91. *The Vicarage, 20 Chapel Lane, Keadby, Scunthorpe, S Humberside DN17 3EZ* Scunthorpe (01724) 783612

GIBBONS, Ven Kenneth Harry. b 31. Man Univ BSc52. Cuddesdon Coll 54. **d** 56 **p** 57. C Fleetwood *Blackb* 56-60; NE Sch Sec SCM 60-62; Hon C Leeds St Pet *Ripon* 60-62; C St Martin-in-the-Fields *Lon* 62-65; V New Addington *Cant* 65-70; V Portsea St Mary *Portsm* 70-81; RD Portsm 73-79; Hon Can Portsm Cathl 76-81; Dir of Post-Ord Tr *Blackb* 81-83; Acting Chapl HM Forces Weeton 81-85; Dir of Ords 82-90; Adn Lanc from 81; P-in-c Weeton 81-85; V St Michaels on Wyre from 85. *The Vicarage, Hall Lane, St Michael's-on-Wyre, Preston PR3 0TQ* St Michaels (01995) 679242

GIBBONS, Paul James. b 37. JP. Chich Th Coll 63. **d** 65 **p** 66. C Croydon St Mich *Cant* 65-72; V Maidstone St Mich from 72. *The Vicarage, 109 Tonbridge Road, Maidstone, Kent ME16 8JS* Maidstone (01622) 752710

GIBBONS, Mrs Susan Janet. b 51. St Mary's Coll Dur BA73 Birm Univ PGCE74. W Midl Minl Tr Course 89. **d** 92 **p** 94. NSM Fladbury, Wyre Piddle and Moor *Worc* from 92. *The Old School, Bricklehampton, Pershore, Worcs WR10 3HJ* Pershore (01386) 710475

GIBBONS, Thomas Patrick. b 59. St Jo Coll Dur BA82. St Steph Ho Ox 88. **d** 92. C Whorlton *Newc* 90-94; C Gosforth St Nic from 94. *71 Church Road, Gosforth, Newcastle upon Tyne NE3 1AQ* 0191-285 7062

GIBBONS, Canon William Simpson. b 32. TCD BA60 MA64. d 61 p 62. I Drumholm and Rossnowlagh *D & R* 65-70; C Dub St Ann w St Steph *D & G* 70-72; I Kill 72-95; Can Ch Ch Cathl Dub 91-95; rtd 95. *Muthaiga, 8 Mount Bernard Drive, Castlederg, Co Tyrone*

GIBBS, Colin Hugh. b 35. St Mich Coll Llan 82. d 84 p 85. C Bistre *St As* 84-87; V Penycae 87-92; rtd 92. *Asaph, 26 Cil y Coed, Ruabon, Wrexham, Clwyd LL14 6TA* Ruabon (01978) 823550

GIBBS, Colin Wilfred. b 39. Man Univ BA62. St Jo Coll Nottm 71. d 73 p 74. C Crowborough *Chich* 73-76; C Rodbourne Cheney *Bris* 76-77; C Bickenhill w Elmdon *Birm* 77-80; CF from 80. *clo MOD (Army), Bagshot Park, Bagshot, Surrey GU19 5PL* Bagshot (01276) 471717 Fax 412834

GIBBS, Canon Derek Norman. b 38. Kelham Th Coll. d 62 p 63. C Newc Ch Ch w St Ann *Newc* 62-65; C Shiremoor 65-67; V New Bentley *Sheff* 67-68; V Sheff Parson Cross St Cecilia 68-80; RD Ecclesfield 75-80; V Cantley 80-92; RD Doncaster 82-92; Hon Can Sheff Cathl 88-92; P-in-c Doncaster Ch Ch 89-91; Cyprus from 93. *Margarita, Agios Demitrianos, Paphos, Cyprus* Paphos (6) 732276

GIBBS, Prof Edmund. b 38. Lon Univ BD62. Fuller Th Sem California DMin81 Oak Hill Th Coll 58. d 63 p 64. C Wandsworth All SS *S'wark* 63-66; Chile 66-70; Sec SAMS 70-73; Educn Sec 73-77; Ch Progr Manager Bible Soc 77-84; USA from 84; Assoc Prof Evang and Ch Renewal Fuller Th Sem 84-94. *Address temp unknown*

GIBBS, Mrs Fiorenza Silvia Elisabetta. b 49. SRN71 Surrey Univ DipHV72. St Alb Minl Tr Scheme 90. d 93. NSM Hitchin *St Alb* from 93. *41 West Lane, Pirton, Hitchin, Herts SG5 3QP* Hitchin (01462) 711846

GIBBS, Ian Edmund. b 47. Lon Univ BEd69. St Steph Ho Ox 72. d 75 p 76. C Stony Stratford *Ox* 75-79; V Forest Town *S'well* 79-83; R Diddlebury w Munslow, Holdgate and Tugford *Heref* from 83; R Abdon from 83. *The Rectory, Munslow, Craven Arms, Shropshire SY7 9ET* Munslow (01584) 841688

GIBBS, Dr James Millard. b 28. Michigan Univ BSE51 Nottm Univ PhD68. Seabury-Western Th Sem BD57. d 57 p 57. Vice-Prin Lich Th Coll 66-71; Lic to Offic *Lich* 66-71; India 72-77; Tutor Qu Coll Birm 78-84; V Stechford *Birm* 84-93; rtd 93; Perm to Offic *Birm* from 93. *14 Metchley Court, Birmingham B17 0JP* 0121-426 2108

✠**GIBBS, Rt Rev John.** b 17. Bris Univ BA42 Lon Univ BD48. Linc Th Coll 55. d 55 p 56 c 73. C Brislington St Luke *Bris* 55-57; Chapl St Matthias's Coll Bris 57-64; Vice-Prin 61-64; Prin Keswick Hall C of E Coll of Educn 64-73; Lic to Offic *Nor* 64-73; Hon Can Nor Cathl 68-73; Suff Bp Bradwell *Chelmsf* 73-76; Bp Cov 76-85; rtd 85; Asst Bp Bris from 85; Asst Bp Glouc from 85. *Farthingloe, Southfield, Minchinhampton, Stroud, Glos GL6 9DY* Brimscombe (01453) 886211

GIBBS, Dr Jonathan Robert. b 61. Jes Coll Ox MA89 Jes Coll Cam PhD90. Ridley Hall Cam 84. d 89 p 90. C Stalybridge H Trin and Ch Ch *Ches* 89-92; Chapl Basle w Freiburg-im-Breisgau *Eur* from 92. *St Johanns-Ring 92, CH-4056, Basle, Switzerland* Basle (61) 321-7477 Fax 321-7476

GIBBS, Mrs Patricia Louise. b 39. S'wark Ord Course 91. d 94. NSM Croydon H Sav *S'wark* from 94; Chapl Asst Mayday Univ Hosp Thornton Heath from 94. *41 Sandringham Road, Thornton Heath, Surrey CR7 7AX* 0181-684 9720

GIBBS, Peter Winston. b 50. Ex Univ BA72 Leic Univ DipSocWork75 CQSW75. St Jo Coll Nottm DipTh. d 90 p 91. C Hampreston *Sarum* 90-94; P-in-c Ipswich St Matt *St E* from 94. *6 Collinsons, Hadleigh Road, Ipswich IP2 0DS* Ipswich (01473) 281364

GIBBS, Canon Philip Roscoe. b 33. Codrington Coll Barbados 57. d 60 p 61. Br Honduras 60-73; Belize 73-74; Hon Can Br Honduras 71-73; Hon Can Belize from 73; V Stoke Newington Common St Mich *Lon* 74-87; New Zealand from 87; rtd 93. *The Vicarage, PO Box 13-253,, 22 Bassett Road, Johnsonville,, Wellington 4, New Zealand* Wellington (4) 478-8384

GIBBS, Canon Robert John. b 43. Dur Univ BA64. Westcott Ho Cam 66. d 68 p 69. C Costessey *Nor* 68-71; C Halesowen *Worc* 71-75; TV 75-76; P-in-c Dudley St Jas 77-79; V 79-82; Dioc Ecum Officer 82-89; R Ribbesford w Bewdley and Dowles 82-91; RD Kidderminster 83-89; Hon Can Worc Cathl 87-91; V Budleigh Salterton *Ex* from 91; RD Aylesbeare from 93. *St Peter's Vicarage, 4A West Hill Lane, Budleigh Salterton, Devon EX9 6AA* Budleigh Salterton (01395) 443195

GIBBS, Canon Roderick Harold. b 25. Leeds Univ BA49. Coll of Resurr Mirfield 49. d 51 p 52. R Stepney St Dunstan and All SS *Lon* 65-72; Dep Hd Master Laindon Sch 72-76; Hon C Langdon Hills *Chelmsf* 74-78; Hd Master Wm Forster Sch Tottenham 77-83; Hon C Bounds Green *Lon* 78-83; P-in-c Purley St Mark Woodcote *S'wark* 83-86; V 86-92; Hon Can S'wark Cathl 89-92; rtd 92. *73 The Crescent, Earley, Reading RG6 2NW* Reading (01734) 264767

GIBBS, Canon William Gilbert. b 31. Bps' Coll Cheshunt 55. d 58 p 59. C Wellington w W Buckland *B & W* 58-61; C Kensington

St Mary Abbots w St Geo *Lon* 61-68; V Guilsborough *Pet* 68; V Guilsborough w Hollowell 68-74; V Guilsborough w Hollowell and Cold Ashby from 74; P-in-c Cottesbrooke w Gt Creaton and Thornby from 83; Can Pet Cathl from 88; P-in-c Maidwell w Draughton, Scaldwell, Lamport etc 88-89. *The Vicarage, Guilsborough, Northampton NN6 8PU* Northampton (01604) 740297

GIBBY, Thomas Rees. b 12. St D Coll Lamp BA33 BD42. St Mich Coll Llan 33. d 35 p 36. V Ivybridge *Ex* 62-75; R Harford 63-75; rtd 75. *Penlon, Cwmann, Lampeter, Dyfed SA48 8DU* Lampeter (01570) 422100

GIBLIN, Brendan Anthony. b 64. K Coll Lon BD86. Wycliffe Hall Ox 90. d 92 p 93. C Tadcaster w Newton Kyme *York* from 92. *3 Heatherdene, Tadcaster, N Yorkshire LS24 8EZ* Tadcaster (01937) 834514

GIBLING, Derek Vivian. b 31. Wadh Coll Ox BA56 MA63. Wycliffe Hall Ox 70. d 72 p 73. C Fisherton Anger *Sarum* 72-74; C Yatton Keynell *Bris* 74-77; C Castle Combe 74-77; C Biddestone w Slaughterford 74-77; P-in-c Youlgreave *Derby* 77-82; P-in-c Stanton-in-Peak 77-82; V Youlgreave, Middleton, Stanton-in-Peak etc 82-88; P-in-c Hartington and Biggin 88-90; V Hartington, Biggin and Earl Sterndale from 90. *The Vicarage, Hartington, Buxton, Derbyshire SK17 0AW* Hartington (01298) 84280

GIBRALTAR AND IBERIA, Archdeacon of. See ROBINSON, John Kenneth

GIBRALTAR IN EUROPE, Bishop of. See HIND, Rt Rev John William

GIBRALTAR, Dean of. See HORLOCK, Very Rev Brian William

GIBSON, Alan. b 35. Birm Univ BSc56 Man Univ MSc72. NW Ord Course 71. d 74 p 75. C Sale St Anne *Ches* 74-77; V Runcorn St Mich 77-82; Educn Adv *Carl* 82-88; P-in-c Hugill 82-88; V Grange-over-Sands from 88. *The Vicarage, Hampsfell Road, Grange-over-Sands, Cumbria LA11 6BE* Grange-over-Sands (015395) 32757

GIBSON, Canon Alan Gordon. b 18. AKC48. d 48 p 49. V S Beddington St Mich *S'wark* 64-76; RD Sutton 70-76; Hon Can S'wark Cathl 74-87; P-in-c Perry Hill St Geo 76-82; RD W Lewisham 79-82; Vice-Chmn Dioc Past Cttee 82-87; RD Clapham and Brixton 83-85; rtd 87. *33 Briarwood Road, London SW4 9PJ* 0171-627 1100

GIBSON, Alan Henry. b 11. MBE44. K Coll Lon BD37 AKC37 Ely Th Coll 37. d 37 p 38. V Sandgate St Paul *Cant* 64-76; rtd 76; Lic to Offic *Cant* 76-87; Chapl St Mary's Hosp Etchinghill 80-87. *14 Orchard Walk, Stoney Lane, Weeke, Winchester, Hants SO22 6DL* Winchester (01962) 883869

GIBSON, Alexander Douglas. b 21. Wycliffe Hall Ox 60. d 62 p 63. V Gresley *Derby* 65-77; V Hartington 77-78; V Biggin 77-78; V Hartington and Biggin 78-88; rtd 88; Perm to Offic *Derby* from 88. *Westmead, Aldern Way, Baslow Road, Bakewell, Derbyshire DE45 1AJ* Bakewell (01629) 812723

GIBSON, Anthony Richard. b 43. Ridley Hall Cam 83. d 85 p 86. C Rushmere *St E* 85-88; P-in-c N Tawton and Bondleigh *Ex* 88; P-in-c Sampford Courtenay w Honeychurch 88; R N Tawton, Bondleigh, Sampford Courtenay etc 88-93; RD Okehampton 92-93; P-in-c Tiverton St Pet 93-95; P-in-c Tiverton St Pet w Chevithorne from 95. *St Peter's Rectory, 32 The Avenue, Tiverton, Devon EX16 4HW* Tiverton (01884) 254079

GIBSON, Catherine Snyder (Kate). b 39. Parson's Sch of Design (NY) 57. Local Minl Tr Course 83. d 86 p 94. Colombia 86-87; C Aber St Marg *Ab* 87-88; USA 88-89; Dioc Hosp Chapl *Ab* 89-92; C Aber St Mary 93-95; Bp's Chapl for Tr and Educn 93-95; P-in-c Aboyne from 95; P-in-c Ballater from 95; P-in-c Braemar from 95. *The Rectory, 7 Invercauld Road, Ballater, Aberdeenshire AB35 5RP* Ballater (013397) 55726 Fax as telephone

GIBSON, Colin Taylor. b 54. Trin Coll Cam BA77. Oak Hill Th Coll DipHE88. d 88 p 89. C Thrybergh w Hooton Roberts *Sheff* 88-91; P-in-c Tinsley from 91. *St Lawrence's Vicarage, 24 Highgate, Sheffield S9 1WL* Sheffield (0114) 244 1740

GIBSON, Dr David Francis. b 36. Magd Coll Cam BA57 BChir60 MB61. SW Minl Tr Course 84. d 90 p 91. NSM Newport, Bishops Tawton and Tawstock *Ex* 90-95; Chapl N Devon Distr Hosp Barnstaple from 95; NSM Pilton w Ashford *Ex* from 95. *North Devon District Hospital, Raleigh Park, Barnstaple, Devon EX31 4JB* Barnstaple (01271) 22577 or 42098

GIBSON, David Innes. b 31. NDD53. Oak Hill Th Coll 56. d 59 p 60. C S Croydon Em *Cant* 59-62; C Washfield *Ex* 62-63; Asst Master and Chapl Blundells Sch Tiverton 63-64; Chapl Sutton Valence Sch Maidstone 64-68; Chapl Dean Close Sch Cheltenham 68-75; Asst Chapl and Ho Master 75-85; Asst Master Brightlands Sch Newnham-on-Severn 85-90; C Cheltenham St Mary, St Matt, St Paul and H Trin *Glouc* from 91. *2 Withyholt Park, Charlton Kings, Cheltenham, Glos GL53 9BP* Cheltenham (01242) 511612

GIBSON, Douglas Harold (Doug). b 20. Portsm Dioc Tr Course. d 87. NSM Portsea St Luke *Portsm* from 87. *83 Middle Street, Southsea, Hants PO5 4BW* Portsmouth (01705) 829769

GIBSON, Ven George Granville. b 36. Cuddesdon Coll 69. d 71 p 72. C Tynemouth Cullercoats St Paul *Newc* 71-73; TV Cramlington 73-77; V Newton Aycliffe *Dur* 77-85; R Bishopwearmouth St Mich w St Hilda 85-90; TR Sunderland 90-93; RD Wearmouth 85-93; Hon Can Dur Cathl 88-93; Adn Auckland from 93. *Glebe House, Sunderland Bridge, Durham DH6 5HB* 0191-378 0273 Fax 378 3885

GIBSON, Henry Edward. b 15. Keble Coll Ox BA41 DipTh42 MA46. St Steph Ho Ox 41. d 43 p 44. V Waterlooville *Portsm* 63-81; rtd 81; Perm to Offic *Portsm* from 81; Perm to Offic *Chich* from 81. *8 Worcester Road, Chichester, W Sussex PO19 4DJ* Chichester (01243) 779194

GIBSON, Ian. b 48. Open Univ BA85. S Dios Minl Tr Scheme 82. d 85 p 86. NSM Uckfield *Chich* 85-88; V Fairwarp 88-93; P-in-c from 94; V High Hurstwood 88-93; P-in-c from 94. *The Vicarage, Fairwarp, Uckfield, Sussex TN29 3BL* Nutley (01825) 712277

GIBSON, Ian David Michael. b 58. NE Lon Poly BSc80. Westcott Ho Cam 84. d 87 p 88. C Castle Camps *Ely* 87-90; C Bartlow 87-90; C Linton 87-90; C Shudy Camps 87-90; NSM Gt w Lt Gidding and Steeple Gidding from 91; NSM Hamerton from 91; NSM Winwick from 91; NSM Upton and Copmanford from 91. *The Community of Christ the Sower, Manor Farm, Little Gidding, Huntingdon PE17 5RJ* Winwick (018323) 674

GIBSON, John George. b 20. Chich Th Coll 47. d 50 p 51. V Gunnersbury St Jas *Lon* 58-70; V Upper Teddington SS Pet and Paul 70-84; rtd 84; Perm to Offic *Chich* from 85. *College of St Barnabas, Blackberry Lane, Lingfield, Surrey RH7 6NJ* Dormans Park (01342) 870703

GIBSON, John Murray Hope. b 35. Dur Univ BA58 DipTh60. Cranmer Hall Dur 58. d 60 p 61. C Ches le Street *Dur* 60-63; C Stockton 63-68; V Denton and Ingleton 68-75; V Swalwell from 75; Chapl Dunston Hill Hosp Dur from 80. *The Vicarage, Whickham Bank, Swalwell, Newcastle upon Tyne NE16 3JL* 0191-488 7538

GIBSON, John Noel Keith. b 22. MBE89. Ch Coll Cam MA48 Lon Univ BD59. Coll of Resurr Mirfield 45. d 47 p 48. Antigua 51-56; Virgin Is from 56; rtd 87; Can All SS Cathl Virgin Is from 89. *PO Box 65, Valley, Virgin Gorda, British Virgin Islands* Virgin Islands (180949) 55216

GIBSON, Kenneth George Goudie. b 54. Glas Univ MA83 Edin Univ BD87. Edin Th Coll 83. d 88 p 89. C Glas St Marg *Glas* 88-90; R E Kilbride from 90. *St Mark's Rectory, Telford Road, East Kilbride, Glasgow G75 0HN* East Kilbride (013552) 25222

GIBSON, Mrs Laura Mary. b 50. N Ord Course 85. d 88 p 94. Par Dn Foley Park *Worc* 88-90; Par Dn Kidderminster St Jo and H Innocents 90-94; TV from 94. *35 Sutton Park Road, Kidderminster, Worcs DY11 6LD* Kidderminster (01562) 748213

GIBSON, Mark. b 48. d 84. OSB from 67; Abbot of Alton 82-90; Perm to Offic *Win* from 84; Hon C Paddington St Sav *Lon* from 90; Acting Bp's Dom Chapl 90-91. *24 Formosa Street, London W9 2QA, or Alton Abbey, Alton, Hants GU34 4AP* 0171-286 4962 or Alton (01420) 62145

GIBSON, Nigel Stephen David. b 53. St Barn Coll Adelaide DipMin87. d 87 p 87. Australia 87-89; C Boston *Linc* 90-91; Lect 90-91; P-in-c Stamford St Mary and St Mich 91-92; P-in-c Stamford Baron 91-92; R Stamford St Mary and St Martin from 92. *The Rectory, Pinfold Lane, Stamford, Lincs PE9 2LS* Stamford (01780) 51233

GIBSON, Paul Saison. b 33. BA LTh. d 56 p 57. C Bloomsbury St Geo w St Jo *Lon* 56-59; Canada from 60. *600 Jarvis Street, Toronto, Ontario, Canada, M4Y 2J6*

GIBSON, Philip Nigel Scott. b 53. St Jo Coll Dur BA78. Cranmer Hall Dur DipTh79. d 79 p 80. C Yardley St Edburgha *Birm* 79-82; C Stratford-on-Avon w Bishopton *Cov* 82-84; Chapl SW Hosp Lon 84-91; Chapl St Thos Hosp Lon 84-91; Assoc Priest Newington St Paul *S'wark* 91-92; Chapl Charing Cross Hosp Lon 92-93; Chapl R Lon Hosp (Whitechapel) 93-94; Chapl Bedf Hosp NHS Trust from 95. *Chaplain's Office, Bedford Hospital, South Wing, Kempston Road, Bedford MK42 9DJ* Bedford (01234) 355122

GIBSON, Raymond. b 23. Ely Th Coll 60. d 62 p 63. Chapl Nottm City Hosp 68-84; V Barlings *Linc* 84-88; rtd 88. *11 Cornell Drive, Nottingham NG5 8RF*

GIBSON, Raymond Frank. b 34. Toronto Bible Coll BTh61 Tyndale Hall Bris 62. d 64 p 65. C Kirk Norton *Bradf* 64-67; C Otley 67-72; V Fairlight *Chich* 72-83; V Hallwood *Ches* 83-85; R Freethorpe w Wickhampton, Halvergate etc *Nor* from 85; P-in-c Reedham w Cantley w Limpenhoe and Southwood from 94. *The Vicarage, 60 Lower Green, Freethorpe, Norwich NR13 3AH* Great Yarmouth (01493) 700322

GIBSON, Canon Robert Swinton. b 26. Wadh Coll Ox BA50 MA55. Wells Th Coll 50. d 53 p 54. R Guisborough *York* 69-83; RD Guisborough 73-83; TR Halifax *Wakef* 83-94; Hon Can Wakef Cathl from 85; RD Halifax 86-92; rtd 94. *The Cottage, Hutton Buscel, Scarborough, N Yorkshire YO13 9LL* Scarborough (01723) 862133

GIBSON, Ven Terence Allen (Terry). b 37. Jes Coll Cam BA61 MA65. Cuddesdon Coll 61. d 63 p 64. C Kirkby *Liv* 63-66; TV 72-75; TR 75-84; Warden Cen 63 66-75; Youth Chapl 66-72; RD Walton 79-84; Adn Suffolk *St E* 84-87; Adn Ipswich from 87. *99 Valley Road, Ipswich IP1 4NF* Ipswich (01473) 250333 Fax 286877

GIBSON, Thomas Thomson. b 23. Sarum Th Coll 62. d 63 p 64. V Rowde *Sarum* 66-74; R Poulshot 67-74; V Badminton w Acton Turville *Glouc* 74-84; P-in-c Hawkesbury 81-84; V Badminton w Lt Badminton, Acton Turville etc 84-93; rtd 93; Perm to Offic *B & W* from 95. *9 Lansdown Place West, Bath BA1 5EZ* Bath (01225) 337903 Fax 483638

GICK, Alan Gladney. b 11. TCD BA38 MA58. d 40 p 41. I Lislimnaghan *D & R* 60-80; rtd 80. *107 Old Manor Road, Rustington, W Sussex BN16 3QD* Rustington (01903) 774140

GIDDENS, Leslie Vernon. b 29. Bps' Coll Cheshunt 54. d 56 p 57. C-in-c Hayes St Nic CD *Lon* 63-94; rtd 94. *6 Ashdown Road, Uxbridge, Middlesex UB10 0HY* Uxbridge (01895) 232406

GIDDEY, Canon William Denys. b 17. Leeds Univ BA39. Coll of Resurr Mirfield 39. d 41 p 42. R Binbrook *Linc* 48-61; R Swinhope w Thorganby 48-61; Chapl Eastbourne Hosp Gp 61-83; Can and Preb Chich Cathl *Chich* 78-90; rtd 82; Perm to Offic *Chich* from 90. *70 Sidley Road, Eastbourne, E Sussex BN22 7JP* Eastbourne (01323) 722918

GIDDINGS, Mrs Jacqueline Mary (Jackie). b 44. St Aid Coll Dur BA67. SW Minl Tr Course 91. d 94. C Plympton St Mary *Ex* from 94. *Church House, 9 Horswell Close, Plympton, Plymouth PL7 3NG* Plymouth (01752) 346485

GIDDINGS, John Norton Cornock. b 22. d 86 p 87. NSM Cromhall w Tortworth and Tytherington *Glouc* 86-90; Hon C Stockland w Dalwood *Ex* from 90. *The Vicarage, Stockland, Honiton, Devon EX14 9EF* Stockland (0140488) 401

✠**GIGGALL, Rt Rev George Kenneth.** b 14. OBE61. Man Univ BA37 St Chad's Coll Dur DipTh38. d 39 p 40 c 73. C Cheetwood St Alb *Man* 39-41; C Reddish 41-45; Chapl RN 45-69; QHC 67-69; Dean Gib *Eur* 69-73; Bp St Helena 73-79; Aux Bp Eur 79-81; Chapl San Remo w Bordighera 80-81; rtd 81; Asst Bp Blackb from 81. *Fosbrooke House, 8 Clifton Drive, Lytham St Annes, Lancs FY8 5RQ* Lytham (01253) 735683

GILBERT, Anthony John David. b 54. LRSC83 Open Univ BA91. Ripon Coll Cuddesdon 83. d 86 p 87. C Exning St Martin w Landwade *St E* 86-89; Chapl RAF from 89. *Chaplaincy Services (RAF), HQ, Personnel and Training Command, RAF Innsworth, Gloucester GL3 1EZ* Gloucester (01452) 712612 Ext 5164 Fax 510828

GILBERT, Arthur John. b 57. LTCL76 GBSM79 Reading Univ PGCE80. Coll of Resurr Mirfield 88. d 91 p 92. C Uppingham w Ayston and Wardley w Belton *Pet* 91-94; C St Bart Armley w St Mary New Wortley *Ripon* from 94. *20 Wesley Road, Leeds LS12 1UN* Leeds (0113) 279 7377

GILBERT, Barry. b 46. Leeds Univ BA67. Coll of Resurr Mirfield 67. d 69 p 70. C Malvern Link w Cowleigh *Worc* 69-73; P-in-c Bromsgrove All SS 73-81; V 81-83; P-in-c Lower Mitton 83-88; V 88-92; V Stourport-on-Severn and Wilden from 92; RD Stourport from 93. *The Vicarage, Stourport-on-Severn, Worcs DY13 9DD* Stourport (01299) 822041

GILBERT, Caroline Margaret. b 62. Nottm Univ BTh90. St Jo Coll Nottm 87. d 90. Hon C Aston SS Pet and Paul *Birm* 90-93. *459 Fleet Lane, St Helens, Mersyside WA9 2NQ* St Helens (01744) 21213

GILBERT, Miss Christine Lesley. b 44. DipHE. Trin Coll Bris 79. dss 85 d 86 p 94. Par Dn Bilston *Lich* 87-94; TV Penkridge Team from 94. *The Vicarage, Top Road, Acton Trussell, Stafford ST17 0RQ* Stafford (01785) 712248

GILBERT, Christopher Anthony. b 60. Aston Univ BSc82. St Jo Coll Nottm 86. d 89 p 90. C Aston SS Pet and Paul *Birm* 89-93; TV Parr *Liv* from 93. *459 Fleet Lane, St Helens, Merseyside WA9 2NQ* St Helens (01744) 21213

GILBERT, Frederick Herbert. b 14. Worc Ord Coll 64. d 66 p 67. C Paignton Ch Ch *Ex* 69-73; TV Offwell, Widworthy, Cotleigh, Farway etc 73-79; rtd 80; Lic to Offic *Ex* from 80. *17 Hoskings Court, Strode Road, Buckfastleigh, Devon TQ11 0PE* Buckfastleigh (01364) 43321

GILBERT, Frederick Joseph. b 29. Lich Th Coll 58. d 59 p 60. R Crumpsall St Matt *Man* 68-75; RD Cheetham 70-74; RD N Man 74-75; V Rochdale St Aid 75-78; TV Rochdale 78-80; V Westhoughton 80-84; TR 84-87; AD Deane 85-87; R W Bowbrook *Worc* 87-89; R Bowbrook N 89-93; rtd 93. *Freshways, Main Road, Peopleton, Pershore, Worcs WR10 2EG* Worcester (01905) 841629

GILBERT, John Edwin. b 28. FCA62. Bps' Coll Cheshunt 54. **d** 57 **p** 58. India 65-71; Perm to Offic *St Alb* 71-77; Lic to Offic 77-86; Hon C Sunnyside w Bourne End 86-89; TV Padgate *Liv* 89-94; rtd 94. *4 Westgate Drive, Bridgnorth, Shropshire WV16 4QF* Bridgnorth (01746) 762611

GILBERT, John Michael. b 06. St Boniface Warminster. **d** 31 **p** 32. V Porthleven *Truro* 63-74; Lic to Offic 74-78; rtd 75. *5 Rigelou Flats, Meade Street, George, 6530 South Africa* George (441) 741748

GILBERT, Joseph. b 12. Chich Th Coll 33. **d** 36 **p** 37. V Lever Bridge *Man* 65-76; rtd 77; Perm to Offic *Man* from 77. *159 Bolton Road, Turton, Bolton BL7 0AF* Bolton (01204) 852736

GILBERT, Mrs Margaret Ann. b 39. Dub Inst of Adult Educn DPastMin89 TCD DipTh91. CITC 89. **d** 92 **p** 93. NSM Dub Clontarf *D & G* from 92. *67 Grange Park Road, Raheny, Dublin 5, Irish Republic* Dublin (1) 848-1340

GILBERT, Michael Victor. b 61. Dur Univ BA84 Westhill Coll Birm CYCW86. Trin Coll Bris DipThe94. **d** 94 **p** 95. C Chapeltown *Sheff* from 94. *9 Maple Place, Chapeltown, Sheffield S30 4QW* Sheffield (0114) 246 1860

GILBERT, Philip Mark. b 62. Liv Univ BA84. Coll of Resurr Mirfield 84. **d** 87 **p** 88. C Frodsham *Ches* 87-89; C Stockton Heath 89-92; R Tangmere and Oving *Chich* from 92. *St Andrew's Vicarage, 21 Gibson Road, Tangmere, Chichester, W Sussex PO20 6JA* Chichester (01243) 785089

GILBERT, Raymond. b 34. AKC61. **d** 62 **p** 63. C Newbold and Dunston *Derby* 62-66; PV and Succ S'wark Cathl *S'wark* 66-68; P-in-c Stuntney *Ely* 68-74; Prec and Sacr Ely Cathl 68-74; Min Can Cant Cathl *Cant* 74-79; Hon Min Can from 79; P-in-c Patrixbourne w Bridge and Bekesbourne 79-81; V from 81; RD E Bridge from 92. *The Vicarage, 23 High Street, Bridge, Canterbury, Kent CT4 5JZ* Canterbury (01227) 830250

GILBERT, Raymond Frederick. b 44. Local NSM Course 91. **d** 93 **p** 94. NSM Stowmarket *St E* from 93. *3 Violet Hill Road, Stowmarket, Suffolk IP14 1NE* Stowmarket (01449) 677700

GILBERT, Roger Charles. b 46. Ex Coll Ox BA69 MA74 Nottm Univ MEd81. St Steph Ho Ox 69. **d** 71 **p** 72. NSM Bridgwater St Mary w Chilton Trinity *B & W* 71-74; NSM Rugeley *Lich* 74-81; NSM Cannock 81-83; NSM Wednesbury St Jas and St Jo from 83. *41 Stafford Road, Cannock, Staffs WS11 2AF* Cannock (01543) 570531

GILBERT, Canon Roger Geoffrey. b 37. K Coll Lon BD69 AKC69. **d** 70 **p** 71. C Walton-on-Thames *Guildf* 70-74; R St Mabyn *Truro* 74-81; P-in-c Helland 74-81; P-in-c Madron 81-86; R Falmouth K Chas from 86; Hon Can Truro Cathl from 94; RD Carnmarth S from 92. *The Rectory, Albany Road, Falmouth, Cornwall TR11 3RP* Falmouth (01326) 314176

GILBERT, Roy Alan. b 48. Birm Univ BEd70 Lon Univ DipTh79. Ripon Coll Cuddesdon 74. **d** 76 **p** 77. C Moseley St Mary *Birm* 76-82; Australia from 82. *Guildford Grammar School, 11 Terrace Road, Guildford, W Australia 6055* Perth (9) 378-1222 or 378-2778 Fax 279-1135

GILBERT, Sidney Horace. b 34. Dur Univ BA58 MA69 Univ of Wales BD62 CertEd83. St Mich Coll Llan 58. **d** 61 **p** 62. C Colwyn Bay *St As* 61-63; C Llanrhos 63-69; R Penley and Bettisfield 69-78; V Brymbo and Bwlchgwyn 78-82; Univ of Wales (Swansea) *S & B* 82-83; R Beeston Regis *Nor* from 84; Holiday Chapl 84-91; Sen Chapl from 91. *All Saints' Rectory, Cromer Road, Beeston Regis, Cromer, Norfolk NR27 9NG* Sheringham (01263) 822163

GILCHRIST, David John. b 51. Mert Coll Ox BA75 MA79. St Jo Coll Nottm DPS79. **d** 79 **p** 80. C Gt Ilford St Andr *Chelmsf* 79-81; C Buckhurst Hill 81-84; Chapl Dover Coll Kent from 84. *24 Folkestone Road, Dover, Kent CT17 9RU* Dover (01304) 205906

GILCHRIST, Gavin Frank. b 53. AKC74. Coll of Resurr Mirfield 76. **d** 77 **p** 78. C Newbold and Dunston *Derby* 77-80; C Addlestone *Guildf* 80-84; V Blackpool St Mary *Blackb* 84-92; P-in-c Carl St Herbert w St Steph *Carl* from 92. *St Herbert's Vicarage, Blackwell Road, Carlisle CA2 4RA* Carlisle (01228) 23375

GILCHRIST, Lawrence Edward. b 29. Liv Univ BSc52. NW Ord Course 74. **d** 76 **p** 77. NSM Buxton w Burbage and King Sterndale *Derby* 76-83; V Chinley w Buxworth 83-94; rtd 94. *18 Miles Hawk Way, Mildenhall, Bury St Edmunds, Suffolk IP28 7SE* Mildenhall (01638) 711360

GILCHRIST, Spencer. b 66. QUB BA88. BTh. **d** 91 **p** 92. C Ballynafeigh St Jude *D & D* from 91. *15 St John's Park, Belfast BT7 3JF* Belfast (01232) 641447

GILDING, James Peter. b 33. Leeds Univ BA64. Ely Th Coll 61. **d** 63 **p** 64. C Chorley St Geo *Blackb* 63-66; C Pemberton St Fran Kitt Green *Liv* 66-69; P-in-c Terrington St John *Ely* 69-73; P-in-c Walpole St Andrew 69-73; V Elm 74-81; TR Stanground and Farcet 81-89; V Haslingfield 89-95; R Harlton 89-95; R Haslingfield w Harlton and Gt and Lt

Eversden from 95. *The Rectory, Broad Lane, Haslingfield, Cambridge CB3 7JF* Cambridge (01223) 870285

GILDING, Richard Herbert. b 11. St Jo Coll Dur LTh46 BA47. ALCD35. **d** 35 **p** 36. V Studley *Sarum* 56-75; rtd 75. *40 East Budleigh Road, Budleigh Salterton, Devon EX9 6EJ* Budleigh Salterton (01395) 443807

GILES, Canon Barry James. b 35. Kelham Th Coll 54. **d** 59 **p** 60. C Leytonstone St Marg w St Columba *Chelmsf* 59-62; Prec Gib Cathl *Eur* 62-66; V Darwen St Geo *Blackb* 66-69; V Forest Gate St Edm *Chelmsf* 69-73; R Jersey St Pet *Win* from 73; Vice-Dean Jersey from 84; Hon Can Win Cathl from 93. *St Peter's Rectory, Jersey, Channel Islands* Jersey (01534) 481805

GILES, Brother. *See* HILL, Michael John

GILES, Brother. *See* SPRENT, Michael Francis

GILES, Edward Alban. b 34. Bps' Coll Cheshunt. **d** 58 **p** 59. S Africa 63-70; Chapl HM Pris Camp Hill 70-75; Chapl HM Pris Stafford 75-83; Chapl HM Young Offender Inst Hollesley Bay Colony from 83; rtd 94; Sub Chapl HM Pris Blundeston from 94. *The Hollies, Ferry Farm Drive, Sutton Hoo, Woodbridge, Suffolk IP12 3DR* Woodbridge (01394) 387486 Fax 411071

GILES, Canon Eric Francis. b 34. Sarum Th Coll 61. **d** 63 **p** 64. C Plympton St Mary *Ex* 63-71; R Dumbleton w Wormington *Glouc* 71-77; P-in-c Toddington w Stanley Pontlarge 71-77; R Dumbleton w Wormington and Toddington 77-79; V Churchdown St Jo from 79; Hon Can Glouc Cathl from 95. *St John's Vicarage, St John's Avenue, Churchdown, Gloucester GL3 2DA* Churchdown (01452) 713421

GILES, Frank Edwin. b 22. St Aid Birkenhead 50. **d** 53 **p** 54. V Sacriston *Dur* 56-70; V Hook *S'wark* 70-81; V Langley St Mich *Birm* 81-88; rtd 88. *5 Victoria Terrace, Bourton-on-the-Water, Cheltenham, Glos GL52 6BN* Cotswold (01451) 820486

GILES, Gordon John. b 66. Lanc Univ BA88 Magd Coll Cam PhD95. Ridley Hall Cam BA95 CTM95. **d** 95. C Chesterton Gd Shep *Ely* from 95. *19 Hurrell Road, Cambridge CB4 3RQ* Cambridge (01223) 464348

GILES, Graeme John. b 56. Linc Th Coll 82. **d** 85 **p** 86. C Prestbury *Glouc* 85-88; C Paulsgrove *Portsm* from 88. *47 Lime Grove, Portsmouth PO6 4DG* Cosham (01705) 219800

GILES (nee WILLIAMS), Mrs Gwenllian (Gwen). b 34. RSCN55 SRN58 SCM60. W Midl Minl Tr Course 88. **d** 92 **p** 94. NSM Bromsgrove St Jo *Worc* from 92. *22 Abbey Close, Parklands, Bromsgrove, Worcs B60 2RA* Bromsgrove (01527) 576221

GILES, Canon John Robert. b 36. Em Coll Cam BA60 MA65. Ripon Hall Ox 60. **d** 61 **p** 62. C Lowestoft St Marg *Nor* 61-65; Chapl UEA 65-72; R Kidbrooke St Jas *S'wark* 72-79; Sub-Dean Greenwich 74-79; V Sheff St Mark Broomhall *Sheff* 79-87; Ind Chapl 79-92; Can Res Sheff Cathl 87-92; V Lee Gd Shep w St Pet *S'wark* from 92. *The Vicarage, 47 Handen Road, London SE12 8NR* 0181-852 5270

GILES, Maurice Alfred Douglas. b 15. Bps' Coll Cheshunt 66. **d** 66 **p** 67. C Southgate St Andr *Lon* 69-71; V New Southgate St Paul 71-75; C Friern Barnet St Jas 75-80; rtd 80; Perm to Offic *Lon* from 80. *66 Granville Road, London N12 0HT* 0181-346 0214

GILES, Peter Michael Osmaston. b 40. Solicitor 65. S Dios Minl Tr Scheme 85. **d** 88 **p** 89. Hon C Wootton Bassett *Sarum* 88-90; Lic to RD Calne from 91. *The Old Vicarage, Honeyhill, Wootton Bassett, Swindon SN4 7AZ* Swindon (01793) 852643

GILES, Canon Richard Stephen. b 40. MRTPI71 Newc Univ BA63 MLitt88. Cuddesdon Coll 64. **d** 65 **p** 66. C Higham Ferrers w Chelveston *Pet* 65-68; Perm to Offic *Ox* 69; C Oakengates *Lich* 70; C Stevenage St Geo *St Alb* 71-75; P-in-c Howdon Panns *Newc* 75-76; TV Willington Team 76-79; Bp's Adv for Planning *Pet* 79-87; V Pet St Jude 79-87; Par Development Officer *Wakef* from 87; P-in-c Huddersfield St Thos 87-94; Hon Can Wakef Cathl from 94; V Huddersfield St Thos from 94. *St Thomas's Vicarage, 78 Bankfield Road, Huddersfield HD1 3HR* Huddersfield (01484) 420660

GILES, Robert Medwin (Bob). b 37. Man Univ BA(Econ)58 PGCE59. Ripon Hall Ox 64. **d** 66 **p** 67. C Peel *Man* 66-69; C Alverstoke *Portsm* 69-71; P-in-c Edale *Derby* 71-79; Warden Champion Ho Youth Tr *Carl* 71-79; Sen Youth Officer *York* 79-86; P-in-c Shipley *Chich* 86-87; V 87-91; Area Sec (Dios Pet & St Alb) USPG 91-92; R Broughton w Loddington and Cransley etc *Pet* from 92. *The Rectory, Gate Lane, Broughton, Kettering, Northants NN14 1ND* Kettering (01536) 791373

GILES, Susan Jane. b 58. BSc. **dss** 83 **d** 92 **p** 94. Balsall Heath St Paul *Birm* 83-85; Asst Chapl Southmead Hosp Bris 86-90; Asst Chapl HM Rem Cen Pucklechurch from 90; Asst Chapl HM Pris Bris from 92. *HM Remand Centre, Pucklechurch, Bristol BS17 3QJ* Bristol (0117) 937 2606 Fax 937 2729

GILES, Timothy David. b 46. FCA60. Oak Hill Th Coll DipTh90. **d** 90 **p** 91. C Ipswich St Marg *St E* 90-94; C Reigate

St Mary *S'wark* from 94. *63 Chart Lane, Reigate, Surrey RH2 7EA* Reigate (01737) 243085

GILFORD, George. b 49. St Kath Coll Liv CertEd72 LTCL86. N Ord Course 88. **d** 91 **p** 92. NSM Gt Crosby St Faith *Liv* from 91. *Flat 2, 17 Alexandra Road, Waterloo, Liverpool L22 1RJ* 0151-920 5744

GILKES, Donald Martin. b 47. St Jo Coll Nottm 78. **d** 80 **p** 81. C Conisbrough *Sheff* 80-84; P-in-c Balne 84-86; P-in-c Hensall 84-86; TV Gt Snaith 86-88; V Whittle-le-Woods *Blackb* from 88. *The Vicarage, Preston Road, Whittle-le-Woods, Chorley, Lancs PR6 7PS* Chorley (01257) 263306

GILKS, Peter Martin. b 51. SRN77 Nottm Univ BMus72. Ripon Coll Cuddesdon 82. **d** 84 **p** 85. C Bitterne Park *Win* 84-87; TV Basingstoke 87-93; R Abbotts Ann and Upper and Goodworth Clatford from 93. *The Rectory, Upper Clatford, Andover, Hants SP11 7QP* Andover (01264) 352906

GILL, Alan Gordon. b 42. Sarum & Wells Th Coll 73. **d** 75 **p** 76. C Wimborne Minster *Sarum* 75-78; R Winterbourne Stickland and Turnworth etc 78-86; V Verwood from 86. *The Vicarage, Dewlands Way, Verwood, Dorset BH31 6JN* Verwood (01202) 822298

GILL, Christopher John Sutherland. b 28. Selw Coll Cam BA52 MA70. Ely Th Coll 52. **d** 54 **p** 55. Chapl St Edm Sch Cant 60-76; Chapl Bennett Memorial Sch Tunbridge Wells from 76; Hon C Tunbridge Wells K Chas *Roch* 77-93; rtd 93. *Flat 1, Hurstleigh, Hurstwood Lane, Tunbridge Wells, Kent TN4 8YA* Tunbridge Wells (01892) 528409

GILL, David Brian Michael. b 55. Southn Univ BTh88. Sarum & Wells Th Coll 83. **d** 86 **p** 87. C Honiton, Gittisham, Combe Raleigh, Monkton etc *Ex* 86-89; C E Teignmouth 89; C W Teignmouth 89; C Teignmouth, Ideford w Luton, Ashcombe etc 90-91; TV Ex St Thos and Em from 91. *Emmanuel Vicarage, 49 Okehampton Road, Exeter EX4 1EL* Exeter (01392) 435840

GILL, Donald Maule Harvell. b 08. Keble Coll Ox BA33 MA39. Wells Th Coll 34. **d** 35 **p** 36. V Micheldever *Win* 45-70; R Minstead 71-80; rtd 80; Perm to Offic *Win* from 80. *4 Hereward Close, Romsey, Hants SO51 5RA* Romsey (01794) 514591

GILL, Mrs Gabrielle Mary (Gay).d 90 **p** 94. NSM Timperley *Ches* from 90. *The Croft, 3 Harrop Road, Hale, Altrincham, Cheshire WA15 9BU* 0161-928 1800

GILL, Gary George. b 44. Culham Coll Ox CertEd70. Cant Sch of Min 85. **d** 87 **p** 88. C Addlestone *Guildf* 87-90; C Buckland in Dover w Buckland Valley *Cant* from 90; Chapl Buckland Hosp Dover from 90. *24 Dryden Road, Dover, Kent CT16 2BX* Dover (01304) 822004

GILL, Geoffrey Fitzell. b 17. Selw Coll Cam BA39 MA43. Linc Th Coll 39. **d** 41 **p** 42. V Enderby *Leic* 51-82; rtd 82. *The Poplars, Port Eynon, Gower, Swansea SA3 1NN* Gower (01792) 390206

GILL, James Joseph. b 45. Pontifical Univ Maynooth BD78. **d** 77 **p** 78. In RC Ch 77-82; C Howden TM *York* 82-83; TV 83-86; P-in-c Wragby w Sharlston *Wakef* 86-88; V Sharlston 88-91; V Tilehurst St Geo *Ox* from 91. *St George's Vicarage, 98 Grovelands Road, Reading RG3 2PD* Reading (01734) 588354 or 509695

✠**GILL, the Rt Rev Kenneth Edward.** b 32. Hartley Victoria Coll. **d** 58 **p** 60 **c** 72. In Ch of S India 58-80; Bp Karnataka Cen 72-80; Asst Bp Newc from 80. *83 Kenton Road, Newcastle upon Tyne NE3 4NL* 0191-285 2220 Fax 213 0728

GILL, Mrs Mary. b 20. Nottm Univ BA42. St Jo Coll Nottm CertCS43. **d** 88. NSM Alston Team *Newc* 88-90; rtd 90. *Old School, Garrigill, Alston, Cumbria CA9 3DP* Alston (01434) 381594

GILL, Michael John. b 59. K Coll Lon BA81 AKC81. St Mich Coll Llan BD85. **d** 85 **p** 86. Min Can St Woolos Cathl *Mon* 85-90; Chapl St Woolos Hosp Newport 87-90; Succ Heref Cathl *Heref* 90-93; C Heref St Jo 90-93; TV Ebbw Vale *Mon* from 93. *The Vicarage, Cwm Road, Waunlwyd, Ebbw Vale, Gwent NP3 6TR* Ebbw Vale (01495) 371258

GILL, Richard Ward. b 26. Lon Univ BD53. Oak Hill Th Coll 53. **d** 54 **p** 55. V St Alb St Paul *St Alb* 65-91; rtd 91; Perm to Offic *Ex* from 92. *50 Woodbury Park, Axminster, Devon EX13 5QY*

GILL, Canon Prof Robin Morton. b 44. K Coll Lon BD66 AKC66 Lon Univ PhD69 Birm Univ MSocSc72. **d** 68 **p** 69. C Rugby St Andr *Cov* 68-71; Papua New Guinea 71-72; Lect Th Edin Univ 72-86; Sen Lect 86-88; Assoc Dean Faculty of Div 85-88; P-in-c Edin SS Phil and Jas *Edin* 73-75; P-in-c Ford *Newc* 75-87; Perm to Offic 87-92; P-in-c Coldstream *Edin* 87-92; Wm Leech Prof Applied Th Newc Univ 88-92; Mich Ramsey Prof Modern Th Kent Univ from 92; Hon Can Cant Cathl *Cant* from 92. *Rutherford College, The University, Canterbury, Kent CT2 7NX* Canterbury (01227) 764000 or 781976 Fax 475473

GILL, Stanley. b 11. Clifton Th Coll 37. **d** 39 **p** 40. V Cornhill w Carham *Newc* 67-74; V Branxton 71-74; rtd 76. *37 Castle Terrace, Berwick-upon-Tweed TD15 1NZ* Berwick-upon-Tweed (01289) 330982

GILL, Stanley. b 34. Sarum Th Coll 66. **d** 68 **p** 69. C Ipswich St Mary at Stoke w St Pet & St Mary Quay *St E* 68-73 and 78-80; TV 80-82; V Bury St Edmunds St Geo 73-78; P-in-c Childe Okeford, Manston, Hammoon and Hanford *Sarum* 82-89; R The Lulworths, Winfrith Newburgh and Chaldon 89-94; R Hazelbury Bryan and the Hillside Par from 94. *The Rectory, Hazelbury Bryan, Sturminster Newton, Dorset DT10 2ED* Hazelbury Bryan (01258) 817251

GILL, Thomas. b 21. St Aid Birkenhead 62. **d** 63 **p** 64. V Burstwick w Thorngumbald *York* 67-78; RD S Holderness 74-78; R Brandesburton 78-86; RD N Holderness 80-86; rtd 87. *Bellfield, Arnold Lane, Arnold, Hull HU11 5HP* Hornsea (01964) 562282

GILL, Timothy Charles (Tim). b 66. Newc Univ BA88. Westcott Ho Cam 89. **d** 92 **p** 93. C N Hull St Mich *York* from 92. *1 St Michael's Church, Orchard Park Road, Hull HU6 9BX* Hull (01482) 804458

GILL, William. b 08. St Aid Birkenhead 59. **d** 60 **p** 61. V Austwick *Bradf* 68-78; rtd 78; Perm to Offic *Bradf* 79-85; Perm to Offic *Linc* from 85. *14 Woodland Avenue, Skellingthorpe, Lincoln LN6 5TE* Lincoln (01522) 682529

GILLAN, Dr Ian Thomson. b 15. Aber Univ MA37 BD40 Edin Univ PhD43. **d** 52 **p** 53. In RC Ch 52-72; C Aber St Andr *Ab* 73-74; P-in-c Fochabers *Mor* 74-75; P-in-c Aberlour 74-75; Provost St Andr Cathl Inverness 75; P-in-c Aber St Clem *Ab* 76-78; rtd 79; Perm to Offic *Ab* from 79. *5 Park Crescent, Oldmeldrum, Aberdeen AB51 0DH* Oldmeldrum (01651) 872308

GILLARD, Geoffrey Vernon (Geoff). b 48. Man Univ BA70 Nottm Univ MPhil80. Trin Coll Umuahia Nigeria 72 St Jo Coll Nottm 74. **d** 78 **p** 79. C Aughton Ch Ch *Liv* 78-81; Hong Kong 81-87; Dir of Studies St Alb Dio Minl Tr Scheme *St Alb* 87-92; Prin St Alb Dio Minl Tr Scheme from 92. *17 Eastmoor Park, Harpenden, Herts AL5 1BN* Harpenden (01582) 762005

GILLESPIE, George Henry. b 20. SS Coll Cam BA46 MA55. Cuddesdon Coll 46. **d** 48 **p** 49. V Allenton and Shelton Lock *Derby* 56-71; Chapl Derby High Sch for Girls 71-78; V Bath Ascension *B & W* 71-78; P-in-c Norton St Philip w Hemington, Hardington etc 78-81; R 81-85; rtd 85; Perm to Offic *B & W* from 86. *18 South Lea Road, Bath BA1 3RW* Bath (01225) 339023

GILLESPIE, Michael David. b 41. E Midl Min Tr Course 86. **d** 89 **p** 90. NSM Countesthorpe w Foston *Leic* from 89. *3 Penfold Drive, Countesthorpe, Leicester LE8 3TP* Leicester (0116) 278 1130

GILLETT, Brian Alan Michael. b 42. ARICS73. Chich Th Coll. **d** 82 **p** 83. C Tupsley *Heref* 82-86; R Kingstone w Clehonger and Eaton Bishop 86-89; P-in-c Thruxton 89; P-in-c Allensmore 89; R Kingstone w Clehonger, Eaton Bishop etc from 89. *The Rectory, Kingstone, Hereford HR2 9EY* Golden Valley (01981) 250350

GILLETT, Canon David Keith. b 45. Leeds Univ BA65 MPhil68. Oak Hill Th Coll 66. **d** 68 **p** 69. C Watford St Luke *St Alb* 68-71; Sec Pathfinders and CYFA N Area 71-74; Lect St Jo Coll Nottm 74-79; Ch of Ireland Renewal Cen 80-82; V Luton Lewsey St Hugh *St Alb* 82-88; Prin Trin Coll Bris from 88; Hon Can Bris Cathl *Bris* from 91. *16 Pembroke Road, Bristol BS9 1BB* Bristol (0117) 968 2646 or 968 2803 Fax 968 7470

GILLETT, Victor Henry John. b 31. Open Univ BA83 BTh87 Open Univ MTh94. Clifton Th Coll 59. **d** 62 **p** 63. C Walton Breck *Liv* 62-65; C Wednesfield Heath *Lich* 65-68; V Tipton St Paul 68-76; V Moulton *Pet* 76-92; TV Worthing Ch the King *Chich* from 92; Chapl Ramsay Hall from 92. *85 Heene Road, Worthing, W Sussex BN11 4PP* Worthing (01903) 218026

GILLETT, Vincent. b 30. FCollP81 Lon Univ BSc55 UEA MSc72 DipSMan76. Chich Th Coll 59. **d** 61 **p** 62. Ghana 63-72; Lic to Offic *Liv* 72-79; Lic to Offic *Ex* 79-84; Hd Master St Wilfrid's Sch *Ex* 79-84; R Atherington and High Bickington 84-94; V Burrington 84-94; rtd 95. *Birchy Barton Lodge, 2 Honiton Road, Heavitree, Exeter EX1 3EA* Exeter (01392) 436393

GILLETT, William Charles. b 05. Sarum Th Coll 28. **d** 31 **p** 32. R E w W Anstey *Ex* 51-78; rtd 78; Perm to Offic *Ex* from 78; Perm to Offic *B & W* 81-93. *Sarum, East Anstey, Tiverton, Devon EX16 9JP* Anstey Mills (013984) 284

GILLHAM, Martin John. b 45. Wilson Carlile Coll IDC66 Qu Coll Birm 72. **d** 75 **p** 76. C Whitley Ch Ch *Ox* 75-78; TV Crowmarsh Gifford w Newnham Murren 78-79; TV Wallingford w Crowmarsh Gifford etc 79-83; V Kintbury w Avington 83-94; Dioc Lay Min Adv and Warden of Readers from 89; Thames Regional Guardian SSF from 93; NSM W Wycombe w Bledlow Ridge, Bradenham and Radnage from 94. *The Rectory, West Wycombe, High Wycombe, Bucks HP14 3AH* High Wycombe (01494) 529988

GILLHAM, Mrs Patricia Anne. b 40. Wilson Carlile Coll IDC66 Ox Min Course CBTS93. **d** 93 **p** 94. Par Dn Kintbury w Avington *Ox* 93-94; C 94-95; C W Wycombe w Bledlow Ridge, Bradenham and Radnage from 95. *The Rectory, West Wycombe, High Wycombe, Bucks HP14 3AH* High Wycombe (01494) 529988

GILLHESPEY, Canon Clive. b 28. Lon Univ DipTh66 BD73. Cranmer Hall Dur 63. **d** 65 **p** 66. V Flookburgh *Carl* 69-74; R Barrow St Geo w St Luke 74-81; TR 81-92; Hon Can Carl Cathl 84-92; rtd 92. *Canon's Court, 43 Holyoake Avenue, Barrow-in-Furness, Cumbria LA13 9LH* Barrow-in-Furness (01229) 839041

GILLIAN, Ronald Trevor. b 57. Ulster Univ DipMus77 MTD78 QUB BEd89 TCD BTh93. CITC 90. **d** 93 **p** 94. C Belf St Donard *D & D* from 93. *17 Kirkliston Drive, Belfast BT5 5NX* Belfast (01232) 651821

GILLIAT, Canon Patrick Neville. b 10. G&C Coll Cam BA32 MA36. Tyndale Hall Bris 32. **d** 34 **p** 35. Can Res Sheff Cathl *Sheff* 69-76; Succ Sheff Cathl 69-76; rtd 76; Perm to Offic *B & W* 76-93. *Amberley, Sleepers Hill, Winchester SO22 4NB* Winchester (01962) 865976

GILLIBRAND, John Nigel. b 60. Ox Univ BA82 MA86 Lon Univ PGCE83. **d** 88 **p** 89. C Dolgellau w Llanfachreth and Brithdir etc *Ban* 88-90; C Llanbeblig w Caernarfon and Betws Garmon etc 90-91; V Ffestiniog w Blaenau Ffestiniog from 91. *The Rectory, The Square, Blaenau Ffestiniog, Gwynedd LL41 3UW* Blaenau Ffestiniog (01766) 831966

GILLIES, Canon Eric Robert. b 19. Worc Ord Coll 61. **d** 63 **p** 64. R Aldrington *Chich* 67-82; RD Hove 77-82; Can and Preb Chich Cathl 81-89; P-in-c Clapham w Patching 82-83; V Findon 82-83; V Findon w Clapham and Patching 83-89; rtd 89; P-in-c Burpham *Chich* 89-94. *330 Findon Road, Worthing, W Sussex BN14 0HB* Arundel (01903) 873330

GILLIES, Dr Robert Arthur (Bob). b 51. Edin Univ BD77 St Andr Univ PhD91. Edin Th Coll 73. **d** 77 **p** 78. C Falkirk *Edin* 77-80; C Edin Ch Ch 80-84; Chapl Napier Coll 80-84; Chapl Dundee Univ *Bre* 84-90; R St Andrews St Andr *St And* from 91. *St Andrew's Rectory, Queen's Terrace, St Andrews, Fife KY16 9QF* St Andrews (01334) 73344

GILLIGAN, Harry. b 07. Dur Univ 56. **d** 58 **p** 59. V Everton St Polycarp *Liv* 66-68; Chapl to the Deaf (Southport) 71-79; rtd 74; Perm to Offic *Win* from 82; Perm to Offic *Portsm* from 88. *4 Lampeter Avenue, Cosham, Portsmouth PO6 2AL* Cosham (01705) 324710

GILLING, John Reginald. b 25. Cam Univ BA49 MA51 MLitt55. Cuddesdon Coll 53. **d** 55 **p** 56. Chapl Ch Ox 62-71; V Pimlico St Mary Graham Terrace *Lon* 71-90; AD Westmr St Marg 79-85; rtd 90. *49 Westgate, Chichester, W Sussex PO19 3EZ* Chichester (01243) 775169

GILLINGHAM, John Bruce. b 48. Ch Ch Ox BA69 MA74. St Jo Coll Nottm BA73. **d** 73 **p** 74. C Plymouth St Andr w St Paul and St Geo *Ex* 73-77; C Ox St Aldate w H Trin *Ox* 78; Chapl Jes Coll Ox 78-88; Chapl Ox Pastorate 79-88; Dioc Missr *Birm* 88-92; R Ox St Clem *Ox* from 92. *St Clement's Rectory, 58 Rectory Road, Oxford OX4 1BW* Oxford (01865) 248735

GILLINGHAM, Michael John. b 46. Univ of Wales (Swansea) DSCE80 Hull Univ MA90. Chich Th Coll 68. **d** 71 **p** 72. C Llanharan w Peterston-super-Montem *Llan* 71-73; C Skewen 73-76; Neath Deanery Youth Chapl 74-76; Perm to Offic 79-80; TV Kirkby *Liv* 76-77; Youth Chapl *Ches* 77-79; Perm to Offic *St Alb* 80-83; Youth Worker 80-83; TV Sheff Manor *Sheff* 83-88; Chapl Sheff Sea Cadets from 87; R Frecheville from 88. *Frecheville Rectory, Brackenfield Grove, Sheffield S12 4XS* Sheffield (0114) 239 9555

GILLINGHAM, Canon Peter Llewellyn. b 14. MVO55. Or Coll Ox BA35 DipTh36 MA39. Wycliffe Hall Ox 35. **d** 37 **p** 38. V Horsham *Chich* 60-77; RD Horsham 74-77; Chapl Sherborne Sch Dorset 78-79; rtd 79; Perm to Offic *St E* from 82. *Maplestead Cottage, Leiston Road, Aldeburgh, Suffolk IP15 5QD* Aldeburgh (01728) 852739

GILLINGS, Ven Richard John. b 45. St Chad's Coll Dur BA67. Linc Th Coll 68. **d** 70 **p** 71. C Altrincham St Geo *Ches* 70-75; P-in-c Stockport St Thos 75-77; R 77-83; P-in-c Stockport St Pet 78-83; TR Birkenhead Priory 83-93; RD Birkenhead 85-93; Hon Can Ches Cathl from 92; V Bramhall 93-94; Adn Macclesfield from 94. *The Vicarage, Robin's Lane, Bramhall, Stockport, Cheshire SK7 2PE* 0161-439 2254

GILLION, Canon Frederick Arthur. b 08. ALCD30 St Jo Coll Dur LTh30 BA31 MA34. **d** 31 **p** 32. R Beeston Regis *Nor* 69-75; rtd 75; Perm to Offic *Nor* from 75. *66 The Street, Ingworth, Norwich NR11 6AE* Aylsham (01263) 732583

GILLION, Robert Alan. b 51. LRAM. Sarum & Wells Th Coll 81. **d** 83 **p** 84. C E Dereham *Nor* 83-86; C Richmond St Mary w St Matthias and St Jo *S'wark* 86-90; Hong Kong from 90. *37A Seahorse Lane, Discovery Bay, Lantau Island, Hong Kong* Hong Kong (852) 987-7106 Fax 987 8691

GILLMAN, Noel Francis. b 26. St D Dioc Tr Course St D Coll Lamp St Mich Coll Llan. **d** 79 **p** 80. NSM Llanelli *St D* 79-83;

C 83-85; TV Tenby 85-91; rtd 91. *4 Oaklands, Swiss Valley, Llanelli, Dyfed SA14 8DA* Llanelli (01554) 772663

GILLMOR, Canon Samuel Frederick. b 29. St Aid Birkenhead. **d** 62 **p** 63. C Carlow Union *C & O* 62-64; I Fenagh Union 64-68; I Maryborough w Dysart Enos 68-79; Preb Ossory Cathl 78-79; Preb Leighlin Cathl 78-79; I Clane w Donadea *M & K* 79-84; I Mullingar, Portnashangan, Moyliscar, Kilbixy etc 84-93; Can Meath 92-93; I Achonry w Tubbercurry and Killoran *T, K & A* from 93; Can Achonry Cathl from 93. *Back Acre, Carrowdubh, Strandhill, Co Sligo, Irish Republic* Sligo (71) 68571

GILLUM, Thomas Alan. b 55. Ex Univ BSc76. Cranmer Hall Dur 87. **d** 89 **p** 90. C Brompton H Trin w Onslow Square St Paul *Lon* 89-94; P-in-c Paddington St Steph w St Luke from 94. *St Stephen's Vicarage, 25 Talbot Road, London W2 5JF* 0171-792 2283

GILMAN, Charles Philip. b 12. Tyndale Hall Bris 39. **d** 41 **p** 42. R Marks Tey *Chelmsf* 64-74; V Leigh *S'wark* 74-81; rtd 81; Perm to Offic *Win* from 81. *36 Canon Street, Winchester, Hants SO23 9JJ* Winchester (01962) 867980

GILMORE, Henry. b 51. Man Univ BA72 TCD BD82. CITC 75. **d** 75 **p** 76. C Arm St Mark w Aghavilly *Arm* 75-78; C Dub St Patr Cathl Gp *D & G* 78-81; I Stranorlar w Meenglas and Kilteevogue *D & R* 81-84; I Achill w Dugort, Castlebar and Turlough *T, K & A* 84-91; I Moville w Greencastle, Donagh, Cloncha etc *D & R* from 91. *The Rectory, Castlebar, Moville, Co Donegal, Irish Republic* Buncrana (77) 82572

GILMORE, Canon Norman. b 16. Leeds Univ BA38. Coll of Resurr Mirfield 38. **d** 40 **p** 41. R Friern Barnet St Jas *Lon* 63-78; RD Cen Barnet 72-78; V Mortimer W End w Padworth *Ox* 78-83; rtd 83; Perm to Offic *Chich* from 83. *12 Ashton Gardens, Rustington, W Sussex BN16 2SH* Rustington (01903) 774683

GILMOUR, Ian Hedley. b 57. Ex Univ LLB Lon Univ BD. Wycliffe Hall Ox 80. **d** 83 **p** 84. C Harold Wood *Chelmsf* 83-86; C Thame w Towersey *Ox* 86-91; V Streatham Vale H Redeemer *S'wark* from 91. *The Vicarage, Churchmore Road, London SW16 5UZ* 0181-764 5808

GILMOUR, John Logan. b 14. Cuddesdon Coll 46. **d** 48 **p** 49. C Reading St Mary V *Ox* 48-51; Min St Barn CD Reading 51-55; Thailand 55-58; V Ellel *Blackb* 58-60; S Africa from 60. *2 Russell Lodge, Main Road, Constantia, 7800 South Africa* Cape Town (21) 794-1523

GILPIN, Jeremy David (Jerry). b 59. Pemb Coll Ox BA80 CertEd82. Trin Coll Bris BA88. **d** 88 **p** 89. C Southsea St Jude *Portsm* 88-92; R Itchingfield w Slinfold *Chich* from 92. *The Rectory, The Street, Slinfold, Horsham, W Sussex RH13 7RR* Horsham (01403) 790197

GILPIN, Richard John. b 45. Lon Univ BSc66 Bris Univ DipTh69. Wells Th Coll 67. **d** 70 **p** 71. C Davyhulme Ch Ch *Man* 70-74; Pastor Gustav Adolf Berlin EKD 74-77; R Heaton Norris Ch w All SS 77-83; R Chorlton-cum-Hardy St Clem from 83. *The Rectory, 6 Edge Lane, Chorlton-cum-Hardy, Manchester M21 1JF* 0161-881 3063

GILPIN, Preb Richard Thomas. b 39. Lich Th Coll 60. **d** 63 **p** 64. C Whipton *Ex* 63-66; C Tavistock and Gulworthy 66-69; V 73-91; V Swimbridge 69-73; Preb Ex Cathl from 82; Sub-Dean Ex Cathl from 92; RD Tavistock 87-90; Dioc Dir of Ords 90-91; Adv for Voc and Dioc Dir of Ords from 91. *Taddyforde Lodge, New North Road, Exeter EX4 4AT* Exeter (01392) 54517

GIMSON, Francis Herbert. b 54. Reading Univ BSc79 LTh. St Jo Coll Nottm 83. **d** 86 **p** 87. C Menston w Woodhead *Bradf* 86-89; C Barnoldswick w Bracewell 89-91; V Langleybury St Paul *St Alb* from 91. *The Vicarage, Langleybury Lane, Kings Langley, Herts WD4 8QR* Kings Langley (01923) 270634

GINEVER, Preb John Haynes. b 20. St Jo Coll Dur. Westcott Ho Cam. **d** 43 **p** 44. V Mill Hill Jo Keble Ch *Lon* 63-70; RD W Barnet 67-70; RD Wolv *Lich* 70-89; P-in-c Wolv St Geo 70-78; P-in-c Wolv All SS 70-78; R Wolv 73-78; Preb Lich Cathl 75-89; P-in-c Wolv St Mark 76-78; P-in-c Wolv St Chad 76-78; TR Wolv 78-89; rtd 89. *Flat 4, 26 Branksome Wood Road, Bournemouth BH4 9JZ* Bournemouth (01202) 763373

GINEVER, Paul Michael John. b 49. AKC71. **d** 72 **p** 73. C Davyhulme Ch Ch *Man* 72-75; Australia 76-77; C Tettenhall Wood *Lich* 77-80; C Halesowen *Worc* 80; TV Halesowen 80-86; P-in-c Gt Malvern Ch Ch from 86. *The Vicarage, 8 Christchurch Road, Malvern, Worcs WR14 3BE* Malvern (01684) 574106

GINGELL, John Lawrence. b 27. Lon Univ BD55. ALCD55. **d** 55 **p** 56. Toc H Staff Padre 61-70; Lic to Offic *Liv* 67-70; V Somercotes *Derby* 70-72; Bp's Ind Adv 72-80; rtd 92. *18 Bournville Road, London SE6 4RN* 0181-690 0148

GINN, Daniel Vivian. b 33. Univ of Wales (Cardiff) BSc55 DipEd56. Llan Dioc Tr Scheme 79. **d** 82 **p** 83. NSM Llantwit Major and St Donat's *Llan* 82-83; NSM Llantwit Major from 83; RD Llantwit Major and Cowbridge from 94. *Chenet, 24 Voss Park Drive, Llantwit Major, S Glam CF61 1YE* Llantwit Major (01446) 792774

GINN

GINN, Richard John. b 51. ACIB Lon Univ BD77 Dur Univ DipTh78. Lambeth STh85 Cranmer Hall Dur 77. **d** 79 **p** 80. C Hornsey Ch Ch *Lon* 79-82; C Highgate St Mich 82-85; V Westleton w Dunwich *St E* from 85; V Darsham from 85. *The Vicarage, Westleton, Saxmundham, Suffolk IP17 3AQ* Westleton (0172873) 271

GINNEVER, Canon John Buckley. b 20. Man Univ BA42. Ridley Hall Cam 46. **d** 48 **p** 49. R Levenshulme St Mark *Man* 57-76; V Chadderton St Matt 76-84; Hon Can Man Cathl 82-85; rtd 85; Perm to Offic *St As* from 85. *22 Glan Ffyddion, Waterfall Road, Dyserth, Rhyl, Clwyd LL18 6EG* Dyserth (01745) 570654

GINNO, Albert Charles. b 31. Lon Coll of Div 66. **d** 68 **p** 69. C Kemp Town St Mark and St Matt *Chich* 68-72; P-in-c E Hoathly 72-83; V Westham from 83. *The Vicarage, Westham, Pevensey, E Sussex BN24 5DE* Eastbourne (01323) 762294

GIRARD, William Nicholas Charles. b 35. Coll of Resurr Mirfield 65. **d** 67 **p** 68. C Yate *Glouc* 67-70; C Westbury-on-Trym St Alb *Bris* 70-73; Chapl K Sch Ely 73-76; V Fenstanton *Ely* 76-85; V Hilton 76-85; R Balsham from 85; P-in-c Horseheath from 85; P-in-c W Wickham from 85; RD Linton 93-94. *The Rectory, Balsham, Cambridge CB1 6DX* Cambridge (01223) 894010

GIRLING, Andrew Martin. b 40. Em Coll Cam BA63 MA67. Wycliffe Hall Ox 63. **d** 65 **p** 66. C Luton w E Hyde *St Alb* 65-69; Chapl Hull Univ *York* 69-75; V Dringhouses from 75. *The Vicarage, Dringhouses, York YO2 2QG* York (01904) 706120

GIRLING, David Frederick Charles. b 33. Edin Th Coll 58. **d** 61 **p** 62. C Caister *Nor* 61-65; C Leigh St Clem *Chelmsf* 65-66; CF 66-83; V Prittlewell St Luke *Chelmsf* from 83. *The Vicarage, St Luke's Road, Southend-on-Sea SS2 4AB* Southend-on-Sea (01702) 467620

GIRLING, Francis Richard (Vincent). b 28. Worc Coll Ox BA52 MA56 Lon Univ BD65. Coll of Resurr Mirfield 55. **d** 57 **p** 59. CR from 57. *House of the Resurrection, Mirfield, W Yorkshire WF14 0BN* Mirfield (01924) 494318

GIRLING, Gordon Francis Hulbert. b 15. TD61. Univ Coll Ox BA37 MA41. Wells Th Coll 39. **d** 46 **p** 47. V Kingsbury H Innocents *Lon* 59-79; rtd 79; Perm to Offic *Chich* from 80. *212 Coast Road, Pevensey Bay, Pevensey, E Sussex BN24 6NR* Eastbourne (01323) 766359

GIRLING, Stephen Paul. b 61. Southn Univ BSc83. Trin Coll Bris BA91. **d** 91 **p** 92. C Ogley Hay *Lich* 91-95; TV S Molton w Nymet St George, High Bray etc *Ex* from 95. *The Vicarage, Chittlehampton, Umberleigh, Devon EX37 9QL* Chittlehamholt (01769) 540654

GIRLING, Timothy Havelock (Tim). b 43. St Aid Birkenhead 63. **d** 67 **p** 68. C Wickford *Chelmsf* 67-70; C Luton w E Hyde *St Alb* 70-74; Chapl Luton and Dunstable Hosp 74-80; C Luton All SS w St Pet *St Alb* 74-80; R Northill w Moggerhanger 80-89; Chapl Glenfield Hosp (NHS) Trust Leic from 89; Chapl Glenfrith Hosp 89-93. *36 Winton Avenue, Leicester LE3 1DH, or Chaplain's Office, Glenfield Hospital, Groby Road, Leicester LE3 9QP* Leicester (0116) 291 3795 or 287 1471

GIRLING, William Havelock. b 18. Ex Coll Ox BA MA46. Ridley Hall Cam. **d** 49 **p** 50. Asst Chapl Bradfield Coll Berks 54-70; P-in-c Stanford Dingley *Ox* 71-86; rtd 86. *Oakthorpe, Charlton Drive, Charlton Kings, Cheltenham, Glos GL53 8ES* Cheltenham (01242) 577364

GISBOURNE, Michael Andrew. b 65. Leeds Univ BA87. St Jo Coll Nottm BTh91 DipMM91. **d** 92 **p** 93. C Gateacre *Liv* 92-95; C Marton *Blackb* from 95. *74 Worcester Road, Blackpool FY3 9SZ* Blackpool (01253) 792118

GITTINGS, Graham. b 46. Qu Coll Birm 75. **d** 78 **p** 79. C Caverswall *Lich* 78-81; C Wolv St Matt 81-82; C Walthamstow St Mary w St Steph *Chelmsf* 82-83; C Dagenham 83-89; V Earl Shilton w Elmesthorpe *Leic* from 89. *The Vicarage, Maughan Street, Earl Shilton, Leicester LE9 7BA* Earl Shilton (01455) 843961

GIVEN, Harold Richard. b 54. Oak Hill Th Coll 75. **d** 78 **p** 79. C Belf St Clem *D & D* 78-80; C Belf St Donard 80-83; I Tamlaght O'Crilly Upper w Lower *D & R* 83-92; I Tamlaghtfinlagan w Myroe from 92. *Finlagan Rectory, 77 Ballykelly Road, Limavady, Co Derry BT49 9DS* Limavady (015047) 62743

GIVEN, John Thornton. TCD Div Sch BA36 Div Test38 MA45. **d** 40 **p** 41. C-in-c Preban w Moyne *C & O* 46-50; Australia from 50; rtd 79. *19 Fourth Avenue, Home Hill, Townsville, Queensland, Australia 4806* Townsville (77) 821983

GLADSTONE, Robert Michael (Rob). b 60. Ch Ch Ox BA82 MA86. Wycliffe Hall Ox DipMin94. **d** 94 **p** 95. C Trentham *Lich* from 94. *4 Oakshaw Grove, Stoke-on-Trent ST4 8UB* Stoke-on-Trent (01782) 643457

✠GLADWIN, Rt Rev John Warren. b 42. Chu Coll Cam BA65 MA68. Cranmer Hall Dur DipTh66. **d** 67 **p** 68 **c** 94. C Kirkheaton *Wakef* 67-71; Tutor St Jo Coll Dur 71-77; Dir Shaftesbury Project 77-82; Lic to Offic *S'well* 77-82; Sec Gen

Syn Bd for Soc Resp 82-88; Preb St Paul's Cathl *Lon* 84-88; Provost Sheff 88-94; Angl Adv Yorkshire TV 88-94; Bp Guildf from 94. *Willow Grange, Woking Road, Guildford, Surrey GU4 7QS* Guildford (01483) 573922 Fax 32663

GLADWIN, Thomas William. b 35. St Alb Minl Tr Scheme 78. **d** 81 **p** 82. NSM Hertf St Andr *St Alb* 81-82; NSM Digswell and Panshanger 82-86; C from 86. *99 Warren Way, Welwyn, Herts AL6 0DL* Welwyn (01438) 714700

GLAISTER, James Richard. b 30. Oak Hill Th Coll 81. **d** 83 **p** 84. NSM Shrub End *Chelmsf* 83-85; NSM Lawshall w Shimplingthorne and Alpheton *St E* 85-87; NSM Lavenham 87-88; C Felixstowe St Jo from 88. *1 Arwela Road, Felixstowe, Suffolk IP11 8DQ* Felixstowe (01394) 271578

GLAISYER, Ven Hugh. b 30. Or Coll Ox BA51 MA55. St Steph Ho Ox 51. **d** 56 **p** 56. C Tonge Moor *Man* 56-62; C Sidcup Ch Ch *Roch* 62-64; V Milton next Gravesend Ch Ch 64-81; RD Gravesend 74-81; V Hove All SS *Chich* 81-91; Can and Preb Chich Cathl 82-91; RD Hove 82-91; P-in-c Hove St Jo 87-91; Adn Lewes and Hastings from 91. *27 The Avenue, Lewes, E Sussex BN7 1QT* Lewes (01273) 479530 Fax 476529 Mobile (0378) 049822

GLANVILLE-SMITH, Canon Michael Raymond. b 38. AKC61. **d** 62 **p** 63. C St Marylebone St Mark w St Luke *Lon* 62-64; C Penzance St Mary *Truro* 64-68; R Worc St Andr and All SS w St Helen *Worc* 68-74; Dioc Youth Chapl 68-74; V Catshill 74-80; P-in-c Worc St Martin w St Pet 80-81; TR Worc St Martin w St Pet, St Mark etc 81-86; TR Worc SE 86-90; Hon Can Worc Cathl 83-90; Can Res Ripon Cathl *Ripon* from 90. *St Wilfred's House, Minster Close, Ripon, N Yorkshire HG4 1QR* Ripon (01765) 700211

GLARE, Michael Francis. b 28. Southn Univ BA54. St Steph Ho Ox 56. **d** 57 **p** 58. C Tamerton Foliot *Ex* 65-70; R Weare Giffard w Landcross 70-76; RD Hartland 74-76; P-in-c Babbacombe 76-80; V 80-87; V Ilsington 87-93; rtd 93; Perm to Offic *Ex* from 94. *Poplar Lodge, 23 Albion Street, Shaldon, Teignmouth, Devon TQ14 0DF* Shaldon (01626) 872679

GLASBY, Alan Langland. b 46. Nottm Univ LTh77. Linc Th Coll DipMin89 St Jo Coll Nottm 74. **d** 77 **p** 78. C Erith St Paul *Roch* 77-80; C Moor Allerton *Ripon* 80-81; TV 81-87; V Middleton St Mary 87-92; V Bilton from 92. *Bilton Vicarage, Bilton Lane, Harrogate, N Yorkshire HG1 3DT* Harrogate (01423) 565129

GLASGOW AND GALLOWAY, Bishop of. *See* TAYLOR, Rt Rev John Mitchell

GLASGOW AND GALLOWAY, Dean of. *See* REID, Very Rev Douglas William John

GLASGOW, Provost of. *See* FRANCIS, Very Rev Peter Brereton

GLASS, Kenneth William. b 23. FRSA68. **d** 57 **p** 58. V Ipswich St Nic *St E* 63-73; P-in-c Ipswich St Helen 73; R Sproughton w Burstall 74-76; Perm to Offic from 76; rtd 83. *19 Chalkeith Road, Needham Market, Ipswich IP6 8HA* Needham Market (01449) 720393

GLASSPOOL, John Martin. b 59. RGN87 Kent Univ BA83. Westcott Ho Cam 88. **d** 90 **p** 91. C Forest Gate Em w Upton Cross *Chelmsf* 90-93; P-in-c Theydon Garnon 93-95; Chapl St Marg Hosp Epping from 93; TV Epping Distr *Chelmsf* from 95. *The Rectory, Theydon Garnon, Epping, Essex CM16 7PQ* Epping (01992) 572680

GLAZEBROOK, Ronald Victor. b 19. FRHistS Keble Coll Ox BA41 MA48 DipEd53. St Steph Ho Ox 41. **d** 43 **p** 44. Perm to Offic *Cant* 70-77; C Beckenham St Barn *Roch* 72-75; Warden St Marg Ho Bethnal Green 76-83; rtd 83. *Flat 1B, 11 Dane Road, St Leonards-on-Sea, E Sussex TN38 0RN*

GLAZEBROOK, William Leng (Bill). b 29. Edin Th Coll 76. **d** 76 **p** 77. C Dollar *St And* 76-82; Dioc Supernumerary 83; Chapl Trin Coll Glenalmond 84; P-in-c Glencarse *Bre* 84-87; Dioc Sec 84-87; Chapl HM Pris Perth 85-87; V Broughton Poggs w Filkins, Broadwell etc *Ox* 87-94; rtd 94. *10 Rose Terrace, Perth PH1 5HA* Perth (01738) 624913

GLEADALL, John Frederick. b 39. Ripon Hall Ox 66 Sarum Th Coll 69. **d** 70 **p** 71. C S Ashford Ch Ch *Cant* 70-76; P-in-c Hothfield 76-83; P-in-c Eastwell w Boughton Aluph 81-83; P-in-c Westwell 81-83; V Westwell, Hothfield, Eastwell and Boughton Aluph from 84. *The Vicarage, Westwell, Ashford, Kent TN25 4LQ* Charing (01233) 712401

GLEDHILL, Alan. b 43. Lon Univ BSc(Econ). N Ord Course 81. **d** 84 **p** 85. C Knaresborough *Ripon* 84-87; P-in-c Easby 87-88; P-in-c Bolton on Swale 87-88; V Easby w Brompton on Swale and Bolton on Swale from 88. *The Vicarage, St Paul's Drive, Brompton on Swale, Richmond, N Yorkshire DL10 7HQ* Richmond (01748) 811840

GLEDHILL, Canon James William. b 27. Dur Univ BA52. Westcott Ho Cam 52. **d** 56 **p** 57. C Mexborough *Sheff* 56-59; CF 59-61; C Bywell St Pet *Newc* 61-65; V Warden w Newbrough from 65; RD Hexham 78-88; Hon Can Newc Cathl from 88. *The Vicarage, Warden, Hexham, Northd NE46 4SL* Hexham (01434) 603910

GLEDHILL, Canon Jonathan Michael. b 49. Keele Univ BA72 Bris Univ MA75. Trin Coll Bris 72. **d** 75 **p** 76. C Marple All SS *Ches* 75-78; C Folkestone H Trin w Ch Ch *Cant* 78-83; V Cant St Mary Bredin from 83; Tutor Cant Sch of Min from 83; RD Cant 88-94; Hon Can Cant Cathl from 92. *St Mary Bredin Vicarage, 57 Nunnery Fields, Canterbury, Kent CT1 3JN* Canterbury (01227) 462479

GLEDHILL, Peter. b 29. Ball Coll Ox BA53 MA54. Cuddesdon Coll 54. **d** 56 **p** 57. Asst Master Cheadle Gr Sch 68-70; Lic to Offic *Lich* 70-71; P-in-c Kingstone w Gratwich 71-83; P-in-c Llanyblodwel and Trefonen 83-84; R 84-89; C Menai and Malltraeth Deanery *Ban* 90-94; NSM from 95; rtd 94. *Yr Hen Felin, Pwllfanogl, Llanfairpwllgwyngyll, Ynys Mon, Gwynedd LL61 6PD* Bangor (01248) 714434

GLEED, Roy Edward. b 19. Linc Coll Ox BA48 MA53. Chich Th Coll. **d** 50 **p** 51. R Dowdeswell and Andoversford w the Shiptons etc *Glouc* 63-74; P-in-c 69-74; R Avening 74-76; R Avening w Cherington 76-84; rtd 84; Perm to Offic *Bris* from 84; Perm to Offic *Glouc* from 84. *9 Court Field, Tetbury, Glos GL8 8LF* Tetbury (01666) 502159

GLEESON, Robert Godfrey. b 49. Man Univ CQSW74. Qu Coll Birm 83. **d** 85 **p** 86. C Hall Green St Pet *Birm* 85-88; Asst Chapl Mental Health & Elderly Care Services Birm HA 88-90; Chapl from 90; Chapl Moseley Hall Hosp Birm 90-94; Chapl Qu Eliz Hosp Birm from 94. *180 Pineapple Road, Birmingham, B30 2TY, or Queen Elizabeth Hospital, Mindelsohn Way, Birmingham B15 2QZ* 0121-444 2793 or 627 2885

GLEN, Robert Sawers. b 25. Qu Coll Cam BA49 MA56. Sarum & Wells Th Coll 79. **d** 81 **p** 82. Chapl Sherborne Sch Dorset 81-86; C Yetminster w Ryme Intrinseca and High Stoy *Sarum* 86-95; RD Sherborne from 92; rtd 95. *Devan Haye, North Road, Sherborne, Dorset DT9 3BJ* Sherborne (01935) 812018

GLENDALOUGH, Archdeacon of. See SWANN, Ven Edgar John

GLENDINING, Canon Alan. b 24. LVO79. Westcott Ho Cam 58. **d** 60 **p** 61. V Raveningham *Nor* 63-70; P-in-c Hales w Heckingham 63-70; R Thurlton w Thorpe next Haddiscoe 63-70; V Norton Subcourse 63-70; P-in-c Aldeby w Wheatacre w Burgh St Peter 66-70; P-in-c Haddiscoe w Toft Monks 68-70; Dom Chapl to The Queen 70-79; Chapl to The Queen from 79; R Sandringham w W Newton *Nor* 70-79; RD Heacham and Rising 72-76; Hon Can Nor Cathl 77-89; TR Lowestoft and Kirkley 79-85; Sen Chapl to Holidaymakers 85-89; V Ranworth w Panxworth and Woodbastwick 85-89; RD Blofield 87-89; rtd 90. *7 Bellfosters, Kings Staithe Lane, King's Lynn, Norfolk PE30 1LZ* King's Lynn (01553) 760113

GLENFIELD, Samuel Ferran. b 54. QUB BA76 TCD MLitt90 BTh91. **d** 91 **p** 92. C Douglas Union w Frankfield *C, C & R* 91-94; I Rathcooney Union from 94. *The Rectory, Ballynaroon, Glounthaune, Cork, Irish Republic*

GLENN, Michael David. b 37. Lich Th Coll 67. **d** 70 **p** 71. C Denton Ch Ch *Man* 70-74; Chapl Oldham Hosps 74-77; P-in-c Moss Side Ch Ch *Man* 77-78; Hon C Drayton Bassett *Lich* 78-82; Hon C Hints 78-82; Perm to Offic *Man* 82-90; TV Corby SS Pet and Andr w Gt and Lt Oakley *Pet* from 90. *The Vicarage, 1 Lovap Way, Great Oakley, Corby, Northants NN18 8JL* Corby (01536) 746266

GLEW, George William. b 24. Oak Hill Th Coll 64. **d** 66 **p** 67. C Willesborough w Hinxhill *Cant* 69-73; R Burlingham St Edmund, St Andr, St Pet etc *Nor* 73-77; V Burlingham St Edmund w Lingwood 77-83; C Horsham *Chich* 83-85; P-in-c Worthing Ch Ch 85-89; rtd 89. Hon CF from 89. *17 Mead Way, Canterbury, Kent CT2 8BB* Canterbury (01227) 472639

GLOUCESTER, Archdeacon of. See WAGSTAFF, Ven Christopher John Harold

GLOUCESTER, Bishop of. See BENTLEY, Rt Rev David Edward

GLOUCESTER, Dean of. See JENNINGS, Very Rev Kenneth Neal

GLOVER, Canon Brian Reginald. b 38. St D Coll Lamp BA60 Sarum Th Coll 60. **d** 62 **p** 63. C Redditch St Steph *Worc* 62-68; V Redditch St Geo 68-74; V Ellistown *Leic* 74-77; V Leic St Aid 77-82; V Fleckney 82-84; V Fleckney and Kilby from 84; RD Gartree II (Wigston) from 89; Hon Can Leic Cathl from 94. *The Vicarage, 12 Saddington Road, Fleckney, Leicester LE8 8AW* Leicester (0116) 240 2215

GLOVER, David. b 50. Coll of Resurr Mirfield 77. **d** 80 **p** 81. C Hope St Jas *Man* 80-83; C Leigh St Mary 83-85; V Cudworth *Wakef* from 85. *The Vicarage, St John's Road, Cudworth, Barnsley, S Yorkshire S72 8DE* Barnsley (01226) 710279

GLOVER, David Charles. b 66. St Jo Coll Dur BA87 St Jo Coll Cam MPhil91. Ridley Hall Cam 87. **d** 90 **p** 91. C Wath-upon-Dearne w Adwick-upon-Dearne *Sheff* 90-92; Chapl Hatf Coll Dur from 92. *Hatfield Cottage, Hatfield College, Durham DH1 3RQ* 0191-374 3175 Fax 374 7472

GLOVER, George Edward. b 58. Strathclyde Univ BSc80 Edin Univ BD83. Edin Th Coll. **d** 83 **p** 86. C Dunblane *St And* 83-84; C Southgate Ch Ch *Lon* 84-85; C Golders Green

85-88; Chapl Sunderland Mental Health Unit 88-90; C Sherburn w Pittington *Dur* 90-92; P-in-c Trimdon Station from 92. *The Vicarage, Trimdon Grange, Trimdon Station, Co Durham TS29 6EX* Wellfield (01429) 880872

GLOVER, Henry Arthur. b 32. Lon Univ BSc58. Wycliffe Hall Ox 59. **d** 61 **p** 62. C Fareham St Jo *Portsm* 61-63; C Liv Our Lady and St Nic *Liv* 63-64. *15 Thorncliffe Road, Wallasey, Merseyside L44 3AA* 0151-638 6018

GLOVER, John. b 48. Kelham Th Coll 67. **d** 71 **p** 72. C Foley Park *Worc* 71-75; TV Sutton *Liv* 75-79; P-in-c Churchill w Blakedown *Worc* 79-84; R 84-87; R Belbroughton w Fairfield and Clent 87-91; Chapl Children's Family Trust from 91; NSM Flint *St As* 92-93; R Halkyn w Caerfallwch w Rhescyae from 93. *The New Rectory, Halkyn, Holywell, Clwyd CH8 8BU* Halkyn (01352) 780670

GLOVER, Michael John Myers. b 28. CEng MICE MSAICE Bradf Tech Coll DipCivEng48 Lon Univ BSc48. Cuddesdon Coll 54. **d** 56 **p** 57. S Africa 60-73 and from 86; TR Northn Em Pet 74-86; Bp's Chapl E Area Northn 73-74; rtd 93. *PO Box 447, Nongoma, 3950 South Africa* (358) 310044

GLOVER, Richard John. b 47. Nottm Univ BTh77. Linc Th Coll 73. **d** 77 **p** 78. C Barrow St Geo w St Luke *Carl* 77-79; C Netherton 79-80; P-in-c Addingham 80-83; P-in-c Edenhall w Langwathby and Culgaith 80-83; V Addingham, Edenhall, Langwathby and Culgaith 83-84; V Bishops Hull *B & W* 84-89; V Shilbottle *Newc* from 89. *The Vicarage, Shilbottle, Alnwick, Northd NE66 2XR* Shilbottle (01665) 575800

GLYN-JONES, Alun. b 38. CCC Cam BA59 MA63. Bps' Coll Cheshunt 60. **d** 61 **p** 62. C Portsea St Mary *Portsm* 61-65; Chapl Hampton Sch Middx 65-76; Hd Master Abp Tenison Gr Sch Croydon 76-88; V Twickenham St Mary *Lon* from 88. *St Mary's Vicarage, Riverside, Twickenham TW1 3DT* 0181-892 2318 or 744 2693

GOALBY, George Christian. b 55. Leeds Univ BA77. St Jo Coll Nottm DPS81. **d** 81 **p** 82. C Wakef St Andr and St Mary *Wakef* 81-84; Asst Chapl HM Pris Wakef 84-85; Chapl HM Youth Cust Cen Deerbolt 85-87; Chapl HM Pris Frankland 87-89; V Swinderby *Linc* from 89. *All Saints' Vicarage, Station Road, Swinderby, Lincoln LN6 6LY* Swinderby (01522) 586430

GOATCHER, Mrs Sara Jacoba Helena. b 46. Oak Hill NSM Course 86. **d** 89 **p** 94. NSM S Croydon Em *S'wark* from 89. *5 Normanton Road, South Croydon, Surrey CR2 7AE* 0181-688 6130 or 688 6676

GOATER, Charles Frederick. b 16. **d** 82 **p** 82. NSM Fishponds St Mary *Bris* 82-89; Perm to Offic from 89. *72 Queensholme Crescent, Bristol BS16 6LH* Bristol (0117) 956 1147

GOATER, Michael Robert. b 46. N Ord Course 89. **d** 92 **p** 93. C Norton *Sheff* 92-94; V Endcliffe from 94; Chapl Sheff Hallam Univ from 95. *St Augustine's Vicarage, 4 Clarke Drive, Sheffield S10 2NS* Sheffield (0114) 266 1932

GOATER, William Arthur. b 12. Chich Th Coll 33. **d** 36 **p** 37. V N Nibley *Glouc* 53-77; V Stinchcombe 55-77; rtd 77; Perm to Offic *Glouc* from 77. *17 Webber House, Shepherd Mead, Gloucester Road, Tewkesbury, Glos GL20 5RR* Tewkesbury (01684) 275411

GOBBETT, Michael George Timothy. b 64. St Chad's Coll Dur BSc86. St Steph Ho Ox BA89. **d** 90 **p** 91. C Hartlepool St Aid *Dur* 90-94; P-in-c Norton St Mich from 94. *The Vicarage, 13 Imperial Avenue, Norton, Stockton-on-Tees, Cleveland TS20 2EW* Stockton-on-Tees (01642) 553984

GOBLE, Clifford David. b 41. Oak Hill Th Coll 69. **d** 72 **p** 73. C Erith St Paul *Roch* 72-76; C Tunbridge Wells St Jas 76-79; R Southfleet from 79; RD Gravesend from 94. *The Rectory, Hook Green Road, Southfleet, Dartford DA13 9NQ* Southfleet (01474) 833252

GODBER, Francis Giles. b 48. Open Univ BA79. Ridley Hall Cam 72. **d** 75 **p** 76. C Blackheath *Birm* 75-78; C Wolv St Matt *Lich* 78-80; TV Washfield, Stoodleigh, Withleigh etc *Ex* 80-85; R Shenley and Loughton *Ox* 85-88; R Watling Valley from 88. *The Rectory, Pitcher Lane, Loughton, Milton Keynes MK5 8AU* Milton Keynes (01908) 666253

GODDARD, Charles Douglas James. b 47. CITC 67. **d** 70 **p** 71. C Orangefield *D & D* 70-73; C Stormont 73-75; Miss to Seamen from 75; Sen Chapl and Sec N Ireland from 77. *7 Abercorn Drive, Carnreagh Road, Hillsborough, Co Down BT26 6LB* Hillsborough (01846) 683592

GODDARD, Christopher. b 45. Sarum & Wells Th Coll 79. **d** 81 **p** 82. C Whitehaven *Carl* 81-83; C Barrow St Geo w St Luke 83-85; P-in-c Hayton St Mary 85-90; V Brigham from 90; V Mosser from 90. *The Vicarage, 1 High Brigham, Cockermouth, Cumbria CA13 0TE* Cockermouth (01900) 825383

GODDARD, Canon Frederick Paul Preston. b 24. Jes Coll Cam BA49 MA51. Westcott Ho Cam 49. **d** 51 **p** 52. Chapl Yeatman and Coldharbour Hosp Dorset 69-87; V Sherborne w Castleton and Lillington *Sarum* 69-87; RD Sherborne 73-77; Can and Preb Sarum Cathl 75-87; rtd 87. *56 West Street, Polruan, Fowey, Cornwall PL23 1PL* Polruan (01726) 870339

GODDARD, Harold Frederick. b 42. Keble Coll Ox BA63 DipTh65 MA69. Cuddesdon Coll 64. **d** 66 **p** 67. C Birm St Pet *Birm* 66-70; Chapl Dudley Road Hosp Birm 66-70; C Alverstoke *Portsm* 70-72; Chapl Gosport Cottage Hosp Portsm 70-72; P-in-c Portsea St Geo CD 72-76; Chapl Portsm Cathl 73-76; P-in-c Stoke Prior *Worc* 76-78; P-in-c Wychbold and Upton Warren 77-78; R Stoke Prior, Wychbold and Upton Warren 78-80; Chapl Forelands Orthopaedic Hosp Worc 77-80; Chapl R Marsden Hosp Lon and Surrey 80-83; R Martley and Wichenford *Worc* 83-88; P-in-c Knightwick w Doddenham, Broadwas and Cotheridge 85-88; R Martley and Wichenford, Knightwick etc 89-90; Bp's Adv on Min of Healing from 87; Chapl St Rich Hospice Worc from 87; RD Martley and Worc W *Worc* 88-90; Chapl Kidderminster Gen Hosp from 90; P-in-c Hallow *Worc* 91-92; P-in-c Sedgeberrow w Hinton-on-the-Green from 92; Chapl Eversham Community Hosp Worc from 93. *The Rectory, Sedgeberrow, Evesham, Worcs WR11 6UE* Evesham (01386) 881291

GODDARD, Canon John William. b 47. St Chad's Coll Dur BA69 DipTh70. **d** 70 **p** 71. C S Bank *York* 70-74; C Cayton w Eastfield 74-75; V Middlesb Ascension 75-82; RD Middlesbrough 81-87; V Middlesb All SS 82-88; Can and Preb York Minster 87-88; Vice-Prin Edin Th Coll 88-92; TR Ribbleton *Blackb* from 92. *The Rectory, 238 Ribbleton Avenue, Ribbleton, Preston PR2 6QP* Preston (01772) 791747

GODDARD, Ms Marion. b 54. Sarum & Wells Th Coll 87. **d** 89 **p** 94. Par Dn Lewisham St Swithun *S'wark* 89-94; C 94-95; Chapl Brook Gen Hosp Lon from 95. *14 Duncrievie Road, London SE13 6TE* 0181-318 7531

GODDARD, Matthew Francis. b 45. Lon Univ DipTh69. Kelham Th Coll 65. **d** 69 **p** 70. C Mansf St Mark *S'well* 69-72; C Northolt Park St Barn *Lon* 72-78; P-in-c Acton Green St Pet 78-87; R Norwood St Mary from 87. *The Rectory, Tentelow Lane, Norwood Green, Southall, Middx UB2 4LE* 0181-574 1362

GODDARD, Stuart David. b 53. Cen Sch of Art Lon BA76 Middx Poly PGCE82. Trin Coll Bris DipHE93. **d** 93 **p** 94. C Watling Valley *Ox* from 93. *2 Littlecote, Great Holm, Milton Keynes MK8 9EZ* Milton Keynes (01908) 560075

GODDARD, Canon Sydney Thomas. b 16. St Aid Birkenhead 46. **d** 49 **p** 50. Warden World Friendship Ho 59-83; V Liv St Sav *Liv* 59-71; Hon Can Liv Cathl 69-83; rtd 84; Perm to Offic *Ban* from 84. *Ynys Thomas, Bronaber, Trawsfynydd, Blaenau Ffestiniog, Gwynedd LL41 4UR* Trawsfynydd (0176687) 413

GODDARD, Canon William. b 09. Kelham Th Coll 29. **d** 34 **p** 35. R Guildf St Nic *Guildf* 59-74; R Catworth Magna *Ely* 74-77; R Covington 75-77; R Tilbrook 75-77; rtd 77; Perm to Offic *Glouc* from 79. *Flat 13, Capel Court, The Burgage, Prestbury, Cheltenham, Glos GL52 3EL* Cheltenham (01242) 528849

GODDARD, William Edwin George. b 14. Clifton Th Coll 66. **d** 68 **p** 69. C Rodbourne Cheney *Bris* 68-71; R Beaford and Roborough *Ex* 71-78; TV Newton Tracey 76-78; R Beaford, Roborough and St Giles in the Wood 78-79; rtd 79; Perm to Offic *Bris* 84-93. *26 Stuart Court, High Street, Kibworth, Leicester LE8 0LE* Leicester (0116) 279 6343

GODDEN, Ven Max Leon. b 23. Worc Coll Ox BA50 MA54. Chich Th Coll 50. **d** 52 **p** 53. V Glynde, W Firle and Beddingham *Chich* 62-82; Adn Lewes 72-76; Adn Lewes and Hastings 75-88; rtd 88. *14 Oak Close, Chichester, W Sussex PO19 3AJ* Chichester (01243) 531344

GODDEN, Peter David. b 47. ARCO70 Leeds Univ BA69. Linc Th Coll 85. **d** 87 **p** 88. C Bearsted w Thurnham *Cant* 87-90; C Hykeham *Linc* 90-91; TV 91-95; P-in-c Linc St Pet-at-Gowts and St Andr from 95. *St Peter-at-Gowts' Vicarage, Sibthorp Street, Lincoln LN5 7SP* Lincoln (01522) 530256

GODDEN, Timothy Richard James (Tim). b 62. Univ Coll Lon BA84. St Jo Coll Nottm DPS89. **d** 89 **p** 90. C Tulse Hill H Trin and St Matthias *S'wark* 89-93; TV Horsham *Chich* from 93. *St Mark's House, North Heath Lane, Horsham, W Sussex RH12 4PJ* Horsham (01403) 254964

GODECK, John William George. b 30. Chich Th Coll 57. **d** 60 **p** 61. C Wadhurst *Chich* 60-62; C Tidebrook 60-62; C Eastbourne 62-63; R Bondleigh *Ex* 63-78; R Zeal Monachorum 63-78; P-in-c Broadwoodkelly 65-67; R 68-78; R Dunchideock and Shillingford St George w Ide from 78; RD Kenn 83-89. *The Rectory, Shillingford St George, Exeter EX2 9UT* Exeter (01392) 832589

GODFREY, Ann Veronica. *See* MACKEITH, Mrs Ann Veronica

GODFREY, Dr Brian Ernest Searles. b 37. Lon Univ BSc60 MSc63 PhD72. S'wark Ord Course 78. **d** 81 **p** 82. NSM Hayes *Roch* 81-86; C 86-88; R Kingsdown 88-93; R Sundridge w Ide Hill from 93; RD Sevenoaks from 95. *The Rectory, Chevening Road, Sundridge, Sevenoaks, Kent TN14 6AB* Westerham (01959) 563749

GODFREY, Canon David Samuel George. b 35. CITC 64. **d** 66 **p** 67. C Londonderry Ch Ch *D & R* 66-68; I Tomregan w Drumlane *K, E & A* 68-71; I Cloonclare 71-79; I Templebreedy *C, C & R* 79-85; I Bray *D & G* from 85; Can Ch Ch Cathl Dub from 95. *The Rectory, Church Road, Bray, Co Wicklow, Irish Republic* Dublin (1) 286-2968

GODFREY, Edward Colin. b 30. Wells Th Coll 63 ADipR62. **d** 65 **p** 66. C Paignton Ch Ch *Ex* 69-73; V Stockland w Dalwood 73-77; Chapl HM Pris Man 77-78; Chapl HM Pris Cant 78-83; Chapl HM Pris Highpoint 83-85 and 90-95; Chapl HM Young Offender Inst Glen Parva 85-90; rtd 95. *11 De Burgh Place, Clare, Sudbury, Suffolk CO10 8QL*

✠**GODFREY, Rt Rev Harold William.** b 48. AKC71. **d** 72 **p** 73 **c** 87. C Warsop *S'well* 72-75; TV Hucknall Torkard 75-86; Dioc Ecum Officer 81-82; SAMS from 86; Adn Montevideo 86-88; Asst Bp Argentina and Uruguay 87-88; Uruguay from 88. *Iglesia Anglicana del Uruguay, Echevariarza 3426, Montevideo, Uruguay*

GODFREY, John Frederick. b 31. Solicitor Lon Univ LLB53 AKC54. Cuddesdon Coll 59. **d** 61 **p** 62. C Battersea St Luke *S'wark* 61-65; Min Reigate St Phil CD 65-72; Public Preacher *St Alb* from 73. *Thicketts, Theobald Street, Radlett, Herts WD7 7LS* Radlett (01923) 855558

GODFREY, Joy. b 33. SW Minl Tr Course. **dss** 85 **d** 87 **p** 94. Devonport St Aubyn *Ex* 85-87; Hon Par Dn 87-94; Hon C from 94. *85 Browning Road, Plymouth PL2 3AW* Plymouth (01752) 564253

GODFREY, Preb Michael. b 49. K Coll Lon BD70 AKC72. **d** 72 **p** 73. C Birtley *Dur* 72-75; Ind Chapl 76-79; Ind Chapl *Lich* 79-93; TV Bilston St Mary 79; TV Bilston 80-86; TV Wolv 86-93; Preb Lich Cathl from 87. *283 Henwood Road, Wolverhampton WV6 8PU* Wolverhampton (01902) 752278

GODFREY, Michael James. b 50. Sheff Univ BEd77. St Jo Coll Nottm DipTh79 CPS79. **d** 82 **p** 83. C Walton H Trin *Ox* 82-86; C Chadderton Ch Ch *Man* 86-91; V Woodlands *Sheff* from 91. *The Vicarage, 9 Great North Road, Woodlands, Doncaster, S Yorkshire DN6 7RB* Doncaster (01302) 723268

GODFREY, Nigel Philip. b 51. MRTPI76 Bris Poly DipTP73 Ox Univ BA78 MA84. Ripon Coll Cuddesdon 77. **d** 79 **p** 80. C Kennington St Jo w St Jas *S'wark* 79-89; Community of Ch the Servant 84-93; V Brixton Rd Ch Ch *S'wark* from 89. *96 Brixton Road, London SW9 6BE* 0171-793 9824 or 587 0375

GODFREY, Mrs Pauline Ann. b 58. LMH Ox BA79 MA83 Ox Univ Inst of Educn PGCE80. S Dios Minl Tr Scheme 89. **d** 92 **p** 94. NSM Headley All SS *Guildf* from 92. *7 Birch Grove, Whitehill, Bordon, Hants GU35 9DG* Bordon (01420) 475971

GODFREY, Canon Robert Bernard. b 16. Wells Th Coll 55. **d** 56 **p** 57. R Ipswich St Mary at Stoke w St Pet & St Mary Quay *St E* 69-76; Hon Can St E Cathl 73-81; RD Samford 75-81; R Sproughton w Burstall 76-81; rtd 81; Perm to Offic *St E* from 81. *Long Acre, London Road, Ipswich IP2 0SS* Ipswich (01473) 689398

GODFREY, Robert John. b 27. ACP St Jo Coll York CertEd48. Sarum Th Coll 52. **d** 54 **p** 55. Chapl Crookham Court Sch Newbury 63-79; P-in-c Yattendon w Frilsham *Ox* 79-80; TV Hermitage and Hampstead Norreys, Cold Ash etc 80-88; Cyprus 88-92; rtd 92; C W Woodhay w Enborne, Hampstead Marshall etc *Ox* from 92. *St Lawrence's Rectory, The Green, West Woodhay, Newbury, Berks RG15 0BL* Inkpen (01488) 668705

GODFREY, Rumley Myles. b 48. S'wark Ord Course. **d** 83 **p** 84. NSM Dorchester *Ox* from 83. *The Old Malthouse, Warborough, Oxon OX10 7DY* Warborough (0186732) 8627

GODFREY, Canon Rupert Christopher Race. b 12. Qu Coll Ox BA34 DipTh35 MA38. Ridley Hall Cam 35. **d** 36 **p** 37. Hon Can St E Cathl *St E* 57-77; V Bury St Edmunds St Mary 59-77; rtd 77; Perm to Offic *St E* from 77. *Archway House, Pytches Road, Woodbridge, Suffolk IP12 1EY* Woodbridge (01394) 382816

GODFREY, Simon Henry Martin. b 55. K Coll Lon BD AKC80. St Steph Ho Ox 80. **d** 81 **p** 82. C Kettering SS Pet and Paul *Pet* 81-84; R Crick and Yelvertoft w Clay Coton and Lilbourne 84-89; V Northn All SS w St Kath from 89. *All Saints' Vicarage, 6 Albion Place, Northampton NN1 1UD* Northampton (01604) 21854 or 32194

GODFREY, Stanley William (Stan). b 24. CEng MIEE67. Qu Coll Birm 71. **d** 74 **p** 74. C Sutton Coldfield St Chad *Birm* 74-78; Hon C Handsworth St Andr 78-86; Hon C Worc City St Paul and Old St Martin etc *Worc* 86-89; Hon C Droitwich Spa from 89. *2 Squires Close, Kempsey, Worcester WR5 3JE* Worcester (01905) 820624

GODIN, Mrs Mary Louise. b 42. SRN64 QN66. Oak Hill NSM Course 89. **d** 92 **p** 94. NSM Surbiton Hill Ch Ch *S'wark* from 92. *58 Surbiton Hill Park, Surbiton, Surrey KT5 8ER* 0181-339 5088 Fax as telephone

GODSALL, Andrew Paul. b 59. Birm Univ BA81. Ripon Coll Cuddesdon 86. **d** 88 **p** 89. C Gt Stanmore *Lon* 88-91; C Ealing All SS 91-94; V Hillingdon All SS from 94. *All Saints' Vicarage, Ryefield Avenue, Uxbridge, Middx UB10 9BT* Uxbridge (01895) 233991

GODSALL, Ralph Charles. b 48. Qu Coll Cam BA71 MA75. Cuddesdon Coll 73. **d** 75 **p** 76. C Sprowston *Nor* 75-78; Chapl Trin Coll Cam 78-84; V Hebden Bridge *Wakef* 84-93; V Westmr St Steph w St Jo *Lon* from 93. *The Vicarage, 21 Vincent Square, London SW1P 2NA* 0171-834 0950

GODSELL, Arthur Norman. b 22. St D Coll Lamp BA47. **d** 49 **p** 50. V Heybridge w Langford *Chelmsf* 62-73; RD Maldon 70-73; R Rochford 73-91; RD Rochford 84-89; rtd 91. *51 Westfa Felinfoel, Llanelli, Dyfed SA14 8DG* Llanelli (01554) 776561

GODSELL, David Brian. b 40. Lon Univ BA62. Coll of Resurr Mirfield 65. **d** 67 **p** 68. C Middlesb All SS *York* 67-73; C Stainton-in-Cleveland 73-75; V Whitby St Ant *Newc* 75-90; P-in-c Brandon *Dur* 90-94; V from 94. *The Vicarage, Sawmill Lane, Brandon, Durham DH7 8NS* 0191-378 0845

GODSELL, Kenneth James Rowland. b 22. Birm Univ DipTh50. Qu Coll Birm. **d** 76 **p** 77. Tutor Westhill Coll of HE Birm from 74; Hon C Selly Hill St Steph *Birm* 76-81; Hon C Selly Park St Steph and St Wulstan 81-94; Perm to Offic from 94. *7 Farqhuar Road East, Birmingham B15 3RD* 0121-454 3737 or 472 7245

GODSON, Alan. b 31. Ch Coll Cam BA61 MA65. Clifton Th Coll 61. **d** 63 **p** 64. C Preston All SS *Blackb* 63-66; Lic to Offic *Man* 66-69; Asst Chapl Emb Ch Paris 69; Dioc Ev *Liv* from 69; P-in-c Edge Hill St Mary 72-78; V from 78. *The Vicarage, Towerlands Street, Liverpool L7 8TT* 0151-709 6710

GODSON, Mark Rowland. b 61. K Coll Lon BD83 AKC83 CertEd84. Linc Th Coll 84. **d** 86 **p** 87. C Hurst Green *S'wark* 86-88; C Fawley *Win* 88-90; TV Wimborne Minster and Holt *Sarum* 90-95; P-in-c Horton and Chalbury 90-95; P-in-c Stalbridge from 95. *The Rectory, Church Walk, Stalbridge, Sturminster Newton, Dorset DT10 2LR* Stalbridge (01963) 62859

GODWIN, David Harold. b 45. Lon Univ DipTh71. Kelham Th Coll 67. **d** 71 **p** 72. C Camberwell St Phil and St Mark *S'wark* 71-75; Asst Chapl The Lon Hosp (Whitechapel) 75-79; Chapl R E Sussex Hosp Hastings 79-86; Chapl Glos R Hosp from 86; Chapl Over Hosp Glouc 86-92. *Gloucestershire Royal Hospital, Great Western Road, Gloucester GL1 3NN* Gloucester (01452) 528555

GODWIN, Canon Michael Francis Harold. b 35. Nottm Univ BSc47. Ely Th Coll 59. **d** 61 **p** 62. C Farnborough *Guildf* 61-65; V Epsom St Barn 66-85; V Bramley and Grafham from 85; Hon Can Guildf Cathl from 89. *The Vicarage, Birtley Rise, Bramley, Guildford, Surrey GU5 0HZ* Guildford (01483) 892109

GODWIN, Canon Noel. b 29. Qu Coll Ox BA52 MA57. St Steph Ho Ox 52. **d** 54 **p** 55. Lic to Offic *Nor* 65-76; RD Depwade 76-77; R Attleborough 77-80; R Attleborough w Besthorpe 80-82; Hon Can Nor Cathl 81-82; V Croydon St Mich w St Jas *Cant* 82-84; V Croydon St Mich w St Jas *S'wark* 85-95; RD Croydon Cen 86-91; Hon Can S'wark Cathl 89-95; rtd 95. *Pendoggett House, Pendoggett, St Kew, Bodmin, Cornwall PL30 3HH* Bodmin (01208) 880465

GODWIN, Peter. b 19. MBE77. Malvern Coll. Ridley Hall Cam 76. **d** 77 **p** 78. C Headley All SS *Guildf* 77-78; Argentina from 78; rtd 88. *Avenida Belgrano 568, 8 Piso A, Buenos Aires, Argentina* Buenos Aires (1) 302287

GOFTON, Canon William Alder. b 31. Dur Univ BA54. Coll of Resurr Mirfield 59. **d** 61 **p** 62. C Benwell St Aid *Newc* 61-64; C N Gosforth 64-69; V Seaton Hirst 69-77; V Newc H Cross 77-89; RD Newc W 85-89; Hon Can Newc Cathl from 88; R Bolam w Whalton and Hartburn w Meldon from 89; P-in-c Netherwitton 89-95; V from 95; Chapl Kirkley Hall Coll from 90. *The Rectory, Whalton, Morpeth, Northd NE61 3UX* Whalton (01670) 75360

GOLBOURNE, Winston George. b 30. Univ of W Indies BA53. Virginia Th Sem STM69 Sarum & Wells Th Coll 71. **d** 73 **p** 74. C Bitterne Park *Win* 73-76; Jamaica 76-79; C Handsworth St Andr *Birm* 79-83; V Perry Hill St Geo *S'wark* from 83. *St George's Vicarage, 2 Woolstone Road, London SE23 2SG* 0181-699 2778

GOLD, Guy Alastair Whitmore. b 16. TD50. Trin Coll Cam BA38 MA48. Qu Coll Birm 55. **d** 55 **p** 56. R Hasketon *St E* 69-76; rtd 76; Perm to Offic *St E* 76-89. *Bridge House, Great Bealings, Woodbridge, Suffolk IP13 6NW* Grundisburgh (01473) 735518

GOLDEN, Stephen Gerard. b 61. Lon Univ BA84. St Steph Ho Ox 84. **d** 86 **p** 87. C Reading St Luke w St Bart *Ox* 86-90; CF 90-94. *Address temp unknown*

GOLDENBERG, Ralph Maurice. b 45. City Univ FBCO67 FBOA67. Trin Coll Bris DipHE90. **d** 90 **p** 91. C Kinson *Sarum* 90-93; C Edgware *Lon* from 93. *St Andrew's Parsonage, 1 Beulah Close, Edgware, Middx HA8 8SP* 0181-958 9730

GOLDIE, Canon David. b 46. Glas Univ MA68 Fitzw Coll Cam BA70 MA74. Westcott Ho Cam 68. **d** 70 **p** 71. C Swindon Ch Ch *Bris* 70-73; C Troon *Glas* 73-75; R Ardrossan 75-82; Miss Priest Irvine 75-82; PM Milton Keynes *Ox* 82-86; V Milton Keynes from 86; RD Milton Keynes 86-90; Hon Can Ch Ch from 90. *7 Alverton, Great Linford, Milton Keynes MK14 5EF* Milton Keynes (01908) 605150

GOLDIE, James Stuart. b 46. Edin Univ BTh73 BEd73. ALCD69. **d** 69 **p** 70. C Blackpool St Paul *Blackb* 69-70; C Gt Sankey *Liv* 70-73; Asst Chapl Greystone Heath Sch 70-73; Chapl Kilmarnock Academy 73-75; V Flixton St Jo *Man* 75-78; Chapl Friars Sch Man 75-78; V Skelmersdale St Paul *Liv* 78-80; Chapl Trin Sch Liv 78-80; Chapl Westbrook Hay Sch Hemel Hempstead 87-89; V Pennington w Lindal and Marton *Carl* 89-90; Chapl Bp Wand Sch *Lon* 90-95. *24 Strath Dee Terrace, West Ferry, Dundee DD5 1QJ*

GOLDING, Piers Edwin Hugh. b 26. RD76. St Aug Coll Cant 48 Edin Th Coll 50. **d** 53 **p** 54. Chapl RNR 62-93; V S Bermondsey St Aug *S'wark* 62-93; rtd 93; Perm to Offic *S'wark* from 95. *College of St Barnabas, Blackberry Lane, Lingfield, Surrey RH7 6NJ* Dormans Park (01342) 870366

GOLDING, Simon Jefferies. b 46. Brasted Place Coll 70. Linc Th Coll 72. **d** 74 **p** 75. C Wilton *York* 74-77; Chapl RN from 77. *Directorate Gen, RN Chapl Services, Room 203, Victory Building, HM Naval Base, Portsmouth PO1 3LS* Portsmouth (01705) 727903 Fax 727112

GOLDING, Stephen. b 57. Keele Univ BA79 CertEd79 Lon Bible Coll BA86. Cant Sch of Min 93. **d** 95. NSM Ramsgate St Luke *Cant* from 95; Chapl St Lawr Coll Ramsgate from 95. *28 College Road, Ramsgate, Kent CT11 7AA* Ramsgate (01843) 850592

GOLDING, Canon Terence Brannigan. b 25. Univ of Ottawa MA. Qu Coll Birm 79. **d** 77 **p** 77. Lesotho 77-79; C Walsall *Lich* 79-83; I Currin w Drum and Newbliss *Clogh* 83-86 and from 88; V Eighton Banks *Dur* 86-88; rtd 94. *Scotshouse Rectory, Clones, Co Monaghan, Irish Republic* Clones (47) 56103

GOLDINGAY, Dr John Edgar. b 42. Keble Coll Ox BA64 Nottm Univ PhD83. Clifton Th Coll 64. **d** 66 **p** 67. C Finchley Ch Ch *Lon* 66-69; Lect St Jo Coll Nottm 70-75; Dir Academic Studies 76-79; Registrar 79-85; Vice-Prin 85-88; Prin St Jo Coll Nottm from 88. *St John's College, Chilwell Lane, Bramcote, Nottingham NG9 3DS* Nottingham (0115) 925 1114/922 4046 Fax 922 0134 or 943 6438

GOLDSMITH, Brian Derek. b 36. Leeds Univ BA64. Coll of Resurr Mirfield 64. **d** 66 **p** 67. C Littlehampton St Mary *Chich* 66-69; C Guildf St Nic *Guildf* 69-73; V Aldershot St Aug 73-81; C-in-c Leigh Park St Clare CD *Portsm* 82-85; C Rowner from 85. *74 Tichborne Way, Gosport, Hants PO13 0BN* Fareham (01329) 238020

GOLDSMITH, John Oliver. b 46. K Coll Lon BD69 AKC69. St Aug Coll Cant 69. **d** 70 **p** 71. C Dronfield *Derby* 70-73; C Ellesmere Port *Ches* 73-74; TV Ellesmere Port 74-81; P-in-c Pleasley *Derby* 81-87; P-in-c Pleasley Hill *S'well* 83-87; V Matlock Bank *Derby* from 87; RD Wirksworth from 92. *All Saints' Vicarage, Smedley Street, Matlock, Derbyshire DE4 3JG* Matlock (01629) 582235

GOLDSMITH, Malcolm Clive. b 39. Birm Univ BSocSc60. Ripon Hall Ox 60. **d** 62 **p** 63. C Balsall Heath St Paul *Birm* 62-64; Chapl Aston Univ 64-72; Bp's Adv on Ind Soc *S'well* 72-78; C Sherwood 78-79; R Nottm St Pet and St Jas 79-85; P-in-c Nottm All SS 85; Gen Sec IVS 85-88; Lic to Offic 85-88; Bp's Personal Exec Asst *Bradf* 88-91; Hon C Edin St Jo *Edin* 92-94; R Edin St Cuth from 94. *6 Westgarth Avenue, Edinburgh EH13 0BD* 0131-441 3557

GOLDSMITH, Mrs Mary Louie. b 48. K Coll Lon BA70 AKC70. Qu Coll Birm 91. **d** 93 **p** 94. NSM Matlock Bank *Derby* from 93. *All Saints' Vicarage, Smedley Street, Matlock, Derbyshire DE4 3JG* Matlock (01629) 582235

GOLDSMITH, Mrs Pauline Anne. b 40. Linc Th Coll 82. dss 84 **d** 87 **p** 94. Waddington *Linc* 86-88; Par Dn 87-88; Par Dn Gt and Lt Coates w Bradley 89-94; TV from 94. *16 Longfield Road, Grimsby, S Humberside DN34 5SB* Grimsby (01472) 751809

GOLDSMITH, Stephen. b 32. Edin Th Coll. **d** 76 **p** 77. SPCK Staff from 53; Bookshops Regional Manager SPCK from 87; NSM Penicuik *Edin* 76-81; NSM Linc St Nic w St Jo Newport *Linc* 81-90; NSM Gt and Lt Coates w Bradley from 90. *16 Longfield Road, Grimsby, S Humberside DN34 5SB* Grimsby (01472) 751809

GOLDSPINK, David. b 35. MBAC88 Open Univ BA81. Lon Coll of Div 62. **d** 65 **p** 66. C St Austell *Truro* 68-70; TV Bramerton w Surlingham *Nor* 70-73; Min Gunton St Pet 73-75; R Mutford w Rushmere w Gisleham w N Cove w

Barnby 75-81; Asst Chapl HM Pris Man 81-82; Chapl HM Youth Cust Cen Hollesley Bay Colony 82-84; Chapl HM Pris Blundeston 84-88; Perm to Offic *St E* from 87; rtd 88; Perm to Offic *Nor* from 88. *14 Deepdale, Carlton Colville, Lowestoft, Suffolk NR33 8TU* Lowestoft (01502) 537769

GOLDSPINK, Canon Robert William. b 23. Fitzw Coll Cam BA52 MA56. Trin Coll Bris 47. **d** 52 **p** 53. V Tunbridge Wells St Jas *Roch* 64-83; Hon Can Roch Cathl 83-87; V Seal St Pet 83-87; rtd 87; Perm to Offic *Nor* from 87. *Bethany, 50 Uplands Close, Carlton Colville, Suffolk NR33 8AD* Lowestoft (01502) 515662

GOLDSTRAW, William Henry. b 15. Lich Th Coll 60. **d** 61 **p** 62. V Alton *Lich* 68-82; V Bradley-in-the-Moors 68-82; V Alton w Bradley-le-Moors 82-84; rtd 84; Perm to Offic *Lich* from 84. *36 The Avenue, Cheddleton, Leek, Staffs ST13 7BJ* Churnet Side (01538) 360204

GOLDTHORPE, Peter Martin. b 36. AKC61. **d** 62 **p** 63. C Lt Ilford St Barn *Chelmsf* 62-66; C Wickford 66-68; P-in-c Luton St Anne *St Alb* 68-78; P-in-c Linby w Papplewick *S'well* 78-82; Perm to Offic 82-92; Midl Sec CMJ 83-92; Perm to Offic *Birm* 85-92; Perm to Offic *Linc* 86-92; V Leaton and Albrighton w Battlefield *Lich* from 93. *The Vicarage, Baschurch Road, Bomere Heath, Shrewsbury SY4 3PN* Bomere Heath (01939) 290259

GOLDTHORPE, Ms Shirley. b 42. Linc Th Coll 70. **dss** 76 **d** 87 **p** 94. Thornhill Lees *Wakef* 76-78; Birkenshaw w Hunsworth 78-80; Batley St Thos 80-85; Batley All SS 80-85; Purlwell 80-92; Par Dn 87-88; D-in-c 88-92; D-in-c Horbury Junction 92-94; P-in-c from 94. *The Vicarage, Millfield Road, Horbury, Wakefield, W Yorkshire WF4 5DU* Wakefield (01924) 275274

GOLIGHTLY, William Michael. b 43. Chich Th Coll 67. **d** 70 **p** 74. C Sleekburn *Newc* 70-71; C Wallsend St Luke 71; C Shiremoor 74-77; C Delaval 77-81; TV Bellingham/Otterburn Gp 81-89; TV N Shields 89-92; Chapl Winterton Hosp Sedgefield from 92. *Winterton Hospital, Sedgefield, Stockton-on-Tees, Cleveland TS21 3EJ* Sedgefield (01740) 620521

GOLLEDGE, Christopher John. b 66. St Mich Coll Llan DipTh92. **d** 92 **p** 93. C Newton Nottage *Llan* 92-95. *32 Bennett Road, Brighton BN3 5JL*

GOLLOP, Michael John. b 58. Keble Coll Ox BA81 MA85. St Mich Coll Llan BD85. **d** 85 **p** 86. C Newport St Mark *Mon* 85-87; C Bassaleg 87-91; V St Hilary Greenway 91-93; V Itton and St Arvans w Penterry and Kilgwrrwg etc from 93. *The Vicarage, St Arvans, Chepstow, Gwent NP6 6EU* Chepstow (01291) 622064

GOLTON, Alan Victor. b 29. St Jo Coll Ox BA51 MA54 DPhil54. Local NSM Course 84. **d** 85 **p** 86. P-in-c Barston *Birm* from 87. *12 Granville Road, Dorridge, Solihull, W Midlands B93 8BY* Knowle (01564) 773058

GOMERSALL, Ian Douglass. b 56. Fitzw Coll Cam BSc77 Fitzw Coll Cam BA80 MA85. Westcott Ho Cam 78. **d** 81 **p** 82. C Darlington St Mark w St Paul *Dur* 81-84; C Barnard Castle w Whorlton 84-86; Chapl HM Young Offender Inst Deerbolt 85-90; P-in-c Cockfield *Dur* 86-88; R 88-90; Dep Chapl HM Pris Wakef 90-91; Chapl HM Pris Full Sutton from 91; P-in-c Kexby w Wilberfoss *York* from 93. *The Chaplain's Office, HM Prison, Full Sutton, York YO4 1PS* Stamford Bridge (01759) 72447 Fax 71206

GOMERSALL, Richard. b 45. FCA68. N Ord Course 90. **d** 93 **p** 94. NSM Thurcroft *Sheff* from 93. *Dale View House, 14 Wignall Avenue, Wickersley, Rotherham, S Yorkshire S66 0AX* Rotherham (01709) 546441 or 376313 Fax 703026 or 836008

GOMPERTZ, Canon Peter Alan Martin. b 40. ALCD63. **d** 64 **p** 65. C Eccleston St Luke *Liv* 64-69; Scripture Union 69-73; C Yeovil *B & W* 73-75; V Northn St Giles *Pet* from 75; Can Pet Cathl from 88. *St Giles's Vicarage, Spring Gardens, Northampton NN1 1LX* Northampton (01604) 34060

GONIN, Christopher Willett. b 33. Man Univ DipRS82 DipA&CE87. AKC56. **d** 60 **p** 61. C Camberwell St Geo *S'wark* 60-64; C Stevenage H Trin *St Alb* 64-69; C Bletchley *Ox* 70-73; R Newington St Mary *S'wark* 73-76; Perm to Offic *Bris* 76-77; Hon C Horfield H Trin 77-89; Hon C City of Bris 89-91; V Milton Ernest *St Alb* from 92; V Thurleigh from 92. *The Vicarage, Thurleigh Road, Milton Ernest, Bedford MK44 1RF* Oakley (01234) 822885

GOOCH, Michael Anthony. b 44. Nottm Coll of Educn TCert66. Cant Sch of Min 90. **d** 93 **p** 94. NSM New Romney w Old Romney and Midley *Cant* from 93. *Little Owls, Tookey Road, New Romney, Kent TN28 8ET* New Romney (01679) 64652

GOOD, Alan Raymond. b 39. Bris Sch of Min 83. **d** 85 **p** 86. NSM Horfield St Greg *Bris* from 85. *177 Filton Road, Horfield, Bristol BS7 0XX* Bristol (0117) 952 1323

GOOD, Andrew Ronald. b 60. Bris Univ BA82. Linc Th Coll 83. **d** 85 **p** 86. C Epping St Jo *Chelmsf* 85-88; C Cheshunt *St Alb* 88-91; R Spixworth w Crostwick *Nor* 91-93; R Frettenham w

Stanninghall 91-92; R Spixworth w Crostwick and Frettenham from 92. *The Rectory, Spixworth, Norwich NR10 3PR* Norwich (01603) 898258

GOOD, Anthony Ernest. b 28. ARIBA51 Heriot-Watt Univ MSc73. Wells Th Coll 54. **d** 56 **p** 57. R Sandhurst *Ox* 61-70; Perm to Offic *Ex* 71-82; TR Wallingford w Crowmarsh Gifford etc *Ox* 82-92; RD Wallingford 85-91; rtd 92. *Cotts Weir Quay, Bere Alston, Yelverton, Devon PL20 7BX* Yelverton (01822) 840524

GOOD, David Howard. b 42. Glouc Sch of Min 84. **d** 87 **p** 88. NSM Bromyard *Heref* 87-92; C Pontesbury I and II 92-95; P-in-c Ditton Priors w Neenton, Burwarton etc from 95. *The Vicarage, Ditton Priors, Bridgnorth, Shropshire WV16 6SQ* Ditton Priors (0174634) 636

GOOD, Florence Rose. b 10. SRN44. **dss** 78 **d** 87 **p** 94. Upper Holloway St Pet w St Jo *Lon* 84-89; Hon Par Dn 87-89; rtd 89. *221 Salisbury Walk, Magdala Avenue, London N19 5DY* 0171-272 8652

GOOD, Geoffrey. b 27. St Aid Birkenhead. **d** 61 **p** 62. V Staincliffe *Wakef* 65-79; V Thornes St Jas w Ch Ch 79-93; rtd 93. *147 Thornes Road, Wakefield, W Yorkshire WF2 8QN* Wakefield (01924) 378273

GOOD, Very Rev George Fitzgerald. b 19. TCD BA41. CITC 42. **d** 42 **p** 43. Dean Derry *D & R* 67-84; rtd 84. *Cliff Cottage, Portnoo, Lifford, Co Donegal, Irish Republic* Portnoo (75) 45268

GOOD, John Hobart. b 43. Bps' Coll Cheshunt 66 Coll of Resurr Mirfield 68. **d** 69 **p** 70. C Ex St Jas *Ex* 69-73; C Cockington 73-75; C Wolborough w Newton Abbot 75-78; P-in-c Exminster 78-80; P-in-c Kenn 78-80; R Exminster and Kenn 80-95; RD Kenn 89-95; TR Axminster, Chardstock, Combe Pyne and Rousdon from 95. *The Rectory, Church Street, Axminster, Devon EX13 5AQ* Axminster (01297) 32264

GOOD, Kenneth Raymond. b 52. TCD BA74 Nottm Univ BA76 NUI HDipEd81 MEd84. St Jo Coll Nottm 75. **d** 77 **p** 78. C Willowfield *D & D* 77-79; Chapl Ashton Sch Cork 79-84; I Dunganstown w Redcross and Conary *D & G* 84-90; I Lurgan Ch the Redeemer *D & D* from 90; RD Shankill from 92. *Shankill Rectory, 62 Banbridge Road, Lurgan, Craigavon, Co Armagh BT66 7HG* Lurgan (01762) 323341 or 325673 Fax 325673

GOOD, Ven Kenneth Roy. b 41. K Coll Lon BD66 AKC66. **d** 67 **p** 68. C Stockton St Pet *Dur* 67-70; Chapl Antwerp Miss to Seamen *Eur* 70-74; Japan 74-79; Hon Can Kobe from 74; Asst Gen Sec Miss to Seamen 79-85; Asst Chapl St Mich Paternoster Royal *Lon* 79-85; V Nunthorpe *York* 85-93; RD Stokesley 90-93; Adn Richmond *Ripon* from 93. *62 Palace Road, Ripon, N Yorkshire HG4 1HA* Ripon (01765) 604342 Fax as telephone

GOOD, Robert Stanley. b 24. TCD BA45 BD47 Kent Univ MA82. **d** 47 **p** 48. Sen Lect Ch Ch Coll Cant 64-78; Fiji 83-87; rtd 87; Perm to Offic *Cant* from 87. *44 Ivanhoe Road, Herne Bay, Kent CT6 6EG* Herne Bay (01227) 363561

GOOD, Stuart Eric Clifford. b 37. Wycliffe Hall Ox 63. **d** 64 **p** 65. C Walton H Trin *Ox* 64-67; Australia from 67. *5 Vigna Place, Ferndale, W Australia 6155* Perth (9) 271-9633

GOOD, Canon William Thomas Raymond. b 13. TCD BA39 MA45. **d** 39 **p** 40. Prec Cloyne Cathl *C, C & R* 69-82; I Carrigrohane Union 73-82; Preb Cork Cathl 79-82; rtd 82. *Grange House, Castlemartyr, Co Cork, Irish Republic* Cork (21) 667349

GOODACRE, Canon David Leighton. b 36. Birm Univ DPS69. AKC59. **d** 60 **p** 61. C Stockton St Chad *Dur* 60-63; C Birtley 63-68; Chapl Sunderland Gen Hosp 69-74; P-in-c Ryhope *Dur* 75-81; V Ovingham *Newc* from 81; Hon Can Newc Cathl from 92. *St Mary's Vicarage, 2 Burnside Close, Ovingham, Prudhoe, Northd NE42 6BS* Prudhoe (01661) 832273

GOODACRE, Norman William. b 07. ARIBA32 Liv Univ BArch31 MA33. Westcott Ho Cam 32. **d** 33 **p** 34. V Coniston Cold *Bradf* 45-58; Lic to Offic *Ripon* 58-75; rtd 75; Perm to Offic *Liv* from 76. *81 Holmefield Road, Liverpool L19 3PF* 0151-724 4176

GOODALL, George. b 24. LCP. **d** 86 **p** 87. NSM Bretby w Newton Solney *Derby* 86-94; Perm to Offic from 94. *6 Brizlincote Lane, Burton-on-Trent, Staffs DE15 0PU* Burton-on-Trent (01283) 562467

GOODALL, John William. b 45. Hull Univ BA69. Ripon Hall Ox 69. **d** 71 **p** 72. C Loughb Em *Leic* 71-74; C Dorchester *Ox* 74-75; TV Dorchester 75-80; Tutor Sarum & Wells Th Coll 80-88; Vice Prin S Dios Minl Tr Scheme 80-88; P-in-c Gt Wishford *Sarum* 80-83; P-in-c Colehill from 88; Dioc Dir of Readers from 88. *The Vicarage, Smugglers Lane, Colehill, Wimborne, Dorset BH21 2RY* Wimborne (01202) 883721

GOODALL, Jonathan Michael. b 61. R Holloway Coll Lon BMus83. Wycliffe Hall Ox 86. **d** 89 **p** 90. C Bicester w Bucknell, Caversfield and Launton *Ox* 89-92; Sacr and Chapl

Westmr Abbey from 92; Lic to Offic *Lon* from 94. *4B Little Cloister, Westminster Abbey, London SW1P 3PL* 0171-222 1386 Fax 233 2072

GOODALL, Malcolm. b 39. Carl Dioc Tr Course 80. **d** 85 **p** 86. NSM Crosscanonby *Carl* 85-88; NSM Allonby 85-88; C Auckland St Andr and St Anne *Dur* 88-90; V Grindon and Stillington from 90. *The Vicarage, Thorpe Thewles, Stockton-on-Tees, Cleveland TS21 3JU* Sedgefield (01740) 30549

GOODBURN, David Henry. b 41. S'wark Ord Course 73. **d** 76 **p** 77. NSM Enfield SS Pet and Paul *Lon* 76-82; Perm to Offic 83-85; NSM Potters Bar *St Alb* 85-88; Chapl RN from 88. *Directorate Gen, RN Chapl Services, Room 203, Victory Building, HM Naval Base, Portsmouth PO1 3LS* Portsmouth (01705) 727903 Fax 727112

GOODCHILD, Andrew Philip. b 55. Oak Hill Th Coll BA85. **d** 85 **p** 86. C Barnston *Ches* 85-88; C Hollington St Leon *Chich* 88-89; P-in-c Millbrook *Ches* 89-94; Chapl Kimbolton Sch Cambs from 94; Head RE from 94. *Longways, 27 Stow Road, Kimbolton, Huntingdon, Cambs PE18 0HU* Huntingdon (01480) 861221

GOODCHILD, Canon John McKillip. b 42. Clare Coll Cam BA64 MA68 Or Coll Ox CertEd69. Wycliffe Hall Ox 67. **d** 69 **p** 70. C Clubmoor *Liv* 69-72; Nigeria 72-83; Hon Can Aba from 74; V Ainsdale *Liv* 83-89; TR Maghull from 89. *The Rectory, 20 Damfield Lane, Maghull, Liverpool L31 6DD* 0151-526 5017

✠GOODCHILD, Rt Rev Ronald Cedric Osbourne. b 10. Trin Coll Cam BA32 MA35. Bps' Coll Cheshunt 34. **d** 34 **p** 35 **c** 64. C Ealing St Mary *Lon* 34-37; Chapl Oakham Sch Leics 37-42; Chapl RAFVR 42-46; W Germany 46-49; Sch Sec SCM 49-53; P-in-c St Helen Bishopsgate w St Martin Outwich *Lon* 51-53; V Horsham *Chich* 53-59; RD Horsham 54-59; Adn Northn *Pet* 59-64; R Ecton 59-64; Can Pet Cathl 62-64; Suff Bp Kensington *Lon* 64-79; Area Bp Kensington 79-80; rtd 80; Asst Bp Ex from 83. *Mead Farm, Welcombe, Hartland, Bideford, Devon EX39 6HH* Morwenstow (0128883) 241

GOODCHILD, Roy John. b 30. Wycliffe Hall Ox 60. **d** 61 **p** 62. C Hayes *Roch* 61-64; C S w N Bersted *Chich* 64-68; R Birdham w W Itchenor 68-73; V Saltdean 74-83; V Hollington St Jo 83-90; V Ticehurst and Flimwell from 90; RD Rotherfield from 95. *The Vicarage, Ticehurst, Wadhurst, E Sussex TN5 7AB* Ticehurst (01580) 200316

GOODDEN, John Maurice Phelips. b 34. Sarum & Wells Th Coll 70. **d** 72 **p** 75. C Weymouth H Trin *Sarum* 72-74; C Harlow New Town w Lt Parndon *Chelmsf* 74-78; Ind Chapl 78-82; Chapl Princess Alexandra Hosp Harlow 78-82; V Moulsham St Jo *Chelmsf* 86-90; R Chipstead S'wark from 90; Adv Rural Min from 90. *The Rectory, Starrock Lane, Chipstead, Coulsdon, Surrey CR5 3QD* Downland (01737) 552157 or 553527

GOODE, Allan Kenneth. b 37. S'wark Ord Course. **d** 72 **p** 73. C Belmont *Lon* 72-74; V Liv St Bride w St Sav *Liv* 74-78; V Eccleston Park 78-89; C Billinge 89-91; P-in-c Scarisbrick 91-94; V from 94. *St Mark's Vicarage, 458A Southport Road, Ormskirk, Lancs L40 9RF* Scarisbrick (01704) 880317

GOODE, Anthony Thomas Ryall. b 42. Ex Coll Ox BA64 MA71. Cuddesdon Coll 65. **d** 67 **p** 68. C Wolvercote *Ox* 67-71; Chapl RAF 71-91; P-in-c Edith Weston w Normanton *Pet* 72-74; Asst Chapl-in-Chief RAF from 91. *Chaplaincy Services (RAF), HQ, Personnel and Training Command, RAF Innsworth, Gloucester GL3 1EZ* Gloucester (01452) 712612 Ext 5164 Fax 510828

GOODE, John Laurence. b 48. W Cheshire Coll of Tech TEng70 Federal Univ Minas Gerais Brazil DipT78. Chich Th Coll 81. **d** 83 **p** 84. C Crewe St Andr *Ches* 83-86; USPG 87-94; Brazil 91-94; TV Ches Team *Ches* from 94. *Christ Church Vicarage, 5 Gloucester Street, Chester CH1 3HR* Chester (01244) 380625

GOODE, Michael Arthur John. b 40. K Coll Lon BD AKC63. **d** 64 **p** 65. C Sunderland Springwell w Thorney Close *Dur* 64-68; C Solihull *Birm* 68-70; R Fladbury, Wyre Piddle and Moor *Worc* 70-75; P-in-c Foley Park 75-81; V 81-83; RD Kidderminster 81-83; TR Crawley *Chich* 83-93; TR Abingdon *Ox* from 93; V Shippon from 93. *The Rectory, St Helen's Court, Abingdon, Oxon OX14 5BS* Abingdon (01235) 520144

GOODE, Canon Peter William Herbert. b 23. Oak Hill Th Coll 60. **d** 62 **p** 63. V Harold Hill St Paul *Chelmsf* 65-76; V Gt Warley Ch Ch 76-93; RD Brentwood 89-93; Hon Can Chelmsf Cathl 90-93; rtd 93. *52 Slimmons Drive, St Albans, Herts AL4 9AP* St Albans (01727) 831904

GOODE, William Aubrey. b 08. Bps' Coll Cheshunt 63. **d** 65 **p** 66. V Kirk Fenton *York* 67-76; rtd 76. *Flat 16, Guardian Court, Water Lane, Clifton, York YO3 6PR* York (01904) 655199

GOODER, Martin Lee. b 37. Sheff Univ BSc58. Oak Hill Th Coll 58. **d** 60 **p** 61. C Barrow St Mark *Carl* 60-63; C Halliwell St Pet *Man* 63-66; R Chorlton on Medlock St Sav 66-71; R Brunswick 71-92; P-in-c Bacup Ch Ch from 92. *Christ Church*

Vicarage, Greensnook Lane, Bacup, Lancs OL13 9DQ Bacup (01706) 878293

GOODERHAM, Daniel Charles. b 24. St Fran Coll Brisbane 49 ACT ThL51. **d** 52 **p** 53. V Ipswich St Bart *St E* 64-71; R Drinkstone 71-78; R Rattlesden 71-78; RD Lavenham 75-78; V Beckenham St Mich w St Aug *Roch* 78-87; P-in-c Whiteparish *Sarum* 87-89; rtd 89. *58 Millfield, Eye, Suffolk IP23 7DE* Eye (01379) 871589

GOODERICK, Peter Handley. b 26. Down Coll Cam BA50 MA52. Linc Th Coll 51. **d** 53 **p** 54. CF (TAVR) 59-74; V Mert St Jas *S'wark* 68-80; P-in-c Baginton *Cov* 80-81; P-in-c Stoneleigh w Ashow 80-81; R Stoneleigh w Ashow and Baginton 81-88; RD Kenilworth 85-88; R Berkswell 88-91; rtd 91; Chapl Malaga w Almunecar and Nerja *Eur* 91-92; Perm to Offic *Cov* from 93. *9 Margetts Close, Barrowfield Lane, Kenilworth, Warks CV8 1EN* Kenilworth (01926) 59855

GOODERSON, William Dennis. b 09. St Pet Hall Ox BA35 MA39. Wycliffe Hall Ox 35. **d** 36 **p** 37. V Cumnor *Ox* 66-77; rtd 77. *6 Gouldland Gardens, Headington, Oxford OX3 9DQ* Oxford (01865) 62387

GOODEY, Philip Julian Frank (Phil). b 61. Glos Coll of Arts & Tech HND83. Aston Tr Scheme 87 Trin Coll Bris DipTh92. **d** 92 **p** 93. C Iver *Ox* 92-94; C Hornchurch St Andr *Chelmsf* from 94. *85 Kenilworth Gardens, Hornchurch, Essex RM12 4SG* Hornchurch (01708) 442275

GOODFELLOW, Dr Ian. b 37. St Cath Coll Cam BA61 MA65 Lon Univ PGCE76 Dur Univ PhD83. Wells Th Coll 61. **d** 63 **p** 64. C Dunstable *St Alb* 63-67; Chapl Haileybury Coll Herts 67-71; Lect, Chapl and Tutor Bede Coll Dur 71-74; Lect SS Hild & Bede Dur 75-78; Sen Counsellor Open Univ (SW Region) from 79; Perm to Offic *Ex* from 80. *Crosslea, 206 Whitchurch Road, Tavistock, Devon PL19 9DQ* Tavistock (01822) 612069

GOODFIELD, Dudley Francis. b 40. AKC65. **d** 66 **p** 67. C Bath Twerton-on-Avon *B & W* 66-69; C Lache cum Saltney *Ches* 69-71; C Portishead *B & W* 71-76; V Weston-super-Mare St Andr Bournville 76-82; V Ruishton w Thornfalcon from 82. *The Vicarage, Church Lane, Ruishton, Taunton, Somerset TA3 5JW* Henlade (01823) 442269

GOODHAND, Richard. b 51. Sarum & Wells Th Coll 88. **d** 90 **p** 91. C Wollaton *S'well* 90-93; P-in-c Clarborough w Hayton from 93; Sub-Chapl HM Pris Ranby from 93. *The Vicarage, Church Lane, Clarborough, Retford, Notts DN22 9NA* Retford (01777) 704781 Fax 702691

GOODHEW, David John. b 65. Collingwood Coll Dur BA86 CCC Ox DPhil92 St Jo Coll Dur BA92 DMinlStuds93. Cranmer Hall Dur 90. **d** 93 **p** 94. C Bedminster *Bris* from 93. *30 Brookdale Road, Bristol BS13 7PZ* Bristol (0117) 964 5817

GOODHEW, Mrs Lindsey Jane Ellin. b 66. UEA BA87 St Jo Coll Dur BA92 DMinlStuds93. Cranmer Hall Dur 90. **d** 93 **p** 94. C Bishopsworth *Bris* from 93. *30 Brookdale Road, Bristol BS13 7PZ* Bristol (0117) 964 5817

GOODHEW, Roy William. b 41. Reading Univ BA. S Dios Minl Tr Scheme. **d** 89 **p** 90. C Southn Maybush St Pet *Win* 89-94; V Hound from 94. *The Vicarage, Grange Road, Netley Abbey, Southampton SO3 5FF* Southampton (01703) 452209

GOODING, Ian Eric. b 42. MIProdE68 CEng69 Leeds Univ BSc63 BCom65. St Jo Coll Nottm 70 Lon Coll of Div LTh72 DPS73. **d** 73 **p** 74. C Wandsworth All SS *S'wark* 73-77; Bp's Ind Adv *Derby* from 77; P-in-c Stanton-by-Dale w Dale Abbey 77-87; R from 87; P-in-c Risley from 94. *The Rectory, Stanton-by-Dale, Ilkeston, Derbyshire DE7 4QA* Nottingham (0115) 932 4584

GOODING, Ian Peter Slade. b 56. MBCS88 Imp Coll Lon BScEng77. Qu Coll Birm DipTh92. **d** 92 **p** 93. C Swindon Dorcan *Bris* from 92. *18 Larksfield, Covingham, Swindon SN3 5AD* Swindon (01793) 520139

GOODING, John Henry. b 47. St Jo Coll Nottm. **d** 84 **p** 85. C Charles w St Matthias Plymouth *Ex* 84-88; C Leeds St Geo *Ripon* 88-93; TV Liskeard, St Keyne, St Pinnock, Morval etc *Truro* 93-94; Consultant Lon and SE CPAS from 94; Hon C Egham *Guildf* from 95. *9 Redwood, Thorpe, Egham, Surrey TW20 8SU* Chertsey (01932) 560407

GOODLAD, Martin Randall. b 39. Sheff City Coll of Educn TDip60. Linc Th Coll 63. **d** 66 **p** 67. C Bramley *Ripon* 66-69; TV Daventry *Pet* 69-71; Asst Dioc Youth Officer 69-71; Asst Dir of Educn *Wakef* 71-74; Youth Work Officer Gen Syn Bd of Educn 74-83; P-in-c Cheam Common St Phil *S'wark* 83-85; V from 85; RD Sutton from 90. *61 Kingsmead Avenue, Worcester Park, Surrey KT4 8UZ* 0181-337 1327

GOODLEY, Christopher Ronald. b 47. K Coll Lon BD72 AKC72. **d** 73 **p** 74. C Shenfield *Chelmsf* 73-77; C Hanley H Ev *Lich* 77-78; TV 78-83; Chapl Whittington Hosp Lon 83-86; Chapl St Crispin's Hosp Northn 88-94; Chapl Princess Marina Hosp Northn from 94. *Princess Marina Hospital, Duston, Northampton NN5 6UN* Northampton (01604) 595087 or 752323

GOODMAN, Preb Denys Charles. b 24. Selw Coll Cam BA49 MA56. Linc Th Coll 49. **d** 51 **p** 52. V Hollinwood *Man* 57-70; R Bath Bathwick St Mary *B & W* 70-78; P-in-c Bath Bathwick St Jo 76-78; R Bath Bathwick 78-91; RD Bath 81-90; Preb Wells Cathl from 82; rtd 91. *Hollinwood, Johnson Close, Wells, Somerset BH5 3NN* Wells (01749) 675011

GOODMAN, Canon Derek George. b 34. Keble Coll Ox BA57 MA60. Ridley Hall Cam 59. **d** 61 **p** 62. C Attenborough *S'well* 61-65; R Eastwood 65-84; Dioc Insp of Schs 65-89; V Woodthorpe 84-89; Dir of Educn *Leic* from 89; Hon Can Leic Cathl from 90. *1 Brown Avenue, Quorn, Loughborough, Leics LE12 8RH* Quorn (01509) 415692

GOODMAN, Ernest Edwin. b 14. BNC Ox BA49 MA53. Chich Th Coll 53. **d** 54 **p** 55. Perm to Offic *Pet* from 66; R Clayton w Keymer *Chich* 71-79; rtd 79. *33 Hatton Hall, Hatton Avenue, Wellingborough, Northants NN8 5AP* Wellingborough (01933) 222912

GOODMAN, John. b 20. Selw Coll Cam BA42 MA46. Linc Th Coll 47. **d** 49 **p** 50. V Salisbury St Mark *Sarum* 68-83; R Wool and E Stoke 83-88; rtd 88. *141 Avon Road, Devizes, Wilts SN10 1PY* Devizes (01380) 721267

GOODMAN, John Dennis Julian. b 35. FCA68. Sarum & Wells Th Coll 74. **d** 76 **p** 77. C Cotmanhay *Derby* 76-79; TV Old Brampton and Loundsley Green 79-86; R Finningley w Auckley *S'well* from 86. *The Rectory, Rectory Lane Finnigley, Doncaster, S Yorkshire DN9 3DA* Doncaster (01302) 770240

GOODMAN, Mark Alexander Scott. b 61. Lanc Univ BA84 Nottm Univ BTh90. Linc Th Coll 87. **d** 90 **p** 91. C Denton St Lawr *Man* 90-93; R Dalkeith *Edin* from 93; R Lasswade from 93. *The Rectory, 7 Ancrum Bank, Dalkeith, Midlothian EH22 3AY* 0131-663 7000

GOODMAN, Peter William (Bill). b 60. St Cath Coll Cam BA82. St Jo Coll Nottm 85. **d** 89 **p** 90. C Stapenhill w Cauldwell *Derby* 89-92; C Ovenden *Wakef* 92-94; V Halifax St Aug from 94. *St Augustine's Vicarage, Hanson Lane, Halifax, W Yorkshire HX1 5PG* Halifax (01422) 65552

GOODMAN, Canon Sidney William. b 10. Kelham Th Coll 27. **d** 33 **p** 34. V Habrough Gp *Linc* 55-71; Can and Preb Linc Cathl 69-79; P-in-c Wold Newton w Hawerby 71-78; rtd 78. *28 Grosvenor Road, Louth, Lincs LN11 0BB* Louth (01507) 603798

GOODMAN, Stephen John. b 67. St Chad's Coll Dur BSc88. Coll of Resurr Mirfield 89. **d** 92 **p** 93. C W Bromwich St Fran *Lich* from 92. *207 Hydes Road, West Bromwich, W Midlands B71 2EF* 0121-556 0713

GOODMAN, Victor Terence (Vic). b 46. MBCS74 CEng92 Liv Univ BSc67. E Midl Min Tr Course 82. **d** 85 **p** 86. NSM Barwell w Potters Marston and Stapleton *Leic* 85-89; NSM Croft and Stoney Stanton 89-94; P-in-c Whetstone from 94. *The Vicarage, Church Lane, Whetstone, Leicester LE8 6LQ* Leicester (0116) 284 8713

GOODRICH, Derek Hugh. b 27. Selw Coll Cam BA48 MA54. St Steph Ho Ox 50. **d** 52 **p** 53. C Willesden St Andr *Lon* 52-57; Guyana from 57; Adn Berlice 81-84; V Gen Dio Guyana 82-94; Dean Georgetown 84-94; rtd 92. *St Aloysius Chapel, 615/6 Penny Lane, South Ruimveldt Gardens, Georgetown, Guyana*

GOODRICH, Canon Peter. b 36. Dur Univ BA58. Cuddesdon Coll 60. **d** 62 **p** 63. C Walton St Jo *Liv* 62-66; C Prescot 66-68; V Anfield St Marg 68-72; V Gt Crosby St Faith 72-83; P-in-c Seaforth 76-80; RD Bootle 78-83; TR Upholland 83-94; Hon Can Liv Cathl from 89; R Halsall from 94; Dioc Dir LNSM from 94. *Gesterfield Farmhouse, Halsall Road, Halsall, Ormskirk, Lancs L39 8RN* Halsall (01704) 841202

✠**GOODRICH, Rt Rev Philip Harold Ernest.** b 29. St Jo Coll Cam BA52 MA56. Cuddesdon Coll 52. **d** 54 **p** 55 **c** 73. C Rugby St Andr *Cov* 54-57; Chapl St Jo Coll Cam 57-61; R S Ormsby w Ketsby, Calceby and Driby *Linc* 61-68; R Harrington w Brinkhill 61-68; R Oxcombe 61-68; R Ruckland w Farforth and Maidenwell 61-68; R Somersby w Bag Enderby 61-68; R Tetford and Salmonby 61-68; V Bromley SS Pet and Paul *Roch* 68-73; Suff Bp Tonbridge 73-82; Dioc Dir of Ords 74-82; Bp Worc from 82. *The Bishop's House, Hartlebury Castle, Kidderminster, Worcs DY11 7XX* Hartlebury (01299) 250214   Fax 250027

GOODRIDGE, Canon Peter David. b 32. Yale Univ STM84 FRSA92. AKC57. **d** 58 **p** 59. C Eastcote St Lawr *Lon* 58-64; V Tottenham St Phil 64-71; V W Drayton 71-85; P-in-c St Michael Penkevil *Truro* 85-88; P-in-c Lamorran and Merther 85-88; Dir of Educn from 85; Hon Can Truro Cathl from 87. *16 Crescent Rise, Truro, Cornwall TR1 3ER* Truro (01872) 70940 or 74352   Fax 222510

✠**GOODRIDGE, Rt Rev Sehon Sylvester.** b 37. K Coll Lon BD66. Huron Coll Ontario DD77 Codrington Coll Barbados 59. **d** 63 **p** 64. St Lucia 64-66; Jamaica 66-71; Warden & Dep Prin United Th Coll W Indies 69-71; Barbados 71-89; Prin Codrington Coll 71-82; Warden, Counsellor & Sen Lect Univ of W Indies 83-89; Hon Can Barbados from 76; Prin

Simon of Cyrene Th Inst 89-94; Chapl to The Queen 93-94; Bp Windward Is from 94. *Bishop's House, PO Box 128, Kingstown, St Vincent, West Indies*

GOODRUM, Mrs Alice. b 30. Lightfoot Ho Dur 58. **dss** 80 **d** 87 **p** 94. Fenham St Jas and St Basil *Newc* 80-91; C 87-91; rtd 91. *58 West Avenue, South Shields, Tyne & Wear NE34 6BD* 0191-427 6746

GOODSELL, Patrick (Pat). b 32. BA88. Linc Th Coll 62. **d** 64 **p** 65. C Thornton Heath St Jude *Cant* 64-65; C Croydon St Jo *S'wark* 65-70; V Tenterden St Mich *Cant* 70-78; P-in-c Sellindge w Monks Horton and Stowting 78-84; P-in-c Lympne w W Hythe 82-84; V Sellindge w Monks Horton and Stowting etc 84-92; V Nonington w Wymynswold and Goodnestone etc from 92. *The Rectory, Vicarage Lane, Nonington, Dover, Kent CT15 4JT* Nonington (01304) 840271

GOODWIN, Dr Barry Frederick John. b 48. Birm Univ BSc69 PhD77. St Jo Coll Nottm LTh88. **d** 88 **p** 89. C Ware Ch Ch *St Alb* 88-91; P-in-c Stanstead Abbots from 91; P-in-c Gt Amwell w St Marg from 95. *The Vicarage, 25 Hoddesdon Road, Stanstead Abbotts, Ware, Herts SG12 8EG* Ware (01920) 870115

GOODWIN, Deryck William. b 27. Birm Univ BSc48 MSc49 PhD51. NW Ord Course 74. **d** 77 **p** 78. Sen Lect York Univ 77-86; Hon C Elvington w Sutton on Derwent and E Cottingwith *York* 77-86; V Burton Pidsea and Humbleton w Elsternwick 86-90; R Middleton w Newton, Levisham and Lockton 90-94; rtd 94. *Linden, Peaslands Lane, Pickering, N Yorkshire YO18 7QX*

GOODWIN, Canon John Fletcher Beckles. b 20. Jes Coll Cam BA43 MA46. Ridley Hall Cam 42. **d** 45 **p** 46. V Mert *Ox* 62-70; V Heanor *Derby* 70-74; V Hazelwood 74-85; V Turnditch 74-85; Adv for In-Service Tr and Chapl to Bp 74-88; Hon Can Derby Cathl 81-85; rtd 85; Perm to Offic *Derby* from 85. *63 Ladyworld Avenue, Belper, Derbyshire DE56 1HT* Belper (01773) 820844

GOODWIN, Ronald Victor (Ron). b 33. S'wark Ord Course. **d** 86 **p** 87. NSM Wickford and Runwell *Chelmsf* from 86. *164 Southend Road, Wickford, Essex SS11 8EH* Wickford (01268) 734447

GOODWIN, Stephen. b 58. Sheff Univ BA80. Cranmer Hall Dur 82. **d** 85 **p** 86. C Lytham St Cuth *Blackb* 85-87; C W Burnley 88-90; TV Headley All SS *Guildf* from 90. *St Mark's Vicarage, 58 Forest Road, Bordon, Hants GU35 0BP* Bordon (01420) 477550

GOODWIN, Mrs Susan Elizabeth. b 51. Leeds Poly BSc74 Leeds Univ MSc76. St Jo Coll Dur 82. **dss** 84 **d** 87 **p** 94. Norton Woodseats St Chad *Sheff* 84-87; Par Dn 87; Chapl Scargill Ho 87-89; NSM W Burnley *Blackb* 89-90; NSM Headley All SS *Guildf* from 90; Past Asst Acorn Chr Healing Trust 91-93. *St Mark's Vicarage, 58 Forest Road, Bordon, Hants GU35 0BP* Bordon (01420) 477550

GOODWINS, Christopher William Hedley. b 36. St Jo Coll Cam BA58 MA62. Linc Th Coll 62. **d** 64 **p** 65. C Lowestoft Ch Ch *Nor* 64-69; V Tamerton Foliot *Ex* from 69; P-in-c Southway 78-82. *St Mary's Vicarage, Tamerton Foliot, Plymouth PL5 4NH* Plymouth (01752) 771033

GOODYER, Edward Arthur (Ted). b 42. Witwatersrand Univ BA63 SS Coll Cam BA67 MA70 Rhodes Univ MTh91. St Pet Coll Grahamstown 68. **d** 68 **p** 69. S Africa 69-92; Can Cape Town Cathl 80-84; R Alverstoke *Portsm* from 92. *The Rectory, Little Anglesey Road, Alverstoke, Gosport, Hants PO12 2JA* Gosport (01705) 581979

GOULD, Peter John. b 44. Lon Univ BD74. St Steph Ho Ox 67. **d** 70 **p** 71. C Chiswick St Nic w St Mary *Lon* 70-73; Chapl Asst R Masonic Hosp Lon 73-74; Chapl Asst Basingstoke Distr Hosp 74-77; Chapl from 80; Chapl R Marsden Hosp Lon and Surrey 77-80. *The North Hampshire Hospital, Aldermaston Road, Basingstoke, Hants RG24 9NA* Basingstoke (01256) 473202

GORDON, Canon Alexander Ronald. b 49. Nottm Univ BPharm71 Leeds Univ DipTh76. Coll of Resurr Mirfield 74. **d** 77 **p** 78. C Headingley *Ripon* 77-80; C Fareham SS Pet and Paul *Portsm* 80-83; V Cudworth *Wakef* 83-85; Hon C Tain *Mor* 85-87; P-in-c Lairg Miss from 87; P-in-c Brora from 88; P-in-c Dornoch from 88; Dioc Dir of Ords from 89; Can St Andr Cathl Inverness from 95. *The Grange, Lochside, Lairg, Sutherland IV27 4EG* Lairg (01549) 402295 or 402374

✠**GORDON, Rt Rev Archibald Ronald McDonald.** b 27. Ball Coll Ox BA50 MA52. Cuddesdon Coll 50. **d** 52 **p** 53 **c** 75. C Stepney St Dunstan and All SS *Lon* 52-55; Chapl Cuddesdon Coll 55-59; Lic to Offic *Ox* 57-59; V Birm St Pet *Birm* 59-68; Lect Qu Coll Birm 60-62; Can Res Birm Cathl *Birm* 67-71; V Ox St Mary V w St Cross and St Pet *Ox* 71-75; Bp Portsm 75-84; Bp at Lambeth (Hd of Staff) *Cant* 84-91; Asst Bp S'wark 84-91; Bp HM Forces 85-90; Can Res and Sub-Dean Ch Ch Ox from 91; Asst Bp Ox from 91. *Christ Church, Oxford OX1 1DP* Oxford (01865) 276278

GORDON, Bruce Harold Clark. b 40. Hull Univ DipMin87. St Jo Coll Dur 65. **d** 68 **p** 69. C Edin St Jas *Edin* 68-71; C Blackheath St Jo *S'wark* 71-74; R Duns *Edin* 74-90; R Lanark *Glas* from 90; R Douglas from 90. *The Rectory, 1 Cleghorn Road, Lanark ML11 7QT* Lanark (01555) 663065

GORDON, David John. b 65. Edin Th Coll CECM93. **d** 93 **p** 94. Chapl St Andr Cathl *Ab* from 93; NSM Aber St Andr from 93. *102 Bonnymuir Place, Aberdeen AB2 4NP* Aberdeen (01224) 635659

GORDON, Donald Ian (Don). b 30. Nottm Univ BA52 PhD64. Westcott Ho Cam 71. **d** 71 **p** 72. NSM Newport *Chelmsf* 71-75; NSM Creeksea w Althorne, Latchingdon and N Fambridge from 76. *Holden House, Steeple Road, Latchingdon, Chelmsford CM3 6JX* Maldon (01621) 740296

GORDON, Edward John. b 32. Univ of Wales BA52. St Mich Coll Llan 52. **d** 55 **p** 56. C Baglan *Llan* 55-61; C Newc 61-65; C Laleston w Tythegston 61-65; V Ynyshir 65-69; C Bramhall *Ches* 69-72; V Cheadle Hulme All SS 72-79; V Tranmere St Paul w St Luke 79-88; V Sandbach Heath from 88; Chapl Arclid Hosp from 90; RD Congleton *Ches* from 92. *The Heath Vicarage, School Lane, Sandbach, Cheshire CW11 0LS* Crewe (01270) 768826

GORDON, Ms Jennifer Anne. b 60. Hull Univ BSc81. S Dios Minl Tr Scheme 90. **d** 93 **p** 94. C Alverstoke *Portsm* from 93. *1 Newlands Avenue, Alverstoke, Gosport, Hants PO12 3QX* Gosport (01705) 522710

GORDON, John Michael. b 30. CITC. **d** 83 **p** 84. NSM Dub St Geo *D & G* 83-85; NSM Dub Irishtown w Donnybrook from 85. *Ferndale House, Rathmichael, Shankill, Co Dublin, Irish Republic* Dublin (1) 282-2421 Fax 282-2934

GORDON, Jonathan Andrew. b 61. Keele Univ BA83 Southn Univ BTh88. Sarum & Wells Th Coll. **d** 87 **p** 88. C Wallingford w Crowmarsh Gifford etc *Ox* 87-91; C Tilehurst St Mich 91-93; TV Stoke-upon-Trent *Lich* from 93. *All Saints Vicarage, 540 Leek Road, Hanley, Stoke-on-Trent ST1 3HH* Stoke-on-Trent (01782) 205713

GORDON, Canon Kenneth Davidson. b 35. Edin Univ MA57. Tyndale Hall Bris 58. **d** 60 **p** 61. C St Helens St Helen *Liv* 60-66; V Daubhill *Man* 66-71; R Bieldside *Ab* from 71; Can St Andr Cathl from 81. *St Devenick's Rectory, Bieldside, Aberdeen AB1 9AP* Aberdeen (01224) 861552

GORDON, Robert Andrew. b 42. Llan Dioc Tr Scheme 82. **d** 84 **p** 85. C Bargoed and Deri w Brithdir *Llan* 84-87; V Aberpergwm and Blaengwrach 87-94; R Johnston w Steynton *St D* from 94. *The Vicarage, Steynton, Milford Haven, Dyfed SA73 1AW* Milford Haven (01646) 692867

GORDON, Robert Douglas (Rob). b 57. Hull Univ BSc. Trin Coll Bris BA87. **d** 87 **p** 88. C Bridgwater St Fran *B & W* 87-90; C Street w Walton 90-93. *1 Newland Avenue, Alverstoke, Gosport, Hants PO12 3QX* Gosport (01705) 522710

GORDON, Robert John. b 56. Edin Univ MA81. Wycliffe Hall Ox 87. **d** 89 **p** 90. C Wilnecote *Lich* 89-91; C Bideford *Ex* 91-95; P-in-c Feniton, Buckerell and Escot from 95. *The Rectory, Feniton, Honiton, Devon EX14 0ED* Honiton (01404) 850253

GORDON, Thomas William. b 57. QUB BEd80 Univ of Ulster MA86 TCD BTh89 DPS. CITC 85. **d** 89 **p** 90. C Ballymacash *Conn* 89-91; Min Can Belf Cathl from 91; Chapl and Tutor CITC from 91. *The Chaplain's Residence, CITC, Braemor Park, Rathgar, Dublin 14, Irish Republic* Dublin (1) 492-3506 or 492-3590 Fax 492-3082

GORDON CLARK, Charles Philip. b 36. Worc Coll Ox BA59 MA61. Cuddesdon Coll 61. **d** 62 **p** 63. C Haslemere *Guildf* 62-65; Chapl Tonbridge Sch Kent 65-68; R Keston *Roch* 68-74; V Tunbridge Wells K Chas 74-86; Perm to Offic *S & B* from 86. *4 Danyrallt, Llaneglwys, Builth Wells, Powys LD2 3BJ* Builth Wells (01982) 560656

GORDON CLARK, John Vincent Michael. b 29. FCA DipRS. S'wark Ord Course 73. **d** 76 **p** 77. NSM Guildf H Trin w St Mary *Guildf* 76-81; NSM Albury w St Martha 81-92; Dioc Chapl to MU from 92; Perm to Offic from 92. *Hillfield, 8 Little Warren Close, Guildford GU4 8PW* Guildford (01483) 69027

GORDON-CUMMING, Henry Ian. b 28. Called to the Bar (Gray's Inn) 56. Oak Hill Th Coll 54. **d** 57 **p** 58. V Virginia Water *Guildf* 68-78; R Busbridge 78-87; V Lynch w Iping Marsh and Milland *Chich* 87-94; rtd 94. *Bay Cottage, Brookside, Runcton, Chichester, W Sussex PO20 6PX* Chichester (01243) 783395

GORDON-KERR, Canon Dr Francis Alexander. b 39. Dur Univ BA64 MA67 Hull Univ PhD81 DipEd. Wycliffe Hall Ox 65. **d** 67 **p** 68. C Heworth St Mary *Dur* 67-70; Chapl Newc Poly *Newc* 70-75; Chapl Hull Univ *York* 75-82; V Welton w Melton 82-92; Clergy Tr Officer E Riding 82-92; AD W Hull from 87; RD Hull from 89; Can and Preb York Minster from 89; V Anlaby St Pet from 92. *The Vicarage, Church Street, Anlaby, Hull HU10 7DG* Hull (01482) 653024

GORDON-TAYLOR, Benjamin Nicholas. b 69. St Jo Coll Dur BA90 Leeds Univ BA94 St Jo Coll Dur MA90. Coll of Resurr Mirfield 92. **d** 95. C Launceston *Truro* from 95. *11 Summerhill*

Road, Launceston, Cornwall PL15 7DU Launceston (01566) 776398

GORE, Canon John Charles. b 29. Leeds Univ BA52. Coll of Resurr Mirfield 52. **d** 54 **p** 55. Zambia 64-75; Can Lusaka 70-75; R Elland *Wakef* 75-84; TR 84-86; Brighouse and Elland 77-86; V Wembley Park St Aug *Lon* 86-95; P-in-c Tokyngton St Mich 89-90; AD Brent 90-95; rtd 95. *The Vicarage, 13 Forty Avenue, Wembley, Middx HA9 8JL* 0181-904 4089

GORE, Canon John Harrington. b 24. Em Coll Cam BA49 MA52. Westcott Ho Cam 49. **d** 51 **p** 52. R Deal St Leon *Cant* 67-75; RD Sandwich 70-78; P-in-c Sholden 74-75; R Deal St Leon w Sholden 75-80; R Southchurch H Trin *Chelmsf* 80-90; RD Southend-on-Sea 84-89; Hon Can Chelmsf Cathl 86-90; rtd 90; Perm to Offic *St E* from 90. *8 De Burgh Place, Clare, Suffolk CO10 8QL* Clare (01787) 278558

GORHAM, Andrew Arthur. b 51. Bris Univ BA73 Birm Univ DipTh78 MA87. Qu Coll Birm 77. **d** 79 **p** 80. C Plaistow St Mary *Roch* 79-82; Chapl Lanchester Poly *Cov* 82-87; TV Warw from 87. *24 Greenway, Warwick CV34 5SG*

GORHAM, Ms Karen Marisa. b 64. Trin Coll Bris BA95. **d** 95. C Northallerton w Kirby Sigston *York* from 95. *1 Ashlands Road, Northallerton, N Yorkshire DL6 1HA* Northallerton (01609) 777385

GORICK, David Charles. b 32. Reading Univ BA55 Nottm Univ DipEd72. E Midl Min Tr Course 81. **d** 84 **p** 85. NSM W Bridgford *S'well* 84-89; P-in-c Gotham from 89; P-in-c Kingston and Ratcliffe-on-Soar from 89. *The New Rectory, 39 Leake Road, Gotham, Notts NG11 0JL* Nottingham (0115) 983 0608

GORICK, Janet Margaret. dss 86 **d** 87 **p** 94. Hon Par Dn W Bridgford *S'well* 87-95; NSM Gotham from 95; NSM Barton in Fabis from 95; NSM Kingston and Ratcliffe-on-Soar from 95; NSM Thrumpton from 95. *The New Rectory, 39 Leake Road, Gotham, Nottingham NG11 0JL* Nottingham (0115) 983 0608

GORICK, Martin Charles William. b 62. Selw Coll Cam BA84 MA88. Ripon Coll Cuddesdon 85. **d** 87 **p** 88. C Birtley *Dur* 87-91; Bp's Dom Chapl *Ox* 91-94; V Smethwick *Birm* from 94. *The Vicarage, 93A Church Road, Smethwick, Warley, W Midlands B67 6EE* 0121-558 1763

GORIN, Walter. b 10. Lon Univ BA32 AKC32. Lich Th Coll 39. **d** 41 **p** 43. R Gt and Lt Saxham w Westley *St E* 69-79; rtd 79; Perm to Offic *St E* from 79. *16 Samuel Street Walk, Bury St Edmunds, Suffolk IP33 2PQ* Bury St Edmunds (01284) 702110

GORING, Charles Robert (Charlie). b 60. Linc Th Coll CMM93. **d** 93 **p** 94. C Thornbury *Glouc* from 93. *50 Park Road, Thornbury, Bristol BS12 1HR* Thornbury (01454) 412656

GORNALL, William Brian. b 36. OStJ SRN58. Ely Th Coll 61. **d** 64 **p** 65. P-in-c Blackb St Pet w All SS *Blackb* 69-75; Hon Chapl and Lect Blackb Coll of Tech 69-75; V Blackb St Pet w All SS 75-79; V Blackpool St Mich 79-84; V Torrisholme 84-91; C Greenhill *Sheff* 91-94; rtd 94. *34 Kemple View, Clitheroe, Lancs BB7 2QD* Clitheroe (01200) 27061

GORRIE, Richard Bingham. b 27. Univ Coll Ox BA49 MA51. Ridley Hall Cam 49. **d** 51 **p** 52. Scripture Union Rep (Scotland) 56-92; Chapl Fettes Coll Edin 60-74; Dir Inter-Sch Chr Fellowship (Scotland) 74-80; rtd 92; Perm to Offic *Glas* from 92. *5 Ashlea Drive, Giffnock, Glasgow G46 6BX* 0141-637 5946

GORRINGE, Timothy Jervis. b 46. St Edm Hall Ox BA69 MPhil75. Sarum Th Coll 69. **d** 72 **p** 73. C Chapel Allerton *Ripon* 72-75; C Ox St Mary V w St Cross and St Pet *Ox* 76-78; India 79-86; Chapl St Jo Coll Ox from 86. *St John's College, Oxford OX1 3JP* Oxford (01865) 277351

GORTON, Anthony David Trevor. b 39. Lon Univ BSc65. Oak Hill Th Coll 78. **d** 81 **p** 82. Hon C Colney Heath St Mark *St Alb* from 81. *Waterdell, Lane End, Hatfield, Herts AL10 9DU* Hatfield (01707) 263605

GORTON, Ian Charles Johnson. b 62. Bp Otter Coll BA84 Sarum & Wells Th Coll 86. **d** 89 **p** 90. C Wythenshawe Wm Temple Ch *Man* 89-92; C Man Apostles w Miles Platting 92-95; P-in-c Abbey Hey from 95. *St George's Rectory, 10 Redacre Road, Abbey Hey, Manchester M18 8RD* 0161-223 1624

GOSDEN, Timothy John. b 50. Open Univ BA86. Chich Th Coll 74. **d** 77 **p** 78. C Cant All SS *Cant* 77-81; Asst Chapl Loughb Univ *Leic* 81-85; Lic to Offic *Cant* 85-87; Chapl Ch Ch Coll Cant 85-87; Chapl (Sen) Hull Univ *York* 87-94; V Taunton Lyngford *B & W* from 94. *St Peter's Vicarage, Eastwick Road, Taunton, Somerset TA2 7HD* Taunton (01823) 275085

GOSHAI, Miss Veja Helena. b 32. SRN57 SCM59 MTD66. Trin Coll Bris 75. **d** 87 **p** 94. Asst Chapl St Bart Hosp Lon 87-95; rtd 91. *7 Freemens Houses, Ferndale Road, London SW9 8AN*

GOSLING, Dr David Lagourie. b 39. MInstP69 CPhys84 Man Univ MSc63 Fitzw Coll Cam MA69 Lanc Univ PhD74.

Ridley Hall Cam 63. **d** 73 **p** 74. Hon C Lanc St Mary *Blackb* 73-74; Hon C Kingston upon Hull St Matt w St Barn *York* 74-77; Hon C Cottingham 78-83; Lic to Offic *Eur* 83-84 and 88-94; Chapl Geneva 84-88; C Cam Gt St Mary w St Mich *Ely* from 89; C Dry Drayton 90-94; India from 95. *Great St Mary's, Cambridge CB2 3PQ, or St Stephen's College, University of Delhi, Delhi 110007, India* Cambridge (01223) 350914 Fax Delhi (11) 725 7965

GOSLING, James Albert. b 41. Oak Hill Th Coll. **d** 84 **p** 85. NSM Victoria Docks St Luke *Chelmsf* from 84. *1 Gardner Road, London E13 8LN* 0171-476 4564

GOSLING, John William Fraser. b 34. St Jo Coll Dur BA58 DipTh60 MA71 Ex Univ PhD78. Cranmer Hall Dur 58. **d** 60 **p** 61. C Plympton St Mary *Ex* 60-68; V Newport 68-78; Org Sec (Dios St Alb and Ox) CECS 78-82; C Stratford sub Castle *Sarum* 83-86; Adv on Cont Minl Educn 83-86; Perm to Offic 86-91; C Swindon Ch Ch *Bris* from 91. *42 Henrietta Court, Marlborough Road, Swindon SN3 1QJ* Swindon (01793) 619782

GOSNELL, Nicholas. b 58. SRN81 Southn Univ BTh91 K Coll Lon MA94. Chich Th Coll 85. **d** 88 **p** 89. C Prestbury *Glouc* 88-91; CF(V) from 89; C Teddington SS Pet and Paul and Fulwell *Lon* 91-94; Chapl and Hd of Div St Jo Sch Leatherhead from 94. *4 Linden Pit Path, Leatherhead, Surrey KT22 7JD* Leatherhead (01372) 361665

GOSNEY, Jeanette Margaret. b 58. Bath Univ BA81 Nottm Univ PGCE82. St Jo Coll Nottm BTh93 MPhil95. **d** 95. C Ipswich St Marg *St E* from 95. *44 Corder Road, Ipswich IP4 2XD* Ipswich (01437) 231137

GOSS, Arthur John Knill. b 10. St Jo Coll Dur BA34 MA37 DipTh37. **d** 35 **p** 36. V Worthing Ch Ch *Chich* 66-71; R Buxted St Marg 71-76; rtd 76. *9 By Sunte, Lindfield, W Sussex RH16 2DG* Haywards Heath (01444) 414471

GOSS, David James. b 52. Nottm Univ BCombStuds. Linc Th Coll. **d** 83 **p** 84. C Wood Green St Mich w Bounds Green St Gabr etc *Lon* 83-86; TV Gleadless Valley *Sheff* 86-89; TR 89-95; V Wheatley Hills from 95. *The Vicarage, Central Boulevard, Doncaster, S Yorkshire DN2 5PE* Doncaster (01302) 342047

GOSS, Kevin Ian. b 56. LRAM75 LTCL76 GRSM77 LGSM80 Hughes Hall Cam PGCE78. S Dios Minl Tr Scheme 89. **d** 92 **p** 93. NSM Ardingly *Chich* from 92; Asst Chapl Ardingly Coll Haywards Heath from 92. *11 Gordon Close, Haywards Heath, W Sussex RH16 1ER* Haywards Heath (01444) 417187

GOSS, Michael John. b 37. Chich Th Coll 62. **d** 65 **p** 66. C Angell Town St Jo *S'wark* 65-68; C Catford St Laur 68-71; P-in-c Lewisham St Swithun 71-81; V Redhill St Jo 81-88; V Dudley St Thos and St Luke *Worc* from 88. *The Vicarage, King Street, Dudley, W Midlands DY2 8QB* Dudley (01384) 252015

GOSS, Very Rev Thomas Ashworth. b 12. St Andr Univ MA36. Ridley Hall Cam 35. **d** 37 **p** 38. R Jersey St Sav *Win* 67-71; Dean Jersey 71-85; Hon Can Win Cathl 71-85; R Jersey St Helier 71-85; rtd 85. *Les Pignons, Mont de la Rosiere, Jersey, Channel Islands JE2 6RG* Jersey (01534) 861433

GOSSWINN, Nicholas Simon. b 50. Birm Poly FGA80. St D Coll Lamp DipTh73. **d** 73 **p** 77. C Abergavenny St Mary *Mon* 73-74; C-in-c Bassaleg 74-80; TV Barrow St Geo w St Luke *Carl* 81-87; C Usworth *Dur* 89-90; TV from 90. *Usworth Vicarage, 14 Prestwick Close, Washington, Tyne & Wear NE37 2LP* 0191-415 0843

GOSWELL, Geoffrey. b 34. SS Paul & Mary Coll Cheltenham CertEd68. Glouc Th Course 70. **d** 71 **p** 72. C Cheltenham Em *Glouc* 71-73; C Lydney w Aylburton 73-76; P-in-c Falfield w Rockhampton 76-79; Chapl HM Det Cen Eastwood Park 76-79; Area Sec CMS (Dios Linc and Pet) 79-86; (Dio Ely) 79-81; CMS Dep Regional Sec (UK) from 86; P-in-c Orton Waterville *Ely* from 90. *The Rectory, 67 Church Drive, Orton Waterville, Peterborough PE2 5HE* Peterborough (01733) 238877

GOTELEE, Peter Douglas. b 28. K Coll Lon 50. **d** 54 **p** 55. P-in-c Badshot Lea CD *Guildf* 65-75; P-in-c Bisley 75-76; V W End 75-76; R Bisley and W End 76-85; V Yarcombe w Membury and Upottery *Ex* 85-93; P-in-c Cotleigh 85-93; rtd 93. *3 Sharpiter Close, Paignton, Devon TQ3 1AR* Paignton (01803) 559150

GOTT, Joseph Desmond. b 26. Ch Ch Ox BA47 MA51 St Chad's Coll Dur DipTh52. **d** 52 **p** 53. V Down Ampney *Glouc* 66-72; PC Poulton 66-69; V 69-72; V Cheltenham St Steph 72-89; rtd 89. *3 Avonmore, 24 Granville Road, Eastbourne, E Sussex BH20 7HA* Eastbourne (01323) 736222

GOTT, Stephen. b 61. St Jo Coll Nottm DipThMin94. **d** 94 **p** 95. C Mt Pellon *Wakef* from 94. *Woodburn Cottage, Albert Road, Pellon, Halifax, W Yorkshire HX2 0BY* Halifax (01422) 369982

GOUGE, Canon Frank. b 16. St Pet Hall Ox BA38 MA45. Wycliffe Hall Ox 38. **d** 40 **p** 41. V Hall Green Ascension *Birm* 67-84; RD Solihull 68-79; Hon Can Birm Cathl 73-84; rtd 84; Perm to Offic *Cov* from 84. *39 Campden Road, Shipston-on-Stour, Warks CV36 4DH* Shipston-on-Stour (01608) 661789

GOUGH, Andrew Stephen. b 60. Sarum & Wells Th Coll 83. **d** 86 **p** 87. C St Leonards Ch Ch and St Mary *Chich* 86-88; C Broseley w Benthall *Heref* 88-90; V Ketley and Oakengates *Lich* 90-93; TV Bickleigh (Plymouth) *Ex* 93; TV Bickleigh (Roborough) and Shaugh Prior 94; P-in-c St Day *Truro* from 94. *The Vicarage, St Day, Redruth, Cornwall TR16 5LD* St Day (01209) 820275

GOUGH, Andrew Walter. b 55. Bris Univ BA78. Trin Coll Bris ADMT92. **d** 92 **p** 93. C Mossley Hill St Matt and St Jas *Liv* 92-94; C Wavertree H Trin from 94. *66 Grant Avenue, Wavertree, Liverpool L15 5AY* 0151-733 6733

GOUGH, Dr Anthony Walter. b 31. Lon Univ DipTh68 Leic Univ MA76. Chicago Th Sem DMin81 Oak Hill Th Coll 57. **d** 60 **p** 61. C Southsea St Simon *Portsm* 60-64; R Peldon *Chelmsf* 64-71; V Rothley *Leic* 71-80; USA 80-81; Chapl St Jo Hosp Aylesbury 81-82; Perm to Offic *Leic* from 82. *410 Hinckley Road, Leicester LE3 0WA* Leicester (0116) 285 4284

GOUGH, Colin Richard. b 47. St Chad's Coll Dur BA69. Cuddesdon Coll 73. **d** 75 **p** 76. C Lich St Chad *Lich* 75-78; C Codsall 78-84; V Wednesbury St Paul Wood Green 84-92; TR Tettenhall Wood from 92. *Christ Church Rectory, 7 Broxwood Park, Tettenhall Wood, Wolverhampton WV6 8LZ* Wolverhampton (01902) 751116

GOUGH, David Norman. b 42. Oak Hill Th Coll 70. **d** 70 **p** 71. C Penn Fields *Lich* 70-73; C Stapenhill w Cauldwell *Derby* 73-77; V Heath 77-86; P-in-c Derby St Chad from 86. *81 Palmerston Street, Derby DE23 6PF* Derby (01332) 760846

GOUGH, Derek William. b 31. Pemb Coll Cam BA55 MA59. St Steph Ho Ox 55. **d** 57 **p** 58. C E Finchley All SS *Lon* 57-60; C Roxbourne St Andr 60-66; V Edmonton St Mary w St Jo from 66. *St John's Vicarage, Dysons Road, London N18 2DS* 0181-807 2767

GOUGH, Canon Ernest Hubert. b 31. TCD BA53 MA57. **d** 54 **p** 55. C Glenavy *Conn* 54-57; C Lisburn Ch Ch 57-61; P-in-c Belf St Ninian 61-62; I 62-71; I Belf St Bart 71-85; I Templepatrick w Donegore from 85; Can Conn Cathl from 91. *The Vicarage, 926 Antrim Road, Templepatrick, Ballyclare, Co Antrim BT39 0AT* Templepatrick (01849) 432300

GOUGH, Frank Peter. b 32. Lon Coll of Div 66. **d** 68 **p** 69. C Weymouth St Mary *Sarum* 68-70; C Attenborough w Chilwell *S'well* 70-73; R Barrow *Ches* 73-77; P-in-c Summerstown *S'wark* 77-88; RD Tooting 80-88; Dioc Past Sec 88-93; Chapl and Tutor Whittington Coll Felbridge from 93. *32 Whittington College, London Road, Felbridge, East Grinstead, W Sussex RH19 2QU* East Grinstead (01342) 322790

✠GOUGH, Rt Rev Hugh Rowlands. b 05. CMG55 OBE42 TD50. Trin Coll Cam BA27 MA31. Lambeth DD59 ACT Hon ThD59 Wycliffe Coll Toronto Hon DD63 Lon Coll of Div 28. **d** 28 **p** 29 **c** 48. C Islington St Mary *Lon* 28-31; V 46-48; R Walcot *B & W* 31-34; V Carlisle St Jas 34-39; V Bayswater *Lon* 39-46; CF (TA) 39-45; RD Islington *Lon* 46-48; Preb St Paul's Cathl 48; Adn W Ham *Chelmsf* 48-58; Suff Bp Barking 48-58; Abp Sydney 58-66; Primate of Australia 59-66; R Freshford w Limpley Stoke *B & W* 67-72; rtd 72. *Forge House, Over Wallop, Stockbridge, Hants SO20 8JF* Andover (01264) 781315

GOUGH, Jonathan Robin Blanning. b 62. Univ of Wales (Lamp) BA83. St Steph Ho Ox 83. **d** 85 **p** 86. C Braunton *Ex* 85-86; C Matson *Glouc* 86-89; CF from 89. *c/o MOD (Army), Bagshot Park, Bagshot, Surrey GU19 5PL* Bagshot (01276) 471717 Fax 412834

GOUGH, Martyn John. b 66. Univ of Wales (Cardiff) 84. St Steph Ho Ox 88. **d** 90 **p** 91. C Port Talbot St Theodore *Llan* 90-92; C Roath St Marg 92-94; Asst Chapl Milan w Genoa and Varese *Eur* from 95. *The European School, Varese, Fermo Pasta 6855, Stabio, Switzerland*

GOUGH, Robert (Bob). b 50. S'wark Ord Course 79. **d** 82 **p** 83. C Heston *Lon* 82-83; C Feltham 83-86; TV Hemel Hempstead *St Alb* 86-90; NSM Kingston All SS w St Jo *S'wark* 90-91; Perm to Offic 91-94. *Pen y Gaer Uchaf, Llanfihangel Glyn Myfr, Corwen, Clwyd LL21 9UH* Corwen (01490) 420791

GOUGH, Stephen William Cyprian. b 50. Alberta Univ BSc71. Cuddesdon Coll BA80. **d** 79 **p** 80. C Walton St Mary *Liv* 79-83; V New Springs 83-87; V Childwall St Dav from 87. *St David's Vicarage, Rocky Lane, Liverpool L16 1JA* 0151-722 4549

GOULD, Alan Charles. b 26. Lon Univ DipTh53. **d** 62 **p** 63. V Audlem and Burleydam *Ches* 67-80; P-in-c Coreley w Doddington *Heref* 80-83; V Knowbury 80-83; P-in-c Berrington and Betton Strange 83-91; P-in-c Cound 83-91; rtd 91. *32 Mytton Oak Road, Shrewsbury SY3 8UD* Shrewsbury (01743) 244820

GOULD, Preb Douglas Walter. b 35. St Jo Coll Cam BA59 MA63. Ridley Hall Cam 59. **d** 61 **p** 62. C Clifton *York* 61-64; C Bridgnorth w Tasley *Heref* 64-67; C Astley Abbotts w Linley 64-67; R Acton Burnell w Pitchford 67-73; P-in-c Cound

68-73; Asst Dioc Youth Officer 68-73; P-in-c Frodesley 69-73; V Bromyard from 73; RD Bromyard from 73; Chapl Bromyard Hosp from 73; P-in-c Ocle Pychard *Heref* 76-88; P-in-c Ullingswick 76-88; P-in-c Stoke Lacy, Moreton Jeffries w Much Cowarne etc 76-83; Preb Heref Cathl from 83. *The Vicarage, 28 Church Lane, Bromyard, Herefordshire HR7 4DZ* Bromyard (01885) 482438

GOULD, Gerald. b 37. S Dios Minl Tr Scheme 84. **d** 86 **p** 87. C Hedge End *Win* 86-89; V St Goran w St Mich Caerhays *Truro* 89-93; P-in-c Crook Peak *B & W* 93-94; R from 94. *The Rectory, Sparrow Hill Way, Weare, Axbridge, Somerset BS26 2LE* Axbridge (01934) 733140

GOULD, Canon Jack. b 15. **d** 45 **p** 47. V Kingswear *Ex* 71-85; rtd 85; Perm to Offic *Ex* from 85. *140 Northfields Lane, Brixham, Devon TQ5 8RH* Brixham (01803) 855397

GOULD, Ms Jan. b 63. Westcott Ho Cam 92. **d** 95. C Pet St Mary *Pet* from 95. *19 Danes Close, Peterborough PE1 5LJ* Peterborough (01733) 53526

GOULD, John Barry. b 38. MICE68. S'wark Ord Course 77. **d** 77 **p** 78. C Streatham St Leon *S'wark* 77-80; V Upper Tooting H Trin 80-87; P-in-c Brockham Green 87-90; P-in-c Betchworth 87-95; P-in-c Buckland 87-95; C-in-c Roundshaw CD from 95. *The Vicarage, Old Reigate Road, Betchworth, Surrey RH3 7DE* Betchworth (01737) 842102

GOULD, Peter Richard. b 34. Univ of Wales BA57. Qu Coll Birm DipTh62. **d** 62 **p** 63. C Rothwell *Ripon* 62-68; V Allerton Bywater 68-73; Lic to Offic *S'well* 73-76; Chapl Lic Victuallers' Sch Ascot 76-93; V Aberavon H Trin *Llan* from 93. *Holy Trinity Vicarage, Fairway, Sandfields, Port Talbot, M Glam SA12 7HG* Port Talbot (01639) 884409

GOULD, Dr Robert Ozburn. b 38. Williams Coll Mass BA59 St Andr Univ PhD63. **d** 78 **p** 83. NSM Edin St Columba *Edin* 78-80; TV from 83; Hon Dioc Supernumerary 80-83. *33 Charterhall Road, Edinburgh EH9 3HS* 0131-667 7230

GOULD, Susan Judith. *See* MURRAY, Mrs Susan Judith

GOULDING, Charles John. b 18. Sarum Th Coll 56. **d** 58 **p** 59. V Ardleigh *Chelmsf* 63-72; V Shrub End 72-84; RD Colchester 81-84; rtd 84; Hon C Fovant, Sutton Mandeville and Teffont Evias etc *Sarum* 84-86; Hon C Mayfield *Chich* 86-89. *Flat 3, 3 Moat Croft Road, Eastbourne, E Sussex BN21 1ND* Eastbourne (01323) 720208

GOULDING, Edward William. b 23. St Aid Birkenhead 54. **d** 56 **p** 57. Chapl HM Pris Birm 69-72; V Gt Harwood St Bart *Blackb* 73-76; Lic to Offic 76-78; V Wray w Tatham Fells 78-87; rtd 88. *2 Crag Bank Road, Carnforth, Lancs LA5 9EG* Carnforth (01524) 735026

GOULDING, John Gilbert. b 29. Univ Coll Dur BA54 MA59. **d** 88 **p** 89. NSM Kemsing w Woodlands *Roch* from 88; Hon Nat Moderator for Reader Tr ACCM 90-91; ABM 91-92; Hon C Sevenoaks St Luke CD 91-93. *Springwood, 50 Copperfields, Kemsing, Sevenoaks, Kent TN15 6QG* Sevenoaks (01732) 762558

GOULDSTONE, Preb Timothy Maxwell. b 46. Ex Univ BSc68 MSc76. Trin Coll Bris 76. **d** 78 **p** 79. C Ware Ch Ch *St Alb* 78-81; P-in-c Ansley *Cov* 81-82; V 82-85; V St Keverne *Truro* from 85; Preb St Endellion from 90. *The Rectory, Tresillian, Truro, Cornwall TR2 4AA* Tresillian (01872) 520431

GOULSTONE, Very Rev Thomas Richard Kerry. b 36. Univ of Wales (Lamp) BA57. St Mich Coll Llan 57. **d** 59 **p** 60. C Llanbadarn Fawr *St D* 59-61; C Carmarthen St Pet 61-64; V 84-93; V Whitchurch w Solva and St Elvis 64-67; V Gors-las 67-76; V Burry Port and Pwll 76-84; Chapl W Wales Gen Hosp Carmarthen 84-93; Can St D Cathl *St D* 86-93; Hon Can St D Cathl from 93; RD Carmarthen 88-92; Adn Carmarthen 91-93; Dean and Lib St As Cathl *St As* from 93. *The Deanery, St Asaph, Clwyd LL17 0RL* St Asaph (01745) 583597

GOUNDRY, Canon Ralph Walter. b 31. St Chad's Coll Dur BA56 DipTh58. **d** 58 **p** 59. C Harton Colliery *Dur* 58-62; Prec Newc Cathl *Newc* 62-65; V Seghill 65-72; V Long Benton from 72; Hon Can Newc Cathl from 94. *The Vicarage, 3 Station Road, Benton, Newcastle upon Tyne NE12 8AN* 0191-266 2015

GOURLEY, William Robert Joseph. b 48. K Coll Lon BD74. CITC 68. **d** 75 **p** 76. C Newtownards *D & D* 75-78; I Currin w Drum and Newbliss *Clogh* 78-81; I Dub St Geo and St Thos, Finglas and Free Ch *D & G* 81-88; RD St Mary 86-88; I Dub Zion Ch from 88. *The Rectory, 18 Bushy Park Road, Rathgar, Dublin 6, Irish Republic* Dublin (1) 492-2365

GOVER, Michael Sydney Richard. b 41. Culham Coll Ox BA63. Chich Th Coll 68. **d** 71 **p** 72. C Ryde All SS *Portsm* 71-75; C Waterlooville 75-83; Perm to Offic 83-91; NSM Portsea Ascension from 91. *333 Twyford Avenue, Portsmouth PO2 8PE* Portsmouth (01705) 671161

GOW, Iain Douglas. b 60. Denver Univ USA BA83 MIM85. Trin Coll Bris DipHE92 MA94. **d** 94 **p** 95. C Kenilworth St Jo *Cov* from 94. *14 Siddeley Avenue, Kenilworth, Warks CV8 1EW* Kenilworth (01926) 59992

GOW, Peter Draffin. b 52. Bede Coll Dur BEd76. St Jo Coll Nottm 83. **d** 85. C Kingston Hill St Paul *S'wark* 85-86; rtd 86. *33 Canbury Avenue, Kingston upon Thames, Surrey KT2 6JP* 0181-549 7942

GOW, Canon William Connell. b 09. Dur Univ LTh36. Edin Th Coll 34. **d** 36 **p** 37. R Dingwall *Mor* 40-77; R Strathpeffer 40-77; Dean Mor 60-77; rtd 77; Hon Can St Andr Cathl Inverness *Mor* from 77. *14 Mackenzie Place, Maryburgh, Ross-shire IV7 8DY* Dingwall (01349) 61832

GOWDEY, Canon Alan Lawrence. b 25. Trin Coll Toronto BA50 Ridley Hall Cam. **d** 52 **p** 53. Ind Chapl *Roch* 62-75; Hon C Gravesend St Geo 66-75; Chapl Heathrow Airport *Lon* 75-82; Hon Can Gib Cathl *Eur* 82-84; Chapl Costa Blanca 82-85; Can Gib Cathl 84-86; Ind Chapl *Roch* 85-86; C Bromley SS Pet and Paul 87-88; rtd 88. *25 Osprey House, Sillwood Place, Brighton BN1 2ND* Brighton (01273) 749459

GOWDEY, Michael Cragg. b 32. Or Coll Ox BA56 MA58 Keele Univ CertEd73. Qu Coll Birm DipTh57. **d** 58 **p** 59. C Ashbourne w Mapleton and Clifton *Derby* 58-63; V Chellaston 63-69; Asst Chapl Ellesmere Coll Shropshire 69-74; Chapl Trent Coll Nottm 74-81; Educn Chapl *Worc* from 81; Chapl K Edw Sixth Form Coll Worcs from 81. *47 Bournheath Road, Fairfield, Bromsgrove, Worcs B61 9HW* Bromsgrove (01527) 570564

GOWEN, John Frank. b 30. **d** 87 **p** 89. NSM Lecale Gp *D & D* 87-91; NSM Cregagh 87-91; Lic to Offic from 91. *36 Downshire Road, Belfast BT6 9JL* Belfast (01232) 701640

GOWER, Christopher Raymond. b 45. FRSA Nottm Univ BA73. St Jo Coll Nottm 70. **d** 73 **p** 74. C Hounslow H Trin *Lon* 73-76; Hon C N Greenford All Hallows 76-77; P-in-c Willesden Green St Gabr 77-82; P-in-c Brondesbury St Anne w Kilburn H Trin 81-82; Perm to Offic 82-84; P-in-c Yiewsley from 84. *The Vicarage, 93 High Street, Yiewsley, Middx UB7 7QH* Uxbridge (01895) 442093

GOWER, Denys Victor. b 33. Cant Sch of Min 85. **d** 87 **p** 88. NSM Gillingham H Trin *Roch* 87-91; NSM Gillingham St Aug 89-91; C Perry Street 91-93; P-in-c Wateringbury w Teston and W Farleigh from 93. *The Rectory, Church Road, Teston, Maidstone, Kent ME18 5AJ* Maidstone (01622) 812494

GOWER, Nigel Plested. b 37. SS Coll Cam BA62 MA65 Lon Univ PGCE68. Ridley Hall Cam 61. **d** 63 **p** 64. C Walthamstow St Jo *Chelmsf* 63-66; CMS 67-78; Nigeria 67-78; P-in-c Loscoe *Derby* 78-79; V 79-88; RD Heanor 84-88; R Bamford from 88; Dioc World Development Officer from 90. *The Rectory, Bamford, Sheffield S30 2AY* Hope Valley (01433) 651375

GOWER, Miss Patricia Ann. b 44. Wilson Carlile Coll IDC79 Sarum & Wells Th Coll 88. **d** 88 **p** 94. Chapl Bris Univ *Bris* 88-91; Par Dn Clifton St Paul 88-91; Par Dn Spondon *Derby* 91-94; C 94-95. *The Rectory, Sudbury, Derby DE6 5HS* Derby (01283) 585302

GOWER, Canon Peter Charles Gwynne. b 24. St D Coll Lamp 61. **d** 63 **p** 64. CF (TAVR) 67-72; TV Cwmbran *Mon* 69-75; V Raglan and Llandenny w Llansoy 75-90; V Raglan w Llandenny and Bryngwyn 85-90; Can St Woolos Cathl 84-90; RD Raglan-Usk 84-90; rtd 90; Lic to Offic *Mon* from 90. *19 Manor Court, Baron Street, Usk, Gwent NP5 1DQ* Usk (01291) 673061

GOWER, Archdeacon of. *See* PIERCE, Ven Anthony Edward

GOWING, Ven Frederick William. b 18. OBE85. TCD BA40. CITC 41. **d** 41 **p** 42. I Mullavilly *Arm* 56-84; Adn Arm 79-84; rtd 84. *40 Old Rectory Park, Portadown, Craigavon, Co Armagh BT62 3QH* Portadown (01762) 330933

GOWING, John Ellis. b 18. Magd Coll Ox BA40 MA45. Westcott Ho Cam 40. **d** 41 **p** 42. C-in-c N Aldrington St Rich CD *Chich* 51-53; Hon C Somers Town St Mary *Lon* 53-73; Lic to Offic 73-79; Perm to Offic *Ox* from 79; rtd 83. *7 Thurne Close, Newport Pagnell, Bucks MK16 9DY* Newport Pagnell (01908) 611500

GOYMOUR, Michael Edwyn. b 29. Selw Coll Cam BA51 McGill Univ Montreal BD53. Montreal Dioc Th Coll 51 Wells Th Coll 53. **d** 53 **p** 54. R Gamlingay *Ely* 60-68; rtd 92. *56 Church Drive, Orton Waterville, Peterborough PE2 5HE* Peterborough (01733) 231535

GRACE, Juliet Christine. b 38. Cam Inst of Educn 60. S Dios Minl Tr Scheme 84. **d** 87 **p** 94. NSM Petersfield *Portsm* 87-93; NSM Steep and Froxfield w Privett from 93; Community Mental Health Chapl Petersfield from 93. *33 Woodbury Avenue, Petersfield, Hants GU32 2ED* Petersfield (01730) 262335

GRACE, Kenneth. b 24. Leeds Univ BA49. Wycliffe Hall Ox 62. **d** 63 **p** 64. R Thwing *York* 66-70; V Wold Newton 66-70; Chapl St Andr Sch Worthing 70-76; R Berwick w Selmeston and Alciston *Chich* 76-81; P-in-c Kingston Buci 81-85; R Westbourne 85-90; rtd 90. *17 Beech Road, Findon, Worthing, W Sussex BN14 0UR* Findon (01903) 877021

GRACE, Richard Maurice. b 29. St Chad's Coll Dur BA53. Chich Th Coll 53. **d** 55 **p** 56. V W Bromwich St Fran *Lich* 62-78; P-in-c Salt 78-84; P-in-c Sandon w Burston 82-84; V Salt and Sandon w Burston 84-93; rtd 94. *Little Owls, 1 Trinity Close, Crewe CW2 8FD* Crewe (01270) 662221

GRACE, Wilfrid Windsor. b 15. ACA39 FCA60. Westcott Ho Cam 52. **d** 53 **p** 54. V Minety w Oaksey *Bris* 57-71; V Oldland 71-76; P-in-c Abbots Leigh w Leigh Woods 76; V 76-80; Chapl Ham Green Hosp 79-87; rtd 80; Perm to Offic *B & W* from 81; Hon Chapl Cheshire Home Axbridge from 81. *Hurn Mead, 71 Woodborough Road, Winscombe, Avon BS25 1BA* Winscombe (01934) 843362

GRACIE, Anthony Johnstone. b 25. Ch Coll Cam BA48 MA51. Linc Th Coll 57. **d** 59 **p** 60. R Lyndon w Manton and Martinsthorpe *Pet* 62-76; R N Luffenham 66-76; V Odiham w S Warnborough *Win* 76; V Odiham w S Warnborough and Long Sutton 76-85; Perm to Offic *Bris* 85-88; rtd 88. *53 Ashford Road, Swindon SN1 3NS* Swindon (01793) 695235

GRACIE, Bryan John. b 45. Open Univ BA81. AKC67. **d** 68 **p** 69. C Whipton *Ex* 68-72; Chapl St Jo Sch Tiffield Northants 72-73; Chapl HM Borstal Stoke Heath 74-78; Asst Chapl HM Pris Liv 74; Chapl HM Youth Cust Cen Feltham 78-85; Chapl HM Pris Birm from 85. *HM Prison, Winson Green Road, Birmingham B18 4AS* 0121-554 3838 Fax 554 7990

GRAEBE, Canon Denys Redford. b 26. Qu Coll Cam BA48 MA51. Westcott Ho Cam 50. **d** 51 **p** 52. R Gt Parndon *Chelmsf* 57-72; V Norton *St Alb* 72-83; R Kimpton w Ayot St Lawrence 83-92; RD Wheathampstead 87-92; Hon Can St Alb Abbey 90-92; rtd 92. *5 Sancroft Way, Fressingfield, Eye, Suffolk IP21 5QN* Fressingfield (01379) 588178

GRAESSER, Adrian Stewart. b 42. Tyndale Hall Bris 63. **d** 67 **p** 68. C Nottm St Jude *S'well* 67-69; C Slaithwaite w E Scammonden *Wakef* 69-72; CF 72-75; V Earlsheaton *Wakef* 75-81; R Norton Fitzwarren *B & W* 81-86; R Bickenhill w Elmdon *Birm* 86-90; R Elmdon St Nic from 90. *Elmdon Rectory, Tanhouse Farm Road, Solihull, W Midlands B92 9EY* 0121-743 6336

GRAFTON, Roger Patrick. b 63. Lon Univ BA85. Trin Coll Bris DipHE90. **d** 91 **p** 92. C Kennington St Mark *S'wark* 91-92; C Dulwich St Barn from 92. *45 Bawdale Road, London SE22 9DL* 0181-693 7587

GRAHAM, Alan Robert. b 44. St Edm Hall Ox BA67 MA71. St Steph Ho Ox 67. **d** 70 **p** 71. C Clifton All SS *Bris* 70-74; C Tadley St Pet *Win* 74-77; P-in-c Upper Clatford w Goodworth Clatford 77-79; R Abbotts Ann and Upper and Goodworth Clatford 79-84; V Lyndhurst and Emery Down 84-92; P-in-c Over Wallop w Nether Wallop from 92. *The Rectory, Over Wallop, Stockbridge, Hants SO20 8HT* Andover (01264) 781345

GRAHAM, Alfred. b 34. Bris Univ BA57. Tyndale Hall Bris. **d** 58 **p** 59. C Chaddesden St Mary *Derby* 58-61; C Bickenhill w Elmdon *Birm* 61-64; V Kirkdale St Lawr *Liv* 64-70; V Stapleford *S'well* 70-83; V Burton Joyce w Bulcote from 83. *The Vicarage, 9 Chestnut Grove, Burton Joyce, Nottingham NG14 5DP* Nottingham (0115) 931 2109

✠**GRAHAM, Rt Rev Andrew Alexander Kenny (Alec).** b 29. St Jo Coll Ox BA52 DipTh53 MA57 Lambeth STh95. Ely Th Coll 53. **d** 55 **p** 56 **c** 77. C Hove All SS *Chich* 55-58; Chapl Lect Th and Tutor Worc Coll Ox 58-70; Can and Preb Linc Cathl *Linc* 70-77; Warden Linc Th Coll 70-77; Suff Bp Bedf *St Alb* 77-81; Bp Newc from 81; Chmn Selectors ACCM 84-87; Chmn Doctrine Commn from 87. *Bishop's House, 29 Moor Road South, Newcastle upon Tyne NE3 1PA* 0191-285 2220 Fax 213 0728

GRAHAM, Canon Anthony Nigel. b 40. Univ of Wales (Abth) BA62 CertEd70. Ripon Hall Ox 62. **d** 64 **p** 65. C Heref H Trin *Heref* 64-67; C Birm St Martin *Birm* 67-69; C Selly Oak St Mary 71-75; V Edgbaston SS Mary and Ambrose 75-83; CMS Miss Partner Nigeria 84-88; Hon Can Jos *Birm* from 88; V Highworth w Sevenhampton and Inglesham etc *Bris* from 88; RD Highworth from 93. *The Vicarage, 23 The Willows, Highworth, Swindon SN6 7PG* Swindon (01793) 763862

GRAHAM, Anthony Stanley David (Tony). b 34. SS Coll Cam BA56 MA60. Cuddesdon Coll 58. **d** 60 **p** 61. C Welwyn Garden City *St Alb* 60-64; Asst Chapl Ipswich Sch 64-65; C Margate St Jo *Cant* 65-68; Chr Aid Area Sec Chich from 68. *48 Springfield Road, Crawley, W Sussex RH11 8AH* Crawley (01293) 526279

GRAHAM, Clifton Gordon. b 53. ARCM72 GRSM74 FRCO75 Coll of Ripon & York St Jo PGCE76. St Steph Ho Ox 90. **d** 92 **p** 93. C Northfield *Birm* 92-93; C Perry Beeches from 93. *45 Epwell Road, Birmingham B44 8DH* 0121-356 3036

GRAHAM, Canon Douglas Wrixon. b 13. TCD BA39. Div Test40. **d** 41 **p** 43. I Roscommon w Donamon, Rathcline, Kilkeevin etc *K, E & A* 66-88; Preb Elphin Cathl 79-88; rtd 88.

6 St Theresa's Terrace, Lisna Nult, Roscommon, Irish Republic Roscommon (902) 25028

GRAHAM, Canon Frederick Lawrence. b 35. TCD BA65 DChCD88. CITC 66. **d** 66 **p** 67. C Belf St Matt *Conn* 66-69; TV Chelmsley Wood *Birm* 69-73; Ch of Ireland Youth Officer 73-78; Bp's C Stoneyford *Conn* 78-88; Bp's C Fahan Lower and Upper *D & R* 88-91; RD Innishowen from 88; Can Raphoe Cathl from 90; I Donagheady from 91. *Earlsgift Rectory, 33 Longland Road, Donamana, Co Tyrone BT82 0PH* Londonderry (01504) 398017

GRAHAM, Frederick Louis Roth. b 20. Selw Coll Cam BA47 MA49. Ridley Hall Cam 48. **d** 50 **p** 51. R Wombwell *Sheff* 61-71; V Thorne 71-77; P-in-c Chilton-s-Polden w Edington *B & W* 77-82; P-in-c Catcott 77-82; V W Poldens 82-86; RD Glastonbury 82-86; rtd 86; Perm to Offic *Win* from 86. *73 Newlands Avenue, Southampton SO15 5EQ* Southampton (01703) 789353

GRAHAM, George David. b 42. Jes Coll Cam BA64 MA68. St Jo Coll Nottm LTh Lon Coll of Div 66. **d** 71 **p** 72. C Corby St Columba *Pet* 71-74; C Deptford St Jo *S'wark* 74-77; P-in-c Deptford St Pet 77-82; C-in-c Wheatley Park St Paul CD *Sheff* 82-87; TV Dunstable *St Alb* 87-92; P-in-c Bromley Common St Luke *Roch* from 92. *St Luke's Vicarage, 20 Bromley Common, Bromley BR2 9PD* 0181-464 2076

GRAHAM, George Edgar. b 55. QUB BA91. Sarum & Wells Th Coll 74 CITC 77. **d** 78 **p** 79. C Lisburn Ch Ch *Conn* 78-81; C Mossley 81-83; I Broomhedge 83-91; I Derriaghy w Colin from 91; RD Derriagh from 94. *The Rectory, 20 Derriaghy Road, Lisburn, Co Antrim BT28 3SH* Belfast (01232) 610859

GRAHAM, George Gordon. b 17. St Chad's Coll Dur BA48 DipTh50 MSc71. **d** 50 **p** 51. V Hunwick *Dur* 69-88; Chapl Homelands Hosp Dur from 80; rtd 88. *3 The Willows, Bishop Auckland, Co Durham DL14 7HH* Bishop Auckland (01388) 602758

GRAHAM, Gordon Cecil. b 31. JP. Ch Coll Cam BA53 MA57. Ripon Hall Ox 53. **d** 55 **p** 56. Chapl Hulme Gr Sch Oldham 67-74; Lic to Offic *Ches* from 72; rtd 92. *21 The Crescent, Davenport, Stockport, Cheshire SK3 8SL* 0161-483 6011

GRAHAM, Ian Maxwell. b 50. CertEd76. Chich Th Coll 86. **d** 88 **p** 89. C Middlesb St Thos *York* 88-90; C Stainton-in-Cleveland 90-93; V Hemlington from 93. *1 Southdene Drive, Hemlington, Middlesbrough, Cleveland TS8 9HH* Middlesbrough (01642) 590496

GRAHAM, James Hamilton. b 54. Solicitor 78 Cam Univ MA76 Ox Univ MA83. Ripon Coll Cuddesdon. **d** 84 **p** 85. C Harlescott *Lich* 84-88; C Moreton Say 88-93; R Hodnet w Weston under Redcastle from 93. *The Rectory, Hodnet, Market Drayton, Shropshire TF9 3NT* Hodnet (01630) 685491

GRAHAM, John. b 24. **d** 84 **p** 84. Hon C Glas St Kentigern *Glas* from 84; Chapl Glas R Infirmary from 84. *121 Garthland Drive, Glasgow G31 2SQ* 0141-554 5718

GRAHAM, John Francis Ottiwell Skelton. b 15. G&C Coll Cam BA37 MA48. Wells Th Coll 37. **d** 39 **p** 40. V Winterbourne Earls w Winterbourne Dauntsey etc *Sarum* 58-72; R Bincombe w Broadwey 72-80; R Bincombe w Broadwey, Upwey and Buckland Ripers 80-81; rtd 81; Perm to Offic *Win* from 81. *15A Belmore Lane, Lymington, Hants SO41 9NL* Lymington (01590) 673256

GRAHAM, John Galbraith. b 21. K Coll Cam BA43 MA46. Ely Th Coll 46. **d** 48 **p** 49. Chapl Reading Univ *Ox* 62-72; C Pimlico St Pet w Westmr Ch Ch *Lon* 72-74; R Houghton w Wyton *Ely* 74-78; rtd 86; Lic to Offic *St E* from 86; Lic to Offic *Ely* from 86. *31 Rectory Lane, Somersham, Huntingdon, Cambs PE17 3EL* Ramsey (01487) 842737

GRAHAM, Very Rev Malcolm Frederick. b 15. TCD BA37 MA69. **d** 40 **p** 41. I Kilbroney *D & D* 60-79; RD Newry and Mourne 61-79; RD Kilbroney 61-79; Preb St Patr Cathl Dub 69-72; Dean Killala *T, K & A* 79-89; I Killala w Dunfeeny, Crossmolina etc 79-89; rtd 89. *Kilbroney, Rathnamaugh, Crossmolina, Co Mayo, Irish Republic* Ballina (96) 31717

GRAHAM, Mrs Marion McKenzie. b 39. St As Minl Tr Course. **d** 89. NSM Bagillt *St As* 89-93; NSM Flint from 93. *Sharondale, Bryntirion Road, Bagillt, Clwyd CH6 6BZ* Flint (01352) 734139

GRAHAM, Canon Matthew. b 30. Univ Coll Dur BSc54. K Coll (NS) BD71 Ridley Hall Cam 54. **d** 56 **p** 57. C Littleover *Derby* 56-59; C Fazakerley Em *Liv* 59-61; V Huyton St Geo 61-65; Canada 65-71; V Sutton Coldfield St Columba *Birm* 71-85; V Warley Woods from 85; RD Warley 87-93; Hon Can Birm Cathl 90-95. *St Hilda's Vicarage, Abbey Road, Smethwick, Warley, W Midlands B67 5NQ* 0121-429 1384

GRAHAM, Michael. b 30. Westcott Ho Cam 61. **d** 61 **p** 62. C Withington St Paul *Man* 61-64; V Lawton Moor 64-87; R Mobberley *Ches* from 87. *The Rectory, Mobberley, Knutsford, Cheshire WA16 7RA* Mobberley (01565) 873218

GRAHAM, Michael. b 51. CITC BTh95. **d** 95. C Cork St Fin Barre's Union *C, C & R* from 95. *23 Firgrove Gardens, Bishopstown, Cork, Republic of Ireland* Cork (21) 345889

GRAHAM, Michael Alistair. b 47. CITC 67. **d** 70 **p** 71. C Dub Clontarf *D & G* 71-75; C Ox St Mich w St Martin and All SS *Ox* 76-78; P-in-c Dub Sandymount *D & G* 80-86; I Stillorgan w Blackrock from 86. *The Rectory, Stillorgan, Blackrock, Co Dublin, Irish Republic* Dublin (1) 288-1091

GRAHAM, Peter. b 32. CEng MIMechE. **d** 86 **p** 87. NSM Minchinhampton *Glouc* from 86. *2 Dr Browns Close, Minchinhampton, Stroud, Glos GL6 9DW* Brimscombe (01453) 886747

GRAHAM, Peter Bartlemy. b 23. K Coll Cam BA47 MA52. Ely Th Coll 50. **d** 52 **p** 53. R Harpenden St Nic *St Alb* 64-73; V Aylesbury *Ox* 73-82; Hon Can Ch Ch 79-82; R Elford *Lich* 82-88; Dioc Adv Past Care and Counselling 82-88; rtd 88. *Carriers Cottage, Buckland Newton, Dorchester, Dorset DT2 7DW* Buckland Newton (01300) 345287

GRAHAM, Canon Robert John. b 15. Lon Univ BD54 Hull Univ DipAdEd. Bp Wilson Coll 39. **d** 42 **p** 43. V Howden *York* 58-78; V Barmby on the Marsh 62-78; V Wressell 62-78; RD Howden 70-78; Can and Preb York Minster 74-78; C Worksop Priory *S'well* 78-80; rtd 80. *Cranley, Flat 11, Wellington Square, Cheltenham, Glos GL50 4JX* Cheltenham (01242) 580608

GRAHAM, Ronald Fleming. b 33. Edin Th Coll 67. **d** 69 **p** 69. Chapl St Andr Cathl *Ab* 69-73; R Glas Gd Shep *Glas* 73-75; R Glas Gd Shep and Ascension 75-76; CF (TA) 74-76; R Peterhead *Ab* 76-80; Chapl RAF 76-80; Bp's Dom Chapl *Arg* 80-84; Itinerant Priest 80-84; R Lanark *Glas* 84-89; R Douglas 84-89; rtd 89; Hon C Glas St Ninian *Glas* from 91. *77 Merryvale Avenue, Merrylee Park, Giffnock, Glasgow G46 6DE* 0141-637 4761

GRAHAM, Ronald Gaven. **d** 90 **p** 91. NSM Adare w Kilpeacon and Croom *L & K* 90-92; Dioc Info Officer (Limerick) 91-95; NSM Rathkeale w Askeaton and Kilcornan from 92. *The Pyramids, Old Schoolhouse Road, Castletroy, Limerick, Irish Republic* Limerick (61) 330190 Fax as telephone

GRAHAM, Roy Richard Arthur. b 39. Lon Univ BD63 Open Univ BA78. ALCD62. **d** 63 **p** 64. C Southsea St Jude *Portsm* 63-66; C Morden *S'wark* 66-70; V Tittensor *Lich* 70-79; R Dinsdale w Sockburn *Dur* from 79; R Hurworth from 79. *The Rectory, 3 Croft Road, Hurworth, Darlington, Co Durham DL2 2HD* Darlington (01325) 720362

GRAHAM-BROWN, John George Francis. b 34. CA60. Wycliffe Hall Ox 60. **d** 63 **p** 64. C Darlington St Cuth *Dur* 63-67; C Rufforth w Moor Monkton and Hessay *York* 67-73; Sec York Dioc Redundant Chs Uses Cttee 69-89; Asst Sec DBF 73-84; Dioc Past Cttee 73-89; Hon C York St Barn 73-85; P-in-c 85-92; TV Marfleet from 92. *St Giles' Vicarage, Church Lane, Marfleet, Hull HU9 5RL* Hull (01482) 783690

GRAHAM-ORLEBAR, Ian Henry Gaunt. b 26. New Coll Ox BA49 MA56. Cuddesdon Coll 60. **d** 62 **p** 63. C Hemel Hempstead *St Alb* 62-70; R Barton-le-Cley w Higham Gobion 70-80; R Barton-le-Cley w Higham Gobion and Hexton 80-92; rtd 92; Perm to Offic *Ex* from 94. *Hole Farm, Bickington, Newton Abbot, Devon TQ12 6PE* Bickington (01626) 821298

GRAIN, Anthony Ernest. b 07. CCC Cam BA31 MA35. Ely Th Coll 31. **d** 32 **p** 33. Jamaica 61-62; S Rhodesia 63-65; Rhodesia 65-80; Zimbabwe 80-86; rtd 73; Perm to Offic *Chich* from 86. *College of St Barnabas, Blackberry Lane, Lingfield, Surrey RH7 6NJ* Dormans Park (01342) 870260

GRAIN, Canon Keith Charles. b 27. St Boniface Warminster 47 AKC51. **d** 52 **p** 53. V Hanging Heaton *Wakef* 60-70; V Heckmondwike 70-82; Hon Can Wakef Cathl 74-82; RD Birstall 79-82; V Gargrave *Bradf* 82-92; rtd 92. *2 Holme Ghyll, Colne Road, Glusburn, Keighley, W Yorkshire BD20 8RG* Cross Hills (01535) 630668

GRAINGE, Alan Herbert. b 16. Dur Univ BA49 MA53. Sarum Th Coll 49. **d** 51 **p** 52. V Immingham *Linc* 61-70; Perm to Offic *Ox* 70-74; Lic to Offic 74-81; SSJE from 76; Lic to Offic *Leic* 80-86; rtd 86; Lic to Offic *Lon* from 86. *St Edward's House, 22 Great College Street, London SW1P 3QA* 0171-222 9234

GRAINGER, Canon Bruce. b 37. Nottm Univ BA62 Hull Univ MA83. Cuddesdon Coll 62. **d** 64 **p** 65. C Bingley All SS *Bradf* 64-67; Chapl K Sch Cant 67-72; Hon Min Can Cant Cathl *Cant* 69-72; V Baildon *Bradf* 72-88; Hon Can Bradf Cathl from 84; V Oxenhope from 88; Dir of Ords from 88. *The Vicarage, Oxenhope, Keighley, W Yorkshire BD22 9SA* Keighley (01535) 642529

GRAINGER, Horace. b 34. Carl Dioc Tr Course 82. **d** 85 **p** 86. NSM Barrow St Matt *Carl* 85-89; C Carl St Herbert w St Steph 89-91; TV Penrith w Newton Reigny and Plumpton Wall from 91. *3 Beacon Park, Penrith, Cumbria CA11 7UB* Penrith (01768) 67053 or 62867

GRAINGER, Ian. b 66. Barrow-in-Furness Coll of FE BTEC NC86. Cranmer Hall Dur 89. **d** 92 **p** 93. C Whitehaven *Carl* 92-94; C Walney Is from 94. *7 Irwell Road, Walney, Barrow-in-Furness, Cumbria LA14 3UZ* Barrow-in-Furness (01229) 474663

GRAINGER, Michael Noel Howard. b 40. Trin Coll Carmarthen. **d** 91 **p** 92. NSM Haverfordwest St Martin w Lambston *St D* 91-95; V Maenclochog w Henry's Moat and Mynachlogddu etc from 95. *The Rectory, New Moat, Clarbeston Road, Dyfed SA63 4RQ* Maenclochog (01437) 532238

GRAINGER, Dr Roger Beckett. b 34. FRAI FRSA Birm Univ MA70 Leeds Univ PhD79 Lon Univ BA80 DD90 Huddersfield Poly MPhil88. Lambeth STh83 Trin Coll Bris PhD92 Lich Th Coll 64. **d** 66 **p** 69. C Walsall *Lich* 69-73; Chapl Stanley Royd Hosp Wakef 73-90; rtd 91; Hon C Wakef St Jo *Wakef* from 93. *7 Park Grove, Horbury, Wakefield, W Yorkshire WF4 6EE* Wakefield (01924) 272742

GRANGER, Canon Ronald Harry (Ron). b 22. Selw Coll Cam BA49 MA53. Cuddesdon Coll 49. **d** 51 **p** 52. V Ryde All SS *Portsm* 63-70; RD E Wight 65-70; Hon Can Portsm Cathl 67-90; V Petersfield 70-90; RD Petersfield 75-80; P-in-c Buriton 79-84; R 84-90; rtd 90. *45 Siskin Close, Bishops Waltham, Hants SO3 1RP* Bishops Waltham (01489) 894378

GRANT, Alistair Sims. b 25. SS Coll Cam BA49 MA64. Sarum Th Coll 49. **d** 51 **p** 52. V Haddenham *Ely* 58-65; rtd 90. *56 The Causeway, Burwell, Cambridge CB5 0DU* Newmarket (01638) 741670

GRANT, Andrew Richard. b 40. Univ of Wales BA62. Chich Th Coll 63. **d** 65 **p** 66. C Kennington St Jo *S'wark* 65-68; Hon C 70-72; Hon C Stockwell Green St Andr 68-70; V Nunhead St Antony 72-79; TR N Lambeth 79-92; USPG from 92; Ghana from 92. *PO Box 17, St Monica's Complex, Ashanti-Mattpong, Ghana* 0171-928 8681 Fax 928 2371

GRANT, Antony Richard Charles. b 34. Ch Ch Ox BA59 MA64. Coll of Resurr Mirfield 72. **d** 74 **p** 75. C St Jo Wood *Lon* 74-77; Novice CR 77-79; CR from 79; Lic to Offic *Wakef* from 80. *House of the Resurrection, Mirfield, W Yorkshire WF14 0BN* Mirfield (01924) 494318

GRANT, Arthur Glyndwr Webber (Glyn). b 28. St Luke's Coll Ex CertEd49. Wells Th Coll 52. **d** 54 **p** 55. C Brighton Gd Shep Preston *Chich* 68-76; C Moulsecoomb 76-80; Chapl HM Pris Northeye 80-83; P-in-c Wartling *Chich* 80-83; C Seaford w Sutton 83-87; Sub-Chapl HM Pris Lewes 86-92; rtd 92. *33 Occombe Valley Road, Paignton, Devon TQ3 1QX* Paignton (01803) 522722

GRANT, David Francis. b 32. Chich Th Coll. **d** 60 **p** 61. C Acton Green St Pet *Lon* 60-63; C Ruislip St Martin 63-68; V Oving w Merston *Chich* 68-75; Bp's Dom Chapl 68-75; R Graffham w Woolavington 75-86; R Hastings St Clem and All SS 86-91; R Petworth 91-94; R Egdean 91-94; RD Petworth 92-94. *Glebeland, Graffham, Petworth, W Sussex GU28 0QE* Petworth (01798) 867289

GRANT, Canon Douglas Wyndham Maling. b 22. Trin Coll Cam BA48 MA52. Edin Th Coll 53. **d** 55 **p** 56. R Lenzie *Glas* 65-70; R Alyth *St And* 70-78; R Blairgowrie 70-78; R Inverurie *Ab* 78-88; R Auchindoir 78-88; R Alford 78-88; P-in-c Kemnay 78-88; Can St Andr Cathl 87-88; Hon Can St Andr Cathl from 88; rtd 88; Perm to Offic *Mor* from 89. *Shewglie, 8 Ardross Place, Inverness IV3 5EL* Inverness (01463) 242870

GRANT, Canon Edward Francis. b 14. TCD BA37. TCD Div Sch Div Test. **d** 40 **p** 41. Prec Ferns Cathl *C & O* 69-85; I Wexford w Ardcolm 70-85; Preb Stagonil St Patr Cathl Dub 76-85; rtd 85. *9 Kingston College, Mitchelstown, Co Cork, Irish Republic* Mitchelstown (25) 84214

GRANT, Canon Geoffrey. b 27. Lich Th Coll 55. **d** 58 **p** 59. V Sherston Magna w Easton Grey *Bris* 67-75; P-in-c Luckington w Alderton 71-75; P-in-c Woolcott Park 75-78; V Cotham St Mary 75-81; V Cotham St Sav w St Mary 78-81; TR Yate New Town 81-88; Hon Can Bris Cathl 82-92; Dir St Jo Home Bris 89-92; rtd 92. *5 Hawthorn Coombe, Worle, Weston-super-Mare, Avon BS22 9EE* Weston-super-Mare (01934) 513295

GRANT, Canon Geoffrey Leslie. b 33. Trin Coll Cam BA57 MA61. Ridley Hall Cam 57. **d** 59 **p** 60. C Chelsea St Luke *Lon* 59-64; Chapl Orwell Park Sch Nacton from 64; R Nacton w Levington *St E* 64-78; P-in-c Bucklesham w Brightwell and Foxhall 75-76; R Nacton and Levington w Bucklesham and Foxhall from 78; RD Colneys from 86; Hon Can St E Cathl from 94. *The Rectory, Nacton, Ipswich IP10 0HY* Ipswich (01473) 659292

GRANT, Dr John Brian Frederick. b 47. FRCS76 Bris Univ BSc68 MB, ChB71 MD76. Coll of Resurr Mirfield 91. **d** 93 **p** 94. C Doncaster Ch Ch *Sheff* 93-95; C Doncaster H Trin from 95. *131 Crathie Road, Doncaster, S Yorkshire DN2 5EG* Doncaster (01302) 328120

GRANT, John Peter. b 19. TD50. Wycliffe Hall Ox. **d** 62 **p** 63. Chapl Warneford Hosp Ox 67-71; Rhodesia 71-80; V Gayton *Nor* 80-82; rtd 82; S Africa from 82. *96 Protea Heuwelsig, PO Box 15223, Verwoerdburg, 0140 South Africa*

GRANT, Kenneth Gordon. b 21. ARCM54. K Coll Lon. **d** 55 **p** 56. C Wotton-under-Edge *Glouc* 55-58; R Charfield from 58. *The Rectory, 36 Wotton Road, Charfield, Wotton-under-Edge, Glos GL12 8TG* Falfield (01454) 260489

GRANT, Very Rev Malcolm Etheridge. b 44. Edin Univ BSc66 BD69. Edin Th Coll 66. **d** 69 **p** 70. C St Mary's Cathl *Glas* 69-72; C Grantham w Manthorpe *Linc* 72; TV Grantham 72-78; P-in-c Invergordon *Mor* 78-81; Provost St Mary's Cathl *Glas* 81-91; Can 81-91; R Glas St Mary 81-91; Provost St Andr Cathl Inverness *Mor* from 91; R Inverness St Andr from 91; P-in-c Culloden St Mary-in-the-Fields from 91; R Strathnairn St Paul from 91. *15 Ardross Street, Inverness IV3 5NS* Inverness (01463) 233535

GRANT, Murray William. b 36. Chich Th Coll 64. **d** 66 **p** 67. C Stanley *Liv* 66-70; C Munster Square St Mary Magd *Lon* 70-74; C Westmr St Sav and St Jas Less 74-82; P-in-c Albany Street Ch Ch 82; P-in-c Hammersmith H Innocents 83-94; V from 94. *Holy Innocents Vicarage, 35 Paddenswick Road, London W6 0VA* 0181-748 5195 or 748 2286

GRANT, Canon Rodney Arthur. b 26. AKC52. **d** 53 **p** 54. R Edin St Jas *Edin* 72-80; P-in-c Edin St Aid Miss Niddrie Mains 60-72; R Edin Ch Ch 72-80; R Edin Ch Ch-St Jas 80-86; R Edin SS Phil and Jas 86-92; Chapl St Columba's Hospice Edin 86-92; Hon Can St Mary's Cathl from 91; rtd 92. *29 Bruntsfield Gardens, Edinburgh EH10 4DY* 0131-229 1857

GRANT, William Frederick (Eric). b 23. Fitzw Ho Cam BA48 MA50 Cam Univ CertEd50. Wycliffe Hall Ox 51. **d** 53 **p** 54. Head RE Therfield Sch Leatherhead 60-84; Perm to Offic *Guildf* from 66; rtd 88; Perm to Offic *S'wark* from 89. *Kingfishers, 24 The Avenue, Brockham, Betchworth, Surrey RH3 7EN* Betchworth (01737) 842551

GRANT, Very Rev William James. b 29. **d** 58 **p** 59. Miss to Seamen 66-70; I Fethard w Tintern and Killesk *C & O* 70-77; I Cong, Ballinrobe and Aasleagh *T, K & A* 77-81; Adn Tuam 80-93; I Tuam w Cong and Aasleagh 81-93; Dean Tuam 81-93; rtd 93. *48 Brazabon House, Sandymount, Dublin 4, Irish Republic* Dublin (1) 269-5071

GRANTHAM, Michael Paul. b 47. Linc Th Coll. **d** 84 **p** 85. C Gainsborough All SS *Linc* 84-87; R S Kelsey Gp 87-94; R Dunster, Carhampton and Withycombe w Rodhuish *B & W* from 94. *The Rectory, St George's Street, Dunster, Minehead, Somerset TA24 6RS* Dunster (01643) 821812

GRANTHAM, Suffragan Bishop of. *See* IND, Rt Rev William

GRASBY, Derek. b 56. Bris Univ BA80 MA82. Wesley Coll Bris 77. E Anglian Mini Tr Course 95. **d** 95. C Harlescott *Lich* from 95. *19 Heron Drive, Harlescott, Shrewsbury SY1 4UG* Shrewsbury (01743) 465431

GRATY, Canon John Thomas. b 33. Univ Coll Ox BA58 MA60. Coll of Resurr Mirfield 58. **d** 60 **p** 61. C Cov St Mark *Cov* 60-63; C Hitchin St Mary *St Alb* 63-67; R Cov St Alb *Cov* 67-75; P-in-c Radway w Ratley 75-77; P-in-c Warmington w Shotteswell 75-77; RD Dassett Magna 76-79; R Warmington w Shotteswell and Radway w Ratley 77-84; Hon Can Cov Cathl from 80; P-in-c Nuneaton St Mary 84-89; V from 89. *St Mary's Abbey Vicarage, Nuneaton, Warks CV11 5JB* Nuneaton (01203) 382936

GRAVELL, Canon John Hilary. b 45. Univ of Wales (Abth) BA65 DipEd66. Burgess Hall Lamp 66. **d** 68 **p** 69. C Abth *St D* 68-72; V Blaenpennal and Llangeitho 73-81; V Betws Leuci 73-81; V Llan-non 81-95; Hon Can St D Cathl from 92; V Llandybie from 95. *The Vicarage, 77 Kings Road, Llandybie, Ammanford, Dyfed SA18 2TL* Llandybie (01269) 850337

GRAVELLE, John Elmer. b 25. St Jo Coll Dur BA50 DipTh51. **d** 51 **p** 52. V Hatf Hyde St Mary *St Alb* 64-71; P-in-c Gt Munden 71-74; Dep Dir Clinical Th Assn 71-80; P-in-c Fryerning w Margaretting *Chelmsf* 80-87; Dep Dir Cathl Cen for Research and Tr 82-84; Bp's Adv in Care and Counselling 87-90; rtd 90. *8 Gordon Road, Chelmsford CM2 9LL* Chelmsford (01245) 491795

GRAVES, Canon Eric Arthur. b 13. Leeds Univ BA34. Coll of Resurr Mirfield 34. **d** 36 **p** 37. V Haverhill *St E* 46-81; RD Clare 72-81; rtd 82; Perm to Offic *St E* from 82. *20 Saxon Rise, Bury St Edmunds, Suffolk IP33 3LF* Bury St Edmunds (01284) 764497

GRAVES, Jonathan Mark. b 57. BEd St Steph Ho Ox. **d** 84 **p** 85. C St Leonards Ch Ch and St Mary *Chich* 84-88; C-in-c N Langley CD 88-95; V Stone Cross St Luke w N Langney from 95; Chapl St Wilfrid's Hospice Eastbourne from 94. *The Vicarage, 8 Culver Close, Eastbourne, E Sussex BN23 8EA* Eastbourne (01323) 764473

GRAVES, Peter. b 33. E Midl Min Tr Course 78. **d** 81 **p** 82. NSM Roughey (or Roffey) *Chich* 81-89; NSM Itchingfield w Slinfold from 89. *2 Coniston Close, Roffey, Horsham, W Sussex RH12 4GU* Horsham (01403) 258363

GRAY, Alan. b 25. LRAM52 DCEd75. Qu Coll Birm 51. **d** 54 **p** 55. R Callander *St And* 66-74; R Killin 66-74; R Lochearnhead 66-74; R Alloa 74-77; Community Educn Officer 76-85; Lic to Offic 77-85; R Alyth 85-90; R Blairgowrie 85-90; R Coupar Angus 85-90; rtd 90. *Ach-na-Coile, Ancaster Road, Callander, Perthshire FK17 8EL* Callander (01877) 30158

GRAY, Alan Eric. b 18. Lich Th Coll 38. **d** 41 **p** 42. V Lower Breeding Chich 61-70; rtd 83. *Appletree Cottage, 81 Belmont Road, Malvern, Worcs WR14 1PN* Malvern (01684) 572453

GRAY, Angela Margery. b 46. St D Coll Lamp DipTh73. **dss** 73 **d** 80. Abth *St D* 73-80; Par Dn Dafen and Llwynhendy 80-90; D-in-c 90-94; D-in-c Llwynhendy from 94. *Clergy House, 10 Bryn Isaf, Llwynhendy, Llanelli, Dyfed SA14 9EX* Llanelli (01554) 774213

GRAY, Arthur Alan Western. b 04. Jes Coll Cam BA26 MA31. Ridley Hall Cam 27. **d** 29 **p** 31. New Zealand 55-61; Australia from 62; rtd 66. *Unit 1, 1 Brandreth Street, Tusmore, S Australia 5065* Adelaide (8) 311947

GRAY, Charles Malcolm. b 38. Lich Th Coll 67. **d** 69 **p** 70. C St Geo-in-the-East St Mary *Lon* 69-72; C Bush Hill Park St Mark 72-75; V Winchmore Hill H Trin from 75. *Holy Trinity Vicarage, King's Avenue, London N21 3NA* 0181-360 2947 Fax as telephone

GRAY, Ms Christine Angela (Kit). b 46. Nottm Univ BA67 CertEd68 Dur Univ DipTh73. Cranmer Hall Dur 71. **dss** 80 **d** 87 **p** 94. Rawthorpe *Wakef* 74-81; Chapl Nottm Univ *S'well* 81-88; C Rushmere *St E* 88-94; P-in-c Ringshall w Battisford, Barking w Darmsden etc from 94. *The Rectory, Main Road, Willisham, Ipswich IP8 4SP* Ipswich (01473) 831274

GRAY, Christopher John. b 64. BA BPhil. Coll of Resurr Mirfield. **d** 92 **p** 93. C Cantril Farm *Liv* 92-95; P-in-c Anfield St Marg from 95. *St Margaret's Vicarage, Rocky Lane, Liverpool L6 4BA* 0151-263 3118

GRAY, Dale Armitage. b 42. Edin Th Coll 62. **d** 92 **p** 93. Dioc Missr *Arg* from 92; Chapl St Jo Cathl Oban from 92; P-in-c Cumbrae (or Millport) from 95. *The College, Millport, Isle of Cumbrae KA28 0HE* Millport (01475) 530353

GRAY, David Bryan. b 28. RD77. Roch Th Coll 59. **d** 61 **p** 62. P-in-c Ropsley *Linc* 67-75; P-in-c Sapperton w Braceby 67-75; P-in-c Somerby w Humby 67-75; R Trimley *St E* 75-82; R Orford w Sudbourne, Chillesford, Butley and Iken 82-94; rtd 94. *30 Roman Way, Felixstowe, Suffolk IP11 9NJ* Felixstowe (01394) 285778

GRAY, David Kenneth. b 22. Sarum Th Coll 53. **d** 55 **p** 56. V Hounslow Heath St Paul *Lon* 65-88; rtd 88. *12 Dart Close, Oadby, Leicester LE2 4JA* Leicester (0116) 271 6357

GRAY, Canon Donald Cecil. b 24. K Coll Lon 46. Linc Th Coll 49. **d** 50 **p** 51. Chapl Cobgates Hosp and Farnham Hosp Guildf 67-89; R Farnham *Guildf* 67-89; RD Farnham 69-74; Hon Can Guildf Cathl 71-89; rtd 89. *13 Benenden Green, Alresford, Hants SO24 9PE* Alresford (01962) 734234

GRAY, Canon Donald Clifford. b 30. TD70. FRHistS88 Liv Univ MPhil80 Man Univ PhD85. AKC55. **d** 56 **p** 57. C Leigh St Mary *Man* 56-60; CF (TA) 58-67; V Westleigh St Pet *Man* 60-67; V Elton All SS 67-74; CF (TAVR) 67-77; QHC 74-77; R Liv Our Lady and St Nic w St Anne *Liv* 74-87; RD Liv 75-81; Hon Can Liv Cathl 82-87; Chapl to The Queen from 82; Can Westmr Abbey from 87; R Westmr St Marg from 87; Chapl to Speaker of Ho of Commons from 87. *1 Little Cloister, Westminster Abbey, London SW1P 3PL* 0171-222 4027 or 222 5152 Fax 233 2072

GRAY, Evan William. b 43. Oak Hill Th Coll 86. **d** 88 **p** 89. C Street w Walton *B & W* 88-92; V Blackpool St Mark *Blackb* from 92. *St Mark's Vicarage, 163 Kingscote Drive, Blackpool FY3 8EH* Blackpool (01253) 392895

GRAY, Frank Harold Castell. b 14. ALCD41. **d** 41 **p** 42. V Watford St Luke *St Alb* 66-79; rtd 79; Perm to Offic *B & W* from 80. *9 Southwell Close, Trull, Taunton, Somerset TA3 7EU* Taunton (01823) 282567

GRAY, Canon Geoffrey Thomas. b 23. Oak Hill Th Coll 40 and 46. **d** 46 **p** 47. V Gillingham St Mary *Roch* 66-75; RD Gillingham 66-75; Perm to Offic 75-80; V Strood St Nic w St Mary 80-87; Hon Can Roch Cathl 82-87; Chapl Huggens' Coll Northfleet 87-91; rtd 88; Hon Bp's Chapl Roch from 90; Hon PV Roch Cathl from 91. *Deanery Lodge, The Precinct, Rochester, Kent ME1 1TG* Medway (01634) 844165

GRAY, George Francis Selby. b 03. Trin Coll Cam BA25 MA29. Westcott Ho Cam 25. **d** 27 **p** 28. V Over *Ely* 69-79; rtd 79; Perm to Offic *Chelmsf* from 79; Perm to Offic *Ely* from 79. *2 Bishop Wynn Close, Ely, Cambs CB7 4BH* Ely (01353) 663032

GRAY, Ven Hugh Henry James. b 21. TCD BA48 Div Test49 MA64. **d** 49 **p** 50. C Enniscorthy *C & O* 49-51; I Fenagh w Myshall 51-60; I Clonenagh w Roskelton 60-80; RD Baltinglass from 62; Preb Ossory & Leighlin Cathls 70-78; Treas 78-80; Chan 80-83; I Clonenagh w Offerlane, Borris-in-Ossory etc from 80; Adn Ossory and Leighlin 83-92. *St Peter's Rectory, Mountrath, Portlaoise, Co Laois, Irish Republic* Portlaoise (502) 32146

GRAY, John. ARCM. **d** 89 **p** 90. NSM Tenbury St Mich *Heref* from 89. *Flat 3, Castlemead, Burford, Tenbury Wells, Worcs WR15 8AH* Tenbury Wells (01584) 810959

GRAY, John David Norman. b 38. Oak Hill Th Coll DipHE86. **d** 86 **p** 87. C Portsdown *Portsm* 86-88; C Worthing St Geo *Chich* 88-91; TV Swanborough *Sarum* from 91. *The Vicarage, Wilcot, Pewsey, Wilts SN9 5NS* Marlborough (01672) 62282

GRAY, John Howard. b 39. St Aid Birkenhead 61. **d** 65 **p** 66. C Old Trafford St Cuth *Man* 65-68; C Urmston 68-74; V Oldham Moorside from 74. *The Vicarage, 1 Glebe Lane, Moorside, Oldham, Lancs OL1 4SJ* 0161-652 6452

GRAY, Mrs Joy Dora. b 24. SRN46 SCM48 HVCert. Gilmore Ho 79. **dss** 81 **d** 87 **p** 95. Newick *Chich* 81-87; Hon Par Dn 87-94; NSM Fletching from 94. *10 High Hurst Close, Newick, Lewes, E Sussex BN8 4NJ* Newick (01825) 722965

GRAY, Julian Francis. b 64. Univ of Wales (Lamp) BA86. Coll of Resurr Mirfield 86. **d** 88 **p** 89. C Newport St Woolos *Mon* 88-91; Min Can St Woolos Cathl 88-91; C Bassaleg 91-93; V Overmonnow w Wonastow and Michel Troy from 93. *St Thomas's Vicarage, Overmonnow, Monmouth, Gwent NP5 3ES* Monmouth (01600) 712869

GRAY, Kenneth Amphlett. b 11. St Jo Coll Dur BA34 MA37 DipTh37. **d** 35 **p** 36. Dorset and Wilts Distr Sec BFBS 62-75; rtd 75; Perm to Offic *Nor* from 81. *Windwhistle, Triple Plea Road, Woodton, Bungay, Suffolk NR35 2NS* Woodton (0150844) 395

GRAY, Martin Clifford. b 44. Westcott Ho Cam 78. **d** 80 **p** 81. C Gaywood, Bawsey and Mintlyn *Nor* 80-84; V Sheringham 84-94; P-in-c Lowestoft and Kirkley 94; TR Lowestoft St Marg from 94; Chapl Lothingland Hosp from 95. *St Margaret's Rectory, Hollingsworth Road, Lowestoft, Suffolk NR32 4BW* Lowestoft (01502) 573046

GRAY, Maurice William Halcro. b 27. Hertf Coll Ox BA48 MA60. Coll of Resurr Mirfield. **d** 60 **p** 61. C Cricklade w Latton *Bris* 60-63; Chapl Ellesmere Coll Shropshire 63-92; Lic to Offic *Lich* 63-93; rtd 92; NSM Ellesmere and Welsh Frankton *Lich* from 93; RD Ellesmere from 95. *The Pynt, Rhosgadfa, Gobowen, Oswestry, Shropshire SY10 7BN* Llanwnda (01286) 831385

GRAY, Melvyn Dixon. b 38. Lon Univ BD86 Dur Univ MA89. NE Ord Course 84. **d** 87 **p** 88. C Richmond w Hudswell *Ripon* 87-90; P-in-c Downholme and Marske 88-90; P-in-c Forcett and Stanwick w Aldbrough 90; P-in-c Forcett and Aldbrough and Melsonby 90-91; R from 91. *The Vicarage, 1 Appleby Close, Aldbrough St John, Richmond, N Yorkshire DL11 7TT* Darlington (01325) 374634

GRAY, Michael Frederick Henry. b 36. Southn Univ CQSW78. Lich Th Coll 62. **d** 65 **p** 66. C Plaistow St Mary *Chelmsf* 67-70; Chapl RN 70-72; Hon C Whyke w Rumboldswhyke and Portfield *Chich* 84-88; TV Crawley 88-95; rtd 95. *Flat 14, Sussex Court, Eaton Road, Hove, E Sussex BN3 3AS* Brighton (01273) 326677

GRAY, Neil Kenneth. b 48. Kelham Th Coll 67. **d** 71 **p** 72. C Chorley St Laur *Blackb* 71-74; C S Shore H Trin 74-78; P-in-c Preston St Oswald 78-83; C Blackpool St Steph 83-87; Chapl Co-ord Bolton HA from 87; Chapl Bolton Gen Hosp from 87. *The Chaplain's Office, Bolton General Hospital, Minerva Road, Bolton BL4 0JR* Bolton (01204) 390770 or 390390

GRAY, Neil Ralph. b 53. MA. St Steph Ho Ox. **d** 82 **p** 83. C Kennington St Jo w St Jas *S'wark* 82-85; C Somers Town St Mary *Lon* 85-88. *3 Parsonage Close, High Wycombe, Bucks HP13 6DT* High Wycombe (01494) 531875

GRAY, Penelope Jane. *See* GRAYSMITH, Mrs Penelope Jane

GRAY, Percy. b 28. OBE94 TD71. Lon Univ BA53 St Cath Soc Ox BA55 MA59. Oak Hill Th Coll 50. **d** 55 **p** 56. C Sutton *Liv* 55-58; C Chelsea Ch Ch Lon 58-59; V Bermondsey St Crispin w Ch Ch *S'wark* from 59; CF (TA) 59-67; CF (TAVR) from 67; CF (ACF) from 76. *St Crispin's Vicarage, 483 Southwark Park Road, London SE16 2HU* 0171-237 5567

GRAY, Philip Charles. b 67. Nottm Univ BA91. St Steph Ho Ox 91. **d** 93 **p** 94. C Scarborough St Martin *York* from 93. *136 Filey Road, Scarborough, N Yorkshire YO11 3AA* Scarborough (01723) 378105

GRAY, Philip Thomas. b 41. Lon Univ BA65. Chich Th Coll 66. **d** 68 **p** 69. C Leigh St Clem *Chelmsf* 68-74; V Mendlesham *St E* from 74; P-in-c Wickham Skeith from 86. *The Vicarage, Mendlesham, Stowmarket, Suffolk IP14 5RS* Stowmarket (01449) 766359

GRAY, Sidney Patrick. b 19. Worc Ord Coll. **d** 63 **p** 63. V Dunholme *Linc* 65-71; R Cliffe at Hoo w Cooling *Roch* 72-78; V Gillingham St Aug 78-84; rtd 84; Perm to Offic *Cant* from 84; Perm to Offic *Roch* from 84. *September Cottage, 168 Loose Road, Maidstone, Kent ME15 7UD*

GRAY-STACK, Martha Mary Stewart. b 35. QUB BA57. **d** 90 **p** 91. NSM Limerick City *L & K* 90-93; Warden of Readers 90-93; NSM Clara w Liss, Moate and Clonmacnoise *M & K* from 93. *St Bridgit's Rectory, Clara, Co Offaly, Irish Republic* Clara (506) 31406

GRAYSHON, Matthew Richard. b 47. St Jo Coll Nottm BTh81. **d** 81 **p** 82. C Beverley Minster *York* 81-85; V Hallwood *Ches*

85-93; R Hanwell St Mary w St Chris *Lon* from 93. *The Rectory, 91 Church Road, London W7 3BJ* 0181-567 6185

GRAYSHON, Paul Nicholas Walton (Nick). b 50. St Jo Coll Dur 81. **d** 83 **p** 84. C Walkden Moor *Man* 83-87; V Radcliffe St Andr from 87. *St Andrew's Vicarage, St Andrew's View, Radcliffe, Manchester M26 4HE* 0161-723 2427

GRAYSMITH (nee GRAY), Mrs Penelope Jane. b 63. SS Hild & Bede Coll Dur BA85 Em Coll Cam MPhil88. Westcott Ho Cam 86. **d** 89 **p** 94. Par Dn Evington *Leic* 89-92; Par Dn Cannock *Lich* 92-94; C from 94. *The Vicarage, 226 Hednesford Road, Heath Hayes, Cannock, Staffs WS12 5DZ* Heath Hayes (01543) 270107

GRAYSMITH (formerly SMITH), Peter Alexander. b 62. UEA BSc83. Westcott Ho Cam 85. **d** 88 **p** 89. C Tettenhall Regis *Lich* 88-89; C Cannock 89-92; TV from 92. *The Vicarage, 226 Hednesford Road, Heath Hayes, Cannock, Staffs WS12 5DZ* Heath Hayes (01543) 270107

GRAYSON, Canon Robert William. b 24. Worc Coll Ox BA48 MA49 DipTh50. Wycliffe Hall Ox 49. **d** 50 **p** 51. V Stanwix *Carl* 66-79; RD Carl 71-79; Hon Can Carl Cathl 76-89; V Appleby 79-89; R Ormside 81-89; rtd 89. *Panorama, North End, Burgh-by-Sands, Carlisle CA5 6BD* Burgh-by-Sands (01228) 576863

GREADY, Andrew John. b 63. Univ Coll Lon BSc84. St Jo Coll Nottm DPS89. **d** 89 **p** 90. C Monkwearmouth St Andr *Dur* 89-92; S Africa from 92. *PO Box 39063, Bramley, 2018 South Africa* Johannesburg (11) 786-0656

GREANY, Richard Andrew Hugh. b 44. Qu Coll Ox BA67 MA83. Coll of Resurr Mirfield 67. **d** 69 **p** 70. C Hartlepool St Oswald *Dur* 69-72; C Clifton All SS *Bris* 72-75; Tutor Coll of Resurr Mirfield 75-78; V Whitworth w Spennymoor *Dur* 78-83; P-in-c Byers Green 78-79; Asst Prin St Alb Minl Tr Scheme 83-88; V Flamstead *St Alb* 83-88; V Hessle *York* 88-94; P-in-c Cam St Mary Less *Ely* 94-95; V from 95. *Saint Mary the Less Vicarage, 4 Newnham Terrace, Cambridge CB3 9EX* Cambridge (01223) 350733

GREASLEY, James Kenneth (Jim). b 39. K Coll Lon BD AKC66. **d** 67 **p** 68. C Stoke upon Trent *Lich* 67-70; Zambia 70-76; Chapl HM Borstal Gaynes Hall 76-81; V Gt Staughton *Ely* 76-81; V Melbourn from 81; V Meldreth from 81; RD Shingay from 82. *The Vicarage, Melbourn, Royston, Herts SG8 6DY* Royston (01763) 260295

GREATBATCH, John Charles. b 56. BA. Coll of Resurr Mirfield. **d** 83 **p** 84. C Wednesbury St Paul Wood Green *Lich* 83-88; C Codsall 88-94; V Tipton St Jo from 94. *St John's Vicarage, Upper Church Lane, Tipton, W Midlands DY4 9ND* 0121-557 1793

GREATHEAD, Canon Edwin Bateson. b 24. Man Univ BA49. Wycliffe Hall Ox 49. **d** 51 **p** 52. V Hatf *Sheff* 61-78; Chapl HM Borstal Hatf 75-78; V Frodingham *Linc* 78-89; Can and Preb Linc Cathl from 87; rtd 89. *17 Bakersfield, Wrawby, Brigg, S Humberside DN20 8SZ* Brigg (01652) 658603

GREATREX, Warren Robert. b 21. Qu Univ Kingston Ontario BCom41. Trin Coll Toronto LTh50 BD51. **d** 50 **p** 51. Canada 50-78; Perm to Offic *Heref* from 78. *The Highlands, Symonds Yat, Ross-on-Wye, Herefordshire HR9 6DY* Symonds Yat (01600) 890318

GREAVES, Arthur Roy Hurst. b 15. Man Univ BA38. Ridley Hall Cam 38. **d** 40 **p** 41. V Diseworth *Leic* 69-78; R Long Whatton and Diseworth 78-82; rtd 82. *Unit 103, 20 Excelsior Street, Shenton Park, W Australia 6008* Perth (9) 382-1198

GREAVES, Canon John Neville. b 29. AAA156 Lon Univ DipTh60. St Aid Birkenhead 58. **d** 61 **p** 62. Min-in-c St Rich Peel Hall (Wythenshawe) 67-69; V Wythenshawe St Rich *Man* 71-73; R Sadberge *Dur* 73-78; V Dur St Cuth 78-94; Chapl New Coll Dur 78-92; Chapl Dur Fire Brigade 85-94; RD Dur 80-93; Hon Can Dur Cathl 91-94; rtd 94. *47 The Beeches, Nantwich, Cheshire CW5 5YP* Nantwich (01270) 628178

GREED, Frederick John. b 44. Trin Coll Bris 79. **d** 81 **p** 82. C Yateley *Win* 81-85; R Ore *Chich* 85-95; R Street w Walton *B & W* from 95. *The Rectory, Vestry Road, Street, Somerset BA16 0HX* Street (01458) 42671

GREEDY, Tegryd Joseph (Teg). b 31. St D Coll Lamp 59. **d** 61 **p** 62. C Newbridge *Mon* 61-64; C Bassaleg 64-66; V Newport St Teilo 66-74; Hon C Newport St Mark 82-90; V Gdlcliffe and Whiston and Nash 83-90; Ind Chapl 83-90; V Marshfield and Peterstone Wentloog etc from 90. *The Vicarage, Church Lane, Marshfield, Cardiff CF3 8UF* Castleton (01633) 680257

GREEN, Alan John Enrique. b 56. Worc Coll Ox BTh77. Linc Th Coll 83. **d** 85 **p** 86. C Kirkby *Liv* 85-88; TV 88-94; Chapl Knowsley Community Coll 87-90; Chapl Worc Coll Ox from 94; Ox St Giles and SS Phil and Jas w St Marg *Ox* from 94. *173 Walton Street, Oxford OX1 2HDB* Oxford (01865) 54586

GREEN, Canon Alan Thomas. b 21. Launde Abbey. **d** 64 **p** 65. V Oaks (Charnwood Forest) *Leic* 67-70; R Braunstone 70-74; P-in-c Loddington 74-83; Hon Can Leic Cathl 78-87; P-in-c Knossington and Cold Overton 81-83; P-in-c Owston and

Withcote 81-83; V Enderby w Lubbesthorpe and Thurlaston 83-87; rtd 87. *22 Main Street, Cold Overton, Oakham, Leics LE15 7QB* Leicester (0116) 445 4345

GREEN, Alfred. b 06. St Aid Birkenhead 47. **d** 48 **p** 49. V Holme-in-Cliviger *Blackb* 66-73; rtd 73; Lic to Offic *Blackb* from 75. *40 Richmond Avenue, Cliviger, Burnley, Lancs BB10 4JL* Burnley (01282) 38429

GREEN, Arthur Edward. b 27. Chich Th Coll 58. **d** 59 **p** 60. R Burgh Parva w Briston *Nor* 67-75; V Middleton 75-76; V Middleton w E Winch 76-84; R Neatishead w Irstead 84-90; V Barton Turf 84-90; R Neatishead, Barton Turf and Irstead 90-92; rtd 92. *2 Clinton Road, Waterlooville, Hants PO7 6DT* Waterlooville (01705) 240789

GREEN, Barrie. b 51. SS Coll Cam BA72 MA76. Wycliffe Hall Ox 75. **d** 78 **p** 79. C Castle Vale *Birm* 78-81; V W Heath from 81; RD Kings Norton 87-93. *St Anne's Vicarage, Lilley Lane, Birmingham B31 3JT* 0121-475 5587

GREEN, Brian Robert. b 31. Bris Univ BA55. Tyndale Hall Bris 52. **d** 56 **p** 57. C Toxteth Park St Philemon *Liv* 56-58; V Toxteth Park St Philemon w St Silas 58-59; P-in-c Toxteth Park St Gabr 64-69; P-in-c Toxteth Park St Jo and St Thos 64-69; P-in-c Toxteth Park St Jas and St Matt 68-69; V Elsenham *Chelmsf* 69-85; V Henham 69-85; P-in-c Ugley 84-85; V Henham and Elsenham w Ugley 85-89; RD Newport and Stansted 87-89; Perm to Offic *Ex* 90-91; V Tidenham w Beachley and Lancaut *Glouc* from 91. *Tidenham Vicarage, Gloucester Road, Tutshill, Chepstow, Gwent NP6 7DH* Chepstow (01291) 622442

GREEN, Mrs Catherine Isabel (Cathy). b 48. Cant Sch of Min 89. **d** 92 **p** 94. Par Dn Willesborough *Cant* 92-94; C from 94. *11 Earlsworth Road, Willesborough, Ashford, Kent TN24 0DF* Ashford (01233) 646202

GREEN, Charles Clisby. b 11. St Aid Birkenhead 46. **d** 48 **p** 49. R Eling *Win* 68-73; R Testwood 68-73; V Marchwood 68-73; TR Eling, Testwood and Marchwood 73-75; rtd 75; Perm to Offic *Man* 77-79; Perm to Offic *Win* 79-85. *Fosbrooke House, 8 Clifton Drive, Lytham, Lytham St Annes, Lancs FY8 5RE* Lytham (01253) 738189

GREEN, Christopher Frederick. b 46. Nottm Univ BTh75 Birm Univ DipEd85. Bp Otter Coll CertEd69 Linc Th Coll 71. **d** 75 **p** 76. C Hodge Hill *Birm* 75-77; C S Lafford *Linc* 77-79; P-in-c Worc St Mich *Worc* 79-82; Hd of Relig Studies & Lib RNIB New Coll Worc from 82. *Darenth, Walkers Lane, Whittington, Worcester WR5 2RE* Worcester (01905) 355714

GREEN, Christopher Martyn. b 58. New Coll Edin BD80. Cranmer Hall Dur 82. **d** 83 **p** 84. C Virginia Water *Guildf* 83-87; C Bromley Ch Ch *Roch* 87-91; Study Asst the Proclamation Trust 91-92; C Surbiton Hill Ch Ch *S'wark* from 92. *181 Elgar Avenue, Surbiton, Surrey KT5 9JX* 0181-399 1503

GREEN, Mrs Clare Noreen. b 30. SW Minl Tr Course 84. **d** 88. NSM Bideford *Ex* 88-90; Perm to Offic from 90. *5 St Margarets Court, Lakenham Hill, Northam, Bideford, Devon EX39 1JW* Bideford (01237) 472960

GREEN, Clifford. b 28. Leeds Univ BA51. Coll of Resurr Mirfield 51. **d** 53 **p** 54. C Solihull *Birm* 53-56; CR from 58; Lic to Offic *Wakef* 59-62 and from 67; S Africa 63-66; Lic to Offic *Ripon* 75-76. *House of the Resurrection, Mirfield, W Yorkshire WF14 0BN* Mirfield (01924) 494318

GREEN, David John. b 32. K Alfred's Coll Win 51 CPC84. Sarum Th Coll 63. **d** 64 **p** 65. C Trowbridge H Trin *Sarum* 64-68; Hd of RE Trowbridge Boys' High Sch 64-68; V Bournemouth St Fran *Win* 68-70; V Weymouth St Paul *Sarum* 70-95; Chapl S Dorset Tech Coll Weymouth 80-85; Chapl Weymouth Coll 85-95. *St Mary's House, 1 Rolfe Crescent, Chickerell, Weymouth, Dorset DT3 4LY* Weymouth (01305) 766700

GREEN, David John. b 54. DCR, MU. SW Minl Tr Course 82. **d** 85 **p** 86. C St Marychurch *Ex* 85-89; C Laira 89-90; V Maughold *S & M* from 90. *The Vicarage, Maughold, Ramsey, Isle of Man IM7 1AS* Ramsey (01624) 812070

GREEN, David Norman. b 37. Magd Coll Cam BA60. Clifton Th Coll 60. **d** 62 **p** 63. SSF from 55; C Islington St Mary *Lon* 62-65; C Burley *Ripon* 65-68; Kenya 69-80; P-in-c Brimscombe *Glouc* 81-90; R Woodchester and Brimscombe from 90. *The Vicarage, Brimscombe, Stroud, Glos GL5 2PA* Brimscombe (01453) 882204

GREEN, David William. b 53. CertEd75 Nottm Univ BCommStuds84. Linc Th Coll 81. **d** 84 **p** 85. C S Merstham *S'wark* 84-88; C Walton-on-Thames *Guildf* 88-91; V Gillingham H Trin *Roch* from 91; Chapl to Lennox Wood Elderly People's Home from 91. *Holy Trinity Vicarage, 2 Waltham Road, Gillingham, Kent ME8 6XQ* Medway (01634) 231690 or 231372

GREEN, Canon Dennis John. b 45. Lich Th Coll 69. **d** 72 **p** 73. C Hampton All SS *Lon* 72-74; P-in-c Leverington *Ely* 75-76; R 76-80; Can Res Ely Cathl from 80; Vice-Dean and Treas Ely Cathl from 84; Dioc Development Officer for Par from 80;

Dioc Development Consultant from 84; Cathl Development Officer from 92. *The Black Hostelry, The College, Ely, Cambs CB7 4DL* Ely (01353) 662612

GREEN, Canon Derek George Wilson. b 27. Bris Univ BA53 MA58. Tyndale Hall Bris 48. **d** 53 **p** 54. R N Pickenham w Houghton on the Hill *Nor* 58-89; R S Pickenham 58-89; R N Pickenham w S Pickenham etc 89-93; Hon Can Nor Cathl 78-93; E Region Co-ord Scripture Union 80-92; rtd 93. *5 Hawkins Meadow, College Fields, Marlborough, Wilts SN8 1UA* Marlborough (01672) 511713

GREEN, Donald Henry. b 31. Selw Coll Cam BA54. Qu Coll Birm 81. **d** 83 **p** 84. C Dudley Holly Hall St Aug *Worc* 83-85; V Dudley St Barn 85-90. *The Cuckoo's Nest, 12 Mill Green, Knighton, Powys LD7 1EE* Knighton (01547) 528289

GREEN, Donald Pentney (Brother Donald). b 25. Leeds Univ BA50. Coll of Resurr Mirfield 50. **d** 52 **p** 53. C Ardwick St Benedict *Man* 52-55; SSF from 55; Sec for Miss SSF from 78; Lic to Offic *Chelmsf* 58-60 and 69-72; Papua New Guinea 60-63; Chapl HM Pris Kingston Portsm 72-76; Lic to Offic *Edin* 76-77; Org Sec Catholic Renewal 77; Lic to Offic *Lich* from 78. *42 Balaam Street, London E13 8AQ* 0171-474 5863

GREEN, Mrs Dorothy Mary. b 36. Westf Coll Lon BA58. Selly Oak Coll 60. **dss** 83 **d** 87 **p** 94. Ryde All SS *Portsm* 83-87; C 87-91; Hon C Hempnall *Nor* from 91. *The Rectory, Hempnall, Norwich NR15 2AD* Hempnall (01508) 498157

GREEN, Douglas Edward. b 17. Sarum Th Coll 47. **d** 50 **p** 51. V Bosbury *Heref* 58-78; R Coddington 59-79; V Wellington Heath 59-79; Hon C Minsterley 78-80; rtd 82; Perm to Offic *Worc* from 83. *St Agnes, Lower Dingle, Malvern, Worcs WR14 4BQ*

GREEN, Duncan Jamie. b 52. Sarum & Wells Th Coll 82. **d** 84 **p** 85. C Uckfield *Chich* 84-87; Youth Chapl *Chelmsf* from 87; Warden and Chapl St Mark's Coll Res Cen from 93. *St Mark's College, Audley End, Saffron Walden, Essex CB11 4JD* Saffron Walden (01799) 522006

GREEN, Edward John. b 35. Lich Th Coll. **d** 59 **p** 60. C Longford *Cov* 59-61; C Wigston Magna *Leic* 61-65; V from 73; V Ellistown 65-73. *The Vicarage, Bushloe End, Wigston, Leics LE18 2BA* Leicester (0116) 288 3419

GREEN, Edward Marcus. b 66. Mert Coll Ox BA88 MA92. Wycliffe Hall Ox 90. **d** 94 **p** 95. C Glyncorrwg w Afan Vale and Cymmer Afan *Llan* from 94. *2 Hillcrest House, Pen-y-Bryn, Cymmer, Port Talbot, W Glam SA11 3SE* Port Talbot (01639) 851135

GREEN, Canon Edward Michael Bankes. b 30. Ex Coll Ox BA53 MA56 Qu Coll Cam BA57 MA61 BD66 Toronto Univ DD92. Ridley Hall Cam 55. **d** 57 **p** 58. C Eastbourne H Trin *Chich* 57-60; Tutor Lon Coll of Div 60-69; Prin St Jo Coll Nottm 69-75; Hon Can Cov Cathl *Cov* 70-78; R Ox St Aldate w H Trin *Ox* 75-82; R Ox St Aldate w St Matt 82-86; Canada 87-92; Prof Evang Regent Coll Vancouver 87-92; Abps' Adv Springboard for Decade of Evang from 92; Six Preacher Cant Cathl *Cant* from 93. *7 The Green, Beeston, Nottingham NG9 5BE* Nottingham (0115) 943 1738 Fax 431737

GREEN, Edward Wallace. b 11. K Coll Lon BA32 AKC33. Ripon Hall Ox 33. **d** 35 **p** 36. Chapl Oakham Sch Leics 54-58; Perm to Offic *Chelmsf* 61-79; rtd 79; Perm to Offic *Win* from 81. *Day House, Alma Road, Romsey, Hants SO51 8EB* Southampton (01703) 557756

GREEN, Mrs Elizabeth Pauline Anne. b 29. Lon Coll of Div DipRK70. **dss** 76 **d** 87 **p** 94. Chorleywood Ch Ch *St Alb* 76-87; Par Dn 87-90; C Chipping Sodbury and Old Sodbury *Glouc* from 90; Asst Dioc Missr from 90. *The Old House, Parks Farm, Old Sodbury, Bristol BS17 6PX* Chipping Sodbury (01454) 311936

GREEN, Eric Kenneth. b 18. Tyndale Hall Bris 40. **d** 45 **p** 47. R All Cannings w Etchilhampton *Sarum* 63-75; V Over Kellet *Blackb* 75-83; rtd 83. *1 Hill Crescent, Burley in Wharfedale, Ilkley, W Yorkshire LS29 7QG* Burley-in-Wharfedale (01943) 864538

GREEN, Ernest James. b 31. Pemb Coll Cam BA55 MA62. Linc Th Coll 55. **d** 57 **p** 58. C Rawmarsh w Parkgate *Sheff* 57-60; Sec Th Colls Dept SCM 60-62; Prec and Sacr Bris Cathl *Bris* 62-65; Min Can 62-65; V Churchill *B & W* 65-78; RD Locking 72-78; V Burrington and Churchill 78-82; Preb Wells Cathl 81-82; V Ryde All SS *Portsm* 82-91; P-in-c Ryde H Trin 82-86; RD E Wight 83-88; TR Hempnall *Nor* from 91. *The Rectory, Hempnall, Norwich NR15 2AD* Hempnall (01508) 498157

GREEN, Ernest Swinfen. b 12. Wells Th Coll 66. **d** 67 **p** 67. V Lower Beeding *Chich* 70-77; rtd 77. *9 Barleycroft, Cowfold, Horsham, W Sussex RH13 8DP* Horsham (01403) 864352

GREEN, Frank Gilbert. b 23. Kelham Th Coll 46. **d** 50 **p** 51. SSM from 52; S Africa 84-88; Lesotho 69-84; Lic to Offic *Ox* from 88; rtd 93. *SSM Priory, Willen, Milton Keynes MK15 9AA* Milton Keynes (01908) 663749 Fax 234546

GREEN, Canon Frederick George (Fred). b 40. Nottm Univ BA62 MA67. Linc Th Coll 64. **d** 66 **p** 67. C Warsop *S'well* 66-70; R 76-89; V Clipstone 70-76; P-in-c Norton Cuckney

85-89; TR Hucknall Torkard from 89; Hon Can S'well Minster from 93; RD Newstead from 93. *The Rectory, Annesley Road, Hucknall, Nottingham NG15 7DE* Nottingham (0115) 963 2033

GREEN, Gary Henry. b 64. Univ of Wales (Cardiff) BD87 DPT95. St Mich Coll Llan 93. **d** 95. C Baglan *Llan* from 95. *35 Crawford Road, Port Talbot, W Glam SA12 8ND* Port Talbot (01639) 814116

GREEN, George Henry Langston. b 12. St Aug Coll Cant 38. **d** 41 **p** 42. V Frodsham *Ches* 55-78; rtd 78; Perm to Offic *Ches* from 78. *River View, Gwespyr, Holywell, Clwyd CH8 9JS* Prestatyn (01745) 857489

GREEN, George James. b 26. Cuddesdon Coll 69. **d** 69 **p** 70. C Handsworth St Mary *Birm* 69-76; R Croughton w Evenley *Pet* 76-88; R Aynho and Croughton w Evenley from 88. *The Rectory, Croughton Road, Aynho, Banbury, Oxon OX17 3BG* Croughton (01869) 810903

GREEN, Gordon Sydney. b 33. Ridley Hall Cam 77. **d** 79 **p** 80. C Ipswich St Marg *St E* 79-83; TV Barton Mills, Beck Row w Kenny Hill etc 83-85; TV Mildenhall 85-86; Perm to Offic *Pet* from 87; rtd 88. *1 Highcliffe Close, High Street, Thornton, Bradford, W Yorkshire BD13 3EH* Bradford (01274) 835001

GREEN, Graham Herbert. b 53. City Univ BSc74. Westcott Ho Cam 75. **d** 78 **p** 79. C Hatcham St Cath *S'wark* 78-82; C S Ashford Ch Ch *Cant* 82-88; V Cheriton All So w Newington from 88. *All Souls' Vicarage, 1 Ashley Avenue, Cheriton, Folkestone, Kent CT19 4PX* Folkestone (01303) 275483

GREEN, Graham Reginald. b 48. Sarum & Wells Th Coll 71. **d** 74 **p** 75. C Chorley St Laur *Blackb* 74-76; C Padiham 76-79; V Osmondthorpe St Phil *Ripon* 79-94. *3 Northwood Gardens, Colton, Leeds LS15 9HH* Leeds (0113) 264 3558

GREEN, Humphrey Christian (Father Benedict). b 24. Mert Coll Ox BA49 MA52. Cuddesdon Coll 50. **d** 51 **p** 82. Lic to Offic *Wakef* from 61; CR from 62; Vice-Prin Coll of Resurr Mirfield 65-75; Prin 75-84; rtd 94. *House of the Resurrection, Mirfield, W Yorkshire WF14 0BN* Mirfield (01924) 494318

GREEN, James Hardman. b 19. Open Univ BA74. **d** 52 **p** 53. R Morcott w S Luffenham *Pet* 65-75; Chapl R Assn for Deaf and Dumb 75-77; V E Boldon *Dur* 77-84; rtd 84. *1 Netherwindings, Towthorpe Road, Haxby, York YO3 3FB* York (01904) 764364

GREEN, James Manton. b 33. E Midl Min Tr Course 82. **d** 85 **p** 86. Hon C Kirby Muxloe *Leic* 85-89; Asst Chapl Glenfield Gen and Glenfrith Hosps from 89. *83 Oakcroft Avenue, Kirby Muxloe, Leicester LE9 2DH* Leicester (0116) 239 3126

GREEN, Miss Jennifer Mary (Jenny). b 55. SEN78 SRN81 RM84. Trin Coll Bris DipHE88 ADPS89. **d** 90 **p** 95. C Tong *Bradf* 90-93; Chapl Bradf Cathl 93; CMS from 94; Uganda from 94. *Muhabura Diocese, PO Box 22, Kisoro, Uganda*

GREEN, Jeremy Nigel. b 52. St Andr Univ MA Nottm Univ DipTh. St Jo Coll Nottm 80. **d** 83 **p** 84. C Dorridge *Birm* 83-86; V Scrooby *S'well* 86-94; V Bawtry w Austerfield and Misson from 94. *The Vicarage, Martin Lane, Bawtry, Doncaster, S Yorkshire DN10 6NJ* Doncaster (01302) 710298

GREEN, John. b 28. AKC54. **d** 55 **p** 56. V Inskip *Blackb* 63-75; V Fairhaven 75-87; rtd 87; Perm to Offic *Blackb* from 87. *42 Westwood Road, Lytham, Lytham St Annes, Lancs FY8 5NX* Lytham (01253) 739288

GREEN, John. b 53. Nottm Univ BCombStuds83. Linc Th Coll 80. **d** 83 **p** 84. C Watford St Mich *St Alb* 83-86; C St Alb St Steph 86-91; Chapl RN from 91. *Directorate Gen, RN Chapl Services, Room 203, Victory Building, HM Naval Base, Portsmouth PO1 3LS* Portsmouth (01705) 727903 Fax 727112

GREEN, John David. b 29. Lon Univ BD66. Roch Th Coll 63. **d** 66 **p** 66. C Roch St Pet w St Marg *Roch* 66-72; V Oxshott *Guildf* 72-85; R Weybridge 85-94; rtd 94. *103 Bitterne Drive, Woking, Surrey GU21 3JX* Woking (01483) 727936

GREEN, John Francis Humphrey. b 44. MIL85 Ex Univ BA65. Westcott Ho Cam CTM93. **d** 93 **p** 94. C Tadworth *S'wark* from 93. *22 Station Approach Road, Tadworth, Surrey KT20 5AD* Tadworth (01737) 812006

GREEN, Canon John Henry. b 44. K Coll Lon BD72 AKC. **d** 73 **p** 74. C Tupsley *Heref* 73-77; Asst Chapl Newc Univ *Newc* 77-79; V Stevenage St Hugh Chells *St Alb* 79-85; V St Jo in Bedwardine *Worc* 85-92; P-in-c Newland, Guarlford and Madresfield from 92; Dir of Ords from 92; Hon Can Worc Cathl from 94. *The Rectory, Madresfield, Malvern, Worcs WR13 5AB* Malvern (01684) 574919

GREEN, John Herbert Gardner-Waterman. b 21. Trin Hall Cam BA48 MA58. Wells Th Coll 58. **d** 59 **p** 60. R Sandhurst w Newenden *Cant* 68-90; RD W Charing 74-81; rtd 90. *Littlefield House, Maytham Road, Rolvenden Layne, Cranbrook, Kent TN17 4NS* Cranbrook (01580) 241579

GREEN, Preb John Stanley. b 12. Keble Coll Ox BA33 MA37. Wells Th Coll 33. **d** 35 **p** 36. R Ex St Jas *Ex* 49-77; Preb Ex Cathl 69-84; rtd 77; Perm to Offic *Ex* from 84. *2 Whiteway Drive, Heavitree, Exeter EX1 3AN* Exeter (01392) 437291

GREEN, Joseph Hudson. b 28. TD76. Dur Univ TCert73. Kelham Th Coll 48. **d** 53 **p** 54. CF (TAVR) 67-77; V Leadgate *Dur* 69-78; V Dudleston *Lich* 78-85; V Criftins 78-85; R Hodnet w Weston under Redcastle 85-93; RD Hodnet 86-93; rtd 93. *3 The Paddocks, Market Drayton, Shropshire TF9 3UE* Market Drayton (01630) 658887

GREEN, Julia Ann. b 58. Nottm Univ BA80. Linc Th Coll 84. **dss** 86 **d** 87 **p** 94. Asst Chapl HM Pris Morton Hall 85-90; Linc St Jo *Linc* 86-87; Hon C 87-88; Hon C Bardney from 88; Chapl Linc Co Hosp from 90; Chapl St Geo Hosp Linc from 90. *The Rectory, 10 Church Lane, Bardney, Lincoln LN3 5TZ* Bardney (01526) 398595

GREEN, Miss Karina Beverley. b 61. Ripon Coll Cuddesdon 87. **d** 90 **p** 94. C Lee-on-the-Solent *Portsm* 90-93; Dioc Youth Officer *Guildf* from 94. *2 South Hill, Godalming, Surrey GU7 1JT* Godalming (01483) 416539

✠**GREEN, Rt Rev Laurence Alexander (Laurie).** b 45. K Coll Lon BD68 AKC68. DMin82 NY Th Sem STM69 St Aug Coll Cant 70. **d** 70 **p** 71 **c** 93. C Kingstanding St Mark *Birm* 70-73; V Erdington St Chad 73-83; Prin Aston Tr Scheme 83-89; Hon C Birchfield *Birm* 84-89; TR Poplar *Lon* 89-93; Area Bp Bradwell *Chelmsf* from 93. *The Bishop's House, Orsett Road, Horndon-on-the-Hill, Stanford-le-Hope, Essex SS17 8NS* Stanford-le-Hope (01375) 673806 Fax 674222

GREEN, Leslie James. b 31. K Coll Lon BD53 AKC54. **d** 56 **p** 57. R Glas St Oswald *Glas* 60-70; Lic to Offic *Dur* 71-73; V Oxclose 73-82; TR Sheff Manor *Sheff* 82-85; V Nether w Upper Poppleton *York* 85-93; rtd 93. *16 Kingsclere, Huntington, York YO3 9SF* York (01904) 769088

GREEN, Mrs Margaret Elizabeth. b 34. DipYL65. St Mich Ho Ox 60. **dss** 84 **d** 87 **p** 94. Ecclesall *Sheff* 84-87; Par Dn 87-90; C Doncaster St Jas 90-94; rtd 95. *91 Littemoor Lane, Doncaster, S Yorkshire DN4 0LQ* Doncaster (01302) 365884

✠**GREEN, Rt Rev Mark.** b 17. MC45. Linc Coll Ox BA40 MA44 Aston Univ Hon DSc80. Cuddesdon Coll 40. **d** 40 **p** 41 **c** 72. C Glouc St Cath *Glouc* 40-42; CF (EC) 43-46; V Newland St Jo *York* 48-53; CF 53-56; V S Bank *York* 56-58; R Cottingham 58-64; Can and Preb York Minster 63-72; Hon Chapl to Abp York 64-72; V Bishopthorpe 64-72; V Acaster Malbis 64-72; RD Ainsty 64-68; Suff Bp Aston *Birm* 72-82; Dioc Dir of Ords 80-82; rtd 82; Asst Bp Chich from 82. *27 Selwyn House, Selwyn Road, Eastbourne, E Sussex BN21 2LF* Eastbourne (01323) 642707

GREEN, Martin Charles. b 59. Bris Univ BA81 MPhil86. Wycliffe Hall Ox 82. **d** 84 **p** 85. C Margate H Trin *Cant* 84-88; V Kingston upon Hull Southcoates St Aid *York* 88-94; P-in-c Bishop's Itchington *Cov* from 94. *The Vicarage, Bishop's Itchington, Leamington Spa CV33 0QT* Harbury (01926) 613466

GREEN, Martyn. b 41. FCA. Ridley Hall Cam 78. **d** 80 **p** 81. C Wetherby *Ripon* 80-83; V Leeds St Cypr Harehills 83-90; V Ossett cum Gawthorpe *Wakef* from 90. *The Vicarage, Fearnley Avenue, Ossett, W Yorkshire WF5 9ET* Wakefield (01924) 274068

GREEN, Canon Maurice Paul. b 34. MCIMA60. Wells Th Coll 68. **d** 70 **p** 71. C Eaton *Nor* 70-74; R N w S Wootton 74-90; RD Lynn 83-89; Hon Can Nor Cathl from 88; V Swaffham from 90. *The Vicarage, White Cross Road, Swaffham, Norfolk PE37 8QY* Swaffham (01760) 721373

GREEN, Neil Howard. b 57. New Coll Ox BA80 PGCE81. Wycliffe Hall Ox 87. **d** 90 **p** 91. C Finchley St Paul and St Luke *Lon* 90-94; C Muswell Hill St Jas w St Matt from 94. *8 St James Lane, London N10 3DB* 0181-883 0636

GREEN, Nicholas Eliot. b 54. Leeds Univ BA76 Lon Univ BD78 AKC. Westcott Ho Cam 78. **d** 79 **p** 80. C Southgate Ch Ch *Lon* 79-82; Chapl Brooklands Tech Coll 82-86; C Weybridge *Guildf* 82-86; V Hilton *Ely* 86-92; V Fenstanton 86-92; R Princes Risborough w Ilmer *Ox* from 92. *The Rectory, 54 Manor Park Avenue, Princes Risborough, Bucks HP27 9AR* Princes Risborough (01844) 344784

GREEN, Paul. b 25. RD. Sarum & Wells Th Coll 72. **d** 74 **p** 75. C Pinhoe *Ex* 74-77; P-in-c 77-79; V 79-85; P-in-c Bishopsteignton 85-88; P-in-c Ideford, Luton and Ashcombe 85-88; rtd 88; Perm to Offic *Ex* from 88. *58 Maudlin Drive, Teignmouth, Devon TQ14 8SB* Teignmouth (01626) 777312

GREEN, Paul Francis. b 48. Cranmer Hall Dur BA78. **d** 79 **p** 80. C Cirencester *Glouc* 79-82; C Lydney w Aylburton 82-85; V Westbury-on-Severn w Flaxley and Blaisdon 85-90; Chapl Carlton Hayes Hosp from 90; Chapl Leics Mental Health Service Unit from 90. *Carlton Hayes Hospital, Forest Road, Narborough, Leics LE9 5ES* Leicester (0116) 286 3481

GREEN, Paul John. b 48. Sarum & Wells Th Coll 72. **d** 73 **p** 74. C Tuffley *Glouc* 73-76; C Prestbury 76-82; P-in-c Highnam w Lassington and Rudford 82-83; P-in-c Tibberton w Taynton 82-83; R Highnam, Lassington, Rudford, Tibberton etc 84-92; Hon Min Can Glouc Cathl from 85; V Fairford from 92; RD Fairford from 93. *The Vicarage, Fairford, Glos GL7 4BB* Cirencester (01285) 712467

GREEN, Peter. b 38. Ex Univ BSc59. Sarum Th Coll 59. **d** 61 **p** 62. C Romford St Edw *Chelmsf* 61-66; Ceylon 66-70; V Darnall H Trin *Sheff* 71-80; TV Stantonbury *Ox* 80-87; TV Stantonbury and Willen 87-91; Dep Chapl HM Pris Belmarsh 91-92; Chapl HM Pris Woodhill from 92. *The Chaplain's Office, HM Prison Woodhill, Tattenhoe Street, Milton Keynes MK4 4DA* Milton Keynes (01908) 501999 Fax 505417

GREEN, Canon Peter Edwin. b 33. Lich Th Coll. **d** 62 **p** 63. C-in-c Heartsease St Fran CD *Nor* 65-73; V Loddon w Sisland 73-91; Hon Can Nor Cathl 86-92; rtd 92; Perm to Offic *Nor* from 92. *Ambleside, Lowestoft Road, Beccles, Suffolk NR34 7DG* Beccles (01502) 717740

GREEN, Peter Geoffrey. b 59. St Andr Univ MA83. Coll of Resurr Mirfield 85. **d** 88 **p** 89. C Pershore w Pinvin, Wick and Birlingham *Worc* 88-91; V Dudley St Barn from 91. *St Barnabas's Vicarage, Middlepark Road, Dudley, W Midlands DY1 2LD* Dudley (01384) 256680

GREEN, Peter Jamie. b 63. Reading Coll of Tech C&G82. Aston Tr Scheme 87 Oak Hill Th Coll BA93. **d** 93 **p** 94. C Brigg *Linc* from 93. *5 Winston Way, Brigg, S Humberside DN20 8UA* Brigg (01652) 655609

GREEN, Philip Charles. b 53. Wigan Coll of Tech HNC77 IMC81. Nor Ord Course 91. **d** 94 **p** 95. C Southport Em *Liv* from 94. *28 Elswick Green, Southport, Merseyside PR9 9XT* Southport (01704) 27294

GREEN, Canon Philip Harry. b 19. ALCD50. **d** 50 **p** 51. V Shipley St Paul *Bradf* 64-77; Hon Can Bradf Cathl 77-82; V Gargrave 77-82; rtd 82; Perm to Offic *Bradf* from 82; Perm to Offic *Carl* from 82. *102 Kentsford Road, Grange-over-Sands, Cumbria LA11 7BB* Grange-over-Sands (015395) 32950

GREEN, Richard Charles. b 49. K Coll Lon 68 St Aug Coll Cant 73. **d** 74 **p** 75. C Broseley w Benthall *Heref* 74-79; TV Heref St Martin w St Fran (S Wye TM) from 80. *Flat 3, St Martin's Parish Centre, Ross Road, Hereford HR2 7RJ* Hereford (01432) 354588 or 353717 Fax 352412

GREEN, Robert Henry. b 57. K Coll Lon BD79. Wycliffe Hall Ox 81. **d** 83 **p** 84. C Norbury *Ches* 83-86 and from 91; C Knutsford St Jo and Toft 86-88; rtd 88. *122 Cavendish Road, Hazel Grove, Stockport, Cheshire SK7 6JH* Poynton (01625) 877042

GREEN, Robert Leonard. b 44. Sarum & Wells Th Coll. **d** 84 **p** 85. C Battersea St Luke *S'wark* 84-89; CF from 89. *c/o MOD (Army), Bagshot Park, Bagshot, Surrey GU19 5PL* Bagshot (01276) 471717 Fax 412834

GREEN, Robert Stanley. b 42. Dur Univ BA65. Wells Th Coll 65. **d** 67 **p** 68. C Ashford *Cant* 67-73; R Otham 73-80; V Bethersden w High Halden 80-87; R Winterbourne Stickland and Turnworth etc *Sarum* from 87. *The Rectory, Winterbourne Stickland, Blandford Forum, Dorset DT11 0NL* Milton Abbas (01258) 880482

GREEN, Robin Christopher William. b 43. Leeds Univ BA64 Fitzw Ho Cam BA67. Ridley Hall Cam 65. **d** 68 **p** 69. C S'wark H Trin *S'wark* 68-71; C Englefield Green *Guildf* 71-73; Chapl Whitelands Coll of HE *S'wark* 73-78; Team Ldr Dioc Lay Tr Team 78-84; V W Brompton St Mary w St Pet *Lon* 84-87; USPG 87-90; Perm to Offic *S'wark* 88-90; NSM from 91. *2 Church Path, Mitcham, Surrey CR4 3BN* 0181-543 0519

GREEN, Rodney William. b 52. Local NSM Course 90. **d** 93 **p** 94. NSM Flixton St Jo *Man* from 93. *9 Fishermore Road, Urmston, Manchester M31 2TU* 0161-748 7238

GREEN, Roger Thomas. b 43. Oak Hill Th Coll DipHE79. **d** 79 **p** 80. C Paddock Wood *Roch* 79-83; R High Halstow w All Hallows and Hoo St Mary 83-89; Chapl HM Pris Brixton 89-90; Chapl HM Pris Standford Hill from 90. *HM Prison Standford Hill, Church Road, Eastchurch, Sheerness, Kent ME12 4AA* Sheerness (01795) 880441 Fax 880267

GREEN, Preb Ronald Henry (Ron). b 27. Lambeth MA86 Bps' Coll Cheshunt 53. **d** 55 **p** 56. RE Adv *Lon* 63-73; V Hampstead St Steph 64-73; RD N Camden (Hampstead) 67-73; V Heston 73-80; Preb St Paul's Cathl 75-83; Jt Dir Lon and S'wark Bd of Educn 79-83; Dir of Educn *Sarum* 83-86; R Chiddingfold *Guildf* 86-91; rtd 91; Perm to Offic *Nor* 91-92; Master St Nic Hosp from 92. *The Master's House, St Nicholas Hospital, Harnham, Salisbury SP1 2SW* Salisbury (01722) 336874

GREEN, Ruth Valerie. See JAGGER, Mrs Ruth Valerie

GREEN, Sidney Leonard. b 44. Lon Univ DipTh70 BD72 MTh86 Montessori Soc DipEd84. Oak Hill Th Coll 68. **d** 72 **p** 73. C Skelmersdale St Paul *Liv* 72-74; C Denton Holme *Carl* 74-76; In Bapt Ch 76-85; Chapl Qu Eliz Gr Sch Blackb 85-91; Perm to Offic *Blackb* 91; Chapl Epsom Coll Surrey from 91; Lic to Offic *Guildf* from 91. *17 Tintagel Close, Epsom, Surrey KT17 4HA* Epsom (01372) 742204

GREEN, Stephen Keith. b 48. Ex Coll Ox BA69 Mass Inst of Tech MSc75. N Ord Course 84. **d** 87 **p** 88. Hong Kong 87-93. *10 Queen Street Place, London EC4R 1BQ or, 44 Scarsdale Villa, London W8 6PP* 0171-336 3354 or 937 3290 Fax 336 3661

GREEN, Steven Douglas. b 57. Univ of Wales (Ban) DipTh81. Sarum & Wells Th Coll 81. **d** 82 **p** 83. C Hawarden *St As* 82-86; V Mostyn 86-93; V Ffynnongroyw 86-93; V Mostyn w Ffynnongroyw from 93. *The Vicarage, Hafod y Ddol Lane, Mostyn, Holywell, Clwyd CH8 9EJ* Mostyn (01745) 560513

GREEN, Stuart. b 57. Nottm Univ BA79. Linc Th Coll 83. **d** 85 **p** 86. C Boultham *Linc* 85-88; R Bardney from 88. *The Rectory, 10 Church Lane, Bardney, Lincoln LN3 5TZ* Bardney (01526) 398595

GREEN, Ms Susan Denise. b 66. TCD BA89 HDipEd90. Irish Sch of Ecum MPhil93. **d** 92 **p** 93. C Antrim All SS *Conn* 92-95; Dio Youth Officer (Cashel) *C&O* from 95. *The Rectory, Castlecomer, Co Kilkenny, Republic of Ireland* Kilkenny (56) 41677

GREEN, Mrs Susan Margaret (Sue). b 54. Univ of Wales (Abth) BSc75. SW Minl Tr Course 92. **d** 95. NSM Wiveliscombe w Chipstable, Huish Champflower etc *B&W* from 95. *North Rodden Cottage, Maundown, Wiveliscombe, Taunton, Somerset TA4 2BU* Wiveliscombe (01984) 623809

GREEN, Trevor Geoffrey Nash. b 45. BA. Oak Hill Th Coll 81. **d** 84 **p** 85. C Stalybridge H Trin and Ch Ch *Ches* 84-89; V from 89. *The Vicarage, Hough Hill Road, Stalybridge, Cheshire SK15 2HB* 0161-303 1984

GREEN, Trevor Howard. b 37. Sarum & Wells Th Coll 72. **d** 74 **p** 75. C Bloxwich *Lich* 74-77; C Willenhall St Steph 77-79; P-in-c 79-80; V 80-82; V Essington 82-90; V Brewood from 90; V Bishopswood from 90; RD Penkridge from 94. *The Vicarage, Sandy Lane, Brewood, Stafford ST19 9ET* Brewood (01902) 850368

GREEN, Vivian Hubert Howard. b 15. DD58. **d** 39 **p** 40. Chapl Linc Coll Ox 51-79; Rector Linc Coll Ox 83-87; rtd 87. *Calendars, Sheep Street, Burford, Oxon OX18 4LS* Burford (01993) 823214

GREEN, William. b 44. Newc Univ BA66 DipEd67 MA77. N Ord Course 87. **d** 90 **p** 91. NSM Utley *Bradf* from 90. *105 Shann Lane, Keighley, W Yorkshire BD20 6DY* Keighley (01535) 605102

GREEN, William John. b 23. Birm Univ BSc43. Roch Th Coll 64. **d** 66 **p** 67. C Standish w Hardwicke and Haresfield *Glouc* 68-70; R Eastington and Frocester 70-80; P-in-c S Cerney w Cerney Wick 80-84; V S Cerney w Cerney Wick and Down Ampney 84-87; P-in-c Maisemore 87-90; rtd 90. *36 Fairfield, Upavon, Pewsey, Wilts SN9 6DZ* Stonehenge (01980) 630798

GREEN, William Lewis. b 12. St Cath Coll Cam BA34 MA39. Cuddesdon Coll 34. **d** 35 **p** 36. Benin 70-76; Nigeria 76-78; Zanzibar and Tanga 79-82; rtd 82; Perm to Offic *Ches* from 82. *20 Dunkirk Drive, Ellesmere Port, South Wirral L65 6QH* 0151-355 5456

GREENACRE, Canon Roger Tagent. b 30. Clare Coll Cam BA52 MA56. Coll of Resurr Mirfield 52. **d** 54 **p** 55. C Hanworth All SS *Lon* 54-59; Chapl Ely Th Coll 59-60; Chapl Summer Fields Sch Ox 60-61; C N Audley Street St Mark *Lon* 62-63; Chapl Liddon Ho Lon 63-65; Chapl Paris St Geo *Eur* 65-75; RD France 70-75; Dioc Ecum Officer *Chich* 75-88; Lect Chich Th Coll 75-89; Can Res and Chan Chich Cathl *Chich* from 75; Chmn Chich Dioc Eur Ecum Cttee from 89. *4 Vicars' Close, Canon Lane, Chichester, W Sussex PO19 1PT* Chichester (01243) 784244 Fax 536190

GREENALL, Canon Ronald Gilbert. b 41. St Aid Birkenhead 61. **d** 64 **p** 65. C Adlington *Blackb* 64-67; C Ribbleton 67-69; R Coppull St Jo 69-84; V Garstang St Thos from 84; RD Garstang from 89; Hon Can Blackb Cathl from 95. *The Vicarage, Church Street, Garstang, Preston PR3 1PA* Garstang (01995) 602162

GREENE, Colin John David. b 50. QUB BA73 Fitzw Coll Cam MA75 Nottm Univ PhD. St Jo Coll Nottm 78. **d** 80 **p** 81. Hon C Sandiacre *Derby* 80-81; C Loughb Em *Leic* 81-84; V Dishley and Thorpe Acre 84-89; Evang Tr Consultant Bible Soc 89-91; Tutor Trin Coll Bris from 91. *Trinity College, Stoke Hill, Bristol BS9 1JP* Bristol (0117) 968 2803

GREENE, David Arthur Kirsopp. b 36. St Pet Coll Ox BA60 MA64 FETC81. Tyndale Hall Bris 61. **d** 63 **p** 64. C Southgate *Chich* 63-66; C Kirby Grindalythe *York* 66-69; C N Grimston w Wharram Percy and Wharram-le-Street 66-69; R Folke, R Long Burton, Folke, N Wootton, Haydon etc 75-80; P-in-c Thornford w Beer Hackett 80-84; P-in-c High Stoy 81-84; R Bradf Abbas and Thornford w Beer Hackett from 84. *The Rectory, Church Road, Thornford, Sherborne, Dorset DT9 6QE* Yetminster (01935) 872382

GREENE, John Howe. b 22. K Coll Lon AKC48 BD49. **d** 49 **p** 50. R Burwash *Chich* 69-75; R Petworth 75-88; RD Petworth 76-88; P-in-c Egdean 76-80; R 80-88; rtd 88; Perm to Offic *Chich* from 88. *37 Wilderness Road, Hurstpierpoint, Hassocks, W Sussex BN6 9XD* Hurstpierpoint (01273) 833051

GREENE, Paul David O'Dwyer. b 53. Brunel Univ BSc78 Southn Univ DASS81 CQSW81. Oak Hill NSM Course 90. **d** 93 **p** 94. NSM Northwood Em *Lon* from 93. *Orchard House,*

50 The Drive, Northwood, Middx HA6 1HP Northwood (01923) 829605

GREENER, Jonathan Desmond Francis. b 61. Trin Coll Cam BA83 MA87. Coll of Resurr Mirfield 89. **d** 91 **p** 92. C S'wark H Trin w St Matt *S'wark* 91-94; Bp's Dom Chapl *Truro* from 94. *The Flat, Lis Escop, Feock, Truro, Cornwall TR3 6QQ* Truro (01872) 862657 or 862680 Fax 862037

GREENFIELD, Canon Martin Richard. b 54. Em Coll Cam MA75. Wycliffe Hall Ox MA78. **d** 79 **p** 80. C Enfield Ch Ch Trent Park *Lon* 79-83; CMS from 84; Nigeria 85-94; Hon Can Aba from 89; C Langdon Hills *Chelmsf* 94-95; R Brampton *Ely* from 95. *The Rectory, 15 Church Road, Brampton, Huntingdon, Cambs PE18 8PF* Huntingdon (01480) 453341

GREENFIELD, Norman John Charles. b 27. Leeds Univ BA51. Chich Th Coll 51. **d** 53 **p** 54. V Littleworth *Ox* 65-71; Asst Stewardship Adv 65-70; V New Marston 71-79; Dioc Stewardship Adv *Chich* 79-88; P-in-c Amberley w N Stoke 79-83; R Guestling and Pett 88-94; rtd 94. *5 Marlborough Close, Eastbourne, E Sussex BN23 8AN* Eastbourne (01323) 769494

GREENHALGH, David Murray. b 13. Jes Coll Cam BA34 MA38 Lon Univ BD47. Ridley Hall Cam 34. **d** 36 **p** 37. V Shirley *Win* 59-78; rtd 78; Perm to Offic *Pet* from 84; Perm to Offic *Linc* from 91. *3 Cricket Lawns, Oakham, Leics LE15 6HT* Oakham (01572) 757238

GREENHALGH, Eric. b 20. Tyndale Hall Bris. **d** 63 **p** 64. V Preston St Mary *Blackb* 68-72; V Partington and Carrington *Ches* 72-81; V Inskip *Blackb* 81-85; rtd 85; Perm to Offic *Blackb* from 85; Perm to Offic *Carl* from 85. *37 Fairgarth Drive, Kirkby Lonsdale, Carnforth, Lancs LA6 2DT* Kirkby Lonsdale (015242) 72122

GREENHALGH, Ian Frank. b 49. Wycliffe Hall Ox 74. **d** 77 **p** 78. C Parr *Liv* 77-80; V Wigan St Barn Marsh Green 80-84; Chapl RAF from 84. *Chaplaincy Services (RAF), HQ, Personnel and Training Command, RAF Innsworth, Gloucester GL3 1EZ* Gloucester (01452) 712612 Ext 5164 Fax 510828

GREENHALGH, Philip Adrian. b 52. Ian Ramsey Coll 75 Wycliffe Hall Ox 76. **d** 79 **p** 80. C Gt Clacton *Chelmsf* 79-82; P-in-c Stalmine *Blackb* 82-86; Perm to Offic *Ely* 86-87; Rep Leprosy Miss E Anglia 86-87; Area Org CECS 88-90; Perm to Offic *Carl* 88-93; NSM Alston Team *Newc* 90-92; NSM Chulmleigh *Ex* 92-93; NSM Chawleigh w Cheldon 92-93; NSM Wembworthy w Eggesford 92-93; P-in-c Gilsland w Nether Denton *Carl* from 93. *The School-House, Gilsland, Carlisle CA6 7AA* Gilsland (016977) 47657

GREENHALGH, Stephen. b 53. Trin Coll Bris 77 Lon Bible Coll BA80. **d** 81 **p** 82. C Horwich H Trin *Man* 81-84; C Horwich 84-85; Chapl RAF 85-93. *Address temp unknown*

GREENHILL, Anthony David. b 39. Bris Univ BSc59. Tyndale Hall Bris 61. **d** 63 **p** 64. C Southsea St Jude *Portsm* 63-65; India 65-78; C Kinson *Sarum* 78-81; V Girlington *Bradf* from 81. *The Vicarage, 27 Baslow Grove, Bradford, W Yorkshire BD9 5JA* Bradford (01274) 544987

GREENHOUGH, Alan Kenneth. b 40. St D Coll Lamp DipTh66. **d** 66 **p** 67. C Allestree *Derby* 66-70; C Ilkeston St Mary 70-73; V Bradwell 73-85; R Twyford w Guist w Bintry w Themelthorpe etc *Nor* 85-95; P-in-c Stibbard 94-95; R Twyford, Guist, Bintree, Themelthorpe etc from 95. *The Rectory, Guist, Dereham, Norfolk NR20 5LU* Foulsham (0136284) 255

GREENHOUGH, Andrew Quentin (Andy). b 68. E Lon Poly BSc89. Wycliffe Hall Ox BTh94. **d** 94 **p** 95. C Partington and Carrington *Ches* from 94. *18 Langdale Road, Partington, Urmston, Manchester M31 4NE* 0161-775 7666

GREENHOUGH, Arthur George. b 30. Fitzw Ho Cam BA52 MA56. Tyndale Hall Bris 55. **d** 57 **p** 58. C Wakef St Andr *Wakef* 57-63; R Birkin w Haddlesey *York* 63-85; RD Selby 77-84; P-in-c Hambleton 84-85; R Haddlesey w Hambleton and Birkin from 85. *The Rectory, Chapel Haddlesey, Selby, N Yorkshire YO8 8QF* Selby (01757) 270245

GREENHOUGH, Geoffrey Herman. b 36. Sheff Univ BA57 Lon Univ BD71. St Jo Coll Nottm 74. **d** 75 **p** 76. C Cheadle Hulme St Andr *Ches* 75-78; R Tilston and Shocklach 78-82; V Hyde St Geo 82-87; V Pott Shrigley from 87. *The Vicarage, Spuley Lane, Pott Shrigley, Macclesfield, Cheshire SK10 5RS* Bollington (01625) 573316

GREENING, Miss Nigella May. b 21. Gilmore Ho 62. **d** 87 **p** 94. C Glouc St Geo w Whaddon *Glouc* 87-89; rtd 89. *Fairfield, Minsterworth, Gloucester GL2 8JG* Gloucester (01452) 750243

GREENISH, Dr Brian Vivian Isitt. b 20. LRCP MRCS Lon Univ MB BSc. **d** 89 **p** 89. NSM Bedf St Pet w St Cuth *St Alb* 89-91; Perm to Offic from 91. *69 Chaucer Road, Bedford MK40 2AW* Bedford (01234) 352498

GREENLAND, Clifford James Gomm. b 09. Clifton Th Coll 63. **d** 64 **p** 65. V Wiggenhall St Mary Magd *Ely* 67-75; rtd 75. *6 Sunset Avenue, Woodford Green, Essex IG8 0ST* 0181-505 8858

GREENLAND, Robin Anthony Clive. b 31. Dur Univ BA53. Linc Th Coll 59. **d** 61 **p** 62. V Holton-le-Clay *Linc* 65-70; V Tetney 65-70; V Embsay w Eastby *Bradf* 70-78; V Earby 78-83; V Firbank, Howgill and Killington 83-94; Hon C Sedbergh, Cautley and Garsdale 83-94; rtd 94; Perm to Offic *Heref* from 94. *19 Worcester Road, Ledbury, Herefordshire HR8 1PL* Ledbury (01531) 631224

GREENLAND, Roy Wilfrid. b 37. St Steph Ho Ox 71. **d** 73 **p** 74. C Wanstead St Mary *Chelmsf* 73-76; V Harlow St Mary Magd 76-83; P-in-c Huntingdon All SS w St Jo *Ely* 83-84; P-in-c Huntingdon St Barn 83-84; P-in-c Huntingdon St Mary w St Benedict 83-84; Bermuda 84-89; V Northn St Alb *Pet* 89-92; R Waldron *Chich* from 92. *The Rectory, Sheepsetting Lane, Waldron, Heathfield, E Sussex TN21 0UY* Heathfield (01435) 862816

GREENLEES, Geoffrey Ian Loudon. b 20. Sarum Th Coll 70. **d** 71 **p** 72. C Wilton w Netherhampton and Fugglestone *Sarum* 71-74; R Woodchurch *Cant* 75-85; rtd 85; Perm to Offic *Cant* from 85. *8 Martin's Close, Tenterden, Kent TN30 7AJ* Tenterden (01580) 762586

GREENMAN, David John. b 35. Lon Univ BA59. Oak Hill Th Coll 57. **d** 61 **p** 62. C Wandsworth St Steph *S'wark* 61-63; C Bishopwearmouth St Gabr *Dur* 63-66; C-in-c Bedgrove CD *Ox* 66-74; P-in-c Macclesfield Ch Ch *Ches* 74-77; V 77-81; P-in-c Glouc All SS *Glouc* 81-85; V Glouc St Jas 81-85; V Bare *Blackb* 85-91; V Market Lavington and Easterton *Sarum* from 91. *The Vicarage, 14 Church Street, Market Lavington, Devizes, Wilts SN10 4DT* Devizes (01380) 813914

GREENSLADE, Keith James Inglis. b 27. St Mich Coll Llan 60. **d** 62 **p** 63. V Upper Stratton *Bris* 68-95; rtd 95. *65 Shakespeare Road, Wootton Bassett, Swindon SN4 8HF* Swindon (01793) 853253

GREENSLADE, Peter Michael. b 37. Bp Burgess Hall Lamp 69. **d** 71 **p** 72. C Llanwnda w Goodwick and Manorowen *St D* 71-73; C Lydiate *Liv* 73-75; V Wigan St Cath 75-76; Chapl Newsham Gen Hosp Liv 76-78; C Knotty Ash St Jo *Liv* 76-78; C Leake cum Saltney *Ches* 78-80; V Barnton 80-84; C Warburton 85-86; Warden Petroc Chr Guest Ho 86-90; rtd 90. *41 Knightswood, Hampton Dene, Hereford HR1 1UZ* Hereford (01432) 359777

GREENSLADE, Timothy Julian (Tim). b 63. St Jo Coll Ox BA86. Oak Hill Th Coll BA95. **d** 95. C Broadwater St Mary *Chich* from 95. *30 Fletcher Road, Worthing, W Sussex BN14 8EX* Worthing (01903) 526370

GREENUP, Basil William. b 08. St Jo Coll Cam BA30 MA37. Bps' Coll Cheshunt 38. **d** 39 **p** 39. Conduct Eton Coll and Master of Choristers 40-64; rtd 69. *Barton Cottage, Coburg Road, Sidmouth, Devon EX10 8NG* Sidmouth (01395) 578586

GREENWAY, John. b 32. Bps' Coll Cheshunt 68 Qu Coll Birm 69. **d** 69 **p** 70. C Luton Ch Ch *St Alb* 69-74; C Pulloxhill w Flitton 75-76; P-in-c Marston Morteyne 76-79; P-in-c Lidlington 77-79; P-in-c Marston Morteyne w Lidlington 80-81; R from 81. *The Vicarage, Lidlington, Bedford MK43 0RN* Ampthill (01525) 403687

GREENWAY, Margaret Hester. b 26. **d** 87. Downend *Bris* 75-79; Oldland 79-82; Stratton St Margaret w S Marston etc 82-86; rtd 86; Perm to Offic *B & W* from 87. *5 Weston Lodge, Lower Bristol Road, Weston-super-Mare, Avon BS23 2PJ* Weston-super-Mare (01934) 623561

GREENWELL, Christopher. b 49. Linc Th Coll 79. **d** 81 **p** 82. C Scarborough St Martin *York* 81-84; V S Bank 84-89; R Bolton by Bowland w Grindleton *Bradf* 89-92; V Nether Hoyland St Andr *Sheff* from 92. *The Vicarage, Market Street, Hoyland, Barnsley, S Yorkshire S74 0ET* Barnsley (01226) 742126

GREENWELL, Paul. b 60. Magd Coll Ox BA81 MA85. St Steph Ho Ox 82. **d** 85 **p** 86. C Hendon and Sunderland *Dur* 85-88; Chapl Univ Coll of Ripon & York St Jo 88-93; Min Can and Prec Ripon Cathl *Ripon* 88-93; V Hunslet St Mary from 93. *The Vicarage, Church Street, Hunslet, Leeds LS10 2QY* Leeds (0113) 271 6991

GREENWOOD, Canon Gerald. b 33. Leeds Univ BA57 Sheff Poly MSc83 Surrey Univ Hon MA93. Linc Th Coll 57. **d** 59 **p** 60. C Rotherham *Sheff* 59-62; V Elsecar 62-69; V Wales 70-77; P-in-c Thorpe Salvin 74-77; Dioc Sch Officer 77-84; P-in-c Bramley and Ravenfield 77-78; P-in-c Hooton Roberts 77-78; R 78-84; Hon Can Sheff Cathl 80-84; Dioc Dir of Educn 81-84; Hon Can S'wark Cathl *S'wark* from 84; Dir of Educn from 84. *15C Paveley Drive, Morgan's Walk, London SW11 3TP* 0171-585 1731 or 407 7911

GREENWOOD, Gordon Edwin. b 44. Trin Coll Bris 78. **d** 80 **p** 81. C Bootle St Matt *Liv* 80-83; V Hunts Cross 83-93; V Skelmersdale St Paul from 93. *The Vicarage, Church Road, Skelmersdale, Lancs WN8 8ND* Skelmersdale (01695) 722087

GREENWOOD, Hilary Peter Frank. b 29. Nottm Univ BA57. Kelham Th Coll 50. **d** 57 **p** 58. SSM from 54; Warden Kelham Th Coll 70-74; Asst Chapl Madrid *Eur* 74-76; Perm to Offic *Blackb* 76-80; Perm to Offic *Man* 80-82; R Longsight St Jo w St Cypr 82-89; rtd 89; Hon Asst Chapl Prague *Eur* from 92.

Buchovcova 5, (2nd Floor, Flat 12), Zizkov, 13000 Prague 3, Czech Republic Prague (2) 827-7824

GREENWOOD, James Peter. b 61. RIBA87 Univ Coll Lon BSc83 DipArch86 St Jo Coll Dur BA90. Cranmer Hall Dur 88. **d** 91 **p** 92. C Belper *Derby* 91-94; CMS from 95. *St Thomas Church, Luqman Hakim Road, G-7/2, Islamabad, Pakistan*

GREENWOOD, John Newton. b 44. St Chad's Coll Dur BA69 DipTh70. **d** 70 **p** 71. C Hartlepool H Trin *Dur* 70-72; Lic to Offic from 72; Hd Master Archibald Primary Sch Cleveland from 84. *1 Brae Head, Eaglescliffe, Stockton-on-Tees, Cleveland TS16 9HP* Eaglescliffe (01642) 783200

GREENWOOD, Leslie. b 37. Dur Univ BA59 DipTh61. St Jo Coll Dur. **d** 61 **p** 62. C Birstall *Wakef* 61-63; C Illingworth 64-70; Chapl H Trin Sch Halifax 64-89; V Charlestown 70-91; TV Upper Holme Valley from 91. *The Vicarage, 2 Ashgrove Road, Holmfirth, Huddersfield HD7 1LR* Huddersfield (01484) 683131

GREENWOOD, Michael Eric. b 44. Oak Hill Th Coll 78. **d** 80 **p** 81. C Clubmoor *Liv* 80-83; V Pemberton St Mark Newtown 83-94; V Grassendale from 94. *St Mary's Vicarage, 22 Eaton Road, Liverpool L19 0PW* 0151-427 1474

GREENWOOD, Norman David. b 52. Edin Univ BMus74 Lon Univ BD78 Nottm Univ MPhil90. Oak Hill Th Coll 76. **d** 78 **p** 79. C Gorleston St Andr *Nor* 78-81; SAMS 81-83; C Cromer *Nor* 83-84; R Appleby Magna and Swepstone w Snarestone *Leic* 84-94; P-in-c Chesterfield H Trin *Derby* 94-95; P-in-c Chesterfield Ch Ch 94-95; R Chesterfield H Trin and Ch Ch from 95. *Christ Church Vicarage, 89 Sheffield Road, Chesterfield, Derbyshire S41 7JH* Chesterfield (01246) 273508

GREENWOOD, Robert John Teale. b 28. Leeds Univ BA53. Coll of Resurr Mirfield 53. **d** 55 **p** 56. Chapl HM Pris Holloway 69-70; Chapl HM Pris Man 71-77; Chapl HM Pris Styal 77-88; Lic to Offic *Ches* 77-93; Perm to Offic *St As* from 89; Perm to Offic *Ban* from 89; rtd 93. *1 Glan y Wern, Pentrefoelas, Betws y Coed, Gwynedd LL24 0LG* Pentrefoelas (016905) 313

GREENWOOD, Canon Dr Robin Patrick. b 47. St Chad's Coll Dur BA68 DipTh69 MA71 Birm Univ PhD92. **d** 70 **p** 71. C Adel *Ripon* 70-73; Min Can and Succ Ripon Cathl 73-78; V Leeds Halton St Wilfrid 78-86; Dioc Can Res Glouc Cathl *Glouc* from 86; Dioc Missr and Dir Lay and Post-Ord Tr 86-95; Min Development Officer *Chelmsf* from 95. *Diocesan Office, Guy Harlings, 53 New Street, Chelmsford CM1 1AT* Chelmsford (01245) 266731

GREENWOOD, Roy Douglas. b 27. Tyndale Hall Bris 58. **d** 60 **p** 61. V Seathwaite w Ulpha *Carl* 63-72; P-in-c Haverthwaite 72-74; C Ulverston St Mary w H Trin 74-78; V Egton w Newland 78-86; Assoc Chapl Palma de Mallorca and Balearic Is *Eur* 86-93; Assoc Chapl Palma de Mallorca 93-95; rtd 95. *Lista de Correos Apt 78, Pollensa, Palma de Mallorca, Spain* Palma de Mallorca (71) 865845

GREER, Eric Gordon. b 52. Pepperdine Univ BA74. Princeton Th Sem MDiv80. **d** 93 **p** 94. C Southgate St Andr *Lon* from 93. *10 The Woodlands, London N14 5RN* 0181-368 3276

GREER, John Edmund. b 32. QUB BSc53 BAgr54 PhD56 TCD BD65 NUU MPhil72. Bps' Coll Cheshunt 56. **d** 58 **p** 59. Chapl NUU 68-72; Lect 72-84; Reader 84-94; rtd 94. *6 Beech Hill, Postboys Walk, Ballymoney, Co Antrim BT53 6DB* Ballymoney (012656) 62368

GREER, James Robert Ferguson. b 34. TCD BA56 MA59. **d** 60 **p** 61. C Dundela *D & D* 60-65; I Castlewellan 65-78; I Castlewellan w Kilcoo from 78; RD Kilmegan from 89; Can Dromore Cathl from 90; Prec from 93. *The Rectory, 58 Mill Hill, Castlewellan, Co Down BT31 9NB* Castlewellan (013967) 78306

GREETHAM, Canon William Frederick. b 40. Bede Coll Dur CertEd. Cranmer Hall Dur 63. **d** 66 **p** 67. C St Annes *Blackb* 66-69; C Ashton-on-Ribble St Andr 69-71; Chapl Aysgarth Sch N Yorkshire 71-81; C Bedale *Ripon* 72-75; V Crakehall 75-82; V Hornby 75-82; V Patrick Brompton and Hunton 75-82; V Kirkby Stephen *Carl* 82-90; R Kirkby Stephen w Mallerstang etc from 90; RD Appleby 86-91; Hon Can Carl Cathl from 89. *The Vicarage, Vicarage Lane, Kirkby Stephen, Cumbria CA17 4QX* Kirkby Stephen (017683) 71204

GREG, John Kennedy. b 24. Trin Coll Cam BA46 MA61. Chich Th Coll 46. **d** 49 **p** 50. V Cumwhitton *Carl* 62-75; C Carl St Barn 75; TV 75-80; Chapl Strathclyde Ho Hosp Carl 80-85; TV Carl H Trin and St Barn *Carl* 80-85; rtd 85; Perm to Offic *Carl* from 86. *113 Wigton Road, Carlisle CA2 7EL* Carlisle (01228) 38837

GREGG, David William Austin. b 37. Lon Univ BD66 Bris Univ MA69. Tyndale Hall Bris 63. **d** 68 **p** 69. C Barrow St Mark *Carl* 68-71; P-in-c Lindal w Marton 71-75; Communications Sec Gen Syn Bd for Miss and Unity 76-81; Prin Romsey Ho Coll Cam 81-88; V Haddenham w Cuddington, Kingsey etc *Ox* from 88. *The Vicarage, 27A The Gables, Haddenham, Aylesbury, Bucks HP17 8AD* Haddenham (01844) 291244

GREGORY, Alan Paul Roy. b 55. K Coll Lon BD77 MTh78 AKC. Ripon Coll Cuddesdon 78. **d** 79 **p** 80. C Walton-on-

Thames *Guildf* 79-82; Tutor and Dir of Studies Sarum & Wells Th Coll 82-88; USA from 88. *4862 Cambridge Drive, Dunwoody, Atlanta, Georgia 30338, USA*

GREGORY, Brian. b 43. Trin Coll Bris. **d** 82 **p** 83. C Burscough Bridge *Liv* 82-85; V Platt Bridge 85-92; V Ben Rhydding *Bradf* from 92. *The Vicarage, Ben Rhydding, Ilkley, W Yorkshire LS29 8PT* Ilkley (01943) 607363

GREGORY, Clive Malcolm. b 61. Lanc Univ BA84 Qu Coll Cam BA87 MA89. Westcott Ho Cam 85. **d** 88 **p** 89. C Margate St Jo *Cant* 88-92; Chapl Warw Univ *Cov* from 92. *92 De Montfort Way, Coventry CV4 7DT* Coventry (01203) 690216 or 523519

GREGORY, Father. *See* DUDDING, Edward Leslie

GREGORY, Graham. b 36. Open Univ BA78 Lon Univ DipTh65. Tyndale Hall Bris 63. **d** 66 **p** 67. C Wandsworth St Mich *S'wark* 66-71; C Hastings Em and St Mary in the Castle *Chich* 71-75; V Douglas St Ninian *S & M* 75-91; Dioc Youth Officer 78-88; Chapl HM Pris Douglas 82-86; RD Douglas *S & M* 86-91; V Wollaton Park *S'well* from 91; V Lenton Abbey from 91. *St Mary's Vicarage, Wollaton Park, Nottingham NG8 1AF* Nottingham (0115) 978 6988

GREGORY, Ian Peter. b 45. Open Univ BA82 Plymouth Univ PGCE92. Bernard Gilpin Soc Dur 66 Chich Th Coll 67. **d** 70 **p** 71. C Tettenhall Regis *Lich* 70-73; C Shrewsbury H Cross 73-76; P-in-c Walsall St Mary and All SS Palfrey 76-80; R Petrockstowe, Petersmarland, Merton, Meeth etc *Ex* 80-85; TV Ex St Thos and Em 87-91; Hon C S Wimbledon All SS *S'wark* from 94. *142 Monkleigh Road, Morden, Surrey SM4 4ER* 0181-401 6148

GREGORY, Ivan Henry. b 31. Leeds Univ BA52. Ely Th Coll 58. **d** 60 **p** 60. V Braunton *Ex* 67-77; V Tintagel *Truro* 77-93; RD Trigg Minor 84-86; rtd 93. *20 Greenfields Avenue, Alton, Hants GU34 2ED* Alton (01420) 542860

GREGORY, John Frederick. b 33. Glouc Sch of Min 75. **d** 78 **p** 78. NSM S Cerney w Cerney Wick *Glouc* 78-81; NSM Coates, Rodmarton and Sapperton etc 81-88; P-in-c Kempsford w Welford from 88. *The Parsonage, Kempsford, Fairford, Glos GL7 4ET* Kempsford (01285) 810241

GREGORY, Miss Pauline Beatrice Joan (Paula). b 20. SRN43. K Coll Lon 47. **dss** 54 **d** 87 **p** 94. CSA 49-57; Jamaica 58-69; Victoria Docks Ascension *Chelmsf* 70-80; Canning Town St Cedd 80-84; Colchester St Botolph w H Trin and St Giles 84-87; Hon Par Dn 87-94; Hon C from 94. *51 St John's Green, Colchester CO2 7EZ* Colchester (01206) 43138

GREGORY, Peter. b 35. Cranmer Hall Dur 59. **d** 62 **p** 63. V Tonge Fold *Man* 68-72; V Hollym w Welwick and Holmpton *York* 72-77; P-in-c Foston w Flaxton 77-80; P-in-c Crambe w Whitwell and Huttons Ambo 77-80; R Whitwell w Crambe, Flaxton, Foston etc 81-94; rtd 94. *6 High Terrace, Northallerton, N Yorkshire DL6 1BG* Northallerton (01609) 776956

GREGORY, Richard Branson. b 33. Fitzw Ho Cam BA58 MA62. Sarum Th Coll 58 Ridley Hall Cam 59. **d** 60 **p** 61. C Sheff St Cuth *Sheff* 60-62; Asst Chapl Leeds Univ *Ripon* 62-64; V Yeadon St Jo *Bradf* 64-71; R Keighley 71-74; TR Keighley St Andr 74-82; Hon Can Bradf Cathl 71-82; RD S Craven 71-73 and 78-82; P-in-c Broadmayne, W Knighton, Owermoigne etc *Sarum* 82-85; R from 85. *The Rectory, Main Street, Broadmayne, Dorchester, Dorset DT2 8EB* Warmwell (01305) 852435

GREGORY, Canon Stephen Simpson. b 40. Nottm Univ BA62 CertEd63. St Steph Ho Ox. **d** 68 **p** 69. C Aldershot St Mich *Guildf* 68-71; Chapl St Mary's Sch Wantage 71-74; R Edgefield *Nor* 74-88; R Holt 74-94; R Holt w High Kelling from 94; RD Holt 79-84 and 93-95; Hon Can Nor Cathl from 94. *The Rectory, Holt, Norfolk NR26 6BB* Holt (01263) 712048 Fax 711397

GREGORY-SMITH, Thomas Gregory. b 08. St Jo Coll Cam BA30 MA34. Lon Coll of Div 33. **d** 34 **p** 35. C-in-c Wimbledon Em Ridgway Prop Chpl *S'wark* 71-76; rtd 76. *46 Sea Road, Barton-on-Sea, New Milton, Hants BH25 7NG* New Milton (01425) 610942

GREGSON, Peter John. b 36. Univ Coll Dur BSc61. Ripon Hall Ox 61. **d** 63 **p** 64. C Radcliffe St Thos *Man* 63-65; C Baguley 65-67; Chapl RN 68-91; V Ashburton w Buckland in the Moor and Bickington *Ex* from 91; RD Moreton from 95. *The Vicarage, Copperwood Close, Ashburton, Newton Abbot, Devon TQ13 7JQ* Ashburton (01364) 652506

GREIG, George Malcolm. b 28. CA53 St Andr Univ BD95. Local NSM Course 75. **d** 81 **p** 82. NSM Dundee St Mary Magd *Bre* 81-84; NSM Dundee St Jo 82-84; P-in-c Dundee St Ninian 84; Hon Chapl St Paul's Cathl Dundee from 85; NSM Dundee St Paul from 85. *61 Charleston Drive, Dundee DD2 2HE* Dundee (01382) 66709

GREIG, John Kenneth. b 38. Natal Univ BA57. St Paul's Grahamstown LTh60. **d** 61 **p** 62. S Africa 61-66 and 71-78; C Friern Barnet St Jas *Lon* 66-69; C Kenton 69-71; Chapl Whitelands Coll of HE *S'wark* 78-84; Area Ecum Officer

(Croydon) from 84; V Purley St Swithun from 84. *Windsor Lodge, Purley Rise, Purley, Surrey CR8 3AW* 0181-660 3744

GREIG, Martin David Sandford. b 45. Bris Univ BSc67. St Jo Coll Nottm 72. **d** 75 **p** 76. C Keresley and Coundon *Cov* 75-79; C Rugby St Andr 79-83; TV 83-86; V Cov St Geo 86-93; TV Southgate *Chich* from 93. *St Andrew's Vicarage, Weald Drive, Crawley, W Sussex RH10 6NU* Crawley (01293) 531828

GRELLIER, Brian Rodolph. b 34. AKC61. **d** 62 **p** 63. C Wandsworth St Paul *S'wark* 62-66; Japan 66-72; Miss to Seamen 72-76; V Freiston w Butterwick *Linc* from 76; Chapl HM Pris N Sea Camp from 89. *Pinchbeck House, Butterwick, Boston, Lincs PE22 0HZ* Boston (01205) 760550 Fax 760098

GRESSWELL, George Gilbert. b 03. Lon Univ BA38. Hartley Victoria Coll. **d** 43 **p** 44. V Laxey *S & M* 59-70; rtd 70; Perm to Offic *S & M* from 70. *Knock Rushen, Ballafesson, Port Erin, Isle of Man IM9 6PT* Port Erin (01624) 832079

GRETTON, Tony Butler. b 29. St Jo Coll Dur BA53. **d** 54 **p** 55. R Norton Fitzwarren *B & W* 57-68; rtd 68; Chapl Glouc Docks Mariners' Ch *Glouc* 73-92; P-in-c Brookthorpe w Whaddon and Harescombe 79-82; Hon C The Edge, Pitchcombe, Harescombe and Brookthorpe 82-89. *18 Clover Drive, Hardwicke, Gloucester GL2 5TG* Gloucester (01452) 721505

GREW, Nicholas David. b 52. Surrey Univ BSc74 MSc75. Wycliffe Hall Ox DipMin95. **d** 95. C Biddulph *Lich* from 95. *48 Thames Drive, Biddulph, Stoke-on-Trent ST8 7HL* Stoke-on-Trent (01782) 522428

GREW, Richard Lewis. b 32. Clare Coll Cam BA54 MA58. Wycliffe Hall Ox 67. **d** 68 **p** 69. C Repton *Derby* 68-73; Asst Chapl Repton Sch Derby 74-93; Lic to Offic *Derby* 73-93; rtd 93; Perm to Offic *Sarum* from 94. *5 Priory Gardens, Spetisbury, Blandford Forum, Dorset DT11 9DS* Sturminster Marshall (01258) 857613

GREWCOCK, Peter Joseph. b 28. Sarum Th Coll. **d** 58 **p** 59. V Howe Bridge *Man* 62-72; P-in-c Werrington, St Giles in the Heath and Virginstow *Truro* 72-73; V Leic St Chad *Leic* 73-76; P-in-c Trotton w Chithurst *Chich* 76-80; C Broadstone *Sarum* 80-84; TV Gillingham 84-88; P-in-c Milborne St Andrew w Dewlish 88-92; rtd 92. *9 Hambledon Close, Blandford Forum, Dorset DT11 7SA* Blandford (01258) 450893

GREY, Canon Edward Alwyn. b 23. Univ of Wales (Swansea) BA48. St D Coll Lamp. **d** 50 **p** 51. R Flint *St As* 69-89; RD Holywell 73-89; Can St As Cathl 76-89; rtd 89. *60 Gronant Road, Prestatyn, Clwyd LL19 9NE* Prestatyn (01745) 855302

GREY, Edwin Charles. b 03. Wycliffe Coll Toronto 46. **d** 49 **p** 50. Canada 49-70; C Bowdon *Ches* 70-76; Asst Chapl Santa Cruz *Eur* 77-78; Perm to Offic *Glouc* 78-88. *Address temp unknown*

GREY, Richard Thomas. b 50. St D Coll Lamp BA73 Ripon Hall Ox 73. **d** 75 **p** 76. C Blaenavon w Capel Newydd *Mon* 75-77; Ind Chapl from 77; C Newport St Paul 77-80; CF (TA) from 78; Chapl Aberbargoed Hosp from 80; V Bedwellty *Mon* 80-88; R Llanwenarth Ultra 88-92; R Govilon w Llanfoist w Llanelen from 92. *The Rectory, Govilon, Abergavenny, Gwent NP7 9PT* Gilwern (01873) 830342

GREY, Canon Roger Derrick Masson. b 38. AKC61. **d** 62 **p** 63. C Darlington H Trin *Dur* 62-63; C Bishopwearmouth St Mich 63-67; V Mabe *Truro* 67-70; Dioc Youth Chapl 67-70; Youth Chapl *Glouc* 70-77; V Stroud H Trin 77-82; Dioc Can Res Glouc Cathl from 82; Dir of Educn 82-94; Bp's Chapl from 94. *4A Millers Green, Gloucester GL1 2BN* Gloucester (01452) 525242

GREY, Stephen Bernard. b 56. Linc Th Coll 86. **d** 88 **p** 89. C Worsley *Man* 88-93; V Bamford from 93. *St Michael's Vicarage, 389 Bury and Rochdale Old Road, Heywood, Lancs OL10 4AT* Heywood (01706) 369610

GREY, Canon Thomas Hilton. b 18. St D Coll Lamp BA39 Keble Coll Ox BA41 MA46. St Mich Coll Llan 41. **d** 42 **p** 43. R Haverfordwest St Thos and Haroldston E St Issell *St D* 64-77; Can St D Cathl 72-84; Treas St D Cathl 80-84; RD Roose 74-84; R Haverfordwest St Mary and St Thos w Haroldston 77-84; rtd 85. *3 Gwscum Park, Burry Port, Dyfed SA16 0DX* Burry Port (01554) 833629

GRIBBEN, John Gibson. b 44. Lon Univ DipTh73 K Coll Lon BD75 QUB MTh81. CITC 73. **d** 75 **p** 76. C Dunmurry *Conn* 75-78; CR from 81; Lic to Offic *Wakef* from 83. *College of the Resurrection, Mirfield, W Yorkshire WF14 0BW* Mirfield (01924) 490441

GRIBBIN, Canon Bernard Byron. b 35. Bradf Univ DipHP76 MPhil84. St Aid Birkenhead 58. **d** 60 **p** 61. C Maghull *Liv* 60-63; C Prescot 63-65; V Denholme Gate *Bradf* 65-71; V Bankfoot 71-79; Dioc Stewardship Adv 79-86; Prec and Chapl Choral Ches Cathl *Ches* 86-91; Hon Can Ches Cathl from 91; V Ringway from 91; Dioc Tourism Officer from 91. *Ringway Vicarage, Halebarns, Altrincham, Cheshire WA15 0HQ* 0161-980 3955

GRIBBLE, Canon Arthur Stanley. b 04. Qu Coll Cam BA27 MA31. Westcott Ho Cam 27. **d** 30 **p** 31. Can Res Pet Cathl *Pet*

67-79; rtd 79; Perm to Offic *Pet* from 79; Perm to Offic *Linc* from 80. *2 Princes Road, Stamford, Lincs PE9 1QT* Stamford (01780) 55838

GRIBBLE, Howard Frank. b 27. Magd Coll Cam BA50 MA56. Ely Th Coll 50. **d** 52 **p** 53. V Harlow St Mary Magd *Chelmsf* 62-70; R Lawhitton *Truro* 70-81; R Lezant 70-81; RD Trigg Major 75-79; P-in-c S Petherwin w Trewen 77-79; Chapl R Cornwall Hosp Truro 81-84; rtd 84. *Westerlies, Marine Drive, Widemouth Bay, Bude, Cornwall EX23 0AQ* Bude (01288) 361528

GRIBBLE, Malcolm George. b 44. Chu Coll Cam BA67 MA71. Linc Th Coll 79. **d** 81 **p** 82. C Farnborough *Roch* 81-84; V Bostall Heath 84-90; V Bexleyheath Ch Ch from 90. *The Vicarage, 113 Upton Road, Bexleyheath, Kent DA6 8LS* 0181-303 3260

GRICE, Charles. b 24. MBE83. **d** 58 **p** 59. Ind Chapl *Sheff* 69-76; V Tinsley 69-73; V Oughtibridge 73-76; Gen Sec Ch Lads' and Ch Girls' Brigade 77-91; R Braithwell w Bramley *Sheff* 88-91; rtd 89. *57 Deepdale Road, Rotherham, S Yorkshire S61 2NR* Rotherham (01709) 557551

GRICE, Canon David Richard. b 32. Keble Coll Ox BA55 MA59. St Steph Ho Ox 55. **d** 57 **p** 58. C Leeds St Aid *Ripon* 57-61; C Middleton St Mary 61-62; V Woodlesford 62-69; V Leeds St Wilfrid 69-78; TR Seacroft 78-93; Hon Can Ripon Cathl from 92; P-in-c Thorner from 93. *The Vicarage, Church View, Thorner, Leeds LS14 3ED* Leeds (0113) 289 2437

GRICE-HUTCHINSON, Canon George Arthur Claude. b 12. Bps' Coll Cheshunt 39. **d** 39 **p** 40. V Benwell St Jas *Newc* 63-74; V N Sunderland 74-79; Hon Can Newc Cathl 77-79; rtd 80. *17 Westacres Crescent, Newcastle upon Tyne NE15 7NY* 0191-274 7975

GRIERSON, Peter Stanley. b 42. Lon Univ BD68 Leeds Univ MPhil74. Linc Th Coll 68. **d** 69 **p** 70. C Clitheroe St Mary *Blackb* 69-71; C Aston cum Aughton *Sheff* 71-74; V Preston St Jude w St Paul *Blackb* 74-81; V Blackb St Luke w St Phil from 89; RD Blackb from 91. *St Luke's Vicarage, Lansdowne Street, Blackburn BB2 1UU* Blackburn (01254) 581402

GRIEVE, David Campbell. b 51. St Jo Coll Dur BA74. Wycliffe Hall Ox 74. **d** 76 **p** 77. C Upton (or Overchurch) *Ches* 76-80; C Selston *S'well* 80-82; V Pelton *Dur* 82-89; rtd 89. *Horn's House Farm, Witton Gilbert, Durham DH7 6TT* 0191-384 1268

GRIEVE (nee BELL), Mrs Judith Margaret. b 52. Golds Coll Lon CertEd73. NE Ord Course 91. **d** 94. NSM Choppington *Newc* from 94. *20 Stobhill Villas, Morpeth, Northd NE61 2SH* Morpeth (01670) 503433

GRIEVE, Robert Andrew Cameron. b 33. ACP65. Edin Th Coll 69. **d** 71 **p** 72. C Leigh St Mary *Man* 71-73; Hon C Chedburgh w Depden and Rede *St E* 73-75; Lic to Offic 75-77; P-in-c Newton 77-79; V Assington 77-79; R Fraserburgh w New Pitsligo *Ab* 79-83; R Corringham *Linc* 83-91; Perm to Offic from 91; V Owston *Sheff* from 91. *The Vicarage, 11 Crabgate Lane, Skellow, Doncaster, S Yorkshire DN6 8LE* Doncaster (01302) 337101

GRIEVES, Anthony Michael. b 47. St Alb Minl Tr Scheme 81. **d** 84 **p** 85. NSM Stevenage St Mary Shephall *St Alb* 84-86; NSM Stevenage St Mary Sheppall w Aston from 86. *27 Falcon Close, Stevenage, Herts SG2 9PG* Stevenage (01438) 727204

GRIEVES, Ian Leslie. b 56. Bede Coll Dur CertEd77 BEd78. Chich Th Coll 82. **d** 84 **p** 85. C Darlington St Mark w St Paul *Dur* 84-87; C Whickham 87-89; V Darlington St Jas from 89. *St James's Vicarage, Vicarage Road, Darlington, Co Durham DL1 1JW* Darlington (01325) 465980

GRIFFIN, Dr Alan Howard Foster. b 44. TCD BA66 MA69 Peterho Cam PhD71. Sarum & Wells Th Coll 75. **d** 78 **p** 79. Asst to Lazenby Chapl and Lect Ex Univ from 78; Sub-Warden from 78; Warden from 81; Sen Warden from 84; Lic to Offic *Ex* from 78. *Duryard House, Duryard Halls, Lower Argyll Road, Exeter EX4 4RG* Exeter (01392) 432164 or 264203

GRIFFIN, Christopher Donald (Chris). b 59. Reading Univ BA80 CertEd81. Wycliffe Hall Ox DipTh85. **d** 85 **p** 86. C Gerrards Cross *Ox* 85-88; Chapl Felsted Sch Essex from 88; Perm to Offic *Chelmsf* from 88. *The Colony, Chelmsford Road, Felsted, Dunmow, Essex CM6 3EP* Gt Dunmow (0371) 820414 or 820258

GRIFFIN, Dennis Gordon. b 24. Worc Ord Coll 66. **d** 68 **p** 69. V Rainbow Hill St Barn *Worc* 69-74; R Broughton *Man* 74-79; V Pendlebury Ch Ch 79-86; rtd 89. *Trevean, Goldsithney, Penzance, Cornwall TR20 9JZ* Penzance (01736) 711320

GRIFFIN, Gerald Albert Francis. b 31. Qu Coll Birm 74. **d** 77 **p** 78. NSM Bushbury *Lich* 77-83; Ind Chapl *Dur* 83-88; Chapl HM Pris Man 88-89; Chapl HM Pris Featherstone 89-93; C Toxteth St Philemon w St Gabr and St Cleopas *Liv* from 93. *221 Caryl Street, Liverpool L8 6RE* 0151-708 8389

GRIFFIN, Harold Rodan Bristow. b 12. Jes Coll Cam BA33 LLB34 MA43. Ridley Hall Cam 43. **d** 45 **p** 46. V Framsden

St E 61-71; R Helmingham 61-71; rtd 77. *Flat 48, Gretton Court, Girton, Cambridge CB3 0QN* Cambridge (01223) 276842

GRIFFIN, Joan Angela. b 35. Qu Coll Birm 82. dss 85 **d** 92 **p** 94. Moseley St Mary *Birm* 85-92; NSM from 92. *389 Wake Green Road, Birmingham B13 0BH* 0121-777 8772

GRIFFIN, Canon John Henry Hugh. b 13. St Cath Coll Cam BA35 MA39. Linc Th Coll 35. **d** 38 **p** 39. R Stratford St Mary *St E* 46-72; C Hadleigh w Layham and Shelley 72-73; P-in-c Gt and Lt Glemham 73-79; P-in-c Blaxhall w Stratford St Andrew and Farnham 73-79; Hon Can St E Cathl 78-79; rtd 79; Perm to Offic *St E* from 79. *3 Church Street, Hadleigh, Ipswich IP7 5DT* Hadleigh (01473) 823100

GRIFFIN, Joseph William. b 48. Univ of Wales (Cardiff) DipTh73 DPS74. St Mich Coll Llan 70. **d** 74 **p** 75. C Killay *S & B* 74-78; C Swansea St Thos and Kilvey 78-81; V Troedrhiwgarth *Llan* 81-91; V Llanrhidian w Llanmadoc and Cheriton *S & B* from 91; RD Gower from 94. *The Vicarage, Llanrhidian, Swansea SA3 1EH* Swansea (01792) 390144

GRIFFIN, Keith. b 66. Nottm Trent Univ BA88. Cranmer Hall Dur BA94. **d** 95. C Gedling *S'well* from 95. *St George's Rectory, Victoria Road, Nottingham NG4 2NN* Nottingham (0115) 961 5566

GRIFFIN, Kenneth Francis. b 21. Lon Univ BSc64. St Jo Coll Nottm 72. **d** 73 **p** 74. C Bexleyheath Ch Ch *Roch* 73-77; R Kingsdown 77-82; rtd 86. *Woodlands, Palmers Cross Hill, Rough Common, Canterbury, Kent CT2 9BL* Canterbury (01227) 457314

GRIFFIN, Malcolm Neil. b 36. Leeds Univ BA57. Coll of Resurr Mirfield 57. **d** 59 **p** 60. C Cheadle *Lich* 59-61; C Bloxwich 61-64; P-in-c Willenhall St Anne 64-69; V Stretton w Claymills 69-75; V Baswich (or Berkswich) 75-85; V Madeley from 85. *The Vicarage, Madeley, Crewe CW3 9PX* Stoke-on-Trent (01782) 750205

GRIFFIN, Malcolm Roger. b 46. Open Univ BA DipRS83 DM90. S'wark Ord Course. **d** 83 **p** 84. NSM Romford St Andr *Chelmsf* 83-87; Hon C Romford St Jo 87-90; Hon C Gt Ilford St Alb from 90. *35 Oak Street, Romford RM7 7BA* Romford (01708) 741089

GRIFFIN, Canon Michael Richard. b 19. CD78. Trin Coll Bris 43. **d** 44 **p** 44. C Tonbridge St Steph *Roch* 44-45; C Tunbridge Wells H Trin 45-47; V Hindley St Pet *Liv* 47-51; Canada from 51; Can Huron from 64; CStJ from 78. *68 Caledonia Street, Stratford, Ontario, Canada, N5A 5W6*

GRIFFIN, Niall Paul. b 37. TCD BA61 Div Test61. **d** 61 **p** 62. C Newtownards *D & D* 61-63; C Arm St Mark *Arm* 63-64; Jamaica 64-66; C Lurgan Ch Ch *D & D* 66-69; Chapl RAF 69-84; Missr Chr Renewal Cen *D & D* 84-89; Ireland and Scotland Network Ldr SOMA from 89. *7 Cloughmore Park, Rostrevor, Newry, Co Down BT34 3AX* Rostrevor (016937) 38959

GRIFFIN, Nigel Charles. b 48. Leic Univ BSc71 Ox Univ DipTh73. Cuddesdon Coll 71. **d** 74 **p** 75. C Wandsworth St Anne *S'wark* 74-77; V Tadworth 77-84; Chapl Gt Ormond Street Hosp for Sick Children Lon 78-84; V Whitworth w Spennymoor *Dur* 84-91; TR St Jo on Bethnal Green *Lon* from 91. *St John's Rectory, 30 Victoria Park Square, London E2 0HU* 0181-980 1742

GRIFFIN, Nigel Robert. b 50. Univ of Wales (Lamp) BA71. Ripon Hall Ox 71. **d** 73 **p** 74. C Burry Port and Pwll *St D* 73-77; C Carmarthen St Pet 77-79; Youth Chapl from 79; V Whitland and Kiffig 80-89; Warden of Ords from 86; V Llangynnwr and Cwmffrwd 89-92; RD Carmarthen 91-92; R Aberporth w Tremain and Blaenporth from 92. *The Rectory, Aberporth, Cardigan, Dyfed SA43 2BX* Aberporth (01239) 810556

GRIFFIN, Robert Maurice. b 13. Tyndale Hall Bris 52. **d** 54 **p** 55. N Area Sec BCMS 70-75; V Withnell *Blackb* 75-79; rtd 79; Lic to Offic *Blackb* from 79. *87 Pirehill Lane, Stone, Staffs ST15 0AS*

GRIFFIN, Canon Roger Thomas Kynaston. b 14. ALCD41. **d** 41 **p** 42. V W Ham *Chelmsf* 61-82; P-in-c Plaistow St Mary 71-72; Chmn RADD 73-86; Hon Can Chelmsf Cathl 80-82; rtd 82; Perm to Offic *B & W* from 83. *Warrenhurst, Church Street, Minehead, Somerset TA24 5JU* Minehead (01643) 706166

GRIFFIN, Canon Rutland Basil. b 16. ALCD41. **d** 41 **p** 42. V Dartford H Trin *Roch* 61-84; RD Dartford 64-84; Hon Can Roch Cathl 70-84; rtd 84; Perm to Offic *Roch* from 84; Perm to Offic *Cant* from 84. *21 The Crescent, Canterbury, Kent CT2 7AQ* Canterbury (01227) 761091

GRIFFIN, Very Rev Victor Gilbert Benjamin. b 24. MRIA TCD BA46 MA57 Hon DD92. CITC 47. **d** 47 **p** 48. Dean St Patr Cathl Dub 68-91; rtd 91. *7 Tyler Road, Limavady, Co Londonderry BT49 0DW* Limavady (015047) 62093

GRIFFIN, William George. b 13. St Pet Hall Ox BA36 MA45. Wycliffe Hall Ox 36. **d** 37 **p** 38. V Church Broughton w Barton and Sutton on the Hill *Derby* 66-72; R Brington w Whilton *Pet* 72-78; rtd 78; Perm to Offic *Pet* from 86. *6 Riverside Drive, Weedon, Northampton NN7 4RT* Weedon (01327) 41585

GRIFFITH, Brian Vann. b 34. Univ Sch Th Abth & Lamp DipTh82 BTh91 MTh94. **d** 82 **p** 83. NSM Abth *St D* 82-87; NSM Llanfihangel w Llanafan and Llanwnnws etc 87-88; NSM Llanbadarn Fawr w Capel Bangor and Goginan 88-93; Public Preacher from 93. *14 Ystwyth Close, Penparcau, Aberystwyth, Dyfed SY23 3RU*

GRIFFITH, Canon David Vaughan. b 36. Univ of Wales (Lamp) BA60. Lich Th Coll 60. **d** 62 **p** 63. C Llanfairfechan *Ban* 62-66; C Dolgellau 66-70; R Llanfair Talhaiarn *St As* 70-82; P-in-c Llangernyw, Gwytherin and Llanddewi 77-85; R Llanfairtalhaiarn and Llansannan 82-85; V Colwyn from 85; Warden of Readers from 91; Can Cursal St As Cathl from 95. *The Vicarage, 28 Bodelwyddan Avenue, Old Colwyn, Colwyn Bay, Clwyd LL29 9NP* Colwyn Bay (01492) 518394

GRIFFITH, Canon Dermot George Wallace. b 13. TCD BA35. **d** 36 **p** 37. I Killyman *Arm* 47-86; RD Dungannon 67-86; Can Arm Cathl 73-86; Treas Arm Cathl 83-86; rtd 86. *The Cottage, 38 Drumkee Road, Dungannon, Co Tyrone BT71 6JA* Coalisland (018687) 48629

GRIFFITH, Donald Bennet. b 17. Dur Univ LTh40. St Aid Birkenhead 36. **d** 40 **p** 41. R Lawford *Chelmsf* 66-73; R Theydon Garnon 73-77; P-in-c Bradfield 77-82; rtd 82. *Porto Cristo, Mill Lane, Thorpe-le-Soken, Clacton-on-Sea, Essex CO16 0ED* Clacton-on-Sea (01255) 861766

GRIFFITH, Frank Michael. b 24. Bris Univ BSc50 Lon Univ DipTh60. St Aid Birkenhead 58. **d** 60 **p** 61. V Rounds Green *Birm* 67-70; R Barford *Cov* 70-78; V Wasperton 70-78; RD Stratford 77-79; R Barford w Wasperton and Sherbourne 78-89; RD Fosse 79-87; rtd 90. *Wusi, Armscote Road, Tredington, Shipston-on-Stour, Warks CV36 4NP* Shipston-on-Stour (01608) 661621

GRIFFITH, Canon Geoffrey Grenville. b 17. Linc Coll Ox BA48 MA56. Chich Th Coll 48. **d** 50 **p** 51. V Chapel-en-le-Frith *Derby* 66-84; RD Buxton 71-78; Hon Can Derby Cathl 80-84; rtd 84; Perm to Offic *Derby* 84-90; Chapl HM Pris Morton Hall 85-90; Chapl St Barn Hospice Linc from 91. *292 Hykenham Road, Lincoln LN6 8BJ* Lincoln (01522) 695683

GRIFFITH, Glyn Keble Gethin. b 37. St D Coll Lamp BA59 Ridley Hall Cam 67. **d** 69 **p** 70. C Derby St Aug *Derby* 69-72; C Coity w Nolton *Llan* 72-75; P-in-c Heage *Derby* 75-81; V Allestree St Nic 81-92; R Wilne and Draycott w Breaston from 92. *The Rectory, 68 Risley Lane, Breaston, Derby DE7 3AU* Derby (01332) 872242

GRIFFITH, Canon Hugh Emrys. b 24. St D Coll Lamp BA53. **d** 54 **p** 55. R Newborough w Llangeinwen w Llangaffo etc *Ban* 61-75; R Llanllyfni 75-81; R Amlwch 81-94; RD Twrcelyn 82-94; Can Ban Cathl from 89; rtd 94. *Llys Caerwynt, Rhosybol, Amlwch, Gwynedd LL68 9TS* Amlwch (01407) 831917

GRIFFITH, John Laurence Powell. b 30. Toronto Univ BA53. Coll of Resurr Mirfield 69. **d** 71 **p** 72. C Gt Berkhamsted *St Alb* 71-79; C Milton Ernest 79-80; P-in-c Wilden w Colmworth and Ravensden 80-81; R 81-88; Canada 88-94; rtd 95. *11 Days Lane, Biddenham, Bedford MK40 4AD* Bedford (01234) 358173

GRIFFITH, Canon John Vaughan. b 33. LTh73. St D Coll Lamp 53. **d** 58 **p** 59. C Holyhead w Rhoscolyn *Ban* 58-63; R Maentwrog w Trawsfynydd 63-68; Chapl RAF 68-72; V Winnington *Ches* 72-76; V Northwich St Luke and H Trin 76-81; V Sandiway from 81; Dioc Communications Officer 84-86; Ed Ches Dioc News from 84; Hon Can Ches Cathl from 89. *The Vicarage, Sandiway, Northwich, Cheshire CW8 2JU* Sandiway (01606) 883286

GRIFFITH, Steven Ellsworth. b 63. St Steph Ho Ox. **d** 87 **p** 88. C Holyhead w Rhoscolyn w Llanfair-yn-Neubwll *Ban* 87-90; CF from 90. *c/o MOD (Army), Bagshot Park, Bagshot, Surrey GU19 5PL* Bagshot (01276) 471717 Fax 412834

GRIFFITH, William Stephen. b 50. Univ of Wales (Ban) BA71. Westcott Ho Cam 71. **d** 73 **p** 74. C Llandudno *Ban* 73-76; C Calne and Blackland *Sarum* 76-78; P-in-c Broadwindsor w Burstock and Seaborough 78-79; TV Beaminster Area 79-81; Lic to Offic 81-83; Chapl St Pet Sch York 83-87; C Leeds St Pet *Ripon* 87; Chapl Bearwood Coll Wokingham 87-92; CMS from 92; Jordan from 92. *The Jordan Chaplaincy, PO Box 2370, Amman, Jordan*

GRIFFITH-JONES, Robin Guthrie. b 56. New Coll Ox BA78 Ch Coll Cam BA88. Westcott Ho Cam 86. **d** 89 **p** 90. C Cantril Farm *Liv* 89-92; Chapl Linc Coll Ox from 92. *Lincoln College, Oxford OX1 3DR* Oxford (01865) 279800

GRIFFITHS, Alan Charles. b 46. Dur Univ BA67 DipTh69. Cranmer Hall Dur 66. **d** 69 **p** 70. C Leic H Apostles *Leic* 69-72; Lic to Offic *York* 73-77; V Lea Hall *Birm* 77-87; Asst Dir of Educn *Sheff* 87-92; V W Bessacarr from 92. *The Vicarage, 39 Sturton Close, Doncaster, S Yorkshire DN4 7JG* Doncaster (01302) 538487

GRIFFITHS, Alec. b 42. St Chad's Coll Dur BA63 DipTh65. **d** 65 **p** 66. C Glas St Ninian *Glas* 65-68; C Greenock 68-72; R

Glas H Cross 72-79; V Birchencliffe *Wakef* 79-83; Chapl Kingston Hosp Surrey from 83; Chapl Tolworth Hosp Surbiton 83-93. *Kingston Hospital, Galsworthy Road, Kingston-upon-Thames, Surrey KT2 7QB*   0181-397 1577 or 546 7711

GRIFFITHS, Arthur Evan. b 27. ACP66. St Deiniol's Hawarden. **d** 69 **p** 70. Hon C Cleobury Mortimer w Hopton Wafers *Heref* 69-83; C 84-86; P-in-c Coreley w Doddington 86-88; P-in-c Knowbury 86-88; rtd 89. *Maryn, Catherton Road, Cleobury Mortimer, Kidderminster, Worcs DY14 8EB* Cleobury Mortimer (01299) 270489

GRIFFITHS, Beatrice Mary. b 29. Chelsea Coll Lon DipPE50 CertEd60 Lon Univ CertRK60. Westcott Ho Cam 85. **dss** 86 **d** 87 **p** 94. W Bridgford *S'well* 86-87; Hon Par Dn Wilford Hill 87-94; Hon C from 94. *7 Stella Avenue, Tollerton, Nottingham NG12 4EX*   Nottingham (0115) 937 4155

GRIFFITHS, Caroline Heidi Ann. *See* PRINCE, Caroline Heidi Ann

GRIFFITHS, David. b 38. St Mich Coll Llan DipTh67. **d** 67 **p** 68. C Llangollen *St As* 67-71; C Rhyl 71-74; V Kerry 74-77; V Kerry and Llanmerewig 77-82; R Caerwys and Bodfari 82-87; V Gresford from 87. *The Vicarage, Gresford, Wrexham, Clwyd LL12 8RG*   Gresford (01978) 852236

GRIFFITHS, David Bruce. b 44. Sussex Univ BA69 Hull Univ MA83. Linc Th Coll. **d** 82 **p** 83. C Springfield All SS *Chelmsf* 82-84; TV Horwich *Man* 84-92; V Heaton Ch Ch from 92. *The Vicarage, 2 Towncroft Lane, Bolton BL1 5EW*   Bolton (01204) 840430

GRIFFITHS, David John. b 53. Bromsgrove F E Coll HND76. St Jo Coll Nottm BTh93 DipMM94. **d** 94 **p** 95. C Retford *S'well* from 94. *1 Chapelgate, Retford, Notts DN22 6PL* Retford (01777) 706792

GRIFFITHS, David Mark. b 41. Univ of Wales (Cardiff) BA67 CertEd71. St Mich Coll Llan 92. **d** 94 **p** 95. C Llwynderw *S & B* from 94. *23 Mayals Avenue, Blackpill, Swansea SA3 5DE* Swansea (01792) 401703

GRIFFITHS, David Mark. b 59. Kent Univ BA80. Chich Th Coll 81. **d** 83 **p** 84. C Clydach *S & B* 83-84; C Llwynderw 84-88; V Swansea St Nic from 88. *St Nicholas' Vicarage, 58A Dyfed Avenue, Townhill, Swansea SA1 6NG*   Swansea (01792) 654272

GRIFFITHS, Ven Dr David Nigel. b 27. RD77. FSA Worc Coll Ox BA52 MA56 Reading Univ PhD91. Linc Th Coll 56. **d** 58 **p** 59. Chapl RNR 63-77; V Linc St Mich *Linc* 67-73; R Linc St Mary Magd w St Paul 67-73; Vice Chan and Lib Linc Cathl 67-73; TR New Windsor *Ox* 73-87; RD Maidenhead 77-82 and 84-87; Chapl to The Queen from 77; Hon Can Ch Ch *Ox* 83-87; Adn Berks 87-92; rtd 92. *2 Middleton's Field, Lincoln LN2 1QP*   Lincoln (01522) 525753

GRIFFITHS, David Percy Douglas. b 25. St Mich Coll Llan. **d** 78 **p** 79. C Betws St Dav w Ammanford *St D* 78-80; V Llanarth w Mydroilyn, Capel Cynon, Talgarreg etc 80-84; V Llanarth and Capel Cynon w Talgarreg etc 84-86; V Newc Emlyn w Llandyfriog and Troed-yr-aur 86-95; rtd 95. *The Poplars, High Street, Newcastle Emlyn, Dyfed SA38 9BU*   Newcastle Emlyn (01239) 711448

GRIFFITHS, David Rowson Hopkin. b 38. Oak Hill Th Coll 59. **d** 62 **p** 63. C Barrow St Mark *Carl* 62-65; OMF from 66; Japan 66-88; The Philippines from 88. *clo OMF, Belmont, The Vine, Sevenoaks, Kent TN13 3TZ*   Sevenoaks (01732) 450747 Fax 456164

GRIFFITHS, David Wynne. b 47. Univ of Wales (Cardiff) BD73. St Mich Coll Llan 69. **d** 73 **p** 74. Hon C Gabalfa *Llan* 73-76; Lic to Offic 77-79; Hon C Tonypandy w Clydach Vale 79-80; Hon C Pontypridd St Cath 80-87; Perm to Offic from 87. *13 Heol Ty'n-y-Cae, Rhiwbina, Cardiff CF4 6DH*

GRIFFITHS, Canon Evan David. b 32. DEdin Cert86 Open Univ BA77 BA78. St D Coll Lamp 64. **d** 66 **p** 67. C Betws St Dav w Ammanford *St D* 66-72; V Newchurch and Merthyr 72-80; V Llanybydder and Llanwenog w Llanwnnen from 80; RD Lamp and Ultra-Aeron from 86; Hon Can St D Cathl from 93. *The Vicarage, Llanybydder, Dyfed SA40 9QE* Llanybydder (01570) 480483

GRIFFITHS, Garrie Charles. b 53. St Jo Coll Nottm LTh77. **d** 77 **p** 78. Canada 77-78; C Stalybridge H Trin and Ch Ch *Ches* 78-81; C Moreton 81-84; V Godley cum Newton Green 84-89; V Bayston Hill *Lich* from 89. *42 Eric Lock Road West, Bayston Hill, Shrewsbury SY3 0QA*   Shrewsbury (01743) 872164

GRIFFITHS, Geoffrey Ernest. b 28. AKC52. **d** 53 **p** 54. Chapl Colston's Sch Bris 59-75; V Atworth *Sarum* 63-72; P-in-c Shaw and Whitley 69-72; V Atworth w Shaw and Whitley 72-94; NSM Breage w Germoe *Truro* from 94; rtd 94. *Breage Vicarage, Helston, Cornwall TR13 9PN*   Helston (01326) 573449

GRIFFITHS, George Brian. b 25. Kelham Th Coll 46. **d** 51 **p** 52. C-in-c Amersham St Mich CD *Ox* 66-73; V Amersham on the Hill from 73; rtd 95. *8 Oak Close, Hexham, Northd NE46 2RE* Hexham (01434) 608946

GRIFFITHS, Canon George Francis. b 09. Edin Th Coll 41. **d** 42 **p** 43. R Weldon w Deene *Pet* 67-77; Can Pet Cathl 74-77; rtd 77; Perm to Offic *S'wark* from 84. *90 Maryon Road, London SE7 8DJ*   0181-317 7467

GRIFFITHS, Gerald Lewis. b 38. Qu Coll Birm. **d** 88 **p** 89. C Wrexham *St As* 88-91; TV 91-95; R Hope from 95. *The Rectory, Kiln Lane, Hope, Wrexham, Clwyd LL12 9HN* Caergwrle (01978) 762127

GRIFFITHS, Gordon John. b 31. Univ of Wales (Cardiff) BA53. S'wark Ord Course 72. **d** 75 **p** 76. NSM Sutton St Nic *S'wark* 75-78; Asst Chapl Eastbourne Coll 78-81; NSM Willingdon *Chich* 81-88. *15 Buckhurst Close, Willingdon, Eastbourne, E Sussex BN20 9EF*   Eastbourne (01323) 505547

GRIFFITHS, Harvey Stephen. b 35. Linc Coll Ox BA58 MA62. Linc Th Coll 62. **d** 62 **p** 63. C Frodingham *Linc* 62-65; P-in-c Darlington St Cuth *Dur* 65-70; Chapl RN 70-92; P-in-c Southwick w Boarhunt *Portsm* from 92. *The White House, High Street, Southwick, Fareham, Hants PO17 6EB* Cosham (01705) 377568

GRIFFITHS, Jack. b 16. St D Coll Lamp BA39. **d** 42 **p** 43. V Ward End *Birm* 60-81; rtd 81; Perm to Offic *Birm* from 81. *21 Dunston Court, 52 Wheeleys Road, Birmingham B15 2LL* 0121-440 5141

GRIFFITHS, John Alan. b 48. CPsychol AFBPsS Univ of Wales BSc72 Cape Town Univ MSc76. St Mich Coll Llan 87. **d** 89 **p** 90. C Neath w Llantwit *Llan* 89-93; V Roath St German from 93. *St German's Clergy House, Metal Street, Roath, Cardiff CA2 1LA*   Cardiff (01222) 494488

GRIFFITHS, John Gareth. b 44. Lich Th Coll 68. **d** 71 **p** 72. C Shotton *St As* 71-73; C Rhyl w St Ann 73-76; V Llanasa 76-95; RD Holywell 89-95; V Rhuddlan from 95. *The Vicarage, Vicarage Lane, Rhuddlan, Rhyl, Clwyd LL18 2UE*   Rhuddlan (01745) 591568

GRIFFITHS, Leonard Lewis Rees. b 09. Lon Coll of Div 27 St Jo Coll Dur BA31 LTh31 MA43. **d** 32 **p** 33. Chapl RN Sch Haslemere 67-75; Antigua 75-76; rtd 76; Perm to Offic *Guildf* from 76. *9 Rosemary Court, Church Road, Haslemere, Surrey GU27 1BH*   Haslemere (01428) 661391

GRIFFITHS, Lewis Eric Holroyd. b 05. Univ Coll Dur BA29. **d** 29 **p** 30. R Tendring *Chelmsf* 59-70; rtd 70. *12 The Cedars, Adelaide Road, Teddington, Middx TW11 0AX*   0181-977 6643

GRIFFITHS, Malcolm. b 47. St Alb Minl Tr Scheme. **d** 82 **p** 83. NSM Hemel Hempstead *St Alb* 82-86; C 86-87; TV Liskeard, St Keyne, St Pinnock, Morval etc *Truro* from 87. *The Parsonage, Tremadden Lane, Liskeard, Cornwall PL14 3DS* Liskeard (01579) 346236

GRIFFITHS, Margaret. *See* MacLACHLAN, Mrs Margaret

GRIFFITHS, Mrs Margarett. b 29. ATCL47 LRAM48. CA Tr Coll 50. **dss** 81 **d** 87. Hackington *Cant* 81-83; Ashford 84-89; Par Dn 87-89; rtd 89. *39 Newington Way, Craven Arms, Shropshire SY7 9PS*   Craven Arms (01588) 673848

GRIFFITHS, Martyn Robert. b 51. Nottm Univ BTh74 St Martin's Coll Lanc PGCE75. Kelham Th Coll 70. **d** 74 **p** 75. C Kings Heath *Birm* 74-77; C-in-c Elmdon Heath CD 77-79; TV Solihull 79-81; Asst Admin Shrine of Our Lady of Walsingham 81-85; V Oldham St Steph and All Martyrs *Man* 85-89; TR Swinton and Pendlebury from 89. *The Rectory, Vicarage Road, Swinton, Manchester M27 3WA*   0161-794 1568 or 727 8175

GRIFFITHS, Meirion. b 38. Clifton Th Coll 63. **d** 66 **p** 67. C Upper Holloway St Pet *Lon* 66-68; C Taunton St Jas *B & W* 68-70; C Radipole *Sarum* 70-74; R Chich St Pancras and St Jo *Chich* 74-82; RD Edeyrnion *St As* 82-88; R Corwen and Llangar 82-88; Australia from 88. *87 Wittenoom Street, Collie, W Australia 6225*   Collie (97) 341049

GRIFFITHS, Mervyn Harrington. b 15. Ripon Hall Ox 53. **d** 54 **p** 55. R Bighton *Win* 59-78; V Bishop's Sutton 59-78; rtd 80; Perm to Offic *Ex* from 80. *Kimberley, Clapps Lane, Beer, Seaton, Devon EX12 3HQ*   Seaton (01297) 22382

GRIFFITHS, Morgan Emlyn. b 17. St D Coll Lamp BA38 St Mich Coll Llan 39. **d** 43 **p** 44. R (Llanfihangel) Cwmdu and Tretower *S & B* 60-78; V Crickhowell w Cwmdu and Tretower 78-83; rtd 83. *10 St John's, Pendre Close, Brecon, Powys LD3 9ED*   Brecon (01874) 611125

GRIFFITHS, Neville. b 39. Univ of Wales BA63. St D Coll Lamp LTh66. **d** 66 **p** 67. C Newport St Mark *Mon* 66-68; C Cardiff St Jo *Llan* 68-70; Chapl Greystoke Th Tr Coll 70-76; C Greystoke w Matterdale *Carl* 70-75; TV Greystoke, Matterdale and Mungrisdale 75-76; Chapl Grey Coll Dur 76-81; C Croxdale *Dur* 76-81; R Didsbury Ch Ch *Man* 81-83; P-in-c Lowther and Askham *Carl* 83-84; R 84-88; V Guernsey St Matt *Win* 88-93; R Guernsey St Pierre du Bois from 93. *The Rectory, St Peter-in-the-Wood, Guernsey, Channel Islands GY7 9SB*   Guernsey (01481) 63544

GRIFFITHS, Paul Edward. b 48. St Jo Coll Nottm 86. **d** 88 **p** 89. C Ipswich St Andr *St E* 88-92; P-in-c Tollerton *S'well* from 92; P-in-c Plumtree from 95. *The Rectory, Tollerton, Nottingham NG12 4FW*   Nottingham (0115) 937 2349

GRIFFITHS, Richard Barre Maw. b 43. CCC Ox BA65 MA69. Cranmer Hall Dur DipTh71 BA71. **d** 71 **p** 72. C Fulwood *Sheff* 71-74; Hon C Sheff St Jo 74-76; Fell Dept of Bibl Studies Sheff Univ 74-76; C Fulham St Matt *Lon* 76-78; P-in-c 78-83; R Chich St Pancras and St Jo *Chich* from 83. *St Pancras's Rectory, 9 St John Street, Chichester, W Sussex PO19 1UR* Chichester (01243) 536390 or 536387

GRIFFITHS, Robert Fred. b 20. St Aid Birkenhead 47. **d** 50 **p** 51. C-in-c Fairfield St Rich CD *Worc* 69-76; rtd 85. *56 Heathfield Road, Norton, Evesham, Worcs WR11 4TQ* Evesham (01386) 870198

GRIFFITHS, Robert Herbert. b 53. Univ of Wales (Ban) DipTh75. Chich Th Coll 75. **d** 76 **p** 77. C Holywell *St As* 76-80; CF(TA) from 79; V Llanfair D C *St As* 80-84; P-in-c Gyffylliog 80-84; Asst Dioc Youth Chapl 81-86; V Llanfair, Derwen, Llanelidan and Efenechtyd 84-88; Dioc Youth Chapl 86-90; V St As and Tremeirchion from 88. *The Vicarage, 1 Llys Trewithan, Mount Road, St Asaph, Clwyd LL17 0DF* St Asaph (01745) 583264

GRIFFITHS, Robert James (Rob). b 52. Nottm Univ BTh82. St Jo Coll Nottm 79. **d** 82 **p** 83. C Kettering St Andr *Pet* 82-85; C Collier Row St Jas *Chelmsf* 85; C Collier Row St Jas and Havering-atte-Bower 86-89; R High Ongar w Norton Mandeville from 89. *The Rectory, The Street, High Ongar, Essex CM5 9NQ* Ongar (01277) 362593

GRIFFITHS, Roger. b 46. Trin Coll Bris 70. **d** 74 **p** 75. C Normanton *Derby* 74-77; C Bucknall and Bagnall *Lich* 77-80; TV 80-83; TV Abth *St D* 83-86; R Letterston w Llanfair Nant-y-Gof etc from 86. *The Rectory, 22 St David's Road, Letterston, Haverfordwest, Dyfed SA62 5SE* Letterston (01348) 840336

GRIFFITHS, Roger Michael. b 47. Wycliffe Hall Ox 83. **d** 86 **p** 87. Min Can St D Cathl *St D* 86-88; V Pen-boyr 88-94; V Fishguard w Llanychar and Pontfaen w Morfil etc from 94. *The Vicarage, High Street, Fishguard, Dyfed SA65 9AU* Fishguard (01348) 872895

GRIFFITHS, Russell Howard. b 22. Glouc Th Course 75. **d** 77 **p** 78. NSM Fownhope w Fawley *Heref* 77-80; NSM Brockhampton 77-80; P-in-c Bridstow w Peterstow 80-81; TV Ross w Brampton Abbotts, Bridstow and Peterstow 81-87; rtd 87. *Green Gables, 239 Ledbury Road, Tupsley, Hereford HR1 1QN* Hereford (01432) 265362

GRIFFITHS, Shirley Thelma. b 48. Open Univ BA83. St Deiniol's Hawarden 79. **d** 82. NSM Dyserth and Trelawnyd and Cwm *St As* 82-91; RE Officer from 89; Min Can St As Cathl from 91. *2 Llys Trewithan, Mount Road, St Asaph, Clwyd LL17 0DF* St Asaph (01745) 583853

GRIFFITHS, Simon Mark. b 62. Ch Ch Coll Cant BA84. Chich Th Coll. **d** 87 **p** 88. C Cardiff St Jo *Llan* 87-91; Sub-Chapl HM Pris Cardiff 87-91; Chapl and Succ Roch Cath *Roch* from 91. *The Succentor's House, 5 St Margaret Street, Rochester, Kent ME1 1TU* Medway (01634) 841482

GRIFFITHS, Canon Stanley Arthur. b 17. Lon Univ BSc38. Cuddesdon Coll 46. **d** 47 **p** 48. V St Neots *Ely* 65-77; RD St Neots 76-82; Hon Can Ely Cathl 76-82; V Buckden 77-82; rtd 82; Perm to Offic *Ely* from 82; Perm to Offic *York* from 82. *17 York Road, Malton, N Yorkshire YO17 0AX* Malton (01653) 697324

GRIFFITHS, Stephen Mark (Steve). b 67. Nottm Univ BTh93. St Jo Coll Nottm 90. **d** 93 **p** 94. C Glascote and Stonydelph *Lich* from 93. *31 Lintly, Tamworth, Staffs B77 4LN* Tamworth (01827) 896363

GRIFFITHS, Miss Sylvia Joy. b 50. Gipsy Hill Coll of Educn CertEd71. St Jo Coll Nottm 85. **dss** 86 **d** 87 **p** 94. Woodthorpe *S'well* 86-87; Par Dn 87-90; Min Bestwood/Rise Park LEP from 90; TD Bestwood 90-94; TR from 94. *The Vicarage, 81 Cherry Orchard Mount, Bestwood, Nottingham NG5 5TJ* Nottingham (0115) 927 6107

GRIFFITHS, Thomas. b AKC57. **d** 58 **p** 59. C Cheadle Hulme All SS *Ches* 58-61; C Oxton 61-63; V Micklehurst 63-72; V Ringway 73-91; V Liscard St Mary w St Columba from 91. *St Mary's Vicarage, 107 Manor Road, Wallasey, Merseyside L45 7LU* 0151-639 1553

GRIFFITHS, Ven Thomas Elwyn. b 12. Univ of Wales BA35 Or Coll Ox BA38 MA45. St Steph Ho Ox 37. **d** 38 **p** 39. Adn Brecon *S & B* 69-78; rtd 78. *27 Parc Pendre, Brecon, Powys LD3 9ES* Brecon (01874) 625756

GRIFFITHS, Thomas Wailes (Tom). b 02. Wadh Coll Ox BA25 MA33. St D Coll Lamp 24. **d** 25 **p** 26. P-in-c Innerleithen *Edin* 67-70; P-in-c Lerwick *Ab* 78-79; P-in-c Burravoe 78-79; rtd 79. *115 Banbury Road, Oxford OX2 6LA* Oxford (01865) 516461

GRIFFITHS, Trefor Idris. b 51. Univ of Wales (Cardiff) BA73 CertEd76 DPS86. St Mich Coll Llan 84. **d** 86 **p** 87. C Aberdare St Jo *Llan* 86-89; V Port Talbot St Agnes w Oakwood 89-94; V Rhymney *Mon* from 94. *The Vicarage, Lawn Terrace, Rhymney, Gwent NP2 5LL* Rhymney (01685) 840500

GRIFFITHS, Tudor Francis Lloyd. b 54. Jes Coll Ox BA76 MA81. Wycliffe Hall Ox 76. **d** 79 **p** 80. C Brecon w Battle *S & B*

79-81; Min Can Brecon Cathl 79-81; C Swansea St Mary w H Trin 81-83; V Llangattock and Llangyndir 83-88; CMS from 89; Uganda from 89. *Bishop Tucker Theological College, PO Box 4, Mukono, Uganda*

GRIFFITHS, Vyrnach Morgan. b 24. Univ of Wales (Lamp) BA50. St Mich Coll Llan 52. **d** 54 **p** 55. V Dinas w Penygraig *Llan* 69-74; R Llanddulas *St As* 74-80; R Llanddulas and Llysfaen 80-89; rtd 89. *27 Wynnstay Road, Old Colwyn, Colwyn Bay, Clwyd LL29 9DS* Colwyn Bay (01492) 512232

GRIFFITHS, William Bevan. b 13. AKC37. **d** 37 **p** 38. R Braunston *Pet* 59-79; rtd 79. *73 Glannant Way, Cimla, Neath, W Glam SA11 3YP* Neath (01639) 635697

GRIFFITHS, William David Aled. b 52. Univ of Wales (Abth) BA74 Man Univ AHA77. St Mich Coll Llan DipTh83. **d** 83 **p** 84. C Carmarthen St Pet *St D* 83-87; Asst Warden of Ords from 84; V Llansadwrn w Llanwrda and Manordeilo 87-92; V Llangynnwr and Cwmffrwd from 92. *The Vicarage, Llangynnwr, Carmarthen, Dyfed SA31 2HY* Carmarthen (01267) 236435

GRIFFITHS, William David Maldwyn. b 23. St D Coll Lamp BA47. **d** 50 **p** 51. V Llanfihangel Geneu'r Glyn *St D* 67-89; RD Llanbadarn Fawr 87-89; rtd 89. *Bro Enlli, Lower Regent Street, Aberaeron, Dyfed SA46 0HZ* Aberaeron (01545) 570176

GRIFFITHS, William Thomas Gordon. b 48. York Univ BA70 Fitzw Coll Cam BA79. Ridley Hall Cam 78. **d** 80 **p** 81. C Dulwich St Barn *S'wark* 80-83; C Egglescliffe *Dur* 83-85; Ind Chapl 85-90; V Stockton St Jas from 90. *243 Darlington Lane, Stockton-on-Tees, Cleveland TS19 8AA* Stockton-on-Tees (01642) 676323

GRIGG, Simon James. b 61. Warw Univ BA82 MA83 Southn Univ BTh90. Chich Th Coll 87. **d** 90 **p** 91. C Cowley St Jas *Ox* 90-94; V W Hampstead St Jas *Lon* from 94. *42 Birchington Road, London NW6 4LJ* 0171-625 9705

GRIGG, Canon Terence George. b 34. Kelham Th Coll 54. **d** 59 **p** 60. C Brookfield St Anne, Highgate Rise *Lon* 59-62; Chapl Lee Abbey 63-66; Chapl and Lect St Luke's Coll Ex 66-70; V Stainton-in-Cleveland *York* 70-83; R Cottingham from 83; Hon Can Koforidua from 84; Can York Minster *York* from 90. *The Rectory, Hallgate, Cottingham, N Humberside HU16 4DD* Hull (01482) 847668

GRIGG, William John Frank. b 27. SSC. Ripon Hall Ox. **d** 66 **p** 67. C Fenton *Lich* 69-74; C St Stephen by Saltash *Truro* 74-76; TV Redruth 76-79; TV Laneast w St Clether and Tresmere 79-81; P-in-c Wendron 81-85; TV Helston and Wendron 85-91; rtd 91. *St Germoe, 23 Dunheved Fields, Launceston, Cornwall PL15 7HS* Launceston (01566) 772878

GRIGGS, Canon Alan Sheward. b 33. Trin Hall Cam BA56 MA60. Westcott Ho Cam 58. **d** 60 **p** 61. C Arnold *S'well* 60-63; Succ S'wark Cathl *S'wark* 63-66; Ind Chapl 66-71; C Leeds H Trin *Ripon* 71-81; V 81-91; Soc and Ind Adv 71-81; Hon Can Ripon Cathl from 84; Soc Resp Officer from 91. *33 Harrowby Road, Leeds LS16 5HZ* Leeds (0113) 275 8100 or 234 3533

GRIGGS, Frederick John. b 20. Peterho Cam BA48 MA53. Linc Th Coll. **d** 50 **p** 51. R Colne Engaine *Chelmsf* 62-80; P-in-c Frating w Thorrington 80-83; rtd 83. *6 Church View, Holton, Halesworth, Suffolk IP19 8PB* Halesworth (01986) 875298

✝**GRIGGS, Rt Rev Ian Macdonald.** b 28. Trin Hall Cam BA52 MA56. Westcott Ho Cam. **d** 54 **p** 55. C Portsea St Cuth *Portsm* 54-59; Youth Chapl *Sheff* 59-64; Bp's Dom Chapl 59-64; V Sheff St Cuth 64-71; V Kidderminster St Mary *Worc* 71-82; Hon Can Worc Cathl 77-84; TR Kidderminster St Mary and All SS etc 82-84; Preb Heref Cathl *Heref* 84-94; Adn Ludlow 84-87; P-in-c Tenbury St Mich 84-87; Suff Bp Ludlow 87-94; rtd 94; Hon Ass Bp Carlisle from 94. *Rookings, Patterdale, Penrith, Cumbria CA11 0NP* Penrith (01768) 482064

GRIGGS, Kenneth Courtenay. b 13. Worc Ord Coll 56. **d** 58 **p** 59. V Dodford *Worc* 64-79; rtd 79; Perm to Offic *Worc* 79-82; Perm to Offic *Glouc* 82-92. *Parton House, Parton Road, Churchdown, Gloucester GL3 2JE* Churchdown (01452) 714775

GRIGOR, David Alexander. b 29. Lon Univ DipTh54. St Aid Birkenhead 51. **d** 54 **p** 55. V Paignton St Paul Preston *Ex* 67-73; Brazil 73-74; Hon C Heavitree *Ex* 74-77; Chapl Ex Sch 74-77; Chapl Brighton Coll 77-89; Chapl Warminster Sch Wilts from 89; rtd 93. *28 Lower Keyford, Frome, Somerset BA11 4AS* Frome (01373) 474147

GRIGSBY, Peter Edward. b 31. Magd Coll Cam MA56 CertEd56. NE Ord Course 85. **d** 88 **p** 89. NSM Haxby w Wigginton *York* 88-90; C Brayton 90-92; TV from 92. *St Francis's Vicarage, 25 Fox Lane, Thorpe Willoughby, Selby, N Yorkshire YO8 9NA* Selby (01757) 703742

GRIGSON, Richard John Stephen. b 60. Man Univ BA83. Qu Coll Birm 86. **d** 88 **p** 89. C W Bromwich St Fran *Lich* 88-92; V Smallthorne from 92. *St Saviour's Vicarage, Smallthorne, Stoke-on-Trent ST6 1NX* Stoke-on-Trent (01782) 835941

GRIMASON, Canon Alistair John. b 57. CITC 76. **d** 79 **p** 80. C Belf H Trin *Conn* 79-82; C Dub Drumcondra w N Strand *D & G* 82-84; I Navan w Kentstown, Tara, Slane, Painestown etc *M & K* 84-91; Dioc Youth Officer (Meath) 90-94; Dioc Info Officer (Meath) from 90; I Tullamore w Durrow, Newtownfertullagh, Rahan etc from 91; Preb Tipper St Patr Cathl Dub from 92. *The Rectory, Hop Hill, Tullamore, Co Offaly, Irish Republic* Tullamore (506) 21731

GRIME, Arthur Michael. b 28. Kelham Th Coll 48. **d** 52 **p** 53. V Chiswick St Paul Grove Park *Lon* 66-88; rtd 89. *9 Portland Mews, St George's Road, Brighton BN2 1EQ*

GRIME, William John Peter. b 38. St Jo Coll Ox BA60 MA66. Cuddesdon Coll 69. **d** 70 **p** 71. C Blackb St Jas *Blackb* 70-74; Chapl St Martin's Coll of Educn 74-77; V Seascale *Carl* 77-78; P-in-c Irton w Drigg 77-78; V Seascale and Drigg from 78. *The Vicarage, The Banks, Seascale, Cumbria CA20 1QT* Seascale (019467) 28217

GRIMES, William Geoffrey. b 33. Cranmer Hall Dur 59. **d** 62 **p** 63. C Preston St Jo *Blackb* 62-65; C Ribbleton 65-68; V New Longton 68-76; Adv on Services for the Deaf Sefton 77-89; Lic to Offic 80-89; Perm to Offic *Liv* 86-89; P-in-c Ingol *Blackb* 89-90; C Ashton-on-Ribble St Mich 90; P-in-c 90-91; P-in-c Ashton-on-Ribble St Mich w Preston St Mark 91-92; V from 92. *St Michael's Vicarage, 2 Edgerton Road, Ashton-on-Ribble, Preston PR2 1AJ* Preston (01772) 726157

GRIMLEY, Robert William. b 43. Ch Coll Cam BA66 MA70 Wadh Coll Ox BA68 MA76. Ripon Hall Ox 66. **d** 68 **p** 69. C Radlett *St Alb* 68-72; Hon C Moseley St Mary *Birm* 72-84; Chapl K Edw Sch Birm 72-84; V Edgbaston St Geo *Birm* from 84. *St George's Vicarage, 3 Westbourne Road, Birmingham B15 3TH* 0121-454 2303

GRIMSBY, Suffragan Bishop of. See TUSTIN, Rt Rev David

GRIMSDALE, Mrs Margaret. b 24. STDip48 Lon Univ STD55. Gilmore Course 80. **dss** 82 **d** 87. Stoke Poges *Ox* 82-87; Hon Par Dn 87-88; Hon Par Dn Burrington and Churchill *B & W* 88-90; rtd 90; Perm to Offic *B & W* 90-94. *6 Chapel Close, Castle Cary, Somerset BA7 7AX* Castle Cary (01963) 50866

GRIMSHAW, Canon Eric Fenton Hall. b 34. Bris Univ BA57. Tyndale Hall Bris 54. **d** 58 **p** 59. C Moss Side St Jas *Man* 58-61; C Leyland St Andr *Blackb* 61-64; V Preston St Mark 64-72; V Mirehouse Carl 72-91; Hon Can Carl Cathl 86-91; V Knowsley *Liv* from 91. *The Vicarage, Tithebarn Road, Prescot, Merseyside L34 0JA* 0151-546 4266

GRIMSTER, Barry John. b 49. Ex Univ BA70. Trin Coll Bris 72. **d** 74 **p** 75. C S Lambeth St Steph *S'wark* 74-77; C New Malden and Coombe 77-82; P-in-c Deptford St Jo 82-84; V Deptford St Jo w H Trin 84-89; V Woking St Pet *Guildf* from 89. *St Peter's Vicarage, 28 High Street, Old Woking, Woking, Surrey GU22 9ER* Woking (01483) 762707

GRIMWADE, Eric Peter. b 14. AKC37. **d** 37 **p** 38. Chapl Cane Hill Hosp Coulsdon 69-78; C Lee-on-the-Solent *Portsm* 78-79; Hon C 79-81; rtd 79; Perm to Offic *Chich* from 82. *50 Brookway, Lindfield, Haywards Heath, W Sussex RH16 2BP* Haywards Heath (01444) 414761

GRIMWADE, Canon John Girling. b 20. Keble Coll Ox BA48 MA52. Cuddesdon Coll 48. **d** 50 **p** 51. R Caversham *Ox* 62-81; Hon Can Ch Ch 73-90; Chapl to The Queen 80-90; R Caversham and Mapledurham *Ox* 81-83; P-in-c Stonesfield 83-89; rtd 89; Perm to Offic *Ox* from 89; Perm to Offic *Glouc* from 89. *88 Alexander Drive, Cirencester, Glos GL7 1UJ* Cirencester (01285) 885767

GRIMWADE, Leslie Frank. b 24. FBIM60. Trin Coll Bris 74. **d** 77 **p** 78. C Taunton St Jas *B & W* 77-80; C Polegate *Chich* 80-83; R Swainsthorpe w Newton Flotman *Nor* 83-90; rtd 90; Hon Min Malmesbury Abbey *Bris* from 90; Chapl Malmesbury Hosp from 90. *Drimwal, Common Road, Malmesbury, Wilts SN16 0HN* Malmesbury (01666) 823541

GRIMWOOD, David Walter. b 48. Lon Univ BA70 K Coll Lon BD73 AKC73. **d** 74 **p** 75. C Newc St Geo *Newc* 74-78; C Whorlton 78-80; TV Totton *Win* 80-93; Adv to Coun for Soc Resp (Dios Cant and Roch) *Cant* from 93. *56 Postley Road, Maidstone, Kent ME15 6TR* Maidstone (01622) 764625

GRINDELL, James Mark. b 43. Nottm Univ BA66 Bris Univ MA69. Wells Th Coll 66. **d** 68 **p** 69. C Bushey Heath *St Alb* 68-72; C Ex St Dav *Ex* 72-74; Chapl St Audries Sch W Quantoxhead 74-83; Chapl Berkhamsted Sch Herts 83-86; Chapl Denstone Coll Uttoxeter 86-91; Chapl Portsm Gr Sch from 92. *Portsmouth Grammar School, High Street, Portsmouth PO1 2LN* Portsmouth (01705) 819125

✠**GRINDROD, Rt Rev John Basil Rowland.** b 19. KBE90. Qu Coll Ox BA49 MA53. Linc Th Coll 49. **d** 51 **p** 52 **c** 66. C Hulme St Mich *Man* 51-54; R Ancoats All SS 56-60; Australia from 60; Adn Rockhampton 60-65; Bp Riverina 66-71; Bp Rockhampton 71-80; Abp Brisbane 80-90; rtd 90. *14B Thomas Street, Murwillumbah, NSW, Australia 2484* Murwillumbah (66) 721320

GRINHAM, Garth Clews. b 36. Oak Hill Th Coll 61. **d** 64 **p** 65. C Beckenham Ch Ch *Roch* 64-68; C Wallington H Trin *S'wark* 68-71; V Erith St Paul *Roch* 71-76; Asst Sec CPAS 76-81; Hon C Knockholt *Roch* 76-81; V Southport Ch Ch *Liv* 81-94; V Douglas St Ninian *S & M* from 94. *St Ninian's Vicarage, 58 Ballanard, Douglas, Isle of Man IM2 5HE* Douglas (01624) 621694

GRINHAM, Julian Clive. b 39. Birkb Coll Lon BA65. Oak Hill Th Coll 79. **d** 81 **p** 82. C Blackb Ch Ch w St Matt *Blackb* 81-83; Nat Sec Pathfinders CPAS 83-89; Dir CYPECS 89-94; V Normanton *Derby* from 94. *St Giles Vicarage, Browning Street, Normanton, Derby DE23 8DN* Derby (01332) 767483

GRINSTED, Richard Anthony. b 43. Leic Univ BSc65. Oak Hill Th Coll 67. **d** 70 **p** 71. C Egham *Guildf* 70-73; C Woodford Wells *Chelmsf* 73-76; P-in-c Havering-atte-Bower 76-84; R Ditton *Roch* 84-94; R Chulmleigh *Ex* from 94; R Chawleigh w Cheldon from 94; R Wembworthy w Eggesford from 94. *The Rectory, Chulmleigh, Devon EX18 7NY* Chulmleigh (01769) 580537

GRISCOME, David. b 47. Oak Hill Th Coll BA88 TCD Div Sch 89. **d** 89 **p** 90. C Glendermott *D & R* 89-91; I Clondehorkey w Cashel 91-95; I Mevagh w Glenalla 91-95; Bp's C Calry *K, E & A* from 95. *Calry Rectory, The Mall, Sligo, Irish Republic* Sligo (71) 46513

GRIST, Anthony John. b 51. Kent Univ BA72. Westcott Ho Cam 73. **d** 76 **p** 77. C Wythenshawe St Martin *Man* 76-79; C Reddish 79-82; V Royton St Anne 82-86. *32 Manchester Road, Mossley, Ashton-under-Lyne, Lancs OL5 0AA*

GRITTEN, Desmond Digby. b 17. ALCD54. **d** 54 **p** 55. V Kenilworth St Jo *Cov* 58-87; RD Kenilworth 63-73; rtd 87; Perm to Offic *Cant* 87-92; Perm to Offic *Ex* from 92. *22 Rumsay Gardens, Barnstaple, Devon EX32 9EY* Barnstaple (01271) 326794

GROOCOCK, Christopher John (Chris). b 59. St Jo Coll Nottm LTh92 DCM92. **d** 92 **p** 93. C Shawbury *Lich* from 92. *10 Bridgeway, Shawbury, Shrewsbury SY4 4PG* Shawbury (01939) 250902

GROSSCURTH, Stephen. b 55. Sarum & Wells Th Coll 81. **d** 84 **p** 85. C Southport H Trin *Liv* 84-87; C Amblecote *Worc* 87-89; V Walton St Jo *Liv* from 89. *St John's Vicarage, Rice Lane, Liverpool L9 2BW* 0151-525 3458

GROSSE, Anthony Charles Bain. b 30. Oak Hill Th Coll 58. **d** 61 **p** 62. C Chislehurst Ch Ch *Roch* 61-65; C Washfield *Ex* 65-71; TV Washfield, Stoodleigh, Withleigh etc 71-73; R Hemyock 73-86; P-in-c Clayhidon 76-86; R Hemyock w Culm Davy and Clayhidon 87-93; R Hemyock w Culm Davy, Clayhidon and Culmstock from 93. *The Rectory, Hemyock, Cullompton, Devon EX15 3RQ* Hemyock (01823) 680244

GROSSE, Richard William. b 52. Solicitor 77 M Essex Tech Coll LLB73. Ridley Hall Cam 86. **d** 88 **p** 89. C Soham *Ely* 88-91; C Bedale *Ripon* 91-93; C-in-c Thornton Watlass w Thornton Steward 91-93; V Barton and Manfield w Cleasby 93-95; V Barton and Manfield and Cleasby w Stapleton from 95. *The Vicarage, Barton, Richmond, N Yorkshire DL10 6JJ* Darlington (01325) 377274

GROSVENOR, Royston Johannes Martin. b 47. K Coll Lon BD70 AKC. **d** 71 **p** 72. C Pontesbury I and II *Heref* 71-75; C Bishopston *Bris* 75-79; P-in-c Croydon St Pet S End *Cant* 79-81; V Croydon St Pet 81-84; V Croydon St Pet *S'wark* 85-87; R Merstham and Gatton from 87. *The Rectory, Gatton Bottom, Merstham, Redhill RH1 3BH* Merstham (01737) 643755

GROVE, Canon John Montgomery. b 13. Magd Coll Cam BA35 MA39. Westcott Ho Cam 39. **d** 39 **p** 40. Chapl Clifton Coll Bris 43-57; Hd Master Chorister Sch Dur 57-78; rtd 74; Hon Can Dur Cathl *Dur* 74-90. *22 South Street, Durham DH1 4OP* 0191-384 4787

GROVE, Ronald Edward. b 32. Oak Hill Th Coll 60. **d** 63 **p** 64. C Bromley St Jo *Roch* 63-66; V Stratford New Town St Paul *Chelmsf* 66-94. *Buttermilk House, Cottage Row, Sandwich, Kent CT13 9HR* Sandwich (01304) 620351

GROVER, Wilfrid John. b 29. Lich Th Coll 55. **d** 58 **p** 59. V Cookham *Ox* 65-85; RD Maidenhead 82-85; Warden Christchurch Retreat Ho *Glouc* 85-93; rtd 89; Hon C Jedburgh *Edin* from 93. *Cairnbrook, Bemersyde, Melrose, Roxburghshire TD6 9DP* St Boswells (01835) 822054

GROVES, James Alan. b 32. CCC Cam BA58 MA62. Wells Th Coll 58. **d** 60 **p** 61. C Milton next Gravesend Ch Ch *Roch* 60-64; C Beckenham St Jas 64-66; V Orpington St Andr from 66. *St Andrew's Vicarage, Anglesea Road, Orpington, Kent BR5 4AN* Orpington (01689) 823775

GROVES, Mrs Jill. b 61. Univ Coll Lon BSc82. St Jo Coll Nottm DTS91 MA93. **d** 93 **p** 94. C Tenbury *Heref* from 93. *23 Castle Close, Burford, Tenbury Wells, Worcs WR15 8AY* Tenbury Wells (01584) 811975

GROVES, Philip Neil. b 62. Man Univ BA84. St Jo Coll Nottm 86. **d** 88 **p** 89. C Holbeck *Ripon* 88-91; CMS from 91; Tanzania from 93. *St Philip's Theological College, PO Box 26, Kongwa, Tanzania*

GROVES, Robert John (Bob). b 42. Trin Coll Bris 74. **d** 76 **p** 77. C Norwood *S'wark* 76-79; P-in-c Clapham Park All SS 79-86; V Anerley *Roch* 86-95; TV Canford Magna *Sarum* from 95. *The Vicarage, Canford Magna, Wimborne, Dorset BH21 3AF* Wimborne (01202) 883382

GROVES, Stephen James Andrew. b 60. Newc Univ BA82. Coll of Resurr Mirfield 83. **d** 86 **p** 87. C Brighton Resurr *Chich* 86-91; C St Leonards Ch Ch and St Mary 91-94; C Petworth 94. *96 London Road, St Leonards-on-Sea, E Sussex TN37 6LR* Hastings (01424) 422738

GROWNS, John Huntley. b 28. Chich Th Coll 57. **d** 60 **p** 61. C-in-c Kempston Transfiguration CD *St Alb* 67-74; R Stevenage St Geo 74-82; R Felpham w Middleton *Chich* 82-88; P-in-c Westmill w Gt Munden *St Alb* 88-89; Dioc Stewardship Adv 88-93; P-in-c Westmill 89-93; rtd 93. *28 Cambridge Road, Ely, Cambs CB7 4HL* Ely (01353) 662263

GRUBB, Greville Alexander. b 36. St Jo Coll Nottm 72. **d** 74 **p** 75. C Rushden w Newton Bromswold *Pet* 74-77; Chapl St D Coll Llandudno 77-89; Chapl Casterton Sch from 90; Lic to Offic *Carl* from 90. *Beckside, Casterton, Carnforth, Lancs LA6 2SB* Kirkby Lonsdale (015242) 71737

GRUBB, Martin John. b 63. Man Univ BA87. Wycliffe Hall Ox 89. **d** 91 **p** 92. C Pennycross *Ex* from 91. *23 Pennycross Park Road, Plymouth PL2 3NP* Plymouth (01752) 772758

GRUNDY, Anthony Brian. b 36. Pemb Coll Cam BA62 MA87. Ridley Hall Cam 61. **d** 63 **p** 64. C Hatcham St Jas *S'wark* 63-66; C Margate H Trin *Cant* 66-68; C Brixton Hill St Sav *S'wark* 68-70; V Assington *St E* 70-76; TV Much Wenlock w Bourton *Heref* 76-81; TV Wenlock 81-82; TR 82-88; RD Condover 86-88; R Burghfield *Ox* from 88. *The Rectory, Hollybush Lane, Burghfield Common, Reading RG7 3BH* Burghfield Common (01734) 834433

GRUNDY, Christopher John. b 49. Trin Coll Bris 74. **d** 77 **p** 78. C Maidstone St Luke *Cant* 77-81; Argentina 81-82; Chile 82-84; Perm to Offic *Guildf* from 84. *The Lyttons, Seale, Farnham, Surrey GU10 1HR* Runfold (01252) 782071

GRUNDY, Jocelyn Pratchitt. b 22. Trin Coll Cam MA. Westcott Ho Cam 64. **d** 66 **p** 67. R Shere *Guildf* 68-73; V Fleet 73-83; C Aldershot St Mich 83-87; rtd 87. *Richmond Cottage, School Hill, Seale, Farnham, Surrey GU10 1HY* Runfold (01252) 782238

GRUNDY, Mrs Judith Michal Towers Mynors. b 54. Lady Spencer Chu Coll of Educn CertEd76 Ox Univ BEd77. Trin Coll Bris DipHE87. **d** 93 **p** 94. NSM Kensal Rise St Mark and St Martin *Lon* 93-95; NSM Snettisham w Ingoldisthorpe and Fring *Nor* from 95. *The Vicarage, 18 Park Lane, Snettisham, King's Lynn, Norfolk PE31 7NW* Dersingham (01485) 541301

GRUNDY, Julian David. b 60. St Andr Univ MA83. Trin Coll Bris BA88. **d** 89 **p** 90. C Lanc St Thos *Blackb* 89-92; C Kensal Rise St Mark and St Martin *Lon* 92-95; R Snettisham w Ingoldisthorpe and Fring *Nor* from 95. *The Vicarage, 18 Park Lane, Snettisham, King's Lynn, Norfolk PE31 7NW* Dersingham (01485) 541301

GRUNDY, Ven Malcolm Leslie. b 44. AKC68 Open Univ BA76. **d** 69 **p** 70. C Doncaster St Geo *Sheff* 69-72; Ind Chapl 72-80; Dir of Educn *Lon* 80-86; TR Huntingdon *Ely* 86-91; Hon Can Ely Cathl 88-94; Dir Avec 91-94; Lic to Offic 91-93; Perm to Offic *Lon* 91-94; Adn Craven *Bradf* from 94. *The Vicarage, Gisburn, Clitheroe, Lancs BB7 4HR* Clitheroe (01200) 445214 Fax 445816

GRUNDY, Paul. b 55. BD77 AKC. Linc Th Coll 79. **d** 80 **p** 81. C Ryhope *Dur* 80-82; C Ferryhill 82-85; TV Cramlington *Newc* 85-87; TV Swinton and Pendlebury *Man* 87-90; V Wingate Grange *Dur* from 90. *The Vicarage, Wingate, Co Durham TS28 5BW* Wellfield (01429) 838338

GRYLLS, Michael John. b 38. Qu Coll Cam BA62 MA66. Linc Th Coll 62. **d** 64 **p** 65. C Sheff Gillcar St Silas *Sheff* 64-67; C-in-c Dunscroft CD 67-70; V Herringthorpe 70-78; V Amport, Grateley, Monxton and Quarley *Win* 78-89; RD Andover 85-89; V Whitchurch w Tufton and Litchfield from 89. *The Vicarage, Church Street, Whitchurch, Hants RG28 7AS* Whitchurch (01256) 892535

GUDGEON, Michael John. b 40. Qu Coll Cam BA63 MA67. Chich Th Coll 65. **d** 66 **p** 67. C Kings Heath *Birm* 66-72; Asst Chapl K Edw Sch Birm 69-72; Chapl and Tutor Cuddesdon Coll 72-75; V Hawley H Trin *Guildf* 75-80; V Minley 75-80; Adult Educn Adv *Chich* 80-87; Can Res Portsm Cathl *Portsm* 87-90; Dioc Dir of Educn 87-90; V Hove St Thos *Chich* 90-93; TV Hove 93-94; Bp's Chapl *Eur* from 94; Dir of Ords from 94. *46 Blackwater Lane, Worth, Crawley, W Sussex RH10 4RN* Crawley (01293) 883051 Fax 884479

GUERNSEY, Dean of. *See* FENWICK, Very Rev Jeffrey Robert

GUEST, David. b 41. Dur Univ BA62. Coll of Resurr Mirfield 70. **d** 72 **p** 73. C Horsforth *Ripon* 72-75; C Richmond 75-76; C Richmond w Hudswell 76-78; R Middleham 78-81; R Middleham and Coverham w Horsehouse 81-86; R W Rainton *Dur* from 86; V E Rainton from 86; RD Houghton from 92. *The Rectory, West Rainton, Houghton le Spring, Tyne & Wear DH4 6PA* 0191-584 3263

GUEST, David Andrew. b 61. Portsm Coll of Tech NDTJ82. Chich Th Coll BTh92. **d** 92 **p** 93. C Prenton *Ches* 92-94; C Ches H Trin from 94. *44 Southway, Chester CH1 5NN* Chester (01244) 373955

GUEST, Derek William. b 55. N Ord Course 90. **d** 93 **p** 94. C Cheadle Hulme St Andr *Ches* from 93. *33 Kingsley Drive, Cheadle Hulme, Cheadle, Cheshire SK8 5LZ* 0161-486 9306

GUEST, Ven Frederick William. b 07. St Aug Coll Cant 27. **d** 32 **p** 33. C Tilbury Docks *Chelmsf* 32-34; Australia from 34; Can Perth 51-73; Adn Canning 61-67; Adn Perth 67-73. *203 Riley House, 20 Excelsior Street, Shenton Park, W Australia 6008* Perth (9) 381-7052

GUEST, John. b 36. Trin Coll Bris 59. **d** 61 **p** 62. C Barton Hill St Luke w Ch Ch *Bris* 61-64; C Liv St Sav *Liv* 65-66; USA from 66. *RD 5 Camp Meeting Road, Sewickley, Pennsylvania 15143, USA*

GUEST, John Andrew Kenneth. b 55. Univ of Wales (Lamp) BA78. Wycliffe Hall Ox 78. **d** 80 **p** 81. C Eastwood *S'wark* 80-84; TV Toxteth St Philemon w St Gabr and St Cleopas *Liv* 84-89; C Cranham Park *Chelmsf* 89-93; P-in-c Stanford-le-Hope w Mucking from 93. *The Rectory, The Green, Stanford-le-Hope, Essex SS17 0EP* Stanford-le-Hope (01375) 672271

GUEST, Leslie Leonard. b 15. Ripon Hall Ox 62. **d** 63 **p** 64. V Norton and Lenchwick *Worc* 66-77; R Inkberrow w Cookhill and Kington w Dormston 77-84; rtd 84; Perm to Offic *Worc* from 84. *35 Husum Way, Kidderminster, Worcs DY10 3QJ* Kidderminster (01562) 745722

GUEST, Simon Llewelyn. b 56. Univ of Wales (Lamp) BA78 CertEd79 DipTh85. St Mich Coll Llan 83. **d** 85 **p** 86. C Bassaleg *Mon* 85-88; C Cwmbran 88-89; R 89-90; V Raglan w Llandenny and Bryngwyn from 90. *The Vicarage, Primrose Green, Raglan, Gwent NP5 2DU* Raglan (01291) 690330

GUEST-BLOFELD, Thomas. b 35. St D Coll Lamp BA59 Cranmer Hall Dur 59. **d** 62 **p** 63. C Ely 68-70; C Pemberton St Jo *Liv* 70-72; V Walton St Jo 72-74; V Barkisland w W Scammonden *Wakef* 74-80; V Smallbridge *Man* 80-82; C Irlam 83-86; rtd 87. *7 The Moat, Wallingford, Oxon OX10* Wallingford (01491) 836829

GUILDFORD, Bishop of. *See* GLADWIN, Rt Rev John Warren

GUILDFORD, Dean of. *See* WEDDERSPOON, Very Rev Alexander Gillan

GUILLAN, Miss Barbara Doris. b 19. S'wark Ord Course 45. **d** 87. NSM St Stythians w Perranarworthal and Gwennap *Truro* 87-89; rtd 89; Perm to Offic *Truro* 89-94. *Address temp unknown*

GUILLE, John Arthur. b 49. Southn Univ BTh79. Sarum & Wells Th Coll 73. **d** 76 **p** 77. C Chandler's Ford *Win* 76-80; P-in-c Bournemouth St Jo 80-84; P-in-c Bournemouth St Mich 83-84; V Bournemouth St Jo w St Mich 84-89; R Guernsey St Andr from 89. *The Rectory, rue des Morts, St Andrew, Guernsey, Channel Islands GY6 8XN* Guernsey (01481) 38568

GUILLEBAUD, Miss Margaret Jean (Meg). b 43. Edin Univ BSc66. All Nations Chr Coll DipRS79 Cranmer Hall Dur 79. dss 80 **d** 87 **p** 94. New Malden and Coombe *S'wark* 80-84; Carlton Colville w Mutford and Rushmere *Nor* 84-87; C 87-91; Par Dn Rodbourne Cheney *Bris* 91-94; C from 94. *21 Newland Road, Swindon SN2 3BP* Swindon (01793) 613734

GUILLOTEAU, Claude. b 32. Ripon Coll Cuddesdon 77. **d** 57 **p** 57. In RC Ch 57-76; C Warmsworth *Sheff* 78-80; C Goole 80-86; C Hatf 86-88; C Ecclesall 88-94; rtd 94. *Residence Frederic Mistral, 3 rue Frederic Mistral, F-81200, Mazamet, France*

GUINNESS, Christopher Paul. b 43. Lon Coll of Div 64. **d** 67 **p** 68. C Farnborough *Guildf* 67-70; C Tulse Hill H Trin *S'wark* 70-74; C Worting *Win* 74-78; P-in-c S Lambeth St Steph *S'wark* 78-89; V 89-91; RD Lambeth 86-90; C Ches Square St Mich w St Phil *Lon* from 91. *4 Victoria Square, London SW1W 0QY* 0171-834 7258

GUINNESS, Garry Grattan. b 40. Em Coll Cam BA64 MA68. Ridley Hall Cam 64. **d** 66 **p** 67. C Wallington H Trin *S'wark* 66-69; C St Marylebone All So w SS Pet and Jo *Lon* 69-72; P-in-c Clifton H Trin, St Andr and St Pet *Bris* 72-79; V Watford St Luke *St Alb* 79-90; TR Worthing Ch the King *Chich* from 90. *4 Shakespeare Road, Worthing, W Sussex BN11 4AL* Worthing (01903) 205185

GUINNESS, Graham Alexander. b 60. Jordan Hill Coll Glas DCE82 Edin Univ LTh85. Edin Th Coll 82. **d** 85 **p** 86. Dioc Youth Chapl *Mor* 85-88; C Elgin w Lossiemouth 85-88; P-in-c Glas St Ninian *Glas* 88-90; R Tighnabruaich *Arg* 90-91; R Dunoon from 90; Miss to Seamen from 90. *The Rectory, Kilbride Road, Dunoon, Argyll PA23 7LN* Dunoon (01369) 2444

GUINNESS, Peter Grattan. b 49. Man Univ BSc71 CertEd73 Nottm Univ DipTh81. St Jo Coll Nottm 80. **d** 82 **p** 83. C Normanton *Wakef* 82-87; V Fletchamstead *Cov* 87-91; V Lanc St Thos *Blackb* from 91. *St Thomas's Vicarage, 33 Belle Vue Terrace, Lancaster LA1 4TY* Lancaster (01524) 32134 Fax 846895

GUINNESS, Canon Robin Gordon. b 38. St Jo Coll Cam MA61. Ridley Hall Cam 63. **d** 63 **p** 64. C Bedworth *Cov* 63-66; CMS 66-68; Canada from 68. *47 Prospect Street, Westmount, Quebec, Canada, H3Z 1W5* Westmount (514) 931-6796

GUISE, John Christopher. b 29. MRPharmS FRSH. W Midl Minl Tr Course 80. **d** 83 **p** 84. NSM Alfrick, Lulsley, Suckley, Leigh and Bransford *Worc* 83-94; NSM Martley and Wichenford, Knightwick etc from 94. *Marsh Cottage, Leigh, Worcs WR6 5LE* Leigh Sinton (01886) 832336

GUISE, Stephen. b 48. Win Sch of Arts BA75. Chich Th Coll 85. **d** 87 **p** 88. C Bexhill St Pet *Chich* 87-90; TV Haywards Heath St Wilfrid 90-94; V Kirdford from 94. *The Vicarage, Kirdford, Billingshurst, W Sussex RH14 0LU* Kirdford (01403) 820605

GUITE, Ayodeji Malcolm. b 57. Pemb Coll Cam BA80 MA84 Newc Poly PGCE82. Ridley Hall Cam 88. **d** 90 **p** 91. C Ely 90-93; TV Huntingdon from 93. *The Vicarage, 3A Longstaffe Way, Hartford, Huntingdon, Cambs PE18 7XT* Huntingdon (01480) 434463

GUITE, Mrs Margaret Ann (Maggie). b 53. Girton Coll Cam BA74 MA78 St Jo Coll Dur PhD81. Cranmer Hall Dur 75. **dss** 79 **d** 87 **p** 94. Warlingham w Chelsham and Farleigh *S'wark* 79-82; Tutor Westcott Ho Cam 82-90; Cherry Hinton St Jo *Ely* 82-86; Tutor Wesley Ho Cam 87-90; Hon Par Dn Ely 90-93; Hon Par Dn Chettisham 90-93; Hon Par Dn Prickwillow 90-93; NSM Huntingdon from 93. *The Vicarage, 3A Longstaff Way, Hartford, Huntingdon, Cambs PE18 7XT* Huntingdon (01480) 434463

GUIVER, Paul Alfred (George). b 45. St Chad's Coll Dur BA68. Cuddesdon Coll 71. **d** 73 **p** 74. C Mill End and Heronsgate w W Hyde *St Alb* 73-76; P-in-c Bishop's Frome *Heref* 76-82; P-in-c Castle Frome 76-82; P-in-c Acton Beauchamp and Evesbatch w Stanford Bishop 76-82; CR from 85. *House of the Resurrection, Mirfield, W Yorkshire WF14 0BN* Mirfield (01924) 494318

GUIVER, Roger William Antony. b 53. Edin Univ MA75 St Chad's Coll Dur BA78. Coll of Resurr Mirfield. **d** 82 **p** 83. C Rekendyke *Dur* 82-85; Chapl Middlesb Gen Hosp 85-93; P-in-c Middlesb St Columba w St Paul *York* 85-94; V Acomb Moor from 94. *The Vicarage, Thanet Road, Dringhouses, York YO2 2PE* York (01904) 706047

GULL, William John. b 42. Ripon Hall Ox 63. **d** 65 **p** 66. C Worksop Priory *S'well* 65-69; C Newark St Mary 69-71; P-in-c Mansf St Lawr 71-77; V 77-78; Chapl HM Young Offender Inst Lowdham Grange 78-90; R Lambley *S'well* 78-91; Chmn Dioc Bd Soc Resp from 86; V Sneinton St Cypr from 91. *St Cyprian's Vicarage, Marston Road, Nottingham NG3 7AN* Nottingham (0115) 987 3425

GULLAND, John Robertson. b 46. ACIB Avery Hill Coll CertEd70 Open Univ BA76 Chelsea Coll Lon MA82. Oak Hill Th Coll 88. **d** 90 **p** 91. NSM Woodside Park St Barn *Lon* 90-92; NSM Castletown *S & M* from 92; Chapl K Wm Coll from 92. *Anchor House, Queens Road, Port St Mary, Isle of Man IM9 5ES* Port Erin (01624) 834548

GULLEY, Hubert Edward Raymond. b 06. Bris Univ BA27. Sarum Th Coll 27. **d** 29 **p** 30. P-in-c Dalry *Glas* 57-75; rtd 75; Perm to Offic *Chich* 84-92. *College of St Barnabas, Blackberry Lane, Lingfield, Surrey RH7 6NJ* Dormans Park (01342) 870430

GULLIDGE, Philip Michael Nowell. b 60. Univ of Wales (Swansea) BSc82 Univ of Wales (Cardiff) BD93. St Mich Coll Llan 90. **d** 93 **p** 94. C Neath w Llantwit *Llan* from 93. *The Parsonage, 35 Trevallen Avenue, Neath, W Glam SA11 3US* Neath (01639) 644434

GULLIFORD, William Douglas. b 69. Selw Coll Cam BA91. Westcott Ho Cam CTM92. **d** 94 **p** 95. C Banstead *Guildf* from 94. *14 Glenfield Road, Banstead, Surrey SM7 2DQ* Burgh Heath (01737) 353938

GULLY, Paul David. b 59. Lon Univ BEd81. Trin Coll Bris BA95. **d** 95. C Radcliffe *Man* from 95. *6 Poolfield Close, Manchester M26 3UE* 0161-723 5460

GULVIN, Philip Christopher. b 53. BSc76. St Jo Coll Nottm 82. **d** 85 **p** 86. C Northwood H Trin *Lon* 85-89; TV Sanderstead All SS *S'wark* from 89. *4 Mitchley Avenue, Purley, Surrey CR8 1EA* 0181-660 8123

GUMBEL, Nicholas Glyn Paul. b 55. Trin Coll Cam MA76 BA85. Wycliffe Hall Ox 83. **d** 86 **p** 87. C Brompton H Trin w Onslow Square St Paul *Lon* from 86. *13 Macaulay Road, London SW4 0QP* 0171-720 3538

GUMMER, Dudley Harrison. b 28. Roch Th Coll 61. **d** 63 **p** 64. C Deptford St Paul *S'wark* 63-65; C Melton Mowbray w Thorpe Arnold *Leic* 65-68; C-in-c E Goscote CD 68-75; V E Goscote 75-78; V Luton St Anne *St Alb* 78-88; R Albury w St Martha *Guildf* from 88. *Yeoman's Acre, Farley Green, Albury, Guildford, Surrey GU5 9DN* Shere (01483) 202465

GUMMER, Selwyn. b 07. Univ of Wales BA34. Wycliffe Hall Ox 39. **d** 39 **p** 40. V Preston *Chich* 65-70; rtd 71. *Winston Grange, Debenham, Stowmarket, Suffolk IP14 6LE* Debenham (01728) 860522

GUNN, Frederick George. b 11. **d** 51 **p** 51. R Witton w Brundall and Braydeston *Nor* 64-79; RD Blofield 74-79; rtd 80; Perm to Offic *Nor* 80-91. *Flat 17, Stuart Court, New Road, Kibworth, Leicester LE8 0LE* Leicester (0116) 279 6367

GUNN, Geoffrey Charles. b 12. Kelham Th Coll 28. **d** 36 **p** 37. V Shotesham *Nor* 56-77; rtd 77; Min Can Nor Cathl *Nor* from 85. *Shepherd's Close, Priory Lane, Shotesham, Norwich NR15 1YH* Brooke (01508) 50285

GUNN, Jeffrey Thomas. b 47. St Chad's Coll Dur BA77 Kent Univ MA95. Coll of Resurr Mirfield 77. **d** 79 **p** 80. C Prestbury *Glouc* 79-82; P-in-c Coldham *Ely* 82-87; P-in-c Elm 82-87; P-in-c Friday Bridge 82-87; V Larkfield *Roch* 87-94; P-in-c Leybourne 87-94; V Petts Wood from 94. *The Vicarage, Willett Way, Orpington, Kent BR5 1QE* Orpington (01689) 829971

GUNN, Robert. b 35. Oak Hill Th Coll 59. **d** 62 **p** 63. Scripture Union 69-71; R Necton w Holme Hale *Nor* 71-77; V Tottenham St Jo *Lon* 77-81; V Gt Cam Road St Jo and St Jas 82-85; V Luton St Fran *St Alb* 85-90; Chapl Luton Airport 90-95; rtd 95. *95 Edgewood Drive, Luton LU2 8ER* Luton (01582) 416151

GUNN-JOHNSON, David Allan. b 49. St Steph Ho Ox 79 Lambeth STh85 MA95. **d** 81 **p** 82. C Oxhey St Matt *St Alb* 81-84; C Cheshunt 84-88; TR Colyton, Southleigh, Offwell, Widworthy etc *Ex* from 88; RD Honiton from 90. *The Vicarage, Colyton, Devon EX13 6LJ* Colyton (01297) 552307

GUNNER, Laurence Francois Pascal. b 36. Keble Coll Ox BA59 MA63. Wells Th Coll 59. **d** 61 **p** 62. C Charlton Kings St Mary *Glouc* 61-65; C Hemel Hempstead *St Alb* 65-69; Chapl Bloxham Sch Oxon 69-86; Sen Chapl Marlborough Coll Wilts from 86. *The Old Rectory, High Street, Marlborough, Wilts SN8 1PA* Marlborough (01672) 512648

GUNNING, George Peter. b 36. Harper Adams Agric Coll NDA58. E Midl Min Tr Course 78. **d** 85 **p** 86. C Winterton Gp *Linc* 85-88; V Alkborough from 88. *The Vicarage, Alkborough, Scunthorpe, S Humberside DN15 9JJ* Scunthorpe (01724) 721126

GUNSTONE, Canon John Thomas Arthur. b 27. St Chad's Coll Dur BA48 MA55. Coll of Resurr Mirfield 50. **d** 52 **p** 53. C-in-c Rush Green St Aug CD *Chelmsf* 58-71; Chapl Barn Fellowship Winterborne Whitechurch 71-75; Tutor Sarum & Wells Th Coll 71-75; Sec Gtr Man Co Ecum Coun 75-92; Lic to Offic *Man* 75-80; Hon Can Man Cathl 80-92; rtd 92. *12 Deneford Road, Didsbury, Manchester M20 8TD* 0161-434 8351

GUNTER, Timothy Wilson. b 37. Leeds Univ BA59 St Jo Coll Cam BA62 MA66. Ridley Hall Cam 59. **d** 62 **p** 63. C Beverley Minster *York* 62-65; C Hornsea and Goxhill 65-70; V Silsden *Bradf* 70-80; V Sunninghill *Ox* from 80. *Sunninghill Vicarage, Church Lane, Ascot, Berks SL5 7DD* Ascot (01344) 20727

GUNYON, Stephen Francis. b 14. Selw Coll Cam BA38 MA48. Linc Th Coll 38. **d** 40 **p** 41. V Hindhead *Guildf* 71-80; rtd 80; Perm to Offic *Pet* from 80. *12 Southgate House, Bury St Edmunds, Suffolk IP33 2RN* Bury St Edmunds (01284) 703156

GUPPY, Kenneth Henry Stanley. b 29. Univ of Wales (Lamp) BA54. St Mich Coll Llan 54. **d** 56 **p** 57. V Llangwm Uchaf w Llangwm Isaf w Gwernesney etc *Mon* 63-85; rtd 85; Lic to Offic *Ox* 88-92; Perm to Offic *B & W* from 94. *11 St Thomas's Court, Woodbury Avenue, Wells, Somerset BA5 2XY*

GURD, Brian Charles (Simon). b 44. Sarum & Wells Th Coll 72. **d** 74 **p** 75. OSP from 67; Lic to Offic *Win* 74-82; Prior Alton Abbey 79-82; C Shepherd's Bush St Steph w St Thos *Lon* 82-84; NSM Willesborough *Cant* 85-87; V Bethersden w High Halden 87-95; R Etchingham *Chich* from 95; V Hurst Green from 95. *The Rectory, High Street, Etchingham, E Sussex TN19 7AH* Etchingham (01580) 819235

GURDON, Mrs June Mary. b 38. Sarum Th Coll 83. **dss** 86 **d** 87 **p** 94. Jersey St Sav *Win* 85-86; Jersey St Mary 86-88; Hon Par Dn 87-88; Hon Par Dn Jersey St Brelade 88-94; Hon C from 94. *The Glade, St Mary, Jersey, Channel Islands* Jersey (01534) 864282

GURNEY, Miss Ann. b 27. Lon Univ DipTh48 STh92. Gilmore Ho 45. **dss** 54 **d** 87 **p** 94. Prin Gilmore Ho 59-70; Bp's Adv for Lay Min *Lon* 70-87; rtd 87; Hon C Eltham H Trin *S'wark* from 94. *35 Archery Road, London SE9 1HF* 0181-850 4083

GURNEY, Dennis Albert John. b 31. Lon Coll of Div. **d** 67 **p** 68. C Boscombe St Jo *Win* 67-69; V Hurstbourne Tarrant and Faccombe 70-77; R Jersey St Ouen w St Geo 77-84; Chapl Intercon Ch Soc from 84; Hon Chapl Miss to Seamen from 84; UAE from 84. *PO Box 7415, Dubai, United Arab Emirates* Dubai (4) 374947

GURNEY, Canon Richmond Harptree. b 24. Worc Coll Ox BA48 MA48. Cuddesdon Coll 48. **d** 50 **p** 51. R Gateshead St Mary *Dur* 66-72; TR Gateshead 72-75; P-in-c Eskdale, Irton, Muncaster and Waberthwaite *Carl* 75-78; V 78-82; Sec Dioc Past and Redundant Chs Uses Cttees 82-87; R Asby 82-89; V Bolton 82-89; V Crosby Ravensworth 82-89; Hon Can Carl Cathl 84-89; rtd 89. *Dunelm, Gelt Road, Brampton, Cumbria CA8 1QH* Brampton (016977) 2516

GURR, Ralph Sydney. b 27. AKC55. **d** 57 **p** 58. V Wyke *Bradf* 69-72; V Edmonton St Mich *Lon* 72-79; R Fordingbridge w Ibsley *Win* 79-82; V Fordingbridge 82-84; C N Stoneham 84-94; P-in-c 89-90; rtd 94. *1 Grosvenor Mansions, Grosvenor Square, Polygon, Southampton SO1 2GQ* Southampton (01703) 339243

GUSH, Laurence Langley. b 23. CChem CEng MICE52 ACGI MRIC Lon Univ BSc44. NW Ord Course 73. **d** 76 **p** 77. NSM Sheff St Matt *Sheff* 76-82; NSM Aston cum Aughton 82-84; NSM Aston cum Aughton and Ulley 84-89; rtd 89. *86 Nursery Crescent, Anston, Sheffield S31 7BR* Dinnington (01909) 567081

GUSSMAN, Robert William Spencer Lockhart. b 50. Ch Ch Ox BA72 MA76. Coll of Resurr Mirfield BA74. **d** 75 **p** 76. C Pinner *Lon* 75-79; C Northolt W End St Jos 79-81; P-in-c Sutton *Ely* 81-82; V 82-89; P-in-c Witcham w Mepal 81-82; R 82-89; RD Ely 86-89; V Alton St Lawr *Win* from 89. *St Lawrence's Vicarage, Church Street, Alton, Hants GU34 2BW* Alton (01420) 83234

GUTCH, John Pitt. b 14. St Edm Hall Ox BA36 MA42. Cuddesdon Coll 37. **d** 38 **p** 39. R Elton *Ely* 67-80; RD Yaxley 72-80; P-in-c Stibbington 75-80; P-in-c Water Newton 76-80; rtd 80. *27 Manor Gardens, Warminster, Wilts BA12 8PN* Warminster (01985) 219258

GUTHRIE, Nigel. b 60. LRAM78 ARCO80 ARCM81 Bris Univ BA82 Ox Univ BA87. Ripon Coll Cuddesdon 85. **d** 88 **p** 89. C Cov St Jo *Cov* 88-91; Chapl Cov Cathl 91-94; V Chellaston *Derby* from 94. *The Vicarage, St Peter's Road, Chellaston, Derby DE7 1UU* Derby (01332) 704835

GUTSELL, Canon David Leonard Nicholas. b 35. Sheff Univ BA59 LTh74. ALCD61. **d** 61 **p** 62. C Clapham Common St Barn *S'wark* 61-65; V Upper Tulse Hill St Matthias 65-76; RD Clapham and Brixton 74-75; V Patcham *Chich* 76-93; Can and Preb Chich Cathl from 89; V Polegate from 93. *St John's Vicarage, 1 Church Road, Polegate, E Sussex BN26 5BX* Polegate (01323) 483259

GUTSELL, Eric Leslie. b 44. Golds Coll Lon TCert65 Ox Univ SDES87. Ox NSM Course. **d** 82 **p** 83. NSM Gt Faringdon w Lt Coxwell *Ox* 82-88; NSM Shrivenham w Watchfield and Bourton from 82. *54 Folly View Road, Faringdon, Oxford SN7 7DH* Faringdon (01367) 240886

GUTTERIDGE, David Frank. b 39. Man Univ BSc61 Lon Inst of Educn PGCE62 DipEd67 Birkb Coll Lon MSc73. W Midl Minl Tr Course 82. **d** 85 **p** 87. NSM Droitwich *Worc* 85-87; NSM Droitwich Spa 87-93; C Shrawley, Witley, Astley and Abberley from 93; Chapl Abberley Hall Sch Worc from 93. *The Rectory, Abberley, Worcester WR6 6BN* Great Witley (01299) 896248

GUTTERIDGE, John. b 34. Oak Hill Th Coll 60. **d** 63 **p** 64. C Southgate *Chich* 66-70; P-in-c Brixton Rd Ch Ch *S'wark* 70-73; P-in-c Manuden w Berden *Chelmsf* 73-76; Distr Sec (N Lon, Herts and Essex) BFBS 76-82; Hon C Walthamstow St Gabr 79-82; V 82-95; Chapl Thorpe Coombe Psycho-Geriatric Hosp 83-95; rtd 95. *St Gabriel's Vicarage, 17 Shernhall Street, London E17 3EU* 0181-520 3411

GUTTERIDGE, John Philip. b 52. QUB BA74. Chich Th Coll 75. **d** 78 **p** 79. C Leeds St Aid *Ripon* 78-82; C Manston 82-85; P-in-c Beeston Hill H Spirit from 85. *Holy Spirit Vicarage, 114 Stratford Street, Leeds LS11 7EQ* Leeds (0113) 271 0390

GUTTERIDGE, Richard Joseph Cooke. b 11. Trin Hall Cam BA32 MA36 BD78. Wells Th Coll 34. **d** 35 **p** 36. C Edgbaston St Bart *Birm* 35-38; Tutor Qu Coll Birm 35-37; Lect Qu Coll Birm 37-38; C Bexhill St Pet *Chich* 38-40; C Temple Balsall *Birm* 40-41; Prin Blue Coat Sch Birm 41-45; R Brampton *Ely* 45-52; Chapl RAF 52-68; Fell Ox Univ 69-72; P-in-c Longstowe *Ely* 72-73; Lic to Offic from 73. *1 Croftgate, Fulbrooke Road, Cambridge CB3 9EG* Cambridge (01223) 352626

GUTTRIDGE, John Arthur. b 26. Trin Hall Cam BA51 MA55. Westcott Ho Cam 51. **d** 53 **p** 54. Dir of Further Tr *Dur* 68-74; Dir of Studies Sarum & Wells Th Coll 74-78; C Bilston St Leon *Lich* 78-79; TV Bilston 80-84; V Wall 84-90; V Stonnall 84-90; rtd 91. *15 St George's Lane North, Worcester WR1 1RD* Worcester (01905) 22175

GUY, Dr Ian Towers. b 47. MRCGP MB BS MSc. NE Ord Course. **d** 83 **p** 84. NSM Saltburn-by-the-Sea *York* 83-88; NSM Skelton w Upleatham 88-92; Perm to Offic from 92. *14 North Terrace, Skelton-in-Cleveland, Saltburn-by-the-Sea TS12 2ES* Guisborough (01287) 650309

GUY, Dr John Richard. b 44. FRHistS80 FRSM81. St D Coll Lamp BA65 PhD85 St Steph Ho Ox 65. **d** 67 **p** 68. C Canton St Cath *Llan* 67-68; C Roath St Sav 68-70; C Machen and Rudry *Mon* 71-74; R Wolvesnewton w Kilgwrrwg and Devauden 74-80; Perm to Offic *B & W* 80-93; V Betws Cedewain and Tregynon and Llanwyddelan *St As* from 93. *The Vicarage, Bettws Cedewen, Newtown, Powys SY16 3DS* Tregynon (01686) 650345

GUY, Kate Anne. b 26. Local NSM Course 87. **d** 88 **p** 94. NSM Welton *Linc* 88-92; NSM Welton and Dunholme w Scothern from 92. *2 Eastfield Close, Welton, Lincoln LN2 3NB* Welton (01673) 860285

GUY, Simon Edward Walrond. b 39. St Andr Univ MA61. St D Coll Lamp LTh67. **d** 67 **p** 68. C Bris St Mary Redcliffe w Temple etc *Bris* 67-68; C Knowle St Martin 68-71; C Bishopston 71-75; V Westwood *Sarum* 75-81; TV Melksham 81-82; TV Wednesfield *Lich* 82-90; R Heaton Moor *Man* from 90. *St Paul's Rectory, 42 Lea Road, Stockport, Cheshire SK4 4JU* 0161-432 1227

GUYMER, Raymond John. b 41. AKC64. **d** 65 **p** 66. C W Bromwich All SS *Lich* 65-70; Chapl HM Borstal Portland 70-78; Chapl HM Youth Cust Cen Hollesley Bay Colony 78-84; Chapl HM Pris Wormwood Scrubs 84-93; Lic to Offic *Lon* 84-93; Chapl HM Pris Win from 93. *HM Prison Winchester, Romsey Road, Winchester, Hants SO22 5DF* Winchester (01962) 854494 Fax 842560

GWILLIAM, Christopher. b 44. St Chad's Coll Dur BA65 DipTh67. **d** 67 **p** 68. C Chepstow *Mon* 67-70; C Risca 70-72; V Cwmtillery 72-75; V Hartlepool St Oswald *Dur* 75-82; Relig Progr Producer Radio Tees 80-87; C Stockton w St Jo 82-83; R Longnewton w Elton 83-87; Relig Progr Producer Radio Nottm *S'well* 87-93; Relig Progr Producer BBC Radio 4 (Man) from 93. *New Broadcasting House, PO Box 27, Oxford Road, Manchester M60 1SJ* 0161-955 3614

GWILLIAM, Canon Oswald Neol. b 03. St Chad's Coll Dur BA24. **d** 26 **p** 27. R Houghton le Spring *Dur* 48-71; Hon Can Dur Cathl 53-71; rtd 71. *Head Farm Caravan, Fenton Lane, How Hill, Carlisle CA4 9LD* Hayton (01228) 70601

GWILLIM, Allan John. b 51. Coll of Resurr Mirfield 87. **d** 89 **p** 90. C Skerton St Luke *Blackb* 89-94; P-in-c Ellel from 94. *St John's Vicarage, Chapel Lane, Galgate, Ellel, Lancaster LA2 0BW* Lancaster (01524) 752017

GWILT, Stephen Gary. d 88 **p** 89. S Africa 88-94; Chapl Glouc Docks Mariners' Ch *Glouc* from 95. *1 Ladywell Close, Gloucester GL2 6XE* Gloucester (01452) 501794

GWINN, Brian Harvey. b 35. MIQA75. St Alb Minl Tr Scheme 83. **d** 86 **p** 87. NSM Wheathampstead *St Alb* 86-88; Ind Chapl 88-95; RD Hatf 93-95; P-in-c Watton at Stone from 95. *The Rectory, Watton at Stone, Hertford SG14 3RD* Ware (01920) 830262

GWYNN, Phillip John. b 57. Univ of Wales BA87 Univ of Wales (Cardiff) DPS89. St Mich Coll Llan 87. **d** 89 **p** 90. C Clydach *S & B* 89-93; V Swansea St Thos and Kilvey from 93. *The Vicarage, Lewis Street, St Thomas, Swansea SA1 8BP* Swansea (01792) 652891

GWYNNE, Robert Durham. b 44. Birm Univ DipTh70. Qu Coll Birm 67. **d** 70 **p** 72. C N Hammersmith St Kath *Lon* 70-75; C Ramsey *Ely* 76-78; TV Old Brumby *Linc* 78-81; C Scartho 81; P-in-c Goxhill 81-83; P-in-c Thornton Curtis 81-83; C Edmonton All SS w St Mich *Lon* 83-84; rtd 86. *Highfield, Station Road, Legbourne, Louth, Lincs LN11 8LL*

GWYTHER, Geoffrey David. b 51. St D Coll Lamp DipTh73. **d** 74 **p** 75. C Pemb Dock *St D* 74-77; C Milford Haven 77-81; V Llawhaden w Bletherston and Llanycefn 81-88; R Prendergast w Rudbaxton from 88. *Prendergast Rectory, 5 Cherry Grove, Haverfordwest, Dyfed SA61 2NT* Haverfordwest (01437) 762625

GWYTHER, Ronald Lloyd. b 23. Lon Univ BA85. St Fran Coll Brisbane ThL47. **d** 47 **p** 48. R Pinxton *Derby* 60-73; V Swanley St Mary *Roch* 73-89; rtd 89. *20 Maylings Farm Road, Fareham, Hants PO16 7QU* Fareham (01329) 230990

GYLE, Alan Gordon. b 65. Aber Univ MA87 Ox Univ BA91. St Steph Ho Ox. **d** 92 **p** 93. C Acton Green *Lon* 92-94; Min Can, Succ and Dean's V Windsor from 94. *3 The Cloisters, Windsor Castle, Windsor, Berks SL4 1NJ* Windsor (01753) 868680

GYTON, Robert Wilfred. b 21. N Ord Course. **d** 78 **p** 79. NSM Repps *Nor* 78-79; C Trunch 79-83; TV 83-88; rtd 88; Perm to Offic *Nor* 88-94; P-in-c Castle Acre w Newton, Rougham and Southacre from 94. *Yamato, 47 Fir Park, Ashill, Thetford, Norfolk IP25 7DE* Thetford (01760) 440305

H

HABERMEHL, Canon Kenneth Charles. b 22. Em Coll Cam BA46 MA48. Chich Th Coll 47. d 49 p 50. V Kempston *St Alb* 65-87; Hon Can St Alb 81-87; rtd 87; Perm to Offic *St Alb* from 87. *34 Bedford Road, Aspley Guise, Milton Keynes MK17 8DH* Milton Keynes (01908) 584710

HABERSHON, Kenneth Willoughby. b 35. New Coll Ox BA57 DipTh58 MA60. Wycliffe Hall Ox 57. d 59 p 60. C Finchley Ch Ch *Lon* 59-66; Sec CYFA 66-74; CPAS Staff 74-90; Hon C Slaugham *Chich* 84-88; Ldr Limpsfield CYFA & Sec Ch Patr Trust from 90. *Truckers Ghyll, Horsham Road, Handcross, Haywards Heath, W Sussex RH17 6DT* Handcross (01444) 400274

HABGOOD, John Gerald Peace. b 18. St Cath Soc Ox BA40 MA45. Cuddesdon Coll 45. d 47 p 48. R Lewes St Thos and All SS *Chich* 68-75; TR Lewes All SS, St Anne, St Mich and St Thos 75-84; rtd 84; Perm to Offic *Chich* from 84. *3 Court Leet, Steyne Road, Seaford, E Sussex BN25 1QT* Seaford (01323) 896832

✠HABGOOD of Calverton, Rt Rev and Rt Hon Lord (John Stapylton). b 27. PC83. K Coll Cam BA48 MA51 PhD52 Dur Univ Hon DD75 Cam Univ Hon DD84 Aber Univ Hon DD88 Huron Coll Hon DD90. Cuddesdon Coll 53. d 54 p 55 c 73. C Kensington St Mary Abbots w St Geo *Lon* 54-56; Vice-Prin Westcott Ho Cam 56-62; R Jedburgh *Edin* 62-67; Prin Qu Coll Birm 67-73; Hon Can Birm Cathl *Birm* 71-73; Bp Dur 73-83; Abp York 83-95; rtd 95. *18 The Mount, Malton, N Yorkshire YO17 0ND*

HABGOOD, Simon. b 60. Nottm Univ BTh88. St Jo Coll Nottm 85. d 88 p 89. C Holbeach *Linc* 88-90; CF (TA) from 89; C Alford w Rigsby *Linc* 90-91; R Rattlesden w Thorpe Morieux and Brettenham *St E* 91-93; V Churchdown *Glouc* 93; V Maenclochog w Henry's Moat and Mynachlogddu etc *St D* 93-94; R Overstrand, Northrepps, Sidestrand & Trimingham *Nor* from 95. *The Rectory, 22A Harbord Road, Overstrand, Cromer, Norfolk NR27 0PN* Overstrand (01263) 579350

HABGOOD, Stephen Roy. b 52. Univ of Wales DipTh77. d 77 p 78. C Eglwyswen and Llanfair Nant-gwyn *St D* 77-81; Perm to Offic *Worc* 85-91. *Oak Thatch, 76 Main Street, Bretforton, Evesham, Worcs WR11 5JJ* Evesham (01386) 830323

HACK, Ms Alison Ruth. b 53. RGN75 RSCN75 RHV80. Sarum & Wells Th Coll 89. d 91. Par Dn St Marylebone, St Paul *Lon* 91-94; C from 94. *St Paul's House, 9A Rossmore Road, London NW1 6NJ* 0171-402 1000

HACK, Canon Rex Hereward. b 28. ACA56 FCA67 Pemb Coll Cam BA50 MA56. Ripon Hall Ox 58. d 59 p 60. V Bramhall *Ches* 69-93; RD Cheadle 87-92; Hon Can Ches Cathl 90-93; rtd 93. *The Oaks, 214 Woodford Road, Woodford, Stockport, Cheshire SK7 1QE* 0161-439 0300

✠HACKER, Rt Rev George Lanyon. b 28. Ex Coll Ox BA52 MA56. Cuddesdon Coll 52. d 54 p 55 c 79. C Bris St Mary Redcliffe w Temple *Bris* 54-59; Chapl St Boniface Coll Warminster 59-64; V Bishopwearmouth Gd Shep *Dur* 64-71; R Tilehurst St Mich *Ox* 71-79; Hon Can Carl Cathl *Carl* 79-94; Suff Bp Penrith 79-94; Episc Adv for the Angl Young People's Assn 87-94; rtd 94; Hon Ass Bp Carlisle from 94. *Keld House, Milburn, Penrith, Cumbria CA10 1TW* Penrith (01768) 361506

HACKER HUGHES, Mrs Katherine Lucy (Katy). b 60. York Univ BA81. Westcott Ho Cam 90. d 92 p 94. Par Dn S Woodham Ferrers *Chelmsf* 92-94; C from 94. *25 Benbow Drive, South Woodham Ferrers, Chelmsford CM3 5FP* Chelmsford (01245) 325593

HACKETT, Bryan Malcolm. b 66. Magd Coll Ox BA88 MA93 Cam Univ BA92. Westcott Ho Cam 90. d 93 p 94. C Willington Team *Newc* from 93. *10 Churchill Street, Wallsend, Tyne & Wear NE28 7SZ* 0191-263 6140

HACKETT, Canon Frank James. b 33. AMIMechE68 MBIM72 MIIM79 HNC54 DMS72 Birm Univ MA77. Bps' Coll Cheshunt 62. d 64 p 65. C Feltham *Lon* 64-69; Ind Chapl *Lich* 69-73; Ind Chapl Port of Lon *Chelmsf* from 73; P-in-c N Ockendon 79-93; Can Chelmsf Cathl from 93; Ind Chapl from 93. *11 Fairfield Avenue, Upminster, Essex RM14 3AZ* Upminster (01708) 221461

HACKETT, John Nigel. b 32. Trin Hall Cam BA55 MA59. Ely Th Coll. d 59 p 60. C Handsworth St Mary *Birm* 59-66; V Handsworth St Jas 66-82; P-in-c Balsall Common 82-83; V 83-95. *Honeymead, Duck Lane, Kenn, Clevedon, Avon BS21 6TP* Clevedon (01275) 876591

HACKETT, Peter Edward. b 25. Magd Coll Ox BA48 MA51 ALCD60. d 60 p 61. R Acton Beauchamp and Evesbatch w Stanford Bishop *Heref* 67-71; VC Heref Cathl 72-76; P-in-c St Weonards w Orcop 76-79; P-in-c Tretire w Michaelchurch and Pencoyd 76-79; P-in-c Garway 76-79; P-in-c Welsh Newton w Llanrothal 77-79; V Rounds Green *Birm* 79-87; rtd

Sutton Coldfield H Trin 87-90; rtd 90; NSM Shipton Moyne w Westonbirt and Lasborough *Glouc* 91-94; Perm to Offic *Birm* from 94. *58 Lodgefield Road, Halesowen, W Midlands B62 8AT* 0121-561 2365

HACKETT, Ronald Glyndwr. b 47. Hatf Coll Dur BA70. Cuddesdon Coll 70. d 72 p 73. C Pemb St Mary and St Mich *St D* 72-75; C Bassaleg *Mon* 75-78; V Blaenavon w Capel Newydd 78-84; Chapl Gwent R Hosp from 84; V Newport St Paul *Mon* 84-90; V Newport Ch Ch from 90. *The Vicarage, Christchurch, Newport, Gwent NP6 1JJ* Newport (01633) 420701

HACKING, Philip Henry. b 31. St Pet Hall Ox BA53 MA57. Oak Hill Th Coll 53. d 55 p 56. C St Helens St Helen *Liv* 55-58; C-in-c Edin St Thos *Edin* 59-68; V Fulwood *Sheff* from 68. *The Vicarage, 2 Chorley Drive, Sheffield S10 3RR* Sheffield (0114) 230 1911

HACKING, Rodney Douglas. b 53. K Coll Lon BD74 AKC74 Man Univ MA83. St Aug Coll Cant 75. d 76 p 78. C Byker St Mich *Newc* 76-77; C Eltham St Jo *S'wark* 77-79; Ind Chapl *Ripon* 80-85; R Upwell St Pet *Ely* 85-88; R Outwell 85-88; Vice Prin S Dios Minl Tr Scheme 89-93; V Bolton le Sands *Blackb* from 93. *The Vicarage, Ancliffe Lane, Bolton-le-Sands, Carnforth, Lancs LA5 8DS* Hest Bank (01524) 822335

HACKING, Stuart Peter. b 60. St Pet Coll Ox BA82 MA. Oak Hill Th Coll 83. d 85 p 86. C Shipley St Pet *Bradf* 85-88; C Darfield *Sheff* 88-91; V Thornton St Jas *Bradf* from 91. *The Vicarage, 300 Thornton Road, Thornton, Bradford, W Yorkshire BD13 3AB* Bradford (01274) 833200

HACKNEY, Bryan William George. b 41. Hull Univ MA80. Linc Th Coll 65. d 68 p 69. C Baildon *Bradf* 68-71; R Gt and Lt Casterton w Pickworth and Tickencote *Pet* 71-74; Lic to Offic *Linc* 74-77; V Barnetby le Wold 77-81; P-in-c Somerby w Humby 77-81; P-in-c Bigby 77-81; Bp's Ind Adv *Derby* 81-85; R Morton and Stonebroom 85-91; V Mackworth St Fran from 91. *St Francis's Vicarage, 78 Collingham Gardens, Mackworth, Derby DE22 4FQ* Derby (01332) 347690

HACKNEY, Archdeacon of. See YOUNG, Ven Clive

HACKSHALL, Brian Leonard. b 33. K Coll Lon BD53 AKC53. d 57 p 58. C Portsea St Mary *Portsm* 57-62; C Westbury-on-Trym St Alb *Bris* 62-64; V Avonmouth St Andr 64-71; Miss to Seamen 71-79; C Crawley *Chich* 79; TV from 79; Ind Chapl from 89. *35 Turnpike Place, Crawley, W Sussex RH11 7UA* Crawley (01293) 513264

HACKWOOD, Paul Colin. b 61. Bradf Coll of Educn DSocStuds82 Huddersfield Poly BSc84 Birm Univ DipTh88. Qu Coll Birm 86. d 89 p 90. C Horton *Bradf* 89-93; Soc Resp Adv *St Alb* from 93. *1 Corinium Gate, St Albans, Herts AL3 4HX* St Albans (01727) 865100

HADDLETON, Peter Gordon. b 53. UEA BA74 Southn Univ BTh80. Sarum & Wells Th Coll 76. d 79 p 80. C Thamesmead *S'wark* 79-83; TV Bridgnorth, Tasley, Astley Abbotts, Oldbury etc *Heref* 83-91; TV Heref St Martin w St Fran (S Wye TM) from 91. *The Vicarage, 1 Holme Lacy Road, Hereford HR2 6DP* Hereford (01432) 277234 or 353717 Fax 352142

HADDOCK, Malcolm George. b 27. Univ of Wales (Cardiff) DipTh53 BA56 CertEd73. St Deiniol's Hawarden 87. d 80 p 81. NSM Newport Ch Ch *Mon* 80-85; NSM Risca 85-87; C 87-89; C Caerleon from 89. *48 Cambria Close, Caerleon, Newport, Gwent NP6 1LF* Caerleon (01633) 422960

HADDON-REECE (nee STREETER), Mrs Christine Mary. b 50. St Jo Coll Nottm BTh81 LTh81. dss 83 d 87 p 94. Monkwearmouth St Andr *Dur* 83-85; Stranton 85-87; Par Dn 87-90; Par Dn Lastingham w Appleton-le-Moors, Rosedale etc *York* 90-94; C from 94. *16 Rosedale Abbey, Pickering, N Yorkshire YO18 8SA* Lastingham (01751) 417721

HADFIELD, Christopher John Andrew. b 39. Jes Coll Cam BA61. Wells Th Coll 63. d 65 p 66. C Wigton w Waverton *Carl* 65-68; Teacher Newlands Sch from 70; Lic to Offic *Mor* from 92. *Newlands School, Seaford, E Sussex BN25 4NP* Seaford (01323) 892209

HADFIELD, Douglas. b 22. K Coll Cam BA44 MA49. St Jo Coll Nottm 84. d 88 p 89. Hon C Lenzie *Glas* 88-92; rtd 92. *Thelema, 8 Church Street, Helmdon, Brackley, Northants NN13 5QJ*

HADFIELD, Graham Francis. b 48. Bris Univ BSc69 St Jo Coll Dur DipTh71. d 73 p 74. C Blackpool St Thos *Blackb* 73-76; CF from 76. *clo MOD (Army), Bagshot Park, Bagshot, Surrey GU19 5PL* Bagshot (01276) 471717 Fax 412834

HADFIELD, Jonathan Benedict Philip John. b 43. Lon Univ BA64 Jes Coll Cam BA67 MA72. Edin Th Coll 66. d 68 p 69. C Fort William *Arg* 68-70; Chapl K Sch Glouc from 70; Hon Min Can Glouc Cathl *Glouc* from 70. *Dulverton House, King's School, Pitt Street, Gloucester GL1 2BG* Gloucester (01452) 521251

HADFIELD, Norman. b 39. Doncaster Coll of Educn TEng78 Univ of Wales (Cardiff) DPS90. St Mich Coll Llan 89 Llan Dioc Tr Scheme 83. **d** 86 **p** 87. NSM Ferndale w Maerdy *Llan* 86-90; C Llanblethian w Cowbridge and Llandough etc 90-92; V Resolven w Tonna from 92. *The Vicarage, Resloven, Neath, W Glam SA11 4AN* Neath (01639) 710354

HADLEY, Charles Adrian. b 50. Trin Coll Cam BA71 MA75. Cuddesdon Coll 73. **d** 75 **p** 76. C Hadleigh w Layham and Shelley *St E* 75-78; C Bracknell *Ox* 78-82; R Blagdon w Compton Martin and Ubley *B & W* 82-92; RD Chew Magna 88-92; R Somerton w Compton Dundon, the Charltons etc from 92. *The Vicarage, Vicarage Lane, Somerton, Somerset TA11 7NQ* Somerton (01458) 72216

HADLEY, Donald Thomas. b 30. Lich Th Coll 55. **d** 58 **p** 59. V S Yardley St Mich *Birm* 66-70; V Tonge Moor *Man* 70-84; C Selly Oak St Mary *Birm* 85-90; rtd 90; Perm to Offic *Birm* from 90. *83 Grosvenor Road, Birmingham B17 9AL* 0121-426 4450

HADLEY, Miss Elizabeth Ann. b 33. DipTh83. St Jo Coll Nottm 80. dss 81 **d** 87 **p** 94. Aspley *S'well* 81-85; Stone St Mich w Aston St Sav *Lich* 85-87; Par Dn 87-92; P-in-c Myddle from 92; P-in-c Broughton from 92; Dioc Voc Officer from 92. *The Rectory, Myddle, Shrewsbury SY4 3RX* Bomere Heath (01939) 290811

HADLEY, John Spencer Fairfax. b 47. Ch Ch Ox BA70 MA73. Coll of Resurr Mirfield BA72. **d** 73 **p** 74. C Stoke Newington St Mary *Lon* 73-77; C High Wycombe *Ox* 77-81; TV 82-87; Chapl Bris Univ *Bris* 87-91; P-in-c Clifton St Paul 87-91. *Hengrave Hall Centre, Bury St Edmunds, Suffolk IP28 6LZ* Bury St Edmunds (01284) 701561

HADLEY, Stuart James. b 55. K Coll Lon BD76 AKC76. St Steph Ho Ox 77. **d** 78 **p** 79. C Mansf St Mark *S'well* 78-82; V Cowbit *Linc* 82-86; Perm to Offic 86-88; NSM W w E Allington and Sedgebrook from 88; NSM Woolsthorpe from 88. *21 Truro Close, Grantham, Lincs NG31 8PH* Grantham (01476) 75854

HADWIN, Alfred. b 34. N Ord Course 85. **d** 88 **p** 89. NSM Lower Darwen St Jas *Blackb* 88-92; NSM Lezayre St Olave Ramsey *S & M* from 92. *St Olave's Vicarage, Ramsey, Isle of Man IM8 3HA* Ramsey (01624) 812104

HAGAN, Kenneth Raymond. b 40. St Jo Coll Morpeth 62 ACT ThDip64. **d** 64 **p** 65. C Charlestown *Man* 64-69; Australia 69-75 and from 89; C Portsea St Mary *Portsm* 75-78; P-in-c Wolvey, Burton Hastings and Stretton Baskerville *Cov* 78-81; OCF 78-81; P-in-c Withybrook w Copston Magna *Cov* 78-81; P-in-c Shilton w Ansty 78-81; Perm to Offic *Leic* 81-83; Perm to Offic *Lon* 82-89. *148 Denison Street, Hamilton, NSW, Australia 2303* Hamilton (49) 611980

HAGGAN, David Anthony. b 25. Barrister-at-Law 70 QUB LLB49. S'wark Ord Course 87. **d** 89 **p** 90. NSM Reigate St Mary *S'wark* from 89. *2 Fairford Close, Brightlands Road, Reigate, Surrey RH2 0EY* Reigate (01737) 246197

HAGGAR, Keith Ivan. b 38. MRPharmS61. Cant Sch of Min 87. **d** 90 **p** 91. NSM Woodnesborough w Worth and Staple *Cant* from 90. *Burtree Cottage, The Street, Worth, Deal, Kent CT14 0DE* Sandwich (01304) 613599

HAGGARD, Amyand Richard. b 21. Jes Coll Ox MA57. Ripon Hall Ox 56. **d** 58 **p** 59. V Battersea St Phil *S'wark* 61-68; rtd 86. *78 Eland Road, London SW11 5LA* 0171-228 8166

✠**HAGGART, Rt Rev Alastair Iain Macdonald.** b 15. Dur Univ LTh41 BA42 MA45 Dundee Univ Hon LLD70. Edin Th Coll 38. **d** 41 **p** 42 **c** 75. C Glas St Mary *Glas* 41-45; C Hendon St Mary *Lon* 45-48; Prec St Ninian's Cathl Perth *St And* 48-51; R Glas St Oswald *Glas* 51-59; P-in-c Glas St Martin 53-58; Can St Mary's Cathl 58-59; Syn Clerk 58-59; Provost St Paul's Cathl Dundee *Bre* 59-71; R Dundee St Paul 59-71; Prin Edin Th Coll 71-75; Can St Mary's Cathl *Edin* 71-75; Bp Edin 75-85; Primus 77-85; rtd 85. *19 Eglinton Crescent, Edinburgh EH12 5BY* 0131-337 8948

HAGGER, Jonathan Paul. b 59. St Jo Coll Nottm BTh95. **d** 95. C Newsham *Newc* from 95. *7 Haven Court, Isabella, Blyth, Northd NE24 5RX* Blyth (01670) 363417

HAGGIE, Deborah. b 58. **d** 92. NSM Mert St Mary *S'wark* from 94. *31 Dennis Park Crescent, London SW20 8QH* 0181-542 9030

HAGGIS, Richard. b 66. Ch Ch Ox BA88. Linc Th Coll DipMM94. **d** 95. C Romford St Edw *Chelmsf* from 95. *54 Parkside Avenue, Romford RM1 4ND* Romford (01708) 727960

HAGGIS, Timothy Robin. b 52. New Coll Ox BA75 MA79. St Jo Coll Nottm DipTh. **d** 82 **p** 83. C Chilwell *S'well* 82-86; TV Hucknall Torkard 86-94; Chapl Trent Coll Nottm from 94. *Trent College, Long Eaton, Nottingham NG10 4AD*

HAGON, Roger Charles. b 58. Nottm Univ BA80. St Steph Ho Ox 82. **d** 85 **p** 86. C Charlton St Luke w H Trin *S'wark* 85-88; C St Helier 88-95; V Kenley from 95. *The Vicarage, 3 Valley Road, Kenley, Surrey CR8 5DJ* 0181-660 3263

HAGUE, David Hallett. b 59. Univ Coll Lon BScEng81 MSc82. Ridley Hall Cam CTM93. **d** 93 **p** 94. C Luton St Mary *St Alb* from 93. *34 Wychwood Avenue, Luton LU2 7HU* Luton (01582) 29902

HAGUE, Eric. b 13. Lon Univ BA52. St Aid Birkenhead 36. **d** 39 **p** 40. R Lt Shelford w Newton *Ely* 69-76; P-in-c Parr Mt *Liv* 76-77; V 77-79; rtd 79. *Guilin, 18 Brookfield Road, Coton, Cambridge CB3 7PW* Madingley (01954) 210233

HAIG, Very Rev Alistair Matthew. b 39. K Coll Lon BD63 AKC63. **d** 64 **p** 65. C Forest Gate St Edm *Chelmsf* 64-67; C Laindon w Basildon 67-71; V S Woodham Ferrers 71-78; P-in-c Bath H Trin *B & W* 78-83; R 83-89; R Bocking St Mary *Chelmsf* from 89; Dean Bocking from 89. *The Deanery, Bocking, Braintree, Essex CM7 5SR* Braintree (01376) 324887 or 553092

HAIG, Andrew Livingstone. b 45. Keble Coll Ox BA67. Coll of Resurr Mirfield 67. **d** 69 **p** 70. C Elton All SS *Man* 69-75; R Brantham *St E* 75-76; R Brantham w Stutton 76-82; RD Samford 81-82; P-in-c Haverhill 82; TR Haverhill w Withersfield, the Wrattings etc 82-90; RD Clare 84-87; Chapl Qu Eliz Hosp K Lynn from 90. *The Chaplain's Office, Queen Elizabeth Hospital, King's Lynn, Norfolk PE30 4ET* King's Lynn (01553) 766266

HAIG, Murray Nigel Francis. b 39. Univ of Wales (Lamp) BA62. Kelham Th Coll 62. **d** 66 **p** 67. C Felixstowe St Jo *St E* 66-72; C Morpeth *Newc* 72-74; V Byker St Mich 74-79; V Byker St Mich w St Lawr 79-81; V Benwell St Jas 81-85; TR Benwell Team 85-91; TR Cramlington from 91. *33 Twyford Close, Cramlington, Northd NE23 9PH* Cramlington (01670) 712259

HAIGH, Alan Bernard. b 42. NE Ord Course 87. **d** 90 **p** 91. NSM Thorner *Ripon* from 90. *4 The Paddock, Thorner, Leeds LS14 3JB* Leeds (0113) 289 2870

HAIGH, Colin. b 15. St Chad's Coll Dur BA40 DipTh41 MA43. **d** 41 **p** 42. V Romford St Alb *Chelmsf* 68-80; rtd 80. *93 Egremont Street, Glemsford, Sudbury, Suffolk CO10 7SG* Glemsford (01787) 281173

HAIGH, John Gibson. b 47. Chich Th Coll 88. **d** 90 **p** 91. C Swinton and Pendlebury *Man* 90-93; C Barton w Peel Green 93; C Richmond w Hudswell *Ripon* from 93; C Downholme and Marske from 93. *1 Wathcote Place, Richmond, N Yorkshire DL10 7SR* Richmond (01748) 826260

HAIGH, Maurice. b 22. St Cath Coll Cam BA46 MA48 Lon Univ BD60. **d** 60 **p** 61. NSM Marton *Blackb* 60-88; rtd 88; Perm to Offic *Blackb* from 88. *20 Doncaster Road, Blackpool FY3 9SQ* Blackpool (01253) 63897

HAIGH, Norman. b 02. Dorchester Miss Coll 27. **d** 30 **p** 31. R Aston Somerville *Glouc* 62-72; V Childswyckham 62-72; rtd 72. *The College of St Barnabas, Blackberry Lane, Lingfield, Surrey RH7 6NJ* Dormans Park (01342) 870260

HAIGH, Owen Quentin. b 15. St Chad's Coll Dur BA43 MA46. **d** 43 **p** 44. R Wiston *Chich* 55-75; R Ashington 55-75; P-in-c Stedham w Iping 75-83; P-in-c Trotton w Chithurst 80-81; rtd 83; Perm to Offic *Chich* from 84. *Chanctonbury, Smuggler's Way, Fairlight, Hastings, E Sussex TN35 4DG* Hastings (01424) 812826

HAIGH, Richard Michael Fisher. b 30. Dur Univ BA57 Birm Univ DPS71. Cranmer Hall Dur DipTh59. **d** 59 **p** 60. C Stanwix *Carl* 59-62; India 63-67 and 68-70; R Salford St Clem w St Cypr Ordsall *Man* 71-75; R Holcombe 75-85; V Unsworth 85-93; R Brough w Stainmore, Musgrave and Warcop *Carl* from 93. *The Rectory, Church Brough, Kirkby Stephen, Cumbria CA17 4EJ* Kirkby Stephen (017683) 41238

HAILES, Derek Arthur. b 38. Coll of Resurr Mirfield. **d** 82 **p** 83. C Sneinton St Cypr *S'well* 82-84; V Kneesall w Laxton 84-85; P-in-c Wellow 84-85; V Kneesall w Laxton and Wellow 85-88; V Sneinton St Steph w St Alb from 88. *The Vicarage, Windmill Lane, Sneinton, Notts NG2 4QB* Nottingham (0115) 958 0508

HAILS, Canon Brian. b 33. JP71. ACMA62 FCMA76. NE Ord Course 77. **d** 81 **p** 82. NSM Harton *Dur* 81-87; Ind Chapl from 87; Hon Can Dur Cathl from 93. *Inhurst, 5 Hepscott Terrace, South Shields, Tyne & Wear NE33 4TH* 0191-456 3490

HAILSTONE, Miss Kitty. b 22. St Andr Ho Portsm 49. dss 81 **d** 87. W Acklam *York* 60-82; rtd 82; Beverley St Mary *York* 82-87; Hon Par Dn 87-95. *26 Corporation Road, Beverley, N Humberside HU17 9HG* Hull (01482) 860223

HAINES, Andrew Philip. b 47. LSE BSc68. Oak Hill Th Coll 84. **d** 87 **p** 88. C Enfield Ch Ch Trent Park *Lon* 87-91; V Hillmorton *Cov* from 91. *The Vicarage, Hoskyn Close, Hillmorton, Rugby, Warks CV21 4LA* Rugby (01788) 576279

HAINES, Dr Daniel Hugo. b 43. TD89. MRCS73 DRCOG78 Lon Univ BDS68 Witwatersrand Univ 78. **d** 79 **p** 84. Swaziland 79-80; Falkland Is 80-82; Hon C Hatcham St Cath *S'wark* from 84. *56 Vesta Road, London SE4 2NH* 0171-635 0305

HAINES, Robert Melvin. b 31. Coll of Resurr Mirfield 71. d 73 p 74. C Derringham Bank *York* 73-76; C Howden 76-79; TV Howden TM 80-82; R Banff *Ab* from 82; R Turriff from 82; R Cuminestown from 82; P-in-c Buckie from 94; P-in-c Portsoy from 94. *The Rectory, Deveron Road, Turriff, Aberdeenshire AB53 7BB* Turriff (01888) 63238

HAINES, Stephen Decatur. b 42. Freiburg Univ MA68 Fitzw Coll Cam BA70 MA74. d 71 p 72. C Fulham St Dionis Parson's Green *Lon* 71-76; C Finchley St Mary 76-78; Hon C Clapham Old Town *S'wark* 83-87; Hon C Clapham TM 87-88; Hon C Camberwell St Giles w St Matt from 88; Hon PV S'wark Cathl from 92. *3 Lyndhurst Square, London SE15 5AR* 0171-703 4239

HAIR, James Eric. b 48. Lon Univ BA69. St Steph Ho Ox 69. d 72 p 73. C Fishponds St Jo *Bris* 72-75; C Bushey *St Alb* 75-79; P-in-c Lake *Portsm* 79-82; V 82-89; P-in-c Shanklin St Sav 79-82; V 82-89; TV Totton *Win* from 89. *The Vicarage, Cooks Lane, Calmore, Southampton SO4 2RU* Southampton (01703) 812702

HAKE, Andrew Augustus Gordon. b 25. Trin Coll Cam BA49 MA54. Wells Th Coll 50. d 51 p 52. Kenya 57-69; Perm to Offic *Bris* from 70; rtd 90. *Stotehayes, Yarcombe, Honiton, Devon EX14 9BB* Honiton (01404) 881200

HAKES, Leslie John. b 25. CEng MRAeS MBIM. Roch Th Coll 60. d 62 p 63. C Swansea St Pet *S & B* 62-67; V Griffin *Blackb* 67-71; V Dolphinholme 71-74; V Dolphinholme w Quernmore from 74. *The Vicarage, Dolphinholme, Lancaster LA2 9AH* Forton (01524) 791300

HALAHAN, Maxwell Crosby. b 30. Lon Univ BSc52 Southn Univ CertEd78 W Sussex Inst of HE ACertEd83. Westcott Ho Cam 54. d 56 p 57. C-in-c Cowes St Faith CD *Portsm* 66-70; V Cowes St Faith 70-77; Hon C Portsea St Sav from 77; rtd 84. *4 Coach House Mews, Old Canal, Southsea, Hants PO4 8HD*

HALDANE-STEVENSON, James Patrick. b 10. TD50. St Cath Soc Ox BA33 MA41. Bps' Coll Cheshunt 35. d 35 p 37. CF 45-55; Australia from 55; Perm to Offic *Chich* 77-78; rtd 83. *3 Argyle Square, Ainslie Avenue, Reid, NSW, Australia 2601* Canberra (6) 248-6951

HALE, Antony Jolyon (Jon). b 56. MRTPI89 Newc Univ BA79. Sarum & Wells Th Coll 86. d 88 p 89. C Monkseaton St Mary *Newc* 88-92; P-in-c Tandridge *S'wark* from 92; C Oxted from 92. *St Peter's Vicarage, Tandridge Lane, Oxted, Surrey RH8 9NN* Oxted (01883) 722932

HALE, Dennis Ernest (Jim). b 26. Southn Univ MA(Ed)66. Sarum & Wells Th Coll 74. d 77 p 78. NSM N Stoneham *Win* 77-86; Assoc Chapl Southn Univ from 86. *12 Field Close, Southampton SO2 3DY* Southampton (01703) 554538

HALE, Elsie Amelia. Gilmore Ho 53. dss 58 d 87. R Devon and Ex Hosps 64-84; Heavitree w Ex St Paul *Ex* 84-88; Perm to Offic from 88. *13 Riverside Court, Colleton Crescent, Exeter EX2 4BZ*

HALE, John. b 37. Ban Coll DBS60 Trin Coll Carmarthen CertEd59. St D Coll Lamp DipTh66. d 66 p 67. C Tenby and Gumfreston *St D* 66-71; R Burton 71-78; R Burton and Rosemarket from 78. *The Rectory, Burton, Milford Haven, Dyfed SA73 1NX* Neyland (01646) 600275

HALE, John Frederick. b 29. Fitzw Ho Cam BA54 MA58. Tyndale Hall Bris. d 55 p 56. V St Leonards St Ethelburga *Chich* 61-79; C Prestonville St Luke 79-90; R Rotherfield w Mark Cross 90-92; rtd 92. *87C Stanmer Park Road, Brighton BN1 7JL* Brighton (01273) 554944

HALE, Keith John Edward. b 53. Sheff Poly BSc75. St Jo Coll Nottm DipTh91. d 91 p 92. C Greasbrough *Sheff* 91-94; P-in-c Tankersley from 94. *The Rectory, 9 Chapel Road, Tankersley, Barnsley, S Yorkshire S75 3AR* Barnsley (01226) 744140

HALE, Peter Raymond Latham. b 30. St Pet Hall Ox BA54 MA58. Linc Th Coll 54. d 56 p 57. C Old Brumby *Linc* 56-59; Prec and Chapl Gib Cathl *Eur* 59-62; V New Cleethorpes *Linc* 62-67; Chapl Sebright Sch Wolverley 67-70; V Dudley St Jas *Worc* 70-76; V Crowthorne *Ox* 76-86; RD Sonning 81-86; P-in-c Cookham 86-90; V Lacey Green from 90. *The Vicarage, Church Lane, Lacy Green, Princes Risborough, Bucks HP27 0PL* Princes Risborough (01844) 347741

HALE, Richard Laurence. b 13. Jes Coll Cam BA35 MA39. Westcott Ho Cam 42. d 43 p 44. V Gt Shelford *Ely* 61-78; rtd 78; Perm to Offic *Nor* from 78. *5 Hare Road, Great Plumstead, Norwich NR13 5DD* Norwich (01603) 721062

HALE, Roger Anthony. b 41. MIH85. Brasted Th Coll 68 Oak Hill Th Coll 70. d 72 p 73. C Blackb Sav *Blackb* 72-75; C Burnley St Pet 75-77; Chapl Burnley Gen Hosp 75-77; V Fence in Pendle *Blackb* 77-82; Chapl Lancs Ind Miss 77-82; NSM Tottenham St Mary *Lon* 88-91; R Cheddington w Mentmore and Marsworth *Ox* from 91. *The Rectory, 29 Mentmore Road, Cheddington, Leighton Buzzard, Beds LU7 0SD* Cheddington (01296) 661358

HALES, Ms Janet (Jan). b 65. TCD BEd85. CITC BTh94. d 94 p 95. C Lisburn Ch Ch Cathl *Conn* from 94. *3 Benford Park, Lisburn, Co Antrim BT27 5HL* Lisburn (01846) 665979

HALFORD, Harry William. b 20. Qu Coll Birm 47. d 50 p 51. V Kimberworth *Sheff* 60-85; rtd 85. *14 Londesborough Way, Metheringham, Lincoln LN4 3HL* Metheringham (01526) 322217

HALFPENNY, Brian Norman. b 36. CB90. St Jo Coll Ox BA60 MA64. Wells Th Coll 60. d 62 p 63. C Melksham *Sarum* 62-65; Chapl RAF 65-83; Sen Chapl RAF Coll Cranwell 82-83; Asst Chapl-in-Chief RAF 83-88; Chapl-in-Chief RAF 88-91; QHC 85-91; Offg Chapl RAF from 91; Can and Preb Linc Cathl *Linc* 89-91; TR Redditch, The Ridge *Worc* from 91. *St Luke's Rectory, 69 Evesham Road, Redditch, Worcs B97 4JX* Redditch (01527) 545521

HALIFAX, Archdeacon of. *See* INWOOD, Ven Richard Neil

HALKES, John Stanley. b 39. SW Minl Tr Course 87. d 90 p 91. NSM St Buryan, St Levan and Sennen *Truro* 90-92; P-in-c Lanteglos by Fowey 92-94; P-in-c from 94. *The Vicarage, Battery Lane, Polruan, Fowey, Cornwall PL23 1PR* Polruan (01726) 870213

HALL, Alan Maurice Frank. b 28. FCCA. Sarum & Wells Th Coll 86. d 89 p 90. NSM Winterbourne Stickland and Turnworth etc *Sarum* from 89. *4 The Knapp, Winterborne Houghton, Blandford Forum, Dorset DT11 0PD* Milton Abbas (01258) 880985

✠HALL, Rt Rev Albert Peter. b 30. St Jo Coll Cam BA53 MA56. Ridley Hall Cam 53. d 55 p 56 c 84. C Birm St Martin *Birm* 55-60; S Rhodesia 60-65; Rhodesia 65-70; R Birm St Martin *Birm* 70-84; Hon Can Birm Cathl 75-84; Suff Bp Woolwich *S'wark* 84-91; Area Bp Woolwich from 91; Chmn Abp's Cttee on UPA from 90. *8B Hillyfields Crescent, London SE4 1QA* 0181-469 0013 Fax 694 8309

HALL, Canon Alfred Christopher. b 35. Trin Coll Ox BA58 MA61. Westcott Ho Cam 58. d 61 p 62. C Frecheville *Derby* 61-64; C Dronfield 64-67; V Smethwick St Matt *Birm* 67-70; V Smethwick St Matt w St Chad 70-75; Can Res Man Cathl *Man* 75-83; Hon Can from 83; Dioc Adult Educn Officer 75-83; Dioc World Development Officer 76-88; V Bolton St Pet 83-90; Chr Concern for One World from 90. *The Knowle, Deddington, Banbury, Oxon OX15 0TB* Deddington (01869) 38225

HALL, Mrs Ann Addington. b 34. Ex Univ CertEd71. SW Minl Tr Course 82. dss 85 d 87 p 94. Ex St Mark *Ex* 85-90; Hon Par Dn 87-90; Perm to Offic 90-92; NSM Cen Ex from 92. *33 Union Road, Exeter EX4 6HU* Exeter (01392) 78717

HALL, Arthur John. b 23. Bris Univ BSc48. Sarum & Wells Th Coll 74. d 76 p 77. Hon C Portishead *B & W* 76-88; Perm to Offic from 88; Chapl St Brandon's Sch Clevedon from 86. *34 Beechwood Road, Portishead, Bristol BS20 8EP* Portishead (01275) 842603

HALL, Barry George. b 38. Solicitor 62. Oak Hill Th Coll 78. d 81 p 82. NSM Stock Harvard *Chelmsf* 81-90; NSM W Hanningfield 90-93; P-in-c from 93. *Harvard Cottage, Swan Lane, Stock, Ingatestone, Essex CM4 9BQ* Stock (01277) 840387

HALL, Brian. b 59. Aston Tr Scheme 90 Oak Hill Th Coll DipHE94. d 94 p 95. C Mansf St Jo *S'well* from 94. *8 Castle Street, Mansfield, Notts NG18 5PP* Mansfield (01623) 20780

HALL, Brian Arthur. b 48. Ex Univ BEd70. Cuddesdon Coll 73. d 75 p 76. C Hobs Moat *Birm* 75-79; V Smethwick 79-93; R Handsworth St Mary from 93. *Handsworth Rectory, 288 Hamstead Road, Birmingham B20 2RB* 0121-554 3407

HALL, Charles Bryan. b 37. Liv Univ BA59. St Mich Coll Llan 59. d 62 p 63. C Prestatyn *St As* 62-64; C Cardiff St Mary *Llan* 64-67; V 73-75; C Hawarden *St As* 67-72; TV 72-73 and 84-86; P-in-c Cardiff St Steph *Llan* 73-75; V Cardiff St Mary w St Steph 75-81; V Penycae *St As* 81-84; R Llandegla and Bryneglwys and Llanarmon-yn-Ial 86-87; R Llandegla and Llanarmon yn Ial from 87. *The Rectory, Llandegla, Wrexham, Clwyd LL11 3AW* Llandegla (01978) 88362

HALL, Charles John. b 40. JP. Lon Coll of Div ALCD68 LTh74. d 68 p 69. C Upton (or Overchurch) *Ches* 68-72; C Morden *S'wark* 72-76; V Hyson Green *S'well* 76-84; V Stapleford from 84; RD Beeston from 90. *The Vicarage, 61 Church Street, Stapleford, Nottingham NG9 8GA* Nottingham (0115) 939 7333

HALL, Christine Mary. b 45. K Coll Lon BD67 MPhil86. d 87. NSM Bickley *Roch* 87-92; Vice-Prin Chich Th Coll from 92. *Mayfield Cottage, 25 Southborough Road, Bromley BR1 2EA* 0181-467 0482

HALL, David Anthony. b 43. Reading Univ BA66. Qu Coll Birm 79. d 81 p 82. C Norton *St Alb* 81-85; TV Hitchin 85-93; P-in-c Bidford-on-Avon *Cov* 93; V from 93. *5 Howard Close, Bidford-on-Avon, Alcester, Warks B50 4EL* Bidford-on-Avon (01789) 772217

HALL, Denis. b 43. Lon Coll of Div 65. **d** 69 **p** 70. C Netherton *Liv* 69-71; C Roby 72-75; V Wigan St Steph 75-90; V Newton-le-Willows from 90. *The Vicarage, 243 Crow Lane East, Newton-le-Willows, Merseyside WA12 9UB* Newton-le-Willows (01925) 224869

HALL, Derek Guy. b 26. Tyndale Hall Bris 50. **d** 51 **p** 52. R Fazakerley Em *Liv* 67-74; TR 74-81; V Langdale *Carl* 81-86; rtd 86; Perm to Offic *Carl* from 86. *14 Gale Park, Ambleside, Cumbria LA22 0BN* Ambleside (015394) 33144

HALL, Desmond. b 27. St Cuth Soc Dur BSc54 PhD58. NE Ord Course 78. **d** 81 **p** 82. NSM Bishopwearmouth St Mich w St Hilda *Dur* 81-82; C Bishopwearmouth St Mary V w St Pet CD 82-85; V Leadgate 85-94; P-in-c Dipton 93-94; rtd 94; NSM Cornwood *Ex* from 94. *1 Abbots Park, Cornwood, Ivybridge, Devon PL21 9PP* Cornwood (01752) 837833

HALL, Edwin George. b 40. Sarum & Wells Th Coll 88. **d** 91 **p** 92. NSM Purton *Bris* from 91. *17 Linley Cottages, Church Path, Purton, Swindon SN5 9DR* Swindon (01793) 770520

HALL, Ernest. b 10. AKC36. **d** 36 **p** 37. V Osmotherley *York* 69-75; rtd 75. *Dulverton Hall, St Martin's Square, Scarborough, N Yorkshire YO11 2DB* Scarborough (01723) 373082

HALL, Geoffrey Hedley. b 33. Bris Univ BA55. St Steph Ho Ox 63. **d** 65 **p** 66. C Taunton H Trin B & W 65-67; CF 67-80; Sen CF 80-86; P-in-c Ambrosden w Arncot and Blackthorn *Ox* 72-75; V Barnsley St Edw *Wakef* from 86. *St Edward's Vicarage, 186 Racecommon Road, Barnsley, S Yorkshire S70 6JY* Barnsley (01226) 203919

HALL, George Richard Wyndham. b 49. Ex Univ LLB71. Wycliffe Hall Ox BA74 MA78. **d** 75 **p** 76. C Walton H Trin *Ox* 75-79; C Farnborough *Guildf* 79-84; Bp's Chapl *Nor* 84-87; R Saltford w Corston and Newton St Loe *B & W* from 87; Chapl Bath Coll of FE from 88. *The Rectory, 12 Beech Road, Saltford, Bristol BS18 3BE* Saltford (01225) 872275

HALL, Canon George Rumney. b 37. Westcott Ho Cam 60. **d** 62 **p** 63. C Camberwell St Phil *S'wark* 62-65; C Waltham Cross *St Alb* 65-67; R Buckenham w Hassingham and Strumpshaw *Nor* 67-74; Chapl St Andr Hosp Thorpe 67-72; Chapl HM Pris *Nor* 72-74; V Wymondham *Nor* 74-87; RD Humbleyard 86-87; Dom Chapl to The Queen from 87; Chapl to The Queen from 89; R Sandringham w W Newton *Nor* 87-94; P-in-c Flitcham 87-94; P-in-c Wolferton w Babingley 87-94; R Sandringham w W Newton and Appleton etc from 95; P-in-c Castle Rising from 87; P-in-c Hillington from 87; Hon Can Nor Cathl from 87; RD Heacham and Rising from 89. *The Rectory, Sandringham, King's Lynn, Norfolk PE35 6EH* Dersingham (01485) 540587

HALL, Mrs Gillian Louise. b 45. N Ord Course 87. **d** 90 **p** 94. NSM Earby *Bradf* from 90. *244 Colne Road, Earby, Colne, Lancs BB8 6TD* Earby (01282) 842593

HALL, Canon Godfrey Charles. b 43. Linc Coll Ox BA66 MA72. Cuddesdon Coll 66. **d** 68 **p** 69. C St Helier *S'wark* 68-72; Asst Chapl Ch Hosp Horsham 72-82; Hd Master Prebendal Sch Chich from 82; Can and Preb Chich Cathl *Chich* from 93. *53 West Street, Chichester, W Sussex PO19 1RT* Chichester (01243) 782026

HALL, Harold Henry Stanley Lawson. b 23. Qu Coll Birm 56. **d** 58 **p** 59. V Newton Aycliffe *Dur* 69-76; R Whitburn 76-89; rtd 89. *9 Balmoral Terrace, East Herrington, Sunderland SR3 3PR* 0191-528 0108

HALL, Harry. b 41. Open Univ BA93. Chich Th Coll 89. **d** 91 **p** 92. C Boston *Linc* 91-92; C Bourne 92-94; P-in-c Sutterton w Fosdyke and Algarkirk from 94. *The Vicarage, Sutterton, Boston, Lincs PE20 2JH* Boston (01205) 460285

HALL, Herbert Alexander. b 05. **d** 61 **p** 62. R Sigglesthorne *York* 70-74; R Sigglesthorne and Rise w Nunkeeling and Bewholme 74-76; rtd 76; Hon C Beverley St Mary *York* from 81. *19 Manor Close, Manor Road, Beverley, N Humberside HU17 7BP* Hull (01482) 867889

HALL, Canon Hubert William Peter. b 35. Ely Th Coll 58. **d** 60 **p** 61. C Louth w Welton-le-Wold *Linc* 60-62; C Gt Grimsby St Jas 62-69; C Gt Grimsby St Mary and St Jas 69-71; Hon Chapl Miss to Seamen from 71; V Immingham *Linc* from 71; RD Haverstoe from 86; Hon Can Linc Cathl from 89. *The Vicarage, 344 Pelham Road, Immingham, Grimsby, S Humberside DN40 1PU* Immingham (01469) 572560

HALL, Ian Michael. b 48. Mansf Coll Ox MA70 Leeds Univ CertEd71. Carl Dioc Tr Course 85. **d** 88 **p** 89. NSM Eskdale, Irton, Muncaster and Waberthwaite *Carl* from 88. *Fisherground Farm, Eskdale, Cumbria CA19 1TF* Eskdale (01946) 23319

HALL, James. b 28. Wollongong Univ BA78. CITC 53. **d** 56 **p** 57. Australia 68-89; R Morley w Deopham, Hackford, Wicklewood etc *Nor* 89-92; R High Oak 92-93; rtd 93. *174 O'Brien's Road, Figtree, NSW, Australia 2525* Wollongong (42) 283239

HALL, Canon James Robert. b 24. TCD BA48 MA54. **d** 49 **p** 50. I Finaghy *Conn* 66-89; Can Belf Cathl 82-89; RD S Belf *Conn*

83-89; rtd 89. *3 Coachman's Way, Hillsborough, Co Down BT26 6HQ* Hillsborough (01846) 689678

HALL, Mrs Jean Margaret. b 38. Bris Univ CertEd59 DipRE59 ACertEd73. Bris Sch of Min 84. **d** 88 **p** 94. Hon C Bris St Andr w St Bart *Bris* 88; Hon C E Bris 88-91; Par Dn Plympton St Mary *Ex* 91-93; Asst Chapl Cant and Thanet Community Healthcare Trust from 93; Asst Chapl Haine Hosp Ramsgate from 93. *Haine Hospital, Haine Road, Ramsgate, Kent CT12 5AD* Ramsgate (01843) 225544 (pager) or 868499

HALL, Jeffrey Ernest. b 42. Linc Th Coll 73. **d** 75 **p** 76. C Brampton St Thos *Derby* 75-78; C New Whittington 78-81; C Whittington 78-81; TV Riverside *Ox* 81-90; R Anstey *Leic* from 90. *The Rectory, 1 Hurd's Close, Groby Road, Anstey, Leicester LE7 7GH* Leicester (0116) 236 2176

HALL, John Barrie. b 41. Sarum & Wells Th Coll 82. **d** 84 **p** 85. Chapl St Edward's Hosp Cheddleton 84-88; C Cheddleton *Lich* 84-88; V Rocester 88-94; V Rocester and Croxden w Hollington from 94; RD Uttoxeter from 91. *The Vicarage, Church Lane, Rocester, Uttoxeter, Staffs ST14 5JZ* Uttoxeter (01889) 590424

HALL, John Bellamy. b 10. Ridley Hall Cam 55. **d** 57 **p** 57. R Daglingworth w the Duntisbournes and Winstone *Glouc* 66-74; P-in-c Kempley w Oxenhall 74-77; rtd 77; Perm to Offic *Chich* 78-83; Perm to Offic *St E* from 83. *14 Riverside, Dunmow, Essex CM6 3AR*

HALL, Dr John Bruce. b 33. St Louis Covenant Th Sem MTh80 DMin85 Lon Coll of Div ALCD60 LTh74. **d** 60 **p** 61. C Kingston upon Hull H Trin *York* 60-67; C Beverley Minster 67-68; V Clapham Park St Steph *S'wark* 68-76; R Tooting Graveney St Nic from 76. *The Rectory, 20A Rectory Lane, London SW17 9QJ* 0181-672 7691

HALL, John Charles. b 46. Hull Univ BA71. Ridley Hall Cam 71. **d** 73 **p** 74. C Bromley Common St Aug *Roch* 73-77; C Westbury-on-Trym St Alb *Bris* 78-80; Oman 80-82; C-in-c Bishop Auckland Woodhouse Close CD *Dur* 82-90; P-in-c Gt and Lt Glemham, Blaxhall etc *St E* 90-91; P-in-c Rodney Stoke w Draycott *B & W* from 91; Dioc Ecum Officer from 91. *The Vicarage, Vicarage Lane, Draycott, Cheddar, Somerset BS27 3SH* Cheddar (01934) 742315

HALL, John Curtis. b 39. CEng73 MIMechE73. Coll of Resurr Mirfield 80. **d** 82 **p** 83. C Pet Ch Carpenter *Pet* 82-86; TV Heavitree w Ex St Paul *Ex* 86-93; R Bow w Broad Nymet from 93; V Colebrooke from 93; R Zeal Monachorum from 93. *The Rectory, Bow, Crediton, Devon EX17 6HS* Bow (01363) 82566

HALL, Canon John Derek. b 25. St Cuth Soc Dur BA50. Linc Th Coll 50. **d** 52 **p** 53. V York St Chad *York* 68-90; Can and Preb York Minster 85-90; rtd 90; Chapl Castle Howard York from 90. *Chanting Hill Farm, Welburn, York YO6 7EF* Whitwell-on-the-Hill (01653) 618345

HALL, John Edmund. b 49. Birm Poly CQSW76 Open Univ BA84. Trin Coll Bris BA89. **d** 89 **p** 90. C Winchmore Hill St Paul *Lon* 89-92; V Edmonton St Aldhelm from 92. *St Aldhelm's Vicarage, Windmill Road, London N18 1PA* 0181-807 5336

HALL, Canon John Kenneth. b 32. Qu Coll Birm 61. **d** 63 **p** 64. C Ilminster w Whitelackington *B & W* 63-66; P-in-c Mackworth St Fran *Derby* 66-69; V Blackford *B & W* 69-76; R Chapel Allerton 69-76; New Zealand from 77; Can St Pet Cathl Waikato from 85. *St Mark's Vicarage, 7 Kenrick Street, Te Aroha, New Zealand* Te Aroha (7) 884-8728

HALL, Dr John MacNicol. b 44. MRCGP75 Glas Univ BSc65 MB, ChB69 St Jo Coll Cam BA73 MA76 Nottm Univ MTh88. Westcott Ho Cam 71. **d** 86 **p** 86. NSM Knighton St Jo *Leic* 86; NSM Clarendon Park St Jo w Knighton St Mich 86-89; Perm to Offic *Ely* 89-91; Perm to Offic *St Alb* 90-92; Perm to Offic *Birm* from 91. *HM Prison, Winson Green Road, Birmingham B18 4AS* 0121-554 3838 Fax 554 7990

HALL, John Michael. b 47. BD. Oak Hill Th Coll 68. **d** 73 **p** 74. C Walthamstow St Mary w St Steph *Chelmsf* 73-76; C Rainham 76-79; P-in-c Woodham Mortimer w Hazeleigh 79-93; P-in-c Woodham Walter 79-93; Ind Chapl 79-93; R Fairstead w Terling and White Notley etc from 93. *The Rectory, New Road, Terling, Chelmsford CM3 2PN* Chelmsford (01245) 433256

HALL, John Michael. b 62. Leeds Univ BA. Coll of Resurr Mirfield 83. **d** 86 **p** 87. C Ribbleton *Blackb* 86-89; C Carnforth 89-92; V Lt Marsden from 92. *St Paul's Vicarage, Bentley Street, Nelson, Lancs BB9 0BS* Nelson (01282) 615888

HALL, John Redvers. b 25. Dur Univ BA59 DipTh62 Man Univ CertEd74. **d** 61 **p** 62. Lic to Offic *Leic* 66-70; Lic to Offic *Blackb* 70-81; P-in-c Ingoldmells w Addlethorpe *Linc* 81-83; V Cholsey *Ox* 83-92; rtd 92. *9 Ruislip Gardens, Aldwick, Bognor Regis, W Sussex PO21 4LB* Pagham (01243) 264865

HALL, Canon John Robert. b 49. St Chad's Coll Dur BA71. Cuddesdon Coll 73. **d** 75 **p** 76. C Kennington St Jo *S'wark* 75-78; P-in-c S Wimbledon All SS 78-84; V Streatham St Pet

84-92; Dir of Educn *Blackb* from 92; Hon Can Blackb Cathl from 92. *St Leonard's House, Potters Lane, Samlesbury, Preston PR5 0UE*   Preston (01772) 877229

HALL, John Wintour. b 17. Leeds Univ BA39. Coll of Resurr Mirfield 39. **d** 41 **p** 41. Chapl Merchant Taylors' Sch Northwood 56-82; rtd 82. *15 Carlton Place, Porthcawl, M Glam CF36 3ET*

HALL, Dr Joseph Hayes. b 30. TD71. FGS53 St Jo Coll Dur BSc53 DipTh55 Liv Univ MA73 ThD90. Wycliffe Hall Ox 55. **d** 55 **p** 56. C Wallasey St Hilary *Ches* 55-59; C Macclesfield St Mich 59-60; CF (TA) 59-72; V Barnton *Ches* 60-67; V New Brighton All SS 67-81; V Woodford from 81. *The Vicarage, Wilmslow Road, Woodford, Stockport, Cheshire SK7 1RH*   0161-439 2286

HALL, Keven Neil. b 47. Auckland Univ BSc PhD74. K Coll Lon BD AKC79. **d** 79 **p** 80. New Zealand 79-87; Chapl Nat Soc for Epilepsy from 91. *1 Coverdale Road, London W12 8JJ*   0181-743 4515

HALL, Leslie. b 37. Man Univ BSc59. E Midl Min Tr Course 83. **d** 86 **p** 87. NSM Freiston w Butterwick *Linc* from 86; Dioc NSM Officer from 94. *29 Brant End Road, Butterwick, Boston, Lincs PE22 0ET*   Boston (01205) 760375

HALL, Mrs Linda Charlotte. b 50. Cam Inst of Educn CertEd72. St Alb Minl Tr Scheme 85 Oak Hill Th Coll 91. **d** 92 **p** 94. NSM St Alb St Steph *St Alb* from 92. *15 Nelsons Avenue, St Albans, Herts AL1 5SE*   St Albans (01727) 869570

HALL, Mrs Margaret Mercia. b 39. Bedf Coll Lon BA61 Cam Univ DipRS78. Gilmore Ho 73. **dss** 80 **d** 87 **p** 94. Gt Chesham *Ox* 81-87; Par Dn 87-94; C from 94. *19 Stanley Avenue, Chesham, Bucks HP5 2JG*   Chesham (01494) 784479

HALL, Mrs Marigold Josephine. b 29. Linc Th Coll 81. **dss** 83 **d** 87. Chapl Asst Hellesdon Hosp Nor from 83; Nor St Pet Parmentergate w St Jo *Nor* 83-87; C 87-94; rtd 90; Perm to Offic *Nor* from 94. *11 Stuart Court, Norwich NR1 1NP*   Norwich (01603) 625933

HALL, Michael Edward. b 32. Fitzw Ho Cam BA57 MA61. Ridley Hall Cam 68. **d** 69 **p** 70. C Aspley *S'well* 69-73; P-in-c Bulwell St Jo 73-75; V 75-81; P-in-c Tylers Green *Ox* 81-90; V from 90. *The Vicarage, Tyler's Green, High Wycombe, Bucks HP10 8HB*   High Wycombe (01494) 813367

HALL, Murray. b 34. K Coll Lon. **d** 61 **p** 62. V Oxshott *Guildf* 67-72; P-in-c Runham *Nor* 72-80; P-in-c Stokesby w Herringby 72-80; R Filby w Thrigby w Mautby 72-80; R Filby w Thrigby, Mautby, Stokesby, Herringby etc 80-94; rtd 94; Perm to Offic *Nor* from 94. *64 Nursery Close, Acle, Norwich NR13 3EH*   Great Yarmouth (01493) 751287

HALL, Nicholas Charles. b 56. **d** 86 **p** 87. C Hyde St Geo *Ches* 86-89; C Cheadle 89-91; NSM from 91. *5 Brooklyn Crescent, Cheadle, Cheshire SK8 1DX*   0161-491 6758

HALL, Canon Nigel David. b 46. Univ of Wales (Cardiff) BA67 BD76 Lon Univ CertEd68. St Mich Coll Llan 73. **d** 76 **p** 77. C Cardiff St Jo *Llan* 76-81; R Llanbadarn Fawr, Llandegley and Llanfihangel etc *S & B* from 81; RD Maelienydd from 89; Can Brecon Cathl from 94. *The Rectory, Llanbadarn Fawr, Crossgates, Llandrindod Wells, Powys LD1 5TT*   Penybont (01597) 851204

HALL (nee WANSTALL), Mrs Noelle Margaret. b 53. Wolfs Coll Cam BEd76. Sarum & Wells Th Coll 84. **dss** 86 **d** 87 **p** 94. Hythe *Cant* 86-87; Par Dn 87-89; Par Dn Reculver and Herne Bay St Bart 89-94; C 94-95; P-in-c Sittingbourne St Mary from 95; Dioc Adv in Women's Min from 95. *St Mary's Vicarage, 88 Albany Road, Sittingbourne, Kent ME10 1EL*   Sittingbourne (01795) 472535

HALL, Peter Douglas. b 60. Ox Poly HND81. Oak Hill Th Coll BA92. **d** 92 **p** 93. C Bromyard *Heref* from 92. *12 Lower Thorn, Bromyard, Herefordshire HR7 4AZ*   Bromyard (01885) 482620

HALL, Philip Edward Robin. b 36. Oak Hill Th Coll 64. **d** 67 **p** 68. C Ware Ch Ch *St Alb* 67-70; C Rayleigh *Chelmsf* 70-73; R Leven w Catwick *York* 73-85; P-in-c Mayfield *Lich* from 85; P-in-c Ilam w Blore Ray and Okeover from 89. *The Vicarage, Mayfield, Ashbourne, Derbyshire DE6 2JR*   Ashbourne (01335) 342855

HALL, Robert Arthur. b 35. Lon Univ BSc66. NW Ord Course 74. **d** 77 **p** 78. C York St Paul *York* 77-79; R Elvington w Sutton on Derwent and E Cottingwith 79-82; Chapl Tiffield Sch Northants 82-84; V Bessingby *York* 84-88; V Carnaby 84-88; V Fulford from 88. *The Vicarage, 1 Fulford Park, Fulford, York YO1 4QR*   York (01904) 633261

HALL, Roger John. b 53. Linc Th Coll. **d** 84 **p** 85. C Shrewsbury St Giles w Sutton and Atcham *Lich* 84-87; CF from 87. *c/o MOD (Army), Bagshot Park, Bagshot, Surrey GU19 5PL*   Bagshot (01276) 471717   Fax 412834

HALL, Ronald Cecil. b 20. St Aid Birkenhead 63. **d** 65 **p** 66. R Talke *Lich* 69-74; V Birstwith *Ripon* 74-90; P-in-c Thornthwaite w Thruscross and Darley 76-77; rtd 90.

Wickham House, Kingsmead, Farm Road, Bracklesham Bay, Chichester, W Sussex PO20 8JU   Bracklesham Bay (01243) 671190

HALL, Mrs Sonia Winifred. b 44. Nottm Univ BSc66 Leeds Univ MSc68. Ox Min Course DipMin94. **d** 94. NSM Ox St Andr *Ox* from 94. *33 Bowness Avenue, Headington, Oxford OX3 0AL*   Oxford (01865) 63639

HALL, Stephen Clarence. b 23. Kelham Th Coll 46. **d** 51 **p** 52. C Killingworth *Newc* 51-53; C Newc H Cross 53-56; S Rhodesia 56-65; Rhodesia 65-80; Zimbabwe from 80; S Africa from 77. *PO Box 10685, Meer-en-See, Zululand, 3901 South Africa*   Richards Bay (351) 32713

HALL, Stephen Philip. b 56. Ripon Coll Cuddesdon. **d** 84 **p** 85. C Camberwell St Giles *S'wark* 84-88; Chapl Brighton Poly *Chich* 88-92; Chapl Brighton Univ 92; TV Bicester w Bucknell, Caversfield and Launton *Ox* from 92; Sub Chapl HM Pris Bullingdon from 92. *75 Ravencroft, Langford Village, Bicester, Oxon OX6 0YQ*   Bicester (01869) 323635

HALL, Prof Stuart George. b 28. New Coll Ox BA52 MA55 BD72. Ripon Hall Ox 53. **d** 54 **p** 55. Lect Th Nottm Univ 62-73; Sen Lect 73-78; Prof Ecclesiastical Hist K Coll Lon 78-90; Perm to Offic *St Alb* 80-86; Perm to Offic *S'wark* 86-90; R Pittenweem *St And* from 90; R Elie and Earlsferry from 90; rtd 93. *Hopedene, 15 High Street, Elie, Leven, Fife KY9 1BY*   Elie (01333) 330145   Fax as telephone

HALL, Timothy Robert. b 52. Dur Univ BA74. St Jo Coll Nottm LTh87. **d** 87 **p** 88. C Hawarden *St As* 87-89; Chapl St Coll Llandudno from 90. *Woodpecker Cottage, St David's College, Llandudno, Gwynedd LL30 1RD*   Llandudno (01492) 581224

HALL, William. b 34. Hull Univ BSc(Econ)56 St Jo Coll Dur CertRS88. NE Ord Course 89. **d** 92 **p** 93. NSM Sunderland *Dur* from 92. *31 Nursery Road, Silksworth Lane, Sunderland SR3 1NT*   0191-528 4843

HALL, Canon William Cameron. b 40. K Coll Lon 60. **d** 65 **p** 66. C Thornaby on Tees St Paul *York* 65-68; Chapl to Arts and Recreation *Dur* from 68; V Grindon 71-80; Hon Can Dur Cathl from 84; Sen Chapl Actors' Ch Union from 89. *59 Western Hill, Durham DH1 4RJ*   0191-386 3177

HALL, William Nawton Sinclair. b 17. Kelham Th Coll 35. **d** 41 **p** 42. R Witton Gilbert *Dur* 55-61; R Lowther w Askham *Carl* 61-84; rtd 83; Perm to Offic *Carl* from 84. *41 Briar Rigg, Keswick, Cumbria CA12 4NN*   Keswick (017687) 74103

HALL, William Norman. b 30. ARIC74 TCD BA52 MA64 BD65. TCD Div Sch Div Test54. **d** 54 **p** 55. Chapl St Jas Choir Sch Grimsby 66-70; Asst Master Hautlieu Sch Jersey 70-73; V Jersey St Mark *Win* 73-92; rtd 92. *La Chansonette, 26 Seafield Avenue, Milbrook, Jersey, Channel Islands JE2 3LZ*   Jersey (01534) 80221

HALL CARPENTER, Leslie Thomas Frank. b 19. Lich Th Coll 55. **d** 57 **p** 58. R Lochgilphead *Arg* 69-70; Area Sec USPG (York) 70-73; P-in-c Well *Ripon* 73-74; V Kirk Hammerton 74-75; R Hunsingore w Cowthorpe 74-75; V Nun Monkton 74-75; R Kirk Hammerton w Nun Monkton and Hunsingore 75-77; P-in-c Hackness w Harwood Dale *York* 77-79; V Melbecks and Muker *Ripon* 79-82; R Twyford w Guist w Bintry w Themelthorpe etc *Nor* 82-84; rtd 84; Perm to Offic *Nor* from 90. *Little Cogden, 6 Old Hall Drive, Dersingham, Norfolk PE31 6JT*   Dersingham (01485) 542271

HALL-MATTHEWS, Preb John Cuthbert Berners. b 33. Queensland Univ BA55 K Coll Lon PGCE65. Coll of Resurr Mirfield 58. **d** 60 **p** 61. C Woodley St Jo the Ev *Ox* 60-63; C Is of Dogs Ch Ch and St Jo w St Luke *Lon* 63-65; Asst Chapl Ch Hosp Horsham 65-72; Chapl R Hosp Sch Ipswich 72-75; V Tupsley *Heref* 75-90; P-in-c Hampton Bishop and Mordiford w Dormington 77-90; RD Heref City 84-90; Preb Heref Cathl 85-90; TR Wolv *Lich* from 90. *St Peter's Rectory, 42 Park Road East, Wolverhampton WV1 4QA*   Wolverhampton (01902) 23140 or 28491

HALL-THOMPSON, Colin Lloyd. b 51. JP. TCD DipTh. **d** 84 **p** 85. C Dub Rathfarnham *D & G* 84-86; Bp's C Clonmel Union *C, C & R* 86-91; Chapl Fort Mitchel Pris from 86; I Kilbride *Conn* from 91; Hon Chapl Miss to Seamen from 91. *Kilbride Rectory, 7 Rectory Road, Doagh, Co Antrim BT39 0PT*   Ballyclare (01960) 340225

HALLAM, Lawrence Gordon. b 31. Lich Th Coll 61. **d** 63 **p** 64. R Cocking w Bepton *Chich* 68-71; V Eastbourne Ch Ch 71-84; V Bexhill St Barn 84-87; rtd 87; Perm to Offic *Chich* 87-92. *1 Viceroy Lodge, Kingsway, Hove, E Sussex BN3 4RA*   Brighton (01273) 772328

HALLAM, Dr Nicholas Francis (Nick). b 48. MRCPath91 Univ Coll Ox BA71 MA81 Glas Univ PhD76 MB, ChB81. Ox NSM Course 84. **d** 87 **p** 88. NSM Ox St Clem *Ox* 87-93; NSM Balerno *Edin* from 93. *11 Ravelrig Park, Edinburgh EH14 7DL*   0131-449 5341

HALLAM, Canon Peter Hubert. b 33. Trin Hall Cam BA56 MA60. Westcott Ho Cam 56. **d** 58 **p** 59. C St Annes *Blackb* 58-62; Asst Chapl and Tutor St Bede Coll Dur 62-67; V Briercliffe *Blackb* from 67; Hon Can Blackb Cathl from 92.

St James's Vicarage, Briercliffe, Burnley, Lancs BB10 2HU Burnley (01282) 423700

HALLAM, Stanley Bywater. b 16. Wells Th Coll 71. **d** 71 **p** 72. C Haughton le Skerne *Dur* 72-74; R Stanhope 74-82; rtd 82. *8 Low Well Park, Wheldrake, York YO4 6DS* Wheldrake (01904) 448803

✠**HALLATT, Rt Rev David Marrison.** b 37. Southn Univ BA59 St Cath Coll Ox BA62 MA66. Wycliffe Hall Ox 59. **d** 63 **p** 64 **c** 94. C Maghull *Liv* 63-67; V Totley *Derby* 67-75; R Didsbury St Jas *Man* 75-80; R Barlow Moor 76-80; TR Didsbury St Jas and Em 80-89; Adn Halifax *Wakef* 89-94; Area Bp Shrewsbury *Lich* from 94; Hon Can Lich Cathl from 94. *Athlone House, 68 London Road, Shrewsbury SY2 6PG* Shrewsbury (01743) 235867 Fax 243296

HALLATT, John Leighton. b 34. St Pet Coll Ox BA58 MA62. Wycliffe Hall Ox 58. **d** 60 **p** 61. C Ipswich St Jo *St E* 60-63; C Warrington St Paul *Liv* 63-66; V Wadsley *Sheff* 66-72; V Hindley St Pet *Liv* 72-75; Area Sec (Scotland and Dios Newc and Dur) CMS 75-83; N Sec CMS 78-83; TR Cramlington *Newc* 83-90; V Monkseaton St Mary from 90. *The Vicarage, 77 Hawthorn Avenue, Whitley Bay, Tyne & Wear NE26 3AG* 0191-252 2484

HALLETT, Howard Adrian. b 43. Man Univ MPhil90. Oak Hill Th Coll BA81. **d** 81 **p** 82. C Walshaw Ch Ch *Man* 81-84; V Stoke sub Hamdon *B & W* from 84; RD Ivelchester from 91. *The Vicarage, 1 East Stoke, Stoke-sub-Hamdon, Somerset TA14 6RQ* Martock (01935) 822529

HALLETT, Miss Jacqueline Victoria (Lyn). b 54. Ex Univ BA75 PGCE76. Linc Th Coll CMinlStuds94. **d** 94 **p** 95. C Crook *Dur* from 94. *Cherry Tree House, Park Avenue, Crook, Co Durham DL15 9HX* Bishop Auckland (01388) 762451

HALLETT, Keith Philip. b 37. Tyndale Hall Bris 61. **d** 64 **p** 65. C Higher Openshaw *Man* 64-68; C Bushbury *Lich* 68-71; P-in-c Drayton Bassett 71-72; R 72-90; V Fazeley 71-90; P-in-c Hints 78-83; V 83-90; C-in-c Canwell CD 78-83; V Canwell 83-90; RD Tamworth 81-90; P-in-c Buckhurst Hill *Chelmsf* from 90. *St John's Rectory, High Road, Buckhurst Hill, Essex IG9 5RX* 0181-504 1931

HALLETT, Peter. b 49. Bath Univ BSc72. Oak Hill Th Coll DPS. **d** 76 **p** 77. C Brinsworth w Catcliffe *Sheff* 76-79; P-in-c Doncaster St Jas 80-81; V 81-86; R Henstridge and Charlton Horethorne w Stowell *B & W* from 86. *The Vicarage, Henstridge, Templecombe, Somerset BA8 0QE* Stalbridge (01963) 362266

HALLETT, Peter Duncan. b 43. CCC Cam BA66 MA68. Westcott Ho Cam 69. **d** 71 **p** 72. C Sawston *Ely* 71-73; C Lyndhurst and Emery Down *Win* 73-78; C Skegness and Winthorpe *Linc* 78-80; P-in-c Samlesbury *Blackb* 80-91; Asst Dir RE 80-94; C Leyland St Ambrose 91-94; Asst Dir RE from 94. *24 Bosburne Drive, Mellor Brook, Blackburn BB2 7PA* Blackburn (01254) 813544

HALLETT, Raymond. b 44. E Midl Min Tr Course 85. **d** 88 **p** 89. NSM Hucknall Torkard *S'well* from 88. *26 Nursery Close, Hucknall, Nottingham NG15 6DQ* Nottingham (0115) 963 3360

HALLETT, Ronald Walter. b 13. Lon Univ BD36. **d** 36 **p** 37. USA 64-80; rtd 80; Chapl Community of St Denys Warminster from 80; Perm to Offic *Lich* from 83; P-in-c N Cerney w Bagendon *Glouc* 85-86. *c/o St Gabriel's Vicarage, Walstead Road, Walsall, W Midlands WS1 1LU* Walsall (01922) 22583

HALLETT, Canon Roy. b 17. St D Coll Lamp BA48. **d** 49 **p** 50. V Caldicot *Mon* 58-71; V Rumney 71-87; RD Bassaleg 82-87; Can St Woolos Cathl 86-87; rtd 87. *247 Llantarnam Road, Cwmbran, Gwent NP44 3BQ* Cwmbran (01633) 874128

HALLIBURTON, Canon Robert John. b 35. Selw Coll Cam BA56 MA60 Keble Coll Ox BA58 DPhil61 MA71. St Steph Ho Ox 58. **d** 61 **p** 62. C Stepney St Dunstan and All SS *Lon* 61-67; Lect St Steph Ho Ox 67-71; Vice-Prin 71-75; Lect Linc Coll Ox 73-75; Prin Chich Th Coll 75-82; Can and Preb Chich Cathl *Chich* 76-82; Wightring Preb and Th Lect 88-90; P-in-c St Margarets on Thames *Lon* 82-90; Can Res and Chan St Paul's Cathl from 90. *1 Amen Court, London EC4M 7BU* 0171-248 1817

HALLIDAY, Christopher Norton Robert. b 48. N Ord Course 82. **d** 85 **p** 86. C Davyhulme St Mary *Man* 85-87; Lect Bolton St Pet 87-90; I Rathdrum w Glenealy, Derralossary and Laragh *D & G* from 90. *The Rectory, Rathdrum, Co Wicklow, Irish Republic* Rathdrum (404) 46160 Fax 46663

HALLIDAY, Mrs Diana Patricia (Di). b 40. ALA66. N Ord Course 89. **d** 92 **p** 94. NSM Burley in Wharfedale *Bradf* from 92. *The Brackens, 6A Walker Road, Baildon, Shipley, W Yorkshire BD17 5BE* Bradford (01274) 582859

HALLIDAY, Edwin James. b 35. NW Ord Course 70. **d** 73 **p** 74. C New Bury *Man* 73-76; V Bolton St Phil 76-82; Dioc Communications Officer 82-88; V Radcliffe St Thos and St Jo 82-90; R Gt Lever from 90. *St Michael's Rectory, 130 Green Lane, Bolton BL3 2HX* Bolton (01204) 26510

HALLIDAY, Paula Patricia. b 50. MEd83 BTh94. **d** 94 **p** 95. C Killala w Dunfeeny, Crossmolina, Kilmoremoy etc *T, K & A* from 94. *The Rectory, Crossmolina, Ballina, Co Mayo, Irish Republic* Mayo (96) 31384

✠**HALLIDAY, Rt Rev Robert Taylor.** b 32. Glas Univ MA54 BD57. Edin Th Coll 55. **d** 57 **p** 58 **c** 90. C St Andrews St Andr *St And* 57-60; R 83-90; C Glas St Marg *Glas* 60-63; Lect NT Edin Th Coll 63-74; R Edin H Cross *Edin* 63-83; Tutor Edin Univ 69-71; Can St Mary's Cathl *Edin* 73-83; R St Andrews St Andr *St And* 83-90; Tutor St Andr Univ 84-90; Bp Bre from 90. *St Paul's Cathedral, 1 High Street, Dundee DD1 1TD, or 35 Carlogie Road, Carnoustie, Angus DD7 6ER* Dundee (01382) 29230/24486 or Carnoustie (01241) 855781

HALLIDIE SMITH, Andrew. b 31. Pemb Coll Cam BA54 MA58. Ely Th Coll 55. **d** 56 **p** 57. Canada 67-70 and 79-81 and from 91; R Alresford *Chelmsf* 70-79; V Elsecar *Sheff* 81-91; rtd 91. *PO Box 765, Big River, Saskatchewan, Canada, S0J 0E0*

HALLING, William Laurence. b 43. Linc Coll Ox BA64 DipTh66 MA68 Lon Univ BD68. Tyndale Hall Bris 66. **d** 68 **p** 69. C Beckenham St Jo *Roch* 68-72; C Walton H Trin *Ox* 72-78; V Barrow St Mark *Carl* 78-86; R Kirkheaton *Wakef* from 86; Chapl Mill Hill Hosp Huddersfield from 86. *The Rectory, Church Lane, Kirkheaton, Huddersfield HD5 0JR* Huddersfield (01484) 532410

HALLIWELL, Christopher Eigil. b 57. Newc Univ BA78. Trin Coll Bris DipHE91. **d** 91 **p** 92. C Mildenhall *St E* 91-94; R Wrentham w Benacre, Covehithe, Frostenden etc from 94. *The Rectory, Wrentham, Beccles, Suffolk NR34 7LX* Wrentham (01502) 75208

HALLIWELL, Ivor George. b 33. St Cath Coll Cam BA57 MA60. Wells Th Coll 58. **d** 60 **p** 60. C Hanworth St Geo *Lon* 60-62; C Willenhall *Cov* 62-65; C-in-c Whitley St Jas CD 65-68; V Whitley 68-72; V Corton *Nor* 72-77; P-in-c Hopton 72-74; V 74-77; Asst Chapl HM Pris Pentonville 77; Chapl HM Pris *Ex* 77-83; Chapl HM Pris Wakef 83-85; P-in-c Bickington *Ex* 85-87; P-in-c Ashburton w Buckland-in-the-Moor 85-87; V Ashburton w Buckland in the Moor and Bickington 87-90; Chapl HM Pris Channings Wood from 90; Lic to Offic *Ex* from 90. *HM Prison Channing Wood, Denbury, Newton Abbot, Devon TQ12 6DW* Ipplepen (01803) 812361 Fax 813175

HALLIWELL, Michael Arthur. b 28. St Edm Hall Ox BA50 MA53. Ely Th Coll 52. **d** 54 **p** 55. C Welling *S'wark* 54-57; C Bournemouth St Alb *Win* 57-59; Asst Gen Sec C of E Coun on Foreign Relns 59-62; C St Dunstan in the West *Lon* 60-62; Chapl Bonn w Cologne *Eur* 62-67; Chapl RAF 66-67; V Croydon St Andr *Cant* 67-71; R Jersey St Brelade *Win* from 71; Chapl HM Pris Jersey 75-80; Vice-Dean Jersey *Win* from 85; Tutor S Dios Minl Tr Scheme from 92. *The Rectory, La Marquanderie, St Brelade, Jersey, Channel Islands JE3 8EP* Jersey (01534) 42302

HALLOWS, John Martin. b 50. Birm Univ BA78 Lon Univ PGCE82 E Lon Univ MSc93. Oak Hill Th Coll 92. **d** 94. C Boxmoor St Jo *St Alb* from 94. *23 Beechfield Road, Boxmoor, Hemel Hempstead, Herts HP1 1PP* Hemel Hempstead (01442) 253102

HALLS, Peter Ernest. b 38. Bris Univ BA62. Tyndale Hall Bris 59. **d** 64 **p** 65. C Blackb St Barn *Blackb* 64-67; C Bromley Ch Ch *Roch* 67-70; V Halvergate w Tunstall *Nor* 70-79; V Freethorpe w Wickhampton 71-79; P-in-c Beighton and Moulton 77-79; V Tuckswood 79-90; RD Nor S 86-90; R Brooke, Kirstead, Mundham w Seething and Thwaite from 90; RD Depwade from 91. *The Vicarage, Brooke, Norwich NR15 1JV* Brooke (01508) 550378

HALMSHAW, Mrs Stella Mary. b 36. TCert57. St Alb Minl Tr Scheme 81. **dss** 84 **d** 87. Radlett *St Alb* 84-87; NSM 87-89 and from 93; Par Dn 90-93; Chapl Herts Univ from 93. *13 The Crosspath, Radlett, Herts WD7 8HR* Radlett (01923) 854314

HALSALL, Mrs Isobel Joan. b 47. Local Minl Tr Course. **d** 94 **p** 95. C Walshaw Ch Ch *Man* from 94. *42 Knowsley Road, Bolton BL2 5PU* Bolton (01204) 894171

HALSALL, Michael John. b 61. Salford Univ BSc83. Wycliffe Hall Ox 88. **d** 91 **p** 92. C Cowley St Jo *Ox* 91-93; CF from 93. *c/o MOD (Army), Bagshot Park, Bagshot, Surrey GU19 5PL* Bagshot (01276) 471717 Fax 412834

HALSE, Raymond Stafford. b 19. Lon Univ BA49. Oak Hill Th Coll 46. **d** 50 **p** 51. V Ramsgate St Luke *Cant* 68-85; P-in-c Ramsgate Ch Ch 85; rtd 85; Hon C Hordle *Win* from 86. *58 Brunel Drive, Preston, Weymouth, Dorset DT3 6NY* Weymouth (01305) 833048

HALSEY, Anthony Michael James (Tony). b 35. Solicitor 64 K Coll Cam BA56 MA62. St Jo Coll Nottm 73. **d** 75 **p** 76. C Derby St Werburgh *Derby* 75-77; Chapl Canford Sch Wimborne 78-87; TV Sanderstead All SS *S'wark* 87-89; Perm to Offic *Portsm* from 89. *Woodlands, South Road, Liphook, Hants GU30 7HS* Liphook (01428) 724459

HALSEY, George John. b 16. Lon Univ BSc36. Wycliffe Hall Ox 38. **d** 39 **p** 40. V Shelford *S'well* 66-68; V Radcliffe-on-Trent

66-68; Lic to Offic *S'wark* 73-81; rtd 81; Perm to Offic *Guildf* from 81. *70 Ashcombe Road, Dorking, Surrey RH4 1NA* Dorking (01306) 886469

✠**HALSEY, Rt Rev Henry David.** b 19. K Coll Lon BA38. Sarum Th Coll 40. **d** 42 **p** 43 **c** 68. C Petersfield w Sheet *Portsm* 42-45; Chapl RN 46-47; C Plymouth St Andr *Ex* 47-50; V Netheravon w Fittleton *Sarum* 50-53; C-in-c Chatham St Steph CD *Roch* 53-59; V Chatham St Steph 59-62; V Bromley SS Pet and Paul 62-68; Chapl Bromley Hosp 62-68; Hon Can Roch Cathl *Roch* 64-68; RD Bromley 65-66; Adn Bromley 66-68; Suff Bp Tonbridge 68-72; Bp Carl 72-89; rtd 89; Asst Bp Portsm from 91. *Bramblecross, Gully Road, Seaview, Isle of Wight PO34 5BY* Isle of Wight (01983) 613583

HALSEY, Brother John Walter Brooke. b 33. Cam Univ BA57 Edin Univ DPT67. Westcott Ho Cam 61. **d** 61 **p** 62. C Stocksbridge *Sheff* 61-65; Community of the Transfiguration Midlothian from 65; Ind Chapl Edin 65-69. *Hermitage of the Transfiguration, 23 Manse Road, Roslin, Midlothian EH25 9LF*

HALSON, Bryan Richard. b 32. Jes Coll Cam BA56 MA60 Liv Univ MA72. Ridley Hall Cam. **d** 59 **p** 60. C Coulsdon St Andr *S'wark* 59-62; Lic to Offic *Ches* from 63; Tutor St Aid Birkenhead 63-65; Sen Tutor 65-69; Vice-Prin 68-69; Lect Alsager Coll of Educn 69-74; Prin Lect Crewe and Alsager Coll of HE from 74. *11 Winston Avenue, Alsager, Stoke-on-Trent ST7 2BE* Alsager (01270) 873998

✠**HAMBIDGE, Most Rev Douglas Walter.** b 27. Lon Univ BD58. ALCD53 Angl Th Coll (BC) DD70. **d** 53 **p** 54 **c** 69. C Dalston St Mark w St Bart *Lon* 53-56; Canada 56-91; Can Caledonia 65-69; Bp Caledonia 69-80; Bp New Westmr 80; Abp New Westmr and Metrop BC 81-93; Prin St Mark's Th Coll Dar es Salaam from 93. *St Mark's Theological College, PO Box 25017, Dar es Salaam, Tanzania*

HAMBIDGE, John Robert. b 29. Sarum Th Coll. **d** 55 **p** 56. C Tynemouth H Trin W Town *Newc* 55-57; C Middlesb St Jo the Ev *York* 58-63; C Clerkenwell H Redeemer w St Phil *Lon* 63-64; C Richmond St Mary *S'wark* 64-66; V Richmond St Jo 66-76; R Swanscombe *Roch* 76-84; V Aberedw w Llandeilo Graban and Llanbadarn etc *S & B* 84-91; P-in-c Sibson w Sheepy and Ratcliffe Culey *Leic* 91-94; P-in-c Orton-on-the-Hill w Twycross etc 92-94; R The Sheepy Gp from 95. *The Rectory, Sheepy Magna, Atherstone, Warks CV9 3QS* Tamworth (01827) 880301

HAMBLEN, John William Frederick. b 24. Sarum Th Coll 64. **d** 65 **p** 66. C Marlborough *Sarum* 68-70; V Chardstock 70-77; P-in-c Lytchett Matravers 77-83; P-in-c Burpham *Chich* 83-89; Dioc Stewardship Adv 83-89; rtd 89; Perm to Offic *Ex* from 89. *73 West Cliff Road, Dawlish, Devon EX7 9QX*

HAMBLETON, Ronald Dalzell. b 27. Ripon Hall Ox 61. **d** 62 **p** 63. V Knowbury *Heref* 65-75; P-in-c Weston under Penyard 75-79; P-in-c Hope Mansell 75-79; R Weston-under-Penyard w Hope Mansel and The Lea 79-92; rtd 92; NSM Portree *Arg* 92-95. *21 Pentaloe Close, Mordiford, Hereford HR1 4LS* Hereford (01432) 870622

HAMBLIN, John Talbot. b 38. St Steph Ho Ox 64. **d** 66 **p** 67. C Newc St Jo *Newc* 66-70; C Covent Garden St Paul *Lon* 70-71; C St Marylebone Ch Ch w St Barn 71-72; C St Marylebone Ch Ch w St Paul 72-73; C Hendon St Mary 73-76; P-in-c Hornsey St Pet 76-77; V Tottenham Ch Ch W Green 76-77; V W Green Ch Ch w St Pet from 77. *Christ Church Vicarage, Waldeck Road, London N15 3EP* 0181-889 9677

HAMBLIN, Roger Noel. b 42. Ripon Hall Ox 67. **d** 70 **p** 71. C Scotforth *Blackb* 70-73; C Altham w Clayton le Moors 73-76; V Cockerham w Winmarleigh 76-87; V Cockerham w Winmarleigh and Glasson from 87. *The Vicarage, 5 Lancaster Road, Cockerham, Lancaster LA2 0EB* Forton (01524) 791390

HAMBORG, Graham Richard. b 52. Bris Univ BSc73 Nottm Univ BA76 MTh77. St Jo Coll Nottm 74. **d** 77 **p** 78. C Tile Cross *Birm* 77-80; C Upton cum Chalvey *Ox* 80-82; TV 82-86; V Ruscombe and Twyford from 86. *The Vicarage, Ruscombe, Reading RG10 9UD* Twyford (01734) 341685

HAMBREY, Canon Frank Bernard. b 14. Leeds Univ BA42. Coll of Resurr Mirfield 43. **d** 44 **p** 45. Can Res Bermuda Cathl 70-75; Perm to Offic *Carl* from 77; rtd 79. *Bully Cottage, Embleton, Cockermouth, Cumbria CA13 9YA* Bassenthwaite Lake (017687) 76379

HAMBREY, Frederick Charles. b 19. Leeds Univ BA41. Coll of Resurr Mirfield 41. **d** 43 **p** 45. V Hanbury *Lich* 59-70; V Colton *Carl* 70-71; V Satterthwaite and Rusland 70-71; V Colton w Satterthwaite and Rusland 71-84; rtd 84; Perm to Offic *Carl* from 85. *Underknott, Blease Road, Threlkeld, Keswick, Cumbria CA12 4RY* Threlkeld (017687) 79604

HAMEL COOKE, Christopher Kingston. b 21. CCC Ox BA49 MA52 Birm Univ DPS67. Cuddesdon Coll 49. **d** 50 **p** 51. V

Bedf St Andr *St Alb* 69-79; P-in-c Bedf St Mary 70-75; R St Marylebone w H Trin *Lon* 79-89; rtd 90; Perm to Offic *Cov* from 90. *The Malt House, Halford, Shipston-on-Stour, Warks CV36 5BT* Stratford-upon-Avon (01789) 740615

HAMER, Andrew Frank. b 07. Wycliffe Hall Ox 65. **d** 66 **p** 67. V Wethersfield *Chelmsf* 71-77; rtd 77; Perm to Offic *B & W* 81-95. *c/o The Revd R J A Hamer, The Vicarage, Manwood Street, London E16 2JY* 0171-476 2388

HAMER, David Handel. b 41. Cape Town Univ BA61 Trin Coll Ox BA66. Coll of Resurr Mirfield 62. **d** 66 **p** 67. S Africa 66-73; Chapl Blundell's Sch Tiverton from 73; Lic to Offic *Ex* from 73. *Mayfield House, 2 Tidcombe Lane, Tiverton, Devon EX16 4DZ* Tiverton (01884) 253098

HAMER, Irving David. b 59. **d** 84 **p** 85. C Newton Nottage *Llan* 84-88; C Roath St Marg 88-90; V Llansawel w Briton Ferry from 90; Miss to Seamen from 90. *The Vicarage, 251 Neath Road, Briton Ferry, W Glam SA11 2SL* Neath (01639) 812200

HAMER, Roderick John Andrew. b 44. K Coll Lon 64. Ridley Hall Cam 67. **d** 68 **p** 69. C Timperley *Ches* 68-72; C Brewood *Lich* 72-74; V Chesterton 74-80; C S Gillingham *Roch* 80-83; Adv Cant and Roch Coun for Soc Resp 83-90; Hon C S Gillingham 83-90; Perm to Offic *Cant* 90-93; ACUPA Link Officer (Dio Roch) 87-90; TR Southend *Chelmsf* 90-94; P-in-c N Woolwich w Silvertown from 94; Ind Chapl from 94. *St John's Vicarage, Manwood Street, London E16 2JY* 0171-476 2388

HAMER, Canon Thomas. b 15. Univ of Wales BA37. St Mich Coll Llan 37. **d** 38 **p** 39. V Maenclochog w Llandeilo, Llanycefn, Henry's Moat *St D* 47-80; Hon Can St D Cathl 79-80; V Maenclochog w Henry's Moat and Mynachlogddu etc 79-80; rtd 80. *Bryngwyn, The Crescent, Narberth, Dyfed SA67 7DL* Narberth (01834) 860455

HAMER, Mrs Valerie Margaret. b 52. Leeds Univ BA74. S'wark Ord Course 83. **dss** 86 **d** 87 **p** 94. Warlingham w Chelsham and Farleigh *S'wark* 86-87; Par Dn 87-88; Par Dn Caterham 88-94; C from 94; RD Caterham from 95. *The Parsonage, 43 Banstead Road, Caterham, Surrey CR3 5QG* Caterham (01883) 342422

HAMERTON, Thomas Patrick. b 13. St Edm Hall Ox BA35 DipTh36 MA50. Cuddesdon Coll 37. **d** 38 **p** 39. R Abington *Pet* 63-76; V Welton w Ashby St Ledgers 76-83; rtd 83; Perm to Offic *Glouc* from 83. *Orchard Cottage, Paxford, Chipping Campden, Glos GL55 6XD* Paxford (0138678) 305

HAMEY, Geoffrey Allan. b 25. Lon Univ BSc47. S'wark Ord Course 75. **d** 78 **p** 79. NSM Pinner *Lon* 78-83; P-in-c Fincham *Ely* 83-84; P-in-c Marham 83-84; P-in-c Shouldham 83-84; P-in-c Shouldham Thorpe 83-84; V 84-88; rtd 88; Hon C Winkleigh *Ex* from 88. *4 East Park Close, Winkleigh, Devon EX19 8LG* Winkleigh (01837) 83455

HAMILL-STEWART, Simon Francis. b 32. Pemb Coll Cam BA56. N Ord Course 77. **d** 80 **p** 81. NSM Neston *Ches* 80-83; C 83-86; V Over St Jo from 86; Dioc Ecum Officer from 92. *St John's Vicarage, Delamere Street, Winsford, Cheshire CW7 2LY* Winsford (01606) 594651

✠**HAMILTON, Rt Rev Alexander Kenneth.** b 15. Trin Hall Cam BA37 MA41. Westcott Ho Cam 37. **d** 39 **p** 40 **c** 65. C Birstall *Leic* 39-41; C Whitworth w Spennymoor *Dur* 41-45; Chapl RNVR 45-47; V Bedminster St Fran *Bris* 47-58; V Newc St Jo *Newc* 58-65; RD Newc Cen 62-65; Suff Bp Jarrow *Dur* 65-80; rtd 80; Asst Bp B & W from 80. *3 Ash Tree Road, Burnham-on-Sea, Somerset TA8 2LB* Burnham (01628) 783823

HAMILTON, Andrew David. b 65. Chester Coll BA86 Liv Inst of Educn PGCE87. Oak Hill Th Coll BA92. **d** 92 **p** 93. C Necton w Holme Hale *Nor* 92-94; C Necton, Holme Hale w N and S Pickenham from 95. *21 Chantry Lane, Necton, Swaffham, Norfolk PE37 8ES* Swaffham (01760) 722694

HAMILTON, Canon Edgar Reid. b 27. TCD BA49 MA52. CITC 51. **d** 51 **p** 52. I Stormont *D & D* 64-93; RD Dundonald 77-93; Can Belf Cathl 85-91; Preb Wicklow St Patr Cathl Dub 90-93; rtd 93. *13 Massey Park, Belfast BT4 2JX* Belfast (01232) 763835

HAMILTON, Gerald Murray Percival. b 14. Ch Coll Cam BA37 MA41. Ridley Hall Cam 37. **d** 39 **p** 40. Prin Lect Coll of Ripon & York St Jo 67-79; R Crayke w Brandsby and Yearsley *York* 78-82; rtd 82. *Tanglewood Cottage, Newton-on-Ouse, York YO6 2BN* Linton-on-Ouse (01347) 848219

HAMILTON, Canon James. b 09. TCD BA31 MA35. **d** 32 **p** 33. I Ban Abbey *D & D* 41-79; Prec Down Cathl 68-79; rtd 79. *31 Bayview Road, Bangor, Co Down BT19 2AR* Bangor (01247) 465976

HAMILTON, Canon James. b 22. Dur Univ LTh48. Tyndale Hall Bris 41. **d** 49 **p** 50. V Eccleston Ch Ch *Liv* 66-87; Hon Can Liv Cathl 76-87; rtd 87. *6 Freckleton Road, St Helens, Merseyside WA10 3AW* St Helens (0744) 57716

HAMILTON, James Davy. b 20. Hatf Coll Dur 38. Edin Th Coll 40. **d** 43 **p** 45. R Sandford w Upton Hellions *Ex* 62-79; P-in-c

Ashprington 79-81; P-in-c Cornworthy 79-81; R Ashprington, Cornworthy and Dittisham 81-83; C Weymouth St Paul *Sarum* 83-85; rtd 85; Perm to Offic *Ex* from 85. *21 Langaton Lane, Pinhoe, Exeter EX1 3SP* Exeter (01392) 66747

HAMILTON, John Frederick. b 57. Leeds Univ BA78. Edin Th Coll 78. **d** 80 **p** 81. C Whitkirk *Ripon* 80-83; C Leeds Belle Is St Jo and St Barn 83-86; V Oulton w Woodlesford 86-94; V Cookridge H Trin from 94. *Holy Trinity Vicarage, 53 Green Lane, Cookridge, Leeds LS16 7LW* Leeds (0113) 267 4921

HAMILTON, John Hans Patrick. b 44. MBIM86 BD66 AKC67 DipAdEd76 DMS85. K Coll Lon 66. **d** 67 **p** 68. C Cleobury Mortimer w Hopton Wafers *Heref* 67-69; C Sanderstead All SS *S'wark* 69-73; V Battersea St Mary-le-Park 73-75; Dir of Educn *Derby* from 90. *31 Rectory Lane, Breadsall Village, Derby DE21 5LL* Derby (01332) 831663

HAMILTON, John Nicholas. b 49. Trin Coll Cam BA71 MA75. Ridley Hall Cam 72. **d** 75 **p** 76. C Ealing Dean St Jo *Lon* 75-79; C Stoughton *Guildf* 79-83; R Denton St Lawr *Man* 83-88; R The Sherbornes w Pamber *Win* from 88. *The Rectory, Sherborne St John, Basingstoke, Hants RG24 9HX* Basingstoke (01256) 850434

HAMILTON, Canon Noble Ridgeway. b 23. TD66. TCD BA45 MA49. **d** 47 **p** 48. I Seapatrick *D & D* 61-89; RD Aghaderg 64-88; Can Dromore Cathl 66-89; Prec 75-84; Chan 84-89; rtd 89; Lic to Offic *D & D* from 90. *67 Meadowvale, Waringstown, Craigavon, Co Armagh BT66 7RL* Waringstown (01762) 882064

HAMILTON, Richard Alexander. b 46. Pemb Coll Cam BA67 MA87. S Dios Minl Tr Scheme 82. **d** 85 **p** 86. NSM Guernsey St Sampson *Win* 85-89; C Highgate St Mich *Lon* 89-91; P-in-c Tottenham H Trin from 91. *Holy Trinity Vicarage, Philip Lane, London N15 4HZ* 0181-801 3021

HAMILTON, Robert Hair. b 26. Oak Hill Th Coll 75. **d** 76 **p** 77. C Bootle St Matt *Liv* 76-78; C Horwich H Trin *Man* 78-81; R Whalley Range St Marg 81-86; Perm to Offic *Ches* from 86; rtd 91. *The Leaves, 47 Statham Road, Birkenhead, Merseyside L43 7XS* 0151-653 7110

HAMILTON, Samuel Derek. b 34. Bris Univ BA58. Tyndale Hall Bris 54. **d** 59 **p** 60. Bp's C Sallaghy *Clogh* 79-83; rtd 83. *12 Cairnshill Court, Saintfield Road, Belfast BT8 4TX*

HAMILTON, William Graham. b 63. New Coll Ox BA86. Wycliffe Hall Ox BA95. **d** 95. C Ivybridge w Harford *Ex* from 95. *5 Orchard Court, Ivybridge, Devon PL21 9UB* Plymouth (01752) 893208

HAMILTON-BROWN, James John (Jimmy). b 35. Lon Univ BSc59. Trin Coll Bris ADipTh90 Ridley Hall Cam 59. **d** 61 **p** 62. C Attenborough w Bramcote *S'well* 61-67; V Bramcote 67-76; R and D Officer Abps' Coun on Evang 76-79; Lic to Offic *Sarum* 76-81; TR Dorchester 81-91; Sec Par and People 91-95; P-in-c Tarrant Valley from 95. *The Old Mill, Spetisbury, Blandford Forum, Dorset DT11 9DF* Blandford (01258) 453939

HAMILTON-MANON, Phillip Robert Christian. b 49. BA88. St Steph Ho Ox 89. **d** 90 **p** 91. C Norton St Mary *Dur* 90-94; P-in-c Cleadon Park from 94. *St Cuthbert's Vicarage, 218 Sunderland Road, South Shields, Tyne & Wear NE34 6AT* 0191-456 0091

HAMLET, Paul Manning. b 42. MCollP Open Univ BA81. Lambeth STh84 Kelham Th Coll 61. **d** 66 **p** 67. C Rumboldswyke *Chich* 66-69; C Ely 69-73; Hon C Ipswich St Bart *St E* 73-84; Chapl Wellington Sch Somerset 84-94; CF(TAVR) from 88; Chapl Ipswich Sch from 94. *Ipswich School, 25 Henley Road, Ipswich IP1 3SG* Ipswich (01473) 255313

HAMLYN, Canon Eric Crawford. b 37. Dur Univ BA60 MA91. Cranmer Hall Dur DipTh62. **d** 62 **p** 63. C Bushbury *Lich* 62-64; C Whitchurch 64-67; V Burslem St Paul 67-72; V Stafford St Paul Forebridge 72-77; V Trentham 77-85; TR Mildenhall *St E* 85-89; P-in-c Boxford 89-91; R from 91; Clergy Tr Officer from 89; Hon Can St E Cathl from 91. *The Rectory, Boxford, Colchester CO6 5JT* Boxford (01787) 210191

HAMMERSLEY, John Goodwin. b 34. Keble Coll Ox BA57 MA60. Westcott Ho Cam 57. **d** 60 **p** 61. C Sheff St Swithun *Sheff* 60-67; Sec Par and People 67-70; P-in-c Linc St Mary-le-Wigford w St Benedict etc *Linc* 70-78; C Tettenhall Regis *Lich* 78-80; TV 80-87; Preb Lich Cathl 81-87; Chapl Metro Cen Gateshead *Dur* 87-94; RD Gateshead W 88-93; TV Langley Marish *Ox* from 94; Dir Thamesway Progr from 94. *Saint Mary's Vicarage, 180 Langley Road, Slough SL3 7EE* Slough (01753) 546659

HAMMERSLEY, Peter. b 41. Lon Univ BD78 Birm Univ MEd87. Kelham Th Coll 60. **d** 65 **p** 66. C Oadby *Leic* 65-69; Jamaica 70-77; Min Can Worc Cathl *Worc* 77-84; Chapl and Hd RE K Sch Worc 77-84; V Foley Park 84-90; TV Kidderminster St Jo and H Innocents 90-91; Vice-Prin Aston Tr Scheme from 91; Warden of Readers *Worc* from 91.

52 Hanbury Road, Droitwich, Worcs WR9 8PD Droitwich (01905) 776197

HAMMERSLEY, Peter Angus Ragsdale. b 35. Linc Th Coll 74. **d** 76 **p** 77. C Stafford *Lich* 76-79; P-in-c W Bromwich St Andr 79-83; V 83-88; P-in-c W Bromwich Ch Ch 85-88; V Streetly from 88; RD Walsall from 90. *The Vicarage, 2 Foley Church Close, Sutton Coldfield, W Midlands B74 3JX* 0121-353 2292

HAMMERTON, Canon Howard Jaggar. b 14. Man Univ BA36 Leeds Univ MA44. Ridley Hall Cam 36. **d** 38 **p** 39. Hon Can Ripon Cathl *Ripon* 63-81; V Leeds H Trin 65-81; rtd 81. *Flat 4, Bramhope Manor, Moor Road, Bramhope, Leeds LS16 9HJ* Leeds (0113) 284 2142

HAMMETT, Barry Keith. b 47. Magd Coll Ox BA71 MA74. St Steph Ho Ox 71. **d** 74 **p** 75. C Plymouth St Pet *Ex* 74-77; Chapl RN 77-86; Staff Chapl to Chapl of The Fleet from 86. *Directorate Gen, RN Chapl Services, Room 203, Victory Building, HM Naval Base, Portsmouth PO1 3LS* Portsmouth (01705) 727903 Fax 727112

HAMMOND, Mrs Barbara Watson. b 33. ACP70 Lanc Univ MA79. Bp Otter Coll TCert53 S'wark Ord Course DipRS92. **d** 92 **p** 94. NSM Upper Norwood St Jo *S'wark* 92-94; Hon C Spring Park All SS from 94. *All Saints' Vicarage, 1 Farm Drive, Croydon CR0 8HX* 0181-777 4447

HAMMOND, Canon Betty Marian. b 27. Gilmore Ho. dss 84 **d** 87 **p** 94. Gosport Ch Ch *Portsm* 84-87; C 87-93; Par Dn 93-94; C from 94; Hon Can Portsm Cathl from 92. *10 Alvara Road, Gosport, Hants PO12 2HY* Gosport (01705) 583068

HAMMOND, Canon Brian Leonard. b 27. Wells Th Coll BSc54. Wells Th Coll 56. **d** 58 **p** 59. C Clapham H Trin *S'wark* 58-62; V Walworth All SS and St Steph 62-72; V S Merstham 72-87; RD Reigate 80-86; Hon Can S'wark Cathl from 83; V Spring Park All SS from 87. *All Saints' Vicarage, 1 Farm Drive, Croydon CR0 8HX* 0181-777 4447

HAMMOND, Charles Kemble. b 10. TCD BA33 MA37. TCD Div Sch Div Test33. **d** 34 **p** 35. C Willowfield *D & D* 35-37; C Belf St Donard 37; Australia from 37. *36 William Street, Avalon Beach, NSW, Australia 2107* Sydney (2) 918-8025

HAMMOND, Eric Penharwood. b 08. St Chad's Coll Dur BA31 DipTh32 MA47. **d** 32 **p** 33. V Mickleton *Glouc* 52-74; rtd 74. *St Francis, Outlands Lane, Curdridge, Southampton SO3 2HD* Botley (01489) 783324

HAMMOND, Frank. b 49. Linc Th Coll 75. **d** 77 **p** 78. C Sutton *Liv* 77-79; C Blundellsands St Nic 80-83. *13 Leicester Avenue, Crosby, Liverpool L22 2BA*

HAMMOND, James Francis. b 48. CITC 69. **d** 72 **p** 73. C Dub St Bart w Ch Ch Leeson Park *D & G* 72-76; C Monkstown 76-79; I Dunboyne w Kilcock, Maynooth, Moyglare etc *M & K* 79-87; I Holmpatrick w Balbriggan and Kenure *D & G* 87-94; I Dub Ch Ch Cathl Gp 94. *4 Northbrook Villas, Ranelagh, Dublin 6, Irish Republic*

HAMMOND, Lindsay John. b 57. Southn Univ BA83. Sarum & Wells Th Coll 84. **d** 86 **p** 87. C Ashford *Cant* 86-90; V Appledore w Brookland, Fairfield, Brenzett etc from 90; P-in-c Wittersham w Stone-in-Oxney and Ebony from 95; RD S Lympne from 95. *The Vicarage, Appledore, Ashford, Kent TN26 2DB* Appledore (01233) 758250

HAMMOND, Mary. b 15. St Aid Coll Dur BA51 Maria Grey Coll Lon CertEd52. Roch and S'wark Dss Ho 40. dss 43 **d** 87. Australia 68-73; Abp Langton Sch Beare Green 73-75; rtd 75; Perm to Offic *Linc* 75-87; Perm to Offic *Win* 87-89. *26 St Martin's Court, Kingston Crescent, Ashford, Middx TW15 3NB* Ashford (01784) 244398

HAMMOND, Canon Peter. b 21. Mert Coll Ox BA48 MA53 Salonica Univ 48. Cuddesdon Coll 50. **d** 51 **p** 52. R Bagendon *Glouc* 56-61; Lic to Offic *York* 62-83; Perm to Offic *Linc* 83-87; Can and Preb Linc Cathl from 87; rtd 90. *Flat 2, 2 Greestone Place, Lincoln LN2 1PP* Lincoln (01522) 543047

HAMMOND, Peter Clark. b 27. Linc Coll Ox BA49 MA53. Wells Th Coll 51. **d** 52 **p** 53. V Walmer *Cant* 66-85; V Rolvenden 85-89; rtd 89. *19 Hardwick Street, Cambridge CB3 9JA* Cambridge (01223) 467425

HAMNETT, Herbert Arnold. b 22. K Coll Lon BSc49. Qu Coll Birm 49. **d** 51 **p** 52. R Yapton w Ford *Chich* 60-87; rtd 87; Perm to Offic *St E* from 87. *Clarence House, Stradbrooke Road, Fressingfield, Eye, Suffolk IP21 5PP*

HAMPEL, Michael Hans Joachim. b 67. Univ Coll Dur BA89. Westcott Ho Cam CTMin93. **d** 93 **p** 94. C Whitworth w Spennymoor *Dur* from 93. *10 Merrington Close, Kirk Merrington, Spennymoor, Co Durham DL16 7HU* Spennymoor (01388) 815061

HAMPSON, David. b 46. Chich Th Coll 69. **d** 72 **p** 73. C Penrith *Carl* 72-78; V Crosscrake 78-95; V Crosscrake and Preston Patrick 95; P-in-c Arnside from 95. *The Vicarage, Church Hill, Arnside, Carnforth, Lancs LA5 0DW* Arnside (01524) 761319

HAMPSON, Miss Judith Elizabeth. b 50. I M Marsh Coll of Physical Educn Liv BEd72 Open Univ BA89. Ripon Coll Cuddesdon 90. **d** 92 **p** 94. C Alnwick St Mich and St Paul *Newc* from 92. *The Old School House, Green Batt, Alnwick, Northd NE66 1TU* Alnwick (01665) 602070

HAMPSON, Michael John. b 67. Jes Coll Ox BA88. Ripon Coll Cuddesdon 88. **d** 91 **p** 92. C W Burnley *Blackb* 91-93; C Harlow St Mary Magd *Chelmsf* from 93. *39 Hadley Grange, Church Langley, Harlow, Essex CM17 9PQ* Harlow (01279) 451382

HAMPSTEAD, Archdeacon of. *See* WHEATLEY, Ven Peter William

HAMPTON, Canon John Waller. b 28. Linc Coll Ox BA51 MA58. Westcott Ho Cam 51. **d** 53 **p** 54. Asst Dir RE *Cov* 65-70; C-in-c Warw St Nic 69-75; Fell Qu Coll Birm 75-76; P-in-c Wetton *Lich* 76-82; P-in-c Alstonfield 76-82; P-in-c Sheen 76-80; RD Alstonfield 80-82; P-in-c Butterton 80-82; P-in-c Warslow and Elkstones 80-82; P-in-c Broadway *Worc* 82-91; V 91-93; RD Evesham 87-93; Hon Can Worc Cathl 88-93; rtd 93. *41 Craigton Terrace, Aberdeen AB1 7RN* Aberdeen (01224) 310074

HAMPTON, Terence Alastair Godfrey Macpherson. b 38. Bris Univ PGCE73. Lon Coll of Div ALCD63 BD68. **d** 64 **p** 65. C Clifton Ch Ch w Em *Bris* 64-66; C Ickenham *Lon* 66-67; C Patchway *Bris* 67-73; TV Jersey St Brelade *Win* 73-83; R Jersey Grouville 83-94. *The Rectory, Grouville, Jersey, Channel Islands* Jersey (01534) 853073

HAMPTON-SMITH, David Charles. b 22. Ch Ch Ox BA48 MA48. Cuddesdon Coll 48. **d** 50 **p** 51. Chapl Woodbridge Sch Suffolk 62-65; Australia from 65; rtd 87. *139 Esplanade, Port Noarlunga South, S Australia 5167* Adelaide (8) 386-1284

HANCE, Stephen John. b 66. Portsm Poly BSc89 Nottm Univ BTh92 MA93. St Jo Coll Nottm 90. **d** 93 **p** 94. C Southsea St Jude *Portsm* from 93. *92 Marmion Road, Southsea, Hants PO5 2BB* Portsmouth (01705) 874278

HANCOCK, Alfred John. b 28. Lon Univ BSc52. Ex & Truro NSM Scheme 74. **d** 77 **p** 78. NSM Phillack w Gwithian and Gwinear *Truro* 77-78 and from 86; NSM Camborne 78-86. *Redlands, Rosewarne Downs, Camborne, Cornwall TR14 0BD* Camborne (01209) 713527

HANCOCK, Bernard. b 13. Wycliffe Hall Ox 61. **d** 62 **p** 63. R Peopleton *Worc* 65-70; R Hagley 70-76; rtd 78. *The Old Post Office, Birlingham, Pershore, Worcs WR10 3AB* Evesham (01386) 750641

HANCOCK, Dr Christopher David. b 54. Qu Coll Ox BA75 MA80 St Jo Coll Dur PhD84. Cranmer Hall Dur BA78. **d** 82 **p** 83. C Leic H Trin w St Jo *Leic* 82-85; Chapl Magd Coll Cam 85-88; USA 88-94; V Cam H Trin *Ely* from 94. *Holy Trinity Vicarage, 1 Selwyn Gardens, Cambridge CB3 0XG* Cambridge (01223) 354774

HANCOCK, David Richard. b 48. Chich Th Coll. **d** 89 **p** 90. C Maidstone All SS and St Phil w Tovil *Cant* 89-93; CF 90-93; P-in-c Sellindge w Monks Horton and Stowting etc *Cant* from 93. *The Vicarage, Harringe Lane, Sellindge, Ashford, Kent TN25 6HP* Sellindge (01303) 813168

HANCOCK, Douglas Charles. b 16. Lon Univ BSc39 PhD52. Wycliffe Hall Ox 59. **d** 60 **p** 61. R Baughurst w Ramsdale *Win* 64-70; V Bournemouth St Andr 70-79; RD Alresford 79-84; R Hinton Ampner w Bramdean and Kilmeston 79-84; rtd 84; Perm to Offic *Win* from 84; Perm to Offic *Sarum* from 86. *Flat 40, Fairhaven Court, 32/34 Sea Road, Bournemouth BH5 1DG* Bournemouth (01202) 301942

HANCOCK, Mrs Frances Margaret. b 34. LMH Ox BA56 MA94 LSE DipPM57. Gilmore Course IDC81. **dss** 81 **d** 87 **p** 94. Isleworth All SS *Lon* 81-87; TD Ross w Brampton Abbotts, Bridstow and Peterstow *Heref* 87-93; Dioc Adv on Women in Min from 93; NSM Peterchurch w Vowchurch, Turnastone and Dorstone from 93; rtd 94. *Brockwell, Peterchurch, Hereford HR2 0TE* Golden Valley (01981) 550457

HANCOCK, Ivor Michael. b 31. Lon Univ BD60. Linc Th Coll 65. **d** 66 **p** 67. C Havant *Portsm* 66-69; V Gosport Ch Ch 69-76; P-in-c Southend St Alb *Chelmsf* 76-80; V Hawley H Trin *Guildf* from 80; V Minley from 80; RD Aldershot 83-88. *The Vicarage, Hawley, Blackwater, Camberley, Surrey GU17 9BN* Camberley (01276) 35287

HANCOCK, John Clayton. b 36. Dur Univ BA58. Cranmer Hall Dur DipTh60. **d** 60 **p** 61. C Newbarns w Hawcoat *Carl* 60-65; V Church Coniston 65-76; R Torver 66-76; P-in-c Heversham 76-77; V 77-93; V Heversham and Milnthorpe from 93. *The Vicarage, Woodhouse Lane, Heversham, Milnthorpe, Cumbria LA7 7EW* Milnthorpe (015395) 63125

HANCOCK, Canon John Mervyn. b 38. St Jo Coll Dur BA61 DipTh64 MA70 Hertf Coll Ox BA63 MA66. Cranmer Hall Dur 63. **d** 64 **p** 65. C Bishopwearmouth St Gabr *Dur* 64-67; V Hebburn St Jo 67-87; RD Jarrow 83-92; V S Westoe from 87; Hon Can Dur Cathl from 88. *St Michael's Vicarage, Westoe Road, South Shields, Tyne & Wear NE33 3PJ* 0191-455 2132

HANCOCK, John Raymond. b 11. FBOA32. **d** 62 **p** 63. R Guernsey St Michel du Valle *Win* 65-79; rtd 79; Perm to Offic *Portsm* from 82. *Kingsomborne, The Broadway, Totland Bay, Isle of Wight PO39 0BL* Isle of Wight (01983) 754321

HANCOCK, Leonard George Edward. b 28. Open Univ BA81 Leic Univ MEd84. ALCD52. **d** 52 **p** 56. V Sheff St Mary w St Simon w St Matthias *Sheff* 63-72; V Michael *S & M* 72-76; R Loughb All SS *Leic* 76-83; R Loughb All SS and H Trin 83-93; rtd 93. *5 Rumsey Close, Quorn, Loughborough, Leics LE12 8EZ* Loughborough (01509) 620012

HANCOCK, Malcolm James. b 50. AGSM73. Sarum & Wells Th Coll 85. **d** 87 **p** 88. C Sandhurst *Ox* 87-90; P-in-c Bradbourne and Brassington *Derby* 90-92; TV Wirksworth 92-95; V Tunbridge Wells K Chas from 95. *King Charles Vicarage, 5D Frant Road, Tunbridge Wells, Kent TN2 5TA* Tunbridge Wells (01892) 525455

HANCOCK, Ms Mary Joy. b 40. Auckland Univ BA61 Auckland Teachers' Coll PGCE62 Man Univ CQSW69. S'wark Ord Course 91. **d** 94. NSM Mert St Mary *S'wark* from 94. *55 Huntspill Street, London SW17 0AA* 0181-946 8984

HANCOCK, Michael John. b 33. Lich Th Coll 55. **d** 58 **p** 59. C Romsey *Win* 69-72; C Moordown 72-75; C Christchurch 75-78; V Guernsey St Jo 78-89; rtd 89. *10 la rue du Tertre, Vale, Guernsey, Channel Islands* Guernsey (01481) 48887

HANCOCK, Nigel John. b 35. K Coll Cam BA63 MA67. E Anglian Minl Tr Course 86. **d** 89 **p** 91. NSM Cam St Mary Less *Ely* from 89; PV St Jo Coll Cam from 95. *5 Atherton Close, Cambridge CB4 2BE* Cambridge (01223) 355828

HANCOCK, Paul. b 43. AKC66. **d** 67 **p** 68. C Wednesbury St Paul Wood Green *Lich* 67-70; C Rugeley 70-73; V Rickerscote 73-75; R Blisland w St Breward *Truro* 75-78; V Mansf St Lawr *S'well* 78-82; P-in-c Charleton *Ex* 82-83; P-in-c E Portlemouth, S Pool and Chivelstone 82-83; R Charleton w Buckland Tout Saints etc 83-95; RD Woodleigh from 88; P-in-c Plymouth Crownhill Ascension from 95. *The Vicarage, 33 Tavistock Road, Plymouth PL5 3AF* Plymouth (01752) 783617

HANCOCK, Paul Byron. b 51. Bris Univ BA71 MA73. Ripon Hall Ox 72. **d** 75 **p** 76. C Croydon *Cant* 75-78; USA from 78. *3200 Woodland Ridge Boulevard, Baton Rouge, Louisiana 70816, USA*

HANCOCK, Peter. b 55. Selw Coll Cam BA76 MA79. Oak Hill Th Coll BA80. **d** 80 **p** 81. C Portsdown *Portsm* 80-83; C Radipole and Melcombe Regis *Sarum* 83-87; V Cowplain *Portsm* from 87; RD Havant from 93. *The Vicarage, Padnell Road, Cowplain, Waterlooville, Hants PO8 8DZ* Waterlooville (01705) 262295

HANCOCK, Peter Ernest. b 33. Man Univ BA54. Qu Coll Birm 54. **d** 56 **p** 57. Dioc Youth Officer *Portsm* 65-73; R Broughton Astley *Leic* 73-86; Dioc Adv for Min of Health and Healing *B & W* 86-93; rtd 94. *24 Mulberry Road, Congresbury, Bristol BS19 5HD* Yatton (01934) 838920

HANCOCK, Peter Thompson. b 31. G&C Coll Cam BA54 MA58. Ridley Hall Cam 54. **d** 56 **p** 57. Asst Chapl and Lect Emb Ch Paris *Eur* 67-70; V Walton H Trin *Ox* 70-80; Canada 80-84; V Northwood H Trin *Lon* 84-94; rtd 94. *Roughwood Oak, Deadhearn Lane, Chalfont St Giles, Bucks HP8 4HG* Chalfont St Giles (01494) 872324

HANCOCK, Reginald Legassicke (Rex). b 28. Trin Coll Cam BA51 MA57. Clifton Th Coll 60. **d** 61 **p** 62. CF 63-82; R Quantoxhead *B & W* 82-93; rtd 93; Perm to Offic *B & W* from 94. *Stowleys, Bossinton Lane, Porlock, Minehead, Somerset TA24 8HD* Porlock (01643) 862327

HANCOCK, Ronald Edward. b 24. MRCS49 LRCP49. **d** 78 **p** 79. Hon C Highbury Ch Ch *Lon* 78; Hon C Highbury Ch Ch w St Jo 79-82; R Puddletown and Tolpuddle *Sarum* 82-90; rtd 90. *9 Churchward Avenue, Weymouth, Dorset DT3 6NZ* Preston (01305) 832558

HANCOCKS, Graeme. b 58. Univ of Wales (Ban) BD79. Linc Th Coll 79. **d** 81 **p** 82. C Denbigh and Nantglyn *St As* 81-84; Asst Chapl Oslo St Edm *Eur* 84-88; Chapl Stockholm w Gavle and Vasteras 89-90; Chapl Marseille 89-90; Chapl Gothenburg w Halmstad, Jonkoping etc 90-93; Chapl R S Hants Hosp from 93; Chapl Countess Mountbatten Hospice from 93. *Royal South Hants Hospital, Graham Road, Southampton S09 4PE* Southampton (01703) 634288

HANCOX, Granville Leonard. b 32. Lich Th Coll 67. **d** 70 **p** 71. C Caverswall *Lich* 70-73; C Norton in the Moors 73-76; P-in-c Leek St Luke 76-79; TV Leek 79-83; V Priors Lee and St Georges from 83. *The Vicarage, Ashley Road, Telford, Shropshire TF2 9LF* Telford (01952) 612923

✠HAND, Most Rev Geoffrey David. b 18. CBE75. Or Coll Ox BA41 MA46. Cuddesdon Coll 40. **d** 42 **p** 43 **c** 50. C Heckmondwike *Wakef* 42-46; Papua New Guinea 46-83; Bp Coadjutor New Guinea 50-63; Adn N New Guinea 50-63; Bp Papua New Guinea 63-77; Abp Papua New Guinea 77-83; Bp Port Moresby 77-83; rtd 83; P-in-c E w W Rudham *Nor* 83-85;

HAND

P-in-c Houghton 83-85. *121 Brackenbury Road, London W6 0BQ*

HAND, Michael Anthony (Tony). b 63. SROT York Univ BA84 DipCOT88. St Jo Coll Nottm MA95. **d** 95. C Lutterworth w Cotesbach *Leic* from 95. *3 Poplar Avenue, Lutterworth, Leics LE17 4TH* Lutterworth (01455) 552443

HAND, Nigel Arthur. b 54. St Jo Coll Nottm. **d** 84 **p** 85. C Birm St Luke *Birm* 84-88; C Walton H Trin *Ox* 88-89; TV from 89. *24 Como Road, Aylesbury, Bucks HP20 1NR* Aylesbury (01296) 85990

HAND, Peter Michael. b 42. Univ Coll Ox BA63 Lon Univ BSc75. Sarum & Wells Th Coll 77. **d** 80 **p** 81. NSM Shaston *Sarum* 80-81; C Tisbury 81-83; C Glastonbury St Jo w Godney *B & W* 83-84; C Glastonbury w Meare, W Pennard and Godney 84-87; V High Littleton from 87; RD Midsomer Norton from 92. *The Vicarage, High Littleton, Bristol BS18 5HG* Timsbury (01761) 472097

✠**HANDFORD, Rt Rev George Clive.** b 37. Hatf Coll Dur BA61. Qu Coll Birm DipTh63. **d** 63 **p** 64 **c** 90. C Mansf St Pet *S'well* 63-67; Lebanon 67-74; Dean Jerusalem 74-78; UAE 78-83; Adn Gulf 78-83; RD Tuxford and Norwell *S'well* 83-84; V Kneesall w Laxton 83-84; P-in-c Wellow 83-84; Adn Nottm 84-90; Suff Bp Warw *Cov* from 90. *Warwick House, 139 Kenilworth Road, Coventry CV4 7AF* Coventry (01203) 416200 Fax 415254

HANDFORD, John Richard. b 32. Sydney Univ BSc52 Univ Coll Lon MSc58 Surrey Univ MA84 Lon Univ DipTh67. Lon Coll of Div 68. **d** 69 **p** 70. Asst Chapl Wellington Coll Berks 69-80; Hon C Windlesham *Guildf* 87-92; Perm to Offic from 92. *Desiderata, 33 Chertsey Road, Windlesham, Surrey GU20 6EW* Bagshot (01276) 472397

HANDFORD, Maurice. b 25. Oak Hill Th Coll 48. **d** 52 **p** 53. C-in-c Buxton Trin Prop Chpl *Derby* 58-87; I Clondevaddock w Portsalon and Leatbeg *D & R* 87-90; Bp's Dom Chapl 88-90; rtd 90; Perm to Offic *Ches* from 90. *9 Birtlespool Road, Cheadle Hulme, Cheadle, Cheshire SK8 5JZ* 0161-485 3138

HANDFORTH, Richard Brereton. b 31. St Pet Coll Ox BA55 MA60. Westcott Ho Cam 63. **d** 64 **p** 65. C Hornchurch St Andr *Chelmsf* 64-65; Hong Kong 65-73; Chapl CMS Fellowship Ho Chislehurst 73-75; Hon C Chislehurst St Nic *Roch* 73-75; Home Educn Sec CMS 75-83; Lic to Offic *Roch* 76-83; V Biggin Hill 83-88; Inter-change Adv CMS from 88. *67 Murray Avenue, Bromley BR1 3DJ* 0181-460 0238 or 0171-928 8681 Fax 0171-401 3215

HANDLEY, Ven Anthony Michael. b 36. Selw Coll Cam BA60 MA64. Chich Th Coll 60. **d** 62 **p** 63. C Thorpe *Nor* 62-66; C Gaywood, Bawsey and Mintlyn 66-72; V Hellesdon 72-81; RD Nor N 80-81; Adn Nor 81-93; Adn Norfolk from 93. *40 Heigham Road, Norwich NR2 3AU* Norwich (01603) 611808

HANDLEY, Dennis Francis. b 57. MIE79 TEng(CEI)80. Coll of Resurr Mirfield 82. **d** 85 **p** 86. C Headingley *Ripon* 85-88; C Rothwell 88-92; V Liversedge *Wakef* from 92. *Christ Church Vicarage, Knowler Hill, Liversedge, W Yorkshire WF15 6LJ* Heckmondwike (01924) 402414

HANDLEY, Harold. b 14. ACIS42 AACCA44 ACWA48. Bps' Coll Cheshunt 62. **d** 63 **p** 64. V Totternhoe *St Alb* 65-79; C Ringwood *Win* 79-80; rtd 79; Perm to Offic *Win* from 80. *Risdene, 16 Barton Court Avenue, New Milton, Hants BH25 7HD* New Milton (01425) 611771

HANDLEY, John. b 38. Oak Hill Th Coll. **d** 83 **p** 84. C Witton w Brundall and Braydeston *Nor* 83-86; R Reedham w Cantley w Limpenhoe and Southwood 86-93; P-in-c E w W Harling and Bridgham w Roudham from 93; P-in-c Garboldisham w Blo' Norton, Riddlesworth etc from 94. *The Rectory, East Harling, Norwich NR16 2NB* East Harling (01953) 717235

HANDLEY, Neil. b 40. St Aid Birkenhead 64. **d** 67 **p** 68. C Ashton Ch Ch *Man* 67-70; C Stretford All SS 70-73; C Tonge 73; C-in-c Bolton St Jo Breightmet CD 74-79; V Bolton St Jo 79-80; R Broughton 80-87; Perm to Offic *Eur* from 90. *La Taire du Grel, 24250 Domme, France* France (33) 53 28 23 42

HANDLEY, Terence Anthony. b 55. Trent Poly HNC Open Univ BA89. Trin Coll Bris 85. **d** 87 **p** 88. C Meole Brace *Lich* 87-91; V Stafford St Paul Forebridge 91-94. *Address temp unknown*

HANDLEY MACMATH, Terence. b 59. Golds Coll Lon BA80 K Coll Cam BA93. Westcott Ho Cam 91. **d** 94 **p** 95. NSM Southwold *St E* from 94. *Manor Garden Cottage, Woodley's Yard, Southwold, Suffolk IP18 6HP* Southwold (01502) 722153

HANDS, Graeme. b 35. Cranmer Hall Dur. **d** 61 **p** 62. C Atherstone *Cov* 61-63; Chapl Aldwickbury Sch Harpenden 63-66; C Cov St Alb *Cov* 66-68; P-in-c Warw St Paul 68-80; V Radford from 80; RD Cov N 87-93. *The Vicarage, 21 Tulliver Street, Coventry CV6 3BY* Coventry (01203) 598449

HANDSCOMBE, Canon Richard John. b 23. Cuddesdon Coll 58. **d** 60 **p** 61. C Shrub End *Chelmsf* 60-63; V Fingringhoe 63-86; P-in-c E Donyland 75-77; R Fingringhoe w E Donyland 86-90; R Fingringhoe w E Donyland and Abberton etc from 90; Hon Can Chelmsf Cathl from 89. *The Rectory, Fingringhoe, Colchester CO5 7BN* Rowhedge (01206) 729383

HANDY, Canon Maurice Arthur. b 04. TCD BA26 MA34. **d** 27 **p** 28. C An Ch Ch Cathl Dub *D & G* 63-72; Warden of Ch's Min of Healing in Ireland 65-72; I Hacketstown *C & O* 72-76; rtd 76. *Rathfarnham Convalescent Home, Stocking Lane, Rathfarnham, Dublin 16, Irish Republic* Dublin (1) 493-3166

HANFORD, Canon William Richard. b 38. Keble Coll Ox BA60 MA64 Lon Univ BD66. St Steph Ho Ox 60. **d** 63 **p** 64. C Roath St Martin *Llan* 63-66; C Llantwit Major 67-68; PV Llan Cathl 68-72; Chapl RN 72-76; Lic to Offic *Eur* 74-76; Hon C Eastbourne St Sav and St Pet *Chich* 76-77; C Brighton St Pet 77-78; Can Res and Prec Guildf Cathl *Guildf* 78-83; V Ewell from 83. *St Mary's Vicarage, 14 Church Street, Ewell, Epsom, Surrey KT17 2AQ* 0181-393 2643

HANKE, Mrs Hilary Claire. b 53. Qu Coll Birm BTh93. **d** 93 **p** 94. C Kempsey and Severn Stoke w Croome d'Abitot *Worc* from 93. *14 Napleton Lane, Kempsey, Worcester WR5 3PT* Worcester (01905) 821381

HANKEY, Miss Dorothy Mary. b 38. CertEd65. Trin Coll Bris 75. **dss** 78 **d** 87 **p** 94. Wigan St Jas w St Thos *Liv* 78-84; Middleton *Man* 84-85; Litherland Ch Ch *Liv* 85-87; Par Dn 87-89; Par Dn Blackpool St Mark *Blackb* 89-94; C from 94. *2 St Mark's Place, Blackpool FY3 7HR* Blackpool (01253) 397735

HANKINS, Clifford James. b 24. Chich Th Coll 70 SSC87. **d** 72 **p** 73. C Henfield *Chich* 72-76; V Fernhurst 76-84; V Mithian w Mt Hawke *Truro* 84-89; rtd 89; Hon C W Wittering and Birdham w Itchenor *Chich* from 90. *2 Kestrel Close, East Wittering, Chichester, W Sussex PO20 8PQ* Bracklesham Bay (01243) 672164

HANMER, Canon Richard John. b 38. Peterho Cam BA61 MA65. Linc Th Coll 62. **d** 64 **p** 65. C Sheff St Swithun *Sheff* 64-69; Bp's Chapl *Nor* 69-73; V Cinderhill *S'well* 73-81; V Eaton *Nor* 81-94; Dioc Chapl MU from 91; Hon Can Nor Cathl from 93; Can Res Nor Cathl from 94. *52 The Close, Norwich NR1 4EG* Norwich (01603) 665210

HANNA, John. b 44. Trin Coll Bris DipHE82 Lon Bible Coll BA83 Westcott Ho Cam 86. **d** 87 **p** 88. C Denton Ch Ch *Man* 87-91; V Higher Walton *Blackb* from 91. *The Vicarage, Blackburn Road, Higher Walton, Preston PR5 4EA* Preston (01772) 35406

HANNA, Peter Thomas. b 45. ACII66 GIFireE75. CITC 85. **d** 88 **p** 89. NSM Cork St Fin Barre's Union *C, C & R* 88-95; Min Can Cork Cathl from 92; Dio Info Officer 94-95. *Mount Windsor, Farnahoe, Inishannon, Co Cork, Irish Republic* Cork (21) 775470

HANNA, Canon Robert Charles. b 49. Oak Hill Th Coll 75. **d** 77 **p** 78. C Coleraine *Conn* 77-82; I Convoy w Monellan and Donaghmore *D & R* 82-94; Can Raphoe Cathl 88-94; I Drumcliffe w Kilnasoolagh *L & K* from 94. *St Columba's Rectory, Bindon Street, Ennis, Co Clare, Irish Republic* Ennis (65) 20109

HANNAFORD, Dr Robert. b 53. Ex Univ BEd76 MA78 PhD87. St Steph Ho Ox 78. **d** 80 **p** 81. C Ex St Jas *Ex* 80-83; Chapl Ex Univ 83-88; Tutor St Steph Ho Ox 89-92; Sen Lect Ch Ch Coll Cant from 92. *25 Goudhurst Close, Canterbury, Kent CT2 7TU* Canterbury (01227) 784148

HANNAH, John Douglas. b 39. St Paul's Grahamstown DipTh71. **d** 71 **p** 72. S Africa 71-85; C Finchley St Mary *Lon* 85-91; V Balsall Heath St Paul *Birm* from 91. *The Vicarage, 26 Lincoln Street, Balsall Heath, Birmingham B12 9EX* 0121-440 2219

HANNAH, Richard. b 24. CCC Ox BA49 MA53. St Mich Coll Llan 49. **d** 51 **p** 52. R Shenington and Alkerton w Shutford *Ox* 69-79; RD Deddington 78-84; P-in-c Deddington w Clifton and Hempton 79-80; V Deddington w Barford, Clifton and Hempton 81-89; rtd 89. *Cwm Brynnau, Riverside, Llyswen, Brecon, Powys LD3 0LJ* Llyswen (01874) 754716

HANNAY, Robert Fleming. b 23. Ch Ch Ox MA49. Cuddesdon Coll 63. **d** 65 **p** 66. R Garsington *Ox* 69-79; R The Claydons 79-85; rtd 88. *The Old Rectory, Yatesbury, Calne, Wilts SN11 8YE* Calne (01249) 817311

HANNEN, Robert John. b 65. W Glam Inst of HE DipHE87 BEd89. St Mich Coll Llan DipTh91 BTh92. **d** 92 **p** 93. C Gorseinon *S & B* 92-95; P-in-c Cwmbwrla from 95. *St Luke's Rectory, 8 Vicarage Lane, Cwmdu, Swansea SA5 8EU* Swansea (01792) 586300

✠**HANNON, Rt Rev Brian Desmond Anthony.** b 36. TCD BA59 MA62. TCD Div Sch Div Test61. **d** 61 **p** 62 **c** 86. C Clooney *D & R* 61-64; I Desertmartin 64-69; I Londonderry Ch Ch 69-82; RD Londonderry 77-82; I Enniskillen *Clogh* 82-86; Preb Clogh Cathl 82-84; Dean Clogh 85-86; Bp Clogh from 86. *The See House, Fivemiletown, Co Tyrone BT75 0QP* Fivemiletown (013655) 21265 Fax as telephone

HANSCOMBE, Derek George. b 33. Chich Th Coll 60. **d** 62 **p** 63. C Illingworth *Wakef* 62-68; Youth Chapl *Lich* 68-74; V

Coseley St Chad 74-78; USPG from 78; Tutor Coll of the Ascension Selly Oak from 78. *5 St Michael's Close, Madeley, Telford, Shropshire TF7 5SD* Telford (01952) 580706 Fax 0121-472 4320

HANSEN, Harold Percy. b 05. St Chad's Coll Dur BA29 DipTh30 MA32. **d** 30 **p** 31. V Shefford *St Alb* 66-70; R Campton 66-70; rtd 70. *Moorlands, Moor Road, Cotherstone, Barnard Castle, Co Durham DL12 9PH* Teesdale (01833) 650726

HANSEN, Mrs Moira Jacqueline. b 55. K Coll Lon BSc76. Oak Hill Th Coll BA88. **d** 88. Par Dn Finchley Ch Ch *Lon* 88-91; Par Dn Broadwater St Mary *Chich* 91-94; Chapl Oak Hill Th Coll from 94. *4 Farm Lane, London N14 4PP, or Oak Hill College, Chase Side, London N14 4PS* 0181-441 5992 or 449 0467

HANSFORD, Gordon John. b 40. Southn Univ BSc61. Trin Coll Bris 77. **d** 79 **p** 80. C Ex St Leon w H Trin *Ex* 79-82; C Shirley *Win* 82-87; R Landcross, Littleham, Monkleigh etc *Ex* from 87. *The Rectory, Weare Giffard, Bideford, Devon EX39 4QP* Bideford (01237) 472017

HANSON, Christopher. b 48. Birm Bible Inst DipMin75 Wycliffe Hall Ox 87. **d** 89 **p** 90. C Heref St Pet w St Owen and St Jas *Heref* 89-91; C Plymouth St Andr w St Paul and St Geo *Ex* 91-93; C Devonport St Mich 93-94; TV Shebbear, Buckland Filleigh, Sheepwash etc from 94. *The Rectory, Petrockstowe, Okehampton, Devon EX20 3HQ* Okehampton (01837) 810499

HANSON, Dale Robert. b 57. Fitzw Coll Cam BA78 MA81 Univ of BC MA80. Ridley Hall Cam 81. **d** 84 **p** 85. C Much Woolton *Liv* 84-87; Hong Kong 87-91; TV Billingham St Aid *Dur* from 91. *17 Shadforth Drive, Billingham, Cleveland TS23 3PW* Stockton-on-Tees (01642) 561870

HANSON, Canon John Westland. b 19. OBE74. St Jo Coll Dur BA41 DipTh43 MA44. **d** 43 **p** 44. Chapl and Lect RAF Flying Coll Manby 50-76; R Grimoldby w Manby *Linc* 50-76; Chief Examiner Relig Studies Cam Univ 66-82; Can and Preb Linc Cathl from 67; RD Louthesk 68-77; V Woodhall Spa and Kirkstead 76-88; P-in-c Langton w Woodhall 76-88; rtd 88. *Brookfield, 28 Tor-o-Moor Road, Woodhall Spa, Lincs LN10 6TD* Woodhall Spa (01526) 352554

HANSON, Michael Beaumont. b 49. Ox Univ MA. N Ord Course. **d** 84 **p** 85. NSM Leeds St Geo *Ripon* from 84; Chapl Leeds Gr Sch from 84. *The Martlets, 9 Orville Gardens, Leeds LS6 2BS* Leeds (0113) 278 5370

HANSON, Peter Richard. b 45. ARCM. Chich Th Coll 72. **d** 75 **p** 76. C Forest Gate St Edm *Chelmsf* 75-79; C Chingford SS Pet and Paul 79-81; V Leytonstone H Trin Harrow Green 81-86; Dep Chapl HM Pris Wandsworth 86-88; Chapl HM Pris Lewes 88-91; rtd 91; Perm to Offic *Chich* from 91. *Flat 2, 39 St Anne's Crescent, Lewes, E Sussex BN7 1SB* Brighton (01273) 471714

HANSON, Richard. b 14. Wells Th Coll 40. **d** 42 **p** 43. Chapl Milan *Eur* 67-72; V Harrow Weald All SS *Lon* 72-77; P-in-c Alfrick w Lulsley and Suckley *Worc* 77-78; P-in-c Leigh w Bransford 77-78; P-in-c Alfrick, Lulsley, Suckley, Leigh and Bransford 78; R 78-82; rtd 82; Perm to Offic *Linc* from 82. *The Rectory Bungalow, Horsington, Lincoln LN3 5EX* Horsington (01526) 388696

HANSON, Robert Arthur. b 35. Keele Univ BA57. St Steph Ho Ox 57 St Mich Coll Llan 59. **d** 60 **p** 61. C Longton St Mary and St Chad *Lich* 60-65; Chapl St Mary's Cathl *Edin* 65-69; R Glas St Matt *Glas* 69-79; R Paisley H Trin 79-87; V Walsall St Andr *Lich* 87-93. *36 Langside Drive, Kilbarchan, Johnstone, Renfrewshire PA10 2EW*

HANSON, Timothy David. b 68. Oak Hill Th Coll BA95. **d** 95. C Boscombe St Jo *Win* from 95. *167 Southcote Road, Bournemouth BH1 3SP* Bournemouth (01202) 397691

HAPGOOD-STRICKLAND, Peter Russell. b 57. BA. St Steph Ho Ox. **d** 83 **p** 84. C Ashford *Cant* 83-86; C Sheerness H Trin w St Paul 86-90; V Blackb St Thos w St Jude *Blackb* from 90. *St Jude's Vicarage, Accrington Road, Blackburn BB1 2AB* Blackburn (01254) 263259

HARBIDGE, Adrian Guy. b 48. St Jo Coll Dur BA70. Cuddesdon Coll 73. **d** 75 **p** 76. C Romsey *Win* 75-80; V Bournemouth St Andr 80-86; V Chandler's Ford from 86; RD Eastleigh from 93. *The Vicarage, Hursley Road, Eastleigh, Hants SO5 2FT* Chandler's Ford (01703) 252597

HARBORD, Paul Geoffrey. b 56. Keble Coll Ox BA78 MA86. Chich Th Coll 81. **d** 83 **p** 84. C Rawmarsh w Parkgate *Sheff* 83-86; C Doncaster St Geo 86-90; C-in-c St Edm Anchorage Lane CD from 90. *St Edmund's House, Anchorage Lane, Sprotborough, Doncaster, S Yorkshire DN5 8DT* Doncaster (01302) 781986

HARBORD, Philip James. b 56. St Cath Coll Ox BA77. Cranmer Hall Dur 78. **d** 80 **p** 81. C Enfield St Andr *Lon* 80-83; CMS 84-88; Pakistan 84-88; C Clay Hill St Jo and St Luke *Lon* 88-91; Chapl Wexham Park Hosp Slough from 91; Chapl Upton Hosp Slough from 91. *Wexham Park Hospital, Slough*

SL2 4HL, *or The School House, Church Road, Farnham Royal, Slough SL2 3AW* Slough (01753) 633000 or 643233

HARBOTTLE, Anthony Hall Harrison. b 25. LVO79. Ch Coll Cam BA50 MA53. Wycliffe Hall Ox 50. **d** 52 **p** 53. C Boxley *Cant* 52-54; C St Peter-in-Thanet 54-60; R Sandhurst w Newenden 60-68; Chapl Royal Chpl Windsor Gt Park 68-81; Chapl to The Queen from 68; R E Dean w Friston and Jevington *Chich* from 81. *The Rectory, East Dean, Eastbourne, E Sussex BN20 0DL* East Dean (01323) 423266

HARCOURT, Giles Sidford. b 36. Westcott Ho Cam 68. **d** 71 **p** 72. C Bishopwearmouth St Mich w St Hilda *Dur* 71-73; C Fishponds St Mary *Bris* 73-75; Bp's Dom Chapl *S'wark* 75-78; Lic to Offic 78-79; V S Wimbledon H Trin and St Pet 79-88; V Greenwich St Alfege w St Pet and St Paul from 88; Chapl RN Coll Greenwich from 89. *The Vicarage, Park Vista, London SE10 9LZ* 0181-858 6828

HARCOURT, Paul George. b 67. Em Coll Cam BA88 MA92. Wycliffe Hall Ox BA91. **d** 92 **p** 93. C Moreton *Ches* 92-95; C Woodford Wells *Chelmsf* from 95. *7 Marion Grove, Woodford Green, Essex IG8 9TA* 0181-505 1431

HARCOURT-NORTON, Michael Clive. See NORTON, Michael Clive Harcourt

HARCUS, Canon Arthur Reginald (Reg). b 38. Lon Univ BD71 MPhil78. Kelham Th Coll 58. **d** 63 **p** 64. C Old Charlton *S'wark* 63-69; C Felpham w Middleton *Chich* 78-80; P-in-c Donnington 80-85; V Fernhurst 85-91; V Bolney from 91; Tutor Lay Educn & Tr from 91; Hon Can Koforidua from 91. *The Vicarage, Bolney, Haywards Heath, W Sussex RH17 5QR* Bolney (01444) 881301

HARDAKER, Canon Ian Alexander. b 32. K Coll Lon BD59 AKC59. **d** 60 **p** 61. C Beckenham St Geo *Roch* 60-65; R Eynsford w Lullingstone 65-70; V Chatham St Steph 70-85; RD Roch 78-85; Hon Can Roch Cathl from 83; Clergy Appts Adv from 86; Hon Chapl to The Queen from 94. *Fielden House, Little College Street, London SW1P 3SH* 0171-222 9544/5 Fax 233 1104

HARDAKER, Leonard. b 24. AKC54 St Boniface Warminster. **d** 54 **p** 55. V Bolney *Chich* 68-81; R Ninfield 81-89; V Hooe 81-89; rtd 89. *7 Dale View, Silsden, Keighley, W Yorkshire BD20 0JP* Keighley (01535) 653871

HARDAKER, Stephen. b 58. Kent Univ BA79 Southn Univ BTh89. Chich Th Coll 86. **d** 89 **p** 90. C Banstead *Guildf* 89-93; R Tillington *Chich* 93-95; R Duncton 93-95; R Up Waltham 93-95; TV Crawley from 95. *St Richard's Vicarage, 1 Crossways, Crawley, W Sussex RH10 1QF* Crawley (01293) 533727

HARDCASTLE, Frank Rata. b 05. Lon Univ BA24 BD30 AKC30. **d** 30 **p** 31. C Welwyn Garden City *St Alb* 69-71; rtd 71; Perm to Offic *Ex* 72-91. *13 Gracey Court, Woodland Road, Broadclyst, Exeter EX5 3LP*

HARDCASTLE, Nigel John. b 47. Reading Univ BSc68. Qu Coll Birm DipTh71. **d** 72 **p** 73. C Weoley Castle *Birm* 72-75; C Handsworth St Andr 75-78; V Garretts Green 78-86; Exec Sec Ch Computer Project BCC 86-89; R Emmer Green *Ox* from 89. *St Barnabas Vicarage, 20 St Barnabas Road, Emmer Green, Reading RG4 8LG* Reading (01734) 478239

HARDCASTLE, Richard. b 08. Leeds Univ BA24 MA31. Coll of Resurr Mirfield 26. **d** 35 **p** 36. V Bilsdale Midcable *York* 60-75; V Bilsdale 60-75; C-in-c Hawnby w Old Byland 63-75; rtd 74. *56 St John's Street, York YO3 7QT* York (01904) 652111

HARDCASTLE, Roger Clive. b 52. Southn Univ BSc73. Qu Coll Birm DipTh77. **d** 78 **p** 79. C Walton St Mary *Liv* 78-82; V Pemberton St Fran Kitt Green 82-94; TV Padgate from 94. *The Vicarage, Admiral's Road, Birchwood, Warrington WA3 6QG* Padgate (01925) 811906

HARDIE, Ven Archibald George. b 08. Trin Coll Cam BA30 MA35. Westcott Ho Cam 30. **d** 34 **p** 35. TR Halifax *Wakef* 60-70; RD Halifax 62-70; Hon Can Wakef Cathl 63-70; Adn W Cumberland *Carl* 70-79; V Haile 71-80; rtd 80. *Westcliff House, Pondicherry, Rothbury, Morpeth, Northd NE65 7YE*

HARDIE, John Blair. b 16. MBE46. LDS FDS MRCS38 MRCSE66. Edin Th Coll 73. **d** 76 **p** 76. Chapl St Paul's Cathl Dundee *Bre* 76-86; rtd 86; Hon C Carnoustie *Bre* from 86. *4 Lammerton Terrace, Dundee DD4 7BW* Dundee (01382) 452247

HARDIE, Stephen. b 41. AKC67. **d** 68 **p** 69. C Roxbourne St Andr *Lon* 68-73; C Colchester St Mary V *Chelmsf* 73-76; R Wivenhoe 76-92; TR Dovercourt and Parkeston from 92; P-in-c Harwich from 92. *The Rectory, 51 Highfield Avenue, Dovercourt, Harwich, Essex CO12 4DR* Harwich (01255) 552033

HARDING, Dr Alan. b 45. St Jo Coll Ox BA67 MA73 Pemb Coll Ox DPhil92. Oak Hill NSM Course 89. **d** 93 **p** 94. NSM Lt Heath *St Alb* from 93. *White Cottage, 41 Quakers Lane, Potters Bar, Herts EN6 1RH* Potters Bar (01707) 652973

HARDING, Alec James. b 61. St Andr Univ MA83 DTh. Cranmer Hall Dur 86. **d** 89 **p** 90. C Thirsk *York* 89-93;

TV Heref St Martin w St Fran (S Wye TM) *Heref* from 93. *The Vicarage, 1 Prinknash Close, Belmont, Hereford HR2 7XA* Hereford (01432) 277364 or 353717

HARDING, Brenda Kathleen. b 39. Bedf Coll Lon BA60 K Coll Lon BD62. St Deiniol's Hawarden 91. **d** 92 **p** 94. NSM Lanc Ch Ch w St Jo and St Anne *Blackb* from 92. *14 Ascot Close, Lancaster LA1 4LT* Lancaster (01524) 66071

HARDING, Brian Edward. b 38. ALCD65. **d** 65 **p** 66. C Chislehurst Ch Ch *Roch* 65-68; P-in-c Baxenden *Blackb* 68-70; V 70-88; V Douglas from 88. *The Vicarage, 5 Tan House Lane, Parbold, Wigan, Lancs WN8 7HG* Parbold (01257) 462350

HARDING, Clifford Maurice. b 22. Leeds Univ BA47. Coll of Resurr Mirfield 46. **d** 48 **p** 49. V Oldham St Jo *Man* 59-65; Lic to Offic *Blackb* from 65; rtd 87. *31 Riley Avenue, St Annes, Lytham St Annes, Lancs FY8 1HZ* St Annes (01253) 725138

HARDING, David Anthony. b 30. St Edm Hall Ox BA54 MA58 Dur Univ MPhil85. Ely Th Coll 54. **d** 56 **p** 57. Chapl Westmr Sch 68-74; Chapl St Bede Coll Dur 74-75; SS Hild and Bede Coll 75-80; Lic to Offic *S'well* 80-91; Asst Chapl Worksop Coll Notts 80-82; Chapl 82-91; Chapl SS Mary and Anne's Sch Abbots Bromley 91-95; rtd 95. *29 King John's Court, King John's Island, Tewkesbury, Glos GL20 6EG* Tewkesbury (01684) 291978

HARDING, Miss Eileen Thelma. b 18. St Mich Ho Ox 58. dss 60 **d** 87. Sec Dioc Bd for Women's Min *Chich* 63-77; Hd Dss 68-81; Dioc Lay Min Adv 77-81; rtd 81; Broadwater St Mary *Chich* 84-87; Hon Par Dn from 87. *199 King Edward Avenue, Worthing, W Sussex BN14 8DW* Worthing (01903) 239867

HARDING, Frederick Arthur. b 16. S'wark Ord Course 75. **d** 77 **p** 78. NSM Oxted *S'wark* from 77. *33 Crabwood, 13 Blue House Lane, Oxted, Surrey RH8 0UA* Oxted (01883) 716454

HARDING, John James. b 08. BEM. Worc Ord Coll 60. **d** 62 **p** 63. V Stourpaine *Sarum* 66-71; P-in-c Bockleton w Leysters *Heref* 71-76; rtd 76. *Flat 4, Trafalgar Court, 2 Richmond Road, Southsea, Hants PO5 2NU* Portsmouth (01705) 839195

HARDING, John Stuart Michael. b 45. St Jo Coll Nottm 79. **d** 81 **p** 82. C Clifton *S'well* 81-87; V Broxtowe from 87. *The Vicarage, Frinton Road, Nottingham NG8 6GR* Nottingham (0115) 927 8837

HARDING, John William Christopher. b 31. St Jo Coll Dur BA55. **d** 58 **p** 59. C Wigan St Cath *Liv* 58-60; C Much Woolton 60-63; V Whiston 63-73; V Birkdale St Jo from 73. *St John's Vicarage, 17 Kirkstall Road, Southport, Merseyside PR8 4RA* Southport (01704) 63318

HARDING, Mrs Marion. b 33. Gilmore Course 75. dss 85 **d** 87 **p** 94. Hertf St Andr *St Alb* 85-87; Par Dn 87-93; rtd 93; NSM Lt Amwell *St Alb* from 93. *41 Calton Avenue, Hertford SG14 2ER* Hertford (01992) 587348

HARDING, Michael Anthony John. b 37. Brasted Th Coll 67 Sarum Th Coll 68. **d** 71 **p** 72. C Forest Hill Ch Ch *S'wark* 71-72; C Catford St Laur 72-74; C Leominster *Heref* 74-77; V Ditton Priors 77-86; R Neenton 77-86; P-in-c Aston Botterell w Wheathill and Loughton 77-86; P-in-c Burwarton w N Cleobury 77-86; R Ditton Priors w Neenton, Burwarton etc 86-94; P-in-c E Budleigh and Bicton *Ex* 94; P-in-c Otterton and Colaton Raleigh 94; V E Budleigh w Bicton and Otterton from 94. *The Vicarage, East Budleigh, Budleigh Salterton, Devon EX9 7EF* Budleigh Salterton (01395) 444060

HARDING, Peter Michael David. b 38. Man Univ BA61. Lich Th Coll 61. **d** 63 **p** 64. C Hednesford *Lich* 63-67; C Blurton 67-70; V Newc St Paul from 70; RD Newc from 87; Preb Lich Cathl from 89. *St Paul's Vicarage, Hawkstone Close, Newcastle, Staffs ST5 1HT* Newcastle-under-Lyme (01782) 617913

HARDING, Peter Edward. b 39. Univ Coll Ox BA61 MA69. Wycliffe Hall Ox 62. **d** 64 **p** 65. C Westlands St Andr CD *Lich* 64-67; C Hinckley H Trin *Leic* 67-69; R Sutton cum Duckmanton *Derby* 69-75; P-in-c Elvaston and Shardlow from 75. *The Vicarage, Elvaston, Thulston, Derby DE7 3EQ* Derby (01332) 571790

HARDING, Peter Gordon. b 45. **d** 79 **p** 80. C Kirkheaton *Wakef* 79-82; NSM New Sleaford *Linc* from 90. *16 The Drove, Sleaford, Lincs NG34 7AS* Sleaford (01529) 307231

HARDING, Peter Richard. b 46. AKC69. St Aug Coll Cant 69. **d** 70 **p** 71. C Chorley St Pet *Blackb* 70-73; C Ribbleton 73-74; C St Marylebone w H Trin *Lon* 74-80; P-in-c St Marylebone St Cypr 80-82; V from 82; AD Westmr St Marylebone 83-92; Sub-Warden Guild of St Raphael from 88. *St Cyprian's Vicarage, 16 Clarence Gate Gardens, London NW1 6AY* 0171-402 6979

HARDING, Richard Michael. b 42. St Alb Minl Tr Scheme. **d** 83 **p** 84. C Pershore w Pinvin, Wick and Birlingham *Worc* 83-86; V Longdon, Castlemorton, Bushley, Queenhill etc 86-95; P-in-c Catshill and Dodford from 95. *The Vicarage, 403 Stourbridge Road, Catshill, Bromsgrove, Worcs B61 9LG* Bromsgrove (01527) 579619

HARDING, Rolf John. b 22. Oak Hill Th Coll 41 Lon Coll of Div 46. **d** 49 **p** 50. V Coopersale *Chelmsf* 61-91; Chapl St Marg Hosp Epping 73-91; Chapl W Essex HA 86-91; rtd 91.

11 Westbrook Park, Weston, Bath BA1 4DP Bath (01225) 484968

HARDING, Miss Sylvia. b 23. St Mich Ho Ox 55. dss 64 **d** 87. Midl Area Sec CPAS 66-71; Patchway *Bris* 71-78; Sec Coun of Women's Min Bris 77-84; rtd 84; Westbury-on-Trym St Alb *Bris* 86-92; Hon Par Dn 87-92; Perm to Offic from 92. *24 Woodhill Road, Portishead, Bristol BS20 9EU* Portishead (01275) 848638

HARDINGHAM, Paul David. b 52. Lon Univ BSc74 Fitzw Coll Cam BA77. Ridley Hall Cam 75. **d** 78 **p** 79. C Cam St Martin *Ely* 78-81; C Jesmond Clayton Memorial *Newc* 81-88; C Harborne Heath *Birm* 88-91; R Ipswich St Matt *St E* from 91. *St Matthew's Rectory, 3 Portman Road, Ipswich IP1 2ES* Ipswich (01473) 251630

HARDMAN, Dr Bryan Edwin. b 29. Lon Univ BD60 Selw Coll Cam PhD64 K Coll Lon MTh75. Moore Th Coll Sydney ThL54. **d** 55 **p** 55. Australia 63-83; Bangladesh 83-86; Singapore 87-95; rtd 94. *clo The Church Commissioners, 1 Millbank, London SW1P 3JZ*

HARDMAN, Mrs Christine Elizabeth. b 51. Lon Univ BSc(Econ)73. St Alb Minl Tr Scheme 81. dss 84 **d** 87 **p** 94. Markyate Street *St Alb* 84-87; Par Dn 87-88; Tutor St Alb Minl Tr Scheme 88-91; Course Dir St Alb Minl Tr Scheme from 91; C Markyate Street from 94. *Cell View, High Street, Markyate, St Albans, Herts AL3 8PD* Markyate (01582) 840285

HARDMAN, Geoffrey James. b 41. Birm Univ BA63. N Ord Course 77. **d** 80 **p** 81. NSM Latchford St Jas *Ches* 80-93; NSM Haydock St Jas *Liv* from 94. *48 Denbury Avenue, Stockton Heath, Warrington WA4 2BW* Warrington (01925) 664064

HARDMAN, Canon Peter George. b 35. Man Univ BSc56. Ridley Hall Cam 58. **d** 60 **p** 61. C Oldham St Paul *Man* 60-63; Lic to Offic 63-67; NW England Area Sec SCM 63-64; NW England Area Sec CEM 64-67; Asst Chapl Marlborough Coll Wilts 67-72; Chapl 72-79; P-in-c Wareham *Sarum* 79-80; TR from 80; Chapl Christmas Close Hosp Wareham from 80; Can and Preb Sarum Cathl from 87; RD Purbeck from 89. *The Rectory, 19 Pound Lane, Wareham, Dorset BH20 4LQ* Wareham (01929) 552684

HARDWICK, Christopher George (Chris). b 57. ACIB79 Open Univ BA94 DASSc94. Ripon Coll Cuddesdon 90. **d** 92 **p** 93. C Worc SE *Worc* 92-95; R Ripple, Earls Croome w Hill Croome and Strensham from 95. *The Rectory, The Cross, Ripple, Tewkesbury, Glos GL20 6HA* Upton-upon-Severn (01684) 592655

HARDWICK, Dennis Egerton. b 27. St Deiniol's Hawarden. **d** 82 **p** 83. NSM Lache cum Saltney *Ches* 82-85; P-in-c Backford 85-88; P-in-c Capenhurst 87-88; R Backford and Capenhurst 88-93; rtd 93. *11 Prime Close, Walberton, Arundel, W Sussex BN18 0PL*

HARDWICK, Graham John. b 42. Qu Coll Birm 68. **d** 70 **p** 71. C Watford St Mich *St Alb* 70-73; C N Mymms 73-75; Youth Officer Cov Cathl *Cov* 75-81; Chapl Lanchester Poly 76-81; V Nuneaton St Nic from 81. *61 Ambleside Way, Nuneaton, Warks CV11 6AU* Nuneaton (01203) 346900

HARDWICK, John Audley. b 28. Em Coll Cam BA51 MA55. Westcott Ho Cam 51. **d** 53 **p** 54. Chapl St Edm Sch Hindhead 62-86; Asst Hd Master 73-90; Lic to Offic *Guildf* 63-90; rtd 93. *Hillcroft, Kettle Lane, Audlem, Crewe CW3 0BX* Audlem (01270) 811545

HARDWICK, Robert (Rob). b 56. St Jo Coll Nottm DCM93. **d** 93 **p** 94. C Beeston *S'well* from 93. *46 Bramcote Road, Beeston, Nottingham NG9 1DW* Nottingham (0115) 925 8825

HARDWICK, Mrs Susan Frances. b 44. Warw Univ BA81. Qu Coll Birm 82. dss 85 **d** 87 **p** 94. Chilvers Coton w Astley *Cov* 85-87; C 87-91; Chapl Hereward Coll from 91. *The Vicarage, New Street, Rugby, Warks CV22 7BE* Rugby (01788) 544011

HARDWICK, Canon William George. b 16. Lich Th Coll 40. **d** 44 **p** 45. C Northn Ch Ch *Pet* 44-46; C Leic St Paul *Leic* 46-49; Basutoland 49-52; S Africa 52-78 and from 79; V Brigstock w Stanion *Pet* 78-79. *24 Lyndhurst Place, Windham, Umkomaas, 4170 South Africa* Scottburgh (323) 31623

HARDWICKE, Stephen Michael. b 57. Herts Coll BA85 Lon Bible Coll MA87 K Coll Lon MTh92. Westcott Ho Cam 93. **d** 95. C Leagrave *St Alb* from 95. *St Luke's House, 39 Butley Road, Luton LU4 9EW* Luton (01582) 572054

HARDY, Ms Alison Jane. b 61. **d** 95. C Flixton St Mich *Man* from 95. *350 Church Road, Flixton, Urmston, Manchester M31 3HR* 0161-748 3568

HARDY, Anthony. b 36. **d** 86 **p** 87. Hon C Malden St Jas *S'wark* from 86. *48 Blake's Lane, New Malden, Surrey KT3 6NR* 0181-949 0703

HARDY, Anthony William. b 56. Man Univ BEd79 MEd86. St Jo Coll Nottm LTh88. **d** 88 **p** 89. C Pennington *Man* 88-91; V Eccleston St Luke *Liv* from 91. *St Luke's Vicarage, Mulberry Avenue, St Helens, Merseyside WA10 4DE* St Helens (01744) 22456

HARDY, Bertram Frank. b 08. Lich Th Coll 51. **d** 52 **p** 52. C-in-c Lovington *B & W* 69-74; C-in-c N w S Barrow 69-74; rtd 74;

Perm to Offic *B & W* from 74. *7 Churchill Avenue, Wells, Somerset BA5 3JE* Wells (01749) 674696

HARDY, Canon Brian Albert. b 31. St Jo Coll Ox BA54 DipTh55 MA58. Westcott Ho Cam 55. d 57 p 58. C Rugeley *Lich* 57-62; Chapl Down Coll Cam 62-66; C-in-c Livingston Miss *Edin* 66-74; Preb Heref Cathl *Heref* 74-78; Ch Planning Officer Telford 74-78; RD Telford Severn Gorge 75-78; Chapl Edin Th Coll 78-82; Chapl Edin R Infirmary 82-86; R Edin St Columba Edin 82-91; Dean Edin 86-91; R St Andrews All SS *St And* from 91; Hon Can St Mary's Cathl *Edin* from 91. *All Saints' Rectory, North Street, St Andrews, Fife KY16 9AQ* St Andrews (01334) 73193

HARDY, Christopher Richard. b 52. R Holloway Coll Lon BMus77 Southn Univ BTh90. Chich Th Coll 87. d 90 p 91. C Kenton *Lon* 90-95; V E Finchley All SS from 95. *All Saints' Vicarage, 1 Twyford Avenue, London N2 1NV* 0181-883 9315

HARDY, Miss Janet Frances. b 59. Newc Univ BA81 CertEd82. Trin Coll Bris 87. d 89 p 94. Par Dn Sheff St Paul Wordsworth Avenue *Sheff* 89-92; TD Gt Snaith 92-94; TV from 94. *31 Saffron Drive, Snaith, Goole, N Humberside DN14 9LH* Goole (01405) 860843

HARDY, John Charles. b 22. Sheff Univ BA48 DipEd49 Lon Univ DipTh53. St Deiniol's Hawarden 66. d 67 p 68. Hon C Chorley St Laur *Blackb* 67-87; rtd 87; Perm to Offic *Blackb* from 87. *4 Glamis Drive, Chorley, Lancs PR7 1LX* Chorley (01257) 265743

HARDY, John Christopher. b 61. St Jo Coll Dur BA83. Coates Hall Edin BD92. d 92 p 93. C Walker *Newc* from 92. *78 Westbourne Avenue, Walker, Newcastle upon Tyne NE6 4HQ* 0191-234 4715

HARDY, Canon John Lewis Daniel. b 26. St Chad's Coll Dur BA51 DipTh52. d 52 p 53. V Sutton in Ashfield St Mary *S'well* 65-85; R Keyworth 85-93; P-in-c Stanton-on-the-Wolds 85-93; RD Bingham S 91-93; Hon Can S'well Minster 92-93; rtd 93. *10 Redhill Lodge Drive, Nottingham NG5 8JH* Nottingham (0115) 926 7370

HARDY, Michael Frederick Bryan. b 36. Selw Coll Cam BA60 MA64. Linc Th Coll 60. d 62 p 63. C Pontefract St Giles *Wakef* 62-66; C Lightcliffe 66-69; V Hightown 69-78; V Birkby 78-85; C Boultham *Linc* 88-89; V Misterton and W Stockwith *S'well* from 89. *The Vicarage, 5 Minster Road, Misterton, Doncaster, S Yorkshire DN10 4AP* Gainsborough (01427) 890270

HARDY, Michael Henry. b 33. Qu Coll Birm 85. d 86 p 87. C Leic St Jas *Leic* 86-88; R Arnesby w Shearsby and Bruntingthorpe 88-94; RD Guthlaxton I (Blaby) 91-94; TR Ratby w Groby from 94. *The Vicarage, 15 Groby Road, Ratby, Leicester LE6 0LJ* Leicester (0116) 239 3009

HARDY, Michael John. b 35. Keble Coll Ox BA58 MA66. Cuddesdon Coll 59. d 61 p 62. C Dalton-in-Furness *Carl* 61-64; C Harborne St Pet *Birm* 64-68; Min Can Ripon Cathl *Ripon* 68-73; Appt and Tr Sec USPG 73-80; R Stretford St Pet *Man* 80-91; P-in-c Newton Hall *Dur* from 91. *31 York Crescent, Durham DH1 5PT* 0191-386 8049

HARDY, Michael Wilfred. b 27. St Chad's Coll Dur BA52. Coll of Resurr Mirfield. d 54 p 55. C Cullercoats St Geo *Newc* 54-57; Africa 58-62; C Ponteland 63; C Seaton Hirst 63-66; C Gosforth All SS 66-69; Australia from 69. *37 Railway Road, Collinsville, Queensland, Australia 4804* Collinsville (77) 855255

HARDY, Canon Paul Richard. b 30. BA52 MA56. St Steph Ho Ox 57. d 59 p 60. Tanzania 64-95; Can Dar-es-Salaam from 74; rtd 95. *249 Kempshott Lane, Basingstoke, Hants RG22 5LZ*

HARDY, Miss Pauline. b 41. CertEd. Linc Th Coll 85. d 87 p 94. Par Dn Walsall Wood *Lich* 87-89; Par Dn Buckm *Ox* 89-93; Par Dn Buckm w Radclive cum Chackmore 93-94; C from 94. *Church House, 2 Chandos Close, Buckingham MK18 1AW* Buckingham (01280) 812160

✠**HARDY, Rt Rev Robert Maynard.** b 36. Clare Coll Cam BA60 MA64. Cuddesdon Coll 60. d 62 p 63 c 80. C Langley St Aid CD *Man* 62-64; C Langley All SS and Martyrs 64-65; Chapl and Lect Th Selw Coll Cam 65-72; V Boreham Wood All SS *St Alb* 72-75; Dir St Alb Minl Tr Scheme 75-80; P-in-c Aspley Guise *St Alb* 75-79; P-in-c Husborne Crawley w Ridgmont 76-79; R Aspley Guise w Husborne Crawley and Ridgmont 80; Suff Bp Maidstone *Cant* 80-87; Bp Linc from 87; Bp HM Pris from 85. *Bishop's House, Eastgate, Lincoln LN2 1QQ* Lincoln (01522) 534701 Fax 511095

HARDY, Thomas Woodburn. b 26. Bp's Univ Lennoxville BA48. d 49 p 50. P-in-c Fulham St Aug *Lon* 68-73; V 73-91; rtd 91. *58 Boston Gardens, Brentford, Middx TW8 9LP* 0181-847 4533

HARDY, Wallis Bertrand. b 03. Lon Univ BSc24. St Steph Ho Ox 53. d 54 p 55. Chapl Community of St Denys Warminster 64-75; rtd 75. *Ingram House, Whiteley Village, Walton-on-Thames, Surrey KT12 4EJ* Walton-on-Thames (01932) 856315

HARDY, William Marshall Conyers. b 25. Linc Th Coll 55. d 56 p 57. V Belford *Newc* 62-77; RD Bamburgh and Glendale

71-77; V Riding Mill 77-90; RD Corbridge 82-88; Hon Can Newc Cathl 88-91; rtd 90. *5 Riding Dene, Mickley, Stocksfield, Northd NE43 7DG* Hexham (01434) 682009

HARE, David (Brother David Columba). b 46. Qu Coll Birm. d 83 p 83. SSF from 67; Bp's Dom Chapl *Birm* 83-87; V Handsworth St Mich from 87. *St Michael's Vicarage, 20 Soho Avenue, Handsworth, Birmingham B18 5LB* 0121-554 3521 or 4090

HARE, Frank Richard Knight. b 22. Trin Hall Cam BA46 MA48. Cuddesdon Coll 46. d 48 p 49. V Steyning *Chich* 62-70; R Ashurst 62-70; TV Raveningham *Nor* 70-71; TR Barnham Broom 71-79; V Buxton w Oxnead 79-86; R Lammas w Lt Hautbois 79-86; rtd 86; Perm to Offic *St E* from 86. *14 Lee Road, Aldeburgh, Suffolk IP15 5HG* Aldeburgh (01728) 453372

HARE, Dr Richard William. b 66. Bris Univ BSc88 PhD94. Cranmer Hall Dur BA95. d 95. C Coulsdon St Jo *S'wark* from 95. *17 Rowley Court, Yorke Gate, Coulsdon Road, Caterham, Surrey CR3 5AY* Caterham (01883) 346761

HARE, Stanley Thomas. b 23. Roch Th Coll. d 62 p 63. V Sheff St Barn *Sheff* 69-73; Chapl Farnborough and Orpington Hosps 73-85; rtd 85. *15 Marshmallan Road, Mount Hawke, Truro, Cornwall TR4 8DL* Porthtowan (01209) 890757

✠**HARE, Rt Rev Thomas Richard.** b 22. Trin Coll Ox BA48 MA53. Westcott Ho Cam 48. d 50 p 51 c 71. C Haltwhistle *Newc* 50-52; Bp's Dom Chapl *Man* 52-59; Can Res Carl Cathl *Carl* 59-65; R Barrow St Geo w St Luke 65-69; Adn Westmorland and Furness 65-71; Hon Can Carl Cathl 65-71; V Winster 69-71; Suff Bp Pontefract *Wakef* 71-92; rtd 92. *Wood Cottage, Mirehouse, Underskiddaw, Keswick, Cumbria CA12 4QE* Keswick (017687) 72996

✠**HARE DUKE, Rt Rev Michael Geoffrey.** b 25. Trin Coll Ox BA49 MA51 St Andr Univ Hon DD94. Westcott Ho Cam 50. d 52 p 53 c 69. C St Jo Wood *Lon* 52-56; V Bury St Mark *Man* 56-62; Past Dir Clinical Th Assn Nottm 62-64; Past Consultant 64-69; V Daybrook *S'well* 64-69; Bp St Andr *St And* 69-94; rtd 94. *2 Balhousie Avenue, Perth PH1 5HN* Perth (01738) 622642

HARES, David Ronald Walter. b 40. Qu Coll Cam BA63 MA67 CertEd. Westcott Ho Cam 64. d 66 p 67. C Cannock *Lich* 66-69; Chapl Peterho Cam 69-72; Asst Master Chesterton Sch Cam 72-74; V Kesgrave *St E* from 74. *The Vicarage, Kesgrave, Ipswich IP5 7JQ* Ipswich (01473) 622181

HAREWOOD, John Rupert. b 24. Man Univ BA48. Sarum & Wells Th Coll 76. d 79 p 80. NSM Taunton St Jas *B & W* 79-82; TV Camelot Par 82-89; rtd 89; Perm to Offic *Ex* from 92. *19 Swains Road, Budleigh Salterton, Devon EX9 6HL* Budleigh Salterton (01395) 445802

HARFORD, Julian Gray. b 29. Univ Coll Ox BA52 MA59 Lon Univ PGCE58. Qu Coll Birm DipTh64. d 64 p 65. C Chearsley w Nether Winchendon *Ox* 67-77; C Chilton All SS 72-77; R Westbury w Turweston, Shalstone and Biddlesden 77-86; C Chenies and Lt Chalfont 86-87; C Chenies and Lt Chalfont, Latimer and Flaunden 87-95; rtd 95. *14 Dial Close, Seend, Melksham, Wilts SN12 6NP* Devizes (01380) 828306

HARFORD, Ven Michael Rivers Dundas. b 26. Trin Coll Cam BA49 MA51. Westcott Ho Cam 50. d 52 p 53. V Childwall St Dav *Liv* 66-71; Australia from 71; Adn Albany 76-79; Adn Swan 86-89; Adn Mitchell 90-91; rtd 91. *3B Tamar Street, Palmyra, W Australia 6157* Palmyra (9) 319-1538

HARFORD, Timothy William. b 58. Nottm Univ BTh89. Linc Th Coll 86. d 89 p 90. C Minehead *B & W* 89-93; R Knebworth *St Alb* from 93. *The Rectory, 15 St Martin's Road, Knebworth, Herts SG3 6ER* Stevenage (01438) 812101

HARGER, Robin Charles Nicholas. b 49. BTh. Sarum & Wells Th Coll 78. d 81 p 82. C Charlton Kings St Mary *Glouc* 81-85; C Folkestone St Mary and St Eanswythe *Cant* 85-89; TV Langley and Parkfield *Man* 89-95; TV Bournemouth St Pet w St Swithun, St Steph etc *Win* from 95. *St Stephen's Vicarage, St Stephen's Way, Bournemouth BH2 6JZ* Bournemouth (01202) 554355

HARGRAVE, Dr Alan Lewis. b 50. Birm Univ BSc73 PhD77. Ridley Hall Cam 87. d 89 p 90. C Cam H Trin w St Andr Gt *Ely* 89-92; C Cam H Trin 92-93; C-in-c Fen Ditton 93-94; V Cambridge Holy Cross from 94. *Holy Cross Vicarage, 192 Peverel Road, Cambridge CB5 8RL* Cambridge (01223) 413343

HARGREAVE, James David. b 44. ALCM89 LTCL90 Lon Univ BA66 CertEd68. Coll of Resurr Mirfield DipTh72. d 73 p 74. C Houghton le Spring *Dur* 73-77; C Gateshead St Cuth w St Paul 77-79; V Trimdon 79-87; C-in-c Stockton Green Vale H Trin CD 87-94; V Hedon w Paull *York* from 94. *The Vicarage, 44 New Road, Hedon, Hull HU12 8BS* Hull (01482) 897693

HARGREAVES, Arthur Cecil Monsarrat. b 19. Trin Hall Cam BA42 MA46. Westcott Ho Cam 47. d 49 p 50. India 70-76;

Gen Sec Conf of Br Miss Socs 76-79; Hon C Croydon St Aug *Cant* 79-81; V Marden 81-86; rtd 86. *Windrush Cottage, 87 Downscourt Road, Purley, Surrey CR8 1BJ* 0181-668 8871

HARGREAVES, Dr Arthur Walsh. b 34. FRCSE FRCS Man Univ MB, ChB. St Deiniol's Hawarden. **d** 90 **p** 91. NSM Baguley *Man* from 90. *Greenways, Woodbourne Road, Sale, Chesire M33 3SX* 0191-973 7674

HARGREAVES, John. b 43. St Jo Coll Nottm 86. **d** 88 **p** 89. C Werneth *Man* 88-91; TV Rochdale from 91. *St Peter's Vicarage, Church Road, Rochdale, Lancs OL16 5NW* Rochdale (01706) 522291

HARGREAVES, Canon John Henry Monsarrat. b 11. Trin Coll Cam BA33 MA37. Westcott Ho Cam 35. **d** 37 **p** 38. CMS (Nigeria) 43-57 and 59-63; SPCK 65-90; C-in-c Sevenoaks St Luke CD *Roch* 65-83; RD Sevenoaks 74-79; Hon Can Roch Cathl 81-83; rtd 83. *20 St Pauls Road West, Dorking, Surrey RH4 2HU* Dorking (01306) 888648

HARGREAVES, John Rodney. b 36. Open Univ BA74. Didsbury Meth Coll 59 St Deiniol's Hawarden 74. **d** 75 **p** 75. In Meth Ch 63-74; C Pontypool *Mon* 75-77; C Llanedeyrn 77-79; Chapl HM Pris Aylesbury 79-83; Sen Chapl HM Pris Stafford 83-88; Asst Chapl Gen of Pris (N) 88-90; Asst Chapl Gen of Pris from 90. *c/o Home Office, Calthorpe House, Hagley Road, Birmingham B16 8QR* 0121-455 9855 Fax 454 6738

HARGREAVES, John Wilson. b 46. Aber Univ BScFor67 Birm Poly DipVG73. Westcott Ho Cam 84. **d** 86 **p** 87. C Rugby St Andr *Cov* 86-90; TV Daventry Pet 90-92; P-in-c Welton w Ashby St Ledgers 90-92; TV Daventry, Ashby St Ledgers, Braunston etc from 92; Chapl Daventry Tertiary Coll from 94. *The Vicarage, 19 High Street, Welton, Daventry, Northants NN11 5JP* Daventry (01327) 705563

HARGREAVES, Ms Marise. b 60. Leeds Univ BA81. Cranmer Hall Dur 82. **d** 94 **p** 95. NSM Bradf St Clem *Bradf* from 94. *58 Exmouth Place, Undercliffe, Bradford BD3 0NA* Bradford (01274) 641551

HARGREAVES, Mark Kingston. b 63. **d** 91 **p** 92. C Highbury Ch Ch w St Jo and St Sav Lon 91-94; C Ealing St Steph Castle Hill from 94. *26 Drayton Gardens, Ealing, London W13 0LQ* 0181-810 7898

HARGREAVES, Raymond. Open Univ BA79. Ripon Hall Ox 72. **d** 73 **p** 74. C Stanwix *Carl* 73-78; Chapl St Olave's Sch York from 78. *21 Oak Tree Lane, Haxby, York YO3 3YL* York (01904) 763127

HARGREAVES-STEAD, Terence Desmond. b 32. Edin Th Coll 60. **d** 63 **p** 64. C Walney Is *Carl* 63-66; Chapl Withington Hosp Man 66-72; V Westleigh St Paul *Man* from 72. *St Paul's Vicarage, Westleigh Lane, Leigh, Lancs WN7 5NW* Atherton (01942) 882883

HARINGTON, Roger John Urquhart. b 48. Trin Hall Cam BA70 MA71. Coll of Resurr Mirfield 72. **d** 75 **p** 76. C Liv Our Lady and St Nic w St Anne *Liv* 75-78; Asst Chapl Leeds Univ and Poly *Ripon* 78-81; C Moor Allerton 81; TV 81-86; Dioc Drama Adv (Jabbok Theatre Co) from 86. *13 Moorfields, Leeds LS13 3JZ* Leeds (0113) 255 2557

HARKER, Harold Aidan. b 35. **d** 82 **p** 83. OSB from 53; C Reading St Giles *Ox* 82-83; Lic to Offic 83-87; C Halstead St Andr w H Trin and Greenstead Green *Chelmsf* 87-89; P-in-c Belchamp St Paul from 89. *The Vicarage, Belchamp St Paul, Sudbury, Suffolk CO10 7BT* Clare (01787) 277210

HARKER, Dr John Hadlett. b 37. CEng FIChemE MInstE CChem MRSC Dur Univ BSc59 Newc Univ PhD67. NE Ord Course 81. **d** 84 **p** 85. C Earsdon *Newc* 84-87; P-in-c Long Horsley 87-91; V Bassenthwaite, Isel and Setmurthy *Carl* 91-94; TR Howden TM *York* from 94. *The Minster Rectory, Howden, Goole, N Humberside DN14 7BL* Howden (01430) 430332

HARKER, Stephan John. b 47. Em Coll Cam BA68 MA72. Westcott Ho Cam 70. **d** 72 **p** 73. C Marton *Blackb* 72-76; C Preston St Matt 76-79; C Fleetwood 79-80; Chapl Charterhouse Godalming from 81. *Lower Oakhurst, Frith Hill Road, Godalming, Surrey GU7 2ED* Godalming (01483) 422155

HARKIN, John Patrick. b 53. Oak Hill Th Coll DipHE89. **d** 89 **p** 90. C Wisley w Pyrford *Guildf* 89-93; P-in-c Mickleham from 93; Chapl Box Hill Sch Surrey from 93. *The Rectory, Mickleham, Dorking, Surrey RH5 6EB* Leatherhead (01372) 378335

HARKINS, Canon James Robert. b 27. Minnesota Univ BA49. Seabury-Western Th Sem MTh53. **d** 52 **p** 52. USA 52-60; 72-91; 91-93; Colombia 60-72; Dominica 79-85; Venezuela 85-91; Chapl Venice w Trieste *Eur* from 94. *253 Dorsoduro, San Gregorio, 30123 Venice, Italy* Venice (41) 520-0571

HARKNESS, Verney Austin Barnett. b 19. Lon Univ BA40 DipTh63. Ridley Hall Cam 46. **d** 47 **p** 48. R Stoke next Guildf St Jo *Guildf* 63-72; Sri Lanka 73-77; P-in-c Walkington *York* 78-79; P-in-c Bishop Burton 78-79; R Bishop Burton w Walkington 79-84; rtd 85. *20 Wylies Road, Beverley, N Humberside HU17 7AP* Hull (01482) 881924

HARLAND, Albert Henry. b 17. Oak Hill Th Coll 57. **d** 59 **p** 61. V Renhold *St Alb* 69-80; rtd 80; Perm to Offic *St Alb* from 80. *123 Putnoe Lane, Bedford MK41 8LB* Bedford (01234) 345831

HARLAND, Canon Harold William James. b 35. Hertf Coll Ox BA59 MA63. Clifton Th Coll 59. **d** 61 **p** 62. C Reigate St Mary *S'wark* 61-64; C Farnborough *Guildf* 64-68; V Walmley *Birm* 68-74; V Bromley Ch Ch *Roch* 74-86; V Foord St Jo *Cant* from 86; Dir of Post-Ord Tr from 94; Hon Can Cant Cathl from 94. *St John's Vicarage, 4 Cornwallis Avenue, Folkestone, Kent CT19 5JA* Folkestone (01303) 253732

✠**HARLAND, Rt Rev Ian.** b 32. Peterho Cam BA56 MA60. Wycliffe Hall Ox 58. **d** 60 **p** 61 **c** 85. C Melton Mowbray w Thorpe Arnold *Leic* 60-63; V Oughtibridge *Sheff* 63-72; V Sheff St Cuth 72-75; P-in-c Brightside All SS 72-75; RD Ecclesfield 73-75; V Rotherham 75-79; RD Rotherham 76-79; Adn Doncaster 79-85; P-in-c Dunscroft Ch 81-83; Hon Can Blackb Cathl *Blackb* 85-89; Suff Bp Lanc 85-89; Bp Carl from 89. *Rose Castle, Dalston, Carlisle CA5 7BZ* Raughton Head (016974) 76274 Fax 76550

HARLEY, Dr Anne Marion. b 39. St Hugh's Coll Ox MA64 DPhil65. Sarum & Wells Th Coll 85. **d** 88 **p** 94. Par Dn Isleworth St Jo *Lon* 88-91; Chapl Asst St Thos Hosp Lon from 91. *12 Canterbury House, Royal Street, London SE1 7LN* 0171-928 9292

HARLEY, Canon Brian Nigel. b 30. Clare Coll Cam BA53 MA57. Cuddesdon Coll 53. **d** 55 **p** 56. TV Basingstoke *Win* 71-73; TR 73-80; C-in-c Southn St Chris Thornhill CD 61-71; V Eastleigh 80-93; RD Eastleigh 85-93; rtd 93; Bp's Dom Chapl *Win* from 94. *18 Phillimore Road, Southampton SO2 2NR* Southampton (01703) 551049

HARLEY, Brother Brian Mortimer. b 25. K Coll Lon 48. **d** 53 **p** 54. SSF from 56; Papua New Guinea 61-79; Australia from 87; Min Gen SSF from 91; rtd 95. *The Hermitage of St Bernadine, Bucketts Wat, Stroud, NSW, Australia 2425* Cessnock (49) 945372 Fax 945404

HARLEY, Dr Christopher David. b 41. Selw Coll Cam BA63 MA69 Bris Univ PGCE64. Columbia Bibl Sem DMin92 Clifton Th Coll 64. **d** 66 **p** 67. C Finchley Ch Ch *Lon* 66-69; Hon C 75-78; Ethiopia 70-75; Hd of UK Miss CMJ 75-78; Lect All Nations Chr Coll Ware 78-85; Prin 85-93; Chmn Lon Inst of Contemporary Christianity 88-89; Chmn CMJ 89-90; Lic to Offic *St Alb* 79-92; Crosslinks from 93; NSM Bromley Ch Ch *Roch* from 94. *5 Ullswater Close, Bromley BR1 4JF* 0181-691 6111 Fax 694 8023

HARLEY, David Bertram. b 22. Down Coll Cam BA50 MA55. Westcott Ho Cam 55. **d** 56 **p** 58. Chapl Stamford Sch Lincs 58-87; Lic to Offic *Linc* from 59; Confrater Browne's Hosp Stamford from 87; rtd 87. *Beggars' Roost, Priory Road, Stamford, Lincs PE9 2ES* Stamford (01780) 63403

HARLEY, Michael. b 50. AKC73 Ch Ch Coll Cant CertEd74. Lambeth STh92 St Aug Coll Cant 74. **d** 75 **p** 76. C Chatham St Wm *Roch* 75-78; C-in-c Weeke *Win* 78-81; V Southn St Mary Extra 81-86; V Hurstbourne Tarrant, Faccombe, Vernham Dean etc from 86; RD Andover from 95. *The Vicarage, Hurstbourne Tarrant, Andover, Hants SP11 0AH* Hurstbourne Tarrant (01264) 736222

HARLEY, Robert Peter. b 59. Leic Univ BA81. Sarum & Wells Th Coll 86. **d** 89 **p** 90. C Thornbury *Glouc* 89-93; C W Drayton *Lon* from 93. *31 Swan Road, West Drayton, Middx UB7 7JY* West Drayton (01895) 422475

HARLEY, Roger Newcomb. b 38. Ely Th Coll 61. **d** 64 **p** 65. C Plymouth St Pet *Ex* 64-66; C Heston *Lon* 66-69; C Maidstone All SS w St Phil and H Trin *Cant* 69-73; R Temple Ewell w Lydden 73-79; P-in-c Shirley St Geo 79-81; V 81-84; V Croydon H Sav *S'wark* 85-95; V Forest Row *Chich* from 95. *The Vicarage, Lewes Road, Forest Row, E Sussex RH18 5AF* Forest Row (01342) 822595

HARLOW, Antony Francis. b 24. Pemb Coll Cam BA50 MA55. Oak Hill Th Coll 84. **d** 85 **p** 86. NSM Watford St Luke *St Alb* 85-86; CMS 86-91; Uganda 86-91; Perm to Offic *St Alb* from 90; NSM Watford St Pet 92-94. *23 Elizabeth Court, 170 Hempstead Road, Watford WD1 3LR* Watford (01923) 239111

HARLOW, Canon Derrick Peter. b 30. St Jo Coll Cam BA53 MA57. Ridley Hall Cam 53. **d** 55 **p** 56. C Barking St Marg *Chelmsf* 55-58; V Leyton Em 58-63; V Goodmayes All SS 63-75; R Thundersley 76-83; TR Saffron Walden w Wendens Ambo and Littlebury from 83; Hon Can Chelmsf Cathl 84-95. *The Rectory, 17 Borough Lane, Saffron Walden, Essex CB11 4AG* Saffron Walden (01799) 523130

HARLOW, Mrs Elizabeth Gilchrist. b 27. MSc. DipTh. **d** 91 **p** 94. Par Dn St Alb St Luke *St Alb* from 91. *23 Elizabeth Court, 170 Hempstead Road, Watford WD1 3LR* Watford (01923) 239111

HARLOW-TRIGG, Richard John St Clair. b 63. Cam Univ BA85 MA88. Cranmer Hall Dur 87. **d** 89 **p** 90. C Hyson Green *S'well* 89-91; C Basford w Hyson Green 91-94; C Mansf St Pet from 94. *85 Delamere Drive, Mansfield, Notts NG18 4DD* Mansfield (01623) 649119

HARLOW, Archdeacon of. *See* FOX, Ven Michael John

HARMAN, Preb John Gordon Kitchener. b 14. Qu Coll Cam BA36 MA40. Lon Coll of Div 36. **d** 37 **p** 38. R Edgware *Lon* 60-75; C-in-c Westbourne Ch Ch Prop Chpl *Win* 75-81; rtd 79; Perm to Offic *Leic* from 82; Perm to Offic *Lon* 84-92. *32 Lansdowne Road, Shepshed, Leics LE12 9RS* Shepshed (01509) 502865

HARMAN, Leslie Davies. b 46. Nottm Univ BTh76. St Jo Coll Nottm LTh75. **d** 76 **p** 77. C Wandsworth All SS *S'wark* 76-78; C Godstone 78-82; V Thorncombe w Winsham and Cricket St Thomas *B & W* 82-87; TV Hitchin *St Alb* 87-95; V Royston from 95. *The Vicarage, 31 Baldock Road, Royston, Herts SG8 5BJ* Royston (01763) 243145

HARMAN, Michael John. b 48. Chich Th Coll 71. **d** 74 **p** 75. C Blackpool St Steph *Blackb* 74-79; Chapl RN from 79. *Directorate Gen, RN Chapl Services, Room 203, Victory Building, HM Naval Base, Portsmouth PO1 3LS* Portsmouth (01705) 727903 Fax 727112

HARMAN, Canon Robert Desmond. b 41. TCD BA65 MA71. CITC 67. **d** 67 **p** 68. C Taney Ch Ch *D & G* 67-73; I Dub Santry w Glasnevin 73-86; I Dub Sandford w Milltown from 86; Can Ch Ch Cathl Dub from 91. *The Rectory, Sandford Close, Ranelagh, Dublin 6, Irish Republic* Dublin (1) 497-2983 Fax as telephone

HARMAN, Theodore Allan. b 27. Linc Coll Ox BA52 MA56 Hatf Coll Dur MA90. Wells Th Coll 52. **d** 54 **p** 55. Lic to Offic *Bradf* from 57; Asst Chapl Sedbergh Sch Cumbria 57-84; Sen Chapl 84-87; Asst Master 57-87; Tutor Hatf Coll Dur from 88; Admissions Tutor 89-90; Lib from 91; Coll Officer from 91; rtd 92. *Flat D1, Hatfield College, North Bailey, Durham DH1 3RQ* 0191-374 3176 Fax 374 7472

HARMER, Timothy James (Tim). b 47. Birm Univ CertEd68. St Jo Coll Nottm BA95. **d** 95. C Studley *Cov* from 95. *3 Westmead Avenue, Studley, Warks B80 7NB* Studley (01527) 857688

HARNISH, Dr Robert George (Rob). b 64. Univ of Ottawa BSc87 Worc Coll Ox DPhil90 MA92. Wycliffe Hall Ox 90. **d** 93 **p** 94. C Chinnor w Emmington and Sydenham etc *Ox* from 93. *44 Cowleaze, Chinnor, Oxford OX9 4TB* Kingston Blount (01844) 353763

HARONSKI, Boleslaw. b 46. Pemb Coll Ox BA68 MA72 DPhil73. St Mich Coll Llan 80 Westcott Ho Cam 82. **d** 82 **p** 83. C Newport Maindee St Jo Ev *Mon* 82-85; V Llanishen w Trelleck Grange and Llanfihangel etc 85-89; V Blackwood 89-92. *45 St Julian's Road, Newport, Gwent NP9 7GN*

HARPER, Canon Alan Edwin Thomas. b 44. Leeds Univ BA65. CITC 75. **d** 78 **p** 79. C Ballywillan *Conn* 78-80; I Moville w Greencastle, Upper Moville etc *D & R* 80-82; I Londonderry Ch Ch 82-86; I Belf Malone St Jo *Conn* from 86; RD S Belf from 89; Preb St Audoen St Patr Cathl Dub from 90. *St John's Rectory, 86 Maryville Park, Belfast BT9 6LQ* Belfast (01232) 666644

HARPER, Alan Peter. b 50. FCA83 Man Univ BA73. Ripon Coll Cuddesdon 86. **d** 88 **p** 89. C Newport w Longford and Chetwynd *Lich* 88-91; P-in-c Wilnecote 91-94; V from 94. *The Vicarage, Glascote Lane, Wilnecote, Tamworth, Staffs B77 2PH* Tamworth (01827) 280806

HARPER, Brian John. b 61. Liv Univ BA82 TCD DipTh85. **d** 85 **p** 86. C Portadown St Columba *Arm* 85-88; C Drumglass 88-89; I Errigle Keerogue w Ballygawley and Killeshil 89-93; Dioc Info Officer from 90; I Mullavilly from 93. *89 Mullavilly Road, Tandragee, Co Armagh BT62 2LX* Tandragee (01762) 840221

HARPER, Clive Stewart. b 35. FCIS71. Ridley Hall Cam 80. **d** 82 **p** 83. C Bromyard *Heref* 82-85; P-in-c Bredenbury and Wacton w Grendon Bishop 85-89; P-in-c Edwyn Ralph and Collington w Thornbury 85-89; P-in-c Pencombe w Marston Stannett and Lt Cowarne 85-89; R Bredenbury w Grendon Bishop and Wacton etc 89-92; R Bilton *Cov* from 92. *The Rectory, Church Walk, Rugby, Warks CV22 7RN* Rugby (01788) 812613

HARPER, David Laurence. b 51. Qu Coll Cam BA73 MA77 PhD78. Wycliffe Hall Ox BA80. **d** 80 **p** 81. C Mansf St Pet *S'well* 80-84; C Wollaton 84-87; V Brinsley w Underwood 87-94; R Bingham from 94. *The Rectory, Bingham, Nottingham NG13 8DR* Bingham (01949) 837335

HARPER, Donald Morrison. b 10. MBE91. Qu Coll Cam BA36 MA41. Ridley Hall Cam 36. **d** 38 **p** 39. R-in-c Brighton St Geo *Chich* 65-70; Nigeria 70-72; Chapl Madeira *Eur* 72-76; rtd 75; Chapl Costa del Sol W *Eur* 76-84; Chapl Tangier 84-85; Chapl Palermo w Taormina 85-90. *Bishop's House, Lansdowne Crescent, Worcester WR3 8JH* Worcester (01905) 723972

HARPER, Geoffrey. b 32. Hertf Coll Ox BA55 MA59. Coll of Resurr Mirfield. **d** 57 **p** 58. C Cov St Pet *Cov* 57-60; C Handsworth St Mich *Birm* 60-62; C-in-c Kingstanding St Mark CD 62-71; V Kingstanding St Mark 71-73; R Sheviock

Truro 73-80; R Antony w Sheviock 80-82; V Paul from 82; Dioc Development Rep from 86. *The Vicarage, Paul, Penzance, Cornwall TR20 8TY* Penzance (01736) 731261

HARPER, Geoffrey Roger. b 57. Jes Coll Cam BA MA DipTh. St Jo Coll Nottm 81. **d** 84 **p** 85. C Belper *Derby* 84-87; C Birstall and Wanlip *Leic* 87-90; TV Tettenhall Regis *Lich* from 90. *St Paul's Vicarage, 1 Talaton Close, Pendeford, Wolverhampton WV9 5LS* Wolverhampton (01902) 787199

HARPER, Gordon. b 32. Oak Hill Th Coll 64. **d** 66 **p** 67. C Halliwell St Pet *Man* 66-71 and from 84; P-in-c Brinsworth *Sheff* 71-75; V Brinsworth w Catcliffe 76-84. *54 Redcar Road, Bolton BL1 6LL* Bolton (01204) 849413

HARPER, Dr Gordon William Robert. b 48. Wellington Univ (NZ) BA70 St Chad's Coll Dur BA74 Nottm Univ PhD89. Coll of Resurr Mirfield 74. **d** 75 **p** 76. C Battyeford *Wakef* 75-76; New Zealand 76-80; P-in-c Byers Green *Dur* 80-83; V Evenwood 83-89; R Wolviston from 89. *The Rectory, 1 Clifton Avenue, Billingham, Cleveland TS22 5DE* Stockton-on-Tees (01642) 551666

HARPER, Horace Frederic. b 37. Lich Th Coll 58. **d** 60 **p** 61. C Stoke upon Trent *Lich* 60-63; C Fenton 63-66; V Coseley Ch Ch 66-75; V Trent Vale 75-88; P-in-c Dresden 88-89; V from 89; P-in-c Normacot from 94. *Dresden Vicarage, 22 Red Bank, Longton, Stoke-on-Trent ST3 4EY* Stoke-on-Trent (01782) 321257

HARPER, Ian. b 54. AKC78. Oak Hill Th Coll 79. **d** 80 **p** 81. C Sidcup St Jo *Roch* 80-83; C Bushey *St Alb* 83-87; TV Thamesmead *S'wark* 87-92; TR N Lambeth from 92. *St Anselm's Rectory, Kennington Road, London SE11 5DU* 0171-735 3415 or 735 3403

HARPER, James. b 35. St Luke's Coll Ex TDip57. SW Minl Tr Course DipTh89. **d** 90 **p** 91. NSM Pendeen w Morvah *Truro* from 90. *11 Carrallack Terrace, St Just, Penzance, Cornwall TR19 7LW* Penzance (01736) 788574

HARPER, John Anthony. b 46. AKC69. **d** 70 **p** 71. C Pet St Mary *Pet* 70-73; C Abington 73-75; V Grendon w Castle Ashby 75-82; Asst Dioc Youth Chapl 75-82; R Castor w Sutton and Upton 82-94; TV Riverside *Ox* from 94. *Saint Andrew's Vicarage, 55 Welley Road, Wraysbury, Staines, Middx TW19 5ER* Staines (01784) 481258

HARPER, John Hugh. b 34. ALAM62 Hertf Coll Ox BA57 MA61. Wells Th Coll 57. **d** 59 **p** 60. C Twerton *B & W* 59-62; R Chapel Allerton 62-69; V Blackford 62-69; V Halsetown *Truro* 69-91; RD Penwith 84-88; P-in-c S Brent *Ex* 91; V S Brent and Rattery from 91. *The Vicarage, Firswood, South Brent, Devon TQ10 9AN* South Brent (01364) 72774

HARPER, Joseph Frank. b 38. Hull Univ BA60 MA86. Linc Th Coll 80. **d** 81 **p** 82. C Preston St Cuth *Blackb* 81-83; C Lanc St Mary 83-87; V Bamber Bridge St Aid 87-92; V Kinsley w Wragby *Wakef* from 92. *The Vicarage, Fitzwilliam, Pontefract, W Yorkshire WF9 5BX* Hemsworth (01977) 610497

HARPER, Malcolm Barry. b 37. Dur Univ BSc59. Wycliffe Hall Ox 59. **d** 61 **p** 62. C Harold Wood *Chelmsf* 61-65; C Madeley *Heref* 65-68; V Slaithwaite w E Scammonden *Wakef* 68-75; V Walmley *Birm* from 75. *The Vicarage, 2 Walmley Road, Sutton Coldfield, W Midlands B76 8QN* 0121-351 1030

HARPER, Martin Nigel. b 48. FRICS88. S Dios Minl Tr Scheme. **d** 86 **p** 87. NSM St Leonards Ch Ch and St Mary Chich 85-94; NSM Rye from 94. *6 St Matthew's Drive, St Leonards-on-Sea, E Sussex TN38 0TR* Hastings (01424) 713631

HARPER, Canon Maurice. b 20. St Steph Ho Ox 60. **d** 62 **p** 63. V Gt Ilford St Mary *Chelmsf* 67-71; R Upminster 71-85; RD Havering 80-85; Hon Can Chelmsf Cathl 84-85; rtd 85; Perm to Offic *Chelmsf* from 85; Perm to Offic *Nor* from 85; Perm to Offic *St E* from 87. *1 Pine Close, Harleston, Norfolk IP20 9DZ* Harleston (01379) 853401

HARPER, Michael Sydney. b 36. Portsm Dioc Tr Course 86. **d** 87. NSM Leigh Park St Clare CD *Portsm* 87-88; NSM Warren Park St Clare from 88. *17 Hampage Green, Warren Park, Havant, Hants PO9 4HJ* Havant (01705) 454275

HARPER, Paul. b 11. Pemb Coll Ox BA34 MA38. Clifton Th Coll 35. **d** 35 **p** 36. Hd Master Colston Prep Sch Bris 61-68; rtd 76. *2 Dawbourne House, Ashford Road, St Michaels, Tenterden, Kent TN30 6PY* Tenterden (01580) 762751

HARPER, Dr Richard Michael. b 53. Lon Univ BSc75 Univ of Wales PhD78. St Steph Ho Ox BA80. **d** 81 **p** 82. C Holt *Nor* 81-84; C-in-c Grahame Park St Aug CD *Lon* 84-88; Sub-Warden & Dir of Studies St Mich Llan 88-93; Lect Ch Hist Univ of Wales (Cardiff) 88-93; R St Leonards Ch Ch and St Mary *Chich* from 94. *14 Stockleigh Road, St Leonards-on-Sea, E Sussex TN38 0JP* Hastings (01424) 422513

HARPER, Robert. b 08. Lon Coll of Div 46. **d** 46 **p** 47. R St Florence and Redberth *St D* 70-78; rtd 78; NSM Maenclochog w Henry's Moat and Mynachlogddu etc *St D* from 95; NSM

New Moat w Llys-y-fran from 95. *South Hill Cottages, Talbenny, Haverfordwest, Dyfed SA62 3XA*   Broad Haven (01437) 781338

HARPER, Roger.FCA BSc. **d** 87 **p** 88. NSM Onchan *S & M* from 87. *Ballahowin House, St Mark's, Ballasalla, Isle of Man IM9 3AS*   Douglas (01624) 851251

HARPER, Thomas Reginald. b 31. Dur Univ BA57 MA67. **d** 58 **p** 59. C Corbridge w Halton *Newc* 58-60; C Byker St Mich 60-62; V Ushaw Moor *Dur* 62-67; Asst Chapl HM Pris Dur 62-67; N Sec CMS 67-74; V Thornthwaite *Carl* 74-75; V Thornthwaite cum Braithwaite and Newlands 76-90; TV Bellingham/Otterburn Gp *Newc* 90-91; TV N Tyne and Redesdale Team 91-92; TR from 92; RD Bellingham from 93. *Bellingham Rectory, Hexham, Northd NE48 2JS*   Hexham (01434) 220019

HARPER, Timothy James Lincoln (Tim). b 54. LRAM Lon Univ BMus76 CertEd DipP&C. Wycliffe Hall Ox 84. **d** 86 **p** 87. C Morden *S'wark* 86-90; V Deptford St Pet from 90. *St Peter's Vicarage, Wickham Road, London SE4 1LT*   0181-691 3334

HARRAP, William Charles (Bill). b 32. BEM86. **d** 72 **p** 74. Hon C Bethnal Green St Jas Less *Lon* from 72. *12 Wedgewood House, Morpeth Street, London E2 0PZ*   0181-980 6887

HARRATT, Philip David. b 56. Magd Coll Ox BA79 MA83. Ripon Coll Cuddesdon 82. **d** 85 **p** 86. C Ewyas Harold w Dulas, Kenderchurch etc *Heref* 85-88; V Chirbury from 88; V Trelystan from 88; V Marton from 88. *The Vicarage, Chirbury, Montgomery, Powys SY15 6BN*   Chirbury (01938) 561218

HARRE, Kenneth Michael. b 25. MA. E Anglian Minl Tr Course. **d** 84 **p** 85. NSM N Walsham w Antingham *Nor* 84-87; P-in-c Nor St Helen from 87. *65 Yarmouth Road, North Walsham, Norfolk NR28 9AU*   North Walsham (01692) 403362

HARREX, David Brian. b 54. DipHE89. Trin Coll Bris 87. **d** 89 **p** 90. C Bedminster St Mich *Bris* 89-93; V Pilning w Compton Greenfield from 93. *The Vicarage, The Glebe, Pilning, Bristol BS12 3LE*   Pilning (01454) 633409

HARRIES, Gwilym David. b 41. Univ of Wales (Lamp) BA63. St Mich Coll Llan 63. **d** 65 **p** 66. C Llangiwg *S & B* 65-68; C Llangyfelach and Morriston 68-71; TV Abth *St D* 71-76; R Hubberston 76-82; R Hubberston w Herbrandston and Hasguard etc 82-84; V Burry Port and Pwll from 84. *The Vicarage, 134 Pencoed Road, Burry Port, Dyfed SA16 0SB*   Burry Port (01554) 832936

HARRIES, Henry Rayner Mackintosh. b 30. MBE67. Chich Th Coll 53. **d** 55 **p** 56. Chapl RAF 58-79; Asst Chapl-in-Chief RAF 79-84; QHC 83-84; P-in-c Gt Brickhill w Bow Brickhill and Lt Brickhill *Ox* 84-86; R 86-94; RD Mursley 91-94; rtd 95. *44 Onslow Gardens, Ongar, Essex CM5 9BQ*   Ongar (01277) 363741

HARRIES, Canon Lewis John. b 27. Univ of Wales BA52. St Mich Coll Llan 51. **d** 53 **p** 54. V Tredegar St Geo *Mon* 64-93; RD Bedwellty 78-93; Can St Woolos Cathl 82-93; rtd 93; Hon Can St Woolos Cathl *Mon* from 93. *14 Hendre Road, Llanelli, Dyfed SA14 9LD*   Llanelli (01554) 773039

✠**HARRIES, Rt Rev Richard Douglas.** b 36. Selw Coll Cam BA61 MA65. Cuddesdon Coll 61. **d** 63 **p** 64. C Hampstead St Jo *Lon* 63-69; Chapl Westf Coll Lon 67-69; Tutor Wells Th Coll 69-71; Warden Sarum & Wells Th Coll 71-72; V Fulham All SS *Lon* 72-81; Dean K Coll Lon 81-87; FKC from 83; Consultant to Abps Cant and York on Inter-Faith Relns from 86; Bp Ox from 87. *Bishop's House, 27 Linton Road, Oxford OX2 6UL*   Oxford (01865) 244566 Fax 790470

HARRINGTON, Charles William. b 04. Linc Th Coll. **d** 42 **p** 43. V Horley w Hornton *Ox* 65-70; C-in-c Hanwell 65-70; V Letcombe Regis w Letcombe Bassett 70-73; rtd 73; Perm to Offic *Cant* 74-88. *Broadleas Retirement Home, 9 Eldorado Road, Cheltenham, Glos GL50 2PU*   Cheltenham (01242) 583232

HARRINGTON, John Christopher Thomas. b 43. Conf Catholic Colls CertRE63. Qu Coll Birm 71. **d** 74 **p** 75. C Northn St Mich *Pet* 74-76; CF (TA) 75-85; C Paston *Pet* 76-79; Chapl Doddington Co Hosp 79-83; R Benwick St Mary *Ely* 79-82; R Doddington 79-82; R Doddington w Benwick 82-83; V Eastbourne St Mich *Chich* from 83. *The Vicarage, 15 Long Acre Close, Eastbourne, E Sussex BN21 1UF*   Eastbourne (01323) 645740

HARRINGTON, Peter Anthony Saunders. b 30. Fitzw Ho Cam BA52 MA58. Ely Th Coll 53. **d** 55 **p** 56. Chapl Dr Challoner's Gr Sch Amersham 67-95; Lic to Offic *Ox* 67-78; Lic to Offic *St Alb* from 78; rtd 95. *5 Linfields, Little Chalfont, Amersham, Bucks HP7 9QH*   Little Chalfont (01494) 763471

HARRINGTON, William Harry. b 33. AKC57. **d** 58 **p** 59. C Childwall All SS *Liv* 58-60; C Sutton 60-64; V Ditton St Mich 64-76; V Mossley Hill St Barn 76-83; V Highfield from 83. *St Matthew's Vicarage, Highfield, Wigan, Lancs WN3 6BL*   Wigan (01942) 222121

HARRIS, Arthur Emlyn Dawson. b 27. Ex Univ BSc47 Lon Univ DipRS86. S'wark Ord Course 83. **d** 86 **p** 87. NSM Frant w Eridge *Chich* 86-87; P-in-c Withyham St Mich 87-95; rtd 95. *The Rectory, Withyham, Hartfield, E Sussex TN7 4BA*   Hartfield (01892) 770241

HARRIS, Basil George. b 17. St Mich Coll Llan 59. **d** 61 **p** 62. Perm to Offic *Llan* 65-71; C St Alb St Sav *St Alb* 71-74; V Middleton St Cross *Ripon* 74-79; R Helpringham w Hale *Linc* 79-83; rtd 83. *12 Blounts Court, Potterne, Devizes, Wilts SN10 5QA*   Devizes (01380) 724570

HARRIS, Bernard Malcolm. b 29. Leeds Univ BA54. Coll of Resurr Mirfield 54. **d** 56 **p** 57. V W Bromwich St Jas *Lich* 66-78; V Sedgley All SS 78-93; rtd 93. *6 Beacon Lane, Sedgley, Dudley, West Midlands DY3 1NB*   Dudley (01902) 663134

HARRIS, Brian. b 33. Man Univ BSc. Qu Coll Birm 79. **d** 80 **p** 81. C St Chad *Lich* 80-81; Perm to Offic *Ches* 82-87; NSM Warburton 87-88; P-in-c 88-92; R Gt and Lt Casterton w Pickworth and Tickencote *Pet* from 92; RD Barnack from 94. *The Rectory, Main Street, Great Casterton, Stamford, Lincs PE9 4AP*   Stamford (01780) 64036

HARRIS, Brian William. b 38. K Coll Lon BD61 AKC61. St Boniface Warminster 61. **d** 62 **p** 63. C Kirkby *Liv* 65-70; V Dalton 70-79; V Aberford w Saxton *York* 79-91; V Hemingbrough 91-95; rtd 95; Perm to Offic *York* from 95; Dom Chapl to Bp Selby from 95. *1 Andrew Drive, Huntington, York YO3 9YF*   York (01904) 422988

HARRIS, Catherine Elizabeth. See EDMONDS, Mrs Catherine Elizabeth

HARRIS, Cedric Herbert. b 13. AKC37. Wycliffe Hall Ox 37. **d** 37 **p** 38. V Thornes St Jas w Ch Ch *Wakef* 57-73; V Shepley 73-78; rtd 78. *44 Rayner Street, Horbury, Wakefield, W Yorkshire WF4 5BD*   Wakefield (01924) 272297

HARRIS, Charles Edward. b 20. Roch Th Coll 63. **d** 65 **p** 66. C Hertf St Andr *St Alb* 65-71; R Sywell w Overstone *Pet* 71-90; rtd 90; Perm to Offic *Chich* from 92. *College of St Barnabas, Blackberry Lane, Lingfield, Surrey RH7 6NJ*   Dormans Park (01342) 870607

HARRIS, Charles Edwin Laurence. b 96. Ridley Hall Cam 46. **d** 47 **p** 48. V Burbage *Sarum* 50-65; rtd 65. *Church House, Sutton, Dover, Kent CT15 5DF*   Deal (01304) 374809

HARRIS, Claude Anthony. b 16. Dur Univ LTh39. Oak Hill Th Coll 36. **d** 39 **p** 40. R Stone St Mich *Lich* 60-82; V Aston 60-82; rtd 82. *Hardwick Cottage, 51 Stafford Road, Stone, Staffs ST15 0HE*   Stone (01785) 815100

HARRIS, Cyril Evans. b 30. Linc Th Coll 61. **d** 63 **p** 64. C Beaconsfield *Ox* 63-68; V Stoke Poges from 68. *The Vicarage, Park Road, Stoke Poges, Slough SL2 4PE*   Farnham Common (01753) 644177

HARRIS, David. b 52. AKC76. St Steph Ho Ox 76. **d** 77 **p** 79. C Wimbledon *S'wark* 77-80; C Coalbrookdale, Iron-Bridge and Lt Wenlock *Heref* 80-82; V Highters Heath *Birm* 82-84; Perm to Offic *Lon* from 85. *35 Paddonswick Road, London W6 0UA*   0181-748 5195

HARRIS, David Rowland. b 46. Ch Ch Ox BA69 DipTh71 MA72. Wycliffe Hall Ox 70. **d** 73 **p** 74. C Virginia Water *Guildf* 73-76; C Clifton Ch w Em *Bris* 76-79; Scripture Union 79-85; V Bedf Ch Ch *St Alb* from 85. *Christ Church Vicarage, 115 Denmark Street, Bedford MK40 3TJ*   Bedford (01234) 359342

HARRIS, Derrick William. b 21. **d** 63 **p** 64. V Billinge *Liv* 67-81; V Walton *Ches* 81-87; rtd 88. *3 Melrose Avenue, Southport, Merseyside PR9 9UY*   Southport (01704) 213828

HARRIS, Donald Bertram. b 04. K Coll Cam BA25 MA29. Cuddesdon Coll 26. **d** 27 **p** 28. V Wilton Place St Paul *Lon* 55-77; rtd 78. *105 Marsham Court, Marsham Street, London SW1P 4LU*   0171-828 1132

HARRIS, Ernest John. b 46. Lon Univ DipTh74 QUB BD75. **d** 75 **p** 76. C Lisburn Ch Ch *Conn* 75-78; C Coleraine 78-83; I Belf St Kath 83-90; I Ballinderry from 90. *The Rectory, 124 Ballinderry Road, Ballinderry Upper, Lisburn, Co Antrim BT28 2NL*   Aghalee (01846) 651310

HARRIS, Evan Rufus. b 21. Univ of Wales (Lamp) BA49. Bp Burgess Hall Lamp. **d** 50 **p** 51. R Barrowby *Linc* 57-86; Offg Chapl RAF 70-76; rtd 86. *Flat 2, 4 Northumberland Road, Barnet, Herts EN5 1ED*   0181-447 0502

HARRIS, Frank Edward. b 33. ACT ThL69 St Fran Coll Brisbane 65. **d** 68 **p** 69. Australia 68-71 and 73-76; C Plymstock *Ex* 71-72; C E Acton St Dunstan w St Thos *Lon* 72-73; C Bodmin *Truro* 76-77; P-in-c Menheniot 77-79; V Winton *Man* 79-87; Guinea 87-89; R Blisland w St Breward *Truro* from 90. *The Rectory, Blisland, Bodmin, Cornwall PL30 4JE*   Bodmin (01208) 851020

HARRIS, Geoffrey Daryl. b 39. Lon Univ DipTh66 Open Univ BA83. St Aid Birkenhead 63. **d** 66 **p** 67. C Eston *York* 66-70; C Iffley *Ox* 70-75; V Bubwith *York* 75-78; V Bubwith w Ellerton and Aughton 78-79; P-in-c Stillingfleet w Naburn 79-80; R Escrick and Stillingfleet w Naburn from 80; Chapl Qu Marg

Sch York from 83. *The Rectory, Escrick, York YO4 6EX* Escrick (01904) 728406

HARRIS, George. b 36. Sarum Th Coll 66. **d** 68 **p** 69. C Shildon *Dur* 68-70; CF 70-74; P-in-c Doddington *Ely* 74-75; R 75-78; R Benwick St Mary 74-78; V Shotton *Dur* 78-86; V Stockton St Mark 86-87; V Chilton Moor 87-94; rtd 94. *8 Longlands Drive, Houghton Park, Houghton le Spring, Tyne & Wear DH5 8LR*

HARRIS, Gerald Alfred. b 29. Qu Coll Birm 80. **d** 84 **p** 85. NSM Pedmore *Worc* 84-86; C Christchurch *Win* 86-94; rtd 94. *7 Wych Court, Hawkchurch, Axminster, Devon EX13 5XE* Hawkchurch (01297) 678503

HARRIS, Jack. b 49. Barrister-at-Law (Lincoln's Inn) 72 St Cath Coll Ox BA70 MA74 Fitzw Coll Cam BA85 MA89. Westcott Ho Cam 83. **d** 86 **p** 87. C Doncaster Ch Ch *Sheff* 86-91; P-in-c 91-92; V 92-95; V Doncaster H Trin from 95. *The Vicarage, 69 Chequer Road, Doncaster, S Yorkshire DN1 2AN* Doncaster (01302) 349684

HARRIS, James Nigel Kingsley. b 37. St D Coll Lamp BA60. Sarum Th Coll. **d** 62 **p** 63. C Painswick *Glouc* 62-65; C Glouc St Paul 65-67; V Slad 67-77; V Cam 77-78; P-in-c Stinchcombe 77-78; V Cam w Stinchcombe 78-82; V Stonehouse from 82; Chapl Standish Hosp Glouc from 92. *The Vicarage, Elms Road, Stonehouse, Glos GL10 2NP* Stonehouse (01453) 822332

HARRIS, James Philip. b 59. Westf Coll Lon BA82. St Mich Coll Llan BD86. **d** 86 **p** 87. C Newport St Paul *Mon* 86-89; C Bedwellty 89-91; V Newport St Matt from 91. *St Matthew's Vicarage, 124 Caerleon Road, Newport, Gwent NP9 7GS* Newport (01633) 262377

HARRIS, Jeremy Michael. b 64. Gwent Coll of HE HNC86. St Steph Ho Ox BTh93. **d** 93 **p** 94. C Newport St Julian *Mon* from 93. *Church House, 142 Old Barn, St Julians, Newport, Gwent NP9 7BQ* Newport (01633) 211791

HARRIS, Very Rev John. b 32. Univ of Wales (Lamp) BA55. Sarum Th Coll 55. **d** 57 **p** 58. V Pontnewynydd *Mon* 57-60; C Bassaleg 60-63; V Penmaen 63-69; V Newport St Paul 69-84; RD Newport 77-93; V Newport Maindee St Jo Ev 84-93; Can St Woolos Cathl 84-93; Dean Brecon *S & B* from 93; V Brecon St Mary and Battle w Llanddew from 93. *Blackstone, 25 Pendre, Brecon, Powys LD3 9EF* Brecon (01874) 624876

HARRIS, John. b 45. St Steph Ho Ox 72. **d** 75 **p** 76. C Wanstead St Mary *Chelmsf* 75-84; V Penponds *Truro* 84-91; V St Gluvias from 91. *The Vicarage, St Gluvias, Penryn, Cornwall TR10 9LQ* Falmouth (01326) 373356

HARRIS, John. b 54. Leeds Univ BSc75. St Jo Coll Nottm LTh86. **d** 86 **p** 87. C Scissett *Wakef* 86-90; V Moldgreen from 90. *The Vicarage, 35 Church Street, Moldgreen, Huddersfield HD5 9DL* Huddersfield (01484) 424432

HARRIS, John Brian. b 53. Hertf Coll Ox BA76. Ripon Coll Cuddesdon 87. **d** 89 **p** 90. C Witton *Ches* 89-93; R Thurstaston from 93. *The Rectory, Thurstaston Road, Irby, Wirral, Merseyside L61 0HQ* 0151-648 1816

HARRIS, Canon John Peter. b 33. St D Coll Lamp BA57. **d** 58 **p** 59. Chapl St Woolos Hosp Newport 58-63; C Newport St Woolos *Mon* 58-60; Chapl St Woolos Cathl 60-63; CF (TA) 59-63; CF 63-82; V Chepstow *Mon* from 82; RD Chepstow from 85; Can St Woolos Cathl from 93. *The Vicarage, 25 Mount Way, Chepstow, Gwent NP6 5NF* Chepstow (01291) 620980

HARRIS, John Stuart. b 29. Hertf Coll Ox BA52 MA56. Wells Th Coll 52. **d** 54 **p** 55. C Epsom St Martin *Guildf* 54-58; C Guildf H Trin w St Mary 58-63; R Bentley 63-72; V Milford 72-87; R Walton-on-the-Hill from 87; Dioc Ecum Officer 87-92. *St Peter's Rectory, Walton-on-the-Hill, Tadworth, Surrey KT20 7SO* Tadworth (01737) 812105

HARRIS, Mrs Judith Helen. b 42. Chelsea Coll Lon TCert64. St Alb Minl Tr Scheme 83. **dss** 86 **d** 87 **p** 94. Leagrave St Alb 86-87; Hon Par Dn 87-91; TD Dunstable 91-94; TV from 94. *95 Evelyn Road, Dunstable, Beds LU5 4NQ* Dunstable (01582) 476536

HARRIS, Canon Kenneth. b 28. NW Ord Course 70. **d** 72 **p** 73. NSM Upton Ascension *Ches* 72-77; NSM Eccleston and Pulford 77-80; P-in-c Hargrave 80-81; V 81-94; Exec Officer Dioc Bd for Soc Resp 84-94; Hon Can Ches Cathl 91-94; rtd 94. *Delsa, Willington Road, Willington, Tarporley, Cheshire CW6 0ND* Tarporley (01829) 751880

HARRIS, Lawrence Rex Rowland. b 35. St Cath Coll Cam BA59 MA63. Ely Th Coll. **d** 61 **p** 62. C Carrington *S'well* 61-63; Chapl Rampton Hosp Retford 63-66; V Sturton w Littleborough *S'well* 66-71; V Bole w Saundby 66-71; R Clowne *Derby* from 71; RD Bolsover and Staveley 81-86. *The Rectory, Rectory Road, Clowne, Chesterfield, Derbyshire S43 4BH* Chesterfield (01246) 810387

HARRIS, Leslie Ernest. b 08. Kelham Th Coll 31. **d** 31 **p** 32. V Swinton *Sheff* 65-76; rtd 76; Perm to Offic *Sheff* from 87. *12 Hesley Grove, Chapeltown, Sheffield S30 4TX* Sheffield (0114) 246 9319

HARRIS, Miss Margaret Claire. b 53. RGN85 Homerton Coll Cam BEd78. Ridley Hall Cam CTM92. **d** 92. Par Dn Stevenage All SS Pin Green *St Alb* 92-94; C from 94. *156 Durham Road, Stevenage, Herts SG1 4HZ* Stevenage (01438) 740621

HARRIS, Martin John. b 54. Trin Coll Cam BA76 MA. Wycliffe Hall Ox 82. **d** 85 **p** 86. C Lindfield *Chich* 85-88; C Galleywood Common *Chelmsf* 88-91; V Southchurch Ch Ch from 91. *Christ Church Vicarage, Warwick Road, Southend-on-Sea SS1 3BN* Southend-on-Sea (01702) 582585

HARRIS (formerly PRATT), Michael. b 34. ACP65 MIL76 St Mark & St Jo Coll Lon CertEd56. Qu Coll Birm. **d** 83 **p** 84. NSM Bournville *Birm* 83-90; NSM Stirchley from 90; Chapl Univ of Cen England in Birm from 92. *3 Teazel Avenue, Bournville, Birmingham B30 1LZ* 0121-459 5236

HARRIS, Michael Andrew. b 53. Ian Ramsey Coll 74 Trin Coll Bris 75. **d** 78 **p** 79. C St Paul's Cray St Barn *Roch* 78-82; C Church Stretton *Heref* 82-87; Res Min Penkridge w Stretton *Lich* 87-90; Res Min Penkridge Team 90-92; V Amington *Birm* from 92. *The Vicarage, 224 Tamworth Road, Amington, Tamworth, Staffs B77 3DE* Tamworth (01827) 62573

HARRIS, Nicholas Bryan. b 60. Down Coll Cam BA81 MA85. Ridley Hall Cam 82. **d** 85 **p** 86. C Walney Is *Carl* 85-88; C S'wark Ch Ch *S'wark* 88-92. *82 Hurst Road, Eastbourne, E Sussex BN21 2PW* Eastbourne (01323) 731922

HARRIS, Owen. b 50. Univ of Wales (Swansea) BSc(Econ)71 PGCE72. St Mich Coll Llan DPT94. **d** 94 **p** 95. C Bassaleg *Mon* from 94. *2 High Cross Drive, Rogerstone, Newport, Gwent NP1 9AB* Rhiwderin (0633) 895441

✠**HARRIS, Rt Rev Patrick Burnet.** b 34. Keble Coll Ox BA58 MA63. Clifton Th Coll 58. **d** 60 **p** 61 **c** 73. C Ox St Ebbe w St Pet *Ox* 60-63; SAMS 63-81; Adn N Argentina 70-73; Bp 73-80; R Kirkheaton *Wakef* 81-85; Asst Bp Wakef 81-85; Sec C of E Partnership for World Miss 86-88; Asst Bp Ox 86-88; Bp S'well from 88. *Bishop's Manor, Southwell, Notts NG25 0JR* Southwell (01636) 812112   Fax 815401

HARRIS, Paul. b 55. BEd79 DipHE84. Oak Hill Th Coll 82. **d** 84 **p** 85. C Billericay and Lt Burstead *Chelmsf* 84-87; TV Cheltenham St Mary, St Matt, St Paul and H Trin *Glouc* 87-93; V Bitterne *Win* from 93. *The Vicarage, 2 Bursledon Road, Southampton SO2 7LW* Southampton (01703) 446488

HARRIS, Paul Ian. b 45. MSc. Qu Coll Birm. **d** 82 **p** 83. C The Quinton *Birm* 82-86; V Atherstone *Cov* from 86. *40 Holte Road, Atherstone, Warks CV9 1HN* Atherstone (01827) 713200

HARRIS, Paul Michael. b 58. Chelsea Coll Lon BSc79 Bath Coll of HE CertEd82. Oak Hill Th Coll BA89. **d** 89. C Finchley Ch Ch *Lon* 89-90; Teacher St Luke's Sch W Norwood 90-91; The Philippines from 91. *Brent International School, Meralco Avenue, Pasig, Manila, The Philippines* Manila (2) 631-1265

HARRIS, Peter Frank. b 43. W Midl Minl Tr Course 89. **d** 92 **p** 93. NSM Lich Ch Ch *Lich* from 92. *94 Ogley Hay Road, Boney Hay, Walsall WS7 8HU* Burntwood (01543) 675258

HARRIS, Peter Malcolm. b 52. Em Coll Cam BA74 MA79. Trin Coll Bris DipHE80. **d** 80 **p** 81. C Upton (or Overchurch) *Ches* 80-83; BCMS 83-93; Crosslinks from 93; Portugal from 83. *Arocha, Cruzinha, Mexilhoeira Grande, 8500 Portimao, Portugal* Portimao (82) 96380

HARRIS, Raymond. b 36. Nottm Univ BA58. Lich Th Coll 58. **d** 60 **p** 61. V Bacup Ch Ch *Man* 66-82; R Dunsby w Dowsby *Linc* 82-87; R Rippingale 82-87; R Rippingale Gp 87-94; rtd 94. *2 The Bungalow, High Street, Swaton, Sleaford, Lincs NG34 0JU* Sleaford (01529) 421343

HARRIS, Canon Raymond John. b 29. Leeds Univ BA51. Coll of Resurr Mirfield 51. **d** 53 **p** 54. V New Swindon St Barn Gorse Hill *Bris* 59-94; Hon Can Bris Cathl 80-94; RD Cricklade 82-88; rtd 94. *46 Courtbrook, Fairford, Glos GL7 4BE* Cirencester (01285) 713965

HARRIS, Rebecca Jane. *See* SWYER, Mrs Rebecca Jane

HARRIS, Ven Reginald Brian. b 34. Ch Coll Cam BA58 MA61. Ridley Hall Cam. **d** 59 **p** 60. C Wednesbury St Bart *Lich* 59-61; C Uttoxeter w Bramshall 61-64; V Bury St Pet *Man* 64-70; V Walmsley 70-80; RD Walmsley 70-80; Adn Man from 80; Can Res Man Cathl from 80. *4 Victoria Avenue, Eccles, Manchester M30 9HA* 0161-707 6444   Fax as telephone

HARRIS, Robert Douglas. b 57. BEd. Chich Th Coll 80. **d** 82 **p** 83. C Portsea St Mary *Portsm* 82-87; V Clevedon St Jo *B & W* 87-92; R Felpham w Middleton *Chich* from 92. *The Rectory, 24 Limmer Lane, Felpham, Bognor Regis, W Sussex PO22 7ET* Bognor Regis (01243) 842522

HARRIS, Robert James. b 45. ALCD73. St Jo Coll Nottm 69. **d** 72 **p** 73. C Sheff St Jo *Sheff* 72-76; C Goole 76-78; V Bramley and Ravenfield 78-91; P-in-c Boulton *Derby* from 91. *The Vicarage, 1 St Mary's Close, Boulton Lane, Alvaston, Derby DE24 0FE* Derby (01332) 571296

HARRIS, Robert William. b 26. Roch Th Coll 64. **d** 66 **p** 67. C Herne Bay Ch Ch *Cant* 66-70 and 77-84; V Nonington 70-73; V Nonington w Barfreystone 73-77; P-in-c Sark *Win* 84-91; rtd 91. *16 Sandown Lees, Sandwich, Kent CT13 9NZ* Sandwich (01304) 613746

HARRIS, Thomas William (Tom). b 54. AKC76. Linc Th Coll 77 Kelham Th Coll. **d** 78 **p** 79. C Norton Woodseats St Chad *Sheff* 78-81; V Barnby Dun 81-91; P-in-c Kirk Bramwith 81-85; P-in-c Fenwick 81-85; Chapl RN 91-94; P-in-c Christian Malford w Sutton Benger etc *Bris* 94; R Draycot from 94. *The Rectory, Church Road, Christian Malford, Chippenham, Wilts SN15 4BW* Seagry (01249) 720466

HARRIS, William Edric Mackenzie. b 46. Sarum & Wells Th Coll 72. **d** 75 **p** 76. C Langney *Chich* 75-79; C Moulsecoomb 80-81; TV 81-85; R W Grinstead from 85. *The Rectory, Steyning Road, West Grinstead, Horsham, W Sussex RH13 8LR* Partridge Green (01403) 710339

HARRIS, Canon William Ernest. b 21. TCD BA48 MA57. **d** 48 **p** 49. I Belf St Pet *Conn* 63-90; Preb St Audoen St Patr Cathl Dub 83-90; rtd 90. *87 Sunnylands Avenue, Carrickfergus, Co Antrim BT38 8JY* Carrickfergus (01960) 368470

HARRIS, William Fergus. b 36. CCC Cam BA59 MA63 Edin Univ DipEd70. Yale Div Sch 59 Westcott Ho Cam 60. **d** 62 **p** 63. Chapl Edin Univ *Edin* 64-71; R Edin St Pet 71-83; R Perth St Jo *St And* 83-90; Hon C from 90; rtd 90. *35 St Mary's Drive, Perth PH2 7BY* Perth (01738) 21379

HARRIS-DOUGLAS, John Douglas. b 34. Ripon Hall Ox 65. **d** 66 **p** 67. C Ringwood *Win* 66-67; C Baswich (or Berkswich) *Lich* 67-71; R St Tudy *Truro* 71-74; R St Tudy w Michaelstow 74-76; Adv in Children's Work and Asst Dir Educn 71-76; R Fiskerton *Linc* 76-79; Dir of Educn and Adv RE 76-79; P-in-c Thormanby *York* 79-84; V Brafferton w Pilmoor and Myton on Swale 79-84; V Brafferton w Pilmoor, Myton on Swale etc from 84. *The Vicarage, Brafferton, York YO6 2QB* Boroughbridge (01423) 360244

HARRIS-EVANS, Canon Francis Douglas Harris. b 07. Keble Coll Ox BA32 MA39. Linc Th Coll 32. **d** 35 **p** 36. V Newtown Linford *Leic* 68-74; rtd 74; Perm to Offic *Leic* from 74; Perm to Offic *Pet* from 74. *5 Mayflower Mews, Uppingham, Leics LE15 9ZZ* Uppingham (01572) 823699

HARRIS-EVANS, William Giles. b 46. AKC68. Bangalore Th Coll DipTh70. **d** 70 **p** 71. C Clapham H Trin *S'wark* 70-74; Sri Lanka 75-78; V Benhilton *S'wark* 78-86; TR Cov E *Cov* 86-93; TR Brighouse and Clifton *Wakef* from 93. *The Vicarage, 11 Slead Avenue, Brighouse, W Yorkshire HD6 2JB* Brighouse (01484) 714032

HARRIS-WHITE, John Emlyn. b 34. St Aid Birkenhead 59. **d** 62 **p** 63. V Heyhouses *Blackb* 69-71; Chapl Roundway Hosp Devizes 71-77; Chapl R Variety Children's Hosp 77-89; Chapl K Coll and Belgrave Hosps Lon 77-89; Regional Community Relns Co-ord 89-93; rtd 94. *11 Leaside Court, Clifton Gardens, Folkestone, Kent CT20 2ED* Folkestone (01303) 245184

HARRISON, Alan George. b 20. Leeds Univ BA49. Coll of Resurr Mirfield 49. **d** 51 **p** 52. V Eastleigh *Win* 68-72; Chapl Guild of Health Lon 72-76; Chapl St Mich Convent Ham 73-86; Sec Coun for Relig Communities 76-86; rtd 86. *10 The Quadrangle, Morden College, London SE3 0PW* 0181-858 5134

HARRISON, Alan William. b 16. Lich Th Coll 38. **d** 41 **p** 42. V Somerby, Burrough on the Hill and Pickwell *Leic* 55-72; R Boxford *St E* 72-82; rtd 82; Perm to Offic *St E* from 82. *10 Meadowlands, Woolpit, Bury St Edmunds, Suffolk IP30 9SE* Elmswell (01359) 41614

HARRISON, Albert Arthur. b 01. FCIT. **d** 63 **p** 64. Chapl Aske Chapelry 65-85; NSM Rokeby w Brignall *Ripon* 67-89; rtd 89. *16 Ronaldshay Drive, Richmond, N Yorkshire DL10 5BN* Richmond (01748) 823072

HARRISON, Mrs Alison Edwina. b 53. Newc Univ BEd75. Linc Th Coll 84. dss 86 **d** 87 **p** 94. Loughb Em *Leic* 86-87; Par Dn 87-89; C Stockton *Dur* 89-92; P-in-c Lynesack 92-95; P-in-c Cockfield 92-95; P-in-c Ebchester from 95. *The New Rectory, Shaw Lane, Consett, Co Durham DH8 0PY* Ebchester (01207) 560301

HARRISON, Alistair Lee. b 22. ALCD51. **d** 51 **p** 52. Asst Chapl Miss to Seamen 67-77; Lic to Offic *D & G* 77-83; Lic to Offic *M & K* 77-83; C Dub St Ann w St Mark and St Steph *D & G* 83-92; rtd 92. *8 Grosvenor Place, Rathgar, Dublin 6, Irish Republic* Dublin (1) 497-6053

HARRISON, Mrs Barbara Ann. b 41. Man Univ BA63 Leic Univ CertEd64. E Midl Min Tr Course 85. **d** 88 **p** 94. C Immingham *Linc* 88-94; P-in-c Habrough Gp from 94. *2 Anglesey Drive, Immingham, Grimsby, S Humberside DN40 1RE* Immingham (01469) 573578

HARRISON, Mrs Barbara Anne. b 34. Westf Coll Lon BA56 CertEd57 Hull Univ MA85. Linc Th Coll 76. dss 79 **d** 87 **p** 94. Lakenham St Jo *Nor* 79-80; Chapl York Univ *York* 80-88; TD Sheff Manor *Sheff* 88-93; Par Dn Holts CD *Man* 93-94; C-in-c

from 94; Dioc UPA Officer from 93. *St Hugh's Vicarage, Wildmoor Avenue, Oldham OL4 5NZ* 0161-620 1646 or 832 5253 Fax 832 2869

HARRISON, Bernard Charles. b 37. St Mich Coll Llan 61. **d** 64 **p** 65. C Toxteth Park St Marg *Liv* 64-69; C Hindley All SS 69-71; V Wigan St Geo from 71. *St George's Vicarage, 6 Wrightington Street, Wigan, Lancs WN1 2BX* Wigan (01942) 44500

HARRISON, Brian John. b 35. FCP. Glouc Sch of Min 83. **d** 86 **p** 89. NSM Broseley w Benthall *Heref* 86-93; Perm to Offic from 94. *17 Hafren Road, Little Dawley, Telford, Shropshire TF4 3HJ* Telford (01952) 591891

HARRISON, Bruce. b 49. Linc Th Coll 86. **d** 88 **p** 89. C Syston *Leic* 88-90; C Whitby *York* 90-93; V Glaisdale from 93. *The Vicarage, Glaisdale, Whitby, N Yorkshire YO21 2PL* Whitby (01947) 897214

HARRISON, Bruce Mountford. b 49. AKC71. **d** 72 **p** 73. C Hebburn St Cuth *Dur* 72-75; C Bethnal Green St Jo w St Simon *Lon* 75-77; P-in-c Bethnal Green St Bart 77-78; TV Bethnal Green St Jo w St Bart 78-80; C-in-c Pennywell St Thos and Grindon St Oswald CD *Dur* 80-85; V Sunderland Pennywell St Thos 85-90; V Gateshead St Helen from 90. *The Vicarage, 7 Carlton Terrace, Gateshead, Tyne & Wear NE9 6DE* 0191-487 6510

HARRISON, Christopher Dennis. b 57. Clare Coll Cam BA79 BA86. Westcott Ho Cam 84. **d** 87 **p** 88. C Camberwell St Geo *S'wark* 87-92; V Forest Hill from 92. *The Vicarage, 20 Gaynesford Road, London SE23 2UQ* 0181-699 2576

HARRISON, Christopher Joseph. b 38. AKC61 Bris Univ BEd75. **d** 62 **p** 63. C Bottesford *Linc* 62-67; C Elloughton *York* 67-68; P-in-c Farmington *Glouc* 69-74; C Tredington w Stoke Orchard and Hardwicke 74-86; Perm to Offic from 87. *Appledore, 93 Stoke Road, Bishops Cleeve, Cheltenham, Glos GL52 4RP* Cheltenham (01242) 673452

HARRISON, Colin Charles. b 32. Nottm Univ BA59. Ripon Hall Ox 59. **d** 61 **p** 62. C Everton St Chad w Ch Ch *Liv* 61-64; Japan 64-66; P-in-c Glas St Gabr *Glas* 66-71; R Clarkston 71-74; Area Sec (Inner Lon) Chr Aid 74-84; Hon C St Nic Cole Abbey *Lon* 74-78; Hon C St Botolph without Bishopgate 78-84; Miss to Seamen from 85; Nigeria 85-86; S Africa 87-88; Korea 88-91; Trinidad and Tobago 91-92; Singapore from 92. *291 River Valley Road, Singapore 0923* Singapore (65) 737-2880 Fax 235-3391

HARRISON, David Henry. b 40. Lon Univ DipTh67. Tyndale Hall Bris 65. **d** 68 **p** 69. C Bolton St Paul *Man* 68-72; V Bircle 72-83; V Southport SS Simon and Jude *Liv* 83-91; TR Fazakerley Em from 91. *The Rectory, Higher Lane, Liverpool L9 9DJ* 0151-525 2689

HARRISON, David Robert. b 31. Bris Univ BSc52 CertEd55. Oak Hill Th Coll 56. **d** 58 **p** 59. C Brixton Hill St Sav *S'wark* 58-60; C Harpurhey Ch Ch *Man* 60-62; Singapore 62-67; V Greenfield *Man* 67-78; V Tonge Fold 78-90; R Tasburgh w Tharston, Forncett and Flordon *Nor* 90-93; C Gorleston St Andr from 93. *1 South Garden, Gorleston, Great Yarmouth, Norfolk NR31 6TL* Great Yarmouth (01493) 669401

HARRISON, David Samuel. b 44. Univ of Wales (Ban) BSc67. St Mich Coll Llan 67. **d** 70 **p** 71. C Canton St Jo *Llan* 70-74; C Witton *Ches* 74-78; V Sutton St Geo from 78. *St George's Vicarage, 88 Byrons Lane, Macclesfield, Cheshire SK11 7JS* Macclesfield (01625) 423209

HARRISON, Miss Doreen. b 32. Leeds Univ BA53 PGCE54 DipRE57 Lanc Univ MLitt78 MA79. **d** 92 **p** 94. NSM Ambleside w Brathay *Carl* from 92. *Fox How, Ambleside, Cumbria LA22 9LL* Ambleside (015394) 33021

HARRISON, Ernest Wilfrid. b 17. Ox Univ MA Toronto Univ MA. Sarum Th Coll. **d** 40 **p** 41. C Roby *Liv* 40-43; C-in-c St D Huyton w Roby 43-45; C Coulsdon St Jo *S'wark* 45-47; Asst Dioc Missr 48-52; Canada from 52. *Apt 331, 1055 Don Mills Road, Don Mills, Ontario, Canada, M3C 1W8*

HARRISON, Francis Russell. b 20. E Anglian Minl Tr Course. **d** 82 **p** 83. NSM Felixstowe St Jo *St E* 82-85; Asst Chapl Ipswich Hosp 85-87; rtd 87; Perm to Offic *St E* from 87. *The Strands, London Road, Copdock, Ipswich IP8 3JF* Copdock (01473) 730292

HARRISON, Fred Graham. b 41. Lon Univ BSc62. Ridley Hall Cam 80. **d** 82 **p** 83. C Lenton *S'well* 82-85; V Ruddington from 85. *The Vicarage, 62 Musters Road, Ruddington, Nottingham NG11 6HW* Nottingham (0115) 921 1505

HARRISON, Guy Patrick. b 58. CA Tr Coll CertRS85 DipEvang85 Sarum & Wells Th Coll DipThMin94. **d** 94 **p** 95. C Wimborne Minster and Holt *Sarum* from 94. *8 Minster View, Wimborne, Dorset BH21 1BA* Wimborne (01202) 885268

HARRISON, Herbert Gerald. b 29. Oak Hill Th Coll 53. **d** 56 **p** 57. Miss to Seamen 64-74; Port Chapl Ipswich 68-74; V Ipswich All SS *St E* 74-81; P-in-c Elmsett w Aldham 81-88; P-in-c Kersey w Lindsey 81-88; R Horringer cum Ickworth

88-94; rtd 94. *15 Lynwood Avenue, Felixstowe, Suffolk IP11 9HS* Felixstowe (01394) 283764

HARRISON, Ian Wetherby. b 39. Kelham Th Coll 59. **d** 64 **p** 65. C Kennington Park St Agnes *S'wark* 64-67; C E Ham w Upton Park *Chelmsf* 67-71; V Walthamstow St Mich 71-78; Dioc Ecum Officer *Wakef* 78-87; P-in-c Upper Hopton 78-87; P-in-c Mirfield Eastthorpe St Paul 82-87; Min St D Cathl *St D* 87-90; Succ St D Cathl 87-90; P-in-c Leic Ascension *Leic* 90-92; V Leic St Anne from 92. *St Anne's Vicarage, 76 Letchworth Road, Leicester LE3 6FH* Leicester (0116) 285 8452

HARRISON, Jack. b 08. Ripon Hall Ox 64. **d** 65 **p** 66. V Downe *Roch* 69-76; rtd 76; Perm to Offic *Chich* from 76. *Jolly Cottage, Langham Road, Robertsbridge, E Sussex TN32 5DY* Robertsbridge (01580) 880374

HARRISON (nee HOLLINRAKE), Mrs Jean Margaret. b 28. Leeds Univ DSocStuds51 Bolton Teacher Tr Coll TCert64. Wakef Dioc Reader Tr 82. **d** 93. NSM Perth St Ninian *St And* from 93. *12 South Inch Terrace, Perth PH2 8AN* Perth (01738) 39464

HARRISON, John. b 49. Fitzw Coll Cam BA71 MA74. Westcott Ho Cam 74. **d** 77 **p** 78. C Nunthorpe *York* 77-81; C Acomb St Steph 81-83; C-in-c St Aid 81-83; V Heptonstall *Wakef* 83-91; R Stamford Bridge Gp of Par *York* from 91. *The Rectory, 8 Viking Road, Stamford Bridge, York YO4 1BR* Stamford Bridge (01759) 71353

HARRISON, Canon John Gordon. b 13. Wadh Coll Ox BA48 MA52. Trin Coll Bris 32. **d** 36 **p** 38. V Gerrards Cross *Ox* 52-84; RD Amersham 70-79; Hon Can Ch Ch 75-84; rtd 84. *The Clock House, Upton Scudamore, Warminster, Wilts BA12 0AH* Warminster (01985) 214744

HARRISON, John Northcott. b 31. St Jo Coll Cam BA54. Westcott Ho Cam 54. **d** 56 **p** 57. C Moor Allerton *Ripon* 56-59; C Bedale 59-61; V Hudswell w Downholme 61-64; Youth Chapl *Dur* 64-68; V Auckland St Andr and St Anne 68-76; Community Chapl Stockton-on-Tees 76-83; TR Southn (City Cen) *Win* 83-88; V Bris Ch the Servant Stockwood *Bris* from 88; RD Brislington from 89; Chapl St Brendan's Sixth Form Coll from 90. *The Vicarage, Goslet Road, Bristol BS14 8SP* Chew Magna (01275) 832633

HARRISON, Joseph Benson. b 11. OBE74. Didsbury Meth Coll. **d** 49 **p** 50. Gen Sec C of E Coun for Soc Aid 55-75; rtd 76. *50A Sedlescombe Road South, St Leonards-on-Sea, E Sussex TN38 0TJ* Hastings (01424) 446241

HARRISON, Lyndon. b 47. St D Coll Lamp DipTh91 St Mich Coll Llan DMinlStuds93. **d** 93 **p** 94. C Ebbw Vale *Mon* from 93. *The Vicarage, 177 Badminton Grove, Beaufort, Ebbw Vale, Gwent NP3 5UN* Ebbw Vale (01495) 304516

HARRISON, Martin. b 58. DCR78 BA89. Trin Coll Bris 86. **d** 89 **p** 90. C Heworth *York* 89-94; P-in-c Skelton w Shipton and Newton on Ouse from 94. *The Rectory, Church Lane, Skelton, York YO3 6XT* York (01904) 470045

HARRISON, Mary Furley. b 21. MBE63. Westf Coll Lon BA42. Moray Ho Edin CertEd43 Edin Dioc NSM Course 79. **dss** 83 **d** 86. Edin H Cross *Edin* 83-86; NSM from 86. *Barnhill, 33 Barnton Avenue, Edinburgh EH4 6JJ* 0131-336 2226

HARRISON, Matthew Henry. b 64. Univ Coll Dur BA85. Union Th Sem (NY) STM93 St Steph Ho Ox BA88 MA92. **d** 89 **p** 90. C Whickham *Dur* 89-92; USA 92-93; C Owton Manor *Dur* 93-95; Asst Chapl Paris St Geo *Eur* from 95. *7 rue Auguste-Vacquerie, 75116 Paris, France* France (33) 47 20 22 51

HARRISON, Michael Burt (Crispin). b 36. Leeds Univ BA59 Trin Coll Ox BA62 MA66. Coll of Resurr Mirfield 62. **d** 63 **p** 64. C W Hartlepool St Aid *Dur* 63-64; C Middlesb All SS *York* 64-66; Lic to Offic *Wakef* 67-69 and 78-87; CR from 68; S Africa 69-77 and from 87; Registrar Coll of the Resurr Mirfield 78-84; Vice-Prin 84-87. *St Peter's Priory, PO Box 991, Southdale, 2135 South Africa* Johannesburg (11) 434-2504

HARRISON, Michael Robert. b 63. Selw Coll Cam BA84 MSc85. Ripon Coll Cuddesdon BA89 Union Th Sem (NY) STM90. **d** 90 **p** 91. C S Lambeth St Anne and All SS *S'wark* 90-94; Chapl Bp's Chapl to Students *Bradf* from 94; Chapl Bradf Univ from 94; Chapl Bradf and Ilkley Community Coll from 94. Anglican Chaplaincy, *Michael Ramsey House, 2 Ashgrove, Bradford, W Yorkshire BD7 1BN* Bradford (01274) 727034

HARRISON, Canon Noel Milburn. b 27. Lon Univ DipTh56 Leeds Univ MPhil75 PhD80. St Aid Birkenhead 54. **d** 57 **p** 58. Hd Master Elmete Hall Sch Leeds 68-84; Hon C Whitgift w Adlingfleet and Eastoft *Sheff* 83-84; Hon C Abbeydale St Jo 84-86; Dioc Dir of Educn 84-94; R Tankersley 86-94; Hon Can Sheff Cathl 88-94; rtd 94. *Aidan House, 118 High Street, Crowle, Scunthorpe, S Humberside DN17 4DR*

HARRISON, Mrs Nona Margaret. b 50. Open Univ BA80. S Dios Minl Tr Scheme 92. **d** 95. NSM Wellow *Win* from 95. *5 Chichester Close, East Wellow, Romsey, Hants SE51 6EY* Romsey (01794) 323101

HARRISON, Miss Patricia Mary. b 35. St Kath Coll Lon CertEd65 DPEd70 Open Univ BA74. St Mich Ho Ox IDC59. **dss** 85 **d** 87 **p** 94. Nunthorpe *York* 85-87; NSM from 87; rtd 95. *22 Lamonby Close, Nunthorpe, Middlesbrough, Cleveland TS7 0QG* Middlesbrough (01642) 313524

HARRISON, Paul Graham. b 53. Sarum & Wells Th Coll 76. **d** 79 **p** 80. C Brixham w Churston Ferrers *Ex* 79-82; C Portsea N End St Mark *Portsm* 82-87; V Tiverton St Andr *Ex* 87-94; P-in-c Astwood Bank *Worc* from 94; Chapl to the Deaf from 94. *The Vicarage, Church Road, Astwood Bank, Redditch, Worcs B96 6EH* Astwood Bank (01527) 892489

HARRISON, Canon Peter George Stanley. b 22. St Jo Coll Dur BA49 DipTh50. **d** 50 **p** 51. P-in-c Routh *York* 68-91; V Beverley Minster 68-91; RD Beverley 73-85; Can and Preb York Minster from 83; rtd 91. *19 Orchard Way, Pocklington, York YO4 2EH* Pocklington (01759) 304112

HARRISON, Peter Graham. b 12. Ch Ch Ox BA34 MA38. Westcott Ho Cam 34. **d** 35 **p** 36. V Gt Torrington *Ex* 58-78; R Lt Torrington 59-78; rtd 78; C-in-c Holne *Ex* 78-85. *5 The Leat, Bishops Lydeard, Taunton, Somerset TA4 3NY* Taunton (01823) 432584

HARRISON, Peter Keith. b 44. Open Univ BA85. St Aid Birkenhead. **d** 68 **p** 69. C Higher Bebington *Ches* 68-71; C Walmsley *Man* 71-74; V Lumb in Rossendale 74-79; V Heywood St Marg 79-87; V Hey 87-95; AD Saddleworth 93-94; Chapl Athens w Kifissia *Eur* from 95. *c/o The British Embassy, Plutarchou 1, 106 75 Athens, Greece* Athens (1) 721-4906

HARRISON, Peter Reginald Wallace. b 39. Selw Coll Cam BA62. Ridley Hall Cam 62. **d** 64 **p** 65. C Barton Hill St Luke w Ch Ch *Bris* 64-69; Chapl Greenhouse Trust 69-77; Dir Northorpe Hall Trust 77-84; Lic to Offic *Wakef* 77-84; TR Drypool *York* from 84; AD E Hull from 88. *The Vicarage, 139 Laburnum Avenue, Hull HU8 8PA* Hull (01482) 74257

HARRISON, Philip Hubert. b 37. Sarum & Wells Th Coll 77. **d** 79 **p** 80. C Wymondham *Nor* 79-83; V Watton w Carbrooke and Ovington 83-92; R Drayton w Felthorpe from 92. *The Rectory, 46 School Road, Drayton, Norwich NR8 6EF* Norwich (01603) 868749

HARRISON, Raymond Harold. b 16. Keble Coll Ox BA41 MA45. St Aug Coll Cant. **d** 42 **p** 43. R Fen Ditton *Ely* 56-75; V W Wratting 75-82; R Weston Colville 76-82; rtd 82. *2 Guntons Close, Soham, Ely, Cambs CB7 5DN* Ely (01353) 720774

HARRISON, Richard Crispin. b 57. Plymouth Poly BSc79. Trin Coll Bris 82. **d** 85 **p** 86. C Southway *Ex* 85-89; TV Kinson *Sarum* from 89. *The Vicarage, 41 Moore Avenue, Bournemouth BH11 8AT* Bournemouth (01202) 581135

HARRISON, Richard Kingswood. b 61. Linc Coll Ox BA83 MA88 Leeds Univ BA90. **d** 91 **p** 92. C Reading St Giles *Ox* 91-93; Asst Chapl Merchant Taylors' Sch Northwood from 93. *Merchant Taylors' School, Northwood, Middx HA6 2HT* Northwood (01923) 820644

HARRISON, Robert Peter. b 28. Chich Th Coll. **d** 60 **p** 61. P-in-c Fulham St Pet *Lon* 66-73; V 73-94; rtd 94. *10 Portland Avenue, Hove, E Sussex BN3 5NG* Brighton (01273) 416254

HARRISON, Robert William. b 62. Mansf Coll Ox BA84. Qu Coll Birm 87. **d** 89 **p** 90. C Sholing *Win* 89-93; Communications Adv to Bp Willesden *Lon* from 93; C Cricklewood St Gabr and St Mich from 93. *31 Olive Road, London NW2 6TJ* 0181-450 8707 or 452 0290 Fax 452 4138

HARRISON, Rodney Lovel Neal. b 46. MBE87. Dur Univ BA67. Ripon Coll Cuddesdon DipMin95. **d** 95. C N w S Wootton *Nor* from 95. *Ambleside, Castle Rising Road, South Wootton, King's Lynn, Norfolk PE30 3JB* King's Lynn (01533) 674632

HARRISON, Roger John Orrell. b 54. K Coll Lon BD76 AKC76. Carl Dioc Tr Inst 86. **d** 88 **p** 89. Asst Chapl Sedbergh Sch Cumbria 88-91; Chapl Trent Coll Nottm 91-94; C Uppingham w Ayston and Wardley w Belton *Pet* 94-95. *41 Ash Close, Uppingham, Oakham, Leics LE15 9PJ* Uppingham (01572) 822528

HARRISON, Rosemary Jane. b 53. Bradf Coll of Educn CertEd76. Trin Coll Bris DipHE85. **d** 87 **p** 94. NSM Southway *Ex* 87-89; NSM Kinson *Sarum* from 89. *The Vicarage, 41 Moore Avenue, Bournemouth BH11 8AT* Bournemouth (01202) 581135

HARRISON, Dr Steven John. b 47. FRMetS74 Univ of Wales (Abth) BSc68 PhD74. St And Dioc Tr Course 87. **d** 90 **p** 91. NSM Alloa *St And* from 90. *46 Westerlea Drive, Bridge of Allan, Stirling FK9 4DQ* Stirling (01786) 833482

HARRISON, Walter Edward. b 1900. Em Coll Saskatoon. **d** 26 **p** 26. V Mossley *Man* 64-68; rtd 68; Perm to Offic *Man* from 68. *Buckley House, Lancaster Road, Didsbury M20 8QU* 0161-998 2550

HARRISON, Walter William. b 28. St Jo Coll Nottm. **d** 71 **p** 72. C Lenton *S'well* 71-74; R Carlton-in-the-Willows 74-93; rtd 93. *20 Conway Gardens, Nottingham NG5 6LR* Nottingham (0115) 920 0766

HARRISON, Canon William Roy. b 34. Dur Univ BA58 DipTh59. Cranmer Hall Dur 57. **d** 59 **p** 60. C Kingswood *Bris* 59-62; Kenya 62-65; P-in-c Gt Somerford *Bris* 66; V Soundwell from 66; Hon Can Bris Cathl from 92. *The Vicarage, 46 Sweets Road, Bristol BS15 1XQ* Bristol (0117) 967 1511

HARRISSON, John Anthony Lomax. b 47. Ex Univ BA72 DipTh85. Qu Coll Birm 72. **d** 74 **p** 75. C Loughton St Jo *Chelmsf* 74-81; V Chingford St Anne from 81. *St Anne's Vicarage, 200A Larkhall Road, London E4 6NP* 0181-529 4740

HARROD, Victor Ralph (Vic). b 33. Oak Hill Th Coll 76. **d** 79 **p** 80. Hon C Latchingdon w Mundon and N Fambridge *Chelmsf* 79; Hon C Creeksea w Althorne, Latchingdon and N Fambridge 79-83; C Tilbury Docks 83-86; R Orsett 86-90; P-in-c Bulphan 86-90; Chapl Orsett Hosp 86-92; R Orsett and Bulphan *Chelmsf* 90-92; V Thorpe-le-Soken 92-94; rtd 94. *63 Hankin Avenue, Oakley Grange, Dovercourt, Harwich, Essex CO12 5HE* Harwich (01255) 553314

HARROLD, Canon Jeremy Robin. b 31. Hertf Coll Ox BA54 BSc56 MA58 DipTh59. Wycliffe Hall Ox. **d** 59 **p** 60. C Rushden *Pet* 59-61; Bp's Dom Chapl *Lon* 61-64; Australia 64-67; V Harlesden St Mark *Lon* 67-72; V Hendon St Paul Mill Hill 72-84; V Stowmarket *St E* from 84; RD Stowmarket from 90; Hon Can St E Cathl from 94. *The Vicarage, 7 Lockington Road, Stowmarket, Suffolk IP14 1BQ* Stowmarket (01449) 613576

HARRON, Gareth Andrew. b 71. QUB BA92. CITC BTh95. **d** 95. C Willowfield *D & D* from 95. *21 Loopland Crescent, Belfast BT6 9EE* Belfast (01232) 452165

HARRON, James Alexander. b 37. GIMechE61 HNC59 St Aid Coll Dur 63. **d** 65 **p** 66. C Willowfield *D & D* 65-69; I Desertmartin *D & R* 69-80; Dep Sec BCMS (Ireland) 80-84; I Aghalee *D & D* from 84; Chapl HM Pris Maghaberry from 86. *39 Soldierstown Road, Aghalee, Craigavon, Co Armagh BT67 0ES* Aghalee (01846) 651210

HARROP, Douglas. b 21. St Aid Birkenhead 62. **d** 64 **p** 65. C Doncaster St Leon and St Jude *Sheff* 67-70; R S Witham *Linc* 70-76; R N Witham 70-76; RD Beltisloe 72-76; V Kirkdale *York* 76-85; rtd 85. Perm to Offic *Linc* from 85. *13 Dovecote, Middle Rasen, Market Rasen, Lincs LN8 3UD* Market Rasen (01673) 843675

HARROP, Preb Joseph Blakemore. b 17. Saltley Tr Coll Birm TCert39. Qu Coll Birm 51. **d** 53 **p** 56. V Foxt w Whiston *Lich* 58-93; NSM from 93; P-in-c Oakamoor w Cotton 78-85; Preb Lich Cathl 93; rtd 93. *Foxt-Whiston Vicarage, Foxt, Stoke-on-Trent ST10 2HN* Ipstones (01538) 266315

HARROP, Stephen Douglas. b 48. St Jo Coll York CertEd74 Man Univ DSPT85 DipAdEd90. Edin Th Coll 77. **d** 79 **p** 82. C Middlesb St Martin *York* 79-80; C N Hull St Mich 80; C Cayton w Eastfield 80-81; C Oldham *Man* 82-84; V Oldham St Barn 84-89; Hong Kong 89-93; TV Kidderminster St Mary and All SS w Trimpley etc *Worc* from 93; Ind Chapl 93-95; Chapl Kidderminster Coll 93-95. *The Chaplain's House, 186 Birmingham Road, Kidderminster, Worcs DY10 2SJ* Kidderminster (01562) 746332

HARRY, Bruce David. b 40. JP77. Culham Coll Ox CertEd60. N Ord Course 83. **d** 86 **p** 87. NSM Liscard St Thos *Ches* 86-91; NSM Eastham 91-94; C New Brighton St Jas from 94; C New Brighton Em from 94. *21 Sandymount Drive, Wallasey, Merseyside L45 0LJ* 0151-639 7232

HART, Allen Sydney George. b 38. Chich Th Coll 64. **d** 67 **p** 68. C N Wembley St Cuth *Lon* 67-71; C W Bromwich All SS *Lich* 71-74; TV Hucknall Torkard *S'well* 74-80; V Annesley Our Lady and All SS 80-86; V Bilborough St Jo from 86; RD Nottm W from 94. *St John's Vicarage, Graylands Road, Nottingham NG8 4FD* Nottingham (0115) 929 3320

HART, Andre Hendrik. b 62. Cape Town Univ BA86. St Steph Ho Ox 89. **d** 91 **p** 92. C Newbold and Dunston *Derby* from 91. *Church House, 27 Willowgarth Road, Chesterfield, Derbyshire S41 8BL* Chesterfield (01246) 275236

HART, Anthony. b 35. St Mich Coll Llan 77. **d** 79 **p** 80. NSM Jersey St Helier *Win* 79-81; C Heref All SS *Heref* 81-82; C Kingstone 82-84; C Eaton Bishop 82-84; C Clehonger 82-84; R Sutton St Nicholas w Sutton St Michael 84-88; R Withington w Westhide 84-88; R Jersey St Mary *Win* from 88. *St Mary's Rectory, Jersey, Channel Islands JE3 3DB* Jersey (01534) 481410

HART, Colin Edwin. b 45. Leeds Univ BA66 PGCE67 Fitzw Coll Cam BA73 MA77 K Coll Lon MTh76 Leeds Univ MPhil89. Trin Coll Bris 74. **d** 74 **p** 75. C Ware Ch Ch *St Alb* 74-78; TV Sheff Manor *Sheff* 78-80; V Wombridge *Lich* 80-87; Lect St Jo Coll Nottm from 87; Public Preacher *S'well* from 87; Hon C Chilwell 87-91; Hon C Trowell from 91. *St John's College, Chilwell Lane, Bramcote, Nottingham NG9 3DS* Nottm (0115) 925 1114 or 943 0774 Fax 943 6438

HART, David. b 48. Edge Hill Coll of HE BEd80 Liv Inst of Educn ADEd84 Liv Univ MEd87. Nor Ord Course BPhil94.

d 94 **p** 95. NSM Ashton-in-Makerfield St Thos *Liv* from 94. *12 Ratcliffe Road, Aspull, Wigan, Lancs WN2 1YE* Wigan (01942) 832918

HART, David Alan. b 54. Keble Coll Ox BA75 MPhil78. Union Th Sem (NY) STM79 Westcott Ho Cam 83. **d** 83 **p** 84. Asst Chapl Gresham's Sch Holt 83-84; Chapl K Edw VI Sch Nor 84-85; Chapl Shrewsbury Sch 85-87; Chapl St Jo Coll Sch Cam 87-88; C Camberwell St Giles w St Matt *S'wark* 88-90; Chapl Loughb Univ *Leic* from 90. *1 Holywell Drive, Loughborough, Leics LE11 3JU* Loughboro' (0509) 232790 or 263171

HART, David John. b 58. K Coll Lon BD80. St Mich Coll Llan. **d** 85 **p** 86. C Denbigh and Nantglyn *St As* 85-88; Chapl RAF 88-89; C Llanrhos *St As* 89-91; V Rhosllannerchrugog from 91. *1 Gerddi, Hall Street, Rhosllanerchrugog, Wrexham, Clwyd LL14 2LG* Rhosllanerchrugog (01978) 840065

HART, David Leonard. b 42. Ripon Hall Ox 68. **d** 71 **p** 72. C Castle Vale *Birm* 71-73; Chapl All SS Hosp Birm from 73. *12 Dorchester Drive, Birmingham, B17 0SW, or All Saint's Hospital, Lodge Road, Birmingham B18 5SD* 0121-427 7828 or 523 5151

HART, David Maurice. b 35. Univ Coll Dur BSc57. Clifton Th Coll 59. **d** 61 **p** 62. C Bolton St Paul *Man* 61-64; C Hamworthy *Sarum* 64-70; R W Dean w E Grimstead 70-81; R Farley w Pitton and W Dean w E Grimstead 81-90; V Steeple Ashton w Semington and Keevil from 90. *The Vicarage, Vicarage Lane, Steeple Ashton, Trowbridge, Wilts BA14 6HH* Devizes (01380) 870344

HART, Canon Dennis Daniel. b 22. Linc Th Coll 45. **d** 48 **p** 49. V St Alb St Sav *St Alb* 55-92; Hon Can St Alb 74-92; RD St Alb 84-90; rtd 92. *7 Bassett Close, Redbourn, Herts AL3 7JY* Redbourn (01582) 794464

HART, Dennis William. b 30. JP. Open Univ BA. Oak Hill Th Coll 75. **d** 78 **p** 79. Hon C Clacton St Paul *Chelmsf* from 78. *15 Albert Gardens, Clacton-on-Sea, Essex CO15 6QN* Clacton-on-Sea (01255) 431794

HART, Edwin Joseph. b 21. Oak Hill Th Coll 56. **d** 58 **p** 59. V Cranham Park *Chelmsf* 69-71; R Markfield *Leic* 71-89; rtd 89. *135 Grace Dieu Road, Thringstone, Coalville, Leics LE67 5AP* Coalville (01530) 222767

HART, Canon Geoffrey William. b 27. Ex Coll Ox BA51 MA55. Ridley Hall Cam 51. **d** 54 **p** 55. V Southport Ch Ch *Liv* 65-73; R Cheltenham St Mary *Glouc* 73-76; TR Cheltenham St Mary, St Matt, St Paul and H Trin 76-93; Hon Can Glouc Cathl 78-93; rtd 93; Perm to Offic *Ex* from 94. *Little Goosemoor, Branscombe, Seaton, Devon EX12 3BU* Branscombe (0129780) 271

HART, Graham Cooper. b 36. S Dios Minl Tr Scheme 88. **d** 91 **p** 92. NSM Filton *Bris* 91-93; Hon C Downend from 93. *The Old Post Office, Hambrook, Bristol BS16 1RF* Bristol (0117) 956 5300

HART, Canon Graham Merril (Merry). b 23. Ridley Coll Melbourne 65. **d** 77 **p** 77. Tanzania 69-84; CMS 72-83; Can Musoma from 85; Chapl Ostend w Knokke and Bruges *Eur* 84-93; Miss to Seamen 84-93; rtd 93; Perm to Offic *S'wark* from 93. *Morden College, 7 Alexander Court, Kidbrook Grove, London SE3 0LH* 0181-858 3731

HART, Henry St John. b 12. St Jo Coll Cam BA34 Qu Coll Cam MA38 BD54. **d** 36 **p** 37. Chapl Qu Coll Cam 36-50; Dean 40-50 and 55-72; Fell from 36; Vice Pres 78-79; Reader in Hebrew Cam Univ 72-79; rtd 80; Lic to Offic *Nor* 80-86; Perm to Offic from 86. *The Retreat, Felbrigg Hall, Norwich NR11 8PR* West Runton (01263) 837652

HART, James (Jim). b 53. MIL84 Dur Univ BA75 DipEd76 DipHE88. Oak Hill Th Coll 86. **d** 88 **p** 89. C Starbeck *Ripon* 88-90; SAMS from 90; Argentina from 90. *Conde 2370, 1428 Buenos Aires, Argentina*

HART, John Peter. b 39. Bris Sch of Min 80. **d** 84 **p** 85. NSM Malmesbury w Westport and Brokenborough *Bris* 84-88; C Yatton Moor *B & W* 89-90; V Bridgwater H Trin from 90. *Holy Trinity Vicarage, Hamp Street, Bridgwater, Somerset TA6 6AR* Bridgwater (01278) 422610

HART, John Charles. b 11. Worc Coll Ox BA34 MA40. Wycliffe Hall Ox 34. **d** 36 **p** 38. V Rudgwick *Chich* 66-77; rtd 77. *68 The Sheeplands, Sherborne, Dorset DT9 4BS* Sherborne (01935) 813921

HART, John Richard. b 16. Ox NSM Course 72. **d** 75 **p** 76. NSM Reading St Matt *Ox* 75-77; NSM Grazeley and Beech Hill 77-88; NSM Spencer's Wood 77-88; NSM Grazeley, Grazeley and Spencers Wood 88-89; Perm to Offic *Portsm* from 89. *14 Elizabeth Court, High Street, Bembridge, Isle of Wight PO35 5SN* Isle of Wight (01983) 874509

HART, Michael Anthony. b 50. AKC71. St Aug Coll Cant 72. **d** 73 **p** 74. C Southwick St Columba *Dur* 73-76; C Hendon St Alphage *Lon* 76-78; P-in-c Eltham Park St Luke *S'wark* 78-83; V 83-85; R Newington St Mary from 85; P-in-c Camberwell St Mich w All So w Em from 85; RD S'wark and Newington from 93. *The Rectory, 57 Kennington Park Road, London SE11 4JQ* 0171-735 1894

HART, Canon Michael Stuart. b 39. Univ of Wales (Lamp) BA61 Lanc Univ MA72. Wycliffe Hall Ox 61. **d** 63 **p** 64. C W Bromwich St Jas *Lich* 63-66; C Tarrington w Stoke Edith *Heref* 66-67; C Putney St Mary *S'wark* 67-70; V Accrington St Mary *Blackb* 70-82; RD Accrington 76-82; Hon Can Blackb Cathl 81-91; V Walton-le-Dale 82-91; P-in-c Samlesbury 91; TR Heavitree w Ex St Paul *Ex* from 91. *The Rectory, 10 Sherwood Close, Exeter EX2 5DX* Exeter (01392) 421841

HART, Peter Osborne. b 57. St Jo Coll Nottm DCM92. **d** 92 **p** 93. C Shipley St Pet *Bradf* from 92. *43 George Street, Saltaire, Shipley, W Yorkshire BD18 4PT* Bradford (01274) 583457

HART, Peter William. b 60. Liv Univ BA82 Universite de Haute Normandie MesL84 Univ of Wales (Swansea) MPhil92. Sarum & Wells Th Coll 86. **d** 88 **p** 89. C Llansamlet *S & B* 88-89; C Sketty 89-92; P-in-c Warndon St Nic *Worc* from 92. *The Vicarage, 4 Daty Croft, Home Meadow, Warndon, Worcester WR4 0JB* Worcester (01905) 616109

HART, Richard. b 49. Or Coll Ox MPhil85 St D Coll Lamp BA82 Qu Coll Birm 84. **d** 85 **p** 86. C Sketty *S & B* 85-87; P-in-c Llanbister and Llanbadarn Fynydd w Llananno 87-88; V 88-92; P-in-c Dymock w Donnington and Kempley *Glouc* from 92; P-in-c Preston from 92. *The Rectory, Dymock, Glos GL18 2AJ* Dymock (01531) 890270

HART, Ronald George (Ron). b 46. BSc Bris Univ DSA72 Lon Univ DASS77 CQSW77. Sarum & Wells Th Coll. **d** 85 **p** 86. C Sittingbourne St Mich *Cant* 85-88; C Walton H Trin *Ox* 88-89; TV from 89. *The Parsonage, 60 Greville Road, Aylesbury, Bucks HP21 8EY* Aylesbury (01296) 24175

HART, Tony. b 36. CCC Cam BA59 MA63. Cuddesdon Coll 59. **d** 61 **p** 62. C Middlesb All SS *York* 61-64; Bp's Dom Chapl *Dur* 64-67; C Owton Manor CD 67-70; V Harton Colliery 70-82; TR S Shields All SS 82-83; RD Jarrow 77-83; Can Res Dur Cathl 83-92; V Easingwold w Raskelfe *York* from 92. *The Vicarage, Easingwold, York YO6 3JT* Easingwold (01347) 821394

HART, Dr Trevor Andrew. b 61. St Jo Coll Dur BA82 Aber Univ PhD89. **d** 88 **p** 88. Lect Aber Univ from 86; NSM Bieldside *Ab* from 88. *66 Tillydrone Avenue, Aberdeen AB2 2TN* Aberdeen (01224) 483433

HARTE, Frederick George (Fred). b 25. AKC53. **d** 54 **p** 55. V Bellingham St Dunstan *S'wark* 60-73; V Plumstead St Nic 73-84; V Sutton Bridge *Linc* 84-90; rtd 90; Master St Jo Hosp Bath and P-in-c of Chpl from 90. *The Master's Lodge, St John's Hospital, Chapel Court, Bath BA1 1SL* Bath (01225) 464972

HARTE, Ven Matthew Scott. b 46. TCD BA70 MA74. CITC 71. **d** 71 **p** 72. C Ban Abbey *D & D* 71-74; C Ballynafeigh St Jude 74-76; I Ardara w Glencolumbkille, Inniskeel etc *D & R* from 76; Adn Raphoe from 83. *The Rectory, Ardara, Lifford, Co Donegal, Irish Republic* Ardara (75) 41124

HARTERINK, Mrs Joy Frances. b 49. DCEG82 Essex Univ BA71 Hughes Hall Cam CertEd72 Lon Univ MSc87. Oak Hill NSM Course 89. **d** 92 **p** 94. NSM Richmond H Trin and Ch Ch *S'wark* from 92. *9 Sandringham House, Courtlands, Sheen Road, Richmond, Surrey TW10 5BG* 0181-948 7579

HARTIN, Canon James. b 30. TCD BA52 MA60. **d** 54 **p** 55. Sub-Warden CITC 63-80; Prin 80-89; Lect in Ch Hist TCD 64-94; Prof of Past Th TCD 80-89; Prec St Patr Cathl Dub 80-89; I Castlemacadam w Ballinaclash, Aughrim etc *D & G* 89-94; RD Rathdrum 90-94; rtd 94. *Castlemacadam, Avoca, Co Wicklow, Irish Republic* Avoca (402) 35690

HARTLAND, David Robson. b 33. Qu Coll Birm 64. **d** 66 **p** 67. C Brierley Hill *Lich* 66-71; V Hartshill 71-76; V Moxley 76-85; V Willenhall St Steph from 85. *St Stephen's Vicarage, Wolverhampton Street, Willenhall, W Midlands WV13 2PS* Willenhall (01902) 605239

HARTLAND, Ian Charles. b 49. K Coll Lon CertEd BD72 AKC72 MTh76. Sarum & Wells Th Coll 83. **d** 84 **p** 85. C Orpington All SS *Roch* 84-87; Lect Ch Ch Coll Cant from 87. *Ivy Lodge, 4 The Terrace, Canterbury, Kent CT2 7AJ* Canterbury (01227) 760877

HARTLESS, Mrs Berengaria Isabella de la Tour (Beren). b 52. Univ of Wales (Cardiff) BSc74 Golds Coll Lon PGCE76. Ox Min Course CBTS93. **d** 93 **p** 94. Par Dn High Wycombe *Ox* 93-94; C from 94. *15 Rupert Avenue, High Wycombe, Bucks HP12 3NG* High Wycombe (01494) 534605

HARTLESS, Gordon Frederick James. b 13. LRAM40 LTCL42. Worc Ord Coll 54. **d** 55 **p** 56. P-in-c Hawnby w Old Byland *York* 69-78; P-in-c Bilsdale Midcable 75-78; R Scawton w Cold Kirby 69-78; Perm to Offic *York* from 78. *11 Beechfields, High Hawsker, Whitby, N Yorkshire YO22 4LQ* Whitby (01947) 880707

HARTLEY, Brian. b 41. N Ord Course 82. **d** 85 **p** 86. NSM Royton St Paul *Man* 85-91; NSM Oldham St Steph and All Martyrs 91-94; TV E Farnworth and Kearsley from 94. *The Vicarage, 93 Bradford Street, Farnworth, Bolton BL4 9JY* Bolton (01204) 73843

HARTLEY, David Michael. b 59. RGN85 Edin Univ BD81. St Steph Ho Ox 87. **d** 89 **p** 90. C Kingswinford St Mary *Lich* 89-92; C Wolstanton 92; TV from 92. *St Andrew's Vicarage, 14 Dorrington Grove, Porthill, Newcastle, Staffs ST5 0HY* Newcastle-under-Lyme (01782) 715001

HARTLEY, Mrs Dianna Lynn. b 57. Santa Ana Community Coll AS76 California Univ BA78. S'wark Ord Course DipRS92. **d** 92 **p** 94. NSM Peckham St Sav *S'wark* from 92. *67 Danby Street, London SE15 4BT* 0171-639 6408 or 732 3435

HARTLEY, Godfrey. b 37. Man Univ 58. Cuddesdon Coll 64. **d** 64 **p** 65. Miss to Seamen 67-94; Portuguese E Africa 67-73; Sen Chapl and Sec for Scotland 74-89; P-in-c Glas St Gabr *Glas* 74-89; Chapl RNR from 74; Chapl Cornwall Miss to Seamen 89-94; rtd 95. *Sandoes Gate, Feock, Truro, Cornwall TR3 6QN* Truro (01872) 865863

HARTLEY, Graham William Harrington. b 21. Ripon Hall Ox 61. **d** 62 **p** 63. V Knowsley *Liv* 66-72; V Langdale *Carl* 72-81; TV Egremont and Haile 81-85; TV Whitehaven 85-88; rtd 88. Perm to Offic *Carl* from 88. *14 Thrang Brow, Chapel Stile, Ambleside, Cumbria LA22 9JN* Langdale (015394) 37322

HARTLEY, Harold Aitken. b 21. Whitaker Sch of Th. **d** 84 **p** 85. USA 84-89; from 92; NSM Fulford *York* 89-92. *5 Sandiago Lane, Palm Coast, Florida 32137, USA*

HARTLEY, Canon Harry. b 02. Birm Univ BSc28 Open Univ BA76. St Steph Ho Ox 28. **d** 30 **p** 31. R Solihull *Birm* 53-70; Perm to Offic *Glouc* from 70; rtd 71. *Flat 1, Capel Court, The Burgage, Prestbury, Cheltenham, Glos GL52 3EL* Cheltenham (01242) 244426

HARTLEY, Herbert. b 28. AKC52. **d** 53 **p** 54. Chapl RN 66-73; C Langley Marish *Ox* 73-77; R Hedsor and Bourne End 77-93; rtd 93. *5 Charlotte Way, Marlow, Bucks SL7 1PJ* Marlow (01628) 478513

HARTLEY, Dr John Peter. b 56. Cam Univ BA78 Leeds Univ PhD82 Dur Univ BA84. Cranmer Hall Dur 82. **d** 85 **p** 86. C Spring Grove St Mary *Lon* 85-88; C Bexleyheath St Pet *Roch* 88-91; P-in-c Hanford *Lich* from 91; Faith in the City Officer (Potteries) from 91. *The Vicarage, Hanford, Stoke-on-Trent, Staffs ST4 4QD* Stoke-on-Trent (01782) 657848

HARTLEY, John William. b 47. St Jo Coll Dur BA69. Linc Th Coll 70. **d** 72 **p** 73. C Poulton-le-Fylde *Blackb* 72-76; C Lanc St Mary 76-79; V Barrowford 79-87; V Salesbury from 87. *St Peter's Vicarage, 49A Ribchester Road, Blackburn BB1 9HU* Blackburn (01254) 248072

HARTLEY, Julian John. b 57. Oak Hill Th Coll BA85. **d** 85 **p** 86. C Eccleston Ch Ch *Liv* 85-89; V Goose Green from 89. *St Paul's Vicarage, Warrington Road, Wigan, Lancs WN1 6QB* Wigan (01942) 42984

HARTLEY, Michael Leslie. b 56. Leeds Univ BSc77. Ripon Coll Cuddesdon 87. **d** 89 **p** 90. C Standish *Blackb* 89-93; V Bamber Bridge St Aid from 93. *St Aidan's Vicarage, Longworth Street, Bamber Bridge, Preston PR5 6GN* Preston (01772) 35310

HARTLEY, Nigel John. b 48. Portsm Poly BA. St Jo Coll Nottm. **d** 83 **p** 84. C Ipswich St Marg *St E* 83-86; P-in-c Hintlesham w Chattisham 86-95; Dioc Radio Officer 86-95; P-in-c Gt Finborough w Onehouse and Harleston from 95. *The Rectory, Woodland Close, Onehouse, Stowmarket, Suffolk IP14 3HL* Stowmarket (01449) 614378

HARTLEY, Nigel Rogers. b 65. Mansf Coll Ox BA86 MA90. Chich Th Coll 87. **d** 89 **p** 90. C Borehamwood *St Alb* 89-91; PV Llan Cathl *Llan* 91-93; R Foundn of St Kath in Ratcliffe from 93. *The Royal Foundation of St Katharine, 2 Butcher Row, London E14 8DS* 0171-790 3540 Fax 702 7603

HARTLEY, Paul. b 51. Nottm Univ BTh88. Linc Th Coll 85. **d** 88 **p** 89. C Clitheroe St Mary *Blackb* 88-91; TV Guiseley w Esholt *Bradf* from 91. *35 Moorway, Tranmere Park, Guiseley, Leeds LS20 8LD* Guiseley (01943) 878828

HARTLEY, Canon Peter. b 44. Avery Hill Coll PGCE67 Ox Univ DipRE74 St Cath Coll Cam BA66 MA69. Sarum & Wells Th Coll 77. **d** 78 **p** 79. Hon C Freemantle *Win* 78-79; Chr Educn Officer *Pet* 79-81; Dir of Educn 81-90; Dir Coun of Educn and Tr *Chelmsf* from 90; Hon Can Chelmsf Cathl from 92. *St Clare, Links Drive, Chelmsford CM2 9AW* Chelmsford (01245) 251461

HARTLEY, Peter Mellodew. b 41. MA MSc. S'wark Ord Course. **d** 83 **p** 84. NSM Salfords *S'wark* from 83. *60 Deerings Road, Reigate, Surrey RH2 0PN* Reigate (01737) 247940

HARTLEY, Stephen William Mark. b 50. St Chad's Coll Dur BA71. Westcott Ho Cam 72. **d** 74 **p** 75. C Holbrooks *Cov* 74-76; C Styvechale 76-79; P-in-c Snitterfield w Bearley 79-81; V 81-83; V Exhall 83-88; V Tilehurst St Cath *Ox* from 88. *The Vicarage, Wittenham Avenue, Tilehurst, Reading RG3 5LN* Reading (01734) 427786

HARTLEY, Stewart John Ridley. b 47. St Jo Coll Nottm 78. **d** 80 **p** 81. C Altham w Clayton le Moors *Blackb* 80-84; P-in-c Nelson St Phil 84-91; V from 91. *St Philip's Vicarage, 1 Victory Close, Chapel Street, Nelson, Lancs BB9 9ED* Nelson (01282) 698161

HARTLEY, Canon William Reginald (Rex). b 19. CCC Cam BA41 MA45. Linc Th Coll 41. **d** 42 **p** 43. R Birch St Jas *Man* 59-74; V Atherton 74-86; Hon Can Man Cathl 76-86; AD Leigh 79-85; rtd 86; Perm to Offic *Bradf* from 86. *21 Easby Close, Ilkley, W Yorkshire LS29 9DJ* Ilkley (01943) 609005

HARTNELL, Canon Bruce John. b 42. Ex Univ BA64 Linacre Coll Ox BA66 MA. Ripon Hall Ox 64. **d** 66 **p** 67. C S Stoneham *Win* 66-69; Chapl and Tutor Ripon Hall Ox 69-74; V Knowl Hill w Littlewick *Ox* 74-78; Chapl Southn Univ *Win* 78-83; V Sholing from 83; RD Southn from 93; Hon Can Win Cathl from 93. *The Vicarage, 41 Station Road, Southampton SO2 8FN* Southampton (01703) 448337

HARTRIDGE, James Bernard Robertson (Jamie). b 44. S Dios Minl Tr Scheme 89. **d** 92 **p** 93. C Portsea St Cuth *Portsm* 92-95. *20 Highgrove Road, Portsmouth PO3 6PR* Portsmouth (01705) 661890

HARVEY, Alan Douglas. b 25. FRSH82. Melbourne Coll of Div 78. **d** 79 **p** 81. Australia 79-86; Perm to Offic *Ely* 86-87; V Wiggenhall St Germans and Islington 88-95; V Wiggenhall St Mary Magd 88-95; rtd 95. *8 Brassey Avenue, Broadstairs, Kent CT10 2DS* Broadstairs (01843) 864080

HARVEY, Ven Anthony Ernest. b 30. Worc Coll Ox BA53 MA56 DD83. Westcott Ho Cam 56. **d** 58 **p** 59. C Chelsea Ch Ch *Lon* 58-62; Ch Ch Ox 62-69; Warden St Aug Coll Cant 69-75; Lect Th Ox 76-82; Chapl Qu Coll Ox 77-82; Can and Lib Westmr Abbey from 82; Adn Westmr from 87; Sub-Dean Westmr from 87. *3 Little Cloister, Westminster Abbey, London SW1P 3PL* 0171-222 4174 or 222 5152 Fax 233 2072

HARVEY, Anthony Peter. b 42. Birm Univ BSc63 MSc64. Wycliffe Hall Ox 79. **d** 81 **p** 82. C Stoke Damerel *Ex* 81-84; Canada 84-90; Chapl HM Young Offender Inst Deerbolt 91-92; Chapl HM Pris Leeds from 92. *HM Prison, Armley, Leeds LS12 2TJ* Leeds (0113) 263 6411 Fax 790151

HARVEY, Arthur Ernest. b 30. Lon Univ DipTh58 MSc80. Oak Hill Th Coll 54. **d** 57 **p** 58. C Rayleigh *Chelmsf* 57-60; C Morpeth *Newc* 60-63; R Pitsea *Chelmsf* 63-74; Bp's Ind Officer 73-80; R Bobbingworth 74-81; Chapl Bordeaux w Riberac, Cahors, Duras etc *Eur* 82-86; V Barnsbury St Andr and H Trin w All SS *Lon* 86-90; TR Barnsbury from 90. *5 Huntingdon Street, London N1 1BU* 0171-607 6895 or 837 6937

HARVEY, Very Rev Brian. b 16. TCD BA38 BD41. TCD Div Sch Div Test39. **d** 40 **p** 41. Can Th Belf Cathl 63-70; I Kilkenny w Aghour and Kilmanagh *C & O* 70-91; Preb Leighlin Cathl from 70; Dean Ossory 70-91; rtd 91. *Alton, Kilbrittain, Co Cork, Irish Republic* Clonakilty (23) 49686

HARVEY, Charles Alma West. b 07. Glas Univ MA29. Edin Th Coll 29. **d** 31 **p** 32. R Gullane *Edin* 57-75; rtd 75. *Flat 23, 17 Kirk Loan, Edinburgh EH12 7HD* 0131-334 7933

HARVEY, Christopher John Alfred. b 41. S'wark Ord Course 66. **d** 69 **p** 70. C Grays Thurrock *Chelmsf* 69-73; C Gt Baddow 73-75; V Berechurch St Marg w St Mich 75-94; R Tendring and Lt Bentley w Beaumont cum Moze from 94. *The Rectory, The Street, Tendring, Clacton-on-Sea, Essex CO16 0BW* Clacton-on-Sea (01255) 830586

HARVEY, Ven Cyril John. b 30. Univ of Wales (Lamp) BA51. Coll of Resurr Mirfield 51. **d** 53 **p** 54. C Caerau w Ely *Llan* 53-57; C Milford Haven *St D* 57-61; V Castlemartin and Warren 61-65; R Begelly w Kilgetty 65-73; V Haverfordwest St Martin w Lambston 73-88; Can St D Cathl from 85; R Tenby from 88; Adn St D from 91. *The Rectory, Church Park, Tenby, Dyfed SA70 7EE* Tenby (01834) 842068

HARVEY, Debra Eileen. b 54. **d** 94 **p** 95. NSM Camborne *Truro* from 94. *Redwin, 11 Roseland Park, Camborne, Cornwall TR14 8LU* Camborne (01209) 716282

HARVEY, Canon Frank Chivas. b 12. Edin Th Coll 46. **d** 49 **p** 50. Dioc Chapl *St And* 69-74; Chapl HM Pris Perth 69-74; Can St Ninian's Cathl Perth *St And* 77-79; rtd 79; Hon Can St Ninian's Cathl Perth *St And* from 79. *10 Pitcullen Terrace, Perth PH2 7EQ* Perth (01738) 28855

HARVEY, Geoffrey George (Geoff). b 46. Lon Univ BSc71. Ridley Coll Melbourne BTh82. **d** 82 **p** 83. Australia from 82. *St Luke's Vicarage, 59-61 Police Road, Mulgrave, Victoria, Australia 3170* Melbourne (3) 546-6533 Fax as telephone

HARVEY, John. b 30. S'wark Ord Course. **d** 65 **p** 66. C Lewisham St Jo Southend *S'wark* 65-73; V Bellingham St Dunstan 73-78; TV Bourne Valley *Sarum* 78-81; TR 81-87; R Kilkhampton w Morwenstow *Truro* 87-90; rtd 90. *50 Essex Road, Longfield, Dartford DA3 7QL* Longfield (01474) 709627

HARVEY, John Christopher. b 65. Univ of Wales (Lamp) BA86 Nottm Univ BTh89. Linc Th Coll 89. **d** 89 **p** 90. C Dwygyfylchi (or Penmaenmawr) *Ban* 89-93; V Llangrannog w Llandysiliogogo w Penbryn *St D* from 93. *The Vicarage, Pontgarreg, Llangranog, Llandyssul, Dyfed SA44 6AJ* Llangranog (01239) 654003

HARVEY, John Mark. b 64. QUB BEd87 TCD BTh93. CITC 90. **d** 93 **p** 94. C Portadown St Columba *Arm* from 93. *14 Ardmore Crescent, Portadown, Craigavon, Co Armagh BT62 4DU* Portadown (01762) 331916

HARVEY, John Wilfred. b 05. Lon Coll of Div 37. **d** 39 **p** 40. C-in-c Sheviock *Truro* 71-72; rtd 73; P-in-c St Martin by Looe *Truro* 77-79. *Chy Morvah, Marine Drive, Looe, Cornwall PL13 2DJ* Looe (01503) 263327

HARVEY, Lance Sydney Crockford. b 25. Ridley Hall Cam 67. **d** 69 **p** 70. C Mortlake w E Sheen *S'wark* 69-74; P-in-c Woolwich St Thos 75-86; V Lee Gd Shep w St Pet 86-92; RD E Lewisham 87-91; rtd 92. *36 Chapel Street, Penzance, Cornwall TR18 4AQ* Penzance (01736) 60967

HARVEY, Leslie Francis. b 02. Birm Univ MSc22 Ball Coll Ox BA25 MA31. Westcott Ho Cam. **d** 30 **p** 32. Chapl and Hd Master The King's Sch Ches 47-64; rtd 68; Lic to Offic *Derby* from 87. *c/o Leeanda House, 19 Station Road, Borrowash, Derby DE7 3LG* Derby (01332) 675856

HARVEY, Margaret Claire. b 41. Univ of Wales (Abth) BA62 DipEd63 Lon Univ BD68. Dalton Ho Bris 66. dss 68 **d** 80. Flint *St As* 68-74; Lect Trin Coll Bris 74-80; Connah's Quay *St As* 79-80; C 80-86; Bp's Adv for Continuing Clerical Educn from 86; Hon C Corwen and Llangar 86-87; D-in-c Bryneglwys from 87. *Coleg y Groes, The College, Corwen, Clwyd LL21 0AU* Corwen (01490) 412169

HARVEY, Maurice. b 31. **d** 70 **p** 71. C Lisburn St Paul *Conn* 70-72; C Ballymacarrett St Patr *D & D* 72-77; I Ballyphilip w Ardquin 77-79; I Ardmore w Craigavon 79-87; I Killyman *Arm* 87-94; Bp's C Acton w Drumbanagher from 94. *Drumbanagher Rectory, 128 Tandragee Road, Newry, Co Down BT35 6LW* Newry (01693) 298

HARVEY, Norman Roy. b 43. Nottm Univ DipAE86. Wycliffe Hall Ox 66. **d** 69 **p** 70. C Clay Cross *Derby* 69-72; C Dronfield 72-76; TV 76-79; Dioc Youth Officer 79-83; P-in-c Rowsley 79-89; Dioc Adv in Adult and Youth Educn 83-89; TR Eckington w Handley and Ridgeway from 89. *The Rectory, Eckington, Sheffield S31 9BG* Eckington (01246) 432196

HARVEY, Oliver Douglas. b 01. Magd Coll Ox BA25 MA45. Wells Th Coll 25. **d** 25 **p** 26. R Puddletown w Athelhampton and Burleston *Sarum* 62-69; rtd 69; Perm to Offic *Roch* from 86. *c/o 74 Poplar Grove, Maidstone, Kent ME16 0AL* Maidstone (01622) 762565

HARVEY, Oliver Paul. b 33. Magd Coll Ox BA55 MA59. Cuddesdon Coll 57. **d** 59 **p** 60. C S Norwood St Mark *Cant* 59-61; C Hythe 61-64; Zambia 64-71; Chapl Cant Coll of Tech 71-77; Hon C Cant St Martin and St Paul *Cant* 73-77; Chapl K Sch Roch 77-88; C Roch 88-90; V Gillingham St Mary from 90. *The Vicarage, 27 Gillingham Green, Gillingham, Kent ME7 1SS* Medway (01634) 850529

HARVEY, Miss Pamela Betty (Pam). b 33. Dalton Ho Bris IDC59 CertRK59. dss 68 **d** 87 **p** 95. Nottm St Ann *S'well* 68-72; Bestwood St Matt 72-76; CPAS Staff 76-93; Dir Consultants Division CPAS from 93; Perm to Offic *Leic* from 92. *37 Tysoe Hill, Leicester LE3 8AR* Leicester (0116) 287 2670 Fax Warwick (01926) 337613

HARVEY, Mrs Patricia Ann (Pat). b 45. Qu Coll Birm. dss 82 **d** 87 **p** 94. Gospel Lane St Mich *Birm* 82-85; Exhall *Cov* 85-87; C 87-89; TD Droitwich Spa *Worc* 89-94; TV from 94. *61 Drovers Way, Droitwich, Worcs WR9 9DA* Droitwich (01905) 771516

HARVEY, Patrick Arnold. b 58. TCD BA DipTh MA. **d** 85 **p** 86. C Bandon Union *C, C & R* 85-88; I Limerick St Mich *L & K* 88-90; Dioc Info Officer 88-90; I Abbeyleix w Old Church, Ballyroan etc *C & O* from 90. *The Rectory, Abbeyleix, Portlaoise, Co Laois, Irish Republic* Portlaoise (502) 31243 Fax as telephone

HARVEY, Canon Peter Harold Noel. b 16. Univ of Wales BA44. St Aug Coll Cant 39. **d** 40 **p** 41. Ed Ch Illustrated Publications 55-70; V Udimore *Chich* 69-76; P-in-c Brede 75-76; R Brede w Udimore 76-83; Can and Preb Chich Cathl 76-89; rtd 83. *Prebenden, 1 Smugglers' Way, Fairlight Cove, Hastings, E Sussex TN35 4DG* Hastings (01424) 813185

HARVEY, Reginald Darwin. b 28. E Anglian Minl Tr Course. **d** 82 **p** 83. NSM Gillingham w Geldeston, Stockton, Ellingham etc *Nor* from 82; Perm to Offic *St E* from 86. *Blaenwern, Mill Road, Ellingham, Bungay, Suffolk NR35 2PY* Kirby Cane (01508) 518663

HARVEY, Robert Martin. b 30. S'wark Ord Course 69. **d** 70 **p** 71. C Sutton New Town St Barn *S'wark* 70-75; C Leatherhead *Guildf* 76-78; V Wadworth w Loversall *Sheff* from 78; RD W Doncaster from 94. *The Vicarage, Vicarage Drive, Wadworth, Doncaster, S Yorkshire DN11 9BW* Doncaster (01302) 851974

HARVEY, Robin Grant. b 43. Clare Coll Cam BA64 MA68 Univ of NSW PhD74. Linc Th Coll 85. **d** 87 **p** 88. C Keynsham *B & W* 87-91; R E w W Harptree and Hinton Blewett from 91. *The Rectory, Church Lane, East Harptree, Bristol BS18 6BD* West Harptree (01761) 221239

HARVEY, Stephen George Kay. b 06. Lon Univ BD39 Ridley Coll Melbourne 32. ACT ThL33. **d** 33 **p** 34. R Wath *Ripon* 60-72; rtd 72. *11 Hannams Close, Lytchett Matravers, Poole, Dorset BH16 6DN* Lytchett Minster (01202) 623481

HARVEY, Steven Charles. b 58. Reading Univ BA79 Ox Univ BA83 MA88. Ripon Coll Cuddesdon 81. **d** 84 **p** 85. C Oldham *Man* 84-87; Chapl and Hd RE St Pet Sch York from 87. *St Peter's School, York YO3 6AB* York (01904) 623213 or 658332

HARVEY, Trevor John. b 43. Sheff Univ BA64. Coll of Resurr Mirfield 64. **d** 66 **p** 67. C Kingswinford St Mary *Lich* 66-72; V Upper Gornal 72-77; V Meir 77-86; Chapl St Geo Choir Sch Windsor from 86; Min Can Windsor from 86. *12 The Cloisters, Windsor Castle, Windsor, Berks SL4 1NJ* Windsor (01753) 842086

HARVEY, Victor Llewellyn Tucker. b 16. Ch Coll Cam BA38 MA42. Ridley Hall Cam 38. **d** 39 **p** 40. Hon CF from 46; R St Marylebone St Mary *Lon* 64-82; rtd 82; Perm to Offic *St E* from 82; P-in-c Hasketon 83-89. *The Boot, Great Bealings, Woodbridge, Suffolk IP13 6PQ* Grundisburgh (01473) 735382

HARVEY-COOK, Miss Elizabeth Ann. b 62. St D Coll Lamp BA90 St Mich Coll Llan DPS91. **d** 92. C Llangiwg *S & B* 92-94; C Morriston from 94. *2 Monmouth Place, Parc Gwernfadog, Morriston, Swansea SA6 6RF* Swansea (01792) 791397

HARVEY-NEILL, Nicola Lisa Jane. b 69. QUB BD91 TCD MPhil95. CITC BTh94. **d** 95. Dioc *C T, K & A* from 95. *77 Knocknacarra Park, Knocknacarra, Galway, Irish Republic* Galway (91) 22998

HARVIE, Paul Johnston. b 36. ARCO74 FTCL73 Melbourne Univ BMusEd80 MMus83. St Mich Th Coll Crafers 58 Trin Coll Melbourne LTh61 ACT ThL. **d** 62 **p** 63. Australia 62-64 and 66-89; C Penton Street St Silas w All SS *Lon* 64-66; Vice-Provost St Paul's Cathl Dundee *Bre* 89-92; R Dundee St Paul 89-92; R Dundee St Salvador from 92. *The Rectory, 9 Minard Crescent, Dundee DD3 6LH* Dundee (01382) 21785

HARWOOD, Frederick Ronald (Fred). b 21. Wells Th Coll 61. **d** 63 **p** 64. V Hessenford *Truro* 66-71; V Hayle 71-87; rtd 87; Hon C Madron *Truro* 88-92; Prec Gib Cathl and Port Chapl *Eur* 92-95. *Ferncliffe, 5 Harbour View, Hayle, Cornwall TR27 4LB*

HARWOOD, Canon John Rossiter. b 26. Selw Coll Cam BA51 MA55. Wycliffe Hall Ox 51. **d** 53 **p** 54. Home Educn Sec CMS 67-75; V Cheltenham Ch Ch *Glouc* 75-91; RD Cheltenham 84-89; Hon Can Glouc Cathl 85-91; rtd 91; Perm to Offic *Ex* from 91. *29 Clarence Hill, Dartmouth, Devon TQ6 9NY* Dartmouth (01803) 835827

HARWOOD, Leslie Thomas Prosser. b 03. Trin Hall Cam BA25 MA30. Westcott Ho Cam 25. **d** 26 **p** 27. R Hickling *S'well* 52-78; V Kinoulton 52-78; rtd 78; Perm to Offic *S'well* from 78. *Glebe Farm Cottage, Hickling, Melton Mowbray, Leics LE14 3AQ* Melton Mowbray (01664) 822267

HARWOOD, Dr Peter James. b 64. Birm Univ MB88 ChB88. Wycliffe Hall Ox BA93. **d** 94 **p** 95. C Cov H Trin *Cov* from 94. *85 Stoney Road, Coventry CV3 6HH* Coventry (01203) 504141

HARWOOD, Thomas Smith. b 10. St Jo Coll Dur 38. **d** 41 **p** 41. V Middleton St Mary *Ripon* 62-75; V E Winch *Nor* 62-75; rtd 75; Perm to Offic *Nor* from 75. *8 Beechwood Close, Watlington, King's Lynn, Norfolk PE33 0HP* King's Lynn (01553) 811463

HASELDEN, Canon Eugene John Charles. b 17. Em Coll Cam BA40 MA44. Ridley Hall Cam 40. **d** 42 **p** 43. V Leamington Priors H Trin *Cov* 58-75; RD Leamington 69-75; V Lymington *Win* 75-83; RD Lyndhurst 78-82; rtd 83; Perm to Offic *Win* from 83. *1 Ashley Meadows, Romsey, Hants SO51 7LT* Romsey (01794) 522688

HASELOCK, Canon Jeremy Matthew. b 51. York Univ BA73 BPhil74. St Steph Ho Ox BA82 MA86. **d** 83 **p** 84. C Pimlico St Gabr *Lon* 83-86; C Paddington St Jas 86-88; Bp's Dom Chapl *Chich* 88-91; P-in-c Boxgrove 91-94; V from 94; Dioc Adv on Liturgy from 91; Can and Preb Chich Cathl from 94. *The Vicarage, Boxgrove, Chichester, W Sussex PO18 0ED* Chichester (01243) 774045

HASKINS, Thomas. b 41. TCD BA72. CITC 71. **d** 73 **p** 74. C Larne and Inver *Conn* 73-78; C Antrim All SS 78-83; I Belf St Mark 83-90; RD M Belf 89-90; I Dub Clontarf *D & G* from 90; RD Fingal from 95. *15 Seafield Road West, Clontarf, Dublin 3, Irish Republic* Dublin (1) 833-1181

HASLAM, Andrew James. b 57. Univ Coll Dur BSc78 Coll of Ripon & York St Jo PGCE79. Lambeth STh84 Trin Coll Bris 80. **d** 83 **p** 84. C Leyland St Andr *Blackb* 83-86; C Hartford *Ches* 86-88; V Grimsargh *Blackb* from 88. *St Michael's Vicarage, Preston Road, Grimsargh, Preston PR2 5SD* Preston (01772) 653283

HASLAM, Canon David. b 31. St Chad's Coll Dur BA57. Wells Th Coll 57. **d** 59 **p** 60. V E and W Wordlham, Hartley Mauditt w Kingsley etc *Win* 65-71; V Boscombe St Andr 71-92; RD

Bournemouth 80-90; Hon Can Win Cathl 84-92; rtd 92. *50 Petersfield Road, Bournemouth BH7 6QJ* Bournemouth (01202) 432330

HASLAM, Canon Frank. b 26. Bris Univ BA50. Tyndale Hall Bris 49. **d** 51 **p** 52. V Blackpool Ch Ch *Blackb* 65-70; V Macclesfield St Mich *Ches* 71-80; Dir of Resources 80-91; Hon Can Ches Cathl 81-91; rtd 91. *Brackendale, Chester Road, Buckley, Clwyd CH7 3AH* Buckley (01244) 294544

HASLAM, James Robert. b 31. Open Univ BA74. Bps' Coll Cheshunt 55. **d** 57 **p** 58. C Penwortham St Mary *Blackb* 57-63; V Cockerham 63-74; V Cockerham w Winmarleigh 74-76; V Gt Harwood St Bart 76-88; V Fairhaven from 88. *Fairhaven Vicarage, 83 Clifton Drive, Fairhaven, Lytham St Annes, Lancs FY8 1BZ* Lytham (01253) 734562

HASLAM, John Gordon. b 32. Birm Univ LLB53. Qu Coll Birm 75. **d** 77 **p** 77. Hon C Bartley Green *Birm* 77-79; Hon C Moseley St Mary from 79; Chapl to The Queen from 89. *34 Amesbury Road, Birmingham B13 8LE* 0121-449 3394

HASLAM, Robert John Alexander. b 34. CCC Cam BA58. Coll of Resurr Mirfield 58. **d** 60 **p** 61. C Rawmarsh w Parkgate *Sheff* 60-66; Perm to Offic *Edin* 66-73; Perm to Offic *Carl* 73-77; P-in-c Peebles *Edin* 77-81; V Darnall H Trin *Sheff* 81-85; Hon C Bermondsey St Hugh CD *S'wark* 86-88; R Clydebank *Glas* from 88. *21 Dunmore Street, Clydebank, Dunbartonshire G81 1RL* 0141-952 0298

HASLAM-JONES, Christopher John. b 28. ALCD53. **d** 53 **p** 54. V Radcliffe St Andr *Man* 68-86; R Colchester Ch Ch w St Mary V *Chelmsf* 86-93; rtd 93. *Ramia, 4A Belle Vue Road, Poole, Dorset BH14 8TW* Parkstone (01202) 767674

HASLEHURST (nee STERLING), Mrs Anne. b 51. Macalester Coll (USA) BA73. E Anglian Minl Tr Course 89. **d** 92 **p** 94. Par Dn Bury St Edmunds St Jo *St E* 92-94; C from 94. *19 Carnoustie Drive, Fornham St Martin, Bury St Edmunds, Suffolk IP28 6UU* Bury St Edmunds (01284) 706328

HASLER, John Joseph (Joe). b 45. Qu Coll Birm 89. **d** 90 **p** 91. C Horfield H Trin *Bris* 90-93; V Bris St Andr Hartcliffe from 93. *St Andrew's Vicarage, Peterson Square, Bristol BS13 0EE* Bristol (0117) 964 3554

HASSALL, William Edwin. b 41. St Jo Coll Nottm 75. **d** 77 **p** 78. C Wellington w Eyton *Lich* 77-80; C Farewell 80-82; V 82-93; C Gentleshaw 80-82; V 82-93; P-in-c Cheddleton 93-94. *17 Ansty Drive, Heath Hayes, Cannock, Staffs WS12 5TZ* Heath Hayes (01543) 275087

HASSELL, David Edwin. b 38. W Midl Minl Tr Course 87. **d** 90 **p** 91. NSM Worc SE *Worc* 90-93; C Abberton, Naunton Beauchamp and Bishampton etc 93-94; P-in-c 94; R Abberton, The Flyfords, Naunton Beauchamp etc from 94. *The Rectory, Bishampton, Pershore, Worcs WR10 2LT* Bishampton (01386) 462648

HASSELL, John Charles. b 44. FCA. Sarum & Wells Th Coll 81. **d** 83 **p** 84. C Tottenham St Paul *Lon* 83-86; C Fingringhoe w E Donyland *Chelmsf* 86-90; V Moulsham St Jo from 90. *St John's Vicarage, Vicarage Road, Moulsham, Chelmsford CM2 9PH* Chelmsford (01245) 352344

HASSEN, Canon Edward William. b 27. TCD. **d** 56 **p** 57. I Muckamore *Conn* 67-94; RD Antrim 74-93; Dioc Stewardship Adv 90-94; Can Belf Cathl 93-94; rtd 94. *Valloire, 8 Parkgate Road, Parkgate, Templepatrick, Co Antrim BT39 0DF* Antrim (01849) 432823

HASTED, Canon John Arthur Ord. b 28. Keble Coll Ox BA50 MA54. Wells Th Coll 51. **d** 53 **p** 54. V Sibton *St E* 64-78; V Yoxford 64-79; RD Saxmundham 74-79; Hon Can St E Cathl 75-79; rtd 79; Perm to Offic *St Alb* from 82. *1 Eton Court, Pemberley Avenue, Bedford MK40 2LH* Bedford (01234) 341402

HASTEY, Erle. b 44. St Mich Coll Llan 66. **d** 68 **p** 69. C Pontefract St Giles *Wakef* 68-71; C Almondbury 71-74; R Purlwell 74-79; P-in-c Batley Carr 76-79; V Ynysbrir *Llan* 79-86; V Tylorstown w Ynyshir 86-87; V Tonyrefail w Gilfach Goch from 87; P-in-c Llandyfodwg from 87. *The Vicarage, High Street, Tonyrefail, M Glam CF39 8PL* Tonyrefail (01443) 670330

HASTIE-SMITH, Timothy Maybury (Tim). b 62. Magd Coll Cam MA84. Wycliffe Hall Ox 85. **d** 88 **p** 89. C Ox St Ebbe w H Trin and St Pet *Ox* 88-91; Chapl Stowe Sch Bucks from 91. *New Field House, Stowe School, Buckingham MK18 5DF* Buckingham (01280) 812446

HASTINGS, David Kerr. b 40. St Luke's Coll Ex CertEd63. Ox NSM Course 84. **d** 87 **p** 88. Hd Master St Edburg's Sch Bicester from 82; Asst Chapl HM Pris Grendon and Spring Hill 87-89; NSM Bicester w Bucknell, Caversfield and Launton *Ox* 87-89; Chapl HM Pris Reading 90-92; P-in-c Gt Wishford *Sarum* 92; P-in-c S Newton 92; P-in-c Stapleford w Berwick St James 92; R Lower Wylye and Till Valley from 92. *The Rectory, Wishford Magna, Salisbury SP2 2PQ* Salisbury (01722) 790363

HASTINGS, Gary Lea. b 56. New Univ of Ulster BA82 MA87 TCD BTh93. CITC 90. **d** 93 **p** 94. C Galway w Kilcummin

T, K & A 93-95; Dom Chapl to Bp of Tuam from 94; I Aughaval w Achill, Knappagh, Dugort etc from 95. *The Rectory, Newport Road, Westport, Co Mayo, Irish Republic* Westport (98) 25127

HASTINGS, Patrick John Alan. b 45. ACIB68 CertEd75 Sussex Univ BEd82. S Dios Minl Tr Scheme 83. **d** 86 **p** 87. NSM Whyke w Rumboldswhyke and Portfield *Chich* 86-87; C Weybridge *Guildf* 87-89; C Verwood *Sarum* 89-93; P-in-c Lytchett Matravers from 93. *The Rectory, Jennys' Lane, Lytchett Matravers, Poole, Dorset BH16 6BP* Morden (01929) 459200

HASTROP, Paul. b 39. Wells Th Coll 70. **d** 72 **p** 73. C Parkstone St Osmund *Sarum* 72-76; C Penzance St Mary w St Paul *Truro* 76-79; V St Blazey 79-87; TV Bournemouth St Pet w St Swithun, St Steph etc *Win* 87-94; TV Thornaby on Tees *York* from 94. *60 Lanehouse Road, Thornaby, Stockton-on-Tees, Cleveland TS17 8ED* Stockton-on-Tees (01642) 679661

HASTWELL, James Sydney (Jim). b 37. Roch Th Coll 67. **d** 69 **p** 70. C Croydon St Aug *Cant* 69-73; C Hurstpierpoint *Chich* 73-75; P-in-c Twineham 76; P-in-c Sayers Common 76; P-in-c Albourne 76; R Albourne w Sayers Common and Twineham 76-88; V Forest Row 88-94. *4 Park Close, Hurstpierpoint, Hassocks, W Sussex BN6 9XA* Hassocks (01273) 835954

HATCH, Canon George Andrew. b 29. Leeds Univ BA. Coll of Resurr Mirfield. **d** 53 **p** 54. C S Farnborough *Guildf* 53-55; Windward Is 55-63; Barbados from 63; Assoc Dir Chr Action Development in Caribbean 73-83. *St James, Barbados* Barbados (1809) 432-1580

HATCH, Richard Francis. b 36. Qu Coll Cam BA60 MA64. Cuddesdon Coll 60. **d** 62 **p** 63. C Leigh St Mary *Man* 62-66; V Peel Green 66-71; V Barton w Peel Green 71-75; Dioc Broadcasting Officer 73-85; R Birch St Jas 75-78; R Fallowfield 75-78; Lic to Offic from 78. *24 Denison Road, Victoria Park, Manchester M14 5RY* 0161-225 0799

HATCHETT, Michael John. b 49. Enfield Coll BSc72 K Coll Lon BD77 AKC77. Linc Th Coll 77. **d** 78 **p** 79. C Halstead St Andr *Chelmsf* 78-79; C Halstead St Andr w H Trin and Greenstead Green 79-81; C Greenstead juxta Colchester 81-85; V Gt Totham from 85. *The Vicarage, 1 Hall Road, Great Totham, Maldon, Essex CM9 8NN* Maldon (01621) 893150

HATCHLEY, Canon Walter John. b 24. Lon Univ BA65. Coll of Resurr Mirfield 64. **d** 66 **p** 67. C Gosforth All SS *Newc* 69-72; C Cullercoats St Geo 72; TV 72-78; V Newc St Fran 78-93; RD Newc E 83-92; Hon Can Newc Cathl 90-93; rtd 93. *4 Woodthorne Road, Jesmond, Newcastle upon Tyne NE2 3PB*

HATCHMAN, Ms Elizabeth Mary (Lizzie). b 63. St Andr Univ MA85 Kent Coll for Careers DCG87. Selly Oak Coll Qu Coll Birm BD92. **d** 93 **p** 94. C Aston SS Pet and Paul *Birm* from 93. *81 Electric Avenue, Birmingham B6 7ED* 0121-327 0113

HATCHMAN, Hugh Alleyne. b 28. Qu Coll Cam BA52 MA56. Ridley Hall Cam 52. **d** 54 **p** 55. V New Catton St Luke *Nor* 63-79; Chapl Bexley Hosp Kent 79-93; rtd 93. *31 Briar Road, Bexley, Kent DA5 2HW* Crayford (01322) 524041

HATCLIFFE, Charles John William Coombes. b 26. St Aid Birkenhead 59. **d** 61 **p** 62. V Stubbins *Man* 64-71; P-in-c Clifton Green 71-74; V 74-82; P-in-c Acton Burnell w Pitchford *Heref* 82-83; P-in-c Condover 82-83; P-in-c Frodesley 82-83; V Bentley *Lich* 83-89; rtd 89. *3 Chestnut Drive, Bayston Hill, Shrewsbury SY3 0QQ*

HATFULL, Ronald Stanley. b 22. CChem42 MChemA48 FRSC48 FRSH65. Qu Coll Birm 79. **d** 82 **p** 83. NSM Castle Church *Lich* 82-89; Kingsmead Hosp Stafford 82-89; rtd 89. *Ridge House, Ridgeway Close, Hyde Lea, Stafford ST18 9BE* Stafford (01785) 52992

HATHAWAY, Canon David Alfred Gerald. b 48. DipTh72. St Mich Coll Llan 69. **d** 72 **p** 73. C Newport St Julian *Mon* 72-74; P-in-c Oakham w Hambleton and Egleton *Pet* 74-77; V Newport St Matt *Mon* 77-83; V Abertillery 83-88; V Rumney from 88; Hon Can St Woolos Cathl from 91. *The Vicarage, 702 Newport Road, Rumney, Cardiff CF3 8DF* Cardiff (01222) 797882

HATHAWAY, John Albert. b 24. Sarum Th Coll 59. **d** 60 **p** 61. V Holmwood *Guildf* 66-71; R Westborough 71-74; V Newmarket All SS *St E* 74-82; V Acton w Gt Waldingfield 82-85; R W Downland *Sarum* 85-90; rtd 90. *3 Nettleand Nursery, Shaftesbury, Dorset SP7 8QS* Shaftesbury (01747) 851950

HATHAWAY, Martin Charles. b 48. St Jo Coll Nottm LTh95. **d** 95. C Weddington and Caldecote *Cov* from 95. *62 Castle Road, Nuneaton, Warks CV10 0EW*

HATHERLEY, Peter Graham. b 46. Univ of Wales (Cardiff) BSc67 PhD70. St Mich Coll Llan 70. **d** 72 **p** 73. C Ystrad Mynach *Llan* 72-75; Hon C Tonyrefail 75-88; Perm to Offic from 88. *Treetops, The Derwen, Bridgend, M Glam CF35 6HD*

HATHERLEY, Victor Charles. b 17. St Aug Coll Cant 63. **d** 64 **p** 64. R E Harptree *B & W* 68-73; R E w W Harptree 73-76; R E w W Harptree and Hinton Blewett 76-82; rtd 82; Perm to Offic

B & W 83-91. *10 Fairview Road, Broadstone, Dorset BH18 9AX* Broadstone (01202) 699371

HATHORNE (nee MARSH), Mrs Carol Ann. b 44. W Midl Coll of Educn BA82. W Midl Minl Tr Course 88. **d** 91 **p** 94. Par Dn Wednesbury St Paul Wood Green *Lich* 91-93; NSM Pensnett *Worc* from 93. *222 High Street, Pensnett, Brierley Hill, W Midlands DY5 4JP* Brierley Hill (01384) 78438

HATHWAY, Richard Peter. b 17. Kelham Th Coll 34. **d** 41 **p** 42. Chapl Highgate Sch Lon 66-81; rtd 81; Perm to Offic *Nor* from 81; Perm to Offic *St E* from 87. *10 Station Road, Harleston, Norfolk IP20 9ES* Harleston (01379) 853590

HATHWAY, Ross Arthur. b 56. DATh87. Moore Th Coll Sydney BTh86. **d** 86 **p** 87. Australia 87-88; C Corby St Columba *Pet* 89-92; R Trull w Angersleigh *B & W* from 92. *The Rectory, Wild Oak Lane, Trull, Taunton, Somerset TA3 7JT* Taunton (01823) 253518

HATREY, David Nigel. b 57. SS Mark & Jo Coll Plymouth CertEd79 CertSc87 BEd90. SW Minl Tr Course 90. **d** 93 **p** 94. NSM S Hill w Callington *Truro* from 93. *8 Lowertown Close, Landrake, Saltash, Cornwall PL12 5DG* Saltash (01752) 851529

HATT, Michael John. b 34. Sarum Th Coll 67. **d** 69 **p** 70. Hon C Ex St Mary Arches *Ex* 70-73; Hon C Cen Ex from 73. *133 Topsham Road, Exeter EX2 4RE* Exeter (01392) 71165

HATTAN, Jeffrey William Rowland. b 49. Cranmer Hall Dur 83. **d** 85 **p** 86. C Eston w Normanby *York* 85-89; TV 89-95; V Hunmanby w Muston from 95. *The Vicarage, 6 Northgate, Hunmanby, Filey, N Yorkshire YO14 0NT* Scarborough (01723) 890294

HATTER, Canon David George. b 21. Lich Th Coll. **d** 57 **p** 58. V Mansf St Mark *S'well* 67-81; V Sutton w Carlton and Normanton upon Trent etc 81-86; P-in-c Caunton 84-86; Hon Can S'well Minster 84-86; RD Tuxford and Norwell 84-86; rtd 86; Perm to Offic *S'well* from 86. *1 North End, Farndon, Newark, Notts NG24 3SX* Newark (01636) 76960

HATTON, Jeffrey Charles. b 49. K Coll Lon BD70 Bris Univ MA72. Westcott Ho Cam 73 Episc Th Sch Cam Mass 74. **d** 74 **p** 75. C Nor St Pet Mancroft *Nor* 74-78; C Earlham St Anne 78-79; Relig Broadcasting Asst IBA 79-82; Hon C Kensington St Barn Lon 79-84; Hon C Fulham All SS 85-89; R Win All SS w Chilcomb and Chesil *Win* 89-94; Dioc Communications Officer 89-94; P-in-c Salisbury St Thos and St Edm *Sarum* from 94. *The Rectory, St Thomas's Square, Salisbury SP1 1BA* Salisbury (01722) 322537

HATTON, Michael Samuel. b 44. St Jo Coll Dur BA72 DipTh74. **d** 74 **p** 75. C Dudley St Jas *Worc* 74-75; C N Lynn w St Marg and St Nic *Nor* 75-77; C Walsall Wood *Lich* 78-79; Min Shelfield St Mark CD 79-89; V Middleton St Cross *Ripon* from 89. *PO Box 78, Bermagui, New South Wales 2546, Australia*

HATTON, Trevor. b 55. Oak Hill Th Coll BA86. **d** 86 **p** 87. C Chilwell *S'well* 86-90; R Trowell from 90. *The Rectory, Nottingham Road, Trowell, Nottingham NG9 3PF* Nottingham (0115) 932 1474

HATWELL, Timothy Rex. b 53. Oak Hill Th Coll BA85. **d** 85 **p** 86. C Tonbridge St Steph *Roch* 85-90; V Cudham and Downe from 90. *The Vicarage, Cudham Lane South, Cudham, Sevenoaks, Kent TN14 7QA* Biggin Hill (01959) 572445

HAUGHAN, John Francis (Frank). b 28. Tyndale Hall Bris 56. **d** 60 **p** 61. V Tewkesbury H Trin *Glouc* 67-92; rtd 92. *Beech View, Lower Road, Yorkley, Lydney, Glos GL15 4TQ* Dean (01594) 562066

HAUGHTON, Peter Steele. b 57. K Coll Lon BD84 MA90 Fitzw Coll Cam DipTh85. Westcott Ho Cam 84. **d** 86 **p** 87. C Cheam Common St Phil *S'wark* 86-90; Chapl Lon Univ Medical Schs 90-94; Educn Adv Lon Univ Medical Schs 94-95; P-in-c Kingston Vale St Jo from 95. *St John's Vicarage, Robin Hood Lane, London SW15 3PY* 0181-546 4079

HAVARD, Alan Ernest. b 28. Qu Coll Birm 79. **d** 81 **p** 82. NSM Rugby St Matt *Cov* 81-84; C Portishead *B & W* 84-86; V Mickleover All SS *Derby* from 86. *All Saints' Vicarage, Etwall Road, Mickleover, Derby DE3 5DL* Derby (01332) 513793

HAVARD, David William. b 56. Man Univ BA84. Qu Coll Birm 84. **d** 85. C Man Clayton St Cross w St Paul *Man* 85-88; Canada from 88. *Apt 211, 517—10th Street, New Westminster, British Columbia, Canada, V3M 3X4*

HAVELL, Edward Michael. b 38. Dur Univ BA65. Ridley Hall Cam 66. **d** 68 **p** 69. C Ecclesall *Sheff* 68-71; C Roch St Justus *Roch* 71-74; P-in-c Holbeach Hurn *Linc* 74-75; C Hollington St Jo *Chich* 75-85; TV Rye 85-92; C E Dereham and Scarning *Nor* 92; 94. *4 Gammons Way, Sedlescombe, Battle, E Sussex TN33 0RQ* Battle (01424) 870864

HAVENS, Mrs Anita Sue. b 44. Mass Univ BSEd67 Clark Univ (USA) MA72 Hughes Hall Cam BA79. Cranmer Hall Dur MA83. **dss** 84 **d** 87 **p** 94. Gateshead Hosps 84-87; Par Dn Cen Telford *Lich* 87-90; Ind Chapl 87-90; Ind Chapl *Liv* from 90. *36 Heathfield Road, Wavertree, Liverpool L15 9EZ* 0151-722 0342

312

HAVILAND, Edmund Selwyn. b 24. K Coll Cam BA49 MA51. Wells Th Coll 49. **d** 51 **p** 52. V E Peckham *Roch* 68-78; R E Peckham and Nettlestead 78-84; S Africa 84-85; Dep Chapl HM Pris Brixton 85-89; rtd 89; Perm to Offic *Guildf* from 89. *Hill Farm, Thursley, Godalming, Surrey GU8 6QQ* Farnham (01252) 702115

HAWES, Andrew Thomas. b 54. Sheff Univ BA77 Em Coll Cam MA79. Westcott Ho Cam 77. **d** 80 **p** 81. FFS from 78; C Gt Grimsby St Mary and St Jas *Linc* 80-84; P-in-c Gedney Drove End 84-86; P-in-c Sutton St Nicholas 84-86; V Lutton w Gedney Drove End, Dawsmere 86-89; V Edenham w Witham-on-the-Hill from 89. *The Vicarage, Church Lane, Edenham, Bourne, Lincs PE10 0LS* Edenham (01778) 591358

HAWES, Canon Arthur John. b 43. UEA BA86 Birm Univ DPS72 DipL&A75. Chich Th Coll 65. **d** 68 **p** 69. C Kidderminster St Jo *Worc* 68-72; P-in-c Droitwich 72-76; R Alderford w Attlebridge and Swannington *Nor* 76-92; Chapl Hellesdon & Dav Rice Hosps and Yare Clinic 76-92; RD Sparham 81-91; Mental Health Act Commr from 86; Hon Can Nor Cathl *Nor* from 88; TR Gaywood St Faith 92-95; TR Gaywood St Faith, Kings Lynn from 95. *St Faith's Rectory, Gaywood, King's Lynn, Norfolk PE30 4DZ* King's Lynn (01553) 774662 Fax 761327

HAWES, Clive. b 37. Univ of Wales BSc59. Coll of Resurr Mirfield 61. **d** 63 **p** 64. C Ynyshir *Llan* 63-65; C Roath St Marg 65-72; V Llanddewi Rhondda w Bryn Eirw 72-75; Chapl Ch Coll Brecon 75-92; V Llantilio Crossenny w Penrhos, Llanvetherine etc *Mon* from 92. *The Vicarage, Llantilio Crossenny, Abergavenny, Gwent NP7 8SU* Llantilio (0160085) 240

HAWES, George Walter. b 10. Lon Coll of Div 39. **d** 41 **p** 42. R Rowner *Portsm* 60-78; rtd 78. *90 Kiln Road, Fareham, Hants PO16 7UJ* Fareham (01329) 286309

HAWES, Joseph Patricius. b 65. St Chad's Coll Dur BA87. St Steph Ho Ox 88. **d** 91 **p** 92. C Clapham TM *S'wark* from 91. *The Glebe House, 6 Rectory Grove, London SW4 0DZ* 0171-720 3370

HAWES, Michael Rowell. b 31. AKC61. **d** 62 **p** 63. C Epsom St Martin *Guildf* 62-65; Chapl RAF 65-86; R Newnham w Nately Scures w Mapledurwell etc *Win* from 86. *The Rectory, Up Nateley, Basingstoke, Hants RG27 9PL* Hook (01256) 762021

HAWKEN, Andrew Robert. b 58. K Coll Lon BD81 AKC81. St Steph Ho Ox 83. **d** 85 **p** 86. C Ex St Dav *Ex* 85-88; TV Witney *Ox* 88-93; V Benson from 93. *The Vicarage, Church Road, Benson, Wallingford, Oxon OX9 6SF* Wallingford (01491) 838254

HAWKEN, Michael Vaughan. b 50. Lon Univ CertEd71 Open Univ BA76. Trin Coll Bris DipHE81 Trin Episc Sch for Min Ambridge Penn 81. **d** 82 **p** 83. C Roxeth Ch Ch and Harrow St Pet *Lon* 82-86; C Ealing St Paul 86-89; P-in-c 89-92; V 92-93; TR Uxbridge 93-95; rtd 95. *15 Edinburgh Close, Ickenham, Uxbridge, Middx UB10 8RA* Uxbridge (01895) 678872

HAWKER, Canon Alan Fort. b 44. Hull Univ BA65 Lon Univ DipTh68. Clifton Th Coll 65. **d** 68 **p** 69. C Bootle St Leon *Liv* 68-71; C Fazakerley Em 71-73; V Goose Green 73-81; TR Southgate *Chich* from 81; Can and Preb Chich Cathl from 94; RD E Grinstead from 94. *The Rectory, Forester Road, Crawley, W Sussex RH10 6EH* Crawley (01293) 523463

HAWKER, Alan John. b 53. BD76 AKC76. Sarum & Wells Th Coll 77. **d** 78 **p** 79. C Coleford w Staunton *Glouc* 78-81; C Up Hatherley 81-84; V Plymouth St Jas Ham *Ex* 84-92; TV Worc SE *Worc* from 92. *The Vicarage, 160 Bath Road, Worcester WR5 3EP* Worcester (01905) 357244

HAWKER, Brian Henry. b 34. AKC61 St Boniface Warminster 61. **d** 62 **p** 63. V W Wycombe *Ox* 69-72; Past Consultant Clinical Th Assn 72-83; Past Consultant 83-94; Public Preacher *S'well* 72-76; Perm to Offic *B & W* 76-83; Perm to Offic *Truro* 83-90; rtd 94. *clo 97 Frederick Street, Loughborough, Leics LE11 3BH* Loughborough (01509) 263542

✠**HAWKER, Rt Rev Dennis Gascoyne.** b 21. Qu Coll Cam BA48 MA53. Cuddesdon Coll 48. **d** 50 **p** 51 **c** 72. C Folkestone St Mary and St Eanswythe *Cant* 50-55; V S Norwood St Mark 55-60; Lic to Offic *Lon* 60-64; Can and Preb Linc Cathl 64-87; V Gt Grimsby St Mary and St Jas 65-72; Suff Bp Grantham 72-87; Dean Stamford 73-87; Chapl RNR from 78; rtd 87; Asst Bp Nor from 93. *Pickwick Cottage, Hall Close, Heacham, King's Lynn, Norfolk PE31 7JT* Heacham (01485) 70450

HAWKER, Peter Charles. b 17. FSA67 Ch Coll Cam BA39 MA43 Univ of W Aus MA43. St Barn Coll Adelaide ThL41. **d** 43 **p** 44. Sec Gen Confraternity of the Blessed Sacrament 56-85; V Linc St Botolph by Bargate *Linc* 69-85; Can and Preb Linc Cathl from 77; rtd 85. *20 Middleton's Field, Lincoln LN2 1QP* Lincoln (01522) 544337

HAWKER, Ven Peter John. b 37. Ex Univ BA59. Wycliffe Hall Ox 69. **d** 70 **p** 71. Chapl Berne w Neuchatel *Eur* 70-89; Adn Switzerland from 86; Can Brussels Cathl from 86; Chapl

Zurich w St Gallen and Winterthur 90-93; Chapl Zurich w Winterthur from 93. *Promenadengasse 9, 8001 Zurich, Switzerland* Zurich (1) 261-2241 or 252-6024 Fax 252-6024

HAWKES, Mrs Elisabeth Anne. b 56. GRNCM78 CertEd80. Linc Th Coll 86. **d** 88. Hon Par Dn Finham *Cov* 88-90; Hon Par Dn Bexhill St Pet *Chich* from 90. *St Michael's House, Glassenbury Drive, Bexhill-on-Sea, E Sussex TN40 2NY* Bexhill-on-Sea (01424) 219937

HAWKES, Keith Andrew. b 28. Oak Hill Th Coll 72. **d** 74 **p** 75. C Gt Yarmouth *Nor* 74-77; C-in-c Bowthorpe CD 77; Chapl Dusseldorf *Eur* 77-83; TV Quidenham *Nor* 83-88; TR 88-90; RD Thetford and Rockland 86-90; R Wickmere w Lt Barningham, Itteringham etc from 90; Dioc Rural Officer 90-94; P-in-c Saxthorpe w Corpusty, Blickling, Oulton etc from 94. *The Rectory, Itteringham, Norwich NR11 7AX* Saxthorpe (0126387) 4262

HAWKES, Ronald Linton. b 54. York Univ CertEd75 Leeds Univ BEd76. Linc Th Coll 85. **d** 87 **p** 88. C Finham *Cov* 87-90; C Bexhill St Pet *Chich* 90; TV from 91. *St Michael's House, Glassenbury Drive, Bexhill-on-Sea, E Sussex TN40 2NY* Bexhill-on-Sea (01424) 219937

HAWKETT, Graham Kenneth. b 20. Bps' Coll Cheshunt 61. **d** 63 **p** 64. V Wyke *Guildf* 67-85; rtd 85; Perm to Offic *Guildf* from 85. *Bede House, Beech Road, Haslemere, Surrey GU27 2BX* Haslemere (01428) 656430

HAWKINGS, Timothy Denison. b 55. Ex Univ BA78 Nottm Univ BA80. St Jo Coll Nottm 78. **d** 81 **p** 82. C Penn *Lich* 81-85; C Stafford 85; TV 85-94; TR Stratton St Margaret w S Marston etc *Bris* from 94. *The Rectory, Kenwin Close, Swindon SN3 4NB* Swindon (01793) 822793

HAWKINS, Alec Borman. b 07. **d** 68 **p** 69. C Boldmere *Birm* 68-79; Perm to Offic from 79. *2 Wrekin Court, Vesey Close, Sutton Coldfield, W Midlands B74 4QN* 0121-308 4625

HAWKINS, Alfred Pryse. b 29. St Mich Coll Llan 57. **d** 59 **p** 60. C Dowlais *Llan* 59-62; C Caerau w Ely 62-66; V Aberaman and Abercwmboi 66-77; R Ebbw Vale *Mon* 77-82; P-in-c Paddington St Dav Welsh Ch *Lon* from 82; V St Benet Paul's Wharf from 82; P-in-c St Jas Garlickhythe w St Mich Queenhithe etc 85-86. *St David's Vicarage, St Mary's Terrace, London W2 1SJ* 0171-723 3104 or 489 8754

HAWKINS, Canon Alun John. b 44. BA66 AKC Univ of Wales (Ban) BD81. St Deiniol's Hawarden 78. **d** 81 **p** 82. C Dwygyfylchi (or Penmaenmawr) *Ban* 81-84; R Llanberis 84-89; Tutor Ban Dioc NSM Course 85-90; Dir of Ords *Ban* 86-90; V Knighton and Norton *S & B* 89-93; Chapl Knighton Hosp 89-93; R Ban from 93; Can Missr Ban Cathl from 93. *The Canonry, Cathedral Close, Bangor, Gwynedd LL57 1LH* Bangor (01248) 370693

HAWKINS, Andrew Robert. b 40. St Andr Univ BSc64 Dur Univ BA68 DipTh69. St Chad's Coll Dur 65. **d** 69 **p** 70. C Sutton St Nic *S'wark* 69-73; C Wimbledon 73-77; TV Cramlington *Newc* 77-81; R Clutton w Cameley *B & W* 81-89; Chapl City of Bath Coll of FE from 90. *18 Wallycourt Road, Chew Stoke, Bristol BS18 8XN* Bristol (0117) 933 2422

HAWKINS, Canon Arthur Herbert. b 06. Lon Univ BD33. Lon Coll of Div 27. **d** 33 **p** 34. R Leven w Catwick *York* 64-73; Can and Preb York Minster 68-73; rtd 73. *clo A J Hawkins Esq, 3 West Stockwell Street, Colchester CO1 1HQ* Colchester (01206) 577767

HAWKINS, Bruce Alexander. b 44. Qu Coll Ox BA66 MA71. Sarum Th Coll 66. **d** 68 **p** 69. C Epsom St Martin *Guildf* 68-71; Dioc Youth Chapl *Cant* 72-81; Hon Min Can Cant Cathl from 75; Dep Dir of Educn 81-86; V Walmer from 86; RD Sandwich from 94. *The Vicarage, St Mary's Road, Deal, Kent CT14 7NQ* Deal (01304) 374645

HAWKINS, Clive Ladbrook. b 53. DHSA79 St Pet Coll Ox BA76 MA79 DipTh82. Trin Coll Bris 80. **d** 82 **p** 83. C Win Ch Ch *Win* 82-86; R Eastrop from 86. *Eastrop Rectory, 2A Wallis Road, Basingstoke, Hants RG21 3DW* Basingstoke (01256) 55507

HAWKINS, David Frederick Cox. b 17. Clare Coll Cam BA38 MA45. Westcott Ho Cam 46. **d** 48 **p** 49. C Leckhampton SS Phil and Jas *Glouc* 69-73; R Clifford Chambers w Marston Sicca 73-79; R Welford w Weston and Clifford Chambers 79-82; rtd 82; Perm to Offic *B & W* 83-94. *Orchard Rise, Back Street, Bradford-on-Tone, Taunton, Somerset TA4 1HH* Bradford-on-Tone (01823) 461331

HAWKINS, Canon David John Leader. b 49. Nottm Univ BTh73 LTh. St Jo Coll Nottm 69 ALCD73. **d** 73 **p** 74. C Bebington *Ches* 73-76; Nigeria 76-82; C Ox St Aldate w St Matt *Ox* 83-86; V Leeds St Geo *Ripon* from 86. *St George's Vicarage, 208 Kirkstall Lane, Leeds LS5 2AB* Leeds (0113) 274 4367 or 243 8498

HAWKINS, David Kenneth Beaumont. b 36. LTh. Em Coll Saskatoon 63. **d** 63 **p** 64. Canada 63-85; C St Alb St Paul *St Alb* 85-87; C Hednesford *Lich* 87-92; R Buildwas and Leighton w Eaton Constantine etc from 92. *The Vicarage, Eaton Constantine, Shrewsbury SY5 6RF* Cressage (01952) 510333

HAWKINS, David Sewell. b 33. Bps' Coll Cheshunt. **d** 58 **p** 59. C Chingford St Anne *Chelmsf* 58-59; C Bridlington Quay Ch Ch *York* 59-63; V Rudston, Grindale and Ergham w Boynton 63-64; P-in-c Boynton 63-64; V Rudston w Boynton 64-68; Chapl RADD 68-77; R Burton Agnes w Harpham *York* 77-80; P-in-c Lowthorpe w Ruston Parva 77-80; P-in-c Kilham 77-80; R Burton Agnes w Harpham, Kilham, Lowthorpe etc 80-85; R Burton Agnes w Harpham and Lowthorpe etc from 85. *The Rectory, Rudston Road, Burton Agnes, Driffield, N Humberside YO25 0NE* Burton Agnes (01262) 490293

HAWKINS, Donald John. b 39. K Coll Lon BD62 AKC62. St Boniface Warminster 62. **d** 63 **p** 64. C Winlaton *Dur* 63-66; C Gateshead St Mary 66-69; C Ryhope 69-71; R Cockfield 71-79; Chapl N Staffs R Infirmary Stoke-on-Trent 79-89; Chapl Stoke-on-Trent City Gen Hosp from 89. *City General Hospital, 578 Newcastle Road, Stoke-on-Trent ST4 6QG* Stoke-on-Trent (01782) 718146 or 71544

HAWKINS, Canon Francis John (Frank). b 36. Ex Coll Ox BA61 MA63. Chich Th Coll 59. **d** 61 **p** 62. C Tavistock and Gulworthy *Ex* 61-64; Lect Chich Th Coll 64-73; Vice-Prin 73-75; V E Grinstead St Mary *Chich* 75-81; Can Res and Treas Chich Cathl from 81; V Sidlesham 81-89; Dir of Ords from 89. *12 St Martin's Square, Chichester, W Sussex PO19 1NR* Chichester (01243) 783509

HAWKINS, Ian Clinton. b 27. Roch Th Coll 63. **d** 65 **p** 66. V Cotmanhay *Derby* 68-77; V Ospringe *Cant* 77-85; P-in-c Eastling 77-85; P-in-c Goodnestone H Cross w Chillenden and Knowlton 85; P-in-c Womenswold 85; V Nonington w Wymynswold and Goodnestone etc 85-92; rtd 92. *7 Main Road, Bradwell, Sheffield S30 2JG* Hope Valley (01433) 621360

HAWKINS, James Reginald. b 39. Ex Univ BA61. Westcott Ho Cam 61. **d** 63 **p** 64. C Cannock *Lich* 63-66; C Wem 66-67; C Cheddleton 67-69; R Yoxall 69-77; R The Quinton *Birm* 77-84; V Bosbury w Wellington Heath etc *Heref* from 84. *The Vicarage, Bosbury, Ledbury, Herefordshire HR8 1QA* Bosbury (01531) 640225

HAWKINS, John. b 27. FASI73 Ox Poly DipArch52. S'wark Ord Course 84. **d** 87 **p** 88. Hon C Carshalton Beeches S'wark 87-89; Perm to Offic from 89. *44 Castlemaine Avenue, South Croydon, Surrey CR2 7HR* 0181-688 9685

HAWKINS, John Arthur. b 45. Lon Univ DipTh69. Kelham Th Coll 64. **d** 69 **p** 70. C Cov St Alb *Cov* 70-73; C Fletchamstead 73-77; V Whitley 77-81; TV Northn Em *Pet* 81-90; TV Gt Chesham *Ox* from 90. *Christ Church Vicarage, 95 Latimer Road, Chesham, Bucks HP5 1QQ* Chesham (01494) 773318

HAWKINS, John Charles Lacey. b 18. Linc Th Coll 40. **d** 42 **p** 43. R Stockton-on-the-Forest w Holtby and Warthill *York* 60-77; R Sigglesthorne and Rise w Nunkeeling and Bewholme 77-83; rtd 83. *Woodlea, 26 Limekiln Lane, Bridlington, N Humberside YO16 5TH* Bridlington (01262) 601760

HAWKINS, John Edward Inskipp. b 63. K Coll Lon BD85. Qu Coll Birm 86. **d** 88 **p** 89. C Birchfield *Birm* 88-92; C Poplar *Lon* 92-93; TV from 93. *St Nicholas' Church Flat, Aberfeldy Street, London E14 0QD* 0171-515 8405

HAWKINS, Canon John Henry. b 13. TCD BA35 BD51. CITC 37. **d** 37 **p** 38. I Agherton *Conn* 67-78; Can Conn Cathl 76-78; rtd 78. *11 Carnreagh Avenue, Hillsborough, Co Down BT26 6LL* Hillsborough (01846) 682565

HAWKINS, Noel. b 46. St Jo Coll Nottm 82. **d** 84 **p** 85. C Worksop St Jo *S'well* 84-86; C Wollaton Park 86-89; TV Billericay and Lt Burstead *Chelmsf* from 89. *The Rectory, Rectory Road, Little Burstead, Billericay, Essex CM12 9TP* Billericay (01277) 656509

HAWKINS, Paul Henry Whishaw. b 46. Ex Coll Ox BA68 MA74 SS Coll Cam MA84. St Steph Ho Ox 70. **d** 72 **p** 73. C Fawley *Win* 72-75; C Ealing St Steph Castle Hill *Lon* 75-77; P-in-c Dorney *Ox* 77-78; TV Riverside 78-81; Lic to Offic *Ely* 82-87; Chapl SS Coll Cam 82-87; V Plymstock *Ex* from 87; RD Plymouth Sutton from 91. *The Vicarage, 5 Cobb Lane, Plymstock, Plymouth PL9 9BQ* Plymouth (01752) 403126

HAWKINS, Canon Peter Edward. b 35. Leeds Univ BA60. Coll of Resurr Mirfield 60. **d** 62 **p** 63. C Forest Gate St Edm *Chelmsf* 62-65; C Sevenoaks St Jo *Roch* 65-68; Chapl Metrop Police Cadet Corps Tr Sch 68-73; P-in-c Knowle H Nativity *Bris* 73; TV Knowle 73-79; V Westbury-on-Trym H Trin 79-87; TR Solihull *Birm* from 87; Hon Can Birm Cathl from 92. *The Rectory, Church Hill Road, Solihull, W Midlands B91 3RQ* 0121-705 0069 or 705 5350

HAWKINS, Peter Michael. b 38. Kelham Th Coll 58. **d** 63 **p** 64. India 63-69; C Manningham St Paul and St Jude *Bradf* 70-72; C Bradf Cathl 72-75; V Allerton 75-90; V Pet H Spirit Bretton *Pet* from 90; P-in-c Marholm from 90. *23 Westhawe, Bretton, Peterborough PE3 8BE* Peterboro' (0733) 264418 or 265705 Fax 332544

✠**HAWKINS, Rt Rev Richard Stephen.** b 39. Ex Coll Ox BA61 MA65 Ex Univ BPhil76. St Steph Ho Ox 61. **d** 63 **p** 64 **c** 88. C Ex St Thos *Ex* 63-66; C Clyst St Mary 66-75; TV Clyst St George, Aylesbeare, Clyst Honiton etc 75-78; Bp's Officer for Min 78-81; Jt Dir Ex & Truro NSM Scheme 78-81; TV Cen Ex 78-81; Dioc Dir of Ords 79-81; Adn Totnes 81-88; P-in-c Oldridge 81-87; P-in-c Whitestone 81-87; Suff Bp Plymouth from 88. *31 Riverside Walk, Tamerton Foliot, Plymouth PL5 4AQ* Plymouth (01752) 769836 Fax 769818

HAWKINS, Richard Whishaw. b 51. Coll of Resurr Mirfield 93. **d** 95. C Weymouth H Trin *Sarum* from 95. *1 Ben Nevis Road, Weymouth, Dorset DT4 0DB* Weymouth (01305) 779088

HAWKINS, Roger David William. b 33. K Coll Lon BD58 AKC58. **d** 59 **p** 60. C Twickenham St Mary *Lon* 59-61; C Heston 61-64; C Dorking w Ranmore *Guildf* 64-65; V Mitcham St Mark *S'wark* 65-74; V Redhill St Matt 74-91; P-in-c Warlingham w Chelsham and Farleigh from 91. *The Rectory, 15 Chapel Road, Warlingham, Surrey CR6 9LH* Upper Warlingham (01883) 624125

HAWKINS, Roger Julian. b 32. Ripon Hall Ox 59. **d** 61 **p** 62. C-in-c Newall Green CD *Man* 61-63; Chapl RAF 63-67; R Mawgan in Pyder *Truro* 67-75; R Lanteglos by Camelford w Advent 75-78; R Newmarket St Mary w Exning St Agnes *St E* 78-85; P-in-c Coltishall w Gt Hautbois *Nor* 85-87; R Coltishall w Gt Hautbois and Horstead 87-90; Chapl Whiteley Village *Guildf* 90-94. *26 New Road, Ringwood, Hants BH24 3AU*

HAWKINS, Timothy St John (Tim). b 59. CCC Ox BA82. Trin Coll Bris BA87. **d** 87 **p** 88. C Cheltenham St Mary, St Matt, St Paul and H Trin *Glouc* 87-90; C Cowplain *Portsm* 90-94; V Pennycross *Ex* from 94. *St Pancras Vicarage, 66 Glentor Road, Plymouth PL3 5TR* Plymouth (01752) 774332

HAWKINS, William Arthur. b 18. Clifton Th Coll 50. **d** 53 **p** 54. R Ashill w Broadway *B & W* 58-74; R Herstmonceux *Chich* 74-83; rtd 83; Perm to Offic *Chich* from 84. *Three Gables, 17 Heighton Road, Newhaven, E Sussex BN9 0RB* Newhaven (01273) 513694

HAWKSBEE, Canon Derek John. b 28. Lon Univ BSc49. S'wark Ord Course 70. **d** 71 **p** 72. C Norbiton *S'wark* 71-75; Cand and S Area Sec SAMS 71-79; Overseas Sec 73-79; Hon Can Paraguay from 73; Hon C Tunbridge Wells St Jo *Roch* 75-79; USA 79-87; R Ravendale Gp *Linc* from 88. *The Rectory, Post Office Lane, Ashby-cum-Fenby, Grimsby, S Humberside DN37 0QS* Grimsby (01472) 822980

HAWKSWORTH, Maldwyn Harry. b 45. Aston Univ CertEd74. St Jo Coll Nottm 87. **d** 89 **p** 90. C Penn *Lich* 89-94; TV Bloxwich from 94. *6 Cresswell Crescent, Bloxwich, Walsall WS3 2UW* Walsall (01922) 476647

HAWKSWORTH, Peter John Dallas. b 54. Solicitor 79 St Jo Coll Ox BA75 MA79. Sarum & Wells Th Coll 89. **d** 91 **p** 92. C Warminster St Denys, Upton Scudamore etc *Sarum* 91-95; P-in-c Salisbury St Mark from 95. *St Mark's Vicarage, 62 Barrington Road, Salisbury SP1 3JD* Salisbury (01722) 323767

HAWLEY, Anthony Broughton. b 41. St Pet Coll Ox BA67 MA71. Westcott Ho Cam 67. **d** 69 **p** 70. C Wolv St Pet *Lich* 69-72; C-in-c Bermondsey St Hugh CD *S'wark* 73-84; Hon PV S'wark Cathl 83-84; TR Kirkby *Liv* from 84; AD Walton from 93. *The Rectory, Mill Lane, Kirkby, Liverpool L32 2AX* 0151-547 2155

HAWLEY, John Andrew. b 50. K Coll Lon BD71 AKC71. Wycliffe Hall Ox 72. **d** 74 **p** 75. C Kingston upon Hull H Trin *York* 74-77; C Bradf Cathl Par *Bradf* 77-80; V Woodlands *Sheff* 80-91; TR Dewsbury *Wakef* from 91. *The Rectory, 16A Oxford Road, Dewsbury, W Yorkshire WF13 4JT* Wakefield (01924) 465491 or 457057 Fax 465491

HAWLEY, Nigel David. b 51. Coll of Resurr Mirfield 77. **d** 80 **p** 81. C Birch w Fallowfield *Man* 80-84; P-in-c Moston St Jo 84-85; R 85-93; R Reddish from 93. *St Elisabeth's Rectory, Bedford Street, Stockport, Cheshire SK5 6DJ* 0161-431 3033

HAWNT, John Charles Frederick. b 30. St Paul's Cheltenham. Selly Oak Coll 52 Westwood Cen Zimbabwe 72. **d** 75 **p** 76. Rhodesia 75-80; Zimbabwe 80-81; C Rugby St Andr *Cov* 81-85; R Lydeard St Lawrence w Brompton Ralph etc *B & W* from 85. *The Rectory, Lydeard St Lawrence, Taunton, Somerset TA4 3SF* Lydeard St Lawrence (019847) 220

HAWORTH, Mrs Betsy Ellen. b 24. Wm Temple Coll Rugby 50. **dss** 80 **d** 89. Walkden Moor *Man* 80-81; Chapl Th Estates Commr 81-88; Lic to Offic 88-89; NSM Astley Bridge from 89. *14 Sharples Hall Fold, Bolton BL1 7EH* Bolton (01204) 591588

HAWORTH, John Luttrell. b 28. **d** 67 **p** 68. C Kilcommick *K, E & A* 67-70; C Ballymacelligott *L & K* 70-71; TV Tralee w Ballymacelligott, Kilnaughtin etc 71-72; I Kinneigh w Ballymoney *C, C & R* 72-76; I Easkey w Kilglass *T, K & A* 77-83; I Monasterevan w Nurney and Rathdaire *M & K* 83-87; I Kiltegan w Hacketstown, Clonmore and Moyne *C & O* 87-92; I Fermoy Union *C, C & R* from 92. *The Rectory, Forglen Terrace, Co Cork, Irish Republic* Fermoy (25) 31016

HAWORTH, Mark Newby. b 50. MICFor81 Aber Univ BSc73. Westcott Ho Cam 88. **d** 90 **p** 91. C Cherry Hinton St Andr *Ely*

90-93; C Teversham 90-93; P-in-c Swaffham Bulbeck and Swaffham Prior w Reach 93-94; V from 94. *St Mary's Vicarage, Swaffham Prior, Cambridge CB5 0JT* Newmarket (01638) 741409

HAWORTH, Paul. b 47. G&C Coll Cam BA68 MA72. Westcott Ho Cam 75. d 78 p 79. C Hornchurch St Andr *Chelmsf* 78-81; C Loughton St Mary and St Mich 81-88; C Waltham H Cross 88; TV 88-92; TR Becontree S from 92. *St Alban's Vicarage, Vincent Road, Dagenham, Essex RM9 6AL* 0181-592 5410

HAWORTH, Stanley Robert. b 48. St Jo Coll Dur BA69. Sarum & Wells Th Coll 71. d 73 p 74. C Skipton H Trin *Bradf* 73-76; C Bradf Cathl 76-78; C Grantham *Linc* 78; TV 78-82; V Deeping St James from 82. *The Vicarage, 16 Church Street, Deeping St James, Peterborough PE6 8HD* Market Deeping (01778) 347995

HAWORTH, Stuart. b 43. Local Minl Tr Course 91. d 94 p 95. C Bradshaw *Man* from 94. *178 Turton Road, Bolton BL2 3EE* Bolton (01204) 594506

HAWTHORN, Ven Christopher John. b 36. Qu Coll Cam BA60 MA64. Ripon Hall Ox 60. d 62 p 63. C Sutton St Jas *York* 62-66; V Kingston upon Hull St Nic 66-72; V Coatham 72-79; V Scarborough St Martin 79-91; RD Scarborough 82-91; Can and Preb York Minster 87-91; Adn Cleveland from 91. *Park House, Rose Hill, Great Ayton, Middlesbrough TS9 6BH* Great Ayton (01642) 723221

HAWTHORN, David. b 63. Chich Th Coll 87. d 90 p 91. C Hartlepool H Trin *Dur* 90-94; C Middlesb All SS *York* 94-95; P-in-c Thornaby on Tees from 95. *The Rectory, 14 White House Road, Thornaby, Stockton-on-Tees, Cleveland TS17 0AJ* Stockton-on-Tees (0642) 761655

HAWTHORNE, Andrew. b 68. Jes Coll Ox BA89 MA93. Chich Th Coll BTh93. d 93 p 94. C Christchurch *Win* from 93. *105B Stour Road, Christchurch, Dorset BH23 1JN* Christchurch (01202) 486782

HAWTHORNE, John William. b 32. St Aug Coll Cant 74. d 77 p 78. C Boxley *Cant* 77-80; P-in-c Langley 80-82; P-in-c Otham 80-82; R Otham w Langley 82-83; TR Preston w Sutton Poyntz and Osmington w Poxwell *Sarum* 83-87; V Tetbury w Beverston *Glouc* from 87. *The Vicarage, The Green, Tetbury, Glos GL8 8DN* Tetbury (01666) 502333

HAWTHORNE, Noel David. b 30. BNC Ox BA53 MA58. Ridley Hall Cam 53. d 55 p 56. V Idle H Trin *Bradf* 61-70; R Colne St Bart *Blackb* 70-91; RD Pendle 85-91; rtd 91. *56 Barrowford Road, Colne, Lancs BB8 9QE* Colne (01282) 869110

HAWTHORNE, William James (Jim). b 46. TCD 66. d 69 p 70. C Gilnahirk *D & D* 69-72; Asst Chapl Miss to Seamen 72-76; Lic to Offic *Win* 73-76; C Boultham *Linc* 76-78; C Bracebridge Heath 78-90; Dioc Adv for Relig Broadcasting 80-90; Chapl Palma de Mallorca and Balearic Is *Eur* 90-93; Chapl Palma de Mallorca from 93. *Nunez de Balboa 6, San Armadans, 07014 Palma de Mallorca, Spain* Palma de Mallorca (71) 737279 Fax 454492

HAWTIN, Ven David Christopher. b 43. Keble Coll Ox BA65 MA70. Wm Temple Coll Rugby 65 Cuddesdon Coll 66. d 67 p 68. C Pennywell St Thos and Grindon St Oswald CD *Dur* 67-71; C Stockton St Pet 71-74; C-in-c Leam Lane CD 74-79; R Washington 79-88; Dioc Ecum Officer 88-91; Adn Newark S'well from 92. *c/o Dunham House, 8 Westgate, Southwell, Notts NG25 0JL* Southwell (01636) 814490 Fax 815882

HAY, David Frederick. b 38. MA67. Qu Coll Birm 82. d 84 p 85. C Prenton *Ches* 84-88; V Stockport St Sav from 88. *St Saviour's Vicarage, 22 St Saviour's Road, Great Moor, Stockport, Cheshire SK2 7QE* 0161-483 2633

HAY, Ian Gordon. b 52. Dundee Univ MA73 Edin Univ BD76 CertEd84. Edin Th Coll 73. d 76 p 77. C Dumfries *Glas* 76-79; Dioc Chapl *Bre* 79-81; R Bre 81-85; Asst Chapl H Trin Sch Halifax 85-88; Dioc Youth Officer *Carl* from 89. *2 Linden Walk, Stainburn, Workington, Cumbria CA14 4UW* Workington (01900) 603213 Fax Carlisle (01228) 48769

HAY, Jack Barr. b 31. Bps' Coll Cheshunt 57. d 60 p 61. C Byker St Ant *Newc* 60-63; C Killingworth 63-68; V Cowgate 68-77; V Woodhorn w Newbiggin from 77. *The Vicarage, 34A Front Street, Newbiggin-by-the-Sea, Northd NE64 6PS* Ashington (01670) 817220

HAY, John. b 43. St D Coll Lamp 63. d 67 p 68. C Ynyshir *Llan* 67-70; C Cardiff St Mary and St Steph w St Dyfrig etc 70-74; V Llanwynno 74-78; P-in-c Weston-super-Mare All SS *B & W* 78-80; TV Weston-super-Mare Cen Par 80-85; P-in-c Handsworth St Mich *Birm* 85-86; NSM Eastbourne St Sav and St Pet *Chich* 88-91; V Buckley *St As* from 91. *St Matthew's Vicarage, Church Road, Buckley, Clwyd CH7 3JN* Buckley (01244) 550645

HAY, Canon John. b 45. CITC 77. d 79 p 80. C Newtownards *D & D* 79-81; I Galloon w Drummully *Clogh* 81-89; I Donacavey w Barr from 89; Preb Clogh Cathl from 91. *Maranatha, The Rectory, Fintona, Co Tyrone BT78 2DA* Fintona (01662) 841644

HAY, Kenneth Gordon. b 14. TD50. Worc Ord Coll 63. d 65 p 66. CF (TA) 66-79; R Kelvedon Hatch *Chelmsf* 68-73; P-in-c Prittlewell St Steph 73-78; V 78-79; rtd 79. *26 Warwick Road, Thorpe Bay, Southend-on-Sea SS1 3BN* Southend-on-Sea (01702) 586496

HAY, Nicholas John. b 56. Sheff Poly BSc85 DPS88. St Jo Coll Nottm 85. d 88 p 89. C Blackb Redeemer *Blackb* 88-91; C Hellesdon *Nor* 91-95; R Widford *Chelmsf* from 95. *The Rectory, 3 Canuden Road, Widford, Chelmsford CM1 2SU* Chelmsford (01245) 355989

HAYBALL, Douglas Reginald. b 18. Oak Hill Th Coll 66. d 68 p 69. C Ilkley All SS *Bradf* 68-72; V Parr Mt *Liv* 72-75; P-in-c Sheepey w Ratcliffe Culey *Leic* 75-76; R Sibson w Sheepy and Ratcliffe Culey 76-86; rtd 86; Perm to Offic *B & W* from 86. *57 Parklands Way, Somerton, Somerset TA11 6JG* Somerton (01458) 73312

HAYCRAFT, Roger Brian Norman. b 43. Oak Hill Th Coll 69. d 73 p 74. C Belsize Park *Lon* 73-76; C Yardley St Edburgha *Birm* 76-79; V Hornchurch H Cross *Chelmsf* from 79. *The Vicarage, 260 Hornchurch Road, Hornchurch, Essex RM11 1PX* Hornchurch (01708) 447790

HAYDAY, Alan Geoffrey David. b 46. Kelham Th Coll 65. d 69 p 70. C Evington *Leic* 69-72; C Spalding *Linc* 72-78; V Cherry Willingham w Greetwell 78-86; RD Lawres 84-86; TR Old Brumby from 86; RD Manlake from 93. *St Hugh's Rectory, 114 Ashby Road, Scunthorpe, S Humberside DN16 2AG* Scunthorpe (01724) 843064

HAYDEN, David Frank. b 47. Lon Univ DipTh69 BD71. Tyndale Hall Bris 67. d 71 p 72. C Silverhill St Matt *Chich* 71-75; C Galleywood Common *Chelmsf* 75-79; R Redgrave cum Botesdale w Rickinghall *St E* 79-84; RD Hartismere 81-84; V Cromer *Nor* from 84; P-in-c Gresham from 84; Chapl Cromer and Distr Hosp Norfolk from 84; Chapl Fletcher Hosp Norfolk from 85; RD Repps *Nor* from 95. *The Vicarage, 30 Cromwell Road, Cromer, Norfolk NR27 0BE* Cromer (01263) 512000

HAYDEN, Eric Henry Ashmore. b 26. ACII65. Sarum & Wells Th Coll 71. d 73 p 74. C Horsham *Chich* 73-78; V Cuckfield 78-92; rtd 92; P-in-c Tilshead, Orcheston and Chitterne *Sarum* from 92. *The Vicarage, High Street, Tilshead, Salisbury SP3 4RZ* Amesbury (01980) 620517

HAYDEN, Canon John Donald. b 40. Lon Univ BD62. Tyndale Hall Bris 63. d 65 p 66. C Macclesfield Ch Ch *Ches* 65-68; Tanzania 68-77; Home Sec USCL 77-83; TV Ipswich St Mary at Stoke w St Pet & St Mary Quay *St E* 83-85; TV Ipswich St Mary at Stoke w St Pet, Stoke Park 85-94; P-in-c Bury St Edmunds St Mary from 94. *78 Hardwick Lane, Bury St Edmunds, Suffolk IP33 2RA* Bury St Edmunds (01284) 706668

HAYDOCK, Canon Alan. b 41. Kelham Th Coll 60. d 65 p 66. C Rainworth *S'well* 65-68; C Hucknall Torkard 68-71; TV 71-74; V Bilborough St Jo 74-80; R E Bridgford 80-82; R E Bridgford and Kneeton from 82; RD Bingham 84-94; Hon Can S'well Minster from 86. *The Rectory, Kirk Hill, East Bridgford, Nottingham NG13 8PE* East Bridgford (01949) 20218

HAYDON, Keith Frank. b 46. Cuddesdon Coll 73. d 75 p 76. C De Beauvoir Town St Pet *Lon* 75-77; C Wells St Thos w Horrington *B & W* 77-80; TV Weston-super-Mare Cen Par 80-84; TV Cowley St Jas *Ox* 84-87; TR 87-95; P-in-c Walsingham and Houghton *Nor* from 95. *The Vicarage, Walsingham, Norfolk NR22 6BL* Walsingham (01328) 820345

HAYES, Brian Richard Walker. b 33. Qu Coll Birm 81. d 83 p 84. C Cheadle Hulme All SS *Ches* 83-87; C Sheff Parson Cross St Cecilia *Sheff* 87-88; C Sheff Norwood St Leon 88-91; V Gazeley w Dalham, Moulton and Kentford *St E* from 91. *The Vicarage, Gazeley, Newmarket, Suffolk CB8 8RB* Newmarket (01638) 750719

HAYES, Charles Gerald. b 01. Jes Coll Cam BA27 MA31. Ridley Hall Cam 27. d 37 p 38. In RC Ch 37-52; Australia from 37. *4 Moore Street, Pasadena, S Australia 5042* Pasadena (8) 277-7338

HAYES, David Malcolm Hollingworth. b 42. K Coll Lon BD68 AKC68. d 69 p 70. C Upper Teddington SS Pet and Paul *Lon* 69-70; C Ruislip St Martin 70-75; P-in-c Ludford *Heref* 75-80; P-in-c Ashford Carbonell w Ashford Bowdler 75-80; V Eastcote St Lawr *Lon* 80-90; R Cant St Pet w St Alphege and St Marg etc *Cant* from 90; Master Eastbridge Hosp from 90. *The Master's Lodge, 58 St Peter's Street, Canterbury, Kent CT1 2BE* Canterbury (01227) 462395

HAYES, David Roland Payton. b 37. Hertf Coll Ox BA62 MA66. Coll of Resurr Mirfield 62. d 64 p 65. C Woodley St Jo the Ev *Ox* 64-67; C Emscote *Cov* 67-69; C Farnham Royal *Ox* 69-75; P-in-c 75-78; P-in-c Lathbury 78-79; P-in-c Newport Pagnell 78-79; R Newport Pagnell w Lathbury 79-85; RD Newport 80-85; Chapl Renny Lodge Hosp 85-87; R Newport Pagnell w Lathbury and Moulsoe *Ox* 85-86; P-in-c 86-87; P-in-c

Bucknell w Buckton, Llanfair Waterdine and Stowe *Heref* 87-91; V Bucknell w Chapel Lawn, Llanfair Waterdine etc 91-94; RD Clun Forest 91-94; P-in-c Presteigne w Discoed, Kinsham and Lingen from 94. *The Rectory, Presteigne, Powys LD8 2BP* Presteigne (01544) 267777

HAYES, John Henry Andrew. b 52. BSc. Wycliffe Hall Ox 82. **d** 84 **p** 85. C Moreton *Ches* 84-87; R Barrow 87-94; Bp's Chapl 87-94; P-in-c Runcorn St Mich from 94; P-in-c Runcorn All SS from 94. *The Vicarage, Highlands Road, Runcorn, Cheshire WA7 4PS* Runcorn (01928) 575666

HAYES, John Philip. b 52. RMN76. Chich Th Coll 79. **d** 82 **p** 84. C Wigston Magna *Leic* 82-83; C Thurmaston 83-85; TV Shirley *Birm* 85-91; V Lee St Aug *S'wark* 91-93; TV Staveley and Barrow Hill *Derby* from 93. *St Columba's Vicarage, 191 Middlecroft Road, Staveley, Chesterfield, Derbyshire S43 3NQ* Chesterfield (01246) 472724

HAYES, Michael Gordon William. b 48. St Cath Coll Cam BA69 MA73 PhD73. Ridley Hall Cam 73. **d** 75 **p** 76. C Combe Down w Monkton Combe *B & W* 75-78; C Cam H Trin *Ely* 78-81; V Bathampton *B & W* 81-88; V Clevedon St Andr and Ch Ch from 88. *The Vicarage, 10 Coleridge Road, Clevedon, Avon BS21 7TB* Clevedon (01275) 872982

HAYES, Canon Reginald Brian Michael. b 40. Univ of Wales (Cardiff) DipTh71. St Mich Coll Llan 67. **d** 71 **p** 72. C Roath St Martin *Llan* 71-77; V Brynmawr *S & B* 77-80; CF (TA) 79-87; Chapl RN 80-87; P-in-c Porthleven *Truro* 80-81; V Porthleven w Sithney 81-87; RD Kerrier 86-87; V Westmr St Matt *Lon* 87-94; PV Westmr Abbey 88-94; Hon Can Sunyani and Tamale from 90. *50 Grande Rue, 83300 Draguignan (Var), France*

HAYES, Richard. b 39. K Coll Lon BD68 AKC68. **d** 69 **p** 70. C Dartford H Trin *Roch* 69-72; C S Kensington St Steph *Lon* 72-76; V Ruislip Manor St Paul 76-82; V Ealing St Pet Mt Park 82-91; R St Edm the King and St Mary Woolnoth etc from 91. *24 Cinnamon Street, London E1 9NJ* 0171-481 9699

HAYES, Richard Henry. b 65. Bp Otter Coll St Jo Coll Nottm 89. **d** 92 **p** 93. C Southborough St Pet w Ch Ch and St Matt *Roch* 92-95; C Downend *Bris* from 95. *15 Glendale, Downend, Bristol BS16 6EQ* Bristol (0117) 956 8109

HAYES, Mrs Rosemarie Eveline. b 51. Brighton Coll of Educn CertEd72. N Ord Course 88. **d** 91 **p** 94. Par Dn Manston *Ripon* 91-94; C from 94. *21 Grange Park Avenue, Leeds LS8 3BA* Leeds (0113) 265 8306 or 264 5530

HAYES, Timothy James. b 62. **d** 89 **p** 90. C Lache cum Saltney *Ches* 89-94; P-in-c Dukinfield St Jo from 94. *37 Harald Avenue, Dukinfield, Cheshire SK16 5NH* 0161-308 4708

HAYLES, Graham David. b 39. Lon Univ DipTh66. Clifton Th Coll 64. **d** 67 **p** 68. C Gipsy Hill Ch Ch *S'wark* 67-70; C Heatherlands St Jo *Sarum* 70-74; V W Streatham St Jas *S'wark* 74-90; TR Hinckley H Trin *Leic* from 90. *Holy Trinity Vicarage, 1 Cleveland Road, Hinckley, Leics LE10 0AJ* Hinckley (01455) 635711

HAYLLAR, Bruce Sherwill. b 23. Trin Hall Cam BA47 MA53. Cuddesdon Coll 48. **d** 50 **p** 51. V Peacehaven *Chich* 63-72; Zambia 72-75; V Moulsecoomb *Chich* 76-81; TR 81-83; R Rotherfield w Mark Cross 83-90; RD Rotherfield 87-90; rtd 90. *Moses Farm Cottage, Piltdown, Uckfield, E Sussex TN22 3XN* Newick (01825) 722006

HAYMAN, Mrs Audrey Doris. b 41. St Mary's Cheltenham 61 Bris Univ CertEd61 Cov Coll of Educn 65. Glouc Sch of Min 88. **d** 91 **p** 94. NSM Matson *Glouc* from 91. *32 Corncroft Lane, St Leonard's Park, Gloucester GL4 9XU* Gloucester (01452) 411786

HAYMAN, Canon Perceval Ecroyd Cobham. b 15. St Jo Coll Cam BA37 MA41. Linc Th Coll 48. **d** 50 **p** 51. V Rogate *Chich* 63-81; R Terwick 63-81; RD Midhurst 72-81; Can and Preb Chich Cathl 77-94; rtd 81. *3 East Street, Beaminster, Dorset DT8 3DS* Beaminster (01308) 862789

HAYMAN, Canon Robert Fleming. b 31. Princeton Univ BA53. Gen Th Sem (NY) MDiv56. **d** 56 **p** 56. USA 56-88; I Drumcliffe w Lissadell and Munninane *K, E & A* 88-92; Preb Elphin Cathl 88-92; rtd 92. *Kingsfort House, Ballintogher, Sligo, Irish Republic* Sligo (71) 64622

HAYNE, Raymond Guy. b 32. Chich Th Coll 57. **d** 60 **p** 61. C Kings Heath *Birm* 60-63; C Clewer St Andr *Ox* 63-67; V Grimsbury 67-76; P-in-c Wardington 71-74; R Brightwell w Sotwell 76-85; RD Wallingford 81-85; R St Breoke and Egloshayle *Truro* 85-90; RD Trigg Minor and Bodmin 88-90; V Reading St Mark *Ox* from 90. *St Mark's Vicarage, 88 Connaught Road, Reading RG3 2UF* Reading (01734) 587400

HAYNES, Clifford. b 33. Cam Univ MA60. Linc Th Coll 80. **d** 82 **p** 83. C Lightcliffe *Wakef* 82-85; V Bradshaw from 85. *The Vicarage, Pavement Lane, Bradshaw, Halifax, W Yorkshire HX2 9JJ* Halifax (01422) 244330

HAYNES, Cyril Michael. b 26. Univ of Wales BEd64. **d** 84 **p** 85. NSM Wenlock *Heref* from 84. *8 Forester Avenue, Much*

Wenlock, Shropshire TF13 6EX* Much Wenlock (01952) 727263

HAYNES, Donald Irwin. b 28. Birm Univ BA51. Ripon Hall Ox 59. **d** 59 **p** 60. Hon C Gillingham St Mary *Roch* 66-71; Lic to Offic *Birm* 71-81; P-in-c Whittington *Derby* 82-85; R 85-90; C Kinver and Enville *Lich* 90-93; rtd 93. *19 Tyrol Close, Wollaston, Stourbridge, W Midlands DY8 3NL* Stourbridge (01384) 444308

HAYNES, Canon John Richard. b 35. Ely Th Coll 60. **d** 63 **p** 64. C Bollington St Jo *Ches* 63-67; C Ches St Jo 67-68; C Davenham 68-70; Rhodesia 70-80; Zimbabwe 80-90; Sub-Dean Bulawayo Cathl 78-83; Hon Can Matabeleland from 90; R Bishop's Stortford *St Alb* from 90. *69 Havers Lane, Bishop's Stortford, Herts CM23 3PA* Bishop's Stortford (01279) 656546

HAYNES, John Stanley. b 30. W Midl Minl Tr Course. **d** 82 **p** 83. NSM Westwood *Cov* 82-84; C Radford Semele and Ufton 84-85; V 85-95; rtd 95. *64 Rugby Road, Cubbington, Leamington Spa, Warks CV32 7JF* Leamington Spa (01926) 330016

HAYNES, Kenneth Gordon. b 09. Worc Ord Coll. **d** 56 **p** 57. R Feltwell *Ely* 70-75; rtd 75; Hon C Steeton *Bradf* 75-79. *73 Carlbury Avenue, Acklam, Middlesbrough, Cleveland TS5 8SY* Middlesbrough (01642) 828080

HAYNES, Leonard Thomas. b 17. **d** 69 **p** 70. C Lutterworth w Cotesbach *Leic* 69-73; C-in-c Swinford w Catthorpe, Shawell and Stanford 73-74; V 74-83; rtd 83; Perm to Offic *Leic* from 83. *10 Warwick Way, Ashby-de-la-Zouch, Leics LE65 1WY* Ashby-de-la-Zouch (01530) 411466

HAYNES, Canon Michael Thomas Avery. b 32. AKC61. St Boniface Warminster 61. **d** 62 **p** 63. C Hebden Bridge *Wakef* 62-64; C Elland 64-68; V Thornhill Lees 68-82; V Lindley from 82; Hon Can Wakef Cathl from 82. *The Vicarage, 2 The Clock Tower, Lindley, Huddersfield HD3 3JB* Huddersfield (01484) 650996

HAYNES, Very Rev Peter. b 25. Selw Coll Cam BA49 MA54. Cuddesdon Coll 50. **d** 52 **p** 53. Asst Dir RE *B & W* 63-70; Youth Chapl 63-70; V Glastonbury St Jo 70-72; V Glastonbury St Jo w Godney 72-74; Adn Wells, Can Res and Preb Wells Cathl 74-82; Dean Heref 82-92; V Heref St Jo 82-92; rtd 92. *1 Brent Road, Cossington, Bridgwater, Somerset TA7 8LF* Chilton Polden (01278) 722276

HAYNES, Peter Nigel Stafford. b 39. Hertf Coll Ox BA62 MA66. Cuddesdon Coll 62. **d** 64 **p** 65. C Norwood All SS *Cant* 64-68; C Portsea N End St Mark *Portsm* 68-72; Asst Chapl Brussels *Eur* 72-76; TV Banbury *Ox* 76-80; Asst Sec (Internat Affairs) Gen Syn Bd Soc Resp 80-85; P-in-c E Peckham and Nettlestead *Roch* 85-92; R Bredgar w Bicknor and Frinsted w Wormshill etc *Cant* from 92. *The Vicarage, Bredgar, Sittingbourne, Kent ME9 8HA* Wormshill (0162784) 387

HAYNES, Philip Mayo. b 25. St Edm Hall Ox BA50 MA50. Cuddesdon Coll 50. **d** 54 **p** 55. C Limpsfield and Titsey *S'wark* 63-70; V Purley St Mark Woodcote 70-82; R Sherington w Chicheley, N Crawley, Astwood etc *Ox* 82-90; rtd 90. *1 Ridgemont Close, Woodstock Road, Oxford OX2 7PJ* Oxford (01865) 58116

HAYNES, Spencer Malcolm. b 46. Sarum & Wells Th Coll DCTM93. **d** 93 **p** 94. C Devonport St Budeaux *Ex* from 93. *5 Buckingham Place, Plymouth PL5 2EN* Plymouth (01752) 368653

HAYTER, Canon John Charles Edwin. b 15. St Edm Hall Ox BA37 MA44. Westcott Ho Cam 37. **d** 38 **p** 39. V Boldre *Win* 55-82; rtd 82; Perm to Offic *Win* from 82. *4 St Thomas Park, Lymington, Hants SO4 9NF* Lymington (01590) 678587

HAYTER, Mary Elizabeth. *See* BARR, Dr Mary Elizabeth

HAYTER, Canon Michael George. b 18. Ch Ch Ox BA39 MA43. Cuddesdon Coll 40. **d** 41 **p** 42. R Steeple Aston *Ox* 46-83; P-in-c Tackley 76-77; rtd 83; Perm to Offic *Pet* from 84. *Felden House, Charlton, Banbury, Oxon OX17 3DL* Banbury (01295) 811426

HAYTER, Raymond William. b 48. Oak Hill Th Coll 74. **d** 77 **p** 78. C Bermondsey St Jas w Ch Ch *S'wark* 77-80; C Sydenham H Trin 81-83; Asst Chapl HM Pris Brixton 83-84; Chapl HM Youth Cust Cen Stoke Heath 84-88; Chapl HM Pris Maidstone 88-91; CF from 91. *clo MOD (Army), Bagshot Park, Bagshot, Surrey GU19 5PL* Bagshot (01276) 471717 Fax 412834

HAYTER, Ronald William Joseph. b 19. Keble Coll Ox BA40 MA44. Wells Th Coll 40. **d** 42 **p** 43. V Wear St Luke *Ex* 55-87; rtd 87; Perm to Offic *Ex* from 92. *85 Swedwell Road, Torquay TQ2 8QL* Torquay (01803) 322903

HAYTER, Mrs Sandra (Sandy). b 46. S Dios Minl Tr Scheme 82. dss 85 **d** 87 **p** 94. Catherington and Clanfield *Portsm* 85-86; Lee-on-the-Solent 86-87; C 87-89; Par Dn Burnham w Dropmore, Hitcham and Taplow *Ox* 89-94; C 94; TV Wallingford w Crowmarsh Gifford etc from 94. *The Vicarage, 34 Thames Mead, Crowmarsh Gifford, Wallingford, Oxon OX10 8EY* Wallingford (01491) 837626

HAYTHORNTHWAITE, Alfred Parker. b 10. Wycliffe Hall Ox 29. d 35 p 36. V Allithwaite *Carl* 67-76; rtd 76; Perm to Offic *Carl* from 80. *St Mary's Cottage, Vicarage Lane, Kirkby Lonsdale, Cumbria LA6 2BA* Kirkby Lonsdale (015242) 71525

HAYTHORNTHWAITE, Robert Brendan. b 31. Solicitor 59 TCD BA53 LLB56 MA64 QUB DipEd71. Edin Th Coll 63. d 64 p 65. C Belf St Jo Laganbank w Orangefield *D & D* 64-66; C Belf St Thos *Conn* 66-68; Lic to Offic 68-75; C Belf Malone St Jo 75-89; I Shinrone w Aghancon etc *L & K* from 89; Dom Chapl to Bp of Killaloe and Clonfert from 89. *St Mary's Rectory, Shinrone, Birr, Co Offaly, Irish Republic* Roscrea (505) 47164

HAYTON, Mark William. b 59. St Steph Ho Ox 85. d 88 p 89. C Sittingbourne St Mich *Cant* 88-91; C Kennington 91-94; R Broadstairs from 94. *The Rectory, Nelson Place, Broadstairs, Kent CT10 1HQ* Thanet (01843) 862921

HAYTON, Norman Joseph Patrick. b 32. ARICS57. Sarum Th Coll 69. d 71 p 72. C Lytham St Cuth *Blackb* 71-74; V Wesham 74-79; V Chorley St Geo 79-80; NSM Kells *Carl* 84-85; P-in-c Flimby 85-90; V Barrow St Jas 90-94; TV Egremont and Haile from 94. *The Vicarage, 1 Bridge End Park, Egremont, Cumbria CA22 2RE* Egremont (01946) 822051

HAYWARD, Canon Alan Richard. b 25. Open Univ BA72. Wycliffe Hall Ox 54. d 56 p 57. V Wollescote *Worc* 65-85; Hon Can Worc Cathl 85-91; R Alvechurch 85-91; rtd 91. *2 St Kenelm's Court, St Kenelm's Road, Romsley, Halesowen, W Midlands B62 0NF* Romsley (01562) 710749

HAYWARD, Alfred Ross. b 20. Clifton Th Coll 52. d 54 p 55. V Woodborough *S'well* 65-70; Warden Braithwaite Gospel Tr Stathern 73-77; V Tugby and E Norton w Skeffington *Leic* 77-81; R Beeston Regis *Nor* 81-83; rtd 83. *4 Somersby Road, Nottingham NG3 5QY* Nottingham (0115) 920 1406

HAYWARD, Canon Christopher Joseph (Chris). b 38. TCD BA63 MA67. Ridley Hall Cam 63. d 65 p 66. C Hatcham St Jas *S'wark* 65-69; Warden Lee Abbey Internat Students' Club Kensington 69-74; Chapl Chelmsf Cathl *Chelmsf* 74-77; P-in-c Darlaston All SS *Lich* 77-83; Ind Chapl 77-83; Can Res Bradf Cathl *Bradf* 83-92; Sec Bd Miss 83-92; R Linton in Craven from 92; Hon Can Bradf Cathl from 92; RD Skipton from 93. *The Rectory, Hebden Road, Grassington, Skipton, N Yorkshire BD23 5LB* Skipton (01756) 752575 Fax 722898

HAYWARD, Clifford. b 08. St Paul's Grahamstown 51. d 52 p 53. S Africa 57-73; C Lewisham St Mary *S'wark* 73-78; rtd 78. *The Charterhouse, Charterhouse Square, London EC1M 6AN* 0171-251 6357

HAYWARD, Preb Edwin Calland. b 11. ATCL30 Lon Univ BSc32 Leeds Univ DipEd44. Linc Th Coll 35. d 36 p 37. RD Tutbury *Lich* 69-81; V Burton St Modwen 69-81; Preb Lich Cathl 72-81; P-in-c Burton Ch Ch 76-81; rtd 81; Perm to Offic *Derby* from 81; Perm to Offic *Lich* from 81. *19 Henhurst Hill, Burton-on-Trent, Staffs DE13 9TB* Burton-on-Trent (01283) 548735

HAYWARD, Canon Jeffrey Kenneth. b 47. Nottm Univ BTh74. St Jo Coll Nottm LTh74. d 74 p 75. C Stambermill *Worc* 74-77; C Woking St Jo *Guildf* 77-83; V Springfield H Trin *Chelmsf* from 83; Chapl HM Pris Chelmsf from 86; Area RD Chelmsf 86-88; RD Chelmsf 88-93; RD Chelmsf N 93-95; Can Chelmsf Cathl from 93. *The Vicarage, 61 Hill Road, Chelmsford CM2 6HW* Chelmsford (01245) 353389 Fax 493041

HAYWARD, Mrs Jennifer Dawn. b 38. W Midl Minl Tr Course 85. d 88 p 94. NSM Gt Malvern St Mary *Worc* 88-90; NSM Gt Malvern Ch Ch 88-90; Par Dn 90-94; C from 94. *St Mary's House, 137 Madresfield Road, Malvern, Worcs WR14 2HD* Malvern (01684) 575994

HAYWARD, Ven John Derek Risdon. b 23. Trin Coll Cam BA56 MA64. Westcott Ho Cam 56. d 57 p 58. V Isleworth All SS *Lon* 64-94; Adn Middx 74-75; Gen Sec Lon Dio 75-93; rtd 94. *5 Sion Hill Place, Lansdown, Bath BA1 5SJ* Bath (01225) 336305

HAYWARD, John Andrew. b 63. MHCIMA83 Nottm Univ BTh89. Linc Th Coll 86. d 89 p 90. C Seaford w Sutton *Chich* 89-92; C St Pancras H Cross w St Jude and St Pet *Lon* from 92. *47A Basement Flat, Argyle Square, London WC1H 8AL* 0171-713 7996

HAYWARD, John David. b 40. AKC63. d 65 p 66. C Westleigh St Pet *Man* 65-68; C Elton All SS 68-72; R Moston St Chad 72-77; TV Stantonbury *Ox* 74-87; TV Stantonbury and Willen 87-89; P-in-c N Springfield *Chelmsf* from 89. *The Vicarage, 32 Oak Lodge Tye, Chelmsford CM1 5GZ* Chelmsford (01245) 466160

HAYWARD, Preb John Talbot. b 28. Selw Coll Cam BA52 MA56. Wells Th Coll 52. d 54 p 55. R Lamyatt *B & W* 58-71; V Bruton w Wyke Champflower and Redlynch 58-71; RD Bruton 62-71; R Weston-super-Mare St Jo 71-75; Preb Wells Cathl 73-92; TR Weston-super-Mare Cen Par 75-92; rtd 92. *5 Chelswood Avenue, Weston-super-Mare, Avon BS22 8QP* Weston-super-Mare (01934) 628431

HAYWARD, Ms Pamela Jane. b 52. RGN82. Westcott Ho Cam 84. d 87 p 94. Par Dn Northn St Mary *Pet* 87-90; Par Dn Bris St Mary Redcliffe w Temple etc *Bris* 90-94; C from 94. *1B Colston Parade, Bristol BS1 6RA* Bristol (0117) 926 2491

HAYWARD, Peter Noel. b 26. Leeds Univ BA48 BD78. Coll of Resurr Mirfield 48. d 50 p 51. C S Elmsall *Wakef* 50-56; C Sheldon *Birm* 56-60; C-in-c Garretts Green CD 60-69; V Garretts Green 69-70; R Hotham *York* from 70; V N Cave w Cliffe from 70; RD Howden 78-86. *The Vicarage, North Cave, Brough, N Humberside HU15 2LJ* North Cave (01430) 422398

HAYWARD, Roynon Albert Oscar James. b 25. d 67 p 68. Hon C Glouc St Paul *Glouc* 67-89; rtd 89; Perm to Offic *Glouc* from 89. *37 Forest View Road, Gloucester GL4 0BX* Gloucester (01452) 521104

HAYWARD, William Richmond. b 42. NY Th Sem BA90. Chich Th Coll 88. d 88 p 90. Bermuda from 88. *8 Seabright Avenue, Paget DV 04, Bermuda* Bermuda (1-809) 236-3221

HAYWOOD, Frank. b 19. St Cath Soc Ox BA40 MA44. Cuddesdon Coll 40. d 42 p 43. V Challock w Molash *Cant* 62-87; rtd 87. *36A St Leonard's Road, Hythe, Kent CT21 6ER* Hythe (01303) 265356

HAYWOOD, James William. b 36. Chich Th Coll 69. d 73 p 74. C Leeds Halton St Wilfrid *Ripon* 73-76; C Workington St Jo *Carl* 76-78; V Clifton 78-84; P-in-c Barrow St Jas 84-85; V 85-89; V Crosby Ravensworth 89-94; R Asby 89-94; V Bolton 89-94. *19 Bramham Road, Whitwood, Castleford, W Yorkshire WF10 5PA*

HAYWOOD, Keith Roderick. b 48. Oak Hill Th Coll 84. d 86 p 87. C Fazeley *Lich* 86-90; TV Leek and Meerbrook from 90. *St Luke's Vicarage, Novi Lane, Leek, Staffs ST13 6NR* Leek (01538) 373306

HAZEL, Sister. See SMITH, Sister Hazel Ferguson Waide

HAZELL, Ven Frederick Roy (Fred). b 30. Fitzw Ho Cam BA53 MA59. Cuddesdon Coll 54. d 56 p 57. V Croydon H Sav *Cant* 68-84; RD Croydon 72-78; Hon Can Cant Cathl 73-84; P-in-c Croydon H Trin 77-80; Adn Croydon 84; Adn Croydon *S'wark* 85-93; rtd 93; P-in-c Chard Furnham w Chaffcombe, Knowle St Giles etc *B & W* from 95. *The Rectory, Furnham Road, Chard, Somerset TA20 1AE* Chard (01460) 63167

HAZELTON, Edwin Geoffrey. b 08. OBE45. St Geo Windsor 50. d 51 p 52. R Wylye, Stockton and Fisherton Delamere *Sarum* 69-73; R Wylye, Fisherton Delamere and the Langfords 73-76; rtd 76. *Flat 7, St Nicholas's Hospital, Salisbury SP1 2SW* Salisbury (01722) 332247

HAZELTON, John. b 35. St Cath Coll Cam BA56 MA60 Bris Univ MLitt74 Newc Univ BPhil80. Wells Th Coll 59. d 61 p 62. C Twerton *B & W* 61-65; V Pitcombe w Shepton Montague 65-72; Lect SS Hild & Bede Dur 72-79; Lic to Offic *Dur* from 79; Dame Allan's Schs Newc 79-89; Chapl from 89; Lic to Offic *Newc* from 89. *36 Orchard Drive, Durham DH1 1LA* 0191-384 6606 or 275 0608

HAZELTON, Dr Michael John. b 53. UEA BA76 Bedf Coll Lon PhD80 Heythrop Coll Lon BD89 Ox Univ 89. d 90 p 90. Asst Chapl Helsinki *Eur* 94-95; Asst Chapl Zurich w Winterthur from 95. *Promenadengasse 9, 8001 Zurich, Switzerland* Zurich (1) 252-6023 Fax as telephone

HAZELTON, Robert Henry Peter. b 22. Wells Th Coll 65. d 67 p 68. C Milton *B & W* 69-76; V Peasedown St John 76-80; V Peasedown St John w Wellow 80-89; rtd 90; Perm to Offic *B & W* from 90. *37 High Meadows, Midsomer Norton, Bath BA3 2RY* Midsomer Norton (01761) 419675

HAZELWOOD, Ms Jillian. b 32. Bp Otter Coll CertEd52 St Alb Minl Tr Scheme 82. d 87 p 94. NSM Wheathampstead *St Alb* from 87. *14 Butterfield Road, Wheathampstead, St Albans, Herts AL4 8PU* Wheathampstead (01582) 833146

HAZLEDINE, Basil William. b 18. St Pet Hall Ox BA42 MA45. Wycliffe Hall Ox 42. d 43 p 44. V Stoughton *Guildf* 60-70; V Westlands St Andr *Lich* 70-77; P-in-c Whatfield w Semer *St E* 77-78; R 78-81; P-in-c Nedging w Naughton 77-81; R Whatfield w Semer, Nedging and Naughton 81-84; rtd 84. *14 Willis Close, Epsom, Surrey KT18 7SS* Epsom (01372) 726615

HAZLEHURST, Anthony Robin. b 43. Man Univ BSc64. Tyndale Hall Bris 65. d 68 p 69. C Macclesfield Ch Ch *Ches* 68-71; C Bushbury *Lich* 71-75; P-in-c New Clee *Linc* 75-85; TV Deane *Man* from 85. *St Andrew's Vicarage, Crescent Avenue, Bolton BL5 1EN* Bolton (01204) 651851

HAZLEHURST, David. b 32. Liv Univ BSc54. St Steph Ho Ox 55. d 57 p 58. V Blackrod *Man* 67-79; V Halliwell St Marg 79-84; R Sutton St Nic *S'wark* 84-94; rtd 94; Perm to Offic *S'wark* from 95. *48 The Orchard, North Holmwood, Dorking, Surrey RH5 4JT* Dorking (01306) 886568

HAZLEHURST, David John Benedict (Benny). b 63. Trin Coll Bris 88. d 91 p 92. C Plumstead St Jo w St Jas and St Paul *S'wark* from 91. *34 Earl Rise, London SE18 7NH* 0181-855 1311

HAZLETT, Stephen David. b 56. TCD BTh88. CITC. d 88 p 89. C Ballywillan *Conn* 88-90; I Rathcoole 90-95; I Dunluce from 95. *Dunluce Rectory, 17 Priestlands Road, Bushmills, Co Antrim BT57 8QP* Bushmills (012567) 31221

HAZLEWOOD, Andrew Lord. b 54. BSc. Wycliffe Hall Ox. d 82 p 83. C Leckhampton SS Phil and Jas w Cheltenham St Jas *Glouc* 82-85; C Waltham H Cross *Chelmsf* 85-89; R Pedmore *Worc* from 89. *The Rectory, Pedmore Lane, Stourbridge, W Midlands DY9 0SW* Hagley (01562) 884856

HAZLEWOOD, Dr David Paul. b 47. Sheff Univ MB, ChB70 Campion Hall Ox BA72 MA77. Wycliffe Hall Ox 70. d 73 p 74. C Chapeltown *Sheff* 73-75; Singapore 76; Indonesia 76-88; R Ipswich St Helen *St E* from 88. *35 Stradbroke Road, Ipswich IP4 4LS* Ipswich (01473) 725458

HAZLEWOOD, Canon George Ian. b 28. St Fran Coll Brisbane 52. d 55 p 56. V Yeovil H Trin *B & W* 67-74; RD Merston 72-74; V Prestbury *Glouc* 74-94; Hon Can Glouc Cathl 88-94; Hon Can Wangaratta from 88; rtd 94. *6 Plymouth Road, Tavistock, Devon PL19 8AY* Tavistock (01822) 612325

✠**HAZLEWOOD, Rt Rev John.** b 24. K Coll Cam BA48 MA52. Cuddesdon Coll 48. d 49 p 50 c 75. C Camberwell St Mich *S'wark* 49-50; Australia 50-53 and from 55; C Camberwell St Mich w All So *S'wark* 53-55; Vice Prin St Fran Th Coll Brisbane 55-60; Dean Rockhampton 61-68; Dean Perth 68-75; Bp Ballarat 75-93; rtd 93. *The Bishop's Registry, PO Box 89, Ballarat, Victoria, Australia 3353* Ballarat (53) 311183 or 392370 Fax 332982

HEAD, David Nicholas. b 55. Pemb Coll Cam BA77 MA81. Westcott Ho Cam 78. d 81 p 82. C Surbiton St Andr and St Mark *S'wark* 81-84; C St Marylebone w H Trin *Lon* 84-89; TV Clapham TM *S'wark* from 89. *49 Voltaire Road, London SW4 6DD* 0171-978 1774

HEAD, Canon Derek Leonard Hamilton. b 34. ALCD58. d 58 p 59. C Bexleyheath Ch Ch *Roch* 58-61; C Wisley w Pyrford *Guildf* 61-66; C-in-c Ewell St Paul Howell Hill CD 66-73; R Headley All SS 73-81; TR 81-82; RD Farnham 80-82; V Chertsey from 82; Hon Can Guildf Cathl from 83; RD Runnymede 88-93; Dir Post-Ord Tr from 90. *The Vicarage, London Street, Chertsey, Surrey KT16 8AA* Chertsey (01932) 563141

HEAD, John Leslie. b 06. Dur Univ LTh31. Sarum Th Coll 29. d 31 p 32. R Leigh St Clem *Chelmsf* 50-72; rtd 72. *Flat 13, Waters Mead, 26 Thorpe Hall Avenue, Southend-on-Sea SS1 3DW* Southend-on-Sea (01702) 589108

HEAD, Peter Ernest. b 38. Lon Univ BSc59. Ridley Hall Cam 61. d 63 p 64. Head RE Shoeburyness Sch Southend-on-Sea 69-74; Lic to Offic *Chelmsf* 69-74; Head RE Bilborough Coll Nottm 74-79; Public Preacher *S'well* 74-79; NSM Bramcote 74-79; Vice-Prin Totton Coll Southn 79-93; Perm to Offic *Win* from 80; rtd 93; NSM Hordle *Win* from 94. *44 Lentune Way, Lymington, Hants SO41 3PF* Lymington (01590) 678097 Fax as telephone

HEAD, William Peter. b 18. St Edm Hall Ox BA46 MA51. Cuddesdon Coll 46. d 48 p 49. Chapl Highfield Sch Liphook 61-74; rtd 83. *3 Ferndale Road, Chichester, W Sussex PO19 4QJ* Chichester (01243) 527075

HEADING, Richard Vaughan. b 43. ARCS65 Lon Univ BSc65. Coll of Resurr Mirfield 66. d 68 p 69. C Heref St Martin *Heref* 68-75; P-in-c Birches Head *Lich* 75-77; P-in-c Northwood 75-77; TV Hanley H Ev 77-82; V Heref H Trin *Heref* 82-92; TR Bedminster *Bris* from 92. *Bedminster Rectory, 287 North Street, Bristol BS3 1JP* Bristol (0117) 966 4025

HEADLAND, James Frederick. b 20. Clifton Th Coll 51. d 53 p 54. P-in-c Smethcott w Woolstaston *Heref* 65-81; R Church Pulverbatch 65-81; P-in-c Cantley w Limpenhoe and Southwood *Nor* 81; R Reedham 81; R Reedham w Cantley w Limpenhoe and Southwood 81-86; rtd 86; Perm to Offic *Heref* from 86; Perm to Offic *Lich* from 88. *3 Ashford Avenue, Pontesbury, Shrewsbury SY5 0QN* Shrewsbury (01743) 790565

HEADLEY, Miss Carolyn Jane. b 50. MCSP71 GDipP71. Lon Bible Coll DipTh76 Oak Hill Th Coll BA83. dss 83 d 87 p 94. Harlesden St Mark *Lon* 83-86; Kensal Rise St Mark and St Martin 86-87; Par Dn 87; Par Dn Uxbridge St Andr w St Jo 87-88; Par Dn Uxbridge 88-90; TD 90-92; Warden of Readers (Willesden Episc Area) 88-92; Tutor Wycliffe Hall Ox from 94. *6 Tanners Court, Dancers Hill, Charlbury, Chipping Norton, Oxon OX7 3RP* Charlbury (01608) 810799

HEADS, John. b 27. Bps' Coll Cheshunt 60. d 62 p 63. C Stockton St Chad *Dur* 65-70; rtd 94. *18 Green Crescent, Golcar, Huddersfield HD7 4RF* Huddersfield (01484) 651232

HEAGERTY, Alistair John. b 42. MBE87. Or Coll Ox BA63 MA67. Lon Coll of Div BD68. d 68 p 69. C Margate H Trin *Cant* 68-72; CF from 72; Chapl R Memorial Chpl Sandhurst from 92. *c/o MOD (Army), Bagshot Park, Bagshot, Surrey GU19 5PL* Bagshot (01276) 471717 Fax 412834

HEAK, Philip George. b 70. QUB BA92. CITC BTh95. d 95. C Ballymacash *Conn* from 95. *11 Fulmar Avenue, Lisburn, Co Antrim BT28 3HS* Lisburn (01846) 678252

HEAL, David Walter. b 37. Ox Univ MA63 Trin Coll Carmarthen 87. d 90 p 91. NSM Henfynyw w Aberaeron and Llanddewi Aberarth *St D* from 90. *Cae Gwair Bach, Llanon, Cardigan, Dyfed SY23 5LZ* Llanon (01974) 202596

HEAL, Miss Felicity Joan. b 42. Brighton Poly DCouns88. Portsm Dioc Tr Course 89. d 92. NSM Bramshott and Liphook *Portsm* from 92. *40 Rushes Road, Petersfield, Hants GU32 3BW* Petersfield (01730) 260410

HEAL, Geoffrey. b 28. Linc Th Coll 54. d 56 p 57. V Peckham St Jo *S'wark* 62-75; V Southfields St Barn 75-88; rtd 88; Perm to Offic *Ex* from 89. *Digby Cottage, 5 Hind Street, Ottery St Mary, Devon EX11 1BW* Ottery St Mary (01404) 814729

HEALD, William Roland. b 40. Birm Univ DPS79. St Jo Coll Auckland LTh74. d 74 p 75. New Zealand 74-78 and 79-93; C Bournville *Birm* 78-79; V S Kensington St Luke *Lon* from 93. *St Luke's Vicarage, 1 Cathcart Road, London SW10 9NL* 0171-352 7553

HEALE, Dr Nicholas James. b 67. St Cath Coll Ox BA89 DPhil95 Leeds Univ BA94. Coll of Resurr Mirfield CPT95. d 95. C Syston TM *Leic* from 95. *1121 Melton Road, Syston, Leics LE7 8JS* Leicester (0116) 260 1670

HEALE, Walter James Grenville. b 40. Wycliffe Hall Ox 77. d 79 p 80. C Walsall *Lich* 79-82; TV Marfleet *York* 82-89; TR 89-94; R Easington w Skeffling, Kilnsea and Holmpton from 94. *The Rectory, Hull Road, Easington, Hull HU12 0TE* Withernsea (01964) 650203

HEALES, John. b 48. K Coll Lon BD71 AKC71 PGCE72 DPS76. St Mich Coll Llan 75. d 76 p 77. C Cwmbran *Mon* 76-78; Chapl Rendcomb Coll Cirencester 78-82; Perm to Offic *Mon* 85-88; V Penhow, St Brides Netherwent w Llandavenny etc from 88. *Flat 1, The Rectory, Llanfaches, Newport, Gwent NP6 3AY* Penhow (01633) 400901

HEALEY, James Christopher. b 44. Linc Th Coll 84. d 86 p 87. C Boultham *Linc* 86-90; TV Gt Grimsby St Mary and St Jas 90-91; I Narraghmore w Timolin, Castledermot and Kinneagh *D & G* 91-93; I New Ross *C & O* from 93. *The Rectory, College Road, New Ross, Co Wexford, Irish Republic* New Ross (51) 25004

HEANEY, James Roland. b 59. DipTh85. d 85 p 86. C Ballynafeigh St Jude *D & D* 85-88; C Lisburn Ch Ch Cathl *Conn* 88-90; I Dunganstown w Redcross and Conary *D & G* from 90. *The Rectory, Redcross, Co Wicklow, Irish Republic* Wicklow (404) 41637

HEANEY, Michael Roger. b 43. TCD BA66 HDipEd67 MA69 DCG83. CITC 74. d 76 p 77. Chapl St Columba's Coll Dub from 76. *Montana, Scholarstown Road, Templeogue, Dublin 16, Irish Republic* Dublin (1) 493-1167 Fax 493-6655

HEANEY, Samuel Stewart. b 44. Open Univ BA79 Ulster Univ BEd83 Lon Univ BD93. Pb Coll Belf 85 St Deiniol's Hawarden 92. d 92 p 93. In Pb Ch 85-92; C Knockbreda *D & D* from 92. *28 Church Road, Belfast BT8 4AQ* Belfast (01232) 641339

HEANEY, Wendy Anne. b 42. d 95. *34 Meadow Way, Letchworth, Herts SG6 3JB* Letchworth (01462) 482852

HEANS, Simon John. b 56. d 94 p 95. Asst Chapl Lancing Coll W Sussex from 94. *Edgewood, Hoe Court, Lancing, W Sussex BN15 0QX* Lancing (01903) 767585

HEAP, David Leonard. b 58. Man Univ BA79. Cranmer Hall Dur 82. d 85 p 86. C Clitheroe St Jas *Blackb* 85-88; C Blackb St Gabr 88-92; V Bare from 92. *St Christopher's Vicarage, 12 Elm Grove, Morecambe, Lancs LA4 6AT* Morecambe (01524) 411363

HEAP, Lt-Col Edward Jocelyne Fortrey. b 07. OBE49. RMA. St Geo Windsor 53. d 54 p 55. V Horton and Chalbury *Sarum* 63-68; rtd 68. *Manor Lodge Rest Home, 8 Portland Avenue, Exmouth, Devon EX8 2BS* Exmouth (01395) 266691

HEAPS, Richard Peter. b 35. Qu Coll Birm 58. d 61 p 62. C Castle Bromwich SS Mary and Marg *Birm* 61-65; C-in-c Erdington St Chad CD 65-70; V Nechells 70-81; RD Aston 75-81; V Marston Green 81-86; P-in-c Shrawley and Witley w Astley *Worc* 86-92; R Shrawley, Witley, Astley and Abberley from 92. *The Rectory, Shrawley, Worcester WR6 6TS* Worcester (01905) 620489

HEAPS, William Henry. b 20. St Deiniol's Hawarden 81. d 83 p 84. NSM Tranmere St Cath *Ches* from 83; NSM Prenton from 86. *7 St Stephen's Court, Prenton Lane, Birkenhead, Merseyside L42 8QD* 0151-608 4253

HEARD, Charles. b 19. S'wark Ord Course 62. d 65 p 66. C Plumstead St Nic *S'wark* 65-71; C Blackheath All SS 71-72; V Barnes H Trin 72-84; rtd 84; Hon C E Wickham *S'wark* from 84. *Flat 5, Elmfield Court, Wickham Street, Welling, Kent DA16 3DF* 0181-855 9809

HEARD, Ross McPherson. b 11. Clifton Th Coll 38. d 41 p 42. R Hatch Beauchamp w Beercrocombe *B & W* 58-76; V W Hatch

62-76; rtd 76. *235 Queen Edith's Way, Cambridge CB1 4NJ* Cambridge (01223) 212252

HEARN, John. b. 49. Trin Coll Bris. **d** 82 **p** 83. C Epsom Common Ch Ch *Guildf* 82-85; C Ringwood *Win* 85-88; Chapl Basingstoke Distr Hosp 88-91; Chapl Luton and Dunstable Hosp from 91. *Luton & Dunstable Hospital, Lewsey Road, Luton LU4 0DT, or 8 Calnwood Road, Luton LU4 0ET* Luton (01582) 494547 or 491122

HEARN, Jonathan. b 58. GradIPM85 Leeds Univ BA81. Westcott Ho Cam 89. **d** 91 **p** 92. C Tuffley *Glouc* 91-94; C Milton *Win* from 94. *St Peter's House, 25 Ashley Common Road, New Milton, Hants BH25 5AJ* New Milton (01425) 612644

HEARN, Canon Peter Brian. b 31. St Jo Coll Dur 52. **d** 55 **p** 56. C Frodingham *Linc* 55-59; R Belton SS Pet and Paul 59-64; V Manthorpe w Londonthorpe 59-64; V Billingborough 64-73; V Sempringham w Pointon and Birthorpe 64-73; V Flixborogh w Burton upon Stather from 73; RD Manlake 87-93; Can Linc Cathl from 92. *The Vicarage, Burton-upon-Stather, Scunthorpe, S Humberside DN15 9DZ* Scunthorpe (01724) 720276

HEARN, Thomas Michael. b 12. Oak Hill Th Coll 55. **d** 57 **p** 58. V Tushingham *Ches* 65-79; P-in-c Whitewell 73-79; R Tushingham and Whitewell 79-83; Chapl High Sheriff Cheshire 68-69; Clwyd 74-75; rtd 83; Perm to Offic *Ches* from 83. *27 Eaton Mews, Chester CH4 7EJ* Chester (01244) 674834

HEARN, Thomas Peter. b 18. Selw Coll Cam BA40 MA45. Linc Th Coll 40. **d** 42 **p** 43. R Stratton w Baunton *Glouc* 62-75; V France Lynch 75-83; rtd 84; Perm to Offic *Glouc* from 84. *9 Cotswold Close, Cirencester, Glos GL7 1XP* Cirencester (01285) 655627

HEARN, Trevor. b 36. Sarum Th Coll 61. **d** 64 **p** 65. C Hounslow St Steph *Lon* 64-67; Miss to Seamen from 67; Lic to Offic *St E* 74-80; Lic to Offic *Bris* 80-92; UAE from 92. *Dubai International Seafarers' Centre, Mina Rashid Road, PO Box 5811, Dubai, Unites Arab Emirates* Dubai (4) 452951 or 452918 Fax 493298

HEARNE, Derrick Kenneth. b 32. FBCS69 K Coll Lon BA68 AKC68. St Mich Coll Llan DMinlStuds. **d** 90 **p** 91. C Llanbadarn Fawr w Capel Bangor and Goginan *St D* 90-91; Miss to Seamen from 92; Jordan from 92. *Port PO Box 568, Aqaba, Jordan* Aqaba (3) 318416 or 318417 Fax 318417

HEARTFIELD, Canon Peter Reginald. b 27. Chich Th Coll 61. **d** 63 **p** 64. V Brighton St Alb Preston *Chich* 67-73; Chapl Kent and Cant Hosp 73-92; Chapl Nunnery Fields Hosp Cant 73-92; Six Preacher Cant Cathl *Cant* 79-84; Hon Can Cant Cathl 84-92; rtd 92; Abp's Adv for Hosp Chapl *Cant* from 92. *13 Lanfranc Gardens, Harbledown, Canterbury, Kent CT2 8NJ* Canterbury (01227) 451621

HEASLIP, William John (Jack). b 44. TCD BA66. CITC 79. **d** 80 **p** 81. Chapl Mt Temple Sch Dub 80-86; Bp's C Aughaval w Burrishoole, Knappagh and Louisburgh *T, K & A* 86-88; I Aughaval w Achill, Knappagh, Dugort etc 88-95; Radio Officer (Tuam) 90-95; I Cork St Luke Union *C, C & R* from 95. *St Luke's Rectory, Mahony's Avenue, Summerhill, Cork, Irish Republic* Cork (21) 501672

HEATH, Henry. b 40. FCII77. Oak Hill Th Coll 77. **d** 80 **p** 81. Hon C Lexden *Chelmsf* 80-86; C Colne Engaine 86-87; Hon C Halstead St Andr w H Trin and Greenstead Green 87-90; NSM W w E Mersea 91-95; V Stanway from 95. *The Rectory, Church Lane, Stanway, Colchester CO3 5LR* Colchester (01206) 210407

HEATH, Mrs Janet. b 45. E Midl Min Tr Course 89. **d** 91 **p** 94. Par Dn Rainworth *S'well* 91-94; C from 94. *17 The Hollies, Sherwood Park, Rainworth, Mansfield, Notts NG21 0FZ* Mansfield (01623) 490422

HEATH, Canon John Gordon. b 08. Lon Univ AKC34. **d** 33 **p** 34. C Bramley *Guildf* 33-36; S Africa from 36; Can Port Elizabeth from 73. *Cottage 10, 77 Water Road, Walmer, Port Elizabeth, 6070 South Africa* Port Elizabeth (41) 515172

HEATH, John Henry. b 41. Chich Th Coll 69. **d** 71 **p** 72. C Crediton *Ex* 71-74; C Tavistock and Gulworthy 74-76; C Brixham 76-77; C Brixham w Churston Ferrers 77-79; R Bere Ferrers 79-85; P-in-c Moretonhampstead, N Bovey and Manaton 85-88; R 88-93; P-in-c Lifton from 93; P-in-c Kelly w Bradstone from 93; P-in-c Broadwoodwidger from 93. *The Rectory, Lifton, Devon PL16 0BJ* Lifton (01566) 784291

HEATH, Canon Peter Henry. b 24. Kelham Th Coll 40. **d** 47 **p** 48. V Glossop *Derby* 66-92; RD Glossop 83-89; Hon Can Derby Cathl 84-92; rtd 92. *Birchinlea, 15 Park Crescent, Glossop, Derbyshire SK13 9BQ* Glossop (01457) 862047

HEATH, Raymond Walker. b 19. Cuddesdon Coll 46. **d** 47 **p** 48. V Rolvenden *Cant* 66-75; Perm to Offic *Glouc* from 79; rtd 84. *High Lodge, Kineton, Guiting Power, Cheltenham, Glos GL54 5UG* Guiting Power (01451) 850440

HEATH, William Walter. b 11. St Jo Coll Ox BA32. **d** 72 **p** 73. Hon C Petworth *Chich* 72-90; Perm to Offic from 90.

Malthouse, Lurgashall, Petworth, W Sussex GU28 9ET Northchapel (01428) 707212

HEATHCOTE, Edgar. b 15. Linc Th Coll 62. **d** 63 **p** 64. R Ashbrittle *B & W* 69-72; R Ashbrittle w Bathealton, Stawley and Kittisford 72-78; Lic to Offic 78-80; rtd 80; Perm to Offic *B & W* from 80. *Willow Cottage, 23 Bath Place, Taunton, Somerset TA1 4ER* Taunton (01823) 271794

HEATLEY, David Henry. b 50. Kent Univ BA72. Qu Coll Birm 86. **d** 88 **p** 89. C Liss *Portsm* 88-91; V Newchurch from 91; V Arreton from 91. *The Vicarage, Newchurch, Sandown, Isle of Wight PO36 0NN* Isle of Wight (01983) 865504

HEATLEY, Henry David. b 24. CITC 66. **d** 68 **p** 69. C Belf St Matt *Conn* 68-72; C-in-c Layde 72-78; C Belf St Mary 78-80; I Belf St Barn 80-92; rtd 92. *Ebenezer, 91 Larne Road, Carrickfergus, Co Antrim BT38 7NH* Carrickfergus (01960) 365382

HEATLEY, William Cecil. b 39. QUB BA61. Ridley Hall Cam 62. **d** 64 **p** 65. C Ballymacarrett St Patr *D & D* 64-69; C Herne Hill St Paul *S'wark* 69-74; TV Sanderstead All SS 75-82; P-in-c Peckham St Sav 82-87; V from 87. *173 Choumert Road, London SE15 4AW* 0171-639 5072 or 732 3435

HEATON, Alan. b 36. K Coll Lon BD64 AKC64 Nottm Univ MTh76. **d** 65 **p** 66. C Stockton St Chad *Dur* 65-68; C Englefield Green *Guildf* 68-70; C Winlaton *Dur* 70-74; Chapl Derby Lonsdale Coll *Derby* 74-79; V Alfreton 79-87; RD Alfreton 81-86; TR Clifton *S'well* 87-93; P-in-c Rolleston w Fiskerton, Morton and Upton from 93. *The Vicarage, 29 Marlock Close, Fiskerton, Southwell, Notts NG25 0UB* Southwell (01636) 830331

HEATON, Very Rev Eric William. b 20. Ch Coll Cam BA44 MA46 Lambeth Hon DD91. **d** 44 **p** 45. Chapl St Jo Coll Ox 60-74; Sen Tutor 66-73; Dean Dur 74-79; Dean Ch Ch *Ox* 79-90; rtd 90. *Tree Cottage, Elsfield, Oxford OX1 1DP* Stanton St John (01865) 351604

HEATON, Julian Roger. b 62. LSE BSc(Econ)83. St Steph Ho Ox BA86 MA92. **d** 87 **p** 88. C Stockport St Thos w St Pet *Ches* 87-90; Chapl Asst Qu Medical Cen Nottm 90-92; Chapl Asst Univ Hosp Nottm 90-92; V Knutsford St Cross *Ches* from 92. *The Vicarage, Mobberley Road, Knutsford, Cheshire WA16 8EL* Knutsford (01565) 632389

HEATON-RENSHAW, Canon Squire Heaton. b 09. TD50. Selw Coll Cam BA30 MusB30 MA34. Westcott Ho Cam 34. **d** 35 **p** 36. V Mert St Mary *S'wark* 52-75; Perm to Offic *Win* 75-93; rtd 76. *Chiltern, 12 Crabtree Drive, Leatherhead, Surrey KT22 8LJ*

✠**HEAVENER, Rt Rev Robert William.** b 05. TCD BA28. CITC 29. **d** 29 **p** 30 **c** 73. C Clones *Clogh* 29-31; Dioc Curate 31-32; C-in-c Lack 32-38; I Derryvullen N 38-46; R Monaghan w Tyholland 46-51; RD Monaghan 46-73; R Monaghan w Tydavnet 51-73; Can St Patr Cathl Dub 62-68; Adn Clogh 68-73; Bp Clogh 73-80; rtd 80. *12 Church Avenue, Jordanstown, Newtownabbey, Co Antrim BT37 0PJ* Whiteabbey (01232) 863242

HEAVER, Derek Cyril. b 47. St Jo Coll Nottm BTh73. **d** 73 **p** 74. C Win Ch Ch *Win* 73-77; CF from 77. *c/o MOD (Army), Bagshot Park, Bagshot, Surrey GU19 5PL* Bagshot (01276) 471717 Fax 412834

HEAVISIDES, Canon Neil Cameron. b 50. Selw Coll Cam BA72 MA76 Ox Univ BA74 MA85. Ripon Hall Ox 72. **d** 75 **p** 76. C Stockton St Pet *Dur* 75-78; Succ S'wark Cathl *S'wark* 78-81; V Seaham w Seaham Harbour *Dur* 81-88; P-in-c Edington and Imber, Erlestoke and E Coulston *Sarum* 88-89; R 89-93; Can Res Glouc Cathl *Glouc* from 93. *7 College Green, Gloucester GL1 2LX* Gloucester (01452) 523987

HEAWOOD, Canon Alan Richard. b 32. G&C Coll Cam BA54 MA58. Union Th Sem (NY) BD56 Ripon Hall Ox 56. **d** 57 **p** 58. C Horwich H Trin *Man* 57-59; C Weaste 59-60; C Beverley Minster *York* 60-62; Chapl and Lect St Pet Coll Saltley 62-65; R Hockwold w Wilton *Ely* 65-72; R Weeting 65-72; V Melbourn 72-80; V Meldreth 72-80; P-in-c Teversham 80-90; Adult Educn Sec 80-89; Dir of Educn from 80; Hon Can Ely Cathl from 80. *The Rectory, 30 Church Road, Teversham, Cambs CB1 5AW* Teversham (01223) 292220

HEBBLETHWAITE, Canon Brian Leslie. b 39. Magd Coll Ox BA61 MA67 Magd Coll Cam BA63 MA68 BD84. Westcott Ho Cam 62. **d** 65 **p** 66. C Elton All SS *Man* 65-68; Chapl and Dean of Chpl Qu Coll Cam from 69; Lic to Offic *Ely* from 69; Asst Lect Cam Univ 73-77; Lect from 77; Can Th Leic Cathl *Leic* from 82. *Queen's College, Cambridge CB3 9ET* Cambridge (01223) 335511

HEBBLETHWAITE, Dr Emma Sian. b 65. CCC Cam BA85 MA91 PhD92. Westcott Ho Cam CTM94. **d** 94 **p** 95. C Framlingham w Saxtead *St E* from 94. *10 Brook Lane, Framlingham, Woodbridge, Suffolk IP13 9RN* Framlingham (01728) 724352

HEBBORN, Roy Valentine Charles.S Dios Minl Tr Scheme 83. **d** 86 **p** 87. NSM Lewes All SS, St Anne, St Mich and St Thos

Chich from 86. *3 St Anne's Terrace, Western Road, Lewes, E Sussex BN7 1RH* Lewes (01273) 474063

HEBDEN, Cynthia. d 94. NSM Llanfairpwll w Penmynydd *Ban* from 94. *Dryll y Bowl, Lon Refail, Llanfairpwllgwyngyll, Gwynedd LL61 5YS* Menai Bridge (01248) 714241

HEBDEN, John Percy. b 18. St Aid Birkenhead 58. **d** 60 **p** 60. V Laxey *S & M* 70-83; V Lonan 80-83; rtd 84; Hon C Douglas St Geo and St Barn *S & M* from 84. *Begra, Clayhead Road, Baldrine, Douglas, Isle of Man IM4 6DN* Laxey (01624) 781296

HEBER-PERCY, Christopher John. b 41. St Jo Coll Cam BA64 MA68. Wells Th Coll 66. **d** 68 **p** 69. C Leigh St Mary *Man* 68-71; Asst Ind Chapl 71-80; P-in-c Oldham St Andr 75-78; TV Oldham 78-80; Ind Chapl *Win* 80-90; N Humberside Ind Chapl *York* from 90. *19 Bellfield Avenue, Hull HU8 9DS* Hull (01482) 702033

HECKINGBOTTOM, John Michael. b 33. Leeds Univ BA55. St Steph Ho Ox 55. **d** 57 **p** 58. C Wigan All SS *Liv* 57-59; Min Can and Succ Ripon Cathl *Ripon* 59-63; P-in-c Seacroft 63-66; V Menston w Woodhead *Bradf* 66-82; P-in-c Bishop Monkton and Burton Leonard *Ripon* 82-88; Chapl Scotton Banks Hosp Knaresborough 86-88; V Collingham w Harewood *Ripon* 88-94; Perm to Offic *Ripon* from 94. *8 Lawson Road, Dringhouses, York YO2 2NE* York (01904) 707916

HECTOR, Noel Antony. b 61. Barrister-at-Law 84 Sheff Univ LLB83. Oak Hill Th Coll BA91. **d** 91 **p** 92. C Rodbourne Cheney *Bris* 91-92; C Bris St Mary Redcliffe w Temple etc 92-95; R Wrington w Butcombe *B & W* from 95. *The Rectory, High Street, Wrington, Bristol BS18 7QD* Wrington (01934) 862201

HEDDLE, Dr Duncan. b 34. Wadh Coll Ox BA57 MA61 DPhil64. **d** 86 **p** 86. Chapl Aber Univ *Ab* from 86; P-in-c Bucksburn from 90. *2 Douglas Place, High Street, Aberdeen AB2 3EA* Aberdeen (01224) 485975 or 272888

HEDGCOCK, Dr Walter Paul. b 09. FRCGP Lon Univ MB, BS32 MD34. S'wark Ord Course 69. **d** 72 **p** 73. C Blakeney w Lt Langham *Nor* 72-73; P-in-c Field Dalling w Saxlingham 73-76; Bp's Scientific Resp Adv 76-83; Hon C Wallingford w Crowmarsh Gifford etc *Ox* from 84. *3 Cherwell Close, Wallingford, Oxon OX10 0HF* Wallingford (01491) 837684

HEDGE, Peter Andrew. b 62. New Coll Ox MA90. Coll of Resurr Mirfield 90. **d** 93 **p** 94. C Thornbury *Bradf* from 93. *69 Upper Ruston Road, Thornbury, Bradford, W Yorkshire BD3 7EU* Bradford (01274) 666875

HEDGER, Graham. b 57. Lon Bible Coll BA Ridley Hall Cam. **d** 83 **p** 84. C Walton *St E* 83-86; TV Mildenhall 86-91; R Swainsthorpe w Newton Flotman *Nor* 91-94; Dioc Evang Officer 91-94. *14 St Peter's Close, Charsfield, Woodbridge, Suffolk IP13 7RG* Charsfield (01473) 737280

HEDGES, Mrs Anne Violet. b 53. Ripon Coll Cuddesdon 87. **d** 89 **p** 94. C Thetford *Nor* 89-94; Chapl Riddlesworth Hall Sch Nor from 93; P-in-c Garboldisham w Blo' Norton, Riddlesworth etc *Nor* from 94. *The Rectory, Back Street, Garboldisham, Diss, Norfolk IP22 2SD* Garboldisham (01953) 818101

HEDGES, Canon Dennis Walter. b 29. Sarum Th Coll. **d** 62 **p** 63. V Blackheath and Chilworth *Guildf* 69-79; R Farncombe 79-94; RD Godalming 84-89; Hon Can Guildf Cathl 92-94; rtd 94; Perm to Offic *Guildf* from 94; Perm to Offic *Win* from 94. *21 Lincoln Green, Alton, Hants GU34 1SX* Alton (01420) 542624

HEDGES, Ian Charles. b 55. Sarum & Wells Th Coll 79. **d** 82 **p** 83. C Chessington *Guildf* 82-85; C Fleet 85-90; V S Farnborough from 90. *The Vicarage, 1 St Mark's Close, Farnborough, Hants GU14 6PP* Farnborough (01252) 544711

HEDGES, Canon Jane Barbara. b 55. St Jo Coll Dur BA78. Cranmer Hall Dur 78. **dss** 80 **d** 87 **p** 94. Fareham H Trin *Portsm* 80-83; Southn (City Cen) *Win* 83-87; Par Dn 87-88; Dioc Stewardship Adv 88-93; Can Res Portsm Cathl from 93. *51 High Street, Portsmouth PO1 2LU* Portsmouth (01705) 731282

HEDGES, Mrs Jane Rosemary. b 44. RGN65. S Dios Minl Tr Scheme 86. **d** 89 **p** 94. NSM Gillingham *Sarum* from 89; Asst Chapl Westmr Memorial Hosp Shaftesbury from 89. *Dene Hollow, Wyke, Gillingham, Dorset SP8 4NG* Gillingham (01747) 822812

HEDGES, John Michael Peter. b 34. Leeds Univ BA60. Ripon Hall Ox 60. **d** 61 **p** 62. C Weaste *Man* 61-65; V Ashton St Pet 65-74; C Easthampstead *Ox* 74-85; V Tilehurst St Geo 85-91; C Thatcham 91-94; TV from 94. *1 Cowslip Crescent, Dunston Park, Thatcham, Berks* Thatcham (01635) 869940

HEDGES, Leslie Norman. b 26. Bris Univ BA51 Lon Univ BD56. Clifton Th Coll 48. **d** 53 **p** 54. V Clapham Park All SS *S'wark* 59-70; V Findern *Derby* 70-82; V Willington 70-82; V Trowbridge St Thos and W Ashton *Sarum* 82-91; rtd 91. *16 Penwerris Road, Truro, Cornwall TR1 3QS* Truro (01872) 79858

HEDLEY, Dr Charles John Wykeham. b 47. R Holloway Coll Lon BSc69 PhD73 Fitzw Coll Cam BA75 MA79. Westcott Ho Cam 73. **d** 76 **p** 77. C Chingford St Anne *Chelmsf* 76-79; C St Martin-in-the-Fields *Lon* 79-84 and 85-86; P-in-c 84-85; Chapl Ch Coll Cam 86-90; TR Gleadless *Sheff* from 90. *The Rectory, 243 Hollinsend Road, Sheffield S12 2EE* Sheffield (0114) 239 0757

HEDLEY, Henry. b 10. St Edm Hall Ox BA32 MA43. Linc Th Coll 33. **d** 34 **p** 35. R Bletchley *Ox* 63-79; rtd 79. *6 Caldersyde, The Banks, Seascale, Cumbria CA20 1QJ* Seascale (019467) 28985

HEDLEY, Ronald. b 27. Codrington Coll Barbados. **d** 64 **p** 65. Trinidad and Tobago 64-92; rtd 92. *6 Ludlow Road, Sunderland SR2 9HH*

HEDLEY, William Clifford. b 35. Tyndale Hall Bris 65. **d** 67 **p** 68. C Hensingham *Carl* 67-69; C Rainhill *Liv* 69-71; C St Helens St Helen 71-73; V Low Elswick *Newc* 73-81; V Kingston upon Hull Southcoates St Aid *York* 81-87; TV Heworth 87-94; V Norton from 94. *The Vicarage, 80 Langton Road, Norton, Malton, N Yorkshire YO17 9AE* Malton (01653) 692741

HEFFER, William John Gambrell. b 30. AKC55. **d** 56 **p** 57. V Luton All SS *St Alb* 67-73; P-in-c Eaton Socon 73-75; V 75-77; Lic to Offic 78-81; R Wingrave w Rowsham, Aston Abbotts and Cublington *Ox* 81-88; R Wilden w Colmworth and Ravensden *St Alb* 88-91; C Leighton Buzzard w Eggington, Hockliffe etc 91-94; rtd 94. *35 Pebblemoor, Edlesborough, Dunstable, Beds LU7 2HZ* Ampthill (01525) 220428

HEFFERNAN, Ms May Olive. b 52. Maria Grey Coll Lon CertEd74 Lon Univ BD93. Aston Tr Scheme 88 Westcott Ho Cam CTMin93. **d** 93 **p** 94. C Duddeston w Nechells *Birm* from 93. *14 Stanley Road, Birmingham B7 5QS* 0121-328 3781

HEGARTY, Gerald. b 52. QUB BA74 BD81. Union Th Coll Belf 78. **d** 86 **p** 87. NSM Leic H Trin w St Jo *Leic* 86-87; P-in-c Sibson w Sheepy and Ratcliffe Culey 87-90; Chapl St Edm Hall Ox from 90. *St Edmund Hall, Queen's Lane, Oxford OX1 4AR* Oxford (01865) 279091 or 274214 Fax 274215

HEGGS, Thomas James. b 40. Inter-American Univ Puerto Rico BA65. Linc Th Coll 75. **d** 77 **p** 78. C Newark St Mary *S'well* 77-80; C Newark w Hawton, Cotham and Shelton 80; R Barwell w Potters Marston and Stapleton *Leic* 80-89; R Upwell St Pet *Ely* 89-94; R Outwell from 89; P-in-c Yaxley from 94. *The Vicarage, Yaxley, Peterborough PE7 3LH* Peterborough (01733) 240339

HEIDT, John Harrison. b 32. Yale Univ BA54 Ox Univ BLitt67 DPhil75. Nashotah Ho BD57 MDiv69. **d** 56 **p** 57. USA 56-75; C Ox St Mary Magd *Ox* 75-80; V Up Hatherley *Glouc* from 80; P-in-c Cheltenham St Steph from 89. *The Vicarage, Hatherley Road, Cheltenham, Glos GL51 6HX* Cheltenham (01242) 516445

HEIDT, Michael Lewis. b 65. K Coll Lon BD86. St Steph Ho Ox 88. **d** 90 **p** 91. C Reading St Luke w St Bart *Ox* 90-94. *Address temp unknown*

HEIL, Miss Janet. b 53. Liv Univ BEd75 St Jo Coll Dur BA84. Cranmer Hall Dur. **dss** 85 **d** 87 **p** 94. Ashton Ch Ch *Man* 85-87; Par Dn 87-91; Par Dn Scotforth *Blackb* 91-94; C from 94. *10 Lawnswood Avenue, Scotforth, Lancaster LA1 4NZ* Lancaster (01524) 65717

HEINZE, Rudolph William. b 31. Concordia Coll (USA) BSc56 CertEd56 De Paul Univ (USA) MA59 Univ of Iowa PhD65. **d** 86 **p** 87. NSM Colney St Pet *St Alb* from 86; Lect Oak Hill Th Coll 86-88; Sen Tutor Oak Hill Th Coll from 88. *3 Farm Lane, Chase Side, London N14 4PP* 0181-449 5969 Fax 441 5996

HELEY, John. b 28. Lon Univ BA72. Bps' Coll Cheshunt 54. **d** 56 **p** 57. Lic to Offic *Ox* 69-72; R E w W Rudham *Nor* 72-75; P-in-c Houghton 72-74; V 74-75; V Hunstanton St Edm 75-82; V Hunstanton St Edm w Ringstead 82-83; rtd 88. *Meadow Cottage, Cradle Hall Farm, Burnham Market, Kings Lynn, Norfolk PE31 8JX* Docking (01485) 518686

HELFT, Gunter. b 23. Lon Univ BA48. Ely Th Coll 46. **d** 48 **p** 49. Hd Master Abp Temple's Sch Lambeth 67-71; Hd Master Don Valley High Sch S Yorkshire 71-80; rtd 80; Perm to Offic *Worc* from 87. *19 Kenwood Avenue, Worcester WR4 9BD* Worcester (01905) 29797

HELLARD, Dawn Yvonne Lorraine. b 47. St Mich Coll Llan 89. **d** 91. C Llantwit Major *Llan* 91-95; TV Cowbridge from 95. *Margam House, St Hilary, Cowbridge, S Glam CF7 7DP* Cowbridge (01446) 772460

HELLEWELL, John. b 63. **d** 94 **p** 95. C Greasbrough *Sheff* from 94. *18 Coach Road, Rotherham, S Yorkshire S61 4ED* Rotherham (01709) 562378

HELLICAR, Hugh Christopher. b 37. Qu Coll Birm 69. **d** 70 **p** 71. C Bromyard *Heref* 70-73; C Bishop's Castle w Mainstone 73-75; Perm to Offic *S'wark* 77-85; Perm to Offic *Chich* 83-93; NSM Hove All SS 93; NSM Hove from 93. *14 Lewes Crescent, Brighton BN2 1FH* Brighton (01273) 676019

HELLIER, Jeremy Peter. b 53. K Coll Lon BD75 AKC75. St Aug Coll Cant 75. **d** 76 **p** 77. C Walton *St E* 76-79; C Ipswich St

Fran 79-80; C Wolborough w Newton Abbot *Ex* 80-82; CF 82-84; R Pendine w Llanmiloe and Eglwys Gymyn w Marros *St D* 84-89; TR Widecombe-in-the-Moor, Leusdon, Princetown etc *Ex* 89-94; CF (TAVR) 90-94; RD Moreton *Ex* 91-94; Chapl Wellington Sch Somerset from 94. *c/o Wellington School, Wellington, Somerset TA21 8NT* Wellington (01823) 668827 or 668837 Fax 668844

HELLIWELL, Christopher John Guiscard. b 60. Hatf Coll Dur BA82 Fitzw Coll Cam BA86. Westcott Ho Cam 84. **d** 87 **p** 88. C Norton St Mary *Dur* 87-91; V Barton and Manfield w Cleasby *Ripon* 91-93. *Address temp unknown*

HELLYER, Ian Anthony. b 66. Plymouth Poly HNC87 Lanc Univ BSc91 Nottm Univ BTh95. Linc Th Coll 92. **d** 95. C Poulton-le-Fylde *Blackb* from 95. *29 Mossbourne Road, Poulton-le-Fylde, Blackpool FY6 7DU* Blackpool (01253) 884298

HELLYER, Stephen John (Steve). b 56. St Cath Coll Cam BA77 MA81. Wycliffe Hall Ox 82. **d** 84 **p** 85. C Plymouth St Andr w St Paul and St Geo *Ex* 84-88; Chapl Lee Abbey 88-89; Consultant Lon and SE CPAS 90-94; C Nottm St Nic *S'well* from 94. *4 Balmoral Avenue, West Bridgford, Nottingham NG2 7QU* Nottingham (0115) 981 5665

HELM, Alistair Thomas. b 53. Aston Univ BSc75. E Anglian Minl Tr Course 88. **d** 91 **p** 92. NSM Leic St Jas *Leic* from 91. *20 Stoughton Drive North, Leicester LE5 5UB* Leicester (0116) 273 0613

HELM, Nicholas. b 57. Surrey Univ BSc81. St Jo Coll Nottm 85. **d** 88 **p** 89. C Old Ford St Paul w St Steph and St Mark *Lon* 88-92; TV Netherthorpe *Sheff* 92-93; V Sheff St Bart from 93. *The Vicarage, 73 Burgoyne Road, Sheffield S6 3QB* Sheffield (0114) 233 6977

HELMS, David Clarke. b 50. Boston Univ AB72. Yale Div Sch MDiv77. **d** 77 **p** 77. USA 77-88; Ind Chapl *Worc* from 88; Chapl NE Worcs Coll from 88. *1 Marlborough Avenue, Bromsgrove, Worcs B60 2PG* Bromsgrove (01527) 872110

HELYER, Patrick Joseph Peter. b 15. FRGS83. ALCD39 Wycliffe Hall Ox 38. **d** 38 **p** 39. Falkland Is 71-75; R Streat w Westmeston *Chich* 75-78; Tristan da Cunha 78-81; rtd 81; Hon C Malborough w S Huish, W Alvington and Churchstow *Ex* 81-84; Perm to Offic *Heref* from 84; Perm to Offic *Glouc* from 84. *Tristan, 4 Gorse Lane, Sling, Coleford, Glos GL16 8JH* Dean (01594) 834990

HEMINGWAY, Peter. b 32. S'wark Ord Course 72. **d** 75 **p** 76. NSM Belmont *S'wark* 75-79; C Herne Hill St Paul 79-81; V Headstone St Geo *Lon* 81-92; V N Harrow St Alb from 87. *St Alban's Vicarage, Church Drive, Harrow, Middx HA2 7NS* 0181-868 6567

HEMMING, Terry Edward. b 47. S Wales Bible Coll DipTh70 Calvin Coll Michigan MA84 S Dios Minl Tr Scheme 88. **d** 90 **p** 91. Hon C Win All SS w Chilcomb and Chesil *Win* from 90. *15 Gordon Avenue, Winchester, Hants SO23 0QE* Winchester (01962) 855701

HEMMING CLARK, Stanley Charles. b 29. Peterho Cam BA52 MA56. Ridley Hall Cam 52. **d** 54 **p** 55. C Redhill H Trin *S'wark* 54-56; C Woking St Jo *Guildf* 56-59; V Crockenhill All So *Roch* from 59. *The Vicarage, Eynsford Road, Swanley, Kent BR8 8JS* Swanley (01322) 662157

HEMMINGS, Roy Anthony. b 48. Wolv Poly HND69 Univ of Wales (Cardiff) BD85 DPS86. St Mich Coll Llan 82. **d** 86 **p** 87. C Rhyl w St Ann *St As* 86-90; CF from 90. *c/o MOD (Army), Bagshot Park, Bagshot, Surrey GU19 5PL* Bagshot (01276) 471717 Fax 412834

HEMMONS, Laurence John. b 19. Worc Ord Coll 64. **d** 66 **p** 66. R Churchstanton *Ex* 69-70; P-in-c Otterford *B & W* 69-70; R Churchstanton w Otterford 70-82; R Churchstanton, Buckland St Mary and Otterford 80-84; rtd 84; Perm to Offic *Ex* from 88. *7 Westview Close, Whimple, Exeter EX5 2TR* Whimple (01404) 822783

HEMPENSTALL, John Albert. b 43. CITC 64. **d** 67 **p** 68. C Carlow w Urglin and Staplestown *C & O* 67-70; Chapl RN from 70. *Directorate Gen, RN Chapl Services, Room 203, Victory Building, HM Naval Base, Portsmouth PO1 3LS* Portsmouth (01705) 727903 Fax 727112

HEMPHILL, John James. b 44. TCD BA68 MA72. Oak Hill Th Coll 71. **d** 73 **p** 74. C Dundonald *D & D* 73-78; I Balteagh w Carrick *D & R* from 78. *Balteagh Rectory, 115 Drumsurn Road, Limavady, Co Londonderry BT49 0PD* Limavady (015047) 63069

HEMS, Canon Richard Brian. b 30. K Coll Lon BD58. St Aug Coll Cant. **d** 59 **p** 60. C Whitnash *Cov* 59-63; C-in-c Tuckswood CD *Nor* 63-69; V Tuckswood 69-78; R Framingham Earl 78-94; R Gt w Lt Poringland and Howe 78-94; P-in-c Bixley 93-94; R Poringland from 94; Hon Can Nor Cathl from 92. *The Rectory, Rectory Lane, Poringland, Norwich NR14 7SL* Framingham Earl (01508) 492215

HEMSLEY, David Ridgway. b 36. AKC61. **d** 61 **p** 62. C Penhill *Bris* 61-64; C Highworth w Sevenhampton and Inglesham etc 64-66; C Surbiton St Andr *S'wark* 67-70; P-in-c Tingewick w

Water Stratford *Ox* 70-75; P-in-c Radclive 72-75; PM N Marston w Granborough etc 75-81; P-in-c Quainton 75-81; TV Schorne 81-90; P-in-c Lt Missenden 90-93; V from 93. *The Vicarage, Little Missenden, Amersham, Bucks HP7 0RA* Great Missenden (01494) 862008

HEMSLEY, Susan Mary. b 59. Cranmer Hall Dur 93. **d** 95. C Wilnecote *Lich* from 95. *5 Avill, Hockley, Tamworth, Staffs B77 5QE* Tamworth (01827) 251816

HEMSTOCK, Julian. b 51. MIProdE CEng Trent Poly BSc74. Sarum & Wells Th Coll 89. **d** 91 **p** 92. C Carrington *S'well* 91-94; C Basford St Aid from 94. *St John's House, 65 Osborne Grove, Nottingham NG5 2HE* Nottingham (0115) 985 6980

HEMSTOCK, Mrs Pat. b 51. Sarum & Wells Th Coll 89. **d** 91 **p** 95. Par Dn Carrington *S'well* 91-94; Par Dn Basford St Aid 94-95; C from 95. *St John's House, 65 Osborne Grove, Nottingham NG5 2HE* Nottingham (0115) 985 6980

HENCHER, John Bredon. b 31. Lich Th Coll 58. **d** 60 **p** 61. C Pershore w Wick *Worc* 60-62; Bp's Dom Chapl 63-64; V Amblecote 64-70; Perm to Offic *Glouc* 72-74; Dioc RE Adv *Heref* 74-80; Perm to Offic 80-87; Perm to Offic *Mon* from 87; Asst Chapl Mon Sch from 87. *The Tank House, Weston, Pembridge, Herefordshire HR6 9JE* Pembridge (015447) 540

HENCKEN, Alfred David. b 15. AKC42. **d** 42 **p** 43. V S Mymms K Chas *Lon* 68-80; rtd 80. *Hays Nursing Home, Shaftesbury, Dorset SP7 9JR* Shaftesbury (01747) 830282

HENDERSON, Canon Alastair Roy. b 27. BNC Ox BA51 MA54. Ridley Hall Cam 52. **d** 54 **p** 55. V Stoke Bishop *Bris* 68-92; Lect Clifton Th Coll 69-71; Lect Trin Coll Bris 71-73; RD Westbury and Severnside *Bris* 73-79; Hon Can Bris Cathl 80-92; rtd 92; Perm to Offic *Ex* from 92. *3 Garden Court, Cricketfield Lane, Budleigh Salterton, Devon EX9 6PN* Budleigh Salterton (01395) 446147

HENDERSON, Andrew Douglas. b 36. MBASW Trin Coll Cam BA60 MA64 Ox Univ DipPSA63 Liv Univ DASS65. Cuddesdon Coll 60. **d** 62 **p** 63. C Camberwell St Paul *S'wark* 62-64; Hon C Camberwell St Luke 65-80; Perm to Offic *Lon* from 85. *178 Lancaster Road, London W11 1QU* 0171-229 6790

HENDERSON, David. b 35. Oak Hill NSM Course. **d** 83 **p** 84. NSM Rush Green *Chelmsf* from 83. *196 Marlborough Road, Romford RM7 8AL* Romford (01708) 765955

HENDERSON, Ven Edward Chance. b 16. Lon Univ BD39. ALCD39. **d** 39 **p** 40. Adn Pontefract *Wakef* 68-81; rtd 81; Perm to Offic *Wakef* from 81; Perm to Offic *Sheff* from 82. *12 Park Lane, Balne, Goole, N Humberside DN14 0EP* Goole (01405) 861934

HENDERSON, Euan Russell Milne. b 42. St Steph Ho Ox 75. **d** 80 **p** 81. NSM Hambleden Valley *Ox* 80-83; C Reading All SS 83-84; C Maidenhead St Luke 84-86; NSM Swyncombe w Britwell Salome from 87. *The Old Forge, Stonor, Henley-on-Thames, Oxon RG9 6HE* Turville Heath (01491) 638566

HENDERSON, Francis Colin. b 35. St Cath Coll Cam BA59 MA63. Cuddesdon Coll 60. **d** 62 **p** 63. C Croydon *Cant* 62-67; V Westwood *Cov* 67-75; V Chilvers Coton w Astley 75-80; P-in-c Wolston 80; P-in-c Church Lawford w Newnham Regis 80; V Wolston and Church Lawford 80-85; USA from 85. *1364 Katella Street, Laguna Beach, California 92651, USA* Laguna Beach (714) 497-2239

✠**HENDERSON, Rt Rev George Kennedy Buchanan.** b 21. MBE74 JP63. St Chad's Coll Dur LTh43 BA47. Edin Th Coll 40. **d** 43 **p** 45 **c** 77. C Glas Ch Ch *Glas* 43-48; Bp's Dom Chapl *Arg* 48-50; P-in-c Kinlochleven 48-50; P-in-c Nether Lochaber 48-50; R Fort William 50-77; Can St Jo Cathl Oban 60-77; Syn Clerk 64-73; Dean *Arg* 73-77; Bp *Arg* 77-92; Primus 90-92; rtd 92. *Benvoulin, 7 Achnalea, Onich, Fort William, Inverness-shire PH33 6SA* Onich (018553) 240 Fax 443

HENDERSON, Ian Robert. b 29. S'wark Ord Course 64. **d** 67 **p** 69. C Ealing St Pet Mt Park *Lon* 67-72; Hon C N Acton St Gabr 72-74; V Ealing Ascension Hanger Hill 74-88; P-in-c W Twyford 85-88; V Hanger Hill Ascension and W Twyford St Mary 88-90; rtd 90. *5 Croyde Avenue, Greenford, Middx UB6 9LS* 0181-578 8917

HENDERSON, James. b 22. Chich Th Coll 51. **d** 54 **p** 55. V Bolton St Geo *Man* 64-70; V Newhey 70-87; rtd 87; Perm to Offic *Man* from 87. *17 Swift Road, Rochdale, Lancs OL11 5RF* Rochdale (01706) 522228

HENDERSON, Miss Janet. b 57. St Jo Coll Dur BA88 RGN82. Cranmer Hall Dur 85. **d** 88 **p** 94. Par Dn Wisbech SS Pet and Paul *Ely* 88-90; Par Dn Bestwood *S'well* 90-93; Tutor St Jo Coll Nottm 92-93; Lect St Jo Coll Nottm from 93; NSM Bramcote *S'well* from 94. *St John's College, Chilwell Lane, Beeston, Nottingham NG9 3DS* Nottingham (0115) 925 1114 or 228356 Fax 436438

HENDERSON, John William. b 13. AKC38. **d** 38 **p** 39. V Wateringbury *Roch* 63-78; rtd 78. *Cumloden, The Triangle, Somerton, Somerset TA11 6QJ* Somerton (01458) 73424

HENDERSON, Judith Ann. b 37. **d** 89 **p** 94. NSM Sheringham *Nor* 89-92; NSM Brampton St Thos *Derby* from 92. *Rose*

HENDERSON

Cottage, Cotton Mill Hill, Chesterfield, Derbyshire S42 7EV Chesterfield (01246) 569106

HENDERSON, Julian Tudor. b 54. Keble Coll Ox BA76 MA81. Ridley Hall Cam 77. **d** 79 **p** 80. C Islington St Mary *Lon* 79-83; V Hastings Em and St Mary in the Castle *Chich* 83-92; V Claygate *Guildf* from 92. *The Vicarage, Church Road, Claygate, Esher, Surrey KT10 0JP* Esher (01372) 463603

HENDERSON, Nicholas Paul. b 48. Selw Coll Cam BA73 MA77. Ripon Hall Ox 73. **d** 75 **p** 76. C St Alb St Steph *St Alb* 75-78; Warden J F Kennedy Ho Cov Cathl 78-79; C Bow w Bromley St Leon *Lon* 79-85; P-in-c W Acton St Martin from 85; P-in-c Ealing All SS from 89. *St Martin's Vicarage, 25 Birch Grove, London W3 9SP* 0181-248 0608 or 992 2333 Fax 993 5812

HENDERSON, Patrick James. b 57. R Holloway Coll Lon BA78. St Steph Ho Ox 83. **d** 86 **p** 87. C Hornsey St Mary w St Geo *Lon* 86-90; V Whetstone St Jo from 90. *St John's Vicarage, 1163 High Road, London N20 0PG* 0181-445 4569

HENDERSON, Very Rev Richard Crosbie Aitken. b 57. Magd Coll Ox MA84 DPhil84. St Jo Coll Nottm 83. **d** 86 **p** 87. C Chinnor w Emmington and Sydenham etc *Ox* 86-89; I Abbeystrewry Union *C, C & R* 89-95; Can Cork and Ross Cathls from 95; I Ross Union from 95; Dean Ross from 95; Preb Cork Cathl from 95. *The Deanery, Rosscarbery, Co Cork, Irish Republic* Cork (23) 48166

HENDERSON, Robert. b 43. TCD 66 Ulster Univ DipG&C87 Lambeth STh94. **d** 69 **p** 70. C Drumglass *Arm* 69-72; Chapl Miss to Seamen 72-78; Kenya 77-78; I Mostrim w Granard, Clonbroney, Killoe etc *K, E & A* 78-82; I Belf St Matt *Conn* 82-92; RD M Belf 90-93; I Kilroot and Templecorran from 92. *Kilroot Rectory, 29 Downshire Gardens, Carrickfergus, Co Antrim BT38 7LW* Carrickfergus (01960) 362387

HENDERSON, Samuel James Noel. b 16. Hertf Coll Ox BA39 MA42. **d** 42 **p** 43. V Hickling *Nor* 65-82; rtd 82; Perm to Offic *Nor* from 82. *96 Church Lane, Beeston Regis, Sheringham, Norfolk NR26 8EY* Sheringham (01263) 825686

HENDERSON, Terry James. b 45. St Deiniol's Hawarden 76. **d** 77 **p** 77. C Wrexham *St As* 77-79; CA Wilson Carlile Coll of Evang 79-81; TV Langtree *Ox* 81-87; P-in-c Aston Cantlow and Wilmcote w Billesley *Cov* 87-90; V from 90. *The Vicarage, Wilmcote, Stratford-upon-Avon, Warks CV37 9XD* Stratford-upon-Avon (01789) 292376

HENDERSON, William Desmond. b 27. TCD BA56 MA64. **d** 56 **p** 57. I Achonry w Tubbercurry and Kilmactigue *T, K & A* 66-75; rtd 75. *8 Tanian College, Mitchelstown, Co Cork, Irish Republic*

HENDERSON, William Ernest (Bill). b 53. CEng81 MICE81 Southn Univ BSc75. St Jo Coll Nottm 87. **d** 89 **p** 90. C Win Ch Ch *Win* 89-93; V Stanley *Wakef* from 93. *The Vicarage, 379 Aberford Road, Stanley, Wakefield, W Yorkshire WF3 4HE* Wakefield (01924) 822143

HENDERSON, William Ralph. b 32. Oak Hill Th Coll 65. **d** 67 **p** 68. C Nottm St Sav *S'well* 68-74; V Alne *York* 75-92; Chapl York Distr Hosp 86-92; rtd 92. *55 Ashley Park Road, Stockton Lane, York YO3 0XJ* York (01904) 426012

HENDERSON-BEGG, Robert John. b 11. Edin Univ MA32. Westcott Ho Cam 32 Qu Coll Birm 37. **d** 37 **p** 39. Asst Master Beds LEA 57-76; Perm to Offic and Chapter Clerk Newport Deanery *Ox* from 73; Perm to Offic *St Alb* from 73; rtd 76. *Stone Cottage, High Street, Carlton, Bedford MK43 7LA* Bedford (01234) 720366

HENDEY, Clifford. b 30. K Coll Lon BD53 AKC53. **d** 54 **p** 55. Trinidad and Tobago 58-71 and 81-82; V Spratton *Pet* 72-77; V Leeds All So *Ripon* 77-80; R Corringham *Linc* 80-81; V Alkham w Capel le Ferne and Hougham *Cant* 82-95; rtd 95. *308 Dover Road, Folkestone, Kent CT19 6NZ*

HENDRICKSE, Clarence David. b 41. CEng MIMechE71 Nottm Univ PGCE73. St Jo Coll Nottm 71. **d** 74 **p** 75. C St Helens St Helen *Liv* 74-76; C Netherley Ch Ch CD 76-77; TV 78-87; V Liv Ch Ch Norris Green 87-93; V Eccleston Ch Ch from 93. *The Vicarage, Chapel Lane, Eccleston, St Helens, Merseyside WA10 5DA* St Helens (01744) 22698 Fax as telephone

HENDRY, Mrs Helen Clare. b 58. Lanc Univ BA79 Cam Univ PGCE80. Reformed Th Sem Mississippi MA85 Oak Hill Th Coll 94. **d** 95. NSM Muswell Hill St Jas w St Matt *Lon* from 95. *7 Byre Road, Chase Side, London N14 4PQ* 0181-441 7805

HENDRY, Leonard John. b 34. Univ of Wales CPT68. St D Coll Lamp DipTh68. **d** 68 **p** 69. C Minchinhampton *Glouc* 68-71; C Bishop's Cleeve 71-74; V Cheltenham St Mich 74-78; V Horsley and Newington Bagpath w Kingscote 78-82; Chapl Salonika *Eur* 82-91; rtd 94. *Sebilles 5, Tsinari, Ano Poli, Salonika 546 33, Greece* Salonika (31) 281193

HENDRY, Philip David. b 48. K Coll Lon BD72 AKC72. St Aug Coll Cant 72. **d** 73 **p** 74. C Benhilton *S'wark* 73-78; TV Catford (Southend) and Downham 78-85; Chapl St Andr Sch Croydon

from 85; P-in-c Croydon St Andr *S'wark* 85-86; V from 86. *St Andrew's Vicarage, 6 St Peter's Road, Croydon CR0 1HD* 0181-688 6011 Fax 667 9540

HENDY, Graham Alfred. b 45. St Jo Coll Dur BA67 MA75 Fitzw Coll Cam CertEd. Sarum Th Coll 67. **d** 70 **p** 71. C High Wycombe *Ox* 70-75; TV 75-78; R Upton cum Chalvey 78-83; TR 83-90; R S Walsham and Upton *Nor* from 90; Dioc Lay Tr Officer from 90. *The Rectory, The Street, South Walsham, Norfolk NR13 6DQ* Norwich (01603) 270455 Fax 270595

HENEY, Ven William Butler. b 22. CITC. **d** 60 **p** 61. C Seagoe *D & D* 60-63; I Carrickmacross *Clogh* 64-73; I Newbridge w Carnalway and Kilcullen *M & K* from 73; Treas Kildare Cathl 81-86; Can Kildare Cathl from 81; Adn Kildare 86-94. *The Rectory, Newbridge, Co Kildare, Irish Republic* Newbridge (45) 431306

HENLEY, Claud Michael. b 31. Keble Coll Ox BA55 MA59. Chich Th Coll 55. **d** 57 **p** 58. C Cowley St Jas *Ox* 57-60; C Wetherby *Ripon* 60-63; C Brighton St Pet *Chich* 63-69; V Brighton St Jo 69-75; V New Groombridge from 75. *The Vicarage, Groombridge, Tunbridge Wells, Kent TN3 9SE* Langton (01892) 864265

HENLEY, David Edward. b 44. Sarum & Wells Th Coll 69. **d** 72 **p** 73. C Fareham H Trin *Portsm* 72-76; C-in-c Leigh Park St Clare CD 76-78; R Freshwater 78-87; RD W Wight 83-87; R Meonstoke w Corhampton cum Exton from 87; R Droxford from 87; RD Bishops Waltham from 93. *The Rectory, Meonstoke, Southampton SO3 1NF* Droxford (01489) 877512

HENLEY, Dean. b 64. St Chad's Coll Dur BA93. Westcott Ho Cam CTM95. **d** 95. C Farncombe *Guildf* from 95. *73 Binscombe Crescent, Farncombe, Godalming, Surrey GU7 3RA* Godalming (01483) 428972

HENLEY, John Francis Hugh. b 48. SS Mark & Jo Coll Chelsea CertEd69. St Mich Coll Llan DipTh82. **d** 82 **p** 83. C Griffithstown *Mon* 82-85; V St Hilary Greenway 85-90; P-in-c Fulham St Etheldreda w St Clem *Lon* from 90. *St Etheldreda's Vicarage, Doneraile Street, London SW6 6EL* 0171-736 3809

✠**HENLEY, Rt Rev Michael Harry George.** b 38. CB91. Lon Coll of Div LTh60. **d** 61 **p** 62 **c** 95. C St Marylebone w H Trin *Lon* 61-64; Chapl RN 64-68 and 74-89; Chapl of the Fleet and Adn for the RN 89-93; Dir Gen Naval Chapl Services 92-93; Chapl St Andr Univ *St And* 68-72; Chapl R Hosp Sch Holbrook 72-74; QHC 89-93; Hon Can Gib Cathl *Eur* 89-93; P-in-c Pitlochry *St And* 94-95; Bp St Andr from 95. *Afton House, Kennedy Gardens, St Andrews KY16 9DJ* St Andrews (01334) 473167

HENLY, Francis Michael. b 25. Sarum Th Coll. **d** 67 **p** 68. C E w W Harnham *Sarum* 67-70; P-in-c Stour Provost w Todbere 70-75; P-in-c Rowde 75-79; V 79-83; R Poulshot 79-83; V Bishop's Cannings, All Cannings etc 83-92; rtd 92. *Oldbury View, Middle Lane, Cherhill, Calne, Wilts SN11 8XX* Calne (01249) 815191

HENNELL, Canon Michael Murray. b 18. St Edm Hall Ox BA40 DipTh41 MA44 Qu Coll Cam MA49. Wycliffe Hall Ox 40. **d** 42 **p** 43. Prin Ridley Hall Cam 63-70; Can Res Man Cathl *Man* 70-84; rtd 84; Perm to Offic *Ches* from 84. *53 Cleveley Road, Meols, South Wirral L47 8XN* 0151-632 4328

HENNING, Mrs Judy. b 49. S Dios Minl Tr Scheme 85. **d** 88. C Catherington and Clanfield *Portsm* 88-91; C Leigh Park 91-92. *36 Sunderton Lane, Clanfield, Waterlooville, Hants PO8 0NU* Horndean (01705) 597034

HENRY, Very Rev Bryan George. b 30. St D Coll Lamp BA51 St Mich Coll Llan 51. **d** 53 **p** 54. Chapl RAF 63-81; Provost Nicosia and Adn Cyprus 81-90; Prov Sec Jerusalem and Middle E 84-90; Exec Officer Ch in Wales 90-95; rtd 95. *51 Parcau Avenue, Bridgend, M Glam CF31 4SZ* Bridgend (01656) 669489

HENRY, Miss Jacqueline Margaret. b 40. Open Univ BA82. Trin Coll Bris DipHE79. **dss** 83 **d** 87 **p** 94. Deptford St Jo *S'wark* 79-82; Catshill and Dodford *Worc* 83-86; The Lye and Stambermill 86-87; Par Dn 87-89; Educn Chapl 89-93; C Tolleshunt Knights w Tiptree and Gt Braxted *Chelmsf* from 94; Chapl amongst Deaf People from 94. *10 Coriander Road, Tiptree, Colchester CO5 0AS* Tiptree (01621) 819825

HENRY, Canon Maurice James Birks. b 14. Dorchester Miss Coll 34. **d** 38 **p** 39. V Chelford w Lower Withington *Ches* 65-81; RD Knutsford 73-80; Hon Can Ches Cathl 76-81; rtd 81; Perm to Offic *Ches* from 81. *Norlands, 56 Holly Tree Road, Plumley, Knutsford, Cheshire WA16 0UJ* Lower Peover (01565) 722721

HENRY, Peter. b 49. BTh. St Jo Coll Nottm. **d** 84 **p** 85. C Sinfin Moor *Derby* 84-89; C Blagreaves St Andr CD 84-89; V Guernsey St Jo *Win* from 89. *St John's Vicarage, Les Amballes, St Peter Port, Guernsey, Channel Islands GY1 1WY* Guernsey (01481) 720289

HENRY, Stephen Kenelm Malim. b 37. Bps' Coll Cheshunt 60. **d** 62 **p** 63. C Leic St Phil *Leic* 62-67; CF 67-70; V Woodhouse *Wakef* from 70. *Christ Church Vicarage, 79 Woodhouse Hill, Huddersfield HD2 1DH* Huddersfield (01484) 424669

HENRY, Trevor. b 09. St Aid Birkenhead 52. **d** 54 **p** 55. V Cookley *Worc* 63-73; rtd 73; Perm to Offic *Heref* from 85. *Northwood, Shatterford, Bewdley, Worcs DY12 1RL* Arley (012997) 249

✠**HENSHALL, Rt Rev Michael.** b 28. St Chad's Coll Dur BA54 DipTh56. **d** 56 **p** 57 **c** 76. C Sewerby w Marton *York* 56-59; C Bridlington Quay H Trin 56-59; C-in-c Micklehurst CD *Ches* 59-62; V Micklehurst 62-63; V Altrincham St Geo 63-76; Hon Can Ches Cathl 72-76; Suff Bp Warrington *Liv* from 76. *Martinsfield, Elm Avenue, Great Crosby, Liverpool L23 2SX* 0151-924 7004 or 708 9480 Fax 931 3307

HENSHALL, Nicholas James. b 62. Wadh Coll Ox BA84 MA88. Ripon Coll Cuddesdon 85. **d** 88 **p** 89. C Blyth St Mary *Newc* 88-92; V Scotswood from 92. *St Margaret's Vicarage, 14 Heighley Street, Newcastle upon Tyne NE15 6AR* 0191-274 6322

HENSHALL, Ronald Keith. b 54. Loughb Coll of Educn CertEd76. Chich Th Coll 87. **d** 89 **p** 90. C Ribbleton *Blackb* 89-92; USPG from 92; St Kitts-Nevis from 92. *PO Box 193, Charleston, St Kitts-Nevis* 0171-928 8681 Fax 928 2371

HENSHAW, George William. b 21. St Edm Hall Ox BA48 MA48. Qu Coll Birm 48. **d** 49 **p** 50. R Man St Paul New Cross *Man* 64-70; rtd 86; Perm to Offic *Man* 86-87. *2A Beauchamp Hill, Leamington Spa, Warks CV32 5LS* Leamington Spa (01926) 426173

HENSHAW, Nicholas Newell. b 49. Rhodes Univ BA72. Cuddesdon Coll 73. **d** 75 **p** 76. C Beaconsfield *Ox* 75-78; Chapl Wellington Coll Berks 78-80; C Pimlico St Pet w Westmr Ch Ch *Lon* 80-82; Chapl Sevenoaks Sch Kent from 82; Hon C Sevenoaks St Nic *Roch* from 82. *Orchards, Solefields Road, Sevenoaks, Kent TN13 1PF* Sevenoaks (01732) 456710

HENSON, Ms Carolyn. b 44. Solicitor 75 Bedf Coll Lon BA65 Nottm Univ MTh88. E Midl Min Tr Course 82. **dss** 85 **d** 87 **p** 94. Braunstone *Leic* 85-87; Hon Par Dn 87; Par Dn 88; Adult Educn and Tr Officer *Ely* from 89. *170 Main Street, Witchford, Ely, Cambs CB6 2HT* Ely (01353) 666741

HENSON, John Richard. b 40. Selw Coll Cam BA62 MA66. Ridley Hall Cam 62. **d** 65 **p** 66. C Ollerton *S'well* 65-68; Univs Sec CMS 68-73; Chapl Scargill Ho 73-78; V Shipley St Paul *Bradf* 78-83; TR Shipley St Paul and Frizinghall 83-91; V Ilkeston St Mary *Derby* from 91. *St Mary's Vicarage, Ilkeston, Derbyshire DE7 5JA* Nottingham (0115) 932 4725

HENSON, Dr Richard Clive. b 41. Univ of Wales (Cardiff) BSc63 PhD66. S'wark Ord Course 77. **d** 88 **p** 89. Hon C Lee St Mildred *S'wark* from 88. *122 Manor Park, London SE13 5RH* 0181-852 4137

HENSTRIDGE, Edward John. b 31. FPhM AFBPsS Ex Coll Ox BA55 MA59. Wells Th Coll 55. **d** 57 **p** 58. C Milton *Portsm* 57-62; V Soberton w Newtown 62-69; Lic to Offic *Derby* 69-71; Perm to Offic *Guildf* 72-84; Lic to Offic from 84. *The White House, Thursley Road, Elstead, Godalming, Surrey GU8 6LW* Elstead (01252) 702272

HENTHORNE, Thomas Roger. b 30. E Anglian Minl Tr Course. **d** 79 **p** 80. Hd Master St Mary's Sch St Neots 67-93; Hon C St Neots *Ely* from 79. *Stapley, 45 Berkeley Street, Eynesbury, St Neots, Huntingdon, Cambs PE19 2NE* Huntingdon (01480) 472548

HENTON, John Martin. b 48. AKC72 St Luke's Coll Ex DipEd73. St Aug Coll Cant 73. **d** 74 **p** 75. C Woolwich St Mary w H Trin *S'wark* 74-77; C Cotham St Mary *Bris* 77-78; C Cotham St Sav w St Mary 78-80; R Filton 80-87; Chapl Ex Sch 87-91; Chapl St Marg Sch Ex 87-91; V Ex St Dav *Ex* from 91. *St David's Vicarage, 95 Howell Road, Exeter EX4 4LH* Exeter (01392) 54396

HENWOOD, Martin John. b 58. Glas Univ BD81. Ripon Coll Cuddesdon. **d** 85 **p** 86. C Dartford H Trin *Roch* 85-88; C St Martin-in-the-Fields *Lon* 88-93; V Dartford H Trin *Roch* 93. *The Vicarage, High Street, Dartford DA1 1RX* Dartford (01322) 222782

HENWOOD, Canon Peter Richard. b 32. St Edm Hall Ox BA55 MA69. Cuddesdon Coll 56. **d** 57 **p** 58. C Rugby St Andr *Cov* 57-62; C-in-c Gleadless Valley CD *Sheff* 62-71; V Plaistow St Mary *Roch* from 71; RD Bromley from 79; Hon Can Roch Cathl from 88. *St Mary's Vicarage, 74 London Lane, Bromley BR1 4HE* 0181-460 1827 Fax as telephone

HENWOOD (nee OAKLEY), Mrs Susan Mary. b 55. Salford Univ BSc76. St Jo Coll Nottm LTh86 DPS87. **d** 87 **p** 94. Par Dn Armthorpe *Sheff* 87-91; C Howell Hill *Guildf* from 91. *18 Nonsuch Walk, Sutton, Surrey SM2 0JY* 0181-393 4019

HEPPER, Christopher Michael Alan. b 55. St Jo Coll Nottm 90. **d** 92 **p** 93. C High Harrogate Ch Ch *Ripon* 92-95; Bp's Dom Chapl from 95. *18 Cathedral Close, Ripon, N Yorkshire HG4 1ND* Ripon (01765) 604518 or 602045 Fax 600758

HEPPLE, Gordon. b 32. Edin Th Coll. **d** 63 **p** 68. C Billingham St Cuth *Dur* 63-64; C Ryhope 64; Perm to Offic 66-68; C Wingate Grange 68-69; C Heworth St Mary 69; C Gateshead St Mary

HENRY, P-in-c Low Team 71-72; R Lyons 72-79; V Basford St Aid *S'well* 79-84; V Blackhill *Dur* 84-95. *66B Ringwood Road, Christchurch, Dorset BH23 5RE* Highcliffe (01425) 279068

HEPWORTH, Canon Ernest John Peter. b 42. K Coll Lon BD65 AKC65 Hull Univ MA87. **d** 66 **p** 67. C Headingley *Ripon* 66-69; Asst Chapl St Geo Hosp Lon 69-71; C Gt Grimsby St Mary and St Jas *Linc* 71-72; TV 72-74; V Crosby 74-80; V Barton upon Humber from 80; RD Yarborough 86-92; Hon Can Linc Cathl from 94. *The Vicarage, Beck Hill, Barton-on-Humber, S Humberside DN18 5EY* Barton-on-Humber (01652) 632202

HEPWORTH, Michael David Albert. b 37. Em Coll Cam BA59 MA63 Lon Inst of Educn CertEd60. Ridley Hall Cam 65. **d** 67 **p** 68. C Eastbourne All SS *Chich* 67-69; Asst Chapl Bedf Sch 69-72; Chapl 72-83; Hd Master Birkdale Sch from 83; Perm to Offic *Sheff* from 83; Perm to Offic *Derby* from 84. *Birkdale School, 4 Oakholme Road, Sheffield S10 3DH* Sheffield (0114) 266 8408

HEPWORTH, Michael Edward. b 29. Leeds Univ BA51. NW Ord Course 74. **d** 77 **p** 78. Hon C Timperley *Ches* from 77. *56 Ridgway Road, Timperley, Altrincham, Cheshire WA15 7HD* 0161-980 5104

HERBERT, Alan. b 33. FPhS62 Open Univ BA80. Paton Congr Coll Nottm 54 Coll of Resurr Mirfield 67. **d** 68 **p** 68. C Cockermouth All SS w Ch Ch *Carl* 68-71; V Clifton 71-77; V Westf St Mary 77-87; R Long Marton w Dufton and w Milburn from 87. *The Rectory, Long Marton, Appleby-in-Westmorland, Cumbria CA16 6BN* Kirkby Thore (017683) 61269

HERBERT, Anthony. b 19. Bris Univ. Qu Coll Birm 46. **d** 48 **p** 49. V Dur St Cuth *Dur* 64-78; V Barrow upon Soar *Leic* 78-83; R Barrow upon Soar w Walton le Wolds 83-84; rtd 84; Perm to Offic *B & W* from 85. *12 Valley View, Clutton, Bristol BS18 4SN* Temple Cloud (01761) 452494

HERBERT, Canon Charles Vernon. b 18. St Jo Coll Dur BA42 DipTh43 MA45. **d** 44 **p** 45. V Portsdown *Portsm* 61-79; RD Havant 72-77; V Hambledon 79-84; rtd 84; Perm to Offic *Portsm* from 84. *6 Farmhouse Way, Horndean, Waterlooville, Hants PO8 9LF* Horndean (01705) 571129

HERBERT, Christopher John. b 37. Dur Univ BA60 DipTh62. Cranmer Hall Dur 60. **d** 62 **p** 63. C Huyton Quarry *Liv* 62-65; C Rainford 65-68; V Impington *Ely* 68-78; RD N Stowe 76-78; V Gt Shelford from 78; RD Shelford 80-85. *The Vicarage, 12 Church Street, Great Shelford, Cambridge CB2 5EL* Cambridge (01223) 843274

HERBERT, Ven Christopher William (Chris). b 44. Univ of Wales (Lamp) BA65. Wells Th Coll 65. **d** 67 **p** 68. C Tupsley *Heref* 67-71; Dioc RE Adv 71-76; Dioc Dir RE 76-81; Preb Heref Cathl 76-81; V Bourne *Guildf* 81-90; Hon Can Guildf Cathl from 85; Adn Dorking from 90. *Littlecroft, Heathside Road, Woking, Surrey GU22 7EZ* Woking (01483) 772713 Fax 757353

HERBERT, Clair Geoffrey Thomas (Geoff). b 36. Tyndale Hall Bris 61. **d** 64 **p** 65. C Nottm St Sav *S'well* 64-67; C Harwell *Ox* 67-70; C Chilton All SS 67-70; V Bucklebury w Marlston 70-80; Chapl Brighton Coll Jun Sch 80-83; Hon C Upton (or Overchurch) *Ches* 85-86; C 86-88; V Collier Row St Jas and Havering-atte-Bower *Chelmsf* from 88. *St James's Vicarage, 24 Lower Bedfords Road, Romford RM1 4DG* Romford (01708) 749891

HERBERT, Clare. b 54. CQSW86 St Hild Coll Dur BA76 New Coll Edin MTh78. Linc Th Coll 79. **d** 87 **p** 94. Hon Par Dn Bris St Mary Redcliffe w Temple etc *Bris* 87-92; Dioc Past Care Adv *Lon* 92-95; Hon C Clapham TM *S'wark* from 94; Dir Willesden Min Tr Progr *Lon* from 95. *5 Landor Road, London SW9 9RX* 0171-326 4687

HERBERT, Canon David Alexander Sellars. b 39. Bris Univ BA60. St Steph Ho Ox 65. **d** 67 **p** 68. C St Leonards Ch Ch *Chich* 67-80; C St Leonards Ch Ch and St Mary 81; V Bickley *Roch* from 81; Hon Can Roch Cathl from 92. *The Vicarage, Bickley Park Road, Bromley BR1 2BE* 0181-467 3809

HERBERT, David Roy. b 51. K Coll Lon BD73 AKC73. **d** 74 **p** 75. C Sheff St Aid w St Luke *Sheff* 74-76; C Sheff Manor 76-78; TV Gleadless Valley 78-83; TV Ellesmere Port *Ches* 83-93; V Tarvin from 93. *St Andrew's Vicarage, Tarvin, Chester CH3 8EB* Tarvin (01829) 740354

HERBERT, Geoffrey William. b 38. Ox Univ MA62 Birm Univ PhD72. Qu Coll Birm DipTh82. **d** 82 **p** 83. C Hall Green Ascension *Birm* 82-85; R Sheldon from 85. *The Rectory, 165 Church Road, Birmingham B26 3TT* 0121-743 2033

HERBERT, Graham Paul. b 54. Birm Univ BA75. Wycliffe Hall Ox BA80 MA. **d** 81 **p** 82. C Crowborough *Chich* 81-85; Chapl Monkton Combe Sch Bath from 85. *Croft House, The Croft, Monkton Combe, Bath BA2 7HG* Bath (01225) 721127

HERBERT, John William. b 42. Sarum & Wells Th Coll 74. **d** 77 **p** 78. C Dudley St Thos and St Luke *Worc* 77-79; TV Malvern Link w Cowleigh 79-83; R Alfrick, Lulsley, Suckley, Leigh and Bransford 83-92; RD Martley and Worc W from 91; V Hallow from 92. *The Vicarage, Hallow, Worcester WR2 6PF* Worcester (01905) 640348

HERBERT, Jonathan Patrick. b 62. Bris Univ BA86. Linc Th Coll 86. **d** 88 **p** 89. C Kirkby *Liv* 88-91; TV Blakenall Heath *Lich* from 91. *St Chad's Vicarage, Edison Road, Beechdale, Walsall WS2 7HT* Walsall (01922) 612081

HERBERT, Kenneth Cyril. b 20. Univ of Wales (Abth) BA41. St D Coll Lamp LTh43. **d** 43 **p** 44. V Llangorwen *St D* 56-89; RD Llanbadarn Fawr 80-86; rtd 89. *68 Ger-y-llan, Penrhyncoch, Aberystwyth, Dyfed SY23 3DW* Aberystwyth (01970) 828207

HERBERT, Malcolm Francis. b 53. K Coll Lon BD74 AKC74 St Mary's Cheltenham CertEd75. Trin Coll Bris 76. **d** 77 **p** 78. C Wotton-under-Edge w Ozleworth *Glouc* 77; C Wotton-under-Edge w Ozleworth and N Nibley 77-79; C Milton *B&W* 79-80; C Worle 80-85; V Woking Ch Ch *Guildf* from 86; RD Woking from 94. *Christ Church Vicarage, 10 Russetts Close, Woking, Surrey GU21 4BH* Woking (01483) 762100

HERBERT, Michael. b 35. Nottm Univ MA57. St D Coll Lamp 59. **d** 61 **p** 62. C Paston *Pet* 61-65; C Northn All SS w St Kath 65-67; R Sutton w Upton 67-72; Asst Youth Chapl 67-72; Ind Chapl 72-84; P-in-c Pitsford 79-84; Ind Chapl *Worc* from 84; TV Redditch, The Ridge from 84; Chapl NE Worcs Coll from 86. *The Parsonage, Church Road, Webheath, Redditch, Worcs B97 5PD* Redditch (01527) 402404

HERBERT, Ronald (Ron). b 53. Worc Coll Ox BA75 MA80 Lon Univ BD78 W Kentucky Univ MA79. Oak Hill Th Coll 75. **d** 79 **p** 80. C Welling *Roch* 79-89; V Falconwood 89-90; V Becontree St Mary *Chelmsf* from 90. *The Vicarage, 191 Valence Wood Road, Dagenham, Essex RM8 3AH* 0181-592 2822

HERBERT, Mrs Rosemary. b 44. Westf Coll Lon BSc65. Qu Coll Birm 81. **dss** 85 **d** 87. Malvern Link w Cowleigh *Worc* 85-87; Hon Par Dn from 87. *4 Cedar Avenue, Malvern, Worcs WR14 2SG* Malvern (01684) 572497

HERBERT, Timothy David (Tim). b 57. Man Univ BA78 MPhil88. Ridley Hall Cam 79. **d** 81 **p** 82. C Macclesfield St Mich *Ches* 81-85; V Wharton 85-93; Asst Continuing Minl Educn Officer 90-93; P-in-c Thanington *Cant* from 93; Dir of Ords from 93. *The Vicarage, 70 Thanington Road, Canterbury, Kent CT1 3XE* Canterbury (01227) 464516 or 785894

✠**HERD, Rt Rev William Brian.** b 31. Clifton Th Coll 55. **d** 58 **p** 59 **c** 76. C Wolv St Luke *Lich* 58-61; Uganda 61-77; Adn Karamoja 70-75; Bp Karamoja 76-77; Deputation Sec (Ireland) BCMS 77-89; C Trin St Mich, Harrow *Lon* 89-93; V Gresley *Derby* from 93. *The Vicarage, 120 Church Street, Church Gresley, Swadlincote, Derbyshire DE11 9NR* Burton-on-Trent (01283) 223983

HEREFORD, Archdeacon of. See MOSS, Ven Leonard Godfrey

HEREFORD, Bishop of. See OLIVER, Rt Rev John Keith

HEREFORD, Dean of. See WILLIS, Very Rev Robert Andrew

HEREWARD, Dr John Owen. b 53. FRCSE82 Lon Univ MB, BS77. Ridley Hall Cam 89. **d** 91 **p** 92. C W Ealing St Jo w St Jas *Lon* 91-95; P-in-c Hanwell St Mellitus w St Mark from 95. *St Mellitus Vicarage, Church Road, London W7 3BA* 0181-567 6535

HERITAGE, Barry. b 35. Clifton Th Coll 59. **d** 61 **p** 62. C Wolv St Jude *Lich* 61-65; C Chaddesden St Mary *Derby* 65-67; V Kidsgrove *Lich* 67-76; NE Area Sec CPAS 76-89; Perm to Offic *Newc* 76-89; Lic to Offic *York* 76-89; V Elloughton and Brough w Brantingham 89-93; C York St Paul from 93. *123 Hamilton Drive, York YO2 4NX* York (01904) 785135

HERITAGE, Canon Thomas Charles. b 08. St Edm Hall Ox BA29 MA44 AMusTCL31. **d** 34 **p** 38. Can Res Portsm Cathl *Portsm* 64-76; rtd 76. *117 The Close, Salisbury SP1 2EY* Salisbury (01722) 329803

HERKLOTS, Canon John Radu. b 31. Trin Hall Cam BA53 MA61. Westcott Ho Cam 54. **d** 55 **p** 56. C Attercliffe w Carbrook *Sheff* 55-60; C Stoke Damerel *Ex* 60-65; V Devonport St Bart 65-72; V Denmead *Portsm* from 72; RD Havant 82-87; Hon Can Portsm Cathl from 86. *The Vicarage, Denmead, Waterlooville, Hants PO7 6NN* Waterlooville (01705) 255490

HERNIMAN, Ven Ronald George. b 23. Birkb Coll Lon BA51. Oak Hill Th Coll. **d** 54 **p** 55. R Washfield *Ex* 61-72; P-in-c Withleigh 61-72; P-in-c Calverleigh 61-72; R Stoodleigh 62-72; P-in-c Oakford 63-72; P-in-c Morebath 63-72; P-in-c Rackenford 65-72; P-in-c Templeton w Loxbeare 66-72; Adn Barnstaple 70-88; R Shirwell w Loxhore 72-82; rtd 89. *Castleland House, Oakford, Tiverton, Devon EX16 9JA*

HERON, Alexander Francis. b 28. Univ of BC BA60. Angl Th Coll (BC) LTh53. **d** 52 **p** 53. C Bush Hill Park St Mark *Lon* 52-53; C Beckenham St Barn *Roch* 54-55; Canada 55-62 and from 77; Chapl RAF 62-77. *102 Porticol Drive, Scarborough, Ontario, Canada, M1G 3R6*

HERON, David George. b 49. AKC72. **d** 73 **p** 74. C Stockton St Chad *Dur* 73-77; C Beamish 77-81; R Willington and Sunnybrow 81-95; V Dipton and Leadgate from 95. *The*

Vicarage, St Ives Road, Leadgate, Consett, Co Durham DH8 7SN Consett (01207) 503918

HERON, George Dobson. b 34. TD. Cranmer Hall Dur 58. **d** 61 **p** 62. V Dunston St Nic *Dur* 68-77; P-in-c Dunston Ch Ch 74-77; V Dunston 77-82; V Gateshead St Helen 82-89; rtd 94. *36 Woodlands Road, Shotley Bridge, Consett, Co Durham DH8 0DE* Consett (01207) 507733

HERON, Nicholas Peter. b 60. Man Univ BA81 Southn Univ BTh86. Sarum & Wells Th Coll. **d** 84 **p** 85. C Brinnington w Portwood *Ches* 84-87; Chapl RAF from 87. *Chaplaincy Services (RAF), HQ, Personnel and Training Command, RAF Innsworth, Gloucester GL3 1EZ* Gloucester (01452) 712612 Ext 5164 Fax 510828

HERON, Raymond (Ray). b 48. Cranmer Hall Dur St Jo Coll Dur CTM94. **d** 94 **p** 95. C Newc H Cross *Newc* from 94. *2A Lanercost Drive, Newcastle upon Tyne NE5 2DE* 0191-274 9574

HERRETT, Graham. b 40. Sarum & Wells Th Coll 75. **d** 77 **p** 78. C Ilkeston St Mary *Derby* 77-80; TV Hucknall Torkard *S'well* 80-84; C Bulwell St Mary 84-87; Chapl HM Pris Nottm 84-87; Chapl HM Pris Aldington 87-88; Chapl HM Pris Cant 87-90; Chapl HM Pris Belmarsh from 91. *The Chaplain's Office, HM Prison Belmarsh, Western Way, London SE28 0EB* 0181-317 2436 Fax 317 2421

HERRICK, Andrew Frederick. b 58. Univ of Wales (Lamp) BA80. Wycliffe Hall Ox 80. **d** 82 **p** 83. C Abth *St D* 82-85; P-in-c Llangeitho and Blaenpennal w Betws Leucu etc 85-86; R 86-88; Youth Chapl 86-88; R Aber-porth w Tre-main and Blaen-porth 88-91; Succ St D Cathl 91-94; Min St D Cathl 91-94; V Betws St Dav w Ammanford from 94. *The Vicarage, College Street, Ammanford, Dyfed SA18 3AB* Ammanford (01269) 592084

HERRICK, David William. b 52. Middx Poly BSc73. St Jo Coll Nottm DipTh80. **d** 82 **p** 83. C Ipswich St Matt *St E* 82-85; C Nor St Pet Mancroft w St Jo Maddermarket *Nor* 85-88; V Bury St Edmunds St Geo *St E* from 88. *The Vicarage, Acacia Avenue, Bury St Edmunds, Suffolk IP32 6HN* Bury St Edmunds (01284) 750321

HERRINGTON, Wilfrid Spencer. b 17. Chich Th Coll 72. **d** 72 **p** 72. C Bedhampton *Portsm* 72-77; P-in-c Holton St Mary w Gt Wenham *St E* 77-86; P-in-c Raydon 77-86; rtd 86; Perm to Offic *Chich* from 86. *1 Roffrey Avenue, Eastbourne, E Sussex BN22 0AE* Eastbourne (01323) 503212

HERRON, Robert Gordon John. b 36. MIPM75. Wycliffe Hall Ox 65. **d** 77 **p** 78. C Ditton St Mich *Liv* 77-80; C W Kirby St Bridget *Ches* 80-82; R Gorton Our Lady and St Thos *Man* from 82. *Our Lady and St Thomas Rectory, 195B Mount Road, Gorton, Manchester M18 7GG* 0161-223 0421

HERTFORD, Suffragan Bishop of. See SMITH, Rt Rev Robin Jonathan Norman

HERVE, John Anthony. b 49. TD94. Open Univ BA81 Birm Univ DPS85 PGCE95. Lich Th Coll 70. **d** 73 **p** 74. C Middlesb All SS *York* 73-76; CF 76-81; P-in-c Handsworth St Andr *Birm* 81-86; Hon C Cowley St Jo *Ox* 86-90; Tutor St Steph Ho Ox 86-90; V Sparkbrook St Agatha w Balsall Heath St Barn *Birm* from 90. *The Clergy House, 288A Ladypool Road, Birmingham B12 8JU* 0121-449 2790

HERVEY, Mary Diana (Di). b 41. St Hugh's Coll Ox BA63. St And Dioc Tr Course 83. **d** 92 **p** 94. Par Dn Cupar *St And* from 92; Asst Chapl St Andr Univ from 94. *Lynwood, Back Lebanon, Cupar, Fife KY15 4JW* Cupar (01334) 52760

HERYET, Dudley. b 18. AKC42. **d** 42 **p** 43. V Blean *Cant* 62-73; V Kennington 73-83; rtd 83; Perm to Offic *Cant* from 83. *4 Chantry Hall, Dane John, Canterbury, Kent CT1 2QS* Canterbury (01227) 451511

HESELTINE, Mrs Barbara Joan. b 42. Keele Univ BA65. S'wark Ord Course 85. **d** 88 **p** 94. NSM Addington S'wark from 88. *Little Manor, Manor Park, The Avenue, Whyteleafe, Surrey CR3 0AQ* 0181-668 0476

HESELWOOD, Eric Harold. b 43. Oak Hill Th Coll 84. **d** 86 **p** 87. C Farnborough *Roch* 86-88; V Biggin Hill from 88. *St Mark's Vicarage, 10 Church Road, Biggin Hill, Westerham, Kent TN16 3LB* Biggin Hill (01959) 572312

HESELWOOD, Mrs Hilda. b 39. CA Tr Coll 61. **dss** 85 **d** 87 **p** 94. Bromley Common St Luke *Roch* 85-87; Par Dn 87-94; Par Dn 94; C from 94. *St Mark's Vicarage, 10 Church Road, Biggin Hill, Westerham, Kent TN16 3LB* Biggin Hill (01959) 572312

HESKETH, Canon Douglas Campbell. b 09. St Pet Hall Ox BA37 MA44. Wycliffe Hall Ox 37. **d** 38 **p** 39. V Mossley Hill St Barn *Liv* 53-75; Hon Can Liv Cathl 73-75; rtd 75; Hon C Southport All SS *Liv* 75-88. *52 Skipton Avenue, Southport, Merseyside PR9 8JP* Southport (01704) 29584

HESKETH, John Arthur. b 14. Lich Th Coll 54. **d** 56 **p** 57. V Millbrook *Ches* 60-75; C Birkenhead St Jas w St Bede 75-84; rtd 84. *25 Danefield Road, Greasby, South Wirral L49 3PB* 0151-606 0570

HESKETH, Dr Philip John. b 64. K Coll Lon BD86 AKC86 PhD94 Richmond Fellowship Coll DipHRel90. Ripon Coll

Cuddesdon DipMin94. **d** 94 **p** 95. C Bearsted w Thurnham *Cant* from 94. *19 Fulbert Drive, Bearsted, Maidstone, Kent ME14 4PU* Maidstone (01622) 631192

HESKETH, Robin Adams Lempriere. b 18. St Cath Soc Ox BA43 MA47. St Steph Ho Ox 43. **d** 45 **p** 46. V S Petherwin w Trewen *Truro* 61-72; V Lewannick 62-71; P-in-c Penponds 72-73; V 73-83; rtd 84. *Camelview, Marshall Road, Nanstallon, Bodmin, Cornwall PL30 5LD* Lanivet (01208) 831892

HESKETH, Ronald David. b 47. Bede Coll Dur BA68. St Mich Coll Llan 69 Ridley Hall Cam. **d** 71 **p** 72. C Southport H Trin *Liv* 71-74; Asst Chapl Miss to Seamen 74-75; Chapl RAF from 75. *Chaplaincy Services (RAF), HQ, Personnel and Training Command, RAF Innsworth, Gloucester GL3 1EZ* Gloucester (01452) 712612 Ext 5164   Fax 510828

HESKINS, Mrs Georgiana Mary. b 48. K Coll Lon BD81 AKC81 K Coll Lon MTh93. Westcott Ho Cam 81. **dss** 83 **d** 87 **p** 94. Cobbold Road St Sav w St Mary *Lon* 83-85; St Botolph Aldgate w H Trin Minories 85-87; Par Dn 87; Perm to Offic *S'wark* 88-93; Par Dn Kidbrooke St Jas 93-95; Tutor S'wark Ord Course 93-94; Hon C Charlton St Luke w H Trin *S'wark* from 95. *The Rectory, 185 Charlton Church Lane, London SE7 7AA* 0181-858 0791

HESKINS, Jeffrey George. b 55. AKC78 Heythrop Coll Lon MA94. Chich Th Coll 80. **d** 81 **p** 82. C Primrose Hill St Mary w Avenue Road St Paul *Lon* 81-85; Enfield Deanery Youth Officer 85-88; C Enfield Chase St Mary 85-88; TV Kidbrooke St Jas *S'wark* 88-95; R Charlton St Luke w H Trin from 95. *The Rectory, 185 Charlton Church Lane, London SE7 7AA* 0181-858 0791

HESLOP, David Anthony. b 45. BSc DipEd DipTh MTh. St Jo Coll Nottm 81. **d** 83 **p** 84. C Willenhall H Trin *Lich* 83-86; V Gresley *Derby* 86-92; V Marston on Dove w Scropton 92-95; Chapl Derby Univ from 95. *The Vicarage, Hazelwood, Duffield, Belper, Derbyshire DE56 4AL* Duffield (01332) 840161

HESLOP, Harold William. b 40. Leeds Univ BA62 Open Univ BA72. Ox NSM Course. **d** 78 **p** 79. NSM Stoke Mandeville *Ox* 78-91; NSM Wendover from 82; NSM Ellesborough, The Kimbles and Stoke Mandeville from 91. *7 Chiltern Road, Wendover, Aylesbury, Bucks HP22 6DB* Wendover (01296) 624812

HESLOP, James Alan. b 37. Codrington Coll Barbados 61. **d** 64 **p** 65. Br Guiana 64-66; Guyana 66-68; Bahamas 68-72; C Haxby w Wigginton *York* 72-74; TV 74-76; V York St Olave w St Giles 76-87; V Northn All SS w St Kath *Pet* 87-88; R Felpham w Middleton *Chich* 88-92; TR Howden TM *York* 92-94; Warden Coll of St Barn Lingfield from 94. *The Lodge, College of St Barnabas, Blackberry Lane, Lingfield, Surrey RH7 6NJ* Lingfield (01342) 870366 or 870260

HESLOP, Michael Andrew. b 47. Trin Coll Bris 73. **d** 76 **p** 77. C Burmantofts St Steph and St Agnes *Ripon* 76-80; V Thorpe Edge *Bradf* 80-87; TV Penrith w Newton Reigny and Plumpton Wall *Carl* 87-91; V Silloth from 91. *The Vicarage, Wigton Road, Silloth, Carlisle CA5 4NJ* Silloth (016973) 31413

HESSELGREAVES, Canon Arthur. b 16. Univ Coll Dur BA38 DipTh40 MA41. Qu Coll Birm 39. **d** 40 **p** 41. R Cumberworth *Wakef* 65-80; RD Kirkburton 71-80; Hon Can Wakef Cathl 74-81; rtd 81; Perm to Offic *Wakef* from 81. *1 Park Avenue, Thornes, Wakefield, W Yorkshire WF2 8DS* Wakefield (01924) 381104

HESTER, Canon John Frear. b 27. St Edm Hall Ox BA48 MA52. Cuddesdon Coll 51. **d** 52 **p** 53. C Southall St Geo *Lon* 52-55; C Clerkenwell H Redeemer w St Phil 55-58; Sec Actors' Ch Union 58-63; Sen Chapl 70-75; Chapl Soc of Sisters of Bethany Lloyd Square 59-62; Dep Min Can St Paul's Cathl 62-75; R Soho St Anne w St Thos and St Pet 63-75; P-in-c Covent Garden St Paul 69-75; P-in-c Brighton St Jo *Chich* 75-80; V Brighton St Pet 75-78; Can and Preb Chich Cathl 76-85; Can Res and Prec Chich Cathl from 85; RD Brighton 76-85; RD Kemp Town 76-83; RD Preston 76-83; P-in-c Brighton Chpl Royal 77-78; V Brighton St Pet w Chpl Royal 78-80; V Brighton St Pet w Chpl Royal and St Jo 80-85; P-in-c Brighton St Nic 84-85; Chapl to The Queen from 84. *The Residentiary, Canon Lane, Chichester, W Sussex PO19 1PX* Chichester (01243) 782961

HETHERINGTON, Andrew. b 50. Sheff Univ BSc71. Wycliffe Hall Ox 71. **d** 74 **p** 75. C Leic H Trin w St Jo *Leic* 74-78; C Leic H Apostles 78-82; V Bootle St Mary w St Paul *Liv* 82-93; TR The Lydiards *Bris* from 93. *The Rectory, Old Shaw Lane, Shaw, Swindon SN5 9PH* Swindon (01793) 770568

HETHERINGTON, Dermot Hugh. b 42. SRN63 RMN65 RM72 Worc Coll of Educn BSc. **d** 78 **p** 79. Hon C Raveningham *Nor* 78-90; Perm to Offic from 90. *1 Whiteways, Wheatacre, Beccles, Suffolk NR34 0AU* Aldeby (0150277) 467

HETHERINGTON, Mrs Glynis Catherine. b 48. E Midl Min Tr Course CTPS93. **d** 93 **p** 94. NSM E and W Leake, Stanford-

on-Soar, Rempstone etc *S'well* from 93. *20 Potters Lane, East Leake, Loughborough, Leics LE12 6NQ* East Leake (01509) 853344

HETHERINGTON, John Carl. b 52. Linc Th Coll. **d** 84 **p** 85. C Crosby *Linc* 84-88; TV Cleethorpes 88-93; Chapl RAF from 93. *Chaplaincy Services (RAF), HQ, Personnel and Training Command, RAF Innsworth, Gloucester GL3 1EZ* Gloucester (01452) 712612 Ext 5164   Fax 510828

HETLING, William Maurice (Bill). b 37. AKC61. **d** 62 **p** 63. C Eltham St Barn *S'wark* 62-66; C Horley 66-71; Jamaica 71-75; C-in-c Farnham Royal S CD *Ox* 75-78; TV W Slough 78-80; TR 80-88; TV 88-91; TV Parkstone St Pet w Branksea and St Osmund *Sarum* from 91. *St Osmund's Vicarage, 83 Bournemouth Road, Poole, Dorset BH14 0ER* Poole (01202) 730940

HEWAT, Patrick Duxbury. b 13. CCC Cam BA35 MA55. K Coll Lon 48. **d** 49 **p** 50. V Grantchester *Ely* 55-70; Perm to Offic from 70; rtd 78. *19 High Street, Bassingbourn, Royston, Herts SG8 5NE* Royston (01763) 247611

HEWER, Sidney Eric. b 24. Nor Ord Course. **d** 78 **p** 79. NSM Grimston w Congham *Nor* 78-91; NSM Grimston, Congham and Roydon 91-92; Perm to Offic from 92. *42 Vong Lane, Pott Row, Grimston, King's Lynn, Norfolk PE32 1BW* Hillington (01485) 600635

HEWES, John. b 29. Nottm Univ BA50. Chich Th Coll 79. **d** 81 **p** 82. C Buckland in Dover w Buckland Valley *Cant* 81-84; P-in-c Elmsted w Hastingleigh 84-89; P-in-c Crundale w Godmersham 84-89; RD W Bridge 88-89; R Lydd 89-95; RD S Lympne 89-95; rtd 95; Perm to Offic *Cant* from 95. *Brambledown, Tamley Lane, Hastingleigh, Ashford, Kent TN25 5HW* Ashford (01233) 750214

HEWETSON, Ven Christopher. b 37. Trin Coll Ox BA60 MA64. Chich Th Coll 67. **d** 69 **p** 70. C Leckhampton St Pet *Glouc* 69-71; C Wokingham All SS *Ox* 71-73; V Didcot St Pet 73-82; R Ascot Heath 82-90; RD Bracknell 86-90; P-in-c Headington Quarry 90-94; Hon Can Ch from 92; RD Cowley 94; Adn Ches from 94. *25 Bartholomew Way, Chester CH4 7RJ* Chester (01244) 675417

HEWETSON, David Geoffrey. b 31. S'wark Ord Course 71. **d** 74 **p** 75. NSM Brighton St Mich *Chich* from 74. *Flat 1, 166 Dyke Road, Brighton BN1 5PU* Brighton (01273) 564483

HEWETSON, Robin Jervis. b 39. AKC63. **d** 64 **p** 65. C Thorpe *Nor* 64-67; C E Dereham w Hoe 67-69; TV Mattishall w Mattishall Burgh 69-72; R Ingham w Sutton 72-78; R Catfield 75-78; R Taverham w Ringland 78-89; P-in-c Marsham 89-92; P-in-c Burgh 89-92; Dioc Ecum Officer from 89; Exec Officer Norfolk Ecum Coun from 89; R Marsham w Burgh-next-Aylsham from 92. *The Rectory, Marsham, Norwich NR10 5PP* Aylsham (01263) 733249   Fax 733799

HEWETSON, Valerie Patricia. b 44. St Mary's Coll Dur BSc66 MSc70 Leeds Univ MA75. Linc Th Coll 89. **d** 91 **p** 94. C Kingston upon Hull St Nic *York* 91-94; R Barmby Moor w Allerthorpe, Fangfoss and Yapham from 94. *The Vicarage, Barmby Moor, York YO4 5HF* Pocklington (01759) 305971

HEWETT, Andrew David. b 63. Univ of Wales (Lamp) BA. Chich Th Coll 84. **d** 86 **p** 87. C Caldicot *Mon* 86-90; Chapl RAF from 90. *Chaplaincy Services (RAF), HQ, Personnel and Training Command, RAF Innsworth, Gloucester GL3 1EZ* Gloucester (01452) 712612 Ext 5164   Fax 510828

HEWETT, Maurice Gordon. b 28. Lon Univ BA53. Oak Hill Th Coll 49. **d** 54 **p** 55. R Chevening *Roch* 60-95; rtd 95. *Rosings, 12 The Thicketts, Sevenoaks, Kent TN13 2SZ* Sevenoaks (01732) 464734

HEWETT, Roger Leroy. b 45. St Mich Coll Llan DPT95. **d** 95. C Whitchurch *Llan* from 95. *10 Keynsham Road, Whitchurch, Cardiff CF4 1TS* Cardiff (01222) 611388

HEWISON, Alan Stuart. b 30. SS Mark & Jo Coll Plymouth BEd82. K Coll Lon. **d** 57 **p** 58. Chapl RN 63-79; Perm to Offic *Ex* from 79; rtd 95. *8 Hazelwood Crescent, Plymouth PL9 8BL*

HEWITT, Charles David. b 38. Or Coll Ox BA60 MA63. Clifton Th Coll 63. **d** 66 **p** 67. C Southport SS Simon and Jude *Liv* 66-70; C Bethnal Green St Jas Less w Victoria Park *Lon* 70-76; Hon C Old Ford St Paul w St Steph 76-82; Ldr Bridge Ho Chr Cen Shaftesbury Soc 76-90; Hon C Old Ford St Paul w St Steph and St Mark 82-90; V Homerton St Luke from 90. *St Luke's Vicarage, 23 Cassland Road, London E9 7AL* 0181-985 2263

HEWITT, Colin Edward. b 52. Man Poly BA80 Em Coll Cam BA82 MA86. Westcott Ho Cam 80. **d** 83 **p** 84. C Radcliffe St Thos and St Jo *Man* 83-84; C Langley and Parkfield 84-86; R Byfield w Boddington *Pet* 86-89; R Byfield w Boddington and Aston le Walls 89-91; Chapl RAF from 91. *Chaplaincy Services (RAF), HQ, Personnel and Training Command, RAF Innsworth, Gloucester GL3 1EZ* Gloucester (01452) 712612 Ext 5164   Fax 510828

HEWITT, David John. b 40. Wells Th Coll 65. **d** 68 **p** 69. C Southsea H Spirit *Portsm* 68-70; C Bramshott 70-72; C Much Wenlock w Bourton *Heref* 72-74; CF 74-78 and 83-87; P-in-c

Hadzor w Oddingley and Tibberton w Bredicot *Worc* 78-83; P-in-c Chew Magna w Dundry *B & W* 87-88; V 88-93. *Address temp unknown*

HEWITT, David Warner. b 33. Selw Coll Cam BA56 MA60. Wells Th Coll 57. **d** 59 **p** 60. C Longbridge *Birm* 59-61; C Sheldon 61-64; V Smethwick Old Ch 64-70; V Smethwick 70-78; P-in-c Littlehampton St Jas *Chich* 78-85; P-in-c Wick 78-85; V Littlehampton St Mary 78-85; TR Littlehampton and Wick 86-89; Perm to Offic *Eur* from 95. *Kleious 21A, 54 633 Thessaloniki, Greece*

HEWITT, Francis John Adam. b 42. St Chad's Coll Dur BA64 DipTh66. **d** 66 **p** 67. C Dewsbury Moor *Wakef* 66-69; C Huddersfield St Jo 69-73; V King Cross 73-81; V Lastingham *York* 81; P-in-c Appleton-le-Moors 81; V Lastingham w Appleton-le-Moors 81-84; P-in-c Rosedale 83-84; V Lastingham w Appleton-le-Moors and Rosedale 84-86; RD Helmsley 85-94; V Lastingham w Appleton-le-Moors, Rosedale etc 86-94; V Pickering from 94; RD Pickering from 94. *The Vicarage, Whitby Road, Pickering, N Yorkshire YO18 7HD* Pickering (01751) 472983

HEWITT, Garth Bruce. b 46. St Jo Coll Dur BA68. Lon Coll of Div LTh70. **d** 70 **p** 71. C Maidstone St Luke *Cant* 70-73; Staff Evang CPAS 73-79; Hon C W Ealing St Jo w St Jas *Lon* 73-81; Dir Amos Trust from 88; Lic to Offic *Guildf* from 88. *10 Manor Way, Guildford GU2 5RN* Godalming (01483) 576717

HEWITT, Geoffrey Williams. b 48. Leeds Univ BA69. Wells Th Coll 70. **d** 72 **p** 73. C Heywood St Luke *Man* 72-74; Ind Chapl 74-77; P-in-c Hulme St Geo 74-77; V Mamhilad and Llanfihangel Pontymoile *Mon* 77-80; Ind Chapl 77-80; V Arthog w Fairbourne *Ban* 80-89; R Llangelynnin w Rhoslefain 87-89; TV Ban 89-94; Dioc Dir of Soc Resp from 89; P-in-c Pentir from 94. *Pentir Vicarage, Pentir, Bangor, Gwynedd LL57 4YB* Bangor (01248) 362016

HEWITT, Canon George Henry Gordon. b 12. BNC Ox BA34 DipTh35 MA38. Wycliffe Hall Ox 34. **d** 36 **p** 37. Can Res Chelmsf Cathl *Chelmsf* 64-78; Chapl to The Queen 69-82; rtd 78. *8 Rainsford Avenue, Chelmsford CM1 2PJ* Chelmsford (01245) 259836

HEWITT, Harold William. b 12. Fitzw Ho Cam BA35 MA39. Wycliffe Hall Ox 36. **d** 38 **p** 39. V Gt Bowden w Welham *Leic* 66-77; rtd 77; Perm to Offic *Ches* from 77. *20 Rectory Close, Bowling Green Court, Nantwich, Cheshire CW5 5SW* Nantwich (01270) 626660

HEWITT, Canon Henry Thomas Maxwell. b 20. TCD BA44 MA63. **d** 44 **p** 45. V Paddington Em Harrow Road *Lon* 61-72; I Abbeyleix w Old Church, Ballyroan etc *C & O* 72-90; Chan Leighlin Cathl 83-89; Chan Ossory Cathl 83-89; rtd 90. *St James's Rectory, Stradbally, Co Waterford, Irish Republic* Stradbally (51) 93129

HEWITT, James Herbert. b 17. Ch Coll Cam BA39 MA42. Ridley Hall Cam 40. **d** 41 **p** 42. V New Beckenham St Paul *Roch* 65-71; R Mereworth w W Peckham 71-75; V Bradf St Aug Undercliffe *Bradf* 75-82; rtd 82; Perm to Offic *Glas* from 82. *73 Georgetown Road, Dumfries DG1 4DG* Dumfries (01387) 63973

HEWITT, John Kaffrell. b 34. St Aid Birkenhead 60. **d** 63 **p** 64. C Woking Ch Ch *Guildf* 63-66; P-in-c Sudbury w Ballingdon and Brundon *St E* 66-70; V 70-80; V Portsdown *Portsm* from 80. *Portsdown Vicarage, Portsdown Hill Road, Cosham, Portsmouth PO6 1BE* Cosham (01705) 375360

HEWITT, Kenneth Victor. b 30. Lon Univ BSc49 CertEd51 MSc53. Cuddesdon Coll 60. **d** 62 **p** 63. C Maidstone St Martin *Cant* 62-64; C Croydon St Mich 64-67; P-in-c S Kensington St Aug *Lon* 67-73; V from 73; Asst Chapl Lon Univ 67-73. *St Augustine's Vicarage, 118 Queen's Gate, London SW7 5LW* 0171-581 1877 or 584 1960

HEWITT, Michael David. b 49. K Coll Lon BD79 AKC79 CertEd. Qu Coll Birm 79. **d** 80 **p** 81. C Bexleyheath Ch Ch *Roch* 80-84; C Buckland in Dover w Buckland Valley *Cant* 84-89; R Ridgewell w Ashen, Birdbrook and Sturmer *Chelmsf* from 89. *The Rectory, Church Lane, Ridgewell, Halstead, Essex CO9 4SA* Ridgewell (0144085) 355

HEWITT, Paul Stephen Patrick. b 59. BA DipTh. **d** 86 **p** 87. C Ballymacash *Conn* 86-89; Bp's C Ballymena w Ballyclug 89-91; I Glencraig *D & D* from 91. *Glencraig Vicarage, 3 Seahill Road, Craigavad, Holywood, Co Down BT18 0DA* Belfast (01232) 422225

HEWITT, Robert Samuel. b 51. QUB BSc73. CITC 77. **d** 80 **p** 81. C Dundela *D & D* 80-84; I Donaghadee 84-92. *3 The Trees, New Road, Donaghadee, Co Down BT21 0EJ* Donaghadee (01247) 882594

HEWITT, Stephen Wilkes. b 49. Fitzw Coll Cam BA71. St Jo Coll Nottm DipTh90. **d** 90 **p** 91. C Eaton *Nor* 90-93; V Warw St Paul *Cov* from 93. *St Paul's Vicarage, 33 Stratford Road, Warwick CV34 6AS* Warwick (01926) 492934

HEWITT, Thomas Peter James. b 24. St Andr Univ MA50. St Steph Ho Ox 50. **d** 52 **p** 53. V Godshill *Portsm* 65-93; rtd 93.

Blue Nile, 14 Fairfield Way, Totland Bay, Isle of Wight PO39 0EF

HEWITT, Timothy James. b 67. St D Coll Lamp BD. Ripon Coll Cuddesdon. **d** 91 **p** 92. C Milford Haven *St D* 91-94; C Llanelli from 94. *4 Hedley Terrace, Llanelli, Dyfed SA15 3RE* Llanelli (01554) 750355

HEWITT, William Patrick (Paddy). b 48. Nottm Univ BTh79. Linc Th Coll 75. **d** 79 **p** 80. C Workington St Jo *Carl* 79-83; V Flookburgh 83-87; V Barrow St Matt 87-90; V Lowick and Kyloe w Ancroft *Newc* from 90; R Ford and Etal from 90; RD Norham from 91. *The Vicarage, 1 Main Street, Berwick-upon-Tweed TD15 2UD* Berwick-upon-Tweed (01289) 88229

HEWLETT, David Bryan. b 49. Bris Univ BEd72. Qu Coll Birm 77. **d** 79 **p** 80. C Ludlow *Heref* 79-81; TV 81-84; V Marden w Amberley and Wisteston 84-92; Lect Glouc Sch for Min 84-92; Field Officer for Lay Min *Heref* 84-91; Continuing Minl Educn Adv 86-92; Dir Post-Ord Tr 91-92; Perm to Offic *Sarum* 92-94; Hd Master St Fran Sch Pewsey 92-94; Co-ord Chapl Frenchay Healthcare Trust from 94. *19 Whiteway Close, St Annes Park, Bristol BS4 4DQ* Bristol (0117) 972 3340. or 970 1212

HEWLETT, Dr David Jonathon Peter. b 57. Dur Univ BA79 PhD83. Ridley Hall Cam 82. **d** 83 **p** 84. C New Barnet St Jas *St Alb* 83-86; Lect CITC 86-90; P-in-c Feock *Truro* from 91; Jt Dir SW Minl Tr Course from 91; Adv Local Ord Min from 91. *The Vicarage, Feock, Truro, Cornwall TR3 6SD* Truro (01872) 862044 Fax Bodmin (01208) 850946

HEWLETT, Michael Edward. b 16. Mert Coll Ox BA39 MA46. Qu Coll Birm 46. **d** 48 **p** 49. C Woolfardisworthy w Kennerleigh *Ex* 69-72; TV Cheriton Fitzpaine, Woolfardisworthy etc 72-76; TV N Creedy 76-86; rtd 86; Perm to Offic *Ex* 86-87; Perm to Offic *St Alb* from 87. *Jasmine Cottage, 3 The Green, Sarratt, Rickmansworth, Herts WD3 6AY* Rickmansworth (01923) 263803

HEWSON, Thomas Robert (Tom). b 45. Man Univ BA66. S'wark Ord Course 85. **d** 89 **p** 90. C Chinnor w Emmington and Sydenham etc *Ox* 89-92; TV Burnham w Dropmore, Hitcham and Taplow from 92. *Hitcham Vicarage, 1 The Precinct, Burnham, Slough SL1 7HU* Burnham (01628) 602881

HEYES, Andrew Robin. b 61. Man Univ BA93. St Steph Ho Ox 93. **d** 95. C Tonge Moor *Man* from 95. *182 Tonge Moor Road, Bolton BL2 2HN* Bolton (01204) 365247

HEYGATE, Jack Lincoln. b 11. CCC Cam BA33 MA36. Cuddesdon Coll 35. **d** 36 **p** 37. R Warbleton *Chich* 65-69; rtd 76. *Windrush, Leafield, Witney, Oxon OX8 5NP* Asthall Leigh (0199387) 659

HEYGATE, Dr Stephen Beaumont. b 48. Loughb Univ BSc71 CQSW73 PhD89. St Jo Coll Nottm LTh88. **d** 88 **p** 89. C Aylestone St Andr w St Jas *Leic* 88-90; V Cosby from 90. *Cosby Vicarage, Main Street, Cosby, Leicester LE9 1UU* Leicester (0116) 286 2313

HEYHOE, Jonathan Peter. b 53. Man Univ BA75. Trin Coll Bris 77. **d** 80 **p** 81. C Woking St Pet *Guildf* 80-83; C Heatherlands St Jo *Sarum* 83-91; Chr Renewal Cen Newry 91-95; Perm to Offic *D & D* from 91. *112 Shore Road, Rostrevor, Newry, Co Down BT34 3AB*

HEYWOOD, David Stephen. b 55. Selw Coll Cam BA76 MA80 SS Hild & Bede Coll Dur PhD89. St Jo Coll Dur 80. **d** 86 **p** 87. C Cheltenham St Luke and St Jo *Glouc* 86-90; TV Sanderstead All SS *S'wark* from 90. *35 Audley Drive, Warlingham, Surrey CR6 9AH* 0181-657 5505

HEYWOOD, Geoffrey Thomas. b 26. St Mich Coll Llan 60. **d** 62 **p** 63. V Caerhun w Llangelynnin *Ban* 67-74; Asst Chapl HM Pris Liv 74-75; Chapl HM Pris Ex 75-77; Chapl HM Pris Wakef 77-79; Chapl HM Young Offender Inst Eastwood Park 79-90; Chapl HM Pris Leyhill 79-90; rtd 90; Perm to Offic *Glouc* from 94. *5 Meadow Road, Leyhill, Wotton-under-Edge, Glos GL12 8HW*

HEYWOOD, John. b 06. Man Egerton Hall 35. **d** 35 **p** 36. V Dunham Massey St Marg *Ches* 53-75; rtd 76; Perm to Offic *Ches* from 76. *Flat 6, Hillcar, St Margaret's Road, Altrincham, Cheshire WA14 2BE* 0161-928 2054

HEYWOOD, Michael Herbert. b 41. Liv Univ BSc63. Clifton Th Coll 63. **d** 65 **p** 66. C Low Elswick *Newc* 65-68; C St Helens St Mark *Liv* 68-75; Lic to Offic *Dur* 75-85; Leprosy Miss Area Org NE & Cumbria 75-85; S Lon, Surrey and Berks from 85; Lic to Offic *S'wark* from 85. *3 Valerie Court, 33 Worcester Road, Sutton, Surrey SM2 6PU* 0181-643 4896

HEYWOOD, Canon Peter. b 29. AKC54. **d** 55 **p** 56. V Sleekburn *Newc* 63-71; V Wallsend St Luke 71-89; V Belford 89-94; Hon Can Newc Cathl 90-94; rtd 94. *3 Hillcrest Gardens, Jesmond, Newcastle upon Tyne NE2 3QR* 0191-284 9161

HEYWOOD, Peter. b 46. Cranmer Hall Dur 72. **d** 75 **p** 76. C Blackley St Andr *Man* 75-78; C Denton Ch Ch 78-80; V Constable Lee from 80. *St Paul's Vicarage, Hollin Lane, Rawtenstall, Rossendale, Lancs BB4 8HT* Rossendale (01706) 228634

HEYWOOD-WADDINGTON, Roger. b 23. Bps' Coll Cheshunt 58. **d** 58 **p** 59. V Neen Savage w Kinlet *Heref* 61-89; rtd 89. *Brook House, St Michaels, Tenbury Wells, Worcs WR15 8TG* Tenbury Wells (01584) 811116

HEZEL, Adrian. b 43. Chelsea Coll Lon BSc64 PhD67. N Ord Course 78. **d** 81 **p** 82. NSM Mirfield *Wakef* 81-89; C 89-90; V Shelley and Shepley from 90. *The Vicarage, 6 Stonecroft Gardens, Shepley, Huddersfield HD8 8EX* Huddersfield (01484) 602640

HIBBERD, Carol Anne. b 59. Kent Univ BA80. S'wark Ord Course 89. **d** 92 **p** 94. NSM Gospel Lane St Mich *Birm* 92-94; C from 94. *12 Elmcroft Road, Birmingham B26 1PJ* 0121-784 8677

HIBBERD, John. b 60. Wadh Coll Ox MA82. Trin Coll Bris BA89. **d** 89 **p** 90. C Northolt St Mary *Lon* 89-92; C-in-c Southall Em CD 92-94; Min of Miss Through Faith Miss *Ely* from 95. *63 Wertheim Way, Stukeley Meadows, Huntingdon, Cambs PE18 6UH* Huntingdon (01480) 433718

HIBBERD, John Charles. b 38. Chich Th Coll 63. **d** 66 **p** 67. C W Drayton *Lon* 66-70; C Noel Park St Mark 70-72; C Ealing St Steph Castle Hill 72-75; V Gunnersbury St Jas 75-84; V Whitton SS Phil and Jas 84-86; Finance and Trust Sec Lon Dioc Fund from 87; Perm to Offic 87-93. *London Diocesan House, 30 Causton Street, London SW1P 4AU* 0171-821 9351 Fax 821 0424

HIBBERT, Miss Anne Mary Elizabeth. b 59. Southn Univ BA81. Trin Coll Bris 81. **dss** 83 **d** 87 **p** 94. Muswell Hill St Jas w St Matt *Lon* 83-86; Leic H Trin w St Jo *Leic* 86-87; Par Dn 87-90; Evang Co-ord and Adv CPAS from 90; Perm to Offic *Cov* from 90. *7 Suffolk Street, Leamington Spa, Warks CV32 5TG* Leamington Spa (01926) 888210

HIBBERT, Charles Dennis. b 24. Linc Th Coll 69. **d** 70 **p** 71. C Radcliffe-on-Trent *S'well* 70-73; P-in-c Ladybrook 73-77; V 77-79; V Boughton 79-85; V Ollerton 79-85; R Nuthall 85-89; rtd 89. *27 Nottingham Road, Kimberley, Nottingham NG16 2NB* Nottingham (0115) 938 6302

HIBBERT, James Raymond. b 10. St Pet Coll Ox BA32 MA36. Wycliffe Hall Ox 32. **d** 34 **p** 35. V Fulwood Ch Ch *Blackb* 45-75; rtd 75; Lic to Offic *Blackb* from 75. *39 Harrison Road, Fulwood, Preston PR2 4QJ* Preston (01772) 719113

HIBBERT, Peter John. b 43. Hull Univ BA71 Lon Univ CertEd72 MA79. Sarum & Wells Th Coll 85. **d** 88 **p** 89. C Newsome and Armitage Bridge *Wakef* 88-92; P-in-c Newton Flowery Field *Ches* from 92. *St Stephen's Vicarage, 154 Bennett Street, Hyde, Cheshire SK14 4SS* 0161-368 3333

HIBBERT, Preb Roy Trevor. b 30. AKC54. **d** 55 **p** 56. C W Bromwich St Fran *Lich* 55-58; C Cannock 58-60; C-in-c Sneyd Green CD 60-62; V Sneyd Green 62-67; V Harlescott 67-81; R Newport w Longford and Chetwynd from 81; RD Edgmond from 82; P-in-c Forton from 84; Preb Lich Cathl from 87. *The Rectory, High Street, Newport, Shropshire TF10 7BH* Newport (01952) 810089

HIBBINS, Neil Lance. b 60. St Anne's Coll Ox BA82 MA87. Univ of Wales (Cardiff) DPS85. St Mich Coll Llan 83. **d** 85 **p** 86. C Griffithstown *Mon* 85-87; C Pontypool 87-88; TV Pontypool 88-92; Asst Chapl Manor Hosp Walsall from 92. *The Chaplain's Office, Manor Hospital, Moat Road, Walsall WS2 9PS* Walsall (01922) 721172

HIBBS, Canon Lawrence Winston. b 14. Kelham Th Coll 31. **d** 37 **p** 38. V Chandler's Ford *Win* 68-75; R Jersey Grouville 75-83; rtd 83; Perm to Offic *Win* from 83. *13 Rectory Close, St Clement, Jersey, Channel Islands JE2 6RF* Jersey (01534) 851394

HICHENS, Anthony. b 29. AKC59. **d** 60 **p** 61. Guyana 67-75; P-in-c Stratton Audley w Godington *Ox* 76-83; P-in-c Finmere w Mixbury 76-78; P-in-c Fringford w Hethe and Newton Purcell 76-83; R Stratton Audley and Godington, Fringford etc 83-95; rtd 95. *86 Horton Drive, Middleton Cheney, Banbury, Oxon OX17 2LL* Banbury (01295) 712826

HICKES, Roy Edward. b 31. Lon Univ DipTh60. St Aid Birkenhead 56. **d** 59 **p** 60. V Smallbridge *Man* 69-79; R Winford *B & W* 79-81; R Winford w Felton Common Hill 81-88; RD Chew Magna 85-88; Chapl Costa Blanca *Eur* 88-92; rtd 92; Perm to Offic *Bris* from 92. *Winford Manor Priory, Winford, Bristol BS18 8DW* Lulsgate (01275) 472262

HICKEY, Canon Francis Joseph. b 20. AKC49. **d** 50 **p** 51. V Tilbury Docks *Chelmsf* 58-87; RD Orsett and Grays 70-83; Hon Can Chelmsf Cathl 79-87; rtd 87. *202 Parkside House, Clarendon Gardens, Malvern Road, Southsea, Hants PO5 2LD* Portsmouth (01705) 750301

HICKFORD, Michael Francis. b 53. Edin Th Coll 84. **d** 86 **p** 87. Chapl St Jo Cathl Oban *Arg* 86-89; R Alexandria *Glas* 89-95; P-in-c Dingwall *Mor* from 95; P-in-c Strathpeffer from 95. *The Parsonage, 4 Castle Street, Dingwall, Ross-shire IV15 9HU* Dingwall (01349) 62204

HICKIN, Canon Leonard Charles. b 05. Magd Coll Cam BA26 MA30. Ridley Hall Cam 26. **d** 28 **p** 29. R Chesham Bois *Ox*

64-73; rtd 72. *Manormead Nursing Home, Tilford Road, Hindhead, Surrey GU26 6RA* Hindhead (01428) 604780

HICKIN, Maurice Whitehouse. b 09. St Cath Coll Cam BA32 MA38 Bonn Univ DPhil33. Ely Th Coll 33. **d** 34 **p** 35. R Runwell *Chelmsf* 61-75; rtd 75. *Calle De Murillo 6, Benidoleig, Alicante 03759, Spain* Alicante (6) 558-3266

HICKLEY, Peter Michael. b 28. Ely Th Coll 56. **d** 59 **p** 60. C Is of Dogs Ch Ch and St Jo w St Luke *Lon* 68-70; R S Hackney St Jo w Ch Ch 70-77; R Euston w Barnham and Fakenham *St E* 77-80; TR Fenny Stratford and Water Eaton *Ox* 80-88; R Benington w Walkern *St Alb* 88-91; rtd 91; Perm to Offic *Birm* from 91. *372 Heath Road South, Birmingham B31 2BH* 0121-476 1705

HICKLING, Canon Colin John Anderson. b 31. K Coll Cam BA53 MA57. Chich Th Coll 56. **d** 57 **p** 58. C Pallion *Dur* 57-61; Asst Tutor Chich Th Coll 61-65; Asst Lect K Coll Lon 65-68; Lect 68-84; Hon C Munster Square St Mary Magd *Lon* 68-69; Dep Min Can St Paul's Cathl 69-78; Hon C E Dulwich St Jo *S'wark* 70-84; Dep P in O 71-74; P-in-O 74-84; Can Th Leic Cathl *Leic* from 81; Tutor Qu Coll Birm 84-85; Lect Linc Th Coll 85-86; V Arksey *Sheff* from 86; Hon Lect Bibl Studies Sheff Univ from 86. *The Vicarage, Station Road, Arksey, Doncaster, S Yorkshire DN5 0SP* Doncaster (01302) 874445

HICKLING, John. b 34. Launde Abbey. **d** 69 **p** 70. C Melton Mowbray w Thorpe Arnold *Leic* 69-71; TV 71-75; R Waltham on the Wolds w Stonesby and Saltby 75-84; R Aylestone St Andr w St Jas 84-93; R Husbands Bosworth w Mowsley and Knaptoft etc from 93. *The Rectory, Honeypot Lane, Husbands Bosworth, Lutterworth, Leics LE17 6LY* Market Harborough (01858) 880351

HICKMAN, George May. b 11. AKC33. **d** 35 **p** 36. R Withycombe *B & W* 68-84; rtd 84; Perm to Offic *B & W* 85-91. *1 The Causeway, Withycombe, Minehead, Somerset TA24 6PZ* Watchet (01984) 640227

HICKMAN, John William. b 38. Barrister-at-Law (Middle Temple) 69 Qu Coll Cam LLM81. Oak Hill NSM Course 92. **d** 95. NSM Sevenoaks St Nic *Roch* from 95. *26 The Rise, Sevenoaks, Kent TN13 1RQ* Sevenoaks (01732) 454546

HICKS, Miss Barbara. b 42. Cranmer Hall Dur BA71. **dss** 85 **d** 87 **p** 94. Norton Woodseats St Paul *Sheff* 85-87; Par Dn Sheff St Jo 87-94; C from 94. *15 Benson Road, Sheffield S2 5EU* Sheffield (0114) 275 9997

HICKS, Francis Fuller (Frank). b 28. Sarum & Wells Th Coll 71. **d** 74 **p** 75. C Broadstone *Sarum* 74-78; P-in-c Kington Magna and Buckhorn Weston 78-79; TV Gillingham 79-86; P-in-c Portland St Jo 86-89; V 89-93; rtd 93. *Windyridge, 21 Castle Road, Sherborne, Dorset DT9 3RW* Sherborne (01935) 814837

HICKS, Herbert. b 10. Bede Coll Dur BA32 MA47. Ridley Hall Cam 34. **d** 36 **p** 37. V Bramhope *Ripon* 55-74; rtd 74. *2 Larkfield Drive, Harrogate, N Yorkshire HG2 0BX* Harrogate (01423) 508675

HICKS, Mrs Joan Rosemary. b 60. Homerton Coll Cam BEd83. Westcott Ho Cam 87. **d** 90 **p** 94. Par Dn Wendover *Ox* 90-94; C 94-95; C Earley St Pet from 95. *33 Clevedon Drive, Reading RG6 2XF* Reading (01734) 871396

HICKS, Richard Barry. b 32. Dur Univ BA55. Sarum Th Coll 59. **d** 61 **p** 62. C Wallsend St Luke *Newc* 61-64; C Tynemouth Ch Ch 64-69; V Tynemouth St Jo 69-75; V Prudhoe 75-82; TV Swanborough *Sarum* 82-86; R Hilperton w Whaddon and Staverton etc from 86. *The Rectory, Hilperton, Trowbridge, Wilts BA14 7RL* Trowbridge (01225) 752804

HICKS, Stuart Knox. b 34. Univ of W Ontario BA56 Huron Coll LTh59 Ox Univ DipEd67. **d** 58 **p** 60. Canada 58-65; C Allerton *Liv* 65-66; Hon C Rye Park St Cuth *St Alb* 68-72; Lic to Offic *B & W* 72-87 and from 88; Chapl Magdalen Chpl Bath 80-86; Chapl Partis Coll Bath 88-91. *Folly Orchard, The Folly, Saltford, Bristol BS18 3JW* Saltford (01225) 873391

HICKS, Mrs Valerie Joy. b 47. SRN69 HVCert70. Cant Sch of Min 82. **dss** 85 **d** 87 **p** 94. Roch 85-87; Hon Par Dn 87-89; Par Dn Thatcham *Ox* 89-93; TD Aylesbury w Bierton and Hulcott 93-94; TV from 94. *St Peter's House, 18 Bronte Close, Aylesbury, Bucks HP19 3LF* Aylesbury (01296) 432677

HICKS, William Trevor. b 47. Hull Univ BA68 Fitzw Coll Cam BA70 MA74. Westcott Ho Cam 68. **d** 70 **p** 71. C Cottingham *York* 70-73; C Elland *Wakef* 73-76; V Walsden 76-81; V Knottingley 81-92; R Castleford All SS from 92; RD Pontefract from 94. *The Rectory, 15 Barnes Road, Castleford, W Yorkshire WF10 5AA* Castleford (01977) 552401

HIDER, David Arthur. b 46. Lon Univ BSc67. Sarum & Wells Th Coll 86. **d** 89 **p** 90. NSM Southbourne w Thorney Chich 89-91; C Goring-by-Sea 91-94; P-in-c Peacehaven from 94; P-in-c Telscombe w Piddinghoe and Southease from 94. *Peacehaven Vicarage, 41 Bramber Avenue, Peacehaven, E Sussex BN10 8HR* Newhaven (01273) 583149

HIGDON, Lewis George. b 36. Dur Univ BA58. Cranmer Hall Dur DipTh60. **d** 60 **p** 61. C Leeds St Pet *Ripon* 60-65; C Shipley St Paul *Bradf* 65-66; V Esholt 67-75; V Kirkstall *Ripon* 75-79;

HIGGINBOTTOM

V Stanwix *Carl* 79-87; V Ambleside w Brathay from 87. *The Vicarage, Millans Park, Ambleside, Cumbria LA22 9AD* Ambleside (015394) 33205

HIGGINBOTTOM, Richard. b 48. Lon Univ BD74. Oak Hill Th Coll DipTh72. **d** 74 **p** 75. C Kenilworth St Jo *Cov* 74-77; C Finham 77-79; P-in-c Attleborough 79-81; V 81-84; Asst Chapl HM Pris Brixton 84-85; Chapl HM Pris Roch 85-92; Chapl HM Pris Camp Hill from 92. *HM Prison, Camp Hill, Newport, Isle of Wight PO30 5PB* Isle of Wight (01983) 527661   Fax 520505

HIGGINBOTTOM, Richard William. b 51. Man Univ BA73 MA75. Edin Th Coll 83. **d** 85 **p** 86. C Knighton St Mary Magd *Leic* 85-87; C Northleach w Hampnett and Farmington *Glouc* 87-89; V Hayfield *Derby* 89-93; Consultant NW England and Scotland CPAS from 93. *60 Huntsfield, Clayton-le-Woods, Chorley, Lancs PR6 7TT* Preston (01772) 315825

HIGGINS, Dr Bernard. b 42. MRPharmS68 Leic Poly BPharm63 PhD66. St Jo Coll Nottm 89. **d** 91 **p** 92. C Stockport St Geo *Ches* 91-94; C Stockport South West 94-95; P-in-c Dunham Massey St Marg and St Mark from 95. *St Margaret's Vicarage, Dunham Road, Altrincham, Cheshire WA14 4AQ* 0161-928 1609

HIGGINS, Bernard George. b 27. Wycliffe Hall Ox 68. **d** 70 **p** 72. C Surbiton St Matt *S'wark* 70-72; C Battersea St Mary 72-76; C Warblington and Emsworth *Portsm* 76-81; C Milton 81-91; rtd 91. *49 Queens Crescent, Stubbington, Fareham, Hants PO14 2QG* Fareham (01329) 667905

HIGGINS, Frank Roylance. b 34. Open Univ BA74 MEd83. Bps' Coll Cheshunt 59. **d** 62 **p** 63. V Smethwick St Mich *Birm* 67-70; V Garretts Green 70-75; Lic to Offic *Worc* 76-84; Perm to Offic *Birm* 81-87; Hon C Feckenham w Bradley *Worc* 84-87; R Ripple, Earls Croome w Hill Croome and Strensham 87-95; RD Upton 92-95; rtd 95; P-in-c Church Lench w Rous Lench and Abbots Morton *Worc* from 95. *The Rectory, Church Lench, Evesham, Worcs WR11 4UB* Evesham (01386) 870345

HIGGINS, Geoffrey Minta. b 27. New Coll Ox BA52 MA56. Cuddesdon Coll 52. **d** 54 **p** 55. C Pet St Mary *Pet* 54-56; CF 56-77; Hong Kong from 77. *12-C Far East Consortium Building, Main Road, Yuen Long, New Territories, Hong Kong* Hong Kong (852) 479-9374

HIGGINS, Canon Godfrey. b 39. St Chad's Coll Dur BA61 DipTh62 DipEd63. **d** 63 **p** 64. C Brighouse *Wakef* 63-66; C Huddersfield St Jo 66-68; R High Hoyland w Clayton W 68-75; V Marsden 75-84; V Pontefract St Giles from 84; Hon Can Wakef Cathl from 93. *The Vicarage, The Mount, Pontefract, W Yorkshire WF8 1NE* Pontefract (01977) 706803

HIGGINS, John. b 44. Trin Coll Bris 71. **d** 73 **p** 74. C Clapham St Jas *S'wark* 73-74; C Ruskin Park St Sav and St Matt 74-77; C Hamworthy *Sarum* 77-80; V Bordesley St Andr *Birm* 80-83; V Bishop Sutton and Stanton Drew and Stowey *B & W* from 83. *The Vicarage, Sutton Hill Road, Bishop Sutton, Bristol BS18 4UR* Chew Magna (01275) 333385

HIGGINS, John Leslie. b 43. BA CQSW Birm Univ MEd89. Lich Th Coll 64. **d** 66 **p** 67. C Sale St Anne *Ches* 66-69; C Bredbury St Mark 69-72; V Wharton 72-74; Hon C Annan *Glas* 75-79; Hon C Lockerbie 75-79; V Coseley Ch Ch *Lich* 79-89; R Arthuret *Carl* from 89. *Arthuret Rectory, Arthuret Drive, Longtown, Carlisle CA6 5SG* Longtown (01228) 791338

HIGGINS, Canon John Norman. b 14. Em Coll Cam BA36 MA40. Wells Th Coll 39. **d** 40 **p** 41. R Sutton St Nic *S'wark* 67-77; Hon Can S'wark Cathl 76-82; R Limpsfield and Titsey 77-82; rtd 82; Perm to Offic *B & W* from 84. *Robin House, 28 College Road, Wells, Somerset BA5 2TE* Wells (01749) 676416

HIGGINS, Kenneth. b 56. TCD BTh93. CA Tr Coll DipEvang83 CITC 90. **d** 93 **p** 94. C Cregagh *D & D* from 93. *St Finnian's Curatage, 54 Rochester Avenue, Belfast BT6 9JW* Belfast (01232) 791296

HIGGINS, Very Rev Michael John. b 35. Birm Univ LLB57 G&C Coll Cam LLB59 PhD62. Ridley Hall Cam 63. **d** 65 **p** 65. C Ormskirk *Liv* 65-67; Selection Sec ACCM 67-74; Hon C St Marylebone St Mark w St Luke *Lon* 69-74; P-in-c Woodlands *B & W* 74-80; V Frome St Jo 74-80; St Preston St Jo *Blackb* 80-91; Dean Ely from 91. *The Deanery, The College, Ely, Cambs CB7 4DN* Ely (01353) 662432

HIGGINS, Richard Ellis. b 63. Univ of Wales BA84. St Mich Coll Llan DipTh88 DPS89. **d** 89 **p** 90. C Bargoed and Deri w Brithdir *Llan* 89-92; Zimbabwe 92-94; V Penmaen and Crumlin *Mon* from 94. *The Vicarage, Central Avenue, Oakdale, Blackwood, Gwent NP2 0JS* Blackwood (01495) 223043

HIGGINS, Rupert Anthony. b 59. Man Univ BA80. Wycliffe Hall Ox 82. **d** 85 **p** 86. C Plymouth St Andr w St Paul and St

Geo *Ex* 85-90; C-in-c St Paul 88-90; C Clifton Ch Ch w Em *Bris* from 90. *62 Clifton Park Road, Bristol BS8 3HN* Bristol (0117) 973 9640

HIGGINS, Timothy John. b 45. Bris Univ BEd70 Lanc Univ MA74 St Jo Coll Dur DipTh79. **d** 79 **p** 80. C Northn All SS w St Kath *Pet* 79-82; V Whitton St Aug *Lon* 82-90; AD Hampton 86-90; TR Aylesbury w Bierton and Hulcott *Ox* from 90; RD Aylesbury from 94. *The Vicarage, Parson's Fee, Aylesbury, Bucks HP20 2QZ* Aylesbury (01296) 24276

HIGGINSON, Arthur Rothwell. b 14. Edin Th Coll 48. **d** 51 **p** 52. V Northn Ch Ch *Pet* 64-74; V Whitewell *Blackb* 74-79; P-in-c Hurst Green and Mitton *Bradf* 76-79; rtd 79; Lic to Offic *Blackb* from 80. *24 Moorlands, Garstang Road, Preston PR1 1NN* Preston (01772) 51660

HIGGINSON, Gerald Scott. b 29. Keele Univ BA54 Birm Univ PhD57. NW Ord Course 73. **d** 76 **p** 77. NSM York St Mary Bishophill Junior w All SS *York* 76-84; P-in-c 84-86; P-in-c York H Trin w St Jo Micklegate and St Martin 84-86; R Micklegate H Trin and Bishophill Junior St Mary from 86. *Holy Trinity Rectory, Micklegate, York YO1 1LE* York (01904) 623798

HIGGINSON, Richard Edwin. b 15. St Jo Coll Dur BA39 MA42 Lon Univ BD51. Tyndale Hall Bris 35. **d** 39 **p** 40. V S Croydon Em *Cant* 69-78; P-in-c Weeton *Blackb* 78-80; rtd 80; Lic to Offic *Blackb* from 81. *30 Pennine Way, Great Eccleston, Preston PR3 0YS* Great Eccleston (01995) 70634

HIGGS, Allan Herbert Morris. b 22. St Jo Coll Dur BA48 DipTh50. **d** 50 **p** 51. V Fenham St Jas and St Basil *Newc* 61-75; Adult Educn Adv *Linc* 75-80; V Stamfordham w Matfen *Newc* 80-88; rtd 88; Perm to Offic *Bradf* from 88. *3 Southfield Lane, Addingham, Ilkley, W Yorkshire LS29 0NX* Addingham (01943) 830167

HIGGS, Andrew Richard Bowen (Andy). b 53. Man Univ BSc76. St Jo Coll Nottm 81. **d** 85 **p** 86. C Droylsden St Mary *Man* 85-88; C Harlow New Town w Lt Parndon *Chelmsf* 88-94; C Harlow Town Centre w Lt Parndon 94-95; TV from 95. *4A The Drive, Netteswell, Harlow, Essex CM20 3QD* Harlow (01279) 437717

HIGGS, Michael John. b 53. Sarum & Wells Th Coll 76. **d** 80 **p** 81. C Cant St Martin and St Paul *Cant* 80-84; C Maidstone St Martin 84-88; R Egerton w Pluckley from 88. *St James's Vicarage, Glebeland, Egerton, Ashford, Kent TN27 9DH* Egerton (01233) 706224

HIGGS, Owen Christopher Goodwin. b 63. St Anne's Coll Ox BA84 MA88. St Steph Ho Ox 90. **d** 93 **p** 94. C Teddington St Mark and Hampton Wick St Jo *Lon* from 93. *198 Broom Road, Teddington, Middx TW11 9PQ* 0181-977 2068

HIGHAM, Gerald Norman. b 40. St Aid Birkenhead 64. **d** 68 **p** 69. C Garston *Liv* 68-71; C Blundellsands St Nic 71-73; V Bolton All So w St Jas *Man* 73-78; V Tonge w Alkrington 78-84; P-in-c Edenfield 84-86; P-in-c Stubbins 84-86; V Edenfield and Stubbins from 86. *St Philip's Vicarage, Chatterton Road, Ramsbottom, Bury, Lancs BL0 0PQ* Ramsbottom (01706) 822079

HIGHAM, Canon Jack. b 33. Linc Coll Ox BA56 MA60 Birm Univ DipTh59. Union Th Sem (NY) STM61 Qu Coll Birm 58. **d** 60 **p** 61. C Handsworth *Sheff* 60-64; V Handsworth Woodhouse 64-70; USA 70-78; R Stoke Bruerne w Grafton Regis and Alderton *Pet* 78-83; RD Towcester 82-83; Can Res, Chan and Lib Pet Cathl from 83. *Canonry House, Minster Precincts, Peterborough PE1 1XX* Peterborough (01733) 62125

HIGHAM, John Leonard. b 39. Liv Univ DipSocSc71. Wycliffe Hall Ox 62. **d** 65 **p** 66. C Prescot *Liv* 65-71; V Hollinfare 71-74; Adult and Youth Service Adv Knowsley 74-76; TV Padgate 76-84; V Farnworth 84-89; TR Sutton from 89. *Sutton Rectory, Eaves Lane, St Helens, Merseyside WA9 3UB* Marshalls Cross (01744) 812347

HIGHAM (nee ANNS), Mrs Pauline Mary. b 49. Bris Univ BEd71. E Midl Min Tr Course 87. **d** 90 **p** 94. Par Dn Wirksworth w Alderwasley, Carsington etc *Derby* 90-92; Par Dn Wirksworth 92; Par Dn Lt Berkhamsted and Bayford, Essendon etc *St Alb* 92-94; C from 94. *1 Berkhamsted Lane, Little Berkhamsted, Hertford SG13 8LU* Tuffley (01707) 875940

HIGHTON, William James. b 31. St Deiniol's Hawarden. **d** 83. NSM Thornton Hough *Ches* 82-84; C Cheadle 84-88; V Walton from 88. *St John's Vicarage, Chester Road, Higher Walton, Warrington WA4 6TJ* Warrington (01925) 662939

HIGTON, Anthony Raymond (Tony). b 42. Lon Univ BD65. Oak Hill Th Coll 65. **d** 67 **p** 68. C Newark Ch Ch *S'well* 67-69; C Cheltenham St Mark *Glouc* 70-75; R Hawkwell *Chelmsf* from 75. *The Rectory, Ironwell Lane, Hawkwell, Hockley, Essex SS5 4JY* Southend-on-Sea (01702) 203870   Fax 207753

HILARY, Sister. See HOPKINS, Hilda

HILARY, Sister. *See* JORDINSON, Vera

HILDAGE, James Francis. b 18. Univ of Wales BA44. Coll of Resurr Mirfield 44. **d** 46 **p** 47. V Earl Sterndale and Monyash *Derby* 56-87; Lect Matlock Coll of HE 66-83; rtd 87; Perm to Offic *Ban* from 88. *Llangwyfan Isaf, Ty Croes, Anglesey, Gwynedd LL63 5YP* Rhosneigr (01407) 810756

HILDITCH, Dr Janet. b 59. St Andr Univ MTh81 PhD87. N Ord Course 92. **d** 94. C Kirkholt *Man* from 94. *58 Friars Crescent, Rochdale, Lancs OL11 2SF*

HILDRED, David. b 61. Bath Univ BSc83 CertEd83. Wycliffe Hall Ox 86. **d** 89 **p** 90. C Westcliff St Mich *Chelmsf* 89-92; C Rayleigh from 92. *13 Sir Walter Raleigh Drive, Rayleigh, Essex SS6 9JB* Rayleigh (01268) 785043

HILES, Douglas Arthur. b 18. St Deiniol's Hawarden 78. **d** 80 **p** 81. C Heaton Ch Ch *Man* 80-83; rtd 86; Hon C Harwood *Man* from 90. *413 Hough Fold Way, Bolton BL2 3PY* Bolton (01204) 24548

HILES, John Michael. b 32. Qu Coll Cam BA57 MA61. Sarum Th Coll 57. **d** 59 **p** 60. C Clifton St Jas *Sheff* 59-62; V Bramley St Fran 62-69; Hon C Holmfirth *Wakef* 69-89; Hon C Upper Holme Valley 89-91; Lic to Offic from 91. *Rosehill, Parkhead Lane, Holmfirth, Huddersfield HD7 1LB* Holmfirth (01484) 683045

HILL, Andrew. **d** 87. NSM Dagenham *Chelmsf* from 87. *2 Wells Gardens, Dagenham, Essex RM10 8HD* 0181-517 6537

HILL, Mrs Anne. b 40. **d** 88 **p** 94. Par Dn Bexleyheath St Pet *Roch* 88-90; Sub-Chapl HM Pris Belmarsh from 93; Hon C Lee St Mildred *S'wark* from 93. *The Vicarage, 1A Helder Grove, London SE12 0RB* 0181-857 5205 or 317 2436 Fax 317 2421

HILL, Mrs Bridget Ann. b 54. Open Univ BA82 CertEd75. E Midl Min Tr Course 83. **dss** 86 **d** 87 **p** 94. Gt and Lt Coates w Bradley *Linc* 86-87; NSM 87-88; Par Dn Louth 88-91; TD 91-94; Chapl Louth Co Hosp from 89; TV Louth *Linc* from 94. *Holy Trinity Vicarage, 24 Grosvenor Road, Louth, Lincs LN11 0BB* Louth (01507) 607991

HILL, Dr Charles Bernard. b 50. Sheff Univ BA71 Qu Coll Ox DPhil76. Cant Sch of Min 91. **d** 94. NSM Sandgate St Paul w Folkestone St Geo *Cant* from 94. *18 Audley Road, Folkestone, Kent CT20 3QA* Folkestone (01303) 253270

HILL, Charles Merrick (Charlie). b 52. Strathclyde Univ BA74. Qu Coll Birm DipTh79. **d** 80 **p** 81. C Silksworth *Dur* 80-83; C Stockton St Pet 83-85; TV Southn (City Cen) *Win* 85-87; V Portsea St Geo *Portsm* 87-94; P-in-c Bodenham w Hope-under-Dinmore, Felton etc *Heref* from 94. *The Vicarage, Bodenham, Hereford HR1 3JX* Bodenham (0156884) 370

HILL, Canon Christopher John. b 45. K Coll Lon BD67 AKC67 MTh68. **d** 69 **p** 70. C Tividale *Lich* 69-73; C Codsall 73-74; Abp's Asst Chapl on Foreign Relns *Cant* 74-81; ARCIC from 74; Sec 74-90; Hon Can Cant Cathl *Cant* 82-89; Abp's Sec for Ecum Affairs 82-89; Chapl to The Queen from 87; Can Res and Prec St Paul's Cathl *Lon* from 89; Select Preacher Ox Univ from 90. *3 Amen Court, London EC4M 7BU* 0171-236 4532

HILL, Preb Dr Colin. b 42. Leic Univ BSc64 Open Univ PhD88. Ripon Hall Ox 64. **d** 66 **p** 67. C Leic Martyrs *Leic* 66-69; C Braunstone 69-71; Lect Ecum Inst Thornaby Teesside 71-72; V Worsbrough St Thos and St Jas *Sheff* 72-78; Telford Planning Officer *Lich* from 78; RD Telford from 80; RD Telford Severn Gorge *Heref* from 80; Preb Heref Cathl from 83. *Parkfield, Park Avenue, Madeley, Telford, Shropshire TF7 5AB* Telford (01952) 585731 Fax 290617

HILL, Canon Colin Arnold Clifford. b 29. Bris Univ 52. Ripon Hall Ox 55. **d** 57 **p** 58. R Easthampstead *Ox* 64-73; Chapl RAF Coll Bracknell 68-73; V Croydon *Cant* 73-84; Chapl Abp Jo Whitgift Foundn 73-84; Hon Can Cant Cathl 75-84; V Croydon St Jo *S'wark* 85-94; Hon Can S'wark Cathl 85-94; Chapl to The Queen 90-94; rtd 94. *Silver Birches, 70 Preston Crowmarsh, Wallingford, Oxon OX10 6SL*

HILL, Canon David. b 25. AKC54. **d** 55 **p** 56. V Battersea St Mich *S'wark* 62-89; RD Battersea 69-76; Hon Can S'wark Cathl 74-89; rtd 89. *70 Gloucester Avenue, Maldon, Essex CM9 6LA* Maldon (01621) 855384

HILL, David Rowland. b 34. Lon Univ BSc55. Qu Coll Birm. **d** 59 **p** 60. C Upper Tooting H Trin *S'wark* 59-61; C Cheam 61-63; C Richmond St Mary 63-68; V Sutton St Nicholas *Linc* 68-82; V Pinchbeck from 82. *The Vicarage, Spalding Road, Pinchbeck, Spalding, Lincs PE11 3ND* Spalding (01775) 768710

HILL, Canon Derek Ingram. b 12. FSA74 Trin Coll Ox BA34 MA38 Kent Univ Hon DD83. Wells Th Coll 34. **d** 35 **p** 36. R Cant St Pet and St Alphege w St Marg *Cant* 63-54; P-in-c Cant St Mildred w St Mary de Castro 72-74; R Cant St Pet w St Alphege and St Marg etc 74-76; Can Res Cant Cathl 76-83; rtd 83. *2 St John's House, 40 Northgate, Canterbury, Kent CT1 1BE* Canterbury (01227) 761954

HILL, Derek Stanley. b 28. AKC53. **d** 53 **p** 54. V Bury St Edmunds St Geo *St E* 67-73; P-in-c Ampton w Lt Livermere and Ingham 68-73; V Gazeley w Dalham 73-75; P-in-c Lidgate

w Ousden 73-74; P-in-c Gt Bradley 74-78; V Gazeley w Dalham and Moulton 75-78; V Gt Barton 78-86; V Bury St Edmunds All SS 86-93; rtd 93. *Whinwillow, 38 Maltings Garth, Thurston, Bury St Edmunds, Suffolk IP31 3PP* Pakenham (01359) 30770

HILL, Elizabeth Jayne Louise. *See* DAVENPORT, Ms Elizabeth Jayne Louise

HILL, Eugene Mark. b 48. Univ of Wales (Lamp) BA71. Sarum Th Coll 71. **d** 73 **p** 74. C Sutton St Nic *S'wark* 73-77; Hon C 77-80; Asst Chapl Em Sch Wandsworth 77-87; Chapl from 87; Hon C St Helier *S'wark* 83-84; Hon C Caterham from 84; Dir Chr Studies Course from 85. *The Rectory, 5 Whyteleafe Road, Caterham, Surrey CR3 5EG* Caterham (01883) 342062

HILL, Frederick Ashton. b 13. Ch Coll Cam BA34 MA38. Chich Th Coll 36. **d** 38 **p** 39. R Gt and Lt Ryburgh w Gateley and Testerton *Nor* 69-93; R Stibbard 69-93; rtd 93. *3B Stibbard Road, Fulmodeston, Fakenham, Norfolk NR21 0LZ* Fakenham (01328) 878717

HILL, Geoffrey Dennison. b 31. Tyndale Hall Bris DipTh55. **d** 56 **p** 57. R Arthuret *Carl* 63-71; V Arnside 71-76; P-in-c Torver 76-79; rtd 91. *Holywath, Coniston, Cumbria LA21 8HN*

HILL, George Ernest. b 25. St Jo Coll Nottm. **d** 85 **p** 87. NSM Selston *S'well* from 85. *105 Main Road, Jacksdale, Nottingham NG16 5HR* Leabrooks (01773) 603446

HILL, Mrs Gillian Beryl (Gill). b 53. Open Univ BA86. S Dios Minl Tr Scheme 87. **d** 90 **p** 94. NSM Southsea St Jude *Portsm* from 90. *27 Inglis Road, Southsea, Hants PO5 1PB* Portsmouth (01705) 811233

HILL, Harold Gordon Haynes. b 15. Tyndale Hall Bris 36. **d** 39 **p** 40. R Reymerston *Nor* 48-81; R Whinburgh w Westf 48-81; P-in-c Cranworth w Letton and Southbergh 78-79; rtd 81. *34 Morley Road, Sheringham, Norfolk NR26 8JE* Sheringham (01263) 824965

HILL, Henry Baxter. b 19. St Alb Minl Tr Scheme 76. **d** 79 **p** 80. Hon C Mill End and Heronsgate w W Hyde *St Alb* 79-84; Asst Chapl Amersham Hosp from 79; Perm to Offic from 84. *Stelling, 66 Quickley Lane, Chorleywood, Rickmansworth, Herts WD3 5AF* Chorleywood (01923) 282309

HILL, Ian Maxwell. b 60. Loughb Univ BSc81 MCIT85. E Midl Min Tr Course DipTh95. **d** 95. NSM Thurnby Lodge *Leic* from 95. *4 Sturrock Close, Thurnby, Leics LE7 9QP* Leicester (0116) 243 1069

HILL, James Arthur. b 47. Ulster Univ BEd85. CITC. **d** 72 **p** 73. C Ballymena w Ballyclug *Conn* 72-74; C Arm St Mark w Aghavilly *Arm* 74-78; C Derg w Termonamongan *D & R* 78-79; I Inver w Mountcharles, Killaghtee and Killybegs 79-87. *53 Dufferin Avenue, Bangor, Co Down BT20 3AB* Bangor (01247) 469090

HILL, James Reginald. b 06. Man Univ BA29. S'wark Ord Course 67. **d** 69 **p** 70. C Purley Ch Ch *S'wark* 69-77; Perm to Offic *Chich* 77-82 and from 88; Perm to Offic from 84. *Bethany, Rosemary Avenue, Steyning, W Sussex BN44 3YS* Steyning (01903) 816012

HILL, John. b 56. S'wark Ord Course. **d** 89 **p** 90. NSM Upper Norwood St Jo *S'wark* 89-94; Chapl RN from 94. *Directorate Gen, RN Chapl Services, Room 203, Victory Building, HM Naval Base, Portsmouth PO1 3LS* Portsmouth (01705) 727903 Fax 727112

HILL, John Michael. b 34. FCA. Oak Hill NSM Course 81. **d** 85 **p** 86. NSM Rayleigh *Chelmsf* from 85; Perm to Offic *Lon* 86-94. *8 High Road, Hockley, Essex SS5 4SX* Southend-on-Sea (01702) 203287

HILL, Kenneth. b 27. Wycliffe Coll Toronto LTh. **d** 58 **p** 59. C Walsall St Gabr Fulbrook *Lich* 67-70; P-in-c Hanley St Jude 70-79; P-in-c Chacewater *Truro* 79-92; rtd 92. *Delmore, Sparnon Close, Redruth, Cornwall TR15 2RJ* Redruth (01209) 219318

HILL, Kenneth James. b 43. Leic Univ BA64 Lon Univ BD68. Oak Hill Th Coll 65. **d** 69 **p** 70. C Southall Green St Jo *Lon* 69-72; C Blackheath Park St Mich *S'wark* 72-75; C Bath Abbey w St Jas *B & W* 75-83; P-in-c Bath St Mich w St Paul 75-82; R 82-83; R Huntspill 83-91; Perm to Offic from 91; Omega Order from 91. *The Omega Order, Winford Manor, Winford, Bristol BS18 8DW* Nailsea (01275) 472262

HILL, Laurence Bruce. b 43. AKC67. **d** 69 **p** 70. C Feltham *Lon* 69-72; C-in-c Hampstead St Steph 72-77; V Finchley H Trin from 77. *Holy Trinity Vicarage, 91 Church Lane, London N2 0TH* 0181-883 8720

HILL, Leslie Hugh. b 23. Westcott Ho Cam 73. **d** 73 **p** 74. NSM Holbrook and Lt Eaton *Derby* 73-79; NSM Loscoe 79-85; P-in-c Denby 85-88; P-in-c Horsley Woodhouse 87-88; rtd 88; Perm to Offic *Derby* from 88. *1 Hunter Drive, Kilburn, Derby DE56 0ND* Derby (01332) 881081

HILL, Malcolm Crawford. b 43. Lon Univ DipTh70. Oak Hill Th Coll 68. **d** 71 **p** 72. C Maidstone St Luke *Cant* 71-74; C Longfleet *Sarum* 74-79; V Bexleyheath St Pet *Roch* 79-90; V Lee St Mildred *S'wark* from 90. *The Vicarage, 1A Helder Grove, London SE12 0RB* 0181-857 5205

HILL

HILL, Mrs Marjorie Ann. b 38. MCSP60. St Jo Coll Nottm 92. **d** 94 **p** 95. Par Dn Hull St Martin w Transfiguration *York* 94; C from 94. *87 Parkfield Drive, Hull HU3 6TF* Hull (01482) 566706

HILL, Dr Martyn William. b 43. MInstP68 CPhys85 Man Univ BSc64 Univ of Wales (Ban) PhD70. Westcott Ho Cam CTM92. **d** 92 **p** 93. C Horninglow *Lich* from 92. *St John's House, 41 Field Lane, Horninglow, Burton-on-Trent, Staffs DE13 0NH* Burton-on-Trent (01283) 66491

HILL, Michael. b 32. TD77. AKC55. **d** 56 **p** 57. C Tynemouth Cullercoats St Paul *Newc* 56-59; C Drayton in Hales *Lich* 59-61; V Milton 61-64; V Preston Gubbals 64-73; V Leaton 64-76; CF (TA) 65-67; CF (TAVR) 67-87; V Oswestry St Oswald *Lich* 76-87; P-in-c Trefonen 80-83; V Sunningdale *Ox* from 87. *The Vicarage, Sidbury Close, Sunningdale, Ascot, Berks SL5 0PD* Ascot (01344) 20061

HILL, Ven Michael Arthur. b 49. Ridley Hall Cam 74. **d** 77 **p** 78. C Addiscombe St Mary *Cant* 77-81; C Slough *Ox* 81-83; P-in-c Chesham Bois 83-90; R 90-92; RD Amersham 89-92; Adn Berks from 92. *Foxglove House, Love Lane, Donnington, Newbury, Berks RG13 2JG* Newbury (01635) 552820 Fax 522165

HILL, Michael John (Brother Giles). b 43. OSB. S Dios Minl Tr Scheme 82. **d** 84 **p** 86. Perm to Offic *Win* from 84. *Alton Abbey, Abbey Road, Beech, Alton, Hants GU34 4AP* Alton (01420) 62145

HILL, Norman. b 20. St Chad's Coll Dur LTh48. Linc Th Coll 45. **d** 49 **p** 50. V Mosborough *Sheff* 59-72; P-in-c Codnor and Loscoe *Derby* 73-79; V 79-85; rtd 85. *10 The Hill, Walsingham, Norfolk NR22 6DP* Walsingham (01328) 820859

HILL, Norman William. b 14. Ch Coll Cam BA36 MA40. Linc Th Coll 43. **d** 45 **p** 46. V Rickmansworth *St Alb* 60-74; P-in-c Northill 74-78; P-in-c Moggerhanger 74-78; P-in-c Northill w Moggerhanger 78-79; RD Biggleswade 75-79; rtd 80. *West Sillywrea, Langley-on-Tyne, Hexham, Northd NE47 5NE* Hexham (01434) 684635

HILL, Canon Peter. b 36. AKC60. St Boniface Warminster 60. **d** 61 **p** 62. C Gt Berkhamsted *St Alb* 61-67; R Bedf St Mary 67-69; P-in-c 69-70; V Goldington 69-79; V Biggleswade 79-90; RD Biggleswade 80-85; Hon Can St Alb 85-90; V Holbeach *Linc* from 90; RD Elloe E from 94. *The Vicarage, Holbeach, Spalding, Lincs PE12 7DT* Holbeach (01406) 22185

HILL, Peter. b 50. Man Univ BSc71 Nottm Univ MTh90. Wycliffe Hall Ox 81. **d** 83 **p** 84. C Porchester *S'well* 83-86; V Huthwaite from 86. *The Vicarage, Blackwell Road, Huthwaite, Sutton-in-Ashfield NG17 2QT* Mansfield (01623) 555053

HILL, Ralph Jasper. b 15. Tyndale Hall Bris 38. **d** 41 **p** 42. Asst Master Hove Gr Sch 65-78; rtd 80; Perm to Offic *Chich* from 82. *19 Gorham Way, Telscombe Cliffs, Newhaven, E Sussex BN10 7BA* Peacehaven (01273) 583729

HILL, Raymond John Walter. b 09. AKC34. **d** 34 **p** 35. V Westbury and Turweston *Ox* 54-77; C-in-c Shalstone w Biddlesden 68-77; rtd 77; Perm to Offic *Glouc* from 78. *15 Shepherds Way, Stow on the Wold, Cheltenham, Glos GL54 1EA* Cotswold (01451) 831028

HILL, Raymond William. b 17. S'wark Ord Course. **d** 63 **p** 64. V Oulton Broad *Nor* 69-84; rtd 84; Perm to Offic *Chich* from 85. *Greenways, New Road, Sundridge, Sevenoaks, Kent TN14 6DJ* Westerham (01959) 562698

HILL, Richard Brian. b 47. Dur Univ BA68 DipTh70. Cranmer Hall Dur 68 Westcott Ho Cam 70. **d** 71 **p** 72. C Cockermouth All SS w Ch Ch *Carl* 71-74; C Barrow St Geo w St Luke 74-76; V Walney Is 76-83; Dir of Clergy Tr 83-90; P-in-c Westward, Rosley-w-Woodside and Welton 83-90; V Gosforth All SS *Newc* from 90. *All Saints' Vicarage, 33 Brackenfield Road, Newcastle upon Tyne NE3 4DX* 0191-285 6345

HILL, Preb Richard Hebert. b 11. Linc Th Coll 34. **d** 36 **p** 37. C-in-c Pencombe w Marston Stannett and Lt Cowarne *Heref* 69-72; R Ledbury 72-78; RD Ledbury 72-78; P-in-c Eastnor 73-78; rtd 78; Perm to Offic *Heref* from 79. *4 Old School, Henley Road, Ludlow, Shropshire SY8 1RA* Ludlow (01584) 874332

HILL, Richard Hugh Oldham. b 52. CCC Ox BA74 BA77 MA78. Wycliffe Hall Ox 75. **d** 78 **p** 79. C Harold Wood *Chelmsf* 78-81; C Hampreston *Sarum* 81-86; TV N Ferriby *York* from 86. *The Vicarage, St Barnabas Drive, Swanland, North Ferriby, N Humberside HU14 3RL* Hull (01482) 631271

HILL, Robert Joseph. b 45. Oak Hill Th Coll BA81. **d** 81 **p** 82. C W Derby St Luke *Liv* 81-84; P-in-c Devonport St Mich *Ex* from 84. *St Michael's Vicarage, 41 Albert Road, Plymouth PL2 1AB* Plymouth (01752) 562967

HILL, Robin. b 35. Cranmer Hall Dur 59. **d** 62 **p** 63. C Aspley *S'well* 62-65; V Mansf St Aug 65-71; R Hulland, Atlow and Bradley *Derby* 71-76; Australia 76-86; P-in-c Alkmonton, Cubley, Marston, Montgomery etc *Derby* 86-93; P-in-c Ticknall, Smisby and Stanton by Bridge from 93; P-in-c Barrow-on-Trent w Twyford and Swarkestone from 94. *The Vicarage, 7 Church Lane, Ticknall, Derby DE7 1JU* Melbourne (01332) 862549

HILL, Roger Anthony John. b 45. Liv Univ BA67 Linacre Coll Ox BA69 MA. Ripon Hall Ox 67. **d** 70 **p** 71. C St Helier *S'wark* 70-74; C Dawley Parva *Lich* 74-75; C Cen Telford 76-77; TV 77-81; TR 81-88; TR Newark w Hawton, Cotham and Shelton *S'well* 88-89; TR Newark-upon-Trent from 89; RD Newark from 90. *The Rectory, 6 Bede House Lane, Newark, Notts NG24 1PY* Newark (01636) 704513

HILL, Sidney John. b 16. MBE45. Oak Hill Th Coll 46. **d** 48 **p** 49. V Wembdon *B & W* 63-74; Chapl Chantilly w Rouen and Le Havre *Eur* 74-78; R Gressenhall w Longham and Bittering Parva *Nor* 78-81; rtd 81. *1 Jarvis Close, Stalbridge, Sturminster Newton, Dorset DT10 2PQ* Stalbridge (01963) 362728

HILL, Simon George. b 53. Reading Univ BSc75 MSc78 Lon Univ DipRS82. S'wark Ord Course 80. **d** 83 **p** 84. Hon C Croydon St Aug *Cant* 83-84; Swaziland 84-86; Fiji 86-88; Hon C Croydon St Aug *S'wark* 88-90; Tanzania 90-94; Uganda from 94. *23 Godstone Road, Oxted, Surrey RH8 9JS*

HILL, Simon James. b 64. Sheff Univ BA85 Ex Univ PGCE86. Ripon Coll Cuddesdon BA84 DipMin95. **d** 95. C Manston *Ripon* from 95. *2 Manston Avenue, Leeds LS15 8BT* Leeds (0113) 264 1301

HILL, Canon Thomas Henry. b 19. Univ of Wales BA41 BD45. **d** 66 **p** 67. R Glyncorrwg w Afan Vale and Cymmer Afan *Llan* 71-74; V Pemb St Mary and St Mich *St D* 74-84; Can St D Cathl 80-84; rtd 84. *29 Mortimer Hill, Tring, Herts HP23 5JB* Tring (01442) 826558

HILL, William Henry George. b 21. S'wark Ord Course 66. **d** 69 **p** 70. C Welling *S'wark* 69-73; C Reigate St Luke S Park 73-76; V Lynsted w Kingsdown *Cant* 76-87; R Norton 76-87; rtd 87. *Little Orchard, 15 Bramley Hill, Bridport, Dorset DT6 3DP* Bridport (01308) 423915

HILL, William James. b 13. Ripon Hall Ox 60. **d** 61 **p** 62. V Chinley w Buxworth *Derby* 68-74; R Whitwell 74-77; P-in-c Denby 77-79; rtd 79; Perm to Offic *Derby* from 79. *Greenstile, 15 Harewood Road, Allestree, Derby DE22 2JP* Derby (01332) 556135

HILL-BROWN, Timothy Duncan. b 65. Westmr Coll Ox BA87. Wycliffe Hall Ox DPS92. **d** 93 **p** 94. C Sparkhill w Greet and Sparkbrook *Birm* from 93. *132 Oakwood Road, Birmingham B11 4HD* 0121-777 6093

HILL-TOUT, Mark Laurence. b 50. AKC73. **d** 74 **p** 75. C Brighton Resurr *Chich* 74-77; C New Shoreham 77-79; C Old Shoreham 77-79; Dioc Stewardship Adv Lewes and Hastings 79-84; P-in-c Stonegate 79-83; R Horsted Keynes 84-89; V St Helens *Portsm* from 89; V Sea View from 89. *The Vicarage, Eddington Road, Seaview, Isle of Wight PO34 5EF* Isle of Wight (01983) 875190

HILLARY, Leslie Tyrone James. b 59. Cranmer Hall Dur 84. **d** 87 **p** 88. C Middlesb All SS *York* 87-89; C Stainton-in-Cleveland 89-91; CF from 91. *c/o MOD (Army), Bagshot Park, Bagshot, Surrey GU19 5PL* Bagshot (01276) 471717 Fax 412834

HILLEBRAND, Frank David. b 46. AKC68. St Boniface Warminster 68. **d** 69 **p** 70. C Wood Green St Mich *Lon* 69-72; C Evesham *Worc* 72-75; V Worc H Trin 75-80; P-in-c Kidderminster St Jo 80-81; V 81-90; TR Kidderminster St Jo and H Innocents 90-91; TV High Wycombe *Ox* 91-95; TR from 95. *The Vicarage, 6 Priory Avenue, High Wycombe, Bucks HP13 6SH* High Wycombe (01494) 525602

HILLIAM, Mrs Cheryl. b 49. E Midl Min Tr Course DipTh94. **d** 94 **p** 95. C Linc St Faith and St Martin w St Pet *Linc* from 94. *46 Yarborough Crescent, Lincoln LN1 3LU* Lincoln (01522) 512650

HILLIARD, David. b 57. BTh. **d** 91 **p** 92. C Holywood *D & D* 91-94; C Seagoe from 94. *71 Seagoe Road, Portadown, Craigavon, Co Armagh BT63 5HS* Craigavon (01762) 331015

HILLIARD, Very Rev George Percival St John. b 45. TCD BA67. **d** 69 **p** 70. C Seapatrick *D & D* 69-73; C Carrickfergus *Conn* 73-76; I Fanlobbus Union *C, C & R* 76-85; Prec Cork Cathl from 85; I Cloyne Union from 85; Dean Cloyne from 85. *The Deanery, Dungourney Road, Midleton, Co Cork, Irish Republic* Cork (21) 631449

HILLIARD, John William Richard (Jack). b 19. St Jo Coll Morpeth 54. **d** 55 **p** 56. I Carbury *M & K* 68-72; C W Bridgford *S'well* 72-78; V Mansf St Aug 78-84; P-in-c Everton and Mattersey w Clayworth 84-87; rtd 87. *Flat 4, Spencer Court, Merton Road, Southsea, Hants PO5 2AJ* Portsmouth (01705) 293918

HILLIARD, Robert Godfrey. b 52. Univ of Wales DipTh75. St Mich Coll Llan. **d** 75 **p** 76. C Whitchurch *Llan* 75-80; Chapl RN from 80. *Directorate Gen, RN Chapl Services, Room 203, Victory Building, HM Naval Base, Portsmouth PO1 3LS* Portsmouth (01705) 727903 Fax 727112

HILLIER, Derek John. b 30. Sarum Th Coll 61. **d** 63 **p** 64. C Salisbury St Mark *Sarum* 63-65; C Weymouth H Trin 65-66; R Caundle Bishop w Caundle Marsh and Holwell 66-75; P-in-c

Pulham 70-78; R The Caundles and Holwell 75-81; R The Caundles w Folke and Holwell from 81. *The Rectory, Bishops Caundle, Sherborne, Dorset DT9 5ND*   Bishops Caundle (01963) 23243

HILLMAN, Jesse James. b 22. S'wark Ord Course 83. **d** 86 **p** 87. Communications Sec CMS 86; NSM Kidbrooke St Jas *S'wark* 86; NSM Peterchurch w Vowchurch, Turnastone and Dorstone *Heref* 86-93; rtd 93; Perm to Offic *Heref* from 93. *Wesley Place, Peterchurch, Hereford HR2 0RY*   Peterchurch (01981) 550609

HILLMAN, John Anthony. b 32. St Chad's Coll Dur BA53. St Mich Coll Llan 54. **d** 55 **p** 56. C Llangollen *St As* 56-60; S Africa 60-86; TV Wolstanton *Lich* 86-91; P-in-c E Goscote w Ratcliffe and Rearsby *Leic* 91-93; TV Syston TM from 93. *The Vicarage, 25 Ling Dale, East Goscote, Leicester LE7 3XW* Leicester (0116) 260 5938

HILLS, John Bucknell. b 21. Glouc Sch of Min. **d** 89 **p** 89. NSM Moreton-in-Marsh w Batsford, Todenham etc *Glouc* 89-94; Perm to Offic from 94. *1 Corders Lane, Moreton-in-Marsh, Glos GL56 0BU*   Moreton-in-Marsh (01608) 651507

HILLS, Kenneth Hugh. b 30. Univ of NZ BCom54. Ripon Hall Ox 55. **d** 57 **p** 58. Ind Chapl *Birm* 67-74; Chapl Aston Univ 74-82; rtd 91; Community Member Cluny Hill Coll from 93. *The Park, Forres, Morayshire IV36 0TZ*   Forres (01309) 672288

HILLS, Mervyn Hyde. b 19. Ch Coll Cam BA40 MA44. Westcott Ho Cam 40. **d** 42 **p** 43. V Bourn *Ely* 53-86; R Kingston 53-86; rtd 86; Perm to Offic *Ely* from 87. *13 Bakers' Close, Comberton, Cambridge CB3 7DJ*   Cambridge (01223) 262993

HILLS, Michael John. b 58. BA82. Westcott Ho Cam 87. **d** 88 **p** 89. C Workington St Jo *Carl* 88-91; C Gosforth All SS *Newc* 91-93; TV Seaton Hirst from 93. *Saint Andrew's Vicarage, Hawthorn Road, Ashington, Northd NE63 9AU*   Ashington (01670) 818691

HILLS, Michael Rae Buchanan. b 52. CQSW83 Univ of Wales (Lamp) BA81 Ex Univ BPhil83. St Steph Ho Ox DipMin94. **d** 94 **p** 95. C Kingston upon Hull St Nic *York* from 94. *242 Anlaby Park Road South, Hull HU4 7BZ*   Hull (01482) 64329

HILLS, Michael William John. b 54. Univ of Wales (Lamp) BA84. Westcott Ho Cam 85. **d** 87 **p** 88. C Reddish *Man* 87-91; V Bolton St Phil from 91. *St Philip's Vicarage, 453 Bridgeman Street, Bolton BL3 6TH*   Bolton (01204) 61533

HILLS, Richard Leslie. b 36. FMA83 Qu Coll Cam MA63 DIC64 Man Univ PhD68. St Deiniol's Hawarden 85. **d** 87 **p** 88. C Urmston *Man* 87-89; C Gt Yarmouth *Nor* 89-90; NSM Mottram in Longdendale w Woodhead *Ches* 90-93; NSM Mottram in Longdendale from 93. *Stamford Cottage, 47 Old Road, Mottram, Hyde, Cheshire SK14 6LW*   Mottram (01457) 763104

HILLS, Roger Malcolm. b 42. Oak Hill Th Coll 83. **d** 86 **p** 87. Hon C Mill Hill Jo Keble Ch *Lon* from 86; NSM Mill Hill St Mich from 86. *22 Sefton Avenue, London NW7 3QD*   0181-959 1931

HILLS, Rowland Jonathan. b 12. Selw Coll Cam BA35 MA39. Cuddesdon Coll 36. **d** 37 **p** 38. R Iffley *Ox* 59-75; rtd 75; Perm to Offic *Ox* from 76; Chapl Venice w Trieste *Eur* 79-80; Chapl San Remo w Bordighera 81. *19 Church Way, Iffley, Oxford OX4 4DY*   Oxford (01865) 771059

HILLYER, Charles Norman. b 21. Lon Univ BD48. Lambeth STh67 ALCD48. **d** 48 **p** 49. V Ponsbourne *St Alb* 59-70; Chapl Tolmers Park Hosp 59-70; Lib Tyndale Ho Cam 70-73; Org Ed UCCF 73-79; Sec Tyndale Fellowship Bibl Research Cam 73-75; P-in-c Hatherleigh *Ex* 79-81; V 81-86; Perm to Offic *Sarum* from 89. *Charters, The Avenue, Sherborne, Dorset DT9 3AJ*   Sherborne (01935) 813357

HILTON, Clive. b 30. K Coll Lon 54. **d** 58 **p** 59. V Oldham St Chad Limeside *Man* 65-70; P-in-c Gravesend H Family *Roch* 70-71; R Killamarsh *Derby* 71-88; R Broughton w Loddington and Cransley etc *Pet* 88-91; rtd 92. *7 Chaudleigh Close, Altrincham, Cheshire WA14 4XE*   0161-941 3010

HILTON, Ian Anthony. b 57. St Jo Coll Nottm 83. **d** 86 **p** 87. C Nottm St Sav *S'well* 86-90; C Aspley from 90. *13 Hilcot Drive, Aspley, Nottingham NG8 5HR*   Nottingham (0115) 978 4990

HILTON, John. b 49. Ex Univ BA70. Cuddesdon Coll 71. **d** 73 **p** 74. C W Derby (or Tuebrook) St Jo *Liv* 73-79; V Orford St Andr from 79. *St Andrew's Vicarage, Poplars Avenue, Orford, Warrington WA2 9UE*   Warrington (01925) 631903

HILTON, John Read. b 41. Lon Univ BD63 AKC65 LSE BSc73. **d** 65 **p** 66. C Cov H Trin *Cov* 65-69; C Hemel Hempstead *St Alb* 69-70; Hon C Catford St Andr *S'wark* 70-81. *89 Arngask Road, London SE6 1XZ*   0181-698 1965

HILTON-TURVEY, Geoffrey Michael. b 34. Oak Hill Th Coll 80. **d** 81 **p** 82. C Bispham *Blackb* 81-85; V Inskip from 85. *St Peter's Vicarage, Preston Road, Inskip, Preston PR4 0TT* Catforth (01772) 690316

HINCHCLIFFE, Garry Anthony Frank. b 68. New Coll Edin BD94. Edin Th Coll CECM93. **d** 94 **p** 95. C Dumfries *Glas* from 94. *39 Barnton Road, Georgetown, Dumfries DG1 4HN* Dumfries (01387) 52158

HINCHEY, Peter John. b 30. LTCL53. Chich Th Coll 55. **d** 58 **p** 59. V Gillingham St Aug *Roch* 67-72; V Bromley St Andr 72-74; Hon Chapl to Bp 74-78; Hon C Lamorbey H Redeemer 76-78; R Foots Cray 78-81; Perm to Offic *Chich* 92-94; rtd 94; Perm to Offic *S'wark* from 94; Hon C Rotherhithe St Mary w All SS from 94. *Clare Parsonage, 130 Rotherhithe New Road, London SE16 2AP*   0171-237 9244

HINCHLIFF, Canon Peter Bingham. b 29. Rhodes Univ BA48 PhD58 Trin Coll Ox BA50 MA54 BD62 DD64. St Paul's Grahamstown 51. **d** 52 **p** 53. Hon Can Grahamstown from 69; Sec Ch Assembly Miss and Ecum Coun 69-72; Fell and Tutor Ball Coll Ox 72-94; Chapl 72-87; Can Th Cov Cathl *Cov* 72-92; rtd 94. *Christ Church, Oxford OX1 1DP*   Oxford (01865) 276236

HINCKLEY, Paul Frederick. b 61. Cranfield Inst of Tech MSc85 Farnborough Tech Coll HND83. Ridley Hall Cam CTM94. **d** 94. C Ovenden *Wakef* from 94. *82 Ashfield Drive, Ovenden, Halifax, W Yorkshire HX3 5PG*   Halifax (01422) 353502

✠**HIND, Rt Rev John William.** b 45. Leeds Univ BA66. Cuddesdon Coll 70. **d** 72 **p** 73 **c** 91. C Catford (Southend) and Downham *S'wark* 72-76; V Forest Hill Ch Ch 76-82; P-in-c Forest Hill St Paul 81-82; Wiccamical Preb Chich Cathl *Chich* 82-91; Prin Chich Th Coll 82-91; Area Bp Horsham *Chich* 91-93; Bp Eur from 93; Asst Bp Chich from 93. *Bishop's Lodge, Worth, Crawley, W Sussex RH10 7RT, or 14 Tufton Street, London SW1P 3QZ*   Crawley (01293) 883051 or 0171-976 8001   Fax 884479 or 0171-976 8002

HIND, Canon Stanley Maurice. b 29. AKC53. **d** 54 **p** 55. V Carleton *Wakef* 67-78; V E Hardwick 72-78; V Morley St Pet w Churwell 78-86; V Womersley 86-87; P-in-c Kirk Smeaton 86-87; V Womersley and Kirk Smeaton 87-94; Hon Can Wakef Cathl 89-94; rtd 94. *1 The Lilacs, Carleton Road, Pontefract, W Yorkshire WF8 3RW*   Pontefract (01977) 700386

HINDLE, Miss Penelope Jane Bowyn. b 45. Trin Coll Bris 76. **dss** 84 **d** 87 **p** 94. Stoneycroft All SS *Liv* 84-87; Par Dn 87-89; Asst Chapl R Free Hosp Lon 89-93; Chapl Lister Hosp Stevenage from 93; C Stevenage St Andr and St Geo *St Alb* from 94. *Oakland, 19 Park Lane, Knebworth, Herts SG3 6PD* Stevenage (01438) 811584 or 314333

HINDLEY, Andrew David. b 59. Univ of Wales (Lamp) BA. Sarum & Wells Th Coll. **d** 82 **p** 83. C Huddersfield St Pet *Wakef* 82-84; C Huddersfield St Pet and All SS 84-86; P-in-c Holmfield 86-91; R Ribchester w Stidd *Blackb* from 91; Bp's Adv for Leisure and Tourism from 91; Chapl Ribchester Hosp from 91. *The Rectory, Riverside, Ribchester, Preston PR3 3XS* Ribchester (01254) 878352

HINDLEY, Anthony Talbot. b 41. Bernard Gilpin Soc Dur 61 Oak Hill Th Coll 62. **d** 66 **p** 67. C Stoke next Guildf St Jo *Guildf* 66-69; Kenya 70-78; C Redhill H Trin *S'wark* 78-79; P-in-c Eastbourne All So *Chich* 79-83; V 83-86; V S Malling from 86. *The Vicarage, Church Lane, South Malling, Lewes, E Sussex BN7 2JA*   Lewes (01273) 474387

HINDLEY, Dr Godfrey Talbot. b 09. Ch Coll Cam BChir34 MB35 MA46. **d** 66 **p** 67. Tanzania 66-70; Kenya 70-75; Perm to Offic *Ex* 81-91. *21 Delves House West, Ringmer, Lewes, E Sussex BN8 5JW*   Lewes (01273) 813597

HINDLEY, John. b 32. UWIST BSc71. **d** 84 **p** 85. NSM Llantilio Crossenny w Penrhos, Llanvetherine etc *Mon* 85-88; P-in-c Tilbrook *Ely* from 88; P-in-c Covington from 88; P-in-c Keyston and Bythorn from 88; P-in-c Catworth Magna from 88; RD Leightonstone from 88; P-in-c Gt w Lt Gidding and Steeple Gidding from 94. *The Rectory, Church Lane, Tilbrook, Huntingdon, Cambs PE18 0JS*   Huntingdon (01480) 860147

HINDLEY, Roger Dennis. b 48. Birm Univ BA70 Ox Univ BA77 MA83. Ripon Coll Cuddesdon 75 Qu Coll Birm 77. **d** 78 **p** 79. C Rubery *Birm* 78-81; C Henbury *Bris* 81-83; V Erdington St Chad *Birm* 83-89; V Hill from 89. *61 Mere Green Road, Sutton Coldfield, W Midlands B75 5BW*   0121-308 0074

HINDLEY, Thomas Richard. b 31. ARIBA54 Sheff Univ BA53 Lon Univ BD66. Clifton Th Coll 61. **d** 63 **p** 64. C Kenilworth St Jo *Cov* 63-67; C Cheadle *Ches* 67-70; R Harpurhey Ch Ch *Man* from 70; R Harpurhey St Steph from 72. *Christ Church Rectory, Church Lane, Manchester M9 1BG*   0161-205 4020

HINDS, Kenneth Arthur Lancelot. b 30. Bps' Coll Cheshunt. **d** 64 **p** 65. C Sawbridgeworth *St Alb* 64-67; C Gt Berkhamsted 67-71; V Boreham Wood St Mich 71-75; Trinidad and Tobago 75-79; P-in-c Gt Ilford St Luke *Chelmsf* 79-81; V from 81. *St Luke's Vicarage, Baxter Road, Ilford, Essex IG1 2HN*   0181-478 1104

HINDS, Paul Anthony. b 62. CA Tr Coll DipEvang94 St Mich Coll Llan DipTh88. **d** 88 **p** 89. C Skewen *Llan* 88-90; C Roath St Marg 90-91; C Stockland Green *Birm* from 94. *St Mark's Vicarage, Bleak Hill Road, Birmingham B23 7EL* 0121-373 0130

HINE, Canon John Timothy Matusch. b 27. TCD BA51 MA54. Linc Th Coll 53. **d** 55 **p** 56. V Asthall and Swinbrook w Widford *Ox* 67-94; RD Witney 76-81 and 87-89; Hon Can Ch Ch 88-94; rtd 94. *Cheriton, Ring Street, Stalbridge, Sturminster Newton, Dorset DT10 2LZ* Stalbridge (01963) 363813

HINE, John Victor. b 36. Open Univ BA82. Carl Dioc Tr Course 85. **d** 88 **p** 89. NSM Dean *Carl* 88-92; NSM Clifton 88-92; C Millom 92-94; P-in-c Gt Broughton and Broughton Moor from 94. *The Vicarage, The Green, Little Broughton, Cockermouth, Cumbria CA13 0YG* Cockermouth (01900) 825317

HINE, Keith Ernest. b 50. Bradf Univ BA Leeds Univ CertEd. N Ord Course 89. **d** 89 **p** 90. C Wilmslow *Ches* 89-94; V Bowdon from 94. *The Vicarage, Church Brow, Bowdon, Altrincham, Cheshire WA14 2SG* 0161-928 2468

HINES, Dr Richard Arthur. b 49. MSc PhD K Coll Lon MTh89. Oak Hill Th Coll 82. **d** 84 **p** 85. C Mile Cross *Nor* 84-87; Lect Oak Hill Th Coll from 87; Perm to Offic Lon from 93. *2 Fant Lane, Chase Side, London N14 4PP* 0181-441 0568 Fax 441 5996

HINEY, Thomas Bernard Felix (Tom). b 35. MC61. RMA 56. Ridley Hall Cam DipTh69. **d** 69 **p** 70. C Edgbaston St Aug *Birm* 69-71; CF 71-91; Chapl R Hosp Chelsea from 91. *The Royal Hospital Chelsea, Royal Hospital Road, London SW3 4SL* 0171-730 0161 Fax 823 6871

HINGE, Canon David Gerald Francis. b 30. FRSA57. Wells Th Coll 64. **d** 66 **p** 67. C Brookfield St Anne, Highgate Rise *Lon* 66-69; C N Greenford All Hallows 69-71; V Winton *Man* 71-78; R Etherley *Dur* from 78; Hon Can Dur Cathl from 90. *The Rectory, Etherley, Bishop Auckland, Co Durham DL14 0HN* Bishop Auckland (01388) 832350

HINGE, Derek Colin. b 36. CChem60 MRSC60 Imp Coll Lon BSc58. St Alb Minl Tr Scheme 84. **d** 88 **p** 89. NSM Bishop's Stortford St Mich *St Alb* from 88. *12 Avenue Road, Bishop's Stortford, Herts CM23 5NU* Bishop's Stortford (01279) 652173

HINGLEY, Bernadette. b 48. Lon Univ BSc70 York Univ CertEd73. St Jo Coll Nottm DPS77 DipTh78. **dss** 81 **d** 87 **p** 94. Ripon Coll Cuddesdon 81-83; W Slough *Ox* 81-83; Chapl Qu Eliz Hosp Birm 84-88; NSM Balsall Heath St Paul *Birm* 84-90; Perm to Offic 90-91; NSM Birm St Luke from 91. *23 Woodview Drive, Birmingham B15 2JF* 0121-444 6343

HINGLEY, Christopher James Howard. b 48. Trin Coll Ox BA69 MA71. Wycliffe Hall Ox 81. **d** 80 **p** 81. Zimbabwe 80-81 and from 87; Lic to Offic *Ox* 85-87. *Address temp unknown*

HINGLEY, Robert Charles. b 46. Ball Coll Ox BA69 MA74 Birm Univ CertEd73. Qu Coll Birm DipTh72. **d** 73 **p** 74. C Old Charlton *S'wark* 73-76; Asst Warden Iona Abbey 76-77; TV Langley Marish *Ox* 77-83; V Balsall Heath St Paul *Birm* 83-90; Perm to Offic 90-91; V Birm St Luke from 91. *23 Woodview Drive, Birmingham B15 2JF* 0121-444 6343

HINGLEY, Roderick Stanley Plant. b 51. St Chad's Coll Dur BA72. St Steph Ho Ox 74. **d** 75 **p** 76. C Lower Gornal *Lich* 75-79; C Tividale 79-82; C Broseley w Benthall *Heref* 82-84; C Wanstead St Mary *Chelmsf* 84-92; V Romford St Alb from 92. *St Alban's Vicarage, 3 Francombe Gardens, Romford RM1 2TH* Hornchurch (01708) 473580

HINKES, Sidney George Stuart. b 25. Lon Univ BA50 BD70. St Steph Ho Ox 50. **d** 52 **p** 53. C-in-c Bayswater St Mary CD *Ox* 66-82; V Headington St Mary 83-90; rtd 90; Perm to Offic *B & W* 90-91; Perm to Offic *Bris* 92-93; Rtd Clergy Officer Swindon Adnry from 93. *1 The Bungalow, Bremilham Road, Malmesbury, Wilts SN16 0DQ* Malmesbury (01666) 825249

HINKSMAN, Barrie Lawrence James. b 41. K Coll Lon BD64 AKC64 Lon Gestalt Cen GDipGP77. St Boniface Warminster 61. **d** 65 **p** 66. C Crosby *Linc* 65-67; Ecum Development Officer Scunthorpe Coun of Chs 67-69; C Chelmsley Wood *Birm* 69-72; TV 72-75; P-in-c Offchurch *Cov* 75-79; Dioc Tr Officer 79; Perm to Offic 89-90; Hon Chapl Cov Cathl from 94. *South Bank House, 67 Cubbington Road, Lillington, Leamington Spa, Warks CV32 7AQ* Leamington Spa (01926) 832312

HINTON, David Hugh. b 31. Tyndale Hall Bris. **d** 63 **p** 64. C Bowling St Steph *Bradf* 67-71; V Denholme Gate 71-79; P-in-c Morton St Luke 79-85; V 85-86; rtd 86; Perm to Offic *Bradf* from 86. *9 Sydenham Place, Bradford, W Yorkshire BD3 0LB* Bradford (01274) 643460

HINTON, Mrs Frances Mary. b 43. EN(G)85. E Midl Min Tr Course 89. **d** 92 **p** 94. Par Dn Hornsey Rise Whitehall Park Team *Lon* 92-94; C from 94. *6 Zoffany Street, London N19 3ER* 0171-263 4217

HINTON, John Dorsett Owen. b 21. Wells Th Coll 59. **d** 61 **p** 62. V Pucklechurch and Abson w Dyrham *Bris* 67-86; rtd 86; Perm to Offic *Bris* from 86. *Tower House, Clifton Down Road, Bristol BS8 4AG* Bristol (0117) 973 9298

HINTON, Michael George. b 27. Mert Coll Ox BA48 MA51 Reading Univ PhD59. S Dios Minl Tr Scheme 81. **d** 83 **p** 84. NSM Weston-super-Mare St Paul *B & W* 83-85; NSM Sibertswold w Coldred *Cant* 85-87; NSM Eythorne and Elvington w Waldershare etc from 87. *The Vicarage, Shepherdswell, Dover, Kent CT15 7LF* Dover (01304) 830245

HINTON, Nigel Keith. b 49. Univ Coll Lon BSc70 Worc Coll of Educn PGCE73 Lon Univ MA87. Oak Hill NSM Course 89. **d** 92 **p** 93. NSM Cudham and Downe *Roch* from 92. *218 Swievelands Road, Biggin Hill, Westerham, Kent TN16 3QS* Biggin Hill (01959) 573017

HINTON, Roger Amos. b 33. Keble Coll Ox BA56 MA60. Ridley Hall Cam 56. **d** 58 **p** 59. C Drypool St Columba *York* 58-61; CMS 62-76; India 62-67; Tutor CMS Tr Coll Chislehurst 67-69; Pakistan 69-76; V Coalville *Leic* 76-78; V Coalville and Bardon Hill 78-85; RD Akeley S (Coalville) 81-84; TR Bushbury *Lich* from 85. *The Rectory, Bushbury Lane, Bushbury, Wolverhampton WV10 8JP* Wolverhampton (01902) 782226

HIPKINS, John Malcolm. b 33. MInstM. Qu Coll Birm 78. **d** 80 **p** 81. C Clayton *Lich* 80; C Derby St Luke *Derby* 81-84; V Chaddesden St Phil 84-88; rtd 88. *1 Kensington Close, Penrhyd, Amlwch, Gwynedd LL68 0RR* Amlwch (01407) 830082

HIPKINS, Leslie Michael. b 35. ACIS60 Univ Coll Dur BA57. Westcott Ho Cam 89 Oak Hill Th Coll 78. **d** 81 **p** 82. NSM Halstead St Andr w H Trin and Greenstead Green *Chelmsf* 81-87; C Tolleshunt Knights w Tiptree and Gt Braxted 87-89; P-in-c Cratfield w Heveningham and Ubbeston etc *St E* from 89. *The Vicarage, Cratfield, Halesworth, Suffolk IP19 0BU* Ubbeston (01986) 798564

HIPWELL, Canon Trevor Senior. b 23. TCD BA47. **d** 47 **p** 48. Min Can St Patr Cathl Dub 64-75; I Dub Mt Merrion *D & G* 56-94; Chapl Univ Coll Dub 75-94; Preb Monmohenock St Patr Cathl Dub 75-94; rtd 94. *123 Dorney Court, Shankill, Co Dublin, Irish Republic* Dublin (1) 282-3879

HIRONS, Malcolm Percy. b 36. Or Coll Ox BA59 MA62. Wycliffe Hall Ox 59. **d** 61 **p** 62. C Edgbaston St Aug *Birm* 61-64; Chapl Warw Sch 64-65; C Beverley Minster *York* 65-69; V Barnby upon Don *Sheff* 69-80; P-in-c Kirk Bramwith 75-80; P-in-c Fenwick 75-80; V Norton Woodseats St Paul from 80. *St Paul's Vicarage, 6 Angerford Avenue, Sheffield S8 9BG* Sheffield (0114) 255 1945

HIRST, Alan. b 44. Leeds Univ CQSW74. Linc Th Coll 79. **d** 81 **p** 82. C Newton Heath All SS *Man* 81-84; Chapl to the Deaf 84-88; V Oldham St Chad Limeside 88-91; Dep Chapl HM Pris Liv 91-92; Chapl HM Pris Ranby from 92. *The Chaplain's Office, HM Prison Ranby, Retford, Notts DN22 8EU* Retford (01777) 706721 Fax 702691

HIRST, Anthony Melville. b 50. Keele Univ BA73. Cuddesdon Coll 74. **d** 77 **p** 78. C S Gillingham *Roch* 77-80; C Coity w Nolton *Llan* 80-83; OSB from 83; R Hallaton w Horninghold, Allexton, Tugby etc *Leic* 83-90; V Arthog w Fairbourne w Llangelynnin w Rhoslefain *Ban* from 90. *The Rectory, Llwyngwril, Gwynedd LL37 2JB* Fairbourne (01341) 250919

HIRST, David William. b 37. Man Univ BA78. Brasted Th Coll 59 St Aid Birkenhead 61. **d** 63 **p** 64. C Clayton *Man* 63-64; C Bury St Jo 64-66; C Wythenshawe Wm Temple Ch 67-70; V Oldham St Chad Limeside 70-79; V Friezland 79-91; R Ashton St Mich 91-95; Chapl HM Pris Buckley Hall from 95. *HM Detention Centre, Buckley Hall, Buckley Road, Rochdale, Lancs* Rochdale (01706) 861610

HIRST, Douglas. b 33. Oak Hill Th Coll 89. **d** 91 **p** 93. NSM Thorley *St Alb* from 91. *Axholme, 68 Cannons Close, Bishop's Stortford, Herts CM23 2BQ* Bishop's Stortford (01279) 651345

HIRST, Canon Godfrey Ian. b 41. MBIM Univ of Wales (Lamp) BA63. Chich Th Coll 63. **d** 65 **p** 66. C Brierfield *Blackb* 65-68; Ind Chapl *Liv* 68-71; TV Kirkby 71-75; Ind Chapl *Blackb* 75-94; P-in-c Treales 75-87; Hon Can Blackb Cathl from 83; Can Res Blackb Cathl 87-94; V Lytham St Cuth from 94. *The Vicarage, Church Road, Lytham St Annes, Lancs FY8 5PX* Lytham (01253) 736168

HIRST, John Adrian. b 49. St Jo Coll Nottm BTh78. **d** 78 **p** 79. C Cheltenham St Mark *Glouc* 78-84; TV 84-85; TV Swan *Ox* 85-89; R Denham from 89. *The Rectory, Ashmead Lane, Denham, Uxbridge, Middx UB9 5BB* Denham (01895) 832771

HIRST, Mrs Judith (Judy). b 54. St Mary's Coll Dur BA76 LMH Ox PGCE77 Hull Univ MA86. Cranmer Hall Dur BA94. **d** 94 **p** 95. C Dur St Oswald *Dur* from 94. *1 Mill Hill Lane, Durham DH1 3LQ* 0191-374 3979

HIRST, Peter Thornton. b 34. Leeds Univ BA59. Ely Th Coll 59. **d** 61 **p** 62. C Brierley Hill *Lich* 61-64; C Wednesfield St Thos 64-66; R Salford St Bart *Man* 66-71; V Sedgley St Mary *Lich* 71-77; TR Billingham St Aid *Dur* 77-86; TR Elland *Wakef*

86-90; Ind Chapl *Ripon* from 93; C Headingley from 93. *49 Headingley Lane, Leeds LS6 1AA* Leeds (0113) 274 3652

HIRST, Reginald Arnold Archer. b 36. St Paul's Grahamstown. **d** 60 **p** 61. S Africa 60-88; R Wickham *Portsm* from 88. *The Rectory, Southwick Road, Wickham, Fareham, Hants PO17 6HR* Fareham (01329) 832134

HIRST, Roland Geoffrey. b 42. St Cath Coll Cam BA63 MA68. NW Ord Course 74. **d** 77 **p** 78. C Beverley St Mary *York* 77-80; P-in-C Flamborough and Bempton 80-83; V 83-86; R Bolton Abbey *Bradf* 86-95; P-in-c Bassenthwaite, Isel and Setmurthy *Carl* from 95. *The Vicarage, Torpenhow, Carlisle CA5 1HT* Torpenhow (016973) 71295

HIRST, Wilfrid. b 11. Roch Th Coll 65. **d** 66 **p** 67. C Shere *Guildf* 69-71; R Kelly w Bradstone *Ex* 71-74; R Exbourne w Jacobstowe 74-77; rtd 77; Perm to Offic *Chich* from 77. *3 Park Drive, Felpham, Bognor Regis, W Sussex PO22 7RD* Middleton-on-Sea (01243) 584058

HISCOCK, David Alan. b 52. Sarum & Wells Th Coll. **d** 85 **p** 86. C Charlton Kings St Mary *Glouc* 85-89; TV Swan *Ox* from 89. *The Rectory, Marsh Gibbon, Bicester, Oxon OX6 0HJ* Stratton Audley (01869) 277297

HISCOCK, Gary Edward. b 43. DipDrama68 Lon Univ DipRS88. Oak Hill Th Coll BA90. **d** 90 **p** 91. C Cheltenham St Luke and St Jo *Glouc* 90-94; C Hardwicke, Quedgeley and Elmore w Longney from 95. *Church House, Cornfield Drive, Hardwicke, Gloucester GL2 6QJ* Gloucester (01452) 720015

HISCOCK, Peter George Harold. b 31. Wadh Coll Ox BA54 MA66. Ely Th Coll 54. **d** 58 **p** 59. Dean of Residence TCD 68-73; India 73-76; TV Jarrow *Dur* 77-82; Chapl Univ Coll Dur 82-87; RD Newc Cen *Newc* 87-94; P-in-c Dinnington 87-88; TV The King in the Dio of Newc 88-94; rtd 94. *8 Banbury Road, London E9 7DU* 0181-986 2252

HISCOX, Edward. b 23. Univ of Wales (Lamp) BA54. Wells Th Coll 54. **d** 56 **p** 57. V Drypool St Columba w St Andr and St Pet *York* 64-75; R Daglingworth w the Duntisbournes and Winstone *Glouc* 75-95; NSM from 95; rtd 95. *The Rectory, Daglingworth, Cirencester, Glos GL7 7AL* Cirencester (01285) 654561

HISCOX, Jonathan Ronald James. b 64. Univ of Wales (Cardiff) DipHT85. Qu Coll Birm 87. **d** 89 **p** 90. C Wiveliscombe *B & W* 89-93; P-in-c Donyatt w Horton, Broadway and Ashill 93-94; TV Ilminster and District from 94. *The Rectory, Broadway, Ilminster, Somerset TA19 9RE* Ilminster (01460) 52559

HITCH, Kim William. b 54. Leic Univ BSc75 K Coll Lon MA94. Trin Coll Bris 76. **d** 78 **p** 79. C Becontree St Mary *Chelmsf* 78-80; C Huyton Quarry *Liv* 80-83; V Hatcham St Jas *S'wark* 83-91; TR Kidbrooke St Jas from 91. *St James's Rectory, 62 Kidbrooke Park Road, London SE3 0DU* 0181-856 3438

HITCHCOCK, David. b 37. S'wark Ord Course 70. **d** 73 **p** 74. NSM Milton next Gravesend Ch Ch *Roch* from 73. *148 Old Road East, Gravesend, Kent DA12 1PF* Gravesend (01474) 361091

HITCHINS, Graham Edward David. b 54. S Dios Minl Tr Scheme 91. **d** 94 **p** 95. C Bishops Waltham *Portsm* from 94. *15 Denewulf Close, Bishops Waltham, Southampton SO3 1GZ* Bishops Waltham (01489) 894729

HITCHINSON, Preb William Henry. b 12. Chich Th Coll 51. **d** 53 **p** 54. V Eastcote St Lawr *Lon* 56-80; Preb St Paul's Cathl 76-80; rtd 80. *66 Waller Drive, Northwood, Middx HA6 1BW* Northwood (01923) 829778

HITCHMAN, Keith John. b 62. Middx Univ BSc90. Trin Coll Bris BA95. **d** 95. C Bestwood *S'well* from 95. *17 Harvest Close, Nottingham NG5 9BW* Nottingham (0115) 975 3378

HITCHMOUGH, William. b 30. N Ord Course. **d** 81 **p** 82. NSM Penketh *Liv* 81-83; Perm to Offic from 83; Chapl Warrington Distr Gen Hosp from 83. *15 Beecroft Close, Warrington WA5 5QX* Warrington (01925) 650541

HIZA, Douglas William. b 38. Richmond Univ Virginia BA60 MDiv63 Mankato State Univ MS70. Virginia Th Sem 60. **d** 63 **p** 64. USA 63-79; Chapl Hackney Hosp Gp *Lon* from 80; Chapl Homerton Hosp Lon from 80. *Homerton Hospital, Homerton Row, London E9 6SR* 0181-985 5555

HJORTH, Rolf Gunnar Leer. b 25. AMICE St Jo Coll Ox BA46 MA50. Wycliffe Hall Ox 61. **d** 62 **p** 63. V Oulton *Lich* 69-78; Chapl Ostend w Knokke and Bruges *Eur* 78-84; Chapl Dusseldorf 85-90; rtd 90; Spain from 94. *Sa Fontansa 104, Begur, 17255 Girona, Spain*

HOAD, Anne Elizabeth. b 42. Bris Univ BA63. dss 69 **d** 94. Asst Chapl Imp Coll *Lon* 69-74; S'wark Lay Tr Scheme 74-77; Brixton St Matt *S'wark* 77-80; Charlton St Luke w H Trin 80-94; Project Worker Community of Women and Men 88-91; Voc Adv Lewisham from 91; Chapl Lewisham Hosp from 92; Hon C Lee Gd Shep w St Pet from 94. *14 Silk Close, Dorville Road, London SE12 8DL* 0181-297 8761

HOAD, Miss Rosemary Claire. b 60. Cranmer Hall Dur 92. **d** 94 **p** 95. C Epsom St Martin *Guildf* from 94. *115 Albert Road, Epsom, Surrey KT17 4EN* Epsom (01372) 741739

HOAR, George Stanley. b 20. Chich Th Coll 47. **d** 50 **p** 53. V Leake *Linc* 60-71; V Castle Bytham 71-91; R Careby w Holywell and Aunby 73-91; R Lt Bytham 73-91; rtd 91. *1 Sulthorpe Road, Ketton, Stamford, Lincs PE9 3SN* Stamford (01780) 720817

HOARE, Carol. b 46. Lon Univ BA68 Birm Univ CertEd69. Qu Coll Birm 86 W Midl Minl Tr Course 86. **d** 91 **p** 94. NSM Curdworth *Birm* from 91. *14 Elms Road, Sutton Coldfield, W Midlands B72 1JF* 0121-354 1117

HOARE, David Albert Sylvester. b 47. **d** 95. Asst Chapl Gib Cathl *Eur* from 95. *The Old Deanery Flat, 3 Governor's Lane, Gibraltar*

HOARE, Canon David Marlyn. b 33. Bps' Coll Cheshunt 60. **d** 63 **p** 64. C Ampthill w Millbrook and Steppingley *St Alb* 63-67; C Bushey 67-70; V Harlington 70-76; V Oxhey All SS 76-81; V Hellesdon *Nor* from 81; Hon Can Nor Cathl from 95. *The Vicarage, Broom Avenue, Hellesdon, Norwich NR6 6LG* Norwich (01603) 426902

HOARE, Janet Francis Mary. See MILES, Ms Janet Francis Mary

HOARE, Patrick Reginald Andrew Reid (Toddy). b 47. TD80 and Bar 88. Hull Univ MA90. Wycliffe Hall Ox 77. **d** 80 **p** 81. C Guisborough *York* 80-83; CF (TA) from 82; P-in-c Felixkirk w Boltby *York* from 83; P-in-c Kirby Knowle from 83; P-in-c Leake w Over and Nether Silton and Kepwick from 83; P-in-c Cowesby from 83. *The Vicarage, Knayton, Thirsk, N Yorkshire YO7 4AZ* Thirsk (01845) 537277

HOARE, Patrick Vernon Keymer. b 35. Oak Hill NSM Course 90. **d** 93 **p** 94. NSM Staines St Mary and St Pet *Lon* from 93. *2 Saxonbury Avenue, Sunbury-on-Thames, Middx TW16 5HP* Sunbury-on-Thames (01932) 788031

HOARE, Roger John. b 38. Tyndale Hall Bris 63. **d** 66 **p** 67. C Stoughton *Guildf* 66-70; C Chesham St Mary *Ox* 70-73; V Bath St Bart *B & W* 73-83; V Gt Faringdon w Lt Coxwell *Ox* 83-89; Deputation Appeals Org (NE Lon) Children's Soc 89-93; P-in-c Lambourne w Abridge and Stapleford Abbotts *Chelmsf* from 93; Ind Chapl from 93. *7 Field Close, Abridge, Romford RM4 1DL* Theydon Bois (01992) 813424 Fax as telephone

✠**HOARE, Rt Rev Rupert William Noel.** b 40. Trin Coll Ox BA61 MA66 Fitzw Ho Cam BA64 MA84 Birm Univ PhD73. Westcott Ho Cam 62. **d** 64 **p** 65 **c** 93. C Oldham St Mary w St Pet *Man* 64-67; Lect Qu Coll Birm 68-72; Can Th Cov Cathl *Cov* 70-76; R Man Resurr *Man* 72-78; Can Res Birm Cathl *Birm* 78-81; Prin Westcott Ho Cam 81-93; Area Bp Dudley *Worc* from 93. *Bishop's House, 336 Halesowen Road, Cradley Heath, Warley, W Midlands B64 7JF* 0121-550 3407

HOARE, Canon Simon Gerard. b 37. AKC61. **d** 62 **p** 63. C Headingley *Ripon* 62-65; C Adel 65-68; R Spofforth 68-71; R Spofforth w Kirk Deighton 71-77; V Rawdon *Bradf* 77-85; Hon Can Bradf Cathl from 85; R Carleton and Lothersdale from 85; Dioc Ecum Officer from 85. *The Rectory, Carleton, Skipton, N Yorkshire BD23 3BY* Skipton (01756) 792789

HOBBS, Antony Ewan Talbot. b 25. Ripon Hall Ox 58. **d** 60 **p** 61. V Staplefield Common *Chich* 64-89; rtd 89. *Chippers, Chalvington, Hailsham, E Sussex BN27 3TE* Ripe (01321) 811243

HOBBS, Basil Ernest William. b 22. St Chad's Coll Dur BA49 DipTh50. **d** 51 **p** 52. Hon C Paddington H Trin w St Paul *Lon* 70-72; Asst Chapl St Mary's Hosp Praed Street Lon 69-72; Novice CR 72-74; Past Consultant Clinical Th Assn 74-84; Lic to Offic *S'well* 74-83; Chapl HM Pris Nottm 81-84; Hon C Nottm St Andr *S'well* 83-84; C 84-86; TV Clifton 86-87; rtd 87; Perm to Offic *S'well* from 87. *10 New Vale Road, Nottingham NG4 2LB* Nottingham (0115) 987 0460

HOBBS, Christopher Bedo. b 61. Jes Coll Cam BA83 BTh90. Ridley Hall Cam 88. **d** 91 **p** 92. C Langham Place All So *Lon* 91-95; C Hull Newland St Jo *York* from 95. *75 Desmond Avenue, Hull HU6 7JX* Hull (01482) 343789

HOBBS, Christopher John Pearson. b 60. Sydney Univ BA82 K Coll Lon BD89 AKC89. Wycliffe Hall Ox 89. **d** 91 **p** 92. C S Mimms Ch Ch *Lon* 91-94; C Jesmond Clayton Memorial *Newc* from 94. *56 Holly Avenue, Jesmond, Newcastle upon Tyne NE2 2QA* 0191-281 9046

HOBBS, James (Jim). b 42. K Alfred's Coll Win CertEd64 C of E Bd Educn RTC 64 Open Univ BA89. Linc Th Coll 66. **d** 68 **p** 69. C Moseley St Mary *Birm* 68-73; V Kingstanding St Mark 73-77; R Rushbrooke *St E* 77-78; R Bradfield St Geo 77-80; P-in-c Bradfield St Clare 77-80; P-in-c Felsham w Gedding 77-80; R Bradfield St George w Bradfield St Clare etc 80-84; P-in-c Gt and Lt Whelnetham 84-85; R Gt and Lt Whelnetham w Bradfield St George 85-90; Chapl for Educn *Linc* from 90; Chapl Grimsby Colls of H&FE from 90. *Chaplain's Lodge, 19 Devonshire Avenue, Grimsby, S Humberside DN32 0BW* Grimsby (01472) 877079

HOBBS, John Antony. b 36. S Dios Minl Tr Scheme. **d** 87 **p** 88. NSM Crowborough *Chich* from 87. *May Cottage, Alice Bright*

Lane, Crowborough, E Sussex TN6 3SQ   Crowborough (01892) 653909

HOBBS, Canon Keith. b 25. Ex Coll Ox BA46 MA51. Wells Th Coll 56. **d** 58 **p** 59. Hon C S Kensington St Steph *Lon* 62-71; C 71-78; Acting Gen Sec Ch Union 78; Bp's Dom Chapl *Chich* 78-81; Adn Chich 81-91; rtd 91; Perm to Offic *Chich* from 91. *10 St Martin's Square, Chichester, W Sussex PO19 1NR* Chichester (01243) 784260

HOBBS, Kenneth Ian. b 50. Oak Hill Th Coll 74. **d** 77 **p** 78. C Southborough St Pet w Ch Ch and St Matt *Roch* 77-80; C Hoole *Ches* 80-84; V Barnston 84-95; P-in-c Bedworth *Cov* 95; TR from 95. *The Rectory, 1 Linden Lea, Bedworth, Nuneaton, Warks CV12 8ES*   Coventry (01203) 310219

HOBBS, Michael Bedo. b 30. Fitzw Ho Cam BA58 MA62. Clifton Th Coll 58. **d** 60 **p** 61. C Southsea St Jude *Portsm* 60-63; Paraguay 63-65; Argentina 65-67; V Potters Green *Cov* 68-75; Distr Sec BFBS 75-82; R Plaxtol *Roch* from 82; Dioc Miss Audits Consultant from 90. *The Rectory, Plaxtol, Sevenoaks, Kent TN15 0QF*   Plaxtol (01732) 810319

HOBBS, Canon Philip Bertram. b 20. MBE81. Wells Th Coll 46. **d** 48 **p** 49. V Glouc St Jas *Glouc* 60-74; Chapl HM Pris Glouc 61-82; V Sevenhampton w Charlton Abbots and Hawling *Glouc* 74-75; P-in-c Whittington 74-75; V Sevenhampton w Charlton Abbotts and Hawling etc 75-95; Hon Can Glouc Cathl 77-95; rtd 95. *5 Woodlands View, Hobbs Lane, Woodmancote, Cirencester, Glos GL7 7EQ*   Cirencester (01285) 831846

HOBBS, Simon John. b 59. Ox Univ MA82. St Steph Ho Ox 80. **d** 83 **p** 84. C Middlesex Ascension *York* 83-85; C Stainton-in-Cleveland 85-88; C St Marylebone All SS *Lon* 88-90; P-in-c Paddington St Pet 90-94; C-in-c Grosvenor Chpl from 94; C Hanover Square St Geo w St Mark from 94. *13 North Audley Street, London W1Y 1WF*   0171-629 3891

HOBDAY, Walter William Henry. b 10. Ely Th Coll 56. **d** 57 **p** 58. R Perivale *Lon* 59-72; P-in-c Lichborough w Maidford *Pet* 72-74; R 74-76; R Lichborough w Maidford and Farthingstone 76-79; rtd 79; Lic to Offic *Pet* 80-86; Perm to Offic from 86; Perm to Offic *St Alb* from 88. *Hardwicke Cottage, 13 The Green, Bromham, Bedford MK43 8JS*   Oakley (01234) 824542

HOBDEN, Brian Charles. b 38. Oak Hill Th Coll 63. **d** 66 **p** 67. C S Lambeth St Steph *S'wark* 66-70; C Cheadle *Ches* 70-76; USA from 76. *3215 Lilac, Portsmouth, Virginia 23703, USA*

HOBDEN, Christopher Martin. b 49. Lon Univ BSc71. Oak Hill Th Coll 80. **d** 87 **p** 88. NSM St Marylebone All So w SS Pet and Jo *Lon* 87-88; NSM Langham Place All So 88-95. *Soldier's Field, Nepcote Lane, Findon, Worthing, W Sussex BN14 0SH* Findon (01903) 872222

HOBDEN, David Nicholas. b 54. K Coll Lon BD76 AKC76 Cam Univ PGCE. Ripon Coll Cuddesdon 77. **d** 78 **p** 79. C Marlborough *Sarum* 78-80; C Salisbury St Thos and St Edm 81-85; V Shalford *Guildf* from 85. *The Vicarage, East Shalford Lane, Shalford, Guildford, Surrey GU4 8AE*   Guildford (01483) 62396

HOBDEN, Geoffrey William. b 46. DipTh. Trin Coll Bris 80. **d** 82 **p** 83. C Ex St Leon w H Trin *Ex* 82-86; V Weston-super-Mare Ch Ch *B & W* from 86; RD Locking from 93. *Christ Church Vicarage, 18 Montpelier, Weston-super-Mare, Avon BS23 2RH*   Weston-super-Mare (01934) 624376

HOBSON, Anthony Peter. b 53. St Jo Coll Cam BA74. St Jo Coll Nottm 75. **d** 77 **p** 78. C Brunswick *Man* 77-82; R Stretford St Bride 82-92; TR Hackney Marsh *Lon* from 92. *St Barnabas' Vicarage, 111 Homerton High Street, London E9 6DL*   0181-985 2764

HOBSON, Anthony John. b 42. Univ of Wales (Abth) BSc64 Birm Univ MSc65. Qu Coll Birm 79. **d** 81 **p** 82. NSM Bilton *Cov* 81-88; P-in-c Grandborough w Willoughby and Flecknoe from 88. *4 Juliet Drive, Rugby, Warks CV22 6LY*   Rugby (01788) 810416

HOBSON, Herbert Leslie. b 09. St Aid Birkenhead 37. **d** 39 **p** 40. V Heath *Derby* 68-75; rtd 75; Perm to Offic *Derby* from 75; Perm to Offic *S'well* from 75. *40 High Tor, Skegby, Sutton-in-Ashfield, Notts NG17 3EX*   Mansfield (01623) 557083

HOBSON, Canon Patrick John Bogan. b 33. MC53. Magd Coll Cam BA56 MA60. S'wark Ord Course 75 Qu Coll Birm 77. **d** 79 **p** 80. C St Jo in Bedwardine *Worc* 79-81; R Clifton-on-Teme, Lower Sapey and the Shelsleys 81-88; TR Waltham H Cross *Chelmsf* from 88; Hon Can Chelmsf Cathl from 95. *The Rectory, Highbridge Street, Waltham Abbey, Essex EN9 1DG* Lea Valley (01992) 762115

HOCKEN, Glen Rundle. b 59. ACA84 Kent Univ BA80 Southlands Coll Lon PGCE90. Wycliffe Hall Ox 90. **d** 92 **p** 93. C Cogges *Ox* 92-94; C Cogges and S Leigh from 94. *145 Manor Road, Witney, Oxon OX8 6UF*   Witney (01993) 775276

HOCKEY, Paul Henry. b 49. Oak Hill Th Coll BA86. **d** 86 **p** 87. C Dalton-in-Furness *Carl* 86-89; R Clifton, Brougham and

Cliburn 89-94; V Fremington *Ex* from 94. *The Vicarage, Fremington, Barnstaple, Devon EX31 2NX*   Barnstaple (01271) 73879

HOCKING, Canon Hugh Michael Warwick. b 12. VRD54. Ch Coll Cam BA34 MA38. Westcott Ho Cam 34. **d** 36 **p** 37. R Guildf H Trin w St Mary *Guildf* 62-77; Chapl St Luke's Hosp Guildf 63-77; rtd 77; Chapl W Cornwall Hosp Penzance from 78. *2 Clarence Place, Penzance, Cornwall TR18 2QA* Penzance (01736) 63229

HOCKING, John Theodore. b 28. Oak Hill Th Coll 61. **d** 63 **p** 64. N Area Sec BCMS 67-71; Hon C Preston All SS *Blackb* 67-71; V Hoghton 71-78; V Blawith w Lowick *Carl* 78-86; rtd 86. *161 Watling Street Road, Fulwood, Preston PR2 8AE*   Preston (01772) 795058

HOCKING, Paul Frederick. b 43. Chich Th Coll 84. **d** 86 **p** 87. C Whitton and Thurleston w Akenham *St E* 86-89; V Ipswich All Hallows 89-91; P-in-c Gt Cornard from 91. *The Vicarage, 95 Bures Road, Great Cornard, Sudbury, Suffolk CO10 0JE* Sudbury (01787) 373579

HOCKLEY, Paul William. b 47. Chu Coll Cam BA68 MA72 Nottm Univ BA73. St Jo Coll Nottm 71. **d** 74 **p** 75. C Chatham St Phil and St Jas *Roch* 74-78; C Tunbridge Wells St Jo 78-81; V Penketh *Liv* from 81. *St Paul's Vicarage, 6 Poplar Avenue, Penketh, Warrington WA5 2EH*   Penketh (01925) 723492

HOCKLEY, Canon Raymond Alan. b 29. LRAM53 Em Coll Cam MA71. Westcott Ho Cam 56. **d** 58 **p** 59. Chapl Em Coll Cam 68-76; Can Res and Prec York Minster *York* 76-95; rtd 95. *2A Sycamore Terrace, York YO3 7DN*   York (01904) 646702

HOCKNULL, Dr Mark Dennis. b 63. Surrey Univ BSc85 Univ Coll Lon PhD89. Cranmer Hall Dur BA93. **d** 94 **p** 95. C Prenton *Ches* from 94. *83 Bramwell Avenue, Birkenhead, Merseyside L43 0RQ*   0151-608 4692

HOCKRIDGE, Joan. b 25. Girton Coll Cam BA47 MA50. St Steph Ho Ox 82. **dss** 83 **d** 87 **p** 94. Ealing Ascension Hanger Hill *Lon* 83-88; Hon C 87-88; Hon C Hanger Hill Ascension and W Twyford St Mary 88-92; Hon C Hillingdon St Jo 92-95; Perm to Offic from 95. *17 Mead Way, Ruislip, Middx HA4 7QW*   Ruislip (01895) 622643

HODDER, John Kenneth. b 45. Edin Univ MA68. Cuddesdon Coll 71. **d** 73 **p** 74. C Kibworth Beauchamp *Leic* 73-76; C Whittlesey *Ely* 76-80; P-in-c Coveney 80-81; R 81-87; R Downham 80-87; R Nunney and Witham Friary, Marston Bigot etc *B & W* from 87. *The Rectory, High Street, Nunney, Frome, Somerset BA11 4LZ*   Frome (01373) 836732

HODDER, Trevor Valentine. b 31. Bps' Coll Cheshunt 65. **d** 67 **p** 68. C Oxhey All SS *St Alb* 67-70; C Digswell 70-73; V Colchester St Anne *Chelmsf* from 74. *St Anne's Vicarage, Compton Road, Colchester CO4 4BQ*   Colchester (01206) 860931

HODGE, Albert. b 40. N Ord Course 84. **d** 87 **p** 88. C Huyton St Geo *Liv* 87-89; P-in-c Widnes St Paul from 89; Chapl Halton Coll of FE from 89. *St Paul's Vicarage, Victoria Square, Widnes, Cheshire WA8 7QU*   0151-424 2221

HODGE, Anthony Charles. b 43. AKC66. **d** 67 **p** 68. C Carrington *S'well* 67-69; C Bawtry w Austerfield 69-72; C Misson 69-72; Grenada 72-74; Trinidad and Tobago 74-76; V Tuckingmill *Truro* 76-78; V Worksop St Paul *S'well* 78-81; P-in-c Patrington w Hollym, Welwick and Winestead *York* 81-86; R 86-88; V York St Olave w St Giles from 88; Chapl York Coll for Girls from 88. *St Olave's Vicarage, 52 Bootham, York YO3 7BZ*   York (01904) 625186

HODGE, Colin. b 39. Sarum & Wells Th Coll. **d** 83 **p** 84. NSM Wareham *Sarum* 84-87; C Parkstone St Pet w Branksea and St Osmund 87-89; V Lilliput from 89. *The Vicarage, 55 Lilliput Road, Poole, Dorset BH14 8JX*   Poole (01202) 708567

HODGE, Dr Graham Anthony. b 49. Univ of Wales MA PhD86. Lambeth STh Linc Th Coll 79. **d** 80 **p** 81. C Hale *Guildf* 80-82; C Christchurch *Win* 82-86; R Chawton and Farringdon from 86. *The Rectory, Farringdon, Alton, Hants GU34 3EE*   Tisted (01420) 588398

HODGE, John Shaw. b 30. Chich Th Coll 78. **d** 80 **p** 81. C Furze Platt *Ox* 80-83; V Kirkwhelpington, Kirkharle, Kirkheaton and Cambo *Newc* 83-84; TV Langley Marish *Ox* 84-87; rtd 87; Perm to Offic *Cant* from 87. *St Peter's, 15 The Street, Ash, Canterbury, Kent CT3 2HH*   Canterbury (01227) 813347

HODGE, Marilyn Elizabeth. See IVEY, Mrs Marilyn Elizabeth

HODGE, Canon Michael Robert. b 34. Pemb Coll Cam BA57 MA61. Ridley Hall Cam 57. **d** 59 **p** 60. C Harpurhey Ch Ch *Man* 59; C Blackpool St Mark *Blackb* 59-62; V Stalybridge Old St Geo *Man* 62-67; R Cobham w Luddesdowne and Dode *Roch* 67-81; Hon Can Roch Cathl from 81; R Bidborough from 81. *The Rectory, Rectory Drive, Bidborough, Tunbridge Wells, Kent TN3 0UL*   Tunbridge Wells (01892) 528081

HODGE, Nigel John. b 61. BTh83 Univ of Wales DPS85. St Mich Coll Llan 83. **d** 85 **p** 86. C Mynyddislwyn *Mon* 85-87; C

334

Machen 87-89; TV Ebbw Vale 89-91; V Abercarn from 91. *The Vicarage, Abercarn, Gwent NP1 5GU* Ebbw Vale (01495) 243919

HODGES, Francis Reginald. b 26. Selw Coll Cam BA48 MA61. Chich Th Coll 48. **d** 50 **p** 51. R St Breoke *Truro* 61-76; rtd 76; C St Kew *Truro* 77-78; P-in-c 78-80. *Tregellist Cottage, St Kew, Bodmin, Cornwall PL30 3HG* Bodmin (01208) 880083

HODGES, Jasper Tor. b 62. Leeds Univ BSc84 Sheff Univ MEng85 Lon Univ PGCE87. Trin Coll Bris BA94. **d** 94 **p** 95. C Holbeck *Ripon* from 94. *23 Park View, Leeds LS11 7AY* Leeds (0113) 277 7528

HODGES, Keith Michael. b 53. Southn Univ BTh82. Chich Th Coll 77. **d** 80 **p** 81. C Sydenham St Phil *S'wark* 80-84; Perm to Offic 85; C Leatherhead *Guildf* 86-89; V Aldershot St Aug from 89. *St Augustine's Vicarage, Holly Road, Aldershot, Hants GU12 4SE* Aldershot (01252) 20840

HODGES, Murray Knowles. b 02. K Coll Cam BA24 MA29. Ridley Hall Cam. **d** 25 **p** 26. V Muncaster w Waberthwaite *Carl* 57-75; rtd 75; Perm to Offic *Carl* from 77. *Eskside, Ravenglass, Cumbria CA18 1SF* Ravenglass (01229) 717259

HODGETTS, Alan Paul. b 54. BSc78. St Steph Ho Ox 79. **d** 82 **p** 83. C Perry Barr *Birm* 82-85; C Broseley w Benthall *Heref* 85-87; V Effingham w Lt Bookham *Guildf* from 87. *The Vicarage, Lower Road, Effingham, Leatherhead, Surrey KT24 5JR* Bookham (01372) 458314

HODGETTS, Colin William. b 40. St D Coll Lamp BA61 Ripon Hall Ox 61. **d** 63 **p** 64. C Hackney St Jo *Lon* 63-68; Hon C St Martin-in-the-Fields 70-76; C Creeksea w Althorne *Chelmsf* 76-79; Perm to Offic *Ex* from 84. *The Small School, Fore Street, Hartland, Bideford, Devon EX39 6AB* Hartland (01237) 441672

HODGETTS, Harry Samuel. b 30. Chich Th Coll 63. **d** 65 **p** 66. C Harton Colliery *Dur* 65-68; C Penzance St Mary *Truro* 68-70; V Penwerris 70-79; V Kettering St Mary *Pet* 79-94. *20 Crofton Close, Christchurch, Dorset BH23 2JN* Christchurch (01202) 474456

HODGINS, George Eric. b 12. ALCD39. **d** 39 **p** 40. R Lt Easton *Chelmsf* 63-73; R Alphamstone w Lamarsh and Pebmarsh 74-77; rtd 77. *Candles, 23 Church Street, Colne Engaine, Colchester CO6 2EX* Earls Colne (01787) 223776

HODGINS, John Henry. b 21. TCD BA43 BD48. TCD Div Sch Div Test44. **d** 45 **p** 46. Educn Org Ch of Ireland 69-71; Can Th Belf Cathl 71-76; Dean Killala *T, K & A* 76-79; Area Sec (Dios Ripon and York) CMS 79-83; C Acomb St Steph *York* 83-86; rtd 86. *57 Sandhurst Drive, Belfast BT9 5AZ* Belfast (01232) 668990

HODGINS, Ven Michael Minden. b 12. Lambeth Hon MA60 Cuddesdon Coll 38. **d** 39 **p** 40. Adn Hackney *Lon* 51-71; rtd 77. *Flat 5, Up The Quadrangle, Morden College, London SE3 0PU* 0181-858 4762

HODGINS, Philip Arthur. b 57. Lanc Univ BA78 Nottm Univ DipTh83 Bradf Univ MBA90 GradIPM91. Linc Th Coll 82. **d** 85 **p** 86. C Norton *Ches* 85-88; C Whitkirk *Ripon* 88-89; Perm to Offic *Bradf* 89-90; Perm to Offic *Chich* from 91; Jo Grooms Assn for Disabled People from 91. *Little Becks, Batts Bridge Road, Maresfield, Uckfield, E Sussex TN22 2HJ* Uckfield (01825) 762767

HODGKINSON, Canon Arthur Edward. b 13. Dur Univ LTh42. Edin Th Coll 36. **d** 39 **p** 40. Provost St Andr Cathl *Ab* 65-78; Hon Can Ch Cathl Connecticut 65-78; Area Sec (S Wales) USPG 78-82; Hon Can St Andr Cathl *Ab* from 81; rtd 82; Hon C Eyemouth *Edin* 82-86; Perm to Offic *Llan* 86-89. *36 Forbes Road, Edinburgh EH10 4ED* 0131-229 7593

HODGKINSON, Frank Cyril. b 18. Lon Univ BA50. Oak Hill Th Coll 46. **d** 51 **p** 52. V Barkby *Leic* 68-74; V Leic St Chris 74-77; V Ryhall w Essendine *Pet* 77-83; rtd 83; Perm to Offic *Nor* from 84. *16 Waveney Close, Wells-next-the-Sea, Norfolk NR23 1HU*

HODGKINSON, Canon John. b 27. Trin Hall Cam BA51 MA55. Linc Th Coll 51. **d** 53 **p** 54. R Old Brumby *Linc* 66-71; V Kendal H Trin *Carl* 71-90; Hon Can Carl Cathl 84-90; rtd 90. *Boxtree Barn, Levens, Kendal, Cumbria LA8 8NZ* Sedgwick (015395) 60806

HODGKINSON, John David. b 57. Birm Univ BA78 Edin Univ BD89. Edin Th Coll 86. **d** 89 **p** 90. C Briercliffe *Blackb* 89-92; C Darwen St Cuth w Tockholes St Steph 92-94; R Harrington *Carl* from 94. *The Rectory, Rectory Close, Harrington, Workington, Cumbria CA14 5PN* Harrington (01946) 830215

HODGKINSON, Oswald Merchant. b 21. Qu Coll Birm 68. **d** 69 **p** 70. C Shard End *Birm* 69-74; V 74-80; TV Wrexham *St As* 80-86; rtd 86; Perm to Offic *St As* from 86; Perm to Offic *Ban* from 86. *12 Arfryn, Llanrhos, Llandudno LL30 1PB* Llandudno (01492) 584419

HODGSON, Anthony Owen Langlois. b 35. Ripon Hall Ox 60. **d** 62 **p** 63. C Blakeney w Lt Langham *Nor* 62-65; C Stiffkey w Morston 62-65; C Paddington Ch Ch *Lon* 66-70; Area Sec (Beds & Cambs) Chr Aid 70-74; (Herts & Hunts) 70-73; (Rutland & Northants) 73-74; V Gt w Lt Gidding and Steeple

Gidding *Ely* 77-81; Warden Dovedale Ho 81-89; P-in-c Ilam w Blore Ray and Okeover *Lich* 81-89; Dir Chr Rural Cen 89-91; C Checkley from 91; C Stramshall from 91. *The New Rectory, Church Lane, Checkley, Stoke-on-Trent ST10 4NJ* Tean (01538) 722732

HODGSON, Anthony William. b 35. Dur Univ BSc56. Wells Th Coll 58. **d** 60 **p** 61. C Gateshead St Mary *Dur* 60-62; C Leeds All SS *Ripon* 62-66; V Hartlepool St Oswald *Dur* 66-75; C-in-c Stockton St Jas CD 75-81; V Easington Colliery 81-89; V Eighton Banks from 89. *St Thomas's Vicarage, 8 Norwood Court, Gateshead, Tyne & Wear NE9 7XF* 0191-487 6927

HODGSON, Antony Robert. b 66. Westcott Ho Cam 90. **d** 93 **p** 94. C Chorley St Geo *Blackb* from 93. *159 Pilling Lane, Chorley, Lancs PR7 3EF* Chorley (01257) 234936

HODGSON, Canon Charles. b 16. St Aid Coll Dur LTh42 St Jo Coll Dur BA43 MA45. St Aid Birkenhead 39. **d** 43 **p** 44. V Middleton *Birm* 60-70; R Wishaw 60-70; Dioc Adult Educn Officer 60-70; Dioc Missr and Tr Officer Ox 70-82; Hon Can Ch Ch *Ox* 81; RD Witney 81-86; rtd 82. *40 Wykeham Way, Haddenham, Aylesbury, Bucks HP17 8BX* Haddenham (01844) 292593

HODGSON, Christopher. b 24. Or Coll Ox BA49 MA54. Qu Coll Birm 50. **d** 52 **p** 53. V Pembury *Roch* 64-82; Chapl Pembury Hosp Tunbridge Wells 66-82; R Aynho w Newbottle and Charlton *Pet* 82-85; Chapl Burrswood Cen for Divine Healing 85-94; C Castle Bromwich St Clem *Birm* 86-94; rtd 94. *30 Shortheath Crest, Farnham, Surrey GU9 8SB* Farnham (01252) 733179

HODGSON, David George. b 54. Coll of Resurr Mirfield. **d** 82 **p** 83. C Stainton-in-Cleveland *York* 82-87; R Loftus 87; P-in-c Carlin How w Skinningrove 87; R Loftus and Carlin How w Skinningrove 87-93; V Middlesb Ascension from 93. *The Ascension Vicarage, Penrith Road, Middlesbrough, Cleveland TS3 7JR* Middlesbrough (01642) 244857

HODGSON, David Peter. b 56. Fitzw Coll Cam BA77 MA81 Nottm Univ BA82 MTh85. St Jo Coll Nottm 80. **d** 83 **p** 84. C Guiseley w Esholt *Bradf* 83-86; Asst Chapl Loughb Univ *Leic* 86-89; P-in-c Hatf Broad Oak *Chelmsf* 89-90; P-in-c Bush End 89-90; P-in-c Hatf Broad Oak and Bush End from 90; Ind Chapl to Harlow from 89. *The Vicarage, Hatfield Broad Oak, Bishop's Stortford, Herts CM22 7HD* Bishop's Stortford (01279) 718274

HODGSON, Derek Cyril. b 29. Hatf Coll Dur BA50 St Chad's Coll Dur DipTh54. **d** 54 **p** 55. C Lindley *Wakef* 54-58; C-in-c Mixenden CD 58-62; V Thurlstone 62-75; V Mytholmroyd from 75. *The Vicarage, Brier Hey Lane, Mytholmroyd, Hebden Bridge, W Yorkshire HX7 5PJ* Halifax (01422) 883130

HODGSON, George. b 36. Qu Coll Birm 75. **d** 78 **p** 79. NSM Wordsley *Lich* 78-93; NSM Wordsley *Worc* from 93; Perm to Offic 84-93. *1 Newfield Drive, Kingswinford, W Midlands DY6 8HY* Kingswinford (01384) 292543

HODGSON, John. b 35. St Jo Coll Cam MA62 Lon Univ BD61. St Deiniol's Hawarden 80. **d** 81 **p** 82. Hon C Padiham *Blackb* 81-84; C W Burnley 85-87; V from 87. *The Vicarage, Padiham Road, Burnley, Lancs BB12 6PA* Padiham (01282) 775629

HODGSON, Ven John Derek. b 31. St Jo Coll Dur BA53. Cranmer Hall Dur DipTh59. **d** 59 **p** 60. C Stranton *Dur* 59-62; C Monkwearmouth St Andr 62-64; V Stillington 64-66; V Consett 66-75; TR Gateshead 75-83; RD Gateshead 76-83; Hon Can Dur Cathl 78-83; Can Res Dur Cathl from 83; Adn Auckland 83-93; Adn Dur from 93. *15 The College, Durham DH1 3EQ* 0191-384 7534

HODGSON, Matthew William. b 13. Lich Th Coll 40. **d** 44 **p** 45. V Woodhorn w Newbiggin *Newc* 71-77; rtd 77; Lic to Offic *Newc* 77-93. *5 Cumming Street, Nairn, Inverness IV12 4NQ* Nairn (01667) 56719

HODGSON, Peter Richard. b 23. Dur Univ BA50. Bps' Coll Cheshunt 49. **d** 52 **p** 53. V Bolsterstone *Sheff* 61-80; V Kirton in Holland *Linc* 80-86; rtd 86. *Omega, Littlemoor Lane, Sibsey, Boston, Lincs PE22 0TU* Boston (01205) 750167

HODGSON, Roger Vaughan. b 27. Magd Coll Cam BA49 MA54. Cuddesdon Coll 55. **d** 56 **p** 57. R Lt Hadham *St Alb* 65-78; Chapl Oporto *Eur* 78-80; Chapl and Lect St Deiniol's Lib Hawarden 81-82; V Coldwaltham *Chich* 82-92; rtd 92; Asst Chapl Costa Blanca *Eur* 92-94. *21 Maltravers Street, Arundel, W Sussex BN18 9AP* Arundel (01903) 884708

HODGSON, Ven Thomas Richard Burnham. b 26. FRMetS88. Lon Coll of Div BD52 ALCD52. **d** 52 **p** 53. V Raughton Head w Gatesgill *Carl* 67-73; Bp's Dom Chapl 67-73; Dir of Ords 70-74; Hon Can Carl Cathl 72-91; V Grange-over-Sands 73-79; RD Windermere 76-79; P-in-c Mosser 79; V 79-83; Adn W Cumberland 79-91; rtd 91. *58 Greenacres, Wetheral, Carlisle CA4 8LD* Carlisle (01228) 561159

HODGSON, Vernon Charles. b 34. MRPharmS58 Lon Univ BPharm58 Univ of Wales (Cardiff) DPS91. St Mich Coll Llan 90 Llan Dioc Tr Scheme 83. **d** 86 **p** 87. NSM Roath St Marg *Llan* 86-91; C Caerphilly 91-93; V Llanbister and Llanbadarn

Fynydd w Llananno *S & B* from 93. *The Vicarage, Llanbister, Llandrindod Wells, Powys LD1 6TN* Llandrindod Wells (01597) 83333

HODKIN, Canon Hedley. b 02. Sheff Univ MA23 Ch Coll Cam BA25 MA31. Westcott Ho Cam 35. **d** 35 **p** 36. Can Res Man Cathl *Man* 57-70; Sub-Dean 66-70; rtd 70; Perm to Offic *Derby* 70-94; Lic to Offic *Sheff* 72-87. *62 Glendridding Drive, Barrow-in-Furness, Cumbria LA14 4PB* Barrow-in-Furness (01229) 825155

HODKINSON, George Leslie. b 48. Qu Coll Birm 86. **d** 88 **p** 89. C Hall Green St Pet *Birm* 88-91; TV Solihull from 91. *St Helen's House, 6 St Helen's Road, Solihull, W Midlands B91 2DA* 0121-704 2878

HODSON, Gordon George. b 35. St Chad's Coll Dur BA59 DipTh60. **d** 60 **p** 61. C Tettenhall Regis *Lich* 60-64; C Rugeley 64-68; V Shrewsbury St Mich 68-74; V Kinnerley w Melverley 74-87; P-in-c Knockin w Maesbrook 75-87; P-in-c Chebsey 87-91; P-in-c Seighford, Derrington and Cresswell 87-91; V Chebsey, Ellenhall and Seighford-with-Creswell from 91. *The Vicarage, Seighford, Stafford ST18 9PQ* Seighford (01785) 282829

HODSON, Keith. b 53. Hatf Coll Dur BA74. Wycliffe Hall Ox 77. **d** 80 **p** 81. C Ashton on Mersey St Mary *Ches* 80-84; C Polegate *Chich* 84-92; V Baddesley Ensor w Grendon *Birm* from 92. *The Vicarage, Baddesley Ensor, Atherstone, Warks CV9 2BY* Atherstone (01827) 715327

HODSON, Miss Margaret Christina. b 39. Linc Th Coll 88. **d** 90 **p** 94. Par Dn Old Trafford St Jo *Man* 90-94; C from 94. *115 Northumberland Road, Manchester M16 9BQ* 0161-876 5055

HODSON, Raymond Leslie. b 42. St Chad's Coll Dur BSc64 DipTh66. **d** 66 **p** 67. C Adlington *Blackb* 66-68; C Cleveleys 68-72; V Ewood 72-77; V Nazeing *Chelmsf* 77-84; R Ampthill w Millbrook and Steppingley *St Alb* 84-95; Chapl Madrid *Eur* from 95. *Sector Officios 31, 2A Tres Cantos, 28760 Madrid, Spain* Madrid (1) 576-5109

HODSON, William. b 42. Man Univ BA. Cranmer Hall Dur 81. **d** 82 **p** 83. C Ashton St Mich *Man* 82-86; V Tintwistle *Ches* 86-93; P-in-c Weston from 93. *All Saints' Vicarage, 13 Cemetery Road, Weston, Crewe CW2 5LQ* Crewe (01270) 582585

HOEY, Canon David Paul. b 57. QUB BD79. CITC 79. **d** 81 **p** 82. C Belf Whiterock *Conn* 81-83; C Portadown St Mark *Arm* 83-84; I Cleenish w Mullaghdun *Clogh* 84-90; I Magheracross from 90; Dir of Ords from 91; Preb Clogh Cathl from 95. *The Rectory, Ballinamallard, Co Fermanagh BT94 2BT* Ballinamallard (01365) 388238

HOEY, Ven Raymond George. b 46. TCD BA70 MA. **d** 72 **p** 73. C Portadown St Mark *Arm* 72-78; I Camlough w Mullaglass from 78; Dom Chapl to Abp Arm from 86; RD Mullabrack 88-92; Adn Arm from 92. *2 Maytown Road, Bessbrook, Newry, Co Down BT35 7LY* Bessbrook (01693) 830301 Fax as telephone

HOEY, Thomas Kenneth (Augustine). b 15. St Edm Hall Ox BA38 MA44. Cuddesdon Coll 39. **d** 40 **p** 41. CR from 50; Master R Foundn of St Kath in Ratcliffe 62-72; Lic to Offic *Man* 73-76; Perm to Offic *Lon* 84-92; rtd 85. *Charterhouse, London EC1M 6AN* 0171-253 9503

HOEY, William Thomas. b 32. CITC 64. **d** 66 **p** 67. C Belf St Mary *Conn* 66-68; C Lisburn Ch Ch 69-72; I Ballinderry 72-78; I Belf St Simon w St Phil from 78. *St Simon's Rectory, 106 Upper Lisburn Road, Belfast BT10 0BB* Belfast (01232) 617562

HOFFMAN, Canon Stanley Harold. b 17. St Edm Hall Ox BA39 MA43 Kent Univ MA82. Linc Th Coll 40. **d** 41 **p** 42. Dir of Educn *Roch* 65-80; Warden of Readers 73-80; Chapl to The Queen 76-88; rtd 82; Perm to Offic *Guildf* 82-94. *Zansizzey, Trevone, Padstow, Cornwall PL28 8QJ* Padstow (01841) 520864

HOFMEESTER, Adrian Sidney. b 13. TCD BA50 MA53. **d** 51 **p** 52. I Conn w Antrim St Patr *Conn* 61-84; RD Ballymena 74-84; rtd 84. *Elstow, 11 Upper Knockbreda Road, Belfast BT6 9QH* Belfast (01232) 792040

HOGAN, Edward James Martin. b 46. Trin Coll Bris. **d** 85 **p** 86. C St Austell *Truro* 85-88; V Gt Broughton and Broughton Moor *Carl* 88-94; V St Stythians w Perranarworthal and Gwennap *Truro* from 94. *The Vicarage, Old Vicarage Close, Stithians, Truro, Cornwall TR3 7DZ* Stithians (01209) 860123

HOGAN, John James. b 24. St Edm Hall Ox BA51 MA56. Wells Th Coll 51. **d** 53 **p** 54. V Woore *Lich* 58-84; P-in-c Norton in Hales 82-84; V Woore and Norton in Hales 84-89; rtd 89. *Wrekin Prospect, Audlem Road, Woore, Crewe CW3 9RJ* Pipe Gate (01630) 647677

HOGAN, William Riddell. b 22. Qu Coll Birm 48. **d** 51 **p** 52. V Greetland *Wakef* 59-73; V Greetland and W Vale 73-80; V Kellington w Whitley 80-87; rtd 87. *15 The Pastures, Carlton, Goole, N Humberside DN14 9QF* Goole (01405) 862233

HOGARTH, Alan Francis. b 58. Oak Hill Th Coll BA89. **d** 89 **p** 90. C Felixstowe SS Pet and Paul *St E* 89-93; R Beckington w

Standerwick, Berkley, Rodden etc *B & W* from 93. *8 Church Street, Beckington, Bath BA3 6TG* Frome (01373) 830314

HOGARTH, Foley James Myddelton. b 16. Ch Ch Ox BA38 MA42. Wells Th Coll 38. **d** 39 **p** 40. C Rainbow Hill St Barn *Worc* 39-41; C Charlton Kings H Apostles *Glouc* 41-42; CF 42-46; V Fordcombe *Roch* 47-52; Asst Hd Master Holmewood Ho Sch Kent 52-53; Australia from 53. *9 Northumberland Street, Heathpool, S Australia 5068* Adelaide (8) 316318

HOGARTH, Joseph. b 32. Edin Th Coll 65. **d** 67 **p** 67. C Walney Is *Carl* 67-71; V Whitehaven St Jas 71-76; V Millom H Trin w Thwaites 76-82; V Maryport 82-91; V Consett *Dur* from 91. *The Vicarage, 10 Aynsley Terrace, Consett, Co Durham DH8 5NF* Consett (01207) 502235

HOGBEN, Ven Peter Graham. b 25. Bps' Coll Cheshunt 60. **d** 61 **p** 62. R Westborough *Guildf* 64-71; V Ewell 71-82; Hon Can Guildf Cathl 79-90; RD Epsom 80-82; Adn Dorking 82-90; rtd 90. *3 School Road, Rowledge, Farnham, Surrey GU10 4EJ* Frensham (01252) 793533

HOGG, Anthony. b 42. Univ of Wales (Lamp) BA63. Linc Th Coll 64 Chich Th Coll 78. **d** 78 **p** 79. NSM Ridgeway *Ox* 78-86; C 90-91; NSM W w E Hanney 86-88; Hd Master New Coll Sch Ox 88-89; P-in-c Hanney, Denchworth and E Challow *Ox* 91-92; V from 92. *The Vicarage, Winter Lane, West Hanney, Wantage, Oxon OX12 0LF* Wantage (01235) 868863

HOGG, Neil Richard. b 46. BSc69. Ridley Hall Cam 82. **d** 84 **p** 85. C Bingham *S'well* 84-87; TV Bushbury *Lich* from 87. *The Vicarage, 17 Goodyear Avenue, Low Hill, Wolverhampton WV10 9JX* Wolverhampton (01902) 731713

HOGG, Peter Stuart. b 42. Ch Coll Cam BA65 MA68. NW Ord Course 74. **d** 77 **p** 78. NSM Bollington St Jo *Ches* 77-88; Chapl Wells Cathl Sch from 88. *18 Vicars' Close, Wells, Somerset BA5 2UJ* Wells (01749) 674527

HOGG, Robert Bell. b 08. **d** 89. NSM Edin St Mary *Edin* from 89. *141 Broughton Road, Edinburgh EH7 4JJ* 0131-557 3350

HOGG, William John. b 49. New Coll Ox MA71 Lon Univ CertEd72 Crewe & Alsager Coll MSc88. Edin Th Coll 86. **d** 88 **p** 89. C Oxton *Ches* 88-93; R Bromborough from 93. *The Rectory, Mark Rake, Bromborough, Wirral, Merseyside L62 2DH* 0151-334 1466

HOGG, William Ritson. b 47. Leeds Univ BSc69. Qu Coll Birm DipTh71. **d** 72 **p** 73. C Bordesley St Oswald *Birm* 72-76; TV Seacroft *Ripon* 76-82; V Hunslet St Mary 82-88; V Catterick from 88. *The Vicarage, High Green, Catterick, Richmond, N Yorkshire DL10 7LN* Richmond (01748) 811462

HOGGARD, Mrs Jean Margaret. b 36. NW Ord Course 76. dss 79 **d** 87 **p** 94. Northowram *Wakef* 79-87; Par Dn 87-94; C from 94. *13 Joseph Avenue, Northowram, Halifax, W Yorkshire HX3 7HJ* Halifax (01422) 201475

HOGGETT, Robert William John. b 13. Worc Ord Coll 65. **d** 67 **p** 68. C Bromsgrove St Jo *Worc* 67-71; V Keelby *Linc* 71-87; V Riby 74-87; V Aylesby 77-87; RD Haverstoe 81-86; rtd 87; Perm to Offic *Linc* from 88. *Lauriston, North Halls, Binbrook, Lincoln LN3 6BW* Binbrook (01472) 398157

HOGWOOD, Brian Roy. b 38. Bps' Coll Cheshunt. **d** 65 **p** 92. NSM Thetford *Nor* 91-93; Hon C from 93. *31 Byron Walk, Thetford, Norfolk IP24 1JX* Thetford (01842) 763579

HOLBROOK, Colin Eric Basford. *See* BASFORD HOLBROOK, Colin Eric

HOLBROOK, John Edward. b 62. St Pet Coll Ox BA83 MA87. Ridley Hall Cam 82. **d** 86 **p** 87. C Barnes St Mary *S'wark* 86-89; C Bletchley *Ox* 89-93; C N Bletchley CD 89-93; V Adderbury w Milton from 93. *The Vicarage, 13 Dog Close, Adderbury, Banbury, Oxon OX17 3EF* Banbury (01295) 810309

HOLBROOKE-JONES, Stanley Charles. b 27. Dur Univ BA58 DipTh60 MA77. Cranmer Hall Dur 58. **d** 60 **p** 61. C Gravesend St Jas *Roch* 60-63; C Streatham Immanuel w St Anselm *S'wark* 63-66; V W Bromwich H Trin *Lich* 66-79; V W Exe *Ex* 79-88; R Poole *Sarum* from 88; Miss to Seamen from 88. *The Rectory, 10 Poplar Close, Poole, Dorset BH15 1LP* Poole (01202) 672694

HOLCOMBE, Graham William Arthur. b 50. ARCM69. St Mich Coll Llan DipTh80. **d** 80 **p** 81. C Neath w Llantwit *Llan* 80-84; Asst Youth Chapl 81-84; PV Llan Cathl 84-86; V Pentyrch from 86. *The Vicarage, Pentyrch, Cardiff CF4 8QF* Cardiff (01222) 890318

HOLDAWAY, Graham Michael. b 51. Southn Univ BSc73. Sarum & Wells Th Coll 74. **d** 77 **p** 78. C Walton-on-Thames *Guildf* 77-81; TV Westborough 81-86; Perm to Offic from 86. *2 Sheerwater Cottages, Sheerwater Road, West Byfleet, Surrey KT14 6AB* Byfleet (01932) 340396

HOLDAWAY, Dr Simon Douglas. b 47. Lanc Univ BA73 Sheff Univ PhD81. N Ord Course 78. **d** 81 **p** 82. NSM Gleadless *Sheff* from 81; Sen Lect in Sociology Sheff Univ from 81. *136 Totley Brook Road, Sheffield S17 3QU* Sheffield (0114) 236 3711

HOLDAWAY, Stephen Douglas. b 45. Hull Univ BA67. Ridley Hall Cam 67. **d** 70 **p** 71. C Southn Thornhill St Chris *Win* 70-73; C Tardebigge *Worc* 73-78; Ind Chapl 73-78; Ind Chapl *Linc* 78-93; Co-ord City Cen Group Min 81-93; TR Louth from 93; RD Louthesk from 95. *The Rectory, Westgate, Louth, Lincs LN11 9YE* Louth (01507) 610247

HOLDCROFT, Ian Thomas. b 46. St Jo Coll Cam BA68 MA71. Westcott Ho Cam 72. **d** 73 **p** 74. C Bris St Mary Redcliffe w Temple etc *Bris* 73-76; Th Educn Sec Chr Aid 76-80; Exec Sec 80-82; Hon C Battersea St Mary *S'wark* 81-86; Dep Sec Gen Syn Bd for Miss and Unity 82-86; V Whitchurch *Bris* 86-92; V Almondsbury from 92; P-in-c Olveston 92-95; P-in-c Littleton on Severn w Elberton from 92. *The Vicarage, Almondsbury, Bristol BS12 4DS* Almondsbury (01454) 613223

HOLDEN, Canon Arthur Stuart James. b 23. ALCD51. **d** 51 **p** 52. V Earls Colne *Chelmsf* 61-82; V White Colne 68-82; V Earls Colne and White Colne 82-88; Hon Can Chelmsf Cathl 80-88; rtd 88. *10 Wroxham Close, Colchester CO3 3RQ* Colchester (01206) 560845

HOLDEN, Geoffrey. b 26. FCII54. Oak Hill Th Coll 57. **d** 59 **p** 60. R Bath St Mich w St Paul *B & W* 66-73; Chapl Bath Gp Hosps 73-91; rtd 91. *10 Marlborough Lane, Bath BA1 2NQ* Bath (01225) 427933

HOLDEN, Geoffrey Ralph. b 25. Ripon Hall Ox 64. **d** 65 **p** 66. C Walsall *Lich* 68-71; R Longton St Jas 71-75; rtd 90. *Aberscethin, Talybont, Gwynedd LL43 2AR* Dyffryn (01341) 247538

HOLDEN, Jack Crawford (Simon). b 30. Leeds Univ BA59. Coll of Resurr Mirfield 59. **d** 61 **p** 61. C Middlesb All SS *York* 61-64; Lic to Offic *Wakef* 65-69; CR from 67; Asst Chapl Univ Coll *Lon* 69-74; Lic to Offic 70-74. *House of the Resurrection, Mirfield, W Yorkshire WF14 0BN* Mirfield (01924) 494318

HOLDEN, Canon Jack Hatherley. b 12. MBE65. St Aug Coll Cant. **d** 41 **p** 42. V Stoke Newington St Andr *Lon* 65-79; rtd 79; P-in-c Islington St Pet *Lon* 80-82; P-in-c Islington St Jas w St Phil 81-82; C St Ethelburga Bishopgate 86-88. *Charterhouse, London EC1M 6AH* 0171-490 0245

HOLDEN, Canon John. b 33. MBE76. Selly Oak Coll 71 Ridley Hall Cam 65. **d** 67 **p** 68. C Flixton St Jo CD *Man* 67-71; Uganda 71-75; V Aston SS Pet and Paul *Birm* 75-87; RD Aston 86-87; Hon Can Birm Cathl 86-87; R Ulverston St Mary w H Trin *Carl* from 87; RD Furness 90-94; Hon Can Carl Cathl 91-94. *The Rectory, 15 Ford Park Crescent, Ulverston, Cumbria LA12 7JR* Ulverston (01229) 584331

HOLDEN, John Norman. b 35. **d** 95. NSM Codicote *St Alb* from 95. *35 Grange Rise, Codicote, Hitchin, Herts SG4 8YL* Codicote (01438) 820124

HOLDEN, John Worrall. b 44. K Coll Lon AKC67 DPS. **d** 70 **p** 71. C Derby St Bart *Derby* 70-72; Lic to Offic 72-74; Hon C St Helier *S'wark* 74-77; Hon C St Marylebone All SS *Lon* 80-83; Hon C St Botolph Aldgate w H Trin Minories from 84. *St Botolph's Vestry, London EC3N 1AB* 0171-283 1670

HOLDEN, Paul Edward. b 53. CEng79 MIM MIBF BSc75 DipHE84. Trin Coll Bris 82. **d** 86 **p** 87. C Harpurhey Ch Ch *Man* 86-88; C Harpurhey St Steph 88-93; Min Harpurhey LEP 88-93. *2 Baywood Street, Harpurhey, Manchester M9 1XX* 0161-205 2938

HOLDEN, Richard Davis. b 03. St Aid Birkenhead 33. **d** 36 **p** 37. R Sidbury *Ex* 60-70; rtd 70; Lic to Offic *Ex* from 70. *The Rectory, High Street, Wellington, Somerset TA21 8RF* Wellington (01823) 662248

HOLDER, John William. b 41. Chester Coll CertEd61 Open Univ BA73 Bath Univ MEd85. Trin Coll Bris MA94. **d** 87 **p** 88. C Brockworth *Glouc* 87-91; P-in-c Avening w Cherington 91-95; V Cinderford St Jo from 95. *St John's Vicarage, 1 Abbots View, Cinderford, Glos GL14 3EG* Dean (01594) 825446

HOLDER, Kenneth William (Ken). b 29. Sarum Th Coll 60. **d** 61 **p** 62. C Crawley *Chich* 61-65; C-in-c Wick CD 65-73; V Hangleton 73-79; R Rotherfield 79-81; R Rotherfield w Mark Cross 81-83; Chapl Eastbourne Coll 83-84; C Farnborough *Roch* 85; TV Mildenhall *St E* 87-92; R Redgrave cum Botesdale w Rickinghall from 92. *The Rectory, Bury Road, Rickinghall, Diss, Norfolk IP22 1HA* Diss (01379) 898685

HOLDING, Kenneth George Frank. b 27. Sarum & Wells Th Coll 75. **d** 77 **p** 78. C Bexley St Mary *Roch* 77-80; Min Joydens Wood St Barn CD 80-85; R Mereworth w W Peckham 85-92; rtd 92. *121 Burden Road, Beverley, N Humberside HU17 9LW* Hull (01482) 872609

HOLDRIDGE, Bernard Lee. b 35. Lich Th Coll 64. **d** 67 **p** 68. C Swinton *Sheff* 67-71; V Doncaster St Jude 71-81; R Rawmarsh w Parkgate 81-88; RD Rotherham 86-88; V Worksop Priory *S'well* 88-94; Adn Doncaster *Sheff* from 94. *Fairview House, 14 Armthorpe Lane, Doncaster, S Yorkshire DN2 5LZ* Doncaster (01302) 325787

HOLDSTOCK, Godfrey. b 48. St Jo Coll Cam BA69 MA72 Ox Univ BA77 MA81. St Steph Ho Ox 76. **d** 78 **p** 79. C Chislehurst Annunciation *Roch* 78-81; Hon C Richmond St Mary w St

Matthias and St Jo *S'wark* 82-85; V Billesdon and Skeffington *Leic* 85-89; TV High Wycombe *Ox* 89-91; Chapl St Paul's Prep Sch Barnes 91-92; NSM Terriers *Ox* 92-93; P-in-c Barnes H Trin *S'wark* from 93. *Holy Trinity Vicarage, 162 Castelnau, London SW13 9ET* 0181-748 5744

HOLDSWORTH, Ian Scott. b 52. Sheff Poly BA75. Oak Hill Th Coll BA81. **d** 81 **p** 82. C Denham *Ox* 81-84; P-in-c S Leigh 84-89; P-in-c Cogges 84-88; V 88-89. *Address temp unknown*

HOLDSWORTH, John Ivor. b 49. Univ of Wales (Abth) BA70 Univ of Wales (Cardiff) BD73 MTh75. St Mich Coll Llan 70. **d** 73 **p** 74. C Newport St Paul *Mon* 73-77; CF (TAVR) 75-90; V Abercraf and Callwen *S & B* 77-86; Bp's Chapl for Th Educn from 80; V Gorseinon from 86; Hon Lect Th Univ of Wales (Swansea) from 88. *The Vicarage, 42 Princess Street, Gorseinon, Swansea SA4 4US* Gorseinon (01792) 892849

HOLDSWORTH, Michael Andrew. b 65. Univ Coll Dur BA88. Ripon Coll Cuddesdon BA92. **d** 93 **p** 94. C Cannock *Lich* from 93. *44 Manor Avenue, Cannock, Staffs WS11 1AA* Cannock (01543) 502896

HOLE, Very Rev Derek Norman. b 33. Linc Th Coll 57. **d** 60 **p** 61. C Knighton St Mary Magd *Leic* 60-62; S Africa 62-64; C Kenilworth St Nic *Cov* 64-67; R Burton Latimer *Pet* 67-73; V Leic St Jas *Leic* 73-92; Hon Can Leic Cathl 83-92; RD Christianity (Leic) S 83-92; Provost Leic from 92; Chapl to The Queen 85-93. *The Provost's House, 1 St Martin's East, Leicester LE1 5FX* Leicester (0116) 262 5294 Fax 262 5295

HOLEHOUSE, Ernest William. b 15. St Aid Birkenhead 38. **d** 41 **p** 42. C Wickenby w Friesthorpe *Linc* 71-80; C Faldingworth w Buslingthorpe 73-80; rtd 80. *Abbey House, 5 Tennyson Road, Worthing, W Sussex BN11 4BY*

HOLFORD, Andrew Peter. b 62. Nottm Univ BSc84. Cranmer Hall Dur 87. **d** 90 **p** 91. C Waltham Cross *St Alb* 90-93; C Northn St Benedict *Pet* 93-95; V Pet Ch Carpenter from 95. *The Vicarage, Chestnut Avenue, Peterborough PE1 4PE* Peterborough (01733) 67140

HOLFORD, John Alexander. b 40. Chich Th Coll 65. **d** 67 **p** 68. C Cottingley *Bradf* 67-71; C Baildon 71-73; P-in-c Bingley H Trin 73-74; V 74-86; V Woodhall 86-93; C Shelf 93-94; TV Shelf St Mich w Buttershaw St Aid from 94. *91A Mandale Road, Bradford, W Yorkshire BD6 3JS* Bradford (01274) 675015

HOLGATE, Dr David Andrew. b 54. Cape Town Univ BA77 Port Eliz Univ BA89 Rhodes Univ MTh90 PhD94. All Nations Chr Coll DipTh82. **d** 82 **p** 84. S Africa 82-93; P-in-c Felsted *Chelmsf* from 93; Continuing Minl Educn Officer from 93. *The Vicarage, Felsted, Dunmow, Essex CM6 3DQ* Great Dunmow (01371) 820242

✠**HOLLAND, Rt Rev Alfred Charles.** b 27. St Chad's Coll Dur BA50 DipTh52. **d** 52 **p** 53 **c** 70. C W Hackney St Barn *Lon* 52-54; Australia 55-93; from 94; Asst Bp Perth 70-77; Bp Newc 78-92; rtd 93; Jerusalem 93-94. *21 Sullivan Crescent, Wanniassa, ACT, Australia 2903* Wanniassa (6) 231-8368

✠**HOLLAND, Rt Rev Edward.** b 36. AKC64. **d** 65 **p** 66 **c** 86. C Dartford H Trin *Roch* 65-69; C Mill Hill Jo Keble Ch *Lon* 69-72; Prec Gib Cathl *Eur* 72-74; Chapl Naples Ch Ch 74-79; Chapl Bromley Hosp 79-86; V Bromley St Mark *Roch* 79-86; Suff Bp Eur 86-95; Dean Brussels 86-95; Area Bp Colchester *Chelmsf* from 95. *1 Fitzwalter Road, Colchester CO3 3SS* Colchester (01206) 576648 Fax 763868

HOLLAND, Glyn. b 59. Hull Univ BA Bris Univ CertEd. Coll of Resurr Mirfield 83. **d** 85 **p** 86. C Brighouse St Martin *Wakef* 85-89; V Ferrybridge from 89; Chapl Pontefract Gen Infirmary Wakef from 89. *St Andrew's Vicarage, 5 Pontefract Road, Ferrybridge, Knottingley, W Yorkshire WF11 8PN* Pontefract (01977) 672772

HOLLAND, Dr Henry Bowlby Tristram. b 11. Edin Univ MB, ChB34. Edin Th Coll 52. **d** 66 **p** 67. Pakistan 66-71; C Edin SS Phil and Jas *Edin* 71-77; C W Linton 77-88; C Penicuik 77-88; rtd 88. *Cuaig, Linton Bank Drive, West Linton, Peeblesshire EH46 7DT* West Linton (01968) 60454

HOLLAND, Jack Newton Charles. b 08. OBE57. St Edm Hall Ox BA30 MA47. Westcott Ho Cam. **d** 31 **p** 32. R St Mabyn *Truro* 69-74; C-in-c Helland 69-74; rtd 74; Perm to Offic *B & W* 75-93. *Manormead Residential Home, Tilford Road, Hindhead, Surrey GU26 6RA* Hindhead (01428) 604780

HOLLAND, John Stuart. b 52. Sarum & Wells Th Coll 77. **d** 80 **p** 81. C Wylde Green *Birm* 80-83; C Swanage and Studland *Sarum* 83-85; P-in-c Handley w Gussage St Andrew and Pentridge 85-88; TV Preston w Sutton Poyntz and Osmington w Poxwell from 88. *The Vicarage, 58 Littlemoor Road, Preston, Weymouth, Dorset DT3 6AA* Weymouth (01305) 833704

HOLLAND, Laurence Frederick Alfred (Fred). b 21. Sarum & Wells Th Coll. **d** 87 **p** 88. NSM Beaminster Area *Sarum* 87-92; Perm to Offic from 94. *18 St Mary Well Street, Beaminster, Dorset DT8 3BB* Beaminster (01308) 862426

HOLLAND, Mrs Linda (Lynne). b 48. Sarum & Wells Th Coll DCM93. **d** 93 **p** 94. Par Dn Queensbury All SS *Lon* 93-94;

HOLLAND

C from 94. *116 Stag Lane, Edgware, Middx HA8 5LL* 0181-204 3044

HOLLAND, Matthew Francis. b 52. Lon Univ BA73. Qu Coll Birm DipTh78. **d** 79 **p** 80. C Ecclesall *Sheff* 79-83; TV Gleadless Valley 83-86; TR 86-88; V Sheff Gillcar St Silas 88-92; V Sheff St Silas Broomhall from 92. *St Silas's Vicarage, 40 Hanover Street, Sheffield S3 7WT* Sheffield (0114) 272 5300

HOLLAND, Paul William. b 55. Coll of Resurr Mirfield 78. **d** 80 **p** 81. C Parkstone St Pet w Branksea and St Osmund *Sarum* 80-83; CR 85-93; Asst Chapl Musgrove Park Hosp 93; Asst Chapl St Helier Hosp Carshalton from 93. *St Helier Hospital, Wrythe Lane, Carshalton, Surrey SM5 1AA* 0181-296 2306 or 644 4343

HOLLAND, Peter Christie. b 36. St Andr Univ BASc60 Dur Univ DipTh62. Cranmer Hall Dur 60. **d** 62 **p** 63. C Darlington St Jo *Dur* 62-64; C Bishopwearmouth Ch Ch 64-69; V Tudhoe 69-77; V New Seaham 77-89; V Totternhoe, Stanbridge and Tilsworth *St Alb* from 89. *The Vicarage, Mill Road, Stanbridge, Leighton Buzzard, Beds LU7 9HX* Leighton Buzzard (01525) 210253

HOLLAND, Simon Geoffrey. b 63. MHCIMA83 Dorset Inst of HE OND81. Trin Coll Bris DipHE90. **d** 91 **p** 92. C Reigate St Mary *S'wark* 91-95; Chapl Lee Abbey from 95. *Lee Abbey, Lynton, Devon EX35 6JJ* Lynton (01598) 52621 Fax 52619

HOLLAND, Simon Paul. b 56. Univ Coll Lon LLB77 Qu Coll Cam BA80 MA84. Westcott Ho Cam 79. **d** 81 **p** 82. C Uckfield *Chich* 81-84; TV Lewes All SS, St Anne, St Mich and St Thos 84-88; TR 88-91; R Glas St Matt *Glas* 91-95; P-in-c Glas St Kentigern from 95. *1A Bower Street, Glasgow G12 8PT* 0141-334 1239

HOLLAND, William Michael Tristram. b 26. Jes Coll Cam BA50 MA52. St Steph Ho Ox 79. **d** 81 **p** 82. C High Wycombe *Ox* 81-84; R Steeple Aston w N Aston and Tackley 84-94; rtd 94. *10 Tree Lane, Iffley, Oxford OX4 4EY*

HOLLAND, William Geoffrey Bretton. b 36. Magd Coll Cam BA59 MA63. Westcott Ho Cam 61. **d** 63 **p** 64. C Cannock *Lich* 63-66; C Paddington Ch Ch Lon 66-69; Chapl Magd Coll Cam 69-73; V Twyford *Win* 74-78; V Twyford and Owslebury and Morestead 78-84; Chapl Twyford Sch Win from 84. *Twyford School, Searles Hill, Twyford, Winchester, Hants SO21 1NW* Twyford (01962) 712269

HOLLANDS, Albert William. b 17. Roch Th Coll 60. **d** 62 **p** 63. R Syderstone *Nor* 66-77; R Tattersett 67-83; P-in-c Tatterford 76-83; R Syderstone w Barmer 77-79; R Syderstone w Barmer and Bagthorpe 79-83; rtd 83; Perm to Offic *Nor* from 84. *25 Renwick Park East, West Runton, Cromer, Norfolk NR27 9LY* West Runton (01263) 837352

HOLLANDS, Derek Gordon. b 45. Chich Th Coll 72. **d** 74 **p** 75. C Banstead *Guildf* 74-77; C Cranleigh 77-79; C Haywards Heath St Wilfrid *Chich* 79-80; TV 80-82; Chapl Hillingdon Area HA 82-86; Chapl W Suffolk Hosp Bury St Edm 86-95; Pres Coll Health Care Chapls 92-94; Chapl R Cornwall Hosp Trust Truro from 95. *Treliske Hospital, Truro, Cornwall TR1 3LJ* Truro (01872) 40438

HOLLANDS, Percival Edwin Macaulay. b 36. Edin Th Coll 57. **d** 60 **p** 61. C Greenock *Glas* 60-64; C Aber St Mary *Ab* 64-65; P-in-c Aber St Clem 65-68; R Cruden Bay 68-70; CF 70-82; C Ribbleton *Blackb* 82-83; TV 83-88; C Longton 88; C Penwortham St Mary 88-92; V Farington from 92. *St Paul's Vicarage, 150 Croston Road, Farington, Preston PR5 3PR* Preston (01772) 38999

HOLLANDS, Ray Leonard. b 42. AMRSH OSB. S'wark Ord Course 68. **d** 71 **p** 72. NSM Hanworth All SS *Lon* 71-77 and 85-91; NSM Hanworth St Geo 77-85; NSM Marshwood Vale TM *Sarum* 81-91. *4 Priscilla House, Staines Road West, Sunbury-on-Thames, Middx TW16 7BE* Sunbury-on-Thames (01932) 781080

HOLLETT, Catherine Elaine. See DAKIN, Mrs Catherine Elaine

HOLLEY, Canon Geoffrey Raymond. b 28. AKC51. **d** 52 **p** 53. V Gt Burstead *Chelmsf* 56-75; Bp's Ecum Officer 71-82; R Loughton St Jo 75-91; TR 91-92; Can Chelmsf Cathl 78-92; RD Epping Forest 82-92; rtd 92. *The Maltings, Park Street, Thaxted, Dunmow, Essex CM6 2NB* Thaxted (01371) 830902

HOLLEY, Preb Graham Frank. b 29. Sarum Th Coll 60. **d** 61 **p** 62. V Much Marcle *Heref* 67-94; P-in-c Lt Marcle 84-86; RD Ledbury 87-90; Preb Heref Cathl 87-94; rtd 94. *40 Barrhill Road, Gourock, Renfrewshire PA1 1LB* Gourock (01475) 632487

HOLLEY, Paul Robert. b 65. St Jo Coll Dur 91. **d** 94 **p** 95. C Tonge w Alkrington *Man* from 94. *18 Highfield Drive, Middleton, Manchester M24 1DJ* 0161-653 0543

HOLLIDAY, Andrew. b 62. St Steph Ho Ox 89. **d** 92 **p** 93. C Marton *Blackb* 92-95; C Poulton-le-Fylde from 95. *24 Roylen Avenue, Poulton-le-Fylde, Blackpool FY6 7PH* Blackpool (01253) 884535

HOLLIDAY, Arthur. b 22. St Jo Coll Dur 80. **d** 81 **p** 82. Hon C Allerton *Bradf* 81-84; Hon C Thornton St Jas from 84. *9 Alston Close, Bradford, W Yorkshire BD9 6AN* Bradford (01274) 487331

HOLLIDAY, Eric Hedley. b 13. ARCS34 Lon Univ BSc35. Ridley Hall Cam 35. **d** 37 **p** 38. V Islington St Paul Ball's Pond *Lon* 55-78; rtd 78; Perm to Offic *Ely* from 78. *4 George Place, Eynesbury, St Neots, Huntingdon, Cambs PE19 2QG* Huntingdon (01480) 215703

HOLLIDAY, Peter Leslie. b 48. FCA79 Birm Univ BCom70 MA92. Qu Coll Birm 81. **d** 83 **p** 84. C Burton *Lich* 83-87; P-in-c Longdon 87-93; PV and Subchanter Lich Cath 87-93; R Stratford-on-Avon w Bishopton *Cov* from 93. *Stratford Vicarage, Old Town, Stratford-upon-Avon, Warks CV37 6BG* Stratford-upon-Avon (01789) 293088

HOLLIDAY, William (Bill). b 33. Qu Coll Cam BA56 MA60 McGill Univ Montreal BD58 LTh58. Montreal Dioc Th Coll 56 Linc Th Coll 58. **d** 58 **p** 59. C Stanningley St Thos *Ripon* 58-63; C Romaldkirk 63-64; India 64-77; V Thwaites Brow *Bradf* 77-86; RD S Craven 82-86; P-in-c Horton from 86; P-in-c Bradf St Oswald Chapel Green from 91; RD Bowling and Horton from 95. *Faith Sawrey's House, 41 Little Horton Green, Bradford, W Yorkshire BD5 0NG* Bradford (01274) 727976

HOLLIMAN, John James. b 44. St D Coll Lamp BA66. **d** 67 **p** 68. C Tideswell *Derby* 67-71; CF from 71. *c/o MOD (Army), Bagshot Park, Bagshot, Surrey GU19 5PL* Bagshot (01276) 471717 Fax 412834

HOLLIN, Ian. b 40. Open Univ BA76 Inst of Counselling DCC91. Sarum Th Coll 67. **d** 70 **p** 71. C Lanc Ch Ch *Blackb* 70-72; C S Shore H Trin 72-75; C Marton Moss 72-75; V Morecambe St Lawr 75-78; V Blackpool St Mary 78-83; PV and Succ Ex Cathl *Ex* 83-87; Counsellor Coun for Chr Care and Tr 87-91; Admin Boniface Cen Ex 91-93; TV Maltby *Sheff* from 93. *The Vicarage, 5 Haids Road, Maltby, Rotherham, S Yorkshire S66 8BH* Rotherham (01709) 814951

HOLLINGDALE, Derek Leslie. b 32. Ex & Truro NSM Scheme. **d** 83 **p** 84. NSM Tuckingmill *Truro* 83-85; NSM Illogan 85-92; NSM Treslothan from 92. *St Margaret's, 11 Atlantic Terrace, Camborne, Cornwall TR14 7AW* Camborne (01209) 714574

HOLLINGHURST, Stephen. b 59. Univ of Wales DipTh. St Jo Coll Nottm 81. **d** 83 **p** 84. C Hyde St Geo *Ches* 83-86; C Cropwell Bishop w Colston Bassett, Granby etc *S'well* 86-90; R Pembridge w Moorcourt, Shobdon, Staunton etc *Heref* from 90; RD Kington and Weobley from 95. *The Rectory, Pembridge, Leominster, Herefordshire HR6 9EB* Pembridge (01544) 388998

HOLLINGS, Miss Patricia Mary. b 39. CertEd59. S'wark Ord Course 84. **d** 87. Par Dn Wyke *Bradf* 87-94; C from 94. *1 Greenacre Way, Wyke, Bradford, W Yorkshire BD12 9DJ* Bradford (01274) 677439

HOLLINGS, Robert George (Bob). b 48. St Jo Coll Nottm DipThMin94. **d** 94 **p** 95. C Cotmanhay *Derby* from 94. *76 Prince Street, Ilkeston, Derbyshire DE7 8QQ* Nottingham (0115) 930 1311

HOLLINGSHEAD, Miss Pauline Carol. b 49. Local Minl Tr Course. **d** 94 **p** 95. NSM Colsterworth Gp *Linc* from 94. *The Lodge, Little Ponton, Grantham, Lincs NG33 5BS* Great Ponton (01476) 530382

HOLLINGSHURST, Robert Peter. b 38. Ridley Hall Cam 64. **d** 67 **p** 68. C Roxeth Ch Ch *Lon* 67-70; C Attenborough w Chilwell *S'well* 70-73; C Ramsgate St Luke 74-75; Chapl to the Deaf 78-80; TV Louth *Linc* 80-84; Chapl to the Deaf *Sarum* 84-87; P-in-c Odstock w Nunton and Bodenham from 84; P-in-c Britford from 89; P-in-c Charlton All Saints from 89. *The Rectory, Nunton, Salisbury SP5 4HP* Salisbury (01722) 330628

HOLLINGSWORTH, Geoffrey. b 53. MIPM85 Leeds Poly 74. N Ord Course 86. **d** 86 **p** 87. C Thorne *Sheff* 86-89; V Rawcliffe from 89. *The Vicarage, 5 The Green, Rawcliffe, Goole, N Humberside DN14 8QE* Goole (01405) 839298

HOLLINGSWORTH, Canon Gerald Frank Lee. b 26. Lon Univ BA53. Oak Hill Th Coll 49. **d** 54 **p** 55. Bp's Ind Adv *St E* 64-75; V Ipswich H Trin 64-72; R Ipswich St Clem w H Trin 72-75; R Gt and Lt Bealings w Playford and Culpho 75-90; RD Woodbridge 76-84; Hon Can St E Cathl 76-90; rtd 90; Perm to Offic *St E* from 90. *The Conifers, Ipswich Road, Grundisburgh, Woodbridge, Suffolk IP13 6TJ* Grundisburgh (01473) 735232

HOLLINGSWORTH, Miss Paula Marion. b 62. Van Mildert Coll Dur BSc83. Trin Coll Bris BA91. **d** 91 **p** 94. C Keynsham *B & W* 91-95; C Balsall Heath St Paul *Birm* from 95. *51 Alpha Close, Balsall Heath, Birmingham B12 9HF* 0121-440 7867

HOLLINGTON, David Mark. b 61. DipEH83 MIEH83. Trin Coll Bris BA94. **d** 94. C Wednesbury St Paul Wood Green *Lich* from 94. *315 Crankhall Lane, Wednesbury, W Midlands WS10 0QQ* 0121-556 7007

338

HOLLINGWORTH, Martin Douglas. b 50. RMCM GRSM73. Trin Coll Bris 73. **d** 77 **p** 78. C Hartford *Ches* 77-78; C Knowle *Birm* 79-81; S Africa 81-93; Chapl Hong Kong Cathl from 93. *Flat D-2, On Lee, 2 Mount Davis Road, Hong Kong* Fax Hong Kong (0852) 521-7830

HOLLINRAKE, Jean Margaret. *See* HARRISON, Mrs Jean Margaret

HOLLINS, John Edgar. b 35. St Jo Coll Cam BA58 MA62. Oak Hill Th Coll 58. **d** 60 **p** 61. C St Alb St Paul *St Alb* 66-71; Hon C Halliwell St Paul *Man* 71-72; C Ravenhill St Jo 72-73; Perm to Offic *Birm* 79-81; V Millbrook *Ches* 81-89; rtd 89. *Tresuan, Meadway, Looe, Cornwall PL13 1JT* Looe (01503) 264062

HOLLINS, Peter Charles. b 31. Wycliffe Hall Ox 61. **d** 62 **p** 63. C Westwood *Sarum* 65-67; Lic to Offic *Roch* 72-77; Perm to Offic *Worc* 79-95; rtd 95. *Ladykey, Holly Green, Upton-upon-Severn, Worcester WR8 0PD* Upton-upon-Severn (01684) 592508

HOLLINSHEAD, Cyril Wyndham. b 09. Linc Th Coll 45. **d** 47 **p** 48. V Peasedown St John *B & W* 54-76; rtd 76; Perm to Offic *B & W* from 76. *65 Ridgeway, Sherborne, Dorset DT9 6DA* Sherborne (01935) 814232

HOLLIS, Anthony Wolcott Linsley. b 40. McGill Univ Montreal BA61 Long Is Univ MA76. Gen Sem (NY) MDiv64. **d** 64 **p** 65. USA 64-92; Bermuda from 92. *PO Box GE 85, St George's GE BX, Bermuda* Bermuda (1-809) 297-0216 Fax 297-8256

HOLLIS, Canon Arnold Thaddeus. b 33. JP87. Stockton State Coll New Jersey BA74 NY Th Sem MDiv74 STM76 DMin78. Codrington Coll Barbados 56. **d** 59 **p** 60. C Wakef St Jo *Wakef* 60-62; Br Guiana 62-64; P-in-c Horbury Bridge *Wakef* 64-66; C Loughton St Jo *Chelmsf* 66-69; USA 69-77; Bermuda from 77; Hon Chapl RN from 77; Chapl HM Pris from 77; Chapl Miss to Seamen from 90; Hon Can Bermuda Cathl from 87. *PO Box MA 74, Sandys MA BX, Bermuda* Bermuda (1-809) 234-0834 or 2025 Fax 234-2723

HOLLIS, Christopher Barnsley. b 28. Clare Coll Cam BA52 MA59. Wells Th Coll 60. **d** 62 **p** 63. C Baildon *Bradf* 62-64; V Esholt 64-66; V Heaton St Barn 66-85; RD Airedale 73-82; Hon Can Bradf Cathl 77-85; Chapl HM Young Offender Inst Medomsley 85-90; V Medomsley *Dur* 85-90; P-in-c Denholme Gate *Bradf* from 90. *The Vicarage, Denholme, Bradford, W Yorkshire BD13 4EN* Bradford (01274) 832813

HOLLIS, Derek. b 60. Loughb Univ BA82. Cranmer Hall Dur 83. **d** 86 **p** 87. C Evington *Leic* 86-89; C Arnold *S'well* 89-93; V Beckingham w Walkeringham from 93; P-in-c Gringley-on-the-Hill from 95. *The Vicarage, Beckingham, Doncaster, S Yorkshire DN10 4PJ* Saundby (0142784) 266

HOLLIS, Douglas John. b 32. S Dios Minl Tr Scheme. **d** 84 **p** 85. NSM Haywards Heath St Wilfrid *Chich* from 84. *2 Northlands Avenue, Haywards Heath, W Sussex RH16 3RT* Haywards Heath (01444) 453688

HOLLIS, Canon Gerald. b 19. Ch Ch Ox BA42 MA45. Wells Th Coll 45. **d** 47 **p** 48. V Rotherham *Sheff* 60-74; Adn Birm 74-84; rtd 84; Perm to Offic *Sarum* from 87. *68 Britford Lane, Salisbury SP2 8AH* Salisbury (01722) 338154

HOLLIS, Jeffrey Norman. b 30. Qu Coll Birm 71. **d** 74 **p** 75. C Inkberrow *Worc* 74-76; C Eastleigh *Win* 76-79; V Jersey St Jas 79-85; V Jersey St Luke 79-85; R Jersey St Sav 85-91; rtd 91. *12 Hill Farm, Stonepit Lane, Inkberrow, Worcester WR7 4EX* Inkberrow (01386) 793334

HOLLIS, Peter. b 20. Jes Coll Cam BA49. Wells Th Coll 49. **d** 51 **p** 52. R Sudbury St Greg and St Pet *St E* 67-81; R Sudbury and Chilton 81-86; rtd 86. *1 New Cottages, Brundon, Sudbury, Suffolk CO10 6XS* Sudbury (01787) 370447

HOLLIS, Timothy Knowles (Tim). b 28. RN Coll Dartmouth 45. St Steph Ho Ox 54. **d** 58 **p** 59. R Sotterley, Willingham, Shadingfield, Ellough etc *St E* 69-76; Gen Sec L'Arche UK 77-93; Perm to Offic from 77; rtd 93. *14 London Road, Beccles, Suffolk NR34 9NH* Beccles (01502) 717266 Fax 711067

HOLLIS, Mrs Valerie Elizabeth. b 40. **d** 92 **p** 94. NSM Kempston Transfiguration *St Alb* from 92. *33 Silverdale Street, Kempston, Bedford MK42 8BE* Bedford (01234) 853397

HOLLOWAY, Canon Alan James. b 23. FPhS64 Lon Univ BD58 MTh67. Oak Hill Th Coll 53. **d** 56 **p** 57. Chapl and Lect St Paul's Coll Cheltenham 69-73; V Maisemore *Glouc* 73-76; Dir of Educn 74-82; Can Res Glouc Cathl 74-82; R Glouc St Mary de Crypt w St Jo and Ch Ch 82-88; rtd 88; Bp's Personal Asst *Glouc* 88-92. *42 Stancliffe Road, Bedford MK41 9AP* Bedford (01234) 261566

HOLLOWAY, Canon David Dennis. b 43. Lich Th Coll 65. **d** 68 **p** 69. C Cricklade w Latton *Bris* 68-71; C Bris St Agnes w St Simon 71-72; C Bris St Agnes and St Simon w St Werburgh 72-74; V Bitton 74-78; TV E Bris 78-80; P-in-c Tormarton w W Littleton 80-83; Sub Chapl HM Pris Bris from 80; Dioc Ecum Officer 83-93; Hon C Bris St Mich 89-93; Hon Can Bris Cathl from 92; V Horfield St Greg from 93. *St Gregory's Vicarage, Filton Road, Horfield, Bristol BS7 0PD* Bristol (0117) 969 2839

HOLLOWAY, David Ronald James. b 39. Univ Coll Ox BA62 MA66. Ridley Hall Cam 65. **d** 67 **p** 68. C Leeds St Geo *Ripon* 67-71; Tutor Wycliffe Hall Ox 71-72; V Jesmond Clayton Memorial *Newc* from 73. *The Vicarage, 7 Otterburn Terrace, Jesmond, Newcastle upon Tyne NE2 3AP* 0191-281 2001

HOLLOWAY, Graham Edward. b 45. Chich Th Coll 69. **d** 72 **p** 73. C W Drayton *Lon* 72-75; P-in-c Hawton *S'well* 75-80; TV Newark w Hawton, Cotham and Shelton 80; V Ladybrook 80-85; P-in-c Babworth 85-87; R Babworth w Sutton-cum-Lound from 87; RD Retford 88-93. *The Rectory, Babworth, Retford, Notts DN22 8ET* Retford (01777) 703253

HOLLOWAY, Howard Robinett. b 06. Keble Coll Ox BA27 MA31. Wells Th Coll 27. **d** 29 **p** 30. R Perranuthnoe *Truro* 70-72; rtd 72. *33 Aldersgate Street, Oxley, Brisbane, Queensland, Australia 4075*

HOLLOWAY, Keith Graham. b 45. Linc Coll Ox BA67 St Jo Coll Dur DipTh72. **d** 73 **p** 74. C Gt Ilford St Andr *Chelmsf* 73-78; Hon C Squirrels Heath 78-80; Min Chelmer Village CD 80-87; V E Springfield 87-89; P-in-c Gt Dunmow from 89. *3 The Charters, Church End, Dunmow, Essex CM6 2SJ* Great Dunmow (01371) 872504

✠**HOLLOWAY, Most Rev Richard Frederick.** b 33. FRSA92 Lon Univ BD63 Aber Univ Hon DD95. NY Th Sem STM68 Edin Th Coll 58. **d** 59 **p** 60. C Glas St Ninian *Glas* 59-63; P-in-c Glas St Marg 63-68; R Edin Old St Paul *Edin* 68-80; USA 80-84; V Ox St Mary Magd *Ox* 84-86; Bp Edin from 86; Primus from 92. *3 Eglinton Crescent, Edinburgh EH12 5DH or, Walpole Hall, Chester Street, Edinburgh EH3 7EN* 0131-226 5099 or 226 3359 Fax 225 3181

HOLLOWAY, Roger Graham. b 33. Selw Coll Cam BA58 MA61. S'wark Ord Course 74. **d** 78 **p** 80. Hong Kong 78-80 and 85-88; Japan 80-84; PV Westmr St Marg from 88; Nat Dir ICF from 91; Lic to Offic *Lon* from 94. *Flat 6, 2 Porchester Gardens, London W2 6JL* 0171-402 4937 Fax 402 4683

HOLLOWAY, Simon Anthony. b 50. Sussex Univ BSc72. Trin Coll Bris 76. **d** 79 **p** 81. C Bushbury *Lich* 79-81; C Castle Church 81-84; P-in-c Sparkbrook Ch Ch *Birm* 84-91; V from 91; RD Bordesley from 92. *Christ Church Vicarage, 34 Grantham Road, Birmingham B11 1LU* 0121-772 6558

HOLLOWOOD, Christopher George. b 54. K Alfred's Coll Win BEd76. Ripon Coll Cuddesdon 83. **d** 86 **p** 87. C Tupsley *Heref* 86-89; R Much Birch w Lt Birch, Much Dewchurch etc 89-92; Hd of Relig Studies Haywood High Sch Heref from 92. *41 Harold Street, Hereford HR1 2QU*

HOLLOWOOD, Lewis William Rye. b 17. Dur Univ 37. Edin Th Coll 37. **d** 40 **p** 41. V Hadlow Down *Chich* 67-74; R Buxted St Marg 72-74; V Bexhill St Barn 75-81; Chapl Community Servants of the Cross Lindfield from 81; Dioc Communications Officer & Dir Soc Resp *Chich* 81-82; rtd 82. *Convent of the Holy Rood, Lindfield, Haywards Heath, W Sussex RH16 2QN* Lindfield (01444) 482345

HOLMAN, Francis Noel. b 37. DSPT90. Sarum Th Coll 62. **d** 65 **p** 66. C Weston Favell *Pet* 65-68; C Eckington *Derby* 68-71; Asst Chapl St Thos Hosp Lon 72-77; Chapl Hope Hosp Salford from 77; Ladywell and Salford Royal Hosps from 77; Chapl Man and Salford Skin Hosp from 88. *90 Rocky Lane, Monton, Eccles, Manchester M30 9LY* 0161-707 1180 or 787 5167

HOLMAN, Geoffrey Gladstone. b 32. AKC56. **d** 57 **p** 58. CF 60-73; Dep Asst Chapl Gen 73-80; Asst Chapl Gen 80-84; QHC 82-84; V Wetwang and Garton-on-the-Wolds w Kirkburn *York* 84-92; RD Harthill 87-92; rtd 92; NSM Askham Bryan *York* from 93. *20 North Parade, Bootham, York YO3 7AB* York (01904) 624419

HOLMDEN, Miss Maria Irene. b 50. Trent Poly TCert72 BEd73 Golds Coll Lon DPEd84. Oak Hill Th Coll DipHE92. **d** 92 **p** 94. Par Dn Stratford St Jo and Ch Ch w Forest Gate St Jas *Chelmsf* 92-94; C from 94. *29 Maryland Park, London E15 1HB* 0181-534 7503

HOLME, Thomas Edmund. b 49. Selw Coll Cam BA71 MA75. Coll of Resurr Mirfield 71. **d** 73 **p** 74. C Wyther Ven Bede *Ripon* 73-76; C Wimbledon *S'wark* 76-78; TV 78-79; V Bermondsey St Anne 79-81; V Stamford Baron *Pet* 83-89; P-in-c Tinwell 83-89; Hon Min Can Pet Cathl 84-89; Prec Worc Cathl *Worc* from 89. *280 Bath Road, Worcester WR5 3ET* Worcester (01905) 353762

HOLMES, Alan Stewart. b 57. MInstPkg88 St Andr Univ BSc80. Ox NSM Course 85. **d** 88 **p** 89. NSM Shinfield *Ox* 88-95; NSM Beech Hill, Grazeley and Spencers Wood from 95. *The Cottage, Church Lane, Three Mile Cross, Reading RG7 1HB* Reading (01734) 882436

HOLMES, Anthony David Robert. b 38. Oak Hill Th Coll 75. **d** 77 **p** 78. C Iver *Ox* 77-81; V Bucklebury w Marlston from 81. *The Vicarage, Bucklebury, Reading RG7 6PL* Woolhampton (01734) 713193

HOLMES, Clive Horace. b 31. Ox NSM Course. **d** 83 **p** 84. NSM Cumnor *Ox* from 83. *62 Westminster Way, Oxford OX2 0LW* Oxford (01865) 249640

HOLMES, David Roy. b 34. FIPM75. Ox NSM Course 81. **d** 84 **p** 85. NSM Ox SS Phil and Jas w St Marg *Ox* 84-85; NSM Ox St Giles and SS Phil and Jas w St Marg from 85. *48 Charlbury Road, Oxford OX2 6UX* Oxford (01865) 510061

HOLMES, Frank. b 22. NW Ord Course 75. **d** 78 **p** 79. NSM Hyde St Geo *Ches* 78-81; C Poynton 81-87; rtd 87; Perm to Offic *Ches* from 87. *277 Stockport Road, Marple, Stockport, Cheshire SK6 6ES* 0161-449 9289

HOLMES, Geoffrey Robert. b 67. Nottm Univ BSc89. Ridley Hall Cam BA92. **d** 93 **p** 94. C Clifton St Jas *Sheff* from 93. *26 Greenwich Court, Rotherham, S Yorkshire S65 1BU* Rotherham (01709) 372079

HOLMES, George Henry. b 07. ATCL34. **d** 42 **p** 44. V N Kelsey *Linc* 50-63; rtd 63. *Lupin Cottage, Withern, Alford, Lincs LN13 0NB* Withern (01507) 450585

HOLMES, Grant Wenlock. b 54. St Steph Ho Ox BA78 MA83. **d** 79 **p** 80. C Benhilton *S'wark* 79-82; C-in-c S Kenton Annunciation CD *Lon* 82-86; Tutor Chich Th Coll 86-87; Bp's Dom Chapl *Chich* 86-88; V Mayfield from 88. *The Vicarage, High Street, Mayfield, E Sussex TN20 6AB* Mayfield (01435) 873180

HOLMES, Canon John Robin. b 42. Leeds Univ BA64. Linc Th Coll 64. **d** 66 **p** 67. C Wyther Ven Bede *Ripon* 66-69; C Adel 69-73; V Beeston Hill St Luke 73-76; V Holbeck 76-86; RD Armley 82-86; V Manston 86-93; Hon Can Ripon Cathl from 89; Dioc Missr from 93. *Churchfields, Main Street, Darley, Harrogate, N Yorkshire HG3 2QF* Harrogate (01423) 780771

HOLMES, Jonathan Michael. b 49. MRCVS73 Qu Coll Cam BA70 VetMB73 MA74 PhD78. Ridley Hall Cam 87. **d** 88 **p** 89. Chapl Qu Coll Cam from 88. *58 Devonshire Road, Cambridge CB1 2BL* Cambridge (01223) 312774

HOLMES, Dr Nigel Ernest Hartley. b 37. Em Coll Cam BA58 MA64 Lon Hosp BChir61 MB62. Ridley Hall Cam 62. **d** 64 **p** 65. C Cam St Phil *Ely* 64-68; I Jersey St Paul Prop Chpl *Win* 68-77; C Cam H Sepulchre w All SS *Ely* 78-80; Perm to Offic *St E* 80-86; Perm to Offic *Ely* 80-86; P-in-c Brinkley, Burrough Green and Carlton 86-92; P-in-c Westley Waterless 86-92; NSM in Evang from 92. *133 Coleridge Road, Cambridge CB1 3PN* Cambridge (01223) 240593

HOLMES, Nigel Peter. b 48. Nottm Univ BTh72 Lanc Univ CertEd72 Lon Univ BD76 Sheff Univ MEd84. Kelham Th Coll. **d** 72 **p** 73. C Barrow St Matt *Carl* 72-75; C Derby St Bart *Derby* 75-78; P-in-c Barlow 78-84; V Carl St Herbert w St Steph *Carl* 84-91; V Keswick St Jo 91-94; V Mexborough *Sheff* from 94. *The Vicarage, Church Street, Mexborough, S Yorkshire S64 0ER* Mexborough (01709) 582321

HOLMES, Peter Anthony. b 55. Univ of Wales (Ban) BA77 Brighton Poly CertEd78. Trin Coll Bris DipHE. **d** 88 **p** 89. C Croydon Ch Ch *S'wark* 88-93; V Norbiton from 93. *The Vicarage, 21 Wolsey Close, Kingston upon Thames, Surrey KT2 7ER* 0181-942 8330

HOLMES, Dr Peter Geoffrey. b 32. Bris Univ BSc59 MSc69 Leic Univ PhD74. St Deiniol's Hawarden 74. **d** 76 **p** 77. NSM Glen Parva and S Wigston *Leic* from 76; Prof Nottm Poly 85-92; Prof City Univ Nottm from 92. *19 Windsor Avenue, Glen Parva, Leicester LE2 9JQ* Leicester (0116) 277 4534

HOLMES, Robert John Geoffrey. b 28. TCD BA53 MA57. Ely Th Coll 56. **d** 57 **p** 58. S Africa 68-74; Perm to Offic *Ely* 74; Perm to Offic *Chich* 74-76; R Telscombe w Piddinghoe and Southease 76-93; P-in-c Barlavington, Burton w Coates, Sutton and Bignor 93-94; rtd 95. *The Rectory, The Street, Sutton, Pulborough, W Sussex RH20 1PS* Pulborough (01798) 869220

HOLMES, Roger Cockburn. b 46. Jes Coll Ox BA70 MA84 Edin Univ BD76. Edin Th Coll 73. **d** 84 **p** 85. Canada 84-88; R Ditchingham w Pirnough *Nor* 88-90; R Hedenham 88-90; R Broome 88-90; R Ditchingham, Hedenham and Broome 90-93; V Helmsley *York* from 93. *Canons Garth, Helmsley, York YO6 5AQ* Helmsley (01439) 770236

HOLMES, Roy Grant. b 37. Ox NSM Course 83. **d** 86 **p** 87. NSM Wokingham St Paul *Ox* from 86. *58 Copse Drive, Wokingham, Berks RG11 1LX* Wokingham (01734) 784141

HOLMES, Stanley Thomas. b 11. Selw Coll Cam BA34 MA46. St Steph Ho Ox 34. **d** 36 **p** 37. V Goring *Ox* 48-84; rtd 84; Perm to Offic *Ox* from 84. *Lower Farm, 8 Dunstan Road, Old Headington, Oxford OX3 9BY* Oxford (01865) 62657

HOLMES, Stephen. b 54. St Andr Univ MTh84. Chich Th Coll 84. **d** 86 **p** 87. C Croydon St Jo *S'wark* 86-89; C Tewkesbury w Walton Cardiff *Glouc* 89-92; P-in-c Bournemouth St Luke *Win* 92-94; V from 94. *St Luke's Vicarage, 31 Lonsdale Road, Bournemouth BH3 7LY* Bournemouth (01202) 516653

HOLMES, Stephen John. b 50. CertEd72 DipHE83. Trin Coll Bris 81 Sarum & Wells Th Coll 88. **d** 89 **p** 90. C Skegness and Winthorpe *Linc* 89-93; P-in-c Mablethorpe w Trusthorpe from 93. *The Rectory, 88 Wellington Road, Mablethorpe, Lincs LN12 1HT* Mablethorpe (01507) 473159

HOLNESS, Edwin Geoffrey Nicholas. b 39. RGN BTA. Sarum Th Coll 68. **d** 71 **p** 72. C Upper Beeding *Chich* 71-74; C Bramber w Botolphs 71-74; C Munster Square St Mary Magd *Lon* 74-75; Perm to Offic *Chich* 75-76; C Brighton Annunciation 76-77; Chapl Brighton Hosp Gp 77-94; Chapl R Sussex Co Hosp Brighton 77-94; Lic to Offic *Chich* from 77. *8 Courcels, Arundel Street, Brighton BN2 5UB*

HOLROYD, Gordon Eric. b 31. SSM. **d** 76 **p** 76. Asst Chapl St Martin's Coll Lanc 76-77; Chapl 77-78; Hon C Sheff St Matt *Sheff* 78-80; Lic to Offic *Man* 80-81; P-in-c Willen *Ox* 81-84; Perm to Offic *Blackb* from 84; NSM Middlesb All SS *York* 89-95; Australia from 95. *Willen Priory, Milton Keynes MK15 9AA* Milton Keynes (01908) 663749

HOLROYD, John Richard. b 54. Liv Univ BA75 PGCE77. Wycliffe Hall Ox 78. **d** 81 **p** 82. C Gt Stanmore *Lon* 81-84; Min Can, VC and Prec St E Cathl *St E* 84-89; TV Wolverton *Ox* from 89. *28 Harvester Close, Greenleys, Milton Keynes MK12 6LE* Milton Keynes (01908) 222802

HOLROYD, Stephen Charles. b 56. UEA BA79. St Jo Coll Nottm 84. **d** 87 **p** 88. C Barton Seagrave w Warkton *Pet* 87-91; V Eye from 91. *The Vicarage, 4 Fountains Place, Eye, Peterborough PE6 7UN* Peterborough (01733) 222334

HOLT, Alan Leonard. b 12. Dur Univ LTh42. Edin Th Coll 39. **d** 42 **p** 43. V Streetly *Lich* 50-77; rtd 77; Perm to Offic *B & W* from 77. *Old Vicarage, Rectory Way, Lympsham, Weston-super-Mare, Avon BS24 0EW* Weston-super-Mare (01934) 750527

HOLT, Brian. b 30. BMin73. Huron Coll Ontario. **d** 70 **p** 71. Canada 70-78; V Glodwick *Man* 78-83; TV E Farnworth and Kearsley 83-87; R Abbey Hey 87-94; rtd 95. *79 Lennox Road, Todmorden, Lancs OL14 8PS* Todmorden (01706) 819672

HOLT, David. b 44. St Jo Coll Dur BSc67 DipTh69. **d** 70 **p** 71. C Blackley St Pet *Man* 70-73; C Radcliffe St Thos 73-74; C Radcliffe St Thos and St Jo 74-75; V Ashton St Pet 75-79; Dioc Youth Officer *Guildf* 80-85; V Bagshot from 85; RD Surrey Heath from 92. *The Vicarage, 43 Church Road, Bagshot, Surrey GU19 5EQ* Bagshot (01276) 473348

HOLT, Douglas Robert. b 49. MA. Ridley Hall Cam. **d** 82 **p** 83. C Cam St Barn *Ely* 82-84; P-in-c 84-86; V 86-91; V Ealing St Mary *Lon* from 91. *Ealing Vicarage, 11 Church Place, London W5 4HN* 0181-567 0414 or 579 7134

HOLT, Francis Thomas (Frank). b 38. Edin Th Coll 79. **d** 81 **p** 82. C Cullercoats St Geo *Newc* 81-83; C Ponteland 83-86; Chapl Worc Coll of HE 86-89; R Worc St Clem *Worc* 86-93; V Finstall from 93. *The Vicarage, 15 Finstall Road, Bromsgrove, Worcs B60 2EA* Bromsgrove (01527) 872459

HOLT, Harold. b 20. **d** 52 **p** 52. V Haslingden St Jo Stonefold *Blackb* 60-72; V Blackb St Aid 72-85; rtd 85; Perm to Offic *Blackb* from 85. *24 Scott Avenue, Baxenden, Accrington, Lancs BB5 2XA* Accrington (01254) 396474

HOLT, Jack Derek. b 38. Trin Coll Bris 71. **d** 73 **p** 74. C Daubhill *Man* 73-76; P-in-c Thornham w Gravel Hole 76-79; V 79-83; P-in-c Talke *Lich* 83-93; V Cotmanhay *Derby* from 93; Chapl Ilkeston Community Hosp from 93. *Cotmanhay Vicarage, Vicarage Street, Cotmanhay, Ilkeston, Derbyshire DE7 8QL* Nottingham (0115) 932 5670

HOLT, Keith. b 37. S'wark Ord Course. **d** 82 **p** 83. NSM Selsdon St Jo w St Fran *Cant* 82-84; NSM Selsdon St Jo w St Fran *S'wark* from 85. *12 Ridge Langley, South Croydon, Surrey CR2 0AR* 0181-651 1815 or 0171-215 8200

HOLT, Michael. b 38. Univ of Wales (Lamp) BA61 DipTh63. **d** 63 **p** 64. C Stand *Man* 63-69; V Bacup St Jo from 69. *St John's Vicarage, Bankside Lane, Bacup, Lancs OL13 8HG* Bacup (01706) 873275

HOLT, Norman Botterill. b 16. Worc Ord Coll 60. **d** 60 **p** 61. R Earls Croome w Hill Croome and Strensham *Worc* 62-83; rtd 83. *19 Nelson Road, Sheringham, Norfolk NR26 8BU* Sheringham (01263) 822624

HOLT, Paul William Charles. b 53. St Jo Coll Dur BA75. Oak Hill Th Coll 75 Ridley Hall Cam 76. **d** 77 **p** 78. C Bexleyheath Ch Ch *Roch* 77-80; C Frimley *Guildf* 80-84; P-in-c Badshot Lea CD 84-91; P-in-c Lt Marlow *Ox* 91-93; V Flackwell Heath 93-94. *9 Downshire Square, Reading RG1 6NJ*

HOLT, Stuart Henry. b 57. Bath Univ BEd78. Ridley Hall Cam 84. **d** 87 **p** 88. C Locks Heath *Portsm* 87-90; Chapl RAF 89-91; C Worthing St Geo *Chich* 91-93; C Portchester *Portsm* from 93. *190 Dove Avenue, Portchester, Fareham, Hants PO16 8EP* Fareham (01329) 288716

HOLTAM, Nicholas Roderick. b 54. Collingwood Coll Dur BA75 K Coll Lon BD78 AKC78 Dur Univ MA89. Westcott Ho Cam 78. **d** 79 **p** 80. C Stepney St Dunstan and All SS *Lon* 79-83; Tutor Linc Th Coll 83-88; V Is of Dogs Ch Ch and St Jo w St Luke *Lon* from 88. *Christ Church Vicarage, Manchester Road, London E14 3BN* 0171-987 1915

HOLTAM, Canon Ralph. b 16. Univ of Wales BA40. St Mich Coll Llan 40. **d** 42 **p** 43. V Roath St Marg *Llan* 65-76; R Sully 76-85; Can Llan Cathl 81-85; rtd 85; Perm to Offic *Llan* from 85. *19 Windsor Road, Barry, S Glam CF62 6AW* Barry (01446) 741567

HOLTBY, Very Rev Robert Tinsley. b 21. FSA St Edm Hall Ox BA43 MA46 BD57 K Coll Cam BA47 MA52. Cuddesdon Coll 43 Westcott Ho Cam 44. d 46 p 47. Sec C of E Schs Coun 67-74; Gen Sec Nat Soc 67-77; Lic to Offic *S'wark* 68-77; Gen Sec Gen Syn Bd of Educn 74-77; Dean Chich 77-89; rtd 89. *4 Hutton Hall, Huttons Ambo, York YO6 7HW* Malton (01653) 696366

HOLTH, Oystein Johan. b 31. Open Univ BA75. AKC54. d 54 p 55. C Greenford H Cross *Lon* 54-56; Br N Borneo and Sarawak 56-63; E Malaysia 63-67; Chapl OHP 67-75; Chapl St Hilda's Sch Whitby 67-75; P-in-c Pimlico St Barn *Lon* from 75; Ind Chapl from 75. *The Clergy House, St Barnabas Street, London SW1W 8PF* 0171-730 5054

HOLYER, Vincent Alfred Douglas. b 28. Ex Univ BA54. Oak Hill Th Coll 54. d 56 p 57. R St Ruan w St Grade *Truro* 65-85; V Constantine 85-91; rtd 91. *The Cornerstone, 7 Tregenning Park, St Keverne, Helston, Cornwall TR12 6QT* Helston (01326) 280691

HOLYHEAD, Rex Noel Humphrey. b 32. d 68 p 69. C Glouc St Mary de Lode and St Nic *Glouc* 68-70; C Christchurch *Win* 70-77; V Win St Jo cum Winnall 77-81; P-in-c Millbrook 81-82; R from 82. *The Rectory, 115 Regents Park Road, Southampton SO1 3NZ* Southampton (01703) 773417

HOLZAPFEL, Peter Rudolph. b 51. St Jo Coll Nottm 84. d 86 p 87. C St Jo in Bedwardine *Worc* 86-89; V Worc St Mich from 89. *St Michael's Vicarage, Burleigh Road, Worcester WR2 5QT* Worcester (01905) 421986

HOMER, Alan Fellows. b 30. Ridley Hall Cam 61. d 63 p 64. C Heref St Jas *Heref* 63-66; Dep Chapl HM Pris Brixton 66-70; V Brixton Hill St Sav *S'wark* 66-73; CF (TA) 70-73; CF 73-76; V Heeley *Sheff* 75-87; R Cheveley *Ely* from 87; R Ashley w Silverley from 87; V Wood Ditton w Saxon Street from 87; V Kirtling from 87; RD Linton from 94. *The Rectory, 130 High Street, Cheveley, Newmarket, Suffolk CB8 9DG* Newmarket (01638) 730770

HOMEWOOD, Michael John. b 33. Wells Th Coll 69. d 71 p 72. C Ilfracombe H Trin *Ex* 71-72; C Ilfracombe, Lee and W Down 72-75; P-in-c Woolacombe 76-78; TV Ilfracombe, Lee, W Down, Woolacombe and Bittadon 78-82; TR S Molton, Nymet St George, High Bray etc from 82; RD S Molton from 93. *The Rectory, Parsonage Lane, South Molton, Devon EX36 3AX* South Molton (01769) 572356

HOMEWOOD, Peter Laurence de Silvie. b 58. Or Coll Ox BA80 MA84. St Steph Ho Ox 90. d 92 p 93. C Ruislip St Martin *Lon* from 92. *34 Midcroft, Ruislip, Middx HA4 8HB* Ruislip (01895) 632605

HOMFRAY, John Bax Tayler. b 29. Keble Coll Ox BA52 MA. Ridley Hall Cam 52. d 54 p 55. C Kingswood *Bris* 54-57; C Leckhampton St Pet *Glouc* 57-64; V Staverton w Boddington 64-86; V Staverton w Boddington and Tredington etc from 87. *The Vicarage, Staverton, Cheltenham, Glos GL51 0TW* Cheltenham (01242) 680307

HONE, Canon Frank Leslie. b 11. Kelham Th Coll 32. d 38 p 39. V Frodingham *Linc* 66-78; Can and Preb Linc Cathl 72-78; rtd 78. *Morcote, 13 Roselea Avenue, Welton, Lincoln LN2 3RT* Welton (01673) 861548

HONES, Simon Anthony. b 54. Sussex Univ BSc75. Qu Coll Birm DipTh78. d 79 p 80. C Win Ch Ch *Win* 79-82; C Basing 82-88; Min Chineham CD 88-90; V Surbiton St Matt *S'wark* from 90. *St Matthew's Vicarage, 20 Kingsdowne Road, Surbiton, Surrey KT6 6JZ* 0181-399 4853

HONEY, Canon Frederick Bernard. b 22. Selw Coll Cam BA48 MA72. Wells Th Coll 48. d 50 p 51. V Wollaston *Worc* 55-87; RD Stourbridge 72-83; Hon Can Worc Cathl 75-87; rtd 87. *38 Park Farm, Bourton-on-the-Water, Cheltenham, Glos GL54 2YF* Cotswold (01451) 822218

HONEY, Thomas David (Tom). b 56. Lon Univ BA78. Ripon Coll Cuddesdon 80. d 83 p 84. C Mill End and Heronsgate w W Hyde *St Alb* 83-86; C Stepney St Dunstan and All SS *Lon* 86-89; TV High Wycombe *Ox* 89-95; P-in-c Headington Quarry from 95. *The Vicarage, Headington Quarry, Oxford OX3 8NU* Oxford (01865) 62931

HONEYBALL, Mark George. b 56. Ch Coll Cam BA78 MA82. Westcott Ho Cam 79. d 81 p 82. C Witham *Chelmsf* 81-84; C Bath Abbey w St Jas *B & W* 84-86; Chapl Fitzw Coll and New Hall Cam 86-90; Chapl and Hd Relig Studies Oundle Sch Pet from 91. *The School, Oundle, Peterborough PE8 4EN* Oundle (01832) 273372 or 272338

HONNER, Canon Robert Ralph. b 15. St Chad's Coll Dur BA37 DipTh38 MA40. d 38 p 39. V Melbourne *Derby* 54-72; V Beeley and Edensor 72-80; rtd 80; Perm to Offic *Derby* from 80. *5 Castle Mews, Blackwell Lane, Melbourne, Derby DE7 1LW* Melbourne (01332) 864356

HONNOR, Mrs Marjorie Rochefort. b 27. Birm Univ BA48. Cranmer Hall Dur 79. dss 81 d 87 p 94. Church Oakley and Wootton St Lawrence *Win* 81-87; Par Dn 87-89; rtd 89. *33C Surrey Road, Bournemouth BH4 9BJ* Bournemouth (01202) 761021

HONOUR, Colin Reginald. b 44. Lanc Univ CertEd69 Man Univ ADEd75 Newc Univ MEd80. N Ord Course 88. d 91 p 92. NSM Walmsley *Man* 91; C Middleton 92-94; R Holcombe from 94. *The Rectory, 12 Carrwood Hey, Ramsbottom, Bury, Lancs BL0 9QT* Ramsbottom (01706) 822312

HONOUR, Derek. b 59. Bath Univ BSc84. St Jo Coll Nottm. d 89 p 90. C High Wycombe *Ox* 89-91; C Brightside w Wincobank *Sheff* 91-94; P-in-c Dawley St Jerome *Lon* from 94. *St Jerome's Lodge, 42 Corwell Lane, Dawley, Uxbridge, Middx UB8 3DE* 0181-573 1895

HONOUR, Ms Joanna Clare (Jo). b 61. Westmr Coll Ox BEd83. St Jo Coll Nottm LTh88 DPS89. d 89 p 94. Par Dn High Wycombe *Ox* 89-91; NSM Brightside w Wincobank *Sheff* 91-92; Par Dn 93-94; C 94; C 94; Perm to Offic *Lon* from 94. *42 Corwell Lane, Uxbridge, Middx UB8 3DE* 0181-573 2084

HOOD, Mrs Doreen. b 38. Open Univ BA90. NE Ord Course 90. d 93 p 94. NSM Cullercoats St Geo *Newc* from 93. *24 Keswick Drive, North Shields, Tyne & Wear NE30 3EW* 0191-253 1762

HOOD, Leslie. b 23. NE Ord Course. d 85 p 85. NSM Seaham w Seaham Harbour *Dur* 85-90; NSM Dalton le Dale 90-93; NSM Hawthorn 90-93; rtd 93; Perm to Offic *Dur* from 93. *3 Queen Street, Seaham, Co Durham SR7 7SR* 0191-581 2658

HOOD, Peter Michael. b 47. Sheff Univ BSc68 St Pet Coll Ox DipTh72. Wycliffe Hall Ox 70. d 73 p 74. C Soundwell *Bris* 73-76; P-in-c Walcot St Andr CD 76-77; TV Swindon St Jo and St Andr 77-80; V Esh *Dur* 80-88; V Hamsteels 80-88; V Stockton St Paul from 88. *65 Bishopton Road, Stockton-on-Tees, Cleveland TS18 4PE* Stockton-on-Tees (01642) 617869

HOOD, Robert Ernest Nathaniel. b 12. TCD BA34 MA42. d 37 p 38. V Holloway Em w Hornsey Road St Barn *Lon* 57-77; rtd 77; Perm to Offic *Cant* 79-93. *6 Bromley College, London Road, Bromley BR1 1PE*

HOOGERWERF, John Constant. b 50. MIH86 Bris Poly BA85. Oscott Coll (RC) 68. d 73 p 74. In RC Ch 73-84; Hon C Davyhulme Ch Ch *Man* 84-93; Perm to Offic *Heref* from 93. *14 Foster Road, Bridgnorth, Shropshire WV16 4LS* Bridgnorth (01746) 766328

HOOK, Ian Kevin. b 57. Trin Coll Bris DipHE95. d 95. C Dalton-in-Furness *Carl* from 95. *9 Fair View, Dalton-in-Furness, Cumbria LA15 8RZ* Dalton-in-Furness (01229) 464402

HOOK, Ronald Arthur. b 10. Or Coll Ox BA33 MA46. Sarum Th Coll 33. d 34 p 35. R Hurstpierpoint *Chich* 65-75; R Albourne 71-75; rtd 75; Perm to Offic *Chich* from 76. *Bramleys, 35 Manor Gardens, Hurstpierpoint, W Sussex BN6 9UG* Hurstpierpoint (01273) 832092

✠**HOOK, Rt Rev Ross Sydney.** b 17. MC45. Peterho Cam BA39 MA43 Bradf Univ Hon DLitt81. Ridley Hall Cam 39. d 41 p 42 c 65. C Milton *Win* 41-43; Chapl RNVR 43-46; Chapl Ridley Hall Cam 46-48; R Chorlton-cum-Hardy St Clem *Man* 48-52; R Chelsea St Luke *Lon* 52-61; RD Chelsea 52-61; Dir Post Ord Tr *Roch* 61-65; Can Res Roch Cathl 61-65; Suff Bp Grantham *Linc* 65-72; Can and Preb Linc Cathl 66-72; Dean Stamford 72; Bp Bradf 72-80; Chief of Staff to Abp Cant 80-84; Asst Bp Cant 80-94; rtd 84; Perm to Offic *Sarum* from 94. *23A White Cliff Mill Street, Blandford Forum, Dorset DT11 7BQ* Blandford (01258) 454349

HOOKER, Canon Roger Hardham. b 34. St Edm Hall Ox BA58 Ox Univ DipTh59. Wycliffe Hall Ox 58. d 60 p 61. C Stockton *Dur* 60-63; India 65-78; Tutor Crowther Hall CMS Tr Coll Selly Oak 79-82; Dioc Missr *Birm* from 82; Miss Partner CMS from 82; Hon Can Birm Cathl *Birm* from 89. *30 Little Moor Hill, Smethwick, W Midlands B67 7BG* 0121-558 3386 or 0171-928 8681 Fax 0171-401 3215

HOOLE, Charles. b 33. St Aid Birkenhead 61. d 63 p 64. V Lostock Hall *Blackb* 69-73; Chapl HM Pris Eastchurch 74-75; V St Annes St Marg *Blackb* 75-81; V S Shore St Pet 81-92; C Laneside 92-94; rtd 95. *32 Hanover Crescent, Blackpool FY2 9DL* Blackpool (01253) 853564

HOOLEY, John Philip. b 45. Hartley Victoria Coll 69 St Deiniol's Hawarden 78. d 79 p 79. In Meth Ch 73-78; C Heref St Martin *Heref* 79-81; CF from 81. *c/o MOD (Army), Bagshot Park, Bagshot, Surrey GU19 5PL* Bagshot (01276) 471717 Fax 412834

HOOPER, Miss Catherine Margaret. b 58. Leic Univ BSc81 St Jo Coll Dur BA84. dss 85 d 87 p 94. Houghton le Spring *Dur* 85-87; Par Dn 87-88; C Millfield St Mark 88-94; D-in-c Heworth St Alb 94; P-in-c from 94. *The Vicarage, Coldwell Park Drive, Felling, Gateshead, Tyne & Wear NE10 9BX* 0191-438 1720

HOOPER, Canon Charles. b 24. Witwatersrand Univ BA46. Coll of Resurr Mirfield 49. d 51 p 52. N Africa 51-68; Swaziland 68-86; Can Swaziland 71-86; CR from 89. *House of the Resurrection, Mirfield, W Yorkshire WF14 0BN* Mirfield (01924) 494318

HOOPER, Preb Derek Royston. b 33. St Edm Hall Ox BA57 MA65. Cuddesdon Coll 57. **d** 59 **p** 60. C Littleham w Exmouth *Ex* 70-72; TV 72-79; R Wrington w Butcombe *B & W* 79-94; Preb Wells Cathl 93-94; rtd 94; Perm to Offic *Ex* from 95. *Beckington, 7 Cyprus Road, Exmouth, Devon EX8 2DZ* Exmouth (01395) 272831

HOOPER, Geoffrey Michael. b 39. K Coll Lon 61. **d** 66 **p** 67. C Chesterfield All SS *Derby* 66-69; Chapl RAF 69-74; P-in-c Hook Norton w Swerford and Wigginton *Ox* 74-80; P-in-c Gt Rollright 75-80; R Hook Norton w Gt Rollright, Swerford etc 80-82; Warden Mansf Ho Univ Settlement Plaistow from 82; Dir from 86. *Mansfield House, 30 Avenons Road, London E13 8HT* 0171-476 2375 or 476 1505

HOOPER, Ian. b 44. St Jo Coll York CertEd67. Trin Coll Bris DipHE88. **d** 88 **p** 89. C Martlesham w Brightwell *St E* 88-92; V Pakenham w Norton and Tostock from 92. *The Vicarage, Church Hill, Pakenham, Bury St Edmunds, Suffolk IP31 2LN* Pakenham (01359) 30287

HOOPER, Preb Michael Wrenford. b 41. Univ of Wales (Lamp) BA63. St Steph Ho Ox 63. **d** 65 **p** 66. C Bridgnorth St Mary *Heref* 65-70; P-in-c Habberley 70-78; R 78-81; V Minsterley 70-81; RD Pontesbury 75-80; Preb Heref Cathl from 81; V Leominster 81-85; TR Leominster from 85; P-in-c Eyton 81-85; RD Leominster from 81; P-in-c Eye, Croft w Yarpole and Lucton from 91. *The Rectory, Church Street, Leominster, Herefordshire HR6 8NH* Leominster (01568) 612124

HOOPER, Paul Denis Gregory. b 52. Man Univ BA75 Ox Univ BA80 MA87. Wycliffe Hall Ox 78. **d** 81 **p** 82. C Leeds St Geo *Ripon* 81-84; Dioc Youth Officer 84-87; Bp's Dom Chapl 87-95; Dioc Communications Officer from 87; V Harrogate St Mark from 95. *The Vicarage, 13 Wheatlands Road, Harrogate, N Yorkshire HG2 8BB* Harrogate (01423) 504959

HOOPER, Peter Guy. b 30. K Coll Lon 51. **d** 55 **p** 56. R Hazelbury Bryan w Stoke Wake etc *Sarum* 72-84; R Yetminster w Ryme Intrinseca and High Stoy 84-93; RD Sherborne 87-91; rtd 93. *Rose Villa, Long Street, Sherborne, Dorset DT9 3DD* Sherborne (01935) 816819

HOOPER, Sydney Paul. b 46. Lanc Univ BA68 CertEd69 QUB. **d** 85 **p** 87. NSM Killaney w Carryduff *D & D* 85-91; Lic to Offic from 91. *20 Rossdale Road, Cairnshill Road, Belfast BT8 4TG* Belfast (01232) 790907

HOOPER, Mrs Valerie Lilian. b 31. Ex & Truro NSM Scheme 79. **dss** 82 **d** 87. Ex St Mark *Ex* 82-85; Cofton w Starcross 85-87; Hon Par Dn 87-89; Perm to Offic from 91. *1 Cofton Hill, Cockwood, Starcross, Exeter EX6 8RB* Starcross (01626) 890046

HOOPER, William Gilbert. b 38. Ex Univ BA60. St Mich Coll Llan DipTh82. **d** 82 **p** 83. C Hubberston w Herbrandston and Hasguard etc *St D* 82-85; R Llangwm and Freystrop from 85. *The Rectory, Butterhill, Llangwm, Haverfordwest, Dyfed SA62 4JP* Johnston (01437) 891317

HOOTON, Arthur Russell. b 23. Moore Th Coll Sydney ACT ThL51. **d** 52 **p** 52. V Stockingford *Cov* 65-89; rtd 89. *18 Chetwynd Drive, Nuneaton, Warks CV11 4TF* Nuneaton (01203) 343281

HOOTON, David James. b 50. St Kath Coll Liv CertEd73 DipRE81. N Ord Course 83. **d** 86 **p** 87. NSM Pemberton St Mark Newtown *Liv* 86-89; C Ashton-in-Makerfield St Thos 89-92; V Bryn from 92. *The Vicarage, 12 Bryn Road, Ashton-in-Makerfield, Wigan, Lancs WN4 0AA* Ashton-in-Makerfield (01942) 727114

HOPCRAFT, Jonathan Richard. b 34. Or Coll Ox BA55 DipEd66 MA66. Westcott Ho Cam 57. **d** 59 **p** 60. C Cannock *Lich* 59-63; N Rhodesia 63-64; S Rhodesia 64-65; Hon C Olton *Birm* 66-68; Antigua 68-72; C Gt Grimsby St Mary and St Jas *Linc* 72; TV 72-76; P-in-c E Stockwith 76-84; V Blyton w Pilham 76-84; P-in-c Laughton w Wildsworth 76-84; TV Bilston *Lich* 84-90; P-in-c Wolv St Jo from 90. *St John's Vicarage, St John's Square, Wolverhampton WV2 4AT* Wolverhampton (01902) 713041

HOPE, Charles Henry. b 64. FRGS89 Regent's Park Coll Ox BA87 MA90. St Jo Coll Dur BA90. **d** 90 **p** 91. C Tynemouth St Jo *Newc* 90-94; V from 94. *St John's Vicarage, Percy Main, North Shields, Tyne & Wear NE29 6HS* 0191-257 1819

HOPE, Colin Frederick. b 49. St Mich Coll Llan 73. **d** 76 **p** 77. C Warrington St Elphin *Liv* 76-80; V Newton-le-Willows 80-84; CSWG from 84; Lic to Offic *Chich* from 88. *The Monastery, Crawley Down, Crawley, W Sussex RH10 4LH* Copthorne (01342) 712074

HOPE, Cyril Sackett. b 24. St Edm Hall Ox BA49 MA54. Ely Th Coll 50. **d** 51 **p** 52. R Dunchideock and Shillingford *Ex* 63-77; Asst Dir of Educn 73-90; P-in-c Stockland w Dalwood 77-79; V 79-90; rtd 90; Perm to Offic *Ex* from 90. *Verbena, Hind Street, Ottery St Mary, Devon EX11 1BW* Ottery St Mary (01404) 815028

✠**HOPE, Most Rev and Rt Hon David Michael.** b 40. PC91. Nottm Univ BA62 Linacre Ho Ox DPhil65. St Steph Ho Ox 62. **d** 65 **p** 66 **c** 85. C W Derby (or Tuebrook) St Jo *Liv* 65-67

and 68-70; Chapl Bucharest *Eur* 67-68; V Orford St Andr *Liv* 70-74; Prin St Steph Ho Ox 74-82; V St Marylebone All SS *Lon* 82-85; Master of Guardians Shrine of Our Lady Walsingham 82-93; Bp Wakef 85-91; Bp Lon 91-95; Dean of HM Chpls Royal and Prelate of OBE from 91; Abp York from 95. *Bishopthorpe, York YO2 1QE* York (01904) 707021/2 Fax 709204

HOPE, Miss Edith. b 43. SRN64 SCM66 HVCert72 Lanc Univ MA86. Wycliffe Hall Ox 89. **d** 91 **p** 94. Par Dn Droylsden St Mary *Man* 91-94; Par Dn Ecclesall *Sheff* 94; C from 94. *11 Mylor Road, Sheffield S11 7PF* Sheffield (0114) 266 2313

HOPE, Robert. b 36. Dur Univ BSc61. Clifton Th Coll 61. **d** 63 **p** 64. Th Students' Sec IVF 68-71; Hon C Wallington H Trin *S'wark* 69-71; C Ox St Ebbe w St Pet *Ox* 71-74; V Walshaw Ch *Man* 74-87; TR Radipole and Melcombe Regis *Sarum* 87-93; rtd 93. *1A Swiss Valley, Felinfael, Llanelli, Dyfed SA14 8BS* Llanelli (01554) 759199

HOPE, Miss Susan. b 49. St Jo Coll Dur BA83. Cranmer Hall Dur 80. **dss** 83 **d** 87 **p** 94. Boston Spa *York* 83-86; Brightside w Wincobank *Sheff* 86-87; Par Dn 87-89; D-in-c 89-94; V from 94. *The Vicarage, 24 Beacon Road, Sheffield S9 1AD* Sheffield (0114) 243 3640

HOPEWELL, Jeffery Stewart. b 52. ACA79 Leic Univ BA75. E Midl Min Tr Course 82. **d** 85 **p** 86. NSM Houghton on the Hill w Keyham *Leic* 85-88; NSM Houghton-on-the-Hill, Keyham and Hungarton 88-91; C Syston 91-93; TV Syston TM from 93; Bp's Ecum Adv from 91. *The Vicarage, Brookside, Barkby, Leicester LE7 3QD* Leicester (0116) 269 5539

HOPKIN, Gerallt. b 12. Univ of Wales BA36. Sarum Th Coll 37. **d** 38 **p** 39. R St Fagans w Michaelston-super-Ely *Llan* 68-77; rtd 77; Perm to Offic *Llan* from 79. *25B Tangmere Drive, Fairwood Chase, Cardiff CF5 2PP* Cardiff (01222) 553985

HOPKIN, Neil Richard. b 67. ONC86 Trent Poly HNC88. St Jo Coll Nottm BTh95. **d** 95. C Easton H Trin w St Gabr and St Lawr and St Jude *Bris* from 95. *7 Villiers Road, Bristol BS5 0JH* Bristol (0117) 952 2894

HOPKINS, Mrs Angela Joan. b 42. Bp Otter Coll Chich CertEd64. S Dios Minl Tr Scheme 92. **d** 95. NSM Kingsbury H Innocents *Lon* from 95. *3 Regal Way, Harrow, Middx HA3 0RZ* 0181-907 1045

HOPKINS, Aubrey Lionel Evan. b 06. Jes Coll Cam BA28 MA32. Ridley Hall Cam 28. **d** 30 **p** 31. V Folkestone H Trin w Ch Ch *Cant* 62-74; rtd 74; Perm to Offic *Roch* from 83. *Wonston, South View Road, Crowborough, E Sussex TN6 1HW* Crowborough (01892) 667471

HOPKINS, Miss Barbara Agnes. b 28. Lon Univ BSc60 Imp Coll Lon DIC66 MPhil67 DipRS80. St Alb Minl Tr Scheme 82. **dss** 85 **d** 87. Bedf All SS *St Alb* 85-86; Chapl Asst Bedf Gen Hosp 86-88; Bedf St Mich *St Alb* 86-88; Hon Par Dn 87-88; Chapl Asst St Jo Hosp Linc 89-91; Perm to Offic *Linc* from 92. *14 Woburn Avenue, Lincoln LN1 3HJ* Lincoln (01522) 513359

HOPKINS, Christopher Freeman. b 41. Dur Univ BA63. Wells Th Coll 63. **d** 65 **p** 66. C Spring Park *Cant* 65-69; S Africa 69-78; Botswana 78-81; R Beckley and Peasmarsh *Chich* from 81. *The Rectory, School Lane, Peasmarsh, Rye, E Sussex TN31 6UW* Peasmarsh (01797) 230255

HOPKINS, Ernest. b 16. Tyndale Hall Bris 68. **d** 69 **p** 70. C Walton Breck *Liv* 69-70; P-in-c Everton St Chrys 70-74; P-in-c Everton St Jo 70-74; P-in-c Everton Em 70-74; V Everton St Chrys 74-79; RD Walton 76-79; V Eccleston St Luke 79-83; rtd 83; Perm to Offic *St As* from 84; Perm to Offic *Ches* from 88. *12 Shetland Drive, Bromborough, Wirral, Merseyside L62 7JZ* 0151-334 4044

HOPKINS, Henry Charles (Harry). b 46. RD87. Edin Th Coll 65. **d** 71 **p** 72. C Dundee St Salvador *Bre* 71-74; C Dundee St Martin 71-74; Chapl RNVR 72-92; R Monifieth *Bre* 74-78; Miss to Seamen 78-94; Kenya 78-85; Singapore 85-92; New Zealand 89-92; V Middlesb St Thos *York* from 94. *The Vicarage, 1A Cherwell Terrace, Middlesbrough, Cleveland TS3 9DQ* Middlesbrough (01642) 244908

HOPKINS, Hilda (Sister Hilary). dss 33 **d** 87. CSA from 49. *St Andrew's House, 2 Tavistock Road, London W11 1BA* 0171-229 2662

HOPKINS, Canon Hugh. b 33. TCD BA. **d** 62 **p** 63. C Ballymena *Conn* 62-64; C Belf Ch Ch 64-67; I Ballintoy 67-72; I Belf St Ninian 72-81; I Mossley 81-86; I Ballywillan from 86; Miss to Seamen from 86; Can Belf Cathl from 94. *The Rectory, 10 Coleraine Road, Portrush, Co Antrim BT56 8EA* Portrush (01265) 824298

HOPKINS, Canon Hugh Graham Beynon. b 18. Jes Coll Ox BA40 MA45. St Mich Coll Llan 40. **d** 42 **p** 43. V Aberavon *Llan* 59-86; Can Llan Cathl 81-86; RD Margam 81-85; rtd 86; Perm to Offic *Llan* from 86. *25B Mary Street, Porthcawl, M Glam CF36 3YL* Porthcawl (01656) 771651

HOPKINS, John Alun. b 33. Univ of Wales (Lamp) BA55. St Steph Ho Ox 55. **d** 57 **p** 58. V Llanelli St Paul *St D* 76-94; R Eglwys Gymyn and Marros 62-76; rtd 94. *5 Langland Mews,*

Langland Road, Llanelli, Dyfed SA15 1BR Llanelli (01554) 773865

HOPKINS, John Dawson. b 39. Chich Th Coll 85. **d** 87 **p** 88. C Walker *Newc* 87-89; C Newc St Fran 89-92; V Horton from 92. *St Benedict's Vicarage, Brierley Road, Cowpen, Blyth, Northd NE24 5AU* Blyth (01670) 367035

HOPKINS, John Edgar Alexander. b 19. TD65. Jes Coll Cam BA46 MA48. Wells Th Coll 46. **d** 48 **p** 49. V Holdenhurst *Win* 65-71; C-in-c Holdenhurst St Barn CD 65-71; Chapl Stonar Sch Melksham 71-80; P-in-c Clyffe Pypard and Tockenham *Sarum* 80-81; P-in-c Broad Town 80-81; R Broad Town, Clyffe Pypard and Tockenham 81-85; rtd 85. *17 Coxstalls, Wootton Bassett, Swindon SN4 7AW* Swindon (01793) 854091

HOPKINS, Canon John Howard Edgar Beynon. b 14. Univ Coll Ox BA36 MA39. St Mich Coll Llan 36. **d** 37 **p** 38. R Bridge of Weir *Glas* 62-75; R Glas St Marg 75-84; Can St Mary's Cathl 79-84; rtd 84; Hon Can St Mary's Cathl *Glas* from 84. *156 Drymen Road, Bearsden, Glasgow G61 3RE* 0141-942 6013

HOPKINS, Dr Kenneth Victor John. b 45. Univ Coll Lon BA66 Lon Univ BD69 Hull Univ PhD84. Tyndale Hall Bris 66. **d** 69 **p** 70. C S Mimms Ch Ch *Lon* 69-72; C Parkstone St Luke *Sarum* 72-76; P-in-c Trowbridge St Thos 76; V 76-81; R Wingfield w Rowley 76-81; Chapl and Lect NE Surrey Coll of Tech Ewell 81-84; Hd Student Services Essex Inst of HE 84-88; Kingston Poly 88-92; Kingston Univ from 92. *Kingston University, Penrhyn Road, Kingston-upon-Thames, Surrey KT1 2EE* 0181-549 1366

HOPKINS, Lionel. b 48. Open Univ BA82. St D Coll Lamp DipTh70. **d** 71 **p** 72. C Llandeilo Tal-y-bont *S & B* 71-74; C Morriston 74-78; P-in-c Waunarllwydd 78-80; V 80-86; Youth Chapl 84-86; V Llangyfelach from 86. *The Vicarage, 64 Heol Pentre Felin, Morriston, Swansea SA6 6BY* Swansea (01792) 774120

HOPKINS, Miss Patricia Mary. b 46. Kingston Poly BEd78. Trin Coll Bris 83. **dss** 85 **d** 87 **p** 94. Gorleston St Andr *Nor* 85-87; C 87-88; C Woking St Jo *Guildf* 88-90; TD Barnham Broom *Nor* 90-94; TV from 94. *The Rectory, Garveston, Norwich NR9 4QR* Dereham (01362) 858377

HOPKINS, Peter. b 54. Nottm Univ BSc75 Imp Coll Lon MSc79. Oak Hill Th Coll BA86. **d** 86 **p** 87. C Gee Cross *Ches* 86-90; R Gt Gonerby *Linc* 90-95; R Barrowby and Gt Gonerby from 95. *The Rectory, 7 Long Street, Great Gonerby, Grantham, Lincs NG31 8LN* Grantham (01476) 65737

HOPKINS, Reginald Evan. b 10. Jes Coll Cam BA33 MA43. Wycliffe Hall Ox 46. **d** 47 **p** 48. V Billingshurst *Chich* 57-73; V Compton w Up Marden 73-79; R E Marden 73-79; R N Marden 73-79; V Compton, the Mardens, Stoughton and Racton 79-81; rtd 81; Perm to Offic *Chich* from 81. *Mardens, Myrtle Road, Crowborough, E Sussex TN6 1EY* Crowborough (01892) 663631

HOPKINS, Robert James Gardner. b 42. St Alb Minl Tr Scheme. **d** 79 **p** 80. NSM Chorleywood Ch Ch *St Alb* 79-83; NSM Parr Mt *Liv* from 83. *38 Lascelles Street, St Helens, Merseyside WA9 1BA* St Helens (01744) 758886

HOPKINSON, Preb Alfred Stephan. b 08. Wadh Coll Ox BA30 MA35. Linc Th Coll 34. **d** 35 **p** 36. R Bobbingworth *Chelmsf* 63-73; rtd 73; Asst Chapl Win Coll 73-90; Hon C Cam Gt St Mary w St Mich *Ely* from 90. *c/o S Thistleton-Smith Esq, Down Place, South Harting, Petersfield, Hants GU31 5PN* Petersfield (01730) 825374

HOPKINSON, Ven Barnabas John (Barney). b 39. Trin Coll Cam BA63 MA67. Linc Th Coll 63. **d** 65 **p** 66. C Langley All SS and Martyrs *Man* 65-67; C Cam Gt St Mary w St Mich *Ely* 67-71; Asst Chapl Charterhouse Godalming 71-75; P-in-c Preshute *Sarum* 75-76; TV Marlborough 76-81; RD Marlborough 77-81; TR Wimborne Minster and Holt 81-86; Can and Preb Sarum Cathl from 83; RD Wimborne 85-86; Adn Sarum from 86; P-in-c Stratford sub Castle from 87. *Russell House, Stratford sub Castle, Salisbury SP1 3LG* Salisbury (01722) 328756

HOPKINSON, Benjamin Alaric (Ben). b 36. Trin Coll Ox BA59. Chich Th Coll 59. **d** 61 **p** 62. C Pallion *Dur* 61-66; Rhodesia 66-67; Botswana 67-74; Hon C Sherwood *S'well* 74-77; Hon C Carrington 74-77; V Lowdham 77-85; R Whitby *York* from 85; Miss to Seamen from 85. *The Rectory, Chubb Hill Road, Whitby, N Yorkshire YO21 2JP* Whitby (01947) 602590

HOPKINSON, Colin Edward. b 57. BA LLB. Ridley Hall Cam. **d** 84 **p** 85. C Chadwell *Chelmsf* 84-87; C Canvey Is 87-90; P-in-c E Springfield from 90; RD Chelmsf N from 95. *The Vicarage, Ashton Place, Chelmsford CM2 6ST* Chelmsford (01245) 469316

HOPKINSON, David John. b 47. Ox NSM Course. **d** 79 **p** 80. NSM Wardington *Ox* 79-80; Hon C Didcot St Pet 80-83; C Headingley *Ripon* 83-87; P-in-c Leeds All So 87-91; R Middleton Tyas w Croft and Eryholme 91-95; V Leeds Belle Is St Jo and St Barn from 95. *The Vicarage, Low Grange View, Leeds LS10 3DT* Leeds (0113) 271 7821

HOPKINSON, William Humphrey. b 48. ARIC73 Lon Univ BSc69 Dur Univ MA78 Nottm Univ MPhil84 Man Poly MSc90. St Jo Coll Dur DipTh76. **d** 77 **p** 78. C Normanton *Derby* 77-80; C Sawley 80-82; V Birtles *Ches* 82-87; Dir Past Studies N Ord Course 82-94; Dir of Course Development 90-94; Continuing Minl Educn Officer *Ches* 87-94; P-in-c Tenterden St Mich *Cant* from 94. *The Vicarage, Ashford Road, St Michaels, Tenterden, Kent TN30 6PY* Tenterden (01580) 764670

HOPLEY, David. b 37. Wells Th Coll 62. **d** 65 **p** 66. C Frome St Mary *B & W* 65-68; R Staunton-on-Arrow w Byton and Kinsham *Heref* 68-81; P-in-c Lingen 68-81; P-in-c Aymestrey and Leinthall Earles w Wigmore etc 72-81; R Dungeon Hill *Sarum* from 81. *The Rectory, Buckland Newton, Dorchester, Dorset DT2 7BY* Buckland Newton (01300) 345456

HOPLEY, Gilbert. b 40. Univ of Wales (Ban) BA62. St D Coll Lamp LTh65. **d** 65 **p** 66. C St As and Tremeirchion *St As* 65-73; Warden Ch Hostel Ban 73-76; Chapl Univ of Wales (Ban) *Ban* 73-76; V Meifod and Llangynyw *St As* 76-79; Chapl St Marg Sch Bushey 79-87; Hd Master St Paul's Cathl Choir Sch from 87. *Flat 5, 173 Queenstown Road, London SW8 3RJ*

HOPLEY, William James Christopher (Bill). b 50. AKC74. St Aug Coll Cant 74. **d** 75 **p** 76. C Kidderminster St Jo *Worc* 75-78; Ind Chapl 78-85; Co-ord Ind Chapl 85-94; TV Worc St Martin w St Pet, St Mark etc 85-86; TV Worc SE 86-94; Sen Chapl W Midl Police *Birm* from 94. *5 Masshouse Lane, Birmingham B38 9AS* Radio pager (0426) 958158

HOPPER, Bernard. b 20. Leeds Univ BA42. Coll of Resurr Mirfield. **d** 44 **p** 45. V Brighton St Mich *Chich* 67-85; rtd 85; Perm to Offic *Chich* from 85. *64 Warren Drive, Lewes, E Sussex BN7 1HD* Lewes (01273) 475303

HOPPER, Peter John. b 37. Univ Coll Dur BSc59 Lon Univ PGCE60. N Ord Course 89. **d** 91 **p** 91. C Aston cum Aughton and Ulley *Sheff* 91-93; C Aston cum Aughton w Swallownest, Todwick & Ulley 93-94; P-in-c Braithwell w Bramley 94-95; TV Bramley and Ravenfield w Hooton Roberts etc from 95. *The Rectory, Micklebring Lane, Braithwell, Rotherham, S Yorkshire S66 7AS* Rotherham (01709) 812665

HOPPER, Robert Keith. b 45. St Jo Coll Dur 74. **d** 77 **p** 78. C Oxclose *Dur* 77-80; C Hebburn St Jo 80-82; V Lobley Hill from 82. *The Vicarage, Rowanwood Gardens, Gateshead, Tyne & Wear NE11 0DB* 0191-460 4409

HOPPERTON, Thomas. b 33. Chich Th Coll 71. **d** 73 **p** 74. C Cheam *S'wark* 73-89; P-in-c Rotherhithe St Kath w St Barn 89-92; P-in-c S Bermondsey St Bart 91-92; V Bermondsey St Kath w St Bart from 92. *St Katharine's Vicarage, 92 Eugenia Road, London SE16 2RA* 0171-237 3679

HOPWOOD, Adrian Patrick. b 37. CBiol MIBiol MIWEM N Lon Poly BSc61. Ox Min Course 87. **d** 90 **p** 91. NSM Chesham Bois *Ox* 90-93; NSM Amersham 93-95; NSM Ridgeway from 95. *The Glebe House, Childrey, Wantage, Oxon OX12 9UP* Wantage (01235) 751518

HOPWOOD OWEN, Mrs Karen. b 58. Padgate Coll of Educn CertEd79 St Martin's Coll Lanc DASE90. Local NSM Course 92. **d** 95. NSM Peel *Man* from 95. *168 Manchester Road, Tyldesley, Manchester M29 8WY* Atherton (01942) 894850

✠**HORAN, Rt Rev Forbes Trevor.** b 05. Trin Hall Cam BA32 MA36. Westcott Ho Cam 33. **d** 33 **p** 34 **c** 60. C Newc St Luke *Newc* 33-36; C Newc St Geo 36-38; C-in-c Balkwell CD 38-40; Chapl RNVR 40-45; V Shrewsbury St Chad *Lich* 45-52; I Huddersfield *Wakef* 52-60; RD 52-60; Hon Can Wakef Cathl 55-60; Suff Bp Tewkesbury *Glouc* 60-73; rtd 73; Asst Bp Glouc from 75. *3 Silverthorne Close, Shurdington Road, Cheltenham, Glos GL53 0JF* Cheltenham (01242) 527313

HORBURY, Dr William. b 42. Or Coll Ox BA64 MA67 Clare Coll Cam BA66 PhD71. Westcott Ho Cam 64. **d** 69 **p** 70. Fell Clare Coll Cam 68-72; CCC Cam from 78; Lic to Offic *Ely* 69-72 and 78-90; R Gt w Lt Gransden 72-78; Lect Div Cam Univ from 84; NSM Cam St Botolph *Ely* from 90. *5 Grange Road, Cambridge CB3 9AS* Cambridge (01223) 63529

HORDERN, Peter John Calveley. b 35. Jes Coll Cam BA59 MA64. Linc Th Coll. **d** 61 **p** 62. C Billingham St Aid *Dur* 61-65; Canada from 65. *346 Aberdeen Avenue, Brandon, Manitoba, Canada, R7A 1N4*

HORE, Michael John. b 50. Man Univ BSc71. Linc Th Coll 75. **d** 78 **p** 79. C Maidstone St Martin *Cant* 78-81; C St Peter-in-Thanet 81-83; R Storrington *Chich* 83-93; RD Storrington 90-93; V Goring-by-Sea from 93. *The Vicarage, 12 Compton Avenue, Goring-by-Sea, Worthing, W Sussex BN12 4UJ* Worthing (01903) 242525

HORLESTON, Kenneth William. b 50. BA86. Oak Hill Th Coll 84. **d** 86 **p** 87. C Wednesfield Heath *Lich* 86-89; V Blagreaves *Derby* from 89. *St Andrew's Vicarage, 5 Greenburn Close, Littleover, Derby DE23 7FF* Derby (01332) 773877

HORLOCK, Very Rev Brian William. b 31. OBE78. Univ of Wales (Lamp) BA55. Chich Th Coll 55. **d** 57 **p** 58. C Chiswick St Nic w St Mary *Lon* 57-61; C Witney *Ox* 61-62; V N Acton St Gabr *Lon* 62-68; Chapl Oslo w Bergen, Trondheim and

Stavanger *Eur* 68-89; RD Scandinavia 75-79; Adn 80-89; Hon Can Brussels Cathl 80-89; Dean Gib from 89; Chapl Gib from 89. *The Deanery, Gibraltar* Gibraltar (350) 78377 Fax 78463

HORN, Colin Clive. b 39. CEng MIMechE. Cant Sch of Min. **d** 83 **p** 84. NSM Yalding w Collier Street *Roch* 83-91; V Kemsing w Woodlands from 91; RD Shoreham from 94. *The Vicarage, High Street, Kemsing, Sevenoaks, Kent TN15 6PY* Sevenoaks (01732) 761351

HORN, David Henry. b 47. Nottm Univ BA69 CQSW71. Qu Coll Birm. **d** 82 **p** 83. C Hamstead St Paul *Birm* 82-84; V Aston St Jas 84-94; Sec Inner Cities Relig Coun from 94; Perm to Offic *Chelmsf* from 94. *49 Cranmer Road, London E7 0JL, or Room P2/125, Dept of Environment, 2 Marsham Street, London SW1P 3EB* 0181-257 1162 or 0171-276 4430 Fax 0171-276 0767

HORN, Michael Leonard. b 32. Oak Hill Th Coll 56. **d** 59 **p** 60. India 62-75; New Zealand 77-86; rtd 94. *903 Dominion Road, Mount Roskill, Auckland 4, New Zealand*

HORNBY, John Hulme. b 24. AKC47. Qu Coll Birm 48. **d** 49 **p** 50. R Stretham w Thetford *Ely* 66-74; P-in-c Bratton Fleming *Ex* 74-89; P-in-c Stoke Rivers 74-89; P-in-c Challacombe 75-89; RD Shirwell 77-80; rtd 89; Perm to Offic *Ex* from 89. *6 Barbican Terrace, Barnstaple, Devon EX32 9HQ* Barnstaple (01271) 75463

HORNE, Anthony Cedric. b 26. MIMechE61 MIEE67. **d** 77 **p** 78. NSM Kingsdown *Bris* 77-83; C Soundwell 83-85; P-in-c Bris St Andr w St Bart 85-92; rtd 92. *88 Church Road, Soundwell, Bristol BS16 4RG* Bristol (0117) 970 1007

HORNE, Brian Lawrence. b 39. FRSA Natal Univ BA60 Dur Univ DipPh62 MLitt68 Lon Univ PhD71. Gen Th Sem (NY) MDiv63 St Chad's Coll Dur 60. **d** 62 **p** 63. Tutor St Chad's Coll Dur 63-66; Lect K Coll Lon from 66. *King's College, Strand, London WC2R 2LS* 0171-274 6222

HORNE, Jack Kenneth. b 20. Linc Th Coll 68. **d** 70 **p** 71. C Danbury *Chelmsf* 70-75; V Frampton *Linc* 75-85; rtd 85. *154 Kenilworth Road, Grantham, Lincs NG31 9UH* Grantham (01476) 78867

HORNE, Simon Timothy. b 62. Ball Coll Ox BA86 MA90 Southn Univ RNMH89. Qu Coll Birm BD94. **d** 95. C Basingstoke *Win* from 95. *1 The Glebe, Church Square, Basingstoke, Hants RG21 7QW* Basingstoke (01256) 466694

HORNER, Eric. b 43. E Midl Min Tr Course 87. **d** 90 **p** 91. C Boultham *Linc* 90-93; P-in-c Kirton in Holland 93-95; P-in-c Frampton 93-95; P-in-c Frampton w Kirton in Holland from 95. *The Vicarage, Willington Road, Kirton, Boston, Lincs PE20 1EH* Boston (01205) 722380

HORNER, Graham. b 57. ACA81 Grey Coll Dur BSc78. St Jo Coll Nottm DTS93. **d** 93 **p** 94. C Longdon-upon-Tern, Rodington, Uppington etc *Lich* from 93. *44 Pemberton Road, Telford, Shropshire TF5 0BL* Telford (01952) 244255

HORNER, John Henry. b 40. Leeds Univ BA62 Lon Univ DipRS74 Middx Poly MA87. Oak Hill Th Coll 76. **d** 79 **p** 80. Hon C Datchworth w Tewin *St Alb* 79-85; Hon C Ware St Mary 85-91; C S Ashford Ch Ch *Cant* 91-94; C Hatf *St Alb* from 94. *St John's House, Bishop's Rise, Hatfield, Herts AL10 9BZ* Hatfield (01707) 262689

HORNER, Peter Francis. b 27. Jes Coll Ox BA51 MA55. Kelham Th Coll 52. **d** 54 **p** 55. Tutor Kelham Th Coll 54-73; Chapl 58-73; C Averham w Kelham *S'well* 54-56; Lic to Offic 56-73; SSM from 58; Lic to Offic *Ox* 74-87; Australia from 87. *14 St John's Priory, Adelaide, Australia 5000* Adelaide (8) 223-2348

HORNER, Philip David Forster. b 30. Tyndale Hall Bris BDip67. **d** 67 **p** 68. C Ulverston St Mary w H Trin *Carl* 67-71; C Princes Risborough w Ilmer *Ox* 71-76; C Wendover 76-89; P-in-c Ellesborough 76-89; P-in-c Gt and Lt Kimble 82-89; C Walton H Trin 89-92; TV from 92. *24 King Edward Avenue, Aylesbury, Bucks HP21 7JD* Aylesbury (01296) 415260

HORNER, Robert William. b 17. RD. St Pet Hall Ox MA46 DipEd. Ripon Hall Ox 56. **d** 57 **p** 58. Chapl RNR 63-74; R Chinnor *Ox* 66-73; R Emmington 66-73; V Sydenham 66-73; R Chinnor w Emmington and Sydenham 73-84; rtd 84; Perm to Offic *Ex* from 84. *29 Lammas Lane, Paignton, Devon TQ3 1PS* Paignton (01803) 528426

HORNSBY, Edgar. b 23. AKC50. **d** 51 **p** 52. Chapl St Mary's Hall and Brighton Coll 69-74; Chapl St Swithun's Sch *Win* 74-88; rtd 88. *The Manor Farmhouse, Littlewindsor, Beaminster, Dorset DT8 3QU*

HOROBIN, Hector Stanley. b 09. Kelham Th Coll 30 Edin Th Coll 46. **d** 46 **p** 47. V Petts Wood *Roch* 62-88; rtd 88. *23 Wentworth Close, Wentworth Close, Lyminge, Folkestone, Kent CT18 8HL* Folkestone (01303) 863095

HOROBIN, Timothy John (Tim). b 60. St Jo Coll Nottm DipThMin94. **d** 94 **p** 95. C Nelson St Phil *Blackb* from 94. *412 Leeds Road, Nelson, Lancs BB9 8ET* Nelson (01282) 697327

HORROCKS, Mrs Judith Anne (Judie). b 53. Calgary Univ BSc76. St Jo Coll Nottm DPS82. **dss** 82 **d** 87 **p** 94. Denton Ch

Ch *Man* 82-85; Whalley Range St Edm 85-87; Par Dn 87-94; C from 94; Chapl Man R Infirmary 88-90. *1 Range Road, Whalley Range, Manchester M16 8FS* 0161-226 1291

HORROCKS, Oliver John. b 30. Clare Coll Cam BA53 MA57. Westcott Ho Cam 53. **d** 55 **p** 56. C Moss Side Ch Ch *Man* 55-58; C Arnold *S'well* 58-60; R Ancoats *Man* 60-67; R Barthomley *Ches* from 67. *Barthomley Rectory, Crewe CW2 5PE* Crewe (01270) 872479

HORROCKS, Robert James. b 56. Grey Coll Dur BSc78. St Jo Coll Nottm DipTh80 DPS82. **d** 82 **p** 83. C Denton Ch Ch *Man* 82-85; R Whalley Range St Edm from 85. *St Edmund's Rectory, 1 Range Road, Whalley Range, Manchester M16 8FS* 0161-226 1291

HORROCKS, Stanley. b 22. Man Univ BA76. Coll of Resurr Mirfield 77. **d** 78 **p** 79. Hon C Man Miles Platting *Man* 78-81; Hon C Lower Broughton St Clem w St Matthias 81-87; rtd 87; NSM Higher Broughton *Man* 87-92; NSM Broughton St Jas w St Clem and St Matthias 92-93; Perm to Offic from 93. *80 Northumberland Street, Salford M7 0DG* 0161-792 1037

HORSEMAN, Christopher Michael. b 54. Bris Sch of Min 84 Trin Coll Bris 87. **d** 88 **p** 89. C Weston-super-Mare Cen Par *B & W* 88-92; TV Yatton Moor from 92. *6 Westaway Park, Yatton, Bristol BS19 4JU* Weston-super-Mare (01934) 834537

HORSEMAN, Colin. b 46. Lon Coll of Div ALCD69 BD70 STh75. **d** 70 **p** 71. C Higher Openshaw *Man* 70-74; C Darfield *Sheff* 75-78; V Stainforth 78-88; V Heeley 88-95; P-in-c Ducklington *Ox* from 95. *The Rectory, 6 Standlake Road, Ducklington, Witney, Oxon OX8 7XG* Witney (01993) 776625

HORSEY, Maurice Alfred. b 30. AIB. S'wark Ord Course 61. **d** 64 **p** 65. C Coulsdon St Jo *S'wark* 67-71; P-in-c Champion Hill St Sav 71-76; Hon C Lewisham St Swithun 84-86; P-in-c Woolwich St Thos 86-90; R 90-94; rtd 94; Spain from 94; Chapl Costa del Sol W *Eur* from 94. *Apartado 106, 29670 San Pedro de Alcantara, Malaga, Spain* Malaga (52) 886091

HORSEY, Stanley Desmond. b 20. Ely Th Coll 46. **d** 49 **p** 50. V Hove St Barn *Chich* 67-77; V Hove St Barn and St Agnes 77-85; rtd 85; Perm to Offic *Chich* from 85. *27A Amesbury Crescent, Hove, E Sussex BN3 5RD* Brighton (01273) 732081

HORSFALL, David John. b 55. Bris Poly BA77. Trin Coll Bris DipHE82 St Jo Coll Nottm DPS89. **d** 89 **p** 90. C Chaddesden St Mary *Derby* 89-92; V Swadlincote from 92. *The Vicarage, Church Street, Swadlincote, Derbyshire DE11 8LF* Burton-on-Trent (01283) 217756

HORSFALL, Keith. b 39. Tyndale Hall Bris 62. **d** 65 **p** 66. C Walton Breck *Liv* 65-68; C Fazakerley Em 68-70; C Mile Cross *Nor* 70-73; V Gayton 73-80; TR Parr *Liv* 80-90; V Leyland St Andr *Blackb* from 90. *St Andrew's Vicarage, Crocus Field, Leyland, Preston PR5 2DY* Preston (01772) 621645

HORSFIELD, Preb Robert Alan. b 38. Leeds Univ BA60 MA66. Coll of Resurr Mirfield 61. **d** 63 **p** 64. C Lower Gornal *Lich* 63-66; C Bridlington Quay H Trin *York* 66-68; C Sewerby w Marton 66-68; C-in-c Gt Grimsby St Matt Fairfield CD *Linc* 68-73; R Scartho 73-79; R Cleobury Mortimer w Hopton Wafers *Heref* 79-94; P-in-c Neen Sollars w Milson 81-94; P-in-c Neen Savage w Kinlet 91-94; R Cleobury Mortimer w Hopton Wafers etc from 95; P-in-c Knowbury 84-86; P-in-c Coreley w Doddington 84-86; RD Ludlow from 89; Preb Heref Cathl from 92. *The Rectory, The Hurst, Cleobury Mortimer, Kidderminster, Worcs DY14 8EG* Cleobury Mortimer (01299) 270264

HORSHAM, Archdeacon of. *See* FILBY, Ven William Charles Leonard

HORSHAM, Area Bishop of. *See* URWIN, Rt Rev Lindsay Goodall

HORSINGTON, Timothy Frederick. b 44. Dur Univ BA66. Wycliffe Hall Ox 67. **d** 69 **p** 70. C Halewood *Liv* 69-72; C Farnworth 72-75; P-in-c Llangarron w Llangrove *Heref* 75-82; P-in-c Whitchurch w Ganarew 77-82; R Llangarron w Llangrove, Whitchurch and Ganarew 83-84; R Highclere and Ashmansworth w Crux Easton *Win* from 84. *The Rectory, 2 Flexford Close, Highclere, Newbury, Berks RG15 9PE* Highclere (01635) 253991

HORSLEY, Canon Alan Avery. b 36. St Chad's Coll Dur BA58 Pacific State Univ MA84 PhD85. Qu Coll Birm 58. **d** 60 **p** 61. C Daventry *Pet* 60-63; C Reading St Giles *Ox* 63-64; C Wokingham St Paul 64-66; V Yeadon St Andr *Bradf* 66-71; R Heyford w Stowe Nine Churches *Pet* 71-78; RD Daventry 76-78; V Oakham w Hambleton and Egleton 78-81; Can Pet Cathl 79-86; V Oakham, Hambleton, Egleton, Braunston and Brooke 81-86; V Lanteglos by Fowey *Truro* 86-88; Provost St Andr Cathl Inverness *Mor* 88-91; R Inverness St Andr 88-91; P-in-c Culloden St Mary-in-the-Fields 88-91; P-in-c Strathnairn St Paul 88-91; V Mill End and Heronsgate w W

Hyde *St Alb* from 91. *St Peter's Vicarage, Berry Lane, Rickmansworth, Herts WD3 2HQ* Rickmansworth (01923) 772785

HORSMAN, Andrew Alan. b 49. Otago Univ BA70 Man Univ MA72 PhD75. St Steph Ho Ox BA80 MA87. **d** 81 **p** 82. C Hillingdon All SS *Lon* 81-84; C Lt Stanmore St Lawr 84-87; TV Haxby w Wigginton *York* from 87. *The Vicarage, 5 Back Lane, Wigginton, York YO3 3ZH* York (01904) 768178

HORSWELL, Kevin George. b 55. Jes Coll Cam BA77 MA81 Nottm Univ BA81. St Jo Coll Nottm. **d** 82 **p** 83. C Bootle Ch Ch *Liv* 82-86; Chapl LMH Ox 86-91; C Ox St Giles and SS Phil and Jas w St Marg *Ox* 86-91; R Dodleston *Ches* from 91. *St Mary's Rectory, Pulford Lane, Dodleston, Chester CH4 9NN* Chester (01244) 660257

HORTON, Alan Michael. b 47. Univ of Wales BScTech71. Linc Th Coll CMinlStuds92. **d** 92 **p** 93. C Bexleyheath Ch Ch *Roch* from 92. *50 Martindene, Bexleyheath, Kent DA6 8NA* 0181-298 1355

HORTON, Andrew Charles. b 50. Ex Univ BA71. Sarum Th Coll 71. **d** 73 **p** 74. C Westbury-on-Trym St Alb *Bris* 73-76; USA 76-90; P-in-c Battersea St Mich *S'wark* 90-92; V from 92; Local Min Officer Kingston Episc Area from 94. *St Michael's Vicarage, 93 Bolingbroke Grove, London SW11 6HA* 0171-228 1990

HORTON, Canon Christopher Peter. b 26. Leeds Univ BA49. Coll of Resurr Mirfield 49. **d** 51 **p** 52. V Grangetown *York* 59-91; Can and Preb York Minster 85-91; rtd 91. *51 Well Ridge Close, Seaton Grange, Whitley Bay, Tyne & Wear NE25 9PN* 0191-251 0742

HORTON, David Harold. b 49. St Jo Coll Dur BA72. NE Ord Course 82. **d** 86 **p** 87. C Enfield St Jas *Lon* 86-90; Min Joydens Wood St Barn CD *Roch* 90-93; V Joydens Wood St Barn from 93. *The Vicarage, 6 Tile Kiln Lane, Bexley, Kent DA5 2BD* Crayford (01322) 528923

HORTON, Jeremy Nicholas Orkney. b 44. Cranmer Hall Dur 64. **d** 68 **p** 69. C Dalton-in-Furness *Carl* 68-70; C Penrith 70-73; V Hudswell w Downholme and Marske *Ripon* 73-75; R Middleton Tyas and Melsonby 75-81; P-in-c Croft 78-81; P-in-c Eryholme 78-81; V Wortley de Leeds 81-93; V Middleton St Mary from 93. *Middleton Vicarage, 198 Town Street, Leeds LS10 3TJ* Leeds (0113) 270 5689

HORTON, John Ward. b 27. Leeds Univ BA50. Coll of Resurr Mirfield 50. **d** 52 **p** 53. C-in-c Acomb Moor CD *York* 58-71; V Acomb Moor 71-93; rtd 93. *39 Billy Mill Lane, North Shields, Tyne & Wear NE26 8BZ* 0191-296 4082

HORTON, Michael John. b 56. St Jo Coll Cam BA80 MA83 Univ of Wales (Swansea) PGCE83 Ox Univ BA88 MA92. Wycliffe Hall Ox 86. **d** 89 **p** 90. C Northallerton w Kirby Sigston *York* 89-92; C Ulverston St Mary w H Trin *Carl* 92-94; V Lightwater *Guildf* from 94. *The Vicarage, 28 Broadway Road, Lightwater, Surrey GU18 5SJ* Bagshot (01276) 472270

HORTON, Ralph Edward. b 41. S'wark Ord Course 75. **d** 78 **p** 79. C Streatham St Leon *S'wark* 78-81; TV Catford (Southend) and Downham 81-88; V Ashford St Matt *Lon* from 88. *The Vicarage, 99 Church Road, Ashford, Middx TW15 2NY* Ashford (01784) 252459

HORTON, Canon Roberta Anne. b 44. Leic Univ BSc66 CertEd67 Nottm Univ BCombStuds82. Linc Th Coll 79. **dss** 82 **d** 87 **p** 94. Cam St Jas *Ely* 82-86; Beaumont Leys *Leic* 86-87; Par Dn 87-91; Dioc Dir of Tr from 91; P-in-c Swithland from 94; Hon Can Leic Cathl from 94. *The Rectory, 157 Main Street, Swithland, Loughborough, Leics LE12 8QT* Woodhouse Eaves (01509) 891173

HORWOOD, Graham Frederick. b 34. Univ of Wales (Cardiff) BA55. Coll of Resurr Mirfield 55. **d** 57 **p** 58. C Llantrisant *Llan* 57-61; C Roath St Sav 61-62; C Roath St Marg 62-66; V Clydach *S & B* 66-77; V Canton St Luke *Llan* from 77. *St Luke's Vicarage, 12 Thompson Avenue, Cardiff CF5 1EY* Cardiff (01222) 562022

HORWOOD, Thomas Gilbert. b 15. Man Univ BA41. Westcott Ho Cam 45. **d** 46 **p** 47. V Brompton w Snainton *York* 68-80; Master St Jo Hosp Bath 85-90; Min Bath St Mich Chpl *B & W* 85-90; rtd 90; Perm to Offic *Chich* from 90. *April Cottage, The Common, Henfield, W Sussex BN5 9RS* Henfield (01273) 492570

HOSKIN, David James. b 63. Hull Univ BA86. Trin Coll Bris BA94. **d** 94 **p** 95. C Southway *Ex* from 94. *5 Treago Gardens, Plymouth PL6 7AZ* Plymouth (01752) 787065

HOSKIN, David William. b 49. Hatf Coll Dur BSc71. Wycliffe Hall Ox 72. **d** 75 **p** 76. C Bridlington Priory *York* 75-78; C Rodbourne Cheney *Bris* 78-79; C Bebington *Ches* 79-82; R Lockington and Lund and Scorborough w Leconfield *York* 82-88; V Beverley St Mary from 88. *The Vicarage, 15 Molescroft Road, Beverley, N Humberside HU17 7DX* Hull (01482) 881437

HOSKIN, Canon Eric James. b 28. St Chad's Coll Dur BA50 DipTh52. **d** 52 **p** 53. C Coney Hill *Glouc* 52-54; C Stroud 54-57; R Ruardean 57-63; P-in-c Lydbrook 61-63; V Cheltenham Em

63-70; R Dursley 70-86; RD Dursley 77-85; Hon Can Glouc Cathl 81-86; R Easington w Liverton *York* from 86. *The Rectory, Easington, Saltburn-by-the-Sea, Cleveland TS13 4NT* Guisborough (01287) 641348

HOSKIN, Henry Brian. b 32. NW Ord Course 72. **d** 75 **p** 76. NSM Chesterfield St Aug *Derby* 75-79; NSM Bolsover 79-83; NSM Old Brampton and Loundsley Green 83-88; P-in-c Barlow 88-94. *25 Barn Close, Chesterfield, Derbyshire S41 8BD* Chesterfield (01246) 201550

HOSKING, Canon Harold Ernest. b 19. Lich Th Coll 51. **d** 53 **p** 54. V Newquay *Truro* 69-74; TR Redruth 74-80; R Redruth w Lanner 80-84; Hon Can Truro Cathl 78-84; rtd 84; Perm to Offic *Ex* from 84. *28 Chantry Close, Teignmouth, Devon TQ14 8FE* Teignmouth (01626) 770329

HOSKINS, Hugh George. b 46. S Dios Minl Tr Scheme. **d** 84 **p** 85. NSM Hilperton w Whaddon and Staverton etc *Sarum* 84-87; C Calne and Blackland 87-90; R W Lavington and the Cheverells from 90. *The Vicarage, White Street, West Lavington, Devizes, Wilts SN10 4LW* Devizes (01380) 818388

HOSKINS, Ian David. b 41. St Chad's Coll Dur BA63 DipTh65 Dur Univ MA88. **d** 65 **p** 66. C Southwick St Cuth CD *Dur* 65-68; C Beamish 68-72; V S Moor 72-77; Asst Chapl HM Pris Dur 76-80; R Witton Gilbert *Dur* 77-88; Chapl Earl's Ho Hosp Dur 79-94; R Dur St Marg *Dur* 88-94; Chapl St Cuth Hospice Dur 88-94. *Tenter House, 17 Tenter Terrace, Durham DH1 4RD* 0191-384 5626

HOSKINS, Canon James Paul. b 07. Lon Univ BA27. Wells Th Coll 30. **d** 31 **p** 32. V Malborough w S Huish *Ex* 67-77; rtd 77; Lic to Offic *Ex* from 77. *Flat 28, Gracey Court, Woodland Road, Broadclyst, Exeter EX5 3LP* Exeter (01392) 460161

HOSKYNS, John Algernon Peyton. b 20. Pemb Coll Cam BA41 MA45. Westcott Ho Cam 47. **d** 49 **p** 50. R Worplesdon *Guildf* 62-72; V St Weonards w Orcop *Heref* 73-76; P-in-c Linton w Upton Bishop 76-78; P-in-c How Caple w Sollers Hope 76-85; P-in-c Sellack and King's Caple w Foy 81-85; rtd 85; Perm to Offic *Heref* from 85. *Riverknoll, Hoarwithy, Hereford HR2 6QF* Carey (01432) 840282

HOST, Mrs Charmaine Anne. b 54. W Midl Minl Tr Course 87. **d** 90 **p** 94. C Westwood *Cov* 90-94; C Whitnash from 94. *13 Palmer Road, Whitnash, Leamington Spa, Warks CV31 2HP* Leamington Spa (01926) 425366

HOTCHEN, Stephen Jeffrie. b 50. Bradf Coll of Educn. Linc Th Coll 85. **d** 87 **p** 88. C Morpeth *Newc* 87-90; TV High Wycombe *Ox* 90-91; R Dingwall *Mor* 91-94; R Strathpeffer 91-94; V Rickerscote *Lich* from 94. *St Peter's Vicarage, 106 Rickerscote Road, Stafford ST17 4HB* Stafford (01785) 52878

HOTCHIN, Mrs Hilary Moya. b 52. Birm Univ CertEd73. W Midl Minl Tr Course 85. **d** 88 **p** 94. NSM Redditch St Steph *Worc* 88-91; Par Dn Handsworth *Sheff* 91-94; C from 94. *Kunwara, The Rectory Grounds, Handsworth, Sheffield S13 9BZ* Sheffield (0114) 269 4516

HOUGH, Dr Adrian Michael. b 59. MRSC CChem AMITD Hertf Coll Ox BA81 MA84 DPhil84. Ripon Coll Cuddesdon BA91. **d** 92 **p** 93. C Martley and Wichenford, Knightwick etc *Worc* from 92. *4 Taberness Close, Broadwas, Worcester WR6 5NF* Knightwick (01886) 821053

HOUGH, Miss Carole Elizabeth. b 59. Lon Hosp SRN81. St Jo Coll Nottm DipMin91. **d** 91 **p** 94. Par Dn Beoley *Worc* 91-94; C 94-95; Chapl Addenbrooke's Hosp Cam from 95. *Addenbrooke's Hospital, Hills Road, Cambridge BC2 2QQ* Cambridge (01223) 217769 or 245151

HOUGH, Edward Lewis. b 38. Univ of Wales (Lamp) BA60. St Mich Coll Llan 60. **d** 62 **p** 63. Ind Chapl *York* 69-72; R Cilybebyll *Llan* 72-93; RD Neath 84-89; Ind Chapl Port Talbot 92-95; V Cadoxton-juxta-Neath 93-95; rtd 95. *14 Alderwood Close, Crynant, Neath, W Glam SA10 8PY*

HOUGH, Canon John Francis. b 06. St Jo Coll Ox BA29 MA32. Westcott Ho Cam 29. **d** 30 **p** 31. V Tenterden St Mildred w Smallhythe *Cant* 66-74; rtd 74; Perm to Offic *Cant* 74-88; Perm to Offic *Chich* 75-88; Perm to Offic *Ely* from 88. *51 Millfield Court, Brampton Road, Huntingdon, Cambs PE18 6TT* Huntingdon (01480) 413149

HOUGH, Michael. b 49. Man Univ. St Jo Coll Nottm. **d** 84 **p** 85. C Newbottle *Dur* 84-87; V Felling from 87. *The Vicarage, Carlisle Street, Felling, Gateshead, Tyne & Wear NE10 0HQ* 0191-469 2440

HOUGH, Peter George. b 40. Dur Univ BA62. Wells Th Coll 62. **d** 64 **p** 65. C Stocking Farm CD *Leic* 64-68; V Leic St Aid 68-76; V Knutton *Lich* from 76; P-in-c Silverdale and Alsagers Bank from 93. *The Vicarage, Church Lane, Newcastle, Staffs ST5 6DU* Newcastle-under-Lyme (01782) 624282

HOUGH, Sidney Stephen Valentine. b 27. G&C Coll Cam BA50 MA54. Ripon Hall Ox 55. **d** 57 **p** 58. V Messing *Chelmsf* 62-72; R Inworth 62-72; V Messing w Inworth 72-77; Chapl Warley Hosp Brentwood 78-79; R Alphamstone w Lamarsh and Pebmarsh *Chelmsf* 79-88; rtd 88. *27 Weavers Court, Weavers Lane, Sudbury, Suffolk CO10 6HY* Sudbury (01787) 374812

HOUGHTBY, Frank. b 12. Chich Th Coll 41. **d** 41 **p** 42. R N Runcton w Hardwick and Setchey *Nor* 60-91; rtd 91. *29 Lodge Way, Grantham, Lincs NG31 8DD* Grantham (01476) 592282

HOUGHTON, Christopher Guy. b 64. W Surrey Coll of Art & Design BA86. Oak Hill Th Coll DipHE88 BA89. **d** 89 **p** 90. C Mossley Hill St Matt and St Jas *Liv* 89-92; C Ashton-in-Makerfield St Thos 92-95; C Southport St Phil and St Paul from 95. *63 Belmont Street, Southport, Merseyside PR8 1JH* Southport (01704) 531615

HOUGHTON, David John. b 47. Edin Univ BSc(Econ)68. Cuddesdon Coll 69. **d** 71 **p** 72. C Prestbury *Glouc* 71-74; Prec Gib Cathl *Eur* 74-76; Chapl Madrid 76-78; C Croydon *Cant* 78-80; Chapl Warw Sch 80-85; P-in-c Isleworth St Fran *Lon* 85-90; USA 90-91; TV Clapham TM *S'wark* from 91; RD Clapham from 93. *15 Elms Road, London SW4 9ER* 0171-622 8703 Fax as telephone

HOUGHTON, Edward Johnson. b 23. Keble Coll Ox BA48 MA48. Linc Th Coll 48. **d** 50 **p** 51. CF (TA) 56-62; Chapl Hellingly and Amberstone Hosps 61-90; rtd 88. *1 Nursery Close, Osborne Park, Hailsham, E Sussex BN27 2PX* Hailsham (01323) 442126

HOUGHTON, Mrs Evelyn Mabel. b 44. **d** 94. NSM Bedf St Jo and St Leon *St Alb* from 94. *29 Turner Way, Bedford MK41 7ND* Bedford (01234) 212525

HOUGHTON, Geoffrey John. b 59. Ridley Hall Cam 87. **d** 90 **p** 91. C Sholing *Win* 90-94; P-in-c Jersey All SS from 94. *All Saints Vicarage, Saville Street, St Helier, Jersey, Channel Islands JE2 3XF* Jersey (01534) 68538

HOUGHTON, Ian David. b 50. Lanc Univ BA71 Newc Univ CertEd74 Man Univ CertRS90. Sarum & Wells Th Coll 80. **d** 82 **p** 83. C Newc St Geo *Newc* 82-85; Chapl Newc Poly 85-92; Chapl Univ of Northumbria at Newc from 92; Master Newc St Thos Prop Chpl from 90. *9 Chester Crescent, Newcastle upon Tyne NE2 1DH* 0191-232 9789 or 232 6002

HOUGHTON, James Robert. b 44. AKC67. **d** 68 **p** 69. C Herrington *Dur* 68-70; Asst Dioc Youth Chapl *Bris* 70-72; Perm to Offic *Ex* 73-74; C Heavitree 74-77; Perm to Offic *Lon* 78-80 and 83-88; C Heavitree w Ex St Paul *Ex* 78; Hon C W Drayton *Lon* 80-83; Chapl Greycoat Hosp Sch 83-88; Chapl Stonar Sch Melksham 88-95; Chapl SS Mary and Anne's Sch Abbots Bromley from 95. *Stonar School, Cottles Park, Atworth, Melksham, Wilts SN12 8NT* Melksham (01225) 702763

HOUGHTON, Canon John Caswell. b 16. Dur Univ BA38 LTh38. St Boniface Warminster 34. **d** 39 **p** 40. Zambia 64-74; Promotions Sec Feed the Minds 74-81; rtd 81; Perm to Offic *Ox* from 82. *18 Cornelia Close, Bletchley, Milton Keynes MK2 3LX* Milton Keynes (01908) 370526

HOUGHTON, Canon Michael Alan. b 49. Lanc Univ BA70 Dur Univ PGCE71 Southn Univ BTh83. Chich Th Coll 78. **d** 80 **p** 81. C Wellingborough All Hallows *Pet* 80-84; St Helena 84-89; Hon Can from 94; Tutor Coll of Ascension Selly Oak 90; V Folkestone St Pet *Cant* from 90. *St Peter's Vicarage, The Durlocks, Folkestone, Kent CT19 6AL* Folkestone (01303) 254472

HOUGHTON, Ven Michael Richard. b 29. CCC Cam BA52 MA56. Cuddesdon Coll 52. **d** 54 **p** 55. C Portsea N End St Mark *Portsm* 54-57; New Zealand from 57; Adn Tamaki 77-81. *47 Tiri Road, Oneroa, Waiheke Island, New Zealand* Auckland (9) 728250

HOUGHTON, Peter Graham. b 51. St Jo Coll Nottm. **d** 87 **p** 88. C Toxteth Park St Clem *Liv* 87-91; Chapl Winwick Hosp Warrington from 91. *The Chaplain's Office, Winwick Hospital, Warrington WA2 8RR* Warrington (01925) 655221

HOUGHTON, Reginald Leighton. b 10. St Chad's Coll Dur BA33 DipTh34 MA36. **d** 34 **p** 35. V Bartley Green *Birm* 60-75; rtd 75; Perm to Offic *Lich* from 77. *Flat 204, The Cedars, Abbey Foregate, Shrewsbury SY2 6BY* Shrewsbury (01743) 246282

HOUGHTON, Thomas. b 17. NW Ord Course 71. **d** 74 **p** 75. NSM Newc w Butterton *Lich* 74-82; Perm to Offic from 82. *Fernyhough, Crewe CW3 9JT* Stoke-on-Trent (01782) 750275

HOULDEN, Prof James Leslie. b 29. Qu Coll Ox BA52 MA56. Cuddesdon Coll 53. **d** 55 **p** 56. Chapl Trin Coll Ox 60-70; Prin Cuddesdon Coll 70-75; V Cuddesdon *Ox* 70-77; Prin Ripon Coll Cuddesdon 75-77; Hon Can Ch Ch *Ox* 76-77; Sen Lect NT Studies K Coll Lon 77-87; Prof Th K Coll Lon 87-94; rtd 94. *33 Raleigh Court, Lymer Avenue, London SE19 1LS* 0181-670 6648

HOULDEN, Kenneth Harry. b 10. Ridley Hall Cam 53. **d** 55 **p** 56. V Bramley *Win* 67-75; rtd 75; Perm to Offic *Win* from 75. *3 Kingfisher Court, Highfield Road, Southampton SO2 1UN* Southampton (01703) 554199

HOULDING, David Nigel Christopher. b 53. AKC76. **d** 77 **p** 78. C Hillingdon All SS *Lon* 77-81; C Holborn St Alb w Saffron Hill St Pet 81-85; V Hampstead St Steph w All Hallows from 85. *All Hallows' House, 52 Courthope Road, London NW3 2LD* 0171-267 7833

HOULDSWORTH, Raymond Clifford. b 30. Bps' Coll Cheshunt 64. **d** 66 **p** 67. C Egham Hythe *Guildf* 66-70; C Cranbrook *Cant* 70-76; V Hernhill 76-82; V Minster w Monkton 82-95; rtd 95. *11 Craig Road, Six Bells, Abertillery, Gwent NP3 2LR* Abertillery (01495) 321934

HOULT, Roy Anthony. b 35. AKC58. **d** 59 **p** 60. C Walton St Mary *Liv* 59-63; Canada from 63; Hon Can Koot 75-79. *381 Huron Street, Toronto, Ontario, Canada, M5S 2G5*

HOUNSFIELD, Thomas Paul. b 15. Lon Coll of Div 46. **d** 47 **p** 48. R Donington *Lich* 61-80; rtd 80; Perm to Offic *Win* from 81. *10 Widden Close, Sway, Lymington, Hants SO41 6AX* Lymington (01590) 682399

HOUSE, Ven Francis Harry. b 08. OBE55. Wadh Coll Ox BA30 MA34. Cuddesdon Coll 34. **d** 35 **p** 36. R Gawsworth *Ches* 67-78; Adn Macclesfield 67-78; rtd 78. *11 Drummond Court, Drummond Avenue, Leeds LS16 5QE* Leeds (0113) 278 3646

HOUSE, Graham Ivor. b 44. BA80. Oak Hill Th Coll 77. **d** 80 **p** 81. C Ipswich St Jo *St E* 80-84; V Ipswich St Andr from 84. *286 Britannia Road, Ipswich IP4 5HF* Ipswich (01473) 728204

HOUSE, Jack Francis. b 35. Bris Univ BEd70 Lon Univ MA80 Univ of Wales MTh94. Bris & Glouc Tr Course 79. **d** 80 **p** 81. NSM Bedminster *Bris* 80-92; Perm to Offic 92-94; NSM Knowle H Nativity from 94. *48 Hendre Road, Bristol BS3 2LR* Bristol (0117) 966 1144

HOUSE, Mrs Janet. b 45. E Anglia Univ BA67 Keswick Hall Coll PGCE68 Sussex Univ MA80. Ripon Coll Cuddesdon 93. **d** 95. C Swindon Ch Ch *Bris* from 95. *58 Upham Road, Swindon SN3 1DN* Swindon (01793) 521296

HOUSE, Simon Hutchinson. b 30. Peterho Cam BA65 MA67. Cuddesdon Coll 61. **d** 64 **p** 65. V Allestree St Nic *Derby* 69-81; RD Duffield 74-81; V Bitterne Park *Win* 81-91; rtd 91. *22 Stanley Street, Southsea, Hants PO5 2DS* Portsmouth (01705) 838592

HOUSE, Vickery Willis. b 45. MA. Kelham Th Coll. **d** 69 **p** 70. C Crediton *Ex* 69-76; TV Sampford Peverell, Uplowman, Holcombe Rogus etc 76-81; R Berwick w Selmeston and Alciston *Chich* 81-90; Chapl Ardingly Coll Haywards Heath 90-94; V Brighton St Bart *Chich* from 94. *16 Richmond Terrace, Brighton BN2 2NA* Brighton (01273) 685142

HOUSEMAN, Ms Patricia Adele. b 39. St D Coll Lamp DipTh90 St Mich Coll Llan DipPTh93. **d** 93. C St Issell's and Amroth *St D* 93-95; C Llanegryn w Aberdyfi w Tywyn *Ban* from 95. *6 Church Street, Towyn, Gwynedd LL36 9DA* Tywyn (01654) 712030

HOUSMAN, Arthur Martin Rowand. b 53. MA CertEd. Trin Coll Bris 81. **d** 83 **p** 84. C Croydon Ch Ch Broad Green *Cant* 83-84; C Croydon Ch Ch *S'wark* 85-87; TV Stratton St Margaret w S Marston etc *Bris* 87-93; Zimbabwe from 94. *Peterhouse, Private Bag 3741, Marondera, Zimbabwe*

HOUSTON, Canon Arthur James. b 54. Trin Coll Bris BA87. **d** 87 **p** 88. C Chatham St Phil and St Jas *Roch* 87-91; I Carrigaline Union *C, C & R* from 91; Preb Cork Cathl from 95; Preb Ross Cathl from 95. *The Rectory, Carrigaline, Co Cork, Irish Republic* Cork (21) 372224

HOUSTON, Edward Davison. b 31. TCD BA56. **d** 57 **p** 58. C Conwall Union *D & R* 57-59; India 59-88; V Whittlebury w Paulerspury *Pet* from 89; P-in-c Wicken from 89. *The Rectory, 2 Tews End Lane, Paulerspury, Towcester, Northants NN12 7NQ* Paulerspury (01327) 333670

HOUSTON (nee LOVELL), Mrs Helen Sarah. b 70. Bris Univ BA91. St Jo Coll Nottm MA95. **d** 95. C Bourne *Guildf* from 95. *64 Weydon Hill Road, Farnham, Surrey GU9 8NY* Farnham (01252) 715250

HOUSTON, Michael Alexander (Mike). b 46. Lanc Univ MA92. Linc Th Coll 86. **d** 88 **p** 89. C Longton *Blackb* 88-91; C Woughton *Ox* 91-92; TV from 92. *2 Braunston, Woughton Park, Milton Keynes MK6 3AU* Milton Keynes (01908) 674742

HOUSTON, Michael James. b 41. **d** 95. NSM *D & D* from 95. *73 Milecross Road, Newtownards, Co Down BT23 4SR* Newtownards (01247) 813395 or 423396

HOUSTON, Dr Samuel Kenneth (Ken). b 43. FIMA73 QUB BSc64 PhD67. CITC 81. **d** 85 **p** 86. NSM Belf St Jas w St Silas *Conn* 85-91; NSM Belf St Andr from 91. *29 North Circular Road, Belfast BT15 5HB* Belfast (01232) 771830

HOUSTON, William Paul. b 54. QUB BSSc76 TCD BTh78. CITC 78. **d** 81 **p** 82. C Carrickfergus *Conn* 81-83; C Ban St Comgall *D & D* 83-86; I Gilford 86-90; I Carnalea from 90. *St Gall's Rectory, 171 Crawfordsburn Road, Bangor, Co Down BT19 1BT* Helens Bay (01247) 853366

HOVENDEN, Gerald Eric. b 53. York Univ BA75 Ox Univ MA85. Wycliffe Hall Ox 78. **d** 81 **p** 82. C Pitsmoor w Ellesmere *Sheff* 81-85; Chapl Lyon w Grenoble and St Etienne *Eur* 85-90; TV S Gillingham *Roch* from 90. *26 Pear Tree Lane, Hempstead, Gillingham, Kent ME7 3PT* Medway (01634) 387892

HOVEY, Richard Michael. b 58. Imp Coll Lon BSc79 ACGI79 Cranfield Inst of Tech MBA84 CEng83 MIEE83. Cranmer

Hall Dur CTM95. **d** 95. C Cheddar *B & W* from 95. *19 Silver Street, Cheddar, Somerset BS27 3LE*   Cheddar (01934) 743527

HOVIL, Richard Guy. b 29. Ex Coll Ox BA51 MA57. Ridley Hall Cam. **d** 55 **p** 56. Staff Worker Scripture Union 58-71; Chapl Monkton Combe Sch Bath 71-83; V Fremington *Ex* 83-94; rtd 94. *37 Upper Marsh Road, Warminster, Wiltshire BA12 9PN* Warminster (01985) 214337

HOW, Canon John Maxloe. b 15. Magd Coll Cam BA37 MA49. Westcott Ho Cam 39. **d** 39 **p** 40. V Barton w Pooley Bridge *Carl* 59-73; RD Penrith 61-73; V Kirkby Lonsdale w Mansergh 73-76; TR Kirkby Lonsdale 76-81; rtd 81; Perm to Offic *Carl* from 81. *4 Kilmidyke Drive, Grange-over-Sands, Cumbria LA11 7AL* Grange-over-Sands (015395) 34117

HOWARD, Alan James. b 45. Bris Univ BA69. Clifton Th Coll. **d** 71 **p** 72. C Welling *Roch* 71-74; C Cromer *Nor* 74-78; V Sidcup St Andr *Roch* 78-86; V Leyton St Cath *Chelmsf* 86-93; V Leyton, St Cath and St Paul from 93. *St Catherine's Vicarage, Fairlop Road, London E11 1BL* 0181-539 6361

HOWARD, Alban Caldicott Morton. b 13. Keble Coll Ox BA35 MA43. Ely Th Coll 36. **d** 37 **p** 38. R York St Mary Bishophill Junior w All SS *York* 60-81; rtd 82. *The Old Rectory, 7A Tanner Row, York YO1 1JB* York (01904) 654316

HOWARD, Charles William Wykeham. b 52. Southn Univ BTh81. Sarum & Wells Th Coll 76. **d** 79 **p** 80. C St Mary-at-Latton *Chelmsf* 79-82; Chapl RN from 82. *Directorate Gen, RN Chapl Services, Room 203, Victory Building, HM Naval Base, Portsmouth PO1 3LS* Portsmouth (01705) 727903 Fax 727112

HOWARD, David John. b 47. Ripon Hall Ox 70. **d** 72 **p** 73. C Benchill *Man* 72-75; C Sedgley All SS *Lich* 75-77; C-in-c Lostock CD *Man* 77-85; V Lt Hulton 85-88; Perm to Offic 90-91; C E Leake *S'well* 91-92; C Costock 91-92; C Rempstone 91-92; C Stanford on Soar 91-92; C W Leake w Kingston-on-Soar etc 91-92; C E and W Leake, Stanford-on-Soar, Rempstone etc 92-94; P-in-c Bilborough w Strelley from 94. *St Martin's Rectory, 11 St Agnes Close, Nottingham NG8 4BJ* Nottingham (0115) 929 1874

HOWARD, David John. b 51. Lon Univ BSc73. Oak Hill Th Coll 74. **d** 77 **p** 78. C Radipole and Melcombe Regis *Sarum* 77-83; R Tredington and Darlingscott w Newbold on Stour *Cov* 83-90; P-in-c Binley 90-94; V from 94; RD Cov E from 95. *Binley Vicarage, 68 Brandon Road, Coventry CV3 2JF* Coventry (01203) 636334

HOWARD, David William. b 43. K Coll Lon 63. **d** 67 **p** 68. C Skegness *Linc* 67-69; C Gainsborough All SS 69-72; Jamaica from 72. *Address temp unknown*

HOWARD, Canon Donald. b 27. K Coll Lon BD58 AKC58. **d** 59 **p** 60. S Africa 62-72; R Haddington *Edin* 72-78; Can St Andr Cathl *Ab* 78-91; Provost St Andr Cathl 78-91; R Aber St Andr 78-91; Chapl Aber Univ 78-82; P-in-c Aber St Ninian 80-91; Angl Adv Grampian TV 84-88; rtd 91; Hon Can St Andr Cathl *Ab* from 91; Perm to Offic *Ripon* from 91. *42 Waterside, Ripon, N Yorkshire HG4 1RA* Ripon (01765) 692144

HOWARD, Mrs Erika Kathryn. b 49. SRN70 SCM72. S Dios Minl Tr Scheme 88. **d** 91 **p** 94. NSM New Shoreham *Chich* 91-94; NSM Old Shoreham 91-94; C Kingston Buci from 94. *207 Upper Shoreham Road, Shoreham-by-Sea, W Sussex BN43 6BE* Shoreham-by-Sea (01273) 881585

HOWARD, Francis Curzon. b 27. St Aid Birkenhead DipH57. **d** 57 **p** 58. Bermuda 65-71; USA from 71; rtd 92. *Trinity Episcopal Church, PO Box 127, Church Street, Tariffville, Connecticut 06081, USA*

HOWARD, Frank Thomas. b 36. Lon Univ BSc57. Bps' Coll Cheshunt 59. **d** 61 **p** 62. C Macclesfield St Mich *Ches* 61-64; C Claughton cum Grange 64-66; V Lache cum Saltney 66-76; R Stanton *St E* from 76; RD Ixworth 79-85. *The Rectory, The Street, Stanton, Bury St Edmunds, Suffolk IP31 2DQ* Stanton (01359) 50239

HOWARD, Geoffrey. b 30. Barrister-at-Law 83 Lon Univ LLB77. E Midl Min Tr Course. **d** 85 **p** 86. NSM Barton *Ely* 85-87; NSM Coton 85-87; C W Walton 87-92; TV Daventry, Ashby St Ledgers, Braunston etc *Pet* from 92. *The Vicarage, 19 Church Street, Staverton, Daventry, Northants NN11 6JJ* Daventry (01327) 702466

HOWARD, Geoffrey. b 45. St Jo Coll Dur BA68 DipTh70. Cranmer Hall Dur 67. **d** 71 **p** 72. C Cheetham Hill *Man* 71-74; C Denton Ch Ch 75-77; V Pendleton St Ambrose 77-91; AD Salford 86-94; TR Pendleton St Thos w Charlestown 91-94. *143 Manchester Road East, Little Hulton, Manchester M38 0AN* 0161-703 9324

HOWARD, George Granville. b 47. Trin Coll Bris. **d** 88 **p** 89. C Downend *Bris* 88-92; V Clifton H Trin, St Andr and St Pet from 92; Bp's Officer for Miss & Evang from 92. *Holy Trinity Vicarage, 6 Goldney Avenue, Clifton, Bristol BS8 4RA* Bristol (0117) 973 4751

HOWARD, John Alexander. b 27. Wesley Coll Leeds 48 Coll of Resurr Mirfield 66. **d** 67 **p** 68. C Almondbury *Wakef* 67-71; V Skelmanthorpe 71-81; R Fortrose *Mor* 81-94; R Cromarty 81-94; R Arpafeelie 81-94; rtd 94. *2 Webbs Cottages, Stratford Road, Mickleton, Chipping Campden, Glos GL55 6SW* Mickleton (01386) 438787

HOWARD, John Robert. b 60. NUI BA HDipEd TCD DipTh. **d** 84 **p** 85. C Donaghcloney w Waringstown *D & D* 84-88; I Belf St Ninian *Conn* 88-94; Bp's Dom Chapl 88-94; Chapl Ulster Univ from 88; I Annahilt w Magherahamlet *D & D* from 94. *Annahilt Rectory, 2 Loughaghery Road, Hillsborough, Co Down BT26 6DB* Baillie's Mills (01846) 638218

HOWARD, Keith. b 55. Univ of Wales (Ban) DipTh81. St Jo Coll Nottm 81. **d** 84 **p** 85. C Llanidloes w Llangurig *Ban* 84-87; R Llansantffraid Glan Conway and Eglwysfach *St As* from 87. *The Rectory, Glan Conway, Colwyn Bay, Clwyd LL29 5ST* Colwyn Bay (01492) 580279

HOWARD, Malcolm. b 29. St Deiniol's Hawarden. **d** 73 **p** 74. NSM Birstall *Leic* 73-82; NSM Birstall and Wanlip 82-90; Chapl Leics Hospice 89-90; rtd 90. *65 Fielding Road, Birstall, Leicester LE4 3AH* Leicester (0116) 267 3046

HOWARD, Canon Michael Charles. b 35. Selw Coll Cam BA58 MA63. Wycliffe Hall Ox 58. **d** 60 **p** 61. C Stowmarket *St E* 60-64; Nigeria 64-71; Hon Can Ondo 70-71; Hon C Southborough St Pet w Ch Ch and St Matt *Roch* 72-73; Lic to Offic *Ox* from 73. *17 Milton Road, Bloxham, Banbury, Oxon OX15 4JD*

HOWARD, Canon Michael Paul Penrose. b 40. Keele Univ BA62 Lon Univ BD69. Lon Coll of Div 66. **d** 69 **p** 70. C Nottm St Nic *S'well* 69-72; C Ox St Aldate w H Trin *Ox* 72-77; Chapl CCC Ox 75-77; V Dartford Ch Ch *Roch* 77-90; Chapl W Hill Hosp Dartford 77-90; P-in-c Cobham w Luddesdowne and Dode *Roch* from 90; Dioc Adv on Evang from 90; Hon Can Roch Cathl from 92. *The Vicarage, Battle Street, Cobham, Gravesend, Kent DA12 3DB* Meopham (01474) 814332

HOWARD, Nicolas John. b 61. Nottm Univ BTh90. Aston Tr Scheme 85 Linc Th Coll 87. **d** 90 **p** 91. C Bracknell *Ox* 90-94; P-in-c Oldham St Chad Limeside *Man* from 94. *St Chad's Vicarage, Lime Green Road, Oldham OL8 3NG* 0161-624 0970

HOWARD, Norman. b 26. AKC57. St Boniface Warminster 57. **d** 58 **p** 59. Jamaica 62-69; USA from 69; rtd 91. *766 Lake Forest Road, Clearwater, Florida 34625, USA* Clearwater (813) 799-3929

HOWARD, Mrs Patricia Anne (Pat). b 38. Ox Min Course CertBS92. **d** 92 **p** 94. NSM Winslow w Gt Horwood and Addington *Ox* from 92. *Rotherby House, Singleborough, Milton Keynes MK17 0RF* Winslow (01296) 712648

HOWARD, Paul David. b 47. Lanchester Poly BA69. St Jo Coll Nottm 74. **d** 77 **p** 78. C Bedworth *Cov* 77-83; V Newchapel *Lich* 83-93; V Stretton w Claymills from 93. *The Vicarage, Church Road, Stretton, Burton-on-Trent, Staffs DE13 0HD* Burton-on-Trent (01283) 65141

HOWARD, Peter Leslie. b 48. Nottm Univ BTh77 Birm Univ MA80 Leeds Univ MEd91. St Jo Coll Nottm LTh77. **d** 77 **p** 78. C Gospel Lane St Mich *Birm* 77-81; P-in-c Nechells 81-85; V Stanley *Wakef* 85-92; P-in-c Nor Heartsease St Fran *Nor* from 92. *The Vicarage, 100 Rider Haggard Road, Norwich NR7 9UQ* Norwich (01603) 702799

HOWARD, Reginald James (Reg). b 33. AKC60. **d** 61 **p** 62. V Morley St Paul *Wakef* 66-75; V Westgate Common 75-93; rtd 93. *41 Oakleigh Avenue, Wakefield, W Yorkshire WF2 9DF* Wakefield (01924) 373020

HOWARD, Canon Robert Weston. b 28. Pemb Coll Cam BA49 MA53. Westcott Ho Cam 51. **d** 53 **p** 54. V Prenton *Ches* 66-75; RD Frodsham 74-82; P-in-c Dunham-on-the-Hill 75-77; V Helsby and Ince 75-77; V Helsby and Dunham-on-the-Hill 77-82; Hon Can Ches Cathl 78-82; V Moseley St Mary *Birm* 82-88; V Chalke Valley W *Sarum* 88-93; rtd 93. *The Coach House, 13 Clun Road, Aston-on-Clun, Craven Arms, Shropshire SY7 8EW* Little Brampton (015887) 630

HOWARD, Ronald. b 40. AMIBF65 EngTech91. Cranmer Hall Dur 86. **d** 88 **p** 89. C Baildon *Bradf* 88-92; P-in-c Sutton from 92. *The Vicarage, Sutton-in-Craven, Keighley, W Yorkshire BD20 7JS* Cross Hills (01535) 633372

HOWARD, Canon Ronald Trevor. b 19. Pemb Coll Cam BA41 MA45. Wells Th Coll 52. **d** 54 **p** 55. R Belchamp Otten w Belchamp Walter and Bulmer *Chelmsf* 59-93; RD Belchamp 75-90; Hon Can Chelmsf Cathl 79-93; rtd 93; Perm to Offic *Nor* from 93. *The Old Rectory, Mendham, Harleston, Norfolk IP20 0NH* Harleston (01379) 852327

HOWARD, Simon Charles. b 60. Birm Univ BA81 Westhill Coll Birm CYCW86. Ridley Hall Cam CTM92. **d** 92 **p** 93. C Cam St Martin *Ely* from 92; Chapl St Bede's Sch from 92. *18 Langham Road, Cambridge CB1 3SE* Cambridge (01223) 414283

HOWARD, Stanley Reginald Kekewich. b 10. St Pet Hall Ox BA31 MA35. Ridley Hall Cam 31. **d** 33 **p** 34. V Cheltenham St Paul *Glouc* 51-76; Chapl Cheltenham Maternity and St Paul's Hosps 61-76; rtd 76; Perm to Offic *Win* from 81. *Selah, 3 Montague Road, Bournemouth BH5 2EW* Bournemouth (01202) 427376

HOWARD, Ms Susan. b 65. Lanc Univ BA86. Ripon Coll Cuddesdon 88. **d** 91 **p** 94. C Ditton St Mich *Liv* 91-94; C Kirkby from 94. *45 Alvanley Road, Kirkby, Liverpool L32 0SZ* 0151-547 2769

HOWARD, Thomas Norman. b 40. St Aid Birkenhead 64. **d** 67 **p** 68. C Farnworth and Kearsley *Man* 67-70; C Prestwich St Marg 70-73; V Heyside 73-85; Warden Lamplugh Ho Angl Conf Cen Thwing 85-90; HonC Langtoft w Foxholes, Butterwick, Cottam etc *York* 85-87; C 87-90; V Fence and Newchurch-in-Pendle *Blackb* from 90; Dioc Ecum Officer from 90. *The Vicarage, 12 Wheatcroft Avenue, Fence, Burnley, Lancs BB12 9QL* Nelson (01282) 617316

HOWARD, William Alfred. b 47. St Jo Coll Dur BA69. Wycliffe Hall Ox 74. **d** 77 **p** 79. C Norbiton *S'wark* 77-80; C Mile Cross *Nor* 80-84; R Grimston w Congham 84-91; R Grimston, Congham and Roydon from 91. *The Rectory, Grimston, King's Lynn, Norfolk PE32 1BQ* Hillington (01485) 600335

HOWARD-COWLEY, Joseph Charles. b 27. Trin Coll Cam BA53 MA56. Wells Th Coll 53. **d** 55 **p** 56. V Aldringham *St E* 61-86; rtd 86; Perm to Offic *St E* 86-93. *Lower Penquite, St Ive, Liskeard, Cornwall PL14 3NE* Liskeard (01579) 83469

HOWARD JONES, Preb Raymond Vernon. b 31. AKC54. **d** 55 **p** 56. C Hutton *Chelmsf* 55-58; CF 58-62; V Walpole St Andrew *Ely* 62-64; Chapl St Crispin's Hosp Northn 64-70; V Brockhampton w Fawley *Heref* 70-86; V Fownhope 70-86; RD Heref Rural 77-81; Preb Heref Cathl from 81; Communications Adv and Bp's Staff Officer from 86. *The Rectory, Stretton Sugwas, Hereford HR4 7PT* Hereford (01432) 279371

HOWARTH, Arthur. b 14. Dur Univ 36. **d** 37 **p** 38. C Aylesbury *Ox* 37-40; C W Wycombe 41-42; C Acton Vale St Thos *Lon* 42-43; C Fulham All SS 43-44; C Hornsey St Mary 44-46; St Vincent 46-51; Perm to Offic *Ox* 51-54; Perm to Offic *Guildf* 54; Nigeria from 55. *Bishop Lasbrey College Irete, PO Box 68, Owerri, Nigeria*

HOWARTH, Benjamin Wrigley. b 20. AKC43. **d** 43 **p** 44. Dep Asst Chapl Gen 67-70 and 73-75; Warden RAChD Cen 70-73; Chapl to The Queen 73-78; Asst Chapl Gen 75-78; R Chew Stoke w Nempnett Thrubwell *B & W* 78-85; R Norton Malreward 78-85; rtd 85; Perm to Offic *B & W* 86-94. *6 Kings Road, Wells, Somerset BA5 3LU* Wells (01749) 674294

HOWARTH, Christopher. b 47. S Dios Minl Tr Scheme. **d** 83 **p** 84. NSM Uckfield *Chich* from 83; NSM Lt Horsted from 83; NSM Isfield from 83. *137 Rocks Park Road, Uckfield, E Sussex TN22 2BD* Uckfield (01825) 765352

HOWARTH, Geoffrey Gifford. b 21. Oak Hill Th Coll 65. **d** 66 **p** 67. P-in-c Bootle St Mary w St Jo *Liv* 69-73; V Newburn *Newc* 73-86; rtd 86. *Beeches, Pickering Road East, Snainton, Scarborough, N Yorkshire YO13 9AF* Scarborough (01723) 859148

HOWARTH, Canon Gerald Simeon. b 10. AKC35. **d** 35 **p** 36. V Milford *Win* 55-75; rtd 75; Perm to Offic *Guildf* from 81. *12 Langton Avenue, Ewell, Epsom, Surrey KT17 1LD* 0181-393 4421

HOWARTH, Jack Raymond. b 13. Leeds Univ BSc34. Coll of Resurr Mirfield 34. **d** 36 **p** 37. R Elland *Wakef* 63-75; V Halifax St Jo Cragg Vale 75-78; rtd 78; Hon C Haydock St Jas *Liv* 78-86; Chapl Wigan R Infirmary 86-94. *13/4 Ladywell Road, Edinburgh EH12 7TA* 0131-334 0594

HOWARTH, Leslie John. b 22. MIEH MRSH. Sarum & Wells Th Coll 75. **d** 78 **p** 79. NSM Plymouth St Gabr *Ex* from 78. *1 Wardlow Gardens, Trevannion Park, Plymouth PL6 5PU* Plymouth (01752) 773641

HOWARTH, Robert Francis Harvey. b 31. S'wark Ord Course 71. **d** 72 **p** 73. C St Marylebone All So w SS Pet and Jo *Lon* 72-73; C St Helen Bishopsgate w St Martin Outwich 73-78; V Harlow St Mary and St Hugh w St Jo the Bapt *Chelmsf* 78-88; P-in-c Victoria Docks Ascension from 88. *23 Burley Road, London E16 3JU* 0171-474 9757

HOWARTH, Canon Ronald. b 26. TCD BA51 MA54. Linc Th Coll 50. **d** 52 **p** 53. Nigeria 55-89; rtd 91. *4 Kingston Court, Walton Street, Oxford OX2 6ES* Oxford (01865) 53046

HOWARTH, Toby Matthew. b 62. Yale Univ BA86 Birm Univ MA91. Wycliffe Hall Ox 89 Qu Coll Birm 90. **d** 92 **p** 93. C Derby St Aug *Derby* from 92. *70 Violet Street, Derby DE23 8SQ* Derby (01332) 762821

HOWAT, Jeremy Noel Thomas. b 35. Em Coll Cam BA59 MA63. Ridley Hall Cam 59. **d** 63 **p** 64. C Sutton *Liv* 63-65; C Kirk Ella *York* 65-66; C Bridlington Quay Ch Ch 66-69; R Wheldrake 69-78; Dioc Youth Officer 70-74; SAMS from 78;

Argentina 78-81 and from 90; P-in-c Newton upon Ouse *York* 81-82; V Shipton w Overton 81-82; P-in-c Skelton by York 81-82; R Skelton w Shipton and Newton on Ouse 82-89. *Almte Brown 2577, (1832) Lomas de Zamora, Prov de Buenos Aires, Argentina*

HOWDEN, Canon Arthur Travis. b 11. Clare Coll Cam BA33 MA37. Wycliffe Hall Ox 33. **d** 34 **p** 35. R Wortham *St E* 71-72; P-in-c Redgrave w Botesdale 71-72; R Redgrave w Botesdale and Wortham 72-76; rtd 76; Perm to Offic *St E* from 76. *Little Thatch, Oak Lane, Rougham, Bury St Edmunds, Suffolk IP30 9JX* Beyton (01359) 70704

HOWDEN, John Travis. b 40. RIBA62. Sarum Th Coll 66. **d** 69 **p** 70. C S Gillingham *Roch* 69-72; C Banbury *Ox* 72-73; Lic to Offic *York* 73-74; Hon C Hull Newland St Jo 74-81; Hon C Stock Harvard *Chelmsf* 82-86; R Doddinghurst and Mountnessing 86-91; P-in-c Pleshey from 91; Warden Pleshey Retreat Ho from 91. *The Vicarage, The Street, Pleshey, Chelmsford CM3 1HA* Pleshey (01245) 237251

HOWE, Alan Raymond. b 52. Nottm Univ BTh79. St Jo Coll Nottm 76. **d** 80 **p** 81. C Southsea St Simon *Portsm* 80-83; C Bexleyheath St Pet *Roch* 83-86; TV Camberley St Paul *Guildf* 86-93; P-in-c Mansf St Jo *S'well* from 93. *The Vicarage, St John Street, Mansfield, Notts NG18 1QH* Mansfield (01623) 25999

HOWE, Alfred William. b 10. St D Coll Lamp BA32. **d** 33 **p** 34. V Forthampton w Chaceley *Glouc* 59-79; rtd 79; Perm to Offic *Glouc* 80-90. *1 Masons Court, Barton Street, Tewkesbury, Glos GL20 5PY* Tewkesbury (01684) 296442

HOWE, Canon Charles. b 30. Lon Univ BD65 Open Univ BA79. Tyndale Hall Bris 55. **d** 58 **p** 59. C Willowfield *D & D* 58-60; C Derryloran *Arm* 60-64; C Belf St Bart *Conn* 64-65; I Tullyaughnish w Kilmacrennan and Killygarvan *D & R* 65-72; I Londonderry St Aug from 73; Can Derry Cathl from 85; Dioc Org and Tutor for Aux Min from 93. *St Augustine's Rectory, 4 Bridgewater, Londonderry BT47 1YA* Londonderry (01504) 47532

HOWE, Canon David Randall. b 24. St Jo Coll Cam BA51 MA55. Wells Th Coll 51. **d** 53 **p** 54. V Rotherwick, Hook and Greywell *Win* 59-70; R Bossington w Broughton 70-81; R Broughton w Bossington and Mottisfont 81-86; R Broughton, Bossington, Houghton and Mottisfont 86-89; Hon Can Win Cathl 87-89; rtd 89. *Little Orchard, Hilldrop Lane, Ramsbury, Marlborough, Wilts SN8 2RB* Marlborough (01672) 20326

HOWE, Miss Frances Ruth. b 28. ACIB67 GSSR91. Cranmer Hall Dur IDC80. **dss** 80 **d** 87 **p** 94. Newc St Andr *Newc* 80-82; Chapl Asst R Victoria Infirmary Newc 80-87; Chapl Wylam and Fleming Ch Hosp 82-87; Chapl St Oswald's Hospice Newc 86-92; C Newc Epiphany *Newc* 87-90; rtd 92; Hon C Delaval Newc from 92. *18 Mason Avenue, Whitley Bay, Tyne & Wear NE26 1AQ* 0191-252 5163

HOWE, Canon George Alexander. b 52. St Jo Coll Dur BA73. Westcott Ho Cam 73. **d** 75 **p** 76. C Peterlee *Dur* 75-79; C Norton St Mary 79-81; V Hart w Elwick Hall 81-85; R Sedgefield 85-91; RD Sedgefield 89-91; V Kendal H Trin *Carl* from 91; RD Kendal from 94; Hon Can Carl Cathl from 94. *Holy Trinity Vicarage, 2 Lynngarth Drive, Kendal, Cumbria LA9 4JA* Kendal (01539) 721541 or 721248

HOWE, Harry Norman. b 10. United Th Coll Limuru. **d** 73 **p** 74. Kenya 74-75; C Fringford w Hethe and Newton Purcell *Ox* 75-76; rtd 76; Perm to Offic *York* 76-80; Perm to Offic *Lich* from 80; Perm to Offic *Wakef* from 84. *28 Vernon Avenue, Huddersfield HD1 5QD* Huddersfield (01484) 516549

HOWE, Canon John. b 36. Ex Coll Ox BA58 MA63. St Steph Ho Ox 58. **d** 61 **p** 62. C Horninglow *Lich* 61-64; C Sedgley All SS 64-66; V Ocker Hill 66-73; V Gnosall 73-79; P-in-c Hoar Cross 79-82; Preb Lich Cathl 83-88; V Hoar Cross w Newchurch 83-88; Can Res Lich Cathl from 88. *20 The Close, Lichfield, Staffs WS13 7LD* Lichfield (01543) 268777

✠**HOWE, Rt Rev John William Alexander.** b 20. St Chad's Coll Dur BA43 MA48 BD48. Gen Th Sem (NY) Hon DD74 Lambeth DD78. **d** 43 **p** 44 **c** 55. C Scarborough All SS *York* 43-46; Ghana 46-50; Vice-Prin Edin Th Coll 50-55; Hon Chapl St Mary's Cathl *Edin* 51-55; Bp St Andr *St And* 55-69; Exec Officer Angl Communion 69-71; Hon Can St Mary's Cathl *Glas* from 69; Sec Gen ACC 71-82; Research Fell 83-85; Can Jerusalem 76-82; rtd 85; Asst Bp Ripon from 85. *Flat 6, Stuart Court, High Street, Kibworth, Leicester LE8 0LE* Leicester (0116) 279 6205

HOWE, Nicholas Simon. b 60. Man Univ BA81 K Coll Lon MTh85. Ridley Hall Cam 86. **d** 88 **p** 89. C Lich St Chad *Lich* 88-92; TV Leeds City *Ripon* from 92. *Holy Trinity Vicarage, 28 Hawkswood Avenue, Leeds LS5 3PN* Leeds (0113) 259 0031

HOWE, Canon Rex Alan. b 29. Ch Coll Cam BA53 MA57. Coll of Resurr Mirfield 53. **d** 55 **p** 56. V Redcar *York* 67-73; V Kirkleatham 67-73; RD Guisborough 67-73; Dean Hong Kong 73-76; Adn 75-76; TR Grantham *Linc* 77-85; RD

Grantham 78-85; Can and Preb Linc Cathl 81-85; V Canford Cliffs and Sandbanks *Sarum* 85-94; RD Poole 92-94; rtd 94. *Little Over, Mead Road, Corfe Castle, Wareham, Dorset BH20 5EW* Wareham (01929) 480528

HOWE, Canon Ronald Douglas. b 38. K Coll Lon BD62 AKC62 LSE DSA63. **d** 64 **p** 65. C Hendon All SS Childs Hill *Lon* 64-67; C Northn St Mary *Pet* 67-69; V Potterspury w Furtho and Yardley Gobion 69-81; R Corby Epiphany w St Jo 81-86; RD Corby 81-90; V Brigstock w Stanion from 86; P-in-c Lowick w Sudborough and Slipton from 94; Can Pet Cathl from 95. *The Vicarage, Brigstock, Kettering, Northants NN14 3EX* Brigstock (01536) 373371

HOWE, Roy William. b 38. ALCD67. **d** 66 **p** 67. C Bradf Cathl *Bradf* 66-70; C Barnoldswick w Bracewell 70-72; V Yeadon St Jo 72-79; P-in-c Bainton *York* 79-86; P-in-c Middleton-on-the-Wolds 79-86; P-in-c N Dalton 79-86; RD Harthill 81-87; C Watton w Beswick and Kilnwick 82-86; R Bainton w N Dalton, Middleton-on-the-Wolds etc 86-87; TV Penrith w Newton Reigny and Plumpton Wall *Carl* 87-92; Dioc Chapl to Agric and Rural Life 87-92; V Cornhill w Carham *Newc* from 92; V Branxton from 92. *The Vicarage, The Old School House, Branxton, Cornhill-on-Tweed, Northd TD12 4SW* Coldstream (01890) 820368

HOWE, William Ernest. b 25. ARICS51. Westcott Ho Cam 68. **d** 70 **p** 71. C Anston *Sheff* 70-73; V 84-92; C Woodsetts 70-73; V Greasbrough 73-84; rtd 92. *21 Broad Bridge Close, Kiveton Park, Sheffield S31 8SL* Worksop (01909) 515252

HOWELL, Alfred. b 32. Wells Th Coll 57. **d** 59 **p** 60. V Sparkbrook Ch Ch *Birm* 66-73; Lic to Offic *Chelmsf* 73-83; P-in-c Brentwood St Geo 83-88; rtd 88. *Windy Corner, Grove Lane, Iden, Rye, E Sussex TN31 7QA* Iden (01797) 280564

HOWELL, Andrew John. b 44. Clifton Th Coll 68. **d** 71 **p** 72. C Halliwell St Pet *Man* 71-77; V Facit 77-95; P-in-c Smallbridge and Wardle from 95. *The Vicarage, 151 Wardle Road, Rochdale, Lancs OL12 9JA* Rochdale (01706) 713529

HOWELL, Canon Basil Rayson. b 20. St Pet Hall Ox BA49 MA53. Wycliffe Hall Ox 49. **d** 51 **p** 52. V Blundellsands St Nic *Liv* 61-81; RD Bootle 69-78; Hon Can Liv Cathl 78-81; rtd 81; Perm to Offic *Cov* from 81. *9 Arlington Court, Arlington Avenue, Leamington Spa, Warks CV32 5HR* Leamington Spa (01926) 314746

HOWELL, David. b 29. Clifton Th Coll 56. **d** 59 **p** 60. V W Bromwich St Paul Golds Hill *Lich* 62-71; V Deptford St Jo *S'wark* 71-81; Dir and Chapl Home of Divine Healing Crowhurst 81-89; rtd 90; Dir Ch Coun for Health and Healing 91-93; Hon Dioc Adv on Health and Healing *B & W* from 93. *60 Andrew Allan Road, Rockwell Green, Wellington, Somerset TA21 9DY* Wellington (01823) 664529

HOWELL (formerly WILLIAMS), David Paul. b 61. Coll of Resurr Mirfield 91. **d** 93 **p** 94. C Leic St Aid *Leic* from 93. *26 Chevin Avenue, Braunstone, Leicester LE3 6PZ* Leicester (0116) 287 2558

HOWELL, Donald Martin. b 32. Lon Univ BD56. **d** 95. NSM Holt w High Kelling *Nor* from 95. *8 The Beeches, Station Road, Holt, Norfolk NR25 6AU* Holt (01263) 713397

HOWELL, Geoffrey Peter. b 52. LTCL82 Selw Coll Cam BA75 MA78. Cranmer Hall Dur 85. **d** 87 **p** 88. C Hartlepool St Luke *Dur* 87-90; TV Burford I *Heref* 90-94; TV Burford II w Greete and Hope Bagot 90-94; TV Burford III w Lt Heref 90-94; TV Tenbury 90-94; TV Tenbury St Mich 94; P-in-c Cradley w Mathon and Storridge from 94. *The Rectory, Cradley, Malvern, Worcs WR13 5LQ* Ridgway Cross (01886) 880438

HOWELL, John Anthony Neil Belville. b 39. Man Univ BA64. St Deiniol's Hawarden 77. **d** 79 **p** 81. C Wistaston *Ches* 79-82; P-in-c Derry Hill *Sarum* 82-83; V Clayton *Bradf* from 83. *The Vicarage, Clayton Lane, Clayton, Bradford, W Yorkshire BD14 6AX* Bradford (01274) 880373

HOWELL, Martin John Hope. b 38. Bris Univ BA62. Tyndale Hall Bris 59. **d** 64 **p** 65. C Bolton St Paul *Man* 64-67; C Bishopsworth *Bris* 67-70; V Swindon St Aug 70-81; TR Stratton St Margaret w S Marston etc 81-93; RD Cricklade 88; RD Highworth 88-93; Chapl Lee Abbey from 93; Lic to Offic *Ex* from 93. *Lee Abbey Fellowship, Lynton, Devon EX35 6JJ* Lynton (01598) 52621

HOWELL, Roger Brian. b 43. ALCD67. **d** 67 **p** 68. C Battersea Park St Sav *S'wark* 67-71; C Southgate *Chich* 71-76; V Pendeen *Truro* 76-81; P-in-c Sancreed 76-81; V Bedgrove *Ox* 81-91; R Purley from 91; RD Bradfield from 94. *The Rectory, 1 Westridge Avenue, Purley, Reading RG8 8DE* Reading (01734) 417727

HOWELL, Ronald William Fullerton. b 51. Man Univ BA72 CertEd Ox Univ BA78 MA. Ripon Coll Cuddesdon 76. **d** 79 **p** 80. C Newc St Fran *Newc* 79-81; C Warmsworth *Sheff* 81-82; Dioc Educn Officer 82-85; V Millhouses H Trin 85-93; R Thornhill and Whitley Lower *Wakef* from 93. *The Rectory,*

51 Frank Lane, Dewsbury, W Yorkshire WF12 0JW Dewsbury (01924) 465064

HOWELL, Preb Walter Ernest. b 17. St D Coll Lamp BA49. **d** 50 **p** 51. V Kentish Town St Benet and All SS *Lon* 68-79; V Alexandra Park St Sav 79-84; rtd 84. *6 Wattlers Close, Copmanthorpe, York YO2 3XR* York (01904) 702615

HOWELL-EVERSON, Douglas Norman. b 19. TD53. Ripon Hall Ox 59. **d** 60 **p** 61. V Stanton-in-Peak *Derby* 62-75; R Bamford 75-85; rtd 85; Perm to Offic *Derby* from 85; Perm to Offic *Sheff* from 85; Perm to Offic *S'well* from 85. *25 Conway Drive, Carlton-in-Lindrick, Worksop, Notts S81 9DG* Worksop (01909) 731499

HOWELL-JONES, Peter. b 62. Huddersfield Poly BMus84 Bretton Hall Coll PGCE85. St Jo Coll Nottm DTS92 DipMM93. **d** 93 **p** 94. C Walsall *Lich* from 93. *164 Birmingham Road, Walsall WS1 2NJ* Walsall (01922) 645445

HOWELLS, Alun. b 24. St D Coll Lamp 62. **d** 64 **p** 65. C Carmarthen St Dav *St D* 64-70; V Llandyssilio and Egremont 70-71; V Llanboidy and Meidrim 71-81; V Meidrim and Llanboidy and Merthyr 81-88; rtd 88. *Aweltwywi Residential Home, Bethlehem Road, Ffairfach, Llandeilo, Dyfed SA19 6SY* Llandeilo (01558) 822556

HOWELLS, Canon Arthur Glyn. b 32. Univ of Wales (Lamp) BA54. St Mich Coll Llan 54. **d** 56 **p** 57. C Oystermouth *S & B* 56-58; C Llangyfelach and Morriston 58-64; V Llandefalle and Llyswen w Boughrood etc 64-69; Youth Chapl 67-71; V Landore 70-80; Dioc Missr 80-89; Can Brecon Cathl 80-89; Dir St Mary's Coll Swansea from 82; V Swansea St Jas *S & B* from 89; Chan Brecon Cathl from 94. *St James's Vicarage, 55 Eaton Crescent, Uplands, Swansea SA1 4QN* Swansea (01792) 470532

HOWELLS, David. b 55. Grey Coll Dur BA78. Ripon Coll Cuddesdon 79. **d** 81 **p** 82. C Birtley *Dur* 81-84; Canada from 84. *112 Main Street, Rockwood, Ontario, Canada, N0B 2K0*

HOWELLS, David Morgan. b 24. Qu Coll Birm 72. **d** 75 **p** 76. NSM Radford *Cov* 75-87; rtd 87; Perm to Offic *Cov* from 87. *21 Banks Road, Coventry CV6 1JT* Coventry (01203) 598118

HOWELLS, Canon Donald Lockwood. b 20. Lon Univ BA43. Oak Hill Th Coll 39. **d** 43 **p** 44. R Tring *St Alb* 66-80; P-in-c Aldbury 78-80; P-in-c Puttenham w Long Marston 79-80; Hon Can St Alb 80-85; RD Berkhamsted 80-85; TR Tring 80-85; rtd 85; Perm to Offic *Cant* from 85. *10 Cadram Close, Canterbury, Kent CT2 7SD* Canterbury (01227) 462835

HOWELLS, Euryl. b 60. Univ of Wales (Cardiff) BD93. St Mich Coll Llan 90. **d** 93 **p** 94. C Newc Emlyn w Llandyfriog and Troed-yr-aur *St D* from 93. *The Vicarage, Llangeler, Llandysul, Dyfed SA44 5EX* Llandyssul (01559) 371170

HOWELLS, Garfield Edwin (Gary). b 18. K Coll Lon 53 St Boniface Warminster 53. **d** 54 **p** 55. R Kingsdown *Roch* 60-64; Australia from 64; rtd 83. *137 Fendam Street, Warnbro, W Australia 6169* Perth (9) 593-1819

HOWELLS, Gordon. b 39. Univ of Wales (Cardiff) BSc61 DipEd62. Ripon Coll Cuddesdon 86. **d** 88 **p** 89. C Atherstone *Cov* 88-89; C Lillington 89-92; V Clympimg and Yapton w Ford *Chich* from 92. *The Rectory, St Mary's Meadow, Yapton, Arundel, W Sussex BN18 0EE* Yapton (01243) 552962

HOWELLS, Lucinda Jane Reid. b 57. Dur Univ BA78. Ripon Coll Cuddesdon 79. **dss** 81 **d** 85 **p** 85. Birtley *Dur* 81-84; Canada from 84. *112 Main Street, Rockwood, Ontario, Canada, N0B 2K0*

HOWELLS, Neil. b 23. Qu Mary Coll Lon BSc48. Bps' Coll Cheshunt 48. **d** 50 **p** 51. R Welford w Wickham *Ox* 68-73; R Welford w Wickham and Gt Shefford 73-77; RD Newbury 73-77; V Bray and Braywood 77-84; rtd 84; Perm to Offic *Sarum* from 85. *19 Loders, Bridport, Dorset DT6 3SA* Bridport (01308) 456490

HOWELLS, Richard Grant. b 62. Univ of Wales (Lamp) BA83. Westcott Ho Cam 83 and 92. **d** 93 **p** 94. NSM Harston w Hauxton *Ely* from 93. *The Old School House, 8 High Street, Harston, Cambridge CB2 5PX* Cambridge (01223) 871902

HOWELLS, Mrs Sandra June. b 52. FBDO77. Local NSM Course. **d** 93. NSM Caerwent w Dinham and Llanfair Discoed etc *Mon* from 93. *3 Lancaster Way, Chepstow, Gwent NP6 5SJ* Chepstow (01291) 620460

HOWELLS, William Gordon. b 26. **d** 61 **p** 62. C Northam *Ex* 67-71; V Bishops Tawton 71-76; V Cofton w Starcross 76-80; R Aveton Gifford 80-86; V Modbury 80-86; TV Lynton, Brendon, Countisbury, Lynmouth etc 86-91; rtd 91; Perm to Offic *Ex* from 91. *Umtali, Golf Links Road, Westward Ho!, Bideford, Devon EX39 1HH* Bideford (01237) 473578

HOWES, Alan. b 49. Chich Th Coll 76. **d** 79 **p** 80. C Bilborough St Jo *S'well* 79-82; TV Newark w Hawton, Cotham and Shelton 82-89; TV Newark-upon-Trent 89-94; P-in-c Coseley St Chad *Worc* from 94. *St Chad's Vicarage, 3 Oak Street, Coseley, Bilston, W Midlands WV14 9TA* Sedgley (01902) 882285

HOWES, David. b 30. Open Univ BA75. Roch Th Coll 62. **d** 64 **p** 65. C Clyst St George *Ex* 67-71; P-in-c Woolfardisworthy w Kennerleigh 71-72; P-in-c Washford Pyne w Puddington 71-72; TR N Creedy 72-73; Perm to Offic 74-77; C Walworth *S'wark* 77-78; C-in-c Roundshaw CD 78-83; R S'wark St Geo 83-90; P-in-c S'wark St Jude 84-90; P-in-c Risley *Derby* 90-93; Bp's Ind Adv 90-93; rtd 93. *44 Ash Grove, Stapleford, Nottingham NG9 7EL* Nottingham (0115) 939 3041

HOWES, Miss Judith Elizabeth. b 44. SRN RSCN. Ripon Coll Cuddesdon 83. **d** 89 **p** 94. Par Dn Ex St Sidwell and St Matt *Ex* 89-92; Par Dn Brixham w Churston Ferrers and Kingswear 92-94; C from 94. *St Mary's Vicarage, 100 Summercourt Way, Brixham, Devon TQ5 0RB* Brixham (01803) 852756

HOWES, Michael John Norton. b 43. Hull Univ BA66. Linc Th Coll 66. **d** 68 **p** 69. C Gt Berkhamsted *St Alb* 68-71; C Ampthill w Millbrook and Steppingley 71-72; Chapl RAF 72-88; V Thurlby w Carlby *Linc* 88-95; V Ness Gp from 95. *The Vicarage, Thurlby, Bourne, Lincs PE10 0EH* Bourne (01778) 422475

HOWES, Canon Norman Vincent. b 36. AKC61. **d** 62 **p** 63. C Radford *Cov* 62-66; V Napton on the Hill 66-72; V Exhall 72-83; R Walton D'Eiville from 83; V Wellesbourne from 83; RD Fosse 87-93; Hon Can Cov Cathl from 89. *The Vicarage, Wellesbourne, Warwick CV35 9LS* Stratford-upon-Avon (01789) 840262

✠**HOWES, Rt Rev Peter Henry Herbert.** b 11. OBE61 PBS63. Kelham Th Coll 29. **d** 34 **p** 35 **c** 76. C Norton St Mich *Dur* 34-37; Sarawak 37-38 and 40-63; Br N Borneo 38-40; Malaysia 63-81; Can Borneo 55-62; Adn Sarawak 61-62; Adn Kuching 62-65; Can Kuching 62-71; Adn Brunei and N Sarawak 65-71; Asst Bp Kuching 76-81; rtd 81. *7 Tower Place, York YO1 1RZ* York (01904) 638050

HOWITT, Canon Alan John. b 26. ARCM49 Leeds Univ BA50. Coll of Resurr Mirfield 50. **d** 53 **p** 54. V Northn St Mary *Pet* 64-75; RD Wootton 70-74; Chapl Pet Distr Hosp 75-88; Can Pet Cathl *Pet* 75-95; V Pet St Jo 75-95; RD Pet 76-87; rtd 95. *8 Wakerley Drive, Orton Longueville, Peterborough PE2 7WF* Peterborough (01733) 391092

HOWITT, Ivan Richard. b 56. Kent Univ BA81. Sarum & Wells Th Coll 83. **d** 85 **p** 86. C Herne Bay Ch Ch *Cant* 85-87; C St Laurence in the Isle of Thanet 87-90; R Owmby and Normanby w Glentham *Linc* 90-91; P-in-c Spridlington w Saxby and Firsby 90-91; R Owmby Gp from 91; P-in-c Hackthorn w Cold Hanworth from 93. *The Rectory, Owmby-by-Spital, Lincoln LN2 3HL* Normanby-by-Spital (01673) 878275

HOWITT, John Leslie. b 28. Lon Coll of Div 60. **d** 62 **p** 63. Chapl Rampton Hosp Retford 66-71; P-in-c Treswell and Cottam *S'well* 68-71; Chapl HM Pris Cardiff 71-75; Chapl HM Youth Cust Cen Dover 75-79; Chapl HM Pris Dartmoor 79-83; Chapl HM Pris Cant 83-87; Chapl HM Det Cen Aldington 83-87; Perm to Offic *Cant* 87-88; V Shobnall *Lich* 88-94; rtd 94. *6 Park View Road, Hove, E Sussex BN3 7BF*

HOWLAND, Miss Ada Lilian. b 08. St Andr Ho Portsm 47. **dss** 50 **d** 87. Australia 52-59; Southsea St Pet *Portsm* 60-74; rtd 74; Portsm Cathl *Portsm* 74-87; Hon Par Dn from 87. *38 Portsmouth Town Court, 115 High Street, Portsmouth PO1 2SX* Portsmouth (01705) 829352

HOWLAND, Ms Pamela Isobel. b 29. Lady Mabel Coll CertEd71. Qu Coll Birm 79. **dss** 82 **d** 87. Thorpe Edge *Bradf* 82-89; Par Dn 87-89; rtd 89. *308 Moorview Way, Skipton, N Yorkshire BD23 2TW* Skipton (01756) 700725

HOWLDEN, Paul Wilfrid. b 41. Trin Coll Cam BA63 MA67. Cuddesdon Coll 64. **d** 66 **p** 67. C Paulsgrove *Portsm* 66-73; Hon C Ealing Ascension Hanger Hill *Lon* 75-87; R Bishops Waltham *Portsm* 87-88; Perm to Offic from 89. *33 Chamberlain Grove, Fareham, Hants PO14 1HH* Fareham (01329) 233035

HOWLES, Kenneth. b 56. Oak Hill Th Coll DipHE93. **d** 93 **p** 94. C Leyland St Andr *Blackb* from 93. *3 Beech Avenue, Leyland, Preston PR5 2AL* Leyland (01772) 622446

HOWLETT, Richard Laurence. b 56. Trin Coll Bris. **d** 94 **p** 95. C Louth *Linc* from 94. *15 Grosvenor Crescent, Louth, Lincs LN11 0BD* Louth (01507) 603635

HOWLETT, Victor John. b 43. S Dios Minl Tr Scheme 90. **d** 93 **p** 94. NSM Bris St Andr w St Bart *Bris* from 93. *12 Cossins Road, Bristol BS6 7LY* Bristol (0117) 942 4904

HOWSE, Elizabeth Ann. *See* SMITH, Mrs Elizabeth Ann

HOWSON, David James. b 34. Kelham Th Coll 54. **d** 58 **p** 59. C Morecambe St Barn *Blackb* 58-61; C Burnley St Pet 61-63; C-in-c Penwortham St Leon CD 63-65; Bp's Youth Officer *Ox* 65-67; V Whitworth *Man* 67-71; R Rufford *Blackb* 71-78; V Mellor 78-83; Lic to Offic *Ox* 83-87; Area Sec (Dio Ox) USPG 83-87; R Cherbury *Ox* from 87; RD Vale of White Horse from 91. *The Rectory, Longworth, Abingdon, Oxon OX13 5DX* Longworth (01865) 820213

HOWSON, Canon George Webster. b 15. Man Univ BA46. Sarum Th Coll 47. **d** 49 **p** 50. V Over St Chad *Ches* 60-80; RD Middlewich 74-80; rtd 80; Perm to Offic *Ches* from 80. *58 Mount Drive, Nantwich, Cheshire CW5 6JQ* Nantwich (01270) 627870

HOY, Michael John. b 30. Reading Univ BSc52. Oak Hill Th Coll 57. **d** 59 **p** 60. C Worthing St Geo *Chich* 59-62; C Tulse Hill H Trin *S'wark* 62-66; R Danby Wiske w Yafforth and Hutton Bonville *Ripon* 66-76; V Camelsdale *Chich* 76-87; V Gt Marsden *Blackb* from 87. *St John's Vicarage, Barkerhouse Road, Nelson, Lancs BB9 9JS* Nelson (01282) 613824

HOY, Stephen Anthony. b 55. Leeds Poly BA76. Linc Th Coll 92. **d** 94 **p** 95. C Glen Parva and S Wigston *Leic* from 94. *163 Little Glen Road, Leicester LE2 8TX* Leicester (0116) 277 4275

HOYAL, Richard Dunstan. b 47. Ch Ch Ox BA67 MA71 BA78. Ripon Coll Cuddesdon 76. **d** 79 **p** 80. C Stevenage St Geo *St Alb* 79-83; V Monk Bretton *Wakef* 83-89; V Ilkley St Marg *Bradf* from 89. *St Margaret's Vicarage, 14 Queen's Road, Ilkley, W Yorkshire LS29 9QJ* Ilkley (01943) 607015

HOYE, Reginald George. b 16. Tyndale Hall Bris 58. **d** 60 **p** 61. V Nottm St Sav *S'well* 62-82; rtd 82; Perm to Offic *S'well* from 82. *1 White Acre, Burton Joyce, Nottingham NG14 5BU* Nottingham (0115) 931 2485

HOYLAND, John Gregory. b 50. Sussex Univ BEd73. Wycliffe Hall Ox 75. **d** 78 **p** 79. C Pudsey St Lawr *Bradf* 78-81; P-in-c Long Preston 81-84; P-in-c Long Preston w Tosside 84; V 84; CPAS Staff 85-87; Chapl Univ Coll of Ripon & York St Jo from 87. *College of Ripon and York, Lord Mayor's Walk, York YO3 7EX* York (01904) 656771

HOYLE, Dr David Michael. b 57. CCC Cam BA80 MA83 DPhil91. Ripon Coll Cuddesdon 84. **d** 86 **p** 87. C Chesterton Gd Shep *Ely* 86-88; Chapl and Fell Magd Coll Cam 88-91; Dean and Fell 91-95; V Southgate Ch Ch *Lon* from 95. *Christ Chuch Vicarage, 1 The Green, London N14 7EG* 0181-886 0384

HOYLE, Lawrence. b 27. St Aid Birkenhead 52. **d** 55 **p** 56. V Wrose *Bradf* 66-70; R Thwing *York* 70-81; V Wold Newton 71-81; Warden Lamplugh Ho Conf Cen 72-85; Dir Angl Renewal Min 81-89; Hon C Starbeck *Ripon* 87-89; rtd 89; Perm to Offic *Ex* from 92. *30 Highfield Drive, Waterside Park, Kingsbridge, Devon TQ7 1JR* Kingsbridge (01548) 856109

HOYLE, Miss Pamela Margaret. *See* CLOCKSIN, Mrs Pamela Margaret

HOYLE, Stephen Jonathan. b 64. Leeds Univ BA87. Ripon Coll Cuddesdon 88. **d** 90 **p** 91. C Lt Stanmore St Lawr *Lon* 90-93; C Lon Docks St Pet w Wapping St Jo from 93. *St Peter's Clergy House, Wapping Lane, London E1 9RW* 0171-481 2985

HRYZIUK, Petro. b 57. Lanc Univ BEd80. St Jo Coll Nottm DipTh89. **d** 90 **p** 91. C Huyton St Geo *Liv* 90-93; C Goose Green from 93. *23 Marus Avenue, Wigan, Lancs WN3 5QR* Wigan (01942) 41485

HUARD, Ven Geoffrey Robert. b 43. Lon Univ DipTh71. Clifton Th Coll 64. **d** 70 **p** 71. C Barking St Marg *Chelmsf* 70-73; C Everton St Ambrose w St Tim *Liv* 73-74; C Everton St Pet 74-76; Australia from 76; Adn Sydney and Cumberland from 89. *27 Hurlstone Avenue, Hurlstone Park, Sydney, NSW, Australia 2193* Sydney (2) 558-5986 or 265-1524

HUBAND, Eric Bob. b 27. Bris Univ BSc50. Sarum Th Coll 50. **d** 52 **p** 53. V Hengrove *Bris* 67-77; R E Horsley *Guildf* 77-92; rtd 92. *23 Hardens Mead, Chippenham, Wilts SN15 3AE* Chippenham (01249) 661219

HUBAND, Richard William. b 39. Trin Coll Cam BA62 MA66. Qu Coll Birm 76. **d** 78 **p** 79. C Norton *St Alb* 78-81; R Aspley Guise w Husborne Crawley and Ridgmont 81-91; V Elstow from 91. *The Abbey Vicarage, Elstow, Bedford MK42 9XT* Bedford (01234) 261477

HUBBARD, Christopher Maurice. b 25. Trin Coll Cam BA49 MA69. Chich Th Coll 51. **d** 53 **p** 54. V Wymeswold *Leic* 65-72; R Lambley *S'well* 72-77; Chapl HM Youth Cust Cen Lowdham Grange 74-77; P-in-c Chilbolton cum Wherwell *Win* 77-79; R 79-90; rtd 90. *2 Wessex Mews, High Street, Stockbridge, Hants SO20 6HE* Andover (01264) 810302

HUBBARD, David Harris. b 33. St Pet Hall Ox BA57 MA61 K Coll Lon MTh88. Ridley Hall Cam 59. **d** 60 **p** 61. C Dalston St Mark w St Bart *Lon* 60-63; C Stoke Newington St Olave 63-67; Hon C 67-68; Hon C Hornsey Ch Ch 69-70; V 70-82; AD W Haringey 78-85; V Highgate All SS from 82. *All Saints' Vicarage, 1B Church Road, London N6 4QH* 0181-340 1123

HUBBARD, Mrs Elisabeth Ann. b 41. E Anglian Minl Tr Course 82. **dss** 85 **d** 87 **p** 94. Cam H Trin w St Andr Gt *Ely* 85-86; Cherry Hinton St Jo 86-87; Par Dn 87-92; Par Dn Milton 92-94; C 94-95; R Willingham from 95; R Rampton from 95. *The Rectory, Willingham, Cambridge CB4 5ES* Willingham (01954) 261225

HUBBARD, Ian Maxwell. b 43. FCollP83 ACP83 Surrey Univ BEd84 Golds Coll Lon MA86. Sarum & Wells Th Coll 69. **d** 73

p 74. Hon C S'wark H Trin w St Matt *S'wark* 73-78; Hon C Camberwell St Mich w All So w Em 78-87; Hon C Dulwich St Barn 87-90; C Battersea St Mary 90-91; C Battersea St Mary 91-92; V Winscombe *B & W* from 92. *The Vicarage, Winscombe Hill, Winscombe, Avon BS25 1DE* Winscombe (01934) 843164

HUBBARD, Judith Frances. *See* JONES, Ms Judith Frances

HUBBARD, Julian Richard Hawes. b 55. Em Coll Cam BA76 MA81. Wycliffe Hall Ox BA80 MA85. **d** 81 **p** 82. C Fulham St Dionis Parson's Green *Lon* 81-84; Tutor Wycliffe Hall Ox 84-89; Chapl Jes Coll Ox 84-89; Selection Sec ACCM 89-91; Sen Selection Sec ABM 91-93; Perm to Offic *Guildf* 89-93; V Bourne from 93. *The Vicarage, 2 Middle Avenue, Farnham, Surrey GU9 8JL* Farnham (01252) 715505

HUBBARD, Laurence Arthur (Laurie). b 36. Qu Coll Cam BA60 MA64. Wycliffe Hall Ox 60 CMS Tr Coll Chislehurst 65 CMS Tr Coll Selly Oak 93. **d** 62 **p** 63. C Widcombe *B & W* 62-65; Kenya 66-73; V Pype Hayes *Birm* 73-79; P-in-c Nor-over-the-Water Colegate St Geo *Nor* 79-85; P-in-c Nor St Aug w St Mary 79-85; CMS from 85; Area Sec (Dios Cant and Roch) CMS 85-93; Perm to Offic *Cant* 85-93; Syria from 93. *All Saints Community Church, PO Box 11129, Damascus, Syria*

HUBBARD, Roy Oswald. b 32. Lich Th Coll 62. **d** 64 **p** 65. C Baswich (or Berkswich) *Lich* 64-68; P-in-c Ash 68-70; V Stevenage St Pet Broadwater *St Alb* 71-78; V Flitwick 78-90; RD Ampthill 87-90; R Sharnbrook and Knotting w Souldrop from 90. *The Rectory, 81 High Street, Sharnbrook, Bedford MK44 1PE* Bedford (01234) 781444

HUBBLE, Canon Raymond Carr (Ray). b 30. Wm Temple Coll Rugby 60. **d** 61 **p** 62. C Newbold and Dunston *Derby* 61-64; Chapl RAF 64-80; Asst Chapl-in-Chief RAF 80-85; QHC 84-85; P-in-c Odiham w S Warnborough and Long Sutton *Win* 85; P-in-c Odiham 85-86; V from 86; RD Odiham from 88; Hon Can Win Cathl from 94. *The Vicarage, Odiham, Basingstoke, Hants RG25 1LZ* Odiham (01256) 703395

HUBBLE, Trevor Ernest. b 46. Chich Th Coll 70. **d** 76 **p** 77. C Eltham St Barn *S'wark* 76-79; Lesotho 80-87; Adn S Lesotho 84-87; S Africa from 87. *PO Box 33, Matatiele, 4730 South Africa* Matatiele (373) 3589

HUBERT, Brother. *See* COPINGER, Stephen Hubert Augustine

HUCKETT, Andrew William. b 50. AKC72. St Aug Coll Cant 72. **d** 73 **p** 74. C Chipping Sodbury and Old Sodbury *Glouc* 73-76; Miss to Seamen from 76; Chapl Flushing Miss to Seamen *Eur* 76-79; Teesside 79-82; Chapl Milford Haven 86-92; Chapl Medway Ports from 92; Perm to Offic *St D* 86-92. *27 The Finches, Sittingbourne, Kent ME10 4PY* Sittingbourne (01795) 472851 Fax as telephone

HUCKLE, John Walford. b 39. E Midl Min Tr Course. **d** 89 **p** 90. Nottm St Pet and St Jas *S'well* from 89. *43 Bingham Road, Radcliffe-on-Trent, Nottingham NG12 2FY* Nottingham (0115) 933 2278

HUCKLE, Peter. b 46. Ox Univ Inst of Educn CertEd69 Auckland Univ DipPE71 DipEd71. **d** 90 **p** 91. New Zealand 90-91; Hon C N Walsham w Antingham *Nor* 91-92; C Gt Yarmouth 92-94; TV from 94. *The Rectory, 4 Barnard Avenue, Great Yarmouth, Norfolk NR30 4DS* Great Yarmouth (01493) 855472

HUCKLE, Stephen Leslie. b 48. Ch Ch Ox BA70 BA72 MA74. Coll of Resurr Mirfield 73. **d** 75 **p** 76. C Wednesbury St Paul Wood Green *Lich* 75-78; C Aylesbury *Ox* 78-85; C Farnham Royal w Hedgerley 85-88; V Fenny Stratford from 88. *The Vicarage, Manor Road, Fenny Stratford, Milton Keynes MK2 2HW* Milton Keynes (01908) 372825

HUCKLE, Sydney George. b 16. Oak Hill Th Coll 76. **d** 79 **p** 80. Hon C Wakes Colne w Chappel *Chelmsf* 79-80; Hon C Aldham 80-81; Hon C Marks Tey 80-81; Hon C Marks Tey w Aldham and Lt Tey from 81. *5 Orchard Close, Hallow, Worcester WR2 6LA* Worcester (01905) 640818

HUDD, Philip Simon. b 68. Westmr Coll Ox BA90. Westcott Ho Cam 91. **d** 93 **p** 94. C Kirkby *Liv* from 93. *14 Wingate Road, Kirkby, Liverpool L33 6UQ* 0151-546 1504

HUDDLESON, Robert Roulston. b 32. QUB BA55 TCD Div Test57. **d** 57 **p** 58. C Ballymena *Conn* 57-59; C Belf St Jas 59-63; Ethiopia 65-69; Exec Asst WCC Geneva 69-75; Dep Sec Gen Syn Bd for Miss and Unity 75-81; Admin Sec *Dur* 81-86; Lic to Offic 81-86; Dioc Sec *Ex* from 86; Lic to Offic from 86. *c/o Diocesan House, Palace Gate, Exeter EX1 1HX* Exeter (01392) 72686 Fax 430923

✠**HUDDLESTON, Most Revd Ernest Urban Trevor.** b 13. Ch Ch Ox BA34 MA38 Aber Univ Hon DD56 Lanc Univ Hon DLitt72. Wells Th Coll 35. **d** 36 **p** 37 **c** 60. C Swindon New Town *Bris* 36-39; CR from 41; Novice Guardian CR Mirfield 56-58; Prior Lon Ho 58-60; S Africa 43-56; Bp Masasi 60-68; Suff Bp Stepney *Lon* 68-78; Bp Mauritius 78-83; Abp Indian Ocean 78-83; rtd 83. *House of the Resurrection, Mirfield, W Yorkshire WF14 0BN* Mirfield (01924) 494318

HUDDLESTON, Geoffrey Roger. b 36. TCD BA63 MA67. Ridley Hall Cam 63. **d** 65 **p** 66. C Tonbridge SS Pet and Paul *Roch* 65-69; Chapl RAF 69-85; V Lyonsdown H Trin *St Alb* from 85; RD Barnet from 94. *Holy Trinity Vicarage, 18 Lyonsdown Road, Barnet, Herts EN5 1JE* 0181-449 0382

HUDGHTON, John Francis. b 56. BA. Cranmer Hall Dur 81. **d** 83 **p** 84. C Stockport St Geo *Ches* 83-85; C Witton 85-87; C Stockport St Alb Hall Street 87-90; V Thornton le Moors w Ince and Elton 90-95. *The Vicarage, Ince Lane, Elton, Chester CH2 4QB* Helsby (01928) 724028

HUDSON, Andrew Julian. b 57. Cranmer Hall Dur CTMin93. **d** 93 **p** 94. C Moldgreen *Wakef* from 93. *3 Forest Road, Huddersfield HD5 8EU* Huddersfield (01484) 514203

HUDSON, Anthony George. b 39. N Ord Course. **d** 84 **p** 85. C Harrogate St Mark *Ripon* 84-87; P-in-c Hampsthwaite from 87; P-in-c Killinghall 87-94. *The Vicarage, Church Lane, Hampsthwaite, Harrogate, N Yorkshire HG3 2HB* Harrogate (01423) 770337

HUDSON, Brainerd Peter de Wirtz Goodwin. b 34. K Coll Lon BD57 AKC57. Westcott Ho Cam 57. **d** 59 **p** 60. C Morden *S'wark* 59-60; Australia 61-65; Asst Sec CCCS 65-68; Lic to Offic *Lon* 65-68; Chapl St Lawr Coll Ramsgate 68-74; Lic to Offic *Cant* 68-74; Chapl Repton Sch Derby 74-94; Lic to Offic *Derby* 74-94; Chile from 94. *Casilla 16144, Santiago 9, Chile*

HUDSON, Christopher John. b 45. Lon Univ BSc68 MIH73. Cranmer Hall Dur DipTh77. **d** 77 **p** 78. C Bath Weston St Jo *B & W* 77-80; P-in-c Baltonsborough w Butleigh and W Bradley 80-84; V 84-87; P-in-c Shirwell w Loxhore *Ex* 87-89; P-in-c Kentisbury, Trentishoe, E Down and Arlington 88-89; RD Shirwell 88-91; TR Shirwell, Loxhore, Kentisbury, Arlington, etc 90-91; P-in-c Trentishoe 90-91; R Huntspill *B & W* 91-94. *28 Laburnum Road, Wellington, Somerset TA21 8EL* Wellington (01823) 664968

HUDSON, Edmund John. b 21. Qu Coll Cam BA46 MA48. Cuddesdon Coll 47. **d** 49 **p** 50. V York St Hilda *York* 56-86; rtd 86. *37 Elmfield Avenue, York YO3 9LX* York (01904) 426164

HUDSON, Canon Gerald Ernest. b 20. Ex Coll Ox BA42 MA46. Westcott Ho Cam 42. **d** 43 **p** 44. V Roehampton H Trin *S'wark* 60-71; Hon Can S'wark Cathl 68-80; Prin S'wark Ord Course 71-80; R St Mary le Bow w St Pancras Soper Lane etc *Lon* 80-85; rtd 85; Dir of Post-Ord Tr *Cant* 86-88. *10 Medina Avenue, Whitstable, Kent CT5 4EN* Whitstable (01227) 276548

HUDSON, Harold Paige. b 05. New Coll Ox BA28 MA32. Westcott Ho Cam 32. **d** 34 **p** 35. R Kirby Muxloe *Leic* 45-50; rtd 75. *La Mouette, Pontac, St Clement, Jersey, Channel Islands JE2 6SE* Jersey (01534) 851684

HUDSON, John. b 47. FRSA CSocStuds. Linc Th Coll. **d** 83 **p** 84. C Mert St Mary *S'wark* 83-86; C Kirk Ella *York* 86-88; P-in-c Lenborough *Ox* 88-93; V Lenborough from 93; P-in-c Tingewick w Water Stratford, Radclive etc 89-93; P-in-c Water Stratford from 93. *The Rectory, Thornborough Road, Padbury, Buckingham MK18 2AH* Buckingham (01280) 813162

HUDSON, John. b 51. Oak Hill Th Coll 84. **d** 86 **p** 87. C Leyland St Andr *Blackb* 86-89; V Coppull from 89. *The Vicarage, Chapel Lane, Coppull, Chorley, Lancs PR7 4NA* Coppull (01257) 791218

HUDSON, John Stephen Anthony. b 49. S Dios Minl Tr Scheme 85 Chich Th Coll 86. **d** 88 **p** 89. C Horsham *Chich* 88-91; TV Littlehampton and Wick from 91. *The Vicarage, 40 Beaconsfield Road, Wick, Littlehampton, W Sussex BN17 6LN* Littlehampton (01903) 724990

HUDSON, Canon John Cecil. b 22. Selw Coll Cam BA46 MA48. Qu Coll Birm BD51. **d** 48 **p** 49. V Padiham *Blackb* 57-68; RD Whalley 68-83; V Clitheroe St Mary 68-85; Hon Can Blackb Cathl 79-85; rtd 85; Perm to Offic *Blackb* from 85; Perm to Offic *Bradf* from 85. *29 Eastfield Drive, West Bradford, Clitheroe, Lancs BB7 4TQ* Clitheroe (01200) 23531

HUDSON, John Leonard. b 44. AKC66. **d** 67 **p** 68. C Dodworth *Wakef* 67-70; Prec Wakef Cathl 70-73; V Ravensthorpe 73-80; V Royston from 80; P-in-c Carlton from 90; RD Barnsley from 93. *The Clergy House, Church Street, Royston, Barnsley, S Yorkshire S71 4QZ* Barnsley (01226) 722410

HUDSON, John Peter. b 42. AKC64. St Boniface Warminster 64. **d** 65 **p** 66. C S Shields St Hilda w St Thos *Dur* 65-68; Chapl RN 68-84; V Mellor *Blackb* from 84. *The Vicarage, Church Lane, Mellor, Blackburn BB2 7JL* Mellor (01254) 812324

HUDSON, Mrs Mary Gertrude. b 29. Univ Coll Lon BA51 CertEd52. Qu Coll Birm 82. **dss** 85 **d** 87 **p** 94. Kings Norton *Birm* 85-87; NSM from 87. *67 Wychall Lane, Birmingham B38 8TB* 0121-458 3128

HUDSON, Philip Howard. b 50. St Steph Ho Ox 89. **d** 91 **p** 92. C Poulton-le-Fylde *Blackb* 91-95; V Blackpool St Wilfrid from 95. *St Wilfrid's Vicarage, 8 Langdale Road, Blackpool FY4 4RT* Blackpool (01253) 761532

HUDSON

HUDSON, Thomas Bernard. b 16. Ch Coll Cam BA38 MA42. Chich Th Coll 38. **d** 40 **p** 41. Madagascar 50-76; C Owton Manor CD *Dur* 77-81; rtd 81; Hon C Lavender Hill Ascension *S'wark* 81-88. *College of St Barnabas, Blackberry Lane, Lingfield, Surrey RH7 6NJ* Dormans Park (01342) 870260

HUDSON, Canon Thomas George. b 32. TCD BA54. CITC Div Test54. **d** 55 **p** 56. C Belf St Matt *Conn* 55-58; C Belf Ch Ch 58-60; C Carlow *C & O* 60-61; I Hacketstown 61-69; I Kinneigh Union *C, C & R* 69-72; I Monasterevan *M & K* 72-83; I Mostrim w Granard, Clonbroney, Killoe etc *K, E & A* from 83; Preb Elphin Cathl from 86. *The Rectory, Edgeworthstown, Co Longford, Irish Republic* Longford (43) 71172

HUDSON, Trevor. b 32. Dur Univ BA56. Cranmer Hall Dur DipTh. **d** 58 **p** 59. V Stannington *Sheff* 64-79; V Abbeydale St Jo 79-88; V Worsbrough 88-95; rtd 95. *Spring Villa Garden, 136A Langsett Road South, Oughtibridge, Sheffield S30 3HA* Sheffield (0114) 286 3559

HUDSON, Wilfred. b 23. St Jo Coll Dur BA49 DipTh. **d** 51 **p** 52. V Anston *Sheff* 64-74; V Woodsetts 64-74; V Sheff Sharrow 74-88; rtd 88. *128 Totley Brook Road, Sheffield S17 3QU* Sheffield (0114) 236 5558

HUDSON, Wilfrid Reginald. b 17. Clifton Th Coll 48 St Aid Birkenhead 49. **d** 51 **p** 52. V Scarisbrick *Liv* 63-78; New Hall Hosp Scarisbrick 63-78; P-in-c Creacombe *Ex* 78; P-in-c Meshaw 78; P-in-c Thelbridge 78; P-in-c W w E Worlington 78; P-in-c Witheridge 78; P-in-c Witheridge, Thelbridge, Creacombe, Meshaw etc 79; V 79-86; rtd 86. *19 Beech Hill, Wellington, Somerset TA21 8ER* Wellington (01823) 662642

HUDSON-WILKIN, Mrs Rose Josephine. b 61. W Midl Minl Tr Course 89. **d** 91 **p** 94. Par Dn Wolv St Matt *Lich* 91-94; C 94-95; C W Bromwich Gd Shep w St Jo from 95; Black Anglican Concern from 95. *St Andrew's Vicarage, Oakwood Street, West Bromwich, W Midlands B70 9SN* 0121-553 1871

HUDSPITH, Ernest. b 26. Open Univ BA73 Birm Univ DipTh64. Qu Coll Birm 61. **d** 64 **p** 65. Prec Gib Cathl *Eur* 67-68; NSM Twickenham St Mary *Lon* 69-74; rtd 94. *Flat 3, 68 Warrior Square, St Leonards-on-Sea, E Sussex TN37 6BP* Hastings (01424) 441760

HUDSPITH, Mrs Susan Mary. b 49. St Alb Minl Tr Scheme 79. **dss** 82 **d** 87 **p** 94. Luton St Chris Round Green *St Alb* 82-87; Par Dn 87-88; NSM 88-92; Perm to Offic 92-94; C Luton St Mary from 94. *171 Hart Lane, Luton LU2 0JH* Luton (01582) 34948

HUELIN, Dr Gordon. b 19. Lon Univ BD42 MTh47 PhD55. **d** 42 **p** 43. Lect K Coll Lon 59-84; FKC from 78; V St Marg Pattens *Lon* 63-84; rtd 84; Archivist and Libr SPCK from 84; Assoc Prof Univ of Notre Dame (USA) from 84; Perm to Offic *Lon* from 92. *44 Warren Road, London E11 2LX* 0181-530 8594 Fax 0171-388 2352

HUETT, Basil George Pringle. b 19. Lon Univ BA39 Man Univ BD42. Roch Th Coll. **d** 62 **p** 62. Ind Chapl *Roch* 62-72; C Erith St Jo 62-72; rtd 84; Perm to Offic *Roch* from 84. *Hazelcroft, Stonehouse Road, Halstead, Sevenoaks, Kent TN14 7HN* Farnborough (01689) 855471

HUGGETT, Christopher Roy. b 49. Hull Univ BA72 CertEd73. Linc Th Coll 79. **d** 93 **p** 94. C Accrington St Jo w Huncoat *Blackb* 93-95; C Cleveleys from 95. *58 Stockdove Way, Thornton-Cleveleys, Blackpool FY5 2AR* Blackpool (01253) 827744

HUGGETT, Dr David John. b 34. Lon Univ BSc56 Southn Univ PhD59. Clifton Th Coll 64. **d** 67 **p** 68. C Heatherlands St Jo *Sarum* 67-70; C Cam St Sepulchre *Ely* 70-73; R Nottm St Nic S'well 73-92; Cyprus from 93. *PO Box 80, Polis Chrysochous, Cyprus*

HUGGETT, John Victor James. b 39. Dur Univ BA64. Tyndale Hall Bris 64. **d** 66 **p** 67. C Worthing St Geo *Chich* 69-71; C Woking St Pet *Guildf* 71-73; C Buckhurst Hill *Chelmsf* 73-76; V Meltham Mills *Wakef* 76-78; V Wilshaw 76-78; rtd 79; Ldr Breath Fellowship 79-84; Perm to Offic *Wakef* 79-84. *Chilston Mead, Pembury Road, Tunbridge Wells, Kent TN2 3QN* Tunbridge Wells (01892) 514112

HUGGETT, Kevin John. b 62. St Jo Coll Dur BA83. Trin Coll Bris DipHE90 ADPS91. **d** 91 **p** 92. C Gt Ilford St Andr *Chelmsf* 91-94; CMS from 94. *49 St Andrew's Road, Ilford, Essex IG1 3PF* 0181-554 7523

HUGGETT, Michael George. b 38. Bris Univ BA60 Birm Univ CertEd61 Nottm Univ DCE83. E Midl Min Tr Course 85. **d** 88 **p** 89. C Sawley *Derby* 88-92; C Chaddesden St Phil 92-93; P-in-c Alkmonton, Cubley, Marston, Montgomery etc from 93. *The Vicarage, Cubley, Ashbourne, Derbyshire DE6 3DL* Ashbourne (01335) 330680

HUGGILL, Cyril Howard. b 20. St Cath Soc Ox BA42 MA46 AKC44. **d** 44 **p** 45. Chapl and Lect Bp Lonsdale Coll Derby 66-70; V Biggin *Derby* 70-76; V Hartington 70-76; V Goostrey *Ches* 76-85; rtd 85. *The Granary, Silver Street, Kirkby Stephen, Cumbria CA17 4RB* Kirkby Stephen (017683) 71068

HUGGINS, John Henry William. b 24. Wadh Coll Ox MA. Cuddesdon Coll 49. **d** 51 **p** 52. R Esher *Guildf* 55-57; rtd 90. *2 The Malthouse, 3 Willow Vale, Frome, Somerset BA11 1BG* Frome (01373) 465845

HUGHES, Adrian John. b 57. Newc Univ BA78 Dur Univ BA82. Cranmer Hall Dur 80. **d** 83 **p** 84. C Shard End *Birm* 83-86; TV Solihull 86-90; TV Glendale Gp *Newc* 90-94; P-in-c Belford from 94. *The Vicarage, North Bank, Belford, Northd NE70 7LT* Belford (016683) 213545

HUGHES, Alan. b 34. St D Coll Lamp BA54 St Mich Coll Llan 58. **d** 60 **p** 61. C Aberavon *Llan* 60-62; Chapl RAF 62-66; CF 66-76; USA from 76. *Address temp unknown*

HUGHES, Alan. b 46. TD. Edin Th Coll 71. **d** 74 **p** 75. C Edin St Cuth *Edin* 74-76; P-in-c Edin St Luke 76-78; C Marske in Cleveland *York* 78-81; V New Marske 81-84; V Kirkbymoorside w Gillamoor, Farndale & Bransdale 84-94; CF from 84; V Berwick H Trin and St Mary *Newc* from 94. *The Vicarage, Parade, Berwick-upon-Tweed TD15 1DF* Berwick-upon-Tweed (01289) 306136

HUGHES, Albert Ashbden. b 10. Univ of Wales BA37. St Mich Coll Llan 38. **d** 39 **p** 40. V Goostrey *Ches* 64-76; rtd 76; Perm to Offic *Ches* from 76. *50 Preston Road, Lytham, Lytham St Annes, Lancs FY8 5AA* Lytham (01253) 795108

HUGHES, Andrew Terrell. b 29. Bris Univ BA56 DipEd. Coll of Resurr Mirfield 64. **d** 66 **p** 67. C Weston-super-Mare St Sav *B & W* 66-70; C Yeovil St Jo w Preston Plucknett 70-73; TV Yeovil 73-83; R Wincanton 83-88; rtd 89. *2 Cove Street, Weymouth, Dorset DT4 8TS* Weymouth (01305) 778639

HUGHES, Miss Angela Mary. b 52. Avery Hill Coll CertEd75. St Steph Ho Ox 90. **d** 92 **p** 94. Par Dn Kidderminster St Mary and All SS w Trimpley etc *Worc* 92-94; C from 94. *44 Broadwater Drive, Kidderminster, Worcs DY10 2RY* Kidderminster (01562) 68533

HUGHES, Arthur Lewis. b 36. St Deiniol's Hawarden 65. **d** 68 **p** 69. C Holywell *St As* 68-71; Lect St Mary Watford 71-75; V Thornton in Lonsdale w Burton in Lonsdale *Bradf* 75-84; V Daubhill *Man* 84-89; V Castle Town *Lich* from 89; Chapl Staffs Univ from 91. *St Thomas's Vicarage, Doxey, Stafford ST16 1EQ* Stafford (01785) 58796

HUGHES, Arthur William Ronald. b 14. Ch Coll Cam BA36 MA40. St Mich Coll Llan 37. **d** 39 **p** 41. V Arthog w Fairbourne *Ban* 67-74; R Machynlleth and Llanwrin 74-77; rtd 77; Perm to Offic *St D* from 77. *4 Clos y Drindod, Buarth Road, Aberystwyth, Dyfed SY23 1LR* Aberystwyth (01970) 623779

HUGHES, Bernard Patrick. b 35. DipTh64. Oak Hill Th Coll 62. **d** 65 **p** 66. C Fulham St Matt *Lon* 65-69; Chapl St Steph Hosp Lon 69-89; Chapl St Mary Abbots Hosp Lon from 69; Chapl Westmr Hosp Lon 89-94; Chapl Chelsea & Westmr Hosp Lon from 94. *Chelsea & Westminster Hospital, Fulham Road, London SW10 9NH, or 9 Walham Grove, London SW6 1QP* 0171-385 1348 or 0181-746 8083

HUGHES, Bertram Arthur Edwin. b 23. Clifton Th Coll 64. **d** 66 **p** 67. C Ramsgate St Luke *Cant* 68-70; Australia 70-76; P-in-c Swanton Abbott w Skeyton *Nor* 76-80; P-in-c Scottow 76-80; Australia 80-83; R Reymerston w Cranworth, Letton, Southburgh etc *Nor* 83-84; rtd 84; Perm to Offic *Ex* from 90. *88 Winslade Road, Sidmouth, Devon EX10 9EZ* Sidmouth (01395) 512452

HUGHES, Miss Carol Lindsay. b 51. Cam Inst of Educn CertEd72 Nottm Univ BEd86. Trin Coll Bris DipHE93. **d** 93 **p** 94. C Ilkeston St Mary *Derby* from 93. *14 Lower Stanton Road, Ilkeston, Derbyshire DE7 4LN* Nottingham (0115) 932 7032

HUGHES, Christopher. b 45. CQSW81. Sarum & Wells Th Coll 86. **d** 88 **p** 89. C Handsworth *Sheff* 88-91; TV Wombourne w Trysull and Bobbington *Lich* from 91. *59 Six Ashes Road, Bobbington, Stourbridge, W Midlands DY7 5DD* Bobbington (01384) 221580

HUGHES, Christopher Clarke. b 40. Lon Coll of Div ALCD65 LTh. **d** 65 **p** 66. C Broadclyst *Ex* 65-68; C Chenies and Lt Chalfont *Ox* 68-70; TV Lydford w Bridestowe and Sourton *Ex* 70-72; TV Lydford, Brent Tor, Bridestowe and Sourton 72-74; V Buckland Monachorum 74-83; R Ashtead *Guildf* from 83. *The Rectory, Dene Road, Ashtead, Surrey KT21 1ED* Ashtead (01372) 272135

HUGHES, Clive. b 54. Univ of Wales BA77 MA82. St Mich Coll Llan BD95. **d** 95. C Carmarthen St Dav *St D* from 95. *26 Knoll Gardens, Carmarthen, Dyfed SA31 3EJ* Carmarthen (01267) 222865

HUGHES, David Anthony. b 25. Trin Coll Cam BA48 MA55. Linc Th Coll 74. **d** 76 **p** 77. C Boston *Linc* 76-78; V Graffoe 78-90; rtd 90; Perm to Offic *Linc* 91-94. *27 St Clement's Road, Ruskington, Sleaford, Lincs NG34 9AF* Ruskington (01526) 832618

HUGHES, David Harwood. b 09. Univ of Wales BA30. St Mich Coll Llan 31. **d** 32 **p** 33. V Thorncombe *Sarum* 69-75; rtd 75;

352

Perm to Offic *Win* from 75. *54 Newstead Road, Bournemouth BH6 3HL* Bournemouth (01202) 428794

HUGHES, David Howard. b 55. Univ of Wales (Ban). St Mich Coll Llan. **d** 79 **p** 80. C Llanrhos *St As* 79-82; C Eckington w Handley and Ridgeway *Derby* 82-83; C Staveley and Barrow Hill 83-85; TV 85-89; V Whitworth *Man* from 89. *St Bartholomew's House, 1 Beech Close, Whitworth, Rochdale, Lancs OL12 8AR* Rochdale (01706) 853551

HUGHES, David Michael. b 41. Oak Hill Th Coll BD67. **d** 68 **p** 69. C Tunbridge Wells St Jo *Roch* 68-73; C Crookes St Thos *Sheff* 73-81; V Normanton *Wakef* 81-90; TR Didsbury St Jas and Em *Man* from 90. *St James's Rectory, 9 Didsbury Park, Manchester M20 0LH* 0161-434 2178

HUGHES, Debbie Ann. *See* PEATMAN, Mrs Debbie Ann

HUGHES, Douglas. b 25. Lon Coll of Div BD54 ALCD54. **d** 54 **p** 55. R Risley *Derby* 68-77; P-in-c Horsley 77-87; P-in-c Kirk Langley 87-91; P-in-c Mackworth All SS 87-91; P-in-c Mugginton and Kedleston 89-91; rtd 91. *44 Chapel Lane, Spondon, Derby DE21 7JU* Derby (01332) 660561

HUGHES, Elfed. b 53. St Mich Coll Llan BD75. **d** 77 **p** 78. C Skewen *Llan* 77-80; TV Ystradyfodwg w Gelli, Rhigos and Tonpentre 80-81; P-in-c Pentre CD 81-85; V Pentre 85-87; Chapl Wales Poly 87-91; V Llantrisant *Llan* from 91. *The Vicarage, Coed yr Esgob, Llantrisant, M Glam CF7 8EL* Llantrisant (01443) 223356

HUGHES, Mrs Elizabeth Jane. b 58. K Coll Lon BD81 AKC81. Ripon Coll Cuddesdon 85. **dss** 83 **d** 87 **p** 94. Chipping Barnet w Arkley *St Alb* 83-86; Dunstable 86-87; Hon Par Dn 87-93; NSM Boxmoor St Jo from 93. *St John's Vicarage, 10 Charles Street, Hemel Hempstead, Herts HP1 1JH* Hemel Hempstead (01442) 255382

HUGHES, Ms Eunice Nesta. b 14. K Coll Lon 38 CertEd51. Lambeth DipTh40 St Chris Coll Blackheath 34. **dss** 61 **d** 87. RE Teacher Darley Gate 62-64; Cheltenham Ladies' Coll 65-74; Cant St Martin and St Paul *Cant* 76-80; Westgate-on-Sea St Sav 80-87; Hon Par Dn 87; Perm to Offic from 87. *Flat 1, 4 Cedric Road, Westgate-on-Sea, Kent CT8 8NZ* Thanet (01843) 831746

HUGHES, Ven Evan Arthur Bertram. b 25. St D Coll Lamp BA48 LTh50. **d** 50 **p** 51. C Llanstadwel *St D* 70-73; Pakistan 73-74; R Johnston w Steynton *St D* 74-80; Can St D Cathl 80-85; V Newc Emlyn 80-81; V Newc Emlyn w Llandyfriog and Troed-yr-aur 81-86; Adn Carmarthen 85-91; V Llanegwad w Llanfynydd 86-88; V Cynwil Elfed and Newchurch 88-91; rtd 91. *104 Bromwydd Road, Carmarthen, Dyfed SA31 2AW* Carmarthen (01267) 237155

HUGHES, Evan Thomas. b 08. FCII36 Lon Univ BD50. **d** 47 **p** 48. Chapl St Mary's Coll Cheltenham 64-70; rtd 70; Perm to Offic *Derby* from 73. *197 Allestree Lane, Derby DE22 2PF* Derby (01332) 556602

HUGHES, Canon Evelyn. b 31. Gilmore Ho 73. **dss** 79 **d** 87 **p** 94. Fetcham *Guildf* 79-82; Dioc Adv Lay Min 82-86; Farnborough 83-87; C 87-92; Bp's Adv for Women's Min from 87; D-in-c Badshot Lea CD 92-94; C-in-c from 94; Hon Can Guildf Cathl from 94. *8 Badshot Park, Badshot Lea, Farnham, Surrey GU9 9JZ* Farnham (01252) 331370

HUGHES, Canon Geraint Morgan Hugh. b 34. Keble Coll Ox BA58 MA63. St Mich Coll Llan 58. **d** 59 **p** 60. C Gorseinon *S & B* 59-63; C Oystermouth 63-68; R Llanbadarn Fawr, Llandegley and Llanfihangel etc 68-76; R Llandrindod w Cefnllys 76-87; R Llandrindod w Cefnllys and Disserth from 87; Can Brecon Cathl from 89; Prec Brecon Cathl from 95. *The Rectory, Broadway, Llandrindod Wells, Powys LD1 5HT* Llandrindod Wells (01597) 822043

HUGHES, Canon Gerald Thomas. b 30. Lon Univ BD63 MTh. Qu Coll Birm 72. **d** 72 **p** 73. Lic to Offic *Cov* 72-80; P-in-c Birdingbury 80-81; P-in-c Leamington Hastings 80-81; V Leamington Hastings and Birdingbury 81-82; V Dunchurch 82-89; RD Rugby 85-89; Can Res Cov Cathl 89-94; rtd 94; Perm to Offic *Cov* from 94. *Loafers' Cottage, Lazy Lane, Fladbury, Pershore, Worcs WR10 2QL* Pershore (01386) 860650

HUGHES, Gwilym Berw. b 42. St Mich Coll Llan DipTh68. **d** 68 **p** 69. C Conwy w Gyffin *Ban* 68-71; V Llandinorwig w Penisarwaun and Llanddeiniolen 71-75; TV Llandudno 75-80; V Dwygyfylchi from 80; RD Arllechwedd from 88. *The Vicarage, Church Road, Penmaenmawr, Gwynedd LL34 6BN* Penmaenmawr (01492) 623300

HUGHES, Canon Gwyndaf Morris. b 36. Univ of Wales (Lamp) BA57. St Steph Ho Ox 58 St Mich Coll Llan 59. **d** 59 **p** 60. C Glanogwen *Ban* 59-62; Chapl RN 62-78; R Llanfairpwll w Penmynydd *Ban* 78-90; RD Tindaethwy from 88; R Beaumaris from 90; Can Ban Cathl from 95. *The Rectory, 5 Tros-y-Afon, Beaumaris, Gwynedd LL58 8BN* Beaumaris (01248) 811402

HUGHES, Canon Harold Mervyn. b 13. St D Coll Lamp BA34. **d** 37 **p** 38. V Hucclecote *Glouc* 46-78; rtd 78; Perm to Offic

Glouc from 83. *13 Woodland Green, Upton St Leonards, Gloucester GL4 8DB* Gloucester (01452) 618301

HUGHES, Miss Hazel. b 45. St Jo Coll Dur 75. **dss** 78 **d** 87 **p** 94. Lower Mitton *Worc* 78-81; Worc St Martin w St Pet, St Mark etc 82-87; Par Dn Worc SE 87-88; D-in-c Wribbenhall 88-94; V 94; P-in-c from 94. *Wribbenhall Vicarage, Trimpley Lane, Bewdley, Worcs DY12 1JJ* Bewdley (01299) 402196

HUGHES, Canon Henry. b 18. Kelham Th Coll 35. **d** 41 **p** 42. V Holbrooks *Cov* 50-89; Hon Can Cov Cathl 73-89; rtd 89; P-in-c Hoar Cross w Newchurch *Lich* from 89. *The Vicarage, Hoar Cross, Burton-on-Trent, Staffs DE13 8QR* Hoar Cross (0128375) 263

HUGHES, Henry Charles William. b 30. K Coll Lon 58. Roch Th Coll 59. **d** 61 **p** 62. C Woodford St Barn *Chelmsf* 64-72; Lic to Offic 72-95; rtd 95. *99 St Anthony's Drive, Chelmsford CM2 9EH* Chelmsford (01245) 265230

HUGHES, Hugh. b 13. St D Coll Lamp BA35 St Mich Coll Llan 35. **d** 36 **p** 37. R Llaneugrad w Llanallgo and Penrhosllugwy etc *Ban* 73-82; RD Twrcelyn 80-82; rtd 82; Perm to Offic *Ban* from 86. *50 Craig-y-Don, Tyn-y-Gongl, Gwynedd LL74 8SN* Tyn-y-Gongl (01248) 853500

HUGHES, Canon Hywel Maldwyn. b 20. Univ of Wales (Swansea) BA42. St Mich Coll Llan 42. **d** 44 **p** 45. V Killay *S & B* 68-87; RD Clyne 79-87; Can Brecon Cathl 81-87; Treas Brecon Cathl 81-83; Chan 83-87; rtd 88; Canada from 95. *142 Three Valleys Drive, Don Mills, Ontario, Canada, M3A 3B9*

HUGHES, Ivor Gordon. b 45. Culham Coll of Educn CertEd68. Ripon Coll Cuddesdon 75. **d** 77 **p** 78. C Newport w Longford *Lich* 77-79; Children's Work Officer CMS 79-82; V Gt and Lt Bedwyn and Savernake Forest *Sarum* 82-86; P-in-c Urchfont w Stert 86-90; TR Redhorn 90-92; Nat Children's Officer Gen Syn Bd of Educn from 90. *62 Hamilton Road, Salisbury SP1 3TQ* Salisbury (01722) 421905

HUGHES, Mrs Jackie Louise. b 50. ACP81 Birm Poly BEd86. W Midl Minl Tr Course 89. **d** 92. NSM Edgbaston St Geo *Birm* from 92. *267 Stoney Lane, Yardley, Birmingham B25 8YG* 0121-628 4184

HUGHES, Miss Jacqueline Monica (Jackie). b 36. Lon Univ TCert56. Dalton Ho Bris 59. **dss** 77 **d** 88. Redditch St Steph *Worc* 77-79; Worc H Trin 79-82; Chapl Asst Worc R Infirmary from 82. *38 Cockshute Hill, Droitwich, Worcs WR9 7QP* Worcester (01905) 775153 or 763333

HUGHES, John Chester. b 24. St Jo Coll Dur BA48 DipTh50 MA51. **d** 50 **p** 51. Provost Leic 63-78; ChStJ from 74; V Bringhurst w Gt Easton *Leic* 78-87; rtd 87. *29 High Street, Hallaton, Market Harborough, Leics LE16 8UD* Hallaton (0185889) 622

HUGHES, Canon John Herbert Vivian. b 28. St D Coll Lamp BA51 LTh53. **d** 53 **p** 54. V Newchurch and Merthyr *St D* 62-71; V Abergwili w Llanfihangel-uwch-Gwili etc 71-89; RD Carmarthen 82-88; Can St D Cathl 87-89; rtd 89. *Deri Deg, 104 Bronwydd Road, Carmarthen, Dyfed SA31 2AR* Carmarthen (01267) 237155

HUGHES, John Malcolm. b 47. Man Univ BSc68 Leeds Univ DipTh70. Coll of Resurr Mirfield 68. **d** 71 **p** 72. C Newton Nottage *Llan* 71-78; V Llanwynno 78-92; R Cadoxton-juxta-Barry from 92. *The Rectory, 21 Rectory Road, Cadoxton, Barry, S Glam CF63 3QB* Barry (01446) 733041

HUGHES, John Patrick. b 41. Oak Hill Th Coll DipTh66. **d** 67 **p** 68. C Chorleywood St Andr *St Alb* 67-71; C E Twickenham St Steph *Lon* 71-76; TV High Wycombe *Ox* 77-92; Chapl Wycombe Hosp 77-83; V Harborne Heath *Birm* from 92. *St John's Vicarage, 99 Wentworth Road, Birmingham B17 9ST* 0121-428 2093

HUGHES, John Stunt Dickson. b 01. Keble Coll Ox BA25 MA48. Cuddesdon Coll 25. **d** 26 **p** 27. V Washington *Chich* 42-70; rtd 70. *5 West Preston Manor, Rustington, Littlehampton, W Sussex BN16 3AX* Rustington (01903) 786062

✠**HUGHES, Rt Rev John Taylor.** b 08. CBE75. Bede Coll Dur BA31 DipTh32 MA35. **d** 31 **p** 32 **c** 56. Asst Chapl and Tutor St Bede Coll Dur 31-34; Lect 34-35; C Shildon *Dur* 34-37; V Hartlepool St Jas 37-48; Warden S'wark Dioc Ho Blackheath and St Sav Coll 48-56; Can Miss S'wark Cathl 48-56; Suff Bp Croydon *Cant* 56-77; Bp HM Forces 66-75; Adn Croydon *Cant* 67-77; rtd 77; Asst Bp Cant 77-86; Asst Bp S'wark from 86. *Hospital of the Holy Trinity, Croydon CR0 1UB* 0181-686 8313

HUGHES, John Tudor. b 59. Nottm Univ BSc81 Univ of Wales (Cardiff) BD84. St Mich Coll Llan 81. **d** 84 **p** 85. C Mold *St As* 84-88; Asst Dioc Youth Chapl from 86; Min Can St As Cathl 88-90; Min St As and Tremeirchion 88-90; V Holt from 90. *The Vicarage, 5 Smithfield Drive, Holt, Wrexham, Clwyd LL13 9AJ* Farndon (01829) 270001

HUGHES, John William George. b 48. MBE93. St Mich Coll Llan DipTh72. **d** 72 **p** 73. C Swansea St Pet *S & B* 72-76; V Cwmddauddwr w St Harmon's and Llanwrthwl 76-79; P-in-c

Caereithin 79; V 80-86; Chapl RAF from 86. *Chaplaincy Services (RAF), HQ, Personnel and Training Command, RAF Innsworth, Gloucester GL3 1EZ* Gloucester (01452) 712612 Ext 5164 Fax 510828

HUGHES, Martin Conway. b 40. Ex Coll Ox BA61 MA67. Chich Th Coll. **d** 63 **p** 64. C Roehampton H Trin *S'wark* 63-67; C Addlestone *Guildf* 67-71; V Burpham 71-88; V Shamley Green from 88; RD Cranleigh from 90. *The Vicarage, Church Hill, Shamley Green, Guildford, Surrey GU5 0UD* Guildford (01483) 892030

HUGHES, Martyn Lawrence. b 19. Magd Coll Cam BA42 MA46 K Coll Cam BA43 MA52. Westcott Ho Cam. **d** 44 **p** 45. Chapl Harrow Sch Middx 61-73; Perm to Offic *Chich* from 73; Hd Relig Studies Rich Collyer Coll Horsham 73-84; rtd 84. *Spindleberry, Broomers, Hill Lane, Pulborough, W Sussex RH20 2DU* Pulborough (01798) 873786

HUGHES, Matthew James. b 66. K Coll Lon BD88. Westcott Ho Cam 89. **d** 91 **p** 92. C Heston *Lon* 91-94; C Fulham All SS from 94. *70A Fulham High Street, London SW6 3LG* 0171-371 7540

HUGHES, Dr Michael John Minto. b 50. Liv Univ MB, ChB74 DRCOG87 Ox Univ MTh94. Wycliffe Hall Ox 76. **d** 79 **p** 80. C Stranton *Dur* 79-82; Peru 82-86; Hon C Gosforth w Nether Wasdale and Wasdale Head *Carl* 87-88; TV Thetford *Nor* from 89. *44 Nunsgate, Thetford, Norfolk IP24 3EL* Thetford (01842) 752075

HUGHES, Neville Joseph. b 52. NUU BA79 MBIM93. **d** 91 **p** 92. NSM Mullabrack w Markethill and Kilcluney *Arm* from 91. *109 Markethill Road, Portadown, Co Armagh BT62 3SL* Portadown (01762) 841500

HUGHES, Owen. b 17. Univ of Wales BA39. St Mich Coll Llan 39. **d** 40 **p** 41. V Wesham *Blackb* 62-70; R Llanbeulan w Llanfaelog and Tal-y-llyn *Ban* 70-71; R Church Kirk *Blackb* 71-74; V Oswaldtwistle All SS 74-82; rtd 82; Lic to Offic *Blackb* from 82. *57 Blackburn Road, Rishton, Blackburn BB1 4EU* Great Harwood (01254) 884165

HUGHES, Paul Vernon. b 53. Ripon Coll Cuddesdon 79. **d** 82 **p** 83. C Chipping Barnet w Arkley *St Alb* 82-86; TV Dunstable 86-93; P-in-c Boxmoor St Jo from 93. *St John's Vicarage, 10 Charles Street, Hemel Hempstead, Herts HP1 1JH* Hemel Hempstead (01442) 255382

HUGHES, Peter John. b 59. Wolv Poly BA83 Lon Univ PGCE85 Inst of Marketing DipM. Wycliffe Hall Ox 90. **d** 92 **p** 93. C Ecclesall *Sheff* from 92. *48 Renshaw Road, Sheffield S11 7PD* Sheffield (0114) 266 2313

HUGHES, Peter Knowles. b 61. Sarum & Wells Th Coll 87. **d** 90 **p** 91. C Whitchurch *Bris* 90-93. *c/o 75 Geraldine Road, Malvern, Worcs WR14 3NX*

HUGHES, Philip. b 47. St Jo Coll Nottm 79. **d** 81 **p** 82. C Dolgellau w Llanfachreth and Brithdir etc *Ban* 81-83; Youth Chapl 82-83; R Llaneugrad w Llanallgo and Penrhosllugwy etc 83-95; R Llanberis w Llanrug from 95. *The Rectory, Llanberis, Caernarfon, Gwynedd LL55 4TF* Llanberis (01286) 870285

HUGHES, Philip Geoffrey John. b 60. Nottm Univ BCombStuds82 Birm Univ DipTh88. Aston Tr Scheme 84 Qu Coll Birm 86. **d** 89 **p** 90. C Sedgley All SS *Lich* 89-93; C Sedgley All SS *Worc* 93-94; V Boscoppa *Truro* from 94. *St Luke's House, 5 Penhaligon Way, St Austell, Cornwall PL25 3AR* St Austell (01726) 69857

HUGHES, Philip Stephen. b 34. Dur Univ BA59. Coll of Resurr Mirfield 59. **d** 62 **p** 63. C Horfield St Greg *Bris* 62-66; C Bedminster St Mich 66-69; P-in-c Chippenham St Pet 69-71; V 71-83; TR Bedminster 83-91; V Ashton Keynes, Leigh and Minety from 91. *The Vicarage, 23 Richmond Court, Ashton Keynes, Swindon SN6 6PP* Cirencester (01285) 861546

HUGHES, Richard Clifford. b 24. Pemb Coll Cam BA57 MA59. Ely Th Coll 48. **d** 50 **p** 51. C Wandsworth St Anne *S'wark* 50-53; S Rhodesia 53-65; S Africa from 65; Adn Pinetown 75-80; Australia from 86. *90 27 Toogoods Rise, Box Hill North, Victoria, Australia 3129* Melbourne (3) 9898 5335

HUGHES, Richard Jeffrey. b 47. Trin Coll Carmarthen CertEd68. St Mich Coll Llan 74. **d** 76 **p** 77. C Llanbeblig w Caernarfon and Betws Garmon etc *Ban* 76-78; Dioc Youth Chapl 78-82; TV Holyhead w Rhoscolyn w Llanfair-yn-Neubwll 78-83; R Llanfachraeth 83-92; R Llangefni w Tregaean and Llangristiolus etc from 92. *The Rectory, Llangefni, Anglesey, Gwynedd LL77 7EA* Llangefni (01248) 723104

HUGHES, Richard Millree. b 33. Univ of Wales BA56 MA79. St Mich Coll Llan 56. **d** 58 **p** 59. C Mold *St As* 58-61; VC St As Cathl 61-64; V Towyn 64-67; Asst Master Marlborough Sch Woodstock 77-79; R Whitchurch St Mary *Ox* from 79. *The Rectory, Whitchurch, Reading RG8 7DF* Pangbourne (01734) 843219

HUGHES, Robert Elistan-Glodrydd. b 32. Trin Coll Ox BA54 MA58 Birm Univ MLitt85. Westcott Ho Cam 55. **d** 57 **p** 58. C Stoke *Cov* 57-61; Ind Chapl *S'wark* 61-64; Birm Univ Birm

64-87; Chapl 64-69; Lodgings Warden and Student Welfare Adv 69-87; Dir Housing Study Overseas Students Trust 88-91; Perm to Offic *Ban* 88-94; V Harlech and Llanfair-juxta-Harlech etc from 94. *Clogwyn Melyn, Talsarnau, Gwynedd LL47 6TP* Harlech (01766) 780257

HUGHES, Dr Robert Guy. b 64. York Univ BSc86 Reading Univ PhD89. Ripon Coll Cuddesdon BA92. **d** 93 **p** 94. C Sandhurst *Ox* from 93. *27 Hopemen Close, College Town, Camberley, Surrey GU15 4XH* Bracknell (01344) 773296

HUGHES, Rodney Thomas. b 39. Dur Univ BA60 St Cath Coll Ox DipTh61. Wycliffe Hall Ox 60. **d** 62 **p** 63. C Edin St Thos *Edin* 62-65; C Harlow New Town w Lt Parndon *Chelmsf* 65-67; R Haworth *Bradf* 67-74; R W Knighton w Broadmayne *Sarum* 74-77; R Broadmayne, W Knighton, Owermoigne etc 77-82; V Crosthwaite Keswick *Carl* from 82. *Crosthwaite Vicarage, Vicarage Hill, Keswick, Cumbria CA12 5QB* Keswick (017687) 72509

HUGHES, Mrs Sheila. b 52. N Ord Course 92. **d** 95. NSM Birkenhead Priory *Ches* from 95. *33 Farndon Way, Birkenhead, Merseyside L43 2NW* 0151-653 9434

HUGHES, Steven Philip. b 52. St Jo Coll Dur BA. Ridley Hall Cam. **d** 82 **p** 83. C Chilvers Coton w Astley *Cov* 82-86; TV Kings Norton *Birm* 86-91. *Cisnadioara nr 38, C-P 2438, Jud Sibiu, Romania, or PO Box 2368, Kings Norton, Birmingham B38 8RZ* Sibiu (69) 561126 or 415181 Fax as telephone

HUGHES, Ms Valerie Elizabeth (Val). b 53. Birm Univ BA75 CertEd76. Wycliffe Hall Ox DipTh86. **d** 87 **p** 94. C Halewood *Ches* 87-90; Par Dn Garston *Liv* 90-93; TD Gateacre 93-94; TV from 94; Asst Chapl Liv Univ 93. *St Mark's Vicarage, Cranwell Road, Liverpool L25 1NX* 0151-487 9634

HUGHES, William Roger. b 47. Trin Coll Carmarthen. **d** 91 **p** 92. NSM Llan-non *St D* 91-93; Dio Officer for Soc Resp from 93; V Llangathen w Llanfihangel Cilfargen etc from 93. *The Vicarage, Llangathen, Carmarthen, Dyfed SA32 8QD* Dryslwyn (01558) 668455

HUGHES, William Albert. b 48. OSB. S Dios Minl Tr Scheme 90. **d** 92 **p** 93. Alton Abbey from 92; Perm to Offic *Win* from 92. *The Abbey of Our Lady and St John, Beech, Alton, Hants GU34 4AP* Alton (01420) 562145 or 563575

HUGHMAN, Dr June Alison. b 58. Kingston Poly BSc81 Southn Univ PhD84. Trin Coll Bris DipHE88. **d** 89 **p** 94. Par Dn Penge St Jo *Roch* 89-93; C Woking Ch Ch *Guildf* from 93. *4 Orchard Drive, Woking, Surrey GU21 4BN* Woking (01483) 771551

HUGO, Canon Keith Alan. b 41. Nottm Univ BA62. Chich Th Coll 62. **d** 64 **p** 65. C Pontefract St Giles *Wakef* 64-68; C Chesterfield All SS *Derby* 68-71; V Allenton and Shelton Lock 71-77; Dioc Communications Officer *Sarum* 77-89; V Worton 77-84; V Potterne 77-84; Can and Preb Sarum Cathl from 84; V Potterne w Worton and Marston 84-89; R Wyke Regis from 89; RD Weymouth from 94. *The Rectory, 1 Portland Road, Weymouth, Dorset DT4 9ES* Weymouth (01305) 784649

HUITSON, Christopher Philip. b 45. Keble Coll Ox BA66 MA70. Cuddesdon Coll 67. **d** 69 **p** 70. C Croydon St Sav *Cant* 69-71; Soc Service Unit St Martin-in-the-Fields Lon 71-73; C St Alb St Pet *St Alb* 73-77; V Cople 77-78; P-in-c Willington 77-78; V Cople w Willington 78-89; V Leavesden All SS from 89. *All Saints' Vicarage, Horseshoe Lane, Garston, Watford WD2 7HJ* Garston (01923) 672375

HULBERT, Charles Donald. b 09. Linc Th Coll 37. **d** 38 **p** 39. R Plaxtol *Roch* 62-74; Perm to Offic *Nor* from 74; rtd 74. *31 Holt Road, Weybourne, Holt, Norfolk NR25 7SU* Weybourne (0126370) 384

HULBERT, Hugh Forfar. b 22. Bris Univ BA49. Tyndale Hall Bris 46. **d** 50 **p** 51. V Portsea St Luke *Portsm* 63-75; V Worthing H Trin *Chich* 75-81; C-in-c Hove H Trin CD 81-85; C Hailsham 86-87; rtd 87; Perm to Offic *Chich* from 87. *43 Milland Road, Hailsham, E Sussex BN27 1TQ* Hailsham (01323) 842215

HULBERT, Canon John Anthony Lovett. b 40. Trin Coll Cam BA63 MA67. Wells Th Coll 64. **d** 66 **p** 67. C Fareham H Trin *Portsm* 66-70; R Wickham 70-79; RD Bishops Waltham 74-79; V Bedf St Andr *St Alb* 79-92; RD Bedf 87-92; Hon Can St Alb from 91; V Leighton Buzzard w Eggington, Hockliffe etc from 92. *The Vicarage, Pulford Road, Leighton Buzzard, Beds LU7 7AB* Leighton Buzzard (01525) 373217

HULBERT, Canon Martin Francis Harrington. b 37. Dur Univ BSc58 MA62. Ripon Hall Ox 58. **d** 62 **p** 63. C Buxton *Derby* 60-63; C Eglingham *Newc* 63-67; C-in-c Loundsley Green Ascension CD *Derby* 67-71; P-in-c Frecheville 71-73; R Frecheville and Hackenthorpe *Sheff* 73-77; P-in-c Hathersage *Derby* 77-83; V 83-90; RD Bakewell and Eyam 81-90; Hon Can Derby Cathl from 89; R Brailsford w Shirley and Osmaston w Edlaston 90-93; V Tideswell from 93. *The Vicarage, Pursglove Drive, Tideswell, Buxton, Derbyshire SK17 8PA* Tideswell (01298) 871317 Fax 872621

HULETT, Mrs Janet Elizabeth Mary. b 48. **d** 91. NSM Broadwater St Mary *Chich* 91-95. *Address temp unknown*

HULETT, Peter. b 31. CEng MIMechE62 Leeds Univ CertEd74. Wycliffe Hall Ox 75. **d** 77 **p** 78. C Eastwood *S'well* 77-80; C Granby w Elton 80-83; V Gilling and Kirkby Ravensworth *Ripon* 83-90; P-in-c Bishop Monkton and Burton Leonard from 90. *The Vicarage, Knaresborough Road, Bishop Monkton, Harrogate, N Yorkshire HG3 3QQ* Ripon (01765) 677372

HULL, David John. b 44. Linc Th Coll 88. **d** 90 **p** 91. C Mansf Woodhouse *S'well* 90-93; P-in-c Mansf St Lawr from 93. *St Lawrence's Vicarage, 3 Shaw Street, Mansfield, Notts NG18 2NP* Mansfield (01623) 23698

HULL, John Hammond. b 36. Sarum Th Coll 60. **d** 61 **p** 62. C Gt Clacton *Chelmsf* 61-66; Lic to Offic 66-75; Area Chapl (E Anglia) Toc H 66-70; (Midl Region) 70-75; Lic to Offic *Ox* from 75; Chapl Toc H HQ 75-82. *66 Grenville Avenue, Wendover, Aylesbury, Bucks HP22 6AL* Wendover (01296) 624487

HULL, Theodore James Nesbitt (Theo). b 57. Southn Univ BTh84. Sarum & Wells Th Coll 80. **d** 82 **p** 83. C Plumstead St Mark and St Marg *S'wark* 82-84; C Surbiton St Andr and St Mark 84-87; V Balham St Mary and St Jo 87-93; Chapl Lt Plumstead Hosp from 94. *Chapel Cottage, Rectory Road, Wood Norton, Dereham, Norfolk NR20 5BA* Dereham (01362) 84837

HULL, Timothy David. b 60. Lon Bible Coll 87. St Jo Coll Nottm BTh90. **d** 90 **p** 91. C Leyton St Mary w St Edw *Chelmsf* 90-95; Chapl Havering Coll of F & HE from 94; C Harold Hill St Geo *Chelmsf* from 95. *18 Petersfield Avenue, Romford RM3 9PA* Romford (01708) 374388

HULL, Suffragan Bishop of. *See* JONES, Rt Rev James Stuart

HULLAH, Peter Fearnley. b 49. FRSA93 K Coll Lon BD71 AKC71. Cuddesdon Coll 73. **d** 74 **p** 75. Asst Chapl St Edw Sch Ox 74-77; C Summertown *Ox* 74-76; C Wolvercote w Summertown 76-77; Chapl Sevenoaks Sch Kent 77-82; Hon C Sevenoaks St Nic *Roch* 77-82; Ho Master Internat Cen Sevenoaks Sch 82-87; Hon C Kippington 82-87; Sen Chapl K Sch Cant 87-92; Hon Min Can Cant Cathl *Cant* 87-92; Hd Master Chetham's Sch of Music from 92; Lic Preacher *Man* from 93; Perm to Offic *Carl* from 87. *Chetham's School of Music, Long Millgate, Manchester M3 1SB* 0161-834 9644 Fax 839 3609

HULLETT, Frederick Graham. b 32. St Jo Coll York CertEd53 Leeds Univ BA58. Coll of Resurr Mirfield 58. **d** 60 **p** 61. P-in-c Haggerston St Aug w St Steph *Lon* 69-73; Lic to Offic 73-84; Perm to Offic *Linc* from 84; rtd 91. *2 Ryland Road, Welton, Lincoln LN2 3LU* Welton (01673) 860839

HULME, Alan John. b 60. Birm Univ BSc81. Wycliffe Hall Ox BA90. **d** 91 **p** 92. C Chilwell *S'well* from 91. *10 College Road, Beeston, Nottingham NG9 4AS* Nottingham (0115) 925 6501

HULME, Ms Juliette Mary. b 57. Whitelands Coll Lon BEd81. Cranmer Hall Dur CTMin94. **d** 94. C Crayford *Roch* from 94. *1A Iron Mill Place, Crayford, Dartford DA1 4RT* Crayford (01322) 558789

HULME, Norman. b 31. Kelham Th Coll 50. **d** 54 **p** 55. C Blackb St Pet *Blackb* 54-57; C Blakenall Heath *Lich* 57-59; V Gannow *Blackb* 59-64; V Anwick *Linc* 64-74; V S Kyme 64-74; V Moulton 74-83; V Earl Shilton w Elmesthorpe *Leic* 83-88; Chapl Harperbury Hosp Radlett from 88. *Harperbury Hospital, Harper Lane, Shenley, Radlett, Herts WD7 9HQ* Radlett (01923) 854861

HULME, Suffragan Bishop of. *See* SCOTT, Rt Rev Colin John Fraser

HULSE, William John (Bill). b 42. Dur Univ BA65. Linc Th Coll 65. **d** 67 **p** 68. C S Westoe *Dur* 67-70; Lic to Offic *Newc* 70-72; C Far Headingley St Chad *Ripon* 72-76; R Swillington 76-88; V Shadwell 88-95; V Oulton w Woodlesford from 95. *The Vicarage, 46 Holmsley Lane, Woodlesford, Leeds LS26 8RY* Leeds (0113) 282 0411

HUMBLE, Joseph Francis. b 24. Univ Coll Ox BA53 MA57. Cuddesdon Coll 53. **d** 55 **p** 56. V Lillington *Cov* 65-76; Chapl Miss to Seamen 76-85; Hong Kong and Singapore 76-80; Argentina 80-85; Hon C Regent's Park St Mark *Lon* 85-88; rtd 87; Perm to Offic *Lon* from 88. *407 Carole House, 80 Regents Park Road, London NW1 8UE* 0171-483 1418

HUME, Miss Clephane Arrol. b 46. Edin Occupational Therapy Tr Cen DipOT68 Jordan Hill Coll Glas CertFE83 Open Univ BA87. Edin Dioc NSM Course 88. **d** 92 **p** 94. NSM Edin St Jo *Edin* from 92. *30 Findhorn Place, Edinburgh EH9 2JP* 0131-667 2996 Fax 317 3256

HUME, Ernest. b 45. Linc Th Coll 77. **d** 79 **p** 80. C Ilkeston St Mary *Derby* 79-81; C Sheff Manor *Sheff* 81-82; TV 82-88; V Norton Woodseats St Chad from 88. *The Vicarage, 9 Linden Avenue, Sheffield S8 0GA* Sheffield (0114) 274 5086

HUME, Leslie Paul. b 09. Kelham Th Coll 27. **d** 32 **p** 33. SSM from 32; C Liv St Nic *Liv* 32-37; Chapl Kelham Th Coll 37-41; C Nottm St Geo w St Jo *S'well* 41-43; S Africa 43-49 and 51-52 and 66-76; Basutoland 50-51 and 62-66; Dir SSM 52-62; Lic to Offic *S'well* 52-62; Perm to Offic *Ox* 76-83. *SSM Priory,*

Willen, Milton Keynes MK15 9AA Milton Keynes (01908) 663749

HUME, Martin. b 54. Grimsby Coll of Tech HND75. Coll of Resurr Mirfield 89. **d** 91 **p** 92. C Brentwood St Thos *Chelmsf* 91-94; P-in-c Corringham from 94. *The Rectory, Church Road, Corringham, Stanford-le-Hope, Essex SS17 9AP* Stanford-le-Hope (01375) 673074

HUMMERSTONE, Jeremy David. Mert Coll Ox BA65 MA70. Wells Th Coll 70. **d** 72 **p** 73. C Helmsley *York* 72-75; C Pockley cum E Moors 72-75; P-in-c Manningford Bruce w Manningford Abbots *Sarum* 75; TV Swanborough 75-80; P-in-c Frithelstock *Ex* 80-81; P-in-c Gt Torrington 80-81; P-in-c Lt Torrington 80-81; V Gt and Lt Torrington and Frithelstock from 81. *The Vicarage, Calf Street, Torrington, Devon EX38 8EA* Torrington (01805) 622166

HUMPHREY, Mrs Betty. b 37. St Mich Ho Ox 59. **d** 90 **p** 94. C Hardwicke, Quedgeley and Elmore w Longney *Glouc* 90-93; D-in-c Swindon w Uckington and Elmstone Hardwicke 93-94; P-in-c from 94. *The Rectory, Swindon, Cheltenham, Glos GL51 9RD* Cheltenham (01242) 329069

HUMPHREY, David Lane. b 57. Maine Univ BA79. St Jo Coll Nottm 84. **d** 88 **p** 89. C Springfield All SS *Chelmsf* 88-91; C Thundersley from 91. *14 Grangeway, Benfleet, Essex SS7 3RP* Rayleigh (01268) 773462

HUMPHREY, Derek Hollis. b 37. Chich Th Coll 69. **d** 72 **p** 73. C Havant *Portsm* 72-75; C Southsea H Spirit 75-78; V Finsbury Park St Thos *Lon* 78-88; V S Patcham *Chich* from 88. *10 Church Close, Brighton BN1 8HS* Brighton (01273) 502385

HUMPHREY, Canon George William. b 38. Lon Bible Coll BD61 Lon Univ CertEd74 Man Univ DipEdG75. Oak Hill Th Coll 61. **d** 62 **p** 63. C Heigham H Trin *Nor* 62-64; P-in-c Buckenham w Hassingham and Strumpshaw 64-67; Chapl St Andr Hosp Norwich 64-67; Asst Master Mexborough Gr Sch 67-69; Hd RE Cheadle Gr Sch 69-76; Hon C Cheadle Hulme St Andr *Ches* 70-76; P-in-c Kellington w Whitley *Wakef* 76-80; Teacher Thurnscoe Comp Sch 76-80; RE Insp Glos Co Coun and Dio *Glouc* 80-93; Dioc RE Adv from 93; Hon Can Glouc Cathl from 95. *The Rectory, Swindon, Cheltenham, Glos GL51 9RD* Cheltenham (01242) 239069

HUMPHREY, Heather Mary. b 46. CertEd68. W Midl Minl Tr Course 87. **d** 90 **p** 94. NSM Overbury w Teddington, Alstone etc *Worc* from 90. *2/3 Saunders Cottages, Kinsham, Tewkesbury, Glos GL20 8HP* Bredon (01684) 72816

HUMPHREY, Timothy Martin. b 62. Ex Univ BA83. St Jo Coll Nottm DipTh87. **d** 89 **p** 90. C Wallington H Trin *S'wark* from 89. *52 Grosvenor Avenue, Carshalton, Surrey SM5 3EW* 0181-647 4310

HUMPHREYS, Mrs Anne-Marie (Anna). b 44. K Coll Lon BD92 AKC92 SRN67. N Ord Course 92. **d** 95. NSM Man Gd Shep *Man* from 95. *16 Clothorn Road, Manchester M20 6BQ* 0161-434 2164

HUMPHREYS, Brian Leonard. d 87 **p** 88. NSM Maughold S & M 87-92; NSM S Ramsey 92-94; Perm to Offic from 94. *Lewaigue Lodge, Port Lewaigue, Maughold, Isle of Man IM7 1AG* Ramsey (01624) 813694

HUMPHREYS, George Bernard. b 10. AKC36. **d** 36 **p** 37. R Fobbing *Chelmsf* 65-78; rtd 78; Perm to Offic *Ex* from 78. *Prestercot, Butts Lane, Christow, Exeter EX6 7NN* Christow (01647) 52595

HUMPHREYS, Dr James Graham. b 36. Liv Univ BEng57 PhD60. Trin Coll Bris 61. **d** 63 **p** 64. V Houghton *Carl* 68-79; V Bramcote *S'well* 79-93; RD Beeston 85-90; rtd 93. *43 Ribblesdale Road, Nottingham NG5 3GY* Nottingham (0115) 926 3471

HUMPHREYS, Canon John Elwyn Price. b 15. OBE77. Univ of Wales BA37. St Mich Coll Llan 38. **d** 39 **p** 41. Chapl Estoril *Eur* 57-80; Can Gib Cathl 67-80; rtd 80. *Casa Contente, Monte Estoril, Estoril, Portugal 2765* Lisbon (1) 468-3238

HUMPHREYS, John Louis. b 51. Jes Coll Cam BA72 MA76 Nottm Univ BA75. St Jo Coll Nottm 73. **d** 76 **p** 77. C W Bromwich Gd Shep w St Jo *Lich* 76-79; C Woodford Wells *Chelmsf* 79-83; V Werrington *Lich* from 83; Chapl HM Young Offender Inst Werrington Ho from 83. *The Vicarage, 360 Ash Bank Road, Werrington, Stoke-on-Trent ST9 0JS* Ash Bank (01782) 302441 Fax 302504

HUMPHREYS, Canon Kenneth Glyn (Ken). b 28. Bps' Coll Cheshunt 64. **d** 66 **p** 67. C Whitley Ch Ch *Ox* 67-70; V Compton 70-74; V Compton w E Ilsley 74-75; R E Ilsley 74; C Wokingham All SS 75-77; Chapl Lucas Hosp Wokingham 77-81; V Caversham *Ox* 81-94; RD Sonning 86-88; Hon Can Ch Ch 91-94; rtd 95. *17 Snowberry Close, Wokingham, Berks RG11 4AQ* Eversley (01734) 772096

HUMPHREYS, Mrs Lydia Ann. b 60. CCSk90. Sarum & Wells Th Coll DCM93. **d** 93 **p** 94. C Gaywood St Faith *Nor* 93-95; C Gaywood St Faith, Kings Lynn from 95. *5 Gayton Road, King's Lynn, Norfolk PE30 4EA* King's Lynn (01553) 768667

HUMPHREYS, Canon Neil Edgar. b 20. St Pet Hall Ox BA48 MA52. Linc Th Coll 48. **d** 50 **p** 51. Asst Chapl Liv Univ *Liv*

69-78; Dioc Planning Officer 72-78; Bp's Planning Adv 78-79; Hon Can Liv Cathl 78-89; TV W Derby St Mary 79-89; rtd 89. *109 Thingwall Road, Liverpool L15 7JX* 0151-722 4114

HUMPHREYS, Canon Philip Noel. b 34. Bps' Coll Cheshunt 62. **d** 64 **p** 65. C Plymouth St Andr *Ex* 64-68; Chapl Lee Abbey 68-73; V Porchester *S'well* 73-82; RD Bingham W 82-87; P-in-c W Leake w Kingston-on-Soar etc 82-87; R W Bridgford from 82; Hon Can S'well Minster from 93. *The Rectory, Church Drive, West Bridgford, Nottingham NG2 6AX* Nottingham (0115) 981 1112

HUMPHREYS, Roger John. b 45. CertEd66 Open Univ BA76. Wycliffe Hall Ox 81. **d** 83 **p** 84. Chapl Dragon Sch Ox 83-87; C Ox St Andr *Ox* 83-87; V Carterton 87-94; R Bladon w Woodstock from 94. *The Rectory, Woodstock, Oxford OX20 1UQ* Woodstock (0993) 811415

HUMPHREYS, Stephen Robert Beresford. b 52. K Coll Lon 74. **d** 76 **p** 77. C Northwood Hills St Edm *Lon* 76-79; C Manningham St Mary and Bradf St Mich *Bradf* 79-81; C Manningham St Paul and St Jude 82; Chapl Bradf R Infirmary 82-86; C Leeds St Pet *Ripon* 87-90; Perm to Offic *B & W* from 94. *Stowey Farm, Timberscombe, Minehead, Somerset TA24 7BW* Timberscombe (01643) 841265

HUMPHREYS, William Alfred. b 18. Lich Th Coll 54. **d** 56 **p** 57. V Prees *Lich* 65-83; P-in-c Fauls 66-70; V 70-83; RD Wem and Whitchurch 80-83; rtd 83; Perm to Offic *Heref* from 83. *Bryncroft, 4 Seabridge Meadow, Bucknell, Shropshire S77 0AP* Bucknell (015474) 597

HUMPHREYS, William Haydn. b 09. AKC36. St D Coll Lamp 29. **d** 36 **p** 37. V Dewsbury St Mark *Wakef* 48-78; Chapl Dewsbury Gen Hosp 50-78; rtd 78. *Flat 24, Marion Court, Lisvane Road, Cardiff CF4 5RZ* Cardiff (01222) 757158

HUMPHRIES, Anthony Roy (Tony). b 49. Lon Univ BSc73. Wycliffe Hall Ox DipMin94. **d** 94 **p** 95. C Worksop St Jo *S'well* from 94. *5 Windermere Close, Worksop, Notts S81 7QE* Worksop (01909) 472397

HUMPHRIES, Benjamin Paul. b 56. FRGS Man Univ BA Birm Univ DipTh. Qu Coll Birm 82. **d** 85 **p** 86. C Hall Green Ascension *Birm* 85-88; P-in-c Belmont *Man* from 88. *St Peter's Vicarage, High Street, Belmont, Bolton BL7 8AF* Belmont Village (01204) 811221

HUMPHRIES, Miss Catherine Elizabeth. b 53. Trin Coll Bris BA87. **d** 87 **p** 94. C Bath Twerton-on-Avon *B & W* 87-90; Personnel Manager and Tr Officer TEAR Fund 90-91; NSM Norbiton *S'wark* from 91. *14 Virginia Close, New Malden, Surrey TW11 8QE* 0181-949 3000

HUMPHRIES, Christopher William. b 52. St Jo Coll Cam BA73 MA77 CertEd DipTh. St Jo Coll Nottm 76. **d** 79 **p** 80. C Eccleshill *Bradf* 79-82; Chapl Scargill Ho 82-86; TV Guiseley w Esholt *Bradf* 86-91; V Filey *York* from 91. *The Vicarage, 5 Belle Vue Crescent, Filey, N Yorkshire YO14 9AD* Scarborough (01723) 512745

HUMPHRIES, David Graham. b 48. Univ of Wales (Cardiff) DipTh70. St Mich Coll Llan 67. **d** 71 **p** 72. C Neath w Llantwit *Llan* 71-72; C Bishop's Cleeve *Glouc* 81-83; C Cirencester 83-87; V Glouc St Steph from 87. *St Stephen's Vicarage, 84 Frampton Road, Gloucester GL1 5QB* Gloucester (01452) 524694

HUMPHRIES, David John. b 51. BSc CertEd BD. Edin Th Coll. **d** 84 **p** 85. C Styvechale *Cov* 84-88; V Greetland and W Vale *Wakef* from 88. *The Vicarage, 2 Goldfields Way, Greetland, Halifax, W Yorkshire HX4 8LA* Halifax (01422) 372802

HUMPHRIES, Donald. b 43. Bris Univ BA66. Clifton Th Coll 66. **d** 68 **p** 69. C Selly Hill St Steph *Birm* 68-74; Chapl Warw Univ *Cov* 74-79; V Bedf Ch Ch *St Alb* 79-85; V Cam H Trin w St Andr Gt *Ely* 85-92; V Cam H Trin 92-94; rtd 94. *56 The Rowans, Milton, Cambridge CB4 6YU*

HUMPHRIES, Miss Dorothy Maud. b 22. Bedf Coll Lon BA44 Lon Univ DipEd45 Cam Univ DipTh50. Gilmore Course 85. **dss** 79 **d** 87 **p** 94. NSM Kidderminster Deanery from 79. *26 Linden Avenue, Kidderminster, Worcs DY10 3AB* Kidderminster (01562) 824459

HUMPHRIES, Frank Charles. b 40. St Chad's Coll Dur BA61 DipTh63. **d** 63 **p** 64. C Tottenham All Hallows *Lon* 63-66; C S Harrow St Paul 66-71; V Hillingdon All SS 71-80; V Preston Ascension from 80; Dir of Ords from 86. *The Vicarage, 319 Preston Road, Harrow, Middx HA3 0QQ* 0181-904 4062

HUMPHRIES, Grahame Leslie. b 44. Lon Coll of Div ALCD70 LTh. **d** 71 **p** 72. C Wandsworth St Mich *S'wark* 71-74; C Slough *Ox* 74-77; P-in-c Arley *Cov* 77-82; R 82-84; Norfolk Churches' Radio Officer *Nor* from 84; P-in-c Bawdeswell w Foxley from 84. *The Rectory, Foxley, Dereham, Norfolk NR20 4QJ* Bawdeswell (01362) 688397

HUMPHRIES, Harold Joseph. b 14. MIEE52. S'wark Ord Course 70. **d** 70 **p** 71. C Mert St Mary *S'wark* 70-71; C Glouc All SS *Glouc* 71-75; Hon C 78-82; C Glouc St Jas 75-77; Hon Min Can Glouc Cathl from 77. *Monument House, St Mary's Street, Gloucester GL1 2QR* Gloucester (01452) 520449

HUMPHRIES, John. b 49. Univ of Wales (Cardiff) DipTh76. St Mich Coll Llan 73. **d** 76 **p** 77. C Pontnewynydd *Mon* 76-78; C Ebbw Vale 78-81; V Pet Ch Carpenter *Pet* 81-86; P-in-c Kings Cliffe 86-87; R King's Cliffe w Apethorpe 87-93; R King's Cliffe from 93. *The Rectory, 3 Hall Yard, King's Cliffe, Peterborough PE8 6XQ* Kings Cliffe (01780) 470314

HUMPHRIES, Miss Marion Betty. b 29. K Coll Lon DipTh50 Open Univ BA84. Selly Oak Coll 51. **dss** 80 **d** 87 **p** 94. Newmarket St Mary w Exning St Agnes *St E* 80-82; Acomb St Steph *York* 83-86; Scarborough St Martin 86-87; Par Dn 87-93; C Cayton w Eastfield 94; rtd 94; Perm to Offic *Nor* from 95. *27 Wells Road, Walsingham, Norfolk NR22 6DL* Walsingham (01328) 820489

HUMPHRIES, William David. b 57. QUB BEd DipTh. **d** 87. C Ballyholme *D & D* 86-90; Min Can Belf Cathl from 89; VC Belf Cathl 90-93; C Belf St Anne *Conn* 90-93; I Stormont *D & D* from 93. *St Molua's Rectory, 64 Wandsworth Road, Belfast BT4 3LU* Belfast (01232) 657667

HUMPHRIS, Richard. b 44. N Glos Tech Coll OND69. Sarum & Wells Th Coll 69. **d** 72 **p** 73. C Cheltenham St Luke and St Jo *Glouc* 72-77; C Lydney w Aylburton 77-82; Chapl RAF 82-85; TV Kippax w Allerton Bywater *Ripon* 85-92. *Address temp unknown*

HUMPHRISS, Canon Reginald George (Reg). b 36. Kelham Th Coll 56. **d** 61 **p** 62. C Londonderry *Birm* 61-63; Asst Dir RE *Cant* 63-66; Dioc Youth Chapl 63-66; V Preston next Faversham 66-72; P-in-c Goodnestone St Bart and Graveney 71-72; V Spring Park 72-76; R Cant St Martin and St Paul 76-90; RD Cant 82-88; Hon Can Cant Cathl from 85; R Saltwood from 90; RD Elham from 93. *The Rectory, Saltwood, Hythe, Kent CT21 4QA* Hythe (01303) 266932

HUMPHRY, Toby Peter. b 66. Man Univ BA88. Ripon Coll Cuddesdon BA90 Qu Coll Birm 92. **d** 93 **p** 94. C Westhoughton *Man* from 93. *1 Furze Avenue, Westhoughton, Bolton BL5 2NW* Westhoughton (01942) 818030

HUMPHRYES, Garry James. b 62. Coll of Resurr Mirfield 92. **d** 95. C Lt Marsden *Blackb* from 95. *3 Rickards Road, Nelson, Lancs BB9 0RN* Nelson (01282) 614451

HUMPLEBY, Peter. b 40. Open Univ BA76 Hull Univ DipTh82. Linc Th Coll 75. **d** 77 **p** 78. C Todmorden *Wakef* 77-80; V Bruntcliffe 80-88; R Aldingham and Dendron and Rampside *Carl* 88-92; V Dodworth *Wakef* from 92. *The Vicarage, Green Road, Dodworth, Barnsley, S Yorkshire S75 3TY* Barnsley (01226) 203838

HUNDLEBY, Alan. b 41. Local NSM Course 86. **d** 86 **p** 87. NSM Fotherby *Linc* from 86. *35 Cheapside, Waltham, Grimsby, S Humberside DN37 0HE* Grimsby (01472) 827159

HUNG, Frank Yu-Chi. b 45. Birm Univ BSc68 BA75 Liv Univ MSc71 Ox Univ DipTh77. Wycliffe Hall Ox 76. **d** 78 **p** 79. C Walton H Trin *Ox* 78-82; C Spring Grove St Mary *Lon* 82-85; TV Wexcombe *Sarum* 85-92; V Hatcham St Jas *S'wark* from 92. *St James's Vicarage, St James's, London SE14 6AD* 0181-692 7774

HUNGERFORD, Robin Nicholas. b 47. CertEd74. Trin Coll Bris DipHE88. **d** 88 **p** 89. C Swindon Dorcan *Bris* 88-92; TV Melbury *Sarum* from 92. *The Vicarage, Corscombe, Dorchester, Dorset DT2 0NU* Corscombe (01935) 891549

HUNNISETT, John Bernard. b 47. AKC73. **d** 73 **p** 74. C Charlton Kings St Mary *Glouc* 73-77; C Portsea St Mary *Portsm* 77-80; V Badgeworth w Shurdington *Glouc* 80-87; R Dursley from 87. *The Rectory, The Broadwell, Dursley, Glos GL11 4JE* Dursley (01453) 542053

HUNNYBUN, Martin Wilfrid. b 44. Oak Hill Th Coll 67. **d** 70 **p** 71. C Ware Ch Ch *St Alb* 70-74; C Washfield, Stoodleigh, Withleigh etc *Ex* 74-75; TV Washfield, Stoodleigh, Withleigh etc 75-80; R Braunston *Pet* 80-85; Australia from 85. *66 Princess Street, Berry, NSW, Australia 2535* Berry (44) 641058

HUNT, Alan. b 31. St Mich Coll Llan 65. **d** 67 **p** 68. C Standish *Blackb* 67-72; V Clitheroe St Paul Low Moor 72-77; Lic to Offic from 77. *68 Coniston Drive, Walton-le-Dale, Preston PR5 4RQ* Preston (01772) 39554

HUNT, Ashley Stephen. b 50. St Jo Coll Nottm 81. **d** 83 **p** 84. C Southchurch H Trin *Chelmsf* 83-86; TV Droitwich *Worc* 86-87; USA 88-91; TV Melton Gt Framland *Leic* 92-93; TV Melton Mowbray from 93. *1 Palmerston Road, Melton Mowbray, Leics LE13 0SS* Melton Mowbray (01664) 64229

HUNT, Bruce Allan. b 32. Nottm Univ BA54 DipEd55 Leic Univ CCouns90. ALCD59. **d** 61 **p** 62. V Lepton *Wakef* 69-81; V Worksop St Jo *S'well* 81-91; rtd 91; Perm to Offic *S'well* from 91. *14 Dunstan Crescent, Worksop, Notts S80 1AF* Worksop (01909) 478214

HUNT, Charles Evans. b 13. Dur Univ LTh44. ALCD37. **d** 37 **p** 38. V Masbrough St Paul *Sheff* 49-73; P-in-c Masbrough St Jo 56-73; V Wentworth 73-79; rtd 79; Lic to Offic *Ely* from 79. *1 Vicarage Lane, Whittlesford, Cambridge CB2 4NA* Cambridge (01223) 833402

HUNT, Mrs Christina. b 24. Qu Mary Coll Lon BSc45. S Dios Minl Tr Scheme 78. **dss** 81 **d** 87 **p** 94. Alderbury and W Grimstead *Sarum* 81-87; Hon Par Dn 87-91; Hon Par Dn Alderbury Team 91-94; rtd 94; Perm to Offic *Sarum* from 94. *The Heather, Southampton Road, Alderbury, Salisbury SP5 3AF* Salisbury (01722) 710601

HUNT, Christopher Paul Colin. b 38. Ch Coll Cam BA62 MA62. Clifton Th Coll 63. **d** 65 **p** 66. C Widnes St Paul *Liv* 65-68; Singapore 68-70; Malaysia 70-71; Hon C Foord St Jo *Cant* 72-73; Iran 74-80; Overseas Service Adv CMS 81-91; Lic to Offic *S'wark* 81-91; P-in-c Claverdon w Preston Bagot *Cov* from 91. *The Vicarage, Church Road, Claverdon, Warks CV35 8PD* Claverdon (01926) 842256

HUNT, David John. b 35. Kelham Th Coll 60. **d** 65 **p** 66. C Bethnal Green St Jo w St Simon *Lon* 65-69; C Mill Hill St Mich 69-73; R Staple Fitzpaine, Orchard Portman, Thurlbear etc *B & W* 73-79; P-in-c E Coker w Sutton Bingham 79-88; V E Coker w Sutton Bingham and Closworth from 88; RD Merston 85-94. *The Vicarage, East Coker, Yeovil, Somerset BA22 9JG* West Coker (01935) 862125

HUNT, Derek Henry. b 38. ALCD61. **d** 62 **p** 63. C Radipole *Sarum* 66-70; P-in-c Shalbourne w Ham 70-72; V Burbage 72-73; V Burbage and Savernake Ch Ch 73-78; P-in-c Hulcote w Salford *St Alb* 78-88; R Cranfield 78-88; R Cranfield and Hulcote w Salford 88-95; rtd 95. *26 Jowitt Avenue, Kempston, Bedford MK42 8NW*

HUNT, Edward Trebble (Ted). b 31. St Mich Coll Llan 56. **d** 58 **p** 59. C Swansea St Thos *S & B* 58-62; C Swansea St Mary and H Trin 62-65; P-in-c Glantawe 65-72; V 72-76; V Swansea Ch Ch from 76; Chapl HM Pris Swansea from 76. *The Vicarage, 226 Oystermouth Road, Swansea SA1 3UH* Swansea (01792) 652606 Fax 642979

HUNT, Ernest Gary. b 36. Univ Coll Dur BA57 DipEd58. Carl Dioc Tr Inst 90. **d** 93 **p** 94. NSM Salesbury *Blackb* 93-95; NSM Blackb St Mich w St Jo and H Trin from 95. *Dunelm, 10 Pleckgate Road, Blackburn BB1 8NN* Blackburn (01254) 52531

HUNT, Ernest William. b 09. St Jo Coll Dur BA31 MA34 Birm Univ BD46 St Cath Soc Ox BLitt51 Ox Univ MLitt90. St Jo Coll Dur DipTh32. **d** 32 **p** 33. Prof St D Coll Lamp 57-69; rtd 75. *16 Peachcroft Road, Abingdon, Oxon OX14 2NA* Abingdon (01235) 521549

HUNT, Giles Butler. b 28. Trin Hall Cam BA51 MA55. Cuddesdon Coll 51. **d** 53 **p** 54. C Pimlico St Pet w Westmr Ch Ch *Lon* 67-72; V Barkway w Reed and Buckland *St Alb* 72-79; V Preston next Faversham, Goodnestone and Graveney *Cant* 79-92; rtd 92; Perm to Offic *Nor* from 92. *The Cottage, The Fairstead, Cley-next-the-Sea, Holt, Norfolk NR25 7RJ* Cley (01263) 740471

HUNT, Canon Ian Carter. b 34. Chich Th Coll 61. **d** 64 **p** 65. C Plymouth St Pet *Ex* 64-67; C Daventry *Pet* 67-70; V Northn St Paul 70-91; Can Pet Cathl from 81; V Wellingborough All Hallows from 91. *The Vicarage, Church Street, Wellingborough, Northants NN8 3PA* Wellingborough (01933) 222002

HUNT, James Allen (Jim). b 49. Linc Th Coll CMinlStuds92. **d** 92 **p** 93. C Huddersfield St Pet and All SS *Wakef* 92-95; V Longwood from 95. *St Mark's Vicarage, 313 Vicarage Road, Huddersfield HD3 4HJ* Huddersfield (01484) 653576

HUNT, Jeremy Mark Nicholas. b 46. FRGS70 Open Univ BA73 Bris Univ DipEd. Ridley Hall Cam 83. **d** 85 **p** 86. C Leckhampton SS Phil and Jas w Cheltenham St Jas *Glouc* 85-87; Asst Chapl Vevey w Chateau d'Oex and Villars *Eur* 87-90; Asst Chapl Chapl Berne w Neuchatel 89-90; Chapl HM Pris Pentonville 94-95; Chapl HM Pris Highpoint from 95. *The Chaplain's Office, HM Prison, Highpoint, Stradishall, Newmarket, Suffolk CB8 9YG* Wickhambrook (01440) 820611 Fax 820203

HUNT, Jessie. b 15. R Holloway Coll Lon BSc37. St Chris Coll Blackheath 44. **dss** 77 **d** 87 **p** 95. Westcliff St Andr *Chelmsf* 77-78; Southend 78-87; Par Dn 87-90; Chapl Asst Southend Gen Hosp from 87; Perm to Offic from 90. *22 Westminster Drive, Westcliff-on-Sea, Essex SS0 9SL* Southend-on-Sea (01702) 343632

HUNT, John Barry. b 46. Lich Th Coll 70 Qu Coll Birm 72. **d** 73 **p** 74. C Auckland St Andr and St Anne *Dur* 73-77; C Consett 77-79; R Lyons 79-89; P-in-c Hebburn St Cuth from 89. *St Cuthbert's Vicarage, Cosserat Place, Hebburn, Tyne & Wear NE31 1RD* 0191-483 2038

HUNT, John Edwin. b 38. ARCO Dur Univ BA60 DipEd. E Midl Min Tr Course 78. **d** 81 **p** 82. NSM Newbold and Dunston *Derby* 81-92; NSM Chesterfield All SS from 92. *4 Ardsley Road, Ashgate, Chesterfield, Derbyshire S40 4DG* Chesterfield (01246) 275141

HUNT, John Stewart. b 37. Nor Ord Course 75. **d** 78 **p** 79. NSM Hunstanton St Edm *Nor* 78-81; NSM Hunstanton St Mary w Ringstead Parva, Holme etc 81-86; NSM Sedgeford w Southmere 84-86; C Lowestoft and Kirkley 86-89; R Blundeston w Flixton and Lound 89-93; P-in-c Kessingland w Gisleham from 93. *The Rectory, 1 Wash Lane, Kessingland, Lowestoft, Suffolk NR33 7QZ* Lowestoft (01502) 740256

HUNT, Dr Judith Mary. b 57. MRCVS80 Bris Univ BVSc80 Lon Univ PhD85 Fitzw Coll Cam BA90. Ridley Hall Cam 88. **d** 91 **p** 94. Par Dn Heswall *Ches* 91-94; C 94-95; P-in-c Tilston and Shocklach from 95. *The Rectory, Inveresk Road, Tilston, Malpas, Cheshire SY14 7ED* Tilston (01829) 250289

HUNT, Kevin. b 59. St Jo Coll Dur BA80 Ox Univ BA84 MA88. St Steph Ho Ox 81. **d** 84 **p** 85. C Mansf St Mark *S'well* 84-85; C Hendon and Sunderland *Dur* 85-88; V Sunderland Springwell w Thorney Close 88-95; V Sunderland St Mary and St Pet from 95. *The Clergy House, Springwell Road, Sunderland SR3 4DY* 0191-528 3754

HUNT, Canon Michael Francis. b 26. Wadh Coll Ox BA49 MA50. St Steph Ho Ox 49. **d** 51 **p** 52. R Dumfries *Glas* 66-73; R Arbroath *Bre* 73-78; R Inverness St Mich *Mor* 78-80; R Inverness St Jo 78-80; Papua New Guinea 80-91; Hon Can St Jo Cathl Port Moresby from 89; rtd 91; P-in-c Tain *Mor* from 91. *St Andrew's Rectory, Manse Street, Tain, Ross-shire IV19 1HE* Tain (01862) 892193

HUNT, Miss Nicola Mary. b 54. SRN77 RSCN77 RHV87. Ripon Coll Cuddesdon DipMin95. **d** 95. C Broughton Astley *Leic* from 95. *1 Aland Gardens, Broughton Astley, Leicester LE9 6NE* Sutton Elms (01455) 286210

HUNT, Paul Edwin. b 47. Ripon Coll Cuddesdon DipMin95. **d** 95. C Cleobury Mortimer w Hopton Wafers etc *Heref* from 95. *The Glebe, New Road Gardens, Cleobury Mortimer, Kidderminster, Worcs DY14 8AW* Cleobury Mortimer (01299) 270559

HUNT, Paul Firth. b 62. Ox Univ MA89 Edin Univ BD89. Edin Th Coll 86. **d** 89 **p** 90. C Leeds Halton St Wilfrid *Ripon* 89-92; C Leeds City from 92. *16 Oatland Green, Leeds LS7 1SN* Leeds (0113) 244 1696

HUNT, Paul Michael. b 57. St Chad's Coll Dur BA79 K Coll Lon PGCE80. Chich Th Coll 91. **d** 92 **p** 93. Chapl Brighton Coll 92-93; NSM St Leonards SS Pet and Paul *Chich* 92-93; Chapl Mill Hill Sch Lon from 93. *The Bungalow, The Ridgeway, London NW7 1QX* 0181-201 1397 or 959 1176 Fax 201 0663

HUNT, Canon Peter John. b 35. AKC58. St Boniface Warminster. **d** 59 **p** 60. C Chesterfield All SS *Derby* 59-61; C Matlock and Tansley 61-63; Chapl Matlock Hosp 61-63; Lect Matlock Teacher Tr Coll 61-63; V Tottington Man 63-65; CF (TA) 65-67 and from 75; V Bollington St Jo *Ches* 69-76; R Wilmslow from 76; Hon Can Ches Cathl from 94. *The Rectory, 12 Broadway, Wilmslow, Cheshire SK9 1NB* Wilmslow (01625) 523127 or 520309

HUNT, Philip Lacey Winter. b 09. St Steph Ho Ox. **d** 68 **p** 69. Chapl to the Deaf *Ox* 68-75; Hon Chapl from 75. *13 Wingfield Court, Glebe Street, Oxford OX4 1DG* Oxford (01865) 248385

HUNT, Richard William. b 46. G&C Coll Cam BA67 MA71. Westcott Ho Cam 68. **d** 72 **p** 73. C Bris St Agnes and St Simon w St Werburgh *Bris* 72-77; Chapl Selw Coll Cam 77-84; V Birchfield *Birm* from 84. *Holy Trinity Vicarage, 213 Birchfield Road, Birmingham B20 3DG* 0121-356 4241

HUNT, Ms Rosalind (Ros). b 55. Man Univ BA76. St Steph Ho Ox 86. **d** 88 **p** 94. Chapl Jes Coll Cam 88-92; Hon Chapl to the Deaf *Ely* from 92. *107 Hemingford Road, Cambridge CB1 3BY* Cambridge (01223) 575778

HUNT, Canon Russell Barrett. b 35. NY Univ Virginia Univ Fitzw Ho Cam. Westcott Ho Cam 73. **d** 75 **p** 76. C Leic St Mary *Leic* 75-78; V Leic St Gabr 78-82; Chapl Leic Gen Hosp 82-95; Hon Can Leic Cathl *Leic* 88-95; rtd 95; Can Emer Leic Cathl *Leic* from 95. *33 Braunstone Avenue, Leicester LE3 0JH* Leicester (0116) 254 9101

HUNT, Simon John. b 60. Pemb Coll Ox BA81 MA85. St Jo Coll Nottm 87. **d** 90 **p** 91. C Stalybridge St Paul *Ches* 90-93; C Heysham *Blackb* from 93. *Blomidon House, 11 Heysham Mossgate Road, Morecambe, Lancs LA3 2JU* Morecambe (01524) 853846

HUNT, Stephen. b 38. Man Univ BSc61 MSc62 PhD64 DSc80. Carl Dioc Tr Inst 88. **d** 91 **p** 92. C Broughton *Blackb* 91-95; V Preston Em from 95. *Emmanuel Vicarage, 2 Cornthwaite Road, Preston PR2 3DA* Preston (01772) 717136

HUNT, Vera Susan Henrietta. b 33. S Dios Minl Tr Scheme 88. **d** 91 **p** 94. Hon Chapl RAD from 91. *27 Redriff Close, Maidenhead, Berks SL6 4DJ* Maidenhead (01628) 23909

HUNTER, Allan Davies. b 36. Univ of Wales (Lamp) BA57. Coll of Resurr Mirfield 57. **d** 59 **p** 60. C Cardiff St Jo *Llan* 59-68; V Llansawel 68-76; Youth Chapl 71-77; V Llansawel w Briton Ferry 76-79; V Canton St Cath from 79. *The Vicarage, 22A Romilly Crescent, Canton, Cardiff CF1 9NR* Cardiff (01222) 382796

✠**HUNTER, Rt Rev Anthony George Weaver.** b 16. Leeds Univ BA39. Coll of Resurr Mirfield 39. **d** 41 **p** 42 **c** 68. C Newc St Geo *Newc* 41-43 and 48-49; S Africa 43-48; V Ashington *Newc* 49-60; V Huddersfield SS Pet and Paul *Wakef* 60-68;

RD Huddersfield 60-68; Hon Can Wakef Cathl 62-68; Bp Swaziland 68-75; R Hexham *Newc* 75-79; Asst Bp Newc 76-81; rtd 81. *Hillside, Main Street, Sheriff Hutton, York YO6 1PS* Sheriff Hutton (01347) 870226

HUNTER, Cyril Stanley Maurice. b 18. Worc Ord Coll 67. **d** 69 **p** 70. C Guisborough *York* 69-72; C Northallerton w Kirby Sigston 72-75; P-in-c Thornton-le-Street w Thornton-le-Moor etc 75-79; R Thornton le Street w N Otterington etc 79-85; rtd 85. *Linden, Upsall Road, South Kilvington, Thirsk, N Yorkshire YO7 2NQ* Thirsk (01845) 522829

HUNTER, David. b 30. Edin Th Coll 60. **d** 64 **p** 65. R Glas Ch Ch *Glas* 67-70 and 75-78; R Coatbridge 70-73; Chapl HM Pris Glas (Barlinnie) 72-84; P-in-c Glas H Trin *Glas* 73-84; R Glas All SS 84-95; rtd 95. *2 Skaterigg Drive, Burlington Gate, Glasgow G13 1SR* 0141-959 3730

HUNTER, David Matheson. b 46. K Coll Lon BD69 AKC69. **d** 76 **p** 77. C Paignton St Jo *Ex* 76-80; C Plymstock 80-82; P-in-c Brinkley, Burrough Green and Carlton *Ely* 84-86; P-in-c Westley Waterless 84-86; R Bressingham w N and S Lopham and Fersfield *Nor* from 87. *The Rectory, Bressingham, Diss, Norfolk IP22 2AT* Bressingham (0137988) 8267

HUNTER, Edwin Wallace. b 43. FCIM NUI BA83 DipCatech DipCIM. **d** 94 **p** 95. NSM Cork St Fin Barre's Union *C, C & R* from 94; Min Can Cork Cathl from 95. *Cedar Lodge, Church Road, Carrigaline, Co Cork, Irish Republic* Cork (21) 372338

HUNTER, Canon Frank Geoffrey. b 34. Keble Coll Ox BA56 MA60 Fitzw Coll Cam BA58 MA62. Ridley Hall Cam 57. **d** 59 **p** 60. C Bircle *Man* 59-62; C Jarrow Grange *Dur* 62-65; V Kingston upon Hull St Martin *York* 65-72; V Linthorpe 72-76; V Heslington from 76; RD Derwent from 78; Can and Preb York Minster from 85. *The Rectory, Heslington, York YO1 5EE* York (01904) 410389

HUNTER, Harold Hamilton. b 23. Dur Univ BSc48. NE Ord Course 76. **d** 79 **p** 80. NSM Corbridge w Halton *Newc* 79-82; NSM Corbridge w Halton and Newton Hall from 82. *15 Carham Close, Corbridge, Northd NE45 5NA* Hexham (01434) 632748

HUNTER, Henry. b 07. Tyndale Hall Bris 32. **d** 45 **p** 46. R Burlingham St Edmund, St Andr, St Pet etc *Nor* 62-73; rtd 73. *Flat 3, Warnes Close, Cromer, Norwich NR27 0AT* Cromer (01263) 511476

HUNTER, Ian Paton. b 20. Em Coll Cam BA46 MA50. Tyndale Hall Bris 40. **d** 43 **p** 47. R Plumpton w E Chiltington *Chich* 67-77; V Burwash Weald 77-83; P-in-c Stonegate 83-85; rtd 85; Perm to Offic *Chich* from 86. *Edzell, 15 Harrow Close, Seaford, E Sussex BN5 3PE* Seaford (01323) 899871

HUNTER, James. b 38. Bible Tr Inst Glas DipTh65 Union Th Coll Belf BD90. **d** 92 **p** 92. In Pb Ch of Ireland 82-92; V Werneth *Man* from 92. *St Thomas's Vicarage, 3 Regency Close, Oldham OL8 1SS* 0161-678 8926

HUNTER, Canon John Gaunt. b 21. St Jo Coll Dur BA49 Leeds Univ MA94. Ridley Hall Cam 49. **d** 51 **p** 52. Dioc Missr *Liv* 65-71; V Altcar 65-78; Abp York's Adv in Miss 71-78; Hon Can Liv Cathl 71-78; R Buckhurst Hill *Chelmsf* 78-79; TR 79-89; Dioc Adv in Evang *Bradf* 89-92; rtd 92. *Westhouse Lodge, Carnforth, Lancs LA6 3NZ* Carnforth (01524) 241305

HUNTER, Lionel Lawledge Gleave. b 24. Liv Coll of Art NDD50. ALCD53. **d** 53 **p** 54. Chile 61-72; R Diddlebury w Bouldon and Munslow *Heref* 72-75; P-in-c Abdon w Clee St Margaret 73-75; P-in-c Holdgate w Tugford 73-75; Canada 75-85; V N Elmham w Billingford *Nor* 85-89; R N Elmham w Billingford and Worthing 89-90; rtd 90. *Araucana, Wyson Lane, Brimfield, Ludlow, Shropshire SY8 4AN* Brimfield (01584) 711463

HUNTER, Dr Michael John. b 45. CCC Cam BA67 MA71 PhD71 Ox Univ BA75. Wycliffe Hall Ox 73. **d** 76 **p** 77. C Partington and Carrington *Ches* 76-79; CMS 80-90; Uganda 80-89; C Penn Fields *Lich* from 90. *100 Bellencroft Gardens, Wolverhampton WV3 8DU* Wolverhampton (01902) 763603

HUNTER, Canon Michael Oram. b 40. K Coll Lon BD64 AKC64. **d** 65 **p** 66. C Tividale *Lich* 65-68; C Harrogate St Wilfrid *Ripon* 68-70; V Hawksworth Wood 70-78; V Whitkirk 78-86; TR Gt Grimsby St Mary and St Jas *Linc* from 86; Hon Can Linc Cathl from 89. *49 Park Drive, Grimsby, S Humberside DN32 0EG* Grimsby (01472) 342933

HUNTER, Paul. b 55. Huddersfield Poly BEd82. Chich Th Coll 86. **d** 88 **p** 90. C Weymouth H Trin *Sarum* 88-92; P-in-c Hucknall Torkard *S'well* 92; TV from 92. *St John's Parsonage, 1 Nottingham Road, Hucknall, Nottingham NG15 7QN* Nottingham (0115) 963 3490

HUNTER, Peter Wells. b 52. Bris Univ BSc73. Trin Coll Bris BA91. **d** 91 **p** 92. C New Boro and Leigh *Sarum* from 91. *7 Ethelbert Road, Wimborne, Dorset BH21 1BH* Wimborne (01202) 889405

HUNTER, Robert. b 36. Man Univ BSc60. Clifton Th Coll. **d** 63 **p** 64. C Chadderton Ch Ch *Man* 63-65; C Balderstone 65-69; C Newburn *Newc* 69-73; TV Sutton St Jas and Wawne *York*

73-81; V Bilton St Pet 81-82; Hon C N Hull St Mich 82-91; TV Howden TM from 91. *3 Thimblehall Lane, Newport, Brough, N Humberside HU15 2PX* Howden (01430) 440546

HUNTER, Rodney Squire. b 33. Ox Univ BA56 MA61. Coll of Resurr Mirfield 56. **d** 58 **p** 59. C Forest Gate St Edm *Chelmsf* 58-61; Lib Pusey Ho Ox 61-65; Zambia 65-74; Malawi from 74. *Box 130, Zomba, Malawi* Malawi (265) 522419

HUNTER-BAILEY, James Ralph. b 11. Ripon Hall Ox 55. **d** 56 **p** 57. R Wychbold and Upton Warren *Worc* 64-71; Lic to Offic *Sarum* 71-78; rtd 76; Perm to Offic *Win* from 78. *46 Erica Drive, Corfe Mullen, Wimborne, Dorset BH21 3TQ* Broadstone (01202) 602260

HUNTER SMART, Ian Douglas. b 60. St Jo Coll Dur BA83. Edin Th Coll 83. **d** 85 **p** 86. C Cockerton *Dur* 85-89; TV Jarrow 89-92; TV Sunderland from 92; Chapl Sunderland Univ from 92. *2 Thornhill Terrace, Sunderland SR2 7JL* 0191-510 8267

HUNTINGDON, Archdeacon of. See SLEDGE, Ven Richard Kitson

HUNTINGDON, Suffragan Bishop of. See ROE, Rt Rev William Gordon

HUNTLEY, David Anthony. Lon Univ BA60. **d** 64 **p** 65. OMF from 65; Singapore 68-77; Hong Kong 77-81; Thailand from 81. *clo OMF, Belmont, The Vine, Sevenoaks, Kent TN13 3TZ* Sevenoaks (01732) 450747 Fax 456164

HUNTLEY, Denis Anthony. b 56. Qu Coll Birm 77. **d** 80 **p** 81. C Llanblethian w Cowbridge and Llandough etc *Llan* 80-83; TV Glyncorrwg w Afan Vale and Cymmer Afan 83-86; R 86-89; Chapl Asst Walsgrave Hosp Cov 89-92; Chapl Halifax Gen Hosp from 92. *Halifax General Hospital, Huddersfield Road, Halifax, W Yorkshire HX3 0PW* Halifax (01422) 357171 or 884160

HUNTRESS, Franklin Elias. b 33. Berkeley Div Sch STM62. **d** 62 **p** 63. USA 62-65 and 73-77 and 81-91; C Ches St Mary *Ches* 65-68; C Waltham Abbey *Chelmsf* 68-73; V Leic St Gabr *Leic* 77-81; C Skegness and Winthorpe *Linc* 91-93; P-in-c Long Bennington w Foston 93-94. *clo The Revd Canon R Rodger, Bishop's House, Eastgate, Lincoln LN2 1QQ* Lincoln (01522) 534701

HUNWICKE, John William. b 41. Hertf Coll Ox BA64 MA67. St Steph Ho Ox. **d** 67 **p** 68. C Beaconsfield *Ox* 67-70; C Newington St Paul *S'wark* 70-73; Asst Chapl Lancing Coll W Sussex from 73. *Hoe Court House, Lancing, W Sussex BN15 0QX* Lancing (01903) 752145

HURCOMBE, Thomas William (Tom). b 45. BD74 AKC76. **d** 76 **p** 77. C Hampstead St Jo Lon 76-79; C Is of Dogs Ch Ch and St Jo w St Luke 79-83; C Bromley All Hallows 83-89; C E Greenwich Ch Ch w St Andr and St Mich *S'wark* from 89; Ind Chapl from 89; Dioc Urban Missr from 90. *81 Charlton Road, London SE3 8TH* 0181-858 9521

HURD, Alun John. b 52. Avery Hill Coll DipHE83. Trin Coll Bris BA86. **d** 86 **p** 87. C Chertsey *Guildf* 86-90; Chapl St Pet Hosp Chertsey 86-90; V W Ewell *Guildf* from 90. *All Saints' Vicarage, 7 Church Road, Epsom, Surrey KT19 9QY* 0181-393 4357

HURD, Arthur Edward Stanley. b 12. St Jo Coll Dur LTh41 BA42 MA45. Tyndale Hall Bris 38. **d** 42 **p** 43. R Southover *Chich* 63-77; rtd 77; Perm to Offic *Chich* from 77; Perm to Offic *B & W* from 79. *9 Wiltons, Wrington, Bristol BS18 7LS* Wrington (01934) 862382

HURD, Brenda Edith. b 44. Sittingbourne Coll DipEd75. Cant Sch of Min 87. **d** 92 **p** 94. NSM Birling, Addington, Ryarsh and Trottiscliffe *Roch* from 92. *Southview, London Road, Ryarsh, West Malling, Kent ME19 5AW* West Malling (01732) 842588

HURD, John Patrick. b 37. CertEd65 Open Univ BA73 Kent Univ MA92. S Dios Minl Tr Scheme 77. **d** 80 **p** 81. NSM Billingshurst *Chich* 80-82 and 89-94; NSM Itchingfield w Slinfold 82-89. *Groomsland Cottage, Parbrook, Billingshurst, W Sussex RH14 9EU* Billingshurst (01403) 782167

HURDMAN, William Richard. b 40. AKC66 Hull Univ MA84. **d** 67 **p** 72. C Portsea St Mary *Portsm* 67-68; C N Walsham w Antingham *Nor* 71-74; V Friskney *Linc* 74-81; TR Bottesford w Ashby 81-88; TR Hackney *Lon* 88-95; P-in-c King's Lynn St Marg w St Nic *Nor* from 95. *St Margaret's Vicarage, St Margaret's Place, King's Lynn, Norfolk PE30 5DL* King's Lynn (01553) 772858

HURFORD, Colin Osborne. b 33. Qu Coll Ox BA55 MA59. Wells Th Coll 55. **d** 57 **p** 58. C Barnoldswick w Bracewell *Bradf* 57-61; C Warrington St Elphin *Liv* 61-63; Malaysia 63-70; P-in-c Annscroft *Heref* 71-79; P-in-c Pontesbury Hamlet of Longden 71-79; P-in-c Pontesbury III 71-79; R Longden and Annscroft 79-85; P-in-c Church Pulverbatch 81-85; R Longden and Annscroft w Pulverbatch 85-86; Tanzania 86-87; TR Billingham St Aid *Dur* from 87. *The Rectory, 12A Tintern Avenue, Billingham, Cleveland TS23 2DE* Stockton-on-Tees (01642) 531740

HURLE, Anthony Rowland (Tony). b 54. Lon Univ BSc Em Coll Cam PGCE. Wycliffe Hall Ox 80. **d** 83 **p** 84. C Ipswich St Mary at Stoke w St Pet, Stoke Park *St E* 83-87; TV Barking St Marg w St Patr *Chelmsf* 87-92; V St Alb St Paul *St Alb* from 92; RD St Alb from 95. *St Paul's Vicarage, 7 Brampton Road, St Albans, Herts AL1 4PN* St Albans (01727) 836810 or 846281

HURLE (nee POWNALL), Mrs Lydia Margaret. b 53. Wycliffe Hall Ox 78. **dss** 81 **d** 94 **p** 95. Ipswich St Mary at Stoke w St Pet & St Mary Quay *St E* 81-83; NSM St Alb St Paul *St Alb* from 93. *St Paul's Vicarage, 7 Brampton Road, St Albans, Herts AL1 4PN* St Albans (01727) 836810

HURLEY, Daniel Timothy. b 37. St Mich Coll Llan 68. **d** 70 **p** 71. C Llanfabon *Llan* 70-73; CF 73-79; R W Walton *Ely* 79-86; V Cwmddauddwr w St Harmon's and Llanwrthwl *S & B* from 86. *The Vicarage, Cwmdeuddwr, Rhayader, Powys LD6 5AP* Rhayader (01597) 810574

HURLEY, Mark Tristan. b 57. Trin Coll Bris DipHE88 BA89 Sarum & Wells Th Coll 89. **d** 91 **p** 92. C Gainsborough All SS *Linc* 91-94; TV Grantham from 94. *The Vicarage, The Grove, Grantham, Lincs NG31 7PU* Grantham (01476) 71276

HURLEY, Patrick Norman. b 15. **d** 47 **p** 48. C Hartlepool H Trin *Dur* 61-82; rtd 82. *Fourways, Nether Compton, Sherborne, Dorset DT9 4QE* Sherborne (01935) 813319

HURLEY, Robert. b 64. Univ of Wales (Cardiff) BD86. Ridley Hall Cam 88. **d** 90 **p** 91. C Dagenham *Chelmsf* 90-93; C Egg Buckland *Ex* from 93. *57 Hermitage Road, Plymouth PL3 4RX*

HURLOCK, Ronald James. b 31. BSc PhD. St Deiniol's Hawarden. **d** 83 **p** 84. C Oxton *Ches* 83-87; Chapl Asst Man R Infirmary 87-91; rtd 91. *78 Garwood Close, Westbrook, Warrington WA5 5TF* Warrington (01925) 444583

HURLSTON, Ronald Wilcox. b 30. St Deiniol's Hawarden 84. **d** 86 **p** 87. NSM Timperley *Ches* 86-90; C 90-95; rtd 95. *1 Heath Road, Timperley, Altrincham, Cheshire WA15 6BH* 0161-973 9205

HURN, Mrs June Barbara. b 32. Birm Univ CertEd53. Cant Sch of Min 87. **d** 90 **p** 94. NSM Chislehurst St Nic *Roch* from 90. *Sandy Ridge, 64 Lubbock Road, Chislehurst, Kent BR7 5JX* 0181-467 2320

HURRELL, John William. b 25. Ripon Hall Ox 65. **d** 66 **p** 67. C Glouc St Geo *Glouc* 68-70; C Thornbury 70-73; V Glouc St Steph 73-86; V Deerhurst, Apperley w Forthampton and Chaceley 86-90; rtd 90. *1 Church View, Porlock, Minehead, Somerset TA24 8NA* Minehead (01643) 862488

HURRELL, Canon Lionel Rex. b 41. Southn Univ BA64. Coll of Resurr Mirfield 64. **d** 66 **p** 67. C St Marychurch *Ex* 66-69; C Dawlish 69-71; Dioc Youth Officer *Cov* 71-75; V Porthleven *Truro* 75-80; RD Kerrier 78-80; P-in-c Sithney 78-80; V Swindon New Town *Bris* 80-88; TR from 88; RD Wroughton from 93; Hon Can Bris Cathl from 94. *St Mark's Rectory, Church Place, Swindon SN1 5EH* Swindon (01793) 522546

HURST, Alaric Desmond St John. b 24. New Coll Ox BA50 MA70. Wells Th Coll 48. **d** 51 **p** 53. V Writtle *Chelmsf* 63-69; rtd 89. *9 Ganderton Court, Pershore, Worcs WR10 1AW* Worcester (01905) 840939

HURST, Antony. b 38. MA MSc. S'wark Ord Course 79. **d** 83 **p** 84. NSM S'wark H Trin w St Matt *S'wark* 83-89; NSM S'wark Ch Ch from 89. *33 Hugh Street, London SW1V 1QT* 0171-828 2844

HURST, Brian Charles. b 58. Nottm Univ BA. Ripon Coll Cuddesdon 82. **d** 84 **p** 85. C Cullercoats St Geo *Newc* 84-87; C Prudhoe 87-88; TV Willington Team 88-95; V Denton from 95. *The Vicarage, Dunblane Crescent, Newcastle upon Tyne NE5 2BE* 0191-267 4376

HURST, Colin. b 49. Linc Th Coll 88. **d** 90 **p** 91. C Wavertree H Trin *Liv* 90-93; C Croft and Stoney Stanton *Leic* from 93. *The Rectory, Stoney Stanton, Leicester LE9 6LR* Sapcote (01455) 274156

HURST, Colin. b 58. Westmr Coll Ox BA90. St Jo Coll Nottm MA95. **d** 95. C Warboys w Broughton and Bury w Wistow *Ely* from 95. *78 Humberdale Way, Warboys, Huntingdon, Cambs PE17 2TP* Warboys (01487) 823878

HURST, Geoffrey. b 30. St Aid Birkenhead 59. **d** 64 **p** 65. C Sheff Parson Cross St Cecilia *Sheff* 64-69; V Wellingborough St Mark *Pet* 69-77; P-in-c Leic St Mark *Leic* 77-82; TV Leic Resurr 82-83; V Willenhall St Steph *Lich* 83-85; V Nether Hoyland St Andr *Sheff* 85-91; V Moorends 91-94. *80 Sunnyvale Road, Sheffield S17 4FB* Sheffield (0114) 236 1407

HURST, Jeremy Richard. b 40. FCP Trin Coll Cam BA61 MA MPhil. Linc Th Coll 62. **d** 64 **p** 65. C Woolwich St Mary w H Trin *S'wark* 64-69; Perm to Offic *Ex* 69-76; Perm to Offic *Ox* 76-84; TV Langley Marish 84-85; TR from 85. *The Rectory, 3 St Mary's Road, Langley, Berks SL3 7EN* Slough (01753) 542068

HURST, John. b 31. NW Ord Course 76. **d** 79 **p** 80. C Flixton St Jo *Man* 79-82; P-in-c Hindsford 82-86; V 86-88; V Halliwell St Paul 88-93; rtd 93. *6 Barrisdale Close, Bolton BL3 4TR* Bolton (01204) 654863

HURST, John Cecil. b 08. Trin Coll Cam BA30 MA37. Westcott Ho Cam 31. **d** 32 **p** 33. R W Meon and Warnford *Portsm* 63-73; rtd 73. *Middle Butts, Rectory Lane, Meonstoke, Southampton SO3 1NF* Droxford (01489) 877309

HURST, John Wilton. b 22. Kent Univ DipTh80. Tyndale Hall Bris 45. **d** 48 **p** 49. V Tunbridge Wells St Pet *Roch* 59-91; Chapl Pembury Hosp Tunbridge Wells 60-65; rtd 91. *Oaklands, Chapel Lane, Corfe Mullen, Wimborne, Dorset BH21 3SL* Wimborne (01202) 691935

HURST-BANNISTER, Michael Barnabas St Leger. b 19. Dorchester Miss Coll 41. **d** 44 **p** 45. CECS Clerical Org Sec Dios Win, Sarum and Portsm 67-78; Sen Chapl Actors' Ch Union 75-89; P-in-c Soho St Anne w St Thos and St Pet *Lon* 78-84; rtd 84. *Barford Lodge, West Street, Barford St Martin, Salisbury SP3 4AS* Salisbury (01722) 742630

HURT, Arnould Herbert. b 04. Man Univ BSc24. Cuddesdon Coll 28. **d** 28 **p** 29. V Scunthorpe Resurr *Linc* 69-71; rtd 71; P-in-c Innerleithen *Edin* 73-77 and 82-92; Hon C Anfield St Marg *Liv* 77-82. *41 St Augustine's Avenue, Grimsby, S Humberside DN32 0LD* Grimsby (01472) 752349

HUSBAND, Terence. b 26. NW Ord Course 72. **d** 75 **p** 76. C Weaste *Man* 75-78; R Gorton St Phil 78-81; V Belford *Newc* 81-88; Lic to Offic from 88; rtd 91. *11 Carham Close, Corbridge, Northd NE45 5NA* Hexham (01434) 633274

HUSBANDS, Canon Norman. b 03. AKC32. St Steph Ho Ox 32. **d** 32 **p** 33. V Roade *Pet* 41-76; Can Pet Cathl 67-76; rtd 76; Lic to Offic *Pet* 76-86; Perm to Offic from 86. *47 Ridge Way, Weston Favell, Northampton NN3 3AP* Northampton (01604) 408024

HUSSELL, Thomas Stanley (Stan). b 13. Univ of Wales BSc34. Sarum Th Coll 35. **d** 37 **p** 38. V Wragby *Wakef* 61-71; Lic to Offic from 71; rtd 78. *22 St John's Grove, Wakefield, W Yorkshire WF1 3SA* Wakefield (01924) 377891

HUSSEY, William Kenneth Alfred. b 27. St Jo Coll Ox BA48 DipEd49 MA52. Wycliffe Hall Ox 51. **d** 52 **p** 53. Chapl Ipswich Sch 60-72; Hd Master Ches Cathl Choir Sch 72-74; Chapl Rendcomb Coll Cirencester 74-78; P-in-c Rendcomb *Glouc* 74-78; Chapl Berkhamsted Sch Herts 78-83; TV Redruth w Lanner *Truro* 83-84; V St Goran w St Mich Caerhays 84-89; rtd 89. *20 Albany Road, Falmouth, Cornwall TR11 3RW* Falmouth (01326) 312343

HUTCHEON, Mrs Elsie. b 39. RGN63 SCM65 RCN79. E Anglian Minl Tr Course 89. **d** 92 **p** 94. NSM Heigham St Thos *Nor* from 92. *Beech Cottage, 103 Norwich Road, Tacolneston, Norwich NR16 1BP* Fundenhall (0150841) 424

HUTCHIN, David William. b 37. LRAM ARCM LTCL Man Univ MusB58 CertEd59 DipEd59. Glouc Sch of Min 85. **d** 88 **p** 89. NSM Northleach w Hampnett and Farmington *Glouc* 88-94; NSM Cold Aston w Notgrove and Turkdean 88-94; NSM Chedworth, Yanworth and Stowell, Coln Rogers etc from 94. *The Vicarage, Chedworth, Cheltenham, Glos GL54 4AE* Cirencester (01285) 720392

HUTCHINGS, Colin Michael. b 36. Clifton Th Coll 66. **d** 68 **p** 69. C Worksop St Jo *S'well* 68-71; C Hampreston *Sarum* 71-76; TV Tisbury 76-82; R Waddesdon w Over Winchendon and Fleet Marston *Ox* from 82. *The Rectory, Waddesdon, Aylesbury, Bucks HP18 0JQ* Aylesbury (01296) 651312

HUTCHINGS, Ian James. b 49. Lon Univ DipTh72. Clifton Th Coll 69 Trin Coll Bris 72. **d** 73 **p** 74. C Parr *Liv* 73-77; C Timperley *Ches* 77-81; V Partington and Carrington from 81. *St Mary's Vicarage, Manchester Road, Partington, Urmston, Manchester M31 4FB* 0161-775 3542

HUTCHINGS, John Denis Arthur. b 29. Keble Coll Ox BA53 MA59 MSc59. Chich Th Coll 58. **d** 60 **p** 61. C St Pancras w St Jas and Ch Ch *Lon* 60-63; Asst Chapl Denstone Coll Uttoxeter 63-67 and 79-83; C Stepney St Dunstan and All SS *Lon* 67-78; V Devonport St Boniface *Ex* 83-86; TR Devonport St Boniface and St Phil 86-93; P-in-c Lydford and Brent Tor from 93. *The Rectory, Lydford, Okehampton, Devon EX20 4BH* Lydford (0182282) 306

HUTCHINGS, Norman Leslie. b 09. MVI. Wycliffe Hall Ox 42. **d** 43 **p** 43. V Ore Ch Ch *Chich* 62-77; rtd 77; Perm to Offic *Chich* from 77; Perm to Offic *Roch* from 77. *6 Sunnyside Road, Rusthall, Tunbridge Wells, Kent TN4 8RB* Tunbridge Wells (01892) 533264

HUTCHINGS, Robert Henry. b 45. Nottm Univ DTPS88. E Midl Min Tr Course 85. **d** 88 **p** 89. NSM Kibworth and Smeeton Westerby and Saddington *Leic* 88-90; NSM Swinford w Catthorpe, Shawell and Stanford 90-92; NSM Newtown Linford 92-94; NSM Husbands Bosworth w Mowsley and Knaptoft etc from 94. *16 Highcroft, Husbands Bosworth, Lutterworth, Leics LE17 6LF* Market Harborough (01858) 880131

HUTCHINSON, Andrew Charles. b 63. Univ of Wales (Ban) BA84. Aston Tr Scheme 85 Chich Th Coll 87. **d** 89 **p** 90. C Burnley St Cath w St Alb and St Paul *Blackb* 89-92;

C Shrewsbury St Chad w St Mary *Lich* 92-94; Chapl Heref Cathl Sch from 94; Succ Heref Cathl *Heref* from 94. *3 Castle Street, Hereford HR1 2NL* Hereford (01432) 273708

HUTCHINSON, Charles William Aldersey. b 10. SS Coll Cam BA32 MA37. Ely Th Coll 33. **d** 33 **p** 34. R Washingborough w Heighington *Linc* 37-86; Chapl RNVR 43-46; rtd 86. *c/o Miss A Hutchinson, Flat 2, 88 Holland Park, London W11 3RZ*

HUTCHINSON, Canon Cyril Peter. b 37. Dur Univ BA61. Wm Temple Coll Rugby 61. **d** 63 **p** 64. Dir Bradf SHARE 69-76; Perm to Offic *Bradf* 69-75; Hon C Manningham 75-76; V Clayton 76-83; RD Bowling and Horton 80-83; TR Keighley St Andr 83-94; Hon Can Bradf Cathl 84-94; rtd 94; Hon C Keighley All SS *Bradf* from 94. *Wellcroft, Laycock, Keighley, W Yorks BD22 0PN* Keighley (01535) 606145

HUTCHINSON, David Bamford. b 29. QUB BSc53 TCD Div Test55 QUB DipEd57. **d** 55 **p** 56. I Kilkeel *D & D* 66-75; I Willowfield 75-82; V Longfleet *Sarum* 82-94; rtd 94. *68 Bracken Road, Ferndown, Dorset BH22 9PF* Ferndown (01202) 664964

HUTCHINSON, Harold. b 36. NE Ord Course. **d** 84 **p** 85. C Auckland St Andr and St Anne *Dur* 84-87; V Coundon from 87. *2 Collingwood Street, Coundon, Bishop Auckland, Co Durham DL14 8LG* Bishop Auckland (01388) 603312

HUTCHINSON, Hugh Edward. b 27. CEng FICE. Bps' Coll Cheshunt. **d** 61 **p** 62. V Ex St Mark *Ex* 67-75; P-in-c Foston on the Wolds *York* 75-77; P-in-c N Frodingham 75-77; R Beeford w Lissett 75-77; R Beeford w Frodingham and Foston 77-80; RD N Holderness 79-80; P-in-c Appleton Roebuck w Acaster Selby 80-84; P-in-c Etton w Dalton Holme 84-91; rtd 91. *33 Limestone Grove, Burniston, Scarborough, N Yorkshire YO13 0DH* Scarborough (01723) 871116

HUTCHINSON, Jeremy Olpherts. b 32. Or Coll Ox BA55 MA60 St Jo Coll Dur DipTh57. **d** 57 **p** 58. C Shoreditch St Leon *Lon* 57-60; V Hoxton St Jo w Ch Ch 60-78; Hon C Hackney 78-85; C Highbury Ch Ch w St Jo and St Sav Lon 85-91; P-in-c Hanley Road St Sav w St Paul 91-92; TV Tollington from 92. *97 Corbyn Street, London N4 3BX* 0171-272 1246

HUTCHINSON, John Charles. b 44. K Coll Lon 64. **d** 69 **p** 70. C Portsea All SS *Portsm* 69-73; TV Fareham H Trin 73-78; P-in-c Pangbourne *Ox* 78-86; P-in-c Tidmarsh w Sulham 84-86; R Pangbourne w Tidmarsh and Sulham from 86. *The Rectory, St James's Close, Pangbourne, Reading RG8 7AP* Pangbourne (01734) 842928

HUTCHINSON, Jonathan Mark. b 45. Cant Sch of Min 85. **d** 89 **p** 90. NSM Wickham Market w Pettistree and Easton *St E* 89-93; V Thorington w Wenhaston, Bramfield & Walberswick from 94. *The Vicarage, Walberswick, Southwold, Suffolk IP18 6UN* Southwold (01502) 722256

HUTCHINSON, Julie Lorraine. b 55. W Midl Minl Tr Course 90. **d** 93 **p** 94. C Northn St Mary *Pet* from 93. *53 Delapre, Crescent Road, Northampton NN4 9NG* Northampton (01604) 767438

HUTCHINSON, Keith. b 40. Keble Coll Ox BA63 MA68. St Steph Ho Ox 63. **d** 66 **p** 67. C Brighouse *Wakef* 66-72; R Workington St Mich *Carl* 72-83; V Mexborough *Sheff* 83-94. *Littlemore, Station Road, Ampleforth, York YO6 4DG*

HUTCHINSON, Paul Edward. b 33. K Coll Lon. **d** 59 **p** 60. C Bromley St Mich *Lon* 59-63; C Mill Hill St Mich 63-66; C Sandridge *St Alb* 66-73; V St Alb St Mary Marshalswick 73-80; V Tunstall *Lich* 80-91; RD Stoke N 82-91; V Lower Gornal 91-93; V Lower Gornal *Worc* from 93. *The Vicarage, Church Street, Lower Gornal, Dudley, W Midlands DY3 2PF* Sedgley (01902) 882023

HUTCHINSON, Miss Pauline. b 49. St Jo Coll Nottm 88. **d** 90 **p** 94. Par Dn Sherwood *S'well* 90-94; C 94-95; TV Newark-upon-Trent from 95. *St Leonard's Vicarage, Lincoln Road, Newark, Notts NG24 2DQ* Newark (01636) 703691

HUTCHINSON, Peter Francis. b 52. Portsm Poly HND74. Sarum & Wells Th Coll 87. **d** 89 **p** 90. C Honiton, Gittisham, Combe Raleigh, Monkton etc *Ex* 89-93; V Valley Park *Win* from 93. *35 Raglan Close, Eastleigh, Hants SO5 3NH* Eastleigh (01703) 255749

HUTCHINSON, Philip Sheldon. b 32. Pemb Coll Cam BA56 MA59. Chich Th Coll 56. **d** 58 **p** 59. C Plumstead St Nic *S'wark* 58-60; C Roehampton H Trin 60-64; USA 64-65; R Old Charlton *S'wark* 65-69; Australia from 69. *14 Acland Street, St Kilda, Victoria, Australia 3182* Melbourne (3) 534-3892

HUTCHINSON, Raymond. b 30. Lon Univ DipTh59. Richmond Th Coll 53. **d** 56 **p** 58. R Duror *Arg* 65-70; R Portnacrois 65-70; R Partney w Dalby *Linc* 70-73; R Ashby by Partney 70-73; V Skendleby 70-73; R Candlesby w Scremby 72-73; Canada from 78; rtd 95. *CP 157, R R 2, Arundel, Quebec, Canada, J0T 1AO*

HUTCHINSON, Raymond John. b 51. Liv Univ BSc73. Westcott Ho Cam 73. **d** 76 **p** 77. C Peckham St Jo *S'wark* 76-78; C Peckham St Jo w St Andr 78-79; C Prescot *Liv* 79-81; V Edge Hill St Dunstan 81-87; P-in-c Waterloo Park 87-89;

P-in-c Litherland Ch Ch 87-89; V Waterloo Ch Ch and St Mary from 90. *Christ Church Vicarage, 22 Crosby Road South, Liverpool L22 1RQ* 0151-920 7791

HUTCHINSON, Very Rev Roland Louis. b 29. TCD BA51 MA61. **d** 52 **p** 53. I Rathmullan w Tyrella *D & D* 65-74; I Magheralin w Dollingstown 74-95; Treas Dromore Cathl 86-90; Prec 90-93; Dean Dromore 93-95; rtd 95. *Summerhill Lodge, 22 Summerhill, Lurgan, Craigavon, Co Armagh BT66 7AW* Waringstown (01762) 881789

HUTCHINSON, Canon Stephen. b 38. St Chad's Coll Dur BA60 DipTh62. **d** 62 **p** 63. C Tividale *Lich* 62-68; V Walsall St Andr 68-73; R Headless Cross *Worc* 73-81; TR Redditch, The Ridge 81-91; RD Bromsgrove 85-91; Hon Can Worc Cathl from 88; V Stourbridge St Thos from 91. *St Thomas's Vicarage, 34 South Road, Stourbridge, W Midlands DY8 3TB* Stourbridge (01384) 392401

HUTCHINSON, Canon William David. b 27. Wycliffe Hall Ox 55. **d** 57 **p** 58. V Ipswich St Aug *St E* 65-76; R Ewhurst *Guildf* 76-81; V Aldeburgh w Hazlewood *St E* 81-92; RD Saxmundham 83-88; Hon Can St E Cathl 87-92; rtd 92. *Hazelwood, 3 Birch Close, Woodbridge, Suffolk IP12 4UA* Woodbridge (01394) 383760

HUTCHINSON-CERVANTES, Ian Charles. b 62. Cant Univ (NZ) BSc84 Reading Univ MSc86 Jes Coll Cam BA88. Westcott Ho Cam 86. **d** 89 **p** 90. C Iffley *Ox* 89-92; USPG from 92; Venezuela from 93. *c/o USPG, Partnership House, 157 Waterloo Road, London SE1 8XA* 0171-928 8681 Fax 928 2371

HUTCHISON, Geoffrey John. b 52. Trin Hall Cam MA76 Lon Univ CertEd76. Ridley Hall Cam 77. **d** 79 **p** 80. C Harold Wood *Chelmsf* 79-83; CF 83-89; Warden Viney Hill Chr Adventure Cen from 89; P-in-c Viney Hill *Glouc* from 89. *The Vicarage, Viney Hill, Lydney, Glos GL15 4NA* Dean (01594) 516162

HUTCHISON, Henry Peter. b 20. FIChemE CCC Ox MA49 TCD MA52 SS Coll Cam MA55. Linc Th Coll 80. **d** 81 **p** 82. Hon C Cam St Barn *Ely* 81-83; Hon C Ashley w Silverley 83-85; P-in-c Abbots Ripton w Wood Walton 85-90; P-in-c Kings Ripton 85-90; rtd 90. *Meadow Lodge, Church Farm Lane, Scarning, Dereham, Norfolk NR19 2NN* Dereham (01362) 698860

HUTT, Colin Villette. b 32. FCA. Glouc Sch of Min 87. **d** 89 **p** 90. NSM Ludlow *Heref* 89-93; C Ludlow, Ludford, Ashford Carbonell etc 93-94; TV Tenbury from 94. *Old Yew Tree Farmhouse, Ashford Bowdler, Ludlow, Shropshire SY8 4DJ* Richards Castle (01584) 74513 Fax as telephone

HUTT, Canon David Handley. b 38. AKC68. **d** 69 **p** 70. C Bedf Park *Lon* 69-70; C Westmr St Matt 70-73; PV and Succ S'wark Cathl *S'wark* 73-78; Chapl K Coll Taunton 78-82; V Bordesley SS Alb and Patr *Birm* 82-86; V St Marylebone All SS *Lon* 86-95; Can Steward Westmr Abbey from 95. *5 Little Cloister, London SW1P 3PL* 0171-222 6939 or 222 5152 Fax 233 2072

HUTTON, Brian Allan. b 40. Bps' Coll Cheshunt. **d** 69 **p** 70. C Newc St Matt w St Mary *Newc* 69-72; C Blyth St Mary 72-75; V Sheff St Cath Richmond Road *Sheff* 75-85; R Paisley St Barn *Glas* from 85; R Paisley H Trin from 87. *11 Tantallon Drive, Paisley, Renfrewshire PA2 9JT* Brediland (0150581) 2359

HUTTON, Canon David James. b 40. Dur Univ BA64 Kent Univ MA79. Coll of Resurr Mirfield 64. **d** 66 **p** 67. C Kirkby Liv 66-70; Asst Chapl Kent Univ *Cant* 70-73; Chapl 73-78; Six Preacher Cant Cathl 74-80; Chapl The Lon Hosp (Whitechapel) 78-83; Can Res and Chan Liv Cathl *Liv* from 83. *4 Cathedral Close, Liverpool L1 7BR* 0151-709 6271 or 708 0938

HUTTON, Griffith Arthur Jeremy. b 31. Trin Hall Cam BA56 MA59. Linc Th Coll 56. **d** 58 **p** 59. C Hexham *Newc* 58-60; C Gosforth All SS 60-65; V Whitegate *Ches* 65-71; V Whitegate w Lt Budworth 71-78; R Dowdeswell and Andoversford w the Shiptons etc *Glouc* 78-91; V Newnham w Awre and Blakeney from 91. *The Vicarage, Unlawater Lane, Newnham, Glos GL14 1BL* Dean (01594) 516648

HUTTON, John Alexander. b 26. Local NSM Course 73. **d** 77 **p** 78. Hon C Edin St Mary *Edin* 77-89; NSM Glenurquhart *Mor* from 89; Dioc Chapl from 89. *St Ninian's House, Glenurquhart, Inverness IV3 6TN* Glenurquhart (01456) 476264

HUTTON, Joseph Charles. b 21. DFC41. Westcott Ho Cam 63. **d** 65 **p** 66. V Warborough *Ox* 67-70; V Earley St Pet 70-75; R Ludgvan *Truro* 75-79; rtd 79. *2 Baines Close, Bourton-on-the-Water, Cheltenham, Glos GL54 2PU*

HUTTON, Patrick George. b 41. Open Univ BA87. Chich Th Coll 65. **d** 68 **p** 69. C Palmers Green St Jo *Lon* 68-71; Guyana 71-80; P-in-c Stow Bardolph w Wimbotsham and Stow Bridge *Ely* 80-88; P-in-c Nordelph 80-88; V E Bedfont *Lon* from 88; AD Hounslow from 93. *St Mary's Vicarage, 9 Hatton Road, Feltham, Middx TW14 8JR* 0181-751 0088

HUTTON, Canon Stanley Peart. b 15. St Jo Coll Dur BA37 DipTh38 MA40. **d** 38 **p** 39. R Knotting w Souldrop *St Alb* 69-80; V Sharnbrook 69-80; rtd 80; Perm to Offic *Ex* from 80. *Flat 2, Coly House, Rosemary Lane, Colyton, Devon EX13 6LS* Colyton (01297) 552744

HUTTON, Miss Susan Elizabeth. b 70. Univ of Wales (Cardiff) BD91. Ripon Coll Cuddesdon 93. **d** 95. C W Parley *Sarum* from 95. *48 Cammel Road, West Parley, Ferndown, Dorset BH22 8SB* Ferndown (01202) 871459

HUTTON-BURY, David. b 44. **d** 94 **p** 95. NSM Geashill w Killeigh and Ballycommon *M & K* from 94. *Chorleyville Farm, Tullamore, Co Offaly, Irish Republic* Offaly (506) 21813

HUXHAM, Hector Hubert. b 29. Bris Univ BA55. Tyndale Hall Bris 52. **d** 56 **p** 57. Chapl St Jas Univ Hosp Leeds 67-94; rtd 94. *3 Oakwell Oval, Leeds LS8 4AL* Leeds (0113) 266 8851

HUXHAM, Canon Peter Richard. b 38. Worc Coll Ox BA61 MA74. St Steph Ho Ox 61. **d** 63 **p** 64. C Gillingham *Sarum* 63-67; C Osmondthorpe St Phil *Ripon* 67-70; V Parkstone St Osmund *Sarum* 70-75; TR Parkstone St Pet w Branksea and St Osmund 75-92; RD Poole 85-92; Can and Preb Sarum Cathl 85-92; Chapl Musgrove Park Hosp from 92; Chapl Taunton & Somerset NHS Trust from 92. *The Chaplain's Office, Musgrove Park Hospital, Taunton, Somerset TA1 5DA* Taunton (01823) 333444

HUXLEY, Keith. b 33. Ch Coll Cam BA57 MA61. Cuddesdon Coll 57. **d** 59 **p** 60. C Bowdon *Ches* 59-61; C Crewe Ch Ch 61-62; C Ches St Pet 62-64; Youth Chapl 62-68; Asst Chapl Ches Cathl 65-68; V Grange St Andr 68-73; TR E Runcorn w Halton 73-77; Home Sec Gen Syn Bd for Miss and Unity 77-83; Chapl to The Queen from 81; TR Gateshead *Dur* from 83; RD Gateshead 88-92. *The Rectory, 91 Old Durham Road, Gateshead, Tyne & Wear NE8 4BS* 0191-477 3990

HUXLEY, Canon Stephen Scott. b 30. Linc Th Coll 53. **d** 56 **p** 57. V Tynemouth Priory *Newc* 65-74; V Warkworth and Acklington 74-78; P-in-c Tynemouth St Jo 78-81; V 81-87; Hon Can Newc Cathl 82-92; V Wylam 87-92; rtd 92. *35 Castle Street, Norham, Berwick-upon-Tweed TD15 2LQ* Berwick-upon-Tweed (01289) 382356

HUXLEY, William Thomas. b 31. Oak Hill Th Coll 60. **d** 63 **p** 64. C Rainham *Chelmsf* 63-66; C Heworth w Peasholme St Cuth *York* 66-67; R The Chignals w Mashbury *Chelmsf* 67-82; V Kirby le Soken 82-86; R Kirby-le-Soken w Gt Holland 86-87. *Address temp unknown*

HUXTABLE, Christopher Michael Barclay. b 61. Ex Univ BA83 Qu Coll Cam PGCE84. St Steph Ho Ox DipMin95. **d** 95. C Chich St Paul and St Pet *Chich* from 95. *St Paul's House, 37 Somerstown, Chichester, W Sussex PO19 4AL* Chichester (01243) 775199

HUXTABLE, Michael George. b 29. St Jo Coll Cam BA50 MA54. S Dios Minl Tr Scheme 87. **d** 90 **p** 91. NSM Fisherton Anger *Sarum* from 90. *124 Bouverie Avenue South, Salisbury SP2 8EA* Salisbury (01722) 334364

HUYTON, Stuart. b 37. St D Coll Lamp BA62 DipTh63. **d** 63 **p** 64. C Kingswinford H Trin *Lich* 63-66; C Leek St Edw 66-69; V Wigginton 69-76; V Wombourne 76-89; RD Trysull 79-84; P-in-c Bobbington 85-89; TR Wombourne w Trysull and Bobbington 89-95; V Lt Aston from 95. *The Vicarage, 3 Walsall Road, Sutton Coldfield, W Midlands B74 3BD* 0121-353 0356

HUYTON, Susan Mary. b 57. Birm Univ BA79 DipTh86. Qu Coll Birm 83. **d** 86. C Connah's Quay *St As* 86-89; C Wrexham 89-90; D-in-c 90-91; TD from 91. *The Vicarage, 55 Princess Street, Wrexham, Clwyd LL13 7US* Wrexham (01978) 266145

HUZZEY, Peter George. b 48. Trin Coll Bris 74. **d** 76 **p** 77. C Bishopsworth *Bris* 76-79; V from 86; C Downend 79-80; TV Kings Norton *Birm* 80-86. *St Peter's Vicarage, 61 Fernsteed Road, Bristol BS13 8HE* Bristol (0117) 964 2734

HYATT, Robert Keith (Bob). b 34. Em Coll Cam BA59 MA63. Ridley Hall Cam 58. **d** 60 **p** 61. C Cheltenham St Mary *Glouc* 60-63; Asst Chapl K Edw Sch Witley 63-65; C Godalming *Guildf* 65-69; Hong Kong 69-78; V Claygate *Guildf* 78-91; TV Whitton *Sarum* from 91. *The Rectory, Back Lane, Ramsbury, Marlborough, Wilts SN8 2QH* Marlborough (01672) 202235

HYDE, Alan. b 09. Lon Univ BSc33. St Aid Birkenhead 46. **d** 48 **p** 51. V Satley *Dur* 70-77; rtd 77. *7 Selby Gardens, Consett, Co Durham DH8 8AS* Consett (01207) 501441

HYDE, Dennis Hugh. b 23. Leeds Univ BA56. Sarum Th Coll 60. **d** 60 **p** 61. V Shottermill *Guildf* 65-74; Past Consultant Clinical Th Assn 74-80; rtd 88. *32 Amis Avenue, New Haw, Addlestone, Surrey KT15 3ET* Weybridge (01932) 345526

HYDE, Edgar Bonsor. b 29. Clifton Th Coll 59. **d** 61 **p** 62. C Weston-super-Mare Ch Ch *B & W* 61-66; C Chipping Campden *Glouc* 66-70; R Longborough w Condicote and Sezincote 70-78; R Longborough, Sezincote, Condicote and the Swells from 78. *The Rectory, Longborough, Moreton-in-the-Marsh, Glos GL56 0QF* Cotswold (01451) 830447

HYDE-DUNN, Keith Frederick. b 43. Sarum Th Coll. **d** 69 **p** 70. Rhodesia 69-72; C Horsham *Chich* 73-77; P-in-c Fittleworth 77-86; P-in-c Graffham w Woolavington from 86. *The Rectory, Graffham, Petworth, W Sussex GU28 0NL* Graffham (017986) 247

HYDER, Geoffrey Frank. b 28. St Jo Coll Dur 49. **d** 53 **p** 54. Regional Org (Gtr Lon) Chr Aid 68-74; R Keston *Roch* 74-83; R Speldhurst w Groombridge and Ashurst 83-93; RD Tunbridge Wells 86-91; rtd 93. *2 Holland House, 16 Pevensey Road, St Leonards-on-Sea, E Sussex TN38 0JY* Hastings (01424) 715350

HYDER-SMITH, Brian John. b 45. MBIM MInstAM. E Anglian Minl Tr Course 84. **d** 87 **p** 88. NSM Huntingdon *Ely* 87-90; P-in-c Abbots Ripton w Wood Walton from 90; P-in-c Kings Ripton from 90. *The Rectory, Abbots Ripton, Huntingdon, Cambs PE17 2LE* Abbots Ripton (014873) 260

HYDON, Mrs Veronica Weldon. b 52. N Lon Poly BA73 Maria Grey Coll Lon CertEd74. Aston Tr Scheme 87 Westcott Ho Cam 89. **d** 91 **p** 94. Par Dn Poplar Lon 91-94; C 94-95; P-in-c Roxwell *Chelmsf* from 95; Dio Lay Development Officer from 95. *The Vicarage, Vicarage Road, Roxwell, Chelmsford CM1 4NB* Good Easter (01245) 231429

HYLAND, Canon Cecil George. b 38. TCD BA62 MA78. **d** 63 **p** 64. C Belf St Nic *Conn* 63-66; C Monkstown *D & G* 66-68; Ch of Ireland Youth Officer 68-73; Chapl TCD 73-79; I Tullow *D & G* 79-90; RD Killiney from 86; I Howth from 90; Dir of Ords (Dub) from 91; Can Ch Ch Cathl Dub 91-95; Preb from 95. *The Rectory, Howth Road, Dublin 13, Irish Republic* Dublin (1) 832-3019 Fax as telephone

HYSLOP, Mrs Catherine Graham Young (Katie). b 53. St Andr Univ CPSS75. Carl Dioc Tr Inst 90. **d** 92 **p** 94. NSM St Bees *Carl* 92-95; NSM Carl St Jo from 95. *St Peter's Vicarage, Cliff Road, Whitehaven, Cumbria CA28 9ET* Whitehaven (01946) 692496

HYSLOP, James Stott Davidson. b 09. Edin Th Coll 60. **d** 62 **p** 63. R Galashiels *Edin* 69-76; rtd 76. *22/6 Ferry Road Avenue, Edinburgh EH4 4BL* 0131-332 9277

HYSLOP, Thomas James (Jim). b 54. St Andr Univ BD76. Edin Th Coll 76. **d** 78 **p** 79. C Whitehaven *Carl* 78-81; C Walney Is 81-83; P-in-c Gt Broughton and Broughton Moor 83-85; V 85-88; V Kells from 88. *St Peter's Vicarage, Cliff Road, Whitehaven, Cumbria CA28 9ET* Whitehaven (01946) 692496

HYSON, Peter Raymond. b 51. Open Univ BA80 BA87. Oak Hill Th Coll 85. **d** 87 **p** 88. C Billericay and Lt Burstead *Chelmsf* 87-92; TV Whitton *Sarum* from 92. *The Vicarage, St Michael's Mount, Aldbourne, Marlborough, Wilts SN8 2BP* Marlborough (01672) 40261

I

I'ANSON, Frederic Mark. b 43. R Agric Coll Cirencester MRAC68. Carl Dioc Tr Inst 89. **d** 92 **p** 93. NSM Sedbergh, Cautley and Garsdale *Bradf* from 92. *The Bowers, Firbank, Sedbergh, Cumbria LA10 5EG* Sedbergh (01539) 620826

IBALL, Canon Charles Herbert. b 12. Leeds Univ BA34. Coll of Resurr Mirfield 34. **d** 36 **p** 37. R Curdworth *Birm* 70-77; rtd 77; Perm to Offic from 77. *Flat 12, Manormead Home, Tilford Road, Hindhead, Surrey GU26 6RA* Hindhead (01428) 606696

IBALL, Charles Martin John. b 40. Lich Th Coll 67. **d** 69 **p** 70. C Dudley St Edm *Worc* 69-73; C W Bromwich St Jas *Lich* 73-76; V Oxley 76-80; Hon C Whittington w Weeford from 86. *75 Carlcroft, Stoneydelph, Tamworth, Staffs B77 4DW* Tamworth (01827) 896644

IBALL, Glyn. b 41. Univ of Wales BSc63. St Mich Coll Llan 63. **d** 65 **p** 66. C Ruabon *St As* 65-71; Hon C Bedf Park Lon from 71; Chapl Latymer Upper Sch Hammersmith from 71. *106 Woodstock Road, London W4 1EG* 0181-994 4351

ICELY, Lawrence Valentine. b 07. Cuddesdon Coll 40. **d** 40 **p** 41. V Hargrave *Ches* 56-74; rtd 74; Perm to Offic *Ches* from 74. *61 Oxford Road, Runcorn, Cheshire WA7 4NU* Runcorn (01928) 577147

IDDON, Roy Edward. b 40. TCert61 Lanc Univ MA88. N Ord Course 83. **d** 83 **p** 84. Hd Teacher St Andr Primary Sch Blackb from 83; NSM Bolton St Matt w St Barn *Man* 83-88; Lic to AD Walmesley 88-93; NSM Walmsley from 93. *28 New Briggs Fold, Egerton, Bolton BL7 9UL* Bolton (01204) 56589

IDLE, Christopher Martin. b 38. St Pet Coll Ox BA62. Clifton Th Coll 62. **d** 65 **p** 66. C Barrow St Mark *Carl* 65-68; C Camberwell Ch Ch *S'wark* 68-71; P-in-c Poplar St Matthias *Lon* 71-76; R Limehouse 76-89; P-in-c Palgrave w Wortham and Burgate *St E* 89; P-in-c Thrandeston, Stuston and Brome w Oakley 89; R N Hartismere from 89. *The Rectory, Oakley, Suffolk IP21 4AV* Diss (01379) 740322

IENT, Peter. b 25. Leeds Univ BA49. Coll of Resurr Mirfield 49. **d** 51 **p** 52. Chapl HM Rem Cen Warrington 69-74; Chapl HM Pris Albany 74-79; Chapl HM Pris Birm 80-84; Chapl HM Pris Coldingley 84-88; rtd 88. *61 Whites Road, Farnborough, Hants GU14 6PB* Farnborough (01252) 540982

IEVINS, Peter Valdis. b 54. Solicitor 79 St Jo Coll Ox BA75 MA81. Westcott Ho Cam 86. **d** 88 **p** 89. C Sawston *Ely* 88-91; C Babraham 88-91. *32 Ledbury Road, Peterborough PE3 9RH* Peterborough (01733) 269029

IKIN, Gordon Mitchell. b 30. AKC57. **d** 58 **p** 59. V Westleigh St Paul *Man* 61-72; V Thornham St Jas 72-95; rtd 95. *3 Thornham Old Road, Royton, Oldham OL2 5UN* 0161-624 2428

ILES, Canon Paul Robert. b 37. FRCO65 Fitzw Coll Cam BA59 MA64 St Edm Hall Ox MA80. Sarum Th Coll 59. **d** 61 **p** 62. Chapl Bp Wordsworth Sch Salisbury 61-67; C Salisbury St Mich *Sarum* 61-64; Min Can Sarum Cathl 64-67; C Bournemouth St Pet *Win* 67-72; R Filton *Bris* 72-79; V Ox SS Phil and Jas w St Marg *Ox* 79-83; Can Res and Prec Heref Cathl *Heref* from 83. *The Canon's House, The Close, Hereford HR1 2NG* Hereford (01432) 266193

ILIFF, Hugh Graham. b 07. Trin Hall Cam BA31 MA35. **d** 32 **p** 33. India 60-72; rtd 72; Chapl Le Touquet *Eur* 73-76; Perm to Offic *Roch* from 77. *Cornford House, Cornford Lane, Pembury, Tunbridge Wells, Kent TN2 4QS* Tunbridge Wells (01892) 824399

ILLING, Eric James. b 33. Kelham Th Coll 54 Chich Th Coll 55. **d** 57 **p** 58. V Middleton St Mary *Ripon* 65-74; R Felpham w Middleton *Chich* 74-81; Chapl R Devon and Ex Hosp (Wonford) 81-94; TR Heavitree w Ex St Paul *Ex* 81-91; R Bradninch and Clyst Hydon 91-94; rtd 94; Clergy Retirement and Widows' Officer *B & W* from 94; Perm to Offic from 94; Perm to Offic *Chich* from 94. *25 Pikes Crescent, Taunton, Somerset TA1 4HS* Taunton (01823) 289203

ILLINGWORTH, John Patrick Paul. b 34. New Coll Ox BA59 DipTh61 MA63. Chich Th Coll 61. **d** 63 **p** 64. C Brighouse *Wakef* 63-66; C Willesden St Andr *Lon* 66-70; Chapl Gothenburg w Halmstad and Jonkoping *Eur* 70-74; Perm to Offic *Chich* 74; V Ryhill *Wakef* 74-82; R Weston Longville w Morton and the Witchinghams *Nor* from 82; P-in-c Alderford w Attlebridge and Swannington from 94. *The Rectory, Weston Longville, Norwich NR9 5JU* Norwich (01603) 880163

ILOTT, Philip Edwin. b 36. Roch Th Coll 66. **d** 68 **p** 69. C Leavesden All SS *St Alb* 68-71; C-in-c Godshill CD *Portsm* 71-77; V Mayfield *Chich* 77-81; V Bexhill St Barn 81-84; rtd 84; Perm to Offic *Chich* from 85. *Albany House, 11 Albany Road, Bexhill-on-Sea, E Sussex TN40 1BY*

ILSON, John Robert. b 37. Leeds Univ BSc59 Lon Univ BD64 CertEd65. ALCD63. **d** 64 **p** 65. C Kennington St Mark *S'wark* 64-67; C Sydenham H Trin 67-70; Asst Dir RE *Sheff* 70-77; R Hooton Roberts 70-75; R Hooton Roberts w Ravenfield 75-77; P-in-c Kidderminster St Geo *Worc* 77-81; TR 81-85; P-in-c Powyke from 85. *The Vicarage, 31 The Greenway, Powick, Worcester WR2 4RZ* Worcester (01905) 830270

ILTON, Mrs Jennifer Jane. b 38. Chelsea Coll Lon DipT60. S Dios Minl Tr Scheme 92. **d** 95. NSM Jersey St Sav *Win* from 95. *38 Maison St Louis, St Saviour, Jersey, Channel Islands JE2 7LX* Jersey (01534) 22327

ILYAS, Marilyn. b 51. Oak Hill Th Coll 92. **d** 95. C Roch from 95. *47 Roebuck Road, Rochester, Kent ME1 1UE* Medway (01634) 826821

IMMS, William George Law. b 11. Lich Th Coll 64. **d** 64 **p** 65. C Swindon New Town *Bris* 69-76; Hon C Cricklade w Latton 76-81; rtd 77. *29 Trewartha Park, Weston-super-Mare, Avon BS23 2RR* Weston-super-Mare (01934) 627586

IMPEY, Miss Joan Mary. b 35. Lon Univ CertRK69. Dalton Ho Bris 65. **dss** 74 **d** 87 **p** 94. Kennington St Mark *S'wark* 67-75; Barking St Marg w St Patr *Chelmsf* 75-81; Harwell w Chilton *Ox* 81-87; Par Dn 87-92; Par Dn Didcot All SS 92-94; C from 94. *12 Trent Road, Ladygrove, Didcot, Oxon OX11 7RB* Abingdon (01235) 819306

IMPEY, Mrs Patricia Irene. b 45. Birm Univ BA67. Carl Dioc Tr Course 88. **d** 90 **p** 94. Par Dn Blackpool St Paul *Blackb* 90-94; C from 94. *St John's Vicarage, 19 Leamington Road, Blackpool FY1 4HD* Blackpool (01253) 20626

IMPEY, Canon Richard. b 41. Em Coll Cam BA63 MA67 Harvard Univ ThM67. Ridley Hall Cam 67. **d** 68 **p** 69. C Birm St Martin *Birm* 68-72; Dir of Tr *B & W* 72-79; Dir of Ords 76-79; V Blackpool St Jo *Blackb* from 79; RD Blackpool 84-90; Hon Can Blackb Cathl from 89. *St John's Vicarage, 19 Leamington Road, Blackpool FY1 4HD* Blackpool (01253) 20626

INALL, Mrs Elizabeth. b 47. MCSP69. St As Minl Tr Course 88. **d** 92 **p** 94. NSM Tring *St Alb* from 92. *Jordans, 27 Park Road, Tring, Herts HP23 6BN* Tring (01442) 823718

INCE, Preb Edgar Kenelm Peter. b 16. DFC45. Wells Th Coll 54. **d** 56 **p** 57. R Ashwater *Ex* 66-73; R Ashwater w Halwill and

Beaworthy 73-86; RD Holsworthy 74-80; Preb Ex Cathl 85-86; rtd 86. *Prispen, Longmeadow Road, Lympstone, Exmouth, Devon EX8 5LF* Exmouth (01395) 266597

INCE, Peter Reginald. b 26. Bp's Coll Calcutta 48. **d** 51 **p** 52. R Loddington w Cransley *Pet* 62-75; V Snibston *Leic* 75-79; R Mickleham *Guildf* 79-92; rtd 92. *Bickerton, 8 Rockdale, Headley Road, Grayshott, Hindhead, Surrey GU26 6TU* Hindhead (01428) 604694

IND, Dominic Mark (Brother Dominic Mark). b 63. Lanc Univ BA87. Ridley Hall Cam 87. **d** 90 **p** 91. C Birch w Fallowfield *Man* 90-93; SSF from 93. *The Friary, Hilfield, Dorchester, Dorset DT2 7BE* Cerne Abbas (01300) 341345

IND, Philip William David. b 35. K Coll Lon BD82. Wycliffe Hall Ox 74 Cranmer Hall Dur 59. **d** 65 **p** 66. C Charlton Kings St Mary *Glouc* 67-71; R Woolstone w Gotherington and Oxenton 71-74; Chapl Alleyn's Sch Dulwich 76-81; C Beckenham St Geo *Roch* 83-85; V Bromley St Jo 85-87; Perm to Offic *Ox* 88-91; P-in-c Hurley 91-92; P-in-c Stubbings 91-92; rtd 92. *Stilegate, Tugwood Common, Cookham, Maidenhead, Berks SL6 9TT* Maidenhead (01628) 477425

✠**IND, Rt Rev William.** b 42. Leeds Univ BA64. Coll of Resurr Mirfield 64. **d** 66 **p** 67 **c** 87. C Feltham *Lon* 66-71; C Northolt St Mary 71-73; TV Basingstoke *Win* 73-87; Vice-Prin Aston Tr Scheme 79-82; Dioc Dir of Ords *Win* 82-87; Hon Can Win Cathl 84-87; Suff Bp Grantham *Linc* from 87; Dean Stamford from 87; Hon Can Linc Cathl from 87. *Fairacre, 243 Barrowby Road, Grantham, Lincs NG31 8NP* Grantham (01476) 64722

INDER, Patrick John. b 30. K Coll Lon BD54 AKC54. St Boniface Warminster. **d** 55 **p** 56. V Hanwell St Mellitus *Lon* 61-77; R Rawmarsh w Parkgate *Sheff* 77-80; rtd 80; Hon C Sheff St Matt *Sheff* 82-88; Perm to Offic *Win* 90-92. *7 Woodlands, Triangle, Sowerby Bridge, W Yorkshire HX6 3PD* Halifax (01422) 831003

INESON, David Antony. b 36. DPS. ALCD62. **d** 62 **p** 63. C Sandal St Helen *Wakef* 62-65; C Birm St Geo *Birm* 66-71; V Horton *Bradf* 71-80; RD Bowling and Horton 78-80; V Sedbergh, Cautley and Garsdale 80-86; C Firbank, Howgill and Killington 81-86; TV Langley and Parkfield *Man* 86-88; TR Banbury *Ox* from 92. *The Vicarage, 89 Oxford Road, Banbury, Oxon OX16 9AJ* Banbury (01295) 262370

INGALL, Heber Doveton. b 18. ALCD43. **d** 43 **p** 44. R Benefield *Pet* 56-70; P-in-c Stoke Doyle 63-67; rtd 70. *Pilgrims Lodge, Pilgrims Way, Canterbury, Kent CT4 7LR*

INGAMELLS, Harold Frankish. b 34. Codrington Coll Barbados 56. **d** 59 **p** 60. P-in-c Horbury Bridge *Wakef* 64-73; V Horbury Junction 65-75; V Monk Bretton 75-83; P-in-c Hoyland Swaine 83-84; V Thurlstone 83-84; Chapl Community of St Pet Woking 84-95; rtd 95. *20 Corbie Way, Pickering, N Yorkshire YO18 7JS* Pickering (01751) 477759

INGAMELLS, Ronald Sidney. b 32. MITD. AKC56. **d** 57 **p** 58. C Leeds Gipton Epiphany *Ripon* 57-59; C Gt Yarmouth *Nor* 59-64; Dioc Youth Officer 64-79; Hon C Nor St Pet Mancroft 64-79; Sec Tr Development and Chr Educn Nat Coun YMCAs from 79; P-in-c Lemsford *St Alb* from 79. *7 High Oaks Road, Welwyn Garden City, Herts AL8 7BJ* Welwyn Garden (01707) 327621

INGE, John Geoffrey. b 55. St Chad's Coll Dur BSc77 Keble Coll Ox PGCE79 Dur Univ MA94. Coll of Resurr Mirfield. **d** 84 **p** 85. Asst Chapl Lancing Coll W Sussex 84-86; Jun Chapl Harrow Sch Middx 86-89; Sen Chapl 89-90; V Wallsend St Luke *Newc* from 90. *St Luke's Vicarage, 148 Park Road, Wallsend, Tyne & Wear NE28 7QS* 0191-262 3723

INGHAM, John Edmund. b 34. Reading Univ BA56. Clifton Th Coll 58. **d** 60 **p** 61. C Rodbourne Cheney *Bris* 60-63; C Tunbridge Wells St Jo *Roch* 63-67; V Sevenoaks Weald 67-82; V Farrington Gurney *B & W* 82-92; V Paulton 82-92; RD Midsomer Norton 88-91; R Aspley Guise w Husborne Crawley and Ridgmont *St Alb* from 92. *The Rectory, Aspley Guise, Milton Keynes MK17 8HN* Milton Keynes (01908) 583169

INGHAM, Russell Edward. b 39. Glas Univ MA61 Keble Coll Ox BA63 MA67. Cuddesdon Coll 63. **d** 64 **p** 65. Chapl St Mary's Cathl *Glas* 64-69; Warden St John's Youth Cen Tuebrook Liv 69-71; R Port Glas 71-77; R St Andrews All SS *St And* 77-91; V Ruislip St Martin *Lon* 91-94. *The Vicarage, 13 Eastcote Road, Ruislip, Middx HA4 8BE* Ruislip (01895) 633040

INGHAM, Stephen Charles. b 49. S'wark Ord Course 75. **d** 78 **p** 79. C Lee St Aug *S'wark* 78-82; R Gt w Lt Yeldham *Chelmsf* 82-84; TV Rye *Chich* 84-90; V Alderney *Win* from 90. *The Vicarage, Alderney, Guernsey, Channel Islands GY9 3UE* Alderney (01481) 822335

INGLEBY, Anthony Richard. b 48. Keele Univ BA72. Trin Coll Bris. **d** 83 **p** 84. C Plymouth St Jude *Ex* 83-88; R Lanreath *Truro* from 88; V Pelynt from 88. *The Rectory, Lanreath, Looe, Cornwall PL13 2NU* Lanreath (01503) 220310

INGLEDEW, Peter David Gordon. b 48. Jo Dalton Coll Man CertEd73 Croydon Coll DASS92 CQSW92. AKC77 St Steph

Ho Ox 77. **d** 78 **p** 79. C Whorlton *Newc* 78-81; C Poplar *Lon* 81-83; TV 83-85; V Tottenham H Trin 85-90; Perm to Offic *Chich* from 93. *Address temp unknown*

INGLESBY, Eric Vredenburg (Paul). b 15. Qu Coll Ox BA46 MA63. Wycliffe Hall Ox 63. **d** 64 **p** 64. R Caythorpe *Linc* 66-70; C Scilly Is *Truro* 70-73; C Plymouth St Andr w St Paul and St Geo *Ex* 73-76; rtd 76. *St Helen's House, 7 Magdalene Street, Glastonbury, Somerset BA6 9EW* Glastonbury (01458) 831596 or 831678

INGLESBY, Richard Eric. b 47. Birm Univ BSc69 Bris Univ CertEd74. Wycliffe Hall Ox 85. **d** 87 **p** 88. C Cheltenham Ch Ch *Glouc* 87-92; P-in-c Paulton *B & W* 92-94; V from 94; P-in-c Farrington Gurney 92-94; V from 94. *The Vicarage, Church Street, Paulton, Bristol BS18 5LG* Midsomer Norton (01761) 416581

INGRAM, Bernard Richard. b 40. Lon Coll of Div 66. **d** 66 **p** 67. C Bromley Common St Aug *Roch* 66-70; C Gravesend St Geo 70-74; Chapl Joyce Green Hosp Dartford 75-83; V Dartford St Edm *Roch* 75-83; V Strood St Fran from 83; RD Strood from 91. *St Francis's Vicarage, Galahad Avenue, Strood, Rochester, Kent ME2 2YS* Medway (01634) 717162

INGRAM, Miss Emmeline Jessica Anne (Emily). b 26. Gilmore Ho 53. **dss** 54 **d** 87. Ind Chapl *Chelmsf* 68-82; rtd 86; Leigh-on-Sea St Jas *Chelmsf* 86-87; Hon Par Dn from 87. *73 Bohemia Chase, Leigh-on-Sea, Essex SS9 4PW* Southend-on-Sea (01702) 520276

INGRAM, Gary Simon. b 58. K Coll Lon BD AKC. Ripon Coll Cuddesdon. **d** 83 **p** 84. Chapl Nelson and Colne Coll from 92; C Spalding *Linc* 83-87; C Heaton Ch Ch *Man* 87-89; V Colne H Trin *Blackb* from 89. *Holy Trinity Vicarage, 49 Penrith Crescent, Colne, Lancs BB8 8JS* Colne (01282) 863431

INGRAM, Michael. b 28. St Jo Coll Dur 49. **d** 53 **p** 54. Chapl RAF 60-76; P-in-c St Enoder *Truro* 76-79; rtd 90. *clo The British Embassy, Bonn, Box 2012, BFPO 105*

INGRAM, Peter Anthony. b 53. N Ord Course 83. **d** 86 **p** 87. C Maltby *Sheff* 86-89; TV Gt Snaith 89-92; R Adwick-le-Street from 92. *The Rectory, Village Street, Adwick-le-Street, Doncaster, S Yorkshire DN6 7AD* Doncaster (01302) 723224

INGRAMS, Peter Douglas. b 56. Wheaton Coll Illinois BA77 Ox Univ BA80. Wycliffe Hall Ox 78. **d** 83 **p** 84. C Rowner *Portsm* 83-86; C Petersfield w Sheet 86-90; V Sheet from 90. *Sheet Vicarage, 2 Pulens Lane, Petersfield, Hants GU31 4DB* Petersfield (01730) 263673

INKPEN, Richard John. b 28. AKC56. **d** 58 **p** 59. Chapl Montreux w Gstaad *Eur* 69-70; V Blackmoor *Portsm* 70-93; RD Petersfield 80-85; rtd 94. *69 St Luke's Road, Newton Abbot, Devon TQ12 4ND* Newton Abbot (01626) 65510

INKPIN, David Leonard. b 32. CChem MRSC55 Liv Univ BSc54. E Midl Min Tr Course 83. **d** 86 **p** 87. NSM Market Rasen *Linc* from 86; NSM Legsby from 86; NSM Linwood from 86. *Weelsby House, Legsby Road, Market Rasen, Lincs LN8 3DY* Market Rasen (01673) 843360

INKPIN, Jonathan David Francis. b 60. Mert Coll Ox MA81. Ripon Coll Cuddesdon BA85. **d** 86 **p** 87. C Hackney *Lon* 86-88; Tutor Ripon Coll Cuddesdon 88-90; C Cuddesdon *Ox* 88-90; TV Gateshead *Dur* from 90. *3 Wordsworth Street, Gateshead, Tyne & Wear NE8 3HE* 0191-478 2730

INMAN, John Phillip. b 12. St Jo Coll Dur BA35 DipTh36 MA38. **d** 36 **p** 37. V Grindon *Dur* 56-60; Lic to Offic *Carl* 60-77; rtd 77; Perm to Offic *Carl* from 77. *16 Collingwood Close, Coniston, Cumbria LA21 8DZ* Coniston (015394) 41629

INMAN, Malcolm Gordon. b 33. Edin Th Coll 58. **d** 60 **p** 61. C Lundwood *Wakef* 60-63; C Heckmondwike 63-70; V Wrenthorpe 70-75; Chapl Cardigan Hosp 70-73; Asst Chapl Pinderfields Gen Hosp Wakef 72-73; V Cleckheaton St Jo *Wakef* from 75. *St John's Vicarage, 33 Ashbourne Avenue, Cleckheaton, W Yorkshire BD19 5JH* Cleckheaton (01274) 874896

INMAN, Mark Henry. b 31. Lon Univ BSc53. E Anglian Minl Tr Course 80. **d** 83 **p** 84. Hon C Orford w Sudbourne, Chillesford, Butley and Iken *St E* 83-85; Chapl HM Young Offender Inst Hollesley Bay Colony 85-91; Hon C Alderton w Ramsholt and Bawdsey *St E* 85-92; P-in-c from 92; P-in-c Shottisham w Sutton from 92. *The Rectory, Church Lane, Shottisham, Woodbridge, Suffolk IP12 3HG* Shottisham (01394) 411748

INMAN, Martin. b 50. K Coll Lon BD72 AKC73. St Aug Coll Cant 72. **d** 73 **p** 74. C Bridgnorth St Mary *Heref* 73-77; C Parkstone St Pet w Branksea and St Osmund *Sarum* 77-79; V Willenhall St Anne *Lich* 79-85; Chapl Yeovil Distr Gen Hosp 85-91; TV Yeovil *B & W* 85-88; R Barwick 88-91; Chapl St Helier Gen Hosp from 91. *The Chaplain's Office, The General Hospital, St Helier, Jersey, Channel Islands JE2 3QS* Jersey (01534) 59000

INMAN, Paul Stuart. b 60. R Agric Coll Cirencester HND82 DipAI83 Nottm Univ BTh90. Linc Th Coll 87. **d** 90 **p** 91. C Hulme Ascension *Man* 90-94; CMS from 94; Nigeria from 94.

Crowther Hall, Weoley Park Road, Selly Oak, Birmingham B29 6QT 0121-472 4228

INMAN, Thomas Jeremy (Tom). b 45. Rhodes Univ BA67. St Steph Ho Ox 67. **d** 69 **p** 70. C Deptford St Paul *S'wark* 69-72; S Africa 72-76; P-in-c Donnington *Chich* 76-80; V Hangleton 80-86; V Bosham from 86; RD Westbourne from 91. *The Vicarage, Bosham, Chichester, W Sussex PO18 8HX* Bosham (01243) 573228

INNES, Donald Keith. b 33. St Jo Coll Ox BA56 MA60 Lon Univ BD58. Clifton Th Coll 56. **d** 58 **p** 59. C Harold Hill St Paul *Chelmsf* 58-61; C Ealing Dean St Jo *Lon* 61-65; V Westacre *Nor* 65-70; R Gayton Thorpe w E Walton 65-70; V Woking St Paul *Guildf* 70-78; R Alfold and Loxwood 78-88; V Doddington w Wychling *Cant* 88-90; V Newnham 88-90; V Doddington, Newnham and Wychling from 90. *The Vicarage, The Street, Doddington, Sittingbourne, Kent ME9 0BH* Doddington (0179586) 265

INNES, Donald John. b 32. St Jo Coll Ox BA54 MA. Westcott Ho Cam 56. **d** 56 **p** 57. C St Marylebone St Mark Hamilton Terrace *Lon* 56-58; C Walton-on-Thames *Guildf* 58-67; Chapl Moor Park Coll Farnham 67-76; P-in-c Tilford *Guildf* from 76. *The Vicarage, Tilford, Farnham, Surrey GU10 2DA* Frensham (01252) 792333

INNES, James Michael. b 32. Lon Univ BA56 BD59. Clifton Th Coll 59. **d** 59 **p** 60. C Blackpool St Thos *Blackb* 59-62; Tutor Clifton Th Coll 62-65; V Burton All SS *Lich* 65-73; V Ashton on Mersey St Mary *Ches* 73-90; P-in-c Brereton w Swettenham 90-91; R from 91; Dioc Clergy Widows and Retirement Officer from 93. *The Rectory, Brereton, Sandbach, Cheshire CW11 9RY* Holmes Chapel (01477) 533263

INNES, Robert Neil. b 59. K Coll Cam BA82 MA85. St Jo Coll Dur BA91 DMinlStuds92. **d** 95. C Dur St Cuth *Dur* from 95; Lect St Jo Coll Dur from 95. *Grosvenor House, Farley Mount, Durham DH1 4DZ* 0191-386 5150

INSLEY, Canon Michael George Pitron. b 47. Trin Coll Ox BA69 MA70 Nottm Univ MPhil85. Wycliffe Hall Ox 69. **d** 72 **p** 73. C Beckenham Ch Ch *Roch* 72-76; P-in-c Cowden 76-79; Lect St Jo Coll Nottm 79-85; Lic to Offic *S'well* 79-85; V Tidebrook *Chich* from 85; V Wadhurst from 85; Can and Preb Chich Cathl from 94; P-in-c Stonegate from 95. *The Vicarage, High Street, Wadhurst, E Sussex TN5 6AA* Wadhurst (01892) 782083

INSTRELL, Robert Llewellyn (Rob). b 65. Portsm Poly BSc87 Birm Univ DipTh92. Qu Coll Birm 89. **d** 92 **p** 93. C Acocks Green *Birm* 92-95; Chapl Northn Gen Hosp from 95. *Chaplain's Office, Northampton General Hospital, Cliftonville, Northampton NN1 5RD* Northampton (01604) 34700

INVERNESS, Provost of. See GRANT, Very Rev Malcolm Etheridge

INWOOD, Ven Richard Neil. b 46. Univ Coll Ox BSc70 MA73 Nottm Univ BA73. St Jo Coll Nottm 71. **d** 74 **p** 75. C Fulwood *Sheff* 74-78; C St Marylebone All So w SS Pet and Jo *Lon* 78-81; V Bath St Luke *B & W* 81-89; R Yeovil w Kingston Pitney 89-95; Preb Wells Cathl 90-95; Adn Halifax *Wakef* from 95. *2 Vicarage Gardens, Brighouse, W Yorkshire HD6 3HD* Brighouse (01484) 714553 Fax 711897

ION, Robert Henry. b 18. Pemb Coll Ox BA41 MA44 BD47. Ripon Hall Ox 46. **d** 42 **p** 49. Hd Div Crewe Coll of Educn 56-65; Sen Lect 65-73; R Church Lawton *Ches* 73-78; rtd 78. *25 Leachfield Road, Galgate, Lancaster LA2 0NX* Lancaster (01524) 751653

IORNS, Derrick John. b 11. AKC33. **d** 34 **p** 35. V Maldon All SS w St Pet *Chelmsf* 53-71; R Gt Warley St Mary 71-72; P-in-c Childerditch w Lt Warley 71-72; R Gt Warley w Childerditch 72-81; P-in-c Ingrave 79-81; rtd 81. *45 South Drive, Brentwood, Essex CM1 4DL* Brentwood (01277) 220777

IPGRAVE, Canon Michael Geoffrey. b 58. Or Coll Ox BA78. Ripon Coll Cuddesdon 79. **d** 82 **p** 83. C Oakham, Hambleton, Egleton, Braunston and Brooke *Pet* 82-85; Japan 85-87; TV Leic Ascension *Leic* 87-90; Dioc Chapl Relns w People of Other Faiths from 91; C Leic H Trin w St Jo 91-92; Bp's Dom Chapl from 92; TV Leic H Spirit from 94; Hon Can Leic Cathl from 94. *27 Tudor Road, Leicester LE3 5JF* Leicester (0116) 262 2628

IPSWICH, Archdeacon of. See GIBSON, Ven Terence Allen

IREDALE, Simon Peter. b 56. Cam Univ BA78 MPhil80. Wycliffe Hall Ox 83. **d** 86 **p** 87. C Thirsk *York* 86-89; Asst Chapl Norfolk and Nor Hosp 89-90; P-in-c Kexby w Wilberfoss *York* 90-93; Sub-Chapl HM Pris Full Sutton 90-93; Chapl RAF from 93. *Chaplaincy Services (RAF), HQ, Personnel and Training Command, RAF Innsworth, Gloucester GL3 1EZ* Gloucester (01452) 712612 Ext 5164 Fax 510828

IRELAND, David Arthur. b 45. MICFRM87 Mert Coll Ox BA67 MA71. Cuddesdon Coll 67. **d** 69 **p** 70. C Chapel Allerton *Ripon* 69-72; C Harpenden St Nic *St Alb* 72-76; R Clifton 76-84; Perm to Offic *Guildf* from 95. *43 Harefield Avenue, Cheam, Surrey SM2 7ND* 0181-642 3781

IRELAND

IRELAND, Leslie Sydney. b 55. York Univ BA76. St Jo Coll Nottm 83. **d** 86 **p** 87. C Harwood *Man* 86-89; C Davyhulme St Mary 89-90; V Bardsley from 90. *The Vicarage, Byrth Road, Oldham OL8 2TJ* 0161-624 9004

IRELAND, Mrs Lucy Annabel. b 53. Univ of Zimbabwe BSc74. St Jo Coll Nottm 81. **dss** 85 **d** 87 **p** 95. Mansf St Jo *S'well* 85-87; Hon Par Dn Harwood *Man* 87-89; Hon Par Dn Bardsley 90-95; Hon C from 95. *The Vicarage, Byrth Road, Oldham OL8 2TJ* 0161-624 9004

IRELAND, Mark Campbell. b 60. St Andr Univ MTh81. Wycliffe Hall Ox 82. **d** 84 **p** 85. C Blackb St Gabr *Blackb* 84-87; C Lanc St Mary 87-89; Chapl HM Pris Lanc 87-89; V Baxenden *Blackb* from 89. *The Vicarage, Langford Street, Baxenden, Accrington, Lancs BB5 2RF* Accrington (01254) 232471

IRESON, Arthur Stanley (John). b 05. St Cath Coll Cam BA30 MA34. Ridley Hall Cam 29 Lich Th Coll 30. **d** 30 **p** 31. C Radford *Cov* 30-32; C Hatf *St Alb* 32-36; V Watford St Jas 36-42; Chapl Watford Hosps 36-45; Chapl RAFVR 40-46; Can Res Cov Cathl *Cov* 46-50; Bp's Dom Chapl 46-47; Relig Adv Nat Assn Boys' Clubs 47-69; Teacher Wyggeston Boys' Sch Leic 55-72; Lic to Offic *Leic* 69-72; Hon C Leic St Jas from 72; Hd Master Laurels Coll Leic 72-79. *Trelawny, 348 Victoria Park Road, Leicester LE2 1FX* Leicester (0116) 270 4715

IRESON, Brian Walter. b 41. St Mich Coll Llan DMinlStuds93. **d** 93 **p** 94. C Pemb St Mary and St Mich *St D* from 93. *Church House, 13 Holyland Drive, Pembroke, Dyfed SA71 4BG* Pembroke (01646) 685544

IRESON, David Christopher. b 45. Man Univ TCert67 Birm Univ BEd80. St Steph Ho Ox DipTh93. **d** 93 **p** 94. C Minehead *B & W* from 93. *75 Summerland Avenue, Minehead, Somerset TA24 5BW* Minehead (01643) 702868

IRESON, Ms Gillian Dorothy. b 39. Gilmore Ho 67. **dss** 72 **d** 87 **p** 94. Stepney St Dunstan and All SS *Lon* 72-87; Par Dn 87-94; C from 94. *St Faith's House, Shandy Street, London E1 4ST* 0171-790 4194

IRESON, Philip. b 52. Newc Univ BSc73. St Jo Coll Nottm LTh84. **d** 84 **p** 85. C Owlerton *Sheff* 84-87; V The Marshland 87-94; Perm to Offic *Linc* from 90; Chapl HM Young Offender Inst Hatf 91-92; R Firbeck w Letwell *Sheff* from 94; V Woodsetts from 94. *The Rectory, Letwell, Worksop, Notts S81 8DF* Worksop (01909) 730346

IRESON, Richard Henry. b 46. Linc Th Coll 69. **d** 71 **p** 72. C Spilsby w Hundleby *Linc* 71-74; TV Grantham w Manthorpe 74-76; R Claypole 76-79; P-in-c Westborough w Dry Doddington and Stubton 76-77; R 77-79; R Bratoft w Irby-in-the-Marsh 79-86; V Burgh le Marsh 79-86; V Orby 79-86; R Welton-le-Marsh w Gunby 79-86; R Wyberton from 86. *The Rectory, Wyberton, Boston, Lincs PE21 7AF* Boston (01205) 353593

IRETON, Robert John. b 56. Bris Univ BEd. Oak Hill Th Coll BA. **d** 84 **p** 85. C Bromley Ch Ch *Roch* 84-87; TV Greystoke, Matterdale, Mungrisdale, etc *Carl* 87-90; V Falconwood *Roch* from 90. *The Vicarage, The Green, Welling, Kent DA16 2PG* 0181-298 0065

IRONS, Barry. b 39. Wilson Carlile Coll 57 Coll of Resurr Mirfield 82. **d** 83 **p** 84. CA from 57; C Willersey, Saintbury, Weston-sub-Edge etc *Glouc* 83-85; R Scalford w Goadby Marwood and Wycombe etc *Leic* 85-88; P-in-c Clun w Chapel Lawn, Bettws-y-Crwyn and Newc *Heref* 88-91; Bp's Officer for Evang 91-94; P-in-c Breinton 91-94; P-in-c Weston-super-Mare Cen Par *B & W* from 94. *The Rectory, 24 All Saints Road, Weston-super-Mare, Avon BS23 2NN* Weston-super-Mare (01934) 621958

IRONSIDE, John Edmund. b 31. Peterho Cam BA55 MA59. Qu Coll Birm 55. **d** 57 **p** 58. C Spring Park *Cant* 57-60; C Guernsey St Sampson *Win* 60-63; Thailand 63-66; V Guernsey St Jo *Win* 66-72; V Sholing 72-82; R Guernsey St Sampson from 82; Miss to Seamen from 82. *The Rectory, Grandes Maisons Road, St Sampson, Guernsey, Channel Islands GY2 4JS* Guernsey (01481) 44710

IRVINE, Christopher Paul. b 51. Nottm Univ BTh75 Lanc Univ MA76 St Martin's Coll Lanc PGCE77. Kelham Th Coll 73. **d** 76 **p** 76. Chapl Lanc Univ *Blackb* 76-77; C Stoke Newington St Mary *Lon* 77-80; Chapl Sheff Univ *Sheff* 80-85; Chapl St Edm Hall Ox 85-90; Tutor St Steph Ho Ox 85-90; Vice-Prin St Steph Ho Ox 91-94; V Cowley St Jo *Ox* from 94. *The Vicarage, 271 Cowley Road, Oxford OX4 2AJ* Oxford (01865) 242396

IRVINE, David John. b 50. Trin Coll Cam BA72 MA75. NE Ord Course 91. **d** 94. C Hexham *Newc* from 94. *3 Dipton Close, Hexham, Northd NE46 1UG* Hexham (01434) 604935

IRVINE, Gerard Philip. b 30. QUB BA52. Edin Th Coll 56. **d** 56 **p** 57. Chapl St Andr Cathl *Ab* 56-58; Prec St Andr Cathl 58-59; C Belf Malone St Jo *Conn* 61-66; Chapl Community of St Jo Ev Dublin 67-77; C Dub Sandymount *D & G* from 77. *c/o YWCA of Ireland, Radcliffe Hall, St John's Road, Sandymount, Dublin 4, Irish Republic* Dublin (1) 353-1269

IRVINE, James Clyde. b 35. QUB BA57 NUU BPhil(Ed)83. CITC 59. **d** 59 **p** 60. C Belf St Luke *Conn* 59-62; C Lisburn Ch Ch Cathl 62-65; R Duneane w Ballyscullion 65-69; I Kilbride 69-74; Chapl Ballyclare High Sch from 73. *1A Rathmena Avenue, Ballyclare, Co Antrim BT39 9HX* Ballyclare (01960) 322933

IRVINE, John Dudley. b 49. Sussex Univ BA70. Wycliffe Hall Ox BA80. **d** 81 **p** 82. C Brompton H Trin w Onslow Square St Paul *Lon* 81-85; P-in-c Kensington St Barn 85-94; V from 94. *St Barnabas's Vicarage, 23 Addison Road, London W14 8LH* 0171-371 1451

IRVINE, Preb John Graham Gerard Charles. b 20. Mert Coll Ox BA42 MA46. St Steph Ho Ox 42. **d** 45 **p** 46. V Westmr St Matt *Lon* 69-86; Preb St Paul's Cathl 82-86; rtd 86. *42 Montpelier Road, Brighton, E Sussex BN1 3BA* Brighton (01273) 730039

IRVINE, Very Rev John Murray. b 24. Magd Coll Cam BA45 MA49. Ely Th Coll 46. **d** 48 **p** 49. Can Res and Chan Heref Cathl *Heref* 65-78; Dir of Ords 65-78; Provost S'well 78-91; P-in-c Edingley w Halam 78-91; P-in-c Rolleston w Fiskerton, Morton and Upton 90-91; rtd 91; Perm to Offic *Ex* from 92. *9 Salston Barton, Strawberry Lane, Ottery St Mary, Devon EX11 1RG* Ottery St Mary (01404) 815901

IRVINE, Stanley. b 35. TCD DipTh83. **d** 83 **p** 84. C Arm St Mark w Aghavilly *Arm* 83-85; I Kilmoremoy w Castleconnor, Easkey, Kilglass etc *T, K & A* 85-94; Dom Chapl to Bp of Tuam 88-94; I Stranorlar w Meenglas and Kilteevogue *D & R* from 94. *The Rectory, Stranorlar, Co Donegal, Irish Republic* Ballybofey (74) 31081

IRVINE, William Barry. b 48. QUB BD75. St Jo Coll Nottm 75. **d** 76 **p** 77. C Belf St Mich *Conn* 76-80; C Mansf St Pet *S'well* 80-84; V Chapel-en-le-Frith *Derby* 84-90; Chapl Cheltenham Gen Hosp from 90; Chapl Delancey Hosp from 90. *29 Brookway Drive, Charlton Kings, Cheltenham, Glos GL53 8AJ* Cheltenham (01242) 581649/222222

IRVINE, Mrs Yvonne Patricia. b 41. Sarum & Wells Th Coll 89. **d** 90 **p** 94. C Walton *St E* 90-91; Par Dn 91-93; Par Dn Beccles St Mich 93-94; TV from 94. *Hillcrest, 17 Upper Grange Road, Beccles, Suffolk NR34 9NU* Beccles (01502) 712317

IRVING, Canon Andrew. b 27. St Deiniol's Hawarden 62. **d** 65 **p** 66. C Langley Marish *Ox* 69-73; V Moulsford 73-81; Canada from 81; rtd 92. *204-4630 Ponderosa Drive, Peachland, British Columbia, Canada, V0H 1X0* Peachland (604) 767-9582

IRVING, Canon Donald Richard (Don). b 31. Lon Univ BSc56. Lon Coll of Div 66. **d** 68 **p** 69. C Leic H Trin *Leic* 68-71; Asst Chapl HM Pris Leic 70-71; Chapl to Leic Students 70-71; E Regional Co-ord CPAS 71-76; Dir Ch Soc 76-82; Gen Sec Intercon Ch Soc 82-92; Hon Can Brussels Cathl *Eur* from 83; rtd 92. *83 Alfred Street, Alfreton, Derby DE55 7JD* Alfreton (01773) 520116

IRVING, Leslie. b 09. Keble Coll Ox BA30 DipTh31 MA46. Wycliffe Hall Ox 30. **d** 32 **p** 33. Chapl St Cath Sch Bramley 67-74; rtd 74; Perm to Offic *Chich* 74-83; Perm to Offic *Nor* 83-88. *2 Capel Court, The Burgage, Prestbury, Cheltenham, Glos GL52 3EL* Cheltenham (01242) 576426

IRVING, Canon Michael John Derek. b 43. BEd80. Qu Coll Birm 80. **d** 81 **p** 82. C Coleford w Staunton *Glouc* 81-84; V Dean Forest H Trin 84-91; RD Forest S 88-91; P-in-c Hempsted from 91; Dir of Ords from 91; Hon Can Glouc Cathl from 94. *The Rectory, Hempsted, Gloucester GL2 6LW* Gloucester (01452) 524550

IRWIN, Albert Samuel. b 14. TCD BA38 MA44. CITC 38. **d** 38 **p** 39. V Stamford Baron *Pet* 61-81; P-in-c Tinwell 77-81; rtd 81; Lic to Offic *Pet* 81-85; Perm to Offic from 85; Perm to Offic *Linc* from 91. *19 Water Street, Stamford, Lincs PE9 2NJ*

IRWIN, Alexander John. b 14. Westcott Ho Cam 71. **d** 71 **p** 72. C S Shalford *Chelmsf* 71-75; P-in-c Shalford 75-77; V Wethersfield w Shalford 77-86; rtd 86. *18 Oak Tree Road, Marlow, Bucks SL7 3EE* Marlow (01628) 481722

IRWIN, Francis William. b 29. St Chad's Coll Dur BA52 DipTh54 MA56. **d** 54 **p** 55. R Aldborough w Thurgarton *Nor* 66-80; P-in-c Gunton St Andr w Hanworth 66-80; P-in-c Gresham w Bessingham 75-80; R Aldborough w Thurgarton, Bessingham, Gunton etc 80; R Shipdham 80-81; P-in-c E w W Bradenham 80-81; R Shipdham w E and W Bradenham 81-94; rtd 94; Perm to Offic *Nor* from 94. *2 Thompson Avenue, Holt, Norfolk NR25 6EN* Holt (01263) 711612

IRWIN, John Nesbitt Cottier. b 27. SEN79 Mert Coll Ox BA50 MA53. SW Minl Tr Course 86. **d** 87 **p** 88. NSM Buckfastleigh w Dean Prior *Ex* from 87. *56 Plymouth Road, Buckfastleigh, Devon TQ11 0DH* Buckfastleigh (01364) 43044

IRWIN, Patrick Alexander. b 55. BNC Ox BA77 MA81 Edin Univ BD81. Edin Th Coll 77 Liturgisches Inst Trier 79. **d** 81 **p** 82. Hon C Cam St Botolph *Ely* 81-84; Chapl BNC Ox 84-92; Lect Th 86-92; Lic to Offic *Ox* 85-92; Lic to Offic *B & W* 87-92; Perm to Offic *D & G* from 87; CF from 92; Chapl Udruga Hvrata Sv Dominik Gorazde 94-95. *c/o MOD (Army), Bagshot Park, Bagshot, Surrey GU19 5PL* Bagshot (01276) 471717 Fax 412834

IRWIN, Stewart. b 53. Sarum & Wells Th Coll 80. **d** 83 **p** 84. C Brighouse *Wakef* 83-87; V Stockton St Jo *Dur* from 87. *168 Durham Road, Stockton-on-Tees, Cleveland TS19 0DE* Stockton-on-Tees (01642) 674119

IRWIN, Miss Susan Elizabeth (Sue). b 47. Cam Univ DipRS79. St Jo Coll Dur 77. **dss** 79 **d** 87 **p** 94. Harborne St Faith and St Laur *Birm* 79-82; Caterham *S'wark* 82-87; Par Dn 87-88; Par Dn Kidlington w Hampton Poyle *Ox* 88-94; C 94-95; TV Gt Marlow w Marlow Bottom, Lt Marlow and Bisham from 95. *18 Oak Tree Road, Marlow, Bucks SL7 3EE* Marlow (01628) 481722

IRWIN, Victor. b 32. Lon Coll of Div 64. **d** 66 **p** 67. C Leic H Trin *Leic* 66-68; CF 68-72; V Quarry Bank *Lich* 72-81; P-in-c Hopesay w Edgton *Heref* 81-85; V Lydbury N 81-85; R Wickenby Gp *Linc* 85-88; R Gartcosh *Glas* 88-91; R Airdrie 88-91; I Garrison w Slavin and Belleek *Clogh* from 91. *Garrison Rectory, Garrison, Enniskillen, Co Fermanagh BT93 4AE* Belleek (013656) 85372

IRWIN, William George. b 53. QUB BSc77. CITC 80. **d** 80 **p** 81. C Lisburn St Paul *Conn* 80-83; C Seagoe *D & D* 83-85; C Newtownards w Movilla Abbey 85-88; I Ballymacash *Conn* from 88; RD Lisburn from 91. *St Mark's Rectory, 97 Antrim Road, Lisburn, Co Antrim BT28 3EA* Lisburn (01846) 662393

IRWIN-CLARK, Peter Elliot. b 49. Univ Coll Lon LLB71 St Jo Coll Dur BA81. Cranmer Hall Dur 81. **d** 81 **p** 82. C Kirkheaton *Wakef* 81-86; V Shirley *Win* from 86. *The Vicarage, Wordsworth Road, Southampton S01 5LX* Southampton (01703) 771755

ISAAC, Arthur Kenneth. b 12. St Aug Coll Cant. **d** 62 **p** 63. R Rode, Rode Hill and Woolverton *B & W* 65-72; R Hutton 72-77; rtd 77; Perm to Offic *Ex* 77-86; Perm to Offic *Chich* from 86. *Bungalow No 2, Terry's Cross, Woodmancote, Henfield, W Sussex BN5 9SX* Henfield (01273) 493006

ISAAC, Bryan Raymund. b 09. MBE46. Ch Coll Cam BA31 MA35. Wycliffe Hall Ox 31. **d** 33 **p** 34. V Cudham *Roch* 62-73; rtd 74. *44 Coneygar Lane, Bridport, Dorset DT6 3AT* Bridport (01308) 456273

ISAAC, Canon David Thomas. b 43. Univ of Wales BA65. Cuddesdon Coll 65. **d** 67 **p** 68. C Llan w Capel Llanilltern *Llan* 67-71; P-in-c Swansea St Jas *S & B* 71-73; Chapl Ch in Wales Youth Coun 73-77; V Llangiwg *S & B* 77-79; Dioc Youth Officer *Ripon* 79-83; Nat Officer for Youth Work Gen Syn Bd of Educn 83-90; Dioc Dir of Educn *Portsm* from 90; Can Res Portsm Cathl from 90. *1 Pembroke Close, Portsmouth PO1 2NX* Portsmouth (01705) 818107

ISAAC, Edward Henry. b 20. Qu Coll Cam BA42 MA46. Ridley Hall Cam 45. **d** 47 **p** 48. V Millom St Geo *Carl* 66-85; rtd 85; Perm to Offic *Carl* from 86. *31 Lowther Road, Millom, Cumbria LA18 4PE* Millom (01229) 772332

ISAAC, Canon Philip Davies. b 16. Univ of Wales (Lamp) BA37. Chich Th Coll 38. **d** 42 **p** 43. R Ellon *Ab* 64-72; P-in-c Stornoway *Arg* 72-74 and 78-81; R Dunoon 75-78; Can St Jo Cathl Oban 78-81; rtd 81; Hon Can Cumbrae *Arg* from 81. *Newtonville, Crescent Road, Nairn IV12 4NB* Nairn (01667) 452794

ISAACS, John Kenneth. b 36. Cam Univ MA. E Anglian Minl Tr Course. **d** 82 **p** 83. NSM Ely 82-85; Chapl K Sch Ely 85-94; Lic to Offic *Ely* 85-94; P-in-c Denver from 94; P-in-c Ryston w Roxham from 94; P-in-c W Dereham from 94. *Denver Rectory, Downham Market, Norfolk PE38 0DP* Downham Market (01366) 382127

ISAM, Miss Margaret Myra Elizabeth. b 35. Nottm Univ BEd73. E Midl Min Tr Course 78. **dss** 81 **d** 87 **p** 94. Humberston *Linc* 81-84; Gt Grimsby St Andr and St Luke 85-87; D-in-c 87-93; D-in-c Gt Grimsby St Andr w St Luke and All SS 94; P-in-c from 94. *St Luke's Vicarage, 17 Heneage Road, Grimsby, S Humberside DN32 9DZ* Grimsby (01472) 358007

ISBISTER, Charles. b 27. Chich Th Coll 58. **d** 60 **p** 61. V Cookridge H Trin *Ripon* 67-93; rtd 93. *2 Church Mount, Horsforth, Leeds LS18 5LE* Leeds (0113) 239 0813

ISDELL-CARPENTER, Philip Wynn Howard. b 11. St Jo Coll Ox BA33 MA37. Westcott Ho Cam 35. **d** 36 **p** 37. R Frimley *Guildf* 60-72; rtd 76; Perm to Offic *B & W* from 86. *3 Church Path, Crewkerne, Somerset TA18 7HX* Crewkerne (01460) 74075

ISHERWOOD, David Owen. b 46. BA68 MPhil87. Ridley Hall Cam 76. **d** 78 **p** 79. C Sanderstead All SS *S'wark* 78-82; C Horley 82-84; TV 84-88; P-in-c Streatham Immanuel and St Andr 88-89; V 89-95; TR Clapham TM from 95. *Holy Trinity Vicarage, The Chase, London SW4 0PN* 0171-498 6879

ISHERWOOD, Robin James. b 56. Hull Univ BA78 Uppsala Univ MDiv92. Ripon Coll Cuddesdon DipMin94. **d** 94 **p** 95. C Bramhall *Ches* from 94. *33 Dawlish Close, Bramhall, Stockport, Cheshire SK7 2JD* 0161-440 8415

ISHERWOOD, Samuel Peter. b 34. Lon Coll of Div ALCD62 LTh74. **d** 62 **p** 63. C Bacup St Sav *Man* 62-65; C Man Albert Memorial Ch 65-67; V Livesey *Blackb* 67-79; V Handforth *Ches* from 79; RD Cheadle from 92. *The Vicarage, 36 Sagars Road, Handforth, Wilmslow, Cheshire SK9 3EE* Wilmslow (01625) 524119 or 532145

ISIORHO, Father The Chief David John Phillip. b 58. Liv Poly BA80 Wolv Poly DipPsych89 Warw Univ MA93. Westcott Ho Cam 87. **d** 90 **p** 91. C Nuneaton St Mary *Cov* 90-93; P-in-c Bradf St Oswald Chapel Green *Bradf* from 93. *St Oswald's Vicarage, Christopher Street, Bradford, W Yorkshire BD5 9DH* Bradford (01274) 522053

ISIORHO (nee NORTHALL), Mrs Linda Barbara. b 50. Birm Univ BA72 Worc Coll of Educn PGCE75. Qu Coll Birm 88. **d** 90 **p** 94. C Wood End *Cov* 90-91; Perm to Offic 91-93; Perm to Offic *Bradf* 93-94; NSM Low Moor St Mark from 94. *St Oswald's Vicarage, Christopher Street, Bradford, W Yorkshire BD5 9DH* Bradford (01274) 522053

ISITT, Canon David Edgar Reid. b 28. K Coll Cam BA49 MA53. Wells Th Coll 51. **d** 53 **p** 54. Chapl St Edw K and Martyr Cam *Ely* 68-77; Asst Chapl Trin Hall Cam 68-77; Can Res Bris Cathl *Bris* 77-86; Dir Dioc Sch of Min 77-86; P-in-c Bris Ch Ch w St Ewen and All SS 80-82; Dioc Dir of Ords 81-86; Lic to Offic *Ely* from 87; Acting Dean Trin Hall Cam 89; Tutor Westcott Ho 90; Chapl Fitzw Coll Cam 90-93; rtd 93. *41 Fulbrooke Road, Cambridge CB3 9EE* Cambridge (01223) 358522

ISITT, Norman. b 34. St Jo Coll Dur BA56. Cranmer Hall Dur DipTh59. **d** 59 **p** 60. Billericay Co Sch 64-90; Squirrels Heath Sch Romford 64-90; Althorpe and Keadby Co Sch 66-95; rtd 95. *21 Cambridge Avenue, Bottesford, Scunthorpe, S Humberside DN16 3LT* Scunthorpe (01724) 851489

ISLE OF WIGHT, Archdeacon of. See TURNER, Ven Antony Hubert Michael

ISON, Canon David John. b 54. Leic Univ BA76 Nottm Univ BA78 K Coll Lon PhD85. St Jo Coll Nottm 76. **d** 79 **p** 80. C Deptford St Nic and St Luke *S'wark* 79-85; Lect CA Tr Coll Blackheath 85-88; V Potters Green *Cov* 88-93; Jt Dir SW Min Tr Course *Ex* 93-95; Dioc Officer for Continuing Minl Educn from 93; Can Res Ex Cathl from 95. *12 The Close, Exeter EX1 1EZ* Exeter (01392) 75745

ISON, Mrs Hilary Margaret. b 55. Leic Univ BA76 Nottm Univ DipTh78. Gilmore Course 77 St Jo Coll Nottm DPS79. **d** 87 **p** 94. NSM Deptford St Nic and St Luke *S'wark* 87-88; NSM Potters Green *Cov* 88-90; C Rugby St Andr 90-93; Chapl Exeter Hospicare from 93; Lic to Offic *Ex* from 93. *32 Barnfield Road, Exeter EX1 1RX* Exeter (01392) 72091

ISON, John. Cranmer Hall Dur 47. **d** 81 **p** 82. NSM Stockton St Jo CD *Dur* 81-83; NSM Hawthorn 83-87; rtd 87; Perm to Offic *Dur* from 87. *32 Limbrick Court, Fairfield, Stockton-on-Tees, Cleveland TS19 7QF* Stockton-on-Tees (01642) 588525

ISRAEL, Dr Martin Spencer. b 27. Witwatersrand Univ MB49 MRCP52. **d** 74 **p** 75. Hon C St Mich Cornhill w St Pet le Poer etc *Lon* 74-77; Hon C S Kensington H Trin w All SS 77-82; P-in-c from 83. *Flat 2, 26 Tregunter Road, London SW10 9LS* 0171-370 5160

ISSBERNER, Cllr Norman Gunther Erich. b 34. Fitzw Ho Cam BA58 MA61. Clifton Th Coll 57. **d** 59 **p** 60. C Croydon Ch Ch Broad Green *Cant* 59-61; C Surbiton Hill Ch Ch *S'wark* 61-66; V Egham *Guildf* 66-75; V Wallington H Trin *S'wark* 75-86; UK Chmn Africa Inland Miss from 77; Adv on Miss and Evang *Chelmsf* 86-91; P-in-c Castle Hedingham 91-93; V Clacton St Paul from 93; RD St Osyth from 94. *The Vicarage, 7 St Alban's Road, Clacton-on-Sea, Essex CO15 6BA* Clacton-on-Sea (01255) 424760

ITALY AND MALTA, Archdeacon of. See DEVENPORT, Rt Rev Eric Nash

IVE, Dr Jeremy George Augustus. b 57. Rhodes Univ BA81 Ch Coll Cam PhD87 K Coll Lon MPhil95. Wycliffe Hall Ox DipTh91. **d** 91 **p** 92. NSM Ivybridge w Harford *Ex* 91-95; P-in-c Abbotskerswell from 95. *The Vicarage, Church Path, Abbotskerswell, Newton Abbot, Devon TQ12 5NY* Newton Abbot (01626) 334445

IVE (nee KNOTT), Mrs Pamela Frances. b 58. BEd79. Wycliffe Hall Ox 88. **d** 90. Par Dn Ivybridge w Harford *Ex* 90-95; Par Dn Abbotskerswell from 95. *The Vicarage, Church Path, Abbotskerswell, Newton Abbot, Devon TQ12 5NY* Newton Abbot (01626) 334445

IVELL, Robert William. b 45. Lon Univ BSc71 Liv Univ CertEd Sheff Univ DBS83. Ridley Hall Cam 83. **d** 85 **p** 86. C Wadsley *Sheff* 85-88; V Laughton w Throapham from 88. *The Vicarage, 1 Church Corner, Laughton, Sheffield S31 7YB* Dinnington (01909) 562300

IVENS, Edmund Masters. b 11. Edin Th Coll 37. **d** 37 **p** 38. R Dunbar *Edin* 52-79; rtd 79. *28 Kingsburgh Gardens, East Linton, East Lothian EH40 3BZ* East Linton (01620) 860283

IVESON, Mrs Patricia Jill (Pat). b 35. Cam Univ CertEd55 K Coll Lon DipTh70 BD76 AKC76. **dss** 81 **d** 87 **p** 94. Wilmington *Roch* 81-87; Hon Par Dn 87-94; Hon C from 94; Chapl W Hill Hosp Dartford from 87. *Bransome, Church Hill, Wilmington, Dartford DA2 7EH*   Dartford (01322) 279100

IVEY (nee HODGE), Mrs Marilyn Elizabeth. b 52. Wilson Carlile Coll IDC82 Carl Dioc Tr Course. **d** 89 **p** 94. CA from 82; Par Dn Millom *Carl* 89-92; Par Dn Egremont and Haile 92-94; C from 94. *St John's House, Bigrigg, Egremont, Cumbria CA22 2TU*   Egremont (01946) 811155

IVIN, Miss Maureen. b 34. Gilmore Ho 60. **dss** 85 **d** 87 **p** 94. Grays Thurrock *Chelmsf* 85-87; Par Dn 87-94; C from 94. *Wendover, College Avenue, Grays, Essex RM17 5UW*   Grays Thurrock (01375) 373468

IVISON, Norman William. b 54. Hull Univ BA75 DipEd76. Trin Coll Bris DipHE81 DipTh82. **d** 82 **p** 83. Ecum Liaison Officer BBC Radio Furness 82-85; C Barrow St Mark *Carl* 82-85; Chapl Barrow Sixth Form Coll 83-85; Dioc Broadcasting Officer *Lich* 85-91; Relig Progr Producer BBC Radio Stoke 85-91; Hon C Bucknall and Bagnall *Lich* 85-91; Asst Producer Relig Progr BBC TV Man from 91; Perm to Offic *Man* from 92. *6 Bournelea Avenue, Burnage, Manchester M19 1AF*   0161-442 6490 or 200 2020   Fax 200 2285 or 236 1005

IVORY, Christopher James. b 54. Reading Univ BSc76. Qu Coll Birm DipTh80. **d** 81 **p** 82. C Waltham Cross *St Alb* 81-84; C Is of Dogs Ch Ch and St Jo w St Luke *Lon* 84-88; V Streatham Ch Ch *S'wark* from 88; Lambeth Adnry Ecum Officer from 90. *Christ Church Vicarage, 3 Christchurch Road, London SW2 3ET*   Bristol (0117) 951 1300

IZZARD, David Antony. b 55. Trin Coll Bris DipHE94. **d** 94 **p** 95. C E Bris from 94. *34 Thurstons Barton, Whitehall, Bristol BS5 7BQ*   Bristol (0117) 951 1300

IZZARD, Susan Amanda. b 59. Hatf Poly BA82. Trin Coll Bris BA86. **dss** 86 **d** 87. Birm St Martin w Bordesley St Andr *Birm* 86-89; Par Dn 87-89; C Handsworth St Jas 89-91; Asst Chapl Qu Eliz Hosp Birm 90-91. *Address temp unknown*

J

JACK, Alexander Richard (Alex). b 30. Leeds Univ BSc55 MSc66. Oak Hill Th Coll 69. **d** 71 **p** 72. C Penn Fields *Lich* 71-78; P-in-c 78-83; R Barnston and Lt Dunmow *Chelmsf* from 83; RD Dunmow from 88. *The Rectory, 3 Hylands Close, Barnston, Dunmow, Essex CM6 1LG*   Great Dunmow (01371) 875237

JACK, Canon Henry Graham. b 21. K Coll Lon AKC48 BD49. **d** 49 **p** 50. Chile 65-74; Hon Can Chile 66-74; R Trowbridge St Jas *Sarum* 74-87; Can and Preb Sarum Cathl 83-87; rtd 87. *285A The Common, Holt, Trowbridge, Wilts BA14 6QJ*   Trowbridge (01225) 782776

JACK, Paul Pembroke. b 19. SS Coll Cam BA41. Linc Th Coll 41. **d** 42 **p** 43. V Primrose Hill St Mary *Lon* 55-57; rtd 84. *39 Warren Hill Road, Woodbridge, Suffolk IP12 4DY*   Woodbridge (01394) 386562

JACK, Robin Watson. b 43. Westcott Ho Cam. **d** 90 **p** 91. C Debenham w Aspall and Kenton *St E* 90-93; P-in-c Bacton w Wyverstone and Cotton from 93. *The Rectory, Church Road, Bacton, Stowmarket, Suffolk IP14 4LJ*   Bacton (01449) 781245

JACKLIN, John Frederick. b 30. Oak Hill Th Coll 72. **d** 72 **p** 72. Chile 72-75; C Roxeth Ch Ch *Lon* 75-78; V Selston *S'well* from 78. *The Vicarage, Church Lane, Selston, Nottingham NG16 6EW*   Ripley (01773) 810247

JACKS, David. b 59. Nottm Univ BTh87. Linc Th Coll 84. **d** 87 **p** 88. C Oakham, Hambleton, Egleton, Braunston and Brooke *Pet* 87-90; V Weedon Bec w Everdon from 90. *The Vicarage, Church Street, Weedon, Northampton NN7 4PL*   Weedon (01327) 340359 or 0850 597891

JACKSON, Alan. b 44. Newc Univ BA67 DipEd68 MEd79. NE Ord Course 79. **d** 81 **p** 82. NSM Jesmond H Trin *Newc* 81-82; Chapl Bp Wand's Sch Sunbury-on-Thames 82-89; V Hanworth St Rich *Lon* from 89. *St Richard's Vicarage, 35 Forge Lane, Hanworth, Middx TW13 6UN*   0181-898 0241

JACKSON, Canon Arthur Malcolm. b 31. TCD BA54 MA60. CITC 54. **d** 54 **p** 55. C Templecorran Union *Conn* 54-57; C Dub Santry Union *D & G* 57-58; Bp's V and Registrar *C & O* 58-61; I Monasterevan *M & K* 61-68; I Narraghmore w Fontstown and Timolin *D & G* 68-88; I Narraghmore w Timolin, Castledermot and Kinneagh 88-91; I Killanne w Killegney, Rossdroit and Templeshanbo *C & O* from 91; Preb Ferns Cathl from 93; Bp's Dom Chapl from 93. *The Rectory,*

Clonroche, Enniscorthy, Co Wexford, Irish Republic   Enniscorthy (54) 44180

JACKSON, Barry. b 30. St Jo Coll Cam BA53 DipEd54 MA57. Westcott Ho Cam 63. **d** 65 **p** 66. C Stockport St Geo Ches 65-68; C Bridgwater St Mary, Chilton Trinity and Durleigh *B & W* 68-70; P-in-c Thurloxton 70-75; Chapl Wycliffe Coll Stonehouse Glos 75-88; V Heathfield *Chich* from 88. *The Vicarage, Old Heathfield, Heathfield, E Sussex TN21 9AB*   Heathfield (01435) 862457

JACKSON, Very Rev Dr Brandon Donald. b 34. Liv Univ LLB56 Bradf Univ Hon DLitt90. Wycliffe Hall Ox DipTh59. **d** 58 **p** 59. C New Malden and Coombe *S'wark* 58-61; C Leeds St Geo *Ripon* 61-65; V Shipley St Pet *Bradf* 65-77; Relig Adv Yorkshire TV 69-79; Provost Bradf 77-89; Dean Linc from 89. *The Deanery, 23 Minster Yard, Eastgate, Lincoln LN2 1QG*   Lincoln (01522) 523608

JACKSON, Christopher John Wilson. b 45. St Pet Coll Ox BA67 MA87. Ridley Hall Cam 69. **d** 72 **p** 73. C Putney St Marg *S'wark* 72-76; C Battersea St Pet and St Paul 76-79; TV Preston St Jo *Blackb* 79-87; P-in-c Sandal St Cath *Wakef* 87-90; V Shenley Green *Birm* from 90; RD Kings Norton from 95. *St David's Vicarage, 49 Shenley Green, Birmingham B29 4HH*   0121-475 4874

JACKSON, Canon David. b 33. Leeds Univ BA60. Coll of Resurr Mirfield 60. **d** 62 **p** 63. C Lewisham St Steph *S'wark* 62-65; P-in-c New Charlton H Trin 65-69; C Old Charlton 69-72; Sen Tutor Coll of the Resurr Mirfield 72-75; R Clapham H Trin 75-78; P-in-c Clapham St Pet 76-78; TR Clapham Old Town 78-84; Hon Can S'wark Cathl from 80; V Battersea St Mary-le-Park 84-89; V Surbiton St Andr and St Mark from 89. *St Mark's Vicarage, 1 Church Hill Road, Surbiton, Surrey KT6 4UG*   0181-399 6053

JACKSON, David. b 48. Open Univ BA85. Nazarene Th Coll Man DipTh73 St Deiniol's Hawarden 91. **d** 91 **p** 92. In Nazarene Ch 73-90; C Scotforth *Blackb* 91-95; C Banbury *Ox* from 95. *4 Longfellow Road, Banbury, Oxon OX16 9LB*   Banbury (01295) 264961

JACKSON, David Hilton. b 62. Stanford Univ BA84 Ox Univ MSt94. Princeton Th Sem MDiv90 Wycliffe Hall Ox DipTh95. **d** 95. C Ox St Andr *Ox* from 95. *5 Squitchey Lane, Oxford OX2 7LD*   Oxford (01865) 53944

JACKSON, David Reginald Estcourt. b 25. OBE. Qu Coll Cam BA45 MA49. St Jo Coll Dur 80. **d** 81 **p** 82. Hon C Douglas *Blackb* 81-82; C 82-87; rtd 90. *64 The Common, Parbold, Wigan, Lancs WN8 7EA*   Parbold (01257) 462671

JACKSON, David Robert. b 51. Lon Univ BDS. Linc Th Coll 81. **d** 83 **p** 84. C Hatcham St Cath *S'wark* 83-87; V Sydenham St Bart 87-93. *23 Birkdale Court, Buckland Road, Maidstone, Kent ME16 0UH*   Maidstone (01622) 662483

JACKSON, David William. b 53. Golds Coll Lon BA75 PGCE76. Cranmer Hall Dur 90. **d** 92 **p** 93. C Desborough *Pet* 92-95; C Eastham *Ches* from 95. *107 Eastham Rake, Eastham, Wirral, Merseyside L62 9AW*   0151-327 7533

JACKSON, Canon Derek. b 26. Ex Coll Ox BA51 MA55. Westcott Ho Cam 51. **d** 53 **p** 54. V Boxmoor St Jo *St Alb* 63-74; V Bishop's Stortford St Mich 74-85; Hon Can St Alb 82-85; Bermuda 85-89; P-in-c Cerne Abbas w Godmanstone and Minterne Magna *Sarum* 89-95; rtd 95; Chapl Menorca *Eur* from 95. *Tramontana 18, Sol del Este, 07220 Es Castell, Menorca, Spain*   Menorca (71) 354280

JACKSON, Canon Derek Reginald. b 49. K Coll Lon BD72 AKC72. **d** 73 **p** 74. C Westhoughton *Man* 73-75; C Kendal H Trin *Carl* 75-78; V Pennington w Lindal and Marton 78-83; Warden of Readers 82-92; V Kendal St Geo 83-94; Hon Can Carl Cathl from 89; V Applethwaite from 94; P-in-c Troutbeck from 94. *St Mary's Vicarage, Ambleside Road, Windermere, Cumbria LA23 1BA*   Windermere (015394) 43032

JACKSON, Derrick Raymond. b 20. ALAM. Worc Ord Coll 63. **d** 65 **p** 66. C Headless Cross *Worc* 68-70; R Mamble w Bayton 70; TV Steeple Morden *Ely* 71-80; V Hunningham *Cov* 80-85; V Wappenbury w Weston under Wetherley 80-85; rtd 85; Perm to Offic *Ex* from 85. *9 Cauleston Close, Exmouth, Devon EX8 3LU*   Exmouth (01395) 266615

JACKSON, Doreen May. S Dios Minl Tr Scheme. **d** 88 **p** 94. NSM Fareham H Trin *Portsm* from 88. *134 Oak Road, Fareham, Hants PO15 5HR*   Titchfield (01329) 841429

JACKSON, Mrs Elizabeth Mary. b 41. Man Univ BA67. Ox Min Course 90. **d** 92 **p** 94. Chapl Asst R Berks Hosp Reading from 86; Chapl Asst Reading Hosps from 86; NSM Reading St Luke w St Bart *Ox* from 92. *2 Belle Avenue, Reading RG6 2BL or, Royal Berkshire Hospital, London Road, Reading RG1 5AN*   Reading (01734) 264149 or 875111

JACKSON, Mrs Frances Anne (Peggy). b 51. FCA81 ACA76 Somerville Coll Ox BA72 MA76. Ripon Coll Cuddesdon 85. **d** 87 **p** 94. C Ilkeston St Mary *Derby* 87-90; TD Hemel Hempstead *St Alb* 90-94; TV from 94. *St Paul's Vicarage, 23 Saturn Way, Hemel Hempstead, Herts HP2 5NY*   Hemel Hempstead (01442) 255023

JACKSON, Frank James. b 48. ACIS76 Man Univ CertEd77 Open Univ BA88. E Anglian Minl Tr Course 88. **d** 91 **p** 92. NSM Coggeshall w Markshall *Chelmsf* from 91. *41 Tilkey Road, Coggeshall, Colchester CO6 1PQ* Coggeshall (01376) 562910

JACKSON, Miss Freda. b 41. Bp Otter Coll TCert61 Local NSM Course 89. **d** 92 **p** 94. NSM Middleton *Man* 92-94; NSM Middleton St Leon w Thornham St Jo from 94. *783 Manchester Old Road, Middleton, Manchester M24 4RE* 0161-653 5876

JACKSON, Frederick George. b 43. Leeds Univ BA70. Cuddesdon Coll 70. **d** 72 **p** 73. C Cirencester *Glouc* 72-74; C Kilburn St Aug w St Jo *Lon* 74-77; C Pimlico St Mary Graham Terrace 77-81; Bp's Dom Chapl *Chich* 81-86; V Brighton St Mich from 86. *St Michael's Clergy House, 6 Montpelier Villas, Brighton BN1 3AH* Brighton (01273) 727362

JACKSON, George. b 10. St Jo Coll Dur LTh33 BA35 MA39. St Aid Birkenhead 30. **d** 35 **p** 36. V Woodplumpton *Blackb* 53-74; C Broughton 74-77; rtd 75. *Fosbrooke House, 8 Clifton Drive, Lytham St Annes FY8 5RE* Lytham (01253) 737680

JACKSON, Harry Francis. b 30. FBOA FSMC FBCO K Coll Lon BD61 AKC61. Sarum Th Coll 61. **d** 62 **p** 62. Bermuda 62-65; C Cobham *Guildf* 65-69; R Ash from 69; Chapl RAF Farnborough from 80. *The Rectory, Church Road, Ash, Aldershot, Hants GU12 6LU* Aldershot (01252) 21517

JACKSON, Hilary Walton. b 17. St Chad's Coll Dur BA40 MA48. **d** 46 **p** 47. V Heighington *Dur* 66-82; rtd 82. *127 Bates Avenue, Darlington, Co Durham DL3 0UE* Darlington (01325) 482746

JACKSON, Hubert Edwyn Alston. b 08. MIEE67. Ripon Hall Ox DipTh56. **d** 58 **p** 59. V Ilton *B & W* 61-79; V Isle Abbots 62-79; rtd 79; Perm to Offic *B & W* 79-94. *6 Ash Court, Stanway Close, Greenway Road, Taunton, Somerset TA2 6NJ* Taunton (01823) 284510

JACKSON, Ian. b 53. Jes Coll Ox BA75. Linc Th Coll 76. **d** 78 **p** 79. C Holbeach *Linc* 78-82; V Newsome *Wakef* 82-85; V Newsome and Armitage Bridge from 85. *The Vicarage, Newsome, Huddersfield HD4 6QU* Huddersfield (01484) 420664

JACKSON, John Edward. b 29. K Coll Lon BD57 AKC57. **d** 58 **p** 59. C Crofton Park St Hilda w St Cypr *S'wark* 58-61; V Bremhill w Foxham *Sarum* 61-69; V Netheravon w Fittleton 69-73; V Netheravon w Fittleton and Enford 73-85; V Salisbury St Mark 85-92; P-in-c Bryngwyn and Newchurch and Llanbedr etc *S & B* from 92. *The Rectory, Rhosgoch, Builth Wells, Powys LD2 3JU* Painscastle (01497) 851260

JACKSON, John Reginald. b 25. Selw Coll Cam BA45 MA49. Ridley Hall Cam 45. **d** 48 **p** 49. R Georgeham *Ex* 67-73; V Abbotsley *Ely* 73-79; V Everton w Tetworth 73-79; V Waresley 73-79; P-in-c Garway *Heref* 79-85; P-in-c St Weonards w Orcop 79-85; P-in-c Tretire w Michaelchurch and Pencoyd 79-85; P-in-c Welsh Newton w Llanrothal 79-85; rtd 85; Perm to Offic *Heref* from 85. *4 Rosemary Gardens, Hereford HR1 1UP* Hereford (01432) 270271

JACKSON, Preb John Wilson. b 14. St Jo Coll Dur BA38. Wycliffe Hall Ox 38. **d** 40 **p** 41. RD Walsall *Lich* 68-81; V Walsall 68-81; Preb Lich Cathl 72-81; rtd 81; Perm to Offic *Birm* from 82. *6 Arnold Grove, Shirley, Solihull, W Midlands B90 3JR* 0121-744 1288

JACKSON, Miss Kathryn Dianne. b 64. Leeds Univ BA87. St Steph Ho Ox 87. **d** 90 **p** 94. Par Dn Headingley *Ripon* 90-94; C 94; C Hawksworth Wood from 94. *St Andrew's House, Butcher Hill, Leeds LS16 5BG* Leeds (0113) 278 4560

JACKSON, Kenneth Evans. b 30. Kelham Th Coll 50. **d** 54 **p** 55. R Lewtrenchard w Thrushelton *Ex* 67-77; P-in-c Stowford 73-77; P-in-c Malborough w S Huish 77-83; P-in-c W Alvington w S Milton 82-83; V Malborough w S Huish, W Alvington and Churchstow 83-86; P-in-c Lustleigh 86-95; NSM from 95; rtd 95. *28 Staddons View, Bovey Tracey, Newton Abbot, Devon TQ13 9HN* Bovey Tracey (01626) 83276

JACKSON, Kenneth William (Ken). b 30. MCSP53. Chich Th Coll 70. **d** 72 **p** 73. C Eastney *Portsm* 72-74; C Portchester 75-79; V Elson from 79. *St Thomas's Vicarage, 21 Elson Road, Gosport, Hants PO12 4BL* Gosport (01705) 582824

JACKSON, Very Rev Lawrence. b 26. AKC50. **d** 51 **p** 52. V Cov H Trin *Cov* 65-73; Hon Can Cov Cathl 67-73; RD Cov N 68-73; Provost Blackb 73-92; rtd 92; Perm to Offic *Cov* from 93. *Northcot, Brook Lane, Newbold on Stour, Stratford-upon-Avon, Warks CV38 8UA* Stratford-upon-Avon (01789) 450721

JACKSON, Margaret Elizabeth. b 47. Lon Univ BSc68 MIPM89. S'wark Ord Course DipRS83. **dss** 83 **d** 92 **p** 94. Surbiton Hill Ch Ch *S'wark* 83-84; Saffron Walden w Wendens Ambo and Littlebury *Chelmsf* 84-85; Dulwich St Barn *S'wark* 86-92; Hon C from 92; Personal Asst to Bp S'wark 92-94. *4 Ferrings, College Road, London SE21 7LU* 0181-299 1872

JACKSON, Mrs Margaret Elizabeth. b 47. Mon Dioc Tr Scheme. **d** 87 **p** 94. C Chepstow *Mon* 87-90; C Exhall *Cov* 90-92; C Leamington Priors All SS from 92. *The Vicarage, Leam Terrace, Leamington Spa, Warks CV31 1BQ* Leamington Spa (01926) 425083

JACKSON, Mrs Margaret Jane. b 50. RGN72 S Bank Poly HDipHV75. S'wark Ord Course 89. **d** 92 **p** 94. Par Dn Hatcham St Cath *S'wark* 92-94; C from 94. *26 Millmark Grove, London SE14 6RQ* 0181-692 4645 or 732 4343

JACKSON, Mark Harding. b 51. Open Univ BA87. Sarum & Wells Th Coll 76. **d** 79 **p** 80. C Hobs Moat *Birm* 79-83; Chapl RN from 83. *Directorate Gen, RN Chapl Services, Room 203, Victory Building, HM Naval Base, Portsmouth PO1 3LS* Portsmouth (01705) 727903 Fax 727112

JACKSON, Martin. b 56. Clare Coll Cam BA77 MA81. Cranmer Hall Dur BA80. **d** 81 **p** 82. C Houghton le Spring *Dur* 81-84; C Bishopwearmouth St Mich w St Hilda 84-86; TV Winlaton 86; V High Spen and Rowlands Gill 86-94; P-in-c Benfieldside from 94. *St Cuthbert's Vicarage, Church Bank, Consett, Co Durham DH8 0NW* Consett (01207) 503019

JACKSON, Michael Geoffrey St Aubyn. b 56. TCD BA79 MA82 St Jo Coll Cam BA81 MA85 PhD86 Ch Ch Ox MA89 DPhil89. CITC 86. **d** 86 **p** 87. C Dub Zion Ch *D & G* 86-89; Chapl Ch Ch Ox from 89. *Christ Church, Oxford OX1 1DP* Oxford (01865) 276236

JACKSON, Canon Michael James. b 25. Trin Hall Cam BA50 MA58. Wells Th Coll 51. **d** 55 **p** 57. V Doncaster St Geo *Sheff* 69-73; Hon Can Sheff Cathl 71-73; RD Nottm *S'well* 73-90; City Dean 86-91; Hon Can S'well Minster 73-91; V Nottm St Mary 73-78; P-in-c Nottm St Cath 75-78; P-in-c N Wilford St Faith 76-83; V Nottm St Mary and St Cath 78-91; rtd 91. *10 Church End, Nether Broughton, Melton Mowbray, Leics LE14 3ET* Melton Mowbray (01664) 822923

JACKSON, Michael James. b 44. CEng69 MICE69 Liv Univ BEng65 Newc Univ PhD84. NE Ord Course 82. **d** 84 **p** 85. C Houghton le Spring *Dur* 84-87; V Millfield St Mark from 87. *The Vicarage, Hylton Road, Sunderland SR4 7BN* 0191-565 6372

JACKSON, Michael Richard. b 31. Selw Coll Cam BA54 MA58. Westcott Ho Cam 54. **d** 56 **p** 57. C Gosforth All SS *Newc* 56-62; R Dinnington *Sheff* 62-76; V Swinton from 76. *The Vicarage, 50 Golden Smithies Lane, Swinton, Mexborough, S Yorkshire S64 8DL* Mexborough (01709) 582259

JACKSON, Neil Lawrence. b 35. ACII Lon Univ BD71. Lon Coll of Div 68 St Jo Coll Nottm 70. **d** 71 **p** 72. C Wealdstone H Trin *Lon* 71-75; C Worthing H Trin *Chich* 75-78; V Bowling St Steph *Bradf* 78-87; RD Bowling and Horton 83-87; V Kensal Rise St Mark and St Martin *Lon* from 87. *Kensal Rise Vicarage, 93 College Road, London NW10 5EU* 0181-969 4598

JACKSON, Canon Noel Benjamin. b 26. TCD BA50 MA55. **d** 51 **p** 52. I Belf Upper Malone (Epiphany) *Conn* 66-82; RD S Belf 79-82; I Carnmoney 82-94; Preb Castleknock St Patr Cathl Dub 86-94; rtd 94. *6 Kingsfort Lodge, Moira, Craigavon, Co Armagh BT67 0GQ* Moira (01846) 619802

JACKSON, Norman. b 14. St Jo Coll Dur BA39 DipTh40 MA42. **d** 40 **p** 41. R St Mewan *Truro* 69-79; rtd 80; Perm to Offic *Carl* from 82. *23 Riverbank Road, Kendal, Cumbria LA9 5JS*

JACKSON, Norman. b 20. CEng MIMechE53. S'wark Ord Course 74. **d** 77 **p** 78. NSM Erith Ch Ch *Roch* 77-82; Hon C Bishopstoke *Win* from 82. *7 Otter Close, Eastleigh, Hants SO5 6NF* Southampton (01703) 695045

JACKSON, Peter. b 39. Open Univ BA81. St Jo Coll Nottm LTh85. **d** 85 **p** 86. C Clifton *York* 85-88; Chapl Clifton Hosp York 85-88; TV Moor Allerton *Ripon* from 88. *73 The Avenue, Leeds LS17 7NP* Leeds (0113) 267 8487

JACKSON, Peter Jonathan Edward. b 53. St Pet Coll Ox BA74 MA78 PGCE78. St Steph Ho Ox 79. **d** 79 **p** 80. C Malvern Link w Cowleigh *Worc* 79-82; Hon C Ox St Mich w St Martin and All SS *Ox* 79-80; Chapl Aldenham Sch Herts 82-89; Chapl and Hd of RE Harrow Sch from 89; Perm to Offic *Lon* from 89. *Field House South, West Street, Harrow, Middx HA1 3ER* 0181-869 1225

JACKSON, Peter Lewis. b 34. Bps' Coll Cheshunt 63. **d** 66 **p** 67. C Stockingford *Cov* 66-67; C Kenilworth St Nic 67-72; P-in-c Napton on the Hill 72-75; V 75-89; V Lower Shuckburgh 75-89; R Napton-on-the-Hill, Lower Shuckburgh etc from 89. *The Vicarage, Napton, Rugby, Warks CV23 8NE* Southam (01926) 812383

JACKSON, Peter William. b 35. Sarum Th Coll 67. **d** 68 **p** 69. C Skelton in Cleveland *York* 68-69; C Upleatham 68-70; Chapl RN 70-92; Miss to Seamen from 92; Japan from 92. *Port PO Box 709, Kobe 651-01, Japan* Kobe (78) 331-1696 Fax 331-1612

JACKSON, Reginald. b 05. Lon Coll of Div 44. **d** 45 **p** 46. V Sissinghurst *Cant* 58-70; rtd 70; Master St Jo Hosp Bath 70-75;

JACKSON

Perm to Offic *B & W* 70-91. *10 The Meads, Milborne Port, Sherborne, Dorset DT9 5DS* Milborne Port (01963) 250279

JACKSON, Reginald Grant. b 03. Birm Univ BA29. Ripon Hall Ox 28. **d** 29 **p** 30. C Bordesley St Andr *Birm* 29-31; C Moseley St Mary 31-32; C Keston *Roch* 32-35; I Saul *D & D* 35-37; I Saul w Whitminster 37-43; V Painswick *Glouc* 43-54; Canada from 62. *200 Main Street, Ailsa Craig, Ontario, Canada, N0M 1A0*

JACKSON, Richard Charles. b 61. CCC Ox BA83 Cranfield Inst of Tech MSc85. Trin Coll Bris DipHE94. **d** 94 **p** 95. C Lindfield *Chich* from 94. *2 Church Close, Frances Road, Lindfield, Haywards Heath, W Sussex RH16 2JB* Lindfield (01444) 483945

JACKSON, Robert Brandon. b 61. Lanchester Poly BA86 Ox Univ BA88. Wycliffe Hall Ox 86. **d** 89 **p** 90. C Bromley Common St Aug *Roch* 89-92; P-in-c Stowe *Ox* from 92; Asst Chapl Stowe Sch Bucks from 92. *Stowe Vicarage, Dadford, Buckingham MK18 5JX* Buckingham (01280) 812285

JACKSON, Robert Fielden. b 35. St D Coll Lamp BA57. Sarum Th Coll 57. **d** 59 **p** 60. C Altham w Clayton le Moors *Blackb* 59-62; C Lytham St Cuth 62-64; V Skerton St Chad 64-69; V Preesall 69-90; RD Garstang 85-89; V Wray w Tatham and Tatham Fells from 90. *The Vicarage, Main Street, Wray, Lancaster LA2 8QF* Hornby (015242) 21030

JACKSON, Ven Robert Stewart. ALCM48 TCD BA53 MA56. CITC 54. **d** 54 **p** 55. C Aghalee *D & D* 54-57; I Derrybrusk *Clogh* 57-61; I Magheracross 61-68; I Lisnaskea 68-91; Chapl to Bp Clogh 73-80; Preb Clogh Cathl 79-85; Preb Donaghmore St Patr Cathl Dub 85-91; Dioc Registrar *Clogh* 89-91; Preb Sligo Cathl *K, E & A* from 91; Adn Elphin and Ardagh from 91; I Templemichael w Clongish, Clooncumber etc from 91; P-in-c Roscommon w Donamon, Rathcline, Kilkeevin etc from 92; Dir of Ords from 93. *St John's Rectory, Battery Road, Longford, Irish Republic* Longford (43) 46442

JACKSON, Robert William. b 49. K Coll Cam MA73 Man Univ MA. St Jo Coll Nottm 78. **d** 81 **p** 82. C Fulwood *Sheff* 81-84; V Grenoside 84-92; Chapl Grenoside Hosp Sheff 84-92; V Scarborough St Mary w Ch Ch and H Apostles *York* from 92. *The Vicarage, The Crescent, Scarborough, N Yorkshire YO11 2PP* Scarborough (01723) 371354

JACKSON, Roger. b 57. Chich Th Coll 85. **d** 88 **p** 89. C Hale *Guildf* 88-92; V Barton w Peel Green *Man* 92-95; P-in-c Long Crendon w Chearsley and Nether Winchendon *Ox* from 95. *The Vicarage, Long Crendon, Aylesbury, Bucks HP18 9AL* Long Crendon (01844) 208363

JACKSON, Canon Roger Brumby. b 31. Dur Univ BSc53 DipEd54. Ridley Hall Cam 57. **d** 59 **p** 60. C Rowner *Portsm* 59-61; C Drypool St Columba w St Andr and St Pet *York* 61-64; Asst Chapl HM Pris Hull 61-64; V Plumstead St Jas w St Jo *S'wark* 65-68; P-in-c Plumstead St Paul 65-68; V Plumstead St Jo w St Jas and St Paul 68-74; Sub-Dean Woolwich 71-74; Chapl Hulton Hosp Bolton from 74; V Deane *Man* 74-80; TR from 80; AD Deane 80-85; Hon Can Man Cathl from 90. *Deane Rectory, 234 Wigan Road, Bolton BL3 5QE* Bolton (01204) 61819

JACKSON, Preb Roland Francis. b 20. Univ of Wales (Lamp) BA42. St Mich Coll Llan 42. **d** 44 **p** 45. V Stafford St Paul Forebridge *Lich* 61-72; RD Eccleshall 72-82; Chapl HM Pris Drake Hall 75-85; V Eccleshall *Lich* 72-85; Preb Lich Cathl 82-85; rtd 85; Perm to Offic *Lich* from 85. *Treginnis, 29 Meadow Drive, Haughton, Stafford ST18 9HQ* Stafford (01785) 780571

JACKSON, Canon Ronald William (Ron). b 37. ALCD. **d** 69 **p** 70. C Crofton *Portsm* 69-74; V Wolv St Matt *Lich* 74-85; V Bloxwich 85-89; C Tamworth 89-92; Bp's Officer for Par Miss & Development *Bradf* from 92; Hon Can Bradf Cathl from 94. *6 Woodvale Crescent, Bingley, W Yorkshire BD16 4AL* Bradford (01274) 565789

JACKSON, Stanley. b 21. St Cath Soc Ox BA48 MA52. Linc Th Coll 48. **d** 50 **p** 51. R Lt Coates *Linc* 68-77; R Bradley 75-77; TR Gt and Lt Coates w Bradley 78; R Ruskington 78-86; V Dorrington 78-82; Can and Preb Linc Cathl from 79; rtd 86. *73A Lincoln Road, Ruskington, Sleaford, Lincs NG34 9AR* Ruskington (01526) 832821

JACKSON, Canon Stephen Alexander. b 18. Keble Coll Ox BA40 MA44. Cuddesdon Coll 40. **d** 42 **p** 43. R Aylestone *Leic* 65-83; RD Christianity (Leic) S 74-81; Hon Can Leic Cathl 74-81; rtd 83; Perm to Offic *Leic* from 83. *34 Bradgate Drive, Wigston, Leics LE18 1HA* Leicester (0116) 288 1564

JACKSON, Thomas Peter. b 27. Univ of Wales (Lamp) BA50. St Mich Coll Llan 50. **d** 52 **p** 53. V Glouc St Steph *Glouc* 60-73; R Upton St Leonards 73-92; RD Glouc N 82-91; rtd 92. *44 Grebe Close, Gloucester GL4 9XL* Gloucester (01452) 306634

JACKSON, William Stafford. b 48. Sunderland Poly DCYW83. Linc Th Coll. **d** 89 **p** 90. C Heworth St Mary *Dur* 89-91; C

Tudhoe Grange 91-92. *10 Merrington Close, Kirk Merrington, Spennymoor, Co Durham DL16 7HU* Spennymoor (01388) 815061

JACKSON, Canon William Stanley Peter. b 39. Univ of Wales DipTh66. St Mich Coll Llan 63. **d** 66 **p** 67. C Llandrindod w Cefnllys *S & B* 66-69; C Gowerton w Waunarlwydd 69-73; V Crickadarn w Gwenddwr and Alltmawr 73-79; V Llanfeugan and Llanthetty and Glyncollwng etc from 79; Dioc GFS Chapl from 84; Can Res Brecon Cathl from 90. *The Rectory, Talybont-on-Usk, Brecon, Powys LD3 7UX* Talybont-on-Usk (0187487) 243

JACKSON-STEVENS, Preb Nigel. b 42. St Steph Ho Ox. **d** 68 **p** 69. C Babbacombe *Ex* 68-73; P-in-c W Buckland 73-75; V Swimbridge 73-75; V Swimbridge and W Buckland 75-84; P-in-c Mortehoe 84-85; P-in-c Ilfracombe, Lee, W Down, Woolacombe and Bittadon 84-85; TR Ilfracombe, Lee, Woolacombe, Bittadon etc from 85; RD Barnstaple from 93; Preb Ex Cathl from 95. *The Vicarage, St Brannock's Road, Ilfracombe, Devon EX34 8EG* Ilfracombe (01271) 863467

JACOB, Mrs Amelia Stanley. b 52. Punjab Univ BA73. Oak Hill Th Coll. **d** 90 **p** 94. NSM Asian Chr Congr All SS Tufnell Park *Lon* 90-92; NSM Alperton from 92. *62 Clifford Road, Wembley, Middx HA0 1AE* 0181-902 4592

JACOB, John Lionel Andrew. b 26. Selw Coll Cam BA50 MA54. Westcott Ho Cam 50. **d** 52 **p** 53. V Sheff St Aid w St Luke *Sheff* 67-75; TR Sheff Manor 75-82; R Waddington *Linc* 82-91; rtd 91; Perm to Offic *Linc* from 91. *1 Woburn Avenue, Lincoln LN1 3HJ* Lincoln (01522) 513772

JACOB, Joseph. b 38. CITC 65. **d** 68 **p** 69. C Belf St Aid *Conn* 68-70; Bp's Dom Chapl 70-71; I Kilscoran *C & O* 71-80; I Geashill *M & K* 80-83; Asst Warden Ch's Min of Healing from 83; Gen Sec (Ireland) CMJ 87-91; I Ardamine w Kiltennel, Glascarrig etc *C & O* from 91. *Ardamine Rectory, Courtown Harbour, Gorey, Co Wexford, Irish Republic* Gorey (55) 25423

JACOB, Canon William Mungo. b 44. Hull Univ LLB66 Linacre Coll Ox BA69 MA73 Ex Univ PhD. St Steph Ho Ox 70. **d** 70 **p** 71. C Wymondham *Nor* 70-73; Asst Chapl Ex Univ *Ex* 73-75; Dir Past Studies Sarum & Wells Th Coll 75-80; Vice-Prin 77-80; Selection Sec and Sec Cttee for Th Educn ACCM 80-86; Warden Linc Th Coll from 85; Can Linc Cathl *Linc* from 86; Hon C Linc Minster Gp from 88. *The Warden's House, Lincoln Theological College, Drury Lane, Lincoln LN1 3BP* Lincoln (01522) 538885

JACOBS, Michael David. b 41. Ex Coll Ox BA63 MA67. Chich Th Coll 63. **d** 65 **p** 66. C Walthamstow St Pet *Chelmsf* 65-68; Chapl Sussex Univ *Chich* 68-72; Student Counsellor Leic Univ 72-84; Lect Adult Educn Dept from 84; Dir Cen for Past Care and Counselling 84-91. *Vaughan College, St Nicholas' Circle, Leicester LE1 4LB* Leicester (0116) 251 7368

JACOBS, Neville Robertson Eynesford. b 32. Lon Coll of Div ALCD59 LTh74. **d** 59 **p** 60. C Chesham St Mary *Ox* 59-62; CMS 62-67; C Keynsham *B & W* 67-71; R Croscombe and Dinder 72-80; R Pilton w Croscombe, N Wootton and Dinder 80-83; V Biddenham *St Alb* 83-89; V Chipping Sodbury and Old Sodbury *Glouc* from 89; RD Hawkesbury 91-94. *The Vicarage, Horse Shoe Lane, Chipping Sodbury, Bristol BS17 6ET* Chipping Sodbury (01454) 313159

JACOBSON, William Walter. b 24. Cant Univ (NZ) LTh51. **d** 51 **p** 52. V Shiphay Collaton *Ex* 59-77; TV Clyst St George, Aylesbeare, Clyst Honiton etc 77-78 and 80-84; R Clyst St Mary, Clyst St George etc 85-89; C Ottery St Mary 79-80; Dioc Communications Officer 83-89; rtd 89; Perm to Offic *Ex* from 89. *5 Clyst Valley Road, Clyst St Mary, Exeter EX5 1DD* Topsham (01392) 874304

JACQUET, Trevor Graham. b 56. Man Univ BSc77. Oak Hill Th Coll BA88. **d** 88 **p** 89. C Deptford St Nic and St Luke *S'wark* 88-92; Chapl HM Pris Brixton from 92. *The Chaplain's Office, HM Prison Brixton, PO Box 369, Jebb Avenue, London SW2 5XF* 0181-674 9811 Fax 674 6128

JACSON, Edward Shallcross Owen. b 38. St Steph Ho Ox 61. **d** 64 **p** 65. C Yate *Glouc* 64-67; C Churchdown 67-71; P-in-c Sandhurst 71-75; V Sherborne w Windrush and the Barringtons 75-76; V Sherborne, Windrush, the Barringtons etc 76-80; TV Shaston *Sarum* 80-87; Perm to Offic from 88. *Grove Farm, Melbury Abbas, Shaftesbury, Dorset SP7 0DE* Shaftesbury (01747) 853688

JAGE-BOWLER, Christopher William. b 61. Nottm Univ BA83 Ch Ch Ox PGCE84 Down Coll Cam BA89. Ridley Hall Cam 87. **d** 90 **p** 91. C Downend *Bris* 90-94; Chapl Bris Univ from 94; C Bris St Mich and St Paul from 94. *21 St Paul's Road, Clifton, Bristol BS8 1LR* Bristol (0117) 973 3963

JAGGER, Ian. b 55. K Coll Cam BA77 MA81 St Jo Coll Dur BA80 MA87. Cranmer Hall Dur 78. **d** 82 **p** 83. C Twickenham St Mary *Lon* 82-85; P-in-c Willen *Ox* 85-87; TV Stantonbury and Willen 87-94; TR Fareham H Trin *Portsm* from 94; Dioc Ecum Officer from 94. *The Rectory, 9 Brook Meadow, Fareham, Hants PO15 5JH* Fareham (01329) 280180

JAGGER, Dr Peter John. b 38. FRHistS78 Leeds Univ MPhil76 PhD87. Lambeth MA71 Wesley Coll Leeds 62 Coll of Resurr Mirfield 67. **d** 68 **p** 69. C Leeds All SS *Ripon* 68-71; V Bolton w Redmire 71-77; Warden and Chief Lib St Deiniol's Lib Hawarden from 77; Dir of Self Supporting Min from 77; Perm to Offic *Ches* from 77; Lic to Offic *St As* from 77. *St Deiniol's Library, Hawarden, Deeside, Clwyd CH5 3DF* Hawarden (01244) 532350 Fax 520643

JAGGER (nee GREEN), Mrs Ruth Valerie. b 56. Ex Univ CertEd77. Ox NSM Course 87. **d** 90 **p** 94. NSM Stantonbury and Willen *Ox* 90-94; NSM Fareham H Trin *Portsm* from 94. *The Rectory, 9 Brook Meadow, Fareham, Hants PO15 5JH* Fareham (01329) 280180

JAGGS, Michael Richard Moore. S Dios Minl Tr Scheme. **d** 95. NSM Hook *Win* from 95. *Turnpike Field, London Road, Hartley Wintney, Hook, Hants RG27 8HY* Hartley Wintney (01252) 842658

JAGO, Alfred Douglas James. b 08. Leeds Univ BA30. Coll of Resurr Mirfield 30. **d** 32 **p** 33. R St Stephen in Brannel *Truro* 65-76; RD St Austell 71-76; rtd 76; Hon C Charlestown *Truro* from 77. *22 Fairbourne Road, St Austell, Cornwall PL25 4NR* St Austell (01726) 75208

JAGO, Christine May. b 52. **d** 94. NSM St Buryan, St Levan and Sennen *Truro* from 94. *Boscarne House, St Buryan, Penzance, Cornwall TR19 6HU*

JAKEMAN, Francis David. b 47. Leeds Univ BSc69 Ealing Coll of Educn DMS81. Cuddesdon Coll 71. **d** 74 **p** 75. C Gt Grimsby St Mary and St Jas *Linc* 74-77; Ind Chapl *Lon* 77-88; V Harrow Weald All SS from 88; Chapl Weald Coll from 88. *The Vicarage, 175 Uxbridge Road, Harrow, Middx HA3 6TP* 0181-954 0247

JALLAND, Hilary Gervase Alexander. b 50. FRSA Ex Univ BA72. Coll of Resurr Mirfield 74. **d** 76 **p** 77. C Ex St Thos *Ex* 76-80; C Ex St Thos and Em 80; C Portsea St Mary *Portsm* 80-86; V Hempton and Pudding Norton *Nor* 86-90; TV Hawarden *St As* 90-93; R Llandysilio and Penrhos and Llandrinio etc from 93. *The Rectory, Rhos Common, Four Crosses, Llanymynech, Powys SY22 6RW* Llanymynech (01691) 830533

JAMES, Alan Raymond. b 30. Roch Th Coll 65. **d** 66 **p** 67. C Ex St Matt *Ex* 66-70; V Kingskerswell w Coffinswell 70-88; rtd 88. *13 Hillside, Appleby Magna, Swadlincote, Derbyshire DE12 7AB* Measham (01530) 270917

JAMES, Andrew Nicholas. b 54. BSc76. Trin Coll Bris 77. **d** 80 **p** 81. C Prescot *Liv* 80-83; C Upholland 83-85; V Hindley Green 85-91; V Dean Forest H Trin *Glouc* from 91. *Holy Trinity Vicarage, Oakland Road, Harrow Hill, Drybrook, Glos GL17 9JX* Dean (01594) 542232

JAMES, Anne Loraine. b 45. St Jo Coll Nottm CertCS. **d** 90 **p** 94. NSM Ellon *Ab* from 90; NSM Cruden Bay from 90. *Millhouse, Nethermill, Hatton, Peterhead, Aberdeenshire AB42 7SN* Cruden Bay (01779) 812609

JAMES, Arthur Kenneth. b 14. St Chad's Coll Dur BA35 DipTh35 MA38. **d** 37 **p** 38. V Marshfield and Peterstone Wentloog etc *Mon* 64-79; rtd 79. *3 Ellis Avenue, Onslow Village, Guildford, Surrey GU2 5SR* Guildford (01483) 38582

JAMES, Barry Paul. b 49. BSc. Sarum & Wells Th Coll. **d** 82 **p** 83. C Bitterne Park *Win* 82-86; V Southn St Mary Extra from 86. *The Vicarage, 65 Peartree Avenue, Southampton SO2 7JN* Southampton (01703) 448353

JAMES, Billie. b 24. St D Coll Lamp BA50 LTh52. **d** 52 **p** 53. V Scrooby *S'well* 61-74; P-in-c Kneesall 74-82; P-in-c Ossington 74-82; V Norwell 74-82; P-in-c Laxton 77-78; V Norwell w Ossington and Cromwell 82-89; rtd 89; Lic to Offic *Heref* from 89. *Wye Knot, 2 Danum Road, Tudor Park, Ross-on-Wye, Herefordshire HR9 5UG* Ross-on-Wye (01989) 765542

JAMES, Brian Percival Harold. b 26. Southn Univ BSc53. Wycliffe Hall Ox 62. **d** 64 **p** 65. C Hartley Wintney and Elvetham *Win* 64-66; C Shelf *Bradf* 66-71; V Oldham St Ambrose *Man* from 71. *The Vicarage, Prince Charlie Street, Oldham OL1 4HJ* 0161-624 7122

JAMES, Brother. See PICKEN, James Hugh

JAMES, Miss Carolyn Anne. b 65. Coll of Ripon & York St Jo BA87 Nottm Univ BTh91. Linc Th Coll 88. **d** 91 **p** 94. Par Dn Middleton St Mary *Ripon* 91-94; C Wetherby from 94. *53 Barleyfields Road, Wetherby, W Yorkshire LS22 7PT* Wetherby (01937) 583628

✠**JAMES, Rt Rev Colin Clement Walter.** b 26. K Coll Cam BA49 MA51. Cuddesdon Coll 50. **d** 52 **p** 53 **c** 73. C Stepney St Dunstan and All SS *Lon* 52-55; Asst Chapl Stowe Sch Bucks 55-56; Chapl 56-59; Asst in Relig Broadcasting BBC 59-60; Relig Broadcasting Org W Region BBC 60-67; V Bournemouth St Pet *Win* 67-73; P-in-c Bournemouth St Steph 70-73; Dir of Tr 72-77; Can Res Win Cathl 73-77; Suff Bp Basingstoke 73-77; Bp Wakef 77-85; Bp Win 85-95; rtd 95; Asst Bp B & W from 95. *5 Hermitage Road, Lansdown, Bath BA1 5SN* Bath (01225) 312702

JAMES, Colin Robert. b 34. IPFA. St Deiniol's Hawarden 84. **d** 87 **p** 88. NSM Llanwnda w Llanfaglan *Ban* 87-88; NSM Arfon Deanery 88-90; NSM Bistre *St As* from 90. *1 Lea Drive, Buckley, Clwyd CH7 2BQ* Buckley (01244) 544392

JAMES, David. b 38. Southn Univ BEd74. **d** 77 **p** 78. NSM Headbourne Worthy *Win* 77-85; NSM King's Worthy 77-85; Asst Chapl K Alfred's Coll Win 85-89; Chapl St Pet High Sch Ex from 89; Lic to Offic *Ex* from 89. *St Peter's High School, Quarry Lane, Exeter EX2 5AP* Exeter (01392) 74383

JAMES, Ven David Brian. b 30. FCA52 Univ of Wales (Swansea) BA63. St Mich Coll Llan 55. **d** 57 **p** 58. C Llandeilo Tal-y-bont *S & B* 57-59; C Newport Ch Ch *Mon* 59-63; V Bryngwyn and Newchurch and Llanbedr etc *S & B* 63-70; V Llanfeugan and Llanthetty and Glyncollwng etc 70-79; V Ilston w Pennard 79-94; Hon Can Brecon Cathl 87-89; RD Gower 89-94; Can Brecon Cathl 89-94; Chan Brecon Cathl 93-94; Adn Brecon from 94; P-in-c Llanllyr-yn-Rhos w Llanfihangel Helygen from 94. *The Vicarage, Highbury, Llanyre, Llandrindod Wells, Powys LD1 6NF* Llandrindod Wells (01597) 822472

JAMES, David Charles. b 45. Ex Univ BSc66 PhD71. St Jo Coll Nottm BA73. **d** 73 **p** 74. C Portswood Ch Ch *Win* 73-76; V from 90; C Goring-by-Sea *Chich* 76-78; Chapl UEA *Nor* 78-82; V Ecclesfield *Sheff* 82-90; Proctor in Convocation Sheff Cathl 85-90; RD Ecclesfield 87-90. *The Vicarage, 36 Brookvale Road, Southampton SO2 1QR* Southampton (01703) 554277

JAMES, David Clive. b 40. Bris Univ BA61 K Coll Lon DipEd87. St Steph Ho Ox 64. **d** 65 **p** 66. C Portslade St Nic *Chich* 65-68; C Haywards Heath St Wilfrid 68-71; Chapl Brighton Poly 71-76; Lic to Offic from 76. *22 Bradford Road, Lewes, E Sussex BN7 1RB* Brighton (01273) 471851

JAMES, David Howard. b 47. Ex Univ BA70 MA73 Pemb Coll Cam CertEd72. Linc Th Coll 81. **d** 83 **p** 84. C Tavistock and Gulworthy *Ex* 83-86; C E Teignmouth 86-88; C W Teignmouth 86-88; P-in-c Bishopsteignton 88-89; P-in-c Ideford, Luton and Ashcombe 88-89; TV Teignmouth, Ideford w Luton, Ashcombe etc 90-95; P-in-c Sidmouth, Woolbrook, Salcombe Regis, Sidbury etc from 95. *The Rectory, Glen Road, Sidmouth, Devon EX10 8RW* Sidmouth (01395) 514223

JAMES, Canon David Walter Skyrme. b 36. Nottm Univ BA61. Wells Th Coll 61. **d** 63 **p** 64. C Sneinton St Cypr *S'well* 63-66; C Newark St Mary 66-69; R Kirkby in Ashfield St Thos 69-77; P-in-c Rempstone 76-84; P-in-c Costock 76-84; P-in-c Stanford on Soar 76-84; R E Leake 77-84; R Wollaton from 84; Hon Can S'well Minster from 88; AD Nottm W 90-91. *St Leonard's Rectory, Russell Drive, Nottingham NG8 2BD* Nottingham (0115) 928 1798

JAMES, David William. b 55. CA Tr Coll CertRS77 Coll of Resurr Mirfield 86. **d** 88 **p** 88. C New Rossington *Sheff* 88-90; V Yardley Wood *Birm* 90-95; P-in-c Allens Cross from 95. *St Bartholomew's Vicarage, 148 Frankley Beeches Road, Birmingham B31 5LW* 0121-475 8329

JAMES, Derek George. b 27. Sarum & Wells Th Coll 72. **d** 74 **p** 75. C Petersfield w Sheet *Portsm* 74-77; P-in-c Gosport Ch Ch 77-81; V from 81; RD Gosport from 90. *Christ Church Vicarage, 7 Elmhurst Road, Gosport, Hants PO12 1PG* Gosport (01705) 581609

JAMES, Dewi Hirwaun. b 41. St Mich Coll Llan 66 Lich Th Coll 67. **d** 70 **p** 72. C Porthmadog St Jo w Borth-y-Gest and Tremadog *Ban* 70-73; C Llanbeblig w Caernarfon and Betws Garmon etc 83-85; C Ban 88-89 and 90-94; C Sheff Parson Cross St Cecilia *Sheff* 89-90; Min Can Ban Cathl *Ban* 90-94; C Holyhead w Rhoscolyn w Llanfair-yn-Neubwll from 94. *St Seiriol's House, Gors Avenue, Holyhead, Gwynedd LL65 1PB* Holyhead (01407) 761725

JAMES, Ven Douglas Gordon. b 22. Univ of Wales (Abth) BA47. Qu Coll Birm 74. **d** 75 **p** 76. C Cwmbach Llan 75-77; C Aberdare St Jo 77-82; V 82-92; Hon Can Llan Cathl 87-92; Adn Margam 88-92; rtd 92; Perm to Offic *Llan* from 92. *31 Abernant Road, Aberdare, M Glam CF44 0PY* Aberdare (01685) 872559

JAMES, Edmund Pollard. b 10. MBE70. St D Coll Lamp LDiv37. **d** 37 **p** 38. R Pyworthy w Pancraswyke *Ex* 46-77; Preb Ex Cathl 60-77; rtd 77. *No 1 Cottage, Castle Farm, Clevedon, Avon BS21 7AA* Clevedon (01275) 873470

JAMES, Canon Eric Arthur. b 25. Trin Coll Cam MA55. Lambeth Hon DD93 K Coll Lon AKC50 BD51. **d** 51 **p** 52. Can Res and Prec S'wark Cathl *S'wark* 66-73; Dioc Missr *St Alb* 73-83; Can Res St Alb 73-83; Hon Can 83-90; FKC from 78; Preacher Gray's Inn from 78; Dir Chr Action 79-90; Hon Dir from 90; Chapl to The Queen 84-95; Extra Chapl to The Queen from 95; rtd 90. *11 Denny Crescent, London SE11 4UY, or 125 Kennington Road, London SE11 6SF* 0171-582 3068 or 735 2372

JAMES, Gareth Hugh. b 40. St D Coll Lamp DipTh66. **d** 66 **p** 67. C Whitchurch *Llan* 68-71; Chapl Llan Cathl Sch 71-93; rtd 93. *Address temp unknown*

JAMES, Godfrey Walter. b 36. Univ of Wales (Lamp) BA58 Univ of Wales (Cardiff) MA60 St Pet Coll Ox DipEd61 BA63 MA67. St Mich Coll Llan 63. **d** 64 **p** 65. C Canton St Jo *Llan* 64-71; V Williamstown 71-85; V Kenfig Hill from 85. *The Vicarage, Kenfig Hill, Bridgend, M Glam CF33 6DR* Bridgend (01656) 740856

JAMES, Gordon Cecil. b 35. Sarum Th Coll 66. **d** 67 **p** 68. C Kew *S'wark* 67-72; P-in-c Weston Longville w Morton and the Witchinghams *Nor* 72-81; R Diss from 81. *The Rectory, 26 Mount Street, Diss, Norfolk IP22 3QG* Diss (01379) 642072

✠**JAMES, Rt Rev Graham Richard.** b 51. Lanc Univ BA72 Ox Univ DipTh74. Cuddesdon Coll 72. **d** 75 **p** 76 **c** 93. C Pet Ch Carpenter *Pet* 75-79; C Digswell *St Alb* 79-82; TV Digswell and Panshanger 82-83; Lic to Offic 83-93; Sen Selection Sec and Sec Cand Cttee ACCM 83-87; Abp's Chapl *Cant* 87-93; Hon Can Dallas from 89; Suff Bp St Germans *Truro* from 93. *32 Falmouth Road, Truro, Cornwall TR1 2HX* Truro (01872) 73190 Fax 77883

JAMES, Henley George. b 31. Sarum & Wells Th Coll 79. **d** 81 **p** 82. C Tottenham H Trin *Lon* 81-85; C Cricklewood St Pet 85-88; P-in-c 88-89; V Bearwood *Birm* from 89. *St Mary's Vicarage, 27 Poplar Avenue, Birmingham B17 8EG* 0121-429 2165

JAMES, Henry Glyn. b 26. Keble Coll Ox BA50 DipTh51 MA62 Toronto Univ MEd74. Wycliffe Hall Ox 50. **d** 52 **p** 53. Canada 68-73; Hon C Kidmore End *Ox* 74-77; K Jas Coll of Henley 74-87; Hon C Remenham *Ox* 77-88; Chapl The Henley Coll 87-88; Chapl Toulouse *Eur* 88-91; rtd 91; Perm to Offic *Win* 93; Hon C Bournemouth St Pet w St Swithun, St Steph etc from 93. *5 St Ives Gardens, Bournemouth BH2 6NS* Bournemouth (01202) 291451

JAMES, Herbert Royston Joseph. b 22. Sarum Th Coll 65. **d** 67 **p** 68. C Whipton *Ex* 67-75; V Shaugh Prior 75-83; V Ipplepen w Torbryan 83-87; rtd 87; Perm to Offic *Ex* from 90. *188 Hamlin Lane, Exeter EX1 2SH*

JAMES, Howard. b 19. Chich Th Coll. **d** 87. Hon C Whitton St Aug *Lon* 87-94; Perm to Offic from 94. *95 Lyndhurst Avenue, Twickenham TW2 6BH* 0181-898 1190

JAMES, Idris Frank. b 20. MISM69 AMBIM70. St D Coll Lamp 52. **d** 55 **p** 59. V Dunton *Chelmsf* 62-79; R Bulphan 64-77; rtd 85. *39 Cae Fardre, Church Village, Pontypridd, M Glam CF38 1DS* Newtown Llantwit (01443) 202834

JAMES, Jeremy Richard. b 52. Jes Coll Cam BA73 MA77 York Univ CertEd77. St Jo Coll Dur 86. **d** 88 **p** 89. C Broxbourne w Wormley *St Alb* 89-91; C Hailsham *Chich* from 91. *15 Howlett Drive, Hailsham, E Sussex BN27 1QW* Hailsham (01323) 846680

JAMES, John Charles. b 37. Keble Coll Ox BA59. Linc Th Coll 68. **d** 70 **p** 71. C S Shields St Hilda w St Thos *Dur* 70-77; P-in-c Jarrow Docks 77-78; Adn Seychelles 78-92; V Mylor w Flushing *Truro* from 92. *The Vicarage, Mylor, Falmouth, Cornwall TR11 5UD* Falmouth (01326) 374408

JAMES, John David. b 23. CCC Cam MA. Wells Th Coll. **d** 50 **p** 51. V Stansted Mountfitchet *Chelmsf* 61-71; V Clacton St Jas 71-84; R Poulshot *Sarum* 84; V Rowde 84; R Rowde and Poulshot 84-88; rtd 88. *15 Beaconsfield Park, Ludlow, Shropshire SY8 4LY* Ludlow (01584) 873754

JAMES, John Hugh Alexander. b 56. St Jo Coll Dur BA78 Univ of Wales DipTh81. St Mich Coll Llan. **d** 81 **p** 82. C Newton Nottage *Llan* 81-84; Prov Youth and Children's Officer Ch in Wales 84-92; V Llanfihangel-ar-arth *St D* from 92. *The Vicarage, Llanfihangel-ar-arth, Pencader, Dyfed SA39 9HU* Pencader (01559) 384858

JAMES, John Morgan. b 21. Lon Univ BD43 MTh45. ALCD43. **d** 44 **p** 45. V Sunbury *Lon* 67-77; Dir Coll of Preachers 77-85; rtd 85. *Fair Winds, 126 Pagham Road, Pagham, Bognor Regis, W Sussex PO21 4NN* Pagham (01243) 264250

JAMES, John Paul. b 30. Sarum Th Coll 58. **d** 60 **p** 61. C Milton *Portsm* 60-65; C Stanmer w Falmer and Moulsecoomb *Chich* 65-69; V Brighton H Trin 69-71; Canada from 71. *10 Church Hill, Westmount, Quebec, Canada, H3Y 2Z9*

JAMES, Joshua John Gerwyn. b 31. St D Coll Lamp BA52. **d** 54 **p** 55. C Haverfordwest St Mary w St Thos *St D* 54-56; C Llanaber w Caerdeon *Ban* 56-57; CF 57-76; V Tidenham w Beachley and Lancaut *Glouc* 76-80; R Aberdovey *Ban* 80-82; V Quinton w Marston Sicca *Glouc* 82-90; RD Campden 88-90; P-in-c Upper Chelsea St Simon *Lon* from 90. *The Vicarage, 34 Milner Street, London SW3 2QF* 0171-589 5747

JAMES, Keith Edwin Arthur. b 38. Sarum & Wells Th Coll 85. **d** 87 **p** 88. C Hempnall *Nor* 87-91; R Roughton and Felbrigg, Metton, Sustead etc from 91. *The Rectory, Church Loke, Roughton, Norwich NR11 8SZ* Cromer (01263) 768075

JAMES, Keith Nicholas. b 69. Leeds Univ BA91 Nottm Univ MA93. St Jo Coll Nottm 91. **d** 93 **p** 94. C Crosby *Linc* from 93. *14 Normanby Road, Scunthorpe, S Humberside DN15 6AL* Scunthorpe (01724) 850845

JAMES, Lewis John. b 20. St D Coll Lamp BA42. **d** 48 **p** 49. V Smalley *Derby* 60-85; P-in-c Morley 72-81; rtd 85; Perm to Offic *Derby* 85-87. *78 Waun Daniel, Rhos, Pontardawe, Swansea SA8 5HR* Swansea (01792) 830796

JAMES, Lionel Dennis. b 07. Qu Coll Birm. **d** 62 **p** 63. V Weedon Bec *Pet* 65-74; R Dodford w Brockhall 66-74; rtd 74. *7 Springfield Park, Mylor Bridge, Falmouth, Cornwall TR11 5SJ* Falmouth (01326) 373743

JAMES, Malcolm. b 37. CEng MICE MIStructE. N Ord Course. **d** 83 **p** 84. NSM Ripponden *Wakef* from 83. *Lower Stones, Bar Lane, Rishworth, Sowerby Bridge, W Yorkshire HX6 4EY* Halifax (01422) 822483

JAMES, Martin. b 40. ACII. **d** 94. NSM Farnborough *Guildf* from 94. *43 Ashley Road, Farnborough, Hants GU14 7HB* Farnborough (01252) 544698

JAMES, Dr Martyn Howard. b 48. FRCS77 Bris Univ MB, ChB71. Coll of Resurr Mirfield 85. **d** 87 **p** 88. C Torquay St Martin Barton *Ex* 87-92; Coll of Resurr Mirfield 92-93; Sheff Parson Cross St Cecilia *Sheff* 93-94; V Doncaster St Jude from 94. *The Vicarage, 132 Shadyside, Doncaster, S Yorkshire DN4 0DG* Doncaster (01302) 852057

JAMES, Michael John. b 29. ALA53 Strathclyde Univ CYCW74 Heriot-Watt Univ CQSW81. Ho of Resurr Mirfield 57. **d** 59 **p** 60. R Lambley w Knaresdale *Newc* 67-72; Rossie Sch Montrose 75-83; Prin Redding Ho Falkirk 83-86; rtd 93. *28 Windsor Street, Edinburgh EH7 5JR* 0131-556 4935

JAMES, Noel Beddoe Walters. b 39. St Mich Coll Llan DipTh68. **d** 69 **p** 69. C Swansea St Nic *S & B* 68-70; C Swansea St Pet 70-72; Chapl RAF 72-93; P-in-c The Heyfords w Rousham and Somerton *Ox* from 93. *The Rectory, Station Road, Lower Heyford, Bicester, Oxon OX6 3PD* Bicester (01869) 340733

JAMES, Paul Dominic Denis. b 48. AKC71 Westmr Coll Ox DipApTh90. **d** 72 **p** 73. C Leytonstone St Marg w St Columba *Chelmsf* 72-74; C Leigh-on-Sea St Marg 74-79; V Walthamstow St Sav from 79. *St Saviour's Vicarage, 210 Markhouse Road, London E17 8EP* 0181-520 2036

JAMES, Paul Maynard. b 31. Univ of Wales (Ban) BA52 Fitzw Ho Cam BA54 MA58. Ridley Hall Cam 56. **d** 57 **p** 58. C Newhaven *Chich* 57-60; Kenya 60-65; SW Area Sec CCCS 65-68; V Shrewsbury St Julian *Lich* 68-76; V Shrewsbury H Trin w St Julian 76-90; P-in-c Woore and Norton in Hales from 90; Adn Salop's Adv on Evang from 90; RD Hodnet from 93. *The Vicarage, Woore, Crewe CW3 9SA* Pipe Gate (01630) 647316

JAMES, Peter David. b 42. Keble Coll Ox BA63 Lon Univ BD67. Tyndale Hall Bris 64. **d** 67 **p** 68. C Haydock St Mark *Liv* 67-69; C Ashton-in-Makerfield St Thos 69-74; V Whiston 74-80; V Harlech and Llanfair-juxta-Harlech etc *Ban* 80-94; R Botwnnog w Bryncroes from 94. *The Rectory, Botwnnog, Pwllheli, Gwynedd LL53 8PY* Pwllheli (0175883) 450

JAMES, Peter Heppell. b 19. Tyndale Hall Bris 39. **d** 42 **p** 43. R Lt Leighs *Chelmsf* 60-70; rtd 84. *57 Tynedale Road, Loughborough, Leics LE11 3TA* Loughborough (01509) 266940

JAMES, Raymond John. b 36. Linc Th Coll 85. **d** 87 **p** 88. C Cov E *Cov* 87-91; V Wolvey w Burton Hastings, Copston Magna etc from 91. *St John's Vicarage, School Lane, Wolvey, Hinckley, Leics LE10 3LH* Hinckley (01455) 220385

JAMES, Richard Andrew. b 44. Mert Coll Ox BA67 MA70. Tyndale Hall Bris DipTh69. **d** 70 **p** 71. C Bebington *Ches* 70-73; C Histon *Ely* 73-77; Chapl Guildf Coll of Tech 77-80; C Guildf St Sav w Stoke-next-Guildf 77-80; Chapl Bedf Coll of HE *St Alb* 81-83; TV Ipsley *Worc* 84-89; R Mulbarton w Kenningham *Nor* 89-92; rtd 93. *5 Kirkby Close, Ripon, N Yorkshire HG4 2DS* Ripon (01765) 604511

JAMES, Richard David. b 45. Lon Coll of Div 67. **d** 70 **p** 71. C Boultham *Linc* 70-74; C Waltham 74-77; C New Waltham 74-77; TV Cleethorpes 77-87; TR E Bris from 87. *St Ambrose Vicarage, Stretford Avenue, Bristol BS5 7AN* Bristol (0117) 951 7299

JAMES, Dr Richard David. b 65. Clare Coll Cam MA88 Lon Hosp MB90 BChir90. Ridley Hall Cam CTM95. **d** 95. C Clifton Ch Ch w Em *Bris* from 95. *First Floor Flat, Linden Gate, Clifton Down Road, Bristol BS8 4AH* Bristol (0117) 973 2128

JAMES, Richard William. b 47. St D Coll Lamp DipTh75. **d** 75 **p** 76. C Hubberston *St D* 75-78; R Pendine w Llanmiloe and Eglwys Gymyn w Marros 78-83; V Caerwent w Dinham and Llanfair Discoed etc *Mon* 83-84; Chapl Gothenburg w Halmstad, Jonkoping etc *Eur* 84-89; P-in-c Shooters Hill Ch Ch *S'wark* from 89. *Christ Church Vicarage, 1 Craigholm, London SE18 3RR* 0181-856 5858

JAMES, Roger Michael. b 44. K Coll Lon BD66 AKC66. **d** 69 **p** 70. C Frindsbury w Upnor *Roch* 69-72; Lic to Offic *St Alb* 73-78; C Digswell 78-81; R Knebworth 81-92; P-in-c Upper

Tean *Lich* from 92; Local Min Adv Stoke Adnry from 92. *The Vicarage, Vicarage Road, Tean, Stoke-on-Trent ST10 4LE* Tean (01538) 722227

JAMES, Stephen Lynn. b 53. Middx Poly DipHCM74 DipPM75. Oak Hill Th Coll BA86. **d** 86 **p** 87. C Heigham H Trin *Nor* 86-89; Canada 89-93; R Bebington *Ches* from 93. *The Rectory, Church Road, Bebington, Wirral, Merseyside L63 3EX* 0151-645 6478

JAMES, William Arthur. b 10. Univ of Wales BA40. St Mich Coll Llan 40. **d** 42 **p** 43. R Bedwas *Mon* 54-77; rtd 77. *c/o Mrs Stephens, 50 Castle View, Simpson Cross, Haverfordwest, Dyfed SA62 6ES* Camrose (01437) 710681

JAMES, William Glynne George. b 39. Trin Coll Carmarthen 82. **d** 85 **p** 86. NSM Gorseinon *S & B* from 85. *23 Cecil Road, Gowerton, Swansea SA4 3DF* Swansea (01792) 872363

JAMESON, David Kingsbury. b 28. Mert Coll Ox BA50 MA55. Qu Coll Birm 50. **d** 53 **p** 54. V Portsea St Cuth *Portsm* 65-70; V Enfield Jes Chpl *Lon* 70-74; RD Nuneaton *Cov* 74-79; V Nuneaton St Nic 74-80; Org Sec (Leics and Northants) CECS 80-82; Lic to Offic *Leic* 80-82; Perm to Offic *Pet* 80-82; P-in-c Forty Hill Jes Ch *Lon* 82-87; V 87-91; rtd 91; Hon C Okehampton w Inwardleigh, Bratton Clovelly etc *Ex* from 94. *St Bridget's Vicarage, Bridestowe, Okehampton, Devon EX20 2ER* Bridestowe (0183786) 612

JAMESON, Canon Dermot Christopher Ledgard. b 27. TCD BA49 MA54. CITC 49. **d** 50 **p** 51. I Donaghcloney w Waringstown *D & D* 62-79; Can Dromore Cathl 77-93; I Kilbroney 79-93; Treas Dromore Cathl 81-83; Prec Dromore Cathl 83-90; Chan Dromore Cathl 90-93; rtd 93. *Concord, 10B Kilbroney Road, Rostrevor, Co Down BT34 3BH* Rostrevor (016937) 39728

JAMESON, Geoffrey Vaughan. b 27. Culham Coll Ox CertEd51 St Luke's Coll Ex ACertEd52. Wycliffe Hall Ox 68. **d** 70 **p** 71. C Buckm *Ox* 70-73; R Exton w Whitwell *Pet* 73-86; V Marystowe, Coryton, Stowford, Lewtrenchard etc *Ex* 86-90; rtd 90; Perm to Offic *Portsm* from 91. *18 Eglantine Walk, Cowplain, Waterlooville, Hants PO8 9BG* Horndean (01705) 571112

JAMESON, Canon John Edward. b 16. Kelham Th Coll 34. **d** 39 **p** 40. V Gosforth All SS *Newc* 62-76; Hon Can Newc Cathl 72-83; R Rothbury 76-83; rtd 83. *Abbeyfield House, Dial Place, Warkworth, Morpeth, Northd NE65 0UR* Morpeth (01665) 712510

JAMESON, Peter. b 31. Trin Coll Cam BA54 MA60. Linc Th Coll. **d** 62 **p** 63. C Earl's Court St Cuth w St Matthias *Lon* 62-68; C Notting Hill St Clem 68-72; C Notting Hill St Clem and St Mark 72-74; TV Notting Hill 74-77; V Stoke Newington St Olave from 77. *St Olave's Vicarage, Woodberry Down, London N4 2TW* 0181-800 1374

JAMIESON, Hugh Gollan. b 20. TCD BA49. CITC 49. **d** 49 **p** 50. I Mothel *C & O* 69-76; I Badoney Lower *D & R* 76-78; I Donagh w Tyholland and Errigal Truagh *Clogh* 78-82; I Killeshandra w Killegar and Derrylane *K, E & A* 82-87; rtd 87. *Rose Cottage, Killyboley, Glaslough, Monaghan, Irish Republic* Monaghan (47) 88231

JAMIESON, Kenneth Euan Oram. b 24. Lon Univ DipTh68. Roch Th Coll 60. **d** 62 **p** 63. R Colchester St Mary Magd *Chelmsf* 66-71; V Bexleyheath St Pet *Roch* 71-78; P-in-c Maidstone St Faith *Cant* 78-83; P-in-c Maidstone St Paul 78-83; Ind Chapl *St Alb* 83-89; rtd 89; Lic to Offic *B & W* from 89. *4 Ashley Road, Taunton, Somerset TA1 5BP* Taunton (01823) 289367

JAMIESON, Mrs Marilyn. b 52. Cranmer Hall Dur IDC80. **d** 91 **p** 94. Par Dn Gateshead St Cuth w St Paul *Dur* 91; Par Dn Bensham 91-93; Par Dn Ryton w Hedgefield 93-94; C 94; Chapl Metro Cen Gateshead from 94. *The Rectory, Barmoor House, Main Road, Ryton, Tyne & Wear NE40 3AJ* 0191-413 4592

JAMIESON, Peter Grant. b 64. Liv Univ BA87. Coll of Resurr Mirfield 90. **d** 93 **p** 94. C Charlton Kings St Mary *Glouc* from 93. *St Mary's House, 3 Copt Elm Road, Charlton Kings, Cheltenham, Glos GL53 8AG* Cheltenham (01242) 519095

JAMIESON, Miss Rosalind Heather. b 49. CertEd71. St Jo Coll Dur 79. **dss** 81 **d** 87 **p** 94. Queensbury All SS *Lon* 81-85; Richmond H Trin and Ch Ch *S'wark* 85-87; Par Dn 87-91; Par Dn Burmantofts St Steph and St Agnes *Ripon* 91-94; C from 94. *52 Shakespeare Grange, Leeds LS9 7VA* Leeds (0113) 248 2606

JAMIESON, Thomas Lindsay. b 53. N Lon Poly BSc74. Cranmer Hall Dur DipTh76. **d** 77 **p** 78. C Gateshead Fell *Dur* 77-80; C Gateshead 80-84; TV 84-90; P-in-c Gateshead St Cuth w St Paul 90-91; TV Bensham 91-93; P-in-c Ryton w Hedgefield from 93; RD Gateshead W from 94. *The Rectory, Barmoor House, Main Road, Ryton, Tyne & Wear NE40 3AJ* 0191-413 4592

JAMIESON, William Douglas. b 38. Oak Hill Th Coll 63. **d** 66 **p** 67. C Shrewsbury St Julian *Lich* 66-68; C Bucknall and

Bagnall 68-70; C Otley *Bradf* 70-74; TV Keighley 74-81; V Utley from 81. *St Mark's Vicarage, Greenhead Road, Keighley, W Yorkshire BD20 6ED* Keighley (01535) 607003

JANES, David Edward. b 40. Lon Univ BSc67. Glouc Sch of Min 86. **d** 89 **p** 90. NSM Church Stretton *Heref* from 89. *15 Watling Street South, Church Stretton, Shropshire SY6 7BG* Church Stretton (01694) 722253

JANICKER, Laurence Norman. b 47. SS Mark & Jo Coll Chelsea DipEd69. Ridley Coll Melbourne 77 St Jo Coll Nottm 83. **d** 85 **p** 86. C Beverley Minster *York* 85-89; R Lockington and Lund and Scorborough w Leconfield 89-94; V Cov St Geo Cov from 94. *St George's Vicarage, 101 Moseley Avenue, Coventry CV6 1HR* Coventry (01203) 591994

JANSMA, Dr Henry Peter. b 57. NE Bible Coll (USA) BA79 Dur Univ PhD91. Westmr Th Sem (USA) MA85 Linc Th Coll CMM91. **d** 91 **p** 92. C Spalding *Linc* from 91. *The Chantry, 7 Church Street, Spalding, Lincs PE11 2PB* Spalding (01775) 722631

JANVIER, Philip Harold. b 57. Trin Coll Bris BA87. **d** 87 **p** 88. C Much Woolton *Liv* 87-90; TV Toxteth St Philemon w St Gabr and St Cleopas from 90. *St Gabriel's Vicarage, 2 Steble Street, Liverpool L8 6QH* 0151-708 7751

JAQUET, Peter Michael. b 23. ARIBA51. Wells Th Coll 56. **d** 57 **p** 58. V Sellindge w Monks Horton and Stowting *Cant* 60-78; C Drypool St Columba w St Andr and St Pet *York* 78-80; TV Drypool 80-86; rtd 86. *20 Harthill Avenue, Leconfield, Beverley, N Humberside HU17 7LN* Hornsea (01964) 550108

JARAM, Peter Ellis. b 45. MIEE77 CEng77 MBIM88 Lon Univ BSc70. Linc Th Coll CMinlStuds94. **d** 94 **p** 95. C Bridlington Priory *York* from 94. *144 Marton Road, Bridlington, N Humberside YO16 5DH* Bridlington (01262) 677450

JARDIN, Kenneth. b 35. TCD 67. **d** 69 **p** 70. Chapl R Sch Arm 69-72; C Arm St Mark *Arm* 69-72; Chapl RAF 72-78; V Barlings *Linc* 78-83; P-in-c Ecchinswell cum Sydmonton 73-79; P-in-c Burghclere w Newtown 78-79; R Burghclere w Newtown and Ecchinswell w Sydmonton 79-87; P-in-c Wonston 87; R Wonston and Stoke Charity w Hunton from 87. *The Rectory, Wonston, Sutton Scotney, Winchester, Hants SO21 3PA* Winchester (01962) 760240

JARDINE, Anthony. b 38. Lon Univ DipTh70. Qu Coll Birm 64. **d** 67 **p** 68. C Baldock w Bygrave and Clothall *St Alb* 67-71; C N Stoneham *Win* 71-73; P-in-c Ecchinswell cum Sydmonton 73-79; P-in-c Burghclere w Newtown 78-79; R Burghclere w Newtown and Ecchinswell w Sydmonton 79-87; P-in-c Wonston 87; R Wonston and Stoke Charity w Hunton from 87. *The Rectory, Wonston, Sutton Scotney, Winchester, Hants SO21 3PA* Winchester (01962) 760240

JARDINE, David Eric Cranswick. b 30. CCC Ox BA53 DipTh54 MA57. Wycliffe Hall Ox 53. **d** 55 **p** 56. C Wavertree St Mary *Liv* 55-58; C Liv All So Springwood 58-62; C Horley *S'wark* 62-65; V Mitcham Ch Ch 65-72; V Iford *Win* 72-89; R Smannell w Enham Alamein from 89. *The Rectory, Dunhills Lane, Enham Alamein, Andover, Hants SP11 6HU* Andover (01264) 352827

JARDINE, David John (Brother David). b 42. QUB BA65. CITC 67. **d** 67 **p** 68. C Ballymacarrett St Patr *D & D* 67-70; Asst Chapl QUB 70-73; SSF from 73; Asst Chapl HM Pris Belf 75-79; Chapl 79-85; USA 85-88; Sen Asst Warden Ch of Ireland Min of Healing 88-92. *St Francis House, 75 Deerpark Road, Belfast BT14 7PW* Belfast (01232) 351480

JARDINE, Norman. b 47. QUB BSc72. Trin Coll Bris 74. **d** 76 **p** 77. C Magheralin *D & D* 76-78; C Dundonald 78-80; Bp's C Ballybeen 80-88; I Willowfield from 88. *The Rectory, 149 My Lady's Road, Belfast BT6 8FE* Belfast (01232) 457654

JARDINE, Thomas Parker. b 44. Oak Hill Th Coll BA87. **d** 87 **p** 88. C Crowborough *Chich* 87-91; R Dersingham w Anmer and Shernborne *Nor* from 91. *The Vicarage, Dersingham, King's Lynn, Norfolk PE31 6JA* Dersingham (01485) 540214

JARMAN, Christopher. b 38. QUB BA63. Wells Th Coll 69. **d** 71 **p** 72. C Leckhampton SS Phil and Jas *Glouc* 71-73; Chapl RN 73-94; R Stirling *Edin* from 94. *29 Parkdyke, Stirling FK7 9LS* Stirling (01786) 471755

JARMAN, John Geoffrey. b 31. IEng. S'wark Ord Course 75. **d** 78 **p** 79. NSM Chigwell *Chelmsf* 78-81; NSM Leytonstone St Marg w St Columba 81-87; C Walthamstow St Sav 87-89; V Gt Bentley 89-92; P-in-c Frating w Thorrington 89-92; C Wanstead St Mary 92-93; C Wanstead St Mary w Ch Ch from 93. *13 Wanstead Place, London E11 2SW* 0181-530 4970

JARMAN, Robert Joseph (Bob). b 59. Van Mildert Coll Dur BA90 Univ of Wales (Cardiff) DPS91. **d** 92 **p** 93. C Llanishen and Lisvane *Llan* 92-93; C Whitchurch 93-94. *47 Penydre, Rhiwbina, Cardiff CF4 6EJ*

JARMY, David Michael. b 49. Cam Univ PGCE90. Chich Th Coll 76. **d** 79 **p** 80. C St Leonards Ch Ch *Chich* 79-80; C St

Leonards Ch Ch and St Mary 81-82; C St Leonards SS Pet and Paul 82-85; V Sidley 85-89; Perm to Offic *Pet* 89-90; Lt Gidding Community 89-90; NSM Oundle *Pet* from 90. *27 Lower Benefield, Oundle, Peterborough PE8 5AE* Oundle (01832) 275287

JARRATT, Robert Michael. b 39. K Coll Lon BD62 AKC62. NY Th Sem DMin85. **d** 63 **p** 64. C Corby St Columba *Pet* 63-67; Lay Tr Officer *Sheff* 67-71; Ind Chapl *S'wark* 72-80; P-in-c Betchworth 76-80; V Ranmoor *Sheff* from 80; RD Hallam 87-94. *The Vicarage, 389A Fulwood Road, Sheffield S10 3GA* Sheffield (0114) 230 1671/ 230 1199

JARRATT, Stephen. b 51. Edin Univ BD76 St Kath Coll Liv CertEd77. **d** 78 **p** 79. C Horsforth *Ripon* 78-81; C Stanningley St Thos 81-84; P-in-c Fishponds St Jo *Bris* 84-85; V 85-92; V Chapel Allerton *Ripon* from 92. *The Vicarage, Wood Lane, Chapel Allerton, Leeds LS7 3QF* Leeds (0113) 268 3072

✠**JARRETT, Rt Rev Martyn William.** b 44. Hull Univ MPhil91. K Coll Lon BD67 AKC67. **d** 68 **p** 69 **c** 94. C Bris St Geo *Bris* 68-70; C Swindon New Town 70-74; C Northolt St Mary *Lon* 74-76; V Northolt W End St Jos 76-81; V Hillingdon St Andr 81-83; P-in-c Uxbridge Moor 82-83; V Uxbridge St Andr w St Jo 83-85; Lic to Offic 85-91; Selection Sec ACCM 85-88; Sen Selection Sec 89-91; V Chesterfield All SS *Derby* 91-94; Hon Can Blackb Cathl *Blackb* from 93; Suff Bp Burnley from 94. *Dean House, 449 Padiham Road, Burnley, Lancs BB12 6TD* Burnley (01282) 423564 Fax 835496

JARRETT, Rene Isaac Taiwo. b 49. TCert79 Lon Inst of Educn BEd94. Sierra Leone Th Hall CPS83. **d** 83 **p** 85. Sierra Leone 83-89; Hon C St Pancras w St Jas and Ch Ch *Lon* from 89. *2 Woburn Mansions, Torrington Place, London WC1E 7HL* 0171-580 5165

JARROW, Suffragan Bishop of. *See* SMITHSON, Rt Rev Alan

JARVIS, David Thomas. b 15. St D Coll Lamp BA36. **d** 38 **p** 39. Jerusalem 69-71; V Turnham Green Ch Ch *Lon* 72-85; rtd 85; Perm to Offic *Heref* from 85. *28 Penn Grove Road, Hereford HR1 2BH* Hereford (01432) 270196

JARVIS, Canon Eric Thomas Noel. b 24. Qu Coll Cam BA52 MA54. Ridley Hall Cam 52. **d** 54 **p** 55. V Roundhay St Edm *Ripon* 68-86; RD Allerton 79-84; Hon Can Ripon Cathl 81-86; R St Olave Hart Street w All Hallows Staining etc *Lon* 86-90; V St Marg Pattens 86-90; rtd 90. *38 Dogget Road, Cherry Hinton, Cambridge CB1 4LF* Cambridge (01223) 213387

JARVIS, Geoffrey Thomas Henry. b 21. Bps' Coll Cheshunt 61. **d** 62 **p** 63. C Abbots Langley *St Alb* 68-70; Chapl to the Deaf 70-86; P-in-c Sandridge 76-79; V 79-86; rtd 86; Perm to Offic *Nor* from 88. *Two Gables, 56 Hempstead Road, Holt, Norfolk NR25 6DG* Holt (01263) 711051

JARVIS, Graham Michael. b 60. Golds Coll Lon BMus81 PGCE83. Trin Coll Bris BA91. **d** 91 **p** 92. C St Keverne *Truro* 91-94; Sweden from 94. *Vastgotagatan 21B, 641 36 Katrineholm, Sweden*

JARVIS, Ian Frederick Rodger. b 38. Bris Univ BA60. Tyndale Hall Bris 61. **d** 63 **p** 64. C Penge Ch Ch w H Trin *Roch* 63-67; C Bilston St Leon *Lich* 67-71; V Lozells St Silas *Birm* 71-76; V Chaddesden St Mary *Derby* 76-95; V Newhall from 95. *The Vicarage, Church Street, Newhall, Swadlincote, Derbyshire DE11 0HY* Burton-on-Trent (01283) 214685

JARVIS, Jeffrey Wallace. b 45. Sarum & Wells Th Coll 73. **d** 75 **p** 76. C Cherry Hinton St Andr *Ely* 76-77; C Nottm St Mary *S'well* 77-78; Australia from 78. *30 Lapraik Street, Albion, Queensland, Australia 4010* Brisbane (7) 262-7976

JARVIS, Kenneth Eric. b 06. AKC33. **d** 33 **p** 35. V Beaulieu *Win* 60-77; rtd 77; Perm to Offic *Chich* from 77. *4 Bramwell Lodge, Terry's Cross, Henfield, W Sussex EN5 9SX* Henfield (01273) 494532

JARVIS, Miss Mary. b 35. Leeds Univ BA57 Lon Univ CertEd59. Cranmer Hall Dur 78. **dss** 80 **d** 87 **p** 94. Low Harrogate St Mary *Ripon* 80-84; Wortley de Leeds 84-87; C 87-88; C Upper Armley 88-94; C Holbeck from 94. *71 Burnsall Croft, Leeds LS12 3LH* Leeds (0113) 279 7832

JARVIS, Wilfrid Harry. b 20. Leeds Univ BA43. Coll of Resurr Mirfield 43. **d** 45 **p** 46. V New Basford *S'well* 65-89; V Basford St Aid 89-93; rtd 93. *35 Cow Lane, Beeston, Nottingham NG9 3DJ* Nottingham (0115) 922 3283

JARVIS, William Grantham. b 13. **d** 66 **p** 67. C Binley *Cov* 67-71; V Clifton upon Dunsmore w Brownsover 71-83; P-in-c 83; rtd 83; Perm to Offic *Chich* from 84. *12 Heathlands, Westfield, Hastings, E Sussex TN35 4QZ* Hastings (01424) 753595

JASPER, Dr David. b 51. Jes Coll Cam BA72 MA76 Keble Coll Ox BD80 Dur Univ PhD83. St Steph Ho Ox BA75 MA79. **d** 76 **p** 77. C Buckm *Ox* 76-79; C Dur St Oswald *Dur* 80; Chapl Hatf Coll Dur 81-88; Dir Cen Study of Lit and Th Dur 88-91; Prin St Chad's Coll Dur 88-91; Lect and Dir Cen Study of Lit and Th Glas Univ from 91; Lic to Offic *Glas* from 91. *Netterwood, 124 Old Manse Road, Wishaw, Lanarkshire ML2 0EP* (01698) 373286 or 0141-330 4445 Fax 0141-330 4601

JASPER, David Julian McLean. b 44. Dur Univ BA66 Nottm Univ DipTh68. Linc Th Coll 66. **d** 68 **p** 69. C Redruth *Truro*

68-72; R 72-74; TV 74-75; V St Just in Penwith 75-86; P-in-c Sancreed 82-86. *Dumplings, 28 Kelsey Avenue, Finchampstead, Wokingham, Berks RG11 4TZ* Wokingham (01734) 730243

JASPER, James Roland. b 32. CA Tr Coll 56 NE Ord Course 82. **d** 84 **p** 84. C Newburn *Newc* 84-86; V Ansley *Cov* from 86. *The Vicarage, Ansley, Nuneaton, Warks CV10 9PS* Chapel End (01203) 396403

JASPER, Jonathan Ernest Farley. b 50. AKC72 DPMSA85. St Aug Coll Cant 73. **d** 73 **p** 74. C Cheshunt *St Alb* 73-75; C Bedf St Paul 75-77; C Bedf St Pet w St Cuth 75-77; Chapl Southn Univ *Win* 77-80; Chapl Lon Univ Medical Students *Lon* 80-86; PV Chich Cathl *Chich* 86-89; P-in-c Earls Colne and White Colne *Chelmsf* 89-94; P-in-c Colne Engaine 89-94; R Earls Colne w White Colne and Colne Engaine from 95. *St Andrew's Rectory, 5 Shut Lane, Earls Colne, Colchester CO6 2RE* Earls Colne (01787) 222262

JAUNDRILL, John Warwick. b 47. MInstM81. Qu Coll Birm 86. **d** 88 **p** 89. C Bistre *St As* 88-91; P-in-c Towyn and St George 91-92; V from 92. *The Vicarage, 11 Chester Avenue, Kinmel Bay, Rhyl, Clwyd LL18 5LA* Rhyl (01745) 350119

JAY, Colin. b 62. Keble Coll Ox BA85 St Jo Coll Dur BA89. Cranmer Hall Dur 87. **d** 90 **p** 91. C Bishopwearmouth St Gabr *Dur* 90-94; C Newton Aycliffe 94; TV from 94. *20 Haslewood Road, Newton Aycliffe, Co Durham DL5 4XF* Aycliffe (01325) 320112

JAY, Edmund Arthur. b 41. St Chad's Coll Dur BA63. **d** 65 **p** 66. C Southwick St Columba *Dur* 69-70; Hon C Westbury-on-Trym H Trin *Bris* 72-73; P-in-c S Shields St Fran *Dur* 73-76; C S Shields St Hilda w St Thos 76-79; Chapl S Shields Gen Hosp 79-85; rtd 88. *9 Broadmeadows, East Herrington, Sunderland SR3 3RF* 0191-522 6938

JAY, Ms Nicola Mary. b 37. SRN58 ONC61. NE Ord Course 88. **d** 91 **p** 94. Par Dn Whitburn *Dur* 91-94; C 94-95; P-in-c Sacriston and Kimblesworth from 95. *The Vicarage, 1A Church Parade, Sacriston, Durham DH7 6AD* 0191-371 1853

JAY, Richard Hylton Michael. b 31. Bris Univ BEd75. Sarum & Wells Th Coll 77. **d** 79 **p** 80. NSM Bath St Barn w Englishcombe *B & W* 79-81; NSM Saltford w Corston and Newton St Loe 81-88; R Hatch Beauchamp w Beercrocombe, Curry Mallet etc from 89. *The Rectory, Hatch Beauchamp, Taunton, Somerset TA3 6AB* Hatch Beauchamp (01823) 480220

JAYNE, Martin Philip. b 49. MRTPI73 Man Univ BA71 Preston Poly DMS80. Carl Dioc Tr Course 87. **d** 90 **p** 91. NSM Natland *Carl* from 90. *12 Longmeadow Lane, Natland, Kendal, Cumbria LA9 7QZ* Sedgwick (015395) 60942

JEAN DAVINA, Sister. *See* WILBY, Mrs Jean Davina

JEANES, Gordon Paul. b 55. Ox Univ BA79 MA82 BD90. St Steph Ho Ox 80. **d** 82 **p** 83. C S Wimbledon H Trin and St Pet *S'wark* 82-85; C Surbiton St Andr and St Mark 85-90; Chapl St Chad's Coll Dur 90-93; Sub-Warden St Mich Coll Llan from 94. *Sub-Warden's Flat, St Michael's College, Llandaff, Cardiff CF5 2YJ* Cardiff (01222) 563379

JEANS, Alan Paul. b 58. MIAAS84 MIBCO84 Southn Univ BTh89. Sarum & Wells Th Coll 86. **d** 89 **p** 90. C Parkstone St Pet w Branksea and St Osmund *Sarum* 89-93; P-in-c Bishop's Cannings, All Cannings etc from 93. *The Vicarage, The Street, Bishop's Cannings, Devizes, Wilts SN10 2LD* Devizes (01380) 860650

JEANS, David Bockley. b 48. Mert Coll Ox BA71 MA80 PGCE73. Trin Coll Bris DipHE85. **d** 85 **p** 86. C Clevedon St Andr and Ch Ch *B & W* 85-88; V Wadsley *Sheff* from 88. *The Vicarage, 91 Airedale Road, Sheffield S6 4AW* Sheffield (0114) 234 8481

JEAPES (nee PORTER), Mrs Barbara Judith. b 47. Cam Inst of Educn TCert68. Carl Dioc Tr Inst 91. **d** 94. NSM Egremont and Haile *Carl* from 94. *15 Millfields, Beckermet, Cumbria CA21 2YY* Beckermet (01946) 841489

JEAVONS, Maurice. b 32. Ely Th Coll 60. **d** 62 **p** 63. C Longton St Jo *Lich* 62-68; V Wednesfield St Greg 68-81; V Lower Gornal 81-90; NSM Willenhall St Anne 92-93; C Tunstall from 93. *7 Park Terrace, Stoke-on-Trent ST6 6BP* Stoke-on-Trent (01782) 819175

JEE, Colin Scott. b 32. Worc Coll Ox BA55 MA59. Clifton Th Coll 55. **d** 57 **p** 58. C Spitalfields Ch Ch w All SS *Lon* 57-62; C New Malden and Coombe *S'wark* 62-66; R Ludgershall *Ox* 66-78; P-in-c Oakley 73-82; RD Waddesdon 73-78; R Ludgershall w Wotton Underwood and Ashendon from 78. *The Rectory, Ludgershall, Aylesbury, Bucks HP18 9PG* Brill (01844) 238335

JEE, Jonathan Noel. b 63. BNC Ox BA84 MA88. Wycliffe Hall Ox 85. **d** 88 **p** 89. C Brampton St Thos *Derby* 88-92; TV Hinckley H Trin *Leic* from 92. *7 Rosemary Way, Hinckley, Leics LE10 0LN* Hinckley (01455) 890473

JEFF, Canon Gordon Henry. b 32. St Edm Hall Ox BA56 MA60. Wells Th Coll 59. **d** 61 **p** 62. C Sydenham St Bart *S'wark* 61-64;

C Kidbrooke St Jas 64-66; V Clapham St Paul 66-72; V Raynes Park St Sav 73-79; RD Merton 77-79; V Carshalton Beeches 79-86; P-in-c Petersham 86-90; Chapl St Mich Convent from 90; Hon Can S'wark Cathl from 93. *43 Ham Common, Richmond, Surrey TW10 7JG* 0181-948 0775

JEFFERIES, Cecil Arthur. b 11. Glouc Th Course 68. **d** 69 **p** 70. Hon C Rodborough *Glouc* 69-78; Hon C Cainscross w Selsley 78-89; rtd 89. *Daytona, 29 Upper Church Road, Cainscross, Stroud, Glos GL5 4JF* Stroud (01453) 758287

JEFFERIES, Michael Lewis (Mike). b 45. St Jo Coll Nottm. **d** 87 **p** 88. C Pudsey St Lawr and St Paul *Bradf* 87-93; V Beckenham St Jo *Roch* from 93. *St John's Vicarage, 249 Eden Park Avenue, Beckenham, Kent BR3 3JN* 0181-650 6110

JEFFERIES, Phillip John. b 42. St Chad's Coll Dur BA65 DipTh67 MA91. **d** 67 **p** 68. C Tunstall Ch Ch *Lich* 67-71; C Wolv St Pet 71-74; P-in-c Oakengates 74-80; V 80-82; P-in-c Ketley 78-82; V Horninglow from 82; Bp's Adv on Hosp Chapl from 82. *Horninglow Vicarage, Rolleston Road, Burton-on-Trent, Staffs DE13 0JZ* Burton-on-Trent (01283) 68613

JEFFERSON, Charles Dudley. b 55. St Pet Coll Ox BA78 MA81. Ridley Hall Cam 79. **d** 81 **p** 82. C Chadkirk *Ches* 81-84; C Macclesfield St Pet 84-85; C Macclesfield Team Par 85-89; R Elworth and Warmingham from 89. *The Rectory, 38 Roman Way, Sandbach, Cheshire CW11 9EW* Crewe (01270) 762415

JEFFERSON, David Charles. b 33. Leeds Univ BA57. Coll of Resurr Mirfield 57. **d** 59 **p** 60. C Richmond St Mary *S'wark* 62-64; Public Preacher from 64; Chapl Wilson's Gr Sch Camberwell 64-93; Chapl Wilson's Sch Wallington from 75; rtd 93. *15 Sandown Drive, Stanley Road, Carshalton, Surrey SM5 4LN* 0181-669 0640

JEFFERY, Arthur Francis. b 11. St D Coll Lamp BA33 St Mich Coll Llan 33. **d** 35 **p** 36. V Rhydymwyn *St As* 68-78; rtd 78; Perm to Offic *St As* from 78. *36 Llys Alyn, Rhydymwyn, Mold, Clwyd CH7 5HW* Mold (01352) 741435

JEFFERY, Graham. b 35. Qu Coll Cam BA58. Wells Th Coll 58. **d** 60 **p** 61. C Southn Maybush St Pet *Win* 60-63; Australia 63-66; C E Grinstead St Swithun *Chich* 66-68; C-in-c Hydneye CD 68-74; V Wick 74-76; C Hove 76-78; P-in-c Newtimber w Pyecombe 78-82; R Poynings w Edburton, Newtimber and Pyecombe 82-92; P-in-c Sullington and Thakeham w Warminghurst from 92. *The Rectory, Thakeham, Pulborough, W Sussex RH20 3EP* West Chiltington (01798) 813121

JEFFERY, Kenneth Charles. b 40. Univ of Wales BA64 Linacre Coll Ox BA67 MA70. St Steph Ho Ox 64. **d** 67 **p** 68. C Swindon New Town *Bris* 67-68; C Summertown *Ox* 68-71; C Brighton St Pet *Chich* 71-77; V Ditchling from 77. *The Vicarage, Ditchling, Hassocks, W Sussex BN6 8TS* Hassocks (01273) 843165

JEFFERY, Michael Frank. b 48. Linc Th Coll 74. **d** 76 **p** 77. C Caterham Valley *S'wark* 76-79; C Tupsley *Heref* 79-82; P-in-c Stretton Sugwas 82-84; P-in-c Bishopstone 83-84; P-in-c Kenchester and Bridge Sollers 83-84; V Whiteshill *Glouc* 84-92; P-in-c Randwick 92; V Whiteshill and Randwick from 93. *The Vicarage, Farmhill Lane, Stroud, Glos GL5 4DD* Stroud (01453) 764757

JEFFERY, Norman. b 42. Bps' Coll Cheshunt. **d** 67 **p** 68. C Putney St Mary *S'wark* 67-71; C Hoddesdon *St Alb* 71-74; P-in-c Roxton w Gt Barford 74-79; V 79-86; V Woburn Sands from 86. *The Vicarage, Church Road, Woburn Sands, Milton Keynes MK17 8TR* Milton Keynes (01908) 582581

JEFFERY, Peter James. b 41. Leeds Univ BSc63. Oak Hill Th Coll 64. **d** 66 **p** 67. C Streatham Park St Alb *S'wark* 66-70; C Northn St Giles *Pet* 70-73; C Rushden St Pet 73-76; C Rushden w Newton Bromswold 77-78; V Siddal *Wakef* 78-85; V Sowerby Bridge w Norland from 85. *The Vicarage, Park Road, Sowerby Bridge, W Yorkshire HX6 2PG* Halifax (01422) 831253

JEFFERY, Peter Noel. b 37. Pemb Coll Ox BA60 MA64. Linc Th Coll 60. **d** 62 **p** 63. C W Smethwick *Birm* 62-64; P-in-c Bordesley St Andr 64-69; R Turvey *St Alb* from 69; P-in-c Stevington from 79. *The Rectory, Turvey, Bedford MK43 8DB* Turvey (01234) 881210

JEFFERY, Richard William Christopher. b 43. Ex Univ BA65. Coll of Resurr Mirfield 66. **d** 68 **p** 69. C Widley w Wymering *Portsm* 68-71; C Salisbury St Mich *Sarum* 71-74; TV Ridgeway 74-80; V Stanford in the Vale w Goosey and Hatford *Ox* 80-89; V Topsham *Ex* from 89. *The Vicarage, Globefields, Topsham, Exeter EX3 0EZ* Exeter (01392) 876120

JEFFERY, Very Rev Robert Martin Colquhoun. b 35. K Coll Lon BD58 AKC58. **d** 59 **p** 60. C Grangetown *Dur* 59-61; C Barnes St Mary *S'wark* 61-63; Asst Sec Miss and Ecum Coun Ch Assembly 64-68; Sec Dept Miss and Unity BCC 68-71; V Headington *Ox* 71-78; RD Cowley 73-78; P-in-c Tong *Lich* 78-83; V 83-87; Dioc Missr 78-80; Hon Can Lich Cathl 80-87; Adn Salop 80-87; Dean Worc from 87. *The Deanery, 10 College Green, Worcester WR1 2LH* Worcester (01905) 27821 Fax 611139

JEFFERY, Canon Robert Michael. b 17. Selw Coll Cam BA39 MA43. Westcott Ho Cam 39. **d** 41 **p** 42. S Africa 46-76; Chapl Prestfelde Sch Shrewsbury 76-85; rtd 83. *23 St Nicholas Hospital, Salisbury SP1 2SW* Salisbury (01722) 321737

JEFFERYES, June Ann. b 37. Dur Univ BA58. W Midl Minl Tr Course 87. **d** 90 **p** 94. NSM Caverswall *Lich* 90-92; NSM Caverswall and Weston Coyney w Dilhorne from 92. *8 Vicarage Crescent, Caverswall, Stoke-on-Trent ST11 9EW* Blythe Bridge (01782) 393309

JEFFERYES, Neil. b 37. St Andr Univ BSc60 Lon Univ BD62. Tyndale Hall Bris 60. **d** 63 **p** 64. C St Helens St Helen *Liv* 63-68; V Barrow St Mark *Carl* 68-77; RD Furness 74-77; P-in-c Tetsworth *Ox* 77-81; P-in-c Adwell w S Weston 77-81; P-in-c Stoke Talmage w Wheatfield 77-81; RD Aston 81-85; R Tetsworth, Adwell w S Weston, Lewknor etc 81-86; V Caverswall *Lich* 86-92; P-in-c Dilhorne 86-92; RD Cheadle from 91; V Caverswall and Weston Coyney w Dilhorne from 92. *8 Vicarage Crescent, Caverswall, Stoke-on-Trent ST11 9EW* Blythe Bridge (01782) 393309

JEFFORD, Brian Harrison. b 30. S Dios Minl Tr Scheme 79. **d** 81 **p** 82. NSM Eastbourne St Jo *Chich* from 81. *Flat 1, 20 Derwent Road, Eastbourne, E Sussex BN20 7PH* Eastbourne (01323) 730265

JEFFORD, Peter Ernest. b 29. AKC53. **d** 54 **p** 55. R Rollesby w Burgh w Billockby *Nor* 62-71; V Watton 71-81; V Watton w Carbrooke and Ovington 81-82; P-in-c Brampford Speke *Ex* 82-83; P-in-c Cadbury 82-83; P-in-c Thorverton 82-83; P-in-c Upton Pyne 82-83; TR Thorverton, Cadbury, Upton Pyne etc 83-92; rtd 92. *27 Ashlong Road, Marston, Oxford OX3 0NH* Oxford (01865) 60593

JEFFORD, Ronald (Ron). b 46. Univ of Wales (Lamp) Univ of Wales (Cardiff) DPS. St Mich Coll Llan DMinlStuds. **d** 91 **p** 92. C Ebbw Vale *Mon* 91-94; TV 94-95; R Bedwas and Rudry from 95. *The Rectory, Bryn Goleu, Bedwas, Newport, Gwent NP1 9AU* Caerphilly (01222) 885220

JEFFREE, Robin. b 29. AKC54. **d** 55 **p** 56. V Hartford *Ely* 67-83; P-in-c Denver 83; R 83-94; P-in-c Ryston w Roxham 83; V 83-94; V W Dereham 83-94; rtd 94; Perm to Offic *Nor* from 94. *3 Church Lane, Hindolveston, Dereham, Norfolk NR20 5BT* Melton Constable (01263) 861857

JEFFREYS, David John. b 45. S Dios Minl Tr Scheme 89. **d** 92 **p** 93. NSM Bexhill St Barn *Chich* 92-95; Chapl Conquest Hosp Bexhill from 95. *Conquest Hospital, The Ridge, St Leonards-on-Sea, E Sussex TN37 7RD* Bexhill-on-Sea (01424) 843672

JEFFREYS, Timothy John. b 58. Man Univ BSc79. Cranmer Hall Dur 82. **d** 86 **p** 87. C Goodmayes All SS *Chelmsf* 86-88; Hon C S Lambeth St Anne and All SS *S'wark* from 93. *29 Park Mansions, South Lambeth Road, London SW8 1TW* 0171-582 8451

JEFFRIES, Keith. b 48. St Steph Ho Ox DipMin93. **d** 93 **p** 94. C St Marychurch *Ex* from 93. *100 Hartop Road, Torquay TQ1 4QJ* Torquay (01803) 311629

JEFFRIES, Canon Peter George Charles. b 28. Qu Coll Birm 54. **d** 56 **p** 57. R The Ampneys w Driffield and Poulton *Glouc* 69-93; RD Fairford 86-93; Hon Can Glouc Cathl 89-93; rtd 93. *14 Lambourne Close, Ledbury, Herefordshire HR8 2HW* Ledbury (01531) 636105

JELBART, Alexander Parismas. b 21. Oak Hill Th Coll DipTh53. **d** 53 **p** 54. TR Chell *Lich* 62-70; V Madeley *Heref* 70-78; V St Helens St Mark *Liv* 78-86; rtd 86; Perm to Offic *Leic* from 86. *7 Stuart Court, High Street, Kibworth Beauchamp, Leics LE8 0LE* Leicester (0116) 279 6340

JELF, Miss Pauline Margaret. b 55. Chich Th Coll 88. **d** 90 **p** 94. Par Dn Clayton *Lich* 90-94; C Knutton from 94; C Silverdale and Alsagers Bank from 94. *St John's Presbytery, High Street, Alsagers Bank, Stoke-on-Trent ST7 8BQ* Stoke-on-Trent (01782) 721259

JELLEY, David. b 25. St Deiniol's Hawarden 86. **d** 87 **p** 88. NSM Evington *Leic* 87-93; rtd 93; P-in-c New Galloway *Glas* from 93. *The Rectory, New Galloway, Castle Douglas, Kirkcudbrightshire DG7 3RP* New Galloway (01644) 235

JELLEY, Ian. b 54. NE Ord Course. **d** 91 **p** 92. C Jarrow *Dur* 91-95; P-in-c Leam Lane from 95. *St Andrew's Vicarage, Whinbrooke, Gateshead, Tyne & Wear NE10 8HR* 0191-469 3257

JELLEY, James Dudley (Jim). b 46. Linc Th Coll 78. **d** 80 **p** 81. C Stockwell Green St Andr *S'wark* 80-85; P-in-c Camberwell St Phil and St Mark 85-90; V 91-93; Perm to Offic from 94. *7 Wilmott Close, Peckham Hill Street, London SE15 6TZ* 0171-635 0870

JELLY, James Hugh. b 08. Selw Coll Cam BA31 MA36. Wells Th Coll 31. **d** 32 **p** 33. R S Petherton *B & W* 58-74; rtd 74; Hon C Malborough w S Huish *Ex* 74-78; Perm to Offic *B & W* 79-91. *53 Hillview Road, Minehead, Somerset TA24 8EF* Minehead (01643) 702041

JENKIN, Hon Charles Alexander Graham. b 54. BScEng. Westcott Ho Cam 81. **d** 84 **p** 85. C Binley *Cov* 84-88; TV Canvey Is *Chelmsf* 88-94; TR Melton Mowbray *Leic* from 94.

The Rectory, 67 Dalby Road, Melton Mowbray, Leics LE13 0BQ Melton Mowbray (01664) 480923

JENKIN, Christopher Cameron. b 36. BNC Ox BA61 MA64. Clifton Th Coll 61. **d** 63 **p** 64. C Walthamstow St Mary *Chelmsf* 63-68; C Surbiton Hill Ch Ch *S'wark* 68-78; V Newport St Jo *Portsm* 78-88; R Newbarns w Hawcoat *Carl* from 88. *St Paul's Rectory, 353 Abbey Road, Barrow-in-Furness, Cumbria LA13 9JY* Barrow-in-Furness (01229) 821546

JENKINS, Dr Allan Kenneth. b 40. Lon Univ BD63 AKC63 MTh69 PhD85. St Mich Coll Llan 63. **d** 64 **p** 65. C Llanblethian w Cowbridge *Llan* 64-70; India 70-76; R Llanarth w Clytha, Llansantffraed and Bryngwyn *Mon* 76-78; Dir of Studies Chich Th Coll 78-83; P-in-c Fowlmere *Ely* 83-87; P-in-c Thriplow 83-87; Sen Tutor E Anglian Minl Tr Course 84-87; Sen Chapl Cardiff Colls 87-95; Dioc Dir Post-Ord Tr *Llan* 88-95; P-in-c Sidlesham *Chich* from 95; Tutor Bp Otter Coll Chich from 95. *The Vicarage, Church Farm Lane, Sidlesham, Chichester, W Sussex PO20 7RE* Chichester (01243) 641237

JENKINS, Miss Anne Christina. b 47. Birm Univ BA70 Hull Univ CertEd71 St Jo Coll Dur BA77 DipTh78. Cranmer Hall Dur 75. **dss** 78 **d** 87 **p** 94. Coatham *York* 78-81; OHP 81-87; Perm to Offic *York* 81-87; Ghana 87-88; Par Dn Beeston *Ripon* 88-93; Par Dn Leeds Gipton Epiphany 93-94; V Leeds St Marg and All Hallows from 94. *The Vicarage, 24 Regent Terrace, Leeds LS6 1NP* Leeds (0113) 242 2205

JENKINS, Clifford Thomas. b 38. IEng MIEleclE. Sarum & Wells Th Coll. **d** 77 **p** 78. Chapl Yeovil Coll 77-92; Hon C Yeovil *B & W* 77-87; Perm to Offic 87-92; Chs FE Liason Officer (Dios B & W, Bris & Glouc) 87-92; FE Adv Gen Syn Bd of Educn & Meth Div from 90; Perm to Offic *S'wark* from 93. *116 Stag Lane, Edgware, Middx HA8 5LL* 0181-204 3044 or 0171-222 9011 Fax 0171-799 2714

JENKINS, Clive Ronald. b 57. Ripon Coll Cuddesdon 81. **d** 84 **p** 85. C E Grinstead St Swithun *Chich* 84-87; C Horsham 87-88; TV 88-90; Dioc Youth Chapl from 90; P-in-c Amberley w N Stoke and Parham, Wiggonholt etc from 93. *The Vicarage, Amberley, Arundel, W Sussex BN18 9ND* Bury (01798) 831500

JENKINS, Cyril. b 27. Univ of Wales (Lamp) BA53. Wells Th Coll 53. **d** 55 **p** 56. V Gnosall *Lich* 69-72; Chapl St Alb Sch Chorley 72-79; Lic to Offic *Blackb* from 73; Hd of Relig Studies Runshaw Coll 74-84; Lect Runshaw Tertiary Coll 84-86; rtd 86. *55 Church Walk, Euxton, Chorley, Lancs PR7 6HL* Chorley (01257) 263973

✠**JENKINS, Rt Rev David Edward.** b 25. Qu Coll Ox BA51 MA54 Dur Univ DD87. Linc Th Coll 52. **d** 53 **p** 54 c 84. C Birm Cathl *Birm* 53-54; Lect Qu Coll Birm 53-54; Chapl Qu Coll Ox 54-69; Lect Th Ox Univ 55-69; Can Th Leic Cathl *Leic* 66-82; Dir WCC Humanum Studies 69-73; Dir Wm Temple Foundn Man 73-78; Jt Dir 79-94; Prof Th and Relig Studies Leeds Univ 79-84; Bp Dur 84-94; rtd 94; Hon Ass Bp Ripon from 94. *Ashbourne, Cotherstone, Barnard Castle, Co Durham DL12 9PR* Teesdale (01833) 650804

JENKINS, David Harold. b 61. SS Coll Cam BA84 MA87 Ox Univ BA88 MA94. Ripon Coll Cuddesdon 86. **d** 89 **p** 90. C Chesterton Gd Shep *Ely* 89-91; C Earley St Pet *Ox* 91-94; V Blackpool St Mich *Blackb* from 94. *St Michael's Vicarage, Calvert Place, Blackpool FY3 7RU* Blackpool (01253) 397755

JENKINS, Canon David Myrddin. b 30. Univ of Wales BEd76. St Mich Coll Llan 59. **d** 61 **p** 62. C Haverfordwest St Mary w St Thos *St D* 61-63; C Pemb Dock 63-67; Japan 67-69; Miss to Seamen 69-71; V Llansteffan and Llan-y-bri etc *St D* 71-78; R Llantwit Major *Llan* from 78; Can Llan Cathl from 89. *The Rectory, Llantwit Major, S Glam CF61 1SS* Llantwit Major (01446) 792324

JENKINS, David Noble. b 25. CCC Cam BA47 MA50. Cuddesdon Coll 48. **d** 50 **p** 51. Chapl Eastbourne Coll 66-74; V Jarvis Brook *Chich* 75-90; rtd 90; USA 90-92. *2 Littlebourne Cottages, London Road, Crowborough, E Sussex TN6 1SR* Crowborough (01892) 661179

JENKINS, David Roland. b 32. Kelham Th Coll 55. **d** 59 **p** 60. C Middlesb St Jo the Ev *York* 59-60; C Kingston upon Hull St Alb 60-64; C Roehampton H Trin *S'wark* 64-68; V Dawley St Jerome *Lon* 68-73; R Harlington from 73. *The Rectory, St Peter's Way, Hayes, Middx UB3 5AB* 0181-759 9569

JENKINS, David Thomas. b 43. RIBA70 Lon Univ DipTh79. S'wark Ord Course 76. **d** 79 **p** 80. NSM Merthyr Tydfil and Cyfarthfa *Llan* 79-86; NSM Brecon St David w Llanspyddid and Llanilltyd *S & B* 86-91; P-in-c Llangiwg 91-92; V from 92. *The Vicarage, 10 Uplands, Pontardwe, Swansea SA5 9PA* Swansea (01792) 862003

JENKINS, Canon David Thomas Ivor. b 28. Birm Univ MA63 K Coll Lon BD52 AKC52. **d** 53 **p** 54. C Bilton *Cov* 53-56; V Wolston 56-61; Asst Dir FE *Carl* 61-63; V Carl St Barn 63-72; V Carl St Cuth 72-76; P-in-c Carl St Mary w St Paul 72-76; Hon Can Carl Cathl 76-91; V Carl St Cuth w St Mary 76-91;

Dioc Sec from 84; Can Res Carl Cathl from 91. *4 The Abbey, Carlisle CA3 8TZ* Carlisle (01228) 590778 or 22573 Fax 48769

JENKINS, Canon Eric Neil. b 23. Univ of Wales BSc43 MSc47. Wycliffe Hall Ox 60. **d** 62 **p** 63. V Hale *Liv* 65-73; Bp's Adv on Soc and Scientific Affairs 73-88; V Hightown 73-88; Hon Can Liv Cathl 83-89; rtd 89. *51 Oulton Road, Liverpool L16 8NP* 0151-722 5515

JENKINS, Ernest Dennis. b 28. S Dios Minl Tr Scheme 80. **d** 83 **p** 84. NSM Lancing St Mich *Chich* 83-86; C E Grinstead St Swithun 86-89; C Portslade St Nic and St Andr 89-94; rtd 94. *61A Upton Road, Worthing, W Sussex BN13 1BY* Worthing (01903) 263911

JENKINS, Very Rev Frank Graham. b 23. St D Coll Lamp BA47 Jes Coll Ox BA49 MA53. St Mich Coll Llan 49. **d** 50 **p** 51. V Risca *Mon* 64-75; Can St Woolos Cathl 67-76; V Caerleon 75-76; Dean Mon 76-90; rtd 90. *Rivendell, 209 Christchurch Road, Newport, Gwent NP9 7QL* Newport (01633) 255278

JENKINS, Frederick Llewellyn. b 14. St D Coll Lamp BA35 St Mich Coll Llan 36. **d** 37 **p** 38. Chapl R Masonic Sch Bushey 64-77; rtd 77; Perm to Offic *Lich* from 77. *Plas Uchaf, Trefonen, Oswestry, Shropshire SY10 9DT* Oswestry (01691) 653918

JENKINS, Garry Frederick. b 48. Southn Univ BTh79. Chich Th Coll 75. **d** 79 **p** 80. C Kingsbury St Andr *Lon* 79-84; C Leigh St Clem *Chelmsf* 84-88; P-in-c Brentwood St Geo 88-94; V from 94. *The Vicarage, 28 Robin Hood Road, Brentwood, Essex CM15 9EN* Brentwood (01277) 213618

JENKINS, Gary John. b 59. York Univ BA80 CertEd81. Oak Hill Th Coll BA89. **d** 89 **p** 90. C Norwood *S'wark* 89-94; P-in-c St Helier 94-95; V from 95. *St Peter's Vicarage, Bishopsford Road, Morden, Surrey SM4 6BH* 0181-648 6050

JENKINS, Canon George Patrick. b 36. Univ of Wales (Lamp) BA61. Lich Th Coll 61. **d** 63 **p** 64. C Dursley *Glouc* 63-66; C Stroud H Trin 66-69; V Churcham w Bulley 69-81; V Churcham w Bulley and Minsterworth from 81; RD Forest N 79-95; Hon Can Glouc Cathl from 90. *The Vicarage, Church Lane, Churcham, Gloucester GL2 8AF* Gloucester (01452) 750252

JENKINS, Jeanette. b 42. St Jo Coll Nottm 83. **dss** 84 **d** 86 **p** 94. NSM Kilmarnock *Glas* from 84; NSM Irvine St Andr from 84; NSM Ardrossan from 84; Asst Chapl Crosshouse Hosp from 86; Chapl Ayrshire Hospice from 90. *4 Gleneagles Avenue, Kilwinning, Ayrshire KA13 6RD* Kilwinning (01294) 53383

JENKINS, John Alfred Morgan. b 36. Univ of Wales (Lamp) BA58 St Cath Coll Ox BA60 MA64. Wycliffe Hall Ox 61 **d** 61 **p** 62. C Sketty *S & B* 61-69; Br Honduras 69-72; V W Byfleet *Guildf* 73-89; R Monken Hadley *Lon* from 89. *The Rectory, Hadley Common, Barnet, Herts EN5 5QD* 0181-449 2414

JENKINS, John Francis. b 46. Ripon Hall Ox 77 Ripon Coll Cuddesdon 75. **d** 77 **p** 78. C Filton *Bris* 77-79; C Bris St Andr Hartcliffe 79-84; P-in-c Bris H Cross Inns Court 84-85; V 85-95; R Odcombe, Brympton, Lufton and Montacute *B & W* from 95. *The Rectory, Street Lane, Higher Odcombe, Yeovil, Somerset BA22 8UP* West Coker (01935) 862224

JENKINS, John Howard David. b 51. Birm Univ BA72. St Steph Ho Ox 72. **d** 74 **p** 75. C Milford Haven *St D* 74-77; PV Llan Cathl *Llan* 77-81; Chapl Lowther Coll St As 81-84; VC St As Cathl *St As* 81-84; C Neath w Llantwit *Llan* 84-86; Chapl Colston's Sch Bris 86-91; Chapl Blue Coat Sch Birm from 91. *Blue Coat School, Metchley Lane, Birmingham B17 0HR* 0121-454 1425

JENKINS, John Morgan. b 33. Mon Dioc Tr Scheme 82. **d** 85 **p** 86. NSM Cwmbran *Mon* from 85. *5 Ridgeway Avenue, Newport, Gwent NP9 5AF* Newport (01633) 259979

JENKINS, John Raymond. b 26. K Coll Lon 52. **d** 53 **p** 54. Hon C Wrexham *St As* 77-82; V Llanfair Caereinion w Llanllugan 67-70; V Llanychaearn w Llanddeiniol *St D* 82-91; rtd 91; Chapl Lanzarote *Eur* from 95. *Casa dos Piedras, Calle Vocanes, Los Mojones, Puerto del Carmen, Lanzarote*

JENKINS, John Richard. b 68. Dundee Univ LLB90. St Steph Ho Ox BA94 DipMin94. **d** 94 **p** 95. C Brighouse and Clifton *Wakef* from 94. *St Martin's House, 34 Stanley Street, Brighouse, W Yorkshire HD6 1SX* Brighouse (01484) 718919

JENKINS, Kenneth Thomas. b 15. St D Coll Lamp BA36 Ripon Hall Ox 36. **d** 38 **p** 39. Chapl R Masonic Sch Bushey 57-59; Australia from 59; rtd 90. *26A Barr Smith Avenue, Myrtle Bank, South Australia 5064*

JENKINS, Lawrence Clifford. b 45. AKC70 Open Univ BA77. St Aug Coll Cant. **d** 71 **p** 72. C Osmondthorpe St Phil *Ripon* 71-74; C Monkseaton St Mary *Newc* 75-78; V Shiremoor 78-84; V Wheatley Hills *Sheff* 84-95; RD Doncaster 92-95; V Greenhill from 95. *St Peter's Clergy House, Reney Avenue, Sheffield S8 7FN* Sheffield (0114) 237 2311

JENKINS, Paul Morgan. b 44. Sussex Univ BEd68 Fitzw Coll Cam BA73 MA76. Westcott Ho Cam 71. **d** 74 **p** 75. C Forest Gate St Edm *Chelmsf* 74-77; P-in-c Stourpaine, Durweston and Bryanston *Sarum* 77-83; Perm to Offic 83-85; Chapl Bryanston Sch Blandford 77-85; Lic to Offic *Derby* 84-91; Asst Chapl and Housemaster Repton Sch Derby 84-89; Dean of Chpl 89-91; R Singleton *Chich* from 91; V E Dean from 91; V W Dean from 91. *The Rectory, Singleton, Chichester, W Sussex PO18 0EZ* Singleton (01243) 811213

JENKINS, Ven Raymond Gordon Finney. b 98. TCD BA23 MA32 BD36. CITC 28 TCD Div Sch Div Test28. **d** 30 **p** 31. I Dub Grangegorman *D & G* 39-76; Lect TCD 39-70; Adn Dub 61-74; Chan St Patr Cathl Dub 62-76; rtd 76; Hon CV Ch Ch Cathl Dub *D & G* from 76. *4 Damer Court, Upper Wellington Street, Dublin 7, Irish Republic* Dublin (1) 830-1156 or 830-7145

JENKINS, Preb Richard David. b 33. Magd Coll Cam BA58 MA. Westcott Ho Cam 59. **d** 61 **p** 62. C Staveley *Derby* 61-64; C Billingham St Aid *Dur* 64-68; V Walsall Pleck and Bescot *Lich* 68-73; R Whitchurch from 73; RD Wem and Whitchurch from 85; P-in-c Tilstock and Whixall 92-95; Preb Lich Cathl from 93. *The Rectory, Church Street, Whitchurch, Shropshire SY13 1LB* Whitchurch (01948) 892342

JENKINS, Richard Morvan. b 44. St Mich Coll Llan DipTh68 DPS69. **d** 69 **p** 70. C Tenby *St D* 69-73; V Llanrhian w Llanhywel and Carnhedryn 73-77; V Llanrhian w Llanhywel and Carnhedryn etc 77-80; R Johnston w Steynton 80-93; V St Ishmael's w Llan-saint and Ferryside from 93. *The Vicarage, Water Street, Ferryside, Dyfed SA17 5RT* Ferryside (01267) 267288

JENKINS, Canon Robert Francis. b 33. BNC Ox BA57 MA59. Wycliffe Hall Ox 57. **d** 59 **p** 60. C Hall Green Ascension Birm 59-63; V Dosthill and Wood End 63-71; V Brandwood 71-85; V Sutton Coldfield St Columba from 85; Hon Can S Malawi from 87. *280 Chester Road North, Sutton Coldfield, W Midlands B73 6RR* 0121-354 5873

JENKINS, Very Rev Thomas Edward. b 02. St D Coll Lamp BA22 BD32. Wycliffe Hall Ox 24. **d** 25 **p** 26. Dean St D 57-72; rtd 72. *clo The Revd Canon D M Jenkins, The Rectory, Llantwit Major, S Glam CF61 1SS* Llantwit Major (01446) 792324

JENKINS, Thomas Glennard Owen. b 22. St Jo Coll Ox BA48 MA52. Wells Th Coll 49 Wycliffe Hall Ox 50. **d** 50 **p** 51. V Hailey w Crawley *Ox* 60-79; V Penbryn and Betws Ifan w Bryngwyn *St D* 79-87; rtd 87. *24 Anwylfan, Aberporth, Cardigan, Dyfed SA43 2EL* Cardigan (01239) 811402

JENKINS, Thomas William. b 14. Univ of Wales BA40. St Mich Coll Llan 40. **d** 42 **p** 43. V Shrewsbury H Trin w St Julian *Lich* 67-75; V Ruyton 75-80; rtd 80; Perm to Offic *Lich* from 80. *4 Larkhill Road, Park Hall, Oswestry, Shropshire SY11 4AW* Oswestry (01691) 659304

JENKINS, Timothy David. b 52. Pemb Coll Ox BA73 MLitt77 MA82 St Edm Ho Cam BA84. Ridley Hall Cam 82. **d** 85 **p** 86. C Kingswood *Bris* 85-87; Sen Chapl Nottm Univ *S'well* 88-92; Dean and Chapl Jes Coll Cam from 92. *Jesus College, Cambridge CB5 8BL* Cambridge (01223) 68611

JENKINS, Canon William David. b 42. Birm Univ BA63. St D Coll Lamp LTh65. **d** 65 **p** 66. C Gorseinon *S & B* 65-67; C Llanelli *St D* 67-72; V Clydach *S & B* 72-82; Chapl Llandudno Gen Hosp from 82; V Llanrhos *St As* from 82; RD Llanrwst from 84; Hon Can St As Cathl from 93. *Llanrhos Vicarage, 2 Vicarage Road, Llandudno, Gwynedd LL30 1PT* Llandudno (01492) 876512

JENKINS, William Frederick. b 08. St Jo Coll Dur BA33 MA38. **d** 35 **p** 36. V Histon *Ely* 60-75; rtd 75; Lic to Offic *Blackb* from 75. *6 Warwick Drive, Clitheroe, Lancs BB7 3LJ* Clitheroe (01200) 22460

JENKINSON, Margaret. b 40. MCSP62. Carl Dioc Tr Inst 89. **d** 92 **p** 94. NSM Preesall *Blackb* from 92. *10 Spruce Cottages, The Conifers, Hambleton, Poulton-le-Fylde, Lancs FY6 9EP* Poulton-le-Fylde (01253) 701788

JENKYNS, Preb Henry Derrik George. b 30. Sarum Th Coll 57. **d** 60 **p** 61. C Kettering SS Pet and Paul *Pet* 60-64; V Shrewsbury St Geo *Lich* 64-71; V Wednesbury St Paul Wood Green 71-76; V Stokesay *Heref* 76-86; P-in-c Acton Scott 76-86; RD Condover 80-86; Preb Heref Cathl from 83; R Kington w Huntington, Old Radnor, Kinnerton etc from 86. *The Vicarage, Kington, Herefordshire HR5 3AG* Kington (01544) 230525

JENKYNS, John Thomas William Basil. b 30. Univ of Wales (Lamp) BA54 St Cath Coll Ox BA57 MA62. Wycliffe Hall Ox 54. **d** 57 **p** 58. C Neasden cum Kingsbury St Cath *Lon* 57-60; C S Lyncombe *B & W* 60-64; V Gt Harwood St Bart *Blackb* 64-66; R Colne St Bart 66-69; V Chard St Mary *B & W* 69-87; Preb Wells Cathl 87; V Swaffham *Nor* 87-89; V Overbury w Teddington, Alstone etc *Worc* from 89. *The Vicarage, Station Road, Beckford, Tewkesbury, Glos GL20 7AD* Evesham (01386) 881380

JENKYNS, Thomas John Blackwell. b 31. St D Coll Lamp BA52. **d** 54 **p** 55. C Llanelli St Paul *St D* 54-58; C New Windsor St Jo *Ox* 58-64; Chapl RAF 64-85; P-in-c Herriard w Winslade and Long Sutton etc *Win* 85-86; V from 86. *The Vicarage,*

Upton Grey, Basingstoke, Hants RG25 2RB Basingstoke (01256) 862469

JENNER, Miss Brenda Ann. b 54. Culham Coll Ox BEd80. St Jo Coll Nottm DPS88. **d** 88. Par Dn Leigh St Mary *Man* 88-92; Par Dn Leic Ch Sav *Leic* 92-94; rtd 94. *18 Chatsworth Avenue, Wigston, Leicester LE18 4LF*

JENNER, Michael Albert. b 37. Oak Hill Th Coll 75. **d** 77 **p** 78. C Mile Cross *Nor* 77-80; P-in-c Easton *Ely* 80-86; P-in-c Ellington 80-86; P-in-c Grafham 80-86; P-in-c Spaldwick w Barham and Woolley 80-86. *Hope Cottage, 12 Main Street, Greetham, Leics LE15 7NL* Oakham (01572) 813415

JENNER, Dr Peter John. b 56. Chu Coll Cam BA77 PhD80 MA81. St Jo Coll Nottm 82. **d** 85 **p** 86. C Upperby St Jo *Carl* 85-88; Chapl Reading Univ *Ox* from 88. *30 Shinfield Road, Reading RG2 7BW* Reading (01734) 871495 or 318797

JENNETT, Maurice Arthur. b 34. St Jo Coll Dur BA60. Cranmer Hall Dur 60. **d** 62 **p** 63. C Marple All SS *Ches* 62-67; V Withnell *Blackb* 67-75; V Stranton *Dur* 75-91; BCMS 91-93; Crosslinks from 93; Zimbabwe from 91. *St Mary Magdalene's Mission, Post Bag 2005, Nyanga, Zimbabwe*

JENNINGS, Miss Anne. b 41. CertEd63 STh Cam Univ CertRK67. Gilmore Ho 65. **dss** 71 **d** 87 **p** 94. Barton w Peel Green *Man* 71-76; Wythenshawe Wm Temple Ch 76-79; Rochdale 79-83; Chapl Rochdale Colls of FE 79-83; Hillock *Man* 83-87; D-in-c 87-88; Chapl Wakef Cathl *Wakef* from 88. *2 Cathedral Close, Margaret Street, Wakefield, W Yorkshire WF1 2DQ* Wakefield (01924) 378179

JENNINGS, Ven David Willfred Michael. b 44. AKC66. **d** 67 **p** 68. C Walton St Mary *Liv* 67-69; C Christchurch *Win* 69-73; V Hythe 73-80; V Romford St Edw *Chelmsf* 80-92; RD Havering 85-92; Hon Can Chelmsf Cathl 87-92; Adn Southend from 92. *136 Broomfield Road, Chelmsford CM1 1RN* Chelmsford (01245) 258257 Fax 250845

JENNINGS, Francis Kingston. b 16. TCD BA39. **d** 41 **p** 41. I Ardee w Charlestown and Collon *Arm* 57-90; RD Creggan and Louth 74-90; rtd 90. *The Rectory, Ardee, Co Louth, Irish Republic* Ardee (41) 53320

JENNINGS, Frederick David. b 48. K Coll Lon BD73 AKC73. St Aug Coll Cant 73. **d** 74 **p** 75. C Halesowen *Worc* 74-77; Perm to Offic *Birm* 78-80; Perm to Offic *Leic* 78-80 and 85-87; P-in-c Snibston 80-85; Community Relns Officer 81-84; P-in-c Burbage w Aston Flamville 87-91; R from 91. *The Rectory, New Road, Burbage, Hinkley, Leics LE10 2AW* Hinkley (01455) 230512

JENNINGS, George. b 20. Lon Univ BD64. Lambeth STh89 Oak Hill Th Coll 46. **d** 51 **p** 52. V Haydock St Mark *Liv* 66-77; V Newburgh 77-89; rtd 89. *97 Watling Street South, Church Stretton, Shropshire SY6 7BH* Church Stretton (01694) 722145

JENNINGS, Harold Andrew. b 15. ATCL35 LTCL36 FTCL37 MRST39 LRAM39. St Deiniol's Hawarden 63. **d** 63 **p** 64. R Aberedw w Llandeilo Graban etc *S & B* 67-79; V Knighton and Norton 79-85; Hon C Llanbister and Llanbadarn Fynydd w Llananno 85-87; rtd 87. *Finsbury, Beaufort Road, Llandrindod Wells, Powys LD1 5EL* Llandrindod Wells (01597) 824892

JENNINGS, Janet. b 38. SCM71 SRN74. Oak Hill Th Coll BA87. **d** 88. Par Dn Stevenage St Pet Broadwater *St Alb* 88-90; NSM Montgomery Adnry *St As* from 92. *Pound House, Forden, Welshpool, Powys SY21 8NU* Welshpool (01938) 580400

JENNINGS, Jonathan Peter. b 61. Lon Univ BD. Westcott Ho Cam. **d** 86 **p** 87. C Peterlee *Dur* 86-89; C Darlington St Cuth 89-92; Dioc Communications Officer *Man* 92-95; Broadcasting Officer Gen Syn from 95. *Church House, Great Smith Street, London SW1P 3NZ* 0171-222 9011 Fax 233 2660

JENNINGS, Very Rev Kenneth Neal. b 30. CCC Cam BA54 MA58. Cuddesdon Coll 54. **d** 56 **p** 57. C Ramsgate H Trin *Cant* 56-59; India 59-66; Vice-Prin Cuddesdon Coll 67-73; V Hitchin St Mary *St Alb* 73-76; TR Hitchin 77-83; Dean Glouc from 83. *The Deanery, Miller's Green, Gloucester GL1 2BP* Gloucester (01452) 524167

JENNINGS, Mervyn. b 39. Sarum & Wells Th Coll 83. **d** 85 **p** 86. C Knowle *Bris* 85-89; P-in-c Cressing *Chelmsf* 89-93; Rural Youth Development Officer from 89; V Barkingside St Fran from 93. *St Francis's Vicarage, 144 Fencepiece Road, Ilford, Essex IG6 2LA* 0181-500 2970

JENNINGS, Paul Warwick. b 55. Birm Univ BSc77. Coll of Resurr Mirfield 77. **d** 80 **p** 81. C Dudley St Jas *Worc* 80-83; TV Halesowen 83-87; Chapl St Marg Hosp Birm 88-89. *220 Birmingham Road, Walsall WS1 2NY* Walsall (01922) 720656

JENNINGS, Peter James. b 28. Univ of Wales (Lamp) BA56. St D Coll Lamp LTh57. **d** 57 **p** 58. Chapl HM Pris Wakef 66-70; Chapl HM Pris Liv 70-76; RD Walton *Liv* 75-76; Chapl HM Pris Styal 76-77 and 88-92; N Regional Chapl 76-82; Asst Chapl Gen (N) 82-88; Perm to Offic *Man* from 77; Perm to

Offic *Ches* from 79; rtd 93. *6 St Anns Road South, Cheadle, Cheshire SK8 3DZ*   0161-437 8828

JENNINGS, Robert Henry. b 46. St Jo Coll Dur BA69 MA79. Qu Coll Birm DipTh71. **d** 72 **p** 73. C Dursley *Glouc* 72-74; C Coleford w Staunton 75-78; TV Bottesford w Ashby *Linc* 78-83; TV Witney *Ox* 83-89; V Lane End w Cadmore End from 89. *The Vicarage, 7 Lammas Way, Lane End, High Wycombe, Bucks HP14 3EX*   High Wycombe (01494) 881913

JENNINGS, Canon Ronald Osmund. b 18. Leeds Univ BA42 Lon Univ BD56. Bps' Coll Cheshunt 42. **d** 44 **p** 45. V St Ives *Ely* 63-82; rtd 83; Perm to Offic *Ely* from 83; Perm to Offic *Linc* from 84; Perm to Offic *Pet* from 87. *3 Viceroy Drive, Pinchbeck, Spalding, Lincs PE11 3TS*   Spalding (01775) 723883

JENNINGS, Thomas Robert. b 24. TCD BA47 MA51. **d** 48 **p** 49. I Killeshandra *K, E & A* 67-70; I Newc w Newtownmountkennedy and Calary *D & G* 70-92; Can Ch Ch Cathl Dub from 88; rtd 92. *Cedarwood House, Woodstock Road, Kilcoole, Greystones, Co Wicklow, Irish Republic*   Dublin (1) 287-5807

JENNINGS, Walter James. b 37. Birm Univ BMus60 MA90. Qu Coll Birm 77. **d** 80 **p** 81. Hon C Hampton in Arden *Birm* 80-84; Chapl St Alb Aided Sch Highgate Birm 84-86; C Wotton-under-Edge w Ozleworth and N Nibley *Glouc* 86-89; V Cheltenham All SS from 89. *All Saints' Vicarage, 66 All Saints Road, Cheltenham, Glos GL52 2HA*   Cheltenham (01242) 523341

JENNISON, Ronald Bernard (Ron). b 27. Chich Th Coll 57. **d** 59 **p** 60. V Bridlington Quay H Trin *York* 69-77; V Sewerby w Marton 69-77; V Bridlington H Trin and Sewerby w Marton 77-79; Chapl Marseille w St Raphael Aix-en-Provence etc *Eur* 79-82; Chapl Nice w Vence 82-84; R Finmere w Mixbury, Cottisford, Hardwick etc *Ox* 84-92; RD Bicester and Islip 85-92; rtd 92. *12 St Mary's Court, Church Lane, Tingewick, Buckingham MK18 4AT*   Buckingham (01280) 848815

JENNO, Charles Henry. b 25. Wells Th Coll 65. **d** 66 **p** 67. C Fishponds St Mary *Bris* 69-73; V Thornes St Jas w Ch Ch *Wakef* 73-78; V Carleton 78-82; V E Hardwick 78-82; rtd 82; Perm to Offic *Wakef* from 82. *32 Tower Avenue, Upton, Pontefract, W Yorkshire WF9 1EE*   Pontefract (01977) 640925

JENSON, Philip Peter. b 56. Ex Coll Ox BA78 MA82 Down Coll Cam BA80 MA86 PhD88. Ridley Hall Cam 80. **d** 87 **p** 88. C Gt Warley Ch Ch *Chelmsf* 87-89; Lect Trin Coll Bris from 89. *77 Reedley Road, Bristol BS9 3TB, or Trinity College, Stoke Hill, Bristol BS9 1JP*   Bristol (0117) 968 2880 or 968 2803

JEPHSON, Douglas Ronald Shipstone. b 17. St Jo Coll Dur BA38 MA43. **d** 40 **p** 41. R Tysoe w Compton Winyates and Oxhill *Cov* 70-81; R Whatcote 76-81; V Tysoe w Oxhill and Whatcote 81-82; rtd 82. *The Old School House, 42 The Village, Thorp Arch, Wetherby, W Yorkshire LS23 7AG*   Boston Spa (01937) 845955

JEPPS, Philip Anthony. b 34. BNC Ox BA58 MA68. Wycliffe Hall Ox 58. **d** 60 **p** 73. C Elton All SS *Man* 60; Perm to Offic *Pet* 70-73; R Church w Chapel Brampton 74-80; P-in-c Harlestone 79-80; V Kettering St Andr 80-94; V Conisbrough *Sheff* from 94. *St Peter's Vicarage, 8 Castle Avenue, Conisbrough, Doncaster, S Yorkshire DN12 3BT*   Rotherham (01709) 864695

JERMAN, Cecil Maldwyn. b 13. St D Coll Lamp BA34 St Mich Coll Llan 34. **d** 36 **p** 37. V New Brighton St Jas *Ches* 55-74; Lic to Offic *Ban* from 75; rtd 78. *Bryn Haul, Llaneilian, Amlwch, Gwynedd LL68 9LR*   Amlwch (01407) 830977

JERMAN, Edward David. b 40. Trin Coll Carmarthen CertEd61. **d** 87 **p** 88. NSM Llandrygarn w Bodwrog and Heneglwys etc *Ban* from 87. *Tryfan, Trefor, Holyhead, Gwynedd LL65 3YT*   Gwalchmai (01407) 720856

JERMY, Jack. b 22. ACP65. Ripon Hall Ox 64. **d** 65 **p** 66. Hd Master SS Simon and Jude Primary Sch Bolton 62-80; C Bolton SS Simon and Jude *Man* 65-74; P-in-c Rivington 74-93; NSM Horwich and Rivington from 93. *8 Mill Lane, Horwich, Bolton BL6 6AT*   Horwich (01204) 696198

JEROME, Canon Charles Stephen. b 17. Linc Th Coll 48. **d** 50 **p** 51. Dioc Dir of Chr Stewardship *Derby* 67-71; V Denby 68-71; Dioc Dir of Chr Stewardship *Ely* 71-83; P-in-c Holywell w Needingworth 71-78; V Impington 78-84; Hon Can Ely Cathl 82-84; rtd 84; Perm to Offic *Ely* from 84. *31 Greengarth, St Ives, Huntingdon, Cambs PE17 4QS*   St Ives (01480) 493133

JERSEY, Dean of. *See* SEAFORD, Very Rev John Nicholas
JERUSALEM, Bishop of. *See* KAFITY, Rt Rev Samir
JERUSALEM, Dean of. *See* TIDY, Very Rev John Hylton
JERVIS, Christopher. b 53. BEd Cam Univ DipTh. Wycliffe Hall Ox. **d** 82 **p** 83. C Woodford Wells *Chelmsf* 82-85; Chapl Felsted Sch Essex 85-87; Chapl Canford Sch Wimborne from 87. *Merryvale, Canford Magna, Wimborne, Dorset BH21 2AF*   Wimborne (01202) 887722 or 841254

JERVIS, Clement Frank Cooper. b 16. St Jo Coll Dur LTh39 BA40 MA45. St Aid Birkenhead 36. **d** 40 **p** 41. V Pensnett *Lich* 56-81; rtd 81; Perm to Offic *Lich* from 81; Perm to Offic *Ches* from 83. *8 Maidensbridge Road, Wall Heath, Kingswinford, W Midlands DY6 0HG*   Kingswinford (01384) 279974

JERVIS, Preb Horace Roland. b 14. St Jo Coll Dur LTh38 BA39. St Aid Birkenhead 35. **d** 39 **p** 40. V Donnington Wood *Lich* 49-79; Preb Lich Cathl 77-79; rtd 79; Perm to Offic *Lich* from 79. *62 Rowan Road, Market Drayton, Shropshire TF9 1RR*   Market Drayton (01630) 654293

JERVIS, William Edward. b 47. ARICS74. Linc Th Coll 74. **d** 77 **p** 78. C W Bromwich All SS *Lich* 77-80; C Horsham *Chich* 80-86; R W Tarring from 86. *West Tarring Rectory, Glebe Road, Worthing, W Sussex BN14 7PF*   Worthing (01903) 235043

JESSETT, David Charles. b 55. K Coll Lon BD77 AKC77 MTh. Westcott Ho Cam 78. **d** 79 **p** 80. C Aveley *Chelmsf* 79-82; C Walthamstow St Pet 82-85; P-in-c Hunningham *Cov* 85-91; P-in-c Wappenbury w Weston under Wetherley 85-91; Progr Dir Exploring Chr Min Scheme 85-91; Dir CME 87-90; Perm to Offic from 90. *Ellis House, New Street, Cubbington, Leamington Spa, Warks CV32 7LA*   Leamington Spa (01926) 312202/450460   Fax 430117

JESSIMAN, Timothy Edward. b 58. Oak Hill Th Coll DipHE91. **d** 91 **p** 92. C Baldock w Bygrave *St Alb* from 91. *60 The Tene, Baldock, Herts SG7 6DQ*   Baldock (01462) 891375

JESSON, Alan Francis. b 47. MBIM82 FLA91 Ealing Coll of Educn ALA70 Loughb Univ MLS77 Cam Univ MA87. E Anglian Minl Tr Course 88. **d** 91 **p** 92. NSM Swavesey *Ely* from 91; Chapl ACF from 92. *25 Market Street, Swavesey, Cambridge CB4 5QG*   Swavesey (01954) 30337

JESSON, George Albert Oswald (Ossie). b 54. NCA73. Trin Coll Bris DipHE92. **d** 92 **p** 93. C Dishley and Thorpe Acre *Leic* from 92. *19 Cothelstone Avenue, Thorpe Acre, Loughborough, Leics LE11 0TS*   Loughborough (01509) 265986

JESSOP, Mrs Gillian Mary. b 48. Hatf Poly BSc71 Nottm Univ MEd85 Homerton Coll Cam PGCE80. E Anglian Minl Tr Course 91. **d** 94 **p** 95. C Gt Yarmouth *Nor* from 94. *31 Blake Road, Great Yarmouth, Norfolk NR30 4LT*   Great Yarmouth (01493) 844161

JESSOP, John Edward. b 46. RMCS BScEng71. S Dios Minl Tr Scheme 87 Ridley Coll Melbourne DBS89. **d** 90 **p** 90. Australia from 90. *5 Queen Street, Blackburn, Victoria, Australia 3130*   Melbourne (3) 878-8536

JESSUP, Gordon Ernest. b 36. Lon Univ BA59. Oak Hill Th Coll 57. **d** 61 **p** 62. C Barnehurst *Roch* 61-64; C Rushden St Pet 64-67; SE Sec CMJ 67-72; Youth Sec CMJ 68-78; Tr Officer CMJ 78-83; Hon C Woodside Park St Barn *Lon* 78-83; TV Bramerton w Surlingham *Nor* 83-88; P-in-c Framingham Pigot 88; P-in-c Bergh Apton w Yelverton 88; P-in-c Ashby w Thurton, Claxton and Carleton 88; R Thurton from 88. *The Rectory, 29 Ashby Road, Thurton, Norwich NR14 6AX*   Thurton (01508) 480738

JESSUP, William Roy. b 27. Lon Univ BSc48 CertEd. Ridley Hall Cam 59. **d** 61 **p** 62. R Tuddenham St Mary w Cavenham *St E* 64-83; P-in-c Eriswell 75-83; Assoc Min Ipswich All SS 83-85; R Toppesfield and Stambourne *Chelmsf* 85-92; rtd 92. *62 Brunwin Road, Rayne, Braintree, Essex CM7 5BU*   Braintree (01376) 322554

JESTY, Mrs Helen Margaret. b 51. York Univ BA72. Cranmer Hall Dur BA81. dss 82 **d** 87. S Lambeth St Steph *S'wark* 82-86; Norbiton 86-93; Par Dn 87-90; Hon Par Dn 91-93. *Fairfield, 1 Downside Road, Winchester, Hants SO22 5LT*   Winchester (01962) 849190

JEVONS, Alan Neil. b 56. Ex Univ BA77 Selw Coll Cam BA80 MA84. Ridley Hall Cam. **d** 81 **p** 82. C Halesowen *Worc* 81-84; C Heywood St Luke w All So *Man* 84-87; TV Heref St Martin w St Fran (S Wye TM) *Heref* 87-93; P-in-c Much Birch w Lt Birch, Much Dewchurch etc from 93. *The Rectory, Much Birch, Hereford HR2 8HT*   Golden Valley (01981) 540558

JEWELL, Alan David John. b 59. St Cath Coll Ox MA86. Wycliffe Hall Ox 83. **d** 86 **p** 87. C Walton H Trin *Ox* 86-91; TV Sutton *Liv* from 91. *St Michael's Vicarage, Gartons Lane, Sutton Manor, St Helens, Merseyside WA9 4RB*   St Helens (01744) 813738

JEWELL, Charles John. b 15. Bps' Coll Cheshunt 46. **d** 49 **p** 50. Tristan da Cunha 71-74; Area Sec (Dios Ex and Truro) USPG 69-71; S Africa 74-87; rtd 87; Perm to Offic *Ex* from 87. *13 Fairfield Avenue, Plymouth PL2 3QF*   Plymouth (01752) 777169

JEWELL, Mrs Maureen Ann. b 34. Reading Univ CertEd72. Chich Th Coll 90. **d** 91 **p** 95. NSM Parklands St Wilfrid CD *Chich* 91-94; NSM Storrington from 94. *3 Garden Close, Storrington, Pulborough, W Sussex RH20 4PL*   Storrington (01903) 742780

JEWITT, Martin Paul Noel. b 44. AKC69. St Aug Coll Cant. **d** 70 **p** 71. C Usworth *Dur* 70-74; TV 77-78; Papua New Guinea 74-77; V Balham Hill Ascension *S'wark* 78-93; R N Reddish

Man from 93. *St Agnes Rectory, 551 Gorton Road, Stockport, Cheshire SK5 6NF* 0161-223 0692

JEYNES, Anthony James. b 44. AKC68. **d** 69 **p** 70. C Ellesmere Port *Ches* 69-73; C Birkenhead St Pet w St Matt 73-75; R Oughtrington 75-80; C Timperley 80-85; C Eastham 85-89; V New Brighton St Jas from 89; P-in-c New Brighton Em from 94. *The Vicarage, 14 Albion Street, Wallasey, Merseyside L45 9LF* 0151-639 5844

JIGNASU, Nallinkumar Hiralal. b 28. Bombay Univ BA48. Bp Tucker Coll Mukono 68. **d** 68 **p** 69. Uganda 68-73; C Leamington Priors St Mary *Cov* 73-75; Nigeria 75-79; P-in-c New Humberstone *Leic* 80-94; rtd 94. *8 Somerby Road, Thurnby, Leicester LE7 9PR* Leicester (0116) 224 18541

JINMAN, Cecil Alfred Keith. b 20. Keble Coll Ox BA48 MA51. Wycliffe Hall Ox 48. **d** 50 **p** 51. V Claines St Geo *Worc* 59-76; rtd 76; Perm to Offic *Worc* from 76. *11 Diglis Avenue, Worcester WR1 2NS* Worcester (01905) 351736

JOACHIM, Dr Margaret Jane. b 49. FGS91 St Hugh's Coll Ox BA70 MA74 W Midl Coll of Educn PGCE71 Birm Univ PhD77. Sarum & Wells Th Coll 91. **d** 94 **p** 95. NSM Ealing St Barn *Lon* from 94. *8 Newburgh Road, London W3 6DQ* 0181-993 0936

JOAN, Sister. *See* DAVIES, Sister Joan Margaret

JOB, Canon Evan Roger Gould. b 36. ARCM55 Magd Coll Ox BA60 MA64. Cuddesdon Coll 60. **d** 62 **p** 63. C Liv Our Lady and St Nic *Liv* 62-65; V New Springs 65-70; Min Can and Prec Man Cathl *Man* 70-74; Prec and Sacr Westmr Abbey 74-79; Can Res, Prec and Sacr Win Cathl *Win* 79-94; Vice-Dean Win 91-94. *Kitwood Farm, Ropley, Alresford, Hants SO24 0DB*

JOBSON, Clifford Hedley. b 31. St Jo Coll Dur BA54 DipTh56 MA81. **d** 56 **p** 57. C Hall Green Ascension *Birm* 56-59; C Ambleside w Rydal *Carl* 59-60; R Arthuret 60-62; CF 62-73; Dep Asst Chapl Gen 73-78; Asst Chapl Gen 78-84; QHC from 80; V Fleet *Guildf* from 84. *The Vicarage, Branksomewood Road, Fleet, Aldershot, Hants GU13 8JU* Fleet (01252) 616361

JOBSON, Canon Paul. b 39. Wells Th Coll 62. **d** 65 **p** 66. C Woolwich St Mary w H Trin *S'wark* 65-68; Chapl Culham Coll Abingdon 68-72; P-in-c Walworth St Pet *S'wark* 72-75; P-in-c Walworth All SS and St Steph 73-75; TR Walworth 75-89; Hon Can S'wark Cathl 83-89; RD S'wark and Newington 85-88; V Seaham w Seaham Harbour *Dur* from 89; Hon Chapl Miss to Seamen from 89. *The Vicarage, Seaham, Co Durham SR7 7SN* 0191-581 3385

JOHN, Andrew Thomas Griffith. b 64. Univ of Wales LLB. St Jo Coll Nottm BA DPS. **d** 89 **p** 90. C Cardigan and Mwnt and Y Ferwig *St D* 89-91; C Abth 91-92; TV from 92. *The Vicarage, Buarth Road, Aberystwyth, Dyfed SY23 1NB* Aberystwyth (01970) 617015

JOHN, Barbara. b 34. Cam Univ DipTh67. Gilmore Ho. **dss** 67 **d** 80. Merthyr Tydfil *Llan* 67-71; Loughton St Jo *Chelmsf* 71-73; Newport St Woolos *Mon* 73-78; Asst Chapl Univ Hosp of Wales Cardiff 78-85; C Radyr *Llan* from 85. *14 Pace Close, Danescourt, Llandaff, Cardiff CF5 2QZ* Cardiff (01222) 552989

JOHN, Beverley Hayes. b 49. Qu Coll Birm 83. **d** 85 **p** 86. C Oystermouth *S & B* 85-87; C Morriston 87-88; V Cefn Coed and Capel Nantddu w Vaynor etc from 88. *The Vicarage, Somerset Lane, Cefn Coed, Merthyr Tydfil, M Glam CF48 2PA* Merthyr Tydfil (01685) 374253

JOHN, Caroline Victoria. b 64. Cam Univ BA86 MA90. St Jo Coll Nottm DPS90. **d** 90. NSM Cardigan and Mwnt and Y Ferwig *St D* 90-91; NSM Abth from 91. *The Vicarage, Buarth Road, Aberystwyth, Dyfed SY23 1NB* Aberystwyth (01970) 617015

JOHN, Daniel Francis. b 09. AKC36. **d** 36 **p** 37. R Stoke Lacy w Much Cowarne and Morton Jeffries *Heref* 53-76; P-in-c Pencombe w Marston Stannett and Lt Cowarne 68-76; rtd 76; Perm to Offic *Heref* from 76. *Winslow Croft, Bromyard, Herefordshire HR7 4SE* Pencombe (01885) 400270

JOHN, Canon David Michael. b 36. Univ of Wales (Lamp) BA57. St Mich Coll Llan 57. **d** 59 **p** 60. V Ystrad Rhondda *Llan* 68-76; V Pontyclun w Talygarn 76-84; R Newton Nottage 84-91; Can Llan Cathl 85-91; rtd 91; Perm to Offic *Llan* from 91. *1 Hornbeam Close, St Mellons, Cardiff CF3 0JA* Cardiff (01222) 797496

JOHN, Canon Elwyn Crebey. b 36. Univ of Wales (Lamp) BA57. St Mich Coll Llan 57. **d** 59 **p** 60. C Llangiwg *S & B* 59-62; C Llandrindod w Cefnllys 62-66; V Beguildy and Heyope 66-79; Youth Chapl 72-79; Chapl Agric & Rural Soc from 77; V Builth and Llanddewi'r Cwm w Llangynog etc from 79; Can Brecon Cathl from 88; Prec 94-95; Treas from 95. *The Vicarage, 1 North Road, Builth Wells, Powys LD2 3BT* Builth Wells (01982) 552355

JOHN, Ven Islwyn David. b 33. St D Coll Lamp BA56. **d** 58 **p** 59. C Brynamman *St D* 58-61; C Carmarthen St Dav 61-64; V 83-93; V Penbryn and Blaenporth 64-68; V Llandysul 68-83;

Can St D Cathl from 88; RD Carmarthen 92-93; Adn Carmarthen from 93; V Cynwil Elfed and Newchurch from 93. *The Vicarage, Cynwyl Elfed, Carmarthen, Dyfed SA33 6TU* Cynwyl Elfed (01267) 281605

JOHN, Canon James Richard (Dick). b 21. Ch Coll Cam BA47 MA49. Cuddesdon Coll 47. **d** 49 **p** 50. V Bolton St Jas w St Chrys *Bradf* 66-78; R Guiseley 78-83; RD Otley 80-86; P-in-c Esholt 82-83; TR Guiseley w Esholt 83-87; Hon Can Bradf Cathl 83-87; rtd 87; Perm to Offic *Bradf* from 87. *37 Croft House Drive, Otley, W Yorkshire LS21 2ER* Otley (01943) 461998

JOHN, Dr Jeffrey Philip Hywel. b 53. Hertf Coll Ox BA75 Magd Coll Ox DPhil84. St Steph Ho Ox BA77 MA78 CPTS78. **d** 78 **p** 79. C Penarth w Lavernock *Llan* 78-80; Lic to Offic 80; Asst Chapl Magd Coll Ox 80-82; Chapl and Lect BNC Ox 82-84; Fell and Dean of Div Magd Coll Ox 84-91; Lic to Offic *Ox* 83-91; V Eltham H Trin *S'wark* from 91; Chapl Thames Poly 91-92; Chapl Greenwich Univ from 92. *Holy Trinity Vicarage, 59 Southend Crescent, London SE9 2SD* 0181-850 1246 or 316 8150

JOHN, Mark Christopher. b 61. SS Mark & Jo Coll Plymouth BA83. St Steph Ho Ox 84. **d** 87 **p** 88. C Treboeth *S & B* 87-90; V Swansea St Mark and St Jo 90-94; Chapl HM Pris Swansea from 91. *60 Risca Road, Newport, Gwent NP9 4HZ* Newport (01633) 244473 Fax 642979

JOHN, Meurig Hywel. b 46. St D Coll Lamp 67. **d** 71 **p** 72. C Llanelli Ch Ch *St D* 71-74; V Penrhyn-coch and Elerch 74-79; V Llanfihangel Aberbythych 79-81; R Cilgerran w Bridell and Llantwyd 81-83; V Gwaun-cae-Gurwen 83-89; V Llanfihangel Genau'r-glyn and Llangorwen from 89. *The Vicarage, Maes y Garn, Bow Street, Aberystwyth, Dyfed SY24 1XX* Aberystwyth (01970) 828638

JOHN, Napoleon. b 55. Punjab Univ BA76. Lahetysteologisen Institute Ryttyla Finland DipHE85 Oak Hill Th Coll BA93. **d** 93. C Leyton St Mary w St Edw *Chelmsf* from 93. *27 Crawley Road, London E10 6RJ*

JOHN, Nigel. b 59. Univ of Wales (Cardiff) BA87 Selw Coll Cam MPhil90. Westcott Ho Cam 88. **d** 91 **p** 92. C Carmarthen St Pet *St D* 91-94; Chapl Roehampton Inst from 94. *Flat 2, Beverley Gate, Whitelands College, West Hill, London SW15 3SN* 0181-392 3516

JOHN, Robert Michael. b 46. Edin Univ BSc67 Man Univ MSc68 PhD70 Otago Univ BD78. St Jo Coll Auckland 76. **d** 78 **p** 79. New Zealand 78-87 and from 88; C Swansea St Jas *S & B* 87-88. *16 Seaview Road, Otumoetai, Tauranga, New Zealand* Tauranga (7) 576-6617

JOHN, Sidney Arthur Charles Bernard. b 13. Jes Coll Ox BA35 MA39. **d** 38 **p** 39. V Barlow *Derby* 65-78; rtd 78; Perm to Offic *Ox* from 87. *2 Willow Road, Chinnor, Oxon OX9 4RA* Kingston Blount (01844) 352321

JOHN, Stephen Michael. b 63. Univ of Wales BA85. Coll of Resurr Mirfield 87. **d** 89 **p** 90. C Coity w Nolton *Llan* 89-91; C Merthyr Dyfan 91-94; V Tredegar St Geo *Mon* from 94. *St George's Vicarage, Church Street, Tredegar, Gwent NP2 3DU* Tredegar (01495) 252672

JOHN, William Glyndwr (Glyn). b 21. Roch Th Coll 60. **d** 60 **p** 61. V Frizinghall *Bradf* 69-73; V Long Preston 73-80; V Sutton 80-84; rtd 84; Perm to Offic *Bradf* from 84. *110 Princes Drive, Skipton, N Yorkshire BD23 1HW* Skipton (01756) 793003

JOHN-CHARLES, Brother. *See* VOCKLER, Rt Rev John Charles

JOHN-FRANCIS, Brother. *See* FRIENDSHIP, Roger Geoffrey

JOHNES, Philip Sydney. b 45. St Mich Coll Llan DMinlStuds92. **d** 92 **p** 93. C Cardigan and Mwnt and Y Ferwig *St D* 92-95; V Llanegwad w Llanfynydd from 95. *Llanegwad Vicarage, Heol Alltyferin, Nantgaredig, Carmarthen, Dyfed SA32 7RA* Nantgaredig (01267) 290142

JOHNS, Adam Aubrey. b 34. TCD BA57 MA70 NUU BA75. CITC 58. **d** 58 **p** 59. C Aghalee *D & D* 58-61; C Derriaghy *Conn* 61-63; I Billy 63-77; I Billy w Derrykeighan from 77. *321 Castlecat Road, Dervock, Ballymoney, Co Antrim BT53 8BP* Dervock (012657) 41241

JOHNS, Bernard Thomas. b 36. Birm Univ BSc58. St Mich Coll Llan 61. **d** 63 **p** 64. C Aberavon *Llan* 63-65; C St Andrew's Major and Michaelston-le-Pit 65-70; V Cardiff St Andr and St Teilo 70-76; Asst Dioc Dir of Educn 72-91; V Roath St Marg 76-88; R Wenvoe and St Lythans from 88; Dioc Dir Community Educn from 91. *The Rectory, 2 Old Port Road, Wenvoe, Cardiff CF5 6AN* Cardiff (01222) 593392

JOHNS, James Dudley. b 09. Selw Coll Cam BA34 MA38. Ridley Hall Cam 34. **d** 36 **p** 37. R Gt w Lt Wymondley *St Alb* 70-80; R Gt and Lt Wymondley w Graveley and Chivesfield 80-81; rtd 81; Perm to Offic *Nor* 82-94. *25A Beeches Close, Saffron Walden, Essex CB11 4BU* Saffron Walden (01799) 527119

JOHNS, Mrs Patricia Holly (Pat). b 33. Girton Coll Cam BA56 MA60 Hughes Hall Cam PGCE57. Ox NSM Course 87. **d** 90 **p** 94. NSM Wantage *Ox* 90-94; NSM Marlborough *Sarum* from 94. *15 Blowhorn Street, Marlborough, Wilts SN8 1BU* Marlborough (01672) 515897

JOHNS, Canon Ronald Charles (Ron). b 37. TD. Dur Univ BA59. Wells Th Coll 59. **d** 61 **p** 62. C Wigan All SS *Liv* 61-66; TV Kirkby 66-75; Ho Master Ruffwood Sch Kirkby 70-75; TV Maghull 75-79; Dep Hd Master Maghull Old Hall High Sch 75-79; P-in-c Borrowdale *Carl* 79-84; V 84-89; RD Derwent 81-89; Hon Can Carl Cathl 87-89; Can Res Carl Cathl 89-94; R Caldbeck, Castle Sowerby and Sebergham from 94. *The Rectory, Caldbeck, Wigton, Cumbria CA7 8EW* Caldbeck (016974) 78233

JOHNS, Thomas Morton (Tom). b 43. Oak Hill Th Coll 67. **d** 70 **p** 71. C N Meols *Liv* 70-73; C Farnborough *Guildf* 73-76; P-in-c Badshot Lea CD 76-83; Lic to Offic *Pet* 83-90; Chapl HM Youth Cust Cen Wellingborough 83-88; Chapl HM Young Offender Inst Swinfen Hall 88-90; Chapl Tr Officer 88-95; Chapl HM Pris Service Coll 90-95; Lic to Offic *Cov* 90-95; Asst Chapl Gen of Pris (Lon) from 95. *HM Prison Service Headquaters, Cleland House, Page Street, London SW1P 4LN* 0171-217 300 Fax 217 6635

JOHNS, Trevor Charles. b 33. St D Coll Lamp BA58. **d** 58 **p** 59. C Pemb St Mary and St Mich *St D* 58-61; R Walwyn's Castle w Robeston W 61-67; CF 67-75; V Spittal and Treffgarne *St D* 75-79; C Tring *St Alb* 79-80; TV Tring 80-85; V Knighton and Norton *S & B* 85-86; V Merthyr Cynog and Dyffryn Honddu etc from 86. *The Vicarage, Lower Chapel, Brecon, Powys LD3 9RE* Brecon (01874 89) 238

JOHNS, Canon Vernon. b 12. St D Coll Lamp BA33 St Mich Coll Llan 34. **d** 35 **p** 36. R Prendergast w Rudbaxton *St D* 67-72; Can St D Cathl 70-78; R Tenby 72-78; rtd 78. *78 Laws Street, Pembroke Dock, Dyfed SA72 6DQ* Pembroke (01646) 686149

JOHNS, William Price. b 28. Keble Coll Ox BA51 DipTh52 MA56. St Mich Coll Llan 52. **d** 53 **p** 54. V Wellington *Heref* 62-78; R Wellington w Pipe-cum-Lyde and Moreton-on-Lugg 78-93; P-in-c Ford 63-69; rtd 93. *12 Deepdale Close, Cardiff CF2 5LR* Cardiff (01222) 483762

JOHNSON, Miss Annie. b 26. Trin Coll Bris 70. **dss** 75 **d** 87 **p** 94. Barnsbury St Andr *Lon* 75-78; Newark Ch Ch *S'well* 79-80; Newark w Hawton, Cotham and Shelton 80-87; Par Dn 87-88; rtd 88; Perm to Offic *S'well* from 88. *1 Carswell Close, Newark, Notts NG24 4HW* Newark (01636) 704299

JOHNSON, Anthony Arthur Derry. b 15. Kelham Th Coll 31. **d** 39 **p** 40. V Mill Hill St Mich *Lon* 60-73; R Chalfont St Giles *Ox* 73-80; rtd 80. *Garden Close, Long Street, Sherborne, Dorset DT9 3DD* Sherborne (01935) 813469

JOHNSON, Anthony Peter. b 45. Lon Univ DipTh71 AKC76 BD76 MTh79. Wells Th Coll 67. **d** 70 **p** 71. C Goldington *St Alb* 70-73; C Hainault *Chelmsf* 73-76; TV Loughton St Mary 76-81; V Scunthorpe All SS *Linc* 81-85; V Alkborough 85-87; Chapl Man Univ *Man* from 87; TV Man Whitworth from 87. *354 Wilbraham Road, Chorlton-cum-Hardy, Manchester M21 0UX* 0161-881 7688 or 236 3311

JOHNSON, Canon Anthony Trevor. b 27. CCC Ox BA51 MA55. Cuddesdon Coll 51. **d** 53 **p** 54. R Upton Scudamore *Sarum* 67-85; V Warminster St Denys 67-85; RD Heytesbury 71-76; Can and Preb Sarum Cathl 75-92; P-in-c Horningsham 76-85; P-in-c Semley and Sedgehill 85-86; R E Knoyle, Semley and Sedgehill 86-92; rtd 92. *Coombe Warren, Hindon Lane, Tisbury, Salisbury SP3 6QQ* Tisbury (01747) 870130

JOHNSON, Anthony Warrington. b 40. Golds Coll Lon CertEd60. St Jo Coll Nottm 86. **d** 88 **p** 89. C Lutterworth w Cotesbach *Leic* 86-92; V Countesthorpe w Foston from 92; P-in-c Arnesby w Shearsby and Bruntingthorpe from 94. *The Vicarage, 102 Station Road, Countesthorpe, Leicester LE8 5TB* Leicester (0116) 278 4442 or 277 8643

JOHNSON, Arthur Victor. b 19. St Aid Birkenhead 62. **d** 64 **p** 65. V Oswaldtwistle All SS *Blackb* 69-73; V Lanc St Jo w St Anne 73-79; V Out Rawcliffe 79-84; rtd 84; Perm to Offic *Blackb* from 84. *25 Heysham Park, Morecambe, Lancs LA3 2UD* Heysham (01524) 852794

JOHNSON, Brian. b 42. DipRS87. S'wark Ord Course 84. **d** 87 **p** 88. NSM Dulwich St Barn *S'wark* 87-92; NSM Herne Hill 92-94; Perm to Offic from 94. *182 Turney Road, London SE21 7JL* 0171-733 8341

JOHNSON, Canon Charles Edmund. b 15. Em Coll Cam BA40 MA42. Ridley Hall Cam 40. **d** 42 **p** 43. C Woking Ch Ch *Guildf* 42-44; Hd Master Seaford Coll Sussex 44-90; Provost from 90; Can and Preb Chich Cathl *Chich* 84-85. *Seaford College, Lavington Park, Petworth, W Sussex GU28 0NB* Graffham (017986) 392

JOHNSON, Christopher Dudley. b 26. Worc Coll Ox BA44 MA51. Cuddesdon Coll 53. **d** 56 **p** 57. V Eton w Eton Wick and Boveney *Ox* 67-88; rtd 91. *White Wings, West Bexington, Dorchester, Dorset DT2 9DE*

JOHNSON, Christopher Frederick. b 43. ARICS67. Ripon Hall Ox 71. **d** 74 **p** 75. C Chatham St Steph *Roch* 74-78; V Slade Green 78-85; V Wilmington from 85. *The Vicarage, Church Hill, Wilmington, Dartford DA2 7EH* Dartford (01322) 220561

JOHNSON, Christopher Paul. b 47. St Jo Coll Nottm BTh74. **d** 74 **p** 75. C Normanton *Wakef* 74-78; P-in-c Dewsbury St Mark 78-82; V Harden and Wilsden *Bradf* 82-88; P-in-c Holbeck *Ripon* from 88. *St Luke's Vicarage, Malvern View, Leeds LS11 8SG* Leeds (0113) 271 7996

JOHNSON, Christopher Robert. b 43. Lon Coll of Div 66. **d** 70 **p** 71. C Everton St Geo *Liv* 70-71; C Childwall All SS 71-75; TV Gateacre 75-76; TV Bushbury *Lich* 76-87; R Burslem from 87. *The Rectory, 16 Heyburn Crescent, Burslem, Stoke-on-Trent ST6 4DL* Stoke-on-Trent (01782) 88932

JOHNSON, Canon Colin Gawman. b 32. Leeds Univ BA59. Coll of Resurr Mirfield 59. **d** 61 **p** 62. C Barrow St Matt *Carl* 61-67; V from 90; V Addingham 67-71; V Carl H Trin 71-80; V Wigton 80-90; Hon Can Carl Cathl from 85. *The Vicarage, Highfield Road, Barrow-in-Furness, Cumbria LA14 5NZ* Barrow-in-Furness (01229) 823569

JOHNSON, Colin Leslie. b 41. Trin Coll Cam MA65. Cheshunt Coll Cam 62. **d** 93 **p** 94. Publications Dir Chr Educn Movement from 89; NSM Brailsford w Shirley and Osmaston w Edlaston *Derby* from 93. *33 The Plain, Brailsford, Ashbourne, Derbyshire DE6 3BZ* Ashbourne (01335) 60591

JOHNSON, Cyril Francis. b 22. St Cath Coll Cam BA49 MA54. Ely Th Coll 50. **d** 52 **p** 53. R Harpole *Pet* 61-87; rtd 87. *16 Blake's Way, Eastbourne, E Sussex BN23 6EW* Eastbourne (01323) 723491

JOHNSON, David Alan. b 43. Lon Univ BSc63 PhD67. Trin Coll Bris 78. **d** 80 **p** 81. C Watford *St Alb* 80-85; V Idle H Trin *Bradf* from 85. *The Vicarage, 470 Leeds Road, Thackley, Bradford, W Yorkshire BD10 9AA* Bradford (01274) 613300

JOHNSON, David Bryan Alfred. b 36. Kelham Th Coll 56. **d** 61 **p** 62. C Streatham St Paul *S'wark* 61-63; Malaysia 63-71; V Worc St Mich *Worc* 71-74; Warden Lee Abbey Internat Students' Club Kensington 74-77; V Plumstead St Mark and St Marg *S'wark* 77-86; Chapl W Park Hosp Epsom from 86. *23 Bramblewood Close, Carshalton, Surrey SM5 1PQ or West Park Hospital, Horton Lane, Epsom, Surrey KT19 8PB* 0181-669 2663 or (01372) 727811

JOHNSON, David Clark. b 15. Tyndale Hall Bris 61. **d** 62 **p** 63. V Bishopsworth *Bris* 65-74; V Stratton St Margaret 75-78; TR Stratton St Margaret w S Marston etc 78-80; rtd 80; Perm to Offic *Bris* from 80. *13 High Kingsdown, Bristol BS2 8EN* Bristol (0117) 929 8894

JOHNSON, David Francis. b 32. Univ Coll Ox BA55 MA59. Westcott Ho Cam 55. **d** 57 **p** 58. C Earlsdon *Cov* 57-59; C Willenhall 59-61; C Attenborough w Bramcote *S'well* 61-62; V Ravenstone w Weston Underwood *Ox* 62-66; V Crewe Ch Ch *Ches* 66-70; P-in-c Crewe St Pet 67-70; V Thornton w Allerthorpe *York* 70-79; V N Hull St Mich 79-81; V Leyburn w Bellerby *Ripon* 81-88; V Coxwold and Husthwaite *York* from 88. *The Vicarage, Coxwold, York YO6 4AD* Coxwold (01347) 868301

JOHNSON, David John. b 49. Lanc Univ BA72. Linc Th Coll 78. **d** 81 **p** 82. C Stockport St Thos *Ches* 81-84; OGS from 83; C Stockton Heath *Ches* 84-88; V Tranmere St Paul w St Luke from 88. *St Paul's Vicarage, Old Chester Road, Birkenhead, Merseyside L42 3XD* 0151-645 3547

JOHNSON, David Richard. b 67. Birm Univ BSc88. Ripon Coll Cuddesdon BA92. **d** 94 **p** 95. C Horfield H Trin *Bris* from 94. *31 Rosling Road, Bristol BS7 8SX* Bristol (0117) 951 9771

JOHNSON, David William. b 40. Lon Univ BD64. Oak Hill Th Coll 60. **d** 65 **p** 66. C Tunbridge Wells St Jas *Roch* 65-68; C Kirby Muxloe *Leic* 68-72; V Burton Joyce w Bulcote *S'well* 72-83; Chapl Northgate Mental Handicap Unit Morpeth 83-87; V Mitford *Newc* 83-87; Asst Chapl R Victoria Infirmary Newc 87-89; Chapl R Hosp Shrewsbury from 89. *Royal Shrewsbury Hospital, Mytton Oak Road, Shrewsbury SY3 8XF* Shrewsbury (01743) 261000

JOHNSON, David William. b 53. Selw Coll Cam BA76. Ripon Coll Cuddesdon 76. **d** 78 **p** 79. C Fulham St Etheldreda w St Clem *Lon* 78-82; Communications Sec Gen Syn Bd for Miss and Unity 82-87; PV Westmr Abbey 85-87; R Gilmorton w Peatling Parva and Kimcote etc *Leic* 87-91; R Cogenhoe *Pet* from 91; R Whiston from 93. *The Rectory, Church Street, Cogenhoe, Northampton NN7 1LS* Northampton (01604) 891166

JOHNSON, Preb Derek John. b 36. St Aid Birkenhead 65. **d** 68 **p** 69. C Eccleshall *Lich* 68-73; C Stafford St Mary 73-75; Chapl New Cross Hosp Wolv from 75; Preb Lich Cathl *Lich* from 83. *The Chaplain's House, New Cross Hospital, Wednesfield Road, Wolverhampton WV10 0QP* Wolverhampton (01902) 307999

JOHNSON, Miss Diana Margaret. b 46. MCSP68 SRP68 GDipP68. Cranmer Hall Dur CTM94. **d** 94 **p** 95. C Birtley *Dur* from 94. *21 Lavers Road, Birtley, Chester le Street, Co Durham DH3 1HH* 0191-492 0884

JOHNSON, Donald Arnold. b 28. Linc Coll Ox BA51 MA59. Cuddesdon Coll 51. **d** 53 **p** 54. C Henfield *Chich* 53-55; C Horsham 55-59; V Oving w Merston 59-68; Bp's Dom Chapl 59-69; V Hellingly 68-78; V Upper Dicker 68-78; R W Stoke from 78; V Funtington and Sennicotts from 78. *The Vicarage, Funtington, Chichester, W Sussex PO19 0LH* Bosham (01243) 575257

JOHNSON, Mrs Dorothy (Dorrie). Leic Univ BSc89 SRN NDN80 FRSH91. Qu Coll Birm 77. **d** 87 **p** 94. Bp's Asst Officer for Soc Resp *Cov* from 87. *The Firs, Stoneleigh Road, Bubbenhall, Coventry CV8 3BS* Coventry (01203) 303712

JOHNSON, Douglas Leonard. b 45. Trin Coll Bris 70 Lon Bible Coll MA95. **d** 73 **p** 74. C New Malden and Coombe *S'wark* 73-76; P-in-c Upper Tulse Hill St Matthias 76-82; CPAS Staff 82-88; Lect and Tutor CA Coll from 88; Hon C Wimbledon Em Ridgway Prop Chpl *S'wark* from 92. *11 Preston Road, London SW20 0SS* 0181-946 2136

JOHNSON, Edward Anthony (Tony). b 32. Univ of Wales (Swansea) BSc54. St Steph Ho Ox 79. **d** 81 **p** 82. C Wolvercote w Summertown *Ox* 81-84; P-in-c Ramsden 84-87; P-in-c Finstock and Fawler 84-87; P-in-c Wilcote 84-87; V Ramsden, Finstock and Fawler, Leafield etc 87-92; rtd 92; Hon C Kennington *Ox* from 92. *15 Cranbrook Drive, Kennington, Oxford OX1 5RR* Oxford (01865) 739751

JOHNSON, Mrs Elizabeth. b 47. St Hild's Coll Ox MA69. Wycliffe Hall Ox 84. **dss** 86 **d** 87 **p** 94. NSM Ox St Aldate w St Matt *Ox* 86-91; NSM Marston 91-94; NSM Ox St Clem from 94. *27 Templar Road, Oxford OX2 8LR* Oxford (01865) 54568

JOHNSON, Eric. b 38. Nottm Univ BSc60 Leeds Univ DipFE73 Open Univ BA92 SS Paul & Mary Coll Cheltenham MA94. Qu Coll Birm 74. **d** 77 **p** 78. Sen Lect Cov Tech Coll 66-91; NSM Earlsdon *Cov* 77-81; NSM Wolston and Church Lawford 81-86; NSM Stoneleigh w Ashow and Baginton from 90; FE Liaison Officer Dios B & W and Glouc 91-93; Dioc Dir of Educn *Worc* from 93. *The Firs, Stoneleigh Road, Bubbenhall, Coventry CV8 3BS* Coventry (01203) 303712

JOHNSON, Geoffrey Stuart. b 39. ALCD65 Wolv Poly DipEd. **d** 65 **p** 66. C Worksop St Jo *S'well* 65-68; Taiwan 68-71; Singapore 71-76; Aber Univ *Ab* 76-78; Perm to Offic *Heref* 78-82; P-in-c Hoarwithy, Hentland and Sellack 82-84; Chapl Horton Hosp Epsom 84-90; Chapl Brighton Gen Hosp from 90; Chapl Chailey Heritage Hosp Lewes from 90. *Brighton General Hospital, Elm Grove, Brighton, E Sussex BN2 3EW* Brighton (01273) 696955

JOHNSON, Geoffrey Kemble. b 22. RD71. Roch Th Coll 62. **d** 64 **p** 65. R Worlingham *St E* 68-84; rtd 84; Perm to Offic *Nor* from 84; Perm to Offic *St E* from 84. *53 St Walstans Road, Taverham, Norwich NR8 6NG* Norwich (01603) 860626

JOHNSON, Gordon. b 20. **d** 43 **p** 44. R Horseheath *Ely* 64-71; R Bartlow 65-71; Hon C S Kensington St Aug *Lon* from 79; rtd 85. *Rosemary Topping, English Bicknor, Coleford, Glos GL16 7PF* Dean (01594) 861181

JOHNSON, Gordon Edward. b 27. Oak Hill Th Coll 76. **d** 77 **p** 78. C Scarborough St Mary w Ch Ch and H Apostles *York* 77-82; V Hutton Cranswick w Skerne 82-86; P-in-c Watton w Beswick and Kilnwick 82-86; V Hutton Cranswick w Skerne, Watton and Beswick 86-88; V Bubwith w Skipwith 88-93; rtd 93. *10 Winston Court, Northallerton, N Yorkshire DL6 1PY* Northallerton (01609) 778625

JOHNSON, Graham. b 37. Westcott Ho Cam 66. **d** 68 **p** 69. C Stafford St Mary *Lich* 68-71; C Wombourne 71-74; Youth Chapl 74-77; P-in-c Tong 76-77; Res Min Wednesfield St Thos 77-78; TV 79-82; P-in-c Gayton w Fradswell 84-88; P-in-c Milwich 82-88; P-in-c Weston upon Trent 82-88; V Fradswell, Gayton, Milwich and Weston 88-90; TV Wolstanton from 90. *St Barnabas's Vicarage, Old Castle Avenue, Newcastle, Staffs ST5 8OG* Newcastle-under-Lyme (01782) 635978

JOHNSON, Graham James. b 43. Leeds Univ BA67. Coll of Resurr Mirfield DipTh69. **d** 70 **p** 71. C Heckmondwike *Wakef* 70-73; C Pet St Jude *Pet* 73-76; V Gt w Lt Harrowden and Orlingbury 76-83; R Daventry 83-92; TR Daventry, Ashby St Ledgers, Braunston etc 92; Chapl Danetre Hosp 83-93; RD Daventry *Pet* 88-92; P-in-c Loddington *Leic* from 93; Warden Launde Abbey from 93; RD Framland (Melton) *Leic* from 94. *Launde Abbey, East Norton, Leicester LE7 9XB* Belton (01572) 717254

JOHNSON, Harold Barnett. b 10. Ex Coll Ox BA34 MA37. Cuddesdon Coll 34. **d** 35 **p** 36. R Waldron *Chich* 60-75; rtd 75; Hon C Eastbourne St Sav and St Pet *Chich* 75-83; Perm to Offic from 83. *Flat 1, Morley House, College of St Barnabas, Lingfield, Surrey RH7 6NJ* Dormans Park (01342) 870440

JOHNSON, Harold Everard. b 14. TCD BA36 MA40 BD46. **d** 38 **p** 39. V Eccles St Andr *Man* 58-79; rtd 79; Perm to Offic *Man* from 80. *368 New Church Road, Bacup, Lancs OL13 0LD* Bacup (01706) 874922

JOHNSON, Harriet Etta.LRAM DipEd40. Trin Coll Bris. **dss** 76 **d** 87. Burundi 76-80; Ipplepen w Torbryan *Ex* 81-87; Hon Par Dn 87-90; Perm to Offic from 90. *10 Fairfield West, Huxtable Hill, Torquay TQ2 6RN* Torquay (01803) 690115

JOHNSON, Mrs Hilary Ann. b 51. RGN72 RHV74 DipRS85. S'wark Ord Course 82. **dss** 85 **d** 87 **p** 94. Hon Par Dn Salfords *S'wark* 85-90; Chapl St Geo Hosp Lon from 90; NSM Wimbledon *S'wark* from 95. *11 West Avenue, Redhill RH1 5BA, or St George's Hospital, Blackshaw Road, London SW17 0QT* Redhill (01737) 766549

JOHNSON, Ian Lawrence. b 44. Wells Th Coll 68. **d** 71 **p** 72. C Benhilton *S'wark* 71-73; C Weymouth H Trin *Sarum* 73-76; R Pewsey 76-81; R Compton Abbas W w Wynford Eagle etc 81; P-in-c Maiden Newton w Frome Vauchurch 81; R Maiden Newton and Valleys 81-83; Sherborne Episc Area Youth Officer 81-83; Dioc Youth Officer 83-88; TR Langley and Parkfield *Man* 88-95; P-in-c Haughton St Anne from 95; Dioc Adv on Evang from 95. *St Anne's Rectory, St Anne's Drive, Denton, Manchester M34 3EB* 0161-336 2374 Fax as telephone

JOHNSON, Ian Leslie. b 51. Bede Coll Dur TCert73. Wycliffe Hall Ox DipMin93. **d** 93 **p** 94. C Evington *Leic* from 93. *14 Fallowfield Road, Leicester LE5 6LQ* Leicester (0116) 241 2833

✠JOHNSON, Rt Rev James Nathaniel. b 32. Wells Th Coll 63. **d** 64 **p** 65 **c** 85. C Lawrence Weston *Bris* 64-66; St Helena 66-72; Hon Can from 75; Area Sec (Dios Ex and Truro) USPG 72-74; R Combe Martin *Ex* 74-80; V Thorpe Bay *Chelmsf* 80-85; Bp St Helena 85-91; R Byfield w Boddington and Aston le Walls *Pet* 91-92; Asst Bp Pet 91-92; V Hockley *Chelmsf* from 92; Asst Bp Chelmsf from 92; Can Chelmsf Cathl from 94. *The Vicarage, 5A High Road, Hockley, Essex SS5 4SY* Southend-on-Sea (01702) 203668

JOHNSON, John David. b 38. St Deiniol's Hawarden 71. **d** 71 **p** 72. C Heref St Martin *Heref* 71-73; P-in-c Ewyas Harold w Dulas 73-79; P-in-c Kilpeck 73-79; P-in-c St Devereux w Wormbridge 73-79; P-in-c Kenderchurch 73-79; P-in-c Bacton 78-79; TR Ewyas Harold w Dulas, Kenderchurch etc 79-81; R Kentchurch w Llangua, Rowlestone, Llancillo etc 79-81; Lic to Offic *St Alb* from 81; Chapl Napsbury Hosp St Alb from 81. *Napsbury Hospital, Napsbury, St Albans, Herts AL2 1AB* Bowmansgreen (01727) 23333

JOHNSON, John Alan. b 51. Ripon Coll Cuddesdon 75. **d** 77 **p** 78. C Boreham Wood All SS *St Alb* 77-79; C Borehamwood 79-80; TV Dunstable 80-85; Toc H from 85; Nat Chapl from 89. *Carreg-y-Saeth, 40 Lionel Avenue, Wendover, Aylesbury, Bucks HP22 6LP* Wendover (01296) 696431 or 623911 Fax 696137

JOHNSON, Canon John Anthony. b 18. Selw Coll Cam BA48 MA53 St Jo Coll Dur DipTh51. **d** 51 **p** 52. V Mansf Woodhouse *S'well* 60-70; V Beeston 70-85; RD Beeston 81-85; Hon Can S'well Minster 82-85; rtd 86. *7 The Spinney, Cranwell Avenue, Lancaster LA1 4JQ* Lancaster (01524) 65137

JOHNSON, John Cecil. b 23. Peterho Cam BA48. Ely Th Coll 57. **d** 59 **p** 60. C Whitton SS Phil and Jas *Lon* 59-70; P-in-c Fulham St Andr Fulham Fields 70-73; V 73-88; rtd 88. *13 Selkirk Drive, Telford, Shropshire TF7 4JE* Telford (01952) 588407

JOHNSON, Joseph Clarke. b 10. Bps' Coll Cheshunt 46. **d** 48 **p** 49. V Beckermet St Bridget w Ponsonby *Carl* 57-78; rtd 78; Perm to Offic *Carl* from 78. *High Moss, Calderbridge, Seascale, Cumbria CH20 1DQ* Beckermet (01946) 841289

JOHNSON, Keith Winton Thomas William. b 37. K Coll Lon BD63 AKC63. **d** 64 **p** 65. C Dartford H Trin *Roch* 64-69; Kuwait 69-73; V Erith St Jo *Roch* 73-80; V Bexley St Jo 80-91; V Royston *St Alb* 91-94; R Sandon, Wallington and Rushden w Clothall from 94. *The Vicarage, Payne End, Sandon, Buntingford, Herts SG9 0QU* Kelshall (01763) 287256

JOHNSON, Kenneth Reginald. b 06. Leeds Univ BA27. Coll of Resurr Mirfield 24. **d** 29 **p** 30. V Newtown St Luke *Win* 60-71; rtd 71. *c/o Messrs Willmett and Co, 27 Sheet Street, Windsor, Berks SL4 1BX* Windsor (01753) 861381

JOHNSON, Kenneth William George. b 53. Hull Univ BA76 PGCE77. E Midl Min Tr Course 92. **d** 95. NSM Ilkeston H Trin *Derby* from 95. *18 Park Avenue, Awsworth, Nottingham NG16 2RA* Nottingham (0115) 930 7830

JOHNSON, Malcolm Arthur. b 36. Univ Coll Dur BA60 MA64. Cuddesdon Coll 60. **d** 62 **p** 63. C Portsea N End St Mark *Portsm* 62-67; Chapl Qu Mary Coll *Lon* 67-74; V St Botolph Aldgate w H Trin Minories 74-92; P-in-c St Ethelburga Bishopsgate 85-89; AD The City 85-90; Master R Foundn of St Kath in Ratcliffe from 93. *The Royal Foundation of St Katharine, Butcher Row, London E14 8DS* 0171-790 3540 Fax 702 7603

JOHNSON, Malcolm Stuart. b 35. AKC60. d 61 p 62. C Catford St Laur *S'wark* 61-64; Hon C Hatcham St Cath 66-76; P-in-c Kingstanding St Luke *Birm* 76-77; V 77-82; P-in-c Peckham St Jo w St Andr *S'wark* 82-92; V from 92. *St John's Vicarage, 10A Meeting House Lane, London SE15 2UN* 0171-639 0084

JOHNSON, Ms Margaret Anne Hope. b 52. Homerton Coll Cam Open Univ BA81 Fitzw Coll Cam BA95. Ridley Hall Cam 93. d 95. C Northn Em *Pet* from 95. *4 Booth Lane North, Northampton NN3 6JG* Northampton (01604) 648974

JOHNSON, Dr Mark. b 62. Leic Poly BSc84 Loughb Univ PhD88. Ripon Coll Cuddesdon 88. d 94 p 95. C Bishop's Cleeve *Glouc* from 94. *2A Orchard Road, Bishops Cleeve, Cheltenham, Glos GL52 4LX* Cheltenham (01242) 675431 Fax 673612

JOHNSON, Michael. b 42. Birm Univ BSc63. S'wark Ord Course 68. d 71 p 72. C Kidbrooke St Jas *S'wark* 71-74; Hon C Eynsford w Farningham and Lullingstone *Roch* 74-90; Hon C Selling w Throwley, Sheldwich w Badlesmere etc *Cant* from 90. *1 Halke Cottages, North Street, Sheldwich, Faversham, Kent ME13 0LR* Faversham (01795) 536583

JOHNSON, Michael Anthony. b 51. Ex Univ BA76. Ripon Coll Cuddesdon 76 Ch Div Sch of the Pacific (USA) 78. d 78 p 79. C Primrose Hill St Mary w Avenue Road St Paul *Lon* 78-81; C Hampstead St Jo 81-85; TV Mortlake w E Sheen *S'wark* 85-93; R Wroughton *Bris* from 93. *The Vicarage, Church Hill, Wroughton, Swindon SN4 9JS* Swindon (01793) 812301 Fax 813273

JOHNSON, Michael Colin. b 37. Lon Univ DipRS80. S'wark Ord Course 77. d 80 p 81. NSM New Eltham All SS *S'wark* 80-84; NSM Woldingham from 84. *The Rectory, Station Road, Woldingham, Caterham, Surrey CR3 7DD* 0181-905 2192

JOHNSON, Michael Gordon. b 45. Lon Univ DipTh68. Kelham Th Coll 64. d 68 p 69. C Holbrooks *Cov* 68-72; C Cannock *Lich* 72-75; V Coseley Ch Ch 75-79; P-in-c Sneyd 79-82; R Longton 82-88; Chapl Pilgrim Hosp Boston from 88. *The Chaplain's Office, Pilgrim Hospital, Sibsey Road, Boston, Lincs PE21 9QT* Boston (01205) 364801

JOHNSON, Nigel Edwin. b 41. AKC64 St Boniface Warminster 64. d 65 p 66. C Poulton-le-Sands *Blackb* 65-68; Chapl RN 68-93; Perm to Offic *Cant* from 93. *Marlborough House, Duke of York's Royal Military School, Dover, Kent CT15 5DS* Dover (01304) 211688

JOHNSON, Nigel Victor. b 48. ARCM68 LTCL75 Cam Univ DipEd69. Linc Th Coll 80. d 82 p 83. C Lindley *Wakef* 82-85; P-in-c Upperthong 85-87; Perm to Offic *Derby* 88-89; NSM Calow and Sutton cum Duckmanton 89-90; R from 90. *The Rectory, Top Road, Calow, Chesterfield S44 5AF* Chesterfield (01246) 273486

JOHNSON, Paul Anthony. b 56. Leeds Univ BA77 Kent Coll for Careers DCG81. Linc Th Coll CMM87. d 88 p 89. C Glouc St Jas and All SS *Glouc* 88-91; C Leckhampton SS Phil and Jas w Cheltenham St Jas 91-93; Perm to Offic from 93. *4 Windermere Road, Gloucester GL2 0HN* Gloucester (01452) 419114

JOHNSON, Canon Peter Frederick. b 41. Melbourne Univ BA63 Ch Ch Ox BA68 MA72. St Steph Ho Ox 68. d 69 p 70. C Banbury *Ox* 69-71; Tutor St Steph Ho Ox 71-74; Chapl St Chad's Coll Dur 74-80; Vice-Prin 78-80; Chapl K Sch Cant 80-90; Perm to Offic *Cant* 80-81; Hon Min Can Cant Cathl 81-90; Can Res Bris Cathl *Bris* from 90. *41 Salisbury Road, Bristol BS6 7AR* Bristol (0117) 944 4464

JOHNSON, Richard Le Bas. b 22. TCD BA50 MA58. Sarum Th Coll 50. d 52 p 53. S Rhodesia 62-65; Rhodesia 65-72; C King's Worthy *Win* 72-74; R Crawley w Littleton 74-84; R Crawley and Littleton and Sparsholt w Lainston 84-90; rtd 90. *13 Anders Road, South Wonston, Winchester, Hants SO21 3EL* Winchester (01962) 884355

JOHNSON, Richard Miles. b 59. Bris Univ BSc82. St Jo Coll Nottm 87. d 90 p 91. C Bromley SS Pet and Paul *Roch* 90-94. *13 Rochester Avenue, Bromley BR1 3DB* 0181-464 9532

JOHNSON, Robert Kenneth. b 48. N Ord Course 83. d 86 p 87. C Hattersley *Ches* 86-88; C Brinnington w Portwood 88-90; V Gospel Lane St Mich *Birm* from 90. *St Michael's Vicarage, 237 Lakey Lane, Birmingham B28 8QT* 0121-777 6132 or 777 8443

JOHNSON, Canon Robin Edward Hobbs. b 39. Fitzw Ho Cam BA61 MA65. Ripon Hall Ox 61. d 63 p 64. C Tyldesley w Shakerley *Man* 63-66; Lic to Offic *Leic* 66-71; V Castleton Moor *Man* 71-77; Dir of Ords 76-81; V Prestwich St Gabr 77-81; V Heaton Ch Ch 81-91; Hon Can Man Cathl 86-91; TR Dorchester *Sarum* from 91. *The Rectory, 56 Prince of Wales Road, Dorchester, Dorset DT1 1PP* Dorchester (01305) 268837

JOHNSON, Ronald. b 40. Wycliffe Hall Ox 69. d 72 p 73. C Deane *Man* 72-74; C N Meols *Liv* 74-75; Chapl St Jo Sch Tiffield Northants 75-82; Warden Eton Coll Dorney Project

JOHNSON, Ronald Alan (Ron). b 32. MITSA. Ox NSM Course 84. d 86 p 87. NSM Beaconsfield *Ox* from 86. *7 Northcroft, Wooburn Green, High Wycombe, Bucks HP10 0BP* Maidenhead (01628) 527141

JOHNSON, Ronald George (Ron). b 33. Chich Th Coll 75. d 76 p 77. Hon C Shipley *Chich* 76-79; C Brighton St Matthias 79-82; P-in-c Barlavington 82; P-in-c Burton w Coates 82; P-in-c Sutton w Bignor 82; R Barlavington, Burton w Coates, Sutton and Bignor 82-93; rtd 93. *First Floor Flat, 36 South Terrace, Littlehampton, W Sussex BN17 5NU*

JOHNSON, Very Rev Samuel Hugh Akinsope. b 30. K Coll Lon BD61. Linc Th Coll 52. d 55 p 56. C St Martin-in-the-Fields *Lon* 60-62; Nigeria from 63; Provost Lagos Cathl from 70; rtd 95. *3 Oba Nle Aro Crescent, Ilupeju, PO Box 10021, Marina, Lagos, Nigeria*

JOHNSON, Stanley. b 42. QUB BSc63 TCD BTh89. CITC 86. d 89 p 90. C Kilmore w Ballintemple, Kildallon etc *K, E & A* from 89. *Kildallon Rectory, Ardlougher, Ballyconnell, Belturbet, Co Cavan, Irish Republic* Cavan (49) 26259

JOHNSON, Terence John. b 44. Cov Poly BA89. Lon Coll of Div ALCD70 LTh74. d 69 p 70. C Woodside *Ripon* 69-72; C Leeds St Geo 72-76; C Heworth *York* 76-81; V Budbrooke *Cov* from 81; Chapl Wroxall Abbey Sch from 83. *The Vicarage, Budbrooke, Warwick CV35 8QL* Warwick (01926) 494002

JOHNSON, Thomas Bernard. b 44. BA CertEd. Oak Hill Th Coll. d 84 p 85. C Birkenhead St Jas w St Bede *Ches* 84-88; R Ashover and Brackenfield *Derby* from 88; Hon Chapl Derbyshire St Jo Ambulance from 91. *The Rectory, Narrowleys Lane, Ashover, Chesterfield, Derbyshire S45 0AU* Chesterfield (01246) 590246

JOHNSON, Canon Thomas Wyndham Page. b 11. BNC Ox BA33. Cuddesdon Coll 34. d 36 p 37. V Kilndown *Cant* 45-83; Hon Can Cant Cathl 79-83; rtd 83; Perm to Offic *Cant* from 83. *Little Park Cottage, Hook Green, Lamberhurst, Kent TN3 8LN* Lamberhurst (01892) 890391

JOHNSON, Victor Edward. b 45. Linc Th Coll 83. d 85 p 86. C Garforth *Ripon* 85-90; Dioc Video Officer 90-92; V Wyther Ven Bede from 92. *Wyther Vicarage, Houghley Lane, Leeds LS13 4AU* Leeds (0113) 279 8014

JOHNSON, Walter. b 21. St Aid Birkenhead. d 59 p 60. V Bracebridge *Linc* 62-73; R Weston sub Edge and Aston sub Edge *Glouc* 73-77; R Willersey, Saintbury, Weston-sub-Edge etc 77-86; rtd 86; Perm to Offic *Win* from 87. *15 Beechey Road, Bournemouth BH8 8LL* Bournemouth (01202) 557063

JOHNSTON, Alan Beere. b 14. Leeds Univ BA36. Coll of Resurr Mirfield 36. d 38 p 39. V Kingston upon Hull St Mary *York* 62-68; rtd 79. *6 Arlington Close, Goring-by-Sea, Worthing, W Sussex BN12 4ST* Worthing (01903) 426590

JOHNSTON, Canon Albert Richard. b 06. K Coll Lon 37. d 41 p 42. V Dedham *Chelmsf* 50-75; Hon Can Chelmsf Cathl 64-75; rtd 75; Perm to Offic *St E* from 76. *6 Yew Tree Court, Bury St Edmunds, Suffolk IP33 2JF* Bury St Edmunds (01284) 769464

JOHNSTON, Alexander Irvine (Alec). b 47. LRAM Keele Univ BA70. St Alb Minl Tr Scheme 77. d 80 p 81. NSM Hockerill *St Alb* from 80. *48 Newtown Road, Bishop's Stortford, Herts CM23 3SD* Bishop's Stortford (01279) 657479

JOHNSTON, Allen Niall. b 61. AMBIM87 MISM87 Southn Univ BTh92. Sarum & Wells Th Coll 89. d 92 p 93. C Roehampton H Trin *S'wark* 92-95; Dir Past Services RTR Healthcare NHS Trust from 95; Tutor SE Inst for Th Educn from 95. *Queen Mary's University Hospital, Roehampton Lane, London SW15 5PN* 0181-789 6611 Fax 780 1089

JOHNSTON, Austin. b 50. Huddersfield Poly CertEd76 BEd90. Chich Th Coll DipThMin94. d 94 p 95. C Peterlee *Dur* from 94. *197 Hatfield Place, Peterlee, Co Durham SR8 5TA* 0191-518 1775

JOHNSTON, Charles Walter. *See* BARR JOHNSTON, Charles Walter

JOHNSTON, Duncan Howard. b 63. Hull Univ BA85 Nottm Univ MA93. St Jo Coll Nottm 91. d 93 p 94. C Werrington *Pet* from 93. *66 Barber's Hill, Werrington, Peterborough PE4 5EP* Peterborough (01733) 323146

JOHNSTON, Edith Violet Nicholl. b 28. d 87. Par Dn Bentley *Sheff* 87-88; rtd 88. *32 Tennyson Avenue, Mexborough, S Yorkshire S64 0AX* Mexborough (01709) 581169

JOHNSTON, Elizabeth Margaret. b 37. QUB BA58 DipTh69 Serampore Univ BD87. dss 81 d 87 p 94. BCMS 81-93; Crosslinks 93; India 81-93; C Belf St Chris *D & D* 93-94; Bp's C from 94. *St Christopher's Rectory, 412 Upper Newtownards Road, Belfast BT4 3EZ* Belfast (01232) 471522

JOHNSTON, Very Rev Frederick Mervyn Kieran. b 11. TCD BA33 MA52. d 34 p 36. Dean Cork *C, C & R* 66-71; rtd 71. *24 Lapps Court, Hartlands Avenue, Cork, Irish Republic* Cork (21) 313264

JOHNSTON, Geoffrey Stanley. b 44. Aston Univ MBA81 Lon Univ DipTh68 Birm Univ CertEd78. Kelham Th Coll 64. d 68 p 69. C Blakenall Heath *Lich* 68-72 and 73-75; C St Buryan, St Levan and Sennen *Truro* 72-73; P-in-c Willenhall St Steph *Lich* 75-76; C W Bromwich All SS 76-77; Lect W Bromwich Coll of Commerce and Tech 78-82; Ind Chapl *Worc* 82-94; TV Halesowen 82-94; NSM Dudley St Fran from 94. *37 Blagdon Road, Halesowen, W Midlands B63 3PT* 0121-602 2080

JOHNSTON, George Ralph Harden. b 23. TCD BA44 MA47. CITC 45. d 45 p 47. I Greenisland *Conn* 64-88; Can Belf Cathl 83-88; rtd 88. *183 Holywood Road, Belfast BT4 2DG* Belfast (01232) 654968

JOHNSTON, James. b 19. FCIB70. Carl Dioc Tr Course. d 82 p 83. NSM Kendal St Geo *Carl* 82-89; Perm to Offic from 89. *8 Sedbergh Drive, Kendal, Cumbria LA9 6BJ* Kendal (01539) 725422

JOHNSTON, Michael David Haigh. b 44. MBCS. S Dios Minl Tr Scheme. d 91 p 92. NSM Wootton *Portsm* 91-95; NSM Ryde H Trin from 95; NSM Swanmore St Mich and All Angels from 95. *7 Dover Street, Ryde, Isle of Wight PO33 2AQ* Isle of Wight (01983) 611291

JOHNSTON, Canon Robert John. b 31. Oak Hill Th Coll 64. d 64 p 65. C Bebington *Ches* 64-68; I Lack *Clogh* from 68; RD Kesh from 87; Can Clogh Cathl 89-91; Preb Clogh Cathl from 91. *The Rectory, Lack, Enniskillen, Co Fermanagh BT93 0DN* Kesh (013656) 360

JOHNSTON, Thomas Cosbey. b 15. Em Coll Cam BA40 MA44. Ridley Hall Cam 40. d 42 p 43. C Handsworth St Mary *Birm* 42-48; New Zealand from 48. *254 Main Road, Moncks Bay, Christchurch 8, New Zealand* Christchurch (3) 841224

JOHNSTON, Dr Walter Barr. b 09. Lon Univ MRCS32 LRCP32 MB, BS33 DTM&H34. Trin Coll Bris 34 Oak Hill Th Coll 67. d 67 p 68. C Dagenham *Chelmsf* 67-70; V Burton Fleming w Fordon *York* 70-84; V Grindale and Ergham 71-84; P-in-c Wold Newton 82-84; rtd 84. *34 Almond Avenue, Leamington Spa, Warks CV32 6QD* Leamington Spa (01926) 330832

JOHNSTON, Canon Wilfred Brian. b 44. TCD BA67 MA70. d 68 p 70. C Seagoe *D & D* 68-73; I Inniskeel *D & D* 73-82; I Castlerock w Dunboe and Fermoyle from 82; Dioc Registrar *D & D* from 89; RD Dungiven and Limavady 91-94; Can Derry Cathl *D & R* from 92. *The Rectory, 52 Main Street, Castlerock, Coleraine, Co Londonderry BT51 4RA* Castlerock (01265) 848242

JOHNSTON, Ven William Derek. b 40. CITC 68. d 68 p 69. VC Derry Cathl *D & R* 68-70; I Swanlinbar w Templeport *K, E & A* 70-73; I Billis Union 73-84; Glebes Sec (Kilmore) from 77; I Annagh w Drumaloor and Cloverhill 84-87; Preb Kilmore Cathl 85-89; I Annagh w Drumgoon, Ashfield etc from 87; Adn Kilmore from 89. *The Rectory, Belturbet, Co Cavan, Irish Republic* Cavan (49) 22142

JOHNSTON, William Francis (Frank). b 30. CB83. TCD BA55 MA69. d 55 p 56. CF 59-77; Asst Chapl Gen 77-80; Chapl Gen 80-87; P-in-c Winslow *Ox* 87-91; RD Claydon 89-94; R Winslow w Gt Horwood and Addington 91-95; rtd 95. *Lower Axehill, Chard Road, Axminster, Devon EX13 5ED* Axminster (01297) 33259

JOHNSTON, William John. b 35. Lon Univ DipTh72 BA85 MA90. CITC 67. d 70 p 71. C Belf St Donard *D & D* 70-72; C Derg *D & R* 72-78; I Drumclamph w Lower and Upper Langfield 78-91; I Kilskeery w Trillick *Clogh* from 91. *The Rectory, 130 Kilskeery Road, Trillick, Omagh, Co Tyrone BT78 3RJ* Trillick (013655) 61228

JOHNSTON-HUBBOLD, Clifford Johnston. b 19. Lon Univ BA76 BD80. St Aid Birkenhead 49. d 52 p 53. R Sedgeberrow *Worc* 59-73; P-in-c Hinton-on-the-Green 72-73; R Sedgeberrow w Hinton-on-the-Green 73-92; rtd 92. *2 Mills Close, Broadway, Worcs WR12 7RB* Broadway (01386) 852199

JOHNSTONE, Ian Douglas. b 42. St Jo Coll Morpeth 67. d 70 p 70. Australia 70-88; V Morley St Paul *Wakef* from 88. *St Paul's Vicarage, 2 Bridge Court, Bridge Street, Morley, Leeds LS27 0BD* Leeds (01532) 529300

JOHNSTONE, Leslie William. b 20. ALCD49. d 49 p 50. R Bexhill St Mark *Chich* 56-85; rtd 85; Perm to Offic *Chich* from 86. *4 Fitzgerald Park, Seaford, E Sussex BN25 1AX* Seaford (01323) 899708

JOHNSTONE, Peter Verney Lovett. b 37. Trin Coll Cam BA61 MA65. Cuddesdon Coll 61. d 63 p 64. C Kennington St Jo *S'wark* 63-66; Asst Chapl Southn Univ *Win* 66-70; P-in-c Earlsfield St Jo *S'wark* 70-79; V Eltham St Jo from 79. *The Vicarage, Sowerby Close, London SE9 6HB* 0181-850 2731 or 859 1242

JOHNSTONE, William James. b 70. Dur Univ BA91. St Steph Ho Ox 93. d 95. C Plymouth St Pet *Ex* from 95. *3 St Paul Street, Plymouth PL1 3RZ* Plymouth (01752) 225640

JOHNSTONE, William John Richard. b 13. Leeds Univ BA48. Coll of Resurr Mirfield. d 50 p 51. V St Neot *Truro* 63-71; V Ruislip Manor St Paul *Lon* 71-76; C Honicknowle *Ex* 76-77; rtd 78; Perm to Offic *Ex* from 82. *c/o Miss A B Smyth, Syon Abbey, South Brent, Devon TQ10 9JX* South Brent (01364) 72256

JOINT, Capt Michael John. b 39. Sarum & Wells Th Coll 79. d 79 p 79. CA from 61; Hon C Chandler's Ford *Win* 79-83; Youth Chapl 79-83; V Lymington from 83. *The Vicarage, Grove Road, Lymington, Hants SO41 9RF* Lymington (01590) 673847

JOLLY, Leslie Alfred Walter. b 16. AKC40. d 40 p 41. R Chaldon *S'wark* 57-85; rtd 85; Perm to Offic *S'wark* 85-94; Perm to Offic *York* from 85. *62 Wharfedale, Filey, N Yorkshire YO14 0DP* Scarborough (01723) 514591

JONAS, Alan Charles. b 56. Leeds Univ BA79 Univ of Wales (Abth) PGCE80. Wycliffe Hall Ox DipMin94. d 94 p 95. C Hersham *Guildf* from 94. *3 Burwood Road, Walton-on-Thames, Surrey KT12 4AA* Walton-on-Thames (01932) 247868

JONAS, Ian Robert. b 54. St Jo Coll Nottm BTh80. d 80 p 81. C Portadown St Mark *Arm* 80-82; C Cregagh *D & D* 82-85; BCMS Sec *D & G* 85-90; V Langley Mill *Derby* from 90. *The Vicarage, 214 Cromford Road, Langley Mill, Nottingham NG16 4HB* Langley Mill (01773) 712441

JONES, Adrian Alfred Burkett. b 37. St Aid Birkenhead 61. d 64 p 65. C Derby St Aug *Derby* 64-68; Chapl RAF 68-87; R Worlingham w Barnby and N Cove *St E* from 87. *The Rectory, Lowestoft Road, Beccles, Suffolk NR34 7DZ* Beccles (01502) 715403

JONES, Alan. b 28. Man Univ LLB48 LLM50. Coll of Resurr Mirfield 53. d 56 p 57. Chapl RN 61-65; rtd 94. *73 Mousehole Lane, Southampton SO18 4FB* Southampton (01703) 550008

JONES, Alan David. b 32. Lon Coll of Div ALCD58 DipTh70 LTh74. d 58 p 59. V Leyton St Cath *Chelmsf* 64-70; V Hatf Broad Oak 70-77; P-in-c Bush End 70-77; V Theydon Bois 77-88; P-in-c Finchingfield and Cornish Hall End 88-93; rtd 94. *7 Cotswold Drive, Long Melford, Sudbury, Suffolk CO10 9LW* Sudbury (01787) 370864

JONES, Alan John. b 47. Nottm Univ BA71. Coll of Resurr Mirfield 71. d 73 p 74. C Sedgley St Mary *Lich* 73-76; C Cov St Jo *Cov* 76-78; V W Bromwich St Fran *Lich* 78-94; V Ettingshall from 94. *The Vicarage, Ettingshall, Wolverhampton WV4 6QH* Sedgley (01902) 884616

JONES, Alban Vaughan. b 24. St D Coll Lamp BA51. d 52 p 53. Area Sec (Dios Ches, Ban, St As and S & M) CMS 65-72; V Ventnor H Trin *Portsm* 72-79; V Ventnor St Cath 72-79; V Marshfield and Peterstone Wentloog etc *Mon* 79-90; RD Bassaleg 87-90; rtd 90. *40 St Hilary Drive, Killay, Swansea SA2 7EH* Swansea (01792) 208178

JONES, Albert. b 13. K Coll Lon 37. d 41 p 42. R Stifford *Chelmsf* 66-72; P-in-c Stondon Massey 72-79; R Doddinghurst 72-79; rtd 79. *29 Seaview Road, Brightlingsea, Colchester CO7 0PP* Brightlingsea (01206) 303994

JONES, Alfred Albert. b 36. St D Coll Lamp BA59. d 61 p 62. C Treherbert *Llan* 61-64; C Horsham *Chich* 64-82; V Shipley 82-86; Chapl Hillingdon Hosp & Mt Vernon Hosp Uxbridge 86-87. *Chantry House, Nuthurst Road, Monks Gate, Horsham, W Sussex RH13 6LG* Lower Beeding (01403) 891218

JONES, Alwyn Humphrey Griffith. b 30. Leeds Univ BSc51. Coll of Resurr Mirfield 53. d 55 p 56. India 65-73; P-in-c Bedminster St Fran *Bris* 73-75; TR Bedminster 75-83; TV Langport Area Chs *B & W* 83-85; Dep Chapl HM Pris Nor 85; Chapl HM Pris Preston 85-89; Chapl HM Pris Ashwell 89-91; C Acton Green *Lon* 91-93; rtd 93; Hon C Langport Area Chs *B & W* from 93. *The Vicarage, New Street, Long Sutton, Langport, Somerset TA10 9JW* Long Sutton (01458) 241260

✠JONES, Most Rev Alwyn Rice. b 34. Univ of Wales (Lamp) BA55 Fitzw Ho Cam BA57 MA61. St Mich Coll Llan 57. d 58 p 59 c 82. C Llanfairisgaer *Ban* 58-62; N Wales Sec SCM 60-62; Staff Sec SCM 62-65; Chapl St Winifred's Sch Llanfairfechan 65-68; Dir RE *Ban* 65-75; Dioc Youth Officer 66-72; Dir of Ords 70-75; Asst Tutor Univ of Wales (Ban) 73-76; V Porthmadog *Ban* 75-79; Hon Can Ban Cathl 75-78; Preb 78-79; Dean Brecon *S & B* 79-82; V Brecon w Battle 79-82; Bp St As from 82; Abp Wales from 91. *Esgobty, St Asaph, Clwyd LL17 0TW* St Asaph (01745) 583503 Fax 584301

JONES, Alyson Elizabeth. *See* DAVIE, Mrs Alyson Elizabeth

JONES, Mrs Andrea Margaret. b 46. Qu Coll Birm 88. d 90 p 94. Par Dn Kidderminster St Geo *Worc* 90-94; C 94; TV from 94. *6 Forester Way, Kidderminster, Worcs DY10 1NT* Kidderminster (01562) 745996

JONES, Andrew. b 61. Univ of Wales (Ban) BD82 PGCE82 TCD BTh85 MA91 Univ of Wales MPhil93. CITC 83 St Geo Coll Jerusalem 84. **d** 85 **p** 86. Min Can Ban Cathl *Ban* 85-88; R Dolgellau w Llanfachreth and Brithdir etc 88-92; Chapl Dolgellau Hosp 88-92; Lect in Th Univ of Wales (Cardiff) *Llan* 92-93; Dir Past Studies St Mich Coll Llan from 92. *St Michael's College, 54 Cardiff Road, Llandaff, Cardiff CF5 2YJ* Cardiff (01222) 563379

JONES, Andrew. b 64. York Univ BA85. Westmr Th Sem (USA) MDiv91 St Jo Coll Nottm 92. **d** 94 **p** 95. C Win Ch Ch *Win* from 94. *18 Sparkford Close, Winchester, Hants SO22 4NH* Winchester (01962) 865051

JONES, Dr Andrew Christopher. b 47. Southn Univ BA69 PhD75. Ridley Hall Cam 78. **d** 80 **p** 81. C Wareham *Sarum* 80-83; P-in-c Symondsbury 83; P-in-c Chideock 83; R Symondsbury and Chideock 84-91; V Shottermill *Guildf* from 91. *The Vicarage, Vicarage Lane, Shottermill, Haslemere, Surrey GU27 1LQ* Haslemere (01428) 642057

JONES, Andrew Collins. b 62. Univ Coll Dur BA83 MA84 MLitt92. St Steph Ho Ox 88. **d** 90 **p** 91. C Llangefni w Tregaean and Llangristiolus etc *Ban* 90-94; C Hartlepool St Aid *Dur* from 94; Chapl Hartlepool Gen Hosp from 94. *St Aidan's Clergy House, St Aidan's Street, Hartlepool, Cleveland TS25 1SN* Hartlepool (01429) 273539

JONES, Preb Andrew Theodore Hugh. b 22. St Cath Soc Ox BA49 MA53. St Steph Ho Ox. **d** 50 **p** 51. V Witheridge *Ex* 66-77; V Creacombe 67-77; R Thelbridge 67-77; R W w E Worlington 67-77; P-in-c Meshaw 69-77; RD S Molton 72-74; P-in-c Limington *B & W* 77-78; P-in-c Ilchester w Northover 77-78; P-in-c Yeovilton 78; R Ilchester w Northover, Limington, Yeovilton etc 78-80; V Bishops Tawton *Ex* 80-85; V Newport 80-85; RD Barnstaple 81-83; Preb Ex Cathl 82-87; TR Newport, Bishops Tawton and Tawstock 85-87; rtd 87; Perm to Offic *Ex* from 87. *Belmont House, King Street, Combe Martin, Ilfracombe, Devon EX34 0AH* Combe Martin (01271) 883135

JONES, Canon Anthony Spacie (Tony). b 34. AKC58. **d** 59 **p** 60. C Bedf St Martin *St Alb* 59-63; Br Guiana 63-66; Guyana 66-71; V Ipswich All Hallows *St E* 72-80; RD Ipswich 78-86; Bp's Dom Chapl 80-82; V Rushmere 82-91; Hon Can St E Cathl from 83; R Brantham w Stutton from 91. *The Rectory, Rectory Lane, Brantham, Manningtree, Essex CO11 1PZ* Colchester (01206) 392646

JONES, Canon Arthur Alexander. b 10. Birm Univ BA35 MA48 Lon Univ BD45 PhD53. **d** 52 **p** 53. Prin Lect RE Avery Hill Coll 62-75; Hon C Eltham St Sav *S'wark* 71-75; Chapl RAEC Wilton Park 75-80; rtd 75; Tutor K Coll Lon 75-80. *16 Heath Road, Beaconsfield, Bucks HP9 1DD* Beaconsfield (01494) 676746

JONES, Arthur Howard Glyn (Tim). b 07. Ripon Hall Ox 53. **d** 55 **p** 56. R Drewsteignton *Ex* 68-76; V Hittisleigh 73-76; V Spreyton 73-76; rtd 76; Hon C Blackawton and Stoke Fleming *Ex* 76-81; Lic to Offic from 91. *15 Fore Street, Bradninch, Exeter EX5 4NN* Exeter (01392) 881383

JONES, Arthur Kenneth Hughes. b 14. Ch Coll Cam BA36 MA46. Wycliffe Hall Ox. **d** 53 **p** 54. V Furze Platt *Ox* 68-79; rtd 79. *107 Farm Road, Maidenhead, Berks SL6 5JQ* Maidenhead (01628) 31909

JONES, Arthur Leslie. b 12. Univ of Wales BA36. Qu Coll Birm 36. **d** 38 **p** 39. R Upwey *Sarum* 60-80; R Buckland Ripers 75-80; rtd 80. *4 St George's Close, Harnham, Salisbury SP2 8HA* Salisbury (01722) 336653

JONES, Barry Mervyn. b 46. St Chad's Coll Dur BA68 DipTh69. **d** 70 **p** 71. C Bloxwich *Lich* 70-72; C Norwood All SS *Cant* 72-76; C New Addington 76-78; Chapl Mayday Univ Hosp Thornton Heath 78-86; Chapl Qu and St Mary's Hosps Croydon 78-86; Chapl Bromsgrove and Redditch DHA from 86; Chapl Alexandra Hosp Redditch from 86. *The Alexandra Hospital, Woodrow Drive, Redditch, Worcs B98 7UB* Redditch (01527) 503030

JONES, Canon Basil Henry. b 26. Bps' Coll Cheshunt 63. **d** 64 **p** 65. V Leagrave *St Alb* 68-74; RD Luton 71-74; P-in-c Bedf St Paul 74-75; V Wigginton 75-93; Hon Can St Alb 82-93; rtd 93. *17 Lochnell Road, Northchurch, Berkhamsted, Herts HP4 3QD* Berkhamsted (01442) 864485

JONES, Ven Benjamin Jenkin Hywel. b 39. Univ of Wales BA61. St Mich Coll Llan 61. **d** 64 **p** 65. C Carmarthen St Pet *St D* 64-70; V Cynwyl Gaeo w Llansawel and Talley 70-79; R Llanbadarn Fawr 79-82; V Llanbadarn Fawr w Capel Bangor and Goginan 82-92; Can St D Cathl 86-90; RD Llanbadarn Fawr 89-90; Adn Cardigan from 90; V Llanychaearn w Llanddeiniol from 92. *The Vicarage, Llanfarian, Aberystwyth, Dyfed SY23 4BX* Aberystwyth (01970) 617100

JONES, Benjamin Tecwyn. b 17. Univ of Wales BA38. K Coll Lon 38. **d** 40 **p** 41. Hd Master and Chapl St Mary's Sch Bexhill-on-Sea 69-71; V Blackb St Luke *Blackb* 71-72; P-in-c Griffin

71-72; V Blackb St Luke w St Phil 72-83; rtd 83; Lic to Offic *Blackb* from 83. *527A Livesey Branch Road, Feniscowles, Blackburn BB2 5DB* Blackburn (01254) 209206

JONES, Bernard Lewis. b 48. Llan Dioc Tr Scheme 89. **d** 93 **p** 94. NSM Aberaman and Abercwmboi w Cwmaman *Llan* from 93. *21 Gladstone Street, Aberaman, Aberdare, M Glam CF44 6SB* Aberdare (01685) 881994

JONES, Brian H. d 94. Lic to Offic *D & D* from 94. *16 Massey Avenue, Belfast BT4 2JS*

JONES, Canon Brian Howell. b 35. St Mich Coll Llan DipTh61. **d** 61 **p** 62. C Llangiwg *S & B* 61-63; C Swansea St Mary and H Trin 63-70; R New Radnor w Llanfihangel Nantmelan etc 70-75; V Llansamlet 75-89; Dioc Dir of Stewardship 82-89; P-in-c Capel Coelbren 89-95; Dioc Missr 89-95; Can Res Brecon Cathl from 89; RD Cwmtawe 89-93; V Killay from 93. *The Vicarage, 30 Geotre Fach Road, Killay, Swansea SA2 7SG* Swansea (01792) 204233

JONES, Brian Michael. b 34. Trin Coll Bris DipHE81 Oak Hill Th Coll BA82. **d** 84 **p** 84. CMS 82-93; Sierra Leone 84-93; C Frimley *Guildf* from 93. *Church House, 4 Warren Rise, Frimley, Camberley, Surrey GU16 5SH* Camberley (01276) 66740

JONES, Canon Brian Noel. b 32. Edin Th Coll 59. **d** 62 **p** 63. C Monkseaton St Mary *Newc* 62-65; C Saffron Walden *Chelmsf* 65-69; P-in-c Swaffham Bulbeck *Ely* 69-75; Dioc Youth Officer 69-75; RD St Ives 75-83 and 87-89; V Ramsey 75-89; V Upwood w Gt and Lt Raveley 75-89; P-in-c Ramsey St Mary's 82-89; Hon Can Ely Cathl from 85; V Cherry Hinton St Jo from 89; RD Cam from 94. *St John's Vicarage, 9 Luard Road, Cambridge CB2 2PJ* Cambridge (01223) 247451

JONES, Brinley Morgan. b 13. St D Coll Lamp BA37. **d** 40 **p** 41. V Pwllgwaun *Llan* 54-71; R Eglwysbrewis and St Athan 71-78; rtd 78; Perm to Offic *Llan* from 78. *228 New Road, Porthcawl, M Glam CF36 5BA* Porthcawl (01656) 716123

JONES, Canon Bryan Maldwyn. b 32. St Mich Coll Llan DipTh62. **d** 62 **p** 63. C Swansea St Barn *S & B* 62-69; V Trallwng and Betws Penpont 69-75; V Trallwng, Bettws Penpont w Aberyskir etc from 75; RD Brecon II 80-91; RD Brecon from 91; Hon Can Brecon Cathl from 92. *The Vicarage, Trallwng, Brecon, Powys LD3 8HP* Sennybridge (01874) 636549

JONES, Bryan William. b 30. Selw Coll Cam BA53 MA57. Linc Th Coll 53. **d** 55 **p** 56. C Bedminster Down *Bris* 55-58; C Filton 58-62; P-in-c Bedminster St Mich 62-65; V 65-72; P-in-c Moorfields 72-75; TV E Bris from 75. *St Matthew's Vicarage, Victoria Avenue, Bristol BS5 9NH* Bristol (0117) 955 7350

JONES, Bryon. b 34. Open Univ BA84. St D Coll Lamp 61. **d** 64 **p** 65. C Port Talbot St Theodore *Llan* 64-67; C Aberdare St Jo 68-69; C Up Hatherley *Glouc* 69-71; C Oystermouth *S & B* 71-74; V Camrose *St D* 74-77; V Camrose and St Lawrence w Ford and Haycastle from 77. *The Vicarage, Camrose, Haverfordwest, Dyfed SA62 6JE* Camrose (01437) 710501

JONES, Charles Derek. b 37. K Coll Lon BD60 AKC60. **d** 61 **p** 62. C Stockton St Chad *Dur* 61-64; C Becontree St Eliz *Chelmsf* 64-66; C S Beddington St Mich *S'wark* 66-73; Lic to Offic *Ex* 73-77; Perm to Offic *Liv* from 77. *8 Millfield Close, Barton Park, Farndon, Chester CH3 6PW* Farndon (01829) 270554

JONES, Charles Emerson Glynne. b 08. Univ of Wales 27. **d** 31 **p** 32. R Middleton Cheney w Chacombe *Pet* 52-75; rtd 75; Hon C N Huish *Ex* 75-83. *31 Y Berllan, Dunvant, Swansea SA2 8RD* Swansea (01792) 201886

JONES, Charles Eurwyn. b 27. Univ of Wales BSc48 DipEd51. St Mich Coll Llan 53. **d** 55 **p** 56. V Carlton *S'well* 67-75; P-in-c Colwick 69-75; V Bunny w Bradmore 75-95; rtd 95. *9 Wentworth Way, Edwalton, Nottingham NG12 4DJ* Nottingham (0115) 923 4119

JONES, Charles Harold Lloyd. b 08. St D Coll Lamp DipTh59. **d** 59 **p** 60. R Llanfairorllwyn and Llangynllo *St D* 61-70; V Llanllawddog w Capel-y-Groes 70-79; rtd 79. *15 Bro Nantlais, Gwyddgrug, Pencader, Dyfed SA39 9BQ* Pencader (01559) 384884

JONES, Charles John Llewelyn. b 11. Jes Coll Cam BA32 MA36. St Aug Coll Cant 56. **d** 56 **p** 57. V Whittlesford *Ely* 65-84; rtd 84; Perm to Offic *Ely* from 86. *4 Bishop Wynn Close, Ely, Cambs CB7 4BH* Ely (01353) 665230

JONES, Christopher Mark. b 56. St Jo Coll Cam BA78 MA82 Ox Univ BA81 MA85. Wycliffe Hall Ox 79. **d** 82 **p** 83. C Walsall *Lich* 82-84; Chapl St Jo Coll Cam 84-89; Chapl Eton Coll Windsor from 89. *Eton College, Windsor, Berks SL4 6DW* Windsor (01753) 862062

JONES, Christopher Howell. b 50. FCCA BA. Oak Hill Th Coll 80. **d** 83 **p** 84. C Leyton St Mary w St Edw *Chelmsf* 83-86; C Becontree St Mary 86-90; P-in-c Bootle St Matt *Liv* 90-93; V from 93. *St Matthew's Vicarage, 418 Stanley Road, Bootle, Merseyside L20 5AE* 0151-922 3316

JONES, Christopher John Stark. b 39. Lon Univ BA60 AKC60. Wells Th Coll 63. **d** 65 **p** 66. C Stanmore *Win* 65-67; C

Bournemouth St Pet 67-71; C W Wycombe *Ox* 71-75; TV High Wycombe 75-77; V Wokingham St Sebastian 77-84; R Didsbury Ch Ch *Man* from 84. *Christ Church Rectory, 35 Darley Avenue, Manchester M20 2ZD* 0161-445 4152

JONES, Christopher Mark. b 54. St Pet Coll Ox BA75 DipTh77 MA79 Selw Coll Cam MPhil80. Ridley Hall Cam 77. **d** 80 **p** 81. C Putney St Marg *S'wark* 80-83; C Ham St Andr 83-86; Chapl HM Rem Cen Latchmere Ho 83-86; Chapl St Jo Coll Dur 87-93; Tutor Cranmer Hall Dur 87-93; Chapl and Fell St Pet Coll Ox from 93. *St Peter's College, Oxford OX1 2DL* Oxford (01865) 278900

JONES, Clifford Albert. b 20. Edin Th Coll 54. **d** 56 **p** 57. V Bradf *B & W* 69-74; V Bridgwater St Jo 74-78; RD Bridgwater 76-80; R Bridgwater St Jo w Chedzoy 78-80; P-in-c Timsbury 80-85; R Timsbury and Priston 85; rtd 85; P-in-c Nor St Geo Tombland *Nor* 85-90; Hon C St Marylebone All SS *Lon* 90-94. *St Fursey's House, All Hallows Convent, Ditchingham, Bungay, Suffolk NR35 2DZ* Bungay (01986) 892308

JONES, Clive. b 51. BA82. Oak Hill Th Coll 79. **d** 82 **p** 83. C Brunswick *Man* 82-85; V Pendlebury St Jo from 85. *St John's Vicarage, 27 Bolton Road, Swinton, Manchester M27 2XS* 0161-736 2176

JONES, Clive Morlais Peter. b 40. LTCL71 Univ of Wales (Cardiff) BA63 CertEd64. Chich Th Coll 64. **d** 66 **p** 67. C Llanfabon *Llan* 66-70; PV Llan Cathl 70-75; R Gelligaer 75-85; Prec and Can Llan Cathl 84-85; R Tilehurst St Mich *Ox* 85-94; Chapl Costa Blanca *Eur* from 94. *Buzon 3, La Cometa 18, 03729 Senija, Alicante, Spain* Sagunto (6) 573-2465

JONES, Colin Stuart. b 56. Southn Univ LLB77. Coll of Resurr Mirfield 81. **d** 84 **p** 85. C Mountain Ash *Llan* 84-86; C Castle Bromwich SS Mary and Marg *Birm* 86-89; V Kingshurst 89-94; V Perry Barr from 94. *Perry Barr Vicarage, Church Road, Birmingham B42 2LB* 0121-356 7998

JONES, Cyril. b 27. Linc Th Coll 67. **d** 69 **p** 70. C Milnrow *Man* 69-71; C Chorlton-cum-Hardy St Werburgh 71-73; V Chadderton St Mark 73-75; R Didsbury Ch Ch 75-81; V Farlam and Nether Denton *Carl* 81-85; P-in-c Kirkbride w Newton Arlosh 85-89; rtd 89. *81 Newlands Avenue, Cheadle Hulme, Cheadle, Cheshire SK8 6NE*

JONES, Cyril Ernest. b 29. St D Coll Lamp BA54. **d** 56 **p** 57. V Llanybydder *St D* 66-73; V Llanybydder and Llanwenog w Llanwnnen 73-78; V Betws St Dav w Ammanford 78-81; V Cynwyl Gaeo w Llansawel and Talley 81-94; rtd 94. *21 Pontardulais Road, Tycroes, Ammanford, Dyfed SA18 3QD* Ammanford (01269) 596421

JONES, David. b 55. St Steph Ho Ox. **d** 85 **p** 86. C Fleur-de-Lis *Mon* 85-87; V Ynysddu 87-93; V Blackwood from 93. *The Vicarage, South View Road, Blackwood, Gwent NP2 1HR* Blackwood (01495) 224214

JONES, David Arthur. b 44. Liv Univ BA66 Sussex Univ MA68. St D Coll Lamp LTh74. **d** 74 **p** 75. C Tenby *St D* 74-76; C Chepstow *Mon* 76-78; P-in-c Teversal *S'well* 78-81; R 81-91; Chapl Sutton Cen 78-89; V Radford All So w Ch Ch and St Mich from 91. *All Souls' Vicarage, 164 Lenton Boulevard, Nottingham NG7 2BZ* Nottingham (0115) 978 5364

JONES, David Emrys. b 21. Lon Univ BD69 Univ of Wales MA74. St D Coll Lamp BA42. **d** 47 **p** 48. V Beddgelert *Ban* 57-72; R Llangystennin *St As* 72-91; rtd 91. *The Rectory, Llanfor, Bala, Gwynedd LL23 7YA* Bala (01678) 520080

JONES, Chan David Frederick Donald. b 19. Univ of Wales (Abth) BA41. Westcott Ho Cam 41. **d** 43 **p** 44. Lect Bp Burgess Th Hall Lamp 59-72; V Betws St Dav w Ammanford *St D* 64-78; RD Dyffryn Aman 72-78; Can St D Cathl 75-88; Chan St D Cathl 83-88; V Felin-foel 78-88; rtd 88. *93 Nun Street, St Davids, Haverfordwest, Dyfed SA62 6NU* St Davids (01437) 720359

JONES, David Hugh. b 34. St D Coll Lamp BA56. St Mich Coll Llan 58. **d** 58 **p** 59. V Llanddewi Ystradenni and Abbey Cwmhir *S & B* 69-75; V Port Eynon w Rhosili and Llanddewi and Knelston 75-83; V Swansea St Barn 83-92; rtd 92. *16 Lon Ger-y-Coed, Cockett, Swansea SA2 0YH*

✠**JONES, Rt Rev David Huw.** b 34. Univ of Wales (Ban) BA55 Univ Coll Ox BA58 MA62. St Mich Coll Llan 58. **d** 59 **p** 60 c 93. C Aberdare St Jo *Llan* 59-61; C Neath w Llantwit 61-65; V Crynant 65-69; V Cwmavon 69-74; Lect Th Univ of Wales (Cardiff) 74-78; Sub-Warden St Mich Coll Llan 74-78; V Prestatyn *St As* 78-82; Dioc Ecum Officer 78-82; Dean Brecon *S & B* 82-93; V Brecon w Battle 82-83; V Brecon St Mary and Battle w Llanddew 83-93; Asst Bp St As from 93. *24 Drws-y-Coed, Coed-y-Glyn, Wrexham, Clwyd LL13 9QB* Wrexham (01978) 357522

JONES, David Ian Stewart. b 34. Selw Coll Cam BA57 MA61. Westcott Ho Cam 57. **d** 59 **p** 60. Chapl Eton Coll Windsor 66-70; Sen Chapl 70-74; Hd Master Bryanston Sch Blandford 74-82; P-in-c Bris Ch Ch w St Ewen and All SS *Bris* 82-84;

P-in-c Bris St Steph w St Nic and St Leon 82-84; P-in-c City of Bris 84; Soc Resp Adv 84-85; Dir Lambeth Endowed Charities 85-94; Hon PV S'wark Cathl *S'wark* 85-94; rtd 94. *127 Kennington Road, London SE11 6SF* 0171-735 2531

JONES, David James Hammond. b 45. Kelham Th Coll DipTh69. **d** 70 **p** 70. C Cheadle *Lich* 70-73; Hon C W Bromwich All SS 78-83. *60 Hembs Crescent, Great Barr, Birmingham B43 5DG*

JONES, David John. b 06. St D Coll Lamp 55. **d** 57 **p** 58. V Brawdy w Haycastle and Llandeloy *St D* 59-71; RD Dewisland and Fishguard 68-71; V Llangyndeyrn 71-76; rtd 76. *73 Heol Marlais, Trimsaran, Kidwelly, Dyfed SA17 4DF* Trimsaran (01554) 810611

JONES, Chan David John. b 18. St D Coll Lamp BA51. **d** 52 **p** 53. V Blaenpennal and Llangeitho *St D* 60-72; R Llanllwchaiarn 72-79; V Llanfihangel Ystrad w Cribyn and Cilcennin 79-82; Can St D Cathl 82-89; V Llanfihangel Ystrad and Cilcennin w Trefilan etc 82-89; RD Glyn Aeron 85-89; Chan St D Cathl 89. *Maerdy, 14 Harford Row, Lampeter, Dyfed SA48 7DG* Lampeter (01570) 423292

JONES, David Jonathan. b 04. St D Coll Lamp BA34. **d** 34 **p** 35. R Nefyn w Pistyll *Ban* 60-73; rtd 73. *Glanrhos Nursing Home, Brynsiencyn, Llanfairpwllgwyngyll, Gwynedd LL61 6TZ*

JONES, David Michael. b 48. Chich Th Coll 75. **d** 78 **p** 79. C Yeovil *B & W* 78-84; C Barwick 81-84; V Cleeve w Chelvey and Brockley 84-92; V Heigham St Barn w St Bart *Nor* from 92. *The Vicarage, Russell Street, Norwich NR2 4QT* Norwich (01603) 627859

JONES, David Noel. b 29. St Deiniol's Hawarden 69. **d** 71 **p** 72. C Llandegfan w Beaumaris and Llanfaes *Ban* 71-74; TV Amlwch, Rhosybol, Llandyfrydog etc 74-77; R Llanfair Mathafarn Eithaf w Llanbedrgoch 77-82; V Porthmadog 82-84; V Ynyscynhaearn w Penmorfa and Porthmadog 84-86; R Llanllyfni 86-95; RD Arfon 89-92; rtd 95. *3 Rhosfryn, Penrhosgarnedd, Bangor, Gwynedd LL54 2DL* Bangor (01248) 354088

JONES, David Ormond. b 46. Llan Dioc Tr Scheme 90. **d** 94 **p** 95. NSM Resolven w Tonna *Llan* from 94. *30 Henfaes Road, Tonna, Neath, W Glam SA11 3EX* Neath (01639) 633642

JONES, David Raymond (Ray). b 34. Univ of Wales (Lamp) BA54 St Cath Coll Ox BA57 MA61. Wycliffe Hall Ox 58. **d** 58 **p** 59. C Ex St Dav *Ex* 58-60; C Bideford 60-63; Chapl Grenville Coll Bideford 63-66; Chapl RN 66-89; Hon Chapl to The Queen from 84; Warden and Dir Ch Min of Healing Crowhurst from 89. *The Old Rectory, Crowhurst, Battle, E Sussex TN33 9AD* Crowhurst (01424) 830204

JONES, David Robert. b 37. MBIM83 Dur Univ BA59 QUB MA83. Cranmer Hall Dur DipTh69. **d** 69 **p** 70. C Middleton *Man* 69-72; CF 72-92; V Staindrop *Dur* from 92. *St Mary's Vicarage, 7 Beechside, Staindrop, Darlington, Co Durham DL2 3PE* Staindrop (01833) 60237

JONES, David Robert Deverell. b 50. Sarum & Wells Th Coll 72. **d** 75 **p** 78. C Altrincham St Geo *Ches* 75-76; C Clayton *Lich* 77-80; Carriacou 80-81; P-in-c Baschurch *Lich* 81-83; R Baschurch and Weston Lullingfield w Hordley from 83; RD Ellesmere 85-95; P-in-c Criftins from 94; P-in-c Dudleston from 94. *The Rectory, Baschurch, Shrewsbury SY4 2EB* Baschurch (01939) 260305

JONES, David Roy. b 47. CQSW76 Hull Univ BA74 Man Univ DipAdEd76 Bradf Univ MA85 Leic Univ DipIR91. Bernard Gilpin Soc Dur 69 N Ord Course 77. **d** 80 **p** 81. C New Bury *Man* 80-83; NSM Ringley St Sav w H Trin Prestolee from 92. *2 Affleck Avenue, Radcliffe, Manchester M26 9HM* Bolton (01204) 796575

JONES, David Sebastian. b 43. St Cath Coll Cam BA67 MA73. Linc Th Coll 66. **d** 68 **p** 69. C Baguley *Man* 68-71; C Bray and Braywood *Ox* 71-73; V S Ascot from 73; Chapl Heatherwood Hosp E Berks from 81. *The Vicarage, Vicarage Gardens, Ascot, Berks SL5 9DX* Ascot (01344) 22388

JONES, David Victor. b 37. Dur Univ BA59. Cranmer Hall Dur DipTh60. **d** 62 **p** 63. C Farnworth *Liv* 62-65; CF 65-68; Asst Master Hutton Gr Sch Preston from 68; Lic to Offic *Blackb* from 70. *10 Houghton Close, Penwortham, Preston PR1 9HT* Preston (01772) 745306

JONES, Capt Derek John. b 43. CA Tr Coll 64 Sarum & Wells Th Coll 82. **d** 83 **p** 84. CA from 66; C Fleur-de-Lis *Mon* 83-85; V Rhymney 85-93; R Ebbw Vale from 93; RD Blaenau Gwent from 94. *The Rectory, Eureka Place, Ebbw Vale, Gwent NP3 6PN* Ebbw Vale (01495) 301723

JONES, Miss Diana. b 46. Qu Coll Birm 89. **d** 91 **p** 94. Par Dn Harnham *Sarum* 91-94; C 94-95; C Tidworth, Ludgershall and Faberstown from 95. *The Rectory, St Georges Road, Tidworth, Hants SP9 7EW* Tidworth (01980) 843889

JONES, Canon Dick Heath Remi. b 32. Jes Coll Cam BA56. Linc Th Coll 56. **d** 58 **p** 59. C Ipswich St Thos *St E* 58-61; C Putney

St Mary *S'wark* 61-65; P-in-c Dawley Parva *Lich* 65-75; P-in-c Lawley 65-75; RD Wrockwardine 70-72; P-in-c Malins Lee 72-75; RD Telford 72-80; P-in-c Stirchley 74-75; TR Cen Telford 75-80; Preb Lich Cathl 76-80; TR Bournemouth St Pet w St Swithun, St Steph etc *Win* from 80; RD Bournemouth from 90; Hon Can Win Cathl from 91; Chapl Bournemouth and Poole Colls *Sarum* from 94. *St Peter's Rectory, 18 Wimborne Road, Bournemouth BH2 6NT* Bournemouth (01202) 554058

JONES, Donald (Don). b 50. BA BSc. St Jo Coll Nottm 79. **d** 82 **p** 83. C Hutton *Chelmsf* 82-86; C E Ham w Upton Park St Alb 86-88; TV from 88. *15 Greenwich Crescent, London E6 4TU* 0171-476 0618

JONES, Canon Douglas Rawlinson. b 19. St Edm Hall Ox BA41 MA45. Lambeth DD Wycliffe Hall Ox 41. **d** 42 **p** 43. Lect Th Dur Univ 51-64; Prof Div 64-85; Can Res Dur Cathl *Dur* 64-85; rtd 85; Lic to Offic *Edin* from 85. *Whitefriars, King's Road, Longniddry, E Lothian EH32 0NN* Longniddry (01875) 52149

JONES, Edgar John. Univ of Wales (Lamp) BA53. St Mich Coll Llan 53. **d** 55 **p** 56. C Holyhead w Rhoscolyn w Llanfair-yn-Neubwll *Ban* 55-61; R Bodedern and Llechcynfarwy 61-70; V Bodedern w Llechgynfarwy and Llechylched etc 70-73; Perm to Offic from 73. *5 Glan Llyn, Llanfachraeth, Holyhead, Gwynedd LL65 4UW* Holyhead (01407) 742322

JONES, Edgar Joseph Basil. b 14. Univ of Wales LLB37 St Jo Coll Ox BA40 MA43. Ripon Hall Ox 40. **d** 41 **p** 42. V Sandiway *Ches* 61-80; rtd 80; Perm to Offic *Ches* from 80. *Fron, 29 Church Walk, Llandudno, Gwynedd LL30 2HL* Llandudno (01492) 876125

JONES, Edward. b 36. Dur Univ BA60. Ely Th Coll 60. **d** 62 **p** 63. C S Shields St Hilda w St Thos *Dur* 62-65; C Cleadon Park 65-68; V Hebburn St Cuth 68-79; R Winlaton from 79. *The Rectory, Winlaton, Tyne & Wear NE21 6PL* 0191-414 3165

JONES, Edward Gareth. b 36. St D Coll Lamp BA59. **d** 61 **p** 62. C Llanbadarn Fawr *St D* 61-66; V Mydroilyn w Dihewyd 66-69; Missr to the Deaf *Mon* 69-70; V Tregaron *St D* 70-75; Chapl to the Deaf (Dios Llan and Mon) 75-83; V Llanilar w Rhostie and Llangwyryfon etc *St D* from 83; RD Llanbadarn Fawr 90-94. *The Vicarage, Llanilar, Aberystwyth, Dyfed SY23 4PD* Llanilar (01974) 241659

JONES, Canon Edward Graham. b 25. St Deiniol's Hawarden 62. **d** 64 **p** 65. C Bargoed w Brithdir *Llan* 64-70; V Caerau St Cynfelin 70-95; Hon Can Llan Cathl 93-95; rtd 95. *41 Tywith Bungalows, Nantyffryllon, Maesteg, Bridgend, M Glam CF34 0TT* Bridgend (01656) 723988

JONES, Edward Harries. b 16. St D Coll Lamp BA38 Ely Th Coll 38. **d** 39 **p** 40. V Ffynnongroyw *St As* 52-81; rtd 81. *16 Coed Pella Road, Colwyn Bay, Clwyd LL29 7BA* Colwyn Bay (01492) 532997

JONES, Edward Wynne. b 45. OBE93. Univ of Wales (Abth) LLB71. St Mich Coll Llan 72. **d** 74 **p** 75. C Llandegfan w Beaumaris and Llanfaes *Ban* 74-76; V Aberffraw and Llangwyfan w Llangadwaladr 76-78; Chapl RN from 78. *Directorate Gen, RN Chapl Services, Room 203, Victory Building, HM Naval Base, Portsmouth PO1 3LS* Portsmouth (01705) 727903 Fax 727112

JONES, Mrs Elaine Joan. b 50. Oak Hill Th Coll. **d** 87 **p** 94. Par Dn Tottenham H Trin *Lon* 87-92; Par Dn Clay Hill St Jo and St Luke 92-94; C St Botolph Aldgate w H Trin Minories from 94. *St John's Vicarage, 14 Kilvinton Drive, Enfield, Middx EN2 0BD* 0181-366 5043

JONES, Elidyr Price. b 26. St D Coll Lamp BA51. **d** 53 **p** 54. Chapl Kelly Coll Tavistock 65-86; rtd 86; Perm to Offic *St D* from 86. *Bronderi, Pontrhydfendigaid, Ystrad Meurig, Dyfed SY25 6EN* Pontrhydfendigaid (019745) 313

JONES, Mrs Elizabeth Mary. b 48. QUB BA69. N Ord Course 88. **d** 91 **p** 94. Par Dn Kippax w Allerton Bywater *Ripon* 91-94; C from 94. *34 Park Villa Court, Leeds LS8 1EB* Leeds (0113) 266 8837

JONES, Elizabeth Somerset. b 49. St Jo Coll Nottm CertCS84. **d** 88 **p** 94. NSM Duns *Edin* from 88; NSM Selkirk from 89. *Ellem Lodge, Duns, Berwickshire TD11 3SG* Longformacus (013617) 316

JONES, Elwyn. b 09. Univ of Wales BA35. St Mich Coll Llan 35. **d** 36 **p** 37. V Meliden and Gwaenysgor *St As* 72-77; rtd 77. *35 Llys Charles, Towyn, Abergele, Clwyd LL22 9NP* Abergele (01745) 355967

JONES, Emile Conrad Modupe Kojo.d 77 **p** 78. Chapl Heidelberg *Eur* from 94. *Theodor-Kornerstr 7, 69124 Eppelheim, Germany*

JONES, Emmanuel Thomas (Tom). b 19. S Dios Minl Tr Scheme. **d** 81 **p** 82. NSM Fareham H Trin *Portsm* 81-89; rtd 89; Perm to Offic *Portsm* from 89. *24 Maylings Farm Road, Fareham, Hants PO16 7QU* Fareham (01329) 281387

JONES, Eric Alexander. b 19. TCD BA40 MA45 BD45. **d** 42 **p** 43. RD N Belf *Conn* 65-70; I Carnmoney 68-76; V Hensall

Sheff 76-84; RD Snaith and Hatf 79-84; rtd 84. *2 Wilson Crescent, Mount Merrion, Blackrock, Co Dublin, Irish Republic* Dublin (1) 288-0136

JONES, Canon Eric Vernon. b 26. Ely Th Coll 57. **d** 59 **p** 60. V Preston St Matt *Blackb* 64-77; R Chorley St Laur 77-91; Hon Can Blackb Cathl 81-91; rtd 91. *8 Glamis Driue, Chorley, Lancs PR7 1LX* Chorley (01257) 230660

JONES, Eric Walter Nathaniel. b 26. Wells Th Coll. **d** 61 **p** 62. C Buckfastleigh w Dean Prior *Ex* 61-64; Warden Trin Youth Cen Ex 64-67; PV Ex Cathl *Ex* 64-67; Lic to Offic from 67. *Mar-y-Vela, 20A Wallaford Road, Buckfastleigh, Devon TQ11 0AR* Buckfastleigh (01364) 43260

JONES, Canon Eric Wilfred. b 22. Linc Coll Ox BA48 MA53. Cuddesdon Coll 48. **d** 50 **p** 51. Solomon Is 69-74; V Binley *Cov* 74-82; Hon Can Cov Cathl 80-87; RD Cov E 80-82; V Hatton w Haseley and Rowington w Lowsonford 82-87; P-in-c Honiley 85-87; R Hatton w Haseley, Rowington w Lowsonford etc 87; rtd 87; Perm to Offic *Bradf* from 87. *13 Park Avenue, Skipton, N Yorkshire BD23 1PN* Skipton (01756) 793302

JONES, Ernest Edward Stephen. b 39. Lon Univ BD76. St D Coll Lamp DipTh66. **d** 66 **p** 67. C N Meols *Liv* 66-69; C Kirkby 69-71; V Farnworth All SS *Man* 71-75; P-in-c Bempton *York* 75-78; R Rufford *Blackb* 78-84; V Cropredy w Gt Bourton and Wardington *Ox* 84-90; R York St Clem w St Mary Bishophill Senior *York* from 90; P-in-c York All SS N Street from 90. *St Clement's Rectory, 13 Nunthorpe Avenue, York YO2 1PF* York (01904) 622425

JONES, Evan Hopkins. b 38. St Mich Coll Llan 65. **d** 67 **p** 68. C Churston Ferrers w Goodrington *Ex* 67-70; C Tavistock and Gulworthy 70-73; R Ashprington 73-78; V Cornworthy 73-78; R S Hackney St Jo w Ch Ch *Lon* 78-92; AD Hackney 84-89; V Islington St Jas w St Pet from 92. *St James's Vicarage, Arlington Square, London N1 7DS* 0171-226 4108

JONES, Canon Evan Trefor. b 32. Univ of Wales (Ban) BA54 HospCC82. Coll of Resurr Mirfield 54. **d** 56 **p** 57. C Ban St Mary *Ban* 56-62; V Llandinorwic 62-71; TV Llanbeblig w Caernarfon and Betws Garmon etc 71-84; Ed Dioc Link Magazine 79-89; R Llanfairfechan w Abergwyngregyn from 84; Can Ban Cathl from 95. *The Rectory, Aber Road, Llanfairfechan, Gwynedd LL33 0HN* Llanfairfechan (01248) 680591

JONES, Canon Evan Trevor. b 18. Univ of Wales BA40. St Mich Coll Llan 40. **d** 42 **p** 43. V Nevern, Bayvil, Moelgrove and Monington *St D* 69-77; V Nevern and Bayvil w Eglwyswrw and Meline 77-83; RD Cemais and Sub-Aeron 80-87; V Nevern and Y Beifil w Eglwyswrw and Meline etc 83-87; Can St D Cathl 86-87; rtd 87. *Nyfer, 73 Pontwillem, Brecon, Powys LD3 9BS* Brecon (01874) 622353

JONES, Frank Llewellyn. b 12. St Pet Hall Ox BA36 MA42. Wycliffe Hall Ox DipTh37. **d** 37 **p** 38. V Widnes St Paul *Liv* 69-77; rtd 77; Perm to Offic *Nor* from 77. *14 Stigands Gate, East Dereham, Norfolk NR19 2HF* Dereham (01362) 693304

JONES, Canon Fred Leslie. b 12. Univ of Wales (Lamp) BA34. St Mich Coll Llan 34. **d** 35 **p** 36. V Newport St Mark *Mon* 67-77; Can St Woolos Cathl 67-79; rtd 77. *4 Stirling Court, 20 Portarlington Road, Bournemouth BH4 8BY* Bournemouth (01202) 768185

JONES, Frederick. b 33. FRHistS76 Man Univ BA54 Selw Coll Cam PhD72 LSE MSc82. St Steph Ho Ox 56. **d** 58 **p** 59. C Belfield *Man* 58-59; C Westmr St Matt *Lon* 59-60; Hon C Cam St Mary Less *Ely* 71-72; Perm to Offic *Win* 72-74; Lic to Offic 74-89. *Casa Renate, Carrer del Pinsa 86, Port de Pollenca, Mallorca, Spain*

JONES, Frederick John. b 32. Wells Th Coll 57. **d** 60 **p** 61. R Heaton Norris All SS *Man* 65-76; R Heaton Norris Ch w All SS 76-77; V Castleton Moor 77-88; C Greenfield 88-93; rtd 93. *69 Manchester Road, Greenfield, Oldham OL3 7SE* Saddleworth (01457) 873954

JONES, Frederick Morgan. b 19. Univ of Wales (Lamp) BA40 BD49. St Mich Coll Llan 42. **d** 42 **p** 43. R Llanbedrog and Penrhos *Ban* 61-74; R Llanbedrog w Llannor w Llanfihangel etc 74-84; C Llangefni w Tregaean and Llangristiolus etc 84-85; rtd 85; Perm to Offic *Ban* from 85. *15 Ponc-y-Fron, Llangefni, Gwynedd LL77 7NY* Llangefni (01248) 722850

JONES, Gareth. b 35. St Aid Birkenhead 59. **d** 61 **p** 62. C Doncaster Ch Ch *Sheff* 61-65; Min Can Ripon Cathl *Ripon* 65-68; Chapl RAF 68-85; Hong Kong 85-89; R Spofforth w Kirk Deighton *Ripon* from 89. *The Rectory, Church Lane, Spofforth, Harrogate, N Yorkshire HG3 1AF* Wetherby (01937) 590251

JONES, Gareth Lewis. b 42. K Coll Lon BD64 AKC64. **d** 65 **p** 66. C Risca *Mon* 65-70; Perm to Offic *Win* 70-74; Perm to Offic *Newc* 74-75; Perm to Offic *Sarum* 75; C Pontesbury I and II *Heref* 75-77; P-in-c Presteigne w Discoed 77-79; TV Hemel Hempstead *St Alb* 79-86; R Longden and Annscroft w Pulverbatch *Heref* 86-93; TV Leominster from 93. *118 Buckfield Road, Leominster, Herefordshire HR6 8SQ* Leominster (01568) 612124

JONES, Chan Gareth Lloyd. b 38. Univ of Wales BA61 Selw Coll Cam BA63 MA67 Yale Univ STM69 TCD BD70 Lon Univ PhD75. Episc Sem Austin Texas Hon DD90 Westcott Ho Cam 62. **d** 65 **p** 66. C Holyhead w Rhoscolyn *Ban* 65-68; USA 68-70; P-in-c Mert *Ox* 70-72; Tutor Ripon Hall Ox 72; Sen Tutor 73-75; Lect Ex Coll Ox 73-77; Tutor and Lib Ripon Coll Cuddesdon 75-77; Lect Th Univ of Wales (Ban) 77-89; Sen Lect from 89; Sub-Dean Faculty of Th 80-89; Dean from 89; Chan Ban Cathl *Ban* from 90; Select Preacher Ox Univ 89. *Nettuno, Mount Street, Menai Bridge, Gwynedd LL59 5BW* Menai Bridge (01248) 712786

JONES, Gareth Thomas. b 14. Open Univ BA75. Clifton Th Coll 32. **d** 37 **p** 38. V Grewelthorpe *Ripon* 56-82; V Mickley 56-82; P-in-c N Stainley 77-82; rtd 82. *14 Mallorie Close, Ripon, N Yorkshire HG4 2QD* Ripon (01765) 605643

JONES, Glyn Evan. b 44. Lon Coll of Div ALCD67 LTh. **d** 67 **p** 68. C Gt Horton *Bradf* 67-70; SAMS 71-78; Argentina 71-78; V Idle H Trin *Bradf* 78-84; V Hyson Green *S'well* 84-87; V Nottm St Steph 84-87; V Hyson Green St Paul w St Steph 87-89; V Hyson Green 89-91; V Basford w Hyson Green 91-92; V Worksop St Jo from 92; RD Worksop from 93. *St John's Vicarage, Shepherd's Avenue, Worksop, Notts S81 0JD* Worksop (01909) 489868 Fax as telephone Mobile (0585) 816697

JONES, Preb Glyn Owen. b 16. St D Coll Lamp BA37 St Mich Coll Llan 38. **d** 39 **p** 40. V Hengoed *Lich* 53-75; Preb Lich Cathl 73-81; V Baschurch 75-81; rtd 81; Perm to Offic *Lich* from 81. *6 Larkhill Road, Park Hall, Oswestry, Shropshire SY11 4AW* Oswestry (01691) 662739

JONES, Canon Glyndwr (Glyn). b 35. St Mich Coll Llan DipTh62. **d** 62 **p** 63. C Clydach *S & B* 62-64; C Llangyfelach 64-67; C Sketty 67-70; V Bryngwyn and Newchurch and Llanbedr etc 70-72; Miss to Seamen from 72; Aux Min Sec from 81; Asst Gen Sec 85-90; Gen Sec from 90; Hon Can Kobe Japan from 88; Chapl to The Queen from 90; V St Mich Paternoster Royal *Lon* from 91. *5 The Close, Grays, Essex RM16 2XU, or c/o St Michael Paternoster Royal, College Hill, London EC4R 2RL* 0171-248 5202 or 248 7442 Fax 248 4761

JONES, Glynn. b 56. NE Ord Course 91. **d** 94. NSM Glendale Gp *Newc* from 94. *Wooler Common Farm, Wooler, Northd NE71 6RH* Wooler (01668) 281825

JONES, Godfrey Caine. b 36. Dur Univ BA59 Lon Univ CertEd60 Birm Univ MEd71. St Deiniol's Hawarden 76. **d** 78 **p** 79. NSM Ruthin w Llanrhydd *St As* 78-81; C 83-84; Lic to Offic *Derby* 81-83; P-in-c Llanfwrog and Clocaenog and Gyffylliog *St As* 84-85; R 85-93; V Ruabon from 93; RD Llangollen from 93. *The Vicarage, Rark Street, Ruabon, Wrexham, Clwyd LL14 6LF* Wrexham (01978) 810176

JONES, Gordon Howlett. b 26. G&C Coll Cam BA47 MA51. Westcott Ho Cam 49. **d** 51 **p** 52. R Northenden *Man* 63-79; P-in-c Hilmarton and Highway *Sarum* 79-83; V Bremhill w Foxham and Hilmarton 83-92; RD Calne 84-88; rtd 92. *63 New Park Street, Devizes, Wilts SN11 8SB* Devizes (01380) 720950

JONES, Gordon Michael Campbell. b 33. St D Coll Lamp BA56 St Jo Coll Dur 56. **d** 58 **p** 59. C Newport Maindee St Jo Ev *Mon* 58-60; C Penhow, St Brides Netherwent w Llandavenny etc 60-63; V Magor w Redwick and Undy 63-68; Australia 68-71; R Kirkby Thore w Temple Sowerby *Carl* 72-73; R Kirkby Thore w Temple Sowerby and Newbiggin 73-79; P-in-c Accrington St Jas *Blackb* 79-81; P-in-c Accrington St Andr 81-83; Kuwait 83-91; R Swardeston w E Carleton, Intwood, Keswick etc *Nor* from 91. *The Vicarage, The Common, Swardeston, Norwich NR14 8AD* Mulbarton (01508) 570550

JONES, Canon Gordon Rowland. b 24. Oak Hill Th Coll 56. **d** 58 **p** 59. R Bath Walcot *B & W* 63-70; Dir Ext Studies St Jo Coll Nottm 70-73; V Orpington Ch Ch *Roch* 73-78; Sec for Chr Educn Tr 78-85; CPAS Evang 78-85; Hon C Southborough St Pet w Ch Ch and St Matt *Roch* 81-85; Hon Can Leic Cathl *Leic* 83-90; Zimbabwe 85-89; C Leic H Trin w St Jo *Leic* 89-90; rtd 91. *58 Queen's Road, Tunbridge Wells, Kent TN4 9JU* Tunbridge Wells (01892) 531336

JONES, Graham Frederick. b 37. Leeds Univ BA60 GradIPM63. ALCD66. **d** 66 **p** 67. C Chesterfield H Trin *Derby* 66-70; C Leeds St Geo *Ripon* 70-73; P-in-c Newc St Geo *Lich* 73-83; New Zealand 83-87; P-in-c Westcote w Icomb and Bledington *Glouc* 89-94; rtd 94. *7 Keynsham Bank, Cheltenham, Glos GL52 6ER* Cheltenham (01242) 238680

JONES, Griffith Bernard. b 20. Univ of Wales (Lamp) BA42. St Mich Coll Llan 42. **d** 44 **p** 45. Perm to Offic *Pet* 64-82; Perm to Offic *St Alb* 74-82; R Llanfallteg w Clunderwen and Castell Dwyran etc *St D* 82-88; rtd 88. *17 Heol Ceirios, Llandybie, Ammanford, Dyfed SA18 2SR* Llandybie (01269) 851060

JONES, Griffith Trevor. b 56. BSc MPS Univ of Wales B42. **d** 87 **p** 88. C Llandrygarn w Bodwrog and Heneglwys etc *Ban* 87-89; R Llangefni w Tregaean and Llangristiolus etc 89-91; TV Ban 91-94; Chapl Ysbyty Gwynedd 91-94; NSM Arfon Deanery

from 94. *8 Carreg-y-Gad, Llanfairpwllgwyngyll, Gwynedd LL61 6YD*

JONES, Preb Griffith Walter Hywyn. b 24. St Mich Coll Llan 47. **d** 50 **p** 51. V Bettws y Coed and Capel Curig *Ban* 70-78; R Holyhead w Rhoscolyn w Llanfair-yn-Neubwll 78-87; Can and Preb Ban Cathl 78-90; RD Llifon and Talybolion 80-85; Spiritual Dir Cursillo Cymru 81-90; V Ynyscynhaearn w Penmorfa and Porthmadog *Ban* 87-90; rtd 90. *The Vicarage, Glyn Ceiriog, Llangollen, Clwyd LL20 7EH* Glyn Ceiriog (01691) 718245

JONES, Canon Griffith William. b 31. St D Coll Lamp BA53 LTh55. **d** 55 **p** 56. C Llanycil w Bala and Frongoch *St As* 55-58; V Llandrillo 58-66; V Llandrillo and Llandderfel from 66; RD Penllyn from 83; Can Cursal St As Cathl from 87. *The Vicarage, Llandrillo, Corwen, Clwyd LL21 0SW* Llandrillo (0149084) 224

JONES, Gwyn Harris. b 19. Univ of Wales (Lamp) BA42. K Coll Lon 42. **d** 43 **p** 44. V Burton St Chad *Lich* 56-79; V Shrewsbury St Geo 79-87; rtd 87; Perm to Offic *Lich* from 87. *18 Kenwood Gardens, Shrewsbury SY3 8AQ* Shrewsbury (01743) 351057

JONES, Gwynfryn Lloyd. b 35. Univ of Wales (Lamp) BA59. St Mich Coll Llan 59. **d** 61 **p** 62. C Rhyl w St Ann *St As* 61-64; C Prestatyn 64-67; V Whitford 67-75; V Llay 75-83; V Northop from 83. *The Vicarage, Northop, Mold, Clwyd CH7 6BS* Northop (01352) 840235

JONES, Gwynn Rees. b 32. St D Coll Lamp BA55. **d** 57 **p** 58. C Llangystennin *St As* 57-59; C Llanrhos 59-64; R Cefn 64-68; R Llanfyllin 68-80; V Bistre 80-89; R Flint from 89. *The Rectory, Allt Goch, Flint, Clwyd CH6 5NF* Flint (01352) 733274

JONES, Gwynne Ifor. b 10. Jes Coll Ox BA36 MA38. **d** 70 **p** 71. Hon C Llangefni w Tregaean and Llangristiolus etc *Ban* 70-81; rtd 81. *Bryn Horton, Greenfield Avenue, Llangefni, Gwynedd LL77 7NU* Llangefni (01248) 723295

JONES, Canon Harold Desmond. b 22. Sarum Th Coll 52. **d** 55 **p** 56. V Thurleigh *St Alb* 64-80; V Milton Ernest 64-80; RD Sharnbrook 70-81; Hon Can St Alb 78-90; P-in-c Knotting w Souldrop 80-82; V Sharnbrook 80-82; R Sharnbrook and Knotting w Souldrop 82-90; P-in-c Felmersham 82-87; RD Sharnbrook 86-90; rtd 90. *24 Towns End Road, Sharnbrook, Bedford MK44 1HY* Bedford (01234) 782524

JONES, Harold Philip. b 49. Leeds Univ BA72 St Jo Coll Dur BA84. Cranmer Hall Dur 82. **d** 85 **p** 86. C Scartho *Linc* 85-88; V Dodworth *Wakef* 88-91; C Penistone and Thurlstone from 91. *19 Grasmere Close, Penistone, Sheffield S30 6HP* Barnsley (01226) 766282

JONES, Harry Gordon. b 18. Bps' Coll Cheshunt 49. **d** 52 **p** 53. V Hurley w Rhoscolyn *Ex* 64-70; V Salcombe *Ex* 70-79; P-in-c Abbotsham 79-83; rtd 83; Perm to Offic *Ex* 83-90. *The Highfield Manor Nursing Home, Bayview Road, Northam, Bideford, Devon EX39 1AY* Bideford (01237) 474563

JONES, Haydn Llewellyn. b 42. Edin Th Coll 63. **d** 65 **p** 66. C Towcester w Easton Neston *Pet* 65-68; C Northn St Matt 68-72; CF from 72. *c/o MOD (Army), Bagshot Park, Bagshot, Surrey GU19 5PL* Bagshot (01276) 471717 Fax 412834

JONES, Haydn Price. See PRICE-JONES, Haydn

✠**JONES, Rt Rev Haydon Harold.** b 20. **d** 47 **p** 48 **c** 76. C Heaton St Barn *Bradf* 47-49; C Tormohun *Ex* 49-51; C Cov St Pet *Cov* 63-64; R Clutton *B & W* 64-75; R Clutton w Cameley 75-76; Bp Venezuela 76-86; rtd 86. *Apartado 17 467, 1015-A, Caracas, Venezuela*

JONES, Howell Arfon. b 31. St Deiniol's Hawarden. **d** 83 **p** 84. Hon C Northwich St Luke and H Trin *Ches* 83-84; C Bromborough 84-86; C Nantwich 86-87; V Church Minshull w Leighton and Minshull Vernon 87-89; rtd 89. *8 Marton Close, Hough, Crewe CW2 5RD* Crewe (01270) 841389

JONES, Hugh Owen. b 14. Coates Hall Edin 45. **d** 47 **p** 48. V Bodenham w Hope-under-Dinmore *Heref* 63-78; R Bodenham w Hope-under-Dinmore, Felton etc 78-80; rtd 80; Perm to Offic *Heref* 80-95. *24 Tudor Court, Tudor Road, Llandudno, Gwynedd LL30 1BU* Llandudno (01492) 872849

JONES, Humphrey Ingham. b 20. St Pet Coll Ox BA42 MA46. Cuddesdon Coll 42. **d** 43 **p** 44. Tutor and Registrar Richmond Fellowship 68-85; Hon C Bermondsey St Mary w St Olave, St Jo etc *S'wark* 73-78; Perm to Offic *Lon* from 79; rtd 85. *28A Granville Gardens, London W5 3PA* 0181-992 2849

JONES, Hywel Tudor. b 13. St D Coll Lamp BA38. **d** 40 **p** 41. V Dafen *St D* 63-73; R Aber-porth w Tre-main and Blaen-porth 74-78; rtd 78. *Ardwyn, 27 Williams Terrace, Burry Port, Dyfed SA16 0PG* Burry Port (01554) 834321

JONES, Ian Andrew. b 65. Lanc Univ BA87. St Mich Coll Llan DPS90. **d** 90 **p** 91. C Caerphilly *Llan* from 90. *71 Bartlett Street, Caerphilly, M Glam CF8 1JT* Caerphilly (01222) 882695

JONES, Idris. b 31. **d** 88 **p** 94. NSM Llanfihangel Ysgeifiog and Llanffinan etc *Ban* from 88. *Rhoslyn, Gaerwen, Gwynedd LL60 6HR* Gaerwen (01248) 421797

JONES, Canon Idris. b 43. Univ of Wales (Lamp) BA64 Edin Univ LTh67. Edin Th Coll 64 NY Th Sem DMin86. **d** 67 **p** 68. C Stafford St Mary *Lich* 67-70; Prec St Paul's Cathl Dundee *Bre* 70-73; P-in-c Gosforth All SS *Newc* 73-80; R Montrose *Bre* 80-89; R Inverbervie 80-89; Can St Paul's Cathl Dundee 84-92; Chapl Angl Students Dundee Univ 89-92; P-in-c Invergowrie 89-92; R Ayr *Glas* from 92. *12 Barns Terrace, Ayr KA7 2DB* Ayr (01292) 262482

JONES, Canon Idwal. b 13. Univ of Wales BA36. St Mich Coll Llan 36. **d** 38 **p** 39. V Leamington Priors All SS *Cov* 63-79; Hon Can Cov Cathl 72-79; rtd 80; Perm to Offic *Cov* from 80. *Leam Cottage, Main Street, Birdingbury, Rugby, Warks CV23 8EL* Marton (01926) 632896

JONES, Ioan Wynne. b 66. Univ of Wales (Ban) DipTh. St Mich Coll Llan. **d** 91 **p** 92. C Llanbeblig w Caernarfon and Betws Garmon etc *Ban* 91-95; P-in-c Glanogwen from 95. *The Vicarage, 7 Rhos-y-Nant Estate, Bethesda, Bangor, Gwynedd LL57 3PP* Bethesda (01248) 600294

JONES, Iorwerth Owen. b 24. St D Coll Lamp BA51. **d** 53 **p** 55. V Tickhill w Stainton *Sheff* 68-80; R Elworth and Warmingham *Ches* 80-89; rtd 89. *22 Kings Oak Court, Wrexham, Clwyd LL13 8QH* Wrexham (01978) 353779

JONES, Ivor Wyn. b 56. Trin Coll Bris DipHE94. **d** 94 **p** 95. C Gabalfa *Llan* from 94. *27 Pen-y-Bryn Road, Cardiff CF4 3LG* Cardiff (01222) 619556

JONES, Jack Kenneth. b 23. DGA MIPD. E Anglian Minl Tr Course 83. **d** 84 **p** 85. C Fakenham w Alethorpe *Nor* 84-88; C Gt w Lt Snoring w Kettlestone and Pensthorpe 84-93; Perm to Offic from 93. *The Tunns, Great Snoring, Fakenham, Norfolk NR21 0HN* Fakenham (01328) 820441

JONES, James Morgan. b 07. TD47. **d** 57 **p** 58. R Coychurch w Llangan and St Mary Hill *Llan* 67-77; rtd 77; Perm to Offic *Llan* from 77. *4 Woodlands Rise, Bridgend, M Glam CF31 4SW* Bridgend (01656) 662070

✠**JONES, Rt Rev James Stuart.** b 48. Ex Univ BA70 PGCE71. Wycliffe Hall Ox 81. **d** 82 **p** 83 **c** 94. C Clifton Ch Ch w Em *Bris* 82-90; V S Croydon Em *S'wark* 90-94; Suff Bp Hull *York* from 94. *Hullen House, Woodfield Lane, Hessle, N Humberside HU3 0ES* Hull (01482) 649019 or 863171 Fax 647449

JONES, Miss Jaqueline Dorian. b 58. K Coll Lon BD80 AKC80. Westcott Ho Cam 84. **dss** 86 **d** 87 **p** 94. Epsom St Martin *Guildf* 86-87; C 87-91; Chapl Chelmsf Cathl *Chelmsf* from 91. *7 Rainsford Avenue, Chelmsford CM1 2PJ* Chelmsford (01245) 350362

JONES, Jennifer Margaret. b 49. Lon Univ CertEd. Cranmer Hall Dur 87. **d** 89 **p** 94. C Musselburgh *Edin* 89-93; D-in-c 93-94; P-in-c from 94; C Prestonpans 89-93; D-in-c 93-94; P-in-c from 94. *12 Windsor Gardens, Musselburgh, Midlothian TD11 3SG* 0131-665 2925

JONES, John Bernard. b 49. Qu Coll Birm 86. **d** 88 **p** 89. C Mold *St As* 88-91; P-in-c Treuddyn and Nercwys and Eryrys 91-92; V Treuddyn w Nercwys from 92; RD Mold from 95. *The Vicarage, Treuddyn, Mold, Clwyd CH7 4LN* Pontybodkin (01352) 770919

JONES, John Douglas Mathias. b 24. Clare Coll Cam BA49 MA51. Chich Th Coll 49. **d** 51 **p** 52. V Cross Stone *Wakef* 67-76; V Hepworth 76-89; Chapl Storthes Hall Hosp Wakef 81-89; rtd 89. *59 Luke Lane, Holmfirth, Huddersfield HD7 2SZ* Holmfirth (01484) 681036

JONES, Canon John Francis Williams. b 26. St D Coll Lamp 48. **d** 52 **p** 53. C Glanadda *Ban* 52-55; V Porthmadog 55-57; V Llandrygarn w Bodwrog 57-62; V Llandrygarn and Bodwrog w Heneglwys 62-74; V Llandrygarn w Bodwrog and Heneglwys etc from 74; RD Menai and Malltraeth from 75; Hon Can Ban Cathl 81-83; Can from 83; Preb from 90. *The Vicarage, Llandrygarn, Llanerchymedd, Gwynedd LL65 3AZ* Gwalchmai (01407) 720234

JONES, John Harries. b 11. **d** 60 **p** 61. R Llanbedr y Cennin w Dolgarrog, Trefriw etc *Ban* 67-74; R Llanbeulan w Llanfaelog and Tal-y-llyn 74-81; rtd 81. *1 Cerrig-y-Gad, Llanfairpwllgwyngyll, Gwynedd LL61 5QF* Llanfairpwll (01248) 713756

JONES, John Hellyer. b 20. Birm Univ LDS43. Westcott Ho Cam 65. **d** 67 **p** 68. C Haddenham *Ely* 67-70; P-in-c Lolworth 70-79 and 81-85; P-in-c Fen Drayton w Conington 75-79; R Houghton w Wyton 79; rtd 85; Perm to Offic *Ely* from 85. *13 High Street, Haddenham, Ely, Cambs CB6 3XA* Ely (01353) 740530

JONES, John Howard. b 48. New Coll Ox BA69 MA73 K Coll Cam CertEd70. Sarum & Wells Th Coll 76. **d** 77 **p** 78. C Salisbury St Mark *Sarum* 77-78; C Morriston *S & B* 78-80; Dir of Ords 80-83; V Gowerton 80-83; V Swansea St Jas 85-89; Chapl Alleyn's Foundn Dulwich from 89. *53 Gilkes Crescent, London SE21 7BP* 0181-299 4826

JONES, John Idris. b 16. St D Coll Lamp BA41. **d** 43 **p** 44. V Llay *St As* 66-75; rtd 75. *7 Patricia Drive, Shrewsbury SY2 5YU*

JONES, Ven John Jenkin. b 15. Univ Coll Dur BA39 DipTh40 MA42. **d** 40 **p** 41. V Holywell *St As* 60-71; RD Holywell 69-71; Can St As Cathl 70-74; V Llanrhos 71-76; Adn St As 74-84; V Whitford 76-80; rtd 84; Perm to Offic *St As* from 84. *Dorlan, Pentre Llanrhaeadr, Denbigh, Clwyd LL16 4YN* Llanynys (0174578) 447

JONES, John Morgan. b 17. Univ of Wales BA39. Ely Th Coll 39. **d** 40 **p** 41. R Adwick-le-Street *Sheff* 60-63; rtd 82; Perm to Offic *St As* from 82. *3 Heol Awel, Abergele, Clwyd LL22 7UQ* Abergele (01745) 823515

JONES, John Samuel. b 11. Univ of Wales BA36. St D Coll Lamp 36. **d** 38 **p** 40. V Llanfair D C *St As* 72-79; rtd 79. *51 Snowden Drive, Ty Gwyn, Wrexham, Clwyd LL11 2YD* Wrexham (01978) 364914

JONES, Ven John Samuel. b 16. Univ of Wales (Lamp) BA37 BD42. St Mich Coll Llan 38. **d** 39 **p** 40. V Llanllwni *St D* 49-86; RD Lamp and Ultra-Aeron 68-82; Can St D Cathl 72-82; Chan 78-82; Adn Cardigan 82-86; rtd 86. *Bryheulwen, Bryn Road, Lampeter, Dyfed SA48 7EE* Lampeter (01570) 423278

JONES, John Trevor. b 14. St D Coll Lamp BA42. **d** 43 **p** 44. V Poulton *Ches* 60-81; rtd 81; Perm to Offic *Ches* from 82. *21 Sandy Lane, Wallasey, Merseyside L45 3JY* 0151-639 4794

JONES (nee HUBBARD), Ms Judith Frances. b 49. St Alb Minl Tr Scheme 79. **dss** 82 **d** 87 **p** 94. Hemel Hempstead *St Alb* 82-86; Longden and Annscroft w Pulverbatch *Heref* 86-87; Hon C from 87; Vice Prin Glouc & Heref Sch for Min from 92. *Moorcott, Ivington Green, Leominster, Herefordshire HR6 0JN* Ivington (01568) 888311 Fax as telephone

JONES, Canon Keith Brynmor. b 44. Selw Coll Cam BA65 MA69. Cuddesdon Coll 67. **d** 69 **p** 70. C Limpsfield and Titsey *S'wark* 69-72; Dean's V St Alb Abbey *St Alb* 72-76; P-in-c Boreham Wood St Mich 76-79; TV Borehamwood 79-82; V Ipswich St Mary le Tower w St Lawr and St Steph *St E* 82-84; V Ipswich St Mary-le-Tower from 84; RD Ipswich from 92; Hon Can St E Cathl from 93. *St Mary le Tower Vicarage, 8 Fonnereau Road, Ipswich IP1 3JP* Ipswich (01473) 252770

JONES, Keith Bythell. b 35. ACP BA DipHE CertEd. Trin Coll Bris. **d** 83 **p** 84. C Bris St Mary Redcliffe w Temple etc *Bris* 83-86; C Filton 86-88; TV Yate New Town from 88. *The Vicarage, Shorthill Road, Westerleigh, Bristol BS17 4QN* Chipping Sodbury (01454) 312152

JONES, Keith Ellison. b 47. Wycliffe Hall Ox 72. **d** 75 **p** 76. C Everton St Chrys *Liv* 75-79; C Buckhurst Hill *Chelmsf* 79-81; TV 81-88; TR Leek and Meerbrook *Lich* from 88. *The Vicarage, 6 Church Street, Leek, Staffs ST13 6AB* Leek (01538) 382515

JONES, Kenneth Elwyn. b 32. Nottm Univ BA54 Sheff Univ CertEd55 DipEd55. Linc Th Coll 80. **d** 82 **p** 83. C Rotherham *Sheff* 82-85; R Harthill and Thorpe Salvin 85-93; V Millhouses H Trin from 93; RD Ecclesall from 94. *Holy Trinity Vicarage, 80 Millhouses Lane, Sheffield S7 2HB* Sheffield (0114) 236 2838

JONES, Kenneth John. b 26. ALCD53. **d** 53 **p** 54. V Creech St Michael *B & W* 65-91; rtd 91; Perm to Offic *B & W* from 91. *43 Wansbeck Green, Taunton, Somerset TA1 2RE* Taunton (01823) 331149

JONES, Canon Kenneth William. b 14. TD61. St D Coll Lamp BA36 St Mich Coll Llan 36. **d** 38 **p** 39. V Hove St Jo *Chich* 66-77; R Buxted St Marg 77-81; P-in-c High Hurstwood 78-81; rtd 82; Perm to Offic *Chich* from 82. *2/13 Grange Gardens, Eastbourne, E Sussex BN20 7DA* Eastbourne (01323) 642553

JONES, Kingsley Charles. b 45. Birm Univ BSc66 Open Univ BA75. Sarum Th Coll 66. **d** 69 **p** 70. C Penwortham St Mary *Blackb* 69-72; C Broughton 72-74; P-in-c Gt Wollaston *Heref* 74-77; Chapl RAF 77-83; V Colwich w Gt Haywood *Lich* 83-94; V Winshill *Derby* from 94. *The Vicarage, Mill Hill Lane, Burton-on-Trent, Staffs DE15 0BB* Burton-on-Trent (01283) 545043

JONES, Leslie Joseph. b 23. Linc Th Coll. **d** 57 **p** 58. V Bedminster St Aldhelm *Bris* 69-75; TV Bedminster 75-80; V Abbots Leigh w Leigh Woods 80-88; rtd 88; Perm to Offic *Bris* from 88. *4 Summerleaze, Bristol BS16 4ER* Bristol (0117) 965 3597

JONES, Leslie Lloyd. b 13. OBE. BA. **d** 39 **p** 41. CF 42-73; Chapl Gov of Gib 68-72; V Yarcombe w Membury *Ex* 73-83; V Yarcombe w Membury and Upottery 83-84; rtd 84; Perm to Offic *Ex* from 84. *Lower Farway, Chardstock, Axminster, Devon EX13 7DD* Chard (01460) 20397

JONES, Miss Mair. b 41. Cartrefle Coll of Educn TCert61 DSpEd73. St Mich Coll Llan DipPTh93. **d** 93. C Llangollen w Trevor and Llantysilio *St As* from 93. *Homelea, Aber Adda, Hill Street, Llangollen, Clwyd LL20 8HE* Llangollen (01978) 861768

JONES, Malcolm Francis. b 44. Open Univ BA88. Chich Th Coll 67. **d** 70 **p** 71. C Prestbury *Ches* 70-73; Chapl RAF 73-81; Perm to Offic *Ox* 75-77; R Heaton Reddish *Man* 81-84; CF (TA) 82-84; Chapl ACF 82-84; OStJ from 84; CF 84-93; Perm to Offic *Guildf* 88-93; TV Cleethorpes *Linc* from 93. *The*

Vicarage, 3 Taylor's Avenue, Cleethorpes, S Humberside DN35 0LF Cleethorpes (01472) 604598

JONES, Malcolm Stuart. b 41. Sheff Univ BA62. Linc Th Coll 64. d 66 p 67. C Monkseaton St Mary *Newc* 66-69; C Ponteland 69-72; Venezuela 73-75; C Hexham *Newc* 75-77; P-in-c Killingworth 77-92; V Delaval from 92. *The Vicarage, Seaton Sluice, Whitley Bay, Tyne & Wear NE26 4QW* 0191-237 1982

JONES, Maldwyn Lloyd. b 17. St D Coll Lamp BA39. d 40 p 41. USA 68-70; Chapl Lon Nautical Sch 71-72; Lic to Offic *Ban* 72-82; rtd 82; Perm to Offic *Ban* from 82. *The Old Post Office, Tirley, Gloucester GL19 4ES*

JONES, Ms Margaret. b 28. TCD BA53 Lon Univ BD66. d 87 p 94. NSM Stanstead Abbots *St Alb* 87-88; NSM Grappenhall *Ches* from 89. *19 Hill Top Road, Grappenhall, Warrington WA4 2ED* Warrington (01925) 261992

JONES, Margaret Mary (Maggi). b 47. Oak Hill Th Coll 92. d 95. C Sydenham H Trin *S'wark* from 95. *56 Sydenham Park Road, London SE26 4DY* 0181-473 3397

JONES, Mark Andrew. b 60. Southn Univ BSc82 Sussex Univ PGCE83. Oak Hill Th Coll BA91. d 91 p 92. C Wolv St Luke *Lich* from 91. *36 Pencombe Drive, Park Hall Estate, Wolverhampton WV4 5EW* Wolverhampton (01902) 337745

JONES, Mark Vincent. b 60. Univ of Wales (Cardiff) DipTh84. St Mich Coll Llan 81. d 84 p 85. C Whitchurch *Llan* 84-89; V Pwllgwaun w Llanddewi Rhondda 89-90; CF from 90. *c/o MOD (Army), Bagshot Park, Bagshot, Surrey GU19 5PL* Bagshot (01276) 471717 Fax 412834

JONES, Mrs Mary Nerissa Anna. b 41. Qu Mary Coll Lon BA86. Ripon Coll Cuddesdon 86. d 88 p 94. Par Dn St Botolph Aldgate w H Trin Minories *Lon* 88-93; P-in-c Wood End *Cov* from 93. *St Chad's Vicarage, Hillmorton Road, Coventry CV2 1FY* Coventry (01203) 612909

JONES, Mary Valerie. b 37. Univ of Wales (Ban) BD84. St Deiniol's Hawarden 84. d 85. C Holyhead w Rhoscolyn w Llanfair-yn-Neubwll *Ban* 85-87; C Ynyscynhaearn w Penmorfa and Porthmadog 87-90; D-in-c Llansantffraid and Llanarmon and Pontfadog *St As* from 90. *The Vicarage, Glyn Ceiriog, Llangollen, Clwyd LL20 7EH* Glyn Ceiriog (01691) 718245

JONES, Maurice Hughes Rowlestone. b 06. d 47 p 48. Chapl Mt Pleasant Hosp 62-75; V Southall H Trin *Lon* 62-75; rtd 75; Perm to Offic *Glouc* 75-90. *75 Medoc Close, Wymans Brook, Cheltenham, Glos GL50 4SP* Cheltenham (01242) 230328

JONES, Maurice Maxwell Hughes. b 32. Lon Univ DipTh58 Univ of Wales (Cardiff) DPS72. Clifton Th Coll 56. d 60 p 61. C Islington St Andr w St Thos and St Matthias *Lon* 60-63; Argentina 63-71; C Whitchurch *Llan* 72-73; Area Sec (NW England) SAMS 73-77; V Haydock St Mark *Liv* 78-87; V Paddington Em Harrow Road *Lon* from 87. *Emmanuel Vicarage, 28 Windermere Avenue, London NW6 6LN* 0181-969 0438

JONES, Melville Kenneth. b 40. Open Univ BA82. St D Coll Lamp DipTh66. d 66 p 67. C Aberdare St Jo *Llan* 66-71; C Caerau w Ely 71-72; Chapl Pontypridd Hosps 72-89; V Graig *Llan* 72-89; P-in-c Cilfynydd 86-89; V Llantwit Fadre from 89; Chapl E Glam Hosp from 89. *The Vicarage, Upper Church Village, Pontypridd, M Glam CF38 1EP* Pontypridd (01443) 202538

JONES, Michael. b 49. Leeds Univ BA71 Man Univ MA73. Qu Coll Birm 83. d 85 p 86. C Leigh St Mary *Man* 85-88; C-in-c Holts CD 88-93; V Hamer from 93. *All Saints' Vicarage, Foxholes Road, Rochdale, Lancs OL12 0EF* Rochdale (01706) 355591

JONES, Michael Denis Dyson. b 39. CCC Cam BA62 MA66 Lon Univ MSc73. Wycliffe Hall Ox DipTh75. d 76 p 77. C Plymouth St Andr w St Paul and St Geo *Ex* 76-81; V Devonport St Budeaux from 81; RD Plymouth Devonport from 93. *The Vicarage, Agaton Road, Plymouth PL5 2EW* Plymouth (01752) 361019

JONES, Dr Michael Emlyn. b 47. MRCP75 Aber Univ MB, ChB72. d 79 p 79. Tanzania 79-82; Hon C Duns *Edin* from 83. *Ellem Lodge, Duns, Berwickshire TD11 3SG* Longformacus (013617) 316 Fax 329

JONES, Canon Neville Charles. b 42. Univ of Wales BA63 K Coll Lon BD66 AKC66. d 67 p 68. C Holywell *St As* 67-69; C Rhyl w St Ann 69-73; C Christchurch *Win* 73-77; V Stanmore 77-84; RD Win 82-84; V Romsey from 84; RD Romsey 89-94; Hon Can Win Cathl from 93. *The Vicarage, Romsey, Hants SO51 8EP* Romsey (01794) 513125

JONES, Canon Neil Crawford. b 29. Selw Coll Cam BA52 MA57. Linc Th Coll 52. d 54 p 55. V Stockton H Trin *Dur* 69-73; TR Cen Stockton 73-76; P-in-c Elton 75-76; R Longnewton 76; R Longnewton w Elton 76-83; P-in-c 87-93; RD Stockton 77-83; Hon Can Dur Cathl 81-93; Chapl Camerton Hosp Hartlepool 83-85; V Heighington *Dur* 83;

Bp's Dom Chapl 85-93; Hon C Norton St Mary 85-87; rtd 93; Perm to Offic *Pet* from 93. *2 Grange Road, Peterborough PE3 6DR* Peterborough (01733) 69830

JONES, Neville George. b 36. Univ of Wales (Ban) BA59. St Mich Coll Llan 59. d 61 p 62. C Broughton *St As* 61-65; C Newc *Llan* 65-68; V Laleston w Tythegston and Merthyr Mawr 68-84; V Llanishen and Lisvane 84-93; V Llanishen from 93. *The Vicarage, 2 The Rise, Llanishen, Cardiff CF4 5RA* Cardiff (01222) 752545

JONES, Nicholas Godwin. b 58. St Jo Coll Cam BA81 MA84 Hughes Hall Cam PGCE90. Ridley Hall Cam CTM93. d 93 p 94. C Cam H Trin *Ely* from 93. *42 Pretoria Road, Cambridge CB4 1HE* Cambridge (01223) 311144

JONES, Nicholas Newman. b 51. K Coll Lon 71 St Aug Coll Cant 74. d 75 p 76. C Derringham Bank *York* 75-78; C Stokesley 78-81; P-in-c Kirby Misperton 81-85; R Normanby w Edston and Salton 83-85; R Kirby Misperton w Normanby, Edston and Salton 85-87; V Eskdaleside w Ugglebarnby and Sneaton from 87; RD Whitby from 92. *The Vicarage, 22 Eskdaleside, Sleights, Whitby, N Yorkshire YO22 5EP* Whitby (01947) 810349

JONES, Nicholas Peter. b 55. St Mich Coll Llan DipTh82. d 82 p 83. C St Andrew's Major and Michaelston-le-Pit *Llan* 82-84; C Aberdare St Jo 84-88; Youth Chapl 85-89; V Abercynon from 88. *The Vicarage, Abercynon, Mountain Ash, M Glam CF45 3NE* Abercynon (01443) 740207

JONES, Nigel Ivor. b 54. Birm Univ CPS89. W Midl Minl Tr Course 91. d 94 p 95. C Shirley *Birm* from 94. *51 Moreton Road, Shirley, Solihull, W Midlands B90 3AH* 0121-745 1325

✠**JONES, Rt Rev Noel Debroy.** b 32. CB86. Univ of Wales (Lamp) BA53. Wells Th Coll 53. d 55 p 56 c 89. C Tredegar St Jas *Mon* 55-57; C Newport St Mark 57-60; Nigeria 60-62; Chapl RN 62-84; Chapl of the Fleet and Adn for the RN 84-89; QHC 83-89; Hon Can Gib Cathl *Eur* 86-89; Bp S & M from 89. *The Bishop's House, Quarterbridge Road, Douglas, Isle of Man IM2 3RF* Douglas (01624) 622108 Fax 672890

JONES, Norman. b 35. St Deiniol's Hawarden 83. d 85 p 86. C Brecon St Mary and Battle w Llanddew *S & B* 85-91; Min Can Brecon Cathl 85-91; V Brynmawr from 91. *The Vicarage, Dumfries Place, Brynmawr, Gwent NP3 2RA* Brynmawr (01495) 312297

JONES, Norman. b 50. Oak Hill Th Coll BA83. d 83 p 84. C Ulverston St Mary w H Trin *Carl* 83-87; Hong Kong 88-92; TR Eccles *Man* from 92; P-in-c Patricroft from 95. *The Rectory, 12B Westminster Road, Eccles, Manchester M30 9EB* 0161-789 1034 Fax 789 1034

JONES, Mrs Patricia Anne. b 55. NNEB75 CSS81. Oak Hill Th Coll 92. d 95. NSM Mill Hill Jo Keble Ch *Lon* from 95. *The Flat, St Paul's School, The Ridgeway, London NW7 1QU* 0181-201 1583

JONES, Patrick Geoffrey Dickson. b 28. Ch Ch Ox MA55. St Deiniol's Hawarden 79. d 82 p 83. Hon C Sandbach *Ches* 82-84; P-in-c Braemar *Ab* 84-94; R Aboyne 84-94; R Ballater 84-94; rtd 94. *12 Bridge Street, Ballater, Aberdeenshire AB35 5QP* Ballater (01339) 755169

JONES, Patrick George. b 42. Lich Th Coll 69. d 72 p 73. C Chesterton St Geo *Ely* 72-75; P-in-c Waterbeach 75-78; P-in-c Landbeach 76-78; R Charlton-in-Dover *Cant* 78-90; Cautley Trust from 90. *Cautley House, 95 Seabrook Road, Seabrook, Hythe, Kent CT21 5QV* Hythe (01303) 230762

JONES, Paul Harwood. b 20. Qu Coll Birm 51. d 53 p 54. V White Notley w Faulkbourne *Chelmsf* 68-81; P-in-c Cressing 75-80; V Finchingfield and Cornish Hall End 81-88; RD Braintree 83-87; rtd 88; Perm to Offic *Chelmsf* from 88. *83 Kenworthy Road, Braintree, Essex CM7 7JJ* Braintree (01376) 343047

JONES, Paul Terence. b 35. Dur Univ BA60. Qu Coll Birm 60. d 62 p 63. C Rainford *Liv* 62-65; C Skelmersdale St Paul 65-68; V Huyton Quarry 68-78; V Widnes St Ambrose from 78. *St Ambrose Vicarage, Hargreaves Court, Widnes, Cheshire WA8 0QA* 0151-420 8044

JONES, Ms Penelope Howson. b 58. LGSM79 Girton Coll Cam BA80 MA83. Ripon Coll Cuddesdon BA85 MA88. dss 86 d 87 p 94. Hackney *Lon* 86-87; Par Dn 87-88; Tutor Ripon Coll Cuddesdon 88-90; Par Dn Cuddesdon *Ox* 88-90; Perm to Offic *Dur* 92-93; Dir of Practical Th NE Ord Course *Newc* from 93. *3 Wordsworth Street, Gateshead, Tyne & Wear NE8 3HE* 0191-478 2730

JONES, Peter Anthony Watson. b 53. AKC75. Sarum & Wells Th Coll 76. d 77 p 78. C Hessle *York* 77-81; C Stainton-in-Cleveland 81-82; P-in-c Weston Mill *Ex* 82-84; Chapl Plymouth Poly 82-90; V Gt Ayton w Easby and Newton in Cleveland *York* 90-92; C Devonport St Aubyn *Ex* from 92. *12 Cumberland Street, Plymouth PL1 4DX* Plymouth (01752) 509605

JONES (formerly TITCOMBE), Peter Charles. b 57. St Mich Coll Llan DipTh83. d 83 p 84. C Pontnewynydd *Mon* 83-85; C Bassaleg 85-86; C Cwmbran 87; TV 87-94; V Blaenavon w

JONES

Capel Newydd from 94. *The Vicarage, Church Road, Blaenavon, Gwent NP4 9BE* Blaenavon (01495) 790292

JONES, Peter David. b 48. S'wark Ord Course 89. d 92 p 93. Hon C Caterham S'wark from 92. *79 Beverley Road, Whyteleafe, Surrey CR3 0DG* 0181-668 6398

JONES, Peter Gordon Lewis. b 31. d 82 p 83. NSM Llangynwyd w Maesteg *Llan* 82-84; Deputation Appeals Org (S & M Glam) CECS 84-87; Appeals Manager (Wales and Glouc) Children's Soc from 87; NSM Pyle w Kenfig *Llan* from 89. *18 Fulmar Road, Porthcawl, M Glam CF36 3UL* Porthcawl (01656) 715455

JONES, Peter Robin. b 42. BA CertEd. E Midl Min Tr Course 79. d 82 p 83. NSM Doveridge *Derby* from 82. *4 Cross Road, Uttoxeter, Staffs ST14 7BN* Uttoxeter (01889) 565123

JONES, Peter Russell. b 48. St Jo Coll Cam BA71 MA75 Univ of Wales MTh86. Wycliffe Hall Ox DipTh72. d 75 p 76. C Northn All SS w St Kath *Pet* 75-79; C Ban Cathl Par *Ban* 79-81; Min Can Ban Cathl 79-81; R Pentraeth and Llanddyfnan 81-85; V Conwy w Gyffin from 85; Lect Univ of Wales (Ban) from 89. *The Vicarage, Conwy, Gwynedd LL32 8LD* Aberconwy (01492) 593402

JONES, Canon Philip Bryan. b 34. St Mich Coll Llan DipTh61. d 61 p 62. C Hope *St As* 61-64; C Llanrhos 64-67; V Kerry 67-74; R Newtown w Llanllwchaiarn w Aberhafesp from 74; RD Cedewain from 76; Sec Ch in Wales Prov Evang Cttee 80-83; Hon Can St As Cathl *St As* 86-93; Can from 93. *The Rectory, Old Kerry Road, Newtown, Powys SY16 1BP* Newtown (01686) 625795

JONES, Philip Hugh. b 51. Solicitor. Chich Th Coll 92. d 94 p 95. C Horsham *Chich* from 94. *18 Queensway, Horsham, W Sussex RG13 5AY* Horsham (01403) 252986

JONES, Phillip Edmund. b 56. Man Poly BA78 Fitzw Coll Cam BA84 MA88. Westcott Ho Cam 82. d 85 p 86. C Stafford St Jo and Tixall w Ingestre *Lich* 85-89; TV Redditch, The Ridge *Worc* 89-95; Ind Chapl from 89; TV Worc SE from 95. *The Vicarage, Walkers Lane, Whittington, Worcs WR5 2RE* Worcester (01905) 358989

JONES, Raymond Blake. b 29. K Coll Lon BD54 AKC54. d 55 p 56. R Braiseworth *St E* 66-76; V Eye 66-76; P-in-c Yaxley 74-77; RD Hartismere 76-77; V Eye w Braiseworth and Yaxley 77; R Ufford 77-82; V Southbourne St Kath *Win* 82-95; rtd 95. *4 Russell Drive, Riverslea, Christchurch, Dorset BH23 3PA* Christchurch (01202) 473205

JONES, Raymond Powell. b 21. JP63. St D Dioc Tr Course. d 82 p 83. NSM Betws St Dav w Ammanford *St D* 82-86; rtd 86. *227 Pen-y-Banc Road, Ammanford, Dyfed SA18 3QP* Ammanford (01269) 592069

JONES, Raymond Sydney. b 35. MSERT71. Glouc Th Course 85. d 87 p 88. NSM Madley *Heref* 87-89; NSM Preston-on-Wye w Blakemere 87-89; NSM Madley w Tyberton, Preston-on-Wye and Blakemere from 89. *Birch Hill, Clehonger, Hereford HR2 9SY* Golden Valley (01981) 250452

JONES, Raymond Trevor (Ray). b 35. Linc Th Coll. d 82 p 83. C Rushmere *St E* 82-85; Bp's Dom Chapl 85-86; CF 86-91; TV Ridgeway *Sarum* from 91; Relig Programmes Producer BBC Wiltshire Sound from 91. *The Vicarage, Ogbourne St George, Marlborough, Wilts SN8 1SU* Ogbourne St George (01672) 841248

JONES, Richard. b 23. St Deiniol's Hawarden 74. d 76 p 77. NSM Welshpool w Castle Caereinion *St As* 76-94; rtd 94. *Sherwood, Rhos Common, Llandrinio, Llanymynech, Powys SY22 6RN* Llanymynech (01691) 830534

JONES, Canon Richard. b 28. St D Coll Lamp 54. d 56 p 57. C Llanaber w Caerdeon *Ban* 56-61; R Aberffraw w Llangwyfan 61-74; CF (TA) 61-71; V Llanfairisgaer *Ban* 74-79; Bp's Private Chapl 78-82; V Llanfair-is-gaer and Llanddeiniolen 79-89; RD Arfon 82-89; Can Ban Cathl from 86; V Llandegfan w Llandysilio from 89; Chapl ATC from 90. *The Vicarage, Mount Street, Menai Bridge, Gwynedd LL57 5BW* Menai Bridge (01248) 712385

JONES, Canon Richard. b 36. Ely Th Coll 61. d 64 p 65. C Blyth St Mary *Newc* 64-67; C Wallsend St Pet 67-69; R Paisley H Trin *Glas* 69-78; R Monifieth *Bre* from 78; Hon Can St Paul's Cathl Dundee from 93. *The Rectory, 29 Princes Street, Monifieth, Angus DD5 4AW* Monifieth (01382) 532266

JONES, Richard Eifion. b 23. St D Dioc Tr Course 80 St Mich Coll Llan 84. d 82 p 83. NSM Llangennech and Hendy *St D* 82-84; C Llanbadarn Fawr w Capel Bangor and Goginan 84-86; V Llangadog and Gwynfe w Llanddeusant 86-91; rtd 91. *Ynysdawel, Church Street, Llangadog, Dyfed SA19 9AA* Llangadog (01550) 777061

JONES, Richard Keith. b 40. Jes Coll Ox BA63. Wycliffe Hall Ox 61. d 63 p 64. C Blaenavon w Capel Newydd *Mon* 63-67; C Mynyddislwyn 67-71; C Pontypool 71; V Abercarn 71-81; V Penhow, St Brides Netherwent w Llandavenny etc 81-88. *3 Llanover Road Close, Blaenavon, Gwent NP4 9LT* Penhow (01633) 400901

JONES, Richard Martin Hugh. b 31. St D Coll Lamp 56. d 58 p 59. C Swansea St Pet *S & B* 58-63; R Llangynllo and Bleddfa 63-70; R Llandefalle w Llyswen, Boughrood etc 70-83; RD Hay 81-85 and 87-90; V Llandefalle and Llyswen w Boughrood etc from 83. *The Rectory, Church Lane, Llyswen, Brecon, Powys LD3 0UU* Llyswen (01874) 754255

JONES, Robert. b 26. Lon Univ BA52 K Coll Lon BD65 Hull Univ MA82. St Deiniol's Hawarden 79. d 80 p 81. NSM Doncaster St Mary *Sheff* 80-81; C Halifax St Jo Bapt *Wakef* 81-82; C Halifax 83; P-in-c Dewsbury St Mark 83-84; TV Dewsbury 84-92; rtd 92; NSM Halifax St Jo Cragg Vale *Wakef* 92-95; Perm to Offic from 95. *4 Lidget Street, Huddersfield HD3 3JB* Huddersfield (01484) 658885

JONES, Robert. b 40. d 80 p 81. C St Laurence in the Isle of Thanet *Cant* 80-83. *76 Southwood Gardens, Ramsgate, Kent CT11 0BQ*

JONES, Robert (Bob). b 45. Culham Coll Ox CertEd67. St Steph Ho Ox. d 85 p 86. C High Wycombe *Ox* 85-89; V Beckenham St Barn *Roch* 89-90; C Swanley St Mary 90-91; C Edenbridge from 91; C Crockham Hill H Trin from 91. *The Vicarage, Crockham Hill, Edenbridge, Kent TN8 6RL* Edenbridge (01732) 866515

JONES, Robert Bernard. b 24. St Jo Coll Dur BA48. Wycliffe Hall Ox. d 50 p 51. V Ringwood *Win* 61-75; R N Stoneham 75-89; rtd 89. *4 Rowden Close, West Wellow, Romsey, Hants SO51 6RF* West Wellow (01794) 22966

JONES, Robert Cecil. b 32. Univ of Wales (Abth) BA54 DipEd55. Qu Coll Birm 84. d 86 p 87. C Llanbadarn Fawr w Capel Bangor and Goginan *St D* 86-88; R Llanllwchaearn and Llanina 88-91; R Newport w Cilgwyn and Dinas w Llanllawer from 91. *The Rectory, Long Street, Newport, Dyfed SA42 0TY* Newport (01239) 820380

JONES, Canon Robert Dwyfor. b 20. Univ of Wales (Ban) BA41. St Mich Coll Llan 46. d 47 p 48. V Conwy w Gyffin *Ban* 69-85; Can and Treas Ban Cathl 76-85; rtd 85; Perm to Offic *St As* from 85; Perm to Offic *Ban* from 85. *Ormlea, 12 Hywel Place, Llandudno, Gwynedd LL30 1EF* Llandudno (01492) 874390

JONES, Robert George. d 95. NSM Treboeth *S & B* from 95. *Green Gables, 42 Heol Fach, Treboeth, Swansea SA5 9DE*

JONES, Robert George. b 55. Hatf Coll Dur BA77 Ox Univ BA79 MA87. Ripon Coll Cuddesdon 77. d 80 p 81. C Foley Park *Worc* 80-84; V Dudley St Fran 84-92; TR Worc St Barn w Ch Ch from 92. *St Barnabas' Vicarage, Church Road, Worcester WR3 8NX* Worcester (01905) 23785

JONES, Robert Ivan. b 33. CertEd CertRK. Westcott Ho Cam 85. d 85 p 86. NSM Wymondham *Nor* 85-86; C Epsom St Martin *Guildf* 87-89; V Hutton Cranswick w Skerne, Watton and Beswick *York* 89-94; RD Harthill from 92; V Wetwang and Garton-on-the-Wolds w Kirkburn from 94. *The Vicarage, Wetwang, Driffield, N Humberside YO25 9XT* Driffield (01377) 236410

JONES, Robert William. b 55. d 79 p 80. C Seapatrick *D & D* 79; C Ban Abbey 81-83; I Drumgath w Drumgooland and Clonduff 83-89; I Finaghy *Conn* 89-93; I Kilwaughter w Cairncastle and Craigy Hill from 94. *Cairncastle Rectory, 15 Cairncastle Road, Ballygally, Larne, Co Antrim BT40 2RB* Larne (01574) 583220

JONES, Robert William Aplin. b 32. FRSC71 CChem72 Univ of Wales (Cardiff) BSc52 MSc65. St Deiniol's Hawarden 72. d 73 p 74. C Bassaleg *Mon* 73-77; V Nantyglo 77-82; Perm to Offic 82-86; R Colwinston w Llandow and Llysworney *Llan* from 86. *The Rectory, Llandow, Cowbridge, S Glam CF7 7NT* Wick (01656) 890205

JONES, Canon Robin Lang Wilson. b 07. Worc Coll Ox BA28 MA33. St Mich Coll Llan 41. d 41 p 42. R Warcop w Musgrave *Carl* 59-72; Hon Can Carl Cathl 64-72; rtd 72; Perm to Offic *Carl* from 77. *Abbeyfield, The Gables, Kirkby Lonsdale, Carnforth, Lancs LA6 2BD* Kirkby Lonsdale (015242) 71576

JONES, Roderick. b 48. Leeds Univ BA70. Oak Hill Th Coll 74. d 76 p 77. C Beckenham Ch Ch *Roch* 76-80; C Uphill *B & W* 80-84; R Springfield All SS *Chelmsf* 84-90; Selection Sec ABM from 91. *76 Thorkhill Road, Thames Ditton, Surrey KT7 0UQ* 0181-339 0114 or 071-222 9011 Fax 0171-799 2714

JONES, Roger. b 49. St Mich Coll Llan 84. d 86 p 87. C Llangynwyd w Maesteg *Llan* 86-90; V Wiston w Walton E and Clarbeston *St D* from 90. *The Vicarage, Wiston, Haverfordwest, Dyfed SA62 4PL* Clarbeston (01437) 731266

JONES, Canon Ronald Albert. b 15. Em Coll Cam BA37 MA41. Qu Coll Birm 37. d 39 p 40. R Loughb All SS *Leic* 57-76; Hon Can Leic Cathl 63-76; P-in-c Stonesfield *Ox* 76-82; RD Woodstock 80-82; rtd 82; Perm to Offic *Ox* from 82. *11 Gwendroc Close, Truro, Cornwall TR1 2BX* Truro (01872) 73064

JONES, Ronald Thomas. b 19. Aristotelian Soc 64 Univ of Wales BA41. Westcott Ho Cam 41. d 43 p 44. Sen Lect Keswick Hall 60-64; Prin Lect 64-80; Hd Religious Studies 64-80; Lic to Offic *Nor* 60-84; rtd 84. *Bissom Bungalow, Penryn, Cornwall TR10 9LQ* Falmouth (01326) 372205

388

JONES, Russell Frederick. b 55. Edin Univ BD84. Edin Th Coll 81. **d** 84 **p** 85. C Croxteth *Liv* 84-87; V Edge Hill St Dunstan from 87. *St Dunstan's Vicarage, Earle Road, Liverpool L7 6HD* 0151-733 4385

JONES, Samuel. b 44. CITC. **d** 86 **p** 87. C Agherton *Conn* 86-88; I Conn w Antrim St Patr from 88. *Connor Rectory, Church Road, Kells, Ballymena, Co Antrim BT42 3JU* Ballymena (01266) 891254

JONES, Mrs Sharon Ann. b 60. Liv Univ BA82. Cranmer Hall Dur 83. **dss** 85 **d** 87 **p** 94. Rubery *Birm* 85-87; Par Dn 87-89; C-in-c Chelmsley Wood St Aug CD 89-92; Perm to Offic *Newc* 92-93; Chapl HM Pris Acklington from 93. *HM Prison Acklington, Morpeth, Northd NE65 9XF* Morpeth (01670) 760411 Fax 761362

JONES, Miss Sian Eira. b 63. Univ of Wales (Lamp) BA84 Southn Univ BTh88. Sarum & Wells Th Coll 85. **d** 88. C Llan-llwch w Llangain and Llangynog *St D* 88-93; D-in-c Llansteffan and Llan-y-bri etc from 93. *The Vicarage, Llansteffan, Carmarthen, Dyfed SA33 5JT* Llansteffan (01267) 241807

JONES, Sian Hilary. See WIGHT, Mrs Sian Hilary

JONES, Simon. b 63. Trin Coll Bris BA89. **d** 89 **p** 90. C Hildenborough *Roch* 89-93; C Crofton *Portsm* from 93. *46 Carisbrooke Avenue, Fareham, Hants PO14 3PR* Stubbington (01329) 668577

JONES, Stephen Frederick. b 43. Wells Th Coll 68. **d** 71 **p** 72. C-in-c Stockton St Jas CD *Dur* 71-74; Chapl Asst St Ebba's Hosp Epsom 74-79; Chapl Warley Hosp Brentwood 79-87; R Leigh St Clem *Chelmsf* from 87. *St Clement's Rectory, 80 Leigh Hill, Leigh-on-Sea, Essex SS9 1AR* Southend-on-Sea (01702) 75305

JONES, Stephen Frederick. b 53. Magd Coll Ox BA75 MA79 Lon Univ BD89. Linc Th Coll 81. **d** 84 **p** 85. C Kingswinford St Mary *Lich* 84-87; Min Can, Succ and Dean's V Windsor 87-94; C Howden TM *York* from 94. *6 Sandholme Way, Howden, Goole, N Humberside DN14 7LN* Howden (01430) 432276

JONES, Stephen Leslie. b 59. Hull Univ BA80. Sarum & Wells Th Coll 82. **d** 85 **p** 86. C Perry Barr *Birm* 85-88; C Blackpool St Steph *Blackb* 88-90; V Greenlands from 90. *St Anne's House, Salmesbury Avenue, Blackpool FY2 0PR* Blackpool (01253) 53900

JONES, Stephen Richard. b 49. Oak Hill Th Coll 72. **d** 75 **p** 76. C Welling *Roch* 75-79; C Cheltenham St Mark *Glouc* 79-82; V Shiregreen St Jas and St Chris *Sheff* 82-86; P-in-c Harold Hill St Geo *Chelmsf* 86-88; V from 88; P-in-c Harold Hill St Paul 94-95. *St George's Vicarage, Chippenham Road, Romford RM3 8HX* Ingrebourne (01708) 343415

JONES, Stephen William. b 46. K Coll Lon BD70 AKC70. **d** 71 **p** 72. C Streatham St Pet *S'wark* 71-76; C Leeds St Pet *Ripon* 76-79; C Leeds Richmond Hill 79-85; R Gourock *Glas* 85-88; V Porthleven w Sithney *Truro* 88-94; Miss to Seamen 88-94; Perm to Offic *Ex* from 95. *1 Holland Road, Exmouth, Devon EX8 4AT* Exmouth (01395) 264830

JONES, Stewart William. b 57. Heriot-Watt Univ BA79 Bris Univ DSA81. Trin Coll Bris DipHE87 BA88. **d** 88 **p** 89. C Stoke Bishop *Bris* 88-92; P-in-c Brislington St Luke from 92. *The Vicarage, St Luke's Gardens, Church Hill, Bristol BS4 4NW* Bristol (0117) 977 7633

JONES, Sydney Clarence. b 60. **d** 95. Chapl Univ of Wales (Swansea) *S & B* from 95; NSM Sketty from 95. *189 Glanmor Road, Sketty, Swansea SA2 0RR*

JONES, Sydney Clarence. b 21. St Cath Soc Ox BA42 MA46 CertEd. Linc Th Coll 43. **d** 44 **p** 45. Lic to Offic *Bradf* 69-71; V Sharow *Ripon* 71-74; Chapl Dame Allan's Schs Newc 74-79; P-in-c Chollerton w Thockrington *Newc* 79-80; V Scholes *Wakef* 80-86; rtd 86. *102 Priest Lane, Ripon, N Yorkshire HG4 1LT* Ripon (01765) 603204

JONES, Tegid Owen. b 27. Univ of Wales (Lamp) BA51. St Deiniol's Hawarden. **d** 68 **p** 69. C Rhosddu *St As* 68-71; C Wrexham 71-75; R Marchwiel 75-83; R Marchwiel and Isycoed 83-92; RD Ban Isycoed 86-92; rtd 92. *Teglys, 2 Bungalow, Pentre, Chirk, Wrexham, Clwyd LL14 5AW*

JONES, Canon Thomas Graham. b 33. St D Coll Lamp BA57. **d** 59 **p** 60. C Llanelli *St D* 59-64; V Ysbyty Cynfyn 64-69; V Ysbyty Cynfyn w Llantrisant 69-72; V Llanelli Ch Ch 72-94; RD Cydweli 89-93; Hon Can St D Cathl from 93; V Carmarthen St Dav from 94. *St David's Vicarage, 4 Penllwyn Park, Carmarthen, Dyfed SA31 3BU* Carmarthen (01276) 234183

JONES, Ven Thomas Hughie. b 27. FRSA Univ of Wales BA49 Lon Univ BD53 Leic Univ MA72. St Deiniol's Hawarden. **d** 66 **p** 67. Hon C Evington *Leic* 66-76; Hon C Kirby Muxloe 76-81; Dioc Adult Educn Officer 81-85; R Church Langton w Thorpe Langton and Tur Langto 81-85; Hon Can Leic Cathl 83-86; R Church Langton w Tur Langton, Thorpe Langton

etc 85-86; Adn Loughb 86-92; rtd 92. *Four Trees, 68 Main Street, Thorpe Satchville, Melton Mowbray, Leics LE14 2DQ* Melton Mowbray (01664) 840262

JONES, Thomas Jenkin. b 19. St Mich Coll Llan 46. **d** 49 **p** 50. V Stokenham w Sherford *Ex* 68-91; rtd 91; Perm to Offic *Ex* from 91. *16 Long Park, Modbury, Ivybridge, Devon PL21 0RP* Modbury (01548) 830859

JONES, Thomas John Rhidian. b 54. Univ of Wales (Abth) LLB75 BA81. Wycliffe Hall Ox 81. **d** 83 **p** 84. C St D Cathl *St D* 83-86; Min Can St D Cathl 83-86; V Llanpumsaint w Llanllawddog 86-95. *The Vicarage, Llanpumsaint, Carmarthen, Dyfed SA33 6BZ* Llanpumsaint (01267) 253205

JONES, Thomas Lloyd. See LLOYD-JONES, Thomas

JONES, Thomas Madoc. b 06. St D Coll Lamp BA27. **d** 29 **p** 30. V Kempley w Oxenhall *Glouc* 66-71; rtd 71. *16 Pontwilliam, Brecon, Powys LD3 9BT* Brecon (01874) 624380

JONES, Thomas Percy Norman Devonshire (Tom). b 34. St Jo Coll Ox BA58 MA61. Cuddesdon Coll 58. **d** 60 **p** 61. C Portsea St Cuth *Portsm* 60-61; C Portsea N End St Mark 61-67; Asst Chapl Portsm Tech Coll 67-70; Chapl Portsm Poly *Portsm* 70-73; USA 73-74; V Folkestone St Sav *Cant* 75-81; V Regent's Park St Mark *Lon* from 81; Dir Art and Chr Enquiry Trust from 94. *4 Regent's Park Road, London NW1 7TX* 0171-485 3077 or 586 1694

JONES, Canon Thomas Peter. b 20. Ex Coll Ox BA43 MA46. St Mich Coll Llan 43. **d** 45 **p** 46. R Erbistock and Overton *St As* 57-83; Can St As Cathl 78-84; Preb and Prec St As Cathl 84-86; RD Ban Isycoed 80-86; R Overton and Erbistock and Penley 83-86; rtd 86; Perm to Offic *Cov* from 86. *49 Oakleigh Road, Stratford-upon-Avon, Warks CV37 0DP* Stratford-upon-Avon (01789) 269340

JONES, Canon Thomas William Warren. b 25. CITC 49. **d** 49 **p** 50. I Belf Ardoyne *Conn* 63-70; I Ballymacash 70-88; Can Belf Cathl 85-88; rtd 88. *21 Manor Drive, Lisburn, Co Antrim BT28 1JH* Lisburn (01846) 662361

JONES, Timothy Llewellyn. b 67. York Univ BA90. Ripon Coll Cuddesdon BA94 DipMin94. **d** 94 **p** 95. C Middlesb St Martin *York* from 94. *127 Oxford Road, Middlesbrough, Cleveland TS5 5EL* Middlesbrough (01642) 825165

JONES, Timothy Richard Nigel (Tim). b 54. Collingwood Coll Dur BSc75 Birm Univ MSc76. Trin Coll Bris DipHE86. **d** 86 **p** 87. C Hailsham *Chich* 86-91; V Madley w Tyberton, Preston-on-Wye and Blakemere *Heref* from 91. *The Vicarage, Madley, Hereford HR2 9LP* Golden Valley (01981) 250245

JONES, Trevor Blandon. b 43. Oak Hill Th Coll 77. **d** 80 **p** 81. Hon C Homerton St Barn w St Paul *Lon* 80-83; Hon C Harlow New Town w Lt Parndon *Chelmsf* 83-90; C 90-92; V Leyton Em from 92. *Emmanuel Vicarage, 149 Hitcham Road, London E17 8HL* 0181-539 2200

JONES, Trevor Charles. b 50. Oak Hill Th Coll DipHE91. **d** 91 **p** 92. C Goodmayes All SS *Chelmsf* 91-93; C Widford from 93. *16 Wood Street, Chelmsford CM2 9AS* Chelmsford (01245) 348816

JONES, Trevor Edwin. b 49. Ripon Coll Cuddesdon 74. **d** 76 **p** 77. C Cannock *Lich* 76-79; C Middlesb Ascension *York* 79-81; V Oldham St Steph and All Martyrs *Man* 81-84; V Perry Beeches *Birm* 84-90; P-in-c Saltley 90-93; P-in-c Shaw Hill 90-93; V Saltley St Sav and Shaw Hill SS Mary and Jo etc from 93. *The Clergy House, St Saviour's Road, Birmingham B8 1HW* 0121-327 0570

JONES, Preb Trevor Pryce. b 48. Southn Univ BEd76 BTh79. Sarum & Wells Th Coll 73. **d** 76 **p** 77. C Glouc St Geo *Glouc* 76-79; Warden Bp Mascall Cen *Heref* 79-84; Dioc Communications Officer 81-86; TR Heref St Martin w St Fran (S Wye TM) from 84; R Dewsall w Callow from 84; V Holme Lacy w Dinedor from 84; V Lt Dewchurch, Aconbury w Ballingham and Bolstone from 84; V Upper and Lower Bullinghope w Grafton from 84; Preb Heref Cathl from 93. *The Rectory, 91 Ross Road, Hereford HR2 7RJ* Hereford (01432) 353275 or 353717 Fax 352412

JONES, Tudor Howell. b 39. St Mich Coll Llan DipTh67 DPS68. **d** 68 **p** 69. C Clydach *S & B* 68-72; C Swansea St Pet 72-75; V Ystradfellte 75-79; V Llangiwg 79-91; V Manselton from 91. *The Vicarage, Manor Road, Manselton, Swansea SA5 9PA* Swansea (01792) 654848

JONES, Victor Harvey. b 25. St D Coll Lamp BA53 Coll of Resurr Mirfield. **d** 55 **p** 56. Chapl RN 62-80; C Pembroke *B & W* 80-83; rtd 83; Perm to Offic *Ex* from 92. *Flat 3, The Old Vicarage, Case Gardens, Seaton, Devon EX12 2AP*

JONES, Canon Victor Howell. b 18. Univ of Wales BA41. St Mich Coll Llan 41. **d** 43 **p** 45. V Laugharne *St D* 54-72; Chapl St D Hosp Carmarthen 72-85; V Llanllwch *St D* 72-77; V Llanllwch w Llangain 77-83; Can St D Cathl 80-85; V Llan-llwch w Llangain and Llangynog 83-85; rtd 85. *Ty Clyd, 13 Picton Terrace, Carmarthen, Dyfed SA31 3BX* Carmarthen (01267) 232352

JONES, Walter. b 14. TCD 63. **d** 65 **p** 66. C Chaddesden St Mary *Derby* 71-72; C Bootle Ch Ch *Liv* 72-75; C Ashton-in-

Makerfield St Thos 75-77; TV Ebbw Vale *Mon* 77-84; rtd 84. *9 Islwyn Close, Hill Top, Ebbw Vale, Gwent NP3 6NB*

JONES, Warwick. b 29. Univ Coll of SW TDip51 Birkb Coll Lon BA54. **d** 91 **p** 92. NSM Saltash *Truro* from 91. *18 Hillside Road, Saltash, Cornwall PL12 6EX* Saltash (01752) 842031

JONES, Preb Wilfred <u>David</u>. b 22. Keble Coll Ox BA47 MA48. St Mich Coll Llan 47. **d** 48 **p** 49. V St Decumans *B & W* 62-76; V Ilminster w Whitelackington 76-92; RD Ilminster 78-87; Preb Wells Cathl from 81; rtd 92. *Dragons, Lambrook Road, Shepton Beauchamp, Ilminster, Somerset TA19 0NA* South Petherton (01460) 40967

JONES, Wilfred Lovell. b 39. Lon Univ BD71 CertEd. St D Coll Lamp DipTh63. **d** 63 **p** 64. C Llanllyfni *Ban* 63-65; C Llanbeblig w Caernarfon 65-68; V Llanwnog w Penstrowed 68-73; V Llanwnnog and Caersws w Carno 73-75; Lic to Offic *Cant* 77-90; Asst Chapl Dover Coll Kent 77-90; Wrekin Coll Shropshire 91-94; V Llangollen w Trevor and Llantysilio *St As* from 94. *The Vicarage, Abbey Road, Llangollen, Clwyd LL20 8SN* Llangollen (01978) 860231

JONES, Canon William. b 30. Univ of Wales (Ban) DipTh54. St Mich Coll Llan 54 BTh92. **d** 55 **p** 56. C Denio w Aber-erch *Ban* 55-60; V Aberdaron and Bodferin 60-66; V Llandwrog 66-71; R Llanstumdwy, Llangybi w Llanarmon 71-74; R Dolbenmaen w Llanystymdwy w Llangybi etc from 74; RD Eifionydd from 75; Can Ban Cathl 84-93; Can and Treas Ban Cathl from 93. *The Rectory, Llanystumdwy, Criccieth, Gwynedd LL52 0SS* Criccieth (01766) 522325

JONES, Canon William <u>David</u>. b 28. Lon Univ BD57 Leeds Univ MA73. St D Coll Lamp BA48 St Mich Coll Llan 48. **d** 51 **p** 52. Hd of Relig Studies Doncaster Coll of Educn 67-74; Lic to Offic *Sheff* 67-74; Vice-Prin St Bede Coll Dur 74; Vice-Prin SS Hild & Bede Coll Dur 75-89; Lect Th Dur Univ 75-89; Lic to Offic *Dur* 80-85; Dir of Miss Ch in Wales 89-93; Hon Can St D Cathl *St D* 90-93; rtd 93. *Hatfield Cottage, 14 Bath Road, Tetbury, Glos GL8 8EF* Tetbury (01666) 504050

JONES, William Alexander. b 13. Univ of Wales BA35. **d** 69 **p** 70. Hon C Llandegfan w Beaumaris and Llanfaes *Ban* 69-75; C 75-76; P-in-c Penmon and Llangoed w Llanfihangel Dinsylwy 76-77; TV Llandegfan and Beaumaris w Llanfaes w Penmon etc 77-81; rtd 81. *Silva, 4 Coedwig Terrace, Penmon, Beaumaris, Gwynedd LL58 8SL* Llangoed (01248) 490509

JONES, William Douglas. b 28. St Fran Coll Brisbane ThL56. **d** 56 **p** 58. Papua New Guinea 58-72; C Manston *Ripon* 72-75; V Middleton St Mary 75-87; V Ireland Wood 87-94; rtd 94. *6 Willow Court, Pool in Wharfedale, Otley, W Yorkshire LS21 1RX* Leeds (0113) 284 2028

JONES, William Edward Benjamin. b 19. TCD BA43 MA53. TCD Div Sch Div Test44. **d** 44 **p** 45. V N Wembley St Cuth *Lon* 59-81; V Ripley *Guildf* 81-87; Chapl HM Pris Send 81-87; rtd 87. *37 Bircham Road, Reepham, Norfolk NR10 4NG* Norwich (01603) 870738

JONES, Canon William Glyndwr. b 17. St D Coll Lamp BA39. **d** 42 **p** 43. R Granston w St Nic *St D* 51-86; V Mathry w St Edrens 69-86; R Jordanston 78-86; Hon Can St D Cathl from 84; rtd 86. *Pencraig, Sladeway, Fishguard, Dyfed SA65 9NY* Fishguard (01348) 874673

JONES, William Hugh. b 13. Univ of Wales BA35. St Mich Coll Llan 35. **d** 38 **p** 39. R Princes Risborough *Ox* 54-73; R Princes Risborough w Ilmer 73-82; RD Aylesbury 77-80; rtd 82; Perm to Offic *Ox* from 82. *64 Ramworth Way, Foxhills, Aylesbury, Bucks HP21 7EY* Aylesbury (01296) 28838

JONES, William John. b 59. St Mich Coll Llan DMinlStuds93. **d** 93 **p** 94. C Pemb Dock *St D* 93; C Pemb Dock w Cosheston w Nash and Upton from 93. *St Michael's House, The Garth, Cosheston, Pembroke Dock, Dyfed SA72 4UD* Pembroke (01646) 682477

JONES, William Lincoln. b 19. St D Coll Lamp BA41 St Mich Coll Llan 41. **d** 43 **p** 44. V Winscombe *B & W* 64-71; V Bishops Lydeard 71-73; V Bishops Lydeard w Cothelstone 73-80; P-in-c Bagborough 78-80; R Bishops Lydeard w Bagborough and Cothelstone 80-84; rtd 84; Perm to Offic *Ex* from 86. *Holme Lea, Well Mead, Kilmington, Axminster, Devon EX13 7SQ* Axminster (01297) 32744

JONES, William Lloyd. b 36. Univ of Wales (Lamp) BA59. Wycliffe Hall Ox 59. **d** 61 **p** 62. C Holyhead w Rhoscolyn *Ban* 61-65; C Porthmadog 65-67; R Llanfaethlu w Llanfwrog and Llanrhuddlad etc 67-74; R Llanengan and Llangian from 74; RD Llyn from 90. *The Rectory, Abersoch, Pwllheli, Gwynedd LL53 7EA* Abersoch (01758) 812871

JONES-CRABTREE, Stephen. b 56. Nottm Univ BTh80. Linc Th Coll 76. **d** 80 **p** 81. C Chorley St Pet *Blackb* 80-83; C Blackpool St Steph 83-84; C Penwortham St Mary 84-88; R Mareham-le-Fen and Revesby *Linc* from 88. *The Rectory, Mareham le Fen, Boston, Lincs PE22 7QU* Louth (01507) 568502

JONES-EVANS, Thomas <u>Dewi</u> Theodore. b 04. MBE54 TD50. Lon Coll of Div 26. **d** 27 **p** 28. Chapl W Park Hosp Epsom

63-72; rtd 72; Lic to Offic *Mon* 72-82; Perm to Offic from 82. *Anzio, 3 Carlton Terrace, Caerleon, Gwent NP6 1AD* Caerleon (01633) 422138

JORDAN, Anthony John (<u>Tony</u>). b 50. Birm Univ BEd73. Local NSM Course. **d** 83 **p** 84. Asst Chapl Uppingham Sch Leics 83-86; Hon C Uppingham w Ayston and Wardley w Belton *Pet* 83-86; Asst Chapl Sherborne Sch Dorset 86-87; NSM Bournemouth St Fran *Win* from 88. *Flat 8, Alverton Court, 26A Wimborne Road, Bournemouth BH2 6NU* Bournemouth (01202) 318346

JORDAN, Miss Avril Marilyn. b 35. Lon Univ DipEd56. SW Minl Tr Course 79. **dss** 82 **d** 87 **p** 94. Highweek and Teigngrace *Ex* 82-87; Par Dn 87-88; Par Dn Ottery St Mary, Alfington, W Hill, Tipton etc 88-94; C from 94. *9 Washbrook View, Ottery St Mary, Exeter EX11 1EP* Ottery St Mary (01404) 814849

JORDAN, Mrs Elizabeth Ann. b 58. New Hall Cam MA82. St Jo Coll Nottm DipTh84. **d** 87 **p** 94. Par Dn Blackpool St Jo *Blackb* 87-90; Par Dn Ewood 90-94; C 94-95; Asst Dir of Ords 90-95; Miss Shelfield St Mark CD *Lich* from 95. *Church House, 25 Green Lane, Shelfield, Walsall WS4 1RN*

JORDAN, John. b 37. CQSW81. N Ord Course 84. **d** 87 **p** 88. C Southport Em *Liv* 87-90; V Abram from 90; V Bickershaw from 90. *The Vicarage, 9 Lee Lane, Abram, Wigan, Lancs WN2 5QU*

JORDAN, Kenneth John. b 31. K Coll Lon. **d** 69 **p** 70. Guyana 69-74; C Roath St Marg *Llan* 74-76; V Nantymoel w Wyndham 76-81; V Cardiff St Mary w St Steph 81-83; V Cardiff St Mary and St Steph w St Dyfrig etc from 83; Miss to Seamen from 83. *St Mary's Clergy House, Bute Street, Cardiff CF1 5HE* Cardiff (01222) 487777

JORDAN, Peter Harry. b 42. Leeds Univ BA64. Cranmer Hall Dur 70. **d** 73 **p** 74. C Nottm St Ann w Em *S'well* 73-77; C Edgware *Lon* 77-82; V Everton St Chrys *Liv* 82-94; V Bootle St Mary w St Paul from 94; Dioc Ev from 94. *The Vicarage, 70 Merton Road, Bootle, Merseyside L20 7AT* 0151-922 1315

JORDAN, Richard William. b 56. Lanchester Poly BSc78. St Jo Coll Nottm DipTh84. **d** 87 **p** 88. C Blackpool St Jo *Blackb* 87-90; V Ewood 90-95. *Church House, 25 Green Lane, Shelfield, Walsall WS4 1RN*

JORDAN, Robert Brian. b 43. Qu Coll Birm 68. **d** 69 **p** 70. C Norton St Mich *Dur* 69-73; C Hastings St Clem and All SS *Chich* 73-74; C Carshalton *S'wark* 74-81; V Catford St Andr from 81. *The Vicarage, 135 Wellmeadow Road, London SE6 1HP* 0181-697 2600

JORDAN, Ronald Henry. b 30. K Coll Lon. **d** 57 **p** 58. Hon C Edmonton St Mary w St Jo *Lon* 86-94; V Wood Green St Mich 69-73; Hon C Finchley H Trin 80-86; Perm to Offic from 94; rtd 95. *120 Church Lane, London N2 0TB* 0181-883 7828

JORDAN, Thomas. b 36. Man Univ DSPT91. NW Ord Course 76. **d** 79 **p** 80. NSM Prenton *Ches* 79-84; NSM Egremont St Jo 84-91; C from 91; Ind Chapl from 91. *31 Willowbank Road, Devonshire Park, Birkenhead, Merseyside L42 7JU* 0151-652 4212

JORDINSON, Vera (<u>Sister Hilary</u>). b 37. Liv Univ BA60 CertEd61. Westcott Ho Cam 88. **d** 89 **p** 94. CSF from 74; Prov Sec from 90; Lic to Offic *Heref* 89-92; Perm to Offic *Lich* 90-92; Perm to Offic *Birm* 92-94; NSM Birchfield from 94. *St Elizabeth's House, 33 Hampton Road, Birmingham B6 6AN* 0121-523 0215

JORY, Joseph Nicholls. b 07. Lon Univ DipTh31. St Andr Whittlesford 40. **d** 40 **p** 41. R Spennithorne *Ripon* 46-66; R Finghall 54-66; R Hauxwell 64-66; rtd 72; Perm to Offic *Ex* from 79. *Shilstone, Chagford, Newton Abbot, Devon TQ13 8JX* Whiddon Down (01647) 231307

JORYSZ, Ian Herbert. b 62. Van Mildert Coll Dur BSc84 MA95 Liv Univ PhD87. Ripon Coll Cuddesdon BA89 MA95. **d** 90 **p** 91. C Houghton le Spring *Dur* 90-93; C Ferryhill from 93. *59 Church Lane, Ferryhill, Co Durham DL17 8LT* Ferryhill (01740) 653029

JOWETT, Very Rev Alfred. b 14. CBE72. St Cath Coll Cam BA35 MA59 Sheff Univ Hon DLitt82. Linc Th Coll 43. **d** 44 **p** 45. Dean Man 64-83; rtd 83; Perm to Offic *Sheff* from 84. *37 Stone Delf, Sheffield S10 3QX* Sheffield (0114) 230 5455

JOWETT, Ms Hilary Anne. b 54. Hull Univ BA75. Cranmer Hall Dur IDC80. **dss** 82 **d** 87 **p** 94. Sheff St Jo *Sheff* 82-83; Brampton Bierlow 83-87; Par Dn 87-89; Hon Par Dn Sheff Sharrow 89-95; Chapl Nether Edge Hosp Sheff 89-95; C Sheff St Mark Broomhill *Sheff* from 95. *Sharrow Vicarage, 45 St Andrew's Road, Sheffield S11 9AL* Sheffield (0114) 255 0533 or 267 9773

JOWETT, Nicholas Peter Alfred. b 44. St Cath Coll Cam BA66 MA Bris Univ CertEd67 Birm Univ DipTh74. Qu Coll Birm 72. **d** 75 **p** 76. C Wales *Sheff* 75-78; TV Sheff Manor 78-83; V Brampton Bierlow 83-89; V Sheff Sharrow from 89. *Sharrow Vicarage, 45 St Andrew's Road, Sheffield S11 9AL* Sheffield (0114) 255 0533

JOWITT, Andrew Robert Benson. b 56. Down Coll Cam BA78 MA81 PGCE79. Wycliffe Hall Ox 88. **d** 90 **p** 91. C Northn Em *Pet* 90-94; C Barking St Marg w St Patr *Chelmsf* from 94. *79 Sparsholt Road, Barking, Essex IG11 7YG* 0181-594 1960

JOWITT, Canon David Arthur Benson. b 25. St Jo Coll Ox BA49 MA53. Sarum Th Coll 49. **d** 51 **p** 52. OGS from 65; Superior OGS 75-81; P-in-c Edin St Ninian *Edin* 69-77; Dioc Supernumerary 77-80; Chapl Edin R Infirmary 77-80; Syn Clerk *Edin* 77-90; Can St Mary's Cathl 77-90; Vice-Provost 81-86; P-in-c S Queensferry 86-90; rtd 90; Hon C Edin Old St Paul *Edin* from 91. *2 Marchmont Crescent, Edinburgh EH9 1HN* 0131-229 0106

JOWITT, John Frederick Benson. b 23. Oak Hill Th Coll 57. **d** 59 **p** 59. CF 63-73; R Thrandeston, Stuston and Brome w Oakley *St E* 73-82; V Docking *Nor* 82-83; P-in-c Gt Bircham 82-83; R Docking w the Birchams 83-88; P-in-c Stanhoe w Barwick 85-88; R Docking w The Birchams and Stanhoe w Barwick 88; rtd 88; Perm to Offic *Nor* from 88; Perm to Offic *St E* from 90. *White Lodge, The Street, North Cove, Beccles, Suffolk NR34 7PN* Barnby (0150276) 404

JOY, Bernard David. b 50. Sarum & Wells Th Coll 90. **d** 92 **p** 93. C Shortlands *Roch* 92-94; C Henbury *Bris* from 94. *42 Charlton Gardens, Bristol BS10 6LX* Bristol (0117) 950 9970

JOY, Canon Leslie John Clifton. b 09. AKC33. St Steph Ho Ox 33. **d** 33 **p** 34. V Blyth St Mary *Newc* 64-83; RD Bedlington 69-83; Hon Can Newc Cathl 70-83; rtd 83; Perm to Offic *Chelmsf* from 83; Perm to Offic *Newc* from 86. *31 Emmbrook Court, Reading RG6 2TZ* Reading (01734) 873855

JOY, Canon Matthew Osmund Clifton. b 40. St Edm Hall Ox BA62 MA66. St Steph Ho Ox 62. **d** 64 **p** 65. C Brinksway *Ches* 64-66; C Southwick St Columba *Dur* 66-69; V Hartlepool H Trin 69-85; V Rotherham Ferham Park *Sheff* 85-88; V Masbrough from 88; RD Rotherham 88-93. *256 Kimberworth Road, Rotherham, S Yorkshire S61 1HG* Rotherham (01709) 557810 or 560844

JOYCE, Mrs Alison Jane. b 59. Univ of Wales (Swansea) BA81 SS Coll Cam PGCE84 Bris Univ MLitt87. Ripon Coll Cuddesdon BA87. **d** 88 **p** 94. Par Dn Chalgrove w Berrick Salome *Ox* 88-90; Tutor W Midl Minl Tr Course from 90; Perm to Offic *Birm* from 90. *88 Willows Road, Balsall Heath, Birmingham B12 9QD* 0121-440 5171 or 454 8597

JOYCE, Anthony Owen (Tony). b 35. Selw Coll Cam BA60 MA64. Wycliffe Hall Ox 60. **d** 62 **p** 63. C Birm St Martin *Birm* 62-67; Rhodesia 67-70; V Birm St Luke *Birm* 70-79; V Downend *Bris* from 79; RD Stapleton 83-89. *The Vicarage, 63 Downend Road, Bristol BS16 5UF* Bristol (0117) 956 8064

JOYCE, Ernest Thomas Chancellor. b 16. Lon Univ LLB67. Chich Th Coll 68. **d** 70 **p** 71. C Southsea H Spirit *Portsm* 70-75; V New Southgate St Paul *Lon* 75-77; Chantry Priest Chpl St Mich and H So Walsingham 77-81; Perm to Offic *Nor* from 77; rtd 81. *16 Cleaves Drive, Walsingham, Norfolk NR22 6EQ* Walsingham (01328) 820612

JOYCE, Gordon Franklin. b 51. Birm Univ BA72. St Jo Coll Nottm 86. **d** 88 **p** 89. C Didsbury St Jas and Em *Man* 88-92; V Tonge w Alkrington from 92. *St Michael's Vicarage, 184 Kirkway, Middleton, Manchester M24 1LN* 0161-643 2891

JOYCE, Graham Leslie. b 49. Lon Univ CertEd71. Trin Coll Bris DipHE89. **d** 89 **p** 90. C Heald Green St Cath *Ches* 89-93; R Church Lawton from 93. *The Rectory, 1 Liverpool Road West, Church Lawton, Stoke-on-Trent ST7 3DE* Alsager (01270) 882103

JOYCE, John Barnabas Altham. b 47. St Chad's Coll Dur BA69 Lon Univ DipEd86. St Steph Ho Ox 72. **d** 74 **p** 75. C Reading St Giles *Ox* 74-77; C Cowley St Jo 77-80; Dioc Youth and Community Officer 80-87; V Hangleton *Chich* 87-94; Dioc Adv for Schools & Dir Educn from 94. *2 Windlesham Road, Brighton BN1 3AG* Brighton (01273) 778083

JOYCE, Kingsley Reginald. b 49. Man Univ BSc70. Cuddesdon Coll 70. **d** 73 **p** 74. C High Wycombe *Ox* 73-76; C Fingest 76-79; C Hambleden 76-79; C Medmenham 76-79; C Fawley (Bucks) 76-79; C Turville 76-79; P-in-c Hambleden Valley 79-80; R 80-87; R Friern Barnet St Jas *Lon* 87-91; CF from 91. *c/o MOD (Army), Bagshot Park, Bagshot, Surrey GU19 5PL* Bagshot (01276) 471717 Fax 412834

JOYCE, Margaret. b 47. Oak Hill NSM Course 86. **d** 89 **p** 94. NSM Chadwell Heath *Chelmsf* 89-92; NSM Bath Odd Down w Combe Hay *B & W* from 92. *69 Bloomfield Rise, Bath BA2 2BN* Combe Down (01225) 840864

JOYCE, Martin Ernest Chancellor. b 50. K Coll Lon 69. **d** 73 **p** 74. C Leigh Park *Portsm* 73-77; C Milton 77-83; TV Cam Ascension *Ely* 83-85; V Blackpool St Mich *Blackb* 85-87. *64 Cowdenhill Road, Glasgow G13 2HE* 0141-954 6078

JOYCE, Dr Melville Henry Bushell. b 14. MRCPsych71 St D Coll Lamp BA39 Bris Univ MB, ChB52 DPM54. Ely Th Coll

40. **d** 41 **p** 42. C Abergavenny H Trin *Mon* 41-43; C St Winnow *Truro* 43-45; C Westbury-on-Trym H Trin *Bris* 45-46; C Henleaze 46-52; Public Preacher 52-69; Perm to Offic *Lon* 55-69; Lic to Offic from 69; Lect Psychiatry Lon Univ 58-61; Surrey Univ 61-79. *7 Stanhope Terrace, London W2 2UB* 0171-262 3718

JOYCE, Canon Norman. b 14. St Jo Coll Dur BA35 MA38 DipTh38. **d** 37 **p** 38. R N Wingfield *Derby* 57-73; TR N Wingfield, Pilsley and Tupton 73-80; Hon Can Derby Cathl 77-80; rtd 80; Perm to Offic *Carl* from 80. *Fell View, Thurstonfield, Carlisle CA5 6HG* Burgh-by-Sands (01228) 576471

JOYCE, Raymond. b 37. Keele Univ BA60 MA67 Linc Coll Ox BA62 MA68. St Steph Ho Ox 78. **d** 80 **p** 81. NSM Normanton *Derby* 80-83; NSM Derby St Alkmund and St Werburgh 83-87; Lic to Offic from 87. *4 South Avenue, Littleover, Derby DE23 6BA* Derby (01332) 768681

JOYCE, Sister. See CROSSLAND, Sister Joyce

JOYCE, Terence Alan. b 57. St Jo Coll Nottm BTh84. **d** 84 **p** 85. C Mansf St Pet *S'well* 84-88; V Greasley from 88. *The Vicarage, 36 Moorgreen, Newthorpe, Notts NG16 2FB* Langley Mill (01773) 712509

JUBB, William Arthur. b 21. Kelham Th Coll 39. **d** 45 **p** 46. V Monk Bretton *Wakef* 52-74; rtd 86. *5 Mauds Terrace, Barnsley, S Yorkshire S71 2EA* Barnsley (01226) 247286

JUCKES, Jonathan Sydney. b 61. St Andr Univ MA83 Selw Coll Cam BA87. Ridley Hall Cam 85. **d** 88 **p** 89. C Sevenoaks St Nic *Roch* 88-92; Proclamation Trust from 92. *14 Arbery Road, London E3 5DD* 0181-981 2594

JUDD, Adrian Timothy. b 67. Lanc Univ BA88. Cranmer Hall Dur BA92 Trin Coll Singapore 92 St Jo Coll Dur DMinlStuds93. **d** 93 **p** 94. C Dudley Holly Hall St Aug *Worc* from 93. *218 Stourbridge Road, Dudley, W Midlands DY1 2EL* Brierley Hill (01384) 74918

JUDD, Colin Ivor. b 35. Dur Univ BA61. Ridley Hall Cam 61. **d** 63 **p** 64. C Stratford St Jo w Ch Ch *Chelmsf* 63-66; C Kimberworth *Sheff* 66-68; Area Sec (Dios Bradf and Wakef) CMS 68-80; V Bradf St Columba w St Andr *Bradf* from 80. *St Columba's Vicarage, 163 Horton Grange Road, Bradford, W Yorkshire BD7 2DN* Bradford (01274) 571975

JUDD, Eric Sinclair Alderton. b 04. **d** 43 **p** 44. V N Willingham w Legsby *Linc* 64-73; rtd 73. *5 Baildon Crescent, North Hykeham, Lincoln LN6 8HU* Lincoln (01522) 687442

JUDD, Mrs Nicola Jane (Nicky). b 51. Birm Coll of Educn CertEd72. S Dios Minl Tr Scheme 87. **d** 90 **p** 94. NSM Abbotts Ann and Upper and Goodworth Clatford *Win* from 90. *13 Belmont Close, Andover, Hants SP10 2DE* Andover (01264) 363364

JUDD, Peter Somerset Margesson. b 49. Trin Hall Cam BA71. Cuddesdon Coll 71. **d** 74 **p** 75. C Salford St Phil w St Steph *Man* 74-76; Chapl Clare Coll Cam 76-81; C Burnham *Ox* 81-82; TV Burnham w Dropmore, Hitcham and Taplow 82-88; R Iffley from 88; RD Cowley from 94. *The Rectory, Mill Lane, Iffley, Oxford OX4 4EJ* Oxford (01865) 773516

JUDGE, James Arthur. b 20. Lon Univ BD50. ALCD50. **d** 50 **p** 51. R Street *B & W* 62-77; V Banwell 77-88; rtd 88. *512 Gipps House, 270 Jersey Road, Woollahra, NSW, Australia 2025*

JUDGE, Mark Rollo. b 60. Chich Th Coll BTh92. **d** 92 **p** 93. C Forest Gate St Edm *Chelmsf* from 92. *64 Henderson Road, London E7 8EF*

JUDGE, Michael Charles. b 42. Southn Univ BTh79. Chich Th Coll 71. **d** 74 **p** 75. C Eastbourne St Mary *Chich* 74-78; C Seaford w Sutton 79-81; R Hurstpierpoint 81-89; V Easebourne from 89; Chapl K Edw VII Hosp Midhurst from 89; RD Midhurst *Chich* from 90. *The Priory, Easebourne, Midhurst, W Sussex GU29 0AJ* Midhurst (01730) 813341

JUDGE, Ralph Stanley. b 13. TCD BA35 MA58. TCD Div Sch Div Test36. **d** 36 **p** 37. I Castlebar *T, K & A* 45-51; Australia from 51; rtd 83. *11 Troon Avenue, Seaton, S Australia 5023* Adelaide (8) 356-5131

JUDSON, Mrs Mary Ruth. b 47. Bretton Hall Coll DipEd68. NE Ord Course 89. **d** 92 **p** 94. Par Dn Lobley Hill *Dur* 92; Par Dn Ches le Street 92-94; C from 94. *2 Glencoe Avenue, Chester le Street, Co Durham DH2 2JJ* 0191-388 0931

JUDSON, Paul Wesley. b 46. Leic Poly DipAD69 ATD71. Cranmer Hall Dur 87. **d** 89 **p** 90. C Lobley Hill *Dur* 89-92; C Ches le Street from 92. *2 Glencoe Avenue, Chester le Street, Co Durham DH2 2JJ* 0191-388 0931

JUKES, Keith Michael. b 54. Leeds Univ BA76. Linc Th Coll 77. **d** 78 **p** 79. C Wordsley *Lich* 82-83; C Wolv 81-83; C-in-c Stoneydelph St Martin CD 83-90; TR Glascote and Stonydelph 90-91; RD Tamworth 90-91; TR Cannock from 91; V Hatherton from 91. *The Rectory, 11 Sherbrook Road, Cannock, Staffs WS11 1HJ* Cannock (01543) 502131

JULIAN, Sister. See WALSH, Julia Christine

JUPE, Canon Derek Robert. b 26. TCD BA53 Div Test54 MA67. **d** 54 **p** 55. Deputation Sec (Ireland) BCMS 65-72; R Man St Jerome w Ardwick St Silas *Man* 72-78; V Ardsley *Sheff* 78-83; I Tempo and Clabby *Clogh* 83-92; Can Clogh Cathl 89-92; rtd 92. *29 St Andrew's Drive, Whitstone, Nuneaton, Warks CV11 6NQ* Nuneaton (01203) 386880

JUPE, Martin Roy. b 27. Lon Univ BD63. St Deiniol's Hawarden. **d** 61 **p** 62. V Penzance St Jo *Truro* 64-92; RD Penwith 73-76; rtd 92. *25 Nancherrow Terrace, St Just, Penzance, Cornwall TR19 7LA* Penzance (01736) 788320

JUPP, Roger Alan. b 56. St Edm Hall Ox BA78 MA82. Chich Th Coll 79. **d** 80 **p** 81. C Newbold and Dunston *Derby* 80-83; C Cowley St Jo *Ox* 83-85; C Islington St Jas w St Phil *Lon* 85-86; V Lower Beeding *Chich* 86-90; Dom Chapl to Area Bp Horsham 86-91; V Burgess Hill St Jo 90-93; TR Burgess Hill St Jo w St Edw 93-94. *10 Ockley Way, Hassocks, W Sussex BN6 8NE* Hassocks (01273) 844122

JUSTICE, Keith Leonard. b 42. CEng83 MIMechE83 Wolv Univ BSc68. Wycliffe Hall Ox DipMin93. **d** 93 **p** 94. C Penwortham St Mary *Blackb* from 93. *9 The Grove, Penwortham, Preston PR1 0UU* Preston (01772) 745152

JUSTICE, Peter John Michael. b 37. Chich Th Coll 60. **d** 63 **p** 64. C Mill End *St Alb* 68-70; V Eaton Bray 70-73; Hon C Prestwood *Ox* 73-84; Chapl to the Deaf 84-90; rtd 90; Perm to Offic *Ox* 90-93; RD Perm to Offic *Ex* 94-95. *8 Theatre Street, Woodbridge, Suffolk IP12 4NE* Woodbridge (01394) 380899

JUSTICE, Simon Charles. b 66. Univ of Wales (Lamp) BD88 Edin Univ MTh90. Cranmer Hall Dur 90. **d** 92 **p** 93. C Tilehurst St Mich *Ox* 92-95; USA from 95. *58 Third Street, Troy, NY 12180, USA* New York (518) 273-7351

JUTSUM, Linda Mary. *See* ELLIOTT, Mrs Linda Mary

K

KAENEL, Brian Herbert. b 19. Coll of Resurr Mirfield 57. **d** 59 **p** 60. Asst Master St Aug Sch Kilburn 69-70; Ravensbourne Sch Bromley 71-79; Perm to Offic *Roch* from 72; rtd 84. *11 Bromley College, London Road, Bromley BR1 1PE* 0181-290 1660

✠**KAFITY, Rt Rev Samir.** Beirut Univ BA57. Near E Sch of Th 57. **d** 57 **p** 58 **c** 86. Jerusalem 57-59; Jordan 59-75; Adn Beirut 74-77; Gen Sec Cen Syn of Episc Ch in JEM 77-86; Adn Jerusalem 77-86; Bp Jerusalem from 86. *St George's Close, PO Box 1248, Jerusalem 91109, Israel* Fax Jerusalem (2) 273847

KAGGWA, Nelson Sonny. b 58. E Lon Univ BA91. Bible Tr Inst Tennessee DipTh84 Bp Tucker Coll Mukono 77. **d** 80 **p** 80. Kenya 80-83; USA 83; Hon C Ox SS Phil and Jas w St Marg *Ox* 84-85; C W Ham *Chelmsf* 86-87; TV Walthamstow St Mary w St Steph 87-92; Perm to Offic *Sheff* 92-95. *7 Fenwick Street, Derby DE24 8FN*

KAMRAN, Ernest P. b 58. **d** 90. C Shoreditch St Leon and Hoxton St Jo *Lon* from 94. *11 Dock Street, London E1 8JN* 0171-481 9179

KANE, Margaret. b 15. Local NSM Course. **d** 87 **p** 94. NSM Billingham St Aid *Dur* 87-95; Perm to Offic from 95. *218 Kennedy Gardens, Billingham, Cleveland TS23 3RL* Stockton-on-Tees (01642) 553940

KANERIA, Rajni. b 57. Bath Univ BPharm82. Wycliffe Hall Ox 83. **d** 86 **p** 87. C Hyson Green *S'well* 86-87; C Hyson Green St Paul w St Steph 87-89; C Harold Hill St Geo *Chelmsf* 89-91; TV Oadby *Leic* from 91. *St Paul's House, Hamble Road, Oadby, Leicester LE2 4NX* Leicester (0116) 271 0519

KARNEY, Gilbert Henry Peter. b 09. Trin Coll Cam BA31 MA36. Cuddesdon Coll 32. **d** 34 **p** 35. V Embleton *Newc* 54-74; P-in-c Rennington w Rock 73-74; rtd 74; Perm to Offic *Ox* 86-89; C W w E Hanney 89-91. *Darden House, Snuggs Lane, East Hanney, Wantage, Oxon OX12 0HG* Abingdon (01235) 868265

KARRACH, Dr Herbert Adolf. b 24. TCD BA46 MB48 BCh48 BAO48 LSHTM DTM&H55. E Anglian Minl Tr Course 85. **d** 88 **p** 89. Hon C Snettisham w Ingoldisthorpe and Fring *Nor* 88-95; Perm to Offic from 95. *Narnia, 5 Docking Road, Fring, King's Lynn, Norfolk PE31 6SQ* Docking (01485) 518346

KARUNARATNA, Charles Winston. b 28. FPhS FRSA Serampore Coll BD60 DTh84 K Coll Lon MTh66 PhD74 Lon Inst of Educn MA90. ALCD51. **d** 51 **p** 52. C Croydon St Matt *Cant* 51-53; NSM Gt Ilford St Jo *Chelmsf* 89-93; Perm to Offic

from 93. *2 Lancelot Road, Ilford, Essex IG6 3BE* 0181-500 4751

KASHOURIS, Peter Zacharias. b 66. Peterho Cam BA89 MA93. St Steph Ho Ox 92. **d** 94 **p** 95. C Hampstead St Jo *Lon* from 94. *1 Holly Bush Vale, London NW3 6TX* 0171-794 6838

KASSELL, Colin George Henry. b 42. DCC90. Valladolid Spain 63 Ripon Coll Cuddesdon 76. **d** 68 **p** 69. In RC Ch 69-75; Perm to Offic *Ox* 76-77; C Denham 77-80; V Brotherton *Wakef* 80-84; Chapl and Past Ldr St Cath Hospice Crawley 84-91; R Rogate w Terwick and Trotton w Chithurst *Chich* 91-94; C Heene from 94; Chapl Worthing Hosp from 94. *34 Ingleside Crescent, Lancing, W Sussex BN15 8EN* Lancing (01903) 764400

KAUNHOVEN, Anthony Peter. b 55. Leeds Univ BA78 PGCE79 Edin Univ DipMin80. Edin Th Coll 79. **d** 81 **p** 82. C Leeds St Aid *Ripon* 81-84; C Hawksworth Wood 84-89; V Upper Nidderdale 89-91. *29 St James Road, Ilkley, W Yorkshire LS29 9PY* Ilkley (01943) 817659

KAVANAGH, Michael Lowther. b 58. CPsychol90 MBPsS90 York Univ BA80 Newc Univ MSc82 Leeds Univ BA86. Coll of Resurr Mirfield 84. **d** 87 **p** 88. C Boston Spa *York* 87-91; V Beverley St Nic from 91; RD Beverley from 95. *St Nicholas' Vicarage, 72 Grovehill Road, Beverley, N Humberside HU17 0ER* Hull (01482) 881458

KAY, Canon Cyril John. b 05. St Aid Birkenhead 44. **d** 46 **p** 47. V Welland *Worc* 54-74; Hon Can Worc Cathl 69-74; rtd 74; Perm to Offic *Glouc* 80-92. *16 Kayte Close, Bishop's Cleeve, Cheltenham, Glos GL52 4AX* Cheltenham (01242) 674306

KAY, George Ronald. b 24. Sarum & Wells Th Coll 74. **d** 77 **p** 78. NSM Bemerton *Sarum* 77-87; rtd 87. *1 Victoria Close, Wilton, Salisbury SP2 0ET* Salisbury (01722) 743884

KAY, Ian Geoffrey. **d** 89 **p** 90. NSM Rochdale *Man* 89-91 and from 95; NSM Heywood St Luke w All So 91-95. *161 Norden Road, Bamford, Rochdale, Lancs OL11 5PT*

KAY, Ronald William. b 28. Liv Univ BEng49 MEng51. Tyndale Hall Bris 59. **d** 61 **p** 62. V Westcombe Park St Geo *S'wark* 65-76; R Doddington *Linc* 76-78; V Skellingthorpe 76-78; R Skellingthorpe w Doddington 78-91; rtd 91; Perm to Offic *Linc* from 91. *18 Abingdon Avenue, Lincoln LN6 3LE* Lincoln (01522) 696275

KAYE, Alistair Geoffrey. b 62. Reading Univ BSc85. St Jo Coll Nottm DPS90. **d** 90 **p** 91. C Gt Horton *Bradf* 90-94; C Rushden w Newton Bromswold *Pet* from 94. *24 Lodge Road, Rushden, Northants NN10 9HA* Rushden (01933) 316834

KAYE, Canon Gerald Trevor. b 32. Man Univ BSc54. Oak Hill Th Coll. **d** 56 **p** 57. C Widnes St Ambrose *Liv* 56-58; C St Helens St Mark 58-62; V Brixton Hill St Sav *S'wark* 62-65; Canada 65-85; Hon Can Keew 70-75; Adn Patricia 75-85; V Slough *Ox* from 85. *St Paul's Vicarage, 196 Stoke Road, Slough SL2 5AY* Slough (01753) 521497

KAYE, Norman. b 15. St Chad's Coll Dur BA47. **d** 49 **p** 50. R Leighton w Eaton Constantine *Lich* 68-80; P-in-c Wroxeter 68-80; rtd 80. *7 Rope Lane, Shavington, Crewe CW2 5DT* Crewe (01270) 664170

KAYE, Timothy Henry. b 52. Linc Th Coll 77. **d** 80 **p** 81. C Warsop *S'well* 80-83; C Far Headingley St Chad *Ripon* 83-86; P-in-c Birkby *Wakef* 86; TV N Huddersfield 86-91; R Stone St Mich w Aston St Sav *Lich* 91-95; V S Kirkby *Wakef* from 95. *The Vicarage, Bull Lane, South Kirkby, Pontefract, W Yorkshire WF9 3QD* Pontefract (01977) 642795

KEANE, Canon James Goldsworthy. b 23. OBE84 JP71. Selw Coll Cam BA47 MA49. Cuddesdon Coll 47. **d** 49 **p** 50. Dir Ch in Wales Publications 65-79; Gen Sec Ch in Wales Prov Educn Coun 65-79; Hon Can Llan Cathl *Llan* 73-92; R St Andrew's Major and Michaelston-le-Pit 79-92; Chan Llan Cathl 90-92; rtd 92; Perm to Offic *Llan* from 92. *3 Tudor Close, Westbourne Road, Penarth, S Glam CF64 5BR*

KEARNS, Mrs Mary Leah. b 38. **d** 87 **p** 94. Par Dn Morden *S'wark* 87-88; Asst Chapl HM Pris Holloway from 88. *25 Leafield Road, London SW20 9AG* 0181-540 1594 Fax 0171-700 0297

KEARNS, Philip Gillin. b 59. Ripon Coll Cuddesdon 90. **d** 92 **p** 93. C Winchmore Hill St Paul *Lon* from 92. *St Paul's Lodge, 58 Church Hill, London N21 1JA* 0181-882 3298

KEARON, Kenneth Arthur. b 53. TCD BA76 MA79 MPhil91. CITC 78. **d** 81 **p** 82. C Raheny w Coolock *D & G* 81-84; Lect TCD 82-90; Dean of Residence TCD 84-90; I Tullow *D & G* from 90. *Tullow Rectory, Brighton Road, Carrickmines, Dublin 18, Irish Republic* Dublin (1) 289-3135

KEAST, William. b 43. Univ Coll Ox BA65 DipEd66. Local NSM Course 86. **d** 88 **p** 89. NSM Scotton w Northorpe *Linc* from 88. *4 Crapple Lane, Scotton, Gainsborough, Lincs DN21 3QT* Scunthorpe (01724) 763190

KEATES, Frederick. b 08. Ball Coll Ox BA35 MA35. Ripon Hall Ox 35. **d** 36 **p** 37. V Four Oaks *Birm* 51-72; rtd 83. *Durley, 30 Four Oaks Road, Sutton Coldfield, W Midlands B74 2TJ* 0121-308 0204

KEATING, Christopher Robin. b 39. K Coll Lon BD AKC84. Sarum Th Coll 62. **d** 65 **p** 66. C Baildon *Bradf* 65-67; CF 67-72; V Thornton Heath St Paul *Cant* 72-79; C Harold Hill St Geo *Chelmsf* 85-89; V Goodmayes All SS from 89. *All Saints' Vicarage, Broomhill Road, Ilford, Essex IG3 9SJ* 0181-590 1476

KEATING, Geoffrey John. b 52. Liv Poly HND79 Open Univ BA94. St Steph Ho Ox 81. **d** 84 **p** 85. C Lanc Ch Ch w St Jo and St Anne *Blackb* 84-85; C Rotherham *Sheff* 85-87; C Mexborough 87; V Bentley 87-91; V Penponds *Truro* from 91. *The Vicarage, Mill Road, Penponds, Camborne, Cornwall TR14 0QH* Camborne (01209) 712329

KEATING, William Edward. b 10. Trin Coll Ox BA32. Lich Th Coll 33. **d** 33 **p** 34. Chapl Hurstwood Park Hosp Haywards Heath 63-75; St Fran Hosp Haywards Heath 63-75; rtd 75. *Manormead, Tilford Road, Hindhead, Surrey GU26 6RP* Hindhead (01428) 607539

KEAY, Alfred David. b 26. Aston Univ MSc72. Qu Coll Birm 76. **d** 79 **p** 80. Hon C Penkridge w Stretton *Lich* 79-82; C Rugeley 82-85; V Cheswardine 85-95; V Hales 85-95; rtd 95. *2 The Coppice, Farcroft Gardens, Market Drayton, Shropshire TF9 3UA* Market Drayton (01630) 657924

KEDDIE, Canon Tony. b 37. Qu Coll Birm 63. **d** 66 **p** 67. C Barnoldswick w Bracewell *Bradf* 66-69; C New Bentley *Sheff* 69-71; TV Seacroft *Ripon* 71-79; V Kippax 79-85; TR Kippax w Allerton Bywater 85-92; R Fountains Gp from 92; Hon Can Ripon Cathl from 94. *Fountains Rectory, Winksley, Ripon, N Yorkshire HG4 3NR* Kirkby Malzeard (01765) 658260

KEE, David. b 04. Linc Th Coll 45. **d** 47 **p** 48. OGS from 55; V Podington w Farndish *St Alb* 64-73; rtd 74; Perm to Offic *St Alb* from 74; Perm to Offic *Win* from 75. *3 Victoria House, Victoria Road, Winchester, Hants SO23 7BP* Winchester (01962) 852156

KEEBLE, Dorothy Deborah. b 20. **d** 87. NSM Glas H Cross *Glas* from 87. *12 Housel Avenue, Glasgow G13 3UR* 0141-959 3102

KEEBLE, Stephen Robert. b 56. K Coll Lon BD84 AKC84 Selw Coll Cam DipTh86. Westcott Ho Cam 85. **d** 87 **p** 88. C Lt Stanmore St Lawr *Lon* 87-90; C Headstone St Geo 90-93; P-in-c from 93. *The Vicarage, 96 Pinner View, Harrow, Middx HA1 4RJ* 0181-427 1253

KEECH, April Irene. b 52. Pennsylvania Univ BA76. Trin Coll Bris BA89. **d** 89 **p** 92. C Walthamstow St Luke *Chelmsf* 89-92; USA 92-95; V Deptford St Jo w H Trin *S'wark* from 95. *St John's Vicarage, St John's Vale, London SE8 4EA* 0181-692 2857

KEEFER, John Samuel. b 46. BA69 MDiv72 ThM79. **d** 72 **p** 73. USA 72-79; Chapl Bucharest w Sofia *Eur* 84-86; Switzerland from 86. *Address temp unknown*

KEEGAN, Ven Donald Leslie. b 37. ACII. CITC 65. **d** 68 **p** 69. C Drumragh w Mountfield *D & R* 68-72; I Birr w Lorrha, Dorrha and Lockeen *L & K* from 72; Can Killaloe Cathl 80-82; Treas Killaloe Cathl 82-87; Prec Limerick and Killaloe Cathls 87-89; Adn Killaloe, Kilfenora, Clonfert etc from 89. *The Rectory, Birr, Co Offaly, Irish Republic* Birr (509) 20021 Fax 21547

KEEGAN, Graham Brownell. b 40. Nottm Univ CertEd68. N Ord Course 81. **d** 84 **p** 85. C Highfield *Liv* 84-87; V Ince St Mary 87-95; V Newton in Makerfield St Pet from 95. *St Peter's Vicarage, Church Street, Newton-le-Willows, Merseyside WA12 9SR* Newton-le-Willows (0925) 224815

KEELER, Alan. b 58. MIEE87 CEng88 City Univ BSc81. St Jo Coll Nottm DTS90. **d** 90 **p** 91. C Paddock Wood *Roch* 90-94; V Blendon from 94. *The Vicarage, 37 Bladindon Drive, Bexley, Kent DA5 3BS* 0181-301 5387

KEELEY, John Robin. b 38. G&C Coll Cam BA62. Clifton Th Coll 62. **d** 64 **p** 65. C Onslow Square St Paul *Lon* 64-66; C Hove Bp Hannington Memorial Ch *Chich* 66-69; C Harborne Heath *Birm* 69-72; V Leic H Trin *Leic* 72-74; P-in-c Leic St Jo 72-74; V Leic H Trin w St Jo 74-80; Perm to Offic *St Alb* 81-86; Tutor E Anglian Minl Tr Course *Ely* from 95. *11 Townsend, Little Dowham, Ely, Cambs CB6 2TA* Ely (01353) 698209

KEELEY, Keith Morgan. b 12. Man Univ BA33 MA36. **d** 49 **p** 50. R Hinstock *Lich* 59-64; rtd 77. *36 College Road, Newport, Isle of Wight PO30 1HB* Isle of Wight (01983) 523465

KEELING, Brian Arnold. b 35. Coll of Resurr Mirfield. **d** 86 **p** 87. NSM Derby St Mark *Derby* from 86. *31 Highfield Lane, Chaddesden, Derby DE21 6DE* Derby (01332) 668987

KEELING, James Michael. b 33. Dur Univ BA55 MA61. Cuddesdon Coll 57. **d** 59 **p** 60. C Pallion *Dur* 59-64; V Appleton Roebuck w Acaster Selby *York* 65-69; Asst Dir WCC Ecum Inst Celigny 69-72; Lect St Andr Univ from 72; Perm to Offic *Glas* from 92. *17 Cowgate, Garlieston, Newton Stewart, Wigtownshire DG8 8BW* Garlieston (019886) 629

KEELING, Peter Frank. b 34. Kelham Th Coll. **d** 58 **p** 59. C S Elmsall *Wakef* 58-63; C Barnsley St Mary 63-67; V Ravensthorpe 67-73; V Cudworth 73-83; R Downham Market

w Bexwell *Ely* from 83; RD Fincham 83-94; V Crimplesham w Stradsett from 85. *The Rectory, Downham Market, Norfolk PE38 9LE* Downham Market (01366) 382187

KEEN, Charles William Ernest. b 14. Chich Th Coll 48. **d** 51 **p** 52. R Ide Hill *Roch* 66-73; Chapl Sundridge Hosp Kent 66-73; rtd 73; Perm to Offic *Cant* from 73. *4 Godwyn Road, Deal, Kent CT14 6QR* Deal (01304) 362187

KEEN, Michael Spencer. b 41. GRSM62 ARCM St Pet Coll Ox BA68 MA72 Reading Univ CertEd. Westcott Ho Cam 68. **d** 73 **p** 74. Hon C W Derby (or Tuebrook) St Jo *Liv* 73-74; Hon C Stanley 74-76; Chs Youth and Community Officer Telford *Lich* 77-82; Dioc Unemployment Officer *Sheff* 82-89; Hon C Brixton Rd Ch Ch *S'wark* 89-92; Employment Development Officer 89-92; Perm to Offic from 92. *114 Lowden Road, London SE24 0BQ* 0171-274 2206

KEENAN, Leslie Herbert. b 32. Cranmer Hall Dur. **d** 66 **p** 67. C Anston *Sheff* 66-70; C Woodsetts 66-70; Chapl HM Borstal Pollington 70-78; V Balne *Sheff* 70-78; V Poughill *Truro* from 78. *The Vicarage, Poughill, Bude, Cornwall EX23 9ER* Bude (01288) 355183

KEENE, Canon David Peter. b 32. Trin Hall Cam BA56 MA60. Westcott Ho Cam. **d** 58 **p** 59. C Radcliffe-on-Trent *S'well* 58-61; C Mansf St Pet 61-64; V Nottm St Cath 64-71; R Bingham 71-81; Dioc Dir of Ords 81-90; Can Res S'well Minster from 81; Dioc Adv for Overseas Affairs from 94. *2 Vicar's Court, Southwell, Notts NG25 0HP* Southwell (01636) 813188 or 812649

KEENE, Mrs Muriel Ada. b 35. dss 83 **d** 87 **p** 94. Dioc Lay Min Adv *S'well* 87-88; Asst Dir of Ords 88-90; D-in-c Oxton 90-93; D-in-c Epperstone 90-94; D-in-c Gonalston 90-94; NSM Lowdham w Caythorpe, and Gunthorpe from 94; rtd 95. *2 Vicar's Court, Southwell, Notts NG25 0HP* Southwell (01636) 813188

KEEP, Andrew James. b 55. Collingwood Coll Dur BA77 Yale Univ STM84. Sarum & Wells Th Coll 78. **d** 80 **p** 81. C Banstead *Guildf* 80-83; Chapl Qu Eliz Hosp Banstead 80-83; USA 83-84; Chapl Cranleigh Sch Surrey from 84; Lic to Offic *Guildf* from 84; Perm to Offic *Win* from 84. *Cranleigh School, Cranleigh, Surrey GU6 8QQ* Cranleigh (01483) 274561

KEEP, Hugh Charles John Martin. b 45. Qu Coll Birm 90. **d** 92 **p** 93. C Aston Cantlow and Wilmcote w Billesley *Cov* from 92. *Rose Cottage, Church Lane, Aston Cantlow, Solihull, W Midlands B95 6JB* Great Alne (01789) 488207

KEETON, Barry. b 40. Dur Univ BA61 MA69 MLitt78 K Coll Lon BD63 AKC63. **d** 64 **p** 65. C S Bank *York* 64-67; C Middlesb St Cuth 67-69; C Kingston upon Hull St Alb 70-71; V Appleton-le-Street w Amotherby 71-74; Dioc Ecum Adv 74-81; R Ampleforth w Oswaldkirk 74-78; P-in-c Barmby on the Marsh 78-79; P-in-c Laxton w Blacktoft 78-79; P-in-c Wressell 78-79; V Howden 78-79; TR Howden TM 80-91; Can and Preb York Minster 85-91; RD Howden 86-91; TR Lewes All SS, St Anne, St Mich and St Thos *Chich* from 91. *St Anne's Rectory, 57 St Anne's Crescent, Lewes, E Sussex BN7 1SD* Lewes (01273) 472545

KEFFORD, Peter Charles. b 44. Nottm Univ BTh74. Linc Th Coll 70. **d** 74 **p** 75. C W Wimbledon Ch Ch *S'wark* 74-77; C All Hallows by the Tower etc *Lon* 77-81; C-in-c Pound Hill CD *Chich* 81; TV Worth 82-83; TR 83-92; V Henfield w Shermanbury and Woodmancote from 92. *The Vicarage, Church Lane, Henfield, W Sussex BN5 9NY* Henfield (01273) 492017

KEGG, Gordon Rutherford. b 45. Reading Univ BSc66 Imp Coll Lon PhD71 DIC71 Lon Univ CertEd74. Oak Hill Th Coll DipHE90. **d** 90 **p** 91. C Luton Lewsey St Hugh *St Alb* 90-94; TV Hemel Hempstead from 94. *St Barnabas Vicarage, Everest Way, Hemel Hempstead, Herts HP2 4HY* Hemel Hempstead (01442) 253681

KEIGHLEY, David John. b 48. CertEd Open Univ BA88. Sarum & Wells Th Coll 82. **d** 83 **p** 84. C Sawbridgeworth *St Alb* 83-86; TV Saltash *Truro* 86-89; V Lanlivery w Luxulyan from 89. *The Vicarage, Luxulyan, Bodmin, Cornwall PL30 5EE* St Austell (01726) 850880

KEIGHLEY, Martin Philip. b 61. Edin Univ MA83. Westcott Ho Cam 86. **d** 88 **p** 89. C Lytham St Cuth *Blackb* 88-91; C Lanc St Mary 91-93; R Halton w Aughton from 93. *The Rectory, 110 High Road, Halton, Lancaster LA2 6PU* Halton-on-Lune (01524) 811370

KEIGHTLEY, Canon Peter Edward. b 17. Leeds Univ BA41. Coll of Resurr Mirfield 41. **d** 43 **p** 44. V Southsea H Spirit *Portsm* 67-76; Chapl St Mary's Hosp Portsm 76-82; Hon Can Portsm Cathl *Portsm* 81-82; rtd 82; Perm to Offic *Portsm* from 83. *11 Dolphin Court, St Helen's Parade, Southsea, Hants PO4 0QL* Portsmouth (01705) 816697

KEIGHTLEY, Thomas. b 44. CITC 79. **d** 79 **p** 80. C Seagoe *D & D* 79-83; I Belvoir from 83. *3 Brerton Crescent, Belfast BT8 4QD* Belfast (01232) 643777

KEILLER, Mrs Jane Elizabeth. b 52. Westmr Coll Ox BEd74 St Jo Coll Dur DipTh78 Bangalore Univ DipTh79. Cranmer

Hall Dur 76. **dss** 80 **d** 87 **p** 94. Cam H Trin w St Andr Gt *Ely* 80-86; Cam St Barn 86-87; NSM from 87. *Chestnut Cottage, 38 Pierce Lane, Cambridge CB1 5DL* Cambridge (01223) 881444

KEIRLE, Michael Robert. b 62. Trin Coll Bris BA89. **d** 89 **p** 90. C Orpington Ch Ch *Roch* 89-92; Zimbabwe 92-95; R Keston *Roch* from 95. *The Rectory, 24 Commonside, Keston, Kent BR2 6BP* Farnborough (01689) 853186

KEITH, Andrew James Buchanan. b 47. Qu Coll Cam BA69 MA73. Wycliffe Hall Ox 71. **d** 74 **p** 75. C Warrington St Elphin *Liv* 74-77; C Southgate *Chich* 77-80; C-in-c Broadfield CD 80-82; P-in-c Walberton w Binsted 82-85; P-in-c Aldingbourne 83-85; Chapl Oswestry Sch from 85. *12 High Lea Close, Oswestry, Shropshire SY11 1SX* Oswestry (01691) 656296 or 655711

KEITH, John. b 25. LRAM50 LGSM50 AGSM51. Cuddesdon Coll 60. **d** 62 **p** 63. C Raynes Park St Sav *S'wark* 65-68; rtd 90. *Leaning Tree, Inchlaggan, Invergarry, Inverness-shire PH35 4HR*

KEITH, Canon John Frederick Butterfield. b 12. Trin Coll Cam BA35 MA44. Cuddesdon Coll 36. **d** 37 **p** 38. C Greenford H Cross *Lon* 37-41; CF (EC) 40-46; R Ashwell *St Alb* 46-51; R Fakenham w Alethorpe *Nor* 51-57; New Zealand from 58; Hon Can Christchurch Cathl 71-80; Prec 81-84. *Flat 2, 76 Bishop Street, Christchurch 1, New Zealand* Christchurch (3) 651101

KELK, Michael Anthony. b 48. Sarum & Wells Th Coll. **d** 83 **p** 84. C Ross w Brampton Abbotts, Bridstow and Peterstow *Heref* 83-86; P-in-c Burghill from 86; P-in-c Stretton Sugwas from 86. *The Vicarage, Burghill, Hereford HR4 7SG* Hereford (01432) 760246

KELLAM, Miss Margaret June. b 32. Trin Coll Bris IDC70. **dss** 77 **d** 87 **p** 94. Heeley *Sheff* 77-89; Par Dn 87-89; Asst Chapl R Hallamshire Hosp Sheff 89-92; rtd 92; Asst Chapl Cen Sheff Univ Hosps NHS Trust from 92; Chapl Sheff Children's Hosp from 92. *170 Westwick Road, Sheffield S8 7BX* Sheffield (0114) 237 6773

KELLAND, Kenneth William Jerome. b 16. S'wark Ord Course 63. **d** 66 **p** 67. C Sholing *Win* 69-74; V Weston 74-82; rtd 82; Hon C Odiham w S Warnborough and Long Sutton *Win* 82-85; Hon C Herriard w Winslade and Long Sutton etc 85-86. *50 Wooteys Way, Alton, Hants GU34 2JZ* Alton (01420) 85325

KELLEN, David. b 52. Univ of Wales (Cardiff) DipTh73. St Mich Coll Llan 70. **d** 75 **p** 76. C Mynyddislwyn *Mon* 75-77; C Risca 77-78; C Malpas 78-81; V Newport All SS 81-88; V St Mellons and Michaelston-y-Fedw from 88. *The Vicarage, Tyr Winch Road, St Mellons, Cardiff CF3 9UP* Cardiff (01222) 796560

KELLETT, Colin. b 25. Worc Ord Coll 65. **d** 67 **p** 68. C Dewsbury Moor *Wakef* 69-72; V Lundwood 72-77; V Gawber 77-88; rtd 88. *11 Hurrell Court, Hurrell Lane, Thornton Dale, Pickering, N Yorkshire YO18 7QR* Pickering (01751) 476487

KELLETT, Neil. b 41. Bps' Coll Cheshunt 64. **d** 66 **p** 67. C Ex St Thos *Ex* 66-72; C Win H Trin *Win* 72-74; P-in-c Redditch St Geo *Worc* 74-77; Canada from 77. *39 Fox Avenue, St John's, Newfoundland, Canada, A1B 2H8* St John's (709) 726-2883

KELLEY, Neil George. b 64. Westcott Ho Cam 88. **d** 91 **p** 92. C E Bedfont *Lon* 91-93; C Chiswick St Nic w St Mary from 93. *St Denys Cottage, Church Street, London W4 2PD* 0181-995 2019 Fax as telephone

KELLY, Canon Albert Norman. b 21. TCD BA43 MA63. **d** 44 **p** 45. C-in-c New Haw CD *Guildf* 66-72; V New Haw 72-78; RD Chertsey 73-75; RD Runnymede 75-78; V Egham Hythe 78-86; Hon Can Guildf Cathl 80-86; rtd 86; USPG Area Sec 88-93. *21 Rosetta Road, Belfast BT6 0LQ* Belfast (01232) 693921

KELLY, Dr Brian Eugene. b 56. Otago Univ BA77 Dunedin Coll PGCE79 Bris Univ PhD93. Trin Coll Bris BA89. **d** 90 **p** 91. NSM Redland *Bris* 90-93; C Scarborough St Mary w Ch Ch and H Apostles *York* from 93. *13 Woodall Avenue, Scarborough, N Yorkshire YO12 7TH* Scarborough (01723) 361188

KELLY, Canon Brian Horace. b 34. St Jo Coll Dur BA57 DipTh58 MA69. **d** 58 **p** 59. C Douglas St Geo and St Barn *S & M* 58-61; V Foxdale 61-64; V Bolton All So w St Jas *Man* 64-73; V Maughold *S & M* 73-77; Dir of Ords from 76; V German from 77; Can and Prec St German's Cathl from 80. *The Cathedral Vicarage, Albany Road, Peel, Isle of Man IM5 1JS* Peel (01624) 842608

KELLY, Christopher Augustine (Kit). b 15. Croix de Guerre 45 TD65. Keble Coll Ox BA37. Ripon Hall Ox 37. **d** 45 **p** 46. V Bolton Breightmet St Jas *Man* 67-76; V Nelson in Lt Marsden *Blackb* 76-83; rtd 83; Perm to Offic *Bradf* from 83. *33 River Place, Gargrave, Skipton, N Yorkshire BD23 3RY* Skipton (01756) 748247

KELLY, Canon Dennis Charles. b 31. Liv Univ BA52. Lich Th Coll 54. **d** 56 **p** 57. C Tranmere St Paul *Ches* 56-59; C-in-c

Grange St Andr CD 59-63; P-in-c Grange St Andr 63-65; V 65-67; R Coppenhall 67-82; R W Kirby St Andr from 82; Hon Can Ches Cathl from 86. *St Andrew's Vicarage, 2 Lingdale Road, West Kirby, Wirral, Merseyside L48 5DQ* 0151-632 4728

KELLY, Desmond Norman (Des). b 42. Oak Hill Th Coll DipHE90. **d** 90 **p** 91. C Braintree *Chelmsf* 90-94; P-in-c Castle Hedingham 94-95; P-in-c Sible Hedingham 94-95; R Sible Hedingham w Castle Hedingham from 95. *The Vicarage, 15 Queen Street, Castle Hedingham, Halstead, Essex CO9 3EZ* Halstead (01787) 60274

KELLY, Canon Edward William Moncrieff (Ted). b 28. AKC57. **d** 57 **p** 58. Hon C Eltham St Jo *S'wark* 69-87; Org Sec New Guinea Miss 69-77; Org Sec Papua New Guinea Ch Partnership 77-87; Hon Can Papua New Guinea from 78; TR Trowbridge H Trin *Sarum* 87-94; Chapl St Jo Hosp Trowbridge 87-94; rtd 94. *133 Borough Road, Petersfield, Hants GU32 3LP* Petersfield (01730) 260399

KELLY, James Ganly Marks. b 16. TCD BA39 MA50. CITC 39. **d** 39 **p** 40. R Siddington w Preston *Glouc* 71-81; rtd 82. *34 Henry Avenue, Rustington, Littlehampton, W Sussex BN16 2PA* Rustington (01903) 770635

KELLY, John Bernal. b 35. K Coll Cam BA57 MA61. Qu Coll Birm 58. **d** 60 **p** 61. C Huyton St Mich *Liv* 60-62; C Gateshead Fell *Dur* 64-68; R Openshaw *Man* 68-75; V Hey 75-87; V Bury St Jo w St Mark 87-93; V Rochdale St Geo w St Alb from 93. *13 Brooklands Court, Bury Road, Rochdale, Lancs OL11 4EJ* Rochdale (01706) 39743

KELLY, John Adrian. b 49. Qu Coll Birm 70. **d** 73 **p** 74. C Formby St Pet *Liv* 73-77; Perm to Offic from 77; Perm to Offic *Blackb* from 77; Org Sec (Dios Liv, Blackb and S & M) CECS 77-92; Deputation Appeals Org (Lancs and Is of Man) 88-92. *159 Forrest Drive, South Park, Lytham, Lytham St Annes, Lancs FY8 4QG* Lytham (01253) 730083

KELLY, John Dickinson. b 42. Nottm Univ BA63. Ripon Hall Ox 63. **d** 65 **p** 66. C Egremont *Carl* 65-67; C Upperby St Jo 67-70; V Arlecdon 70-73; V Barrow St Aid 73-79; V Milnthorpe 79-83; V Beetham and Milnthorpe 83-85; V Camerton St Pet 85-88; P-in-c Camerton H Trin W Seaton 86-88; V Camerton, Seaton and W Seaton from 88. *The Vicarage, Ling Beck Park, Seaton, Workington, Cumbria CA14 1JQ* Workington (01900) 602162

KELLY, John Graham. b 60. Lanc Univ LLB82 Man Poly Solicitor 84. St Jo Coll Nottm BTh91. **d** 94 **p** 95. C Normanton *Derby* from 94. *211 Village Street, Derby DE23 8DE* Derby (01332) 767407

KELLY, John Henry. b 20. Vancouver Sch of Th STh65. **d** 55 **p** 59. C Hall Green St Pet *Birm* 69-70; V Smethwick St Mich 71-78; P-in-c Smethwick St Steph 72-78; V Selly Oak St Wulstan 78-80; R Over Whitacre w Shustoke 80-86; rtd 86; Perm to Offic *Ches* from 86. *61 Hallfields Road, Tarvin, Chester CH3 8ET* Tarvin (01829) 741218

KELLY, Canon John Norman Davidson. b 09. FBA65 Glas Univ MA31 Hon DD58 Qu Coll Ox BA34 BD51 DD51. St Steph Ho Ox 33. **d** 34 **p** 35. Lic to Offic *Ox* from 35; Can and Preb Chich Cathl *Chich* 48-93; Prin St Edm Hall Ox 51-79; rtd 75. *7 Crick Road, Oxford OX2 6QJ* Oxford (01865) 512907

KELLY, John Rowe. b 32. Edin Th Coll. **d** 85 **p** 86. C Blyth St Mary *Newc* 85-88; C Slaley 88-91; C Healey 88-91; TV Alston Team from 91; Chapl Alston Cottage Hosp from 91. *The Parsonage, Brampton Road, Alston, Cumbria CA9 3AA* Hexham (01434) 381458

KELLY, Malcolm Bernard. b 46. St Mich Coll Llan 72. **d** 74 **p** 75. C Tranmere St Paul w St Luke *Ches* 74-77; Chapl Bebington Hosp from 76; C Barnston *Ches* 77-80; R Thurstaston 80-92; R Grappenhall from 92. *The Rectory, 17 Hill Top Road, Grappenhall, Warrington WA4 3EDD* Warrington (01925) 261546

KELLY, Martin Herbert. b 55. Selw Coll Cam MA90. Aston Tr Scheme 78 Ripon Coll Cuddesdon 80. **d** 83 **p** 84. C Clapham Old Town *S'wark* 83-87; Chapl and Fell Selw Coll Cam 87-92; Chapl Newnham Coll Cam 87-92; C Limpsfield and Titsey *S'wark* from 95. *St Andrew's House, Limpsfield Chart, Oxted, Surrey RH8 0TB* Oxted (01883) 723153

KELLY, Nigel James. b 60. N Staffs Poly BSc83. Ripon Coll Cuddesdon 83. **d** 86 **p** 87. C Cen Telford *Lich* 86-90; TV 90-92; Chapl RN from 92. *Directorate Gen, RN Chapl Services, Room 203, Victory Building, HM Naval Base, Portsmouth PO1 3LS* Portsmouth (01705) 727903 Fax 727112

KELLY, Norman James. b 11. K Coll Lon BD36 AKC36. Wycliffe Hall Ox 36. **d** 36 **p** 37. C Champion Hill St Sav *S'wark* 36-39; C Newhaven *Chich* 39-40; C E Grinstead St Swithun 40-46; V Westf 46-50; New Zealand 50-57; V Canewdon w Paglesham *Chelmsf* from 57. *The Vicarage, High Street, Canewdon, Rochford, Essex SS4 3QA* Southend-on-Sea (01702) 258217

KELLY, Paul Maitland Hillyard. b 24. Ball Coll Ox BA50 MA54. Wells Th Coll 50. **d** 52 **p** 53. P-in-c Preston St Pet

Blackb 67-70; V Ottershaw *Guildf* 70-77; R Ickenham *Lon* 77-94; rtd 94. *37 Dodd Avenue, Wells, Somerset BA5 3JU* Wells (01749) 673334

KELLY, Peter Hugh. b 46. Sarum & Wells Th Coll 81. **d** 84 **p** 85. C Fareham H Trin *Portsm* 84-87; Chapl and Prec Portsm Cathl 87-90; V Eastney from 90. *St Margaret's Vicarage, 13 Cousins Grove, Southsea, Hants PO4 9RP* Portsmouth (01705) 731316

KELLY, Richard Peter. b 47. BA PhD. CITC BTh90. **d** 90 **p** 91. C Dromore Cathl *D & D* 90-93; C Gweedore, Carrickfin and Templecrone *D & R* from 93. *The Rectory, Bunbeg, Letterkenny, Co Donegal, Irish Republic* Bunbeg (75) 31043

KELLY, Stephen Paul. b 55. Keble Coll Ox BA77. Linc Th Coll 77. **d** 79 **p** 80. C Illingworth *Wakef* 79-82; C Knottingley 82-84; V Alverthorpe 84-93; Dioc Ecum Officer 88-93; TR Bingley All SS *Bradf* from 93. *The Vicarage, Hallbank Drive, Bingley, W Yorkshire BD16 4BZ* Bradford (01274) 563113

KELLY, Canon William. b 35. Dur Univ BA58 St Cath Coll Ox DipTh59. Lambeth STh75 Wycliffe Hall Ox 58. **d** 60 **p** 61. C Walney Is *Carl* 60-66; R Distington 66-71; V Barrow St Matt 71-81; RD Furness 77-81; Hon Can Carl Cathl from 79; Dir of Ords from 81; V Dalston 81-92; RD Carl 83-88; P-in-c Raughton Head w Gatesgill 86-92; P-in-c Maryport from 92; P-in-c Flimby from 93. *The Vicarage, Church Street, Maryport, Cumbria CA15 6HE* Maryport (01900) 813077

KELLY, William Edward (Bill). b 37. Univ of Wales (Lamp) BA57 St Cath Soc Ox BA59 MA63. St Steph Ho Ox 57. **d** 60 **p** 61. C S Bank *York* 60-63; C Ingoldisthorpe *Nor* 63-66; C Heacham 63-66; Chapl RAF 66-82; Chapl Woodbridge Sch Suffolk 82-88; V Newport St Paul *Mon* from 90. *11B Victoria Place, Newport, Gwent NP9 4DZ* Newport (01633) 266657

KELLY, William Frederick Paul. b 12. Ch Ch Ox BA35 MA49. Sarum Th Coll 63. **d** 64 **p** 65. R Reepham and Hackford w Whitwell and Kerdiston *Nor* 68-80; rtd 80; P-in-c Thurning w Wood Dalling *Nor* 80-81; Chapl to Rtd Clergy and Clergy Widows Officer from 81. *40 Catton Grove Road, Norwich NR3 3NW* Norwich (01603) 424961

KELLY, William Norman. b 21. St Aid Birkenhead. **d** 64 **p** 65. V Wingates *Man* 69-75; Perm to Offic 76-84; Chapl HM Pris Liv 77-78; Chapl HM Borstal Stoke Heath 78-84; V Castletown *S & M* 84-92; rtd 92. *Crossag Villa, St Mark's Road, Ballasalla, Isle of Man IM9 3EF* Castletown (01624) 825582

KELLY, William Ralston. b 27. TCD BA52 MA55. Lich Th Coll 52. **d** 54 **p** 55. Hd of RE Bablake Sch Cov 60-92; rtd 92. *108 Duncroft Avenue, Coventry CV6 2BW* Coventry (01203) 336807

KELLY, Canon William Robert. b 28. QUB BSc57 BTh. CITC 62. **d** 62 **p** 63. C Lurgan Ch Ch *D & D* 62-66; I Clondehorkey *D & R* 66-70; I Raheny w Coolock *D & G* 70-75; Peru 75-83; I Ballinderry *Conn* 83-89; Hon Can Peru 83; I Belf St Aid *Conn* from 89; Can Belf Cathl from 94. *St Aidan's Rectory, 35 Eglantine Avenue, Belfast BT9 6DW* Belfast (01232) 666741

KELSEY, Michael Ray. b 22. FEPA57. Wycliffe Hall Ox 60. **d** 62 **p** 63. V Scarborough St Jas *York* 68-71; Asst to the Gen Sec USCL 71-74; V Blackheath St Jo *S'wark* 74-87; rtd 87; Perm to Offic *St E* from 88. *25 Prospect Place, Leiston, Suffolk IP16 4AL* Leiston (01728) 830975

KELSHAW, Terence. b 36. Lon Univ DipTh67. Oak Hill Th Coll. **d** 67 **p** 68. C Clifton Ch Ch w Em *Bris* 67-71; C Woking St Jo *Guildf* 71-73; V Bris H Trin *Bris* 73-75; P-in-c Easton St Gabr w St Laur 73-75; V Easton H Trin w St Gabr and St Lawr 75-80; P-in-c Barton Hill St Luke w Ch Ch 76-80; USA from 80. *4304 Carlisle Northeast, Albuquerque, New Mexico 87107-4811, USA*

KELSO, Andrew John (Andy). b 47. LRAM73 Lon Univ BA70. St Jo Coll Nottm 83. **d** 85 **p** 86. C Gorleston St Mary *Nor* 85-87; C Hellesdon 87-90; TV Ipsley *Worc* from 90. *Matchborough Vicarage, Winward Road, Redditch, Worcs B98 0SX* Redditch (01527) 29098

KELSO, William Thomas Proctor. b 19. TCD BA41 MA45. CITC 43. **d** 43 **p** 44. R Blendworth, Chalton and Idsworth *Portsm* 63-70; V Balham Hill Ascension *S'wark* 70-78; Perm to Offic *Chich* 78-84; Chapl and Tutor Whittington Coll Felbridge 78-84; rtd 84; Perm to Offic *S'wark* 84-92. *12 Brunswick Place, Lymington, Hants SO41 9EQ* Lymington (01590) 677939

KEMM, William St John (Bill). b 39. Birm Univ BA62 MA65. Ridley Hall Cam 62. **d** 64 **p** 65. C Kingswinford H Trin *Lich* 64-68; C Hednesford 68-71; V Hanbury 71-76; R Berrow and Breane *B & W* 76-92; V Hertf All SS *St Alb* from 92. *All Saints' Vicarage, Churchfields, Hertford SG13 8AE* Hertford (01992) 582096

KEMP, Allan. b 43. Bps' Coll Cheshunt 65 Oak Hill Th Coll 67. **d** 68 **p** 69. C Tunbridge Wells St Jas *Roch* 68-76; V Becontree St Mary *Chelmsf* 76-90; RD Barking and Dagenham 81-86; V Gt

w Lt Chesterford from 90. *The Vicarage, Great Chesterford, Saffron Walden, Essex CB10 1NP* Saffron Walden (01799) 530317

KEMP, Allan James. b 22. Fitzw Ho Cam BA48. Wells Th Coll 49. **d** 50 **p** 51. C Speke All SS *Liv* 50-54; V Askern *Sheff* 54-58; New Zealand from 58. *Branwell, 138 Bethels Road, RD 1, Henderson, New Zealand* Henderson (9) 810-9898

KEMP, Ms Audrey. b 26. MSR49. Gilmore Ho 62. **dss** 69 **d** 87 **p** 94. S Ockendon Hosp 70-71; N Greenford All Hallows *Lon* 71-72; Feltham 72-80; Brentford St Faith 80-83; Hanworth All SS 83-85; Hanworth St Geo 85-87; Par Dn 87-88; rtd 88; Perm to Offic *B & W* 88-89; Hon Par Dn Ditcheat w E Pennard and Pylle 89-94; P-in-c 94-95. *25 Victoria Court, Castle Cary, Somerset BA7 7BX* Castle Cary (01963) 51276

KEMP, Barry. b 48. St Edm Hall Ox BA70 MA75 Nottm Univ DipTh73 Newc Univ CertEd82. Linc Th Coll 71. **d** 74 **p** 75. C Ashton Ch Ch *Man* 74-77; CF 77-81; C Dunston *Dur* 81-83; Perm to Offic *Newc* 83-87; C Monkseaton St Mary 88; Chapl Ld Wandsworth Coll Basingstoke from 92. *Kimbers, Lord Wandsworth College, Long Sutton, Basingstoke, Hants RG25 1TB* Basingstoke (01256) 862201

KEMP, Canon Bernard Henry. b 06. St Chad's Coll Dur BA26 MA46 DipTh46. **d** 29 **p** 30. V Guernsey St Steph *Win* 63-81; rtd 81; Perm to Offic *Win* from 81. *Carrefour, La Haye du Puits, Castel, Guernsey, Channel Islands GY5 7HX* Guernsey (01481) 56081

KEMP, Christopher Michael. b 48. K Coll Lon BD71 AKC71. St Aug Coll Cant 75. **d** 76 **p** 77. C Weaverham *Ches* 76-79; C Latchford St Jas 79-82; P-in-c Sandbach Heath 82-88; V Macclesfield St Paul 88-89; C Cheadle Hulme All SS 89-93; C Oxton from 93. *36 Noctorum Dell, Birkenhead, Merseyside L43 9UL* 0151-652 8050

KEMP, Clive Warren. b 36. Sheff Univ BSc60. Clifton Th Coll 62. **d** 64 **p** 65. C Wandsworth All SS *S'wark* 64-67; C Normanton *Wakef* 67-71; V Sandal St Cath 71-76; C Chapeltown *Sheff* 85-87; V Sheff St Jo from 87. *49 Norfolk Park Avenue, Sheffield S2 2RA* Sheffield (0114) 275 9998

KEMP, Eric Nelson. b 05. Lich Th Coll 37. **d** 40 **p** 41. USA 68-70; C Hawksworth w Scarrington *S'well* 70-71; rtd 71; P-in-c Morley *Derby* 81-82. *29 Capel Court, The Burgage, Prestbury, Cheltenham, Glos GL52 3EL* Cheltenham (01242) 261339

✠**KEMP, Rt Rev Eric Waldram.** b 15. FRHistS51 Ex Coll Ox BA36 MA40 BD44 DD61 Sussex Univ Hon DLitt. St Steph Ho Ox 36. **d** 39 **p** 40 **c** 74. C Newtown St Luke *Win* 39-41; Lib Pusey Ho 41-46; Chapl Ch Ch Ox 43-46; Tutor and Chapl Ex Coll Ox 46-69; Can and Preb Linc Cathl *Linc* from 52; Chapl to The Queen 67-69; Dean Worc 69-74; Bp Chich from 74. *The Palace, Chichester, W Sussex PO19 1PY* Chichester (01243) 782161 Fax 531332

KEMP, Geoffrey Bernard. b 20. Lon Univ BD43. ALCD42. **d** 43 **p** 44. V Hadleigh St Barn *Chelmsf* 60-79; R Kelvedon Hatch 79-86; V Navestock 79-86; rtd 86; Perm to Offic *St E* from 86; Perm to Offic *Chelmsf* from 86. *24 Roman Way, Felixstowe, Suffolk IP11 9NJ* Felixstowe (01394) 276691

KEMP, Jack Noel. b 14. Univ Coll Lon BA36 MA38. Wycliffe Hall Ox 55. **d** 55 **p** 56. V Four Elms *Roch* 68-80; rtd 80; Perm to Offic *Cant* from 81. *L'Ancresse, 16 Church Street, Whitstable, Kent CT5 1PJ* Whitstable (01227) 265379

KEMP, John Graham Edwin. b 29. Bris Univ BA51 PGCE52 Lon Univ BD65. Wells Th Coll 63. **d** 65 **p** 66. C Maidenhead St Luke *Ox* 65-70; R Rotherfield Greys 70-78; V Highmore 70-78; Dep Dir Tr Scheme for NSM 78-84; P-in-c Taplow 78-82; TV Burnham w Dropmore, Hitcham and Taplow 82-84; Prin E Anglian Minl Tr Course 84-92; rtd 92. *Lea Cottage, Middleton, Saxmundham, Suffolk IP17 3NJ* Saxmundham (01728) 648324

KEMP, John Robert Deverall. b 42. City Univ BSc65 BD69. Oak Hill Th Coll 66. **d** 70 **p** 71. C Fulham Ch Ch *Lon* 70-73; C Widford *Chelmsf* 73-79; P-in-c New Thundersley 79-84; V from 84; Chapl HM Pris Bullwood Hall from 79. *St George's Vicarage, 89 Rushbottom Lane, Benfleet, Essex SS7 4DN* South Benfleet (01268) 792088 Fax Southend-on-Sea (01702) 207464

KEMP, Michael Rouse. b 36. Called to the Bar (Gray's Inn) 59. Sarum & Wells Th Coll 70. **d** 72 **p** 73. C Brompton H Trin *Lon* 72-76; V Crookes St Tim *Sheff* 76-81; V Norton Woodseats St Chad 81-87; P-in-c Mottingham St Andr *S'wark* 87-95; rtd 95. *24 Homefield Close, Swanley, Kent BR8 7JH* Swanley (01322) 667299

KEMP, William Frederick. b 13. St Aug Coll Cant 38. **d** 40 **p** 41. R Denton w Wootton and Swingfield *Cant* 64-79; rtd 79; Perm to Offic *Cant* 79-80; Hon Min Can Cant Cathl from 80. *12 Chantry Court, St Radigund's Street, Canterbury, Kent CT1 2AD* Canterbury (01227) 462261

KEMPSTER, Robert Alec. b 29. Selw Coll Cam MA53. Coll of Resurr Mirfield 53. **d** 55 **p** 56. C-in-c S'wark All Hallows CD *S'wark* 57-70; Chapl Evelina Children's Hosp 57-70; Chapl Guy's Hosp Lon 70-81; Chapl Nat Hosp for Nervous Diseases

Lon 81-89; Chapl Convent Companions Jes Gd Shep W Ogwell 89; rtd 90; Perm to Offic *Ex* from 90. *15A Seymour Road, Newton Abbot, Devon TQ12 2PT*   Newton Abbot (01626) 61720

KEMPTHORNE, Renatus. b 39. Wadh Coll Ox BA60 DipTh61 MA64. Wycliffe Hall Ox 60. **d** 62 **p** 63. C Stoke *Cov* 62-65; New Zealand 65-68 and from 83; R Wytham *Ox* 68-75; Chapl Bp Grosseteste Coll Linc 75-83. *140 Nile Street, Nelson, New Zealand*   Christchurch (3) 546-7447

KENCHINGTON (nee BALLANTYNE), Mrs Jane Elizabeth Ballantyne. b 58. Hull Univ BSc79 Cam Univ PGCE83. Westcott Ho Cam 88. **d** 90 **p** 94. C Winchcombe, Gretton, Sudeley Manor etc *Glouc* 90-94; C from 94. *Minstrels, 23 The Hyde, Winchcombe, Cheltenham, Glos GL54 5QR* Cheltenham (01242) 604268

KENCHINGTON, Paul Henry. b 54. Worc Coll Ox MA76. St Jo Coll Nottm BA81. **d** 82 **p** 83. C Scarborough St Mary w Ch Ch and H Apostles *York* 82-85; C Caversham and Mapledurham *Ox* 85-89; V Hucclecote *Glouc* from 89. *128 Hucclecote Road, Gloucester GL3 3SB*   Gloucester (01452) 610568

KENDAL, Henry David. b 59. ASVA83 Bris Poly DipVal&EstM80. Lon Bible Coll 90 Oak Hill NSM Course 92. **d** 94 **p** 95. NSM Roxeth *Lon* 94-95; C from 95. *21 Butler Avenue, Harrow, Middx HA1 4EJ*   0181-422 5270

KENDAL, Stephen. b 35. Leeds Univ BA59. Coll of Resurr Mirfield 59. **d** 61 **p** 62. C Seaton Hirst *Newc* 61-63; C Newc St Geo 63-66; C Gosforth All SS 66-70; Ind Chapl *Llan* 70-78; Ind Chapl *Dur* 78-91; Hon C Houghton le Spring 78-90; Ind Chapl *Worc* from 91. *15 St John's Avenue, Kidderminster, Worcs DY11 6AT*   Kidderminster (01562) 823929

KENDALL, Alastair Geoffrey. b 55. BSc DipTh. St Jo Coll Nottm DPS. **d** 84 **p** 85. C Glouc St Aldate *Glouc* 84-87; C Sheff St Jo *Sheff* 87-92; V Bream *Glouc* from 92. *The Vicarage, Bream, Lydney, Glos GL15 6ES*   Dean (01594) 562376

KENDALL, Canon Cosmo Norman. b 13. Keble Coll Ox BA38 MA42. Cuddesdon Coll 38. **d** 39 **p** 40. R Buxhall w Shelland *St E* 49-84; P-in-c 84-95; Hon Can St E Cathl from 77; rtd 84. *The Rectory, Buxhall, Stowmarket, Suffolk IP14 3DJ* Rattlesden (01449) 736236

KENDALL, Edward Oliver Vaughan (Ted). b 33. Dur Univ BA59. Ridley Hall Cam 59. **d** 61 **p** 62. Chapl HM Borstal Portland 68-71; Lic to Offic *Bradf* from 71; rtd 94. *Aldby House, Stackhouse Lane, Settle, N Yorkshire BD24 0DW* Settle (01729) 823555

KENDALL, Frank. b 40. FRSA90 CCC Cam BA62 MA68. S'wark Ord Course 74. **d** 74 **p** 75. NSM Lingfield *S'wark* 74-75 and 78-82; NSM Sketty *S & B* 75-78; NSM Limpsfield and Titsey *S'wark* 82-84; Lic to Offic *Man* 84-89; Lic to Offic *Liv* from 89. *Cromwell Villa, 260 Prescot Road, St Helens, Merseyside WA10 3HR*   St Helens (01744) 27626

KENDALL, George Vincent. b 21. Edin Th Coll 46. **d** 48 **p** 49. P-in-c Gretna *Glas* 56-90; P-in-c Langholm 56-90; rtd 90; Perm to Offic *Glas* from 90. *9 Kestrel Hill, Gretna, Dumfriesshire DG16 5DH*   Gretna (01461) 338268

KENDALL, Gordon Sydney. b 41. **d** 72 **p** 74. Hon C Old Ford St Paul w St Steph and St Mark *Lon* 72-82; Hon C Homerton St Luke 86-92; Chapl Hackney Hosp Gp Lon 87-92; Chapl Asst Homerton Hosp Lon 87-92; Chapl Torbay Hosp Torquay from 92; Lic to Offic *Ex* from 92. *Torbay Hospital, Lawes Bridge, Newton Road, Torquay TQ2 7AA, or 19 Arden Drive, Torquay TQ2 6DZ*   Torquay (01803) 614567 or 616119

KENDALL, Miss Jacqueline Ann. b 63. Univ of Wales (Abth) BA85. Cranmer Hall Dur 88. **d** 91 **p** 94. Par Dn Stockport St Sav *Ches* 91-94; C 94-95; C Acton & Worleston, Church Minshull & Wettenhall from 95. *The School House, Church Lane, Aston juxta Mondrum, Nantwich, Cheshire CW5 7PS* Nantwich (01270) 624546

KENDRA, Kenneth Ernest. b 13. OBE66. Leeds Univ BA41 MA48. Linc Th Coll 40. **d** 42 **p** 43. QHC 70; RD Alverstoke *Portsm* 71-79; V Lee-on-the-Solent 71-80; rtd 80. *Highfields, Castle Hill Lane, Mere, Warminster, Wilts BA12 6JB*   Mere (01747) 860823

KENDREW, Dr Neil Stuart. b 46. FITD84 Leeds Univ BA67 Univ of Wales (Swansea) DipAD72 Bradf Univ MSc80 PhD84. Linc Th Coll 67. **d** 69 **p** 70. C Allerton *Liv* 69-72; Ldr Leeds City Cen Detached Youth Work Project 73-75; Dioc Youth Officer *Ripon* 75-77; Lect Ilkley Coll 77-78; Sen Lect Bradf and Ilkley Community Coll 78-88; Hd Community & Youth Studies St Martin's Coll from 88. *St Martin's College, Lancaster LA1 3JD*   Lancaster (01524) 63446

KENDREW, Geoffrey David. b 42. K Coll Lon BD66 AKC66. **d** 67 **p** 68. C Bourne *Guildf* 67-70; C Haslemere 70-76; V Derby St Barn *Derby* from 76. *St Barnabas' Vicarage, 122 Radbourne Street, Derby DE22 3BU*   Derby (01332) 342553

KENDRICK, Dale Evans. b 62. Ch Ch Coll Cant BA86 Nottm Univ MA87 Leeds Univ MA95. Coll of Resurr Mirfield CPT94. **d** 95. C Tividale *Lich* from 95. *14 Gladstone Drive, Tividale, Warley, W Midlands B69 3LF*   0121-557 5402

KENDRICK, Canon Desmond Max. b 22. Leeds Univ BA47. Wycliffe Hall Ox 50. **d** 52 **p** 53. Chapl Leeds Road Hosp Bradf 54-77; V Bradf St Clem *Bradf* 54-77; RD Bradf 63-73; Hon Can Bradf Cathl 64-89; V Otley 77-89; Chapl Wharfdale Gen Hosp 77-90; rtd 89. *26 Ashtofts Mount, Guiseley, W Yorkshire LS20 9DB*   Guiseley (01943) 870430

KENDRICK, Ronald Horace. b 35. Univ of Wales (Ban) BD78 DPS79. St Deiniol's Hawarden. **d** 82 **p** 83. C Wrexham *St As* 82-85; R Llanelian and Betws-yn-Rhos from 85. *The Rectory, Rhodfa Sant Elian, Colwyn Bay, Clwyd LL29 1XX*   Colwyn Bay (01492) 517274

KENNARD, Mark Philip Donald. b 60. Man Univ BSc82. Cranmer Hall Dur 85. **d** 88 **p** 89. C Newark w Hawton, Cotham and Shelton *S'well* 88-89; C Newark-upon-Trent 89-91; C Cropwell Bishop w Colston Bassett, Granby etc 91-93; P-in-c Shireoaks from 93; Chapl Bassetlaw Hosp & Community Services NHS Trust from 93. *1 Potters Nook, Shireoaks, Worksop, Notts S81 8NF*   Worksop (01909) 486537

KENNARD, Ronald Malcolm. b 15. ACA39 FCA60. Chich Th Coll 74. **d** 75 **p** 76. Hon C Cuckfield *Chich* 75-79; P-in-c Elsted w Treyford and Didling 79-83; Perm to Offic from 83. *35 Harberton Crescent, Chichester, W Sussex PO19 4NY* Chichester (01243) 528623

KENNEDY, Anthony Reeves. b 32. Lon Univ DipTh67. Roch Th Coll 64. **d** 67 **p** 68. C Ross *Heref* 67-69; C Marfleet *York* 69-71; TV 72-76; V Lightwater *Guildf* 76-83; V W Ham *Chelmsf* 83-89; V Lutton w Gedney Drove End, Dawsmere Linc 89-94. *10 Cavendish Street, Chichester, West Sussex PO19 1DS*   Chichester (01243) 774558

KENNEDY, Arthur. b 57. St Pet Coll Ox BA79 MA83. St Jo Coll Nottm 83. **d** 85 **p** 86. C Nor Heartsease St Fran *Nor* 85-89; C Tadley St Pet *Win* 89-91; R Farmborough, Marksbury and Stanton Prior *B & W* from 91. *The Rectory, Church Lane, Farmborough, Bath BA3 1AN*   Timsbury (01761) 470727

KENNEDY, Brian McMahon. b 11. TCD BA33 MA38. **d** 34 **p** 35. I Clonmel Union *C, C & R* 68-85; Chapl Cork Miss to Seamen & Chapl Irish Navy 68-85; rtd 85. *22 Strathearn Park, Belfast BT4 2GN*   Belfast (01232) 768046

KENNEDY, Miss Carolyn Ruth. b 59. Univ of Wales (Ban) BA81 GradCertEd(FE)85. Ripon Coll Cuddesdon BA90. **d** 91 **p** 94. C Frodingham *Linc* 91-95; Chapl Cov Univ *Cov* from 95. *The Chaplaincy, Coventry University, Priory Street, Coventry CV1 5FB*   Coventry (01203) 838315

KENNEDY, David George. b 46. Hull Univ BEd71 MA76. Linc Th Coll 77. **d** 79 **p** 80. C Linc St Faith and St Martin w St Pet *Linc* 79-82; V Bilton St Pet *York* 82-90; V New Seaham *Dur* 90-92; Chapl Humberside Univ *York* from 92. *141 Cranbrook Avenue, Hull HU6 7SS*   Hull (01482) 809696

KENNEDY, David John. b 57. St Jo Coll Dur BA78 Nottm Univ MTh81. St Jo Coll Nottm 79. **d** 81 **p** 82. C Tudhoe Grange *Dur* 81-87; C Merrington 84-87; Tutor Qu Coll Birm from 88. *The Queen's College, Somerset Road, Edgbaston, Birmingham B15 2QH*   0121-454 8180 or 452 1805

KENNEDY, Francis Robert Dixon. b 14. Wadh Coll Ox BA38 MA43. Wycliffe Hall Ox 42. **d** 43 **p** 44. Chapl Shoreham Gr Sch 49-71; R Caythorpe *Linc* 71-81; rtd 81; Perm to Offic *Chich* 81-93. *8 Ripley Road, Worthing, W Sussex BN11 5NQ* Worthing (01903) 249498

KENNEDY, James Ernest. b 20. TCD BA46 MA51. CITC 46. **d** 46 **p** 47. I Errigal w Desertoghill *D & R* 67-81; rtd 81. *38 Prospect Road, Portstewart, Co Derry BT55 7LQ* Portstewart (01265) 832052

KENNEDY, John Wilkinson. b 20. TCD BA44 LLB44 MA50. Qu Coll Birm 48. **d** 50 **p** 51. V Doncaster St Jas *Sheff* 60-70; V Anlaby St Pet *York* 70-80; V Cloughton 80-85; P-in-c Hackness w Harwood Dale 81-85; rtd 85. *5 North Grove Approach, Wetherby, W Yorkshire LS22 7GA*   Wetherby (01937) 584524

KENNEDY, Canon Michael Charles. b 39. TCD BA63 MA79 BD79 Open Univ PhD87. TCD Div Sch 61. **d** 63 **p** 64. C Drumglass *Arm* 63-66; I Lisnadill w Kildarton from 66; Warden Dioc Guild of Lay Readers from 74; Hon VC Arm Cathl from 75; Tutor for Aux Min (Arm) from 82; Preb Yagoe St Patr Cathl Dub from 92. *Lisnadill Rectory, 60 Newtownhamilton Road, Armagh BT60 2PW*   Armagh (01861) 523630

KENNEDY, Paul Alan. b 67. ACA92 Brighton Poly. St Steph Ho Ox BA95. **d** 95. C Romford St Andr *Chelmsf* from 95. *24 Eastbury Road, Romford RM7 9AL*   Romford (01708) 734047 Fax 737791

KENNEDY, Paul Joseph Alan. b 57. Newc Univ MA93. Sarum & Wells Th Coll. **d** 84 **p** 85. C Shildon *Dur* 84-85; C Shildon w Eldon 85-86; C Shotton *St As* 86-88; V Waterhouses *Dur* 88-93; V Denton *Newc* 93-95; CF from 95. *c/o MOD (Army), Bagshot Park, Bagshot, Surrey GU19 5PL*   Bagshot (01276) 471717 Fax 412834

KENNEDY, Ross Kenneth. b 40. Edin Th Coll 83. **d** 85 **p** 86. C Hexham *Newc* 85-89; TV Glendale Gp 89-93; TR Ch the King in the Dio of Newc from 93. *North Gosforth Vicarage, Wideopen, Newcastle upon Tyne NE13 6NH* 0191-236 2280

KENNEDY, William Edmund. b 20. QUB BA43 TCD BA45 MA48. **d** 45 **p** 46. I Ballyculter w Kilclief *D & D* 57-85; rtd 85. *Shalom, 8 Dunnanew Road, Seaforde, Downpatrick, Co Down BT30 6PJ* Seaforde (01396) 811706

KENNEDY-BELL, Preb Winnington Douglas. b 15. Keble Coll Ox BA38 MA42. Wells Th Coll 38. **d** 39 **p** 40. Overseas Relig Broadcasting Org BBC 48-75; Reader of The Temple (Lon) from 55; Preb St Paul's Cathl *Lon* from 73; Dep P in O 76-86; rtd 80. *1 Victoria Cottages, Kew Gardens, Richmond, Surrey TW9 3NW* 0181-940 5385

KENNERLEY, Mrs Katherine Virginia (Ginnie). Somerville Coll Ox BA58 MA65 Irish Sch of Ecum DipEcum84 TCD BA86. CITC 86. **d** 88 **p** 90. Lect Applied Th CITC 88-93; NSM Bray *D & G* 88-93; I Narraghmore w Timolin, Castledermot and Kinneagh from 93. *The Rectory, Timolin, Co Kildare, Irish Republic* Athy (507) 24278

KENNETT-ORPWOOD, Jason Robert. b 55. St Mich Coll Llan DipTh77 DPS78. **d** 78 **p** 79. Chapl St Woolos Cathl *Mon* 78-82; Chapl St Woolos Hosp Newport 79-82; Dioc Youth Chapl *Mon* 82-85; V Cwmcarn 82-85; TV Wrexham *St As* 85-89; V Bistre from 89. *Bistre Vicarage, Mold Road, Buckley, Clwyd CH7 2NH* Buckley (01244) 550947

KENNEY, Peter. b 50. Edin Univ BD75. Edin Th Coll 73. **d** 76 **p** 77. C Cullercoats St Geo *Newc* 76-81; TV Whorlton 81-88; P-in-c N Gosforth 88; TR Ch the King in the Dio of Newc 88-93; P-in-c Newc St Jo from 93. *3 Crossway, Jesmond, Newcastle upon Tyne NE2 3QH* 0191-212 0181

KENNING, Michael Stephen. b 47. St Chad's Coll Dur BA68. Westcott Ho Cam 69. **d** 71 **p** 72. C Hythe *Cant* 71-75; TV Bow w Bromley St Leon *Lon* 75-77; C-in-c W Leigh CD *Portsm* 77-81; V Lee-on-the-Solent 81-92; R N Waltham and Steventon, Ashe and Deane *Win* from 92. *The Rectory, North Waltham, Basingstoke, Hants RG25 2BQ* Dummer (01256) 379256

KENNINGTON, John Paul. b 61. Collingwood Coll Dur BA85. St Steph Ho Ox BA87 MA92. **d** 88 **p** 89. C Headington *Ox* 88-91; C Dulwich St Clem w St Pet *S'wark* 91-94; TV Mortlake w E Sheen from 94. *All Saints Vicarage, 86 East Sheen Avenue, London SW14 8AU* 0181-876 4201

KENNY, Canon Charles John. b 39. LGSM74 QUB BA61 MEd78. CITC 69. **d** 69 **p** 70. C Belf St Paul *Conn* 69-71; Hd of RE Grosvenor High Sch 71-94; Lic to Offic from 84; VC Belf Cathl from 94; Can Treas from 95. *45 Deramore Drive, Belfast BT9 5JS* Belfast (01232) 669632

KENNY, Frederick William Bouvier. b 28. TCD BA53 DipEd54 MA56 LTh. **d** 56 **p** 57. C Ballymacarrett St Patr *D & D* 56-58; C Blackpool St Jo *Blackb* 58-61; Chapl Preston Hosp N Shields 61-66; V Preston St Paul *Blackb* 61-66; Youth Adv CMS (Lon) 66-70; Youth Sec (Ireland) CMS 70-75; I Belf St Clem *D & D* 75-80; V Preston St Cuth *Blackb* 80-86; TV Bushbury *Lich* 86-90; P-in-c Stambridge *Chelmsf* from 90; Chapl Rochford Hosp from 90. *The Rectory, Stambridge, Rochford, Essex SS4 2AR* Southend-on-Sea (01702) 258272

KENNY, Thomas Patrick Francis. b 49. Univ of Wales (Cardiff) DipTh76. St Mich Coll Llan 73. **d** 76 **p** 77. C Rochdale *Man* 76-80; R Abbey Hey 80-86; V Stockton Heath *Ches* from 86. *The Vicarage, 91 Walton Road, Stockton Heath, Warrington WA4 6NR* Warrington (01925) 661396

KENNY, Canon Thomas Percival Robert. b 27. TCD BA48 MA51. **d** 50 **p** 51. I Magherafelt *Arm* 66-74; I Derryloran 74-82; CMS 83-88; Nigeria 83-88; Hon Can Owerri from 84; I Clooonclare w Killasnett and Drumlease *K, E & A* 88-90; rtd 90. *26 Clanbrassil Drive, Portadown, Craigavon, Co Armagh BT63 5EH* Portadown (01762) 336479

KENRICK, Kenneth David Norman. b 44. Liv Univ RMN. Ripon Hall Ox 70 NW Ord Course 77. **d** 77 **p** 78. C Stockport St Geo *Ches* 77-83; R Stockport St Thos 83-85; R Stockport St Thos w St Pet from 86. *St Thomas Rectory, 25 Heath Road, Stockport, Cheshire SK2 6JJ* 0161-483 2483

KENSINGTON, Area Bishop of. Vacant

KENT, Dr Christopher Alfred. b 48. CEng77 MIChemE77 Birm Univ BSc69 PhD72 Nottm Univ DipTh83. St Jo Coll Nottm 82. **d** 84 **p** 85. C Bucknall and Bagnall *Lich* 84-86; Hon C Halesowen *Worc* from 86. *40 County Park Avenue, Halesowen, W Midlands B62 8SP* 0121-550 3132

KENT, David. b 44. CEng MIMechE. N Ord Course. **d** 83 **p** 84. NSM Huddersfield St Pet and All SS *Wakef* from 83. *118 Woodside Road, Huddersfield HD4 5JW* Huddersfield (01484) 654058

KENT, Frank. b 44. ARCM76 Open Univ BA82. Ridley Hall Cam. **d** 86 **p** 87. C Faversham *Cant* 86-89; R Lyminge w Paddlesworth, Stanford w Postling etc from 89. *The Rectory, Rectory Lane, Lyminge, Folkestone, Kent CT18 8EG* Lyminge (01303) 862432

KENT, Keith Meredith. b 32. Lon Univ DipTh57. St Aid Birkenhead 55. **d** 58 **p** 59. P-in-c Everton St Polycarp *Liv* 68-74; V Liv All So Springwood 74-78; V Carr Mill 78-86; V Beddgelert *Ban* 86-91; rtd 91. *73 Egerton Road, Ashton-on-Ribble, Preston PR2 1AL* Preston (01772) 722508

KENT, Canon Michael Patrick. b 27. St Edm Hall Ox BA50 MA52. Cuddesdon Coll 50. **d** 52 **p** 53. C-in-c Pennywell St Thos and Grindon St Oswald CD *Dur* 57-70; V Cockerton 70-93; RD Darlington 79-84; Hon Can Dur Cathl 83-93; rtd 93; Chapl St Chad's Coll Dur from 94. *5 Ferens Close, Durham DH11 1JX* 0191-386 2835

KENT, Preb Neville. b 40. Sarum & Wells Th Coll 70. **d** 72 **p** 73. C Taunton St Andr *B & W* 72-77; R Bradf w Oake, Hillfarrance and Heathfield 77-89; Adv on Soc Concerns 80-87; RD Tone 87-89; V Worle 89-93; TR from 93; Preb Wells Cathl from 94. *The Vicarage, 93 Church Road, Worle, Weston-super-Mare, Avon BS22 9EA* Weston-s-Mare (01934) 510694/515922

KENT, Richard Hugh. b 38. Worc Coll Ox BA61 MA65. Chich Th Coll 61. **d** 63 **p** 64. C Emscote *Cov* 63-66; C Finham 66-70; V Dean Forest St Paul *Glouc* 70-75; V Glouc St Aldate 75-86; Chapl and Warden Harnhill Healing Cen from 86. *Harnhill Manor, Harnhill, Cirencester, Glos GL7 5PX* Cirencester (01285) 850283

KENT, Roger Anthony Edward. b 56. Kent Univ BA78. St Steph Ho Ox 79. **d** 81 **p** 82. C Ipswich All Hallows *St E* 81-84; C Poplar *Lon* 84-88; V Newington w Hartlip and Stockbury *Cant* 88-95; Chapl Prague *Eur* from 95. *Terronska 536/10, 160 00 Praha 6, Czech Republic* Prague (2) 312 4208

KENT, Ronald. b 21. St Jo Coll Dur BA43 MA46. St Steph Ho Ox 79. **d** 45 **p** 46. Chapl Univ Coll of Ripon & York St Jo 65-76; Lic to Offic *Dur* 76-88; rtd 86; P-in-c Nidd *Ripon* 88-95. *The Vicarage, Nidd, Harrogate, N Yorkshire HG3 3BN* Harrogate (01423) 770060

KENTIGERN-FOX, Canon William Poyntere Kentigern. b 38. AKC63. **d** 64 **p** 65. C S Mimms St Mary and Potters Bar *Lon* 64-67; C S Tottenham 67-70; P-in-c Duddington w Tixover *Pet* 70-76; R Barrowden and Wakerley 70-76; P-in-c Morcott w S Luffenham 75-77; R Barrowden and Wakerley w S Luffenham 77-79; R Byfield w Boddington 79-86; V Northn St Mich w St Edm from 86; Can Pet Cathl from 94. *St Michael's Vicarage, 19 St Michael's Avenue, Northampton NN1 4JQ* Northampton (01604) 37928

KENWARD, Roger Nelson. b 34. Selw Coll Cam BA58 MA62. Ripon Hall Ox 58. **d** 60 **p** 61. C Paddington St Jas *Lon* 60-63; Chapl RAF 64-82; Asst Chapl-in-Chief RAF 82-89; P-in-c Lyneham w Bradenstoke *Sarum* 72-76; Hon Chapl to The Queen 85-89; R Laughton w Ripe and Chalvington *Chich* from 90; Chapl Laughton Lodge Hosp 90-95. *The Rectory, Church Lane, Laughton, Lewes, E Sussex BN8 6AH* Eastbourne (01323) 811642

KENWAY, Dr Ian Michael. b 52. Leeds Univ BA74 Bris Univ PhD86. Coll of Resurr Mirfield 74. **d** 76 **p** 77. C Cov E *Cov* 76-79; C Southmead *Bris* 79-81; P-in-c Shaw Hill *Birm* 82-88; Asst Sec Gen Syn Bd for Soc Resp 88-93; Chapl Essex Univ *Chelmsf* from 93; Dir of Studies Cen for the Study of Th from 93. *Mariners, Rectory Hill, Wivenhoe, Colchester CO7 9LB* Colchester (01206) 823549

KENWAY, Robert Andrew. b 56. Bris Univ BA78. Westcott Ho Cam 80. **d** 82 **p** 83. C Birchfield *Birm* 82-85; C Queensbury All SS *Lon* 87-89; R Birm St Geo *Birm* from 89. *St George's Rectory, 100 Bridge Street West, Birmingham B19 2YX* 0121-359 2000

KENYON, Stanley Robert. b 31. Kelham Th Coll 51. **d** 55 **p** 56. P-in-c Grimsby St Steph *Linc* 61-71; V Habrough 71-82; V E Halton 73-82; V Killingholme 73-82; V Barnetby le Wold Gp 82-94; rtd 94. *Machindor, 47 Highfields, Crowle, S Humberside DN17 4NP* Scunthorpe (01724) 711435

KEOGH, Anthony. b 35. St Mich Coll Llan 63. **d** 66 **p** 67. C Aberaman and Abercwmboi *Llan* 66-70; Hon C Penarth All SS 70-76; R Jersey H Trin *Win* from 76. *Holy Trinity Rectory, Jersey, Channel Islands* Jersey (01534) 861110

KEOGH, Henry James. b 39. TCD BA61 NUI BMus65. **d** 62 **p** 63. C Cork St Fin Barre's Cathl *C, C & R* 62-65; C Belf St Luke *Conn* 65-66; C Dromore Cathl *D & D* 66-68; I Castlecomer *C & O* 68-85; I Kilscoran w Killinick and Mulrankin from 85; Hon Chapl Miss to Seamen from 85. *The Rectory, Killinick, Co Wexford, Irish Republic* Wexford (53) 58989

KEOGH, Robert Gordon. b 56. TCD DipTh84. **d** 84 **p** 85. C Mossley *Conn* 84-87; I Taunagh w Kilmactranny, Ballysumaghan etc *K, E & A* 87-90; I Swanlinbar w Tomregan, Kinawley, Drumlane etc from 90. *The Rectory, Swanlinbar, Co Cavan, Irish Republic* Swanlinbar (49) 23404

KER, Desmond Agar-Ellis. b 15. Wells Th Coll 58. **d** 58 **p** 59. V Bovey Tracey St Jo *Ex* 70-80; rtd 80; Perm to Offic *S'wark* 84-92. *Flat 1, 42 Wellington Square, Hastings, E Sussex TN34 1PN* Hastings (01424) 444288

KERLEY, Brian Edwin. b 36. St Jo Coll Cam BA57 MA61. Linc Th Coll 59. **d** 61 **p** 62. C Sheerness H Trin w St Paul *Cant* 61-64; C St Laurence in the Isle of Thanet 64-69; C Coulsdon St Andr *S'wark* 69-76; P-in-c Fulbourn *Ely* 76-77; R from 77; RD Quy 83-93; P-in-c Gt Wilbraham from 86; P-in-c Lt Wilbraham from 86. *The Rectory, Apthorpe Street, Fulbourn, Cambridge CB1 5EY* Cambridge (01223) 880337

KERLEY, Patrick Thomas Stewart. b 42. Linc Th Coll. **d** 85 **p** 86. Hon C Thorpe *Nor* 85-90; C Wymondham 90-94; Gt Yarmouth from 94. *The Rectory, Somerton Road, Winterton-on-Sea, Great Yarmouth, Norwich NR29 4AW* Great Yarmouth (01493) 393227

KERR, Andrew Harry Mayne. b 41. TCD BA63 Birm Univ DPS72. **d** 65 **p** 66. C Belf St Luke *Conn* 65-68; SCM Sec (Ireland) 68-72; C Clooney *D & R* 72-74; Australia from 74. *38 Bundoran Parade, Box Hill North, Victoria, Australia 3129* Melbourne (3) 890-3019

KERR, Anthony. Sheff Univ BA64 Man Univ CertEd65. N Ord Course. **d** 85 **p** 86. NSM Greenfield *Man* 85-87; NSM Leesfield from 87. *16 Netherlees, Spring Lane, Oldham OL4 5BA* 0161-620 6512

KERR, Arthur Henry. LRAM47 TCD BA48 DA65. **d** 49 **p** 50. C Templemore *D & R* 49-50; C Dub Harold's Cross *D & G* 50-57; ICM 57-60; Chapl Rotunda Hosp 60-75; Lic to Offic *Conn* 88-94; P-in-c Clondevaddock w Portsalon and Leatbeg *D & R* from 94. *Halothane, 172 Mountsandel Road, Coleraine, Co Londonderry BT52 1JE* Coleraine (01265) 44940

KERR, Charles Alexander Gray. b 33. Open Univ BA75 Birm Univ MA83 MA88. Edin Th Coll 63. **d** 67 **p** 68. C Hawick *Edin* 67-70; C Edgbaston St Geo *Birm* 70-72; Chapl Birm Skin Hosp 70-75; P-in-c Quinton Road W St Boniface *Birm* 72-79; V 79-84; R Musselburgh *Edin* 84-86; P-in-c Prestonpans 84-86; NSM Reighton w Speeton *York* 91-95; P-in-c Burton Pidsea and Humbleton w Elsternwick 91-95; V Anlaby Common St Mark from 95. *St Mark's Vicarage, 1055 Anlaby Road, Hull HU4 7PP* Hull (01482) 51977

KERR, David James. b 36. TCD BA58 MA61 BD61 HDipEd. **d** 60 **p** 61. C Belf Trin Coll Miss *Conn* 60-63; Dean's V St Patr Cathl Dub 63-66; Chapl Beechwood Park Sch St Alb from 66; C Flamstead *St Alb* from 74. *Beechwood Park School, Markyate, St Albans, Herts AL3 8AW* Luton (01582) 841191

KERR, Derek Preston. b 64. TCD BTh90. Oak Hill Th Coll. **d** 90 **p** 91. C Belf St Donard *D & D* 90-93; C Carrickfergus *Conn* from 93. *20 Northlands, Carrickfergus, Co Antrim BT38 8NH* Carrickfergus (01960) 367739

KERR, Miss Dora Elizabeth. b 41. QUB BA65 Southn Univ DipEd66 Nottm Univ DipTh83. St Jo Coll Nottm 82. **dss** 84 **d** 87 **p** 94. Becontree St Mary *Chelmsf* 84-87; Par Dn 87-88; Par Dn Rushden w Newton Bromswold *Pet* 88-93; Par Dn Finham *Cov* 94; Chapl Cov and Warks Hosp from 94; C Finham *Cov* from 94. *145 Green Lane, Coventry CV3 6EB* Coventry (01203) 413674

KERR, George Cecil. b 36. TCD BA60 MA65. CITC 60. **d** 60 **p** 61. C Coleraine *Conn* 60-63; Div Master Annandale Sch Belf 63-65; Dean of Residences QUB 65-74; Lic to Offic *D & D* from 75. *Christian Renewal Centre, Shore Road, Rostrevor, Co Down BT34 3ET* Rostrevor (016937) 38492 Fax 38996

KERR, Mrs Jean. b 46. SS Hild & Bede Coll Dur CertEd69. N Ord Course 84. **d** 87 **p** 94. NSM Peel *Man* 87-93; Par Dn Dixon Green 88-89; Par Dn New Bury 89-93; Par Dn Gillingham St Mark *Roch* 93-94; C from 94. *The Garden House, Vicarage Road, Gillingham, Kent ME7 5JA* Medway (01634) 853687

KERR, John Maxwell. b 43. MSOSc88 Toronto Univ BSc66 Leeds Univ MSc70 Nottm Univ DipTh76. Linc Th Coll 75. **d** 77 **p** 78. C New Windsor *Ox* 77-80; Asst Chapl Cheltenham Coll 80-81; Chapl 81-82; Asst Chapl Win Coll 82-93; Hon C Win St Lawr and St Maurice w St Swithun *Win* from 84. *68 Kingsgate Street, Winchester, Hants SO23 9PE* Winchester (01962) 862317

KERR, Joseph Reid. b 43. St Steph Ho Ox 70. **d** 72. C Ox SS Phil and Jas *Ox* 72-74; Jamaica from 75. *The Rectory, King Street, Kingston, Jamaica W1* Jamaica (1809) 26888

KERR, Nicholas Ian. b 46. Em Coll Cam BA68 MA72. Westcott Ho Cam 74. **d** 77 **p** 78. C Mert St Mary *S'wark* 77-80; C Rainham *Roch* 80-84; Chapl Joyce Green Hosp Dartford 84-90; V Dartford St Edm *Roch* 84-90; V Lamorbey H Redeemer from 90. *The Vicarage, 64 Days Lane, Sidcup, Kent DA15 8JR* 0181-300 1508

KERR, Paul Turner. b 47. Cranmer Hall Dur 68. **d** 71 **p** 72. C Kingston upon Hull St Martin *York* 71-72; C Linthorpe 72-76; C Cherry Hinton St Jo *Ely* 76-78; Chapl Addenbrooke's Hosp Cam 76-78; TV Rochdale *Man* 78-84; Chapl Birch Hill Hosp Rochdale 78-84; V New Bury 84-87; TR 87-93; C Gillingham St Mark *Roch* from 93. *The Garden House, Vicarage Road, Gillingham, Kent ME7 5JA* Medway (01634) 853687

KERR, Peter Albert Calvin. b 09. MC40. Called to the Bar (Gray's Inn) 62 Lon Univ BD30 LLB60 St Cath Soc Ox BA32

MA37. Qu Coll Birm 37. **d** 37 **p** 37. C Aston SS Pet and Paul *Birm* 37-39; CF (TA - R of O) 39-59; Perm to Offic *Mon* from 81. *Hillside, Llanishen, Chepstow, Gwent NP6 6QD* Trelleck (01600) 860723

KERR, Canon Stephen Peter. b 46. TCD BA68 Edin Univ BD71 MPhil80. **d** 71 **p** 72. C Belf H Trin *Conn* 72-76; C Ballywillan 76-78; Lect Linc Th Coll 78-87; Dioc Officer for Adult Educn and Minl Tr *Worc* from 87; P-in-c Ombersley w Doverdale from 87; Hon Can Worc Cathl from 92. *The Rectory, Ombersley, Droitwich, Worcs WR9 0EW* Droitwich (01905) 620950

KERRIDGE, Donald George. b 32. Bede Coll Dur CertEd72 Hull Univ BA84. Wesley Coll Leeds 57 Bps' Coll Cheshunt 61. **d** 62 **p** 63. C Manston *Ripon* 62-66; C Hawksworth Wood 66-71; Asst Chapl Brentwood Sch Essex 72-74; Lic to Offic *Linc* 81-89; R Tetney, Marshchapel and N Coates 89-91; P-in-c Linc St Swithin 91-95; P-in-c Linc St Swithin w All SS from 95; Asst Chapl Linc Co Hosp from 91. *St Swithin's Vicarage, Croft Street, Lincoln LN2 5AZ* Lincoln (01522) 527540

KERRIN, Albert Eric. b 26. Aber Univ MA51. Edin Th Coll 51. **d** 53 **p** 54. P-in-c Portpatrick *Glas* 69-91; P-in-c Stranraer 69-91; rtd 91. *15 London Road, Stranraer, Wigtownshire DG9 8AF* Stranraer (01776) 702822

KERRISON, Mrs Anne Edmonstone. b 23. Cranmer Hall Dur 69. **dss** 77 **d** 87 **p** 94. Hellesdon *Nor* 77-78; Ind Miss 78-79; Lic to Offic 79-88; Perm to Offic 88-94; NSM Hevingham w Hainford and Stratton Strawless from 94. *Sloley Lodge, Sloley, Norwich NR12 8HE* Swanton Abbott (01692) 538253

KERRY, Martin John. b 55. Ox Univ MA78 Nottm Univ BA81 MTh83. St Jo Coll Nottm 79. **d** 82 **p** 83. C Everton St Geo *Liv* 82-85; Lic to Offic *S'well* from 85; Chapl Asst Nottm City Hosp 85-89; Chapl from 89. *The Chaplains' Office, City Hospital, Hucknall Road, Nottingham NG5 1BP* Nottingham (0115) 969 1169 or 962 7616

KERSHAW, John Harvey. b 51. Coll of Resurr Mirfield 84. **d** 86 **p** 87. C Hollinwood *Man* 86-89; V Audenshaw St Hilda from 89. *St Hilda's Vicarage, Denton Road, Audenshaw, Manchester M34 5BL* 0161-336 2310

KERSHAW, Savile. b 37. Bernard Gilpin Soc Dur 60 Chich Th Coll 61. **d** 64 **p** 65. C Staincliffe *Wakef* 64-66; C Saltley *Birm* 66-68; C Birm St Aid Small Heath 68-72; NSM Bordesley SS Alb and Patr 88-93; Perm to Offic from 93. *74 Longmore Road, Shirley, Solihull, W Midlands B90 3EE* 0121-744 3470

KERSLEY, Stuart Casburn. b 40. CEng MIEE. Trin Coll Bris. **d** 82 **p** 83. C Lancing w Coombes *Chich* 82-87; TV Littlehampton and Wick 87-90; R Kingston Buci from 90. *The Rectory, Rectory Road, Shoreham-by-Sea, W Sussex BN43 6EB* Brighton (01273) 592591

KERSWILL, Anthony John. b 39. Lambeth STh85 Linc Th Coll 72. **d** 73 **p** 73. C Boultham *Linc* 73-76; P-in-c N Kelsey 76-83; P-in-c Cadney 76-83; V Gainsborough St Geo 83-91; V Bracebridge from 91. *The Vicarage, 60 Chiltern Road, Bracebridge, Lincoln LN5 8SE* Lincoln (01522) 532636 Fax as telephone

KESLAKE, Peter Ralegh. b 33. Sarum & Wells Th Coll. **d** 83 **p** 84. C Glouc St Geo w Whaddon *Glouc* 83-86; P-in-c France Lynch 86-91; V Chalford and France Lynch from 91. *The Vicarage, Brantwood Road, Chalford Hill, Stroud, Glos GL6 8BS* Brimscombe (01453) 883154

KESSLER, Edward Scharps. b 26. Princeton Univ BA47 Chicago Univ MA51 St Chad's Coll Dur DipTh66. **d** 66 **p** 67. C Hendon St Ignatius *Dur* 68-70; Dioc Planning Officer 70-75; P-in-c Kimblesworth 74-80; Perm to Offic *Sheff* from 87; rtd 89. *44 Hinde Street, Sheffield S4 8HJ* Sheffield (0114) 244 6827

KESTELL-CORNISH, Geoffrey. b 03. Bp's Univ Lennox LST32. **d** 32 **p** 33. V Bishops Tawton *Ex* 48-53; rtd 53; C Ilfracombe H Trin *Ex* 57-68; Perm to Offic from 68. *Flat 13, Mill Court, Mill Road, Barnstaple, Devon EX31 1JQ* Barnstaple (01271) 42566

KESTER, Jonathan George Frederick. b 66. Ex Univ BA90. Coll of Resurr Mirfield CPT93. **d** 93 **p** 94. C Cheshunt *St Alb* from 93. *156 Churchgate, Cheshunt, Waltham Cross, Herts EN8 9DX* Waltham Cross (01992) 620659

KESTERTON, David William. b 59. Man Univ BSc80. Cranmer Hall Dur 85. **d** 88 **p** 89. C Cheddleton *Lich* 88-92; TV Dunstable *St Alb* from 92; Chapl Dunstable Coll from 92. *St Fremund's Vicarage, 22 Prince's Street, Dunstable, Beds LU6 3AX* Luton (01582) 668996 or 696127

KESTON, Dr Marion. b 44. Glas Univ MB, ChB68. St And Dioc Tr Course 87. **d** 90 **p** 94. NSM Dunfermline *St And* from 90; NSM W Fife Team Min from 90. *119 Rose Street, Dunfermline, Fife KY12 0QT* Dunfermline (01383) 620314

KETLEY, Christopher. b 62. Aston Tr Scheme 91 Coll of Resurr Mirfield 93. **d** 95. C Gt Crosby St Faith *Liv* from 95. *31 Allenby Road, Liverpool L23 0SU*

KETLEY, Michael James. b 39. DipHE81. Oak Hill Th Coll 79. **d** 81 **p** 82. C Bedhampton *Portsm* 81-85; R St Ive w Quethiock *Truro* 85-86; C Barkingside St Cedd *Chelmsf* 90-92; P-in-c from 92. *10 Marston Road, Ilford, Essex IG5 0LY* 0181-551 3406

KETTLE, Alan Marshall. b 51. Leeds Univ BA72. Wycliffe Hall Ox MA78. **d** 78 **p** 79. C Llantwit Fadre *Llan* 78-81; Prov RE Adv Ch in Wales 81-84; Chapl Llandovery Coll 84-92; P-in-c Cilycwm and Ystrad-ffin w Rhandir-mwyn etc *St D* 85-92; Chapl W Buckland Sch Barnstaple from 92; Lic to Offic *Ex* from 92. *2 West Close, West Buckland, Barnstaple, Devon EX32 0ST* Filleigh (01598) 760314 or 760560

KETTLE, David John. b 47. Bris Univ BSc69 MLitt86 Fitzw Coll Cam BA75 MA79. Westcott Ho Cam 73. **d** 76 **p** 77. C Bris St Andr Hartcliffe *Bris* 76-79; C Fishponds All SS 79-80; P-in-c 81-83; Perm to Offic *St E* from 83; New Zealand from 91. *22 Goodwin Crescent, Palmerston North, New Zealand* Levin (6) 357-8749

KETTLE, Martin Drew. b 52. New Coll Ox BA74 Selw Coll Cam BA76 Cam Univ MA85. Ridley Hall Cam 74. **d** 77 **p** 78. C Enfield St Andr *Lon* 77-80; Chapl Ridley Hall Cam 80-84; V Hendon St Paul Mill Hill *Lon* from 85; AD W Barnet 90-95. *St Paul's Vicarage, Hammers Lane, London NW7 4EA* 0181-959 1856 or 959 8551

KETTLE, Mrs Patricia Mary Carole. b 41. Worc Coll of Educn CertEd61 Lon Univ DipTh68. Dalton Ho Bris 66. **d** 87 **p** 94. C Wonersh *Guildf* from 87. *Wakehurst Cottage, Links Road, Bramley, Surrey GU5 0AL* Guildford (01483) 898856

KETTLE, Peter. b 51. K Coll Lon BD74 AKC74. St Aug Coll Cant 74. **d** 75 **p** 76. C Angell Town St Jo *S'wark* 75-78; C Putney St Mary 78-80; V Raynes Park St Sav 80-85; Perm to Offic from 85. *46 Allenswood, Albert Drive, London SW19 6JX* 0181-785 3797

KEULEMANS, Andrew Francis Charles. b 68. Univ of Wales (Abth) BSc90. St Jo Coll Nottm BTh93. **d** 94 **p** 95. C Mold *St As* from 94. *2 Harrowby Road, Mold, Clwyd CH7 1DN* Mold (01352) 753624

KEVILL-DAVIES, Christopher Charles. b 44. AKC69. St Aug Coll Cant 70. **d** 70 **p** 71. C Folkestone St Sav *Cant* 70-75; V Yaxley *Ely* 75-78; R Chevington w Hargrave and Whepstead w Brockley *St E* 78-86; Appeals Manager Dr Barnardos 86-88; Appeals Manager St Nich Hospice Bury St Edmunds 88-89; Perm to Offic *St Alb* 86-89; NSM Stansted Mountfitchet *Chelmsf* 87-89; R Barkway, Reed and Buckland w Barley *St Alb* from 89. *The Rectory, 135 High Street, Barkway, Royston, Herts SG8 8ED* Barkway (01763) 848077

KEVIS, Lionel William Graham. b 55. York Univ BA. Wycliffe Hall Ox 83. **d** 86 **p** 87. C Plaistow St Mary *Roch* 86-90; R Ash from 90; R Ridley from 90. *The Rectory, The Street, Ash, Sevenoaks, Kent TN15 7HA* Ash Green (01474) 872209

KEW, William Richard. b 45. Lon Univ BD69. Lon Coll of Div LTh68. **d** 69 **p** 70. C Finchley St Paul Long Lane *Lon* 69-72; C Stoke Bishop *Bris* 72-76; USA from 76. *PO Box 879, Sewanee, Tennessee 37375-0879, USA* Chattanooga (615) 598-1103

KEY, Christopher Halstead (Chris). b 56. St Jo Coll Dur BA77 K Coll Lon MTh78. Ridley Hall Cam 79. **d** 81 **p** 82. C Balderstone *Man* 81-84; C Wandsworth All SS *S'wark* 84-88; C-in-c W Dulwich Em CD 88-93; V W Dulwich Em from 93. *Emmanuel Vicarage, 94 Clive Road, London SE21 8BU* 0181-670 2793

KEY, John Christopher. b 36. Pemb Coll Cam BA60 MA65. **d** 62 **p** 63. C Rugby St Andr *Cov* 62-67; Papua New Guinea 68-71; V Cov St Geo *Cov* 71-76; RD Cov N 73-76; P-in-c Redditch St Steph *Worc* 76-81; Dioc Ecum Officer 80-81; Australia from 81. *16 Dunbar Close, Normanhurst, NSW, Australia 2076* Sydney (2) 635-7922 or 487-3910

KEY, Robert Frederick. b 52. Bris Univ BA73. Oak Hill Th Coll 74. **d** 76 **p** 77. C Ox St Ebbe w St Pet *Ox* 76-80; C Wallington H Trin *S'wark* 80-85; P-in-c Eynsham *Ox* 85; V Eynsham and Cassington 85-91; V Ox St Andr from 91. *The Vicarage, 46 Charlbury Road, Oxford OX2 6UX or St Andrew's Church, Linton Road, Oxford OX2 6UG* Oxford (01865) 311695 or 311212

KEY, Roderick Charles (Rod). b 57. MTh. **d** 84 **p** 85. C Up Hatherley *Glouc* 84-87; V Glouc St Paul from 87. *St Paul's Vicarage, 2 King Edward's Avenue, Gloucester GL1 5DA* Gloucester (01452) 523732

KEYES, Alfred Edward de Hault. b 18. Keble Coll Ox BA39. Lich Th Coll 40. **d** 41 **p** 42. V Goathland *York* 63-73; R Rockbourne w Whitsbury *Win* 73-83; rtd 83; Perm to Offic *Ex* from 84. *7 Seaway Gardens, Paignton, Devon TQ3 2PE* Paignton (01803) 550303

KEYES, Graham George. b 44. St Cath Coll Cam BA65 MA68 Lanc Univ MA74 Nottm Univ MTh85 MPhil92. E Midl Min Tr Course 82. **d** 84 **p** 85. C Evington St Denys *Leic* 84-86; Vice-Prin NE Ord Course 86-89; C Monkseaton St Mary *Newc* 86-89; P-in-c

Newc St Hilda 89-94; TV Ch the King in the Dio of Newc from 94. *27 Polwarth Drive, Newcastle upon Tyne NE3 5NH* 0191-236 4995

KEYES, Mrs Iris Doreen. b 28. SRN. Gilmore Ho 69. **dss** 76 **d** 87 **p** 94. Egham Hythe *Guildf* 76-78; Chapl Asst St Pet Hosp Chertsey 78-82; Addlestone 83-86; Walton-on-Thames 86-87; C 87-89; rtd 89; NSM Addlestone *Guildf* 94-95; Perm to Offic from 95. *36 Finlay Gardens, Addlestone, Surrey KT15 2XN* Weybridge (01932) 846912

KEYES, William Pascall. b 68. Heythrop Coll Lon BD90. Chich Th Coll 92 St Steph Ho Ox DipMin95. **d** 95. C Pimlico St Pet w Westmr Ch Ch *Lon* from 95. *3 St Peter's House, 119 Eaton Square, London SW1W 9AL* 0171-235 4480

KEYS, John Francis. b 47. Goethe Inst Lon DipGL73. Sarum & Wells Th Coll CECM93. **d** 93 **p** 94. NSM Brighton St Mich *Chich* from 93. *1 Arundel House, 22 The Drive, Hove, E Sussex BN3 3JD* Brighton (01273) 771848

KEYTE, Douglas Joseph Henry. b 18. St Jo Coll Cam BA40 MA46. Wycliffe Hall Ox 46. **d** 48 **p** 49. Asst Master Co Gr Sch for Girls Sale 61-75; Hon C Charlestown *Man* 75-89; rtd 83; Hon C Pendleton St Thos w Charlestown *Man* from 89. *26 Heathfield Close, Sale, Cheshire M33 2PQ* 0161-973 2844

KHAMBATTA, Neville Holbery. b 48. St Chad's Coll Dur BA74. S'wark Ord Course 81. **d** 84 **p** 85. NSM Thornton Heath St Jude w St Aid *S'wark* 84-87; Asst Chapl Em Sch Wandsworth 84-87; Asst Warden Horstead Cen from 87; NSM Coltishall w Gt Hautbois and Horstead *Nor* from 87. *Horstead Conference Centre, Rectory Road, Horstead, Norwich NR12 7EP* Norwich (01603) 737215

KHOO, Boon-Hor. b 31. FBCO. Llan Dioc Tr Scheme. **d** 87 **p** 88. NSM Llan w Capel Llanilltern *Llan* from 87. *38 The Cathedral Green, Llandaff, Cardiff CF5 2EB* Cardiff (01222) 561478

KICHENSIDE, Mark Gregory. b 53. Nottm Univ BTh83. St Jo Coll Nottm 80. **d** 83 **p** 84. C Orpington Ch Ch *Roch* 83-86; C Bexley St Jo 86-90; V Blendon 90-93; V Welling from 93. *St John's Vicarage, Danson Lane, Welling, Kent DA16 2BQ* 0181-303 1107

KIDD, Anthony John Eric (Tony). b 38. Solicitor. Oak Hill NSM Course. **d** 89 **p** 90. NSM Rawdon *Bradf* 89-91; C Ilkley All SS 91-93; Perm to Offic 93-95; Perm to Offic *York* from 95. *Woodford House, Middle Street, Kilham, Driffield, N Humberside YO25 0RL* Kilham (01262) 420792

KIDD, Miss Carol Ivy. b 47. Trent Park Coll of Educn CertEd69. Oak Hill Th Coll DipHE94. **d** 95. C Bootle St Mary w St Paul *Liv* from 95. *35 Jersey Close, Bootle, Merseyside L20 4BP* 0151-922 8119

KIDD, John Alan. b 32. Pemb Coll Cam BA58 MA61. Ridley Hall Cam 57. **d** 61 **p** 62. P-in-c Mayfair Ch Ch *Lon* 69-75; V 75-79; V Virginia Water *Guildf* 79-88; Lic to Offic *York* from 94. *Jesmond House, Main Street, Alne, York YO6 2LD* Tollerton (0347) 838537

KIDD, Maurice Edward. b 26. Lon Coll of Div ALCD54 LTh. **d** 55 **p** 56. Chapl Guild of Health Lon 69-72; R Hanworth St Geo *Lon* 72-82; R Chartham *Cant* 82-91; rtd 91. *The Chantry, St Nicholas' Hospital, Harbledown, Canterbury, Kent CT2 9AD* Canterbury (01227) 761655

KIDD, Timothy. b 24. St Chad's Coll Dur BA48 DipTh50 MA53 Nottm Univ MA57 MPhil71 MEd80. Lambeth STh74. **d** 50 **p** 51. Prin Lect Kesteven Coll of Educn 65-79; Hon C Harlaxton *Linc* 66-72; Hon C Lt Ponton 66-72; Hon C Stroxton 66-72; Gen Preacher from 73; Visiting Lect Univ Evansville (USA) 79-86; Teacher K Sch Grantham 80-90; Perm to Offic *Linc* from 89; rtd 90. *14 Woodlands Drive, Grantham, Lincs NG31 9DJ* Grantham (01476) 63273

KIDDLE, John. b 58. Qu Coll Cam BA80 MA83. Ridley Hall Cam 79. **d** 82 **p** 83. C Ormskirk *Liv* 82-86; V Huyton Quarry 86-91; V Watford St Luke *St Alb* from 91. *St Luke's Vicarage, Devereux Drive, Watford WD1 3DD* Watford (01923) 231205

KIDDLE, Mark Brydges. b 34. ACP61. Wycliffe Hall Ox. **d** 63 **p** 64. C Scarborough St Luke *York* 63-66; C Walthamstow St Sav *Chelmsf* 66-71; V Nelson St Bede *Blackb* 71-76; V Perry Common *Birm* 76-79; R Grayingham *Linc* 79-84; V Kirton in Lindsey 79-84; R Manton 79-84; Hon C St Botolph Aldgate w H Trin Minories *Lon* 85-91; Hon C St Clem Eastcheap w St Martin Orgar from 91. *31 Caledonian Wharf, Saundersness Road, London E14 3EN* 0171-515 0637

KIDDLE, Martin John. b 42. Lon Univ DipTh75 Open Univ BA80. St Jo Coll Nottm 74. **d** 76 **p** 77. C Gt Parndon *Chelmsf* 76-80; Asst Chapl HM Pris Wakef 80-81; Asst Chapl HM Youth Cust Cen Portland 81-88; Chapl HM Pris Cardiff from 88. *HM Prison Cardiff, Knox Road, Cardiff CF2 1UG* Cardiff (01222) 491212 Fax 489079

KIDDLE, Canon Peter. b 22. Fitzw Ho Cam BA50 MA54. Clifton Th Coll 57. **d** 57 **p** 58. Kenya 57-72; Hon Can Nairobi Cathl 72; V Worthing St Paul *Chich* 73-87; rtd 87; P-in-c Milton Lilbourne w Easton Royal *Sarum* 87-90. *64 Damask Way, Warminster, Wilts BA12 9PP* Warminster (01985) 214572

KIDDLE, Miss Susan Elizabeth. b 44. Birm Univ BSc66 Nottm Univ CertEd67. Local NSM Course 86. **d** 89 **p** 95. NSM Waddington *Linc* from 89. *16 Sycamore Drive, Brant Road, Lincoln LN5 9DR* Lincoln (01522) 722010

KIDNER, Frank Derek. b 13. ARCM33 Ch Coll Cam BA40 MA44. Ridley Hall Cam 40. **d** 41 **p** 42. Warden Tyndale Ho Cam 64-78; rtd 78; Perm to Offic *Ely* from 79. *56 Manor Park, Histon, Cambridge CB4 4JT* Cambridge (01223) 232579

KIGHTLEY, David John. b 39. AKC67. **d** 68 **p** 69. C Plymouth St Andr *Ex* 68-70; C Ex St Dav 70-73; Chapl Greenwich Distr Hosp & Brook Gen Hosp Lon 73-76; P-in-c Chippenham *Ely* from 76; P-in-c Snailwell from 76; P-in-c Isleham from 76. *The Vicarage, High Street, Chippenham, Ely, Cambs CB7 5PP* Newmarket (01638) 720550

KILBEY, Mrs Sarah. b 39. Edin Univ MA75 Man Poly CertEdD82. Bp Otter Coll TDip59 Edin Dioc NSM Course 84. **d** 93. NSM Edin St Columba *Edin* from 93. *15 Cluny Avenue, Edinburgh EH10 4RN* 0131-447 2378

KILDARE, Archdeacon of. *See* LAWRENCE, Ven Patrick Henry Andrew

KILDARE, Dean of. *See* TOWNLEY, Very Rev Robert Keith

KILFORD, John Douglas. b 38. Oak Hill Th Coll 73. **d** 75 **p** 76. C Beckenham St Jo *Roch* 75-80; P-in-c Sinfin Moor *Derby* 80-83; V Penge St Jo *Roch* 83-92; Staff Member Ellel Min from 92. *6 Milford Close, Catterall, Preston PR3 0GE* Garstang (01995) 604656

KILFORD, William Roy. b 38. BA. Sarum & Wells Th Coll. **d** 84 **p** 85. C Herne *Cant* 84-87; Chapl Wm Harvey Hosp Ashford 87-93; R Mersham w Hinxhill *Cant* 87-93; P-in-c Sevington 87-93; V Reculver and Herne Bay St Bart 93-95; Chapl Paphos from 95. *c/o The Anglican Church, PO Box 1083, Paphos, Cyprus* Fax Paphos (6) 653090

KILGOUR, Richard Eifl. b 57. Edin Univ BD85. Edin Th Coll 81. **d** 85 **p** 86. C Wrexham *St As* 85-88; V Whitford from 88; Ind Chapl from 89. *The Vicarage, Upper Downing Road, Whitford, Holywell, Clwyd CH8 9AJ* Mostyn (01745) 560976

KILLALA AND ACHONRY, Archdeacon of. *See* STRATFORD, Ven Ralph Montgomery

KILLALA, Dean of. *See* ARDIS, Very Rev Edward George

KILLALOE, KILFENORA AND CLONFERT, Dean of. *See* PERDUE, Very Rev Ernon Cope Todd

KILLALOE, KILFENORA, CLONFERT AND KILMACDUAGH, Archdeacon of. *See* KEEGAN, Ven Donald Leslie

KILLE, Canon Vivian Edwy. b 30. Tyndale Hall Bris 60. **d** 62 **p** 63. C Dub Miss Ch *D & G* 62-66; I Emlaghfad *T, K & A* 66-74; I Aghadrumsee w Clogh and Drumsnatt *Clogh* from 74; Preb Clogh Cathl from 93. *Sunshine Rectory, 16 Dangary Road, Roslea, Co Fermanagh BT92 7QY* Roslea (013657) 51206

KILLICK, Brian Anthony Hugh. b 29. Sarum Th Coll 69. **d** 70 **p** 71. C Kingsbury St Andr *Lon* 70-74; C Selston *S'well* 74-76; P-in-c Scarcliffe *Derby* 76-77; P-in-c Sutton cum Duckmanton 77-80; V Stanley 80-94; rtd 94. *40 Oakover Drive, Allestree, Derby DE22 2PR* Allestree (01332) 550562

KILLINGBACK, Oliver Edwin. b 44. S'wark Ord Course 75. **d** 77 **p** 78. C Kingston All SS w St Jo *S'wark* 77-80; C Horley 80-82; NSM Weston Favell *Pet* 87-93; Perm to Offic from 93. *18 Wansford Walk, Northampton NN3 4YF*

KILLOCK, Alfred Kenneth. b 26. Cranmer Hall Dur 72. **d** 74 **p** 75. C Moor Allerton *Ripon* 74-79; Hon C Bolton St Jas w St Chrys *Bradf* 79-83; P-in-c Oakenshaw cum Woodlands 84-90; P-in-c Allerton 90-91; rtd 91. *15 Warwick Road, Bradford, W Yorkshire BD4 7RA* Bradford (01274) 394492

KILLWICK, Simon David Andrew. b 56. K Coll Lon BD80 AKC80. St Steph Ho Ox 80. **d** 81 **p** 82. C Worsley *Man* 81-84; TV from 84. *The Vicarage, 8 Landrace Drive, Boothstown, Worsley, Manchester M28 4UY* 0161-799 1208

KILMORE, Archdeacon of. *See* JOHNSTON, Ven William Derek

KILMORE, Dean of. *See* COMBE, Very Rev John Charles

KILMORE, ELPHIN AND ARDAGH, Bishop of. *See* MAYES, Rt Rev Michael Hugh Gunton

KILNER, Canon Frederick James (Fred). b 43. Qu Coll Cam BA65 MA69. Ridley Hall Cam 67. **d** 70 **p** 71. C Harlow New Town w Lt Parndon *Chelmsf* 70-74; C Cam St Andr Less *Ely* 74-79; P-in-c Milton 79-88; R 88-94; Hon Can Ely Cathl from 88; RD Quy from 93; P-in-c Ely from 94; P-in-c Chettisham from 94; P-in-c Prickwillow from 94; P-in-c Stretham w Thetford from 94; P-in-c Stuntney from 95. *The Vicarage, St Mary's Street, Ely, Cambs CB7 4ER* Ely (01353) 662308

KILPIN, Stanley Leonard. b 09. Worc Ord Coll 67. **d** 69 **p** 70. C Littlehampton St Mary *Chich* 69-75; P-in-c Coldwaltham 75-80; rtd 80; Perm to Offic *Chich* 80-91. *20 Cedar Grove, Beverley, N Humberside HU17 7EP* Hull (01482) 875549

KILSBY, Alfred Daniel Joseph. b 29. St Chad's Coll Dur BA54 Golds Coll Lon PGCE64 Lon Univ BA68 MSc75. Westcott Ho Cam 54. **d** 56 **p** 57. Lect Educn Battersea Coll of Educn

KIMBER, Geoffrey Francis (Geoff). b 46. Univ Coll Lon BA67 PGCE70 DipTh74. St Jo Coll Nottm 86. **d** 88 **p** 89. C Buckhurst Hill *Chelmsf* 88-92; R Arley *Cov* from 92. *The Rectory, Arley, Coventry CV7 8FL* Fillongley (01676) 40378

KIMBER, Mrs Gillian Margaret. b 48. Bedf Coll Lon BA70. Oak Hill Th Coll 89. **d** 91. NSM Buckhurst Hill *Chelmsf* 91-92; C Arley *Cov* from 92. *The Rectory, Arley, Coventry CV7 8FL* Fillongley (01676) 40378

KIMBER, John Keith. b 45. Bris Univ BSc66. St Mich Coll Llan. **d** 69 **p** 70. C Caerphilly *Llan* 69-72; Chapl Birm Univ *Birm* 72-75; TR Bris St Agnes and St Simon w St Werburgh *Bris* 75-82; P-in-c Bris St Paul w St Barn 80-82; Hon C Westbury-on-Trym H Trin 82-83; Area Sec (Wales) USPG 83-89; TR Halesowen *Worc* 89-92; Chapl Geneva *Eur* from 92. *15 Chemin du Vieux Port, 1290 Versoix, Geneva, Switzerland* Geneva (22) 755-4883 or 731-5155

KIMBER, Stuart Francis. b 53. Qu Eliz Coll Lon BSc74 Fitzw Coll Cam BA79 MA83. Ridley Hall Cam 77. **d** 80 **p** 81. C Edgware *Lon* 80-83; C Cheltenham St Mark *Glouc* 83-84; TV 84-92; C Hawkwell *Chelmsf* from 92. *Emmanuel Vicarage, 29 Elizabeth Close, Hockley, Essex SS5 4NQ* Southend-on-Sea (01702) 205939

KIMBERLEY, John Harry. b 49. Brasted Th Coll 72 St Steph Ho Ox 74. **d** 76 **p** 77. C W Tarring *Chich* 76-79; C Portslade St Nic 79-82; C-in-c Findon Valley CD 82-89; V Findon Valley 89-90; V E Preston w Kingston 90-95; Chapl Eastbourne Distr Gen Hosp from 95. *Eastbourne District General Hospital, Kings Drive, Eastbourne, E Sussex BN21 2UD* Eastbourne (01323) 417400

KIMBERLEY, Canon Wilfred Harry. b 19. St Steph Ho Ox 51. **d** 53 **p** 54. V Marsworth *Ox* 65-72; V Buckm 72-78; TR High Wycombe 78-84; Hon Can Ch Ch 79-84; rtd 84; Perm to Offic *Glouc* from 85; Perm to Offic *Ox* from 86. *Rosemary Cottage, Naunton, Cheltenham, Glos GL54 3AA* Guiting Power (01451) 850711

KIME, Thomas Frederick. b 28. Linc Coll Ox BA50 MA53. Cuddesdon Coll 54. **d** 56 **p** 57. S Africa 58-74; R Ellisfield w Farleigh Wallop and Dummer *Win* 74-83; P-in-c Cliddesden 82-83; R Cliddesden and Ellisfield w Farleigh Wallop etc 83-94; rtd 94. *7 Sparkford Close, Winchester, Hants SO22 4NH* Winchester (01962) 870240

KINAHAN, Timothy Charles. b 53. Jes Coll Cam BA75. CITC 77. **d** 78 **p** 79. C Carrickfergus *Conn* 78-81; Papua New Guinea 81-84; I Belf Whiterock *Conn* 84-90; I Gilnahirk *D & D* from 90. *237 Lower Braniel Road, Belfast BT5 7NQ* Belfast (01232) 791748

KINCHIN-SMITH, John Michael. b 52. Fitzw Coll Cam MA. Ridley Hall Cam 79. **d** 82 **p** 83. C Sanderstead All SS *S'wark* 82-87; TV Halesworth w Linstead, Chediston, Holton etc *St E* 87-92; R Mursley w Swanbourne and Lt Horwood *Ox* from 92. *The Rectory, Mursley, Milton Keynes MK17 0RT* Mursley (01296) 720056

KINDER, Mark Russell. b 66. Univ of Wales (Swansea) BA(Econ)88. St Jo Coll Nottm 91. **d** 94 **p** 95. C Pheasey *Lich* from 94. *33 Morland Road, Great Barr, Birmingham B43 7JH* 0121-360 1723

KING, Anthony Richard. b 34. Trin Hall Cam BA58. Ely Th Coll 58 Linc Th Coll 61. **d** 62 **p** 63. C Benwell St Jas *Newc* 62-64; C Thirsk w S Kilvington *York* 64-67; V Halifax St Aug *Wakef* 67-74; R Upton-upon-Severn *Worc* from 74; RD Upton 86-92. *The Rectory, Upton-upon-Severn, Worcester WR8 0JQ* Upton-upon-Severn (01684) 592148

KING, Brian Henry. b 39. Chich Th Coll 63. **d** 65 **p** 66. C Castle Bromwich SS Mary and Marg *Birm* 65-67; C Southwick *Chich* 68-70; V Southwater 70-73; C Brighton St Alb Preston 73-74; TV Brighton Resurr 74-75; V Eastbourne St Elisabeth from 75. *The Vicarage, 266 Victoria Drive, Eastbourne, E Sussex BN20 9QX* Eastbourne (01323) 720068

KING, Cecil John. b 46. Selw Coll Cam BA67 MA71. Coll of Resurr Mirfield 81. **d** 81 **p** 84. Zambia 81-85; SSF from 85; Ghana 86-88; C N Harrow St Alb *Lon* 88-89; C Leeds Gipton Epiphany *Ripon* 91-93. *30 Pembroke Grange, Leeds LS9 6RH* Leeds (0113) 240 2319

KING, Charles John. b 14. CEng46 MIEE Lon Univ BSc39. Ox NSM Course 73. **d** 76 **p** 77. NSM Cuddesdon *Ox* 76-78; NSM Wantage Downs from 78. *48 Ardington, Wantage, Oxon OX12 8PY* Abingdon (01235) 833671

KING, Christopher John. b 56. Chelsea Coll Lon BSc78 CertEd79. St Jo Coll Nottm LTh87. **d** 88 **p** 89. C Wandsworth All SS *S'wark* 88-92; Canada from 92. *PO Box 233, 228 Power Street, Geraldton, Ontario, Canada, P0T 1M0*

KING, Clare Maria. b 68. St Mary's Coll Dur BD91 St Andr Univ. Westcott Ho Cam 91. **d** 94. Hon C Norbury St Phil

S'wark from 94; Chapl Croydon Coll from 95. *4 Turnstone Close, Selsdon, Surrey CR2 8SP*   0181-651 4930

KING, Mrs Daphne Eileen. b 37. E Midl Min Tr Course 78. **dss** 81 **d** 87 **p** 94. Theddlethorpe *Linc* 84-87; D-in-c 87-89; Saltfleetby 84-87; D-in-c 87-89; D-in-c Healing and Stallingborough 89-94; P-in-c from 94. *The Rectory, 1A The Avenue, Healing, Grimsby, S Humberside DN37 7NA* Grimsby (01472) 883481

KING, David Charles. b 52. K Coll Lon 73 Coll of Resurr Mirfield 77. **d** 78 **p** 79. C Saltburn-by-the-Sea *York* 78-81; Youth Officer 81-85; P-in-c Crathorne 81-85; Par Educn Adv *Wakef* 85-91; Min Coulby Newham Ecum Project *York* 91-94; V Egton w Grosmont from 94. *St Hilda's Vicarage, Egton, Whitby, N Yorkshire YO21 1UT*   Whitby (01947) 895315

KING, David Frederick. b 32. Southn Coll of Tech DMA70. Sarum Th Coll 59. **d** 61 **p** 72. C Hanworth All SS *Lon* 60-62; Hon C Andover St Mich *Win* 71-83; P-in-c 83-88; V 88-90; Chapl R S Hants Hosp 90-92; Chapl Countess Mountbatten Hospice 90-92; Chapl Andover War Memorial NHS Trust from 92; Lic to Offic *Win* from 92. *158 Weyhill Road, Andover, Hants SP10 3BG*   Andover (01264) 334319

KING, David Russell. b 42. Univ of Wales (Lamp) BA67. St D Coll Lamp DipTh68. **d** 68 **p** 69. C Barrow St Geo w St Luke *Carl* 68-72; P-in-c Kirkland 72-74; V Edenhall w Langwathby 72-73; P-in-c Culgaith 72-73; V Edenhall w Langwathby and Culgaith 73-74; V Flookburgh 75-79; V Barrow St Jas 79-82; P-in-c Bolton w Ireby and Uldale 82-83; R 83-90; R Burgh-by-Sands and Kirkbampton w Kirkandrews etc from 90. *The Rectory, Burgh-by-Sands, Carlisle CA5 6AW*   Burgh-by-Sands (01228) 576324

KING, David William Anthony. b 42. Ch Ch Ox BA63 MA68. Westcott Ho Cam 63. **d** 65 **p** 66. C Cayton w Eastfield *York* 65-68; C Southbroom *Sarum* 68-71; R Holton Parva 71-72; V Holt St Jas 71-72; V Holt St Jas and Hinton Parva 72-75; P-in-c Horton and Chalbury 73-75; R Holt St Jas, Hinton Parva, Horton and Chalbury 75-79; TV Melton Mowbray w Thorpe Arnold *Leic* 79-83; V Foxton w Gumley and Laughton and Lubenham 83-90; P-in-c Boreham *Chelmsf* from 90. *The Vicarage, Church Road, Boreham, Chelmsford CM3 3EG*   Chelmsford (01245) 467281

KING, Dennis. b 31. ACA53 FCA64. E Midl Min Tr Course 73. **d** 76 **p** 77. NSM Chesterfield All SS *Derby* from 76. *Hillcrest, Stubben Edge, Ashover, Chesterfield, Derbyshire S45 0EU* Chesterfield (01246) 590279

KING, Dennis Charles. b 27. Chich Th Coll 53. **d** 55 **p** 56. Jamaica 66-77; V Bromham w Oakley *St Alb* 77-84; TR St Marylebone Ch Ch *Lon* 84-89; V Flamstead *St Alb* 89-93; rtd 93. *Te Deum, 36 Manor Road, Toddington, Dunstable, Beds LU5 6AH* Toddington (01525) 873557

KING, Dennis Keppel. b 33. Lich Th Coll 63. **d** 65 **p** 66. C Eccleston St Thos *Liv* 65-68; C W Derby St Mary 68-71; V Aintree St Giles from 71. *St Giles Vicarage, 132 Aintree Lane, Aintree, Liverpool L10 8LE*   0151-526 7908

KING, Dr Derek Edwin Noel. b 30. Qu Mary Coll Lon BSc54 Birkb Coll Lon PhD60. Local NSM Course 91. **d** 93 **p** 94. NSM Nacton and Levington w Bucklesham and Foxhall *St E* from 93. *Vindelis, 1 Eastcliff, Felixstowe, Suffolk IP11 9TA* Felixstowe (01394) 270815

KING, Donald (Malcolm Charles). b 32. Chich Th Coll. **d** 86. NSM Forton *Portsm* from 86. *8 Burnett Road, Gosport, Hants PO12 3AH* Gosport (01705) 523440

KING, Fergus John. b 62. St Andr Univ MA Edin Univ BD89. Edin Th Coll 86. **d** 89 **p** 90. Chapl St Jo Cathl Oban *Arg* 89-92; C Oban St Jo 89-92; Tanzania from 92. *clo St Mark's Theological College, PO Box 25017, Dar-es-Salaam, Tanzania*

KING, Frederick William. b 24. CertEd74. Richmond Th Coll 46 Qu Coll Birm 49. **d** 50 **p** 51. Chapl RAF 55-70; Chapl The Leas Sch Hoylake 70-72; Chapl Wirral Gr Sch 74-75; Chapl Summer Fields Sch Ox 75; rtd 89. *31 Saint Yves, 22580 Plouha, France*

KING, George Henry. b 24. MRHS55 NDH55. St Alb Minl Tr Scheme. **d** 79 **p** 80. Hon C Flamstead *St Alb* from 79; Dioc Agric Chapl from 90. *Chad Lane Farm, Chad Lane, Flamstead, St Albans, Herts AL3 8HW*   Luton (01582) 841648

KING, Mrs Gillian Daphne. b 38. E Midl Min Tr Course 79. **dss** 83 **d** 87 **p** 94. Knighton St Jo *Leic* 83-85; Clarendon Park St Jo w Knighton St Mich 86-87; Par Dn 87-89; Chapl Kingston and Esher Mental Health Services 89-93; Chapl Kingston and Esher Community Health Unit from 93; Chapl Long Grove Hosp Epsom 90-92; Chapl Tolworth Hosp Surbiton from 91; Chapl Kingston and Distr Community NHS Trust from 94. *517 Hook Road, Chessington, Surrey KT19 1QW*   0181-390 0102 or 397 1305   Fax 390 1236

KING, Harry William. b 15. Oak Hill Th Coll 38. **d** 41 **p** 42. V Sandon *St Alb* 64-67; V Wallington w Rushden 64-67; Perm to Offic from 67; rtd 80. *318 Hempstead Road, Watford WD1 3NA*   Watford (01923) 232360

KING, Jeffrey Douglas Wallace. b 43. AKC67. **d** 68 **p** 69. C S Harrow St Paul *Lon* 68-71; C Garforth *Ripon* 71-74; V

Potternewton 74-83; TR Moor Allerton from 83; RD Allerton 85-89; Hon Can Ripon Cathl from 90. *St John's Vicarage, Fir Tree Lane, Leeds LS17 7BZ*   Leeds (0113) 268 4598

KING, Dr Jennifer Mary. b 41. Lon Univ BDS65 MSc75 PhD. Ripon Coll Cuddesdon 86. **d** 88 **p** 94. NSM S Hackney St Mich w Haggerston St Paul *Lon* from 88; Chapl Lon Univ Medical Students from 91; Chapl Qu Mary Coll from 91; Chapl Westf Coll from 91. *5 Louisa Gardens, London E1 4NS*   0171-982 6325 or 980 1204

KING, Jeremy Norman. *See* CLARK-KING, Jeremy Norman

KING, John. b 38. S'wark Ord Course DipRS77. **d** 80 **p** 81. C S Gillingham *Roch* 80-85; Min Joydens Wood St Barn CD 85-90; V Borstal from 90; Chapl HM Pris Cookham Wood from 90; Chapl The Foord Almshouses from 90. *The Vicarage, 76 Borstal Street, Rochester, Kent ME1 3HL*   Medway (01634) 845948   Fax 828921

KING, John Andrew. b 50. Qu Coll Birm 72. **d** 75 **p** 76. C Halesowen *Worc* 74-77; C Belper Ch Ch and Milford *Derby* 78-81; Perm to Offic from 87. *11 Well Lane, Milford, Belper, Derbyshire DE56 0QQ*   Derby (01332) 841810

KING, John Charles. b 27. St Pet Hall Ox BA51 MA55. Oak Hill Th Coll 51. **d** 53 **p** 54. Lic to Offic *St Alb* 60-70; Teacher St Fran Bacon Sch St Alb 68-71; Boston Gr Sch 71-88; Lic to Offic *Linc* from 74; rtd 92. *6 Somersby Way, Boston, Lincs PE21 9PQ*   Boston (01205) 363061

KING, John Colin. b 39. Cuddesdon Coll 69. **d** 71 **p** 72. C Cookham Ox 71-75; Youth Chapl *B & W* 75-80; P-in-c Merriott 76-80; P-in-c Hinton w Dinnington 79-80; R Merriott w Hinton, Dinnington and Lopen from 80. *The Vicarage, Church Street, Merriott, Somerset TA16 5PS* Crewkerne (01460) 73226

KING, John David. b 37. Univ of Wales DipTh63. St Aid Birkenhead 67. **d** 69 **p** 70. C Whitfield *Derby* 69-71; C St Laurence in the Isle of Thanet *Cant* 71-76; V Alkham w Capel le Ferne and Hougham 76-82; R Deal St Andr from 82. *St Andrew's Rectory, St Andrew's Road, Deal, Kent CT14 6AS* Deal (01304) 374354

KING, John Michael Stuart. b 22. St Edm Hall Ox BA48 MA52. Cuddesdon Coll 48. **d** 50 **p** 51. R Hinderwell w Roxby *York* 60-71; V Hibaldstow *Linc* 71-88; rtd 88; Perm to Offic *Linc* from 88. *Old School House, Church Lane, Saxby-all-Saints, Brigg, S Humberside DN20 0QE*   Saxby-all-Saints (065261) 693

KING, Joseph Stephen. b 39. St Chad's Coll Dur BA62 DipTh63 MPhil83. **d** 64 **p** 65. C Lewisham St Mary *S'wark* 64-69; Hon C Milton next Gravesend Ch Ch *Roch* 70-85; V from 85. *The Vicarage, 48 Old Road East, Gravesend, Kent DA12 1NR* Gravesend (01474) 352643

KING, Mrs Katharine Mary. b 63. St Hugh's Coll Ox BA85 MA89 SS Coll Cam BA88. Ridley Hall Cam 86. **d** 89 **p** 94. C Ipswich St Aug *St E* 89-91. *18 Fitzmaurice Road, Ipswich IP3 9AX*   Ipswich (01473) 719562

KING, Lawrence Norman. b 38. FRICS. St Deiniol's Hawarden. **d** 80 **p** 81. NSM Lt Bowden St Hugh *Leic* 80-84; NSM Fleckney and Kilby 84-89; R Scalford w Goadby Marwood and Wycombe etc from 89. *The Rectory, 16 Church Street, Scalford, Melton Mowbray, Leics LE14 4DL*   Scalford (01664) 76319

KING, Malcolm Charles. b 37. Chich Th Coll 67. **d** 70 **p** 71. C Mill End *St Alb* 70-72; Chapl RAF 72-76; R W Lynn *Nor* 76-81; V Croxley Green All SS *St Alb* 81-90; V Grimsby St Aug *Linc* from 90; Asst Local Min Officer from 90; OGS from 90. *St Augustine's Vicarage, 145 Legsby Avenue, Grimsby, S Humberside DN32 0LA*   Grimsby (01472) 877109

KING, Malcolm Stewart. b 56. Sarum & Wells Th Coll 77. **d** 80 **p** 81. C Farnham *Guildf* 80-83; C Chertsey 83-86; Chapl St Pet Hosp Chertsey 83-86; V Egham Hythe *Guildf* 86-91; P-in-c Cove St Jo 91; TR from 91; RD Aldershot from 93. *The Rectory, 55 Cove Road, Farnborough, Hants GU14 0EX* Farnborough (01252) 544544

KING, Martin Quartermain. b 39. Reading Univ BA61. Cuddesdon Coll 62. **d** 64 **p** 65. C S Shields St Hilda w St Thos *Dur* 64-66; C Newton Aycliffe 66-71; V Chilton Moor 71-78; R Middleton St Geo 78-91; R Sedgefield from 91; RD Sedgefield from 91. *The Rectory, Sedgefield, Stockton-on-Tees, Cleveland TS21 3DW*   Sedgefield (01740) 20274

KING, Maurice Charles Francis. b 32. ACP58 Em Coll Cam BA55 MA59. Chich Th Coll 78. **d** 79 **p** 80. C Burnley St Cath *Blackb* 79-81; C Burnley St Cath w St Alb and St Paul 81-83; C Sheff Parson Cross St Cecilia *Sheff* 83-88; V New Bentley 88-94; rtd 94. *204 Wordsworth Court, Cockermouth, Cumbria CA13 0EB*   Cockermouth (01900) 827503

KING, Michael Charles. Worc Coll Ox BA56 MA60. Coll of Resurr Mirfield. **d** 62 **p** 63. Hon C Hampstead All So *Lon* 62-65; C Thorpe *Nor* 66-69; Ed Sec BRF 69-90; NSM Queensbury All SS *Lon* 69-79; Hon C Lt Stanmore St Lawr 80-90; R Cawston w Haveringland, Booton and Brandiston *Nor* from 91; P-in-c Saxthorpe w Corpusty, Blickling, Oulton etc 94. *The Rectory, Ames Court, Cawston, Norwich NR10 4AN* Norwich (01603) 871282

KING, Nathan Richard. b 68. Whitelands Coll Lon BA89 Liv Univ DipSocSc91. St Mich Coll Llan DipTh93 BTh94. **d** 94 **p** 95. C Hawarden *St As* from 94. *1 Church Cottage, Rectory Lane, Hawarden, Deeside, Clwyd CH5 3NN* Hawarden (01244) 538715

KING, Nicholas Bernard Paul. b 46. Wycliffe Hall Ox 72. **d** 75 **p** 76. C Pitsmoor w Wicker *Sheff* 75-78; C Erdington St Barn *Birm* 78-80; C Sutton Coldfield H Trin 80-84; V Lynesack *Dur* 84-92; rtd 93. *21 Arthur Terrace, Bishop Auckland, Co Durham DL14 6BL* Bishop Auckland (01388) 605614

KING, Noel Quinton. b 22. St Pet Hall Ox BA47 MA48 Nottm Univ PhD54. Wycliffe Hall Ox. **d** 50 **p** 51. C E Retford *S'well* 50-51; C Nottm St Pet and St Jas 51-53; Lect Ch Hist Nottm Univ 51-55; C Shelford *S'well* 53-55; Uganda from 55. *Address temp unknown*

KING, Peter Duncan. b 48. TD. K Coll Lon LLB70 AKC70 Fitzw Coll Cam BA72 MA77. Westcott Ho Cam 70. **d** 80 **p** 81. Hon C Notting Hill *Lon* 80-84; Hon C Mortlake w E Sheen *S'wark* from 84. *49 Leinster Avenue, London SW14 7JW* 0181-876 8997

KING, Peter George. b 24. Lon Univ LLB52. ALCD55. **d** 55 **p** 56. V Leyton St Paul *Chelmsf* 68-85; rtd 85. *10 Barrington Mead, Sidmouth, Devon EX10 8QW* Sidmouth (01395) 578172

KING, Canon Philip David. b 35. Keble Coll Ox BA57 MA61. Tyndale Hall Bris 58. **d** 60 **p** 61. C Redhill H Trin *S'wark* 60-63; C Wallington H Trin 63-68; V Fulham Ch Ch *Lon* 68-74; Lic to Offic *S'wark* 74-86; Gen Sec SAMS 74-86; V Roxeth Ch Ch and Harrow St Pet *Lon* 86-89; Gen Sec Gen Syn Bd for Miss from 89. *31 Myrtle Avenue, Ruislip, Middx HA4 8SA* 0171-429 0636 or 222 9011 Fax 799 2714

KING, Miss Philipa Ann. b 65. Heythrop Coll Lon. Westcott Ho Cam CTM95. **d** 95. C Cam Ascension *Ely* from 95. *36 Alpha Road, Cambridge CB4 3DG*

KING, Rawlins Henry Pyne. b 16. ALCD42. **d** 42 **p** 43. V Hailsham *Chich* 68-81; rtd 81; Perm to Offic *Chich* from 81. *24 Nutley Crescent, Goring-by-Sea, Worthing, W Sussex BN12 4LA* Worthing (01903) 246206

KING, Richard Andrew. b 51. Linc Th Coll. **d** 84 **p** 85. C Bramhall *Ches* 84-87; V Heald Green St Cath 87-92; P-in-c Ashprington, Cornworthy and Dittisham *Ex* from 92. *The Rectory, Prior View, Cornworthy, Totnes, Devon TQ9 7HN* Totnes (01803) 732384

KING, Richard David. b 63. Oak Hill Th Coll 87. **d** 90 **p** 91. C Foord St Jo *Cant* 90-94; P-in-c Orlestone w Snave and Ruckinge w Warehorne from 94. *The Rectory, Cock Lane, Ham Street, Ashford, Kent TN26 2HU* Ham Street (01233) 732274

KING, Robert Dan (Bob). b 57. Sarum & Wells Th Coll 92. **d** 94 **p** 95. C Heref H Trin *Heref* from 94. *79 Bridle Road, Kings Acre, Hereford HR4 0DW* Hereford (01432) 341033

KING, Robin Lucas Colin. b 59. Dundee Univ MA81. Ridley Hall Cam 87. **d** 89 **p** 90. C Ipswich St Aug *St E* 89-92; V Bures from 92. *The Vicarage, Bures, Suffolk CO8 5AA* Bures (01787) 227315

KING, Canon Stuart John Langley. b 33. Selw Coll Cam BA57 MA61. Linc Th Coll 57. **d** 59 **p** 60. C Plymouth Crownhill Ascension *Ex* 59-62; C Horsham *Chich* 62-67; V Devonport St Mark Ford *Ex* 67-77; RD Plymouth 74-77; Can Res Cov Cathl *Cov* 77-84; V Tooting All SS *S'wark* from 84. *All Saints' Vicarage, 84 Franciscan Road, London SW17 8DQ* 0181-672 3706

KING, Terence Reginald. b 33. St Steph Ho Ox 58. **d** 61 **p** 62. C Thornhill Lees *Wakef* 61-65; V Glasshoughton 65-77; V W Ardsley from 77. *St Mary's Vicarage, Woodkirk, Dewsbury, W Yorkshire WF12 7JL* Batley (01924) 472375

KING, Canon Thomas George. b 10. OBE67. Univ of Wales (Lamp) BA32 Jes Coll Ox BA34 MA38. Lambeth DD79 St Steph Ho Ox 34. **d** 34 **p** 35. R Stoke Charity and Hunton *Win* 46-87; Hon Can Win Cathl 58-87; rtd 87. *33 Western Road, Winchester, Hants SO22 5AJ* Winchester (01962) 861415

KING, Thomas James Richard. b 27. LGSM64 ACP66. St Jo Coll Nottm. **d** 85 **p** 86. Hon C Enderby w Lubbesthorpe and Thurlaston *Leic* from 85. *6 Copt Oak Road, Narborough, Leicester LE9 5EF* Leicester (0116) 286 4250

KING, Timothy William. b 52. CertEd. Ripon Coll Cuddesdon. **d** 81 **p** 82. C Ludlow *Heref* 81-83; C Walton-on-Thames *Guildf* 83-86; C Hammersmith St Paul *Lon* 86-88; V Send *Guildf* 88-95; R Farncombe from 95. *The Rectory, 38 Farncombe Hill, Godalming, Surrey GU7 2AU* Godalming (01483) 416091

KING, Tony Christopher. b 62. Lanc Univ BA83. Coll of Resurr Mirfield 83. **d** 86 **p** 87. C Stansted Mountfitchet *Chelmsf* 86-89; USPG 89-92; Botswana 90-92; C Chingford SS Pet and Paul *Chelmsf* 92-93. *Address temp unknown*

KING, Preb Walter Raleigh. b 45. New Coll Ox BA67 MA74. Cuddesdon Coll 71. **d** 74 **p** 75. C Wisbech SS Pet and Paul *Ely*

74-77; C Barrow St Geo w St Luke *Carl* 77-79; P-in-c Clifford *Heref* 79-83; P-in-c Cusop 79-83; P-in-c Hardwick 79-83; P-in-c Whitney w Winforton 81-84; R Cusop w Clifford, Hardwicke, Bredwardine etc 83-86; R Heref St Nic 86-92; Dir of Ords 86-92; Preb Heref Cathl 86-92; TR Huntingdon *Ely* from 92; RD Huntingdon from 94. *The Rectory, 1 The Walks East, Huntingdon, Cambs PE18 6AP* Huntingdon (01480) 412674

KING-SMITH, Giles Anthony Beaumont. b 53. Univ Coll Ox BA75. Trin Coll Bris DipHE88. **d** 88 **p** 89. C Gtr Corsham *Bris* 88-92; V Two Mile Hill St Mich from 92. *St Michael's Vicarage, Two Mile Hill, Bristol BS15 1BE* Bristol (0117) 967 1371

KING-SMITH, Philip Hugh (Brother Robert Hugh). b 28. CCC Cam BA52 MA56. Cuddesdon Coll 52. **d** 54 **p** 55. C Stockton St Pet *Dur* 54-59; V Bishopwearmouth Gd Shep 59-64; SSF from 64; USA from 66. *San Damiano, 573 Dolores Street, San Francisco, California 94110, USA* San Francisco (415) 861-1372

KINGCOME, John Parken. b 18. CEng50 MIMechE50. Sarum Th Coll 65. **d** 67 **p** 68. C Melksham *Sarum* 67-70; P-in-c Woodborough w Manningford Bohun etc 70-72; R Swanborough 72-75; TR Swanborough 75-79; RD Pewsey 75-84; Custos St Jo Hosp Heytesbury 79-84; rtd 84; Perm to Offic *B & W* from 85; Perm to Offic *Bris* from 92. *Stonecrop, The Butts, Biddestone, Chippenham, Wilts SN14 7DY* Chippenham (01249) 713412

KINGHAM, Derek Henry. b 29. Oak Hill Th Coll 56. **d** 58 **p** 59. C Deptford St Jo *S'wark* 58-60; C Normanton *Derby* 60-63; R Gaulby w Kings Norton and Stretton Parva *Leic* 63-73; V Bacup St Sav *Man* from 73. *St Saviour's Vicarage, 10 Park Crescent, Bacup, Lancs OL13 9RL* Bacup (01706) 873362

KINGHAM, Canon John Arthur. b 14. Ch Coll Cam BA36 MA40. Ridley Hall Cam 36. **d** 38 **p** 39. V Gt Baddow *Chelmsf* 51-82; rtd 82. *63 Tensing Gardens, Billericay, Essex CM12 9JY* Billericay (01277) 652475

KINGHAM, Mair Josephine. See TALBOT, Mrs Mair Josephine

KINGHORN, Richard. b 16. CCC Cam BA38 MA42. Linc Th Coll 39. **d** 40 **p** 46. Chapl K Coll Sch Wimbledon 58-77; rtd 77; Tutor Open Univ 78-89. *5 Edge Hill, London SW19 4LR* 0181-946 0393

KINGMAN, Paul Henry Charles. b 64. Reading Univ BSc86. Wycliffe Hall Ox BTh95. **d** 95. C Whitton *Sarum* from 95. *8 Knowledge Crescent, Ramsbury, Marlborough, Wilts SN8 2QZ* Marlborough (01672) 521282

KINGS, Canon Graham Ralph. b 53. Hertf Coll Ox BA77 MA80 Selw Coll Cam DipTh80. Ridley Hall Cam 78. **d** 80 **p** 81. C Harlesden St Mark *Lon* 80-84; CMS 85-91; Kenya 85-91; Dir Studies St Andr Inst Kabare 85-88; Vice Prin 89-91; Lect in Missiology Cam Federation Th Colls from 91; Overseas Adv Henry Martyn Trust from 91. *York House, 43 Belvoir Road, Cambridge CB4 1JH* Cambridge (01223) 353040 or 355397

KINGS, Mrs Jean Alison. b 63. RGN85. Cranmer Hall Dur BA90. **d** 91 **p** 94. Chapl Bris Poly *Bris* 91-92; Chapl Univ of the W of England, Bris 92-95; Hon C Bris Lockleaze St Mary Magd w St Fran 91-95; C Fishponds All SS from 95. *36 Timberdene, Trendlewood, Bristol BS16 1TJ* Bristol (0117) 965 6725

KINGS, Peter Robert. b 33. AKC61. **d** 62 **p** 63. Dep Dir of Educn *Lon* 66-70; Dep Dir of Educn *S'wark* 66-70; Lic to Offic *Nor* 79-95; rtd 86. *113 Gaywood Road, King's Lynn, Norfolk PE30 2PU* King's Lynn (01553) 772404

KINGSBURY, Canon Richard John. b 41. Lon Univ BA63. Linc Th Coll 65. **d** 67 **p** 68. C Wallsend St Luke *Newc* 67-69; C Monkseaton St Mary 69-70; Chapl K Coll Lon 70-75; V Hungerford and Denford *Ox* 75-83; R Caversham and Mapledurham from 83; Hon Can Ch Ch from 92. *The Rectory, 20 Church Road, Reading RG4 7AD* Reading (01734) 479130 or 471703

KINGSLAND, Desmond George. b 23. Sarum Th Coll 75. **d** 78 **p** 79. Hon C Bournemouth H Epiphany *Win* from 78. *Windy Ridge, 23 Granby Road, Bournemouth BH9 3NZ* Bournemouth (01202) 526011

KINGSLEY, Brian St Clair. b 26. St Steph Ho Ox 56. **d** 59 **p** 60. C Tilehurst St Mich *Ox* 59-63; CSWG from 63; Prior from 85; Lic to Offic *Chich* from 66. *The Monastery of Christ the Saviour, 23 Cambridge Road, Hove, E Sussex BN3 1DE* Brighton (01273) 726698

KINGSLEY-SMITH, John Sydney. b 45. ARCM. Ridley Hall Cam 78. **d** 80 **p** 81. C Nailsea H Trin *B & W* 80-84; TV Whitton *Sarum* 84-91; V Chorleywood Ch Ch *St Alb* from 91. *Christ Church Vicarage, Chorleywood Common, Rickmansworth, Herts WD3 5SG* Chorleywood (01923) 282149

KINGSNORTH, Canon Eric John. b 11. FIA38. Wells Th Coll 45. **d** 47 **p** 48. R Newark St Mary *S'well* 63-74; P-in-c Bradpole

Sarum 74-78; rtd 78; Perm to Offic *Win* from 78. *11 The Cloisters, Belmore Lane, Lymington, Hants SO41 3QX* Lymington (01590) 678397

KINGSTON, Canon Albert William (Bertie). b 47. Bernard Gilpin Soc Dur 68 Oak Hill Th Coll 69. **d** 72 **p** 73. C Walton Breck *Liv* 72-74; C Templemore *D & R* 74-76; I Kildallon w Newtowngore and Corrawallen *K, E & A* 76-82; Bp's C Ardagh w Tashinny, Shrule and Kilcommick from 82; Preb Sligo Cathl from 95. *The Rectory, Tashinny, Colehill, Ballymahon, Co Longford, Irish Republic* Mullingar (44) 57434

KINGSTON, Mrs Avril Dawson. b 34. Local Minl Tr Course 91. **d** 94 **p** 95. NSM Douglas Union w Frankfield *C, C & R* from 94. *Ballymartin House, Glencairn, Co Waterford, Irish Republic* Waterford (58) 56227

KINGSTON, Canon Eric. b 24. **d** 69 **p** 70. C Ballymacarrett St Patr *D & D* 69-72; C Knock 72-76; I Annahilt w Magherahamlet 76-93; rtd 93; Can and Prec Dromore Cathl *D & D* 93. *38 Kinedale Park, Ballynahinch, Co Down BT24 8YS* Ballynahinch (01238) 565715

KINGSTON, George Mervyn. b 47. CITC 70. **d** 73 **p** 74. C Comber *D & D* 73-77; C Belf St Donard 77-80; Min Can Down Cathl 80-84; I Ardglass w Dunsford 82-84; Bp's C Belf St Andr *Conn* 84-90; I Ballymascanlan w Creggan and Rathcor *Arm* from 90. *1 Whitemill Road, Lower Faughart, Dundalk, Co Louth, Irish Republic* Dundalk (42) 71921

KINGSTON, John Desmond George. b 40. TCD BA63 MA66. CITC 64. **d** 64 **p** 65. C Arm St Mark *Arm* 64-70; Hon VC Arm Cathl 69-70; Chapl Portora R Sch Enniskillen from 70; Lic to Offic *Clogh* from 70. *Ambleside, 45 Old Rossory Road, Enniskillen, Co Fermanagh BT74 7LF* Enniskillen (01365) 324493

KINGSTON, Kenneth Robert. b 42. TCD BA65 MA69. **d** 66 **p** 67. C Enniscorthy *C & O* 66-69; C Ballymena *Conn* 70-72; C Drumragh w Mountfield *D & R* 72-78; I Badoney Lower w Greenan and Badoney Upper 78-84; I Desertmartin w Termoneeny from 84. *25 Dromore Road, Desertmartin, Magherafelt, Co Londonderry BT45 5JZ* Magherafelt (01648) 32455

KINGSTON, Michael Joseph. b 51. K Coll Lon BD73 AKC73. St Aug Coll Cant 73. **d** 74 **p** 75. C Reading H Trin *Ox* 74-77; C New Eltham All SS *S'wark* 77-83; V Plumstead Ascension 83-94; Sub-Dean Greenwich N 92-94; V Sydenham St Bart from 94. *St Bartholomew's Vicarage, 4 Westwood Hill, London SE26 6QR* 0181-778 5290

KINGSTON, Robert George. b 46. TCD BA68 Div Test69. **d** 69 **p** 72. C Belf St Thos *Conn* 69-72; C Kilkenny St Canice Cathl *C & O* 72-75; I Ballinasloe w Taughmaconnell *L & K* 77-79; I Maryborough w Dysart Enos and Ballyfin *C & O* 79-85; I Lurgan w Billis, Killinkere and Munterconnaught *K, E & A* 85-88; Registrar Kilmore 87-92; I Lurgan etc w Ballymachugh, Kildrumferton etc 88-92; I Tallaght *D & G* from 92; Warden of Readers from 93. *6 Sally Park, Firhouse Road, Tallaght, Dublin 24, Irish Republic* Dublin (1) 451-5884

KINGSTON, Roy William Henry. b 31. Chich Th Coll 60. **d** 62 **p** 63. C Leeds St Aid *Ripon* 62-66; S Africa 66-73; V Bramley *Ripon* 74-81; TR Hemel Hempstead *St Alb* 81-85; TR Fareham H Trin *Portsm* 85-93; RD Alverstoke 89-90; RD Fareham 90-93; P-in-c Hambledon from 93. *The Vicarage, Church Lane, Hambledon, Portsmouth PO7 4RT* Portsmouth (01705) 632717

KINGSTON, Mrs Shirley Alexandra. b 42. Ch of Ireland Tr Coll DPEd61 TCD BA68 HDipEd70. CITC 90. **d** 93 **p** 94. NSM Castlemacadam w Ballinaclash, Aughrim etc *D & G* 93-95; NSM Rathdrum w Glenealy, Derralossary and Laragh from 95. *Kilpatrick House, Redcross, Wicklow, Irish Republic* Wicklow (404) 47137

KINGSTON, William Ypres. b 19. TCD BA40 MA43 BD46. TCD Div Sch. **d** 43 **p** 44. V Albany Street Ch Ch *Lon* 55-80; C Weeke *Win* 80-85; rtd 85. *20 Cedar Court, Crown Street, Egham, Surrey TW20 9DB* Egham (01784) 431605

KINGSTON-UPON-THAMES, Area Bishop of. *See* WHARTON, Rt Rev John Martin

KINGTON, David Bruce. b 45. Trin Coll Bris 72. **d** 72 **p** 73. C Wellington w Eyton *Lich* 72-77; C Boscombe St Jo *Win* 77-81; R Michelmersh, Timsbury, Farley Chamberlayne etc from 81; RD Romsey from 95. *The Rectory, Braishfield, Romsey, Hants SO5 0PR* Braishfield (01794) 368335

KINNA, Michael Andrew. b 46. Chich Th Coll 84. **d** 86 **p** 87. C Leominster *Heref* 86-90; TV Wenlock 90-93; P-in-c Broseley w Benthall 93; P-in-c Jackfield 93; P-in-c Linley w Willey and Barrow 93; R Broseley w Benthall, Jackfield, Linley etc from 94. *The Rectory, Church Street, Broseley, Shropshire TF12 5DA* Telford (01952) 882644

KINNAIRD, Keith. b 42. Chich Th Coll 72. **d** 75 **p** 76. C Didcot St Pet *Ox* 75-78; C Abingdon w Shippon 78-82; Chapl Abingdon Hosp 79-92; P-in-c Sunningwell *Ox* 82-90; P-in-c Radley 88-90; R Radley and Sunningwell 90-95; SBStJ from 91; Oxon

Co Chapl OStJ 91-95; V New Shoreham *Chich* from 95; V Old Shoreham from 95. *The Vicarage, Church Street, Shoreham-by-Sea, W Sussex BN43 5DQ* Shoreham-by-Sea (01273) 452109

KINSEY, Bruce Richard Lawrence. b 59. K Coll Lon BD81 AKC81 MTh86. Wycliffe Hall Ox. **d** 84 **p** 85. C Gt Stanmore *Lon* 84-88; C Shepherd's Bush St Steph w St Thos 88-91; Chapl and Fell Down Coll Cam from 91. *Downing College, Cambridge CB2 1DQ* Cambridge (01223) 334800

KINSEY, Paul. b 56. Nottm Univ BTh89. Linc Th Coll 86. **d** 89 **p** 90. C Connah's Quay *St As* 89-91; Min Can St As Cathl 91-94; Asst Chapl Middx Hosp Lon from 94. *Middlesex Hospital, Mortimer Street, London W1N 8AA* 0171-636 8333

KINSEY, Russell Frederick David. b 34. Sarum Th Coll 59. **d** 62 **p** 63. C N Cadbury *B & W* 66-76; C Yarlington 66-76; P-in-c Compton Pauncefoot w Blackford 66-76; P-in-c Maperton 66-76; P-in-c N Cheriton 66-76; TV Camelot Par 76-79; V Pill 79-82; P-in-c Easton in Gordano w Portbury and Clapton 80-82; V Pill w Easton in Gordano and Portbury 82-92; rtd 94. *Flat 5, 5 Lovers Walk, Weston-super-Mare, Avon BS23 2AF* Weston-super-Mare (01934) 644087

KINSMEN, Barry William. b 40. Chan Sch Truro. **d** 74 **p** 75. NSM Padstow *Truro* 74-78; Dioc Adv in RE 79-95; P-in-c St Issey 80-81; P-in-c Lt Petherick 80-81; R St Issey w St Petroc Minor 81-95; rtd 95. *12A Old South Court, School Hill, Padstow, Cornwall PL28 8ED* Padstow (01841) 532507

KIPPAX, Michael John. b 48. Open Univ BA82. SW Minl Tr Course 89. **d** 92 **p** 93. C Camborne *Truro* 92-95; C Woughton *Ox* from 95. *49 Garraways, Coffee Hall, Milton Keynes MK6 5DD* Milton Keynes (01908) 670427

KIRBY, Bernard William Alexander (Alex). b 39. Keble Coll Ox BA62. Coll of Resurr Mirfield 62. **d** 65 **p** 72. C Is of Dogs Ch Ch and St Jo w St Luke *Lon* 65-66; Hon C Battersea St Phil S'wark 72; Hon C Battersea St Phil w St Bart 73-76; Perm to Offic 76-78 and from 83. *31 Ashness Road, London SW11 6RY* 0171-223 4000

KIRBY, David Anthony. b 42. Dur Univ BA64 PhD68. N Ord Course 84. **d** 87 **p** 88. NSM Crosland Moor *Wakef* from 87. *9 Fenay Crescent, Almondbury, Huddersfield HD5 8XY* Huddersfield (01484) 533312

KIRBY, David Graham. b 58. Univ of Wales (Cardiff) BA80 Ox Univ BA83. Wycliffe Hall Ox 83. **d** 86 **p** 87. C Northallerton w Kirby Sigston *York* 86-89; C Southport Ch Ch *Liv* 89-92; R Bishop Burton w Walkington *York* from 92. *The Rectory, Walkington, Beverley, N Humberside HU17 8SP* Hull (01482) 868379

KIRBY, Mrs Joan Florence. b 32. St Hugh's Coll Ox MA57 Lon Univ BA66. St Alb Minl Tr Scheme 79. **d** 87 **p** 94. NSM Hemel Hempstead *St Alb* 87-90; C Blisland w St Breward *Truro* 90-94; rtd 92; NSM Cardynham *Truro* from 94. *Penrose, Tresarrett, Blisland, Bodmin, Cornwall PL30 4QY* Bodmin (01208) 851003

KIRBY, John Howard Anthony. b 60. Oak Hill Th Coll BA91. **d** 91 **p** 92. C Grantham *Linc* 91-95. *33 Ypres Road, Allestree, Derby DE3 2NA* Derby (01332) 556051

KIRBY, John Patrick. b 24. Leeds Univ BA50. Coll of Resurr Mirfield 50. **d** 52 **p** 53. P-in-c Buildwas *Lich* 68-77; P-in-c Lt Wenlock *Heref* 68-77; V Coalbrookdale 68-77; C S Gillingham *Roch* 77-83; V New Brompton St Luke 83-89; rtd 89. *2 Allen Court, Hauxton Road, Cambridge CB2 2LU* Cambridge (01223) 845303

KIRBY, Maurice William Herbert. b 31. K Coll Lon DipTh CertEd AKC. **d** 55 **p** 56. V Burcombe *Sarum* 68-70; V Salisbury St Mich 70-73; Chapl SS Helen and Kath Sch Abingdon 73-79; Chapl Wrekin Coll Shropshire 79-84; Hd of Relig Studies 79-84; V Frensham *Guildf* 84-93; Dir of Reader Tr 84-93; rtd 93; Perm to Offic *Ex* 93-94. *c/o 36 Ridgewood Avenue, Saltdean, Brighton BN2 8HH* Brighton (01273) 304863

KIRBY, Paul Michael. b 51. Wycliffe Hall Ox 74. **d** 76 **p** 77. C Gateacre *Liv* 76-79; C Barton Seagrave w Warkton *Pet* 79-83; V Bidston *Ches* 83-93; V Ormskirk *Liv* from 93. *The Vicarage, Park Road, Ormskirk, Lancs L39 3AJ* Ormskirk (01695) 572143

KIRBY, Stennett Roger. b 54. St Pet Coll Ox BA75 MA79. Sarum & Wells Th Coll 75. **d** 77 **p** 78. C Belsize Park *Lon* 77-79; NSM Plumstead St Nic *S'wark* 88; C Leic Ch Sav *Leic* 90-91; TV Hanley H Ev *Lich* 91-95; P-in-c Walsall St Pet from 95. *St Peter's Vicarage, 22 Bloxwich Road, Walsall WS2 8DB* Walsall (01922) 23995

KIRK, Gavin John. b 61. Southn Univ BTh. Chich Th Coll 83. **d** 86 **p** 87. C Seaford w Sutton *Chich* 86-89; Chapl and Succ Roch Cath *Roch* 89-91; Min Can Roch Cathl 89-91; Hon PV Roch Cathl from 91; Asst Chapl K Sch Roch from 91. *5 St Margaret's Street, Rochester, Kent ME1 1TU* Medway (01634) 814479

KIRK, Geoffrey. b 45. Keble Coll Ox BA67. Coll of Resurr Mirfield 71. **d** 72 **p** 73. C Leeds St Aid *Ripon* 72-74; C St

Marylebone St Mark w St Luke *Lon* 74-76; C Kennington St Jo *S'wark* 77-79; C Kennington St Jo w St Jas 79-81; P-in-c Lewisham St Steph and St Mark 81-87; V from 87. *St Stephen's Vicarage, Cressingham Road, London SE13 5AG* 0181-318 1295

KIRK, George. b 14. Kelham Th Coll 32. **d** 38 **p** 39. R Aston cum Aughton *Sheff* 56-80; V Ulley 65-80; RD Laughton 72-79; rtd 80; Chapl to Rtd Clergy and Clergy Widows Officer *Sheff* 80-86; Lic to Offic from 86. *3 Borrowdale Crescent, North Anston, Sheffield S31 7JW* Dinnington (01909) 566774

KIRK, Miss Geraldine Mercedes. b 49. Hull Univ MA89. **d** 87 **p** 94. Ind Chapl *Linc* from 87. *364 Laceby Road, Grimsby, S Humberside DN34 5LU* Grimsby (01472) 873435

KIRK, Henry Logan. b 52. Adelaide Univ BA74 New Coll Edin BD77. **d** 80 **p** 81. S Africa 80-85; Asst Master Haileybury Sch Herts 86; Asst Chapl Rugby Sch Warks 86-93; Dep Head Dulwich Coll Prep Sch 93-94; NSM S Dulwich St Steph *S'wark* 93-94; C Linslade *Ox* from 94. *32 Camberton Road, Leighton Buzzard, Beds LU7 7UP* Leighton Buzzard (01525) 376249

KIRK, John Andrew. b 37. Lon Univ BD61 AKC61 MPhil75 Fitzw Ho Cam BA63. Ridley Hall Cam 61. **d** 63 **p** 64. C Finchley Ch Ch *Lon* 63-66; Argentina 66-79; SAMS 79-81; CMS 82-90; Dean of Miss Selly Oak Coll Birm from 90. *Department of Mission, Selly Oak Colleges, Birmingham B29 6LQ* 0121-472 4231

KIRK, Peter Fenwick. b 30. **d** 83 **p** 84. NSM Bathgate *Edin* 83-91; NSM Linlithgow 83-91; NSM Bathgate from 92. *18 Inch Crescent, Bathgate, West Lothian EH48 1EU* Bathgate (01506) 55369

KIRK, Steven Paul. b 59. Ex Univ LLB80 Univ of Wales (Cardiff) BD87 LLM94. St Mich Coll Llan 84. **d** 87 **p** 88. C Ebbw Vale *Mon* 87-89; PV Llan Cathl *Llan* 89-91; PV and Succ 91-94; V Port Talbot St Agnes w Oakwood from 94. *St Agnes Vicarage, 29 Ynys Street, Port Talbot, W Glam SA13 1YW* Port Talbot (01639) 883630

KIRK-DUNCAN, Ven Brian Andrew Campbell. Pemb Coll Ox BA46 MA47 TCD MA59 DPhil64. Cuddesdon Coll 39. **d** 41 **p** 42. C Summertown *Ox* 41-43; Asst Chapl Dragon Sch Ox 41-43; C Headington Quarry *Ox* 43-44; V Sevenhampton w Charlton Abbots and Hawling *Glouc* 44-47; R Bredon w Bredon's Norton *Worc* 47-62; R St Mary at Hill w St Andr Hubbard etc *Lon* from 62; Prin Becket Coll Lon 63-67; Dep Min Can St Paul's Cathl *Lon* from 69; Perm to Offic *St E* from 91. *The Rectory, St Mary-at-Hill, London EC3R 8EE* 0171-626 4184   Fax 283 4421

KIRK-SMITH, Harold. b 17. Sheff Univ BA39 MA46 PhD53. Lich Th Coll 39. **d** 41 **p** 42. Chapl Rossall Sch Fleetwood 65-72; Hd of Relig Instruction Qu Mary Sch Lytham 72-82; rtd 82. *20 Lowick Drive, Poulton-le-Fylde, Lancs FY6 8HB* Poulton-le-Fylde (01253) 886709

KIRKBY, John Victor Michael. b 39. Lon Univ BScEng62 DipMaths64 BD73. Ridley Hall Cam 65. **d** 67 **p** 68. C Muswell Hill St Jas *Lon* 67-70; Chapl Hatf Poly *St Alb* 71-75; V Wootton 75-86; RD Elstow 82-86; R Byfleet *Guildf* 86-92; P-in-c Potten End w Nettleden *St Alb* from 92. *The Vicarage, Church Road, Potten End, Berkhamsted, Herts HP4 2QY* Berkhamsted (01442) 865217

KIRKBY, Reginald Gresham. b 16. Leeds Univ BA40. Coll of Resurr Mirfield 40. **d** 42 **p** 43. V Bow Common *Lon* 51-94; rtd 94. *7 St James' Court, Bishop Street, London N1 8PH* 0171-226 6992

KIRKE, Clive Henry. b 51. Ridley Hall Cam. **d** 83 **p** 84. C Ainsdale *Liv* 83-86; Gen Asst Bootle Deanery 86-89; P-in-c Litherland St Andr from 89. *St Andrew's Vicarage, St Andrew's Road, Bootle, Merseyside L20 5EX* 0151-922 7916

KIRKER, Richard Ennis. b 51. Sarum & Wells Th Coll 72. **d** 77. C Hitchin *St Alb* 77-78; Gen Sec LGCM from 79. *c/o LGCM, Oxford House, Derbyshire Street, London E2 6HG* 0171-739 1249 or 791 1802

KIRKHAM, Clifford Gerald Frank. b 34. Open Univ BA90. Sarum & Wells Th Coll 72. **d** 74 **p** 75. C Worle *B & W* 74-76; C E Preston w Kingston *Chich* 76-78; C Goring-by-Sea 78-80; C-in-c Maybridge CD 80-82; V Maybridge 82-88; R N Chapel w Ebernoe from 88; Chapl for Rural Affairs from 89. *Northchapel Rectory, Petworth, W Sussex GU28 9HP* Northchapel (01428) 707373

✠**KIRKHAM, Rt Rev John Dudley Galtrey.** b 35. Trin Coll Cam BA59 MA63. Westcott Ho Cam 60. **d** 62 **p** 63 **c** 76. C Ipswich St Mary le Tower *St E* 62-65; Bp's Chapl *Nor* 65-69; P-in-c Rockland St Mary w Hellington 67-69; Papua New Guinea 69-70; C St Martin-in-the-Fields *Lon* 70-72; C Westmr St Marg 70-72; Abp's Dom Chapl *Cant* 72-76; Suff Bp Sherborne *Sarum* 76-81; Area Bp Sherborne from 81; Can and Preb Sarum Cathl from 77; Abp's Adv to the Headmasters' Conf

from 90; Bp HM Forces from 92. *Little Bailie, Dullar Lane, Sturminster Marshall, Wimborne, Dorset BH21 4AD* Sturminster Marshall (01258) 857659   Fax 857961

KIRKLAND, Richard John. b 53. Leic Univ BA75. St Jo Coll Dur 76. **d** 79 **p** 80. C Knutsford St Jo and Toft *Ches* 79-82; C Bebington 82-89; V Poulton Lancelyn H Trin from 89. *6 Chorley Way, Spital, Bebington, Wirral, Merseyside L63 9LS* 0151-334 6780

KIRKMAN, Canon Harold. b 11. Man Univ BA43 BD47. Man Egerton Hall 35. **d** 36 **p** 37. TR Oldham *Man* 55-72; RD Oldham 63-76; Perm to Offic *Wakef* from 72; rtd 76; Perm to Offic *Man* from 76. *3 Black Dyke, Mankinholes Bank, Todmorden, Lancs OL14 6JA* Todmorden (01706) 813499

KIRKMAN, Richard Marsden. b 55. Cranmer Hall Dur. **d** 88. C Bridlington Priory *York* 87-90; TV Thirsk from 90. *The Vicarage, Carlton Miniott, Thirsk, N Yorkshire YO7 4NJ* Thirsk (01845) 522003

KIRKPATRICK, Errol Francis. b 28. TCD. **d** 52 **p** 53. R Kentchurch w Llangua *Heref* 66-77; V Rowlestone w Llancillo 66-77; V Walterstone 66-77; RD Abbeydore 72-77; R Porlock w Stoke Pero *B & W* 77-83; R Lapworth *Birm* 83-89; R Baddesley Clinton 83-89; rtd 89; Perm to Offic *B & W* from 89. *51 Runnymede Road, Yeovil, Somerset BA21 5RY* Yeovil (01935) 31713

KIRKPATRICK, James Michael. b 46. Chich Th Coll 70. **d** 73 **p** 74. C Elgin w Lossiemouth *Mor* 73-76; C Devonport St Mark Ford *Ex* 76-77; P-in-c 77-80; TV Ilfracombe, Lee, W Down, Woolacombe and Bittadon 80-83; V Whitleigh from 83; RD Plymouth Moorside from 93. *St Chad's Presbytery, 17 Whitleigh Green, Plymouth PL5 4DD* Plymouth (01752) 773547

KIRKPATRICK, Jonathan Richard. b 58. CA81 Golds Coll Lon BA85. Wilson Carlile Coll IDC81 S'wark Ord Course 83. **d** 85 **p** 85. C Lewisham St Mary *S'wark* 85-87; Chapl Lewisham Hosp 85-87; Selection Sec and Voc Adv ACCM 88-91; Sec Aston Tr Scheme 89-91; Hon C Noel Park St Mark *Lon* 88-91; New Zealand from 91. *St Michael's Vicarage, 84 Oxford Terrace, Christchurch, New Zealand* Christchurch (3) 795749

KIRKPATRICK, Roger James (Brother Damian). b 41. FCA. **d** 86 **p** 87. SSF from 66; Guardian Belf Friary 80-88; Birm 89-93; Prov Min 91-93; NSM Belf St Pet *Conn* 86-88; Chapl R Victoria Hosp Belf 86-88; Lic to Offic *Linc* from 94. *St Francis House, Normanby Road, Scunthorpe, S Humberside DN15 6AR* Scunthorpe (01724) 953899

KIRKPATRICK, William John Ashley. b 27. SEN SRN RMN. Sarum Th Coll 63. **d** 68 **p** 70. NSM St Mary le Bow w St Pancras Soper Lane etc *Lon* 68-70; NSM Soho St Anne w St Thos and St Pet 70-75; SSF 76-79; NSM S Kensington St Aug *Lon* 79-80; NSM Earl's Court St Cuth w St Matthias from 80. *Flat 3B, Langham Mansions, Earl's Court Square, London SW5 9UP* 0171-373 1330

KIRKUP, Nigel Norman. b 54. K Coll Lon BD79 AKC79. **d** 80 **p** 80. Hon C Catford (Southend) and Downham *S'wark* 80-83; Hon C Surbiton St Andr and St Mark 83-85; Hon C Shirley St Geo from 85. *The Vicarage, The Glade, Croydon CR0 7QJ* 0181-654 8747

KIRKWOOD, Alexander David. b 58. Ex Coll Ox BA81 Dur Univ CertEd82. Linc Th Coll 83. **d** 85 **p** 86. C Linc St Faith and St Martin w St Pet *Linc* 85-88; C Farnborough *Roch* 88-91; V Mitcham St Barn *S'wark* from 91. *St Barnabas' Vicarage, Thirsk Road, Mitcham, Surrey CR4 2BD* 0181-648 2571

KIRKWOOD, David Christopher. b 40. Pemb Coll Ox BA63. Clifton Th Coll 63. **d** 65 **p** 66. C Wilmington *Roch* 65-68; C Green Street Green 68-72; Youth and Area Sec BCMS 72-73; Educn and Youth Sec 73-80; Hon C Sidcup Ch Ch *Roch* 74-80; V Rothley *Leic* 80-92; RD Goscote II 84-88; RD Goscote 88-90; P-in-c Toxteth St Philemon w St Gabr and St Cleopas *Liv* 92-95; TR from 95. *St Philemon's Vicarage, 40 Devonshire Road, Liverpool L8 3TZ* 0151-727 1248

KIRKWOOD, Jack. b 21. Worc Ord Coll 62. **d** 63 **p** 64. V Torpoint *Truro* 66-73; V Turton *Man* 73-81; P-in-c Castleton All So 81-82; Hon C Heywood St Luke 82-84; rtd 86; Perm to Offic *Blackb* 86-89; Perm to Offic *York* 89-94. *2 Westover Grove, Warton, Carnforth, Lancs LA5 9QR* Carnforth (01524) 732552

KIRTLEY, Georgina. b 44. St Jo Coll Dur BA94. Cranmer Hall Dur. **d** 95. NSM Barnard Castle w Whorlton *Dur* from 95. *Ryelands, Stainton, Barnard Castle, Co Durham DL12 8RB* Barnard Castle (01833) 631192

KIRTON, Canon Richard Arthur. b 43. Dur Univ BA67 MA73 DipTh68. Wycliffe Hall Ox 68. **d** 69 **p** 70. C Warsop *S'well* 69-72; C Newark St Mary 72-75; Malaysia 75-83; Dean of Studies Th Sem Kuala Lumpur 79-82; P-in-c Bleasby w Halloughton *S'well* 83-89; V Thurgarton w Hoveringham 83-89; V Thurgarton w Hoveringham and Bleasby etc 89-91; Bp's Adv on Overseas Relns 85-91; Hon Can St Mary's Cathl

Kuala Lumpur from 88; Tutor CA Wilson Carlile Coll of Evang from 91. *Wilson Carlile College of Evangelism, 50 Cavendish Street, Sheffield S3 7RZ* Sheffield (0114) 278 7020

KISSELL, Barrington John. b 38. Lon Coll of Div 64. d 67 p 68. C Camborne *Truro* 67-71; C Chorleywood St Andr *St Alb* from 71; Dir Faith Sharing Min from 74. *Wick Cottage, Quickley Lane, Chorleywood, Rickmansworth, Herts WD3 5AF* Chorleywood (01923) 282188

KITCHEN, Alan. b 39. Coll of Resurr Mirfield 72. d 74 p 75. C Shelf *Bradf* 74-77; P-in-c Tong 77-79; TR 79-84; TR Manningham 84-92; P-in-c Embsay w Eastby from 92. *The Vicarage, 21 Shires Lane, Skipton, N Yorkshire BD23 6SB* Skipton (01756) 792755

KITCHEN, Harold Malcolm. b 33. Trin Coll Cam BA57 MA61. Tyndale Hall Bris 57. d 59 p 60. R Burythorpe, Acklam and Leavening w Westow *York* 66-71; V Wollaton Park *S'well* 71-85; P-in-c Lenton Abbey 77-85; V Thornton in Lonsdale w Burton in Lonsdale *Bradf* 85-89; P-in-c Cofton w Starcross *Ex* 89; P-in-c Kenton w Mamhead and Powderham 89; R Kenton, Mamhead, Powderham, Cofton and Starcross 89-92; rtd 92. *The Vicarage, 5 Morven Drive, Exmouth, Devon EX8 3LZ* Exmouth (01395) 278538

KITCHEN, Leslie Wilson. b 16. Man Univ BA38 MA39. Bps' Coll Cheshunt 39. d 41 p 42. R Garforth *Ripon* 60-72; R Cockley Cley w Gooderstone *Nor* 72-78; V Didlington 75-78; R Gt and Lt Cressingham w Threxton 75-78; R Hilborough w Bodney 75-78; R Oxborough w Foulden and Caldecote 75-78; V Pool w Arthington *Ripon* 78-84; rtd 84. *3 West Terrace, Burton Leonard, Harrogate, N Yorkshire HG3 3RR* Ripon (01765) 677396

KITCHEN, Canon Dr Martin. b 47. N Lon Poly BA71 K Coll Lon BD76 AKC77 Man Univ PhD88. S'wark Ord Course 77. d 79 p 80. Lect CA Tr Coll Blackheath 79-83; Hon C Kidbrooke St Jas *S'wark* 79-83; Chapl Man Poly *Man* 83-88; TV Man Whitworth 83-86; TR 86-88; Adv In-Service Tr *S'wark* from 88; Can Res S'wark Cathl from 88. *17 Stradella Road, London SE24 9HN* 0171-274 4918

KITCHENER, Christopher William. b 46. Open Univ BA. Sarum & Wells Th Coll 82. d 84 p 85. C Bexleyheath Ch Ch *Roch* 84-88; V Gravesend St Mary from 88. *The Vicarage, 57 New House Lane, Gravesend, Kent DA11 7HJ* Gravesend (01474) 352162

KITCHENER, Mrs Evarina Carol. b 51. Stockwell Coll of Educn CertEd70. Cant Sch of Min 89. d 92 p 94. NSM Gravesend St Mary *Roch* from 92. *The Vicarage, 57 New House Lane, Gravesend, Kent DA11 7HJ* Gravesend (01474) 352162

KITCHENER, Canon Michael Anthony. b 45. Trin Coll Cam BA67 MA70 PhD71. Cuddesdon Coll 70. d 71 p 72. C Aldwick *Chich* 71-74; C Caversham *Ox* 74-77; Tutor Coll of Resurr Mirfield 77-83; Prin NE Ord Course *Dur* 83-90; Hon Can Newc Cathl *Newc* 84-90; Can Res and Chan Blackb Cathl *Blackb* 90-95; Warden Rydal Hall *Carl* from 95; P-in-c Rydal from 95. *The Warden's House, Rydal Hall, Ambleside, Cumbria LA22 9LX* Rydal (015394) 32050 Fax 34887

KITCHIN, Kenneth. b 46. Trin Coll Bris. d 89 p 90. C Barrow St Mark *Carl* 89-93; C Dalton-in-Furness from 93. *4 Fair View, Dalton-in-Furness, Cumbria LA15 8RZ* Dalton-in-Furness (01229) 864402

KITCHING, David Monro. b 26. New Coll Ox BA49. Ridley Hall Cam 80. d 82 p 83. C Hornchurch St Andr *Chelmsf* 82-86; P-in-c Graveley w Papworth St Agnes w Yelling etc *Ely* 86-90; rtd 91. *20 Victoria Park, Cambridge CB4 3EL* Cambridge (01223) 65687

KITCHING, Paul. b 53. GTCL LTCL. Coll of Resurr Mirfield 80. d 83 p 84. C Hessle *York* 83-86; Youth Officer from 86; P-in-c Crathorne from 86. *The Rectory, Crathorne, Yarm, Cleveland TS15 0BB* Middlesbrough (01642) 701158

KITELEY, Robert John. b 51. Hull Univ BSc73 Univ of Wales (Abth) MSc75 Lon Univ PhD82. Trin Coll Bris DipTh83. d 83 p 84. C Bebington *Ches* 83-88; C Hoole 88-91; V Plas Newton from 91. *22 Plas Newton Lane, Chester CH2 1PA* Chester (01244) 319677

KITLEY, David Buchan. b 53. St Jo Coll Dur BA. Trin Coll Bris 78. d 81 p 82. C Tonbridge St Steph *Roch* 81-84; C-in-c Southall Em CD *Lon* 84-91; V Dartford Ch Ch *Roch* from 91; Chapl W Hill Hosp Dartford from 91. *The Vicarage, 67 Shepherds Lane, Dartford DA1 2NS* Dartford (01322) 220036

KITNEY, Miss Joan Olive Lily. b 22. Gilmore Ho 50. dss 60 d 87. Hermitage and Hampstead Norreys, Cold Ash etc *Ox* 80-87; NSM Staines St Mary and St Pet *Lon* 87-89; rtd 89. *9 John Childs' Close, Newbury, Berks RG14 7PZ* Newbury (01635) 36416

KITTERINGHAM, Canon Ian. b 35. CCC Cam BA59 MA63. Westcott Ho Cam 59. d 61 p 62. C Rotherham *Sheff* 61-64; C Eltham H Trin *S'wark* 64-66; V Battersea St Mary-le-Park 66-73; V Reigate St Mark 73-80; V Caterham Valley 80-85;

RD Caterham 84-85; V Wandsworth Common St Mary from 85; RD Tooting 88-93; Hon Can S'wark Cathl from 95. *The Vicarage, 291 Burntwood Lane, London SW17 0AP* 0181-874 4804

KITTS, Joseph. b 27. Tyndale Hall Bris 59. d 60 p 61. V Southport SS Simon and Jude *Liv* 66-74; USA 74-94; rtd 92. *Roseleigh, 6 Trumpley Street, Ellesmere, Shropshire SY12 0AE* Ellesmere (01691) 622100

KITWOOD, Thomas Morris. b 37. K Coll Cam BA60 MA64. Wycliffe Hall Ox 62. d 63 p 64. Asst Chapl Sherborne Sch Dorset 63-69; Uganda from 69. *PO Box 14123, Kampala, Uganda*

KIVETT, Michael Stephen. b 50. Bethany Coll W Virginia BA72. Chr Th Sem Indiana MDiv76 Sarum & Wells Th Coll 76. d 77 p 78. C Harnham *Sarum* 77-80; C E Dereham *Nor* 80-83; R S Walsham 83-88; V Upton 83-88; Chapl Lt Plumstead Hosp 84-88; V Chard St Mary *B & W* from 88; RD Crewkerne and Ilminster from 93. *The Vicarage, 2 Forton Road, Chard, Somerset TA20 2HJ* Chard (01460) 62320

KLIMAS, Miss Lynda. b 58. Jes Coll Cam BA89 MA93. Cranmer Hall Dur 89. d 90 p 94. Par Dn Sandy *St Alb* 90-93; Par Dn Bishop's Stortford St Mich 93-94; C from 94. *Cowell House, 24 Apton Road, Bishop's Stortford, Herts CM23 3SM* Bishop's Stortford (01279) 654414

✠**KLYBERG, Rt Rev Charles John.** b 31. ARICS57. Linc Th Coll. d 60 p 61 c 85. C E Dulwich St Jo *S'wark* 60-63; N Rhodesia 63-64; Zambia 64-67 and 77-85; V Battersea St Steph *S'wark* 67-71; P-in-c Battersea Ch Ch and St Steph 71-72; V 72-77; Dean Lusaka Cath 77-85; Suff Bp Fulham *Lon* from 85; Adn Charing Cross from 90. *4 Cambridge Place, London W8 5PB* 0171-937 2560 Fax 937 6876

KNAPMAN, Preb Hugh William Hartly. b 07. St D Coll Lamp BA33. d 32 p 33. Preb Wells Cathl *B & W* 67-87; R Charlton Adam w Charlton Mackrell 69-75; rtd 75; Perm to Offic *B & W* 75-94. *24 Kings Gardens, Honiton, Devon EX14 8FL* Honiton (01404) 44743

KNAPP, Antony Blair. b 48. Imp Coll Lon BSc68. N Ord Course 86. d 89 p 90. C Bolton St Jas w St Chrys *Bradf* 89-92; V Kettlewell w Conistone, Hubberholme etc from 92. *The Vicarage, Kettlewell, Skipton, N Yorkshire BD23 5QU* Kettlewell (01756) 760237

KNAPP, Bryan Thomas. b 61. Trin Coll Bris DipHE90 BA91. d 91 p 92. NSM S Gillingham *Roch* 91-93; C from 93. *Old School Cottage, 79 New Road, Ditton, Maidstone, Kent ME20 6AE* Sevenoaks (01732) 847669

KNAPP (nee STOCKER), Mrs Rachael Ann. b 64. Bris Univ BA86. Trin Coll Bris DipHE90 BA91. d 91 p 94. C Ditton *Roch* from 91. *Old School Cottage, 79 New Road, Ditton, Maidstone, Kent ME20 6AE* Sevenoaks (01732) 847669

✠**KNAPP-FISHER, Rt Rev Edward George.** b 15. Trin Coll Ox BA36 MA40 Cam Univ MA49. Wells Th Coll 38. d 39 p 40 c 60. C Brighouse *Wakef* 40-42; Chapl RNVR 42-46; Chapl Cuddesdon Coll 46-49; Prin 52-60; Lic to Offic *Ely* 49-52; Chapl St Jo Coll Cam 49-52; V Cuddesdon *Ox* 52-60; RD Cuddesdon 58-60; S Africa 60-75; Bp Pretoria 60-75; Adn Westmr 75-87; Can Westmr Abbey 75-87; Asst Bp S'wark 75-87; Asst Bp Lon 76-86; Sub-Dean Westmr 82-87; rtd 87; Asst Bp Chich from 87; Custos St Mary's Hosp Chich from 87. *2 Vicars' Close, Canon Lane, Chichester, W Sussex PO19 1PT* Chichester (01243) 789219

KNARESBOROUGH, Suffragan Bishop of. See MENIN, Rt Rev Malcolm James

KNEE, Geoffrey. b 31. Whitelands Coll Lon CertEd71. CA Tr Coll 56 Glouc Sch of Min 91. d 92 p 93. SSF from 86; NSM Hampton *Worc* from 92. *8 Mayfair, Fairfield, Evesham, Worcs WR11 6JJ* Evesham (01386) 443574

KNEE, Jacob Samuel. b 66. LSE BSc(Econ)87 MSc(Econ)88 Ox Univ BA92. Ripon Coll Cuddesdon 90. d 93 p 94. C Ashby-de-la-Zouch St Helen w Coleorton *Leic* from 93. *38 Avenue Road, Ashby-de-la-Zouch, Leics LE65 2FE* Ashby-de-la-Zouch (01530) 411721

KNEEN, Michael John. b 55. Univ Coll Lon BSc76 MSc77 St Jo Coll Dur BA85. Cranmer Hall Dur 83. d 86 p 87. C Bishop's Castle w Mainstone *Heref* 86-90; TV Bridgnorth, Tasley, Astley Abbotts, Oldbury etc from 90. *41 Innage Lane, Bridgnorth, Shropshire WV16 4HS* Bridgnorth (01746) 766418 or 767174

KNELL, John George. b 35. Cant Sch of Min. d 82 p 83. NSM Sheerness H Trin w St Paul *Cant* 82-87; NSM Minster in Sheppey from 87. *11 Uplands Way, Queenborough Road, Sheerness, Kent ME12 3EF* Sheerness (01795) 665945

KNELL, Canon Raymond John. b 27. Qu Coll Cam BA48 MA52. Ridley Hall Cam 50. d 52 p 53. V Castleside *Dur* 67-76;

V Heworth St Mary 76-93; RD Gateshead 83-87; Hon Can Dur Cathl 87-93; rtd 93. *40 St Andrew's Drive, Low Fell, Gateshead, Tyne & Wear NE9 6JU* 0191-487 6958

KNIBBS, Norman Vivian. b 27. Ely Th Coll 61. **d** 63 **p** 64. V Northn St Dav *Pet* 67-73; TV Kingsthorpe w St Dav Northn 73-79; R Brington w Whilton and Norton 79-92; rtd 92. *18 Harbridges Lane, Long Buckby, Northampton NN6 7QL* Long Buckby (01327) 842857

KNIGHT, Alan Keith. b 27. Ripon Coll Cuddesdon 75. **d** 76 **p** 77. C Swindon Ch Ch *Bris* 76-80; R Mark w Allerton *B & W* 80-83; rtd 83. *22 Chalice Way, Glastonbury, Somerset BA6 8EX* Glastonbury (01458) 831738

KNIGHT, Ven Alexander Francis (Alec). b 39. St Cath Coll Cam BA61 MA65. Wells Th Coll. **d** 63 **p** 64. C Hemel Hempstead *St Alb* 63-68; Chapl Taunton Sch Somerset 68-75; Dir Bloxham Project 75-81; Dir of Studies Aston Tr Scheme 81-83; P-in-c Easton and Martyr Worthy *Win* 83-91; Adn Basingstoke from 90; Can Res Win Cathl from 91. *1 The Close, Winchester, Hants SO23 9LS* Winchester (01962) 869374 Fax 841815

KNIGHT, Andrew James. b 50. Grey Coll Dur BA72 Ox Univ BA74 MA81. Wycliffe Hall Ox 72. **d** 75 **p** 76. Min Can Brecon Cathl *S & B* 75-78; C Brecon w Battle 75-78; C Morriston 78-82; V from 89; V Llanwrtyd w Llanddulas in Tir Abad etc 82-89. *The Vicarage, Vicarage Road, Morriston, Swansea SA6 6DR* Swansea (01792) 771329

KNIGHT, Mrs Ann. b 54. Lanc Univ CertEd75. Trin Coll Bris DipHE83 DPS84. **dss** 84 **d** 87 **p** 94. Wigan St Jas w St Thos *Liv* 84-87; Par Dn 87-90; C Costessey *Nor* from 90. *St Helen's House, Gurney Road, New Costessey, Norwich NR5 0HH* Norwich (01603) 744285

KNIGHT, Arthur Clifford Edwin. b 42. Univ of Wales BSc64. Wells Th Coll 64. **d** 66 **p** 67. C Oystermouth *S & B* 68-73; Chapl RAF 73-95; rtd 95. *Chaplaincy Services (RAF), HQ, Personnel and Training Command, RAF Innsworth, Gloucester GL3 1EZ* Gloucester (01452) 712612 Ext 5164 Fax 510828

KNIGHT, Mrs Barbara. b 46. St Alb Minl Tr Scheme 86. **d** 90 **p** 94. NSM Weston *St Alb* 90-95; NSM Ardeley 90-95; C Norton from 95. *63 Kimberley, Letchworth, Herts SG6 4RB* Weston (01462) 672256 Fax as telephone

KNIGHT, Benjamin Edward. b 10. St Cath Coll Cam BA34 MA38. Wells Th Coll 34. **d** 36 **p** 37. R Symondsbury *Sarum* 65-78; V Chideock 72-78; rtd 78. *The Coach House, Bothenhampton Old Rectory, Bridport, Dorset DT6 4BT* Bridport (01308) 424909

KNIGHT, Dr Christopher Colson. b 52. MSOSc Ex Univ BSc73 Man Univ PhD77 SS Coll Cam MA90. Sarum & Wells Th Coll BTh83. **d** 81 **p** 82. Chapl St Mary's Cathl *Edin* 81-84; V Chesterton *Cov* 84-87; R Lighthorne 84-87; V Newbold Pacey w Moreton Morrell 84-87; Chapl, Fellow and Dir Studies in Th SS Coll Cam 87-92; Sen Research Assoc St Edm Coll Cam from 92. *Hope Cottage, Hindringham Road, Great Walsingham, Norfolk NR22 6DR* Walsingham (01328) 820108

KNIGHT, David Alan. b 59. Lanc Univ BA81. Ripon Coll Cuddesdon 82. **d** 85 **p** 86. C Stretford All SS *Man* 85-88; C Charlestown 88-89; TV Pendleton St Thos w Charlestown 89-94; V Tysoe w Oxhill and Whatcote *Cov* from 94. *The Vicarage, Peacock Lane, Tysoe, Warwick CV35 0SE* Tysoe (01295) 680201

KNIGHT, David Charles. b 32. Clare Coll Cam BA55 MA59. Tyndale Hall Bris 55. **d** 57 **p** 58. V Lannarth *Truro* 69-75; RD Carnmarth N 72-75; V Fremington *Ex* 75-83; C Edmonton All SS w St Mich *Lon* 83; Chapl N Middx Hosp 83; rtd 94. *Magnolia Cottage, Cage End, Hatfield Broad Oak, Bishop's Stortford, Herts CM22 7HT* Bishop's Stortford (01279) 718650

KNIGHT, Canon David Charles. b 45. ATCL63 Lon Univ BA66 St Edm Hall Ox BA68 MA73. St Steph Ho Ox 68. **d** 70 **p** 71. C Northwood H Trin *Lon* 70-73; C Stevenage All SS Pin Green *St Alb* 73-77; C Cippenham CD *Ox* 77-78; TV W Slough 78-83; Dep Min Can Windsor from 81; Ecum Officer to Bp Willesden 83-91; R Lt Stanmore St Lawr *Lon* 83-91; Prec and Can Res Chelmsf Cathl *Chelmsf* from 91. *The Precentor's House, Rainsford Avenue, Chelmsford CM1 2PJ* Chelmsford (01245) 257306

KNIGHT, David Lansley. b 33. Em Coll Cam BA58 MA61 PGCE76. Ridley Hall Cam 57. **d** 59 **p** 60. C Chatham St Steph *Roch* 59-63; C Plymouth St Andr *Ex* 63-65; V Gravesend St Aid *Roch* 65-71; V Bexley St Mary from 71; RD Sidcup from 93. *The Vicarage, 29 Hill Crescent, Bexley, Kent DA5 2DA* Dartford (01322) 523457

KNIGHT, Donald. b 31. Bris Univ BA55 Man Univ DASE73. Tyndale Hall Bris 51 Qu Coll Birm 82. **d** 83 **p** 84. C Chell Lich 83-87; R St Ruan w St Grade and Landewednack *Truro* 87-91; R High Offley and Norbury *Lich* from 91. *The Rectory, Newport Road, Woodseaves, Stafford ST20 0NP* Woodseaves (01785) 284392

KNIGHT, Canon Donald Martin. b 13. Lon Univ BSc34 St Cath Soc Ox DipTh39. Wycliffe Hall Ox 38. **d** 39 **p** 41. R Harlow New Town w Lt Parndon *Chelmsf* 57-86; RD Harlow 60-73; Chapl Harlow Hosp 65-78; Hon Can Chelmsf Cathl *Chelmsf* 71-86; rtd 86; Perm to Offic *Ox* from 86. *Bethany, 18 Lollards Close, Amersham, Bucks HP6 5JL* Amersham (01494) 727138

KNIGHT, Eric Frank Walter. b 19. St Paul's Grahamstown. **d** 51 **p** 52. V Charlton All Saints *Sarum* 68-89; rtd 89. *9 Constable Way, Salisbury SP2 8LN* Salisbury (01722) 331480

KNIGHT, Henry Christian. b 34. Lon Univ HNC57 Fitzw Ho Cam BA62 MA66. Ridley Hall Cam 62. **d** 63 **p** 64. Israel 67-79; CMJ 79-86; V Allithwaite *Carl* 86-93; rtd 93. *20 Saxon Way, Ashby-de-la-Zouch, Leics LE65 2JR* Ashby-de-la-Zouch (01530) 560180

KNIGHT, Herbert John. b 15. Univ of Wales BA38. Ely Th Coll 38. **d** 39 **p** 41. V Knaith *Linc* 58-82; R Lea 58-82; V Upton 61-82; R Gate Burton 78-82; RD Corringham 78-82; rtd 82. *2 Gainas Avenue, Gainsborough, Lincs DN21 2RD* Gainsborough (01427) 612097

KNIGHT, John Bernard. b 34. ACIS60. Oak Hill Th Coll 61 Fuller Th Sem California DMin91. **d** 65 **p** 66. C Morden *S'wark* 65-69; USA 69-71; V Summerfield *Birm* from 71. *Christ Church Vicarage, 64 Selwyn Road, Birmingham B16 0SW* 0121-454 2689

KNIGHT, John Francis Alan MacDonald. b 36. Coll of Resurr Mirfield 59. **d** 61 **p** 62. S Rhodesia 61-65; Rhodesia 65-80; Zimbabwe 80-87; Dean Mutare 81-87; TR Northn Em *Pet* from 87; RD Northn 88-92. *12 Jersey Court, Northampton NN3 3TB* Northampton (01604) 414136 or 402150

KNIGHT, Jonathan Morshead. b 59. Wycliffe Hall Ox 86. **d** 88 **p** 89. C Hillingdon St Jo *Lon* 88-91; NSM Baslow *Derby* 91-92; NSM Curbar and Stoney Middleton 91-92; Lect Bibl Studies Sheff Univ 91-92; Research Fell 92-94; NSM Sheff St Paul Wordsworth Avenue *Sheff* 92-94; Bp's Research Asst *Ely* from 94. *Farthing Cottage, 38 High Street, Harston, Cambridge CB2 5PX* Cambridge (01223) 870914

KNIGHT, Mrs June. b 28. Glouc Sch of Min 85. **d** 87 **p** 94. NSM Leckhampton SS Phil and Jas w Cheltenham St Jas *Glouc* from 87. *31 St Michael's Road, Woodlands, Cheltenham, Glos GL51 5RP* Cheltenham (01242) 517911

KNIGHT, Mrs June Elizabeth. b 42. St Alb Minl Tr Scheme 90. **d** 93 **p** 94. NSM Stanstead Abbots *St Alb* from 93. *The White Cottage, Albury Hall Park, Albury, Ware, Herts SG11 2HX* Albury (01279) 771756

KNIGHT, Keith Kenneth. b 36. Southn Univ BSc58. Wycliffe Hall Ox 59. **d** 62 **p** 63. C Lower Darwen St Jas *Blackb* 62-64; C Leyland St Andr 64-68; P-in-c Blackb All SS 68-71; Dioc Youth Chapl 71-88; Hon C Burnley St Pet 71-74; Warden Scargill Ho from 88. *Scargill House, Kettlewell, Skipton, N Yorkshire BD23 5HU* Kettlewell (01756) 760234 or 760315

KNIGHT, Kenneth William. b 15. TD50. Wycliffe Hall Ox. **d** 61 **p** 62. V Holberton *Ex* 63-91; rtd 91; Perm to Offic *Ex* from 91. *Buckleberry, Shebbear, Beaworthy, Devon EX21 5SA* Shebbear (01409) 281423

KNIGHT, Mrs Margaret Owen. b 34. Oak Hill Th Coll 78. **dss** 80 **d** 87 **p** 94. Chorleywood St Andr *St Alb* 80-87; Par Dn 87-94; C from 94. *15A Blacketts Wood Drive, Chorleywood, Rickmansworth, Herts WD3 5PY* Chorleywood (01923) 283832

KNIGHT, Michael Richard. b 47. St Jo Coll Dur BA69 MA79 Fitzw Coll Cam BA73 MA78 St Cross Coll Ox MA92. Westcott Ho Cam 71. **d** 74 **p** 75. C Bishop's Stortford St Mich *St Alb* 74-75; C Bedf St Andr 75-79; Chapl Angl Students Glas 79-85; P-in-c Riddings *Derby* 86; P-in-c Ironville 86; V Riddings and Ironville 86-91; Lib Pusey Ho 91-94; V Chesterfield All SS *Derby* from 94. *28 Cromwell Road, Chesterfield, Derbyshire S40 4TH* Chesterfield (01246) 232937

KNIGHT, Paul James Joseph. b 50. Oak Hill Th Coll. **d** 84 **p** 85. C Broadwater St Mary *Chich* 84-87; R Itchingfield w Slinfold 87-92; Chapl Highgate Sch Lon from 92. *15A Bishopswood Road, London N6 4PB* 0181-348 9211 or 340 1524

KNIGHT, Capt Paul Jeremy. b 53. **d** 94 **p** 95. CA from 77; C Moreton Say *Lich* from 94. *The Rectory, Moreton Say, Market Drayton, Shropshire TF9 3RS* Market Drayton (01630) 638110

KNIGHT, Peter John. b 51. Lon Univ AKC73 CertEd77. Sarum & Wells Th Coll 79. **d** 80 **p** 81. C Greenford H Cross *Lon* 80-83; C Langley Marish *Ox* 83; NSM W Acton St Martin 89-90; C E Acton St Dunstan w St Thos 90-92; V Malden St Jo *S'wark* from 92. *The Vicarage, 329 Malden Road, New Malden, Surrey KT3 6AL* 0181-942 3297

KNIGHT, Dr Peter Malcolm. b 55. DA81 DRCOG83 MRCGP85 DTM&H86 Cam Univ BA76 Lon Hosp MB, BS76. Trin Coll Bris BA94. **d** 94 **p** 95. C Quidenham *Nor* from 94. *The Vicarage, Mill Road, Old Buckenham, Attleborough, Norfolk NR17 1SG* Attleborough (01953) 860047

KNIGHT, Peter Michael. b 47. St Luke's Coll Ex BEd71. Trin Coll Bris DipHE92. **d** 92 **p** 93. C Bris Ch the Servant Stockwood *Bris* from 92; Chapl St Brendan's Sixth Form Coll 92-94. *78 Bifield Road, Stockwood, Bristol BS14 8TW* Whitchurch (01275) 833617

KNIGHT, Philip Stephen. b 46. Oak Hill Th Coll 75. **d** 77 **p** 78. C Pennycross *Ex* 77-80; C Epsom St Martin *Guildf* 80-83; V Clay Hill St Jo *Lon* 83-86; TV Washfield, Stoodleigh, Withleigh etc *Ex* 86-90; Chapl S Warks Hosps from 90. *37 Lodge Crescent, Warwick CV34 6BK, or South Warwickshire Hospital, Lakin Road, Warwick CV34 5BW* Warwick (01926) 403053 or 495321

KNIGHT, Canon Roger George. b 41. Culham Coll Ox CertEd63. Linc Th Coll 65. **d** 67 **p** 68. C Bris St Andr Hartcliffe *Bris* 67-69; Hd Master Twywell Sch Kettering 69-74; Lic to Offic *Pet* 69-74; V Naseby 74-79; P-in-c Haselbeech 74-79; R Clipston w Naseby and Haselbech 79-82; P-in-c Kelmarsh 79-82; TR Corby SS Pet and Andr w Gt and Lt Oakley 82-88; R Irthlingborough from 88; RD Higham 89-94; Can Pet Cathl from 92. *The Rectory, 79 Finedon Road, Irthlingborough, Wellingborough NN9 5TY* Wellingborough (01933) 650278

KNIGHT, Roger Ivan. b 54. K Coll Lon BD79 AKC79. Ripon Coll Cuddesdon 79. **d** 80 **p** 81. C Orpington All SS *Roch* 80-84; C St Laurence in the Isle of Thanet *Cant* 84-87; R Cuxton and Halling *Roch* from 87. *The Rectory, Rochester Road, Cuxton, Rochester, Kent ME2 1AF* Medway (01634) 717134

KNIGHT, Canon Sydney Frederick Harrold. b 06. Leeds Univ BA29. Coll of Resurr Mirfield 25. **d** 33 **p** 34. C Haydock St Jas *Liv* 33-37; S Africa from 37; Hon Can St John's from 86. *PO Box 334, George, 6530 South Africa* George (441) 5472

KNIGHT, Canon Terence. b 38. Lich Th Coll 60. **d** 63 **p** 64. C Portsea St Alb *Portsm* 63-67; C Basingstoke *Win* 67-72; P-in-c Birches Head *Lich* 72-75; P-in-c Northwood 72-75; V Portsea St Sav *Portsm* from 75; RD Portsm 89-93; Hon Can Portsm Cathl from 90. *St Saviour's Vicarage, Twyford Avenue, Portsmouth PO2 8PB* Portsmouth (01705) 663664

KNIGHT, Thomas. b 20. OBE60. Linc Th Coll 69. **d** 71 **p** 72. C Earlsdon *Cov* 71-74; R Southam 74-77; RD Southam 77-82; R Southam w Stockton 77-82; rtd 82. *5 Cedar Vale, Kirkbymoorside, York YO6 6BU* Kirkbymoorside (01751) 31922

KNIGHT, William Lawrence (Bill). b 39. Univ Coll Lon BSc61 PhD65. Coll of Resurr Mirfield 75. **d** 77 **p** 78. C Hatf *St Alb* 77-81; Asst Chapl Brussels Cathl *Eur* 81-84; V Pet H Spirit Bretton *Pet* 84-89; P-in-c Marholm 84-89; TR Riverside *Ox* from 89. *St Mary's Vicarage, London Road, Datchet, Slough SL3 9JW* Slough (01753) 580467

KNIGHTS, Dr Christopher Hammond. b 61. St Jo Coll Dur BA83 PhD88. Linc Th Coll 87. **d** 89 **p** 90. C Stockton St Pet *Dur* 89-92; C Chich St Paul and St Pet *Chich* 92-94; Tutor Chich Th Coll 92-94; V Ashington *Newc* from 94. *Holy Sepulchre Vicarage, Wansbeck Road, Ashington, Northd NE63 8HZ* Ashington (01670) 813358

KNIGHTS, James William. b 34. AKC66. **d** 67 **p** 68. C Kettering St Andr *Pet* 67-71; V Braunston w Brooke 71-81; V Dudley St Jo *Worc* from 81. *St John's Vicarage, 8A New Rowley Road, Dudley, W Midlands DY2 8AS* Dudley (01384) 253807

KNIGHTS, Philip Alan. b 60. Wadh Coll Ox BA83 MA82 Leeds Univ BA87. Coll of Resurr Mirfield 85. **d** 88 **p** 89. C Seaton Hirst *Newc* 88-91; Chapl Northd Coll of Arts and Tech 88-91; C Leytonstone St Marg w St Columba *Chelmsf* 91-93; Chapl Keble Coll Ox 94; TV Cowley St Jas *Ox* from 94. *Saint Luke's House, 85 Temple Road, Oxford OX4 2EX* Oxford (01865) 748915

KNIGHTS JOHNSON, Nigel Anthony. b 52. BA75. Wycliffe Hall Ox 78. **d** 80 **p** 81. C Beckenham Ch Ch *Roch* 80-84; CF from 84. *c/o MOD (Army), Bagshot Park, Bagshot, Surrey GU19 5PL* Bagshot (01276) 471717 Fax 412834

KNILL-JONES, Jonathan Waring (Jack). b 58. Univ Coll Lon BSc79 St Jo Coll Nottm DTS90. **d** 90 **p** 91. C Northolt W End St Jos *Lon* 90-94; C Hayes St Nic CD from 94. *St Nicholas Vicarage, Raynton Drive, Hayes, Middx UB4 8BG* 0181-573 4122

KNOCK, Dr Andrew Henry Drysdale. b 49. Lon Univ BA71 Stirling Univ PhD78 Edin Univ BD78. Edin Th Coll 75. **d** 78 **p** 79. Chapl St Ninian's Cathl Perth *St And* 78-80; C Alloa 80-84; P-in-c from 85; Chapl Stirling Univ 80-84; C Bridge of Allan 80-84; C Dollar 81-84. *St John's Rectory, 29 Redwell Place, Alloa, Clackmannanshire FK10 2BT* Alloa (01259) 215113 or 724559

KNOPP, Alexander Edward Robert. b 09. St Jo Coll Cam BA33 MA37. Ridley Hall Cam 32. **d** 34 **p** 35. R Gt Yeldham *Chelmsf* 68-73; R Gt w Lt Snoring *Nor* 73-76; rtd 76; Perm to Offic *Ely* from 77. *6 Rose Lane, Melbourn, Royston, Herts SG8 6AD* Royston (01763) 262143

KNOTT, Christopher Rodney. b 42. Open Univ BA77. Kelham Th Coll 64. **d** 68 **p** 69. C Withycombe Raleigh *Ex* 68-72; TV Aylesbeare and Farringdon 72-75; TV Woodbury Salterton

72-75; TV Clyst St George, Aylesbeare, Clyst Honiton etc 75-76; TR Lynton, Brendon, Countisbury, Lynmouth etc 76-81; R Highweek and Teingrace from 81. *The Rectory, 15 Stoneleigh Close, Newton Abbot, Devon TQ12 1PX* Newton Abbot (01626) 54949

KNOTT, Mrs Gladys Phoebe. b 15. Wolsey Hall DipRS64 Glouc Sch of Min 80. dss 81 **d** 87. Stroud H Trin *Glouc* 81-85; Minchinhampton 85-87; Hon C from 87. *7 Dr Brown's Close, Minchinhampton, Stroud, Glos GL6 9DG* Brimscombe (01453) 885259

KNOTT, Graham Keith. b 53. Oak Hill Th Coll 77. **d** 80 **p** 81. C Normanton *Derby* 80-83; C Ripley 83-87; TV Newark w Hawton, Cotham and Shelton *S'well* 87-89; TV Newark-upon-Trent from 89. *The Vicarage, Boundary Road, Newark, Notts NG24 4AJ* Newark (01636) 704969

KNOTT, Janet Patricia. b 50. Avery Hill Coll CertEd71. S Dios Minl Tr Scheme MTS91. **d** 92 **p** 94. NSM Clutton w Cameley *B & W* from 92; Chapl R Sch Bath from 94. *3/4 Sunnyside, Clutton Hill, Clutton, Bristol BS18 4QG* Mendip (01761) 452597

KNOTT, John Wensley. b 51. FIA84 Fitzw Coll Cam MA75. S Dios Minl Tr Scheme 87. **d** 90 **p** 91. NSM Canford Magna *Sarum* 90-94; Perm to Offic *St Alb* from 94. *11 Shrublands Road, Berkhamstead, Herts HP4 3JH* Berrkhamstead (0442) 875005

KNOTT, Montague Hardwick. b 05. Oak Hill Th Coll 54. **d** 55 **p** 56. V Blackmore *Chelmsf* 57-80; P-in-c Stondon Massey 80; V Blackmore and Stondon Massey 80-85; rtd 85. *1 Wadham Close, Ingatestone, Essex CM4 0DL* Ingatestone (01277) 352024

KNOTT, Pamela Frances. *See* IVE, Mrs Pamela Frances

KNOTT, Robert Michael. b 35. MCIBSE MRIPHH. Clifton Th Coll 67. **d** 70 **p** 70. C Rolleston *Lich* 70-72; C Anslow 70-72; C Uphill *B & W* 73-75; C Weston-super-Mare St Paul 77-79; P-in-c Burgate *St E* 79-82; P-in-c Palgrave 79-82; P-in-c Wortham 79-82; P-in-c Palgrave w Wortham and Burgate 82-87; rtd 88; Perm to Offic *Nor* from 91. *Oak Dene Luana, High Road, Bressingham, Diss, Norfolk IP22 2AT*

KNOWD, George Alexander. St Deiniol's Hawarden. **d** 88 **p** 89. NSM Aghalurcher w Tattykeeran, Cooneen etc *Clogh* 88-91; Dioc Info Officer 89-90 and from 92; NSM Ballybay w Mucknoe and Clontibret 91-92; C 92-94; I from 94. *The Rectory, Knocknamaddy, Ballybay, Co Monaghan, Irish Republic* Ballybay (42) 41102 Fax as telephone

KNOWERS, Stephen John. b 49. K Coll Lon BD72 AKC72. **d** 73 **p** 74. C Hatf *St Alb* 73-77; C Cheshunt 77-81; P-in-c Barnet Vale St Mark 81-83; V 83-85; Hon PV S'wark Cathl *S'wark* from 85; Chapl S Bank Poly 85-92; Chapl S Bank Univ 92-94; V Croydon St Pet from 94. *20 Haling Park Road, South Croydon, Surrey CR2 6NE* 0181-688 4715

KNOWLES, Andrew William Allen. b 46. St Cath Coll Cam BA68 MA72. St Jo Coll Nottm 69. **d** 71 **p** 72. C Leic H Trin *Leic* 71-74; C Cam H Trin *Ely* 74-77; C Woking St Jo *Guildf* 77-81; V Goldsworth Park 81-93; V Wyke from 93; Dioc Officer Educn & Development of Lay People from 93. *Wyke Vicarage, Guildford Road, Normandy, Guildford, Surrey GU3 2DA* Guildford (01483) 811332

KNOWLES, Charles Howard. b 43. Sheff Univ BSc65 Fitzw Coll Cam BA69 MA73. Westcott Ho Cam 67. **d** 69 **p** 70. C Bilborough St Jo *S'well* 69-72; VC S'well Minster 72-82; V Cinderhill 82-94; AD Nottm W 91-94; V Cov St Mary *Cov* from 94. *St Mary Magdalen's Vicarage, Craven Street, Coventry CV5 8DT* Coventry (01203) 675838

KNOWLES, Clifford. b 35. Open Univ BA82. NW Ord Course 74. **d** 77 **p** 78. C Urmston *Man* 77-80; V Chadderton St Luke 80-87; V Heywood St Luke w All So from 87; AD Heywood and Middleton 92-95. *12B Far Lane, Coleby, Lincoln LN5 0AH* Lincoln (01522) 810720

KNOWLES, Dorothy Joy. b 20. MCThA. Gilmore Ho 64. dss 69 **d** 89. Finham *Cov* 69-72; Canley 72-76; Styvechale 76-84; rtd 84; Asst Chapl Harnhill Cen for Chr Healing 88-93. *27 Corinium Gate, Cirencester, Glos GL7 2PX* Cirencester (01285) 654852

KNOWLES, Eric Gordon. b 44. W Midl Minl Tr Course. **d** 82 **p** 83. NSM Gt Malvern St Mary *Worc* 82-83; NSM Malvern H Trin and St Jas 83-90; NSM Lt Malvern, Malvern Wells and Wyche from 90. *45 Wykewane, Malvern, Worcs WR14 2XD* Malvern (01684) 567439

KNOWLES, Ven George Woods Atkin. b 21. TCD BA44 MA47. **d** 44 **p** 45. I Drumachose *D & R* 63-89; Can Derry Cathl 75-86; Adn Derry 86-89; rtd 89. *22 Shanreagh Park, Limavady, Co Londonderry BT49 0SF* Limavady (015047) 22298

KNOWLES, Ven Graeme Paul. b 51. AKC73. St Aug Coll Cant 73. **d** 74 **p** 75. C St Peter-in-Thanet *Cant* 74-79; C Leeds St Pet *Ripon* 79-81; Chapl and Prec Portsm Cathl *Portsm* 81-87; Chapter Clerk 85-87; V Leigh Park 87-93; RD Havant 90-93; Adn Portsm from 93. *Victoria Lodge, 36 Osborn Road, Fareham, Hants PO16 7DS* Fareham (01329) 280101

KNOWLES, Mrs Jane Frances. b 44. GGSM66 Lon Inst of Educn TCert67. Ox Min Course CBTS93. **d** 93 **p** 94. NSM Sandhurst *Ox* from 93. *75 Mickle Hill, Little Sandhurst, Camberley, Surrey GU17 8QU* Crowthorne (01344) 774593

KNOWLES, John. b 28. Sarum & Wells Th Coll 84. **d** 73 **p** 74. NSM Magor w Redwick and Undy *Mon* 73-81; NSM Risca 82-83; NSM Marshfield and Peterstone Wentloog etc 83-85; C St Mellons 85-86; V Tredunnoc and Llantrisant w Llanhennock etc 86-94; rtd 94. *5 St Andrews Walk, Tredunnoc, Usk, Gwent NP5 1LZ* Tredunnock (01633) 450509

KNOWLES, Melvin Clay. b 43. Stetson Univ (USA) BA66 Ex Univ MA73 Ox Univ DipTh76. Ripon Coll Cuddesdon 75. **d** 77 **p** 78. C Minchinhampton *Glouc* 77-80; St Helena 80-82; TV Haywards Heath St Wilfrid *Chich* 82-88; Adult Educn Adv 88-94; TR Burgess Hill St Jo w St Edw from 94. *St John's Vicarage, 68 Park Road, Burgess Hill, W Sussex RH15 8HG* Burgess Hill (01444) 232582

KNOWLES, Very Rev Philip John. b 48. MA BTh. CITC 76. **d** 76 **p** 77. C Lisburn St Paul *Conn* 76-79; I Cloonclare w Killasnett and Lurganboy *K, E & A* 79-87; I Gorey w Kilnahue *C & O* 87-89; I Gorey w Kilnahue, Leskinfere and Ballycanew 89-95; Preb Ferns Cathl 91-95; Dean Cashel from 95; I Cashel w Magorban, Tipperary, Clonbeg etc from 95; Chan Waterford Cathl from 95; Chan Lismore Cathl from 95. *The Deanery, Cashel, Co Tipperary, Irish Republic* Tipperary (62) 61232

KNOWLES, Stephen. b 56. Dur Univ BA81 Ox Univ MSc88. Coll of Resurr Mirfield. **d** 83. C Denton *Newc* 83; C Tynemouth Cullercoats St Paul 84. *53 Hotspur Road, Wallsend, Tyne & Wear NE28 9HB* 0191-234 3626

KNOWLES-BROWN, Canon John Henry. b 30. AKC53. **d** 54 **p** 55. V Farley Hill St Jo *St Alb* 69-72; V Totteridge 72-95; RD Barnet 79-89; Hon Can St Alb 85-95; rtd 95. *1 Ascerton Close, Sidmouth, Devon EX10 9BS* Sidmouth (01395) 579286

KNOWLING, Richard Charles. b 46. K Coll Lon BSc67 St Edm Hall Ox BA70 MA89. St Steph Ho Ox 69. **d** 71 **p** 72. C Hobs Moat *Birm* 71-75; C Shrewsbury St Mary w All SS and St Mich *Lich* 75-77; V Rough Hills 77-83; Dir Past Th Coll of Resurr Mirfield 83-90; V Palmers Green St Jo *Lon* from 90. *St John's Vicarage, 1 Bourne Hill, London N13 4DA* 0181-886 1348

KNOX, Geoffrey Martin. b 44. Dur Univ BA66 DipTh67 Sheff City Coll of Educn DipEd73. St Chad's Coll Dur 63. **d** 67 **p** 68. C Newark St Mary *S'well* 67-72; Perm to Offic *Derby* 72-74; V Woodville 74-81; RD Repton 79-81; V Long Eaton St Laur from 81. *The Vicarage, Regent Street, Long Eaton, Nottingham NG10 1JX* Nottingham (0115) 973 3154

KNOX, Iain John Edward. b 46. TCD BA70 MA74 Hull Univ BPhil76. Irish Sch of Ecum 74 CITC 71. **d** 71 **p** 72. C Belf Malone St Jo *Conn* 71-74; Bp's Dom Chapl 72-74; Perm to Offic *D & R* 74-76; I Gweedore Union 76-80; I Clonmel w Innislounagh, Tullaghmelan etc *C & O* from 80; Bp's Dom Chapl from 82; Press & Radio Officer (Cashel) from 90; Dioc Info Officer (Cashel and Waterford) from 92. *St Mary's Rectory, 2 Western Road, Clonmel, Co Tipperary, Irish Republic* Clonmel (52) 21369

KNOX, Canon Ian Carroll. b 32. St Jo Coll Dur BA54 DipTh55. **d** 55 **p** 56. C Illingworth *Wakef* 55-58; C Lightcliffe 58-60; V Rastrick St Matt 60-77; Hon Can Wakef Cathl 76-89; RD Huddersfield 77-89; V Huddersfield St Pet 77-84; V Huddersfield St Pet and All SS 84-89; Can Res Wakef Cathl from 89; Dir of Educn from 89; Dir Ecum Affairs from 94. *5 Kingfisher Grove, Wakefield, W Yorkshire WF2 6SD* Wakefield (01924) 255832

KNOX, Thomas Anthony. b 31. BA. Ely Th Coll. **d** 56 **p** 57. C Poplar All SS w St Frideswide *Lon* 56-59; C Eastbourne St Andr *Chich* 59-61; C Welwyn *St Alb* 61-66; V Boreham Wood St Mich 66-71; R Puttenham w Long Marston 71-79; R Toddington from 79. *The Rectory, 41 Leighton Road, Toddington, Dunstable, Beds LU5 6AL* Toddington (01525) 872298

KOHNER, Canon Jeno George. b 31. K Coll Lon BD56 AKC56. Westcott Ho Cam 56. **d** 57 **p** 58. C Eccleston St Thos *Liv* 57-60; Canada from 60; Hon Can Montreal from 75. *31 Prince Edward Avenue, Point Clare, Quebec, Canada, H9R 4C4*

KOMOR, Michael. b 60. Univ of Wales BSc83. Chich Th Coll 83. **d** 86 **p** 87. C Mountain Ash *Llan* 86-89; C Llantwit Major 89-91; TV from 91. *The Vicarage, Trepit Road, Wick, Cowbridge, S Glam CF7 7QL* Wick (01656) 890471

KONIG, Peter Montgomery. b 44. Westcott Ho Cam 80. **d** 82 **p** 83. C Oundle *Pet* 82-86; Chapl Westwood Ho Sch Pet 86-92; Lic to Offic *Pet* 86-94; Chapl Pet High Sch 92-95; Chapl Worksop Coll Notts from 95. *Worksop College, Worksop, Notts S80 3AP* Worksop (01909) 479306

KOPSCH, Hartmut. b 41. Sheff Univ BA63 Univ of BC MA66 Lon Univ PhD70 DipHE. Trin Coll Bris 78. **d** 80 **p** 81. C Cranham Park *Chelmsf* 80-85; V Springfield *Birm* 85-92; V Dover St Martin *Cant* from 92. *St Martin's Vicarage, 339 Folkestone Road, Dover, Kent CT17 9JG* Dover (01304) 205391

KORNAHRENS, Wallace Douglas. b 43. The Citadel Charleston BA66 Gen Th Sem (NY) STB69. **d** 69 **p** 70. USA 69-72; C Potters Green *Cov* 72-75; Chapl Community of Celebration Wargrave Oxon 75-76; P-in-c Cumbrae (or Millport) *Arg* 76-78; R Grantown-on-Spey *Mor* 78-83; R Rothiemurchus 78-83; R Edin H Cross *Edin* from 83. *Holy Cross Rectory, 18 Barnton Gardens, Edinburgh EH4 6AF* 0131-336 2311

KOTHARE, Jayant. b 41. Bombay Univ BA Heidelberg Univ MDiv. **d** 86 **p** 87. C Handsworth St Mich *Birm* 86-89; C Southall St Geo *Lon* 89-92; TV Thamesmead *S'wark* from 92. *15 Camelot Close, London SE28 0ES* 0181-854 2382 or 310 6814

KOVOOR, George Iype. b 57. Delhi Univ BA77 Serampore Univ BD80 Chr Medical Assn of India DCHospC85. Union Bibl Sem Yavatmal 78. **d** 80 **p** 80. India 80-90; Dean St Paul's Cathl Ambala 84-88; C Derby St Aug *Derby* 90-94; Min Derby Asian Chr Min Project 90-94; Tutor Crowther Hall CMS Tr Coll Selly Oak from 94. *Crowther Hall, Weoley Park Road, Selly Oak, Birmingham B29 6QT* 0121-472 4228 or 415 5738

KROLL, Dr Una Margaret Patricia. b 25. Girton Coll Cam MB51 BChir51. S'wark Ord Course 68. **d** 88. Par Dn Mon from 88. *St Mary's Lodge, Priory Street, Monmouth, Gwent NP5 3BR* Monmouth (01600) 713465

KRONENBURG, Selwyn Thomas Denzil. b 32. Univ of Wales BA54 St Cath Soc Ox BA57 MA60 Leic Univ MA73. Wycliffe Hall Ox. **d** 57 **p** 58. C Surbiton St Matt *S'wark* 57-60; C Luton w E Hyde *St Alb* 60-62; P-in-c Loscoe *Derby* 62-65; Lect RE Bulmershe Coll 65-67; Whitelands Coll from 67; Perm to Offic *Guildf* from 77. *58 Woodfield Lane, Ashtead, Surrey KT21 2BS* Ashtead (01372) 272505

KRZEMINSKI, Stefan. b 51. Nottm Univ BTh77. Linc Th Coll 74. **d** 77 **p** 78. C Sawley *Derby* 77-79; Asst Chapl Blue Coat Sch Nottm from 79; Hon C W Hallam and Mapperley *Derby* from 84; Hd of RE Nottm High Sch from 88. *12 Newbridge Close, West Hallam, Ilkeston, Derbyshire DE7 6LY* Nottingham (0115) 930 5052

KUHRT, Ven Gordon Wilfred. b 41. Lon Univ BD63. Oak Hill Th Coll. **d** 67 **p** 68. C Illogan *Truro* 67-70; C Wallington H Trin *S'wark* 70-73; V Shenstone *Lich* 73-79; P-in-c S Croydon Em *Cant* 79-81; V S Croydon Em *S'wark* 81-89; RD Croydon Cen *Cant* 81-86; Hon Can S'wark Cathl *S'wark* 87-89; Adn Lewisham from 89. *3A Court Farm Road, London SE9 4JH* 0181-857 7982

KURTI, Peter Walter. b 60. Qu Mary Coll Lon LLB82 K Coll Lon MTh89. Ripon Coll Cuddesdon 83. **d** 86 **p** 87. C Prittlewell *Chelmsf* 86-90; Chapl Derby Coll of HE *Derby* 90-92; Chapl Derby Univ 92-94; Dep Hd Relig Resource and Research Cen 90-94; Australia from 94. *Address temp unknown*

KYBIRD, Paul. b 49. Selw Coll Cam BA72 MA75. Qu Coll Birm 72. **d** 74 **p** 76. C Loughb Em *Leic* 74-78; Overseas 78-81; Tutor Crowther Hall CMS Tr Coll Selly Oak 82-86; P-in-c Wreay Carl from 86; Lay Tr Adv from 86; P-in-c Dalston from 92; P-in-c Raughton Head w Gatesgill from 92. *The Vicarage, Townhead Road, Dalston, Carlisle CA5 7JF* Dalston (01228) 710215 or 38086 Fax 48769

KYLE, Laurence Arthur Nelson. b 14. S'wark Ord Course 64. **d** 67 **p** 68. R Hopton w Market Weston *St E* 70-72; P-in-c Barningham w Coney Weston 70-72; R Hopton, Market Weston, Barningham etc 72-79; RD Ixworth 73-79; rtd 79; Perm to Offic *Nor* from 79. *Flat 3, Ellesborough Manor, Butlers Cross, Aylesbury, Bucks HP17 0XF* Aylesbury (01296) 696047

KYLE, Miss Sharon Patricia Culvinor. b 55. Aber Coll of Comm HND75 Open Univ BA89. Coates Hall Edin BD94. **d** 94. C Edin St Jas *Edin* from 94. *43 Scotland Street, Edinburgh EH3 6PY* 0131-557 3797

KYRIACOU, Brian George. b 42. Lon Univ LLB64. Oak Hill Th Coll 79. **d** 81 **p** 82. C Becontree St Mary *Chelmsf* 81-83; C Becontree St Cedd 83-85; C Becontree W 85; TV 85-87; V Shiregreen St Jas and St Chris *Sheff* 87-92; TV Schorne *Ox* from 92. *The Vicarage, Church Street, North Marston, Bucks MK18 3PH* North Marston (01296) 670298

KYRIAKIDES-YELDHAM, Anthony Paul Richard (Tony). b 48. CPsychol91 Birkb Coll Lon BSc82 Golds Coll Lon DASS83 CQSW83 Warw Univ MSc90. K Coll Lon BD73 AKC73. **d** 74 **p** 75. C Dalston H Trin w St Phil *Lon* 74-78; NSM Lon Docks St Pet w Wapping St Jo 79-81; NSM Hackney Wick St Mary of Eton w St Aug 81-85; NSM Wandsworth Common St Mary *S'wark* 85-87; Chapl Wandsworth Mental Health Unit 87-93; Chapl Springfield Hosp Lon 87-93; Lect and Co-ord Dip in Counselling Plymouth Univ from 93; RD Perm to Offic *Ex* from 94. *Liesse, Grange Road, Buckfast, Buckfastleigh, Devon TQ11 0EH* Buckfastleigh (01364) 42189

L

LA TOUCHE, Francis William Reginald. b 51. Linc Th Coll 73. d 76 p 77. C Yate *Bris* 76-77; C Yate New Town 77-79; Chapl Vlissingen (Flushing) Miss to Seamen etc *Eur* 79-83; Lic to Offic *York* 83-91; Miss to Seamen 83-91; V Burstwick w Thorngumbald *York* from 91. *The Vicarage, Main Road, Thorngumbald, Hull HU12 9NA* Withernsea (01964) 626509

LABDON, John. b 32. Oak Hill Th Coll. d 84 p 85. C Formby H Trin *Liv* 84-87; P-in-c St Helens St Mark from 87. *St Mark's Vicarage, 160 North Road, St Helens, Merseyside WA10 2TZ* St Helens (01744) 23806

LACEY, Allan John. b 48. Wycliffe Hall Ox. d 82 p 83. C Greasbrough *Sheff* 82-85; R Treeton 85-92; V Thorpe Hesley from 92. *The Vicarage, 30 Barnsley Road, Thorpe Hesley, Rotherham, S Yorkshire S61 2RR* Sheffield (0114) 246 3487/ 245 7564

LACEY, Ven Clifford George. b 21. AKC49. d 50 p 51. V Eltham St Jo *S'wark* 66-79; Sub-Dean Eltham 70-79; Boro Dean Greenwich 79-85; Adn Lewisham 85-89; rtd 89; Perm to Offic *Nor* 89-91; Perm to Offic *St E* from 90; Bp's Officer for Rtd Clergy and Widows *Nor* from 91. *31 Kerridges, East Harling, Norwich NR16 2QA* East Harling (01953) 718458

LACEY, Eric. b 33. Cranmer Hall Dur 69. d 71 p 72. C Blackpool St Jo *Blackb* 71-75; V Whittle-le-Woods 75-88; R Heysham from 88. *St Peter's Rectory, Main Street, Morecambe, Lancs LA3 2RN* Heysham (01524) 851422

LACEY, Canon Frank Gordon. b 26. Magd Coll Cam BA47 MA51. Ely Th Coll 48. d 50 p 51. V Ockbrook *Derby* 69-73; Dir Past Studies N Ord Course 73-81; V Birtles *Ches* 73-82; Can Res Sheff Cathl *Sheff* 82-91; rtd 91. *6 Barnes Avenue, Dronfield Woodhouse, Sheffield S18 5YG* Dronfield (01246) 416589

LACEY, Graeme Alexander Warner. b 15. Wycliffe Hall Ox. d 63 p 64. V Bexley St Jo *Roch* 67-73; R Cuxton 73-76; R Cuxton and Halling 76-80; rtd 80; Perm to Offic *Chich* from 80. *122 Westminster Drive, Bognor Regis, W Sussex PO21 3RZ* Pagham (01243) 266631

LACEY, Nigel Jeremy. b 59. St Jo Coll Nottm BTh94. d 94 p 95. C Mildenhall *St E* from 94. *Church House, 8 Church Walk, Mildenhall, Bury St Edmunds, Suffolk IP28 7ED* Mildenhall (01638) 715112

LACK, Catherine Mary. b 59. Clare Coll Cam BA81. Qu Coll Birm 90. d 92 p 94. Par Dn Leiston *St E* 92-94; C 94-95; TV Ipswich St Mary at Stoke w St Pet, Stoke Park from 95. *St Mary's House, 6 Stone Lodge Lane, Ipswich IP2 9PA* Ipswich (01473) 601617

LACK, Leonard James Westbrook. b 16. Ripon Hall Ox 65. d 66 p 67. C Leighton Buzzard *St Alb* 66-81; rtd 81; Perm to Offic *Bris* from 81. *1 Pulford Road, Leighton Buzzard, Beds LU7 7AB* Leighton Buzzard (01525) 850480

LACK, Martin Paul. b 57. St Jo Coll Ox MA79 MSc80. Linc Th Coll 83. d 86 p 87. C E Bowbrook *Worc* 86-89; C W Bowbrook 86-89; C Bowbrook S 89-90; C Bowbrook N 89-90; R Teme Valley S from 90. *Hanley Rectory, Broadheath, Tenbury Wells, Worcs WR15 8QW* Upper Sapey (01886) 853286

LACKEY, Michael Geoffrey Herbert. b 42. Oak Hill Th Coll 73. d 75 p 76. C Hatcham St Jas *S'wark* 75-81; V New Barnet St Jas *St Alb* 81-91; V Hollington St Jo *Chich* from 91. *The Vicarage, 94 Lower Glen Road, St Leonards-on-Sea, E Sussex TN37 7AR* Hastings (01424) 751103

LACKEY, William Terence Charles. b 32. St Mich Coll Llan 80. d 82 p 83. C Wrexham *St As* 82-85; V Gwersyllt 85-93; R Trefnant from 93. *The Rectory, Denbigh Road, Trefnant, Denbigh, Clwyd LL16 5UG* Trefnant (01745) 730584

LADD, Mrs Anne de Chair. b 56. Nottm Univ BA78 Birm Univ CQSW80 DipSocWork80. St Jo Coll Nottm LTh DPS86. dss 86 d 87 p 94. Bucknall and Bagnall *Lich* 86-87; Par Dn 87-91; NSM Bricket Wood *St Alb* from 91. *20 West Riding, Bricket Wood, St Albans, Herts AL2 3QP* Garston (01923) 681107 or 676401

LADD, John George Morgan. b 36. Univ of Wales (Ban) BA58 MA65. Trin Coll Carmarthen St Mich Coll Llan. d 90 p 91. NSM Nevern and Y Beifil w Eglwyswrw and Meline etc *St D* 90-92; NSM Llandysilio w Egremont and Llanglydwen etc 92-93; V Gwaun-cae-Gurwen from 93. *The Vicarage, 118 Heol Caegurwen, Gwauncaegurwen, Ammanford, Dyfed SA18 1PD* Amman Valley (01269) 822430

LADD, Nicholas Mark. b 57. Ex Univ BA78 Selw Coll Cam BA81. Ridley Hall Cam 79. d 82 p 83. C Aston SS Pet and Paul *Birm* 82-86; TV Bucknall and Bagnall *Lich* 86-91; V Bricket Wood *St Alb* from 91. *20 West Riding, Bricket Wood, St Albans, Herts AL2 3QP* Garston (01923) 681107 or 676401

LADDS, Canon Robert Sidney. b 41. LRSC72 Lon Univ BEd71. Cant Sch of Min 79. d 80 p 81. C Hythe *Cant* 80-83; R

Bretherton *Blackb* 83-91; Chapl Bp Rawstorne Sch Croston Preston 83-87; Bp's Chapl for Min and Adv Coun for Min *Blackb* 86-91; P-in-c Preston St Jo from 91; Hon Can Blackb Cathl from 93. *The Rectory, 13 Ribblesdale Place, Preston PR1 3NA* Preston (01772) 252528

LADIPO, Adeyemi Olalekan. b 37. Trin Coll Bris 63. d 66 p 76. C Bilston St Leon *Lich* 66-68; Nigeria 68-84; V Canonbury St Steph *Lon* 85-87; BCMS Sec for Internat Miss 87-90; Hon C Bromley SS Pet and Paul *Roch* 89-90; V Herne Hill *S'wark* from 90. *8 Ruskin Walk, London SE24 9LZ* 0171-274 5741

LAING, Canon Alexander Burns. b 34. RD90. Edin Th Coll 57. d 60 p 61. C Falkirk *Edin* 60-62; C Edin Ch Ch 62-70; Chapl RNR 64-91; P-in-c Edin St Fillan *Edin* 70-74; Chapl Edin R Infirmary 74-77; Dioc Supernumerary *Edin* from 77; R Helensburgh *Glas* from 77; Can St Mary's Cathl from 87. *The Rectory, 16 William Street, Helensburgh, Dunbartonshire G84 8BD* Helensburgh (01436) 72500

LAING, James. b 18. AKC49. d 50 p 51. V Southgate St Andr *Lon* 69-87; rtd 87; Hon C Hinxworth w Newnham and Radwell *St Alb* 87-91; Hon C Ashwell w Hinxworth and Newnham from 91. *The Rectory, 10 New Inn Road, Hinxworth, Baldock, Herts SG7 5HG* Baldock (01462) 742770

LAING, Canon William Sydney. b 32. TCD BA54 MA62. CITC 55. d 55 p 56. C Crumlin *Conn* 55-59; C Dub St Ann *D & G* 59-65; I Carbury *M & K* 65-68; I Dub Finglas *D & G* 68-80; I Tallaght 80-91; Can Ch Ch Cathl Dub 90-94; Preb from 94; I Dub Crumlin w Chapelizod from 91. *St Mary's Rectory, Kimmage Road West, Dublin 12, Irish Republic* Dublin (1) 455-5639

LAIRD, Alisdair Mark. b 60. Auckland Univ BA84. Trin Coll Bris BA92. d 92 p 93. C Linthorpe *York* from 92. *23 Linden Grove, Middlesbrough, Cleveland TS5 5NF* Middlesbrough (01642) 815961

LAIRD, Canon John Charles. b 32. Sheff Univ BA53 MA54 St Cath Coll Ox BA58 MA62 Lon Univ DipEd70. Ripon Hall Ox 56. d 58 p 59. C Cheshunt *St Alb* 58-62; Chapl Bps' Coll Cheshunt 62-64; Vice-Prin 64-67; Prin 67-69; V Keysoe w Bolnhurst and Lt Staughton *St Alb* from 69; Hon Can St Alb from 87. *The Vicarage, Church Road, Keysoe, Bedford MK44 2HW* Bedford (01234) 708251

LAIRD, Robert George (Robin). b 40. TCD Div Sch 58 Edin Th Coll 63. d 65 p 66. C Drumragh *D & R* 65-68; CF 68-93; QHC 91-93; Sen Chapl Sedbergh Sch Cumbria from 93. *Sedbergh School, Sedbergh, Cumbria LA10 5HG* Sedbergh (015396) 20983 Fax 21301

LAIRD, Stephen Charles Edward. b 66. Or Coll Ox BA88 MA92 MSt93 K Coll Lon MTh91. Wycliffe Hall Ox DipMin94. d 94 p 95. C Ilfracombe, Lee, Woolacombe, Bittadon etc *Ex* from 94. *St Peter's House, Highfield Road, Ilfracombe, Devon EX34 9LH* Ilfracombe (01271) 864119

LAISTER, Peter. b 27. St D Coll Lamp BA54. St Steph Ho Ox 54. d 56 p 57. Chapl Middx Hosp Lon 66-70; V Clerkenwell H Redeemer w St Phil *Lon* 70-86; USA 86-93; rtd 92. *6 Bishop Street, London N1 8PH* 0171-354 2741

LAKE, Canon David Eurwyn. b 17. TD60. St D Coll Lamp BA39. d 40 p 41. V Skewen *Llan* 62-84; rtd 84; Perm to Offic *Llan* from 84. *Fairwell, 42 Brecon Road, Ystradgynlais, Swansea SA9 1HF* Swansea (01792) 849541

LAKE, Miss Eileen Veronica. b 58. Lon Univ CCouns93. Aston Tr Scheme 85 Sarum & Wells Th Coll 85. d 88 p 94. Par Dn Islington St Mary *Lon* 88-92; Asst Chapl Homerton Hosp Lon 92-94; Asst Chapl Hackney Hosp Gp 92-94; P-in-c Brondesbury Ch Ch and St Laur *Lon* from 94. *The Rectory, Chevening Road, London NW6 6DU* 0181-969 5961

LAKE, Stephen David. b 63. Chich Th Coll 85. d 88 p 89. C Sherborne w Castleton and Lillington *Sarum* 88-92; P-in-c Branksome St Aldhelm from 92; RD Poole from 94. *The Vicarage, St Aldhelm's Road, Poole, Dorset BH13 6BT* Poole (01202) 764420

LAKE, Vivienne Elizabeth. b 38. Lon Univ DHistA78. Westcott Ho Cam 84. dss 86 d 87 p 94. Chesterton Gd Shep *Ely* 86-87; 87-90; NSM Bourn Deanery from 90. *The Vicarage Flat, School Lane, Barton, Cambridge CB3 7BG* Cambridge (01223) 264147

LAKER, Mrs Grace. b 39. SRN63. Sarum & Wells Th Coll BTh91. d 91 p 94. C Helston and Wendron *Truro* 91-95; Chapl Oldchurch Hosp Romford from 95. *Oldchurch Hospital, Oldchurch Road, Romford RM7 0BE, or 14 Hillcourt, Main Road, Romford RM1 3DA* Romford (01708) 746090

LAKER, Leopold Ernest. b 38. Sarum & Wells Th Coll 77. d 77 p 78. C Rainham *Roch* 77-80; V Horton Kirby from 80. *The Vicarage, Horton Kirby, Dartford DA4 9BN* Farningham (01322) 862201

LAMB, Bruce. b 47. Keble Coll Ox BA69 MA73 Leeds Univ DipTh72. Coll of Resurr Mirfield 70. **d** 73 **p** 74. C Romford St Edw *Chelmsf* 73-76; C Canning Town St Cedd 76-79; V New Brompton St Luke *Roch* 79-83; Chapl RN 83-87; C Rugeley *Lich* 87-88; V Trent Vale 88-92. *16 Epworth Road, Portsmouth PO2 0HD*

LAMB, Bryan John Harry. b 35. Leeds Univ BA60 Aston Univ DCouns72. Coll of Resurr Mirfield 60. **d** 62 **p** 63. C Solihull *Birm* 88-89; Asst Master Malvern Hall Sch Solihull 65-74; Alderbrook Sch & Hd of Light Hall Adult Ed Cen 74-88; V Wragby *Linc* 89; Dioc Dir of Readers 89; Perm to Offic *Birm* from 89; rtd 95. *35 Rectory Road, Solihull, W Midlands B91 3RJ* 0121-705 2489

LAMB, Canon Christopher Avon. b 39. Qu Coll Ox BA61 MA65 Birm Univ MA78 PhD87. Wycliffe Hall Ox BA63. **d** 63 **p** 64. C Enfield St Andr *Lon* 63-69; Pakistan 69-75; Tutor Crowther Hall CMS Tr Coll Selly Oak 75-78; Lic to Offic *Birm* 75-87; Co-ord BCMS/CMS Other Faiths Th Project 78-87; Dioc Community Relns Officer *Cov* 87-92; Can Th Cov Cathl from 92; Sec Inter-Faith Relns Bd of Miss and Unity from 92. *5 Waterloo Street, Coventry CV1 5JS* Coventry (01203) 257523

LAMB, David Andrew. b 60. Liv Inst of Educn BA94. Nor Ord Course 90. **d** 94 **p** 95. C Formby H Trin *Liv* from 94. *19 Hampton Road, Formby, Liverpool L37 6EJ* Formby (01704) 876557

LAMB, Ms Jean Evelyn. b 57. Reading Univ BA79 Nottm Univ MA88. St Steph Ho Ox 81. **dss** 84 **d** 88. Leic H Spirit *Leic* 84; Beeston S'well88; Par Dn 88-91; C Nottm St Mary and St Cath from 92. *13 Melbourne Road, Nottingham NG2 5BG* Nottingham (0115) 981 2478

LAMB, John Romney. b 21. Ch Ch Ox BA48 MA53. Wells Th Coll 49. **d** 50 **p** 51. CF 55-70; V Horsell *Guildf* 70-76; V Dorking w Ranmore 76-82; P-in-c Charing Heath w Egerton *Cant* 82-83; P-in-c Pluckley w Pevington 82-83; R Egerton w Pluckley 84-87; rtd 87. *Wayside, Budds Hill, Singleton, Chichester, W Sussex PO18 0HD* Singleton (01243) 811516

LAMB, Peter Francis Charles. b 15. St Cath Coll Cam BA37 MA41. Wells Th Coll 37. **d** 38 **p** 39. R Mells w Vobster, Whatley and Chantry *B & W* 70-77; rtd 77; Perm to Offic *B & W* from 77. *6 Parsons Close, Long Sutton, Langport, Somerset TA10 9LN* Langport (01458) 241481

LAMB, Philip Richard James. b 42. Sarum & Wells Th Coll. **d** 83 **p** 84. C Wotton-under-Edge w Ozleworth and N Nibley *Glouc* 83-86; TV Worc SE *Worc* 86-91; R Billingsley w Sidbury, Middleton Scriven etc *Heref* from 91. *The Rectory, Sidbury, Bridgnorth, Shropshire WV16 6PY* Bridgnorth (01746) 718625

LAMB, Scott Innes. b 64. Edin Univ BSc86 Fitzw Coll Cam BA92. Aston Tr Scheme 88 Ridley Hall Cam CTMin93. **d** 93 **p** 94. NSM Trin St Mich, Harrow *Lon* 93; C E Ham w Upton Park St Alb *Chelmsf* from 93. *2A Navarre Road, London E6 3AQ* 0181-548 1522

LAMB, William Robert Stuart. b 70. Ball Coll Ox BA91 MA95 Peterho Cam MPhil94. Westcott Ho Cam CTM95. **d** 95. C Wakef St Jo *Wakef* from 95. *15 Savile Drive, Halifax, W Yorkshire HX1 2EU* Halifax (01422) 346027

LAMBERT, David Francis. b 40. Oak Hill Th Coll 72. **d** 74 **p** 75. C Paignton St Paul Preston *Ex* 74-77; C Woking Ch Ch *Guildf* 77-84; P-in-c Willesden Green St Gabr *Lon* 84-91; P-in-c Cricklewood St Mich 85-91; V Cricklewood St Gabr and St Mich 92-93; R Chenies and Lt Chalfont, Latimer and Flaunden *Ox* from 93. *The Rectory, Chenies, Rickmansworth, Herts WD3 6ER* Chorleywood (01923) 284433

LAMBERT, David Hardy. b 44. AKC66. **d** 67 **p** 68. C Marske in Cleveland *York* 67-72; V from 85; V N Ormesby 73-85; RD Guisborough 86-91. *The Vicarage, 6 Windy Hill Lane, Marske-by-the-Sea, Redcar, Cleveland TS11 7BN* Middlesbrough (01642) 482896

LAMBERT, David Nathaniel. b 34. Headingley Meth Coll 58 Linc Th Coll 66. **d** 66 **p** 67. R Saltfleetby All SS w St Pet *Linc* 69-73; R Saltfleetby St Clem 70-73; V Skidbrooke 70-73; V Saltfleetby 73-80; R Theddlethorpe 74-80; RD Louthesk 76-82; R N Ormsby w Wyham 80; R Fotherby 81-94; rtd 94. *The Rowans, 17 Stenton Lane, Louth, Lincs LN11 8RZ* Louth (01507) 606220

LAMBERT, Donald William. b 19. Keble Coll Ox BA40 MA44. St Steph Ho Ox 40. **d** 43 **p** 44. V Acton Green St Pet *Lon* 71-77; rtd 77; Perm to Offic *Chich* from 77. *8 Christ Church House, 34 Christ Church Road, Worthing, W Sussex BN11 1JA* Worthing (01903) 206978

LAMBERT, Gordon. b 32. Univ of Wales (Lamp) BA56. Wycliffe Hall Ox 56. **d** 58 **p** 59. C Newbarns w Hawcoat *Carl* 58-63; C-in-c Barrow St Aid CD 63-67; V Barrow St Aid 67-68; R Ousby w Melmerby 68-71; V Farlam 71-76; TV Thirsk w S Kilvington and Carlton Miniott etc *York* 76-77; TV Thirsk

77-89; RD Thirsk 81-89; V Belvedere All SS *Roch* from 89. *All Saints' Vicarage, Nuxley Road, Belvedere, Kent DA17 5JE* Erith (01322) 432169

LAMBERT, Ian Anderson. b 43. Lon Univ BA72 Nottm Univ MTh87. Ridley Hall Cam 66. **d** 67 **p** 68. C Bermondsey St Mary w St Olave, St Jo etc *S'wark* 67-70; Jamaica 71-75; Chapl RAF from 75. *Chaplaincy Services (RAF), HQ, Personnel and Training Command, RAF Innsworth, Gloucester GL3 1EZ* Gloucester (01452) 712612 Ext 5164 Fax 510828

LAMBERT, John Clement Antony. b 28. St Cath Coll Cam BA48 MA52. Cuddesdon Coll 50. **d** 52 **p** 53. R Carlton-in-Lindrick *S'well* 59-93; rtd 93. *139 Longedge Lane, Wingerworth, Chesterfield, Derbyshire S42 6PR* Chesterfield (01246) 551774

LAMBERT, Malcolm Eric. b 58. RMN84 Leic Univ BSc80 Fitzw Coll Cam BA89. Ridley Hall Cam 87. **d** 90 **p** 91. C Humberstone *Leic* 90-94; R S Croxton Gp from 94. *The Rectory, 19 Main Street, South Croxton, Leicester LE7 3RJ* Melton Mowbray (01664) 840245

LAMBERT, Michael Roy. b 25. Univ Coll Dur BSc49. Cuddesdon Coll 52. **d** 52 **p** 53. V Saltburn-by-the-Sea *York* 64-72; P-in-c Shaftesbury H Trin *Sarum* 72-73; R Shaston 74-78; R Corfe Mullen 78-91; rtd 91. *16 Pheasant Way, Cirencester, Glos GL7 1BL* Cirencester (01285) 654657

LAMBERT, Norman. b 39. ACP66 Ch Ch Coll Cant 62 Lon Inst of Educn TCert65. Chich Th Coll 67. **d** 70 **p** 71. C Ocker Hill *Lich* 70-73; C Dudley St Edm *Worc* 73-76; P-in-c Darby End 76-77; V from 77. *St Peter's Vicarage, 25 Brooksbank Drive, Gawne Lane, Cradley Heath, W Midlands B64 5QG* Cradley Heath (01384) 637662

LAMBERT, Miss Olivia Jane. b 48. Matlock Coll of Educn BEd70. Trin Coll Bris DipHE86. **dss** 86 **d** 87 **p** 94. York St Luke *York* 86-87; Par Dn 87-90; Chapl York Distr Hosp 86-90; Par Dn Huntington *York* 90-94; C 94-95; TV from 95. *22 Park Avenue, New Earswick, York YO3 8DB* York (01904) 764306

LAMBERT, Peter George. b 29. Coll of Resurr Mirfield 86. **d** 87 **p** 88. NSM Rothwell w Orton, Rushton w Glendon and Pipewell *Pet* 87-93; P-in-c Corby Epiphany w St Jo from 93. *4 Cogan Crescent, Rothwell, Kettering, Northants NN14 6AS* Kettering (01536) 710692

LAMBERT, Philip Charles. b 54. St Jo Coll Dur BA75 Fitzw Coll Cam BA77 MA81. Ridley Hall Cam 75. **d** 78 **p** 79. C Upper Tooting H Trin *S'wark* 78-81; C Whorlton *Newc* 81-84; P-in-c Alston cum Garrigill w Nenthead and Kirkhaugh 84-87; TV Alston Team 87-89; R Curry Rivel w Fivehead and Swell *B & W* from 89. *The Rectory, Curry Rivel, Langport, Somerset TA10 0HQ* Langport (01458) 251375

LAMBERT, Stephen Uvedale. b 49. FRICS77 Magd Coll Cam BA70 MA75. Ox NSM Course 87. **d** 90 **p** 91. NSM Lt Compton w Chastleton, Cornwell etc *Ox* from 90. *Harcomb, Chastleton, Moreton-in-Marsh, Glos GL56 0SU* Barton-on-the-Heath (0160874) 354

LAMBERT, Stuart Winston. b 46. Southn Univ BTh83 Man Univ MA(Theol)93. **d** 82 **p** 83. C Whyke w Rumboldswhyke and Portfield *Chich* 82-83; Bermuda from 83. *PO Box DD 185, St David's DD BX, Bermuda* Bermuda (1-809) 297-2085 Fax as telephone

LAMBERT, Sydney Thomas. b 17. Keble Coll Ox BA39 MA44. Wells Th Coll 40. **d** 41 **p** 42. R Rendcomb *Glouc* 67-73; V Colesbourne 67-73; P-in-c Cheltenham St Pet 73-78; P-in-c Todenham w Lower Lemington 78-83; P-in-c Bourton on the Hill 78-83; rtd 83; Perm to Offic *Worc* from 83; Perm to Offic *Glouc* from 83. *97 Elm Road, Evesham, Worcs WR11 5DR* Evesham (01386) 446725

LAMBETH, Archdeacon of. See BIRD, Ven Colin Richard Bateman

LAMBOURNE, John Brian. b 36. Chich Th Coll 62. **d** 65 **p** 66. C Cant St Greg *Cant* 65-67; C St Mary in the Marsh 67-68; C E Grinstead St Swithun *Chich* 68-70; C Storrington 70-76; C Sullington 70-76; V Salehurst from 76; CF (TA) from 87; Bp's Adv on Rural Affairs *Chich* from 89; Agric Chapl from 89. *St Mary's Vicarage, Fair Lane, Robertsbridge, E Sussex TN32 5AR* Robertsbridge (01580) 880408

LAMDIN, Keith Hamilton. b 47. Bris Univ BA69. Ripon Coll Cuddesdon 86. **d** 86 **p** 87. Adult Educn Officer *Ox* from 86; Team Ldr Par Resources Dept from 88; Dioc Dir Tr from 94. *41 Stapleton Road, Headington, Oxford OX3 3LX* Oxford (01865) 61760

LAMMAS, Miss Diane Beverley (Di). b 47. Trin Coll Bris 76. **dss** 79 **d** 87 **p** 94. Lenton Abbey *S'well* 79-84; Wollaton Park 79-84; E Regional Co-ord CPAS 84-89; Sec for Voc and Min CPAS 84-89; Hon C Cam St Paul *Ely* 87-90; Voc and Min Adv CPAS 89-92; Sen Voc and Min Adv CPAS from 92; Perm to Offic

Cov from 89. *3 Riversleigh Road, Leamington Spa, Warks CV32 6BG* Leamington Spa (01926) 427637 Fax Warwick (01926) 337613

LAMONT, Roger. b 37. Jes Coll Ox BA60 MA62. St Steph Ho Ox 59. **d** 61 **p** 62. C Northn St Alb *Pet* 61-66; V Mitcham St Olave *S'wark* 66-73; V N Sheen St Phil and All SS 73-85; P-in-c Richmond St Luke 82-85; Chapl St Lawr Hosp Caterham 85-91; Chapl Lifecare NHS Trust (Caterham) from 91. *Lifecare NHS Trust, Coulsdon road, Caterham, Surrey CR3 5YA* Caterham (01883) 340803 or 346411

LAMONT, Ms Veronica Jane (Ronni). b 56. Bp Grosseteste Coll CertEd77. St Jo Coll Nottm 90. **d** 92 **p** 94. Par Dn St Alb St Pet *St Alb* 92-94; C from 94. *48 Catherine Street, St Albans, Herts AL3 5BU* St Albans (01727) 843085

LANCASHIRE, Allan. b 32. Birm Univ BA54. Lich Th Coll. **d** 63 **p** 64. C Birstall *Wakef* 63-67; V Wrenthorpe 67-70; P-in-c Wolverton H Trin *Ox* 70-73; TV 73-76; Educn Officer 73-76; Dioc Schs Officer *Lich* 76-85; P-in-c Drayton St Pet (Oxon) *Ox* 85-90; P-in-c Horley w Hornton 85-90; R Horley w Hornton and Hanwell, Shenington etc from 90. *The Vicarage, Horley, Banbury, Oxon OX17 6BH* Banbury (01295) 738165

LANCASHIRE, Douglas. b 26. SOAS Lon BA50 MA58 K Coll Lon BD55. **d** 61 **p** 79. New Zealand 65-81; R Boxted w Langham *Chelmsf* 81-91; rtd 91. *15 Cecil Avenue, Enfield, Middx EN1 1PT* 0181-363 0718

LANCASTER, Frederick Charles Thomas. b 16. Bps' Coll Cheshunt 48. **d** 51 **p** 52. R Ascot Heath *Ox* 67-81; rtd 81; Perm to Offic *Ox* 82-94. *College of St Barnabas, Blackberry Lane, Lingfield, Surrey RH7 6NJ* Dormans Park (01342) 870260

LANCASTER, John Rawson. b 47. BSc. N Ord Course. **d** 82 **p** 83. C Bolton St Jas w St Chrys *Bradf* 82-86; V Barnoldswick w Bracewell from 86. *The Vicarage, 131 Gisburn Road, Barnoldswick, Colne, Lancs BB8 5JU* Barnoldswick (01282) 812028

LANCASTER, Norman. b 13. Leeds Univ BA36. Coll of Resurr Mirfield 36. **d** 38 **p** 39. V Aylesby *Linc* 71-77; R Gt Coates 71-77; rtd 77; Perm to Offic *Linc* from 77. *50 Westminster Drive, Grimsby, S Humberside DN34 4TY* Grimsby (01472) 361587

LANCASTER, Ronald. b 31. MBE93. FRSC CChem St Jo Coll Dur BA53 MA56. Cuddesdon Coll 55. **d** 57 **p** 58. C Morley St Pet w Churwell *Wakef* 57-60; C High Harrogate St Pet *Ripon* 60-63; Lic to Offic *Ely* 63-88; Chapl Kimbolton Sch Cambs 63-88; Asst Chapl 88-91; Perm to Offic *Ely* from 88. *7 High Street, Kimbolton, Huntingdon, Cambs PE18 0HB* Huntingdon (01480) 860498 Fax 861277

LANCASTER, Mrs Susan Louise. b 47. Leic Univ BA79 CPES81. E Midl Min Tr Course 88. **d** 92 **p** 94. NSM Clarendon Park St Jo w Knighton St Mich *Leic* from 93. *5 Hartopp Road, Leicester LE2 1WE* Leicester (0116) 270 9726

LANCASTER, Archdeacon of. See GIBBONS, Ven Kenneth Harry

LANCASTER, Suffragan Bishop of. See NICHOLLS, Rt Rev John (Jack)

LAND, Michael Robert John. b 43. Ripon Hall Ox 70. **d** 72 **p** 73. C Newbury St Nic *Ox* 72-75; TV Chigwell *Chelmsf* 75-80; V Walthamstow St Andr from 80. *St Andrew's Vicarage, 37 Sutton Road, London E17 5QA* 0181-527 3969

LANDALL, James Norman. b 57. St Jo Coll Dur 85. **d** 88 **p** 89. C Nailsea H Trin *B & W* 88-92; CF from 92. *clo MOD (Army), Bagshot Park, Bagshot, Surrey GU19 5PL* Bagshot (01276) 471717 Fax 412834

LANDEN, Edgar Sydney. b 23. ARCM46 FRCO46 St Jo Coll Dur BA54 BMus55 DipTh55. **d** 55 **p** 56. C Cirencester *Glouc* 69-76; Min Can Ch Ch *Ox* 76-88; R Wytham 76-88; rtd 88; Perm to Offic *B & W* from 88. *Cheriton Lodge, 4 Allandale Road, Burnham-on-Sea, Somerset TA8 2HG* Burnham-on-Sea (01278) 783062

LANDMAN, Denis Cooper. b 21. MBE60 OM(Ger)80. DipEd52. St Deiniol's Hawarden 79. **d** 82 **p** 83. Hon C Tranmere St Paul w St Luke *Ches* 82-86; Australia from 86. *1/24 Sretton Drive, Helensvale, Queensland, Australia 4210* Gold Coast (75) 734660

LANDRETH, Canon Derek. b 20. TD63. K Coll Cam BA47 MA52. Bps' Coll Cheshunt 47. **d** 48 **p** 49. CF (TA) 51-75; V Richmond St Mary *S'wark* 59-70; Hon Can S'wark Cathl 68-76; R Sanderstead All SS 70-74; TR 74-77; Can Res S'wark Cathl 77-82; Vice-Chmn Dioc Past Cttee 77-82; Chapl to The Queen 80-90; P-in-c Icklesham *Chich* 82-83; V 83-88; RD Rye 84-88; P-in-c Fairlight 84-86; rtd 89; Perm to Offic *Chich* from 89. *Gossamer Cottage, Slindon, Arundel, W Sussex BN18 0QT* Slindon (01243) 814224

LANDRETH, Mrs Mavis Isabella (Isabel). b 32. SEN81. Gilmore Ho 67. **dss** 74 **d** 87. Walthamstow St Sav *Chelmsf* 70-75; Sanderstead All SS *S'wark* 76-79; Sheff St Cuth *Sheff*

84-85; N Gen Hosp Sheff 84-85; Icklesham *Chich* 86-87; Hon Par Dn 87-89; Perm to Offic from 89. *Gossamer Cottage, Slindon, Arundel, W Sussex BN18 0QT* Slindon (01243) 814224

LANE, Andrew Harry John. b 49. Lanc Univ BA71. Cuddesdon Coll 71. **d** 73 **p** 74. C Abingdon w Shippon *Ox* 73-78; Chapl Abingdon Sch 75-78; Chapl RAF 78-94; rtd 94; Perm to Offic *Nor* from 94. *32B Beeston Common, Sheringham, Norfolk NR26 8ES* Sheringham (01263) 825623

LANE, Anthony James. b 29. Leeds Univ BA53. Coll of Resurr Mirfield 53. **d** 55 **p** 56. R Handley w Gussage St Andrew and Pentridge *Sarum* 64-80; V Thurmaston *Leic* 80-85; TV Bournemouth St Pet w St Swithun, St Steph etc *Win* 85-93; rtd 93. *5 Richards Way, Salisbury SP2 8NT* Salisbury (01722) 332163

LANE, Antony Kenneth. b 58. Ripon Coll Cuddesdon 84. **d** 87 **p** 88. C Crediton and Shobrooke *Ex* 87-90; C Amblecote *Worc* 90-94; C Sedgley All SS 94-95; TV from 95. *St Andrew's Vicarage, 22 The Straits, Lower Gornal, Dudley, W Midlands DY3 3AB* Sedgley (01902) 885508

LANE, Christopher George (Chris). b 48. NDH. Sarum & Wells Th Coll 84. **d** 86 **p** 87. C Petersfield *Portsm* 86-90; P-in-c Barton from 90. *St Paul's Vicarage, Barton, Newport, Isle of Wight PO30 2HZ* Isle of Wight (01983) 522075

LANE, David John. b 35. Magd Coll Ox BA58 MA62 BD89. Coll of Resurr Mirfield 60. **d** 62 **p** 62. Barbados 61-65; C Wolvercote *Ox* 65-66; Asst Chapl Pemb Coll Ox 66-68; Lect 68-71; Tutor St Steph Ho Ox 68-71; Canada 71-83; Assoc Prof Univ of Toronto 71-83; Tutor Coll of Resurr Mirfield from 83; Dir of Studies from 84; Vice-Prin 87-90; Prin from 90. *College of the Resurrection, Mirfield, W Yorkshire WF14 0BW* Mirfield (01924) 490441

LANE, Denis John Victor. b 29. Lon Univ LLB49 BD55. Oak Hill Th Coll 50. **d** 53 **p** 54. OMF 60-94; Singapore 66-94; Lic to Offic *Chich* from 91; rtd 94. *2 Parry Drive, Rustington, Littlehampton, W Sussex BN16 2QY* Rustington (01903) 785430 Fax as telephone

LANE, Dennis Charles William. b 17. Lon Univ BD40 AKC40. **d** 40 **p** 41. V Tandridge *S'wark* 64-91; RD Godstone 71-76; rtd 91. *7 Branksome Close, New Milton, Hants BH25 6BQ* New Milton (01425) 613302

LANE, Mrs Elizabeth Jane Holden (Libby). b 66. St Pet Coll Ox BA89. Cranmer Hall Dur DMinlStuds93. **d** 93 **p** 94. C Blackb St Jas *Blackb* from 93. *48 The Croft, Blackburn BB1 8DY* Blackburn (01254) 696546

LANE, George David Christopher. b 68. St Pet Coll Ox BA89. Cranmer Hall Dur DMinlStuds93. **d** 93 **p** 94. C Blackb St Jas *Blackb* from 93. *48 The Croft, Blackburn BB1 8DY* Blackburn (01254) 696546

LANE, Canon Gerald. b 29. Bede Coll Dur BA52. Sarum Th Coll 52. **d** 54 **p** 55. V Gillingham St Aug *Roch* 73-78; V Plumstead St Nic *S'wark* 78-73; V Hadlow *Roch* 78-94; Hon Can Roch Cathl 87-94; rtd 94; Perm to Offic *Roch* from 94. *1 Nursery Close, Sevenoaks, Kent TN13 3PR* Sevenoaks (01732) 450281

LANE, Canon Harold. b 09. MBE56. St Chad's Coll Dur BA33 LTh33 MA47. St Paul's Coll Burgh 27. **d** 33 **p** 35. Bahamas 67-80; rtd 80. *20 Mallard Way, Haxby, York YO3 3NG* York (01904) 763558

LANE, Iain Robert. b 61. CCC Ox BA83. Ripon Coll Cuddesdon BA86 MA88. **d** 87 **p** 88. C Rotherhithe St Mary w All SS *S'wark* 87-91; V Bierley *Bradf* from 91. *St John's Vicarage, Bierley Lane, Bierley, Bradford, W Yorkshire BD4 6AA* Bradford (01274) 681397

LANE, John Dormon. b 28. CEng67 MIMechE61 MIProdE61 MBIM75 FBPICS75 FAA77 FIIM81 FICM81 MIEE91 MIMfgE91 Lon Univ BScEng54. Local NSM Course. **d** 92 **p** 93. NSM Northill w Moggerhanger *St Alb* from 92. *11 Garner Close, Northill, Biggleswade, Beds SG18 9AF* Northill (01767) 627354 Fax Huntingdon (01480) 216319

LANE, John Ernest. b 39. OBE94. MBIM76 Cranfield Inst of Tech MSc80. Handsworth Coll Birm 58. **d** 80 **p** 80. In Meth Ch 62-80; Hon C Peckham St Jo w St Andr *S'wark* from 80; Dir St Mungo Housing Assn from 80. *24 Harcourt Road, London SE4 2AJ* 0181-692 9959 or 0171-286 1358

LANE, Mrs Linda Mary. b 41. ACIB66 Cam Univ DipRK70 Lon Univ BD87. Gilmore Ho 67. **dss** 82 **d** 87 **p** 94. Hadlow *Roch* 82-94; Hon Par Dn 87-94; Perm to Offic from 94. *1 Nursery Close, Sevenoaks, Kent TN13 3PR* Sevenoaks (01732) 450281

LANE, Martin John. b 69. Coll of Resurr Mirfield 92. **d** 95. C Liss *Portsm* from 95. *13 Woodbourne Close, Liss, Hants GU33 7BA* Liss (01730) 892764

LANE, Richard Peter. b 60. Linc Th Coll 85. **d** 88 **p** 89. C Towcester w Easton Neston *Pet* 88-91; Asst Chapl Oslo w Bergen, Trondheim, Stavanger etc *Eur* 91-93; V Writtle w

Highwood *Chelmsf* from 93. *The Vicarage, 19 Lodge Road, Writtle, Chelmsford CM1 3HY* Chelmsford (01245) 421282

LANE, Ms Rosalind Anne. b 69. Trevelyan Coll Dur BA91 Heythrop Coll Lon MTh93. Westcott Ho Cam CTM95. **d** 95. C Huddersfield St Pet and All SS *Wakef* from 95. *38 Clement Street, Huddersfield HD1 5HE* Huddersfield (01484) 534204

LANE, Roy Albert. b 42. Bris Sch of Min 82. **d** 85 **p** 86. NSM Bedminster *Bris* from 85. *20 Ashton Drive, Bristol BS3 2PW* Bristol (0117) 983 0747

LANE, Simon. *See* DOUGLAS LANE, Charles Simon Pellew

LANE, Stephen Toller. b 29. SS Coll Cam BA52 MA56. Lon Coll of Div ALCD54 LTh74. **d** 54 **p** 55. V Eccleston St Luke *Liv* 63-71; R Bradfield *Ox* 71-85; R Snettisham w Ingoldisthorpe and Fring *Nor* 85-94; rtd 94. *3 Meadow Road, Newbury, Berks RG14 7AH* Newbury (01635) 528257

LANE, William Michael. b 19. BNC Ox MA47. **d** 79 **p** 80. Asst Chapl Clifton Coll Bris 79-82; P-in-c Bris St Mich *Bris* 82-88; C 88-89; rtd 89; Perm to Offic *Bris* from 89. *8 Fremantle Square, Bristol BS6 5TL* Bristol (0117) 924 7925

LANG, Geoffrey Wilfrid Francis. b 33. St Jo Coll Ox BA56 MA61. Cuddesdon Coll 56. **d** 58 **p** 59. C Spalding *Linc* 58-61; Asst Chapl Leeds Univ *Ripon* 61-62; C Chesterton St Luke *Ely* 62-63; C-in-c Chesterton Gd Shep CD 63-69; V Chesterton Gd Shep 69-72; V Willian *St Alb* 72-76; Dioc Dir of Educn 72-76; R N Lynn w St Marg and St Nic *Nor* 77-86; V Hammersmith St Pet *Lon* from 86. *17 Ravenscourt Road, London W6 0UH* 0181-748 1781 or 741 4848 Fax 748 6610

LANG, Very Rev Dr John Harley. b 27. LRAM Em Coll Cam MA60 K Coll Lon AKC49 BD60 Keele Univ DLitt88. St Boniface Warminster 49. **d** 52 **p** 53. Hd of Relig Progr BBC Radio 67-71; Hd Relig Broadcasting BBC 71-80; C Sacombe *St Alb* 73-80; Chapl to The Queen 77-80; Dean Lich 80-93; rtd 93. *South Barn, Stanway Road, Stanton, Broadway, Worcs WR12 7NQ* Stanton (0138673) 251

LANG, William David. b 51. K Coll Lon BD74 AKC74. St Aug Coll Cant 74. **d** 75 **p** 76. C Fleet *Guildf* 75-79; C Ewell St Fran 79-82; C W Ewell 79-82; V Holmwood 82-92; R Elstead from 92; V Thursley from 92. *The Rectory, Thursley Road, Elstead, Godalming, Surrey GU8 6DG* Elstead (01252) 703251

LANGAN, Mrs Eleanor Susan. b 56. Homerton Coll Cam BEd78. Ripon Coll Cuddesdon 84. **d** 87 **p** 94. Hon Par Dn Grays Thurrock *Chelmsf* 87-89; Lic to Offic 89-94; NSM Creeksea w Althorne, Latchingdon and N Fambridge from 94. *The Vicarage, 18 Victoria Road, South Woodham Ferrers, Chelmsford CM3 5LR* Chelmsford (01245) 320201

LANGAN, Michael Leslie. b 54. Cam Univ BA PGCE. Cranmer Hall Dur. **d** 84 **p** 85. C Grays Thurrock *Chelmsf* 84-89; V Creeksea w Althorne, Latchingdon and N Fambridge 89-95; RD Maldon and Dengie 92-95; P-in-c S Woodham Ferrers from 95. *The Vicarage, 18 Victoria Road, South Woodham Ferrers, Chelmsford CM3 5LR* Chelmsford (01245) 320201

LANGDON, John Bonsall. b 21. Linc Coll Ox BA51 MA55. Ripon Hall Ox 52. **d** 54 **p** 55. R Swillington *Ripon* 63-75; P-in-c Wrangthorn 75-76; V Leeds All Hallows w St Simon 75-76; V Leeds All Hallows w Wrangthorn 76-87; P-in-c Woodhouse St Mark 85-87; V Woodhouse and Wrangthorn 87-92; rtd 92. *32 Magdalene Road, Ripon, N Yorkshire HG4 1HT* Ripon (01765) 606814

LANGDON, Canon William Ancell Martin. b 14. Selw Coll Cam BA36 MA41. Wells Th Coll 36. **d** 38 **p** 39. V Charminster *Sarum* 69-81; rtd 81. *32B Burlington Road, Swanage, Dorset BH19 1LT* Swanage (01929) 424167

LANGFORD, David Laurence. b 51. Local NSM Course 86. **d** 88 **p** 89. NSM Scotton w Northorpe *Linc* from 88. *1 Westgate, Scotton, Gainsborough, Lincs DN21 3QX* Scunthorpe (01724) 763139

LANGFORD, Prof Michael John. b 31. New Coll Ox BA54 MA58 Cam Univ MA59 Lon Univ PhD66. Westcott Ho Cam 55. **d** 56 **p** 57. C Bris St Nath w St Kath *Bris* 56-59; Chapl Qu Coll Cam 59-63; C Hampstead St Jo *Lon* 63-67; Canada from 67; Prof Philosophy Newfoundland Univ from 82; Prof Medical Ethics from 87. *8 Dartmouth Place, St John's, Newfoundland, Canada, A1B 2W2* St John's (709) 739-5746

LANGFORD, Peter Francis. b 54. Sarum & Wells Th Coll 76. **d** 79 **p** 80. C N Ormesby *York* 79-82; Ind Chapl 83-91; V Middlesb St Chad from 91. *St Chad's Vicarage, 9 Emerson Avenue, Linthorpe, Middlesbrough, Cleveland TS5 7QW* Middlesbrough (01642) 819854

LANGFORD, Peter Julian. b 33. Selw Coll Cam BA58. Westcott Ho Cam 59. **d** 60 **p** 61. C E Ham St Mary *Chelmsf* 60-67; Hon C 67-71; Hon C Beccles St Mich *St E* 71-76; Warden Ringsfield Hall Suffolk 71-87; P-in-c Ringsfield w Redisham *St E* 76-80; TV Seacroft *Ripon* from 87. *St Richard's Vicarage, Ramshead Hill, Leeds LS14 1BX* Leeds (0113) 265 6388

LANGHAM, John Godfrey. b 22. Lon Univ DipTh60. Oak Hill Th Coll. **d** 60 **p** 61. V Burton in Kendal *Carl* 63-79; rtd 79;

Perm to Offic *Ex* from 80. *61 Holmdale, Sidmouth, Devon EX10 8DN* Sidmouth (01395) 516417

LANGHAM, Paul Jonathan. b 60. Ex Univ BA81 DipTh83 Fitzw Coll Cam BA86 MA91. Ridley Hall Cam 84. **d** 87 **p** 88. C Bath Weston All SS w N Stoke *B & W* 87-91; Chapl and Fell St Cath Coll Cam from 91. *St Catharine's College, Cambridge CB2 1RL* Cambridge (01223) 338346

LANGLEY, Canon Dr Myrtle Sarah. b 39. FRAI TCD BA61 HDipEd62 MA67 Bris Univ PhD76 Lon Univ BD66. Dalton Ho Bris 64. **d** 88 **p** 94. Dir Chr Development for Miss *Liv* 87-89; Dir of Tr Inst *Carl* from 90; Dioc Dir of Tr from 90; Hon Can Carl Cathl from 91. *92 Greenacres, Wetheral, Carlisle CA4 8LD* Wetheral (01228) 561478 or 22573 Fax 48769

LANGLEY, Canon Robert (Bob). b 37. St Cath Soc Ox BA61. Steph Ho Ox. **d** 63 **p** 64. C Aston cum Aughton *Sheff* 63-68; Midl Area Sec Chr Educn Movement 68-71; HQ Sec Chr Educn Movement 71-74; Prin Ian Ramsey Coll Brasted 74-77; Dir St Alb Minl Tr Scheme 77-85; Can Res St Alb 77-85; Can Res Newc Cathl *Newc* from 85. *16 Towers Avenue, Jesmond, Newcastle upon Tyne NE2 3QE* 0191-281 0714

LANGMAN, Barry Edward. b 46. Master Mariner 73. Cant Sch of Min 87. **d** 90 **p** 91. NSM St Margarets-at-Cliffe w Westcliffe etc *Cant* 90-92; C Sandgate St Paul 92; C Sandgate St Paul w Folkestone St Geo from 92. *The Vicarage, 10 Meadowbrook, Sandgate, Folkestone, Kent CT20 3NY* Folkestone (01303) 248675

✠**LANGRISH, Rt Rev Michael Laurence.** b 46. Birm Univ BSocSc67 Fitzw Coll Cam BA73 MA77. Ridley Hall Cam 71. **d** 73 **p** 74 **c** 93. C Stratford-on-Avon w Bishopton *Cov* 73-76; Chapl Rugby Sch Warks 76-81; P-in-c Offchurch *Cov* 81-87; Dioc Dir of Ords 81-87; P-in-c Rugby St Andr 87-91; Hon Can Cov Cathl 90-93; TR Rugby St Andr 91-93; Suff Bp Birkenhead *Ches* from 93. *Bishop's House, 67 Bidston Road, Birkenhead, Merseyside L34 6TA* 0151-652 2741 Fax 651 2330

LANGSTAFF, James Henry. b 56. St Cath Coll Ox BA77 MA81 Nottm Univ BA80. St Jo Coll Nottm 78. **d** 81 **p** 82. C Farnborough *Guildf* 81-84; P-in-c 84-85; C 85-86; P-in-c Duddeston *Birm* 86; P-in-c Duddeston w Nechells 86; V from 87; RD Birm City from 95. *St Matthew's Vicarage, Duddeston Manor Road, Birmingham B7 4QD* 0121-359 6965

LANGSTON, Clinton Matthew. b 62. Derby Coll of Educn BCombStuds86. Qu Coll Birm 87. **d** 90 **p** 91. C Shirley *Birm* 90-94; CF from 94. *c/o MOD (Army), Bagshot Park, Bagshot, Surrey GU19 5PL* Bagshot (01276) 71717 Fax 412834

LANGTON, Canon Kenneth. b 26. Open Univ BA76. St Aid Birkenhead 52. **d** 55 **p** 56. V Stalybridge *Man* 69-71; R Radcliffe St Mary 71-83; Hon Can Man Cathl 80-91; V Tyldesley w Shakerley 83-91; rtd 91. *889 Walmersley Road, Bury, Lancs BL9 5LE* 0161-764 1552

LANGTON, Canon Maurice Charles. b 09. Trin Coll Cam BA30 MA34. Sarum Th Coll 33. **d** 34 **p** 35. Dir RE and Tr of Ord Cand *Chich* 56-77; Can and Preb Chich Cathl 63-77; rtd 77. *3 Caithness Road, Stamford, Lincs PE9 2TE* Stamford (01780) 51004

LANHAM, Geoffrey Peter. b 62. Cam Univ MA84 Ox Univ MPhil86. Wycliffe Hall Ox 86. **d** 89 **p** 90. C Southborough St Pet w Ch Ch and St Matt *Roch* 89-92; C Harborne Heath *Birm* from 92. *33 Margaret Road, Birmingham B17 0EU*

LANHAM, Richard Paul White. b 42. Dur Univ BA64. Wycliffe Hall Ox 65. **d** 67 **p** 68. C Horwich H Trin *Man* 69-72; V Worsley 72-74; V Accrington St Andr *Blackb* 74-80; V Shillington *St Alb* 80-85; V Upper w Lower Gravenhurst 80-85; rtd 85; Perm to Offic *St Alb* from 85. *10 Alexander Close, Clifton, Shefford, Beds SG17 5RB* Hitchin (01462) 813520

LANKEY, David. b 41. MBCS68 CEng88 Southn Univ BSc62. S'wark Ord Course 79. **d** 82 **p** 83. NSM W Wimbledon Ch Ch *S'wark* 82-92; C Tooting All SS 92-95; R Long Ditton from 95. *The Rectory, 67 St Mary's Road, Surbiton, Surrey KT6 5HB* 0181-398 1583

LANSDALE, Charles Roderick. b 38. Leeds Univ BA59. Coll of Resurr Mirfield 59. **d** 61 **p** 62. C Nunhead St Antony *S'wark* 61-65; Swaziland 65-71; V Benhilton *S'wark* 72-78; TR Catford (Southend) and Downham 78-87; TR Moulsecoomb *Chich* from 87. *St Andrew's Rectory, Hillside, Brighton BN2 4TA* Brighton (01273) 680680

LANSLEY, Paul Sanford. b 33. Trin Coll Cam BA56 MA61. St Steph Ho Ox 56. **d** 58 **p** 59. C N Acton St Gabr *Lon* 58-60; Hon C Colchester St Jas, All SS, St Nic and St Runwald *Chelmsf* from 69; Asst Chapl Colchester Hosps from 86. *31A King Coel Road, Colchester CO3 5AQ* Colchester (01206) 562813

LANTSBERY, Colin. b 39. Chich Th Coll 70. **d** 72 **p** 73. C Wednesfield St Thos *Lich* 72-75; C W Bromwich All SS 75-77; V Normacot 77-84; V Longton St Mary and St Chad 84-94. *18 Riverside View, Truro, Cornwall TR1 1UZ* Truro (01872) 70155

LANYON JONES, Keith. b 49. Southn Univ BTh79. Sarum & Wells Th Coll 74. **d** 77 **p** 78. C Charlton Kings St Mary *Glouc* 77-81; Sen Chapl Rugby Sch Warks from 81; Lic to Offic *Truro* from 83. *11 Horton Crescent, Rugby, Warks CV22 5DJ* Rugby (01788) 544939

LAPAGE, Michael Clement. b 23. Selw Coll Cam BA47 MA73. Clifton Th Coll 60. **d** 61 **p** 62. Kenya 61-72; Chapl Bedf Sch 73-75; Chapl Lyon w Grenoble *Eur* 76-79; V Walford w Bishopswood *Heref* 79-88; P-in-c Goodrich w Welsh Bicknor and Marstow 83-88; rtd 88; Perm to Offic *Ex* from 88. *Moorlands, 20 Watts Road, Tavistock, Devon PL19 8LG* Tavistock (01822) 615901

LAPAGE, Canon Peter Reginald. b 17. MC45. Selw Coll Cam BA41 MA44. Ridley Hall Cam 46. **d** 48 **p** 49. Area Sec (Dios Lon and S'wark) CMS 66-82; rtd 82; Perm to Offic *S'wark* 82-94. *37A Trinity Road, London SW19 8QS* 0181-542 9737

LAPHAM, Canon Fred. b 31. Univ of Wales (Lamp) BA53. Vancouver Sch of Th LTh55 BD58. **d** 55 **p** 55. V Over St Jo *Ches* 62-70; V Upton Ascension 70-82; R Grappenhall 82-91; RD Gt Budworth 85-91; Hon Can Ches Cathl 88-91; rtd 91. *1 Coppice Gate, Lyth Hill, Shrewsbury SY3 0BT* Shrewsbury (01743) 722284

LAPWOOD, Robin Rowland John. b 57. Selw Coll Cam MA. Ridley Hall Cam 80. **d** 82 **p** 83. C Bury St Edmunds St Mary *St E* 82-86; P-in-c Bentley w Tattingstone 86-93; P-in-c Copdock w Washbrook and Belstead 86-93; TV High Wycombe *Ox* from 93. *15 The Brackens, High Wycombe, Bucks HP11 1EB* High Wycombe (01494) 531628

LARGE, Preb Denis Henry. b 18. Sarum Th Coll 39. **d** 42 **p** 43. R Clyst St Mary *Ex* 61-75; R Clyst St George 61-75; Adv Chr Stewardship 64-81; V Woodbury Salterton 67-75; V Rockbeare 67-75; R Aylesbeare and Farringdon 67-75; R Clyst Honiton 67-75; R Sowton 67-75; RD Aylesbeare 73-76; TR Clyst St George, Aylesbeare, Clyst Honiton etc 75-83; rtd 83; Perm to Offic *Ex* from 83. *30 Higher Shapter Street, Topsham, Devon EX3 0AW* Topsham (01392) 873295

LARGE, William Roy. b 40. Dur Univ BA DipEd. Edin Th Coll 82. **d** 84 **p** 85. C Leamington Priors All SS *Cov* 84-88; V Bishop's Tachbrook from 88; Warden of Readers and Sen Tutor from 88. *The Vicarage, 24 Mallory Road, Bishop's Tachbrook, Leamington Spa, Warks CV33 9QX* Leamington Spa (01926) 426922

LARK, William Donald Starling. b 35. Keble Coll Ox BA59 MA63. Wells Th Coll 59. **d** 61 **p** 62. C Wyken *Cov* 61-64; C Christchurch *Win* 64-66; V Yeovil St Mich *B & W* 66-75; C Earley St Pet *Ox* 75-85; V Prittlewell *Chelmsf* 85-88; V Dawlish *Ex* from 88. *The Vicarage, 13 West Cliff Road, Dawlish, Devon EX7 9EB* Dawlish (01626) 862204

LARKIN, Peter John. b 39. ALCD62. **d** 62 **p** 63. C Liskeard w St Keyne *Truro* 62-65; C Rugby St Andr *Cov* 65-67; Sec Bp Cov Call to Miss 67-68; V Kea *Truro* 68-78; P-in-c Bromsgrove St Jo *Worc* 78-81; R Torquay St Matthias, St Mark and H Trin *Ex* from 81; Can Sokoto Nigeria from 91. *The Rectory, Wellswood Avenue, Torquay TQ1 2QE* Torquay (01803) 293280

LARKINS, Mary Herve. b 14. IDC. Coll of Ascension 39. **dss** 46 **d** 87. Gt Ayton w Easby and Newton in Cleveland *York* 46-73; rtd 74; Perm to Offic *Guildf* 76-86; Perm to Offic *Glouc* from 87. *25 Capel Court, The Burgage, Prestbury, Cheltenham, Glos GL52 3EL* Cheltenham (01242) 576460

LARNER, Gordon Edward Stanley. b 30. Brasted Th Coll 54 Oak Hill Th Coll 55. **d** 59 **p** 60. V Lower Sydenham St Mich *S'wark* 68-73; Ind Chapl 73-84; Lic to Offic *S'well* 84-92; Chapl HM Pris Ranby 84-92; rtd 92. *29 Brook Street, Chipping Sodbury, Bristol BS17 6AZ*

LARSEN, Clive Erik. b 55. St Jo Coll Nottm LTh90. **d** 90 **p** 91. C Weaverham *Ches* 90-92; C Helsby and Dunham-on-the-Hill from 92. *The Vicarage, 47 Arden Lea, Warrington WA6 9EQ* Warrington (01925) 722012

LARTER, John William. b 29. Lon Univ BSc51. Coll of Resurr Mirfield. **d** 54 **p** 55. R Middleton Stoney *Ox* 65-70; R Bucknell 69-70; V N Hinksey 70-77; V Eye w Braiseworth and Yaxley *St E* 77-84; RD Hartismere 78-81; P-in-c Occold w Redlingfield 80-84; V Hunstanton St Edm w Ringstead *Nor* 84-91; V Wormingford, Mt Bures and Lt Horkesley *Chelmsf* 91-94; rtd 94; Perm to Offic *Nor* from 94; Perm to Offic *S'well* from 94; Perm to Offic *St E* from 95. *16 Highfield, Eye, Suffolk IP23 7BP*

LASHBROOKE, David. b 60. Ex Univ BA87. Ripon Coll Cuddesdon 90. **d** 92 **p** 93. C Sherborne w Castleton and Lillington *Sarum* from 92. *4 Askwith Close, Sherborne, Dorset DT9 6DX* Sherborne (01935) 815043

LASHBROOKE, John. b 28. Kelham Th Coll 49. **d** 53 **p** 54. R Corby Epiphany w St Jo *Pet* 69-80; V Rubery *Birm* 80-88; V Horam *Chich* 88-93; rtd 93; Perm to Offic *Ex* from 94. *Applegarth, Longmeadow Road, Lympstone, Exmouth, Devon EX8 5LF* Exmouth (01395) 268594

LASKEY, Cyril Edward. b 44. RMN71 RGN74. Llan Dioc Tr Scheme 85. **d** 88 **p** 89. NSM Troedrhiwgarth *Llan* 88-93; NSM Caerau St Cynfelin from 94. *207 Bridgend Road, Maesteg, M Glam CF34 0NL* Maesteg (01656) 734639

LAST, Eric Cyril. b 30. Oak Hill Th Coll 77. **d** 79 **p** 80. C Wandsworth All SS *S'wark* 79-83; V Earlsfield St Andr 83-88; V S Merstham from 88; Asst RD Reigate from 92. *The Vicarage, Battlebridge Lane, South Merstham, Redhill RH1 3LH* Merstham (01737) 642722

LAST, Harold Wilfred. b 17. ARCM52 ARCO53 CCC Cam BA38 MA42. Linc Th Coll 39. **d** 40 **p** 41. Dir of Music St Bees, St Olave's & Felstead Schs 53-73; rtd 73. *81 Dales View Road, Ipswich IP1 4HJ* Ipswich (01473) 745135

LAST, Michael Leonard Eric. b 60. St Jo Coll Nottm DipThMin94. **d** 94 **p** 95. C Tettenhall Wood *Lich* from 94. *283 Henwood Road, Wolverhampton WV6 8PU* Wolverhampton (01902) 746481

LAST, Norman Percy George. b 31. BA CertEd ATPL. Sarum & Wells Th Coll 77 Wycliffe Hall Ox 80. **d** 81 **p** 82. C Walton-on-Thames *Guildf* 81-83; C Farnham 83-87; R Monks Eleigh w Chelsworth and Brent Eleigh etc *St E* 87-90; P-in-c Bradworthy *Ex* from 91. *Lashbrook, Thornbury, Holsworthy, Devon EX22 7BA* Holsworthy (01409) 281287

LATHAM, Christine Elizabeth. b 46. S'wark Ord Course 87. **d** 90 **p** 94. Par Dn Battersea St Pet and St Paul *S'wark* 90-94; Par Dn S'wark Ch Ch 94; C from 94. *30A Dolben Street, London SE1 0UQ* 0171-620 1374

LATHAM, Henry Nicholas Lomax (Harry). b 64. Reading Univ BA86. Wycliffe Hall Ox BTh93. **d** 93 **p** 94. C Abth *St D* from 93. *Ael-y-Bryn, 25 High Street, Aberystwyth, Dyfed SY23 1JG* Aberystwyth (01970) 624537

LATHAM, John Westwood. b 31. Ely Th Coll 57. **d** 60 **p** 61. C Cleckheaton St Jo *Wakef* 60-63; C Hemel Hempstead *St Alb* 63-65; C Wakef Cathl *Wakef* 65-67; V Outwood 67-72; TV Daventry w Norton *Pet* 72-79; V Flore w Dodford and Brockhall from 79. *The Vicarage, Flore, Northampton NN7 4LZ* Weedon (01327) 340510

LATHAM, Robert Norman. b 53. Qu Coll Birm 82. **d** 85 **p** 86. C Tamworth *Lich* 85-89; TV Wordsley 89-93; TV Wordsley *Worc* from 93. *25 Middleway Avenue, Wordsley, Stourbridge, W Midlands DY8 5NH* Kingswinford (01384) 293350

LATHAM, Trevor Martin. b 56. BD84. Ripon Coll Cuddesdon 84. **d** 86 **p** 87. C Cantril Farm *Liv* 86-89; TV W Derby St Mary from 89. *The Vicarage, 1 Sandicroft Road, Liverpool L12 0LX* 0151-549 2202

LATHE, Canon Anthony Charles Hudson. b 36. Jes Coll Ox BA59 MA64 UEA DipSoc68. Lich Th Coll 59. **d** 61 **p** 62. C Selby Abbey *York* 61-63; V Hempnall *Nor* 63-72; R Woodton w Bedingham 63-72; R Fritton w Morningthorpe w Shelton and Hardwick 63-72; R Topcroft 63-72; R Banham 72-76; TR Quidenham 76-83; P-in-c New Buckenham 78-79; V Heigham St Thos 83-94; Hon Can Nor Cathl from 87; RD Nor S 90-94; P-in-c Sheringham from 94. *The Vicarage, 10 North Street, Sheringham, Norfolk NR26 8LW* Sheringham (01263) 822089

LATTIMORE, Anthony Leigh. b 35. Dur Univ BA57. Lich Th Coll 60. **d** 62 **p** 63. C Aylestone *Leic* 62-66; C-in-c Eyres Monsell CD 66-69; V Eyres Monsell 69-73; V Somerby, Burrough on the Hill and Pickwell 73-86; RD Goscote I 80-86; R Glenfield from 86. *The Rectory, Main Street, Glenfield, Leicester LE3 8DG* Leicester (0116) 287 1604

LAUGHTON, Derek Basil. b 24. Worc Coll Ox BA49 MA52. Westcott Ho Cam 49. **d** 51 **p** 52. Chapl Wellington Sch Somerset 64-73; Chapl Ardingly Coll Haywards Heath 73-77; R Plumpton w E Chiltington *Chich* 77-88; Perm to Offic *B & W* from 88; rtd 89. *13 Pyles Thorne Road, Wellington, Somerset TA21 8DX* Wellington (01823) 667386

LAURENCE, Ven John Harvard Christopher. b 29. Trin Hall Cam BA53 MA57. Westcott Ho Cam 53. **d** 55 **p** 56. V Crosby *Linc* 59-74; Can and Preb Linc Cathl 74-79 and 85-94; Dioc Missr 74-79; Bp's Dir of Clergy Tr *Lon* 80-85; Adn Lindsey *Linc* 85-94; rtd 94. *5 Haffenden Road, Lincoln LN2 1RP* Lincoln (01522) 531444

LAURENCE, Julian Bernard Vere. b 60. Kent Univ BA82. St Steph Ho Ox 86. **d** 88 **p** 89. C Yeovil St Mich *B & W* 88-91; Chapl Yeovil Coll from 90; Chapl Yeovil Distr Gen Hosp from 91; P-in-c Barwick *B & W* 91-94; V Taunton H Trin from 94. *Holy Trinity Vicarage, 18 Holway Avenue, Taunton, Somerset TA1 3AR* Taunton (01823) 337890

LAURENCE, Vere Deacon. b 11. Ex Coll Ox BA33 BSc34 MA37. Sarum Th Coll 34. **d** 36 **p** 37. V Upper Sunbury St Sav *Lon* 53-74; R Jacobstow w Warbstow and Treneglos *Truro*

74-83; RD Stratton 77-83; rtd 83; Perm to Offic *B & W* from 85. *12 Westbrook Road, Weston-super-Mare, Avon BS22 8JU* Weston-super-Mare (01934) 415143

LAURENCE, William Gregory (Bill). b 10. St Andr Whittlesford 40. **d** 40 **p** 41. R Aynho *Pet* 65-74; V Newbottle 65-74; rtd 74. *Flat 14, Ellesborough Manor, Butlers Cross, Aylesbury, Bucks HP17 0XF* Aylesbury (01296) 696466

LAURIE, Donovan Hugh (Don). b 40. Man Univ MSc. Oak Hill NSM Course. **d** 82 **p** 83. NSM Cudham and Downe *Roch* 82-84; C Tunbridge Wells St Jas 84-88; P-in-c Ventnor St Cath *Portsm* from 88; P-in-c Ventnor H Trin from 88. *The Vicarage, Park Avenue, Ventnor, Isle of Wight PO38 1LD* Isle of Wight (01983) 852130

LAURIE, James Andrew Stewart (Jim). b 26. Selw Coll Cam BA51 MA55. Ridley Hall Cam 51. **d** 53 **p** 54. P-in-c Ilam w Blore Ray and Okeover *Lich* 65-71; V Wetton 65-71; V Alstonfield 65-71; P-in-c Calton 66-71; V Charsfield w Debach and Monewden w Hoo *St E* 83-86; V Charsfield w Debach, Monewden, Hoo etc 86-90; rtd 90. *Richmond Grove, Birds Green, Bury St Edmunds, Suffolk IP30 0RT* Rattlesden (01449) 736165

LAUT, Graham Peter. b 37. Chich Th Coll 63. **d** 67 **p** 68. C Corringham *Chelmsf* 67-68; C Leytonstone St Marg w St Columba 68-71; P-in-c Leytonstone St Andr 71-75; V 75-80; V Romford Ascension Collier Row from 80. *The Ascension Vicarage, 68 Collier Row Road, Romford RM5 2BA* Romford (01708) 741658

LAVENDER, Cyril Norman. b 01. St Aug Coll Cant 32. **d** 35 **p** 35. V Warham w Wighton *Nor* 60-69; rtd 69; P-in-c Nor St Helen *Nor* 74-84; Perm to Offic from 84. *18 Elaine Herbert House, The Great Hospital, Norwich NR1 4EL* Norwich (01603) 622022

LAVERACK, John Julian. b 51. Keele Univ BA CertEd Bris Univ BA. Bris Bapt Coll 76 Ex & Truro NSM Scheme 81. **d** 82 **p** 83. In Bapt Ch 79-81; C Braunton *Ex* 82-84; V Ex St Mark 84-92; Perm to Offic from 92. *4 Coronation Terrace, Starcross, Exeter EX6 8QA*

LAVERTY, Walter Joseph Robert. b 49. CITC 70 Glouc Th Course 73. **d** 73 **p** 74. C Belf St Donard *D & D* 73-77; C Ballymacarrett St Patr 77-82; I Kilwarlin Upper w Kilwarlin Lower 82-86; I Orangefield w Moneyreagh from 86; RD Dundonald from 91. *397 Castlereagh Road, Belfast BT5 6AB* Belfast (01232) 704493

LAVERY, Edward Robinson. Lon Univ BA DipTh. St Aid Birkenhead 65. **d** 67 **p** 68. C Belf Trin Coll Miss *Conn* 67-69; C Belf St Mary Magd 69-71; CF (TA) from 70; I Belf St Phil *Conn* 71-74; I Craigs w Dunaghy and Killagan 74-83; I Ballymoney w Finvoy and Rasharkin from 83; Dioc Info Officer from 83; RD Coleraine from 94. *The Rectory, Queen Street, Ballymoney, Co Antrim BT53 6JA* Ballymoney (012656) 62149

LAVERY, Leonard. b 06. St Aid Birkenhead 49. **d** 50 **p** 51. V Kenwyn St Jo *Truro* 64-73; rtd 73. *Glan-Mor, Falmouth Road, Truro, Cornwall TR1 2BL* Truro (01872) 72895

LAVILLE, Jocelyn Roger. b 30. Ball Coll Ox BA53 MA62. St Jo Coll Lon ALCD64. **d** 64 **p** 65. C Gillingham St Mark *Roch* 64-69; C Thorpe Edge *Bradf* 69-72; The Philippines from 72. *PO Box 464, Manila, The Philippines 1502* Manila (2) 722-2764

LAW, Andrew Philip. b 61. BNC Ox BA83 MA93 G&C Coll Cam PGCE86. W of England Minl Tr Course 90. **d** 93 **p** 94. C Tupsley w Hampton Bishop *Heref* from 93; Chapl Hereford Sixth Form Coll from 93. *4 Kentchurch Close, Hereford HR1 1QS* Hereford (01432) 267651

LAW, Bryan. b 36. Leeds Univ BA59 Lon Univ BD76. Coll of Resurr Mirfield 59. **d** 61 **p** 62. C Winshill *Derby* 61-64; R Gorton St Phil *Man* 64-70; Lic to Offic 70-71; Perm to Offic *Ox* from 71; Hd Master Page Hill Co Middle Sch Buckm from 81. *35 Little Meadow, Loughton, Milton Keynes MK5 8EH* Milton Keynes (01908) 661333

LAW, Canon Donald Edward Boughton. b 22. Lon Coll of Div 67. **d** 69 **p** 70. C Leic H Apostles *Leic* 69-73; V Cosby 73-81; RD Guthlaxton I (Blaby) 75-81; V Melton Mowbray w Thorpe Arnold 81-86; Hon Can Leic Cathl 81-88; RD Framland II 84-88; TR Melton Gt Framland 86-88; rtd 88; Perm to Offic *Pet* from 88. *36 Mill Grove, Whissendine, Oakham, Leics LE15 7EY* Whissendine (0166479) 411

LAW, Gordon James. b 19. Worc Ord Coll 67. **d** 69 **p** 70. C Hillingdon St Jo *Lon* 69-72; C Brixham *Ex* 72-76; R Drewsteignton 76-79; V Hittisleigh 76-79; V Spreyton 76-79; C Aldershot St Mich *Guildf* 79-82; rtd 82; Perm to Offic *Ex* 83-89; Perm to Offic *Ab* from 83. *69 Maunsell Way, Wroughton, Swindon SN4 9JF* Swindon (01793) 812948

LAW, Gordon Peter. b 35. Bernard Gilpin Soc Dur 59 Chich Th Coll 60. **d** 64 **p** 65. C Walthamstow St Barn and St Jas Gt *Chelmsf* 64-67; C Southchurch H Trin 67-68; C Plaistow St

Andr 68-69; Chapl Aldersbrook Medical Unit 69-83; P-in-c Forest Gate All SS 69-74; V 74-83; V Romford St Jo from 83. *St John's Vicarage, Mawney Road, Romford RM7 7BH* Romford (01708) 742265

LAW, Herbert James Wentworth. b 12. Dur Univ BA39 DipTh39 MA42. **d** 40 **p** 41. V Barton *Ely* 69-78; rtd 78. *37 Westlands, Comberton, Cambridge CB3 7EH* Cambridge (01223) 263406

LAW, Jeremy Thomson. b 61. Univ of Wales (Abth) BSc82 Southn Univ BTh89. Sarum & Wells Th Coll 84. **d** 87 **p** 88. C Wimborne Minster and Holt *Sarum* 87-90; C Highfield *Ox* 90-94; Chapl Ex Univ *Ex* from 94. *University of Exeter, Theology Department, Queens Building, Queens Drive, Exeter EX4 4QE* Exeter (01392) 264240 or 435384   Fax 264377

LAW, Jim. b 20. Lon Coll of Div 49. **d** 52 **p** 53. V Gt Singleton *Blackb* 61-87; rtd 87; Perm to Offic *Blackb* from 87. *30 Cedar Avenue, Poulton-le-Fylde, Lancs FY6 8DQ* Poulton-le-Fylde (01253) 886188

LAW, John Michael. b 43. Open Univ BA79. Westcott Ho Cam 65. **d** 68 **p** 69. C Chapel Allerton *Ripon* 68-72; C Ryhope *Dur* 72-73; Lic to Offic *Ely* from 74; Chapl Fulbourn Hosp Cam from 74; Chapl Ida Darw Hosp Cam from 74; Mental Health Fell Bethlem R & Maudsley Hosps from 82. *Fulbourn Hospital, Fulbourn, Cambridge CB1 5EF, or 1 The Maples, Fulbourn, Cambridge CB1 5DW* Cambridge (01223) 218598 or 248074

LAW, John Francis. b 35. Bps' Coll Cheshunt 65. **d** 67 **p** 68. C Styvechale *Cov* 67-71; P-in-c Cov St Anne and All SS 71-73; TV Cov E 73-77; P-in-c Fillongley 77-82; P-in-c Corley 77-82; V Fillongley and Corley from 82; RD Nuneaton from 90. *The Vicarage, Holbeche Crescent, Fillongley, Coventry CV7 8ES* Fillongley (01676) 40320

LAW, Kenneth. b 16. St Jo Coll Dur LTh39 BA40 MA43. St Aid Birkenhead 36. **d** 40 **p** 41. V Ossett cum Gawthorpe *Wakef* 54-81; CF (TA) 64-81; rtd 81; Perm to Offic *Wakef* from 81. *Heathdene, Cromwell Place, Ossett, W Yorkshire WF5 9LP* Wakefield (01924) 262740

LAW, Nicholas Charles. b 58. BA89. Trin Coll Bris 86. **d** 89 **p** 90. C Goldington *St Alb* 89-92; C Teignmouth, Ideford w Luton, Ashcombe etc *Ex* from 92. *51 Higher Coombe Drive, Teignmouth, Devon TQ14 9LR* Teignmouth (01626) 776607

LAW, Peter James. b 46. Ridley Hall Cam 85. **d** 87 **p** 88. C Bournemouth St Jo w St Mich *Win* 87-91; V Chineham from 91; Min Chineham LEP from 91. *The Vicarage, 1 Hartswood, Chineham, Basingstoke, Hants RG24 8SJ* Basingstoke (01256) 474280

LAW, Peter Leslie. b 25. Bede Coll Dur BA48 DipEd49. Qu Coll Birm 53. **d** 55 **p** 56. Chapl St Luke's Sch Southsea 69-79; Chapl Portsm Cathl *Portsm* 69-79; V Eastney 79-90; rtd 90; Perm to Offic *Portsm* from 90. *123 Hayling Avenue, Portsmouth PO3 6DY* Portsmouth (01705) 619913

LAW, Richard Lindsay. b 34. Univ Coll Ox BA58 MA63 St Pet Coll Birm GradDipEd70. Cuddesdon Coll 58. **d** 60 **p** 61. C Leighton Buzzard *St Alb* 60-63; Trinidad and Tobago 63-67; V Stottesdon *Heref* 67-72; P-in-c Farlow 67-72; Chapl Framlingham Coll Suffolk 72-83; V Leigh-on-Sea St Marg *Chelmsf* 83-91; Warden Framlingham Ho of Prayer and Retreat from 91. *Niggles House, Broadwater, Framlingham, Woodbridge, Suffolk IP13 9LS* Framlingham (01728) 723800

LAW, Robert Frederick. b 43. St Aid Birkenhead 67. **d** 69 **p** 70. C Bengeo *St Alb* 69-72; C Sandy 72-76; P-in-c St Ippolyts 76-81; Chapl Jersey Gp of Hosps 81-84; V Crowan w Godolphin *Truro* 84-92; RD Kerrier 90-91; R St Columb Major w St Wenn from 92. *The Rectory, St Columb, Cornwall TR9 6AE* St Columb (01637) 880252

LAW, Dr Robert James. b 31. Lon Univ MB, BS55. Ridley Hall Cam 62. **d** 64 **p** 65. C Barnehurst *Roch* 64-66; C Edgware *Lon* 66-72; V Halwell w Moreleigh *Ex* 72-94; P-in-c Woodleigh and Loddiswell 79-94; R 79-94. *38 Wheatlands Road, Paignton, Devon TQ4 5HU* Paignton (01803) 559450

LAW, Timothy Robert Kelway. b 63. Peterho Cam BA85 Hughes Hall Cam PGCE88 St Jo Coll Dur MA95. Cranmer Hall Dur DMS95. **d** 95. C Oswestry *Lich* from 95; C Rhydycroesau from 95. *5 High Lea Close, Oswestry, Shropshire SY11 1SX* Oswestry (01691) 662125

LAW-JONES, Peter Deniston. b 55. Newc Univ BA77 Man Univ CertEd81 Nottm Univ BTh87. Linc Th Coll 84. **d** 87 **p** 88. C Chorley St Laur *Blackb* 87-91; V Fenscliffe from 91. *The Vicarage, St Francis Road, Fenscliffe, Blackburn BB2 2TZ* Blackburn (01254) 201757

LAWES, David Alan. b 33. Lon Bible Coll BD57 PGCE58 AcDipEd66 Lon Inst of Educn MA70. Cranmer Hall Dur 90. **d** 91 **p** 92. NSM Shaston *Sarum* 91-94; Hon C Diptford, N Huish, Harberton and Harbertonford *Ex* from 94. *The Vicarage, Harberton, Totnes, Devon TQ9 7SA* Totnes (01803) 867117

LAWES, Geoffrey Hyland. b 37. St Jo Coll Dur BA58 DipTh62 Hertf Coll Ox BA60 MA64 Newc Univ PGCE76 MEd79. Cranmer Hall Dur 61. **d** 63 **p** 64. C Millfield St Mark *Dur* 63-66; C Jarrow Grange 66-69; Hon C 69-86; Lic to Offic 86-90; V Collierley w Annfield Plain from 90. *Collierley Vicarage, Annfield Plain, Stanley, Co Durham DH9 8QS* Stanley (01207) 236254

LAWES, Stephen George. b 40. Nottm Univ PGCE75. St Jo Coll Nottm BTh74. **d** 82 **p** 83. NSM Hillmorton *Cov* 82-86; Perm to Offic *Pet* from 85. *Oak Tree Cottage, 34 Stowe Nine Churches, Northampton NN7 4SQ* Weedon (01327) 40401

LAWES, Timothy Stanley. b 57. Nottm Univ BTh88. Linc Th Coll 85. **d** 88 **p** 89. C Wymondham *Nor* 88-92; R Felmingham, Skeyton, Colby, Banningham etc from 92. *The Rectory, Felmingham, North Walsham, Norfolk NR28 0LD* North Walsham (01692) 402382

LAWLESS, Mrs Patricia Elizabeth (Pat). b 36. Bris Univ BA58 PGCE59 Lon Univ DipSocSc77. S Dios Minl Tr Scheme 91. **d** 93 **p** 94. NSM Frome Ch Ch *B & W* from 93. *9 Sunnyside, Frome, Somerset BA11 1LD* Frome (01373) 463204

LAWLEY, Peter Gerald Fitch. b 52. Chich Th Coll 77. **d** 80 **p** 81. C Pet St Jo *Pet* 80-83; C Daventry 83-87; P-in-c Syresham w Whitfield 87-90; TV Cen Telford *Lich* from 90. *15 Carwood, Stirchley, Telford TF3 1VA* Telford (01952) 595482

LAWLOR, Colin Robert. b 63. Lanc Univ BA89 St Martin's Coll Lanc PGCE90. Chich Th Coll DMinlTh93. **d** 93 **p** 94. C Moulsecoomb *Chich* from 93. *204 Bevendean Crescent, Brighton BN2 4RD* Brighton (01273) 694335

LAWRANCE, David. b 26. Man Univ BA51 BD66 St Cath Soc Ox BA53 MA57. Wycliffe Hall Ox 51. **d** 53 **p** 54. V Oldham Moorside *Man* 61-73; Ind Chapl *Sheff* 74-85; C Wetherby *Ripon* 85-91; Chapl HM Young Offender Inst Wetherby 89-93; rtd 91. *Kinver House, The Green, Kirklington, Bedale, N Yorkshire DL8 2NQ* Thirsk (01845) 567431

LAWRANCE, Hugh Norcliffe. b 40. N Riding Coll of Educn BEd79. Linc Th Coll 83. **d** 85 **p** 86. C Lindley *Wakef* 85-87; C Barkisland w W Scammonden 87-92; C Ripponden 87-92; V Knottingley from 92. *The Vicarage, Chapel Street, Knottingley, W Yorkshire WF11 9AN* Pontefract (01977) 672267

LAWRANCE, Robert William. b 63. Jes Coll Ox BA85 MA89. Ripon Coll Cuddesdon BA87. **d** 88 **p** 89. C Astley *Man* 88-91; Lect Bolton St Pet 91-94; V Bury St Jo w St Mark from 94. *St John's Vicarage, 270 Walmersley Road, Bury, Lancs BL9 6NH* 0161-764 3412

LAWRENCE, Charles Anthony Edwin. b 53. AKC75. St Aug Coll Cant 75. **d** 76 **p** 77. C Mitcham St Mark *S'wark* 76-80; C Haslemere *Guildf* 80-82; P-in-c Ashton H Trin *Man* 82-84; V 84-93; AD Ashton-under-Lyne from 91; V Saddleworth from 93. *The Vicarage, Station Road, Uppermill, Oldham OL3 6HQ* Saddleworth (01457) 872412

LAWRENCE, David Ian. b 48. AIMLS71 MIBiol76 Univ Coll Lon BSc74. Glouc Sch of Min 84 Sarum & Wells Th Coll 87. **d** 88 **p** 89. C Wotton St Mary *Glouc* 88-91; P-in-c Cheltenham St Mich 91-93; V from 93. *St Michael's Vicarage, Severn Road, Cheltenham, Glos GL52 5QA* Cheltenham (01242) 222644

LAWRENCE, David John. b 53. Leeds Poly BEd77. Linc Th Coll. **d** 86 **p** 87. C Gt and Lt Coates w Bradley *Linc* 86-89; P-in-c Hemingby 89-91; R from 91. *The Rectory, Hemingby, Horncastle, Lincs LN9 9QF* Grimsby (01472) 354240

LAWRENCE, George Leslie. b 11. Bp Wilson Coll 38. **d** 41 **p** 42. R Crofton *Wakef* 69-78; rtd 79; Perm to Offic *Wakef* from 79. *702 Doncaster Road, Crofton, Wakefield, W Yorkshire WF4 1PX* Wakefield (01924) 862174

LAWRENCE, Canon Harold. b 12. Univ Coll Dur LTh35 BA36. St Aug Coll Cant 31. **d** 36 **p** 37. C Gt Stanmore *Lon* 36-38; S Africa from 39; Adn Durban 61-74; Hon Can Natal from 74. *7 Chapter Close, Pietermaritzburg, 3201 South Africa* Pietermaritzburg (331) 945686

LAWRENCE, Miss Helen. b 30. St Mich Ho Ox 62. dss 74 **d** 87 **p** 94. Braintree *Chelmsf* 74-87; Par Dn 87-90; rtd 90; Perm to Offic *Chelmsf* 93-94; NSM Frinton from 94. *6 Reynards Close, Kirby Cross, Frinton-on-Sea, Essex CO13 0RA* Frinton-on-Sea (01255) 673837

LAWRENCE, Miss Ida Eugenia Laura. b 14. Open Univ BA81. Gilmore Ho 45. dss 78 **d** 87 **p** 94. Rayleigh *Chelmsf* 78-87; NSM from 87. *Dilkusha, Hardwick Close, Rayleigh, Essex SS6 7QP* Rayleigh (01268) 773059

LAWRENCE, James Conrad. b 62. St Jo Coll Dur BA85. Ridley Hall Cam 85. **d** 87 **p** 88. Min Bar Hill LEP *Ely* 87-93; Deanery Adv in Evang 90-93; CPAS Evang from 93; Perm to Offic *Cov* from 93. *236 Cubbington Road, Leamington Spa, Warks CV32 7AY* Leamington Spa (01926) 316368/334242 Fax Warwick (01926) 337613

LAWRENCE, Mrs Janet Maureen. b 43. Hockerill Teacher Tr Coll TCert64. Ox Min Course CBTS92. **d** 92 **p** 94. Hon Par Dn Bletchley *Ox* 92-94; NSM N Bletchley CD from 94. *20 The Elms, Bletchley, Milton Keynes MK3 6DB* Milton Keynes (01908) 377660

LAWRENCE, John Graham Clive. b 47. ACIB. Trin Coll Bris DipTh78. **d** 78 **p** 79. C Chatham St Phil and St Jas *Roch* 78-83; V Roch St Justus from 83; Asst Chapl HM Pris Roch from 83. *St Justus's Vicarage, 1 Binnacle Road, Rochester, Kent ME1 2XR* Medway (01634) 841183

LAWRENCE, John Shaw. b 27. W Midl Minl Tr Course. **d** 81. NSM Birm St Martin *Birm* 81-85; Chapl Coun for Soc Aid 84-89; NSM Birm St Martin w Bordesley St Andr 85-89; rtd 89. *208 Hay Green Lane, Birmingham B30 1SG* 0121-451 3425

LAWRENCE, Canon Leonard Roy. b 31. Keble Coll Ox BA56 MA59. Westcott Ho Cam 56. **d** 58 **p** 59. C Stockport St Geo *Ches* 58-62; V Thelwall 62-68; V Hyde St Geo 68-75; V Prenton from 75; Hon Can Ches Cathl from 86. *The Vicarage, 1 Reservoir Road, Birkenhead, Merseyside L42 8QX* 0151-608 1808

LAWRENCE, Leslie. b 44. Lon Univ DipRS84. S'wark Ord Course 86. **d** 88 **p** 89. NSM Stanwell *Lon* 88-92; NSM Hounslow H Trin w St Paul from 92. *Witlocke Lodge, 16 Balfour Road, Hounslow TW3 1JX* 0181-572 6280

LAWRENCE, Norman. b 45. Lon Univ BEd75. S'wark Ord Course 77. **d** 80 **p** 81. NSM Hounslow H Trin *Lon* 80-88; NSM Hounslow H Trin w St Paul from 88. *89 Bulstrode Avenue, Hounslow TW3 3AN* 0181-572 6292

LAWRENCE, Ven Patrick Henry Andrew. b 51. TCD BA81. CITC 76. **d** 81 **p** 82. C Templemore *D & R* 81-84; C Kilkenny St Canice Cathl *C & O* 84-85; I Templebreedy w Tracton and Nohoval *C, C & R* 85-92; I Geashill w Killeigh and Ballycommon *M & K* from 92; Can Kildare Cathl from 92; Adn Kildare from 93. *The Rectory, Geashill, Co Offaly, Irish Republic* Tullamore (506) 43879 Fax as telephone

LAWRENCE, Peter Anthony. b 36. Lich Th Coll 67. **d** 69 **p** 70. C Oadby *Leic* 69-74; P-in-c Northmarston and Granborough *Ox* 74-81; P-in-c Hardwick St Mary 74-81; P-in-c Quainton 76-81; P-in-c Oving w Pitchcott 76-81; TR Schorne 81-91; RD Claydon 84-88; V Ivinghoe w Pitstone and Slapton from 91. *The Vicarage, Station Road, Ivinghoe, Leighton Buzzard, Beds LU7 9EB* Cheddington (01296) 668260

LAWRENCE, Peter Halliday. b 47. ALCM K Alfred's Coll Win CertEd69 Nottm Univ BTh76. St Jo Coll Nottm 72. **d** 76 **p** 77. C Birm St Luke *Birm* 76-79; V Burney Lane 79-93; TV Canford Magna *Sarum* 93-95; TR from 95. *The Vicarage, 359 Sopwith Crescent, Wimborne, Dorset BH21 1XQ* Wimborne (01202) 886320

LAWRENCE, Ralph Guy. b 55. Trin Coll Bris DipHE89. **d** 89 **p** 90. C Cotmanhay *Derby* 89-93; P-in-c Tansley, Dethick, Lea and Holloway from 93. *Lea Vicarage, Matlock, Derbyshire DE4 5JP* Dethick (01629) 534275

LAWRENCE, Timothy Hervey. b 25. Ripon Hall Ox 58. **d** 60 **p** 61. V Kentford w Higham Green *St E* 62-84; P-in-c Herringswell 78-84; rtd 84. *13 South Street, Risby, Bury St Edmunds, Suffolk IP28 6QU* Bury St Edmunds (01284) 810083

LAWRENCE, Victor John. b 43. ACII. Oak Hill Th Coll. **d** 83 **p** 84. C Paddock Wood *Roch* 83-87; R Milton next Gravesend w Denton from 87. *The Rectory, Church Walk, Milton, Gravesend, Kent DA12 2QU* Gravesend (01474) 533434

LAWRENCE-MARCH, David Lawrence. b 61. Univ of Wales (Lamp) BA83. Coll of Resurr Mirfield 83. **d** 85 **p** 86. C Pet St Jude *Pet* 85-89; C Kilburn St Aug w St Jo *Lon* 89-90; Chapl St Aug Sch Kilburn 89-92; C Paddington St Mary *Lon* 90-92; Chapl Bearwood Coll Wokingham from 92. *Bearwood College, Wokingham, Berks RG11 5BG* Wokingham (01734) 794329

LAWRENSON, James Percival. b 12. Kelham Th Coll 30. **d** 36 **p** 37. Chapl Berkhamsted Sch Herts 56-78; rtd 78; Perm to Offic *St Alb* from 78; Perm to Offic *Ox* 87-90. *Downside, Torrington Road, Berkhamsted, Herts HP4 3DD* Berkhamsted (01442) 865999

LAWRENSON, Michael. b 35. Leeds Univ BA60 Liv Univ CSocStuds65 Newc Univ DASS69. Coll of Resurr Mirfield 60. **d** 74 **p** 74. NSM Glenrothes *St And* 74-90; Dioc Supernumerary from 90; Chapl HM Pris Perth from 91. *Hollyburn, West Port, Falkland, Cupar, Fife KY7 7BW* Falkland (01337) 857311

LAWRENSON, Ronald David. b 41. CITC 68. **d** 71 **p** 72. C Seapatrick *D & D* 71-78; Min Can Down Cathl 78-79; VC Belf Cathl 79-86; Bp's C Tynan w Middletown *Arm* 86-93; Hon VC Arm Cathl from 87; I Arm St Mark w Aghavilly 92-93; I Donaghmore w Upper Donaghmore from 93; RD Aghaloo from 94. *St Michael's Rectory, 66 Main Street, Castlecaulfield, Dungannon, Co Tyrone BT70 3NP* Donaghmore (01868) 761214

LAWREY, Leslie John. b 18. Em Coll Cam MA45 Lon Univ CertEd65 DipSocWork69. Ridley Hall Cam 45. **d** 47 **p** 48. Travelling Sec Inter-Sch Chr Fellowship 53-63; Perm to Offic *Sarum* 67-70; Perm to Offic *Ex* 70-73; NSM Tredington and Darlingscott w Newbold on Stour *Cov* 73-82; Warden Shaftesbury Soc Housing from 83; rtd 93. *clo P A Toombs Esq, High Pavement, Trent, Sherborne, Dorset DT9 4SW* Sherborne (01935) 851341

LAWRIE, Paul Edward. b 12. Freiburg Univ LLD35 St Cath Soc Ox BA48 MA53. Wycliffe Hall Ox 46. **d** 48 **p** 49. R Todwick *Sheff* 64-78; rtd 78; Chapl Rotherham Distr Gen Hosp 78-85; Hon C Handsworth Woodhouse *Sheff* from 85. *15 Haddon Way, Aston, Sheffield S31 0EH* Sheffield (0114) 287 4864

LAWRIE, Peter Sinclair. b 39. Clifton Th Coll 62. **d** 65 **p** 66. C Derby St Chad *Derby* 65-68; C Toxteth Park St Philemon w St Silas *Liv* 68-71; V Ramsey St Mary's w Ponds Bridge *Ely* 71-81; V Whitwick St Jo the Bapt *Leic* from 81. *The Vicarage, 37 North Street, Whitwick, Coalville, Leics LE67 5HB* Coalville (01530) 836904

LAWRY, Mrs Fianach Alice Moir. b 35. St And Dioc Tr Course 85. **d** 88 **p** 94. NSM Dollar *St And* from 88; Chapl HM Pris Glenochil from 91. *Sunnybank, Muckhart, Dollar, Clackmannanshire FK14 7JH* Dollar (01259) 781426

LAWRY, Samuel John Lockhart. b 11. CCC Cam BA33 MA38. Wells Th Coll 34. **d** 35 **p** 36. V E Meon *Portsm* 57-68; Perm to Offic from 68; rtd 76. *Broadlands House, Petersfield, Hants GU31 4BA* Petersfield (01730) 262134

LAWS, Clive Loudon. b 54. UEA BEd76. Wycliffe Hall Ox 79. **d** 82 **p** 83. C Newc w Butterton *Lich* 82-85; C Gabalfa *Llan* 85-88; R Pendine w Llanmiloe and Eglwys Gymyn w Marros *St D* 89-94. *46 Down Road, Portishead, Bristol BS20 8BH* Portishead (01275) 848109

LAWS, Edwin Kingsley. b 06. LVO53 KPM39. Bps' Coll Cheshunt 56. **d** 57 **p** 58. R Milton Abbas w Winterborne Whitechurch etc *Sarum* 60-74; Custos St Jo Hosp Heytesbury 74-79; rtd 79. *9 Stoberry Crescent, Wells, Somerset BA5 2TG* Wells (01749) 673544

LAWSON, Preb Clifford John. b 21. St Cath Soc Ox BA45 MA47. Qu Coll Birm 45. **d** 47 **p** 48. V Eccleshall *Lich* 57-71; Chapl HM Pris Drake Hall 58-71; RD Eccleshall *Lich* 65-71; Preb Lich Cathl 70-86; R Stafford St Mary 72-74; P-in-c Stafford St Chad 72-74; RD Stafford 72-77; R Stafford St Mary and St Chad 74-77; RD Oswestry 77-82; R Rhydycroesau 77-86; R Selattyn 77-86; rtd 86; Perm to Offic *Lich* from 86. *The Burwains, 22 Port Hill Drive, Shrewsbury SY3 8RS* Shrewsbury (01743) 354085

LAWSON, David McKenzie. b 47. Glas Univ MA69 Edin Univ BD76. Edin Th Coll 73. **d** 76 **p** 77. C Glas St Mary *Glas* 76-82; V Keighley All SS *Bradf* 82-85; Chapl Asst Univ Coll Hosp Lon 85-91; Hon C St Pancras w St Jas and Ch Ch *Lon* 86-91; R Smithfield St Bart Gt 91-93. *Address temp unknown*

LAWSON, David William. b 50. ACA DipHE. Linc Th Coll. **d** 82 **p** 83. C Stafford *Lich* 82-85; TV Redruth w Lanner *Truro* 85-87; Chapl Whitley Hosp Cov from 87; Chapl Gulson Road Hosp Cov from 87; Chapl Cov and Warks Hosp from 87; P-in-c Whitley *Cov* 87-93; V S Leamington St Jo from 93. *St John's Vicarage, Tachbrook Street, Leamington Spa, Warks CV31 3BN* Leamington Spa (01926) 422208

LAWSON, Canon Frederick Quinney. b 45. Leic Univ BA. St Steph Ho Ox. **d** 83 **p** 84. Hon C Loughb Em *Leic* 83-86; NSM Somerby, Burrough on the Hill and Pickwell 86-87; NSM Burrough Hill Pars 87; USA from 87; Hon Can Salt Lake City from 87; Perm to Offic *Leic* 88. *4294 Adonis Drive, Salt Lake City, Utah 84124, USA* Salt Lake City (801) 277-9623 Fax 278-5903

LAWSON, Gary Austin. b 53. Man Univ BA80. Ripon Coll Cuddesdon 80. **d** 82 **p** 83. C Nunhead St Antony *S'wark* 82-86; Hon C Reddish *Man* 86-87; Hon C Longsight St Jo w St Cypr 87-88; V Wythenshawe St Rich from 88. *St Richard's Vicarage, 42 Lomond Road, Manchester M22 5JD* 0161-499 2022

LAWSON, John Alexander. b 62. Sheff Univ BA84. St Jo Coll Nottm DPS87. **d** 87 **p** 88. C Wellington, All SS w Eyton *Lich* 87-92; TV Dewsbury *Wakef* from 92. *St John's Vicarage, 68 Staincliffe Road, Dewsbury, W Yorkshire WF13 4EF* Dewsbury (01924) 463131

LAWSON, Jonathan Halford (Jon). b 68. St Chad's Coll Dur BA90. Westcott Ho Cam CTM93. **d** 93 **p** 94. C Sedgefield *Dur* from 93. *9 Belsay Court, Sedgefield, Stockton-on-Tees, Cleveland TS21 2JA* Sedgefield (01740) 20829

LAWSON, Matthew James. b 67. St Andr Univ MTh91 Ox Univ. Ripon Coll Cuddesdon 92. **d** 94 **p** 95. C Bedf St Andr *St Alb* from 94. *5 St Minver Road, Bedford MK40 3DQ* Bedford (01234) 217330/(0421) 502901

LAWSON, Michael Charles. b 52. Sussex Univ BA75. Trin Coll Bris 75. **d** 78 **p** 79. C Horsham *Chich* 78-81; C St Marylebone

All So w SS Pet and Jo *Lon* 81-87; V Bromley Ch Ch *Roch* from 87. *Christ Church Vicarage, 18 Highland Road, Bromley BR1 4AD* 0181-313 9882

LAWSON-TANCRED, Christopher. b 24. Trin Coll Cam BA49 MA65. Chich Th Coll 63. **d** 65 **p** 66. C Uckfield *Chich* 65-70; R Wrington *B & W* 70-73; R Wrington w Butcombe 73-79; Perm to Offic *Chich* 80-92; Hon C Battersea St Luke *S'wark* 83-89; rtd 89. *Flat 3, Minterne House, Dorchester, Dorset DT2 7AX* Cerne Abbas (01300) 341328

LAWTON, Canon John Stewart. b 19. Ox Univ MA BD DPhil50. St Steph Ho Ox 40. **d** 42 **p** 43. Warden and Chief Lib St Deiniol's Lib Hawarden 62-73; V Lt Leigh and Lower Whitley *Ches* 73-75; Dir of Min 74-84; Can Res Ches Cathl 75-84; rtd 84; Perm to Offic *Ches* from 84. *7 Ormonde Road, Chester CH2 2AH* Chester (01244) 376092

LAXON, Colin John. b 44. Cant Sch of Min 86. **d** 89 **p** 90. C Folkestone St Mary and St Eanswythe *Cant* 89-94; P-in-c Barrow St Jas *Carl* from 94. *St James's Vicarage, 150 Abbey Road, Barrow-in-Furness, Cumbria LA14 5AB* Barrow-in-Furness (01229) 821475

LAXTON, Joseph Henry. b 13. Leeds Univ BA36. Coll of Resurr Mirfield 36. **d** 38 **p** 39. R Tidmarsh w Sulham *Ox* 71-78; rtd 78; Perm to Offic *Heref* from 78. *27 Charlton Rise, Sheet Road, Ludlow, Shropshire SY8 1ND* Ludlow (01584) 874409

LAY, Brian Robert. b 37. Bernard Gilpin Soc Dur 59 Chich Th Coll 60. **d** 63 **p** 64. C Battyeford *Wakef* 63-66; C Belhus Park *Chelmsf* 66-73; P-in-c Sutton on Plym *Ex* 73-80; V from 80. *St John's Vicarage, 3 Alma Street, Cattedown, Plymouth PL4 0NL* Plymouth (01752) 664191

LAY, Geoffrey Arthur. b 54. Leic Poly BA77 Man Univ MA83 Lon Univ BD88. Ridley Hall Cam CTM92. **d** 92 **p** 93. C St Neots *Ely* 92-95; P-in-c Long Stanton w St Mich from 95; P-in-c Dry Drayton from 95. *The Chalet, St Michael's Road, Longstanton, Cambridge CB4 5BZ* Crafts Hill (01954) 782580

LAYBOURNE, Michael Frederick. b 37. Qu Coll Birm 81. **d** 83 **p** 84. C High Elswick St Phil *Newc* 83-85; C High Elswick St Phil and Newc St Aug 86; C Cramlington 86-87; TV from 87. *1 Cateran Way, Cramlington, Northd NE23 6EX* Cramlington (01670) 714261

LAYCOCK, Charles. b 37. Open Univ BA88. N Ord Course. **d** 83 **p** 84. C Astley Bridge *Man* 83-86; R Crumpsall 86-94; V Ashton Ch Ch from 94. *The Vicarage, Vicarage Road, Ashton-under-Lyne, Lancs OL7 9QY* 0161-330 1601

LAYCOCK, Lawrence. b 42. HNC. St Deiniol's Hawarden 86. **d** 89 **p** 90. C Blackpool St Mich *Blackb* 89-94; P-in-c Worsthorne from 94. *The Vicarage, Gorple Road, Worsthorne, Burnley, Lancs BB10 3NN* Burnley (01282) 428478

LAYTON, Miss Norene. b 39. Trin Coll Bris DipHE86. dss 86 **d** 87 **p** 94. Lindfield *Chich* 86-87; Par Dn 87-92; Par Dn Loughb Em *Leic* 92-94; C from 94. *47 Brookfield Avenue, Loughborough, Leics LE11 3LN* Loughborough (01509) 261070

LAZONBY, Canon Alan Frederick. b 19. TD64. St Jo Coll Dur BA40 DipTh41 MA43. **d** 42 **p** 43. R Haughton le Skerne *Dur* 57-84; RD Darlington 74-78; Hon Can Dur Cathl from 71; rtd 84. *16 Loraine Crescent, Darlington, Co Durham DL1 5TF* Darlington (01325) 485876

LE CRAS, Allan. b 20. Linc Th Coll 83. **d** 84 **p** 85. Hon C Toynton All Saints w Toynton St Peter *Linc* 84-88; Hon C Marden Hill Gp 88-90; Perm to Offic from 90. *Snipe Dales Cottage, Lusby, Spilsby, Lincs PE23 4JB* Winceby (01507) 588636

LE DIEU, Miss Heather Muriel. b 41. Birm Univ BA62 MA67 DipTh. St Jo Coll Dur 77. dss 79 **d** 87. Birchfield *Birm* 79-82; Kings Heath 82-84; Walsall Pleck and Bescot *Lich* 84-88; Par Dn 87-88; rtd 88. *8 Hubert Croft, Hubert Road, Birmingham B29 6DU* 0121-471 3566

LE FEUVRE, Henry Mauger. b 21. Lich Th Coll. **d** 62 **p** 63. P-in-c Dorrington *Heref* 69-72; P-in-c Stapleton 69-72; P-in-c Cardington 69-72; R Jersey St Lawr *Win* 72-80; R Risby w Gt and Lt Saxham and Westley *St E* 80-85; rtd 85; Perm to Offic *St E* from 85. *18 Southgate Street, Bury St Edmunds, Suffolk IP33 2AF* Bury St Edmunds (01284) 703524

LE GRICE, Elizabeth Margaret. b 53. Man Univ BA75 MA(Theol)78. Nor Bapt Coll 75 Westcott Ho Cam 87. **d** 88. In Bapt Ch 78-82; C Whitchurch *Llan* from 88. *16 St John's Crescent, Whitchurch, Cardiff CF4 7AF* Cardiff (01222) 625947

LE GRYS, Alan Arthur. b 51. K Coll Lon BD73 AKC73 MTh90. St Aug Coll Cant 73. **d** 74 **p** 75. C Harpenden St Jo *St Alb* 74-77; C Hampstead St Jo *Lon* 77-81; Chapl Westf Coll and Bedf Coll 81-84; V Stoneleigh *Guildf* 84-91; Lect Ripon Coll Cuddesdon from 91. *Flat 2, New Building, Ripon College, Cuddesdon, Oxford OX44 9EX* Wheatley (01865) 875688

LE PAGE, Canon Dallas Arthur des Reaux. b 17. Keble Coll Ox BA49 MA53. Cuddesdon Coll 49. **d** 51 **p** 52. C Hampstead St

Steph *Lon* 53-58; S Africa from 58; rtd 86. *24 Maynard Street Gardens, Cape Town, 8001 South Africa* Cape Town (21) 452221

LE PREVOST, Carl Andrew. b 63. Sarum & Wells Th Coll 85. **d** 88 **p** 89. C Chandler's Ford *Win* 88-91; C Southn Maybush St Pet 91; Asst Chapl Bryanston Sch Blandford 91-93; R Burghclere w Newtown and Ecchinswell w Sydmonton *Win* from 93. *The Rectory, Well Street, Burghclere, Newbury, Berks RG15 9HS* Burghclere (01635) 278470

LE ROSSIGNOL, Richard Lewis. b 52. Aston Univ BSc75. Oak Hill Th Coll BA79. **d** 79 **p** 80. C E Ham St Paul *Chelmsf* 79-81; C Willesborough w Hinxhill *Cant* 81-85; Perm to Offic 85-94; Hon C Brabourne w Smeeth from 94. *64 Osborne Road, Willesborough, Ashford, Kent TN24 0EF* Ashford (01233) 625193

LE SUEUR, Paul John. b 38. Lon Univ BSc59. Wycliffe Hall Ox 60. **d** 62 **p** 63. C Mortlake w E Sheen *S'wark* 62-65; C Witney *Ox* 65-69; R Sarsden w Churchill 69-74; P-in-c Clifton Hampden 74-77; P-in-c Rotherfield Greys H Trin 77-82; V 82-90; V Blacklands Hastings Ch Ch and St Andr *Chich* from 90. *Christ Church Vicarage, 28 Laton Road, Hastings, E Sussex TN34 2ES* Hastings (01424) 421821

LE VASSEUR, Mrs Linda Susan. b 48. Shenstone Coll of Educn CertEd70. S Dios Minl Tr Scheme 92. **d** 95. NSM Guernsey Ste Marie du Castel *Win* from 95; NSM Guernsey St Matt from 95. *Coin des Arquets, Les Arquets, Rue de Catillion, St Pierre du Bois, Guernsey, Channel Islands GY7 9HE* Guernsey (01481) 64047

LE VAY, Dr Clare Forbes Agard Bramhall Joanna. b 41. St Anne's Coll Ox BA64 MA66 Univ of Wales (Abth) MSc72 PhD86. Westcott Ho Cam 86. **d** 88 **p** 94. C Stamford Hill St Thos *Lon* 88-89; C Hackney 89-92; Asst Chapl Brook Gen Hosp Lon 92-95; Asst Chapl Greenwich Distr Hosp Lon 92-95; Chapl Greenwich Healthcare NHS Trust from 95; Chapl Greenwich Distr Hosp Lon from 95. *91 Mildenhall Road, London E5 0RY, or Brook Hospital, Shooters Hill Road, London SE18 4LW* 0181-856 5555 or 985 3150

LEA, His Honour Christopher Gerald. b 17. MC. RMC Called to the Bar (Inner Temple) 48. Ox Min Course 91. **d** 92 **p** 93. NSM Stratfield Mortimer *Ox* from 92. *Simms Farm House, Simms Lane, Mortimer, Reading RG7 2JP* Mortimer (01734) 332360

LEA, Canon Montague Brian. b 34. St Jo Coll Cam BA55 Lon Univ BD71. St Jo Coll Nottm 68. **d** 71 **p** 72. C Northwood Em *Lon* 71-74; Chapl Barcelona *Eur* 74-79; V Hove Bp Hannington Memorial Ch *Chich* 79-86; Adn N France *Eur* 86-94; Chapl Paris St Mich 86-94; Hon Can Gib Cathl from 95; R Chiddingly w E Hoathly *Chich* from 94. *The Rectory, East Hoathly, Lewes, E Sussex BN8 6EG* Halland (01825) 840270

LEA, Norman. b 42. Univ of Wales (Lamp) BA67. Coll of Resurr Mirfield 66. **d** 68 **p** 69. C Aberavon *Llan* 68-71; C Oystermouth 71-73; C Brecon w Battle 73-74; TV Cwmbran *Mon* 74-77; V Talgarth and Llanelieu *S & B* 77-84; V Port Talbot St Theodore *Llan* from 84; Hon Chapl Miss to Seamen from 84. *St Theodore's Vicarage, Talbot Road, Port Talbot, W Glam SA13 1LB* Port Talbot (01639) 883935

LEA, Canon Richard John Rutland. b 40. Trin Hall Cam BA63 MA67. Westcott Ho Cam 63. **d** 65 **p** 66. C Edenbridge *Roch* 65-68; C Hayes 68-71; V Larkfield 71-86; P-in-c Leybourne 76-86; RD Malling 79-84; V Chatham St Steph 86-88; Can Res and Prec Roch Cathl from 88. *2 Kings Orchard, The Precinct, Rochester, Kent ME1 1TG* Medway (01634) 841491

LEACH, Alan William Brickett. b 28. CEng FIStructE FASI FICE MSc. S'wark Ord Course. **d** 89 **p** 90. NSM Forest Row *Chich* from 89. *Hathaway, Ashdown Road, Forest Row, E Sussex RH18 5BN* Forest Row (01342) 823775

LEACH, Gerald. b 27. Sarum & Wells Th Coll 85. **d** 73 **p** 74. NSM Cyncoed *Mon* 73-86; C 86-87; V Dingestow and Llangovan w Penyclawdd etc 87-94; rtd 94. *19 Grange Park, Whitchurch, Ross-on-Wye, Herefordshire HR9 6EA* Symonds Yat (01600) 890397

LEACH, John. b 52. K Coll Lon BD79 AKC79 St Jo Coll Dur MA. **d** 81 **p** 82. C N Walsham w Antingham *Nor* 81-85; C Crookes St Thos *Sheff* 85-89; V Styvechale *Cov* from 89. *The Vicarage, 16 Armorial Road, Coventry CV3 6GJ* Coventry (01203) 692299

LEACH, Robert Neville. b 54. Trin Coll Bris DipHE93. **d** 93 **p** 94. C Towcester w Easton Neston *Pet* from 93. *42 St Lawrence Road South, Towcester, Northants NN12 7DR* Towcester (01327) 352486

LEACH, Stephen Lance. b 42. St Steph Ho Ox 66. **d** 69 **p** 70. C Higham Ferrers w Chelveston *Pet* 69-72; TV Ilfracombe H Trin *Ex* 72-74; V Barnstaple St Mary 74-77; R Goodleigh 74-77; P-in-c Barnstaple St Pet w H Trin 76-77; P-in-c Landkey 77-79; TR Barnstaple and Goodleigh 77-79; TR Barnstaple, Goodleigh and Landkey 79-82; V Paignton St Jo

82-95; Gen Sec ACS from 95. *Gordon Browning House, 8 Spitfire Road, Birmingham B24 9PB* 0121-382 5533 or 354 9885 Fax 382 6999

LEACH, Stephen Windsor. b 47. St Chad's Coll Dur BSc70 Linacre Coll Ox BA72 MA76. Ripon Hall Ox 70. **d** 73 **p** 74. C Swinton St Pet *Man* 73-77; C Oldham St Chad Limeside 77-79; V Shaw 79-87; V St Just in Penwith *Truro* from 87; V Sancreed from 87. *The Vicarage, St Just, Penzance, Cornwall TR19 7UB* Penzance (01736) 788672

LEACH, Timothy Edmund (Tim). b 41. Dur Univ BA63. Ridley Hall Cam 63. **d** 65 **p** 66. C Ecclesfield *Sheff* 65-68; C Stocksbridge 68-71; C-in-c W Bessacarr CD 71-80; V Goole from 80; Hon Chapl Miss to Seamen from 80. *The Vicarage, 22 Clifton Gardens, Goole, N Humberside DN14 6AS* Goole (01405) 764259

LEACH, William Howard. b 07. Em Coll Cam BA29 MA33. Ridley Hall Cam 29. **d** 31 **p** 32. V Lydney w Aylburton *Glouc* 61-75; rtd 75; Perm to Offic *Worc* from 80. *Perrins House, Moorlands Road, Malvern, Worcs WR14 2TZ* Malvern (01684) 568173

LEADBEATER, Michael John. b 45. Nottm Univ BTh72 St Martin's Coll Lanc CertEd73. Kelham Th Coll 68. **d** 73 **p** 74. C Manston *Ripon* 73-77; C Holbrooks *Cov* 77-79; V Tipton St Jo *Lich* 79-89; V Rushall from 89. *Rushall Vicarage, 10 Tetley Avenue, Walsall WS4 2HE* Walsall (01922) 24677

LEADBEATER, Canon Nicolas James. b 20. Univ of Wales BA43. St Steph Ho Ox 43. **d** 45 **p** 46. V Westcote *Glouc* 67-72; P-in-c Icomb 67-72; V Westcote w Icomb 72-79; V Westcote w Icomb and Bledington 79-88; Hon Can Glouc Cathl 83-88; rtd 88. *11 Pitt Street, Gloucester GL1 2BH* Gloucester (01452) 309644

LEAFE, Maurice Stanley Damian. b 28. Chich Th Coll 72. **d** 74 **p** 75. C Allens Cross *Birm* 74-76; C Solihull 76-81; TV 81-84; V Wellingborough St Barn *Pet* 84-88; R Harpole 88-94; rtd 94. *Address excluded by request*

LEAH, William Albert. b 34. K Coll Lon BA56 AKC57 K Coll Cam MA63. Ripon Hall Ox 60. **d** 62 **p** 63. C Falmouth K Chas *Truro* 62-63; Chapl K Coll Cam 63-67; Min Can Westmr Abbey 67-74; V Hawkhurst *Cant* 74-83; Hon Min Can Cant Cathl 78-83; V St Ives *Truro* 83-94. *Trerice Cottage, Sancreed Newbridge, Penzance, Cornwall TR20 8QR* St Buryan (01736) 810987

LEAHY, David Adrian. b 56. Open Univ BA90. Qu Coll Birm. **d** 85 **p** 86. C Tile Cross *Birm* 85-88; C Warley Woods 88-91; V Hobs Moat from 91. *St Mary's House, 30 Hobs Meadow, Solihull, W Midlands B92 8PN* 0121-743 4955

LEAK, Harry Duncan. b 30. St Cath Coll Cam BA53 MA57. Ely Th Coll 53. **d** 54 **p** 55. V Hanley All SS *Lich* 68-71; R Swynnerton 71-80; Perm to Offic from 80; rtd 92. *15 Sutherland Road, Tittensor, Stoke-on-Trent ST12 9JQ*

LEAK, John Michael. b 42. St Jo Coll Nottm. **d** 84 **p** 85. NSM Beeston *Ripon* 84-87; C Far Headingley St Chad 87-88; Hon C 88-90; C Headingley from 90. *10 St Chad's Rise, Leeds LS6 3QE* Leeds (0113) 275 8229

+LEAKE, Rt Rev David. b 35. ALCD59. **d** 59 **p** 60 **c** 69. C Watford *St Alb* 59-61; Lect 61-63; SAMS from 63; Argentina 63-69; Asst Bp Paraguay 69-73; Asst Bp N Argentina 69-80; Bp 80-90; Bp Argentina from 90. *Iglesia Anglicana, Casilla 4293, Correo Central, 100 Buenos Aires, Argentina* Buenos Aires (1) 344618

LEAKE, Duncan Burton. b 49. Leeds Univ BA71 Leeds and Carnegie Coll PGCE72 Birm Univ ADipRE78 Keele Univ MA85. Oak Hill Th Coll 90. **d** 92 **p** 93. C Stanwix *Carl* from 92. *St Mark's House, 77 Bracken Ridge, Carlisle CA3 9TB* Carlisle (01228) 402625 or 511430

LEAKEY, Ian Ramond Arundell. b 24. K Coll Cam BA47 MA49. Ridley Hall Cam 48. **d** 50 **p** 51. Rwanda Miss 53-73; V Cudham *Roch* 73-76; P-in-c Downe 76; V Cudham and Downe 76-89; rtd 89. *5 Pine Close, Beech Grange, Landford, Salisbury SP5 2AW* Romsey (01794) 390561

LEAKEY, Peter Wippell. b 39. Lon Univ BSc60. Trin Coll Bris 73. **d** 75 **p** 76. C Colne St Bart *Blackb* 75-79; V Copp 79-85; V Pennington *Man* from 85; AD Leigh from 93. *The Vicarage, Schofield Street, Leigh, Lancs WN7 4HT* Leigh (01942) 673619

LEAL, Malcolm Colin. b 33. Chich Th Coll 72. **d** 75 **p** 76. Hon C Shoreham St Giles CD *Chich* 75-87; Chapl NE Surrey Coll Guildf 87-95; Hon C Arundel w Tortington and S Stoke *Chich* 88-95; Perm to Offic from 95. *8 West Park Lane, Goring-by-Sea, Worthing, W Sussex BN12 4EK* Worthing (01903) 244160

LEAMING, Ralph Desmond. b 21. Ripon Coll Cuddesdon 79. **d** 81 **p** 82. C Darlington H Trin *Dur* 81-84; V Hamsterley 84-92; rtd 92. *3 Farnley Ridge, Durham DH1 4HB* 0191-384 2049

LEAMY, Stuart Nigel. b 46. Pemb Coll Ox BA68 MA73. Sarum Th Coll 68. **d** 70 **p** 71. Lic to Offic *Lon* 71-81; Hon C Upholland

Liv 72-78. *28 Church Street, Hampton, Middx TW12 2EG* 0181-941 3930

LEAN, David Jonathan Rees. b 52. Univ of Wales (Lamp) DipTh74. Coll of Resurr Mirfield 74. **d** 75 **p** 76. C Tenby *St D* 75-81; V Llanrhian w Llanhywel and Carnhedryn etc 81-88; V Haverfordwest St Martin w Lambston from 88. *St Martin's Vicarage, Barn Street, Haverfordwest, Dyfed SA61 1TD* Haverfordwest (01437) 762509

LEANING, Very Rev David. b 36. Lich Th Coll 58. **d** 60 **p** 61. C Gainsborough All SS *Linc* 60-65; R Warsop *S'well* 65-76; RD Kington and Weobley *Heref* 76-80; R Kington w Huntington 76-80; Adn Newark *S'well* 80-91; Provost S'well from 91; P-in-c Rolleston w Fiskerton, Morton and Upton 91-93. *The Residence, Southwell, Notts NG25 0HP* Newark (01636) 812593 or 812649 Fax 815904

LEARMOUTH, Michael Walter. b 50. FCA. Oak Hill Th Coll 84. **d** 84 **p** 85. C Harlow St Mary and St Hugh w St Jo the Bapt *Chelmsf* 84-89; V Hainault from 89. *St Paul's Vicarage, Arrowsmith Road, Chigwell, Essex IG7 4NZ* 0181-500 3366

LEARY, Thomas Glasbrook. b 42. AKC66. **d** 67 **p** 68. C W Bromwich All SS *Lich* 67-70; TV Croydon *Cant* 70-75; C Limpsfield and Titsey *S'wark* 75-83; V Sutton New Town St Barn 83-92; V Mert St Mary from 92. *The Vicarage, 3 Church Path, London SW19 3HJ* 0181-543 6192

LEATHARD, Brian. b 56. Sussex Univ BA Cam Univ MA. Westcott Ho Cam 79. **d** 82 **p** 83. C Seaford w Sutton *Chich* 82-85; Chapl Loughb Univ *Leic* 85-89; V Hampton Hill *Lon* from 89. *The Vicarage, St James's Road, Hampton Hill, Hampton, Middx TW12 1DQ* 0181-979 2069

LEATHERBARROW, Ronald. b 35. Chester Coll TCert59. NW Ord Course 71. **d** 75 **p** 76. C Eccleston Ch Ch *Liv* 75-80; C Eccleston St Thos 80-83; R Kirklinton w Hethersgill and Scaleby *Carl* 83-86; R Blackley White Moss St Mark *Man* from 86. *St Mark's Rectory, 70 Booth Hall Road, Manchester M9 2BL* 0161-740 7558

LEATHERLAND, Brian. b 43. Nottm Univ BTh73 St Martin's Coll Lanc DipEd. Kelham Th Coll 69. **d** 74 **p** 75. C Higham Ferrers w Chelveston *Pet* 74-76; C Pet St Paul 76-78; V Kings Heath 78-83; V Raunds 83-94. *102 Finedon Road, Irthlingborough, Wellingborough, Northants NN9 5TZ*

LEATHERS, Brian Stanley Peter. b 61. Nottm Univ BSc83. Oak Hill Th Coll BA89. **d** 89 **p** 90. C Watford *St Alb* 89-92; C Welwyn w Ayot St Peter from 92. *St Michael's House, 3 London Road, Woolmer Green, Knebworth, Herts SG3 6JU* Stevenage (01438) 813043

LEATHES, David Burlton de Mussenden. b 49. R Agric Coll Cirencester DipEM70. St Jo Coll Nottm DCM92. **d** 92 **p** 93. C Kirkby Stephen w Mallerstang etc *Carl* from 92; C Brough w Stainmore, Musgrave and Warcop from 94. *Low Beck House, Rookby, Kirkby Stephen, Cumbria CA17 4HX* Kirkby Stephen (017683) 71713

LEATHLEY, Hubert Brian. b 28. MBE91. Linc Th Coll 79. **d** 81 **p** 82. Chapl Automobile Assn from 81; C Basingstoke *Win* 81-83; Chapl Basingstoke Coll of Tech 81-91; TV Basingstoke *Win* 83-91; Ind Chapl 83-91; V Kingsclere from 91. *The Vicarage, Fox's Lane, Kingsclere, Newbury, Berks RG15 8SL* Kingsclere (01635) 298272

LEATHLEY, Susan Mary (Sue). b 57. Bath Univ BPharm78 MRPharmS. Oak Hill Th Coll DTPS94. **d** 94. C Weston-super-Mare Ch Ch *B & W* from 94. *44 Beamond Avenue, Weston-super-Mare, Avon BS23 2TF* Weston-super-Mare (01934) 641639

LEAVER, David Noel. b 63. Hatf Coll Dur BA85. Wycliffe Hall Ox 89. **d** 91 **p** 92. C Blackheath Park St Mich *S'wark* from 91. *1A Pond Road, London SE3 9JL* 0181-852 9564

LEAVER, Prof Robin Alan. b 39. Clifton Th Coll 62. **d** 64 **p** 65. C Gipsy Hill Ch Ch *S'wark* 64-67; C Gt Baddow *Chelmsf* 67-71; C-in-c Reading St Mary Castle Street Prop Chpl *Ox* 71-77; Chapl Luckley-Oakfield Sch Wokingham 73-75; P-in-c Cogges *Ox* 77-84; USA from 84; Prof Ch Music Westmr Choir Coll from 84. *Westminster Choir College, Princeton, New Jersey 08540, USA*

LEAVES (nee CRAIG), Julie Elizabeth. b 63. Southn Univ BTh87. Sarum & Wells Th Coll 82. **dss** 86 **d** 87 **p** 92. Thatcham *Ox* 86-87; Par Dn 87-88; Hong Kong 88-92; Australia from 92. *clo Anglican Church Office, GPO Box W2067, Perth, W Australia 6001* Perth (9) 325-7455 Fax 325-6741

LEAVES, Nigel. b 58. Keble Coll Ox MA80 K Coll Lon MA86. Sarum & Wells Th Coll 84. **d** 86 **p** 87. C Boyne Hill *Ox* 86-88; Hong Kong 88-92; Australia from 92. *clo Anglican Church Office, GPO Box W2067, Perth, W Australia 6001* Perth (9) 325-7455 Fax 325-6741

LEAWORTHY, John Owen. b 40. Univ of Wales (Swansea) BSc62. Oak Hill Th Coll DipHE82. **d** 82 **p** 83. C Compton Gifford *Ex* 82-85; C Plymouth Em w Efford 85-86; P-in-c Marks Tey w Aldham and Lt Tey *Chelmsf* 86-88; R 88-89;

Chapl HM Pris Full Sutton 89-91. *Grafham Water Residential Centre, Perry, Huntingdon, Cambs PE18 0BX* Huntingdon (01480) 810521 Fax 812739

LECKEY, Very Rev Hamilton. b 29. TCD BA51 MA58. **d** 51 **p** 52. C Ballymacarrett St Martin *D & D* 51-55; C Ban Abbey 55-60; I from 79; I Drumgooland w Kilcoo 60-62; Private Chapl Bp Down 62-73; Dir of Ords 62-87; I Comber 62-79; Can Down Cathl from 74; Dean Down from 87; I Down Cathl from 87. *The Abbey Rectory, 5 Downshire Road, Bangor, Co Down BT20 3TW* Bangor (01247) 460173

LEDGARD, Canon Frank William Armitage. b 24. Wells Th Coll 49. **d** 52 **p** 53. R Bedale *Ripon* 66-87; RD Wensley 79-85; Hon Can Ripon Cathl 80-89; Bp's Adv on Chr Healing 87-89; rtd 89. *Bridge House, 19 Swinton Terrace, Masham, Ripon, N Yorkshire HG4 4HS* Ripon (01765) 689375

LEDGARD, Canon Thomas Callinan. b 16. St Jo Coll Cam BA38 MA50. Westcott Ho Cam 38. **d** 39 **p** 40. V Cartmel *Carl* 69-79; Hon Can Carl Cathl 70-82; P-in-c Warcop, Musgrave, Soulby and Crosby Garrett 79-82; rtd 82; Perm to Offic *Carl* from 83. *Tetley Cottage, Allithwaite Road, Cartmel, Grange-over-Sands, Cumbria LA11 7SB* Cartmel (015395) 36455

LEDGER, James Henry. b 23. Oak Hill Th Coll 68. **d** 70 **p** 71. C Spitalfields Ch Ch w All SS *Lon* 70-75; V Chitts Hill St Cuth 75-91; rtd 91. *6 Acorn Street, Hunsdon, Ware, Herts SG12 8PB* Much Hadham (01279) 842878

LEDWARD, John Archibald. b 30. FRSA85 Lon Univ BD85 Man Univ DSPT78 MA81 ThD. ALCD57. **d** 58 **p** 59. C St Helens St Helen *Liv* 58-62; V Daubhill *Man* 71-77; R Newc w Butterton *Lich* 77-88; P-in-c Rockland St Mary w Hellington *Nor* 88; R Rockland St Mary w Hellington, Bramerton etc 88-94; P-in-c Kirby Bedon w Bixley and Whitlingham 92-94; R Rockland St Mary w Hellington, Bramerton etc from 94; RD Loddon 92-95. *The Rectory, Rectory Lane, Rockland St Mary, Norwich NR14 7EY* Surlingham (01508) 538619

LEE, Alan Charles. b 32. S'wark Ord Course 77. **d** 79 **p** 80. NSM Acton Green St Pet *Lon* 79-82; Chapl RADD 82-83; P-in-c St Magnus the Martyr w St Marg New Fish Street *Lon* 83-84; NSM Barnes St Mich *S'wark* 84-90; Perm to Offic *Lon* 89-91; C Brighton St Pet and St Nic w Chpl Royal *Chich* 90-92; rtd 92. *Flat 1, 8 Chichester Terrace, Brighton, E Sussex BN2 1FH*

LEE, Anthony Maurice. b 35. Bps' Coll Cheshunt 62. **d** 65 **p** 66. C Pinner *Lon* 65-71; Asst Youth Chapl *Glouc* 71-72; V Childswyckham 72-73; R Aston Somerville 72-73; V Childswyckham w Aston Somerville 73-91; P-in-c Buckland 88-91; P-in-c Stanton w Snowshill 88-91; R Childswyckham w Aston Somerville, Buckland etc 91-94; RD Winchcombe 86-94; rtd 94. *2 Close Garden, Condicote, Cheltenham, Glos GL54 1ES*

LEE, Arnold John. b 17. St Edm Hall Ox BA40 DipTh41 MA43. Wycliffe Hall Ox 40. **d** 42 **p** 43. V Ox St Andr *Ox* 69-78; V E Boldre w S Baddesley *Win* 78-82; rtd 82; Perm to Offic *Ox* 82-95. *30 Capel Court, The Burgage, Prestbury, Cheltenham, Glos GL52 3EL* Cheltenham (01242) 518625

LEE, Canon Arthur Gordon. b 32. Univ of Wales (Swansea) BA52. St Mich Coll Llan 53. **d** 55 **p** 56. C Brynmawr *S & B* 55-57; C Llangyfelach and Morriston 57-60; V Llanddewi Ystradenni and Abbey Cwmhir 60-69; V Swansea St Pet from 69; RD Penderi from 90; Hon Can Brecon Cathl 91-95; Can Res Brecon Cathl from 95. *The Vicarage, 59 Station Road, Fforestfach, Swansea SA5 5AU* Swansea (01792) 581514

LEE, Brian. b 37. Linc Th Coll 78. **d** 80 **p** 81. C Duston *Pet* 80-84; P-in-c Spratton 84-89; V from 89; P-in-c Maidwell w Draughton, Lamport w Faxton from 89; RD Brixworth from 94. *The Vicarage, 2 Church Road, Spratton, Northampton NN6 8HR* Northampton (01604) 847212

LEE, Brian Ernest. b 32. ACA59 FCA70. Linc Th Coll 60. **d** 62 **p** 63. C Birch St Jas *Man* 62-65; C Withington St Paul 65-66; R Abbey Hey 66-70; Hon C Gatley *Ches* 86-88; V Egremont St Jo from 88; RD Wallasey from 91; OGS from 93. *St John's Vicarage, 7 Silverbeech Road, Wallasey, Merseyside L44 9BT* 0151-638 4360

LEE, Brian John. b 51. K Coll Lon BD78 AKC78. Coll of Resurr Mirfield 78. **d** 79 **p** 80. C Ham St Rich *S'wark* 79-82; C Surbiton St Andr and St Mark 82-85; V Shirley St Geo 85-93; V St Botolph Aldgate w H Trin Minories *Lon* from 93. *St Botolph's Vestry, Aldgate, London EC3N 1AB* 0171-283 1670 or 283 1950 Fax 283 9302

LEE, Christopher Garfield (Chris). b 41. St Deiniol's Hawarden 80. **d** 80 **p** 81. C Swansea St Pet *S & B* 80-81; C Oystermouth 81-83; R Cromhall w Tortworth and Tytherington *Glouc* 83-93; R Bishopston *S & B* from 93; UK Field Dir Educn for Min Progr from 93. *The Rectory, 4 Portway, Bishopston, Swansea SA3 3JR* Swansea (01792) 232140 Fax 233123

LEE, Clive Warwick. b 34. St Pet Coll Ox BA58 MA62 Ox Univ PGCE73. Coll of Resurr Mirfield 58. **d** 60 **p** 61. Lic to Offic

Chich from 69; Chapl Vinehall Sch E Sussex 69-94; rtd 94. *2 Barracks Cottages, Robertsbridge, E Sussex TN32 5JH* Robertsbridge (01580) 880675

LEE, Colin John Willmot. b 21. Wycliffe Hall Ox 57. **d** 59 **p** 59. Bp's Ind Adv *Derby* 67-91; P-in-c Stanton by Dale 69-76; V Ilkeston St Jo 76-91; rtd 91; Perm to Offic *S'well* from 91. *3 Buttermead Close, Trowell, Nottingham NG9 3QT* Nottingham (0115) 949 0100

LEE, Cyril Herbert. b 16. St Jo Coll Dur BA38 DipTh39 MA41. **d** 39 **p** 40. Chapl Oakwood Hosp Maidstone 64-66; Perm to Offic *Cant* from 74; rtd 81; Chapl HM Pris Standford Hill 81-82. *80 Church Lane, Newington, Sittingbourne, Kent ME9 4JU* Newington (01795) 842704

LEE, David Hartley. b 28. St Deiniol's Hawarden 61. **d** 63 **p** 64. C Merthyr Dyfan *Llan* 63-65; C Penarth All SS 65-70; Miss to Seamen from 70; Canada 70-84 and from 90. *c/o Herring Cove PO, Halifax, Nova Scotia, Canada, B0J 1S0*

LEE, David John. b 46. Bris Univ BSc67 Lon Univ DipTh73 Fitzw Coll Cam BA76. Ridley Hall Cam 74. **d** 77 **p** 78. C Putney St Marg *S'wark* 77-80; Uganda 80-86; Tutor Crowther Hall CMS Tr Coll Selly Oak 86-91; Lic to Offic *Birm* 87-91; P-in-c Wishaw from 91; P-in-c Middleton from 91. *The Vicarage, Coppice Lane, Middleton, Tamworth, Staffs B78 2AR* 0121-323 3022

LEE, Ven David Stanley. b 30. Univ of Wales (Cardiff) BSc51. St Mich Coll Llan 56. **d** 57 **p** 58. C Caerau w Ely *Llan* 57-60; C Port Talbot St Agnes 60-70; Ind Chapl 60-70; R Merthyr Tydfil 70-72; Chapl Merthyr Tydfil Hosp 70-91; R Merthyr Tydfil and Cyfarthfa *Llan* 72-91; RD Merthyr Tydfil 82-91; Can Llan Cathl from 84; Adn Llan from 91; R Llanfabon from 91. *Llanfabon Rectory, High Street, Nelson, M Glam CF46 6HA* Nelson (01443) 450335

LEE, David Wight Dunsmore. b 39. Wells Th Coll 61. **d** 63 **p** 64. C Middlesb St Oswald *York* 63-67; C Northallerton w Kirby Sigston 67-69; Malawi 69-75; V Newington Transfiguration *York* 76-81; P-in-c Sheriff Hutton 81-85; P-in-c Sheriff Hutton and Farlington from 85. *The Vicarage, New Lane, Sheriff Hutton, York YO6 1QU* Sheriff Hutton (01347) 870336

LEE, Donald Hugh Thomson. b 48. Bard Coll (NY) BA70 Keble Coll Ox BA73 MA78. St Steph Ho Ox 72. **d** 74 **p** 75. C Swindon New Town *Bris* 74-79; C W Hampstead St Jas *Lon* 79-83; V Haggerston St Chad from 83. *St Chad's Vicarage, Dunloe Street, London E2 8JR* 0171-739 3878

LEE, Edmund Hugh. b 53. Trin Coll Ox BA75 Golds Coll Lon BMus83. Ripon Coll Cuddesdon 93. **d** 95. C Malden St Jas *S'wark* from 95. *15 Knightwood Crescent, New Malden, Surrey KT3 5SR*

LEE, Francis George (Frank). b 37. Univ of Wales (Ban). St Aid Birkenhead 62. **d** 65 **p** 66. C Wavertree H Trin *Liv* 65-69; Bahamas 69-72; 81-84; V Knowsley *Liv* 72-76; Australia 76-81; V Middle Rasen Drax *Linc* 84-88; Miss to Seamen 88-92; R Maybole *Glas* 88-92; R Girvan 88-92; P-in-c Pinmore 88-92; TV Upper Holme Valley *Wakef* from 92. *The Vicarage, Kirkroyds Lane, New Mill, Huddersfield HD7 7LS* Holmfirth (01484) 683375

LEE, Frederick Roydon. b 13. OBE69. S'wark Ord Course 76. **d** 77 **p** 78. NSM Sundridge w Ide Hill *Roch* 77-81; rtd 81; Perm to Offic *Roch* from 81. *Tranquil, Combe Bank, Sundridge, Sevenoaks, Kent TN14 6AD* Westerham (01959) 563552

LEE, Frederick William Maxwell. b 15. Dur Univ LTh40 St Pet Hall Ox BA47 MA51 Ox Univ Inst of Educn CertEd68. Lambeth STh89 St Aid Birkenhead 37. **d** 40 **p** 41. Perm to Offic the *Nor* 68-70; Asst Master Thorpe Gr Sch 68-70; Hitchin Girls' Gr Sch 70-80; C St Alb St Sav *St Alb* 74-80; rtd 80; Perm to Offic *St Alb* from 80. *13 Sandpit Lane, St Albans, Herts AL1 4DY* St Albans (01727) 857353

LEE, Gilbert (Sai Kuen). b 51. Hong Kong BD80. **d** 80 **p** 81. Hong Kong 80-88; NSM St Martin-in-the-Fields *Lon* from 88; Chapl to Chinese in London from 88. *3 Strutton Court, 54 Great Peter Street, London SW1P 2HH* 0171-233 0723

LEE, Hector. b 33. Leeds Univ CertEd60. Kelham Th Coll 53. **d** 57 **p** 58. SSM from 57; Tutor Kelham Th Coll 60-63; Basutoland 63-66; Lesotho 66-69; S Africa 69-88; Can Bloemfontein Cathl 80-88; V Burnley St Cuth *Blackb* from 88. *The Vicarage, Barbon Street, Burnley, Lancs BB10 1TS* Burnley (01282) 424978

LEE, Henry. b 31. St Chad's Coll Dur BA53 DipTh55 CertEd. **d** 55 **p** 56. V Medomsley *Dur* 65-75; Chapl Darlington Memorial Hosp 75-79; V Darlington H Trin *Dur* 75-82; V Brompton w Deighton *York* 82-90; rtd 90. *103 Benfieldside Road, Consett, Co Durham DH8 0RS* Consett (01207) 592170

LEE, Miss Hoe Lynley. b 52. St Jo Coll Nottm BTh89. **d** 90 **p** 94. Par Dn Pitsea *Chelmsf* 90-95; C Pitsea w Nevendon 95. *112 Mallgraves, Pitsea, Basildon, Essex SS13 3QE* Basildon (01268) 551725

LEE, Hugh Gordon Cassels. b 41. St Andr Univ BSc64. Edin Th Coll 64. **d** 67 **p** 68. C Dumfries *Glas* 67-70; C Totteridge *St Alb* 70-73; R Glas St Jas *Glas* 73-80; R Bishopbriggs 80-86; R St

Fillans *St And* 86-89; P-in-c Muthill 86-90; R Comrie from 86; R Crieff from 86; P-in-c Lochearnhead from 89. *Ainsdale, 10 Dollerie Terrace, Crieff, Perthshire PH7 3ED* Crieff (01764) 653898

LEE, Miss Iris Audrey Olive. b 26. St Andr Coll Southsea 54. dss 76 **d** 87. N Weald Bassett *Chelmsf* 76-87; rtd 87; NSM Clacton St Jas *Chelmsf* from 87. *30 Marine Court, Marine Parade West, Clacton-on-Sea, Essex CO15 1ND* Clacton-on-Sea (01255) 423719

LEE, John Charles Hugh Mellanby. b 44. Trin Hall Cam BA66 MA69 Brunel Univ MTech71. Ox NSM Course 78. **d** 81 **p** 82. NSM Amersham on the Hill *Ox* 81-88; NSM Ox St Aldate w St Matt 88-93; NSM Wheatley w Forest Hill and Stanton St John from 93. *12 Walton Street, Oxford OX1 2HG* Oxford (01865) 511382

LEE, John Foden. b 34. AKC61. **d** 61 **p** 62. C Pet All SS *Pet* 61-63; C Sudbury St Andr *Lon* 63-65; C Sherborne w Castleton and Lillington *Sarum* 65-67; V Erlestoke 67-68; R Gt Cheverell 67; V Erlestoke and Gt Cheverell 68-79; V Seend and Bulkington 79-86; Ind Chapl *Derby* from 86; V Derby St Paul from 86. *St Paul's Vicarage, Old Chester Road, Chester Green, Derby DE1 3SA* Derby (01332) 381116

LEE, John Michael Andrew. b 62. Leeds Univ BA84. Trin Coll Bris 88. **d** 90 **p** 91. C Norbiton *S'wark* 90-94; C Leic H Trin w St Jo *Leic* from 94. *25 Holbrook Road, Leicester LE2 3LG* Leicester (0116) 270 0732

LEE, John Royden. b 47. MInstGA87 Univ of Wales (Swansea) BSc70 MSc73. Ripon Hall Ox 73. **d** 75 **p** 76. C Swansea St Pet *S & B* 75-78; C St Botolph Aldgate w H Trin Minories *Lon* 79-84; P-in-c Chiddingstone w Chiddingstone Causeway *Roch* 84-89; R from 89. *The Rectory, Chiddingstone, Edenbridge, Kent TN8 7AH* Penshurst (01892) 870478

LEE, John Samuel. b 47. Chich Th Coll 74. **d** 77 **p** 78. C Bramley *Ripon* 77-80; C Bideford *Ex* 81-84; TV Littleham w Exmouth 84-90; P-in-c Sidbury 90-91; TV Sidmouth, Woolbrook, Salcombe Regis, Sidbury etc from 91. *The Vicarage, Harcombe Lane, Sidford, Sidmouth, Devon EX10 9QN* Sidmouth (01395) 579520

LEE, Kenneth Peter. b 45. Em Coll Cam BA67 MA71. Cuddesdon Coll 67. **d** 69 **p** 70. C Stoke Poges *Ox* 69-72; C Witton *Ches* 72-74; V Frankby w Greasby 74-92; R Christleton from 92. *The Rectory, Birch Heath Lane, Christleton, Chester CH3 7AP* Chester (01244) 335663

LEE, Luke Gun-Hong. b 37. Univ of Yon Sei BTh62. St Jo Coll Morpeth 64. **d** 67 **p** 68. Korea 67-79; C Bloxwich *Lich* 79-83; TV Dunstable *St Alb* 83-90; V Croxley Green All SS from 90. *All Saints' Vicarage, Croxley Green, Rickmansworth, Herts WD3 3HJ* Rickmansworth (01923) 772109

LEE, Nicholas Knyvett. b 54. MA. Cranmer Hall Dur. **d** 85 **p** 86. C Brompton H Trin w Onslow Square St Paul *Lon* from 85. *St Paul's Church House, Onslow Square, London SW7 3NX* 0171-589 3933

LEE, Peter Alexander. b 44. Hull Univ BSc(Econ)65. Ex & Truro NSM Scheme 80. **d** 83 **p** 84. NSM Ex St Sidwell and St Matt *Ex* 83-89; NSM Ex St Dav from 90. *Windyridge, Beech Avenue, Exeter EX4 6HF* Exeter (01392) 54118

✠LEE, Rt Rev Peter John. b 47. St Jo Coll Cam BA69 CertEd70 MA73. Ridley Hall Cam 70 St Jo Coll Nottm 72. **d** 73 **p** 74 **c** 90. C Onslow Square St Paul *Lon* 73-76; S Africa from 76; V-Gen and Bp Ch the K from 90. *PO Box 1653, Rosettenville, 2130 South Africa* Johannesburg (11) 435-0097

LEE, Peter Kenneth. b 44. Selw Coll Cam BA66 MA69. Cuddesdon Coll 67. **d** 69 **p** 70. C Manston *Ripon* 69-72; C Bingley All SS *Bradf* 72-77; Chapl Bingley Coll of Educn 72-77; V Cross Roads cum Lees *Bradf* 77-90; V Auckland St Pet *Dur* from 90; Tutor NE Ord Course from 91. *St Peter's Vicarage, 39 Etherley Lane, Bishop Auckland, Co Durham DL14 7QZ* Bishop Auckland (01388) 661856

LEE, Canon Raymond John. b 30. St Edm Hall Ox BA53 MA57. Tyndale Hall Bris 54. **d** 56 **p** 57. V Woking St Mary *Guildf* 62-70; V Gt Crosby St Luke *Liv* 70-82; Dioc Adv NSM 79-95; V Allerton 82-94; Hon Can Liv Cathl 89-95; P-in-c Altcar from 94; rtd 95. *15 Barkfield Lane, Formby, Liverpool L37 1LY* Formby (01704) 872670

LEE, Reginald Wilfred. b 09. Kelham Th Coll 27. **d** 32 **p** 33. C Upper Norwood All SS w St Marg *Cant* 58-71; rtd 71. *College of St Barnabas, Blackberry Lane, Lingfield, Surrey RH7 6NJ* Dormans Park (01342) 870260

LEE, Richard Alexander. b 63. St Jo Coll Nottm BTh91. **d** 91 **p** 92. C Gt Stanmore *Lon* 91-95; C Edgware from 95. *50 Fairfield Crescent, Edgeware, Middx HA8 9AH* 0181-952 1243

LEE, Robert David. b 53. QUB BD75. CITC 77. **d** 77 **p** 78. C Comber *D & D* 77-83; I Mt Merrion 83-87; CMS 89-92; Egypt from 89. *PO Box 87, Zamalek, Cairo, Egypt*

LEE, Robert William. b 31. Keele Univ BA54 St Cath Soc Ox BA58 MA63. Ripon Hall Ox 56. **d** 59 **p** 60. C Dawley St Jerome *Lon* 59-62; C Bromley H Trin *Roch* 62-65; R Clayton

Man 65-70; P-in-c Man St Paul 65-70; TV Hemel Hempstead *St Alb* 70-72; TV Corby SS Pet and Andr w Gt and Lt Oakley *Pet* 72-80; V Weedon Lois w Plumpton and Moreton Pinkney etc 80-88; R Thornhams Magna and Parva, Gislingham and Mellis *St E* from 88. *The Rectory, Orchard Close, Gislingham, Eye, Suffolk IP23 8JW* Mellis (01379) 783652

LEE, Roderick James. b 50. Linc Th Coll 88. **d** 90 **p** 91. C Rushden w Newton Bromswold *Pet* 90-93; C Kingsthorpe w St Dav Northn 93-95; TV from 95. *42 Fallow Walk, Northampton NN2 8DE* Northampton (01604) 846215

LEE, Simon Margeison. b 43. Brighton Coll of Educn TCert66. Cant Sch of Min 90. **d** 93 **p** 94. NSM Walmer *Cant* from 93. *26 Greenacre Drive, Deal, Kent CT14 7UQ* Deal (01304) 362585

LEE, Steven Michael. b 56. Dur Univ BA. Trin Coll Bris 80. **d** 83 **p** 84. C Beckenham St Jo *Roch* 83-86; C Leic Martyrs *Leic* 86-90; V Coalville and Bardon Hill 90-95; P-in-c Kibworth and Smeeton Westerby and Saddington from 95. *The Rectory, 25 Church Road, Kibworth, Leicester LE8 0NB* Kibworth (0116) 279 9244

LEE, Terence. b 46. FCA. Ox NSM Course. **d** 83 **p** 84. NSM Calcot *Ox* 83-87; NSM Burghfield 87-88; Perm to Offic from 88. *45 Christchurch Road, Reading RG2 7AN* Reading (01734) 312512

LEE, Thomas Richard. b 52. AKC73. St Aug Coll Cant 74. **d** 75 **p** 76. C Leam Lane CD *Dur* 75-80; Chapl RAF from 80. *Chaplaincy Services (RAF), HQ, Personnel and Training Command, RAF Innsworth, Gloucester GL3 1EZ* Gloucester (01452) 712612 Ext 5164 Fax 510828

LEE, William George. b 11. TCD BA33 MA48. **d** 34 **p** 35. V Chislehurst Ch Ch *Roch* 61-76; rtd 76. *Dale Garth, Harmby, Leyburn, N Yorkshire DL8 5PD* Wensleydale (01969) 622649

LEE WARNER, Canon Theodore John. b 22. Univ Coll Ox BA49 MA54. Wells Th Coll 50. **d** 51 **p** 52. V Darlington H Trin *Dur* 63-74; Chapl Darlington Memorial Hosp 63-74; V Norton St Mary *Dur* 74-80; RD Barnard Castle 80-87; V Gainford 80-87; R Winston 80-87; Hon Can Dur Cathl 83-87; rtd 87. *112 Cleveland Terrace, Darlington, Co Durham DL3 8JA* Darlington (01325) 467585

LEECE, Roderick Neil Stephen. b 59. ARCM85 Wadh Coll Ox BA81 MA85 Leeds Univ BA84. Coll of Resurr Mirfield 82. **d** 85 **p** 86. C Portsea St Mary *Portsm* 85-91; V Stamford Hill St Bart *Lon* from 91. *St Bartholomew's Vicarage, Craven Park Road, London N15 6AA* 0181-800 1554

LEECH, Christopher. b 16. Linc Th Coll 37. **d** 39 **p** 40. R Combe Pyne w Rousdon *Ex* 60-76; P-in-c 76-82; rtd 82; Perm to Offic *Ex* from 82. *Nestor, Hillhead, Colyton, Devon EX13 6HH* Colyton (01297) 552034

LEECH, Kenneth. b 39. Lon Univ BA61 AKC61 Trin Coll Ox BA63 MA71. St Steph Ho Ox 62. **d** 64 **p** 65. C Hoxton H Trin w St Mary *Lon* 64-67; C Soho St Anne w St Thos and St Pet 67-71; Tutor St Aug Coll Cant 71-74; R Bethnal Green St Matt *Lon* 74-79; Field Officer Community & Race Relns Unit BCC 80; Race Relns Officer Gen Syn Bd for Soc Resp 81-87; Hon C Notting Hill St Clem and St Mark *Lon* 82-85; Hon C Notting Dale St Clem w St Mark and St Jas 85-88; Dir Runnymede Trust 87-90; St Botolph Aldgate w H Trin Minories *Lon* from 91. *St Botolph's Vestry, Aldgate, London EC3N 1AB* 0171-377 0721

LEECH, Miss Peggy Irene. b 29. CA Tr Coll 56. **dss** 85 **d** 87 **p** 94. Oxhey All SS *St Alb* 86-87; C from 87; rtd 91. *9 The Mead, Carpenters Park, Watford WD1 5BY* 0181-428 6136

LEEDS, Archdeacon of. *See* OLIVER, Ven John Michael

LEEFIELD, Michael John. b 37. Liv Univ BA60 K Coll Lon BD65 AKC65. St Boniface Warminster 62. **d** 66 **p** 67. C Gt Yarmouth *Nor* 66-70; V Trowse 70-75; V Arminghall 70-75; R Caistor w Markshall 70-75; Chapl Norfolk and Nor Hosp 70-75; V Lydney w Aylburton *Glouc* 75-84; RD Forest S 82-84; Lic to Offic from 85. *Brays Court, Awre, Newnham, Glos GL14 1EP* Longhope (01594) 510483

LEEKE, Charles Browne. b 39. TCD DipTh CertEd. **d** 83 **p** 84. C Ballymoney w Finvoy and Rasharkin *Conn* 83-86; I Faughanvale *D & R* from 86; Miss to Seamen from 92; Bp's Dom Chapl *D & R* from 92. *21 Main Street, Eglinton, Londonderry BT47 3AB* Eglinton (01504) 810217

LEEKE, Stephen Owen. b 50. E Anglian Minl Tr Course 82 Ridley Hall Cam 83. **d** 84 **p** 85. C Cherry Hinton St Andr *Ely* 84-87; P-in-c Warboys 87-91; P-in-c Wistow 87-91; P-in-c Bury 87-91; R Warboys w Broughton and Bury w Wistow from 91; RD St Ives from 92. *The Rectory, 15 Church Road, Warboys, Huntingdon, Cambs PE17 2RJ* Ramsey (01487) 822237

LEEMAN, John Graham. b 41. N Ord Course 78. **d** 80 **p** 81. NSM Hull Sculcoates St Mary *York* from 80. *1 Snuff Mill Lane, Cottingham, N Humberside HU16 4RY* Hull (01482) 840355

LEEMING, Jack. b 34. Kelham Th Coll 56. **d** 61 **p** 62. C Sydenham St Phil *S'wark* 61-64; Chapl RAF 64-68; Chapl

Salisbury Gen Infirmary 84-89; R Barford St Martin, Dinton, Baverstock etc *Sarum* from 89. *The Rectory, Barford St Martin, Salisbury SP3 4AS* Salisbury (01722) 743385

LEEMING, John Maurice. b 24. CEng MIMechE MIProdE FIED. NW Ord Course 72. **d** 75 **p** 76. NSM Endcliffe *Sheff* 75-78; C Norton 78-80; V Bolsterstone 80-89; Jt Min Stocksbridge Chr Cen LEP 80-89; Ind Chapl 81-89; rtd 89; Perm to Offic *S'well* from 89. *Beck House, Toftdyke Lane, Clayworth, Retford, Notts DN22 9AH* Retford (01777) 817795

LEEMING, Peter. b 23. Leeds Univ BA50. Bps' Coll Cheshunt 50. **d** 52 **p** 53. C Moordown *Win* 68-71; C Hawarden *St As* 71-78; TV 78-89; rtd 89. *2 Church Cottages, Rectory Drive, Hawarden, Deeside, Clwyd CH5 3NN* Hawarden (01244) 531186

LEES, Charles Alan. b 38. RGN OND FETC. W Midl Minl Tr Course 78. **d** 81 **p** 82. NSM Yardley St Cypr Hay Mill *Birm* 81-84 and 86-87; Hon C Dorridge 84-86; Chapl E Birm Hosp 85-87; Hon C Leamington Spa and Old Milverton *Cov* 89-90; Perm to Offic *Birm* from 95. *49 Gordon Street, Leamington Spa, Warks CV31 1HR* Leamington Spa (01926) 332199

LEES, John Raymond. b 57. Selw Coll Cam BA78 MA82. St Steph Ho Ox 89. **d** 91 **p** 92. C Eastbourne St Mary *Chich* 91-93; Min Can and Succ St Paul's Cathl *Lon* from 93. *8A Amen Court, London EC4M 7BU* 0171-248 6115

LEES, Mrs Kathleen Marion. b 30. Birkb Coll Lon BA60 DipRS80. S'wark Ord Course 77. **dss** 80 **d** 87 **p** 94. Epping St Jo *Chelmsf* 80-86; Hon C Hunstanton St Mary w Ringstead Parva, Holme etc *Nor* 87-88; Perm to Offic 88-94; NSM Gaywood St Faith 94-95; NSM Gaywood St Faith, Kings Lynn from 95; Chapl Qu Eliz Hosp K Lynn from 94. *12 Cherry Tree Road, Snettisham, King's Lynn, Norfolk PE31 7NZ* Dersingham (01485) 540364

LEES, Stephen. b 55. St Jo Coll York CertEd77 BEd78. St Jo Coll Nottm 88. **d** 90 **p** 91. C Mansf St Jo *S'well* 90-93; TV Bestwood from 93. *45 Pine Hill Close, Nottingham NG5 9DA* Nottingham (0115) 927 7229

LEES, Stuart Charles Roderick. b 62. Trin Coll Bris BA. **d** 89 **p** 90. C Woodford Wells *Chelmsf* 89-93; C Brompton H Trin w Onslow Square St Paul *Lon* from 93. *clo Holy Trinity Vicarage, 73 Prince's Gate Mews, London SW7 2PP* 0171-584 8957

LEES-SMITH, Christopher John (Brother Edward). b 21. CCC Ox BA49 MA65. Cuddesdon Coll 48. **d** 50 **p** 51. SSF from 54; Perm to Offic *Newc* 62-74; Guardian Alnmouth Friary 65-74; Chapl to the Third Order SSF 74-91; rtd 91. *42 Balaam Street, London E13 8AQ* 0171-476 5189

LEESE, Arthur Selwyn Mountford. b 09. K Coll Lon BD31 AKC31 St Cath Soc Ox BA33 MA44. Ripon Hall Ox 31. **d** 33 **p** 34. V Hawkhurst *Cant* 51-74; rtd 74; Perm to Offic *Chich* from 76; Perm to Offic *Cant* from 77. *84 Wickham Avenue, Bexhill-on-Sea, E Sussex TN39 3ER* Bexhill-on-Sea (01424) 213137

LEESE, Frederick Henry Brooke. b 24. AKC47. **d** 47 **p** 48. V Pagham *Chich* 60-70; V Chorley *Ches* 70-82; R Rogate w Terwick and Trotton w Chithurst *Chich* 82-90; RD Midhurst 85-90; rtd 90; Perm to Offic *B & W* from 90. *Treetops, Furnham Crescent, Chard, Somerset TA20 1AZ* Chard (01460) 65524

LEESON, Bernard Alan. b 47. MIMgt92 FCollP92 FRSA92 Bris Univ CertEd68 Open Univ BA75 Southn Univ MA78. E Midl Min Tr Course 84. **d** 87 **p** 88. Dep Hd Master Ripley Mill Hill Sch 80-91; NSM Breadsall *Derby* 87-91; Hd St Aid CE High Sch Lancs from 91; Perm to Offic *Blackb* 91-92; Lic to Offic from 92; NSM Officer from 92. *The Lodge, Daggers Lane, Preesall, Poulton-le-Fylde, Lancs FY6 0QN* Knott End (01253) 811020 or 810504 Fax 810244

LEESON, David Harry Stanley. b 45. Glouc Th Course 82. **d** 85 **p** 86. NSM Stratton w Baunton *Glouc* 85-94; NSM N Cerney w Bagendon 91-94; NSM Stratton, N Cerney, Baunton and Bagendon from 95. *83 Cheltenham Road, Stratton, Cirencester, Glos GL7 2JB* Cirencester (01285) 651186

LEESON, Mrs Sally Elizabeth. b 57. Sussex Univ BA79. Westcott Ho Cam 83. **dss** 85 **d** 87 **p** 94. Battersea St Pet and St Paul *S'wark* 85-87; Par Dn 87-90; Par Dn Limpsfield and Titsey 90-94; C 94; Perm to Offic from 94. *32 Albany Road, New Malden, Surrey KT3 3NY*

LEFEVER, Dr Henry Charles. b 06. Lon Univ BA30 BD32 Tubingen Univ PhD34. **d** 65 **p** 66. Hon C Blackheath Ascension *S'wark* 69-75; rtd 75; Perm to Offic *Cant* from 76. *10 Mulberry Court, Stour Street, Canterbury, Kent CT1 2NT* Canterbury (01227) 768304

LEFFLER, Christopher. b 33. Em Coll Cam BA57 MA61. Linc Th Coll. **d** 59 **p** 60. C Bermondsey St Mary w St Olave and St Jo *S'wark* 59-60; C Herne Hill St Paul 60-63; C-in-c Canley CD *Cov* 63-67; R Gt and Lt Glemham *St E* 67-72; R Badwell Ash w Gt Ashfield, Stowlangtoft etc 72-82; R Trimley from 82. *The Rectory, Church Lane, Trimley, Ipswich IP10 0SW* Felixstowe (01394) 286188

LEFFLER, Jeremy Paul (Jem). b 62. Westmr Coll Ox BEd88. Wycliffe Hall Ox BTh94. **d** 94 **p** 95. C Ormskirk *Liv* from 94. *18 Lea Crescent, Ormskirk, Lancs L39 1PQ* Ormskirk (01695) 570874 or 571832

LEFROY, Christopher John Elton. b 25. Clare Coll Cam BA46 MA49. Ridley Hall Cam 47. **d** 49 **p** 50. V Highbury Ch Ch *Lon* 65-78; V Highbury Ch Ch w St Jo 79-82; V Highbury Ch Ch w St Jo and St Sav Lon 82-90; rtd 90. *12 Rodmill Drive, Eastbourne, E Sussex BN21 2SG* Eastbourne (01323) 640294

LEFROY, John Perceval. b 40. Trin Coll Cam BA62. Cuddesdon Coll 64. **d** 66 **p** 67. C Maidstone St Martin *Cant* 66-69; C St Peter-in-Thanet 69-74; V Barming Heath 74-82; V Upchurch w Lower Halstow from 82; P-in-c Iwade from 95. *The Vicarage, 15 Oak Lane, Upchurch, Sittingbourne, Kent ME9 7AT* Medway (01634) 387227

LEFROY (nee CLARK), Mrs Kathleen Christine. b 33. Newton Park Coll Bris TCert53 Lon Univ DipTh58. St Mich Ho Ox 56 Trin Coll Bris 90. **d** 90. Personnel Sec SAMS 83-91; Asst Gen Sec 87-92; NSM Eastbourne H Trin *Chich* from 90; Chmn SEAN (Internat) and SOMA (UK) from 91; rtd 92; Dioc Voc Adv *Chich* from 92. *12 Rodmill Drive, Eastbourne, E Sussex BN21 2SG* Eastbourne (01323) 640294

LEGG, Adrian James. b 52. St Jo Coll Nottm LTh82 BTh82. **d** 82 **p** 83. C Haughton le Skerne *Dur* 82-85; C Llanishen and Lisvane *Llan* 85-89; V Llanwddyn and Llanfihangel and Llwydiarth *St As* 89-93; V Llansadwrn w Llanwrda and Manordeilo *St D* from 93. *The Vicarage, Llanwrda, Dyfed SA19 8HD* Llangadog (01550) 777343

LEGG, Joanna Susan Penberthy. *See* PENBERTHY, Ms Joanna Susan

LEGG, John Andrew Douglas. b 32. Selw Coll Cam BA55 MA57. Wells Th Coll 57. **d** 59 **p** 59. Solomon Is 70-71; Asst Master Lt Ilford Comp Sch 72-83; P-in-c Stapleford Tawney w Theydon Mt *Chelmsf* 78-83; R Hemingby *Linc* 83-88; Greece from 88; rtd 92. *Prastos, Kynorias, Arkadia, Greece 22006* Arkadia (755) 51693

LEGG, Reginald John. b 26. LRAM50 TCert45. Wells Th Coll 61. **d** 63 **p** 64. Miss to Seamen 67-74; V Methwold *Ely* 74-80; RD Feltwell 75-80; P-in-c Preston *Glouc* 80-91; P-in-c Dymock w Donnington and Kempley 80-91; rtd 91. *3 Shottsford Close, Swanage, Dorset BH19 2LH* Swanage (01929) 427989

LEGG, Dr Richard. b 37. Selw Coll Cam BA62 MA66 Brunel Univ MPhil77. NY Th Sem DMin Coll of Resurr Mirfield 63. **d** 65 **p** 66. C Ealing St Pet Mt Park *Lon* 65-68; Chapl Brunel Univ 68-78; C Chipping Barnet w Arkley *St Alb* 81-83; TV 83-85; R St Buryan, St Levan and Sennen *Truro* 85-93; Subwarden St Deiniol's Lib Hawarden 93; Perm to Offic *Ches* 93; TV Beaminster Area *Sarum* from 93. *The Vicarage, 20 Orchard Way, Mosterton, Beaminster, Dorset DT8 3LT* Broadwindsor (01308) 868090

LEGG, Robert Richard. b 16. MBE45. Open Univ BA78. St Aug Coll Cant 36. **d** 59 **p** 60. V W w E Tytherley *Win* 62-71; V Kingsclere 71-83; rtd 83; Perm to Offic *Win* from 83. *The Furrow, Evingar Road, Whitchurch, Hants RG28 7EU* Whitchurch (01256) 892126

LEGG, Roger Keith. b 35. Lich Th Coll 61. **d** 63 **p** 64. C Petersfield w Sheet *Portsm* 63-66; C Portsea St Mary 66-70; Rhodesia 70-75; V Clayton *Lich* from 75. *The Vicarage, Clayton Lane, Newcastle, Staffs ST5 3DW* Newcastle-under-Lyme (01782) 614500

LEGG, Miss Ruth Helen Margaret. b 52. Hull Univ BA74 Homerton Coll Cam CertEd75. Trin Coll Bris DipHE88. **d** 88 **p** 94. C Clevedon St Andr and Ch Ch *B & W* 88-92; C Nailsea Ch Ch from 92. *32 Southfield Road, Nailsea, Bristol BS19 1JB* Nailsea (01275) 855789

LEGGATE, Colin Archibald Gunson. b 44. Bris Sch of Min 86. **d** 88 **p** 89. NSM Brislington St Luke *Bris* from 88. *20 Pendennis Park, Bristol BS4 4JN* Bristol (0117) 971 4301

LEGGE, Frederick John (Fred). b 10. Ridley Hall Cam 58. **d** 59 **p** 59. R E Leake *S'well* 63-76; P-in-c Rempstone 70-76; P-in-c Costock 70-76; P-in-c Stanford on Soar 70-76; rtd 76. *Flat 11, Ellesborough Manor, Butlers Cross, Aylesbury, Bucks HP17 0XF* Aylesbury (01296) 696001

LEGGETT, James Henry Aufrere. b 61. Oak Hill Th Coll DipHE93. **d** 93 **p** 94. C Hensingham *Carl* from 93. *13 West View, Hensingham, Whitehaven, Cumbria CA28 8QY* Whitehaven (01946) 67030

LEGGETT, Vanessa Gisela. *See* CATO, Ms Vanessa Gisela

LEGOOD, Giles Leslie. b 67. K Coll Lon BD88 AKC88. Ripon Coll Cuddesdon 90. **d** 92 **p** 93. C N Mymms *St Alb* 92-95; Chapl Lon Univ Medical Students *Lon* from 95. *15 Ormonde Mansions, 106 Southampton Row, London WC1B 4BP* 0171-242 2574

LEICESTER, Archdeacon of. *See* EDSON, Ven Michael (Mike)
LEICESTER, Bishop of. *See* BUTLER, Rt Rev Thomas Frederick
LEICESTER, Provost of. *See* HOLE, Very Rev Derek Norman

LEIGH, Mrs Alison Margaret. b 40. CertEd63 Golds Coll Lon BEd75. Sarum & Wells Th Coll 85. **d** 87 **p** 94. C Chessington *Guildf* 87-90; C Green Street Green *Roch* 90-92; D-in-c E Peckham and Nettlestead 92-94; P-in-c from 94. *The Rectory, Bush Road, East Peckham, Tonbridge, Kent TN12 5LL* East Peckham (01622) 871278

LEIGH, Arnold Robert. b 36. AKC60. **d** 61 **p** 62. C Lewisham St Mary *S'wark* 61-66; C Stockwell Green St Andr 66-69; V 69-72; TV Withycombe Raleigh *Ex* 72-74; TR 74-80; V Devonport St Bart 80-93; P-in-c Moretonhampstead, N Bovey and Manaton from 93. *The Rectory, 3 Grays Meadow, Moretonhampstead, Newton Abbot, Devon TQ13 8NB* Moretonhampstead (01647) 440977

LEIGH, Dennis Herbert. b 34. Lon Univ BSc56 DipTh68. Chich Th Coll 58. **d** 60 **p** 61. C Roehampton H Trin *S'wark* 60-62; C E Wickham 62-67; C Plumstead St Mark and St Marg 67-73; C Corby Epiphany w St Jo *Pet* 73-74; C Paston 84-86; C Aylestone St Andr w St Jas *Leic* from 86. *58 Belvoir Drive, Leicester LE2 8PA* Leicester (0116) 283 9246

LEIGH, Canon James Ronald. b 32. S'wark Ord Course 63. **d** 67 **p** 68. C Purley St Barn *S'wark* 67-71; Prec St Ninian's Cathl Perth *St And* 71-73; R Leven 73-79; R Kirkcaldy from 79; R Kinghorn from 81; Can St Ninian's Cathl Perth from 90. *1 Longbraes Gardens, Kirkcaldy, Fife KY2 5YJ* Kirkcaldy (01592) 263314

LEIGH, Martin Francis. b 40. Sheff Univ BSc63. Cuddesdon Coll 65. **d** 67 **p** 68. C St Mary-at-Lambeth *S'wark* 67-70; C Bakewell *Derby* 70-74; V Ockbrook 74-82; RD Ilkeston 78-82; V Baslow 82-92; Bp's Exam Officer 82-92; TR Kings Norton *Birm* from 92. *The Rectory, 273 Pershore Road South, Birmingham B30 3EX* 0121-458 7522 or 458 3289

LEIGH, Mrs Mary Elizabeth. b 42. K Coll Lon BA64 LSE DSA65. Westcott Ho Cam 89. **d** 91 **p** 94. NSM Chesterfield All SS *Derby* 91-92; C Hall Green Ascension *Birm* 92-94; C Yardley St Edburgha from 94. *The Rectory, Kings Norton, Birmingham B30 7BA* 0121-458 7522 or 778 6835

LEIGH, Raymond. b 37. Lon Univ BEd81. Clifton Th Coll 65. **d** 68 **p** 69. C Chadwell *Chelmsf* 68-71; Chapl RAF 71-77; NSM Hillingdon St Jo *Lon* 87-88; C Rowley Regis *Birm* 88-90; V Londonderry 90-95; R Westbury w Turweston, Shalstone and Biddlesden *Ox* from 95. *The Vicarage, Westbury, Brackley, Northants NN13 5JT* Brackley (01280) 704964

LEIGH, Roy Stephen. b 28. Imp Coll Lon BSc49. S'wark Ord Course 87. **d** 90 **p** 92. NSM Green Street Green *Roch* 90-92; NSM E Peckham and Nettlestead from 92. *The Rectory, Bush Road, East Peckham, Tonbridge, Kent TN12 5LL* East Peckham (01622) 871278

LEIGH-HUNT, Edward Christopher. b 22. Univ Coll Dur BA47. Ely Th Coll 48. **d** 50 **p** 51. Chapl Asst St Bart Hosp Lon 66-73; C St Bart Less *Lon* 66-73; Chapl Middx Hosp 73-86; rtd 87. *14 Cain Court, Castlebar Mews, London W5 1RY* 0181-991 1171

LEIGH-HUNT, Nicolas Adrian. b 46. MIEx70. Qu Coll Birm 85. **d** 87 **p** 88. C Tilehurst St Geo *Ox* 87-91; TV Wexcombe *Sarum* from 91. *The Vicarage, 5 Eastcourt, Burbage, Marlborough, Wilts SN8 3AG* Marlborough (01672) 810258

LEIGH-WILLIAMS, Owen Charles. b 32. BNC Ox BA56 MA60. Wycliffe Hall Ox 56. **d** 58 **p** 59. C Southgate *Chich* 64-62; C Gt Warley Ch Ch *Chelmsf* 64-68; Asst Chapl Warley Hosp Brentwood 64-68; C Dagenham *Chelmsf* 68-72; P-in-c Basildon St Andr 72-86. *309A Church Road, Basildon, Essex SS14 2NE* Basildon (01268) 521628

LEIGHLIN, Dean of. *See* FAULL, Very Rev Cecil Albert

LEIGHTON, Adrian Barry. b 44. LTh. Lon Coll of Div 65. **d** 69 **p** 70. C Erith St Paul *Roch* 69-72; C Ipswich St Marg *St E* 72-75; P-in-c Ipswich St Helen 75-82; R 82-88; P-in-c Holbrook w Freston and Woolverstone from 88; RD Samford 90-93; P-in-c Wherstead from 94. *The Rectory, Holbrook, Ipswich IP9 2QZ* Holbrook (01473) 328900

LEIGHTON, Alan Granville Clyde. b 37. MInstM AMIDHE Lon Univ DipRS. S'wark Ord Course 73. **d** 76 **p** 77. C Silverhill St Matt *Chich* 76-79; C Eston *York* 79-82; V 82-84; TR Eston w Normanby from 84. *429 Normanby Road, Normanby, Middlesbrough, Cleveland TS6 0ED* Eston Grange (01642) 460613

LEIGHTON, Canon Anthony Hindess. b 23. Lon Univ BSc44. Wells Th Coll 47. **d** 49 **p** 50. R Girton *Ely* 61-88; RD N Stowe 68-76; Hon Can Ely Cathl 82-88; rtd 88. *Eastleigh, Parkhall Road, Somersham, Huntingdon, Cambs PE17 3HF* Ramsey (01487) 842750

LEIGHTON, Anthony Robert. b 56. Trin Coll Bris BA88. **d** 88 **p** 89. C Trin St Mich, Harrow *Lon* 88-92; TV Ratby w Groby *Leic* 92-94; TR from 94. *The Rectory, 39 Pymm Ley Lane, Groby, Leicester LE6 0GZ* Leicester (0116) 231 3090

LEIGHTON, John Thomas. b 08. **d** 76 **p** 77. C W Derby St Mary *Liv* 76-77; Hon C Knowsley from 77; Hon C Litherland St Phil from 84. *22 Newlyn Avenue, Litherland, Liverpool L21 9LD* 0151-928 1957

LEIGHTON, Mrs Susan. Bretton Hall Coll BEd80. Trin Coll Bris BA89. **d** 89 **p** 94. Par Dn Harrow Weald All SS *Lon* 89-92; NSM Ratby w Groby *Leic* from 92. *The Rectory, 58 Pymm Ley Lane, Groby, Leicester LE6 0GZ* Leicester (0116) 231 3090

LEIPER, Nicholas Keith. b 34. SS Coll Cam BA55 MB58 BChir58 MA65. St Jo Coll Nottm LTh82. **d** 84 **p** 85. C Bidston *Ches* 84-87; TV Gateacre *Liv* 87-92; P-in-c Bickerstaffe 92-94; P-in-c Melling 92-94; V Bickerstaffe and Melling from 94. *The Vicarage, Intake Lane, Bickerstaffe, Ormskirk, Lancs L39 0EB* Skelmersdale (01695) 22304

LEITCH, Peter William. b 36. FCA58 ATII59. Coll of Resurr Mirfield 83. **d** 85 **p** 86. C Newsome *Wakef* 85; C Newsome and Armitage Bridge 85-88; P-in-c Upper Hopton 88-91; P-in-c Mirfield Eastthorpe St Paul 88-91; Chapl Rouen Miss to Seamen *Eur* 92-94; Sen Chapl 94-95; Chapl Pernis Miss to Seamen from 95. *The Missions to Seamen, Vondelingenweg 524, 319 KK Rotterdam, The Netherlands* Rotterdam (10) 438-7043

LEMMON, Canon Rowland. b 09. Keble Coll Ox BA31 MA40. Wells Th Coll 31. **d** 32 **p** 33. R Hexham *Newc* 62-75; rtd 75; Perm to Offic *Ex* from 82. *4 Arundel Close, Alphington, Exeter EX2 8UQ* Exeter (01392) 70365

LEMPRIERE, Norman Everard. b 28. Liv Univ BEng54. Ridley Hall Cam 55. **d** 57 **p** 58. R Nymet Rowland w Coldridge *Ex* 69-75; R Denton w S Heighton and Tarring Neville *Chich* 75-81; R Sullington and Thakeham w Warminghurst 81-92; rtd 92. *38 Woodbury Avenue, Wells, Somerset BA5 2XP* Wells (01749) 673368

LENDRUM, Canon William Henry. b 24. TCD BA50 MA62. CITC 50. **d** 50 **p** 51. I Belf St Mary Magd *Conn* 69-91; Can Conn Cathl from 87; rtd 91. *38 Lancefield Road, Belfast BT9 6LL* Belfast (01232) 665872

LENG, Bruce Edgar. b 38. St Aid Birkenhead 68. **d** 69 **p** 70. C Sheff St Swithun *Sheff* 69-74; TV Speke St Aid *Liv* 74-78; TV Yate New Town *Bris* 78-82; R Handsworth *Sheff* 82-95; P-in-c Thrybergh w Hooton Roberts 95; R Thrybergh from 95. *The Rectory, Handsworth Road, Handsworth, Sheffield S13 9BZ* Sheffield (0114) 269 2403

LENNARD, Edward Stuart Churchill. b 21. Ex Coll Ox MA42. Cuddesdon Coll 47. **d** 54 **p** 55. SSJE from 54; S Africa 57-59; Lic to Offic *Ox* 59-86; Perm to Offic from 86; rtd 88. *Green Gates Nursing Home, 2 Hernes Road, Summertown, Oxford OX2 7PT* Oxford (01865) 58815

LENNARD, Mrs Elizabeth Jemima Mary Patricia. b 21. Edin Dioc NSM Course 78. **dss** 82 **d** 86 **p** 94. Falkirk *Edin* 82-86; Hon C 86-91; Asst Dioc Supernumerary from 91. *36 Heugh Street, Falkirk FK1 5QR* Falkirk (01324) 623240

LENNARD, Thomas Jay. b 21. MBE54. Edin Dioc NSM Course 74. **d** 76 **p** 77. Hon C Kelso *Edin* 76-82; Hon C Falkirk 82-91; Asst Dioc Supernumerary from 91. *36 Heugh Street, Falkirk FK1 5QR* Falkirk (01324) 623240

LENNON, Alfred Dennis. b 32. Oak Hill Th Coll 72. **d** 74 **p** 74. C Cam H Sepulchre w All SS *Ely* 74-77; P-in-c Cam St Barn 77-83; I Edin St Thos *Edin* 83-90; P-in-c Burghwallis w Skelbrooke *Sheff* from 90; Dioc Adv for Evang from 90. *St Helen's Rectory, Burghwallis, Doncaster, S Yorkshire DN6 9JL* Doncaster (01302) 700227

LENNOX, James. b 12. TCD BA36 MA40. CITC 37. **d** 38 **p** 39. V Bingley All SS *Bradf* 63-77; rtd 77; Perm to Offic *Bradf* from 77. *30 Hazel Beck, Cottingley Bridge, Bingley, W Yorkshire BD16 1LZ* Bradford (01274) 560189

LENNOX, William Ernest Michael. b 28. Selw Coll Cam BA52 MA63 Leeds Univ CertEd55. K Coll Lon 62. **d** 63 **p** 64. C Margate St Jo *Cant* 66-71; R Kingsnorth 71-73; R Shadoxhurst 71-73; R Kingsnorth w Shadoxhurst 73-93; rtd 93. *6 Rue Aux Savons, Le Boisle, 80150 Crecy en Ponthieu, France*

LENON, Philip John FitzMaurice. b 24. ARIBA52 Lon Univ BD60. Wycliffe Hall Ox 55. **d** 57 **p** 58. V Crowborough *Chich* 67-89; rtd 89. *Snowhill Cottage, Dinton, Salisbury SP3 5HN* Teffont (01722) 716754

LENOX-CONYNGHAM, Andrew George. b 44. Magd Coll Ox BA65 MA70 CCC Cam PhD73. Westcott Ho Cam 72. **d** 74 **p** 75. C Poplar *Lon* 74-77; TV Poplar 77-80; Chapl Heidelberg *Eur* 80-82 and from 91; Chapl Ch Coll Cam 82-86; Lic to Offic *Ely* 83-91; Chapl and Fell St Cath Coll Cam 86-91. *Augustastrasse 3, 69126 Heidelberg, Germany* Heidelberg (6221) 393216

LENS VAN RIJN, Robert Adriaan. b 47. St Jo Coll Nottm 78. **d** 80 **p** 81. C Gt Baddow *Chelmsf* 80-83; C Edgware *Lon* 83-86; C Derby St Pet and Ch Ch w H Trin *Derby* 86-90; Chapl Eindhoven *Eur* from 91. *Chopinlaan 41, 5653 ET Eindhoven, The Netherlands* Eindhoven (40) 573523

LENTON, Colin William. b 23. CertEd. Cuddesdon Coll 80. **d** 81 **p** 81. Hon C Cowley St Jo *Ox* 81-82; Hon C Oakley 82-85; V Langtoft w Foxholes, Butterwick, Cottam etc *York* 85-89;

rtd 89. *Flat 3, 24 South Drive, Harrogate HG2 8AU* Harrogate (01423) 564751

LENTON, Robert Vincent. b 15. Clifton Th Coll 62. **d** 63 **p** 63. V Lacock w Bowden Hill *Bris* 71-83; rtd 83; Perm to Offic *Liv* 83-95. *College of St Barnabas, Blackberry Lane, Lingfield, Surrey RH7 6NJ* Dormans Park (01342) 870260

LENYGON, Canon Herbert Edward. b 11. Lon Univ BD53. Kelham Th Coll 32. **d** 38 **p** 39. Chapl Newc United Hosps 49-74; rtd 74; Perm to Offic *Cov* 74-93. *48 Foxes Way, Warwick CV34 6AY* Warwick (01926) 493954

LEONARD, Ms Ann Cressey. b 50. Open Univ BA90. S Dios Minl Tr Scheme 90. **d** 94 **p** 95. C Portsea St Cuth *Portsm* from 94. *223 Queens Road, Portsmouth PO2 7LX* Portsmouth (01705) 699226

LEONARD, John Francis. b 48. Lich Th Coll 69. **d** 72 **p** 73. C Chorley St Geo *Blackb* 72-75; C S Shore H Trin 75-80; V Marton Moss 81-89; V Kingskerswell w Coffinswell *Ex* from 89. *The Vicarage, Pound Lane, Kingskerswell, Newton Abbot, Devon TQ12 5DW* Kingskerswell (01803) 872305

LEONARD, John James. b 41. Southn Univ BSc62. Sarum Th Coll 63. **d** 65 **p** 66. C Loughb Em *Leic* 65-70; V New Humberstone 70-78; C-in-c Rushey Mead CD 78-85; V Leic St Theodore from 85. *St Theodore's House, 4 Sandfield Close, Leicester LE4 7RE* Leicester (0116) 266 9956

LEONARD, Peter Michael. b 47. MRTPI Portsm Poly BSc Trent Poly DipTP. Sarum & Wells Th Coll 82. **d** 84 **p** 85. C Llantwit Major *Llan* 84-88; V Cymmer and Porth from 88. *The Vicarage, Maesgwyn, Porth, M Glam CF39 9HW* Porth (01443) 682219

LEONARD, Stanley Gwyn. b 15. Univ of Wales (Lamp) BA36. Ripon Hall Ox 36. **d** 41. C Hengoed *Lich* 41; Lic to Offic *Mon* 49-84; Hon C Trevethin 84-87. *Address temp unknown*

LEONARD-JOHNSON, Philip Anthony. b 35. Selw Coll Cam BA58 MA62. Linc Th Coll 63. **d** 65 **p** 66. C Wymondham *Nor* 65-68; Rhodesia 68-80; Zimbabwe 80-82; R Adderley *Lich* 82-92; V Drayton in Hales 82-92; P-in-c Moreton Say 88-92; S Africa from 92. *Holy Trinity Rectory, PO Box 256, King William's Town, 5600 South Africa* King William's Town (433) 24154 or 23259

LEONARDI, Jeffrey. b 49. Warw Univ BA71 Aston Univ DCouns79. Carl Dioc Tr Course 85. **d** 88 **p** 89. C Netherton *Carl* 88-91; V Crosscanonby 91; V Allonby from 91. *Crosscanonby Vicarage, Crosby, Maryport, Cumbria CA15 6SJ* Maryport (01900) 814192

LEPINE, Jeremy John. b 56. BA. St Jo Coll Nottm 82. **d** 84 **p** 85. C Trin St Mich, Harrow *Lon* 84-88; TV Horley *S'wark* from 88. *St Wilfrid's Vicarage, Horley Row, Horley, Surrey RH6 8DF* Horley (01293) 771869

LEPINE, Peter Gerald. b 27. St Fran Coll Brisbane ThL56. **d** 57 **p** 58. SSF 63-91; Papua New Guinea 67-76; Solomon Is 76; Perm to Offic *Conn* 76-80; P-in-c Belf H Redeemer 80-87; Lic to Offic *Newc* from 88; rtd 92. *Flat 1, 2 Queen's Road, Jesmond, Newcastle upon Tyne NE2 2PP* 0191-281 1156

LEPPARD, Miss Myra Anne. b 47. Chich Th Coll. **d** 90. Asst Chapl Brighton Hosp Gp from 90; Par Dn Brighton Gd Shep Preston *Chich* 91-92; Par Dn S Patcham 92-94; C Rustington from 94. *23 Henry Avenue, Rustington, Littlehampton, W Sussex BN16 2PA* Rustington (01903) 787612

LEPPINGTON, Ms Dian. b 46. Leeds Univ BA85. Cranmer Hall Dur 81. **dss** 83 **d** 87 **p** 94. Potternewton *Ripon* 83-87; Par Dn from 88; Ind Chapl from 85. *52 Newton Court, Leeds LS8 2PH* Leeds (0113) 248 5011 or 242 4886

LERRY, Keith Doyle. b 49. Univ of Wales (Cardiff) DipTh72. St Mich Coll Llan 69. **d** 72 **p** 73. C Caerau w Ely *Llan* 72-75; C Roath St Martin 75-84; V Glyntaff from 84. *The Vicarage, Glyntaff, Pontypridd, M Glam CF37 4AS* Pontypridd (01443) 402535

LERVY, Hugh Martin. b 68. **d** 91 **p** 92. C Brecon St Mary and Battle w Llanddew *S & B* 91-93; C Oystermouth 93-95; V Glantawe from 95. *The Vicarage, 122 Mansell Road, Bon-y-Maen, Swansea SA1 7JR* Swansea (01792) 652839

LESITER, Ven Malcolm Leslie. b 37. Selw Coll Cam BA61 MA65. Cuddesdon Coll 61. **d** 63 **p** 64. C Eastney *Portsm* 63-66; C Hemel Hempstead *St Alb* 66-71; TV 71-73; V Leavesden All SS 73-88; RD Watford 81-88; V Radlett 88-93; Hon Can St Alb Abbey 90-93; Adn Bedf from 93. *17 Lansdowne Road, Luton LU3 1EE* Luton (01582) 30722 Fax as telephone

LESLIE, David Rodney. b 43. AKC67. **d** 68 **p** 69. C Belmont *Lon* 68-71; C St Giles Cripplegate w St Bart Moor Lane etc 71-75; TV Kirkby *Liv* 76-84; TR Ditton St Mich from 84. *339 Ditchfield Road, Widnes, Cheshire WA8 8XR* 0151-424 2502

LESLIE, Richard Charles Alan. b 46. ACIB71. St Alb Minl Tr Scheme 76. **d** 79 **p** 91. NSM Redbourn *St Alb* 79-88; Hon C Newport Pagnell w Lathbury and Moulsoe *Ox* from 88; Stewardship Adv St Alb Adnry *St Alb* from 94. *49 Broad Street, Newport Pagnell, Bucks MK16 0AW* Newport Pagnell (01908) 612333

LESTER, Preb Geoffrey. b 16. Trin Coll Cam BA39 MA43. Wycliffe Hall Ox 41. **d** 42 **p** 43. R Bath Abbey w St Jas *B & W* 60-89; RD Bath 61-71; Preb Wells Cathl 62-93; rtd 89. *29 Woodland Grove, Claverton Down, Bath BA2 7AT* Bath (01225) 469860

LESTER, Trevor Rashleigh. b 50. CITC 83 St Deiniol's Hawarden 92. **d** 89 **p** 90. NSM Douglas Union w Frankfield *C, C & R* 89-93; C Kilkenny w Aghour and Kilmanagh *C & O* 93-95; Bp's V Ossory Cathl 93-95; Dioc Registrar (Ossory, Ferns and Leighlin) 93-95; Dioc Lib St Canice's Lib 93-95; I Abbeystrewry Union *C, C & R* from 95. *The Rectory, Skibbereen, Co Cork, Republic of Ireland* Cork (28) 21234

L'ESTRANGE, Canon Guy James Albert. b 24. TCD BA47 MA50. CITC. **d** 47 **p** 48. R Saltwood *Cant* 68-89; RD Elham 74-80; Hon Can Cant Cathl 81-89; Sec to Dioc Bd of Min 86-89; rtd 89; Guardian of The Greyfriars Cant from 93. *36 St Stephen's Hill, Canterbury, Kent CT2 7AX* Canterbury (01227) 763226

L'ESTRANGE, Canon Hilary Cecil Hurford. b 21. St Paul's Coll Barton 42. **d** 45 **p** 46. C Edin St Salvador *Edin* 51-54; S Africa from 54; Hon Can George from 85; rtd 88. *51 Drostdy Street, Swellendam, 6740 South Africa* Swellendam (291) 42326

L'ESTRANGE, Timothy John Nicholas. b 67. Surrey Univ BA90 Ox Univ BA92. St Steph Ho Ox 90. **d** 93 **p** 94. C Halesworth w Linstead, Chediston, Holton etc *St E* from 93. *St Ursula House, 64 Old Station Road, Halesworth, Suffolk IP19 8JQ* Halesworth (01986) 874480

LETALL, Ronald Richard. b 29. ACII76. Linc Th Coll 82. **d** 84 **p** 85. C Scarborough St Martin *York* 84-86; C Middlesb St Thos 86-88; R Kirby Misperton w Normanby, Edston and Salton 88-90; TV Louth *Linc* 90-94; rtd 94. *4 Pavilion Close, Brierley, Barnsley, S Yorkshire S72 9LR* Barnsley (01226) 715433

LETCHER, Canon David John. b 34. K Coll Lon 54. Chich Th Coll 56. **d** 58 **p** 59. C St Austell *Truro* 58-62; C Southbroom *Sarum* 62-64; R Odstock w Nunton and Bodenham 64-72; RD Alderbury 68-73 and 77-82; V Downton 72-85; Can and Preb Sarum Cathl from 79; TV Dorchester from 85; RD Dorchester 89-95. *St George's Vicarage, 50 High Street, Dorchester, Dorset DT1 1LB* Dorchester (01305) 262394

LETFORD, Peter Arthur. b 36. Oak Hill Th Coll 68. **d** 70 **p** 71. C Maidstone St Faith *Cant* 70-72; CF 72-75; C Ramsgate St Luke *Cant* 75-77; P-in-c Eastling 77-79; P-in-c Becontree St Eliz *Chelmsf* 79-84; P-in-c Clay Cross *Derby* 84-90; TV N Wingfield, Clay Cross and Pilsley 90-94; Chapl Casablanca *Eur* from 94. *25 Rue Mohamed Adjahim (ex Massena), Maarif Casablanca, Morocco* Morocco (2) 253171

LETHBRIDGE, Christopher David. b 43. N Ord Course 90. **d** 93 **p** 94. NSM S Elmsall *Wakef* 93-95; C Knottingley from 95. *Mylor, Chapel Lane, Knottingley, W Yorkshire WF11 9AN* Knottinley (01977) 677010

LETHEREN, William Neils. b 37. Lon Univ DipTh63. St Aid Birkenhead 61. **d** 64 **p** 65. C Liv St Mich *Liv* 64-67; V 71-75; C Kirkdale St Athanasius 67-69; C Walsall Wood *Lich* 69-71; V W Derby St Jas *Liv* 75-84; R Newton in Makerfield Em 84-88; V Garston from 88. *The Vicarage, Horrocks Avenue, Garston, Liverpool L19 5NY* 0151-427 4204

LETSON, Barry. b 55. Univ of Wales BA77. St Deiniol's Hawarden 82. **d** 83 **p** 84. C Flint *St As* 83-86; V Llansantffraid and Llanarmon and Pontfadog 86-89; R Montgomery and Forden and Llandyssil from 89; RD Pool from 92. *The Rectory, Montgomery, Powys SY16 6PT* Montgomery (01686) 668243

LETTON, Stanley Gladstone. b 17. Local NSM Course 81. **d** 82 **p** 94. NSM Bre from 82; NSM Tarfside from 82; NSM Auchmithie from 82. *12 Latch Road, Brechin, Angus DD9 6JE* Brechin (01356) 622519

LETTS, Gerald Vincent. b 33. Univ of Wales BA63 Birm Univ DipTh65. NY Th Sem DMin Qu Coll Birm 63. **d** 65 **p** 66. C Birstall *Leic* 65-68; V Belgrave St Mich 68-75; V Sheff St Cuth *Sheff* 75-91; R Bradfield from 91. *The Rectory, Bradfield, Sheffield S6 6LG* Sheffield (0114) 285 1225

LETTS, Kenneth John (Ken). b 42. Melbourne Univ BA65 Leeds Univ DipTh71 Melbourne Univ DipEd67. Coll of Resurr Mirfield 68. **d** 71 **p** 72. Australia 71-94; Chapl Nice w Vence *Eur* from 94. *11 rue de la Buffa, 06000 Nice, France* France (33) 93 87 19 83

LEUNG, Dr Peter. Trin Coll Singapore BTh60 St Andr Univ PhD73. SE Asia Sch of Th MTh69. **d** 60 **p** 61. Singapore 60-62 and 65-76; Br N Borneo 62-63; Malaysia 63-65; Lect Congr Coll Man 76-77; USPG 77-83; Perm to Offic *Roch* 83-89; BCC 83-90; CCBI from 90; Perm to Offic *S'wark* 88-94; Hon C Shortlands *Roch* from 90; Regional Sec (S and E Asia) CMS from 91. *14 Uplands, Beckenham, Kent BR3 3NB* 0181-650 4157 or 0171-928 8681 Fax 0171-401 3215

LEVER, Edmund Arthur (Ted). b 23. Sarum Th Coll 55. **d** 57 **p** 58. V Brentwood St Geo *Chelmsf* 64-73; Chapl S Ockendon

Hosp 73-78; rtd 88. *42 Pear Tree Close, South Ockendon, Essex RM15 6PR* South Ockendon (01708) 852933

LEVER, Julian Lawrence Gerrard. b 36. Fitzw Coll Cam BA60 MA64. Sarum Th Coll 60. **d** 62 **p** 63. C Amesbury *Sarum* 62-66; R Corfe Mullen 66-78; RD Wimborne 73-75; P-in-c Wilton w Netherhampton and Fugglestone 78-82; R 82-86; R Salisbury St Martin 86-94. *6 St John's Close, Wimborne, Dorset BH21 1LY* Wimborne (01202) 848249

LEVERTON, Michael John. b 52. K Coll Lon BD76 AKC76 MTh77. Cant Sch of Min 84. **d** 87 **p** 88. NSM Elham w Denton and Wootton *Cant* 87-92; C Yelverton, Meavy, Sheepstor and Walkhampton *Ex* 92-93; TV from 93. *The Vicarage, 1 Manor Farm, Dousland, Yelverton, Devon PL20 6NR* Yelverton (01822) 855076

LEVERTON, Peter James Austin (Jim). b 33. Nottm Univ BA55. Ripon Coll Cuddesdon 79. **d** 81 **p** 82. C St Jo in Bedwardine *Worc* 81-84; V Worc St Mich 84-88; TR Worc St Barn w Ch Ch 88-92; V Riddings and Ironville *Derby* from 92. *The Vicarage, Vicarage Lane, Ironville, Nottingham NG16 5PT* Leabrooks (01773) 602241

LEVERTON, Peter Robert. b 25. Lich Th Coll 59. **d** 60 **p** 61. V Marshchapel *Linc* 70-73; V Grainthorpe w Conisholme 70-73; R N Coates 70-73; Miss to Seamen 73-77; P-in-c Brislington St Luke *Bris* 77-84; V Avonmouth St Andr 84-87; Ind Chapl 84-87; P-in-c Ugborough *Ex* 87-91; P-in-c Ermington 88-91; rtd 91; Perm to Offic *Ex* 91-95. *4 Drakes Avenue, Sidford, Sidmouth, Devon EX10 9QY* Sidmouth (01395) 579835

LEVETT, Colin Andrew. b 13. **d** 69 **p** 71. Par Dn Hatch End St Anselm *Lon* 69-71; AP N Wembley St Cuth 71-73; P-in-c Dollis Hill St Paul 73-78; rtd 78. *19 Wilmington Court, Bath Road, Worthing, W Sussex BN11 3QN* Worthing (01903) 210744

LEVETT, Canon Howard. b 44. K Coll Lon AKC67. **d** 68 **p** 69. C Rotherhithe St Mary w All SS *S'wark* 68-72; P-in-c Walworth St Jo 72-77; V Walworth St Jo 77-80; P-in-c Walworth Lady Marg w St Mary 78; RD S'wark and Newington 78-80; Adn Egypt 80-94; Miss to Seamen from 80; JMECA from 80; V Holborn St Alb w Saffron Hill St Pet *Lon* from 94. *St Alban's Clergy House, Brooke Street, London EC1N 7RD* 0171-405 1831 Fax as telephone

LEVEY, Canon Colin Russell. b 35. Open Univ BA76. S'wark Ord Course 63. **d** 66 **p** 67. C Rusthall *Roch* 66-71; Youth Chapl 71-75; Hon C Riverhead 71-75; V Lamorbey H Redeemer 75-81; V Milton next Gravesend Ch Ch 81-85; P-in-c Elmley Lovett w Hampton Lovett and Elmbridge etc *Worc* 87-91; P-in-c Hartlebury 87-91; P-in-c Wilden 87-91; R Orton and Tebay w Ravenstonedale etc *Carl* from 91; RD Appleby from 93; Hon Can Carl Cathl from 94. *The Vicarage, Orton, Penrith, Cumbria CA10 3RQ* Orton (015396) 24532

LEVICK, Brian William. b 30. Westcott Ho Cam 63. **d** 64 **p** 65. C Deeping St James *Linc* 69-70; C Hemel Hempstead *St Alb* 70-71; TV 71-77; Hon C Sedbergh, Cautley and Garsdale *Bradf* 77-83; V Firbank, Howgill and Killington 77-83; V Cononley w Bradley 83-90; C Kettlewell w Conistone, Hubberholme etc 90-93; rtd 93; Hon C New Sleaford *Linc* from 93; Dioc Ecum Officer from 93. *11 Rowan Drive, Silk Willoughby, Sleaford, Lincs NG34 8PQ* Sleaford (01529) 303207

LEVICK, Canon Frank Hemsley. b 29. Kelham Th Coll 49. **d** 54 **p** 55. V Ribbleton *Blackb* 67-80; TR 80-85; Hon Can Blackb Cathl 75-90; R Ribchester w Stidd 85-90; rtd 90. *The Old Nurseries, Low Street, Beckingham, Doncaster, S Yorkshire DN10 4PS* Saundby (01427) 848668

LEVY, Christopher Charles. b 51. Southn Univ BTh82. Sarum & Wells Th Coll 79. **d** 82 **p** 83. C Rubery *Birm* 82-85; C Stratford-on-Avon w Bishopton *Cov* 85-87; TV Clifton *S'well* 87-95; V Egmanton from 95; R Kirton from 95; V Walesby from 95. *St Edmunds Vicarage, Walesby, Newark, Notts NG22 9PA* New Ollerton (01623) 860522

LEWERS, Very Rev Benjamin Hugh (Ben). b 32. Selw Coll Cam BA60 MA64. Linc Th Coll. **d** 62 **p** 63. C Northn St Mary *Pet* 62-65; C Hounslow Heath St Paul *Lon* 65-68; C-in-c Hounslow Gd Shep Beavers Lane CD 65-68; Chapl Heathrow Airport 68-75; R Newark St Mary *S'well* 75-80; P-in-c Averham w Kelham 79-81; TR Newark w Hawton, Cotham and Shelton 80-81; Provost Derby from 81. *Provost's House, 9 Highfield Road, Derby DE22 1GX* Derby (01332) 341201 or 342971

LEWES AND HASTINGS, Archdeacon of. See GLAISYER, Ven Hugh

LEWES, Area Bishop of. See CUNDY, Rt Rev Ian Patrick Martyn

LEWIS, Ven Albert John Francis. b 21. Univ Coll of S Wales BA(Econ)45. St Mich Coll Llan 46. **d** 48 **p** 49. Dioc Dir RE *Llan* 60-91; V Pendoylan 61-73; P-in-c Welsh St Donats 70-73; V Pendoylan and Welsh St Donats 73-81; RD Llan 69-81; Can Llan Cathl 76-81; Treas 81-88; Adn Margam 81-88; Adn Llan 88-91; rtd 91; Chapl to Rtd Clerics and Widows of Clergy *Llan* from 91. *11 Downs View Close, Aberthin, Cowbridge, S Glam CF7 7HG* Cowbridge (01446) 773320

LEWIS, Canon Alexander Thomas (Alex). b 20. Univ of Wales (Ban) BA51. St Mich Coll Llan 50. **d** 52 **p** 53. V Llandegai St Ann, Bethesda w Tregarth *Ban* 56-89; RD Arllechwedd 73-89; Hon Can Ban Cathl 82-84; Can 84-89; rtd 89. *91 Wellfield Road, Culcheth, Warrington WA3 4BX* Culcheth (01925) 762899

LEWIS, Ann Theodora Rachel. b 33. Univ of Wales (Ban) BA55. Qu Coll Birm 78. **d** 80. C Swansea St Mary w H Trin *S & B* from 80; Chapl St Mary's Coll from 90. *St Mary's Vicarage, Eden Avenue, Swansea SA2 0PS* Swansea (01792) 298616

LEWIS, Canon Arthur Griffith. b 15. Univ of Wales (Lamp) BA40. **d** 47 **p** 48. V Ystalyfera *S & B* 63-87; RD Cwmtawe 79-85; Hon Can Brecon Cathl 80-89; Can 81-85; P-in-c Capel Coelbren 85-89; rtd 89. *14 Pontwillim, Brecon, Powys LD3 9BT* Brecon (01874) 622869

LEWIS, Arthur Jenkin Llewellyn. b 42. Univ of Wales (Cardiff) MPS67 BPharm. Coll of Resurr Mirfield 71. **d** 73 **p** 74. C Cardiff St Jo *Llan* 73-78; C Christchurch *Win* 78-82; R Lightbowne *Man* from 82. *St Luke's Rectory, Kenyon Lane, Manchester M10 9HS* 0161-681 1308

LEWIS, Arthur Roland. b 20. St Edm Hall Ox BA41 MA45. St Steph Ho Ox 41. **d** 43 **p** 44. S Rhodesia 58-65; Rhodesia 65-80; S Africa 80-87; rtd 87; Perm to Offic *Birm* from 88. *54 Lyndon Road, Solihull, W Midlands B92 7RQ*

LEWIS, Ven Benjamin Alec. b 12. St D Coll Lamp BA34. **d** 36 **p** 37. Adn St D 70-82; Can St D Cathl 70-82; rtd 82. *4 St Non's Close, St Davids, Haverfordwest, Dyfed SA62 6RL* St Davids (01437) 720446

LEWIS, Very Rev Bertie. b 31. Univ of Wales (Lamp) BA54 St Cath Soc Ox BA57 MA60. Wycliffe Hall Ox 54. **d** 57 **p** 58. C Cwmaman *St D* 57-60; C Abth St Mich 60-62; V Llanddewi Brefi w Llanbadarn Odwyn 62-65; V Henfynyw w Aberaeron and Llanddewi Aberarth 65-75; V Lamp 75-80; Can St D Cathl 78-86; Chapl Abth Hosps 80-88; R Abth *St D* 80-88; Adn Cardigan 86-90; V Nevern and Y Beifil w Eglwyswrw and Meline etc 88-90; V from 94; Dean St D 90-94; V St D Cathl 90-94; Hon Can St D Cathl from 94. *The Vicarage, Nevern, Newport, Dyfed SA42 0NF* Newport (01239) 820427

LEWIS, Brian James. b 52. Cant Univ (NZ) BA75. St Jo Coll Auckland 76. **d** 78 **p** 79. New Zealand 78-80; C Shrub End *Chelmsf* 80-82; P-in-c Colchester St Barn 82-84; V 84-88; P-in-c Romford St Andr 88-90; R from 90; RD Havering from 93. *St Andrew's Rectory, 119 London Road, Romford RM7 9QD* Romford (01708) 764192

LEWIS, Very Rev Christopher Andrew. b 44. Bris Univ BA69 CCC Cam PhD74. Westcott Ho Cam 71. **d** 73 **p** 74. C Barnard Castle *Dur* 73-76; Dir Ox Inst for Ch and Soc 76-79; Tutor Ripon Coll Cuddesdon 76-79; P-in-c Aston Rowant w Crowell *Ox* 78-81; Sen Tutor Ripon Coll Cuddesdon 79-81; Vice-Prin 81-82; V Spalding *Linc* 82-87; Can Res Cant Cathl *Cant* 87-94; Dir of Minl Tr 89-94; Dean St Alb from 94. *The Deanery, Sumpter Yard, St Albans, Herts AL1 1BY* St Albans (01727) 852120

LEWIS, Canon Christopher Gouldson. b 42. K Coll Cam BA64 MA68. Cuddesdon Coll 65. **d** 67 **p** 68. C Gosforth All SS *Newc* 67-71; Sarawak 71-74; V Luton St Chris Round Green *St Alb* 74-80; RD Reculver *Cant* 80-86 and 92-93; V Whitstable All SS w St Pet 80-84; TR Whitstable 84-93; Dir of Post-Ord Tr 88-93; Hon Can Cant Cathl 91-93; Can Res Bradf Cathl *Bradf* from 93; Bp's Officer for Min and Tr from 93. *2 Cathedral Close, Bradford, W Yorkshire BD1 4EG* Bradford (01274) 727806

LEWIS, Christopher Thomas Samuel. b 08. CCC Cam BA30 MA39. Cuddesdon Coll 30. **d** 32 **p** 33. R Cheriton Bishop *Ex* 61-74; rtd 74. *Manormead, Tilford Road, Hindhead, Surrey GU26 6RA* Hindhead (01428) 607863

LEWIS, David Antony. b 48. Dur Univ BA69 Nottm Univ MTh84. St Jo Coll Nottm 81. **d** 83 **p** 84. C Gateacre *Liv* 83-86; V Toxteth St Cypr w Ch Ch from 86; AD Liv N from 94. *The Vicarage, 48 John Lennon Drive, Liverpool L6 9HT* 0151-260 3262

LEWIS, David Austin. b 09. St D Coll Lamp BA31. **d** 32 **p** 33. R Llanwenarth Ultra *Mon* 64-76; rtd 76; Lic to Offic *Mon* from 77. *29 Fairfield, Penperlleni, Pontypool, Gwent NP4 0AP* Nantyderry (01873) 880101

LEWIS, Very Rev David Gareth. b 31. Univ of Wales (Ban) BA52 DipEd53 Or Coll Ox BA59 MA63. St Mich Coll Llan 56. **d** 60 **p** 61. C Neath w Llantwit *Llan* 60-63; Chapl Sarum Th Coll 63-64; Vice-Prin 64-69; Dean Belize 69-78; V Newport St Mark *Mon* 78-82; Can St Woolos Cathl 81-90; Dioc Missr 81-90; Clerical Sec Governing Body Ch in Wales from 85; Dean Mon from 90; V Newport St Woolos from 90. *The Deanery, Stow Hill, Newport, Gwent NP9 4ED* Newport (01633) 263338

LEWIS, David Glyn. b 09. Univ of Wales BA36. Ripon Hall Ox 36. **d** 39 **p** 40. V Cubbington *Cov* 68-79; rtd 80; Perm to Offic

Cov from 80. *4 St James Close, Stratford-upon-Avon, Warks CV37 7RH* Stratford-upon-Avon (01789) 205559

LEWIS, David Hugh. b 45. Oak Hill Th Coll 88. **d** 90 **p** 91. C Oakham, Hambleton, Egleton, Braunston and Brooke *Pet* 90-94; R Ewhurst *Guildf* from 94. *The Rectory, Ewhurst, Cranleigh, Surrey GU6 7PX* Cranleigh (01483) 277584

LEWIS, David Roy. b 18. Univ of Wales (Lamp) BA39. St Mich Coll Llan 40. **d** 40 **p** 41. V Seven Sisters *Llan* 66-77; R Colwinston w Llandow and Llysworney 77-86; rtd 86. *Rockleigh, Colwinstone, Cowbridge, S Glam CF7 7NL* Bridgend (01656) 654797

LEWIS, David Tudor. b 61. Jes Coll Cam BA83. Trin Coll Bris BA88. **d** 88 **p** 89. C Tile Cross *Birm* 88-91; C Woking St Jo *Guildf* 91-95; TV Carl H Trin and St Barn *Carl* from 95. *104 Housesteads Road, Carlisle CA2 7XG* Carlisle (01228) 36710

LEWIS, David Tudor Bowes. b 63. Keele Univ BA85 Univ of Wales (Cardiff) BTh90. St Mich Coll Llan 87. **d** 90 **p** 91. C Llangollen w Trevor and Llantysilio *St As* 90-93; C Bistre from 93. *9 Ffordd Offa, Mynydd Isa, Mold, Clwyd CH7 6UF* Mold (01352) 750713

LEWIS, Canon David Vaughan. b 36. Trin Coll Cam BA60 MA64. Ridley Hall Cam 60. **d** 62 **p** 63. C Rugby St Matt *Cov* 62-65; Asst Chapl K Edw Sch Witley 65-71; Hon C Rainham *Chelmsf* 71-76; V Stoke Hill *Guildf* 76-87; V Wallington H Trin *S'wark* from 87; Hon Can S'wark Cathl from 95. *Holy Trinity Vicarage, Maldon Road, Wallington, Surrey SM6 8BL* 0181-647 7605

LEWIS, David Watkin. b 40. Univ of Wales (Lamp) BA61 Univ of Wales (Swansea) DipYL65. Wycliffe Hall Ox 61. **d** 63 **p** 64. C Skewen *Llan* 63-66; Field Tr Officer Prov Youth Coun Ch in Wales 66-68; C Gabalfa 68-71; P-in-c Marcross w Monknash and Wick 71-73; R 73-83; RD Llantwit Major and Cowbridge 81-83; V Baglan from 83. *The Vicarage, 29 Church Road, Port Talbot, W Glam SA12 8ST* Port Talbot (01639) 821199

LEWIS, Canon Donald Edward (Don). b 30. Univ of Wales (Lamp) BA53. Wycliffe Hall Ox 53. **d** 55 **p** 56. C Wrexham *St As* 55-59; R Castle Caereinion 59-62; Area Sec (Dios Ches, Ban, St As and S & M) CMS 62-65; India 62-65; V Hale *Ches* 65-77; V Swansea St Mary and H Trin *S & B* 77-79; V Swansea St Mary w H Trin and St Mark 79-83; V Swansea St Mary w H Trin from 83; RD Swansea from 78; Hon Can Brecon Cathl 79-81; Can 81-95; Treas 94-95; Prec Brecon Cathl 90-94. *The Vicarage, Eden Avenue, Swansea SA2 0PS* Swansea (01792) 298616

LEWIS, Edward John. b 15. Qu Coll Cam BA36 MA40. Ridley Hall Cam 36. **d** 38 **p** 39. V Swanwick and Pentrich *Derby* 56-74; P-in-c Longstone 74-80; rtd 80; Perm to Offic *Derby* from 80; Perm to Offic *Liv* from 80. *5 Old Hall Gardens, Rainford, St Helens, Merseyside WA11 8NS* Rainford (01744) 882242

LEWIS, Edward John. b 58. Univ of Wales BEd80 BA82. Chich Th Coll 82. **d** 83 **p** 84. C Llangiwg *S & B* 83-85; C Morriston 85-87; V Tregaron w Ystrad Meurig and Strata Florida *St D* 87-89; Chapl Manor Hosp Walsall from 89; Distr Co-ord Chapl Walsall Hosps from 90. *The Chaplain's Office, Manor Hospital, Moat Road, Walsall WS2 9PS* Walsall (01922) 721172 or 656834

LEWIS, Elinor Glenys. b 11. CBE93. SRN34 SCM35. St Chris Coll Blackheath 44. **dss** 49 **d** 78 **p** 78. New Zealand from 60; rtd 71. *10a Heybridge Lane, Christchurch 2, New Zealand* Christchurch (3) 332-6808

LEWIS, Elsie Leonora. b 26. Cranmer Hall Dur 72. **dss** 78 **d** 84 **p** 94. S Westoe *Dur* 78-80; Ryton 80-86; rtd 86. *53 Cushy Cow Lane, Ryton, Tyne & Wear NE40 3NL* 0191-413 5845

LEWIS, Eric. b 36. Sarum & Wells Th Coll 74. **d** 77 **p** 78. NSM Oldbury *Sarum* 77-92; C Weymouth St Paul 92-94; P-in-c Portland St Jo from 94; Chapl Weymouth Coll from 94. *St John's Vicarage, Ventnor Road, Portland, Dorset DT5 1JE* Portland (01305) 820103

LEWIS, Evan David Dyfrig. b 17. TD67. Univ of Wales BA47. St Mich Coll Llan 47. **d** 49 **p** 50. CF (TA) 52-88; R Llanmaes and Llanmihangel *Llan* 58-88; rtd 88; Perm to Offic *Llan* from 88. *5 Oak Grove, Eglwysbrewis, St Athan, Barry, S Glam CF62 4QR* St Athan (01446) 750123

LEWIS, Evan Edgar. b 07. K Coll Cam BA31 MA35. St D Coll Lamp BA28. **d** 31 **p** 32. V Stoke St Milburgh w Heath *Heref* 57-73; R Abdon w Clee St Margaret 57-73; R Cold Weston 57-73; rtd 73; Perm to Offic *Heref* 73-90. *The Granary, Stoke St Milborough, Ludlow, Shropshire SY8 2EJ* Stoke St Milborough (0158475) 219

LEWIS, Evan Thomas Derwen. b 10. Univ of Wales BA34. St D Coll Lamp 34. **d** 35 **p** 36. V Glasbury St Pet *S & B* 46-83; rtd 83. *43 Gwernyfed Avenue, Three Cocks, Brecon, Powys LD3 0RT* Glasbury (01497) 847229

LEWIS, Francis Edward Walter. b 17. Univ of Wales BA40. St Mich Coll Llan 41. **d** 42 **p** 43. V Linslade *Ox* 65-73; V

Maidenhead St Luke 73-81; rtd 81. *13 Courtlands Road, Shipton-under-Wychwood, Chipping Norton, Oxon OX7 6DF* Shipton-under-W'wood (01993) 830604

LEWIS, Frederick. b 09. FRAI40 Univ of Wales BA31. St Mich Coll Llan 30. **d** 32 **p** 33. Chapl and Tutor Whittington Coll Felbridge 55-68; rtd 68. *7 Shearman Road, Hadleigh, Suffolk IP7 3JW* Hadleigh (01473) 827089

LEWIS, Frederick Norman. b 23. Leeds Univ BA47. Coll of Resurr Mirfield 47. **d** 49 **p** 50. V Kingswinford St Mary *Lich* 69-88; rtd 88. *27 Bramblewood Drive, Finchfield, Wolverhampton WV3 9DB* Wolverhampton (01902) 334934

LEWIS, Gary. b 61. Lanc Univ BA85. Ripon Coll Cuddesdon 86. **d** 89 **p** 90. C Blackb St Mich w St Jo and H Trin *Blackb* 89-92; C Altham w Clayton le Moors 92-95; V Lea from 95. *St Christopher's Vicarage, 848 Blackpool Road, Lea, Preston PR2 1XL* Preston (01772) 683587

LEWIS, Hubert Godfrey. b 33. Univ of Wales (Lamp) BA59 DipTh60. **d** 60 **p** 61. C Merthyr Tydfil *Llan* 60-64; C Caerphilly 64-66; Perm to Offic *S'wark* 66-76; Perm to Offic *Cant* 76-82; Hon C Shirley St Jo *S'wark* from 82. *4 East Way, Croydon CR0 8AH* 0181-777 6587

LEWIS, Dr Ian. b 33. MRCS LRCP Lon Univ MB, BS57. Oak Hill Th Coll 61. **d** 63 **p** 64. C Heatherlands St Jo *Sarum* 63-66; Ethiopia 66-73; Hon C Bath Walcot *B & W* 75-77; Lic to Offic 78-84. *22C Ashley Road, Bathford, Bath BA1 7TT* Bath (01225) 859818

LEWIS, Ian Richard. b 54. Sheff Univ BA76 Ox Univ BA83 MA87. Wycliffe Hall Ox 81. **d** 84 **p** 85. C Rusholme *Man* 84-88; C Sandal St Helen *Wakef* 88-91; V Bath St Bart *B & W* from 91. *St Bartholomew's Vicarage, 5 Oldfield Road, Bath BA2 3NB* Bath (01225) 422070

LEWIS, Jacob Brian. b 33. Univ of Wales BA54 Fitzw Ho Cam BA56 MA60. Wells Th Coll 56. **d** 57 **p** 58. C Cardiff St Mary *Llan* 57-61; S Africa 61-63; C Cowley St Jo *Ox* 63-67; V Gladstone Park St Fran *Lon* 67-76; V Compton w E Ilsley *Ox* from 76. *The Vicarage, Compton, Newbury, Berks RG16 0RD* Compton (01635) 578256

LEWIS, James Edward. b 22. St D Coll Lamp BA50. **d** 51 **p** 52. V Brynamman *St D* 61-72; R Llangathen w Llanfihangel Cilfargen 72-82; V Llangathen w Llanfihangel Cilfargen etc 82-90; RD Llangadog and Llandeilo 85-89; rtd 90. *The Flat, 3 St Mary Street, Carmarthen, Dyfed SA31 1TN* Carmarthen (01267) 221660

LEWIS, John Jocelyn Vivien. b 49. Trevelyan Coll Dur BSc70 Sheff Univ PhD75. E Midl Min Tr Course DTPS94. **d** 94 **p** 95. NSM Brimington *Derby* from 94. *10 Rother Avenue, Brimington, Chesterfield, Derbyshire S43 1LE* Chesterfield (01246) 279050

LEWIS, Ven John Arthur. b 34. Jes Coll Ox BA56 MA60. Cuddesdon Coll 58. **d** 60 **p** 61. C Prestbury *Glouc* 60-63; C Wimborne Minster *Sarum* 63-66; R Eastington and Frocester *Glouc* 66-70; V Nailsworth 70-78; Chapl Memorial and Querns Hosp Cirencester 78-88; V Cirencester *Glouc* 78-88; RD Cirencester 84-88; Hon Can Glouc Cathl from 85; Adn Cheltenham from 88. *Westbourne, 283 Gloucester Road, Cheltenham GL51 7AD* Cheltenham (01242) 522923 Fax 235925

LEWIS, John Edward. b 31. SS Mark & Jo Coll Chelsea CertEd53. Qu Coll Birm 83. **d** 85 **p** 86. C Leominster *Heref* 85-87; TV from 87. *The Vicarage, 1A School Road, Leominster, Herefordshire HR6 8NS* Leominster (01568) 612124

LEWIS, John Herbert. b 42. Selw Coll Cam BA64 MA68. Westcott Ho Cam 64. **d** 66 **p** 67. C Wyken *Cov* 66-70; C Bedf St Andr *St Alb* 70-73; Lib Pusey Ho 73-77; Bp's Chapl for Graduates *Ox* 73-77; TV Woughton 78-82; TV Gt Chesham 82-88; P-in-c Newport Pagnell w Lathbury and Moulsoe 88-91; R from 91. *New Rectory, 81 High Street, Newport Pagnell, Bucks MK16 8AB* Newport Pagnell (01908) 611145

LEWIS, John Horatio George. b 47. Southn Univ BEd72 MA85. Ox NSM Course 86. **d** 89 **p** 90. NSM Newbury *Ox* from 89. *36 Glendale Avenue, Newbury, Berks RG14 6RU* Newbury (01635) 34721

✠LEWIS, Rt Rev John Hubert Richard. b 43. AKC66. **d** 67 **p** 68 **c** 92. C Hexham *Newc* 67-70; Ind Chapl 70-77; Communications Officer *Dur* 77-82; Chapl for Agric *Heref* 82-87; Adn Ludlow 87-92; Suff Bp Taunton *B & W* from 92. *Sherford Farm House, Sherford, Taunton, Somerset TA1 3RF* Taunton (01823) 288759 Fax 257085

LEWIS, John Malcolm. b 41. Reading Univ BEd. Trin Coll Bris. **d** 82 **p** 83. C Kingswood *Bris* 82-85; TV Weston-super-Mare Cen Par *B & W* 85-91; Dioc Children's Adv *Nor* from 91. *25 Lackford Close, Brundall, Norwich NR13 5NG* Norwich (01603) 714829 or 880853 Fax 881083

LEWIS, Very Rev John Percival. b 19. TCD BA44. CITC 47. **d** 47 **p** 48. I Knappagh *T, K & A* 51-74; RD Tuam 56-91; Can

Tuam Cathl from 70; I Omey w Ballynakill, Errislannan and Roundstone 73-91; Provost Tuam 73-91; rtd 91. *Albany, Pheasant Hill, Castlebar, Co Mayo, Irish Republic* Castlebar (94) 22747

LEWIS, John Pryce. b 65. Trin Coll Carmarthen BA87. Wycliffe Hall Ox 92. **d** 94 **p** 95. C Carmarthen St Pet *St D* from 94. *St Peter's Clergy House, 10A The Parade, Carmarthen, Dyfed SA31 1LY* Carmarthen (01267) 237303

LEWIS, John Thomas. b 47. Jes Coll Ox BA69 MA73 St Jo Coll Cam BA72. Westcott Ho Cam 71. **d** 73 **p** 74. C Whitchurch *Llan* 73-77; C Llanishen and Lisvane 77-80; Asst Chapl Univ of Wales (Cardiff) 80-85; Warden of Ords 81-85; V Brecon St David w Llanspyddid and Llanilltyd *S & B* 85-91; Sec Prov Selection Panel & Bd Ch in Wales from 87; V Bassaleg *Mon* from 91. *The Vicarage, 1 Church View, Bassaleg, Newport, Gwent NP1 9ND* Newport (01633) 893258

LEWIS, Kenneth Lionel. b 22. Keble Coll Ox BA50 MA54 Ch Coll Cam CertEd52. Wycliffe Hall Ox 52. **d** 52 **p** 53. C Bromley St Jo *Roch* 52-55; C Streatham Hill St Marg *S'wark* 55-57; R Tatsfield 57-72; Lic to Offic 72-78 and from 89; Perm to Offic *Roch* 75-78 and from 83; Perm to Offic *Cant* 75-78. *9 Nostle Road, Northleach, Cheltenham, Glos GL54 3PF* Cotswold (01451) 860118

LEWIS, Leslie. b 25. Qu Coll Birm 82. **d** 83 **p** 84. NSM Garretts Green *Birm* 83-88; NSM Coleshill 88-92; NSM Maxstoke 88-92; rtd 92; Perm to Offic *Birm* from 92. *54 Bellevue Road, Birmingham B26 2QA* 0121-742 3662

LEWIS, Leslie. b 28. LRAM56. St Aid Birkenhead 61. **d** 63 **p** 64. C Eastham *Ches* 63-66; C W Kirby St Bridget 66-72; V Rainow w Saltersford 72-73; V Rainow w Saltersford and Forest from 73; Dioc Clergy Widows and Retirement Officer 88-93. *The Vicarage, Rainow, Macclesfield, Cheshire SK10 5TZ* Bollington (01625) 572013

LEWIS, Maureen. b 50. Chester Coll BA92. St Jo Coll Nottm DipMM94. **d** 94 **p** 95. C Ellesmere Port *Ches* from 94. *The Vicarage, Seymour Drive, Ellesmere Port, South Wirral L65 9LZ* 0151-355 3988

LEWIS, Michael Augustine Owen. b 53. Mert Coll Ox BA75 MA79. Cuddesdon Coll 75. **d** 78 **p** 79. C Salfords *S'wark* 78-80; Chapl Thames Poly 80-84; V Welling 84-91; TR Worc SE *Worc* from 91; RD Worc E from 93. *The Rectory, 6 St Catherine's Hill, Worcester WR5 2EA* Worcester (01905) 355119 or 358083

LEWIS, Michael David Bennett. b 41. Univ of Wales DipTh68. St Mich Coll Llan 65. **d** 68 **p** 69. C Penarth w Lavernock *Llan* 68-72; Chapl RAF 72-74; C Llanishen and Lisvane *Llan* 74-77; V Penyfai w Tondu 77-82; Chapl Ardingly Coll Haywards Heath 82-90; R Merrow *Guildf* from 90; RD Guildf from 94. *The Rectory, 232 Epsom Road, Merrow, Guildford, Surrey GU4 7AA* Guildford (01483) 504311

LEWIS, Michael Douglas. b 35. Hertf Coll Ox BA57 MA60. Sarum Th Coll 58. **d** 59 **p** 60. C Stogursey *B & W* 59-65; V N Curry 65-86; V Taunton H Trin 86-94. *Coombe Corner, Adsborough, Taunton, Somerset TA2 8RP* Taunton (01823) 413560

LEWIS, Michael John. b 37. LLAM86. St Aid Birkenhead 64. **d** 66 **p** 67. C Whitnash *Cov* 66-69; C Nuneaton St Nic 69-73; TV Basildon St Martin w H Cross and Laindon *Chelmsf* 73-79; V W Bromwich St Jas *Lich* 79-85; TV Buxton w Burbage and King Sterndale *Derby* from 85. *St Mary's House, 2A New Market Street, Buxton, Derbyshire SK17 6LP* Buxton (01298) 24179

LEWIS, Norman Eric. b 34. SRN55 Open Univ BA77. Roch Th Coll 59 Lich Th Coll 60. **d** 63 **p** 64. V Hindsford *Man* 67-77; V Bolton SS Simon and Jude 77-90; rtd 90. *Millbank Cottage, Kirby Misperton, Malton, N Yorkshire YO17 0XZ* Kirby Misperton (0165386) 526

LEWIS, Paul Wilfred. b 37. Ch Ch Ox BA60 DipEd61 MA64 DipTh72. Chich Th Coll 62. **d** 64 **p** 65. C St Pancras H Cross w St Jude and St Pet *Lon* 64-66; C Tottenham St Jo 66-68; Barbados 68-71; Lect Sarum & Wells Th Coll 72-74; Chapl Sarum & Wells Th Coll 73-74; Chapl LSE *Lon* 74-80; Chapl St Chris Hospice Lon 80-86; C St Giles Cripplegate w St Bart Moor Lane etc *Lon* 86-89; Chapl Nat Hosp for Neurology & Neurosurgery Lon from 89. *The National Hospital, Queen Square, London WC1N 3BG* 0171-837 3611 or 278 3706

LEWIS, Peter Anthony. b 25. Sarum & Wells Th Coll 76. **d** 79 **p** 80. Hon C Southsea St Simon *Portsm* from 79. *2 Selsey Avenue, Southsea, Hants PO4 9QL* Portsmouth (01705) 732394

LEWIS, Canon Peter Goulstone. b 25. Univ of Wales (Lamp) BA48. **d** 50 **p** 51. V Tongwynlais *Llan* 66-79; V Llantrisant 79-90; Can Llan Cathl 85-91; RD Pontypridd 88-90; rtd 91; Perm to Offic *Llan* from 91. *73 Pinecroft Avenue, Cwmbach, Aberdare, M Glam CF44 0NB* Aberdare (01685) 882257

LEWIS, Peter Graham. b 40. Linc Th Coll 70. **d** 81 **p** 82. C Gt and Lt Coates w Bradley *Linc* 81-85; TV 85-87; P-in-c Southoe w Hail Weston *Ely* 87-89; R 89-90; P-in-c Lt Paxton 87-89; V from 89; P-in-c Diddington 87-89; V from 89; R Southoe from 90. *The Vicarage, 24 St James's Road, Little Paxton, St Neots, Huntingdon, Cambs PE19 4QW* Huntingdon (01480) 214280

LEWIS, Peter Richard. b 40. Dur Univ BA62 Birm Univ DipTh64. Qu Coll Birm 62. **d** 64 **p** 65. C Moseley St Mary *Birm* 64-67; C Sherborne w Castleton and Lillington *Sarum* 67-71; P-in-c Bishopstone w Stratford Tony 72-80; V Amesbury from 80; Offg Chapl RAF from 80. *The Vicarage, Church Street, Amesbury, Salisbury SP4 7EU* Amesbury (01980) 623145

LEWIS, Miss Rachel Veronica Clare. b 59. St Jo Coll Dur BA80 Man Univ PGCE81 Univ of Wales (Cardiff) MSc. Sarum & Wells Th Coll 86. **d** 86 **p** 94. C Caereithin *S & B* 86-88; Par Dn Bolton St Pet *Man* 88-91; Chapl Bolton Colls of FE 88-91; Chapl Trin Coll Carmarthen 91-94; C Yatton Keynell *Bris* from 94; C Nettleton w Littleton Drew from 94; C Biddestone w Slaughterford from 94; C Castle Combe from 94; C W Kington from 94. *2 Coopers Meadow, Yatton Keynell, Chippenham, Wilts SN14 7PZ* Chippenham (01249) 782306

LEWIS, Ray Arthur. b 63. Oak Hill Th Coll 87. **d** 90 **p** 91. C Holloway St Mary Magd *Lon* 90-93; TV W Ham *Chelmsf* from 93. *St Matthew's Vicarage, 38 Dyson Road, London E15 4JX* 0181-519 2504

LEWIS, Raymond James. b 34. Univ of Wales (Cardiff) BA Open Univ BSc. St Mich Coll Llan. **d** 91 **p** 92. C Llanelli *St D* 91-94. *4 Hedley Terrace, Llanelli, Dyfed SA15 3RE* Llanelli (01554) 750355

LEWIS, Very Rev Richard. b 35. Fitzw Ho Cam BA78 MA63. Ripon Hall Ox 58. **d** 60 **p** 61. C Hinckley St Mary *Leic* 60-63; C Sanderstead All SS *S'wark* 63-66; V S Merstham 67-72; V S Wimbledon H Trin 72-74; P-in-c S Wimbledon St Pet 72-74; V S Wimbledon H Trin and St Pet 74-79; V Dulwich St Barn 79-90; Chapl Alleyn's Foundn Dulwich 79-90; RD Dulwich *S'wark* 83-90; Hon Can S'wark Cathl 87-90; Dean Wells *B & W* from 90; Warden of Readers from 91. *The Dean's Lodging, 25 The Liberty, Wells, Somerset BA5 2SU* Wells (01749) 670278 Fax 679184

LEWIS, Canon Richard Charles. b 44. Lon Univ DipTh68 DipSocSc78. ALCD69. **d** 69 **p** 70. C Kendal H Trin *Carl* 69-72; C Chipping Barnet *St Alb* 72-76; V Watford Ch Ch from 76; Hon Can St Alb Abbey from 90. *Christ Church Vicarage, Leggatts Way, Watford WD2 6BQ* Garston (01923) 672240

LEWIS, Robert (Bob). b 38. St Pet Coll Ox BA62 MA66. Cuddesdon Coll 62. **d** 64 **p** 65. C Kirkby *Liv* 64-67 and 70-71; TV 71-75; Chapl St Boniface Coll Warminster 68-69; Tutor St Aug Coll Cant 69-70; Abp's Dom Chapl *York* 76-79; Dir of Ords 76-79; TR Thirsk 79-92; Chapl Oslo w Bergen, Trondheim, Stavanger etc *Eur* from 93. *Harald Harfagresqt 2, 0363 Oslo, Norway or c/o The British Embassy, BFPO 50, Oslo, Norway* Oslo (2) 692214 or 552400

LEWIS, Robert George. b 53. Lanc Univ BEd76. Ripon Coll Cuddesdon. **d** 78 **p** 79. C Liv Our Lady and St Nic w St Anne *Liv* 78-81; Asst Dir of Educn 81-88; P-in-c Newchurch 88-89; R Newchurch 94; P-in-c Glazebury 88-89; R Newchurch and Glazebury 89-94; R Winwick from 94. *The Rectory, Golborne Road, Winwick, Warrington WA2 8SZ* Warrington (01925) 632760

LEWIS, Canon Robert Hugh Cecil. b 25. New Coll Ox BA50 MA50. Westcott Ho Cam 50. **d** 52 **p** 53. V Poynton *Ches* 63-91; RD Stockport 72-85; Hon Can Ches Cathl 75-91; RD Cheadle 85-87; Dioc Ecum Officer 87-91; Chapl to The Queen from 85; rtd 91. *78 Dean Drive, Wilmslow, Cheshire SK9 2EY* Wilmslow (01625) 524761

LEWIS, Roger Edward. b 24. Qu Coll Cam BA45 MA49. Ridley Hall Cam 47. **d** 49 **p** 50. V Clacton St Paul *Chelmsf* 58-71; V Surbiton St Matt *S'wark* 71-89; rtd 89; Perm to Offic *S'wark* from 89. *Rose Cottage, 40 Grove Road, Horley, Surrey RH6 8EL* Horley (01293) 771197

LEWIS, Roger Gilbert. b 49. St Jo Coll Dur BA70. Ripon Hall Ox 70. **d** 72 **p** 73. C Boldmere *Birm* 72-76; C Birm St Pet 76-77; TV Tettenhall Regis *Lich* 77-81; V Ward End *Birm* 81-91; rtd 91; Perm to Offic *Birm* from 91. *8 Tudor Terrace, Ravenhurst Road, Birmingham B17 8SB* 0121-427 4915

LEWIS, Preb Ronald Llewellyn. b 12. Leeds Univ BSc35. Coll of Resurr Mirfield 35. **d** 37 **p** 38. V Taunton H Trin *B & W* 63-77; Preb Wells Cathl from 73; rtd 77. *Rose Cottage, 23 Burton Place, Taunton, Somerset TA1 4HE* Taunton (01823) 274778

LEWIS, Stuart William. b 54. Newc Univ BA79. Edin Th Coll. **d** 86 **p** 87. C Ledbury w Eastnor *Heref* 86-89; Chapl Malvern Coll Worcs from 89. *The Chaplain's House, College Road, Great Malvern, Worcs WR14 3DD* Malvern (01684) 892694

LEWIS, Terence Arnold. b 15. Jes Coll Ox BA37 MA41 BD51. St Mich Coll Llan 38. **d** 39 **p** 40. R Aston Clinton w Buckland and Drayton Beauchamp *Ox* 64-86; rtd 86; Perm to Offic *Ox* 86-87 and from 90. *5 Villiers Close, Moreton Grange, Buckingham MK18 1JH* Buckingham (01280) 815849

LEWIS, Thomas Peter. b 45. Selw Coll Cam BA67 MA. Ripon Hall Ox 68. **d** 70 **p** 71. C Hatf *St Alb* 70-74; C Boreham Wood All SS 74-78; Chapl Haileybury Coll Herts 78-85; Chapl Abingdon Sch from 86. *25 Park Road, Abingdon, Oxon OX14 1DA* Abingdon (01235) 526034

LEWIS, Thomas James. b 17. Univ of Wales BA49. St D Coll Lamp 49. **d** 51 **p** 52. V Clyro w Bettws, Llowes and Glasbury All SS *S & B* 66-73; RD Hay 66-73; V Llanyrnewydd 73-82; rtd 82. *34 St Nicholas Court, Gower Road, Killay, Swansea SA2 7AG* Swansea (01792) 297866

LEWIS, Timothy John. b 56. Univ of Wales (Swansea) BA76. Sarum & Wells Th Coll 83. **d** 86 **p** 87. C Taunton St Mary *B & W* 86-89; Chapl RN from 89. *Directorate Gen, RN Chapl Services, Room 203, Victory Building, HM Naval Base, Portsmouth PO1 3LS* Portsmouth (01705) 727903 Fax 727112

LEWIS, Trevor Charlton Haselden. b 22. Qu Coll Birm 49. **d** 51 **p** 52. R Dursley *Glouc* 65-70; Chapl RN 70-71; USA from 71; rtd 94. *190 Park Drive, Gunnison, Colorado 81230, USA*

LEWIS, Vera Elizabeth. b 45. Lon Univ BA66 Univ of Wales (Abth) DipEd67 DipLib73. St As Minl Tr Course 82. **d** 85. NSM Garthbeibio and Llanerfyl and Llangadfan *St As* 85-86; C 87-88; NSM Llanfair Caereinion w Llanllugan 85-86; C 87-88; D-in-c Llanrhaeadr-ym-Mochnant and Llanarmon etc from 88. *The Vicarage, Llanrhaeadr-ym-Mochnant, Oswestry, Shropshire SY10 0JZ* Llanrhaeadr (01691) 780247

LEWIS, Walter Arnold. b 45. NUI BA68 TCD MPhil91. TCD Div Sch 71. **d** 71 **p** 72. C Belf Whiterock *Conn* 71-73; C Belf St Mark 73-80; Bp's C Belf St Andr 80-84; I Belf St Thos from 84. *St Thomas's Rectory, 1A Eglantine Avenue, Belfast BT9 6DW* Belfast (01232) 668360 Fax as telephone

LEWIS, William George Melville. b 31. Open Univ BA. S'wark Ord Course. **d** 69 **p** 70. C Coulsdon St Jo *S'wark* 69-71; C Perry Hill St Geo 71-74; V Eltham St Barn 74-80; V Reigate St Mark 80-89; V Ham St Rich from 89. *The Vicarage, Ashburnham Road, Ham, Richmond, Surrey TW10 7NL* 0181-948 3758

LEWIS, William George Rees. b 35. Hertf Coll Ox BA59 MA63. Tyndale Hall Bris 61. **d** 63 **p** 64. C Tenby w Gumfreston *St D* 63-66; C Llanelli St Paul 66-69; R Letterston 69-84; R Jordanston w Llanstinan 73-78; R Punchestown and Lt Newc 78-84; R Hubberston w Herbrandston and Hasguard etc 84-90; Prov Officer for Evang and Adult Educn 90-94; V Gabalfa *Llan* from 94. *St Mark's Vicarage, 208 North Road, Cardiff CF4 3BL* Cardiff (01222) 613286

LEWIS, William Rhys. b 20. St Mich Coll Llan 53. **d** 55 **p** 56. R Ebbw Vale *Mon* 64-73; V Llangattock and Llangyndir *S & B* 73-78; V Cwmbwrla 78-85; rtd 85; Perm to Offic *Llan* from 85. *6 Beech Avenue, Llantwit Major, S Glam CF61 1RT* Llantwit Major (01446) 796741

LEWIS-ANTHONY, Justin Griffith. b 64. LSE BA86. Ripon Coll Cuddesdon BA91. **d** 92 **p** 93. C Cirencester *Glouc* from 92. *15 Partridge Way, Cirencester, Glos GL7 1BH* Cirencester (01285) 654779

LEWIS LLOYD, Canon Timothy David (Tim). b 37. Clare Coll Cam BA58 MA62. Cuddesdon Coll 58. **d** 60 **p** 61. C Stepney St Dunstan and All SS *Lon* 60-64; C St Alb Abbey *St Alb* 64-67; Prec St Alb Abbey 67-69; V St Paul's Walden 69-78; V Braughing w Furneux Pelham and Stocking Pelham 78-79; P-in-c Lt Hadham 78-79; V Braughing, Lt Hadham, Albury, Furneux Pelham etc 79-82; V Cheshunt from 82; RD Cheshunt 89-94; Hon Can St Alb from 94. *The Vicarage, Churchgate, Cheshunt, Waltham Cross, Herts EN8 9DY* Waltham Cross (01992) 623121

LEWIS-NICHOLSON, Russell John. b 45. Caulfield Inst of Tech DipCivEng68. Oak Hill Th Coll DipTh81. **d** 81 **p** 82. C Clayton *Bradf* 81-84; Australia from 84. *121 Albert Street, Geelong West, Victoria, Australia 3218* Geelong (52) 216694

LEWISHAM, Archdeacon of. See KUHRT, Ven Gordon Wilfred

LEWORTHY, Graham Llewelyn. b 47. Reading Univ BA69. S Dios Minl Tr Scheme 91. **d** 94 **p** 95. NSM Sark *Win* from 94. *La Baleine, Sark, Channel Islands* Sark (01481) 832140

LEWTHWAITE, David. b 39. K Coll Lon BD75. St Aid Birkenhead 63. **d** 65 **p** 66. C Standish *Blackb* 65-68; S Africa 68-71; P-in-c Blackb All SS *Blackb* 71-72; C Kentish Town St Jo *Lon* 72-75; P-in-c Wilden w Colmworth and Ravensden *St Alb* 75-79; V Knottingley *Wakef* 79-81; R Maulden *St Alb* from 81; RD Ampthill from 90. *The Rectory, Clophill Road, Maulden, Bedford MK45 2AA* Ampthill (01525) 403139

LEY, John Andrew. b 16. St Deiniol's Hawarden 70. **d** 72 **p** 73. Hon C Leintwardine *Heref* 72-76; Hon C Wigmore Abbey 76-77; AP Pulloxhill w Flitton *St Alb* 77-79; Lic to Offic *Blackb* 80-81; C Stoke Lacy, Moreton Jeffries w Much Cowarne etc *Heref* 81-87; rtd 87; Perm to Offic *Lich* from 87. *4 Winchester Close, Lichfield, Staffs WS13 7SL* Lichfield (01543) 255941

LEYLAND, Derek James. b 34. Lon Univ BSc55 Birm Univ DipTh60. Qu Coll Birm 58. d 60 p 61. V Ashton-on-Ribble St Andr *Blackb* 80-87; V Pendleton 67-74; Ind Youth Chapl 70-74; R Brindle 74-80; V Garstang St Helen Churchtown 87-94; Sec SOSc 90-94; rtd 94. *Greystocks, Goosnargh Lane, Goosnargh, Preston PR3 2BP*

LEYLAND, Tyrone John. b 49. Aston Univ BSc68. St Jo Coll Nottm 89. d 91 p 92. C Lich St Mary w St Mich *Lich* 91-94; C Willenhall H Trin from 94. *The Vicarage, 129 Essington Road, Willenhall, W Midlands WV12 5DT* Willenhall (01902) 473321

LEYSHON, Simon. b 63. Trin Coll Carmarthen BA86 Southn Univ BTh89. Sarum & Wells Th Coll. d 89 p 90. C Tenby *St D* 89-92; TV from 92. *The Vicarage, Penally, Tenby, Dyfed SA70 7PN* Tenby (01834) 842416

LIBBY, John Ralph. b 55. Trin Coll Cam BA(Econ)83. Ridley Hall Cam 89. d 91 p 92. C Enfield St Andr *Lon* 91-93; C Northwood Em from 93. *4 Church Close, Northwood, Middx HA6 1AG* Northwood (01923) 835255

LICHFIELD, Archdeacon of. *See* NINIS, Ven Richard Betts

LICHFIELD, Bishop of. *See* SUTTON, Rt Rev Keith Norman

LICHFIELD, Dean of. *See* WRIGHT, Very Rev Dr Nicholas Thomas (Tom)

LICKESS, Canon David Frederick. b 37. St Chad's Coll Dur BA63 DipTh65. d 65 p 66. C Howden *York* 65-70; V Rudby in Cleveland w Middleton from 70; Can and Preb York Minster from 90; RD Stokesley from 93. *The Vicarage, Hutton Rudby, Yarm, Cleveland TS15 0HY* Stokesley (01642) 700223

LIDDELL, Peter Gregory. b 40. St Andr Univ MA63 Linacre Ho Ox BA65 MA70. Andover Newton Th Coll DMin75 Ripon Hall Ox 63. d 65 p 66. C Hatf *St Alb* 65-71; USA 71-76; P-in-c Kimpton w Ayot St Lawrence *St Alb* 77-83; Dir of Past Counselling from 80. *The Coach House, The Old Vicarage, Kimpton, Hitchin, Herts SG4 8EF* Kimpton (01438) 832266

LIDDELOW, Peter William. b 33. Oak Hill NSM Course. d 82 p 83. NSM Finchley Ch Ch *Lon* 82-84; NSM S Mimms Ch Ch from 84. *23 King's Road, Barnet, Herts EN5 4EP* 0181-441 2968

LIDDLE, George. b 48. NE Ord Course 88. d 90 p 91. C Auckland St Andr and St Anne *Dur* 90-92; C Crook 92-94; C Stanley 92-94; P-in-c Evenwood from 94. *St Paul's Vicarage, Evenwood, Bishop Auckland, Co Durham DL14 9RA* Bishop Auckland (01388) 832348

LIDDLE, Harry. b 36. Wadh Coll Ox BA57 MA61. Wycliffe Hall Ox 62. d 64 p 65. C Withington St Paul *Man* 64-68; R Broughton 68-73; V Balby *Sheff* 73-82; R Firbeck w Letwell 82-94; V Woodsetts 82-94; TV Aston cum Aughton w Swallownest, Todwick & Ulley from 94. *9 Horbiry End, Todwick, Sheffield S31 0HH* Worksop (01909) 515360

LIDDLE, Stephen John. b 60. St Jo Coll Ox BA81 PGCE82. Linc Th Coll 88. d 91 p 92. C Morpeth *Newc* 91-95; P-in-c Byker St Mich w St Lawr from 95. *St Michael's Vicarage, Headlam Street, Newcastle upon Tyne NE6 2DX* 0191-265 3720

LIDDON, Alfred James. b 21. Lon Univ BA49. Oak Hill Th Coll 46. d 51 p 52. R Gunton St Pet *Nor* 65-77; RD Lothingland 76-80; R Bradwell 77-88; rtd 88; Perm to Offic *Nor* from 88. *6 Pennine Way, Oulton, Lowestoft, Suffolk NR32 3HD* Lowestoft (01502) 518247

LIDSTONE, Vernon Henry. b 43. SW Minl Tr Course 89. d 92 p 93. NSM Bovey Tracey SS Pet, Paul and Thos w Hennock *Ex* 92-94; Sub-Chapl HM Pris Channings Wood from 92; Asst Dioc Stewardship Adv 92-93; Dioc Stewardship Adv from 93. *The Elms, Willand, Cullompton, Devon EX15 2RL* Cullompton (01884) 3551

LIDWILL, Mark Robert. b 57. TCD DipTh87. d 87 p 88. C Annagh w Drumgoon, Ashfield etc *K, E & A* 87-90; I Urney w Denn and Derryheen from 90; Dioc Youth Adv from 92. *The Rectory, Co Cavan, Irish Republic* Cavan (49) 61016

LIFTON, Norman Reginald. b 22. ALSM. Worc Ord Coll 62. d 64 p 65. C Milford Haven *St D* 68-70; R Spexhall w Wissett *St E* 70-77; V Berkeley *Glouc* 77-84; C Malborough w S Huish, W Alvington and Churchstow *Ex* 84-87; V Ticknall, Smisby and Stanton by Bridge *Derby* 87-92; rtd 92; Perm to Offic *Ex* from 92. *Woodleigh, 6 Cotmore Way, Chillington, Kingsbridge, Devon TQ7 2HU* Kingsbridge (01548) 580264

LIGHTFOOT, Very Rev Vernon Keith. b 34. St Jo Coll Dur BA58. Ripon Hall Ox 58. d 60 p 61. C Rainhill *Liv* 60-62; C Liv Our Lady and St Nic 62-65; V Stanley 65-75; New Zealand from 75; Dean Waikato from 86. *The Deanery, 6 Tisdall Street, Hamilton, PO Box 338, New Zealand* Hamilton (7) 839-4683

LIGHTOWLER, Joseph Trevor. b 33. d 79 p 80. Hon C Leverstock Green *St Alb* 79-80; Hon C Chambersbury (Hemel Hempstead) 80-84; C Woodmansterne *S'wark* 84-88; R Odell and Pavenham *St Alb* from 88. *The Rectory, 3 Church Lane, Odell, Bedford MK43 7AA* Bedford (01234) 720234

LIKEMAN, Canon Martin Kaye. b 34. St Mich Coll Llan 55. d 57 p 58. C Llanwnog w Penstrowed *Ban* 57-60; C Llandudno 60-64; V Llanrhian w Llanhywel and Carnhedryn *St D* 64-73; RD Dewisland and Fishguard 71-73; V Llanstadwel from 73; Can St D Cathl from 88. *The Vicarage, Llanstadwel, Milford Haven, Dyfed SA73 1AW* Neyland (01646) 600227

LILES, Malcolm David. b 48. Nottm Univ BA69. St Steph Ho Ox 69. d 71 p 72. C Corby Epiphany w St Jo *Pet* 71-74; C New Cleethorpes *Linc* 74-76; TV Lt Coates 76-77; TV Gt and Lt Coates w Bradley 78-82; Soc Resp Sec 82-93; Hon C Gt Grimsby St Mary and St Jas 82-93; P-in-c Grimsby All SS 88-93; TV Dronfield w Holmesfield *Derby* from 93. *The Vicarage, Main Road, Holmesfield, Sheffield S18 5WT* Sheffield (0114) 289 0243

LILEY, Christopher Frank. b 47. Nottm Univ BEd70. Linc Th Coll 72. d 74 p 75. C Kingswinford H Trin *Lich* 74-79; TV Stafford 79-84; V Norton *St Alb* from 84; RD Hitchin 89-94. *The Vicarage, 17 Norton Way North, Letchworth, Herts SG6 1BY* Letchworth (01462) 685059

LILEY, Peter James. b 60. Liv Univ BA82 Westmr Coll Ox PGCE83. Oak Hill Th Coll DipHE93. d 93 p 94. C Exning St Martin w Landwade *St E* from 93. *3 Norfolk Avenue, Newmarket, Suffolk CB8 0DE* Newmarket (01638) 661120

LILLEY, Alan Charles. b 34. Nottm Univ BA55 MA67 St Cath Soc Ox DipTh59. Wycliffe Hall Ox 57. d 59 p 60. C Leic H Apostles *Leic* 59-63; C New Humberstone 63-65; V Copt Oak 65-78; Perm to Offic from 80; Student Counsellor Loughb Univ 78-88; Dir from 88. *12 Shepherd Walk, Kegworth, Derby DE74 2HS* Loughborough (01509) 673967

LILLEY, Christopher Howard (Chris). b 51. FCA75 FTII83. St Jo Coll Bramcote DCM93 Local NSM Course 83. d 85 p 86. Hon C Skegness and Winthorpe *Linc* 85-93; C Gt Limber w Brocklesby from 93; Perm to Offic *S'well* from 93. *The Glebe House, Church Lane, Limber, Grimsby, S Humberside DN37 8JN* Roxton (01469) 61082

LILLEY, Ivan Ray. b 32. Bps' Coll Cheshunt 58. d 61 p 62. C Kettering SS Pet and Paul *Pet* 61-64; C Gt Yarmouth *Nor* 64-75; P-in-c Tottenhill w Wormegay *Ely* 76-83; P-in-c Watlington 76-83; P-in-c Holme Runcton w S Runcton and Wallington 76-83; V Tysoe w Oxhill and Whatcote *Cov* 83-86; C Langold *S'well* 87-91; P-in-c from 91. *St Luke's Vicarage, Church Street, Langold, Worksop, Notts S81 9NW* Worksop (01909) 730398

LILLEY, John. b 36. Liv Univ DipAdEd70. d 81 p 82. NSM Holyhead w Rhoscolyn w Llanfair-yn-Neubwll *Ban* 81-84; Chapl Scargill Ho 84-87; TV Beaminster Area *Sarum* 87-93; RD Beaminster 89-93; P-in-c Fradswell, Gayton, Milwich and Weston *Lich* from 93; P-in-c Hixon w Stowe-by-Chartley from 93. *The Vicarage, Weston, Stafford ST18 0HX* Weston (01889) 270490

LILLIAN, Sister. *See* MORRIS, Sister Lillian Rosina

LILLIE, Judith Virginia. *See* THOMPSON, Mrs Judith Virginia

LILLINGTON, Brian Ray. b 36. RMN60 FRSH84 Ex Univ DSA65 Lon Univ DipMentH67. S Dios Minl Tr Scheme 87. d 90 p 91. NSM Yateley *Win* from 90. *Kaos, Little Vigo, Yateley, Camberley, Surrey GU17 7ES* Yateley (01252) 872760

LILLINGTON (nee POLLIT), Mrs Ruth Mary. b 65. SS Paul & Mary Coll Cheltenham BA88. St Jo Coll Nottm DPS90. d 90 p 94. Par Dn Caverswall *Lich* 90-92; Par Dn Caverswall and Weston Coyney w Dilhorne 92-93; Par Dn Luton St Mary *St Alb* 93-94; C from 94; Chapl Luton Univ from 93. *72 Crawley Green Road, Luton LU2 0QU* Luton (01582) 35548

LILLISTONE, Brian David. b 38. SS Coll Cam BA61 MA65. St Steph Ho Ox 61. d 63 p 64. C Ipswich All Hallows *St E* 63-66; C Stokesay *Heref* 66-71; P-in-c Lyonshall w Titley 71-76; R Martlesham w Brightwell *St E* from 76. *The Rectory, 17 Lark Rise, Martlesham Heath, Ipswich IP5 7SA* Ipswich (01473) 622424

LIMBERT, Kenneth Edward. b 25. CEng69 MIMechE. S'wark Ord Course 72. d 75 p 76. NSM Northwood Hills St Edm *Lon* 75-90; Perm to Offic from 90. *55 York Road, Northwood, Middx HA6 1JJ* Northwood (01923) 825791

LIMBRICK, Gordon. b 36. Open Univ BA88. St Jo Coll Nottm CertCS90. d 87 p 91. NSM Troon *Glas* 87-90; NSM Yaxley *Ely* from 90. *271 Broadway, Yaxley, Peterborough PE7 3NR* Peterborough (01733) 243170

LIMERICK AND ARDFERT, Dean of. *See* SIRR, Very Rev John Maurice Glover

LIMERICK, Archdeacon of. *See* NUTTALL, Ven Michael John Berkeley

LIMERICK, ARDFERT, AGHADOE, KILLALOE, KILFENORA, CLONFERT, KILMACDUAGH AND EMLY, Bishop of. *See* DARLING, Rt Rev Edward Flewett

LINAKER, David Julian John Ramage. b 65. Ripon Coll Cuddesdon BTh95. **d** 95. C Colehill *Sarum* from 95. *37 Bridle Way, Colehill, Wimborne, Dorset BH21 2UP* Wimborne (01202) 849364

LINCOLN, Archdeacon of. *See* BRACKENBURY, Ven Michael Palmer

LINCOLN, Bishop of. *See* HARDY, Rt Rev Robert Maynard

LINCOLN, Dean of. *See* JACKSON, Very Rev Dr Brandon Donald

LIND-JACKSON, Peter Wilfrid. b 35. Leeds Univ BA67. Linc Th Coll 67. **d** 68 **p** 69. C Heref St Martin *Heref* 68-71; P-in-c Burghill 71-78; V 78-82; P-in-c Whorlton *Dur* 82-83; V Barnard Castle 82-83; V Barnard Castle w Whorlton from 83. *The Vicarage, Barnard Castle, Co Durham DL12 8NW* Teesdale (01833) 37018

LINDARS, Frank. b 23. Wycliffe Hall Ox 54. **d** 56 **p** 57. V Shadwell *Ripon* 61-80; RD Allerton 73-78; V Masham and Healey 80-88; rtd 88. *Hope Cottage, Reeth, Richmond, N Yorkshire DL11 6SF* Richmond (01748) 884685

LINDECK, Peter Stephen. b 31. Oak Hill Th Coll 57. **d** 59 **p** 60. V Toxteth Park St Bede *Liv* 68-74; Nigeria 74-76; C Netherton *Liv* 76-77; C Ollerton *S'well* 77-80; C Boughton 77-80; V Whitgift w Adlingfleet and Eastoft *Sheff* 80-86; P-in-c Swinefleet 81-86; V Kilnhurst 86-94; Chapl Montagu Hosp Mexborough from 86; rtd 94. *41 Church Lane, Doncaster, S Yorkshire DN4 0XB* Doncaster (01302) 855957

LINDEN, Gregory. b 25. Roch Th Coll. **d** 66 **p** 66. C Roundhay St Edm *Ripon* 65-68; C Highweek *Ex* 68-72; V Brampford Speke 72-82; R Upton Pyne 72-82; R Middleton-in-Teesdale *Dur* 82-85; V Eggleston from 85; R Middleton-in-Teesdale w Forest and Frith from 85. *The Rectory, Middleton-in-Teesdale, Barnard Castle, Co Durham DL12 0QW* Teesdale (01833) 40267

LINDISFARNE, Archdeacon of. *See* BOWERING, Ven Michael Ernest

LINDLEY, Geoffrey. b 22. St Jo Coll Ox BA45 MA47. Westcott Ho Cam 47. **d** 47 **p** 48. V Ox St Marg *Ox* 56-72; P-in-c Pyrton w Shirburn 72-79; P-in-c Lewknor 72-79; P-in-c Milton-under-Wychwood 79-80; P-in-c Shipton-under-Wychwood 79-80; V Shipton-under-Wychwood w Milton-under-Wychwood 80-85; Perm to Offic from 86; rtd 87. *St John's Home, St Mary's Road, Oxford OX4 1QE* Oxford (01865) 247725

LINDLEY, Harold Thomas. b 28. St Jo Coll Ox BA51 MA73. Wells Th Coll 51. **d** 53 **p** 54. V Longstone *Derby* 68-74; P-in-c Barrow w Twyford 74-84; V Barrow-on-Trent w Twyford and Swarkestone 84-93; rtd 93. *Gorwel, 35 Nant Bychan, Moelfre, Gwynedd LL72 8HE* Moelfre (01248) 410484

LINDLEY, Ven Ralph Adrian. b 20. CBE75. St Jo Coll Dur BA51 DipTh53. **d** 53 **p** 54. Chapl RAF 55-70; UAE 70-78; Adn Gulf 70-78; Gen Sec JMECA 78-85; rtd 86. *Taffrail, Lower Road, St Briavels, Lydney, Glos GL15 6SA* Dean (01594) 530230

LINDLEY, Richard Adrian. b 44. MBIM92 Hull Univ BA65 Birm Univ DPS68 Man Univ MA79 Birm Poly DMS91. Cuddesdon Coll 66. **d** 68 **p** 69. C Ingrow cum Hainworth *Bradf* 68-70; Perm to Offic *Birm* 70-74; TV Ellesmere Port *Ches* 74-79; R Westborough *Guildf* 79-80; TR 80-84; Dir of Educn *Birm* from 84. *60 Peterbrook Road, Shirley, Solihull, W Midlands B90 1ED* 0121-474 2001 or 427 5141 Fax 428 1114

LINDO, Leithland Oscar. b 29. St Aug Coll Cant 57 St Pet Coll Jamaica 53. **d** 56 **p** 57. Jamaica 56-58; C Edmonton St Mary w St Jo *Lon* 58-62; C Heston 62-66; V Staines Ch Ch from 66. *Christ Church Vicarage, Kenilworth Gardens, Staines, Middx TW18 1DR* Staines (01784) 455457

LINDOP, Andrew John. b 57. Cam Univ MA. Cranmer Hall Dur 80. **d** 82 **p** 83. C Brinsworth w Catcliffe *Sheff* 82-85; C S Shoebury *Chelmsf* 85-89; V Mosley Common *Man* from 89. *St John's Vicarage, Mosley Common Road, Worsley, Manchester M28 4AN* 0161-790 2957

LINDOP, Kenneth. b 45. Linc Th Coll 71. **d** 74 **p** 75. C Leic St Phil *Leic* 74-77; C Cov H Trin *Cov* 77-80; P-in-c Cubbington 80-82; V from 82; RD Warw and Leamington from 91. *The Vicarage, Rugby Road, Cubbington, Leamington Spa, Warks CV32 7JL* Leamington Spa (01926) 423056

LINDSAY, Alexandra Jane (Sandra). b 43. CITC 90. **d** 93 **p** 94. Lic to Offic *K, E & A* 93-94; NSM Bailieborough w Knockbride, Shercock and Mullagh from 94. *Clementstown House, Cootehill, Co Cavan, Irish Republic* Cootehill (49) 52207 Fax as telephone

LINDSAY, Anthony. b 38. Trin Coll Bris DipHE93 St Jo Coll Nottm CertCS88. **d** 89 **p** 90. CMS 76-92; Sierra Leone 88-92; C Rainham w Wennington *Chelmsf* from 93. *8A Frederick Road, Rainham, Essex RM13 8NT* Rainham (01708) 554458

LINDSAY, Cecil. b 43. Iona Coll (NY) BBA68. CITC 85. **d** 88 **p** 88. NSM Kilmore w Ballintemple, Kildallon etc *K, E & A* 88-90; Lic to Offic 90-92; NSM Roscommon w Donamon,

Rathcline, Kilkeevin etc from 92. *Clementstown House, Cootehill, Co Cavan, Irish Republic* Cootehill (49) 52207 Fax as telephone

LINDSAY, David Macintyre. b 46. Trin Hall Cam BA68 MA72 Ox Univ DipTh70. Cuddesdon Coll 68. **d** 71 **p** 72. C Gosforth All SS *Newc* 71-74; C Keele *Lich* 74-78; Perm to Offic *St E* 79-80; Chapl Haberdashers' Aske's Sch Elstree from 80. *36 Cranbourne Drive, Harpenden, Herts AL5 1RU* Harpenden (01582) 765660

LINDSAY, Eric Graham. b 30. Witwatersrand Univ BA51 Lon Univ DipAdEd78 MA80 Heythrop Coll Lon DipTh82. Coll of Resurr Mirfield 55. **d** 57 **p** 59. Perm to Offic *Roch* 65-72; Perm to Offic *Chelmsf* 72-84; C Stepney St Dunstan and All SS *Lon* 84-85; R Bridge of Weir *Glas* from 85; R Kilmacolm from 85; rtd 95. *St Fillan's Rectory, 4 Balmore Court, Kilmacolm, Renfrewshire PA13 4LX* Kilmacolm (01505) 872961

LINDSAY, John Carruthers. b 50. Edin Univ MA72 BD82. Edin Th Coll 79. **d** 82 **p** 83. C Broughty Ferry *Bre* 82-84; C Edin St Hilda *Edin* 84-85; TV 85-88; C Edin St Fillan 84-85; TV 85-88; R N Berwick from 88; R Gullane from 88. *The Rectory, 2 May Terrace, North Terrace, East Lothian EH39 4BA* North Berwick (01620) 2154

LINDSAY, Richard John. b 46. Sarum & Wells Th Coll 74. **d** 78 **p** 79. C Aldwick *Chich* 78-81; C Almondbury *Wakef* 81-82; C Almondbury w Farnley Tyas 82-84; V Mossley *Man* from 84. *The Vicarage, Stamford Street, Mossley, Ashton-under-Lyne, Lancs OL5 0LP* Mossley (01457) 832219

LINDSAY, Canon Richard John Alan. b 24. TCD BA46 BD52. **d** 49 **p** 50. R Chich St Pancras and St Jo *Chich* 68-74; Chapl Maisons-Laffitte *Eur* 74-82; Can Brussels Cathl 81-89; Chapl The Hague w Leiden and Voorschoten 82-89; rtd 89; Perm to Offic *Heref* from 89. *Japonica Cottage, King's Acre Road, Breinton, Hereford HR4 0SG* Hereford (01432) 50230

LINDSAY, Canon Robert. b 16. St Jo Coll Dur BA37 DipTh38 MA40. **d** 39 **p** 40. RD Derwent *Carl* 70-81; V Loweswater w Buttermere 74-81; rtd 81; Perm to Offic *Ex* from 81. *58 Primley Road, Sidmouth, Devon EX10 9LF* Sidmouth (01395) 577882

LINDSAY, Robert Ashley Charles. b 43. Leeds Univ BA66 Ex Univ BPhil81. Coll of Resurr Mirfield 66. **d** 68 **p** 69. C Mill Hill Jo Keble Ch *Lon* 68-72; C Sherborne w Castleton and Lillington *Sarum* 73-78; Chapl Coldharbour Hosp Dorset 73-78; Perm to Offic *Leic* from 87. *79 Castledine Street, Loughborough, Leics LE11 2DX* Loughborough (01509) 264360

LINDSAY-PARKINSON, Michael. b 28. Edin Th Coll 66. **d** 67 **p** 68. C Edin Ch Ch *Edin* 67-70; C Helensburgh *Glas* 70-72; R Lockerbie 72-83; R Annan 72-83; S Africa 83-88; V Alsager St Mary *Ches* 88-93; rtd 93. *10 Cherry Tree Avenue, Church Lawton, Stoke-on-Trent ST7 3EL* Alsager (01270) 875574

LINDSEY, Archdeacon of. Vacant

LINES, John Anthony. b 31. Man Univ BA54 MA55 Birm Univ PhD74. St Jo Sem Wonersh 80 E Midl Min Tr Course. **d** 84 **p** 85. NSM Derby St Bart *Derby* 84-87; C Market Bosworth, Cadeby w Sutton Cheney etc *Leic* 87-90; C Wigston Magna 90-91; R Happisburgh w Walcot, Hempstead, Lessingham etc *Nor* 91-95; R Happisburgh, Walcot, Hempstead w Eccles etc from 95. *The Vicarage, The Hill, Happisburgh, Norwich NR12 0AB* Walcott (01692) 650313

LINFORD, Preb John Kenneth. b 31. Liv Univ BA52. Chich Th Coll 54. **d** 56 **p** 57. V Tunstall Ch Ch *Lich* 61-70; V Sedgley All SS 70-78; Chapl Chase Hosp Cannock 78-91; TR Cannock *Lich* 78-91; V Hatherton 80-91; Preb Lich Cathl from 88; rtd 91. *16 School Lane, Hill Ridware, Rugeley, Staffs WS15 3QN* Armitage (01543) 492831

LING, Andrew Joyner. b 35. ACP69 St Luke's Coll Ex TCert63 Open Univ BA80. SW Minl Tr Course 83. **d** 86 **p** 87. NSM St Mellion w Pillaton *Truro* 86-87; NSM Landulph 86-87; NSM St Dominic 86-87; NSM St Dominic, Landulph and St Mellion w Pillaton 87-90; C Saltash 90-94; TV from 94. *The Vicarage, St Stephens, Saltash, Cornwall PL12 4AB* Saltash (01752) 842323

LING, Timothy Charles. b 61. Ex Univ BA85 Selw Coll Cam BA91. Ridley Hall Cam CTM92. **d** 92 **p** 93. C Gerrards Cross and Fulmer *Ox* from 92. *24 Fulmer Drive, Gerrards Cross, Bucks SL9 7HJ* Gerrards Cross (01753) 887587

LINGARD, Colin. b 36. Kelham Th Coll 58. **d** 63 **p** 64. C Middlesb St Martin *York* 63-66; C Stainton-in-Cleveland 66-71; V Eskdaleside w Ugglebarnby 71-77; P-in-c Redcar w Kirkleatham 77; V Kirkleatham 78-86; RD Guisborough 83-86; V Linc St Botolph by Bargate *Linc* 86-89; Dioc Dir of Readers 86-89; R Washington *Dur* 89-93; P-in-c Middleton St Geo from 93. *The Rectory, 8 Westacres, Neasham Road, Middleton St George, Darlington, Co Durham DL2 1LJ* Dinsdale (01325) 332557

LINGARD, Keith Patrick. b 30. AKC53. **d** 54 **p** 55. V S Farnborough *Guildf* 65-75; R Glaston w Bisbrooke *Pet* 75-76;

R Morcott w Glaston and Bisbrooke 77-95; rtd 95. *13 Woodside East, Thurlby, Bourne, Lincs PE10 0HT* Bourne (01778) 425572

LINGS, George William. b 49. Nottm Univ BTh74 Ox Univ PGCE75. Lambeth Hon MLitt93 St Jo Coll Nottm 70. d 75 p 76. C Harold Wood *Chelmsf* 75-78; C Reigate St Mary *S'wark* 78-85; V Deal St Geo *Cant* from 85. *The Vicarage, 8 St George's Road, Deal, Kent CT14 6BA* Deal (01304) 372587

LINGWOOD, David Peter. b 51. Lon Univ BEd73 Southn Univ BTh80. Sarum & Wells Th Coll 75. d 78 p 79. C Ashford St Hilda *Lon* 78-81; C Astwood Bank w Crabbs Cross *Worc* 81; TV Redditch, The Ridge 81-86; TR Blakenall Heath *Lich* from 86. *Christ Church Rectory, Blakenall Heath, Walsall WS3 1HT* Bloxwich (01922) 479593

LINN, Frederick Hugh. b 37. Em Coll Cam BA61 MA65. Ripon Hall Ox 61. d 63 p 64. C Bramhall *Ches* 63-68; V Liscard St Mary 68-71; V Liscard St Mary w St Columba 71-74; V Wybunbury 74-82; R Eccleston and Pulford from 82. *The Rectory, Eccleston, Chester CH4 9HT* Chester (01244) 674703

LINN, John David Alan. b 29. MC51. Ridley Hall Cam 73. d 75 p 76. C Ely 75-77; P-in-c Kennett 77-81; R 81-82; P-in-c Fordham St Pet 77-81; V 81-82; P-in-c Guilden Morden 82-88; P-in-c Litlington w Abington Pigotts 82-88; P-in-c Steeple Morden 82-88; P-in-c Tadlow 82-88; P-in-c Wendy w Shingay 82-88; R Fincham 88-94; V Shouldham 88-94; V Shouldham Thorpe 88-94; V Marham 88-94; rtd 94. *50 Forehill, Ely, Cambs CB7 4AQ* Ely (01353) 669535

LINNEGAN, Canon John McCaughan. ACCS48 ACIS70 TCD BA55. d 57 p 58. I Cappagh *D & R* 59-80; I Cappagh w Lislimnaghan 80-90; Can Derry Cathl 82-90; rtd 90. *46 Lisanelly Park, Omagh, Co Tyrone BT79 7DE* Omagh (01662) 249643

LINNEGAR, George Leonard. b 33. CGA. Kelham Th Coll 63. d 62 p 63. C Wellingborough St Mary *Pet* 62-65; Lic to Offic *Lich* 65-69; Lic to Offic *B & W* 69-80; Hon C Lewes All SS, St Anne, St Mich and St Thos *Chich* 80-86; C from 87. *20 Morris Road, Lewes, E Sussex BN7 2AT* Lewes (01273) 478145

LINNEY, Ven Gordon Charles Scott. b 39. CITC 66. d 69 p 70. C Agherton *Conn* 69-72; Min Can Down Cathl *D & D* 72-75; I Dub St Cath w St Jas *D & G* 75-80; Preb Tipperkevin St Patr Cathl Dub 77-80; I Glenageary *D & G* from 80; Adn Dub from 88; Lect CITC 89-93. *St Paul's Vicarage, Silchester Road, Glenageary, Co Dublin, Irish Republic* Dublin (1) 280-1616 Fax as telephone

LINNING, Alexander. b 19. Birm Univ BA40 Lon Univ BD42. d 61 p 62. Hon C W Bridgford *S'well* 61-80; Lic to Offic from 80. *7 Kingston Road, Nottingham NG2 7AQ* Nottingham (0115) 981 2959

LINSKILL, Martin Paul Richard. b 50. Magd Coll Ox BA72 MA75. St Steph Ho Ox 73. d 75 p 76. C Pinner *Lon* 75-80; C Greenhill *Sheff* 80-82; C Penistone *Wakef* 82-83; Tutor St Steph Ho Ox 84-91; Chapl Bede Ho Stapleharst 91; V Bedf St Martin *St Alb* from 91. *St Martin's Vicarage, 76 Clapham Road, Bedford MK41 7PN* Bedford (01234) 357862

LINTERN, John. b 61. Linc Th Coll BTh93. d 93 p 94. C Preston on Tees *Dur* from 93. *18 Elmwood Road, Eaglescliffe, Stockton-on-Tees, Cleveland TS16 0AQ* Eaglescliffe (01642) 782665

LINTON, Alan Ross. b 28. Lon Univ DipTh60. St Aid Birkenhead 57. d 60 p 61. C Douglas *Blackb* 69-71; P-in-c Appley Bridge All SS CD 71-76; P-in-c Scorton 76-85; P-in-c Calder Vale w Admarsh 76-85; R Hoole 85-93; rtd 93. *12 Clive Road, Penwortham, Preston PR1 0AT* Preston (01772) 747813

LINTON, Joseph Edmund. b 19. St Andr Univ MA46. Sarum Th Coll 46. d 48 p 49. V Beltingham w Henshaw *Newc* 59-93; rtd 93. *4 Dipton Close, Eastwood Grange, Hexham, Northd NE46 1UG* Hexham (01434) 601457

LINTON, Sydney. b 07. Pemb Coll Ox BA30 MA34. Westcott Ho Cam 31. d 32 p 33. V Barnes H Trin *S'wark* 57-71; R Codford *Sarum* 71-73; R Codford, Upton Lovell and Stockton 73-77; rtd 77. *clo Lord Harris Court, Wokingham, Berks RG11 5EA* Wokingham (01734) 787496

LINTOTT, William Ince. b 36. St Cath Coll Cam BA58. Ely Th Coll 58. d 60 p 61. C Brighton St Wilfrid *Chich* 60-62; C Chingford SS Pet and Paul *Chelmsf* 62-66; Lic to Offic *Ely* from 66; Chapl Fulbourn Hosp Cam 66-73. *7 Haverhill Road, Stapleford, Cambridge CB2 5BX* Cambridge (01223) 842008

LINZEY, Prof Andrew. b 52. FRSA93 K Coll Lon BD73 AKC73 Univ of Wales (Cardiff) DPS74 PhD86 Ox Univ MA92. St Aug Coll Cant 75. d 75 p 76. C Charlton-by-Dover SS Pet and Paul *Cant* 75-77; Chapl and Lect Theol NE Surrey Coll of Tech Guildf 77-81; Chapl Essex Univ *Chelmsf* 81-92; Dir of Studies Cen for Study of Th 87-92; Sen Research Fell Mansf Coll Ox from 92; Tutor Chr Ethics from 93; Special Prof Th Nottm Univ from 92. *Mansfield College, Oxford OX1 3TF* Oxford (01865) 270999

LIPPIATT, Michael Charles. b 39. Oak Hill Th Coll BD71. d 71 p 72. C Ardsley *Sheff* 71-74; C Lenton *S'well* 74-78; V Jesmond H Trin *Newc* from 78. *Holy Trinity Vicarage, 63 Roseberry Crescent, Jesmond, Newcastle upon Tyne NE2 1EX* 0191-281 1663

LIPPIETT, Dr Peter Vernon. b 47. DRCOG79 MRCGP80 Lon Univ MB, BS73. Ripon Coll Cuddesdon 86. d 88 p 89. C Pinner *Lon* 88-91; V Twyford and Owslebury and Morestead *Win* from 91. *The Vicarage, Church Lane, Twyford, Winchester, Hants SO21 1NT* Twyford (01962) 712208

LIPSCOMB, Timothy William. b 52. Chich Th Coll 82. d 85 p 86. C Sevenoaks St Jo *Roch* 85-89; C Stanningley St Thos *Ripon* 89-92; V St Bart Armley w St Mary New Wortley from 92. *Armley Vicarage, Wesley Road, Leeds LS12 1SR* Leeds (0113) 263 8620

LIPSCOMBE, Brian. b 37. Bris Univ BA62. Tyndale Hall Bris 62. d 64 p 65. C Eccleston Ch Ch *Liv* 64-66; C Halliwell St Pet *Man* 66-69; C Frogmore H Trin *St Alb* 69-72; V Richmond Ch Ch *S'wark* 72-75; TV Mortlake w E Sheen 76-80; P-in-c Streatham Vale H Redeemer 80-88; V 85-91; R Norris Bank *Man* from 91. *St Martin's Rectory, 110 Crescent Park, Stockport, Cheshire SK4 2JE* 0161-432 3537

LISEMORE, Canon Frederick John Henry. b 11. St Cath Soc Ox BA37 MA38. Ripon Hall Ox 36. d 37 p 38. V Foremark *Derby* 70-77; V Repton 70-77; Perm to Offic *Lich* from 78; rtd 78. *36 Church Lane, Barton under Needwood, Burton-on-Trent, Staffs DE13 8HU* Barton under Needwood (01283) 712554

LISK, Stewart. b 62. Regent's Park Coll Ox BA84 MA88 Univ of Wales (Cardiff) DPS87. St Mich Coll Llan 86. d 88 p 89. C Glan Ely *Llan* 88-92; Chapl Cardiff Inst of HE from 92; Chapl Welsh Coll of Music and Drama from 92; Asst Chapl Univ of Wales (Cardiff) from 92. *St Teilo's Vicarage, Flora Street, Cardiff CF2 4EP* Cardiff (01222) 232407 or 761001

LISMORE, Dean of. *See* WEEKES, Very Rev Cecil William

LISTER, Anthony Galen. b 27. RIBA DipArch. NE Ord Course. d 83 p 84. Hon C Anlaby St Pet *York* 83-87. *Ballachan, Glenuig, Lochailort, Inverness-shire PH38 4NB* Lochailort (016877) 242

LISTER, David Ian. b 26. Roch Th Coll 61. d 62 p 64. V Tufnell Park St Geo *Lon* 68-83; V Tufnell Park St Geo and All SS 83-92; rtd 92. *8 Stonethwaite, Woodthorpe, York YO2 2SY* York (01904) 704586

LISTER, Edmund. b 08. AKC35. d 35 p 36. R Dunsfold *Guildf* 67-73; rtd 73; C Bladon w Woodstock *Ox* 73-75. *The Leys, Ware Lane, Lyme Regis, Dorset DT7 3EL* Lyme Regis (01297) 443060

LISTER, Frederick William. b 07. Wells Th Coll 71. d 71 p 72. Asst Chapl The Hague w Leiden *Eur* 71-75; Chapl Gothenburg w Halmstad and Jonkoping 75-78; rtd 78; Hon C High Harrogate St Pet *Ripon* 78-82. *8 Tudor Court, Prince of Wales Mansions, Harrogate, N Yorkshire HG1 1JB* Harrogate (01423) 502162

LISTER, Mrs Jennifer Grace (Jenny). b 44. Totley Hall Coll CertEd65. Nor Ord Course 87. d 92 p 94. C Cowgate *Newc* 92-95; NSM Lich St Mary w St Mich *Lich* from 95; NSM Wall from 95. *3 Bracken Close, Lichfield, Staffs WF14 9RU* Lichfield (01543) 417179

LISTER (nee AISBITT), Mrs Joanne. b 69. St Jo Coll Dur BA91. St Steph Ho Ox 91. d 93. NSM Mill End and Heronsgate w W Hyde *St Alb* from 93. *St Thomas House, 46 Chalfont Road, Rickmansworth, Herts WD3 2TB* Rickmansworth (01923) 771022

LISTER, Very Rev John Field. b 16. Keble Coll Ox BA38 MA42. Cuddesdon Coll 38. d 39 p 41. V Brighouse *Wakef* 54-71; Adn Halifax 61-72; RD Wakef 72-80; Provost Wakef 72-82; rtd 82; Perm to Offic *Cant* from 82. *5 Larkscliff Court, The Parade, Birchington, Kent CT7 9NB* Thanet (01843) 42543

LISTER, Joseph Hugh. b 38. Tyndale Hall Bris. d 64 p 65. C Pemberton St Mark Newtown *Liv* 64-68; Hon C Braintree *Chelmsf* 68-71; Hon C Darfield *Sheff* 71-73; P-in-c Sheff St Swithun 73-76; TV Sheff Manor 76-80; P-in-c Burston *Nor* 80-81; P-in-c Tivetshall 80-81; P-in-c Gissing 80-81; TR Winfarthing w Shelfanger 80-81; R Winfarthing w Shelfanger w Burston w Gissing etc 81-88; P-in-c Sandon, Wallington and Rushden w Clothall *St Alb* 88-89; R 89-93; R Nether and Over Seale *Derby* from 93; V Lullington from 93. *The Rectory, Neatherseal, Swandlincote, Derbyshire DE12 9AF* Burton (01524) 761179

LISTER, Miss Mary Phyllis. b 28. St Andr Ho Portsm 52. dss 80 d 87. Inkberrow w Cookhill and Kington w Dormston *Worc* 80-82; Ancaster *Linc* 82-87; C 87-88; rtd 88; Perm to Offic *Worc* from 88. *7 Byfield Rise, Worcester WR5 1BA* Worcester (01905) 29683

LISTER, Peter. b 42. Leeds Univ BA64 Newc Univ PGCE75. Coll of Resurr Mirfield 63. d 65 p 66. C Monkseaton St Pet *Newc* 65-68; C Cramlington 68-70; Hon C 71-78; C Morpeth 79-83; V Shilbottle 83-88; Asst Dioc Dir of Educn 83-88; Dir of Educn 88-95; Hon Can Newc Cathl 88-95; Dioc Dir of Educn

Lich from 95. *3 Bracken Close, Lichfield, Staffs WS14 9RU* Lichfield (01543) 417179

LISTER, Father William Bernard. b 67. Keble Coll Ox BA88 MA92. St Steph Ho Ox BA91. **d** 92 **p** 93. C Mill End and Heronsgate w W Hyde *St Alb* from 92. *St Thomas House, 46 Chalfont Road, Rickmansworth, Herts WD3 2TB* Rickmansworth (01923) 771022

LISTON, Scott Carnie. b 62. Edin Univ BD87. Edin Th Coll. **d** 88 **p** 88. C Edin St Martin *Edin* 88-91; C Edin St Luke 88-91; C Edin St Dav 91-92; Chapl HM Young Offender Inst Guys Marsh from 92. *HM Young Offender Institution, Guys Marsh, Shaftesbury, Dorset SP7 0AH* Shaftesbury (01747) 853344 Fax 851584

LITHERLAND, Norman Richard. b 30. Lon Univ BA51 Man Univ MEd72. N Ord Course 78. **d** 81 **p** 82. NSM Flixton St Mich *Man* 81-94; rtd 94. *1 Overdale Crescent, Urmston, Manchester M31 3GR* 0161-748 4243

LITHERLAND, Terence (Terry). b 46. Local NSM Course 90. **d** 93 **p** 94. NSM Horwich *Man* 93; NSM Horwich and Rivington from 93. *61 Tomlinson Street, Horwich, Bolton BL6 5QR* Bolton (01204) 692201

LITTLE, Andrew. b 27. Open Univ BA83. AKC51. **d** 52 **p** 53. V Northwood *Lich* 61-72; P-in-c Hixon 72-86; V Stowe 72-86; V Hixon w Stowe-by-Chartley 86-89; rtd 89; Perm to Offic *Nor* from 89. *5 Damocles Court, Norwich NR2 1HN* Norwich (01603) 662241

LITTLE, Ms Christine. b 60. Lanc Univ BA83. St Jo Coll Nottm DTS90 DPS91. **d** 91 **p** 94. Par Dn Meltham *Wakef* 91-94; C Hatcham St Jas *S'wark* from 94. *Flat 3, St Michael's Centre, Desmond Street, London SE14 6JF* 0181-691 2167

LITTLE, David John. b 65. Oak Hill Th Coll BA94. **d** 94 **p** 95. C Chislehurst Ch Ch *Roch* from 94. *56 Walden Road, Chislehurst, Kent BR7 5DL* 0181-467 6283

LITTLE, Denis Theodore. b 15. St Jo Coll Dur BA36 MA39. **d** 39 **p** 40. V Lythe *York* 61-72; R Dunnington 72-80; RD Bulmer 78-80; rtd 80; C Bulmer *York* 84-86; C Bulmer w Dalby, Terrington and Welburn 86. *92 The Village, Strensall, York YO3 5BX* York (01904) 490695

LITTLE, Derek Peter. b 50. St Jo Coll Dur BA72 DipTh75. Trin Coll Bris. **d** 75 **p** 76. C Bradley *Wakef* 75-78; C Kidderminster St Geo *Worc* 78-82; V Lepton *Wakef* 82-85; E Regional Sec CPAS 85-88; Lic to Offic *Ely* 86-88; V Canonbury St Steph *Lon* from 88. *St Stephen's Vicarage, 9 River Place, London N1 2DE* 0171-226 7526

LITTLE, Canon George Nelson. b 39. CITC 70. **d** 72 **p** 73. C Portadown St Mark *Arm* 72-76; I Newtownhamilton w Ballymoyer and Belleek 76-80; I Aghadery w Donaghmore *D & B* 80-81; I Aghadery w Donaghmore and Scarva from 81; RD Aghaderg from 88; Can Dromore Cathl from 93; Treas from 93. *Aghaderg Rectory, 32 Banbridge Road, Loughbrickland, Banbridge, Co Down BT32 3YB* Ballinaskeagh (018206) 24073

LITTLE, Harold Clifford. b 18. Lon Univ BD42. ALCD42. **d** 42 **p** 43. V S Dulwich St Steph *S'wark* 56-87; Lect Bibl and Relig Studies Lon Univ 61-87; rtd 87; Perm to Offic *Ex* from 88. *Howden Lodge, Willand Old Village, Cullompton, Devon EX15 2RJ* Cullompton (01884) 32663

LITTLE, Herbert Edwin Samuel. b 21. Lon Univ BA54 BD68. NE Ord Course 79. **d** 80 **p** 81. NSM Dur St Cuth *Dur* 80-88; rtd 88. *3 Whitesmocks Avenue, Durham DH1 4HP* 0191-384 2897

LITTLE, Ian Arthur Langley. b 24. ARICS52. S'wark Ord Course 63. **d** 66 **p** 67. NSM Bromley St Andr *Roch* 69-77; Perm to Offic from 77; rtd 86. *23 Vale Road, Bickley, Kent BR1 2AL* 0181-467 4899

LITTLE, Ian Dawtry Torrance. b 49. SW Minl Tr Course. **d** 85 **p** 86. NSM St Stythians w Perranarworthal and Gwennap *Truro* from 85. *Kernyk, Crellow Fields, Stithians, Truro, Cornwall TR3 7RE*

LITTLE, James Harry. b 57. York Univ BA79 Birm Univ DipTh86. Qu Coll Birm 84. **d** 87 **p** 88. C Wollaton *S'well* 87-90; C N Wheatley, W Burton, Bole, Saundby, Sturton etc 90-93; R E Markham w Askham, Headon w Upton and Grove from 93. *The Rectory, Lincoln Road, East Markham, Newark, Notts NG22 0SH* Tuxford (01777) 871731

LITTLE, Canon John Richardson. b 28. Magd Coll Ox BA49 MA53 DipTh50. Westcott Ho Cam 52. **d** 54 **p** 55. V Newc H Cross *Newc* 65-77; RD Newc W 74-77; V Gosforth All SS 77-89; Hon Can Newc Cathl 82-93; V Heddon-on-the-Wall 89-93; rtd 93. *34 Winchester Walk, Woodlands Park, Newcastle upon Tyne NE13 6JP* 0191-236 6535

LITTLE, Stephen Clifford. b 47. Man Univ MEd81. AKC72. **d** 72 **p** 73. C Grange St Andr *Ches* 72-73; C E Runcorn w Halton 73-75; P-in-c Newbold *Man* 75-77; P-in-c Broughton and Milton Keynes *Ox* 77-82; Sector Min Milton Keynes Chr Coun 77-84; TR Warw *Cov* 84-93; R Harvington, Norton and Lenchwick *Worc* from 93. *The Rectory, Station Road, Harvington, Evesham, Worcs WR11 5NJ* Evesham (01386) 871068

LITTLECHILD, William Bryant. b 02. St Geo Windsor 52. **d** 53 **p** 54. V Sutton Courtenay w Appleford *Ox* 55-67; rtd 67; P-in-c Chaffcombe *B & W* 76-77; P-in-c Knowle St Giles w Cricket Malherbie 76-77; Perm to Offic 77-94. *Kerris Vean, Chaffcombe, Chard, Somerset TA20 4AH* Chard (01460) 62062

LITTLEFAIR, David. b 38. ACCA71 FCCA85 Lon Univ BD79. Trin Coll Bris 76. **d** 79 **p** 80. C Bursledon *Win* 79-82; V Charles w St Matthias Plymouth *Ex* 82-89; Warden Lee Abbey Internat Students' Club Kensington 89-94; V Malmesbury w Westport and Brokenborough *Bris* from 94. *The Abbey Vicarage, Crudwell Road, Malmesbury, Wilts SN16 9BA* Malmesbury (01666) 823126

LITTLER, Eric Raymond. b 36. AMIC93 Lon Univ DipTh67. Roch Th Coll 65. **d** 68 **p** 69. C Hatf Hyde St Mary *St Alb* 68-73; Chapl Welwyn Garden City Hosp 70-73; TV Pemberton St Jo *Liv* 73-78; Chapl Billinge Hosp Wigan 76-81; V Pemberton St Fran Kitt Green *Liv* 78-81; V White Notley, Faulkbourne and Cressing *Chelmsf* 81-88; V Westcliff St Andr from 81; Chapl Westcliff Hosp from 88; Chapl Southend HA from 89. *St Andrew's Vicarage, 65 Electric Avenue, Westcliff-on-Sea, Essex SS0 9NN* Southend-on-Sea (01702) 342868

LITTLER, Dr Keith Trevor. b 35. Lon Univ BSc(Soc)63 TCert64 York Univ MA82 Hull Univ PhD88 Trin Coll Carmarthen 89. Local NSM Course 89. **d** 92 **p** 93. NSM Betws St Dav w Ammanford *St D* 92-94; C 94; R Pendine w Llanmiloe and Eglwys Gymyn w Marros from 94. *The Rectory, Pendine, Carmarthen, Dyfed SA33 4PD* Pendine (01994) 453405

LITTLER, Malcolm Kenneth. b 34. Univ of Wales (Lamp) BA55. **d** 57 **p** 58. V Llanwnda w Goodwick and Manorowen *St D* 68-74; V Llanfynydd 74-78; V The Suttons w Tydd *Linc* 87-90; V Graffoe 90-94; rtd 94. *Ivy Cottage, Chapel Lane, Lincoln LN1 3BA*

LITTLEWOOD, Miss Jacqueline Patricia (Jacquie). b 52. Linc Th Coll 77. **dss** 80 **d** 87 **p** 94. Crayford *Roch* 80-84; Gravesend H Family w Ifield 84-87; Par Dn 87-93; rtd 93; NSM Gravesend St Aid *Roch* from 93. *25 Beltana Drive, Gravesend, Kent DA12 4BT* Gravesend (01474) 560106

LITTLEWOOD, John Edward. b 50. UEA BSc71. Ridley Hall Cam 72. **d** 75 **p** 76. C Hellesdon *Nor* 75-78; C Eaton 78-81; Hon C S Hill w Callington *Truro* 83-89; Hon C Linkinhorne 86-89; Hon C Stoke Climsland 89-91. *Address temp unknown*

LITTLEWOOD, John Richard. b 37. Ridley Hall Cam 69. **d** 72 **p** 73. C Rushden w Newton Bromswold *Pet* 72-75; Chapl Scargill Ho 75-77; V Werrington *Pet* 77-91; V Highbury Ch Ch w St Jo and St Sav Lon from 91. *Christ Church Vicarage, 155 Highbury Grove, London N5 1SA* 0171-226 4544

LITTLEWOOD, Philip Nigel. b 59. Sarum & Wells Th Coll 87. **d** 90 **p** 91. C Frome St Jo and St Mary *B & W* 90-95; P-in-c Keinton Mandeville w Lydford-on-Fosse etc from 95. *The Rectory, Church Street, Keinton Mandeville, Somerton, Somerset TA11 6EP* Charlton Mackrell (01458) 223216

LITTON, Alan. b 42. Ridley Hall Cam 66. **d** 69 **p** 70. C Bolton St Bede *Man* 69-71; C Ashton St Mich 71-73; V Haslingden St Jo Stonefold *Blackb* 73-77; Ind Chapl *York* 77-81; V Crewe All SS and St Paul *Ches* 81-84; Ind Chapl *Liv* 84-89; V Spotland *Man* 89-94; R Newchurch *Liv* from 94. *The Rectory, 17 Jackson Avenue, Newchurch, Culcheth, Warrington WA3 4DZ* Culcheth (01925) 766300

LIVERPOOL, Archdeacon of. *See* METCALF, Ven Robert Laurence (Bob)

LIVERPOOL, Bishop of. *See* SHEPPARD, Rt Rev David Stuart

LIVERPOOL, Dean of. *See* WALTERS, Very Rev Rhys Derrick Chamberlain

LIVERSUCH, Ian Martin. b 56. St Jo Coll Dur BA79 DPS83. Wycliffe Hall Ox 79. **d** 83 **p** 84. C Newport St Mark *Mon* 83-85; C Risca 85-88; P-in-c Newport All SS 88-91; Canada from 91. *PO Box 606, Hemmingford, Quebec, Canada, J0L 1H0*

LIVESEY, Kenneth. b 29. Codrington Coll Barbados 57. **d** 59 **p** 60. Guyana 66-72 and 84-89; P-in-c Royton St Paul *Man* 72-73; V 73-81; P-in-c Bury H Trin 81-82; TR Bury Ch King w H Trin 82-84; V Oldham St Steph and All Martyrs 89-91; rtd 91. *2 Malvern Close, Royton, Oldham OL2 5HH* 0161-628 8617

LIVINGSTON, Bertram. TCD BA56. **d** 57 **p** 58. C-in-c Derryvolgie *Conn* 63-78; I 78-79; I Monaghan *Clogh* 79-86; I Desertlyn w Ballyeglish *Arm* 86-94; rtd 94. *40 Ballynagamick Road, Portadown, Craigavon, Co Armagh BT63 5NR* Lurgan (01762) 831859

LIVINGSTON, Richard. b 46. Qu Coll Birm. **d** 83 **p** 84. C Hobs Moat *Birm* 83-87; V Droylsden St Martin *Man* from 87. *St Martin's Vicarage, Greenside Lane, Droylsden, Manchester M35 7SJ* 0161-370 9833

LIVINGSTONE, Canon Francis Kenneth. b 26. TCD BA48 MA64. TCD Div Sch Div Test49. **d** 49 **p** 50. Hon VC Arm Cathl *Arm* 63-92; I Portadown St Sav 66-78; I Kilmore St Aid w St Sav 78-83; I Donaghmore w Upper Donaghmore 83-92;

Preb Yagoe St Patr Cathl Dub 85-92; rtd 92. *9 Castle Parade, Richhill, Armagh BT61 9QQ* Richhill (01762) 871574

LIVINGSTONE, Canon John Morris. b 28. Peterho Cam BA53 MA56. Cuddesdon Coll 53. **d** 55 **p** 56. V Notting Hill St Jo *Lon* 63-74; P-in-c Notting Hill St Mark 66-73; P-in-c Notting Hill All SS w St Columb 67-74; P-in-c Notting Hill St Clem 68-74; TR Notting Hill 74-75; Chapl Paris St Geo *Eur* 75-84; Adn N France 79-84; Adn Riviera 84-93; Chapl Nice w Vence 84-93; Chapl Biarritz from 93; rtd 93. *47 Perspective de la Côte des Basques, 64200, Biarritz, France* France (33) 59 24 71 18 Fax as telephone

LLANDAFF, Archdeacon of. *See* LEE, Ven David Stanley

LLANDAFF, Bishop of. *See* DAVIES, Rt Rev Roy Thomas

LLANDAFF, Dean of. *See* ROGERS, Very Rev John

✠**LLEWELLIN, Rt Rev John Richard Allan.** b 38. Fitzw Ho Cam BA64 MA78. Westcott Ho Cam 61. **d** 64 **p** 65 **c** 85. C Radlett *St Alb* 64-68; S Africa 68-71; V Waltham Cross *St Alb* 71-79; R Harpenden St Nic 79-85; Hon Can Truro Cathl *Truro* 85-92; Suff Bp St Germans 85-92; Suff Bp Dover *Cant* from 92. *Upway, 52 St Martin's Hill, Canterbury, Kent CT1 1PR* Canterbury (01227) 464537 or 459382 Fax 784985

LLEWELLIN DAVIES, Dr Lawrence John David. b 16. Jes Coll Ox BA39 MA43 DipEd59 Bonn Univ ThD58. Ripon Hall Ox 39. **d** 39 **p** 40. Dean Chpl & Hd Div Hall Sir Wm Herschel Gr Sch 59-80; Lic to Offic *Ox* 67-81; rtd 81; Perm to Offic *Ox* from 81. *Deans Lodge, Hollybush Hill, Stoke Poges, Slough SL2 4PZ* Fulmer (01753) 662495

LLEWELLYN, Brian Michael. b 47. ARICS73. Sarum & Wells Th Coll 78. **d** 80 **p** 81. C Farncombe *Guildf* 80-83; Chapl RAF 83-87; R Hethersett w Canteloff w Lt and Gt Melton *Nor* 87-95; RD Humbleyard 94-95; P-in-c Smallburgh w Dilham w Honing and Crostwight from 95. *The Rectory, Honing, North Walsham, Norfolk NR28 9AB* Smallburgh (01692) 536466

LLEWELLYN, Christine Ann. b 46. Univ of Wales (Ban) BA69 DipEd70. **d** 89. NSM Arthog w Fairbourne w Llangelynnin w Rhoslefain *Ban* 90-93; NSM Holyhead w Rhoscolyn w Llanfair-yn-Neubwll 93-94; C from 94. *The Old School, Rhoscolyn, Holyhead, Gwynedd LL65 2RQ* Valley (01407) 741593

LLEWELLYN, David John Patrick. b 16. AKC40. Wells Th Coll. **d** 46 **p** 47. I Kinneigh Union *C, C & R* 76-83; rtd 83. *Anne's Cottage, Hamilton Row, Courtmacsherry, Bandon, Co Cork, Irish Republic* Courtmacsherry (23) 46381

LLEWELLYN, Neil Alexander. b 55. LWCMD78. Westcott Ho Cam 79 Sarum & Wells Th Coll 83. **d** 84 **p** 85. C Heref St Martin *Heref* 84-86; Chapl Rotterdam Miss to Seamen *Eur* 86-89; R Docking w The Birchams and Stanhoe w Barwick *Nor* 89-92; Chapl Ypres *Eur* from 92; Toc H from 92. *Maloulaan 13, 8900 Ypres, Belgium* Ypres (57) 216212

LLEWELLYN, Richard Morgan. b 37. CB91 OBE79 MBE76. FIMgt81. Sarum & Wells Th Coll DCTM93. **d** 93 **p** 94. C Brecon St Mary and Battle w Llanddew *S & B* from 93; Min Can Brecon Cathl from 93. *The Almonry, Cathedral Close, Brecon, Powys LD3 9DP* Brecon (01874) 622972

LLEWELLYN, William David. b 22. Univ of Wales (Lamp) BA43. **d** 48 **p** 49. V Treharris *Llan* 63-70; V Penmaen *Mon* 70-77; V St Mellons 77-87; rtd 87. *262 Cardiff Road, Newport, Gwent NP9 3AH*

✠**LLEWELLYN, Rt Rev William Somers.** b 07. Ball Coll Ox BA29 DipTh34 MA37. Wycliffe Hall Ox. **d** 35 **p** 36 **c** 63. C Chiswick St Nic w St Mary *Lon* 35-37; V Badminton w Acton Turville *Glouc* 37-49; CF (EC) 40-46; CF (TA) 48-51; V Tetbury w Beverston *Glouc* 49-61; Hon C 77-85; CF (R of O) 51-62; RD Tetbury *Glouc* 56-61; Adn Lynn *Nor* 61-72; C Blakeney w Lt Langham 62-63; C Stiffkey w Morston 62-63; Suff Bp Lynn 63-72; rtd 73; Asst Bp Glouc from 73; P-in-c Boxwell w Leighterton 73-76. *Glebe House, Leighterton, Tetbury, Glos GL8 8UN* Tetbury (01666) 890236

LLEWELYN, John Dilwyn. b 18. St D Coll Lamp BA40 AKC42. **d** 42 **p** 43. V Plymouth St Simon *Ex* 61-82; rtd 82; Perm to Offic *Ex* from 84. *25 Oakley Close, Pinhoe, Exeter EX1 3SB* Exeter (01392) 67169

LLEWELYN, Robert Charles. b 09. Pemb Coll Cam BA32 MA36. **d** 36 **p** 37. India 51-71; Adn Poona 69-71; Warden Bede Ho Staplehurst 72-75; rtd 74; Chapl Shrine of St Julian 76-90. *80A King Street, Norwich NR1 1PQ* Norwich (01603) 662600

LLEWELYN, Canon Robert John. b 32. Keble Coll Ox BA54 MA58. Cuddesdon Coll 65. **d** 66 **p** 67. C Bedf St Andr *St Alb* 66-69; C Cheltenham St Luke and St Jo *Glouc* 69-75; V S Cerney w Cerney Wick 75-80; V Glouc St Cath from 80; P-in-c Glouc St Mark 87-89; Hon Can Glouc Cathl from 94. *St Catharine's Vicarage, 29 Denmark Road, Gloucester GL1 3JQ* Gloucester (01452) 524497

LLOYD, Canon Bernard James. b 29. AKC56. **d** 57 **p** 58. V E Ham St Geo *Chelmsf* 65-82; RD Newham 76-82; Hon Can Chelmsf Cathl 92-94; R Danbury 82-94; P-in-c Woodham Ferrers 87-90; rtd 94. *Chanterelle, 47 Seaview Avenue, West Mersea, Colchester CO5 5SE* West Mersea (01206) 383892

LLOYD, Ven Bertram Trevor. b 38. Hertf Coll Ox BA60 MA64. Clifton Th Coll 62. **d** 64 **p** 65. C S Mimms Ch Ch *Lon* 64-70; V Wealdstone H Trin 70-84; RD Harrow 77-82; P-in-c Harrow Weald St Mich 80-84; V Trin St Mich, Harrow 84-89; Adn Barnstaple *Ex* from 89. *Stage Cross, Whitemoor Hill, Bishops Tawton, Barnstaple, Devon EX33 0BE* Barnstaple (01271) 75475 Fax as telephone

LLOYD, Bertram John (Bert). b 26. DipTh83. St Mich Coll Llan. **d** 83 **p** 84. C Malpas *Mon* 83-85; V Blaenavon w Capel Newydd 85-93; rtd 93. *22 St Helen's Crescent, Llanellen, Abergavenny, Gwent NP7 9HN* Abergavenny (01873) 857003

LLOYD, Canon Charles Henry. b 13. TCD BA34. CITC 36. **d** 36 **p** 37. I New Ross *C & O* 70-82; Preb Tassagard St Patr Cathl Dub 73-82; rtd 82. *74 The Rise, Woodpark, Ballinteer, Dublin 16, Irish Republic* Dublin (1) 295-1181

LLOYD, Crewdson Howard. b 31. Ex Coll Ox BA54 MA64. Wells Th Coll 64. **d** 66 **p** 67. C Ex St Dav *Ex* 66-69; C Cirencester *Glouc* 69-72; Perm to Offic *Ox* from 72; Summoner of Preachers Ox Univ 81-89. *36 Thackley End, 119 Banbury Road, Oxford OX2 6LB* Oxford (01865) 511032

LLOYD, David John. b 52. Lon Univ BD82. St D Coll Lamp DipTh76. **d** 76 **p** 77. C Pemb St Mary and St Mich *St D* 76-77; C Llanelli 77-80; V Cilycwm and Ystrad-ffin w Rhandir-mwyn etc 80-82; Oman 82-84; R Llanllwchaearn and Llanina *St D* 84-88; V Llangennech and Hendy 88-90; Perm to Offic *St Alb* from 91. *30 Elm Grove, Bihop's Stortford, Herts CM23 5JB* Bishop's Stortford (01279) 652702

LLOYD, David John Silk. b 37. Univ of Wales (Lamp) BA62. St Steph Ho Ox 71. **d** 73 **p** 74. C Brentwood St Thos *Chelmsf* 73-77; C Hockley 77-80; C Wickford 80-81; C Wickford and Runwell 81-83; TV 83-88; Chapl Runwell Hosp Essex 81-88; S Africa from 88; Perm to Offic *Chelmsf* from 88. *4 Argyll House, Seaforth Road, Westcliff-on-Sea, Essex SS0 7SJ*

LLOYD, David Peter. b 58. Kingston Poly BA81 DipArch84. Sarum & Wells Th Coll 88. **d** 90 **p** 91. C N Dulwich St Faith *S'wark* 90-94; TV Bedminster *Bris* from 94. *St Dunstan's Vicarage, 66 Bedminster Down Road, Bristol BS13 7AA* Bristol (0117) 963 5977

LLOYD, Dr Dennis John. b 46. BSc70 MSc74 PhD81. S Dios Minl Tr Scheme. **d** 90 **p** 91. C Hamworthy *Sarum* 90-92; Chapl UEA *Nor* from 92. *42 Heigham Road, Norwich NR2 3AU* Norwich (01603) 625734 or 56161

LLOYD, Edward Gareth. b 60. K Coll Cam BA81 MA85. Ridley Hall Cam 85. **d** 88 **p** 89. C Jarrow *Dur* 88-91; C Monkwearmouth St Pet 91-92; P-in-c from 92. *St Peter's Vicarage, St Peter's Way, Sunderland SR6 0DY* 0191-567 3726

LLOYD, Miss Eileen. b 50. FIMLS74 Liv Poly HNC72. N Ord Course 88. **d** 91 **p** 94. C Heref St Martin w St Fran (S Wye TM) *Heref* 91-95; P-in-c Bucknell w Chapel Lawn, Llanfair Waterdine etc from 95. *The Vicarage, Bucknell, Shropshire SY7 0AD* Bucknell (015474) 340

LLOYD, Mrs Elizabeth Jane. b 52. CChem GRIC74 MRIC77 HND73 Nottm Univ DipTh79. Linc Th Coll 77. **dss** 80 **d** 87 **p** 94. Linc St Nic w St Jo Newport *Linc* 80-81; Lic to Offic *Sarum* 81-87; Chapl Poole Gen Hosp from 85; Hon Par Dn Lytchett Matravers *Sarum* 87-92. *The Rectory, 19 Springfield Road, Poole, Dorset BH14 0LG* Parkstone (01202) 748860 or 442167

LLOYD, Miss Glenys Elizabeth Barrett. b 43. CertEd67. Cranmer Hall Dur 79. **dss** 82 **d** 87 **p** 94. Rainham *Roch* 82-86; Cov Caludon *Cov* 86-92; TD 87-92; C Childs Ercall *Lich* 92-95; C Stoke upon Tern 92-95; C Cheswardine, Childs Ercall, Hales, Hinstock etc from 95. *The Vicarage, Childs Ercall, Market Drayton, Shropshire TF9 2DA* Childs Ercall (0195278) 229

LLOYD, Graham. b 36. Brasted Th Coll 62 St Aid Birkenhead 64 Glouc Sch of Min 86. **d** 89 **p** 90. NSM Churchstoke w Hyssington and Sarn *Heref* from 89. *The Pullets Cottage, Church Stoke, Montgomery, Powys SY15 6TL* Church Stoke (01588) 620285

LLOYD, Gwilym Wyn. b 50. Leic Univ BA72 Birm Univ MSc73 Lon Univ BD88. Trin Coll Bris DipHE85. **d** 87 **p** 88. C Bexleyheath Ch Ch *Roch* 87-91; R Darlaston St Lawr *Lich* from 91. *The Rectory, Darlaston, Wednesbury, W Midlands WS10 8AA* 0121-526 2240

LLOYD, Hamilton William John Marteine. b 19. Jes Coll Ox BA41 MA45. Ripon Hall Ox. **d** 43 **p** 44. V Whitchurch w Tufton and Litchfield *Win* 68-71; V Lyndhurst 71-73; V Lyndhurst and Emery Down 73-84; rtd 84; Perm to Offic *Win* from 86. *Post Office House, North Litchfield, Whitchurch, Hants RG28 7PR* Whitchurch (01256) 893507

LLOYD, Harry James. b 22. Univ of Wales (Lamp) BA50. **d** 51 **p** 52. V Kingston *Sarum* 60-83; V Worth Matravers 60-83; C Milton Abbas, Hilton w Cheselbourne etc 83-87; rtd 87. *Linden, Streetway Lane, Cheselbourne, Dorchester, Dorset DT2 7NU* Milborne St Andrew (0125887) 331

431

LLOYD

LLOYD, Very Rev Henry Morgan. b 11. DSO41 OBE59. Or Coll Ox BA33 MA37. Cuddesdon Coll 33. **d** 35 **p** 36. Dean Truro 60-81; rtd 81. *3 Hill House, The Avenue, Sherborne, Dorset DT9 3AJ* Sherborne (01935) 812037

LLOYD, Canon Herbert James. b 31. TD. St D Coll Lamp BA57. **d** 58 **p** 59. C Wrexham *St As* 58-65; TV 71-74; R Llanferres 65-67; R Llanferres, Nercwys and Eryrys 67-71; V Rhyl w St Ann from 74; CF (TA) from 74; Can St As Cathl *St As* from 81; Prec St As Cathl from 89. *The Vicarage, Bath Street, Rhyl, Clwyd LL18 3LU* Rhyl (01745) 353732

LLOYD, John Everard. b 27. FCMA60 LSE BSc50. St Alb Minl Tr Scheme 84. **d** 87 **p** 88. NSM Harpenden St Nic *St Alb* 87-90; Hon C Addingham *Bradf* from 90. *2 High Springs, Owler Park Road, Ilkley, W Yorkshire LS29 0BG* Ilkley (01943) 609267

LLOYD, John James. b 14. St D Coll Lamp BA36. **d** 37 **p** 38. V Cadoxton-juxta-Neath *Llan* 63-79; rtd 79; Perm to Offic *Llan* from 79. *16 Spoonbill Close, Rest Bay, Porthcawl, M Glam CF36 3UR* Porthcawl (01656) 715470

LLOYD, John Philip. b 15. St Chad's Coll Dur BA37 DipTh38 MA40. **d** 38 **p** 39. V Bickerton *Ches* 69-77; rtd 77; Perm to Offic *Ches* from 77. *17 Wesley Close, Bowling Green Court, Nantwich, Cheshire CW5 5SN* Nantwich (01270) 626771

LLOYD, Jonathan Wilford. b 56. Surrey Univ and City of Lon Poly BSc80 Golds Coll Lon CQSW82 DASS82 N Lon Poly MA86. S'wark Ord Course 87. **d** 90 **p** 91. Hon C Sydenham St Bart *S'wark* 90-94; Dir of Soc Resp 91-95; PV S'wark Cathl from 91; Bp's Officer for Ch in Soc from 95. *Trinity House, 4 Chapel Court, Borough High Street, London SE1 1HW* 0171-403 8686 Fax 403 2242

LLOYD, Michael Francis. b 57. Down Coll Cam BA79 MA82 St Jo Coll Dur BA83. Cranmer Hall Dur 81. **d** 84 **p** 85. C Locks Heath *Portsm* 84-87; Asst Chapl Worc Coll Ox 89-90; Chapl Ch Coll Cam 90-94. *Address temp unknown*

LLOYD, Nigel James Clifford. b 51. Nottm Univ BTh81 Lambeth STh90. Linc Th Coll 77. **d** 81 **p** 82. C Sherborne w Castleton and Lillington *Sarum* 81-84; R Lytchett Matravers 84-92; TR Parkstone St Pet w Branksea and St Osmund from 92. *The Rectory, 19 Springfield Road, Poole, Dorset BH14 0LG* Parkstone (01202) 748860

LLOYD, Oscar Wynn. b 17. St D Coll Lamp BA43. **d** 45 **p** 47. V Helsby *Ches* 66-74; V Ince 66-74; R Dodleston 74-82; rtd 82; Perm to Offic *Ches* from 82. *12 Hawarden Drive, Drury, Buckley, Clwyd CH7 3ED* Buckley (01244) 549650

LLOYD, Mrs Pamela Valpy. b 25. Gilmore Ho 48 St Aug Coll Cant 76. dss 76 **d** 87 **p** 94. Chartham Cant 76-78; Cant All SS 78-85; rtd 85; Chapl Asst Kent and Cant Hosp 87; Chapl Chaucer Hosp Cant 87-90; NSM Elham w Denton and Wootton Cant 87-93; Sub-Chapl HM Pris Cant from 88; Hon C Cant St Martin and St Paul from 93. *Cavendish House, 9 North Holmes Road, Canterbury, Kent CT1 1QJ* Canterbury (01227) 457782

LLOYD, Canon Peter John. b 32. TD78. Leic Univ DipSocSc53. Wells Th Coll 59. **d** 61 **p** 62. CF (TA) 62-73 and 77-87; R Brinkley, Burrough Green and Carlton *Ely* 69-73; CF 73-77; V Chessington *Guildf* 77-85; RD Epsom 82-87; V Epsom St Martin 85-92; rtd 92; Hon Can Guildf Cathl *Guildf* from 92. *74 Southover, Wells, Somerset BA5 1UH* Wells (01749) 672213

LLOYD, Peter Vernon James. b 36. St Jo Coll Cam BA60 MA. Ridley Hall Cam 60. **d** 62 **p** 63. C Keynsham w Queen Charlton *B & W* 62-65; Perm to Offic *Sarum* from 65; NSM Bournemouth St Jo w St Mich 84-87; NSM Bournemouth St Pet w St Swithun, St Steph etc 90-91; Perm to Offic from 91. *18 Cornelia Crescent, Branksome, Poole, Dorset BH12 1LU* Bournemouth (01202) 741422

LLOYD, Raymond David (Brother Ramon). b 35. Univ of Wales (Cardiff) DipTh61 Edin Univ MPhil74. Zurich Th Sem BD69 Edin Th Coll 71. **d** 72 **p** 72. C Glas St Mary *Glas* 72-76; Chapl Glas Univ 74-76; SSF from 78. *St Mary at the Cross, Glasshampton, Shrawley, Worcester WR6 6TQ* Great Witley (01299) 896345

LLOYD, Rex Edward Ambrose. b 04. Worc Coll Ox BA26 DipTh27 MA32. Wycliffe Hall Ox 29. **d** 29 **p** 30. R Hamsey *Chich* 64-70; Chapl HM Pris Lewes 65-69; rtd 70. *clo R V S Lloyd Esq, Shingleberry, Tag Lane, Hare Hatch, Reading RG10 9ST* Reading (01734) 402157

LLOYD, Richard Leslie Harris. b 09. Peterho Cam BA31 MA35 Mert Coll Ox BA32 MA36 BLitt36. St Steph Ho Ox 32. **d** 36 **p** 37. Chapl St Bede Coll Dur 63-74; rtd 74. *8 Homebryth House, Front Street, Sedgefield, Stockton-on-Tees, Cleveland TS21 3BW* Sedgefield (01740) 22468

LLOYD, Robert Graham. b 42. St Jo Coll Nottm 82. **d** 84 **p** 85. C Tonyrefail *Llan* 84-87; V Martletwy w Lawrenny and Minwear and Yerbeston *St D* 87-91; V Monkton from 91. *Priory Vicarage, Monkton, Pembroke, Dyfed SA71 4LW* Pembroke (01646) 682723

LLOYD, Robert James Clifford. b 18. Selw Coll Cam BA41 MA49. Linc Th Coll 46. **d** 47 **p** 48. R Chartham *Cant* 66-81;

RD W Bridge 75-81; Hon C Elham w Denton and Wootton from 82; rtd 83. *Cavendish House, 9 North Holmes Road, Canterbury, Kent CT1 1QJ* Canterbury (01227) 457782

LLOYD, Roger Bernard. b 58. K Coll Lon BA. Cranmer Hall Dur. **d** 84 **p** 85. C Hornchurch St Andr *Chelmsf* 84-87; C Gt Parndon 87-94; V Elm Park St Nic Hornchurch from 94. *The Vicarage, 17 St Nicholas Avenue, Elm Park, Hornchurch, Essex RM12 4PT* Hornchurch (014024) 51451

LLOYD, Ronald. b 37. St Mich Coll Llan. **d** 83 **p** 84. C Penarth All SS *Llan* 83-85; V Cwmbach 85-91; Perm to Offic from 91. *23 Teilo Street, Cardiff CF1 9JN*

LLOYD, Ronald Henry. b 32. Univ of Wales (Lamp) BA52 LTh54. **d** 54 **p** 56. C Manselton *S & B* 54-56; C Sketty 56-59; C Swansea St Mary 59-63; CF (TA) 59-65; V Elmley Castle w Netherton and Bricklehampton *Worc* 63-69; Chapl Dragon Sch Ox 69-82; Chapl St Hugh's Coll Ox 75-80; P-in-c Ox St Marg *Ox* 75-76; Chapl Magd Coll Ox 75-82; Prec and Chapl Ch Ch *Ox* 82-87; R Alvescot w Black Bourton, Shilton, Holwell etc from 87; P-in-c Broughton Poggs w Filkins, Broadwell etc 94-95. *The Vicarage, Shilton, Burford, Oxon OX18 4AE* Carterton (01993) 845954

LLOYD, Samuel. b 07. Univ of Wales BA48. St Deiniol's Hawarden 69. **d** 69 **p** 70. C Llangynwyd w Maesteg *Llan* 70-83; rtd 83; Perm to Offic *Llan* from 83. *9 Station Street, Maesteg, M Glam CF34 9AE* Maesteg (01656) 732386

LLOYD, Mrs Sandra Edith. b 48. Sarum & Wells Th Coll 83. dss 86 **d** 87 **p** 94. Freshwater *Portsm* 86-87; C 87-89; C Whitwell 89-95; V from 95; C Niton 89-95; P-in-c from 95. *The Vicarage, Whitwell, Ventnor, Isle of Wight PO38 2PP* Isle of Wight (01983) 730745

LLOYD, Simon David. b 58. Portsm Poly BA. Wycliffe Hall Ox. **d** 83 **p** 84. C Cotmanhay *Derby* 83-85; Chapl Asst Nottm City Hosp 85-87; Chapl Basford Hosp Nottm 85-87; Perm to Offic *Birm* from 91. *2 Ash Mews, Acocks Green, Birmingham B27 6TB* 0121-706 5784

LLOYD, Stephen Russell. b 47. Worc Coll Ox BA69 MA77 CertEd DipTh. Oak Hill Th Coll 76. **d** 77 **p** 78. C Canonbury St Steph *Lon* 77-80; C Braintree *Chelmsf* 80-92; V Braintree St Paul from 92. *St Paul's Parsonage, Hay Lane, Braintree, Essex CM7 6DY* Braintree (01376) 325095

LLOYD, Stuart George Errington. b 49. TCD BA72. **d** 75 **p** 76. C Cloughfern *Conn* 75-79; C Cregagh *D & D* 79-82; I Eglantine *Conn* 82-89; I Ballymena w Ballyclug from 89. *St Patrick's Rectory, 102 Galgorm Road, Ballymena, Co Antrim BT42 1AE* Ballymena (01266) 652253

LLOYD, Timothy David Lewis. See LEWIS LLOYD, Canon Timothy David

LLOYD-JAMES, Duncan Geraint. b 66. St Steph Ho Ox BTh94. **d** 94. C St Leonards Ch Ch and St Mary *Chich* from 94. *31 Alfred Street, St Leonards-on-Sea, E Sussex TN38 0HD* Hastings (01424) 443956

LLOYD-JAMES, John Eifion. b 39. Clifton Th Coll 63. **d** 65 **p** 66. C Burgess Hill St Andr *Chich* 65-68; C-in-c Portslade Gd Shep Mile Oak CD 68-74; V Lancing St Mich 74-88; V Billingshurst 88-93; V Kemp Town St Mary from 93. *St Mary's Vicarage, 11 West Drive, Brighton BN2 2GD* Brighton (01273) 698601

LLOYD JONES, Ieuan. b 31. FBIM St Cath Coll Cam BA51 MA54. Sarum & Wells Th Coll 80. **d** 83 **p** 84. Hon C Claygate *Guildf* 83-89; Perm to Offic *Ox* from 89. *11 Southcroft, Old Marston, Oxford OX3 0PF* Oxford (01865) 793098

LLOYD-JONES (formerly JONES), Thomas (Tom). b 20. Univ Coll Ox BA42 MA44. Coll of Resurr Mirfield 42. **d** 44 **p** 45. V Bishop's Stortford H Trin *St Alb* 63-70; V Welwyn Garden City 70-85; rtd 85. *12 Golden Dell, Welwyn Garden City, Herts AL7 4EB* Welwyn Garden (01707) 338305

LLOYD-RICHARDS, David Robert. b 48. Open Univ BA84 Hull Univ MA87. St D Coll Lamp DipTh70. **d** 71 **p** 72. C Skewen *Llan* 71-73; C Neath w Llantwit 73-76; Miss to Seamen 76-77; V Pontlottyn w Fochriw *Llan* 77-84; R Merthyr Dyfan 84-90; Chapl Barry Neale-Kent Hosp 84-90; Sen Chapl Univ Hosp of Wales Cardiff from 90; Tutor Open Univ from 85. *77 Rhydhelig Avenue, Heath Park, Cardiff CF4 4DB* Cardiff (01222) 620957 or 744854

LLOYD WILLIAMS, Martin Clifford. b 65. Westmr Coll Lon BEd87. Trin Coll Bris BA93. **d** 93 **p** 94. C Bath Walcot *B & W* from 93. *5 The Linleys, Bath BA1 2XE* Bath (01225) 316572

LOASBY, Preb Edgar Harold. b 13. BNC Ox BA35 MA46. Cuddesdon Coll 35. **d** 36 **p** 37. R Chelsea St Luke *Lon* 61-82; Preb St Paul's Cathl 71-82; rtd 82; Perm to Offic *Lon* from 82. *31 Oakley Gardens, London SW3 5QH* 0171-352 8828

LOAT, Andrew Graham. b 61. Aber Univ BD83. St Jo Coll Nottm DPS87. **d** 87 **p** 88. C Llangynwyd w Maesteg *Llan* 87-90; C Llansamlet *S & B* 90-91; V Whitton and Pilleth and Cascob etc from 91. *The Rectory, Whitton, Knighton, Powys LD7 1NP* Knighton (01547) 528566

LOBANOV-ROSTOVSKY, Andrew Russell. b 17. Qu Coll Ox BA38 MA55. Cuddesdon Coll 56. **d** 57 **p** 58. Chapl St Bede's

432

Ch for the Deaf Clapham 64-75; Chapl to the Deaf *Guildf* 75-82; rtd 82; Perm to Offic *Chich* 86-89; Perm to Offic *Glas* 89-91. *10 Aikenhead House, Kings Park, Carmunnock Road, Glasgow G44 5HL*   0141-633 0479

LOBB, Edward Eric. b 51. Magd Coll Ox BA74 MA76. Wycliffe Hall Ox 73. **d** 76 **p** 77. C Haughton St Mary *Man* 76-80; C Rusholme 80-84; P-in-c Whitfield *Derby* 84-90; V 90-92; V Stapenhill w Cauldwell from 92. *6 Clay Street, Stapenhill, Burton-on-Trent, Staffs DE15 9BB*   Burton-on-Trent (01283) 561437

LOCK, David Stephen. b 28. **d** 63 **p** 64. C Streatham Vale H Redeemer *S'wark* 63-66; C Hatcham St Jas 66-75; V Leyton All SS *Chelmsf* from 75. *All Saints' Vicarage, 47 Melbourne Road, London E10 7HF*   0181-539 2170

LOCK, Graham Robert. b 39. Hertf Coll Ox BA63. Ridley Hall Cam 62. **d** 64 **p** 65. C Bexleyheath St Pet *Roch* 64-66; C Roch St Justus 66-71; C St Mary Cray and St Paul's Cray 71-75; V Chatham St Paul w All SS 75-83; R Lambourne w Abridge and Stapleford Abbotts *Chelmsf* 83-92; V Barkingside St Laur from 92. *St Laurence's Vicarage, Donington Avenue, Ilford, Essex IG6 1AJ*   0181-554 2003

LOCK, Paul Alan. b 65. St Chad's Coll Dur BA86. Coll of Resurr Mirfield 87. **d** 89 **p** 90. C Upholland *Liv* 89-92; C Teddington SS Pet and Paul and Fulwell *Lon* from 92. *4 Bychurch End, Teddington, Middx TW11 8PS*   0181-977 5518

LOCK, Canon Peter Harcourt D'Arcy. b 44. AKC67. **d** 68 **p** 69. C Meopham *Roch* 68-72; C Wigmore w Hempstead 72; C S Gillingham 72-77; R Hartley 77-83; R Fawkham and Hartley 83-84; V Dartford H Trin 84-93; Hon Can Roch Cathl from 90; V Bromley SS Pet and Paul from 93. *The Vicarage, 9 St Paul's Square, Bromley BR2 0XH*   0181-460 6275

LOCKE, Brian Henry. b 38. AKC61. **d** 62 **p** 63. C Westleigh St Pet *Man* 62-65; C Marske in Cleveland *York* 65-68; V Boosbeck w Moorsholm 68-72; Perm to Offic *Man* 78-82; P-in-c Kirkholt 82-86; V from 86; Chapl HM Young Offender Inst Buckley Hall 85-89; AD Rochdale *Man* from 92. *St Thomas's Vicarage, Cavendish Road, Rochdale, Lancs OL11 2QX*   Rochdale (01706) 45962

LOCKE, Richard Nigel. b 61. Coll of Resurr Mirfield 92. **d** 94 **p** 95. C Middlesbr Ascension *York* from 94. *The Ascension Vicarage, Penrith Road, Middlesbrough, Cleveland TS3 7JR*   Middlesbrough (01642) 244857

LOCKE, Robert Andrew. b 62. St Steph Ho Ox 89. **d** 92 **p** 93. C Colchester St Jas, All SS, St Nic and St Runwald *Chelmsf* 92-95; CF from 95. *c/o MOD (Army), Bagshot Park, Bagshot, Surrey GU19 5PL*   Bagshot (01276) 471717   Fax 412834

LOCKE, Stephen John. b 60. St Chad's Coll Dur BA82. Sarum & Wells Th Coll 84. **d** 86 **p** 87. C Blackb St Mich w St Jo and H Trin *Blackb* 86-89; C Oswaldtwistle Immanuel and All SS 89-92; V Blackb St Mich w St Jo and H Trin from 92. *St Michael's Vicarage, Whalley New Road, Blackburn BB1 6LB*   Blackburn (01254) 257121

LOCKER, Dorothea Isobel Leslie. b 19. MRPharmS41 Heriot-Watt Coll PhC41. Local NSM Course 79. **dss** 85 **d** 87. NSM Edin St Pet *Edin* 85-91; rtd 91. *4C Mayfield Gardens, Edinburgh EH9 2BU*   0131-667 3509

LOCKETT, Paul. b 48. Sarum & Wells Th Coll 73. **d** 76 **p** 77. C Horninglow *Lich* 76-78; C Tewkesbury w Walton Cardiff *Glouc* 78-81; P-in-c W Bromwich St Pet *Lich* 81-90; R Norton Canes 90-95; Dean's V Lich Cathl from 91; V Longton St Mary and St Chad from 95. *St Mary and St Chad's Presbytery, 269 Anchor Road, Stoke-on-Trent ST3 5DH*   Stoke-on-Trent (01782) 313142

LOCKETT, Canon William Ernest Alfred. b 16. ARCA39 ATD51 FRSA70 FIBD NRD Florence Academy. Linc Th Coll 44. **d** 45 **p** 46. Sen Lect Liv Univ 56-82; Can Th Liv Cathl *Liv* 72-82; rtd 82; Perm to Offic *Liv* from 82. *The Croft, Ruff Lane, Ormskirk, Lancs L39 4QZ*   Ormskirk (01695) 572119

LOCKEY, Malcolm. b 45. FRSA75 Sunderland Poly BA67 Newc Univ DipEd68. NE Ord Course 87. **d** 90 **p** 91. NSM Yarm *York* from 90. *26 Blackfriars, Yarm, Cleveland TS15 9HG*   Eaglescliffe (01642) 782696

LOCKHART, Antony William Clapesdon. b 25. GIMechE. Wells Th Coll 63. **d** 65 **p** 66. C Worplesdon *Guildf* 69-73; V Weston 73-79; TV Westborough 79-84; V Shamley Green 84-87; RD Cranleigh 85-87; Dioc Widows Officer *Cant* 89-90; rtd 90. *10 Beverley Road, Canterbury, Kent CT2 7EN*   Canterbury (01227) 760980

LOCKHART, Clare Patricia Anne (Sister Clare). b 44. Bris Univ BA74. St Jo Coll Dur 84. **d** 87 **p** 94. Sisters of Charity from 63; Chapl Asst Sunderland Distr Gen Hosp 84-89; Chapl from 89; NSM N Hylton St Marg Castletown *Dur* from 87. *Sunderland District General Hospital, Sunderland SR4 7TP*, or *6 North View, Castletown, Sunderland SR5 3AF*   0191-565 6256 or 516 0406

LOCKHART, David. b 68. QUB BSc90 TCD BTh93. CITC 90. **d** 93 **p** 94. C Belf St Mary w H Redeemer *Conn* from 93.

15 Westway Park, Ballygomartin Road, Belfast BT13 3NW   Belfast (01232) 710584

LOCKHART, Ms Michelle. b 68. Man Univ BA89. Ripon Coll Cuddesdon 90. **d** 92 **p** 94. Par Dn Leigh St Mary *Man* 92-94; Asst Chapl HM Pris Full Sutton from 95. *The Chaplain's Office, HM Prison, Full Sutton, York YO4 1PS*   Stamford Bridge (01759) 372447   Fax 371206

LOCKHART, Raymond William. b 37. Qu Coll Cam BA58 LLB60 MA61. St Jo Coll Nottm 72. **d** 74 **p** 75. C Aspley *S'well* 74-76; V 81-88; R Knebworth *St Alb* 76-81; Dir CMJ Stella Carmel from 88; Jerusalem from 88. *c/o CMJ, 30C Clarence Road, St Albans, Herts AL1 4JJ*   St Albans (01727) 833114

LOCKHART, Very Rev Robert Joseph Norman. b 24. TCD BA46 MA53. **d** 46 **p** 48. I Belf St Donard *D & D* 62-70; I Lurgan Ch the Redeemer 70-89; Prec Dromore Cathl 71-75; Dean Dromore 75-89; rtd 89; Lic to Offic *D & D* from 90. *30 Church Road, Belfast BT8 4AQ*   Belfast (01232) 491588

LOCKLEY, Ven Harold. b 16. Lon Univ BA37 BD43 MTh49 Nottm Univ PhD55 Em Coll Cam MLitt91. Westcott Ho Cam 46. **d** 46 **p** 47. Dir of Ords *Leic* 51-79; V Leic All SS 63-78; Adn Loughb 63-86; rtd 86. *21 Saxon Close, Market Harborough, Leics LE16 7PR*   Market Harborough (01858) 465605

LOCKWOOD, David Nicholas. b 23. Birm Univ MA81. St D Coll Lamp BA51 Qu Coll Birm 51. **d** 53 **p** 54. V Hanley Castle w Hanley Swan *Worc* 64-79; V Hanley Castle, Hanley Swan and Welland 79-81; Perm to Offic *S & B* from 81; rtd 88. *Church Row, Llowes, Hereford HR3 5JB*   Glasbury (01497) 847664

LOCKWOOD, Wilfred Eric. b 18. Leeds Univ BA49. Coll of Resurr Mirfield 49. **d** 51 **p** 52. V Leeds Ch Ch and St Jo and St Barn Holbeck *Ripon* 62-71; R Ducklington *Ox* 71-83; rtd 83; Perm to Offic *Nor* from 83. *15A Wells Road, Walsingham, Norfolk NR22 6DL*   Walsingham (01328) 820723

LOCKYER, David Ralph George. b 41. Wells Th Coll 65. **d** 67 **p** 68. C Bottesford *Linc* 67-69; C Eling *Win* 69-73; TV Eling, Testwood and Marchwood 73-77; TR Speke St Aid *Liv* 77-84; V Halifax St Jude *Wakef* from 84; Chapl Halifax R Infirmary from 84. *St Jude's Vicarage, Kensington Road, Savile Park, Halifax, W Yorkshire HX3 0HN*   Halifax (01422) 354842

LOCKYER, Desmond Edward Weston. b 18. AKC49. **d** 50 **p** 51. V Eastbourne St Mich *Chich* 68-75; V Preston 75-87; rtd 87; Perm to Offic *Chich* from 87. *Pilgrims, Nep Town Road, Henfield, W Sussex BN5 9DY*   Brighton (01273) 493681

LOCKYER, Maurice David. b 19. AKC43. **d** 43 **p** 44. V Huncote *Leic* 64-77; rtd 77. *21 Smith Close, London SE16 1PB*

LOCKYER, Peter Weston. b 60. Linc Coll Ox BA80 MA87. St Jo Coll Nottm 84. **d** 87 **p** 88. C Rowner *Portsm* 87-90; C Beaconsfield *Ox* 90-91; TV 91-95; Dep Chapl HM Young Offender Institution, Glen Parva from 95. *HM Young Offender Institution, Glen Parva, Tigers Road, Wigston, Leicester LE18 4TN*   Leicester (0116) 277 2022   Fax 247 7679

LOCOCK, Jillian Maud (Jill). b 33. Lon Univ BSc55. N Ord Course 81. **dss** 84 **d** 87 **p** 95. Didsbury Ch Ch *Man* 84-86; Chapl Asst Man R Infirmary 85-87; Chapl Asst Withington Hosp 86-88; Chapl Asst RN from 88; NSM Dumbarton *Glas* from 93. *20C Queen Street, Helensburgh, Dunbartonshire G84 9LG*   Helensburgh (01436) 71252

LODER, Sister Helen. b 43. Golds Coll Lon 65. S'wark Ord Course 91. **d** 94 **p** 95. NSM from 70; NSM S Hackney St Mich w Haggerston St Paul *Lon* from 94. *St Saviour's Priory, 18 Queensbridge Road, London E2 8NS*   0171-739 9976

LODGE, Anthony William Rayner. b 26. Wadh Coll Ox BA51 MA55. Cuddesdon Coll 63. **d** 66 **p** 67. Chapl Ripon Gr Sch 68-91; rtd 91; Perm to Offic *Heref* from 92. *Church Cottage, Diddlebury, Craven Arms, Shropshire SY7 9DH*   Munslow (01584) 841340

LODGE, Canon John Alfred Ainley. b 29. Wells Th Coll 54. **d** 57 **p** 58. C-in-c Mixenden CD *Wakef* 69-75; V Mixenden 75-76; V Almondbury 76-79; RD Almondbury 76-79; V Warmfield 79-88; Bp's Dom Chapl 79-87; Hon Can Wakef Cathl 85-92; RD Kirkburton 88-92; P-in-c Emley 88-92; rtd 92; Perm to Offic *Ripon* from 92. *Bygate, 2 Station Court, Morton on Swale, Northallerton, N Yorkshire DL7 9TQ*   Northallerton (01609) 778551

LODGE, Michael John. b 53. Wycliffe Hall Ox 87. **d** 89 **p** 90. C Highworth w Sevenhampton and Inglesham etc *Bris* 89-93; P-in-c Cheltenham St Luke and St Jo *Glouc* from 93. *St Luke's Vicarage, 38 College Road, Cheltenham, Glos GL53 7HX*   Cheltenham (01242) 513940

LODGE, Robin Paul. b 60. Bris Univ BA82 Ch Ch Coll Cant PGCE83. Chich Th Coll 88. **d** 90 **p** 91. C Calne and Blackland *Sarum* 90-94; Asst Chapl St Mary's Sch Calne 90-94; TV Wellington and Distr *B & W* from 94. *All Saints Vicarage, 8 Exeter Road, Wellington, Somerset TA21 9DH*   Wellington (01823) 472742

LODGE, Roy Frederick. b 38. BTh Birm Univ DipSoc62. Tyndale Hall Bris 63. **d** 66 **p** 67. C Tardebigge *Worc* 66-67; Chapl and Warden Probation Hostel Redditch 67-69;

433

LODWICK

Chapl RAF 69-75; C Kinson *Sarum* 76; Lic to Offic *Pet* 76-77; Asst Chapl HM Pris Stafford 77-78; Chapl HM Pris Ranby 78-84; Chapl HM Pris Long Lartin 84-93; Chapl HM Young Offender Inst Hewell Grange from 93; Chapl HM Rem Cen Brockhill from 93. *HM Young Offender Institution, Hewell Grange, Redditch, Worcs B97 6QQ* Redditch (01527) 550843 Fax 550169

LODWICK, Brian Martin. b 40. Leeds Univ BA61 MPhil76 Linacre Coll Ox BA63 MA67 Univ of Wales PhD87. St Steph Ho Ox 61. **d** 64 **p** 65. C Aberaman *Llan* 64-66; C Newton Nottage 66-73; R Llansannor and Llanfrynach w Penllyn etc 73-94; RD Llantwit Major and Cowbridge 83-94; Chan Llan Cathl from 92; R Llandough w Leckwith from 94. *The Rectory, Llandough Hill, Llandough, Penarth, S Glam CF64 2NA* Penarth (01222) 703349

LODWICK, Stephen Huw. b 64. Plymouth Univ BSc85. St Mich Coll Llan DipTh94. **d** 94 **p** 95. C Clydach *S & B* from 94. *37 Kelvin Road, Clydach, Swansea SA6 5JP* Swansea (01792) 845397

LOEWENDAHL, David Jacob (Jake). b 50. SS Coll Cam BA74 MA77. Ripon Coll Cuddesdon 75. **d** 77 **p** 78. C Walworth *S'wark* 77-80; Chapl St Alb Abbey *St Alb* 80-83; Chapl St Alb Sch 80-83; Team Ldr Community Service Volunteers 84-90; Perm to Offic *Lon* 83-90; R E and W Tilbury and Linford *Chelmsf* from 90. *The Rectory, Princess Margaret Road, East Tilbury, Grays, Essex RM18 8PB* Tilbury (01375) 842220

LOFT, Edmund Martin Boswell. b 25. St Jo Coll Cam BA49 MA55. Ely Th Coll 49. **d** 51 **p** 52. V Fillongley *Cov* 62-77; V Earlsdon 77-90; rtd 90. *10 Quarry Road, Sheffield S17 4DA* Sheffield (0114) 236 0759

LOFTHOUSE, Canon Alexander Francis Joseph. b 30. Keble Coll Ox BA54 MA58. St Steph Ho Ox 54. **d** 56 **p** 57. V Airedale w Fryston *Wakef* 60-70; V Maryport *Carl* 70-78; P-in-c Helsington 78; V 78-95; P-in-c Underbarrow 78; V 78-95; P-in-c Levens 78; V 78-95; Hon Can Carl Cathl 85-95; rtd 95. *Hazel Grove House, Yealand Redmayne, Carnforth, Lancs LA5 9RW*

LOFTHOUSE, Miss Brenda. b 33. RGN60 RM62 RNT69. N Ord Course 84. **d** 87 **p** 94. Hon Par Dn Greengates *Bradf* 87-89; Par Dn Farsley 89-94; V Bolton St Jas w St Chrys from 94. *St James's Vicarage, 1056 Bolton Road, Bradford, W Yorkshire BD2 4LH* Bradford (01274) 637193

LOGAN, Kevin. b 43. Oak Hill Th Coll 73. **d** 75 **p** 76. C Blackb Sav *Blackb* 75-78; C Leyland St Andr 78-82; V Gt Harwood St Jo 82-91; V Accrington Ch Ch from 91. *Christ Church Vicarage, 3 Bentcliff Gardens, Accrington, Lancs BB5 2NX* Accrington (01254) 235089

LOGAN, Samuel Desmond. b 39. TEng. CITC. **d** 78 **p** 79. NSM Belvoir *D & D* 78-85; NSM Knock 85-87; NSM Belf St Brendan 87-91; Lic to Offic 91-95; C Ban Abbey from 95. *8 Casaeldona Crescent, Belfast BT6 9RE* Belfast (01232) 795473

LOGUE, Mrs Rosemary Christine. TCD BTh93. CITC 90. **d** 93 **p** 94. C Clooney w Strathfoyle *D & R* from 93. *17 Dunhugh Park, Victoria Road, Londonderry BT47 2NL* Londonderry (01504) 47480

LOMAS, David Xavier. b 39. St Jo Coll Dur BA78. Cranmer Hall Dur 75. **d** 78 **p** 79. C Ches le Street *Dur* 78-81; C-in-c Newton Hall LEP 81-85; Chapl Scunthorpe Distr HA 85-93; Chapl Linc Co Hosp Gp from 93. *The County Hospital, Greetwell Road, Lincoln LN2 5QY* Lincoln (01522) 573402 or 512512

LOMAS, John Derrick. b 58. St Mich Coll Llan DPT94. **d** 94 **p** 95. C Rhyl w St Ann *St As* from 94. *The Close, Paradise Street, Rhyl, Clwyd LL18 3LW* Rhyl (01745) 337130

LOMAS, Paul Roy. b 54. Man Univ TCert75. N Ord Course 86. **d** 89 **p** 90. C Hollinwood *Man* 89-92; R Failsworth H Family from 92. *The Rectory, 190 Lord Lane, Failsworth, Manchester M35 0PG* 0161-681 3644

LOMAX, Canon Barry Walter John. b 39. Lambeth STh Lon Coll of Div 63. **d** 66 **p** 67. C Sevenoaks St Nic *Roch* 66-71; C Southport Ch Ch *Liv* 71-73; V Bootle St Matt 73-78; P-in-c Litherland St Andr 76-78; V New Boro and Leigh *Sarum* 78-94; Can and Preb Sarum Cathl from 91; R Blandford Forum and Langton Long from 94. *The Rectory, 2 Portman Place, Deer Park, Blandford Forum, Dorset DT11 7DG* Blandford (01258) 480092

LOMAX, Canon Frank. b 20. Leeds Univ BA42. Coll of Resurr Mirfield 42. **d** 44 **p** 45. V Prudhoe *Newc* 64-74; Singapore from 75; Hon Can Singapore from 75; rtd 87. *142 Killiney Road, 04-146 Devonshire Court, Singapore 0923* Singapore (65) 737-8329

LONDON (St Paul's), Dean of. See EVANS, Very Rev Thomas Eric

LONDON, Archdeacon of. See CASSIDY, Ven George Henry

LONDON, Bishop of. *Vacant*

LONG, Miss Anne Christine. b 33. Leic Univ BA56 Ox Univ DipEd57 Lon Univ BD65. **dss** 80 **d** 87 **p** 94. Lect St Jo Coll Nottm 73-84; Acorn Chr Healing Trust from 85; Stanstead Abbots *St Alb* 85-92; Hon Par Dn 87-92; Hon Par Dn Camberley St Paul *Guildf* 92-94; Hon C from 94. *8 Loweswater Walk, Camberley, Surrey GU15 1BH* Camberley (01276) 677591 Fax Bordon (01420) 478122

LONG, Anthony Auguste (Tony). b 45. Linc Th Coll 79. **d** 81 **p** 82. C Kingswinford St Mary *Lich* 81-84; TV Ellesmere Port *Ches* 84-87; V Witton from 87. *The Vicarage, 61 Church Road, Northwich, Cheshire CW9 5PB* Northwich (01606) 42943

LONG, Anthony Robert. b 48. SS Mark & Jo Coll Chelsea CertEd70 Southn Univ BTh93. Chich Th Coll 74. **d** 77 **p** 78. C Chiswick St Nic w St Mary *Lon* 77-80; C Earley St Pet *Ox* 80-85; P-in-c Worstead w Westwick and Sloley *Nor* 85-92; P-in-c Tunstead w Sco' Ruston from 85; R Worstead, Westwick, Sloley, Swanton Abbot etc from 92. *The Vicarage, Worstead, North Walsham, Norfolk NR28 9SE* Smallburgh (01692) 536800

LONG, Christopher William. b 47. OBE94. Nottm Univ BTh78 Open Univ BA80. Linc Th Coll 75. **d** 78 **p** 79. C Shiregreen St Jas and St Chris *Sheff* 78-81; V 81-82; Chapl RAF from 82; Perm to Offic *St E* from 91. *Chaplaincy Services (RAF), HQ, Personnel and Training Command, RAF Innsworth, Gloucester GL3 1EZ* Gloucester (01452) 712612 Ext 5164 Fax 510269

LONG, Canon Colin Angus. b 17. St D Coll Lamp BA38 St Mich Coll Llan 39. **d** 40 **p** 43. V Newport Maindee St Jo Ev *Mon* 62-83; Can St Woolos Cathl 77-83; rtd 83. *18 Newport Road, New Inn, Pontypool, Gwent NP4 0NT* Pontypool (01495) 753624

LONG, David William. b 47. K Coll Lon 67. St Aug Coll Cant 70. **d** 72 **p** 73. C Stanley *Liv* 72-73; C W Derby St Luke 73-76; C Cantril Farm 76-79; V Warrington St Barn 79-81; C-in-c Westbrook St Jas CD 82; V Westbrook St Jas from 82. *The Vicarage, 302 Hood Lane, Great Sankey, Warrington WA5 1UQ* Warrington (01925) 633873

LONG, Edward Percy Eades (Bill). b 14. Liv Univ BA36 MA38. Linc Th Coll 73. **d** 73 **p** 74. C Sedbergh, Cautley and Garsdale *Bradf* 73-84; rtd 85; Perm to Offic *Bradf* from 85. *4 Derry Cottages, Sedbergh, Cumbria LA10 5SN* Sedbergh (015396) 20577

LONG, Frederick Hugh. b 43. E Midl Min Tr Course 90. **d** 90 **p** 91. NSM Grantham *Linc* from 90. *65 Barrowby Road, Grantham, Lincs NG31 8AB* Grantham (01476) 67278

LONG, Geoffrey Lawrence. Portsm Dioc Tr Course 88. **d** 89. NSM Whippingham w E Cowes *Portsm* from 89. *10 Minerva Road, East Cowes, Isle of Wight PO32 6DH* Isle of Wight (01983) 295917

LONG, Harry. b 27. BEM. QUB DBS. **d** 79 **p** 80. NSM Carryduff *D & D* 79-86; NSM Newtownards 86; NSM Belvoir 87-91; Lic to Offic from 91. *28 Cadger Road, Carryduff, Belfast BT8 8AU* Belfast (01232) 812348

LONG, Ven John Sanderson. b 13. Qu Coll Cam BA35 MA39. Cuddesdon Coll 35. **d** 36 **p** 37. Hon Can Ely Cathl *Ely* 70-81; Adn Ely 70-81; R Cam St Botolph 70-81; rtd 81. *23 Thornton Road, Girton, Cambridge CB3 0NP* Cambridge (01223) 276421

LONG, Canon John Sydney. b 25. Lon Univ BSc49. Wycliffe Hall Ox 50. **d** 51 **p** 52. V Barnoldswick w Bracewell *Bradf* 64-85; Hon Can Bradf Cathl 77-91; RD Skipton 83-90; R Broughton, Marton and Thornton 85-91; rtd 91. *1 Church Villa, Carleton, Skipton, N Yorkshire BD23 3DQ* Skipton (01756) 799095

LONG, Kingsley Edward. b 41. CITC 90. **d** 93 **p** 94. NSM Howth *D & G* from 93. *Crimond, 125 Seapark, Malahide, Co Dublin, Irish Republic* Dublin (1) 845-3179

LONG, Michael David Barnby. b 32. AKC55. **d** 56 **p** 57. C Whitby *York* 56-59; C Cottingham 59-61; V Elloughton 61-66; P-in-c Brantingham 61-66; V Sheff Parson Cross St Cecilia *Sheff* 66-68; V Flamborough *York* 68-73; R Litcham w Kempston w E and W Lexham *Nor* 73-75; P-in-c York St Luke *York* 75-77; V 77-80; V Hatton w Haseley and Rowington w Lowsonford *Cov* 80-82; V Derringham Bank *York* 82-85; V Castle Acre w Newton *Nor* 85; R Southacre 85; R Castle Acre w Newton, Rougham and Southacre 85-86; TV Grantham *Linc* 86-89; V Cayton w Eastfield *York* from 89; RD Scarborough from 94. *The Vicarage, Eastfield, Scarborough, N Yorkshire YO11 3EE* Scarborough (01723) 582428

LONG, Peter Ronald. b 48. Nottm Univ BA69 Man Univ CertEd70 DPT71. Cuddesdon Coll 71. **d** 73 **p** 74. Chapl RAFVR from 74; C Bodmin *Truro* 75-76; C Newquay 75-76; Asst Youth Chapl 75-76; Dioc Youth Chapl 76-79; Perm to Offic *Eur* 76 and 78-85 and from 87; P-in-c Mawgan w St Martin-in-Meneage *Truro* 76 and 79-82; Chapl Helston-Meneage Community and Geriatric Hosp 80-95; Miss to Seamen from 80; P-in-c Cury w Gunwalloe *Truro* 80-82; R

Cury and Gunwalloe w Mawgan from 83; Perm to Offic *Ex* 82-93. *The Rectory, Mawgan, Helston, Cornwall TR12 6AD* Mawgan (01326) 221291   Fax 240478

LONG, Dr Roger Eric. b 36. Univ Coll Dur BSc59 PhD62. NE Ord Course 90. **d** 93 **p** 94. C Street TM *York* from 93. *The Vicarage, Church Lane, Amotherby, Malton, N Yorkshire YO17 0NT*   Malton (01653) 693503

LONG, Canon Samuel Ernest. b 18. JP68. ALCD50. **d** 49 **p** 50. I Dromara w Garvaghy *D & D* 56-85; Can Dromore Cathl 81-85; Treas 82-85; rtd 85. *9 Cairnshill Court, Saintfield Road, Belfast BT8 4TX*   Belfast (01232) 793401

LONG, Simon Richard. b 40. Birm Univ DPS69. Bernard Gilpin Soc Dur 61 Ely Th Coll 62 Coll of Resurr Mirfield 64. **d** 65 **p** 66. C Bournemouth St Fran *Win* 54-68; Belgium 68; USA 69-88; P-in-c Medbourne cum Holt w Stockerston and Blaston *Leic* 88-89; P-in-c Bringhurst w Gt Easton 88-89; R Six Saints circa Holt from 90; RD Gartree I (Harborough) from 93. *The Rectory, Rectory Lane, Medbourne, Market Harborough, Leics LE16 8DZ*   Medbourne Green (0185883) 419

LONG, William Thomas. b 53. TCD DipTh81 Dur Univ MA88. **d** 81 **p** 82. C Orangefield *D & D* 81-84; C Portadown St Mark *Arm* 84-86; I Dromara w Garvaghy *D & D* 86-91; I Aghalurcher w Tattykeeran, Cooneen etc *Clogh* from 91. *St Ronan's Rectory, Killarbran, Fivemiletown, Co Tyrone BT75 0SR*   Brookeborough (013655) 31822

LONGBOTHAM, Richard Ashley. b 14. AKC36. Sarum Th Coll 37. **d** 37 **p** 38. Rhodesia and S Africa 47-80; rtd 81. *PO Box 366, Hermanus C P, 7200 South Africa*

LONGBOTTOM, Canon Frank. b 41. Lon Univ DipTh68 Birm Univ DPS74. Ripon Hall Ox 65. **d** 68 **p** 69. C Epsom St Martin *Guildf* 68-72; Asst Chapl St Ebbas Hosp Epsom 68-72; Asst Chapl Qu Mary's Hosp Carshalton 68-72; Asst Chapl Henderson Hosp Sutton 68-72; Chapl Highcroft Hosp Birm 72-94; Chapl Northcroft Hosp Birm 74-94; Dioc Adv for Past Care of Clergy & Families from 89; Bp's Adv from 94; Hon Can Birm Cathl *Birm* from 91. *46 Sunnybank Road, Sutton Coldfield, W Midlands B73 5RE*   0121-350 5823 or 378 2211

LONGBOTTOM, Paul Edward. b 44. AKC67. **d** 68 **p** 69. C Rainham *Roch* 68-71; C Riverhead 71-75; C Dunton Green 71-75; V Penge Lane H Trin 75-84; V Chatham St Wm 84-94; V Shorne from 94; Dioc Dir of Ords from 94. *The Vicarage, Butchers Hill, Shorne, Gravesend, Kent DA12 3EB*   Shorne (01474) 822234

LONGFOOT, Richard. b 46. Oak Hill Th Coll 76. **d** 78 **p** 79. C Chaddesden St Mary *Derby* 78-81; C Cam St Martin *Ely* 81-83; R Folksworth w Morborne 83-89; R Stilton w Denton and Caldecote 83-89; R Stilton w Denton and Caldecote etc from 90. *The Rectory, Stilton, Peterborough PE7 3RF* Peterborough (01733) 240282

LONGFORD, Canon Edward de Toesny Wingfield. b 25. Ch Ch Ox BA48 MA53. Wells Th Coll 49. **d** 51 **p** 52. P-in-c Everton w Tetworth *Ely* 68-71; V 71-73; R Gamlingay 68-80; P-in-c Hatley 78-80; Hon Can Ely Cathl 79-90; R Gamlingay w Hatley St Geo and E Hatley 80-90; RD St Neots 82-90; rtd 90. *9 Philippa Close, Ely, Cambs CB6 1BT*   Ely (01353) 667495

LONGMAN, Edward. b 37. Hatf Coll Dur BSc62 Fitzw Ho Cam BA66. Clifton Th Coll 62 Ridley Hall Cam 64. **d** 66 **p** 67. C Lower Homerton St Paul *Lon* 66-72; C Parr *Liv* 72-73; TV 74-85; Perm to Offic from 86. *66 Hard Lane, Dentons Green, St Helens, Merseyside WA10 2LA*   St Helens (01744) 55667

LONGMAN, Canon Edward George (Ted). b 35. St Pet Hall Ox BA58 MA62. Westcott Ho Cam 59. **d** 61 **p** 62. C Sheff St Mark Broomhall *Sheff* 61-65; V Brightside St Thos 65-74; V Yardley St Edburgha *Birm* 74-84; RD Yardley 77-84; Hon Can Birm Cathl from 81; R Sutton Coldfield H Trin from 84; Chapl Gd Hope Distr Gen Hosp Sutton Coldfield 84-90; RD Sutton Coldfield *Birm* from 94. *16 Coleshill Street, Sutton Coldfield, W Midlands B72 1SH*   0121-354 3607

LONGRIDGE, Richard Nevile. b 15. Sarum Th Coll 46. **d** 48 **p** 49. R Spetisbury w Charlton Marshall *Sarum* 67-77; rtd 77; Perm to Offic *Ex* from 78. *27 East Avenue, Exeter EX1 2DX* Exeter (01392) 435866

LONGUET-HIGGINS, John. b 62. Leeds Univ BA85. St Jo Coll Nottm DTS90 DPS91. **d** 91 **p** 92. C Kidlington w Hampton Poyle *Ox* from 91. *4 Court Close, Kidlington, Oxon OX5 2DG* Kidlington (01865) 374021

LONGWORTH, Arthur Victor. b 24. Trin Coll Ox BA48 MA51. St Steph Ho Ox 48. **d** 49 **p** 50. CR from 54; C Rubery *Birm* 69-70; Vice-Prin Chich Th Coll 70-73; V Walsgrave on Sowe *Cov* 73-75; Dioc Dir of Ords 73-80; V Bishop's Tachbrook 75-80; V Sheff St Matt *Sheff* 80-89; Ind Chapl 80-87; rtd 89. *18 Sycamore Avenue, Garstang, Preston PR3 1FR*   Garstang (01995) 603145

LONGWORTH-DAMES, Canon Francis Robert. b 12. Jes Coll Cam BA34 MA38. Westcott Ho Cam 36. **d** 37 **p** 38. R Warlingham w Chelsham and Farleigh *S'wark* 65-73; V Catford St Andr 74-81; rtd 81. *17 Capel Court, The Burgage,*

Prestbury, Cheltenham, Glos GL52 3EL   Cheltenham (01242) 239830

LONSDALE, Canon Rupert Philip. b 05. Ridley Hall Cam 47. **d** 48 **p** 49. V Thornham w Titchwell *Nor* 65-70; rtd 70; Chapl Puerto de la Cruz Tenerife *Eur* 70-73. *Reepham House, Bastion Square, Mdina RBT 12, Malta*

LOOKER, Miss Clare Margaret. b 55. Liv Univ CertEd DipRE. Westcott Ho Cam 85. **d** 87. Par Dn Prestwood and Gt Hampden *Ox* 87-90; rtd 90; Hon C Olney w Emberton *Ox* from 90. *56 Christian Court, Willen, Milton Keynes MK15 9HY*

LOONE, Sean Joseph Patrick. b 60. Cov Poly BA83 Wolv Poly CertEd84 Leeds Univ BA88. Coll of Resurr Mirfield 86. **d** 89 **p** 90. C Solihull *Birm* 89-92; Hd RE Bromsgrove Jun Sch Worcs from 93. *9 Broomfield Road, Solihull, W Midlands B91 2ND*   0121-705 5117

LOPDELL-BRADSHAW, Canon Humphrey Maitland. b 32. Edin Th Coll 58. **d** 61 **p** 62. C Edin H Cross *Edin* 61-65; C Edin St Barn 65-67; P-in-c Oldbury *Birm* 67-68; V 68-72; R Edin St Hilda *Edin* 72-77; R Hawick 77-88; R Huntly *Mor* from 88; R Aberchirder from 88; R Keith from 88; Can St Andr Cathl Inverness from 91. *The Rectory, Seafield Avenue, Keith, Banffshire AB55 3BS*   Keith (01542) 882782

LOPEZ-FERREIRO, Serafin Julio. b 35. Dur Univ BA74 DipTh71. St Jo Coll Dur. **d** 71 **p** 72. C S Lambeth St Steph *S'wark* 71-75; C Upper Tooting H Trin 76-78; P-in-c Tooting St Aug 78-83; V from 83. *St Augustine's Vicarage, 99 Broadwater Road, London SW17 0DY*   0181-672 4712

LORAINE, Kenneth. b 34. Cranmer Hall Dur 63. **d** 66 **p** 67. C Hartlepool All SS Stranton *Dur* 66-69; C Darlington St Cuth 69-72; V Preston on Tees 72-79; V Staindrop 79-87; P-in-c Haynes *St Alb* from 87; Dioc Stewardship Adv from 87. *The Vicarage, 4A North Lane, Haynes, Bedford MK45 3PW* Haynes (0123066) 235

LORD, Alexander. b 13. ALCD43. **d** 43 **p** 44. R Illogan *Truro* 70-81; rtd 81; C Letton w Staunton, Byford, Mansel Gamage etc *Heref* 81-84. *43 Narrow Lane, Llandudno Junction, Gwynedd LL31 9SZ*   Aberconwy (01492) 584647

LORD, Canon John Fairbourne. b 19. Kelham Th Coll 38. **d** 43 **p** 44. RD Holt *Nor* 64-79; R Thornage w Brinton w Hunworth and Stody 64-84; Hon Can Nor Cathl 77-84; rtd 84; Perm to Offic *Nor* from 84. *25 Melton Road, Hindolveston, Dereham, Norfolk NR20 5DB*   Melton Constable (01263) 860819

LORD, Kenneth Frank. b 14. Clifton Th Coll 34. **d** 38 **p** 40. V Skelton cum Newby *Ripon* 53-81; rtd 81. *The Vicarage, Skelton-on-Ure, Ripon, N Yorkshire HG4 5AJ* Boroughbridge (01423) 322864

LORD, Stuart James. b 59. K Coll Lon BD81 AKC81. Sarum & Wells Th Coll 83. **d** 85 **p** 86. C Darwen St Pet w Hoddlesden *Blackb* 85-88; C Otley *Bradf* 88-93; P-in-c Low Moor St Mark from 93. *St Mark's Vicarage, 1 Park Bottom, Low Moor, Bradford, W Yorkshire BD12 0UA*   Bradford (01274) 677754

LORIMER, Eileen Jean. b 35. CertEd56. Dalton Ho Bris 62. **dss** 84 **d** 89 **p** 94. Chiddingstone w Chiddingstone Causeway *Roch* 84-89; NSM from 89. *The Nursery Flat, Hoath House, Chiddingstone Hoath, Edenbridge, Kent TN8 7DB*   Cowden (01342) 850784

LOSACK, Marcus Charles. b 53. Ch Coll Cam BA76 MA78 MPhil. Sarum & Wells Th Coll 78. **d** 80 **p** 81. C Hattersley *Ches* 80-82; C Dub Zion Ch *D & G* 83-86; Libya 86-89; CMS 89-92; Jerusalem 89-92; P-in-c Dub Sandymount *D & G* 92-93; I Newc w Newtownmountkennedy and Calary from 93. *The Rectory, Newcastle, Greystones, Co Wicklow, Irish Republic* Dublin (1) 281-9300   Fax as telephone

LOSEBY, Everitt James Carnall. b 22. Launde Abbey. **d** 66 **p** 67. C Thurmaston *Leic* 66-70; R Seagrave w Walton le Wolds 70-75; V Thurnby Lodge 75-84; V Swinford w Catthorpe, Shawell and Stanford 84-87; rtd 87; Perm to Offic *Leic* from 87. *63 Willow Road, Blaby, Leicester LE8 4BG*   Leicester (0116) 277 1983

LOTT, Dr Eric John. b 34. Lon Univ BA65 Lanc Univ MLitt70 PhD77. Richmond Th Coll BD59. **d** 60 **p** 61. India 60-88; Prof United Th Coll Bangalore 77-88; Wesley Hall Ch and Community Project Leics 88-94; rtd 94; Perm to Offic *Leic* from 94. *16 Main Road, Old Dalby, Melton Mowbray, Leics LE14 3LR*   Melton Mowbray (01664) 822405

LOUDEN, Canon Terence Edmund (Terry). b 48. Ch Coll Cam BA70 MA74. Sarum & Wells Th Coll 72. **d** 75 **p** 76. C Portsea N End St Mark *Portsm* 75-78; C-in-c Leigh Park St Clare CD 78-81; R Chale 81-88; R Niton 81-88; P-in-c Whitwell 82-84; V Cosham from 88; Hon Can Portsm Cathl from 92. *St Philip's Vicarage, Hawthorn Crescent, Cosham, Portsmouth PO6 2TL* Cosham (01705) 326179

LOUGHBOROUGH, Archdeacon of. See STANES, Ven Ian Thomas

LOUGHEED, Canon Brian Frederick Britain. b 38. TCD BA60. CITC 61. **d** 61 **p** 62. C Dub St Pet w St Audoen *D & G* 61-63; C Glenageary 63-66; I Rathmolyon Union *M & K* 66-79;

I Killarney w Aghadoe and Muckross *L & K* from 79; Can Limerick and Killaloe Cathls 87-95; Preb Taney St Patr Cathl Dub from 89; Dioc Info Officer (Limerick) *L & K* 90-91; Radio Officer from 91. *St Mary's Rectory, Rookery Road, Ballycasheen, Killarney, Co Kerry, Irish Republic* Killarney (64) 31832 Fax as telephone

LOUGHLIN, Canon Alfred. b 10. Clifton Th Coll 37. **d** 39 **p** 40. R Kinson *Sarum* 54-81; rtd 81. *18 Donnelly Road, Bournemouth BH6 5NW* Bournemouth (01202) 422306

LOUGHLIN, George Alfred Graham. b 43. Lon Univ DipTh68. Clifton Th Coll 65. **d** 69 **p** 70. C Plumstead All SS *S'wark* 69-73; C Bromley Ch Ch *Roch* 73-76; P-in-c Bothenhampton w Walditch *Sarum* 76-79; TV Bridport 79-83; V Heatherlands St Jo from 83. *St John's Vicarage, 72 Alexandra Road, Poole, Dorset BH14 9EW* Parkstone (01202) 741276

LOUGHTON, Michael. b 34. K Coll Lon BD58 AKC58. **d** 59 **p** 60. C Chingford SS Pet and Paul *Chelmsf* 59-62; C Eastbourne St Elisabeth *Chich* 62-65; R Lewes St Jo sub Castro 65-74; Perm to Offic from 87. *Follers Manor, Seaford Road, Alfriston, Polegate, E Sussex BN26 5TT* Alfriston (01323) 870252

LOUIS, Peter Anthony. b 41. St Cath Coll Ox BA63 MA77 Jes Coll Cam CertEd64 Man Univ MPhil85. Wells Th Coll 66. **d** 68 **p** 70. C E Grinstead St Mary *Chich* 68-75; C Radcliffe-on-Trent *S'well* 75-80; Hd Master Blue Coat Comp Sch Cov 80-85; V Welwyn Garden City *St Alb* from 85; Chapl Oaklands Coll from 93. *The Vicarage, 48 Parkway, Welwyn Garden City, Herts AL8 6HH* Welwyn Garden (01707) 323316

LOUW, Paul Leonard. b 32. Leeds Univ BA56 Port Eliz Univ MA79. Coll of Resurr Mirfield 56. **d** 58 **p** 59. C Solihull *Birm* 58-61; S Africa from 61. *55 Main Road, Walmer, Port Elizabeth, 6070 South Africa* Port Elizabeth (41) 513588

LOVATT, Bernard James. b 31. Lich Th Coll 64. **d** 65 **p** 66. C Burford III w Lt Heref 65-67; C Cleobury Mortimer w Hopton Wafers 67-68; C Bradford-on-Avon *Sarum* 68-69; C Wootton Bassett 69-72; C Broad Town 69-72; R Bishopstrow and Boreham 72-79; P-in-c Brighton St Geo *Chich* 79-83; V Brighton St Anne 79-83; V Brighton St Geo and St Anne 83-86; P-in-c Kemp Town St Mark and St Matt 85-86; V Brighton St Geo w St Anne and St Mark from 86. *St George's Vicarage, 33 Eaton Place, Brighton BN2 1EG* Brighton (01273) 699779

LOVATT, William Robert. b 54. SS Coll Cam MA75 K Coll Lon PGCE77 MA78. Oak Hill Th Coll 85. **d** 87 **p** 88. C Devonport St Budeaux *Ex* 87-90; Asst Chapl Paris St Mich *Eur* 90-94; P-in-c Lenton *S'well* from 94. *The Vicarage, 35A Church Street, Nottingham NG7 2FH* Nottingham (0115) 970 1059

LOVE, Ms Anette. b 53. Matlock Coll of Educn CertEd74 Nottm Univ BEd75. St Jo Coll Dur 88. **d** 90 **p** 94. Par Dn Gresley *Derby* 90-92; C Heanor 92-94; C Loscoe from 94. *The Vicarage, High Street, Loscoe, Heanor, Derbyshire DE75 7LE* Langley Mill (01773) 765631

LOVE, Richard Angus. b 45. AKC67. **d** 68 **p** 69. C Balham Hill Ascension *S'wark* 68-71; C Amersham *Ox* 71-73; R Scotter w E Ferry *Linc* 73-79; P-in-c Petham w Waltham and Lower Hardres w Nackington *Cant* 79-85; R Petham and Waltham w Lower Hardres etc 85-90; V Sittingbourne H Trin w Bobbing from 90. *Holy Trinity Vicarage, 47 London Road, Sittingbourne, Kent ME10 1NQ* Sittingbourne (01795) 472724

LOVE, Dr Robert (Bob). b 45. Bradf Univ BSc68 PhD74 NE Lon Poly PGCE89. Trin Coll Bris DipTh75. **d** 75 **p** 76. C Bowling St Jo *Bradf* 75-79; TV Forest Gate St Sav w W Ham St Matt *Chelmsf* 79-85; P-in-c Becontree St Eliz from 85. *St Elizabeth's Vicarage, Hewett Road, Dagenham, Essex RM8 2XT* 0181-517 0355

LOVEDAY, Joseph Michael. b 54. AKC75. St Aug Coll Cant 75. **d** 78 **p** 79. C Kettering SS Pet and Paul *Pet* 78-81; C Upper Teddington SS Pet and Paul *Lon* 81-84; CF from 84. *c/o MOD (Army), Bagshot Park, Bagshot, Surrey GU19 5PL* Bagshot (01276) 471717 Fax 412834

LOVEGROVE, Mrs Anne Maureen. b 44. DipHE90. Oak Hill Th Coll 88. **d** 90 **p** 94. Par Dn Thorley *St Alb* 90-94; C 94-95; V Croxley Green St Oswald from 95. *The Vicarage, 159 Baldwins Lane, Croxley Green, Rickmansworth, Herts WD3 3LL* Watford (01923) 232387

LOVEGROVE, Walter John. b 19. Dur Univ LTh44. St Aug Coll Cant 38. **d** 42 **p** 43. S Africa 47-72 and 83-93; V Chaddesden St Phil *Derby* 72-75; P-in-c Tintinhull *B & W* 75; R Tintinhull w Chilthorne Domer, Yeovil Marsh etc 75-80; RD Martock 78-80; P-in-c Norbury St Phil *Cant* 80-81; V 81-83; rtd 86. *59 Holloway Road, Dorchester, Dorset DT1 1LF* Dorchester (01305) 260180

LOVEJOY, Geoffrey William. b 08. St Chad's Coll Dur BA31 LTh31 MA47. Dorchester Miss Coll 28. **d** 32 **p** 33. R Stoke Goldington w Gayhurst *Ox* 65-72; P-in-c Ravenstone w Weston Underwood 67-72; rtd 73; Chapl Sevenoaks Hosp

73-79; Hon C Sevenoaks St Jo *Roch* 73-88; Perm to Offic from 88. *61 Old Mill Close, Eynsford, Dartford DA4 0BN* Farningham (01322) 866186

LOVEJOY, James Allan. b 06. Jes Coll Cam BA28 MA35. Westcott Ho Cam 35. **d** 36 **p** 37. V Westleton w Dunwich *St E* 67-74; V Darsham 71-74; rtd 74; Perm to Offic *St E* from 74. *28 Pembroke Road, Framlingham, Woodbridge, Suffolk IP13 9HA* Framlingham (01728) 723214

LOVEJOY, John Geoffrey. b 35. K Coll Lon BD60 AKC60. **d** 61 **p** 62. C Byker St Laur *Newc* 61-64; C Choppington 64-66; C Usworth *Dur* 66-70; Perm to Offic *Carl* 73-77; Algeria 77-78; Australia 79-84 and 86-88; NSM Isla-Deveron *Mor* 85-86; Perm to Offic *S'wark* from 88. *30 Woodside Road, Sutton, Surrey SM1 3SU* 0181-644 4151

LOVELAND, John Michael. b 30. Roch Th Coll 65. **d** 67 **p** 68. C Ashford St Hilda CD *Lon* 67-71; P-in-c Earley St Nic *Ox* 71-76; V 76-79; V Kennington 79-84; V Reading St Mark 84-89; P-in-c Drayton St Pet (Berks) 89-92; rtd 92. *Chantry House, Radley Road, Abingdon, Oxon OX14 3SN*

LOVELESS, Christopher Hugh. b 61. Trin Coll Ox BA84 MA91. Linc Th Coll 89. **d** 91 **p** 92. C Willingdon *Chich* 91-95; C Goring-by-Sea from 95. *19 Angus Road, Goring-by-Sea, Worthing, W Sussex BN12 4BL* Worthing (01903) 241052

LOVELESS, Martin Frank. b 46. Wycliffe Hall Ox 72. **d** 75 **p** 76. C Caversham *Ox* 75-81; V Carterton 81-86; Chapl RAF from 86. *Chaplaincy Services (RAF), HQ, Personnel and Training Command, RAF Innsworth, Gloucester GL3 1EZ* Gloucester (01452) 712612 Ext 5164 Fax 510828

LOVELESS, Robert Alfred. b 43. Birm Univ BA66. Westcott Ho Cam 66. **d** 68 **p** 69. C Kenilworth St Nic *Cov* 68-72; C Costessey *Nor* 73-75; R Colney 75-80; R Lt w Gt Melton, Marlingford and Bawburgh 75-80; V Lt and Gt Melton w Bawburgh 80-82; P-in-c Westwood *Sarum* 82-83; Chapl Stonar Sch Melksham 82-87; P-in-c Wingfield w Rowley *Sarum* 82-83; R Westwood and Wingfield 83-87; R Paston *Pet* 87-93; V Nassington w Yarwell and Woodnewton from 93. *The Vicarage, 34 Station Road, Nassington, Peterborough PE8 6QG* Stamford (01780) 782271

LOVELESS, Canon William Harry. b 21. Lon Univ BSc60. Ridley Hall Cam 61. **d** 63 **p** 64. V Cam St Mark *Ely* 67-87; RD Cam 81-84; Hon Can Ely Cathl 81-87; rtd 87. *103 High Street, Swaffham Bulbeck, Cambridge CB5 0LX*

LOVELL, Charles Nelson. b 34. Or Coll Ox BA57 MA61. Wycliffe Hall Ox. **d** 59 **p** 60. C Walsall St Matt *Lich* 59-63; C St Giles-in-the-Fields *Lon* 63; Argentina 64-67; C Cam H Trin *Ely* 64; V Esh *Dur* 67-75; V Hamsteels 67-75; Chapl Winterton Hosp Sedgefield 75-83; R Stanhope *Dur* 83-86; Chapl Horn Hall Hosp Weardale from 83; R Stanhope w Frosterley *Dur* from 86; V Eastgate w Rookhope from 86; RD Stanhope from 87. *The Rectory, Stanhope, Bishop Auckland, Co Durham DL13 2UE* Weardale (01388) 528308

LOVELL, David John. b 38. JP89. Univ of Tasmania BEcon86. Qu Coll Birm 60. **d** 60 **p** 62. C Glouc St Steph *Glouc* 60-64; C Lower Tuffley St Geo CD 64-67; V Lydbrook 67-73; Australia from 73. *23 Lucas Street, Kingston, Tasmania, Australia 7050* Tasmania (29) 5709

LOVELL, Frederick Arthur. b 07. Chich Th Coll 31. **d** 34 **p** 35. R Combe Martin *Ex* 53-73; rtd 74. *Lynfield House, Middle Warberry Road, Torquay TQ1 1RN* Torquay (01803) 201313

LOVELL, Helen Sarah. *See* HOUSTON, Mrs Helen Sarah

LOVELL, Keith Michael Beard. b 43. K Coll Lon 67. **d** 68 **p** 69. C Romford St Edw *Chelmsf* 68-73; P-in-c Elmstead 73-79; V Tollesbury w Salcot Virley from 79. *The Vicarage, 12 King's Walk, Tollesbury, Maldon, Essex CM9 8XH* Maldon (01621) 869393 or 868441

LOVELL, Laurence John. b 31. St D Coll Lamp BA54 Tyndale Hall Bris 54. **d** 56 **p** 57. V St Keverne *Truro* 63-68; Australia from 68; rtd 95. *1/64 Cambridge Street, Penshurst, NSW, Australia 2222* Sydney (2) 580-7454

LOVELUCK, Allan (Illtyd). b 30. Queensland Univ MSocWork72. St D Coll Lamp BA53 St Mich Coll Llan 53. **d** 55 **p** 56. C Dowlais *Llan* 55-58; SSF 58-79; Lic to Offic *Chelmsf* 62-64; Australia from 64. *230 Buckland Road, Nundah, Queensland, Australia 4812* Brisbane (7) 260-6460

LOVELUCK, Dr Graham David. b 34. CChem FRSC Univ of Wales (Abth) BSc55 PhD58. St Deiniol's Hawarden 77. **d** 78 **p** 79. Hon C Llanfair Mathafarn Eithaf w Llanbedrgoch Ban 78-87; Hon C Llaneugrad w Llanallgo and Penrhosllugwy etc 87-93; C 93-94; C Twrcelyn from 95. *Gwenallt, Marianglas, Gwynedd LL73 8PE* Tyn-y-Gongl (01248) 853741

LOVELY, Leslie Walter. b 09. Dur Univ LTh32. **d** 32 **p** 33. C Southn St Alb *Win* 32-35; Egypt 35-43; S Africa from 43. *158 Darrenwood Village, Private Bag X5, Linden, 2014 South Africa* Johannesburg (11) 678-7303

LOVERIDGE, Douglas Henry. b 52. Sarum & Wells Th Coll. **d** 84 **p** 85. C Earley St Pet *Ox* 84-88; V Hurst from 88. *The Vicarage, Church Hill, Hurst, Reading RG10 0SJ* Twyford (01734) 340017

LOVERING, Mrs Jennifer Mary (Jen). b 39. Eastbourne Tr Coll CertEd59. Wycliffe Hall Ox 81. **dss** 84 **d** 87 **p** 94. Abingdon w Shippon *Ox* 84-87; Par Dn Abingdon 87-94; C from 94. *39 The Mote, Abingdon, Oxon OX14 3NZ* Abingdon (01235) 521371

LOVERING, Martin. b 35. Imp Coll Lon BScEng57 DMS66. Wycliffe Hall Ox 82. **d** 84 **p** 85. NSM Abingdon w Shippon *Ox* 84-88; C Abingdon 88-89; TV from 89. *39 The Mote, Abingdon, Oxon OX14 3NZ* Abingdon (01235) 521371

LOVETT, Francis Roland. b 25. Glouc Th Course. **d** 85 **p** 86. NSM Ludlow *Heref* 85-91; rtd 92. *7 Poyner Road, Ludlow, Shropshire SY8 1QT* Ludlow (01584) 872871

LOVETT, Ian Arthur. b 43. NE Lon Poly BSc74 Ox Poly DipTP78. Linc Th Coll 85. **d** 87 **p** 88. C Uppingham w Ayston and Wardley w Belton *Pet* 87-91; R Polebrook and Lutton w Hemington and Luddington from 91. *The Rectory, Polebrook, Peterborough PE8 5LN* Oundle (01832) 274941

LOVETT, Ian James. b 49. S'wark Ord Course 73. **d** 76 **p** 77. NSM Gravesend St Geo *Roch* 76-77; NSM Willesborough w Hinxhill *Cant* 77-83; Perm to Offic *Ex* 83-85; C Compton Gifford 85; C Plymouth Em w Efford 85-86; TV 86-92; TV Plymouth Em, Efford and Laira from 93. *28A Sefton Avenue, Lipson, Plymouth PL4 7HB* Plymouth (01752) 663484

LOVEWELL, Robert Antony. b 34. Lich Th Coll. **d** 62 **p** 63. C Endcliffe *Sheff* 62-65; Miss to Seamen 65-79; Portuguese E Africa 65-73; V Wilton *York* 73-79; TV Thornaby on Tees 79-81; Ind Chapl *Ex* from 81. *65 Easterdown Close, Plymstock, Plymouth PL9 8SR* Plymouth (01752) 552323 or 402103

LOVITT, Gerald Elliott. b 25. St Mich Coll Llan 59. **d** 61 **p** 62. C Whitchurch *Llan* 66-71; V Grangetown 71-76; V Rockfield and Llangattock w St Maughan's *Mon* 76-83; V Rockfield and St Maughen's w Llangattock etc 83-93; rtd 93. *78 Ninian Road, Penylan, Cardiff CF2 5EN*

LOW, Dr Alastair Graham. b 43. Brunel Univ BSc68 Reading Univ PhD74. Ripon Coll Cuddesdon 90. **d** 92 **p** 93. C Brighton Gd Shep Preston *Chich* from 92. *56 Reigate Road, Brighton BN1 5AH* Brighton (01273) 889419

LOW, David Anthony. b 42. AKC66. **d** 67 **p** 68. C Gillingham St Barn *Roch* 67-70; V 82-88; C Wallingford *Ox* 70-73; V Spencer's Wood 73-82; P-in-c Grazeley and Beech Hill 77-82; Chapl Medway Hosp Gillingham 86-88; V Hoo St Werburgh *Roch* from 88. *The Vicarage, Hoo, Rochester, Kent ME3 9BB* Medway (01634) 250291

LOW, David John. b 32. Bris Univ BA53. Wells Th Coll 55. **d** 57 **p** 58. C Bradf Ch Ch *Man* 57-59; C Benchill 59-62; V Newbold 62-75; R Moston St Mary from 75. *St Mary's Rectory, 47 Nuthurst Road, Moston, Manchester M10 0EW* 0161-681 1201

LOW, David Michael. b 39. Cape Town Univ BA60. Cuddesdon Coll 61. **d** 63 **p** 64. C Portsea St Cuth *Portsm* 63-65; S Africa 65-69; C Havant *Portsm* 69-72; V St Helens 72-88; P-in-c Sea View 80-81; V 81-88; V Sandown Ch Ch from 88. *The Vicarage, 26 Nunwell Street, Sandown, Isle of Wight PO36 9DE* Isle of Wight (01983) 402548

LOW, Peter James. b 52. Nottm Univ BTh89. Linc Th Coll 86. **d** 89 **p** 90. C Dartford H Trin *Roch* 89-92; C Plympton St Mary *Ex* 92-94; TR Devonport St Boniface and St Phil from 94. *St Boniface Vicarage, 1 Normandy Way, Plymouth PL5 1SW* Plymouth (01752) 361137

LOW, Stafford. b 42. N Lon Poly BSc65. Trin Coll Bris 82. **d** 85 **p** 86. C Yeovil *B & W* 85-88; C Glastonbury w Meare, W Pennard and Godney 88-92; R Berrow and Breane from 92. *The Rectory, 1 Manor Way, Coast Road, Berrow, Burnham-on-Sea, Somerset TA8 2RG* Greendown (01278) 751744

LOW, Terence John Gordon (Terry). b 37. Oak Hill Th Coll 75. **d** 77 **p** 78. C Kensal Rise St Martin *Lon* 77-79; C Longfleet *Sarum* 79-83; P-in-c Maiden Newton and Valleys 83-84; TV Melbury 84-88; TV Buckhurst Hill *Chelmsf* 88-92; R Gt Hallingbury and Lt Hallingbury from 92. *The Rectory, Wright's Green Lane, Little Hallingbury, Bishop's Stortford, Herts CM22 7RE* Bishop's Stortford (01279) 723341

LOW, William Roberson (Robbie). b 50. MFFS Pemb Coll Cam BA73 MA77. Westcott Ho Cam 76. **d** 79 **p** 80. FFS from 78; C Poplar *Lon* 79-83; Chapl St Alb Abbey *St Alb* 83-88; V Bushey Heath from 88. *St Peter's Vicarage, 19 High Road, Bushey Heath, Watford WD2 1EA* 0181-950 1424 Fax 950 1547

LOWATER, Mrs Jennifer Blanche (Jenny). b 34. Eastbourne Tr Coll TCert54. Sarum & Wells Th Coll 82. **dss** 85 **d** 87 **p** 94. Locks Heath *Portsm* 85-87; Hon C 87-88; NSM Southsea St Pet 88-94; Asst Dir of Ords from 91; NSM Hook w Warsash from 94. *Lower Gubbles, Hook Lane, Warsash, Southampton SO3 9HH* Locks Heath (01489) 572156

LOWCOCK, Brian Walter. b 23. Man Univ LLB43. Linc Th Coll 56. **d** 57 **p** 58. Perm to Offic *Linc* 68-73; Lic to Offic *Ely* 70-74; P-in-c Holbeach Marsh *Linc* 74-81; P-in-c Witham on the Hill 81; P-in-c Edenham 81; V Edenham w Witham-on-the-Hill 82-85; rtd 85; Perm to Offic *Ely* from 86. *2 The Chase, Ely, Cambs CB6 3DS* Ely (01353) 667641

LOWE, Miss Alison Margaret. b 56. Linc Th Coll. **dss** 84 **d** 89. Knottingley *Wakef* 84-86; Par Educn Adv 86-90; Par Dn Edin Ch Ch *Edin* 90-91. *10 Heath Park Place, Selkirk TD7 4DN*

LOWE, Anthony Richard (Tony). b 45. York Univ BA66 Birm Univ DipTh68. Qu Coll Birm 66. **d** 69 **p** 70. C Greasbrough *Sheff* 69-71; C Thrybergh 71-75; P-in-c Sheff St Mary w St Simon w St Matthias 75-78; V Shiregreen St Hilda 78-85; V Hoxne w Denham St Jo and Syleham *St E* 85-89; P-in-c Wingfield 86-89; R Hoxne w Denham, Syleham and Wingfield from 90. *The Vicarage, Church Hill, Hoxne, Eye, Suffolk IP21 5AT* Hoxne (01379) 75246

LOWE, Mrs Brenda June. b 53. Cranmer Hall Dur 75. **d** 88 **p** 94. Chapl to Families Trin Coll and Mortimer Ho Bris 88-91; NSM Marple All SS *Ches* from 91. *The Vicarage, 155 Church Lane, Marple, Stockport, Cheshire SK6 7LD* 0161-449 0950 or 427 2378

LOWE, David Charles. b 43. Kelham Th Coll 62. **d** 67 **p** 68. C Wingerworth *Derby* 67-70; C Greenhill St Pet 70-73; TV Eckington 73-74; TV Eckington w Handley and Ridgeway 74-78; V Bury St Edmunds St Geo *St E* 78-86; V Leiston from 86; RD Saxmundham from 88. *St Margaret's Vicarage, 2 King Edward Road, Leiston, Suffolk IP16 4HQ* Leiston (01728) 831059

LOWE, David Reginald. b 42. K Coll Lon BD65 AKC65. St Boniface Warminster 65. **d** 66 **p** 67. C Tupsley *Heref* 66-69; C Lewes St Anne *Chich* 69-73; C Heref H Trin *Heref* 73-77; P-in-c Lyonshall w Titley 77-88; V Lyonshall w Titley, Almeley and Kinnersley from 88. *The Vicarage, Lyonshall, Kington, Herefordshire HR5 3LN* Lyonshall (01544) 340212

LOWE, Derrick. b 34. Codrington Coll Barbados 58. **d** 60 **p** 61. Br Guiana 60-64; R Kirkwall *Ab* 65-69; R Ardwick St Benedict *Man* 69-95. *36 Oak Drive, Denton Tameside, Manchester M34 2JS*

LOWE, Donald. b 33. Lich Th Coll 57. **d** 60 **p** 61. S Africa 73-81; V Gannow *Blackb* 70-73; V Colne H Trin 81-89; TV Melbury *Sarum* 89-94; RD Beaminster 93-94; rtd 94. *28 High Bank, Threshfield, Skipton, N Yorkshire BD23 5BU* Skipton (01756) 752346

LOWE, Canon Eric. b 29. Trin Coll Ox BA50 MA54. St Steph Ho Ox 50. **d** 52 **p** 53. Lic to Offic *Ches* 65-88; Lic to Offic *Ban* 65-88; Area Sec (Dios Ches, Ban and St As) USPG 65-88; (Dio Liv) 73-85; Perm to Offic *Liv* 73-88; V Frodsham *Ches* 88-95; Can Ndola (Zambia) from 88; rtd 95. *55 Wetherby Way, Little Sutton, South Wirral L66 4TB* 0151-339 1648

LOWE, Canon John Bethel. b 30. TCD BA52 BD65. Ridley Hall Cam 55. **d** 55 **p** 56. C Belf St Mary Magd *Conn* 55-57; Sudan 59-64; Uganda 64-74; Warden CMS Fellowship Ho Foxbury 74-76; V Kippington *Roch* from 76; Dioc Dir of Ords from 82; Hon Can Roch Cathl from 85. *The Vicarage, 59 Kippington Road, Sevenoaks, Kent TN13 2LL* Sevenoaks (01732) 452112

LOWE, John Forrester. b 39. Nottm Univ BA61. Lich Th Coll 61. **d** 64 **p** 65. C N Woolwich *Chelmsf* 64-70; V Marks Gate 70-74; V Moulsham St Jo 74-79; V N Woolwich w Silvertown 79-82; V Birm St Pet *Birm* 82-86; Gen Sec SOMA 86-91; V Heckmondwike *Wakef* from 92. *The Vicarage, Church Street, Heckmondwike, W Yorkshire WF16 0AX* Heckmondwike (01924) 405881

LOWE, Keith Gregory. b 50. Sarum & Wells Th Coll DCM93. **d** 93 **p** 94. C Wallasey St Hilary *Ches* 93-94; C W Kirby St Bridget from 94. *13 Caldy Road, West Kirby, Wirral, Merseyside L48 2HE* 0151-625 2731

LOWE, Michael Arthur (Mike). b 46. Lon Univ BD67 Hull Univ MA85. Cranmer Hall Dur DipTh75. **d** 76 **p** 77. C Thorpe Edge *Bradf* 76-79; C N Ferriby *York* 79-84; TV 84-86; Dir Past Studies Trin Coll Bris 86-91; V Marple All SS *Ches* from 91. *The Vicarage, 155 Church Lane, Marple, Stockport, Cheshire SK6 7LD* 0161-449 0950 or 427 2378

LOWE, Michael Sinclair. b 35. Open Univ BA75. AKC61. **d** 62 **p** 63. C Wythenshawe Wm Temple Ch CD *Man* 62-66; V Facit 66-70; V Bath St Barn w Englishcombe *B & W* 70-79; V Bathford 79-86; V Branksome Park All SS *Sarum* 86-95; C Christchurch *Win* from 95. *All Saints House, 22 Kestrel Drive, Christchurch, Dorset BH23 4DE* Highcliffe (01425) 276267

LOWE, Raymond John. b 12. OBE67. St Edm Hall Ox BA34 MA38. Sarum Th Coll 34. **d** 36 **p** 37. R Padworth *Ox* 70-77; V Mortimer W End 70-77; rtd 77; Perm to Offic *Ox* 77-93. *Flat 11, Stuart Court, Kibworth Beauchamp, Leics LE8 0LE* Leicester (0116) 279 2508

LOWE, Canon Reginald Kenneth William. b 09. TCD BA31. **d** 32 **p** 33. I Blessington *D & G* 65-79; Treas Ch Ch Cathl Dub 74-79; rtd 79. *Glenbride Cottage, Kilpedder, Co Wicklow, Irish Republic* Dublin (1) 281-9211

LOWE, Canon Richard (Christopher). b 23. Birm Univ BSc44. Coll of Resurr Mirfield 46. **d** 48 **p** 49. Lic to Offic *Wakef* from 86; CR from 67; Lic to Offic *Lon* 69-93; Master R Foundn of St Kath in Ratcliffe 82-92; Warden Community of St Denys Warminster 83-87; rtd 93. *House of the Resurrection, Mirfield, W Yorkshire WF14 0BN* Mirfield (01924) 494318

LOWE, Samuel (Sam). b 35. St D Coll Lamp. **d** 65 **p** 66. C Tenby w Gumfreston *St D* 65-67; C Lower Mitton *Worc* 67-69; C Halesowen 69-72; R Droitwich St Nic w St Pet 72-73; TV Droitwich 73-77; P-in-c Claines St Geo 77-78; P-in-c Worc St Mary the Tything 77-78; P-in-c Worc St Geo w St Mary Magd 78-84; V from 84. *St George's Vicarage, Worcester WR1 1HX* Worcester (01905) 22698

LOWE, Stephen Arthur. b 49. Nottm Univ BSc71 DipTh. Cuddesdon Coll 71. **d** 74 **p** 75. C Mansf St Mark *S'well* 74-77; Papua New Guinea 77-79; V Kirkby Woodhouse *S'well* 80-86; V Beeston from 86. *The Vicarage, Middle Street, Beeston, Nottingham NG9 1GA* Nottingham (0115) 925 4571

LOWE, Ven Stephen Richard. b 44. Lon Univ BSc66. Ripon Hall Ox 68. **d** 68 **p** 69. C Gospel Lane St Mich *Birm* 68-72; C-in-c Woodgate Valley CD 72-75; V E Ham w Upton Park *Chelmsf* 75-76; TR E Ham w Upton Park St Alb 76-88; Hon Can Chelmsf Cathl 85-88; Adn Sheff from 88. *23 Hill Turretts Close, Sheffield S11 9RE* Sheffield (0114) 235 0191 Fax 235 2275

LOWELL, Ian Russell. b 53. AKC75. St Aug Coll Cant 75. **d** 76 **p** 77. C Llwynderw *S & B* 76-79; C Swansea St Mary w H Trin and St Mark 79-81; Chapl Ox Hosps 81-83; TV Gt and Lt Coates w Bradley *Linc* 83-88; V Wellingborough St Mark *Pet* from 88; Chapl Northants Ambulance Service from 92. *St Mark's Vicarage, Queensway, Wellingborough, Northants NN8 3SD* Wellingborough (01933) 673893

LOWEN, David John. b 42. Sussex Univ BSc74 Univ of Wales (Lamp) MA84. Llan Dioc Tr Scheme 86. **d** 88 **p** 89. C Carmarthen St Pet *St D* 88-90; P-in-c Walwyn's Castle w Robeston W 90-92; R from 92. *The Rectory, Walwyn's Castle, Haverfordwest, Dyfed SA26 3ED* Haverfordwest (01437) 781257

LOWEN, John Michael. b 47. Nottm Univ BTh77. Linc Th Coll 73. **d** 77 **p** 78. C Stapleford *S'well* 77-80; C Stratford-on-Avon w Bishopton *Cov* 80-82; V Monkseaton St Mary *Newc* 82-90; V Ponteland 90-95; Chapl HM Pris Leeds from 95. *HM Prison, Armley, Leeds LS12 2TJ* Leeds (0113) 263 6411 Fax 790151

LOWERSON, John Ridley. b 41. FR HistS83 Leeds Univ BA62 MA65. S Dios Minl Tr Scheme 85. **d** 88 **p** 89. NSM Ringmer *Chich* from 88. *9 Bradford Road, Lewes, E Sussex BN7 9RB* Brighton (01273) 473413

LOWLES, Martin John. b 48. Thames Poly BSc72. St Jo Coll Dur DipTh78. **d** 78 **p** 79. C Leyton St Mary w St Edw *Chelmsf* 78-81; C Waltham Abbey 81-85; V E Ham St Paul 85-95; Asst AD Newham 91-95; TR N Huddersfield *Wakef* from 95. *The Vicarage, 75 St John's Road, Huddersfield HD1 5EA* Huddersfield (01484) 427071

LOWMAN, Canon David Walter. b 48. K Coll Lon BD73 AKC73. St Aug Coll Cant 73. **d** 75 **p** 76. C Notting Hill *Lon* 75-78; C Kilburn St Aug w St Jo 78-81; Selection Sec and Voc Adv ACCM 81-86; TR Wickford and Runwell *Chelmsf* 86-93; Dioc Dir of Ords from 93; C Chelmsf All SS from 93; C Chelmsf Ascension from 93; Hon Can Chelmsf Cathl from 93. *25 Roxwell Road, Chelmsford CM1 2LY* Chelmsford (01245) 264187 Fax 348789

LOWNDES, Charles. b 22. MISW57 CQSW72 Rotherham Poly DDW57. **d** 87 **p** 88. NSM Hanley H Ev *Lich* from 87. *7 Beacon Rise, Stone, Staffs ST15 0AL* Stone (01785) 812698

LOWNDES, Richard Owen Lewis. b 63. Univ of Wales (Ban) BD86. Coll of Resurr Mirfield 87. **d** 89 **p** 90. C Milford Haven *St D* 89-91; C Roath St German *Llan* 91-94; Chapl Cardiff R Infirmary 91-94; V Tylorstown w Ynyshir from 94. *The Vicarage, Craig Road, Ynyshir, Porth, M Glam CF39 0NS* Porth (01443) 684149

LOWRIE, Robert Colledge. b 33. Leeds Univ DipTh57. Chich Th Coll 68. **d** 69 **p** 70. C Sidmouth St Nic *Ex* 69-73; C Sidmouth, Woolbrook and Salcombe Regis 73-74; V W Hill 74-81; RD Ottery 77-82; TR Sidmouth, Woolbrook and Salcombe Regis 81-86; V Redlynch and Morgan's Vale *Sarum* from 86. *The Vicarage, Redlynch, Salisbury SP5 2PE* Downton (01725) 510439

LOWRIE, Ronald Malcolm (Ron). b 48. Ripon Hall Ox 70. **d** 72 **p** 73. C Knowle *Birm* 72-75; C Bourton-on-the-Water w Clapton *Glouc* 75-79; R Broadwell, Evenlode, Oddington and Adlestrop 79-81; TV Trowbridge H Trin *Sarum* 81-88; P-in-c Westwood and Wingfield 88-90; R from 90; Chapl Westwood Hosp Bradf from 88. *The Rectory, Westwood, Bradford-on-Avon, Wilts BA15 2AF* Bradford-on-Avon (01225) 863109

LOWRY, Canon Christopher Somerset. TCD BA47 MA65. **d** 47 **p** 48. I Grange *Arm* 52-80; Chapl St Luke's Mental Hosp Arm 56-91; RD Tynan 71-91; Can Arm Cathl from 79; Treas 86-88; Prec 88-91; I Loughgall w Grange 80-91; rtd 91. *Fairlow, 10 Mellifont Drive, Armagh BT61 9ES* Armagh (01861) 527704

LOWRY, Canon Robert Harold. b 19. TCD BA44 MA49. CITC 44. **d** 44 **p** 45. I Willowfield *D & D* 62-75; RD Hillsborough 70-75; I Lambeg *Conn* 75-89; Can Conn Cathl from 82; rtd 90; Lic to Offic *D & D* from 90. *2 Winchester Drive, Carryduff, Belfast BT8 8QD* Belfast (01232) 813927

LOWRY, Stephen Harold. QUB BSc CertEd TCD DipTh. **d** 85 **p** 86. C Coleraine *Conn* 85-88; Bp's Dom Chapl from 87; I Greenisland from 88. *The Rectory, 4 Tinamara, Upper Station Road, Greenisland, Carrickfergus, Co Antrim BT38 8FE* Whiteabbey (01232) 863421

LOWSON, Christopher. b 53. AKC75. Berkeley Div Sch STM78 St Aug Coll Cant 76. **d** 77 **p** 78. C Richmond St Mary *S'wark* 77-79; C Richmond St Mary w St Matthias and St Jo 79-82; P-in-c Eltham H Trin 82-83; V 83-91; V Petersfield *Portsm* from 91; R Buriton from 91. *The Vicarage, Shackleford House, 12 Dragon Street, Petersfield, Hants GU31 1AB* Petersfield (01730) 264138

LOWTON, Nicholas Gerard. b 53. St Jo Coll Ox BA76. Glouc Sch of Min 86. **d** 89 **p** 90. Chapl Cheltenham Coll from 89; NSM Prestbury *Glouc* 89-94. *Hazelwell, College Road, Cheltenham, Glos GL53 7JD* Cheltenham (01242) 522665

LOXHAM, Geoffrey Richard. b 40. Hull Univ BA62. Cranmer Hall Dur. **d** 65 **p** 66. C Darwen St Barn *Blackb* 65-68; C Leyland St Andr 68-72; V Preston St Mark 72-79; V Edgeside *Man* 79-91; P-in-c Withnell *Blackb* 91; P-in-c Heapey St Barnabas and Withnell St Paul 91-92; V from 92. *1 Balmoral Drive, Brinscall, Chorley, Lancs PR6 8ST* Brinscall (01254) 832017

LOXLEY, Harold. b 43. N Ord Course 79. **d** 82 **p** 83. NSM Sheff Parson Cross St Cecilia *Sheff* 82-87; C Gleadless 87-90; V Sheff St Cath Richmond Road from 90. *St Catherine's Vicarage, 300 Hastilar Road South, Sheffield S13 8EJ* Sheffield (0114) 239 9598

LOXLEY, Ronald Alan Keith. b 26. St Jo Coll Ox BA51 MA55. Wm Temple Coll Rugby 66 Cuddesdon Coll 67. **d** 68 **p** 69. C Swindon Ch Ch *Bris* 68-71; Ind Chapl *Lon* 71-83; Ind Chapl *Chelmsf* 83-92; P-in-c Theydon Garnon 83-92; rtd 92; Perm to Offic *Linc* from 92. *15 Wainwell Mews, Winnowsty Lane, Lincoln LN2 4BF* Lincoln (01522) 511738

LOXTON, John Sherwood. b 29. Bris Univ BSc50 Birm Univ BA53. Handsworth Coll Birm 50 Chich Th Coll 80. **d** 80 **p** 81. In Meth Ch 50-80; C Haywards Heath St Wilfrid *Chich* 80-82; TV 82-89; V Turners Hill from 89. *The Vicarage, Turners Hill, Crawley, W Sussex RH10 4PB* Copthorne (01342) 715278

LUBBOCK, David John. b 34. S'wark Ord Course. **d** 87 **p** 88. NSM Tulse Hill H Trin and St Matthias *S'wark* from 87. *78 Claverdale Road, London SW2 2DL* 0181-674 6146

LUBKOWSKI, Richard Jan. b 51. Westmr Coll Ox BEd75 Warw Univ MA79. St Jo Coll Dur 86. **d** 88 **p** 89. C Duston *Pet* 88-90; C Hellesdon *Nor* 90-91; Perm to Offic *Sheff* from 91. *22 Almond Tree Avenue, Carlton, Goole, N Humberside DN14 9QQ* Goole (01405) 862558

LUCAS, Anthony Stanley. b 41. Man Univ BA62. Qu Coll Birm 63. **d** 65 **p** 66. C N Hammersmith St Kath *Lon* 65-69; C W Wimbledon Ch Ch *S'wark* 69-74; C Caterham 74-78; P-in-c Stockwell St Mich 78-86; V 86-91; P-in-c S'wark St Geo 91; R S'wark St Geo the Martyr w St Jude 91-94; P-in-c S'wark St Alpheage 92-94; R S'wark St Geo the Martyr w St Alpheage & St Jude from 95. *St George's Rectory, Manciple Street, London SE1 4LW* 0171-407 2796

LUCAS, Arthur Edgar. b 24. Clifton Th Coll 60. **d** 62 **p** 63. V Willoughby-on-the-Wolds w Wysall *S'well* 66-74; P-in-c Widmerpool 71-74; R Collyhurst *Man* 75-80; V Heapey *Blackb* 80-91; rtd 91. *18 Parkway, Standish, Wigan, Lancs WN6 0SJ*

LUCAS, Ven Brian Humphrey. b 40. CB93. FRSA93 Univ of Wales (Lamp) BA62. St Steph Ho Ox 62. **d** 64 **p** 65. C Neath w Llantwit *Llan* 67-70; Chapl RAF 70-87; Asst Chapl-in-Chief RAF 87-91; Chapl-in-Chief RAF 91-95; QHC from 88; Perm to Offic *Llan* from 88; Can and Preb Linc Cathl *Linc* from 91; rtd 95. *Pen-y-Coed, 6 Arnhem Drive, Caythorpe, Grantham, Lincs NG32 3DQ* Loveden (01400) 272085

LUCAS, Mrs Janet Rosemary. b 46. Open Univ BA76. S Dios Minl Tr Scheme 84. **dss** 86 **d** 87 **p** 94. N Wembley St Cuth *Lon* 86-87; Par Dn 87-88; Par Dn Northolt W End St Jos 88-90; Asst Chapl Ealing Gen Hosp from 90; Par Dn Hanwell St Mary 90-91; Par Dn Hanwell St Chris 90-91; Par Dn Hanwell St Mary w St Chris 91-94; C from 94. *117 Wood End Lane, Northolt, Middx UB5 4JP* 0181-422 4543

LUCAS, John Maxwell. b 34. TD85. Cranmer Hall Dur 59. **d** 62 **p** 63. V Blackb St Aid *Blackb* 68-72; V Sparkhill St Jo *Birm* 72-78; CF (TAVR) from 73; V Edgbaston St Aug *Birm* 78-85; V Slyne w Hest *Blackb* 85-89; Chapl HM Young Offender Inst Stoke Heath 89-93; rtd 93. *2 Glendon Close, Market Drayton, Shropshire TF9 1NX* Market Drayton (01630) 652977

LUCAS, Canon John Arthur. b 07. Keble Coll Ox BA29 MA45. Cuddesdon Coll 29. **d** 33 **p** 34. V Ox St Thos *Ox* 47-74; P-in-c 74-79; Hon Can Ch Ch 70-85; rtd 74; Hon C Ox St Mary V w St Cross and St Pet *Ox* 78-85; Perm to Offic from 85. *12 Lucas Place, Iffley, Oxford OX4 4HA* Oxford (01865) 774508

LUCAS, Kenneth Ashley. b 18. Wells Th Coll 68. d 69 p 70. C Rye *Chich* 69-73; C Rye w Rye Harbour and Playden 73; R W Chiltington 74-83; rtd 83; Perm to Offic *Chich* from 83. *12 Delves House West, Delves Close, Ringmer, Lewes, E Sussex BN8 5JW* Ringmer (01273) 813150

LUCAS, Mark Wesley. b 62. Man Univ BSc83. Oak Hill Th Coll BA94. d 94 p 95. C Harold Wood *Chelmsf* from 94. *8 Archibald Road, Harold Wood, Romford RM3 0RH*

LUCAS, Canon Paul de Neufville. b 33. Ch Ch Ox BA59 MA59 Cam Univ MA63. Cuddesdon Coll 57. d 59 p 60. C Westmr St Steph w St Jo *Lon* 59-63; Chapl Trin Hall Cam 63-69; V Greenside *Dur* 69-73; Chapl Shrewsbury Sch 73-77; V Batheaston w St Cath *B & W* 78-88; Preb Wells Cathl 87-88; Can Res and Prec from 88. *4 The Liberty, Wells, Somerset BA5 2SU* Wells (01749) 673188

LUCAS, Peter Stanley. b 21. Sarum Th Coll 48. d 50 p 51. C Gillingham *Sarum* 50-53; Min Heald Green St Cath CD *Ches* 53-58; V Heald Green St Cath 58-62; V Egremont St Jo 62-65; Canada from 66. *Apt 404, 1241 Fairfield Road, Victoria, British Columbia, Canada, V8V 3B3*

LUCAS, Raymond Charles Henry. b 15. ALCD41. d 41 p 42. R Branston *Linc* 61-76; R Parkham, Alwington and Buckland Brewer *Ex* 76-79; rtd 80. *3 Walnut Court, Walnut Road, Chelston, Torquay TQ2 6HS* Torquay (01803) 606703

LUCAS, Preb Richard Charles (Dick). b 25. Trin Coll Cam BA49 MA57. Ridley Hall Cam. d 51 p 52. C Sevenoaks St Nic *Roch* 51-55; Cand Sec CPAS 55-61; Asst Sec 61-67; R St Helen Bishopsgate w St Martin Outwich *Lon* 61-80; P-in-c St Andr Undershaft w St Mary Axe 77-80; R St Helen Bishopsgate w St Andr Undershaft etc from 80; Preb St Paul's Cathl from 85. *The Rectory, 33 Great St Helen's, London EC3A 6AT* 0171-283 2231 Fax 626 0911

LUCAS, Ronald James. b 38. St Aid Birkenhead 64. d 67 p 68. C Swindon Ch Ch *Bris* 67-71; C Knowle St Martin 71-74; V Swindon St Jo 74-77; TR Swindon St Jo and St Andr 77-81; R Wroughton 81-83; TV Liskeard w St Keyne, St Pinnock and Morval *Truro* 83-87; R St Ive w Quethiock 87-91; R St Ive and Pensilva w Quethiock from 91. *The Rectory, St Ive, Liskeard, Cornwall PL14 3LX* Liskeard (01579) 382327

LUCAS, Mrs Vivienne Kathleen. b 44. Sarum & Wells Th Coll 84. d 87 p 94. Chapl Asst W Middx Univ Hosp Isleworth 87-92; Par Dn Whitton St Aug *Lon* 87-94; C Isleworth St Jo from 94. *224 High Street, Feltham, Middx TW13 4HX* 0181-890 4482

LUCAS, William Wallace. b 29. Sarum Th Coll 56. d 59 p 60. V Norton St Mich *Dur* 63-81; R Broseley w Benthall *Heref* 81-93; P-in-c Jackfield 81-93; P-in-c Linley w Willey and Barrow 81-93; rtd 93. *105 Side Cliff Road, Sunderland SR6 9JR* 0191-549 1573

LUCK, Benjamin Paul. b 53. BD. St Mich Coll Llan 80. d 83 p 84. C Blakenall Heath *Lich* 83-87; C Torpoint *Truro* 87-89; V Tuckingmill from 89. *All Saints' Vicarage, 35 Roskear, Camborne, Cornwall TR14 8DG* Camborne (01209) 712114

LUCKCUCK, Anthony Michael. b 47. Lon Univ BA70. Wycliffe Hall Ox 70. d 77 p 78. C Mansf Woodhouse *S'well* 77-79; C Beeston 79-82; V Harworth 82-85; V Carlton from 85. *St John's Vicarage, 261 Oakdale Road, Nottingham NG4 1BP* Nottingham (0115) 987 4882

LUCKRAFT, Christopher John. b 50. K Coll Lon BD80 AKC80. Ripon Coll Cuddesdon. d 81 p 82. C Sherborne w Castleton and Lillington *Sarum* 81-84; Bermuda 84-87; Chapl RN from 87. *Directorate Gen, RN Chapl Services, Room 203, Victory Building, HM Naval Base, Portsmouth PO1 3LS* Portsmouth (01705) 727903 Fax 727112

LUDLOW, Canon Arthur Percival. b 26. Chich Th Coll 48. d 51 p 52. C Manston *Ripon* 51-54; C Seacroft 54-58; V Stanground *Ely* 58-72; R Somersham w Pidley and Oldhurst 72-88; P-in-c Gt w Lt Stukeley from 88; Chapl Hinchingbrooke Hosp from 88; Hon Can Ely Cathl *Ely* from 89. *The Rectory, Great Stukeley, Huntingdon, Cambs PE17 5AL* Huntingdon (01480) 453016

LUDLOW, Christopher George. b 18. AKC42. d 42 p 43. Chapl K Alfred Coll *Win* 57-70; Prin Lect Relig Studies 57-76; rtd 83. *23 Penair View, Truro, Cornwall TR1 1XR* Truro (01872) 41898

LUDLOW, Archdeacon of. See SAXBEE, Rt Rev John Charles

LUDLOW, Suffragan Bishop of. See SAXBEE, Rt Rev John Charles

LUFF, Canon Alan Harold Frank. b 28. ARCM77 Univ Coll Ox DipTh52 MA54. Westcott Ho Cam 54. d 56 p 57. C Stretford St Matt *Man* 56-59; C Swinton St Pet 59-61; Prec Man Cathl 61-68; V Dwygyfylchi (or Penmaenmawr) *Ban* 68-79; Prec and Sacr Westmr Abbey 79-86; Prec 86-92; Can Res Birm Cathl *Birm* from 92. *119 Selly Park Road, Birmingham B29 7HY* 0121-472 0146 or 236 4333

LUFF, Mrs Caroline Margaret Synia. b 44. St Hild Coll Dur BA65 Bris Univ CertEd66. SW Minl Tr Course 87. d 90 p 94. Par Dn Teignmouth, Ideford w Luton, Ashcombe etc *Ex* from 90. *The Rectory, 30 Dawlish Road, Teignmouth, Devon TQ14 8TG* Teignmouth (01626) 774495

LUFF, Philip Garth. b 42. St Chad's Coll Dur BA63 DipTh64. d 65 p 66. C Sidmouth St Nic *Ex* 65-69; C Plymstock 69-71; Asst Chapl Worksop Coll Notts 71-74; V Gainsborough St Jo *Linc* 74-80; V E Teignmouth *Ex* 80-89; P-in-c W Teignmouth 85-89; TR Teignmouth, Ideford w Luton, Ashcombe etc from 90. *The Rectory, 30 Dawlish Road, Teignmouth, Devon TQ14 8TG* Teignmouth (01626) 774495

LUGG, Donald Arthur. b 31. St Aid Birkenhead 56. d 59 p 60. Iran 67-73; V Cliftonville *Cant* 74-94; rtd 94; Reculver *Cant* from 94. *Redcroft, Vulcan Close, Whitstable, Kent CT9 1DF* Whitstable (01227) 770434

LUGG, Stuart John. b 26. Glouc Th Course 74. d 76 p 77. NSM Fairford *Glouc* 76-79; P-in-c Kempsford w Welford 80-88; Perm to Offic from 88. *Content, Station Road, South Cerney, Cirencester, Glos GL7 5UB* Cirencester (01285) 860498

LUKE, Anthony (Tony). b 58. Down Coll Cam BA81 MA85 Geneva Univ CES84. Ridley Hall Cam 82. d 84 p 85. C Allestree *Derby* 84-87; C Oakham, Hambleton, Egleton, Braunston and Brooke *Pet* 87-88; V Allenton and Shelton Lock *Derby* from 88. *St Edmund's Vicarage, Sinfin Avenue, Allenton, Derby DE24 9JA* Derby (01332) 701194

LUMB, David Leslie. b 28. Jes Coll Cam BA52 MA56. Oak Hill Th Coll 52. d 54 p 55. V Handforth *Ches* 60-71; V Plymouth St Jude *Ex* 71-87; V Southminster *Chelmsf* 87-93; rtd 93. *13 Glebe Close, Redditch, Worcs B98 0AW* Redditch (01527) 28623

LUMB, Dennis. b 36. Oak Hill Th Coll 77. d 79 p 80. C Penn Fields *Lich* 79-84; P-in-c Tibberton, Kinnersley and Preston Wealdmoors 84-89; R Tibberton w Bolas Magna and Waters Upton 89-91; P-in-c Saltfleetby *Linc* from 91; P-in-c Theddlethorpe from 91. *The Rectory, Main Road, Saltfleetby, Louth, Lincs LN11 7RU* Saltfleetby (01507) 338074

LUMBY, Jonathan Bertram. b 39. Em Coll Cam BA62 MA66 Lon Univ PGCE66. Ripon Hall Ox 62. d 64 p 65. C Moseley St Mary *Birm* 64-65; Asst Master Enfield Gr Sch 66-67; C Hall Green Ascension 67-70; V Melling *Liv* 70-81; P-in-c Milverton w Halse and Fitzhead *B & W* 81-82; R 82-86; P-in-c Gisburn *Bradf* 90-93; Dioc Rural Adv 90-93; P-in-c Easton w Colton and Marlingford *Nor* from 95; Dioc Missr from 95. *Riverside Cottage, Banburgh Road, Marlingford, Norwich NR9 5AG* Norwich (01603) 880197

LUMGAIR, Michael Hugh Crawford. b 43. Lon Univ BD71. Oak Hill Th Coll 66. d 71 p 72. C Chorleywood Ch Ch *St Alb* 71-74; C Prestonville St Luke *Chich* 74-75; C Attenborough *S'well* 75-80; R Tollerton 80-91; V Bexleyheath St Pet *Roch* from 91. *St Peter's Vicarage, 50 Bristow Road, Bexleyheath, Kent DA7 4QA* 0181-303 8713

LUMLEY, William. b 22. TCD BA44 MA49 BD49 QUB PhD77. Edgehill Th Coll Belf 49. d 50 p 51. I Ballybay *Clogh* 66-73; I Derryvullen S w Garvary 73-82; I Killucan w Clonard and Castlelost *M & K* 82-88; rtd 88. *Gallows Hill, 104 Ballyquinn Road, Limavady, Co Londonderry BT49 9EY* Limavady (015047) 66174

LUMMIS, Elizabeth Howieson. See McNAB, Mrs Elizabeth Howieson

LUMSDEN, Frank. b 20. Edin Th Coll 51. d 53 p 54. V Lynesack *Dur* 56-76; R Castle Eden w Monkhesleden 76-86; rtd 86; Perm to Offic *Dur* from 86; Perm to Offic *Ripon* from 90. *Cloud High, Eggleston, Barnard Castle, Co Durham DL12 0AU* Teesdale (01833) 50644

LUMSDON, Keith. b 45. Linc Th Coll 68. d 71 p 72. C S Westoe *Dur* 71-74; C Jarrow St Paul 74-77; TV Jarrow 77-88; V Ferryhill from 88. *St Luke's Vicarage, Church Lane, Ferryhill, Co Durham DL17 8LT* Ferryhill (01740) 651438

LUND, David Peter. b 46. N Ord Course 88. d 91 p 92. C Maghull *Liv* 91-94; V Hindley All SS from 94. *The Vicarage, 192 Atherton Road, Hindley, Wigan, Lancs WN2 3XA* Wigan (01942) 551757

LUND, John Edward. b 48. St Jo Coll Dur 78. d 80 p 81. C Peterlee *Dur* 80-83; C Bishopton w Gt Stainton 83-85; C Redmarshall 83-85; C Grindon and Stillington 83-85; V Hart w Elwick Hall from 85; Hon Chapl Miss to Seamen from 85. *The Vicarage, Hart, Hartlepool, Cleveland TS27 3AP* Hartlepool (01429) 262340

LUNGLEY, Canon John Sydney. b 41. St Pet Coll Ox BA64 MA70. St Steph Ho Ox 64. d 66 p 67. C Burslem St Werburgh *Lich* 66-70; C Codsall 70-73; V Ocker Hill 73-88; RD Wednesbury 84-88; V Kingswinford St Mary 88-93; V Kingswinford St Mary *Worc* from 93; Hon Can Worc Cathl from 94. *The Vicarage, 17 Penzer Street, Kingswinford, W Midlands DY6 7AA* Kingswinford (01384) 273716

LUNN, Brooke Kingsmill. b 32. TCD BA62 MA66. Chich Th Coll 62. d 64 p 65. C Northolt Park St Barn *Lon* 64-66; C N St Pancras All Hallows 66-68; P-in-c Hornsey St Luke 68-79; V Stroud Green H Trin from 79; AD W Haringey 90-95. *The Vicarage, Granville Road, London N4 4EL* 0181-340 2051

LUNN, Christopher James Edward. b 34. AKC58. **d** 59 **p** 60. C Clapham H Trin *S'wark* 59-62; C Cranleigh *Guildf* 63-64; C Ham St Andr *S'wark* 64-66; V Ham St Rich 66-75; V Coulsdon St Andr from 75. *St Andrew's Vicarage, Julien Road, Coulsdon, Surrey CR5 2DN* 0181-660 0398

LUNN, David. b 47. Bris Univ BSc69 Dur Univ BA73 DipTh74. St Jo Coll Dur 71. **d** 74 **p** 75. C Aigburth *Liv* 74-77; C Slough *Ox* 77-81; P-in-c Haversham w Lt Linford 81-84; R Haversham w Lt Linford, Tyringham w Filgrave 84-93; RD Newport 86-92; TR Walton Milton Keynes from 93. *The Rectory, Walton Road, Wavendon, Milton Keynes MK17 8LW* Milton Keynes (01908) 582839

✠**LUNN, Rt Rev David Ramsay.** b 30. K Coll Cam BA53 MA57. Cuddesdon Coll 53. **d** 55 **p** 56 **c** 80. C Sugley *Newc* 55-59; C N Gosforth 59-63; Chapl Linc Th Coll 63-66; Sub-Warden 66-70; V Cullercoats St Geo *Newc* 71-72; TR 72-80; RD Tynemouth 75-80; Bp Sheff from 80. *Bishopscroft, Snaithing Lane, Sheffield S10 3LG* Sheffield (0114) 230 2170 Fax 263 0110

LUNN, Leonard Arthur. b 42. Trin Coll Bris 69. **d** 72 **p** 73. C Walthamstow St Mary w St Steph *Chelmsf* 72-75; V Collier Row St Jas 75-85; V Collier Row St Jas and Havering-atte-Bower 86-87; Sen Chapl St Chris Hospice Sydenham *S'wark* from 87. *St Christopher's Hospice, 51-59 Lawrie Park Road, London SE26 6DZ* 0181-778 9252 or 699 3305 Fax 659 8680

LUNN, Canon William Bell. b 21. Edin Th Coll 47. **d** 50 **p** 51. R Edin St Mark *Edin* 57-75; Can St Mary's Cathl 68-75; R Fochabers *Mor* 75-86; R Aberlour 75-86; Can St Andr Cathl Inverness 79-86; Hon Can from 86; rtd 86. *67 Woodside Drive, Forres, Morayshire IV36 0UF* Forres (01309) 675208

LUNNEY, Canon Henry. b 31. ACIB57. Wycliffe Hall Ox 73. **d** 74 **p** 75. C Ipswich St Aug *St E* 74-77; P-in-c Westerfield w Tuddenham St Martin 77-83; R Westerfield and Tuddenham St Martin w Witnesham from 83; Asst Dioc Chr Stewardship Adv 78-83; Hon Can St E Cathl from 92. *The Rectory, Westerfield, Ipswich IP6 9AG* Ipswich (01473) 251073

LUNNON, Robert Reginald. b 31. K Coll Lon BD55 AKC55. St Boniface Warminster 55. **d** 56 **p** 57. C Maidstone St Mich *Cant* 56-58; C Deal St Leon 58-62; V Sturry 63-68; V Norbury St Steph 68-77; V Orpington All SS *Roch* from 77; RD Orpington from 79. *The Vicarage, 1A Keswick Road, Orpington, Kent BR6 0EU* Orpington (01689) 824624

LUNT, Derek. b 32. St Jo Coll Dur 51. St Aid Birkenhead 55. **d** 57 **p** 58. R Pembridge w Moor Court and Shobdon *Heref* 67-74; Chapl Lucton Sch Herefordshire 71-74; rtd 91; Perm to Offic *Worc* from 93. *The Firs, 243 West Malvern Road, Malvern, Worcs WR14 4BE* Malvern (01684) 573932

LUNT, Dr Margaret Joan. b 44. Leeds Univ MBChA68. Cranmer Hall Dur CTMin91. **d** 94. C Stanford-le-Hope w Mucking *Chelmsf* from 94. *Glebe House, Wharf Road, Stanford-le-Hope, Essex SS17 0BY*

LUNT, Canon Ronald Sowden. b 30. Leeds Univ BA56. Ely Th Coll 56. **d** 58 **p** 59. C Stockport St Thos *Ches* 58-61; C Ellesmere Port 61-65; V Newton in Mottram 65-78; RD Ches 78-95; TR Ches Team from 78; Hon Can Ches Cathl from 82. *The Rectory, 1 Vicar's Lane, Chester CH1 1QX* Chester (01244) 326357

LURIE, Miss Gillian Ruth (Gill). b 42. LRAM62 GNSM63 ACertCM80. Gilmore Ho 68. **dss** 74 **d** 87 **p** 94. Camberwell St Phil and St Mark *S'wark* 74-76; Haddenham *Ely* 76-79; Dioc Lay Min Adv 79-86; Longthorpe *Pet* 79-81; Pet H Spirit Bretton 81-86; Bramley *Ripon* 86-87; C 87-88; TD 88-93; P-in-c Methley w Mickletown from 93. *The Rectory, Church Side, Methley, Leeds LS26 9BJ* Castleford (01977) 515278

LURKINGS, Edward Henry. b 28. AKC53 Lon Univ BSc68 MSc70 PhD81. **d** 54 **p** 55. Ind Chapl *Lon* 62-71; Hon C Luton St Mary *St Alb* 72-84; V Potterspury, Furtho, Yardley Gobion and Cosgrove *Pet* 84-92; rtd 92. *Glasfryn, Abercych, Boncath, Dyfed SA37 0JL* Llechryd (0123987) 576

LURY, Anthony Patrick. b 49. K Coll Lon BD71 AKC71. St Aug Coll Cant 71. **d** 72 **p** 73. C Richmond St Mary *S'wark* 72-76; P-in-c Streatham Hill St Marg 76-81; V Salfords 81-90; V Emscote *Cov* from 90. *All Saints' Vicarage, Vicarage Fields, Warwick CV34 5NJ* Warwick (01926) 492073

LURY, Denys Patrick. b 15. Dur Univ LTh48. Bps' Coll Cheshunt 36. **d** 38 **p** 39. V Maidstone St Mich *Cant* 63-72; Chapl St Monica's Home of Rest Westbury-on-Trym 72-80; rtd 80; Perm to Offic *Bris* from 80. *14 Gerrish Avenue, Bristol BS16 5PN* Bristol (0117) 956 7514

LUSBY, Dennis John. b 27. Brentwood Coll of Educn CertEd70. **d** 93 **p** 94. NSM Grayshott *Guildf* from 93. *Squirrels Dray, Waggoners Way, Grayshott, Hindhead, Surrey GU26 6DX* Hindhead (01428) 604419

LUSCOMBE, John Nickels. b 45. AKC68. **d** 69 **p** 70. C Stoke Newington St Faith, St Matthias and All SS *Lon* 69-74; V

Tottenham St Phil 74-81; Zimbabwe 82-86; V Queensbury All SS *Lon* from 86. *The Vicarage, Waltham Drive, Edgware, Middx HA8 5PQ* 0181-952 4536 or 952 0744

✠**LUSCOMBE, Rt Rev Lawrence Edward (Ted).** b 24. ACA52 FSA80 Dundee Univ LLD87 MPhil91 PhD93. K Coll Lon 63. **d** 63 **p** 64 **c** 75. C Glas St Marg *Glas* 63-66; R Paisley St Barn 66-71; Provost St Paul's Cathl Dundee *Bre* 71-75; R Dundee St Paul 71-75; Bp Bre 75-90; Primus 85-90; OStJ from 85; rtd 90; Perm to Offic *Bre* from 90. *Woodville, Kirkton of Tealing, Dundee DD4 0RD* Tealing (01382) 380331

LUSTED, Jack Andrew. b 58. Sussex Univ BSc79 PGCE81. St Steph Ho Ox 88. **d** 90 **p** 91. C Moulsecoomb *Chich* 90-93; C Southwick from 93. *Church House, 1 Church House Close, Southwick, Brighton BN42 4WQ* Brighton (01273) 594084

LUSTY, Ronald Henry. b 23. Ox NSM Course. **d** 84 **p** 85. NSM Tilehurst St Mary *Ox* 84-88; NSM Reading H Trin from 88. *St Benedict's, 11 Juniper Way, Tilehurst, Reading RG3 6NB* Reading (01734) 428669

LUTHER, Richard Grenville Litton (Dick). b 42. Lon Univ BD64. Tyndale Hall Bris 66. **d** 68 **p** 69. C Preston St Mary *Blackb* 68-70; C Bishopsworth *Bris* 70-71; C Radipole *Sarum* 72-76; TV Radipole and Melcombe Regis 77-90; TR Hampreston from 90. *The Rectory, 9 Pinewood Road, Ferndown, Wimborne, Dorset BH22 9RW* Wimborne (01202) 872084

LUTHER, Stuart Frank. b 26. MIEE60 CEng66 FIEE77 Lon Univ BSc57 Southn Univ BA88. Ripon Hall Ox 66. **d** 69 **p** 70. C Bexhill St Aug *Chich* 69-72; Hon C Romsey *Win* 72-90. *Address temp unknown*

LUTTON, Percy Theodore Bell Boyce. b 24. TCD BA45 MA48. **d** 46 **p** 48. V Wribbenhall *Worc* 61-80; R Castlemorton, Hollybush and Birtsmorton 80-89; rtd 89. *23 Bridgeman Road, Oswestry, Shropshire SY11 2JP* Oswestry (01691) 656425

✠**LUXMOORE, Rt Rev Christopher Charles.** b 26. Trin Coll Cam BA50 MA54. Chich Th Coll 50. **d** 52 **p** 53 **c** 84. C Newc St Jo *Newc* 52-55; C-in-c Newsham St Bede CD 55-57; V Newsham 57-58; Trinidad and Tobago 58-66; V Headingley *Ripon* 67-81; Hon Can Ripon Cathl 80-81; Can Res and Prec Chich Cathl *Chich* 81-84; Bp Bermuda 84-89; Adn Lewes and Hastings *Chich* 89-91; Provost Woodard Corp (S Division) 89-91; rtd 91. *42 Willowbed Drive, Chichester, W Sussex PO19 2JB* Chichester (01243) 784680

LYALL, Canon Graham. b 37. Univ of Wales (Lamp) BA61 Birm Univ DipTh63. Qu Coll Birm 61. **d** 63 **p** 64. C Middlesb Ascension *York* 63-67; C Kidderminster St Mary *Worc* 67-72; V Dudley Holly Hall St Aug 72-79; P-in-c Barbourne 79-81; V 81-93; RD Worc E 83-89; Hon Can Worc Cathl from 85; TR Malvern Link w Cowleigh from 93. *St Matthias' Rectory, 12 Lambourne Avenue, Malvern, Worcs WR14 1NL* Malvern (01684) 573834

LYDDON, David Andrew. b 47. LDSRCSEng70 Lon Univ BDS70. SW Minl Tr Course 90. **d** 93 **p** 94. NSM Tiverton St Pet *Ex* 93-95; NSM Tiverton St Pet w Chevithorne from 95. *Hightrees, 19 Patches Road, Tiverton, Devon EX16 5AH* Tiverton (01884) 257250

LYDON, Mrs Barbara. b 34. Gilmore Ho 64. **dss** 72 **d** 87 **p** 94. Rastrick St Matt *Wakef* 72-85; Upper Hopton 85-87; Par Dn 87; D-in-c Kellington w Whitley 87-94; P-in-c 94-95; rtd 95. *17 Garlick Street, Brighouse, W Yorkshire HD6 3PW* Brighouse (01484) 722704

LYES-WILSDON, Mrs Patricia Mary (Pat). b 45. ALA65 Open Univ BA86. Glouc Th Course 84 Qu Coll Birm 86. **d** 87 **p** 94. C Thornbury *Glouc* 87-94; P-in-c Cromhall w Tortworth and Tytherington from 94; Dioc Voc Officer from 94. *The New Rectory, Rectory Lane, Cromhall, Wotton-under-Edge, Glos GL12 8AN* Wickwar (01454) 294767

LYNAS, Mrs Judith (Judy). b 53. Hollings Coll Man HND74. S Dios Minl Tr Scheme 89. **d** 92 **p** 94. Par Dn Lytchett Minster *Sarum* 92-94; C from 94. *15 Guest Road, Upton, Poole, Dorset BH16 5LQ* Poole (01202) 623637

LYNAS, Very Rev Norman Noel. b 55. St Andr Univ MTh78. CITC 78. **d** 79 **p** 80. C Knockbreda *D & D* 79-81; C Holywood 81-85; I Portadown St Columba *Arm* 85-91; Dioc Info Officer 86-89; Tutor for Aux Min (Arm) 88-91; Radio Officer (Arm) 90-91; I Kilkenny w Aghour and Kilmanagh *C & O* from 91; Dean Ossory from 91. *The Deanery, Kilkenny, Irish Republic* Kilkenny (56) 21516

LYNAS, Stephen Brian. b 52. St Jo Coll Nottm BTh77. **d** 78 **p** 79. C Penn *Lich* 78-81; Relig Progr Org BBC Radio Stoke-on-Trent 81-84; C Hanley H Ev 81-82; C Edensor 82-84; Relig Progr Producer BBC Bris 85-88; Lic to Offic *Bris* 85-92; Relig Progr Sen Producer BBC S & W England 88-91; Hd Relig Progr TV South 91-92; Community (and Relig) Affairs Ed Westcountry TV from 92; Perm to Offic *Cant* 91-92; Perm to Offic *Ex* from 92. *Shippen House, Brownston, Rattery, South Brent, Devon TQ10 9LQ* Buckfastleigh (01364) 642015

LYNCH, Preb Donald MacLeod. b 11. CBE72. Pemb Coll Cam BA34 MA37. Wycliffe Hall Ox. **d** 35 **p** 36. Chief Sec CA 60-76;

Preb St Paul's Cathl *Lon* 64-76; Chapl to The Queen 69-81; P-in-c Seal St Lawr *Roch* 74-85; rtd 76; RD Sevenoaks *Roch* 79-84; P-in-c Underriver 80-85; Perm to Offic *Chich* from 86; Perm to Offic *Roch* from 86. *Flat 2, 20 Grassington Road, Eastbourne, E Sussex BN20 7BJ* Eastbourne (01323) 720849

LYNCH-WATSON, Graham Leslie. b 30. AKC55. **d** 56 **p** 57. V Purley St Barn *S'wark* 67-77; C Caversham *Ox* 77-81; C Caversham and Mapledurham 81-85; P-in-c Warw St Paul *Cov* 85-86; V 86-92; rtd 92. *11 Crouch Street, Banbury, Oxon OX16 9PP* Banbury (01295) 263172

LYNDS, Thomas George. b 34. Lon Coll of Div ALCD62 LTh74. **d** 62 **p** 63. C Eastbourne All So *Chich* 62-65; C Edgware *Lon* 65-72; V Wimbledon St Luke *S'wark* 72-85; P-in-c Rainham *Chelmsf* 85-92; P-in-c Wennington 85-92; R Rainham w Wennington from 92. *The Vicarage, Broadway, Rainham, Essex RM13 9YW* Rainham (01708) 552752

LYNE, Peter. b 27. Sheff Univ BA51. Qu Coll Birm 51. **d** 53 **p** 54. V Elvaston and Shardlow *Derby* 69-74; P-in-c Ashbourne St Jo 74-80; P-in-c Kniveton w Hognaston 75-80; P-in-c Fenny Bentley, Thorpe and Tissington 77-78; P-in-c Osmaston w Edlaston 78-80; P-in-c Lt Eaton 80-84; V P-in-c Holbrooke 80-84; V Holbrook and Lt Eaton 84-91; rtd 91. *3 Vicarage Close, High Street, Belper, Derbyshire DE56 1TB* Belper (01773) 829188

LYNE, Roger Howard. b 28. Mert Coll Ox BA52 MA56. Oak Hill Th Coll 52. **d** 54 **p** 55. C Bucknall and Bagnall *Lich* 76-81; Perm to Offic *Win* from 82; rtd 88. *21 Copse Road, Burley, Ringwood, Hants BH24 4EG* Burley (01425) 402232

LYNETT, Anthony Martin (Tony). b 54. K Coll Lon BD75 AKC75 Darw Coll Cam PGCE76. Sarum & Wells Th Coll 77. **d** 78 **p** 79. C Swindon Ch Ch *Bris* 78-81; C Leckhampton SS Phil and Jas w Cheltenham St Jas *Glouc* 81-83; Asst Chapl HM Pris Glouc 83-88; Chapl from 91; V Coney Hill *Glouc* 83-88; Chapl HM Young Offender Inst Deerbolt 88-91; P-in-c Glouc St Mark *Glouc* from 91. *St Mark's Vicarage, Sandhurst Lane, Gloucester GL2 9AB* Gloucester (01452) 523843 Fax 310302

LYNN, Mrs Antonia Jane. b 59. Girton Coll Cam BA80 MA84. St Steph Ho Ox 82. dss 84 **d** 87. Portsm Cathl *Portsm* 84-87; D-in-c Camberwell St Mich w All So w Em *S'wark* 87-91; Par Dn Newington St Mary 87-91; Perm to Offic 91-94; Chapl Horton Hosp Epsom 91-94; Hon Par Dn Ewell *Guildf* from 94. *St Dunstan's Cottage, 4 Tudor Close, Cheam, Surrey SM3 8QS* 0181-641 7911 or 0171-580 2492

LYNN, Dixon. b 09. Ely Th Coll 46. **d** 47 **p** 48. V Birtley *Newc* 62-75; R Wark 62-75; rtd 75; Perm to Offic *Newc* from 75. *Bridge House, Newbrough, Hexham, Northd NE47 5AR* Newbrough (01434) 674219

LYNN, Edward Brown. b 14. Dur Univ BA35. Lich Th Coll 37. **d** 37 **p** 38. V Market Weighton *York* 66-77; R Goodmanham 66-77; RD Weighton 68-76; V Trimdon Grange *Dur* 77-79; V Trimdon Station 77-79; rtd 80. *53 Alderside Crescent, Lanchester, Co Durham DH7 0PZ* Lanchester (01207) 521456

LYNN, Frank Trevor. b 36. Keble Coll Ox BA61 MA63. St Steph Ho Ox 61. **d** 63 **p** 64. C W Derby St Mary *Liv* 63-65; C Chorley *Ches* 65-68; V Altrincham St Jo 68-72; Chapl RN 72-88; Hon C Walworth St Jo *S'wark* 88-90; C Cheam from 90. *4 Tudor Close, Sutton, Surrey SM3 8QS* 0181-641 7911

LYNN, Jeffrey. b 39. E Midl Min Tr Course 76 Moore Th Coll Sydney. **d** 79 **p** 80. C Littleover *Derby* 79-80; Hon C Allestree 80-85; Chapl HM Pris Man 85-86; Lic to Offic *Man* 85-86; Chapl HM Pris Kirkham 86-93; Chapl HM Pris Wakef from 93. *HM Prison Wakefield, 5 Love Lane, Wakefield, W Yorkshire WF2 9AG* Wakefield (01924) 378282 Fax 384391

LYNN, John Cairns. b 40. Surrey Univ BSc63 Lon Univ MSc66. NW Ord Course 73. **d** 76 **p** 77. NSM Hunts Cross *Liv* 76-80; Chapl Liv Cathl from 80. *2 Bancroft Close, Hunts Cross, Liverpool L25 0LS* 0151-486 7833

LYNN, Peter Anthony. b 38. Keele Univ BA62 St Jo Coll Cam BA64 MA68 PhD72. Westcott Ho Cam 67. **d** 68 **p** 69. C Soham *Ely* 68-72; Min Can St Paul's Cathl *Lon* 72-78; Perm to Offic *St Alb* 78-86; Min Can and Sacr St Paul's Cathl *Lon* 86-88; C Westmr St Matt 89-91; V Glynde, W Firle and Beddingham *Chich* from 91. *The Parsonage, Firle, Lewes, E Sussex BN8 6NP* Glynde (01273) 858227

LYNN, Archdeacon of. *See* FOOTTIT, Ven Anthony Charles
LYNN, Suffragan Bishop of. *See* CONNER, Rt Rev David John
LYON, Adrian David. b 55. Coll of Resurr Mirfield 84. **d** 87 **p** 88. C Crewe St Andr *Ches* 87-90; C Altrincham St Geo 90-91; TV Accrington *Blackb* from 91. *St Peter's Vicarage, 151 Willows Lane, Accrington, Lancs BB5 0NH* Accrington (01254) 231758

LYON, Christopher David. b 55. Strathclyde Univ LLB75 Edin Univ BD81. Edin Th Coll 78. **d** 81 **p** 82. C Dumfries *Glas* 81-84; P-in-c Alexandria 84-88; R Greenock from 88. *St John's Rectory, 24 Forsyth Street, Greenock, Renfrewshire PA16 9DZ* Greenock (01475) 20750

LYON, Dennis. b 36. Lon Univ DipTh66. Wycliffe Hall Ox 64. **d** 67 **p** 68. C Woodthorpe *S'well* 67-70; Warden Walton Cen 70-72; V W Derby Gd Shep *Liv* 72-81; V Billinge from 81; AD Wigan W from 89. *91 Newton Road East, Billinge, Wigan, Lancs WN5 7LB* Billinge (01744) 892210

LYON, Canon Donald Robert. b 24. Trin Coll Cam BA41 PhD44 MA45. Linc Th Coll 46. **d** 47 **p** 48. V Glouc St Mark *Glouc* 52-85; Hon Can Glouc Cathl 74-85; RD Glouc City 77-83; rtd 85. *12 Doverdale Drive, Longlevens, Glos GL2 0NN* Gloucester (01452) 524070

LYON, John Forrester. b 39. Edin Th Coll CertEd95. **d** 95. C Gourock *Glas* from 95. *15 Jacobson Terrace, Dundee DD3 9TD* Dundee (01382) 819065

LYON, John Harry. b 51. S Dios Minl Tr Scheme 86. **d** 89 **p** 90. NSM S Patcham *Chich* 89-91; C Chich St Paul and St Pet 91-94; R Earnley and E Wittering from 94. *The Rectory, East Wittering, Chichester, W Sussex PO20 8PS* Bracklesham Bay (01243) 672260

LYON, Stephen Paul. b 49. Univ of Wales (Swansea) BSc71. Trin Coll Bris 74. **d** 77 **p** 78. C Hull Newland St Jo *York* 77-81; Chapl Lee Abbey 81-84; V Norbiton *S'wark* 84-92; RD Kingston 88-92; Prin S'wark LNSM Scheme from 92. *11 Cupar Road, London SW11 4JW* 0171-622 4925 oe 378 7506

LYONS, Bruce Twyford. b 37. Lon Univ DipTh69. Tyndale Hall Bris 67. **d** 70 **p** 71. C Virginia Water *Guildf* 70-73; Chapl Ostend w Knokke and Bruges *Eur* 73-78; V E Ham St Paul *Chelmsf* 78-85; V St Alb Ch Ch *St Alb* 85-91; Chapl St Albans City Hosp 88-91; Chapl Wellingborough Sch from 92. *38 Castle Street, Wellingborough, Northants NN8 1LW, or The School, Wellingborough, Northants NN8 2BX* Wellingborough (01933) 276028/222427

LYONS, Edward Charles. b 44. Nottm Univ BTh75 LTh. St Jo Coll Nottm 71. **d** 75 **p** 76. C Cam St Martin *Ely* 75-78; P-in-c Bestwood Park *S'well* 78-85; R W Hallam and Mapperley *Derby* from 85. *The Rectory, The Village, West Hallam, Ilkeston, Derbyshire DE7 6GR* Nottingham (0115) 932 4695

LYONS, Margaret Rose Marie. b 47. Local NSM Course 89. **d** 89. NSM Gainsborough All SS *Linc* 89-91. *1C Common Road, Low Moor, Bradford BD12 0NT*

LYONS, Paul Benson. b 44. Qu Coll Birm 68. **d** 69 **p** 70. C Rugby St Andr *Cov* 69-70; C Moston St Jo *Man* 70-72; PV Llan Cathl *Llan* 73-74; C Brookfield St Anne, Highgate Rise *Lon* 74-75; Perm to Offic 76-82; C Westmr St Sav and St Jas Less 82-86; V Gt Cam Road St Jo and St Jas from 86. *St John's Vicarage, 113 Creighton Road, London N17 8JS* 0181-808 4077

LYONS, William. b 22. Local NSM Course 78. **d** 80 **p** 81. NSM Glenrothes *St And* 80-81; NSM Kirkcaldy 81-91; NSM Kinghorn 81-91; rtd 91. *44 Annandale Gardens, Glenrothes, Fife KY6 1JD* Glenrothes (01592) 751905

†LYTH, Rt Rev Richard Edward. b 16. St Edm Hall Ox BA38 MA55. Oak Hill Th Coll. **d** 56 **p** 57 **c** 67. C Arthuret *Carl* 56-59; Uganda 59-72; Bp Kigezi 67-72; C Chorleywood St Andr *St Alb* 74-81; rtd 81. *31 Backwoods Lane, Lindfield, Haywards Heath, W Sussex RH16 2EQ* Lindfield (01444) 482500

LYTH, Canon Richard Francis. b 05. Dur Univ LTh25 BA27. Edin Th Coll 22. **d** 28 **p** 29. R Uddingston *Glas* 39-75; rtd 75; Hon Can St Mary's Cathl *Glas* from 79. *26 Gardenside Street, Uddingston, Glasgow G71 7BY* Uddingston (01698) 812536

LYTLE, Canon John Deaville. b 23. Wadh Coll Ox BA50 MA52. Wycliffe Hall Ox 50. **d** 51 **p** 52. V Bradbourne and Brassington *Derby* 59-89; RD Wirksworth 78-88; Hon Can Derby Cathl 82-89; rtd 89; Perm to Offic *Derby* from 89. *14 Manor Road, Ashbourne, Derbyshire DE6 1EH* Ashbourne (01335) 346588

M

McADAM, Alexander William. b 15. Univ of Wales BA37 Jes Coll Ox BA40 MA43. St Mich Coll Llan 39. **d** 41 **p** 42. V Grosmont and Skenfrith *Mon* 50-85; rtd 85. *Sally Ruck, Rectory Lane, Grosmont, Abergavenny, Gwent NP7 8LW* Golden Valley (01981) 240421

McADAM, Gordon Paul. b 66. QUB BSc88 TCD BTh93. CITC 90. **d** 93 **p** 94. C Drumglass w Moygashel *Arm* from 93. *Kinore, 84 Killyman Road, Dungannon, Co Tyrone BT71 6QD* Dungannon (018687) 27131

McADAM

McADAM, Canon Michael Anthony. b 30. K Coll Cam BA52 MA56. Westcott Ho Cam 54. **d** 56 **p** 57. C Towcester w Easton Neston *Pet* 56-59; Chapl Hurstpierpoint Coll Hassocks 60-68; Bp's Dom Chapl *Lon* 69-73; R Much Hadham *St Alb* from 73; Hon Can St Alb 89-95. *The Rectory, High Street, Much Hadham, Herts SG10 6DA* Much Hadham (01279) 842609

✠**McADOO, Most Rev Henry Robert.** b 16. TCD BA38 PhD40 BD48 DD49. Seabury-Western Th Sem Hon STD62. **d** 39 **p** 40 **c** 62. C Waterford H Trin *C & O* 39-43; I Castleventry w Ardfield *C, C & R* 43-48; I Kilmocomogue 48-52; RD Glansalney W & Bere 48-52; Preb Cork Cathl 49-52; Can Cloyne Cathl 49-52; Dean Cork 52-62; Can St Patr Cathl Dub 59-62; Bp Ossory, Ferns and Leighlin 62-77; Dean Leighlin *C & O* 62-63; Abp Dub *D & G* 77-85; rtd 85. *2 The Paddocks, Dalkey, Co Dublin, Irish Republic* Dublin (1) 280-0063

McALEESE, William Henry. b 27. TCD BA53. St Aug Coll Cant 60. **d** 60 **p** 61. I Billis *K, E & A* 68-71; C W Byfleet *Guildf* 71-74; C Gt Bookham 74-77; C Epsom Common Ch 77-80; C Leatherhead 80-86; rtd 86; Perm to Offic *D & D* from 87; Perm to Offic *Conn* from 90. *Hollygate Lodge, 21 Hollygate Park, Carryduff, Belfast BT8 8DN*

McALISTER, David. b 39. St Jo Coll Nottm 83. **d** 87 **p** 88. NSM Arpafeelie *Mor* 87-93; NSM Cromarty 87-93; NSM Fortrose 87-93; C Broughty Ferry *Bre* from 93. *6 Bridge Street, Broughty Ferry, Dundee DD5 2ST* Dundee (01382) 78537

McALISTER, Kenneth Bloomer. b 25. TCD BA51. **d** 51 **p** 53. R Ripley *Ripon* 62-91; rtd 91. *31 Wetherby Road, Knaresborough, N Yorkshire HG5 8LH* Harrogate (01423) 860705

MacALISTER, Randall George Leslie. b 41. TCD BA63 MA66. **d** 64 **p** 66. C Portadown St Mark *Arm* 64-67; I Keady w Armaghbreague and Derrynoose 67-74; R Kirriemuir *St And* 74-81; R Greenock *Glas* 81-87; R Forfar *St And* 87-95; R Lunan Head 87-95; Chapl Sophia Antipolis *Eur* from 95. *6 Traverse deî Tourdres, Haut Sartoux, 06560 Valbonne, France* France (33) 93 65 38 63

McALISTER, Thomas George. b 20. TCD BA42 MA47. **d** 43 **p** 44. Chapl Wispers Sch Surrey 69-79; R Haslemere *Guildf* 69-79; V Slyne w Hest *Blackb* 79-85; rtd 85; Perm to Offic *Guildf* from 86; Perm to Offic *Portsm* from 86; P-in-c Linchmere *Chich* 92-93. *Bywoods, Bunch Lane, Haslemere, Surrey GU27 1ET* Haslemere (01428) 643516

McALLEN, James. b 38. Lon Univ BD71. Oak Hill Th Coll 63. **d** 66 **p** 67. C Blackheath St Jo *S'wark* 66-69; C Edin St Thos *Edin* 69-73; V Selby St Jas *York* 73-80; V Wistow 75-80; V Houghton *Carl* 80-91; Gen Sec Lon City Miss 92-93; Dir 93-94; Hon C Blackheath St Jo *S'wark* from 94. *192 Charlton Road, London SE7 7DW* 0181-856 7306

McALLEN, Robert. b 41. Bps' Coll Cheshunt 62. **d** 65 **p** 66. C Seagoe *D & D* 65-68; C Knockbreda 68-70; CF from 70; Chapl R Memorial Chpl Sandhurst 87-92. *c/o MOD (Army), Bagshot Park, Bagshot, Surrey GU19 5PL* Bagshot (01276) 471717 Fax 412834

MACAN, Peter John Erdley. b 36. Bp Gray Coll Cape Town 58 LTh60. **d** 60 **p** 61. S Africa 60-67; C S Lambeth St Ann *S'wark* 68-71; V Nunhead St Silas 72-81; P-in-c Clapham H Spirit 81-87; TV Clapham TM 87-90; V Dulwich St Clem w St Pet from 90. *St Clement's Vicarage, 140 Friern Road, London SE22 0AY* 0181-693 1890

McARDLE, Thomas. b 16. Edin Th Coll 47. **d** 48 **p** 49. V Pokesdown St Jas *Win* 71-77; P-in-c Bentworth cum Shalden 77-78; P-in-c Bentworth and Shalden and Lasham 78-79; R 79-81; rtd 81; Perm to Offic *Win* from 81. *77 Broadway, Bournemouth BH6 4EG* Bournemouth (01202) 426854

MACARTNEY, Prof Fergus James. b 40. MRCP68 FACC76 FRCP77 Qu Coll Cam BA62 MA84 St Thos Hosp Cam BCh66 MB67. E Anglian Minl Tr Course 86 SW Minl Tr Course 88. **d** 90 **p** 91. Chapl Lee Abbey 90-91; NSM Shirwell, Loxhore, Kentisbury, Arlington, etc *Ex* 90-91; Asst Chapl Amsterdam w Den Helder and Heiloo *Eur* from 91. *Angsteloord 46, 1391 EG Abcoude, The Netherlands* Abcoude (2946) 4233

MACARTNEY, William Horne. b 08. Qu Coll Cam BA30 MA34. Ridley Hall Cam 31. **d** 33 **p** 34. CMS 68-70; Uganda 68-73; rtd 73; Perm to Offic *Carl* from 74. *56 Crow Green Lane, Pilgrims Hatch, Brentwood, Essex CM15 9RL* Brentwood (01277) 373090

McATEER, John Alexander. b 18. TCD BA44 MA50. CITC 44. **d** 44 **p** 45. V Hammersmith H Innocents *Lon* 59-83; rtd 83; Perm to Offic *Lon* 83-93. *162 Sutton Court Road, London W4 3HR* 0181-995 5317

MACAULAY, John Roland. b 39. Man Univ BSc61. Wells Th Coll 61. **d** 63 **p** 64. C Padgate Ch Ch *Liv* 63-66; C Upholland 66-73; TV 73-75; V Hindley St Pet 75-81; Chapl Liv Coll from 81. *36 Glenmore Avenue, Mossley Hill, Liverpool L18 4QF* 0151-724 3785 or 724 1563

MACAULAY, Kenneth Lionel. b 55. Edin Univ BD78. Edin Th Coll 74. **d** 78 **p** 79. C Glas St Ninian *Glas* 78-80; Dioc Youth Chapl 80-87; P-in-c Glas St Matt 80-87; R Glenrothes *St And* 87-89; Chapl St Mary's Cathl *Glas* 89-92; Min Glas St Mary 89-92; Min Glas St Serf from 92. *25 Cullen Street, Glasgow G32 7UP* 0141-778 9703 or 778 9733

McAUSLAND, Canon William James. b 36. Edin Th Coll 56. **d** 59 **p** 60. C Dundee St Mary Magd *Bre* 59-64; R 71-79; R Glas H Cross *Glas* 64-71; Chapl St Marg Old People's Home 79-85; R Dundee St Marg *Bre* from 79; Chapl St Mary's Sisterhood 82-87; Chapl Dundee Hosps from 85; Hon Can St Paul's Cathl Dundee *Bre* from 93. *19 Ancrum Road, Dundee DD2 2JL* Dundee (01382) 67227

McAVOY, George Brian. b 41. MBE78. TCD BA61 MA72. **d** 63 **p** 65. C Cork St Luke w St Ann *C, C & R* 63-66; I Timoleague w Abbeymahon 66-68; Chapl RAF 68-88; Asst Chapl-in-Chief RAF from 88; QHC from 92; NSM St Mary-le-Strand w St Clem Danes *Lon* from 93. *St Clement Danes Church, London WC2R 1DH* 0171-242 8282

McAVOY, Philip George. b 63. Imp Coll Lon BSc85 SS Coll Cam BA90. Westcott Ho Cam 88. **d** 91 **p** 92. C W End *Win* 91-95; TV Swanage and Studland *Sarum* from 95. *The Vicarage, 130 Victoria Avenue, Swanage, Dorset BH19 1AX* Swanage (01929) 422916

McBAY, Canon Walter Ernest. b 17. St Aid Birkenhead 47. **d** 49 **p** 50. R The Shelsleys *Worc* 67-72; V Farndon *S'well* 72-78; R Thorpe 72-78; V Swinefleet *Sheff* 78-80; C Cleethorpes *Linc* 80-83; rtd 83; Perm to Offic *Ex* from 83. *Flat 10, Ellesborough Manor, Butlers Cross, Aylesbury, Bucks HP17 0XF* Aylesbury (01296) 622324

McBRIDE, Stephen Richard. b 61. QUB BSc84 TCD DipTh87 BTh89. CITC 84. **d** 87 **p** 88. C Antrim All SS *Conn* 87-90; I Belf St Pet from 90; Bp's Dom Chapl from 94. *St Peter's Rectory, 17 Waterloo Park South, Belfast BT15 5HX* Belfast (01232) 777053

McCABE, Alan. b 37. Lon Univ BScEng61. Ridley Hall Cam 61. **d** 63 **p** 64. C Bromley SS Pet and Paul *Roch* 63-67; PV Roch Cathl 67-70; V Bromley H Trin 70-77; V Westerham 77-88; V Eastbourne St Jo *Chich* from 88. *St John's Vicarage, 9 Buxton Road, Eastbourne, E Sussex BN20 7LL* Eastbourne (01323) 721105

McCABE, Canon John Trevor. b 33. RD78. Nottm Univ BA55 St Cath Soc Ox DipTh59. Wycliffe Hall Ox 57. **d** 59 **p** 60. C Compton Gifford *Ex* 59-63; P-in-c Ex St Martin, St Steph, St Laur etc 63-66; Chapl RNR from 63; Chapl Ex Sch 64-66; V Capel *Guildf* 66-71; V Scilly Is *Truro* 71-74; TR 74-81; Can Res Bris Cathl *Bris* 81-83; V Manaccan w St Anthony-in-Meneage and St Martin *Truro* from 83; RD Kerrier 87-90 and from 94; Chmn Cornwall NHS Trust for Mental Handicap from 91; Hon Can Truro Cathl from 93. *The Vicarage, Manaccan, Helston, Cornwall TR12 6HA* Manaccan (01326) 231261

McCABE, Terence John. b 46. Sarum Th Coll 71. **d** 74 **p** 75. C Radford *Cov* 74-77; P-in-c Bris St Paul w St Barn *Bris* 77-80; TV E Bris 80-84; USA 84-90; R Eynesbury *Ely* from 90. *The Rectory, 7 Howitt's Lane, Eynesbury, St Neots, Huntingdon, Cambs PE19 2AJ* St Ives (01480) 403884

McCABE, Thomas Stephen (Tom). b 56. QUB BSc77. St Jo Coll Nottm DTS91. **d** 91 **p** 92. C Broadheath *Ches* 91-95; C Bramhall from 95. *17 Syddal Road, Bramhall, Stockport, Cheshire SK7 1AB* 0161-439 0994

McCABE, Dr William Alexander Beck. b 27. QUB BA50 PhD65. **d** 74 **p** 74. Sec Sheff Coun of Chs 74-80; Hon C Millhouses H Trin *Sheff* 74-80; TV Sheff Manor 80-83; C Mosborough 83; C Portsea St Cuth *Portsm* 83-86; C S w N Hayling 86-87; V Mickleover St Jo *Derby* 87-91; rtd 91. *Tawelfan, Ruthin Road, Cadole, Mold, Clwyd CH7 5LQ* Mold (01352) 810435

McCAFFERTY, Canon Christine Ann. b 43. FCA76. Gilmore Course 76. dss 79 **d** 87 **p** 94. Writtle *Chelmsf* 79-81; Writtle w Highwood 81-87; C 87-94; NSM Officer from 88; Bp's Dom Chapl (Bradwell) from 88; Hon Can Chelmsf Cathl from 91; TR Wickford and Runwell from 94. *The Rectory, 120 Southend Road, Wickford, Essex SS11 8EB* Wickford (01268) 733147

McCAGHREY, Mark Allan. b 66. Warw Univ BSc87. St Jo Coll Nottm BTh93. **d** 94 **p** 95. C Byfleet *Guildf* from 94. *118 Rectory Lane, Byfleet, Surrey KT14 7LY* Byfleet (01932) 354627

McCALLA, Robert Ian. b 31. AKC55. St Boniface Warminster 52. **d** 56 **p** 57. C Barrow St Jo *Carl* 56-58; C Penrith St Andr 58-61; R Greenheys St Clem *Man* 61-64; V Glodwick 64-71; R Distington *Carl* 71-73; V Howe Bridge *Man* 73-87; Chapl Atherleigh Hosp from 75; R Heaton Mersey *Man* 87-92; V Tyldesley w Shakerley from 92. *St George's Vicarage, 203 Manchester Road, Tyldesley, Manchester M29 8WT* Atherton (01942) 882914

MacCALLUM, Norman Donald. b 47. Edin Univ LTh70. Edin Th Coll 67. **d** 71 **p** 72. TV Livingston LEP *Edin* 71-82; P-in-c Bo'ness from 82; R Grangemouth from 82; Miss to Seamen from 82. *33 Carronflats Road, Grangemouth, Stirlingshire FK3 9DG* Grangemouth (01324) 482438

McCAMLEY, Gregor Alexander. b 42. TCD BA64 MA67. CITC 65. **d** 65 **p** 66. C Holywood *D & D* 65-68; C Ban St Comgall 68-72; I Carnalea 72-80; I Knock from 80; Stewardship Adv from 89; Can Down Cathl from 90; Dioc Registrar from 90. *The Rectory, 29 King's Road, Belfast BT5 6JG* Belfast (01232) 471514

McCAMMON, Canon John Taylor. b 42. QUB BSc65 Lon Univ BD70. Clifton Th Coll 67. **d** 71 **p** 72. C Lurgan Ch Ch *D & D* 71-75; I Kilkeel 75-82; I Lisburn Ch Ch Cathl *Conn* from 82; Treas from 94; Can Conn Cathl from 85. *Cathedral Rectory, 2 Clonevin Park, Lisburn, Co Antrim BT28 3BL* Lisburn (01846) 662865

McCANDLESS, John Hamilton Moore. b 24. QUB BA Ulster Poly BEd. **d** 63 **p** 64. C Jordanstown *Conn* 69-70; I Ballinderry w Tamlaght and Arboe *Arm* 70-74; I Kilbarron w Rossnowlagh and Drumholm *D & R* 84-87; rtd 87. *20 Whinsmoor Park, Broughshane, Ballymena, Co Antrim BT42 4JG* Broughshane (01266) 861898

McCANN, David Terence. b 44. Dur Univ BA67 DipTh69. St Chad's Coll Dur 63. **d** 69 **p** 70. C Tonge Moor *Man* 69-73; C Failsworth St Jo 73-76; Sub-Chapl HM Pris Man 76-94; P-in-c Cheetwood St Alb 76-82; C Higher Broughton 76-82; P-in-c Prestwich St Hilda 82-85; V 85-94. *3 Highfield Avenue, Worsley, Manchester M28 1AL*

McCANN, Michael Joseph. b 61. Man Univ BSc82 TCD BTh91. **d** 91 **p** 92. C Derryloran *Arm* 91-94; I Dunmurry *Conn* from 94. *27 Church Avenue, Dunmurry, Belfast BT17 9RS* Belfast (01232) 610984

McCANN, Roland Neil. b 39. Serampore Coll BD73. Bp's Coll Calcutta DipTh70. **d** 70 **p** 73. India 70-74; C Earley St Bart *Ox* 74-77; C-in-c Harlington Ch Ch CD *Lon* from 77. *192 Waltham Avenue, Hayes, Middx UB3 1TF* 0181-573 0112

McCANN, Thomas Alan George. b 66. CITC 90. **d** 93 **p** 94. C Carrickfergus *Conn* from 93. *7 Macroom Gardens, Carrickfergus, Co Antrim BT38 8NB* Carrickfergus (01960) 362126

McCARRAHER, Seymour. b 26. Magd Coll Cam BA48 MA55. St Steph Ho Ox. **d** 55 **p** 56. Chapl RN 59-75; C Christchurch *Win* 75-81; V Darton *Wakef* 81-92; rtd 92. *34 Moorside, Boston Spa, Wetherby, W Yorkshire LS23 6PN* Boston Spa (01937) 843948

McCARTHY, Brendan. QUB BD MTh PhD94 TCD DipTh81. **d** 81 **p** 82. C Drumglass *Arm* 81-83; I Ardtrea w Desertcreat 83-90; I Drumragh w Mountfield *D & R* from 90. *Drumragh Rectory, 21 Church Street, Omagh, Co Tyrone BT78 1DG* Omagh (01662) 242130

McCARTHY, David William. b 63. Edin Th Coll BD88. **d** 88 **p** 89. C Edin St Paul and St Geo *Edin* 88-91; P-in-c S Queensferry from 91. *12 Springfield Place, South Queensferry, West Lothian EH30 9XE* 0131-319 1099

McCARTHY, Ian Christopher. b 52. Liv Univ BA73. Chich Th Coll 84. **d** 86 **p** 87. C Barbourne *Worc* 86-88; C Halesowen 88-90; V Worksop St Paul *S'well* 90-94. *1 Hazelbury Road, Nailsea, Bristol BS19 2JT*

McCARTHY, Very Rev John Francis. b 38. TCD BA61 MA72. **d** 62 **p** 63. C Seapatrick *D & D* 62-66; C Seagoe 66-71; I Moira 71-75; I Dundalk *Arm* 75-86; I Enniskillen *Clogh* 86-94; Dean Clogh 89-94; USA from 94. *St John's Anglican Church, 7th and Hampshire Street, Quincy, Illinois 62301, USA*

McCARTHY, Peter James. b 25. OBE. Cranmer Hall Dur. **d** 85 **p** 86. Hon C Farnham w Scotton, Staveley, Copgrove etc *Ripon* 85-87; V Startforth w Bowes 87-92; rtd 92; C Dufftown *Ab* from 92. *St Michael's Rectory, Conval Street, Dufftown, Keith, Banffshire AB55 4AH* Dufftown (01340) 20621

MacCARTHY, Very Rev Robert Brian. b 40. TCD BA63 MA66 PhD83 NUI MA65 Ox Univ MA82. Cuddesdon Coll 77. **d** 79 **p** 80. C Carlow w Urglin and Staplestown *C & O* 79-81; Lic to Offic (Cashel, Waterford and Lismore) 81-86; Lib Pusey Ho 81-82; Fell St Cross Coll Ox 81-82; C Bracknell *Ox* 82-83; TV 83-86; C Kilkenny w Aghour and Kilmanagh *C & O* 86-88; Bp's V and Lib Kilkenny Cathl 86-88; Chapl Kilkenny Coll 86-88; Bp's Dom Chapl 86-89; I Castlecomer w Colliery Ch, Mothel and Bilbo 88-95; RD Carlow 88-95; Dioc Info Officer (Ossory and Leighlin) 88-90; Glebes Sec (Ossory and Leighlin) 92-94; Preb Monmohenock St Patr Cathl Dub from 94; Provost Tuam *T, K & A* from 95; I Galway w Kilcummin from 95. *The Rectory, Taylor's Hill, Galway, Irish Republic* Galway (91) 21914 or 64648

McCARTHY, Terence Arthur (Terry). b 46. Kelham Th Coll 66. **d** 70 **p** 71. C Gt Burstead *Chelmsf* 70-74; C Wickford 74-76; TV E Runcorn w Halton *Ches* 76-80; V Runcorn H Trin 80-84; Chapl HM Pris Liv 84; Chapl HM Pris Acklington 84-92; Chapl HM Pris Holme Ho from 92. *The Chaplain's Office, HM Prison Holme House, Stockton-on-Tees, Cleveland TS18 2QU* Stockton-on-Tees (01642) 673759 Fax 674598

McCARTNEY, Adrian Alexander. b 57. Stranmillis Coll BEd79 TCD BTh88. St Jo Coll Nottm LTh86. **d** 88 **p** 89. C Jordanstown w Monkstown *Conn* 88-91; Bp's C Monkstown 91-94; I from 94. *22 Rosemount Crescent, Jordanstown, Newtownabbey, Co Antrim BT37 0NH* Belfast (01232) 865160

McCARTNEY, Robert Charles.TCD DipTh85. **d** 85 **p** 85. C Portadown St Mark *Arm* 85-88; I Errigle Keerogue w Ballygawley and Killeshil 88-89; CF from 89. *clo MOD (Army), Bagshot Park, Bagshot, Surrey GU19 5PL* Bagshot (01276) 471717 Fax 412834

McCARTY, Dr Colin Terence. b 46. Loughb Univ BTech68 PhD71 Lon Univ PGCE73 FRSA89. E Anglian Minl Tr Course 91. **d** 94 **p** 95. NSM Exning St Martin w Landwade *St E* from 94. *1 Seymour Close, Newmarket, Cambs CB8 8EL* Newmarket (01638) 669400 Fax Cambridge (01223) 325537

MacCARTY, Paul Andrew. b 34. Sarum & Wells Th Coll 73. **d** 75 **p** 76. Ind Chapl *Win* 75-80; C Bournemouth St Andr 75-84; Hon C Christchurch 80-91; C from 91. *3 Douglas Avenue, Christchurch, Dorset BH23 1JT* Christchurch (01202) 483807

McCAUGHEY, Canon Robert Morley. b 07. MA35. **d** 35 **p** 36. V Wisbech SS Pet and Paul *Ely* 61-74; Hon Can Ely Cathl 72-74; rtd 74; Perm to Offic *D & R* from 76. *51 Ballinahone House, Knockcloughrim, Magherafelt, Co Londonderry BT45 8PT* Magherafelt (01648) 42110

McCAUSLAND, Norman. b 58. TCD BTh89. CITC 89. **d** 89 **p** 90. C Portadown St Columba *Arm* 89-91; P-in-c Clonmel Union *C, C & R* 91-94; Miss to Seamen 91-94; CMS from 94. *Church Mission Society, Partnership House, 157 Waterloo Road, London SE1 8UU* 0171-928 8681 Fax 401 3215

McCAY, Alexander Wilson Michael. b 16. Keble Coll Ox BA41 MA45. Cuddesdon Coll 41. **d** 43 **p** 44. Lic to Offic *Wore* 67-81; Chapl St Mich Sch Barnstaple 78-81; R Peebles *Edin* 81-89; rtd 89. *2E, 22 Springbank Gardens, Dunblane, Perthshire FK15 9JX* Dunblane (01786) 825018

McCLATCHEY, Alfred Henry Bailey. b 20. BNC Ox BA48 MA48. **d** 67 **p** 68. V Escomb *Dur* 69-74; V Witton Park 69-74; Bp's Dom Chapl 69-74; Bp's Dom Chapl *Worc* 74-79; R Hartlebury 74-86; rtd 86; Perm to Offic *Worc* from 86. *10 Bellars Lane, Malvern, Worcs WR14 2DN* Malvern (01684) 560336

McCLATCHIE, Canon Donald William. b 40. TCD BA65. CITC 66. **d** 66 **p** 67. C Dub Clontarf *D & G* 66-68; CV Ch Ch Cathl Dub 68-71 and 75-80; P-in-c Dub St Audh 71-75; Prec Ch Ch Cathl Dub 80-89. *Luicelle, Killiney Hill Road, Killiney, Co Dublin, Irish Republic* Dublin (1) 282-6474

McCLAUGHRY, Victor Thomas. b 13. TCD BA34 MA46. **d** 36 **p** 37. V E Preston w Kingston *Chich* 70-79; rtd 79. *16 Woodland Avenue, High Salvington, Worthing, W Sussex BN13 3AF* Worthing (01903) 692971

McCLAY, David Alexander. b 59. TCD DipTh87. **d** 87 **p** 88. C Magheralin w Dollingstown *D & D* 87-90; I Kilkeel from 90. *The Rectory, 44 Manse Road, Kilkeel, Newry, Co Down BT34 4BN* Kilkeel (016937) 62300

McCLEAN, Robert Mervyn. b 38. Greenwich Univ BTh91. Edgehill Th Coll Belf 57. **d** 85 **p** 88. NSM Seapatrick *D & D* from 85. *2 Kiloanin Crescent, Lurgan Road, Banbridge, Co Down BT32 4NU* Banbridge (018206) 27419

McCLOUGHLIN, Joshua. b 27. CITC 69. **d** 70 **p** 71. C Magheraculmoney *Clogh* 70-72; C Cloughfern *Conn* 73-77; I Dunfanaghy *D & R* 77-79; I Drumkeeran w Templecarne and Muckross *Clogh* 79-83; I Aghavea from 83. *The Rectory, Brookeborough, Enniskillen, Co Fermanagh BT94 4EZ* Brookeborough (013653) 210

McCLURE, Robert (Roy). b 30. Open Univ BA92. TCD Div Sch 68. **d** 70 **p** 71. C Monaghan *Clogh* 70-72; C Belf St Matt *Conn* 72-76; Chapl HM Pris Liv 76-77; Chapl HM Pris Preston 77-82; V Foulridge *Blackb* 82-88; rtd 88; Perm to Offic *Liv* from 89. *4 Mill Lane Crescent, Southport, Merseyside PR9 7PF* Southport (01704) 27476

McCLURE, Canon Timothy Elston (Tim). b 46. St Jo Coll Dur BA68. Ridley Hall Cam 68. **d** 70 **p** 71. C Kirkheaton *Wakef* 70-73; C Chorlton upon Medlock *Man* 74-79; Chapl Man Poly 74-82; TR Man Whitworth 79-82; Gen Sec SCM 82-92; Perm to Offic *Birm* 83-92; Bp's Soc & Ind Adv & Team Ldr Soc & Ind Min LEP *Bris* from 92; Hon Can Bris Cathl from 92. *7 South Road, Bristol BS6 6QP* Bristol (0117) 955 7430 or 942 5264

McCLUSKEY, Miss Lesley. b 45. Hull Univ LLB72 Bolton Coll of Educn PGCE77. N Ord Course 89. **d** 92 **p** 94. C Bootle St Mary w St Paul *Liv* 92-94; C Wigan St Anne from 94. *33 Guildford Crescent, Beech Hill, Wigan, Lancs WN6 8NG* Wigan (01942) 33794

McCOLLUM, Charles James. b 41. TCD BTh89. CITC 85. **d** 89 **p** 90. C Larne and Inver *Conn* 89-91; Bp's C Belf Whiterock from 91. *St Columba's Rectory, 194 Ballygomartin Road, Belfast BT13 3NF* Belfast (01232) 721134

McCOLLUM, Canon Robert George. b 20. TCD BA43 MA60. **d** 44 **p** 45. I Dub Clontarf *D & G* 62-89; Can Ch Ch Cathl Dub 83-89; RD Fingal 84-89; I Rathmolyon w Castlerickard, Rathcore and Agher *M & K* 89-94; rtd 94. *16 Park View, Athboy, Co Meath, Irish Republic* Meath (46) 32747

McCOMB, Samuel. b 33. CITC 70. **d** 71 **p** 72. C Belf St Mich *Conn* 71-74; C Lisburn Ch Ch 74-79; I from 83; I Ballinderry *Arm* 79-83. *Christ Church Rectory, 27 Hillsborough Road, Lisbury, Co Antrim BT28 1JL* Lisburn (01846) 662163

McCONACHIE, Robert Noel. b 40. Golds Coll Lon BA86. Oak Hill Th Coll 86. **d** 88 **p** 89. C Larkfield *Roch* 88-93; R Mereworth w W Peckham from 93. *The Rectory, The Street, Mereworth, Maidstone, Kent ME18 5NA* Maidstone (01622) 812214

McCONKEY, Brian Robert. b 62. Carl Dioc Tr Inst 92. **d** 95. C Blackb St Gabr *Blackb* from 95. *St Gabriel's House, 100 Highbank, Blackburn BB1 9SX* Blackburn (01254) 662818

McCONNELL, Brian Roy. b 46. St Paul's Grahamstown DipTh71. **d** 71 **p** 72. S Africa 71-77 and 79-85; C Prestwich St Marg *Man* 77-79; V Liscard St Mary w St Columba *Ches* 85-90; V Altrincham St Geo from 90. *St George's Vicarage, Townfield Road, Altrincham, Cheshire WA14 4DS* 0161-928 1279

McCONNELL, Peter Stuart. b 54. Linc Th Coll 89. **d** 91 **p** 92. C N Shields *Newc* 91-95; V Balkwell from 95. *St Peter's Vicarage, The Quadrant, North Shields, Tyne & Wear NE29 7JA* 0191-257 0952

McCONNELL, Robert Mark. b 60. Oak Hill Th Coll BA88. **d** 89 **p** 90. C Bedf Ch Ch *St Alb* 89-92; C Ban St Comgall *D & D* 92-94; I Killyleagh from 94. *The Rectory, 34 Irishbeg, Killyleagh, Downpatrick, Co Down BT30 9TR* Killyleagh (01396) 828231

McCORMACK, Canon David Eugene. b 34. Wells Th Coll 66. **d** 68 **p** 69. C Lillington *Cov* 68-71; C The Lickey *Birm* 71-75; V Highters Heath 75-82; V Four Oaks from 82; Hon Can Birm Cathl from 95. *The Vicarage, 2 Walsall Road, Sutton Coldfield, W Midlands B74 4QJ* 0121-308 5315

McCORMACK, George Brash. b 32. ACIS65 FCIS75 Lon Univ DipRS85. S'wark Ord Course 82. **d** 85 **p** 86. Hon C Crofton St Paul *Roch* 85-89; C Crayford 89-91; R Fawkham and Hartley from 91. *The Rectory, 3 St John's Lane, Hartley, Dartford DA3 8ET* Longfield (01474) 703819

McCORMACK, John Heddon. b 58. Chich Th Coll 85. **d** 88 **p** 89. C Cleobury Mortimer w Hopton Wafers *Heref* 88-90; C Lymington *Win* 90-92; C Portsea N End St Mark *Portsm* 92-95; Chapl St Barn Hospice Worthing from 95. *St Barnabas Hospice, Columbia Drive, Worthing, W Sussex BN13 2QF, or, 17 St Elmo Road, Worthing BN14 7EJ* Worthing (01903) 264221

McCORMACK, Kevan Sean. b 50. Chich Th Coll 77. **d** 80 **p** 81. C Ross *Heref* 80-81; C Ross w Brampton Abbotts, Bridstow and Peterstow 81-83; C Leominster 83; TV 84-87; Chapl R Hosp Sch Holbrook from 87. *The Housemaster's Flat, Nelson House, Royal Hospital School, Holbrook, Ipswich IP9 2RX* Holbrook (01473) 328851

McCORMACK, Mrs Lesley Sharman. b 50. E Anglian Minl Tr Course. **d** 88 **p** 94. Hon Par Dn Chevington w Hargrave and Whepstead w Brockley *St E* 88-95; Asst Chapl W Suffolk Hosp Bury St Edm 88-95; Chapl Kettering Gen and St Mary's Hosps from 95. *Kettering General Hospital, Rothwell Road, Kettering, Northants NN16 8UZ* Kettering (01536) 492000

McCORMICK, Mrs Anne Irene. b 67. Sheff Univ BA89 Hull Univ PGCE90. Ripon Coll Cuddesdon 90. **d** 92 **p** 94. C Spalding *Linc* from 92. *33 Spalding Road, Holbeach, Spalding, Lincs PE12 7HG* Holbeach (01406) 490310

McCORMICK, David Mark. b 68. Univ of Wales (Ban) BD89. Ripon Coll Cuddesdon 90. **d** 92 **p** 93. C Holbeach *Linc* from 92. *33 Spalding Road, Holbeach, Spalding, Lincs PE12 7HG* Holbeach (01406) 490310

McCOSH, Duncan Ian. b 50. Edin Dioc NSM Course 82. **d** 91 **p** 92. C Dalkeith *Edin* from 91; C Lasswade from 91. *4 Eldindean Place, Bonnyrigg, Midlothian EH19 2EY* 0131-663 6682

McCOUBREY, Prof Hilaire. b 53. Trin Coll Cam BA75 MA78 Nottm Univ PhD90 Solicitor 78. E Midl Min Tr Course 92. **d** 95. Prof Law Hull Univ from 95; NSM Rowley w Skidby *York* from 95. *University of Hull Law School, Hull HU6 7RX* Hull (01482) 466323 Fax 466388

McCOUBREY, William Arthur. b 36. CEng MIMechE. Sarum & Wells Th Coll 86. **d** 89 **p** 90. C Bedhampton *Portsm* 89-92; V Stokenham w Sherford *Ex* from 92. *The Vicarage, Stokenham, Kingsbridge, Devon TQ7 2ST* Kingsbridge (01548) 580385

McCOULOUGH, David. b 61. Man Univ BA84 St Jo Coll Dur BA88. Cranmer Hall Dur 86. **d** 89 **p** 90. C Man Apostles w Miles Platting *Man* 89-92; C Elton All SS 92-94; V Halliwell St Marg from 94. *The Vicarage, 1 Somerset Road, Bolton BL1 4NE* Bolton (01204) 840880

McCOULOUGH, Thomas Alexander. b 32. AKC59. **d** 60 **p** 61. C Norton St Mich *Dur* 60-63; India 63-67; P-in-c Derby St Jas *Derby* 67-72; Ind Chapl *York* 72-82; P-in-c Sutton on the Forest from 82; Dioc Sec for Local Min 82-89; Lay Tr Officer

from 89. *The Vicarage, Sutton on the Forest, York YO6 1DW* Easingwold (01347) 810251

McCREA, Basil Wolfe. b 21. QUB BA49. Wycliffe Hall Ox 51. **d** 53 **p** 54. I Cork H Trin *C, C & R* 68-72; I Carrigaline Union 72-90; rtd 90. *30 Somerville, Carrigaline, Co Cork, Irish Republic* Cork (21) 371538

McCREA, Francis. b 53. BTh. **d** 91 **p** 92. C Dundonald *D & D* 91-94; I Belf St Brendan from 94. *St Brendan's Rectory, 36 Circular Road, Belfast BT4 2GA* Belfast (01232) 763458

McCREADY, Kennedy Lemar. b 26. FIEE56 Garnett Coll Lon TCert54 Woolwich Poly CEng56 Birkb Coll Lon BSc59 Sussex Univ DBS92. Chich Th Coll 91. **d** 92. NSM Mayfield *Chich* from 92. *Quarry House, Groomsbridge, Tunbridge Wells, Kent TN3 9PS* Tunbridge Wells (01892) 864297

McCREADY, Marcus Diarmuid Julian. b 63. NUU BA85 TCD BTh88 MA MPhil. **d** 88 **p** 89. C Seagoe *D & D* 88-91; I Clonallon w Warrenpoint from 91. *Clonallon Rectory, Donaghaguy Road, Warrenpoint, Newry, Co Down BT34 3RZ* Warrenpoint (016937) 72267

McCREADY, Maurice Shaun. b 55. MA. Ripon Coll Cuddesdon. **d** 83 **p** 84. C Bridgwater St Fran *B & W* 83-86; C Walton-on-Thames *Guildf* 86-88; C Elm Park St Nic Hornchurch *Chelmsf* 88-93; NSM from 93. *39 Woodcote Avenue, Elm Park, Hornchurch, Essex RM12 4PY* Hornchurch (01708) 452740

McCREERY, Canon William Robert Desmond. b 35. QUB BD. Oak Hill Th Coll 59. **d** 62 **p** 63. C Dundonald *D & D* 62-66; C Belf St Donard 66-69; I Annalong 69-78; I Knockbreda 78-89; Can Belf Cathl from 88; I Ban St Comgall *D & D* from 89. *2 Raglan Road, Bangor, Co Down BT20 3TL* Bangor (01247) 465230

McCRORY, Canon Peter. b 34. Chich Th Coll 63. **d** 67 **p** 68. C St Marychurch *Ex* 67-72; R Kenn w Mamhead 72-76; R Kenn 76-78; Bp's Dom Chapl *S'wark* 78-81; V Kew from 81; RD Richmond and Barnes 84-89; Hon Can S'wark Cathl from 90. *The Vicarage, 278 Kew Road, Kew, Richmond, Surrey TW9 3EE* 0181-940 4616

McCRORY, Walter Edward. b 38. TCD 66. **d** 69 **p** 70. C Carrickfergus *Conn* 69-73; C Ballywillan 73-76; I Armoy w Loughguile and Drumtullagh from 76. *The Rectory, 181 Glenshesk Road, Armoy, Ballymoney, Co Antrim BT53 8RJ* Armoy (012657) 51226

McCRUM, Malcolm Scott. **d** 93. Perm to Offic *Nor* 93-94; NSM Chesham Bois *Ox* from 94. *67A Woodley Hill, Chesham, Bucks HP5 1SP* Chesham (01494) 774868

McCUBBIN, Very Rev David. b 29. AKC54. St Boniface Warminster 54. **d** 55 **p** 56. R Kirkcaldy *St And* 63-70; R Wallsend St Pet *Newc* 70-79; R Aber St Jo *Ab* 79-81; R Glas St Bride *Glas* 81-87; Provost Cumbrae Cathl *Arg* 87-94; R Cumbrae (or Millport) 87-94; Can St Jo Cathl Oban 87-94; Syn Clerk 88-94; rtd 94. *137 Marlborough Avenue, Glasgow G11 7JE* 0141-357 1553

McCULLAGH, Ms Elspeth Jane Alexandra. b 68. Man Univ BSc90. Wycliffe Hall Ox BTh95. **d** 95. C Huddersfield H Trin *Wakef* from 95. *60 Imperial Road, Huddersfield HD1 4PG* Huddersfield (01484) 548340

McCULLAGH, John Eric. b 46. TCD BA68 BTh88 QUB DipEd70. **d** 88 **p** 89. C Stillorgan w Blackrock *D & G* 88-91; Chapl and Hd of RE Newpark Sch Dub from 90; I Clondalkin w Rathcoole from 91. *The Rectory, Monastery Road, Clondalkin, Dublin 22, Irish Republic* Dublin (1) 459-2160

McCULLAGH, Canon Mervyn Alexander. b 44. TCD BA68 BEng68. CITC 79. **d** 79 **p** 80. C Larne and Inver *Conn* 79-83; C Ballymacash 83-85; C Dub St Ann w St Mark and St Steph *D & G* 85-88; I Baltinglass w Ballynure etc *C & O* from 88; Warden of Readers from 90; Preb Ossory and Leighlin Cathls from 92. *The Rectory, Baltinglass, Co Wicklow, Irish Republic* Baltinglass (508) 81321

McCULLOCH, Alistair John. b 59. Univ of Wales (Lamp) BA81 Leeds Univ BA86. Coll of Resurr Mirfield 84. **d** 87 **p** 88. C Portsm Cathl *Portsm* 87-90; C Portsea St Mary 90-94; V Reading St Matt *Ox* from 94. *St Matthew's Vicarage, 205 Southcote Lane, Reading RG3 3AX* Reading (01734) 573755

MacCULLOCH, Dr Diarmaid Ninian John. b 51. FSA78 FRHistS82 Chu Coll Cam BA72 MA76 PhD77 Liv Univ DAA72. Ripon Coll Cuddesdon DipTh87. **d** 87. NSM Clifton All SS w St Jo *Bris* 87-88. *28 William Street, Bristol BS3 4TT* Bristol (0117) 971 2422

McCULLOCH, Geoffrey Kenneth. b 10. OBE57. Lon Coll of Div 62. **d** 64 **p** 65. V Kingston upon Hull St Matt w St Barn *York* 71-79; rtd 79; Perm to Offic Lon from 79. *5 Roy Road, Northwood, Middx HA6 1EQ* Northwood (01923) 827438

✠**McCULLOCH, Rt Rev Nigel Simeon.** b 42. Selw Coll Cam BA64 MA69. Cuddesdon Coll 64. **d** 66 **p** 67 **c** 86. C Ellesmere Port *Ches* 66-70; Dir Th Studies Ch Coll Cam 70-75; Chapl 70-73; Dioc Missr *Nor* 73-78; P-in-c Salisbury St Thos and St

Edm *Sarum* 78-81; R 81-86; Adn Sarum 79-86; Can and Preb Sarum Cathl 79-86; Suff Bp Taunton *B & W* 86-92; Preb Wells Cathl 86-92; Bp Wakef from 92. *Bishop's Lodge, Woodthorpe Lane, Wakefield, W Yorkshire WF2 6JL* Wakefield (01924) 255349 Fax 250202

McCULLOCK, Mrs Patricia Ann. b 46. CertEd72. E Midl Min Tr Course 87. **d** 90 **p** 94. C Bottesford w Ashby *Linc* 90-95; P-in-c Wragby from 95. *The Rectory, Snelland Road, Wickenby, Lincoln LN3 5AB* Wickenby (01673) 885721

McCULLOUGH, Roy. b 46. Linc Th Coll 70. **d** 73 **p** 74. Chapl Highfield Priory Sch Lancs 73-77; C Ashton-on-Ribble St Andr *Blackb* 73-77; V Rishton 77-86; V Burnley (Habergham Eaves) St Matt w H Trin from 86; RD Burnley from 91. *St Matthew's Vicarage, Harriet Street, Burnley, Lancs BB11 4JH* Burnley (01282) 424849

McCULLOUGH, Sidney. b 31. QUB BA53 DipEd61 MEd74. CITC. **d** 89 **p** 91. NSM Glencraig *D & D* 89-91; Lic to Offic 91; I Ballyphilip w Ardquin from 91. *The Rectory, 8 Cloughey Road, Portaferry, Newtownards, Co Down BT22 1ND* Portaferry (012477) 28349

McCURDY, Hugh Kyle. b 58. Portsm Poly BA Univ of Wales (Cardiff) PGCE. Trin Coll Bris. **d** 85 **p** 86. C Egham *Guildf* 85-88; C Woking St Jo 88-91; V Histon *Ely* from 91; RD N Stowe from 94. *The Vicarage, 9A Church Street, Histon, Cambridge CB4 4EP* Cambridge (01223) 232255

McCUTCHEON, Irene. *See* TEMPLETON, Irene

McDERMID, Ven Norman George Lloyd Roberts. b 27. St Edm Hall Ox BA49 MA52. Wells Th Coll 49. **d** 51 **p** 52. Dioc Stewardship Adv *Ripon* 64-76; R Kirkby Overblow 64-80; Hon Can Ripon Cathl 72-93; Dioc Stewardship Adv *Wakef* 73-76; Dioc Stewardship Adv *Bradf* 73-76; RD Harrogate *Ripon* 77-83; V Knaresborough 80-83; Adn Richmond 83-93; rtd 93. *Greystones, 10 North End, Bedale, N Yorkshire DL8 1AB* Bedale (01677) 422210

MACDONALD, Alan Hendry. b 49. St Steph Ho Ox 86. **d** 88 **p** 89. C Heavitree w Ex St Paul *Ex* 88-91; C Withycombe Raleigh 91-92; TV from 92. *St John's Vicarage, 3 Diane Close, Exmouth, Devon EX8 5PG* Exmouth (01395) 270094

MACDONALD, Alastair Douglas. b 48. St Jo Coll Dur 71. **d** 74 **p** 75. C Mottingham St Andr *S'wark* 74-78; C Woolwich St Mary w St Mich 78-81; V S Wimbledon St Andr 81-89; V Brighton St Matthias *Chich* 89-94; Chapl Southn Community Mental Hosp from 94. *Knowle Hospital, Fareham, Hants PO17 5NA* Fareham (01329) 832271 Fax 834486

MACDONALD, Cameron. b 51. Open Univ BA89. Wilson Carlile Coll 76 NE Ord Course 89. **d** 90 **p** 91. CA from 76; C Nairn *Mor* 90-92; P-in-c 92-95; CF from 95. *c/o MOD (Army), Bagshot Park, Bagshot, Surrey GU19 5PL* Bagshot (01276) 71717 Fax 412834

MACDONALD, Christopher Kenneth. b 57. Ex Univ BA79 PGCE80. Trin Coll Bris DipHE93. **d** 93 **p** 94. C Eastbourne All SS *Chich* from 93. *1F Grassington Road, Eastbourne, E Sussex BN20 7BP* Eastbourne (01323) 721231

MACDONALD, Colin. b 47. St Jo Coll Nottm 87. **d** 89 **p** 90. C Gt Limber w Brocklesby *Linc* 89-92; P-in-c Barrow and Goxhill from 92. *The Vicarage, Thornton Street, Barrow-on-Humber, S Humberside DN19 7DG* Barrow-on-Humber (01469) 30357

MacDONALD, Derek. b 45. Lon Univ DipTh77 Murdoch Univ Aus BA86 MA88. Oak Hill Th Coll 74. **d** 77 **p** 78. C Braunstone *Leic* 77-80; Australia from 80. *94 Armstrong Road, Wilson, W Australia 6107* Perth (9) 458-2674

MACDONALD, Donald Courtenay. b 45. Nottm Univ BTh74 St Martin's Coll Lanc CertEd75. Kelham Th Coll 70. **d** 75 **p** 76. C Clifton All SS w Tyndalls Park *Bris* 75-78; C Clifton All SS w St Jo 78-79; Chapl Derby Lonsdale Coll *Derby* 79-84; V Derby St Andr w St Osmund from 84; RD Derby S from 89; Dioc Communications Officer 89-93. *St Osmund's Vicarage, London Road, Derby DE24 8UW* Derby (01332) 571329

McDONALD, Douglas Mark. b 28. Linc Coll Ox BA54 MA59. Wells Th Coll 68. **d** 69 **p** 70. C Horsham *Chich* 69-76; TV Kirkby Lonsdale *Carl* 76-79; P-in-c Tidmarsh w Sulham *Ox* 79-83; Chapl St Audries Sch W Quantoxhead 83-91; rtd 91. *18 Lower Park, Minehead, Somerset TA24 8AX* Minehead (01643) 703104

McDONALD, Gordon James Joseph. b 17. Wycliffe Hall Ox 50. **d** 52 **p** 53. V Pemberton St Mark Newtown *Liv* 63-80; R Easton w Letheringham *St E* 80-83; rtd 83. *91 Ridgeway, Sherborne, Dorset DT9 6DB* Sherborne (01935) 813011

MACDONALD, Henry George Warren. b 20. TCD BA42 MA46 BD46. Div Test43. **d** 43 **p** 44. Chapl RN 49-75; QHC from 74; C Fulford *York* 75-79; Perm to Offic *Ex* from 79; OCF from 87; rtd 92. *12 Little Ash Road, Plymouth PL5 1JT* Plymouth (01752) 361271

McDONALD, Canon Ian Henry. b 40. TD. St Aid Birkenhead 65. **d** 68 **p** 69. C Kingston upon Hull H Trin *York* 68-70; C Drumglass *Arm* 70-73; I Eglish w Killylea 73-80; I Maghera w

Killelagh *D & R* 80-91; I Killowen from 91; CF (TAVR) from 91; Can Derry Cathl *D & R* from 94. *St John's Rectory, Laurel Hill, Coleraine, Co Londonderry BT51 3EE* Coleraine (01265) 42629

McDONALD, James Damian. b 66. Pemb Coll Cam BA87 MA91 SS Hild & Bede Coll Dur PGCE88. Qu Coll Birm 90. **d** 92 **p** 93. C Camberwell St Geo *S'wark* 92-95; Chapl G&C Coll Cam from 95. *Gonville and Caius College, Cambridge CB2 1TA* Cambridge (01223) 332482

McDONALD, James Stewart. b 31. St Mich Coll Llan 59. **d** 62 **p** 63. C Haslingden w Haslingden Grane *Blackb* 62-66; V Preston St Jude 66-73; V Blackpool St Wilfrid 73-85; V Blackb St Aid from 85. *St Aidan's Vicarage, St Aidan's Avenue, Blackburn BB2 4EA* Blackburn (01254) 253519

MacDONALD, John. b 16. St Cath Soc Ox BA38 MA42 BLitt58. St Steph Ho Ox 39. **d** 41 **p** 42. Chapl Burgess Hall Lamp 60-76; Sub-Warden 62-76; V Edstaston *Lich* 76-82; V Whixall 76-82; Chapl Choral Ches Cathl *Ches* 82-85; rtd 85. *47 The Links, Gwernaffield, Mold, Clwyd CH7 5DZ* Mold (01352) 740015

MACDONALD, John Alexander. b 07. Tyndale Hall Bris. **d** 41 **p** 42. V Byker St Mark *Newc* 53-80; rtd 80. *135 Bosworth Gardens, Newcastle upon Tyne NE6 5UP* 0191-265 7486

McDONALD, John Richard Burleigh. b 17. TCD BA40 BD41 MA. **d** 41 **p** 42. Hd of RE Stranmillis Coll Belf 66-86; Dir Post-Ord Tr *Conn* 86-94; rtd 94. *76 Osborne Drive, Belfast BT9 6LJ* Belfast (01232) 666737

McDONALD, Lawrence Ronald. b 32. St Alb Minl Tr Scheme 84. **d** 87 **p** 88. NSM Sharnbrook and Knotting w Souldrop *St Alb* 87-90; C Bromham w Oakley and Stagsden 90-93; P-in-c Renhold from 93. *The Vicarage, 46 Church End, Renhold, Bedford MK41 0LU* Bedford (01234) 771317

MACDONALD, Malcolm James. b 42. Sarum Th Coll 70. **d** 71 **p** 73. C Hounslow St Steph *Lon* 71-72; C Hammersmith St Sav 72-76; P-in-c Hammersmith St Luke 76-79; V 79-87; V Kirkby Woodhouse *S'well* from 87. *The Vicarage, 57 Skegby Road, Kirkby-in-Ashfield, Nottingham NG17 9JE* Mansfield (01623) 759094

MACDONALD, Canon Murray Somerled. b 23. Pemb Coll Cam BA46 MA49. Ely Th Coll 47. **d** 48 **p** 49. V Fenstanton *Ely* 62-70; V Hilton 62-70; RD Huntingdon 69-76; R Huntingdon All SS w St Jo 70-82; R Huntingdon St Mary w St Benedict 71-82; Hon Can Ely Cathl 72-82; Can Res 82-88; rtd 89; Perm to Offic *Linc* from 89. *4 Hacconby Lane, Morton, Bourne, Lincs PE10 0NT* Morton (01778) 570711

MACDONALD, Ranald Alexander (Alec). b 23. Fitzw Ho Cam BA50 MA55. Westmr Coll Cam 48 Lon Coll of Div 63. **d** 63 **p** 63. In Pb Ch 51-62; R Parham & Wiggonholt w Greatham *Chich* 67-83; P-in-c Bolam w Whalton *Newc* 83-86; P-in-c Hartburn and Meldon 83-86; P-in-c Netherwitton 83-88; R Bolam w Whalton and Hartburn w Meldon 86-88; rtd 88; Perm to Offic *Chich* 88-93. *2 Redbarn Cottages, High Street, Henfield, W Sussex BN5 9HP* Henfield (01273) 493370

MACDONALD, Stephen Calliss. b 35. Selw Coll Cam BA58. Westcott Ho Cam 58. **d** 60 **p** 61. C Norwood All SS *Cant* 60-64; Chapl Cov Cathl *Cov* 64-68; Chr Aid 68-70. *Crossways, Breachwood Green, Hitchin, Herts SG4 8PL* Kimpton (01438) 833210

MacDONALD, Trevor John. b 33. Hertf Coll Ox BA55 MA59. Chich Th Coll 92. **d** 93 **p** 94. NSM Hove St Barn and St Agnes *Chich* from 93. *31 Orchard Gardens, Hove, E Sussex BN3 7BH* Brighton (01273) 771228

MACDONALD, Warren. Melbourne Univ BEng MPhil. Trin Coll Bris DipHE95. **d** 95. NSM Iford *Win* from 95. *40 Ringer Road, Bournemouth BH7 6LX* Bournemouth (01202) 422131

MACDONALD-MILNE, Brian James. b 35. CCC Cam BA58 MA62 St Pet Coll Ox MA81. Cuddesdon Coll 58. **d** 60 **p** 61. C Fleetwood *Blackb* 60-63; Solomon Is 64-78; New Hebrides 78-80; Acting Chapl Trin Coll Ox 81; Acting Chapl St Pet Coll Ox 81-82; Asst Chapl HM Pris Grendon and Spring Hill 81-82; Research Fell Qu Coll Birm 82-83; Hon AP Bordesley SS Alb and Patr *Birm* 82-83; R Landbeach *Ely* 83-88; V Waterbeach 83-88; OCF 83-88; R Radwinter w Hempstead *Chelmsf* from 88; RD Saffron Walden from 91; P-in-c The Sampfords from 95. *The Rectory, Radwinter, Saffron Walden, Essex CB10 2SW* Radwinter (01799) 599332

MACDONALD-STEELE, Arthur Henry. b 14. Selw Coll Cam BA36. Linc Th Coll 38. **d** 38 **p** 39. P-in-c N Tuddenham *Nor* 69-75; P-in-c Hockering 69-75; rtd 75. *Amble, 6 Brentwood, Norwich NR4 6PW* Norwich (01603) 56925

McDONOUGH, David Sean. b 55. **d** 89 **p** 90. C Moseley St Mary *Birm* 89-92; TV Glascote and Stonydelph *Lich* from 92. *90 Briar, Tamworth, Staffs B77 4DZ* Tamworth (01827) 52754

McDONOUGH, John Terence. b 57. St Jo Coll Nottm LTh86. **d** 89 **p** 90. C Linthorpe *York* 89-94; TV Heworth from 94. *6 Forest Way, Stockton Lane, York YO3 0BJ* York (01904) 425678

McDOUGAL

McDOUGAL, John Anthony Phelps Standen. *See* STANDEN McDOUGALL, Canon John Anthony Phelps

McDOUGALL, David <u>Robin</u>. b 61. Avery Hill Coll CertEd BEd84. Ridley Hall Cam 85. **d** 87 **p** 88. C Bletchley *Ox* 87-91; C High Wycombe 91-93; C E Twickenham St Steph *Lon* from 93. *17 Sandycoombe Road, Twickenham TW1 2LU* 0181-891 0729

MacDOUGALL, Iain Ferguson. b 27. OBE JP. Clare Coll Cam BA51 MA55. Sarum & Wells Th Coll 85. **d** 86 **p** 87. NSM Langport Area Chs *B & W* 86-88; NSM Sedbergh, Cautley and Garsdale *Bradf* 88-90; NSM Appleby Deanery *Carl* 90-91; NSM Kirkby Stephen w Mallerstang etc from 91; OCF from 90. *Sandford Lodge, Sandford, Appleby-in-Westmorland, Cumbria CA16 6NR* Appleby (017683) 52978

MacDOUGALL, Canon Iain William. b 20. TCD BA43 MA59. CITC 43. **d** 43 **p** 44. I Mullingar, Portnashangan, Moyliscar, Kilbixy etc *M & K* 58-85; Can Meath 81-85; rtd 85. *18 Denville Court, Killiney, Co Dublin, Irish Republic* Dublin (1) 285-4751

McDOUGALL, Stuart Ronald. b 28. Leeds Univ DipAdEd MEd84. Roch Th Coll 64. **d** 66 **p** 67. C Wells St Thos w Horrington *B & W* 69-70; TV Tong *Bradf* 70-73; V Cononley w Bradley 73-82; C Thornthwaite w Thruscross and Darley *Ripon* 82-83; P-in-c Dacre w Hartwith 83-86; rtd 86. *Portman Chase Lodge, Chalbury, Wimborne, Dorset BH21 7EU* Witchampton (01258) 840558

MACDOUGALL, William Duncan. b 47. Nottm Univ BTh74 LTh74. St Jo Coll Nottm 69. **d** 74 **p** 75. C Highbury New Park St Aug *Lon* 74-77; C Tunbridge Wells St Jo *Roch* 78; SAMS 77 and 78-82; Argentina 78-82; V Rashcliffe and Lockwood *Wakef* 83-87; V Tunbridge St Steph *Roch* from 87. *St Stephen's Vicarage, 6 Brook Street, Tonbridge, Kent TN9 2PJ* Tonbridge (01732) 353079

McDOWALL, Julian Thomas. b 39. CCC Cam BA62 MA67. Linc Th Coll 62. **d** 64 **p** 65. C Rugby St Andr *Cov* 64-70; C-in-c Stoke Hill CD *Guildf* 70-72; V Stoke Hill 72-76; R Elstead 76-91; V Thursley 82-91; TV Wellington and Distr *B & W* 91-93; C Lymington *Win* from 93. *20 Solent Avenue, Lymington, Hants SO41 3SD* Lymington (01590) 676750

McDOWALL, Robert Angus (<u>Robin</u>). b 39. AKC66. **d** 67 **p** 68. CF from 69; Sen CF 80-94; QHC from 93; rtd 94. *c/o MOD (Army), Bagshot Park, Bagshot, Surrey GU19 5PL* Bagshot (01276) 471717 Fax 412834

McDOWALL, Roger Ian. b 40. AKC64. **d** 65 **p** 66. C Peterlee *Dur* 65-68; C Weaste *Man* 68-70; C Tonge Moor 70-73; V Whitworth 73-80; TV Torre *Ex* 80-88; V Torre All SS from 88. *All Saints' Vicarage, 45 Barton Road, Torquay TQ1 4DT* Torquay (01803) 328865

McDOWELL, Charles. b 16. BEM65. Bps' Coll Cheshunt 64. **d** 66 **p** 67. C Hilborough w Bodney *Nor* 66-70; R Colkirk 70-74; P-in-c Whissonsett w Horningtoft 71-74; R Colkirk w Oxwick, Whissonsett and Horningtoft 74-77; P-in-c Harpley 77-79; R 79-81; R Gt Massingham 77-81; rtd 81; Hon C Emscote *Cov* 85-90; Clergy Widows Officer and Chapl from 90. *4 Margetts Close, Kenilworth, Warks CV8 1EN* Kenilworth (01926) 58567

McDOWELL, Ian. b 67. Ch Coll Cam MA88 BA92. Westcott Ho Cam CTM93. **d** 93 **p** 94. C Hackney *Lon* from 93. *21B Blurton Road, London E5 0NL* 0181-986 5668

McDOWELL, Peter Kerr. b 69. QUB BA91. CITC BTh94. **d** 94 **p** 95. C Lisburn St Paul *Conn* from 94. *12 Belvoir Crescent, Lisburn, Co Antrim BT28 1VA* Lisburn (01846) 664189

McEACHRAN, Peter. b 20. **d** 75 **p** 76. Pakistan 75-79; Area Sec (Dios Ox and St Alb) CMS from 79; Hon C Haddenham w Cuddington, Kingsey etc *Ox* from 79; rtd 86. *107 Sheerstock, Haddenham, Aylesbury, Bucks HP17 8EY* Haddenham (01844) 291436

McENDOO, Canon Neil Gilbert. b 50. TCD BA72. CITC 75. **d** 75 **p** 76. C Cregagh *D & D* 75-79; C Dub St Ann *D & G* 79-82; I Dub Rathmines w Harold's Cross from 82; Can Ch Ch Cathl Dub from 92. *The Rectory, Purser Gardens, Church Avenue, Rathmines, Dublin 6, Irish Republic* Dublin (1) 497-1797

McENERY, Michael Joseph (<u>Mike</u>). b 35. Cant Sch of Min 77. **d** 80 **p** 81. C Smarden *Cant* 80-83; P-in-c 83-85; P-in-c Biddenden 83-85; P-in-c Harrietsham 85-86; P-in-c Ulcombe 85-86; R Harrietsham w Ulcombe 86-90; R Willesborough from 90. *The Rectory, 66 Church Road, Willesborough, Ashford, Kent TN24 0JG* Ashford (01233) 624064

McEVITT, Peter Benedict. b 58. Coll of Resurr Mirfield 91. **d** 93 **p** 94. C Swinton and Pendlebury *Man* from 93. *St Augustine's Vicarage, 23 Hospital Road, Pendlebury, Manchester M27 1EY* 0161-794 2962

McFADDEN, Canon Ronald Bayle. b 30. TCD BA53 MA55. **d** 54 **p** 55. V Pateley Bridge and Greenhow Hill *Ripon* 64-73; V Knaresborough St Jo 73-79; P-in-c Knaresborough H Trin 78-79; Can Res Ripon Cathl 79-90; rtd 90; Chapl Qu Mary's Sch Baldersby Park from 90. *12 Ure Bank Terrace, Ripon, N Yorkshire HG4 1JG* Ripon (01765) 604043

McFADYEN, Phillip. b 44. K Coll Lon BD69 AKC69 MTh70 ATD. St Aug Coll Cant 69. **d** 71 **p** 72. C Sheff St Mark Broomhall *Sheff* 71-74; Chapl Keswick Hall Coll Nor 74-79; V Swardeston *Nor* 79-81; P-in-c E Carleton 79-81; P-in-c Intwood w Keswick 79-81; R Swardeston w E Carleton w Intwood and Keswick 81-85; R Swardeston w E Carleton, Intwood, Keswick etc 85-90; V Ranworth w Panxworth and Woodbastwick from 90; Dioc Clergy Tr Officer from 90. *The Vicarage, Ranworth, Norwich NR13 6HT* Norwich (01603) 270263 Fax 270597

McFARLAND, Alan Malcolm. b 24. Lon Univ BA53. Bris Sch of Min 82. **d** 85 **p** 86. NSM Westbury-on-Trym H Trin *Bris* 85-88; Asst Lect Bris Sch of Min 85-88; Perm to Offic *Glouc* 88-89; NSM Lechlade 89-93; Perm to Offic *Lon* from 92; Perm to Offic *Sarum* from 93. *11 The Sea Horse, Higher Sea Lane, Charmouth, Bridport, Dorset DT6 6BB* Charmouth (01297) 560414

McFARLANE, Beverly. b 50. RGN. Edin Th Coll 90 Brechin NSM Ord Course 85. **d** 87. NSM Dundee St Martin *Bre* 87-90; Par Dn Edin H Cross *Edin* 92-94; All SS Convent Ox from 94. *All Saints Convent, St Mary's Road, Oxford OX4 1RU* Oxford (01865) 249127

McFARLANE, Ms Janet Elizabeth. b 64. Sheff Univ BMedSci87 St Jo Coll Dur BA92. Cranmer Hall Dur DMinlStuds93. **d** 93 **p** 94. Par Dn Stafford *Lich* 93-94; C from 94. *9 Brunswick Terrace, Stafford ST16 1BB* Stafford (01785) 43995

MACFARLANE, William Angus. b 17. Worc Coll Ox BA39 MA43. Wycliffe Hall Ox 39. **d** 40 **p** 41. V Bexleyheath Ch Ch *Roch* 71-79; Perm to Offic *B & W* from 79; Chapl Sandhill Park Hosp Taunton 80-87; rtd 82. *Moorlands, Blue Anchor, Minehead, Somerset TA24 6JZ* Dunster (01643) 821564

McFIE, Canon James Ian. b 28. Lich Th Coll 59. **d** 61 **p** 62. V Hey *Man* 65-75; V Elton All SS 75-85; V Walmsley 85-95; AD Walmsley 85-95; Hon Can Man Cathl 90-95; rtd 95. *4 Devonshire Road, Millom, Cumbria LA18 4JF* Millom (01229) 775192

McGANITY, Steven. b 61. Nottm Univ BTh93. St Jo Coll Nottm 90. **d** 93 **p** 94. C Gateacre *Liv* from 93. *24 Lee Vale Road, Liverpool L25 3RW* 0151-487 9391

McGARAHAN, Kevin Francis. b 51. Oak Hill Th Coll BA84. **d** 84 **p** 85. C Balderstone *Man* 84-87; Sports Chapl 86-87; C Stoughton *Guildf* 87-89; C Ashton St Mich *Man* 89-92; TV Madeley *Heref* from 92. *The Woodside Vicarage, 40 Park Lane, Madeley, Telford, Shropshire TF7 5HN* Telford (01952) 588958

McGEARY, Peter. b 59. K Coll Lon BD AKC. Chich Th Coll 84. **d** 86 **p** 87. C Brighton St Pet and St Nic w Chpl Royal *Chich* 86-90; C St Marylebone All SS *Lon* from 90. *6 Margaret Street, London W1N 7LG* 0171-636 1788

McGEE, Preb Peter John. b 36. Trin Coll Cam BA60 MA. Chich Th Coll 60. **d** 62 **p** 63. C N Keyham *Ex* 62-63; C St Marychurch 63-65; C Townstall w Dartmouth 65-68; C Cockington 68-71; V Exminster 71-78; V Alfington 78-82; V Ottery St Mary 78-82; RD Ottery 82-90; Preb Ex Cathl from 82; TR Ottery St Mary, Alfington and W Hill 82-87; TR Ottery St Mary, Alfington, W Hill, Tipton etc from 87. *The Vicar's House, 7 College Road, Ottery St Mary, Devon EX11 1DQ* Ottery St Mary (01404) 812062

McGEE, Very Rev Stuart Irwin. b 30. TCD BA53 MA68. **d** 53 **p** 54. C Belf St Simon *Conn* 53-55; Singapore 55-58; I Drumholm and Rossnowlagh *D & R* 58-65; CF 65-77; Dep Asst Chapl Gen 77-88; Can Achonry Cathl *T, K & A* 89-92; I Achonry w Tubbercurry and Killoran 89-92; Dean Elphin and Ardagh *K, E & A* from 92; I Sligo w Knocknarea and Rosses Pt from 92. *The Cathedral Rectory, Strandhill Road, Sligo, Irish Republic* Sligo (71) 62263

McGILL, Francis Leonard (<u>Frank</u>). b 31. **d** 93 **p** 94. NSM Howell Hill *Guildf* from 93. *27 Hampton Grove, Ewell, Epsom, Surrey KT17 1LA* 0181-393 2226

MacGILLIVRAY, Canon Alexander Buchan. b 33. Edin Univ MA55 Aber Univ DipEd67. Edin Th Coll 55. **d** 57 **p** 58. Chapl St Ninian's Cathl Perth *St And* 57-59; Chapl Aberlour Orphanage 59-62; C Aberlour *Mor* 59-62; R Oldmeldrum *Ab* from 62; R Whiterashes from 62; R Fyvie from 74; R Insch from 74; Can St Andr Cathl from 78. *The Rectory, Oldmeldrum, Inverurie, Aberdeenshire AB51 0AD* Oldmeldrum (01651) 872208

MacGILLIVRAY, Jonathan Martin. b 53. Aber Univ MA75. Coll of Resurr Mirfield. **d** 80 **p** 81. C Hulme Ascension *Man* 80-84; P-in-c Birch St Agnes 84-85; R 85-91; V Hurst from 91. *St John's Vicarage, King's Road, Ashton-under-Lyne, Lancs OL6 8EZ* 0161-330 1935

McGINLEY, Jack Francis. b 36. ALCD65. **d** 65 **p** 66. C Erith St Paul *Roch* 65-70; C Morden S'wark 70-74; V New Catton Ch Ch *Nor* 74-94; RD Nor N 84-89; Hon Can Nor Cathl 90-94; R Carlton-in-the-Willows *S'well* from 94. *St Paul's Rectory, Church Street, Nottingham NG4 1BJ* Nottingham (0115) 961 6169

446

McGIRR, Canon William Eric. b 43. CITC 68. **d** 71 **p** 72. C Carrickfergus *Conn* 71-74; C Mt Merrion *D & D* 74-77; I Donacavey w Barr *Clogh* 77-88; RD Kilskeery 86-88; I Ballybeen *D & D* 88-94; I Magheraculmoney *Clogh* from 94; Can Clogh Cathl from 95. *The Rectory, Kesh, Enniskillen, Co Fermanagh BT93 1TF* Kesh (013656) 32221

McGLASHAN, Alastair Robin. b 33. MSAnPsych90 Ch Ch Ox BA57 MA58 St Jo Coll Cam BA59 MA63. Ridley Hall Cam 58. **d** 60 **p** 61. C St Helens St Helen *Liv* 60; C Ormskirk 60-62; India 63-74; USA 74-75; C Lamorbey H Redeemer *Roch* 75-77; Chapl W Park Hosp Epsom 77-85; Chapl Maudsley Hosp Lon 85-87; Perm to Offic *S'wark* from 86. *102 Westway, London SW20 9LS* 0181-542 2125

McGLINCHEY, Patrick Gerard. b 59. **d** 95. C Barton Seagrave w Warkton *Pet* from 95. *8 Rannoch Close, Kettering, Northants NN15 5BS* Kettering (01536) 516414

McGONIGLE, Canon Thomas. b 22. TCD BA45 MA65. TCD Div Sch 43. **d** 46 **p** 47. I Magherafelt *Arm* 74-88; I Portadown St Mark 61-74; Can Arm Cathl 72-88; Treas 79-83; Chan 83-88; Prec 88; rtd 88; Lic to Offic *Arm* from 88. *91 Kernan Gardens, Portadown, Craigavon, Co Armagh BT63 5RA* Portadown (01762) 330892

McGOWAN, Anthony Charles. b 57. Jes Coll Cam BA79 MA. Coll of Resurr Mirfield. **d** 82 **p** 83. C Milford Haven *St D* 82-85; C Penistone *Wakef* 85-86; C Thurlstone 85-86; C Penistone and Thurlstone 86-88; CR from 88; Asst Chapl Radcliffe Infirmary Ox 91-94; Chapl from 94. *Radcliffe Infirmary, Woodstock Road, Oxford OX2 6HE* Oxford (01865) 224664 or 311188

McGOWAN, James Rutherford. b 30. Trin Hall Cam BA53 MA58. Ely Th Coll 53. **d** 55 **p** 56. Chapl K Sch Ely 70-73; R Duxford *Ely* 73-79; P-in-c Ickleton 78-79; V Buckland *Ox* 79-80; V Littleworth 79-80; R Pusey 79-80; R Warbleton and Bodle Street Green *Chich* 84-93; rtd 93. *8 Lovell Court, Mill Road, Eastbourne, W Sussex BN21 2LW* Eastbourne (01323) 643188

McGOWAN, Michael Hugh. b 35. St Cath Coll Cam BA58 MA62. Clifton Th Coll. **d** 60 **p** 61. C Islington St Mary *Lon* 60-63; Chapl Lyon w Grenoble and Aix-les-Bains *Eur* 63-67; Chapl Chantilly, Rouen, Caen and Le Havre 63-65; Asst Chapl Chapl Paris St Mich 63-67; V Maidenhead St Andr and St Mary Magd *Ox* 68-81; V S Mimms Ch Ch *Lon* from 82; AD Cen Barnet from 91. *Christ Church Vicarage, St Albans Road, Barnet, Herts EN5 4LA* 0181-449 0832

McGOWN, Robert Jackson. b 20. Keble Coll Ox BA42 MA46. Linc Th Coll 42. **d** 45 **p** 46. C W Kirby St Bridget *Ches* 64-71; Perm to Offic from 76; rtd 85. *16 Church Road, West Kirby, Wirral, Merseyside L48 0RW* 0151-625 9481

McGRANAGHAN, Patrick Joseph Colum. b 46. Glas Univ BSc68 Lanc Univ MA72. St Alb Minl Tr Scheme. **d** 85 **p** 86. NSM Markyate Street *St Alb* from 85. *Clovelly Court, Glencairn Road, Kilmacolm, Renfrewshire PA13 4NR* Kilmacolm (01505) 872733

McGRATH, Prof Alister Edgar. b 53. Wadh Coll Ox BA75 Mert Coll Ox MA78 DPhil78 BD83. Westcott Ho Cam 78. **d** 80 **p** 81. C Wollaton *S'well* 80-83; Tutor Wycliffe Hall Ox from 83; Prin from 95; Chapl St Hilda's Coll Ox 83-87; Research Lect in Th Ox Univ from 93; Prof Systematic Th Regent Coll Vancouver from 93. *Wycliffe Hall, 54 Banbury Road, Oxford OX2 6PW* Oxford (01865) 274209 or 244658 Fax 311346 or 274215

McGRATH, Dr Gavin John. b 53. Marietta Coll (USA) BA76 Trin Episc Sch for Min MDiv81 Dur Univ PhD90. **d** 81 **p** 82. USA 81-87; C Fulwood *Sheff* from 87. *1 Silver Birch Avenue, Sheffield S10 3TA* Sheffield (0114) 263 0926

McGRATH, Ian Denver. b 47. Leeds Univ CertEd72. Local NSM Course 85. **d** 87 **p** 88. NSM Ancaster *Linc* 87-89; NSM Ancaster Wilsford Gp 89-92; C Spilsby w Hundleby from 92. *48 Boston Road, Spilsby, Lincs PE23 5HQ* Spilsby (01790) 54146

McGRATH, John. b 49. Salford Univ BSc78 Man Poly CertEd79. N Ord Course 82. **d** 85 **p** 86. C Horwich *Man* 85-88; P-in-c Hillock 88-89; V 89-94; V York St Luke *York* from 94. *St Luke's Vicarage, 79 Burton Stone Lane, York YO3 6BZ* York (01904) 630354

McGREGOR, Alistair Darrant. b 45. ALCD69. **d** 69 **p** 70. C Streatham Immanuel w St Anselm *S'wark* 69-73; Bermuda 73-76; Warden St Mich Cen New Cross 76-80; C Hatcham St Jas *S'wark* 76-80; V Nor Heartsease St Fran *Nor* 80-87; TR Thetford from 87; P-in-c Kilverstone 87-90; P-in-c Croxton 87-90; RD Thetford and Rockland from 90. *The Rectory, 6 Redcastle Road, Thetford, Norfolk IP24 3NF* Thetford (01842) 762291

MacGREGOR, Colin Highmoor. b 19. Lon Univ BSc45 Magd Coll Cam BA47 MA50. Wells Th Coll 54. **d** 56 **p** 57. V Clapham St Pet *S'wark* 60-73; V Riddlesdown 73-87; rtd 87. *Flat 3, Longacre Court, 21 Mayfield Road, South Croydon, Surrey CR2 0BG* 0181-651 2615

MACGREGOR, Donald Alexander Thomson (Don). b 52. Loughb Univ BSc75 Leic Univ CertEd78. St Jo Coll Nottm DTS93. **d** 93 **p** 94. C Walmley *Birm* from 93. *90 Walmley Ash Road, Sutton Coldfield, W Midlands B76 8JB* 0121-351 1245

✠**MACGREGOR, Rt Rev Gregor.** b 33. St Andr Univ MA64 BD67. **d** 77 **p** 77 **c** 94. NSM Elie and Earlsferry *St And* 77-81; NSM Pittenweem 77-81; R Glenrothes 81-86; C Cumbrae (or Millport) *Arg* 86; P-in-c Dollar *St And* 87-90; Miss Priest Wester Hailes St Luke *Edin* 91-94; TV Edin St Luke 91-94; Bp Mor from 94. *Bishop's House, 34 Rangemore Road, Inverness IV3 5EA* Inverness (01463) 231059

MacGREGOR, Neil. b 35. Keble Coll Ox BA60 MA80. Wells Th Coll. **d** 65 **p** 66. C Bath Bathwick St Mary w Woolley *B & W* 65-70; R Oare w Culbone 70-74; P-in-c Kenn w Kingston Seymour 74-76; R 76-80; V Lee Brockhurst *Lich* from 80; V Wem from 80; P-in-c Loppington w Newtown from 95. *The Rectory, Ellesmere Road, Wem, Shrewsbury SY4 5TU* Wem (01939) 232550

McGREGOR, Nigel Selwyn. b 47. FCA69. Sarum & Wells Th Coll 87. **d** 89 **p** 90. C Charlton Kings St Mary *Glouc* 89-92; P-in-c Seale *Guildf* from 92; P-in-c Puttenham and Wanborough from 92. *The Rectory, Seale, Farnham, Surrey GU10 1JA* Runfold (01252) 782302

McGUFFIE, Dr Duncan Stuart. b 45. Man Univ MA70 Regent's Park Coll Ox DPhil80. S Dios Minl Tr Scheme 84. **d** 85 **p** 85. C Sholing *Win* 85-89; V Clavering w Langley and Arkesden *Chelmsf* from 89. *The Vicarage, 54 Pelham Road, Clavering, Saffron Walden, Essex CB11 4PQ* Clavering (01799) 550703

McGUINNESS, Gordon Baxter. b 57. St Andr Univ BSc79 BNC Ox MSc80. Oak Hill NSM Course 86. **d** 89 **p** 90. NSM Loudwater *Ox* 89-92; C Chilwell *S'well* from 92. *Church House, Barncroft, Chilwell, Nottingham NG9 4HU* Nottingham (0115) 922 1879

McGUIRE, Alec John. b 51. Societas Liturgica 85 MRSH86 BAC Accred90 K Coll Cam BA73 MA76. Westcott Ho Cam 74. **d** 78 **p** 79. C Hungerford and Denford *Ox* 78-81; Prec Leeds St Pet *Ripon* 81-86; Perm to Offic 86-90. *34 Gledhow Wood Road, Leeds LS8 4BZ* Leeds (0113) 240 0336

McGUIRE, John. b 31. Oak Hill Th Coll 59. **d** 62 **p** 65. C Tooting Graveney St Nic *S'wark* 62-64; C Normanton Derby 64-67; N Area Sec ICM 67-71; Chapl RNR 67-81; R Biddulph Moor *Lich* from 71. *The Rectory, Hot Lane, Biddulph Moor, Stoke-on-Trent ST8 7HP* Stoke-on-Trent (01782) 513323

McHAFFIE, Alistair. b 57. Oak Hill Th Coll DipHE94. **d** 94 **p** 95. C Braintree *Chelmsf* from 94. *183 Notley Road, Braintree, Essex CM7 3HG* Braintree (01376) 322578

McHARDY, Canon Iain William Thomson Duff. b 13. St Andr Univ MA36. Ely Th Coll 37. **d** 38 **p** 39. P-in-c Invergordon *Mor* 52-74; Can St Andr Cathl Inverness 64-80; R Fortrose 74-80; Dean Mor 77-80; rtd 80; Hon Can St Andr Cathl Inverness *Mor* from 80. *Beech Tree Cottage, Navity, Cromarty, Ross-shire IV11 8XY* Cromarty (01381) 600451

McHUGH, Brian Robert. b 50. FSS77 AFIMA83 York Univ BA72 Keele Univ CertEd73 Southn Univ CEurStuds78 Portsm Poly CertComp84 DPSE90. S Dios Minl Tr Scheme 79. **d** 82 **p** 83. NSM Sarisbury *Portsm* 82-86; NSM Shedfield from 86. *28 Siskin Close, Bishops Waltham, Southampton SO3 1RQ* Bishops Waltham (01489) 896658

MACINNES, Canon David Rennie. b 32. Jes Coll Cam BA55 MA59. Ridley Hall Cam 55. **d** 57 **p** 58. C Gillingham St Mark *Roch* 57-61; C St Helen Bishopsgate w St Martin Outwich *Lon* 61-67; Prec Birm Cathl *Birm* 67-78; Angl Adv ATV 67-82; Angl Adv Cen TV from 82; Dioc Missr *Birm* 79-87; Hon Can Birm Cathl 81-87; R Ox St Aldate w St Matt *Ox* 74; R Ox St Aldate from 95. *St Aldate's Parish Centre, 40 Pembroke Street, Oxford OX1 1BP* Oxford (01865) 244713

MACINTOSH, Andrew Alexander. b 36. St Jo Coll Cam BA59 MA63 BD80. Ridley Hall Cam 60. **d** 62 **p** 63. C S Ormsby Gp *Linc* 62-64; Lect St D Coll Lamp 64-67; Lic to Offic *Ely* from 67; Chapl St Jo Coll Cam from 67; Asst Dean 69-79; Dean from 79; Lect Th from 70. *St John's College, Cambridge CB2 1TP* Cambridge (01223) 338600

McINTOSH, Andrew Malcolm Ashwell. b 43. Chich Th Coll 67. **d** 70 **p** 71. C Brentwood St Thos *Chelmsf* 70-74; C Chingford SS Pet and Paul 74-79; P-in-c Maldon St Mary w Mundon 79-83; R from 83. *St Mary's Rectory, Park Drive, Maldon, Essex CM9 7JG* Maldon (01621) 857191

McINTOSH, David Henry. b 45. St Jo Coll Dur BSc67 DipTh69 LTCL87. Cranmer Hall Dur 67. **d** 70 **p** 71. C Sutton *Liv* 70-74; TV 74-75; Chapl Bethany Sch Goudhurst 75-80; V Douglas St Thos *S & M* 80-87; Dir RE and Adv in Children's Work 80-87; TV Ellesmere Port *Ches* 88-94; P-in-c Barnton from 94. *The Vicarage, Barnton, Northwich, Cheshire CW8 4JH* Northwich (01606) 74358

MacINTOSH, George Grant. b 41. St Jo Coll Dur BA75 DipTh76. **d** 76 **p** 77. C Ecclesall *Sheff* 76-79; Hon C Sheff St Oswald 79-81; Dioc Adult Educn Officer from 81; V Crookes St Tim 81-88; V Abbeydale St Jo from 88; RD Ecclesall 89-94. *St John's Vicarage, 2 Devonshire Glen, Sheffield S17 3NY* Sheffield (0114) 236 0786

McINTOSH, Canon Hugh. b 14. Hatf Coll Dur LTh41 BA42 MA45. Edin Th Coll 38. **d** 42 **p** 42. Provost St Mary's Cathl *Glas* 66-70; Can 70-83; R Lanark 70-83; rtd 83; Hon Can St Mary's Cathl *Glas* from 83. *2 Ridgepark Drive, Lanark ML11 7PG* Lanark (01555) 663458

McINTOSH, Ian MacDonald. b 64. Jes Coll Cam BA86. Trin Coll Bris BA90. **d** 90 **p** 91. C Belmont *Lon* 90-92; C Pinner from 92. *37 Eastcote Road, Pinner, Middx HA5 1EL* 0181-429 4426

McINTOSH, Mrs Nicola Ann. b 60. Trin Coll Bris DipHE89 ADPS90. **d** 90 **p** 94. Par Dn Queensbury All SS *Lon* 90-93; Par Dn Ruislip Manor St Paul 93-94; C from 94. *37 Eastcote Road, Pinner, Middx HA5 1EL* 0181-429 4426

MACINTYRE, Angus Greer. b 14. Linc Coll Ox BA36 DipTh39 MA41. Wycliffe Hall Ox 38. **d** 39 **p** 40. V Harborne St Pet *Birm* 68-76; St Helena 76-79; rtd 79; Hon C Edin Ch Ch *Edin* 79-90. *12 Inverleith Place, Edinburgh EH3 5PZ* 0131-551 3287

McINTYRE, James Whitelaw. b 37. Lon Univ BD66. Edin Th Coll 59. **d** 62 **p** 63. P-in-c Cumbernauld *Glas* 66-74; R Stirling *Edin* 74-93; rtd 93. *24 Cedar Avenue, Stirling FK8 2PQ* Stirling (01786) 474380

McINTYRE, Robert Mark. b 69. Nottm Univ BA91. Coll of Resurr Mirfield 92. **d** 94 **p** 95. C Wednesbury St Jas and St Jo *Lich* from 94. *18 Dawn Drive, Tipton, W Midlands DY4 0DT* 0121-502 6296

McKAE, William John. b 42. Liv Univ BSc63 St Mark & St Jo Coll Lon PGCE64 Bris Univ DipTh70. Wells Th Coll 68. **d** 71 **p** 72. C Tranmere St Paul w St Luke *Ches* 71-74; C Midsomer Norton *B & W* 74-75; TV Birkenhead Priory *Ches* 75-80; R Oughtrington 80-91; Chapl Asst Hope, Salford R and Ladywell Hosps Man 91-92; Lic Preacher *Man* 91-92; R Heaton Reddish from 92. *The Rectory, St Mary's Drive, Stockport, Cheshire SK5 7AX* 0161-477 6702

McKAVANAGH, Dermot James. b 51. TCD BA75 MA78 K Coll Lon BD78 AKC78. **d** 78 **p** 79. C Croydon H Sav *Cant* 78-82; Asst Chapl Wellington Coll Berks 82-87; Lic to Offic *Ox* 85-87; Chapl RAF from 87. *Chaplaincy Services (RAF), HQ, Personnel and Training Command, RAF Innsworth, Gloucester GL3 1EZ* Gloucester (01452) 712612 Ext 5164 Fax 510828

McKAY, Brian Andrew. b 39. Sarum Th Coll 69. **d** 71 **p** 72. C Walker *Newc* 71-74; C Wooler Gp 74-77; TV 77-81; V Long Benton St Mary 81-89; TV Bellingham/Otterburn Gp 89-91; TV N Tyne and Redesdale Team from 91. *The Vicarage, Otterburn, Newcastle upon Tyne NE19 1NP* Otterburn (01830) 520212

MACKAY, Canon Douglas Brysson. b 27. Edin Th Coll 56. **d** 58 **p** 59. Prec St Andr Cathl Inverness *Mor* 58-61; P-in-c Fochabers 61-70; R 70-72; Chapl Aberlour Orphanage 64-67; P-in-c Aberlour 64-72; Syn Clerk 65-72; Can St Andr Cathl Inverness 65-72; Hon Can from 72; R Carnoustie *Bre* from 72; Can St Paul's Cathl Dundee from 81; Syn Clerk from 81. *Hollyrood Rectory, Carnoustie, Angus DD7 6AB* Carnoustie (01241) 52202

MACKAY, Hedley Neill. b 27. St Aid Birkenhead 53. **d** 56 **p** 57. Nigeria 61-70; C Wawne *York* 70-71; TV Sutton St Jas and Wawne 72-76; V Huntington 76-82; TR 82-93; rtd 93; Dioc Rtd Clergy and Widows Officer *York* from 94. *2 Elmfield Terrace, Heworth, York YO3 0EH* York (01904) 412971

MACKAY, Ian Stuart Reay. b 31. St Aid Birkenhead 56. **d** 58 **p** 59. V Bolton Sav *Man* 66-71; Lect Liv Educn Authority 71-74; Regional Officer Nat Assn for Teachers in F&HE 75-91; rtd 92. *5 East Meade, Chorltonville, Manchester M21 2DX* 0161-881 1228

MACKAY, James Alexander Nigel. b 11. TCD BA38. Edin Th Coll 38. **d** 41 **p** 42. V Weasenham *Nor* 62-67; V Rougham 62-67; Perm to Offic *Lon* 72-76; rtd 76. *29 Howbury Street, Bedford MK40 3QU*

McKAY, John Andrew. b 38. HDipEd. Chich Th Coll. **d** 74 **p** 75. C Primrose Hill St Mary w Avenue Road St Paul *Lon* 74-77; V Battersea Ch Ch and St Steph *S'wark* 77-82; I Rathkeale w Askeaton and Kilcornan *L & K* 82-85; I Dub St Bart w Ch Ch Leeson Park *D & G* from 85. *12 Merlyn Road, Ballsbridge, Dublin, Irish Republic* Dublin (1) 269-4813

McKAY, John William. b 41. Aber Univ MA62 Keble Coll Ox BA64 Selw Coll Cam PhD69. Ridley Hall Cam 66. **d** 70 **p** 71. Lect Th Hull Univ 69-82; Hon C Cottingham *York* 70-79; Hon C Willerby 79-82; R Prestwick *Glas* 82-85; Dir of Studies Roffey Place Chr Tr Cen Horsham from 85; Lic to Offic *Chich* from 85. *Kingdom Faith Ministries, Roffey Place, Crawley Road, Faygate, Horsham, W Sussex RH12 4SA* Faygate (01293) 851543 Fax 851330

McKEARNEY, Andrew Richard. b 57. Selw Coll Cam MA. Edin Th Coll 81. **d** 82 **p** 83. Prec St Ninian's Cathl Perth *St And* 82-84; Chapl St Mary's Cathl *Edin* 84-88; R Hardwick Ely 88-94; R Toft w Caldecote and Childerley 88-94; V Chesterton Gd Shep from 94. *The Good Shepherd Vicarage, 51 Highworth Avenue, Cambridge CB4 2BQ* Cambridge (01223) 312933

McKECHNIE, John Gregg. b 30. Em Coll Cam BA54 MA57. Ridley Hall Cam 54. **d** 55 **p** 56. V Reading St Jo *Ox* 68-85; RD Reading 83-85; V Lindfield *Chich* 85-95; rtd 95. *3 The Courtyard, Stockbridge Road, Chichester, W Sussex PO19 2GP* Chichester (01243) 531703

McKEE, Canon Harold Denis. b 30. TCD BA53 MA57. **d** 54 **p** 55. Can Res and Prec Sheff Cathl *Sheff* 65-86; C Preston St Jo *Blackb* 86-87; TV 87-92; rtd 92. *200 Cobden View Road, Sheffield S10 1HT* Sheffield (0114) 267 8214

McKEE, Patrick Joseph. b 49. Ripon Coll Cuddesdon DipMin94. **d** 94 **p** 95. C Oakham, Hambleton, Egleton, Braunston and Brooke *Pet* from 94. *45 Trent Road, Oakham, Leics LE15 6HE* Oakham (01572) 756086

McKEE, William Thomas. b 18. CITC 64. **d** 65 **p** 66. C Willowfield *D & D* 68-73; Bp's C Magherally w Annaclone 73-77; I 77-85; rtd 85. *Flat 15, Fold Mews, 22 Ballyholme Road, Bangor, Co Down BT20 5JS* Bangor (01247) 459598

McKEEMAN, David Christopher. b 36. AKC58 DipEd76. **d** 60 **p** 61. C Catford St Andr *S'wark* 60-64; P-in-c W Dulwich Em 64-69; Lic to Offic *Win* 70-82; R Silchester from 82. *The Rectory, Silchester, Reading RG7 2LU* Silchester (01734) 700322

McKEGNEY, John Wade. b 47. TCD BA70 MA81. CITC 70. **d** 72 **p** 73. C Ballynafeigh St Jude *D & D* 72-75; C Ban St Comgall 75-80; I Drumgath w Drumgooland and Clonduff 80-83; I Gilnahirk 83-90; I Arm St Mark w Aghavilly *Arm* from 90. *St Mark's Rectory, 14 Portadown Road, Armagh BT61 9EE* Armagh (01861) 522970

MACKEITH (nee GODFREY), Mrs Ann Veronica. b 35. Bris Univ BSc57 CertEd. Gilmore Course 78. **dss** 79 **d** 87 **p** 94. Bishopwearmouth Ch Ch *Dur* 79-83; Bishopwearmouth St Gabr 83-86; Ryhope 86-88; Par Dn 87-88; Par Dn Darlington H Trin 88-94; C from 94. *135 Hummersknott Avenue, Darlington, Co Durham DL3 8RR* Darlington (01325) 463481

McKELLAR, John Lorne. b 19. Sarum Th Coll 70. **d** 72 **p** 73. C Warminster St Denys *Sarum* 72-75; USA 75-79 and 81-84; P-in-c Colchester St Barn *Chelmsf* 79-81; rtd 84. *Corrie, 105A Clay Street, Crockerton, Warminster, Wilts BA12 8AG* Warminster (01985) 213161

McKELVEY, Canon Robert Samuel James Houston. b 42. QUB BA65 MA(Ed)88. CITC 67. **d** 67 **p** 68. C Dunmurry *Conn* 67-70; CF (TAVR) from 70; P-in-c Kilmakee *Conn* 70-77; I 77-81; N Ireland Educn Org from 81; Preb Newc St Patr Cathl Dub from 89. *19 Upper Lisburn Road, Belfast BT10 0GW* Belfast (01232) 619008 or 301130

McKELVIE, Canon Alfred. b 10. TCD BA34 MA43. CITC 35. **d** 35 **p** 36. I Ballynafeigh St Jude *D & D* 56-80; Adn Down 70-75; Chan Down Cathl 75-80; rtd 80. *50 Blenheim Park, Carryduff, Belfast BT8 8NN* Belfast (01232) 812682

McKEMEY, Alfred Douglas. b 18. Tyndale Hall Bris 38. **d** 42 **p** 43. V Burgess Hill St Andr *Chich* 68-84; RD Hurst 80-84; rtd 84; Perm to Offic *Chich* from 85; P-in-c Henfield w Shermanbury and Woodmancote 91-92. *45 Parsonage Road, Henfield, W Sussex BN5 9JG* Henfield (01273) 493222

McKEMEY, Canon Robert. b 15. St Aid Birkenhead 50. **d** 52 **p** 53. I Aghadowey w Kilrea *D & R* 69-73; R Meysey Hampton w Marston Meysey *Glouc* 73-81; RD Fairford 77-81; rtd 81. *3 Sevenoaks Road, Reading RG6 2NT* Reading (01734) 660501

McKENNA, Dermot William. TCD BA63 MA66. CITC 64. **d** 64 **p** 65. I Killeshin *C & O* 66-84; rtd 84. *20 Sherwood, Pollerton, Carlow, Irish Republic* Carlow (503) 32003

McKENNA, Lindsay Taylor. b 62. Glas Univ MA83 Aber Univ BD86. Edin Th Coll 87. **d** 87 **p** 88. C Broughty Ferry *Bre* 87-90; C Wantage *Ox* 90-93; V Illingworth *Wakef* from 93. *St Mary's Vicarage, 157 Keighley Road, Illingworth, Halifax, W Yorkshire HX2 9LL* Halifax (01422) 244322

MACKENNA, Richard William. b 49. Pemb Coll Cam BA71 MA75. Ripon Coll Cuddesdon BA77 MA81. **d** 78 **p** 79. C Fulham St Dionis Parson's Green *Lon* 78-81; C Paddington St Jas 81-85; Tutor Westcott Ho Cam 85-89; V Kingston All SS w St Jo *S'wark* 90-91. *187 Lichfield Court, Sheen Road, Richmond, Surrey TW9 1BB* 0181-940 0893

MACKENNA, Robert Christopher Douglass (Chris). b 44. Or Coll Ox BA72 MA75 MBAP85. Cuddesdon Coll 71. **d** 73 **p** 74. C Farncombe *Guildf* 73-77; C Tattenham Corner and Burgh Heath 77-80; P-in-c Hascombe 80-90; R from 90; RD Godalming from 91. *The Rectory, The Street, Hascombe, Godalming, Surrey GU8 4JA* Hascombe (01483) 208362

MACKENZIE, Canon Alan George Kett Fairbairn. b 11. OBE81. Univ of Wales BSc32. **d** 41 **p** 42. Chapl Miss and Coun to Deaf and Dumb 41-74; P-in-c Corscombe *Sarum* 75-77; P-in-c Halstock and the Chelboroughs 77; rtd 77. *Flat 3, 70 Richmond Road, Worthing, W Sussex BN11 4AF* Worthing (01903) 239780

MACKENZIE, Alfred Arthur. b 25. Bps' Coll Cheshunt 61. d 61
p 62. C Waltham Abbey Chelmsf 61-64; V Barking St
Erkenwald 64-72; V Broomfield 72-83; P-in-c Willerby w
Ganton and Folkton York 83-91; R from 91. The Vicarage,
Staxton, Scarborough, N Yorkshire YO12 4SF Sherburn
(01944) 710364
MACKENZIE, Andrew John Kett. b 46. Southn Univ BA68.
Local NSM Course 88. d 91 p 92. Fullbrook Sch New Haw
from 76; NSM Woodham Guildf from 91. 250 Albert Drive,
Sheerwater, Woking, Surrey GU21 5TY Byfleet (01932)
346712
MACKENZIE, Miss Ann. b 54. CertEd76 DipHE82 DPS86.
Trin Coll Bris 82. dss 85 d 87 p 94. Normanton Wakef 85-87;
Par Dn 87-90; Par Dn Bletchley Ox 90-94; C from 94. 13 Burns
Road, Bletchley, Milton Keynes MK3 5AN Milton Keynes
(01908) 366729
MACKENZIE, David Stuart. b 45. Linc Th Coll 66. d 69 p 70. C
Bishopwearmouth St Mary V w St Pet CD Dur 69-72; C
Pontefract St Giles Wakef 72-74; Chapl RAF from 74.
Chaplaincy Services (RAF), HQ, Personnel and Training
Command, RAF Innsworth, Gloucester GL3 1EZ Gloucester
(01452) 712612 Ext 5164 Fax 510828
MACKENZIE, George. b 09. MBE46 TD50. Worc Coll Ox
BA31 MA35. Wells Th Coll 32. d 33 p 34. R Sullington Chich
52-74; R Storrington 53-74; rtd 74; Perm to Offic Chich from
74. 21 The Martlets, West Chiltington, Pulborough, W Sussex
RH10 2QB West Chiltington (01798) 812771
MACKENZIE, Canon Iain MacGregor. b 37. Qu Coll Ox BA59
MA63 Edin Univ MTh69. Wycliffe Hall Ox. d 63 p 64. C
Southn St Mary w H Trin Win 63-66; C Christchurch 66-69; R
Dunoon Arg 69-75; V Pokesdown All SS Win 75-78; C
Woolston 78-79; C St Giles-in-the-Fields Lon 79-82; R St
Marylebone St Mary 82-89; Can Res Worc Cathl Worc from
89. 2 College Green, Worcester WR1 2LH Worcester (01905)
25238
McKENZIE, Ian Colin. b 31. CA56 Nottm Univ CTPS92.
E Midl Min Tr Course 89. d 93. NSM Edin St Mark Edin from
93; NSM Edin St Andr and St Aid from 93. 7 Highfield Close,
Ravenshead, Nottingham NG15 9DZ Mansfield (01623)
792162
MACKENZIE, Ian William (Bill). b 46. Trin Coll Bris DipHE95.
d 95. C Bideford Ex from 95. 61 Hanson Park, Bideford, Devon
EX39 3SB Bideford (01237) 477482
McKENZIE, Jack Llewellyn. b 29. FRSH AMIEHO MAMIT.
S'wark Ord Course. d 79 p 80. Hon C Stonebridge St Mich
Lon 79-88; Hon C Willesden St Mary from 88. 2 Beckett
Square, Chiltern Park, Berkhamsted, Herts HP4 1BZ
Berkhamsted (01442) 874265
MACKENZIE, Preb Lawrence Duncan. b 30. St Aid Birkenhead
52. d 55 p 56. C Blackb St Gabr Blackb 55-58; C Burnley St Pet
58-60; C St Giles-in-the-Fields Lon 60-63; V Queensbury All
SS 63-85; V Hillingdon St Jo from 85; Preb St Paul's Cathl
from 89. St John's Vicarage, Royal Lane, Uxbridge, Middx
UB8 3QR Uxbridge (01895) 233932
MacKENZIE, Peter Stirling. b 65. Univ Coll Lon BSc88. Oak
Hill Th Coll BA95. d 95. C Roxeth Lon from 95. 69 Southdown
Crescent, Harrow, Middx HA2 0QT
MACKENZIE, Peter Thomas. b 44. Lon Univ LLB67 Nottm
Univ DipTh68. Cuddesdon Coll 68. d 70 p 71. C Leigh Park
Portsm 70-75; P-in-c Sittingbourne St Mary Cant 75-82; V
Folkestone St Sav 82-90; RD Elham 89-90; R Cant St Martin
and St Paul from 90; RD Cant from 95. The Rectory,
13 Ersham Road, Canterbury, Kent CT1 3AR Canterbury
(01227) 462686
McKENZIE, Mrs Priscilla Ann (Cilla). b 47. St Jo Coll Nottm
87. d 93 p 94. NSM Ellon Ab from 93; NSM Cruden Bay from
93. High-Hame, 20 Bredero Drive, Ellon, Aberdeenshire
AB41 9QF Ellon (01358) 723484
MACKENZIE, Reginald James Sterling. b 11. Sarum Th Coll
55. d 57 p 58. V St Kew Truro 67-73; P-in-c St Hilary 73-78;
P-in-c Perranuthnoe 73-78; P-in-c St Hilary w Perranuthnoe
78-81; rtd 81. 7 Lindsey Court, Bognor Regis, W Sussex
PO22 8JQ
MACKENZIE, Richard Graham. b 49. St Aug Coll Cant 72. d 73
p 74. C Deal St Leon Cant 73-75; C Deal St Leon w Sholden
75-78; C Herne 78-81; Canada from 81. 46 Victoria Street,
Petawawa, Ontario, Canada, K8H 2G6
MACKENZIE, Simon Peter Munro. b 52. Univ Coll Ox BA74.
Coll of Resurr Mirfield 82. d 85 p 86. C Tipton St Jo Lich
85-91; V Perry Beeches Birm from 91. St Matthew's Vicarage,
313 Beeches Road, Birmingham B42 2QR 0121-360 2100
McKEON, Canon James Ernest. b 22. TCD BA45 HDipEd49
Div Test. d 46 p 47. Warden Wilson's Hosp Sch
Multyfarnham 64-83; Can Kildare Cathl M & K 83-88; Prec
87-88; P-in-c Geashill w Killeigh and Ballycommon 83-88; rtd

88; Dioc Info Officer (Meath) M & K 90-91; Radio Officer
from 91. Church House, Collinstown, Mullingar, Co
Westmeath, Irish Republic Collinstown (44) 66229
McKEON, Canon Victor Edward Samuel. b 39. FCA65 Lon
Univ BD. CITC. d 68 p 69. C Enniskillen Clogh 68-72;
Accountant to Conn & D & D 72-79; P-in-c Magherahamlet
D & D 77-79; I Derryvullen N w Castlearchdale Clogh 79-91;
Dioc Treas from 83; Can Clogh Cathl 86-89; Preb 89-95; Chan
from 95; I Monaghan w Tydavnet and Kilmore 91-95; RD
Monaghan 91-95; I Trory w Killadeas from 95. Trory Rectory,
Rossfad, Ballinamallard, Co Fermanagh BT94 2LS
Ballamallard (01365) 388477
MACKERACHER, Alasdair John. b 22. Linc Th Coll 69. d 71
p 72. C Oakdale St Geo Sarum 71-73; C Swanage 73-78; V W
Alvington w S Milton Ex 78-81; R Ashreigney 81-85; R
Broadwoodkelly 81-85; V Brushford 81-85; V Winkleigh
81-85; V Swimbridge and W Buckland 85-88; rtd 88. 2 Peak
Coach House, Cotmaton Road, Sidmouth, Devon EX10 8SY
MACKEY, John. b 34. Lich Th Coll. d 64 p 65. C Kells Carl
64-67; C Barrow St Matt 67-70; R Clayton Man 70-75; V Low
Marple Ches 75-83; R Coppenhall from 83. The Rectory,
Coppenhall, Crewe CW1 3TN Crewe (01270) 215151
MACKEY, Lionel John. b 47. FCA76 AITI78 TCD BTh93.
CITC 90. d 93 p 94. C Raheny w Coolock D & G from 93.
115 Ayrfield Drive, Dublin 13, Irish Republic Dublin (1)
847-3250 Fax as telephone
MACKEY, William John Noel. b 07. TCD BA28 MA51. CITC
30. d 31 p 32. Ch of Ireland Ind Officer 61-74; rtd 75; Perm to
Offic D & D from 75. 86 North Road, Belfast BT4 3DJ Belfast
(01232) 658470
McKIBBIN, Gordon. b 29. Lon Univ DipTh57. St Aid
Birkenhead 55. d 58 p 59. C Dundela D & D 58-60; C Knotty
Ash St Jo Liv 61-64; V Gt Sankey from 64. The Parsonage,
Parsonage Way, Great Sankey, Warrington WA5 1RP
Penketh (01925) 723235
MacKICHAN, Gillian Margaret (Gill). b 34. Bedf Teacher Tr
Coll DipPE56 Cam Univ CertEd56 Lon Univ DSocStuds76
CQSW80. S Dios Minl Tr Scheme 90. d 93 p 94. NSM Upper
Kennett Sarum from 93. West Bailey, Lockeridge,
Marlborough, Wilts SN8 4ED Marlborough (01672) 861629
MACKIE, Ian William. b 31. Lon Univ BSc53 Ex Univ PGCE54.
Linc Th Coll 81. d 83 p 84. C Market Rasen Linc 83-87; V
Bracebridge Heath from 87; RD Christianity from 92.
1 Churchill Avenue, Bracebridge Heath, Lincoln LN4 2JX
Lincoln (01522) 546451
McKIE, Kenyon Vincent. b 60. Aus Nat Univ BA83 Canberra
Coll DipEd84. ACT BTh88 DipMin89. d 86 p 87. Australia
86-89; Hon C Coulsdon St Andr S'wark from 89. 23 Rickman
Hill, Coulsdon, Surrey CR5 3DS Downland (01737) 557732
McKINLEY, Canon Arthur Horace Nelson. b 46. TCD BA69
MA79. CITC 70. d 70 p 71. C Taney Ch Ch D & G 71-76; I Dub
Whitechurch from 76; Preb Dunlavin St Patr Cathl Dub from
91. Whitechurch Vicarage, Whitechurch Road, Rathfarnham,
Dublin 16, Irish Republic Dublin (1) 493-3953
McKINLEY, George Henry. b 23. TCD BA44 MA51. d 46 p 47.
R Hackney St Jo Lon 65-72; TR Hackney 72-77; V Painswick
w Sheepscombe Glouc 77-83; Bp's Chapl 83-87; C Sandhurst
83-85; C Twigworth, Down Hatherley, Norton, The Leigh etc
85-87; rtd 88. The Chaplain's House, Laslett's Almshouses,
Union Street, Worcester WR1 2AS Malvern (01684) 568652
McKINNEL, Nicholas Howard Paul. b 54. Qu Coll Cam BA75
MA79. Wycliffe Hall Ox BA79 MA86. d 80 p 81. C Fulham St
Mary N End Lon 80-83; Chapl Liv Univ Liv 83-87; P-in-c
Hatherleigh Ex 87-88; R Hatherleigh, Meeth, Exbourne and
Jacobstowe 88-94; P-in-c Plymouth St Andr w St Paul and St
Geo 94-95; TR Plymouth St Andr and St Paul Stonehouse
from 95. St Andrew's Vicarage, 13 Bainbridge Avenue,
Plymouth PL3 5QZ Plymouth (01752) 772139 or 661414
McKINNEY, James Alexander. b 52. Ex Univ BA74 Hull Univ
MA87. Ripon Coll Cuddesdon 75. d 78 p 79. C Wath-upon-
Dearne w Adwick-upon-Dearne Sheff 78-82; V Doncaster
Intake 82-87; Ind Chapl 84-87; Chapl Bramshill Police Coll
Win 87-92; V Cleator Moor w Cleator Carl from 92; Chapl
Cumbria Constabulary from 93; P-in-c Frizington and
Arlecdon from 94. The Vicarage, Trumpet Road, Cleator,
Cumbria CA23 3EF Cleator Moor (01946) 810510
McKINNEY, Mervyn Roy. b 48. St Jo Coll Nottm. d 81 p 82. C
Tile Cross Birm 81-84; C Bickenhill w Elmdon 84-89; V
Addiscombe St Mary S'wark 89-93; V Addiscombe St Mary
Magd w St Martin from 93. St Mary Magdalene Vicarage,
Canning Road, Croydon CR0 6QD 0181-654 3459
McKINNEY, Dr Richard William Alexander. b 38. QUB BA62
New Coll Edin BD65 Ch Ch Ox DPhil70. d 83 p 84. Australia
from 84. Trinity College, Royal Parade, Parkville, Victoria,
Australia 3052 Melbourne (3) 349-0124 Fax 347-1610
McKINNON, Archibald Vincent. b 07. d 77 p 78. Hon C
Tranmere St Paul w St Luke Ches 77-79; Hon C W Kirby St

MACKINNON

Bridget 79-88; rtd 88; Perm to Offic *Ches* from 88. *4 Caldy Court, Caldy Road, Wirral, Merseyside L48 2HG*

MacKINNON, Mrs Karen Audrey. b 64. Ex Univ BA85. Linc Th Coll CMM92. **d** 92 **p** 94. Par Dn Filton *Bris* 92-93; Par Dn Bris Lockleaze St Mary Magd w St Fran 93-94; C from 94. *211 Romney Avenue, Bristol BS7 9SZ* Bristol (0117) 951 3098

McKINNON, Neil Alexander. b 46. Wycliffe Hall Ox 71. **d** 74 **p** 75. C Deptford St Nic w Ch Ch *S'wark* 74-76; C St Helier 76-79; Min W Dulwich All SS and Em 79-81; TV Thameshead from 87. *5 Finchale Road, London SE2 9PG* 0181-310 5614

MACKINNON, Ross Cameron. b 52. St Steph Ho Ox 86. **d** 88 **p** 89. C Monk Bretton *Wakef* 88-91. *4 Cornwall Close, Barnsley, S Yorkshire S71 2ND* Barnsley (01226) 281275

MACKINTOSH, Æneas. b 27. Kelham Th Coll 44. **d** 52 **p** 53. R Edin St Jo *Edin* 69-81; Can St Mary's Cathl 75-87; R Gullane 81-87; R N Berwick 81-87; Info Officer & Communications Adv to the Gen Syn 87-92; rtd 92. *31 St Albans Road, Edinburgh EH9 2LT* 0131-667 4160

MACKINTOSH, Robin Geoffrey James. b 46. Rhodes Univ BCom71 Cranfield Inst of Tech MBA78 Ox Univ BA85 MA91. Ripon Coll Cuddesdon 83. **d** 86 **p** 87. C Cuddesdon *Ox* 86; C Cannock *Lich* 86-89; R Girton *Ely* from 89. *The Rectory, 40 Church Lane, Girton, Cambridge CB3 0JP* Cambridge (01223) 276235 Fax as telephone

McKITTRICK, Douglas Henry. b 53. St Steph Ho Ox 74. **d** 77 **p** 78. C Deptford St Paul *S'wark* 77-80; C W Derby (or Tuebrook) St Jo *Liv* 80-81; TV St Luke in the City 81-89; V Toxteth Park St Agnes and St Pancras from 89. *St Agnes's Vicarage, 1 Buckingham Avenue, Liverpool L17 3BA* 0151-733 1742

McKITTRICK, Noel Thomas Llewellyn. b 28. TCD BA50 MA57 BD71. **d** 51 **p** 53. V Glastonbury St Benedict *B & W* 59-82; V Weston-super-Mare St Paul 82-92; rtd 93; Perm to Offic *Ex* from 94. *Priory Lodge, Latimer Road, Exeter EX4 7JP* Exeter (01392) 496744

McKNIGHT, John Andrew. b 49. **d** 78 **p** 79. Australia 78-89; C Eltham St Sav *S'wark* 89-90; C Catford St Laur 91-93; C Bellingham St Dunstan 91-93. *75 Bexhill Road, London SE4 1SJ* 0181-690 2904

McKNIGHT, Thomas Raymond. b 48. QUB BEd71. CITC 74. **d** 77 **p** 78. C Lisburn Ch Ch Cathl *Conn* 77-80; C Carrickfergus 80-82; I Kilcronaghan w Draperstown and Sixtowns *D & R* 82-86; I Magheragall *Conn* 86-91; RD Lisburn 88-91; CF from 91. *c/o MOD (Army), Bagshot Park, Bagshot, Surrey GU19 5PL* Bagshot (01276) 471717 Fax 412834

MACKRIELL, Peter John. b 64. Mansf Coll Ox BA85 MA93 Man Univ PGCE87. St Jo Coll Nottm BTh93 MA94. **d** 94 **p** 95. C Hale and Ashley *Ches* from 94. *St Peter's House, 233 Ashley Road, Hale, Altrincham, Cheshire WA15 9SS* 0161-941 1824

MACKRILL, Robert John. b 51. RIBA79 Univ Coll Lon BSc73 DipArch76. E Midl Min Tr Course 92. **d** 93 **p** 94. NSM Stamford All SS w St Jo *Linc* from 93. *110 Lonsdale Road, Stamford, Lincs PE9 2SF* Stamford (01780) 54490

MacLACHLAN (nee GRIFFITHS), Mrs Margaret. b 44. SRN67 Birm Poly CertEd81 Open Univ BA82. W Midl Minl Tr Course 92. **d** 95. NSM Tile Cross *Birm* from 95. *Wayside, 17 Chester Road, Birmingham B36 9DA* 0121-747 2340

MACLACHLAN, Michael Ronald Frederic. b 39. Wycliffe Hall Ox 75. **d** 77 **p** 78. C Mansf St Pet *S'well* 77-80; P-in-c Newark Ch Ch 80; TV Newark w Hawton, Cotham and Shelton 80-86; P-in-c Sparkhill St Jo *Birm* 86-90; P-in-c Sparkbrook Em 86-90; V Sparkhill w Greet and Sparkbrook 90-92; RD Bordesley 90-92; Canada from 92. *St Andrew's Mission, Coppermine, NWT, Canada, X0E 0E0*

McLACHLAN, Ms Sheila Elizabeth. b 52. SRN73 Kent Univ MA89. Wycliffe Hall Ox 80. **dss** 83 **d** 87 **p** 94. Chapl Kent Univ Cant 83-94; Dep Master Rutherford Coll 87-94; D-in-c Kingsnorth w Shadoxhurst 94; P-in-c from 94. *The Rectory, Church Hill, Kingsnorth, Ashford, Kent TN23 3EG* Ashford (01233) 620433

MacLAREN, Ms Clare. b 67. Edin Univ LLB88. Linc Th Coll BTh95. **d** 95. C Benchill *Man* from 95. *St Luke's House, Brownley Road, Manchester M22 4PT* 0161-945 7399

MacLAREN, Duncan Arthur Spencer. b 69. Or Coll Ox BA90. Oak Hill Th Coll 92. **d** 94 **p** 95. C Ox St Clem *Ox* from 94. *Family Centre Flat, Cross Street, Oxford OX4 1DA* Oxford (01865) 245385

MACLAREN, Grant. b 12. St Cath Coll Cam BA37 MA41. Wycliffe Hall Ox 37. **d** 39 **p** 40. V Derby St Pet and Ch Ch w H Trin *Derby* 57-73; V Stanley 73-80; rtd 80; Perm to Offic *Derby* from 80. *21 Tennessee Road, Chaddesden, Derby DE21 6LE* Derby (01332) 661226

MACLAREN (nee ALEXANDER), Mrs Jane Louise. b 69. LMH Ox BA90. Oak Hill Th Coll BA95. **d** 95. C Ox St Clem *Ox* from 95. *The Flat, St Clement's Family Centre, Cross Street, Oxford OX4 1DA* Oxford (01865) 790837

McLAREN, Mrs Jeanette Moira. b 59. **d** 95. C Dulwich St Clem w St Pet *S'wark* from 95. *9 Grass Mount, London SE23 3UW*

McLAREN, Richard Francis. b 46. Mansf Coll Ox DSocStuds69. S'wark Ord Course 72. **d** 75 **p** 76. C Charlton St Luke w H Trin *S'wark* 75-78; C Kensington St Mary Abbots w St Geo *Lon* 78-81; Hon C St Marylebone w H Trin from 82. *84 Clarence Gate Gardens, London NW1 6QR* 0171-262 4586

McLAREN, Robert Ian (Rob). b 62. Bris Univ BSc84 St Jo Coll Dur BA87. Cranmer Hall Dur 85. **d** 88 **p** 89. C Birkenhead Ch Ch *Ches* 88-90; C Bebington 90-95; V Cheadle All Hallows from 95. *All Hallows' Vicarage, 222 Councillor Lane, Cheadle, Cheshire SK8 2JG* 0161-428 9071

McLAREN, Ronald. b 31. Kelham Th Coll. **d** 59 **p** 60. C Redcar *York* 59-62; C Hornsea and Goxhill 62-65; V Middlesb St Thos 65-70; Chapl RN 70-73; Australia from 73. *56 Lincoln Street, Lindisfarne, Tasmania, Australia 7015* Hobart (2) 438134

McLAREN, William Henry. b 27. OBE94. Edin Th Coll 55. **d** 56 **p** 57. R Aber St Mary *Ab* 68-73; P-in-c Newland St Aug *York* 73-74; V 74-75; V Hull St Cuth 75-81; V Hedon w Paull 81-94; RD S Holderness 84-94; rtd 94. *Kirklea, Ottringham Road, Keyingham, Hull HU12 9RX* Withernsea (01964) 624159

McLARNON, Mrs Sylvia Caroline Millicent. b 45. S Dios Minl Tr Scheme 92. **d** 95. NSM Burgess Hill St Andr *Chich* from 95. *75 Cants Lane, Burgess Hill, W Sussex RH15 0LX* Burgess Hill (01444) 233902

McLAUGHLIN, Hubert James Kenneth. Greenwich Univ BTh93. **d** 88 **p** 89. NSM Donagheady *D & R* 88-89; NSM Glendermott from 89. *9 Cadogan Park, Kilfennan, Londonderry BT47 1QW* Londonderry (01504) 48916

MACLEAN, Alexander James. b 28. CEng MIStructE53. St Aid Birkenhead 52. **d** 55 **p** 56. R Largs *Glas* 69-71; V E Crompton *Man* 71-79; V Turners Hill *Chich* 79-89; rtd 89. *22 College Road, Ardingly, Haywards Heath, W Sussex RH17 6TY* Haywards Heath (01444) 892199

MACLEAN, Very Rev Allan Murray. b 50. Edin Univ MA72. Cuddesdon Coll 72. **d** 76 **p** 77. Chapl St Mary's Cathl *Edin* 76-81; Tutor Edin Univ 77-80; R Dunoon *Arg* 81-86; R Tighnabruaich 84-86; Provost St Jo Cathl Oban from 86; Can from 86; Can Cumbrae from 86; R Oban St Jo from 86; R Ardbrecknish from 86; R Ardchattan from 89; Miss to Seamen from 86. *The Rectory, Ardconnel Terrace, Oban, Argyll PA34 5DJ* Oban (01631) 62323

McLEAN, Dr Bradley Halstead. b 57. McMaster Univ Ontario BSc Toronto Univ MDiv MTh PhD. **d** 83 **p** 84. C Dur St Giles *Dur* 83-84; Canada from 84. *38 Tweedsmuir Road, Winnipeg R3P 1Z2, or St John's College, 400 Dysart Road, Winnipeg, Manitoba, Canada R3T 2M5*

MACLEAN, Donald Allan Lachlan. b 05. Linc Coll Ox BA27 MA31. Linc Th Coll 27. **d** 28 **p** 29. R Pitlochry *St And* 63-70; rtd 70; Perm to Offic *Mor* from 70. *Hazelbrae House, Glenurquhart, Inverness IV3 6TJ* Glenurquhart (01456) 476267

McLEAN, Canon Donald Stewart. b 48. TCD BA70. CITC 70. **d** 72 **p** 73. C Glendermott *D & R* 72-75; I Castledawson 75-87; Dioc Dir of Ords from 79; I Londonderry Ch Ch from 87; Can Derry Cathl from 91. *Christ Church Rectory, 80 Northland Road, Londonderry BT48 0AL* Londonderry (01504) 263279

MACLEAN, Dorothy. b 31. Dundee Coll DipEd70. **d** 86. NSM Kirriemuir *St And* from 82. *84 Slade Gardens, Kirriemuir, Angus DD8 5AG* Kirriemuir (01575) 72396

McLEAN, Mrs Eileen Mary. b 44. City Univ BSc67. N Ord Course 85. **d** 88 **p** 94. Par Dn Burley in Wharfedale *Bradf* 88-92; Par Dn Nottm St Pet and St Jas *S'well* 92-94; C from 94. *15 Hamilton Drive, The Park, Nottingham NG7 1DF* Nottingham (0115) 924 3354

McLEAN, Miss Frances Ellen. b 21. RGN44 SCM45. Edin Dioc NSM Course 85. **d** 88 **p** 94. NSM Penicuik *Edin* from 88; NSM W Linton from 88. *56 Cuikenburn, Penicuik, Midlothian EH26 0JQ* Penicuik (01968) 675029

MACLEAN, Kenneth John Forbes. b 31. St Deiniol's Hawarden 80. **d** 81 **p** 82. C Sedgley All SS *Lich* 81-85; V Shareshill 85-90; R Bicton, Montford w Shrawardine and Fitz from 90. *The Rectory, 15 Brookside, Bicton, Shrewsbury SY3 8EP* Shrewsbury (01743) 850519

MACLEAN, Lawrence Alexander Charles. b 61. K Coll Lon BD84 AKC84. Chich Th Coll 86. **d** 88 **p** 89. C Cirencester *Glouc* 88-91; C Prestbury from 91. *8 Boulton Road, Cheltenham, Glos GL50 4RZ* Cheltenham (01242) 523177

McLEAN, Ms Margaret Anne (Maggie). b 62. Birm Univ BA91. Qu Coll Birm 88. **d** 91 **p** 94. Par Dn Bedf All SS *St Alb* 91-94; C 94; Chapl St Alb High Sch for Girls from 94. *St Peter's Vicarage, Barnet Road, Barnet, Herts EN5 3JF* 0181-440 2046

McLEAN, Canon Michael Stuart. b 32. Dur Univ BA57. Cuddesdon Coll 57. **d** 59 **p** 60. C Camberwell St Giles *S'wark* 59-61; Lic to Offic *Nor* 61-68; R Marsham 68-74; R Burgh 68-74; RD Ingworth 70-74; P-in-c Nor St Pet Parmentergate w

St Jo 74-75; TV 75-78; TR 78-86; Hon Can Nor Cathl 82-86; Can Res Nor Cathl 86-94; P-in-c Nor St Mary in the Marsh 87-94; Perm to Offic from 94. *10 Fountain Court, Ipswich Road, Norwich NR1 2QA* Norwich (01603) 630398

McLEAN, Peter. d 94 **p** 95. C Mold *St As* from 94. *Trelawney, Bryn Coch Lane, Mold, Clwyd CH7 1PS* Mold (01352) 757337

McLEAN, Robert Hedley. b 47. St Jo Coll Dur BA69. Ripon Hall Ox 69. **d** 71 **p** 72. C Redhill St Jo *S'wark* 71-74; C S Beddington St Mich 74-77; C-in-c Raynes Park H Cross CD 77; P-in-c Motspur Park 77-80; V 80-84; V Tadworth from 84; Asst RD Reigate 92-93; RD Reigate from 93. *The Vicarage, The Avenue, Tadworth, Surrey KT20 5AS* Tadworth (01737) 813152

McLEAN-REID, Robert. b 43. Oak Hill Th Coll DipHE83. **d** 83 **p** 84. C Rainham *Chelmsf* 83-86; R Challoch w Newton Stewart *Glas* 86-87; R Aber St Pet *Ab* 87-90; P-in-c Aber St Clem 89-90; V Easington Colliery *Dur* 90-95; rtd 95. *The Vicarage, Easington Colliery, Peterlee, Co Durham SR8 3PJ* 0191-527 0272

MacLEAY, Angus Murdo. b 59. Solicitor 83 Univ Coll Ox BA81 MA86 Man Univ MPhil92. Wycliffe Hall Ox 85. **d** 88 **p** 89. C Rusholme *Man* 88-92; V Houghton *Carl* from 92. *The Vicarage, Houghton, Carlisle CA6 4HZ* Carlisle (01228) 810076 or 515972

MACLEAY, Very Rev John Henry James. b 31. St Edm Hall Ox BA54 MA60. Coll of Resurr Mirfield 55. **d** 57 **p** 58. C E Dulwich St Jo *S'wark* 57-60; C Inverness St Mich *Mor* 60-62; R 62-70; P-in-c Grantown-on-Spey 70-78; P-in-c Rothiemurchus 70-78; Can St Andr Cathl Inverness 77-78; R Fort William *Arg* from 78; Can St Jo Cathl Oban from 80; Can Cumbrae from 80; Syn Clerk 80-87; Dean Arg from 87. *St Andrew's Rectory, Parade Road, Fort William, Inverness-shire PH33 6BA* Fort William (01397) 702979

McLELLAN, Eric Macpherson Thompson. b 16. St Jo Coll Dur BA38 DipTh39 MA41. **d** 39 **p** 40. Chapl Br Emb Ch Paris *Eur* 70-80; Adn N France 79-80; Perm to Offic *Chich* from 80; Perm to Offic *Roch* from 80; rtd 81. *7 Stainer Road, Tonbridge, Kent TN10 4DS* Tonbridge (01732) 356491

MACLEOD, Alan Roderick Hugh (Roddie). b 33. St Edm Hall Ox BA56 MA61 Ox Univ DipEd62 Lon Univ DipCD69. Wycliffe Hall Ox 56. **d** 58 **p** 59. C Bognor St Jo *Chich* 58-61; Chapl Wadh Coll Ox 62; Hd of RE Picardy Boys' Sch Erith 62-68; C Erith St Jo *Roch* 63-69; Dean Lonsdale Coll Lanc Univ 70-72; Lic to Offic *Blackb* 70-72; Hd of RE K Edw VI Sch Totnes 72-73; Perm to Offic *Ex* 72-73; St Helier Boys' Sch Jersey 73-84; Lic to Offic *Win* 73-84; V Shipton Bellinger from 84. *St Peter's Vicarage, Shipton Bellinger, Tidworth, Hants SP9 7UF* Stonehenge (01980) 842244

MACLEOD, Everton William. b 57. DCR78. Oak Hill Th Coll DipHE91. **d** 91 **p** 92. C New Ferry *Ches* 91-93; C Moreton from 93. *40 Carnsdale Road, Moreton, Wirral, Merseyside L46 9QR* 0151-605 1241

MacLEOD, John Malcolm (Jay). b 61. Harvard Univ BA84 Pemb Coll Ox BA87. Linc Th Coll MDiv93. **d** 93 **p** 94. C Chesterfield St Aug *Derby* from 93. *32 Davian Way, Walton, Chesterfield, Derbyshire S40 3JG* Chesterfield (01246) 203776

MacLEOD, Kenneth. b 22. St Chad's Coll Dur BA50 DipTh52. **d** 52 **p** 53. C Holsworthy w Cookbury *Ex* 52-55; C Braunton 55-58; R Milton Damerel and Newton St Petrock etc 58-70; RD Holsworthy 66-70; V Kirkby Fleetham *Ripon* 70-89; R Langton on Swale 70-89; P-in-c Scruton 88-89; R Kirkby Fleetham w Langton on Swale and Scruton from 90. *The Rectory, Kirkby Fleetham, Northallerton, N Yorkshire DL7 0SB* Northallerton (01609) 748251

McLEOD, Canon Ronald. b 17. Lon Univ BA39 BA50 BD71 Ex Univ BA56 Man Univ MA59. Bps' Coll Cheshunt 39. **d** 41 **p** 42. Prin RAF Chapl Sch and Asst Chapl-in-Chief 69-73; QHC 72-73; R Itchen Abbas cum Avington *Win* 73-91; Hon Can Win Cathl 84-91; rtd 91. Perm to Offic *Ex* from 92. *Melfort, High Wall, Barnstaple, Devon EX31 2DP* Barnstaple (01271) 43636

McLEOD, Ms Susan Margaret. b 48. SEN69 Sheff Poly CQSW89 DipSocWork89. N Ord Course MTh95. **d** 95. NSM Charlesworth and Dinting Vale *Derby* from 95. *30 Lee Vale Drive, Charlesworth, Broadbottom, Hyde, Cheshire SK14 6HD* Glossop (01457) 866640

McLOUGHLIN, Ian Livingstone. b 38. CEng MICE64. Carl Dioc Tr Course 78. **d** 83 **p** 84. NSM Stanwix *Carl* 83-88; C Barrow St Geo w St Luke 88-90; R Kirkby Thore w Temple Sowerby and Newbiggin from 90. *The Rectory, Kirkby Thore, Penrith, Cumbria CA10 1UR* Kirkby Thore (017683) 61248

McLUCKIE, John Mark. b 67. St Andr Univ BD89. Edin Th Coll MTh91. **d** 91 **p** 92. C Perth St Ninian *St And* 91-94; Chapl K Coll Cam from 94. *52 Storey's Way, Cambridge CB3 0DX* Cambridge (01223) 327723 or 331251

MACLURE, Canon Andrew Seaton. b 15. Ch Coll Cam BA37 MA41. Lon Coll of Div 37. **d** 39 **p** 40. Uganda 41-86; Dean

Mvara 69-72; rtd 86; Perm to Offic *Chich* from 87. *42 Jonas Drive, Wadhurst, E Sussex TN5 6RL* Wadhurst (01892) 782708

McMAHON, Brian Richard. b 39. ACII. Oak Hill NSM Course 84. **d** 87 **p** 88. NSM Colney Heath St Mark *St Alb* from 87. *23 Bluebridge Avenue, Brookmans Park, Hatfield, Herts AL9 7RY* Potters Bar (01707) 655351

McMANN, Duncan. b 34. Jes Coll Ox BA55 MA60. Clifton Th Coll 55. **d** 58 **p** 59. C Newburn *Newc* 58-60; C Bishopwearmouth St Gabr *Dur* 60-62; N Area Sec BCMS 62-66; Midl and E Anglia Area Sec 66-92; Support Co-ord 84-92; Lic to Offic *Man* 62-66; Lic to Offic *Cov* 66-92; P-in-c Awsworth w Cossall *S'well* from 92; Chapl Notts Constabulary from 93. *The Vicarage, The Lane, Awsworth, Nottingham NG16 2QP* Nottingham (0115) 944 4887

McMANNERS, John. b 16. FRHistS73 FBA78 St Edm Hall Ox BA39 MA45 DLitt77 St Chad's Coll Dur DipTh47 Hon DLitt84. **d** 47 **p** 48. Regius Prof Ecclesiastical Hist Ox Univ 72-84; Can Res Ch Ch *Ox* 72-84; rtd 84; Chapl All So Coll Ox from 85. *71 Cunliffe Close, Oxford OX2 7BJ, or All Souls College, Oxford OX1 4AL* Oxford (01865) 279368

McMANUS, James Robert. b 33. Man Univ DPT82. Wycliffe Hall Ox 56. **d** 59 **p** 60. C Leic H Trin *Leic* 58-60; C Aylestone 60-63; India 66-79; V Oldham St Barn *Man* 79-83; Asst Regional Sec CMS 83-85; V Wolv St Matt *Lich* 85-93; V Lapley w Wheaton Aston from 93; P-in-c Blymhill w Weston-under-Lizard from 93. *The Vicarage, Pinfold Lane, Lapley, Stafford ST19 9PD* Wheaton Aston (01785) 840395

McMASTER, James Alexander. b 43. **d** 69 **p** 70. C Dundonald *D & D* 69-73; C Antrim All SS *Conn* 73-78; I Tempo and Clabby *Clogh* 78-83; I Knocknamuckley *D & D* 83-95; I Carrickfergus *Conn* from 95. *The Rectory, 12 Harwood Gardens, Carrickfergus, Co Antrim BT38 7US* Carrickfergus (01960) 363244

McMASTER, Richard Ian. b 32. Edin Th Coll 57. **d** 60 **p** 61. C Carl H Trin *Carl* 60-63; Tanganyika 63-64; Tanzania 64-66; V Broughton Moor *Carl* 66-69; V Burnley St Steph *Blackb* 69-77; V New Longton 77-89; P-in-c Woodhall Spa and Kirkstead *Linc* 89-91; P-in-c Langton w Woodhall 89-91; P-in-c Bucknall w Tupholme 89-91; P-in-c Horsington w Stixwould 89-91; R Woodhall Spa Gp from 92. *The Vicarage, Alverston Avenue, Woodhall Spa, Lincs LN10 6SL* Woodhall Spa (01526) 353856

McMASTER, William Keith. b 57. TCD. **d** 82 **p** 84. C Portadown St Columba *Arm* 82-84; C Erdington St Barn *Birm* 84-87; TV Shirley from 87. *1 Mappleborough Road, Shirley, Solihull, Birmingham B90 1AG* 0121-744 3123

McMICHAEL, Andrew Hamilton. b 48. Univ of Wales (Ban) BA77 Mansf Coll Ox DSocStuds74. Chich Th Coll 87. **d** 89 **p** 90. C Chorley St Geo *Blackb* 89-92; C Burnley St Andr w St Marg 92-94; Chapl Burnley Healthcare NHS Trust from 92; R Eccleston *Blackb* from 94. *The Rectory, Eccleston, Chorley, Lancs PR7 6NA* Eccleston (01257) 451206

McMONAGLE, William Archibald. b 36. CITC 65. **d** 68 **p** 69. C Magheralin *D & D* 68-71; C Ban Abbey 71-81; I Grey Abbey w Kircubbin from 81. *90 Newtownards Road, Greyabbey, Co Down BT22 2QJ* Greyabbey (012477) 88216

✠**McMULLAN, Rt Rev Gordon. b** 34. ACIS57 QUB BSc61 PhD71 Cam Univ DipRS78 Irish Sch of Ecum ThD87 TCD MPhil90 Univ of the South (USA) DMin. Ridley Hall Cam 61. **d** 62 **p** 63 **c** 80. C Ballymacarrett St Patr *D & D* 62-67; Cen Adv on Chr Stewardship to Ch of Ireland 67-70; C Knock 70-71; I 76-80; I Belf St Brendan 71-76; Offg Chapl RAF 71-78; Bp's Dom Chapl *D & D* 73-80; Adn Down 79-80; Bp Clogh 80-86; Bp *D & D* from 86. *The See House, 32 Knockdene Park South, Belfast BT5 7AB* Belfast (01232) 471973 Fax 650584

McMULLEN, Alan John. b 14. K Coll Cam BA36 MA41. Cuddesdon Coll 39. **d** 40 **p** 41. VC York Minster *York* 49-81; rtd 81. *2 Ramsey Avenue, Acaster Lane, Bishopthorpe, York YO2 1SQ* York (01904) 701121

McMULLEN, Philip Kenneth. b 55. RMN80 Glam Univ DMS92. St Mich Coll Llan DipTh95. **d** 95. C Coity w Nolton *Llan* from 95. *100 Fairfield Road, Bridgend, M Glam CF31 3DS* Bridgend (01656) 652948

McMULLEN, Ronald Norman. b 36. MBAC89 TCD BA61 MA66 Liv Univ DSocStuds73 York Univ DipCommW74 California Inst of Integral Studs San Francisco MA92. Ridley Hall Cam 61. **d** 63 **p** 64. C Fulham St Mary N End *Lon* 63-67; C Cam St Sepulchre *Ely* 67-70; C Everton St Ambrose w St Tim *Liv* 70-73; Community Work Course & Research Asst York Univ 73-75; P-in-c Heanor *Derby* 75-79; V 79-88; RD Heanor 76-83; USA 88-93. *18 Fleetwood Avenue, Holland-on-Sea, Clacton-on-Sea, Essex CO15 5SD* Clacton-on-Sea (01255) 815354

McMULLON, Andrew Brian. b 56. Sheff Univ BSc DipTh. St Jo Coll Nottm. **d** 83 **p** 84. C Stainforth *Sheff* 83-86; V Blackb Redeemer *Blackb* 86-90; Chapl RAF from 90. *Chaplaincy*

Services (RAF), HQ, Personnel and Training Command, RAF Innsworth, Gloucester GL3 1EZ   Gloucester (01452) 712612 Ext 5164   Fax 510828

McNAB (nee LUMMIS), Mrs Elizabeth Howieson. b 44. Lon Univ LDSRCSEng68 BDS68. St Jo Coll Nottm CertCS88. **d** 88 **p** 95. NSM Lerwick *Ab* from 88; NSM Burravoe from 88. *9 Blydoit, Scalloway, Shetland ZE1 0UG*   Scalloway (01595) 88327

MACNAB, Kenneth Edward. b 65. LMH Ox BA87 MA91. Coll of Resurr Mirfield 89. **d** 91 **p** 92. C Northn All SS w St Kath *Pet* 91-93; Lib Pusey Ho from 93. *Pusey House, Oxford OX1 3LZ*   Oxford (01865) 278415

McNAMARA, Michael Ian. b 59. Van Mildert Coll Dur BA81. Ridley Hall Cam 83. **d** 85 **p** 86. C Bedf Ch Ch *St Alb* 85-89; BCMS 89-92; Tanzania 89-92; TV Bolton St Paul w Em *Man* from 93. *Emmanuel Vicarage, Edward Street, Bolton BL3 5LQ*   Bolton (01204) 393282

McNAMEE, William Graham. b 38. Birm Univ BSocSc59. Cranmer Hall Dur BA74 DipTh. **d** 75 **p** 76. C Tonbridge St Steph *Roch* 75-78; C Fazeley *Lich* 78-87; Chapl Staffs Poly 87-92; Chapl Staffs Univ from 92. *19 Paragon Avenue, Westbury Park, Clayton, Newcastle, Staffs ST5 4EX*   Newcastle-under-Lyme (01782) 625544

MACNAUGHTON, Alexander. b 15. SS Coll Cam BA37 MA41. Linc Th Coll 40. **d** 41 **p** 42. India 48-73; C Derby St Thos *Derby* 74-80; Chapl Derbyshire R Infirmary 75-80; rtd 80; Perm to Offic *Derby* 80-92. *Flat 10, 40 Drummond Place, Edinburgh EH3 6NR*   0131-558 1700

MACNAUGHTON, Canon Donald Allan. b 17. Or Coll Ox BA40 MA43. Westcott Ho Cam 40. **d** 41 **p** 42. Hon Can Newc Cathl *Newc* 71-82; V Berwick H Trin 71-82; RD Norham 71-82; rtd 82; Chapl Marseille w St Raphael Aix-en-Provence etc *Eur* 82-87. *Flat 2, 18 Fidra Road, North Berwick, East Lothian EH39 4NG*   North Berwick (01620) 2841

MACNAUGHTON, James Alastair. b 54. St Jo Coll Ox BA78 Fitzw Coll Cam BA80. Ridley Hall Cam 78. **d** 81 **p** 82. C Rounds Green *Birm* 81-85; TV Bestwood Park *S'well* 85-86; TV Bestwood 86-90; V Amble *Newc* from 90. *The Vicarage, Church Street, Amble, Morpeth, Northd NE65 0DY*   Alnwick (01665) 710273

McNAUGHTON, John. b 29. St Chad's Coll Dur DipTh54. **d** 54 **p** 55. C Thorney Close CD *Dur* 54-58; C-in-c E Herrington St Chad CD 58-62; V E Herrington 62-66; CF from 66; V Hutton Cranswick w Skerne, Watton and Beswick *York* from 94. *47 Southgate, Hutton Cranswick, Driffield, N Humberside YO25 9QX*   Driffield (01377) 270869

MACNAUGHTON, William Malcolm. b 57. Qu Coll Cam BA80. Ridley Hall Cam 79. **d** 81 **p** 82. C Haughton le Skerne *Dur* 81-85; P-in-c Newton Hall 85-90; TV Shoreditch St Leon and Hoxton St Jo *Lon* from 90; AD Hackney from 94. *St John's Vicarage, Crondall Street, London N1 6PT*   0171-739 9823

McNEE, William Creighton. FIPM TCD DipTh Univ of Wales (Cardiff) DipPM Ulster Univ MA NUU MA. **d** 82 **p** 83. C Larne and Inver *Conn* 82-84; I Donagheady *D & R* 84-91; I Kilwaughter w Cairncastle and Craigy Hill *Conn* 91-93; I Ardstraw w Baronscourt, Badoney Lower etc *D & R* from 93. *2 Bunbeg Road, Newtownstewart, Omagh, Co Tyrone BT78 4NQ*   Newtownstewart (016626) 61342   Fax as telephone

McNEIGHT, Herbert Frank. b 14. Chich Th Coll. **d** 79 **p** 80. Hon C Southwick *Chich* from 79; Chapl Southlands Hosp Shore by Sea from 83. *12 Mile Oak Crescent, Southwick, Brighton BN42 4QP*   Brighton (01273) 592765

McNEIL, Mrs Ann. b 41. **d** 89 **p** 94. NSM Henfield w Shermanbury and Woodmancote *Chich* from 89. *Lancasters, West End Lane, Henfield, W Sussex BN5 9RB*   Henfield (01273) 492606

McNEILE, Donald Hugh. b 30. Trin Coll Cam BA53. Coll of Resurr Mirfield 53. **d** 55 **p** 56. C W Derby Gd Shep *Liv* 57-61; rtd 95. *Manor Farm Household, North Hinksey, Oxford OX2 0NA*   Oxford (01865) 245473

MACNEILL, Nicholas Terence. b 62. St Steph Ho Ox BTh93. **d** 93 **p** 94. C Ex St Thos and Em *Ex* from 93. *13 Sydney Road, Exeter EX2 9AJ*   Exeter (01392) 439501

McNEISH, Canon John. b 34. Edin Th Coll 58. **d** 61 **p** 62. C Kirkcaldy *St And* 61-64; Prec St Andr Cathl *Ab* 64-66; Chapl RAF 66-72; C Wootton Bassett *Sarum* 72-75; P-in-c Stour Provost w Todbere 75-79; TR Gillingham from 79; RD Blackmore Vale 81-86; Can and Preb Sarum Cathl from 92. *The Rectory, High Street, Gillingham, Dorset SP8 4AH*   Gillingham (01747) 822435

McNICOL, Andrew Keith. b 45. Westmr Coll of Educn CertEd69 Westmr Coll Ox DipApTh89 MA90 Open Univ BA79. Westmr Coll Cam 70 Westcott Ho Cam 92. **d** 92 **p** 93. In URC 73-92; C Whitstable *Cant* 92-95; V Ferring *Chich* from 95. *The Vicarage, 19 Grange Park, Ferring, Worthing, W Sussex BN12 5LS*   Worthing (01903) 241645

McNIVEN, Mrs Betty. b 47. Lanc Univ BA68. N Ord Course 83. **dss** 86 **d** 87 **p** 94. Baguley *Man* 86-87; Par Dn 87-88; Par Dn Newton Heath All SS 88-91; Par Dn E Farnworth and Kearsley 91-94; TV 94-95; P-in-c Spotland from 95. *10 Little Flatt, Rochdale, Lancs OL12 7AU*   Rochdale (01706) 48972

MACONACHIE, Canon Alwyn. b 21. TCD BA43 MA47 BD47. CITC 44. **d** 44 **p** 45. N Sec (Ireland) CMS 64-70; Gen Sec 70-74; I Glencraig *D & D* 74-91; RD Ban 78-91; Can Down Cathl 82-91; Prec 87-90; Chan 90-91; rtd 91. *16 Springhill Road, Bangor, Co Down BT20 3NR*   Bangor (01247) 466999

MACONACHIE, Canon Charles Leslie. b 27. TCD BA71 MA74 MDiv85 PhD90. Em Coll Saskatoon 47. **d** 50 **p** 51. C Clooney *D & R* 50-54; P-in-c Lower Tamlaght O'Crilly 54-61; Chapl Newsham Gen Hosp Liv 61-63; Chapl RAF 63-67; C Londonderry Ch Ch *D & R* 69-75; I Belmont 75-78; Warden for Min of Healing from 75; I Culmore w Muff and Belmont from 78; Warden Irish Internat Order of St Luke Physician from 82; Can Derry Cathl from 85. *The Rectory, Culmore Road, Heathfield, Londonderry BT47 8JD*   Londonderry (01504) 352396

MACOURT, Ven William Albany. b 19. TCD BA40 MA46. **d** 42 **p** 43. I Ballymacarrett St Patr *D & D* 64-89; Preb Swords St Patr Cathl Dub 75-89; adn Down *D & D* 80-89; Chan Belf Cathl 85-89; rtd 89; Dioc Info Officer *D & D* from 89. *4 Barnett's Road, Belfast BT5 7BA*   Belfast (01232) 794282

McPHATE, Dr Gordon Ferguson. b 50. Aber Univ MB, ChB74 Fitzw Coll Cam BA77 MA81 MD88 Surrey Univ MSc86 Edin Univ MTh94. Westcott Ho Cam 75. **d** 78 **p** 79. Hon C Sanderstead All SS *S'wark* 78-81; Hon PV S'wark Cathl 81-86; Lect Lon Univ 81-86; Hon C Edin St Mich and All SS *Edin* 86-89; Chapl and Lect St Andr Univ *St And* from 86; Sen Lect from 93. *68 Winram Place, St Andrews, Fife KY16 8XH*   St Andrews (01334) 476983

MacPHEE, Roger Hunter. b 43. Leeds Univ BSc65. E Anglian Minl Tr Course. **d** 86 **p** 87. NSM Trunch *Nor* from 86. *8 Lawn Close, Knapton, North Walsham, Norfolk NR28 0SD*   Mundesley (01263) 720045

McPHERSON, Andrew Lindsay (Andy). b 58. MIPM84 St Jo Coll Dur BA79. St Jo Coll Nottm DPS88. **d** 88 **p** 89. C Bitterne *Win* 88-92; V Weston from 92. *The Vicarage, Weston Lane, Southampton SO2 9HG*   Southampton (01703) 448421

MACPHERSON, Anthony Stuart. b 56. Qu Coll Birm 77. **d** 80 **p** 81. C Morley St Pet w Churwell *Wakef* 80-84; C Penistone 84-85; P-in-c Thurlstone 85-86; TV Penistone and Thurlstone 86-88; V Grimethorpe 88-95; P-in-c Westgate Common from 95. *St Michael's Vicarage, 166 Horbury Road, Wakefield, W Yorkshire WF2 8BQ*   Wakefield (01924) 380689

MACPHERSON, Archibald McQuarrie. b 27. Edin Th Coll 50. **d** 52 **p** 53. R Dumbarton *Glas* 63-92; rtd 92. *29 Bramblehedge Path, Alexandria, Dunbartonshire G83 8PH*   Alexandria (01389) 53981

MacPHERSON, David Alan John. b 42. Lon Univ DipTh71 BD75 Open Univ BA83 Hatf Poly MSc89. Clifton Th Coll 69 Trin Coll Bris 72. **d** 72 **p** 73. C Drypool St Columba w St Andr and St Pet *York* 72-76; Asst Chapl HM Pris Hull 72-76; P-in-c Bessingby *York* 76-78; P-in-c Carnaby 76-78; Chapl RAF 78-83; P-in-c Chedgrave w Hardley and Langley *Nor* 83-87; R from 87; Chapl Langley Sch Nor from 83. *The Rectory, Chedgrave, Norwich NR14 6NE*   Loddon (01508) 20535

MACPHERSON, Ewan Alexander. b 43. Toronto Univ BA74. Wycliffe Coll Toronto MDiv78. **d** 78 **p** 79. Canada 78-86; V Westbury sub Mendip w Easton *B & W* from 86; V Priddy from 86. *The Vicarage, Crow Lane, Westbury sub Mendip, Wells, Somerset BA5 1HL*   Wells (01749) 870254

MACPHERSON, John. b 28. Lon Univ BSc50 Ex Univ DipEd51 Univ of W Indies HDipEd65. St Alb Minl Tr Scheme 82. **d** 89 **p** 90. NSM Gt Berkhamsted *St Alb* from 89. *Southways, 5 Kingsdale Road, Berkhamsted, Herts HP4 3BS*   Berkhamsted (01442) 866262

MACPHERSON, Peter Sinclair. b 44. Lich Th Coll 68. **d** 71 **p** 72. C Honiton, Gittisham and Combe Raleigh *Ex* 71-72; C Bideford 72-74; C Devonport St Mark Ford 74-75; V Thorncombe *Sarum* 75-79; TV Dorchester 79-85; Chapl Jersey Gp of Hosps 85-90; Chapl Derriford Hosp Plymouth from 90; Lic to Offic *Ex* from 90. *Bymoor House, Down Lane, Buckland Monachorum, Yelverton, Devon PL20 7LN*   Plymouth (01752) 777111

McQUADE, William. b 09. BSP46. **d** 49 **p** 50. V Allhallows *Carl* 66-76; rtd 76; Perm to Offic *K, E & A* from 76. *Ballinafad, Via Boyle, Co Sligo, Irish Republic*

MacQUAIDE, Arthur John Allan. b 13. TCD BA37. **d** 38 **p** 39. I Garrison w Slavin and Belleek *Clogh* 60-80; Bp Dom Chapl 67-73; Preb Clogh Cathl 73-80; rtd 80; C Steeton *Bradf* 84-89. *Address temp unknown*

MACQUARRIE, Canon John. b 19. TD62. FBA84 Glas Univ MA40 BD43 PhD54 DLitt64 Hon DD69 Ox Univ MA70 DD81. **d** 65 **p** 65. USA 65-70; Lady Marg Prof of Div Ox Univ

70-86; Can Res Ch Ch *Ox* 70-86; rtd 86. *206 Headley Way, Oxford OX3 7TA*   Oxford (01865) 61889

MACQUIBAN, Gordon Alexander. b 24. Univ of Wales (Lamp) BA49 Crewe Coll of Educn CertEd72. Ely Th Coll 49. **d** 51 **p** 52. V Ches Ch Ch *Ches* 64-71; Hon C Ches H Trin 71-85; Hon C Runcorn All SS 85-87; Hon C Frodsham 87-88; rtd 88. *4 Avon Close, Hoveland Park, Taunton, Somerset TA1 4SU*   Taunton (01823) 282602

McQUILLAN, Miss Martha. b 33. St Mich Ho Ox 66. **dss** 70 **d** 87 **p** 94. Barnsbury St Andr *Lon* 70-72; Nottm St Ann w Em *S'well* 72-79; Chapl Asst Univ Hosp Nottm 79-90; Chapl Asst Nottm Gen Hosp 79-90; rtd 90. *27 Penarth Rise, Nottingham NG5 4EE*   Nottingham (0115) 962 1760

McQUILLEN, Brian Anthony. b 45. Ripon Hall Ox 73. **d** 75 **p** 76. C Northfield *Birm* 75-78; C Sutton Coldfield H Trin 78-80; V Bearwood 80-89; V Glouc St Geo w Whaddon *Glouc* from 89. *St George's Vicarage, Grange Road, Gloucester GL4 0PE*   Gloucester (01452) 520851

McQUILLEN-WRIGHT, Christopher Charles (Chris). b 71. Kent Univ BA92. Westcott Ho Cam CTM95. **d** 95. C Phillack w Gwithian and Gwinear *Truro* from 95; C Hayle from 95; C St Erth from 95. *Godrevy House, Penpol Avenue, Hayle, Cornwall TR27 4NQ*   Hayle (01736) 755870

MACRAE, Charles. b 27. RD71. Edin Univ BDS62. S Dios Minl Tr Scheme 88. **d** 91 **p** 92. NSM Heene *Chich* 91-94; NSM Portsea St Alb *Portsm* from 94. *64 Stone Lane, Worthing, W Sussex BN13 2BQ*   Worthing (01903) 693877

McRAE, Keith Alban. b 44. S'wark Ord Course 68. **d** 73 **p** 74. NSM Crawley *Chich* 73-78; NSM Ifield 78-90. *Plough Cottage, Ifield Street, Ifield, Crawley, W Sussex RH10 0NN*   Crawley (01293) 513629

MacRAE, Mrs Rosalind Phyllis. b 41. Sarum & Wells Th Coll 81. **dss** 84 **d** 94 **p** 94. Feltham *Lon* 84-87; Par Dn 87; Asst Chapl R Cornwall Hosp Truro 87-88; Chapl Mt Edgcumbe Hospice 88-92; Chapl St Austell Hosp 88-92; Chapl Penrice Hosp St Austell 88-92; NSM St Austell *Truro* 88-92; Chapl R Cornwall Hosp Trust Truro 92-95. *Christmas Cottage, 7 Church Lane, Mevagissey, St Austell, Cornwall PL26 6SX*   St Austell (01726) 842046

McREYNOLDS, Kenneth Anthony. b 48. TCD DipTh83. **d** 83 **p** 84. C Ballymena w Ballyclug *Conn* 83-86; I Rathcoole 86-90; I Lambeg from 90. *Lambeg Rectory, 58 Belfast Road, Lisburn, Co Antrim BT27 4AT*   Hillsborough (01846) 663872

MACROW-WOOD, Anthony Charles. b 60. ACA86 York Univ BA82 Jes Coll Cam BA91. Westcott Ho Cam CTM92. **d** 92 **p** 93. C Swindon St Jo and St Andr *Bris* from 92. *62 Purley Avenue, Parks South, Swindon SN3 2DS*   Swindon (01793) 619656

McSPARRON, Cecil. b 35. Regent Coll Vancouver MCS87 Bible Tr Inst Glas DipMin63 Trin Th Coll Singapore DipMin68 MMin77 MDiv86. **d** 68 **p** 69. C Glendermott *D & R* 68-70; Singapore 70-77 and 83-89; C Portadown St Mark *Arm* 78-80; UK Regional Dir OMF 80-87; Tutor Miss Studies Lon Bible Coll 90-93. *London Bible College, Green Lane, Northwood, Middx HA6 2UW*   Northwood (01923) 826061

McTEER, Robert Ian. b 56. Chich Th Coll 90. **d** 92 **p** 93. C S Shields All SS *Dur* 92-95; P-in-c Auckland St Helen from 95; Chapl Tindale Crescent Hosp Dur from 95. *The Vicarage, 8 Manor Road, Bishop Auckland, Co Durham DL14 9EN*   Bishop Auckland (01388) 604152

McVEAGH, Paul Stuart. b 56. Southn Univ BA78. Oak Hill Th Coll BA88. **d** 88 **p** 89. C Bebington *Ches* 88-92; BCMS 92-93; Crosslinks 93-95; Portugal 92-95; R High Halstow w All Hallows and Hoo St Mary *Roch* from 95. *The Rectory, Cooling Road, High Halstow, Rochester, Kent ME3 8SA*   Medway (01634) 250637

McVEETY, Ian. b 46. N Ord Course 82. **d** 85 **p** 86. NSM Langley and Parkfield *Man* 85-86; C 87-89; V Castleton Moor from 89. *The Vicarage, Vicarage Road North, Rochdale, Lancs OL11 2TE*   Rochdale (01706) 32353

McVEIGH, Miss Dorothy Sarah. b 67. QUB BA89 TCD BTh93. CITC 90. **d** 93 **p** 94. C Belf St Matt *Conn* from 93. *45 Lyndehurst Park, Belfast BT13 3PG*   Belfast (01232) 721581

McVEIGH, Samuel. b 49. CITC 77. **d** 79 **p** 80. C Drumragh w Mountfield *D & R* 79-82; I Dromore *Clogh* 82-90; RD Kilskeery 89-90; I Drumachose *D & R* from 90. *49 Killane Road, Limavady, Co Londonderry BT49 0DJ*   Limavady (015047) 62680

McVICAR, Sandra. See BUTLER, Mrs Sandra

MACVICAR, Miss Mary. b 23. Edin Univ MA44 Ox Univ DipEd45. Ripon Coll Cuddesdon 85. **dss** 86 **d** 87 **p** 94. Bishops Waltham *Portsm* 86-89; Hon C 87-89; Perm to Offic 89-94; Hon C Portsm Cathl 94-95; rtd 95; Perm to Offic *Portsm* from 95. *15 Roman Row, Bank Street, Bishops Waltham, Southampton SO32 1RW*   Bishops Waltham (01489) 895955

McWATT, Glenn Ellsworth. b 48. Birkb Coll Lon DipRS92. Lon Bible Coll 70 S'wark Ord Course 89. **d** 92 **p** 93. Hon C Tulse Hill H Trin and St Matthias *S'wark* from 92. *32 Brockwell Court, Effra Road, London SW2 1NA*   0171-274 5521 or 620 4444

MacWILLIAM, Very Rev Alexander Gordon. b 23. Univ of Wales BA43 Lon Univ BD47 PhD52. St Mich Coll Llan 43. **d** 45 **p** 46. Lect Trin Coll Carmarthen 58-84; Lic to Offic *St D* 60-78; Can St D Cathl 78-84; Prec, V, and Dean 84-90; rtd 90. *Pen Parc, Smyrna Road, Llangain, Carmarthen, Dyfed SA33 5AD*   Llansteffan (01267) 241333

McWILLIAM, Charles Denis. b 24. Clare Coll Cam BA49 MA52. Cuddesdon Coll 49. **d** 51 **p** 52. Perm to Offic *Sarum* 67-73; Perm to Offic *Eur* 73-80; V Heyhouses *Blackb* 80-88; V Sabden and Pendleton 88-89; rtd 89. *Standen Hall Farm House, Clitheroe, Lancs BB7 1PR*   Clitheroe (01200) 26442

MABBS, Miss Margaret Joyce. b 24. St Hilda's Coll Ox BA45 MA47 DipEd46 DipRS82. S'wark Ord Course 79. **dss** 82 **d** 87 **p** 94. Eltham Park St Luke *S'wark* 82-87; NSM from 87. *70 Westmount Road, London SE9 1JE*   0181-850 4621

MACCLESFIELD, Archdeacon of. See GILLINGS, Ven Richard John

MACE, Alan Herbert. b 28. Lon Univ BA49 Ex Inst of Educn TCert50. Wycliffe Hall Ox 59. **d** 60 **p** 61. C Folkestone H Trin w Ch Ch *Cant* 63-67; Lic to Offic *Win* from 67; rtd 93. *15 Bassett Heath Avenue, Southampton SO1 7GP*   Southampton (01703) 768161

MACE, Mrs Helen Elizabeth. b 31. Ox Univ MA52 Solicitor 56. Coll of Ascension 62. **dss** 74 **d** 87 **p** 94. Tadcaster *York* 77-84; Asst Chapl Leeds Gen Infirmary from 84; rtd 91; C Woodhouse and Wrangthorn *Ripon* from 94. *25 Grosvenor Park Gardens, Leeds LS6 2PL*   Leeds (0113) 276 0645

MACE, Robert Alfred Beasley. b 16. Leeds Univ BA49. Coll of Resurr Mirfield 48. **d** 50 **p** 51. V Barnsley St Pet *Wakef* 65-72; V Barnsley St Pet and St Jo 72-84; rtd 85; Perm to Offic *Wakef* from 85. *90 Blenheim Road, Barnsley, S Yorkshire S70 6AS*   Barnsley (01226) 283831

MACEY, Anthony Keith Frank. b 46. Univ of Wales (Cardiff) DipTh69. St Steph Ho Ox 69. **d** 71 **p** 72. C Ex St Thos *Ex* 71-76; V Wembury 76-88; RD Ivybridge 83-91; V Cockington from 88. *The Vicarage, 22 Monterey Close, Torquay TQ2 6QW*   Torquay (01803) 607957

MACEY, Ralph Arthur. b 14. TD63. Leeds Univ BA38. Coll of Resurr Mirfield 38. **d** 40 **p** 41. Hd of RE Newc Ch High Sch 67-80; Hon C Gosforth All SS *Newc* 67-76; Hon C Cullercoats St Geo from 76; rtd 79. *11 Trafalgar House, Oxford Street, Tynemouth, Tyne & Wear NE30 4PR*   0191-257 0019

MACHIN, Roy Anthony. b 38. BA79. Oak Hill Th Coll 76. **d** 79 **p** 80. C Halliwell St Pet *Man* 79-83; V Eccleston St Luke *Liv* 83-91; V Kendal St Thos *Carl* from 91; V Crook from 91. *St Thomas's Vicarage, South View Lane, Kendal, Cumbria LA9 4PL*   Kendal (01539) 721509

MACK, Mrs Gillian Frances (Gill). b 50. SCM72. Cant Sch of Min 84. **d** 87 **p** 94. NSM Deal St Geo *Cant* 87-88; NSM Deal St Leon and St Rich and Sholden 88-92; Par Dn 93-94; C from 94. *St Richard's Lodge, 73 St Richard's Road, Deal, Kent CT14 9JR*   Deal (01304) 374674

MACKLIN, Reginald John. b 29. Bris Univ BA52. Ely Th Coll 54. **d** 55 **p** 56. C W Hackney St Barn *Lon* 55-58; C E Ham St Mary *Chelmsf* 58-61; C Northolt St Mary *Lon* 61-64; Jordan 64-68; Palma de Mallorca and Balearic Is *Eur* 68-69; P-in-c Hammersmith St Matt *Lon* 69-70; V Stanwell 70-82; V Kimbolton *Ely* 82-88; V Stow Longa 82-88; RD Leightonstone 82-88; P-in-c Keyston and Bythorn 85-88; P-in-c Catworth Magna 85-88; P-in-c Tilbrook 85-88; P-in-c Covington 85-88; R Coveney from 88; R Downham from 88; RD Ely from 89. *The Rectory, Little Downham, Ely, Cambs CB6 2ST*   Pymore (01353) 699337

MACKNEY, John Pearson. b 17. Univ of Wales BA39 Lon Univ PGCE73 MA81. St D Coll Lamp 39. **d** 41 **p** 42. C Gelligaer *Llan* 41-44; CF 44-47; C Llangeinor *Llan* 47-49; P-in-c Cardiff All SS 49-58; Chapl HM Pris Cardiff 49-58; V Mountain Ash *Llan* 58-69; Hon C Streatley w Moulsford *Ox* from 81. *Merlebank, Reading Road, Moulsford, Wallingford, Oxon OX10 9JG*   Cholsey (01491) 651347

MADDEN, Robert Willis. b 14. TCD BA36 MA40. CITC 38. **d** 39 **p** 40. R Misterton w Walcote *Leic* 66-79; rtd 79; Perm to Offic *Derby* from 79. *22A Duffield Road, Little Eaton, Derby DE21 5DS*   Derby (01332) 832388

MADDEX, Patrick John. b 31. Edin Univ BSc54. Bps' Coll Cheshunt 55. **d** 57 **p** 58. C Baldock w Bygrave and Clothall *St Alb* 57-61; C Oxhey All SS 61-64; V Codicote 64-82; R Gt and Lt Wymondley w Graveley and Chivesfield from 82. *The Rectory, Great Wymondley, Hitchin, Herts SG4 7ES*   Stevenage (01438) 353305

MADDISON, Norman. b 12. St Jo Coll Dur BA34. **d** 35 **p** 36. R Wolsingham and Thornley *Dur* 64-77; rtd 77. *Whitfield Place, Wolsingham, Bishop Auckland, Co Durham DL13 3AJ*   Bishop Auckland (01388) 527127

MADDOCK, Mrs Audrey. b 27. Lon Univ CertEd79 Open Univ BA80. Bris Sch of Min 81. dss 84 d 87 p 94. Stanton St Quintin, Hullavington, Grittleton etc *Bris* 84-87; Par Dn 87-94; C 94; P-in-c Nettleton w Littleton Drew from 95. *1 Brookside, Hullavington, Chippenham, Wilts SN14 6HD* Malmesbury (01666) 837275

MADDOCK, David John Newcomb. b 36. Qu Coll Cam BA60 MA64. Oak Hill Th Coll 60. d 62 p 63. C Bispham *Blackb* 62-65; R 82-93; Canada 65-70; R Walsoken *Ely* 70-77; V Ore Ch Ch *Chich* 77-82; RD Blackpool *Blackb* 90-93; V Fowey *Truro* from 93. *The Vicarage, Church Avenue, Fowey, Cornwall PL23 1BU* Fowey (01726) 833535

MADDOCK, Eric John. b 99. Oak Hill Th Coll 54. d 54 p 55. V Preston St Mary *Blackb* 62-66; rtd 69. *The Vicarage, Fowey, Cornwall PL23 1BU* Fowey (01726) 833535

MADDOCK, Francis James Wilson. b 14. Bris Univ BA36 Wadh Coll Ox BA38 MA42. Cuddesdon Coll 39. d 40 p 41. R Boscastle w Davidstow *Truro* 64-74; TR 74-78; P-in-c Port Isaac 78-79; rtd 79; Perm to Offic *Ex* from 87. *8 Sylvan Close, Exmouth, Devon EX8 3BQ* Exmouth (01395) 274381

MADDOCK, Nicholas Rokeby. b 47. ABSM72 Birm Coll of Educn CertEd73. Linc Th Coll 82. d 82 p 83. C Romford St Edw *Chelmsf* 82-87; V Sway *Win* 87-94; V Taunton St Mary B & W from 94. *St Mary's Vicarage, Church Square, Taunton, Somerset TA1 1SA* Taunton (01823) 272441

MADDOCK, Norman. b 15. St Jo Coll Dur BA38 DipTh39 MA41. d 39 p 40. V Chatburn *Blackb* 69-79; Perm to Offic *Blackb* from 79. R Warton St Oswald w Yealand Conyers 79-84; rtd 80. *22 Norbroom Drive, Newport, Shropshire TF10 7TD* Newport (01952) 814256

MADDOCK, Philip Arthur Louis. b 47. Open Univ BA82. Oak Hill Th Coll 75. d 78 p 79. C New Ferry *Ches* 78-81; C Barnston 81-82; V Over St Jo 82-85; Chapl to the Deaf 85-88; V Norley 85-88; P-in-c Treales *Blackb* from 88; Chapl to the Deaf from 88. *The Vicarage, Church Road, Treales, Preston PR4 3SH* Preston (01772) 682219

MADDOCK, Canon Philip Lawrence. b 20. Bris Univ BA42. Cuddesdon Coll 42. d 43 p 44. Chapl St Lawr Hosp Bodmin 69-76; Can Res and Treas Truro Cathl *Truro* 76-88; rtd 88. *31 Trenethick Avenue, Helston, Cornwall TR13 8LU* Helston (01326) 564909

✠**MADDOCKS, Rt Rev Morris Henry St John.** b 28. Trin Coll Cam BA52 MA56. Chich Th Coll. d 54 p 55 c 72. C Ealing St Pet Mt Park *Lon* 54-55; C Uxbridge St Andr w St Jo 55-58; V Weaverthorpe w Helperthorpe and Luttons *York* 58-61; V Scarborough St Martin 61-72; Suff Bp Selby 72-83; Adv Min Health and Healing to Abps Cant and York from 83; Asst Bp B & W 83-87; Asst Bp Chich from 87; Jt Founding Dir Acorn Chr Healing Trust from 91; Can and Preb Chich Cathl from 92. *Acorn Christian Healing Trust, Whitehill Chase, High Street, Bordon, Hants GU35 0AP* Bordon (01420) 478121 or 472779 Fax 478122

MADDOX, Preb Bernard Thomas. b 31. Kelham Th Coll 48 St Steph Ho Ox 53. d 55 p 56. V Burslem St Werburgh *Lich* 60-74; Chapl Haywood and Stanfield Hosps Stoke-on-Trent 60-74; P-in-c Shrewsbury All SS *Lich* 74-76; P-in-c Shrewsbury St Mich 74-76; P-in-c Shrewsbury St Mary 74-76; V Shrewsbury St Mary w All SS and St Mich 76-87; V Shrewsbury All SS w St Mich 87-91; RD Shrewsbury 82-91; Preb Lich Cathl from 86; I St Jo Hosp Lich 91-93; rtd 93. *The Master's House, St John's Hospital, Lichfield, Staffs WS13 6PB* Lichfield (01543) 264169

MADDOX, David John. b 34. AIMLS58. Sarum & Wells Th Coll 92. d 81 p 93. In RC Ch 81-91; NSM Wimborne Minster and Holt *Sarum* 93-95; NSM Canford Magna from 95. *298 Wimborne Road, Poole, Dorset BH15 3EG* Poole (01202) 672597

MADDOX, David Morgan. b 22. Univ of Wales (Lamp) BA42 Trin Coll Cam BA61 MA64. St Mich Coll Llan 42. d 45 p 46. V Trumpington *Ely* 56-90; rtd 90. *48 High Street, Barton, Cambridge CB3 7BG* Cambridge (01223) 264127

MADDOX, Edwin Joseph Crusha. b 09. Dorchester Miss Coll 38. d 41 p 42. V Walthamstow St Sav *Chelmsf* 61-71; V Leigh-on-Sea St Jas 71-77; rtd 77. *43 Barnard Road, Leigh-on-Sea, Essex SS9 3PH* Southend-on-Sea (01702) 776822

MADDOX, Goronwy Owen. b 23. Univ of Wales (Swansea) BA52 DipEd53. Sarum Th Coll 67. d 70 p 71. Hd Master H Trin Sch Calne 57-82; Hon C Calne and Blackland *Sarum* 70-82; C 82-83; V Llywel and Traean-glas w Llanulid S & B 83-92; rtd 92. *4 St Matthews Close, Rowde, Devizes, Wilts SN10 2PG* Devizes (01380) 728965

MADDOX, Hugh Inglis Monteath. b 37. CCC Cam BA60. Westcott Ho Cam 61. d 63 p 64. C Attercliffe *Sheff* 63-66; C Maidstone All SS w St Phil *Cant* 66-67; C Folkestone St Mary and St Eanswythe 67-69; C St Martin-in-the-Fields *Lon* 69-73; R Sandwich *Cant* 73-81; V St Peter-in-Thanet 81-84; V Red Post *Sarum* from 84. *The Vicarage, Morden, Wareham, Dorset BH20 7DR* Morden (01929) 459244

MADDY, Kevin. b 58. GRNCM79 Selw Coll Cam BA83. Westcott Ho Cam 81. d 85 p 86. C St Peter-in-Thanet *Cant* 85-88; Perm to Offic *Nor* from 88; Chapl RAF from 88. *Chaplaincy Services (RAF), HQ, Personnel and Training Command, RAF Innsworth, Gloucester GL3 1EZ* Gloucester (01452) 712612 Ext 5164 Fax 510828

MADELEY, Mark Keith. b 68. Oak Hill Th Coll BA93. d 93 p 94. C Mickleover All SS *Derby* from 93. *7 Barnwood Close, Mickleover, Derby DE3 5QY* Derby (01332) 511340

MADGE, Francis Sidney. b 35. AKC58. d 59 p 60. C York St Mary Bishophill Senior *York* 59-62; C Sutton St Mich 62-64; C Ex St Jas *Ex* 64-69; R Sutton by Dover w Waldershare *Cant* 69-78; P-in-c W Wickham St Mary 78-81; V 81-84; V W Wickham St Mary *S'wark* from 85. *St Mary's Vicarage, The Avenue, West Wickham, Kent BR4 0DX* 0181-777 3137

MAGAHY, Canon Gerald Samuel. b 23. TCD BA45 MA61 LLD80 Univ Coll Galway HDipEd55. d 53 p 54. Chapl and Hd Master K Hosp Sch Dub 61-83; Treas St Patr Cathl Dub 80-89; Chan 89-91; Prec 91-95; rtd 95. *Seacrest, Bray Head, Co Wicklow, Irish Republic* Skibbereen (28) 67231

MAGEE, Francis Malcolm. b 24. Edin Univ MA49. d 54 p 55. Lic to Offic *S'wark* 71-75; Hon C Abbey Wood 75-78; C Mottingham St Andr 79-81; C Rotherhithe St Mary w All SS 81-83; C Rotherhithe St Kath w St Barn 83-89; rtd 89. *33 Apthorpe Street, Fulbourn, Cambs CB1 5EY* Cambridge (01223) 880218

MAGEE, Frederick Hugh. b 33. Yale Univ BA57. Westcott Ho Cam 58. d 59 p 60. C Bury St Mark *Man* 59-62; USA 63-64 and from 87; Chapl St Paul's Cathl Dundee *Bre* 74-79; P-in-c Invergowrie 76-79; R St Andrews St Andr *St And* 79-83; R Lunan Head 83-87; R Forfar 83-87. *220 Cottage Avenue, Box 351, Cashmere, Washington 98815-1004, USA* Cashmere (509) 782-2786

MAGEE, John Lawrence. b 19. Lon Univ BA52. d 78 p 78. Hon C Westbury-on-Severn w Flaxley and Blaisdon *Glouc* 78-89; rtd 89; Perm to Offic *Glouc* from 89. *Sharon, Blaisdon, Longhope, Glos GL17 0AL* Gloucester (01452) 831217

MAGEE, Canon Patrick Connor. b 15. K Coll Cam BA37 MA41. Westcott Ho Cam 38. d 39 p 40. Chapl Bryanston Sch Blandford 60-70; V Ryde All SS *Portsm* 70-72; Chapl Tiffin Sch Kingston-upon-Thames 72-73; V Salisbury St Mich *Sarum* 73-75; TR Bemerton 75-84; rtd 84. *16A Donaldson Road, Salisbury SP1 3AD* Salisbury (01722) 324278

MAGILL, Robert James Henderson (Bobby). b 59. Paisley Coll of Tech BSc81. Sarum & Wells Th Coll DipThMin94. d 94 p 95. C W Moors *Sarum* from 94. *21 Weavers Close, West Moors, Ferndown, Dorset BH22 0PG* Ferndown (01202) 891816

MAGILL, Walter Brian Brendan. b 20. TCD BA42 BD45. d 44 p 45. Lect Div Nottm Coll of Educn 62-75; Hd of Dept Trent Poly 75-85; Lic to Offic *S'well* from 66; rtd 85. *16 Parkcroft Road, Nottingham NG2 6FN* Nottingham (0115) 923 3293

MAGNESS, Anthony William John. b 37. New Coll Ox BA62 MA65. Coll of Resurr Mirfield 78. d 80 p 81. C Gt Crosby St Faith *Liv* 80-83; C Newc St Jo *Newc* 83-85; P-in-c Newc St Luke 85-88; P-in-c Newc St Andr 88; V Newc St Andr and Newc St Luke from 89; Chapl Hunters Moor Hosp from 89. *The Vicarage, 15 Claremont Street, Newcastle upon Tyne NE2 4AH* 0191-232 3341

MAGOR, Robert Jolyon. b 47. Wilson Carlile Coll IDC82 Sarum & Wells Th Coll DCTM93. d 93. C Plaistow *Chelmsf* from 93. *181 Balaam Street, London E13 8AA* 0181-470 2531

MAGOWAN, Alistair James. b 55. Leeds Univ BSc77 DipHE. Trin Coll Bris 78. d 81 p 82. C Owlerton *Sheff* 81-84; C Dur St Nic *Dur* 84-89; Chapl St Aid Coll Dur 85-89; V Egham *Guildf* from 89; RD Runnymede from 93. *The Vicarage, Vicarage Road, Egham, Surrey TW20 9JN* Egham (01784) 432066

MAGOWAN, Harold Victor. b 34. ACII69 FCII73 Chartered Insurance Practitioner 89 QUB BA55 BSc(Econ)66 DipEd69. TCD Div Sch Div Test57. d 57 p 58. C Antrim All SS w Muckamore *Conn* 57-59. *95A Groomsport Road, Bangor, Co Down BT20 5NG*

MAGSON, Thomas Symmons. b 09. MA. d 75 p 76. NSM Highworth w Sevenhampton and Inglesham etc *Bris* 75-88; Perm to Offic from 88. *21 Cricklade Road, Highworth, Swindon SN6 7BW* Swindon (01793) 762579

MAGUIRE, Canon Brian William. b 35. Hull Univ BTh84 MA88. Coll of Resurr Mirfield 70. d 72 p 73. C Guisborough *York* 72-76; TV Haxby w Wigginton 76-77; TR 78-89; V Huddersfield St Pet and All SS *Wakef* from 89; Hon Can Wakef Cathl from 94. *59 Lightridge Road, Huddersfield HD2 2HF* Huddersf'd (0484) 544558 or 427964

MAHONEY, William Denis. b 35. Sem of the Immaculate Conception (NY) 77. d 79. In RC Ch 79-87; USA 79-87; NSM Egremont and Haile *Carl* 92-93; NSM Kells from 93. *Manresa, 8 Priory Road, St Bees, Cumbria CA27 0HB* Egremont (01946) 822262

MAHONY, Conal Martin. b 38. Pontificio Ateneo Antoniano Rome LicSTh64 Lateran Univ Rome ThD66. Franciscan Ho of Studies 57. d 62 p 63. In RC Ch 62-89; Dir Folkestone

Family Care Cen 86-92; Lic to Offic *Cant* 89-92; C Hempnall *Nor* 92-94; TV from 94. *24 Triple Plea Road, Woodton, Bungay, Suffolk NR35 2NS* Woodton (01508) 482397

MAHOOD, Canon Brian Samuel. b 12. St Jo Coll Dur BA39 MA42. **d** 39 **p** 40. V Squirrels Heath *Chelmsf* 53-79; Hon Can Chelmsf Cathl 76-79; rtd 79. *Jesmond Dene Cottages, 79 Tenterfield Road, Maldon, Essex CM9 7EN* Maldon (01621) 855366

MAIDEN, Charles Alistair Kingsley. b 60. Trent Poly BSc84. St Jo Coll Nottm LTh88. **d** 89 **p** 90. C Porchester *S'well* 89-93; C Selston from 93. *The Parsonage, Church Hill, Jacksdale, Notts NG16 5HR* Ripley (01773) 602800

MAIDMENT, Thomas John Louis (Tom). b 43. Lon Univ BSc65. St Steph Ho Ox. **d** 67 **p** 68. C Westmr St Steph w St Jo *Lon* 67-73; P-in-c Twickenham Common H Trin 73-77; V 77-80; V Heston from 80. *The Vicarage, 147 Heston Road, Hounslow TW5 0RD* 0181-570 2288

MAIDSTONE, Archdeacon of. *See* EVANS, Ven Patrick Alexander Sidney

MAIDSTONE, Suffragan Bishop. *See* REID, Rt Rev Gavin Hunter

MAIN, David. b 16. Man Univ BA40 St Jo Coll Ox BA48 MA53. Cuddesdon Coll 40. **d** 41 **p** 42. R Bracon Ash w Hethel *Nor* 57-73; rtd 73. *3 Low Farm Cottages, Keswick Road, Norwich NR4 6TX* Norwich (01603) 58109

MAIN, Canon David Murray. b 28. Univ Coll Ox BA52 MA56. St Deiniol's Hawarden 73. **d** 73 **p** 74. C Glas St Marg *Glas* 73-75; R Challoch w Newton Stewart 75-79; R Kilmarnock 79-93; Can St Mary's Cathl 85-93; rtd 93; Hon Can St Mary's Cathl *Glas* from 93; Hon C Challoch w Newton Stewart from 94. *Sunnybrae, 50 Abercromby Road, Castle Douglas, Kirkcudbrightshire DG7 1BA* Castle Douglas (01556) 504669

MAINA, Simon Mwangi. b 52. Nairobi Univ 85. **d** 80 **p** 81. Kenya 80-95; C Acton St Mary *Lon* from 95. *39 Derwentwater Road, London W3 6DF* 0181-993 8201

MAINES, Trevor. b 40. Leeds Univ BSc63. Ripon Hall Ox 63. **d** 65 **p** 66. C Speke All SS *Liv* 65-70; C Stevenage St Geo *St Alb* 70-73; V Dorridge *Birm* 73-78; Org Sec (Dio Ex) CECS 79-80; Hon C Tiverton St Pet *Ex* 79-80; Org Sec (Wales) CECS 80-87; Hon C Newton Nottage *Llan* 81-83; Perm to Offic *Mon* 83-87; V Arlesey w Astwick *St Alb* 87-95; RD Shefford 91-95; V Goldington from 95. *St Mary's Vicarage, Church Lane, Goldington, Bedford MK41 0AP* Bedford (01234) 355024

MAINEY, Ian George. b 51. CertEd73. Oak Hill Th Coll DipHE86 BA87. **d** 87 **p** 88. C Denton Holme *Carl* 87-91; V Hensingham from 91. *The Vicarage, Egremont Road, Hensingham, Whitehaven, Cumbria CA28 8QW* Whitehaven (01946) 692822

MAINWARING, Islwyn Paul. b 52. Univ of Wales (Swansea) BD75 DPS79. St Mich Coll Llan 77. **d** 79 **p** 80. C Llanilid w Pencoed *Llan* 79-82; C Llanishen and Lisvane 82-85; TV Cwmbran *Mon* 85-88; V Troedyrhiw w Merthyr Vale *Llan* 88-91. *Pennant, 109 Penygroes Road, Blaenau, Ammanford, Dyfed SA18 3BZ* Ammanford (01269) 850350

MAINWARING, William Douglas. b 26. Univ of Wales (Swansea) DipTh73. St Mich Coll Llan 72. **d** 74 **p** 75. C Aberdare St Fagan *Llan* 76-78; V Seven Sisters 78-80; rtd 80; Perm to Offic *Llan* from 80. *3 Rhiw Nant, Abernant, Aberdare, M Glam CF44 0QB* Aberdare (01685) 878409

MAIR, Canon James Fraser. b 25. St Pet Hall Ox BA49 MA53. Wycliffe Hall Ox 49. **d** 51 **p** 52. R Bacton w Wyverstone *St E* 67-80; V Thurston 80-89; Hon Can St E Cathl 87-89; rtd 89; Perm to Offic *St E* from 90. *The Maltings, Shop Green, Bacton, Stowmarket, Suffolk IP14 4LF* Bacton (01449) 781896

MAIRS, Adrian Samuel. b 43. DipHE. Oak Hill Th Coll 76. **d** 78 **p** 79. C Rugby St Matt *Cov* 78-82; P-in-c Mancetter 82-84; V from 84. *The Vicarage, Quarry Lane, Mancetter, Atherstone, Warks CV9 1NL* Atherstone (01827) 713266

MAITIN, Ito. b 36. Lon Univ DipTh67 BA. Kelham Th Coll 63. **d** 68 **p** 69. C Longton St Jo *Lich* 68-69; C Leek St Edw 69-71; C Lich St Chad 71-74; C Tamworth 74-81; V Penkhull from 81. *The Vicarage, 214 Queen's Road, Stoke-on-Trent ST4 7LG* Stoke-on-Trent (01782) 414092

MAITLAND, Sydney Milivoge Patrick. b 51. Edin Univ BSc Strathclyde Univ DipTP. Glas Univ BSc St Geo *Glas* from 86. *14 Kersland Street, Glasgow G12 8BL* 0141-339 4573

MAJOR, Maurice Edward. b 23. E Anglian Minl Tr Course. **d** 84 **p** 85. NSM Field Dalling w Saxlingham *Nor* 84-87; NSM Sharrington 84-87; NSM Gunthorpe w Bale 84-87; NSM Gunthorpe w Bale w Field Dalling, Saxlingham etc 87-89; Perm to Offic *St As* 89-93; Perm to Offic *Nor* from 93. *Endymion, Creake Road, Burnham Market, King's Lynn, Norfolk PE31 8EW* Fakenham (01328) 738757

MAJOR, Richard James Edward. b 54. DipTh. Trin Coll Bris 78. **d** 81 **p** 82. C Parr *Liv* 81-84; V Burton Fleming w Fordon *York* 84-85; V Grindale and Ergham 84-85; P-in-c Wold Newton

84-85; V Burton Fleming w Fordon, Grindale etc 85-91; V Bilton St Pet from 91. *The Vicarage, 116 Main Road, Bilton, Hull HU11 4AD* Hull (01482) 811441

MAJOR, Dr Richard John Charles. b 63. Ex Coll Ox BA91 MA93 Magd Coll Cam DPhil91 Massey Univ (NZ) MA85. St Steph Ho Ox 92. **d** 94. C Truro Cathl *Truro* from 94. *14 Merrick Avenue, Truro, Cornwall TR1 1NF* Truro (01872) 27576 or 76782 Fax 77788

MAKAMBWE, Francis James. b 40. St Jo Sem Lusaka. **d** 65 **p** 67. Zambia 65-91; C Waterloo St Jo w St Andr *S'wark* from 92; Miss Partner CMS from 91. *1 Cranfield Row, Gerridge Street, London SE1 7QN* 0171-928 4871 or 928 8681 Fax 401 3215

MAKEL, Arthur. b 39. Sheff Poly DMS75. AKC63. **d** 64 **p** 65. C Beamish *Dur* 64-68; Ind Chapl *York* 68-72; P-in-c Scotton w Northorpe *Linc* 72-81; Ind Chapl 72-81; R Epworth 81-89; P-in-c Wroot 81-89; R Epworth and Wroot 89-92; R Sigglesthorne and Rise w Nunkeeling and Bewholme *York* from 92. *The Rectory, Sigglesthorne, Hull HU11 5QA* Hornsea (01964) 533033

MAKEPEACE, David Norman Harry. b 51. Magd Coll Ox BA74. Trin Coll Bris 83. **d** 85 **p** 86. C Romford Gd Shep Collier Row *Chelmsf* 85-88; Tanzania 88-89; C York St Paul *York* 89-91; TV Radipole and Melcombe Regis *Sarum* from 91. *The Vicarage, 106 Spa Road, Weymouth, Dorset DT3 5ER* Weymouth (01305) 771938

MAKEPEACE, James Dugard. b 40. Keble Coll Ox BA63 MA67. Cuddesdon Coll 63. **d** 65 **p** 66. C Cullercoats St Geo *Newc* 65-68; Chapl Wadh Coll Ox 68-72; Lib Pusey Ho 68-72; V Romford St Edw *Chelmsf* 72-79; V Tettenhall Regis *Lich* 79-80; TR from 80; RD Trysull from 87. *The Vicarage, 2 Lloyd Road, Tettenhall, Wolverhampton WV6 9AU* Wolverhampton (01902) 751622

MAKIN, Hubert. b 18. ACP66 Open Univ BA74. NW Ord Course. **d** 78 **p** 79. Hon C Mt Pellon *Wakef* 78-91; Hon C King Cross 91-94; Perm to Offic from 94. *46 Upper Highfield, Mount Tabor, Halifax, W Yorkshire HX2 0UG* Halifax (01422) 244642

MAKIN, Miss Pauline. b 45. Cranmer Hall Dur 75. **dss** 78 **d** 87 **p** 94. Ashton-in-Makerfield St Thos *Liv* 78-87; Par Dn 87-89; Par Dn Rainford 89-94; C from 94; Asst Dioc Chapl to the Deaf from 89. *23 Windermere Drive, Rainford, St Helens, Merseyside WA11 7LD* Rainford (01744) 884254

MAKIN, Valerie Diana. Lon Univ DipRS83. S'wark Ord Course 86. **d** 88 **p** 94. Hon Par Dn Bryanston Square St Mary w St Marylebone St Mark *Lon* 88-95; Chapl St Marylebone Healing and Counselling Cen 88-94; NSM Godalming *Guildf* 94-95; Perm to Offic from 95; Perm to Offic *Lon* from 95. *Crowts, Tuesley, Godalming, Surrey GU7 1UD* Godalming (01483) 416613

MAKOWER, Canon Dr Malory. b 38. TCD BA61 MA68 St Jo Coll Ox MA64 DPhil64. Ridley Hall Cam 64. **d** 66 **p** 67. C Onslow Square St Paul *Lon* 66-69; Tutor Ridley Hall Cam 69-71; Sen Tutor 71-76; P-in-c Lode and Longmeadow *Ely* 76-84; Warden E Anglian Minl Tr Course 77-79; Prin 79-84; Dir of Post-Ord Tr for NSM *Nor* 84-90; C Gt Yarmouth 84-89; TV from 89; Dioc NSM Officer from 88; Prin LNSM Tr Scheme from 94; Hon Can Nor Cathl from 94. *Ludham House, 55 South Beach Parade, Great Yarmouth, Norfolk NR30 3JP* Great Yarmouth (01493) 853622 Fax 766476

MALAN, Victor Christian de Roubaix. b 39. Cape Town Univ BA60 Linacre Coll Ox BA63 MA68. Wycliffe Hall Ox 61. **d** 63 **p** 64. C Springfield *Birm* 63-66; P-in-c 66-67; C New Windsor *Ox* 67-69; Chapl St Jo Coll Cam 69-74; V Northn All SS w St Kath *Pet* 74-86; V Stockport St Geo *Ches* 86-89; R N Mundham w Hunston and Merston *Chich* from 89. *The Rectory, Church Lane, Hunston, Chichester, W Sussex PO20 6AJ* Chichester (01243) 782003

MALBON, John Allin. b 36. Oak Hill Th Coll 62. **d** 65 **p** 66. C Wolv St Jude *Lich* 65-68; C Hoole *Ches* 68-71; P-in-c Crewe Ch Ch 71-75; V 75-79; V Plemstall w Guilden Sutton from 79. *The Vicarage, Guilden Sutton, Chester CH3 7EL* Mickle Trafford (01244) 300306

MALCOLM, Brother. *See* FOUNTAIN, David Roy

MALCOLM, Miss Mercia Alana. b 54. St Andr Univ MA77 Lon Univ DipRS87. S'wark Ord Course 84. **d** 87 **p** 94. C Dartford Ch Ch *Roch* 87-91; Par Dn Stockport St Geo *Ches* 91-94; C 94; C Stockport South West 94; Chapl Ulster Univ from 95; C Jordanstown *Conn* from 95. *6 Mount Pleasant Road, Jordanstown, Newtownabbey, Co Antrim BT37 0NQ* Whiteabbey (01232) 853524

MALE, David Edward. b 62. Southn Univ BA83. St Jo Coll Dur BA90 Cranmer Hall Dur 88. **d** 91 **p** 92. C Leic St Chris *Leic* 91-94; C Kirkheaton *Wakef* from 94. *423 Wakefield Road, Huddersfield HD5 8DB* Huddersfield (01484) 429885

MALE, John. b 28. ACA54 FCA65. Linc Th Coll 59. **d** 61 **p** 62. Bp's Dom Chapl *Linc* 61-72; C Linc St Pet in Eastgate w St Marg 68-70; R Riseholme 70-72; S Africa 72-85; Chapl

Heathfield Sch Ascot 86-87; Chapl Lucas Hosp Wokingham from 86; rtd 89. *44 Simkins Close, Winkfield Row, Bracknell, Berks RG12 6QS* Bracknell (01344) 886026

MALINS, Peter. b 18. Down Coll Cam BA40 MA47. Ridley Hall Cam 40. **d** 42 **p** 43. CF 47-73; QHC 72-73; V Greenwich St Alfege w St Pet and St Paul *S'wark* 73-87; P-in-c Greenwich H Trin and St Paul 76-84; Sub-Dean Greenwich 79-81; rtd 87. *12 Ridgeway Drive, Dorking, Surrey RH4 3AN* Dorking (01306) 882035

MALKINSON, Christopher Mark. b 47. Chich Th Coll 84. **d** 86 **p** 87. C Stroud and Uplands w Slad *Glouc* 86-89; V Cam w Stinchcombe from 89. *The Vicarage, Church Road, Cam, Dursley, Glos GL11 5PQ* Dursley (01453) 542084

MALKINSON, Michael Stephen. b 43. St Steph Ho Ox 65. **d** 68 **p** 69. C New Addington *Cant* 68-71; C Blackpool St Steph *Blackb* 71-74; V Wainfleet St Mary *Linc* 74-81; R Wainfleet All SS w St Thos 74-81; P-in-c Croft 80-81; V Lund *Blackb* 81-93; V Heyhouses on Sea from 93. *St Annes Vicarage, 2 Headroomgate Road, St Annes, Lytham St Annes, Lancs FY8 3BD* St Annes (01253) 722725

MALLESON, Michael Lawson. b 42. Univ of Wales (Swansea) BA64 Nottm Univ DipTh68. Linc Th Coll 67. **d** 70 **p** 71. C Wakef St Jo *Wakef* 70-73; C-in-c Holmfield St Andr CD 73-75; V Holmfield 75-80; V Heworth St Alb *Dur* 80-93; V Killingworth *Newc* from 93. *The Vicarage, Killingworth, Newcastle upon Tyne NE12 0BL* 0191-268 3242

MALLETT, John Christopher. b 44. E Anglian Minl Tr Course. **d** 82 **p** 83. NSM Hethersett w Canteloff *Nor* 82-85; NSM Hethersett w Canteloff w Lt and Gt Melton 85-90; Chapl Wayland Hosp Norfolk from 88. *2 Bailey Close, Hethersett, Norwich NR9 3EU* Norwich (01603) 811010

MALLETT, Michael William. b 18. St Deiniol's Hawarden. **d** 69 **p** 70. C Hyde St Geo *Ches* 69-75; V Broadheath 75-84; rtd 84; Perm to Offic *Carl* 84-94. *4 Ellesborough Manor, Butlers Cross, Aylesbury, Bucks HP17 0XF* Aylesbury (01296) 696018

MALLETT, Ven Peter. b 25. CB78. AKC50. **d** 51 **p** 52. Dep Asst Chapl Gen 68-72; Asst Chapl Gen 73-74; Chapl Gen 74-80; OStJ from 76; Man Dir Inter-Ch Travel 81-86; rtd 90. *Hawthorne Cottage, Hampstead Lane, Yalding, Maidstone, Kent ME18 6HJ* Maidstone (01622) 812607

MALLIN, Very Rev Stewart Adam Thomson. b 24. Edin Th Coll 59. **d** 61 **p** 62. P-in-c Thurso *Mor* 68-77; R Wick 68-77; CSG from 74; Can St Andr Cathl Inverness *Mor* 74-91; R Dingwall 77-91; R Strathpeffer 77-91; Syn Clerk 81-83; Dean Mor 83-91; rtd 91; Hon Can St Andr Cathl Inverness *Mor* from 91; Hon C Strathnairn St Paul from 91. *St Paul's Parsonage, Croachy, Strathnairn, Inverness IV15 9HU* Farr (018083) 397

MALLINSON, Canon Ralph Edward. b 40. Or Coll Ox BA63 MA66. St Steph Ho Ox 63. **d** 66 **p** 67. C Bolton St Pet *Man* 66-68; C Elton All SS 68-72; V Bury St Thos 72-76; V Bury Ch K ing 76-81; P-in-c Goodshaw 81-82; V 82-84; V Goodshaw and Crawshawbooth 84-93; AD Rossendale 83-93; Hon Can Man Cathl from 92; V Unsworth from 93. *St George's Vicarage, Hollins Lane, Bury, Lancs BL9 8JJ* 0161-766 2429

MALLOCH, Elizabeth Gilmour. b 10. Edin Univ MA33 DipEd34. dss 85 **d** 86 **p** 94. NSM Edin St Mary *Edin* 85-95; rtd 95. *173/101 Comely Bank Road, Edinburgh EH4 1DH* 0131-343 6100

MALLON, Allister. b 61. Sheff Univ BA83 TCD DipTh87 BTh89 MA. CITC. **d** 87 **p** 88. C Ballymoney w Finvoy and Rasharkin *Conn* 87-90; C Belf St Mary w H Redeemer 90-92; Bp's C Belf St Mary Magd from 92. *St Mary Magdalene Rectory, 56 Windsor Avenue, Belfast BT9 6EJ* Belfast (01232) 667516

MALLORY, George Henry. b 14. JP. Lon Univ BSc63. St Deiniol's Hawarden. **d** 80 **p** 81. NSM Oaks in Charnwood and Copt Oak *Leic* 80-88; rtd 88; Perm to Offic *Leic* 88-91; Perm to Offic *Worc* from 91. *Claudina, Bewdley Road North, Stourport-on-Severn, Worcs DY13 8PX* Stourport (01299) 827969

MALONEY, Ms Fiona Elizabeth. b 60. Bradf Univ BSc2. Cranmer Hall Dur BA91 N Ord Course 91. **d** 92 **p** 94. Par Dn Castleton Moor *Man* 92-94; C 94-95. *54 Tweedle Hill Road, Higher Blackley, Manchester M9 8LG* 0161-740 6774

MALONEY, Terence Mark. b 63. York Univ BSc84. Cranmer Hall Dur 88. **d** 91 **p** 92. C Blackley St Andr *Man* from 91. *54 Tweedle Hill Road, Higher Blackley, Manchester M9 3LG* 0161-740 6774

MALPASS, Clive William. b 36. AKC60. **d** 61 **p** 62. C Malden St Jo *S'wark* 61-64; C Horley 64-69; Youth Chapl *Dur* 69-72; Adv in Lay Tr 72-76; V Wyther Ven Bede *Ripon* 76-82; V Askrigg w Stallingbusk from 82; RD Wensley from 94. *The Vicarage, Askrigg, Leyburn, N Yorkshire DL8 3HZ* Wensleydale (01969) 650301

MALSOM, Laurence Michael. b 31. Selw Coll Cam BA55 MA59. Cuddesdon Coll 55. **d** 57 **p** 58. V Harberton *Ex* 64-71; V Harbertonford 64-71; RD Totnes 70-75; V S Brent 71-75; V

St Marychurch 75-79; P-in-c Plymouth Crownhill Ascension 79-80; V 80-94; rtd 94. *The Village, St Mellion, Saltash, Cornwall PL12 6RJ* Liskeard (01579) 51219

MALTA, Dean of. *Vacant*

MALTBY, Geoffrey. b 38. Leeds Univ BA62. Wells Th Coll 68. **d** 70 **p** 71. C Mansf St Mark *S'well* 70-73; V Skegby 73-78; V Carrington 78-87; C Rainworth 87-90; Chapl for People with a Mental Handicap from 90. *18 Beverley Close, Rainworth, Mansfield, Notts NG21 0LW* Mansfield (01623) 797095

MALTBY, Dr Judith Diane. b 57. Illinois Univ BA79 Newnham Coll Cam PhD92. S Dios Minl Tr Scheme 89. **d** 92 **p** 94. Tutor Sarum & Wells Th Coll 87-93; Hon Par Dn Wilton w Netherhampton and Fugglestone *Sarum* 92-93; Chapl and Fell CCC Ox from 93. *Corpus Christi College, Oxford OX1 4JF* Oxford (01865) 276722

MALTIN, Basil St Clair Aston. b 24. Qu Coll Cam BA49 MA54. Westcott Ho Cam 50. **d** 51 **p** 52. V Bishops Lydeard *B & W* 63-71; R Pulborough *Chich* 71-90; RD Storrington 84-89; rtd 90. *13 Somerstown, Chichester, W Sussex PO19 4AG* Chichester (01243) 786740

MAN, Archdeacon of. *See* WILLOUGHBY, Ven David Albert

MANCE, Herbert William. b 19. St Jo Coll Cam BA40 MA44. Oak Hill Th Coll 47. **d** 49 **p** 50. Nigeria 58-71; Can Ibadan 70-71; C Buckhurst Hill *Chelmsf* 71-75; P-in-c Roydon 75-79; V 79-85; rtd 85. *52 Redwood Avenue, Stone, Staffs ST15 0DB* Stone (01785) 816128

MANCHESTER, Canon Charles. b 28. Univ Coll Lon BD54. Oak Hill Th Coll 50. **d** 55 **p** 56. V Aldershot H Trin *Guildf* 67-87; RD Aldershot 73-78; R Newdigate 87-93; Hon Can Guildf Cathl 89-93; rtd 93. *12 Fulmar Road, Christchurch, Dorset BH23 4BJ*

MANCHESTER, John Charles. b 45. Lon Univ BD69. ALCD68. **d** 69 **p** 70. C Scarborough St Martin *York* 69-73; C Selby Abbey 73-76; P-in-c Old Malton 76-79; V from 79; RD Bulmer and Malton 85-91. *The Gannock House, Old Malton, Malton, N Yorkshire YO17 0HB* Malton (01653) 692121

MANCHESTER, Archdeacon of. *See* HARRIS, Ven Reginald Brian

MANCHESTER, Bishop of. *See* MAYFIELD, Rt Rev Christopher John

MANCHESTER, Dean of. *See* RILEY, Very Rev Kenneth Joseph (Ken)

MANDER, Dennis Stanley. b 18. Bps' Coll Cheshunt 60. **d** 62 **p** 63. S Africa 69-78; R Lanteglos by Camelford w Advent *Truro* 78-85; rtd 85. *12 Menheniot Crescent, Langore, Launceston, Cornwall PL15 8PD* Launceston (01566) 772853

MANDER, Peter John. b 52. Liv Univ BA85. Sarum & Wells Th Coll 85. **d** 87 **p** 88. C Hale and Ashley *Ches* 87-90; TV Grantham *Linc* from 90. *114 Manthorpe Road, Grantham, Lincs NG31 8DL* Grantham (01476) 76047

MANDER, Canon Thomas Leonard Frederick. b 33. Ely Th Coll 60. **d** 62 **p** 63. V Bishop's Tachbrook *Cov* 66-70; V Earlsdon 70-76; V Chesterton 76-83; R Lighthorne 76-83; V Newbold Pacey w Moreton Morrell 76-83; Hon Can Cov Cathl 80-92; P-in-c S Leamington St Jo 83-84; V 84-92; rtd 92; Perm to Offic *Cov* from 92. *59 Murcott Road East, Whitnash, Leamington Spa, Warks CV31 2JJ* Leamington Spa (01926) 339950

MANDERSON, Dr Robert Dunlop (Leslie). b 35. FDS68 FRCSEd68 Dur Univ LDS59. Ox Min Course 92. **d** 94. NSM Maidenhead St Andr and St Mary Magd *Ox* from 94. *Squirrels, Sandisplatt Road, Maidenhead, Berks SL6 4NB* Maidenhead (01628) 38505

MANHIRE, Ashley Lewin. b 31. AKC55. **d** 56 **p** 57. C Plymouth St Gabr *Ex* 56-59; C Cockington 59-66; V Torquay St Martin Barton 66-83; RD Ipplepen 82-87; V Shaldon from 83. *The Vicarage, Torquay Road, Shaldon, Teignmouth, Devon TQ14 0AX* Shaldon (01626) 872396

MANHOOD, Mrs Phyllis. b 32. Aston Tr Scheme 78 Qu Coll Birm 79. dss 82 **d** 87 **p** 94. Harwich *Chelmsf* 82-83; Dovercourt and Parkeston 83-85; Fawley *Win* 85-87; Par Dn 87-92; P-in-c Bournemouth St Aug from 92. *St Augustine's Vicarage, 2A St Anthony's Road, Bournemouth BH2 6PD* Bournemouth (01202) 556861

✠**MANKTELOW, Rt Rev Michael Richard John.** b 27. Cu Coll Cam BA48 MA52. Chich Th Coll 51. **d** 53 **p** 54 **c** 77. C Boston *Linc* 53-56; Chapl Ch Coll Cam 57-61; Chapl Linc Th Coll 61-63; Sub-Warden 64-66; V Knaresborough St Jo *Ripon* 66-73; RD Harrogate 72-77; V Harrogate St Wilfrid 73-77; P-in-c Harrogate St Luke 75-77; Hon Can Ripon Cathl 75-77; Suff Bp Basingstoke *Win* 77-93; Can Res Win Cathl 77-91; Hon Can 91-93; Vice-Dean 87-93; rtd 93; Asst Bp Chich from 94; Asst Bp Eur from 94. *2 The Chantry, Canon Lane, Chichester, W Sussex PO19 1PZ* Chichester (01243) 531096

MANLEY, Canon Gordon Russell Delpratt. b 33. Ch Coll Cam BA56 MA60. Linc Th Coll 57. **d** 59 **p** 60. C Westbury-on-Trym St Alb *Bris* 59-61; Chapl Ch Coll Cam 61-66; V Radlett *St Alb*

66-75; V Faversham *Cant* from 75; RD Ospringe 84-90; Hon Can Cant Cathl from 90. *The Vicarage, Preston Street, Faversham, Kent ME13 8PG* Faversham (01795) 532592

MANLEY, Michael Alan. b 60. SS Hild & Bede Coll Dur BA82. Trin Coll Bris DipTh86. **d** 86 **p** 87. C Accrington St Jo *Blackb* 86-89; C Huncoat 88-89; C Accrington St Jo w Huncoat 89-90; V Preston St Luke and St Oswald from 90. *The Vicarage, 60 Harewood Road, Preston PR1 6XE* Preston (01772) 795395

MANLEY-COOPER, Simon James. b 46. S Dios Minl Tr Scheme 91. **d** 94 **p** 95. NSM Soho St Anne w St Thos and St Pet *Lon* from 94; Perm to Offic St Alb from 94. *19 Barnfield Road, Harpenden, Herts AL5 5TH* Harpenden (01582) 460797

MANLEY-HARRIS, Eric Francis. b 34. Ex Univ CertEd68 Jas Cook Univ Townsville BA90. Sarum Th Coll 61. **d** 64 **p** 65. C Plymstock *Ex* 64-66; C Ex St Mary Arches 67-68; Chapl RN 68-74; Australia 74-94; Perm to Offic *Truro* from 94. *c/o The Rectory, Blisland, Bodmin, Cornwall PL30 4JE* Bodmin (01208) 851020

MANN, Ms Angela. b 58. Bath Univ BA80 Bris Univ PGCE83. Trin Coll Bris DipHE94. **d** 94 **p** 95. C Marlborough *Sarum* from 94. *10 Alexandra Terrace, Marlborough, Wilts SN8 1DA* Marlborough (01672) 515244

MANN, Lt-Comdr Anthony James. b 34. Open Univ BA76. St Jo Coll Nottm 85. **d** 88 **p** 89. NSM Helensburgh *Glas* from 88. *The Anchorage, Portkil, Kilcreggan, Helensburgh, Dunbartonshire G84 0LF* Helensburgh (01436) 842623

MANN, Canon Charmion Anne Montgomery. b 36. Liv Univ BA57 CertEd62 DipEd79. Trin Coll Bris 80. **dss** 82 **d** 87 **p** 94. Bris St Nath w St Kath *Bris* 82-84; Bris St Matt and St Nath 84-85; Asst Chapl City Cen Hosps Bris 85-88; Chapl Bris Maternity Hosp 88-94; Chapl Bris R Hosp for Sick Children 88-94; Chapl Bris R Infirmary 88-94; Hon Can Bris Cathl *Bris* from 93; P-in-c Lacock w Bowden Hill from 94. *The Vicarage, Folly Lane, Lacock, Chippenham, Wilts SN15 2LL* Chippenham (01249) 730272 Fax 730130

MANN, Christopher John. b 57. Glas Univ BSc79. Westcott Ho Cam 83. **d** 86 **p** 87. C Worc SE *Worc* 86-89; Min Can and Sacr St Paul's Cathl *Lon* from 89. *7A Amen Court, London EC4M 7BU* 0171-236 3871

MANN, David. b 57. BA. Ridley Hall Cam. **d** 82 **p** 83. C Monkwearmouth St Andr *Dur* 82-86; Chapl Sheff Cathl *Sheff* 86-87; C Leeds St Geo *Ripon* 87-94; V Ripon H Trin from 94. *Holy Trinity Vicarage, College Road, Ripon, N Yorkshire HG4 2AE* Ripon (01765) 605865

MANN, David Peter. b 29. Ho of Sacred Miss 51. **d** 55 **p** 56. V Shieldfield Ch Ch *Newc* 59-75; V Kingsbury St Andr *Lon* 75-89; rtd 89. *14 Grove Street, Norton, Malton, N Yorkshire YO17 9BG*

MANN, Donald Leonard. b 22. Westcott Ho Cam. **d** 47 **p** 48. V Sheen *Lich* 69-76; P-in-c Calton 72-76; P-in-c Ellastone 76; rtd 76. *Bungalow 24, Lyme Green Settlement, Macclesfield, Cheshire SK11 0LD* Sutton (01260) 252209

MANN, Gary. b 63. Nottm Univ BTh90. Linc Th Coll 87. **d** 90 **p** 91. C Knottingley *Wakef* 90-93; TV Brighouse and Clifton from 93. *The Vicarage, 31 Robin Hood Way, Brighouse, W Yorkshire ND6 4LA* Brighouse (01484) 713290

MANN, Ivan John. b 52. Brunel Univ BTech74 Southn Univ BTh80. Sarum & Wells Th Coll 75. **d** 78 **p** 79. C Hadleigh w Layham and Shelley *St E* 78-81; C Whitton and Thurleston w Akenham 81-83; V Leiston 83-86; Perm to Offic 86-89; R Aldringham w Thorpe, Knodishall w Buxlow etc 89-93; V Ipswich St Jo from 93. *St John's Vicarage, Cauldwell Hall Road, Ipswich IP4 4QE* Ipswich (01473) 728034

MANN, John. b 35. ISO91. Lon Univ DipEcon66. Oak Hill NSM Course 89. **d** 92 **p** 93. NSM Springfield All SS *Chelmsf* from 92. *18 Humber Road, Chelmsford CM1 5PE* Chelmsford (01245) 259596

MANN, John Owen. b 55. QUB BD77 MTh86. CITC 79. **d** 79 **p** 81. C Cloughfern *Conn* 79-82; C Knock *D & D* 82-85; I Ballyrashane w Kildollagh *Conn* 85-89; R Bentworth and Shalden and Lasham *Win* 89-93; RD Alton 92-93; I Cloughfern *Conn* from 93. *Cloughfern Rectory, 126 Doagh Road, Newtownabbey, Co Antrim BT37 9QR* Belfast (01232) 862437

✠**MANN, Rt Rev Michael Ashley.** b 24. KCVO89. CBIM RMA 42 Harvard Univ AMP73. Wells Th Coll 55. **d** 57 **p** 58 **c** 74. C Wolborough w Newton Abbot *Ex* 57-59; V Sparkwell 59-62; Nigeria 62-67; Home Sec Miss to Seamen 67-69; Can Res Nor Cathl *Nor* 69-74; Vice-Dean 73-74; Dioc Ind Adv 69-74; Suff Bp Dudley *Worc* 74-76; Dean of Windsor and Dom Chapl to The Queen 76-89; rtd 89. *Lower End Farm Cottage, Eastington, Northleach, Glos GL54 3PN* Cotswold (01451) 860767

MANN, Peter Eric. b 51. St Jo Coll Dur BA73. Westcott Ho Cam 73. **d** 75 **p** 76. C Barrow St Jo *Carl* 75-78; C Egremont 78-80; V Carl St Luke Morton 80-86; TR Egremont and Haile 86-93; P-in-c Barrow St Geo w St Luke from 93; RD Furness

from 94. *The Rectory, 98 Roose Road, Barrow-in-Furness, Cumbria LA13 9RL* Barrow-in-Furness (01229) 821641

MANN, Ralph Norman. b 27. BNC Ox BA51 MA55 DipEd52. Ox NSM Course 79. **d** 82 **p** 83. NSM Kingham w Churchill, Daylesford and Sarsden *Ox* 82-85; S Area Sec BCMS 82-89; P-in-c Broadwell, Evenlode, Oddington and Adlestrop *Glouc* from 89. *The Rectory, Broadwell, Moreton-in-Marsh, Glos GL56 0TU* Cotswold (01451) 831866

MANN, Robert Francis Christopher Stephen. b 17. K Coll Lon BD56 PhD60. Kelham Th Coll 36. **d** 40 **p** 41. Asst Master Kilmorie Co Sch Lon 61-65; USA from 65; Dean St Mary's Sem and Univ Baltimore 70-83; rtd 82. *107 East Chase Street, Baltimore, Maryland 21202, USA* Baltimore (410) 837-7362

MANN, Robin. b 45. RMTPI73 DipTP72 Fitzw Coll Cam BA76 MA80. Ridley Hall Cam 73. **d** 77 **p** 78. C Wetherby *Ripon* 77-80; V Hipswell 80-86; V Mamble w Bayton, Rock w Heightington etc *Worc* from 86. *The Vicarage, Far Forest, Kidderminster, Worcs DY14 9TT* Rock (01299) 266580

MANN, Terence John (Terry). b 47. GGSM68 LRSM79 Lon Univ PGCE69 Trin Coll Cam FTCL79 Miami Univ MA80. Ox Min Course CBTS94. **d** 94. NSM Kingham w Churchill, Daylesford and Sarsden *Ox* from 94. *The Baliffe's House, Kingham Hill, Kingham, Chipping Norton, Oxon OX7 6TE* Chipping Norton (01608) 658450 Fax 658658

MANNALL, Michael John Frederick. b 37. St Mich Coll Llan 61. **d** 63 **p** 64. C-in-c Cricklewood St Pet CD *Lon* 69-73; R Broughton *Pet* 73-75; Hon C Kingston St Luke S'wark 76-94; rtd 84. *The Blessings, 55 Sculthorpe Road, Fakenham, Norfolk NR21 9ET* Fakenham (01328) 863496

MANNERS, Kenneth. b 29. N Ord Course. **d** 84 **p** 85. NSM Brayton *York* from 84. *16 Wistow Road, Selby, N Yorkshire YO8 0LY* Selby (01757) 702129

MANNING, Mrs Ann. b 42. Liv Univ CertEd75. St Jo Coll Nottm CTM94 N Ord Course 94. **d** 95. NSM Grasmere *Carl* from 95. *The Vicarage, Chapel Stile, Ambleside, Cumbria LA22 9JG* Ambleside (015394) 37267

MANNING, Arthur Philip. b 35. Chester Coll BEd74. St Jo Coll Nottm 88. **d** 89 **p** 90. C Eastham *Ches* 89-90; NSM Lache cum Saltney 91-95; NSM Langdale *Carl* from 95. *12 Butterbache Road, Huntington, Chester CH3 6BZ* Chester (01244) 314432

MANNING, Brian Hawthorne. b 29. AMCT52 CEng59 MIStructE59. NW Ord Course 70. **d** 73 **p** 74. NSM Birch St Jas *Man* 73-75; NSM Prestwich St Gabr 75-80; NSM Prestwich St Mary 80-85; NSM Marple All SS *Ches* 85-88; R Cockfield w Bradfield St Clare, Felsham etc *St E* from 88; RD Lavenham from 93. *The Rectory, Howe Lane, Cockfield, Bury St Edmunds, Suffolk IP30 0HA* Cockfield Green (01284) 828385

MANNING, David Godfrey. b 47. Trin Coll Bris 73. **d** 76 **p** 77. C Richmond H Trin and Ch Ch S'wark 76-79; C Anston *Sheff* 79-83; V Blackpool St Mark *Blackb* 83-91; V Creech St Michael *B & W* from 91. *The Vicarage, Creech St Michael, Taunton, Somerset TA3 5PP* Henlade (01823) 442237

MANNING, Neville Alexander. b 41. Lon Univ BD68. ALCD68. **d** 68 **p** 69. C Belvedere All SS *Roch* 68-71; C Hollington St Leon *Chich* 71-73; C Hersham *Guildf* 73-77; V Dawley St Jerome *Lon* 77-94; R Denton w S Heighton and Tarring Neville *Chich* from 94. *The Rectory, 6 Heighton Road, Newhaven, E Sussex BN9 0RB* Newhaven (01273) 514319

✠**MANNING, Rt Rev William James.** b 16. TCD BA44 MA47 Or Coll Ox MA50. TCD Div Sch Div Test44. **d** 44 **p** 45 **c** 78. C Dub Donnybrook *D & G* 44-47; C Cork St Fin Barre's Cathl C, C & R 47-49; Chapl Thos Coram Sch Berkhamsted 49-51; Bermuda 51-64; Can Res Bermuda Cathl 53-64; Zurich *Eur* 64-66; S Africa from 67; Dean George 72-77; Bp George 78-87. *Liamslea, 10 Dalmore Road, Tokai, 7945 South Africa* Cape Town (21) 757811

MANNINGS, Andrew James. b 52. Trent Park Coll of Educn CertEd73. St Jo Coll Nottm DCM92. **d** 92 **p** 94. C Over St Chad *Ches* 92-93; C Sale St Anne from 93. *141 Conway Road, Sale, Cheshire M33 2TL* 0161-976 6168

MANNS, Edwin Ernest (Eddie). b 30. Portsm Dioc Tr Course 84. **d** 85. C Paulsgrove *Portsm* 85-95; Chapl St Mary's Hosp Portsm 90-91; Team Chapl Portsm Hosp 91-95; rtd 95. *17 Kelvin Grove, Portchester, Fareham, Hants PO16 8LQ* Cosham (01705) 324818

MANSBRIDGE, Ven Michael Winstanley. b 32. Southn Univ BA54. Ridley Hall Cam 56. **d** 58 **p** 59. C Ware St Mary *St Alb* 58-60; C Claverdon w Preston Bagot *Cov* 60-62; Kenya 62-65; V Chilvers Coton w Astley *Cov* 65-75; RD Nuneaton 67-74; V Leamington Priors H Trin 75-83; UAE from 83; Miss to Seamen from 83. *St Andrew's Vicarage, PO Box 262, Abu Dhabi, United Arab Emirates* Abu Dhabi (2) 461631 or 464591

MANSEL, Canon James Seymour Denis. b 07. KCVO79. Ex Coll Ox BA32 MA41. Westcott Ho Cam. **d** 41 **p** 42. Dom Chapl to The Queen 65-79; Sub Dean of HM Chpls Royal 65-79; Sub Almoner and Dep Clerk of the Closet 65-79; Can and Preb Chich Cathl *Chich* 71-79; rtd 79; Extra Chapl to The Queen from 79; Hon C Westmr St Marg 80-88; PV Westmr Abbey 83-88. *15 Sandringham Court, London W9 1UA* 0171-286 3052

MANSELL, Clive Neville Ross. b 53. Solicitor 77 Leic Univ LLB74. Trin Coll Bris DipHE81. **d** 82 **p** 83. C Gt Malvern St Mary *Worc* 82-85; Min Can Ripon Cathl *Ripon* 85-89; R Kirklington w Burneston and Wath and Pickhill from 89. *The Rectory, Kirklington, Bedale, N Yorkshire DL8 2NJ* Thirsk (01845) 567429

MANSFIELD, Gordon Reginald. b 35. Lon Univ DipTh61 CertEd BA. Clifton Th Coll 58. **d** 63 **p** 64. C Carl St Jo *Carl* 63-65; C Westcombe Park St Geo *S'wark* 65-68; C Rashcliffe *Wakef* 68-70; V Woodlands *Sheff* 70-80; V Steeple Bumpstead and Helions Bumpstead *Chelmsf* from 80. *The Vicarage, Church Street, Steeple Bumpstead, Haverhill, Suffolk CB9 7EA* Haverhill (01440) 730257

MANSFIELD, Julian Nicolas. b 59. K Coll Lon BD AKC. Edin Th Coll 83. **d** 85 **p** 86. C Kirkby *Liv* 85-89; TV Ditton St Mich from 89. *St Thomas's Vicarage, 154 Liverpool Road, Widnes, Cheshire WA8 7JB* 0151-420 6614

MANSFIELD, Robert William. b 45. Local NSM Course 89. **d** 88 **p** 89. NSM Louth *Linc* from 88. *The Old Railway House, Stewton, Louth, Lincs LN11 8SD* Louth (01507) 327533

MANSFIELD, Simon David. b 55. Brunel Univ BSc81 Lon Univ MA94. Ripon Coll Cuddesdon 88. **d** 90 **p** 91. C N Harrow St Alb *Lon* 90-93; C Birchington w Acol and Minnis Bay *Cant* from 93. *29 Hunting Gate, Birchington, Kent CT7 9JA* Thanet (01843) 843750

MANSFIELD, Stephen McLaren. b 59. FGA DipRJ GDip. Cranmer Hall Dur 86. **d** 89 **p** 90. C Poynton *Ches* 89-92; C Bromborough 92-94; V Bidston from 94. *The Vicarage, 6 Statham Road, Birkenhead, Merseyside L43 7XS* 0151-652 4852

MANSHIP, Canon David. b 27. ARCO Keble Coll Ox BA52 MA58. Qu Coll Birm 52. **d** 54 **p** 55. Clergy Tr Officer 68-70; Dir of Educn *Win* 70-79; Hon Can Win Cathl 74-79; R Old Alresford 76-79; V Abingdon w Shippon *Ox* 79-89; TR Abingdon 89-93; V Shippon 89; rtd 93. *Woodlyn, Faringdon Road, Southmoor, Abingdon, Oxon OX13 5AF* Longworth (01865) 820885

MANSLEY, Colin Edward. b 56. Edin Univ MA80 BA85. Ripon Coll Cuddesdon 83. **d** 86 **p** 87. C Worle *B & W* 86-89; C Baguley *Man* 89-91; C Radcliffe St Mary 91; TV Radcliffe from 91. *The Rectory, Rectory Close, Radcliffe, Manchester M26 9QB* 0161-723 2460

MANSON-BRAILSFORD, Andrew Henry. b 64. NUU BA86. Ripon Coll Cuddesdon 87. **d** 90 **p** 91. C Warrington St Elphin *Liv* 90-93; C Torrisholme *Blackb* from 93. *14 Lambrigg Close, Morecambe, Lancs LA4 4UE* Morecambe (01524) 422249

MANTHORP, Brian Robert. b 34. Pemb Coll Ox BA55 MA59. Westcott Ho Cam. **d** 61 **p** 62. C Busbridge *Guildf* 61-62; Lic to Offic *S'wark* 62-65; Asst Master Framlingham Coll 66-68; India 68-70; Master Oakbank Sch Keighley 70-73; Hd Master H Trin Sch Halifax 73-80; Worc Coll for the Blind 80-87; Prin RNIB New Coll Worc from 87; Perm to Offic *Worc* 84-94. *RNIB New College, Whittington Road, Worcester WR5 2JX* Worcester (01905) 763933

MANTLE, John Ambrose Cyril. b 46. St Andr Univ MTh74 CertEd75 Kent Univ MA90. Edin Th Coll 66. **d** 69 **p** 70. C Broughty Ferry *Bre* 69-71; Perm to Offic 71-75; Perm to Offic *Edin* 75-77; Chapl St Andr Univ *St And* 77-80; P-in-c Pittenweem 78-80; P-in-c Elie and Earlsferry 78-80; Chapl and Fell Fitzw Coll Cam 80-86; Tutor Cant Sch of Min 86-91; Vice Prin 91-93; C Boxley w Detling *Cant* 86-93; Lect Rob Gordon Univ Aber 94; Dioc Avd for Educn and Tr of Adults *Chich* from 94. *18 Nizells Avenue, Hove, E Sussex BN3 1PL* Brighton (01273) 736389

MANTLE, Canon Rupert James. b 15. Edin Univ MA37. Edin Th Coll 38. **d** 40 **p** 41. R Aber St Pet *Ab* 67-81; Hon C 84-87; Can St Paul's Cathl Dundee *Bre* 70-76; Can St Andr Cathl *Ab* 78-81; rtd 81; Hon Can St Andr Cathl *Ab* from 81. *32 Craigiebuckler Terrace, Aberdeen AB1 7SS* Aberdeen (01224) 316636

MANTON, Paul Arthur. b 45. Lon Univ DipTh75 BD77. Oak Hill Th Coll 73. **d** 77 **p** 78. C Wolv *Lich* 77-80; C Penn Fields 80; Ind Chapl *Lon* 80-87; Hon C St Marylebone All So w St Pet and Jo 80-87. *Address temp unknown*

MANTON, Peter Geoffrey Kevitt. b 20. Wycliffe Hall Ox. **d** 61 **p** 62. R Jersey St Jo *Win* 65-85; rtd 85; Perm to Offic *Win* 85-90. *9 Clos de Gouray, Gorey, Jersey, Channel Islands JE3 9EN* Jersey (01534) 853204

MAPLE, David Charles. b 34. Sarum Th Coll 64. **d** 66 **p** 66. C Buckland in Dover *Cant* 66-67; C St Laurence in the Isle of Thanet 67-71; Chapl RAF 71-75; P-in-c Ivychurch 75-76; P-in-c Newchurch *Cant* 75-78; P-in-c Burmarsh 75-78; C St Mary in the Marsh 75-76; R Dymchurch 76-78; R Dymchurch w Burmarsh and Newchurch 78-81; Hon Min Can Cant Cathl

from 79; Abp's Dioc Chapl 81-91; Chapl St Jo Hosp Cant from 91. *5D St John's Hospital, Canterbury, Kent CT1 1BG* Canterbury (01227) 764935

MAPLE, John Philip (Jack). b 50. Chich Th Coll 71. **d** 74 **p** 79. C Notting Hill St Mich and Ch Ch *Lon* 74-75; Lic to Offic 78-79; C Barnsbury St Dav w St Clem 79-80; C Cotham St Sav w St Mary *Bris* 80-83; TV St Marylebone Ch Ch *Lon* 83-91; R St Marylebone, St Paul from 91. *St Paul's House, 9 Rossmore Road, London NW1 6NJ* 0171-262 9443

MAPLES, Ven Jeffrey Stanley. b 16. Down Coll Cam BA38 MA46. Chich Th Coll 39. **d** 40 **p** 41. V Milton *Portsm* 67-73; Adn Swindon *Bris* 74-82; rtd 82. *Flat 1, 95 Crane Street, Salisbury SP1 2PU* Salisbury (01722) 323848

MAPLEY, Mrs Barbara Jean. b 46. Guy's Hosp Medical Sch MCSP69. Oak Hill NSM Course 86. **d** 89 **p** 94. NSM Kelvedon *Chelmsf* 89-93; C Witham 93-94; TV from 94. *2 Janmead, Witham, Essex CM8 2EN* Witham (01376) 516872

MAPPLEBECKPALMER, Richard Warwick. b 32. CCC Cam BA56 MA60. Cuddesdon Coll 56. **d** 58 **p** 59. C Redcar *York* 58-60; C Drypool St Jo 61-63; V Pendleton St Ambrose *Man* 63-77; P-in-c Piddington *Ox* 77; P-in-c Ambrosden w Arncot and Blackthorn 77; P-in-c Mert 77; V Ambrosden w Mert and Piddington 77-88; USA from 88. *Address temp unknown*

MAPSON, Preb John Victor. b 31. Lon Univ BA60. Oak Hill Th Coll 55. **d** 60 **p** 61. C Littleover *Derby* 60-62; C Wandsworth St Mich *S'wark* 62-65; R Willand *Ex* 65-71; P-in-c Axmouth 71-72; V 72-75; V Axmouth w Musbury 75-77; RD Honiton 76-77; V Cullompton 77-89; R Kentisbeare w Blackborough 77-89; RD Cullompton 81-89; P-in-c Sidmouth All SS from 89; Preb Ex Cathl from 91; RD Ottery from 94. *All Saints' Vicarage, All Saints' Road, Sidmouth, Devon EX10 8ES* Sidmouth (01395) 515963

MAPSTONE, Trevor Anthony. b 63. Lanc Univ BSc84. St Jo Coll Nottm LTh88 DPS89. **d** 89 **p** 90. C Hoole *Ches* 89-92; C Lanc St Thos *Blackb* from 92. *77 Ulster Road, Lancaster LA1 4LH* Lancaster (01524) 381510

MARAJH, Brian Melvin.BA. **d** 86 **p** 87. S Africa 86-94; Perm to Offic *Glas* from 94. *c/o The Diocesan Office, 5 St Vincent Place, Glasgow G1 2DH* 0141-221 572

MARCER, Graham John. b 52. Ripon Coll Cuddesdon 75. **d** 78 **p** 79. C Sherborne w Castleton and Lillington *Sarum* 78-81; C Christchurch *Win* 81-84; V Southn St Jude 84-90; P-in-c Moordown 90-91; C Sheff Parson Cross St Cecilia *Sheff* 91-93; V Balby from 93. *St John's Vicarage, 6 Greenfield Lane, Doncaster, S Yorkshire DN4 0PT* Doncaster (01302) 853278

MARCETTI, Alvin Julian. b 41. San Jose State Univ BA66 Santa Clara Univ MA76. Cranmer Hall Dur 85. **d** 87 **p** 88. C Stepney St Dunstan and All SS *Lon* 87-91; Chapl City of Lon Poly 91-92; Chapl Lon Guildhall Univ from 92. *1 The Crescent, Tower Hill, London EC3N 2LY* 0171-481 1749 or 320 1379

MARCH, Charles Anthony Maclea (Tony). b 32. CCC Cam BA55 MA70. Oak Hill Th Coll 55. **d** 57 **p** 58. C S Croydon Em *Cant* 57-60; C Eastbourne H Trin *Chich* 60-63; V Whitehall Park St Andr Hornsey Lane *Lon* 63-67; V Tunbridge Wells H Trin w Ch Ch *Roch* 67-82; V Prestonville St Luke *Chich* from 82. *St Luke's Vicarage, 64 Old Shoreham Road, Brighton BN1 5DD* Brighton (01273) 552267

MARCH, Gerald. b 44. Nottm Univ BA75. Oak Hill Th Coll 92. **d** 95. NSM Sandgate St Paul w Folkestone St Geo *Cant* from 95. *20 Durnford Close, Canterbury, Kent CT2 7RY* Canterbury (01227) 454113

MARCH, John Vale. b 39. CCC Cam BA62 MA76. Linc Th Coll 62. **d** 64 **p** 65. C Sheldon *Birm* 64-68; C Hodge Hill 68-72; TV 72-85; C Handsworth St Jas from 85. *168 Albert Road, Birmingham B21 9JT* 0121-523 0317

MARCHAND, Canon Rex Anthony Victor (Toby). b 47. K Coll Lon BD69 AKC69. St Aug Coll Cant 69. **d** 70 **p** 71. C Leigh Park *Portsm* 70-73; C Hatf St Alb 73-80; R Deal St Leon and St Rich and Sholden *Cant* 80-95; RD Sandwich 91-94; Hon Can Cant Cathl 94-95; V Bishop's Stortford St Mich *St Alb* from 95. *61 Larksway, Bishop's Park, Bishop's Stortford, Herts* Bishop's Stortford (01279) 651415

MARCHANT, Ven George John Charles. b 16. St Jo Coll Dur LTh38 BA39 MA42 BD64. Tyndale Hall Bris 35. **d** 39 **p** 40. V Dur St Nic *Dur* 54-74; RD Dur 64-74; Hon Can Dur Cathl 72-74; Adn Auckland 74-83; Can Res Dur Cathl 74-83; rtd 83; Perm to Offic *Nor* from 83. *28 Greenways, Eaton, Norwich NR4 6PE* Norwich (01603) 58295

MARCHANT, Canon Iain William. b 26. Wells Th Coll 59. **d** 60 **p** 61. V Hawkesbury *Glouc* 63-76; R Newent 76-85; Hon Can Glouc Cathl 84-92; R Newent and Gorsley w Cliffords Mesne 85-92; rtd 92. *Daisy Green, Daisy Lane, Howley, Wotton-under-Edge, Glos GL12 7PF* Dursley (01453) 844779

MARCHANT, Canon Ronald Albert. b 26. Em Coll Cam BA50 MA52 PhD57 BD64. Ridley Hall Cam 50. **d** 54 **p** 55. V

Laxfield *St E* 59-92; RD Hoxne 73-78; Hon Can St E Cathl 75-92; P-in-c Wilby w Brundish 86-92; rtd 92. *34 The Paddock, Boroughbridge Road, York YO2 6AW* York (01904) 798446

MARDEN, Peter Edgar. b 40. Univ of Wales (Lamp) BA61 Linacre Coll Ox BA64 MA68. St Steph Ho Ox 62. **d** 65 **p** 66. C Catford St Laur *S'wark* 65-70; C Mortlake w E Sheen 70-73; V Sydenham St Phil 73-75; Lic to Offic *Cant* from 76; Perm to Offic *Roch* from 81. *Rock Cottage, Pye Corner, Ulcombe, Maidstone, Kent ME17 1EH* Maidstone (01622) 675861

MARGAM, Archdeacon of. *See* WILLIAMS, Ven Martin Infeld

MARINER, Aris. b 43. Alexandria Univ BSc65. St Alb Minl Tr Scheme 84. **d** 87. NSM Stevenage H Trin *St Alb* from 87. *13 Church Lane, Stevenage, Herts SG1 3QS* Stevenage (01438) 365596

MARK, Brother. *See* SHARPE, John Brebber

MARK, Timothy John. b 34. Bris Univ BA57 MLitt68 MEd71 Leeds Univ PhD79. Didsbury Meth Coll 54. **d** 59 **p** 61. India 59-64 and 65-69; Perm to Offic *Sheff* from 73. *15 Fieldhouse Road, Sprotborough, Doncaster, S Yorkshire DN5 7RN* Doncaster (01302) 853022

MARKBY, Archibald Campbell. b 15. Em Coll Cam BA37 MA41. Ridley Hall Cam 37. **d** 39 **p** 39. V Damerham *Sarum* 71-80; V Martin 71-80; rtd 80. *2 Church Farm, Church Sreet, Fordingbridge, Hants SP6 1BQ* Fordingbridge (01425) 656141

MARKBY, Peter John Jenner. b 38. Em Coll Cam BA60. Clifton Th Coll 62. **d** 64 **p** 65. C Tufnell Park St Geo *Lon* 64-68; C Crowborough *Chich* 68-73; C Polegate 73-77; R Southover from 77. *The Rectory, Southover High Street, Lewes, E Sussex BN7 1HT* Lewes (01273) 472018

MARKE, Christopher Andrew Burrows. b 42. MIEaclE FRSA93 Open Univ BA81. Oak Hill NSM Course. **d** 84 **p** 85. NSM Brighstone and Brooke w Mottistone *Portsm* 84-86; NSM Shorwell w Kingston 85-93; NSM Gatcombe 87-93; NSM Chale 89-93; Asst Chapl Dunkerque Miss to Seamen *Eur* 94; Chapl Rouen Miss to Seamen from 94. *Foyer de Marins, 16 rue Duguay Trouin, 76000 Rouen, France* France (33) 35 70 51 63 Fax 35 07 12 65

MARKHAM, David Christopher. b 17. Clifton Th Coll 67. **d** 69 **p** 70. C Eastbourne H Trin *Chich* 69-74; R Elmswell *St E* 74-78; P-in-c Danehill *Chich* 78-83; V 83-88; rtd 88. *16 Wilmar Way, Seal, Sevenoaks, Kent TN15 0DN* Sevenoaks (01732) 762163

MARKHAM, Deryck O'Leary. b 28. Oak Hill Th Coll 66. **d** 68 **p** 69. C Purley Ch Ch *S'wark* 68-72; V E Budleigh and Bicton *Ex* 72-93; RD Aylesbeare 89-93; rtd 93. *86 Granary Lane, Budleigh Salterton, Devon EX9 6ER* Budleigh Salterton (01395) 443340

MARKHAM, Canon Gervase William. b 10. Trin Coll Cam BA32 MA36. Westcott Ho Cam 34. **d** 36 **p** 37. V Morland w Thrimby and Gt Strickland *Carl* 65-84; Hon Can Carl Cathl 72-84; rtd 84; Perm to Offic *Carl* from 84. *The Garden Flat, Morland House, Penrith, Cumbria CA10 3AZ* Morland (01931) 714654

MARKHAM, John Gabriel. b 06. Linc Coll Ox BA30 MA70. Ely Th Coll 30. **d** 31 **p** 32. Chapl Reading and Distr Hosps 60-74; rtd 74. *22 Watlington Road, Benson, Oxford OX10 6LS* Wallingford (01491) 835597

MARKHAM, John William. b 12. St Aid Birkenhead 34. **d** 37 **p** 38. V Teynham *Cant* 60-75; rtd 75; Perm to Offic *Cant* 75-93. *16 Oaten Hill Place, Canterbury, Kent CT1 3HJ* Canterbury (01227) 453988

MARKLAND, Vincent Hilton. b 33. Univ of Wales (Lamp) BA55 Leic Univ PGCE58. Ripon Hall Ox 67. **d** 68 **p** 69. C Worsley *Man* 68-83; V Monton from 83; AD Eccles 93-95. *The Vicarage, 3 Egerton Road, Monton, Eccles, Manchester M30 9LR* 0161-789 2420

MARKS, Alfred Howard. b 02. Qu Coll Cam BA25 MA29. Ridley Hall Cam 25. **d** 26 **p** 27. Hon CF from 45; V Ipswich St Marg *St E* 70-79; rtd 70; Lic to Offic *St E* 70-80; Lic to Offic *Worc* 81-84; 84-91. *28 Stuart Court, High Street, Kibworth, Leicester LE8 0LE* Leicester (0116) 279 6357

MARKS, Allan Willi. b 56. Cranmer Hall Dur CTM94. **d** 94 **p** 95. C Barnoldswick w Bracewell *Bradf* from 94. *81 Rainhall Road, Barnoldswick, Colne, Lancs BB8 6AA* Barnoldswick (01282) 812494

MARKS, Anthony Alfred (Tony). b 28. AKC53. **d** 54 **p** 55. Chapl RN 63-83; QHC from 81; P-in-c Bradninch *Ex* 83-88; R Bradninch and Clyst Hydon 88-90; rtd 90. *Bryony Cottage, The Combe, Compton Martin, Bristol BS18 6JD*

MARKS, Anthony Wendt. b 43. G&C Coll Cam BA63 MA67 PhD70 BNC Ox DPhil72. St John's Coll Nottm. **d** 72 **p** 73. C Withington St Crispin *Man* 72-75; Chapl Lon Univ Medical Students *Lon* 75-80; Warden Liddon Ho Lon 80-92; C-in-c Grosvenor Chpl *Lon* 80-92; V Shrewsbury All SS w St Mich *Lich* from 92. *All Saints Presbytery, 5 Lingen Close, Shrewsbury SY1 2UN* Shrewsbury (01743) 458820

MARKS, David Frederick. b 14. Univ of Wales BA37 Jes Coll Ox BA40 MA45. St Mich Coll Llan 40. **d** 41 **p** 42. Sen Lect St D Coll Lamp 74-82; rtd 82. *Wyngarth, Bryn Road, Lampeter, Dyfed SA48 7EF* Lampeter (01570) 422474

MARKS, John Alexander Rishworth. b 19. TCD BA41 MA61. CITC 43. **d** 43 **p** 44. Chapl RN 46-69; rtd 69; Perm to Offic *St Alb* from 77. *1 Linten Close, Hitchin, Herts SG4 9PA*

MARKS, Timothy John. b 45. Man Univ BA76. **d** 88 **p** 89. NSM Burton and Sopley *Win* 88-91; R Croxton and Eltisley *Ely* from 91; R Graveley w Papworth St Agnes w Yelling etc from 91. *The Vicarage, Eltisley, St Neots, Huntingdon, Cambs PE19 4TQ* Croxton (0148087) 252

MARKWELL, Donald Stanley. b 30. Victoria Univ Wellington MA53. **d** 79 **p** 80. Hon C Kingston Hill St Paul *S'wark* 79-82; Hon C Ham St Andr from 82. *12 Albany Mews, Albany Park Road, Kingston upon Thames, Surrey KT2 5SL* 0181-546 0740

MARLEY, Alan Gordon. b 59. Birm Univ BA89. **d** 89 **p** 90. C Blandford Forum and Langton Long *Sarum* 89-93; Chapl HM Young Offender Inst Aylesbury from 93. *HM Young Offender Institution, Bierton Road, Aylesbury, Bucks HP20 1EH* Aylesbury (01296) 24435 Fax 434139

MARLEY, Neville William Arthur. b 24. Em Coll Cam BA46 MA51. Ridley Hall Cam 48. **d** 50 **p** 51. V Telford Park St Thos *S'wark* 56-89; CF (TA - R of O) 64-67; rtd 89. *12 The Headlands, Darlington, Co Durham DL3 8RP* Darlington (01325) 357559

MARLOW, Preb Walter Geoffrey. b 29. AKC57. **d** 57 **p** 58. C Long Eaton St Laur *Derby* 57-61; C Mackworth St Fran 61-63; R Stoke Albany w Wilbarston *Pet* 63-68; V Calow *Derby* 68-73; R Wingerworth 73-82; P-in-c Islington St Jas w St Phil *Lon* 82-87; P-in-c Islington St Pet 82-87; V Islington St Jas w St Pet 87-92; AD Islington 84-90; Preb St Paul's Cathl 87-92; Bp's Dom Chapl *B & W* from 92; Preb Wells Cathl from 92. *North Wing, The Palace, Wells, Somerset BA5 2PD* Wells (01749) 672341 Fax 679355

MARNHAM, Charles Christopher. b 51. Jes Coll Cam BA73 MA77. Cranmer Hall Dur DipTh76. **d** 77 **p** 78. C Brompton H Trin *Lon* 77-78; C Brompton H Trin w Onslow Square St Paul 78-80; C Linthorpe *York* 80-84; R Haughton le Skerne *Dur* from 84. *The Rectory, Haughton Green, Darlington, Co Durham DL1 2DD* Darlington (01325) 468142

MARNS, Nigel Geoffrey. b 63. Univ of Wales (Abth) BSc(Econ)85 Birm Univ BD92. Qu Coll Birm 90. **d** 93 **p** 94. C Addington *S'wark* from 93. *56 Viney Bank, Courtwood Lane, Croydon CR0 9JT* 0181-657 2478

MARQUEZ, Edilberto (Eddie). b 57. Instituto Biblico Alianza Lima BA80 Westmr Coll Ox MA93. St Steph Ho Ox 92. **d** 94 **p** 95. C Reading St Jo *Ox* from 94. *1 Church House, Orts Road, Reading RG1 3JN* Reading (01734) 669545

MARR, Canon Donald Radley. b 37. K Coll Lon 57. St Aid Birkenhead 61. **d** 64 **p** 65. V Marthall *Ches* 67-72; C W Kirby St Bridget 72-76; R Waverton 76-83; R Nantwich 83-87; RD Nantwich 86-87; RD Malpas 87-91; V Bunbury 87-91; Hon Can Ches Cathl 91-92; Dioc Rural Officer from 91; rtd 91. *St Boniface, 5 Hockenhull Crescent, Tarvin, Chester CH3 8LJ* Tarvin (01829) 741302

MARR, Mrs Joan Mary. b 36. SRN58 SCM75 HVCert78 NDN79. St Jo Coll Nottm CertCS91. **d** 91. Par Dn Moffat *Glas* from 91. *Auburn Cottage, Templand, Lockerbie, Dumfriesshire DG11 1TG* Dumfries (01387) 810734

MARR, Peter. b 36. Reading Univ PhD78. Ox NSM Course 84. **d** 87 **p** 88. NSM Reading St Giles *Ox* 87-89; C Beverley Minster *York* 90-92; P-in-c Beckenham St Barn *Roch* from 92. *St Barnabas' Vicarage, Oak Hill Road, Beckenham, Kent BR3 2NG* 0181-650 3332

MARRETT, Hedley Charles Guille. b 09. St Boniface Warminster 29. **d** 34 **p** 35. V Jersey St Simon *Win* 50-77; P-in-c Jersey All SS 67-77; rtd 77. *11 Bell Meadow, Hook, Basingstoke, Hants RG27 9HG* Hook (01256) 763176

MARRIOTT (nee REID), Mrs Amanda Joy (Mandy). b 63. DipRSAMDA83 Nottm Univ BTh92. Linc Th Coll 89. **d** 92. Par Dn Rothwell *Ripon* 92-94; C 94-95; C Manston from 95. *21 Pendas Grove, Leeds LS15 8HE* Leeds (0113) 264 9666

MARRIOTT, Frank Lewis. b 29. Lich Th Coll 57. **d** 60 **p** 61. R Tysoe w Compton Winyates and Oxhill *Cov* 64-70; P-in-c Cov St Marg 70-77; R Ufton 77-83; V Long Itchington 77-83; RD Southam 82-89; V Long Itchington and Marton 83-95; rtd 95. *12 Traherne Close, Ledbury, Herefordshire HR8 2JF* Ledbury (01531) 634576

MARRIOTT, Stanley Richard. b 36. AKC60 Warw Univ MA92. **d** 61 **p** 62. C Coleshill *Birm* 61-64; C Maxstoke 61-64; V Ansley *Cov* 64-78; Org Sec (E Midl) CECS 79-83; P-in-c Baxterley *Birm* 83; P-in-c Merevale w Bentley 83; P-in-c Baxterley w Hurley and Wood End and Merevale etc 83-84; R 84-87; R Newton Regis w Seckington and Shuttington from 87. *The Rectory, Newton Regis, Tamworth, Staffs B79 0PH* Tamworth (01827) 830254

MARRISON, Geoffrey Edward. b 23. Lon Univ BA48 PhD67. Bps' Coll Cheshunt 49 Kirchliche Hochschule Th Coll Berlin 50. **d** 51 **p** 52. C Wormley *St Alb* 51-52; Malaya 52-55; Singapore 55-56; C Radlett *St Alb* 56-57; C St Botolph Aldgate w H Trin Minories *Lon* 57-58; V Crookes St Tim *Sheff* 58-61; India 62-64; Perm to Offic *Cant* 64-69; Lic to Offic 69-82; Perm to Offic *Carl* from 83; Tutor Carl Dioc Tr Course from 83. *1 Ainsworth Street, Ulverston, Cumbria LA12 7EU* Ulverston (01229) 586874

MARROW, David Edward Armfield. b 42. Nottm Univ BA65 MA. Tyndale Hall Bris 65. **d** 67 **p** 68. C Clifton Ch Ch w Em *Bris* 67-70; Ethiopia 70-75; N Area Sec BCMS 75-77; C-in-c Ryde St Jas Prop Chpl *Portsm* 77-84; V Worthing St Geo *Chich* from 84. *The Vicarage, 20 Seldon Road, Worthing, W Sussex BN11 2LN* Worthing (01903) 203309

MARSDEN, Andrew Philip. b 63. Keble Coll Ox BA85 MA90 Birm Univ MA86. Wycliffe Hall Ox BA90. **d** 91 **p** 92. C Newport St Jo *Portsm* 91-94; C Cowplain from 94. *24 Wincanton Way, Cowplain, Waterlooville, Hants PO7 8NW* Waterlooville (01705) 257915

MARSDEN, Andrew Robert. b 49. AKC71. St Aug Coll Cant 68. **d** 72 **p** 73. C New Addington *Cant* 72-75; C Prudhoe *Newc* 75-77; Asst Chapl HM Pris Wakef 77; Chapl HM Borstal Portland 77-82; Chapl HM Young Offender Inst Onley 82-89; V Ulceby Gp *Linc* from 89. *The Vicarage, Church Lane, Ulceby, S Humberside DN39 6TB* Wootton (01469) 588239

MARSDEN, Mrs Carole. b 44. Avery Hill Coll TCert65 Sheff Poly DipEd87. N Ord Course 88. **d** 91 **p** 94. NSM Saddleworth *Man* 91-92; Par Dn 92-94; C 94-95; P-in-c Oldham St Paul from 95. *St Paul's Vicarage, 55 Belgrave Road, Oldham OL8 1LU* 0161-624 1068

MARSDEN, Geoffrey (Geoff). b 26. Lon Univ CertEd50 DipTh54 Open Univ BA79. E Anglian Minl Tr Course. **d** 86 **p** 87. NSM Higham *St E* 86-89; NSM Stratford St Mary 86-89; P-in-c Polstead from 89. *Mwaiseni, 5 Upper Street, Stratford St Mary, Colchester CO7 6LR* Colchester (01206) 322316

MARSDEN, George Henry. b 28. TCD BA57 MA60. Em Coll Saskatoon LTh51. **d** 51 **p** 52. R Berners Roding and Willingale w Shellow *Chelmsf* 61-82; rtd 82; Perm to Offic *Cant* 82-94. *43 Castle Street, Canterbury, Kent CT1 2PY* Canterbury (01227) 457917

MARSDEN, John Joseph. b 53. York Univ BA74 Nottm Univ DipTh78 MTh81 Kent Univ PhD88. St Jo Coll Nottm 77. **d** 80 **p** 81. C Leigh St Mary *Man* 80-83; Hon C Chatham St Steph *Roch* 83-91; Ind Chapl 83-91; Lect Systematic Th CITC from 91. *3 Sugarloaf Terrace, Veray Road, Bray, Co Wicklow, Irish Republic* Dublin (1) 492-3506 or 286-9054 Fax 492-3082

MARSDEN, John Robert. b 22. Linc Coll Ox BA48 MA49. Ripon Hall Ox 57. **d** 58 **p** 59. Chapl Dur Sch 61-85; rtd 85. *Prebends, High Kilburn, York YO6 4AJ* Coxwold (01347) 868597

MARSDEN, Miss Joyce. b 47. Trin Coll Bris DipHE80. dss 83 **d** 87 **p** 94. Wavertree H Trin *Liv* 83-85; Much Woolton 85-87; Par Dn 87-94; C from 94. *25 Linkside Road, Liverpool L25 9NX* 0151-428 6935

MARSDEN, Michael John. b 59. St Mich Coll Llan 78. **d** 82 **p** 83. C Neath w Llantwit *Llan* 82-85; Asst Chapl Univ Hosp of Wales Cardiff 85-89; V Graig *Llan* 89-93; P-in-c Cilfynydd 89-93; R Merthyr Tydfil St Dav from 93. *The Rectory, Bryntirion Road, Thomastown, Merthyr Tydfil, M Glam CF47 0ER* Merthyr Tydfil (01685) 722992

MARSDEN, Robert. b 59. Ch Ch Ox BA81 PGCE82. Oak Hill Th Coll BA92. **d** 92 **p** 93. C Sevenoaks St Nic *Roch* from 92. *40 South Park, Sevenoaks, Kent TN13 1EJ* Sevenoaks (01732) 454221

MARSDEN, Robert James. b 56. Ch Ch Coll Cant BEd79. Oak Hill Th Coll DipHE92. **d** 94 **p** 95. C Margate H Trin *Cant* from 94. *20 Millmead Avenue, Cliftonville, Margate, Kent CT9 3LP* Thanet (01843) 224408

MARSDEN, Canon Robert William. b 24. TCD BA49 MA52. CITC 50. **d** 50 **p** 51. I Clones w Killeevan *Clogh* 66-94; Prec Clogh Cathl 86-94; rtd 94. *30 Claremont Park, Sandymount, Dublin 4, Irish Republic* Dublin (1) 668-0210

MARSDEN, Samuel Edward. b 44. Keble Coll Ox BA66 MA85. Linc Th Coll 66. **d** 68 **p** 69. C Liskeard w St Keyne *Truro* 68-72; R Gerrans w St Antony in Roseland 72-77; Hong Kong 77-81; P-in-c Ingrave *Chelmsf* 81-82; P-in-c Gt Warley w Childerditch 81-82; R Gt Warley w Childerditch and Ingrave 82-89; Australia from 89. *The Rectory, Wamboin Street, Gilgandra, NSW, Australia 2827* Gilgandra (68) 472064 or 471100

MARSDEN-JONES, Watkin David. b 22. Univ of Wales (Lamp) BA48. **d** 49 **p** 50. V Copthorne *Chich* 56-70; RD E Grinstead 66-70; V Bosham 70-86; rtd 86; Perm to Offic *Chich* from 86. *10 Fairfield Road, Bosham, Chichester, W Sussex PO18 8JH* Bosham (01243) 575053

MARSH, Anthony David. b 29. Roch Th Coll 64. **d** 66 **p** 67. R Wrentham w Benacre and Covehithe *St E* 69-75; R Wrentham

w Benacre, Covehithe, Frostenden etc 75-80; P-in-c Beyton and Hessett 80-86; C Felixstowe St Jo 86-88; rtd 88. *7 Lime Tree Avenue, Felixstowe Beach Holiday Park, Walton Avenue, Felixstowe IP11 8HE* Felixstowe (01394) 283393

MARSH, Ven Bazil Roland. b 21. Leeds Univ BA42. Lambeth MLitt91 Coll of Resurr Mirfield 42. **d** 44 **p** 45. Can Pet Cathl *Pet* 64-91; R Northn St Pet w Upton 64-91; Adn Northn 64-91; rtd 91. *12 Parkway, Northampton NN3 3BS* Northampton (01604) 406644

MARSH, Carol Ann. *See* HATHORNE, Mrs Carol Ann

MARSH, Colin Arthur. b 54. St Jo Coll Nottm. **d** 82 **p** 83. C Kirkby *Liv* 82-86; TV St Luke in the City 86-91; USPG from 91; Zambia from 91. *clo USPG, Partnership House, 157 Waterloo Road, London SE1 8XA* 0171-928 8681 Fax 928 2371

MARSH, David. b 32. St Jo Coll Dur BA54 DipTh57. **d** 57 **p** 58. C Bilston St Leon *Lich* 57-62; Kenya 63-66 and 70-72; Chapl Scargill Ho 67-69; Adn S Maseno 70-72; V Meole Brace *Lich* 72-77; V Westlands St Andr 77-86; V Trentham from 86. *The Vicarage, Trentham Park, Stoke-on-Trent ST4 8AE* Stoke-on-Trent (01782) 658194

MARSH, Donald. b 35. W Midl Minl Tr Course. **d** 90 **p** 91. NSM Wednesbury St Bart *Lich* from 90. *Holly Rise, 19 Trouse Lane, Wednesbury, W Midlands WS10 7HR* 0121-556 0095

MARSH, Dr Francis John. b 47. ATCL ARCM ARCO York Univ BA69 DPhil76 Selw Coll Cam 73. Oak Hill Th Coll 72. **d** 75 **p** 76. C Cam St Matt *Ely* 75-78; C Pitsmoor w Wicker *Sheff* 79; C Pitsmoor w Ellesmere 79-81; C Crookes St Thos 81-85; V S Ossett *Wakef* from 85; RD Dewsbury from 93. *The Vicarage, 36 Manor Road, Ossett, W Yorkshire WF5 0AU* Wakefield (01924) 264818 or 263311

MARSH, Geoffrey John. b 38. K Coll Lon BD60 AKC60 Birm Univ PGCE66. **d** 61 **p** 62. C Upper Teddington SS Pet and Paul *Lon* 61-63; C Brierley Hill *Lich* 63-66; Asst Master Borough Green Sch 67-69; P-in-c Bracknell *Ox* 69-73; P-in-c Speen 73-74; P-in-c Stockcross 73-74; R Boxford w Stockcross and Speen 74-80; PV Truro Cathl *Truro* 80-82; Chapl Truro Cathl Sch 80-82; Chapl SS Mary and Anne's Sch Abbots Bromley 82-85; Chapl Heref Cathl Sch from 85. *4 Castle Street, Hereford HR1 2NL* Hereford (01432) 273757 or 266679

MARSH, Gordon Bloxham. b 25. Cant Sch of Min 82. **d** 85 **p** 86. NSM Loose *Cant* 85-86; NSM New Romney w Old Romney and Midley 86-90; NSM Asst to RD S Lympne 90-94; rtd 94; Perm to Offic *Cant* from 94. *Westleton, St John's Road, New Romney, Kent TN28 8EN* New Romney (01797) 366506

MARSH, Harry Carter. b 14. Chich Th Coll 48. **d** 49 **p** 50. V Sholing *Win* 60-71; R Michelmersh w Eldon w Timsbury 71-74; R Michelmersh w Mottisfont, Timsbury and Eldon 74-79; Perm to Offic 79-94; rtd 80; Perm to Offic *Portsm* 82-94. *Manormead Residential Home, Tilford Road, Hindhead, Surrey GU26 6RA* Hindhead (01428) 604780

MARSH, Jack Edmund Bruce. b 08. MA. **d** 73 **p** 74. NSM Yatton Keynell *Bris* 73-88; NSM Biddestone w Slaughterford 73-88; NSM Castle Combe 73-88; NSM W Kington 73-88; Perm to Offic from 88. *St Peter's House, The Green, Biddestone, Chippenham, Wilts SN14 7DG* Corsham (01249) 712835

MARSH, Lawrence Allan. b 36. Sarum Th Coll 66. **d** 67 **p** 68. C Waterlooville *Portsm* 67-70; V Shedfield 70-76; R Fen Ditton *Ely* from 76; P-in-c Horningsea from 83. *The Rectory, 16 High Street, Fen Ditton, Cambridge CB5 8ST* Teversham (01223) 293257

MARSH, Leonard Stuart Alexander. b 55. Hull Univ BA77. Linc Th Coll 77. **d** 79 **p** 80. C Eltham St Barn *S'wark* 79-81; C Camberwell St Giles 81-83; Hon C Clifton St Paul *Bris* 83-86; Chapl Bris Univ 83-86; Area Sec (Dio S'wark) USPG 86-91; Chapl City Univ *Lon* from 91; NSM Clerkenwell H Redeemer and St Mark from 94. *15 Ormonde Mansions, 106 Southampton Row, London WC1B 4BP* 0171-242 2574 or 477 8000

MARSH, Mrs Margaret Ann. b 37. Nottm Univ BSc59 Ox Univ DipEd60 Newc Univ MA93. Carl Dioc Tr Course 86 Lambeth STh87. **d** 87. Asst Chapl Garlands Hosp 87-92; Dn Carl Cathl *Carl* 87-93; NSM Carl St Luke Morton 93-94; NSM Cumbria Ind Chapl Team from 94. *34 Moorville Drive South, Carlisle CA3 0AW* Carlisle (01228) 45717

MARSH, Miss Maxine Dorothy. b 49. Bretton Hall Coll TCert72. Westcott Ho Cam 90. **d** 92 **p** 94. C Kings Norton *Birm* 92-95; P-in-c Kingsbury from 95. *The Vicarage, Church Lane, Kingsbury, Tamworth, Staffs B78 2LR* Tamworth (01827) 873500

MARSH, Peter Derek. b 29. Em Coll Saskatoon. **d** 59 **p** 60. Lic to Offic *Lon* 64-71; P-in-c Kilburn St Mary 71-81; rtd 81; Perm to Offic *St Alb* from 87. *231 Handside Lane, Welwyn Garden City, Herts AL8 6TF* Welwyn Garden (01707) 325105

MARSH, Ralph. b 42. ACP65 Chester Coll CertEd63 Birm Univ BPhil77. St Deiniol's Hawarden 86. **d** 88 **p** 89. NSM Tranmere St Paul w St Luke *Ches* 88-90; C Guiseley w Esholt *Bradf*

90-92; V Broughton *St As* 92-94; C Ribbleton *Blackb* from 94. *St Anne's House, Waddington Road, Preston PR2 6HU* Preston (01772) 792993

MARSH, Dr Richard.d 94. Hon C Westmr St Steph w St Jo *Lon* from 94. *4 The Cooperage, Rita Road, London SW8 1HP* 0171-582 8026

MARSH, Dr Richard St John Jeremy. b 60. Keble Coll Ox BA82 MA86 Dur Univ PhD91. Coll of Resurr Mirfield 83. **d** 85 **p** 86. C Grange St Andr *Ches* 85-87; Fell and Chapl Univ Coll Dur 87-92; Abp's Asst Sec for Ecum Affairs *Cant* from 92; Lic to Offic *Lon* from 93. *4 The Cooperage, Regents Bridge Gardens, London SW8 1HP* 0171-582 8026

MARSH, Robert Christopher. b 53. Ex Univ BEd76. St Steph Ho Ox 86. **d** 88 **p** 89. C St Leonards Ch Ch and St Mary *Chich* 88-91; TV Crawley from 91. *Peterhouse, 128 Ifield Road, Crawley, W Sussex RH11 7BW* Crawley (01293) 520921

MARSH, Roger Philip. b 44. K Coll Lon BD72 AKC72. St Aug Coll Cant 73. **d** 73 **p** 74. C Leagrave *St Alb* 73-76; Asst Youth Officer 76-77; Resources Officer 77-80; Chapl Marlborough Coll Wilts 80-86; Master Ardingly Coll Jun Sch Haywards Heath from 86. *Junior School, Ardingly College, Haywards Heath, W Sussex RH17 6SQ* Ardingly (01444) 892279

MARSH, Mrs Shelley Ann. b 54. SRN75 SCM76. St Jo Coll Nottm CertCS87. **d** 89 **p** 94. Hon C Glas Gd Shep and Ascension *Glas* from 89. *44 Atholl Crescent, Paisley, Renfrewshire PA1 3AW* 0141-883 8668

MARSH, Simon Robert. b 59. Sarum & Wells Th Coll 79. **d** 82 **p** 83. C Mottram in Longdendale w Woodhead *Ches* 82-85; Bp's Dom Chapl *Bradf* 85-87; V Ashton Hayes *Ches* 87-90; V Macclesfield St Paul from 90. *St Paul's Vicarage, Swallow Close, Lark Hall Road, Macclesfield, Cheshire SK10 1QN* Macclesfield (01625) 422910

MARSHALL, Alan John. b 48. Carl Dioc Tr Course. **d** 89 **p** 90. NSM Carl St Luke Morton *Carl* 89-92. *12 Thornton Road, Stanwix, Carlisle CA3 9HZ* Carlisle (01228) 25338

MARSHALL, Alexander Robert. b 43. Glouc Sch of Min 84. **d** 87 **p** 88. NSM Newtown w Llanllwchaiarn w Aberhafesp *St As* from 87. *3 Churchill Drive, Newtown, Powys SY16 2LQ* Newtown (01686) 628375

MARSHALL, Ms Alison Rose Marie. b 60. Leic Univ BA83 Birkb Coll Lon MA86 E Anglia Univ PGCE87. Ridley Hall Cam CTM95. **d** 95. C Whittlesey and Pondersbridge *Ely* from 95. *The Vicarage, St Mary's Street, Whittlesey, Peterborough PE7 1BG* Peterborough (01733) 203676

MARSHALL, Mrs Angela. b 48. Trin Coll Bris 74. **d** 88. Hon Par Dn Newc St Geo *Lich* 88-92; Lic to Offic *Eur* 92-94; Dn Versailles St Mark from 94. *31 rue du Pont Colbert, 78000 Versailles, France* France (331) 39 02 79 45

MARSHALL, Arthur. b 25. Oak Hill Th Coll 66. **d** 68 **p** 69. C Worksop St Jo *S'well* 68-72; R Trowell 72-78; R Abbas and Templecombe w Horsington *B & W* 78-80; V Pemberton St Mark Newtown *Liv* 80-82; V Creeksea w Althorne, Latchingdon and N Fambridge *Chelmsf* 82-86; R Epperstone *S'well* 86-89; R Gonalston 86-89; P-in-c Oxton *S'well* 86-89; rtd 89. *Flat 2, Coombe Court, Tadworth, Surrey KT20 5AL* Tadworth (01737) 813347

MARSHALL, Basil Eustace Edwin. b 21. OBE69. Westcott Ho Cam 71. **d** 73 **p** 74. C Edenbridge *Roch* 73-78; P-in-c Matfield 78-85; P-in-c Lamberhurst 78-85; C Farnborough 85-86; rtd 86; Hon C Speldhurst w Groombridge and Ashurst *Roch* from 86. *7 Boyne Park, Tunbridge Wells, Kent TN4 8EL* Tunbridge Wells (01892) 521664

MARSHALL, Bernard Godfrey Graham. b 35. Birm Univ BA56. Qu Coll Birm DipTh59. **d** 60 **p** 61. C Hampton *Worc* 60-63; P-in-c Fairfield St Rich CD 63-65; Deanery Youth Chapl 62-65; Chapl RN 65-91; V Ashford Hill w Headley *Win* from 91. *The Vicarage, Ashford Hill, Newbury, Berks RG15 8AZ* Headley (01635) 268217

MARSHALL, Canon Bryan John. b 40. Chich Th Coll 63. **d** 65 **p** 66. C Poulton-le-Fylde *Blackb* 65-68; C S Shore H Trin 68-70; V Wesham 70-74; P-in-c Chich Cathl *Chich* 74-82; V Boxgrove 82-91; P-in-c Tangmere 82-84; R 84-91; R Westbourne from 91; Can and Preb Chich Cathl from 94. *The Rectory, Westbourne Road, Westbourne, Emsworth, Hants PO10 8UL* Emsworth (01243) 372867

MARSHALL, Christopher John. b 56. Edge Hill Coll of HE BEd79. St Alb Minl Tr Scheme 83. **d** 86 **p** 87. C Biggleswade *St Alb* 86-89; Chapl Asst S Beds Area HA 89-91; Chapl St Helier Hosp Carshalton from 91; Sen Chapl St Helier NHS Trust from 93. *32 Gauntell Road, Sutton, Surrey SM1 4RY, or St Helier Hospital, Carshalton, Surrey SM5 1AA* 0181-296 2306

MARSHALL, Preb Christopher John Bickford (Chris). b 32. TD78. AKC56. **d** 57 **p** 58. C Leatherhead *Guildf* 57-60; C Crewkerne *B & W* 60-63; V Long Sutton 63-72; V Long Sutton w Long Load 72-76; V Wiveliscombe 76-93; RD Tone 78-87; Preb Wells Cathl from 88; P-in-c Chipstable w Huish Champflower and Clatworthy 93; R Wiveliscombe w

Chipstable, Huish Champflower etc from 93. *The Vicarage, South Street, Wiveliscombe, Taunton, Somerset TA4 2LZ* Wiveliscombe (01984) 623309

MARSHALL, Christopher Robert. b 49. St Chad's Coll Dur BA71. Sarum & Wells Th Coll 72. **d** 74 **p** 75. C Sheff Parson Cross St Cecilia *Sheff* 74-77; C Walsall St Gabr Fulbrook *Lich* 77-78; C Upper Gornal 78-80; V Walsall St Andr 80-86; V Willenhall St Giles from 86. *St Giles's Vicarage, Walsall Street, Willenhall, W Midlands WV13 2ER* Willenhall (01902) 605722

MARSHALL, David. b 66. St Kath Coll Liv CertRS88 Liv Univ BA88. Ripon Coll Cuddesdon 89. **d** 92 **p** 93. C Dovecot *Liv* from 92. *97 Broadoak Road, Liverpool L14 0NP* 0151-252 0388

MARSHALL, David Charles. b 52. St Chad's Coll Dur BA73. Trin Coll Bris 74. **d** 76 **p** 77. C Meole Brace *Lich* 76-78; C W Teignmouth *Ex* 78-80; C Broadwater St Mary *Chich* 80-84; V Newc St Geo *Lich* 84-92; Chapl Versailles w Chevry *Eur* from 92. *31 rue du Pont Colbert, 78000 Versailles, France* France (331) 39 02 79 45 Fax 39 50 97 29

MARSHALL, David Evelyn. b 63. New Coll Ox BA85 Birm Univ MA88. Ridley Hall Cam 88. **d** 90 **p** 91. C Roundhay St Edm *Ripon* 90-92; Chapl Ex Coll Ox from 95. *Exeter College, Oxford OX1 3DP* Oxford (01865) 279600

MARSHALL, Eric. b 20. E Midl Min Tr Course. **d** 82 **p** 83. Chapl Grimsby Distr Hosps from 82; Hon C Gt Grimsby St Mary and St Jas *Linc* from 85. *Morn Tide, Waithe Lane, Grimsby, S Humberside DN37 0RJ* Grimsby (01472) 823681

MARSHALL, Canon Geoffrey Osborne (Geoff). b 48. St Jo Coll Dur BA71. Coll of Resurr Mirfield 71. **d** 73 **p** 74. C Waltham Cross *St Alb* 73-76; C Digswell 76-78; P-in-c Belper Ch Ch and Milford *Derby* 78-86; V Spondon 86-93; Chapl Derby High Sch for Girls from 87; RD Derby N *Derby* from 90; Can Res Derby Cathl from 93. *24 Kedleston Road, Derby DE22 1GU* Derby (01332) 343144

MARSHALL, Mrs Gillian Kathryn. b 54. Glouc Sch of Min 84. **d** 87. NSM Newtown w Llanllwchaiarn w Aberhafesp *St As* from 87. *42 Churchill Drive, Newtown, Powys SY16 2LQ* Newtown (01686) 628375

MARSHALL, Graham George. b 38. Dur Univ BA60 St Chad's Coll Dur DipTh65. **d** 65 **p** 66. C Ashton-on-Ribble St Mich *Blackb* 65-67; C Lanc St Mary 67-71; R Church Eaton *Lich* 71-75; Prec Man Cathl *Man* 75-78; R Reddish 78-85; V Chadderton St Luke from 87. *St Luke's Vicarage, Queen's Road, Chadderton, Oldham OL9 9HU* 0161-624 3562

MARSHALL (nee CHADWICK), Mrs Helen Jane. b 63. UEA BA84 Nottm Univ MTh91. St Jo Coll Nottm LTh88 DPS91. **d** 91 **p** 94. Par Dn Easton H Trin w St Gabr and St Lawr and St Jude *Bris* 91-94; C 94-95. *6 Stanley Road, Oxford OX4 1QZ* Oxford (01865) 242831

MARSHALL, Canon Hugh Phillips. b 34. SS Coll Cam BA57 MA61. Linc Th Coll 57. **d** 59 **p** 60. C Westmr St Steph w St Jo *Lon* 59-65; V Tupsley *Heref* 65-74; V Wimbledon *S'wark* 74-78; TR 78-87; RD Merton 79-86; V Mitcham SS Pet and Paul 87-90; Hon Can S'wark Cathl 89-90; Chief Sec ABM from 90. *30 Woodville Road, Morden, Surrey SM4 5AF, or Church House, Great Smith Street, London SW1P 3NZ* 0181-542 3962 or 0171-222 9011 Fax 0171-799 2714

MARSHALL, Mrs Jean. b 36. SW Minl Tr Course 84. **d** 87 **p** 94. NSM Stratton *Truro* 87-89; NSM Bodmin w Lanhydrock and Lanivet 89-94; NSM Lezant w Lawhitton and S Petherwin w Trewen from 94. *The Vicarage, South Petherwin, Launceston, Cornwall PL15 7JA* Launceston (01566) 773782

MARSHALL, John. b 37. Kelham Th Coll 53. **d** 62 **p** 63. C Winshill *Derby* 62-64; C Chaddesden St Phil 64-65; Chapl HM Borstal Morton Hall 65-75; V Swinderby *Linc* 66-77; R Church Aston *Lich* 77-84; V Auckland St Andr and St Anne *Dur* from 84; P-in-c Hunwick 88-90; Chapl Bishop Auckland Gen Hosp from 84. *St Andrew's Vicarage, Park Street, Bishop Auckland, Co Durham DL14 7JS* Bishop Auckland (01388) 604397

MARSHALL, John. b 50. St Luke's Coll Ex CertEd74 W Lon Inst of HE DipEdHChild79. S'wark Ord Course 88. **d** 91 **p** 92. Hon C Brixton Hill St Sav *S'wark* from 91. *57A Kingscourt Road, London SW16 1JA* 0181-769 3665

MARSHALL, John Dixon. b 17. Dur Univ LTh43. Edin Th Coll 40. **d** 43 **p** 44. R Fortrose *Mor* 65-74; R Cromarty 65-74; R Baillieston *Glas* 74-82; R Glas St Serf 74-82; rtd 82; Perm to Offic *Mor* from 82. *17 Mackenzie Terrace, Rosemarkie, Fortrose, Ross-shire IV10 8UH* Fortrose (01381) 20924

MARSHALL, John Douglas. b 23. Univ of Wales (Cardiff) BA43. **d** 79 **p** 80. Hon C Radlett *St Alb* 79-86; Lic to Offic *Llan* from 86. *Meiros, 3 River Walk, Cowbridge, S Glam CF7 7DW* Cowbridge (01446) 773930

MARSHALL, John Linton. b 42. Worc Coll Ox BA64 MA68 Bris Univ MLitt75. Wells Th Coll 66. **d** 68 **p** 69. C Bris St Mary Redcliffe w Temple etc *Bris* 68-71; Tutor Sarum & Wells Th Coll 71-73; Perm to Offic *Pet* 74-77; Lic to Offic *S'well* 77-81;

VC S'well Minster 79-81; R Ordsall 81-88; P-in-c Grove 84-88; RD Retford 84-88; V Northowram *Wakef* from 88. *The Vicarage, Back Clough, Northowram, Halifax, W Yorkshire HX3 7HH* Halifax (01422) 202551

MARSHALL, John William. b 24. St And NSM Tr Scheme. **d** 73 **p** 74. NSM Inverkeithing *St And* 73-90; NSM Lochgelly 73-90; NSM Rosyth 73-90; rtd 90. *33 Whyte Street, Lochgelly, Fife KY5 9DA* Lochgelly (01592) 780769

MARSHALL, Kirstin Heather. b 64. St Jo Coll Nottm 90. **d** 93 **p** 95. NSM Glas St Marg *Glas* from 93. *St Margaret's Church House, 351 Kilmarnock Road, Glasgow G43 2DS* 0141-636 1131

MARSHALL, Lionel Alan. b 41. TEng. St Deiniol's Hawarden 84 Qu Coll Birm 86. **d** 87 **p** 88. C Llandudno *Ban* 87-90; V Rhayader and Nantmel *S & B* from 90. *The Vicarage, Dark Lane, Rhayader, Powys LD6 5DA* Rhayader (01597) 810223

MARSHALL, Canon Maurice Peter. b 23. Oak Hill Th Coll 59. **d** 61 **p** 62. V New Ferry *Ches* 64-79; V Hartford 79-89; Hon Can *Ches* Cathl 87-89; rtd 89. *27 East Lane, Sandiway, Northwich, Cheshire CW8 2QQ* Northwich (01606) 888591

MARSHALL, Michael David. b 51. BSc. Trin Coll Bris. **d** 84 **p** 85. C Kennington St Mark *S'wark* 84-88; V Streatham Park St Alb from 88; RD Tooting from 93. *St Alban's Vicarage, 5 Fayland Avenue, London SW16 1SR* 0181-677 4521 or 769 5415

✠**MARSHALL, Rt Rev Michael Eric.** b 36. Ch Coll Cam BA58 MA62. Cuddesdon Coll 58. **d** 60 **p** 61 **c** 75. C Birm St Pet *Birm* 60-62; Tutor Ely Th Coll 62-64; Min Can Ely Cathl *Ely* 62-64; Chapl Lon Univ *Lon* 64-69; V St Marylebone All SS 69-75; Suff Bp Woolwich *S'wark* 75-84; Asst Bp Lon from 84; Episc Dir Angl Inst Missouri 84-92; Can and Preb Chich Cathl *Chich* from 90; Asst Bp Chich from 92; Abps' Adv Springboard for Decade of Evang from 92. *The Gatehouse, Palace Yard, Canon Lane, Chichester, W Sussex PO19 1PX*

MARSHALL, Canon Peter Arthur. b 31. AKC58. **d** 59 **p** 60. Chapl Orchard View and Kingsmead Court Hosps 66-94; R Lexden *Chelmsf* 66-94; RD Colchester 88-93; Hon Can *Chelmsf* Cathl 90-94; rtd 94. *21 Manor Close, Wickham, Fareham, Hants PO17 5BZ* Fareham (01329) 832988

MARSHALL, Peter James. b 48. Qu Coll Birm 78. **d** 80 **p** 81. C Ormskirk *Liv* 80-83; V Dallam from 83. *St Mark's Vicarage, Longshaw Street, Warrington WA5 5DY* Warrington (01925) 631193

MARSHALL, Canon Peter Jerome. b 40. McGill Univ Montreal. Westcott Ho Cam 61. **d** 63 **p** 64. C E Ham St Mary *Chelmsf* 63-66; C Woodford St Mary 66-71; C-in-c S Woodford 66-71; V Walthamstow St Pet 71-81; Dep Dir of Tr 81-84; Can Res Chelmsf Cathl 81-85; Dioc Dir of Tr *Ripon* from 85; Can Res Ripon Cathl from 85. *12 Clotherholme Road, Ripon, N Yorkshire HG4 2DA* Ripon (01765) 604835

MARSHALL, Peter John. b 33. K Coll Lon 56. Codrington Coll Barbados 57. **d** 61 **p** 62. CF 67-88; rtd 88. *c/o MOD (Army), Bagshot Park, Bagshot, Surrey GU19 5PL* Bagshot (01276) 471717 Fax 412834

MARSHALL, Peter John Charles. b 35. Bris Univ BA60. Ridley Hall Cam 60. **d** 62 **p** 63. C Lindfield *Chich* 62-65; Travelling Sec Scripture Union 65-83; Hon C Nottm St Nic *S'well* 65-67; Hon C Cheadle Hulme St Andr *Ches* 67-83; V Ilkley All SS *Bradf* from 83; RD Otley from 92. *The Vicarage, 58 Curly Hill, Ilkley, W Yorkshire LS29 0BA* Ilkley (01943) 607537

MARSHALL, Robert Paul (Rob). b 60. Sheff Univ BA81 Dur Univ MA85. Cranmer Hall Dur 81. **d** 83 **p** 84. C Kirkstall *Ripon* 83-85; C Otley *Bradf* 85-87; Dioc Communications Officer 87-91; P-in-c Embsay w Eastby 87-91; Dioc Communications Officer *Lon* from 91. *110 Ellesmere Road, London NW10 1JS* 0181-452 7939 or 0171-233 8681 Fax 0171-233 8670

MARSHALL, Simon. b 54. Kingston Poly BSc77 Leeds Univ PGCE78 MA(Ed)79. Qu Coll Birm DipTh93. **d** 93. C Gt Clacton *Chelmsf* from 93. *St Mark's House, 112 Woodlands Close, Great Clacton, Clacton-on-Sea, Essex CO15 4RU* Clacton-on-Sea (01255) 430520

MARSHALL, Canon Timothy James. b 26. Barrister-at-Law (Middle Temple) 50 BNC Ox BA48 BCL49 MA53. St Steph Ho Ox DipTh51. **d** 52 **p** 53. V Shirebrook *Derby* 60-92; Hon Can Derby Cathl 86-92; rtd 92. *43 Charleston Road, Penrhyn Bay, Llandudno, Gwynedd LL30 3HB* Colwyn Bay (01492) 543541

MARSHALL, Timothy John. b 53. GRSM74. Oak Hill Th Coll BA79. **d** 79 **p** 80. C Muswell Hill St Jas w St Matt *Lon* 79-85; V Hammersmith St Simon 85-92; V Bovingdon *St Alb* from 92. *The Vicarage, Bovingdon, Hemel Hempstead, Herts HP3 0LP* Hemel Hempstead (01442) 833298

MARSHALL, Canon William John. b 35. TCD BA57 BD61 PhD75. TCD Div Sch 59. **d** 59 **p** 60. C Ballyholme *D & D* 59-61; India 62-72; Asst Dean of Residence TCD 73-76; I Rathmichael *D & G* 76-92; Can Ch Ch Cathl Dub 90; Chan from 91; Vice-Prin CITC from 92. *99 Landscape Park,*

Churchtown, Dublin 14, Irish Republic Dublin (1) 298-6989 or 492-3506 Fax 492-3082

MARSHALL, William Michael (Bill). b 30. Pemb Coll Ox BA53 MA57 DipEd65 Lon Univ DipTh67 Bris Univ MLitt72 PhD79 DipTh. Sarum & Wells Th Coll 79. **d** 80 **p** 81. Asst Chapl Millfield Sch Somerset from 65; Hon C Glastonbury St Jo w Godney *B & W* 80-84; Hon C Glastonbury w Meare, W Pennard and Godney from 84. *The Long House, Baltonsborough, Glastonbury, Somerset BA6 8QP* Baltonsborough (01458) 50288

MARSHALL-TAYLOR, Aubrey. b 11. Dur Univ LTh35. Tyndale Hall Bris 32. **d** 41 **p** 42. R Graveley w Chivesfield *St Alb* 55-78; rtd 78; Perm to Offic *St Alb* from 79; Perm to Offic *Ox* from 87. *10 Halifax House, Little Chalfont, Amersham, Bucks HP7 9NG* Little Chalfont (01494) 763749

MARSTON, David Howarth. b 48. St Jo Coll Dur BA69. Edin Th Coll 69. **d** 71 **p** 72. C Kendal H Trin *Carl* 71-75; Perm to Offic *Glas* 75-78; Hon C Barrow St Matt *Carl* 79-93; NSM Southport All SS *Liv* 93-94; NSM Southport All So 93-94; NSM Southport All SS and All So from 94. *28 Hillsview Road, Southport, Merseyside PR8 3PN* Southport (01704) 576138

MARSTON, William Thornton. b 59. Worc Coll Ox BA81 MA85 Cam Univ CertEd83. St Steph Ho Ox BA87. **d** 88 **p** 89. C Beckenham St Geo *Roch* 88-92; TV Ifield *Chich* from 92. *St Alban's Vicarage, Gossops Drive, Crawley, W Sussex RH11 8LD* Crawley (01293) 529848

MART, Terence Eugene. b 47. CertEd76 BA82. St Jo Coll Nottm LTh87. **d** 87 **p** 88. C Prestatyn *St As* 87-91; Chapl Theatr Clwyd Mold 87-91; R Llangystennin from 91. *The Rectory, Glyn y Marl Road, Llandudno Junction, Gwynedd LL31 9NS* Aberconwy (01492) 583579

MARTIN, Alexander Lewendon. b 26. Em Coll Cam BA47 MA51. Ridley Hall Cam 56. **d** 57 **p** 58. Chapl Felsted Sch Essex 64-74; Chapl Sedbergh Sch Cumbria 74-84; R Askerswell, Loders and Powerstock *Sarum* 84-89; RD Lyme Bay 86-89; rtd 89; Perm to Offic *Ex* from 89. *Thirtover, 7 Alexandra Way, Crediton, Devon EX17 2EA* Crediton (01363) 776206

MARTIN, Canon Anthony Bluett. b 29. St Jo Coll Cam BA52 MA56. Ridley Hall Cam 52. **d** 54 **p** 55. V Hoole *Ches* 63-84; Hon Can Ches Cathl 83-94; V Bowdon 84-94; rtd 94. *8 Eaton Mews, Chester CH4 7EJ* Chester (01244) 680307

MARTIN, Anthony George. b 20. Nottm Univ LTh74. ALCD42. **d** 43 **p** 45. R Ilchester w Northover *B & W* 69-72; R Limington 69-72; R Axbridge 72-74; R Axbridge w Shipham and Rowberrow 74-80; rtd 81; Perm to Offic *B & W* from 81. *5 Lawpool Court, Wells, Somerset BA5 2AN* Wells (01749) 675739

MARTIN, Brother. *See* COOMBE, John Morrell

MARTIN, Christopher John. b 45. Ball Coll Ox BA67 MA87. Wycliffe Hall Ox 86. **d** 88 **p** 89. C Edin St Thos *Edin* 88-90; R Duns from 90. *The Rectory, Wellfield, Duns, Berwickshire TD11 3EH* Duns (01361) 82209

MARTIN, Christopher John Neville. b 32. Trin Coll Ox BA54 MA57. St Deiniol's Hawarden 82 S'wark Ord Course. **d** 83 **p** 84. NSM Man St Ann *Man* 83-84; NSM N Sheen St Phil and All SS *S'wark* 84-87; NSM Petersham 87-89; C Fryerning w Margaretting *Chelmsf* 89-92; P-in-c St Ippolyts *St Alb* from 92. *The Vicarage, Stevenage Road, St Ippolyts, Hitchin, Herts SG4 7PE* Hitchin (01462) 457552

MARTIN, Prof David Alfred. b 29. LSE BSc PhD. Westcott Ho Cam. **d** 83 **p** 84. Hon C Guildf Cathl *Guildf* from 83. *174 St John's Road, Woking, Surrey GU21 1PQ* Woking (01483) 762134

MARTIN, David Geoffrey. b 34. K Coll Lon BD60 AKC61. **d** 61 **p** 62. C Liv Our Lady and St Nic *Liv* 61-63; Australia 63-66; Chapl and Lect K Coll Lon 66-70; V Kennington St Jo *S'wark* 70-77; P-in-c Camberwell St Jas 76-77; Hon C Clapham Ch Ch and St Jo 77-81; Lic to Offic 81-85; V S Wimbledon All SS 85-90; V Upper Norwood St Jo from 90. *St John's Vicarage, 2 Sylvan Road, London SE19 2RX* 0181-653 0378

MARTIN, David Howard. b 47. Worc Coll Ox BEd79. AKC70 St Aug Coll Cant 70. **d** 71 **p** 72. C Sedgley All SS *Lich* 71-75; Dioc Youth Chapl *Worc* 75-81; P-in-c Worc St Andr and All SS w St Helen 75-81; R Newland, Guarlford and Madresfield 81-91; R Alvechurch from 91. *The Rectory, Alvechurch, Birmingham B48 7SB* 0121-445 1087

MARTIN, Donald Dales. b 30. Sarum Th Coll 53. **d** 55 **p** 56. V Manfield w Cleasby *Ripon* 60-73; V Melbecks and Muker 73-78; R Romaldkirk w Laithkirk 78-83; V Broughton and Duddon *Carl* 83-89; rtd 89; R Iona *Arg* 89-95; Lic to Offic *Mor* from 89. *The Grove, Ewanfield, Crieff, Perthshire PH7 3DA* Crieff (01764) 652228

MARTIN, Donald Philip Ralph. b 30. Trin Coll Toronto MA55 STB55. **d** 54 **p** 55. Canada 54-57; Tutor Kelham Th Coll 57-73; SSM from 60; P-in-c Willen *Ox* 73-81; Japan 81-82; Ghana 83-89; Dir Cleveland Lay Tr Course from 89; C Middlesb All SS *York* 89-91; NSM from 91. *All Saints' Vicarage, Grange*

Road, Middlesbrough, Cleveland TS1 2LR Middlesbrough (01642) 245035

MARTIN, Edward Eldred William. b 37. Cranfield Inst of Tech MSc84. S'wark Ord Course 65. **d** 68 **p** 69. C Greenwich St Alfege w St Pet *S'wark* 68-71; C Kidbrooke St Jas 71-75; V Peckham St Jo 75-78; P-in-c Peckham St Andr w All SS 76-78; V Peckham St Jo w St Andr 78-81; Hon PV S'wark Cathl from 81; Chapl Guy's Hosp Lon 81-88. *22 Jerningham Road, London SE14 5NX* 0171-639 1402

MARTIN, Edwin John. b 43. JP89. TEng MIIExE89. **d** 83 **p** 84. NSM Cwmbran *Mon* 83-85; NSM Griffithstown 85-87; NSM Cwmbran from 87. *168 Rowleaze, Greenmeadow, Cwmbran, Gwent NP44 4LG* Cwmbran (01633) 485575

MARTIN, Miss Eileen Susan Kirkland. b 45. LCST66. Lon Bible Coll DipTh71 Cranmer Hall Dur 77. dss 83 **d** 86. C Kilmarnock *Glas* 84-86; Par Dn Heanor *Derby* 87-92; Perm to Offic from 92. *20 The Nook, Loscoe, Heanor, Derbyshire DE75 7LQ* Langley Mill (01773) 760220

MARTIN, George Cobain. b 34. TCD BA57 MA65. **d** 57 **p** 58. I Kircubbin *D & D* 64-74; R Ashby by Partney *Linc* 75-78; R Partney w Dalby 75-78; V Skendleby 75-78; P-in-c Candlesby w Scremby 77-78; R Partney 78-95; rtd 95. *Southwold, Main Road, East Keal, Spilsby, Lincs PE23 4BA* Spilsby (01790) 752988

MARTIN, Glenn. b 52. Qu Coll Birm 84. **d** 86 **p** 87. C Chatham St Wm *Roch* 86-89; Chapl Pastures Hosp Derby 89-94; Chapl Kingsway Hosp Derby from 89. *14 Barnwood Close, Mickleover, Derby DE3 5QY, or Kingsway Hospital, Kingsway, Derby DE22 3LZ* Derby (01332) 510869 or 362221

MARTIN, Canon Gordon Albion John. b 30. AKC54. **d** 55 **p** 56. C Enfield Chase St Mary *Lon* 55-59; C Palmers Green St Jo 59-61; V Edmonton St Martin 61-64; V Culham *Ox* 64-67; Bp's Youth Chapl *St Alb* 67-73; P-in-c Wareside 69-73; V Harpenden St Jo from 73; RD Wheathampstead 76-87; Hon Can St Alb from 85. *St John's Vicarage, 5 St John's Road, Harpenden, Herts AL5 1DJ* Harpenden (01582) 712776

MARTIN, Graham Rowland. b 39. LCP FRSA Liv Univ CertEd58 Nottm Univ DipRE65 Lon Univ DipTh BD70 Bris Univ BEd73 Bris Poly DipEdMan80. Wells Th Coll 71. **d** 71 **p** 72. Hon C Glouc St Cath *Glouc* 71-76; P-in-c Brookthorpe w Whaddon 76-78; Perm to Offic 78-80; Hon C Hucclecote 80-82; Hon C Tuffley 82-88; NSM Hardwicke, Quedgeley and Elmore w Longney 88-89; V Kemble, Poole Keynes, Somerford Keynes etc from 89. *The Vicarage, Kemble, Cirencester, Glos GL7 6AG* Cirencester (01285) 770049

MARTIN, Dr James Davidson. b 35. Glas Univ MA57 BD60 PhD70. **d** 89 **p** 89. NSM St Andrews St Andr *St And* from 89; Chapl St Andr Univ from 89. *32 Craigievar Drive, Glenrothes, Fife KY7 4PH* Glenrothes (01592) 772956

MARTIN, James Smiley. b 32. TCD 65. **d** 67 **p** 68. C Glenavy *Conn* 67-70; C Belf St Mary 70-73; I Carnmoney 73-74; I Mallusk 74-94; rtd 94. *c/o 21 Dundesert Road, Nutts Corner, Crumlin, Co Antrim BT29 4SL* Glengormley (01232) 825636

MARTIN, John. b 32. Roch Th Coll 61. **d** 64 **p** 65. C Barrow St Matt *Carl* 64-66; C Netherton 66; C Bishopwearmouth St Mich *Dur* 66-67; C Wigan All SS *Liv* 67-73; C-in-c Croxteth St Paul CD 73-80; C Stockport St Alb Hall Street *Ches* 80-82; P-in-c Hyde St Thos from 82. *St Thomas's Vicarage, 14 Walker Lane, Hyde, Cheshire SK14 5PL* 0161-368 1406

MARTIN, John Albert. TCD DipTh85. **d** 85 **p** 86. C Drumachose *D & R* 85-88; I Cumber Upper w Learmount from 88; Bp's Dom Chapl from 94. *Alla Rectory, 87 Cumber Road, Claudy, Co Londonderry BT47 4JA* Claudy (01504) 338214

MARTIN, John Henry. b 42. St Jo Coll Cam BA63 MA67. St Jo Coll Nottm BA73. **d** 73 **p** 74. C Ecclesall *Sheff* 73-77; C Hednesford *Lich* 77-82; V Walsall Pleck and Bescot 82-92; V Whittington w Weeford from 92. *The Vicarage, Whittington, Lichfield, Staffs WS14 9LH* Whittington (01543) 432233

MARTIN, John Hunter. b 42. AKC64. **d** 65 **p** 66. C Mortlake w E Sheen *S'wark* 65-69; C-in-c Bermondsey St Hugh CD 69-72; V Bermondsey St Anne 72-78; P-in-c Lt Ouse *Ely* 78; V Littleport 78-89; V Attercliffe *Sheff* 89-90; P-in-c Darnall H Trin 89-90; TR Darnall-cum-Attercliffe from 90. *The Vicarage, 25/27 Industry Road, Sheffield S9 5FP* Sheffield (0114) 256 2337

MARTIN, John Keith. b 32. Sarum & Wells Th Coll 76. **d** 79 **p** 80. C Bath Bathwick *B & W* 79-82; V Weston-super-Mare St Andr Bournville 82-85; V Cinderford St Jo *Glouc* 85-94. *Glen Cairn, 39 Laflouder Fields, Mullion, Helston, Cornwall TR12 7EJ* Helston (01326) 240613

MARTIN, Canon John Pringle. b 24. Bris Univ BA50. Clifton Th Coll 50. **d** 52 **p** 53. V Congleton St Pet *Ches* 59-81; RD Congleton 74-85; Hon Can Ches Cathl 80-90; R Brereton w Swettenham 81-90; rtd 90. *49 Parkhouse Road, Minehead, Somerset TA24 8AD* Minehead (01643) 706769

MARTIN, John Stuart. b 11. St Jo Coll Dur BA34. Wycliffe Hall Ox. **d** 35 **p** 36. V Upottery *Ex* 65-72; TV Farway w Northleigh and Southleigh 72-73; rtd 73. *Church Villa, 8 Church Road,*

Bawdrip, Bridgwater, Somerset TA7 8PU Puriton (01278) 684092

MARTIN, Canon John Tidswell. b 24. Em Coll Cam BA48 MA52. Kelham Th Coll 48. **d** 53 **p** 54. V Kingston All SS *S'wark* 68-76; V Kingston All SS w St Jo 76-89; Hon Can S'wark Cathl 87-89; rtd 89. *175 Lincoln Avenue, Twickenham TW2 6NL*

MARTIN, John William. b 12. Clifton Th Coll 37. **d** 37 **p** 38. R Itchingfield *Chich* 51-82; rtd 82; Perm to Offic *Win* from 82. *23 Chawton Close, Harestock, Winchester, Hants SO22 6HY* Winchester (01962) 883061

MARTIN, Jonathan Patrick McLeod. b 55. Leic Univ BA81. Sarum & Wells Th Coll 84. **d** 86 **p** 87. C Southn Thornhill St Chris *Win* 86-89; Perm to Offic 89-92; C Heatherlands St Jo *Sarum* from 92. *35 Stanfield Road, Parkstone, Poole, Dorset BH12 3HR* Poole (01202) 746744

MARTIN, Joseph Edward. b 35. NDD55. Bps' Coll Cheshunt 58. **d** 60 **p** 61. C Short Heath *Birm* 60-62; C Caterham Valley *S'wark* 63-66; R W Hallam and Mapperley *Derby* 66-70; P-in-c Mapperley 66-67; V Wykeham and Hutton Buscel *York* 71-78; Chapl HM Pris Askham Grange 78-82; V Askham Bryan w Askham Richard *York* 78-82; R Amotherby w Appleton and Barton-le-Street 82-84; C Banbury *Ox* 85-88; C Warsop *S'well* 88-90; V Tuxford w Weston and Markham Clinton from 90. *The Vicarage, Lincoln Road, Tuxford, Newark, Notts NG22 0HP* Tuxford (01777) 870497

MARTIN, Kenneth. b 20. Univ of Wales (Lamp) BA47. **d** 48 **p** 49. C Rumney *Mon* 48-49; C Griffithstown 49-51; CF (TA) from 52. *21 Earls Court Road, Penylan, Cardiff CF3 7DE* Cardiff (01222) 493796

MARTIN, Kenneth Cyril. b 31. AIGCM53. S'wark Ord Course 71. **d** 73 **p** 74. C Hollington St Leon *Chich* 73-76; C Horsham 76-79; P-in-c Broadwaters *Worc* 79-81; V 81; P-in-c Worc H Trin 81-86; R Stoulton w Drake's Broughton and Pirton etc 86-91; rtd 91. *6 Scobell Close, Pershore, Worcs WR10 1AN* Pershore (01386) 556734

MARTIN, Canon Kenneth Roger. b 16. AKC40. **d** 40 **p** 41. R Wokingham All SS *Ox* 69-81; RD Sonning 78-81; rtd 81; Perm to Offic *Ex* from 81; Perm to Offic *Ox* from 81. *1 Indio Road, Bovey Tracey, Devon TQ13 9BT* Bovey Tracey (01626) 832605

MARTIN, Miss Marion. b 47. Oak Hill Th Coll DipHE85. dss 86 **d** 87. Ditton *Roch* 86-88; C 87-88; rtd 88; Perm to Offic *Glouc* 89-95. *33 Campden Road, Cheltenham, Glos GL51 6AA* Cheltenham (01242) 239477

MARTIN, Nicholas Roger. b 53. St Jo Coll Dur BA74. Ripon Coll Cuddesdon 75. **d** 77 **p** 78. C Wolvercote w Summertown *Ox* 77-80; C Kidlington 80-82; TV 82-84; V Happisburgh w Walcot *Nor* 84-85; P-in-c Hempstead w Lessingham and Eccles 84-85; R Happisburgh w Walcot, Hempstead, Lessingham etc 85-89; R Blakeney w Cley, Wiveton, Glandford etc from 89. *The Rectory, Wiveton Road, Blakeney, Holt, Norfolk NR25 7NJ* Cley (01263) 740686

MARTIN, Nicholas Worsley. b 52. Sarum & Wells Th Coll 71. **d** 75 **p** 76. C Llan w Capel Llanilltern *Llan* 75-79; C Cardiff St Jo 79; C Caerphilly 79-83; TV Hemel Hempstead *St Alb* 83-93; Chapl Hemel Hempstead Gen Hosp 83-93. *Pilgrims Cottage, The Street, Graffham, Petworth, W Sussex GU28 0NP* Graffham (01798) 867397

MARTIN, Norman George. b 22. Sarum & Wells Th Coll 74. **d** 77 **p** 78. NSM Long Ashton *B & W* 77-81; NSM Walton in Gordano 81-82; NSM E Clevedon and Walton w Weston w Clapton 82-87; Perm to Offic from 87; Chapl Barrow Hosp from 87; Chapl Farleigh Hosp from 87. *7 Clynder Grove, Castle Road, Clevedon, Avon BS21 7DF* Clevedon (01275) 873124

MARTIN, Mrs Penelope Elizabeth. b 44. Cranmer Hall Dur 83. dss 86 **d** 87 **p** 94. Seaham w Seaham Harbour *Dur* 86-87; Par Dn 87-89; Par Dn Cassop cum Quarrington 89-93; Par Dn Sherburn w Pittington 93-94; C from 94. *26 Telford Close, High Shincliffe, Durham DH1 2YJ* 0191-386 1742

MARTIN, Peter. b 50. MIH75. Linc Th Coll 82. **d** 84 **p** 85. C Taunton H Trin *B & W* 84-86; C Bath Bathwick 86-88; R Cannington, Otterhampton, Combwich and Stockland from 88; Chapl Cannington Coll from 89; Chapl Somerset Coll of Agric & Horticulture from 89. *The Rectory, 27 Brook Street, Cannington, Bridgwater, Somerset TA5 2HP* Combwich (01278) 652953

MARTIN, Peter. b 66. Univ of Wales (Ban) BD89. Qu Coll Birm 90. **d** 92 **p** 93. C Kingswinford St Mary *Lich* 92-93; C Kingswinford St Mary *Worc* from 93. *4 The Village, Kingswinford, W Midlands DY6 8AY* Dudley (01384) 273397

MARTIN, Philip James. b 58. Cam Univ BA. Coll of Resurr Mirfield. **d** 84 **p** 85. C Pontefract St Giles *Wakef* 84-88; C Wantage *Ox* 88-90; C Didcot All SS 90; V Alderholt *Sarum* from 90. *The Vicarage, Draggons Road, Alderholt, Fordingbridge, Hants SP6 3DN* Fordingbridge (01425) 653179

MARTIN, Raymond William. b 32. MBIM Lon Univ BSc66 DMA. Glouc Th Course 73. **d** 76 **p** 76. C Glouc St Mary de Lode and St Nic *Glouc* 76-77; Hon C Redmarley D'Abitot, Bromesberrow w Pauntley etc 77-84; R 84-91; P-in-c Falfield w Rockhampton from 91; P-in-c Oldbury-on-Severn from 91; Chapl HM Pris Eastwood Park from 91. *The Vicarage, Sundayshill Lane, Falfield, Wotton-under-Edge, Glos GL12 8DQ* Falfield (01454) 260033 Fax 261027

MARTIN, Richard. b 34. Rhodes Univ BA54 Em Coll Cam BA57 MA58. Wells Th Coll 57. **d** 59 **p** 60. C Portsea St Mary *Portsm* 59-60; S Africa 60-87; C Aldershot St Mich *Guildf* 87-94; R Wick *Mor* from 94; P-in-c Thurso from 94. *5 Naver Place, Thurso, Caithness KW14 7PZ* Thurso (01847) 63393

MARTIN, Richard Charles de Villeval. b 41. St Jo Coll Ox BA63 MA67. Ox Ord Course. **d** 84 **p** 85. NSM Ox St Thos w St Frideswide and Binsey *Ox* from 84; Asst Chapl Highgate Sch 86-92; Asst Master Magd Coll Sch Ox 92-94; Chapl from 94. *11 Benson Place, Oxford OX2 6QH* Oxford (01865) 510694

MARTIN, Richard Hugh. b 55. Dur Univ BA78. St Jo Coll Nottm BA81 DPS82. **d** 82 **p** 83. C Gateshead *Dur* 82-85; C Redmarshall 85-88; V Scarborough St Jas w H Trin *York* from 88. *St James's Vicarage, 24 Seamer Road, Scarborough, N Yorkshire YO12 4DT* Scarborough (01723) 361469

MARTIN, Robert David Markland. b 49. FCA80 Trin Coll Cam BA71 MA74. Trin Coll Bris BA91. **d** 91 **p** 92. C Kingswood *Bris* from 91. *1 Downend Road, Bristol BS15 1RT* Bristol (0117) 967 6122

MARTIN, Robert Paul Peter. b 58. Chich Th Coll. **d** 83 **p** 84. C Anfield St Columba *Liv* 83-86; C Orford St Marg 86-87; R Blackley H Trin *Man* 87-90; C Oseney Crescent St Luke *Lon* 90-93; C Kentish Town from 93. *The Church House, Ospringe Road, London NW5 2JB* 0171-267 4720

MARTIN, Robin Hugh. b 35. Rhodes Univ BA56 Birm Univ DipRTS57. **d** 58 **p** 59. C-in-c Kimberworth Park *Sheff* 62-65; Lic to Offic *Newc* 67-71; Perm to Offic *Man* 79-93; rtd 93. *Address temp unknown*

MARTIN, Roger Ivor. b 42. DMS76 MIMgt. Cant Sch of Min. **d** 85 **p** 86. NSM Saltwood *Cant* 85-90; P-in-c Crundale w Godmersham from 90; Dioc Exec Officer for Adult Educn and Lay Tr from 90. *The Forge, Godmersham Park, Godmersham, Canterbury, Kent CT4 7DT* Canterbury (01227) 738177 Fax as telephone

MARTIN, Mrs Rosanna Stuart. b 60. Bris Univ BA81. Wycliffe Hall Ox 89. **d** 92 **p** 94. Par Dn Stanford in the Vale w Goosey and Hatford *Ox* 92-94; C from 94. *7 Limetrees, Chilton, Didcot, Oxon OX11 1AH* Didcot (01235) 821861

MARTIN, Roy Ernest. b 29. FCA54. Qu Coll Birm 74. **d** 77 **p** 77. NSM Marston Green *Birm* 77-85; NSM Sheldon 85-89; Perm to Offic from 89. *14 Walcot Green, Dorridge, Solihull, W Midlands B93 8BU* Knowle (01564) 772943

MARTIN, Rupert Gresley. b 57. Worc Coll Ox BA78. Trin Coll Bris DipHE91. **d** 91 **p** 92. C Yateley *Win* 91-95; V Sandal St Helen *Wakef* from 95. *Woodlands Cottage, 2 Castle Road, Wakefield, W Yorkshire WF2 7LU* Wakefield (01924) 255441

MARTIN, Russell Derek. b 47. St Jo Coll Dur 71. **d** 74 **p** 75. C Hartlepool H Trin *Dur* 74-78; C Swindon St Jo and St Andr *Bris* 78-79; V Penhill 79-91; V Haselbury Plucknett, Misterton and N Perrott *B & W* from 91. *The Rectory, North Perrott, Crewkerne, Somerset TA18 7TB* Crewkerne (01460) 72063

MARTIN, Mrs Sara Galloway. b 19. MCSP40. N Ord Course 71. **dss** 79 **d** 87 **p** 94. Ainsworth *Man* 79-82; Tottington 82-87; Par Dn 87-88 and from 94; rtd 89; Perm to Offic *Man* 89-94. *36 Victoria Street, Tottington, Bury, Lancs BL8 4AG*

MARTIN, Miss Susan (Sue). b 56. Nottm Univ BA77. Edin Th Coll 86. **d** 88 **p** 94. C Leigh Park *Portsm* 88-91; C Sandown Ch Ch 91-94; C Portsea St Cuth from 94. *15 Grays Court, Portsmouth PO1 2PN* Portsmouth (01705) 733575

MARTIN, Sylvia. b 24. **dss** 75 **d** 87 **p** 94. NSM Selsdon St Jo w St Fran *S'wark* from 87. *42 Upper Selsdon Road, Selsdon, Croydon CR2 8DE* 0181-657 3422

MARTIN, Terry Allan. b 64. GRSM85 DipRCM85. Chich Th Coll 85. **d** 88 **p** 89. C Hangleton *Chich* 88-91; C New Shoreham 91-95; C Old Shoreham 91-95; V Lower Beeding from 95; Dom Chapl to Area Bp Horsham 95. *The Vicarage, Plummers Plain, Lower Beeding, Horsham, W Sussex RH13 6NU* Lower Beeding (01403) 891367

MARTIN, Thomas Robin. b 40. Bps' Coll Cheshunt 64. **d** 67 **p** 68. C Ripley *Derby* 67-70; C Ilkeston St Mary 70-74; V Chinley w Buxworth 74-83; V Knighton St Mich *Leic* 83-85; V Thurmaston from 85. *The Vicarage, 828 Melton Road, Thurmaston, Leicester LE4 8BE* Leicester (0116) 269 2555

MARTIN, William Harrison. b 38. **d** 87 **p** 88. NSM Rushen *S & M* 87-92; C German from 92. *3 Peverill Avenue, Peel, Isle of Man IM5 1QB* Peel (01624) 843588

MARTIN, William Henry Blyth. b 10. Keble Coll Ox BA33 MA36. Cuddesdon Coll 35. **d** 36 **p** 37. V Long Eaton St Laur *Derby* 62-80; rtd 81; Perm to Offic *Cov* from 81; Perm to Offic *Pet* from 85. *93 Crick Road, Hillmorton, Rugby, Warks CV21 4DZ*

MARTIN, William Matthew (Bill). b 28. C&G81 FETC81 Ch Coll Cam BA52 MA56. Ridley Hall Cam 52. **d** 54 **p** 55. CF 61-82; Dep Asst Chapl Gen 73-82; Asst Master St Jo Southworth RC High Sch Preston 82-88; Lic to Offic *Blackb* from 82; rtd 93. *40 Jepps Avenue, Barton, Preston PR3 5AS* Broughton (01772) 862166

MARTIN-DOYLE, Mrs Audrey Brenda. b 35. Cranmer Hall Dur 80. **dss** 82 **d** 87. The Lye and Stambermill *Worc* 82-86; Chapl Lee Abbey 86-88; Ldr Aston Cottage Community from 88; NSM Cheltenham St Mark *Glouc* 94; NSM Cheltenham St Mary, St Matt, St Paul and H Trin from 94. *4 Jenners Walk, St George's Place, Cheltenham, Glos GL50 3LD* Cheltenham (01242) 514419

MARTINDALE, Mrs Patricia Ann. b 24. Qu Coll Birm. **dss** 84 **d** 87 **p** 94. Rugby St Andr *Cov* 84-87; NSM from 87. *54 Hillmorton Road, Rugby, Warks CV22 5AD* Rugby (01788) 543038

MARTINEAU, Canon Christopher Lee (Chris). b 16. Trin Hall Cam BA38 MA70. Linc Th Coll 39. **d** 41 **p** 42. R Skipton H Trin *Bradf* 65-83; rtd 83; Perm to Offic *Bradf* from 83. *6 Greenhead Avenue, Utley, Keighley, W Yorkshire BD20 6EY* Keighley (01535) 609247

MARTINEAU, Canon David Richards Durani. b 36. AKC59. **d** 60 **p** 61. C Ches St Jo *Ches* 60-64; S Africa 64-69; C Jarrow St Paul *Dur* 69-72; TV 72-75; TR Jarrow 76-85; V Gildersome *Wakef* from 85; Hon Can Wakef Cathl from 94. *St Peter's House, 2A Church Street, Gildersome, Morley, Leeds LS27 7AF* Leeds (0113) 253 3339

MARTINEAU, Jeremy Fletcher. b 40. K Coll Lon BD65 AKC65. **d** 66 **p** 67. C Jarrow St Paul *Dur* 66-73; Bp's Ind Adv 69-73; P-in-c Raughton Head w Gatesgill *Carl* 73-80; Chapl to Agric 73-80; Ind Chapl *Bris* 80-90; Abps' Rural Officer *Cant* 90-93; Nat Rural Officer Gen Syn Bd of Miss from 94. *The Arthur Rank Centre, National Agricultural Centre, Stoneleigh, Coventry CV8 2LZ* Warwick (01926) 812130 or 696969

✠**MARTINEAU, Rt Rev Robert Arnold Schurhoff.** b 13. Trin Hall Cam BA35 MA39. Westcott Ho Cam 36. **d** 38 **p** 39 **c** 66. C Melksham *Sarum* 38-41; Chapl RAFVR 41-46; V Ovenden *Wakef* 46-52; V Allerton *Liv* 52-66; Hon Can Liv Cathl 61-66; RD Childwall 64-66; Suff Bp Huntingdon *Ely* 66-72; Bp Blackb 72-81; rtd 81. *Gwenallt, Park Street, Denbigh, Clwyd LL16 3DB* Denbigh (01745) 814089

MARTINSON, Peter Stephen Douglas. b 15. K Coll Lon BA42 AKC48. **d** 49 **p** 50. Area Sec (Dio Guildf) USPG 66-80; rtd 80; Perm to Offic *Portsm* from 86. *25 Yeomans Lane, Liphook, Hants GU30 7PN* Liphook (01428) 722498

MARTLEW, Andrew Charles. b 50. Nottm Univ BTh76 Lanc Univ MA80. Linc Th Coll 72. **d** 76 **p** 77. C Poulton-le-Fylde *Blackb* 76-79; Hon C Lanc Ch Ch 79-80; Malaysia 81-83; V Golcar *Wakef* 83-89; Dioc Schs Officer 89-95; V Warmfield 89-95; Dioc Dir of Educn *York* from 95. *The Vicarage, Crayke, York YO6 4TA*

MARVELL, John. b 32. Lon Univ BD63 Leic Univ MEd73 PhD85. Oak Hill Th Coll 79. **d** 80 **p** 81. NSM Colchester Ch Ch w St Mary V *Chelmsf* 80-85; Perm to Offic 85-87; P-in-c Stisted w Bradwell and Pattiswick from 87. *The Rectory, Water Lane, Stisted, Braintree, Essex CM7 8AP* Braintree (01376) 551839

MASCALL, Mrs Margaret Ann. b 43. LRAM64 Bris Univ CertEd65 St Jo Coll Dur BA71 MA79. Cranmer Hall Dur 69. **dss** 76 **d** 87 **p** 94. Hertf St Andr *St Alb* 75-79; Herne Bay Ch Ch *Cant* 79-82; Seasalter 82-84; Whitstable 84-87; Par Dn 87-90; Perm to Offic 91-94; Hon C Hackington from 94. *58 Pigeon Lane, Herne Bay, Kent CT6 7ES* Canterbury (01227) 362942

MASDING, John William. b 39. Magd Coll Ox BA61 MA65 DipEd63 Univ of Wales (Cardiff) LLM94. Ridley Hall Cam 63. **d** 65 **p** 66. C Boldmere *Birm* 65-71; V Hamstead St Paul from 71. *Hamstead Vicarage, 840 Walsall Road, Birmingham B42 1ES* 0121-357 1259 Fax 357 8328

MASH, William Edward John (Bill). b 54. ARCS MCIT81 Imp Coll Lon BSc75. St Jo Coll Nottm 87. **d** 89 **p** 90. C Beverley Minster *York* 89-93; V Elloughton and Brough w Brantingham from 93. *The Vicarage, Church Lane, Elloughton, Brough, N Humberside HU15 1HN* Hull (01482) 667431

MASHEDER, Peter Timothy Charles. b 49. AKC71. St Aug Coll Cant 71. **d** 72 **p** 73. C Barkingside St Fran *Chelmsf* 72-75; C Chingford SS Pet and Paul 75-91; P-in-c High Laver w Magdalen Laver and Lt Laver etc from 91. *The Lavers Rectory, Magdalen Laver, Ongar, Essex CM5 0ES* Harlow (01279) 426774

MASHEDER, Richard. b 36. AKC59. **d** 60 **p** 61. C Preston St Matt *Blackb* 60-62; C Padiham 62-65; P-in-c Worsthorne 65; V 65-74; CF (TA) 65-67; P-in-c Blackb St Jude *Blackb* 74-78; V

Blackb St Thos 76-78; V Blackb St Thos w St Jude 78-82; V Silverdale from 82. *The Vicarage, St John's Grove, Silverdale, Carnforth, Lancs LA5 0RH* Silverdale (01524) 701268

MASKELL, John Michael. b 45. Sarum & Wells Th Coll 86. **d** 88 **p** 89. C Swanborough *Sarum* 88-91; Chapl RAF 91-95; P-in-c Ollerton w Boughton *S'well* from 95. *The Vicarage, 65 Larch Road, New Ollerton, Newark, Notts NG22 9SX* Mansfield (01623) 860323

MASKREY, Mrs Susan Elizabeth. b 43. Cranmer Hall Dur IDC70 St Jo Coll Dur CertRK70. **dss** 76 **d** 92 **p** 94. Littleover *Derby* 76-77; Sec to Publicity Manager CMS Lon 77-78; Stantonbury and Willen *Ox* 78-88; Billingham St Aid *Dur* 88-95; C 92-95; Asst Chapl HM Pris Holme Ho 94-95; Asst Chapl HM Pris Preston from 95. *HM Prison, 2 Ribbleton Lane, Preston PR1 5AB* Preston (01772) 57734 Fax 556643

MASLEN (formerly CHILD), Mrs Margaret Mary. b 44. ALA76 Open Univ BA79. S Dios Minl Tr Scheme 89. **d** 92 **p** 94. C Portishead *B & W* 92-93; C Ilminster w Whitelackington 93-94; C Ilminster and District from 94. *145 Blackdown View, Ilminster, Somerset TA19 0BG* Ilminster (01460) 53427

MASLEN, Richard Ernest. b 34. S Dios Minl Tr Scheme 89. **d** 92 **p** 93. NSM Sherston Magna, Easton Grey, Luckington etc *Bris* 92-93; NSM Ilminster w Whitelackington *B & W* 93-94; NSM Ilminster and District from 94. *145 Blackdown View, Ilminster, Somerset TA19 0BG* Ilminster (01460) 53427

MASLEN, Canon Stephen Henry. b 37. CCC Ox BA62 MA65. Ridley Hall Cam 62. **d** 64 **p** 65. C Keynsham w Queen Charlton *B & W* 64-67; C Cheltenham St Mary *Glouc* 67-71; P-in-c St Mary-at-Lambeth *S'wark* 72-74; TV N Lambeth 74-79; V Horley 79-84; TR 84-94; RD Reigate 86-91; R Coulsdon St Jo from 94; Hon Can S'wark Cathl from 95. *232 Coulsdon Road, Coulsdon, Surrey CR5 1EA* Downland (01737) 552152

MASLEN, Trevor. b 51. Chich Th Coll 77. **d** 80 **p** 81. C Harlow St Mary Magd *Chelmsf* 80-83; C Huntingdon St Barn *Ely* 83-86; P-in-c Huntingdon 86-87; TV 87-92; V Southn St Jude Win from 92. *The Vicarage, 94 Chestnut Road, Southampton S01 6BU* Southampton (01703) 774603

MASON, Adrian Stanley. b 54. Hatf Poly BSc77. Ripon Coll Cuddesdon 77. **d** 80 **p** 81. C Mill End and Heronsgate w W Hyde *St Alb* 80-83; P-in-c Chardstock *Ex* 83; TV Axminster, Chardstock, Combe Pyne and Rousdon 83-87; TV Halesworth w Linstead, Chediston, Holton etc *St E* 87-88; R Brandon and Santon Downham 88-91; R Glem Valley United Benefice 91-95; NSM Clare Deanery from 95. *The Rectory, Glemsford, Sudbury, Suffolk CO10 7RF* Glemsford (01787) 280361

MASON, Alan Hambleton. b 27. Lon Univ BD59. Wycliffe Hall Ox 56. **d** 59 **p** 60. V Thornton St Jas *Bradf* 63-73; V Norbiton *S'wark* 73-84; V Wavertree St Thos *Liv* 84-92; rtd 92. *17 Lovelace Road, Liverpool L19 1QE* 0151-427 5678

MASON, Charles Godfrey. b 24. CEng71 FInstE74 Open Univ BA84. CITC 85 D & D Ord Course 85. **d** 87 **p** 89. NSM Ban St Comgall *D & D* 87-90; NSM Lecale Gp 87-91; NSM Donaghadee 90-91; Lic to Offic from 91. *20 Seymour Avenue, Bangor, Co Down BT19 1BN* Bangor (01247) 465096

MASON, Charles Oliver. b 51. Jes Coll Cam BA73 St Jo Coll Dur BA79. **d** 80 **p** 81. C Cheltenham St Mary, St Matt, St Paul and H Trin *Glouc* 80-84; C Enfield Ch Ch Trent Park *Lon* 84-88; P-in-c W Hampstead St Cuth 88-93; V from 93. *St Cuthbert's Vicarage, 13 Kingscroft Road, London NW2 3QE* 0181-452 1913

MASON, Dr Christina. b 42. Univ of Wales BMus63 MA65 BSc(Econ)70 CertCS82 Dundee Univ PhD84 MSW91 CQSW91. **dss** 82 **d** 86. Lic to Offic *Bre* from 82. *Maywood, Main Street, Longforgan, Dundee DD2 5EP* Longforgan (0182622) 337

MASON, Mrs Christine Mary. b 43. Sarum & Wells Th Coll 91. **d** 93 **p** 94. Par Dn Blakenall Heath *Lich* 93-94; C from 94. *27 Smithfield Road, Walsall WS3 1ND* Walsall (01922) 477013

MASON, Christopher David. b 51. Lanc Univ BA72 MEd82. E Anglian Minl Tr Course 91. **d** 94 **p** 95. NSM Pet St Mary *Pet* from 94. *21 Bakers Lane, Woodston, Peterborough PE2 9QW* Peterborough (01733) 342116

MASON, Clive Ray. b 34. St Chad's Coll Dur BA57. Qu Coll Birm 57. **d** 59 **p** 60. V Darlington St Jo *Dur* 64-74; P-in-c Southwick H Trin 75-84; R 84-89; V Bearpark 89-95; rtd 95; Perm to Offic *Dur* from 95. *41 Harbour View, Littlehaven, South Shields, Tyne & Wear NE33 1LS* 0191-454 0234

MASON, David Gray. b 37. **d** 95. NSM Biddenham *St Alb* from 95. *2A Devon Road, Bedford MK40 3DF* Bedford (01234) 357036

MASON, David John. b 42. Sarum & Wells Th Coll 72. **d** 74 **p** 75. C S Hackney St Jo w Ch Ch *Lon* 75-78; C Haggerston All SS 78-80; V Canning Town St Cedd *Chelmsf* 80-83; Chapl Springfield Hosp Southwick 83-87; Chapl Middx Hosp Lon

from 87. *Middlesex Hospital, Mortimer Street, London W1N 8AA* 0171-636 8333

MASON, Dennis Wardell. b 28. Ox NSM Course 83. **d** 86 **p** 87. NSM Ox St Barn and St Paul *Ox* from 86. *26 John Lopes Road, Eynsham, Witney, Oxon OX8 1JR* Oxford (01865) 880440

MASON, Mrs Elizabeth Ann. b 42. Cam Inst of Educn TCert64 Open Univ BA90. Ox Min Course CBTS94. **d** 94. NSM Worminghall w Ickford, Oakley and Shabbington *Ox* from 94. *20 Clifden Road, Wormingham, Aylesbury, Bucks HP18 9JP* Ickford (01844) 339640

MASON, Ernest Walter. b 20. S'wark Ord Course 74. **d** 77 **p** 78. NSM Clapham H Spirit *S'wark* 77-87; NSM Clapham TM 87-88; rtd 88; Perm to Offic *S'wark* from 88. *35 Klea Avenue, London SW4 9HG* 0181-673 5575

MASON, Francis Robert Anthony. b 56. Trin Coll Bris BA90. **d** 90 **p** 91. C Denham *Ox* 90-94; P-in-c Jersey Grouville *Win* from 94. *The Rectory, Grouville, Jersey, Channel Islands JE3 9DA* Jersey (01534) 853073

MASON, Frederic. b 13. SS Coll Cam MA38 Malaya Univ LLD60. St Aug Coll Cant 60. **d** 61 **p** 62. Prin Ch Ch Coll Cant 61-75; Hon C Hackington *Cant* 61-67; Lic to Offic 67-75; Perm to Offic *Ex* 75-88; Perm to Offic *Sarum* from 88. *Downsview House, 63 St Mark's Avenue, Salisbury SP1 3DD* Salisbury (01722) 325165

MASON, Frederick Michael Stewart. b 15. Kelham Th Coll 32. **d** 39 **p** 40. V Thornton N Radford *Cov* 59-86; rtd 86; Perm to Offic *Glouc* from 86. *Brinsworth, 2 Mercia Road, Winchcombe, Cheltenham, Glos GL54 5QD* Cheltenham (01242) 602709

MASON, Geoffrey Charles. b 48. K Coll Lon BD74 AKC74. St Aug Coll Cant 74. **d** 75 **p** 76. C Hatcham Park All SS *S'wark* 75-78; V Bellingham St Dunstan 78-87; RD E Lewisham 82-87; C Catford (Southend) and Downham 87-88; Bp's Adv for Min Development from 88. *32 King's Orchard, London SE9 5TJ* 0181-859 7614 or 0171-378 7506 Fax 0171-403 6497

MASON, John Evans. b 32. RD. Linc Th Coll 57. **d** 59 **p** 60. C Putney St Mary *S'wark* 59-62; C Berry Pomeroy *Ex* 62-64; Chapl RN 64-68; V Hopton *Nor* 68-72; Chapl RNR 69-82; P-in-c Roydon St Remigius *Nor* 72-76; R Diss 72-80; Dir YMCA Cam 80-85; Prin YMCA Dunford Coll 85-88; Perm to Offic *Glouc* from 88; Perm to Offic *Ox* from 89. *Westerley Cottage, Burford Street, Lechlade, Glos GL7 3AP* Faringdon (01367) 252642

MASON, John Martin. b 41. UMIST BSc63. Glouc Sch of Min 80 Qu Coll Birm 82. **d** 84 **p** 85. C Tuffley *Glouc* 84-87; P-in-c Willersey, Saintbury, Weston-sub-Edge etc 87-92; R from 92. *The Rectory, Weston-sub-Edge, Chipping Campden, Glos GL55 6QH* Evesham (01386) 840292

MASON, Jonathan Patrick. b 55. Edin Th Coll 90. **d** 92 **p** 93. C Edin Ch Ch *Edin* 92-94; C Edin Old St Paul from 94. *48 India Street, Edinburgh EH3 6HD* 0131-225 6472

MASON, Ms Josephine Margaret. b 41. Edin Univ BMus64. W Midl Minl Tr Course 88. **d** 93 **p** 94. Chapl Asst Highcroft and Northcroft Hosps *Birm* from 91; C Birm St Jo Ladywood from 93. *340 Selly Oak Road, Birmingham B30 1HP* 0121-451 1412

MASON, Julia Ann. b 43. St Jo Coll Nottm 89. **d** 91 **p** 95. NSM Troon *Glas* 91-93; NSM Ayr from 93; NSM Maybole from 93; NSM Girvan from 93. *2 Balcomie Crescent, Troon, Ayrshire KA10 7AR* Troon (01292) 311707

MASON, Canon Kenneth Staveley. b 31. ARCS53 Lon Univ BSc53 BD64. Wells Th Coll 56. **d** 58 **p** 59. C Kingston upon Hull St Martin *York* 58-61; C Pocklington w Yapham-cum-Meltonby, Owsthorpe etc 61-63; C Millington w Gt Givendale 61-63; V Thornton w Allerthorpe 63-69; Sub-Warden St Aug Coll Cant 69-76; Dir Cant Sch of Min 77-81; Sec to Dioc Bd of Min Cant 77-87; Six Preacher Cant Cathl 79-84; Prin Cant Sch of Min 81-89; Hon Can Cant Cathl 84-89; Prin Edin Th Coll from 89; Can St Mary's Cathl *Edin* from 89. *St Colm's, 21 Inverleith Terrace, Edinburgh EH3 5NS* 0131-343 2038

MASON, Nigel Frederick. b 60. Wycliffe Hall Ox DipMin95. **d** 95. C Highbury Ch Ch w St Jo and St Sav Lon from 95. *7 Lyndon Court, Kelvin Road, London N5 2PP* 0171-359 1799

MASON, Paul. b 51. Cranmer Hall Dur CTMin93. **d** 93 **p** 94. C Handforth *Ches* from 93. *61 Pickmere Road, Wilmslow, Cheshire SK9 3TB* Wilmslow (01625) 529570

MASON, Peter Charles. b 45. K Coll Lon BD72 AKC72 Birm Univ PGCE89. St Aug Coll Cant 72. **d** 73 **p** 74. C Ilkeston St Mary *Derby* 73-76; C Bridgnorth St Mary *Heref* 76-78; TV Bridgnorth, Tasley, Astley Abbotts, Oldbury etc 78-88; RE Teacher from 89; Perm to Offic from 89. *4 Woodberry Close, Bridgnorth, Shropshire WV16 4PT*

MASON, Canon Peter Joseph. b 34. Lon Univ BA58. Coll of Resurr Mirfield 58. **d** 60 **p** 61. C Belhus Park CD *Chelmsf* 60-63; Lic to Offic *Eur* 63-64; Asst Chapl Lon Univ Lon 64-70; Chapl City Univ 66-70; R Stoke Newington St Mary 70-78; V Writtle *Chelmsf* 78-81; P-in-c Highwood 78-81; V Writtle w Highwood 81-86; R Shenfield 86-93; Hon Can Chelmsf Cathl from 89; P-in-c Maldon All SS w St Pet from 93; RD Maldon and Dengie from 95. *All Saints' Vicarage, Church Walk, Maldon, Essex CM9 7PY* Maldon (01621) 854179

MASON, Ven Richard John. b 29. Linc Th Coll 55. **d** 58 **p** 59. C Hatf *St Alb* 58-64; Bp's Dom Chapl *Lon* 64-69; V Riverhead *Roch* 69-73; P-in-c Dunton Green 69-73; V Edenbridge 73-83; Hon Can Roch Cathl from 77; Adn Tonbridge from 77; P-in-c Crockham Hill H Trin 81-83; C-in-c Sevenoaks St Luke CD from 83. *St Luke's House, 30 Eardley Road, Sevenoaks, Kent TN13 1XT* Sevenoaks (01732) 452462

MASON, Robert Herbert George (Bob). b 48. Oak Hill Th Coll 82. **d** 84 **p** 85. C Ware Ch Ch *St Alb* 84-88; V Eastbourne All So *Chich* from 88. *The Vicarage, 53 Susan's Road, Eastbourne, E Sussex BN21 3TH* Eastbourne (01323) 731366

MASON, Roger Arthur. b 41. Lon Univ BSc65 K Coll Lon BD68 AKC68. **d** 69 **p** 70. C Enfield St Andr *Lon* 69-72; P-in-c Westbury *Heref* 72-78; P-in-c Yockleton 72-78; P-in-c Gt Wollaston 77-78; V Willesden St Mary *Lon* 78-88; V Prittlewell *Chelmsf* from 88; P-in-c Prittlewell St Steph from 92. *Prittlewell Vicarage, 489 Victoria Avenue, Southend-on-Sea SS2 6NL* Southend-on-Sea (01702) 343470

MASON, Simon Duncan. b 61. Strathclyde Univ BA83 St Jo Coll Dur PhD89 Nottm Univ BTh92. Linc Th Coll 89. **d** 92 **p** 93. C Grays Thurrock *Chelmsf* from 92. *48 Parker Road, Grays, Essex RM17 5YN* Grays Thurrock (01375) 379309

MASON, Stephen David. b 65. Univ of Wales (Lamp) BA87. Ripon Coll Cuddesdon 89. **d** 92 **p** 93. C Gt Grimsby St Mary and St Jas *Linc* from 92. *3 Grosvenor Street, Grimsby, S Humberside DN32 0QH* Grimsby (01472) 356931

MASON, Thomas Edward. b 52. Bris Univ MEd80. Trin Coll Bris BA91. **d** 91 **p** 92. C Glouc St Jas and All SS *Glouc* 91-94; V Churchdown from 94. *The Vicarage, 5 Vicarage Close, Churchdown, Gloucester GL3 2NE* Churchdown (01452) 713203

MASON, Thomas Henry Ambrose. b 51. BA86. **d** 86 **p** 87. C W Drayton *Lon* 86-89; Field Officer Oak Hill Ext Coll 89-94; Eur Sec Intercon Ch Soc from 94; Lic to Offic *Eur* from 95. *72 Byne Road, London SE26 5JD* 0181-659 3249

MASON, William Frederick. b 48. Linc Th Coll 75. **d** 78 **p** 79. C Ipswich St Aug *St E* 78-81; TV Dronfield *Derby* 81-88; V Ellesmere St Pet *Sheff* 88-91; V Bedgrove *Ox* from 91. *The Vicarage, 252 Wendover Road, Aylesbury, Bucks HP21 9PD* Aylesbury (01296) 22214

MASSEY, Frederick. b 02. Univ of Wales BA30. **d** 30 **p** 31. P-in-c Saltdean *Chich* 60-66; rtd 66; Perm to Offic *Chich* 66-76; Perm to Offic *Derby* from 77. *2A St Mary's Close, Alvaston, Derby DE24 0GF* Derby (01332) 752442

MASSEY, George Douglas. b 44. St Jo Coll Nottm DCM93. **d** 93 **p** 94. C Higher Bebington *Ches* from 93. *Christ Church House, 3 Beech Road, Bebington, Wirral, Merseyside L36 8PE* 0151-645 9074

MASSEY, Keith John. b 46. Oak Hill Th Coll 69. **d** 72 **p** 73. C Bermondsey St Jas w Ch Ch *S'wark* 72-76; C Benchill *Man* 76-82; V Clifton Green from 82. *St Thomas's Vicarage, Delamere Avenue, Clifton, Swinton, Manchester M27 2GL* 0161-794 1986

MASSEY, Nigel John. b 60. Birm Univ BA81 MA82. Wycliffe Hall Ox. **d** 87 **p** 88. C Bearwood *Birm* 87-90; C Warley Woods 90; C Tottenham St Paul *Lon* 91-94; USA from 94. *French Church Du St Spirit, 111 East 60th Street, New York, New York 10022* Bronx (212) 838-5680

MASSEY, Preb William Cyril. b 32. Lich Th Coll 58. **d** 61 **p** 62. C Heref St Martin *Heref* 61-66; V Kimbolton w Middleton-on-the-Hill 66-75; V Alveley 75-83; P-in-c Quatt 81-83; R Alveley and Quatt 84-85; R Llangarron w Llangrove, Whitchurch and Ganarew from 85; Preb Heref Cathl from 92. *The Vicarage, Llangrove, Ross-on-Wye, Herefordshire HR9 6EZ* Llangarron (01989) 770341

MASSHEDAR, John Frederick. b 50. Dur Univ BEd74. Linc Th Coll 76. **d** 78 **p** 79. C Pocklington w Yapham-cum-Meltonby, Owsthorpe etc *York* 78-81; C Middlesb Ascension 81-82; V 82-85; V Eskdaleside w Ugglebarnby and Sneaton 85-87; V Shotton *Dur* from 87. *The Vicarage, Shotton Colliery, Durham DH6 2JW* 0191-526 1156

MASSHEDAR, Richard Eric. b 57. Nottm Univ BTh86. Linc Th Coll 83. **d** 86 **p** 87. C Cassop cum Quarrington *Dur* 86-89; C Ferryhill 89-91; V Leam Lane 91-94; P-in-c Hartlepool St Paul from 94. *St Paul's Vicarage, 6 Hutton Avenue, Hartlepool, Cleveland TS26 9PN* Hartlepool (01429) 272934

MASSINGBERD-MUNDY, John. b 07. Pemb Coll Cam BA30 MA46. Cuddesdon Coll 31. **d** 32 **p** 33. V Gt Limber w Brocklesby *Linc* 65-72; V Kirmington 65-72; rtd 72. *79 Wolverton Road, Newport Pagnell, Bucks MK16 8BH* Newport Pagnell (01908) 617242

MASSINGBERD-MUNDY, Roger William Burrell. b 36. TD. Univ of Wales (Lamp) BA59. Ridley Hall Cam 59. **d** 61 **p** 62. C Benwell St Jas *Newc* 61-64; CF (TA) 63-68; CF (TAVR) 71-83; C Whorlton *Newc* 64-72; TV 73; P-in-c Healey 73-85; Dioc

Stewardship Adv 73-85; Hon Can Newc Cathl 82-85; R S Ormsby w Ketsby, Calceby and Driby *Linc* 85-86; P-in-c Harrington w Brinkhill 85-86; P-in-c Haugh 85-86; P-in-c Oxcombe 85-86; P-in-c Ruckland w Farforth and Maidenwell 85-86; P-in-c Somersby w Bag Enderby 85-86; P-in-c Tetford and Salmonby 85-86; R S Ormsby Gp from 86; RD Bolingbroke from 88. *The Rectory, South Ormsby, Louth, Lincs LN11 8QT* Louth (01507) 480236

MASSON, Philip Roy. b 52. Hertf Coll Ox BA75 Leeds Univ BA77. Coll of Resurr Mirfield 75. **d** 78 **p** 79. C Port Talbot St Theodore *Llan* 78-82; V Penyfai w Tondu 82-92; Dioc Dir Post-Ord Tr 85-88; Warden of Ords from 88; R Newton Nottage from 92. *The Rectory, 64 Victoria Avenue, Porthcawl, M Glam CF36 3HE* Porthcawl (01656) 712042

MASTERMAN, Malcolm. b 49. K Coll Lon 73. Chich Th Coll 76. **d** 77 **p** 78. C Peterlee *Dur* 77-80; Chapl Basingstoke Distr Hosp 80-85; Chapl Freeman Hosp Newc from 85. *Freeman Hospital Chaplaincy, Freeman Road, Newcastle upon Tyne NE7 7DN* 0191-284 3111

MASTERMAN, Miss Patricia Hope (Pat). b 28. St Mich Ho Ox 59. **dss** 79 **d** 87. Asst CF 79-90; rtd 90. *33 Sea Lane Gardens, Ferring, Worthing, W Sussex BM12 5EQ* Worthing (01903) 245231

✠**MASTERS, Rt Rev Brian John.** b 32. Qu Coll Cam BA55 MA59. Cuddesdon Coll 62. **d** 64 **p** 65 **c** 82. C Stepney St Dunstan and All SS *Lon* 64-69; V Hoxton H Trin w St Mary 69-82; P-in-c Hoxton St Anne w St Sav and St Andr 69-75; P-in-c Hoxton St Anne w St Columba 75-80; Suff Bp Fulham 82-84; Area Bp Edmonton from 85. *1 Regent's Park Terrace, London NW1 7EE* 0171-267 4455 Fax 267 4404

MASTERS, Kenneth Leslie (Ken). b 44. Leeds Univ BA68. Cuddesdon Coll 68. **d** 70 **p** 71. C Wednesbury St Paul Wood Green *Lich* 70-71; C Tettenhall Regis 71-75; TV Chelmsley Wood *Birm* 75-79; R Harting *Chich* 79-87; V Rustington from 87. *The Vicarage, Claigmar Road, Rustington, Littlehampton, W Sussex BN16 2NL* Rustington (01903) 784749

MASTERS, Leslie. b 31. Ripon Hall Ox 73. **d** 75 **p** 76. C Hanham *Bris* 75-78; TV Bris St James and St Simon w St Werburgh 78-84; Asst Chapl HM Pris Man 84; Chapl HM Pris Northeye 84-88; Chapl HM Pris Littlehey 88-94; rtd 94; NSM St Goran w St Mich Caerhays *Truro* from 94. *The Vicarage, Gorran, St Austell, Cornwall PL26 6HN* St Austell (01726) 842229

MASTERS, Canon Raymond Austin. b 26. Kelham Th Coll 45. **d** 52 **p** 53. SSM from 51; S Africa 52-65; Can Bloemfontein Cathl 58-65; Perm to Offic *Blackb* 65-68; Chapl St Martin's Coll of Educn Lanc 68-70; Asst Sec Gen Syn Bd for Miss and Unity 71-77; Inc C Harrow St Pet *Lon* 72-77; TV Cen Ex 78-82; Dioc Miss and Ecum Officer 78-82; Warden Windsor Convent from 79; Can Res Heref Cathl *Heref* 82-93; Treas 85-93; Bp's Co-ord for Min 82-93. *The Cottage, The Convent, Hatch Lane, Windsor, Berks SL4 3QS* Slough (01753) 860449

MASTERS, Stephen Michael. b 52. St Chad's Coll Dur BA75. Coll of Resurr Mirfield 85. **d** 87 **p** 88. C Primrose Hill St Mary w Avenue Road St Paul *Lon* 87-90; C Hornsey St Mary w St Geo 90-91; Bp's Dom Chapl *Chich* from 91. *Monk's Cottage, Palace Yard, Canon Lane, Chichester, W Sussex PO19 1PX* Chichester (01243) 780982 or 782161 Fax 531332

MASTERTON, Paul Robert. b 35. Clifton Th Coll 63. **d** 66 **p** 67. C Selly Hill St Steph *Birm* 66-68; C Sutton Coldfield H Trin 68-72; C Aldridge *Lich* 72-74; C Gt Crosby St Luke *Liv* 74-76; P-in-c Manuden w Berden *Chelmsf* 76-86; R Helpringham w Hale *Linc* from 86. *2 Vicarage Lane, Helpringham, Sleaford, Lincs NG34 0RP* Swaton (01529) 421435

MASTIN, Brian Arthur. b 38. Peterho Cam BA60 MA63 BD80 Mert Coll Ox MA63. Ripon Hall Ox 62. **d** 63 **p** 64. Asst Lect Hebrew Univ Coll of N Wales (Ban) 63-65; Lect Hebrew 65-82; Sen Lect from 82; Chapl Ban Cathl *Ban* 63-65; Lic to Offic from 65. *Department of Religious Studies, University College, Bangor, Gwynedd LL57 2DG* Bangor (01248) 351151

MATCHETT, Edward James Boyd. b 19. TCD BA43 MA60. **d** 43 **p** 44. C Belf St Mary *Conn* 43-45; Miss to Seamen from 45; Iraq 47-50; New Zealand 64-69; Regional Dir Miss to Seamen (E Region) 69-74; Hong Kong 74-83; Chapl Cornish Ports 83-86; Perm to Offic *Nor* from 86. *10 Southern Reach, Mulbarton, Norwich NR14 8BU* Mulbarton (01508) 70337

MATHER, Bernard Herbert. b 26. Univ Coll Dur BA51. Sarum Th Coll 53. **d** 55 **p** 56. C Wallsend St Luke *Newc* 55-60; USPG 60-94; India 60-94; rtd 94. *clo Mrs L Boundy, Kilaganoon, Kerry Road, Montgomery, Powys SY15 6HW* Montgomery (01686) 668277

MATHER, Cuthbert. b 15. Tyndale Hall Bris 36. **d** 40 **p** 41. V Needham w Rushall *Nor* 57-80; rtd 80; Perm to Offic *Nor* from 80. *2 Church Close, Hunstanton, Norfolk PE36 6BE* Hunstanton (01485) 533084

MATHER, David Jonathan. b 65. New Coll Ox BA88 MA95. St Steph Ho Ox BTh95. **d** 95. C Pickering *York* from 95.

74 Eastgate, Pickering, N Yorkshire YO18 7DY   Pickering (01751) 475472

MATHER, Mrs Elizabeth Ann (Libby). b 45. Dalton Ho Bris IDC70 St Jo Coll Nottm 92. **d** 94 **p** 95. NSM Littleover *Derby* from 94. *The Vicarage, 35 Church Street, Littleover, Derby DE23 6GF*   Derby (01332) 767802

MATHER, James Malcolm. b 31. Trin Coll Cam BA54 MA59. Cuddesdon Coll 54. **d** 56 **p** 57. C S Bank *York* 56-60; C Sutton St Mich 60-61; C Hanwell St Thos *Lon* 61-63; V Ilkeston H Trin *Derby* 63-72; P-in-c Upper Langwith 73-77; R 77-80; P-in-c Whaley Thorns 77-80; R Upper Langwith w Langwith Bassett etc 80; P-in-c Watlington *Ox* 80-81; V Watlington w Pyrton and Shirburn 81-86; R Harome w Stonegrave, Nunnington and Pockley *York* from 86. *The Rectory, Harome, York YO6 5JS*   Helmsley (01439) 70163

MATHER, James William. b 63. Sheff Univ BA86. St Steph Ho Ox 88. **d** 91 **p** 92. C Doncaster St Leon and St Jude *Sheff* 91-94; C Cantley from 94. *40 Cantley Manor Avenue, Cantley, Doncaster, S Yorkshire DN4 6TN*   Doncaster (01302) 531520

MATHER, Stephen Albert. b 54. Qu Coll Birm 85. **d** 87 **p** 88. C Sutton *Liv* 87-90; TV from 90. *316 Reginald Road, Sutton Leach, St Helens, Merseyside WA9 4HS*   St Helens (01744) 812380

MATHER, William Bernard George. b 45. St Jo Coll Nottm 77. **d** 79 **p** 80. C St Leonards St Leon *Chich* 79-82; TR Netherthorpe *Sheff* 82-90; V Littleover *Derby* from 90. *The Vicarage, 35 Church Street, Littleover, Derby DE23 6GF*   Derby (01332) 767802

MATHERS, Alan Edward. b 36. FPhS Lon Univ BA. Oak Hill Th Coll 61. **d** 64 **p** 65. C Ox St Matt *Ox* 64-66; C Bootle St Leon *Liv* 66-68; C Hampreston *Sarum* 68-70; P-in-c Damerham 70-71; V Queniborough *Leic* 71-76; USA 76-77; P-in-c Tipton St Paul *Lich* 77-84; V 85-86; V Tipton St Matt 77-86; V Sutton Ch Ch *S'wark* 86-95; Chapl Cannes *Eur* from 95. *Residence Kent, rue du General Ferrie, 06400 Cannes, France*   France (33) 93 94 54 61

MATHERS, David Michael Brownlow. b 43. Em Coll Cam BA65 MA69. Clifton Th Coll 65. **d** 67 **p** 68. C Branksome St Clem *Sarum* 67-70; C Bromley Ch Ch *Roch* 70-73; V Bures St E 73-80; Brazil 80-82; P-in-c Old Newton w Stowupland *St E* 82-86; V 87-90; V Thurston from 90; RD Ixworth from 94. *Thurston Vicarage, Bury St Edmunds, Suffolk IP31 3RU*   Pakenham (01359) 30301

MATHERS, Derek. b 48. N Ord Course 82. **d** 85 **p** 86. C Huddersfield St Jo *Wakef* 85-86; C N Huddersfield 86-88; TV Almondbury w Farnley Tyas 88-92; V Marsden from 92. *The Vicarage, 20A Station Road, Marsden, Huddersfield HD7 6DG*   Huddersfield (01484) 847864

MATHERS, Kenneth Ernest William. b 56. Portsm Coll of Tech TDip82 HND84. Trin Coll Bris DipHE95. **d** 95. C Bournemouth St Jo w St Mich *Win* from 95. *101A Surrey Road, Poole, Dorset BH12 1HQ*

MATHERS (nee STEWART), Mrs Kim Deborah. b 61. Southn Univ LLB82. ASCAT DipApTh86 Trin Coll Bris DipHE88 ADPS89. **d** 89 **p** 94. Par Dn Bitterne *Win* 89-93; Hon C Stoke Bishop *Bris* 93-95; Hon C Bournemouth St Jo w St Mich *Win* from 95. *101A Surrey Road, Poole, Dorset BH12 1HQ*

MATHESON, David Melville. b 23. McGill Univ Montreal BA55 BD61. Linc Th Coll 77. **d** 77 **p** 78. Chapl Blue Coat Sch Reading 77-85; Hon C Verwood *Sarum* 85-88; C Stratfield Mortimer *Ox* 88-92; Perm to Offic from 93. *7 Highfield Court, Reading Road, Reading RG7 3YP*   Burghfield Common (01734) 834039

MATHESON, Canon Ronald Stuart. b 29. Lon Univ BA50. Ely Th Coll 52. **d** 54 **p** 55. R Glenrothes *St And* 69-73; R Dundee St Marg *Bre* 73-80; Belize 79-80; Chapl Sliema *Eur* 81-82; Chapl Costa del Sol E 82-94; Hon Can Gib Cathl from 90; Chapl Sliema from 94; rtd 94. *Bishop's House, 75 Rodolphe Street, SLM 14, Sliema, Malta*   Malta (356) 330575 Fax 339656

MATHEWS, Richard Twitchell. b 27. Bps' Coll Cheshunt 57. **d** 59 **p** 60. V Riddlesden *Bradf* 67-74; Australia 74-78; P-in-c Medbourne cum Holt w Stockerston and Blaston *Leic* 78-82; Chapl Alassio *Eur* 82-83; Chapl San Remo 82-83; Chapl Palma and Balearic Is w Ibiza etc 83-87; P-in-c Witchford w Wentworth *Ely* 87-91; rtd 91. *19 Dorset House, Hastings Road, Bexhill-on-Sea, E Sussex TN40 2HJ*   Bexhill-on-Sea (01424) 213185

MATHEWS, Ronald Peel Beresford. b 24. TCD DBS DipYL. **d** 64 **p** 65. I Clonbroney w Killoe *K, E & A* 66-71; I Drumgoon and Ashfield 71-74; Dep Sec Leprosy Miss 74-84; I Kinneigh Union *C, C & R* 84-93; rtd 93. *19 Kingston College, Mitchelstown, Co Cork, Irish Republic*   Cork (25) 84779

MATHEWS, Trevor John. b 50. HonLMStJ83. UEA PPAC93. St Steph Ho Ox 87. **d** 89 **p** 90. C Cheltenham St Steph *Glouc* 89-91; C Up Hatherley 89-91. *Community Drug Team, New Writtle Street Centre, Chelmsford CM2 0RW*   Chelmsford (01245) 351441 Fax 357494

MATHIAS, John Maelgwyn. b 15. St D Coll Lamp BA38 St Mich Coll Llan 40. **d** 40 **p** 41. R Cellan w Llanfair Clydogau *St D* 54-83; Lect St Jo Ch Coll Ystrad Meurig 67-77; rtd 83. *Bronallt, Capel Seion Road, Drefach, Llanelli, Dyfed SA14 4BN*

MATHIE, Patricia Jean (Mother Donella). b 22. CertEd49. dss 79 **d** 87. CSA from 74; Asst Superior 82-94; Mother Superior from 94; Notting Hill St Jo *Lon* 79-80; Abbey Ho Malmesbury 81-82; Notting Hill St Clem and St Mark 82-84; Kensal Town St Thos w St Andr and St Phil 85-87; Hon C from 87. *St Andrew's House, 2 Tavistock Road, London W11 1BA*   0171-229 2662

MATON, Oswald. b 24. St Aug Coll Cant 75. **d** 77 **p** 78. Hon C Chatham St Steph *Roch* from 77. *304 Maidstone Road, Chatham, Kent ME4 6JJ*   Medway (01634) 843568

MATTEN, Derek Norman William. b 30. Man Univ BA51. Wycliffe Hall Ox 54. **d** 56 **p** 57. W Germany 69-90; Germany 90-93; Lic to Offic *Eur* 69-93; Perm to Offic *Ex* from 90; rtd 93. *7 Mount Plym, Plymouth Road, Totnes, Devon TQ9 5PH*   Totnes (01803) 866732

MATTHEW, Canon Andrew Foster. b 45. Oak Hill Th Coll 68. **d** 70 **p** 71. C St Alb St Paul *St Alb* 70-74; C Harwell *Ox* 74-76; C Chilton All SS 74-76; C Harwell w Chilton 76-77; V St Keverne *Truro* 77-84; RD Kerrier 81-84; V St Austell from 84; Hon Can Truro Cathl from 89. *The Vicarage, 1 Carnsmerry Crescent, St Austell, Cornwall PL25 4NA*   St Austell (01726) 73839

MATTHEWS, Barry Alan. b 46. AKC68. St Boniface Warminster St Paul's Grahamstown. **d** 69 **p** 70. S Africa 69-74 and 77-83; C Leeds St Aid *Ripon* 74-77; C Shotton *St As* 83-84; Zimbabwe from 84. *St Margaret's Rectory, 2 Greenfield Square, North End, Bulawayo, Zimbabwe*

MATTHEWS, Brian. b 32. ARIC55. Cranmer Hall Dur 59. **d** 62 **p** 63. C Belgrave St Pet *Leic* 62-65; C Whitwick St Jo the Bapt 65-69; C Kirby Muxloe 69-71; P-in-c Bardon Hill 71-78; V Thringstone St Andr from 78. *The Vicarage, 49 Loughborough Road, Thringstone, Coalville, Leics LE67 8LQ*   Coalville (01530) 222380

MATTHEWS, Canon Brian Benjamin. b 14. OBE73. Ox Univ MA. Chich Th Coll 35. **d** 37 **p** 38. Chapl Monte Carlo w Beaulieu *Eur* 58-83; Can Malta Cathl from 73; Adn Riviera 76-83; rtd 83; Chapl Beaulieu-sur-Mer *Eur* from 83. *47 Boulevard Marechal Joffre, 06310 Beaulieu-sur-Mer, France*   France (33) 93 01 63 46

MATTHEWS, Canon Campbell Thurlow. b 33. Lon Univ BA56 Dur Univ DipEd57. St Jo Coll Nottm 70. **d** 71 **p** 72. C Ryton *Dur* 71-74; Chapl R Victoria Infirmary Newc 74-82; V Greenside *Dur* 74-82; R Wetheral w Warw *Carl* 82-93; RD Brampton 83-91; P-in-c Farlam and Nether Denton 87-93; P-in-c Gilsland 87-93; Hon Can Carl Cathl from 87; P-in-c Thornthwaite cum Braithwaite and Newlands from 93. *Thornthwaite Vicarage, Braithwaite, Keswick, Cumbria CA12 5RY*   Braithwaite (01768) 78243 Fax Carlisle (01228) 48769

MATTHEWS, Celia Inger. b 30. St Chris Coll Blackheath 50. **d** 86 **p** 94. Dioc Missr *St And* from 86. *24 Barossa Place, Perth PH1 5HH*   Perth (01738) 23578

MATTHEWS, Preb Clarence Sydney. b 11. Lon Univ BA30 AKC32 BD38. **d** 34 **p** 35. V Ealing St Steph Castle Hill *Lon* 54-81; RD Ealing E 68-79; rtd 81; Perm to Offic *Cant* 81-92; Perm to Offic *Lon* 84-93. *8 Swanbrook Court, Bridge Avenue, Maidenhead, Berks SL6 1YZ*   Maidenhead (01628) 789287

MATTHEWS, Colin John. b 44. Jes Coll Ox BA67 MA71 Fitzw Coll Cam BA70 MA74. Ridley Hall Cam 68. **d** 71 **p** 72. C Onslow Square St Paul *Lon* 71-74; C Leic H Apostles *Leic* 74-78; Bible Use Sec Scripture Union 78-89; Dir St Sav Ch Cen Guildf 89-95; V Burpham *Guildf* from 95. *6 Manor Way, Onslow Village, Guildford, Surrey GU2 5RN*   Guildford (01483) 33412

MATTHEWS, David Charles. b 61. TCD BA84 HDipEd86 MA87 Lille Univ LesL85. CITC BTh95. **d** 95. C Arm St Mark w Aghavilly *Arm* from 95. *6 Ashley Avenue, Armagh BT60 1HD*   Armagh (01861) 522389

MATTHEWS, Mrs Diana Elizabeth Charlotte. b 43. MCSP65. Local NSM Course 92. **d** 93. NSM Merrow *Guildf* from 93. *Ravenswood, 22 Tangier Road, Guildford, Surrey GU1 2DF*   Guildford (01483) 568845

MATTHEWS, Mrs Francilla Lacey (Cilla). b 37. S'wark Ord Course 83. dss 86 **d** 87 **p** 94. Bromley St Mark *Roch* 86-87; Hon Par Dn 87-90; Par Dn Hayes 90-94; C from 94. *71 Hayes Road, Bromley BR2 9AE*   0181-464 4083

MATTHEWS, Frederick Peter. b 45. Grey Coll Dur BA66 MA68 K Coll Lon PGCE68 Lon Univ BSc(Econ)75. Sarum & Wells Th Coll 70. **d** 72 **p** 73. C W Wickham St Jo *Cant* 72-74; C Sholing *Win* 74-77; Lic to Offic 78-79; V Woolston from 79. *St Mark's Vicarage, 117 Swift Road, Southampton SO2 9ER*   Southampton (01703) 326908

MATTHEWS, George Charles Wallace. b 27. Sarum Th Coll 58. **d** 60 **p** 61. V Wheelock *Ches* 67-76; V Mossley 76-93; rtd 93. *20 Leyland Grove, Haslington, Crewe CW1 1ZE* Crewe (01270) 587463

MATTHEWS, Gerald Lancelot. b 31. Bris Univ LLB50. Ripon Hall Ox 55. **d** 57 **p** 58. V Brent Tor *Ex* 63-72; P-in-c Lydford w Bridestowe and Sourton 70-72; TR Lydford, Brent Tor, Bridestowe and Sourton 72-78; P-in-c Black Torrington, Bradf w Cookbury etc 78-90; Perm to Offic from 90; rtd 94. *The Larches, Black Torrington, Beaworthy, Devon EX21 5PU* Black Torrington (01409) 231228

MATTHEWS, Gilbert Brian Reeves. b 19. Keble Coll Ox BA42 MA48. St Steph Ho Ox 41. **d** 44 **p** 45. R Rushton and Glendon *Pet* 58-79; P-in-c Thorpe Malsor 76-79; R Rushton and Glendon w Thorpe Malsor 79-81; C Spondon *Derby* 81-87; rtd 87. *Christchurch Parsonage, Redhill, Bristol BS18 7SL*

MATTHEWS, Harold James. b 46. Leeds Univ BSc68 Fitzw Coll Cam BA70 MA74. Westcott Ho Cam 68. **d** 71 **p** 72. C Mossley Hill St Matt and St Jas *Liv* 71-74; C Stanley 74-76; TV Hackney *Lon* 76-78; Chapl Forest Sch Snaresbrook 78-83; Hd Master Vernon Holme Sch Cant 83-88; Perm to Offic *Cant* 83-88; Hd Master Heath Mt Sch Hertf from 88; Perm to Offic *St Alb* from 88. *Heath Mount School, Woodhall Park, Watton at Stone, Hertford SG14 3NG* Ware (01920) 830230 or 830541

MATTHEWS, Mrs Heather Ann. b 49. Bris Univ BA71 Lon Univ CertEd72. Trin Coll Bris 87. **d** 89 **p** 94. C Blagdon w Compton Martin and Ubley *B & W* 93-93; D-in-c 93-94; P-in-c 94; R from 94. *The Rectory, High Street, Blagdon, Bristol BS18 6TA* Blagdon (01761) 462495

MATTHEWS, Mrs Joan Muriel. b 53. N Ord Course 89. **d** 92 **p** 94. C Aughton St Mich *Liv* from 92. *92 Delph Park, Ormskirk, Lancs L39 5DQ* Aughton Green (01695) 422908

MATTHEWS, Canon John. b 22. TD66. Trin Coll Cam BA48 MA51. Bps' Coll Cheshunt 49. **d** 51 **p** 52. CF (TA) from 53; P-in-c Lt Canfield *Chelmsf* 62-70; V Gt Dunmow 62-88; P-in-c Gt Easton 70-83; RD Dunmow 75-88; Hon Can Chelmsf Cathl 85-88; rtd 88. *Moorside Cottage, The Common, Walberswick, Southwold, Suffolk IP18 6TE* Southwold (01502) 722783

MATTHEWS, Lewis William (Bill). b 29. St Jo Coll Dur BA53 DipTh55 MSc76. **d** 55 **p** 56. R Braunstone *Leic* 64-70; V Thornaby on Tees St Paul *York* 70-72; TR Thornaby on Tees 72-78; Dir Dioc Bd for Soc Resp *Lon* 79-84; Perm to Offic 84-94; Warden Durning Hall Chr Community Cen Forest Gate 84-94; rtd 94. *Gouray Vicarage, Gorey Village, Grouville, Jersey JE3 6EB* Jersey (01534) 853255

MATTHEWS, Melvyn William. b 40. St Edm Hall Ox BA63 MA68. K Coll Lon BD66 AKC67. **d** 67 **p** 68. C Enfield St Andr *Lon* 67-70; Asst Chapl Southn Univ *Win* 70-73; Kenya 75-76; V Highgate All SS *Lon* 76-79; P-in-c Clifton St Paul *Bris* 79-87; Sen Chapl Bris Univ 79-87; Dir Ammerdown Cen for Study and Renewal 87-93; V Chew Magna w Dundry *B & W* from 93. *The Vicarage, 24 High Street, Chew Magna, Bristol BS18 8PW* Chew Magna (01275) 332199

MATTHEWS, Oswald John. b 13. St Edm Hall Ox BA37 MA40. Ripon Hall Ox 35. **d** 37 **p** 38. C Beverley Minster *York* 37-41; V Drypool St Andr and St Pet 41-48; Chapl RAF 41-45; V Fridaythorpe w Fimber and Thixendale *York* 48-52; Miss to Seamen 52-64; Argentina 52-54; New Zealand from 54. *55A Jellicoe Street, Wanganui, New Zealand* Wanganui (06) 343-9540

MATTHEWS, Paul. b 47. Brunel Univ BTech70 S Bank Poly DipEEngD72. S Dios Minl Tr Scheme 89. **d** 92 **p** 93. Hon C Goring-by-Sea *Chich* from 92. *Rose Cottage, The Court House, Sea Lane, Goring-by-Sea, Worthing, W Sussex BN12 4NY* Worthing (01903) 502011

MATTHEWS, Canon Percival Charles Halls. b 15. Em Coll Cam BA37 MA41. Wycliffe Hall Ox 37. **d** 38 **p** 39. V Douglas St Geo and St Barn *S & M* 57-80; RD Douglas 71-80; Can St German's Cathl 75-80; rtd 80; Perm to Offic *S & M* 80-81; Hon C German St Jo 81-94. *Edelweiss, Glen Lough Circle, Glen Vine, Douglas, Isle of Man IM4 4AX* Marown (01624) 851860

MATTHEWS, Peter Henry. b 22. Sarum Th Coll 62. **d** 64 **p** 65. R Hilperton w Whaddon *Sarum* 70-78; P-in-c Staverton 71-72; V 72-78; P-in-c Milborne St Andrew w Dewlish 78-87; rtd 87. *Holmlands, Lambrook Road, Shepton Beauchamp, Ilminster, Somerset TA19 0LZ* South Petherton (01460) 40938

MATTHEWS, Rodney Charles. b 36. Sarum Th Coll 62. **d** 64 **p** 65. C Gt Clacton *Chelmsf* 64-68; C Loughton St Mary 68-74; TV 74-76; V Goodmayes All SS 76-87; V Woodford Bridge from 87; Hon Chapl Sail Tr Assn from 89; P-in-c Barkingside St Cedd 90-92. *St Paul's Vicarage, 4 Cross Road, Woodford Green, Essex IG8 8DX* 0181-504 3815

MATTHEWS, Roger Charles. b 54. MBCS82 CEng90 Man Univ BSc75 CDipAF78. Trin Coll Bris 87. **d** 89 **p** 90. C Gt

Baddow *Chelmsf* 89-93; P-in-c Chigwell Row 93-94; TV Chigwell and Chigwell Row from 94. *All Saints Rectory, Romford Road, Chigwell, Essex IG7 4QD* 0181-500 2805

MATTHEWS, Canon Roy Ian John. b 27. TD71. St Cath Soc Ox BA52 MA56. St Steph Ho Ox 52. **d** 54 **p** 55. CF (TA) 58-92; V Penistone w Midhope *Wakef* 65-72; V Brighouse 72-84; Hon Can Wakef Cathl 76-92; V Darrington w Wentbridge 84-92; Dioc Schs Officer 84-89; Dep Dir of Educn 85-89; rtd 92; Perm to Offic *Wakef* from 92; Perm to Offic *York* from 92. *14 Spring Walk, Brayton, Selby, N Yorkshire YO8 9DS* Selby (01757) 707259

MATTHEWS, Royston Peter. b 39. Univ of Wales (Lamp) BA61 DipTh64. St Mich Coll Llan 61. **d** 64 **p** 65. C Fairwater CD *Llan* 64-67; C Cadoxton-juxta-Barry 67-71; V Bettws *Mon* 71-84; V Abergavenny H Trin from 84. *Holy Trinity Vicarage, Baker Street, Abergavenny, Gwent NP7 5BH* Abergavenny (01873) 853203

MATTHEWS, Canon Stuart James. b 37. St Jo Coll Dur BA60. Bps' Coll Cheshunt 60. **d** 62 **p** 63. C Horsham *Chich* 62-65; C Rednal *Birm* 65-67; Min Brandwood St Bede Statutory Distr 67-68; C Northfield 68-73; V Thurcroft *Sheff* 73-82; RD Laughton 79-82; R Sprotbrough from 82; RD Adwick 84-89; Hon Can Sheff Cathl from 92. *The Rectory, 42A Spring Lane, Sprotborough, Doncaster, S Yorkshire DN5 7QG* Doncaster (01302) 853203

MATTHEWS, Terence Leslie. b 35. Handsworth Coll Birm 55. **d** 61 **p** 62. V Horden *Dur* 64-72; R Witton Gilbert 72-77; P-in-c Grangetown 77-85; V Cleadon 85-86; V Hebburn St Cuth 86-88; rtd 88. *7 Holmlands Park South, Sunderland SR2 7SG* 0191-522 6466

MATTHEWS, Canon William Andrew (Bill). b 44. Reading Univ BA65. St Steph Ho Ox 65. **d** 67 **p** 68. C Westbury-on-Trym St Alb *Bris* 67-70; C Marlborough *Sarum* 70-73; P-in-c Winsley 73-75; V 75-81; V Bradford-on-Avon from 81; RD Bradf 84-94; Can and Preb Sarum Cathl from 88. *Holy Trinity Vicarage, 18A Woolley Street, Bradford-on-Avon, Wilts BA15 1AF* Bradford-on-Avon (01225) 864444

MATTHEWS, William Temple Atkinson. b 47. E Midl Min Tr Course 86. **d** 83 **p** 83. SSF 83-86; C Brinsley w Underwood *S'well* 86-89; TV Hitchin *St Alb* from 89. *The Vicarage, 31 Meadowbank, Hitchin, Herts SG4 0HY* Hitchin (01462) 432179

MATTHEWS-LOYDALL, Mrs Elaine. b 63. Bp Otter Coll BA85 St Jo Coll Nottm LTh89 DPS90. **d** 90 **p** 94. Par Dn Nottm All SS *S'well* from 90; Asst Chapl to the Deaf 91-93; Chapl to the Deaf from 93. *Pumpkin Cottage, 54 Wilne Road, Sawley, Notts NG10 3AN* Nottingham (0115) 972 8943

MATTHEWS-PAYNE, James. b 19. St D Coll Lamp BA41. Lich Th Coll 41 St Mich Coll Llan 46. **d** 46 **p** 47. V Woolston *Win* 60-65; Australia from 65; rtd 80. *22/11 Freedman Road, Mount Lawley, W Australia 6050* Perth (9) 272-5253

MATTHIAE, David. b 40. Fitzw Ho Cam BA63 MA69. Linc Th Coll 63. **d** 65 **p** 66. C New Addington *Cant* 65-70; C Charlton-by-Dover SS Pet and Paul 70-75; V Cant All SS 75-84; P-in-c Tunstall 84-87; R Tunstall w Rodmersham from 87; RD Sittingbourne 88-94. *The Rectory, Tunstall, Sittingbourne, Kent ME9 8DU* Sittingbourne (01795) 423907

MATTHIAS, Edwin (Eddie). b 23. AKC50. **d** 51 **p** 52. R Chailey *Chich* 65-92; rtd 92. *Oak Cottage, Hunters End, Lewes, E Sussex BN8 4AT* Lewes (01273) 400894

MATTHIAS, George Ronald. b 30. CertEd51. St Deiniol's Hawarden 76. **d** 78 **p** 79. NSM Broughton *St As* 78-83; NSM Wrexham 83-85; C 85-87; V Brymbo from 87. *The Vicarage, Brymbo, Wrexham, Clwyd LL11 5LF* Wrexham (01978) 758107

MATTHIAS, John Rex. b 61. St Mich Coll Llan DMS94. **d** 94 **p** 95. C Llandrillo-yn-Rhos *St As* from 94. *5 Conway Close, Rhos-on-Sea, Colwyn Bay, Clwyd LL28 4JE* Colwyn Bay (01492) 546373

MATTHIAS, Paul. b 47. Philippa Fawcett Coll CertEd75 Kent Univ DipEd84. Cant Sch of Min 92. **d** 94 **p** 95. NSM Gillingham St Aug *Roch* from 94; Head RE Hever Sch Maidstone from 94. *3 Malvern Road, Gillingham, Kent ME7 4BA* Medway (01634) 576197

MATTOCK, Colin Graham. b 38. Chich Th Coll. **d** 84 **p** 85. C Hove All SS *Chich* 84-87; C Bexhill St Pet 87-90; V Henlow *St Alb* from 90. *The Vicarage, 12 Church Road, Henlow, Beds SG16 6AN* Hitchin (01462) 816296

MATTY, Horace Anthony (Tony). b 36. Ely Th Coll 61. **d** 63 **p** 64. C Minchinhampton *Glouc* 63-66; C Hunslet St Mary and Stourton *Ripon* 66-69; TV Wendy w Shingay *Ely* 69-71; V Parson Drove 71-74; V Southea cum Murrow 71-74; V Coven *Lich* 74-82; TV Hednesford 82-85; TV Basildon, St Martin of Tours w Nevendon *Chelmsf* 85-92; P-in-c Basildon St Andr w H Cross 85-92; P-in-c Sandon from 92; P-in-c E Hanningfield from 92. *The Rectory, Sandon, Chelmsford CM2 7SQ* Chelmsford (01245) 472262

MAUCHAN, Andrew. b 44. Hertf Coll Ox BA65 MA69 Man Univ CertEd66. Oak Hill Th Coll DipHE90. **d** 90 **p** 91. C Bridlington Priory *York* 90-94; V Alverthorpe *Wakef* from 94. *The Vicarage, St Paul's Drive, Wakefield, W Yorkshire WF2 0BT* Wakefield (01924) 371300

MAUDE, Canon Alan. b 41. Lon Univ DipTh67 BD69 Newc Univ MSc90. Lambeth STh74 Oak Hill Th Coll 66. **d** 69 **p** 70. C Balderstone *Man* 69-73; Asst Chapl Crumpsall and Springfield Hosps 73-75; C Crumpsall St Matt 73-75; Chapl R Victoria Infirmary Newc from 75; Hon Can Newc Cathl *Newc* from 88. *Royal Victoria Infirmary, Queen Victoria Road, Newcastle upon Tyne NE1 4LP* 0191-284 4966 or 232 5131

MAUDE, Ralph Henry Evelyn. b 09. St Pet Hall Ox BA33 MA37. St Steph Ho Ox 32. **d** 33 **p** 34. V Devizes St Pet *Sarum* 66-74; rtd 74. *4 Manor Court, Swan Road, Pewsey, Wilts SN9 5DW* Marlborough (01672) 63186

MAUDLIN, David. b 39. E Anglian Minl Tr Course 92. **d** 95. NSM Bury St Edmunds St Jo *St E* from 95. *6 Norton Road, Thurston, Bury St Edmunds, Suffolk IP31 3PB* Pakenham (01359) 231772

MAUDSLEY, Canon George Lambert. b 27. St Jo Coll Nottm 74. **d** 75 **p** 76. C Binley *Cov* 75-77; Chapl Barn Fellowship Winterborne Whitechurch 77-83; V Salford Priors *Cov* 83-94; RD Alcester 87-92; Hon Can Cov Cathl 91-94; rtd 94. *7 Flax Piece, Upton Snodsbury, Worcester WR7 4PA* Worcester (01905) 381034

MAUDSLEY, Keith. b 51. York Univ BA72. Ripon Hall Ox 72. **d** 75 **p** 76. C Rugby St Andr *Cov* 75-79; C Cam Gt St Mary w St Mich *Ely* 79-82; Chapl Girton Coll 79-82; P-in-c Binley *Cov* 82-89; RD Cov E 87-89; P-in-c Leek Wootton 89-91; Dioc Policy Development Adv 89-91; Dioc Adv on UPA *Liv* from 91; Soc Resp Officer from 91. *8 The Parchments, Newton-le-Willows, Merseyside WA12 0DY* Newton-le-Willows (01925) 220586

MAUDSLEY, Michael Peter. b 38. St Andr Univ BSc61. Oak Hill Th Coll 65. **d** 67 **p** 68. C Blackpool St Mark *Blackb* 67-70; C Hartford *Ches* 70-72; R Balerno *Edin* 72-82; V Stapenhill w Cauldwell *Derby* 82-91; TV Edin St Paul and St Geo *Edin* 91-95; R from 95. *21 Barony Street, Edinburgh EH3 6PD* 0131-558 1157

MAUGHAN, Geoffrey Nigel (Geoff). b 48. CCC Cam BA69 MA73. Oak Hill Th Coll 75. **d** 77 **p** 78. C New Malden and Coombe *S'wark* 77-81; C Abingdon w Shippon *Ox* 81-89; TV Abingdon from 89. *69 Northcourt Road, Abingdon, Oxon OX14 1NR* Abingdon (01235) 520115 or 522549

MAUGHAN, John. b 28. Keble Coll Ox BA51 MA55. Linc Th Coll 51. **d** 53 **p** 54. R Penshaw *Dur* 59-72; V Cleadon Park 72-93; rtd 93. *2 Struddar's Farm Court, Bates Lane, Blaydon-on-Tyne, Tyne & Wear NE21 5TF* 0191-414 8350

✠**MAUND, Rt Rev John Arthur Arrowsmith.** b 09. CBE75 MC46. Leeds Univ BA31. Coll of Resurr Mirfield 31. **d** 33 **p** 34 **c** 50. C Evesham *Worc* 33-36; C Blackheath All SS *S'wark* 36-38; S Africa 39-50; Bp Basutoland 50-66; Bp Lesotho 66-76; Asst Bp St E 76-83; Asst Bp Worc from 84; rtd 86. *1 Warden's Lodge, Beauchamp Community, The Quadrangle, Newland, Malvern, Worcs WR13 5AX* Malvern (01684) 568072

MAUND, Margaret Jennifer. b 42. SRN SCM. Llan Dioc Tr Scheme. **d** 94. NSM Cymmer and Porth *Llan* from 94. *27 Mill Street, Tonyrefail, Porth, M Glam CF39 8AB* Tonyrefail (01443) 670085

MAUNDER, Alan John. b 52. UWIST BSc74. Oak Hill Th Coll DipHE88. **d** 90 **p** 91. C Birkenhead Ch Ch *Ches* 90-95; P-in-c Poulton from 95. *St Luke's Vicarage, Mill Lane, Wallasey, Merseyside L44 3BP* 0151-638 4663

MAUNDRELL, Canon Wolseley David. b 20. New Coll Ox BA41 DipTh42 MA45. **d** 43 **p** 44. Can Res and Treas Win Cathl *Win* 61-70; Vice-Dean Win 66-70; Asst Chapl Brussels *Eur* 70-71; V Icklesham *Chich* 72-82; RD Rye 78-84; Can and Preb Chich Cathl 81-89; TR Rye 82-89; rtd 89; P-in-c Stonegate *Chich* 89-95. *13 North Walls, Chichester, W Sussex PO19 1DA* Chichester (01243) 537359

MAUNSELL, Colin Wray Dymock. b 33. Pemb Coll Cam BA56 MA59 Lon Univ DipTh58. Tyndale Hall Bris 56. **d** 58 **p** 59. BCMS 60-93; Ethiopia 61-79 and from 91; Portugal 81-91; Crosslinks 93-94; rtd 94. *clo St Matthew's Church, PO Box 109, Addis Ababa, Ethiopia* Addis Ababa (1) 112623

MAURICE, Kenneth. b 07. St D Coll Lamp BA34. **d** 33 **p** 34. R Cruwys Morchard *Ex* 57-68; rtd 68; Perm to Offic *Ex* from 85. *clo Little Knowle, Hillside Road, Sidmouth, Devon EX10 8JD*

MAURICE, Peter David. b 51. St Chad's Coll Dur BA72. Coll of Resurr Mirfield. **d** 75 **p** 76. C Wandsworth St Paul *S'wark* 75-79; TV Mortlake w E Sheen 79-85; V Rotherhithe H Trin from 85; RD Bermondsey from 91. *Holy Trinity Vicarage, Bryan Road, London SE16 1HE* 0171-237 3963

MAWBEY, Miss Diane. b 55. Cranmer Hall Dur. **d** 89 **p** 94. Par Dn Menston w Woodhead *Bradf* 89-92; C Barnoldswick w Bracewell 92-93; Chapl Asst Birm Children's Hosp from 93; Chapl Asst Birm Maternity Hosp from 93. *101 Leahurst Crescent, Birmingham B17 0LD* 0121-428 1624 or 454 4851

MAWER, David Ronald. b 32. Keble Coll Ox BA55 MA58 Dur Univ BA57 McGill Univ Montreal PhD77. Wells Th Coll 58. **d** 59 **p** 60. Canada 61-92; Co-ord Angl Studies St Paul Univ Ottawa 81-92; Can Ottawa from 85; rtd 92. *Moorside, Church Lane, Thropton, Morpeth, Northd NE65 7JA* Rothbury (01669) 620597

MAWSON, Canon Arthur Cyril. b 35. St Pet Coll Ox BA56 MA61. Wycliffe Hall Ox 61. **d** 62 **p** 63. C Walsall *Lich* 62-66; V Millhouses H Trin *Sheff* 66-73; Selection Sec ACCM 73-79; Can Res and Treas Ex Cathl *Ex* from 79; Dioc Dir of Ords from 81. *9 The Close, Exeter EX1 1EZ* Exeter (01392) 79367

MAWSON, David Frank. b 44. Selw Coll Cam BA65 MA69. Linc Th Coll 79. **d** 80 **p** 81. C Tunstall *Lich* 80-83; C Blakenall Heath 83-84; TV 84-90; Chapl Goscote Hosp Walsall 87-90; V Pelsall *Lich* 90-94; V Tividale from 94. *St Michael's Vicarage, Tividale, Warley, W Midlands B69 2LQ* 0121-520 7766

MAWSON, Frank. b 18. ACIS70. NW Ord Course 74. **d** 77 **p** 78. NSM Stockport St Mary *Ches* 77-79; P-in-c Harthill and Burwardsley 79-82; rtd 82; Perm to Offic *Ches* from 82; Perm to Offic *St As* from 82; Perm to Offic *Lich* from 88. *Flat 16, College Court, Ludlow, Shropshire SY8 1BZ* Ludlow (01584) 873869

MAXTED, Neil Andrew. b 58. GradIMI80. Sarum & Wells Th Coll CMinlStuds92. **d** 92 **p** 93. C Folkestone St Sav *Cant* from 92. *209 Downs Road, Folkestone, Kent CT19 5PX* Folkestone (01303) 254474

MAXWELL, Christopher John Moore (Bill). b 31. MRCS59 LRCP59 Qu Coll Cam MA75. Trin Coll Bris 74. **d** 75 **p** 76. Chile 75-81; C Clevedon Ch Ch *B & W* 75; Hon C Homerton St Luke *Lon* 81-94; Chapl Ibiza *Eur* from 94. *clo Supermercado Magon, Port des Torrent, 07820 San Antonio, Ibiza, Spain*

MAXWELL, Ian Charles. b 17. Ch Coll Cam BA40 MA44. Ridley Hall Cam 40. **d** 42 **p** 43. R Stanhope *Dur* 61-74; R Gt w Lt Somerford and Seagry *Bris* 74-82; rtd 82; Perm to Offic *Chich* from 82. *22 Hastings Avenue, Seaford, E Sussex BN25 3LQ* Seaford (01323) 890453

MAXWELL, Marcus Howard. b 54. Liv Univ BSc76 Man Univ MPhil89. St Jo Coll Nottm BA79. **d** 80 **p** 81. C Chadderton St Matt *Man* 80-84; V Bircle 84-93; P-in-c Heaton Mersey from 93. *St John's Rectory, 15 Priestnall Road, Stockport, Cheshire SK4 3HR* 0161-432 2165

MAXWELL, Ralph. b 21. CEng MIMechE. **d** 86 **p** 87. NSM Belf St Mich *Conn* 86-87; Lic to Offic 87-89; NSM Belf St Jas w St Silas from 89. *69 Woodvale Road, Belfast BT13 3BN* Belfast (01232) 742421

MAXWELL, Richard Renwick. b 23. Mert Coll Ox BA49 MA49. Westcott Ho Cam 49. **d** 51 **p** 52. R Harrietsham *Cant* 67-73; V Blean 73-84; Hon C Hindhead *Guildf* 84-88; Perm to Offic *Cant* from 85; rtd 88. *4 St Birinus Road, Woodfalls, Salisbury SP5 2LE* Downton (01725) 22037

MAY, Anthony John (Tony). b 30. Sarum Th Coll 62. **d** 63 **p** 64. P-in-c Woolwich St Thos *S'wark* 69-74; Chapl Warlingham Park Hosp Croydon 74-81; Field Worker Surrey Community Development Trust 81-85; Admin Nat Assn for Voluntary Hostels 85-92; rtd 93. *3 St Mary's Road, Reigate, Surrey RH2 7JH* Reigate (01737) 248826

MAY, Arthur John. b 16. Linc Th Coll 40. **d** 42 **p** 43. V Belhus Park *Chelmsf* 68-83; rtd 83. *19 Warriner Avenue, Hornchurch, Essex RM12 4LH* Hornchurch (01708) 458421

MAY, Charles Henry. b 29. Lon Coll of Div ALCD58 LTh74. **d** 58 **p** 59. V Homerton St Luke *Lon* 67-80; Home Sec SAMS 80-84; V Fulham Ch Ch *Lon* 84-94; rtd 94. *16 Kilverstone, Werrington, Peterborough PE4 5DX* Peterborough (01733) 328108

MAY, Denis Harry. b 31. ARICS56. S'wark Ord Course. **d** 63 **p** 64. C Eltham St Jo *S'wark* 63-65; Hon C Charing w Lt Chart *Cant* 66-70; Lic to Offic from 70. *19 Malvern Road, Ashford, Kent TN24 8JA* Ashford (01233) 638816

MAY, Donald Charles Leonard. b 25. Chich Th Coll 72. **d** 73 **p** 74. C Barkingside H Trin *Chelmsf* 73-77; V Aldersbrook 77-91; rtd 92. *236 Prospect Road, Woodford Green, Essex IG8 7NQ* 0181-504 6119

MAY, George Louis. b 27. Selw Coll Cam BA52 MA55 Cam Univ PGCE67 ADEd78. Ridley Hall Cam 52. **d** 54 **p** 55. Asst Master Guthlaxton Sch Wigston 67-70; Ixworth Sch 70-72; Thurston Upper Sch 73-74; Perias Sch New Alresford 75-85; Hon C Ropley w W Tisted *Win* 78-79; Perm to Offic from 79; rtd 92. *High View, Gundleton, Alresford, Hants SO24 9SW* Alresford (01962) 733887

MAY, John Alexander Cyril. b 52. K Coll Lon BD77 Ox Univ PGCE78. Linc Th Coll 79. **d** 80 **p** 81. C Tynemouth Ch Ch

Newc 80-82; C Tynemouth Ch Ch w H Trin 82-85; C Tynemouth St Aug 82-85; TV Glendale Gp 85-90; V Wottonunder-Edge w Ozleworth and N Nibley *Glouc* from 90. *The Vicarage, Culverhay, Wotton-under-Edge, Glos GL12 7LS* Dursley (01453) 842175

MAY, Peter Dudfield. b 12. St Jo Coll Cam BA34 LLB35 LLM. Ripon Hall Ox 38. **d** 39 **p** 40. R Stoke Abbott *Sarum* 53-82; V Netherbury 54-82; rtd 82. *The Parsonage Farmhouse, Dinnington, Hinton St George, Somerset TA17 8SU* Ilminster (01460) 53880

MAY, Peter Richard. b 43. MICE70 St Jo Coll Cam BA64 MA68. Trin Coll Bris 77. **d** 79 **p** 80. C Lanc St Thos *Blackb* 79-85; V Darwen St Barn 85-91; Chapl Lyon w Grenoble *Eur* 91-92; Chapl Lyon 92-94; Perm to Offic *S'wark* 94-95; TR Horley from 95. *4 Russells Crescent, Horley, Surrey RH6 7DN* Horley (01293) 783509

MAY, Simon George. b 47. FCA77 Ex Univ BA69 Univ of Wales (Ban) CertEd72. Sarum & Wells Th Coll 86. **d** 88 **p** 89. C Tamworth *Lich* 88-92; V Whitchurch *Ex* from 92. *The Vicarage, 204 Whitchurch Road, Tavistock, Devon PL19 9DQ* Tavistock (01822) 610364

MAY, Dr Stephen Charles Arthur. b 52. Mert Coll Ox BA73 Edin Univ BD78 Aber Univ PhD86. Ridley Hall Cam 84. **d** 86 **p** 87. C Sawley *Derby* 86-88; Lect Systematic Th St Jo Coll Auckland from 88. *179B St John's Road, Auckland 5, New Zealand* Auckland (9) 521-0063

MAYBURY, David Kaines. b 32. G&C Coll Cam BA55 MA59. Ridley Hall Cam 55. **d** 57 **p** 58. C Sydenham H Trin *S'wark* 57-60; C Rainham *Chelmsf* 60-63; R Edin St Jas *Edin* 63-75; R Jedburgh 75-84; NSM Duns 84-91; Warden Whitchester Conf Cen 84-91; Warden Whitchester Chr Guest Ho and Retreat Cen from 91; NSM Hawick *Edin* from 91. *Whitchester Christian Centre, Borthaugh, Hawick, Roxburghshire TD9 7LN* Hawick (01450) 371080 Fax as telephone

MAYBURY, Doreen Lorna. b 33. RGN54 SCM56. Edin Th Coll 76. **dss** 81 **d** 95. Jedburgh *Edin* 81-84; Duns 84-91; Warden Whitchester Conf Cen 84-91; Warden Whitchester Chr Guest Ho and Retreat Cen from 91; Hawick *Edin* 91-95; NSM from 95. *Whitchester Christian Centre, Borthaugh, Hawick, Roxburghshire TD9 7LN* Hawick (01450) 371080 Fax as telephone

MAYBURY, Canon John Montague. b 30. G&C Coll Cam BA53 MA57. Ridley Hall Cam 53. **d** 55 **p** 56. C Allerton *Liv* 55-59; C Rowner *Portsm* 59-62; V Wroxall 62-67; V Southsea St Simon 67-78; V Crofton 78-91; Hon Can Portsm Cathl from 81; C Locks Heath from 91. *19 Netley Road, Titchfield Common, Fareham, Hants PO14 4PE* Locks Heath (01489) 584168

MAYBURY, Paul. b 31. St Deiniol's Hawarden 87. **d** 88 **p** 90. NSM Sutton St Geo *Ches* 88-94; rtd 94. *29 Westbury Drive, Macclesfield, Cheshire SK11 8LR* Macclesfield (01625) 424475

MAYBURY, Paul Dorian. b 58. Trin Coll Bris DipHE95. **d** 95. C Spondon *Derby* from 95. *Prospect House, 27 Park Road, Spondon, Derby DE21 7LN* Derby (01332) 662990

MAYCOCK, Ms Jane Ellen. b 66. Somerville Coll Ox BA90. Cranmer Hall Dur 90. **d** 92 **p** 94. Par Dn Trin St Mich, Harrow *Lon* 92-94; C 94-95; C Kendal H Trin *Carl* from 95. *7 Wattsfield Road, Kendal, Cumbria LA9 5JH* Kendal (01539) 729572

MAYELL, Howard John. b 50. Bris Sch of Min 81. **d** 84 **p** 88. NSM Patchway *Bris* 84-86; NSM Weston-super-Mare Cen Par *B & W* 87-88; C N Stoneham *Win* 88-91; P-in-c Black Torrington, Bradf w Cookbury etc *Ex* from 91. *The Rectory, Black Torrington, Beaworthy, Devon EX21 5PU* Black Torrington (01409) 231279

MAYER, Alan John. b 46. AKC70. St Aug Coll Cant 70. **d** 71 **p** 72. C Stanningley St Thos *Ripon* 71-74; C St Helier *S'wark* 74-79; TV Wimbledon 79-85; V Reigate St Luke S Park from 85. *St Luke's Vicarage, Church Road, Reigate, Surrey RH2 8HY* Reigate (01737) 246302

MAYER, Graham Keith. b 46. St Cath Coll Ox BA68 Nottm Univ CertEd69 Ex Univ MA93 DCouns94. Linc Th Coll 78. **d** 80 **p** 81. C Paignton St Jo *Ex* 80-93; Perm to Offic from 93. *9 York Gardens, Paignton, Devon TQ4 5NP* Paignton (01803) 554593

MAYER, Mrs Paula Denise. b 45. St Hilda's Coll Ox BA68 Nottm Univ CertEd69. SW Minl Tr Course 84. **d** 88. Hon Par Dn Paignton St Jo *Ex* 88-90; Par Dn 90-93; Perm to Offic from 93. *9 York Gardens, Paignton, Devon TQ4 5NP* Paignton (01803) 554593

MAYERSON, Dr Paul Strom. b 28. PhD MEd MusBac. Ridley Hall Cam 80. **d** 82 **p** 83. C New Romney w Old Romney and Midley *Cant* 82-85; P-in-c Ospringe 85; P-in-c Eastling 85; R Eastling w Ospringe and Stalisfield w Otterden 85-90; rtd 90. *168 Piper Hill Road, Ashland, New Hampshire NH03217, USA*

MAYES, Andrew Dennis. b 56. K Coll Lon BD79 AKC79. St Steph Ho Ox 80. **d** 81 **p** 82. C Hendon St Alphage *Lon* 81-84; C

Hockley *Chelmsf* 84-87; V Kingstanding St Mark *Birm* 87-92; V Saltdean *Chich* from 92. *St Nicholas' Vicarage, Saltdean, Brighton BN2 8HE* Brighton (01273) 302345

MAYES, Very Rev Gilbert. b 15. TCD BA43 MA61. CITC 44. **d** 44 **p** 45. Dean Lismore *C & O* 61-87; I Lismore w Cappoquin, Kilwatermoy, Dungarvan etc 61-87; Prec Waterford Cathl 84-87; Preb Stagonil St Patr Cathl Dub 85-87; rtd 87. *Woodford, Ballybride Road, Rathmichael, Shankill, Co Dublin, Irish Republic* Dublin (1) 282-4089

MAYES, Canon John Charles Dougan. b 44. Bps' Coll Cheshunt 63. **d** 67 **p** 68. C Portadown St Mark *Arm* 67-74; I Aghadowey w Kilrea *D & R* 74-86; USPG Area Sec 77-94; I Clooney w Strathfoyle from 86; Can Derry Cathl from 92. *All Saints' Rectory, 20 Limavady Road, Londonderry BT47 1JD* Londonderry (01504) 44306

MAYES, Leonard Harry. b 25. Ely Th Coll 59. **d** 61 **p** 62. V Watford St Mich *St Alb* 69-78; V Liscard St Mary w St Columba *Ches* 78-82; R Moreton and Church Eaton *Lich* 82-90; rtd 90. *11 Covert Close, Great Haywood, Stafford ST18 0RN* Little Haywood (01889) 882994

✠**MAYES, Rt Rev Michael Hugh Gunton.** b 41. TCD BA62 Lon Univ BD85. TCD Div Sch Div Test64. **d** 64 **p** 65 **c** 93. C Portadown St Columba *Arm* 64-68; Japan 68-74; Area Sec (Dios Cashel, Cork, Lim and Tuam) USPG 75-93; I Cork St Mich Union *C, C & R* 75-86; I Moviddy Union 86-88; Adn Cork, Cloyne and Ross 86-93; I Rathcooney Union 88-93; Preb Elphin Cathl *K, E & A* from 93; Bp *K, E & A* from 93. *The See House, Kilmore, Cavan, Irish Republic* Cavan (49) 31336 Fax 62829

MAYES, Stephen Thomas. b 47. St Jo Coll Nottm 67. **d** 71 **p** 72. C Cullompton *Ex* 71-75; C Cheltenham St Mark *Glouc* 76-84; P-in-c Water Orton *Birm* 84-91; V from 91. *The Vicarage, Water Orton, Birmingham B46 1RX* 0121-747 2751

✠**MAYFIELD, Rt Rev Christopher John.** b 35. G&C Coll Cam BA57 MA61 Linacre Ho Ox DipTh63 Cranfield Inst of Tech MSc83. Wycliffe Hall Ox 61. **d** 63 **p** 64 **c** 85. C Birm St Martin *Birm* 63-67; Lect 67-71; V Luton St Mary *St Alb* 71-80; RD Luton 74-80; Adn Bedf 80-85; Suff Bp Wolv *Lich* 85-92; Area Bp Wolv 92-93; Hon Can Lich Cathl 85-93; Bp Man from 93. *Bishopscourt, Bury New Road, Manchester M7 0LE* 0161-792 2096 Fax 792 6826

MAYFIELD, Timothy James Edward (Tim). b 60. LMH Ox BA82. Trin Coll Bris BA88. **d** 88 **p** 89. C Ovenden *Wakef* 88-92; V Mt Pellon from 92. *The Vicarage, Church Lane, Halifax, W Yorkshire HX2 0EF* Halifax (01422) 365027

MAYHEW, Canon Charles. b 40. K Coll Lon BD64 AKC64. **d** 65 **p** 66. R Cawston *Nor* 69-74; P-in-c Felthorpe w Haveringland 69-74; R Barnack w Ufford and Bainton *Pet* 74-86; RD Barnack 77-86; Can Pet Cathl 83-94; V Oakham, Hambleton, Egleton, Braunston and Brooke 86-94; Chapl Catmose Vale & Rutland Memorial Hosps 86-94; rtd 94. *Thorndon Green, Church Road, Lyndon, Oakham, Leics LE15 8TU* Oakham (01572) 722108

MAYHEW, David Francis. b 51. Ch Ch Ox BA72 MA76 Newc Poly DCG76. Wycliffe Hall Ox BA75 NE Ord Course 89. **d** 91 **p** 92. NSM High Elswick St Paul *Newc* 91-94; Toc H 91-94; V Mitford *Newc* from 94; Chapl Northgate Mental Handicap Unit Morpeth from 94. *The Vicarage, Stable Green, Mitford, Morpeth, Northd NE61 3PZ* Morpeth (01670) 512527

MAYHEW, Peter. b 10. MBE46. Lon Univ BSc31 Ox Univ MLitt79. Ely Th Coll 34. **d** 35 **p** 36. Australia 70-74; Chapl Soc of All SS Sisters of the Poor Ox 74-84; rtd 84; Perm to Offic *Ox* from 84; C Sandford-on-Thames 87. *St John's Home, St Mary's Road, Oxford OX4 1QE* Oxford (01865) 724309

MAYLAND, Mrs Jean Mary. b 36. JP77. TCert60 LMH Ox BA58 DipTh59 MA61. St Deiniol's Hawarden 91. **d** 91 **p** 94. NSM York Minster *York* 91-93; Lect and Tutor N Ord Course from 91; Dioc Ecum Officer *Dur* from 93; Local Unity Officer Dur Ecum Relns Gp from 93. *The Rectory, Brancepeth, Durham DH7 8EL* 0191-378 0503

MAYLAND, Canon Ralph. b 27. Ripon Hall Ox 57. **d** 59 **p** 60. Chapl RNR 61-94; V Brightside St Marg *Sheff* 68-72; Ind Chapl 68-81; V Ecclesfield 72-81; Can Res and Treas York Minster *York* 82-94; rtd 94; NSM Brancepeth *Dur* from 94. *The Rectory, Brancepeth, Durham DH7 8EL* 0191-378 0503

MAYLOR, David Charles. b 59. Lanc Univ BSc80 Edge Hill Coll of HE PGCE81. St Jo Coll Nottm 89. **d** 91 **p** 92. C Hindley All SS *Liv* 91-94; P-in-c Spalding St Paul *Linc* from 94. *St Paul's Vicarage, 65 Holbeach Road, Spalding, Lincs PE11 2HY* Spalding (01775) 722532

MAYNARD, John William. b 37. Lon Univ BSc58. Ripon Hall Ox 60. **d** 62 **p** 63. C St Laurence in the Isle of Thanet *Cant* 62-67; C S Ashford Ch Ch 67-70; V Pagham *Chich* from 70. *The Vicarage, Church lane, Pagham, Bognor Regis, W Sussex PO21 4NX* Pagham (01243) 262713

MAYNARD, Raymond. b 30. S'wark Ord Course 75 Ox Ord Course 76. **d** 77 **p** 78. NSM Hedsor and Bourne End *Ox* 77-80;

C Newport Pagnell w Lathbury 80-83; P-in-c Lacey Green 83-89; V 89; Perm to Offic *Guildf* from 90. *9 Forestdale, Grayshott, Hindhead, Surrey GU26 6TA*   Hindhead (01428) 604565

MAYNARD, Canon Richard Edward Buller. b 42. AKC66. **d** 67 **p** 68. C St Ives *Truro* 67-71; C Falmouth K Chas 71-74; V St Germans 74-84; V Tideford 74-84; RD E Wivelshire 81-85; Hon Can Truro Cathl from 82; V St Germans 84-85; TR Saltash from 85; Chapl St Barn Hosp Saltash from 90. *The Vicarage, 11 Higher Port View, Saltash, Cornwall PL12 4BU*   Saltash (01752) 843142

MAYNARD, Robert Walter. b 38. St Alb Minl Tr Scheme. **d** 85 **p** 86. NSM Chorleywood St Andr *St Alb* from 85. *Carmel, 4 Haddon Road, Chorleywood, Rickmansworth, Herts WD3 5AN*   Chorleywood (01923) 282522

MAYNE, Brian John. b 52. LTCL75 ARICS81 Univ of Wales (Cardiff) BA73. NE Ord Course 82 Coll of Resurr Mirfield 84. **d** 85 **p** 86. C Stainton-in-Cleveland *York* 85-89; P-in-c Rounton w Welbury from 89; Chapl HM Young Offender Inst Northallerton from 89. *St Leonard's House, 7 Spring Hill, Northallerton, N Yorkshire DL6 2SQ*   East Harlsey (01609) 882401   Fax Northallerton (01609) 779664

MAYNE, Canon John Andrew Brian. b 34. QUB BA55 Lon Univ BD62. CITC 57. **d** 57 **p** 58. C Ballymoney *Conn* 57-60; C Knock *D & D* 60-62; P-in-c Knocknagoney 62-68; P-in-c Belvoir 68-71; I 71-80; Dean Waterford *C & O* 80-84; I Lecale Gp *D & D* from 84; Can Down Cathl from 85; Prec Down Cathl from 91. *Saul Rectory, 9 Quoile Road, Downpatrick, Co Down BT30 6SE*   Downpatrick (01396) 613101 or 614922

MAYNE, Very Rev Michael Clement Otway. b 29. CCC Cam BA55 MA58. Cuddesdon Coll 55. **d** 57 **p** 58. C Harpenden St Jo *St Alb* 57-59; Bp's Dom Chapl *S'wark* 59-65; V Norton *St Alb* 65-72; Hd of Relig Progr BBC Radio 72-79; Hon Can S'wark Cathl *S'wark* 75-79; V Cam Gt St Mary w St Mich *Ely* 79-86; Dean Westmr from 86. *The Deanery, Westminster Abbey, London SW1P 3PA*   0171-222 2953   Fax 233 2072

MAYO, Christopher Paul (Chris). b 68. Heythrop Coll Lon BD91. Qu Coll Birm 91. **d** 93 **p** 94. C Wednesfield *Lich* 93-94; C Bilston from 94. *107 Wellington Road, Bilston, W Midlands WV14 6BQ*   Wolverhampton (01902) 353428

MAYO, Mrs Deborah Ann. b 67. Newc Univ BA89 Birm Univ BD92. Qu Coll Birm 90. **d** 93 **p** 94. Par Dn Bloxwich *Lich* 93-94; C from 94. *67 Nairn Road, Bloxwich, Walsall WS3 3XB*   Walsall (01922) 479145

MAYO, Canon Gordon Edwin. b 18. St Jo Coll Dur LTh42 BA45 MA61. Oak Hill Th Coll. **d** 42 **p** 43. Warden Lee Abbey Internat Students' Club Kensington 64-71; R Coulsdon St Jo *S'wark* 71-78; Dir of Chr Stewardship 78-85; Hon Can S'wark Cathl 83-85; rtd 85; P-in-c Limpsfield and Titsey *S'wark* 85-89; Perm to Offic *Chich* 90-94. *160 New Street, Horsham, W Sussex RH13 5EG*   Horsham (01403) 273508

MAYO, Inglis John. b 46. FCA. Ripon Coll Cuddesdon 74. **d** 77 **p** 78. C Bitterne Park *Win* 77-81; C Christchurch 81-86; P-in-c Sturminster Marshall *Sarum* 86-89; P-in-c Kingston Lacy and Shapwick 86-89; V Sturminster Marshall, Kingston Lacy and Shapwick from 89. *The Vicarage, Newton Road, Sturminster Marshall, Wimborne, Dorset BH21 4BT*   Sturminster Marshall (01258) 857255

MAYO, Robert William (Bob). b 61. Keble Coll Ox BA83. Cranmer Hall Dur 85. **d** 87 **p** 88. C Luton Lewsey St Hugh *St Alb* 87-90; Hd Cam Univ Miss 90-95; Hon C Bermondsey St Jas w Ch Ch *S'wark* 90-95; Chapl S Bank Univ from 95. *1 St Alphege Clergy House, Pocock Street, London SE16 0BJ*   0171-928 8912

MAYOH, John Harrison. b 23. Southn Univ BA50. Wycliffe Coll Toronto 50. Wycliffe Hall Ox 52. **d** 53 **p** 54. V Bridlington Quay Ch Ch *York* 69-80; R Aythorpe w High and Leaden Roding *Chelmsf* 80-87; rtd 87. *5 Keswick Close, Chester CH2 2PP*   Chester (01244) 328789

MAYOH, Margaret Evelyn. b 38. Open Univ BA87. Trin Coll Bris DipHE82. **dss** 82 **d** 87 **p** 94. Halliwell St Paul *Man* 82-87; Hon Par Dn 87-91; Hon Par Dn Walmersley 91-94; Hon C from 94. *40 Hillside Avenue, Bromley Cross, Bolton BL7 9NJ*   Bolton (01204) 55423

MAYOR, Henry William. b 39. Or Coll Ox BA62 Birm Univ DPS67. Westcott Ho Cam 62. **d** 64 **p** 65. C The Quinton *Birm* 64-66; C Dudley St Thos *Worc* 67-71; R Birch St Agnes *Man* 71-83; Community Chapl Aylesbury *Ox* 83-89; Community Chapl Aylesbury w Bierton and Hulcott 89; R Cheetham St Luke and Lower Crumpsall St Thos *Man* from 89. *26 Saltire Gardens, Tetlow Lane, Salford M7 0DG*   0161-792 3123

MAYOSS, Anthony (Aidan). b 31. Leeds Univ BA55. Coll of Resurr Mirfield 55. **d** 57 **p** 58. C Meir *Lich* 57-62; Lic to Offic *Wakef* 62-72 and from 78; CR from 64; S Africa 73-75; Asst Chapl Lon Univ *Lon* 76-78; Bursar CR 84-90. *House of the Resurrection, Mirfield, W Yorkshire WF14 0BN*   Mirfield (01924) 494318

MAYOSS-HURD, Mrs Susan Patricia. b 59. Lanc Univ BA81. Cranmer Hall Dur 82. **dss** 84 **d** 87 **p** 94. Ribbesford w Bewdley and Dowles *Worc* 84-88; Par Dn 87-88; C W Heath *Birm* from 88; Chapl W Heath Hosp from 88. *33 Burley Way, Birmingham B38 8JJ*   0121-459 5327

MDUMULLA, Jonas Habel. b 50. Nairobi Univ Hull Univ BTh87 MA89. St Phil Coll Kongwa DipTh74. **d** 74 **p** 75. Tanzania 74-82; C Sutton St Jas and Wawne *York* from 82. *73 Grandale, Hull HU7 4BL*   Hull (01482) 838222

MEACHAM, John David. b 24. AKC51 Open Univ MPhil90. Lambeth STh77. **d** 52 **p** 53. V Sittingbourne St Mich *Cant* 58-74; V Brenchley *Roch* 74-83; Bp's Chapl and Research Asst 83-86; P-in-c Gt Wishford *Sarum* 83-88; P-in-c S Newton 83-88; Sec C of E Doctrine Commn 84-89; rtd 88. *20 Chiselbury Grove, Salisbury SP2 8EP*   Salisbury (01722) 332217

MEAD, Arthur Hugh. b 39. K Coll Cam BA60 MA64 New Coll Ox BLitt66. St Steph Ho Ox 61. **d** 80 **p** 80. NSM Hammersmith St Jo *Lon* from 80; Chapl St Paul's Sch Barnes from 82; Dep P in O 85-90 and from 95; P in O 90-95. *22 Spencer Road, London W4 3SN*   0181-994 4112 or 748 9142

MEAD, Colin Harvey. b 26. FCA. S Dios Minl Tr Scheme. **d** 84 **p** 85. NSM Talbot Village *Sarum* from 84. *59 Alyth Road, Bournemouth BH3 7HB*   Bournemouth (01202) 763647

MEAD, Canon John Harold. b 37. Wells Th Coll 69. **d** 71 **p** 72. C Charlton Kings St Mary *Glouc* 71-75; R Stratton w Baunton 75-82; R Bishop's Cleeve from 82; RD Tewkesbury from 88; Hon Can Glouc Cathl from 90. *The Rectory, Bishops Cleeve, Cheltenham, Glos GL52 4NG*   Cheltenham (01242) 675103

MEAD, Nicholas Charles. b 50. Newc Univ BEd73 Reading Univ MA76. Ridley Hall Cam 83. **d** 85 **p** 86. C Bilton *Cov* 85-88; C Whittlesey *Ely* 88-89; Perm to Offic from 89. *11 Marne Road, Whittlesey, Peterborough PE7 1UQ*   Peterborough (01733) 350212

MEAD, Nigel Gerrish. b 31. Tyndale Hall Bris 62. **d** 64 **p** 65. C Shirley *Win* 64-67; C Alverdiscott w Huntshaw *Ex* 67-71; C Yarnscombe 67-71; C Beaford and Roborough 67-71; C St Giles in the Wood 67-71; R Shebbear, Buckland Filleigh, Sheepwash etc 71-88; TR Shebbear, Buckland Filleigh, Sheepwash etc from 89; P-in-c Langtree 85-86; RD Torrington 86-93. *The Rectory, Shebbear, Beaworthy, Devon EX21 5RU*   Shebbear (01409) 281424

MEADEN, Philip George William. b 40. Open Univ BA75. Lich Th Coll 64. **d** 66 **p** 67. C Aston SS Pet and Paul *Birm* 66-70; V Lozells St Paul 70-76; Asst Chapl HM Pris Brixton 76-77; Chapl HM Pris Lewes 77-84; Chapl HM Pris Aylesbury 84-88; Chapl HM Pris Wandsworth from 88. *HM Prison Wandsworth, PO Box 757, Heathfield Road, London SW18 3HS*   0181-874 7292   Fax 877 0358

MEADER, Philip John. b 44. Oak Hill Th Coll 73. **d** 75 **p** 76. C E Ham St Paul *Chelmsf* 75-77; CMJ 77-90; TV Lowestoft and Kirkley *Nor* 90-94; V Lowestoft St Andr from 94. *The Vicarage, 51 Beresford Road, Lowestoft, Suffolk NR32 2NQ*   Lowestoft (01502) 511521

MEADOWS, John Michael. b 27. St Jo Coll Cam BA50. Ridley Hall Cam 51. **d** 53 **p** 54. Overseas Miss Fellowship 56-87; Vietnam 62-75; Refugee Reception Cen Sopley *Win* 79-82; NSM Canford Magna *Sarum* 86-88; C Radipole and Melcombe Regis 89-94; rtd 94. *18 Wellington Avenue, Southampton SO2 5DD*   Southampton (01703) 465167

MEADOWS, Canon Stanley Percival. b 14. TD61. St D Coll Lamp BA46. **d** 47 **p** 48. R Man St Geo w St Barn *Man* 61-72; R Man Miles Platting 72-82; RD Ardwick 77-82; rtd 82; Perm to Offic *Man* from 82. *287 Charlestown Road, Manchester M9 7BB*   0161-795 9478

MEADS, William Ivan. b 35. ACIS67 ACMA75 Qu Mary Coll Lon BA56. Linc Th Coll 75. **d** 77 **p** 78. C Pentonville St Luke and St Jo *Glouc* 77-81; Chapl HM Pris Pentonville 81-82; Preston 82-85; Wakef 85-88; P-in-c Wroxton w Balscote and Shenington w Alkerton *Ox* 88-90; R Broughton w N Newington and Shutford 90-95; P-in-c Week St Mary w Poundstock and Whitstone *Truro* from 95. *The Rectory, The Glebe, Week St Mary, Holsworthy, Devon EX22 6UY*   Week St Mary (0128884) 265

MEADWAY, Dr Jeanette Valerie. b 47. FRCP87 FRCPEd87 Edin Univ MB, ChB69. Oak Hill NSM Course 89. **d** 93. NSM Stratford St Jo and Ch Ch w Forest Gate St Jas *Chelmsf* from 93. *4 Glebe Avenue, Woodford Green, Essex IG8 9HB*   0181-504 1958

MEAGER, Frederick William. b 18. St Mich Coll Llan 46. **d** 48 **p** 49. V Watford St Pet *St Alb* 64-83; RD Watford 70-75; rtd 83; Perm to Offic *St Alb* from 83; Perm to Offic *Ely* from 84. *31 Home Manor House, Cassio Road, Watford WD1 7BS*   Watford (01932) 237032

MEAKIN, Canon Anthony John (Tony). b 28. TD76. Down Coll Cam BA52 MA56. Westcott Ho Cam 52. **d** 54 **p** 55. V Alnwick St Paul *Newc* 60-71; V Edlingham 62-71; CF (TA) 63-83; R Whickham *Dur* 71-88; RD Gateshead W 78-88; Hon Can Dur

Cathl 83-93; Bp's Sen Chapl and Exec Officer for Dioc Affairs 88-93; rtd 93. *73 Oakfields, Burnopfield, Newcastle upon Tyne NE16 6PQ* Burnopfield (01207) 70429

MEAKIN, David John. b 61. Hull Univ BA82 Hughes Hall Cam PGCE83 Lambeth STh88. Westcott Ho Cam 86. **d** 88 **p** 89. C Upminster *Chelmsf* 88-92; Prec and Sacr Dur Cathl *Dur* from 92. *8 The College, Durham DH1 3EQ* 0191-386 4733

MEAKIN, Ven John Ernest. b 13. Kelham Th Coll 30. **d** 36 **p** 37. Singapore 51-55; Australia from 55; rtd 80. *Staddle Stones, Elder Street, Moonta Mines, S Australia 5557* Moonta Mines (88) 252816

MEANLEY, Hubert Edward Sylvester. b 10. Trin Coll Cam BA32. **d** 34 **p** 35. R Settrington *York* 68-76; P-in-c Thorpe Bassett 72-76; rtd 76. *5 Cherry Tree Close, Skelton-on-Ure, Ripon, N Yorkshire HG4 5AL* Boroughbridge (01423) 324918

MEARA, David Gwynne. b 47. Or Coll Ox BA70 MA73. Lambeth STh76 Cuddesdon Coll 71. **d** 73 **p** 74. C Whitley Ch Ch *Ox* 73-77; Chapl Reading Univ 77-82; V Basildon 82-87; P-in-c Aldworth and Ashampstead 85-87; V Basildon w Aldworth and Ashampstead 87-94; RD Bradfield 90-94; V Buckm w Radclive cum Chackmore from 94; RD Buckm from 95. *The Rectory, 39 Fishers Field, Buckingham MK18 1SF* Buckingham (01280) 813178

MEARDON, Dr Brian Henry. b 44. Reading Univ BSc66 PhD71. Oak Hill Th Coll DipHE79 MPhil84. **d** 79 **p** 80. C Reading St Jo *Ox* 79-82; V Warfield from 82. *The Vicarage, Church Lane, Warfield, Bracknell, Berks RG12 6EE* Winkfield Row (01344) 882228

MEARNS, Christopher Lee. b 30. Worc Coll Ox BA54 MA58. Ripon Hall Ox BTh56. **d** 57 **p** 58. C Greenhill St Jo *Lon* 57-60; Canada 60-62; Lect Ripon Coll of Educn 63-75; Sen Lect Coll of Ripon and York St Jo 75-85; USA 87 and 89; Tutor Ridley Hall Cam 88; Seychelles 88 and 89-90; Perm to Offic *Ripon* from 90. *14 Primrose Drive, Ripon, N Yorkshire HG4 1EY* Ripon (01765) 602695

✠**MEARS, Rt Rev John Cledan.** b 22. Univ of Wales (Abth) BA43 Univ of Wales MA48. Wycliffe Hall Ox 43. **d** 47 **p** 48 **c** 82. C Mostyn *St As* 47-49; C Rhosllannerchrugog 49-56; V Cwm 56-59; Lic to Offic *Llan* 59-73; Chapl St Mich Coll Llan 59-67; Lect Th Univ of Wales (Cardiff) 59-73; Sub-Warden St Mich Coll Llan 67-73; V Gabalfa *Llan* 73-82; Hon Can Llan Cathl 81-82; Bp Ban 82-92; rtd 92. *Isfryn, 23 Avonridge, Cardiff CF4 9AU* Cardiff (01222) 615505

MEARS, Phillip David. b 40. Dur Univ BA62 DipTh63. **d** 65 **p** 66. C Sandylands *Blackb* 65-68; C Chorley St Geo 68-71; V Leyland St Ambrose 71-81; Perm to Offic *Ches* from 81; Chapl Warrington Distr Gen Hosp from 81. *Warrington District General Hospital, Lovely Lane, Warrington WA5 1QC* Warrington (01925) 664082 or 35911

MEASEY, George. b 08. Roch Th Coll 67. **d** 68 **p** 69. C Rowner *Portsm* 68-72; C Worthing St Geo *Chich* 72-78; rtd 78; Perm to Offic *Chich* from 78. *15 Westbrooke Court, Crescent Road, Worthing, W Sussex BN11 1RG*

MEATH AND KILDARE, Bishop of. See EMPEY, Most Rev Walton Newcome Francis

MEATH, Archdeacon of. See CORRIGAN, Ven Thomas George

MEATS, Canon Alan John. b 41. Univ of Wales (Cardiff) BA62 DipEd63 Lon Univ BD70. St Mich Coll Llan 68. **d** 70 **p** 71. C Pontypridd St Cath *Llan* 70-73; TV Ystradyfodwg 73-75; Dioc Insp of Schs 73-75 and 83-89; V Llandeilo Tal-y-bont *S & B* 75-83; RD Llwchwr 81-83; V Aberdare St Fagan *Llan* 83-89; V Felin-foel *St D* from 89; Asst Dioc Dir of Educn from 89; Hon Can St D Cathl from 94. *The Vicarage, Swiss Valley Road, Felinfoel, Llanelli, Dyfed SA14 8BS* Llanelli (01554) 773559

MEDCALF, James Gordon (Jim). b 31. CB. Solicitor 63. S'wark Ord Course 87. **d** 90 **p** 91. NSM Shortlands *Roch* from 90. *14B Bromley Grove, Bromley BR2 0LN* 0181-464 2211

MEDCALF, John Edward. b 19. Oak Hill Th Coll 47. **d** 50 **p** 51. V Wednesfield Heath *Lich* 61-85; rtd 85; Perm to Offic *Heref* from 86. *Cee View, Kilforge, Bolstone, Hereford HR2 6NE* Hereford (01432) 840339

MEDCALF, William Henry. b 15. TCD BA45 MA49. CITC 46. **d** 46 **p** 47. CMJ 50-80; rtd 80. *185 Dibdin House, London W9 1QQ* 0171-328 3133

MEDFORTH, Allan Hargreaves. b 27. Qu Coll Cam BA48 MA52. Westcott Ho Cam 50. **d** 51 **p** 52. C Hexham *Newc* 51-55; PV S'well Minster *S'well* 55-59; V Farnsfield 59-72; RD S'well 66-72; V St Alb St Pet *St Alb* from 72; RD St Alb 74-84. *The Vicarage, 23 Hall Place Gardens, St Albans, Herts AL1 3SB* St Albans (01727) 851464

MEDHURST, Prof Kenneth Noel (Ken). b 38. Edin Univ MA61 Man Univ PhD69. **d** 91 **p** 93. NSM Shipley St Paul and Frizinghall *Bradf* from 91. *100 Langley Lane, Baildon, Shipley, W Yorkshire BD17 6TD* Bradford (01274) 598273

MEDHURST, Dr Leslie John. b 56. TCD DipTh85 BTh90 MA93 Open Univ BA91 Greenwich Univ PhD93. **d** 85 **p** 86. C Seapatrick *D & D* 85-90; I Belf St Mark *Conn* from 90. *St*

Mark's Rectory, 119 Ligoniel Road, Belfast BT14 8DN Belfast (01232) 713151

MEDLEY, Philip Roger. b 46. ANCA FTC69 Birm Univ CertEd73. SW Minl Tr Course. **d** 85 **p** 86. NSM Ottery St Mary, Alfington and W Hill *Ex* 85-86; C S Hill w Callington Truro 86-89; C Linkinhorne 86-89; V from 89; Dioc Officer for Evang from 93. *The Vicarage, Linkinhorne, Callington, Cornwall PL17 7LY* Liskeard (01579) 62560 Fax as telephone

MEE, Colin Henry. b 36. Reading Univ BSc58. Bris Sch of Min 83. **d** 85 **p** 86. NSM Stanton St Quintin, Hullavington, Grittleton etc *Bris* 85-87; C Swindon Ch Ch 88-90; TV Washfield, Stoodleigh, Withleigh etc *Ex* 90-95; TR from 95. *The Rectory, Withleigh, Tiverton, Devon EX16 8JG* Tiverton (01884) 252357

MEED, Henry Robert (Harry). b 15. Ripon Hall Ox 50. **d** 51 **p** 52. P-in-c Thornborough *Ox* 69-75; R Wingrave w Rowsham, Aston Abbotts and Cublington 75-81; rtd 81; Perm to Offic *St E* from 81. *Blyth Cottage, Church Road, Felsham, Bury St Edmunds, Suffolk IP30 0PJ* Rattlesden (01449) 737818

MEEHAN, Cyril Frederick. b 52. St Jo Coll Nottm BTh80. **d** 80 **p** 81. C Keresley and Coundon *Cov* 80-83; P-in-c Linton and Castle Gresley *Derby* 83-90; P-in-c Alvaston from 90. *The Vicarage, 8 Church Street, Alvaston, Derby DE24 0PR* Derby (01332) 571143

MEEK, Anthony William (Tony). b 45. ACIB. Ox NSM Course 80. **d** 83 **p** 84. NSM Gt Chesham *Ox* from 83. *Elmcroft, Ley Hill, Chesham, Bucks HP5 3QR* Chesham (01494) 772816

MEEK, George Edward. b 08. Leeds Univ BA30. Coll of Resurr Mirfield 26. **d** 32 **p** 33. P-in-c Newton Longville *Ox* 68-75; P-in-c Whaddon w Tattenhoe 68-75; R Newton Longville w Stoke Hammond, Whaddon etc 75-77; rtd 77; Perm to Offic *Chich* from 77. *28 Titian Road, Hove, E Sussex BN3 5QS* Brighton (01273) 773065

MEEK, John Conway. b 33. Lon Univ BSc55 AKC56 St Cath Soc Ox BA59 MA63. Wycliffe Hall Ox 57. **d** 59 **p** 60. C Streatham Immanuel w St Anselm *S'wark* 59-62; C Bilston St Leon *Lich* 63-65; Chapl Kent and Cant Hosp 65-73; V Cant St Mary Bredin *Cant* 65-82; RD Cant 76-82; Hon Can Cant Cathl 79-82; R Bridlington Priory *York* from 82; RD Bridlington from 83; Can York Minster from 94. *The Rectory, Church Green, Bridlington, N Humberside YO16 5JX* Bridlington (01262) 672221

MEERE, Mrs Alison Elizabeth. b 44. SRN65 HVCert67. Ripon Coll Cuddesdon 85. **d** 87 **p** 94. Par Dn Hengrove *Bris* 87-88; Par Dn Winterbourne 88-91; Par Dn Southmead 91-93; Par Dn Hackney *Lon* 93-94; TV from 94. *St James's House, 59A Kenninghall Road, London E5 8BS* 0181-985 1804

MEERING, Laurence Piers Ralph. b 48. Man Univ BSc70. Trin Coll Bris 79. **d** 81 **p** 82. C Downend *Bris* 81-84; C Crofton *Portsm* 84-87; V Witheridge, Thelbridge, Creacombe, Meshaw etc *Ex* 87-94; TV Southgate *Chich* from 94. *21 Anglesey Close, Crawley, W Sussex RH11 9HG* Crawley (01293) 537976

MEGAHEY, Alan John. b 44. Selw Coll Cam BA65 MA69 QUB PhD69. Westcott Ho Cam 69. **d** 70 **p** 71. Asst Chapl Wrekin Coll Shropshire 70-72; Ho Master Cranleigh Sch Surrey 72-83; Zimbabwe 83-93; Chapl Uppingham Sch Leics from 93. *Pentire House, 48 High Street West, Uppingham, Oakham, Leics LE15 9QD* Uppingham (01572) 822144

✠**MEHAFFEY, Rt Rev Dr James.** b 31. TCD BA52 MA56 BD56 QUB PhD75. **d** 54 **p** 55 **c** 80. C Ballymacarrett St Patr *D & D* 54-56; C Deptford St Jo *S'wark* 56-58; C Down Cathl *D & D* 58-60; C-in-c Ballymacarrett St Chris 60-62; I Kilkeel 62-66; I Cregagh 66-80; Bp's Private Chapl 72-76; Preb Down Cathl 76-80; Dioc Missr 76-80; Bp D & R from 80. *The See House, 112 Culmore Road, Londonderry BT48 8JF* Londonderry (01504) 262440 Fax 352554

MEIKLE, Canon David Skene. b 39. St Cath Coll Cam BA60 MA89. Westcott Ho Cam. **d** 63 **p** 64. C Hawick *Edin* 63-67; C Edin SS Phil and Jas 67-72; C Banbury *Ox* 72-73; TV 74-78; R Ipswich St Matt *St E* 78-91; Hon Can St E Cathl from 90; TR Mildenhall from 91. *The Vicarage, Barton Mills, Bury St Edmunds IP28 6AP* Mildenhall (01638) 716044

MEIN, Canon James Adlington. b 38. Nottm Univ BA60. Westcott Ho Cam 61. **d** 63 **p** 64. C Edin St Columba *Edin* 63-67; Bp's Dom Chapl 65-67; Malawi 67-72; R Grangemouth *Edin* 72-82; P-in-c Bo'ness 76-82; TV Livingston LEP 82-90; R Edin Ch Ch from 90; Can St Mary's Cathl from 90. *4 Morningside Road, Edinburgh EH10 4DD* 0131-229 6556

MEIRION-JONES, Huw Geraint. b 39. R Agric Coll Cirencester NDA61 MRAC61 K Coll Lon AKC69 BD71 MA84. St Aug Coll Cant 69. **d** 70 **p** 71. C Harlescott *Lich* 70-73; C Worplesdon *Guildf* 73-77; V Ash Vale 77-85; Dioc Press Officer from 85; TR Westborough from 85. *Westborough Rectory, Beckingham Road, Guildford, Surrey GU2 6BU* Guildford (01483) 504228

MEISSNER, Canon Charles Ludwig Birbeck Hill. b 26. TCD 60. d 62 p 63. C Monaghan *Clogh* 62-64; C Kildallon *K, E & A* 64-65; I 65-71; I Kinawley w Drumany and Crom 71-85; I Mohill w Farnaught, Aughavas, Oughteragh etc from 85; Preb Elphin Cathl from 87. *St Mary's Rectory, Mohill, Co Leitrim, Irish Republic* Carrick-on-Shannon (78) 31012

MELANIPHY, Miss Angela Ellen. b 55. SRN79. Cranmer Hall Dur 87. d 90 p 94. Par Dn Leytonstone St Jo *Chelmsf* 90-94; C from 94. *86 Mornington Road, London E11 3DX* 0181-539 3935

MELBOURNE, Brian Kenneth. b 45. York Univ Toronto 77. Trin Coll Toronto LTh82. d 82 p 82. Canada 82-87; Bermuda 88-94; P-in-c Biddenden and Smarden *Cant* from 94. *The Rectory, High Street, Biddenden, Ashford, Kent TN27 8AH* Biddenden (01580) 291454

MELBOURNE, Miss Thelma. b 08. Dalton Ho Bris 68. dss 77 d 87 p 94. Earlham St Anne *Nor* 77-87; C from 94; Perm to Offic 87-94. *333 Earlham Road, Norwich NR2 3RQ* Norwich (01603) 53008

MELDRUM, Andrew John Bruce. b 66. Univ of Wales (Abth) LLB89. Westcott Ho Cam CTM94. d 94 p 95. C Paddington St Jas *Lon* from 94. *8 St James's Court, 75 Gloucester Terrace, London W2 3DH* 0171-706 2796

MELHUISH, Douglas. b 12. St Pet Hall Ox BA34 MA38. Wycliffe Hall Ox 39. d 39 p 40. Asst Master Haberdashers' Aske's Sch Hampstead 37-40; St Jo Sch Leatherhead 40-42; Lic to Offic *Guildf* 40-42; Asst Master Bedford Sch 42-46; Chapl 43-46; Lic to Offic *St Alb* 42-46; Lect & Tutor Trin Coll Carmarthen 46-48; CMS 48-68; Kenya 48-68; Perm to Offic *York* 69-74; Perm to Offic *Win* 70-74; P-in-c St Lawrence *Portsm* 74-79; Perm to Offic *B & W* from 85. *27 Sturford Lane, Corsley, Warminster, Wilts BA12 7QR* Chapmanslade (01373) 832396

MELINSKY, Canon Michael Arthur Hugh. b 24. Ch Coll Cam BA47 MA49. Ripon Hall Ox 57. d 57 p 59. Hon Can Nor Cathl and Can Missr *Nor* 68-73; Chief Sec ACCM 73-78; Prin N Ord Course 78-88; rtd 88; Perm to Offic *Nor* from 88. *15 Parson's Mead, Norwich NR4 6PG* Norwich (01603) 55042

MELLING, John Cooper. b 44. ALCD73. St Jo Coll Nottm 68. d 72 p 73. C Enfield St Andr *Lon* 72-76; C Didsbury St Jas and Em *Man* 76-79; R Gt Lever 79-84; V Seamer w E Ayton *York* from 84. *The Vicarage, 3 Stockshill, Seamer, Scarborough, N Yorkshire YO12 4QG* Scarborough (01723) 863102

MELLING, Canon Leonard Richard. b 13. St Aid Birkenhead 38. d 41 p 42. V Osbaldwick w Murton *York* 67-78; RD Bulmer 72-78; Malaysia 78-81; Dean Kuching 78-81; rtd 81. *12 Heslington Road, York YO1 5AT* York (01904) 627593

MELLISH, John. b 26. Cranmer Hall Dur 67. d 69 p 70. C Ulverston St Mary w H Trin *Carl* 69-72; V Bromfield 72-73; V Bromfield w Waverton 73-79; P-in-c Allonby w W Newton 77-79; V Shap w Swindale 79-86; RD Appleby 82-86; V Bassenthwaite, Isel and Setmurthy 86-90; rtd 90. *Wyndham, 3 Old Road, Longtown, Cumbria CA6 5TH* Longtown (01228) 791441

MELLISS, Laurence John Albert. b 21. DSM45 RD69. AKC52. d 53 p 54. Chapl RNR 59-76; V Littlehampton St Mary *Chich* 64-76; RD Arundel 75-76; V Findon 76-81; R Catsfield and Crowhurst 81-86; rtd 86; Perm to Offic *Cant* from 86; Dioc Widows Officer from 89. *Chanctonbury, Church Road, New Romney, Kent TN28 8EX* New Romney (01679) 63605

MELLOR, David John. b 49. SSC Nottm Univ BTh72. Kelham Th Coll 68. d 72 p 73. C Horninglow *Lich* 72-74; C Tividale 74-77; C Stafford St Mary and St Chad 77-79; TV Stafford 79-82; Chapl Stafford Gen Infirmary 77-82; V Burslem St Werburgh 82-92; Chapl Haywood and Stanfield Hosps Stoke-on-Trent 82-92; V Derby St Luke *Derby* from 92. *St Luke's Vicarage, 48 Peet Street, Derby DE22 3RF* Derby (01332) 345720 Fax 203233

MELLOR, Miss Dorothy Lilian. b 38. Birm Univ BA61. N Ord Course 86. d 89 p 94. NSM Stockton Heath *Ches* from 89; Chapl HM Young Offender Inst Thorn Cross from 92. *100 Bridge Lane, Appleton, Warrington, Cheshire WA4 3AL* Warrington (01925) 267683 Fax 262153

MELLOR, Frederick Charles Walter (Tony). b 24. Oak Hill NSM Course 80. d 83 p 84. NSM Loughton St Jo *Chelmsf* from 83; Chapl Asst Whipps Cross Hosp Lon from 87. *4 Scotland Road, Buckhurst Hill, Essex IG9 5NR* 0181-504 6203

MELLOR, Canon Kenneth Paul. b 49. Southn Univ BA71 Leeds Univ MA72. Cuddesdon Coll 72. d 73 p 74. C Cottingham *York* 73-76; C Ascot Heath Ox 76-80; V Tilehurst St Mary 80-85; V Menheniot *Truro* 85-94; RD W Wivelshire from 88; Hon Can Truro Cathl from 90; Can Treas from 94; Can Res and Treas Truro Cathl from 94. *Lemon Lodge, Lemon Street, Truro, Cornwall TR1 2PE* Truro (01872) 72094

MELLOR, Robert Frederick. b 14. ACIS37 Dur Univ LTh42. Tyndale Hall Bris 38. d 41 p 42. V Tranmere St Cath *Ches*

65-79; rtd 79; Perm to Offic *Ches* from 80. *5 Fleet Croft Road, Arrowe Park, Wirral, Merseyside L49 5LY* 0151-678 7717

MELLORS, Derek George. b 38. Bris Univ CertEd60 Lon Univ BSc71 Nottm Univ DipEd74 Liv Univ MEd83. N Ord Course 81. d 84 p 85. NSM Eccleston Ch Ch *Liv* 84-92; C Lowton St Mary 92-93; V Ashton-in-Makerfield St Thos from 93. *The Vicarage, 18 Warrington Road, Ashton-in-Makerfield, Wigan, Lancs WN4 9PL* Ashton-in-Makerfield (01942) 727275

MELLORS, Canon James. b 32. Kelham Th Coll 52. d 56 p 57. V Scholes *Wakef* 61-72; V Mirfield 72-88; Hon Can Wakef Cathl 83-88; V Leyburn w Bellerby *Ripon* 88-93; rtd 93. *Langthwaite Cottage, Main Street, West Witton, Leyburn, N Yorkshire DL8 4LR* Wensleydale (01969) 622452

MELLOWS, Canon Alan Frank. b 23. Qu Coll Cam BA45 MA49. Tyndale Hall Bris 47. d 49 p 50. R Mileham *Nor* 62-74; R Beeston next Mileham 66-74; P-in-c Stanfield 62-74; P-in-c Gt w Lt Dunham 70-73; R Ashill 74-79; P-in-c Saham Toney 78-79; R Ashill w Saham Toney 79-88; Hon Can Nor Cathl 82-88; rtd 88; Perm to Offic *Nor* from 88. *8 Smugglers Close, Hunstanton, Norfolk PE36 6JU* Hunstanton (01485) 534271

MELLOWSHIP, Robert John. b 52. St Mich Coll Llan BD92. d 92 p 93. C Brecon St Mary and Battle w Llanddew *S & B* 92-94; Min Can Brecon Cathl 92-94; C Pontypool *Mon* 94-95; TV from 95. *St James' Vicarage, Hanbury Road, Pontypool, Gwent NP4 6JL* Pontypool (01495) 769772

MELLUISH, Mark Peter. b 59. Oak Hill Th Coll. d 89 p 90. C Ashtead *Guildf* 89-93; V Ealing St Paul *Lon* from 93. *St Paul's Vicarage, 102 Elers Road, London W13 9QE* 0181-567 4628 or 579 5953

MELLUISH, Stephen. b 60. Trin Coll Bris DipHE93. d 93 p 94. C Gipsy Hill Ch Ch *S'wark* from 93. *34 Woodland Hill, London SE19 1PB* 0181-761 7924

MELLY, Aleck Emerson. b 24. Oak Hill Th Coll 50. d 53 p 54. R Kemberton w Sutton Maddock *Lich* 68-80; P-in-c Stockton 74-80; R Kemberton, Sutton Maddock and Stockton 81-89; rtd 89. *47 Greenfields Road, Bridgnorth, Shropshire WV16 4JG* Bridgnorth (01746) 762711

MELROSE, Kenneth Mark Cecil. b 15. Ex Coll Ox BA37 DipTh38 MA41. Ripon Hall Ox 37. d 39 p 40. V Portswood St Denys *Win* 63-71; V Bovey Tracey SS Pet and Paul *Ex* 71-85; rtd 85; Perm to Offic *Cant* from 85. *88 Wells Way, Faversham, Kent ME13 7QU* Faversham (01795) 536115

MELROSE, Michael James Gervase. b 47. St Chad's Coll Dur BA69 DipTh70. d 71 p 72. C Chelmsf All SS *Chelmsf* 71-74; C Pimlico St Pet w Westmr Ch Ch *Lon* 74-80; R Man Victoria Park *Man* 80-94; P-in-c Cheetwood St Alb 85-91; R Reading St Giles *Ox* from 94. *St Giles's Rectory, Church Street, Reading RG1 2SB* Reading (01734) 572831

MELTON, Mrs Anne. b 44. N Riding Coll of Educn CertEd65. St Jo Coll Dur 80. dss 83 d 87 p 94. Newton Aycliffe *Dur* 83-87; Par Dn 87-88; Par Dn Shildon w Eldon 88-94; Asst Dir of Ords 88-94; C Shildon w Eldon 94; P-in-c Usworth from 94. *4 Highbury Close, Springwell, Gateshead, Tyne & Wear NE9 7PU* 0191-416 3533

MELVILLE, Dominic. b 63. Sussex Univ BA84 Southn Univ BTh90. Sarum & Wells Th Coll 87. d 90 p 91. C Willenhall H Trin *Lich* 90-94; V Wednesfield St Greg from 94. *St Gregory's Vicarage, 112 Long Knowle Lane, Wednesfield, Wolverhampton WV11 1JQ* Wolverhampton (01902) 731677

MELVILLE, Malcolm Charles Crompton. b 13. Ancient Soc of Coll Youths 37 Birm Univ BSc36. Lich Th Coll 37. d 39 p 40. C Heacham *Nor* 65-67; Perm to Offic *St Alb* from 67; rtd 78. *45 Beverley Crescent, Bedford MK40 4BX* Bedford (01234) 266060

MELVIN, Gordon Thomas. b 55. BA86. Sarum & Wells Th Coll 86. d 88 p 89. C Linc St Faith and St Martin w St Pet *Linc* 88-91; TV Horsham *Chich* 91-94; Chapl Horsham Gen Hosp 91-94; Chapl Ipswich Hosp from 94. *50 Constable Road, Ipswich IP4 2UZ, or Ipswich Hospital, Heath Road, Ipswich IP4 5PD* Ipswich (01473) 704100 or 233517

MEMBERY, Donald Percy. b 20. K Coll Lon BSc50 DipEd51 AKC51. Ox NSM Course. d 79 p 80. NSM Aston Rowant w Crowell Ox 79-81; P-in-c Swyncombe 81-85; R Swyncombe w Britwell Salome 85-88; rtd 88; Perm to Offic *Ripon* from 88. *11 Carr Manor Gardens, Leeds LS17 5DQ* Leeds (0113) 269 1578

MENDEL, Thomas Oliver (Tom). b 57. Down Coll Cam BA79 MA82. Cranmer Hall Dur 79. d 81 p 82. Lic to Offic *Ely* 81-86; Chapl Down Coll Cam 81-86; Hon C Ely 81-86; V Minsterley *Heref* 86-92; Chapl Costa del Sol W *Eur* 92-93; Chapl Shrewsbury Sch 93-95; Chapl Milan w Genoa and Varese *Eur* from 95. *via Plino 34, 20129 Milan, Italy* Milan (2) 204-9298

MENEY, Brian James. b 42. Glas Univ MA63. Edin Th Coll 63. d 65 p 66. Lic to Offic *Edin* 69-71; C Edin H Cross 71-73; Asst Sec Rep Ch Coun 73-81; P-in-c Edin St Barn 73-81; Chapl Bede Ho Staplehurst 81-82; P-in-c Plaistow SS Phil and Jas w St Andr *Chelmsf* 82-83; TR Plaistow 83-90; V Leeds Gipton Epiphany *Ripon* 90-95; rtd 95. *Spofforth Hall Cheshire Home,*

Wetherby Road, Harrogate, W Yorkshire HG3 1BX
Wetherby (01937) 590669

✠**MENIN, Rt Rev Malcolm James.** b 32. Univ Coll Ox BA55 MA59. Cuddesdon Coll 55. **d** 57 **p** 58 **c** 86. C Southsea H Spirit *Portsm* 57-59; C Fareham SS Pet and Paul 59-62; V Nor St Jas w Pockthorpe *Nor* 62-72; P-in-c Nor St Martin 62-74; P-in-c Nor St Mary Magd 68-72; V Nor St Mary Magd w St Jas 72-86; RD Nor E 81-86; Hon Can Nor Cathl 82-86; Suff Bp Knaresborough *Ripon* from 86. *16 Shaftesbury Avenue, Leeds LS8 1DT* Leeds (0113) 266 4800

MENNISS, Andrew Philip. b 49. Univ of Wales (Swansea) BSc73. Sarum & Wells Th Coll 83. **d** 85 **p** 86. C Horsell *Guildf* 85-89; V Bembridge *Portsm* from 89; RD E Wight from 95. *The Vicarage, Bembridge, Isle of Wight PO35 5NA* Isle of Wight (01983) 872175

MENON, Nicholas Anthony Thotekat. b 39. Mert Coll Ox BA61 MA65 DipTh62. St Steph Ho Ox 61. **d** 63 **p** 64. C Paddington Ch Ch *Lon* 63-66; Hon C 66-70; V Thorpe *Guildf* 70-76; V Ox SS Phil and Jas w St Marg *Ox* 76-79; Chapl Surrey Univ *Guildf* 79-81; Chapl and Ho Master Cranleigh Sch Surrey from 82. *Loveday House, Cranleigh School, Cranleigh, Surrey GU6 8PZ* Cranleigh (01483) 272510

MENTZEL, Kevin David. b 60. Reading Univ BSc82 Down Coll Cam BA87 MA91. Ridley Hall Cam 85. **d** 88 **p** 89. C Ditton *Roch* 88-91; Asst Chapl Eton Coll Windsor 91-93; Asst Chapl R Hosp Sch Ipswich 93-94; Past Asst Fulham St Dionis Parson's Green *Lon* from 94. *16 Parson's Green, London SW6 4TS* 0171-736 4849

MEPHAM, Kevin Aubrey. b 55. Sarum & Wells Th Coll 85. **d** 88 **p** 89. NSM Sidley *Chich* 88-90; C Hollington St Leon 90-94; V Horam from 94. *The Vicarage, Horebeech Lane, Horam, Heathfield, E Sussex TN21 0DT* Horam Road (01435) 812563

MEPHAM, Stephen Richard. b 64. K Coll Lon BD85 AKC85. Linc Th Coll 87. **d** 89 **p** 90. C Newark-upon-Trent *S'well* 89-92; C Cheshunt *St Alb* from 92. *St Clement's House, 44 Hillview Gardens, Cheshunt, Waltham Cross, Herts EN8 0PE* Waltham Cross (01992) 625098

MEPSTED, Leonard Charles. b 34. Leeds Univ BA61. Coll of Resurr Mirfield 61. **d** 63 **p** 64. C Goldthorpe *Sheff* 63-65; C S Shields St Hilda w St Thos *Dur* 65-69; C Woodston *Ely* 69-71; V Friday Bridge 71-72; C Moss Side Ch Ch *Man* 72-74; P-in-c Farnworth All SS 75-76; C Lawton Moor 76-78; P-in-c Falinge 78-87; R Eastchurch w Leysdown and Harty *Cant* from 87. *The Rectory, Warden Road, Eastchurch, Sheerness, Kent ME12 4EJ* Eastchurch (01795) 880205

✠**MERCER, Rt Rev Eric Arthur John.** b 17. Kelham Th Coll. **d** 47 **p** 48 **c** 65. C Coppenhall *Ches* 47-51; C-in-c Heald Green St Cath CD 51-53; R Stockport St Thos 53-59; R Ches St Bridget w St Martin 59-65; Dioc Missr 59-65; Hon Can Ches Cathl 64-65; Suff Bp Birkenhead 65-73; Bp Ex 73-85; rtd 85; P-in-c E Knoyle, Hindon w Chicklade and Pertwood *Sarum* 85-86; P-in-c Hindon w Chicklade and Pertwood 86-88. *Frickers House, Cow Drove, Chilmark, Salisbury SP3 5AJ* Teffont (01722) 716400

MERCER, Canon John James Glendinning. b 20. TCD BA49 MA55. **d** 50 **p** 51. I Ballyholme *D & D* 55-90; Can Belf Cathl 76-88; Preb Wicklow St Patr Cathl Dub 88-90; rtd 90. *6 Hillfoot, Groomsport, Bangor, Co Down BT19 6JJ* Bangor (01247) 472979

✠**MERCER, Rt Rev Robert William Stanley.** b 35. St Paul's Grahamstown LTh59. **d** 59 **p** 60 **c** 77. S Rhodesia 59-63; Lic to Offic *Wakef* 64-66; CR from 65; Perm to Offic *Llan* 66-68; S Africa 68-70; Rhodesia 70-80; Zimbabwe 80-87; Sub-Prelate OStJ from 81; Bp Matabeleland 77-87; Canada from 87; Asst Bp Angl Catholic Ch of Canada 88-89; Dioc Bp from 89. *225 First Avenue, Ottawa, Ontario, Canada, K15 2G5*

MERCER, Timothy James. b 54. Fitzw Coll Cam BA76 MA80. Westcott Ho Cam 78. **d** 81 **p** 82. C Bromley SS Pet and Paul *Roch* 81-85; R Swanscombe from 85. *The Rectory, Swanscombe Road, Swanscombe, Kent DA10 0JZ* Greenhithe (01322) 843160

MERCERON, Daniel John. b 58. Lon Univ BA81. Westcott Ho Cam 88. **d** 90 **p** 91. C Clevedon St Jo *B & W* 90-94; CF from 94. *c/o MOD (Army), Bagshot Park, Bagshot, Surrey GU19 5PL* Bagshot (01726) 471717 Fax 412834

MERCHANT, David Clifford. b 17. Univ of Wales BA37 Birm Univ MA70. St Mich Coll Llan 45. **d** 46 **p** 47. Chapl Westhill Coll of HE Birm 65-82; Hon C Northfield *Birm* 74-92; rtd 82; Perm to Offic *Birm* from 92. *28 Weoley Park Road, Birmingham B29 6QU* 0121-472 0910

MERCHANT, Canon William Moelwyn. b 13. FRSL Univ of Wales BA33 MA50 DLitt60 Wittenberg Univ USA Hon DHL70. **d** 40 **p** 41. Chan Sarum Cathl *Sarum* 67-70; Can and Preb Sarum Cathl 67-73; V Llanddewi Brefi w Llanbadarn Odwyn *St D* 74-78; rtd 78. *32 Willes Road, Leamington Spa, Warks CV31 1BN* Leamington Spa (01926) 314253

MERCIER, David Cuthbert. b 10. St Pet Hall Ox BA32 MA36. Wycliffe Hall Ox 35. **d** 37 **p** 38. C Edge Hill St Mary *Liv* 37-41; C Gt Sankey 41-44; C Parr 44-49; V Langford Budville w

Runnington *B & W* 49-54; R Phillack w Gwithian *Truro* 55-59; New Zealand from 59. *44 Haumoana Road, Haumoana, Hawkes Bay, New Zealand* Levin (6) 875-0147

MERCURIO, Frank James Charles. b 46. Webster Univ (USA) BA73 MA75. St Alb Minl Tr Scheme 87. **d** 89 **p** 90. C Cheshunt *St Alb* 89-93; TV Hitchin from 93; RD Hitchin from 94. *Holy Saviour Vicarage, St Anne's Road, Hitchin, Herts SG5 1QB* Hitchin (01462) 456140

MEREDITH, Andrew James MacPherson. b 59. St Jo Coll Nottm DCM93. **d** 93 **p** 94. C Killay *S & B* from 93. *The Parsonage, 79 Ashgrove, Killay, Swansea SA2 7QZ* Swansea (01792) 206631

MEREDITH, Claison Charles Evans. b 26. Univ of Wales (Lamp) BA51. **d** 54 **p** 55. V Weston Zoyland *B & W* 69-80; V Puriton and Pawlett 80-91; rtd 91. *38 Riverside, Southwell, Notts NG25 0HA* Southwell (01636) 812517

MEREDITH, James Noel Michael Creed. b 17. Keble Coll Ox BA40 MA43. Westcott Ho Cam 39. **d** 40 **p** 42. R Stoke Cov 61-71; RD Cov E 69-71; V Hessle *York* 71-78; R Milton Abbas, Hilton w Cheselbourne etc *Sarum* 78-80; TV Llandudno *Ban* 80-84; rtd 82. *11 Pascoe Close, Poole, Dorset BH14 0NT* Poole (01202) 737108

MEREDITH, Robert. b 21. Bps' Coll Cheshunt 56. **d** 58 **p** 59. V Kimpton *St Alb* 67-75; RD Wheathampstead 72-76; R Kimpton w Ayot St Lawrence 75-76; R Hunsdon 76-80; R Widford 76-80; R Hunsdon w Widford and Wareside 80-84; P-in-c Braughing, Lt Hadham, Albury, Furneux Pelham etc 84-88; R Braughing w Furneux Pelham and Stocking Pelham 88-90; rtd 90; Perm to Offic *St Alb* from 90. *19 Cowper Crescent, Hertford SG14 3DZ* Hertford (01992) 558847

MEREDITH, Canon Roland Evan. b 32. Trin Coll Cam BA55 MA59. Cuddesdon Coll 55. **d** 57 **p** 58. V Hitchin St Mary *St Alb* 63-72; V Preston St Jo *Blackb* 72-76; TR 76-79; RD Preston 72-79; Hon Can Blackb Cathl 77-79; TR Witney *Ox* 79-94; P-in-c Hailey w Crawley 79-82; RD Witney from 89; Hon Can Ch Ch from 92; rtd 94. *1 Deanery Court, Broad Street, Bampton, Oxford OX18 2LY* Witney (01993) 851142

MEREDITH, Ronald Duncan d'Esterre. b 09. K Coll Lon BD32 AKC32. **d** 32 **p** 33. V Seasalter *Cant* 68-76; rtd 76; Perm to Offic *Cant* from 76. *64 Beacon Road, Broadstairs, Kent CT10 3DG* Thanet (01843) 869883

MEREDITH-JONES, Richard. b 26. JP79. K Coll Lon 50. **d** 54 **p** 55. Ind Chapl *Wakef* 66-70; Chapl Glenside Hosp Bris 70-92; Perm to Offic *Glouc* 70-88; CF (TAVR) 78-91; Perm to Offic *Ban* 88-93; rtd 91. *18 Wetlands Lane, Portishead, Bristol BS20 8NA* Portishead (01275) 817217

MERIONETH, Archdeacon of. *See* DAVIES, Ven Francis James Saunders

MERIVALE, Charles Christian Robert. b 44. Cranmer Hall Dur 76. **d** 78 **p** 79. C Highbury Ch Ch *Lon* 78; C Highbury Ch Ch w St Jo 79-81; P-in-c Hawes *Ripon* 81-82; P-in-c Hardrow and St Jo w Lunds 81-82; V Hawes and Hardraw 82-84; Chapl R Cornwall Hosp Truro 85-92; Lic to Offic *Truro* 85-92; rtd 92. *Welham House, Welham, Castle Cary, Somerset BA7 7NE* Castle Cary (01963) 350264

MERRETT, Jonathan Charles. b 55. Univ of Wales (Ban) BMus77 MMus78. Ripon Coll Cuddesdon 78. **d** 81 **p** 82. C Kenilworth St Nic *Cov* 81-84; C Grandborough w Willoughby and Flecknoe 84-87; Asst Dioc Educn Officer from 87. *18 St Mary's Crescent, Leamington Spa, Warks CV31 1JL* Leamington Spa (01926) 885146

MERRICK, John. b 51. New Univ of Ulster BA72 DipAdEd75 TCD HDipEd73. CITC 89. **d** 92 **p** 93. Hd Master Sligo Gr Sch from 92; Lic to Offic *K, E & A* from 92. *The Headmaster's Residence, Sligo Grammar School, The Mall, Sligo, Irish Republic* Sligo (71) 42775

MERRINGTON, Bill. b 55. BSc. Cranmer Hall Dur. **d** 83 **p** 84. C Harborne Heath *Birm* 83-88; V Leamington Priors St Paul *Cov* from 88. *The Vicarage, 15 Lillington Road, Leamington Spa, Warks CV32 5YS* Leamington Spa (01926) 335331

MERRY, David Thomas (Tom). b 48. St Chad's Coll Dur BA70. AKC73. **d** 74 **p** 75. C Cirencester *Glouc* 74-78; TV Bridgnorth, Tasley, Astley Abbotts and Oldbury *Heref* 78-83; P-in-c Quatford 81-83; P-in-c Stroud H Trin *Glouc* from 83; Chapl Stroud Gen Hosp from 83. *Holy Trinity Vicarage, 10 Bowbridge Lane, Stroud, Glos GL5 2JW* Stroud (01453) 764551

MERRY, Ivor John. b 28. W Midl Minl Tr Course. **d** 87 **p** 88. NSM Redditch, The Ridge *Worc* 87-94; NSM Astwood Bank from 94. *5 Church Road, Astwood Bank, Redditch, Worcs B96 6EH* Redditch (01527) 892887

MERRY, Canon James Thomas Arthur. b 38. Toronto Univ BA58 Saskatchewan Univ LLB74. Wycliffe Coll Toronto BTh62. **d** 61 **p** 62. Canada 61-89; I Ematris w Rockcorry, Aghabog and Aughnamullan *Clogh* from 89; Dioc Registrar from 91; Can Clogh Cathl from 95. *The Rectory, Dartrey, Cootehill, Co Cavan, Irish Republic* Castleblayney (42) 42484

MERRY, Rex Edwin. b 38. AKC67. d 68 p 69. C Spalding St Jo *Linc* 68-73; C Boxmoor St Jo *St Alb* 73-83; TV Hemel Hempstead 83-95; V Farley Hill St Jo from 95. *The Vicarage, 47 Rotheram Avenue, Luton LU1 5PP* Luton (01582) 29466

MERWOOD, Raymond George. b 27. K Coll Lon. d 54 p 56. V Newton Poppleford w Harpford *Ex* 67-91; rtd 91; Perm to Offic *Ex* from 92. *53 Carter Avenue, Exmouth, Devon EX8 3EF* Exmouth (01395) 279432

MESSENGER, Paul. b 38. Univ of Wales (Lamp) BA63. Coll of Resurr Mirfield 63. d 65 p 66. C Battersea St Luke *S'wark* 65-69; C Ainsdale *Liv* 69-71; V Wigan St Steph 71-74; Asst Chapl St Marg Convent E Grinstead 74-76; Chapl Kingsley St Mich Sch W Sussex 74-76; P-in-c Southwater *Chich* 76-81; V from 81. *The Vicarage, Southwater, Horsham, W Sussex RH13 7BT* Horsham (01403) 730229

MESSENGER, Canon Reginald James. b 13. Univ Coll Dur LTh38 BA39 MA57. St Aug Coll Cant 35. d 39 p 40. India 39-80; rtd 80; Perm to Offic *Chich* from 80. *58 Oakcroft Gardens, Littlehampton, W Sussex BN17 6LT* Littlehampton (01903) 715982

MESSER, Ralph Edwin. b 32. NW Ord Course 76. d 79 p 80. NSM Escrick and Stillingfleet w Naburn *York* 79-81; Area Sec (Dio York) USPG 79-81; Ind Chapl *York* from 81; P-in-c Cawood from 81; P-in-c Ryther from 81. *The Vicarage, Cawood, Selby, N Yorkshire YO8 0TP* Cawood (01757) 268273

MESSOM, Alan George. b 42. St Chad's Coll Dur BA63 DipTh65. d 65 p 66. C Newc St Gabr *Newc* 65-68; Korea 69-77; V Derby St Bart *Derby* from 78. *St Bartholomew's Vicarage, Addison Road, Derby DE24 8FH* Derby (01332) 347709

METCALF, Preb Michael Ralph. b 37. Clare Coll Cam BA61 MA65 Birm Univ MA80. Ridley Hall Cam 63. d 64 p 65. C Downend *Bris* 64-67; Perm to Offic *Birm* 68-78; Perm to Offic *Lich* 72-81; Dioc Dir of Educn 83-94; Preb Lich Cathl from 91; V Stafford St Paul Forebridge from 94. *St Paul's Vicarage, 31 The Oval, Stafford ST17 4LQ* Stafford (01785) 51683

METCALF, Ven Robert Laurence (Bob). b 35. Dur Univ BA60. Cranmer Hall Dur DipTh62. d 62 p 63. C Bootle Ch Ch *Liv* 62-65; C Farnworth 65-67; V Wigan St Cath 67-75; R Wavertree H Trin 75-94; Chapl Blue Coat Sch Liv 75-94; Dir of Ords *Liv* from 82; Hon Can Liv Cathl from 87; Adn Liv from 94. *38 Menlove Avenue, Allerton, Liverpool L18 2EF* 0151-734 3956

METCALFE, Alan. b 22. St Aid Birkenhead 49. d 52 p 53. V Dewsbury St Matt and St Jo *Wakef* 69-71; Warden Bridgehead Hostel Cardiff 71-73; Field View Hostel Stoke Prior 73-75; McIntyre Ho Nuneaton 75-79; C Southam w Stockton *Cov* 79-84; P-in-c Kinwarton w Gt Alne and Haselor 84-87; rtd 87; Perm to Offic *Ex* from 88. *32 High Road, Trimley, Ipswich IP10 0SZ* Felixstowe (01394) 271585

METCALFE, James. b 17. St Pet Hall Ox BA39 MA44. Wycliffe Hall Ox 39. d 41 p 42. R Wickersley *Sheff* 71-82; rtd 82; Perm to Offic *Bradf* from 83. *Scar Field, The Mains, Giggleswick, Settle, N Yorkshire BD24 0AX* Settle (01729) 823983

METCALFE, Reginald Herbert. b 38. d 79. Hon C Aspley Guise *St Alb* 79; Hon C Aspley Guise w Husborne Crawley and Ridgmont 80-84; Hon C Bovingdon from 84. *30 Manorville Road, Aspley, Hemel Hempstead, Herts HP3 0AP* Hemel Hempstead (01442) 242952

METCALFE, Canon Ronald. b 41. BA. Edin Th Coll 67. d 69 p 70. C Saltburn-by-the-Sea *York* 69-72; P-in-c Crathorne 73-77; Youth Officer 73-77; Dioc Adult Tr Officer 78-88; Can Res York Minster from 88; Sec for Miss and Min from 88. *5 Minster Yard, York YO1 2JE* York (01904) 642542

METCALFE, William Bernard. b 47. St Jo Coll Cam BA69 MA73 Ball Coll Ox BA71. Ripon Hall Ox 70. d 72 p 73. C Caversham *Ox* 72-75; C Aylesbury 75-79; Ind Chapl 75-79; TV Thamesmead *S'wark* 79-84; TR Totton *Win* 84-94; R Gt Bentley and Frating w Thorrington *Chelmsf* from 94. *The Rectory, Moors Close, Great Bentley, Colchester CO7 8QL* Great Bentley (01206) 250476

METCALFE, Canon William Nelson. b 15. St Jo Coll Dur BA39 MA54. St Aid Birkenhead LTh38. d 39 p 40. R Bottesford and Muston *Leic* 62-82; RD Framland I 60-80; Hon Can Leic Cathl 75-82; rtd 82. *62 Church Lane, Sutton-on-Sea, Mablethorpe, Lincs LN12 2JB* Sutton-on-Sea (01507) 442331

METHUEN, John Alan Robert. b 47. BNC Ox BA69 MA74. Cuddesdon Coll 69. d 71 p 72. C Fenny Stratford *Ox* 71-73; C Fenny Stratford and Water Eaton 74; Asst Chapl Eton Coll Windsor 74-77; P-in-c Dorney *Ox* 74-77; Warden Dorney/Eton Coll Conf Cen 74-77; V Reading St Mark 77-83; R Hulme Ascension *Man* from 83. *The Ascension Rectory, Royce Road, Manchester M15 5FQ* 0161-226 5568

METHVEN, Alexander George. b 26. Lon Univ BD52 Em Coll Cam BA54 MA58. ACT ThL47 Lon Coll of Div 50. d 53 p 53. V Lower Sydenham St Mich *S'wark* 60-67; Australia from 68;

rtd 91. *PO Box 494, Belgrave, Victoria, Australia 3160* Victoria (3) 754-8056

METIVIER, Robert John. b 31. Lon Univ BA68. Lambeth STh61 Ch Div Sch of the Pacific (USA) BD66 MDiv69 Codrington Coll Barbados 56. d 60 p 61. Trinidad and Tobago 61-64 and 68-78; USPG 66-67; C Gt Berkhamsted *St Alb* 78-82; V Goff's Oak St Jas 82-90; V Tokyngton St Mich *Lon* from 90. *The Vicarage, St Michael's Avenue, Wembley, Middx HA9 6SL* 0181-902 3290

METTERS, Anthony John Francis. b 43. AKC65. d 68 p 69. C Heavitree *Ex* 68-74; V Plymouth Crownhill Ascension 74-79; RD Plymouth 77-79; Chapl RN from 79. *Directorate Gen, RN Chapl Services, Room 203, Victory Building, HM Naval Base, Portsmouth PO1 3LS* Portsmouth (01705) 727903 Fax 727112

METTHAM, Maurice Desmond. b 20. Sarum & Wells Th Coll 73. d 74 p 75. C Guernsey St Sav *Win* 74-81; Perm to Offic from 81. *c/o La Masse Residential Home, Grande Capelles Road, St Sampsons, Guernsey, Channel Islands* Guernsey (01481) 49334

MEW, Ms Jacqueline Mary (Jackie). b 57. Southn Univ MPhil90 MBCS83. S Dios Minl Tr Scheme 92. d 95. NSM Hythe *Win* from 95. *9 Birchdale, Hythe, Southampton SO45 3HX* Southampton (01703) 840132 Fax as telephone

MEWIS, David William. b 47. Leeds Inst of Educn CertEd68 Leeds Poly BEd83. N Ord Course 87. d 90 p 91. C Skipton Ch Ch *Bradf* 90-92; R Bolton by Bowland w Grindleton from 92. *The Rectory, Sawley Road, Grindleton, Clitheroe, Lancs BB7 4QS* Clitheroe (01200) 41154

MEWS, Stuart Paul. b 44. Leeds Univ BA64 MA67 Trin Hall Cam PhD74 FRHistS75. Westcott Ho Cam 86. d 87 p 88. Lect Lanc Univ 68-92; NSM Caton w Littledale *Blackb* 87-90; Hon C Lanc St Mary 88-92; Reader Relig Studies Chelt & Glouc Coll of HE from 92; Perm to Offic *Glouc* from 93. *Cheltenham and Gloucester College, PO Box 220, The Park Campus, Cheltenham, Glos GL50 2QF* Cheltenham (01242) 543358

MEYER, Stuart Thomas. b 45. GLCM69 Open Univ BA85. Trin Coll Bris 76. d 78 p 79. C Heref St Pet w St Owen *Heref* 78-79; C Heref St Pet w St Owen and St Jas 79-80; Chapl K Coll Cam 80-84; Chapl Lon Univ Medical Schs *S'wark* 84-87; Chapl Dulwich Hosp 87-93; Chapl Camberwell Distr HA 90-93; Chapl K Coll Hosp Lon 90-93; Chapl King's Healthcare NHS Trust from 93. *King's College Hospital, Denmark Hill, London SE5 9PJ* 0171-346 3522

MEYER, William John. b 46. ACIB. Cranmer Hall Dur 83. d 85 p 86. C Merrow *Guildf* 85-89; V Grayshott from 89. *The Vicarage, Grayshott, Hindhead, Surrey GU26 6NH* Hindhead (01428) 604540

MEYNELL, Andrew Francis. b 43. Westcott Ho Cam 70. d 73 p 74. C Cowley St Jas *Ox* 73-79; TV 79-81; P-in-c Halton 81-95; V Wendover 81-95; P-in-c Monks Risborough from 95. *The Rectory, Mill Lane, Monks Risborough, Princes Risborough, Bucks HP27 9JE* Princes Risborough (01844) 342556

MEYNELL, Mrs Honor Mary. b 37. E Midl Min Tr Course 84. d 87 p 94. NSM Kirk Langley *Derby* from 87. *Meynell Langley, Kirk Langley, Ashbourne, Derbyshire DE6 4NT* Kirk Langley (01332) 824207

MEYNELL, Canon Mark. b 14. Ch Ch Ox BA37 MA44. Cuddesdon Coll. d 40 p 41. V Leamington Hastings *Cov* 65-79; R Birdingbury 74-79; Can Th Cov Cathl 73-78; rtd 79; Perm to Offic *St E* from 80. *2 Double Street, Framlingham, Woodbridge, Suffolk IP13 9BN* Framlingham (01728) 723898

MEYRICK, Cyril Jonathan. b 52. St Jo Coll Ox BA73 MA77. Sarum & Wells Th Coll 74. d 76 p 77. C Bicester *Ox* 76-78; Bp's Dom Chapl 78-81; Barbados 81-84; TV Burnham w Dropmore, Hitcham and Taplow *Ox* 84-90; TR Tisbury *Sarum* from 90. *The Rectory, Park Road, Tisbury, Salisbury SP3 6LF* Tisbury (01747) 870312

MEYRICK, Thomas Henry Corfe. b 67. Magd Coll Ox BA88 MA92. St Steph Ho Ox BA94. d 95. C Bierley *Bradf* from 95. *12 Thurley Road, Bradford, W Yorkshire BD4 7AT* Bradford (01274) 729084

MIALL, Peter Brian. b 30. Scawsby Coll of Educn TCert69. d 89 p 89. Hon C Bolsterstone *Sheff* from 89. *Waldershaigh Cottage, Heads Lane, Bolsterstone, Sheffield S30 5ZH* Sheffield (0114) 288 5558

MICHAEL, Brother. See FISHER, Rt Rev Reginald Lindsay

MICHAEL, Ian MacRae. b 40. Aber Univ MA62 Hertf Coll Ox DPhil66. Westcott Ho Cam 77. d 79 p 80. C Kings Heath *Birm* 79-82; Vice-Provost St Paul's Cathl Dundee *Bre* 82-88; V Harborne St Faith and St Laur *Birm* from 88; RD Edgbaston from 91. *The Vicarage, 115 Balden Road, Birmingham B32 2EL* 0121-427 2410

MICHAELS, David Albert Emmanuel. b 49. Barrister-at-Law (Inner Temple) 73 Bede Coll Dur BA72. Westcott Ho Cam 86. d 88 p 89. C Hampstead St Jo *Lon* 88-91; TV Wolvercote w

Summertown *Ox* from 91. *The Vicarage, 2 Mere Road, Wolvercote, Oxford OX2 8AN* Oxford (01865) 515640 Fax 516440

MICHELL, Canon Douglas Reginald. b 19. St Jo Coll Dur BA41 MA44. Westcott Ho Cam 41. **d** 43 **p** 44. V Evington *Leic* 61-80; Hon Can Leic Cathl 67-84; RD Christianity (Leic) N 74-79; V Billesdon w Goadby and Rolleston 80-82; RD Gartree I (Harborough) 81-84; V Billesdon and Skeffington 82-84; rtd 85; Perm to Offic *St Alb* from 85. *The Old Smithy, The Green, Harrold, Bedford MK43 7DB* Bedford (01234) 721063

MICHELL, Francis Richard Noel. b 42. St Cath Coll Cam BA64 MA68. Tyndale Hall Bris 64. **d** 66 **p** 67. C Northn St Giles *Pet* 66-69; C Gateacre *Liv* 69-72; V Litherland St Paul Hatton Hill 72-79; V Rainhill 79-88; V Rainford from 88. *The Vicarage, Church Road, Rainford, St Helens, Merseyside WA11 8HD* Rainford (01744) 882200

MICHELL, Canon Jocelyn Ralph Stamerham. b 21. Trin Coll Cam BA43 MA55. Ridley Hall Cam 45. **d** 51 **p** 55. V Longstock w Leckford *Win* 70-79; Nigeria 79-82; Hon Can Asaba from 81; R Hale w S Charford *Win* 83-86; rtd 86. *4 The Crescent, Darby Green Road, Camberley, Surrey GU17 0EA* Yateley (01252) 877953

MICKLETHWAITE, Andrew Quentin. b 67. Univ Coll Dur BA89. Trin Coll Bris BA94. **d** 94 **p** 95. C Abington *Pet* from 94. *21 Lime Avenue, Northampton NN3 2HA* Northampton (01604) 711264

MICKLETHWAITE, Jane Catherine. b 56. Lanc Univ BSc78. Trin Coll Bris DipHE94. **d** 95. NSM Kings Heath *Pet* from 95. *21 Lime Avenue, Northampton NN3 2HA* Northampton (01604) 711264

MICKLETHWAITE, Peter William. b 62. Peterho Cam BA84 MA88. St Jo Coll Nottm DipTh89 DPS90. **d** 90 **p** 91. C Leatherhead *Guildf* 90-93; C Wisley w Pyrford from 93. *33 Engliff Lane, Woking, Surrey GU22 8SU* Byfleet (01932) 351070

MIDDLEBROOK, Bryan. b 33. Dur Univ BA55 DipEd58 Newc Univ MEd74. NE Ord Course 85. **d** 88 **p** 88. NSM Dur St Cuth *Dur* from 88. *5 Fieldhouse Terrace, Durham DH1 4NA* 0191-386 6665

MIDDLEDITCH, Terry Gordon. b 30. Univ of Wales (Lamp) BA62. **d** 63 **p** 64. C Poulton-le-Fylde *Blackb* 63-67; C-in-c Heysham 65-67; C Cheltenham St Pet *Glouc* 75-77; Perm to Offic 77-82; Hon C Badgeworth w Shurdington 82-87; C Poulton-le-Sands w Morecambe St Laur *Blackb* 88-91; V Stalmine from 91. *The Vicarage, Carr End Lane, Stalmine, Poulton-le-Fylde, Lancs FY6 0LQ* Blackpool (01253) 702538

MIDDLEMISS, Fritha Leonora. b 47. Man Univ BA68 CertEd69. Glouc Sch of Min 86. **d** 89 **p** 94. NSM Bengeworth *Worc* 89-94; NSM Stoulton w Drake's Broughton and Pirton etc from 94. *Vine Cottage, Kennel Bank, Cropthorne, Pershore, Worcs WR10 3NB* Pershore (01386) 860330

MIDDLESEX, Archdeacon of. See RAPHAEL, Ven Timothy John

MIDDLETON, Alan Derek. b 46. St Jo Coll Dur BA68 MA85. Qu Coll Birm DipTh71 DPS72. **d** 72 **p** 73. C Cannock *Lich* 72-76; Warden St Helen's Youth & Community Cen Bp Auckd 76-79; V Darlington St Jo *Dur* 79-89; TR E Darlington 89-90; V Upper Norwood All SS *S'wark* from 90. *All Saints' Vicarage, 12 Beulah Hill, London SE19 3LS* 0181-653 2820

MIDDLETON, Barry Glen. b 41. Lich Th Coll 68. **d** 70 **p** 71. C Westhoughton *Man* 70-73; C Prestwich St Marg 73-74; TV Buxton w Burbage and King Sterndale *Derby* 74-77; Chapl Worc R Infirmary 77-83; Fairfield Hosp Hitchin 83-85; P-in-c Erpingham w Calthorpe *Nor* 85-86; P-in-c Erpingham w Calthorpe, Ingworth, Aldborough etc 86; R 86-92; R Badingham w Bruisyard, Cransford and Dennington *St E* from 92. *The Rectory, 5 Orchard Rise, Badingham, Woodbridge, Suffolk IP13 8LN* Badingham (0172875) 784

MIDDLETON, Hugh Charles. b 50. Nottm Univ BTh77. Linc Th Coll 73. **d** 77 **p** 78. C New Sleaford *Linc* 77-81; C Grantham 81; TV 81-83; R Caythorpe 83-95. *The Rectory, Gorse Hill Lane, Caythorpe, Grantham, Lincs NG32 3DU* Loveden (01400) 73114

MIDDLETON, Kenneth Frank. b 28. Keble Coll Ox BA52 MA64. St Steph Ho Ox 52. **d** 55 **p** 56. C Leic St Matt *Leic* 55-58; C W Hackney St Barn *Lon* 58-60; V Leic St Matt and St Geo *Leic* 60-82; RD Christianity (Leic) N 79-82; P-in-c Leic St Alb 80-82; Hon Can Leic Cathl 80-82; P-in-c Belgrave St Mich 81-82; TR Bridgnorth, Tasley, Astley Abbotts, Oldbury etc *Heref* 82-87; P-in-c Quatford 83; RD Bridgnorth 83-87; TR Littleham w Exmouth *Ex* from 87. *The Rectory, 1 Maer Road, Exmouth, Devon EX8 2DA* Exmouth (01395) 272227

MIDDLETON, Leonard James. b 33. Bps' Coll Cheshunt 55. **d** 58 **p** 59. C Beckenham St Geo *Roch* 58-60; C Wallingford St Mary w All Hallows and St Leon *Ox* 60-64; V Codnor and Loscoe *Derby* 64-71; P-in-c W Tilbury *Chelmsf* 71-77; V E

Tilbury 71-77; R Copford w Easthorpe 77-91; R Gayton Gp of Par *Nor* from 91. *The Vicarage, Gayton, King's Lynn, Norfolk PE32 1QA* Gayton (01553) 636227

MIDDLETON, Ven Michael John. b 40. Dur Univ BSc62 Fitzw Ho Cam BA66 MA70. Westcott Ho Cam 63. **d** 66 **p** 67. C Newc St Geo *Newc* 66-69; V 77-85; S Africa 69-72; Chapl K Sch Tynemouth 72-77; R Hexham *Newc* 85-92; Hon Can Newc Cathl 90-92; Adn Swindon *Bris* from 92. *2 Louviers Way, Swindon SN1 4DU* Swindon (01793) 644556 Fax 495352

MIDDLETON, Rodney. b 54. St Andr Univ BD80. St Steph Ho Ox 80. **d** 82 **p** 83. C Walton St Mary *Liv* 82-87; C-in-c Kew St Fran of Assisi CD 87-94; V Kew 94-95; Chapl Southport and Formby Distr Gen Hosp 87-95; V Haydock St Jas from 95. *The Vicarage, 169 Church Road, Haydock, St Helens, Merseyside WA11 0NJ* Ashton-in-Makerfield (01942) 727956

MIDDLETON, Thomas Arthur. b 36. AKC61. **d** 62 **p** 63. C Sunderland *Dur* 62-63; C Auckland St Helen 63-67; C Winlaton 67-70; C-in-c Pennywell St Thos and Grindon St Oswald CD 70-79; R Boldon from 79; Adv in Stewardship Dur Adnry from 87. *Boldon Rectory, Rectory Green, West Boldon, Tyne & Wear NE36 0QD* 0191-536 7370

MIDDLETON-DANSKY, Brother Serge Wladimir. b 45. Cuddesdon Coll 74. **d** 77 **p** 78. C Wisbech SS Pet and Paul *Ely* 77-79; Lic to Offic Adnry Riviera *Eur* from 80; C Ox St Giles and SS Phil and Jas w St Marg *Ox* 83-86; Perm to Offic 86-88; Perm to Offic *Truro* 88-90; P-in-c Zennor from 90; P-in-c Towednack from 90. *The Vicarage, Zennor, St Ives, Cornwall TR26 3BY* Penzance (01736) 796955

MIDDLETON, Suffragan Bishop of. *See* VENNER, Rt Rev Stephen Squires

MIDDLEWICK, Robert James. b 44. K Alfred's Coll Win CertEd67 Lon Univ BD76. Ripon Coll Cuddesdon 75. **d** 77 **p** 78. C Bromley SS Pet and Paul *Roch* 77-81; C Belvedere All SS 81-84; P-in-c Lamberhurst 85-88; P-in-c Matfield 85-88; V Lamberhurst and Matfield from 88. *The Vicarage, Old Town Hill, Lamberhurst, Tunbridge Wells, Kent TN3 8EL* Lamberhurst (01892) 890324

MIDGLEY, Edward Graham. b 23. St Edm Hall Ox BA47 MA48 BLitt50. Cuddesdon Coll 56. **d** 56 **p** 57. Lic to Offic *Ox* 56-89; Dean St Edm Hall Ox 56-78; Vice-Prin 70-78; Chapl 78-86; Chapl St Hugh's Coll Ox 86-89. *4 St Lawrence Road, South Hinksey, Oxford OX1 5AZ* Oxford (01865) 735460

MIDGLEY, George William. b 38. N Ord Course. **d** 83 **p** 84. C Penistone and Thurlstone *Wakef* 83-89; TV 89-94; TR from 94. *The Vicarage, Shrewbury Road, Penistone, Sheffield S30 6DY* Barnsley (01226) 763241

MIDLANE, Colin John. b 50. Qu Mary Coll Lon BA72. Westcott Ho Cam 73 Sarum & Wells Th Coll 77. **d** 78 **p** 79. C Bethnal Green St Pet w St Thos *Lon* 78-82; P-in-c Haggerston All SS 82-88; Chapl Hengrave Hall Cen, Bury St Edmunds 88-89; Priest Counsellor St Botolph Aldgate *Lon* 89-94; C St Botolph Aldgate w H Trin Minories 93-94; TV Haywards Heath St Wilfrid *Chich* from 94. *The Vicarage, Gravelye Lane, Haywards Heath, W Sussex RH16 3RL* Haywards Heath (01444) 456894

MIDWINTER, Sister Josie Isabel. b 46. Open Univ BA84. CA Tr Coll IDC71 ACT DipTh77. **d** 87. CA from 71; CMS 84-93; Uganda 85-91; Kenya from 92. *Church Army Training College, PO Box 72584, Nairobi, Kenya* Nairobi (2) 558596 or 554970 Fax 554970

MIDWOOD, Peter Stanley. b 47. Linc Th Coll 80. **d** 82 **p** 83. C Garforth *Ripon* 82-85; C-in-c Grinton w Arkengarthdale, Downholme and Marske 85-86; C-in-c Melbecks and Muker 85-86; P-in-c Swaledale 86; V from 86. *The Vicarage, Reeth, Richmond, N Yorkshire DL11 6TR* Richmond (01748) 884706

MIELL, David Keith. b 57. BSc PhD BA. Westcott Ho Cam 83. **d** 86 **p** 87. C Blackbird Leys CD *Ox* 86-89; C Walton 89-90; TV Walton Milton Keynes from 90; RD Milton Keynes from 93. *The Rectory, Broughton, Milton Keynes MK10 9AA* Milton Keynes (01908) 667846

MIGHALL, Robert. b 33. St Pet Coll Ox BA57 MA61. Wycliffe Hall Ox 57. **d** 58 **p** 59. C Stoke *Cov* 58-62; C Rugby St Andr 62-64; V Newbold on Avon 64-76; V Combroke w Compton Verney from 76; V Kineton from 76. *The Vicarage, Kineton, Warwick CV35 0LL* Kineton (01926) 640248

MIHILL, Dennis George. b 31. St Alb Minl Tr Scheme 78. **d** 81 **p** 82. NSM Harpenden St Nic *St Alb* 81-86; C Sawbridgeworth 86-89; V Motspur Park *S'wark* from 89. *The Vicarage, 2 Douglas Avenue, New Malden, Surrey KT3 6HT* 0181-942 3117

MILBURN, John Frederick. b 56. Westmr Coll Ox BA84. Sarum & Wells Th Coll 84. **d** 86 **p** 87. C Leavesden All SS *St Alb* 86-89; C Broxbourne w Wormley 89-93; CF (TA) 90-94; Australia from 94. *PO Box 106, Texas, Queensland, Australia 4385*

MILBURN, Very Rev Robert Leslie Pollington. b 07. FSA SS Coll Cam BA30 MA34. **d** 34 **p** 35. Master of The Temple (Lon) 68-80; rtd 80; Perm to Offic *Heref* 81-88; Perm to Offic *Worc* from 85. *5 St Barnabas House, Newland, Malvern, Worcs WR13 5AX* Malvern (01684) 561044

MILES, Canon Charles Reginald (Reg). b 12. Tyndale Hall Bris 36. **d** 39 **p** 40. R Dibden *Win* 46-92; Hon Can Win Cathl 75-92; rtd 92. *10 Redwood Close, Dibden Purlieu, Southampton SO4 5SN* Southampton (01703) 848202

MILES, Gerald Christopher Morgan. b 36. CEng MIEE Peterho Cam BA57 MA72 Cranfield Inst of Tech MSc72. Wycliffe Hall Ox 74. **d** 76 **p** 77. C Tunbridge Wells St Jas *Roch* 76-80; V Leigh 80-90; R Addington w Trottiscliffe 90-91; P-in-c Ryarsh w Birling 90-91; R Birling, Addington, Ryarsh and Trottiscliffe from 91. *The Vicarage, Birling Road, Ryarsh, West Malling, Kent ME19 5LS* West Malling (01732) 842249

MILES (nee HOARE), Ms Janet Francis Mary. b 48. St Aid Coll Dur BA70 Bris Univ MEd84. Sarum & Wells Th Coll DipMin93. **d** 93 **p** 94. C Bruton and Distr *B & W* from 93. *30 Priory Mead, Bruton, Somerset BA10 0DZ* Bruton (01749) 813822

MILES, Keith Robert George. b 53. Sarum & Wells Th Coll. **d** 89 **p** 90. NSM Fishponds St Mary *Bris* from 89. *6 Langdale Road, Bristol BS16 2DG* Bristol (0117) 958 5815

MILES, Malcolm Robert. b 36. AKC60. **d** 61 **p** 62. C Northn St Mary *Pet* 61-63; C E Haddon 63-67; R Broughton 67-73; Asst Chapl Nottm Univ *S'well* 73-78; V Northn H Trin *Pet* 75-84; V Painswick w Sheepscombe *Glouc* from 84; RD Bisley 90-94. *The Vicarage, Orchard Mead, Painswick, Stroud, Glos GL6 6YD* Painswick (01452) 812334

MILES, Mrs Marion Claire. b 41. S Dios Minl Tr Scheme 86. **d** 88 **p** 94. Hon Par Dn Blandford Forum and Langton Long *Sarum* 88-94; Hon C from 94; Chapl Blandford Community Hosp from 88. *20 Alexandra Street, Blandford Forum, Dorset DT11 7JE* Blandford (01258) 452010

MILES, Canon Robert William. b 27. Magd Coll Cam BA50 MA55. Westcott Ho Cam 50. **d** 52 **p** 53. R Dalmahoy *Edin* 65-70; R Batsford w Moreton-in-Marsh *Glouc* 70-77; rtd 77; Perm to Offic *Glouc* from 79. *Boilingwell, Winchcombe, Cheltenham, Glos GL54 5JB* Cheltenham (01242) 603337

MILES, Miss Ruth Cecilia. b 11. dss 40 **d** 87. Adv in Children's RE *Linc* 60-71; rtd 71; Perm to Offic *Glouc* from 83. *The Abbeyfield House, 326 Prestbury Road, Cheltenham, Glos GL52 3DD* Cheltenham (01242) 516357

MILFORD, Mrs Catherine Helena. b 39. LMH Ox BA61 DipTh62 MA65. Gilmore Course 81. dss 82 **d** 87 **p** 94. Heaton St Barn *Bradf* 82-87; Par Dn 87-88; Adult Educn Adv *Win* from 88. *Church House, 9 The Close, Winchester, Hants SO23 9LS* Winchester (01962) 844644

MILLAM, Peter John. b 36. Univ of Wales (Lamp) BA58. Ridley Hall Cam 58. **d** 63 **p** 64. Falkland Is 66-70; V Pulloxhill w Flitton *St Alb* 70-79; V Luton St Paul 79-89; V Chipping Campden w Ebrington *Glouc* 89-94; rtd 94. *22 Willowhale Avenue, Aldwick, Bognor Regis, W Sussex PO21 4AY* Bognor Regis (01243) 268316

MILLAR, Alan Askwith. b 26. Qu Coll Birm 59. **d** 60 **p** 61. V Middlesb St Aid *York* 64-72; V Cayton w Eastfield 72-88; Chapl to RD of Scarborough 88-89; rtd 89; Perm to Offic *Bradf* from 89. *23 Rowan Court, Old Bridge Rise, Ilkley, W Yorkshire LS29 9HH* Ilkley (01943) 602081

MILLAR, Andrew Charles (Andy). b 48. Hull Univ BSc69. Cuddesdon Coll 71. **d** 73 **p** 74. C Rushmere *St E* 73-76; C Ipswich All Hallows 76-79; Youth Chapl *Sheff* 79-83; Youth Chapl *Win* 83-92; V Colden from 92. *The Vicarage, Colden Common, Winchester, Hants SO21 1TL* Twyford (01962) 712505

MILLAR, Christine. See WHEELER, Mrs Christine

MILLAR, Frank. b 38. N Lon Poly CQSW63. Sarum Th Coll 67. **d** 69 **p** 70. C S'wark H Trin *S'wark* 69-72; C Saltdean *Chich* 72-74; CECS 74-75; P-in-c Beaumont and Moze *Chelmsf* 76-80; P-in-c Gt Oakley 76-77; P-in-c Tendring 76-80; R Tendring and Lt Bentley w Beaumont cum Moze 80-83; R Rivenhall 83-87; Chapl Palma de Mallorca w Menorca *Eur* 87-90; Perm to Offic *S'wark* 90-94; P-in-c Takeley w Lt Canfield *Chelmsf* from 94. *The Rectory, Parsonage Road, Takeley, Bishop's Stortford, Herts CM22 6QX* Bishop's Stortford (01279) 870837

MILLAR, Gary. b 67. Wales Poly HND88. St Mich Coll Llan 88. **d** 91 **p** 92. C Tonyrefail w Gilfach Goch *Llan* 91-93; C Barry All SS from 93. *5 Cledwen Close, Barry, S Glam CF62 7TE* Barry (01446) 746899

MILLAR, John Alexander Kirkpatrick (Sandy). b 39. Trin Coll Cam BA62 MA66. St Jo Coll Dur 74. **d** 76 **p** 77. C Brompton H Trin *Lon* 76-78; C Brompton H Trin w Onslow Square St Paul 78-85; V from 85; AD Chelsea 89-94. *Holy Trinity Vicarage, 73 Prince's Gate Mews, London SW7 2PP* 0171-584 8957 or 581 8255

MILLARD, Albert George. b 17. Chich Th Coll. **d** 64 **p** 65. V Kintbury w Avington *Ox* 71-82; rtd 82. *8 Crown Mews, 15 Clarence Road, Gosport, Hants PO12 1DH* Gosport (01705) 511934

MILLARD, Canon Jane Mary. b 43. Open Univ BA80. Edin Dioc NSM Course 81. **d** 90 **p** 94. NSM Edin St Mary *Edin* from 90; Chapl HIV/AIDS from 90; Can St Mary's Cathl from 95. *Honeybrae, Ninemileburn, Penicuik, Midlothian EH26 9ND*

MILLARD, Jonathan Neil. b 62. Barrister-at-Law (Gray's Inn) 84 Aston Univ BSc83. Wycliffe Hall Ox 89. **d** 92 **p** 93. C Haddenham w Cuddington, Kingsey etc *Ox* 92-94; USA from 94. *23 Stonemarker Drive, Washington, PA 15301-2745, USA*

MILLARD, Malcolm Edoric. b 38. Lon Univ BA60 AKC60 Lon Inst of Educn PGCE61. St Jo Coll Nottm 88. **d** 77 **p** 81. Gambia 77-95; CMS 89-94; C S Shoebury *Chelmsf* from 95. *Bryn Avon, Glebe Road, Ramsden Bellhouse, Billericay, Essex CM11 1RL* Ramsden Heath (01268) 710081

MILLARD, Canon Murray Clinton. b 29. Ex Coll Ox BA50 DipTh52 MA58. St Steph Ho Ox 51. **d** 53 **p** 54. C Horfield St Greg *Bris* 53-55; C Guernsey St Steph *Win* 55-61; R Jersey St Mary 61-71; R Guernsey St Sampson 71-82; V Guernsey St Steph from 82; Hon Can Win Cathl from 83. *St Stephen's Vicarage, De Beauvoir, St Peter Port, Guernsey, Channel Islands GY1 1RN* Guernsey (01481) 720268

MILLARD, Richard Stuart Marsh. b 33. St Pet Coll Ox BA57 MA. Oak Hill NSM Course 90. **d** 93 **p** 94. NSM Laleham *Lon* 93-94; Hon C Neatishead, Barton Turf and Irstead *Nor* from 94; NSM C to RD Tunstead from 94. *The Rectory, Butcher's Common, Neatishead, Norwich NR12 8XH* Horning (01602) 630645

MILLER, Anthony Talbot. b 37. Univ of Wales (Lamp) BA59. Coll of Resurr Mirfield. **d** 61 **p** 62. V Holme Cultram St Mary *Carl* 65-76; Lic to Offic *Lich* 76-78; P-in-c Wrockwardine Wood 78-80; R 80-94; OCF 92-94; rtd 94. *7 Bron yr Afon, Conwy, Llandudno, Gwynedd LL32 8LP* LLandudno (0492) 573757

MILLER, Barry. b 42. Bede Coll Dur TCert63 Open Univ BA79 Leic Univ MEd86. Linc Th Coll 63. **d** 65 **p** 66. C Greenside *Dur* 65-68; C Auckland St Andr and St Anne 68-71; Adv in Educn *Leic* 71-77; C Leic St Nic 77-80; Asst Chapl Leic Univ 77-80; Children's Officer Gen Syn Bd of Educn 80-84; Hd of Relig Studies W Midl Coll of HE 84-89; Hd Initial Teacher Educn Wolv Poly 89-92; Wolv Univ from 92; Perm to Offic *Leic* from 90. *Kirkstone House, 48 Top Street, Appleby Magna, Swadlincote, Derbyshire DE12 2AH* Measham (01530) 273722

MILLER, Charles Irvine. b 35. Nottm Univ BEd76. Bps' Coll Cheshunt 61. **d** 63 **p** 64. R Ingoldmells w Addlethorpe *Linc* 68-72; P-in-c Bishop Norton 72-76; V Scunthorpe St Jo 76-83; Chapl Manor Hosp Walsall 83-89; rtd 89. *68 Station Road, Kennett, Newmarket, Suffolk CB8 7QF* Newmarket (01638) 552576

MILLER, Darren Noel. b 67. Birm Univ BSocSc89. Chich Th Coll BTh95 Coll of Resurr Mirfield 94. **d** 95. C Weoley Castle *Birm* from 95. *34 Shenley Lane, Birmingham B29 5PL* 0121-476 3990

MILLER, David George. b 54. Or Coll Ox BA76 MA80. Ripon Coll Cuddesdon 78. **d** 81 **p** 82. C Henfield w Shermanbury and Woodmancote *Chich* 81-84; C Monk Bretton *Wakef* 84-87; V Rastrick St Jo 87-93; TR Helston and Wendron *Truro* from 93. *St Michael's Rectory, Church Lane, Helston, Cornwall TR13 8PF* Helston (01326) 572516

MILLER, David James Tringham. b 45. AKC70. Sarum & Wells Th Coll 76. **d** 77 **p** 78. C Abington *Pet* 77-80; TV Corby SS Pet and Andr w Gt and Lt Oakley 80-83; V Kettering All SS 83-94; RD Kettering 87-94; V Pet All SS from 94. *All Saints' Vicarage, 208 Park Road, Peterborough PE1 2UJ* Peterborough (01733) 54130

MILLER, David John. b 37. Louvain Univ Belgium LicScCat67. Chich Th Coll 60. **d** 62 **p** 63. C Southsea H Spirit *Portsm* 62-65; C Roehampton H Trin *S'wark* 67-68; Chapl Luxembourg *Eur* 68-72; Chapl Lausanne 72-91; Asst Chapl Lausanne 91-93; Perm to Offic from 94. *Avenue de l'Eglise Anglaise 1 bis, 1006 Lausanne, Switzerland* Lausanne (21) 616-2636

MILLER, Preb David Reginald. b 29. AKC54. **d** 55 **p** 56. V Pill *B & W* 61-70; V Wedmore 70-74; V Wedmore w Theale 74-78; RD Axbridge 77-89; P-in-c Blackford 77-78; V Wedmore w Theale and Blackford 78-95; Preb Wells Cathl from 85; Warden of Readers 85-91; rtd 95. *Whitelake Lodge, Lower Street, Pilton, Shepton Mallet, Somerset BA4 4DD*

MILLER, David Samuel. b 31. Lich Th Coll 62. **d** 63 **p** 64. C Southbourne St Kath *Win* 66-71; V E and W Worldham, Hartley Mauditt w Kingsley etc 71-76; TV Buckhurst Hill *Chelmsf* 76-80; V Elm Park St Nic Hornchurch 80-93; rtd 93. *Apartado 716, 03180 Torrevieja, Alicante, Spain* Alicante (65) 976185

MILLER, Edward Jeffery. b 24. St Jo Coll Cam BA48 MA50. Wells Th Coll 48. **d** 50 **p** 51. P-in-c Wootton Courtenay *B & W*

MILLER

68-74; R 74-83; P-in-c Timberscombe 68-74; V 74-83; P-in-c Selworthy 79-83; R Selworthy and Timberscombe and Wootton Courtenay 83-93; P-in-c Luccombe 86; R 86-93; rtd 93. *Lodge Rocks Cottage, Old Cleeve, Minehead, Somerset TA24 6RD* Washford (01984) 41228

MILLER, Dr Ernest Charles. b 56. Franklin & Marshall Coll (USA) BA78 Michigan Univ MA79 Keble Coll Ox DPhil90. Nashotah Ho MDiv82. d 82 p 83. USA 82-84; Warden Ho of SS Greg and Macrina 84-90; Asst Chapl Keble Coll Ox 84-88; Lic to Offic *Ox* 87-91; P-in-c New Marston from 91. *New Marston Vicarage, 8 Jack Straw's Lane, Oxford OX3 0DL* Oxford (01865) 242803

MILLER, Francis Rogers. b 54. Ex Univ BA86. St Steph Ho Ox 86. d 88 p 89. C Wednesfield *Lich* 88-93; P-in-c Caldmore from 93; C Walsall St Mary and All SS Palfrey from 93. *St Michael's Vicarage, St Michael's Street, Walsall WS1 3RQ* Walsall (01922) 23445

MILLER, Geoffrey Edward. b 28. Leeds Univ BA56. Coll of Resurr Mirfield 53. d 57 p 58. R Claypole *Linc* 63-76; R Westborough w Dry Doddington and Stubton 65-76; P-in-c Bierley *Bradf* 76-78; V 78-91; rtd 91; Chantry Priest Chpl St Mich & H So Walsingham from 91; Perm to Offic *Nor* from 91. *20 Cleaves Drive, Little Walsingham, Norfolk NR22 6EQ* Walsingham (01328) 820591

MILLER, Geoffrey Vincent. b 56. BEd. St Jo Coll Nottm. d 83 p 84. C Jarrow *Dur* 83-86; TV Billingham St Aid 86-92; Dioc Urban Development Officer from 91; Community Chapl Stockton-on-Tees 92-94; P-in-c Darlington St Cuth from 94. *26 Upsall Drive, Darlington, Co Durham DL3 8RB* Darlington (01325) 358911

MILLER, Ven George Charles Alexander. b 20. TCD BA45. CITC 46. d 46 p 47. I Urney w Denn and Derryheen *K, E & A* 65-89; Preb Kilmore Cathl 77-87; Adn Kilmore 87-89; rtd 89. *Wavecrest, Blenacup, Cavan, Irish Republic* Cavan (49) 61270

MILLER, Canon Harold Creeth. b 50. TCD BA73 MA78 Nottm Univ BA75. St Jo Coll Nottm 73. d 76 p 77. C Carrickfergus *Conn* 76-79; Dir Ext Studies St Jo Coll Nottm 79-84; Chapl QUB 84-89; I Carrigrohane Union *C, C & R* from 89; Bp's Dom Chapl from 91; Can Cork and Cloyne Cathls from 94. *The Rectory, Carrigrohane, Co Cork, Irish Republic* Cork (21) 871106 Fax as telephone

MILLER (nee BLUNDEN), Jacqueline Ann. b 63. Leic Univ BA86 SS Coll Cam BA90. Ridley Hall Cam 88. d 91. Par Dn Bedf St Paul *St Alb* 91-94; C 94-95. *The Mission House, Mitchley Road, London N17 9HG* 0181-801 7976

MILLER, James Ivimey. b 33. Trin Hall Cam BA55 MA59. Ridley Hall Cam 56. d 61 p 62. C Kirk Ella *York* 67-73; R Cockfield *St E* 73-78; rtd 78; Perm to Offic *St E* from 78. *3 Grosvenor Gardens, Bury St Edmunds, Suffolk IP33 2JS* Bury St Edmunds (01284) 762839

MILLER, John David. b 50. Nottm Univ BTh73 Lanc Univ CertEd74. Kelham Th Coll 68. d 74 p 75. C Horden *Dur* 74-79; C Billingham St Aid 79-80; TV 80-84; TR S Shields All SS from 84. *The Rectory, Tyne Terrace, South Shields, Tyne & Wear NE34 0NF* 0191-456 1851

MILLER, John Douglas. b 24. FCA60. N Ord Course 74. d 77 p 78. C Prestbury *Ches* 77-80; V Ashton Hayes 80-87; rtd 87; Perm to Offic *Ex* from 87. *35 Branscombe Close, Colyford, Colyton, Devon EX13 6RF* Colyton (01297) 553581

MILLER, John Forster. b 32. Ox NSM Course. d 83 p 84. NSM Patcham *Chich* 83-86; NSM Radlett *St Alb* 86-93; Perm to Offic from 93. *4 Craigweil Avenue, Radlett, Herts WD7 7EU* Radlett (01923) 857148

MILLER, John Selborne. b 32. RMN70 Lon Univ DBS68. S'wark Ord Course 64. d 71 p 72. C Kenton *Lon* 71-74; C Fulham St Etheldreda w St Clem 74-78; Asst at Convent of the Epiphany Truro 79-81; Hon C Pimlico St Sav 81-84; C Shirley *Birm* 84-86; rtd 86; Perm to Offic *Nor* from 86. *28 Knight Street, Walsingham, Norfolk NR22 6DA* Walsingham (01328) 820824

MILLER, John Stephen Corfield. b 16. Selw Coll Cam BA38 MA41. Westcott Ho Cam 39. d 40 p 41. Australia 61-78; Asst Master Bp Reindorp Sch Guildf 78-81; rtd 81. *Brierley, 8 St Omer Road, Guildford, Surrey GU1 2DB* Guildford (01483) 60359

MILLER, Kenneth Huitson. b 30. Dur Univ BA55 DipEd. Lich Th Coll 58. d 60 p 61. C Newc St Geo *Newc* 60-63; C N Gosforth 63-67; Subchanter and Sacr Lich Cathl *Lich* 67-75; Chapl Lich Cathl Sch 70-75; V Wolstanton *Lich* 75-79; RD Newc 77-87; TR Wolstanton from 79. *The Rectory, Wolstanton, Knutton Road, Newcastle, Staffs ST5 0HU* Newcastle-under-Lyme (01782) 717561

MILLER, Kenneth Leslie. b 50. Lanc Univ BEd74 Liv Univ BPhil94 FRSA. N Ord Course 78. d 80 p 81. NSM Formby St Pet *Liv* 80-87; Chapl St Marg High Sch from 86; NSM Anfield St Columba from 87. *9 Hampton Road, Formby, Liverpool L37 6EJ* Formby (01704) 831256

MILLER, Luke Jonathan. b 66. SS Coll Cam BA87 MA91. St Steph Ho Ox BA90. d 91 p 92. C Oxhey St Matt *St Alb* 91-94;

C Tottenham St Mary *Lon* from 94. *The Mission House, Mitchley Road, London N17 9HG* 0181-801 7976

MILLER, Dr Michael Daukes. b 46. MRCGP74 DRCOG Qu Coll Cam MA71 Lon Univ BCh70 MB71 DCH. Glouc Th Course 82. d 85 p 94. NSM Lydney w Aylburton *Glouc* 85-95; NSM Lydney from 95. *Highmead House, Blakeney, Glos GL15 4DY* Dean (01594) 516668

MILLER, Patrick Figgis. b 33. Ch Coll Cam BA56 MA60. Cuddesdon Coll 56. d 58 p 59. C Portsea St Cuth *Portsm* 58-61; C Cam Gt St Mary w St Mich *Ely* 61-63; Hd Dept Man Gr Sch 63-69; Can Res and Lib S'wark Cathl *S'wark* 69-72; Dir of Studies Qu Mary's Coll Basingstoke 72-79; Prin Sunbury Coll 79-80; Prin Esher Coll from 81; Lic to Offic *Guildf* from 84. *31 Hare Lane, Claygate, Esher, Surrey KT10 9BT* Esher (01372) 467563

MILLER, Paul. b 49. Oak Hill Th Coll 71. d 74 p 75. C Upton *Ex* 74-77; C Farnborough *Guildf* 77-78; P-in-c Torquay St Luke *Ex* 78-81; V 81-86; V Green Street Green *Roch* 86-94; V Green Street Green and Pratts Bottom from 94. *The Vicarage, 46 Worlds End Lane, Orpington, Kent BR6 6AG* Farnborough (01689) 852905

MILLER, Paul Richard. b 37. K Coll Lon BSc60 AKC60. Linc Th Coll 60. d 62 p 63. C Sheff St Geo *Sheff* 62-65; C Bottesford *Linc* 65-67; Bp's Youth Chapl 67-69; C Corringham 67-69; Dioc Youth Officer *Ripon* 69-74; Hd Youth Nat Coun of Soc Services 74-79; P-in-c Battlesden and Pottesgrove *St Alb* 79-80; P-in-c Eversholt w Milton Bryan 79-80; P-in-c Woburn 79-80; V Woburn w Eversholt, Milton Bryan, Battlesden and from 80. *The Vicarage, Park Street, Woburn, Milton Keynes MK17 9PG* Woburn (01525) 290225

MILLER, Canon Paul William. b 18. Qu Coll Birm DipTh50. d 50 p 51. Can Res Derby Cathl *Derby* 66-83; Chapl to The Queen 81-89; rtd 83; Perm to Offic *Derby* from 83. *15 Forester Street, Derby DE1 1PP* Derby (01332) 344773

MILLER, Peter Tennant. b 21. Keble Coll Ox BA47 MA63. Ripon Hall Ox 62. d 63 p 64. V Worksop St Paul *S'well* 68-73; P-in-c Nottm St Cath 74-75; C Nottm St Mary 75-77; R Edith Weston w N Luffenham and Lyndon w Manton *Pet* 77-86; rtd 86; Perm to Offic *Cov* 86-90. *Regency Cottage, 9 Cross Road, Leamington Spa, Warks CV32 5PD* Leamington Spa (01926) 314236

MILLER, Philip Harry. b 58. Leeds Univ BA79. Chich Th Coll 80. d 82 p 83. C Reddish *Man* 82-86; R Lower Broughton Ascension 86-94; P-in-c Cheetwood St Alb 91-94. *4 Jeffreys Drive, Dukinfield, Cheshire SK16 4BZ*

MILLER, Philip Howard. b 40. Tyndale Hall Bris 67. d 72 p 73. Argentina 72-73; C Rusholme *Man* 73-74; Paraguay 74-77; C Toxteth St Cypr w Ch Ch *Liv* 78-80; V Burscough Bridge 80-85; V Woodbridge St Jo *St E* 85-91; P-in-c Combs 91-92 and from 93; Chapl Burrswood Cen for Divine Healing 92-93. *The Rectory, 135 Poplar Hill, Combs, Stowmarket, Suffolk IP14 2AY* Stowmarket (01449) 612076

MILLER, Richard Bracebridge. b 45. Wycliffe Hall Ox 68. d 70 p 71. C Lee Gd Shep w St Pet *S'wark* 70-74; C Roehampton H Trin 74-77; C Earley St Pet *Ox* 77-80; V Aldermaston w Wasing and Brimpton from 80. *The Vicarage, Aldermaston, Reading RG7 4LX* Reading (01734) 712281

MILLER, Robert George. b 15. Bris Univ BA37. Bible Churchmen's Coll 37. d 39 p 40. V Upper Edmonton St Jas *Lon* 47-79; Chapl N Middx Hosp 48-81; rtd 79; Perm to Offic *Lon* 80-89. *9 Marley Court, Aspley, Brisbane, Queensland, Australia 4034* Brisbane (7) 263-8114

MILLER, Robert Stephen. b 71. QUB BSc92. CITC BTh95. d 95. C Shankill *D & D* from 95. *Shankhill Parish Curatage, 136 Lough Road, Lurgan, Craigavon, Co Armagh BT66 6JL* Craigavon (01762) 325962

MILLER, Ronald Anthony. b 41. CEng CPA MRAeS City Univ BSc63. S'wark Ord Course 69. d 72 p 80. NSM Crookham *Guildf* 72-73 and 80-85; NSM New Haw from 85. *Glen Anton, Horsley Road, Downside, Cobham, Surrey KT11 3NY* Cobham (01932) 863394

MILLER, Ms Rosamund Joy. b 56. Lon Univ BSc77 Whitelands Coll Lon PGCE80. E Midl Min Tr Course CTPS92. d 94. NSM Grantham *Linc* from 94. *48 North Parade, Grantham, Lincs NG31 8AN* Grantham (01476) 79242

MILLER, Mrs Rosslyn Leslie. b 43. St Andr Univ MA65 Ox Univ DipEd66 Cam Univ DipRK69. dss 72 d 87. Dir of Studies Inst of Chr Studies 72; St Marylebone All SS *Lon* 72; Adult Educn Officer 73-78; Alford w Rigsby *Linc* 86-87; C 87-90; Dioc Dir of Readers from 90. *120A Station Road, Waddington, Lincoln LN5 9QS* Lincoln (01522) 720819

MILLER, Roy. b 29. d 88 p 93. NSM Leic Cathl *Leic* 88-91; NSM Leic H Apostles from 91. *5 Bratmyr, Fleckney, Leicester LE8 0BJ* Leicester (0116) 240 2004

MILLER, Stephen Michael. b 63. NE Lon Poly BSc86 Nottm Univ BTh91. Linc Th Coll 88. d 91 p 92. C Dudley St Fran *Worc* 91-94; V Sedgley St Mary from 94. *St Mary's Vicarage, St Mary's Close, Hurst Hill, Dudley, W Midlands DY3 1LD* Sedgley (01902) 883310

MILLER, William David. b 45. Man Univ BA66. Linc Th Coll 69. **d** 71 **p** 72. C Newc St Geo *Newc* 71-74; C Corbridge w Halton 74-77; C N Gosforth 77-81; TV Whorlton 81-90; Chapl K Sch Tynemouth from 90. *7 Strawberry Terrace, Hazelrigg, Newcastle upon Tyne NE13 7AR* 0191-236 5024 or 258 5995

MILLETT, Canon Francis Henry Walter. b 19. AKC48. **d** 49 **p** 50. R Nor St Jo Timberhill w All SS *Nor* 61-75; V Nor St Jo Sepulchre 61-75; RD Nor E 70-81; TR Nor St Pet Parmentergate w St Jo 75-77; Hon Can Nor Cathl 77-86; V Nor St Giles 77-86; rtd 87; Perm to Offic *Nor* from 87. *203A Unthank Road, Norwich NR2 2PH* Norwich (01603) 52641

MILLETT, William Hugh. b 21. AKC49. **d** 50 **p** 51. R Richard's Castle *Heref* 58-78; P-in-c Stoke Lacy, Moreton Jeffries w Much Cowarne etc 78-82; Perm to Offic *Worc* from 83; rtd 86. *151 Upper Welland Road, Malvern, Worcs WR14 4LB* Malvern (01684) 567056

MILLGATE, Victor Frederick. b 44. St Mich Coll Llan 81. **d** 83 **p** 84. C Pemb St Mary and St Mich *St D* 83-85; V Manobier and St Florence w Redberth from 85. *The Vicarage, Manorbier, Tenby, Dyfed SA70 7TN* Manorbier (01834) 871617

MILLICHAMP, Mrs Penelope Mary. b 39. CertEd60. W Midl Minl Tr Course 82. **dss** 85 **d** 87 **p** 94. Wednesfield *Lich* 85-94; Par Dn 87-90; TD 90-94; Perm to Offic 94-95; NSM Longdon-upon-Tern, Rodington, Uppington etc from 95. *9 The Buck, Sheinton, Cressage, Shrewsbury SY5 6DJ* Cressage (01952) 510403

MILLIER, Gordon. b 28. St Aid Birkenhead 63. **d** 65 **p** 66. P-in-c Badgworth w Biddisham *B & W* 69-76; R Weare w Badgworth and Biddisham 76-84; R Pilton w Croscombe, N Wootton and Dinder 84-93; rtd 93. *28 Withy Close, Canal Hill, Tiverton, Devon EX16 4HZ* Tiverton (01884) 253128

MILLIGAN, William Edward. b 03. TCD BA25 MA29. CITC 28. **d** 28 **p** 29. I Bright w Ballee and Killough *D & D* 68-73; rtd 73. *2 Blackwood Court, Helen's Bay, Bangor, Co Down BT19 1TJ* Helens Bay (01247) 852795

MILLIGAN, Canon William John (Barney). b 28. OBE95. Em Coll Cam BA49. Cuddesdon Coll 53. **d** 55 **p** 56. V New Eltham All SS *S'wark* 62-71; V Roehampton H Trin 71-79; Can Res St Alb 79-86; Chapl Strasbourg *Eur* 86-95; Angl Rep Eur Insts 90-95; rtd 95; Perm to Offic *S'wark* from 95. *29 Stirling Road, London SW9 9EF* 0171-274 4827

MILLINER, Llewelyn Douglas. b 14. Univ of Wales BSc35. **d** 38 **p** 39. C-in-c Chelmsf St Luke CD *Chelmsf* 66-69; Perm to Offic 69-80; rtd 80; Perm to Offic *Ex* from 80. *Fordings, Weare Giffard, Bideford, Devon EX39 4QS* Bideford (01237) 473729

MILLING, David Horace. b 29. Or Coll Ox BA51 MA54 Cam Univ PhD73. Cuddesdon Coll 54. **d** 56 **p** 57. Lect St D Coll Lamp 73-75; C Caversham *Ox* 77-81; C Mapledurham 77-81; C Caversham St Andr 81-86; TV Upper Kennett *Sarum* 86-88; rtd 88. *10 The Maples, Cirencester, Glos GL7 1TQ* Cirencester (01285) 650400

MILLINGTON, Robert William Ernest. b 51. Sheff Univ BA73 St Jo Coll Dur DipTh75. **d** 76 **p** 77. C Ormskirk *Liv* 76-79; C Litherland St Paul Hatton Hill 79-81; V Bootle Ch Ch 81-88; Chapl K Edw Sch Witley from 88. *Queen's House, 3 Gurdon's Lane, Wormley, Godalming, Surrey GU8 5TF* Wormley (01428) 684298

MILLINGTON, Stuart. b 45. Lich Th Coll 67. **d** 70 **p** 71. C Boulton *Derby* 70-73; C Moseley St Mary *Birm* 73-76; TV Staveley and Barrow Hill *Derby* 76-82; R Wingerworth from 82; RD Chesterfield from 91. *The Rectory, Longedge Lane, Wingerworth, Chesterfield, Derbyshire S42 6PU* Chesterfield (01246) 234242

MILLINS, Leslie Albert. b 20. St Paul's Grahamstown. **d** 53 **p** 54. V Old St Pancras w Bedf New Town St Matt *Lon* 69-76; V Edmonton St Alphege 76-89; rtd 89; Perm to Offic *Chich* from 90. *68 Parkstone Road, Hastings, E Sussex TN34 2NT*

MILLS, Alan Francis. b 29. Ch Coll Cam BA52 MA91. Linc Th Coll 52. **d** 54 **p** 55. C Hucknall Torkard *S'well* 54-58; C Bath Bathwick St Jo *B & W* 58-70; V Drayton 70-76; V Muchelney 70-76; V Alcombe from 76. *The Vicarage, Bircham Road, Alcombe, Minehead, Somerset TA24 6BE* Minehead (01643) 703285

MILLS, Alexandra. b 56. Univ of Wales (Abth) BMus78 CertEd79. Ripon Coll Cuddesdon 88. **d** 90 **p** 94. Par Dn Earlsfield St Andr *S'wark* 90-94; C 94; C Kingston All SS w St Jo from 94. *2 Grove Lane, Kingston-upon-Thames, Surrey KT1 2SU* 0181-546 9882

MILLS, Anthony James. b 55. Nottm Univ BA. Linc Th Coll. **d** 84 **p** 85. C Mexborough *Sheff* 84-86; C Howden TM *York* 86-89; V Fylingdales and Hawsker cum Stainsacre 89-95; V Scarborough St Sav w All SS from 95. *St Saviour's Vicarage, 1 Manor Road, Scarborough, N Yorkshire YO12 7RZ* Scarborough (01723) 360648

MILLS, Canon Clifford James Holden. b 13. AKC39. **d** 39 **p** 40. Hon Can St E Cathl *St E* 63-81; V Reydon 70-78; RD

Halesworth 73-81; rtd 78. *16 St Peter's Path, Holton, Halesworth, Suffolk IP19 8NB* Halesworth (01986) 872884

MILLS, David Bryn. b 49. Ox NSM Course. **d** 83 **p** 84. NSM Stantonbury *Ox* 83-87; NSM Stantonbury and Willen from 87. *3 Tuffnell Close, Willen, Milton Keynes MK15 9BL* Milton Keynes (01908) 605171

MILLS, David Francis. b 51. DipHE78. Oak Hill Th Coll 76. **d** 79 **p** 80. C Rodbourne Cheney *Bris* 79-82; C Wolv St Matt *Lich* 82-85; CF 85-88; TV Braunstone *Leic* 88-95; Past Asst to Adn Leic from 95. *36 Woodcote Road, Leicester LE3 2WD* Leicester (0116) 282 5272

MILLS, Geoffrey Charles Malcolm. b 33. Wycliffe Hall Ox 59. **d** 61 **p** 62. C Buckhurst Hill *Chelmsf* 61-65; C Ecclesall *Sheff* 65-69; V Endcliffe 69-78; R Whiston from 78. *The Rectory, Whiston, Rotherham, S Yorkshire S60 4JA* Rotherham (01709) 364430

MILLS, Miss Glenys Christine. b 38. Open Univ BA81. Dalton Ho Bris DipTh64. **d** 87 **p** 94. Par Dn Clifton Ch Ch w Em *Bris* 87-94; C 94-95; P-in-c Gt w Lt Abington *Ely* from 95; Chapl Arthur Rank Hospice Cam from 95. *The Vicarage, 35 Church Lane, Little Abington, Cambridge CB1 6BQ* Cambridge (01223) 891350

MILLS, Gordon Derek. b 35. Lich Th Coll 60. **d** 63 **p** 64. C W Derby St Mary *Liv* 63-65; C Clifton w Glapton *S'well* 65-67; V N Wilford St Faith 67-72; V Farnsfield 72-82; P-in-c Kirklington w Hockerton 77-82; Asst Dir of Educn *Blackb* 82-86; P-in-c Brindle 82-86; V Gt Budworth *Ches* 86-88; P-in-c Appleton Thorn and Antrobus 87-88; V Gt Budworth and Antrobus 88-92; V Gt Budworth from 92. *The Vicarage, Great Budworth, Northwich, Cheshire CW9 6HF* Comberbach (01606) 891324

MILLS, Canon Hubert Cecil. b 44. TCD BA66 MA71. CITC 67. **d** 67 **p** 68. C Dub Rathfarnham *D & G* 67-72; Min Can St Patr Cathl Dub 69-92; Succ 72-92; Preb Rathmichael St Patr Cathl Dub from 92; C Dub St Steph and St Ann *D & G* 72-77; I Holmpatrick w Balbriggan and Kenure 77-86; I Killiney H Trin 86-93. *Holy Trinity Rectory, Killiney Road, Killiney, Co Dublin, Irish Republic* Dublin (1) 285-2695

MILLS, Jack Herbert. b 14. Selw Coll Cam BA38 MA42. Cuddesdon Coll 39. **d** 40 **p** 41. New Zealand 52-56 and 59-61 and from 87; Australia 57-59 and 62-73; Hd Master St Wilfrid's Sch Ex 74-79; Chapl Community of St Wilfrid 74-79; Hon C Ewhurst *Chich* 79-81; Hon C Bodiam 79-81; Perm to Offic *Ex* 81-85; Perm to Offic *Chich* 85-87; rtd 87. *St Chad's Square, Selwyn Village, Point Chevalier, Auckland 2, New Zealand* Auckland (9) 892243

MILLS, Jennifer Clare. *See* TOMLINSON, Mrs Jennifer Clare

MILLS, Canon John. b 21. Keble Coll Ox BA45 MA47 DipTh48 Lon Univ BD57. Wycliffe Hall Ox 47. **d** 49 **p** 50. V Prescot *Liv* 63-88; RD Prescot 72-84; Hon Can Liv Cathl 74-88; rtd 88. *3 The Stables, Station Lane, Guilden Sutton, Chester CH3 7SY* Mickle Trafford (01244) 300027

MILLS, John Kettlewell. b 53. BA. Cranmer Hall Dur. **d** 84 **p** 85. C Ashton on Mersey St Mary *Ches* 84-87; TV Didsbury St Jas and Em *Man* from 87. *453 Parrswood Road, East Didsbury, Manchester M20 0NE* 0161-445 1310

MILLS, Leslie. b 17. Open Univ BSc94 Reading Univ MA95. Wycliffe Hall Ox 68. **d** 68 **p** 69. C Basingstoke *Win* 68-77; C Basing 78-80; C York Town St Mich *Guildf* 80-84; rtd 84; Perm to Offic *Win* from 84; Perm to Offic *Guildf* from 85; Perm to Offic *Ox* from 86. *21 Mill Lane, Yateley, Camberley, Surrey GU17 7TE* Yateley (01252) 870689

MILLS, Michael Henry. b 51. AKC73. St Aug Coll Cant. **d** 74 **p** 75. C Newton Aycliffe *Dur* 74-78; C Padgate *Liv* 78-79; TV from 79. *The Vicarage, 1 Briers Close, Fearnhead, Warrington WA2 0DN* Padgate (01925) 823108

MILLS, Peter John. b 52. Sarum & Wells Th Coll 87. **d** 89 **p** 90. C Chatham St Wm *Roch* 89-92; V Perry Street from 92. *All Saints' Vicarage, Perry Street, Northfleet, Gravesend, Kent DA11 8RD* Gravesend (01474) 534398

MILLS, Roger Conrad. b 58. Selw Coll Cam BA79 MA83. St Jo Coll Nottm DPS85. **d** 85 **p** 86. C Jesmond H Trin *Newc* 85-88; C Alnwick St Mich and St Paul 88-91; Chapl Newc Univ from 91. *52 Fern Avenue, Jesmond, Newcastle upon Tyne NE2 2QX* 0191-281 5166 or 222 6341

MILLS, Walter Charles. b 30. Oak Hill Th Coll 82. **d** 85 **p** 86. NSM Broomfield *Chelmsf* 85-88; C Pleshey 88-95; rtd 95. *29 Mill Lane, Broomfield, Chelmsford CM1 7BQ* Chelmsford (01245) 441117

MILLS-POWELL, Mark Oliver McLay. b 55. Edin Th Sem Virginia. **d** 83 **p** 84. C Huyton St Mich *Liv* 83-86; USA 86-95; P-in-c Basildon w Aldworth and Ashampstead *Ox* from 95. *The Vicarage, Upper Basildon, Reading RG8 8LS* Upper Basildon (01491) 671223

MILLSON, Mrs Margaret Lily. b 41. CertEd61. E Midl Min Tr Course 83. **dss** 86 **d** 87 **p** 94. NSM Bottesford w Ashby *Linc* from 86. *65 Timberland, Bottesford, Scunthorpe, S Humberside DN16 3SH* Scunthorpe (01724) 865489

MILLWARD, Mark Anthony. b 61. Leeds Poly BSc. St Steph Ho Ox. **d** 86 **p** 87. C Sunderland Red Ho *Dur* 86-89; C Leic Ch Sav *Leic* 89-90; V Sunderland Pennywell St Thos *Dur* from 90. *St Thomas's Vicarage, Parkhurst Road, Pennywell, Sunderland SR4 9DB*   0191-534 2100

MILLWARD, Miss Pauline Freda. b 50. AMA74. N Ord Course 89. **d** 92 **p** 94. NSM Warley *Wakef* from 92. *8 Hill Park Mount, Kebroyd, Sowerby Bridge, W Yorkshire HX6 3JB*   Halifax (01422) 823576

MILLWOOD, Stephen Grant. b 44. Sheff Tech Coll HNC66 Sheff City Coll of Educn CertEd77 Open Univ BA92. St Jo Coll Nottm DipThMin92. **d** 94 **p** 95. C Anston *Sheff* from 94. *20 St James Avenue, Anston, Sheffield S31 7DR*   Dinnington (01909) 550579

MILLYARD, Alexander John. b 29. St Jo Coll Dur BA53. Qu Coll Birm 53. **d** 54 **p** 55. Chapl HM Pris Ex 69-71; Chapl HM Pris Wandsworth 72-73; V Snibston *Leic* 73-75; V Leic All So 75-79; V Blakesley and Adstone *Pet* 79-89; R Blakesley w Adstone and Maidford etc 89-91; rtd 91. *Flat 6, Gainsborough House, Eaton Gardens, Hove, E Sussex BN3 3UA*   Brighton (01273) 728722

✠**MILMINE, Rt Rev Douglas.** b 21. CBE83. St Pet Hall Ox BA46 MA46. Clifton Th Coll 47. **d** 47 **p** 48 **c** 73. C Ilfracombe SS Phil and Jas *Ex* 47-50; C Slough *Ox* 50-53; Chile 54-69; Adn N Chile, Bolivia and Peru 63-69; Hon Can Chile from 69; Area Sec SAMS 69-72; Bp Paraguay 73-85; rtd 86. *1C Clive Court, 24 Grand Parade, Eastbourne, E Sussex BN21 3DD*   Eastbourne (01323) 734159

MILMINE, Neil Edward Douglas. b 46. Kent Univ BSc70. Wycliffe Hall Ox 80. **d** 82 **p** 83. C Hailsham *Chich* 82-86; C Horsham 86; TV 86-93; V Patcham from 93. *The Vicarage, 12 Church Hill, Brighton BN1 8YE*   Brighton (01273) 552157

MILN, Dr Peter. b 43. MBIM Univ of Wales (Swansea) BA65 Nottm Univ MTh81 PhD89. E Midl Min Tr Course 76. **d** 79 **p** 80. NSM Uttoxeter w Bramshall *Lich* 79-85; CF (TAVR) from 82. *41 Balance Street, Uttoxeter, Staffs ST14 8JQ*   Uttoxeter (01889) 565110

MILNE, Alan. b 54. RMN SRN FETC. Cranmer Hall Dur 89. **d** 91 **p** 92. C Hartlepool St Luke *Dur* 91-94; P-in-c Dalton le Dale from 94; P-in-c Hawthorn from 94. *The Vicarage, Church Lane, Murton, Seaham, Co Durham SR7 9RD*   0191-526 2410

MILNE, Miss Christine Helen. b 48. LTCL71 Lon Univ DipRS86. S'wark Ord Course 83. **dss** 86 **d** 87. S Lambeth St Steph S'wark 86-89; Par Dn 87-89; New Zealand from 89. *1/13 Faulke Avenue, Wainuiomata, New Zealand*   Wellington (4) 642186

MILNE, Glenn Alexander Roscoe. b 62. Or Coll Ox BA85 MA89. Westcott Ho Cam 87. **d** 89 **p** 90. C Hexham *Newc* 89-92; CF 92-95; I Castlepollard and Oldcastle w Loughcrew etc *M & K* from 95. *St Michael's Rectory, Castlepollard, Mullingar, Co Westmeath, Irish Republic*   Mullingar (44) 61123

MILNER, David. b 38. St Aid Birkenhead 63. **d** 66 **p** 67. C Ulverston H Trin *Carl* 66-68; C Mickleover All SS *Derby* 68-71; C Mickleover St Jo 68-71; V 71-82; P-in-c Sandiacre 82-86; P-in-c Doveridge from 86; RD Longford from 86; P-in-c Sudbury and Somersal Herbert from 92. *The Vicarage, Church Lane, Doveridge, Ashbourne, Derbyshire DE6 5NN*   Uttoxeter (01889) 563420

MILNER, Eric. b 10. Mert Coll Ox BA33 MA37. Linc Th Coll 35. **d** 36 **p** 37. V Bentley *Sheff* 67-80; rtd 80; Perm to Offic *Wakef* from 86. *30 Hillcrest Avenue, Ossett, W Yorkshire WF5 9PP*   Wakefield (01924) 271740

MILNER, Leslie. b 35. MBE93. Birm Univ BSc57 St Jo Coll Cam BA59. Wells Th Coll 61. **d** 63 **p** 64. C Yardley St Edburgha *Birm* 63-66; C Seacroft *Ripon* 66-71; Dir St Basil's Cen Deritend from 71; Lic to Offic *Birm* 71-86; Perm to Offic from 86. *St Basil's Centre, Heathmill Lane, Birmingham B9 4AX*   0121-772 2483

✠**MILNER, Rt Rev Ronald James.** b 27. Pemb Coll Cam BA49 MA52. Wycliffe Hall Ox 51. **d** 53 **p** 54 **c** 88. Succ Sheff Cathl *Sheff* 53-58; V Westwood *Cov* 58-64; V Fletchamstead 64-70; R Southn St Mary w H Trin *Win* 70-72; P-in-c Southn St Matt 70-72; Lic to Offic 72-73; TR Southn (City Cen) 73-83; Hon Can Win Cathl 75-83; Adn Linc 83-88; Can and Preb Linc Cathl 83-88; Suff Bp Burnley *Blackb* 88-93; rtd 93; Asst Bp S'well from 94. *7 Crafts Way, Southwell, Notts NG25 0BL*   Southwell (01636) 816256

MILNER, William David. b 52. St Jo Coll Nottm DCM93. **d** 93 **p** 94. C Wollaton S'well from 93. *4 Woodbank Drive, Nottingham NG8 2QU*   Nottingham (0115) 928 2779

MILNES, David Ian. b 45. Chich Th Coll 74. **d** 76 **p** 77. C Walthamstow St Sav *Chelmsf* 76-80; C Chingford SS Pet and Paul 80-83; P-in-c Gt Ilford St Alb 83-87; V from 87. *The Vicarage, 99 Albert Road, Ilford, Essex IG1 1HS*   0181-478 2428

MILROY, Mrs Ethel Doreen. b 33. Bedf Coll Lon BSc54 Bris Univ PGCE69 Nottm Univ MEd79. N Ord Course 88. **d** 91 **p** 94. NSM Tideswell *Derby* from 91. *Barn Cottage, Parke Road, Tideswell, Buxton, Derbyshire SK17 8NS*   Tideswell (01298) 872242

MILTON, Andrew John. b 54. BD. St Steph Ho Ox. **d** 83 **p** 84. C Highfield *Ox* 83-87; TV Banbury 87-95; P-in-c Thorney Abbey *Ely* from 95. *The Abbey Vicarage, The Green, Thorney, Peterborough PE6 0QD*   Peterborough (01733) 270388

MILTON, Miss Angela Daphne. b 50. Oak Hill Th Coll 84. **d** 87 **p** 94. NSM Watford *St Alb* from 87. *34 Woodhurst Avenue, Garston, Watford WD2 6RQ*   Garston (01923) 228311

MILTON, Claudius James Barton. b 29. K Coll Lon BD52 AKC53. **d** 53 **p** 54. Chapl Cranbrook Sch Kent 65-74; Asst Master and Housemaster 65-74; Chapl & Asst Master Clayesmore Sch Blandford 74-89; Clayesmore Prep Sch 74-89; rtd 89. *28 Oakwood Drive, Iwerne Minster, Blandford Forum, Dorset DT11 8QT*   Fontmell Magna (01747) 811791

MILTON, Derek Rees. b 45. Open Univ BA76 Lon Univ BD80. St Jo Sem Wonersh 63. **d** 68 **p** 69. In RC Ch 68-84; Hon C Luton Lewsey St Hugh *St Alb* 84-85; Hon C Houghton Regis 85-86; C 86-89; TV Brixham w Churston Ferrers and Kingswear *Ex* from 89. *All Saints' Vicarage, 16 Holwell Road, Brixham, Devon TQ5 9NE*   Brixham (01803) 855549

MILTON-THOMPSON, Dr David Gerald. b 17. OBE76. MRCS LRCP42 Em Coll Cam BA39 MA MB BChir49. Lon Coll of Div 62. **d** 63 **p** 64. CMS 49-81 and 85-88; Kenya 52-81; C Chadwell *Chelmsf* 81-82; Hon C 82-85; Uganda 85-88; rtd 88; Hon C Sevenoaks St Nic *Roch* from 88. *1 The Glebe, Oak Lane, Sevenoaks, Kent TN13 1NN*   Sevenoaks (01732) 462977

MILTON-THOMPSON, Jonathan Patrick. b 51. Nottm Univ BA76. Oak Hill Th Coll 86. **d** 88 **p** 89. C Bispham *Blackb* 88-92; C Darfield *Sheff* 92; C-in-c Gt Houghton CD from 92. *16 High Street, Great Houghton, Barnsley, S Yorkshire S72 0AB*   Barnsley (01226) 752320

MILVERTON, Frederic Jack. b 15. Lon Univ BSc37 Leeds Univ MEd40. Ripon Hall Ox 56. **d** 57 **p** 58. Lic to Offic *Sarum* 70-79; Hd of Educn Weymouth Coll of Educn 70-76; Dean Educn Dorset Inst of HE 76-79; TV Oakdale St Geo 79-82; rtd 82. *Flat 4, Compass South, Rodwell Road, Weymouth, Dorset DT4 8QT*   Weymouth (01305) 788930

MILVERTON, Mrs Ruth Erica. b 32. Open Univ BA78 Southn Univ MA82. Sarum Th Coll 83. **dss** 86 **d** 87 **p** 95. Weymouth H Trin *Sarum* 86-87; Hon Par Dn 87-95; NSM from 95. *4 Compass South, Rodwell Road, Weymouth, Dorset DT4 8QT*   Weymouth (01305) 788930

MILVERTON of Lagos and Clifton, Rev and Rt Hon Lord (Fraser Arthur Richard Richards). b 30. Bps' Coll Cheshunt. **d** 57 **p** 58. R Christian Malford w Sutton Benger etc *Bris* 67-93; Public Preacher 93-95; rtd 95. *7 Betjeman Road, Barton Park, Marlborough, Wilts SN8 1TL*   Marlborough (01672) 866568

MILWARD, Terence George. b 23. Ripon Hall Ox 66. **d** 68 **p** 69. C Selly Oak St Mary *Birm* 68-70; C Edgbaston St Bart 70-75; TV Bournemouth St Pet w St Swithun, St Steph etc *Win* 75-81; R Smannell w Enham Alamein 81-88; rtd 88; Perm to Offic *Guildf* from 88. *Church House Flat, Church Lane, Witley, Godalming, Surrey GU8 5PN*   Wormley (01428) 685308

MINALL, Peter. b 26. Lon Univ BSc47. Bps' Coll Cheshunt 51. **d** 53 **p** 54. V Stroud *Glouc* 69-84; RD Bisley 78-84; P-in-c Barnwood 84-91; Chapl Coney Hill Hosp Glouc 86-91; Lic to Offic *Glouc* from 91; rtd 91. *Amberwood, Knapp Lane, Painswick, Stroud, Glos GL6 6YE*   Painswick (01452) 813730

MINAY, Francis Arthur Rodney. b 44. Edin Coll of Art DA65. Westcott Ho Cam 66. **d** 68 **p** 69. C Edenbridge *Roch* 68-73; C Bromley St Mark 73-75; V Tudeley w Capel 75-79; TV Littleham w Exmouth *Ex* 79-82; P-in-c Bolton Percy *York* from 82; Asst Chapl to Arts and Recreation in the NE from 82. *The Rectory, Bolton Percy, York YO5 7AL*   Appleton Roebuck (01904) 744213

MINCHER, John Derek Bernard. b 31. **d** 60 **p** 61. OSB 54-80; Lic to Offic *Ox* 60-80; Perm to Offic *St E* 81-87; C Halesworth w Linstead, Chediston, Holton etc 87-90; P-in-c Worlingworth, Southolt, Tannington, Bedfield etc 90-91; R from 91. *The Rectory, Worlingworth, Woodbridge, Suffolk IP13 7NT*   Worlingworth (0172876) 8102

MINCHEW, Donald Patrick. b 48. Univ of Wales (Cardiff) BD76. St Mich Coll Llan 72. **d** 76 **p** 77. C Glouc St Aldate *Glouc* 76-80; P-in-c Sharpness CD 80-81; V Sharpness w Purton and Brookend from 81; Miss to Seamen from 81. *The Vicarage, Sanigar Lane, Newtown, Berkeley, Glos GL13 9NF*   Dursley (01453) 811360

MINCHIN, Anthony John. b 35. St Cath Coll Cam BA59 MA. Wells Th Coll 59. **d** 61 **p** 62. C Cheltenham St Pet *Glouc* 61-64; C Bushey *St Alb* 64-67; V Cheltenham St Mich *Glouc* 67-74; V Lower Cam 74-82; V Tuffley 82-92; R Huntley and Longhope from 92. *The Rectory, 56 Byford Road, Huntley, Glos GL19 3EL*   Gloucester (01452) 831044

MINCHIN, Charles Scott. b 51. Trin Coll Cam BA72 MA75. Linc Th Coll 73. **d** 75 **p** 76. C Gt Wyrley *Lich* 75-78; TV Wilnecote 78-82; C Tamworth 82-84; C-in-c Glascote CD 84-88; R Brierley Hill 88-93; R Brierley Hill *Worc* from 93. *The Rectory, 2 Church Hill, Brierley Hill, W Midlands DY5 3PX* Brierley Hill (01384) 78146

MINCHIN, Canon George Reginald. b 05. TCD BA31 MA43. **d** 31 **p** 32. I Camus-juxta-Bann *D & R* 65-75; Can Derry Cathl 70-75; rtd 75. *4 Fortview, Portballintrae, Bushmills, Co Antrim BT57 8TJ* Bushmills (012657) 31607

MINGINS, Canon Marion Elizabeth. b 52. Birm Univ BSocSc73 CQSW75. Cam DipRS78. **d** 87 **p** 94. CA from 79; NSM Battersea Park All SS *S'wark* 87-89; Sen Selection Sec ACCM 87-89; OHP from 89; Asst Dioc Dir of Ords and Voc Adv *St E* from 91; Chapl St E Cathl 91-93; Min Can 91-92; Hon Can St E Cathl 92-93; Can Res St E Cathl from 93. *2 Abbey Precincts, The Churchyard, Bury St Edmunds, Suffolk IP33 1RS* Bury St Edmunds (01284) 753396

MINHINNICK, Leslie. b 18. Jes Coll Ox BA39 MA43. Wycliffe Hall Ox 40. **d** 41 **p** 42. V Lytham St Jo *Blackb* 66-81; rtd 83; Perm to Offic *Ban* from 83. *The Old School House, Cemaes, Anglesey, Gwynedd LL67 0NG* Cemaes Bay (01407) 710601

MINION, Arthur. b 65. TCD BTh92. CITC 89. **d** 92 **p** 93. C Bandon Union *C, C & R* 92-95; I Taunagh w Kilmactranny, Ballysumaghan etc *K, E & A* from 95. *The Rectory, Riverstown, Via Boyle, Co Sligo, Irish Republic* Sligo (71) 65368

MINNS, John Alfred. b 38. Oak Hill Th Coll 63. **d** 68 **p** 69. C Cheadle Hulme St Andr *Ches* 68-72; C Hartford 72-74; V Wharton 74-85; V Halliwell St Paul *Man* 85-87; C Halliwell St Pet 87-91; rtd 91. *39 Hambidge Lane, Lechlade, Glos GL7 3BJ* Faringdon (01367) 253549

MINNS, John Charles. b 42. E Anglian Minl Tr Course. **d** 85 **p** 86. NSM Heigham St Barn w St Bart *Nor* 85-91; NSM Nor St Geo Tombland from 91; Asst Chapl Norfolk & Nor Hosp from 92. *18 Thunder Lane, Thorpe St Andrew, Norwich NR7 0JW* Norwich (01603) 37000

MINORS, Graham Glyndwr Cavill. b 44. Glouc Sch of Min. **d** 79 **p** 79. Hon C Lower Cam *Glouc* 79-83; C Leckhampton SS Phil and Jas w Cheltenham St Jas 83-89; V Cainscross w Selsley from 89. *The Vicarage, 58 Cashes Green Road, Stroud, Glos GL5 4RA* Stroud (01453) 755148

MINSHALL, Douglas Arthur. b 24. E Midl Min Tr Course 78. **d** 81 **p** 82. NSM Worksop Priory *S'well* 81-85; NSM E Retford 85-87; C 87-88; NSM W Retford 85-87; C 87-88; P-in-c Clarborough w Hayton 88-93; rtd 93. *3 Avon Rise, Retford, Notts DN22 6QH* Retford (01777) 869872

MINSHALL, Neville David. b 37. Wolv Poly MA86. AKC64. **d** 65 **p** 66. C Wolv St Paul *Lich* 65-66; C Stafford St Mary 66-68; C Rugeley 68-69; C Shrewsbury H Cross 69-73; P-in-c Wrockwardine Wood 73-77; R Brierley Hill 77-81; R Hope w Shelve *Heref* from 81; V Middleton from 81; R Worthen from 81. *The Rectory, Worthen, Shrewsbury SY5 9HW* Worthen (01743) 891476

MINSON, Roger Graham. b 41. Leeds Univ BA64 Bris Univ DSA69. Coll of Resurr Mirfield 64. **d** 66 **p** 67. C Horfield St Greg *Bris* 66-70; C Southmead 70-73; V Lawrence Weston 74-81; TV Knowle 81-93; V Knowle St Martin 93-95; V Fishponds St Mary from 95. *St Mary's Vicarage, Vicar's Close, Bristol BS16 3TH* Bristol (0117) 965 4462

MINTER, Richard Arthur. b 05. Worc Coll Ox BA29 MA33 BD55. St Steph Ho Ox 29. **d** 32 **p** 33. V Stow w Quy *Ely* 46-85; rtd 85; P-in-c Stow w Quy *Ely* from 85. *The Vicarage, Quy, Cambridge CB5 9AD* Cambridge (01223) 811277

MINTON, Richard Reginald. b 09. Bible Churchmen's Coll 32. **d** 35 **p** 36. R Corley *Cov* 65-76; rtd 76; Chapl All Hallows Sch Rousdon 78-81. *c/o C Minton Esq, 57 Orchard Road, Tewin, Welwyn, Herts AL6 0HL* Welwyn (01438) 798700

MINTY, Kenneth Desmond. b 25. Ch Ch Ox BA48 MA51. Lich Th Coll 71 Qu Coll Birm 72. **d** 73 **p** 74. Asst Chapl Wrekin Coll Shropshire 73-84; Chapl 84-86; Hon C Lawley *Lich* 74-75; Hon C Cen Telford 75-81; Hon C Longdon-upon-Tern, Rodington, Uppington etc 81-89; V Ercall Magna from 89; V Rowton from 89. *The Vicarage, High Ercall, Telford, Shropshire TF6 6BE* Telford (01952) 770206

MINTY, Selwyn Francis. b 34. St D Coll Lamp 58. **d** 61 **p** 62. C Tonyrefail *Llan* 61-66; C Pontypridd St Cath 66-69; V Cilfynydd 69-84; V Crynant from 84. *The Vicarage, 35 Main Road, Crynant, Neath, W Glam SA10 8NT* Neath (01639) 750226

MIR, Amene Rahman. b 58. Man Univ BA81 PhD93. Coll of Resurr Mirfield 81. **d** 83 **p** 84. C Walton St Mary *Liv* 83-87; Chapl Walton Hosp Liv 83-87; Perm to Offic *Man* 87-90; Asst Chapl Salford Mental Health Unit 90-94; Chapl Salford Mental Health Services (NHS Trust) from 94. *87 Carrington Lane, Sale, Cheshire M33 5WH* 0161-973 1836 or 787 5709

MITCHAM, Andrew Mark. b 66. Kent Univ BA87 Leeds Univ BA90. Coll of Resurr Mirfield 88. **d** 91 **p** 92. C Downham Market w Bexwell *Ely* 91-94; Shrine of Our Lady of Walsingham from 94. *The College, Walsingham, Norfolk NR22 6EF* Walsingham (01328) 820266

MITCHELL, Albert George. b 48. TCD BA. **d** 88 **p** 89. Bp's C Skreen w Kilmacshalgan and Dromard *T, K & A* from 88. *The Glebe, Kilglass, Co Sligo, Irish Republic* Kilglass (96) 36258

MITCHELL, Allan. b 52. Kelham Th Coll 74 Linc Th Coll 78. **d** 78 **p** 79. C Kells *Carl* 78-81; C Upperby St Jo 81-83; V Pennington w Lindal and Marton 83-88; V Westf St Mary from 88. *St Mary's Vicarage, Salisbury Street, Workington, Cumbria CA14 3TR* Workington (01900) 603227

MITCHELL, Andrew Patrick (Paddy). b 37. Ripon Coll Cuddesdon 84 English Coll Valladolid 59. **d** 64 **p** 65. In RC Ch 64-85; C Woolwich St Mary w St Mich *S'wark* 85-87; V E Wickham 87-94; P-in-c Walsall St Andr *Lich* from 94. *119 Hollyedge Lane, Walsall WS2 8PU* Walsall (01922) 721658

MITCHELL, Cecil Robert. b 32. QUB BScEng54. CITC 65. **d** 65 **p** 66. Dioc Sec *Conn* 70-74; Dioc Sec *D & D* 70-74; I Ballywalter 74-82; V Malew *S & M* 82-84; I Bright w Ballee and Killough *D & D* 84-89; I Killyleagh 89-94; rtd 94. *20 Innisfayle Crescent, Bangor, Co Down BT19 1DT* Bangor (01247) 466167

MITCHELL, Christopher Allan (Chris). b 51. Newc Univ BA72. Oak Hill Th Coll 82. **d** 84 **p** 85. C Guisborough *York* 84-87; C Thornaby on Tees 87-88; TV 88-92; V Dent w Cowgill *Bradf* from 92. *The Vicarage, Dent, Sedbergh, Cumbria LA10 5QR* Dent (015396) 25226

MITCHELL, Christopher Ashley. b 69. **d** 95. Min Can St As Cathl *St As* from 95. *13 Llys Clwyd, Elwy Park, St Asaph, Clwyd LL17 0UA*

MITCHELL, Christopher Derek. b 61. Univ of Wales (Lamp) BA85 Leic Univ MA86 Qu Coll Cam BA88 MA92. Westcott Ho Cam 87. **d** 89 **p** 90. C Streetly *Lich* 89-92; C Brookfield St Mary *Lon* from 92. *The Vicarage, 106 Highgate West Hill, London N6 6AP* 0181-340 5190

MITCHELL, Canon David George. b 35. QUB BA56. Sarum Th Coll 59. **d** 61 **p** 62. C Westbury-on-Trym H Trin *Bris* 61-64; C Cricklade w Latton 64-68; V Fishponds St Jo 68-77; RD Stapleton 76-77; TR E Bris 77-87; Hon Can Bris Cathl from 87; R Syston 87-94; V Warmley 87-94; P-in-c Bitton 87-94; R Warmley, Syston and Bitton from 94; RD Bitton 87-93. *The Rectory, Church Avenue, Bristol BS15 5JJ* Bristol (0117) 967 3965

MITCHELL, Preb David Norman. b 35. Tyndale Hall Bris 64. **d** 67 **p** 68. C Marple All SS *Ches* 67-70; C St Helens St Helen *Liv* 70-72; V S Lambeth St Steph *S'wark* 72-78; P-in-c Brixton Rd Ch Ch 73-75; SE Area Sec CPAS 78-81; R Uphill *B & W* 81-92; TR from 92; Chapl Weston-super-Mare Gen Hosp from 86; Preb Wells Cathl *B & W* from 90. *The Rectory, 3 Old Church Road, Uphill, Weston-super-Mare, Avon BS23 4UH* Weston-super-Mare (01934) 620156

MITCHELL, Edwin. b 44. St Jo Coll Nottm BTh74. **d** 74 **p** 75. C Worksop St Jo *S'well* 74-77; C Waltham Abbey *Chelmsf* 77-80; V Whiston *Liv* 80-91; R Wombwell *Sheff* from 91. *The Rectory, 1 Rectory Close, Wombwell, Barnsley, S Yorkshire S73 8EY* Barnsley (01226) 752166

MITCHELL, Eric Sidney. b 24. S Dios Minl Tr Scheme 77. **d** 80 **p** 81. NSM Portland All SS w St Pet *Sarum* 80-83; C 88-92; Bermuda 83-88; Chapl HM Pris The Verne from 91; rtd 92. *10 Underhedge Gardens, Portland, Dorset DT5 2DX* Portland (01305) 821059

MITCHELL, Frank. b 21. Ely Th Coll 49. **d** 51 **p** 52. V Scarborough St Sav *York* 62-73; V Scarborough St Sav w All SS 73-83; rtd 83. *6 Sitwell Street, Scarborough, N Yorkshire YO11 5EX* Scarborough (01723) 367948

MITCHELL, Canon Frank Leonard. b 14. St Cath Soc Ox BA39 MA47. Wycliffe Hall Ox 46. **d** 48 **p** 49. R Hayes *Roch* 66-77; C Speldhurst w Groombridge and Ashurst 77-79; rtd 79; Perm to Offic *Chich* from 80; Perm to Offic *Roch* from 82. *10 Beechwood Close, Burwash, Etchingham, E Sussex TN19 7BS* Burwash (01435) 882601

MITCHELL, Geoffrey. b 36. CEng66 FCIT92 FIMechE76 SS Coll Cam BA60 MA64. E Midl Min Tr Course 88. **d** 91 **p** 92. NSM Oaks in Charnwood and Copt Oak *Leic* 91-94; NSM Loughb All SS and H Trin from 94. *36 Brick Kiln Lane, Shepshed, Loughborough, Leics LE12 9EL* Shepshed (01509) 502280

MITCHELL, Geoffrey Peter. b 30. Liv Univ BEng57 Man Univ MSc68. Wells Th Coll 57. **d** 59 **p** 60. Hon C Unsworth *Man* 68-86; V Woolfold 86-95; rtd 95. *14 Redfern Wood, Caldershaw, Oldham OL12 7GA* Oldham (01706) 38180

MITCHELL, Canon George Alfred. b 23. TCD BA45 MA56. **d** 46 **p** 47. I Carrickfergus *Conn* 59-70; I Ban St Comgall *D & D* 70-88; Can Belf Cathl 78-88; rtd 88. *2 Glendun Park, Bangor, Co Down BT20 4UX* Bangor (01247) 460882

MITCHELL, Gordon Frank Henry. b 26. QFSM. FIFireE. Sarum & Wells Th Coll 74. **d** 77 **p** 78. NSM Alderbury and W Grimstead *Sarum* 77-91; NSM Alderbury Team from 91. *Seefeld, Southampton Road, Whaddon, Salisbury SP5 3EB* Salisbury (01722) 710516

MITCHELL, Graham Bell. b 40. Otago Univ BA64 MA65 Worc Coll Ox BA73 MA76. St Chad's Coll Dur 66. **d** 68 **p** 69. C Bris St Agnes w St Simon *Bris* 68-71; C Bedminster St Mich 73-76; V Auckland St Pet *Dur* 76-78; Vice-Prin Chich Th Coll 78-83; C Brighton St Pet w Chpl Royal and St Jo *Chich* 83-86; P-in-c Scaynes Hill from 86. *The Vicarage, Scaynes Hill, Haywards Heath, W Sussex RH17 7PB* Haywards Heath (01444) 831265

MITCHELL, Canon Henry Gordon. b 20. St Chad's Coll Dur BA44 DipTh45 MA47. **d** 45 **p** 46. R Fulbeck *Linc* 52-72; RD Loveden 64-72; Can and Preb Linc Cathl 67-85; P-in-c Carlton Scroop w Normanton 69-72; V New Sleaford 72-85; rtd 85; Perm to Offic *Linc* from 85. *3 Lime Grove, Caythorpe, Grantham, Lincs NG32 3DH* Loveden (01400) 73346

MITCHELL, Jolyon Peter. b 64. Selw Coll Cam BA88 MA90. St Jo Coll Dur MA93. **d** 93 **p** 94. NSM St Mary's Cathl *Edin* from 93; Lecturer Edin Univ from 93. *4 Bruntsfield Terrace, Edinburgh EH10 4EX* 0131-229 8154

MITCHELL, Miss Josephine Dorothy (Jose). b 36. Dalton Ho Bris 65. **dss** 76 **d** 87 **p** 94. Hailsham *Chich* 75-85; Enfield St Jas *Lon* 85-87; Par Dn 87-94; C from 94. *170 Addison Road, Enfield, Middx EN3 5LE* 0181-805 1271

MITCHELL, Kevin. b 49. Newc Univ BSc71 Ox Univ BA83. Ripon Coll Cuddesdon 81. **d** 83 **p** 84. C Cantril Farm *Liv* 83-86; Chapl N Middx Hosp from 86; C Gt Cam Road St Jo and St Jas *Lon* 86-90; P-in-c Cricklewood St Pet from 90. *St Peter's Vicarage, 5 Farm Avenue, London NW2 2EG* 0181-450 9043

MITCHELL, Very Rev Patrick Reynolds. b 30. FSA81 Mert Coll Ox BA52 MA56. Wells Th Coll 52. **d** 54 **p** 55. C Mansf St Mark *S'well* 54-57; Chapl Wells Th Coll 57-61; PV Wells Cathl *B & W* 57-61; V Milton *Portsm* 61-67; V Frome St Jo *B & W* 67-73; P-in-c Woodlands 67-73; Dir of ords 70-74; Dean Wells 73-89; Dean of Windsor and Dom Chapl to The Queen from 89. *The Deanery, Windsor Castle, Windsor, Berks SL4 1NJ* Windsor (01753) 865561 or 865538

MITCHELL, Peter Derek. b 30. Roch Th Coll 67. **d** 69 **p** 70. C Wargrave *Ox* 69-72; V Lund *Blackb* 72-80; V Badsey w Aldington and Wickhamford *Worc* from 80. *The Vicarage, Badsey, Evesham, Worcs WR11 5EW* Evesham (01386) 830343

MITCHELL, Richard John Anthony. b 64. St Martin's Coll Lanc BA85 PGCE86. Sarum & Wells Th Coll 88. **d** 91 **p** 92. C Kendal H Trin *Carl* 91-95; TV Kirkby Lonsdale from 95. *The Vicarage, Vicarage Lane, Kirkby Lonsdale, Carnforth, Lancs LA6 2BA* Carnforth (015242) 72078

MITCHELL, Robert Hugh. b 53. Ripon Coll Cuddesdon. **d** 82 **p** 83. C E Dulwich St Jo *S'wark* 82-86; C Cam Gt St Mary w St Mich *Ely* 86-90; Chapl Girton Coll Cam 86-90; Asst Chapl Win Coll 90-91; Assoc Chapl Addenbrooke's Hosp Cam 91-93; Chapl Portsm Hosps NHS Trust from 93; Chapl St Mary's Hosp Portsm from 93. *The Chaplains' Office, St Mary's Hospital, Milton Road, Portsmouth P03 6AD* Portsmouth (01705) 822331

MITCHELL, Robert McFarlane. b 50. Man Univ BA72. Wycliffe Hall Ox 73. **d** 75 **p** 76. C Tonbridge SS Pet and Paul *Roch* 75-80; CF from 80. *c/o MOD (Army), Bagshot Park, Bagshot, Surrey GU19 5PL* Bagshot (01276) 471717 Fax 412834

MITCHELL, Roger Sulway. b 36. Chich Th Coll 70. **d** 71 **p** 71. C Sidcup St Jo *Roch* 71-74; C Pembury 74-76; Lic to Offic *Truro* from 76; Chapl St Lawr Hosp Bodmin from 76; Chapl Cornwall and Is of Scilly Mental Health Unit from 88. *St Lawrence's Hospital, Bodmin, Cornwall PL31 2QT, or 12 Beacon Road, Bodmin, Cornwall PL31 1AS* Bodmin (01208) 73281 or 76357

MITCHELL, Stephen Andrew John. b 56. Ch Ch Coll Cant CertEd78 K Coll Lon AKC77 BD80 Lambeth STh90. Coll of Resurr Mirfield 80. **d** 82 **p** 83. C Chatham St Steph *Roch* 82-87; C Edenbridge 87-91; V from 91; P-in-c Crockham Hill H Trin 91-94. *The Vicarage, Mill Hill, Edenbridge, Kent TN8 5DA* Edenbridge (01732) 862258

MITCHELL, Stephen John. b 51. Ex Univ BA73 Fitzw Coll Cam BA78 MA. Ridley Hall Cam 76. **d** 79 **p** 80. C Gt Malvern St Mary *Worc* 79-81; Prec Leic Cathl *Leic* 82-85; R Barrow upon Soar w Walton le Wolds from 85. *The Rectory, 27 Cotes Road, Barrow on Soar, Loughborough, Leics LE12 8JP* Quorn (01509) 412471

MITCHELL, Steven. b 58. BTh. St Jo Coll Nottm. **d** 83 **p** 84. C Ovenden *Wakef* 83-87; V Gawthorpe and Chickenley Heath from 87. *The Vicarage, 73 Chickenley Lane, Dewsbury, W Yorkshire WF12 8QD* Wakefield (01924) 451547

MITCHELL, Dr Stuart Ian. b 50. Wadh Coll Ox BA71 DPhil74. S'wark Ord Course DipRS84. **d** 85 **p** 87. NSM Charlton St Luke w H Trin *S'wark* 85-86; NSM Kidbrooke St Jas 86-88; NSM Newbold and Dunston *Derby* 88-94; C from 94. *1 Hollens Way, Holme Hall, Chesterfield, Derbyshire S40 4XR* Chesterfield (01246) 211053

MITCHELL, Tom Good. b 21. K Coll (NS) STh62. **d** 63 **p** 64. Canada 63-81; V Misterton and W Stockwith *S'well* 81-87; rtd 87; Perm to Offic *Glouc* from 87. *Ashbury, Binyon Road, Winchcombe, Cheltenham, Glos GL54 5QQ* Cheltenham (01242) 604279

MITCHELL, Wilfred Christopher. b 15. Lich Th Coll 51. **d** 53 **p** 54. V Linc All SS *Linc* 69-81; rtd 81. *51A Downview Road, Worthing, W Sussex BN11 4QH* Worthing (01903) 502745

MITCHELL, William Blanchard. b 26. Lon Univ DipTh54. CF Aid Birkenhead 53. **d** 55 **p** 56. CF 61-77; V Nicholforest and Kirkandrews on Esk *Carl* 77-84; R Kirkby Thore w Temple Sowerby and Newbiggin 84-89; rtd 89. *Koi Hai, 23 Longlands Road, Carlisle CA3 9AD* Carlisle (01228) 42630

MITCHELL-INNES, Charles William. b 47. Pemb Coll Cam BA69 MA73. Sarum Th Coll 83. **d** 86 **p** 87. Asst Chapl Sherborne Sch Dorset 86-89; Perm to Offic *Sarum* from 86; Chapl Milton Abbey Sch Dorset from 90. *Monmouth House, Milton Abbey School, Blandford Forum, Dorset DT11 0DA* Milton Abbas (01258) 880676

MITCHELL-INNES, James Alexander. b 39. Ch Ch Ox BA64 MA66. Lon Coll of Div 65. **d** 67 **p** 68. C Cullompton *Ex* 67-71; Nigeria 71-75; P-in-c Puddletown w Athelhampton and Burleston *Sarum* 75-78; R Puddletown and Tolpuddle 78-82; V Win Ch Ch *Win* 82-92; V Titchfield *Portsm* from 92. *The Vicarage, 24 Castle Street, Titchfield, Fareham, Hants PO14 4DU* Titchfield (01329) 842324

MITCHINSON, Frank. b 37. AKC60. **d** 61 **p** 62. C Cross Heath *Lich* 61-64; C Forrabury w Minster and Trevalga *Truro* 64-68; C Harpenden St Nic *St Alb* 68-70; R Southwick *Chich* 70-83; V Billingshurst 83-88; V Preston from 88. *35 Preston Drove, Brighton BN1 6LA* Brighton (01273) 555033

MITCHINSON, Canon Ronald (Ron). b 35. Westmr Coll Ox MA91. Linc Th Coll 66. **d** 68 **p** 69. C Heworth St Mary *Dur* 68-72; C Banbury *Ox* 72-73; TV 73-76; New Zealand 76-82; TR Banbury *Ox* 82-86; RD Deddington 84-86; Ind Chapl 86-92; Hon Can Ch Ch 90-92; TV Brayton *York* from 92; Sen Ind Chapl Selby Coalfield from 92. *20 Mayfield Drive, Brayton, Selby, N Yorkshire YO8 9JZ* Selby (01757) 706239

MITFORD, Bertram William Jeremy (Bill). b 27. Wells Th Coll 62. **d** 64 **p** 65. C Frome St Jo *B & W* 68-71; V Cleeve 72-74; V Cleeve w Chelvey and Brockley 74-79; Chapl HM Pris Shepton Mallet from 79; C Shepton Mallet *B & W* 79-84; C Shepton Mallet w Doulting 84-92; rtd 92. *2 Charlton Road, Shepton Mallet, Somerset BA4 5NY* Shepton Mallet (01749) 342825

MITRA, Avijit. b 53. Keble Coll Ox BA76. Ox NSM Course 84. **d** 88 **p** 89. NSM Abingdon *Ox* from 88; Asst Chapl Abingdon Sch from 88. *Waste Court, 76 Bath Street, Abingdon, Oxon OX14 1EB* Abingdon (01235) 520326

MITRA, Mrs Nicola Jane. b 54. St Hugh's Coll Ox BA76 PGCE77 MA81. Ox Min Course DipMin94. **d** 94. NSM Abingdon *Ox* from 94. *Waste Court, 76 Bath Street, Abingdon, Oxon OX14 1EB* Abingdon (01235) 520326

MITSON, Mrs Carol Mae. b 46. Oak Hill NSM Course 89. **d** 93. NSM Lawford *Chelmsf* from 93. *Drift Cottage, The Drift, Dedham, Colchester CO7 6AH* Colchester (01206) 323116

MITSON, John Dane. b 29. Solicitor 56 SS Coll Cam MA53 LLM54. Oak Hill Th Coll 91 E Anglian Minl Tr Course 93. **d** 94. Dio Registrar and Legal Sec to Bp St E&I from 75; NSM Greenstead juxta Colchester *Chelmsf* from 94. *Drift Cottage, The Drift, Dedham, Colchester CO7 6AH* Colchester (01206) 323116 Fax 230524

MITSON, Miss Joyce. b 37. Man Univ CertEd64. Trin Coll Bris DipHE79. **dss** 79 **d** 87 **p** 94. Wellington w Eyton *Lich* 79-85; Farnworth *Liv* 85-87; Par Dn 87-91; TD Bilston *Lich* 91-94; TV 94; Lich Local Min Adv 91-94; C W Bromwich St Jas from 94. *St Paul's Vicarage, 93 Bagnall Street, West Bromwich, W Midlands B70 0TS*

MITTON, Michael Simon. b 53. Ex Univ BA75. St Jo Coll Nottm 76. **d** 78 **p** 79. C High Wycombe *Ox* 78-82; C Kidderminster St Geo *Worc* 82; TV 82-89; Dir Angl Renewal Min from 89; Angl Renewal Min Adv *Ripon* 90-91. *30 Bromley Street, Derby DE22 1HJ* Derby (01332) 368062 or 200175 Fax 200185

MOAT, Terry. b 61. Nottm Univ BTh92. Aston Tr Scheme 86 Linc Th Coll 88. **d** 92 **p** 93. C Caterham *S'wark* from 92. *70 Spencer Road, Caterham, Surrey CR3 5LB* Caterham (01883) 340882

MOATE, Gerard Grigglestone. b 54. BA. Oak Hill Th Coll 79. **d** 82 **p** 83. C Mildmay Grove St Jude and St Paul *Lon* 82-85; C Hampstead St Jo 85-88; P-in-c Pinxton *Derby* 88; V Charlesworth and Dinting Vale 88-95; V Dedham *Chelmsf* from 95. *The Vicarage, High Street, Dedham, Colchester CO7 6DE* Colchester (01206) 322136

MOATE, Phillip. b 47. SRN DN RNT. N Ord Course 87. **d** 90 **p** 91. NSM Upper Holme Valley *Wakef* 90-94; NSM Honley 94-95; P-in-c Roos and Garton in Holderness w Tunstall etc *York* from 95. *The Rectory, Roos, Hull HU12 0LD* Withernsea (01964) 670362

MOATT, Richard Albert. b 54. K Coll Lon BD76 AKC76. Linc Th Coll 80. **d** 81 **p** 82. C Egremont and Haile *Carl* 81-85; V Addingham, Edenhall, Langwathby and Culgaith from 85. *The Vicarage, Langwathby, Penrith, Cumbria CA10 1LW* Langwathby (01768) 881212

MOBBERLEY, Keith John. b 56. BA. Westcott Ho Cam. **d** 84 **p** 85. C Cov Caludon *Cov* 84-87; C Kenilworth St Nic 87-92; V Keresley and Coundon from 92. *The Vicarage, 34 Tamworth Road, Coventry CV6 2EL* Keresley (01203) 332717

MOBBERLEY, Mrs Susan. b 57. Kent Univ BA79. Westcott Ho Cam 81. dss 84 **d** 90 **p** 94. Cov Caludon *Cov* 84-87; Lic to Offic 87-92; NSM Keresley and Coundon from 92. *The Vicarage, 34 Tamworth Road, Coventry CV6 2EL* Keresley (01203) 332717

MOBBS, Bernard Frederick. b 26. S'wark Ord Course 71. **d** 72 **p** 73. C Purley St Barn *S'wark* 72-74; Vice-Prin S'wark Ord Course 74-80; P-in-c Sydenham St Bart *S'wark* 80-87; V Dormansland 87-92; rtd 92. *Fair Havens, Fletching Street, Mayfield, E Sussex TN20 6TH* Mayfield (01435) 872910

MOBERLY, Richard Hamilton. b 30. Trin Hall Cam BA53 MA57. Cuddesdon Coll 53. **d** 55 **p** 56. V Kennington Cross St Anselm *S'wark* 67-73; TV N Lambeth 74-80; Ind Chapl 80-95; rtd 95. *5 Atherfold Road, London SW9 9LL* 0171-733 6754

MOBERLY, Robert Walter Lambert. b 52. New Coll Ox MA77 Selw Coll Cam MA80 Trin Coll Cam PhD81. Ridley Hall Cam 74. **d** 81 **p** 82. C Knowle *Birm* 81-85; Lect Dur Univ from 85. *8 Princes Street, Durham DH1 4RP* 0191-386 4255 or 374 2067

MOBLEY, Ronald John. b 15. Worc Ord Coll. **d** 62 **p** 63. V Eastleach w Southrop *Glouc* 68-73; V Newland w Redbrook 74-80; rtd 80; Hon C St Mary-le-Strand w St Clem Danes *Lon* 85-86. *35 Church Street, Eastbourne, E Sussex BN21 1HN*

MOCKFORD, John Frederick. b 28. Em Coll Cam BA52 MA56. Ridley Hall Cam 52. **d** 54 **p** 55. CMS 65-73; Uganda 66-73; Can Missr Kampala 72-73; V Bushbury *Lich* 73-77; TR 77-84; Preb Lich Cathl 81-84; Dir Miss and Past Studies Ridley Hall Cam 84-88; V Ipswich St Marg *St E* 88-93; rtd 93. *10 Castle Brooks, Framlingham, Woodbridge, Suffolk IP13 9RN* Framlingham (01728) 724193

MOCKFORD, Peter John. b 57. Nottm Univ BSc79 St Jo Coll Dur BA88. Cranmer Hall Dur 86. **d** 89 **p** 90. C Tamworth *Lich* 89-94; V Blurton from 94. *The Vicarage, School Lane, Stoke-on-Trent ST3 3DU* Stoke-on-Trent (01782) 312163

MOESEL, Joseph Sams. b 65. Villanova Univ USA BA90 Ox Univ BTh93. Ripon Coll Cuddesdon DipMin95. **d** 95. C Twigworth, Down Hatherley, Norton, The Leigh etc *Glouc* from 95. *The Glebe House, Sandhurst Lane, Gloucester GL1 9NP* Gloucester (01452) 730447

MOFFAT, George. b 46. Edin Univ BD77 Open Univ BA87. Edin Th Coll 67. **d** 72 **p** 73. C Falkirk *Edin* 73-76; C Edin St Pet 76-81; Chapl Edin Univ 77-81; C Heston *Lon* 81-84; V S Elmsall *Wakef* 84-93; TR Manningham *Bradf* from 93. *The Rectory, 63 St Paul's Road, Manningham, Bradford, W Yorkshire BD8 7LS* Bradford (01274) 487042

MOFFATT, Neil Thomas. b 46. Fitzw Coll Cam BA68 MA72. Qu Coll Birm 69. **d** 71 **p** 72. C Old Charlton *S'wark* 71-74; C Walworth St Pet 74-75; C Walworth 75-77; C Dormansland 77-86; TR Padgate *Liv* from 86. *The Rectory, Station Road, Padgate, Warrington WA2 0PD* Padgate (01925) 821555

MOFFATT, Canon Percy Elliott. b 15. St Aug Coll Cant 38. **d** 40 **p** 41. R Stoke *Cov* 71-75; TR Cov Caludon 76-78; Hon Can Cov Cathl 76-82; V Dunchurch 78-82; rtd 82; Perm to Offic *Cov* from 82. *49 Dalehouse Lane, Kenilworth, Warks CV8 2EP* Kenilworth (01926) 55881

MOFFETT, Mrs Marie-Louise. b 25. St Andr Univ MA46 Cam Univ DipRS76. **d** 87 **p** 94. St Andr Univ Angl Chapl Team 87-91. *10 Queen's Gardens, St Andrews, Fife KY16 9TA* St Andrews (01334) 73678

MOFFITT, Mrs Vivien Louisa. b 37. LSE BSc59 DipPM60. Sarum & Wells Th Coll 90. **d** 91 **p** 94. NSM Chandler's Ford *Win* from 91. *13 Velmore Road, Eastleigh, Hants SO5 3HD* Chandler's Ford (01703) 265327

MOGER, Peter John. b 64. Mert Coll Ox BA85 BMus86 MA89 St Jo Coll Dur BA93. Cranmer Hall Dur 89. **d** 93 **p** 94. C Whitby *York* from 93. *31 George Street, Whitby, N Yorkshire YO21 1EW* Whitby (01947) 820827

MOGFORD, Canon Stanley Howard. b 13. St Pet Hall Ox BA35 DipTh36 MA39. Westcott Ho Cam 36. **d** 37 **p** 38. V Llanblethian w Cowbridge and Llandough etc *Llan* 63-80; rtd

80; Perm to Offic *Llan* from 80. *Fortis Green, 19 Plas Treoda, The Common, Whitchurch, Cardiff CF4 1PT* Cardiff (01222) 618839

MOGRIDGE, Christopher James. b 31. Culham Coll of Educn CertEd62 LCP70 FCollP86. St Steph Ho Ox 93. **d** 94 **p** 95. NSM Wellingborough St Andr *Pet* from 94. *April Cottage, Little Harrowden, Wellingborough, Northants NN9 5BB* Wellingborough (01933) 678412

MOIR, David William. b 38. St Aid Birkenhead 64. **d** 67 **p** 68. C Danbury *Chelmsf* 67-70; C Bollington St Jo *Ches* 70-72; V Sutton St Jas 72-81; V Prestbury 81-95; RD Macclesfield from 88; P-in-c Bosley and N Rode w Wincle and Wildboarclough from 95. *The Vicarage, Wincle, Macclesfield, Cheshire SK11 0QH* Wincle (01260) 227234

MOIR, Nicholas Ian. b 61. G&C Coll Cam BA82 MA86 Ox Univ BA86. Wycliffe Hall Ox 84. **d** 87 **p** 88. C Enfield St Andr *Lon* 87-91; Bp's Dom Chapl *St Alb* 91-94; Chapl St Jo Coll Cam from 94. *St John's College, Cambridge CB2 1TP* Cambridge (01223) 338600

MOLE, Arthur Penton. b 10. Witwatersrand Univ BA30. Bps' Coll Cheshunt 33. **d** 35 **p** 36. R Old Alresford *Win* 71-76; rtd 76; Perm to Offic *Worc* from 76. *15 Garden Styles, Pershore, Worcs WR10 1JW* Pershore (01386) 554167

MOLE, David Eric Harton. b 33. Em Coll Cam BA54 MA58 PhD62. Ridley Hall Cam 55. **d** 59 **p** 59. C Selly Hill St Steph *Birm* 59-62; Tutor St Aid Birkenhead 62-63; Chapl Peterho Cam 63-69; Ghana 69-72; Lect Qu Coll Birm 72-76; Tutor USPG Coll of the Ascension Selly Oak 76-87; C Burton *Lich* 87-93; Chapl Burton Gen Hosp 87-93; Chapl Ostend w Knokke and Bruges *Eur* from 93. *Ganzestraat 20/2, B-8000 Brugge, Belgium* Brugge (50) 347677

MOLE, Jennifer Vera. b 49. CertEd70. Qu Coll Birm 82. **d** 84. C Pontypool *Mon* 84-87; C Cyncoed 87-88; TD from 88. *100 Hill Rise, Llanedeyrn, Cardiff CF2 6UL* Cardiff (01222) 733915

MOLESWORTH, Canon Anthony Edward Nassau. b 23. Pemb Coll Cam BA45 MA48. Coll of Resurr Mirfield 45. **d** 46 **p** 47. Swaziland 52-68; Can 68-71; R Huish Episcopi w Pitney *B & W* 71-78; P-in-c High Ham 76-78; TR Langport Area Chs 78-84; R Charlton Musgrove, Cucklington and Stoke Trister 84-90; RD Bruton 86-90; rtd 90; Perm to Offic *B & W* from 90. *3 Barrow Hill, Stourton Caundle, Sturminster Newton, Dorset DT10 2LD* Stalbridge (01963) 362337

MOLL, David Henry. b 27. St Chad's Coll Dur 50. **d** 54 **p** 55. R Gt w Lt Poringland and Howe *Nor* 69-75; R Framingham Earl 79-92; rtd 92. *48 Sadler Road, Norwich NR6 6PQ* Norwich (01603) 406992

MOLL, Randell Tabrum. b 41. Lon Univ BD65. Wycliffe Hall Ox 62. **d** 66 **p** 67. C Drypool St Columba w St Andr and St Pet *York* 66-70; Asst Chapl HM Pris Hull 66-70; Asst Master Hull Gr Sch 66-70; C Netherton *Liv* 70-74; C Sefton 70-72; Ind Chapl 70-74 and from 92; Belgium 75-76; P-in-c Brockmoor *Lich* 76-81; Team Ldr Black Country Urban Ind Miss 76-81; Dir Chilworth Home Services 81-84; Asst Master Bp Reindarp Sch Guildf 84-90; France and Iraq 91; Chapl Sedbergh Sch Cumbria 92; Sen Chapl Miss in the Economy (Merseyside) from 92. *79 Moor Lane, Crosby, Liverpool L23 2SQ* 0151-932 0507 or 709 5586   Fax 709 7596

MOLLER, Canon George Brian. b 35. TCD BA60 MA64 Lon Univ BD84. **d** 61 **p** 62. C Belf St Pet *Conn* 61-64; C Larne and Inver 64-68; P-in-c Rathcoole 68-69; I 69-86; I Belf St Bart from 86; Chapl Stranmillis Coll of Educn Belf from 88; Preb Conn Cathl *Conn* from 90. *St Bartholomew's Rectory, 16 Mount Pleasant, Belfast BT9 5DS* Belfast (01232) 669995

MOLLOY, Mrs Heather. b 54. Bradf Univ BTech76. Local NSM Course 92. **d** 95. NSM Harwood *Man* from 95. *7 Fellside, Bolton BL2 4SH* Bolton (01204) 520395

MOLONY, Nicholas John. b 43. St Jo Coll Dur BA67 Birm Univ DipTh70 MA78. Qu Coll Birm 68. **d** 71 **p** 72. C Beaconsfield *Ox* 70-75; P-in-c Chesham Ch Ch 75-80; TV Gt Chesham 80-81; P-in-c Weston Turville 81-90; P-in-c Stoke Mandeville 87-89; P-in-c Gt Marlow 90-93; P-in-c Bisham 90-93; TR Gt Marlow w Marlow Bottom, Lt Marlow and Bisham from 93. *12 Thamesfield Gardens, Marlow, Bucks SL7 1PZ* Marlow (01628) 482660

MONBERG, Ms Ulla Stefan. b 52. BA79. Westcott Ho Cam 88. **d** 90 **p** 94. C Westmr St Jas *Lon* 90-94; Dean Women's Min and Area Dir of Ords Cen Lon from 94; Dean Women's Min Kensington from 94; Sec Dioc Bd of Women Candidates for Ord from 94. *London Diocesan House, 36 Causton Street, London SW1P 4AU* 0171-488 4318

MONCUR, Henry Alexander. b 11. AKC43. **d** 43 **p** 44. V Stoke Golding w Dadlington *Leic* 57-79; rtd 79; Perm to Offic *Pet* from 80. *16 Beaufort Drive, Kettering, Northants NN15 6SF* Burton Latimer (01536) 725791

MONK, Mrs Mary. b 38. CertEd58. S'wark Ord Course 85. **d** 88 **p** 94. NSM Lee Gd Shep w St Pet *S'wark* from 88. *9 Horn Park Lane, London SE12 8UX* 0181-318 5802

MONK, Nicholas John. b 32. Westcott Ho Cam 61. **d** 63 **p** 64. C Bris H Cross Inns Court *Bris* 63-67; C Stoke Bishop 67-69;

V Swindon All SS 69-75; V Ashton Keynes w Leigh 75-87; P-in-c Minety w Oaksey 82-87; RD Malmesbury 85-88; V Ashton Keynes, Leigh and Minety 87-91; TR Swindon St Jo and St Andr from 91. *The Vicarage, Verwood Close, Swindon SN3 2LE* Swindon (01793) 611473

MONKS, Ian Kay. b 36. K Coll Lon BA60 Lon Inst of Educn PGCE61. Oak Hill NSM Course 90. **d** 93. NSM Woodford Bridge *Chelmsf* from 93. *46 Summit Drive, Woodford Green, Essex IG8 8QP* 0181-550 2390

MONKS, John Stanley. b 12. AKC42. St D Coll Lamp 38. **d** 42 **p** 43. V Blyth St Cuth *Newc* 66-83; rtd 83. *56 West Dene Drive, North Shields, Tyne & Wear NE30 2SZ* 0191-257 0157

MONKS, Roger James. b 39. G&C Coll Cam BA61. Coll of Resurr Mirfield 61. **d** 63 **p** 64. C Higham Ferrers *Pet* 63-66; C Cheshunt *St Alb* 68-70; Chapl Dartington Hall Sch 70-71. *18 Coleson Hill Road, Wrecclesham, Farnham, Surrey GU10 4QQ*

MONMOUTH, Archdeacon of. See WOODMAN, Ven Peter Wilfred

MONMOUTH, Bishop of. See WILLIAMS, Rt Rev Rowan Douglas

MONMOUTH, Dean of. See LEWIS, Very Rev David Gareth

MONROE, James Allen. b 35. Stranmillis Coll TCert57. St Aid Birkenhead 63. **d** 64 **p** 65. C Belf St Mich *Conn* 64-68; C Coleraine 68-71; I 77-86; I Ballynure and Ballyeaston 71-77; I Holywood *D & D* from 86; RD Holywood from 89; Can Belf Cathl from 91. *The Vicarage, 156 High Street, Holywood, Co Down BT18 9HT* Belfast (01232) 422069 or 423622

MONTAGUE, Mrs Juliet. b 52. Nottm Univ BTh82. Linc Th Coll 78. **dss** 82 **d** 87 **p** 94. Gainsborough All SS *Linc* 82-86; Chapl Linc Cathl 86-92; Chapl Linc Colls of FE 86-92; D-in-c Whaplode Drove 92-94; D-in-c Gedney Hill 92-94; P-in-c from 94. *The Vicarage, Whaplode Drove, Spalding, Lincs PE12 0TN* Holbeach (01406) 330392

MONTAGUE-YOUENS, Canon Hubert Edward. b 30. Ripon Hall Ox 55. **d** 58 **p** 59. V Kidderminster St Geo *Worc* 69-72; R Ribbesford w Bewdley and Dowles 72-81; RD Kidderminster 74-81; Hon Can Worc Cathl 78-81; TR Bridport *Sarum* 81-86; RD Lyme Bay 82-86; V Easebourne *Chich* 86-89; Chapl K Edw VII Hosp Midhurst 86-89; rtd 89; Perm to Offic *Glouc* from 89; Perm to Offic *Worc* from 89. *71 Gloucester Road, Tewkesbury, Glos GL20 5SS* Tewkesbury (01684) 292363

✠**MONTEFIORE, Rt Rev Hugh William.** b 20. St Jo Coll Ox BA46 MA47 SS Coll Cam BD63 Aber Univ Hon DD77 Birm Univ Hon DD85. Westcott Ho Cam 48. **d** 49 **p** 50 **c** 70. C Newc St Geo *Newc* 49-51; Chapl and Tutor Westcott Ho Cam 51-53; Vice-Prin 53-54; Dean G&C Coll Cam 54-63; Asst Lect Th Cam Univ 56-59; Lect 59-63; Can Th Cov Cathl *Cov* 59-69; V Cam Gt St Mary w St Mich *Ely* 63-70; Hon Can Ely Cathl 69-70; Suff Bp Kingston-upon-Thames *S'wark* 70-78; Bp Birm 78-87; rtd 87; Asst Bp S'wark from 87. *White Lodge, 23 Bellevue Road, London SW17 7EB* 0181-672 6697

MONTEITH, David Robert Malvern. b 68. St Jo Coll Dur BSc89 Nottm Univ BTh92 MA93. St Jo Coll Nottm 90. **d** 93 **p** 94. C Kings Heath *Birm* from 93. *14 All Saints' Road, Birmingham B14 7LL* 0121-444 2491

MONTGOMERIE, Alexander (Sandy). b 47. St Jo Coll Nottm CertCS94. **d** 94. NSM Irvine St Andr *Glas* from 94. *105 Sharphill Road, Saltcoats, Ayrshire KA21 5QU* Saltcoats (01294) 465193

MONTGOMERIE, Andrew Simon. b 60. Keble Coll Ox BA82. Ridley Hall Cam 83. **d** 85 **p** 86. C Childwall All SS *Liv* 85-87; C Yardley St Edburgha *Birm* 87-90; TV Solihull from 90. *St Michael's Church Centre, Oak Cottage, Bryanston Road, Solihull, W Midlands B91 1BS* 0121-704 4730

MONTGOMERY, Canon Anthony Alan. b 33. Trin Hall Cam BA56. Edin Th Coll 56. **d** 58 **p** 59. C Dumfries *Glas* 58-63; P-in-c Airdrie 63-66; R 66-68; Asst Chapl Gordonstoun Sch from 68; Can St Andr Cathl Inverness *Mor* from 81. *Easter Hillside, Mosstowie, Elgin, Morayshire IV30 3XE* Alves (0134385) 282

MONTGOMERY, Charles George Greathead. b 08. AKC33. **d** 33 **p** 34. V Poundstock *Truro* 44-45; rtd 75. *Jasmine Cottage, Ash Cross, Bradworthy, Holsworthy, Devon EX22 7SP*

MONTGOMERY (nee YOUATT), Mrs Jennifer Alison. b 49. St Aid Coll Dur BSc70 Homerton Coll Cam PGCE71. N Ord Course 89. **d** 92 **p** 94. NSM Ripon H Trin *Ripon* from 92. *Washington House, Littlethorpe, Ripon, N Yorkshire HG4 3LJ* Ripon (01765) 605276

MONTGOMERY, Canon John Alexander. b 11. TCD BA34. **d** 35 **p** 36. RD Newtownforbes *K, E & A* 67-80; I Ardagh w Kilcommick 67-80; Preb Elphin Cathl 67-80; rtd 80; Hon C Bathgate *Edin* 83-91; Hon C Linlithgow 83-91. *6 Watson Place, Armadale, Bathgate, West Lothian EH48 2NJ* Armadale (01501) 731470

MONTGOMERY, Pembroke John Charles. b 24. Codrington Coll Barbados. **d** 53 **p** 55. St Vincent 55-73; Can Kingstown

Cathl 63-73; P-in-c Derby St Jas *Derby* 73-74; V 74-90; rtd 90. *37 Church Street, Tetbury, Glos GL8 8JG* Tetbury (01666) 504817

MONTGOMERY, Miss Rachel. b 63. Reading Univ BA85. Wycliffe Hall Ox BTh94. **d** 94 **p** 95. C Tufnell Park St Geo and All SS *Lon* from 94. *35 Weatherbury House, Wedmore Street, London N19 4RB* 0171-272 3057

MONTGOMERY, Stanley. b 18. St Cath Coll Cam BSc. Lich Th Coll. **d** 52 **p** 53. P-in-c Hitcham w Lt Finborough *St E* 93-95; Perm to Offic from 95. *34 Drovers Rise, Stanton, Bury St Edmunds, Suffolk IP31 2BW* Stanton (01359) 250359

MONTGOMERY, Thomas Charles Osborne. b 59. Edin Univ BD81. Edin Th Coll 77. **d** 82 **p** 83. C Glas St Mary *Glas* 82-85; C Dumfries 85-88; R Hamilton from 88. *The Rectory, 4C Auchingramont Road, Hamilton, Lanarkshire ML3 6JT* Hamilton (01698) 429895

MONTGOMERY, Timothy Robert (Tim). b 59. Hull Univ BA82 Cam Univ PGCE83. E Anglian Minl Tr Course 90. **d** 93 **p** 94. NSM Cam St Phil *Ely* from 93; Dir Romsey Mill Community Cen 93-94. *21 Coleridge Road, Cambridge CB1 3PH* Cambridge (01223) 248806 Fax 415855

MONTGOMERY, Archdeacon of. See PRITCHARD, Ven Thomas William

MOODY, Aubrey Rowland. b 11. Coll of Resurr Mirfield 53. **d** 55 **p** 56. C Wanstead St Mary *Chelmsf* 55-57; V Feering from 57. *Feering Vicarage, Colchester, Essex CO5 9NL* Kelvedon (01376) 570226

MOODY, Christopher John Everard (Chris). b 51. New Coll Ox BA72 Lon Univ MSc90. Cuddesdon Coll BA74. **d** 75 **p** 76. C Fulham All SS *Lon* 75-79; C Surbiton St Andr and St Mark *S'wark* 79-82; Chapl K Coll Lon 82-87; V S Lambeth St Anne and All SS *S'wark* 87-95; RD Lambeth 90-95; P-in-c Market Harborough *Leic* from 95; P-in-c Market Harborough Transfiguration from 95. *The Rectory, Rectory Lane, Market Harborough, Leics LE16 8AS* Market Harborough (01858) 462926

MOODY, Colin John. b 36. Chich Th Coll 61. **d** 63 **p** 64. C Hove All SS *Chich* 63-69; C Dulwich St Barn *S'wark* 69-70; Perm to Offic *Bris* 70-71; Perm to Offic *Chich* 72-78 and from 90; Lic to Offic *Ely* 78-93. *11 Hewitts, Henfield, W Sussex BN5 9TD* Henfield (01273) 495062

MOODY, Derek Frank. b 41. Univ of Wales BA62. Chich Th Coll 63. **d** 65 **p** 66. C Ellesmere Port *Ches* 65-69; C Lewisham St Jo Southend *S'wark* 69-73; TV Catford (Southend) and Downham 73-75; V Ham St Rich 75-83; V Catford St Laur 83-88; TV Brighton St Pet and St Nic w Chpl Royal *Chich* from 88. *5 Clifton Road, Brighton BN1 3HP* Brighton (01273) 321399

MOODY, Preb George Henry. b 27. ACIS56 ARCA68 DipChD77. Cranmer Hall Dur 69. **d** 71 **p** 72. C Marske in Cleveland *York* 71-74; Chapl to the Deaf *Lich* 74-89; Preb Lich Cathl 83-89; rtd 89. *21 Priestcrofts, Marske-by-the-Sea, Redcar, Cleveland TS11 7HW* Redcar (01642) 489660

MOODY, Ivor Robert. b 57. K Coll Lon BD AKC. Coll of Resurr Mirfield. **d** 82 **p** 83. C Leytonstone St Marg w St Columba *Chelmsf* 82-85; C Leigh-on-Sea St Marg 85-88; V Tilbury Docks from 88. *St John's Vicarage, Dock Road, Tilbury, Essex RM18 7PP* Tilbury (01375) 842417

MOOKERJI, Michael Manoje. b 45. Baring Union Coll Punjab BSc69. Ridley Hall Cam 83. **d** 85 **p** 86. C Heanor *Derby* 85-92; V Codnor and Loscoe 92-93; V Codnor from 93. *The Vicarage, Codnor, Ripley, Derbyshire DE5 9SN* Ripley (01773) 742516

MOON, Arthur Thomas. b 22. ACP53 LCP56 Lon Univ DipTh66. Sarum Th Coll 65. **d** 66 **p** 67. C Fulwood Ch Ch *Blackb* 66-71; Hon C Bispham 71-80; C 80-87; rtd 87; Perm to Offic *Blackb* from 87. *15 Kirkstone Drive, Blackpool FY5 1QQ* Blackpool (01253) 853521

MOON, John Charles. b 23. Sarum Th Coll 49. **d** 51 **p** 52. V Spalding St Jo *Linc* 67-82; V Spalding St Jo w Deeping St Nicholas 82-86; rtd 86. *14 Harrox Road, Moulton, Spalding, Lincs PE12 6PR* Holbeach (01406) 370111

MOON, Philip Russell. b 56. Em Coll Cam BA78 MA81 Reading Univ PGCE79. Wycliffe Hall Ox BA82. **d** 85 **p** 86. C Crowborough *Chich* 85-87; Hd of CYFA (CPAS) 87-94; C Lowestoft Ch Ch *Nor* from 94. *The Vicarage, 16 Corton Road, Lowestoft, Suffolk NR32 4PL* Lowestoft (01502) 572444

MOON, Thomas Arnold. b 24. Lon Univ BA51. Oak Hill Th Coll 49. **d** 52 **p** 53. V Everton St Benedict *Liv* 56-70; V Formby St Luke 70-95; rtd 95. *8 Harington Road, Formby, Liverpool L37 1NU* Formby (01704) 872249

MOONEY, Canon Paul Gerard. b 58. **d** 84 **p** 85. In RC Ch 84-90; Korea 90-94; Miss to Seamen 90-94; Chapl Antwerp Seafarers' Cen *Eur* from 94; Asst Chapl Antwerp St Boniface from 94. *Hoevensebaan 253, 2950 Kapellen, Antwerp, Belgium* Antwerp (3) 665-1122 or 233-3475

MOOR, David Drury. b 18. St Edm Hall Ox BA39 MA44. Wells Th Coll 46. **d** 48 **p** 49. V Bournemouth St Mich *Win* 69-83; rtd 83; Perm to Offic *Sarum* from 83; Perm to Offic *Win* from 83. *93 Western Avenue, Bournemouth BH10 6HG* Bournemouth (01202) 512455

MOOR, Maurice Albert Charles. b 03. St Paul's Coll Burgh 30. **d** 34 **p** 35. V Chute w Chute Forest *Sarum* 45-62; Lic to Offic *Ban* from 63; rtd 68. *Edensor Lodge, Llwyngwril, Gwynedd LL37 2JJ* Fairbourne (01341) 250495

MOOR, Simon Alan. b 65. Nottm Univ BTh93. Linc Th Coll 90. **d** 93 **p** 94. C Skegness and Winthorpe *Linc* from 93. *55 St Andrew's Drive, Skegness, Lincs PE25 1DJ* Skegness (01754) 768617

MOORE, Albert William (Bill). b 47. Birm Poly FTC72. W Midl Minl Tr Course 91. **d** 94. C Hobs Moat *Birm* from 94. *18 Newbold Close, Bentley Heath, Solihull, W Midlands B93 9BS* Knowle (01564) 775145

MOORE, Andrew Jonathon. b 57. York Univ BA82. Wycliffe Hall Ox BA84 MA89. **d** 86 **p** 86. Australia 86-90; Asst Chapl Worc Coll Ox 91-94; Chapl Jes Coll Ox from 94. *Jesus College, Oxford OX1 3DW* Oxford (01865) 279757 Fax 274215

MOORE, Anthony Harry. b 34. Westcott Ho Cam 88. **d** 90 **p** 91. C Eyke w Bromeswell, Rendlesham, Tunstall etc *St E* 90-93; V Aldeburgh w Hazlewood from 93. *The Vicarage, Church Walk, Aldeburgh, Suffolk IP15 5DU* Aldeburgh (01728) 452223

MOORE, Anthony Richmond (Tony). b 36. Clare Coll Cam BA59 MA63. Linc Th Coll 59. **d** 61 **p** 62. C Roehampton H Trin *S'wark* 61-66; C New Eltham All SS 66-70; PM Blackbird Leys CD *Ox* 70-81; Dioc Ecum Officer from 80; TV Dorchester 81-93; V Enstone and Heythrop from 93. *The Vicarage, Little Tew Road, Church Enstone, Chipping Norton, Oxon OX7 4NL* Chipping Norton (01608) 677319

MOORE, Dr Arthur Lewis. b 33. Dur Univ BA58 PhD64. Cranmer Hall Dur DipTh59. **d** 62 **p** 63. C Stone *Roch* 62-66; C Clevedon St Andr *B & W* 66-68; Chapl Wycliffe Hall Ox 68-70; Vice-Prin 70-83; P-in-c Ampfield *Win* 83-84; V Hursley and Ampfield 84-92; TV Ewyas Harold w Dulas, Kenderchurch etc *Heref* 92-94; P-in-c from 94. *The Rectory, Ewyas Harold, Hereford HR2 0EY* Golden Valley (01981) 240484

MOORE, Arthur Robert (Bob). b 15. Sarum Th Coll 62. **d** 63 **p** 64. V Steeple Ashton w Semington *Sarum* 67-79; V Keevil 72-79; P-in-c Southwick w Boarhunt *Portsm* 79-91; rtd 84. *1 High Street, Southwick, Fareham, Hants PO17 6EB* Cosham (01705) 382113 Fax 370991

MOORE, Canon Bernard Geoffrey. b 27. New Coll Ox BA47 MA52. Ely Th Coll 49. **d** 51 **p** 52. V Morecambe St Barn *Blackb* 67-81; R Standish 81-88; Hon Can Blackb Cathl 86-92; RD Chorley 86-92; V Charnock Richard 88-92; rtd 92; Perm to Offic *Ex* from 92. *29 Wiltshire Close, Exeter EX4 1LU* Exeter (01392) 58686

MOORE, Bernard George. b 32. Qu Coll Birm 57. **d** 60 **p** 61. C Middlesb St Columba *York* 60-62; S Africa 62-70; Chapl RN 70-74; C Milton *Portsm* 74-76; New Zealand from 76. *45 Feasegate Street, Manurewa, New Zealand* Auckland (9) 267-6924

MOORE, Brian Philip. b 51. AKC72. St Aug Coll Cant 72. **d** 74 **p** 75. C Hatf *St Alb* 74-78; C Radlett 78-81; V Eaton Bray w Edlesborough 81-92; RD Dunstable 85-90; V St Alb St Sav from 92. *St Saviour's Vicarage, 25 Sandpit Lane, St Albans, Herts AL1 4DF* St Albans (01727) 851526

✠**MOORE, Rt Rev Bruce Macgregor.** b 31. Univ of NZ BA55. Coll of Resurr Mirfield. **d** 57 **p** 58 **c** 92. C Blackpool St Steph *Blackb* 57-61; New Zealand from 61; Asst Bp Auckland from 92. *4 Lemonwood Place, Manurewa, Auckland 1702, New Zealand* Auckland (9) 268-1805 or 377-1989 Fax 268-1905

MOORE, Charles David (Charlie). b 59. RIBA86 Dundee Univ BSc82 BArch85. St Jo Coll Nottm DTS93. **d** 93 **p** 94. C Deane *Man* from 93. *281 Deane Church Lane, Bolton BL3 4ES* Bolton (01204) 64313

MOORE, Preb Clive Granville. b 31. St Pet Hall Ox BA54 MA58. Wycliffe Hall Ox 54. **d** 55 **p** 56. R Radstock *B & W* 69-71; P-in-c Writhlington 69-71; R Radstock w Writhlington 71-83; RD Midsomer Norton 81-83; R S Petherton w the Seavingtons 83-95; RD Crewkerne 83-92; RD Crewkerne and Ilminster 93; Preb Wells Cathl 90-95; rtd 95. *Mowries Stable, West Street, Somerton, Somerset TA11 6NA* Somerton (01458) 274649

MOORE, Colin Frederick. b 49. CITC 69. **d** 72 **p** 73. C Drumglass w Moygashel *Arm* 72-80; I Newtownhamilton w Ballymoyer and Belleek 80-87; I Newtownhamilton w Ballymoyer and Pomeroy etc 87-91; I Newtownhamilton w Ballymoyer and Belleck from 91; Hon VC Arm Cathl from 85; RD Mullabrack from 92. *71 Ballymoyer Road, Whitecross, Armagh BT60 2LA* Glenanne (01861) 507256

MOORE, David. b 36. Univ of Wales (Lamp) BA61 Magd Coll Cam BA63 MA68. Linc Th Coll 63. **d** 65 **p** 66. C Saltburn-by-the-Sea *York* 65-69; C Northallerton w Kirby Sigston 69-72; V Kirklevington from 72; V High and Low Worsall from 73;

Chapl HM Det Cen Kirklevington 72-89; Chapl HM Young Offender Inst Kirklevington Grange from 89. *The Vicarage, Kirk Levington, Yarm, Cleveland TS15 9LQ* Eaglescliffe (01642) 782439 Fax 790530

MOORE, David James Paton. b 60. Sheff Univ BEng82. Cranmer Hall Dur 88. **d** 91 **p** 92. C Pemberton St Mark Newtown *Liv* 91-94; C St Helens St Helen from 94. *75 King Edward Road, St Helens, Merseyside WA10 2AR* St Helens (01744) 613122

MOORE, David Leonard. b 51. **d** 80 **p** 82. Hon C Brixton St Matt *S'wark* 80-82; C 82-84; TV Bris St Agnes and St Simon w St Werburgh *Bris* 84-86; Perm to Offic 86-88; Perm to Offic *Blackb* from 88. *154 Victoria Road, Fulwood, Preston PR2 4NQ*

MOORE, Dr David Metcalfe. b 41. Hull Univ BA64 PhD69. Trin Coll Bris 76. **d** 78 **p** 79. C Marple All SS *Ches* 78-82; V Loudwater *Ox* 82-90; V Chilwell *S'well* 90-93; rtd 93. *10 Cromwell Avenue, Thame, Oxon OX9 3TD* Thame (01844) 217556

MOORE, David Roy. b 39. Clare Coll Cam BA61. Ripon Hall Ox 61. **d** 63 **p** 64. C Melton Mowbray w Thorpe Arnold *Leic* 63-66; Dep Dir The Samaritans 66-73; C St Steph Walbrook and St Swithun etc *Lon* 66-73; C Daybrook *S'well* 77-80; V 80-87; V Ham St Andr *S'wark* from 87. *The Vicarage, Ham Common, Richmond, Surrey TW10 5HG* 0181-940 9017

MOORE, Dr Deborah Claire Patricia. b 62. Essex Univ BSc83 Liv Univ PhD88 SS Coll Cam BA89. Ridley Hall Cam 87. **d** 90 **p** 94. Par Dn Hale and Ashley *Ches* 90-94; C 94; C Prenton from 94. *91 Woodchurch Lane, Prenton, Birkenhead, Merseyside L42 9PL* 0151-608 9793

MOORE, Canon Dennis Charles. b 19. Lon Univ BD46. Tyndale Hall Bris 39. **d** 43 **p** 44. V Wellington w Eyton *Lich* 62-70; RD Wrockwardine 66-70; V Watford St Mary *St Alb* 70-73; P-in-c Watford St Jas 70-73; V Watford 73-84; RD Watford 75-81; rtd 84; Perm to Offic *Nor* from 84. *82 Greenways, Eaton, Norwich NR4 6HF* Norwich (01603) 502492

MOORE, Donald John. b 31. Chich Th Coll 86. **d** 87 **p** 88. C Uckfield *Chich* 87-88; C Southwick 88-90; Bermuda from 90. *PO Box DD 188, St David's DD 01, Bermuda* Bermuda (1-809) 297-1231

MOORE, Douglas Gregory. b 49. Bris Univ BA71 CertEd72. Coll of Resurr Mirfield 87. **d** 89 **p** 90. C Hessle *York* 89-93; P-in-c Micklefield 93-94; P-in-c Micklefield w Aberford 94-95; V from 95. *The Vicarage, Great North Road, Micklefield, Leeds LS25 4AG* Leeds (0113) 286 2154

✠**MOORE, Rt Rev Edward Francis Butler.** b 06. TCD BA28 MA40 PhD44 Hon DD59. **d** 30 **p** 31 **c** 59. C Bray *D & G* 30-32; Hon CV Ch Ch Cathl Dub 31-35; C Dub Clontarf 32-34; I Castledermot w Kinneagh 34-40; I Greystones 40-58; RD Delgany 50-58; Can Ch Ch Cathl Dub 51-58; Adn Glendalough 57-58; Bp K, E & A 59-81; rtd 81. *Drumlona, Sea Road, Kilcoole, Co Wicklow, Irish Republic* Dublin (1) 287-6648

MOORE, Canon Edward James. b 32. TCD BA56 MA59. **d** 56 **p** 57. C Belf St Luke *Conn* 56-59; CF 59-62; C Dunmurry *Conn* 62-64; P-in-c Kilmakee 64-70; I Belf H Trin 70-80; I Jordanstown w Monkstown 80-91; I Jordanstown from 91; RD N Belf from 88; Can Belf Cathl from 90. *120A Circular Road, Newtownabbey, Co Antrim BT37 0RH* Belfast (01232) 862119

MOORE, Canon Fred. b 11. St Jo Coll Dur LTh42 BA44. St Aid Birkenhead 39. **d** 43 **p** 44. V Camerton, Seaton and W Seaton *Carl* 54-72; RD Maryport 67-70; Hon Can Carl Cathl 70-77; RD Solway 70-75; V Gt Broughton 72-77; rtd 77; Perm to Offic *Carl* from 77. *30 Braeside, Seaton, Workington, Cumbria CA14 1EH* Workington (01900) 62358

MOORE, Canon Henry James William. b 33. TCD BA55 MA70. **d** 56 **p** 57. C Mullabrack *Arm* 56-61; C Drumglass 61-63; I Clogherney 63-81; I Ballinderry w Tamlaght and Arboe from 81; Preb Arm Cathl from 90. *10 Brookmount Road, Coagh, Cookstown, Co Tyrone BT80 0BB* Ballyronan (01648) 418255

✠**MOORE, Rt Rev Henry Wylie.** b 23. Liv Univ BCom50 Leeds Univ MA72. Wycliffe Hall Ox 50. **d** 52 **p** 53 **c** 83. C Farnworth *Liv* 52-54; C Middleton *Man* 54-56; CMS 56-60; Iran 57-60; R Burnage St Marg *Man* 60-63; R Middleton 60-74; Home Sec CMS 74-80; Exec Sec CMS 80-83; Bp Cyprus and the Gulf 83-86; Gen Sec CMS 86-90; rtd 90; Asst Bp Dur 90-94. *Fern Hill Cottage, Hopesay, Craven Arms, Shropshire SY7 8HD* Craven Arms (015882) 248

MOORE, Preb Hugh Desmond. b 37. St Cath Soc Ox BA58 MA64. St Steph Ho Ox 58. **d** 61 **p** 62. C Kingston St Luke *S'wark* 61-68; Asst Chapl Lon Univ *Lon* 68-70; Chapl Edgware Gen Hosp from 70; V Hendon St Alphage *Lon* from 70; AD W Barnet 85-90; Preb St Paul's Cathl from 95. *The Vicarage, Montrose Avenue, Edgware, Middx HA8 0DN* 0181-952 4611

MOORE, Ivan.MA BTh. **d** 90 **p** 91. C Knock *D & D* 90-93. *3 Sandown Park South, Knock, Belfast BT5 6HE*   Belfast (01232) 653370

✠**MOORE, Rt Rev James Edward. b** 33. TCD BA54 MA64. **d** 56 **p** 57 **c** 95. C Knock *D & D* 56-60; C Ban St Comgall 60-62; P-in-c Belvoir 62-68; I Groomsport 68-75; I Dundela 75-95; Can Down Cathl 85-89; Treas 87-89; Adn Down 89-95; Chan Belf Cathl 89-95; Bp Conn from 95. *Temp address: Bishop's House, 22 Deramore Park, Belfast BT9 5JU*   Belfast (01232) 668442

MOORE, James Frederick. b 12. Sheff Univ BSc35 MSc36. **d** 38 **p** 40. Lic to Offic *Bradf* 55-84; rtd 77. *215 Bradford Road, Riddlesden, Keighley, W Yorkshire BD20 5JR*   Keighley (01535) 606094

MOORE, Canon James Kenneth. b 37. AKC62. St Boniface Warminster 62. **d** 63 **p** 64. C W Hartlepool St Oswald *Dur* 63-66; C-in-c Manor Park CD *Sheff* 66-76; TV Sheff Manor 76-78; R Frecheville and Hackenthorpe 78-87; V Bilham 87-91; V Sheff St Oswald from 91; Hon Can Sheff Cathl from 93. *St Oswald's Vicarage, 2 Bannerdale Road, Sheffield S7 2DL*   Sheffield (0114) 250 8226   Fax as telephone

MOORE, John. b 22. St Aid Birkenhead 54. **d** 57 **p** 58. I Templepatrick *Conn* 68-85; rtd 85. *Cuthona, 67 Prospect Road, Portstewart, Co Londonderry BT55 7NQ*   Portstewart (01265) 833905

MOORE, John. b 26. Univ of Wales (Lamp) BA51. Oak Hill Th Coll 51. **d** 53 **p** 54. V Retford *S'well* 67-73; R Aspenden and Layston w Buntingford *St Alb* 73-86; V Stanstead Abbots 86-91; rtd 91. *20 Radley Road, Abingdon, Oxon OX14 3PQ*   Abingdon (01235) 532518

MOORE, John Arthur. b 33. Cuddesdon Coll 70. **d** 71 **p** 72. Hon C Gt Burstead *Chelmsf* 71-74; Chapl Barnard Castle Sch from 74. *Littlemoor, Mount Eff Lane, Barnard Castle, Co Durham DL12 8UW*   Teesdale (01833) 38601

MOORE, Canon John Cecil. b 37. TCD BA61 MA67 BD69. CITC 62. **d** 62 **p** 63. C Belf St Matt *Conn* 62-65; C Holywood *D & D* 65-70; I Ballyphilip w Ardquin 70-77; I Mt Merrion 77-79; I Donaghcloney w Waringstown from 79; Treas Dromore Cathl 90-93; Chan from 93. *54 Banbridge Road, Waringstown, Lurgan, Co Armagh BT66 7QD*   Waringstown (01762) 881218

MOORE, John David (Dick). b 30. St Chad's Coll Dur BA54 DipTh55 DipEd56. **d** 56 **p** 57. C Wallsend St Pet *Newc* 56-60; C Leamington Priors All SS *Cov* 60-62; V Longford 62-75; P-in-c Nuneaton St Mary 75-77; V 77-83; V St Ives *Ely* from 83. *The Vicarage, Westwood Road, St Ives, Huntingdon, Cambs PE17 4DH*   St Ives (01480) 463254

MOORE, John Ernest. b 24. Oak Hill NSM Course. **d** 84 **p** 85. NSM Hornchurch H Cross *Chelmsf* 84-86; NSM S Woodham Ferrers 86-91; NSM Canvey Is from 91. *14 St Peter's Road, Canvey Island, Essex SS8 9NQ*   Canvey Island (01268) 690261

MOORE, John Henry. b 35. Nottm Univ BMus56 CertEd57 MA61. E Midl Min Tr Course 87. **d** 90 **p** 91. NSM Gotham *S'well* from 90; NSM Kingston and Ratcliffe-on-Soar from 90. *19 Hall Drive, Gotham, Nottingham NG11 0JT* Nottingham (0115) 983 0670

MOORE, John Keith. b 26. Sarum & Wells Th Coll 78. **d** 81 **p** 82. NSM Guildf All SS *Guildf* 81-86; NSM Guildf H Trin w St Mary 86-94; Dean of Chapter 90-94; Perm to Offic from 94. *6 Oakhurst, Crossways Road, Grayshott, Hindhead, Surrey GU26 6JW*   Hindhead (01428) 607174

MOORE, John Michael. b 48. Em Coll Cam BA70 MA73. Cuddesdon Coll 72. **d** 74 **p** 75. C Almondbury *Wakef* 74-78; TV Basingstoke *Win* 78-88; P-in-c Southn St Alb 88-91; V Swaything from 91. *St Alban's Vicarage, 357 Burgess Road, Southampton SO2 3BD*   Southampton (01703) 554231

MOORE, Canon John Richard. b 35. LTh59. St Jo Coll Nottm 56. **d** 59 **p** 60. C Northwood Em *Lon* 59-63; V Burton Dassett *Cov* 63-66; Youth Chapl 63-71; Dir Lindley Lodge Educn Trust Nuneaton 71-82; TR Kinson *Sarum* 82-88; Dir CPAS from 88; Hon Can Cov Cathl *Cov* from 95. *clo CPAS, Athena Drive, Tachbrook Park, Warwick CV34 6NG*   Warwick (01926) 334242   Fax 337613

MOORE, John Richard. b 45. Linc Th Coll 80. **d** 82 **p** 83. C Gt Grimsby St Mary and St Jas *Linc* 82-86; V Skirbeck Quarter 86-95; Miss to Seamen from 86; P-in-c Coningsby w Tattershall *Linc* from 95. *The Rectory, 22 High Street, Coningsby, Lincoln LN4 4RA*   Coningsby (01526) 342223

MOORE, Leonard Richard. b 22. Leeds Univ BA47. Coll of Resurr Mirfield 47. **d** 49 **p** 50. Lic to Offic *St Alb* 68-70; P-in-c Bedf H Trin 70-74; rtd 87; Hon C Cardington *St Alb* from 87. *22 Dart Road, Bedford MK41 7BT*   Bedford (01234) 357536

MOORE, Mrs Margaret Doreen. b 37. Westf Coll Lon BA58 CertEd59 BD63. Dalton Ho Bris 61. **dss** 85 **d** 87 **p** 94. Harold Hill St Paul *Chelmsf* 85-87; Hon Par Dn S Woodham Ferrers

MOORE, Matthew Edward George. b 38. Oak Hill Th Coll 77. **d** 77 **p** 78. C Larne and Inver *Conn* 77-80; I Desertmartin *D & R* 80-84; I Milltown *Arm* from 84. *10 Derrylileagh Road, Portadown, Craigavon, Co Armagh BT62 1TQ*   Annaghmore (01762) 851246

MOORE, Canon Mervyn. b 18. Leeds Univ BA40. Coll of Resurr Mirfield 40. **d** 42 **p** 43. C Middlesb St Martin *York* 42-45; C Helmsley 45-49; V Osbaldwick w Murton 49-54; S Africa from 54. *Canonsgarth, 11A Twelfth Avenue, Parktown North, 2193 South Africa*   Johannesburg (11) 298724

MOORE, Canon Michael Mervlyn Hamond. b 35. Pemb Coll Ox BA60 MA63. Wells Th Coll 60. **d** 62 **p** 63. C Bethnal Green St Matt *Lon* 62-66; Chapl Bucharest w Sofia and Belgrade *Eur* 66-67; Asst Gen Sec C of E Coun on Foreign Relns 67-70; Gen Sec 70-72; Abp's Asst Chapl on Foreign Relns *Cant* 72-82; Hon C Walworth St Pet *S'wark* 73-80; Hon Can Cant Cathl *Cant* 74-90; Chapl Chpl Royal Hampton Court Palace from 82; Dep P in O from 92. *Hampton Court Palace, West Molesey, Surrey KT8 9AU*   0181-977 2762

MOORE, Norman Butler. b 25. St Jo Coll Dur BA50 DipTh52. **d** 52 **p** 53. V Hazelwell *Birm* 69-75; V Watford St Andr *St Alb* 75-94; rtd 94. *5 Vicarage Close, St Albans, Herts AL1 2PU*   St Albans (01727) 863219

MOORE, Dr Paul. b 59. Ball Coll Ox BA82 DPhil86. Wycliffe Hall Ox DipTh87. **d** 89 **p** 90. C Ox St Andr *Ox* 89-93; V Kildwick *Bradf* from 93. *The Vicarage, Kildwick, Keighley, W Yorkshire BD20 9BB*   Cross Hills (01535) 633307

MOORE, Peter. b 21. Leeds Univ BA47. Coll of Resurr Mirfield 46. **d** 48 **p** 49. R Mundford w Lynford *Nor* 65-76; P-in-c Ickburgh w Langford 65-76; P-in-c Cranwich 65-76; V Whitley *Newc* 76-86; rtd 86; Perm to Offic *Newc* from 86. *31 Glebelands, Corbridge, Northd NE45 5DS*   Hexham (01434) 633207

MOORE, Very Rev Peter Clement. b 24. OBE93. FSA Ch Ch Ox BA45 MA48 DPhil54. Cuddesdon Coll 45. **d** 47 **p** 48. Can Res Ely Cathl *Ely* 67-73; Vice-Dean 71; Dean St Alb 73-93; rtd 93. *Thruxton House, Thruxton, Hereford HR2 9AX*   Wormbridge (0198121) 376

MOORE, Raymond. b 47. QUB BSc70. **d** 87 **p** 88. NSM Belf All SS *Conn* from 87. *14 Osborne Park, Belfast BT9 6JN*   Belfast (01232) 669168

MOORE, Canon Richard Noel. b 34. TCD BA56 MA60. **d** 57 **p** 58. C Derry Cathl *D & R* 57-60; I Clondehorkey 60-66; I Stranorlar w Meenglas and Kilteevogue 66-76; I Glendermott from 76; Can Derry Cathl from 89. *Glendermott Rectory, Altnagelvin, Londonderry BT47 2LS*   Londonderry (01504) 43001

MOORE, Richard Norman Theobald. b 39. St Andr Univ BSc62 Lon Univ BD66. Clifton Th Coll. **d** 66 **p** 67. C Stowmarket *St E* 66-69; C New Humberstone *Leic* 69-72; P-in-c Leic Martyrs 73; V 73-84; Chapl Manor Hosp Epsom 84-94; Chapl St Ebba's Hosp Epsom from 94. *72 Newton Wood Road, Ashtead, Surrey KT21 1NO, or St Ebba's Hospital, Hook Road, Epsom, Surrey KT19 8NL*   Ashtead (01372) 272525 or 722212

MOORE, Robert Allen. b 32. Univ of the Pacific BA54 Boston Univ STB58 STM59. **d** 63 **p** 63. USA 63-80; V Farington *Blackb* 80-83; TV Preston St Jo 83-85; P-in-c Fleetwood 85-87; V Leyland St Jas from 87. *St James's Vicarage, 201 Slater Lane, Leyland, Preston PR5 3SH*   Leyland (01772) 421034

MOORE, Canon Robert Denholm. b 23. TCD BA45 Div Test46. **d** 46 **p** 47. I Tamlaghtfinlagan w Myroe *D & R* 65-92; Chapl HM Pris Magilligan 72-92; Can Derry Cathl *D & R* 80-92; rtd 92. *22 Tyler Road, Limavady, Co Londonderry BT49 0DR* Limavady (015047) 68597

MOORE, Canon Robert George Chaffey. b 11. Kelham Th Coll 28. **d** 39 **p** 40. R Compton Abbas *Sarum* 49-73; Can and Preb Sarum Cathl from 72; TV Shaston 73-77; rtd 77. *Ashton House, 20 Stratford Road, Salisbury SP1 3JH*   Salisbury (01722) 338018

MOORE, Robin Alan. b 42. Portsm Coll of Tech DBS65 Lon Univ BA71 Garnett Coll Lon CertEd75 Open Univ AdDipEdMan87. S Dios Minl Tr Scheme 91. **d** 94 **p** 95. NSM Barcombe *Chich* from 94. *Yew Tree House, School Path, Barcombe, Lewes, E Sussex BN8 5DN*   Barcombe (01273) 400747

MOORE, Robin Hugh. b 52. CertEd BEd QUB BD TCD DipTh. **d** 84 **p** 85. C Derryloran *Arm* 84-86; C Knock *D & D* 86-89; Bp's C Belf St Steph w St Luke *Conn* 89-94; I from 94. *92 Lansdowne Road, Belfast BT15 4AB*   Belfast (01232) 774119

MOORE, Ronald Spencer. b 09. Leeds Univ BA33. Coll of Resurr Mirfield 33. **d** 35 **p** 36. R Warburton *Ches* 63-74; rtd 74. *2 Russell Avenue, Sale, Cheshire M33 2ET*   0161-973 2157

MOORE, Very Rev Thomas Robert. b 38. TCD 65. Lambeth DipTh79 MA84. **d** 68 **p** 69. C Dub Drumcondra w N Strand *D & G* 68-70; C Portadown St Columba *Arm* 70-72; I Kilskeery w Trillick *Clogh* 72-85; RD Kilskeery 81-86; Dioc Sec from 83; I Trory w Killadeas 85-95; Can Clogh Cathl 86-89; Preb 89-91; Preb Donaghmore St Patr Cathl Dub 91-95; Dean Clogh from 95; I Clogh w Errigal Portclare from 95. *The Deanery, 10 Augher Road, Clogher, Co Tyrone BT76 0AD* Clogher (016625) 48235 Fax as telephone

MOORE, Mrs Wendy. b 44. Westcott Ho Cam CTM94. **d** 94 **p** 95. C Rotherham *Sheff* from 94. *3 Reneville Road, Rotherham, S Yorkshire S60 2AR* Rotherham (01709) 364729

MOORE, William Henry. b 14. K Coll Lon 34. **d** 38 **p** 39. Perm to Offic *Nor* 62-71; Asst Master Mildenhall Sec Sch 68-73; Heartsease Sch Nor 73-75; C Mildenhall *St E* 71-73; rtd 79; Hon C Thorpe *Nor* from 88. *21 Green Court, Avenue Green, Norwich NR7 0DN* Norwich (01603) 32758

MOORE, Canon William James Foster. b 26. TCD BA50. **d** 50 **p** 51. I Broomhedge *Conn* 66-83; I Dunluce 83-95; Can Belf Cathl 88-95; rtd 95. *2 Dunluce Park, Portballintrae, Bushmills, Co Antrim BT57 8YZ* Bushmills (012657) 32645

MOORE, William Morris. b 33. QUB BSc55 TCD. **d** 61 **p** 62. C Belf St Mich *Conn* 61-64; I 70-80; C Belf All SS 64-70; I Ballynafeigh St Jude *D & D* from 80. *10 Mornington, Annadale Avenue, Belfast BT7 3JS* Belfast (01232) 491602

MOORE, William Thomas Sewell. b 21. MRCS LRCP MA. Westcott Ho Cam. **d** 82 **p** 83. Chapl Countess Mountbatten Ho Southn 84-90; Hon C Shedfield *Portsm* from 84; rtd 90. *Crossways, Blind Lane, Wickham, Fareham, Hants PO17 5HD* Wickham (01329) 832119

MOORGAS, Geoffrey Gordon. b 30. Sarum & Wells Th Coll 80. **d** 81 **p** 82. C Brixton St Matt *S'wark* 81-84; C Clapham Old Town 84-87; C Clapham TM 87; Namibia 87-94; rtd 95. *St Silvan's House, Red Lane, Oxted, Surrey RH8 0RS*

MOORHEAD, Michael David. b 52. BSc BA. St Steph Ho Ox. **d** 83 **p** 84. C Kilburn St Aug w St Jo *Lon* 83-87; C Kenton 87-89; V Harlesden All So from 89; P-in-c Willesden St Matt from 92. *All Souls' Vicarage, 3 Station Road, London NW10 4UJ* 0181-965 4988

MOORHOUSE, Christine Susan. b 49. K Coll Lon BD71. W Midl Minl Tr Course. **dss** 86 **d** 87 **p** 94. NSM Stourbridge St Thos *Worc* from 86. *20 High Street, Stourbridge, W Midlands DY8 4NJ* Stourbridge (01384) 395381

MOORHOUSE, Humphrey John. b 18. Oak Hill Th Coll 37. **d** 41 **p** 42. R Grayne *Chelmsf* 45-83; rtd 83. *12 Waverley Road, Benfleet, Essex SS7 4AZ* South Benfleet (01268) 754952

MOORHOUSE, Llewellyn Owen. b 14. Ely Th Coll 63 St Deiniol's Hawarden. **d** 64 **p** 65. V Grayrigg *Carl* 68-75; P-in-c Sawrey 75-80; rtd 80. *Regent House, 17 Church Street, Beaumaris, Gwynedd LL58 8AB* Beaumaris (01248) 810628

MOORHOUSE, Peter. b 42. Liv Univ BSc64 Hull Univ CertEd. Linc Th Coll 79. **d** 81 **p** 82. C Horsforth *Ripon* 81-85; R Ackworth *Wakef* from 85. *The Rectory, Ackworth, Pontefract, W Yorkshire WF7 7EJ* Pontefract (01977) 602751

MOORSOM, Christopher Arthur Robert. b 55. Ox Univ BA. Sarum & Wells Th Coll 79. **d** 82 **p** 83. C Bradford-on-Avon *Sarum* 82-85; R Broad Town, Clyffe Pypard and Tockenham 85-89; V Banwell *B & W* from 89. *The Vicarage, 3 East Street, Banwell, Weston-super-Mare, Avon BS24 6BN* Banwell (01934) 822320

MOORSOM, Robert Coverdale. b 23. ARCM48. Cuddesdon Coll 49. **d** 50 **p** 51. V Bierley *Bradf* 65-71; C Wareham *Sarum* 71-80; TV Gillingham 80-83; R The Lulworths, Winfrith Newburgh and Chaldon 83-89; rtd 89. *4 Hodges Close, Poole, Dorset BH17 7QE* Poole (01202) 684897

MORALEE, Thomas Edward (Tony). b 33. S'wark Ord Course. **d** 82 **p** 83. NSM Wandsworth All SS *S'wark* 82-90; NSM Gt Bookham *Guildf* 91-92; Perm to Offic from 92. *71 Eastwick Park, Leatherhead, Surrey KT23 3NH* Leatherhead (01372) 454433

MORAY, ROSS AND CAITHNESS, Bishop of. *See* MACGREGOR, Rt Rev Gregor

MORAY, ROSS AND CAITHNESS, Dean of. *See* FORREST, Very Rev Robin Whyte

MORCOM, Canon Anthony John. b 16. Clare Coll Cam BA38 MA42. Cuddesdon Coll 38. **d** 39 **p** 40. V Cam St Mary Less *Ely* 66-73; RD Cam 71-73; Can Res Ely Cathl 74-83; rtd 84; Lic to Offic *Ely* from 84. *33 Porson Road, Cambridge CB2 2ET* Cambridge (01223) 62352

MORDECAI, Mrs Betty. b 27. Birm Univ BA48 Cam Univ CertEd49. Wycliffe Hall Ox 85. **dss** 86 **d** 87 **p** 94. Leamington Priors All SS *Cov* 86-87; Hon Par Dn 87-89; C Worc City St Paul and Old St Martin etc *Worc* 89-94; rtd 94. *8 Swains Crofts, Leamington Spa, Warks CV31 1YW* Leamington Spa (01926) 882001

MORDECAI, Thomas Huw. b 59. Bris Univ BA81 St Jo Coll Dur BA85. Cranmer Hall Dur 83. **d** 87 **p** 88. C Gillingham St Mary *Roch* 87-90; Chapl Warw Sch from 90. *21 Calder Walk, Leamington Spa, Warks CV31 1SA* Leamington Spa (01926) 886042/493298

MORE, Richard David Antrobus. b 48. St Jo Coll Dur BA70 DipTh71. Cranmer Hall Dur 70. **d** 72 **p** 73. C Macclesfield St Mich *Ches* 72-77; Chapl Lee Abbey 77-82; V Porchester *S'well* from 82; RD Gedling from 90. *The Vicarage, Marshall Hill Drive, Nottingham NG3 6FY* Nottingham (0115) 960 6185

MORECROFT, Michael William. b 40. MIBiol Man Univ MEd. W Midl Minl Tr Course. **d** 86 **p** 87. Hd Master Polesworth Sch Warks from 86; Hon C Wylde Green *Birm* 86-89; Hon C Castle Bromwich St Clem from 89. *St Clement's Vicarage, Lanchester Way, Birmingham B36 9JG* 0121-747 4460

MORETON, Mark. b 39. Jes Coll Cam BA64 MA68. Westcott Ho Cam. **d** 65 **p** 66. C Portsea All SS *Portsm* 65-70; C St Martin-in-the-Fields *Lon* 70-72; Chapl Jes Coll Cam 72-77; R Stafford St Mary and St Chad *Lich* 77-79; P-in-c Stafford Ch Ch 77-79; P-in-c Marston w Whitgreave 77-79; TR Stafford 79-91; V W Bromwich All SS from 91. *All Saints' Vicarage, 90 Hall Green Road, West Bromwich, W Midlands B71 3LB* 0121-588 2647

MORETON, Dr Michael Bernard. b 44. St Jo Coll Cam BA66 MA70 Ch Ch Ox BA66 MA69 DPhil69. St Steph Ho Ox 66. **d** 68 **p** 69. C Banstead *Guildf* 68-74; R Alburgh *Nor* 74-75; R Denton 74-75; R Middleton Cheney w Chacombe *Pet* 75-87. *Penny Royal, 19 Thorpe Road, Chacombe, Banbury, Oxon OX17 2JW* Banbury (01295) 710631

MORETON, Preb Michael Joseph. b 17. Univ Coll Lon BA40 Ch Ch Ox BA47 MA53. Wells Th Coll 47. **d** 48 **p** 49. Lect Th Ex Univ 57-86; R Ex St Mary Steps *Ex* 59-86; P-in-c 86-92; RD Christianity 83-89; Preb Ex Cathl from 85; rtd 86. *3 Glenthorne Road, Duryard, Exeter EX4 4QU* Exeter (01392) 438083

MORETON, Philip Norman Harley. b 28. Linc Th Coll. **d** 57 **p** 58. V Linc St Giles *Linc* 65-70; V Bracebridge Heath 71-77; V Seasalter *Cant* 77-84; TV Whitstable 84-88; rtd 88. *The Cottage, 2 Broad Lane, Howden, Goole, N Humberside DN14 7DN* Howden (01430) 430552

MORETON, Rupert Robert James. b 66. TCD BA89. CITC BTh92. **d** 92 **p** 93. C Dub Ch Ch Cathl Gp *D & G* from 92. *32 Shandon Drive, Dublin 7, Irish Republic* Dublin (1) 838-0469

✠**MORGAN, Rt Rev Alan Wyndham.** b 40. Univ of Wales (Lamp) BA62. St Mich Coll Llan 62. **d** 64 **p** 65 **c** 89. C Llangyfelach and Morriston *S & B* 64-69; C Swansea St Pet 69-72; C Cov E *Cov* 72-73; TV 73-83; Bp's Officer for Soc Resp 78-83; Adn Cov 83-89; Suff Bp Sherwood *S'well* from 89. *Sherwood House, High Oakham, Mansfield, Notts NG18 5AJ* Mansfield (01623) 657491 Fax 662526

MORGAN, Anthony Hogarth. b 42. St Josef Missiehuis Holland 60 St Jos RC Coll Lon 62. **d** 65 **p** 66. In RC Ch 66-93; NSM Handsworth Woodhouse *Sheff* 93-94; C Sheff Norwood St Leon from 94. *St Hilda's House, 2 Firth Park Crecsent, Sheffield S5 6HE* Sheffield (0114) 243 6308

✠**MORGAN, Rt Rev Dr Barry Cennydd.** b 47. Lon Univ BA69 Selw Coll Cam BA72 MA74 Univ of Wales PhD86. Westcott Ho Cam 70. **d** 72 **p** 73 **c** 93. Chapl Bryn-y-Don Community Sch 72-75; C St Andrew's Major and Michaelston-le-Pit *Llan* 72-75; Ed Welsh Churchman 75-82; Lect Th Univ of Wales (Cardiff) 75-77; Chapl and Lect St Mich Coll Llan 75-77; Warden Ch Hostel Ban 77-84; Chapl and Lect Th Univ of Wales (Ban) 77-84; In-Service Tr Adv *Ban* 78-84; Dir of Ords 82-84; Can Ban Cathl 83-84; R Wrexham *St As* 84-86; Adn Meirionnydd *Ban* 86-93; R Criccieth w Treflys 86-93; Bp Ban from 93. *Tyr Esgob, Bangor, Gwynedd LL57 2SS* Bangor (01248) 362895 Fax 354866

MORGAN, Bernard Spencer Trevor. b 32. AKC55. **d** 56 **p** 57. R Kessingland *Nor* 65-83; RD Lothingland 71-76; R St Just in Roseland w Philleigh *Truro* 83-87; V Ludham w Potter Heigham *Nor* 87-93; RD Waxham 89-93; rtd 93; Perm to Offic *Nor* from 93. *7 Stuart Drive, Beccles, Suffolk NR24 9SB* Beccles (01502) 715654

MORGAN, Miss Beryl. b 30. **dss** 83 **d** 87 **p** 94. Hd Dss 70-87; Dioc Lay Min Adv *Lich* 70-93; Willenhall H Trin 80-87; Par Dn 87-93; rtd 93. *11A Church Hill, Penn, Wolverhampton WV4 5NP* Wolverhampton (01902) 337173

MORGAN, Brian. b 35. Lon Univ BA58. Wells Th Coll 59. **d** 61 **p** 62. C Withington *Man* 61-63; C Rochdale 63-65; Trinidad and Tobago 65-69; V Heywood St Jas *Man* 69-74; Miss to Seamen 74-80; Kenya 74-77; Chapl Pernis Miss to Seamen *Eur* 77-78; Antwerp 78-80; V Skerton St Chad *Blackb* 80-84; P-in-c Oswaldtwistle Immanuel 84-87; P-in-c Oswaldtwistle All SS 84-87; V Barrowford from 87. *The Vicarage, Wheatley Lane Road, Barrowford, Nelson, Lancs BB9 6QS* Nelson (01282) 613206

MORGAN, Christopher Heudebourck. b 47. Lon Univ DipTh70 Lanc Univ BA73 Heythrop Coll Lon MTh91. Kelham Th Coll 66. **d** 73 **p** 74. C Birstall *Leic* 73-76; Asst Chapl Brussels *Eur* 76-80; P-in-c Redditch St Geo *Worc* 80-81; TV Redditch, The

Ridge 81-85; V Sonning *Ox* from 85; Prin Berks Chr Tr Scheme 85-89; Dir Past Studies Ox Min Course from 92. *The Vicarage, Thames Street, Sonning, Reading RG4 0UR* Reading (01734) 693298

MORGAN, Christopher John. b 46. Brasted Th Coll 68 Linc Th Coll 70. **d** 72 **p** 73. C Earley St Pet *Ox* 72-76; C Epsom St Martin *Guildf* 76-79; V Stoneleigh 79-83; Ind Chapl *York* 83-87; NACRO 87-91; V York St Hilda *York* from 92. *St Hilda's Vicarage, 155 Tang Hall Road, York YO1 3SD* York (01904) 413150

MORGAN, David Farnon Charles. b 43. Leeds Univ BA68. Coll of Resurr Mirfield 68. **d** 70 **p** 71. C Swinton St Pet *Man* 70-73; C Langley All SS and Martyrs 73-75; R Salford St Clem w St Cypr Ordsall 75-76; R Salford Ordsall St Clem 76-86; V Adlington *Blackb* from 86. *St Paul's Vicarage, Railway Road, Adlington, Chorley, Lancs PR6 9QZ* Adlington (01257) 480253

MORGAN, David Joseph (Joe). b 47. Bp Burgess Hall Lamp 66 St Deiniol's Hawarden 74. **d** 74 **p** 75. C Pemb Dock *St D* 74-77; C Burry Port and Pwll 77-80; Miss to Seamen from 80; Sen Chapl and Sec Welsh Coun from 85. *25 Glanmor Park Road, Sketty, Swansea SA2 0QG* Swansea (01792) 206637

MORGAN, David Watcyn. b 14. St D Coll Lamp. **d** 64 **p** 65. R Herbrandston and St Ishmael w Hasguard *St D* 70-83; rtd 83. *31 Glenalla Road, Llanelli, Dyfed SA15 1EE* Llanelli (01554) 776572

MORGAN, Denis. b 36. Cuddesdon Coll 67. **d** 69 **p** 70. C Bush Hill Park St Steph *Lon* 69-72; C Stevenage St Nic *St Alb* 72-75; V Croxley Green St Oswald 75-85; V Shillington from 85. *All Saints' Vicarage, Shillington, Hitchin, Herts SG5 3LS* Hitchin (01462) 711240

MORGAN, Canon Edgar Francis Andrew. b 07. St Jo Coll Dur BA34 MA38. **d** 34 **p** 35. V Coleshill *Birm* 61-75; V Maxstoke 61-75; rtd 75; Perm to Offic *B & W* from 75. *34 Severn Avenue, Weston-super-Mare, Avon BS23 4DQ* Weston-super-Mare (01934) 621299

MORGAN, Enid Morris Roberts. b 40. St Anne's Coll Ox BA61 Univ of Wales (Ban) MA73. United Th Coll Abth BD81. **d** 84. C Llanfihangel w Llanafan and Llanwnnws etc *St D* 84-86; D-in-c 86-93; Dir Bd of Miss Ch in Wales from 93. *The Church in Wales Centre, Woodland Place, Penarth, S Glam CF64 2EX* Cardiff (01222) 708234 Fax 712413

MORGAN, Gareth Morison Kilby. b 33. Bris Univ BA56. Cuddesdon Coll 57 Bangalore Th Coll. **d** 61 **p** 62. C St Helier *S'wark* 61-65; Chapl Scargill Ho 65-70; Dir RE *Linc* 71-74; Dir of Educn *St E* 74-81; TR Hanley H Ev *Lich* 81-89; TR Cen Telford 89-92; Warden Glenfall Ho *Glouc* from 92. *Glenfall House, Harp Hill, Cheltenham, Glos GL54 4EP* Cheltenham (01242) 583654 Fax 251314

MORGAN, Geoffrey. b 51. AKC72. St Aug Coll Cant 73. **d** 74 **p** 75. C Hulme Ascension *Man* 74-77; C Nantwich *Ches* 77-79; R Hatf *St Alb* 79-86; Chapl S Beds HA 86-91; Chapl Luton and Dunstable Hosp 86-91; Chapl Cov Poly *Cov* 91-92; Chapl Cov Univ 92-95; rtd 95. *9 Spencer Road, Coventry CV5 6PA* Coventry (01203) 670124

MORGAN, Glyn. b 21. Oak Hill Th Coll 73. **d** 76 **p** 77. Hon C Barton Seagrave w Warkton *Pet* from 76. *St Edmund's House, Warkton, Kettering, Northants NN15 5AB* Kettering (01536) 520610

MORGAN, Glyn. b 33. Univ of Wales (Ban) BA55 MA69. Coll of Resurr Mirfield 55. **d** 57 **p** 58. C Dolgellau *Ban* 57-60; C Conway 60-63; V Corris 63-68; Hd of RE Friars' Sch Ban 69-70; Lic to Offic 70-71; Hd of RE Oswestry Boys' Modern Sch 70-74; Hd of RE Oswestry High Sch for Girls 74-79; Hon C Oswestry H Trin *Lich* 71-79; Hd of RE Fitzalan Sch Oswestry 79-88; Perm to Offic 79-84; Perm to Offic *St As* 84-88; V Meifod and Llangynyw from 88; RD Caereinion from 89. *The Vicarage, Meifod, Powys SY22 6DH* Meifod (0193884) 231

MORGAN, Graham. b 47. S'wark Ord Course. **d** 83 **p** 84. NSM S Kensington St Steph *Lon* 83-90; NSM Hammersmith H Innocents from 90. *24 Charville Court, Charville Road, London W14 9JG* 0171-381 3211

MORGAN, Canon Gwilym Owen. b 17. LSE BSc47. Westcott Ho Cam 46. **d** 48 **p** 49. Chapl Salford R Hosp 51-71; R Salford St Phil w St Steph *Man* 59-71; RD Salford 57-71; Hon Can Man Cathl 62-71; Can Res 71-85; Sub-Dean 72-85; rtd 86; Perm to Offic *Man* from 86. *20 Lyndhurst Road, Didsbury Village, Manchester M20 0AA* 0161-434 2732

MORGAN, Harold Evan. b 17. St D Coll Lamp BA38. **d** 40 **p** 41. V Newc *Llan* 68-82; rtd 83; Perm to Offic *Llan* from 82. *28 Seaview Drive, Ogmore-by-Sea, Bridgend, M Glam CF32 0PB* Southerndown (01656) 880467

MORGAN, Henry. b 45. Hertf Coll Ox BA68. Westcott Ho Cam 68. **d** 70 **p** 71. C Lee St Marg *S'wark* 70-73; C Newington St

Paul 73-76; V Camberwell St Mich w All So w Em 76-84; V Kingswood 84-93; Perm to Offic from 93. *4 Glebe Gardens, New Malden, Surrey KT3 5RY* 0181-942 4362

MORGAN, Ian David John. b 57. LTCL75 Hull Univ BA78. Ripon Coll Cuddesdon 80. **d** 83 **p** 84. C Heref H Trin *Heref* 83-86; C New Shoreham *Chich* 86-88; Researcher, Producer & Presenter BBC Local Radio 88-92; V Ipswich All Hallows *St E* 92-95; TR Ipswich St Mary at Stoke w St Pet, Stoke Park from 95. *The Rectory, 74 Ancaster Road, Ipswich IP2 9AJ* Ipswich (01473) 601895

MORGAN, Ian Stephen. b 50. Open Univ BA88. Sarum & Wells Th Coll 86. **d** 88 **p** 89. C Baldock w Bygrave *St Alb* 88-91; C Rumburgh w S Elmham w the Ilketshalls *St E* 91-92; C S Elmham and Ilketshall 92-95; V Bungay H Trin w St Mary from 95. *The Vicarage, 3 Trinity Gardens, Bungay, Suffolk NR35 1HH* Bungay (01986) 892110

MORGAN, James Geoffrey Selwyn. b 59. Ex Univ BA81 PGCE82 Dur Univ CCSk91. Cranmer Hall Dur 88. **d** 91 **p** 92. C Reading St Agnes w St Paul *Ox* 91-93; C Bromham w Oakley and Stagsden *St Alb* from 94. *St Mary's House, 65 Lincroft, Oakley, Bedford MK43 7SS* Oakley (01234) 826153

MORGAN, John Aeron. b 15. St D Coll Lamp BA37. **d** 40 **p** 41. R Harley w Kenley *Heref* 62-73; P-in-c Hughley 65-73; V Pencarreg and Llanycrwys *St D* 73-86; rtd 86. *46 Penybryn, Cwmann, Lampeter, Dyfed SA48 8HG* Lampeter (01570) 422198

MORGAN, John Geoffrey Basil. b 21. Wells Th Coll 59. **d** 60 **p** 61. V Ensbury *Sarum* 69-82; C W Parley 82-86; rtd 86. *40 Sheppards Field, Wimborne, Dorset BH21 1PX* Wimborne (01202) 848120

MORGAN, John Roland. b 31. Birm Univ BA54. Bps' Coll Cheshunt 54. **d** 55 **p** 56. V Balsall Common *Birm* 68-82; V N Leigh *Ox* 82-95; RD Woodstock 87-92; rtd 95. *Dyn Caryn, 2 Hayling Close, Godmanchester, Huntingdon, Cambs PE18 8XB* Huntingdon (01480) 459522

MORGAN, John William Miller. b 34. Lon Univ BSc56. Wycliffe Hall Ox 61. **d** 63 **p** 64. C St Alb Ch Ch *St Alb* 63-68; V Luton St Matt High Town 68-79; V Mangotsfield *Bris* 79-90; P-in-c Stanton St Quintin, Hullavington, Grittleton etc from 90. *The Rectory, 1 Rectory Close, Stanton St Quintin, Chippenham, Wilts SN14 6DE* Malmesbury (01666) 837187

MORGAN, Katharine. b 41. **d** 91. NSM Lougher *S & B* from 91. *68 Borough Road, Lougher, Swansea SA4 6RT*

MORGAN, Kenneth James. b 14. Selw Coll Cam BA36 MA43. Wells Th Coll 36. **d** 38 **p** 39. V Shalford *Guildf* 66-84; rtd 84; Perm to Offic *Guildf* from 85. *Greenwood, The Close, Wonersh, Guildford, Surrey GU5 0PA* Guildford (01483) 898791

MORGAN, Mark Anthony. b 58. LLB. Chich Th Coll. **d** 84 **p** 85. C Thorpe *Nor* 84-87; C Eaton 87-90; V Southtown 90-92; Perm to Offic from 92. *86 Yarmouth Road, Norwich NR7 0QZ* Norwich (01603) 702186

MORGAN, Martin Paul. b 46. St Steph Ho Ox 71. **d** 73 **p** 74. C Kettering St Mary *Pet* 73-76; C Fareham SS Pet and Paul *Portsm* 76-80; V Portsea Ascension 80-94; V Rottingdean *Chich* from 94. *The Vicarage, Steyning Road, Rottingdean, Brighton BN2 7GA* Brighton (01273) 309216

MORGAN, Mervyn Thomas. b 24. Ch Coll Cam BA48 MA71. Chich Th Coll 79. **d** 80 **p** 81. NSM Lewes All SS, St Anne, St Mich and St Thos *Chich* 80-82; P-in-c Glynde, W Firle and Beddingham 82-84; V Burwash Weald 84-89; R Alphamstone w Lamarsh and Pebmarsh *Chelmsf* 89-92; rtd 92. *Suncroft, Chapel Road, Otley, Ipswich IP6 9NX* Ipswich (01473) 890143

MORGAN, Michael. b 32. Lon Univ BSc57 MSc67 PhD63. **d** 74 **p** 75. NSM Portsdown *Portsm* from 74. *1 Widley Road, Cosham, Portsmouth PO6 2DS* Cosham (01705) 377442

MORGAN, Michael John. b 45. Nottm Univ BA66 MEd71. Linc Th Coll 80. **d** 82 **p** 83. C Bulkington *Cov* 82-83; C Bulkington w Shilton and Ansty 83-85; V Longford 85-89; R Norton *Sheff* from 89. *The Rectory, Norton, Sheffield S8 8JQ* Sheffield (0114) 274 5066

MORGAN, Morley Roland. b 47. Univ of Wales (Lamp) BA76. St Steph Ho Ox 76. **d** 77 **p** 78. C Merthyr Dyfan *Llan* 77-78; C Llantrisant 78-80; TV Cov Caludon *Cov* 80-86; Chapl N Man Gen Hosp from 86. *North Manchester General Hospital, Delaunays Road, Crumpsall, Manchester M8 6RB* 0161-795 4567 or 720 2990

MORGAN, Nicholas John. b 50. K Coll Lon BD71 AKC71 CertEd. St Aug Coll Cant 72. **d** 73 **p** 74. C Wythenshawe Wm Temple Ch *Man* 73-76; C Southam w Stockton Cov 76-79; V Brailes from 79; R Sutton under Brailes from 79; RD Shipston from 90. *The Vicarage, Brailes, Banbury, Oxon OX15 5HT* Brailes (01608) 685230

MORGAN, Nicola. b 64. Nottm Univ BA86. Linc Th Coll BTh95. **d** 95. C Lillington *Cov* from 95. *34 Lime Avenue, Leamington Spa, Warks CV32 7DF* Leamington Spa (01926) 37710

MORGAN, Philip. b 51. Lon Univ BSc75 Univ of Wales (Cardiff) BD78. St Mich Coll Llan 75. **d** 78 **p** 79. C Swansea St Nic *S & B* 78-81; C Morriston 81-83; C Swansea St Mary w H Trin 83-84; USA from 84. *705 Sixth, Box 374, Howe, Indiana 46746, USA*

MORGAN, Canon Philip Brendan. b 35. G&C Coll Cam BA59 MA63. Wells Th Coll 59. **d** 61 **p** 62. C Paddington Ch Ch *Lon* 61-66; C Trunch w Swafield *Nor* 66-68; P-in-c Nor St Steph 68-72; Sacr Nor Cathl 72-74; Can Res and Sub-Dean St Alb 74-81; Hon Can St Alb 81-94; R Bushey 81-94; RD Aldenham 91-94; Can Res and Treas Win Cathl *Win* from 94. *8 The Close, Winchester, Hants SO23 9LS* Winchester (01962) 854771

MORGAN, Canon Philip Reginald Strange. b 27. St D Coll Lamp BA51 Keble Coll Ox BA53 MA57. Wells Th Coll 57. **d** 57 **p** 58. CF (TA) 62-74; R Machen and Rudry *Mon* 66-75; R Machen 75-76; V Caerleon 76-95; Can St Woolos Cathl 84-95; rtd 95. *4 Anthony Drive, Caerleon, Newport, Gwent NP6 1DS* Caerleon (01633) 422238

MORGAN, Philip Richard Llewelyn. b 27. Wadh Coll Ox BA50 MA52. St Steph Ho Ox 53. **d** 55 **p** 56. Chapl Haileybury Coll Herts 58-73; Hd Master Haileybury Jun Sch Berks 73-87; R The Deverills *Sarum* 87-94; rtd 94. *6 Phillips Close, Headley, Bordon, Hants GU35 8LY* Bordon (01428) 712194

MORGAN, Canon Reginald Graham. b 25. St D Coll Lamp BA46 LTh48. **d** 48 **p** 49. V Rhuddlan *St As* 66-94; RD St As 78-94; Hon Can St As Cathl 83-89; Can from 89; rtd 94. *Manafon, Plot 64, The Fairlands, Rhuddlan, Rhyl, Clwyd LL18 2SR* Rhuddlan (01745) 591036

MORGAN, Reginald Graham Tharle. b 46. St D Jo Coll Nottm LTh75. **d** 75 **p** 76. C Oadby *Leic* 76-79; S Africa from 80. *PO Box 112, Greytown, Natal, 3500 South Africa* Greytown (334) 32192

MORGAN, Richard Mervyn. b 50. Wadh Coll Ox BA73 MA75 K Alfred's Coll Win PGCE74. **d** 92 **p** 93. CMS from 85; Kenya 88-94; Perm to Offic *S'wark* from 95. *26 Thackeray Manor, Manor Park Road, Sutton, Surrey SM1 4AH* 0181-286 0575

MORGAN, Robert Chowen. b 40. St Cath Coll Cam BA63 MA. St Chad's Coll Dur 64. **d** 66 **p** 67. C Lanc St Mary *Blackb* 66-76; Lect Lanc Univ 67-76; Lect Th Ox Univ from 76; P-in-c Sandford-on-Thames *Ox* from 87. *Lower Farm, Sandford-on-Thames, Oxford OX4 4YR* Oxford (01865) 748848

MORGAN, Canon Robert Harman. b 28. OBE94. Univ of Wales (Cardiff) BA55. Coll of Resurr Mirfield 55. **d** 57 **p** 58. C Penarth w Lavernock *Llan* 57-61; C Caerau w Ely 61-67; V Glan Ely from 67; Hon Can Llan Cathl from 94. *Church House, Grand Avenue, Ely, Cardiff CF5 4HX* Cardiff (01222) 591633

MORGAN, Robert Hugh. b 49. **d** 91 **p** 92. C Swansea St Pet *S & B* 91-94; V Oxwich w Penmaen and Nicholaston from 94. *The Rectory, Penmaen, Swansea SA3 2HH* Penmaen (01792) 371241

MORGAN, Roger. b 32. Bris Univ BA59. Tyndale Hall Bris 56. **d** 61 **p** 62. C Chitts Hill St Cuth *Lon* 61-64; R Kingham *Ox* 64-69; R Kingham and Daylesford 69-78; P-in-c Sarsden w Churchill 74-78; V W Hampstead St Cuth *Lon* 78-87; P-in-c Fyfield *Chelmsf* 87-89; R Fyfield and Moreton w Bobbingworth 90-93; P-in-c Willingale w Shellow and Berners Roding 88-93; R Fyfield, Moreton w Bobbingworth & Willingale etc from 93. *The Rectory, Fyfield, Ongar, Essex CM5 0SD* Fyfield (01277) 899255

MORGAN, Roger William. b 40. Mert Coll Ox BA62 Cam Univ MA67. Ridley Hall Cam 80. **d** 81 **p** 82. NSM Cam St Paul *Ely* 81-84; V Corby St Columba *Pet* 84-90; V Leic H Trin w St Jo *Leic* from 90. *29 Holmfield Road, Leicester LE2 1SE* Leicester (0116) 270 4986

MORGAN, Canon Samuel. b 07. St D Coll Lamp BA32. **d** 32 **p** 33. V Felin-foel *St D* 64-77; Can St D Cathl 72-79; rtd 77. *10 Ty'r Fran Avenue, Llanelli, Dyfed SA15 3LP* Llanelli (01554) 772977

MORGAN, Simon John. b 58. Univ of Wales (Swansea) BA81 Univ of Wales (Cardiff) BD86 MA93. **d** 86 **p** 87. C Penarth All SS *Llan* 86-87; C Port Talbot St Theodore 87-89; C Gelligaer 89-91; R Dowlais from 91. *The Rectory, Dowlais, Merthyr Tydfil, M Glam CF48 3NA* Merthyr Tydfil (01685) 722118

MORGAN, Steve Shelley. b 48. Univ of Wales DipTh70. St Mich Coll Llan 67. **d** 71 **p** 72. C Llan w Capel Llanilltern *Llan* 71-74; C Llanharan w Peterston-super-Montem 71-74; C Neath w Llantwit 74-77; TV Merthyr Tydfil and Cyfarthfa 77-91; V Merthyr Tydfil Ch Ch from 91; RD Merthyr Tydfil from 93. *Christchurch Vicarage, Heol S O Davies, Merthyr Tydfil, M Glam CF48 1DR* Merthyr Tydfil (01685) 371995

MORGAN, Thomas John Walford. b 16. Univ of Wales BA37. St D Coll Lamp 37. **d** 39 **p** 40. V Swallowfield *Ox* 71-81; rtd 81. *57 Felinfoel Road, Llanelli, Dyfed SA15 3JQ* Llanelli (01554) 752303

MORGAN, Verna Ireta. b 42. NE Ord Course. **d** 89 **p** 94. NSM Potternewton *Ripon* 89-92; Par Dn Longsight St Luke *Man* 92-94; C from 94. *54 Bletchley Close, Longsight, Manchester M13 9BH* 0161-272 7138

MORGAN, William John. b 38. Selw Coll Cam BA62 MA66. Cuddesdon Coll 62. **d** 65 **p** 66. C Cardiff St Jo *Llan* 65-68; Asst Chapl Univ of Wales (Cardiff) 68-70; Perm to Offic *Lon* 70-73; C Albany Street Ch Ch 73-78; P-in-c E Acton St Dunstan 78-80; V E Acton St Dunstan w St Thos from 80. *The Vicarage, 54 Perryn Road, London W3 7NA* 0181-743 4117

MORGAN, Canon William Charles Gerwyn. b 30. Univ of Wales (Lamp) BA52. St Mich Coll Llan 52. **d** 56 **p** 57. Miss to Seamen 68-93; V Fishguard w Llanychar *St D* 68-85; V Fishguard w Llanychar and Pontfaen w Morfil etc 85-93; Can St D Cathl 85-93; Chan 91-93; rtd 93. *Wrth y Llan, Pontycleifion, Cardigan, Dyfed SA43 1DW* Cardigan (01239) 613943

MORGAN, William Stanley Timothy. b 41. Univ of Wales (Lamp) BA63. Wycliffe Hall Ox 63. **d** 66 **p** 67. C Abth St Mich *St D* 66-69; V Ambleston w St Dogwells 69-70; V Ambleston, St Dogwells, Walton E and Llysyfran 70-74; V Llan-non 74-80; V Lamp 80-87; V Lamp Pont Steffan w Silian from 87. *The Vicarage, Lampeter, Dyfed SA48 7EJ* Lampeter (01570) 422460

MORGAN-JONES, Christopher John (Chris). b 43. Bris Univ BA66 Chicago Univ MBA68 McMaster Univ Ontario MA69. Cuddesdon Coll 70. **d** 73 **p** 74. C Folkestone St Sav *Cant* 73-76; P-in-c Swalecliffe 76-82; V Addington 82-84; V Addington S'wark 85-92; RD Croydon Addington 85-90; V Maidstone All SS and St Phil w Tovil *Cant* from 92. *The Vicarage, Priory Road, Maidstone, Kent ME15 6NL* Maidstone (01622) 756002

MORGAN-JONES, Richard James. b 46. Em Coll Cam BA68. Ripon Hall Ox 73. **d** 75 **p** 76. C Bromley St Mark *Roch* 75-77; Perm to Offic 77-84. *15 Wendover Road, Bromley BR2 9JU*

MORGANS, Paul Hywel. b 61. LWCMD83. Chich Th Coll 86. **d** 90 **p** 91. C Johnston w Steynton *St D* 90-92; C Caerau w Ely *Llan* 92-95; V Pentre from 95. *The Vicarage, 7 Llewellyn Street, Pentre, M Glam CF41 7BY* Bargoed (01443) 433651

MORISON, John Donald. b 34. ALCD60. **d** 61 **p** 62. C Rayleigh *Chelmsf* 61-64; C St Austell *Truro* 64-67; V Meltham Mills *Wakef* 67-71; Youth Chapl *Cov* 71-76; S Africa 76-82; Can Port Elizabeth 80-82; Bardsley Missr 82-86; Lic to Offic *S'wark* 82-86; Dioc Missr *Derby* from 86; V Quarndon from 86. *St Paul's Vicarage, 149 Church Road, Quarndon, Derby DE22 5JA* Derby (01332) 559333

MORLEY, Athelstan John. b 29. Linc Coll Ox BA52 MA56. Ridley Hall Cam. **d** 54 **p** 55. R Hadleigh St Jas *Chelmsf* 69-94; rtd 94; Hon C Prittlewell *Chelmsf* from 94. *29 Tattersall Gardens, Leigh-on-Sea, Essex SS9 2QS* Southend-on-Sea (01702) 551494

MORLEY, Frank. b 15. Worc Ord Coll 63. **d** 65 **p** 66. V Overton w Fyfield and E Kennett *Sarum* 68-73; V Urchfont w Stert 74-81; rtd 81; Perm to Offic *Heref* 81-86; Perm to Offic *Worc* 86-91; C Much Birch w Lt Birch, Much Dewchurch etc *Heref* 86. *5 Barton Lodge, Station Road, Barton under Needwood, Burton-on-Trent, Staffs DE13 8DR* Burton-on-Trent (01283) 716304

MORLEY, Miss Gillian Dorothy. b 21. Greyladies Coll 49. **dss** 70 **d** 87. Lewisham St Swithun *S'wark* 70-82; Sturry w Fordwich and Westbere w Hersden *Cant* 82-87; Perm to Offic from 87. *28 Glen Iris Avenue, Canterbury, Kent CT2 8HP* Canterbury (01227) 459992

MORLEY, John. b 43. AKC67 St Deiniol's Hawarden 67. **d** 68 **p** 69. C Newbold on Avon *Cov* 69-73; C Solihull *Birm* 73-77; C-in-c Elmdon Heath CD 76-77; Chapl RAF 77-93; TR Wallingford w Crowmarsh Gifford etc *Ox* from 93. *The Rectory, 22 Castle Street, Wallingford, Oxon OX10 8DW* Wallingford (01491) 837280

MORLEY, Keith. b 44. St Chad's Coll Dur BA66 DipTh67 Open Univ BSc93. **d** 67 **p** 68. C S Yardley St Mich *Birm* 67-70; C Solihull 70-73; V Shaw Hill 73-77; P-in-c Burton Coggles *Linc* 77-79; P-in-c Boothby Pagnell 77-79; V Lenton w Ingoldsby 77-79; P-in-c Bassingthorpe w Bitchfield 77-79; R Ingoldsby 79-87; RD Beltisloe 84-87; P-in-c Old Dalby and Nether Broughton *Leic* 87-94; RD Framland (Melton) 88-90. *11 Swallow Close, Quarrington, Sleaford, Lincs NG34 7UU*

MORLEY, Canon Leonard. b 04. Man Egerton Hall 35. **d** 37 **p** 38. V Kingsley *Ches* 56-72; rtd 72; Perm to Offic *Cant* 79-93; Perm to Offic *Chich* 81-93. *The College of St Barnabas, Blackberry Lane, Lingfield, Surrey RH7 6NJ* Dormans Park (01342) 870260

MORLEY, Canon Leslie James. b 45. K Coll Lon BD67 AKC67 MTh68. **d** 69 **p** 70. C Birm St Pet *Birm* 69-72; C W Brompton St Mary *Lon* 72; C W Brompton St Mary w St Pet 73-74; Chapl Nottm Univ *S'well* 74-80; Dir of Post-Ord Tr 80-85; Can Res and Vice-Provost S'well Minster 80-85; Hon Can from 85;

Chapl Blue Coat Sch Nottm 85-90; R Nottm St Pet and St Jas *S'well* from 85; AD Nottm Cen 90-93. *3 King Charles Street, Nottingham NG1 6GB*   Nottingham (0115) 947 4891

MORLEY, Peter. b 36. St Jo Coll Nottm 81. **d** 83 **p** 84. C Sheff St Jo *Sheff* 83-87; Chapl Shrewsbury Hosp Sheff 85-87; V Worsbrough Common 87-93; Chapl Mt Vernon Hosp Barnsley 87-93; R Harthill and Thorpe Salvin *Sheff* from 93. *The Rectory, 36 Union Street, Harthill, Sheffield S31 8YH*   Worksop (01909) 770279

MORLEY, Terence Martin Simon. b 49. SS Hild & Bede Coll Dur CertEd78. St Steph Ho Ox 71. **d** 74 **p** 75. C Kingston upon Hull St Alb *York* 74-76; C Middlesb All SS 76-77; Perm to Offic *Dur* 77-78; Hon C Worthing St Andr *Chich* 78-80; C Brighton Ch Ch 80-82; C Hove St Patr 80-82; C Ayr *Glas* 83-86; C Maybole 83-86; P-in-c Coatbridge 86-88; R 88-92; Perm to Offic 92-93; V Plymouth St Jas Ham *Ex* from 93. *St James's Vicarage, Ham Drive, Plymouth PL2 2NJ*   Plymouth (01752) 362485

MORLEY, Trevor. b 39. MPS62 MRSH84 Man Univ BSc62. Ripon Hall Ox 65. **d** 67 **p** 68. C Compton Gifford *Ex* 67-70; Chapl Hammersmith Hosp Lon 70-83; Hon C N Hammersmith St Kath *Lon* 70-83; Chapl Univ Coll Hosp Lon from 83; Hon Chapl St Luke's Hosp for the Clergy from 89. *University College Hospital, Gower Street, London WC1E 6AU*   0171-387 9300

MORLEY-BUNKER, John Arthur. b 27. Wells Th Coll 67. **d** 68 **p** 69. C Horfield H Trin *Bris* 68-71; P-in-c Easton All Hallows 71-75; V 75-82; RD Bris City 74-79; V Horfield St Greg 82-93; rtd 93. *1 Knoll Court, Knoll Hill, Bristol BS9 1QX*   Bristol (0117) 968 5837

MORLING, David Arthur. b 45. CertEd66 Open Univ BA78. S Dios Minl Tr Scheme 83. **d** 85 **p** 86. NSM Parklands St Wilfrid CD *Chich* from 85. *52 Worcester Road, Chichester, W Sussex PO19 4DZ*   Chichester (01243) 782281

MORPHET, George Thexton. b 12. ACT ThL47. **d** 38 **p** 39. Australia 53-62 and from 68; Miss to Seamen 53-77; rtd 77. *68 Spowers Street, Bribie Island, Queensland, Australia 4507*

MORPHY, George David. b 49. Lon Univ BA Birm Univ BEd. W Midl Minl Tr Course. **d** 89 **p** 90. NSM Ribbesford w Bewdley and Dowles *Worc* from 89. *41 Hallow Road, Worcester WR2 6BX*   Worcester (01905) 422007

MORPHY, Michael John. b 43. Newc Univ BSc65 Dur Univ MSc66 QUB PhD73. Ripon Coll Cuddesdon 82. **d** 84 **p** 85. C Halifax *Wakef* 84-86; V Luddenden w Luddenden Foot from 86. *The Vicarage, 50 Carr Field Drive, Luddenden, Halifax, W Yorkshire HX2 6RJ*   Halifax (01422) 882127

MORRELL, Geoffrey Bernard. b 45. AKC68. **d** 69 **p** 71. C W Leigh CD *Portsm* 69-76; V Shedfield from 76; RD Bishops Waltham 82-88. *The Vicarage, Church Road, Shedfield, Southampton SO3 2HY*   Wickham (01329) 832162

✠**MORRELL, Rt Rev James Herbert Lloyd.** b 07. AKC30. Ely Th Coll 30. **d** 31 **p** 32 **c** 59. C Hendon St Alphage *Lon* 31-36; C Brighton St Mich *Chich* 36-40; Chapl Supt Brighton Boys' Hostel 40-41; Chapl for Work among Men and Boys 40-41; Lect C of E Moral Welfare Coun 41-44; V Roughey (or Roffey) 44-46; Adn Lewes 46-49; Suff Bp Lewes 59-77; Can and Preb Chich Cathl 59-84; FKC from 60; rtd 77; Asst Bp Chich from 77. *83 Davigdor Road, Hove, E Sussex BN3 1RA*   Brighton (01273) 733971

MORRELL, Mrs Jennifer Mary. b 49. N Ord Course 84. **d** 87 **p** 94. Par Dn Crewe All SS and St Paul *Ches* 87-90; Par Dn Padgate *Liv* 90-94; C 94-95; TV Kirkby from 95. *St Martins House, Peatwood Avenue, Kirkby, Liverpool L32 7PR*   0151-546 2387

MORRELL, Nigel Paul. b 38. S'wark Ord Course 73. **d** 76 **p** 77. C Letchworth St Paul w Willian *St Alb* 76-85; V Farley Hill St Jo 85-95; RD Luton 90-94; V Cardington from 95. *The Vicarage, Cardington, Bedford MK44 3SS*   Bedford (01234) 838203

MORRELL, Paul Rodney. b 49. S RN70. SW Minl Tr Course 90. **d** 93 **p** 94. NSM Heavitree w Ex St Paul *Ex* from 93. *65 Quarry Park Road, Exeter EX2 5PD*   Exeter (01392) 431367

MORRELL, Robin Mark George. b 29. Cuddesdon Coll 58. **d** 60 **p** 61. C-in-c Stockwood CD *Bris* 63-71; Lic to Offic 71-72; R Honiton, Gittisham and Combe Raleigh *Ex* 72-78; Lay Tr Officer *S'wark* 78-81; Asst Chapl HM Pris Brixton 81-85; Past Counsellor from 85; Hon C Hatcham St Cath *S'wark* from 91; rtd 94. *46 Erlanger Road, London SE14 5TG*   0171-252 9346

MORRIS, Alan Ralph Oakden. b 29. Roch Th Coll 59. **d** 61 **p** 62. C Wrotham *Roch* 66-74; V Biggin Hill 74-82; R Kingsdown 82-88; V Seal St Pet 88-92; rtd 92; P-in-c Renhold *St Alb* 92-93. *46 Old Mill Close, Eynsford, Dartford DA4 0BN*   Dartford (01322) 863153

MORRIS, Albert George. b 15. Tyndale Hall Bris 47. **d** 48 **p** 49. C-in-c Bridgemary CD *Portsm* 67-80; rtd 81; Perm to Offic *Portsm* from 82. *1 Ashcroft Court, Winton Road, Petersfield, Hants GU32 3HE*   Petersfield (01730) 265190

MORRIS, Canon Alexander Dorner. b 23. Jes Coll Cam BA48 MA53. Linc Th Coll 49. **d** 51 **p** 52. V Bexley St Mary *Roch* 63-71; V Leatherhead *Guildf* 71-89; RD Leatherhead 72-77; Hon Can Guildf Cathl 86-89; rtd 89. *9 Roses Cottages, West Street, Dorking, Surrey RH4 1QL*   Dorking (01306) 882485

MORRIS, Arthur Ronald. b 17. Jes Coll Ox BA38 MA42. St Steph Ho Ox 38. **d** 40 **p** 41. V Edmonton St Mich *Lon* 66-71; Australia from 71; rtd 82. *118 The Palms, Melody Court, Warana, Queensland, Australia 4575*

MORRIS, Bernard Lyn. b 28. St Aid Birkenhead 55. **d** 58 **p** 59. R Aylton w Pixley, Munsley and Putley *Heref* 69-79; P-in-c Tarrington w Stoke Edith 72-77; R 77-79; P-in-c Queen Camel, Marston Magna, W Camel, Rimpton etc *B & W* 79-80; R 80-87; R Queen Camel w W Camel, Corton Denham etc 87-95; rtd 95. *Canterbury Bells, Ansford Hill, Castle Cary, Somerset BA7 7JL*   Castle Cary (01963) 351154

MORRIS, Beti Elin. b 36. CertEd57. Sarum & Wells Th Coll 87. **d** 89. C Llangeitho and Blaenpennal w Betws Leucu etc *St D* 89-92; C-in-c Pencarreg and Llanycrwys from 92. *Hafdir, Llanwnen Road, Lampeter, Dyfed SA48 7JP*   Lampeter (01570) 422385

MORRIS, Brian Michael Charles. b 32. S Dios Minl Tr Scheme 82. **d** 85 **p** 86. NSM Denmead *Portsm* 85-89; C S w N Hayling from 89. *27 Seaview Road, Hayling Island, Hants PO11 9PD*   Hayling Island (01705) 466342

MORRIS, Christopher John. b 45. K Coll Lon AKC67 BD68. **d** 68 **p** 69. C W Bromwich All SS *Lich* 68-72; C Porthill 72-74; Min Can Carl Cathl *Carl* 74-77; Ecum Liaison Officer BBC Radio Carl 74-77; Dioc Communications Officer *Carl* 77-83; V Thursby 77-83; Angl Adv Border TV from 82; V Upperby St Jo *Carl* 83-91; P-in-c Lanercost w Kirkcambeck and Walton from 91. *The Vicarage, Lanercost, Brampton, Cumbria CA8 2HQ*   Brampton (016977) 2478

MORRIS, Christopher Mangan. b 47. Chich Th Coll 71. **d** 73 **p** 74. C Athersley *Wakef* 73-76; C Kippax *Ripon* 76-78; TV Seacroft 78-81; V Oulton w Woodlesford 81-86; V Hawksworth Wood 86-93; V Rawdon *Bradf* from 93. *The Vicarage, Rawdon, Leeds LS19 6QQ*   Leeds (0113) 250 3263

MORRIS, Prof Colin. b 28. FRHistS71 Qu Coll Ox BA48 MA53. Linc Th Coll 51. **d** 53 **p** 54. Chapl Pemb Coll Ox 53-69; Prof Medieval Hist Southn Univ from 69; Lic to Offic *Win* from 69. *53 Cobbett Road, Southampton SO2 4HJ*   Southampton (01703) 227258

MORRIS, Canon David Edmond. b 27. Univ of Wales (Cardiff) BA55. St D Coll Lamp 55. **d** 57 **p** 58. CF 61-81; QHC 78-93; V Penllergaer *S & B* 81-93; RD Llwchwr 86-93; Can Brecon Cathl 90-93; Hon Can from 93; rtd 93. *21 Delfryn, Derwydd Road, Ammanford, Dyfed SA18 3LJ*   Ammanford (01269) 832306

MORRIS, David Freestone (Brother Augustine). b 05. Lon Univ 22. **d** 36 **p** 37. OSB from 24; Abbot 48-74; Lic to Offic *Ox* from 54; rtd 74. *Elmore Abbey, Church Lane, Speen, Newbury, Berks RG13 1SA*   Newbury (01635) 33080

MORRIS, Preb David Meeson. b 35. Trin Coll Ox BA56 MA60. Chich Th Coll 57. **d** 60 **p** 61. C Westmr St Steph w St Jo *Lon* 60-65; Lib Pusey Ho 65-68; Chapl Wadh Coll Ox 67-68; C Sheff Norwood St Leon *Sheff* 68-69; Ind Chapl 68-72; C Brightside St Marg 69-72; R Adderley *Lich* 72-82; V Drayton in Hales 72-82; RD Tutbury 82-95; Chapl Burton Gen Hosp 82-90; P-in-c Burton St Modwen *Lich* 82; V Burton from 82; Preb Lich Cathl from 93; P-in-c Shobnall from 94. *The Vicarage, Rangemore Street, Burton-on-Trent, Staffs DE14 2ED*   Burton-on-Trent (01283) 36235

MORRIS, David Michael. b 59. Ox Univ MA84. Sarum & Wells Th Coll 82. **d** 84 **p** 85. C Angell Town St Jo *S'wark* 84-87; C Mitcham SS Pet and Paul 87-90; V Llandygwydd and Cenarth w Cilrhedyn etc *St D* from 90. *The Vicarage, Llechryd, Cardigan, Dyfed SA43 2NE*   Llechryd (01239) 682552

MORRIS, David Pryce. b 39. Univ of Wales (Ban) DipTh62. Kelham Th Coll 55 St Mich Coll Llan 62. **d** 63 **p** 64. C Colwyn Bay *St As* 63-70; R St George 70-76; Dioc Children's Adv 75-87; V Bodelwyddan and St George 76-79; V Connah's Quay from 79; St As Dioc Adult Lay Tr Team from 88; Ed St As Dioc News from 89; Dioc Info Officer from 90. *The Vicarage, Church Hill, Connah's Quay, Deeside, Clwyd CH5 1AZ*   Deeside (01244) 830224

MORRIS, Dennis Gordon. b 41. ALCM58 DipTh67. St D Coll Lamp 64. **d** 67 **p** 68. C Neath w Llantwit *Llan* 67-92; V Troedrhiwgarth from 92. *Garth Vicarage, 72 Bridgend Road, Maesteg, M Glam CF34 0NL*   Bridgend (01656) 732441

MORRIS, Dr Edward. b 42. **d** 72 **p** 73. C Darlington H Trin *Dur* 72-75; Tutor St Steph Ho Ox 75-82; Sen Tutor 79-82; R Shadforth *Dur* 82-86; Chapl Hammersmith Hosp Lon from 86; Chapl Qu Charlotte's Hosp Lon from 86. *The Chaplain's Office, Hammersmith Hospital, Du Cane Road, London W12 0HS*   0181-743 2030

MORRIS, Canon Edwin Alfred. b 32. Wells Th Coll 62. **d** 64 **p** 65. C Wood End *Cov* 64-66; Lic to Offic 66-68; Ind Chapl 68-85;

P-in-c Churchover w Willey 74-85; RD Rugby 78-85; R City of Bris from 85; Hon Can Bris Cathl from 89; RD Bris City 91-94. *2 Fremantle Square, Bristol BS6 5TL* Bristol (0117) 942 7546 or 927 7977

MORRIS, Mrs Elizabeth Mary. b 22. Univ Coll Lon BSc50 DipRS82. S'wark Ord Course 82. dss 83 d 87 p 94. Purley St Mark Woodcote *S'wark* 83-87; Hon Par Dn Littleham w Exmouth *Ex* 87-94; Hon C from 94. *7 Strawberry Hill, Lympstone, Exmouth, Devon EX8 5JZ* Exmouth (01395) 265727

MORRIS, Canon Frank Leo. b 20. St Steph Ho Ox 50. d 53 p 54. R Wyddial *St Alb* 65-79; P-in-c 79-82; V Gt w Lt Hormead 65-79; RD Buntingford 68-75; V Gt w Lt Hormead, Anstey, Brent Pelham etc 79-82; V Hormead, Wyddial, Anstey, Brent Pelham etc 82-89; Hon Can St Alb 85-89; rtd 89. *9 Manland Avenue, Harpenden, Herts AL5 4RG* Harpenden (01582) 462348

MORRIS, Geoffrey David. b 43. Fitzw Coll Cam BA65 MA69 Westmr Coll Ox DipEd67. N Ord Course. d 82 p 83. C Man Clayton St Cross w St Paul *Man* 82-85; V Lower Kersal from 85. *St Aidan's Vicarage, Littleton Road, Salford M7 0TN* 0161-792 3072

MORRIS, George Erskine. b 34. Codrington Coll Barbados Qu Coll Birm 60. d 62 p 63. C Kidderminster St Jo *Worc* 62-66; Canada from 66. *11203-68 Street NW, Edmonton, Alberta, Canada, T5B 1N6*

MORRIS, Graham Edwin. b 60. Sarum & Wells Th Coll 83. d 86 p 87. C Coalbrookdale, Iron-Bridge and Lt Wenlock *Heref* 86-90; TV Bilston *Lich* from 90. *8 Cumberland Road, Bilston, Wolverhampton WV14 6LT* Bilston (01902) 497794

MORRIS, Canon Gwilym Alun. b 09. CBE64. Qu Coll Birm 38. d 39 p 40. V Coxwold *York* 70-75; rtd 75; Hon Can Bahrain from 88. *Captain Cook's Cottage, Grape Lane, Whitby, N Yorkshire YO22 4BA* Whitby (01947) 602434

MORRIS, Henry James. b 47. Lon Univ BSc69. Wycliffe Hall Ox MA. d 79 p 80. C Woodford Wells *Chelmsf* 79-82; C Gt Baddow 82-87; R Siddington w Preston *Glouc* from 87. *The Rectory, Preston, Cirencester, Glos GL7 5PR* Cirencester (01285) 654187

MORRIS, Ian Henry. b 42. Sarum & Wells Th Coll 73. d 75 p 76. C Lawrence Weston *Bris* 75-78; C St Buryan, St Levan and Sennen *Truro* 78-81; P-in-c Lanteglos by Fowey 81-84; V 84-85; R Lanteglos by Camelford w Advent from 85; RD Trigg Minor and Bodmin from 93. *The Rectory, Trefrew Road, Camelford, Cornwall PL32 9TQ* Camelford (01840) 212286

MORRIS, Ian James Patrick. b 43. Dur Univ BA65. Westcott Ho Cam 67. d 69 p 70. C Wisbech SS Pet and Paul *Ely* 69-72; C Gaywood, Bawsey and Mintlyn *Nor* 72-76; Asst Chapl Basingstoke Distr Hosp 76-78; Chapl Meanwood Park Hosp Gp Leeds 78-88; Chapl Addenbrooke's Hosp Cam from 88. *Addenbrooke's Hospital, Hills Road, Cambridge CB2 2QQ* Cambridge (01223) 217769 or 245151

MORRIS, Ivor Leslie. b 50. Chich Th Coll 82. d 84 p 85. C Southend *Chelmsf* 84-87; C Somers Town St Mary *Lon* 87-90; P-in-c Chelmsf Ascension *Chelmsf* from 90; P-in-c Chelmsf All SS from 92. *The Vicarage, 57 Maltese Road, Chelmsford CM1 2PD* Chelmsford (01245) 353914

MORRIS, Miss Jane Elizabeth. b 52. York Univ BA71 CertEd72 MSc80. NE Ord Course CMinlStuds92. d 92 p 94. NSM York St Mich-le-Belfrey *York* 92-95; C Leeds St Geo *Ripon* from 95. *4 Hunt Court, York YO1 2DE* York (01904) 654288

MORRIS, Dr Jeremy Nigel. b 60. Ball Coll Ox MA81 DPhil86 Clare Coll Cam BA92. Westcott Ho Cam CTM93. d 93 p 94. C Battersea St Mary *S'wark* from 93. *35 Kerrison Road, London SW11 2QG* 0171-223 6880

MORRIS, Canon John. b 25. Westcott Ho Cam. d 65 p 66. V Leverstock Green *St Alb* 68-80; TR Chambersbury (Hemel Hempstead) 80-82; V N Mymms 82-90; RD Hatf 83-88; Hon Can St Alb 89-90; rtd 90; Perm to Offic *Nor* 92-94; P-in-c Barney, Fulmodeston w Croxton, Hindringham etc 94-95. *Elba, Croxton Road, Fulmodeston, Fakenham, Norfolk NR21 0NJ* Fakenham (01328) 878685

MORRIS, John Derrick. b 18. MRCS43 LRCP43. Lon Coll of Div 62. d 64 p 65. V Broadway *Worc* 67-71; Hon C St Leonards St Leon *Chich* 71-83; rtd 83; Perm to Offic *Chich* from 84. *21 Heathfield Green, Midhurst, W Sussex GU29 9QA* Midhurst (01730) 814084

MORRIS, Dr John Douglas (Johnny). b 37. Cam Univ BA58 Lon Inst of Educn PGCE60 Univ of E Africa MEd67 Ex Univ PhD87. S Dios Minl Tr Scheme 94. d 95. NSM Twyford and Owslebury and Morestead *Win* from 95. *Gifford House, St Giles Hill, Winchester, Hants SO23 0JH* Winchester (01962) 869720

MORRIS, John Dudley. b 33. Ball Coll Ox BA57 DipTh59 MA61. Wycliffe Hall Ox 58. d 60 p 61. C Tonbridge SS Pet and Paul *Roch* 60-65; C Enfield Ch Ch Trent Park *Lon* 65-69;

Chapl Elstree Sch Woolhampton 70-74; Hd Master Handcross Park Sch W Sussex 74-89; V Rudgwick *Chich* from 89; RD Horsham from 93. *The Vicarage, Rudgwick, Horsham, W Sussex RH12 3DD* Rudgwick (01403) 822127

MORRIS, John Edgar. b 20. Keble Coll Ox BA42 MA50. Wycliffe Hall Ox 42. d 44 p 45. V Ainsdale *Liv* 66-82; R Broadwell, Evenlode, Oddington and Adlestrop *Glouc* 82-88; rtd 89. *29 Letch Hill Drive, Bourton-on-the-Water, Cheltenham, Glos GL54 2DQ* Cotswold (01451) 820571

MORRIS, John Owen. b 56. Nottm Univ BCom82. Linc Th Coll 79. d 82 p 83. C Morriston *S & B* 82-84; C Kingstone w Clehonger and Eaton Bishop *Heref* 84-87; P-in-c Lugwardine w Bartestree and Weston Beggard 87-92; Chapl RN from 92. *Directorate Gen, RN Chapl Services, Room 203, Victory Building, HM Naval Base, Portsmouth PO1 3LS* Portsmouth (01705) 727903 Fax 727112

MORRIS, Canon John Richard. b 23. Or Coll Ox BA48 MA52. Westcott Ho Cam 48. d 50 p 51. R Sanderstead All SS *S'wark* 64-70; Warden Caius Ho Miss 70-88; V Battersea St Mary 70-88; Hon Can S'wark Cathl 76-88; RD Battersea 76-81; Hon C Battersea St Mary-le-Park 76-79; Hon C Battersea Park All SS 84-88; rtd 88; Master Abp Holgate Hosp Pontefract from 88. *Archbishop Holgate Hospital, Robin Lane, Hemsworth, Pontefract, W Yorkshire WF9 4PP* Hemsworth (01977) 610434

MORRIS, Kenneth Owen. b 12. Univ of Wales BA34. St Mich Coll Llan 35. d 37 p 38. V Aston w Benington *St Alb* 59-60; Lic to Offic 60-77; rtd 77. *20 Middle Mead, Hook,, Hants RG27 9TE* Basingstoke (01256) 762228

MORRIS, Kevin John. b 63. Univ of Wales (Ban) BMus84. Westcott Ho Cam 85. d 88 p 89. C Roath St Marg *Llan* 88-91; C Holborn St Alb w Saffron Hill St Pet *Lon* from 91. *St Alban's Clergy House, Brooke Street, London EC1N 7RD* 0171-405 1831

MORRIS, Leslie Heber. b 26. Ox Univ MA47. Qu Coll Birm 83. d 84 p 93. NSM W Leigh *Portsm* 84-85; NSM Warblington and Emsworth from 86. *3 Park Crescent, Emsworth, Hants PO10 7NT* Emsworth (01243) 373389

MORRIS, Sister Lillian Rosina. b 29. dss 70 d 87. CSA from 68; Mother Superior 82-94; Sherston Magna w Easton Grey *Bris* 71-73; Notting Hill All SS w St Columb *Lon* 74-82. *St Andrew's House, 2 Tavistock Road, London W11 1BA* 0171-229 2662

MORRIS, Margaret Jane.E Midl Min Tr Course 86. d 89 p 94. NSM Quorndon *Leic* from 89; Chapl to People affected by AIDS/HIV from 94. *10 Toller Road, Quorn, Loughborough, Leics LE12 8AH* Quorn (01509) 412092

MORRIS, Canon Martin Geoffrey Roger. b 41. Trin Coll Cam BA63 MA67. St D Coll Lamp 63. d 66 p 67. C Newport St Paul *Mon* 66-72; R Lamp Velfrey *St D* 72-74; R Lamp Velfrey and Llanddewi Velfrey from 74; RD St Clears from 83; Hon Can St D Cathl 91-92; Can St D Cathl from 92. *The Rectory, Lampeter Velfrey, Narberth, Dyfed SA67 8UH* Llanteg (0183483) 241

MORRIS, Ms Mary. b 27. Birm Univ BA49 CertEd50 MA56. dss 65 d 87 p 94. Kinver *Lich* 83-87; Hon Par Dn Kinver and Enville 87-94; Hon C from 94. *Lyndhurst, Dunsley Road, Kinver, Stourbridge, W Midlands DY7 6LN* Kinver (01384) 877245

MORRIS, Michael Alan. b 46. Jes Coll Cam BA70 MA74. Coll of Resurr Mirfield 79. d 81 p 82. C Leamington Priors All SS *Cov* 81-83; C Milton *Portsm* 83-88; R Petworth *Chich* 88-90; R Egdean 88-90; Chapl St Pet Hosp Chertsey 90-95; Hon C Thorpe *Guildf* 90-95; P-in-c Harbledown *Cant* from 95; Chapl St Nic Hosp Cant from 95. *The Rectory, Summer Hill, Harbledown, Canterbury, Kent CT2 8NW* Canterbury (01227) 464117

MORRIS, Norman Foster Maxwell. b 46. Ex Univ BA68 MA72 Leic Univ PGCE69 K Coll Lon MTh85 Univ of Wales (Cardiff) MA91. S'wark Ord Course 75. d 78 p 79. C Hackbridge and N Beddington *S'wark* 78-81; Chapl Tonbridge Sch Kent 81-85; Chapl Mon Sch from 85; Lic to Offic *Mon* from 87; Asst Warden Jones Almshouses Mon from 89. *The Chaplain's House, The Burgage, Old Dixton Road, Monmouth, Gwent NP5 3DP* Monmouth (01600) 713506

MORRIS, Paul David. b 56. St Jo Coll Nottm BTh79. d 80 p 81. C Billericay and Lt Burstead *Chelmsf* 80-84; C Luton Lewsey St Hugh *St Alb* 84-89; Bp's Adv on Evang *S'well* from 89. *39 Davies Road, Nottingham NG2 5JE* Nottingham (0115) 981 1311

MORRIS, Peter. b 45. Leeds Univ CertEd66. Tyndale Hall Bris 68. d 71 p 72. C Southport SS Simon and Jude *Liv* 71-74; Min-in-c Ch Ch Netherley LEP 74-76; V Bryn 76-91; R Redenhall, Harleston, Wortwell and Needham *Nor* from 91. *The Rectory, 10 Swan Lane, Harleston, Norfolk IP20 9AN* Harleston (01379) 852068

MORRIS, Canon Peter Arthur William. b 23. Bps' Coll Cheshunt 57. d 58 p 59. V Sawbridgeworth *St Alb* 62-74;

V S Gillingham *Roch* 74-79; Warden Pleshey Retreat Ho 79-85; P-in-c Pleshey *Chelmsf* 79-85; Hon Can Chelmsf Cathl 81-85; P-in-c Rumburgh w S Elmham w the Ilketshalls *St E* 85-89; rtd 89; Perm to Offic *St E* from 90. *The Cottage on the Common, Westleton, Saxmundham, Suffolk IP17 3AZ* Westleton (0172873) 788

MORRIS, Canon Peter Michael Keighley. b 27. St Jo Coll Ox BA49 MA56. Westcott Ho Cam 51. **d** 54 **p** 55. Lic to Offic *St D* 55-85; Lect Univ of Wales (Lamp) 55-69; Sen Lect 69-90; Dean Faculty of Th 77-81; Can St D Cathl 85-90; rtd 90; Treas St D Cathl *St D* from 92. *Hafdir, Llanwnen Road, Lampeter, Dyfed SA48 7JP* Lampeter (01570) 422385

MORRIS, Philip Gregory. b 50. Leeds Univ BA71 MPhil74. Coll of Resurr Mirfield 71. **d** 73 **p** 74. C Aberdare St Jo *Llan* 74-77; C Neath w Llantwit 77-80; V Cymmer and Porth 80-88; Dioc Missr from 88; TV Llantwit Major from 88. *60 Ham Lane South, Llantwit Major, S Glam CF1 1RN* Llantwit Major (01446) 793770 Fax as telephone

MORRIS, Raymond. b 48. Open Univ HND70 BA88. N Ord Course 80. **d** 83 **p** 84. C Tonge w Alkrington *Man* 83-86; R Blackley St Paul 86-91; V Heyside from 91. *St Mark's Vicarage, Heyside, Royton, Oldham OL2 6LS* Shaw (01706) 844502

MORRIS, Raymond Arthur (Ray). b 42. Trin Coll Ox BA64 MA66 Lon Univ LLB71 CQSW72. Clifton Th Coll 66. **d** 67 **p** 91. C Greenstead juxta Colchester *Chelmsf* 67-68; Perm to Offic *York* 69-91; NSM Linthorpe from 91. *3 Medina Gardens, Middlesbrough, Cleveland TS5 8BN* Middlesbrough (01642) 593726

MORRIS, Raymond John Walton. b 08. OBE69. Em Coll Cam BA33 MA37. Lon Coll of Div 33. **d** 34 **p** 35. V Brompton H Trin *Lon* 69-75; rtd 75. *3 Nettlebed Nursery, Shaftesbury, Dorset SP7 8QZ* Shaftesbury (01747) 853422

MORRIS, Reginald Brian. b 31. St Mich Coll Llan 56. **d** 59 **p** 60. CF 62-78; V Cheswardine *Lich* 78-84; V Hales 78-84; Perm to Offic 84-86; C Cen Telford 86-89; rtd 89. *Woodside Cottage, School Lane, Prees, Whitchurch, Shropshire SY13 2BU* Whitchurch (01948) 840090

MORRIS, Richard Samuel. b 10. TCD BA35 MA39. Edgehill Th Coll Belf 31. **d** 58 **p** 59. I Kilsaran w Drumcar, Dunleer and Dunany *Arm* 69-75; rtd 75. *20 Kerrington Court, 119 Marlborough Park South, Belfast BT9 6HN* Belfast (01232) 662261

MORRIS, Robert John. b 45. Leeds Univ BA67. Coll of Resurr Mirfield 74. **d** 76 **p** 77. C Beeston Hill St Luke *Ripon* 76; C Holbeck 76-78; C Moseley St Mary *Birm* 78-83; P-in-c Handsworth St Jas 83-88; V from 88; P-in-c Handsworth St Mich 86-87; RD Handsworth from 92. *St James's Vicarage, Austin Road, Birmingham B21 8NU* 0121-554 4151

MORRIS, Canon Robin Edward. b 32. St Jo Coll Ox BA55 MA60. Westcott Ho Cam 55. **d** 57 **p** 58. C Halliwell St Thos *Man* 57-61; V Castleton Moor 61-71; V Stalybridge 71-80; R Heswall *Ches* from 80; Hon Can Ches Cathl from 91; RD Wirral N from 93. *The Rectory, Heswall, Wirral, Merseyside L60 0DZ* 0151-342 3471

MORRIS, Roger Anthony Brett. b 68. ARCS89 Imp Coll Lon BSc89 Trin Coll Cam BA92. Ridley Hall Cam CTM93. **d** 93 **p** 94. C Northleach w Hampnett and Farmington *Glouc* from 93; C Cold Aston w Notgrove and Turkdean from 93. *High View, Farmington Road, Northleach, Cheltenham, Glos GL54 3JA* Cotswold (01451) 860096

MORRIS, Stanley James. b 35. Keble Coll Ox BA58 MA63. Chich Th Coll 59. **d** 61 **p** 62. C Tunstall Ch Ch *Lich* 61-64; C W Bromwich All SS 64-67; V Wilnecote 67-88; V Alrewas from 88; V Wychnor from 88. *The Vicarage, Alrewas, Burton-on-Trent, Staffs DE13 7BT* Burton-on-Trent (01283) 790486

MORRIS, Stephen Bryan. b 54. Linc Th Coll 88. **d** 90 **p** 91. C Glouc St Geo w Whaddon *Glouc* 90-94; C Glouc St Mary de Crypt w St Jo and Ch Ch 94-95; C Glouc St Mary de Crypt w St Jo, Ch Ch etc from 95; Chapl Deaf from 94. *2 High View, Gloucester GL2 6LN* Gloucester (01452) 416178

MORRIS, Stephen Francis. b 52. St Jo Coll Nottm BTh79. **d** 79 **p** 80. C N Hinksey *Ox* 79-82; C Leic H Apostles *Leic* 82-85; TV Shenley and Loughton *Ox* 85-88; TV Watling Valley 88-95; V Chatham St Wm *Roch* from 95. *The Vicarage, 18 Marion Close, Chatham, Kent ME5 9QA* Medway (01634) 861975

MORRIS, Canon Stuart Collard. b 43. AKC66. St Boniface Warminster 66. **d** 67 **p** 68. C Hanham *Bris* 67-71; C Whitchurch 71-74; P-in-c Wapley w Codrington and Dodington 74-77; P-in-c Westerleigh 74-77; P-in-c Holdgate w Tugford *Heref* 77-82; P-in-c Abdon w Clee St Margaret 77-82; R Diddlebury w Bouldon and Munslow 77-82; P-in-c Sotterley, Willingham, Shadingfield, Ellough etc *St E* 82-87; RD Beccles and S Elmham 83-94; P-in-c Westhall w Brampton and Stoven 86-88; P-in-c Flixton w Homersfield and S Elmham 86-92; Hon Can St E Cathl from 87; V Bungay H

Trin w St Mary 87-94; P-in-c Hadleigh w Layham and Shelley from 94; RD Hadleigh from 94. *The Deanery, Hadleigh, Ipswich IP7 5DT* Hadleigh (01473) 822218

MORRIS, Canon Thomas Ernest Gilbert. b 06. Ex Coll Ox. St D Coll Lamp BA28. **d** 30 **p** 31. Hon Can Accra from 55; V Rockfield and Llangattock w St Maughan's *Mon* 69-77; rtd 77. *24 Brunswick Gardens, London W8 4AL*

MORRIS, Canon Thomas Gordon. b 25. CertEd48. St Mich Coll Llan 80. **d** 83 **p** 85. NSM Morriston *S & B* 83-86; C Caereithin 86-87; P-in-c 87-88; V from 88; Hon Can Brecon Cathl from 95. *The Vicarage, 64 Cheriton Close, Portmead, Swansea SA5 5LA* Swansea (01792) 583646

MORRIS, Very Rev Timothy David. b 48. Lon Univ BSc69. Trin Coll Bris DipTh75. **d** 75 **p** 76. C Edin St Thos *Edin* 75-77; R Edin St Jas 77-83; R Troon *Glas* 83-85; R Galashiels *Edin* from 85; Dean Edin from 92. *The Rectory, Parsonage Road, Galashiels, Selkirkshire TD1 3HS* Galashiels (01896) 3118

MORRIS, Mrs Valerie Ruth. b 46. St Hugh's Coll Ox BA68 MA72. Qu Coll Birm 76. **dss** 78 **d** 87. Burton *Lich* 82-87; Par Dn 87-90; Hon Par Dn from 90. *The Vicarage, Rangemore Street, Burton-on-Trent, Staffs DE14 2ED* Burton-on-Trent (01283) 36235

MORRIS, William Humphrey Francis. b 29. FRAS84 FInstP92 Univ of Wales BA54 MA72 Birm Univ DipTh58 Trin Coll Cam BA62 MA66 Man Univ MEd76 Trin Coll Cam PhD75 Man Univ PhD80 Ox Univ DPhil85 DD88. Qu Coll Birm 56. **d** 58 **p** 59. V Sandbach Heath *Ches* 65-68; Lic to Offic from 69; rtd 84; Lic to Offic *Lich* from 93. *Stonyflats Farm, Smallwood, Sandbach, Cheshire CW11 0XH* Smallwood (01477) 500354

MORRIS, William James. b 23. St Deiniol's Hawarden 72. **d** 73 **p** 74. NSM Brecon Adnry 73-78; NSM Crickhowell w Cwmdu and Tretower *S & B* 78-93. *The School House, Cwmdu, Crickhowell, Powys NP8 1RU* Bwlch (01874) 730355

MORRIS, William Richard Price. b 23. FCollP82. Glouc Sch of Min. **d** 88 **p** 89. Hon C Bussage *Glouc* 88-90; Perm to Offic 90-91; Hon C France Lynch 91; Hon C Chalford and France Lynch 91-93; rtd 93; Perm to Offic *Glouc* from 93. *Langendum House, Burleigh View, Bussage, Stroud, Glos GL6 8DD* Brimscombe (01453) 886382

MORRISON, Alexander Grant (Alex). b 37. St Fran Coll Brisbane ThL ACT St Columb's Hall Wangaratta. **d** 66 **p** 67. Australia 66-82; C Hayes St Mary *Lon* 83-84; R Black Notley *Chelmsf* from 84. *The Rectory, 71 Witham Road, Black Notley, Braintree, Essex CM7 8LJ* Braintree (01376) 349619

MORRISON, Andrew Leslie. b 11. TD53. Pemb Coll Ox BA33 MA37. Westcott Ho Cam 33. **d** 35 **p** 36. V Bury and Houghton *Chich* 64-76; rtd 76; Perm to Offic *Chich* from 76. *14 Guildford Place, Chichester, W Sussex PO19 4DU* Chichester (01243) 784310

MORRISON, Barry John. b 44. Pemb Coll Cam BA66 MA70. ALCD69. **d** 69 **p** 70. C Stoke Bishop *Bris* 69-72; C Edgware *Lon* 72-76; Chapl Poly Cen Lon 76-83; Hon C Langham Place All So 76-83; P-in-c W Hampstead St Luke 83-88; V from 88; Chapl Westf Coll 84-92. *St Luke's Vicarage, 12 Kidderpore Avenue, London NW3 7SU* 0171-794 2634

MORRISON, Iain Edward. b 36. St Steph Ho Ox 76. **d** 78 **p** 79. C Brighton St Aug and St Sav *Chich* 78-81; C Felpham w Middleton 81-83; P-in-c Barnham and Eastergate 83-85; R Aldingbourne, Barnham and Eastergate 85-91; V Jarvis Brook from 91. *The Vicarage, Tubwell Lane, Jarvis Brook, Crowborough, E Sussex TN6 3RH* Crowborough (01892) 652639

MORRISON, James Wilson Rennie (Jimmy). b 42. Aber Univ MA65. Linc Th Coll 76. **d** 78 **p** 79. C Whitley Ch Ch *Ox* 78-81; R Bagshot *Guildf* 81-88. *clo MOD (Army), Bagshot Park, Bagshot, Surrey GU19 5PL* Bagshot (01276) 471717 Fax 412834

MORRISON, John. b 18. Local NSM Course 73. **d** 76. Chapl St Paul's Cathl Dundee *Bre* 76-82; Hon C Dundee St Martin 82-92. *Address temp unknown*

MORRISON, Ven John Anthony. b 38. Jes Coll Cam BA60 MA64 Linc Coll Ox MA68. Chich Th Coll 61. **d** 64 **p** 65. C Birm St Pet *Birm* 64-68; C Ox St Mich *Ox* 68-71; Chapl Linc Coll Ox 68-74; C Ox St Mich w St Martin and All SS *Ox* 71-74; V Basildon 74-82; RD Bradfield 78-82; V Aylesbury 82-89; RD Aylesbury 85-89; TR Aylesbury w Bierton and Hulcott 89-90; Adn Buckm from 90. *60 Wendover Road, Aylesbury, Bucks HP21 9LW* Aylesbury (01296) 23269 Fax 397324

MORRISON, Richard James. b 55. Sarum & Wells Th Coll 87. **d** 89 **p** 90. C Boston *Linc* 89-93; P-in-c Digby from 93. *The Vicarage, 3 Beck Street, Digby, Lincoln LN4 3NE* Metheringham (01526) 320235

MORRISON, Robin Victor Adair. b 45. Nottm Univ BA67. Bucharest Th Inst 67 Ripon Hall Ox 68. **d** 70 **p** 71. C Hackney St Jo *Lon* 70-73; Chapl Newc Univ *Newc* 73-76; P-in-c Teversal *S'well* 76-78; Chapl Sutton Cen 76-78; Asst Hd Deans Community Sch Livingston *Edin* 78-80; R Edin St Columba 80-81; Chapl Birm Univ *Birm* 81-88; Prin Soc Resp

Officer *Derby* from 88. *216 Derby Road, Sandiacre, Nottingham NG10 5HE* Nottingham (0115) 939 2243

MORRISON, Walter Edward. b 15. ALCD41. **d** 41 **p** 42. V Bath St Luke *B & W* 66-81; rtd 81; Perm to Offic *B & W* from 81. *15 Ashley Road, Clevedon, Avon BS21 7UX* Clevedon (01275) 876088

MORRISON, Walter John Raymond (Ray). b 30. Jes Coll Cam BA55 MA58. Westcott Ho Cam 55. **d** 57 **p** 58. V Letchworth St Paul *St Alb* 63-71; RD Hitchin 70-71; R Ludlow *Heref* 72-83; RD Ludlow 78-83; Preb Heref Cathl 78-83; P-in-c Ludlow, Ludford, Ashford Carbonell etc 80-83; Chapl St Thos Hosp Lon 83-86; Chapl Eastbourne Distr Gen Hosp 86-95; rtd 95. *190 Farleigh Road, Pershore, Worcs WT10 1LY* Pershore (01386) 556542

MORRISON-WELLS, Canon John Frederick Pritchard. b 42. Univ of Wales (Lamp) BA65. Coll of Resurr Mirfield 65. **d** 67 **p** 68. C Bartley Green *Birm* 67-70; C Handsworth St Andr 70-73; V Perry Barr 73-80; RD Bordesley 80-90; V Birm St Aid Small Heath 80-92; P-in-c Small Heath St Greg 83-85 and 89-92; Hon Can Birm Cathl 83-92; P-in-c Bordesley St Oswald 91-92; V Ox St Giles and SS Phil and Jas w St Marg *Ox* from 92. *The Vicarage, Church Walk, Oxford OX2 6LY* Oxford (01865) 510460

MORROW, David. b 63. NUU BSc86 TCD BTh89. CITC 86. **d** 89 **p** 90. C Portadown St Mark *Arm* 89-91; C Ballymena w Ballyclug *Conn* 91-94; I Tempo and Clabby *Clogh* from 94. *The Rectory, Clabby, Fivemiletown, Co Tyrone BT75 0RD* Fivemiletown (013655) 21697

MORROW, Canon Edward Sidney (Ed). b 34. Qu Coll Birm 73. **d** 74 **p** 75. Namibia 75-78 and 79-87 and 89-90; C Truro St Paul *Truro* 78-79; Chapl to Namibians in Eur 87-89; C W Hackney St Barn *Lon* 87-89; Hon Can Windhoek from 87; V Stamford Hill St Thos *Lon* from 90. *The Vicarage, 37 Clapton Common, London E5 9AA* 0181-806 1463

MORROW, Canon Henry Hugh (Harry). b 26. TCD BA49 MA67 Flinders Univ Aus BSocAdmin76. TCD Div Sch Div Test49. **d** 49 **p** 50. C Dub St Thos *D & G* 49-53; I Rathmolyon *M & K* 53-58; I Killoughter *K, E & A* 58-63; C Portadown St Columba *Arm* 63-65; I Ballinderry w Tamlaght 65-70; Australia from 70; Can Adelaide from 84. *5 Allen Dale Grove, Stony Fell, S Australia 5066* Adelaide (8) 332-5890

MORROW, Joseph John. b 54. JP87. Edin Univ BD79. NY Th Sem DMin87 Edin Th Coll 76. **d** 79 **p** 80. Chapl St Paul's Cathl Dundee *Bre* 79-82; P-in-c Dundee St Martin 82-85; R 85-90; P-in-c Dundee St Jo from 85. *Braidwood, Strathmore Road, Glamis, Forfar, Angus DD8 1RX* Glamis (01307) 40582

MORSE, Mrs Elisabeth Ann. b 51. New Hall Cam MA73 Qu Eliz Coll Lon MSc74. S'wark Ord Course 91. **d** 94. C Wimbledon *S'wark* from 94. *9 Thornton Road, London SW19 4NE* 0181-946 4494

MORSE, Harry Arthur Carminowe. b 59. St Jo Coll Dur BA81 SS Paul & Mary Coll Cheltenham PGCE85. Oak Hill Th Coll BA91. **d** 91 **p** 92. C Summerfield *Birm* 91-92; C Hamstead St Bernard from 92. *33 Hamstead Road, Great Barr, Birmingham B43 5BA* 0121-357 4741

MORSHEAD, Ivo Francis Trelawny. b 27. ACA52 FCA63. Cuddesdon Coll 61. **d** 63 **p** 64. C Wimbledon *S'wark* 68-73; V Elham *Cant* 73-78; V Whitchurch *Ex* 78-91; rtd 91. *28 Edge Street, London W8 7PN* 0171-727 5975

MORSON, Mrs Dorothy Mary. b 29. Linc Th Coll 71. **d** 87. Par Dn Cen Telford *Lich* 87-89; rtd 89; Perm to Offic *Lich* from 89. *Ashleigh, Hunter Street, Shrewsbury SY3 8QN* Shrewsbury (01743) 369225

MORSON, John. b 41. **d** 88 **p** 92. NSM Eyemouth *Edin* 88-92; NSM Duns 88-89; CF 89-92; R Stromness *Ab* from 92; R Kirkwall from 92. *The Rectory, Dundas Crescent, Kirkwall, Isle of Orkney KW15 1JQ* Kirkwall (01856) 872024

MORT, Alister. b 52. BSc BA. Oak Hill Th Coll. **d** 82 **p** 83. C Cheadle Hulme St Andr *Ches* 82-85; C Rodbourne Cheney *Bris* 86-87; TV 87-90; V New Milverton *Cov* from 90. *2 St Mark's Road, Leamington Spa, Warks CV32 6DL* Leamington Spa (01926) 421004

MORT, Ivan Laurence (Laurie). b 61. Nottm Univ BTh87. Linc Th Coll 84. **d** 87 **p** 88. C Aston cum Aughton and Ulley *Sheff* 87-90; C Greenstead juxta Colchester *Chelmsf* 90-94; Chapl Toulouse *Eur* from 94. *1 Rue Pasteur, 31700 Cornebarrieu, Toulouse, France* France (33) 61 85 17 67

✠**MORT, Rt Rev John Ernest Llewelyn.** b 15. CBE65. St Cath Coll Cam BA38 MA42 Ahmadu Bello Univ Zaria Hon LLD70. Westcott Ho Cam 38. **d** 40 **p** 41 **c** 52. C Dudley St Thos *Worc* 40-44; Bp's Dom Chapl 44-52; V St Jo in Bedwardine 48-52; Bp N Nigeria 52-69; Can Res and Treas Leic Cathl *Leic* 70-88; Asst Bp Leic from 72; rtd 88. *271 Forest Road, Woodhouse, Loughborough, Leics LE12 8TZ*

MORTER, Ian Charles. b 54. AKC77. Coll of Resurr Mirfield 77. **d** 78 **p** 79. C Colchester St Jas, All SS, St Nic and St Runwald *Chelmsf* 78-82; C Brixham w Churston Ferrers *Ex* 82-83; TV 84-86; TV Brixham w Churston Ferrers and

Kingswear 86; TV Sidmouth, Woolbrook and Salcombe Regis 86-91; TV Sidmouth, Woolbrook, Salcombe Regis, Sidbury etc from 91. *St Francis' Vicarage, Woolbrook Road, Sidmouth, Devon EX10 9XH* Sidmouth (01395) 514522

MORTIMER, Anthony John. b 42. Sarum & Wells Th Coll 68. **d** 71 **p** 72. C Heref St Martin *Heref* 71-79; V Kingstone 79-85; P-in-c Clehonger 80-85; P-in-c Eaton Bishop 80-85; TR Pinhoe and Broadclyst *Ex* from 85. *The Rectory, 9 Church Hill, Pinhoe, Exeter EX4 9ER* Exeter (01392) 67541

MORTIMER, Charles Philip. b 38. Linc Th Coll 68. **d** 70 **p** 71. C Penistone w Midhope *Wakef* 70-74; V Luddenden 74-77; P-in-c Luddenden Foot 74-77; Chapl RAF 77-91; Asst Chapl-in-Chief RAF 91-93; V Staincliffe *Wakef* from 93. *The Vicarage, Staincliffe Hall Road, Batley, W Yorkshire WF17 7QX* Batley (01924) 473343

MORTIMER, Very Rev Hugh Sterling. b 23. TCD BA44 MA53. **d** 46 **p** 47. Hon VC 57-85; I Arm St Mark *Arm* 66-83; Can Arm Cathl 67-72; Treas 72-73; Chan 73-75; Prec 75-83; Dean Elphin and Ardagh *K, E & A* 83-91; I Sligo w Knocknarea and Rosses Pt 83-91; rtd 91; Perm to Offic *Conn* from 91. *95 Sharman Road, Belfast BT9 5HE* Belfast (01232) 669184

MORTIMER, Jonathan Michael. b 60. Bris Univ BA83. Oak Hill Th Coll BA92. **d** 92 **p** 93. C Rugby St Matt *Cov* from 92. *14 York Street, Rugby, Warks CV21 2BL* Rugby (01788) 568359 or 535208

MORTIMER, Lawrence George. b 45. St Edm Hall Ox BA67 MA71 St Chad's Coll Dur DipTh68. **d** 70 **p** 71. C Rugby St Andr *Cov* 70-75; V Styvechale 75-89; Dioc Broadcasting Officer 80-89; Dioc Communications Officer from 89; P-in-c Wootton Wawen from 95. *The Vicarage, Wootton Wawen, Solihull, W Midlands B95 6BD* Henley-in-Arden (01564) 792659

MORTIMER, William Raymond. b 31. GradIEE58 AMIEE66. St Deiniol's Hawarden 68. **d** 69 **p** 70. C Flint *St As* 69-71; Lic to Offic 72-73; V Llanwddyn and Llanfihangel and Llwydiarth 73-85; RD Llanfyllin 83-84; R Llanrwst and Llanddoget and Capel Garmon from 85. *The Rectory, Llanrwst, Gwynedd LL26 0DW* Llanrwst (01492) 640223

MORTIMORE, David Jack. b 42. Master Mariner 69. St Mich Coll Llan. **d** 91 **p** 92. C Pemb St Mary and St Mich *St D* 91-92; C Bargoed and Deri w Brithdir *Llan* from 92. *61 Park Road, Bargoed, M Glam CF8 8SR* Bargoed (01443) 821386

MORTIMORE, Robert Edward. b 39. Kelham Th Coll 61 Wells Th Coll 66. **d** 69 **p** 70. C Byfleet *Guildf* 69-72; New Zealand from 72. *25 St Judes Street, Airondale, New Zealand* Auckland (9) 828-7520

MORTON, Alan McNeile. b 28. Lon Univ BD49 AKC51 MTh68 BA78. St Boniface Warminster. **d** 52 **p** 53. Chapl Reading Sch 69-78 and 83-88; Hd Master St Sebastian's Sch Wokingham 78-83; rtd 93. *8 Blenheim Drive, Oxford OX2 8DG* Oxford (01865) 56371

MORTON, Albert George. b 34. Saskatchewan Univ BA61 McGill Univ Montreal MA73. Em Coll Saskatoon 56. **d** 61 **p** 61. Canada 61-65; C Stanford-le-Hope *Chelmsf* 66-69; V Linc St Geo Swallowbeck *Linc* 69-82; R Lt Munden w Sacombe *St Alb* 82-89; R The Mundens w Sacombe from 89. *The Rectory, Little Munden, Dane End, Ware, Herts SG12 0NT* Dane End (01920) 438766

MORTON, Alfred Bruce. b 21. TCD BA42 MA47. Linc Th Coll 43. **d** 44 **p** 45. R Northfield *Birm* 57-73; RD Kings Norton 62-73; Chapl Partis Coll Bath 73-84; C Marksbury *B & W* 81-83; P-in-c Melling w Tatham *Blackb* 84-87; rtd 87; Perm to Offic *Blackb* from 87. *6 Stanley Drive, Hornby, Lancaster LA2 8NA* Hornby (015242) 21999

MORTON, Andrew Edward. b 51. Lon Univ BA72 BD74 AKC74 Univ of Wales (Cardiff) MPhil93. St Aug Coll Cant 75. **d** 76 **p** 77. C Feltham *Lon* 76-79; C Pontlottyn w Fochriw *Llan* 79-81; V Ferndale w Maerdy 81-88; V Tylorstown w Ynyshir 88-93; Dir of Studies Llan Ord Course 91-93; R Llangybi and Coedypaen w Llanbadoc *Mon* from 93; Chapl Gwent Tertiary Coll from 93. *The Rectory, Parc Road, Llangybi, Usk, Gwent NP5 1NL* Newport (01633) 450214

MORTON, Arthur. b 15. CVO79 OBE61. Jes Coll Cam BA36 MA40. Wycliffe Hall Ox 36. **d** 38 **p** 39. Dir NSPCC 54-79; rtd 80; Perm to Offic *Portsm* from 85. *25 Cottes Way, Fareham, Hants PO14 3NF* Stubbington (01329) 663511

MORTON, Mrs Christine Mary. b 39. Linc Th Coll 78. **dss** 80 **d** 87 **p** 94. Ore *Chich* 80-84; Southwick 84-85; Winchmore Hill St Paul *Lon* 85-87; Par Dn 87-94; C from 94. *122 Bourne Hill, London N13 4BD* 0181-886 3157

MORTON, Clive Frederick. b 47. Lon Univ BA70. St Jo Coll Dur 78. **d** 80 **p** 81. C Countesthorpe w Foston *Leic* 80-83; C Glen Parva and S Wigston 83-86; V Birm St Pet *Birm* from 86. *St Peter's Vicarage, 32 George Street West, Birmingham B18 7HF* 0121-523 8000

MORTON, Howard Knyvett. b 30. St Jo Coll Cam BA51 MA67. Linc Th Coll 55. **d** 57 **p** 58. Head RE Heaton Gr Sch Newc 60-66 and 72-75; CMS 66-72; Heworth Grange Sch Dur 75-83; Regional Org Oxfam 88-91; Grainger Gr Sch Newc 91-94;

Lic to Offic *Newc* 73-93; Dioc World Development Officer from 94; rtd 95. *Fellfoot Cottage, Wall, Hexham, Northd NE46 4DX*   Hexham (01434) 681331

MORTON, Mrs Jenny. b 50. Bedf Coll Lon BA72 Leic Univ PGCE73. E Midl Min Tr Course 87. **d** 90 **p** 94. C New Mills *Derby* 90-94; Chapl Asst Nottm City Hosp from 94. *56 Marshall Drive, Bramcote, Nottingham NG9 3LD* Nottingham (0115) 939 5784

MORTON, John Francis Eric. b 17. Leeds Univ BA38. Coll of Resurr Mirfield 38. **d** 40 **p** 41. V Beeston Hill H Spirit *Ripon* 60-77; rtd 77. *1 Deanery Close, Minster Road, Ripon, N Yorkshire HG4 1LZ*   Ripon (01765) 701227

MORTON, Canon John Ivan. b 32. Linc Coll Ox BA55 MA59. Wells Th Coll. **d** 57 **p** 58. C Shrewsbury St Chad *Lich* 57-60; C Dunham Massey St Marg *Ches* 60-62; V Derby St Luke *Derby* 62-70; R W Kirby St Andr *Ches* 70-75; V Northn St Matt *Pet* from 75; RD Northn 79-88; Can Pet Cathl from 82. *St Matthew's Vicarage, St Matthew's Parade, Northampton NN2 7HF*   Northampton (01604) 713615 or 791251

MORTON, Canon John Peter Sargeson. b 12. Keble Coll Ox BA35 MA39. Lich Th Coll 35. **d** 36 **p** 37. V Ambleside w Rydal and Brathay *Carl* 67-78; rtd 78; Perm to Offic *Glouc* from 78. *35 Gretton Road, Winchcombe, Cheltenham, Glos GL54 5EG* Cheltenham (01242) 603384

MORTON, Mark Paul. b 58. Univ of Wales (Swansea) BA79. Ridley Hall Cam CTM92. **d** 92 **p** 93. C Daventry, Ashby St Ledgers, Braunston etc *Pet* 92-95; CF (TA) 93-95; CF from 95. *c/o MOD (Army), Bagshot Park, Bagshot, Surrey GU19 5PL* Bagshot (01276) 471717   Fax 412834

MORTON, Sister Rita. b 34. Wilson Carlile Coll. **dss** 85 **d** 87 **p** 94. CA from 76; Par Dn Harlow New Town w Lt Parndon *Chelmsf* 87-89; C Harold Hill St Geo 89-94; rtd 94. *16 Cheviot Road, Hornchurch, Essex RH11 1LP*

MORTON, Robert Hart (Bob). b 28. Moray Ord Course 91. **d** 94. Hon C St Andr Cathl Inverness *Mor* from 94. *75 Fairfield Road, Inverness IV3 5LJ*   Inverness (01463) 223525

MORTON, Rupert Neville. b 25. St Steph Ho Ox 51. **d** 54 **p** 55. V Bramley *Guildf* 62-79; V Grafham 62-79; RD Cranleigh 71-76; R Haslemere 79-91; rtd 91. *Rock House, Wormley, Godalming, Surrey GU8 5SN*   Wormley (01428) 682614

MORTON, Mrs Sheila. b 44. Leeds Univ DipTh92. Sarum & Wells Th Coll 79. **dss** 84 **d** 87 **p** 94. HM Forces Dusseldorf 84-86; Cov St Mary *Cov* 86-87; Par Dn 87-89; Par Dn Boston Spa *York* 89-92; Par Dn Flitwick *St Alb* 93-94; C from 94. *32 St Albans Close, Flitwick, Bedford MK45 1UA*   Flitwick (01525) 718561

MORTON, Canon William Derek. b 28. Wells Th Coll 67. **d** 69 **p** 70. C Kibworth Beauchamp *Leic* 69-72; Ind Chapl *Nor* 72-93; Hon Can Nor Cathl 90-93; RD Nor E 90-93; rtd 93; Perm to Offic *Nor* from 93. *55 Cameron Green, Taverham, Norwich NR8 6UA*   Norwich (01603) 861240

MORTON, Canon William Wright. b 56. ALAM TCD BTh88. **d** 88 **p** 89. C Drumachose *D & R* 88-91; I Conwal Union w Gartan from 91; Bp's Dom Chapl from 92; Can Raphoe Cathl from 94. *Conwal Rectory, Magherennan, Letterkenny, Co Donegal, Irish Republic*   Letterkenny (74) 22573

MOSEDALE, Hugh Alfred. b 14. AKC48. **d** 49 **p** 50. C W Derby St Mary *Liv* 49-52; C Lewisham St Mary S'wark 52-55; C Walton St Mary *Liv* 55-57; V Middleton Junction *Man* 57-61; R Boxworth *Ely* from 61; R Elsworth w Knapwell from 61; RD Bourn 72-81. *The Rectory, Boxworth, Cambridge CB3 8LZ*   Elsworth (019547) 226

MOSELEY, Arthur William. b 27. Lich Th Coll. **d** 60 **p** 61. V Bradley St Martin *Lich* 66-72; C Stoke upon Trent 73-74; V Brown Edge 74-85; V Criftins 85-93; V Dudleston 85-93; rtd 93. *Pentre Collen, 2 Cil-y-Coed, Ruabon, Wrexham, Clwyd LL14 4EN*

MOSELEY, Colin Francis. b 40. FRICS ACIArb. **d** 79 **p** 80. NSM Fishponds St Mary *Bris* 79-84; Hon C Winterbourne Down 84-86; Hon C Frenchay and Winterbourne Down from 86. *2 Prospect Close, Winterbourne Down, Bristol BS17 1BD* Winterbourne (01454) 778064

MOSELEY, David John Reading. b 30. Univ Coll Ox BA54 MA58. Wells Th Coll 54. **d** 56 **p** 57. C Farnworth and Kearsley *Man* 56-59; Trinidad and Tobago 59-63; V Bedminster St Paul *Bris* 63-75; TV Bedminster 75-78; V Kilmington w Shute *Ex* from 78; P-in-c Stockland w Dalwood 90. *The Vicarage, Kilmington, Axminster, Devon EX13 7RF*   Axminster (01297) 33156

MOSELEY, Hugh Martin. b 47. St Jo Coll Dur BA70. Westcott Ho Cam 71. **d** 73 **p** 74. C Hythe *Cant* 73-77; P-in-c Eythorne w Waldershare 77-83; V Ringmer *Chich* from 83; RD Lewes and Seaford from 93. *The Vicarage, Ringmer, Lewes, E Sussex BN8 5LA*   Ringmer (01273) 812243

MOSELEY, Roger Henry. b 38. Edin Th Coll 60. **d** 63 **p** 64. C Friern Barnet All SS *Lon* 63-66; C Grantham St Wulfram *Linc*

66-69; P-in-c Swaton w Spanby 69-73; P-in-c Horbling 69-73; V Soberton w Newtown *Portsm* 73-80; V Sarisbury from 80. *The Vicarage, 149 Bridge Road, Sarisbury Green, Southampton SO3 7EN*   Locks Heath (01489) 572207

MOSELING, Peter. b 48. W Midl Minl Tr Course 92. **d** 95. C Daventry, Ashby St Ledgers, Braunston etc *Pet* from 95. *48 Trinity Close, Daventry, Northants NN11 4RN*   Daventry (01327) 78697

MOSELING, Stephen. b 57. Chich Th Coll 83. **d** 86 **p** 87. C Burnley St Cath w St Alb and St Paul *Blackb* 86-89; C Rawmarsh w Parkgate *Sheff* 89-91; V Colindale St Matthias *Lon* 91-94. *47 New Road, London N22 5ET*   0181-889 1832

MOSES, Very Rev Dr John Henry. b 38. Nottm Univ BA59 PhD65. Linc Th Coll 62. **d** 64 **p** 65. C Bedf St Andr *St Alb* 64-70; P-in-c Cov St Pet *Cov* 70-73; P-in-c Cov St Mark 71-73; TR Cov E 73-77; RD Cov E 73-77; Adn Southend *Chelmsf* 77-82; Provost Chelmsf from 82; Chmn Coun of Cen for Th Study Essex Univ from 87. *Provost's House, 3 Harlings Grove, Waterloo Lane, Chelmsford CM1 1YQ*   Chelmsford (01245) 354318 or 263660   Fax 496802

MOSES, Leslie Alan. b 49. Hull Univ BA71 Edin Univ BD76. Edin Th Coll 73. **d** 76 **p** 77. C Edin Old St Paul *Edin* 76-79; R 85-95; R Leven *St And* 79-85; P-in-c Edin St Marg *Edin* 86-92; V St Marylebone All SS *Lon* from 95. *All Saints' Vicarage, 7 Margaret Street, London W1N 8JQ*   0171-636 1788 or 636 9961   Fax 436 4470

MOSES, Norman. b 12. AKC37. **d** 37 **p** 38. V Grangetown *Dur* 58-77; rtd 77. *1 Wayside, Sunderland SR2 7QJ* 0191-514 2150

MOSFORD, Denzil Huw Erasmus. b 56. St D Coll Lamp DipTh77 AKC78 Sarum & Wells Th Coll 77. **d** 79 **p** 80. C Clydach *S & B* 79-82; V from 82; Jamaica 82-85; V Ystalyfera *S & B* 85-87; RD Cwmtawe from 93. *The Vicarage, 53 Bryntawe Road, Ynystawe, Swansea SA6 5AD*   Swansea (01792) 843202

MOSFORD, Denzil Joseph. b 28. **d** 86 **p** 87. C Manselton *S & B* 86-89; V Port Eynon w Rhosili and Llanddewi and Knelston from 89. *The Rectory, Port Eynon, Swansea SA3 1NL* Swansea (01792) 390456

MOSLEY, Edward Peter. b 38. Clifton Th Coll 62. **d** 67 **p** 68. C Mirehouse *Carl* 67-69; C Newbarns w Hawcoat 69-72; R Aikton 72-77; R Orton St Giles 72-77; V Silloth 77-78; CF from 78; Hon C Grantown-on-Spey *Mor* from 94; Hon C Rothiemurchus from 94. *Tigh-na-Drochaid, Nethy Bridge, Inverness-shire PH25 3DW*   Nethy Bridge (01479) 821666

MOSS, Very Rev Basil Stanley. b 18. Qu Coll Ox BA41 MA45. Linc Th Coll 42. **d** 43 **p** 44. Hon Can Bris Cathl *Bris* 66-73; Chief Sec ACCM 66-73; Provost Birm 73-85; rtd 85; Perm to Offic *Worc* from 85; Perm to Offic *Birm* from 86. *25 Castle Grove, Stourbridge, W Midlands DY8 2HH*   Stourbridge (01384) 378799

MOSS, Christopher Ashley. b 52. Ex Univ BA73 York Univ DSA77 Southn Univ DASS78 CQSW78. Wycliffe Hall Ox 89. **d** 91 **p** 92. C Malvern H Trin and St Jas *Worc* from 91. *23 Tennyson Drive, Malvern, Worcs WR14 2TQ*   Malvern (01684) 893118

MOSS, Dr Clement Frederick. b 16. OBE73. Ludhiana Chr Med Coll LSMF55. Cliff Th Coll 38 Ridley Hall Cam 81. **d** 81 **p** 81. Hon C Bedf St Jo and St Leon *St Alb* 81-89; NSM Sharnbrook Deanery 82-93; Perm to Offic from 93. *22 Meadway, Harrold, Bedford MK43 7DR*   Bedford (01234) 720608   Fax 720087

MOSS, David Glyn. b 62. St Anne's Coll Ox BA83 Em Coll Cam BA89. Westcott Ho Cam 87. **d** 90 **p** 91. C Halesowen *Worc* 90-93; Tutor St Steph Ho Ox from 93. *St Stephen's House, 16 Marston Street, Oxford OX4 1JX*   Oxford (01865) 247874

MOSS, David Sefton. b 59. MRPharmS81 Sunderland Poly BSc80. Ridley Hall Cam CTM93. **d** 93 **p** 94. C Highworth w Sevenhampton and Inglesham etc *Bris* from 93. *24 Lismore Road, Highworth, Swindon SN6 7HU*   Swindon (01793) 764729

MOSS, Denis. b 32. St Jo Coll Auckland LTh83. **d** 74 **p** 75. New Zealand 74-92; Chapl Budapest *Eur* from 92. *Budenz Utca 4/B, Budapest 1021, Hungary*

MOSS, Harold George Edward. b 20. Glouc Th Course 79. **d** 80 **p** 81. NSM Cirencester *Glouc* 80-83; NSM Brimpsfield, Cranham, Elkstone and Syde 83-89; rtd 89. *57 Queen Elizabeth Road, Cirencester, Glos GL7 1DH*   Cirencester (01285) 652857

MOSS, Ivan Douglas Francis. b 24. Chich Th Coll. **d** 76 **p** 77. Hon C Crawley *Chich* 76-93; rtd 93. *14 Normanhurst Close, Three Bridges, Crawley, W Sussex RH10 1YL*   Crawley (01293) 522172

MOSS, James Wilfred. b 15. Oak Hill Th Coll 75. **d** 76 **p** 77. Hon C Frogmore H Trin *St Alb* 76-78 and 81-93; Hon C Watford St Luke 78-81; Perm to Offic from 93. *8A The Rise, Park Street, St Albans, Herts AL2 2NT*   St Albans (01727) 872467

MOSS, Preb Kenneth Charles. b 37. ARCS59 Lon Univ BSc59 DIC62 PhD62. d 66 p 67. Canada 66-73; Chapl Ex Univ *Ex* 73-83; V St Marychurch from 83; RD Ipplepen 87-93; Preb Ex Cathl from 92. *The Vicarage, Hampton Avenue, St Marychurch, Torquay TQ1 3LA* Torquay (01803) 327661 or 329054

MOSS, Ven Leonard Godfrey. b 32. K Coll Lon BD59 AKC59. d 60 p 61. C Putney St Marg *S'wark* 60-63; C Cheam 63-67; R Much Dewchurch w Llanwarne and Llandinabo *Heref* 67-72; Dioc Ecum Officer 69-83; V Marden w Amberley 72-80; V Marden w Amberley and Wisteston 80-84; P-in-c 92-94; Preb Heref Cathl from 79; Can Heref Cathl 84-91; Dioc Soc Resp Officer 84-91; Adn Heref from 91. *The Archdeacon's House, The Close, Hereford HR1 2NG* Hereford (01432) 272873

MOSS, Mrs Nelva Elizabeth. b 44. Bp Grosseteste Coll TCert66 Sussex Univ BEd73. S Dios Minl Tr Scheme 90. d 93 p 94. NSM Bincombe w Broadwey, Upwey and Buckland Ripers *Sarum* from 93. *64 Elwell Street, Weymouth, Dorset DT3 5QF* Weymouth (01305) 814347

MOSS, Peter Hextall. b 34. Clare Coll Cam BA59 MA62. Linc Th Coll 59. d 61 p 62. C Easington Colliery *Dur* 61-63; C Whickham 63-65; C-in-c Town End Farm CD 65-72; TV Mattishall *Nor* 72-75; P-in-c Welborne 75-84; P-in-c Mattishall w Mattishall Burgh 75-84; TR Hempnall 84-89. *High House Cottage, Gunn Street, Foulsham, Dereham, Norfolk NR20 5RN* Foulsham (0136284) 823

MOSS, Peter John. b 41. K Coll Cam BA64 MA67. Westcott Ho Cam 63. d 84 p 85. Hon C Leighton Buzzard w Eggington, Hockliffe etc *St Alb* 84-93; NSM Luton St Sav from 93. *84 Regent Street, Leighton Buzzard, Beds LU7 8JZ* Leighton Buzzard (01525) 372904

MOSS, Stephen. b 51. Lon Univ BSc69. S'wark Ord Course. d 85 p 86. NSM Clapham Ch Ch and St Jo *S'wark* 85-87; NSM Clapham TM from 87. *59A Bromfelde Road, London SW4 6PP* 0171-720 3152

MOSS, Victor Charles. b 25. Oak Hill Th Coll BD65. d 66 p 67. C Belper *Derby* 69-71; V Chesterfield Ch Ch 71-93; rtd 93. *16 Nether Croft Road, Brimington, Chesterfield, Derbyshire S43 1QD* Chesterfield (01246) 206260

MOSS, Wilfrid Maurice. b 10. St Jo Coll Dur LTh34 BA35 MA41. Tyndale Hall Bris 31. d 35 p 36. V Sidcup Ch Ch *Roch* 50-75; rtd 75; Perm to Offic *Ex* 75-85; Perm to Offic *B & W* from 85. *Stonehaven, 4 West View Close, Middlezoy, Bridgwater, Somerset TA7 0NP* Burrowbridge (01823) 698851

MOSSE, Mrs Barbara Ann. b 51. CertEd73 Open Univ BA77. CA Tr Coll IDC81 Lambeth STh83. d 90 p 95. NSM Southbourne w W Thorney *Chich* 90-93; Perm to Offic 93-95; Community Mental Health Chapl Fareham/Gosport from 94; NSM Purbrook *Portsm* from 95. *8 Long Copse Court, Long Copse Lane, Emsworth, Hants PO10 7UW* Emsworth (01243) 376155

MOSSMAN, Preb Donald Wyndham Cremer. b 13. OBE65. Lon Coll of Div LTh39. d 39 p 40. Preb St Paul's Cathl *Lon* 60-86; RD W Haringey 67-71; C Highgate St Mich 69-71; R St Jas Garlickhythe w St Mich Queenhithe etc 71-84; Hon C Warsaw *Eur* 77-84; Hon Can Brussels Cathl 81-84; rtd 84. *The Charterhouse, Charterhouse Square, London EC1M 6AN* 0171-251 8002

MOSSOP, Henry Watson. b 08. Lich Th Coll 52. d 54 p 55. V Twyford w Guist *Nor* 66-73; rtd 73; Perm to Offic *Nor* 74-93; from 93. *Crossing Cottage, Pond Lane, Antingham, North Walsham, Norfolk NR28 0NH* North Walsham (01692) 403561

MOSSOP, Patrick John (Pat). b 48. Solicitor St Jo Coll Cam MA LLB. Linc Th Coll BTh93. d 93. C Halstead St Andr w H Trin and Greenstead Green *Chelmsf* from 93. *47 Tidings Hill, Halstead, Essex CO9 1BL* Halstead (01787) 475528

MOSSOP, Canon Robert Owen. b 09. Peterho Cam BA30 MA35. Westcott Ho Cam 32. d 33 p 34. V Constantine *Truro* 50-73; RD Kerrier 60-73; Hon Can Truro Cathl 69-84; rtd 73. *Westwood, Carnmenellis, Redruth, Cornwall TR16 6PB* Stithians (01209) 860288

MOTE, Gregory Justin. b 60. Oak Hill Th Coll BA83. d 86 p 87. C W Ealing St Jo w St Jas *Lon* 86-90; C St Helen Bishopsgate w St Andr Undershaft etc from 90. *64 Arbery Road, London E3 5DD* 0181-983 1079

MOTH, Miss Susan. b 44. Leic Univ BA65 K Coll Lon CertEd66. Linc Th Coll 83. dss 85 d 87 p 94. Churchdown St Jo *Glouc* 85-87; C 87-93; D-in-c The Rissingtons 93-94; P-in-c from 94. *The Rectory, Great Rissington, Cheltenham, Glos GL54 2LL* Cotswold (01451) 810611

MOTHERSOLE, John Robert. b 25. Chich Th Coll. d 84 p 85. NSM Hayes St Anselm *Lon* 84-93; NSM Hayes St Edm from 93. *116 Nestles Avenue, Hayes, Middx UB3 4QD* 0181-848 0626

MOTT, Julian Ward. b 52. Loughb Univ BSc77. Ripon Coll Cuddesdon 78. d 81 p 82. C Aylestone *Leic* 81-84; C Gt Ilford

St Mary *Chelmsf* 84-88; R Chevington w Hargrave and Whepstead w Brockley *St E* from 88. *The Rectory, Chevington, Bury St Edmunds, Suffolk IP29 5QL* Chevington (01284) 850204

MOTT, Peter John. b 49. Ch Coll Cam BA70 MA75 Dundee Univ PhD73 Nottm Univ BA79. St Jo Coll Nottm 77. d 80 p 81. C Hull Newland St Jo *York* 80-83; C Selly Park St Steph and St Wulstan *Birm* 83-87; C Mosborough *Sheff* 87-92; R Colne St Bart *Blackb* from 92. *The Rectory, Albert Road, Colne, Lancs BB8 0AE* Colne (01282) 863479

MOTTERSHEAD, Derek. b 39. Open Univ BA74 BEd. Chich Th Coll 65. d 69 p 70. C Walthamstow St Barn and St Jas Gt *Chelmsf* 69-72; C Chelmsf All SS 72-77; P-in-c Cold Norton w Stow Maries 77-80; V Leytonstone St Andr 80-92; V Eastbourne St Sav and St Pet *Chich* from 92; Miss to Seamen from 92. *St Saviour's Vicarage, Spencer Road, Eastbourne, E Sussex BN21 4PA* Eastbourne (01323) 722317

MOTTRAM, Andrew Peter. b 53. AKC77. Ripon Coll Cuddesdon 77. d 78 p 79. C E Bedfont *Lon* 78-81; C Hatf St Alb 81-84; V Milton Ernest 84-91; V Thurleigh 84-91; P-in-c Heref All SS *Heref* from 91. *All Saints' Vicarage, 45 Venns Lane, Hereford HR1 1DE* Hereford (01432) 266588 or 355088 Fax 344428

MOTYER, John Alexander. b 24. TCD BA46 MA51 BD51. Wycliffe Hall Ox 47. d 47 p 48. V W Hampstead St Luke *Lon* 65-70; Dep Prin Tyndale Hall Bris 70-71; Prin and Dean Trin Coll Bris 71-81; Min Westbourne Ch Ch Prop Chpl *Win* 81-89; rtd 89; Perm to Offic *Ex* from 90. *10 Littlefield, Bishopsteignton, Teignmouth, Devon TQ14 9SG* Teignmouth (01626) 770986

MOTYER, Stephen. b 50. Pemb Coll Cam BA73 MA77 Bris Univ MLitt79. Trin Coll Bris 73. d 76 p 77. Lect Oak Hill Th Coll 76-83; C Braughing, Lt Hadham, Albury, Furneux Pelham etc *St Alb* 83-87; Perm to Offic from 87; Lect Lon Bible Coll from 87. *12 Lower Tail, Carpenders Park, Watford WD1 5DD* 0181-428 9422

MOUGHTIN, Ross. b 48. St Cath Coll Cam BA70 St Jo Coll Dur BA75. d 76 p 77. C Litherland St Paul Hatton Hill *Liv* 76-79; C Heswall *Ches* 79-84; Chapl Edw Unit Rochdale Infirmary 83-92; V Thornham w Gravel Hole *Man* 84-92; V Aughton Ch Ch *Liv* from 92. *Christ Church Vicarage, 22 Long Lane, Aughton, Ormskirk, Lancs L39 5AT* Aughton Green (01695) 422175

MOULD, Mrs Jacqueline. b 66. QUB BD88. d 91 p 92. C Belf St Aid *Conn* 91-94; C Drumragh w Mountfield *D & R* from 94. *12 Crevenagh Way, Omagh, Co Tyrone BT79 0JE* Omagh (01662) 247200

MOULD, Jeremy James. b 63. Nottm Univ BA85. d 91 p 92. C Mossley *Conn* 91-94; C Drumragh w Mountfield *D & R* from 94. *12 Crevenagh Way, Omagh, Co Tyrone BT79 0JE* Omagh (01662) 247200

MOULDER, Kenneth. b 53. Lon Univ BEd75. Ridley Hall Cam 78. d 81 p 82. C Harold Wood *Chelmsf* 81-84; C Darfield *Sheff* 84-88; V Walkergate *Newc* 88-92; P-in-c Byker St Mark 90-92; V Byker St Mark and Walkergate St Oswald from 92. *St Oswald's Parsonage, Woodhead Road, Newcastle upon Tyne NE6 4RX* 0191-263 6249

MOULE, Prof Charles Francis Digby. b 08. CBE. FBA66 Em Coll Cam BA29 MA34 St Andr Univ Hon DD58. Ridley Hall Cam 31. d 33 p 34. Lady Marg Prof Div Cam Univ 51-76; Can Th Leic Cathl *Leic* 55-76; rtd 76; Perm to Offic *Chich* from 81. *1 King's Houses, Pevensey, E Sussex BN24 5JR* Eastbourne (01323) 762436

MOULE, George William Henry. b 04. Em Coll Cam BA26 MA30. d 36 p 37. V Damerham *Sarum* 59-70; rtd 70; Perm to Offic *Carl* from 77. *Herne Cottage, Abbey Road, St Bees, Cumbria CA27 0ED*

MOULE, Kevin David. b 54. Coll of Resurr Mirfield 77. d 80 p 81. C E Finchley All SS *Lon* 80-84; C Notting Hill St Mich and Ch Ch 84-91; P-in-c Isleworth St Fran 91-94; P-in-c Walham Green St Jo w St Jas from 94. *The Vicarage, 40 Racton Road, London SW6 1LP* 0171-385 3676 Fax 385 7634

MOULT, Jane Elizabeth Kate. b 61. Trin Coll Bris DipHE93. d 94 p 95. NSM St Jo in Bedwardine *Worc* from 94. *16 Heron Close, Worcester WR2 4BW* Worcester (01905) 429641

MOULT, Simon Paul. b 66. Nene Coll Northampton DipChir88. Trin Coll Bris BA94. d 94 p 95. C St Jo in Bedwardine *Worc* from 94. *16 Heron Close, Worcester WR2 4BW* Worcester (01905) 429641

MOULTON, Paul Oliver. b 43. BSc. N Ord Course 77. d 80 p 81. C Wilmslow *Ches* 80-85; V Knutsford St Cross 85-92; Chapl Mary Dendy Hosp Knutsford 86-92; V Gatley *Ches* from 92. *St James's Vicarage, 11 Northenden Road, Cheadle, Cheshire SK8 4EN* 0161-428 4764

MOULTON, William Arthur. b 11. Man Univ Leic Univ MEd64. Wells Th Coll 47. d 48 p 49. Asst Chapl & Sen Lect Coll SS Mark & Jo Chelsea 48-62; Prin Lect Bp Grosseteste

Coll Linc 62-76; Hon PV Linc Cathl *Linc* from 76. *Bungalow 7, Terrys Cross, Woodmancote, Henfield, W Sussex BN5 9SX* Henfield (01273) 493091

MOUNCER, David Peter. b 65. Univ of Wales (Abth) BA86. Oak Hill Th Coll BA94. **d** 94 **p** 95. C Foord St Jo *Cant* from 94. *126 Lucy Avenue, Folkestone, Kent CT19 5TN* Folkestone (01303) 250280

MOUNSEY, William Lawrence Fraser. b 51. St Andr Univ BD75. Edin Th Coll 76. **d** 78 **p** 79. C Edin St Mark *Edin* 78-81; Chapl RAF 81-90; R Dalmahoy *Edin* from 90; Chapl Heriot-Watt Univ from 90. *The Rectory, Dalmahoy, Kirknewton, Midlothian EH27 8EB* 0131-333 1683

MOUNSTEPHEN, Philip Ian. b 59. Southn Univ BA80 Magd Coll Ox MA87. Wycliffe Hall Ox 85. **d** 88 **p** 89. C Gerrards Cross and Fulmer *Ox* 88-92; V W Streatham St Jas *S'wark* from 92. *St James' Vicarage, 236 Mitcham Lane, London SW16 6NT* 0181-677 3947

MOUNT, Canon Judith Mary. b 35. Bedf Coll Lon BA56 Lon Univ CertEd57. Ripon Coll Cuddesdon 81. **dss** 83 **d** 87 **p** 94. Carterton *Ox* 83-85; Charlton on Otmoor and Oddington 85-87; Dioc Lay Min Adv and Asst Dir of Ords 86-89; Par Dn Islip w Charlton on Otmoor, Oddington, Noke etc 87-94; C 94-95; Assoc Dioc Dir Ords & Adv for Women in Ord Min 89-95; Hon Can Ch Ch 92-95; rtd 95; Hon C Shill Valley and Broadshire *Ox* from 95. *The Vicarage, Filkins, Lechlade, Glos GL7 3JQ* Faringdon (01367) 860460

MOUNTFORD, Brian Wakling. b 45. Newc Univ BA66 Cam Univ MA73 Ox Univ MA90. Westcott Ho Cam 66. **d** 68 **p** 69. C Westmr St Steph w St Jo *Lon* 68-69; C Paddington Ch Ch 69-73; Chapl SS Coll Cam 73-78; V Southgate Ch Ch *Lon* 78-86; V Ox St Mary V w St Cross and St Pet *Ox* from 86. *12 Mansfield Road, Oxford OX1 3TA* Oxford (01865) 243806

MOUNTFORD, John. b 55. Nottm Univ BEd77 Birm Univ MA80 Ex Univ MPhil86. Linc Th Coll 73. **d** 78 **p** 79. C Wombourne *Lich* 78-80; C Upper Gornal 80-82; C Paignton St Jo *Ex* 82-86; Papua New Guinea 86-87; Chapl Blue Coat Sch Birm 87-90; Perm to Offic *Birm* 88-90; Australia 91-94. *Address temp unknown*

MOUNTNEY, Frederick Hugh. b 14. St Chad's Coll Dur BA36 MA39. Lich Th Coll 36. **d** 37 **p** 38. V Heref All SS *Heref* 56-75; Chapl Victoria Eye Hosp Heref 56-75; Chapl Bonn w Cologne *Eur* 75-79; rtd 79; Perm to Offic *Heref* 79-90; Perm to Offic *St E* from 82; Perm to Offic *Nor* from 82; Perm to Offic *Eur* from 90. *St Martin's, 44 London Road, Harleston, Norfolk IP20 9BW* Harleston (01379) 853744

MOUNTNEY, John Michael. b 47. St Chad's Coll Dur BA69 MA84. Cuddesdon Coll 69. **d** 71 **p** 72. C Morpeth *Newc* 71-75; C Longbenton St Bart 75-77; Sub-Warden Community of All Hallows Ditchingham 77-83; R Blundeston w Flixton and Lound *Nor* 83-87; TR Nor St Pet Parmentergate w St Jo 87-93; Warden Julian Shrine 87-93; V Embleton w Rennington and Rock *Newc* from 93. *The Vicarage, Embleton, Alnwick, Northd NE66 3UW* Embleton (01665) 576660

MOURANT, Julia Caroline. b 58. Sheff Univ BA79. St Jo Coll Nottm DPS84. **dss** 84 **d** 92 **p** 94. Cropwell Bishop w Colston Bassett, Granby etc *S'well* 84-86; Marple All SS *Ches* 86-89; Harlow St Mary and St Hugh w St Jo the Bapt *Chelmsf* 89-92; NSM from 92. *St Mary's Vicarage, 5 Staffords, Harlow, Essex CM17 0JR* Harlow (01279) 450633

MOURANT, Sidney Eric. b 39. DipTh70. Oak Hill Th Coll BD73. **d** 89 **p** 90. C Oxton *Ches* 89-92; V Douglas St Thos *S & M* from 92. *St Thomas's Vicarage, Princes Road, Douglas, Isle of Man* Douglas (01624) 675609

MOURANT, Stephen Philip Edward. b 54. Nottm Univ BTh83. St Jo Coll Nottm. **d** 83 **p** 84. C Cropwell Bishop w Colston Bassett, Granby etc *S'well* 83-86; C Marple All SS *Ches* 86-89; P-in-c Harlow St Mary and St Hugh w St Jo the Bapt *Chelmsf* 89-90; V from 90. *St Mary's Vicarage, 5 Staffords, Harlow, Essex CM17 0JR* Harlow (01279) 450633

MOVERLEY, Ruth Elaine. b 55. K Alfred's Coll Win 73. Llan Dioc Tr Scheme 85. **d** 90. C Llangynwyd w Maesteg *Llan* 90-95; C Glan Ely from 95. *2 Deere Close, Ely, Cardiff CF5 4NU*

MOWAT, Geoffrey Scott. b 17. CCC Ox BA39 MA49. Ripon Hall Ox 58. **d** 59 **p** 60. V Coln St Aldwyn w Hatherop and Quenington *Glouc* 64-77; RD Fairford 74-77; Malaysia 77-83; rtd 83; Perm to Offic *B & W* 86-87; from 92; Min Bath St Mary Magd Holloway 87-92. *3 Chedworth Close, Bath BA2 7AF* Bath (01225) 833310

MOWBRAY, David. b 38. Fitzw Ho Cam BA60 MA64 Lon Univ BD62. Clifton Th Coll. **d** 63 **p** 64. C Northn St Giles *Pet* 63-66; Lect Watford St Mary *St Alb* 66-70; V Broxbourne 70-77; R Broxbourne w Wormley 77-84; V Hertf All SS 84-91; V Darley Abbey *Derby* from 91; Asst Chapl Derby R Infirmary from 91. *Darley Abbey Vicarage, 25 Church Lane, Derby DE22 1EX* Derby (01332) 553192

MOWBRAY, Derek David Whitfield. b 19. Lon Univ BD42 Dur Univ MLitt52 Sheff Univ PhD58 Leeds Univ PhD59. ALCD42. **d** 42 **p** 43. R Bris St Jo w St Mary-le-Port *Bris* 71-74; Perm to Offic from 75; rtd 84. *20 Glynderwen Close, Derwen Fawr, Swansea SA2 8EQ* Swansea (01792) 208708

MOWER, Miss Marguerite Mary. b 36. Bris Univ BA57. Cant Sch of Min 90. **d** 93 **p** 94. NSM Eythorne and Elvington w Waldershare etc *Cant* from 93. *Meadow Bank, Eythorne Road, Shepherdswell, Dover, Kent CT15 7PN* Dover (01304) 830226

MOWLL, John William Rutley. b 42. Sarum Th Coll 63. **d** 66 **p** 67. C Oughtibridge *Sheff* 66-69; C Hill *Birm* 69-73; Ind Chapl *Worc* 73-78; V Upper Arley 73-78; P-in-c Upton Snodsbury and Broughton Hackett etc 78-81; R 81-83; V Boughton under Blean w Dunkirk *Cant* 83-89; V Boughton under Blean w Dunkirk and Hernhill from 89. *The Vicarage, 101 The Street, Boughton-under-Blean, Faversham, Kent ME13 9BG* Canterbury (01227) 751410

MOXLEY, Cyril Edward. b 09. Ch Coll Cam BA32 MA37. Ely Th Coll 33. **d** 35 **p** 37. V S Stoneham *Win* 65-74; rtd 74; Hon Chapl Win Cathl from 79. *20 King Alfred Place, Winchester, Hants SO23 7DF* Winchester (01962) 865534

MOXON, Canon Michael Anthony. b 42. Lon Univ BD78. Sarum Th Coll 67. **d** 70 **p** 71. C Kirkley *Nor* 70-74; Min Can St Paul's Cathl *Lon* 74-81; Sacr 77-81; Warden Coll of Min Canons 79-81; V Tewkesbury w Walton Cardiff *Glouc* 81-90; Chapl to The Queen from 86; Can Windsor from 90; Chapl Royal Chpl Windsor Gt Park from 90. *The Chaplain's Lodge, The Great Park, Windsor, Berks SL4 2HP* Egham (01784) 432434

MOXON, William James. b 25. Qu Coll Birm 68. **d** 69 **p** 70. C Letchworth St Paul *St Alb* 69-72; C-in-c N Brickhill CD 72-76; Chapl Puerto de la Cruz Tenerife *Eur* 76-78; Egypt 78-80; V Altrincham St Jo *Ches* 80-90; rtd 90. *75 Overn Avenue, Buckingham MK18 1LU* Buckingham (01280) 823132

MOY, Mrs Joy Patricia. b 35. Cant Sch of Min 87. **d** 90 **p** 94. NSM Cranbrook *Cant* from 90. *1 Dobells, Cranbrook, Kent TN17 3EL* Cranbrook (01580) 713066

MOYNAGH, Dr David Kenneth. b 46. LRCP70 MRCS70 MRCGP76 Lon Univ MB, BS70. S Dios Minl Tr Scheme 88. **d** 91 **p** 92. NSM Ore *Chich* from 91. *Stalkhurst Farm, Ivyhouse Lane, Hastings, E Sussex TN35 4NN* Hastings (01424) 751314

MOYNAGH, Michael Digby. b 50. Southn Univ BA73 Lon Univ MA74 Aus Nat Univ PhD78 Bris Univ MA85. Trin Coll Bris DipHE84. **d** 85 **p** 86. C Northwood Em *Lon* 85-89; P-in-c Wilton *B & W* 89-90; TR from 90. *The Vicarage, Fons George, Wilton, Taunton, Somerset TA1 3JT* Taunton (01823) 284253

MOYNAN, David George. b 53. DipTh. **d** 86 **p** 87. C Seagoe *D & D* 86-88; C Taney *D & G* 88-89; I Arklow w Inch and Kilbride 89-94; Miss to Seamen from 89; Dioc Stewardship Adv *D & G* from 92; I Kilternan from 94. *The Rectory, Kilternan, Co Dublin, Irish Republic* Dublin (1) 295-5603

MOYNAN, Canon William John. b 20. TCD BA44. **d** 44 **p** 45. I Swords w Donabate and Killsallaghan *D & G* 68-90; Can Ch Ch Cathl Dub 83-90; Chapl Shelton Abbey Pris 89-90; rtd 90. *The Rectory, Church Road, Tramore, Co Waterford, Irish Republic* Tramore (51) 81301

MOYSE, Mrs Pauline Patricia. b 42. Ex Univ CertEd62. S Dios Minl Tr Scheme 88. **d** 91 **p** 94. Hon C Fleet *Guildf* 91-92; C from 93. *38 Oasthouse Drive, Ancell's Farm, Fleet, Aldershot, Hants GU13 8UL* Fleet (01252) 629976

MPUNZI, Nduna Ananias. b 46. Birm Univ DPS79 Glas Univ LTh84. St Pet Coll Alice 69. **d** 71 **p** 72. S Africa 71-78; C Bilston *Lich* 84-86; TV 86-90; P-in-c Walsall St Mary and All SS Palfrey from 90; P-in-c Caldmore 90-93; C from 93. *Palfrey Vicarage, Dale Street, Walsall WS1 4AN* Walsall (01922) 33451

MUDDIMAN, John Bernard. b 47. Keble Coll Ox BA67 MA72 DPhil76 Selw Coll Cam BA71 MA75. Westcott Ho Cam 69. **d** 72 **p** 73. Hon C Ox St Giles *Ox* 72-83; Chapl New Coll Ox 72-76; Tutor St Steph Ho Ox 76-83; Vice-Prin 80-83; Lect Th Nottm Univ 83-90; Fell Mansf Coll Ox from 90; Lic to Offic *Ox* from 90. *Mansfield College, Oxford OX1 3TF* Oxford (01865) 270999

MUDGE, Frederick Alfred George. b 31. Leeds Univ BSc58 Univ of Wales BD67. St Mich Coll Llan 58. **d** 61 **p** 62. C Cwmavon *Llan* 61-64; PV Llan Cathl 64-70; R Llandough w Leckwith 70-88; V Penarth All SS from 88. *All Saints' Vicarage, 2 Lower Cwrt-y-Vil Road, Penarth, S Glam CF64 3HQ* Penarth (01222) 708952

MUDIE, Martin Bruce. b 54. Golds Coll Lon BA76. Sarum & Wells Th Coll CMinlEd92. **d** 92 **p** 93. C Bromley St Mark *Roch* from 92. *25 Matfield Close, Bromley BR2 9DY* 0181-466 5827

MUGGLETON, Major George. b 25. Chich Th Coll 55. **d** 57 **p** 58. R Stisted w Bradwell and Pattiswick *Chelmsf* 69-87; rtd 87. *Curvalion House, Creech St Michael, Taunton, Somerset TA3 5QF* Henlade (01823) 443842

MUIR, David Murray. b 49. Glas Univ MA70 Nottm Univ BA72. St Jo Coll Nottm 70. **d** 76 **p** 77. C Fulham St Mary N End *Lon* 76-80; C Aspley *S'well* 80; India 81-85; Dir Ext Studies St Jo Coll Nottm from 85. *St John's College, Chilwell Lane, Bramcote, Nottingham NG9 3DS* Nottingham (0115) 925 1117/4 Fax 220134 or 436438

MUIR, Canon David Trevor. b 49. TCD MA MLitt93. CITC. **d** 78 **p** 79. C Dub Clontarf *D & G* 78-80; C Monkstown St Mary 80-83; I Kilternan 83-94; I Delgany from 94; Can Ch Ch Cathl Dub from 95. *The Rectory, Delgany, Co Wicklow, Irish Republic* Dublin (1) 287-4515

MUIR, John Johnston. b 20. Strathclyde Univ BSc81. St Jo Coll Nottm 83. **d** 85 **p** 87. Hon C Glas St Marg *Glas* 85-91; rtd 91; Perm to Offic *B & W* from 93. *265 Milton Road, Weston-super-Mare, Avon BS22 8JA* Weston-super-Mare (01934) 622036

MUIR, John William. b 38. Dur Univ BA59 Mansf Coll Ox MA65. Chich Th Coll 78. **d** 78 **p** 79. In Congr Ch (England & Wales) 62-70; In United Ch of Zambia 70-78; C Brighouse *Wakef* 78-80; V Northowram 80-87; V Sowerby from 87. *The Vicarage, Towngate, Sowerby, Sowerby Bridge, W Yorkshire HX6 1JJ* Halifax (01422) 831036

MUKHERJEE (or MUKHOPADHYAY), Supriyo. b 42. Calcutta Univ BA70. Serampore Th Coll BD76 Bp's Coll Calcutta 70. **d** 75 **p** 76. India 75-91; C Crook *Dur* 91-92; V Nelson in Lt Marsden *Blackb* 92-95; Dioc Community Relns Adv *Cov* from 95; TV Cov E from 95. *St Barnabas Vicarage, 55 St Paul's Road, Coventry CV6 5DE* Coventry (01203) 688264

MULCOCK, Edward John. b 16. Leeds Univ BA37. Coll of Resurr Mirfield 37. **d** 39 **p** 40. V Fulham St Jo Walham Green *Lon* 66-76; V Fulham St Jas Moore Park 69-76; V Walham Green St Jo w St Jas 76-83; rtd 84. *Flat 2, Gardens Court, 57 Parkstone Road, Poole, Dorset BH15 2NX* Poole (01202) 673162

MULHOLLAND, Nicholas Christopher John (Chris). b 44. Chich Th Coll 77. **d** 79 **p** 80. C Thornbury *Glouc* 79-83; R Boxwell, Leighterton, Didmarton, Oldbury etc from 83. *The Rectory, Leighterton, Tetbury, Glos GL8 8UW* Leighterton (01666) 890283

MULKERN, Richard Neville. b 39. S'wark Ord Course 88. **d** 91 **p** 92. NSM Leytonstone St Andr *Chelmsf* 91-93; Min Sec and Welfare Officer Miss to Seamen 91-93; Welfare Sec 93-94; Dir N Region from 94. *14 Northwood Park, Woodlesford, Leeds LS26 8PF* Leeds (0113) 282 1668 or 270 5578

MULLARD, George Edward. b 14. St D Coll Lamp BA38 Sarum Th Coll 38. **d** 39 **p** 40. V E Coker w Sutton Bingham *B & W* 69-79; rtd 79; Perm to Offic *B & W* from 79. *Alvington Cottage, Brympton, Yeovil, Somerset BA22 8TH* Yeovil (01935) 71752

MULLEN, Charles William. b 64. CITC BTh92. **d** 92 **p** 93. C Lecale Gp *D & D* 92-95; I Gorey w Kilnahue, Leskinfere and Ballycanew *C & O* from 95. *Christ Church Rectory, The Avenue, Gorey, Co Wexford, Irish Republic* Gorey (55) 21283

MULLEN, Peter John. b 42. Liv Univ BA70. **d** 70 **p** 71. C Manston *Ripon* 70-72; C Stretford All SS *Man* 72-73; C Oldham St Mary w St Pet 73-74; Lic to Offic 74-77; V Tockwith and Bilton w Bickerton *York* 77-89. *16 Whin Road, Dringhouses, York YO2 2JZ*

MULLENGER, Canon Alan Edward Clement. b 15. Lon Univ BD64. Kelham Th Coll 35. **d** 40 **p** 41. SSM from 40; C Sheff Parson Cross St Cecilia *Sheff* 40-48; S Africa 48-56; Basutoland 56-61; Wycliffe Hall Ox 63-64; Perm to Offic *Ox* 63-64; Perm to Offic *Nor* 64-65; St Aug Coll Walsingham 64-65; Ghana 65-74; Hon Can Kumasi 73-74; Lesotho from 74; Hon Can Lesotho Cathl from 88. *PO Box 122, Roma 180, Lesotho* Lesotho (266) 315079

MULLENGER, William. b 44. Linc Th Coll 68. **d** 69 **p** 70. C Clapham St Jo *S'wark* 69-73; C Hook 73-81; P-in-c Camberwell St Phil and St Mark 81-85; V Hackbridge and N Beddington 85-93; rtd 93. *30 Constance Crescent, Bromley BR2 7QJ*

MULLENS, John Langford. b 06. Selw Coll Cam BA28 MA52. Westcott Ho Cam 29. **d** 29 **p** 30. R Farthinghoe w Thenford *Pet* 54-71; rtd 71; Perm to Offic *Roch* from 72; Perm to Offic *Cant* from 72; Perm to Offic *Chich* from 72. *Brentwood Court, 29D Frant Road, Tunbridge Wells, Kent TN2 5JT* Tunbridge Wells (01892) 527770

MULLER, Vernon. b 40. Natal Univ BA61 St Chad's Coll Dur DipTh64. **d** 64 **p** 65. S Africa 64-76; Chapl Friern Hosp Lon 77-91; Chapl R Berks Hosp Reading from 91; Chapl Battle Hosp Reading from 91. *The Chaplain's Office, Royal Berkshire Hospital, London Road, Reading RG1 5AN* Reading (01734) 875111

MULLER, Wolfgang Wilhelm Bernard Heinrich Paul. b 28. ALCD54. **d** 55 **p** 56. V Wigmore w Hempstead *Roch* 65-72; V S Gillingham 72-73; W Germany 73-90; Germany from 90; rtd 93. *Krokusweg 14, 34431 Marsberg 14, Germany*

MULLETT, John St Hilary. b 25. St Cath Coll Cam BA47 MA49. Linc Th Coll. **d** 50 **p** 51. V Oxton *Ches* 69-77; R

Ashwell *St Alb* 77-90; RD Buntingford 82-88; rtd 90; Fell St Cath Coll Cam from 90. *13 Church Lane, Madingley, Cambridge CB3 8AF* Madingley (01954) 211670

MULLINEAUX, John. b 16. Man Univ BA38. Kelham Th Coll 38. **d** 41 **p** 42. V Caton w Littledale *Blackb* 67-81; rtd 81; Lic to Offic *Blackb* from 81. *10 Ashfield Avenue, Lancaster LA1 5DZ* Lancaster (01524) 36769

MULLINER, Denis Ratliffe. b 40. BNC Ox BA62 MA66. Linc Th Coll 70. **d** 72 **p** 73. C Sandhurst *Ox* 72-76; Chapl Bradfield Coll Berks from 76. *Great Oaks, Bradfield, Reading RG7 6AR* Bradfield (01734) 744263

MULLINS, Joe. b 20. MC45. Trin Coll Ox BA49 MA59. Ridley Hall Cam 48. **d** 50 **p** 51. India 52-74; Australia from 74; rtd 86. *24 Bunny Street, Weston, ACT, Australia 2611* Canberra (6) 288-9973

MULLINS, Malcolm David. b 42. St Edm Hall Ox BA63. St Steph Ho Ox 63. **d** 65 **p** 66. C Lamorbey H Redeemer *Roch* 69-75; C Solihull *Birm* 75-77; rtd 77. *PO Box 3127, London NW7 3SZ*

MULLINS, Mrs Margaret. b 49. Southn Univ CertEd70 K Alfred's Coll Win DSpEd87. Sarum & Wells Th Coll DCTM94. **d** 94 **p** 95. C Bishopstoke *Win* from 94. *5 Harding Lane, Fair Oak, Eastleigh, Hants SO50 8GL* Eastleigh (01703) 601031

MULLINS, Peter Matthew. b 60. Ch Ch Ox BA32 MA86 Birm Univ DPS84 Irish Sch of Ecum MPhil90. Qu Coll Birm 82. **d** 84 **p** 85. C Caversham and Mapledurham *Ox* 84-88; Perm to Offic *E d S* 88-89; TV Old Brumby *Linc* 89-94; Clergy Tr Adv from 94. *1 St Giles, Lincoln LN2 4PE* Lincoln (01522) 528199

MULLINS, Timothy Dougal. b 59. Dur Univ. Wycliffe Hall Ox 83. **d** 85 **p** 86. C Reading Greyfriars *Ox* 85-89; C Haughton le Skerne *Dur* from 89; Chapl Eton Coll Windsor from 95. *2 Church Close, High Street, Eton, Windsor, Berks SL4 6AP* Windsor (01753) 671373

MULLIS, Robert Owen (Bob). b 49. Bris Univ BA71 CertEd71 Birm Univ ACertEd91. St Mich Coll Llan DMinlStuds93. **d** 93 **p** 94. NSM Llangenni and Llanbedr Ystrad Yw w Patricio *S & B* from 93. *3 Pontfaen, Llanbedr, Crickhowell, Powys NP8 1SJ* Crickhowell (01873) 811927

MULRAINE, Miss Margaret Haskell. b 24. Birm Univ BA45 DipEd46. Sarum Th Coll 83. **dss** 86 **d** 87 **p** 94. Wareham *Sarum* 86-87; Hon Par Dn 87-93; Perm to Offic from 93. *5 Trinity Close, Trinity Lane, Wareham, Dorset BH20 4LL* Wareham (01929) 552523

MULRENAN, Richard John. b 12. ACA36 FCA60. Tyndale Hall Bris 37. **d** 46 **p** 47. V Braintree *Chelmsf* 66-77; rtd 77; Perm to Offic *Ox* from 83. *36 Emmbrook Court, Woolacombe Drive, Reading RG6 2TZ* Reading (01734) 861453

MUMFORD, Albert Edward. b 47. MCIT. Qu Coll Birm 85. **d** 87 **p** 88. C Leic Ascension *Leic* 87-91; C Burbage w Aston Flamville 91-94. *Address temp unknown*

MUMFORD, Dr David Bardwell. b 49. MRCPsych86 St Cath Coll Cam BA71 MA75 Bris Univ MB, ChB81 Edin Univ MPhil89. Bp's Coll Calcutta 71 Cuddesdon Coll 73. **d** 75. C Bris St Mary Redcliffe w Temple etc *Bris* 75-76; NSM 76-82; NSM Edin St Columba *Edin* 82-86; NSM Calverley *Bradf* 86-92. *Address temp unknown*

MUMFORD, David Christopher. b 47. Mert Coll Ox BA68 MA74 York Univ MSW CQSW81. Linc Th Coll 84. **d** 86 **p** 87. C Shiremoor *Newc* 86-89; C N Shields 89-91; V Byker St Ant from 91. *St Anthony's Vicarage, Enslin Gardens, Newcastle upon Tyne NE6 3ST* 0191-265 1605

MUMFORD, Grenville Alan. b 34. Richmond Th Coll DipTh. **d** 78 **p** 78. C Witham *Chelmsf* 78-81; C-in-c Gt Ilford St Marg CD 81-85; V Gt Ilford St Marg 85-87; P-in-c Everton and Mattersey w Clayworth *S'well* 87-89; R from 89; RD Bawtry from 93. *The Rectory, Abbey Lane, Mattersey, Doncaster, S Yorkshire DN10 5DX* Retford (01777) 817364

MUMFORD, Canon Hugh Raymond. b 24. Oak Hill Th Coll 50. **d** 53 **p** 54. V Nether Cerne *Sarum* 69-71; R Godmanstone 69-71; R Cerne Abbas w Upcerne 69-71; R Minterne Magna 69-71; V Cerne Abbas w Godmanstone and Minterne Magna 71-89; RD Dorchester 75-79; Can and Preb Sarum Cathl 77-89; rtd 89. *10 South Walks Road, Dorchester, Dorset DT1 1ED* Dorchester (01305) 264971

MUMFORD, John Alexander. b 52. St Andr Univ MTh75. Ridley Hall Cam 75. **d** 77 **p** 78. C Canford Magna *Sarum* 77-82; C Ches Square St Mich w St Phil *Lon* 82-85; USA 85-87; SW Lon Vineyard Chr Fellowship from 87. *572 Kingston Road, London SW20 8DR*

MUMFORD, Michael David. b 29. **d** 79 **p** 80. Chapl Lister Hosp Stevenage 79-83; C Royston *St Alb* 83-87; P-in-c Kelshall 83-88; P-in-c Therfield 83-88; C Barkway, Reed and Buckland w Barley 87-88; R Ewhurst *Chich* 88-94; R Bodiam 88-94; RD Rye 90-91; rtd 94. *6 Whydown Place, Bexhill-on-Sea, E Sussex TN39 4RA* Bexhill-on-Sea (02424) 845278

MUNBY, Philip James. b 52. Pemb Coll Ox BA75 MA80. St Jo Coll Nottm 76. **d** 78 **p** 79. C Gipsy Hill Ch Ch *S'wark* 78-82;

C-in-c W Dulwich Em CD 82-88; V Barnsley St Geo *Wakef* from 88. *St George's Vicarage, 100 Dodworth Road, Barnsley, S Yorkshire S70 6HL* Barnsley (01226) 203870

MUNCEY, William. b 49. BA80. Oak Hill Th Coll. **d** 80 **p** 81. C Wandsworth St Mich *S'wark* 80-84; C Morden 84-88; TV from 88. *5 Willows Avenue, Morden, Surrey SM4 5SG* 0181-646 2002

MUNCHIN, David Leighfield. b 67. Imp Coll Lon BSc88. Ripon Coll Cuddesdon 89. **d** 92 **p** 93. C Golders Green *Lon* 92-94; C Golders Green from 94. *1 St Albans Close, North End Road, London NW11 7RA* 0181-458 5846

MUNDEN, Alan Frederick. b 43. Nottm Univ BTh74 Birm Univ MLitt80 Dur Univ PhD87. St Jo Coll Nottm LTh74. **d** 74 **p** 75. C Cheltenham St Mary *Glouc* 74-76; C Cheltenham St Mary, St Matt, St Paul and H Trin 76; Hon C Jesmond Clayton Memorial *Newc* 76-80; C 80-83; V Cheylesmore *Cov* from 83. *Christ Church Vicarage, 11 Frankpledge Road, Coventry CV3 5GT* Coventry (01203) 502770

MUNDY, Ms Katherine Ann. b 52. Croydon Coll HND73 CQSW80 DipSocSc80. Oak Hill Th Coll 87. **d** 92. Ind (Retail) Chapl *Lon* 92-95; C W Bromwich All SS *Lich* from 95; Ind Chapl from 95. *7 Hopkins Drive, West Bromwich, W Midlands B71 3RR* 0121-588 3744

MUNGAVIN, David Stewart. b 60. Stirling Univ BA80. Edin Th Coll 87. **d** 90 **p** 91. C Glas St Marg *Glas* 90-92; P-in-c Airdrie from 92; P-in-c Coatbridge from 92; P-in-c Gartcosh from 92. *24 Etive Drive, Airdrie, Lanarkshire ML6 9QQ* Airdrie (01236) 756550

MUNGAVIN, Canon Gerald Clarence. b 27. Edin Th Coll 51. **d** 54 **p** 55. Chapl RAF 62-75; R Turriff *Ab* 75-81; R Cuminestown 75-81; R Banff 75-81; R Banchory 81-92; R Kincardine O'Neil 81-92; Can St Andr Cathl from 89; rtd 92. *Craigleith, Bowfield Road, Howwood, Johnstone, Renfrewshire PA9 1BS* Kilbarchan (015057) 2461

MUNN, Carole Christine. b 45. E Midl Min Tr Course 83. **d** 90 **p** 94. NSM Long Bennington w Foston *Linc* from 90. *The Rectory, Claypole, Newark, Notts NG23 5BH* Newark (01636) 626224

MUNN, George. b 44. MM72. Linc Th Coll 85. **d** 87 **p** 88. C Boston *Linc* 87-90; R Claypole from 90. *The Rectory, Claypole, Newark, Notts NG23 5BH* Newark (01636) 626224

MUNN, Richard Probyn. b 45. Selw Coll Cam BA67 MA69. Cuddesdon Coll 67. **d** 69 **p** 70. C Cirencester *Glouc* 69-71; USPG 71-79; Zambia 71-79; Adn S Zambia 79; P-in-c Kings Stanley *Glouc* 80-83; R Lezant w Lawhitton and S Petherwin w Trewen *Truro* 84-92; Lesotho from 93. *PO Box 249, Leribe, Lesotho* Lesotho (266) 400731

MUNNS, Stuart Millington. b 36. OBE77. MIDPM91 St Cath Coll Cam BA58 MA62. Cuddesdon Coll 58. **d** 60 **p** 61. C Allenton and Shelton Lock *Derby* 60-63; C Brampton St Thos 63-65; C-in-c Loundsley Green Ascension CD 65-66; Bp's Youth Chapl 66-72; Nat Dir of Community Industry 72-77; Hon C Hornsey Ch Ch *Lon* 72-77; Dioc Missr *Liv* 77-82; V Knowsley 77-82; P-in-c Stramshall *Lich* 82-88; V Uttoxeter w Bramshall 82-88; RD Uttoxeter 82-87; P-in-c Kingstone w Gratwich 84-88; P-in-c Marchington w Marchington Woodlands 84-88; P-in-c Checkley 86-88; Perm to Offic *B & W* 88-90; NSM Wells St Thos w Horrington 90-94; P-in-c Ditcheat w E Pennard and Pylle from 94. *The Rectory, Ditcheat, Shepton Mallet, Somerset BA4 6RE* Wells (01749) 860429 Fax as telephone

MUNRO, Basil Henry. b 40. Ripon Hall Ox 73. **d** 75 **p** 76. C N Mymms *St Alb* 75-78; C St Alb St Steph 78-80; V 80-87; R Aston-on-Trent and Weston-on-Trent *Derby* from 87; Chapl Aston Hall Hosp Derby from 87. *The Rectory, Rectory Gardens, Aston-on-Trent, Derby DE72 2AZ* Derby (01332) 792658

MUNRO, Donald Alexander. b 08. Clifton Th Coll. **d** 46 **p** 47. V Kilmington *B & W* 69-83; rtd 84; Perm to Offic *B & W* 84-90. *182 Harepath Road, Seaton, Devon EX12 2HE* Seaton (01297) 20567

MUNRO, Duncan John Studd. b 50. Magd Coll Ox BA72 MA76. Wycliffe Hall Ox 73. **d** 76 **p** 77. C Ecclesall *Sheff* 76-77; C Sheff St Barn and St Mary 78-80; Lic to Offic from 80. *Poppyfields, Church Road, Crowle, Worcester WR7 4AT* Worcester (01905) 381893

MUNRO, Canon Louis Cecil Garth. b 16. Leeds Univ BA40. Coll of Resurr Mirfield 40. **d** 42 **p** 43. V Forton *Portsm* 55-81; rtd 81; Perm to Offic *Portsm* from 81. *7 St Helens Road, Alverstoke, Gosport, Hants PO12 2RL* Gosport (01705) 585494

MUNRO, Robert Speight. b 63. Bris Univ BSc84 Man Univ PGCE81. All So Coll of Applied Th DipApTh86 Oak Hill Th Coll BA93. **d** 93 **p** 94. C Hartford *Ches* from 93. *71 School Lane, Hartford, Northwich, Cheshire CW8 1PF* Northwich (01606) 784755

MUNRO, Canon Terence George. b 34. Jes Coll Cam BA56 MA60. Linc Th Coll 59. **d** 61 **p** 62. C Far Headingley St Chad

Ripon 61-64; Jamaica 64-70; R Methley w Mickletown *Ripon* 70-79; V Hunslet Moor St Pet and St Cuth 79-85; R Barwick in Elmet 85-93; V Woodhouse and Wrangthorn from 93; Dioc Ecum Officer from 93; Hon Can Ripon Cathl from 94. *St Mark's Vicarage, St Mark's Avenue, Leeds LS2 9BN* Leeds (0113) 245 4893 Fax as telephone

MUNT, Cyril. b 27. AKC52. **d** 53 **p** 54. R Harbledown *Cant* 68-83; R Porlock w Stoke Pero *B & W* 83-92; rtd 92. *Applegarth, 26 Hood Close, Glastonbury, Somerset BA6 8ES* Glastonbury (01458) 831842

MUNT, Canon Donald James. b 20. ALCD53 St Jo Coll Nottm LTh74. **d** 53 **p** 54. V Deptford St Pet *S'wark* 69-76; R Litcham w Kempston w E and W Lexham *Nor* 76-83; P-in-c Mileham 81-83; P-in-c Beeston next Mileham 81-83; P-in-c Stanfield 81-83; R Litcham, Kempston, Lexham, Mileham, Beeston etc 84-87; RD Brisley and Elmham 85-87; Hon Can Nor Cathl 87-88; rtd 88; Perm to Offic *Nor* from 88. *7 Irwin Close, Reepham, Norwich NR10 4EQ* Norwich (01603) 870618

MUNT, Mrs Linda Christine. b 55. NE Ord Course DipHE95. **d** 95. NSM Beverley St Nic *York* from 95. *5 Saunders Croft, Walkington, Beverley, N Humberside HU17 8TG* Hull (01482) 869945

MUNT, Canon Neil. b 20. AKC43. Linc Th Coll 43. **d** 44 **p** 45. V Godmanchester *Ely* 62-74; Hon Can Ely Cathl 74-86; V Ely 74-86; V Prickwillow 76-86; V Chettisham 76-86; RD Ely 82-86; rtd 86; Perm to Offic *Ely* from 86. *8A Wood Street, Doddington, March, Cambs PE15 0SA* March (01354) 740738

MURCH, Robin Norman. b 37. Wells Th Coll. **d** 67 **p** 68. C Wisbech St Aug *Ely* 67-70; C Basingstoke *Win* 70-73; C Whitstable All SS *Cant* 73-76; V Queenborough from 76. *The Vicarage, North Road, Queenborough, Kent ME11 5ET* Sheerness (01795) 662648

MURDIN, Frank Laurence. b 11. Leeds Univ BA34. Coll of Resurr Mirfield 34. **d** 36 **p** 37. V Greetham w Stretton and Clipsham *Pet* 65-76; rtd 76. *48 Pinewood Close, Bourne, Lincs PE10 9RL* Bourne (01778) 423696

MURDOCH, Alexander Edward Duncan. b 37. Oak Hill Th Coll 68. **d** 71 **p** 72. C Kensington St Helen w H Trin *Lon* 71-72; C Kensington St Barn 73-74; CF 74-78; C W Kirby St Bridget *Ches* 78-84; V N Shoebury *Chelmsf* 84-87; V W Poldens *B & W* from 87. *The Vicarage, Holy Well Road, Edington, Bridgwater, Somerset TA7 9LE* Bridgwater (01278) 722055

MURDOCH, David John. b 58. Birm Univ BSocSc81. Ripon Coll Cuddesdon 81. **d** 84 **p** 85. C Penwortham St Leon *Blackb* 84-87; C Wirksworth w Alderwasley, Carsington etc *Derby* 87-89; R Shirland from 89. *The Rectory, Shirland, Alfreton, Derbyshire DE55 6BB* Alfreton (01773) 836003

MURFET, Edward David. b 36. Qu Coll Cam BA59 MA63. Chich Th Coll 59. **d** 61 **p** 62. C Croydon St Mich *Cant* 61-64; C Hunslet St Mary and Stourton *Ripon* 64-65; C Hackney Wick St Mary of Eton w St Aug *Lon* 65-69; Chapl Berne *Eur* 69-71; Chapl Naples 71-74; Chapl Rome 74-77; Lic to Offic *Bris* 78-81; Gen Sec CEMS 81-86; C Leeds St Pet *Ripon* 87-89; P-in-c 89-90; V Leeds City 91-93; Min Can Ripon Cathl from 93. *17 High St Agnesgate, Ripon, N Yorkshire HG4 1QR* Ripon (01765) 602609

MURFET, Gwyn. b 44. Linc Th Coll 71. **d** 74 **p** 75. C Scalby w Ravenscar and Staintondale *York* 74-77; P-in-c S Milford 77-83; R 83-84; V Kirkby Ireleth *Carl* from 84. *The Vicarage, School Road, Kirkby-in-Furness, Cumbria LA17 7UQ* Kirkby-in-Furness (01229) 889256

MURGATROYD, Canon Eric. b 17. Open Univ BA77. Lich Th Coll 43. **d** 46 **p** 46. V Cottingley *Bradf* 66-77; Hon Can Bradf Cathl 77-83; V Woodhall 77-83; rtd 83; Perm to Offic *Bradf* from 83. *34 Ferncliffe Drive, Baildon, Shipley, W Yorkshire BD17 5AQ* Bradford (01274) 594072

MURIEL, Sister. See ARTHINGTON, Sister Muriel

MURPHIE, Andrew Graham. b 65. Reading Univ BA86. St Jo Coll Nottm BTh91 MA92. **d** 92 **p** 93. C Boulton *Derby* from 92. *14 Courtland Drive, Alvaston, Derby DE24 0GJ* Derby (01332) 756466

MURPHY, Alexander Charles. b 28. St Edm Coll Ware 50. **d** 55 **p** 56. NSM Edin St Jas *Edin* 88-90; TV Edin St Mark 90-93; TV Edin St Andr and St Aid 90-93; TV Edin St Marg from 93. *6 London Road, Dalkeith, Midlothian EH22 1DR* 0131-660 1574

MURPHY, David. b 14. Lon Univ BA50 BD52. **d** 49 **p** 50. V Haverton Hill *Dur* 67-73; V W Pelton 73-82; rtd 82. *8 St Helier's Way, Stanley, Co Durham DH9 0UR* Stanley (01207) 230639

MURPHY, Jack. b 27. N Ord Course 83. **d** 86 **p** 87. C St Bart Armley w St Mary New Wortley *Ripon* 86-90; C Hawksworth Wood 90-94; rtd 94. *70 Avocet Way, Bridlington, N Humberside YO15 3NT* Bridlington (01262) 609477

MURPHY, Dr James Royse. b 54. DRCOG80 MRCGP81 Bris Univ MB, ChB77. Glouc Sch of Min 88. **d** 92 **p** 94. NSM Glouc St Cath *Glouc* from 92. *31 Plock Court, Gloucester GL2 9DW* Gloucester (01452) 411772

MURPHY, Canon John Gervase Maurice Walker (Gerry). b 26. LVO. TCD BA52 MA55. **d** 52 **p** 53. CF 55-73; Asst Chapl Gen 73-77; V Ranworth w Panxworth *Nor* 77-79; RD Blofield 79; Dom Chapl to The Queen 79-87; Chapl to The Queen from 87; R Sandringham w W Newton *Nor* 79-87; RD Heacham and Rising 85-87; Hon Can Nor Cathl 86-87; Chapl Intercon Ch Soc 87-91; Falkland Is 87-91; Miss to Seamen 87-91; rtd 91; Chapl St Pet-ad-Vincula at HM Tower of Lon from 91; Dep P in O from 92. *The Chaplain's Residence, HM Tower of London, London EC3N 4AB* 0171-488 5689 Fax 702 2214

MURPHY, Maurice Vincent. b 49. Van Mildert Coll Dur BSc70. **d** 85 **p** 86. NSM Malpas *Mon* 85-86; Perm to Offic *Man* 86-90; NSM Bolton Breightmet St Jas 90-94; NSM Rawtenstall St Mary from 94. *18 Higher Ridings, Bromley Cross, Bolton BL7 9HP*

MURPHY, Owen. b 52. Open Univ BA85. Chich Th Coll 92. **d** 94 **p** 95. C Oxhey St Matt *St Alb* from 94. *6 Lime Close, Oxhey, Watford WD1 4HD* Watford (01923) 251841

MURPHY, Peter Frederick. b 40. AKC65. **d** 67 **p** 68. C Paddington St Jo w St Mich *Lon* 67-72; P-in-c Basingstoke *Win* 72-76; TV 76-81; V Hythe 81-92; V Lyndhurst and Emery Down from 92. *The Vicarage, 5 Forest Gardens, Lyndhurst, Hants SO43 7AF* Lyndhurst (01703) 282154

MURPHY, Philip John Warwick. b 65. Kent Univ BA87. Chich Th Coll 88. **d** 91 **p** 92. C Broadstone *Sarum* 91-94; C Teddington SS Pet and Paul and Fulwell *Lon* from 94. *The Priests House, Clonmell Road, Teddington, Middx TW11 0SD* 0181-977 2853

MURPHY, Ronald Frederick. b 38. **d** 84 **p** 85. P-in-c N Cerney w Bagendon *Glouc* 87-90. *70 Tattershall, Toot Hill, Swindon SN5 8BX* Swindon (01793) 694870

MURPHY, William Albert. b 43. Lon Univ BD73 QUB MTh78. **d** 73 **p** 74. C Lisburn Ch Ch *Conn* 73-79; Supt & Chapl Ulster Inst for the Deaf from 79; Chapl HM Pris Maze from 82; Dioc Dir Ords *Conn* from 92. *Ulster Institute for the Deaf, 5-6 College Square North, Belfast BT1 6AR* Belfast (01232) 321733 Fax 233868

MURRAY, Alan. b 37. Sarum Th Coll 62. **d** 64 **p** 65. C High Elswick St Phil *Newc* 64-68; C Seaton Hirst 68-74; V Seghill from 74. *The Vicarage, Seghill, Cramlington, Northd NE23 7EA* 0191-237 1601

MURRAY, Alan. b 61. St Jo Coll Nottm BTh92. **d** 92 **p** 93. C Wombwell *Sheff* 92-95; C Mortomley St Sav High Green from 95. *161 Mortomley Lane, High Green, Sheffield S30 4HT* Sheffield (0114) 284 6668

MURRAY, Mrs Christine Jean. b 57. Qu Coll Birm 93. **d** 95. C Milton *Win* from 95. *15 Conway Close, New Milton, Hants BH25 6HL* New Milton (01425) 620409

MURRAY, Christopher James. b 49. Open Univ BA78. St Jo Coll Nottm 79. **d** 81 **p** 82. C Heatherlands St Jo *Sarum* 81-84; C Hamworthy 84-90; R Passenham *Pet* from 90. *The Rectory, Deanshanger, Milton Keynes MK19 6JP* Milton Keynes (01908) 262371

MURRAY, David McIlveen. b 36. ALCD61. **d** 61 **p** 62. C Mortlake w E Sheen *S'wark* 61-64; C Lyncombe *B & W* 64-67; C Horsham *Chich* 67-73; V Devonport St Bart *Ex* 73-79; R Chalfont St Peter *Ox* from 79; RD Amersham 86-89. *The Vicarage, 4 Austen Way, Chalfont St Peter, Gerrards Cross, Bucks SL9 8NW* Gerrards Cross (01753) 882389

MURRAY, Gordon Stewart. b 33. Birkb Coll Lon BSc72. Ripon Coll Cuddesdon 76. **d** 78 **p** 79. C Kenilworth St Nic *Cov* 78-81; V Potterspury w Furtho and Yardley Gobion *Pet* 81-83; V Potterspury, Furtho, Yardley Gobion and Cosgrove 84; TV Wolvercote w Summertown *Ox* 84-90; P-in-c Walworth *S'wark* 90-95; TR Walworth St Pet from 95. *St Peter's Rectory, Liverpool Grove, London SE17 2HH* 0171-703 3139

MURRAY, Ian Hargrave. b 48. Man Univ BSc71. St Jo Coll Nottm 79. **d** 81 **p** 82. C Erith St Paul *Roch* 81-84; C Willenhall H Trin *Lich* 84-87; TV 87-92; P-in-c Moxley from 92. *The Vicarage, 5 Sutton Road, Moxley, Wednesbury, W Midlands WS10 8SG* Bilston (01902) 491807

MURRAY, Ian William. b 32. Lon Univ BA53 PGCE54. Oak Hill NSM Course 80. **d** 83 **p** 84. NSM Pinner *Lon* from 83. *4 Mansard Close, West End Lane, Pinner, Middx HA5 3FQ* 0181-866 2984

MURRAY, Canon John Desmond. b 16. TCD BA38 MA46. CITC 39. **d** 39 **p** 40. I Milltown *D & G* 70-82; Can Ch Ch Cathl Dub 79-82; rtd 82. *3 Adare Close, Killincarrig, Greystones, Co Wicklow, Irish Republic* Dublin (1) 287-6359

MURRAY, John Douglas. b 16. Keble Coll Ox BA38 MA46. Bps' Coll Cheshunt 38. **d** 40 **p** 41. Tutor St Pet Coll of Educn Birm 50-78; Lic to Offic *Birm* 50-79; P-in-c Streat w Westmeston *Chich* 79-86; rtd 81; Perm to Offic *Birm* from 87. *104 Sunnybank Road, Sutton Coldfield, W Midlands B73 5RL* 0121-354 9488

MURRAY, Ven John Grainger. b 45. CITC 67. **d** 70 **p** 71. C Carlow *C & O* 70-72; C Limerick St Mary *L & K* 72-77; I Rathdowney w Castlefleming, Donaghmore etc *C & O* from 77; Preb Leighlin Cathl 83-88; Chan 89-90; Prec 90-92; Preb Ossory Cathl 83-88; Chan 89-90; Prec 90-92; Adn Ossory and Leighlin from 92; Adn Cashel, Waterford and Lismore from 94. *The Rectory, Rathdowney, Portlaoise, Co Laois, Irish Republic* Rathdowney (505) 46311 Fax 46540

MURRAY, John Louis. b 47. Keble Coll Ox BA67 MA69. **d** 82 **p** 83. Asst Chapl Strasbourg *Eur* from 82. *10 rue du General Gourard, 67000 Strasbourg, France* France (33) 88 36 12 25

MURRAY, John Thomas. b 33. Edin Th Coll 63. **d** 66 **p** 67. C Golcar *Wakef* 66-69; Guyana 70-74; Perm to Offic *S'wark* 74-75; Perm to Offic *Lon* 75-79; Hon C Paddington St Mary Magd 79-82; Asst Chapl Athens w Kifissia *Eur* 82-83; Chapl Br Emb Ankara 83-85; R Johnstone *Glas* 86-91; Perm to Offic *Sheff* from 91; Perm to Offic *Wakef* from 91. *135 Cambridge Street, South Elmsall, Pontefract, W Yorkshire WF9 2AW* Pontefract (01977) 608223

MURRAY, Mrs Margaret Janice. b 46. Carl Dioc Tr Course. dss 86 **d** 87 **p** 94. Walney Is *Carl* 86-87; Hon Par Dn 87-89; Par Dn Carl H Trin and St Barn 89-94; C 94; Chapl Cumberland Infirmary 90-94; C Harraby *Carl* from 94; Chapl Garlands Hosp from 94; Chapl to the Deaf and Hard of Hearing *Carl* from 94. *398 London Road, Carlisle CA1 3ER* Carlisle (01228) 596427

MURRAY, Paul Ridsdale. b 55. BEd. St Steph Ho Ox. **d** 83 **p** 84. C Hartlepool St Oswald *Dur* 83-86; C S Shields All SS 86-88; V Sacriston and Kimblesworth 88-94; P-in-c Esh w Hamsteels from 94. *21 The Wynds, Esh Winning, Durham DH7 9DT* 0191-373 4273

MURRAY, Mrs Ruth Elizabeth. b 55. Dur Univ BA77 Man Coll of Educn CertEd78. **d** 94 **p** 95. NSM Alloa *St And* from 94; Chapl Stirling Univ from 94. *29 Craigview, Sauchie, Alloa, Clackmannanshire FK10 3HE* Alloa (01259) 217432

MURRAY (nee GOULD), Mrs Susan Judith. b 61. BSc83. St Jo Coll Nottm DTS90. **d** 91 **p** 94. Par Dn Stokesley *York* 91-94; CMS from 94; Perm to Offic *Birm* 94-95; Argentina from 95. *Mision Anglicana, Casilla 9, 3636 Ingeniero Juarez, Prov de Formosa, Argentina*

MURRAY, William Robert Craufurd. b 44. St Chad's Coll Dur BA66 DipTh68. **d** 68 **p** 69. C Workington St Mich *Carl* 68-71; C Harrogate St Wilfrid *Ripon* 71-74; P-in-c Sawley 74; V Winksley cum Grantley and Aldfield w Studley 74; R Fountains 74-81; New Zealand from 81. *St Barnabas's Vicarage, 7 Makora Street, Fendalton, Christchurch 4, New Zealand* Christchurch (3) 351-7064

MURRAY-LESLIE, Adrian John Gervase. b 46. Lich Th Coll 67. **d** 69 **p** 70. C Sheff St Cuth *Sheff* 69-73; C Mosborough 73-75; C-in-c Mosborough CD 75-80; Warden Champion Ho Youth Cen Edale from 80; P-in-c Edale *Derby* from 80. *The Vicarage, Edale, Sheffield S30 2ZA* Hope Valley (01433) 670254

MURRELL, Canon John Edmund. b 28. Westcott Ho Cam. **d** 66 **p** 67. C Ivychurch w Old Romney and Midley *Cant* 66-70; R Bardwell *St E* 70-75; Perm to Offic *Ely* 75-77; V Wenhaston w Thorington and Bramfield w Walpole *St E* 77-86; V Thorington w Wenhaston and Bramfield 86-92; P-in-c Walberswick w Blythburgh 86-92; V Thorington w Wenhaston, Bramfield & Walberswick 92-93; RD Halesworth 85-90; Hon Can St E Cathl 89-93; rtd 93. *Blyth Reach, The Street, Walberswick, Southwold, Suffolk IP18 6UN*

MURRIE, Clive Robert. b 44. Ripon Coll Cuddesdon. **d** 79 **p** 80. C Kenton Ascension *Newc* 79-80; C Prudhoe 80-83; V Burnopfield *Dur* 83-87; R Stella 87-91; V Coalpit Heath *Bris* 91-95; P-in-c Sittingbourne St Mich *Cant* from 95. *St Michael's Vicarage, Valenciennes Road, Sittingbourne, Kent ME10 1EN* Sittingbourne (01795) 472874

MURRIN, Robert Staddon (Bob). b 42. RMA 62 Reading Univ BA68 Birm Univ DPS93. W of England Minl Tr Course 90 Birm Bible Inst DipRS92. **d** 93. NSM Peterchurch w Vowchurch, Turnastone and Dorstone *Heref* from 93. *Albion Cottage, Peterchurch, Hereford HR2 0RP* Peterchurch (01981) 550467 Fax 550432

MURSELL, Alfred Gordon. b 49. ARCM74 BNC Ox BA70 MA73 BD87. Cuddesdon Coll 71. **d** 73 **p** 74. C Walton St Mary *Liv* 73-77; V E Dulwich St Jo *S'wark* 77-86; Tutor Sarum Th Coll 87-91; TR Stafford *Lich* from 91. *The Rectory, 32 Rowley Avenue, Stafford ST17 9AG* Stafford (01785) 58511

MUSGRAVE, Canon James Robert Lord. b 20. TCD BA43 MA51. **d** 44 **p** 45. I Magheragall *Conn* 64-85; Can Conn Cathl 82-85; Bp's C Killead w Gartree 87-95; rtd 95. *61 Crumlin Road, Aldergrove, Crumlin, Co Antrim BT29 4AQ* Crumlin (01849) 453532

MUSHEN, Canon Francis John. b 34. Birm Univ BA60. Ripon Hall Ox 60. **d** 62 **p** 63. C Foleshill St Laur *Cov* 62-65;

C Halesowen *Worc* 65-69; V Stourbridge Norton St Mich 69-81; Hon Can Worc Cathl from 81; P-in-c Bromsgrove St Jo 81-87; V 87-92; R Kempsey and Severn Stoke w Croome d'Abitot from 92. *The Vicarage, Old Road South, Kempsey, Worcester WR5 3NJ* Worcester (01905) 820202

MUSINDI, Philip. b 63. Bp Tucker Coll Mukono DipTh87 BD91 St Mich Coll Llan 91. d 87 p 90. Uganda 87-92; C Builth and Llanddewi'r Cwm w Llangynog etc *S & B* 92-94; C Newport St Teilo *Mon* from 94. *c/o St Teilo's Vicarage, 1 Aberthaw Road, Newport, Gwent NP9 9NS* Newport (01633) 273593

MUSK, Dr Bill Andrew. b 49. Ox Univ BA70 MA75 Univ of S Africa D Litt et Phil84 Lon Univ DipTh73. Fuller Th Sem California ThM80 Trin Coll Bris DipTh81. d 81 p 82. Egypt 81-86; CMS 88-89; TV Maghull *Liv* from 89. *St Peter's Vicarage, 1 St Peter's Row, Moorhey Road, Liverpool L31 5LU* 0151-526 3434

MUSKETT, David John. b 63. Southn Univ BA85. Ripon Coll Cuddesdon 87. d 90 p 91. C Kempston Transfiguration *St Alb* 90-93; C Ampthill w Millbrook and Steppingley from 93. *18 Russell Drive, Ampthill, Bedford MK45 2UA* Ampthill (01525) 405812

MUSPRATT, Oscar. b 06. Ridley Coll Melbourne ThL29. d 29 p 30. V Penn *Ox* 45-89; rtd 90. *1 Penn Mead, Church Road, Penn, High Wycombe, Bucks HP10 8NY* High Wycombe (01494) 813200

MUSSELWHITE, Edward Charles. b 15. d 64 p 65. V Bream *Glouc* 66-75; R Dowdeswell and Andoversford w the Shiptons etc 75-77; rtd 78; Perm to Offic *B & W* from 80. *13 Channel Heights, Bleadon, Weston-super-Mare, Avon BS24 9LX* Bleadon (01934) 812566

MUSSON, David John. b 46. Open Univ BA86. Linc Th Coll 70. d 73 p 74. C New Sleaford *Linc* 73-76; C Morton 76-80; P-in-c Thurlby 80-86; P-in-c Silk Willoughby from 86; R Quarrington w Old Sleaford from 86. *The Rectory, 77 Grantham Road, Quarrington, Sleaford, Lincs NG34 7NP* Sleaford (01529) 306776

MUSSON, Dr John Keith. b 39. CEng MIMechE Nottm Univ BSc61 PhD66. St As Minl Tr Course 85. d 88 p 89. Assoc Prin NE Wales Inst of HE from 80; NSM Holywell *St As* 88-93; C 93-95; R Caerwys and Bodfari from 95. *The Rectory, Pen y Cefn Road, Caerwys, Mold, Clwyd CH7 5AQ* Caerwys (01352) 720223

MUSSON, William John. b 58. UMIST BSc80. St Jo Coll Nottm 88. d 91 p 92. C Nantwich *Ches* 91-94; C Finchley Ch Ch *Lon* from 94. *622 High Road, London N12 0NU* 0181-445 6988

MUST, Albert Henry. b 27. Clifton Th Coll 61. d 63 p 64. V Highbury Vale St Jo *Lon* 68-78; V Highbury New Park St Aug 78-84; V Walthamstow St Jo *Chelmsf* 84-93; rtd 93; Perm to Offic *Cant* from 93. *24 Nightingale Avenue, Whitstable, Kent CT5 4TR* Whitstable (01227) 772160

MUST, Mrs Shirley Ann. b 35. St Mich Ho Ox 61. dss 82 d 87 p 94. Highbury New Park St Aug *Lon* 82-84; Walthamstow St Jo *Chelmsf* 84-87; Hon Par Dn 87-93; Perm to Offic *Cant* 93-94; Hon C Herne Bay Ch Ch from 94. *24 Nightingale Avenue, Whitstable, Kent CT5 4TR* Whitstable (01227) 772160

MUSTOE, Alan Andrew. b 52. Man Univ BA74. Qu Coll Birm DipTh77. d 78 p 79. C Chatham St Wm *Roch* 78-82; R Burham and Wouldham 82-88; Dioc Info Officer 83-88; V Strood St Nic w St Mary from 88. *The Vicarage, 3 Central Road, Strood, Rochester, Kent ME2 3HF* Medway (01634) 719052

MUSTON, David Alan. b 33. Nottm Univ BA60. Ridley Hall Cam 62. d 64 p 65. C Tankersley *Sheff* 64-67; C Goole 67-70; Asst Sec Ind Cttee of Gen Syn Bd for Soc Resp 70-76; Ind Chapl *Win* 77-79; V Leigh St Mary *Man* 79-83; R Otham w Langley *Cant* from 83. *The Rectory, Church Road, Otham, Maidstone, Kent ME15 8SB* Maidstone (01622) 861470

MUSTON, James Arthur. b 48. Leic Univ CertRS91 Open Univ BA92. E Midl Min Tr Course 89. d 91 p 92. NSM Chaddesden St Mary *Derby* 91-95; C Gt Grimsby St Andr w St Luke and All SS *Linc* from 95. *August House, 18 Vivian Road, Grimsby, S Humberside DN32 8QF* Grimsby (01472) 200545

MUTCH, Miss Sylvia Edna. b 36. St Mich Ho Ox 57. dss 79 d 87 p 94. Clifton *York* 79-95; Par Dn 87-94; C 94-95; Chapl Clifton Hosp York 81-94; R Elvington w Sutton on Derwent and E Cottingwith *York* from 95. *The Rectory, Church Lane, Elvington, York YO4 5AD* Elvington (01904) 608462

MUXLOW, Canon George. b 19. Qu Coll Birm. d 55 p 56. R Oakdale St Geo *Sarum* 63-82; TR 82-84; rtd 84. *9 Cuthburga Road, Wimborne, Dorset BH21 1LH* Wimborne (01202) 887940

MYATT, Andrew William Gilchrist. b 62. Wycliffe Hall Ox 85. d 88 p 89. C Cogges *Ox* 88-91; C S Leigh 88-91; Vineyard Ministries from 91. *144A London Road, Oxford OX3 9ED* Oxford (01865) 742131

MYATT, Edwin Henry. b 54. MA. Ripon Coll Cuddesdon. d 84 p 85. C W Bromwich St Fran *Lich* 84-88; C Sedgley All SS 88-93; V Trent Vale 93-94. *The Conifers, 5 Prestwick Road, Kingswinford, W Midlands ST4 6JY*

MYATT, Francis Eric (Fran). b 60. St Jo Coll Nottm LTh92. d 92 p 93. C W Derby St Luke *Liv* 92-95; TV Sutton from 95. *80 Waterdale Crescent, St Helens, Merseyside WA9 3PH* Marshalls Cross (01744) 815158

MYATT, Philip Bryan. b 29. Wycliffe Hall Ox 54. d 57 p 58. R Woodchester *Glouc* 64-70; R Bath Walcot *B & W* 70-91; R The Edge, Pitchcombe, Harescombe and Brookthorpe *Glouc* 91-94; rtd 94. *West Cottage, Amberley, Glos GL5 5AL*

MYCOCK, Geoffrey John Arthur. b 22. Open Univ BA76. St Deiniol's Hawarden 76. d 77 p 78. Hon C Ches H Trin *Ches* 77-79; Bp's Dom Chapl 79-80; P-in-c Hargrave 79-80; V Sandbach Heath 80-82; Chapl and Lect St Deiniol's Lib Hawarden 82-85; V Holt *St As* 85-90; rtd 90; Perm to Offic *St As* from 90; Perm to Offic *Ches* from 91. *20 Eaton Close, Broughton, Chester CH4 0RF* Chester (01244) 531214

MYERS, Canon Arnold George. b 23. Keble Coll Ox BA44 DipTh46 MA48. St Steph Ho Ox. d 47 p 48. R W Derby St Mary *Liv* 62-79; TR 79-84; RD W Derby 71-78; Hon Can Liv Cathl 74-84; rtd 84; Perm to Offic *Liv* from 84. *10 Surrey Drive, West Kirby, Wirral, Merseyside L48 2HP* 0151-625 2250

MYERS, Duncan Frank. b 57. Warw Univ BSc. St Jo Coll Nottm. d 84 p 85. C Upton cum Chalvey *Ox* 84-86; C Farnborough *Guildf* 86-90; Chapl Nottm Poly *S'well* 90-92; Chapl Nottm Trent Univ 92-95; Sen Past Adv Nottm Trent Univ from 95. *3 Carisbrooke Drive, Nottingham NG3 5DS* Nottingham (0115) 960 5447 or 418418

MYERS, John Bulmer. b 19. Worc Ord Coll 64. d 66 p 67. NSM Huddersfield St Jo *Wakef* 74-76; C 76-79; V Cornholme 79-88; rtd 88. *284 Burnley Road, Todmorden, Lancs OL14 8EW* Todmorden (01706) 812224

MYERS, Paul Henry. b 49. ALA72. Qu Coll Birm 74. d 77 p 78. C Baildon *Bradf* 77-80; C W Bromwich All SS *Lich* 80-83; Chapl RAF 83-86; V Milton *Lich* 87-92. *Address temp unknown*

MYERS, Peter John. b 60. St Jo Coll Dur BA81. Linc Th Coll CMM84. d 84 p 85. C Bulwell St Mary *S'well* 84-88; C Shrewsbury H Cross *Lich* 88-92; rtd 92. *7 Peace Cottages, Old Coleham, Shrewsbury SY3 7BD* Shrewsbury (01743) 360791

MYERS, Robert William John. b 57. Aus Nat Univ BSc80 Newc Univ Aus DipEd82. Trin Coll Bris DipHE95. d 95. C Addiscombe St Mary Magd w St Martin *S'wark* from 95. *68 Elgin Road, Croydon CR0 6XA* 0181-654 6925

MYERSCOUGH, Robin Nigel. b 44. K Coll Lon BD69 Nottm Univ PGCE70. Coll of Resurr Mirfield 66. d 81 p 92. Hon C Diss *Nor* 81-84; Chapl Nor Sch 81-84; Hd Relig Studies Sedbergh Sch Cumbria 84-85; Chapl and Hd Relig Studies Dur Sch 85-92; Chapl Gresham's Sch Holt from 92. *10 Kelling Road, Holt, Norfolk NR25 6RT* Holt (01263) 713234

MYHILL, Christopher John. b 47. Oak Hill Th Coll DipHE79. d 79 p 80. C Stanford-le-Hope w Mucking *Chelmsf* 79-82; C Leyton St Luke 82-87; V Chatteris *Ely* from 87. *The Vicarage, Church Lane, Chatteris, Cambs PE16 6JA* Chatteris (01354) 692173

MYLES, Peter Rodney. b 42. K Coll Lon 61 St Aug Coll Cant 70. d 71 p 72. C Tideswell *Derby* 71-74; C W Brompton St Mary w St Pet *Lon* 74-79; P-in-c Notting Hill St Pet 79-82; Chapl to Bp Kensington 82-87; C Kensington St Mary Abbots w St Geo 82-92; P-in-c Isleworth St Jo from 92. *The Vicarage, St John's Road, Isleworth, Middx TW7 6NY* 0181-560 4916

MYLNE, Denis Colin. b 31. Jordan Hill Coll Glas CYCW75. Kelham Th Coll 69. d 71. Perm to Offic *Glas* 74-84; Perm to Offic *Ab* 84-88; C Bedf All SS *St Alb* 88-91; C Harpenden St Jo from 91. *2 Linwood Road, Harpenden, Herts AL5 1RR* Harpenden (01582) 767551

MYNETT, Colin. b 25. Roch Th Coll 61. d 63 p 64. R Lifton *Ex* 66-71; R Kelly w Bradstone 66-71; TV Devonport St Aubyn 71-75; V Cinderford St Jo *Glouc* 75-84; P-in-c Cheltenham All SS 84-89; rtd 89. *5 Heron Close, Cheltenham, Glos GL51 6HA* Cheltenham (01242) 523341

MYNETT, John Alan. b 37. CEng MIMechE67 Bris Univ BSc59 MSc61. N Ord Course 82. d 85 p 86. NSM Poynton *Ches* 85-90; NSM Macclesfield Team Par from 90. *46 Barber Street, Macclesfield, Cheshire SK11 7HT* Macclesfield (01625) 614103

MYNORS, James Baskerville. b 49. Peterho Cam BA70 MA74. Ridley Hall Cam 70 St Jo Coll Nottm 77. d 78 p 80. Hon C Leic H Apostles *Leic* 78-79; C Virginia Water *Guildf* 79-83; C Patcham *Chich* 83-88; P-in-c Fowlmere *Ely* from 88; P-in-c Thriplow from 88; Sen Tutor E Anglian Minl Tr Course 88-90; Vice-Prin from 90. *The Rectory, Fowlmere, Royston, Herts SG8 7SU* Fowlmere (01763) 208195

N

NADEN, Anthony Joshua. b 38. Jes Coll Ox BA62 MA64 SOAS Lon PhD73. Wycliffe Hall Ox 60. **d** 62 **p** 63. C Rowner *Portsm* 62-66; C Fisherton Anger *Sarum* 70-72; Ghana from 72. *PO Box 3, Walewale, NR Ghana*

NADERER, Gordon Kenneth Charles Maximilian. b 14. Wycliffe Hall Ox. **d** 44 **p** 45. R Rodmell w Southease *Chich* 58-74; V Westham 74-83; rtd 83; Perm to Offic *Chich* from 83. *65 Church Lane, South Bersted, Bognor Regis, W Sussex PO22 9QA* Bognor Regis (01243) 866885

NADIN, Dennis Lloyd. b 37. St D Coll Lamp BA60 Man Univ MEd81. Ridley Hall Cam 63. **d** 64 **p** 65. C Childwall All SS *Liv* 64-67; C Seacroft *Ripon* 67-69; Project Officer Grubb Inst 69-70; Lect CA Tr Coll Blackheath 70-72; Community Educn Essex Co Coun 73-80; Public Preacher *Chelmsf* from 73. *The Hermitage, 201 Willowfield Road, Harlow, Essex CM18 6RZ* Harlow (01279) 430176

NAGEL, Lawson Chase Joseph. b 49. ARHistS75 Michigan Univ BA71 K Coll Lon PhD82. Sarum & Wells Th Coll. **d** 83 **p** 84. C Chiswick St Nic w St Mary *Lon* 83-86; Sec Gen Confraternity of the Blessed Sacrament from 85; C Horsham *Chich* 86; TV 86-91; OStJ from 89; V Aldwick *Chich* from 91. *The Vicarage, 25 Gossamer Lane, Aldwick, Bognor Regis, W Sussex PO21 3AT* Pagham (01243) 262049

NAIDU, Michael Sriram. b 28. Univ of the South (USA) 81. Ridley Hall Cam 86. **d** 80 **p** 85. Acting Chapl Stuttgart *Eur* 85-91; Chapl Stuttgart from 91. *Kloster Kinchberg, 72172 Sulz am Neckar, Stuttgart, Germany* Stuttgart (7454) 883136 or 883105

NAIRN, Frederick William. b 43. TCD 64. Luther NW Th Sem DMin88. **d** 67 **p** 68. C Larne and Inver *Conn* 67-70; Chapl RAF 70-74; P-in-c Harmston *Linc* 75-77; V 77-84; V Coleby 78-84; USA from 84. *4900 Nathan Lane, Plymouth, Minnesota 55442, USA*

NAIRN, Stuart Robert. b 51. K Coll Lon BD75 AKC75. St Aug Coll Cant 75. **d** 76 **p** 77. C E Dereham *Nor* 76-80; TV Hempnall 80-88; V Narborough w Narford from 88; V Pentney St Mary Magd w W Bilney from 88; RD Lynn from 91. *The Vicarage, Narborough, King's Lynn, Norfolk PE32 1TE* Narborough (01760) 338552

NAIRN-BRIGGS, Canon George Peter. b 45. AKC69. St Aug Coll Cant 69. **d** 70 **p** 71. C Catford St Laur *S'wark* 70-73; C Raynes Park St Sav 73-75; V Salfords 75-81; V St Helier 81-87; Dioc Soc Resp Adv *Wakef* from 87; Can Res Wakef Cathl from 92. *21 Willow Park, Wakefield, W Yorkshire WF1 2JP or, Church House, Wakefield, W Yorkshire WF1 1LP* Wakefield (01924) 824393 or 371802 Fax 364834

NAISH, Timothy James Neville. b 57. St Jo Coll Ox BA80 MA88. W Midl Minl Tr Course 86. **d** 87 **p** 88. CMS from 81; C Cov H Trin *Cov* 87; Zaire 88-91; Perm to Offic *Birm* 91-93; Uganda from 93. *Bishop Tucker Theological College, PO Box 4, Mukono, Uganda*

NAISMITH, Mrs Carol. b 37. St Andr Univ MA59. Edin Dioc NSM Course 85. **d** 90 **p** 94. NSM Edin Old St Paul *Edin* from 90; NSM Edin St Marg from 90. *38 Castle Avenue, Edinburgh EH12 7LB* 0131-334 4486

NANCARROW, Mrs Rachel Mary. b 38. Cam Inst of Educn TCert59. E Anglian Minl Tr Course 87. **d** 90 **p** 94. NSM Girton *Ely* 90-95; NSM Foxton from 95. *1 Oakington Road, Girton, Cambridge CB3 0QH* Cambridge (01223) 232693

NANKIVELL, Christopher Robert Trevelyan. b 33. Jes Coll Ox BA55 MA63. Linc Th Coll 56. **d** 58 **p** 59. C Bloxwich *Lich* 58-60; C Stafford St Mary 60-64; P-in-c Malins Lee 64-72; Soc Welfare Sector Min to Milton Keynes Chr Coun 73-76; Lic to Offic *Ox* 73-76; Lect Qu Coll Birm 76-81. *424 King's Road, Birmingham B44 0UJ* 0121-354 6520

NAPIER, Charles John Lenox. b 29. Univ Coll Ox BA52 MA57. Philosophical and Th Coll of Soc of Jes Louvain STL60. **d** 60 **p** 60. In RC Ch 60-63; C Illogan *Truro* 63-66; Tutor Lon Coll of Div 66-70; Tutor St Jo Coll Nottm 70-73; TV S Molton w Nymet St George *Ex* 73-75; TV S Molton, Nymet St George, High Bray etc 75-80; R Drewsteignton from 80; V Hittisleigh from 80; V Spreyton from 80. *The Rectory, Drewsteignton, Exeter EX6 6QW* Drewsteignton (01647) 281227

NAPIER, Lady Jennifer Beryl. b 39. S Dios Minl Tr Scheme 89. **d** 93. NSM Itchen Valley *Win* from 93. *Upper Chilland House, Martyr Worthy, Winchester, Hants SO21 1EB* Itchen Abbas (01962) 779307 Fax as telephone

NAPLEY, David John. b 13. S'wark Ord Course 65. **d** 68 **p** 69. C Hurst Green *S'wark* 68-71; C Ham St Andr 71-74; TV Quidenham w Eccles and Snetterton *Nor* 74-77; P-in-c Earsham 77-79; R Earsham w Alburgh and Denton 79-83; rtd 83; Perm to Offic *Nor* 84-90; Perm to Offic *St E* 87-88.

Wainford Nursing Home, 1 Saltgate, Beccles, Suffolk NR34 9AN Beccles (01502) 714975

NARUSAWA, Masaki Alec. b 53. K Coll Lon BD77 AKC77. Linc Th Coll 77. **d** 78 **p** 79. C Hendon St Alphage *Lon* 78-81; C Eastcote St Lawr 81-84; V Glodwick *Man* from 84. *St Mark's Vicarage, 1 Skipton Street, Oldham OL8 2JF* 0161-624 4964

NASH, Alan Frederick. b 46. Sarum & Wells Th Coll 72. **d** 75 **p** 76. C Foley Park *Worc* 75-79; P-in-c Mildenhall *Sarum* 79-82; Dioc Youth Officer 79-82; TV N Wingfield, Pilsley and Tupton *Derby* 82-85; Perm to Offic 85-87. *85 Brighton Terrace Road, Sheffield S10 1NT*

NASH, Brian John. b 54. St Jo Coll Dur BSc75. St Jo Coll Nottm 77. **d** 80 **p** 81. C Birm St Luke *Birm* 80-84; C Bucknall and Bagnall *Lich* 84; TV 84-92. *191 Selly Oak Road, Birmingham B30 1HU* 0121-486 3169

NASH, David. b 25. K Coll Lon BD51 AKC51. **d** 52 **p** 53. R Rivenhall *Chelmsf* 66-83; P-in-c Boscastle w Davidstow *Truro* 83-85; TR 85-90; rtd 90. *9 Boscundle Avenue, Falmouth, Cornwall TR11 5BU*

NASH, David John. b 41. Pemb Coll Ox BA64 MA70. Wells Th Coll 65. **d** 67 **p** 68. C Preston Ascension *Lon* 67-70; TV Hackney 70-75; TV Clifton *S'well* 76-82; V Winchmore Hill St Paul *Lon* from 82; AD Enfield 87-91. *St Paul's Vicarage, Church Hill, London N21 1JA* 0181-886 3545

NASH, Mrs Ingrid. b 36. SRN57 RNT80 BEd78 CCouns89. S'wark Ord Course 91. **d** 94. NSM Eltham Park St Luke *S'wark* from 94; Chapl Bromley Hosp Trust Roch from 94. *13 Crookston Road, London SE9 1YH* 0181-850 0750

NASH, Paul Alexander. b 20. Glouc Th Course 73. **d** 76 **p** 76. NSM Coleford w Staunton *Glouc* 76-88. *16 Orchard Road, Coombs Park, Coleford, Glos GL16 8AU* Dean (01594) 832758

NASH, Reginald Frank. b 15. **d** 66 **p** 67. P-in-c Sharpness *Glouc* 69-75; V Dymock w Donnington 75-77; R Dymock w Donnington and Kempley 77-80; rtd 80; Perm to Offic *Glouc* from 80. *Holcombe Glen Cottage, Minchinhampton, Stroud, Glos GL6 9AJ* Stroud (01453) 835635

NASH, Richard Edward. b 10. Westcott Ho Cam 54. **d** 56 **p** 57. V Eridge Green *Chich* 68-72; R Winterborne Came *Sarum* 73-75; P-in-c Stinsford 73-75; rtd 75. *7 Herbert Terrace, Wookey Hole Road, Wells, Somerset BA5 2NN* Wells (01749) 675306

NASH, Robin Louis. b 51. Open Univ BA87. Chich Th Coll 82. **d** 84 **p** 85. C Lymington *Win* 84-86; C Andover w Foxcott 86-90; R Kegworth *Leic* from 90. *The Rectory, 24 Nottingham Road, Kegworth, Derby DE74 2FH* Kegworth (01509) 672349 Fax as telephone Mobile (0378) 638989

NASH, Ven Trevor Gifford. b 30. Clare Coll Cam BA53 MA57. Cuddesdon Coll 53. **d** 55 **p** 56. Chapl St Geo Hosp Lon 67-73; R Win St Lawr and St Maurice w St Swithun *Win* 73-82; Bp's Adv Min of Healing from 73; P-in-c Win H Trin 77-82; RD Win 75-82; Hon Can Win Cathl 80-95; Adn Basingstoke 82-90; Acorn Trust Exec Co-ord from 90; rtd 95. *The Corner Stone, 50B Hyde Street, Winchester, Hants SO23 7DY* Winchester (01962) 861759

NASH, William Paul. b 48. St Mich Coll Llan 86. **d** 87 **p** 88. C Pemb Dock *St D* 87-89; P-in-c Llawhaden w Bletherston and Llanycefn 89-90; V 90-92; P-in-c E Brixton St Jude *S'wark* from 92. *St Jude's Vicarage, Dulwich Road, London SE24 0PA* 0171-274 3183

NASH, William Henry. b 31. Oak Hill Th Coll 58. **d** 61 **p** 62. C New Milverton *Cov* 61-64; C Toxteth Park St Philemon w St Silas *Liv* 64-67; V Bryn 67-76; NW Area Sec CPAS 76-82; V Penn Fields *Lich* from 82. *St Philip's Vicarage, Church Road, Bradmore, Wolverhampton WV3 7EN* Wolverhampton (01902) 341943

NASH, William Warren. b 09. TCD BA35 MA58. CITC 36. **d** 36 **p** 38. I Aghadrumsee *Clogh* 51-74; rtd 74. *Strathmore, 45 Mulberry Green, Harlow, Essex CM17 0EY*

NASH-WILLIAMS, Piers le Sor Victor. b 35. Trin Hall Cam BA57 MA61. Cuddesdon Coll 59. **d** 61 **p** 62. C Milton *Win* 61-64; Asst Chapl Eton Coll Windsor 64-66; Perm to Offic *Chich* 66-68; C Furze Platt *Ox* 69-73; V Newbury St Geo Wash Common 72-73; TV Newbury 73-91; R Ascot Heath from 91. *The Rectory, Ascot Heath, Ascot, Berks SL5 8DQ* Ascot (01344) 21200

NASON, David. b 44. ACA68 FCA78 Open Univ BA92. Ripon Coll Cuddesdon 84. **d** 86 **p** 87. C Banstead *Guildf* 86-89; PV Chich Cathl *Chich* from 89; Chapl Prebendal Sch Chich from 89. *1 St Richard's Walk, Canon Lane, Chichester, W Sussex PO19 1QA* Chichester (01243) 775615

NATERS, Charles James Reginald (Brother James). b 20. Selw Coll Cam BA45 MA47. Coll of Resurr Mirfield 46. **d** 47 **p** 48. SSJE from 54; S Africa 59-68; Lic to Offic *Ox* 69-76; Lic to Offic *Lon* 76-85 and from 88; Lic to Offic *Leic* from 85; rtd 90; Superior Gen SSJE from 91. *St Edward's House, 22 Great College Street, London SW1P 3QA* 0171-222 9234

NATHANAEL, Brother. See THOMPSON, Nathanael

NATHANAEL, Martin Moses. b 43. Lon Univ BEd73 K Coll Lon MTh77. Ripon Coll Cuddesdon 77. **d** 79 **p** 80. C Hampton All SS *Lon* 79-82; P-in-c Kensal Town St Thos w St Andr and St Phil 82-83; Hd Div Bp Stopford Sch Lon 83-91; TV Tring *St Alb* from 91. *The Vicarage, Watery Lane, Wilstone, Tring, Herts HP23 4PH* Tring (01442) 823008

NATHANIEL, Ivan Wasim. Punjab Univ MA65. Bp's Coll Calcutta 59. **d** 62 **p** 64. India 62-68; C Newland St Aug *York* 68-70; Hon C Crawley *Chich* from 70; Chapl H Trin Sch Crawley from 70; Hd of Relig Studies from 91. *13 Haywards, Crawley, W Sussex RH10 3TR*

NATTRASS, Michael Stuart. b 41. Man Univ BA62. Cuddesdon Coll 62. **d** 64 **p** 65. C Easington Colliery *Dur* 64-65; C Silksworth 65-68; Perm to Offic *S'well* 68-72; Lic to Offic *Dur* 72-76; Perm to Offic *Lon* 76-78; Hon C Pinner from 78. *81 Cecil Park, Pinner, Middx HA5 5HL* 0181-866 0217

NAUMANN, Canon David Sydney. b 26. Ripon Hall Ox 54. **d** 55 **p** 56. Dioc Youth Chapl *Cant* 63-70; Warden St Gabr Retreat Ho Westgate 68-70; V Littlebourne 70-82; RD E Bridge 78-82; Hon Can Cant Cathl from 81; R Sandwich 82-91; RD Sandwich 85-90; rtd 91. *2 The Forrens, The Precincts, Canterbury, Kent CT1 2ER* Canterbury (01227) 458939

NAUNTON, Hugh Raymond. b 38. Whitelands Coll Lon CertEd69 Open Univ BA75. Bernard Gilpin Soc Dur 59 Chich Th Coll 60. **d** 63 **p** 64. C Stanground *Ely* 63-66; NSM Woolwich St Mary w H Trin *S'wark* 66-67; NSM Wandsworth St Anne 67-69 and 71-73; NSM Paddington St Sav *Lon* 69-71; NSM Cuddington *Guildf* 73-78; Hon C Cheam Common St Phil *S'wark* 79-95; C Cheam from 95. *35 Farm Way, Worcester Park, Surrey KT4 8RN* 0181-330 6303

NAYLOR, Frank. b 36. Lon Univ BA58 Liv Univ MA63. NW Ord Course 75. **d** 75 **p** 76. NSM Eccleston Ch Ch *Liv* 75-92; Asst Dioc Chapl to the Deaf 92-94; Sen Chapl from 94. *27 Daresbury Road, Eccleston, St Helens, Merseyside WA10 5DR* St Helens (01744) 57034

NAYLOR, Frederick. b 11. St Aug Coll Cant 34. **d** 38 **p** 39. V Bishop Burton *York* 66-77; rtd 78. *2 York Road, Bishop Burton, Beverley, N Humberside HU17 8QF* Hornsea (01964) 550226

NAYLOR, Ian Frederick. b 47. AKC70 Open Univ BA92. St Aug Coll Cant 70. **d** 71 **p** 72. C Camberwell St Giles *S'wark* 71-74; OSB 74-86; Chapl RN from 86. *Directorate Gen, RN Chapl Services, Room 203, Victory Building, HM Naval Base, Portsmouth PO1 3LS* Portsmouth (01705) 727903 Fax 727112

NAYLOR, James Barry. b 50. Lon Univ BSc71 St Benet's Hall Ox BA75. Wycliffe Hall Ox 72. **d** 76 **p** 76. C Catford (Southend) and Downham *S'wark* 76-79; TV 79-82; P-in-c Lewisham St Swithun 82-87; V E Dulwich St Jo from 87; RD Dulwich from 90. *St John's Vicarage, 62 East Dulwich Road, London SE22 9AU* 0171-639 3807 Fax 358 0799

NAYLOR, Miss Jean. b 29. Linc Th Coll 77. **dss** 79 **d** 87. Charlton St Luke w H Trin *S'wark* 79-84; Crofton Park St Hilda w St Cypr 84-89; Par Dn 87-89; rtd 89. *12 Winter Terrace, Barnsley, S Yorkshire S75 2ES* Barnsley (01226) 204767

NAYLOR, John Watson. b 26. Trin Hall Cam BA52 MA56. Ripon Hall Ox 64. **d** 66 **p** 67. C Otterburn w Elsdon and Horsley w Byrness *Newc* 69-72; R Husborne Crawley w Ridgmont *St Alb* 72-76; Chapl Caldicott Sch Farnham Royal 76-80; P-in-c Chollerton w Thockrington *Newc* 80-82; R Chollerton w Birtley and Thockrington 82-91; rtd 91. *Abbeyfield House, Bellingham, Hexham, Northd NE48 2BS* Hexham (01434) 220106

NAYLOR, Canon Peter Aubrey. b 33. Kelham Th Coll 54 Ely Th Coll 57. **d** 58 **p** 59. C Shepherd's Bush St Steph *Lon* 58-62; C Portsea N End St Mark *Portsm* 62-66; Chapl HM Borstal Portsm 64-66; V Foley Park *Worc* 66-74; V Maidstone All SS w St Phil and H Trin *Cant* 74-81; P-in-c Tovil 79-81; V Maidstone All SS and St Phil w Tovil 81-91; Hon Can Cant Cathl 79-93; RD Sutton 80-86; R Biddenden and Smarden 91-93; P-in-c Leic St Marg and All SS *Leic* from 93; P-in-c Leic St Aug from 93. *The Vicarage, 8 Pool Road, Leicester LE3 9GD* Leicester (0116) 251 9679

NAYLOR, Peter Edward. b 30. Linc Th Coll 58. **d** 61 **p** 62. C S Beddington St Mich *S'wark* 61-64; V S Lambeth St Ann 64-77; V Nork *Guildf* 77-90; R Ecton *Pet* from 90; Warden Ecton Ho from 90. *The Rectory, 23 West Street, Ecton, Northampton NN6 0QE* Northampton (01604) 416322 or 406442 Fax 787052

NAYLOR, Peter Henry. b 41. MIMechE HND64. Chich Th Coll 64. **d** 67 **p** 68. C Filton *Bris* 67-70; C Brixham *Ex* 70-72; C Leckhampton St Pet *Glouc* 72-76; V Brockworth 76-94; P-in-c Gt Witcombe 91-94; RD Glouc N 91-94; P-in-c The Ampneys w Driffield and Poulton from 94. *The Rectory, Ampney St Peter, Cirencester, Glos GL7 5SH* Cirencester (01285) 851240

NAYLOR, Robert James. b 42. Liv Univ CQSW66. N Ord Course 74. **d** 77 **p** 78. C Aigburth *Liv* 77-80; Soc Resp Officer

Glouc 80-85; Leonard Cheshire Foundn (Lon) 85-93. *The Stable Family Home Trust, The Stables, Bisterne, Ringwood, Hants BH24 3BN* Ringwood (01425) 478043

NAYLOR, Russell Stephen. b 45. Leeds Univ BA70 St Chad's Coll Dur DipTh72. Ho of Resurr Mirfield 64. **d** 72 **p** 73. C Chapel Allerton *Ripon* 72-75; Ind Chapl *Liv* 75-81; P-in-c Burtonwood 81-83; V from 83. *The Vicarage, Chapel Lane, Burtonwood, Warrington WA5 4PT* Newton-le-Willows (01925) 225371

NAYLOR, Stanley. b 29. NW Ord Course 76. **d** 79 **p** 80. NSM Girlington *Bradf* 79-80; C Tong 80-83; C Ingrow cum Hainworth 83-85; P-in-c Bradf St Clem 85-93; C Baildon from 93. *9 Coach Road, Baildon, Shipley, W Yorkshire BD17 5JE* Bradford (01274) 593441

NAYLOR, Ms Vivien Frances Damaris (Liz). b 55. RGN86 DTM89 New Hall Cam BA78 MA82. Ripon Coll Cuddesdon DipMin93. **d** 93 **p** 94. C Northn St Jas *Pet* 93-95; Chapl Asst Southn Univ Hosps NHS Trust from 95. *31 Winnington, Fareham, Hants PO15 6HP* Fareham (01329) 239664

NAZER, Raymond. b 20. St Chad's Coll Dur LTh42 BA43. Edin Th Coll 39. **d** 43 **p** 44. V Ipswich All Hallows *St E* 62-72; V Castle Acre w Newton *Nor* 72-84; R Southacre 72-84; P-in-c Rougham 82-84; rtd 84; Perm to Offic *Nor* from 84. *12 Malsters Close, Mundford, Thetford, Norfolk IP26 5HJ* Thetford (01842) 878329

✠NAZIR-ALI, Rt Rev Dr Michael James. b 49. Karachi Univ BA70 St Edm Hall Ox BLitt74 MLitt81 Fitzw Coll Cam MLitt76. ACT PhD83 Ridley Hall Cam 70. **d** 74 **p** 76 **c** 84. Tutorial Supervisor Th Cam Univ 74-76; C Cam H Sepulchre w All SS *Ely* 74-76; Pakistan 76-86; Sen Tutor Karachi Th Coll 76-81; Provost Lahore 81-84; Bp Raiwind 84-86; Asst to Abp Cant 86-89; Co-ord of Studies and Ed Lambeth Conf 86-89; Hon C Ox St Giles and SS Phil and Jas w St Marg *Ox* 86-89; Hon C Limpsfield and Titsey *S'wark* 89-94; Gen Sec CMS 89-94; Asst Bp S'wark 89-94; Can Th Leic Cathl *Leic* from 92; Bp Roch from 94. *Bishopscourt, Rochester, Kent ME1 1TS* Medway (01634) 842721 Fax 831136

NEAL, Alan. b 27. Trin Coll Bris DipTh84. **d** 84 **p** 85. Hon C Broughty Ferry *Bre* 84-85; P-in-c Dundee St Ninian 85-86; R Annan *Glas* 86-94; R Lockerbie 86-94. *Address temp unknown*

NEAL, Canon Anthony Terrence. b 42. BA CertEd. Chich Th Coll 65. **d** 68 **p** 69. C Cross Green St Sav and St Hilda *Ripon* 68-73; NSM Hawksworth Wood 73-78; Asst Chapl & Hd RE Abbey Grange High Sch Leeds 73-81; NSM Farnley 78-81; Dioc Adv in RE *Truro* 81-85; Children's Officer 85-87; Stewardship Adv 87-88; P-in-c St Erth 81-84; V from 84; P-in-c Phillack w Gwithian and Gwinear from 94; P-in-c Hayle from 94; Hon Can Truro Cathl from 94. *The Rectory, Forth An Tewennow, St Mary's Gardens, Phillack, Hayle, Cornwall TR27 4QE* Hayle (01736) 753541

NEAL, Christopher Charles. b 47. St Pet Coll Ox BA69. Ridley Hall Cam 69. **d** 72 **p** 73. C Addiscombe St Mary *Cant* 72-76; C Camberley St Paul *Guildf* 76-83; TV 83-86; V Thame w Towersey *Ox* from 86. *The Vicarage, Lashlake Lane, Thame, Oxon OX9 3AB* Thame (01844) 212225

NEAL, Canon Geoffrey Martin. b 40. AKC63. **d** 64 **p** 65. C Wandsworth St Paul *S'wark* 64-66; USA 66-68; C Reigate St Mark *S'wark* 68-70; P-in-c Wandsworth St Faith 70-72; V 72-75; V Houghton Regis *St Alb* from 75; Hon Can St Alb from 93. *The Vicarage, Bedford Road, Houghton Regis, Dunstable, Beds LU5 5DJ* Luton (01582) 867593

NEAL, James Christian. b 62. Trin Coll Cam BA84 MA88. Coll of Resurr Mirfield 95. **d** 95. C Lt Stanmore St Lawr *Lon* from 95. *18 Milford Gardens, Edgware, Middx HA8 6EY* 0181-951 3662

NEAL, John Edward. b 44. Nottm Univ BTh74. Linc Th Coll 70. **d** 74 **p** 75. C Lee St Marg *S'wark* 74-77; C Clapham St Jo 77; C Clapham Ch Ch and St Jo 77-81; P-in-c Eltham St Barn 81-83; V from 83; Sub-Dean Eltham 89-91; Sub-Dean Greenwich S from 91. *St Barnabas Vicarage, 449 Rochester Way, London SE9 6PH* 0181-856 8294

NEAL, Stephen Charles. b 44. MIMgt76 K Coll Lon BSc66. N Ord Course 90. **d** 93 **p** 94. C Walmsley *Man* from 93. *38 Queens Avenue, Bromley Cross, Bolton BL7 9BL* Bolton (01204) 303080

NEALE, Alan James Robert. b 52. LSE BSc(Econ)73 Ox Univ BA76 MA81. Wycliffe Hall Ox 74. **d** 77 **p** 78. C Plymouth St Andr w St Paul and St Geo *Ex* 77-80; C Portswood Ch Ch *Win* 80-82; V Stanstead Abbots *St Alb* 82-85; Asst Master Chelmsf Hall Sch Eastbourne 85-88; USA from 88. *Address temp unknown*

NEALE, David. b 50. Lanchester Poly BSc72. St Mich Coll Llan BD83. **d** 83 **p** 84. Min Can St Woolos Cathl *Mon* 83-87; Chapl St Woolos Hosp Newport 85-87; R Blaina and Nantyglo *Mon* 87-91; Video Production Officer Bd of Miss from 91. *Church in Wales Centre, Woodlands Place, Penarth, S Glam CF64 2EX* Penarth (01222) 705278 or 708234

NEALE, Geoffrey Arthur. b 41. Brasted Th Coll 61 St Aid Birkenhead 63. **d** 65 **p** 66. C Stoke *Cov* 65-68; C Fareham H

Trin *Portsm* 68-71; TV 71-72; R Binstead 72-77; TR Bottesford w Ashby *Linc* 77-80; V Horncastle w Low Toynton 80-90; V Brigg 90-95; V Blockley w Aston Magna and Bourton on the Hill *Glouc* from 95; Local Min Officer from 95. *The Vicarage, Blockley, Moreton-in-Marsh, Glos GL56 9ES* Blockley (01386) 700283

NEALE, Canon James Edward McKenzie (Eddie). b 38. Selw Coll Cam BA61. Clifton Th Coll 61. **d** 63 **p** 64. C Everton St Ambrose w St Tim *Liv* 63-72; Relig Adv BBC Radio Merseyside 72-76; V Bestwood St Matt *S'well* 76-86; Dioc Urban Officer 86-91; V Nottm St Mary and St Cath from 91; Hon Can S'well Minster from 91. *St Mary's Vicarage, Standard Hill, Nottingham NG1 6GA* Nottingham (0115) 947 2476

NEALE, Mrs Jan Celia. b 42. E Midl Min Tr Course CTPS92. **d** 92 **p** 94. C Gt and Lt Coates w Bradley *Linc* from 92. *26 Meadowbank, Great Coates, Grimsby, S Humberside DN37 9PL* Grimsby (01472) 280162

✠**NEALE, Rt Rev John Robert Geoffrey.** b 26. AKC54 St Boniface Warminster 54. **d** 55 **p** 56 **c** 74. C St Helier *S'wark* 55-58; Chapl Ardingly Coll Haywards Heath 58-62; Recruitment Sec CACTM 63-66; ACCM 66-68; R Hascombe *Guildf* 68-74; Can Missr and Dir Post-Ord Tr 68-74; Hon Can Guildf Cathl 68-74; Adn Wilts *Sarum* 74-80; Suff Bp Ramsbury 74-81; Area Bp Ramsbury 81-88; Hon Can Sarum Cathl 74-88; Sec Partnership for World Miss 89-91; Asst Bp S'wark 89-91; Asst Bp Lon 89-91; rtd 91; Asst Bp B & W from 91; Asst Bp Bris from 92. *26 Prospect, Corsham, Wilts SN13 9AF* Corsham (01249) 712557

NEALE, Martyn William. b 57. G&C Coll Cam BA78 MA82. Ripon Coll Cuddesdon 78. **d** 81 **p** 82. C Perry Hill St Geo *S'wark* 81-83; C Purley St Mark Woodcote 83-85; V Abbey Wood from 85. *The Vicarage, 1 Conference Road, London SE2 0YH* 0181-311 0377

NEAUM, Canon David. b 12. Lich Th Coll 34. **d** 37 **p** 38. C Burton All SS *Lich* 37-39; C Cannock 39-43; R Kingstone w Gratwich 43-46; R Leigh 46-52; Tristan da Cunha 52-56; S Rhodesia 56-65; Rhodesia 65-80; Zimbabwe 80-81; St Helena 81-84; Australia from 84. *Holy Trinity Rectory, Ararat, Victoria, Australia 3377* Ararat (53) 521109

NEAVE, Garry Reginald. b 51. Leic Univ MA73 PGCE74. S'wark Ord Course DipRS DipPSE. **d** 82 **p** 83. Hon C Harlow St Mary Magd *Chelmsf* from 82; Chapl Harlow Tertiary Coll from 84; Hon C St Mary-at-Latton *Chelmsf* from 87. *35 Perry Springs, Harlow, Essex CM17 9DQ* Harlow (01279) 435684

NEECH, Canon Alan Summons. b 15. Dur Univ LTh37. Tyndale Hall Bris 34. **d** 39 **p** 40. BCMS (India) 39-65; Gen Sec BCMS 66-81; Hon C Slough *Ox* 75-81; rtd 80; RD Loddon *Nor* 85-90; Perm to Offic from 90. *The Gardens Cottage, Rockland St Mary, Norwich NR14 7HQ* Surlingham (01508) 538519

NEED, Philip Alan. b 54. AKC75. Chich Th Coll 76. **d** 77 **p** 78. C Clapham Ch Ch and St Jo *S'wark* 77-79; C Luton All SS w St Pet *St Alb* 80-83; V Harlow St Mary Magd *Chelmsf* 83-89; P-in-c Chaddesden St Phil *Derby* 89-91; Bp's Dom Chapl *Chelmsf* from 91. *Willowdene, Maldon Road, Margaretting, Ingatestone, Essex CM4 9JW* Ingatestone (01277) 352472

NEEDHAM, George Oswald. b 18. Man Univ BA49. Wycliffe Hall Ox 49. **d** 51 **p** 52. R Thurstaston *Ches* 64-79; rtd 79; Perm to Offic *Ches* from 79. *14 Gills Lane, Barnston, Wirral, Merseyside L61 1AD* 0151-648 6732

NEEDHAM, Miss Patricia. b 32. **d** 87 **p** 94. Par Dn Warmsworth *Sheff* 87-89; Par Dn Norton Woodseats St Chad 89-92; Chapl Beauchief Abbey from 89; rtd 92. *14 Dalewood Drive, Sheffield S8 0EA* Sheffield (0114) 236 2688

NEEDHAM, Brother Peter Douglas. b 56. Chich Th Coll 86. **d** 88 **p** 88. SSF from 80; C S Moor *Dur* 88-90; Chapl RN 91-93. *The Friary, Alnmouth, Alnwick, Northd NE66 3NJ* Alnmouth (01665) 830213

NEEDLE, Paul Robert. b 45. Lon Univ DipTh70. Oak Hill Th Coll 67. **d** 70 **p** 71. C Gt Horton *Bradf* 70-74; C Pudsey St Lawr 74-77; Chapl St Luke's Hosp Bradf 78-80; Hon C Horton *Bradf* 78-80; NSM Irthlingborough *Pet* 87-90; NSM Gt w Lt Addington from 90. *The Rectory, Woodford Road, Great Addington, Kettering, Northants NN14 4BS* Cranford (01536) 78257

NEEDS, Dr Michael John. b 42. Open Univ BA82 Univ of Wales (Swansea) MSc84 PhD87. Wycliffe Hall Ox 91. **d** 93 **p** 94. C Abth *St D* from 93. *St Anne's Vicarage, Penparcau, Aberystwyth, Dyfed SY23 1RZ* Aberystwyth (01970) 617819

NEELY, Dr William George. b 32. Lon Univ BD62 QUB PhD. **d** 56 **p** 57. C Cregagh *D & D* 56-62; C-in-c M Merrion 62-68; I 68-76; Dioc Missr (Down) 70-76; Can Down Cathl 74-76; I Kilcooley w Littleton, Crohane and Killenaule *C & O* 76-84; P-in-c Fertagh 79-84; I Keady w Armaghbreague and Derrynoose *Arm* from 84; Tutor for Aux Min (Arm) from 86; RD Tynan from 91. *31 Crossmore Road, Keady, Armagh BT60 3JY* Keady (01861) 531230

NEIL, Richard Wilfred. b 16. Lon Univ DipTh57. Lon Coll of Div 51. **d** 53 **p** 54. V Devonport St Mich *Ex* 60-81; rtd 81; Lic to Offic *Ex* from 81. *22 Park Street, Plymouth PL3 4BL* Plymouth (01752) 558974

NEIL-SMITH, John Christopher. b 20. Pemb Coll Cam BA43 MA46. Westcott Ho Cam 43. **d** 44 **p** 45. V S Hampstead St Sav *Lon* 59-91; rtd 91. *40 Madeley Road, London W5 2LH* 0181-991 2971

NEILL, Charles Christopher Stanley. b 33. G&C Coll Cam BA57 MA60. Cuddesdon Coll 65. **d** 66 **p** 67. C Heref St Jo *Heref* 66-67; VC Heref Cathl and Chapl Heref Cathl Sch 67-78; Chapl Abingdon Sch 78-80; TV Wolvercote w Summertown *Ox* 80-84; Chapl St Edw Sch Ox 80-91; R W Woodhay w Enborne, Hampstead Marshall etc *Ox* from 91. *The Rectory, Enborne, Newbury, Berks RG15 0HD* Newbury (01635) 34427

NEILL, Canon Erberto Mahon. b 16. TCD BA40 MA Div Test. **d** 39 **p** 40. I Castleknock w Mulhuddart, Clonsilla etc *D & G* 61-75; I Dub Harold's Cross 77-81; I Boyle Union *K, E & A* 81-87; Preb Elphin Cathl 83-87; rtd 87. *2 The Court, Newtownpark House, Blackrock, Co Dublin, Irish Republic*

NEILL, Very Rev Ivan Delacherois. b 12. CB63 OBE58. Jes Coll Cam BA35 MA38. Lon Coll of Div 35. **d** 36 **p** 37. Provost Sheff 66-74; Perm to Offic *Glouc* 74-86; rtd 77; Perm to Offic *S'wark* 86-94. *Fair Oak, Aviemore Road, Crowborough, E Sussex TN6 1QU* Crowborough (01892) 662928

NEILL, James Purdon. b 41. Lon Univ DipTh63. Oak Hill Th Coll 60. **d** 64 **p** 65. C Kendal St Thos *Carl* 64-68; Chapl Park Hill Flats Sheff 68-71; P-in-c Mansf St Jo *S'well* 71-77; V Nottm St Ann w Em from 77. *St Ann's Vicarage, 17 Robin Hood Chase, Nottingham NG3 4EY* Nottingham (0115) 950 5471

✠**NEILL, Rt Rev John Robert Winder.** b 45. TCD BA66 MA69 Jes Coll Cam BA68 MA72. Ridley Hall Cam 67. **d** 69 **p** 70 **c** 86. C Glenageary *D & G* 69-71; Lect CITC 70-71 and 82-84; Dioc Registrar (Ossory, Ferns and Leighlin) *C & O* 71-74; Bp's V, Lib and Chapter Registrar Kilkenny Cathl 71-74; I Abbeystrewry *C, C & R* 74-78; I Dub St Bart w Ch Ch Leeson Park *D & G* 78-84; Chapl Community of St Jo the Ev 78-84; Dean Waterford *C & O* 84-86; Prec Lismore Cathl 84-86; Adn Waterford 84-86; I Waterford w Killea, Drumcannon and Dunhill 84-86; Bp T, K & A from 86. *Bishop's House, Knockglass, Crossmolina, Co Mayo, Irish Republic* Ballina (96) 31317 Fax 31775

NEILL, Richard Walter. b 67. Wadh Coll Ox BA89 Em Coll Cam BA92. Westcott Ho Cam CTM93. **d** 93 **p** 94. C Abbots Langley *St Alb* from 93. *40 Kindersley Way, Abbots Langley, Herts WD5 0DG* Kings Langley (01923) 265729

NEILL, Robert Chapman. b 51. Lon Univ BD82. CITC 77. **d** 77 **p** 78. C Lurgan Ch the Redeemer *D & D* 77-82; I Tullylish 82-88; I Mt Merrion from 88. *The Rectory, 122 Mount Merrion Avenue, Belfast BT6 0FS* Belfast (01232) 644308

NEILL, Stephen Mahon. b 69. TCD BA91 MLitt93. CITC 91. **d** 93 **p** 94. C Monkstown *D & G* 93-95; Dom Chapl to Bp of Killaloe and Clonfert *L & K* from 95; C Limerick City from 95. *14 Springfield Drive, Dooradoyle, Limerick, Irish Republic* Limerick (61) 302038 Fax as telephone

NEILL, Ven William Barnet. b 30. TCD BA61. **d** 63 **p** 64. C Belf St Clem *D & D* 63-66; C Dundonald 66-72; I Drumgath 72-80; I Drumgooland 76-80; I Mt Merrion 80-83; I Dromore Cathl from 83; Adn Dromore from 85. *Dromore Cathedral Rectory, 20 Church Street, Dromore, Co Down BT25 1AA* Dromore (01846) 692275

NEILL, Very Rev William Benjamin Alan. b 46. Open Univ BA76. CITC 68. **d** 71 **p** 72. C Dunmurry *Conn* 71-74; C Coleraine 75-77; C Dub St Ann w St Steph *D & G* 77-78; I Convoy w Monellan and Donaghmore *D & R* 78-81; I Faughanvale 81-86; I Waterford w Killea, Drumcannon and Dunhill *C & O* from 86; Dean Waterford from 86; Prec Lismore Cathl from 86; Prec Cashel Cathl from 87. *The Deanery, 41 Grange Park Road, Waterford, Irish Republic* Waterford (51) 74119 Fax as telephone

NELLIST, Mrs Valerie Ann. b 48. SRN69 SCM71. St And Dioc Tr Course 87. **d** 90 **p** 94. NSM Dunfermline *St And* from 90; NSM W Fife Team Min from 90. *28 Glamis Gardens, Dalgety Bay, Dunfermline, Fife KY11 5TD* Dalgety Bay (01383) 824066

NELMES, Mrs Christine. b 41. St Mary's Cheltenham DipT63. S Dios Minl Tr Scheme 92. **d** 95. NSM Winscombe *B & W* from 95. *23 Sidcot Lane, Winscombe, Avon BS25 1LA* Winscombe (01934) 844300 Fax 842973

NELSON, Canon Allen James. b 29. CITC 53. **d** 55 **p** 56. C Glenageary *D & G* 55-57; C Dub Clontarf 57-60; I Bailieborough w Mullagh *K, E & A* 60-75; P-in-c Knockbride 66-72; P-in-c Knockbride w Shercock 72-75; I Julianstown w Colpe *M & K* 75-81; I Julianstown and Colpe w Drogheda and

Duleek from 81; Dioc Glebes Sec from 81; Can Meath from 84. *The Rectory, Eastham Road, Bettystown, Co Meath, Irish Republic* Drogheda (41) 27345

NELSON, Christopher James. b 57. Preston Poly HNC80 Nottm Univ BTh88. Aston Tr Scheme 83 St Jo Coll Nottm 85. **d** 88 **p** 89. C Blackpool St Thos *Blackb* 88-90; C Altham w Clayton le Moors 90-92; V Knuzden from 92. *St Oswald's Vicarage, Bank Lane, Blackburn BB1 2AP* Blackburn (01254) 698321

NELSON, Frank. b 12. Jes Coll Ox BA35 MA40 Lon Univ BSc44. Ox NSM Course. **d** 78 **p** 78. NSM Sutton Courtenay w Appleford *Ox* 78-89; Lic to Offic from 89. *6 Tullis Close, Sutton Courtenay, Abingdon, Oxon OX14 4BD* Abingdon (01235) 848567

NELSON, Graham William. b 61. Birm Univ CYCW85. St Jo Coll Nottm BA91. **d** 91 **p** 92. C Pype Hayes *Birm* 91-93; C Lanc St Mary *Blackb* from 94. *24 Milkingstile Lane, Lancaster LA1 5QB* Lancaster (01524) 382362

NELSON, Jane. b 42. **d** 94. Par Dn Muchalls *Bre* from 94; Asst Chapl Grampian Health Care from 93. *4 St Michael's Road, Newtonhill, Stonehaven, Kincardineshire AB3 2RW* Newtonhill (01569) 730967

NELSON, Kenneth Edmund. b 10. St Jo Coll Cam BA33 MA36. Qu Coll Birm 46. **d** 47 **p** 48. R Crayke w Brandsby and Yearsley *York* 68-78; rtd 78. *Flat 1, Holly Mount, 23B Ripon Road, Harrogate, N Yorkshire HG1 2JL* Harrogate (01423) 568460

NELSON, Mark Richard. b 61. Ushaw Coll Dur BA84. NE Ord Course 89. **d** 84 **p** 85. In RC Ch 84-89; C Birtley *Dur* 91-94; P-in-c Middlesb St Cuth *York* from 94; Urban Development Officer from 94. *95 Southwell Road, Middlesbrough, Cleveland TS5 6NG* Middlesbrough (01642) 820838

NELSON, Canon Michael. b 44. Lon Univ BD66. Coll of Resurr Mirfield 66. **d** 68 **p** 69. C Newbold and Dunston *Derby* 68-72; C N Gosforth *Newc* 72-77; V Seaton Hirst 77-83; V Blyth St Mary 83-93; P-in-c Horton 86-87; RD Bedlington 88-93; R Hexham from 93; Hon Can Newc Cathl from 94. *The Rectory, Eilansgate, Hexham, Northd NE46 3EW* Hexham (01434) 603121

NELSON, Canon Nelson John. b 21. Ripon Hall Ox 64. **d** 65 **p** 66. V W Smethwick *Birm* 68-90; RD Warley 79-86; Hon Can Birm Cathl 83-90; rtd 90. *68 Pembroke Way, Stourport-on-Severn, Worcs DY13 8QZ* Stourport (01299) 822821

NELSON, Sister Norma Margaret. b 34. Liv Univ DASS77 CQSW77. CA Tr Coll IDC60. **d** 93 **p** 94. TD Kirkby *Liv* 93-94; TV from 94. *St Mark's Vicarage, Brook Hey Drive, Kirkby, Liverpool L33 9TE* 0151-546 2645

NELSON, Paul John. b 52. Nottm Univ BCombStuds84. Linc Th Coll 81. **d** 84 **p** 85. C Waltham Cross *St Alb* 84-87; C Sandridge 87-90; V from 90. *The Vicarage, 2 Anson Close, House Lane, Sandridge, St Albans, Herts AL4 9EN* St Albans (01727) 866089

NELSON, Ralph Archbold. b 27. St Cuth Soc Dur BA50. Bps' Coll Cheshunt 50. **d** 52 **p** 53. V Featherstone *Wakef* 58-80; V Kirkham *Blackb* 80-92; RD Kirkham 88-91; rtd 92. *6 Blundell Lane, Penwortham, Preston PR1 0EA* Preston (01772) 742573

NELSON, Robert Gibson. b 34. ALCD61. **d** 61 **p** 62. Australia 69-72; V Guernsey St Jo *Win* 72-78; R Guernsey Ste Marie du Castel 78-86; V Guernsey St Matt 84-86; rtd 86. *Le Petit Feugre, Clos des Mielles, Castel, Guernsey, Channel Islands* Guernsey (01481) 52726

NELSON, Robert Towers. b 43. MSOSc Liv Coll of Tech BSc65. NW Ord Course 76. **d** 79 **p** 80. NSM Liv Our Lady and St Nic w St Anne *Liv* 79-83; NSM Liscard St Thos *Ches* 83-87; P-in-c from 87; Dioc Ind Missr from 87; Asst Sec SOSc from 89. *5 Sedbergh Road, Wallasey, Merseyside L44 2BR* 0151-630 2830

NELSON, Roger Charles. b 44. ATII74 Newc Univ LLB66 Solicitor 69. Cant Sch of Min 88. **d** 91 **p** 92. NSM Deal St Leon and St Rich and Sholden *Cant* from 91. *377 London Road, Deal, Kent CT14 9PS* Dover (01304) 366681

NELSON, Warren David. b 38. TCD BA67. **d** 68 **p** 69. C Belf St Mich *Conn* 68-70; I Kilcooley w Littleton, Crohane, Killenaule etc *C & O* 70-76; Chapl Coalbrook Fellowship Hosp Ho Thurles 76-94; Perm to Offic (Cashel, Waterford and Lismore) 93-94; I Lurgan etc w Ballymachugh, Kildrumferton etc *K, E & A* from 94. *The Rectory, Virginia, Co Cavan, Irish Republic* Cavan (49) 47389

NELSON, William. b 38. Oak Hill Th Coll 74. **d** 76 **p** 77. C Hensingham *Carl* 76-81; V Widnes St Paul *Liv* 81-89; R Higher Openshaw *Man* from 89. *St Clement's Rectory, Ashton Old Road, Manchester M11 1HJ* 0161-370 1538

NENER, Canon Thomas Paul Edgar. b 42. FRCSEd71 FRCS71 Liv Univ MB, ChB. Coll of Resurr Mirfield 78. **d** 80 **p** 81. C Warrington St Elphin *Liv* 80-83; V Haydock St Jas 83-95; V W Derby (or Tuebrook) St Jo from 95; Hon Can Liv Cathl from 95. *St John's Vicarage, Tuebrook, Liverpool L13 7EA* 0151-228 2023

NENO, David Edward. b 62. SS Mark & Jo Coll Plymouth BA85. Ripon Coll Cuddesdon 85. **d** 88 **p** 89. C Chapel Allerton *Ripon* 88-91; C Acton St Mary *Lon* 91-94; V Kingsbury H Innocents from 94. *The Vicarage, 54 Roe Green, London NW9 0PJ* 0181-204 7531

NESBITT, Charles Howard. b 09. St Jo Coll Dur LTh34 BA35. Bp Wilson Coll 31. **d** 35 **p** 36. V Stalmine *Blackb* 68-74; rtd 75. *Sunnyside Eventide Home, 75 South Oswald Road, Edinburgh EH9 2HH* 0131-667 6831

NESBITT, Heather Hastings. b 48. S'wark Ord Course 88. **d** 90 **p** 94. Par Dn Camberwell St Luke *S'wark* 90-94; C Addiscombe St Mary Magd w St Martin from 94. *97 Stretton Road, Croydon CR0 6ET* 0181-662 0282

NESBITT, Ronald. b 58. Sheff Univ LLB TCD DipTh85. CITC 82. **d** 85 **p** 86. C Ballymena w Ballyclug *Conn* 85-88; C Holywood *D & D* 88-90; I Helen's Bay from 90. *2 Woodland Avenue, Helens Bay, Bangor, Co Down BT19 1TX* Helens Bay (01247) 853601

NESHAM, George Dove. b 20. ALCD50. Lon Coll of Div. **d** 50 **p** 51. V W Ardsley *Wakef* 62-77; V Ripponden 77-80; V Satley *Dur* 80-87; RD Stanhope 81-87; rtd 87. *29 Ettrick Road, Jarrow, Tyne & Wear NE32 5SL* 0191-489 8071

✠NESTOR, Rt Rev Donald Patrick. b 38. Ex Coll Ox BA63 MA66 Birm Univ DipTh65. Qu Coll Birm 63. **d** 65 **p** 66 **c** 79. C W Ardsley *Wakef* 65-68; C Forton *Lich* 68-72; Lesotho 72-79; Chapl Nat Univ 74-77; Warden Angl Sem Roma 74-79; Bp Lesotho 79-92; Asst Bp Blackb from 92; P-in-c Bretherton from 92. *The Rectory, 156 South Road, Bretherton, Preston PR5 7AH* Croston (01772) 600206

NETHERWOOD, Mrs Anne Christine. b 43. ARIBA68 Liv Univ BArch66 Lon Univ BD92. St Deiniol's Hawarden 88. **d** 91 **p** 94. NSM Ellesmere and Welsh Frankton *Lich* 91-94; C Criftins from 94; C Dudleston from 94. *The Vicarage, Criftins, Ellesmere, Shropshire SY12 9LN* Dudleston Heath (0169175) 212

NEUDEGG, Mrs Joan Mary. b 36. Cant Sch of Min 81. **dss** 84 **d** 87 **p** 94. Chalk *Roch* 84-86; Hon C Dean Forest H Trin *Glouc* 87-90; Hon C Woolaston w Alvington 90-95; Hon C Woolaston w Alvington and Aylburton from 95. *The Rectory, Main Road, Alvington, Lydney, Glos GL15 6AT* Netherend (01594) 529387

NEUDEGG, Leslie. b 35. Lon Univ DipRS83 Open Univ BA84. S'wark Ord Course 77. **d** 80 **p** 81. Hon C Chalk *Roch* 80-86; Area Org CECS 86-89; P-in-c Woolaston w Alvington *Glouc* 89-95; R Woolaston w Alvington and Aylburton from 95. *The Rectory, Main Road, Alvington, Lydney, Glos GL15 6AT* Netherend (01594) 529387

NEVELL, Frederick George. b 24. Lon Univ BA51. Oak Hill Th Coll 46. **d** 51 **p** 52. V W Kilburn St Luke w St Simon and St Jude *Lon* 64-73; V Clapham Common St Barn *S'wark* 73-90; rtd 90. *19 Bolton Road, Folkestone, Kent CT19 5RX* Folkestone (01303) 241428

NEVILL, James Michael. b 50. Cranmer Hall Dur 84. **d** 86 **p** 87. C Sowerby Bridge w Norland *Wakef* 86-91; CF 91-94; TV Broadwater St Mary *Chich* from 94. *80 Dominion Road, Worthing, W Sussex BN14 8JT* Worthing (01903) 230759

NEVILLE, Alfred John. b 21. K Coll Lon BA40. Sarum & Wells Th Coll. **d** 83 **p** 84. NSM Weston-super-Mare St Paul *B & W* 83-93; Perm to Offic from 93. *12 Woodford Court, 21 Clarence Road North, Weston-super-Mare, Avon BS23 4AW* Weston-super-Mare (01934) 631176

NEVILLE, David Bruce. b 61. Ravensbourne Coll of Art & Design BA83. St Jo Coll Nottm LTh89. **d** 91 **p** 92. C Broxtowe *S'well* 91-94; C Attenborough 94-95. *29 Osbourne Street, Nottingham NG7 5LY*

NEVILLE, Canon Graham. b 22. CCC Cam BA47 MA49 CertEd Cam Univ BD94. Chich Th Coll 48. **d** 50 **p** 51. Chapl Sutton Valence Sch Kent 68-73; Prin Lect Relig Studies Eastbourne Coll of Educn 73-80; Dir of Educn *Linc* 80-87; Can and Preb Linc Cathl 82-88; rtd 87; Perm to Offic *Linc* from 88. *16 Silverdale Avenue, Worcester WR5 1PY* Worcester (01905) 360319

NEVILLE, Michael Robert John. b 56. Hatf Coll Dur BA80 Hughes Hall Cam PGCE81. Wycliffe Hall Ox 82. **d** 85 **p** 86. C E Twickenham St Steph *Lon* 85-88; Asst Dir Proclamation Trust 88-93; R Fordham *Chelmsf* from 93. *The Rectory, Wood Lane, Fordham Heath, Colchester CO3 5TR* Colchester (01206) 240221

NEVIN, Alan Joseph. MIPM. CITC BA. **d** 92 **p** 93. NSM Youghal Union *C, C & R* 92-94; NSM Waterford w Killea, Drumcannon and Dunhill *C & O* 94-95; C from 95. *8 Monea Crescent, Ardmore, Co Waterford, Irish Republic* Ardmore (24) 94291

NEVIN, Ronald. b 32. DMin88. Wesley Coll Leeds Linc Th Coll 63. **d** 64 **p** 65. R Cockfield *Dur* 66-70; USA from 70; rtd 95. *19879 Gator Creek Court, Nth Fort Myers, FL 33903, USA* Fort Myers (941) 731 8843

NEW, David John. b 37. Lon Univ BSc58. Chich Th Coll 65. d 67 p 68. C Folkestone St Mary and St Eanswythe *Cant* 67-72; C Kings Heath *Birm* 72-74; V S Yardley St Mich 74-83; V Moseley St Agnes from 83. *St Agnes' Vicarage, 5 Colmore Crescent, Birmingham B13 9SJ* 0121-449 0368

NEW, Derek. b 30. d 86 p 87. NSM Brondesbury St Anne w Kilburn H Trin *Lon* from 86. *20 Lynton Road, London NW6 6BL* 0171-328 0187

NEW, John Bingley. b 29. Lon Univ BD70. Chich Th Coll 77. d 77 p 78. C Sholing CD *Win* 77-79; C Sholing 79; V Micheldever and E Stratton, Woodmancote etc 79-91; rtd 91. *Duffield, Church Road, Kings Somborne, Stockbridge, Hants SO20 6NX* Romsey (01794) 388406

NEW, John. b 08. St Jo Coll Dur LTh32 BA33. St Aid Birkenhead 29. d 33 p 34. R Beckingham *S'well* 69-73; P-in-c Walkeringham 69-73; rtd 73; Perm to Offic *S'well* from 73. *17 Muir Avenue, Tollerton, Nottingham NG12 4EZ* Nottingham (0115) 937 5406

NEW, Canon Thomas Stephen. b 30. K Coll Cam BA52 MA56. Cuddesdon Coll 52. d 54 p 55. V Guildf All SS *Guildf* 64-72; V Banstead 72-93; RD Epsom 76-80; Hon Can Guildf Cathl 79-93; Sub-Chapl HM Pris Downview 88-93; rtd 93; Perm to Offic *Ex* from 94. *St Katharine's, North Street, Denbury, Newton Abbot, Devon TQ12 6DJ* Ipplepen (01803) 813775

NEWALL, Arthur William. b 24. Univ of Wales (Lamp) BA49. Chich Th Coll 49. d 51 p 52. R Foots Cray *Roch* 68-78; V Henlow *St Alb* 78-89; rtd 89. *38 Fairhaven Road, Southport, Merseyside PR9 9UH* Southport (01704) 26045

NEWALL, Richard Lucas. b 43. AKC66. d 66 p 67. C Roby *Liv* 66-69; C Douglas St Geo and St Barn *S & M* 69-71; Lic to Offic *Man* 72-75; C Ban St Mary *Ban* 75-77; R Newborough w Llangeinwen w Llangaffo etc from 77. *Newborough Rectory, Anglesey, Gwynedd LL61 6RP* Newborough (01248) 440285

NEWARK, Archdeacon of. *See* HAWTIN, Ven David Christopher

NEWBON, Eric. b 23. Fitzw Ho Cam BA51 MA55. Ridley Hall Cam 51. d 53 p 54. V Southport All So *Liv* 65-85; rtd 85; Perm to Offic *Ches* from 86. *33 Haymakers Way, Saughall, Chester CH1 6AR* Saughall (01244) 880123

NEWBON, Kenneth. b 29. Wells Th Coll 67. d 69 p 70. C Church Stretton *Heref* 69-72; P-in-c Cressage w Sheinton 72-75; R Braunstone *Leic* 75-81; TR 81-84; P-in-c Eardisley w Bollingham and Willersley *Heref* 84-88; P-in-c Brilley w Michaelchurch on Arrow 84-88; P-in-c Whitney w Winforton 84-88; RD Kington and Weobley 87-95; R Eardisley w Bollingham, Willersley, Brilley etc from 88. *The Rectory, Church Street, Eardisley, Hereford HR3 6LB* Eardisley (01544) 327440

NEWBON, Michael Charles. b 59. Oak Hill Th Coll DipHE94. d 94 p 95. C Bedf St Jo and St Leon *St Alb* from 94. *53 Hillesdon Avenue, Elstow, Bedford MK42 9AJ* Bedford (01234) 358307

NEWBURY, Canon Robert. b 22. St D Coll Lamp BA46. d 48 p 49. V Manselton *S & B* 63-84; V Manselton w Hafod 84-90; Hon Can Brecon Cathl from 85; rtd 91. *4 Cobham Close, Gorseinon, Swansea SA4 4FA* Swansea (01792) 654848

NEWBY, Peter Gordon. b 23. d 64 p 65. R Lt Bowden St Nic *Leic* 69-72; V Jersey Gouray St Martin *Win* 72-77; Chapl Jersey Gp of Hosps 78-80; R Much Birch w Lt Birch, Much Dewchurch etc *Heref* 80-88; rtd 89; Perm to Offic *Ex* from 90. *18 Woodfields, Seaton, Devon EX12 2UX* Seaton (01297) 24562

NEWCASTLE, Bishop of. *See* GRAHAM, Rt Rev Andrew Alexander Kenny

NEWCASTLE, Provost of. *See* COULTON, Very Rev Nicholas Guy

NEWCOMBE, John Adrian. b 61. Univ of Wales (Lamp) BA83 SS Paul & Mary Coll Cheltenham PGCE85. Ripon Coll Cuddesdon 90. d 92 p 93. C Stroud and Uplands w Slad *Glouc* from 92. *St Hugh's Lodge, 11 Hillier Close, Uplands, Stroud, Glos GL5 1XS* Stroud (01453) 751935

NEWCOMBE, Kenneth Harry. b 27. Ridley Hall Cam 70. d 72 p 73. C Melton Mowbray w Thorpe Arnold *Leic* 72-78; P-in-c W Bridgford *S'well* 78-84; V Radcliffe-on-Trent 84-85; V Shelford 84-85; P-in-c Holme Pierrepont w Adbolton 84-85; R Radcliffe-on-Trent and Shelford etc 85. *The Rectory, Radcliffe-on-Trent, Nottingham NG12 2FB* Nottingham (0115) 933 2203

NEWCOMBE, Timothy James Grahame. b 47. AKC75. St Aug Coll Cant 75. d 76 p 77. C Heref St Martin *Heref* 76-79; C Hitchin *St Alb* 79-85; R Croft and Stoney Stanton *Leic* 85-91; P-in-c Launceston *Truro* 91-92; V Launceston from 92. *St Mary's Vicarage, Dunheved Road, Launceston, Cornwall PL15 9JE* Launceston (01566) 772974

NEWCOME, Canon James William Scobie. b 53. Trin Coll Ox BA74 MA78 Selw Coll Cam BA77 MA81. Ridley Hall Cam 75. d 78 p 79. C Leavesden All SS *St Alb* 78-82; P-in-c Bar Hill LEP *Ely* 82-92; V Bar Hill 92-93; Tutor Ridley Hall Cam

83-88; P-in-c Dry Drayton *Ely* 89-94; RD N Stowe 93-94; V Bar Hill 94; Can Res Ches Cathl and Dioc Dir of Ords from 94. *5 Abbey Street, Chester CH1 2JF* Chester (01244) 315532

NEWELL, Aubrey Francis Thomas. b 20. St D Coll Lamp BA43. d 45 p 46. V Gawcott and Hillesden *Ox* 62-77; P-in-c Radclive 69-72; RD Buckm 70-76 and 82-84; P-in-c Padbury w Adstock 72-77; V Lenborough 77-87; rtd 87. *5 Church View, Steeple Claydon, Buckingham MK18 2QR* Aylesbury (01296) 738271

NEWELL, Christopher David. b 53. CCouns92. S'wark Ord Course DipRS87. d 87 p 88. C Stockwell St Mich *S'wark* 87-90; Asst Chapl R Lon Hosp (Whitechapel) 90-92; Asst Chapl R Lon Hosp (Mile End) 90-92; R Birch St Agnes *Man* from 92; P-in-c Longsight St Jo w St Cypr from 94. *St Agnes's Rectory, Slade Lane, Manchester M13 0GN* 0161-224 2596

NEWELL, Dr Edmund John. b 61. Univ Coll Lon BSc83 Nuff Coll Ox DPhil88 MA89. Ox Min Course 89 Ripon Coll Cuddesdon 92. d 94 p 95. C Deddington w Barford, Clifton and Hempton *Ox* from 94. *16 Broad Close, Barford St Michael, Banbury, Oxon OX15 0RW* Deddington (01869) 338988

NEWELL, Gerald Frederick Watson. b 34. Sarum Th Coll 56. d 59 p 61. C Southn Maybush St Pet *Win* 59-61; C Overton w Laverstoke and Freefolk 61-63; CF (TA) 61-63; CF 63-66; R Spennithorne *Ripon* 66-68; R Finghall 66-68; R Hauxwell 66-68; Hon C Steyning *Chich* 74-78; Perm to Offic *Ex* from 93; P-in-c Breamore *Win* from 95. *The Rectory, Breamore, Fordingbridge, Hants SP6 2BY* Downton (01725) 513098

NEWELL, Jack Ernest. b 26. CEng FIChemE ARCS BSc. Glouc Th Course 80. d 83 p 84. NSM Hempsted *Glouc* from 83. *Hempsted House, Hempsted, Gloucester GL2 6LW* Gloucester (01452) 523320

NEWELL, Kenneth Ernest. b 22. S Dios Minl Tr Scheme 77. d 79 p 80. NSM Lynton, Brendon, Countisbury, Lynmouth etc *Ex* 79-85; TR 85-89; RD Shirwell 84-89; rtd 89; Perm to Offic *Ex* from 89. *Mole End, Lydiate Lane, Lynton, Devon EX35 6HE*

NEWELL, Samuel James (Jim). b 28. TCD BA53 MA63. TCD Div Sch Div Test54. d 54 p 55. V Chesham Ch Ch *Ox* 63-74; P-in-c Wraysbury 74-78; TV Riverside 78-94; rtd 94. *41 Redford Road, Windsor, Berks SL4 5ST* Windsor (01753) 862300

NEWELL PRICE, Dr John Charles. b 29. MRCGP64 SS Coll Cam BA50 MB, ChB53. Local NSM Course 88. d 91 p 94. NSM Frensham *Guildf* from 91. *Dragon Lodge, Millbridge, Frensham, Farnham, Surrey GU10 3DQ* Frensham (01252) 793317

NEWHAM, Jill. b 37. Oak Hill NSM Course. d 89. NSM W w E Mersea *Chelmsf* 89-91 and from 95; NSM Peldon w Gt and Lt Wigborough from 91. *Lingwood, Church Road, Peldon, Colchester CO5 7PT* Peldon (01206) 735515

NEWHOUSE, Ven Robert John Darrell. b 11. Worc Coll Ox BA35 MA38. Cuddesdon Coll 35. d 36 p 37. Adn Totnes *Ex* 66-76; Can Res Ex Cathl 66-76; Treas 70-76; rtd 76; Perm to Offic *Ex* from 76. *Pound Cottage, Northlew, Okehampton, Devon EX20 3NR* Beaworthy (01409) 221532

✠NEWING, Rt Rev Kenneth Albert. b 23. Selw Coll Cam BA53 MA57. Coll of Resurr Mirfield 53. d 55 p 56 c 82. C Plymstock *Ex* 55-63; R Plympton St Maurice 63-82; RD Plympton 71-76; Preb Ex Cathl 75-82; Adn Plymouth 78-82; Suff Bp Plymouth 82-88; Lic to Offic *Ox* 88-93; OSB from 89; rtd 93. *Elmore Abbey, Church Lane, Newbury, Berks RG13 1SA* Newbury (01635) 33080

NEWING, Dr Peter. b 33. FSAScot59 FRSA60 ACP67 MCollP86 Birm Univ CertEd55 Dur Univ BA63 Bris Univ BEd76 NY State Univ BSc85 EdD88 Cam Univ DipRS91. Cranmer Hall Dur 63. d 65 p 66. C Blockley w Aston Magna *Glouc* 65-69; P-in-c Taynton 69-75; P-in-c Tibberton 69-75; R Brimpsfield w Elkstone and Syde 75-83; R Brimpsfield, Cranham, Elkstone and Syde from 83; P-in-c Daglingworth w the Duntisbournes and Winstone from 95. *The Rectory, Brimpsfield, Gloucester GL4 8LD* Gloucester (01452) 863621

NEWLANDS, Christopher William. b 57. Bris Univ BA79. Westcott Ho Cam 81. d 84 p 85. C Bishops Waltham *Portsm* 84-87; Hon C Upham 85-87; Prec, Sacr and Min Can Dur Cathl *Dur* 87-92; Chapl Bucharest w Sofia *Eur* from 92. *Church of the Resurrection, Str Xenopol 2, Bucharest, Romania* Bucharest (1) 615-1392 or 210-2937 Fax 111634

NEWLANDS, Prof George McLeod. b 41. Edin Univ MA63 Heidelberg Univ BD66 PhD70 Ch Coll Cam MA73. d 82 p 82. Lect Cam Univ 73-86; Lic to Offic *Ely* from 82; Fell and Dean Trin Hall Cam 82-86; Prof Div Glas Univ from 86; Perm to Offic *Glas* from 86. *8 Hills Avenue, Cambridge CB1 4XA, or The University, Glasgow G12 8QQ* Cambridge (01223) 248631 or 0141-339 8855

NEWLYN, Canon Edwin. b 39. AKC64. d 65 p 66. C Belgrave St Mich *Leic* 65-68; Miss to Seamen 68-81; Brazil 68-69; C Glas St Gabr *Glas* 69-73; S Africa 73-76; V Fylingdales *York* 81; P-in-c Hawsker 81; V Fylingdales and Hawsker cum Stainsacre 81-88; RD Whitby 85-92; P-in-c Goathland from

88; Can York Minster from 90. *The Vicarage, Goathland, Whitby, N Yorkshire YO22 5AN* Whitby (01947) 896227 or 896239 Fax 896316

NEWMAN, Adrian. b 58. Bris Univ BSc80 DipHE85 MPhil89. Trin Coll Bris 82. **d** 85 **p** 86. C Forest Gate St Mark *Chelmsf* 85-89; V Hillsborough and Wadsley Bridge *Sheff* from 89; RD Hallam from 94. *Christ Church Vicarage, 218 Foxhill Road, Sheffield S6 1HJ* Sheffield (0114) 231 1576

NEWMAN, Alan George. b 18. Lich Th Coll 41. **d** 44 **p** 45. V Bradford-on-Avon Ch Ch *Sarum* 56-76; R Monkton Farleigh w S Wraxall 76-84; rtd 84; Perm to Offic *Sarum* from 84. *14 White Horse Road, Winsley, Bradford-on-Avon, Wilts BA15 2JZ* Bradford-on-Avon (01225) 854119

NEWMAN, Alfred John Gordon. b 19. Qu Coll Birm 71. **d** 74 **p** 74. Hon C Hall Green St Pet *Birm* 74-84; Perm to Offic *St E* from 84. *Willowmere, Rectory Road, Middleton, Saxmundham, Suffolk IP17 3NW* Westleton (0172873) 457

NEWMAN, Cecil Ernest. b 21. Bris Univ BA58 DipTh58. Roch Th Coll 61. **d** 62 **p** 63. Lic to Offic *Roch* 67-86; Chapl Darenth Park Hosp Dartford 67-86; rtd 86. *27 Nursery Road, Meopham, Gravesend, Kent DA13 0LR* Meopham (01474) 812955

NEWMAN, David Malcolm. b 54. FSAScot81 Aber Univ LTh BTh. St Steph Ho Ox 89. **d** 91 **p** 92. C St Mary-at-Latton *Chelmsf* 91-94; R Weeley and Lt Clacton from 94. *The Vicarage, 2 Holland Road, Little Clacton, Clacton-on-Sea, Essex CO16 9RS* Clacton-on-Sea (01255) 860241

NEWMAN, David Maurice Frederick. b 54. Hertf Coll Ox BA75 MA79. St Jo Coll Nottm. **d** 79 **p** 80. C Orpington Ch Ch *Roch* 79-83; C Bushbury *Lich* 83-86; V Ockbrook *Derby* from 86. *The Vicarage, 265 Victoria Avenue, Ockbrook, Derby DE7 3RL* Derby (01332) 662352

NEWMAN, Mrs Diana Joan. b 43. Sarum Th Coll 81. **dss** 84 **d** 87 **p** 94. Parkstone St Pet w Branksea and St Osmund *Sarum* 84-87; Hon Par Dn 87-94; Hon C from 94. *62 Vale Road, Poole, Dorset BH14 9AU* Parkstone (01202) 745136

NEWMAN, Eric William. b 26. Vancouver Sch of Th STh65. **d** 56 **p** 57. Miss to Seamen 67-91; Chapl Newport, Gwent 68-78; Chapl Tyne & Wear 78-91; rtd 91. *1 Sunnycroft, Portskewett, Chepstow, Gwent NP6 4RY* Caldicot (01291) 420679

NEWMAN, Geoffrey Maurice. b 22. Ox NSM Course 77. **d** 80 **p** 81. NSM Binfield *Ox* 80-84; Chapl St Geo Sch Ascot 82-84; V Teynham *Cant* 84-87; rtd 87. *55 St Mildred's Road, Westgate-on-Sea, Kent CT8 8RJ* Thanet (01843) 833837

NEWMAN, Graham Anthony. b 44. Ripon Coll Cuddesdon 79. **d** 81 **p** 82. C Walker *Newc* 81-84; C Whorlton 84-87; V Warkworth and Acklington 87-94; V Haltwhistle and Greenhead from 94; Chapl Northumberland HA from 94. *The Vicarage, Edens Lawn, Haltwhistle, Northd NE49 0AB* Haltwhistle (01434) 320215

NEWMAN, James Edwin Michael. b 59. Nottm Univ BA80 Ox Univ BA90. Wycliffe Hall Ox 88. **d** 91 **p** 92. C Bidston *Ches* 91-95; C Cheadle from 95. *4 Cuthbert Road, Cheadle, Cheshire SK8 2DT* 0161-428 3983

NEWMAN, John Humphrey. b 17. ALCD49. **d** 49 **p** 50. V Penge St Jo *Roch* 64-74; R Knockholt 74-82; rtd 82; Perm to Offic *Chich* from 84. *Stonegarth, Pett Level Road, Fairlight, Hastings, E Sussex TN35 4EA* Hastings (01424) 812518

NEWMAN, Laurence Victor. b 23. Wells Th Coll. **d** 66 **p** 67. C Milton *Win* 69-71; Asst Chapl HM Pris Wandsworth 71-72; Chapl HM Rem Cen Ashford 72-77; Chapl HM Pris Win 77-88; Chapl Las Palmas *Eur* 88-89; Chapl Algarve 89-91; rtd 91. *41 Nuns Road, Winchester, Hants SO23 7EF* Winchester (01962) 867699

NEWMAN, Michael Alan. b 40. Chich Th Coll 67. **d** 70 **p** 71. C Kilburn St Aug *Lon* 70-73; C St Geo-in-the-East St Mary 75-78; rtd 78. *April Cottage, Georges Lane, Storrington, Pulborough, W Sussex RH20 3JH* Storrington (01903) 744354

NEWMAN, Michael John. b 50. Leic Univ BA72 MA75 Ex Coll Ox DipTh74. Cuddesdon Coll 73. **d** 75 **p** 76. C Tettenhall Regis *Lich* 75-79; C Uttoxeter w Bramshall 79-82; R Norton Canes 82-89; TR Rugeley from 89. *The Rectory, 20 Church Street, Rugeley, Staffs WS15 2AB* Rugeley (01889) 582149

NEWMAN, Paul Anthony. b 48. Lon Univ BSc70 Leeds Univ DipTh75. Coll of Resurr Mirfield 73. **d** 76 **p** 77. C Catford St Laur *S'wark* 76-81; TV Grays All SS *Chelmsf* 81-83; TV Lt Thurrock St Mary 81-83; W Ham Adnry Youth Chapl 83-87; P-in-c Forest Gate All SS 83-89; V 89-91; Dep Chapl HM Pris Wormwood Scrubs 91-92; Chapl HM Pris Downview from 92. *HM Prison Downview, Sutton Lane, Sutton, Surrey SM2 5PD* 0181-770 7500 Fax 770 7673

NEWMAN, Richard David. b 38. BNC Ox BA60 MA63. Lich Th Coll 60. **d** 62 **p** 63. C E Grinstead St Swithun *Chich* 62-66; C Gt Grimsby St Jas *Linc* 66-69; C Gt Grimsby St Mary and St Jas 69-73; TV 73-74; V St Nicholas at Wade w Sarre *Cant* 74-75; P-in-c Chislet w Hoath 74-75; V St Nicholas at Wade w Sarre

and Chislet w Hoath 75-81; V S Norwood H Innocents 81-84; V S Norwood H Innocents *S'wark* from 85. *Holy Innocents' Vicarage, 192A Selhurst Road, London SE25 6XX* 0181-653 2063

NEWNHAM, Eric Robert. b 43. Sarum & Wells Th Coll 70. **d** 75 **p** 76. Hon C Blackheath Ascension *S'wark* from 75. *27 Morden Hill, London SE13 7NN* 0181-692 6507 or 691 6559

NEWNS, Donald Frederick. b 07. St Aid Birkenhead 34. **d** 37 **p** 38. R Litcham w Kempston w E and W Lexham *Nor* 61-72; rtd 73. *Lexham, 2 Walkergate, Alnwick, Northd NE66 1NB* Alnwick (01665) 602872

NEWPORT, Derek James. b 39. Acadia Univ (NS) BA82 MEd84. Sarum & Wells Th Coll 74. **d** 76 **p** 77. C Tavistock and Gulworthy *Ex* 76-78; Canada 78-86; V Malborough w S Huish, W Alvington and Churchstow *Ex* from 86. *The Vicarage, Malborough, Kingsbridge, Devon TQ7 3RR* Kingsbridge (01548) 561234

NEWPORT, Archdeacon of. *See* TYTE, Ven Keith Arthur Edwin

NEWSAM, Peter William. b 62. Called to the Bar (Gray's Inn) 84 Ex Univ LLB83. St Steph Ho Ox 85. **d** 88 **p** 89. C Whitleigh *Ex* 88-91; C-in-c Middleton-on-Sea CD *Chich* from 91. *St Nicholas House, 106 Elmer Road, Middleton-on-Sea, Bognor Regis, W Sussex PO22 6LJ* Bognor Regis (01243) 586348

NEWSOME, David Ellis. b 55. St Jo Coll Dur BA77. Westcott Ho Cam 80. **d** 82 **p** 83. C Finchley St Mary *Lon* 82-85; C Fulham All SS 85-87; Bp's Dom Chapl *Birm* 87-91; V Gravelly Hill from 91; P-in-c Stockland Green from 93; RD Aston from 95. *All Saints' Vicarage, Broomfield Road, Birmingham B23 7QA* 0121-373 0730

NEWSOME, John Keith. b 49. Mert Coll Ox BA73 MA76. Ripon Coll Cuddesdon 73. **d** 76 **p** 77. C Bywell St Pet *Newc* 76-78; C Berwick H Trin 78-82; Chapl Bonn w Cologne *Eur* 86-93; Chapl Hamburg from 93. *Beim Grunen Jager 16, 2000 Hamburg 36, Germany* Hamburg (40) 439-2334

NEWSON, John David. b 32. MIAAP85 MAJA85 Southn Univ BSc53 PhD57. Cuddesdon Coll 64. **d** 65 **p** 66. Hon C Cant All SS *Cant* 65-77; Lect Ch Ch Coll Cant 65-80. *Address temp unknown*

NEWSTEAD, Dominic Gerald. b 65. Wycliffe Hall Ox BTh95. **d** 95. C Windlesham *Guildf* from 95. *c/o The Rectory, Windlesham, Surrey GU20 6AA*

NEWSUM, Alfred Turner Paul. b 28. Coll of Resurr Mirfield 52. **d** 53 **p** 54. P-in-c Small Heath St Greg *Birm* 68-78; V Birm St Aid Small Heath 72-80; V Stockland Green 80-93; rtd 93. *Ty Offeiriad, 2 Almond Drive, Pentwyn, Cardiff CF2 7HD*

NEWTH, Barry Wilfred. b 33. Bris Univ BA56. ALCD58. **d** 58 **p** 59. C Upton (or Overchurch) *Ches* 58-62; C Kimberworth *Sheff* 62-63; V Clifton *Man* 63-72; V Radcliffe St Thos 72-74; V Radcliffe St Thos and St Jo 74-81; R Heaton Mersey 81-86; V Kirkby Malham *Bradf* 86-87; P-in-c Coniston Cold 86-87; V Kirkby-in-Malhamdale w Coniston Cold from 87. *The Vicarage, Kirkby Malham, Skipton, N Yorkshire BD23 4BS* Airton (01729) 830215

NEWTH, Canon Frederick John. b 07. Keble Coll Ox BA28 MA35. Cuddesdon Coll 28. **d** 30 **p** 31. S Africa 50-83; Adn Heidelberg 57-61; rtd 68; Hon Can Johannesburg 68-83. *Lot 4, Beckmans Road, Tewantin, Queensland, Australia 4565* Tewantin (74) 740200

NEWTON, Miss Ann. b 46. Trin Coll Bris 75. **d** 87 **p** 94. Par Dn Rothley *Leic* 87-91; Par Dn Becontree St Mary *Chelmsf* 91-94; C from 94. *19 Bosworth Road, Dagenham, Essex RM10 7NU* 0181-593 6780

NEWTON, Barrie Arthur. b 38. Dur Univ BA61. Wells Th Coll 61. **d** 63 **p** 64. C Walton St Mary *Liv* 63-67; C N Lynn w St Marg and St Nic *Nor* 67-69; Chapl Asst The Lon Hosp (Whitechapel) 69-71; Chapl K Coll Hosp Lon 72-77; P-in-c Bishops Sutton w Stowey *B & W* 77-81; P-in-c Compton Martin w Ubley 79-81; P-in-c Bridgwater St Jo w Chedzoy 81-83; Chapl St Mary's Hosp Praed Street Lon from 83. *St Mary's Hospital, Praed Street, London W2 1NY* 0171-725 6666 or 725 1508

NEWTON, Brian Karl. b 30. Keble Coll Ox BA55 MA59. Wells Th Coll 56. **d** 58 **p** 59. Trinidad and Tobago 71-77; Gen Ed USPG 69-71; P-in-c Gt Coates *Linc* 77; TV Gt and Lt Coates w Bradley 78-88; V Burgh le Marsh 88-94; R Bratoft w Irby-in-the-Marsh 88-94; V Orby 88-94; R Welton-le-Marsh w Gunby 88-94; rtd 94. *27 Somersby Way, Boston, Lincs PE21 9PQ* Boston (01205) 362433

NEWTON, Canon Christopher Wynne. b 25. Trin Hall Cam BA46. Westcott Ho Cam 48. **d** 50 **p** 51. TR Hemel Hempstead *St Alb* 66-72; RD Milton Keynes *Ox* 72-77; TV Swan 78-84; RD Claydon 78-84; Dioc Ecum Officer 79-84; Hon Can Ch Ch 80-83; P-in-c Lt Gaddesden *St Alb* 84-86; rtd 86; Perm to Offic *St Alb* from 86. *24 Slade Court, Watling Street, Radlet, Herts WD7 7BT* Radlett (01923) 859131

NEWTON, David Ernest. b 42. Sarum & Wells Th Coll 72. **d** 74 **p** 75. C Wigan All SS *Liv* 74-80; VC York Minster *York* 80-85; R Ampleforth w Oswaldkirk 85-86; P-in-c E Gilling 85-86; R Ampleforth and Oswaldkirk and Gilling E from 86; RD Helmsley from 94. *The Rectory, Ampleforth, York YO6 4DU* Ampleforth (01439) 788264

NEWTON, Derek. b 50. Sunderland Poly HND72. NE Ord Course 89. **d** 92 **p** 93. NSM Houghton le Spring *Dur* from 92. *Pinelodge, Warwick Drive, Houghton le Spring, Tyne & Wear DH5 8JR* 0191-584 9169

NEWTON, Derek Lewis. b 14. K Coll Lon BA36. Wycliffe Hall Ox 54. **d** 55 **p** 56. Nigeria 58-78; C Woodford St Mary w St Phil and St Jas *Chelmsf* 78-85; rtd 85; Perm to Offic *Chelmsf* from 85. *13 Dorcester Court, Buckingham Road, London E18 2NG* 0181-505 8157

NEWTON, George Peter Howgill. b 62. Pemb Coll Cam BA84 MA88. Oak Hill Th Coll BA93. **d** 93 **p** 94. C Blackpool St Thos *Blackb* from 93. *8 Collingwood Avenue, Blackpool FY3 8BZ* Blackpool (01253) 302679

NEWTON, Gerald Blamire. b 30. Lich Th Coll. **d** 69 **p** 70. C Leeds Halton St Wilfrid *Ripon* 69-73; C Gt Yarmouth *Nor* 73-74; P-in-c Cattistock w Chilfrome and Rampisham w Wraxall *Sarum* 74-77; V Coney Hill *Glouc* 77-79; V Bryneglwys and Llandegla *St As* 79-80; R Llandegla and Bryneglwys and Llanarmon-yn-Ial 80-86; P-in-c Burythorpe, Acklam and Leavening w Westow *York* 86-95; rtd 95. *9 Ropery Walk, Malton, N Yorkshire YO17 0JS* Burythorpe (01653) 692084

NEWTON, Graham Hayden. b 47. AKC69. St Aug Coll Cant 70. **d** 70 **p** 71. C St Mary-at-Lambeth *S'wark* 70-73; TV Catford (Southend) and Downham 73-78; P-in-c Porthill *Lich* 78-79; TV Wolstanton 79-86; V Stevenage H Trin *St Alb* from 86. *Holy Trinity Vicarage, 18 Letchmore Road, Stevenage, Herts SG1 3JD* Stevenage (01438) 353229

NEWTON, John. b 39. AKC65. **d** 66 **p** 67. C Whipton *Ex* 66-68; C Plympton St Mary 68-74; V Broadwoodwidger 74-81; P-in-c Kelly w Bradstone 74-81; R Lifton 74-81; Chapl All Hallows Sch Rousdon from 81; Lic to Offic *Ex* from 81. *Home Farm, Allhallows School, Rousdon, Lyme Regis, Dorset DT7 3RA* Seaton (01297) 21606

NEWTON, John Richard. b 25. FBIM. St Jo Coll Dur 76 Cranmer Hall Dur. **d** 78 **p** 79. C Cottingham *York* 78-80; R Beeford w Frodingham and Foston 80-86; R Todwick *Sheff* 86-92; rtd 92; Perm to Offic *Linc* from 92. *Quiet Corner, 12 Pelham Close, Sudbrooke, Lincoln LN2 2SQ* Lincoln (01522) 595123

NEWTON, Canon Keith. b 52. K Coll Lon BD73 AKC73 Ch Ch Coll Cant PGCE75. St Aug Coll Cant 74. **d** 75 **p** 76. C Gt Ilford St Mary *Chelmsf* 75-78; TV Wimbledon *S'wark* 78-85; Malawi 85-91; Dean Blantyre 86-91; Can S Malawi from 86; P-in-c Knowle *Bris* 91-93; V Knowle H Nativity from 93. *Holy Nativity Vicarage, 41 Lilymead Avenue, Bristol BS4 2BY* Bristol (0117) 977 4260

NEWTON, Louis Kalbfield. b 44. N Texas State Univ BA73. Westcott Ho Cam CTM93. **d** 93 **p** 94. C Walthamstow St Pet *Chelmsf* from 93. *1 Beech Court, Bisterne Avenue, London E17 3QX* 0181-521 3333

NEWTON, Nigel Ernest Hartley. b 38. St Jo Coll Nottm CertCS87. **d** 89 **p** 90. Hon C Largs *Glas* 89-92; Asst Chapl Ashbourne Home Largs 89-92; P-in-c Eyemouth *Edin* 92-95; Chapl Miss to Seamen from 92; P-in-c Challoch w Newton Stewart *Glas* from 95. *All Saints Rectory, Challoch, Newton Stuart, Wigtownshire DG8 6RB* Newton Stuart (01671) 2107

NEWTON, Miss Pauline Dorothy. b 48. Southn Univ BA70 PGCE71 MPhil79. Sarum Th Coll 79. **dss** 82 **d** 87 **p** 94. Bemerton *Sarum* 82-87; Hon Par Dn 87-94; C from 94; Perm to Offic *Worc* from 86; Dep Hd Malvern Girls' Coll Worcs from 86. *13 Highbury Avenue, Salisbury SP2 7EX* Salisbury (01722) 325707

NEWTON, Peter. b 35. Sarum & Wells Th Coll 74. **d** 77 **p** 78. Hon C Reading St Barn *Ox* 77-79; C Bracknell 79-83; TV 83-85; V Knowl Hill w Littlewick from 85. *St Peter's Vicarage, Knowl Hill, Reading RG10 9YD* Littlewick Green (01628) 822732

NEWTON, Peter. b 39. St Jo Coll Nottm 73. **d** 75 **p** 76. C Porchester *S'well* 75-79; R Wilford from 79. *The Rectory, Main Road, Wilford, Nottingham NG11 7AJ* Nottingham (0115) 981 5661

NEWTON, Raymond David. b 43. K Coll Lon BSc65. Linc Th Coll 65. **d** 67 **p** 68. C Ipswich St Matt *St E* 67-71; C E w W Barkwith *Linc* 71-74; R Chelmondiston w Harkstead *St E* 74-78; R Chelmondiston w Harkstead and Shotley w Erwarton 78-91; R Chelmondiston and Erwarton w Harkstead from 91. *The Rectory, Chelmondiston, Ipswich IP9 1HY* Woolverstone (01473) 780214

NEWTON, Richard. b 47. Lon Univ DipTh72. Trin Coll Bris 72. **d** 73 **p** 74. C Fareham St Jo *Portsm* 73-76; C Cheltenham St Mark *Glouc* 76-83; P-in-c Malvern St Andr *Worc* 83-95; TR Kingswood *Bris* from 95. *Holy Trinity Vicarage, High Street, Kingswood, Bristol BS15 4AD* Bristol (0117) 967 3627

NEWTON, Richard John Christopher. b 60. Bris Univ BSc81. Qu Coll Birm 85. **d** 88 **p** 89. C Bris Ch the Servant Stockwood *Bris* 88-92; C Dorking w Ranmore *Guildf* from 92. *79 Ashcombe Road, Dorking, Surrey RH4 1LX* Dorking (01306) 882065

NEWTON, Robert Keith. b 61. Man Univ BA83. St Steph Ho Ox 86. **d** 89 **p** 90. C Ludlow *Heref* 89-91; Egypt from 92. *Flat 17, 15 Ahmed Sabri, Zamalek, Cairo, Egypt*

NEWTON, William (Bill). b 51. Chich Th Coll 86. **d** 88 **p** 89. C Leigh-on-Sea St Marg *Chelmsf* 88-92; V Belhus Park 92-94. *35 Elmdon Road, South Ockendon, Essex RM15 5BF* South Ockendon (01708) 671335

NEWTON, Canon William Ronald. b 12. Birm Univ BA43. Westcott Ho Cam 41. **d** 43 **p** 44. Hon Can Truro Cathl *Truro* 71-83; V Penzance St Mary w St Paul 73-82; rtd 82; Perm to Offic *Chich* from 83. *52 Rutland Court, New Church Road, Hove, E Sussex BN3 4BB* Brighton (01273) 773422

NEY, Ven Reginald Basil. b 22. OBE78. ARCM55. Lich Th Coll 41. **d** 45 **p** 46. Chapl Madrid *Eur* 56-87; Can Gib Cathl 62-87; Adn Gib 63-87; rtd 87. *Apartmento 24, Bloque A-3, Colonia Ducal, Playa de Gandia, Valencia, Spain*

NIAS, John Charles Somerset. b 18. Worc Coll Ox BA40 MA45 BD46. Wells Th Coll 40. **d** 41 **p** 42. V Finstock and Fawler *Ox* 56-83; V Ramsden 56-83; Dir of Studies Cen Readers' Bd 63-73; rtd 83; Perm to Offic *Win* from 83; Perm to Offic *Portsm* from 83; Perm to Offic *Chich* from 88. *29 Southleigh Road, Warblington, Havant, Hants PO9 2QG* Havant (01705) 453186

NIBLETT, David John Morton. b 24. Wells Th Coll 51. **d** 54 **p** 55. V Barnstaple St Pet w H Trin *Ex* 65-75; V S Brent 75-90; rtd 90; Perm to Offic *B & W* from 90. *2 Beretun Orchard, Glastonbury, Somerset BA6 8AX* Glastonbury (01458) 833101

NICE, John Edmund. b 51. Univ of Wales (Ban) BA73. Coll of Resurr Mirfield 74. **d** 76 **p** 77. C Oxton *Ches* 76-79; C Liscard St Mary w St Columba 79-82; V Latchford St Jas 82-92; R Holyhead w Rhoscolyn w Llanfair-yn-Neubwll *Ban* from 92. *The Rectory, Newry Street, Holyhead, Anglesey, Gwynedd LL65 1HS* Holyhead (01407) 763001

NICHOL, William David. b 58. Hull Univ BA84. Ridley Hall Cam 84. **d** 87 **p** 88. C Hull Newland St Jo *York* 87-90; C Kirk Ella 90-92; TV from 92. *2A Chestnut Avenue, Willerby, Hull HU10 6PA* Hull (01482) 658974

NICHOLAS, Canon Arnold Frederick. b 34. Jes Coll Cam BA58 MA62. Ely Th Coll 58. **d** 60 **p** 61. C Wisbech St Aug *Ely* 60-63; P-in-c Lt Massingham *Nor* 63-65; Youth Chapl 63-67; Chapl Bp Otter Coll Chich 67-70; R Westbourne *Chich* 70-76; V Stansted 70-76; Can and Preb Chich Cathl 76-82; RD Chich 76-80; P-in-c Chich St Pet 76-81; V Chich St Paul and St Bart 80-81; V Chich St Paul and St Pet 81-82; V Wisbech SS Pet and Paul *Ely* 82-90; RD Wisbech 82-90; V Fordham St Pet 90-95; P-in-c Kennett 90-95. *Westbourne Cottage, 6 Gold's Pightle, Ringstead, Hunstanton, Norfolk PE36 5LD*

NICHOLAS, Brian Arthur. b 19. St Edm Hall Ox BA47 MA53. Wycliffe Hall Ox 62. **d** 64 **p** 65. V Chudleigh Knighton *Ex* 69-76; V Ex St Mark 76-84; rtd 84; Perm to Offic *Ex* from 84. *Windyridge, 4 Little Johns Cross Hill, Exeter EX2 9PJ* Exeter (01392) 219222

NICHOLAS, Ernest Milton. b 25. ACP50 Newc Univ DipAdEd69 Lanc Univ MA78. NE Ord Course 85. **d** 86 **p** 87. NSM Hexham *Newc* from 86. *Hillside, Eilansgate, Hexham, Northd NE46 3EW* Hexham (01434) 603609

NICHOLAS, Herbert Llewellyn. b 19. St D Coll Lamp 51. **d** 53 **p** 54. V Pontypridd St Matt *Llan* 65-89; rtd 89; Perm to Offic *Llan* from 89. *47 Meadow Crescent, Tonteg, Pontypridd, M Glam CF38 1NL* Pontypridd (01443) 206563

NICHOLAS, Malcolm Keith. b 46. FIMLS71 Open Univ BA79. S Dios Minl Tr Scheme 81. **d** 84 **p** 85. NSM Gatcombe *Portsm* 84-92; NSM Shorwell w Kingston 88-92; C Hartley Wintney, Elvetham, Winchfield etc *Win* from 92. *40 Pool Road, Hartley Wintney, Basingstoke, Hants RG27 8RD* Hartley Wintney (01252) 843602

NICHOLAS, Maurice Lloyd. b 30. Kelham Th Coll 54. **d** 58 **p** 59. Chapl RADD 65-75; C Northolt St Mary *Lon* 75-85; rtd 85; Hon C Upper Teddington SS Pet and Paul *Lon* 85-90; Hon C Teddington SS Pet and Paul and Fulwell from 90. *58 Elton Close, Hampton Wick, Kingston-upon-Thames, Surrey KT1 4EE* 0181-977 9340

NICHOLAS, Paul James. b 51. Univ of Wales (Lamp) DipTh73 BA. Coll of Resurr Mirfield 73. **d** 74 **p** 75. C Llanelli *St D* 74-78; C Roath St Marg *Llan* 78-84; P-in-c Leic St Pet *Leic* 84-87; V Shard End *Birm* from 87. *The Vicarage, 47 Shustoke Road, Birmingham B34 7BA* 0121-747 3299

NICHOLL, Joseph Edward Chancellor. b 20. MC45. Qu Coll Cam BA46 MA48. Ridley Hall Cam. d 48 p 49. Asst Chapl Stowe Sch Bucks 62-72; Chapl 72-75; P-in-c Stowe Ox 75-81; R Angmering Chich 82-85; rtd 85; Perm to Offic Chich from 86. *24 Rufus Close, Lewes, E Sussex BN7 1BG* Lewes (01273) 479164

NICHOLLS, Alan Fryer. b 26. Univ Coll Ex BA50. Sarum Th Coll 50. d 52 p 53. Asst Chapl and Ho Master Woodbridge Sch Suffolk 66-86; TV Bruton and Distr *B & W* 86-92; rtd 92. *9 Southover, Wells, Somerset BA5 1UG* Wells (01749) 677513

NICHOLLS, Brian Albert. b 39. LBIPP LMPA. St Jo Coll Nottm CertCS84 W Midl Minl Tr Course 90. d 93 p 94. NSM Oakham, Hambleton, Egleton, Braunston and Brooke *Pet* from 93. *10 Uppingham Road, Oakham, Leics LE15 6JD* Oakham (01572) 757884

NICHOLLS, David Gwyn. b 36. Lon Univ BSc57 K Coll Cam PhD62 Yale Univ STM62 Ox Univ MA73. Chich Th Coll 61. d 62 p 63. C Bloomsbury St Geo w St Jo *Lon* 62-66; Trinidad and Tobago 66-73; Chapl Lect and Fell Ex Coll Ox 73-78; P-in-c Littlemore *Ox* 78-86; V from 86. *The Vicarage, St Nicholas' Road, Oxford OX4 4PP* Oxford (01865) 749939

✠**NICHOLLS, Rt Rev John (Jack).** b 43. AKC66. d 67 p 68 c 90. C Salford St Clem Ordsall *Man* 67-69; C Langley All SS and Martyrs 69-72; V 72-78; Dir Past Th Coll of Resurr Mirfield 78-83; Lic to Offic *Wakef* 79-83; Can Res Man Cathl *Man* 83-90; Suff Bp Lanc *Blackb* from 90. *Wheatfield, 7 Dallas Road, Lancaster LA1 1TN* Lancaster (01524) 32897 Fax 66095

NICHOLLS, John Gervase. b 15. Qu Coll Cam BA38 MA42. Lon Coll of Div 38. d 39 p 40. Cyprus 67-75; R Ipswich St Clem w H Trin *St E* 75-81; rtd 81; P-in-c Wilby w Brundish *St E* 81-84; Perm to Offic *Chich* 85-88; Perm to Offic *Nor* from 88. *17 Moorfield Road, Mattishall, Dereham, Norfolk NR20 3NZ* Dereham (01362) 858501

NICHOLLS, Leonard Samuel. b 07. Ex Coll Ox BA29 MA34. Bps' Coll Cheshunt 30. d 32 p 33. R Etwall w Egginton *Derby* 68-71; rtd 71. *Old Post House, Framfield, Uckfield, E Sussex TN22 5PN* Framfield (01825) 890311

NICHOLLS, Mark Richard. b 60. LSE BSc82 Leeds Univ BA88. Coll of Resurr Mirfield 86. d 89 p 90. C Warrington St Elphin *Liv* 89-92; V Wigan St Andr from 92. *St Andrew's Vicarage, 3A Mort Street, Wigan, Lancs WN6 7AU* Wigan (01942) 43514

NICHOLLS, Mark Simon. b 57. Down Coll Cam MA79. Ripon Coll Cuddesdon 92. d 94 p 95. C Farnham *Guildf* from 94. *23 Hazell Road, Farnham, Surrey GU9 7BW* Farnham (01252) 714521

NICHOLLS, Michael Stanley. b 34. AKC59. St Boniface Warminster 59. d 60 p 61. C Torquay St Martin Barton CD *Ex* 60-63; C E Grinstead St Mary *Chich* 63-66; C-in-c Salfords CD *S'wark* 66-68; V Salfords 68-75; V Tunbridge Wells St Barn Roch from 75. *The Vicarage, 31 Lansdowne Road, Tunbridge Wells, Kent TN1 2NQ* Tunbridge Wells (01892) 523609

NICHOLLS, Neil David Raymond. b 65. Univ Coll Lon BA86. Wycliffe Hall Ox BA90. d 91 p 92. C Westmr St Steph w St Jo *Lon* 91-94; C Islington St Mary from 94. *108 Liverpool Road, London N1 0RE* 0171-226 0854

NICHOLLS, Roy Meacham. b 29. CEng MIMechE62. Glouc Sch of Min 85. d 88 p 89. NSM Pershore w Pinvin, Wick and Birlingham *Worc* 88-94; Perm to Offic from 94. *5 Paddock Close, Pershore, Worcs WR10 1HJ* Pershore (01386) 553508

NICHOLLS, Stanley Charles. b 28. St Chad's Coll Dur BA53. Bps' Coll Cheshunt 53. d 54 p 55. V Ruswarp w Sneaton *York* 68-78; V Kirkby-in-Cleveland 78-88; rtd 88. *1 Brecks Close, Wigginton, York YO3 3TW* York (01904) 765114

✠**NICHOLLS, Rt Rev Vernon Sampson.** b 17. Clifton Th Coll 38. d 41 p 41 c 74. C Bedminster Down *Bris* 41-42; C Liskeard w St Keyne *Truro* 42-44; CF (EC) 44-46; V Meopham *Roch* 46-56; RD Cobham 54-56; V Walsall *Lich* 56-67; RD Walsall 56-67; Chapl Walsall Gen Hosp 56-67; Preb Lich Cathl *Lich* 64-67; Adn Birm 67-74; Dean St German's Cathl *S & M* 74-83; Bp *S & M* 74-83; rtd 83; Asst Bp Cov from 83. *Apartment 18, Lucy's Mill, Mill Lane, Stratford-upon-Avon, Warks CV37 6DE* Stratford-upon-Avon (01789) 294478

NICHOLS, Albert Percival. b 18. Tyndale Hall Bris. d 57 p 57. P-in-c Chiselborough w W Chinnock *B & W* 60-70; R E Chinnock 60-77; R Middle Chinnock 60-70; R Middle w W Chinnock 70-78; RD Martock 75-78; P-in-c Norton sub Hamdon w Chiselborough 77-78; R Norton sub Hamdon, W Chinnock, Chiselborough etc 78-86; rtd 86; Perm to Offic *B & W* from 86; Perm to Offic *Sarum* from 86. *53 East Street, Beaminster, Dorset DT8 3DS* Beaminster (01308) 862871

NICHOLS, Dennis Harry. b 25. Kelham Th Coll 47. d 52 p 53. V Bury H Trin *Man* 61-81; V St Gluvias *Truro* 81-90; RD Carnmarth S 85-90; rtd 90. *11 Marlborough Crescent, Falmouth, Cornwall TR11 2RJ* Falmouth (01326) 312243

NICHOLS, Derek Edward. b 33. Lon Univ BD58 Monash Univ Aus DipEd82. Chich Th Coll 73. d 72 p 73. C S w N Hayling

Portsm 73-75; Perm to Offic *Linc* 75-77; Australia from 80; Prec Gippsland from 92. *89 Market Street, Sale, Victoria, Australia 3850* Moe (51) 442635

NICHOLS, Canon Raymond Maurice. b 22. ALCD53. d 53 p 54. Home Sec SPCK 64-71; Overseas Sec 67-73; Publisher 73-74; P-in-c Dorchester *Ox* 74-78; P-in-c Newington 77-78; TR Dorchester 78-87; V Warborough 78-87; rtd 87. *12 Abbey Court, Cerne Abbas, Dorchester, Dorset DT2 7JH* Cerne Abbas (01300) 341456

NICHOLSON, Brian Warburton. b 44. St Jo Coll Nottm 70 Lon Coll of Div ALCD73 LTh74. d 73 p 74. C Canford Magna *Sarum* 73-77; C E Twickenham St Steph *Lon* 77-80; V Colchester St Jo *Chelmsf* from 80. *St John's Vicarage, Evergreen Drive, Colchester CO4 4HU* Colchester (01206) 843232

NICHOLSON, Miss Clare. b 46. RMN80 Keele Univ BA70 CertEd70 Lon Univ DN80. St Jo Coll Nottm DPS85. dss 85 d 87 p 94. Bletchley *Ox* 85-87; Par Dn 87-89; Par Dn Milton Keynes 89-90; Par Dn Prestwood and Gt Hampden 90-94; C from 94. *28 St Peter's Close, Prestwood, Great Missenden, Bucks HP16 9ET* Great Missenden (01494) 866351

NICHOLSON, David. b 57. Sarum & Wells Th Coll 80. d 83 p 84. C Trevethin *Mon* 83-85; C Ebbw Vale 85-87; V Newport St Steph and H Trin 87-95; Hon Chapl Miss to Seamen from 87; V Abertillery *Mon* from 95. *The Vicarage, Church Street, Abertillery, Gwent NP3 1DA* Abertillery (01495) 212246

NICHOLSON, Canon Donald. b 10. St Chad's Coll Dur BA32 DipTh34 MA35. d 33 p 34. Hon Can St Mary's Cathl *Edin* 64-84; Chapl Stacklands Retreat Ho W Kingsdown 71-75; rtd 75; Perm to Offic *Edin* from 75; Perm to Offic *Mor* from 80; Chapl St Marg Convent Aber from 80; Hon Can St Andr Cathl *Ab* from 84. *The Chaplaincy, St Margaret's Convent, 17 Spital, Aberdeen AB2 3HT* Aberdeen (01224) 638407

NICHOLSON, Dorothy Ann. b 40. S'wark Ord Course 81. dss 84 d 87 p 94. Carshalton Beeches *S'wark* 84-87; Par Dn 87-88; Par Dn Brixton Rd Ch Ch 88-89; C Malden St Jo 89-95; V Balham St Mary and St Jo from 95. *St Mary's Vicarage, 35 Elmsfield Road, London SW17 8AG* 0181-673 1188

NICHOLSON, Dr Ernest Wilson. b 38. TCD BA60 MA64 Glas Univ PhD64 Cam Univ BD71 DD78. Westcott Ho Cam 69. d 69 p 70. Lect Div Cam Univ 67-79; Fell Chapl and Dir of Th Studies Pemb Coll Cam 69-79; Dean 73-79; Prof of Interpr of H Scripture Or Coll Ox 79-90; Provost from 90; Lic to Offic *Ox* from 84. *The Provost's Lodgings, Oriel College, Oxford OX1 4EW* Oxford (01865) 276533

NICHOLSON, Harold Sydney Leonard. b 35. Leic Univ HNC65 Garnett Coll Lon PGCE67 Open Univ BA77. S'wark Ord Course DipRS86 Oak Hill NSM Course 92. d 94 p 95. NSM Stanwell *Lon* from 94. *7 Academy Court, Fordbridge Road, Sunbury-on-Thames, Middx TW16 6AN* Sunbury-on-Thames (01932) 787690

NICHOLSON, John Paul. b 57. Sarum Th Coll. d 82 p 83. C Kirkby *Liv* 82-85; TV Speke St Aid from 85. *62 East Millwood Road, Speke, Liverpool L24 6SQ* 0151-425 4398

NICHOLSON, Joseph. b 14. LRAM45 St Jo Coll Dur BA35 DipTh37 MA38. d 37 p 38. Asst Master Penhill Sec Sch Swindon 69-75; Perm to Offic *Bris* 69-75; Perm to Offic *Mon* 75-77; P-in-c Blaenavon w Capel Newydd 77-79; rtd 79. *52 Seacroft Road, Mablethorpe, Lincs LN12 2DJ* Mablethorpe (01507) 477574

NICHOLSON, Kevin Smith. b 47. CQSW76. Edin Th Coll 89. d 91 p 92. C Burntisland *St And* from 91; C W Fife Team Min from 91. *Lovedale Cottage, Abbotsford Road, Lochore, Lochgelly, Fife KY5 8DT* Burntisland (01592) 861331

NICHOLSON, Nigel Patrick. b 46. Sarum & Wells Th Coll 72. d 75 p 76. C Farnham *Guildf* 75-78; C Worplesdon 78-81; P-in-c Compton 81-85; R Compton w Shackleford and Peper Harow 85-89; R Cranleigh from 89. *The Rectory, High Street, Cranleigh, Surrey GU6 8AS* Cranleigh (01483) 273620

NICHOLSON, Miss Pamela Elizabeth. b 47. Ripon Coll Cuddesdon. d 92 p 94. C Balsall Heath St Paul *Birm* 92-95; V Smethwick St Matt w St Chad from 95. *1 St Matthew's Road, Smethwick, Warley, W Midlands B66 3TN* 0121-558 1653

NICHOLSON, Canon Peter Charles. b 25. OBE92. Lambeth Hon MA89 Chich Th Coll 57. d 59 p 60. V Wroxham w Hoveton *Nor* 67-74; V Lyme Regis *Sarum* 74-80; Gen Sec St Luke's Hosp for the Clergy 80-93; NSM Harlington *Lon* 80-87; Hon PV S'wark Cathl *S'wark* from 87; Can and Preb Chich Cathl *Chich* 89-93; rtd 93. *St Luke's Cottage, 13 Brearley Close, Uxbridge, Middx UB8 1JJ* Uxbridge (01895) 233522

NICHOLSON, Peter Charles. b 44. Oak Hill Th Coll 74. d 76 p 77. C Croydon Ch Ch Broad Green *Cant* 76-80; C Gt Baddow *Chelmsf* 80-88; TV from 88. *42 Riffams Drive, Great Baddow, Chelmsford CM2 7QH* Chelmsford (01245) 471516

NICHOLSON, Rodney. b 45. Mert Coll Ox BA68 MA71. Ridley Hall Cam 69. d 72 p 73. C Colne St Bart *Blackb* 72-75; C

Blackpool St Jo 75-78; V Ewood 78-90; V Clitheroe St Paul Low Moor from 90. *The Vicarage, St Paul's Street, Clitheroe, Lancs BB7 2LS* Clitheroe (01200) 22418

NICHOLSON, Roland. b 40. Sarum & Wells Th Coll 72. **d** 74 **p** 75. C Morecambe St Barn *Blackb* 74-78; V Feniscliffe 78-90; V Sabden and Pendleton from 90. *St Nicholas's Vicarage, Westley Street, Sabden, Lancs BB7 9EH* Burnley (01282) 771384

NICHOLSON, Trevor Parry. b 35. St Edm Hall Ox BA58 MA. Wycliffe Hall Ox 58. **d** 60 **p** 61. C Eastbourne Ch Ch *Chich* 60-63; C Ifield 63-67; Asst Youth Chapl *Win* 67-73; Chapl Shoreham Gr Sch 73-78; P-in-c Capel *Guildf* 78-85; V 85-90; Chapl Qu Anne's Sch Caversham from 90. *2 Henley Road, Caversham, Reading RG4 0DY* Reading (01734) 474191 or 471582

NICHOLSON, Miss Velda Christine. b 44. CertEd65. Birm Bible Inst DipTh69 Cranmer Hall Dur 81. **dss** 82 **d** 87 **p** 94. GD and Lt Driffield *York* 82-86; Newby 86-87; Par Dn 87-88; TD Cramlington *Newc* 88-94; TV from 94. *9 Megstone Avenue, Cramlington, Northd NE23 6TU* Cramlington (01670) 732681

NICHOLSON, William Surtees. b 15. Coll of Resurr Mirfield 39. **d** 41 **p** 42. R Ashington *Chich* 61-74; V Bamburgh and Lucker *Newc* 74-81; rtd 81. *Pepperclose Cottage, The Wynding, Bamburgh, Northd NE69 7DB* Bamburgh (016684) 437

NICKALLS, Frederick William (Fred). b 13. Oak Hill Th Coll 49. **d** 51 **p** 52. R Nailsea H Trin *B & W* 67-78; rtd 78; Perm to Offic *Win* 82-90. *34 Suffolk Place, Woodbridge, Suffolk IP12 1XB* Woodbridge (01394) 380539

NICKLESS, Christopher John (Chris). b 58. Univ of Wales BA79. Coll of Resurr Mirfield 79. **d** 81 **p** 82. C Bassaleg *Mon* 81-85; TV Ebbw Vale 85-93; V Newport St Teilo from 93. *St Teilo's Vicarage, 1 Aberthaw Road, Newport, Gwent NP9 9NS* Newport (01633) 273593

NICKLESS, Canon Victor George. b 08. Dur Univ BA34 LTh34. Lon Coll of Div 30. **d** 34 **p** 35. R Wrotham *Roch* 63-77; rtd 77. *East Wing, Ford Place, Ford Lane, Wrotham Heath, Sevenoaks, Kent TN15 7SE* West Malling (01732) 844172

NICKLIN, Ivor. b 41. FRSA68 BEd MTh73 PhD76 MA84. Wycliffe Hall Ox. **d** 84 **p** 85. NSM Weaverham *Ches* 84-89; P-in-c Kings Walden *St Alb* 89-91; P-in-c Offley w Lilley 89-91; V King's Walden and Offley w Lilley 91-93; V Basford *Lich* from 93. *211 Basford Park Road, Basford, Newcastle, Staffs ST5 0PG* Newcastle (013967) 619045

NICKOLS-RAWLE, Peter John. b 44. St Luke's Coll Ex CertEd73. Sarum & Wells Th Coll 76. **d** 78 **p** 79. C Ex St Thos *Ex* 78-80; C Ex St Thos and Em 80; C Old Shoreham *Chich* 80-86; C New Shoreham 80-86; P-in-c Donnington 86-90; Chapl RAF 90-92; TV Ottery St Mary, Alfington, W Hill, Tipton etc *Ex* from 92. *The Vicarage, Bendarrock Road, West Hill, Ottery St Mary, Devon EX11 1WW* Ottery St Mary (01404) 812094

NICOL, Ernest. b 25. S'wark Ord Course 71. **d** 74 **p** 75. NSM Hornsey Ch Ch *Lon* 74-75; NSM Hornsey St Geo 76-84; C Hendon Ch Ch 85-90; rtd 90; C Steeton *Bradf* from 90; Asst Chapl Airedale Hosp Bradf from 90. *12 Parkway, Steeton, Keighley, W Yorkshire BD20 6SX* Keighley (01535) 654270

NICOLE, Bruce. b 54. ACIB. Wycliffe Hall Ox 89. **d** 91 **p** 92. C Headley All SS *Guildf* from 91. *7 Windmill Drive, Bordon, Hants GU35 8AL* Headley Down (01428) 714565

NICOLL, Alexander Charles Fiennes. b 34. Lon Univ DipTh66. Lon Coll of Div 66. **d** 68 **p** 69. C Trentham *Lich* 68-71; C Hednesford 72-74; P-in-c Quarnford 74-84; V Longnor 74-84; P-in-c Sheen 80-84; V Longnor, Quarnford and Sheen from 85. *The Vicarage, Longnor, Buxton, Derbyshire SK17 0PA* Longnor (01298) 83316

NICOLL, Miss Angela Olive. b 50. Linc Th Coll 77. **dss** 79 **d** 87 **p** 94. Catford St Laur *S'wark* 79-83; Peckham St Jo w St Andr 83-87; Par Dn 87-88; Par Dn New Addington 88-94; C from 94. *78 Gascoigne Road, Croydon CR0 0NE* Lodge Hill (01689) 848123

NICOLL, George Lorimer. b 23. Local NSM Course 75. **d** 75. NSM Clydebank *Glas* from 75. *19 McKenzie Avenue, Clydebank, Dunbartonshire G81 2AT* 0141-952 5116

NICOLSON, Paul Roderick. b 32. Cuddesdon Coll 65. **d** 67 **p** 68. C Farnham Royal *Ox* 67-70; Lic to Offic *St Alb* 70-82; C Hambleden Valley *Ox* from 82. *The Vicarage, Turville, Henley-on-Thames, Oxon RG9 6QU* Turville Heath (01491) 638240

NIE, Miss Muriel Rose. b 29. St Mich Ho Ox IDC57. **d** 87 **p** 94. NSM Leyton All SS *Chelmsf* from 87. *2 Queens Court, Manor Road, London E10 7HP* 0181-556 0457

NIELSEN, Ronald Marius Boniface. b 09. **d** 51 **p** 52. OSB from 46; Lic to Offic *Ox* from 51. *Elmore Abbey, Speen, Newbury, Berks RG13 1SA* Newbury (01635) 33080

NIGHTINGALE, John Brodie. b 42. Pemb Coll Ox BA64 Bris Univ DSocStuds65 Qu Coll Cam BA67. Westcott Ho Cam 65. **d** 67 **p** 68. C Wythenshawe St Martin *Man* 67-70; Nigeria 70-76; P-in-c Amberley w N Stoke *Chich* 76-79; Adult Educn Adv 76-79; Asst Home Sec Gen Syn Bd for Miss and Unity 80-84; Miss Sec 84-87; P-in-c Wolverton w Norton Lindsey and Langley *Cov* 87-95; Dioc Miss Adv 87-95; V Rowley Regis *Birm* from 95. *St Giles' Vicarage, 192 Hanover Road, Rowley Regis, Warley, W Midlands B65 9EQ* 0121-559 1251

NIGHTINGALE, Mrs Susan (Sue). b 44. Keele Univ BA66 DipSocSc66 Coll of Ripon & York St Jo CertC85. S'wark Ord Course 90. **d** 93 **p** 94. NSM St Giles Cripplegate w St Bart Moor Lane etc *Lon* from 93. *31 Shakespeare Tower, London EC27 8DR* 0171-638 5440

NIGHTINGALE, William Hirst. b 11. ACCS52. St Aug Coll Cant. **d** 61 **p** 63. Ind Chapl *S'wark* 65-76; Hon C Wimbledon 70-81; rtd 82; Perm to Offic *S'wark* from 84. *14 Melbury Gardens, London SW20 0DJ* 0181-946 8361

NIKKEL, Marc Randall. b 50. Fuller Th Sem California MDiv80 Gen Th Sem (NY) STM85. **d** 85 **p** 86. Sudan 81-87; Kenya 88; NSM Edin St Pet *Edin* 89-90; NSM Stoke Newington St Olave *Lon* 91-93. *430 Seven Sisters Road, London N4 2RE* 0181-809 6860

NIMMO, Alexander Emsley. b 53. Aber Univ BD76 Edin Univ MPhil83. Edin Th Coll 76. **d** 78 **p** 79. Prec St Andr Cathl Inverness *Mor* 78-81; P-in-c Stornoway *Arg* 81-83; R 84; R Edin St Mich and All SS *Edin* 84-90; Chapl HM Pris Saughton 87-90; R Aber St Marg *Ab* from 90. *St Margaret's Rectory, Gallowgate, Aberdeen AB1 1EA* Aberdeen (01224) 644969

NIND, Canon Anthony Lindsay. b 26. MBE86. Ball Coll Ox BA50 MA50. Cuddesdon Coll 50. **d** 52 **p** 53. R Langton Matravers *Sarum* 61-70; Brazil 70-75; Chapl Vienna *Eur* 75-80; Adn Switzerland 80-86; Chapl Zurich w St Gallen and Winterthur 80-86; Hon Can Brussels Cathl 81-89; Dean Gib 86-89; rtd 89. *7 Trinity Close, Trinity Lane, Wareham, Dorset BH20 4LL* Wareham (01929) 553434

NIND, Robert William Hampden. b 31. Ball Coll Ox BA54 MA60. Cuddesdon Coll 54. **d** 56 **p** 57. C Spalding *Linc* 56-60; Jamaica 60-67; P-in-c Battersea St Bart *S'wark* 67-70; V Brixton St Matt 70-82; Lic to Offic 82-84 and from 89; Ind Chapl 84-89; Ind Chapl *Ox* from 89. *1 Ivy Crescent, Cippenham Lane, Slough SL1 5DA* Slough (01753) 528131

NINEHAM, Canon Prof Dennis Eric. b 21. Qu Coll Ox BA43 MA46 Cam Univ BD64 Birm Univ Hon DD72. Linc Th Coll 44. **d** 44 **p** 45. Warden Keble Coll Ox 69-79; Hon Can Bris Cathl *Bris* 80-86; Prof Th Bris Univ 80-86; rtd 86; Perm to Offic *Ox* from 87. *4 Wootten Drive, Iffley Turn, Oxford OX4 4DS* Oxford (01865) 715941

NINIS, Ven Richard Betts. b 31. Linc Coll Ox BA53 MA62. Linc Th Coll 53. **d** 55 **p** 56. C Poplar All SS w St Frideswide *Lon* 55-62; V Heref St Martin *Heref* 62-71; V Upper and Lower Bullinghope w Grafton 68-71; R Dewsall w Callow 68-71; Dioc Missr 69-74; Preb Heref Cathl 70-74; Telford Planning Officer *Lich* 70-74; Can Res and Treas Lich Cathl from 74; Adn Stafford 74-80; Adn Lich from 80. *24 The Close, Lichfield, Staffs WS13 7LD* Lichfield (01543) 258813 Fax 419478

NISBETT, Canon Thomas Norman. b 25. OBE91. Codrington Coll Barbados. **d** 62 **p** 63. Barbados 62-64; Bermuda from 65; Hon Can Bermuda Cathl from 81. *PO Box DV 401, Devonshire DV BX, Bermuda* Bermuda (1-809) 236-0537 Fax as telephone

NIXON, Mrs Annette Rose. b 37. K Coll Lon BD58 Newc Univ CertEd73. **d** 88 **p** 94. Dioc Youth Officer *Ox* 84-90; Par Dn Earley St Pet 88-93; Par Dn Olney w Emberton 93-94; C from 94. *4 Oxleys, Olney, Bucks MK46 5PH* Bedford (01234) 241529

NIXON, Canon Bernard Lawrence. b 26. St Jo Coll Dur BA55 DipTh56. **d** 56 **p** 57. C Goole *Sheff* 56-60; Chapl Wm Baker Tech Coll 60-67; V Silsoe *St Alb* 67-82; V Silsoe, Pulloxhill and Flitton from 82; RD Ampthill 75-87; Hon Can St Alb from 79. *The Vicarage, Silsoe, Bedford MK45 4ED* Silsoe (01525) 860438

NIXON, Canon Charles Hunter. b 07. Keble Coll Ox BA30 MA47. Dorchester Miss Coll 31. **d** 33 **p** 34. Hon Can Ely Cathl *Ely* 70-78; R Coveney 73-78; rtd 78; Perm to Offic *Nor* from 78. *23 Cleeves Drive, Walsingham, Norfolk NR22 6EQ* Walsingham (01328) 820310

NIXON, David John. b 59. St Chad's Coll Dur BA81. St Steph Ho Ox 88. **d** 91 **p** 92. C Plymouth St Pet *Ex* 91-94; Chapl Ex Univ from 94. *29 Barnardo Road, Exeter, Devon EX2 4ND* Exeter (01392) 420162

NIXON, Frances (Isobel). b 34. TCD BA62. **d** 94 **p** 95. NSM Rossory *Clogh* from 94. *63 Granshaugh Road, Enniskillen, Co Fermanagh BT92 2BL* Enniskillen (01365) 348723

NIXON, John David. b 38. CEng70 MICE Leeds Univ BSc60. Linc Th Coll 76. **d** 78 **p** 79. C Rugby St Andr *Cov* 78-83; TV 83-86; TV Bicester w Bucknell, Caversfield and Launton *Ox* from 86. *The Vicarage, The Spinney, Launton, Bicester, Oxon OX6 0EP* Bicester (01869) 252377

NIXON, Phillip Edward. b 48. Ch Ch Ox MA73 DPhil73 Trin Coll Cam BA80. Westcott Ho Cam 78. **d** 81 **p** 82. C Leeds Halton St Wilfrid *Ripon* 81-84; V Goring *Ox* 84; V Goring w S Stoke from 84; RD Henley from 94. *The Vicarage, Manor Road, Goring, Reading RG8 9DR* Goring-on-Thames (01491) 872196

NIXON, Rosemary Ann. b 45. Bp Grosseteste Coll CertEd66 Dur Univ MA83. Dalton Ho Bris IDC72 DipTh72 BD73. **d** 87 **p** 94. Tutor St Jo Coll w Cranmer Hall Dur 75-89; Dir St Jo Coll Ext Progr 82-89; NSM Ches le Street *Dur* 87-89; TD Gateshead 89-92; Dir Cranmer Hall Urban Studies Unit 89-92; Staff Member Edin Th Coll from 92. *The Theological Institute, Rosebery Crescent, Edinburgh EH12 5JT* 0131-337 0478 or 337 3838

NIXSON, Peter. b 27. Ball Coll Ox BA51 MA59 Ex Univ PGCE67 DipEd72. Coll of Resurr Mirfield 51. **d** 53 **p** 54. Perm to Offic *Ex* 70-85; Hon C Oswestry H Trin *Lich* 69-70; Sch Coun Tiverton 70-75; Newton Abbot 75-85; V Winkleigh *Ex* 85-92; R Ashreigney 85-92; R Broadwoodkelly 85-92; V Brushford 85-92; RD Chulmleigh 87-93; rtd 93; Perm to Offic *Ex* from 93. *34 Osney Crescent, Paignton, Devon TQ4 5EY* Paignton (01803) 522698

NIXSON, Ms Rosemary Clare (Rosie). b 57. Westf Coll Lon BA79 Liv Univ MA80 MPhil82. Aston Tr Scheme 89 Trin Coll Bris BA94. **d** 94 **p** 95. C E Bris 94; C Bris St Andr Hartcliffe from 94. *404 Bishport Avenue, Hartcliffe, Bristol BS13 0HX* Bristol (0117) 978 4052

✠NOAKES, Most Rev George. b 24. Univ of Wales (Abth) BA48 Univ of Wales Hon DD90. Wycliffe Hall Ox 49. **d** 50 **p** 52 **c** 82. C Lamp *St D* 50-56; V Eglwyswrw and Meline 56-59; V Tregaron 59-67; V Cardiff Dewi Sant *Llan* 67-76; R Abth *St D* 76-80; Can *St D* Cathl 77-79; Adn Cardigan 79-82; V Llanychaearn w Llanddeiniol 80-82; Bp St D 82-91; Abp Wales 87-91; rtd 91. *Hafod-Lon, Rhydargaeau, Carmarthen, Dyfed SA32 7DT* Llanpumsaint (01267) 253302

NOBBS, John Ernest. b 35. Tyndale Hall Bris 60. **d** 63 **p** 64. C Wakef St Andr and St Mary *Wakef* 69-71; C Tooting Graveney St Nic *S'wark* 71-74; C Woking St Pet *Guildf* 74-78; C Worthing St Geo *Chich* 78-88; C Rayleigh *Chelmsf* 88-94; rtd 94. *89 Panfield Lane, Braintree, Essex CM7 5RP* Braintree (01376) 322901

NOBLE, Alexander Frederick Innes (Sandy). b 30. Selw Coll Cam BA53 MA58. Lon Coll of Div ALCD55. **d** 55 **p** 56. Chapl Blundell's Sch Tiverton 66-72; St Jo C of E Sch Cowley 73-77; Chapl Cranbrook Sch Kent 77-81; Chapl St Geo Sch Harpenden 81-90; Hon C Henriard w Winslade and Long Sutton etc *Win* 90-94; rtd 95. P-in-c Oare w Culbone *B & W* from 95. *The Rectory, Oare, Lynton, Devon EX35 6NX* Brendon (015987) 270

NOBLE, Canon Arthur. b 12. TCD BA35 MA38. TCD Div Sch Div Test. **d** 36 **p** 37. I Lisburn Ch Ch *Conn* 61-82; Preb Conn Cathl 74-79; Prec 79-82; rtd 82. *38 King's Road, Knock, Belfast BT5 6LF* Belfast (01232) 652815

NOBLE, Christopher John Lancelot. b 58. Aston Tr Scheme 88 Oak Hill Th Coll DipHE90. **d** 90 **p** 91. C Tonbridge SS Pet and Paul *Roch* 90-95; R Stansted w Fairseat and Vigo from 95. *The Rectory, 9 The Coach Drive, Meopham, Gravesend, Kent DA13 0SZ* Fairseat (01732) 822494

NOBLE, David. b 37. S Dios Minl Tr Scheme 84. **d** 87 **p** 88. C Alverstoke *Portsm* 87-89; Australia from 90. *Anglican Rectory, Lancaster Road, PO Box 139, Jerramungup, W Australia 6337* Albany (98) 351175

NOBLE, Mrs Eileen Joan. b 45. NE Ord Course 90. **d** 93 **p** 94. C Gosforth All SS *Newc* from 93. *1 Northfield Road, Gosforth, Newcastle upon Tyne NE3 3UL* 0191-284 8568

NOBLE, Francis Alick. b 10. Trin Coll Cam BA33 MA37. Linc Th Coll 33. **d** 36 **p** 37. R Guiseley *Bradf* 67-78; rtd 78; Perm to Offic *St As* from 78. *16 Aberconwy Parc, Prestatyn, Clwyd LL19 9HH* Prestatyn (01745) 856820

NOBLE, Graham Edward. b 49. SS Paul & Mary Coll Cheltenham CertEd71 Open Univ BA74. E Anglian Minl Tr Course 85. **d** 88 **p** 89. C Kesgrave *St E* 88-90; P-in-c Gt and Lt Blakenham w Baylham and Nettlestead 90-95; P-in-c Debenham w Aspall and Kenton from 95. *The Vicarage, 34 Gracechurch Street, Debenham, Stowmarket, Suffolk IP14 6RE* Debenham (01728) 860265

NOBLE, Paul Vincent. b 54. Leeds Univ BA75 PGCE76 Ox Univ BA81 MA85. St Steph Ho Ox 79. **d** 82 **p** 83. C Prestbury *Glouc* 82-85; P-in-c Avening w Cherington 85-90; V The

Suttons w Tydd *Linc* from 90. *The Vicarage, Sutton St James, Spalding, Lincs PE12 0EE* Sutton St James (0194585) 457

NOBLE, Peter Hirst. b 37. Lon Univ BD68 Leeds Univ MPhil72. Cranmer Hall Dur 65. **d** 68 **p** 69. C Honley *Wakef* 68-72; P-in-c Moss *Sheff* 72-81; V Askern 72-92; rtd 92. *40 Broome Close, Huntington, York YO3 9RH* York (01904) 766203

NOBLE, Philip David. b 46. Glas Univ BSc67 Edin Univ BD70. Edin Th Coll 67. **d** 70 **p** 71. C Edin Ch Ch *Edin* 70-72; Papua New Guinea 72-75; R Cambuslang *Glas* 76-83; R Uddingston 76-83; Ev Prestwick 83-85; R Prestwick from 85. *56 Ayr Road, Prestwick, Ayrshire KA9 1RR* Prestwick (01292) 77108

NOBLE, Robert. b 43. TCD BA66 BD73. **d** 68 **p** 69. C Holywood *D & D* 68-71; Chapl RAF from 71. *Chaplaincy Services (RAF), HQ, Personnel and Training Command, RAF Innsworth, Gloucester GL3 1EZ* Gloucester (01452) 712612 Ext 5164 Fax 510828

NOBLETT, William Alexander. b 53. Southn Univ BTh78. Sarum & Wells Th Coll 74. **d** 78 **p** 79. C Sholing *Win* 78-80; I Ardamine w Kiltennel, Glascarrig etc *C & O* 80-82; Chapl RAF 82-84; V Middlesb St Thos *York* 84-87; Asst Chapl HM Pris Wakef 87-89; Chapl 89-92; Chapl HM Pris Nor from 92. *HM Prison, Mousehold, Norwich NR1 4LU* Norwich (01603) 37531 Fax 300867

NOCK, Peter Arthur. b 15. Keble Coll Ox BA36 MA42. Bps' Coll Cheshunt 37. **d** 39 **p** 40. V Maney *Birm* 71-81; rtd 81; Perm to Offic *Carl* from 81. *West View, Dufton, Appleby, Cumbria CA16 6DB* Appleby (017683) 51413

NOCK, Roland George William. b 62. St Andr Univ BSc84 BD89. Edin Th Coll 91. **d** 91 **p** 92. C Dunfermline *St And* 91-93; C W Fife Team Min 91-93; R Cupar from 93. *33 Millbank, Cupar, Fife KY15 5DP* Cupar (01334) 52372

NOCKELS, Donald Reginald. b 09. Leeds Univ BA32. Coll of Resurr Mirfield 32. **d** 34 **p** 35. V Cononley w Bradley *Bradf* 63-73; rtd 73. *Ellesborough Manor, Butlers Cross, Aylesbury, Bucks HP17 0XF*

NOCKELS, John Martin. b 46. Lich Th Coll Qu Coll Birm 73. **d** 73 **p** 74. C Eccleshill *Bradf* 73-76; C Fawley *Win* 76-78; V Southn St Jude 78-84; R Tadley St Pet from 84. *The Rectory, The Green, Tadley, Basingstoke, Hants RG26 6PB* Tadley (01734) 814860

NODDER, Jonathan James Colmore. b 37. Lon Univ DipTh64. Tyndale Hall Bris 63. **d** 65 **p** 66. C Bebington *Ches* 65-71; V Stockport St Mark 71-88; V Burton in Kendal *Carl* 88-90; V Burton and Holme from 90. *St James's Vicarage, Glebe Close, Burton-in-Kendal, Carnforth, Lancs LA6 1PL* Carnforth (01524) 781391

NODDER, Thomas Arthur (Brother Arnold). b 20. K Coll Lon 58. **d** 60 **p** 61. Brotherhood of the H Cross from 49; SSF from 63; C Plaistow St Andr *Chelmsf* 66-68; Lic to Offic *Newc* 69-70; Perm to Offic *Birm* 70-83; Perm to Offic from 90; Lic to Offic *Sarum* 83-89; rtd 90. *c/o The Provincial Bursar, 113 Gillott Road, Birmingham B16 0ET* 0121-454 8302

NODDINGS, John Henry. b 39. Chich Th Coll 80. **d** 81 **p** 82. C Southborough St Pet w Ch Ch and St Matt *Roch* 81-83; C Prittlewell *Chelmsf* 83-86; V Clay Hill St Jo *Lon* 86-88; V Clay Hill St Jo and St Luke from 88; Chapl Chase Farm Hosp Enfield from 88. *St Luke's Vicarage, 92 Browning Road, Enfield, Middx EN2 0HG* 0181-363 6055

NOEL, Brother. *See* ALLEN, Noel Stephen

NOEL, Canon Frank Arthur. b 20. TCD BA44 MA49. CITC 45. **d** 45 **p** 46. I Mullabrack w Kilcluney *Arm* 63-75; RD Mullabrack 75-88; I Acton w Drumbanagher 75-88; Preb Arm Cathl 86-88; rtd 88; Lic to Offic *Arm* from 90. *31 Woodford Drive, Armagh BT60 7AY* Armagh (01861) 527787

NOEL-COX, Edward Lovis. b 99. Bps' Coll Cheshunt 22. **d** 23 **p** 25. Chapl Qu Mary's Hosp Carshalton 51-64; rtd 64; Perm to Offic *Chich* 66-93. *1 Stirling Court, 20 Portarlington Road, Bournemouth BH4 8BY* Bournemouth (01202) 765461

NOKES, Peter Warwick. b 48. Leic Univ BA71. Westcott Ho Cam 79. **d** 81 **p** 82. C Northfield *Birm* 81-84; C Ludlow *Heref* 84-87; P-in-c Writtle w Highwood *Chelmsf* 87-91; V 91-92; P-in-c Epping St Jo 92-95; P-in-c Coopersale 93-95; TR Epping Distr from 95. *The Vicarage, Hartland Road, Epping, Essex CM16 4PD* Epping (01992) 572906

NOKES, Robert Harvey. b 39. Keble Coll Ox BA61 MA65 Birm Univ DipTh63. Qu Coll Birm 61. **d** 63 **p** 64. C Totteridge *St Alb* 63-67; C Dunstable 67-73; V Langford 73-90; R Braughing w Furneux Pelham and Stocking Pelham from 90. *The Rectory, 7A Green End, Braughing, Ware, Herts SG11 2PG* Ware (01920) 822619

NOLAN, James Charles William. b 44. Chich Th Coll 75. **d** 77 **p** 78. C Crewe St Andr *Ches* 77-79; C Sale St Anne 79-83; R Holme Runcton w S Runcton and Wallington *Ely* from 83; V Tottenhill w Wormegay from 83; R Watlington from 83. *The Rectory, Downham Road, Watlington, King's Lynn, Norfolk PE33 0HS* King's Lynn (01553) 810305

NOLAN, James Joseph. b 16. Cranmer Hall Dur. **d** 61 **p** 62. V Heworth w Peasholme St Cuth *York* 66-72; CPAS Staff 72-74; R Bridlington Priory *York* 74-82; rtd 82. *9 Vicarage Close, Seamer, Scarborough, N Yorkshire YO12 4QS* Scarborough (01723) 862443

NOLAN, Canon John. b 25. TCD BA51 MA55. CITC 51. **d** 51 **p** 52. VC 55-79; Min Can 60-88; Can from 88; C Belf Upper Falls *Conn* 79-92; RD Derriaghy 90-92; rtd 92. *Apartment 32, Mount Royal, Millisle Road, Donaghadee, Co Down BT21 0HY* Donaghadee (01247) 882655

NOLAN, Marcus. b 54. Bris Univ BEd. Ridley Hall Cam. **d** 83 **p** 84. C Dagenham *Chelmsf* 83-86; C Finchley St Paul and St Luke *Lon* 86-90; V W Hampstead Trin from 90. *Holy Trinity Church Office, Finchley Road, London NW3 5HT* 0171-435 0083 or 794 2975

NOLLAND, Dr John Leslie. b 47. New England Univ (NSW) BSc67 Clare Coll Cam PhD78. Moore Th Coll Sydney ThL70 BD71. **d** 71 **p** 72. Australia 71-78; Canada 78-86; Asst Prof NT Studies Regent Coll Vancouver 78-86; Tutor Trin Coll Bris from 86; Vice Prin from 91. *129 Reedley Road, Stoke Hill, Bristol BS9 1BE* Bristol (0117) 968 4053

NOON, Canon Edward Arthur. b 16. Selw Coll Cam BA38 MA42. Bps' Coll Cheshunt 38. **d** 40 **p** 41. V Horley *S'wark* 65-77; Hon Can S'wark Cathl 72-83; P-in-c Purley St Barn 77-83; rtd 83; Hon C Overbury w Teddington, Alstone etc *Worc* 83-86; Perm to Offic *Glouc* from 86. *40 Shepherds Leaze, Wotton-under-Edge, Glos GL12 7LQ* Dursley (01453) 844978

NORBURN, Very Rev Richard Evelyn Walter. b 21. Witwatersrand Univ BA44 TDip44. St Paul's Grahamstown 49. **d** 51 **p** 53. V Norbury St Phil *Cant* 65-75; V Addington 75-81; Hon Can Cant Cathl 79-81; RD Croydon Addington 81; Dean Botswana 81-88; rtd 89. *Tebogong, 2 Rectory Cottages, Middleton, Saxmundham, Suffolk IP17 3NR* Saxmundham (01728) 73721

NORBURN, Canon Richard Henry. b 32. St Edm Hall Ox BA57 DipTh58. Wycliffe Hall Ox 57. **d** 59 **p** 59. C Sudbury St Greg and St Pet *St E* 59-65; Dioc Youth Officer 65-74; P-in-c Gt Livermere 74-81; R Ampton w Lt Livermere and Ingham 74-81; RD Thingoe 78-88; Hon Can St E Cathl from 81; R Ingham w Ampton and Gt and Lt Livermere 81-92; TV Blackbourne from 92. *The Rectory, Ingham, Bury St Edmunds, Suffolk IP31 1NS* Culford (01284) 728430

NORFOLK, Ven Edward Matheson. b 21. Leeds Univ BA44. Coll of Resurr Mirfield 41. **d** 46 **p** 47. R Gt Berkhamsted *St Alb* 69-81; Hon Can St Alb 72-82; V Kings Langley 81-82; Adn St Alb 82-87; rtd 87; Perm to Offic *Ex* from 87. *5 Fairlawn Court, Sidmouth, Devon EX10 8UR* Sidmouth (01395) 514222

NORFOLK, Archdeacon of. *See* HANDLEY, Ven Anthony Michael

✠**NORGATE, Rt Rev Cecil Richard.** b 21. St Chad's Coll Dur BA47 DipTh49. **d** 49 **p** 50 **c** 84. C Wallsend St Pet *Newc* 49-54; Tanganyika 54-64; Tanzania from 64; UMCA 54-57; V-Gen Masasi 77-84; Bp Masasi 84-92; rtd 92. *St Cyprian's College, Rondo, PO Box 212, Lindi, Tanzania*

NORGATE, Norman George. b 32. Qu Coll Cam BA55 MA58. Ridley Hall Cam. **d** 57 **p** 58. C Erith St Paul *Roch* 57-60; C E Twickenham St Steph *Lon* 60-63; V Bexleyheath St Pet *Roch* 63-71; V Woking St Mary *Guildf* 71-83; V Tunbridge Wells St Jas *Roch* 83-92; TR Tunbridge Wells St Jas w St Phil from 92. *The Vicarage, 12 Shandon Close, Tunbridge Wells, Kent TN2 3RE* Tunbridge Wells (01892) 530687

NORKETT, Alan. b 45. Sarum & Wells Th Coll 85. **d** 87 **p** 88. C Shrewsbury St Giles w Sutton and Atcham *Lich* 87-90; V Mow Cop 90-94. *21 Bedford Road, Kidsgrove, Stoke-on-Trent ST7 1HQ*

NORMAN, Andrew Herbert. b 54. K Coll Lon BD77 AKC77 Lon Univ PhD88. St Steph Ho Ox 77. **d** 78 **p** 79. C Deal St Leon w Sholden *Cant* 78-81; C Maidstone All SS and St Phil w Tovil 81-84; V Tenterden St Mich 84-93; Chapl Benenden Hosp Kent 86-91; Dir of Post-Ord Tr *Cant* 91-93; R Guildf St Nic *Guildf* from 93. *The Rectory, 3 Flower Walk, Guildford, Surrey GU2 5EP* Guildford (01483) 504895

NORMAN, Arthur Leslie Frayne. b 08. Sarum Th Coll 29. **d** 31 **p** 33. Chapl HM Pris Swansea 58-75; rtd 75. *4 Malvern Terrace, Brynmill, Swansea SA2 0BE* Swansea (01792) 465310

NORMAN, Catherine. b 51. Nottm Univ BSc73 N Counties Coll Newc CertEd74. Linc Th Coll CMinlStuds95. **d** 95. C Scartho *Linc* from 95. *25 Waltham Road, Grimsby, S Humberside DN33 2LY* Grimsby (01472) 870373

NORMAN, Canon Edward Robert. b 38. FRHistS72 Selw Coll Cam BA61 PhD64 MA65 BD67 DD78. Linc Th Coll 65. **d** 65 **p** 71. Fell Jes Coll Cam 64-71; Lect Cam Univ 64-88; Lic to Offic *Ely* 65-95; Fell and Dean Peterho 71-88; Six Preacher Cant Cathl Cant 84-89; Chapl Ch Ch Coll Cant 88-95; Can Res and Treas York Minster *York* from 95. *3 Minster Court, York YO1 2JJ* York (01904) 625599

NORMAN, Ven Garth. b 38. St Chad's Coll Dur BA62 DipTh63 MA68 Cam Inst of Educn PGCE68 UEA MEd84. **d** 63 **p** 64. C Wandsworth St Anne *S'wark* 63-66; CT runch w Swafield *Nor* 66-71; R Gimingham 71-77; RD Repps 75-83; TR Trunch 77-83; Prin Chiltern Chr Tr Course *Ox* 83-87; C W Wycombe w Bledlow Ridge, Bradenham and Radnage 83-87; Dir of Tr *Roch* 88-94; Hon Can Roch Cathl from 91; Adn Bromley from 94. *6 Horton Way, Farningham, Kent DA4 0DQ* Farningham (01322) 864522

NORMAN, Jillianne Elizabeth. b 59. DCR80. Ridley Hall Cam 85. **d** 88 **p** 94. Par Dn Fishponds St Jo *Bris* 88-92; Perm to Offic from 92; Hon C Warmley, Syston and Bitton from 94. *74 Blackhorse Road, Mangotsfield, Bristol BS17 3AY* Bristol (0117) 956 1551

NORMAN, Canon John Ronald. b 15. GradIT Lon Univ BA40. Linc Th Coll 40. **d** 42 **p** 43. R Dunnington *York* 61-72; R Bolton Percy 72-82; Dioc Worship Adv 72-82; Can and Preb York Minster 77-92; rtd 82. *Iona, 5 Northfield Close, Pocklington, York YO4 2EG* Pocklington (01759) 303170

NORMAN, Linda Mary. b 48. Man Univ BSc69 CertEd70 St Jo Coll Dur BA82. **dss** 83 **d** 87. York St Mich-le-Belfrey *York* 83-88; Par Dn 87-88; rtd 88. *23 Ainsty Avenue, Dringhouses, York YO2 2HH* York (01904) 706152

NORMAN, Michael Heugh. b 18. Qu Coll Cam BA48 Kent Univ MA. Westcott Ho Cam 48. **d** 50 **p** 51. C St Peter-in-Thanet *Cant* 50-52; S Africa from 52. *5 Rosedale Cottage, Lower Nursery Road, Rosebank, 7700 South Africa* Cape Town (21) 685-3622

NORMAN, Michael John. b 59. Southn Univ LLB82. Wycliffe Hall Ox 82. **d** 85 **p** 86. C Woodley St Jo the Ev *Ox* 85-89; C Uphill *B & W* 89-92; TV from 92. *2 Westbury Crescent, Weston-super-Mare, Avon BS23 4RB* Weston-super-Mare (01934) 623195

NORMAN, Michael John (Mick). b 61. St Jo Coll Ox BSc83 Univ Coll Lon MSc84. Aston Tr Scheme 89 St Jo Coll Nottm 91. **d** 93 **p** 94. C Haughton le Skerne *Dur* from 93. *1 Aviemore Court, Darlington, Co Durham DL1 2TF* Darlington (01325) 486382

NORMAN, Peter John. b 59. Chich Th Coll 84. **d** 87 **p** 88. C Farncombe *Guildf* 87-91; C Cockington *Ex* 91-94; V Winkleigh from 94; R Ashreigney from 94; R Broadwoodkelly from 94; V Brushford from 94. *The Vicarage, Torrington Road, Winkleigh, Devon EX19 8HR* Winkleigh (01837) 83719

NORMAN, Roy Albert. b 23. **d** 65 **p** 66. C Thornbury *Glouc* 67-70; P-in-c Woolaston w Alvington 70-80; R 80-88; rtd 88. *William Annett's Dwelling, Crossways, Ruardean, Glos GL17 9XB* Dean (01594) 542503

NORMAN, Canon William Beadon. b 26. Trin Coll Cam BA49 MA55. Ridley Hall Cam 52. **d** 52 **p** 53. V Alne *York* 65-74; RD Warley *Birm* 74-79; V Blackheath 74-79; Hon Can Birm Cathl 78-91; TR Kings Norton 79-91; RD Kings Norton 82-87; Warden Dioc Readers Bd 84-91; rtd 91; Perm to Offic *S'wark* from 91; Perm to Offic *Lon* from 94; Preacher Lincoln's Inn from 94. *37 Cloudesdale Road, London SW17 8ET* 0181-673 9134 Fax 675 6890

NORMAN, William John. b 08. St Andr Whittlesford. **d** 44 **p** 45. Area Sec CMS 56-74; R Buriton *Portsm* 74-79; rtd 79. *22 Middlehill Road, Colehill, Wimborne, Dorset BH21 2SD* Wimborne (01202) 884775

NORMAND, Stephen Joseph William. b 48. N Texas State Univ BSEd80. Sarum & Wells Th Coll 90. **d** 92 **p** 93. C Norton *St Alb* 92-94; C St Alb St Pet from 95. *4 The Willows, St Albans, Herts AL1 1UL* St Albans (01727) 858120

NORMINGTON, Eric. b 16. S'wark Ord Course. **d** 63 **p** 64. V Bath Weston All SS *B & W* 71-78; P-in-c N Stoke 76-78; R Bath Weston All SS w N Stoke 78-81; rtd 81; Perm to Offic *Ex* from 81. *53 Higher Woolbrook Park, Sidmouth, Devon EX10 9ED* Sidmouth (01395) 512016

NORRIS, Mrs Alison. b 55. St Andr Univ MTheol77 Dur Univ CertEd78. Cant Sch of Min. **dss** 82 **d** 87 **p** 94. Warlingham w Chelsham and Farleigh *S'wark* 83-85; Willingham *Ely* 85-87; Hon Par Dn 87-90; Hon Par Dn Worle *B & W* 90-94; NSM Milverton w Halse and Fitzhead from 94. *The Vicarage, Parsonage Lane, Milverton, Taunton, Somerset TA4 1LR* Milverton (01823) 400305

NORRIS, Allan Edward. b 43. St Jo Coll Dur BA72 DipTh73. Cranmer Hall Dur 69. **d** 73 **p** 74. C Plumstead St Jo w St Jas and St Paul *S'wark* 73-78; C Battersea Park St Sav 78-82; C Battersea St Geo w St Andr 78-82; V Grain w Stoke *Roch* 82-92; V Sissinghurst w Frittenden *Cant* from 92. *The Rectory, Oakleaves, Frittenden, Cranbrook, Kent TN17 2DD* Frittenden (0158080) 275

NORRIS, Andrew David. b 54. CPsychol St Andr Univ BSc78 Lon Univ MPhil80. E Anglian Minl Tr Course 87. **d** 90 **p** 91. C Worle *B & W* 90-94; R Milverton w Halse and Fitzhead from 94. *The Vicarage, Parsonage Lane, Milverton, Taunton, Somerset TA4 1LR* Milverton (01823) 400305

NORRIS, Andrew Peter. b 62. Aston Univ BSc83. St Jo Coll Nottm BA86 DPS87. **d** 87 **p** 88. C Mountsorrel Ch Ch and St Pet *Leic* 87-90; C Harborne Heath *Birm* 90-91; P-in-c Edgbaston St Germain 91-92; V from 92. *St Germain's Vicarage, 180 Portland Road, Birmingham B16 9TD* 0121-429 3431

NORRIS, Barry John. b 46. Nottm Univ CQSW75 MTh86 Open Univ BA80. St Jo Sem Wonersh. **d** 70 **p** 71. In RC Ch 70-72; C Wisbech SS Pet and Paul *Ely* 76-78; TV E Ham w Upton Park St Alb *Chelmsf* 78-81; Chapl RAF 81-87; V N Tadley St Mary *Win* from 87. *St Mary's Vicarage, Bishopswood Road, Tadley, Basingstoke, Hants RG26 6HQ* Tadley (01734) 814435

NORRIS, Clifford Joseph. b 29. Codrington Coll Barbados. **d** 61 **p** 68. Antigua 61-62; C Penton Street St Silas w All SS *Lon* 68-70; C Stepney St Dunstan and All SS 70-73; P-in-c Bethnal Green St Jas the Gt w St Jude 73-82; V Aveley and Purfleet *Chelmsf* from 82. *The Vicarage, Mill Road, Aveley, South Ockendon, Essex RM15 4SR* Purfleet (01708) 864865

NORRIS, Eric Richard. b 43. MICFM86. Bernard Gilpin Soc Dur 65 Ripon Hall Ox 66. **d** 69 **p** 70. C Huyton St Mich *Liv* 69-72; C Mexborough *Sheff* 72-74; V Dalton 74-78; Org Sec (Dio Carl) CECS 78-89; Area Appeals Manager N Co 89-93; Lic to Offic *Carl* 78-93; Lic to Offic *Dur* 89-93; TR Thirsk *York* from 93. *The Rectory, Thirsk, N Yorkshire YO7 1PR* Thirsk (01845) 523183

NORRIS, Mark. b 68. Brunel Univ BEng90. Oak Hill Th Coll DipHE92 BA93. **d** 93 **p** 94. C Roby *Liv* from 93. *42 Buttermere Road, Liverpool L16 2NN* 0151-489 5910

NORTH, Albert. b 13. Lon Univ BA35. Sarum Th Coll 64. **d** 65 **p** 66. V Gt w Lt Saling *Chelmsf* 70-72; V St Osyth 72-81; rtd 81; Perm to Offic *B & W* from 86. *18 Nelson House, Nelson Place West, Bath BA1 2BA* Bath (01225) 330896

NORTH, Barry Albert. b 46. **d** 82 **p** 83. C Brampton St Thos *Derby* 82-84; C Chesterfield St Aug 84-88; P-in-c Derby St Mark 88-91; R Coalbrookdale, Iron-Bridge and Lt Wenlock *Heref* from 91. *The Vicarage, Coalbrookdale, Telford, Shropshire TF8 7NR* Ironbridge (01952) 433309

NORTH, David Roland. b 45. Lich Th Coll 70 Qu Coll Birm 72. **d** 73 **p** 74. C Salesbury *Blackb* 73-76; C Marton 76-79; V Penwortham St Leon 79-87; R Whittington St Jo *Lich* from 87. *The Rectory, Whittington, Oswestry, Shropshire SY11 4DF* Oswestry (01691) 652222

NORTH, Philip John. b 66. York Univ BA88. St Steph Ho Ox BA91. **d** 92 **p** 93. C Sunderland Springwell w Thorney Close *Dur* 92-95; C Sunderland St Mary and St Pet from 95. *The Clergy House, Springwell Road, Sunderland SR3 4DY* 0191-528 3754

NORTH, Preb Robert. b 54. Lon Univ BSc77. Ripon Coll Cuddesdon 78. **d** 81 **p** 82. C Leominster *Heref* 81-86; TV Heref St Martin w St Fran (S Wye TM) 86-92; TV Dewsall w Callow 86-92; TV Holme Lacy w Dinedor 86-92; TV Lt Dewchurch, Aconbury w Ballingham and Bolstone 86-92; TV Upper and Lower Bullinghope w Grafton 86-92; P-in-c Heref St Nic from 92; Dir of Ords from 92; Preb Heref Cathl from 94. *St Nicholas's Rectory, 76 Breinton Road, Hereford HR4 0JY* Hereford (01432) 273810

NORTH, Canon Vernon Leslie. b 26. Bps' Coll Cheshunt 61. **d** 63 **p** 64. V Stotfold *St Alb* 68-91; RD Shefford 79-91; Hon Can St Alb 89-92; R Stotfold and Radwell 91-92; rtd 92. *Hunters Moon, 10 High Street, Little Paxton, St Neots, Huntingdon, Cambs PE19 4HA* Huntingdon (01480) 471146

NORTH WEST EUROPE, Archdeacon of. See ALLEN, Ven Geoffrey Gordon

NORTHALL, Malcolm Walter. b 26. Cheshunt Coll Cam 59 Ely Th Coll 63. **d** 64 **p** 65. V Blockley w Aston Magna *Glouc* 67-82; P-in-c Churchdown 82; V 82-92; rtd 92; Perm to Offic *Ban* from 92. *5 Maethlon Close, Tywyn, Gwynedd LL36 0BN* Tywyn (01654) 710123

NORTHAM, Cavell Herbert James Cavell. See CAVELL-NORTHAM, Canon Cavell Herbert James

NORTHAM, Mrs Susan Jillian (Jill). b 36. Oak Hill Th Coll DipHE87. **d** 89. NSM Enfield Ch Ch Trent Park *Lon* 89-91; Par Dn 91-94; C from 94. *22 Crescent East, Barnet, Herts EN4 0EN* 0181-449 4483

NORTHAMPTON, Archdeacon of. See CHAPMAN, Ven Michael Robin

NORTHCOTT, Canon Geoffrey Stephen. b 21. Leeds Univ BA42. Coll of Resurr Mirfield 40. **d** 47 **p** 48. V Luton St Sav *St Alb* 68-89; Hon Can St Alb 72-89; RD Luton 82-89; rtd 89. *8 Nelson House, Nelson Place West, Bath BA1 2BA* Bath (01225) 338296

NORTHCOTT, Dr Michael Stafford. b 55. St Chad's Coll Dur BA76 MA77 PhD. St Jo Coll Dur 80. **d** 81 **p** 82. C Chorlton-cum-Hardy St Clem *Man* 81-84; Malaysia 84-89; Lect Chr Ethics New Coll Edin Univ 89-91; NSM Edin Old St Paul *Edin* 89-91; NSM Edin St Jas 91-93; TV Edin St Marg from 93. *8 Dudley Gardens, Edinburgh EH6 4PY* 0131-554 1651

NORTHCOTT, William Mark. b 36. Clifton Th Coll 61. **d** 64 **p** 65. C Walthamstow St Luke *Chelmsf* 64-68; C Idle H Trin *Bradf* 68-70; N Sec CMJ 70-79; V Withnell *Blackb* 79-90; P-in-c Glenrothes *St And* 90-91; Asst Dioc Supernumerary 90-91; Perm to Offic *Blackb* from 91. *30 The Laund, Leyland, Preston PR5 3XX* Preston (01772) 620331

NORTHERN FRANCE, Archdeacon of. See DRAPER, Ven Martin Paul

NORTHFIELD, Stephen Richmond. b 55. Lon Univ BSc77 Southn Univ BTh84. Sarum & Wells Th Coll 79. **d** 82 **p** 83. C Colchester St Jas, All SS, St Nic and St Runwald *Chelmsf* 82-85; C Chelmsf All SS 85-89; V Ramsey w Lt Oakley and Wrabness from 89. *The Vicarage, Ramsey Road, Ramsey, Harwich, Essex CO12 5EU* Ramsey (01255) 880291

NORTHING, Capt Ross. b 58. Wilson Carlile Coll DipEvang87 St Steph Ho Ox DipMin94. **d** 94 **p** 95. CA from 87; C Up Hatherley *Glouc* from 94; C Cheltenham St Steph from 94. *28 Davallia Drive, Cheltenham, Glos GL51 5XB* Cheltenham (01242) 863019

NORTHOLT, Archdeacon of. See BROADBENT, Ven Peter Alan (Pete)

NORTHOVER, Kevin Charles. b 57. Coll of Resurr Mirfield 89. **d** 91 **p** 92. C Kingston upon Hull St Alb *York* 91-94; V Moorends *Sheff* from 94. *The Vicarage, West Road, Moorends, Doncaster, S Yorkshire DN8 4LH* Thorne (01405) 741758

NORTHRIDGE, Canon Herbert Aubrey Hamilton. b 16. TCD BA40 MA43. **d** 41 **p** 42. I Derg *D & R* 50-81; Can Derry Cathl 72-81; rtd 81. *Goblusk, Ballinamallard, Co Fermanagh BT94 2LW* Ballinamallard (0136581) 676

NORTHUMBERLAND, Archdeacon of. See ELLIOTT, Ven Peter

NORTHWOOD, Michael Alan. b 36. Lon Univ BSc60. Wells Th Coll 62. **d** 64 **p** 65. C Eastbourne St Mary *Chich* 64-66; C Sanderstead All SS *S'wark* 66-68; P-in-c Alton Barnes w Alton Priors etc *Sarum* 69-75; Lic to Offic 76-86; Perm to Offic *Ox* from 86. *Saratoga, Long Grove, Seer Green, Beaconsfield, Bucks HP9 2QH* Beaconsfield (01494) 671127

NORTON, Anthony Bernard. b 40. Man Univ BA62. Linc Th Coll 63. **d** 65 **p** 66. C Westbury-on-Trym H Trin *Bris* 65-68; C Bris St Agnes w St Simon 68-70; P-in-c Bris St Werburgh 70-72; TV Bris St Agnes and St Simon w St Werburgh 72-77; V Lakenham St Alb *Nor* 77-85; TV Trunch 85-93; TV Halesworth w Linstead, Chediston, Holton etc *St E* from 93. *The Vicarage, Spexhall, Halesworth, Suffolk IP19 0RQ* Halesworth (01986) 875453

NORTON, James Herbert Kitchener. b 37. Qu Coll Birm 78. **d** 81 **p** 82. NSM Donnington Wood *Lich* 81-83; C Matson *Glouc* 83-86; V New Mills *Derby* from 86; RD Glossop from 93. *St George's Vicarage, Church Lane, New Mills, Stockport, Cheshire SK12 4NP* New Mills (01663) 743225

NORTON, John Colin (Andrew). b 25. Magd Coll Ox BA50 MA54. Cuddesdon Coll 50. **d** 52 **p** 53. V Clifton All SS w Tyndalls Park *Bris* 68-78; Hon Can Bris Cathl 77-80; V Clifton All SS w St Jo 78-80; V Penistone *Wakef* 80-83; CR from 85; rtd 95. *House of the Resurrection, Mirfield, W Yorkshire WF14 0BN* Mirfield (01924) 494318

NORTON, Leslie Miles. b 10. Sarum Th Coll 46. **d** 48 **p** 49. V Dulwich Common St Pet *S'wark* 55-83; rtd 83; Perm to Offic *Bris* from 83. *46 St Dennis Road, Malmesbury, Wilts SN16 9BH* Malmesbury (01666) 824767

NORTON (or HARCOURT-NORTON), Michael Clive Harcourt. b 34. MACE84 Selw Coll Cam BA58 MA60 Univ of NSW MCom81. Union Th Sem (NY) STM69 Wells Th Coll 56. **d** 58 **p** 59. C Gt Ilford St Jo *Chelmsf* 58-62; Australia 62-68 and from 69; USA 68-69. *2 Ambrose Street, Hunters Hill, Sydney, NSW, Australia 2110* Sydney (2) 817-2167 Fax 879-4051

NORTON, Michael James Murfin. b 42. Lich Th Coll 66. **d** 67 **p** 68. C W Bromwich St Fran *Lich* 67-70; C Wellington Ch Ch 70-72; C Norwood All SS *Cant* 72-76; V Elstow *St Alb* 76-82; Asst Chapl HM Pris Wakef 82-83; Chapl HM Pris Camp Hill 83-86; Chapl HM Pris Parkhurst 86-88; Chapl HM Pris Win 88-93; V Somborne w Ashley *Win* from 93. *The Vicarage, Winchester Road, Kings Somborne, Stockbridge, Hants SO20 6PF* Romsey (01794) 388223

NORTON, Paul James. b 55. BA86. Oak Hill Th Coll 83. **d** 86 **p** 87. C Luton St Fran *St Alb* 86-89; C Bedworth *Cov* from 89. *St Andrew's House, Smorrall Lane, Bedworth, Nuneaton, Warks CV12 0JN* Bedworth (01203) 363322

NORTON, Peter Eric Pepler. b 38. TCD BA61 G&C Coll Cam PhD64. St Jo Coll Dur 78. **d** 80 **p** 81. C Ulverston St Mary w H Trin *Carl* 80-83; P-in-c Warcop, Musgrave, Soulby and Crosby Garrett 83-84; R 84-90; OCF 83-90; V Appleby *Carl* from 90; R Ormside from 90. *The Vicarage, Appleby-in-Westmorland, Cumbria CA16 6QW* Appleby (017683) 51461

NORTON, William Fullerton. b 23. Selw Coll Cam BA46 MA52. Wycliffe Hall Ox 46. **d** 48 **p** 49. C Tooting Graveney St Nic *S'wark* 68-71; V Hanley Road St Sav w St Paul *Lon* 71-89; rtd 89. *21 Peel Road, Brighton BN2 5ND* Brighton (01273) 677332

NORTON, Archdeacon of. *See* OFFER, Ven Dr Clifford Jocelyn

NORWICH, Bishop of. *See* NOTT, Rt Rev Peter John

NORWICH, Dean of. *See* PLATTEN, Very Rev Stephen George

NORWOOD, Andrew David. b 65. Lon Bible Coll BA91 Cranmer Hall Dur DMS94. **d** 94. C Headingley *Ripon* from 94. *5 Derwentwater Grove, Leeds LS6 3EN* Leeds (0113) 275 8937

NORWOOD, David John. b 40. SS Paul & Mary Coll Cheltenham BEd82. Linc Th Coll 65. **d** 68 **p** 69. C Hitchin St Mary *St Alb* 68-71; Zambia 72-76; C Littlehampton St Jas *Chich* 76-77; P-in-c Chacewater *Truro* 77-79; Chapl R Cornwall Hosp Treliske 77-79; Head RE Red Maids Sch Bris 82-85; Appeals Organiser Children's Soc 86-94; P-in-c Clarkston *Glas* from 94. *St Aidan's Rectory, 8 Golf Road, Clarkston, Glasgow G76 7LZ* 0141-638 2860

NORWOOD, Philip Geoffrey Frank. b 39. Em Coll Cam BA62 MA66. Cuddesdon Coll 63. **d** 65 **p** 66. C New Addington *Cant* 65-69; Abp's Dom Chapl *Cant* 69-72; V Hollingbourne 72-78; P-in-c Wormshill 74-78; P-in-c Bredgar w Bicknor and Huckinge 74-78; P-in-c St Laurence in the Isle of Thanet 78-82; V 82-88; RD Thanet 86-88; V Spalding *Linc* from 88. *The Parsonage, Church Street, Spalding, Lincs PE11 2PB* Spalding (01775) 722772

NOTLEY, Michael James. b 41. St Edm Hall Ox BA63 MA68. E Midl Min Tr Course 84. **d** 87 **p** 88. Hon C Oadby *Leic* from 87. *1 Berkeley Close, Oadby, Leicester LE2 4SZ* Leicester (0116) 271 3872

NOTT, George Thomas Michael. b 34. Ex Coll Ox BA58 MA62 Birm Univ MEd88. Coll of Resurr Mirfield. **d** 60 **p** 61. C Solihull *Birm* 60-69; Min Can Worc Cathl *Worc* 69-77; Chapl K Sch Worc 69-77; P-in-c Worc St Nic *Worc* 77-84; P-in-c Worc St Andr and All SS w St Helen 82-84; Children's Officer 84-87; Droitwich Spa 87-89; V Broadheath, Crown E and Rushwick from 89; Chapl Worc Coll of HE from 89. *The Vicarage, Crown East Lane, Rushwick, Worcester WR2 5TU* Worcester (01905) 428801

✠**NOTT, Rt Rev Peter John.** b 33. Fitzw Ho Cam BA61 MA65. Westcott Ho Cam 58. **d** 61 **p** 62 **c** 77. C Harpenden St Nic *St Alb* 61-64; Chapl Fitzw Coll Cam 64-69; Fell 66-69; Chapl New Hall Cam 66-69; R Beaconsfield *Ox* 69-76; TR 76-77; Preb Wells Cathl *B & W* 77-85; Suff Bp Taunton 77-85; Bp Nor from 85. *The Bishop's House, Norwich NR3 1SB* Norwich (01603) 629001 Fax 761613

NOTTAGE, Terence John. b 36. Oak Hill Th Coll 62. **d** 65 **p** 66. C Finchley St Paul Long Lane *Lon* 65-68; C Edgware 68-72; V Harlesden St Mark 72-86; V Kensal Rise St Mark and St Martin 86; TR Plymouth Em w Efford *Ex* 86-92; P-in-c Laira 88-92; TR Plymouth Em, Efford and Laira from 93. *Emmanuel Rectory, 9 Seymour Drive, Plymouth PL3 5BG* Plymouth (01752) 663321

NOTTINGHAM, Dr Birman. b 29. St Chad's Coll Dur BA53 MA56 MEd66 DipClinPs58 DipEd61 MBPsS66 Lanc Univ PhD75. Ely Th Coll 53. **d** 55 **p** 56. Lic to Offic *Dur* 58-70; St Martin's Coll Lanc 66-94; Lic to Offic *Blackb* from 66; rtd 94. *33 Newlands Road, Lancaster LA1 4JE* Lancaster (01524) 66949

NOTTINGHAM, Archdeacon of. *See* WALKER, Ven Thomas Overington (Tom)

NOURSE, John. b 22. St Jo Coll Cam BA43 ACertCM90 St Jo Coll Cam MA47. Wells Th Coll 48. **d** 49 **p** 51. Min Can and Prec Cant Cathl *Cant* 69-73; V Charing w Lt Chart 73-83; V Charing w Charing Heath and Lt Chart 84-88; rtd 88; Perm to Offic *Ex* from 90. *High Mead, Greenhill Avenue, Lympstone, Exmouth, Devon EX8 5HW* Exmouth (01395) 264480

NOWELL, John David. b 44. AKC67. **d** 68 **p** 69. C Lindley *Wakef* 68-70; C Lightcliffe 70-72; V Wyke *Bradf* 72-80; V Silsden 80-92; V Baildon from 92. *The Vicarage, Baildon, Shipley, W Yorkshire BD17 6BY* Bradford (01274) 594941

NOY, Frederick William Vernon. b 47. Sarum Th Coll 67. **d** 71 **p** 72. C Swindon St Jo *Bris* 71-75; Chapl to the Deaf *Sarum* 75-80; P-in-c Stinsford, Winterborne Came w Whitcombe etc 76-80; Perm to Offic from 80. *54 Casterbridge Road, Dorchester, Dorset DT1 2AG* Dorchester (01305) 264269

NOYCE, Colin Martley. b 45. Brasted Th Coll 73 Ridley Hall Cam 74. **d** 76 **p** 77. C Cam St Jas *Ely* 76-78; Chapl RN 78-82; R Mistley w Manningtree *Chelmsf* 82-86; Miss to Seamen 86-90; Kenya 86-89; Trinidad and Tobago 89-90; V Four Marks *Win* from 90. *The Vicarage, 22 Lymington Bottom, Four Marks, Alton, Hants GU34 5AA* Alton (01420) 563344

NOYCE, Graham Peter. b 62. Bedf Coll Lon BSc84. Trin Coll Bris BA92. **d** 92 **p** 93. C Sketty *S & B* 92-94; C Swansea St Jas from 94. *21 Ffynone Drive, Swansea SA1 6DB* Swansea (01792) 470248

NOYES, Roger. b 39. Linc Th Coll 65. **d** 67 **p** 68. C Adel *Ripon* 67-70; Chapl Aldenham Sch Herts 70-74; V Aldborough w Boroughbridge and Roecliffe *Ripon* 74-89; Rural Min Adv 89-90. *Rose Cottage, Moor End, Nun Monkton, York YO5 8DY* Harrogate (01423) 330846

NUDDS, Douglas John. b 24. St Aid Birkenhead 48. **d** 51 **p** 52. Chapl Leic R Infirmary 68-72; High Royds Hosp Menston 72-79; V Bradf St Wilfrid Lidget Green *Bradf* 79-84; Lic to Offic *St Alb* from 84; Chapl Shenley Hosp Radlett Herts 84-89; rtd 89; Perm to Offic *Nor* from 89. *Longview, Southgate Close, Wells-next-the-Sea, Norfolk NR23 1HG* Fakenham (01328) 711926

NUGENT, Canon Alan Hubert. b 42. Dur Univ BA65 MA78. Wycliffe Hall Ox 65 United Th Coll Bangalore DipTh66. **d** 67 **p** 68. C Mossley Hill St Matt and St Jas *Liv* 67-71; C Bridgnorth St Mary *Heref* 71-72; Chapl Dur Univ *Dur* 72-78; P-in-c Bishopwearmouth Ch Ch 78-85; P-in-c Brancepeth 85-94; Dioc Dir of Educn from 85; Hon Can Dur Cathl from 86. *20 Dickens Wynd, Durham DH1 3QY* 0191-386 0473

NUGENT, David Richard. b 54. MInstPS84 Liv Poly BA87. Oak Hill Th Coll BA95. **d** 95. C Birkenhead St Jas w St Bede *Ches* from 95. *3 Buckingham Avenue, Birkenhead, Merseyside L43 8TD* 0151-652 9180

NUGENT, Eric William. b 26. Bps' Coll Cheshunt 56. **d** 58 **p** 59. V Eastwood St Dav *Chelmsf* 66-79; P-in-c Weeley 79-81; V Lt Clacton 80-81; R Weeley and Lt Clacton 81-93; rtd 93. *1 King's Court, King's Road, Dovercourt, Harwich, Essex CO12 4DS* Harwich (01255) 552640

NUNN, Andrew Peter. b 57. Leic Poly BA79 Leeds Univ BA82. Coll of Resurr Mirfield 80. **d** 83 **p** 84. C Manston *Ripon* 83-87; C Leeds Richmond Hill 87-91; Chapl Agnes Stewart C of E High Sch Leeds 87-95; V Leeds Richmond Hill *Ripon* 91-95; Personal Asst to Bp S'wark from 95. *70 Pollards Hill North, London SW16 4NY* 0181-679 4908

NUNN, Geoffrey William John. b 24. St Jo Coll Dur BA51. **d** 52 **p** 53. C Upminster *Chelmsf* 52-58; V Dagenham St Martin 58-94; C 95; R Becontree S from 95. *St Martin's Vicarage, Goresbrook Road, Dagenham, Essex RM9 6UX* 0181-592 0967

NUNN, Peter. b 32. Kelham Th Coll 53. **d** 57 **p** 58. Chapl Winwick Hosp Warrington 65-90; rtd 90. *1 Rylands Street, Springfield, Wigan, Lancs WN6 7BL* Wigan (01942) 35407

NUNN, Canon Peter Michael. b 38. Sarum Th Coll 64. **d** 66 **p** 67. C Hornsey St Geo *Lon* 66-71; C Cleator Moor w Cleator *Carl* 71-72; V Carl St Luke Morton 72-79; V Wotton St Mary *Glouc* from 79; Offg Chapl RAF from 80; RD Glouc City *Glouc* 88-94; Hon Can Glouc Cathl from 90. *Holy Trinity Vicarage, Church Road, Longlevens, Gloucester GL2 0AJ* Gloucester (01452) 524129

NUNN, Peter Rawling. b 51. Ox Univ BA73 Sheff Univ MSc74 BA85. Oak Hill Th Coll 82. **d** 85 **p** 86. C Bispham *Blackb* 85-87; C-in-c Anchorsholme 87-89; V from 89. *The Vicarage, 36 Valeway Avenue, Thornton Cleveleys, Lancs FY5 3RN* Blackpool (01253) 856646

NUNN, Mrs Sheila Jean. b 43. Southn Univ DipT64. Sarum & Wells Th Coll DipMin94. **d** 94 **p** 95. C Caversham and Mapledurham *Ox* from 94. *25 Ilkley Road, Reading RG4 7BD* Reading (01734) 472070

NUNN, Stephen Robert. b 64. St Jo Coll Nottm BTh92. **d** 92 **p** 93. C Hailsham *Chich* 92-95; C Hollington St Leon from 95. *158 Old Church Road, St Leonards-on-Sea, E Sussex TN38 9HD* Hastings (01424) 852486

NUNNERLEY, William John Arthur. b 27. Univ of Wales (Lamp) BA54 St Chad's Coll Dur DipTh56. **d** 56 **p** 57. Chapl RN 60-81; QHC from 79; R Barnoldby le Beck *Linc* 81-92; R Waltham 81-92; rtd 92. *Juniper Cottage, 82B Lower Street, Merriott, Somerset TA16 5NW* Crewkerne (01460) 76049

NUNNEY, Miss Sheila Frances. b 49. NNEB69 SRN74 RSCN74 SCM75 RCN STDip81. Oak Hill Th Coll BA92. **d** 92 **p** 94. C Swaffham *Nor* from 92. *8 Hoveton Drive, Swaffham, Norfolk PE37 7SQ* Swaffham (01760) 722717

NURSER, Canon John Shelley. b 29. Peterho Cam BA50 MA54 PhD58. Wells Th Coll 58. **d** 58 **p** 59. Australia 68-74; R Freckenham w Worlington *St E* 74-76; Can Res and Chan Linc Cathl *Linc* 76-92; Can and Preb Linc Cathl 92-94; P-in-c Shudy Camps *Ely* 92-94; rtd 94. *Shudy Camps Vicarage, Cambridge CB1 6RE* Saffron Walden (01799) 584809

NURTON, Robert. b 44. Univ of Wales (Lamp) BA67. Ridley Hall Cam 67. **d** 69 **p** 70. C Bris St Andr Hartcliffe *Bris* 69-73; C Ipswich St Mary at Stoke w St Pet & St Mary Quay *St E* 73-77;

Chapl RN from 77. *Directorate Gen, RN Chapl Services, Room 203, Victory Building, HM Naval Base, Portsmouth PO1 3LS* Portsmouth (01705) 727903 Fax 727112

NUTH, Stephen William. b 55. Nazarene Th Coll Man CertRS87 St Jo Coll Nottm LTh95. **d** 95. C Wadhurst *Chich* from 95; C Stonegate from 95. *The Vicarage, Stonegate, Wadhurst, E Sussex TN5 7EJ* Ticehurst (01580) 200515

NUTTALL, George Herman. b 31. St Jo Coll Dur BA59 DipTh61. Cranmer Hall Dur 59. **d** 61 **p** 62. C Eccleshill *Bradf* 61-65; V Oldham St Barn *Man* 65-70; Area Sec (Dios Derby and Lich) CMS 70-81; V Derby St Aug *Derby* 81-84; Chapl Bournemouth and Poole Colls *Sarum* from 85; Chapl Dorset Inst of HE 85-90; Chapl Bournemouth Poly *Win* 90-92; Chapl Bournemouth Univ from 92. *14 Crescent Road, Poole, Dorset BH14 9AS* Poole (01202) 745806 or 524111

NUTTALL, Ven Michael John Berkeley. b 36. AKC60. St Boniface Warminster 61. **d** 61 **p** 62. C Chapel Allerton *Ripon* 61-64; C Stanningley St Thos 64-68; V Leeds Gipton Epiphany 68-76; P-in-c Stainby w Gunby *Linc* 76-83; R N Witham 76-83; R S Witham 76-83; TV Bottesford w Ashby 83-88; I Adare w Kilpeacon and Croom *L & K* from 88; Adn Limerick from 92. *The Rectory, Adare, Co Limerick, Irish Republic* Limerick (61) 396227

NUTTALL, Wilfrid. b 29. ACP59 Open Univ BA82. Chich Th Coll 82. **d** 84 **p** 85. C Accrington St Jo *Blackb* 84-86; C Darwen St Cuth w Tockholes St Steph 86-89; V Foulridge 89-92; rtd 92. *15 Hope Road, Deal, Kent CT14 7DG*

NYE, Canon David Charles. b 39. K Coll Lon BD65. **d** 63 **p** 64. C Charlton Kings St Mary *Glouc* 63-67; C Yeovil St Jo w Preston Plucknett *B & W* 67-70; V Lower Cam *Glouc* 70-74; Min Can Glouc Cathl 74-79; Dir of Ords 74-79; Prin Glouc Th Course 74-79; V Glouc St Mary de Lode and St Nic *Glouc* 74-76; V Maisemore 76-79; Chapl Grenville Coll Bideford 79-81; V Leckhampton SS Phil and Jas w Cheltenham St Jas *Glouc* from 81; Hon Can Glouc Cathl from 88; RD Cheltenham from 89. *St Philip's Vicarage, 80 Painswick Road, Cheltenham, Glos GL50 2EW* Cheltenham (01242) 525460

NYE, Ven Nathaniel Kemp (Niel). b 14. AKC36. Cuddesdon Coll 36. **d** 37 **p** 38. Tait Missr Cant 66-72; Adn Maidstone *Cant* 72-79; rtd 79. *Lees Cottage, Boughton Lees, Ashford, Kent TN25 4HX* Ashford (01233) 626175

O

OADES, Michael Anthony John. b 45. Brasted Th Coll 69 Sarum & Wells Th Coll 71. **d** 73 **p** 74. C Eltham Park St Luke *S'wark* 73-78; C Coulsdon St Andr 78-81; P-in-c Mert St Jas 81-85; V 85-87; V Benhilton from 87. *All Saints' Vicarage, All Saints' Road, Sutton, Surrey SM1 3DA* 0181-644 9070

OADES, Canon Peter Robert. b 24. Fitzw Ho Cam BA47 CertEd48 MA53. **d** 67 **p** 67. VC Sarum Cathl *Sarum* 68-74; Chapl Sarum Cathl Sch 68-74; P-in-c Sturminster Newton and Hinton St Mary *Sarum* 74-75; V 75-81; R Stock and Lydlinch 75-81; RD Blackmore Vale 78-81; V Woodford Valley 81-89; Can and Preb Sarum Cathl 85-89; rtd 89; Perm to Offic *Sarum* from 89; Hon Chapl to the Deaf from 89; Perm to Offic *Win* from 89. *28 Mulberry Gardens, Fordingbridge, Hants SP6 1BP* Fordingbridge (01425) 657113

OAKE, Barry Richard. b 47. ARICS71. Ripon Coll Cuddesdon 83. **d** 85 **p** 86. C Wantage *Ox* 85-88; C Warlingham w Chelsham and Farleigh *S'wark* 88-91; R N w S Wootton *Nor* from 91. *The Rectory, Castle Rising Road, South Wootton, King's Lynn, Norfolk PE30 3JA* King's Lynn (01553) 671381

OAKES, Graham. b 42. Leeds Univ DipTh68. Chich Th Coll 68. **d** 70 **p** 71. C Hulme Ascension *Man* 70-74; C Clifton All SS w Tyndalls Park *Bris* 74-76; P-in-c Chadderton St Mark *Man* 76-78; V 78-82; V King Cross *Wakef* 82-95; R Bath H Trin *B & W* from 95. *Holy Trinity Rectory, 9 Marlborough Lane, Bath BA1 2NQ* Bath (01225) 422311

OAKES, Miss Jennifer May. b 43. Trin Coll Bris DipHE80. **dss** 82 **d** 87 **p** 94. Wilnecote *Lich* 82-85; Stoneydelph St Martin CD 82-85; Bentley 85-87; Par Dn 87-89; NSM Hixon w Stowe-by-Chartley 89-93; Par Dn 93-94; Par Dn Fradswell, Gayton, Milwich and Weston 93-94; C Hixon w Stowe-by-Chartley from 94; C Fradswell, Gayton, Milwich and Weston from 94. *Church House, 10 Meadow Glade, Hixton, Stafford ST8 0NT* Weston (01889) 271068

OAKES, Jeremy Charles. b 51. ACA75 FCA81. Westcott Ho Cam 75. **d** 78 **p** 79. C Evington *Leic* 78-81; C Ringwood *Win*

81-84; P-in-c Thurnby Lodge *Leic* 84-89; TV Oakdale St Geo *Sarum* 89-95; P-in-c Canford Cliffs and Sandbanks from 95. *The Vicarage, 14 Flaghead Road, Poole, Dorset BH13 7JW* Canford Cliffs (01202) 700341

OAKES, John Cyril. b 49. AKC71. St Aug Coll Cant 71. **d** 72 **p** 73. C Broseley w Benthall *Heref* 72-76; C Cannock *Lich* 76-79; TV 79-83; V Rough Hills from 83; P-in-c Wolv St Steph from 94. *St Martin's Vicarage, Dixon Street, Wolverhampton WV2 2BG* Wolverhampton (01902) 341030

OAKES, Canon Leslie John. b 28. AKC53. **d** 54 **p** 55. V Longbridge *Birm* 64-93; Hon Can Birm Cathl 84-93; rtd 93; Perm to Offic *Birm* from 93. *108 Hole Lane, Birmingham B31 2DF* 0121-476 8514

OAKES, Melvin. b 36. Linc Th Coll 77. **d** 79 **p** 80. C Lt Ilford St Mich *Chelmsf* 79-82; V Highams Park All SS from 82. *All Saints' Vicarage, 12A Castle Avenue, London E4 9QD* 0181-527 3269

OAKES, Robert. b 47. Ex & Truro NSM Scheme. **d** 82 **p** 83. NSM Probus, Ladock and Grampound w Creed and St Erme *Truro* 82-84; TV Bodmin w Lanhydrock and Lanivet 85-88; R S Hill w Callington from 88; P-in-c Linkinhorne 88-89; RD E Wivelshire from 95. *The Rectory, Liskeard Road, Callington, Cornwall PL17 7JD* Liskeard (01579) 383341

OAKHAM, Archdeacon of. *See* FERNYHOUGH, Ven Bernard

OAKLEY, Barry Wyndham. b 32. TD72. SS Coll Cam BA53 MA57. Ridley Hall Cam 56. **d** 58 **p** 59. C Alverstoke *Portsm* 58-61; C Bermondsey St Mary w St Olave and St Jo *S'wark* 61-63; V Crofton *Portsm* 63-78; V Edmonton All SS *Lon* 78-82; P-in-c Edmonton St Mich 80-82; V Edmonton All SS w St Mich from 82. *All Saints' Vicarage, 43 All Saints' Close, London N9 9AT* 0181-803 9199

OAKLEY, Hilary Robert Mark. b 53. Univ of Wales (Ban) BSc75 Ox Univ BA78. Ripon Coll Cuddesdon 76. **d** 79 **p** 80. C Birm St Pet *Birm* 79-82; C Cam Gt St Mary w St Mich *Ely* 82-86; Chapl Girton Coll Cam 82-86; Chapl Zurich w St Gallen and Winterthur *Eur* 86-88; NSM Lon 88-92; Perm to Offic *St Alb* from 92. *40 Kimberley Road, St Albans, Herts AL3 5PX* St Albans (01272) 834072

OAKLEY, Mark David. b 68. K Coll Lon BD90 AKC90. St Steph Ho Ox 90. **d** 93 **p** 94. C St Jo Wood *Lon* from 93. *3 Cochrane Street, London NW8 7PA* 0171-722 4766

OAKLEY, Richard John. b 46. AKC69 St Aug Coll Cant 69. **d** 70 **p** 71. C Wythenshawe Wm Temple Ch *Man* 70-75; V Ashton H Trin 75-80; CR 80-93; Lic to Offic *Lon* 88-93; V Cantley *Sheff* from 93. *St Wilfrid's Vicarage, 200 Cantley Lane, Doncaster, S Yorkshire DN4 6PA* Doncaster (01302) 535133

OAKLEY, Robert Paul. b 51. Sheff Univ BScTech72 PGCE74. St Jo Coll Nottm DipTh89. **d** 89 **p** 90. C Heatherlands St Jo *Sarum* 89-92; V Burton All SS w Ch Ch *Lich* from 92. *242 Blackpool Street, Burton-on-Trent, Staffs DE14 3AU* Burton-on-Trent (01283) 65134

OAKLEY, Robin Ian. b 37. Ripon Hall Ox 68. **d** 70 **p** 71. C Leighton Buzzard *St Alb* 70-73; C Watford St Mich 73-76; R Ickleford 76-80; R Ickleford w Holwell from 80. *The Rectory, 36 Turnpike Lane, Ickleford, Hitchin, Herts SG5 3XB* Hitchin (01462) 432925

OAKLEY, Susan Mary. *See* HENWOOD, Mrs Susan Mary

OAKLEY, Timothy Crispin (Tim). b 45. Qu Coll Cam BA66 MA70. St Jo Coll Nottm 73. **d** 76 **p** 77. C Bromley Common St Aug *Roch* 76-79; C Fairfield *Liv* 79-81; CMS 82-90; Kenya 82-90; P-in-c Beaford, Roborough and St Giles in the Wood *Ex* from 91. *The Vicarage, Beaford, Winkleigh, Devon EX19 8NN* Beaford (018053) 213

OATES, Alan. b 32. S'wark Ord Course 79. **d** 80 **p** 81. NSM Rayleigh *Chelmsf* 80-87; TV Jarrow *Dur* 87-92; P-in-c Stella from 92. *The Rectory, Shibdon Road, Blaydon-on-Tyne, Tyne & Wear NE21 5AE* 0191-414 2720

OATES, Austin Edwin. b 17. Worc Ord Coll. **d** 63 **p** 64. V Plemstall w Guilden Sutton *Ches* 67-74; V Crowton 74-88; rtd 88. *31 Haleview Road, Helsby, Warrington WA6 9PH* Helsby (01928) 723908

OATES, Canon John. b 30. Kelham Th Coll 53. **d** 57 **p** 58. C Hackney Wick St Mary of Eton w St Aug *Lon* 57-60; Development Officer C of E Youth Coun 60-64; Sec C of E Coun Commonwealth Settlement 64-65; Gen Sec 65-72; Sec C of E Cttee on Migration & Internat Affairs 68-72; Hon Can Bunbury from 69; V Richmond St Mary *S'wark* 70-79; P-in-c Richmond St Jo 76-79; V Richmond St Mary w St Matthias and St Jo 79-84; RD Richmond and Barnes 79-84; R St Bride Fleet Street w Bridewell etc *Lon* from 84. *St Bride's Rectory, Fleet Street, London EC4Y 8AU* 0171-353 1301 or 583 0239 Fax 583 4867

OATES, John Francis Titus. b 27. SSC Worc Coll Ox BA50 MA54. Qu Coll Birm 50. **d** 52 **p** 53. Chapl RN 56-67; USA from 67; rtd 92. *RR1, Box 878, Belfast, Maine 04915, USA* Belfast (207) 338-4796

OATES, Michael Graham. b 62. Leic Poly BSc84. Aston Tr Scheme 87. Cranmer Hall Dur 89. **d** 92 **p** 93. C Enfield St Andr

Lon from 92. *159 Parsonage Lane, Enfield, Middx EN1 3UJ* 0181-364 6628

OATEY, Canon Michael John. b 31. Chich Th Coll 57. **d** 60 **p** 61. C W Drayton *Lon* 60-66; V Chiswick St Mich 66-74; R St Sampson *Truro* from 74; V Tywardreath w Tregaminion from 74; Hon Can Truro Cathl from 88. *The Vicarage, Tywardreath, Par, Cornwall PL24 2PL* Par (01726) 812998

OBAN, Provost of. *See* MACLEAN, Very Rev Allan Murray

OBEE, Douglas Walter. b 18. Roch Th Coll 65. **d** 67 **p** 68. C Beckenham St Geo *Roch* 67-71; R Whitestone *Ex* 71-75; V Oldridge 72-75; P-in-c Harford 76-87; V Ivybridge 76-87; V Ivybridge w Harford 87; rtd 87; Perm to Offic *Ex* from 88. *16 Kerswill Road, Exeter EX4 1NY* Exeter (01392) 439405

O'BENEY, Robin Mervyn. b 35. Ely Th Coll 61. **d** 64 **p** 65. Hon C Wymondham *Nor* 74-76; R Swainsthorpe w Newton Flotman 76-80; NSM Sparkenhoe Deanery *Leic* 87-90; V Billesdon and Skeffington 90-91; rtd 95. *Tigh Na Bochd, Bunessan, Isle of Mull PA67 6DH* Bunessan (01681) 700281

OBERST, Simon Julian. b 57. ACA83 Trin Coll Cam BA79 MA82. Wycliffe Hall Ox DipTh90. **d** 91 **p** 92. C S Croydon Em *S'wark* 91-95; V Chipping Campden w Ebrington *Glouc* from 95. *The Vicarage, Chipping Campden, Glos GL55 6HU* Evesham (01386) 840671

O'BRIEN, Andrew David. b 61. Nottm Univ BTh88. Linc Th Coll 85. **d** 88 **p** 89. C Clare w Poslingford *St E* 88-89; C Clare w Poslingford, Cavendish etc 89-91; V Belton All SS *Linc* from 91. *The Vicarage, Belton, Doncaster, S Yorkshire DN9 1NS* Epworth (01427) 872207

O'BRIEN, Donogh Smith. b 34. St Pet Hall Ox BA56 MA60. Ripon Hall Ox 56. **d** 57 **p** 58. C Gt Sankey *Liv* 57-63; C Farnworth 63-66; Lic to Offic from 66; Asst Master Wade Deacon Gr Sch Widnes from 66. *Fourways, 178 Lunts Heath Road, Farnworth, Widnes, Cheshire WA8 9AZ* 0151-424 0147

O'BRIEN, George Edward. b 32. Clifton Th Coll 61. **d** 64 **p** 65. V Castle Town *Lich* 68-88; Chapl St Geo Hosp Stafford from 88; Chapl Kingsmead Hosp Stafford from 88; rtd 92. *185 Tixall Road, Stafford ST16 3XJ* Stafford (01785) 44261

O'BRIEN, Canon James Henry. b 10. Bps' Coll Cheshunt 42. **d** 44 **p** 45. R D Darwen *Blackb* 64-75; V Darwen St Cuth 67-75; Hon Can Blackb Cathl 73-75; rtd 75; C Adlington *Blackb* 75-79; Lic to Offic from 79. *21 Suffolk Street, Blackburn BB2 4ES* Blackburn (01254) 264799

O'BRIEN, John. b 41. St Jo Coll Cam BA63 MA67. Ridley Hall Cam 63. **d** 65 **p** 66. C Wotton St Mary *Glouc* 65-69; Youth Chapl 67-69; Lect Coll of SS Paul and Mary Cheltenham 69-85; V Twigworth, Down Hatherley, Norton, The Leigh etc *Glouc* from 85; RD Glouc N from 94. *The Rectory, Twigworth, Gloucester GL2 9PQ* Gloucester (01452) 731483

O'BRIEN, Mary. b 68. Leeds Univ BSc90. St Jo Coll Nottm BTh93 DipMM94. **d** 94 **p** 95. C Middleton St Mary *Ripon* from 94. *40 Manor Farm Gardens, Leeds LS10 3RA* Leeds (0113) 277 5276

O'BRIEN, Shelagh Ann. *See* STACEY, Mrs Shelagh Ann

O'BYRNE, Francis Michael. b 12. Tyndale Hall Bris 41. **d** 44 **p** 45. I Athboy Union *M & K* 56-81; Can Meath 76-81; rtd 81. *Birch Lea, Old Connaught Avenue, Bray, Co Wicklow, Irish Republic* Dublin (1) 282-4429

OCKFORD, Paul Philip. b 46. St Chad's Coll Dur BA67. St Steph Ho Ox 68. **d** 70 **p** 71. C Streatham St Pet *S'wark* 70-74; C Cheam 74-77; P-in-c Eastrington *York* 77-79; TV Howden TM 80-83; R Sherburn and W and E Heslerton w Yedingham 83-92; V Bampton, Morebath, Clayhanger and Petton *Ex* from 92. *The Vicarage, Bampton, Tiverton, Devon EX16 9NG* Bampton (01398) 331385

OCKWELL, Canon Herbert George Grant. b 12. Kelham Th Coll 30. **d** 36 **p** 37. R Blendworth, Chalton and Idsworth *Portsm* 70-81; rtd 81; Perm to Offic *Portsm* from 81; Perm to Offic *Chich* from 82. *72 Bowes Hill, Rowland's Castle, Hants PO9 6BS* Rowland's Castle (01705) 412301

O'CONNELL, Miss Mary Joy. b 49. York Univ BA71 Leeds Univ CertEd74. Chich Th Coll 84. **dss** 86 **d** 87 **p** 94. Cinderhill *S'well* 86-87; Par Dn 87-94; C 94; P-in-c from 94. *The Vicarage, Nuthall Road, Nottingham NG8 6AD* Nottingham (0115) 978 1514

O'CONNOR, Canon Alfred Stanley. b 20. TCD BA43 MA60. **d** 43 **p** 44. I Drumglass *Arm* 65-85; Can Arm Cathl 83-85; rtd 85. *Highfield, Greenhill Road, Brookeborough, Enniskillen, Co Fermanagh BT94 4EZ* Brookeborough (0136553) 725

O'CONNOR, Canon Brian Michael McDougal. b 42. St Cath Coll Cam BA67 MA69. Cuddesdon Coll 67. **d** 69 **p** 70. C Headington *Ox* 69-71; Sec Dioc Past and Redundant Chs Uses Cttees 72-79; P-in-c Mert 72-76; V Rainham *Roch* from 79; RD Gillingham 81-88; Hon Can Roch Cathl from 89. *The Vicarage, 80 Broadview Avenue, Gillingham, Kent ME8 9DE* Medway (01634) 231534

O'CONNOR, Canon Dr Daniel. b 33. Univ Coll Dur BA54 MA67 St Andr Univ PhD81. Cuddesdon Coll 56. **d** 58 **p** 59. C Stockton St Pet *Dur* 58-62; C W Hartlepool St Aid 62-63;

CMD 63-70; USPG 70-72; India 63-72; Chapl St Andr Univ *St And* 72-77; R Edin Gd Shep *Edin* 77-82; Prin Coll of the Ascension Selly Oak 82-90; Dir Scottish Chs Ho (Chs Together in Scotland) 90-93; Can Res Wakef Cathl *Wakef* from 93; Bp's Adv on Inter-Faith Issues from 93. *3 Cathedral Close, Margaret Street, Wakefield, W Yorkshire WF1 2DQ* Wakefield (01924) 374349

O'CONNOR, Edward Howard. b 32. AIMLS59 FRSH65. Linc Th Coll 81 Immanuel Coll Ibadan 76. **d** 77 **p** 79. Nigeria 77-81; P-in-c Newchurch *Portsm* 81-83; V 83-91; P-in-c Arreton 82-83; V 83-91; Chapl HM Pris Kingston (Portsm) from 91; rtd 92. *23 Arundel Road, Ryde, Isle of Wight PO33 1BW* Isle of Wight (01983) 617062

O'CONNOR, John Goodrich. b 34. Keble Coll Ox BA58 MA60. Lich Th Coll. **d** 61 **p** 62. C Blackpool St Steph *Blackb* 61-66; C Holbeck *Ripon* 66-68; C Hendon St Mary *Lon* 68-73; TV Thornaby on Tees *York* 73-79; TR 79-89; V Blyth St Cuth *Newc* from 89; Chapl Wellesley Nautical Sch from 89. *The Vicarage, 29 Ridley Avenue, Blyth, Northd NE24 3BA* Blyth (01670) 352410

O'CONNOR, Nigel George. b 25. TD66. Linc Th Coll 53. **d** 55 **p** 56. CF (TA) 62-71; R Ivychurch w Old Romney and Midley *Cant* 65-74; V Brenzett w Snargate and Snave 65-74; R Newchurch 65-74; R St Mary in the Marsh 65-74; R Burmarsh 65-74; V Brookland w Fairfield 65-74; CF (R of D) 71-91; V S w N Hayling *Portsm* 74-85; V Corby Glen *Linc* 85-91; rtd 91. *Winterbourne House, Allington, Salisbury SP4 0BZ* Idmiston (01980) 611453

ODDY, Canon Frederick Brian. b 29. Univ of Wales (Lamp) BA50. Linc Th Coll 50. **d** 52 **p** 53. C Preston Em *Blackb* 52-55; C St Annes 55-57; V Chorley St Jas 57-64; V Warton St Oswald 64-76; P-in-c Yealand Conyers 74-76; V Warton St Oswald w Yealand Conyers from 76; RD Tunstall 84-90; Hon Can Blackb Cathl from 89. *St Oswald's Vicarage, Warton, Carnforth, Lancs LA5 9PG* Carnforth (01524) 732946

ODLING-SMEE, Dr George William. b 35. FRCS68 K Coll Dur MB, BS59. **d** 77 **p** 78. NSM Belf St Thos *Conn* 77-90; NSM Belf St Geo from 90. *10 Deramore Park South, Belfast BT9 5JY* Belfast (01232) 669275

ODLUM, Michael Julian. b 24. DFC45. St Mich Coll Llan 55. **d** 56 **p** 57. V Sampford Arundel *B & W* 67-74; Asst Chapl HM Pris Wandsworth 74; Chapl HM Pris Standford Hill 74-81; Chapl HM Pris Leic 82-89; rtd 89. *67A Main Street, Kirby Muxloe, Leicester LE9 2AN*

O'DONNELL, Kevin George. b 57. Man Univ BA78 Didsbury Coll Man PGCE79. St Steph Ho Ox 86. **d** 88 **p** 89. C Tokyngton St Mich *Lon* 88-90; C Ascot Heath *Ox* 90-92; Perm to Offic from 94. *74 Fernbank Road, Ascot, Berks SL5 8HE* Ascot (01344) 882296

O'DONOVAN, Canon Oliver Michael Timothy. b 45. Ball Coll Ox BA68 MA71 DPhil75. Wycliffe Hall Ox 68. **d** 72 **p** 73. Tutor Wycliffe Hall Ox 72-77; Canada 77-82; Can Res Ch Ch *Ox* from 82; Regius Prof Moral and Past Th Ox Univ from 82. *Christ Church, Oxford OX1 1DP* Oxford (01865) 276219

OEHRING, Anthony Charles. b 56. Sheff City Poly BA79 CQSW79. Ridley Hall Cam 86. **d** 88 **p** 89. C Gillingham *Sarum* 88-91; TV S Gillingham *Roch* from 91. *60 Parkwood Green, Gillingham, Kent ME8 9PP* Snodland (01634) 235837

OEPPEN, John Gerard David. b 44. St D Coll Lamp DipTh67. **d** 67 **p** 68. C-in-c Cwmmer w Abercregan CD *Llan* 67-70; TV Glyncorrwg w Afan Vale and Cymmer Afan 70-71; C Whitchurch 71-74; V Aberavon H Trin 74-78; V Bargoed and Deri w Brithdir 78-86; R Barry All SS from 86. *The Rectory, 3 Park Road, Barry, M Glam CF62 6NU* Barry (01446) 734629

OESTREICHER, Canon Paul. b 31. OM(Ger)95. Univ of NZ BA53 MA56 Cov Poly Hon DLitt91. Linc Th Coll 56. **d** 59 **p** 60. C Dalston H Trin w St Phil *Lon* 59-61; C S Mymms K Chas 61-68; Asst in Relig Broadcasting BBC 61-64; Assoc Sec Internat Affairs Dept BCC 64-69; V Blackheath Ascension *S'wark* 68-81; Dir of Tr 69-72; Hon Can S'wark Cathl 78-81; Lic to Offic 81-86; Asst Gen Sec BCC 81-86; Can Res Cov Cathl *Cov* from 86; Dir of Internat Min from 86; Humboldt Fell, Inst of Th, Free Univ of Berlin 92-93; Lic to Offic *Eur* 92-93. *20 Styvechale Avenue, Coventry CV5 6DX* Coventry (01203) 673704 or 634531 Fax 631448

O'FERRALL, Very Rev Basil Arthur. b 24. CB79. TCD BA48 MA65. TCD Div Sch Div Test48. **d** 48 **p** 49. Chapl RN 51-75; Chapl of the Fleet and Adn for the RN 75-80; QHC 75-80; Hon Can Gib Cathl *Eur* 77-80; Chapl to The Queen 80-85; V Ranworth w Panxworth and Woodbastwick *Nor* 80-85; Bp's Chapl Norfolk Broads 80-85; Hon Can Win Cathl *Win* 85-93; R Jersey St Helier 85-93; Dean Jersey 85-93; Pres Jersey Miss to Seamen 85-93; Angl Adv Channel TV 85-93; rtd 93. *The Stone House, Barrack Square, Winchelsea, E Sussex TN36 4EG* Rye (01797) 223458

OFFER, Ven Dr Clifford Jocelyn. b 43. Ex Univ BA67. Westcott Ho Cam 67. **d** 69 **p** 70. C Bromley SS Pet and Paul *Roch* 69-74;

TV Southn (City Cen) *Win* 74-83; TR Hitchin *St Alb* 83-94; Adn Nor from 94; Can Res Nor Cathl from 94. *26 The Close, Norwich NR1 4DZ* Norwich (01603) 620375

OGDEN, Cyril Newton. b 12. AKC39. **d** 39 **p** 40. V Holbeach Fen *Linc* 69-77; V Whaplode 60-77; rtd 77; Perm to Offic *Linc* 77-88; Perm to Offic *Glouc* from 88. *1 Chapelside, Clapton Row, Bourton-on-the-Water, Cheltenham, Glos GL54 2DN* Cotswold (01451) 821440

OGDEN, Eric. b 34. NW Ord Course 73. **d** 76 **p** 77. NSM Lydgate St Anne *Man* 76-92; NSM St Anne Lydgate w Ch Ch Friezland from 92. *40 Burnedge Lane, Grasscroft, Oldham OL4 4EA* Saddleworth (01457) 873661

OGDEN, Canon Eric Grayson. b 06. AKC32. St Steph Ho Ox 32. **d** 32 **p** 33. R Upper St Leonards St Jo *Chich* 65-72; rtd 72; Chapl Costa del Sol E *Eur* 72-76; Chapl Malaga w Almunecar and Nerja 76-78; Hon C Worthing St Andr *Chich* from 79. *Fernbank, 25 Gratwicke Road, Worthing, W Sussex BN11 4BJ*

OGDEN, Harry. b 30. AKC57. **d** 58 **p** 59. V Farnworth and Kearsley *Man* 69-72; V Oldham St Steph and All Martyrs 72-79; R Moss Side Ch Ch 79-95; rtd 95. *16 Tysoe Gardens, Salford M3 6BL* 0161-839 1761

OGDEN-SWIFT, Geoffrey William. b 21. Pemb Coll Cam BA46 MA48. Cuddesdon Coll 47. **d** 49 **p** 50. V Soham *Ely* 66-80; RD Fordham 70-78; P-in-c Over 80-86; rtd 87. *40 Station Road, Fulbourn, Cambridge CB1 5ES* Cambridge (01223) 881571

OGILVIE, Canon Gordon. b 42. Glas Univ MA64 Lon Univ BD67. ALCD66. **d** 67 **p** 68. C Ashtead *Guildf* 67-72; V New Barnet St Jas *St Alb* 72-80; Dir Past Studies Wycliffe Hall Ox 80-87; P-in-c Harlow New Town w Lt Parndon *Chelmsf* 87-89; R 89-94; TR Harlow Town Centre w Lt Parndon from 94; Chapl Princess Alexandra Hosp Harlow from 88; Hon Can Chelmsf Cathl *Chelmsf* from 94. *The Rectory, 43 Upper Park, Harlow, Essex CM20 1TW* Harlow (01279) 424616

OGILVIE, Ian Douglas. b 37. Em Coll Cam BA59 MA63. Linc Th Coll 59. **d** 61 **p** 62. C Clapham H Trin *S'wark* 61-63; C Cam Gt St Mary w St Mich *Ely* 63-66; Chapl Sevenoaks Sch Kent 66-77; Hon C Sevenoaks St Nic *Roch* 67-77; Chapl Malvern Coll Worcs 77-84; Hd Master St Geo Sch Harpenden 84-87; Lic to Offic *St Alb* 84-87; Bp's Dom Chapl 87-89; P-in-c Aldenham 87-91; Appeals Dir Mind 89-91; Fund Raising Dir Br Deaf Assn from 91; NSM Tring *St Alb* 92-94; Perm to Offic from 94. *The White House, 19 Lower Icknield Way, Marsworth, Tring, Herts HP23 4LN* Cheddington (01296) 661479

OGLE, Ms Catherine. b 61. Leeds Univ BA82 MPhil85 Fitzw Coll Cam BA87. Westcott Ho Cam 85. **d** 88 **p** 94. C Middleton St Mary *Ripon* 89-91; Relig Progr Ed BBC Radio Leeds 91-95; NSM Leeds St Marg and All Hallows 91-95; P-in-c Woolley *Wakef* from 95. *The Vicarage, Church Street, Wakefield, W Yorkshire WF4 2JU* Barnsley (01226) 382550

OGLESBY, Canon Leslie Ellis (Les). b 46. Univ Coll Ox BA69 MA73 City Univ MPhil73 Fitzw Coll Cam BA73 MA77. Ripon Coll Cuddesdon 77. **d** 78 **p** 79. C Stevenage St Mary Shephall *St Alb* 78-80; Dir St Alb Minl Tr Scheme 80-87; V Markyate Street *St Alb* 80-87; Dir Continuing Minl Educn 87-94; Hon Can St Alb from 93; TR Hitchin from 94. *The Rectory, 21 West Hill, Hitchin, Herts SG5 2HZ* Hitchin (01462) 434017 or 452758

OGLEY, John. b 40. Oak Hill Th Coll 62. **d** 65 **p** 66. C Ardsley *Sheff* 65-68; C Carlton-in-the-Willows *S'well* 68-71; P-in-c Tollerton 71-79; V Skegby 79-93; R Carlton-in-Lindrick from 93. *The Rectory, Carlton-in-Lindrick, Worksop, Notts S81 9EF* Worksop (01909) 730222

O'GORMAN, Paul Anthony. b 46. Portsm Poly BSc79. Oak Hill Th Coll DipHE81. **d** 81 **p** 82. C Leyton St Mary w St Edw *Chelmsf* 81-83; C Rayleigh 83-84; CF 84-87; R Northiam *Chich* 87-93; V Hastings Em and St Mary in the Castle from 93. *The Vicarage, Vicarage Road, Hastings, E Sussex TN34 3NA* Hastings (01424) 421543

O'HANLON, Canon William Douglas. b 11. Peterho Cam BA32 MA37. Clifton Th Coll 32. **d** 37 **p** 38. Can and Preb Sarum Cathl *Sarum* 61-82; R Studland 72-82; rtd 82. *Crown Hill, 14 Bon Accord Road, Swanage, Dorset BH19 2DT* Swanage (01929) 425416

OHS, Lt-Comdr Douglas Fredrick. b 49. Saskatchewan Univ BA74. Em Coll Saskatoon LTh75. **d** 74 **p** 75. C Bridgwater St Mary w Chilton Trinity *B & W* 75-77; Canada from 77. *Chaplain (P), CFB Suffield, PO Box 239, Ralston, Alberta, Canada, T0J 2N0*

OJI, Dr Erasmus Oluchukwu. b 43. LRCP70 MRCS70 FRCS76 Lon Univ BSc66. Oak Hill Th Coll 75. **d** 78 **p** 79. C Ealing Dean St Jo *Lon* 78-80; Nigeria 80-90; Asst Chapl Rotherham Distr Gen Hosp 90-91; Perm to Offic *Sheff* from 92. *369 Fulwood Road, Sheffield S10 3BS* Sheffield (0114) 266 1360

OKE, Michael John. b 42. Ox Min Course 89. **d** 92 **p** 93. NSM Stratfield Mortimer *Ox* from 92. *Gladstone Cotage,*

18 Windmill Road, Mortimer, Reading RG7 3RN Reading (01734) 332829

OKEKE, Canon Ken Sandy Edozie. b 41. Nigeria Univ BSc67. **d** 76 **p** 76. Nigeria 76-80 and 87-89; Chapl to Nigerians in UK and Irish Republic 80-87; Hon Can Kwara from 85; C Man Whitworth *Man* from 89; Chapl Insts Higher Learning Man from 89. *296 Wilbraham Road, Chorlton-cum-Hardy, Manchester M21 1UU* 0161-881 5771 or 273 1465

OKELLO, Modicum. b 53. Nairobi Sch of Miss DipMiss82 Haggaih Inst of Chr Leadership DipCL86 Wycliffe Hall Ox 86 Trin Coll Bris BA90 St Paul's Coll Limuru DipTh78. **d** 78 **p** 79. Kenya 78-80; Uganda 80-86; NSM Goodmayes All SS *Chelmsf* 91-92; C Barking St Marg w St Patr from 92. *12 Thorpe Road, Barking, Essex IG11 9XJ* 0181-591 1238

OLD, Arthur Anthony George (Tony). b 36. Clifton Th Coll 69. **d** 71 **p** 72. C Clitheroe St Jas *Blackb* 71-73; C Bispham 73-77; V Haslingden St Jo Stonefold 77-81; TV Lowestoft and Kirkley *Nor* 81-83; Chapl to the Deaf *Cant* from 83; P-in-c Hernhill 83-85; C Preston next Faversham, Goodnestone and Graveney from 85. *25 Dence Park, Herne Bay, Kent CT6 6BQ* Herne Bay (01227) 360948

OLDALE, Harry. b 17. Bps' Coll Cheshunt 51. **d** 53 **p** 54. R Edgefield *Nor* 60-71; V Weybourne w Upper Sheringham 71-76; R Kelling w Salthouse 76-83; V Weybourne w Upper Sheringham 76-83; rtd 83; Perm to Offic *Nor* from 85. *St Stephen's, 24 Station Road, Holt, Norfolk NR25 6BS* Holt (01263) 713964

OLDEN, Canon Aidan Ronald Cuming. b 17. TCD BA38 MA41. CITC 39. **d** 40 **p** 41. Can Meath *M & K* 58-92; I Kells w Balrathboyne, Moynalty etc 60-92; Preb Tipper St Patr Cathl Dub 64-92; RD Clonard and Trim *M & K* 67-92; rtd 92. *Balreask New, Navan, Co Meath, Irish Republic* Navan (46) 27874

OLDFIELD, Roger Fielden. b 45. Qu Coll Cam BA67 MA71 City of Lon Poly DMS69 Lon Univ BD75. Trin Coll Bris 75. **d** 75 **p** 76. C Halliwell St Pet *Man* 75-80; V from 80; AD Bolton from 93. *St Peter's Vicarage, 1 Sefton Road, Harpers Lane, Bolton BL1 6HT* Bolton (01204) 849412 Fax 849440

OLDHAM, Canon Arthur Charles Godolphin. b 05. AKC33. **d** 34 **p** 34. Dir of Ords *Guildf* 58-71; Can Res Guildf Cathl 61-71; rtd 71; Perm to Offic *Guildf* 81-92. *The Lawn, Holybourne, Alton, Hants GU34 4ER* Alton (01420) 544293

OLDHAM, Charles Harry. b 14. St D Coll Lamp BA47. **d** 48 **p** 49. V Goff's Oak St Jas *St Alb* 68-79; rtd 79. *94 Prestbury Drive, Warminster, Wilts BA12 9LE* Warminster (01985) 213678

OLDHAM, Canon John. b 19. Kelham Th Coll 38. **d** 44 **p** 45. V Derby St Barn *Derby* 64-72; V Buxton 72-74; TR Buxton w Burbage and King Sterndale 74-84; Hon Can Derby Cathl 79-85; rtd 84; Perm to Offic *Derby* from 84. *Rose Cottage, Holt Lane, Lea, Matlock, Derbyshire DE4 5GQ* Dethick (01629) 534469

OLDLAND, Dr Hubert Charles (Peter). b 29. ARCS53 FRIC62 FRACI67 Imp Coll Lon BSc53 PhD56 DIC56. Ridley Coll Melbourne ThL85. **d** 83 **p** 84. Australia from 83. *5 Abbott Street, North Balwyn, Victoria, Australia 3104* Melbourne (3) 857-8768

OLDNALL, Frederick Herbert. b 16. Ripon Hall Ox 56. **d** 57 **p** 58. V Rosliston w Coton in the Elms *Derby* 62-83; rtd 83; Perm to Offic *Cov* from 93. *19 Keeling Road, Kenilworth, Coventry, Warks CV8 2JP* Kenilworth (01926) 52417

OLDROYD, Preb Colin Mitchell. b 30. Down Coll Cam BA54 MA60. Wells Th Coll 60. **d** 61 **p** 62. C Elton All SS *Man* 61-63; C Ex St Dav *Ex* 63-66; P-in-c Neen Sollars w Milson *Heref* 66-78; P-in-c Coreley w Doddington 66-78; R Cleobury Mortimer w Hopton Wafers 66-78; RD Ludlow 75-78; P-in-c Eastnor 78-81; R Ledbury 78-81; R Ledbury 78-81; Chapl Ledbury Cottage Hosp Heref from 79; R Ledbury w Eastnor *Heref* from 81; Preb Heref Cathl from 84; P-in-c Lt Marcle from 85. *The Rectory, Ledbury, Herefordshire HR8 1PL* Ledbury (01531) 632571

OLDROYD, David Christopher Leslie. b 42. FRICS. S Dios Minl Tr Scheme. **d** 85 **p** 86. NSM Four Marks *Win* 85-90; rtd 90. *Hill House, Spring Lane, Farnham, Surrey GU9 0JD* Farnham (01252) 737586

OLDROYD, James Healey. b 08. Worc Ord Coll. **d** 55 **p** 56. V Worc St Mark *Worc* 61-75; rtd 75; Perm to Offic *Worc* from 75. *7 Magnolia Close, Worcester WR5 3SJ* Worcester (01905) 355603

OLDROYD, Trevor. b 33. Hatf Coll Dur BA55 Lon Univ BD60. Wycliffe Hall Ox 60. **d** 61 **p** 62. W Germany 68-73; Chapl Dudley Sch 73-80; Asst Chapl Wellington Coll Berks 80-82; P-in-c Rendcomb *Glouc* 82-86; Chapl Rendcomb Coll 82-86; Chapl Wrekin Coll Shropshire 86-90; V Deptford St Jo w H Trin *S'wark* 91-94; rtd 94. *3 Dolphin Court, Northbrook Road, Swanage, Dorset BH19 1QJ* Swanage (01929) 427954

OLHAUSEN, William John. b 37. TCD BA60 MA63. Ridley Hall Cam 60. **d** 62 **p** 63. C Grassendale *Liv* 62-66; Asst Chapl

Dur Univ *Dur* 66-70; Lect Dur Univ 66-70; V Hazlemere *Ox* 70-89; RD Wycombe 78-83; Perm to Offic 89-93. *7 The Brae, Groomsport, Co Down BT19 6JG* Bangor (01247) 464454

OLIVE, Dan. b 29. ARIBA54. Sarum & Wells Th Coll 79. **d** 82 **p** 83. NSM Wells St Cuth w Wookey Hole *B & W* 82-85; C Yatton Moor 86-88; R Mells w Buckland Dinham, Elm, Whatley etc from 88; RD Frome from 93. *The Rectory, Mells, Frome, Somerset BA11 3PT* Mells (01373) 812320

OLIVER, Arthur Norman. b 16. Worc Ord Coll 63. **d** 65 **p** 66. C W Worthing St Jo *Chich* 69-71; R Etchingham 71-85; V Hurst Green 72-85; rtd 85; Perm to Offic *Ely* 86-89; Perm to Offic *Chich* from 89. *1 April Place, Buckhurst Road, Bexhill-on-Sea, E Sussex TN40 1UE* Bexhill-on-Sea (01424) 219838

OLIVER, Bernard John. b 31. CEng65 MIMechE. S'wark Ord Course 75. **d** 78 **p** 79. NSM Chipping Ongar *Chelmsf* 78-81; C Waltham Abbey 81-85; C High Ongar w Norton Mandeville 85-87; C Somerton w Compton Dundon, the Charltons etc *B & W* 87-88. *1 Orchard Way, Mosterton, Beaminster, Dorset DT8 3LT* Broadwindsor (01308) 868037

OLIVER, Canon David Ryland. b 34. Univ of Wales (Lamp) BA56 St Cath Coll Ox BA58 MA62. Wycliffe Hall Ox 56. **d** 58 **p** 59. C Carmarthen St Pet *St D* 58-61; C Llangyfelach and Morriston *S & B* 61-63; R Aberedw w Llandeilo Graban etc 63-66; R Llanbadarn Fawr, Llandegley and Llanfihangel etc 66-67; Lic to Offic *Llan* 68-70; Lic to Offic *Ban* 70-73; V Nefyn w Pistyll w Tudweiliog w Llandudwen etc 73-74; V Abercraf and Callwen *S & B* 74-77; V Llangyfelach 77-79; R Llanllwchaearn and Llanina *St D* 79-83; V Cwmaman 83-94; Can St D Cathl from 90; RD Dyffryn Aman 93-94; V Cynwyl Gaeo w Llansawel and Talley from 94. *The Vicarage, Talley, Llandeilo, Dyfed SA19 7YP* Talley (01558) 685229

OLIVER, Graham Frank. b 42. St Barn Coll Adelaide. **d** 68 **p** 69. Australia 68-86; C Ealing Ch the Sav *Lon* 86-93; Perm to Offic from 94. *19 Bond Street, London W5 5AP*

OLIVER, John Andrew George. b 28. OBE83. St Jo Coll Dur BA53 DipTh55. **d** 55 **p** 56. Chapl RN 61-83; QHC 79-83; R Guisborough *York* 83-89; Chapl and Tutor Whittington Coll Felbridge 89-93; rtd 93. *Allandale, Thacka Lane, Penrith, Cumbria CA11 9HX* Penrith (01768) 892096

OLIVER, Ven John Graham Wyand. b 47. Ridley Hall Cam 76. **d** 78 **p** 79. C Shortlands *Roch* 78-81; C Hammersmith St Paul *Lon* 81-85; Zambia from 85; Adn S Zambia from 89. *c/o USPG, Partnership House, 157 Waterloo Road, London SE1 8XA* (0171-928 8681 Fax 928 2371

✠OLIVER, Rt Rev John Keith. b 35. G&C Coll Cam BA59 MA63 MLitt65. Westcott Ho Cam. **d** 64 **p** 65 **c** 90. C Hilborough w Bodney *Nor* 64-68; Chapl Eton Coll Windsor 68-72; R S Molton w Nymet St George *Ex* 73-75; P-in-c Filleigh w E Buckland 73-75; P-in-c Warkleigh w Satterleigh and Chittlehamholt 73-75; P-in-c High Bray w Charles 73-75; RD S Molton 74-80; TR S Molton, Nymet St George, High Bray etc 75-82; P-in-c N Molton w Twitchen 77-79; TR Cen Ex 82-85; Adn Sherborne *Sarum* 85-90; P-in-c W Stafford w Frome Billet 85-90; Can Res Sarum Cathl 85-90; Bp Heref from 90. *Bishop's House, The Palace, Hereford HR4 9BN* Hereford (01432) 271355 Fax 343047

OLIVER, John Michael. b 39. Univ of Wales (Lamp) BA62. Ripon Hall Ox 62. **d** 64 **p** 65. C High Harrogate St Pet *Ripon* 64-67; C Bramley 67-72; V Low Harrogate St Mary 72-78; V Beeston 78-82; RD Armley 86-92; Hon Can Ripon Cathl from 87; Adn Leeds from 92. *Archdeacon's Lodge, 2 Halcyon Hill, Leeds LS7 3PU* Leeds (0113) 269 0594 Fax as telephone

OLIVER, Paul Robert. b 41. Lon Univ DipTh65. Tyndale Hall Bris 63. **d** 66 **p** 67. C Virginia Water *Guildf* 66-70; Scripture Union (E Region) 70-74; TV Thetford *Nor* 75-83; V Earlham St Anne from 83; RD Nor S from 94. *The Vicarage, Bluebell Road, Norwich NR4 7LP* Norwich (01603) 52922

OLIVER, Philip Maule. b 38. Birm Univ LLB59. Wells Th Coll 62. **d** 64 **p** 65. C Chesterton *Lich* 64-67; C Tettenhall Wood 67-71; V Milton 71-78; V Ixworth and Bardwell *St E* 78-92; P-in-c Honington w Sapiston and Troston 81-92; TR Blackbourne from 92; RD Ixworth 85-94. *The Vicarage, Ixworth, Bury St Edmunds, Suffolk IP31 2HE* Pakenham (01359) 30311

OLIVER, Mrs Philippa Mary Olive (Penny). b 30. R Holloway Coll Lon BA52. Cant Sch of Min 89. **d** 92 **p** 95. NSM Eythorne and Elvington w Waldershare etc *Cant* from 92. *34 Milner Road, Elvington, Dover, Kent CT15 4EL* Shepherdswell (01304) 831166

OLIVER, Roland John. b 29. Ex Univ TCert54. Lich Th Coll. **d** 59 **p** 60. V Weston Rhyn *Lich* 62-77; V Lt Aston 77-94; rtd 94. *1 Perivale Close, Radbrook, Shrewsbury SY3 6DH*

OLIVER, Stephen John. b 48. AKC69. St Aug Coll Cant 70. **d** 71 **p** 72. C Clifton w Glapton *S'well* 71-75; P-in-c Newark Ch Ch 75-79; R Plumtree 79-85; Sen Producer BBC Relig Broadcasting Dept Lon 85-87; Chief Producer 87-91; Perm to

Offic *Pet* 87-91; TR Leeds City *Ripon* from 91. *Leeds Rectory, 1 Vicarage View, Leeds LS5 3HF* Leeds (0113) 278 6237 or 245 2036

OLIVER, Canon Terence Maule. b 07. Univ Coll Dur BA32. Linc Th Coll 31. **d** 36 **p** 37. V Shilbottle *Newc* 66-76; rtd 76; Lic to Offic *Newc* from 76; Hon Can Kuala Lumpur Cathl from 87. *Restharrow, Longhorsley, Morpeth, Northd NE65 8SY* Longhorsley (0167088) 253

OLIVER, Thomas Gordon. b 48. Nottm Univ BTh72 LTh74 DipAdEd80. St Jo Coll Nottm 68 ALCD72. **d** 72 **p** 73. C Thorpe Edge *Bradf* 72-76; C Woodthorpe *S'well* 76-80; V Huthwaite 80-85; Dir Past Studies St Jo Coll Nottm 85-94; Dir of Tr *Roch* from 94. *18 King's Avenue, Rochester, Kent ME1 3DS* Medway (01634) 841232

OLIVEY, Hugh Charles Tony. b 35. St Mich Coll Llan 77. **d** 79 **p** 80. C St Winnow *Truro* 79-81; C Lanhydrock 81-82; C Lostwithiel 81-82; C Lanivet 81-82; P-in-c 82-83; TV Bodmin w Lanhydrock and Lanivet 84-89; P-in-c St Neot 89-90; P-in-c Warleggan 89-90; R St Neot and Warleggan from 90. *The Vicarage, St Neot, Liskeard, Cornwall PL14 6NG* Liskeard (01579) 20472

OLLIER, Cecil Rupert. b 13. St Edm Hall Ox BA34 MA42. Ely Th Coll 34. **d** 36 **p** 37. V Fenton *Lich* 58-73; R Moreton Say 73-78; rtd 78; Hon C Kettering SS Pet and Paul *Pet* 78-80; Chapl Berkeley's Hosp Worc 80-82; Master Abp Holgate's Hosp Hemsworth from 83. *20 Ludwall Road, Normacot, Longton, Stoke-on-Trent ST3 7HU* Stoke-on-Trent (01782) 333592

OLLIER, Timothy John Douglas. b 44. Trin Hall Cam BA66 MA69. Cuddesdon Coll 66. **d** 68 **p** 69. C Silksworth *Dur* 68-71; C St Marylebone w H Trin *Lon* 71-74; C Winlaton *Dur* 74-77; V Bishopton w Gt Stainton 77-88; R Redmarshall 77-88; P-in-c Grindon and Stillington 83-88; RD Barnard Castle from 88; V Gainford from 88; R Winston from 88; Hon Can Dur Cathl from 94. *The Vicarage, Gainford, Darlington, Co Durham DL2 3DS* Darlington (01325) 730261

OLLIFF, Rowland. b 61. Coll of Resurr Mirfield CPS95. **d** 95. C Bickleigh (Roborough) and Shaugh Prior *Ex* from 95. *47 The Heathers, Roborough, Plymouth PL6 7QS* Plymouth (01752) 777168

O'LOUGHLIN, Gordon Raymond. b 32. Linc Coll Ox BA56 MA60. Wells Th Coll 56. **d** 58 **p** 59. C Bournemouth St Fran *Win* 58-62; C Tunbridge Wells St Barn *Roch* 62-65; Chapl Roch Th Coll 65-67; Sub-Warden 67-69; V Kingston upon Hull St Alb *York* 69-78; Dir of Post-Ord Tr 77-82; Can and Preb York Minster 78-81; TV York All SS Pavement w St Crux and St Martin etc 78-82; V Bromley St Andr *Roch* 82-87; P-in-c Brighton St Paul *Chich* 87-94; V from 94. *St Paul's Parsonage, 9 Russell Place, Brighton BN1 2RG* Brighton (01273) 739639

O'LOUGHLIN, Dr Michael Wilfred Bryan. b 23. Ch Coll Cam BA47 MA58 PhD64. **d** 81 **p** 82. NSM Linton *Ely* from 81; Chapl Addenbrooke's Hosp Cam 84-88; NSM Shudy Camps from 84; NSM Castle Camps from 84; Chmn Dioc Bd Soc Resp from 88. *Ditches Close, 42 The Grip, Linton, Cambridge CB1 6NR* Cambridge (01223) 891357

OLSEN, Arthur Barry. b 37. Univ of NZ BA61. Melbourne Coll of Div BD73 ACT ThL64. **d** 64 **p** 64. New Zealand 64-81; C Hersham *Guildf* 81-84; P-in-c Botleys and Lyne 84-95; V from 95; P-in-c Long Cross 84-95; V from 95. *The Vicarage, Lyne Lane, Lyne, Chertsey, Surrey KT16 0AJ* Ottershaw (01932) 874405

OLUMIDE, Oluseye Abiola Abisogun Okikiade (Seye). b 42. Westhill Coll Birm CertCEd66 Bradf Univ BA89 MSc92. Clifton Th Coll 68. **d** 71 **p** 72. C Halliwell St Pet *Man* 71-72; C Collyhurst St Oswald and St Cath 71; C Salford St Phil w St Steph 72; C Wood Green St Mich *Lon* 73; P-in-c 73; C Stanmer w Falmer and Moulsecoomb *Chich* 73-76; C Moss Side St Jas w St Clem *Man* 76; C Hulme Ascension 76-77; Chapl Asst N Man Gen Hosp 77-80; Chapl St Bernard's Hosp Southall 80-86; Chapl Bradf R Infirmary from 86; Chapl Lynfield Mt Hosp Bradf from 86; Chapl St Luke's Hosp Bradf from 86. *29 Haslingden Drive, Heaton, Bradford, W Yorkshire BD9 5HT* Bradford (01274) 483054 or 542200

OLYOTT, Ven Leonard Eric (Len). b 26. Lon Univ BA50. Westcott Ho Cam 50. **d** 52 **p** 53. V Crewkerne *B & W* 68-71; R Crewkerne w Wayford 71-77; RD Crewkerne 72-77; Preb Wells Cathl from 76; Adn Taunton 77-92; rtd 92. *5 Greendale, Ilminster, Somerset TA19 0EB* Ilminster (01460) 55062

O'MALLEY, Brian Denis Brendan. b 40. Oscott Coll (RC) Coll of Resurr Mirfield 82. **d** 77 **p** 83. In RC Ch 77-81; Warden St Greg Retreat Rhandirmwyn *St D* 81-82; Lic to Offic 82-83; Chapl and Min Can St D Cathl 83-85; V Wiston w Ambleston, St Dogwells, Walton E etc 85-89; V Wiston w Clarbeston and Walton E 89; R Walton W w Talbenny and Haroldston W from 89. *All Saints' Rectory, Walton West, Haverfordwest, Dyfed SA62 3UB* Broad Haven (01437) 781279

OMAN, Brian Malcolm. b 14. Qu Coll Cam BA36 MA46. Chich Th Coll 36. **d** 37 **p** 38. OGS from 39; R Greenford H Cross *Lon* 62-74; V Kings Sutton *Pet* 74-88; rtd 88; Perm to Offic *Pet* from 88. *The Old Post Office, Church Street, Sulgrave, Banbury, Oxon OX17 2RP* Sulgrave (01295) 768317

O'NEILL, Christopher John. b 53. ALAM LGSM MSAPP Worc Coll Ox BA75 MA80 CertEd91 CCouns91 DipTHPsych91. Ripon Coll Cuddesdon 77. **d** 78 **p** 79. Asst Chapl Rugby Sch Warks 78-80; Chapl Charterhouse Godalming from 81. *14 Chapelfields, Charterhouse Road, Godalming, Surrey GU7 2BF* Godalming (01483) 414437

O'NEILL, Edward Daniel (Eddie). b 42. Man Univ BA62 Bradf Univ MSc76. N Ord Course 89. **d** 92 **p** 93. NSM Prenton *Ches* from 92. *Holmhurst, 24 Column Road, West Kirby, Wirral, Merseyside L48 8AX* 0151-625 7704

O'NEILL, Gary. b 57. K Coll Lon BD79 AKC79. Westcott Ho Cam 80. **d** 81 **p** 82. C Oldham *Man* 81-84; C Birch w Fallowfield 84-87; R Moston St Chad from 87. *The Rectory, 30 Hawthorn Road, New Moston, Manchester M40 3RH* 0161-681 3203

O'NEILL, Irene. *See* CARTER, Mrs Irene

ONIONS, Martin Giles. b 63. TC. Chich Th Coll 85. **d** 88 **p** 89. C Eastbourne St Mary *Chich* 88-91; C-in-c Hydneye CD from 91. *St Peter's House, The Hydneye, Eastbourne, E Sussex BN22 9BY* Eastbourne (01323) 504392

ONSLOW, Sister Denzil Octavia. b 19. CertRK58. dss 61 **d** 87 **p** 94. CSA from 56; Novice Guardian 68-73 and 90-94; R Foundn of St Kath in Ratcliffe 73-79; Notting Hill St Jo and St Pet *Lon* 80-87; Hon Par Dn 87-94; Hon C from 94. *St Andrew's House, 2 Tavistock Road, London W11 1BA* 0171-229 2662

ORAM, Canon Geoffrey William James. b 14. Em Coll Cam BA37 MA40. Ridley Hall Cam 36. **d** 38 **p** 39. V Aldeburgh w Hazlewood *St E* 64-80; rtd 80; Perm to Offic *St E* 80-81 and from 86; P-in-c Ipswich St Mich 81-86. *Pantiles, Spring Meadow, Hillfarm Road, Playford, Ipswich IP6 9ED* Ipswich (01473) 622566

ORAM, John Ernest Donald. b 34. Open Univ BA74. Tyndale Hall Bris. **d** 61 **p** 62. C Cheetham Hill *Man* 61-64; C Gt Baddow *Chelmsf* 64-67; V Blackb St Barn *Blackb* 67-72; Bp's Chapl for Soc Resp *Sheff* 72-86; Chapl Psychotherapist 79-86; Perm to Offic from 86. *12 Montgomery Road, Sheffield S7 1LQ* Sheffield (0114) 258 2332 /268 2883

✠**ORAM, Rt Rev Kenneth Cyril.** b 19. Lon Univ BA39 AKC41. Linc Th Coll 42. **d** 42 **p** 43 **c** 74. C Cranbrook *Cant* 42-45; S Africa 46-87; Adn Bechuanaland 53-60; Dean Kimberley 60-64; Dean and Adn Grahamstown 64-74; Bp 74-87; Asst Bp Lich from 87; rtd 93. *10 Sandringham Road, Stafford ST17 0AA* Stafford (01785) 53974

ORAM, Roland Martin David. b 45. ARCM70 Trin Coll Cam BA68. Cranmer Hall Dur DipTh78. **d** 78 **p** 79. C Aspley *S'well* 78-81; Chapl Alleyn's Sch Dulwich 81-88; Chapl Versailles w Grandchamp and Chevry *Eur* 88-92; Chapl Denstone Coll Uttoxeter from 92. *Denstone College, Uttoxeter, Staffs ST14 5HN* Rocester (01889) 590484 Fax 591295

ORAM, Stephen John. b 58. **d** 84 **p** 85. C Kidderminster St Jo *Worc* 84-88; Chapl RAF 88-92; P-in-c Brislington St Anne *Bris* from 92. *The Vicarage, 23 First Avenue, Bristol BS4 4DU* Bristol (0117) 977 6667

ORCHARD, Canon George Richard. b 41. Ex Coll Ox BA62 BA64 MA66. Ripon Hall Ox 62. **d** 65 **p** 66. C Greenhill St Pet *Derby* 65-70; Member Ecum Team Min Sinfin Moor 70-78; V Sinfin Moor 76-78; TR Dronfield 78-86; Can Res Derby Cathl 86-92; Hon Can Derby Cathl from 92; P-in-c Baslow 92-93; P-in-c Curbar and Stoney Middleton 92-93; V Baslow w Curbar and Stoney Middleton from 93. *The Vicarage, Curbar Lane, Calver, Sheffield S30 1YF* Hope Valley (01433) 630387

ORCHARD, Harry Frank. b 23. Roch Th Coll. **d** 63 **p** 64. V Preston *Sarum* 67-71; R Teffont Evias and Teffont Magna 71-73; V Dinton 71-73; C Fovant w Compton Chamberlayne etc 76-78; Lic to Offic 78-80 and from 82; RD Chalke 80-82; rtd 88. *Downstream, Burcombe, Salisbury SP2 0EJ* Salisbury (01722) 742322

ORCHARD, Nigel John. b 56. CertEd78. St Steph Ho Ox 82. **d** 85 **p** 86. C Tottenham St Paul *Lon* 85-89; C Is of Dogs Ch Ch and St Jo w St Luke 89-90; TV 90-92; P-in-c Southall Ch Redeemer from 92. *Christ The Redeemer Vicarage, 299 Allenby Road, Southall, Middx UB1 2HE* 0181-578 2711

ORCHARD, Mrs Tryphena Jane. b 35. Westf Coll Lon BA57. S'wark Ord Course 87. **d** 92 **p** 94. NSM Shaston *Sarum* from 92. *Old Cann Rectory, Salisbury Road, Shaftesbury, Dorset SP7 8ER* Shaftesbury (01747) 855228 Fax as telephone

ORCHIN, Robert Andrew. b 71. K Coll Lon BD92. Ripon Coll Cuddesdon DipMin95. **d** 95. C Leigh Park *Portsm* from 95. *13 Riders Lane, Havant, Hants PO9 4QS* Havant (01705) 475746

O'REILLY, Clare Maria. *See* KING, Clare Maria

O'REILLY, Philip Jonathon. b 66. ARICS Portsm Poly BSc87. Westcott Ho Cam CTMin93. **d** 93 **p** 94. C Selsdon St Jo w St Fran *S'wark* from 93. *4 Turnstone Close, South Croydon, Surrey CR2 8SP* 0181-651 4930

ORFORD, Barry Antony. b 49. St Steph Ho Ox 71. **d** 73 **p** 74. C Mon 73-77; VC St As Cathl *St As* 77-81; C St As and Tremeirchion 77-81; CR from 83. *House of the Resurrection, Mirfield, W Yorkshire WF14 0BN* Mirfield (01924) 494318

ORFORD, Keith John. b 40. FCIT. E Midl Min Tr Course 76. **d** 79 **p** 80. NSM Matlock Bank *Derby* from 79. *27 Lums Hill Rise, Matlock, Derbyshire DE4 3FX* Matlock (01629) 55349

ORLAND, Canon Ernest George. b 28. Lich Th Coll 61. **d** 62 **p** 63. R Corby SS Pet and Andr *Pet* 69-72; TR Corby SS Pet and Andr w Gt and Lt Oakley 72-81; RD Corby 79-81; Can Pet Cathl 79-93; V Pet All SS 81-93; rtd 93. *43 Godsey Lane, Market Deeping, Peterborough PE6 8HY* Market Deeping (01778) 380724

ORME, John. b 29. Sarum Th Coll 58. **d** 60 **p** 61. C Heald Green St Cath *Ches* 60-64; C Ellesmere Port 64-67; Chapl Harperbury Hosp Radlett 67-73; P-in-c Luton All SS w St Pet *St Alb* 73-79; V 79-87; V Oxhey St Matt from 87. *The Vicarage, St Matthew's Close, Eastbury Road, Oxhey, Watford WD1 4PT* Watford (01923) 241420

ORME, Stewart. b 22. Leeds Univ BA49 Open Univ BA75. St Steph Ho Ox 50. **d** 52 **p** 53. R Albury w St Martha *Guildf* 59-87; rtd 87. *The Spinney, Hawksford Lane West, Fernhurst, Haslemere, Surrey GU37 3NT* Haslemere (01428) 654789

ORME, Sydney. b 27. Oak Hill Th Coll 54. **d** 58 **p** 59. V Friarmere *Man* 61-73; V Knypersley *Lich* 73-92; rtd 92. *10 Elworth Road, Sandbach, Cheshire CW11 9HQ* Crewe (01270) 759233

ORMEROD, Henry Lawrence. b 35. Pemb Coll Cam BA58 MA63. Qu Coll Birm DipTh59. **d** 60 **p** 61. C Chigwell *Chelmsf* 60-64; C Thundersley 64-68; C Canvey Is 68-72; V Stanground *Ely* 72-77; TR Stanground and Farcet 77-81; TR Swindon St Jo and St Andr *Bris* 81-90; TR N Wingfield, Clay Cross and Pilsley *Derby* from 90. *The Rectory, St Lawrence Road, North Wingfield, Chesterfield, Derbyshire S42 5HX* Chesterfield (01246) 851181

ORMISTON, Albert Edward. b 26. AMCT46. Oak Hill Th Coll 53. **d** 56 **p** 57. R Gateacre *Liv* 67-73; V Tonbridge St Steph *Roch* 73-86; V Dent w Cowgill *Bradf* 86-91; rtd 91. *29 Bollin Drive, Congleton, Cheshire CW12 3RR* Congleton (01260) 276828

ORMROD, Paul William. b 57. Liv Univ BA80. Westcott Ho Cam 80. **d** 83 **p** 84. C Prescot *Liv* 83-86; TV Padgate 86-95; V Formby St Pet from 95. *St Peter's Vicarage, Cricket Path, Formby, Liverpool L37 7DP* Formby (01704) 873369

ORMSBY, Diana Clare. b 21. CertEd41. Sarum & Wells Th Coll 77 Gilmore Course 78. dss 80 **d** 87 **p** 94. Lydford, Brent Tor, Bridestowe and Sourton *Ex* 80-87; Hon C Lydford and Brent Tor from 87. *Lipscliffe, Coryton, Okehampton, Devon EX20 4AB* Tavistock (01822) 860344

ORMSBY, Robert Daly. b 22. CCC Ox BA42 MA48. Sarum & Wells Th Coll 77. **d** 78 **p** 79. Hon C Lydford and Brent Tor *Ex* from 78. *Lipscliffe, Coryton, Okehampton, Devon EX20 4AB* Tavistock (01822) 860344

ORMSTON, Derek. b 43. Univ of Wales (Lamp) DipTh67. **d** 67 **p** 68. C Ogley Hay *Lich* 67-70; C Tettenhall Regis 70-74; P-in-c Leek All SS 74-79; TV Leek and Meerbrook 79-83; Youth Chapl *Bris* 83-87; R Brinkworth w Dauntsey from 87; Chapl New Coll Swindon from 87. *The Rectory, Brinkworth, Chippenham, Wilts SN15 5AS* Malmesbury (01666) 510207

ORMSTON, Richard Jeremy. b 61. Southlands Coll Lon BA83. Oak Hill Th Coll BA87. **d** 87 **p** 88. C Rodbourne Cheney *Bris* 87-91; R Collingtree w Courteenhall and Milton Malsor *Pet* from 91. *The Rectory, Collingtree, Northampton NN4 0NF* Northampton (01604) 761895

O'ROURKE, Brian Joseph Gerard. b 58. TCD BA82 HDipEd83. CITC 89. **d** 92 **p** 93. Chapl Glendalough Sch from 90; C Newc w Newtownmountkennedy and Calary *D & G* from 92. *Windy Ridge, 102 Glebemount, Wicklow, Co Wicklow, Irish Republic* Wicklow (404) 69608 Fax 68180

ORPIN, Mrs Gillian. b 32. SRN53. Oak Hill Th Coll 82. **d** 87 **p** 95. Par Dn Passenham *Pet* 92; NSM Oban St Jo *Arg* from 92. *Gual Reidh, Taynuilt, Argyll PA35 1JQ* Taynuilt (018662) 281

ORR, Andrew Dermot Harman. b 66. Sheff Univ BSc89. CITC BTh92. **d** 92 **p** 93. C Ballymacash *Conn* 92-95; I Castlecomer w Colliery Ch, Mothel and Bilbo *C & O* from 95. *The Rectory, Castlecomer, Co Kilkenny, Republic of Ireland* Kilkenny (56) 41677

ORR, Very Rev David Cecil. b 33. TCD BA56 MA68. **d** 57 **p** 58. C Drumragh *D & R* 57-60; I Convoy 60-70; RD Raphoe 66-70; I Maghera 70-80; I Drumragh w Mountfield 80-84; Dean

Derry from 84; I Templemore from 84; Miss to Seamen from 84. *The Deanery, 30 Bishop Street, Londonderry BT48 6PP* Londonderry (01504) 262746

ORRELL, Joseph Albert (Joe). b 30. Lon Univ BD56 Wigan Coll of Tech HNC52. Headingley Coll Leeds 53 Lich Th Coll 60. **d** 61 **p** 62. V Hollinfare *Liv* 63-71; V New Springs 71-76; Lic to Offic 77-92; Asst Master Aspull High Sch 77-81; Hd of RE Wigan Deanery C of E High Sch 81-92; C Billinge 92-94; rtd 94. *1 Whitecroft Avenue, Lowton, Warrington WA3 2TA* Wigan (01942) 712804

ORTON, Richard. b 33. Keble Coll Ox BA56 MA60 Leeds Univ. Lich Th Coll 60. **d** 61 **p** 64. C Penistone w Midhope *Wakef* 61-62; Hon C Meltham 62-69; Hon C Horsforth *Ripon* 69-72; C Far Headingley St Chad 72-75; V Hellifield *Bradf* 75-80; RD Bowland 78-80; R Hutton *Chelmsf* 80-87; R Wallasey St Hilary *Ches* from 87; Dioc Ecum Officer from 92. *St Hilary's Rectory, Church Hill, Wallasey, Merseyside L45 3NH* 0151-638 4771

OSBORN, Miss Anne. b 40. Reading Univ BA62 MA64 Lon Univ PGCE67. Oak Hill NSM Course 87. **d** 92. Chapl Lon Univ *Lon* 92-94; Chapl Lon Guildhall Univ from 94; Chapl Univ Westmr 94-95. *8 Beaufort House, Talbot Road, London N15 4DR* 0181-801 0115

OSBORN, David Ronald. b 42. Bris Univ BA66 Leeds Univ CertEd77 Bath Univ MEd80. Clifton Th Coll 62. **d** 66 **p** 67. C Farndon *S'well* 66-69; P-in-c W Bridgford 69-72; Asst Dioc Dir Educn *Carl* 72-77; P-in-c Kirkandrews-on-Eden w Beaumont and Grinsdale 72-77; Hd RE and Chapl Dauntsey's Sch Devizes 77-83; USA 83; V Southbroom *Sarum* 83-86; Consultant to Lay Tr Schemes *Ox* 86; Hd RE Bexhill High Sch 86-90; TV Langtree from 93. *The Vicarage, Crabtree Corner, Ipsden, Oxford OX10 6BN* Wallingford (01491) 681129 Fax 682191

OSBORN, David Thomas. b 58. PGCE80 K Coll Lon BD79 AKC79. Linc Th Coll 82. **d** 83 **p** 84. C Bearsted w Thurnham *Cant* 83-86; Chapl RAF 86-90; R Bassingham *Linc* 90-91; V Aubourn w Haddington 90-91; V Carlton-le-Moorland w Stapleford 90-91; R Thurlby w Norton Disney 90-91; Chapl RAF from 91. *Chaplaincy Services (RAF), HQ, Personnel and Training Command, RAF Innsworth, Gloucester GL3 1EZ* Gloucester (01452) 712612 Ext 5164 Fax 510828

OSBORN, Mrs Diana Marian. b 52. R Holloway Coll Lon BSc74 CertEd75. NE Ord Course 81. **dss** 84 **d** 87 **p** 94. Malden St Jo *S'wark* 84-89; Par Dn 87-89; Par Dn Brampton *Ely* 89-92; Par Dn Richmond H Trin and Ch Ch *S'wark* 92-93; Chapl Ridley Hall Cam from 94; C Milton *Ely* from 95. *30 Chestnut Close, Brampton, Huntingdon, Cambs PE18 8TP* Huntingdon (01480) 411389

OSBORN, Preb John Geoffrey Rowland. b 33. Jes Coll Cam BA55 MA59. Wells Th Coll 63. **d** 65 **p** 66. C Easthampstead *Ox* 65-68; Lic to Offic *Blackb* 68-70; Brunei 70-75; Asst Dir RE *Blackb* 75-77; V Tockholes 75-77; Dir RE *B & W* 77-83; Dir and Sec Lon Dioc Bd for Schs *Lon* from 83; Preb St Paul's Cathl from 86. *c/o London Diocesan House, 30 Causton Street, London SW1P 4AU* 0171-821 9311 Fax as telephone

OSBORN, Maurice. b 25. Univ of Wales BA50. Wycliffe Hall Ox 55. **d** 55 **p** 56. Chapl Dauntsey's Sch Devizes 57-72; Asst Master 58-78; P-in-c Bishop's Lavington *Sarum* 79-83; P-in-c Lt Cheverell 82-83; P-in-c W Lavington and the Cheverells 83-90; rtd 90. *Greensand Cottage, West Lavington, Devizes, Wilts SN10 4LB* Devizes (01380) 813244

OSBORN, Peter George. b 14. Sydney Univ BA35. Cuddesdon Coll 61. **d** 63 **p** 64. Australia from 75; Chapl Abingdon Sch 68-73; P-in-c Hawley H Trin *Guildf* 74-75; rtd 79. *Unit 8, 33 Buxton Street, North Adelaide, Australia 5006* Adelaide (8) 239-0959

OSBORNE, Alexander Deas. b 34. Liv Univ BSc54 PhD57. Oak Hill NSM Course 78. **d** 81 **p** 82. NSM Redbourn *St Alb* from 81. *19 Rickyard Meadow, Redbourn, St Albans, Herts AL3 7HT* Redbourn (01582) 793749

OSBORNE, Canon Anthony Russell. b 47. Sarum & Wells Th Coll 77. **d** 79 **p** 80. C Heref St Martin *Heref* 79-81; TV 82-86; TV Hanley H Ev *Lich* 86-92; Dioc Soc Resp Officer *Heref* from 92; Can Heref Cathl from 92. *1 Carter Grove, Hereford HR1 1NT* Hereford (01432) 265465 or 355248

OSBORNE, Arthur Frederick. b 09. K Coll Lon BD44 AKC44. K Coll Lon 28. **d** 33 **p** 34. Chapl and Prin Lect Kirkby Fields Coll of Educn 65-72; Chapl Northn Coll of Educn 72-75; rtd 75. *1 Braham Court, 11 Nuns Close, Hitchin, Herts SG5 1EP* Hitchin (01462) 433976

OSBORNE, Canon Brian Charles. b 38. St Andr Univ MA61 Lon Univ DipTh80. Clifton Th Coll 61. **d** 63 **p** 64. C Skirbeck H Trin *Linc* 63-68; V from 80; P-in-c New Clee 68-71; V 71-75; V Derby St Aug *Derby* 75-80; Chapl Pilgrim Hosp Boston 84-88; RD Holland E *Linc* 85-95; Can Linc Cathl from 92. *Holy Trinity Vicarage, 64 Spilsby Road, Boston, Lincs PE21 9NS* Boston (01205) 363657

OSBORNE, Christopher Hazell (Chris). b 60. Aston Tr Scheme 89 Sarum & Wells Th Coll DCM93. **d** 93 **p** 94. C Paignton St Jo *Ex* from 93. *St Boniface House, Belfield Road, Paignton, Devon TQ3 3UZ* Paignton (01803) 556612

OSBORNE, David Champernowne. b 61. Coll of Resurr Mirfield 90. **d** 93 **p** 94. C W Leigh *Portsm* from 93. *4 Whiteoak Walk, Havant, Hants PO9 5PL* Havant (01705) 781449

OSBORNE, David Robert. b 50. Birm Univ BSc71 MEd86 Nottm Univ DipTh72 Bris Univ PGCE73. St Jo Coll Dur 78. **d** 80 **p** 81. C Penkridge w Stretton *Lich* 80-85; R Longdon-upon-Tern, Rodington, Uppington etc 85-94; R Pilton w Croscombe, N Wootton and Dinder *B & W* from 94. *The Rectory, High Meadows, Pilton, Shepton Mallet, Somerset BA4 4DX* Shepton Mallet (01225) 317535

OSBORNE, David Victor. b 36. Dur Univ BA59. Cranmer Hall Dur DipTh62. **d** 62 **p** 63. C Kennington Cross St Anselm *S'wark* 62-66; C Sandal St Helen *Wakef* 66-67; R Ancoats *Man* 67-73; V Claremont H Angels 73-80; R Breedon cum Isley Walton and Worthington *Leic* 80-87; V Beaumont Leys 87-92; V Billesdon and Skeffington from 92. *The Vicarage, Church Street, Billesdon, Leicester LE7 9AE* Leicester (0116) 259 6321

OSBORNE, Derek James. b 32. Tyndale Hall Bris 53. **d** 57 **p** 58. C Weymouth St Mary *Sarum* 57-60; C Southgate *Chich* 60-63; V Croydon Ch Ch Broad Green *Cant* 63-71; V Cromer *Nor* 71-83; P-in-c Gresham w Bessingham 71-80; Hon Can Nor Cathl 77-83; V Northwood Em *Lon* 83-94; Chapl Lee Abbey from 94. *Lee Abbey, Lynton, Devon EX35 6JJ* Lynton (01598) 52621 Fax 52619

OSBORNE, Hayward John. b 48. New Coll Ox BA70 MA73. Westcott Ho Cam 71. **d** 73 **p** 74. C Bromley SS Pet and Paul *Roch* 73-77; C Halesowen *Worc* 77-80; TV 80-83; TR Worc St Barn w Ch Ch 83-88; V Moseley St Mary *Birm* from 88; RD Moseley from 94. *St Mary's Vicarage, 18 Oxford Road, Birmingham B13 9EH* 0121-449 1459 or 449 2243

OSBORNE, Mrs June. b 53. Man Univ BA74. St Jo Coll Nottm. **dss** 80 **d** 87 **p** 94. Birm St Martin *Birm* 80-84; Old Ford St Paul w St Steph and St Mark *Lon* 84-87; Par Dn 87-94; P-in-c from 94. *36 Tredegar Road, London E3 5AE* 0181-980 2839

OSBORNE, Mark William. b 67. Univ of Wales BA89. Coll of Resurr Mirfield CPT94. **d** 94 **p** 95. C Goldthorpe w Hickleton *Sheff* from 94. *179 Doncaster Road, Goldthorpe, Rotherham, S Yorkshire S63 9JD* Rotherham (01709) 881468

OSBORNE, Ralph. b 38. Kent Univ DipTh80. Bernard Gilpin Soc Dur 62 Clifton Th Coll 63. **d** 66 **p** 67. C Harpurhey Ch Ch *Man* 66-68; C Chorlton on Medlock St Sav 68-71; C Wilmington *Roch* 71-74; V St Mary Cray and St Paul's Cray 74-85; P-in-c Bath St Steph *B & W* 85-88; P-in-c Charlcombe 86-88; R Charlcombe w Bath St Steph from 88. *St Stephen's Rectory, Richmond Place, Lansdown, Bath BA1 5PZ* Bath (01225) 317535

OSBORNE, Canon Robin Orbell. b 29. Leeds Univ BA54. Coll of Resurr Mirfield 52. **d** 54 **p** 55. V Cheshunt *St Alb* 65-82; RD Cheshunt 70-81; Hon Can St Alb 76-82; V Penzance St Mary w St Paul *Truro* 82-88; Can Res and Treas Truro Cathl 88-94; Perm to Offic *B & W* from 94; rtd 94. *7 The Judge's Lodgings, 19 New Street, Wells, Somerset BA5 2LD* Wells (01749) 672326

OSBOURNE, David John. b 56. Linc Th Coll 78. **d** 79 **p** 80. C Houghton le Spring *Dur* 79-82; C Spalding St Jo *Linc* 82-83; C Spalding St Jo w Deeping St Nicholas 83-84; V Swineshead 84-94; RD Holland W 86-92; P-in-c Boultham from 94. *The Rectory, 2A St Helen's Avenue, Lincoln LN6 7RA* Lincoln (01522) 682026

OSBOURNE, Steven John. b 59. St Jo Coll Nottm 92. **d** 94 **p** 95. C Bushbury *Lich* from 94. *11 Wistwood Hayes, Wolverhampton WV10 8QU* Wolverhampton (01902) 784907

OSGERBY, Dr John Martin. b 34. Sheff Univ BSc56 PhD59. Linc Th Coll 75. **d** 77 **p** 78. C Rotherham *Sheff* 77-80; C-in-c W Bessacarr CD 80-84; V W Bessacarr 84-87; Warden of Readers from 86; R Fishlake w Sykehouse, Kirk Bramwith, Fenwick etc from 87. *The Vicarage, Fishlake, Doncaster, S Yorkshire DN7 5JW* Doncaster (01302) 841396

OSGOOD, Graham Dean. b 39. Lon Univ BSc62. ALCD71 St Jo Coll Nottm 71. **d** 71 **p** 72. C Bebington *Ches* 71-76; V Gee Cross from 76. *The Vicarage, Higham Lane, Hyde, Cheshire SK14 5LX* 0161-368 2337

OSMAN, David Thomas. b 49. Bradf Univ BTech72. Trin Coll Bris 75. **d** 78 **p** 79. C Stranton *Dur* 78-81; C Denton Holme *Carl* 81-84; V Preston on Tees *Dur* from 84. *The Vicarage, Quarry Road, Eaglescliffe, Stockton-on-Tees, Cleveland TS16 9BD* Stockton-on-Tees (01642) 780516

OSMAN, Ernest. b 35. St Aid Birkenhead 61. **d** 64 **p** 65. C Heaton Ch Ch *Man* 64-68; V Farnworth St Pet 68-77; V St Martin's *Lich* 77-85; V Endon w Stanley from 85. *The Vicarage, Leek Road, Endon, Stoke-on-Trent ST9 9BH* Stoke-on-Trent (01782) 502166

OSMAN, Stephen William. b 53. Matlock Coll of Educn CertEd74 Teesside Poly CQSW80. St Jo Coll Dur 88. **d** 90 **p** 91. C Newbarns w Hawcoat *Carl* 90-93; TV Marfleet *York* from 93. *St Phillip's House, 107 Amethyst Road, Hull HU9 4JG* Hull (01482) 762087

OSMASTON, Miss Amiel Mary Ellinor. b 51. Ex Univ BA73 St Jo Coll Dur BA84. St Jo Coll Nottm DPS77 Cranmer Hall Dur 82. **dss** 84 **d** 87 **p** 94. Ches le Street *Dur* 84-87; Par Dn 87-88; Dir Miss and Past Studies Ridley Hall Cam from 89. *Ridley Hall, Sidgwick Avenue, Cambridge CB3 9HG* Cambridge (01223) 311672

OSMOND, David Methuen. b 38. Qu Coll Birm 75. **d** 77 **p** 78. C Yardley St Edburgha *Birm* 77-80; V Withall 80-89; R W Coker w Hardington Mandeville, E Chinnock etc *B & W* from 89. *The Rectory, 7 Cedar Fields, West Coker, Yeovil, Somerset BA22 9DB* West Coker (01935) 862328

OSMOND, Mrs Heather Christine. b 44. ABSM64 ARCM65 Birm Poly CertEd65. Qu Coll Birm 83. **dss** 84 **d** 87. Brandwood *Birm* 84-85; Withall 85-87; Par Dn 87-89; Perm to Offic *B & W* from 89. *The Rectory, 7 Cedar Fields, West Coker, Yeovil, Somerset BA22 9DB* West Coker (01935) 862328

OSMOND, Oliver Robert. b 44. Ch Coll Cam BA66 MA70. Cuddesdon Coll 66 Trin Coll Toronto STB69. **d** 69 **p** 70. Canada 69-81; V Mill Hill Jo Keble Ch *Lon* from 81. *John Keble Vicarage, 142 Deans Lane, Edgware, Middx HA8 9NT* 0181-959 1312

OSSORY AND LEIGHLIN, Archdeacon of. *See* MURRAY, Ven John Grainger

OSSORY, Dean of. *See* LYNAS, Very Rev Norman Noel

OSTLE, Arthur John. b 08. St Aid Birkenhead 38. **d** 38 **p** 39. C Gt Crosby St Luke *Liv* 38-40; CF (EC) 40-46; C Sefton *Liv* 46-47; V Bootle St Mary w St Jo 47-51; Canada from 52. *311-400 Sandringham Crescent, London, Ontario, Canada, N6C 5A8*

O'SULLIVAN, Mrs Hazel. b 50. S Dios Minl Tr Scheme 91. **d** 94 **p** 95. C Cove St Jo *Guildf* from 94. *1 Mariners Drive, Farnborough, Hants GU14 8DA* Farnborough (01252) 544127

OSWALD, John Edward Guy. b 39. Qu Coll Cam BA63 MA67. Ridley Hall Cam. **d** 68 **p** 69. C Chippenham St Paul w Langley Burrell *Bris* 68-72; C Hengrove 72-75; P-in-c Hardenhuish 75-79; P-in-c Kington 75-79; TV Chippenham St Paul w Hardenhuish etc 79-82; P-in-c Gt w Lt Somerford and Seagry 82-86; P-in-c Corston w Rodbourne 84-86; R Gt Somerford, Lt Somerford, Seagry, Corston etc from 86. *The Rectory, Frog Lane, Great Somerford, Chippenham, Wilts SN15 5JA* Seagry (01249) 720220

OSWALD, Ronald William. b 17. TCD BA38 MA53 BD57 BA59. TCD Div Sch. **d** 55 **p** 56. V Castle Hedingham *Chelmsf* 67-80; R Panfield 80-87; rtd 87; Perm to Offic *B & W* from 87. *1 Abbey Cottages, Galhampton, Yeovil, Somerset BA22 7AQ* Castle Cary (01963) 50623

OSWIN, Frank Anthony (Tony). b 43. Chich Th Coll 69. **d** 71 **p** 72. C Radford *Cov* 71-74; C Shrub End *Chelmsf* 74-76; V Layer-de-la-Haye 76-80; V Eastwood St Dav 80-93; TR Withycombe Raleigh *Ex* from 93. *The Rectory, 74 Withycombe Village Road, Exmouth, Devon EX8 3AE* Exmouth (01395) 264182

OTTAWAY, Bernard Wyndham. b 15. Keble Coll Ox BA38 MA43. Cuddesdon Coll 38. **d** 39 **p** 40. R Loughton St Jo *Chelmsf* 55-71; R Birdbrook w Sturmer 71-76; P-in-c Ashen w Ridgewell 74-76; R Ridgewell w Ashen, Birdbrook and Sturmer 76-81; P-in-c Farnham 81-85; rtd 85; Perm to Offic *Guildf* 86-89; Perm to Offic *Chelmsf* from 89. *Wash Farm House, Ridgewell, Halstead, Essex CO9 4PJ* Ridgewell (0144085) 593

OTTAWAY, Michael John. b 17. Mert Coll Ox BA40 MA44. Cuddesdon Coll 40. **d** 41 **p** 42. V Wolvercote *Ox* 49-76; TV Wolvercote w Summertown 76-83; rtd 83; Perm to Offic *Chich* from 84. *13 Bishopstone Road, Seaford, E Sussex BN25 2UB* Seaford (01323) 899179

OTTER, Anthony Frank. b 32. Kelham Th Coll 54. **d** 59 **p** 60. C Bethnal Green St Jo w St Simon *Lon* 59-63; C Aylesbury *Ox* 63-68; V Hanslope w Castlethorpe 68-77; P-in-c N w S Moreton 77-79; P-in-c Aston Tirrold w Aston Upthorpe 77-79; R S w N Moreton, Aston Tirrold and Aston Upthorpe from 79. *The Rectory, South Moreton, Didcot, Oxon OX11 9AF* Didcot (01235) 812042

OTTERWELL, Anthony David. b 40. **d** 89 **p** 90. NSM Brighton Resurr *Chich* from 89. *11 Welesmere Road, Rottingdean, Brighton BN2 7DN* Brighton (01273) 301339

OTTEWELL, Dr David. b 42. Sheff Univ BSc65 Leic Univ PhD69. N Ord Course 90. **d** 93 **p** 94. NSM Barnby Dun *Sheff* from 93. *10 The Grove, Barnby Dun, Doncaster, S Yorkshire DN3 1EB* Doncaster (01302) 890345

OTTEY, Canon John Leonard. b 34. AKC60 Nottm Univ BA70. **d** 61 **p** 62. C Grantham St Wulfram *Linc* 61-64; R Keyworth *S'well* 70-85; P-in-c Stanton-on-the-Wolds 71-85; P-in-c E Retford 85-87; V from 87; P-in-c W Retford 85-87; R from 87;

Hon Can S'well Minster from 93. *The Rectory, Rectory Road, Retford, Notts DN22 7AY* Retford (01777) 703116

OTTLEY, David Ronald. b 57. Lanc Univ BA78. Sarum & Wells Th Coll 79. **d** 81 **p** 82. C Urmston *Man* 81-85; Lect Bolton St Pet 85-87; P-in-c Halliwell St Thos 87-88; V Bolton St Thos from 88. *St Thomas's Vicarage, Cloister Street, Bolton BL1 3HA* Bolton (01204) 841731

OTTLEY, Ronald. b 28. St Deiniol's Hawarden 81. **d** 83 **p** 84. Hon C Prestbury *Ches* from 83. *The Beeches, 4 Salisbury Place, Tytherington, Macclesfield, Cheshire SK10 2HP* Macclesfield (01625) 432649

OTTO, Francis James Reeve. b 42. New Coll Ox BA64 BA68 Ex Univ 82. St Steph Ho Ox 66 Wells Th Coll 68. **d** 69 **p** 70. C St Stephen by Saltash *Truro* 69-72; C Newquay 72-73; V Lanteglos by Fowey 73-79; V St Goran w St Mich Caerhays 79-82; Chapl St Mary's Hall Brighton 82-88; Chapl Reading Sch 88-90; Teacher The Abbey Sch Reading 91-93; Chapl Lic Victuallers' Sch Ascot 93-94; Lic to Offic *Ox* 89-95; C Boyne Hill 95; P-in-c Cocking, Bepton and W Lavington *Chich* from 95. *The Rectory, Mill Lane, Cocking, Midhurst, W Sussex GU29 0HJ* Midhurst (01730) 817340

OTTOSSON, Krister Alexander. b 39. Lon Univ BSc61. Wycliffe Hall Ox 62 Ch Div Sch of the Pacific (USA) MDiv65. **d** 65 **p** 66. C Ches le Street *Dur* 65-68; NW Area Sec Chr Educn Movement 68-71; Educn Sec BCC 71-76; Adv in Lay Tr *Dur* 76-81; Adult Educn Officer Gen Syn Bd of Educn 81-82; City Cen Chapl *Newc* from 82. *71 Longdean Park, Chester le Street, Co Durham DH3 4DG* 0191-388 9622

OUGH, John Christopher. b 51. Lon Univ CertEd Open Univ BA. SW Minl Tr Course 91. **d** 94. C Plymouth Em, Efford and Laira *Ex* from 94. *27 Efford Crescent, Plymouth PL3 6NH* Plymouth (01752) 786250

OULD, Julian Charles. b 57. MHCIMA77. Coll of Resurr Mirfield 80. **d** 83 **p** 84. C Hebburn St Cuth *Dur* 83-86; C Pet H Spirit Bretton *Pet* 86-90; R Peakirk w Glinton from 90. *The Rectory, 11 Lincoln Road, Glinton, Peterborough PE6 7JR* Peterborough (01733) 252265

OULESS, John Michael. b 22. AKC49. Ridley Hall Cam 49. **d** 50 **p** 51. V Southwick w Glapthorn *Pet* 62-71; Chapl Glapthorn Road Hosp Oundle 63-71; R Cogenhoe *Pet* 71-89; R Whiston 71-89; rtd 89. *2 Clos du Roncherez, St Brelade, Jersey, Channel Islands JE3 8FG* Jersey (01534) 44916

OUTEN (nee BAILEY), Mrs Joyce Mary Josephine. b 33. St Gabr Coll Lon CertEd69 DipRS83. S'wark Ord Course 80. **dss** 83 **d** 87 **p** 94. Par Dn Woolwich St Mary w St Mich *S'wark* 87-89; Par Dn Rusthall *Roch* 89-94; C from 94. *6 Ashley Gardens, Rusthall, Tunbridge Wells, Kent TN4 8TY* Tunbridge Wells (01892) 512587

OUTHWAITE, Stephen Anthony (Tony). b 35. Wells Th Coll 62. **d** 64 **p** 65. C Bitterne Park *Win* 64-67; C-in-c N Tadley CD 67-71; R Milton 71-93; RD Christchurch 82-90; V Win St Cross w St Faith from 93; Master St Cross Hosp from 93. *The Master's Lodge, St Cross Hospital, Winchester, Hants SO23 9SD* Winchester (01962) 852888

OUTRAM, David Michael. b 42. Univ of Wales (Ban) BA77 BD79. Coll of Resurr Mirfield 79. **d** 80 **p** 81. C Llandegfan and Beaumaris w Llanfaes w Penmon etc *Ban* 80-82; Chapl Prebendal Sch Chich 82-86; PV Chich Cathl *Chich* 82-86; Asst Chapl Wellington Coll Berks 86-89; Hd Div from 87; Chapl from 89. *7 Chaucer Road, Wellington Chase, Crowthorne, Berks RG11 7QN* Crowthorne (01344) 778373 or 772262

OVENDEN, Edward Clifford Lewis. b 10. Chich Th Coll 31. **d** 33 **p** 34. V Epping St Jo *Chelmsf* 55-75; rtd 76; Perm to Offic *Chich* from 76. *Nazareth House, Wrestwood Road, Bexhill-on-Sea, E Sussex TN40 2ND* Bexhill-on-Sea (01424) 219618

OVENDEN, John Anthony. b 45. Open Univ BA80 BA93. Sarum & Wells Th Coll 71. **d** 74 **p** 75. C Handsworth *Sheff* 74-77; C Isfield *Chich* 77-80; C Uckfield 77-80; P-in-c Stuntney *Ely* 80-85; Min Can, Prec and Sacr Ely Cathl 80-85; V Primrose Hill St Mary w Avenue Road St Paul *Lon* from 85; Dir English Hymnal Co from 93. *St Mary's Vicarage, 44 King Henry's Road, London NW3 3RP* 0171-722 3062 or 722 3238

OVENDEN, Richard Reginald. b 1900. Sarum Th Coll 24. **d** 27 **p** 28. V W Alvington *Ex* 54-69; rtd 69. *St Clare, 12 Rodney Road, Backwell, Bristol BS19 3HW* Flax Bourton (01275) 833161

OVEREND, Alan. b 53. Sheff Univ BA75. Oak Hill Th Coll 84. **d** 86 **p** 87. C Aughton St Mich *Liv* 86-89; P-in-c Eccleston Park 89-92; V from 92. *St James's Vicarage, 159A St Helen's Road, Prescot, Merseyside L34 2QB* 0151-426 6421

OVEREND, Barry Malcolm. b 49. K Coll Lon BD71 AKC71 DipMin88. St Aug Coll Cant 71. **d** 72 **p** 73. C Nailsworth *Glouc* 72-74; C High Harrogate Ch Ch *Ripon* 75-78; V Collingham w Harewood 78-87; V Far Headingley St Chad from 87. *St Chad's Vicarage, Otley Road, Leeds LS16 5JT* Leeds (0113) 275 2224 or 274 4322

OVEREND, Paul. b 66. Coll of Ripon & York St Jo BA88. Coll of Resurr Mirfield 88. **d** 93 **p** 94. C Cayton w Eastfield *York*

from 93. *4 Hawson Close, Sarcborough, N Yorkshire YO11 3QW* Scarborough (01723) 583282

OVERINGTON, David Vernon. b 34. W Aus Advanced Ed Coll DipRE90. ALCD60. **d** 60 **p** 61. C Penge Ch Ch w H Trin *Roch* 60-62; C Lenton *S'well* 62-65; P-in-c Brackenfield w Wessington *Derby* 65-71; P-in-c Cubley w Marston Montgomery 71-76; Australia from 76. *52 Pangbourne Street, Wembley, W Australia 6014*

OVERTHROW, Royston John (Roy). b 45. Southn Univ BTh94. Portsm Dioc Tr Course 84. **d** 85. NSM Portsm Cathl *Portsm* 85-91; Perm to Offic 91-94; Dn to Bp Sarum from 94. *11 Burford Road, Salisbury SP2 8AN* Salisbury (01722) 338146

OVERTHROW, Canon Terence Reginald Charles (Terry). b 36. Glouc Th Course 76. **d** 79 **p** 79. NSM Glouc St Geo *Glouc* 79-82; NSM Hardwicke, Quedgeley and Elmore w Longney 82-87; C Twigworth w Down Hatherley 87; R Pebworth w Dorsington and Honeybourne from 87; RD Campden from 90; Hon Can Glouc Cathl from 95. *The Vicarage, Stratford Road, Honeybourne, Evesham, Worcs WR11 5PP* Evesham (01386) 830302

OVERTON, Charles Henry. b 51. CCC Ox BA74 MA77 Fitzw Coll Cam PGCE75 BA79 MA85. Ridley Hall Cam 77. **d** 80 **p** 81. C Tonbridge SS Pet and Paul *Roch* 80-84; Lic to Offic *Cant* 84-87; Asst Chapl St Lawr Coll Ramsgate 84-87; P-in-c Aythorpe w High and Leaden Roding *Chelmsf* 88-95; P-in-c Hughenden *Ox* from 95. *The Vicarage, Valley Road, Hughenden Valley, High Wycombe, Bucks HP14 4PF* Naphill (01494) 563439

OVERTON, David Malcolm. b 52. Chich Th Coll. **d** 84 **p** 85. C Ches H Trin *Ches* 84-86; C Woodchurch 86-88; C Coppenhall 88-91; C Croydon St Jo *S'wark* 91-94; C-in-c 91-94. *90 Cambridge Road, Teddington, Middx TW11 8DJ* 0181-977 1294

OVERTON, Keith Charles. b 28. E Anglian Minl Tr Course 78. **d** 81 **p** 82. NSM Duxford *Ely* 81-84; NSM Whittlesford 84-88; P-in-c 88-94; P-in-c Pampisford 88-90; Perm to Offic *Bris* from 94. *86 Pittsfield, Cricklade, Swindon SN6 6AW* Swindon (01793) 750321

OVERTON, Thomas Vincent Edersheim. b 34. New Coll Ox BA58 DipTh59 MA61. Wycliffe Hall Ox 58. **d** 60 **p** 61. C W Hampstead Trin *Lon* 60-63; C Leeds St Geo *Ripon* 63-67; Perm to Offic *Lon* 68-71; Thailand 71-78; R Knossington and Cold Overton *Leic* 78-81; V Owston and Withcote 78-81; R Bedf St Jo and St Leon *St Alb* 81-90; Perm to Offic *B & W* 90-91; V Leigh *Roch* from 91. *The Vicarage, Leigh, Tonbridge, Kent TN11 8QJ* Hildenborough (01732) 833022

OVERY, Arthur William. b 19. JP. Nor Ord Course 73. **d** 76 **p** 77. NSM Lowestoft St Marg *Nor* 76-78; NSM Lowestoft and Kirkley 79-89; Perm to Offic from 89. *The Hollies, Warren Road, Lowestoft, Suffolk NR32 4QD* Lowestoft (01502) 561289

OVEY, Michael John. b 58. Ball Coll Ox BA81 BCL82. Ridley Hall Cam 88. **d** 91 **p** 92. C Crowborough *Chich* 91-95; Australia from 95. *39 King Street, Newtown, Sydney, NSW 2042 Australia*

OWEN, Bryan Philip. b 47. CertEd70. Cant Sch of Min 83. **d** 86 **p** 87. NSM Deal St Geo *Cant* 86-87; C Herne 87-89; R Clarkston *Glas* 89-93; Warden Scottish Chs Ho (Chs Together in Scotland) from 93. *The Warden's Lodge, Scottish Churches House, Kirk Road, Dunblane, Perthshire FK15 0AJ* Dunblane (01786) 823588 Fax 825844

OWEN, Christine Rose. b 62. Univ of Wales (Ban) BA83 PGCE84. Qu Coll Birm 86. **d** 88 **p** 94. C Ynyscynhaearn w Penmorfa and Porthmadog *Ban* 88-90; Chapl Lon Univ *Lon* from 90; Hon C St Marylebone w H Trin from 94. *14 Rokeby House, Lamb's Conduit Street, London WC1N 3LX* 0171-404 0926

OWEN, Canon Cledwyn. b 15. Univ of Wales BA36. Dorchester Miss Coll 36. **d** 38 **p** 39. R Newtown w Llanllwchaiarn w Aberhafesp *St As* 64-74; V Llangollen w Trevor and Llantysilio 74-82; Chan St As Cathl 76-82; rtd 82; Perm to Offic *Lich* from 83. *14 Green Lane, Bayston Hill, Shrewsbury SY3 0NS* Shrewsbury (01743) 873506

OWEN, Canon David William. b 31. Down Coll Cam BA55 MA58. Linc Th Coll 55. **d** 57 **p** 58. C Salford St Phil w St Steph *Man* 57-61; C Grantham St Wulfram *Linc* 61-65; V Messingham 65-70; V Spilsby w Hundleby 70-77; R Aswardby w Sausthorpe 71-77; R Langton w Sutterby 71-77; R Halton Holgate 73-77; P-in-c Firsby w Gt Steeping 75-77; P-in-c Lt Steeping 75-77; TR Louth 77-92; Chapl Louth Co Hosp 77-92; RD Louthesk *Linc* 82-89; Can and Preb Linc Cathl 85-92; TR Swan *Ox* from 92; RD Claydon from 94. *The Rectory, Grendon Underwood, Aylesbury, Bucks HP18 0SY* Grendon Underwood (01296) 770240

OWEN, Derek Malden. b 29. Oak Hill Th Coll 74. **d** 76 **p** 77. C Eastbourne H Trin *Chich* 76-78; C Walthamstow St Mary w St

Steph *Chelmsf* 78-81; R Ditcheat w E Pennard and Pylle *B & W* 81-83; rtd 94; Hon C Fairlight, Guestling and Pett *Chich* from 94. *Church House, Waites Lane, Fairlight, Hastings, E Sussex TN35 4AX* Hastings (01424) 813104

OWEN, Edgar. b 26. W Midl Minl Tr Course. **d** 82 **p** 83. NSM Garretts Green *Birm* 82-88; NSM Stechford 88-94; rtd 94; Perm to Offic *Birm* from 94. *Flat 1, 41 Averill Road, Birmingham B26 2EG* 0121-783 5603

✠**OWEN, Rt Rev Edwin.** b 10. TCD BA32 MA41. **d** 34 **p** 35 **c** 72. C Glenageary *D & G* 34-36; C Dub Ch Ch Leeson Park 36-38; Min Can St Patr Cathl Dub 35-36; Chan V 36-38; Succ 38-42; I Birr w Eglish *L & K* 42-57; RD Lower Ormond 46-57; Can Killaloe Cathl 54-57; Dean Killaloe 57-72; Dioc Sec (Killaloe etc) 57-72; RD Upper O'Mullod and Traderry 57-60; RD Kilfenora and Corkovasker 60-72; Bp Killaloe 72-76; Bp *L & K* 76-81; rtd 81. *5 Frankfort Avenue, Rathgar, Dublin 6, Irish Republic* Dublin (1) 497-2205

OWEN, Emyr. b 69. Lancs Poly BSc91. Westcott Ho Cam BA94 CTM95. **d** 95. C Llanbeblig w Caernarfon and Betws Garmon etc *Ban* from 95. *The Vicarage, Maesincla, Caernarfon, Gwynedd LL55 1DD* Caernarfon (01286) 675604

OWEN, Ethelston John Charles. b 20. St D Coll Lamp BA42. **d** 48 **p** 49. V Clehonger *Heref* 60-80; R Eaton Bishop 60-80; rtd 80; Perm to Offic *Heref* from 81. *3 Yew Tree Close, Kingstone, Hereford HR2 9HG* Golden Valley (01981) 250785

OWEN, Canon Eugene. b 33. Singapore Teaching Coll DipT52. Trin Coll Bris DipTh85. **d** 90 **p** 90. The Philippines from 86; Can Maria Clara Ch Ch Cathl from 92. *38 Haddo House, Haddo Street, London SE10 9SG* 0181-858 9269 Fax 692 2107

OWEN, Geoffrey Neill. b 55. Chich Th Coll. **d** 85 **p** 86. C Streatham St Pet *S'wark* 85-89; C Battersea Ch Ch and St Steph 89-91; TV Surbiton St Andr and St Mark from 91. *St Andrew's Vicarage, 1 The Mall, Surbiton, Surrey KT6 4EH* 0181-399 6806

OWEN, Gerald. b 16. St D Coll Lamp BA49. **d** 50 **p** 51. V Wednesbury St Bart *Lich* 64-83; rtd 83. *35 Troon Place, Wordsley, Stourbridge, W Midlands DY8 5EN* Kingswinford (01384) 294952

OWEN, Gordon Campbell. b 41. FRMetS65 MRAeS66 Univ of Wales (Ban) BD76 PGCE77. Ban Ord Course 79. **d** 81 **p** 82. Hd RE Eirias High Sch Colwyn Bay 77-88; Chapl RAFVR from 81; AP Ban Cathl *Ban* 82-88; Chapl St Kath Coll and Liv Inst of HE 88-91; Dioc Liaison Officer for RE *Liv* 88-91; V Llanfair-is-gaer and Llanddeiniolen *Ban* from 91; Educn Officer from 91. *The Vicarage, Port Dinorwic, Gwynedd LL56 4SQ* Bangor (01248) 671513

OWEN, Graham Anthony. b 54. Birm Univ BA77. Trin Coll Bris DipHE94. **d** 94 **p** 95. C Wiveliscombe w Chipstable, Huish Champflower etc *B & W* from 94. *29 Lion d'Angers, Wiveliscombe, Taunton, Somerset TA4 2PN* Wiveliscombe (01984) 624164

OWEN, Graham Wynne. b 46. GTCL67 FTCL70 Lon Inst of Educn MA81. Cant Sch of Min 90. **d** 93 **p** 94. C Eltham H Trin *S'wark* from 93. *25 Parkhill Road, Sidcup, Kent DA15 7NJ* 0181-300 8079 or 859 6274

OWEN, Harry Dennis. b 47. Oak Hill Th Coll 73. **d** 76 **p** 77. C Fulham Ch Ch *Lon* 76-81; V Byker St Mark *Newc* 81-89; V Plumstead All SS *S'wark* from 89. *All Saints' Vicarage, 106 Herbert Road, London SE18 3PU* 0181-854 2995

OWEN, James Thomas. b 48. Linc Th Coll 77. **d** 80 **p** 81. C Palmers Green St Jo *Lon* 80-84; C Timperley *Ches* 84-87; C Bramhall 87-92; V Latchford St Jas from 92. *St James's Vicarage, Manx Road, Warrington WA4 6AJ* Warrington (01925) 631893

OWEN, John Edward. b 52. Middx Poly BA75. Sarum & Wells Th Coll BTh81. **d** 81 **p** 82. C S Ashford Ch Ch *Cant* 81-85; TV Bemerton *Sarum* 85-91; V St Leonards and St Ives *Win* 91-95; R N Stoneham from 95. *The Rectory, 62 Glen Eyre Road, Southampton S02 3NL* Southampton (01703) 768123

OWEN, John Peregrine. b 19. Univ of Wales (Swansea) BA41. St Mich Coll Llan 41. **d** 43 **p** 44. R Dowlais *Llan* 59-76; RD Merthyr Tydfil 69-76; R Wenvoe and St Lythans 76-87; RD Penarth and Barry 85-87; rtd 87; Perm to Offic *Llan* from 87. *3 Pen-y-Maes, Forest View, Morriston, Swansea SA6 9DG* Swansea (01792) 793011

OWEN, Keith Robert. b 57. Warw Univ BA Ox Univ BA MA85 Hull Univ MA(Ed)89. St Steph Ho Ox 79. **d** 82 **p** 83. C Headingley *Ripon* 82-85; Chapl Grimsby Colls of H&FE 85-90; Chapl for Educn *Linc* 85-90; P-in-c Linc St Botolph by Bargate 90-95; Chapl to Caring Agencies Lin City Cen 90-95; V Steeton *Bradf* from 95; Chapl Airedale Hosp Bradf from 95. *The Vicarage, 2 Halsteads Way, Steeton, Keighley, W Yorkshire BD20 6SN* Steeton (01535) 652004

OWEN, Kenneth Phillip. b 56. **d** 95. C Heswall *Ches* from 95. *The Croft, Croftsway, Heswall, Wirral, Merseyside L60 9JP* 0151-342 4841

OWEN, Lionel Edward Joseph. b 19. S'wark Ord Course 66. **d** 69 **p** 70. C Hythe *Cant* 69-73; C Deal St Leon 73-75; V Teynham 75-84; RD Ospringe 80-84; rtd 84; Perm to Offic *Cant* from 84. *Green Hayes, London Road, Hythe, Kent CT21 4JH* Hythe (01303) 267642

OWEN, Preb Noah. b 10. St D Coll Lamp BA34. **d** 34 **p** 35. RD Chew Magna *B & W* 71-77; R Chew Stoke w Nempnett Thrubwell 73-77; R Norton Malreward 77; rtd 77; Perm to Offic *B & W* 79-80; Preb Wells Cathl 76-77 and from 80. *West Grove, Crewkerne, Somerset TA18 7ES* Crewkerne (01460) 74023

OWEN, Owen Thomas. b 19. Liv Univ 37 Lanc Univ MA77. St Chad's Coll Dur DipTh45. **d** 45 **p** 46. Lic to Offic *Liv* 62-84; Prin 65-84; rtd 84. *1 Oakwood Road, Halewood, Liverpool L26 1XD* 0151-486 8672

OWEN, Peter Russell. b 35. St Mich Coll Llan DipTh63. **d** 63 **p** 64. C Wrexham *St As* 63-64; C Connah's Quay 64-65; Asst Chapl Miss to Seamen 66-69; P-in-c Upper Norwood All SS w St Marg *Cant* 69-72; C Hawarden *St As* 72-75; V Cilcain and Nannerch 75-79; R Cilcain and Nannerch and Rhyd-y-mwyn 79-83; V Brymbo and Bwlchgwyn 83-87; R Llangynhafal and Llanbedr Dyffryn Clwyd from 87. *The Rectory, Llanbedr Dyffryn Clwyd, Ruthin, Clwyd LS15 1UP* Ruthin (01824) 704051

OWEN, Phillip Clifford. b 42. G&C Coll Cam BA65 MA69. Ridley Hall Cam 71. **d** 73 **p** 74. C Stowmarket *St E* 73-76; C Headley All SS *Guildf* 76-81; TV 81-89; R Clifton-on-Teme, Lower Sapey and the Shelsleys *Worc* from 89. *The Rectory, Clifton-on-Teme, Worcester WR6 6DJ* Shelsley Beauchamp (01886) 812483

OWEN, Raymond Philip. b 37. Man Univ BScTech60 AMCT60 Teesside Poly DMS83. Chich Th Coll 65. **d** 67 **p** 68. C Elland *Wakef* 67-70; C Lindley 70-73; V Bradshaw 73-80; Ind Chapl *Dur* 80-91; TR Hanley H Ev *Lich* from 91. *The Rectory, 35 Harding Road, Stoke-on-Trent ST1 3BQ* Stoke-on-Trent (01782) 266031

OWEN, Richard Ellis. b 12. Clifton Th Coll 48. **d** 50 **p** 51. V Badminton w Acton Turville *Glouc* 61-71; V Kemble w Poole Keynes 71-73; R Pebworth w Dorsington 73-79; R Pebworth w Dorsington and Marston Sicca 79-83; rtd 83; Perm to Offic *Glouc* 83-94. *40 Ballards Close, Mickleton, Chipping Campden, Glos GL55 6TN* Mickleton (01386) 438755

OWEN, Canon Richard Llewelyn. b 27. Univ of Wales (Lamp) BA51. St Mich Coll Llan 51. **d** 53 **p** 54. V Penrhyndeudraeth and Llanfrothen *Ban* 67-77; R Llangefni w Tregaean and Llangristiolus etc 77-89; Can Ban Cathl 82-93; Treas 86-93; Can Missr and V Bangor Cathl Par 89-93; RD Arfon 92-93; rtd 93; Hon Can Ban Cathl from 93. *Bodowen, Great Ormes Road, Llandudno, Gwynedd LL30 2BW* Llandudno (01492) 872765

OWEN, Richard Matthew. b 49. Sheff Univ BA70 Leeds Univ CertEd73. N Ord Course 84. **d** 87 **p** 88. NSM Chorlton-cum-Hardy St Werburgh *Man* 87-89; C N Reddish 89-91; Perm to Offic *York* from 91. *9 Albion Street, Skeldergate, York YO1 1HJ* York (01904) 679989

OWEN, Robert David Glyn. b 06. Bps' Coll Cheshunt 37. **d** 39 **p** 40. V Burslem St Paul *Lich* 63-67; rtd 67. *18 Bromley College, High Street, Bromley BR1 1PE* 0181-460 2570

OWEN, Robert Glynne. b 33. St Mich Coll Llan 56. **d** 58 **p** 59. C Machynlleth and Llanwrin *Ban* 58-62; C Llanbeblig w Caernarfon 62-65; V Carno and Trefeglwys 65-69; Hon C Dorking w Ranmore *Guildf* 69-75; Perm to Offic *St As* 75-94; V Broughton from 94. *The Vicarage, Bryn y Gaer Road, Pentre, Broughton, Wrexham, Clwyd LL11 6AT* Wrexham (01978) 756210

OWEN, Robert Lee. b 56. Univ of Wales (Cardiff) BD79. Qu Coll Birm 79. **d** 81 **p** 82. C Holywell *St As* 81-84; Perm to Offic *Birm* 85-87; Chapl Blue Coat Sch Birm 85-87; Chapl St Elphin's Sch Matlock 87-94; Chapl Qu Marg Sch York from 94. *Queen Margarets School, Escrick Park, Escrick, York YO4 6EU* York (01904) 728261

OWEN, Ronald Alfred. b 44. Sarum & Wells Th Coll 80. **d** 81 **p** 82. C Wotton St Mary *Glouc* 81-83; CF from 83; Perm to Offic *S'wark* from 94. *c/o MOD (Army), Bagshot Park, Bagshot, Surrey GU19 5PL* Bagshot (01276) 471717 Fax 412834

OWEN, Roy Meredith. b 21. Univ of Wales BA43. St Mich Coll Llan 43. **d** 45 **p** 46. V Pontyclun w Talygarn *Llan* 62-75; C Cadoxton-juxta-Barry 82-85; rtd 85; Perm to Offic *Llan* 86-88. *20 Mary Street, Llandaff North, Cardiff CF4 2JQ* Cardiff (01222) 569427

OWEN, Canon Stanley Alfred George. b 17. Worc Ord Coll 57. **d** 59 **p** 60. R Bickenhill w Elmdon *Birm* 60-86; rtd 86; Perm to Offic *Birm* from 86; Chmn and Sec Assn Ch Fellowships from 88. *Bickenhill House, 154 Lode Lane, Solihull, W Midlands B91 2HP* 0121-704 9281

OWEN, Tuddy. b 12. Univ of Wales (Ban) BA35. St Mich Coll Llan 36. **d** 36 **p** 37. V Tywyn *Ban* 57-77; rtd 77; Canada from

81. *120 Poplar Street, PO Box 1424, Stellarton, Novia Scotia, Canada, B0K 1S0* New Glasgow (902) 755-4036

OWEN, William. b 05. OBE. Lon Univ BD55. Tyndale Hall Bris 27. **d** 30 **p** 31. Kenya 54-81; rtd 81; Perm to Offic *Cant* 81-94. *51 Bridge Down, Bridge, Canterbury, Kent CT4 5BA* Canterbury (01227) 830625

OWEN, William David. b 17. Univ of Wales BA39. Wycliffe Hall Ox 40. **d** 41 **p** 42. V Claines St Jo *Worc* 63-94; rtd 94. *Ball Mill Bunglow, Main Road, Hallow, Worcester WR2 6LS* Worcester (01905) 640385

OWEN-JONES, Peter Charles. b 57. Ridley Hall Cam 92. **d** 94 **p** 95. C Leverington *Ely* from 94; C Wisbech St Mary from 94. *The Vicarage, Church Road, Wisbech St Mary, Wisbech, Cambs PE13 4RN* Wisbech (01945) 410814

OWEN-JONES, Peter John. b 47. CEng84 MIMechE84 MBIM87 FPWI90 RMCS BScEng68. E Midl Min Tr Course 85. **d** 88 **p** 89. NSM Holbrook and Lt Eaton *Derby* from 88. *6 Station Road, Little Eaton, Derby DE21 5DN* Derby (01332) 831423

OWENS, Mrs Ann Lindsay. b 47. **d** 95. NSM New Bury *Man* from 95. *St James's Rectory, Highfield Road, Farnworth, Bolton BL4 0AJ*

OWENS, Ashby. b 43. Man Univ BA65 Fitzw Ho Cam BA67 MA71. Ridley Hall Cam 65. **d** 68 **p** 69. C Chorley *Ches* 68-71; C Barnston 71-74; V Alsager St Mary 74-83; V Brinnington w Portwood 83-94; TR New Bury *Man* from 94. *507 Plodder Lane, Farnworth, Bolton BL4 0JZ* Farnworth (01204) 791577

OWENS, Christopher Lee. b 42. Coll of Ripon & York St Jo 61 Lon Inst of Educn TCert. Linc Th Coll 66. **d** 69 **p** 70. C Dalston H Trin w St Phil *Lon* 69-72; C Portsea N End St Mark *Portsm* 72-81; TV E Ham w Upton Park St Alb *Chelmsf* 81-92; C Is of Dogs Ch Ch and St Jo w St Luke *Lon* from 92. *St Luke's House, Strafford Street, London E14 8LT* 0171-515 9888

OWENS, Philip Roger. b 47. Univ of Wales (Ban) DipTh70. Wells Th Coll 71. **d** 71 **p** 72. C Colwyn Bay *St As* 71-74; C Wrexham 74-77; TV 77-80; P-in-c Yoxford *St E* 80-85; Asst Stewardship and Resources Adv 80-85; R Ban Monachorum and Worthenbury *St As* from 85; Dioc Stewardship Officer from 89; RD Ban Isycoed from 92. *The Rectory, 8 Ludlow Road, Bangor-on-Dee, Wrexham, Clwyd LL13 0JG* Bangor-on-Dee (01978) 780608

OWENS, Canon Rodney Stones. b 19. Lon Univ BA53. Bps' Coll Cheshunt 48. **d** 50 **p** 51. Perm to Offic *St E* 65-74; Asst Master Ipswich Sch 65-74; R Coddenham 74-75; R Gosbeck 74-75; P-in-c Hemingstone w Henley 74-75; R Coddenham w Gosbeck and Hemingstone w Henley 75-84; RD Bosmere 78-84; Hon Can St E Cathl 81-84; rtd 84; Perm to Offic *St E* from 85. *10 Warren Lane, Martlesham Heath, Ipswich IP5 7SH* Ipswich (01473) 623411

OWENS, Stephen Graham Frank. b 49. Ch Coll Cam BA71 CertEd72 MA75. Qu Coll Birm 73. **d** 75 **p** 76. C Stourbridge Norton St Mich *Worc* 75-80; Tanzania 80-88; V Dudley Wood *Worc* from 88. *The Vicarage, 57 Lantern Road, Dudley, W Midlands DY2 0DL* Cradley Heath (01384) 569018

OWERS, Ian Humphrey. b 46. Em Coll Cam BA68 MA72. Westcott Ho Cam 71. **d** 73 **p** 74. C Champion Hill St Sav *S'wark* 73-77; V Peckham St Sav 77-82; P-in-c E Greenwich Ch Ch w St Andr and St Mich 82-83; V 83-94; P-in-c Westcombe Park St Geo 85-94; RD Greenwich 92-94. *Address temp unknown*

OWST, Clifford Samuel. b 09. FCII34. Linc Th Coll 77. **d** 77 **p** 78. Hon C Mablethorpe w Stain *Linc* 77-78; Hon C Mablethorpe w Trusthorpe 78-83; New Zealand from 83. *1/1062 Beraih Road, Torbay, Auckland 10, New Zealand* Auckland (9) 403-8599

OXBORROW, Paul Leonard. b 54. Bris Univ BA76. Coll of Resurr Mirfield 84. **d** 86 **p** 87. C Watford St Mich *St Alb* 86-89; C Royston 89-92; C Burgess Hill St Jo *Chich* 92-93; C Burgess Hill St Jo w St Edw from 93. *St Andrew's House, 7 Dunstall Avenue, Burgess Hill, W Sussex RH15 8PJ* Burgess Hill (01444) 241300

OXBROW, Mark. b 51. Reading Univ BSc72 Fitzw Ho Cam BA75 MA79. Ridley Hall Cam 73. **d** 76 **p** 77. C Luton Ch Ch *Roch* 76-80; TV Newc Epiphany *Newc* 80-88; Chapl Newc Mental Health Unit 80-88; Regional Sec Eur CMS from 88; Communication Resources Sec CMS from 94. *10 Nettleden Avenue, Wembley, Middx HA9 6DP, or CMS, Partnership House, 157 Waterloo Road, London SE1 8UU* 0181-900 2485 or 0171-928 8681 Fax 0171-401 3215

OXENFORTH, Colin Bryan. b 45. St Chad's Coll Dur BA67 DipTh69. **d** 69 **p** 70. C Bromley St Andr *Roch* 69-72; C Nunhead St Antony *S'wark* 72-76; V Toxteth St Marg *Liv* 76-89; V Brixton St Matt *S'wark* from 89. *The Vicarage, 5 St Matthew's Road, London SW2 1ND* 0171-274 3553

OXFORD (Christ Church), Dean of. See DRURY, Very Rev John Henry

OXFORD, Victor Thomas. b 41. Chich Th Coll 65. **d** 68 **p** 69. C Norton in the Moors *Lich* 68-73; C Norton Canes 73-75; TV

Cannock 75-81; V Chesterton from 81. *The Vicarage, Church Street, Chesterton, Newcastle, Staffs ST5 7HJ* Newcastle-under-Lyme (01782) 562479

OXFORD, Archdeacon of. *See* WESTON, Ven Frank Valentine

OXFORD, Bishop of. *See* HARRIES, Rt Rev Richard Douglas

OXLEY, Cecil Robert. b 23. TEng72. Coll of Resurr Mirfield 84. **d** 84 **p** 85. NSM Derby St Luke *Derby* 84-92; rtd 92. *8 Top Farm Court, Highfield Road, Kilburn, Belper, Derbyshire DE56 0PU* Derby (01332) 781079

OXLEY, Christopher Robert. b 51. Sheff Univ BA73 PGCE74 Ox Univ BA78 MA83. Wycliffe Hall Ox 76. **d** 79 **p** 80. C Greasbrough *Sheff* 79-82; C Doncaster St Leon and St Jude 82-84; Asst Chapl Brussels *Eur* 84-87; V Humberstone *Leic* 87-93; V Beaumont Leys from 93. *5 Beacon Close, Leicester LE4 1BN* Leicester (0116) 235 2667

OXLEY, David William. b 63. TCD BA85 BTh89. CITC 85. **d** 89 **p** 90. C Dub Ch Ch Cathl Gp *D & G* 89-92; CV Ch Ch Cathl Dub 90-92; I Templebreedy w Tracton and Nohoval *C, C & R* from 92; Min Can Cork Cathl from 95. *The Rectory, Crosshaven, Co Cork, Irish Republic* Crosshaven (21) 831236

OXLEY, Martin Neil. b 65. Birm Univ BA86 Edin Univ BD95. CECM95. **d** 95. C Glas St Mary *Glas* from 95; C Clydebank from 95. *42 Hillhead Street, Glasgow G12 8PZ* 0141-339 8904

OXLEY, Mrs Paula Jane. b 51. Sheff Univ BA74 CertEd75. E Midl Min Tr Course 90. **d** 93 **p** 94. NSM Birstall and Wanlip *Leic* 93-95; NSM Beaumont Leys from 95. *5 Beacon Close, Leicester LE4 1BN* Leicester (0116) 235 2667

OYET, Canon Julius Isotuk. b 39. Concordia Coll (USA) MA79. Immanuel Coll Ibadan DipTh70. **d** 70 **p** 72. Nigeria 70-90; C Warblington and Emsworth *Portsm* from 91; Miss Partner CMS from 91. *Parish House, 41 Woodlands Avenue, Emsworth, Hants PO10 7QB* Emsworth (01243) 370115

P

PACEY, Edgar Prentice. b 29. Edin Univ MA50. Edin Th Coll 52. **d** 54 **p** 55. R Coatbridge *Glas* 61-70; Perm to Offic 70-77; Hon C Glas St Martin 77-83; P-in-c Rothesay *Arg* 83-93; R Tighnabruaich 91-93; Perm to Offic *Glas* from 91; rtd 93. *Dunstan, 16 Broomfield Drive, Dunoon, Argyll PA23 7LJ*

PACEY, Graham John. b 52. Leeds Univ CertEd74 Open Univ BA81 Teesside Poly ADEd85. NE Ord Course 90. **d** 93 **p** 94. C Kirkleatham *York* from 93. *44 Ayton Drive, Redcar, Cleveland TS10 4LR* Redcar (01642) 490475

PACKER, Prof James Innell. b 26. CCC Ox BA48 MA52 DPhil55. Wycliffe Hall Ox 49. **d** 52 **p** 53. Lic to Offic *Bris* 70-79; Prin Tyndale Hall Bris 70-72; Assoc Prin Trin Coll Bris 72-79; Prof Hist Th Regent Coll Vancouver 79-89; Prof Th from 89; rtd 91. *6017 Holland Street, Vancouver, Canada, V6N 2B2*

PACKER, Ven John Richard. b 46. Keble Coll Ox BA67 MA. Ripon Hall Ox 67. **d** 70 **p** 71. C St Helier *S'wark* 70-73; Chapl Abingdon St Nic *Ox* 73-77; Tutor Ripon Hall Ox 73-75; Tutor Ripon Coll Cuddesdon 75-77; V Wath-upon-Dearne w Adwick-upon-Dearne *Sheff* 77-86; RD Wath 83-86; TR Sheff Manor 86-91; RD Attercliffe 90-91; Assoc Prin Trin Coll from 91. *Moorside, 50 Stainburn Road, Workington, Cumbria CA14 1SN* Workington (01900) 66190 Fax as telephone

PACKER, Canon John William. b 18. K Coll Lon BA40 AKC40 BD41 MTh48. **d** 41 **p** 42. Hd Master Can Slade Gr Sch Bolton 53-77; Lic to Offic *Man* 53-77; Hon Can Man Cathl 75-78; rtd 77; Perm to Offic *Cant* from 78. *Netherbury, Meadow Close, Bridge, Canterbury, Kent CT4 5AT* Canterbury (01227) 830364

PACKER, Roger Ernest John. b 37. ARCO59 Pemb Coll Cam BA60 MA64. Cuddesdon Coll 60. **d** 62 **p** 63. C Chippenham St Andr w Tytherton Lucas *Bris* 62-65; C Caversham *Ox* 65-70; R Sandhurst 70-91; V Bridgwater St Mary, Chilton Trinity and Durleigh *B & W* from 91; RD Bridgwater from 94. *The Vicarage, 7 Durleigh Road, Bridgwater, Somerset TA6 7HU* Bridgwater (01278) 422437 or 424972

PACKHAM, Ms Elizabeth Daisy. b 33. Golds Coll Lon BSc54 CertEd55. N Ord Course. **dss** 83 **d** 87 **p** 94. Fairfield *Derby* 83-84; Buxton w Burbage and King Sterndale 84-87; Par Dn 87-94; C 94-95; P-in-c Chinley w Buxworth from 95. *The Vicarage, Buxworth, Stockport, Cheshire SK12 7NH* Whaley Bridge (01663) 732243

PADDICK, Graham. b 47. S'wark Ord Course. **d** 89 **p** 90. C St Helier *S'wark* 89-93; P-in-c Thornton Heath St Paul from 93.

The Vicarage, 1 Norbury Avenue, Thornton Heath, Surrey CR7 8AH 0181-653 2762

PADDISON, Michael David William. b 41. Oak Hill Th Coll 75. **d** 77 **p** 78. C Gt Warley Ch Ch *Chelmsf* 77-80; C Rayleigh 80-83; R Scole, Brockdish, Billingford, Thorpe Abbots etc *Nor* 83-95; RD Redenhall 89-95; R Reepham, Hackford w Whitwell, Kerdiston etc from 95. *The Rectory, Station Road, Reepham, Norwich NR10 4LJ* Norwich (01603) 870220

PADDOCK, Canon Gerald Alfred. b 39. Oak Hill Th Coll 66. **d** 69 **p** 70. C Whitehall Park St Andr Hornsey Lane *Lon* 69-73; C Edgware 73-76; P-in-c Ab Kettleby w Wartnaby and Holwell *Leic* 76-81; Dioc Missr 80-87; Hon Can Leic Cathl from 80; V Oaks in Charnwood and Copt Oak from 81; Police Liaison Officer from 81; Dioc Voc Officer from 81. *The Vicarage, Oaks Road, Oaks-in-Charnwood, Loughborough, Leics LE12 9YD* Shepshed (01509) 503246

PADDOCK, John Allan Barnes. b 51. Liv Univ BA74 MA91 Man Univ PGCE75. St Steph Ho Ox BA77 MA81. **d** 80 **p** 81. C Matson *Glouc* 80-82; Asst Chapl Madrid *Eur* 82-83; Chapl R Gr Sch Lanc 83-86; Chapl RAF 86-91; Offg Chapl RAF from 92; Chapl St Olave's Gr Sch Orpington 91-94; Perm to Offic *Blackb* from 94. *35 Cork Road, Lancaster LA1 1AY*

PADGET, William Thomas. b 19. **d** 77 **p** 78. NSM Rodbourne Cheney *Bris* 77-90; rtd 90; Perm to Offic *Bris* from 90. *39 George Tweed Gardens, Ramleaze Drive, Swindon SN5 9PX* Swindon (01793) 723789

PAGAN, Canon Keith Vivian. b 37. St Jo Coll Dur BA60 MA66. Chich Th Coll 60. **d** 62 **p** 63. C Clacton St Jas *Chelmsf* 62-64; C Wymondham *Nor* 64-70; P-in-c Guestwick 70-80; P-in-c Kettlestone 70-79; V Hindolveston 70-80; R Islay *Arg* from 80; R Campbeltown from 80; Miss to Seamen from 80; Can St Jo Cathl Oban *Arg* from 85; Can Cumbrae from 85. *The Rectory, Argyll Street, Campbeltown, Argyll PA28 6AY* Campbeltown (01586) 553846

PAGE, Canon Alan George. b 24. Em Coll Cam BA48 MA52. Wycliffe Hall Ox 49. **d** 51 **p** 52. Kenya 53-71; Hon Can Mt Kenya 71-75; Hon Can Mt Kenya S 75-84; C S Lyncombe *B & W* 71-72; R Freshford w Limpley Stoke 72-76; R Freshford, Limpley Stoke and Hinton Charterhouse 76-84; Can Mt Kenya Cen from 84; C Fulham St Mary N End *Lon* 87-89; rtd 89. *45 Ashley Avenue, Bath BA1 3DS* Bath (01225) 310532

PAGE, Alan Richard Benjamin. b 38. Univ of Wales (Lamp) BA60 BSc. St Mich Coll Llan 60. **d** 62 **p** 63. C Cardiff St Andr and St Teilo *Llan* 62-64; C Newport St Julian *Mon* 64-67; C Hoxton H Trin w St Mary *Lon* 67-69; C Winchmore Hill H Trin 69-71; V Camden Town St Mich w All SS and St Thos from 71. *St Michael's Vicarage, 1 Bartholomew Road, London NW5 2AH* 0171-485 1256

PAGE, Arthur Henry. b 21. Open Univ BA79. Sarum & Wells Th Coll. **d** 82 **p** 82. NSM Gtr Corsham *Bris* 82-87; Perm to Offic *Dur* 88; NSM Shadforth 89-91; Perm to Offic from 91. *9 Foxton Way, High Shincliffe, Durham DH1 2PJ* 0191-386 2141

PAGE, David. b 48. Bris Univ BA70 Leic Univ MA74 Southn Univ PGCE74 Nottm Univ DipTh82. St Jo Coll Nottm 81. **d** 83 **p** 84. C Morden *S'wark* 83-86; V Wimbledon St Luke 86-91; P-in-c Clapham Common St Barn 91-92; V from 92. *St Barnabas' Vicarage, 12 Lavender Gardens, London SW11 1DL* 0171-223 5953

✠**PAGE, Rt Rev Dennis Fountain.** b 19. G&C Coll Cam BA41 MA45. Linc Th Coll 41. **d** 43 **p** 44 **c** 75. C Rugby St Andr *Cov* 43-49; R Weeting *Ely* 49-65; R Hockwold w Wilton 49-65; RD Feltwell 53-65; Hon Can Ely Cathl 63-65 and 68-75; V Yaxley 65-75; Adn Huntingdon 65-75; Suff Bp Lanc *Blackb* 75-85; rtd 85; Perm to Offic *St E* from 85. *Larkrise, Hartest, Bury St Edmunds, Suffolk IP29 4ES* Bury St Edmunds (01284) 830694

PAGE, Mrs Dorothy Jean. b 29. Portsm Poly CertEd50. Ox NSM Course 84. **d** 87 **p** 94. NSM Wantage Downs *Ox* from 87. *11 North Street, Marcham, Abingdon, Oxon OX13 6NG* Frilford Heath (01865) 391462

PAGE, Ian George. b 62. Ex Univ BSc84 York Univ PGCE85. Edin Th Coll 87. **d** 90 **p** 91. C Blackpool St Steph *Blackb* 90-92; Perm to Offic *Ex* from 92. *31 Winston Park, South Molton, Devon EX36 3AY* South Molton (01769) 572895

PAGE, Mrs Irene May. b 38. Birm Univ BA58. NE Ord Course 85. **d** 87 **p** 94. Par Dn Cockfield *Dur* 87-90; Par Dn Waterloo St Jo w St Andr *S'wark* 90-94; C 94-95; R Woolwich St Thos from 95. *The New Rectory, Maryon Road, London SE7 8DJ* 0181-855 1718

PAGE, John Jeremy. b 56. Keble Coll Ox BA79 MA83 Edin Univ BD86. Edin Th Coll 83. **d** 86 **p** 87. C Wetherby *Ripon* 86-89; TV Wrexham *St As* 89-92; Chapl Hymers Coll Hull from 92. *46 Sunny Bank, Hull HU3 1LQ* Hull (01482) 43555

PAGE, John Laurance Howard. b 40. ALCD. **d** 65 **p** 66. C Spitalfields Ch Ch w All SS *Lon* 65-69; C Win Ch Ch *Win* 69-72; C Ringwood 72-76; V Lockerley and E Dean w E and W

Tytherley 76-89; RD Romsey 85-89; V Lord's Hill from 89. *1 Tangmere Drive, Southampton SO1 8GY*   Southampton (01703) 731182

PAGE, Canon Michael John. b 42. K Coll Lon BD66 AKC66. **d** 67 **p** 68. C Rawmarsh w Parkgate *Sheff* 67-72; C-in-c Gleadless Valley CD 72-74; TR Gleadless Valley 74-77; V Lechlade *Glouc* 77-86; RD Fairford 81-86; V Winchcombe, Gretton, Sudeley Manor etc from 86; Hon Can Glouc Cathl from 91; RD Winchcombe from 94. *The Vicarage, Langley Road, Winchcombe, Cheltenham, Glos GL54 5QP* Cheltenham (01242) 602368

PAGE, Owen Richard. b 53. FIMLS83 Trent Poly HNC77 Derby Coll of Educn DMS85. Linc Th Coll 89. **d** 91 **p** 92. C Gt Bookham *Guildf* 91-94; V Kings Heath *Pet* from 94. *The Vicarage, Church Green, Northampton NN5 7LS* Northampton (01604) 407074

PAGE, Canon Richard Dennis. b 23. G&C Coll Cam BA48 MA50. Ridley Hall Cam 48. **d** 50 **p** 51. V Ecclesfield *Sheff* 64-71; RD Ecclesfield 66-71; P-in-c Holkham w Egmere and Waterden *Nor* 71-78; R Wells next the Sea 71-78; RD Burnham and Walsingham 72-78; V Hemsby 78-83; P-in-c Brooke w Kirstead 83-85; P-in-c Mundham w Seething 83-85; P-in-c Thwaite 83-85; R Brooke, Kirstead, Mundham w Seething and Thwaite 85-89; Hon Can Nor Cathl 87-89; rtd 90. *The Greyhound, Back Street, Reepham, Norfolk NR10 4SJ* Norwich (01603) 870886

PAGE, Robert William Charles. b 67. St Steph Ho Ox 90. **d** 93 **p** 94. C Hockerill *St Alb* from 93. *17 Legions Way, Bishop's Stortford, Herts CM23 2AU*   Bishop's Stortford (01279) 657261

PAGE, Teehan Dawson. b 61. Ch Ch Ox BA83 MA87. St Steph Ho Ox 91. **d** 93 **p** 94. C Surbiton St Andr and St Mark *S'wark* from 93. *33 Cheyne Hill, Surbiton, Surrey KT5 8BL*   0181-399 7948

PAGE, Thomas William. b 57. Sarum & Wells Th Coll 84. **d** 87 **p** 88. C Caterham *S'wark* 87-91; C Cheam 91-95; P-in-c Cranham *Chelmsf* from 95. *All Saints House, 51 Courtney Gardens, Upminster, Essex RM14 1DM*   Upminster (01708) 228200

PAGE, Canon Trevor Melvyn. b 41. Dur Univ BA63 Fitzw Coll Cam BA72 Westcott Ho Cam 64. **d** 67 **p** 68. C Millhouses H Trin *Sheff* 67-69; Chapl Sheff Univ 69-74; V Doncaster Intake 74-82; Dioc Dir of Ords from 82; Dioc Dir of In-Service Tr from 82; Can Res Sheff Cathl from 82; Dioc Dir of Min from 89. *393 Fulwood Road, Sheffield S10 3GE* Sheffield (0114) 230 5707

PAGE, William George. b 42. Linc Th Coll 83. **d** 85 **p** 86. C Boston *Linc* 85-89; V Sibsey w Frithville from 89; RD Holland E from 95. *The Vicarage, Sibsey, Boston, Lincs PE22 0RT*   Boston (01205) 750305

PAGE-CHESTNEY, Michael William. b 47. Linc Th Coll 80. **d** 82 **p** 83. C Barton upon Humber *Linc* 82-85; TV Gt Grimsby St Mary and St Jas 85-91; V E Stockwith from 91; V Blyton w Pilham 91-93; V Laughton w Wildsworth 91-93; V Corringham and Blyton Gp from 93. *The Vicarage, Church Lane, Blyton, Gainsborough, Lincs DN21 3JZ*   Laughton (01427) 628216

PAGE-CHESTNEY, Mrs Susan Valerie. b 49. E Midl Min Tr Course DipTh86. **dss** 86 **d** 87 **p** 94. NSM Gt Grimsby St Mary and St Jas *Linc* 86-91; NSM Blyton w Pilham 91-93; NSM Laughton w Wildsworth 91-93; NSM Corringham and Blyton Gp from 93; NSM E Stockwith from 91. *The Vicarage, Church Lane, Blyton, Gainsborough, Lincs DN21 3JZ*   Laughton (01427) 628216

PAGE-TURNER, Edward Gregory Ambrose Wilford. b 31. Qu Coll Birm 57. **d** 60 **p** 61. C Helmsley *York* 60-64; C Kensington St Phil Earl's Court *Lon* 64-67; C Walton-on-Thames *Guildf* 67-70; V Seend *Sarum* 70-71; V Seend and Bulkington 71-79; R Bladon w Woodstock *Ox* 79-87; P-in-c Begbroke 80-86; P-in-c Shipton-on-Cherwell 80-86; P-in-c Hampton Gay 80-85; RD Woodstock 84-87; P-in-c Wootton by Woodstock 85-87; R Patterdale *Carl* 87-89; R Askerswell, Loders and Powerstock *Sarum* from 89; RD Lyme Bay from 89; RD Beaminster from 94. *The Vicarage, Loders, Bridport, Dorset DT6 3SA* Bridport (01308) 427175

PAGET, Alfred Ivor. b 24. St Aid Birkenhead 56. **d** 59 **p** 60. R Gt and Lt Henny w Middleton *Chelmsf* 66-74; C Gt Holland 74-79; V Holland-on-Sea 79-92; rtd 92. *94 Wellfield Road, London SW16 2BP*   0181-769 3394

PAGET, David Rolf. b 54. Worc Coll Ox BA78. St Steph Ho Ox BA80. **d** 81 **p** 82. C Sheerness H Trin w St Paul *Cant* 81-84; C E Bedfont *Lon* 84-88; P-in-c Fulham St Andr Fulham Fields 88-89; V from 89. *St Andrew's Vicarage, 10 St Andrew's Road, London W14 9SX*   0171-385 5578

PAGET, Richard Campbell. b 54. Collingwood Coll Dur BA76 Rob Coll Cam BA87. Ridley Hall Cam 85. **d** 88 **p** 89. C Gipsy

Hill Ch Ch *S'wark* 88-92; R Chatham St Mary w St Jo *Roch* from 92. *The Rectory, 65 Maidstone Road, Chatham, Kent ME4 6DP*   Medway (01634) 843632

PAGET, Robert James Innes. b 35. AKC59. **d** 60 **p** 61. C Attenborough w Bramcote *S'well* 60-63; C Cheltenham St Mark *Glouc* 63-72; P-in-c Pilsley *Derby* 72-73; TV N Wingfield, Pilsley and Tupton 73-89; R Pinxton from 89. *The Rectory, Town Street, Pinxton, Nottingham NG16 6HH* Ripley (01773) 580024

PAGET-WILKES, Ven Michael Jocelyn James. b 41. NDA64. ALCD69. **d** 69 **p** 70. C Wandsworth All SS *S'wark* 69-74; V Hatcham St Jas 74-82; V Rugby St Matt *Cov* 82-90; Adn Warw from 90. *10 Northumberland Road, Leamington Spa, Warks CV32 6HA*   Leamington Spa (01926) 313337 or 674328

PAGETT, Andrew Stephen. b 45. Bris & Glouc Tr Course. **d** 82 **p** 83. NSM Swindon New Town *Bris* from 82. *93 Lansdown Road, Swindon SN1 3ND*   Swindon (01793) 539283

PAICE, Michael Antony. b 35. Kelham Th Coll 55. **d** 60 **p** 61. C Skegby *S'well* 60-62; C Carlton 62-66; V Misterton and W Stockwith 66-81; P-in-c Littleton on Severn w Elberton *Bris* 81-83; V Olveston 81-83; Deputation Appeals Org CECS 83-89; R Sutton St Nicholas w Sutton St Michael *Heref* from 89; R Withington w Westhide from 89. *The Rectory, Sutton St Nicholas, Hereford HR1 3BA*   Hereford (01432) 880253

PAICE, William Henry. b 08. Worc Ord Coll. **d** 57 **p** 58. C-in-c Gurnard All SS CD *Portsm* 68-73; rtd 73. *Garden House, The Laurels, Church Street, Shelfanger, Diss, Norfolk IP22 2DG* Diss (01379) 651128

PAIN, Canon David Clinton. b 36. K Coll Lon 56. **d** 64 **p** 64. Benin 64-67; Ghana 67-86; Hon Can Accra 80-86; V Kemp Town St Mary *Chich* 86-93; Chapl St Mary's Hall Brighton from 88; V Billingshurst *Chich* from 93. *The Vicarage, East Street, Billingshurst, W Sussex RH14 9PY*   Billingshurst (01403) 782332

PAIN, Lawrence Percy Bernard. b 11. Lon Univ BA32. Wells Th Coll 48. **d** 49 **p** 50. V Rowledge *Guildf* 70-81; rtd 81; Perm to Offic *Portsm* from 89. *62 Forest Close, Waltham Chase, Southampton SO3 2NB*   Bishops Waltham (01489) 894972

PAIN, Michael Broughton George. b 37. Dur Univ BA61. Wycliffe Hall Ox 61. **d** 63 **p** 64. C Downend *Bris* 63-67; C Swindon Ch Ch 67-70; V Alveston 70-78; V Guildf Ch Ch *Guildf* 78-90; TR Melksham *Sarum* from 90; Chapl Melksham Hosp from 90. *The Rectory, Canon Square, Melksham, Wilts SN12 6LX*   Melksham (01225) 703262

PAIN, Richard Edward. b 56. Bris Univ BA79 Univ of Wales (Cardiff) BD84. St Mich Coll Llan 81. **d** 84 **p** 85. C Caldicot *Mon* 84-86; P-in-c Cwmtillery 86-88; V 88-91; V Six Bells 88-91; V Risca from 91. *The Vicarage, 1 Gelli Crescent, Risca, Newport NP1 6QG*   Risca (01633) 612307

PAINE, Dr David Stevens. b 24. St Jo Coll Cam MB47 BChir47 MA52. Ridley Hall Cam 52. **d** 54 **p** 55. C Rowner *Portsm* 54-56; C Freshwater 56-59; V S Cerney w Cerney Wick *Glouc* 59-64. *42 Newton Road, Cambridge CB1 5EF*   Cambridge (01223) 353300

PAINE, Kevin Adrian Martin. b 56. Univ of Wales (Cardiff) DipTh81. St Mich Coll Llan. **d** 81 **p** 82. Chapl St Woolos Cathl *Mon* 81-85; Perm to Offic 85-93; Miss to the Deaf and Dumb 93-94. *35 Risca Road, Newport, Gwent CF2 5AX*   Newport (01633) 258197

PAINE, Peter Stanley. b 46. K Coll Lon BD69 AKC69. Linc Th Coll DipMin89 Cuddesdon Coll 69. **d** 71 **p** 72. C Leeds St Aid *Ripon* 71-74; C Harrogate St Wilfrid 74-78; V Beeston Hill H Spirit 78-82; TV Seacroft 82-90; V Martham w Repps w Bastwick *Nor* 90-94; V Martham and Repps with Bastwick, Thurne etc from 94. *The Vicarage, Martham, Great Yarmouth, Norfolk NR29 4PR*   Great Yarmouth (01493) 740240

PAINE, William Barry. b 58. TCD DipTh84. CITC. **d** 84 **p** 85. C Glendermott *D & R* 84-86; C Lurgan St Jo *D & D* 86-88; I Kilbarron w Rossnowlagh and Drumholm *D & R* 88-91; CF from 91. *c/o MOD Chaplains (Army), Bagshot Park, Bagshot, Surrey GU19 5PL*   Bagshot (01276) 471717

PAINE DAVEY, Nathan Paul. b 64. Barrister-at-Law 88 Birm Poly LLB86. St Steph Ho Ox 89. **d** 92 **p** 93. C Palmers Green St Jo *Lon* 92-95; C Kentish Town St Silas from 95; C Haverstock Hill H Trin w Kentish Town St Barn from 95. *30A Hadley Street, London NW1 8SS*   0171-482 1170

PAINTER, Canon David Scott. b 44. LTCL65 Worc Coll Ox BA68 MA72. Cuddesdon Coll 68. **d** 70 **p** 71. C Plymouth St Andr *Ex* 70-73; Chapl Plymouth Poly 71-73; C St Marylebone All SS *Lon* 73-76; Abp's Dom Chapl *Cant* 76-80; Dir of Ords 76-80; V Roehampton H Trin *S'wark* 80-91; PV Westmr Abbey 81-91; RD Wandsworth *S'wark* 85-90; Perm to Offic 91; Can Res and Treas S'wark Cathl from 91; Dioc Dir of Ords from 91. *22 Rochelle Close, London SW11 2RX*   0181-871 1118 or 0171-403 8686

PAINTER, John. b 25. Selw Coll Cam BA48 MA53. Ripon Hall Ox 48. **d** 50 **p** 51. V Sandown Ch Ch *Portsm* 66-72; R Keinton Mandeville *B & W* 72-77; P-in-c Lydford-on-Fosse 76-77; R

Keinton Mandeville w Lydford on Fosse 77-90; RD Cary 81-90; RD Bruton 82-85; rtd 90; Perm to Offic *B & W* from 90. *1 Fairview Terrace, Station Road, Castle Cary, Somerset BA7 7BX* Castle Cary (01963) 50756

PAIRMAN, David Drummond. b 47. GGSM CertEd. Chich Th Coll 82. **d** 84 **p** 85. C Cowes St Mary *Portsm* 84-87; C Marshwood Vale *Sarum* 87-90; C Hawkchurch 87-90; C Marshwood Vale TM from 90. *The Rectory, Hawkchurch, Axminster, Devon EX13 5XD* Axminster (01297) 678225

PAISEY, Gerald Herbert John. b 31. Wm Booth Memorial Coll 51 Lon Univ CertRS60 Leic Univ CertEd62 Nottm Univ DipRE68 DipAdEd70 MPhil77 Lanc Univ MA78 K Coll Lon PhD91. St Alb Minl Tr Scheme 80. **d** 88 **p** 90. NSM Montrose *Bre* 88-90; NSM Inverbervie 88-90; NSM Stonehaven from 90; NSM Catterline from 90. *20 St Michael's Way, Newtonhill, Stonehaven, Kincardineshire AB3 2GS* Stonehaven (01569) 730322

PAISEY, Jeremy Mark. b 58. Aber Univ LLB81 Solicitor 83. Coates Hall Edin 92. **d** 94. C Turriff *Ab* from 94; C Buckie from 94; C Banff from 94; C Cuminestown from 94; C Portsoy from 94. *All Saints House, Clunie Square, Buckie, Banffshire AB56 1HA* Buckie (01542) 832312

PAISH, Miss Muriel Dorothy. b 21. Birm Univ CertEd41. Glouc Sch of Min. **dss** 85 **d** 87 **p** 94. Uley w Owlpen and Nympsfield *Glouc* 85-87; Hon C from 87. *5 Woodstock Terrace, Uley, Dursley, Glos GL11 5SW* Dursley (01453) 860429

PAISLEY, James. b 05. Edin Th Coll 27. **d** 29 **p** 30. V Hampstead Norris *Ox* 47-70; V Compton 47-70; rtd 70; Perm to Offic *Ex* from 70. *15 Wilton Way, Abbotskerswell, Newton Abbot, Devon TQ12 5PG* Newton Abbot (01626) 53728

PAISLEY, Ronald Gordon. b 15. Clifton Th Coll 50. **d** 52 **p** 53. V Becontree St Alb *Chelmsf* 60-73; V Toxteth Park St Clem *Liv* 73-80; rtd 80; Perm to Offic *Carl* from 86. *Glen Rosa, Station Road, Brampton, Cumbria CA8 1EX* Brampton (016977) 3022

PAISLEY, Samuel Robinson (Robin). b 51. Man Univ BSc72. Edin Th Coll BD91. **d** 91 **p** 92. C St Mary's Cathl *Glas* 91-95; P-in-c Bishopbriggs from 95. *St James's Rectory, 9 Meadowburn, Bishopbriggs, Glasgow G64 3HA* 0141-772 4514

PAKENHAM, Charles Wilfrid. b 18. Trin Coll Ox BA40 MA52. Wycliffe Hall Ox 40. **d** 41 **p** 42. V Litherland Ch Ch *Liv* 52-84; rtd 84; P-in-c W Woodhay w Enborne, Hampstead Marshall etc *Ox* 91-92. *15 Cook Road, Albourne, Marlborough, Wilts SN8 2EG* Marlborough (01672) 40531

PAKENHAM, Stephen Walter. b 29. Qu Coll Cam BA57 MA61. Linc Th Coll 57. **d** 59 **p** 60. V Donnington *Chich* 64-75; V Appledram 64-75; V Durrington 75-81; V St Mary Bourne and Woodcott *Win* 81-88; rtd 88. *The Malthouse, Frogmore, Kingsbridge, Devon TQ7 2PG* Frogmore (01548) 531703

PALIN, John Edward. b 47. Univ of Wales (Cardiff) DipTh70 DPS71 Open Univ BA83 Leeds Univ MA89. St Mich Coll Llan 67. **d** 71 **p** 72. C Staveley *Derby* 71-74; C Nottm St Mary *S'well* 75-77; P-in-c Thistleton 77-79; V Greetham w Stretton and Clipsham *Pet* 77-79; V Greetham and Thistleton w Stretton and Clipsham 79-83; TR Staveley and Barrow Hill *Derby* 83-87; Chapl R Hallamshire Hosp Sheff 87-88; Perm to Offic *Sheff* 88-90; C Bramley *Ripon* 90-91; TV 91-93; Chapl Doncaster Health Care NHS Trust from 93; Chapl Tickhill Road Hosp Doncaster from 93. *Tickhill Road Hospital, Tickhill Road, Doncaster, S Yorkshire DN4 8QL* Doncaster (01302) 853241

PALIN, Roy. b 34. Man Univ BA56. Ripon Hall Ox 65. **d** 67 **p** 68. C Ilkeston St Mary *Derby* 67-70; C Wollaton *S'well* 70-71; V Harby w Swinethorpe 71-79; V Thorney w Wigsley and Broadholme 71-79; P-in-c N Clifton 75-79; R Harby w Thorney and N and S Clifton 79-80; V Tuxford 80-81; P-in-c Laxton 80-81; P-in-c Markham Clinton 80-81; P-in-c Weston 80-81; V Tuxford w Weston and Markham Clinton 81-90; R Nuthall from 90. *The Rectory, 24 Watnall Road, Nuthall, Nottingham NG16 1DU* Nottingham (0115) 938 4987

PALK, Mrs Deirdre Elizabeth Pauline. b 41. AIL77 Reading Univ BA63 City of Lon Poly DipBS74 DipRS84. S'wark Ord Course 81. **dss** 84 **d** 87. Wanstead H Trin Hermon Hill *Chelmsf* 84-87; Hon Par Dn from 87; Hon Par Dn Walthamstow St Pet from 88. *3 Ashdon Close, Woodford Green, Essex IG8 0EF* 0181-505 3547

PALLANT, Canon Roger Frank. b 35. Trin Coll Cam BA57 MA61. Wells Th Coll 57. **d** 59 **p** 60. C Stafford St Mary *Lich* 59-62; C Ipswich St Mary le Tower *St E* 62-65; Dioc Youth Chapl 62-65; Dev Officer C of E Youth Coun 65-70; Hon C Putney St Mary *S'wark* 66-71; Org Sec New Syn Gp 70-71; R Hintlesham w Chattisham *St E* 71-80; V Ipswich All Hallows 80-88; Hon Can St E Cathl from 85; P-in-c Sproughton w Burstall from 88; Dioc Officer for Local NSM from 88; RD Samford from 93. *The Rectory, Glebe Close, Sproughton, Ipswich IP8 3BQ* Ipswich (01473) 241078

PALLETT, Ian Nigel. b 59. Leeds Univ BA80. Linc Th Coll 81. **d** 84 **p** 85. C Halesowen *Worc* 84-88; C Mansf Woodhouse *S'well* 88-91; R Morton and Stonebroom *Derby* from 91. *The Vicarage, 14 High Street, Stonebroom, Alfreton, Derbyshire DE55 6JY* Ripley (01773) 872353

PALMER, Alister Gordon. b 46. Univ of Tasmania BA73 DipEd74. Trin Coll Bris 78 Ridley Hall Cam 80. **d** 80 **p** 81. C Patchway *Bris* 80-83; C Bushbury *Lich* 83-86; V Wednesfield Heath 86-93. *St Stephen's Vicarage, Hilton Street, Wolverhampton WV10 0LF*

PALMER, Angus Douglas. b 40. St Chad's Coll Dur BA62 DipTh63. **d** 63 **p** 64. C Wallsend St Pet *Newc* 63-66; C Newc H Cross 66-69; C Bottesford *Linc* 69-70; R Penicuik *Edin* 70-83; R W Linton 77-83. *6 Hackworth Gardens, Wylam, Northd NE41 8EJ* Wylam (01661) 853786

PALMER, Bernard Joseph. b 20. St Cath Soc Ox BA49 MA64. Worc Ord Coll 64. **d** 66 **p** 67. R Harvington *Worc* 69-78; V Stoulton w Drakes Broughton and Pirton 78-85; rtd 85; Perm to Offic *Ex* from 85. *Belvedere, Treloyhan Park Road, St Ives, Cornwall TR26 2AH* Penzance (01736) 796846

PALMER, Canon David Henry. b 33. Bris Univ BA54. Linc Th Coll 54. **d** 58 **p** 59. C E Dulwich St Jo *S'wark* 58-62; C Pet All SS *Pet* 62-68; V Northn H Trin 68-74; Chapl Br Emb Ankara *Eur* 74-77; Chapl Rome 77-84; Can Malta Cathl 79-84; Hon Can Malta Cathl from 84; V Brighton St Matthias *Chich* 84-88; P-in-c Upper Teddington SS Pet and Paul *Lon* 88-90; P-in-c Fulwell St Mich and St Geo 88-90; V Teddington SS Pet and Paul and Fulwell from 90; AD Hampton from 90. *The Vicarage, 1 Bychurch End, Teddington, Middx TW11 8PS* 0181-977 3330

PALMER, David Philip. b 50. Sarum & Wells Th Coll. **d** 84 **p** 85. C St Ives *Ely* 84-86; C Luton All SS w St Pet *St Alb* 86-88; V Stocksbridge *Sheff* from 88. *The Vicarage, Victoria Road, Stocksbridge, Sheffield S30 5FX* Sheffield (0114) 288 6964

PALMER, David Roderick. b 34. St Jo Coll Dur BA56 Birm Univ DipTh58 Trin Coll Ox. Qu Coll Birm 56. **d** 60 **p** 61. C Loughton St Jo *Chelmsf* 60-63; C Pimlico St Gabr *Lon* 63-64; Miss to Seamen 64-67; CF 67-74; Chapl Luxembourg *Eur* 74-80; P-in-c Exton and Winsford and Cutcombe w Luxborough *B & W* 80-82; P-in-c Wrington w Butcombe 82-84; Dep Dir of Tr Inst Wednesbury St Jas *Lich* 84-86; C Gt Wyrley 86-89; V Wilshamstead and Houghton Conquest *St Alb* from 90. *The Vicarage, Wilshamstead, Bedford MK45 3EU* Bedford (01234) 740423

PALMER, Canon Derek George. b 28. Selw Coll Cam BA50 MA54. Wells Th Coll 50. **d** 52 **p** 53. C Stapleton *Bris* 52-54; C Bishopston 54-58; C-in-c Hartcliffe St Andr CD 58-62; V Bris St Andr Hartcliffe 62-68; V Swindon Ch Ch 68-76; Hon Can Bris Cathl 74-76; Adn Roch 77-83; Can Res Roch Cathl 77-83; Hon Can 83-87; Home Sec Gen Syn Bd for Miss and Unity 83-87; TR Dronfield *Derby* 87-90; TR Dronfield w Holmesfield from 90; Chapl to The Queen from 90; Hon Can Derby Cathl *Derby* from 92. *The Rectory, Church Street, Dronfield, Sheffield S18 6QB* Dronfield (01246) 411531

PALMER, Derek James. b 54. Man Univ BA77. Qu Coll Birm 77. **d** 79 **p** 80. C Leek *Lich* 79-83; CF 83-92. *Address temp unknown*

PALMER, Miss Elizabeth Anne. b 46. Reading Univ BA68 Nottm Univ PGCE69 MEd78. St Jo Coll Nottm DTS91. **d** 91 **p** 94. C Scartho *Linc* from 91. *25 Waltham Road, Grimsby, S Humberside DN33 2LY* Grimsby (01472) 870373

PALMER, Preb Francis Harvey. b 30. Jes Coll Cam BA52 MA56. Wycliffe Hall Ox 53. **d** 55 **p** 56. V Cam H Trin *Ely* 64-71; Chapl to Cam Pastorate 64-71; Prin Ridley Hall Cam 71-72; R Worplesdon *Guildf* 72-80; Bp's Ecum Officer 74-80; P-in-c Blymhill w Weston-under-Lizard *Lich* 80-82; Dioc Missr and Sec to Bd for Miss and Unity 80-90; Preb Lich Cathl 86-89; TV Walsall 87-90; rtd 90. *The Old Vicarage, Claverley, Wolverhampton WV5 7DT* Claverley (01746) 710746

PALMER, Graham. b 31. Em Coll Cam BA53 MA57. Qu Coll Birm 56. **d** 58 **p** 59. C Camberwell St Giles *S'wark* 58-61; C Kilburn St Aug *Lon* 61-67; P-in-c Fulham St Alb 67-73; V 73-92; V Fulham St Alb w St Aug from 92. *St Alban's Vicarage, 4 Margravine Road, London W6 8HJ* 0171-385 0724

PALMER, Hugh. b 50. Pemb Coll Cam BA72 MA76. Ridley Hall Cam 73. **d** 76 **p** 77. C Heigham H Trin *Nor* 76-80; Bp's Chapl for Tr and Miss 80-84; C St Helen Bishopsgate w St Andr Undershaft etc *Lon* from 85. *30 Tredegar Square, London E3 5AG* 0171-283 2231

PALMER, Hugh Maurice Webber. b 28. Magd Coll Cam BA51 MA55. Cuddesdon Coll 51. **d** 53 **p** 54. Rhodesia 65-70; C Headbourne Worthy *Win* 70-71; P-in-c Stratton Strawless *Nor* 72-77; R Hainford 72-77; R Haynford w Stratton Strawless 77-80; Chapl HM Pris Stafford 80-82; Chapl HM Pris Standford Hill 82-89; Sub-Chapl HM Pris Nor 89-91; rtd 91. *2B Millfield Road, North Walsham, Norfolk NR29 0EB* North Walsham (01692) 403664

PALMER

PALMER, Ian Stanley. b 50. K Coll Lon BD71. Cranmer Hall Dur 73. **d** 75 **p** 76. C Huyton St Mich *Liv* 75-78; Chapl Dur Univ *Dur* 78-83; V Collierley w Annfield Plain 83-90; Australia from 90. *The Bishop's Registry, 48 Church Street, Newcastle, NSW, Australia 2300* Newcastle (49) 293094

PALMER, Mrs Jacqueline Merrill. b 60. Leeds Univ BA82. Cranmer Hall Dur 83. **dss** 85 **d** 87. Asst Chapl Hull Univ *York* 85-87. *60 Magnolia Road, Southampton SO2 7LH* Southampton (01703) 432591

PALMER, John Richard Henry. b 29. AKC52. **d** 53 **p** 54. Chapl Holloway Sanatorium Virginia Water 66-70; Chapl Brookwood Hosp Woking 70-94; rtd 94. *Lightning Ridge, Pentreath Road, The Lizard, Helston, Cornwall TR12 7NY* The Lizard (01326) 290654

PALMER, John Russell. b 25. Birm Univ BSc46. Cuddesdon Coll 70. **d** 71 **p** 72. C Weeke *Win* 71-76; V Four Marks 76-90; rtd 90. *33 Montague Road, Bournemouth BH5 2EW* Bournemouth (01202) 426536

PALMER, Malcolm Leonard. b 46. Sarum & Wells Th Coll. **d** 82 **p** 83. C Cannock *Lich* 82-85; Chapl RAF 85-89; Asst Chapl HM Pris Dur 89-90; Chapl HM Young Offender Inst Hewell Grange 90-93; Chapl HM Rem Cen Brockhill 90-93; Chapl HM Pris Blakenhurst from 93. *HM Prison Blakenhurst, Hewell Grange, Redditch, Worcester B97 6QS* Redditch (01527) 543348 Fax 546382

PALMER, Marion Denise. b 42. SRN64 SCM66 Open Univ BA82. Linc Th Coll 84. **dss** 86 **d** 87 **p** 94. Poplar *Lon* 86-87; Par Dn 87-90; Par Dn Gillingham St Mary *Roch* 90-94; C from 94. *146 Woodlands Road, Gillingham, Kent ME7 2SX* Medway (01634) 571197

PALMER, Dr Maureen Florence. b 38. Qu Eliz Coll Lon BSc60 PhD64 DipRS79. Ripon Coll Cuddesdon DipTh84. **dss** 85 **d** 87 **p** 94. Tupsley *Heref* 85-87; C 87-88; Par Dn Talbot Village *Sarum* 88-91; Chapl Birm Cathl *Birm* from 91. *114 Cherry Orchard Road, Birmingham B20 2JY* 0121-515 2250

PALMER, Michael Christopher. b 43. AKC67. **d** 68 **p** 69. C Easthampstead *Ox* 68-71; Miss to Seamen 71-73; Hong Kong 73; Lic to Offic *Ox* 76-79; Lic to Offic *Truro* 79-83; Dioc Soc Resp Adv from 83; Bp's Dom Chapl 85-87; V Devoran from 87. *The Vicarage, Devoran, Truro, Cornwall TR3 6PA* Truro (01872) 863116

PALMER, Norman Ernest. b 28. Lon Univ DipTh56 BD59. Roch Th Coll 66. **d** 67 **p** 67. V Bozeat w Easton Maudit *Pet* 69-90; rtd 90. *4 St Augustine's Close, Bexhill-on-Sea, E Sussex TN39 3AZ* Bexhill-on-Sea (01424) 218573

PALMER, Canon Peter Malcolm. b 31. Chich Th Coll 56. **d** 59 **p** 60. C Leighton Buzzard *St Alb* 59-63; C Apsley End 63-65; C Hitchin H Sav 65-69; R Ickleford 69-76; V Oxhey St Matt 76-86; V Kensworth, Studham and Whipsnade from 86; Hon Can St Alb from 94. *The Vicarage, Clay Hall Road, Kensworth, Dunstable, Beds LU6 3RF* Whipsnade (01582) 872223

PALMER, Peter Parsons. b 27. **d** 59 **p** 61. SSJE from 59; Canada 59-79; Perm to Offic *Leic* 80-86; Perm to Offic 86-94; Lic to Offic from 94. *SSJE Priory, 228 Iffley Road, Oxford OX4 1SE* Oxford (01865) 242227

PALMER, Philip Edward Hitchen. b 35. St Jo Coll Cam MA61 DipAdEd74. Ridley Hall Cam 61 E Anglian Minl Tr Course 87. **d** 90 **p** 91. NSM Gt Oakley w Wix *Chelmsf* from 90. *Glebe House, Great Oakley, Harwich, Essex CO12 5BJ* Clacton-on-Sea (01255) 880737

PALMER, Robert William. b 28. DMS. Wells Th Coll 63. **d** 65 **p** 66. P-in-c Cov St Mark *Cov* 69-71; Chapl Cov and Warks Hosp 69-71; Hon C Binley *Cov* 72-76; V Sheff St Paul Wordsworth Avenue *Sheff* 76-84; V Deepcar 84-93; rtd 93. *Moorlands, 26 Coal Pit Lane, Stocksbridge, Sheffield S30 5AW*

PALMER, Canon Stephen Charles. b 47. Oak Hill Th Coll 71. **d** 74 **p** 75. C Crofton *Portsm* 74-77; Bp's Dom Chapl 77-80; Chapl RNR from 78; R Brighstone and Brooke w Mottistone *Portsm* 80-91; P-in-c Shorwell w Kingston 82-86; RD W Wight 87-91; Hon Can Portsm Cathl from 91; Falkland Is from 91; Intercon Ch Soc from 91. *The Deanery, Stanley, Falkland Islands* Falkland Islands (500) 21100 Fax 21842

PALMER, Steven Roy. b 51. Birm Univ BSc71. W Midl Minl Tr Course 91. **d** 94 **p** 95. C Sheldon *Birm* from 94. *151 Church Road, Birmingham B26 3TT* 0121-743 6956

PALMER, Terence Henry James (Terry). b 34. St Edm Hall Ox BA65 MA69. St D Coll Lamp BA55 LTh57. **d** 57 **p** 58. C Griffithstown *Mon* 57-60; Min Can and C St D Cathl *St D* 60-63; Perm to Offic *Ox* 63-65; Perm to Offic *B & W* 63-65; C Mon 65-69; C-in-c St Hilary Greenway CD 69-72; R Roggiett w Llanfihangel Roggiett 72-80; R Portskewett and Roggiett w Llanfihangel Rogiett from 80; RD Netherwent from 89; Dir NSM Studies from 91. *The Rectory, 19 Main Road, Portskewett, Newport, Gwent NP6 4SG* Caldicot (01291) 420313

PALMER, William Frederick. b 15. Kelham Th Coll 33. **d** 40 **p** 41. R Chalfont St Giles *Ox* 68-73; V Mill Hill St Mich *Lon* 73-81; rtd 81; Perm to Offic *St Alb* from 81. *22 The Sycamores, Baldock, Herts SG7 5BJ* Baldock (01462) 892456

PALMER-PALMER-FFYNCHE, Barry Marshall. b 23. Hertf Coll Ox BA47 MA48. Westcott Ho Cam 47. **d** 49 **p** 50. Chapl Westmr Hosp Lon 66-73; V Chipping Sodbury and Old Sodbury *Glouc* 73-88; rtd 88; Perm to Offic *Glouc* from 89; Perm to Offic *Bris* from 89; Perm to Offic *Lon* from 90. *Finch's Folly, Home Farm Stables, 45 Hay Street, Marshfield, Chippenham, Wilts SN14 8PF* Bath (01225) 891096

PAMMENT, Canon Gordon Charles. b 31. TCD BA54. Linc Th Coll 56. **d** 58 **p** 60. I Macroom Union *C, C & R* 65-72; I Rathcormac Union 72-78; I Fermoy Union 78-91; Preb Ross Cathl 89-91; Preb Cork Cathl 89-91; rtd 91. *5 Langford Place, Co Cork, Irish Republic*

PAMPLIN, Dr Richard Lawrence. b 46. Lon Univ BScEng68 Dur Univ BA75. NY Th Sem DMin85 Wycliffe Hall Ox 75. **d** 77 **p** 78. C Greenside *Dur* 77-80; C Sheff St Barn and St Mary *Sheff* 80-84; R Wombwell 84-90; P-in-c Madeley *Heref* 90-91; TR from 91. *St Michael's Vicarage, Church Street, Madeley, Telford, Shropshire TF7 5BN* Telford (01952) 585718

PANG, Wing-On. b 43. BA67 Lon Univ MA70. Oak Hill Th Coll 87. **d** 87 **p** 88. C Pennycross *Ex* 87-91; TV Mildenhall *St E* from 91. *11 The Green, Tuddenham, Bury St Edmunds, Suffolk IP28 6SD* Mildenhall (01638) 712376

PANGBOURNE, John Godfrey. b 36. Ridley Hall Cam 82. **d** 84 **p** 85. C Ashtead *Guildf* 84-88; V Ore Ch Ch *Chich* from 88. *Christ Church Vicarage, 76 Canute Road, Ore, Hastings, E Sussex TN35 5HT* Hastings (01424) 421439

PANKHURST, Donald Araunah. b 28. Qu Coll Birm DipTh64. **d** 64 **p** 65. V Aspull *Liv* 68-76; R Newchurch 76-88; R Winwick 88-94; rtd 94. *4 St Mary's Park, Windermere, Cumbria LA23 1AY* Windermere (015394) 46390

PANNELL, Roy Charles. b 45. AKC69. **d** 70 **p** 71. C Sheff Parson Cross St Cecilia *Sheff* 70-75; V New Bentley 75-82; V Greenhill 82-94. *74 Sandygate Road, Sheffield S10 5RZ* Sheffield (0114) 268 6471

PANNETT, Philip Anthony. b 36. MPS59 AKC63. **d** 64 **p** 65. C Stanmer w Falmer and Moulsecoomb *Chich* 64-68; C Hangleton 68-72; Teacher Bodiam Manor Sch 74-76. *35 Dudley Road, Brighton BN1 7GN* Brighton (01273) 551431

PANTER, Canon Noel. b 09. Ex Coll Ox BA31 DipTh32 MA35. Wycliffe Hall Ox 31. **d** 33 **p** 34. Hon Can Worc Cathl *Worc* 66-77; V Gt Malvern Ch Ch 68-77; rtd 77; Perm to Offic *Heref* from 78; Perm to Offic *Glouc* 79-93. *2 Park View, Oatleys Road, Ledbury, Herefordshire HR8 2BN* Ledbury (01531) 632789

PANTER, Richard James Graham. b 48. Oak Hill Th Coll 73. **d** 76 **p** 77. C Rusholme *Man* 76-80; C Toxteth St Cypr w Ch Ch *Liv* 80-85; V Clubmoor from 85. *St Andrew's Vicarage, 176 Queen's Drive, Liverpool L13 0AL* 0151- 226 1977

PANTER MARSHALL, Mrs Susan Lesley. b 49. Portsm Poly BSc72 Grad L184. S Dios Minl Tr Scheme 88. **d** 91 **p** 94. NSM Southover *Chich* from 91. *30 South Way, Lewes, E Sussex BN7 1LY* Lewes (01273) 474670

PANTING, John. b 36. K Coll Cam BA60 MA64. Ridley Hall Cam 60. **d** 63 **p** 63. C Woking St Pet *Guildf* 63-65; Chapl Dean Close Sch Cheltenham 65-68; Lic to Offic *York* 68-70; C Stratford-on-Avon w Bishopton *Cov* 70-75; TV 75-79; V Keresley and Coundon 79-92; R Earlham St Eliz *Nor* from 92; BAGUPA Link Officer from 95. *St Elizabeth's Vicarage, 75 Cadge Road, North Earlham, Norwich NR5 8DQ* Norwich (01603) 250764

PANTON, Alan Edward. b 45. K Coll Lon BD67 AKC67. **d** 68 **p** 69. C Eltham St Jo *S'wark* 68-73; C Horley 73-78; V Dallington *Pet* from 78. *The Vicarage, The Barton's Close, Dallington, Northampton NN5 7HQ* Northampton (01604) 751478

PANTRY, John Richard. b 46. Oak Hill NSM Course DipTh93. **d** 93. NSM Alresford *Chelmsf* from 93. *2 Conifers Close, Alresford, Colchester CO7 8AW* Colchester (01206) 824257

PAPANTONIOU, Ms Frances Caroline (Fran). b 52. S Dios Minl Tr Scheme 89. **d** 92 **p** 94. Par Dn Harrow Weald All SS *Lon* 92-94; C from 94. *159 Kenton Lane, Harrow, Middx HA3 8TL* 0181-907 0771

PAPE, Timothy Vernon Francis (Tim). b 39. Lon Univ BSc63. Wells Th Coll 63. **d** 65 **p** 66. C Pershore w Wick *Worc* 65-69; Perm to Offic *Bris* 69-73; Hon C Southbroom *Sarum* from 75; Hd Master Chirton Primary Sch Wilts from 81. *Mallards, Chirton, Devizes, Wilts SN10 3QX* Devizes (01380) 840593

PAPWORTH, John. b 21. Lon Univ BSc(Econ). **d** 75 **p** 76. Zambia 76-81; Hon C Paddington St Sav *Lon* 81-83; Hon C St Marylebone St Mark Hamilton Terrace from 85. *24 Abercorn Place, London NW8 9XP* 0171-286 4366

PAPWORTH, Miss Shirley Marjorie. b 33. CA Tr Coll. **d** 88 **p** 94. Par Dn Hornchurch H Cross *Chelmsf* 88-93; rtd 93; NSM Hornchurch H Cross *Chelmsf* from 94. *4 Gosport Drive, Hornchurch, Essex RM12 6NU* Rainham (01708) 524348

526

PARADISE, Bryan John. b 49. Southn Univ BSc Lon Bible Coll BA. Cranmer Hall Dur. **d** 82 **p** 83. C High Harrogate Ch Ch *Ripon* 82-86; Dioc Adult Educn Officer *Guildf* from 86; P-in-c Dunsfold 86-90; R 90-93; R E Horsley from 93. *The Rectory, Ockham Road South, East Horsley, Leatherhead, Surrey KT24 6RL* East Horsley (01483) 282359

PARE, Stephen Charles. b 53. Sussex Univ BEd75. St Mich Coll Llan DipTh80. **d** 80 **p** 81. C Cardiff St Jo *Llan* 80-83; P-in-c Marcross w Monknash and Wick 83; TV Llantwit Major 83-91; V Penmark w Porthkerry from 91. *The Vicarage, 6 Milburn Close, Rhoose, Barry, S Glam CF62 3EJ* Barry (01446) 711713

PARFITT, Brian John. b 49. Ex Coll Ox BA71 MA76. Wycliffe Hall Ox 71. **d** 74 **p** 75. C Newport St Mark *Mon* 74-78; R Blaina 78-83; R Blaina and Nantyglo 83-86; Chapl Blaina and Distr Hosp Gwent 83-86; Consultant W Midlands and Wales CPAS 86-95; V Magor w Redwick and Undy *Mon* from 95. *The Vicarage, Magor, Newport, Gwent NP6 3BZ* Newport (01633) 880266

PARFITT, Graeme Stanley. b 36. Qu Coll Birm 77. **d** 79 **p** 80. C Fishponds St Jo *Bris* 79-82; V Southmead 82-91; V Stockwell St Mich *S'wark* from 91. *St Michael's Vicarage, 78 Stockwell Park Road, London SW9 0DA* 0171-274 6357

PARFITT, John Arthur. b 49. St Jo Coll Nottm BTh81. **d** 81 **p** 82. C Radcliffe-on-Trent *S'well* 81-84; C Chilwell 84-86; V Awsworth w Cossall 86-91; Perm to Offic from 91. *133 Parkside, Nottingham NG8 2NL* Nottingham (0115) 928 1907

PARFITT, Preb John Hubert. b 29. Birm Univ DipTh66 Southn Univ MA72 BPhil. Qu Coll Birm 78. **d** 80 **p** 81. C Fladbury, Wyre Piddle and Moor *Worc* 80-82; C Malvern Link w Cowleigh 82; V Hanley Castle, Hanley Swan and Welland 82-83; Dir RE *B & W* 84-93; Preb Wells Cathl 85-93; rtd 93. *Keturah, Jury Road, Dulverton, Somerset TA22 9EJ*

PARFITT, Canon Keith John. b 44. K Coll Lon BD68 AKC68. St Aug Coll Cant 69. **d** 70 **p** 71. C Kettering St Andr *Pet* 70-74; Asst Soc and Ind Adv *Portsm* 74-89; RD Alverstoke 79-86; C-in-c Bridgemary CD 81-82; V Bridgemary 82-89; Dioc UPA Officer *Blackb* from 89; Can Res Blackb Cathl from 94. *37 Buncer Lane, Blackburn BB2 6SN* Blackburn (01254) 254910

PARGETER, Canon Muriel Elizabeth. b 28. St Mich Ho Ox 53. **dss** 82 **d** 87 **p** 95. Hd Dss *Roch* 82-87; Dioc Dir of Ords 87-90; Hon Can Roch Cathl 87-90; rtd 90; NSM Worthing Ch the King *Chich* from 95. *63 Pavilion Road, Worthing, W Sussex BN45 7EE* Worthing (01903) 214476

PARISH, George Richard. b 33. ACIB60 Qu Coll Cam BA56 MA60. S'wark Ord Course 85. **d** 88 **p** 89. NSM Sunninghill *Ox* from 88. *The Shieling, Heathfield Avenue, Ascot, Berks SL5 0AL* Ascot (01344) 25840

PARISH, Nicholas Anthony. b 58. Oak Hill Th Coll BA84 Ridley Hall Cam 84. **d** 86 **p** 87. C Eltham H Trin *S'wark* 86-89; C Barnes St Mary 89-91; V Streatham St Paul from 91. *St Paul's Vicarage, Chillerton Road, London SW17 9BE* 0181-672 5536

PARISH, Stephen Richard. b 49. Oak Hill Th Coll DipTh77. **d** 77 **p** 78. C Chadderton Ch Ch *Man* 77-81; C Chell *Lich* 81-82; TV 82-88; V Warrington St Ann *Liv* from 88. *St Ann's Vicarage, 1A Hartherbert Street, Warrington WA2 7QG* Warrington (01925) 631781

PARK, Ernest Winston. b 10. St Paul's Cheltenham CertEd31. Moray Ord Course 89. **d** 92. C Poolewe *Mor* from 92. *Whindley, Auchtercairn, Gairloch, Ross-shire IV21 2BN* Gairloch (01445) 2340

PARK, Tarjei Erling Alan. b 64. W Lon Inst of HE BA88 Lanc Univ MA89. Ripon Coll Cuddesdon DipMin94. **d** 94 **p** 95. C Lanc St Mary *Blackb* from 94. *25 Bishopdale Road, Lancaster LA1 5NF* Lancaster (01524) 844672

PARK, Canon Trevor. b 38. Lon Univ BA64 Open Univ PhD90. Lambeth STh81 Linc Th Coll 64. **d** 66 **p** 67. C Crosthwaite Kendal *Carl* 66-68; Asst Chapl Solihull Sch Warks 69-71; Chapl St Bees Sch Cumbria 71-77; V St Bees *Carl* 71-77; V Dalton-in-Furness 77-84; V Natland from 84; Hon Can Carl Cathl from 86; RD Kendal 89-94. *The Vicarage, Natland, Kendal, Cumbria LA9 7QQ* Sedgwick (015395) 60355

PARKE, W/Cdr Edmund George. b 14. JP71. TCD BA37 MA47. **d** 38 **p** 39. Chapl RAF 42-69; Chapl Soc Work Dept Dundee Corp 69-75; Tayside Regional Coun 75-79; rtd 79; Perm to Offic *St And* from 79; Perm to Offic *Bre* from 79. *9 Netherlea Place, Newport-on-Tay, Fife DD6 8NW* Newport-on-Tay (01382) 542048

PARKE, Canon George Reginald. b 09. Linc Th Coll 40. **d** 42 **p** 43. Hon Can Newc Cathl *Newc* 70-80; V Beadnell 73-80; rtd 80. *West House, Dunstan, Alnwick, Northd NE66 3TB* Embleton (01665) 576257

PARKE, Simon Frederick Fenning. b 57. MA. Wycliffe Hall Ox. **d** 84 **p** 85. C Isleworth St Jo *Lon* 84-87; C St Marylebone All So w SS Pet and Jo 87-88; C Langham Place All So 88-93; V Tufnell Park St Geo and All SS from 93. *The Vicarage,*

72 Crayford Road, London N7 0ND   0171-609 1645 or 387 1360

PARKER, Alfred. b 20. Man Univ BA47. Wycliffe Hall Ox 47. **d** 49 **p** 50. V Belmont *Man* 65-87; rtd 87. *21 Edgeley Road, Whitchurch, Shropshire SY13 1EU*

PARKER, Angus Michael Macdonald. b 53. Bris Univ BSc74. St Jo Coll Nottm DipTh81 DPS83. **d** 83 **p** 84. C Northn St Giles *Pet* 83-86; C Attenborough *S'well* from 86. *120 Seaburn Road, Beeston, Nottingham NG9 6HJ* Nottingham (0115) 973 5655

PARKER, Mrs Ann Jacqueline. b 41. Dur Inst of Educn TCert63 Sunderland Poly TCert65 Open Univ BA82. W of England Minl Tr Course 91. **d** 95. NSM Pilning w Compton Greenfield *Bris* from 95. *Wyngarth, Easter Compton, Bristol BS12 3RA* Pilning (01454) 632329

PARKER, Arthur Townley. b 14. Worc Ord Coll 59. **d** 61 **p** 62. Chapl Hostel of God Clapham 71-73; rtd 74; Perm to Offic *Blackb* from 87. *30 Langdale Road, Morecambe, Lancs LA4 5XA* Morecambe (01524) 419183

PARKER, Carole Maureen. b 45. N Ord Course. **d** 87 **p** 95. NSM Coalville and Bardon Hill *Leic* 87-90; Perm to Offic 90-95; NSM Dishley and Thorpe Acre from 95. *165 Leicester Road, Mountsorrel, Loughborough, Leics LE12 7DB* Leicester (0116) 230 2790

PARKER, David Arthur. b 48. Lon Univ DipTh71. Kelham Th Coll. **d** 71 **p** 72. C Newc Ch Ch *Newc* 71-74; C Hendon *Dur* 74-79; C-in-c Southwick St Cuth CD 79-84; V Sunderland Red Ho 84-88; rtd 88. *Sisters of Charity, St Elizabeth House, Longbrook Street, Plymouth PL7 3NL* Plymouth (01752) 336112

PARKER, Dr David Charles. b 53. St Andr Univ MTh75 Em Coll Cam DipTh76 Univ of Leiden DTh90. Ridley Hall Cam 75. **d** 77 **p** 78. C Hendon St Paul Mill Hill *Lon* 77-80; C Bladon w Woodstock *Ox* 80-85; C-in-c Shipton-on-Cherwell 80-85; C-in-c Begbroke 80-85; C-in-c Hampton Gay 80-85; Perm to Offic *Birm* 85-89; Lic to Offic from 89; Lect Qu Coll Birm 85-93; Sen Angl Tutor 89-93; Lect Birm Univ from 93. *Department of Theology, PO Box 363, Birmingham University, Birmingham B15 2TT* 0121-414 3344

PARKER, David John. b 33. St Chad's Coll Dur BA55 Hull Univ MA85. Linc Th Coll 57. **d** 59 **p** 60. C Tynemouth Ch Ch *Newc* 59-60; C Ponteland 60-63; C Byker St Mich 63-64; C-in-c Byker St Martin CD 64-69; V Whorlton 69-73; TR 73-80; Ind Chapl *Linc* 80-84; Master St Thos the Martyr Newc 84-89; C-in-c Newc St Thos Prop Chpl *Newc* 84-89; Exec Officer Dioc Bd Soc Resp *Man* from 90. *43 Acresfield Road, Salford M6 7GE* 0161-737 6891 or 832 5253

PARKER, David Louis. b 47. Lon Univ LLB70 Ox Univ MA82. Wycliffe Hall Ox BA79. **d** 80 **p** 81. C Broadwater St Mary *Chich* 80-84; TV Ifield from 84. *The Vicarage, Ifield, Crawley, W Sussex RH11 0NN* Crawley (01293) 520843

PARKER, David William. b 21. SEN CQSW MBASW. Glouc Th Course 77 Sarum & Wells Th Coll 81. **d** 81 **p** 81. Chapl HM Pris Leyhill 81-84; NSM Cromhall w Tortworth *Glouc* 81-83; NSM Wickwar w Rangeworthy 83-87; Perm to Offic from 88. *22 Durham Road, Charfield, Wotton-under-Edge, Glos GL12 8TH* Falfield (01454) 260253

PARKER, Dennis. b 22. Tyndale Hall Bris 63. **d** 64 **p** 65. C-in-c Reading St Mary Castle Street Prop Chpl *Ox* 68-70; R Newdigate *Guildf* 70-87; rtd 87. *Cleve House, Flint Hill, Dorking, Surrey RH4 2LL* Dorking (01306) 889458

PARKER, Frank Maxwell Lewis. b 12. St Deiniol's Hawarden 66. **d** 67 **p** 68. V Temple Fortune St Barn *Lon* 71-76; V Long Buckby w Watford *Pet* 76-82; rtd 82; Lic to Offic *Pet* 83-85; Perm to Offic from 85. *4 Station Road, West Haddon, Northampton NN6 7AU* West Haddon (01788) 510385

PARKER, George Jeffrey. b 24. LCP69. Cuddesdon Coll 70. **d** 70 **p** 71. Hd Master St Nic Sch Codsall 70-76; Hon C Codsall *Lich* 70-76; Hon C Lapley w Wheaton Aston 76-80; Lic to Offic 80-82; R Hepworth *St E* 82-86; P-in-c Hinderclay w Wattisfield 82-86; P-in-c Thelnetham 82-86; R Hepworth, Hinderclay, Wattisfield and Thelnetham 86-89; rtd 89. *Cranham, 42 Sheringham Covert, Beaconside, Staffs ST16 3YL* Stafford (01785) 58223

PARKER, George William. b 29. BS53 BD57 Lon Univ PGCE67. K Coll (NS) 49. **d** 53 **p** 54. Canada 68-71 and 78-93; C Portsea N End St Mark *Portsm* 72-75; V Darlington St Jo *Dur* 75-78; rtd 91. *Spider Cottage, RR3 Newport, Nova Scotia, Canada, B0N 2A0*

PARKER, Hugh James. b 30. ACP55 TCD MA57 NUU DASE74. **d** 63 **p** 64. Lic to Offic *Conn* 63-70; Dioc C from 70; Hd Master Larne High Sch 81-92. *29 Ransevyn Drive, Whitehead, Co Antrim BT38 8NW* Whitehead (01960) 378106

PARKER, John Bristo. b 26. Edin Th Coll 61. **d** 64 **p** 65. V Sledmere *York* 68-74; R Cowlam 68-74; P-in-c Wetwang 69-74; V Sledmere and Wetwang w Cowlan 74-79; V Kirkby Ireleth *Carl* 79-83; V Rillington w Scampston, Wintringham etc *York* 83-87; R Bishop Wilton w Full Sutton, Kirby Underdale etc 87-91; rtd 91. *East Lodge, Sledmere, Driffield, N Humberside YO25 0XQ* Driffield (01377) 86325

PARKER, Canon John William. b 06. AKC34. Sarum Th Coll 34. **d** 35 **p** 36. V Coates *Linc* 62-75; R Willingham 62-75; R Stow in Lindsey 62-75; Can and Preb Linc Cathl from 74; rtd 75. *Flat 7, Ellesborough Manor, Butlers Cross, Aylesbury, Bucks HP17 0XF*

PARKER, Preb Joseph French. b 09. St Chad's Coll Dur BA37 DipTh38 MA40. **d** 38 **p** 39. RD W Bromwich *Lich* 61-76; V W Bromwich All SS 61-76; Preb Lich Cathl 67-76; rtd 76; Perm to Offic *Carl* from 77. *36 Glebe Farm Court, Up Hatherley, Cheltenham, Glos GL51 5EB* Cheltenham (01242) 863273

PARKER, Julian Roderick. b 57. Essex Univ BA80. Sarum & Wells Th Coll DipMin93. **d** 93 **p** 94. C Gillingham *Sarum* from 93. *The Clough, Wyke Road, Gillingham, Dorset SP8 4NH* Gillingham (01747) 822767

PARKER, Miss Margaret. b 27. Lightfoot Ho Dur 54. **dss** 60 **d** 87 **p** 94. Ryhope *Dur* 60-61; Monkwearmouth St Andr 61-79; Adv for Accredited Lay Min 74-87; Adv for Accredited Lay Min *Newc* 79-87; Newc St Geo 79-87; C 87; Tutor Cranmer Hall Dur 87-92; Hon Dn Dur Cathl *Dur* 92-94; Min Can Dur Cathl 93; NSM Dur Cathl 94; Chapl St Mary's Coll Dur from 95. *53 Devonshire Road, Durham DH1 2BJ* 0191-386 3233

PARKER, Margaret Grace. *See* TORDOFF, Mrs Margaret Grace

PARKER, Matthew John. b 63. Man Univ BA85 SS Coll Cam BA88. Ridley Hall Cam 85. **d** 88 **p** 89. C Twickenham St Mary *Lon* 88-91; C Stockport St Geo *Ches* 91-93; Chapl Stockport Gr Sch from 91; P-in-c Stockport St Mark *Ches* 93-94; TV Stockport South West from 94. *St Mark's Vicarage, 66 Berlin Road, Stockport, Cheshire SK3 9QS* 0161-480 5896

PARKER, Canon Michael John. b 54. Cam Coll of Art and Tech BA76 Lon Univ BD85. Trin Coll Bris 82. **d** 85 **p** 86. C Leic H Trin w St Jo *Leic* 85-88; P-in-c Edin Clermiston Em *Edin* 88-90; Chapl Edin St Thos from 90; Can St Mary's Cathl from 94. *16 Belgrave Road, Edinburgh EH12 6NF* 0131-334 1309

PARKER, Michael John. b 57. BSc. Wycliffe Hall Ox 80. **d** 83 **p** 84. C Heigham H Trin *Nor* 83-86; C Muswell Hill St Jas w St Matt *Lon* 86-90; R Bedf St Jo and St Leon *St Alb* from 90. *St John's Rectory, 36 St John's Street, Bedford MK42 0DH* Bedford (01234) 354818

PARKER, Peter Edward. b 32. FRSA Edin Univ MA55 Lon Univ PGCE56. Sarum & Wells Th Coll 73. **d** 74 **p** 75. C Kirkby Lonsdale w Mansergh *Carl* 74-76; C Kingston St Jo *S'wark* 76; C Kingston All SS w St Jo 76-80; Chapl S Bank Poly 80-85; Ind Chapl *Chelmsf* 85-90; Chapl Chelmsf Cathl 85-90; R Mistley w Manningtree and Bradfield from 90. *The Rectory, 21 Malthouse Road, Mistley, Manningtree, Essex CO11 1BY* Colchester (01206) 392200

PARKER, Ramon Lewis (Brother Raphael). b 36. Kelham Th Coll 56. **d** 61 **p** 62. C Tonge Moor *Man* 61-64; C Clerkenwell H Redeemer w St Phil *Lon* 64-65; V Prestwich St Hilda *Man* 65-71; SSF from 71; Chapl St D Univ Coll Lamp *St D* 81-86; Lic to Offic *Sarum* from 87. *The Friary, Hilfield, Dorchester, Dorset DT2 7BE* Cerne Abbas (01300) 341345

PARKER, Richard Bryan. b 64. Sheff Poly BA87. Coll of Resurr Mirfield 92. **d** 95. C Norton *Sheff* from 95. *6 Hazlebarrow Close, Sheffield S8 8AL* Sheffield (0114) 237 6273

PARKER, Richard Frederick. b 36. Oak Hill Th Coll 72. **d** 74 **p** 75. C Wootton *St Alb* 74-76; C Hove Bp Hannington Memorial Ch *Chich* 76-81; R Northwood *Portsm* 81-88; V W Cowes H Trin 81-88; V Aldershot H Trin *Guildf* from 88. *2 Cranmore Lane, Aldershot, Hants GU11 3AS* Aldershot (01252) 20618

PARKER, Robert Lawrence (Bob). b 34. ALCD59. **d** 59 **p** 60. C Chippenham St Paul *Bris* 59-61; C Swindon Ch Ch 61-63; New Zealand 63-71; P-in-c Over Stowey w Aisholt *B & W* 71-73; V Nether Stowey 71-73; V Nether Stowey w Over Stowey 73-93; RD Quantock 87-93; V Pitminster w Corfe from 93. *The Vicarage, Pitminster, Taunton, Somerset TA3 3AZ* Blagdon Hill (01823) 421232

PARKER, Robert William. b 18. Linc Th Coll 81. **d** 81 **p** 82. NSM Mablethorpe w Trusthorpe *Linc* 81-83; NSM Alford w Rigsby 83-86; NSM Alberbury w Cardeston *Heref* 87-90; NSM Ford 87-90; rtd 90; Perm to Offic *Linc* from 90. *17 The Glade, Sandilands, Sutton-on-Sea, Lincs SN12 2RZ* Sutton-on-Sea (01507) 442572

PARKER, Roger Thomas Donaldson. b 55. Simon Frazer Univ BC BA80 Univ of Wales (Cardiff) LLB84 Univ Coll Lon

LLM85. Coll of Resurr Mirfield CPT95. **d** 95. C Swinton and Pendlebury *Man* from 95. *St Matthew's House, 46 Townsend Road, Swinton, Manchester M27 6SH* 0161-794 1808

PARKER, Roland John Graham. b 48. AKC72 Hull Univ BA(Ed)83. St Aug Coll Cant 71. **d** 74 **p** 75. C Linc St Faith and St Martin w St Pet *Linc* 74-78; V Appleby 78-84; Ind Chapl 78-84; V N Kelsey 84-92; V Cadney 84-92; P-in-c Waddington from 92. *The Rectory, Waddington, Lincoln LN5 9RS* Lincoln (01522) 720323

PARKER, Russell Edward. b 48. Lon Univ DipTh77 Man Univ BA80 Nottm Univ MTh82. St Jo Coll Nottm 80. **d** 81 **p** 82. C Walmsley *Man* 81-85; V Coalville and Bardon Hill *Leic* 85-90; Acorn Chr Healing Trust from 90; Perm to Offic *Leic* from 90. *165 Leicester Road, Mountsorrel, Loughborough, Leics LE12 7DB* Leicester (0116) 230 2790

PARKER, Thomas Henry Louis. b 16. Em Coll Cam BA38 MA42 BD50 DD61. Lon Coll of Div 38. **d** 39 **p** 40. V Oakington *Ely* 61-71; Lect Dur Univ 71-81; rtd 81. *72 Windsor Road, Cambridge CB4 3JN* Cambridge (01223) 312215

PARKER, Thomas Richard (Tom). b 52. Imp Coll Lon BScEng73 Keele Univ MEd83. Cranmer Hall Dur CTM94. **d** 94 **p** 95. C Chadkirk *Ches* from 94. *29 Urwick Road, Romiley, Stockport, Cheshire SK6 3JS* 0161-494 0547

PARKER, Timothy Percy. b 58. Man Univ BA. St Jo Coll Nottm DipTh. **d** 85 **p** 86. C Pitsmoor Ch Ch *Sheff* 85-87; C Kimberworth 87-89; C Brightside w Wincobank 89-91; C Upper Armley *Ripon* from 91. *Ascension Vicarage, 117 Foundry Mill Street, Leeds LS14 6EJ* Leeds (0113) 232 6652

PARKER, William Albert Stuart. b 26. Wells Th Coll 68. **d** 70 **p** 71. C Bartley Green *Birm* 70-72; C Sutton Coldfield H Trin 72-75; V Allens Cross 75-82; V Lydbrook *Glouc* 82-88; V Holbeach Marsh *Linc* 88-93; rtd 93. *78 Wold Road, Pocklington, York YO4 2QG* Pocklington (01759) 304032

PARKER, William Joseph. b 10. Man Univ BA37. Ridley Hall Cam 35. **d** 37 **p** 38. R Barnburgh *Sheff* 66-77; rtd 77; Perm to Offic *St As* from 78; Perm to Offic *Ban* from 78. *23 Victoria Park, Colwyn Bay, Clwyd LL29 7AX* Colwyn Bay (01492) 532057

PARKES, Kevin. b 62. Trent Poly BA84. Sarum & Wells Th Coll BTh90. **d** 88 **p** 89. C Wandsworth St Anne *S'wark* 88-92; USPG from 92; Trinidad and Tobago from 93. *St Patrick's Vicarage, Tobago, Trinidad and Tobago* 0171-928 8681 Fax 928 2371

PARKES, Canon Norman John. b 36. Edin Th Coll 78. **d** 76 **p** 76. In Bapt Ch 70-76; Hon C E Kilbride *Glas* 76-78; C Glas St Marg 78-80; R from 85; R Challoch w Newton Stewart 80-85; Can St Mary's Cathl from 95. *St Margaret's Rectory, 22 Monreith Road, Glasgow G43 2NY* 0141-632 3292 Fax 632 8441

PARKES, Robert Stephen. b 12. Selw Coll Cam BA35 MA40. Linc Th Coll 37. **d** 38 **p** 39. R Pangbourne *Ox* 65-77; rtd 78; Perm to Offic *Win* from 78. *22 Arle Close, Alresford, Hants SO24 9BG* Alresford (01962) 734109

PARKHILL, Alan John. b 43. TCD BA66. CITC 68. **d** 67 **p** 68. C Knockbreda *D & D* 67-70; Asst Warden Elswick Lodge Newc 71-72; C Ban St Comgall 73-78; Bp's C Kilmore 78-82; I Kilmore w Inch 82-86; I Clonfeacle w Derrygortreavy *Arm* from 86. *4 Clonfeacle Road, Benburb, Dungannon, Co Tyrone BT71 7LQ* Benburb (01861) 548239

PARKIN, George David. b 37. Cranmer Hall Dur BA60 DipTh62. **d** 62 **p** 63. C Balderstone *Man* 62-65; C Tunstead 65-67; C Gateshead Fell *Dur* 69-73; Nigeria 74-76; V Walton Breck *Liv* 80-92; V Rawtenstall St Mary *Man* from 92. *2 Melia Close, Rawtenstal, Rossendale, Lancs BB4 6RQ* Rossendale (01706) 215585

PARKIN, John Edmund. b 44. Open Univ BA73. St Jo Coll Nottm 83. **d** 85 **p** 86. C Aberavon *Llan* 85-90; R Eglwysilan from 90. *The Rectory, Brynhafod Road, Abertridwr, Caerphilly, M Glam CF8 2BH* Senghenydd (01222) 830220

PARKIN, John Francis. b 40. Linc Th Coll 65. **d** 68 **p** 69. C Cullercoats St Geo *Newc* 68-72; C Stony Stratford *Ox* 72-73; TV Lt Coates *Linc* 73-76; Perm to Offic 88-93; C Horncastle w Low Toynton from 93. *The Firs, 68 Louth Road, Horncastle, Lincs LN9 5LJ* Horncastle (01507) 523208

PARKIN, Trevor Kinross. b 37. Cranmer Hall Dur 63. **d** 66 **p** 67. C Kingston upon Hull St Martin *York* 66-69; C Reading St Jo *Ox* 69-73; Ind Chapl *Lon* 73-80; Hon C Langham Place All So 73-80; Ind Chapl *Ely* 80-82; V Maidenhead St Andr and St Mary Magd *Ox* from 82. *St Mary's Vicarage, 14 Juniper Drive, Maidenhead, Berks SL6 8RE* Maidenhead (01628) 24908

PARKINSON, Andrew. b 56. Keble Coll Ox BA77 MA80. Westcott Ho Cam 78. **d** 80 **p** 81. C S Shore H Trin *Blackb* 80-85; V Lea 85-94; V Longton from 94. *Longton Vicarage, Birchwood Avenue, Hutton, Preston PR4 5EE* Longton (01772) 612179

PARKINSON, Arthur Norman. b 09. TCD BA32. **d** 33 **p** 34. I Acton w Drumbanagher *Arm* 63-75; Prec Arm Cathl 73-75; rtd 75. *34 Old Rectory Park, Portadown, Craigavon, Co Armagh BT62 3QH* Portadown (01762) 336491

PARKINSON, Miss Brenda. b 40. Lancs Poly CQSW. Dalton Ho Bris 65. **dss** 74 **d** 87 **p** 94. Ribbleton *Blackb* 75-80; Ingol 82-87; Par Dn 87-88; Par Dn Ashton-on-Ribble St Mich 88-91; Par Dn Ashton-on-Ribble St Mich w Preston St Mark 91-92; Par Dn Gt Marsden 92-94; C from 94. *11 Hallam Crescent, Nelson, Lancs BB9 9PD* Nelson (01282) 615819

PARKINSON, David Thomas. b 42. Linc Th Coll 77. **d** 79 **p** 80. C Yate New Town *Bris* 79-82; TV Keynsham *B & W* 82-88; R Bleadon from 88. *The Rectory, Coronation Road, Bleadon, Weston-super-Mare, Avon BS24 0PG* Bleadon (01934) 812297

PARKINSON, Derek Leslie. b 29. Ripon Hall Ox 64. **d** 66 **p** 67. P-in-c Preston St Sav *Blackb* 69-74; P-in-c Preston St Jas 69-74; P-in-c Fontmell Magna *Sarum* 74-81; P-in-c Ashmore 74-81; P-in-c Kingswood w Alderley and Hillesley *Glouc* 81-82; R 82-94; rtd 94. *The Old Manse, Ludgate Hill, Wotton-under-Edge, Glos GL12 7JJ*

PARKINSON, Edward James. b 19. TCD BA50 MA54. **d** 51 **p** 52. C Belf St Mary *Conn* 51-53; C Lanc St Mary *Blackb* 53-55; CF (TA) from 54; R Limehouse St Anne *Lon* 55-60; V Hampton St Mary 60-69; Lic to Offic *Newc* 74-80; Master of the Charterhouse Hull 80-95; AD Cen & N Hull *York* 87-89; rtd 95. *100 High Street, Weston, Bath BA1 4DQ* Bath (01225) 425463

PARKINSON, Francis Wilson (Frank). b 37. DCouns88 Open Univ BA79. Bernard Gilpin Soc Dur 58 St Aid Birkenhead DipTh62. **d** 62 **p** 63. C Monkwearmouth St Andr *Dur* 62-64; C Speke All SS *Liv* 64-67; CF 67-93; Perm to Offic *Ox* from 93. *9 Priory Mead, Longcot, Faringdon, Oxon SN7 7TJ* Swindon (01793) 784406

PARKINSON, George Stanley. b 20. St Jo Coll Dur BA47 DipTh48. **d** 48 **p** 49. V Pennington *Man* 58-71; V Eccles St Mary 71-80; V Churt *Guildf* 80-90; RD Farnham 82-88; rtd 90. *12 Bevere Court, Bevere, Worcester WR3 7RE* Worcester (01905) 457106

PARKINSON, Ian Richard. b 58. Univ Coll Dur BA79 *Lon* Univ BD84. Wycliffe Hall Ox 80. **d** 83 **p** 84. C Hull Newland St Jo *York* 83-86; C Linthorpe 86-92; V Saltburn-by-the-Sea from 92. *The Vicarage, Greta Street, Saltburn-by-the-Sea, Cleveland TS12 1LS* Guisborough (01287) 622007

PARKINSON, Very Rev John Fearnley. b 30. MBE90. ALCD54. **d** 55 **p** 56. Relig Adv Westward TV 62-81; CF (TA) 63-77; V Kenton *Ex* 66-75; R Kenton w Mamhead 75-79; R Kenton w Mamhead and Powderham 79-83; Preb Ex Cathl 75-83; Relig Adv SWTV 82-83; Provost St Chris Cathl Bahrain 83-89; CMS 90-95; Hon Chapl Br Emb Israel 90-95; Dean Jerusalem 90-93; rtd 95. *6 Priory Gardens, Dawlish, Devon EX7 9JN* Dawlish (01626) 862415

PARKINSON, John Reginald. b 32. Qu Coll Birm 79. **d** 81 **p** 82. NSM Catshill *Worc* 81-85; C Knightwick w Doddenham, Broadwas and Cotheridge 85-88; C Martley and Wichenford 85-88; P-in-c Berrow w Pendock and Eldersfield 88-89; R Berrow w Pendock, Eldersfield, Hollybush etc from 89; RD Upton from 95. *The Vicarage, Berrow, Malvern, Worcs WR13 6JN* Birtsmorton (01684) 833237

PARKINSON, Joseph Greenwood. b 10. Tyndale Hall Bris 30. **d** 34 **p** 36. V Onecote cum Bradnop *Lich* 58-75; rtd 75. *Dulverton Hall, St Martin's Square, Scarborough, N Yorkshire YO11 2DB* Scarborough (01723) 373082

PARKINSON, Peter. b 23. Roch Th Coll 61. **d** 63 **p** 64. V Newton-on-Trent *Linc* 68-73; R Kettlethorpe 68-73; V Grainthorpe w Conisholme 74-83; V Marshchapel 74-83; R N Coates 74-83; V Buckt 83-88; rtd 88. *11 Waltham Road, Doddington Park, Lincoln LN6 0SD* Lincoln (01522) 680604

PARKINSON, Raymond Neville. b 21. Bris Univ BA53. Tyndale Hall Bris 50. **d** 54 **p** 55. V Ashby-de-la-Zouch H Trin *Leic* 69-79; V Swannington St Geo and Coleorton 79-87; rtd 87; Perm to Offic *Leic* from 87; Perm to Offic *Linc* from 88. *45 Kipling Drive, Mablethorpe, Lincs LN12 2RF* Sutton-on-Sea (01507) 441140

PARKINSON, Simon George Denis. b 39. Univ of Wales (Lamp) BA66. Westcott Ho Cam 65. **d** 67 **p** 68. C Rothwell *Ripon* 67-70; Chapl RAF 70-73; C Leeds St Pet *Ripon* 74-75; V Horbury Junction *Wakef* 76-83; V Hanging Heaton 83-92; P-in-c Upper Hopton 92; V Eastthorpe and Upper Hopton from 92. *The Vicarage, 4 Hopton Hall Lane, Mirfield, W Yorkshire WF14 8EL* Mirfield (01924) 493569

PARKINSON, Thomas Alan. b 40. St Jo Coll York CertEd61 DipTh62. NW Ord Course 75. **d** 78 **p** 79. NSM Sheff Parson Cross St Cecilia *Sheff* 78-82; NSM Goldthorpe w Hickleton 82-90; C Cantley from 90. *10 Manse Close, Cantley, Doncaster, S Yorkshire DN4 6QX* Doncaster (01302) 539783

PARKINSON, Vivian Leslie (Viv). b 54. St Luke's Coll Ex CertEd76 Brighton Poly BEd87. St Jo Coll Nottm 92. **d** 94

p 95. C Cowbridge *Llan* from 94. *12 Gray's Walk, Cowbridge, S Glam CF7 7BQ* Cowbridge (01446) 773515

PARLETT, Gordon Alec. b 14. Oak Hill Th Coll 46. **d** 49 **p** 50. R Buckland in Dover *Cant* 56-72; Hon Chapl Miss to Seamen 58-72; Chapl Buckland Hosp Dover 59-72; V Loose *Cant* 72-87; rtd 87; Perm to Offic *Cant* from 89; Perm to Offic *Chich* from 89. *St Giles's Parsonage, Bodiam, Robertsbridge, E Sussex TN32 5UJ* Staplecross (01580) 830793

PARMENTER, Mrs Deirdre Joy. b 45. E Anglian Minl Tr Course 91. **d** 94 **p** 95. C Ipswich St Aug *St E* from 94. *18 Fitzmaurice Road, Ipswich IP3 9AX* Ipswich (01473) 719562

PARNELL-HOPKINSON, Clive. b 46. Sarum & Wells Th Coll 75. **d** 78 **p** 79. C Maldon All SS w St Pet *Chelmsf* 78-81; C Chandler's Ford *Win* 81-84; Chapl RAF from 84. *Chaplaincy Services (RAF), HQ, Personnel and Training Command, RAF Innsworth, Gloucester GL3 1EZ* Gloucester (01452) 712612 Ext 5164 Fax 510828

PARR, Frank. b 35. Nottm Univ BCombStuds82 Lanc Univ MA86. Linc Th Coll 79. **d** 82 **p** 83. C Padiham *Blackb* 82-85; P-in-c Accrington St Andr 85-88; V Oswaldtwistle Immanuel and All SS from 88. *Immanuel Vicarage, New Lane, Oswaldtwistle, Accrington, Lancs BB5 3QN* Accrington (01254) 233962

PARR, George. b 12. MC45. St Jo Coll Dur BA37. **d** 38 **p** 39. V Ripon H Trin *Ripon* 59-78; rtd 78. *Pollensa, 22 South Grange Road, Ripon, N Yorkshire HG4 2NH* Ripon (01765) 604163

PARR, Canon James Edwin Cecil. b 20. TCD BA42 MA47. **d** 43 **p** 44. I Cloughfern *Conn* 59-82; Can Conn Cathl 80-82; rtd 82. *Cloughfern Cottage, 26B Feumore Road, Ballinderry Upper, Lisburn, Co Antrim BT28 2LH* Aghalee (01846) 651851

PARR, Dr John. b 53. St Edm Hall Ox BA74 MA87 Lon Univ BD79 Sheff Univ PhD90. Trin Coll Bris 75. **d** 79 **p** 80. C Gt Crosby St Luke *Liv* 79-82; C Walton St Mary 82-84; V Ince St Mary 84-87; Tutor and Lect Ridley Hall Cam 87-95; Chapl 87-93; Dir Studies 93-95; P-in-c Harston w Hauxton *Ely* from 95. *The Vicarage, Church Street, Harston, Cambridge CB2 5NP* Cambridge (01223) 872496

PARRATT, Dennis. b 53. St Steph Ho Ox. **d** 84 **p** 85. C Cainscross w Selsley *Glouc* 84-88; C Old Shoreham *Chich* 88-91; C New Shoreham 88-91. *17 Colvill Avenue, Shoreham-by-Sea, W Sussex BN43 5WN* Shoreham-by-Sea (01273) 464528

PARRETT, Mrs Rosalind Virginia. b 43. Cant Sch of Min 84. **d** 87 **p** 94. NSM Selling w Throwley, Sheldwich w Badlesmere etc *Cant* 87-91; Asst Chapl Cant Hosp 87-91; Par Dn Stantonbury and Willen *Ox* 91-94; TV from 94. *The Cross and Stable Church House, 1 Stable Yard, Downs Barn, Milton Keynes MK14 7RZ* Milton Keynes (01908) 663346

PARRETT, Simon Christopher. b 60. Sarum & Wells Th Coll. **d** 87 **p** 88. C Ifield *Chich* 87-91; Chapl to the Deaf *Sarum* 91-94. *90 Wareham Road, Lytchett Matravers, Poole, Dorset BH16 6DT* Poole (01202) 622477

PARRETT, Stanley Frederick Donald. b 24. **d** 78 **p** 79. NSM Whitchurch w Ganarew *Heref* 78-83; C Goodrich w Welsh Bicknor and Marstow 83-86; C Walford w Bishopswood 83-86; R Pembridge w Moorcourt, Shobdon, Staunton etc 86-89; rtd 89. *4 Manley Lane, Pembridge, Leominster, Herefordshire HR6 9EE*

PARRISH, Robert Carey. b 57. St Steph Ho Ox 89. **d** 91 **p** 92. C Abington *Pet* 91-94; C Leckhampton SS Phil and Jas w Cheltenham St Jas *Glouc* from 94. *72 Salisbury Avenue, Cheltenham, Glos GL51 5DH* Cheltenham (01242) 517057

PARROTT, David Wesley. b 58. Oak Hill Th Coll BA. **d** 84 **p** 85. C Thundersley *Chelmsf* 84-87; C Rainham 87-89; P-in-c Heydon w Gt and Lt Chishill 89-90; P-in-c Elmdon w Wendon Lofts and Strethall 89-90; P-in-c Chrishall 89-90; R Heydon, Gt and Lt Chishill, Chrishall etc from 91. *1 Hall Lane, Great Chishill, Royston, Herts SG8 8SG* Royston (01763) 838703

PARROTT, George. b 37. Leeds Univ BA61. Bps' Coll Cheshunt 61. **d** 63 **p** 64. C Lower Mitton *Worc* 63-65; C-in-c Fairfield St Rich CD 65-68; Zambia 68-70; C Cleethorpes *Linc* 70-75; R Withern 75-80; P-in-c Gayton le Marsh 76-80; P-in-c Strubby 76-80; P-in-c Authorpe w Tothill 76-80; P-in-c Belleau w Aby and Claythorpe 76-80; P-in-c N and S Reston w Castle Carlton 76-80; P-in-c Swaby w S Thoresby 76-80; R Withern 80-90; V Reston 80-90; V Messingham 90-93; P-in-c Fincham *Ely* from 95; P-in-c Marham from 95; P-in-c Shouldham from 95; P-in-c Shouldham Thorpe from 95. *The Rectory, High Street, Fincham, Downham Market, Norfolk PE33 9EL* Fincham (01366) 347491

PARROTT, Canon Gerald Arthur. b 32. St Cath Coll Cam BA56 MA60. Chich Th Coll. **d** 58 **p** 59. C Ashington *Newc* 58-61; C Brighton St Pet *Chich* 61-63; V Leeds St Wilfrid *Ripon* 63-68; R Lewisham St Jo Southend *S'wark* 69-73; TR Catford (Southend) and Downham 73-77; RD E Lewisham 75-77; Can

Res and Prec S'wark Cathl 77-88; TR Wimbledon 88-95; rtd 95. *10 Palings Way, Fernhurst, Haslemere, Surrey GU27 3HJ*

PARROTT, Martin William. b 57. Keele Univ BA79 Lon Univ PGCE80. Ripon Coll Cuddesdon 82. **d** 85 **p** 86. C Birchfield *Birm* 85-88; Chapl Lon Univ *Lon* 88-93; P-in-c Univ Ch Ch the K Lon 90-93; V Hebden Bridge *Wakef* from 93. *St James's Vicarage, Church Lane, Hebden Bridge, W Yorkshire HX7 6DL* Halifax (01422) 842138

PARRY, Canon Bryan Horace. b 33. St Mich Coll Llan 65. **d** 67 **p** 68. C Holyhead w Rhoscolyn w Llanfair-yn-Neubwll *Ban* 67-71; TV 71-73; P-in-c Small Heath St Greg *Birm* 73-78; V 78-80; V Perry Barr 80-94; RD Handsworth 83-91; P-in-c Kingstanding St Luke 86-92; Hon Can Birm Cathl 87-94; rtd 94; Perm to Offic *Nor* from 94. *St Seiriol, Old Crown Yard, Walsingham, Norfolk NR22 6BU* Walsingham (01328) 820019

PARRY, Brychan Vaughan. b 13. Univ of Wales DipTh37. St Andr Coll Pampisford 41. **d** 42 **p** 42. V Gt Barton *St E* 69-78; rtd 78. *64 Cuckmere Road, Seaford, E Sussex BN25 4DJ* Seaford (01323) 898273

PARRY, David Allan. b 62. Bris Univ BSc83 Univ of Wales (Cardiff) CQSW88 DASS88. Trin Coll Bris DipHE94. **d** 94 **p** 95. C Withywood *Bris* from 94. *74 Gatehouse Avenue, Withywood, Bristol BS13 9AE* Bristol (0117) 964 2668

PARRY, David Thomas Newton. b 45. Selw Coll Cam BA67 MA71. Lambeth STh76 Cuddesdon Coll 67. **d** 69 **p** 70. C Oldham St Mary w St Pet *Man* 69-73; C Baguley 73-74; Tutor Sarum & Wells Th Coll 74-78; V Westleigh St Pet *Man* 78-88; TR E Farnworth and Kearsley from 88. *The Rectory, Church Street, Farnworth, Bolton BL4 8AQ* Farnworth (01204) 72819

PARRY, Denis. b 34. Sarum & Wells Th Coll 83. **d** 85 **p** 86. C Hubberston w Herbrandston and Hasguard etc *St D* 85-89; P-in-c Herbrandston and Hasguard w St Ishmael's 89-90; R from 90. *The Rectory, Herbrandston, Milford Haven, Dyfed SA73 3SJ* Milford Haven (01646) 693263

PARRY, Canon Dennis John. b 38. Univ of Wales (Lamp) BA60. St Mich Coll Llan 60. **d** 62 **p** 63. C Caerphilly *Llan* 62-64; C Aberdare St Fagan 64-67; Canada 67-69; R Gelligaer *Llan* 69-75; V Llanwnnog and Caersws w Carno *Ban* 75-89; V Llanidloes w Llangurig from 89; RD Arwystli from 89; Hon Can Ban Cathl from 90. *The Vicarage, Llanidloes, Powys SY18 6HZ* Llanidloes (01686) 412370 Fax as telephone

PARRY, Derek Nugent Goulding. b 32. Ely Th Coll 60. **d** 63 **p** 64. C Portsea N End St Mark *Portsm* 67-74; P-in-c Piddletrenthide w Plush, Alton Pancras etc *Sarum* 74-92; rtd 92. *Farthing Cottage, 12 Fordington Green, Dorchester, Dorset DT1 1LU* Dorchester (01305) 269794

PARRY, John Idris. b 16. St D Coll Lamp BA37. **d** 52 **p** 53. Warden CMS Fellowship Ho Foxbury 68-74; V Langton Green *Roch* 74-81; rtd 81. *Abbeyfield House, 39 East Parade, Rhyl, Clwyd LL18 3AN* Rhyl (01745) 332890

PARRY, John Seth. b 22. Tyndale Hall Bris 40 and 47. **d** 48 **p** 49. V Chaddesden St Mary *Derby* 60-76; V Ravenhead *Liv* 76-87; rtd 87. *22 Thingwall Lane, Liverpool L14 7NX* 0151-228 6832

PARRY, Keith Melville. b 31. ARICS65 Lon Univ DipRS83. S'wark Ord Course 80. **d** 83 **p** 84. NSM Bexley St Jo *Roch* 83-88; C Orpington All SS from 88. *12 Mosyer Drive, Orpington, Kent BR5 4PW* Orpington (01689) 838599

PARRY, Canon Kenneth Charles. b 34. Ripon Hall Ox 56. **d** 58 **p** 59. C Stoke *Cov* 58-61; Chapl RN 61-65; V Cradley *Worc* 65-70; V Gt Malvern H Trin 70-83; RD Malvern 74-83; Hon Can Worc Cathl 80-83; V Budleigh Salterton *Ex* 83-91; Can Res Ex Cathl from 91. *6 The Close, Exeter EX1 1EZ* Exeter (01392) 72498

PARRY, Ms Manon Ceridwen. b 69. Wales Poly BA90 Selw Coll Cam BA93. Ridley Hall Cam CTM94. **d** 94. C Llandudno *Ban* from 94. *66 Rhuddlan Avenue, Llandudno, Gwynedd LL30 1LN* Llandudno (01492) 875646

PARRY, Marilyn Marie. b 46. W Coll Ohio BA68 Man Univ MA77. Episc Th Sch Cam Mass BA68 Gilmore Ho 76. **dss** 79 **d** 87 **p** 94. Westleigh St Pet *Man* 79-85; Chapl Asst N Man Gen Hosp 85-90; Tutor N Ord Course from 90; Lic Preacher *Man* 90-94; Hon C E Farnworth and Kearsley from 94. *The Rectory, 55 Church Street, Farnworth, Bolton BL4 8AQ* Farnworth (01204) 72819

PARRY, Nicholas John Sinclair. b 56. Sarum & Wells Th Coll 82. **d** 85 **p** 86. C Hendon St Mary *Lon* 85-87; C Verwood *Sarum* 87-90; TV Witney *Ox* from 90. *The Vicarage, 17 Chestnut Avenue, Witney, Oxon OX8 6PD* Witney (01993) 705061

PARRY, Mrs Olwen Margaret. b 45. Cardiff Coll of Educn CertEd67. Llan Dioc Tr Scheme 88. **d** 92. NSM Newc *Llan* from 92. *17 Wernlys Road, Pen-y-Fai, Bridgend, M Glam CF31 4NS* Bridgend (01656) 721860

PARRY, Richard Nigel. b 56. Univ of Wales (Cardiff) BD86. St Mich Coll Llan 82. **d** 86 **p** 87. C Holywell *St As* 86-89; V Berse

and Southsea from 89. *The Vicarage, Smithy Lane, Southsea, Wrexham LL11 6PN* Wrexham (01978) 750150

PARRY, Miss Violet Margaret. b 30. Selly Oak Coll 53. **dss** 82 **d** 87. W Kilburn St Luke w St Simon and St Jude *Lon* 82-83; St Marylebone St Mary 83-86; Stamford All SS w St Jo *Linc* 86-87; C 87-90; rtd 90; Perm to Offic *Linc* from 90. *4 Torkington Gardens, Stamford, Lincs PE9 2EW* Stamford (01780) 52831

PARRY, William Daniel. b 09. St Chad's Coll Dur BA31 DipTh32 MA34. **d** 32 **p** 33. V Llandinam 48-72; V Llandinam w Trefeglwys w Penstrowed *Ban* 72-78; RD Arwystli 53-73; Can Ban Cathl from 60; Chan 70-78; rtd 78. *14 Cae Mawr, Penrhyncoch, Aberystwyth, Dyfed SY23 3EJ* Aberystwyth (01970) 828118

PARRY CHIVERS, Stanley. b 06. St Paul's Coll Burgh 25. **d** 29 **p** 30. V Brondesbury St Laur *Lon* 47-71; rtd 71; Perm to Offic *Ex* 71-73 and 74-91; P-in-c Barnstaple St Mary 73-74. *c/o Mrs W I Lim, 1 Hobart Cottages, Great Hampden, Great Missenden, Bucks HP16 9RQ* Great Missenden (01494) 488625

PARRY-JENNINGS, Christopher William. b 34. Lon Coll of Div 57. **d** 60 **p** 62. C Claughton cum Grange *Ches* 60-63; C Folkestone H Trin w Ch Ch *Cant* 63-67; New Zealand from 67. *39 Major Hornbrook Road, Mount Pleasant, Christchurch, New Zealand* Christchurch (3) 3841-253

PARRY JONES, Leonard. b 29. Univ of Wales (Ban) BA52. St Mich Coll Llan 52. **d** 54 **p** 55. V Llanynys w Llanychan *St As* 65-71; V Brynmaen w Trofarth 71-94; RD Rhos 77-94; rtd 94. *The Cottage, Kerry, Newtown, Powys SY16 4NU* Kerry (01686) 670822

PARSELL, Howard Vivian. b 60. Univ of Wales (Lamp) BA87 Univ of Wales (Swansea) PGCE88. St Mich Coll Llan DPT93. **d** 94 **p** 95. C Builth and Llanddewi'r Cwm w Llangynog etc *S & B* from 94. *14 Penybryn, Brecon Road, Builth Wells, Powys LD2 5LF* Builth Wells (01982) 553864

PARSELLE, Stephen Paul. b 53. LTh. St Jo Coll Nottm. **d** 82 **p** 83. C Boscombe St Jo *Win* 82-86; CF from 86. *c/o MOD (Army), Bagshot Park, Bagshot, Surrey GU19 5PL* Bagshot (01276) 471717 Fax 412834

PARSLOW, Ven John Henry. b 18. MBE74. Qu Coll Birm 47. **d** 50 **p** 51. V Worc H Trin *Worc* 58-60; Nyasaland 60-64; Malawi from 64; rtd 84. *PO Box 30642, Chichiri, Blantyre 3, Malawi* Malawi (265) 640489

PARSONAGE, Robert Leslie. b 20. St Aid Birkenhead 43. **d** 46 **p** 47. CF 52-74; V Bayswater *Lon* 74-83; rtd 83; Perm to Offic *Lon* 83-88; Preacher Newland Almshouses Glos from 88; Lic to Offic *Glouc* from 88. *The Lecturer's House, 11 Almshouse Road, Newland, Coleford, Glos GL16 8NL* Dean (01594) 832441

PARSONS, Andrew David. b 53. UEA BA74 Fitzw Coll Cam BA77 MA81. Westcott Ho Cam 75. **d** 78 **p** 79. C Hellesdon *Nor* 78-82; C Eaton 82-85; P-in-c Burnham Thorpe w Burnham Overy 85-87; R Burnham Sutton w Burnham Ulph etc 85-87; R Burnham Gp of Par 87-93; P-in-c Wroxham w Hoveton and Belaugh 93; R from 93. *The Vicarage, Church Lane, Wroxham, Norwich NR12 8SH* Norwich (01603) 782678

PARSONS, Andrew Philip. b 50. RIBA80 Aston Univ BSc75 DipArch76. St Jo Coll Nottm DipThMin95. **d** 95. C Langdon Hills *Chelmsf* from 95. *4 Little Berry Lane, Langdon Hills, Basildon, Essex SS16 6TL* Basildon (01268) 418275

PARSONS, Arthur. b 45. St Jo Coll Nottm LTh. **d** 75 **p** 76. C Cuddington *Guildf* 75-78; C Liskeard w St Keyne and St Pinnock *Truro* 78-81; P-in-c Ludgvan 81-83; R from 83; Chapl Falmouth Fire Brigade from 91; P-in-c Perranuthnoe from 93. *The Rectory, Ludgvan, Penzance, Cornwall TR20 8EZ* Penzance (01736) 740784

PARSONS, Arthur Gordon Boyd (Bob). b 20. TD50. SSC MIPM47 MRCO83. Ripon Hall Ox BA54. **d** 56 **p** 57. Offg Chapl RAF 65-74; V Friskney *Linc* 69-74; R Tansor w Cotterstock and Fotheringhay *Pet* 74-76; V Forest Town S'well 76-78; V Sutton cum Lound 78-85; rtd 85; P-in-c Sampford Courtenay w Honeychurch *Ex* 85-87; P-in-c Exbourne w Jacobstowe 85-87; Hon C Holsworthy w Hollacombe and Milton Damerel 87-88; Hon C Bude Haven *Truro* 88-89; Hon C Stratton and Launcells 89-95; Perm to Offic *Linc* from 95. *La Casita, Mill Field, Trusthorpe, Mablethorpe, Lincs LN12 2PG* Mablethorpe (01507) 473632

PARSONS, Bernard. b 26. Ely Th Coll 60. **d** 62 **p** 63. V W Pinchbeck *Linc* 64-71; V Sutton Bridge 71-83; R Coningsby w Tattershall 83-93; rtd 93; Perm to Offic *Linc* from 93. *2 St Peter's Drive, Woodhall Spa, Lincs LN10 6SY* Woodhall Spa (01526) 353027

PARSONS, Christopher James Hutton. b 54. Univ of Wales (Ban) BA75 Birm Univ DipTh78. Qu Coll Birm. **d** 79 **p** 80. C Crowthorne *Ox* 79-83; V Tilehurst St Cath 83-88; P-in-c Wrentham w Benacre, Covehithe, Frostenden etc *St E* 89-91; R 91-94. *35 Tufton Gardens, West Molesey, Surrey KT8 1TD*

PARSONS, David. b 37. Qu Coll Cam BA61. Ridley Hall Cam. d 62 p 63. C Ormskirk *Liv* 62-65; C Beccles St Mich *St E* 65-68; V Woodbridge St Jo 68-73; Chapl Edgarley Hall Sch Glastonbury 73-78; Asst Master Bruton Sch for Girls from 78; Chapl Bruton Sch for Girls from 86. *13 Ivythorn Road, Street, Somerset BA16 0TE* Street (01458) 46110

PARSONS, David Norman. b 39. FCIB83. Trin Coll Bris 92. d 94 p 95. NSM Swindon Dorcan *Bris* from 94. *7 Sedgebrook, Swindon SN3 6EY* Swindon (01793) 642077

PARSONS, Desmond John. b 25. Coll of Resurr Mirfield 65. d 66 p 67. C Purley St Mark Woodcote *S'wark* 66-70; V W Dulwich All SS and Em 71-83; R Limpsfield and Titsey from 83. *The Rectory, Limpsfield, Oxted, Surrey RH8 0DG* Oxted (01883) 712512

PARSONS, Geoffrey Fairbanks. b 35. Trin Coll Cam BA58 MA68. Ridley Hall Cam 59. d 61 p 62. C Over St Chad *Ches* 61-64; C Heswall 64-69; V Congleton St Steph 69-75; V Weaverham 75-94; P-in-c Backford and Capenhurst from 94. *The Vicarage, Grove Road, Mollington, Chester CH2 4DG* Great Mollington (01244) 851071

PARSONS, George Edward. b 35. St D Coll Lamp BA60 Ripon Hall Ox 60. d 62 p 63. C Leominster *Heref* 62-66; NSM Bromfield 67-72; NSM Culmington w Onibury 67-72; NSM Stanton Lacy 67-72; NSM Ludlow 72-77; P-in-c Caynham 77-79; NSM Bishop's Cleeve *Glouc* 79-91; Sub-Chapl HM Pris Glouc 88-91; P-in-c Hasfield w Tirley and Ashleworth from 91; P-in-c Maisemore from 91. *Ballalona, 1 Goodrich Hill, Ashleworth, Gloucester GL19 4JD* Cheltenham (01242) 700659

PARSONS, George Horace Norman. b 19. S'wark Ord Course 65. d 68 p 69. C Hatcham St Cath *S'wark* 68-72; C Horley 72-76; P-in-c S Wimbledon All SS 76-78; P-in-c Caterham 78-81; C 82-84; Chapl St Lawr Hosp Caterham 82-84; rtd 85. *8 Russell Road, Mitcham, Surrey CR4 2YS* 0181-646 4386

PARSONS, Gilbert Harvey. b 20. St Pet Hall Ox BA46 MA46. Cuddesdon Coll 48. d 50 p 51. V Stokenchurch and Cadmore End *Ox* 61-72; P-in-c Ibstone w Fingest 65-72; RD Aston 66-72; V Burford w Fulbrook 72-74; V Burford w Fulbrook and Taynton 74-85; rtd 85. *Windrush, 23 Highlands Way, Whiteparish, Salisbury SP5 2SZ* Whiteparish (01794) 884832

PARSONS, Dr Jennifer Anne (Jeni). b 53. Univ of Wales (Lamp) BA76 MA78 Jes Coll Cam PhD90. Westcott Ho Cam CTM94. d 94 p 95. C Halesowen *Worc* from 94. *Alton House, 30 Tenterfields, Halesowen, W Midlands B63 3LH* 0121-550 2278

PARSONS, John Banham. b 43. Selw Coll Cam BA65 MA68. Ridley Hall Cam 65. d 67 p 68. C Downend *Bris* 67-71; Public Preacher Withywood LEP 71-77; P-in-c Hengrove 77-78; V 78-85; V Letchworth St Paul w Willian *St Alb* 85-94; P-in-c Barking St Marg w St Patr *Chelmsf* from 94. *The Rectory, 166 Longbridge Road, Barking, Essex IG11 8SS* 0181-594 2932

PARSONS, John Christopher. b 27. Keble Coll Ox BA52 MA56 CQSW77. St Steph Ho Ox 52. d 54 p 55. Lic to Offic *Chelmsf* 69-71; Chapl RADD Essex Area 69-71; Chapl to the Deaf 71-85; Lic to Offic *Truro* 71-74; Perm to Offic *Ex* 73-74; P-in-c Godolphin *Truro* 74-80; P-in-c St Enoder 80-92; rtd 92; Perm to Offic *Cant* from 92. *78 Poplar Drive, Greenhill, Herne Bay, Kent CT6 7QA* Herne Bay (01227) 741516

PARSONS, Laurie. b 19. Keble Coll Ox BA41. Wells Th Coll 41. d 43 p 44. V Radford Semele *Cov* 70-83; V Radford Semele and Ufton 83-84; rtd 84; Perm to Offic *Cov* from 84; Perm to Offic *Pet* from 84. *86 Bull Baulk, Middleton Cheney, Banbury, Oxon OX17 2SR* Banbury (01295) 711829

PARSONS, Mrs Margaret Anne. b 31. Sheff Poly CQSW77. E Midl Min Tr Course 73. dss 77 d 87 p 94. Dronfield *Derby* 77-87; Par Dn 87-89; Par Dn Tidworth, Ludgershall and Faberstown *Sarum* 89-94; C 94-95; P-in-c Wold-Marsh Gp *Linc* from 95. *The Rectory, Church Lane, Withern, Alford, Lincs LN13 0NG* Alford (01507) 450814

PARSONS, Canon Marlene Beatrice. b 43. Wilson Carlile Coll. dss 76 d 87 p 94. Coulsdon St Jo *S'wark* 76-79; Hill *Birm* 79-86; Dioc Lay Min Adv 80-90; Vice Prin W Midl Minl Tr Course 86-90; Hon Can Birm Cathl from 89; Dioc Dir of Ords from 90; Dean of Women from 90. *257 Gillott Road, Birmingham B16 0RX* 0121-454 3974

PARSONS, Martin. b 07. Qu Coll Cam BA28 MA32. Lon Coll of Div 29. d 30 p 31. Ext Sec CMJ 69-72; rtd 72. *61 Elm Tree Road, Locking, Weston-super-Mare, Avon BS24 8EL* Banwell (01934) 822090

PARSONS, Miss Mary Elizabeth. b 43. Wilson Carlile Coll 65. dss 78 d 87 p 94. Chapl Asst Chu Hosp Ox 78-89; Chapl 89-93; rtd 93. *21 Woodlands Road, Oxford OX3 7RU* Oxford (01865) 63909

PARSONS, Dr Michael William Semper. b 47. St Cath Coll Ox BA69 MA74 DPhil74 Selw Coll Cam BA77 MA81. Ridley

Hall Cam 75. d 78 p 79. C Edmonton All SS *Lon* 78-81; SPCK Research Fell Dur Univ 81-84; Hon Th Lect 84-85; SPCK Fell N of England Inst for Chr Educn 84-85; Lic to Offic *Dur* 81-85; P-in-c Derby St Aug *Derby* from 85; Dioc Voc Adv from 86. *St Augustine's Vicarage, 155 Almond Street, Derby DE23 6LY* Derby (01332) 766603 Fax 270837

PARSONS, Richard Edgar. b 46. K Coll Lon BD69 AKC69 MTh70 MPhil84. d 71 p 72. C Doncaster Intake *Sheff* 71-73; Hon C Blackheath All SS *S'wark* 73-84; Lect CA Tr Coll Blackheath 73-79; Selection Sec ACCM 79-84; V Hendon St Mary *Lon* from 84; V Hendon Ch Ch from 84; Dir of Ords from 85. *The Vicarage, Parson Street, London NW4 1QR* 0181-203 2884

PARSONS, Canon Robert Martin. b 43. Qu Coll Cam BA65 MA69. ALCD68. d 68 p 69. C Chapeltown *Sheff* 68-71; C Sheff St Jo 71-75; V Swadlincote *Derby* 75-91; RD Repton 81-91; P-in-c Gresley 82-86; R Etwall w Egginton 91-93; Can Res Derby Cathl from 93. *22 Kedleston Road, Derby DE22 1GU* Derby (01332) 385552

PARSONS, Roger John. b 37. Sarum Th Coll 62. d 65 p 66. C Bitterne Park *Win* 65-69; C Clerkenwell H Redeemer w St Phil *Lon* 69-72; C Willesden St Andr 72-76; C St Laurence in the Isle of Thanet *Cant* 76-81; Chapl Luton and Dunstable Hosp 81-86; Chapl St Mary's Hosp Luton 81-86; C Luton All SS w St Pet *St Alb* 81-86; Trustee St Benedict's Trust from 85; TV E Dereham *Nor* 86-88; TV E Dereham and Scarning 89; Perm to Offic 89-93. *16 Cremer Street, Sheringham, Norfolk NR26 8DZ* Sheringham (01263) 825849

PARSONS, Stephen Christopher. b 45. Keble Coll Ox BA67 MA72 BLitt78. Cuddesdon Coll 68. d 70 p 71. C Whitstable All SS *Cant* 70-71; C Croydon St Sav 71-74; Perm to Offic *Ox* 74-76; C St Laurence in the Isle of Thanet *Cant* 76-79; V Lugwardine w Bartestree and Weston Beggard *Heref* 79-87; V Lechlade *Glouc* from 87. *The Vicarage, Sherbourne Street, Lechlade, Glos GL7 3AH* Faringdon (01367) 252262

PARSONS, Stephen Drury. b 54. Qu Mary Coll Lon BSc76 CCC Cam MSc79. Westcott Ho Cam 79. d 82 p 83. C Stretford All SS *Man* 82-85; C Newton Heath All SS 85-86; V Ashton St Jas 86-90. *8 Ripponden Street, Oldham OL1 4JG*

PARSONS, Dr Victor. b 29. RD75. FRCP72 BNC Ox MA53 MB, ChB53 DM72. Coll of Resurr Mirfield 90. d 91 p 92. Hon C Upper Norwood All SS *S'wark* from 91. *15 Glyn Close, London SE25 6DT* 0181-653 2182

PARSONS, William George. b 20. Em Coll Cam BA47 MA50. Wells Th Coll 49. d 51 p 52. V Warmley *Bris* 68-71; P-in-c Syston 68-71; Lic to Offic 71-76; P-in-c Luckington w Alderton 76-80; C N Stoneham *Win* 80-84; Chapl St Cross Hosp Win 84-87; rtd 85; Perm to Offic *Win* from 86. *c/o J W Parsons Esq, 105 Woolsbridge Road, Ashley Heath, Ringwood, Hants BH24 2LZ* Ringwood (01425) 474829

PARTINGTON, Canon Brian Harold. b 36. St Aid Birkenhead 60. d 63 p 64. C Barlow Moor *Man* 63-66; C Deane 66-68; V Patrick *S & M* from 68; Bp's Youth Chapl 68-76; P-in-c German St Jo 77-78; V from 78; P-in-c Foxdale 77-78; V from 78; Can St German's Cathl from 85. *The Vicarage, Patrick, Peel, Isle of Man IM5 3AW* Peel (01624) 842637 Fax 843374

PARTINGTON, Kenneth. b 41. Lanc Univ MA86. Ripon Hall Ox. d 70 p 71. C Atherton *Man* 70-72; C Kippax *Ripon* 72-75; V Cartmel Fell *Carl* from 75; V Crosthwaite Kendal from 75; V Witherslack from 75; V Winster from 78. *The Vicarage, Crosthwaite, Kendal, Cumbria LA8 8HT* Crosthwaite (015395) 68276

PARTINGTON, Kevin. b 51. Huddersfield Poly BA73. St Jo Coll Nottm DCM93. d 93 p 94. C Salterhebble All SS *Wakef* from 93. *315 Skircoat Green Road, Halifax, W Yorkshire HX3 0NA* Halifax (01422) 341476

PARTINGTON, Peter John. b 57. Peterho Cam MA. St Jo Coll Nottm 79. d 81 p 82. C Cov H Trin *Cov* 81-85; C Woking St Jo *Guildf* 85-87; C from 94; R Busbridge 87-94; Dir of Ords from 94. *13 Heath Drive, Brookwood, Woking, Surrey GU24 0HG* Woking (01483) 799284

PARTRIDGE, Anthony John. b 38. Univ of Wales (Lamp) BA61 Linacre Ho Ox BA63 K Coll Lon PhD77. St Steph Ho Ox 61. d 64 p 65. C Sydenham All SS *S'wark* 64-67; Hon C 68-74; Lic to Offic from 74; Prin Lect Thames Poly 75-92; Greenwich Univ from 92. *40 Upwood Road, London SE12 8AN, or University of Greenwich, Wellington Street, London SE18 6PF* 0181-318 9901 or 854 2030

PARTRIDGE, Canon David John Fabian. b 36. Ball Coll Ox BA60 MA. Westcroft Ho Cam 60. d 62 p 63. C Halliwell St Thos *Man* 62-65; C St Martin-in-the-Fields Lon 65-69; R Warblington and Emsworth *Portsm* from 69; Hon Can Portsm Cathl from 84. *The Rectory, 20 Church Path, Emsworth, Hants PO10 7DP* Emsworth (01243) 372428

PARTRIDGE, Ian Starr. b 36. Linc Th Coll 87. **d** 89 **p** 90. C Barton upon Humber *Linc* 89-92; P-in-c Barkwith Gp from 92. *Barkwith Rectory, East Barkwith, Lincoln LN3 5RY* Wragby (01673) 858291

PARTRIDGE, Miss Margaret Edith. b 35. Birm Univ DipTh68. Gilmore Ho 63. **dss** 85 **d** 87 **p** 94. Amblecote *Worc* 85-87; Par Dn 87-89; C Borehamwood *St Alb* 89-94; TV from 94. *35 Winstre Road, Borehamwood, Herts WD6 5DR* 0181-207 6603

PARTRIDGE, Martin David Waud. b 38. Ox NSM Course 86. **d** 89 **p** 90. NSM Wargrave *Ox* from 89. *Ellums, Cockpole Green, Wargrave, Reading RG10 8NE* Wargrave (01734) 403849

PARTRIDGE, Michael John. b 61. St Edm Hall Ox BA83 MA89 St Jo Coll Dur BA86. Cranmer Hall Dur 84. **d** 87 **p** 88. C Amington *Birm* 87-90; C Sutton Coldfield H Trin 90-93; P-in-c W Exe *Ex* from 93. *St Paul's Vicarage, Bakers Hill, Tiverton, Devon EX16 5NE* Tiverton (01884) 255705

PARTRIDGE, Ronald Malcolm (Ron). b 49. Lon Univ DipTh73 DAC94. Bris Bapt Coll LTh74 Cuddesdon Coll 74. **d** 75 **p** 76. C Bris St Andr Hartcliffe *Bris* 75-78; C E Bris 78-82; V Easton All Hallows 82-85; TV Brighton St Pet w Chpl Royal and St Jo Chich 85-86; TV Brighton St Pet and St Nic w Chpl Royal 86-88; C-in-c Bermondsey St Hugh CD *S'wark* 88-90; Asst Chapl Gt Ormond Street Hosp for Children NHS Trust from 91. *The Hospital for Sick Children, Great Ormond Street, London WC1N 3JH* 0171-405 9200

PARTRIDGE, Canon Timothy Reeve. b 39. Lon Univ BSc60 AKC60. Wells Th Coll 60. **d** 62 **p** 63. C Glouc St Cath *Glouc* 62-65; C Sutton St Nicholas *Linc* 65-74; R Bugbrooke *Pet* 74-95; P-in-c Kislingbury w Rothersthorpe 95; R Bugbrooke w Rothersthorpe from 95; RD Daventry 81-88; Can Pet Cathl from 83. *The Rectory, Church Lane, Bugbrooke, Northampton NN7 3PB* Northampton (01604) 830373

PASCHAL, Brother. See WORTON, David Reginald

PASKETT, Ms Margaret Anne. b 45. York Univ BSc81 Leeds Univ MEd83. NE Ord Course 84. **d** 87 **p** 94. Par Dn Marske in Cleveland *York* 87-91; C from 92; Dioc Adv for Diaconal Mins from 92. *5 Howard Drive, Marske-by-the-Sea, Redcar, Cleveland TS11 7JE* Redcar (01642) 474528

PASKINS, David James. b 52. Univ of Wales (Lamp) BA73 Trin Hall Cam BA76 MA81. Westcott Ho Cam 74. **d** 77 **p** 78. C St Peter-in-Thanet *Cant* 77-80; C Swanage *Sarum* 80-82; R Waldron *Chich* 82-92; R Bere Ferrers *Ex* from 92. *The Rectory, Bere Alston, Yelverton, Devon PL20 7HH* Tavistock (01822) 840229

PASLEY, Canon Charles Victor. b 19. Lon Bible Coll. **d** 58 **p** 59. I Skreen w Kilmacshalgan and Dromard *T, K & A* 61-87; RD Straid 66-87; Dom Chapl to Bp of Tuam 69-87; Can Achonry Cathl 75-87; rtd 87. *51 Beaumont Avenue, Churchtown, Dublin 14, Irish Republic* Dublin (1) 298-8903

PASSANT, Keith. b 39. St Jo Coll Dur BA62 CertEd70. St Alb Minl Tr Scheme 77. **d** 87 **p** 88. C Hatf Hyde St Mary *St Alb* 87-93; rtd 93. *26 Monk's Rise, Welwyn Garden City, Herts AL8 7NF* Welwyn Garden (01707) 332869

PASSINGHAM, Eric Albert. b 27. Wells Th Coll 69. **d** 70 **p** 71. C Chatham St Steph *Roch* 70-74; C Crawley *Chich* 74-79; TV 79-86; P-in-c Rusper from 86. *The Rectory, High Street, Rusper, Horsham, W Sussex RH12 4PX* Rusper (01293) 871251

PASTERFIELD, Canon Dunstan Patrick. b 17. Clare Coll Cam BA49 MA53. Cuddesdon Coll 49. **d** 51 **p** 51. C Dennington *St E* 51-53; Canada from 53; Hon Can Calgary 78-82. *Box 212, Arcola, Saskatchewan, Canada, S0C 0G0* Saskatchewan (306) 455-2785 Fax 455-2210

✠**PASTERFIELD, Rt Rev Philip John.** b 20. Trin Hall Cam BA49 MA53. Cuddesdon Coll 49. **d** 51 **p** 52 **c** 74. C Streatham St Leon *S'wark* 51-54; Chapl K Edw VII Hosp Midhurst 54-60; V W Lavington *Chich* 54-60; R Woolbeding 55-60; V Oxton *Ches* 60-68; RD Birkenhead 66-68; Can Res St Alb 68-74; RD St Alb 71-74; Suff Bp Crediton *Ex* 74-84; rtd 84; Asst Bp Ex from 84. *2 Brixton Court, Brixton, Plymouth PL8 2AH* Plymouth (01752) 880817

PATCHELL, Miss Gwendoline Rosa (Wendy). b 49. Golds Coll Lon BA69 TCert70. Trin Coll Bris DipHE92. **d** 92 **p** 94. C Ashton on Mersey St Mary *Ches* from 92. *12 Willoughby Close, Sale, Cheshire M33 1PJ* 0161-962 5204

PATCHING, Colin John. b 47. Linc Th Coll 84. **d** 86 **p** 87. C Farnley *Ripon* 86-89; C Didcot St Pet *Ox* 89-92; P-in-c Steventon w Milton from 92. *The Vicarage, 73 Field Gardens, Steventon, Abingdon, Oxon OX11 6TF* Abingdon (01235) 831243

PATE, Barry Emile Charles. b 50. NE Lon Poly BA80 CQSW80. S'wark Ord Course 85. **d** 88 **p** 89. NSM E Dulwich St Jo *S'wark* 88-92; C Farnborough *Roch* 92-94; C Broxbourne w Wormley *St Alb* from 94. *St Laurence's House, 11 Wharf Road, Broxbourne, Herts EN10 6HU* Hoddesdon (01992) 442356

PATEL, Miss Urmila Devi. b 59. Essex Univ BSc82. Chich Th Coll 90. **d** 92 **p** 94. Par Dn Leek and Meerbrook *Lich* 92-94; C from 94. *132 Trinity Rise, London SW2 2QT* 0181-674 3551

PATEMAN, Donald Herbert. b 15. ALCD48. **d** 48 **p** 49. C Bethnal Green St Jas Less *Lon* 48-51; Hon Sec Soc for Relief of Distress 52-66; C Bromley All Hallows 54-56; V Dalston St Mark w St Bart from 56. *St Mark's Vicarage, Sandringham Road, London E8 2LL* 0171-254 4741

PATEMAN, Edward Brian. b 29. Leeds Univ BA51. Qu Coll Birm 51. **d** 53 **p** 54. V Dalton le Dale *Dur* 65-93; RD Houghton 72-75; R Hawthorn 88-93; rtd 93. *27 Atherton Drive, Houghton le Spring, Tyne & Wear DH4 6TA* 0191-385 3168

PATEN, Richard Alfred. b 32. CEng MICE61 Ch Coll Cam BA56 MA60. Ripon Hall Ox 61. **d** 63 **p** 64. C Oadby *Leic* 63-67; C Pet St Mark *Pet* 67-71; Chapl Community Relns 71-93; Bp's Dioc Chapl 73-85; Perm to Offic from 93. *198 Lincoln Road, Peterborough PE1 2NQ* Peterborough (01733) 66288

PATERNOSTER, Canon Michael Cosgrove. b 35. Pemb Coll Cam BA59 MA63. Cuddesdon Coll 59. **d** 61 **p** 62. C Surbiton St Andr *S'wark* 61-63; Chapl Qu Coll Dundee 63-68; Dioc Supernumerary *Bre* 63-68; Chapl Dundee Univ 67-68; Sec Fellowship of SS Alb and Sergius 68-71; R Dollar *St And* 71-75; R Stonehaven *Bre* 75-90; Hon Can St Paul's Cathl Dundee from 81; R Aber St Jas *Ab* from 90. *31 Gladstone Place, Aberdeen AB1 6UX* Aberdeen (01224) 322631

PATERSON, David. b 33. Ch Ch Ox BA55 MA58. Linc Th Coll 56. **d** 58 **p** 59. C Kidderminster St Mary *Worc* 58-60; C Wolv St Geo *Lich* 60-64; V Loughb St Pet *Leic* from 64. *St Peter's Vicarage, 129 Ashby Road, Loughborough, Leics LE11 3AB* Loughborough (01509) 263047

PATERSON, Douglas Monro. b 30. Em Coll Cam BA54 MA57. Tyndale Hall Bris 55. **d** 57 **p** 58. Rwanda 67-73; C Edin St Thos *Edin* 73-75; Lect Northumbria Bible Coll 73-94; Perm to Offic *Edin* 75-94; Lic to Offic *Newc* 76-94; rtd 94. *3 Penn Mead, Church Road, Penn, High Wycombe, Bucks HP10 8NY* High Wycombe (01494) 812496

PATERSON, Gordon Ronald (Ron). b 16. MBE57. Ripon Hall Ox 58. **d** 59 **p** 60. V Swanmore St Barn *Portsm* 62-85; RD Bishops Waltham 79-82; rtd 85; Perm to Offic *Win* from 85; Perm to Offic *Portsm* from 85. *28 Eastways, Bishops Waltham, Southampton SO3 1EX* Bishops Waltham (01489) 895671

PATERSON, James Beresford. b 21. DSC42. St Andr Univ MPhil85. Westcott Ho Cam 59. **d** 61 **p** 62. R Broughty Ferry *Bre* 64-72; Dioc Supernumerary 72-79; Sec Scottish Ch Action for World Development 72-79; P-in-c Glencarse 76-84; Dioc Sec 79-84; Hon Can St Paul's Cathl Dundee 79-89; rtd 84. *67 Ipswich Road, Woodbridge, Surrey IP12 4BT* Woodbridge (01394) 383512

PATERSON, Mrs Jennifer Ann. b 49. Brooklands Tech Coll 69. S Dios Minl Tr Scheme 83. **d** 88. C Hale *Guildf* 88-92; Perm to Offic from 94. *4 St George's Close, Badshot Lea, Farnham, Surrey GU9 9LZ* Aldershot (01252) 316775

PATERSON, Very Rev John Thomas Farquhar. b 38. TCD BA61 MA64 BD71. CITC 63. **d** 63 **p** 64. C Drumglass *Arm* 63-65; C Dub St Bart *D & G* 66-68; Min Can St Patr Cathl Dub 67-83; Asst Dean of Residence TCD 68-72; C-in-c Dub St Mark *D & G* 68-71; I Dub St Bart w Ch Ch Leeson Park 72-78; Dean Kildare *M & K* 78-89; I Kildare w Kilmeague and Curragh 78-89; Lect Past Liturgy CITC 85-91; Hon Sec Gen Syn 85-91; Dean Ch Ch Cathl Dub *D & G* from 89; I Dub Ch Ch Cathl Gp from 89; Dio Radio Officer 91-94. *The Deanery, St Werburgh Street, Dublin 8, Irish Republic* Dublin (1) 478-1797 or 677-8099 Fax 679-8991

PATERSON, Rex Douglas Trevor. b 27. AKC54. **d** 55 **p** 56. V Woodingdean *Chich* 62-73; V Ferring 73-94; rtd 94. *4 Clapham Close, Clapham, Worthing, W Sussex BN13 3XA* Patching (0190674) 396

PATERSON, Robert Mar Erskine. b 49. St Jo Coll Dur BA71 DipTh72 MA82. **d** 72 **p** 73. C Harpurhey St Steph *Man* 72-73; C Sketty *S & B* 73-78; V Llangattock and Llangyndir 78-83; V Gabalfa *Llan* 83-94; R Cowbridge from 94. *The Vicarage, 85 Broadway, Llanblethian, Cowbridge, S Glam CF7 7EY* Cowbridge (01446) 775597 or 772302

PATERSON, Robin Fergus. b 32. Moore Th Coll Sydney 83. **d** 87 **p** 89. Singapore 87-88; NSM Crieff *St And* 88-92; NSM Comrie 88-92; R Dunkeld from 93; R Strathtay from 93. *St Mary's Rectory, St Mary's Road, Birnam, Dunkeld, Perthshire PH8 0BJ* Dunkeld (01350) 727329

PATERSON, Robin Lennox Andrew. b 43. N Ord Course 84. **d** 87 **p** 88. C Manston *Ripon* 87-91; P-in-c Leeds All So 91-95; V from 95. *All Souls' Vicarage, Blackman Lane, Leeds LS2 9EY* Leeds (0113) 245 3078

PATERSON, Stuart Maxwell. b 37. Kelham Th Coll 57 Lich Th Coll 58. **d** 60 **p** 61. C Ilkeston St Mary *Derby* 60-64; V

Somercotes 64-70; R Wingerworth 70-73; P-in-c Hawick *Edin* 92-95; R from 95. *The Rectory, 2 Trystside, Hawick, Roxburghshire TD9 0DX* Hawick (01450) 72043

PATERSON, Mrs Susan Ann. b 57. St Hilda's Coll Ox MA84. E Midl Min Tr Course DTPS95. d 95. Hon C Evington *Leic* from 95. *82 Pine Tree Avenue, Leicester LE5 1AL* Leicester (0116) 276 0422

PATERSON, Canon William John McCallum. b 19. Leeds Univ BA41. Coll of Resurr Mirfield 41. d 43 p 44. R Finghall *Ripon* 69-79; R Hauxwell 69-79; R Spennithorne 69-79; Hon Can Ripon Cathl 75-84; R Kirk Hammerton w Nun Monkton and Hunsingore 79-84; rtd 84. *Dellwood, Ampleforth, York YO6 4DA* Ampleforth (014393) 645

PATEY, Very Rev Edward Henry. b 15. Liv Univ Hon LLD80. d 39 p 40. Dean Liv 64-82; rtd 82; Perm to Offic *Bris* from 82. *139 High Street, Malmesbury, Wilts SN16 9AL* Malmesbury (01666) 822482

PATIENT, Peter Leslie. b 39. Chich Th Coll 63. d 66 p 67. C Headington *Ox* 66-69; C Stroud *Glouc* 69-72; C Welwyn *St Alb* 72-75. *28 Young's Rise, Welwyn Garden City, Herts AL8 6RU* Welwyn Garden (01707) 328830

PATON, George Hemsell. b 23. Wadh Coll Ox MA49. Oak Hill Th Coll 50. d 52 p 53. V Kemp Town St Mark and St Matt *Chich* 67-71; R Ripe w Chalvington 71-76; R Laughton w Ripe and Chalvington 77-78; V Iford w Kingston and Rodmell 78-90; rtd 90. *77 Springett Avenue, Ringmer, Lewes, E Sussex BN8 5QT* Ringmer (01273) 812754

PATON, Ian Fisher. b 13. Leeds Univ BA36. Coll of Resurr Mirfield 36. d 38 p 39. C Blandford Forum *Sarum* 38-41; C Hanover Square St Geo *Lon* 41-44; Chapl RNVR 44-47; Chapl RN 47-57; Perm to Offic *Bris* 58-62; C St Teath *Truro* 62-67; Australia from 67. *Address temp unknown*

PATON, Canon Ian James. b 57. Jes Coll Cam MA78 PGCE79. Westcott Ho Cam MA81. d 82 p 83. C Whitley Ch Ch *Ox* 82-84; Bp's Dom Chapl 84-86; Chapl Wadh Coll Ox 86-90; C Ox St Mary V w St Cross and St Pet *Ox* 86-90; Can and Vice-Provost St Mary's Cathl Edin 90-94; R Edin St Mary 90-94; R Haddington from 94; R Dunbar from 94. *The Rectory, Church Street, Haddington, East Lothian EH41 3EX* Haddington (01620) 822023

PATON, John David Marshall. b 47. Barrister 70. St Steph Ho Ox 81. d 83 p 84. C Bethnal Green St Matt *Lon* 83-84; C Bethnal Green St Matt w St Jas the Gt 84-86; P-in-c St Geo-in-the-East St Mary 86-89; V 89-92; AD Tower Hamlets from 92; Dir Post-Ord Tr from 92; P-in-c Bethnal Green St Barn from 92. *16 Rhondda Grove, London E3 5AP* 0181-980 8628 Fax as telephone

PATON, John William Scholar. St Steph Ho Ox. d 95. C Sherborne w Castleton and Lillington *Sarum* from 95. *Askwith House, 1 Quarr Drive, Sherborne, Dorset DT9 4HZ* Sherborne (01935) 814277

PATON, Ven Michael John Macdonald. b 22. Magd Coll Ox BA49 MA54. Linc Th Coll 52. d 54 p 55. Sen Chapl Sheff United Hosps 67-70; Chapl Weston Park Hosp Sheff 70-78; V Sheff St Mark Broomhall *Sheff* 70-78; Adn Sheff 78-87; Can Res Sheff Cathl 78-87; rtd 88. *947 Abbeydale Road, Sheffield S7 2QD* Sheffield (0114) 236 6148

PATON-WILLIAMS, David Graham. b 58. Warw Univ BA81 Trin Coll Ox DipTh82 Selw Coll Cam BA86 MA90. Ridley Hall Cam 84. d 87 p 88. C S Westoe *Dur* 87-90; C Newton Aycliffe 90-91; TV 91-93; Chapl Univ Coll of Ripon & York St Jo from 93; Min Can Ripon Cathl *Ripon* from 93. *5 Crescent Parade, Ripon, N Yorkshire HG4 2JE* Ripon (01765) 607346

PATRICIA, Sister. *See* PERKINS, Sister Patricia Doris

PATRICK, Hugh Joseph. b 37. TCD BA62 MA66. d 63 p 64. C Dromore Cathl *D & D* 63-66; C Lurgan Ch Ch 66-70; C Rothwell *Ripon* 70-73; V Thurnscoe St Hilda *Sheff* 73-78; V Wales from 78; P-in-c Thorpe Salvin 78-82; RD Laughton from 93. *The Vicarage, Manor Road, Wales, Sheffield S31 8PD* Worksop (01909) 771111

PATRICK, John Andrew. b 62. St Jo Coll Dur BA84. Ripon Coll Cuddesdon 87. d 89 p 90. C Frankby w Greasby *Ches* 89-92; C Boston *Linc* from 92. *2 Tower Street, Boston, Lincs PE21 8RX* Boston (01205) 362524

PATRICK, John Peter. b 23. AKC. d 52 p 53. V Upperthong *Wakef* 59-75; V Slaithwaite w E Scammonden 75-80; V Donington *Linc* 80-92; rtd 92; Perm to Offic *Linc* from 92. *Little Paddock, 140 Main Road, Hundleby, Spilsby, Lincs PE23 5NQ* Spilsby (01790) 52304

PATRICK, Robert Charles. b 64. Leeds Univ BA86 Fitzw Coll Cam BA91. Ridley Hall Cam 89. d 92 p 93. C Barton upon Humber *Linc* from 92. *7 West Grove, Barton-on-Humber, S Humberside DN18 5AG* Barton-on-Humber (01652) 32697

PATSTON, Raymond Sidney Richard. b 26. Kelham Th Coll 47. d 51 p 52. C Hammersmith H Innocents *Lon* 51-53; C Acton Green St Pet 53-56; Area Sec E Counties UMCA 56-62; C Chesterton St Luke *Ely* 56-59; R Downham Market w Bexwell

61-71; V Clee *Linc* from 71. *Old Clee Rectory, 202 Clee Road, Grimsby, S Humberside DN32 8NG* Grimsby (01472) 691800

PATTEN (nee STARNS), Mrs Helen Edna. b 43. St Hilda's Coll Ox BA65 Lon Univ CertEd70 DipTh75. Trin Coll Bris 73 Oak Hill Th Coll 81. dss 82 d 87 p 94. Tunbridge Wells St Jo *Roch* 82-86; Patcham *Chich* 86-87; Par Dn 87-91; Par Dn Eckington w Handley and Ridgeway *Derby* 91-94; C from 94. *The Vicarage, 1 Aintree Avenue, Eckington, Sheffield S31 9JA* Eckington (01246) 436673

PATTEN, John. b 27. Qu Coll Birm 74. d 76 p 77. NSM Armitage *Lich* 76-79; NSM Lich St Mary w St Mich from 79. *31 Trent Valley Road, Lichfield, Staffs WS13 6EZ* Lichfield (01543) 268245

PATTENDEN, Henry Albert. b 11. Lich Th Coll 53. d 54 p 55. C Etruria *Lich* 67-72; C Widley w Wymering *Portsm* 72-73; rtd 76. *55 Compton Close, Lichfield Road, Stafford ST17 6PW* Stafford (01785) 47355

PATTERSON, Alfred Percy. d 85 p 87. NSM Aghalee *D & D* 85-91; C Gilford 91-93; Bp's C 93-95; I from 95. *The Vicarage, 18 Scarva Road, Gilford, Craigavon, Co Armagh BT63 6BG* Craigavon (01762) 831130

PATTERSON, Andrew John. b 56. Master Mariner 85 Riversdale Coll OND76. Qu Coll Birm 85. d 88 p 89. C Newc St Phil and St Aug *Newc* 88-92; Asst Chapl R Victoria Infirmary Newc from 92. *25 Kingsway, Newcastle upon Tyne NE4 9UH, or Royal Victoria Infirmary, Newcastle upon Tyne NE1 4LP* 0191-274 4100 or 232 5131

PATTERSON, Anthony. b 43. Moore Th Coll Sydney BTh82. d 83 p 83. Australia 83-91; C Darfield *Sheff* 91-94; TR Marfleet *York* from 94. *St George's Rectory, 33 Carden Avenue, Hull HU9 4RT* Hull (01482) 791291

PATTERSON, Charles David Gilliat. b 40. Lon Univ DipTh74. Oak Hill Th Coll 71. d 74 p 75. C Brompton H Trin *Lon* 74-77; C Spring Grove St Mary 77-80; V Bures *St E* 80-92; R Bath Weston St Jo w Kelston *B & W* from 92. *The Rectory, 177 Newbridge Hill, Bath BA1 3PY* Bath (01225) 427206

PATTERSON, Colin Hugh. b 52. CertEd75 St Pet Coll Ox MA77 Univ of Wales (Cardiff) MPhil90. Trin Coll Bris DipHE86. d 87 p 88. C Blackb Sav *Blackb* 87-90; C Haughton le Skerne *Dur* 90-93; Adult Educn Adv from 93. *24 Monks Crescent, Durham DH1 1HD* 0191-386 1691

PATTERSON, Colin Peter Matthew. b 62. Newc Poly HND82 BA84. St Steph Ho Ox 92. d 94 p 95. C Cullercoats St Geo *Newc* from 94. *42 Shorestone Avenue, North Shields, Tyne & Wear NE30 3NE* 0191-253 4847

PATTERSON, Mrs Diane Rosemary. b 46. W Midl Minl Tr Course 88. d 91 p 94. C Hill *Birm* 91-95; Perm to Offic from 95. *3 Dower Road, Sutton Coldfield, W Midlands B75 6UA* 0121-308 0759

PATTERSON, Hugh John. b 38. Southn Univ MPhil76. AKC63. d 64 p 65. C Epsom St Martin *Guildf* 64-65; Chapl Ewell Coll 65-68; Asst Chapl and Lect Bp Otter Coll Chich 68-71; Lect Dudley Coll of Educn 71-77; Lect Wolv Poly 77-92; Wolv Univ from 92; Chapl Wolv Univ *Lich* from 89; Hon C Morville w Aston Eyre *Heref* from 82; Hon C Upton Cressett w Monk Hopton from 82; Hon C Acton Round from 82. *6 Victoria Road, Bridgnorth, Shropshire WV16 4LA* Bridgnorth (01746) 765298

PATTERSON, Ian Francis Riddell. b 31. TCD BA55. d 55 p 56. C Belf St Mary *Conn* 55-59; C Finaghy 59-63; I Craigs w Dunaghy and Killagan 63-66; Belf Trin Coll Miss 66-68; I Belf H Redeemer 68-80; I Kilroot 80-90; I Kilroot and Templecorran 90-92; I Donagh w Tyholland and Errigal Truagh *Clogh* from 92. *The Rectory, Glaslough, Co Monaghan, Irish Republic* Monaghan (47) 88277

PATTERSON, Jennifer Mary. *See* TAYLOR, Sister Jennifer Mary

PATTERSON, John. b 27. MBIM76 Regent St Poly Lon DMS58. Bps' Coll Cheshunt 60. d 61 p 62. Chapl RAF 65-72; V Ashton St Jas *Man* 72-78; USA 78-90; C Somercotes and Grainthorpe w Conisholme *Linc* 90-92; rtd 92. *44 Simpson Close, Barrow-upon-Humber, S Humberside DN19 7BL* Barrow-on-Humber (01469) 30867

PATTERSON, John Norton (Jack). b 39. TCD BA64 MA68. d 65 p 66. C Belf St Paul *Conn* 65-68; C Larne and Inver 68-72; I Ballintoy w Rathlin and Dunseverick from 72; Miss to Seamen from 72. *The Rectory, 2 Ballinlea Road, Ballintoy, Ballycastle, Co Antrim BT54 6NQ* Ballycastle (012657) 62411

PATTERSON, Marjorie Jean. *See* BROWN, Mrs Marjorie Jean

PATTERSON, Norman John. b 47. Peterho Cam BA69. Lon Coll of Div ALCD DPS St Jo Coll Nottm 70. d 73 p 74. C Everton St Ambrose w St Tim *Liv* 73-74; C Everton St Pet 74-78; TV 79-84; C Aigburth 84-92; Dioc Adv Past Care and Counselling from 84; V Gt Crosby All SS from 92. *All Saints' Vicarage, 17 Moor Coppice, Crosby, Liverpool L23 2XJ* 0151-924 6436

PATTERSON, Patric Douglas MacRae. b 51. Wycliffe Hall Ox 73. **d** 76 **p** 77. C Bebington *Ches* 76-79; Canada from 79. *156 Barrie Street, Kingston, Ontario, Canada, K7L 3J9*

PATTERSON, Philip Fredrick. b 50. Ulster Univ BSc QUB BD. **d** 82 **p** 83. C Lurgan Ch the Redeemer *D&D* 82-86; I Carrowdore w Millisle 86-89; I Knockbreda from 89. *Knockbreda Rectory, 69 Church Road, Belfast BT8 4AN* Belfast (01232) 641493

PATTERSON, Trevor Harold. b 60. QUB BA82 Stranmillis Coll PGCE83. Trin Coll Bris DipHE93. **d** 93 **p** 94. C Ashtead *Guildf* from 93. *17 Loraine Gardens, Ashtead, Surrey KT21 1PD* Ashtead (01372) 273819

PATTERSON, William Alfred. b 54. Wycliffe Hall Ox 77. **d** 79 **p** 80. C Partington and Carrington *Ches* 79-81; Canada from 81. *Box 125, The Pas, Manitoba, Canada, R9A 1K3*

PATTERSON, Canon William James. b 30. CBE91. Ball Coll Ox BA53 MA57. Ely Th Coll 53. **d** 55 **p** 56. R Esher *Guildf* 65-72; RD Emly 68-72; R Downham *Ely* 72-80; P-in-c Coveney 78-80; Adn Wisbech 79-84; V Wisbech St Mary 80-84; Dean Ely 84-90; V Everton w Tetworth 90-93; V Abbotsley 90-93; V Waresley 90-93; Hon Can Ely Cathl 90-93; rtd 93. *1 Watledge Close, Tewkesbury, Glos GL20 5RJ*

PATTINSON, Sir William Derek. b 30. Kt90. Qu Coll Ox BA52 MA56. St Deiniol's Hawarden 90. **d** 91 **p** 92. NSM Westmr St Gabr *Lon* from 91. *4 Strutton Court, Great Peter Street, London SW1P 2HH* 0171-222 6307

PATTISON, Anthony. b 50. MRPharmS73 Heriot-Watt Univ BSc72. Sarum & Wells Th Coll 85. **d** 87 **p** 88. C Cullercoats St Geo *Newc* 87-89; Ind Chapl from 89; C Cramlington 89-91; TV from 91. *24 Lindsey Close, Beaconhill Glade, Cramlington, Northd NE23 8EJ* Cramlington (01670) 715464

PATTISON, George Linsley. b 50. Edin Univ MA72 BD77 Dur Univ PhD. Edin Th Coll 74. **d** 77 **p** 78. C Benwell St Jas *Newc* 77-80; P-in-c Kimblesworth *Dur* 80-83; R Badwell Ash w Gt Ashfield, Stowlangtoft etc *St E* 83-91; Dean of Chapl K Coll Cam from 91. *King's College, Cambridge CB2 1ST* Cambridge (01223) 350411

PATTISON, Graham Bentley. b 39. Open Univ BA75. Kelham Th Coll 59. **d** 64 **p** 65. C Beamish *Dur* 64-66; C Benfieldside 66-67; C Barnsley St Mary *Wakef* 67-70; TV Tong *Bradf* 70-74; TR 74-77; Master Sherburn Hosp *Dur* from 77; Soc Resp Officer *Dur* 77-94. *The Master's House, Sherburn Hospital, Durham DH1 2SE* 0191-372 0332

PATTISON, Stephen Bewley. b 53. Selw Coll Cam BA76. Edin Th Coll 76. **d** 78 **p** 80. C Gosforth All SS *Newc* 78-79; NSM St Nic Hosp *Newc* 78-82; Hon C *Newc* St Thos Prop Chpl *Newc* 80-82; Chapl Edin Th Coll 82-83; Lect Past Studies Birm Univ 83-88; Perm to Offic *Birm* 83-86 and from 87; Hon C Moseley St Mary 86-87. *15 Forest Court, Forest Road, Birmingham B13 9DL* 0121-449 4762 or 233 1810

PATTMAN, Andrew. b 53. Didsbury Coll Man BEd75. Westcott Ho Cam CTM95. **d** 95. C Washington *Dur* from 95. *40 Waskerley Road, Washington, Tyne & Wear NE38 8EP*

PATTON, Ven Desmond Hilton. b 12. TCD BA35. **d** 36 **p** 37. I Carlow w Urglin and Staplestown *C&O* 59-77; Adn Ossory and Leighlin 62-76; rtd 76; Chapl Mageough Home *D&G* from 88. *Littleholme, Delgany, Co Wicklow, Irish Republic* Dublin (1) 287-5207

PATTON, Eugene Smith. b 19. MDiv MEd MLS. **d** 92. NSM Monasterevan w Nurney and Rathdaire *M&K* 92-93. *The Rectory, Monasterevan, Co Kildare, Irish Republic* Monasterevan (45) 25411

PAUL, Brother. *See* SINGLETON, Ernest George

PAUL, Canon John Douglas. b 28. Edin Univ MA52. Ely Th Coll 52. **d** 54 **p** 55. Portuguese E Africa 60-70; Adn Metangula 65-70; R Castle Douglas *Glas* 70-75; R Edin St Mark *Edin* 75-80; R Elgin w Lossiemouth *Mor* 80-92; Syn Clerk 89-91; Hon Can St Andr Cathl Inverness from 89; Dean Mor 91-92; rtd 92. *2 The Avenue, Gifford, Haddington, East Lothian EH41 4QX* Gifford (0162081) 547

PAUL, John Matthew. b 61. K Coll Lon BA82 Fitzw Coll Cam BA88 MA92. Westcott Ho Cam 86. **d** 89 **p** 90. C Writtle w Highwood *Chelmsf* 89-94; Min Can and Chapl St Paul's Cathl *Lon* from 94. *7B Amen Court, London EC4M 7BU* 0171-248 6151

PAUL, John Wilfred. b 30. St Jo Coll Morpeth LTh52 BA82. **d** 51 **p** 52. Australia 51-57; C Mitcham Ascension *S'wark* 57-59; V Clapham St Jo 59-65; CF (TA) 60-67; V Balham St Mary *S'wark* 66-85; V Balham St Mary and St Jo 85-86; R St Andr-by-the-Wardrobe w St Ann, Blackfriars *Lon* from 86; R St Jas Garlickhythe w St Mich Queenhithe etc from 86. *St Andrew's House, St Andrew's Hill, London EC4V 5DE* 0171-248 7546 Fax 329 3632

PAUL, Naunihal Chand (Nihal). b 40. Allahabad Univ MA. Bangalore Th Coll BD. **d** 69 **p** 70. India 70-74; C Urmston *Man* 75-77; P-in-c Farnworth St Pet 77-80; TV E Farnworth and Kearsley 80-83; TV Laindon St Martin and St Nic w Nevendon *Chelmsf* 83-90; R Laindon w Dunton from 90.

38 Claremont Road, Laindon, Basildon, Essex SS15 5PZ Basildon (01268) 411190

PAUL, Roger Philip. b 53. Clare Coll Cam BA74 CertEd76 MA88. Westcott Ho Cam 78. **d** 81 **p** 82. C Cov Caludon *Cov* 81-85; R Warmington w Shotteswell and Radway w Ratley from 85. *The Rectory, Warmington, Banbury, Oxon OX17 1BT* Farnborough (0129589) 213

PAUL, Simon Nicholas. b 56. Hull Univ BA81 PGCE82. Trin Coll Bris BA95. **d** 95. C Cranleigh *Guildf* from 95. *22 Orchard Gardens, Cranleigh, Surrey GU6 7LG* Guildford (01483) 272573

PAULEY, Denniss Franklyn. b 19. Chich Th Coll. **d** 57 **p** 58. C Pentonville St Silas w All SS and St Jas *Lon* 69-84; rtd 84; Hon C Pentonville St Silas w All SS and St Jas *Lon* from 84. *87A Richmond Avenue, London N1 0LX* 0171-607 2865

PAVEY, Mrs Angela Mary. b 55. Hull Univ BA77 Nottm Univ BCombStuds84. Linc Th Coll 81. dss 84 **d** 87 **p** 94. Linc St Faith and St Martin w St Pet *Linc* 84-86; Chapl Boston Coll of FE from 87; Asst Min Officer 89-95; Dioc Dir of Ords from 94. *The Rectory, Fishtoft, Boston, Lincs PE21 0RZ* Boston (01205) 363216

PAVEY, Gordon Sidney Alfred. b 19. Lon Univ BD47 Leeds Univ MEd58. Chich Th Coll 40. **d** 42 **p** 43. V Huddersfield St Thos *Wakef* 54-64; Youth Chapl 54-57; Lic to Offic *Bris* from 68; Prin Lect Th Bris Poly 77-92; Prin Lect Th Univ of the W of England, Bris from 92; rtd 84. *2 Carey's Close, Clevedon, Avon BS21 6BA* Clevedon (01275) 872623

PAVEY, John Bertram. b 51. Keele Univ BA73 Hull Univ PGCE74. Linc Th Coll 81. **d** 83 **p** 84. C Boultham *Linc* 83-86; R Fishtoft from 86. *The Rectory, Fishtoft, Boston, Lincs PE21 0RZ* Boston (01205) 363216

PAVEY, Michael Trevor. b 32. ALCD59. **d** 59 **p** 60. C Nor St Pet Mancroft *Nor* 59-61; C N Walsham w Antingham 61-63; Chapl RAF 63-83; R Mark w Allerton *B&W* from 83. *The Rectory, Vicarage Lane, Mark, Highbridge, Somerset TA9 4NN* Mark Moor (01278) 641258

PAVLIBEYI, Andrew Christos. b 53. Trent Poly CertEd76. Oak Hill Th Coll BA88 Wycliffe Hall Ox 84. **d** 86 **p** 87. C Finchley Ch Ch *Lon* 86-89; Chapl Lon Univ 89-92; V S Hampstead St Sav 92-93; P-in-c from 93. *St Saviour's Vicarage, 30 Eton Villas, London NW3 4SQ* 0171-722 4621

PAWSEY, Jack Edward. b 35. Trin Coll Ox BA59 MA65. Westcott Ho Cam 64. **d** 66 **p** 67. Sec Coun Soc Aid *S'wark* 66-75; Race Relns Worker 75-78; Acting Sec Coun Soc Aid 78-82; Perm to Offic 84-86; Hon C Camberwell St Geo from 86. *20 Addington Square, London SE5 7JZ* 0171-701 2769 or 735 5871

PAWSON, Preb John Walker. b 38. Kelham Th Coll 58. **d** 63 **p** 64. C N Hull St Mich *York* 63-67; C Lower Gornal *Lich* 67-70; V Tipton St Jo 70-78; V Meir Heath from 78; RD Stoke from 88; Preb Lich Cathl from 93. *St Francis's Vicarage, Meir Heath, Stoke-on-Trent ST3 7LH* Blythe Bridge (01782) 393189

PAXMAN, Denis James. b 24. FRMetS82 St Edm Hall Ox BA49 DipTh51 MA54. Ely Th Coll 52. **d** 53 **p** 54. Warden St Mich Coll Tenbury 65-77; V Tenbury St Mich *Heref* 65-77; Chapl & Hd Relig Studies Howell's Sch Denbigh 77-83; V Lakenheath *St E* 83-87; R Tain *Mor* 87-91; Prin Moray Ord Course 87-91; rtd 89. *Corriegills, Brough Sowerby, Kirkby Stephen, Cumbria CA17 4EG* Brough (017683) 41427

PAXON, Robin Michael Cuninghame. b 46. St Jo Coll Dur BA69. Westcott Ho Cam 69. **d** 71 **p** 72. C Croydon St Pet S End *Cant* 71-77; C Saffron Walden w Wendens Ambo and Littlebury *Chelmsf* 77-80; P-in-c Plaistow St Mary 80-83; TV Plaistow 83-89; TV Dovercourt and Parkeston from 90. *20 Park Road, Harwich, Essex CO12 3BJ*

PAXTON, Cyril. b 14. S'wark Ord Course 64. **d** 67 **p** 68. C Riddlesdown *S'wark* 67-74; C Uckfield *Chich* 74-77; C Isfield 74-77; C S Petherton w the Seavingtons *B&W* 77-83; rtd 79; Perm to Offic *B&W* from 83. *Cobblers, Hinton St George, Somerset TA17 8SA* Crewkerne (01460) 72741

PAXTON, John Ernest. b 49. Ex Univ BA71. Westcott Ho Cam 74. **d** 74 **p** 75. C Redditch St Steph *Worc* 74-77; UAE 77-81; C Bolton St Pet *Man* 81-91; Ind Missr 81-91; TV Southn (City Cen) *Win* from 91. *22 Gordon Avenue, Southampton SO9 3RX* Southampton (01703) 584301

PAY, Norman John. b 50. St Jo Coll Dur BA72 DipTh73. Cranmer Hall Dur. **d** 74 **p** 75. C S Moor *Dur* 74-78; C Rawmarsh w Parkgate *Sheff* 78-80; C-in-c New Cantley CD 80-82; V New Cantley 82-89; V Doncaster St Leon and St Jude from 89; Asst Clergy In-Service Tr Officer from 90. *St Leonard's Vicarage, Barnsley Road, Doncaster, S Yorkshire DN5 8QE* Doncaster (01302) 784858

PAYN, Peter Richard. b 33. Moore Th Coll Sydney LTh59. **d** 60 **p** 60. Australia 60-79; C Blackb Ch Ch w St Matt *Blackb* 79-81; V Lowestoft Ch Ch *Nor* 81-92; V Tunbridge Wells St Pet *Roch* from 92. *St Peter's Vicarage, Bayhall Road, Tunbridge Wells, Kent TN2 4TP* Tunbridge Wells (01892) 530384

PAYNE, Alan Frank. b 19. Bps' Coll Cheshunt 63. **d** 65 **p** 66. V Oulton w Woodlesford *Ripon* 69-80; V Thurgoland *Wakef* 80-82; rtd 82; Perm to Offic *Wakef* from 82. *602 King Lane, Alwoodley Park, Leeds LS17 7AN* Leeds (0113) 266 0221

PAYNE, Arthur Edwin. b 37. K Alfred's Coll Win CertEd59 Ban Coll DipRE60 Univ of Wales (Swansea) ACertEd68. St Mich Coll Llan 86. **d** 87 **p** 88. C Swansea St Gabr *S & B* 87-90; Chapl Univ of Wales (Swansea) 89-90; V Brynmawr 90-91; TV Wickford and Runwell *Chelmsf* 91-94; Chapl Runwell Hosp Essex 91-94; P-in-c Wraxall *B & W* from 94. *The Rectory, Wraxall, Bristol BS19 1NA* Bristol (0117) 985 7086

PAYNE, Canon Charles Thomas Leonard. b 11. Kelham Th Coll 29. **d** 34 **p** 35. V Streatham Ch Ch *S'wark* 42-79; Chapl CA Hostel Streatham 48-79; RD Streatham *S'wark* 73-79; Hon Can S'wark Cathl 75-79; rtd 79; Perm to Offic *St E* from 79. *6 Cedar Walk, Acton, Sudbury, Suffolk CO10 0UN* Sudbury (01787) 376812

PAYNE, Cyril Douglas. b 16. Sarum Th Coll 46. **d** 49 **p** 50. V Wellingborough All SS *Pet* 63-82; rtd 82; Perm to Offic *Cant* from 82. *32 London Road, Canterbury, Kent CT2 8LN* Canterbury (01227) 765694

PAYNE, Cyril Gordon. b 26. Bris Univ BA53. Linc Th Coll 53. **d** 55 **p** 56. V Otterbourne *Win* 63-75; V Milford 75-90; rtd 90. *11 Oaklands, Lymington, Hants SO41 3TH* Lymington (01590) 671274

PAYNE, David Charles. b 62. Univ of Wales (Abth) BLib84. St Jo Coll Nottm MA95. **d** 95. C Horncastle w Low Toynton *Linc* from 95. *St Mary's House, 6 Park Road, Horncastle, Lincs LN9 5EF* Horncastle (01507) 524564

PAYNE, David James. b 31. Clare Coll Cam BA54 MA61. Wycliffe Hall Ox 60. **d** 62 **p** 63. R Shackleford *Guildf* 66-73; R Peper Harow 66-73; R Odell *St Alb* 73-78; V Pavenham 73-78; Warden Home of Divine Healing Crowhurst 78-84; R Wraxall *B & W* 84-92; rtd 92. *Langet End, Upper Up, South Cerney, Cirencester, Gloucester GL7 5US* Cirencester (01285) 860677

PAYNE, David Ronald. b 49. DMS77 Open Univ BA87. St Mich Coll Llan. **d** 90 **p** 91. C Oystermouth *S & B* 90-93; V Penllergaer from 93. *The Vicarage, 16 Swansea Road, Penllergaer, Swansea SA4 1AQ* Gorseinon (01792) 862603

PAYNE, Canon Denis Alfred. b 22. Or Coll Ox BA50 MA53. Wells Th Coll 50. **d** 51 **p** 52. Min Sec ACCM 67-69; Sen Selection Sec 69-73; Dir Post-Ord Tr and Further Tr for Clergy *St E* 73-84; Dioc Dir of Ords 73-87; Can Res St E Cathl 73-89; rtd 89; Perm to Offic *St E* from 90. *The Crooked House, Brussels Green, Darsham, Saxmundham, Suffolk IP17 3RN* Yoxford (0172877) 705

PAYNE, Francis Michael Ambrose. b 18. Keble Coll Ox BA39 MA43. Ely Th Coll 39. **d** 41 **p** 42. R Henley *Ox* 63-78; RD Henley 73-78; R Ecton *Pet* 78-83; rtd 83; Perm to Offic *Nor* from 83. *The Monastery, Happisburgh, Norwich NR12 0AB* Walcott (01692) 650076

PAYNE, Frederick Gates (Eric). b 19. Jes Coll Cam BA40 MA43. Lon Coll of Div 40. **d** 42 **p** 43. Ethiopia 48-67; SW Org Sec CMJ 68-85; rtd 84; Perm to Offic *B & W* from 85. *83 Penn Lea Road, Bath BA1 3RQ* Bath (01225) 423092

PAYNE, James John Henry (Jim). b 26. MBE69. St Pet Hall Ox BA53 MA59. Tyndale Hall Bris 48 Linc Th Coll 53. **d** 53 **p** 54. Nigeria 57-87; Hon Can Lagos 71-88; rtd 88; Perm to Offic *Ox* 88-93. *1 Timberyard Cottages, Shellingford, Faringdon, Oxon SN7 7QA* Stanford in the Vale (01367) 710274

PAYNE, John. b 58. Glas Univ BSc80 Edin Univ BD84. Edin Th Coll 81. **d** 90 **p** 90. C Dur St Nic *Dur* 90-94; Australia from 94. *c/o H Jones Esq, Rms 3680, Hansen Road, Rochester, Victoria 3651, Australia* Bendigo (54) 862321

PAYNE, John Charles. b 04. St Aid Birkenhead 50. **d** 51 **p** 52. V Preston St Sav *Blackb* 62-69; rtd 69. *c/o 84 Ackworth Road, Pontefract, W Yorkshire WF8 4NG*

PAYNE, John Percival. b 49. Nottm Univ BA70. Cuddesdon Coll 70. **d** 72 **p** 73. C Tilehurst St Mich *Ox* 72-76; C Cross Green St Sav and St Hilda *Ripon* 76-79; Chapl St Hilda's Priory Sneaton, Whitby 79-83; V Leeds Belle Is St Jo and St Barn *Ripon* 83-88; Chapl St Hilda's Sch Whitby from 88. *Ugthorpe Grange, Guisborough Road, Ugthorpe, Whitby, N Yorkshire YO21 2BE* Whitby (01947) 895285

PAYNE, John Rogan. b 44. Episc Th Coll Sao Paulo. **d** 78 **p** 79. Brazil 78-86; C Ilkley All SS *Bradf* 86-88; R Elvington w Sutton on Derwent and E Cottingwith *York* 88-94. *Manor Farm House, East Flotmanby Road, Filey, N Yorkshire YO14 0HX* Scarborough (01723) 513969

PAYNE, Canon Joseph Marshall. b 17. TCD BA38 MA52. **d** 40 **p** 41. Asst Chapl-in-Chief RAF 65-72; V Malew *S & M* 72-82; RD Castletown 77-82; Can St German's Cathl 78-84; Treas 80-84; rtd 82; Perm to Offic *S & M* from 84. *Ard-ny-Shee, 3 Viking Close, Ballakillowey, Colby, Isle of Man IM9 4BH* Port Erin (01624) 832039

PAYNE, Kenneth Alan. b 45. Pemb Coll Ox BA68 MA71. Qu Coll Birm 71. **d** 74 **p** 74. Hon C Perry Barr *Birm* 74-78; Hon C Ruislip Manor St Paul *Lon* 78-79; C Hawksworth Wood

PAYNE, Leonard John. b 49. St Jo Coll Nottm DipThMin95. **d** 95. C Trimley *St E* from 95. *3 Black Barns, Trimley, Ipswich IP10 0XT* Trimley (01394) 274015

PAYNE, Leonard Vivian. b 20. St D Coll Lamp BA42 Lich Th Coll 42. **d** 44 **p** 46. V Weston-super-Mare St Paul *B & W* 62-81; rtd 81. *23 Downs View, Aberthin, Cowbridge, S Glam CF7 7HF* Cowbridge (01446) 775130

PAYNE, Mark James Townsend. b 69. Van Mildert Coll Dur BA90. Ridley Hall Cam CTM94. **d** 94 **p** 95. C Angmering Chich from 94. *Vestry Cottage, Arundel Road, Angmering, Littlehampton, W Sussex BN16 4JR* Littlehampton (01903) 776529

PAYNE, Michael Frederick. b 49. NE Surrey Coll of Tech HND72. St Jo Coll Nottm 81. **d** 83 **p** 84. C Hyson Green *S'well* 83-86; P-in-c Peckham St Mary Magd *S'wark* 86-90; V from 90. *St Mary's Vicarage, 22 St Mary's Road, London SE15 2DW* 0171-639 4596

PAYNE, Ralfe Dudley. b 22. Lon Univ BA50. Qu Coll Birm 50. **d** 52 **p** 53. V Brockmoor *Lich* 63-75; C Kinver 76-79; R Himley 79-89; V Swindon 79-89; rtd 89. *Highfield, Dunsley, Kinver, Stourbridge, W Midlands DY7 6LY* Kinver (01384) 873612

PAYNE, Richard Derek. b 29. K Coll Lon 51. **d** 55 **p** 56. R Telscombe w Piddinghoe *Chich* 63-75; R Telscombe w Piddinghoe and Southease 75-76; Chapl Holmewood Ho Sch Tunbridge Wells 76-78; Perm to Offic *Chich* from 78; Perm to Offic *Cant* from 79; Org Sec (SE England) CECS 78-93; rtd 93; Chapl Lanzarote *Eur* 94-95. *Greystones, Duddleswell, Uckfield, E Sussex TN22 3BH* Nutley (01825) 712314

PAYNE, Robert Christian. b 42. St Mich Coll Llan DipTh65. **d** 65 **p** 66. C Charlton Kings St Mary *Glouc* 65-69; C Waltham Cross *St Alb* 69-71; V Falfield *Glouc* 71-72; P-in-c Rockhampton 71-72; V Falfield w Rockhampton 72-76; Chapl HM Det Cen Eastwood Park 71-76; Chapl HM Youth Cust Cen Everthorpe 76-79; Chapl HM Youth Cust Cen Glen Parva 79-85; Pris Service Chapl Tr Officer 85-88; Chapl HM Pris Swinfen Hall 85-88; Asst Chapl Gen of Pris (SW) 88-90; Asst Chapl Gen of Pris from 90. *c/o Home Office, Calthorpe House, Hagley Road, Birmingham B16 8QR* 0121-455 9855 Fax 454 6738

PAYNE, Robert Harold Vincent (Bob). b 44. St Jo Coll Nottm 77. **d** 79 **p** 80. C Didsbury St Jas *Man* 79-80; C Didsbury St Jas and Em 80-83; V Southchurch Ch Ch *Chelmsf* 83-90; P-in-c Charles w St Matthias Plymouth *Ex* 90-94; Warden Lee Abbey from 94. *Garden Lodge, Lee Abbey, Lynton, Devon EX35 6JJ* Lynton (01598) 52621 Fax 52619

PAYNE, Robert Sandon. b 48. ARICS72 Reading Univ BSc69. Ripon Coll Cuddesdon 77. **d** 80 **p** 81. C Bridgnorth, Tasley, Astley Abbotts and Oldbury *Heref* 80-83; P-in-c Wistanstow 83-92; P-in-c Acton Scott 86-92; P-in-c Dorrington 92-94; P-in-c Leebotwood w Longnor 92-94; P-in-c Smethcott w Woolstaston 92-94; P-in-c Stapleton 92-94; R Dorrington w Leebotwood, Longnor, Stapleton etc from 94. *The Rectory, Dorrington, Shrewsbury SY5 7JL* Dorrington (01743) 718578

PAYNE, Victor Harold. b 27. S'wark Ord Course 82. **d** 85 **p** 86. Hon C Sanderstead All SS *S'wark* 85-95; rtd 95; Perm to Offic *S'wark* from 95. *8 Langley Oaks Avenue, South Croydon, Surrey CR2 8DH* 0181-657 5658

PAYNE, Victor John. b 45. Open Univ BA81. St Mich Coll Llan DipTh69 DPS70. **d** 70 **p** 71. C Ystrad Mynach *Llan* 70-72; C Whitchurch 72-75; CF (TA) 74-75; CF 75-85 and 87-93; V Talgarth and Llanelieu *S & B* 85-87; C Bassaleg *Mon* from 93. *99 The Uplands, Rogerstone, Newport, Gwent NP1 9FE* Newport (01633) 893357

PAYNE, Walter Richard Stanley. b 29. FRSC64 Lon Univ BSc54 PhD63 DipRS78. S'wark Ord Course 78. **d** 78 **p** 79. NSM Lamorbey H Trin *Roch* 78-85; Perm to Offic from 85. *120 Hurst Road, Sidcup, Kent DA15 9AF* 0181-302 0267

PAYNE, Warwick Martin. b 26. AKC51. **d** 52 **p** 53. C Mansf St Pet *S'well* 52-56; Gambia 56-58; C Winlaton *Dur* 59-62; S Africa from 63. *PO Box 207, Eshowe, 3815 South Africa* Eshowe (354) 41532

PAYNE COOK, John Andrew Somerset. b 43. St Pet Coll Ox BA65 MA. Coll of Resurr Mirfield 65. **d** 68 **p** 69. C St Mary-at-Latton *Chelmsf* 68-71; C Gt Berkhamsted *St Alb* 71-76; C-in-c N Brickhill CD 76-82; V N Brickhill and Putnoe 83-85; TR Tring from 85; RD Berkhamsted from 92. *The Rectory, Church Yard, Tring, Herts HP23 5AE* Tring (01442) 822170

PAYNTER, Stephen Denis. b 59. Bath Univ BSc82 CertEd82. Trin Coll Bris BA89. **d** 89 **p** 90. C Nailsea Ch Ch *B & W* 89-92; C Farnborough *Guildf* from 92. *The Parsonage, 45 Sand Hill, Farnborough, Hants GU14 8ER* Farnborough (01252) 543789

PAYNTON, Paul Alexander. b 42. Hull Univ DipMin88. Linc Th Coll 72. **d** 74 **p** 75. C Uppingham w Ayston *Pet* 74-77; P-in-c Market Overton w Thistleton 77-79; R Teigh w Whissendine 77-79; R Teigh w Whissendine and Market

Overton 79-95; V Irchester from 95. *The Vicarage, 19 Station Road, Irchester, Wellingborough, Northants NN9 7EH* Rushden (01933) 312674

PAYTON, Canon Arthur Edward. b 16. Lambeth MA81. **d** 39 **p** 41. Hon C Kelvedon *Chelmsf* 69-82; Hon Can Gib Cathl *Eur* 73-84; rtd 81; P-in-c Wickmere w Lt Barningham and Itteringham *Nor* 84-88; Perm to Offic from 88. *The Grange, Sandy Lane, West Runton, Cromer, Norfolk NR27 9LT* West Runton (01263) 837400

PAYTON, John Vear. b 36. Bps' Coll Cheshunt 60. **d** 63 **p** 64. C Hatf Hyde St Mary *St Alb* 63-72; V Farley Hill St Jo 72-84; Counsellor (Inner Healing) 84-91. *41 Trowbridge Gardens, Luton LU2 7JY* Luton (01582) 450612

PEACE, Brian. b 38. St Jo Coll Nottm DCM92. **d** 92 **p** 93. C Huddersfield H Trin *Wakef* from 92. *60 Imperial Road, Edgerton, Huddersfield HD1 4PG* Huddersfield (01484) 548340

PEACE, Geoffrey. b 23. S'wark Ord Course. **d** 68 **p** 69. NSM Ashford St Hilda CD *Lon* 68-73; NSM Ashford St Hilda 73-80; C Spilsby w Hundleby *Linc* 80-83; C Sandhurst *Ox* 83-85; V Owlsmoor 85-88; rtd 88. *21 Balfour Road, Bournemouth BH9 2AZ* Bournemouth (01202) 525700

PEACH, Malcolm Thompson. b 31. St Chad's Coll Dur BA56. Sarum Th Coll 56. **d** 58 **p** 59. C Beamish *Dur* 58-61; Chapl Dur Univ 61-65; NE England Sec SCM 61-65; C-in-c Stockton St Mark CD *Dur* 65-72; P-in-c Bishopwearmouth St Nic 72-81; V 81-85; V S Shields St Hilda w St Thos from 85; Hon Chapl Miss to Seamen from 85; P-in-c S Shields St Aid w St Steph *Dur* from 92. *St Hilda's Vicarage, 40 Lawe Road, South Shields, Tyne & Wear NE33 2EU* 0191-454 1414

PEACHELL, David John. b 45. Oak Hill Th Coll 85. **d** 86 **p** 87. C Prescot *Liv* 86-89; CF from 89. *c/o MOD (Army), Bagshot Park, Bagshot, Surrey GU19 5PL* Bagshot (01276) 471717 Fax 412834

PEACOCK, David. b 39. Liv Univ BA61 Lanc Univ MA71. Westcott Ho Cam 84. **d** 84 **p** 85. Prin Lect St Martin's Coll Lanc 84-85; Hon C Lanc St Mary *Blackb* 84-85; Hon C Roehampton H Trin *S'wark* 85-92; Prin Whitelands Coll of HE from 85; Hon C Putney St Mary from 92. *Whitelands College, West Hill, London SW15 3SN* 0181-392 3501 or 788 4195

PEACOCK, David Christopher. b 57. York Univ BA78 DPhil83. Wycliffe Hall Ox 89. **d** 91 **p** 92. C Old Brumby *Linc* 91-95; TV Bottesford w Ashby from 95. *St Peter's Vicarage, Old School Lane, Bottesford, Scunthorpe, S Humberside DN16 3RD* Scunthorpe (01724) 840616

PEACOCK, John. b 35. ALCD60. **d** 60 **p** 61. C Addiscombe St Mary *Cant* 60-62; C Felixstowe St Jo *St E* 62-65; Chapl RAF 65-70; Australia from 71. *4A Lockerbie Road, Thornleigh, NSW, Australia 2120* Sydney (2) 484-3589 or 816-0222

PEACOCK, Thomas Edward. b 35. Dur Univ BSc55 PhD58. **d** 64 **p** 65. C S'wark St Sav w All Hallows *S'wark* 64-67; Australia 67-68 and from 70; C Jarrow *Dur* 68-69. *9 Bergamot Street, Bald Hills, Queensland, Australia 4036* Brisbane (7) 261-1711

PEACOCK, William John. b 15. Worc Ord Coll 65. **d** 67 **p** 68. C Netherton St Andr *Worc* 69-74; R Ebbw Vale *Mon* 74-78; V Caerwent w Dinham and Llanfair Discoed 78-83; rtd 83; Perm to Offic *Chich* from 87. *2 Dickens Way, Eastbourne, E Sussex BN23 7TG* Eastbourne (01323) 763897

PEACOCKE, Canon Dr Arthur Robert. b 24. MBE93. Ex Coll Ox BA45 BSc47 MA48 DPhil48 DSc62 DD82 Birm Univ DipTh60 BD71. **d** 71 **p** 71. Fell and Tutor St Pet Hall Ox 65-73; Dean Clare Coll Cam 73-84; Lic to Offic *Ely* 73-85; Lic to Offic *Ox* from 85; Dir Ian Ramsey Cen Ox 85-88; Warden SOSc from 87; Hon Chapl Ch Ch Ox from 88; Hon Can Ch Ch from 94. *55 St John's Streett, Oxford OX1 2LQ, or Exeter College, Oxford OX1 3DP* Oxford (01865) 512041

PEAD, Charles Henry. b 31. **d** 87 **p** 88. NSM Llanfrechfa and Llanddewi Fach w Llandegveth *Mon* 87-92; NSM Mamhilad and Llanfihangel Pontymoile from 92. *Jasmine, Caerleon Road, Llanfrechfa, Cwmbran, Gwent NP44 8DQ* Cwmbran (01633) 482685

PEAKE, Charles Clifford. b 17. St Jo Coll Ox BA38 Leeds Univ MA88. Qu Coll Birm 38. **d** 40 **p** 41. V Starbeck *Ripon* 68-78; R Farnham w Scotton and Staveley and Copgrove 78-82; rtd 82. *8 Burke Street, Harrogate, N Yorkshire HG1 4NR* Harrogate (01423) 522265

PEAKE, Robert Ernest. b 27. Univ Coll Lon BSc51 FSS. Coll of Resurr Mirfield 83. **d** 85 **p** 86. C Linslade *Ox* 85-88; TV Gt Chesham 88-89; rtd 89; Hon C Princes Risborough w Ilmer *Ox* from 93. *Butley Cottage, Chestnut Way, Longwick, Princes Risborough, Bucks HP27 9SD* Princes Risborough (01844) 344952

PEAKE, Ven Simon Jeremy Brinsley. b 30. Worc Coll Ox BA54 MA56. St Steph Ho Ox 53. **d** 57 **p** 58. C Eastbourne St Andr *Chich* 57-60; S Africa 60-69; Zambia 69-77; Chapl Athens w Kifissia *Eur* 77-87; Chapl Vienna w Budapest and Prague

87-91; Chapl Vienna w Budapest 91-93; Chapl Vienna from 93; Hon Can Malta Cathl 87-92; Can Malta Cathl from 92; Adn Aegean from 95. *Thugutstrasse 21/2, 1020 Vienna 2, Austria* Vienna (1) 720-7973 or 712-9193 Fax 714-7824

PEAL, Jacqueline (Jackie). b 46. MCSP70. Cant Sch of Min 88. **d** 91 **p** 94. NSM Bexley St Jo *Roch* from 91; NSM Crayford 91-94; C from 94. *St John's Vicarage, 29 Park Hill Road, Bexley, Kent DA5 1HX* Crayford (01322) 521786

PEAL, John Arthur. b 46. K Coll Lon BD70 AKC. **d** 71 **p** 72. C Portsea All SS w St Jo Rudmore *Portsm* 71-74; C Westbury *Sarum* 71-77; V Borstal *Roch* 77-82; Chapl HM Pris Cookham Wood 78-82; Chapl Erith and Distr Hosp from 82; V Erith Ch Ch *Roch* 82-91; P-in-c Erith St Jo 86-91; V Bexley St Jo from 91. *St John's Vicarage, 29 Park Hill Road, Bexley, Kent DA5 1HX* Crayford (01322) 521786

PEAL, William John. b 26. K Coll Lon BSc47 AKC PhD52. St Jo Coll Nottm 79. **d** 80 **p** 81. C Coalville and Bardon Hill *Leic* 80-83; TV Melton Mowbray w Thorpe Arnold 83-86; TV Melton Gt Framland 86-90; rtd 90. *20 Conway Road, Knypersley, Stoke-on-Trent ST8 7AL* Stoke-on-Trent (01782) 513580

PEARCE, Adrian Francis. b 55. S Dios Minl Tr Scheme 92. **d** 95. NSM Jersey St Jas *Win* from 95; NSM Jersey St Luke from 95. *24 Richelieu Park, Tower Road, St Helier, Jersey, Channel Islands JE2 3HT* Jersey (01534) 873115

PEARCE, Alfred Edward. b 16. AKC48. **d** 48 **p** 49. R Hackington *Cant* 67-87; rtd 87. *12 Mead Way, Canterbury, Kent CT2 8BB* Canterbury (01227) 464048

PEARCE, Mrs Angela Elizabeth. b 36. K Coll Lon BSc58 CertEd59 BD79 AKC79. **dss** 79 **d** 87. Chapl Raines Sch 79-87; Homerton St Barn w St Paul *Lon* 79-85; Upper Chelsea St Simon 85-89; Hon Par Dn 87-89; Hon Par Dn Limehouse from 89. *Limehouse Rectory, 5 Newell Street, London E14 7HP* 0171-987 1502

PEARCE, Brian Edward. b 39. Kelham Th Coll 59. **d** 64 **p** 65. C Smethwick St Matt *Birm* 64-68; C Kings Norton 68-72; TV 73-80; TR Swindon Dorcan *Bris* 80-91; Min Withywood CD 91-94; RD Bedminster from 92; V Withywood from 94. *Withywood Church House, 63 Turtlegate Avenue, Bristol BS13 8NN* Bristol (0117) 964 7763

PEARCE, Clive. b 40. Univ of Wales (Lamp) BA63. St Steph Ho Ox 63. **d** 65 **p** 66. C Acton Green St Pet *Lon* 65-67; C Eastcote St Lawr 67-73; V Hatch End St Anselm from 73. *The Vicarage, 50 Cedar Drive, Pinner, Middx HA5 4DE* 0181-428 4111

PEARCE, Canon Denis William Wilfrid. b 25. Bps' Coll Cheshunt 55. **d** 58 **p** 59. C-in-c Leytonstone St Aug CD *Chelmsf* 65-74; V Leytonstone H Trin Harrow Green 65-81; P-in-c Leyton St Luke 78-81; R Capel w Lt Wenham *St E* 81-86; P-in-c Lavenham 86-89; R 89-93; RD Lavenham 87-93; Hon Can St E Cathl 90-93; rtd 93; Clergy Retirement Officer *St E* from 93. *74 Hintlesham Drive, Felixstowe, Suffolk IP11 8YL* Felixstowe (01394) 279189

PEARCE, Desmond. b 30. Univ of Wales (Abth) BA52. E Midl Min Tr Course 85. **d** 88 **p** 89. NSM Chellaston *Derby* 88-90; NSM Walsall St Gabr Fulbrook *Lich* 90; C Stoke Lacy, Moreton Jeffries w Much Cowarne etc *Heref* from 91. *Shalom, Ullingswick, Hereford HR1 3JG* Hereford (01432) 820385

PEARCE, Preb Dr Eustace Kenneth Victor. b 13. FRAI64 Univ Coll Lon BSc65 St Pet Coll Ox DipAnth64 Florida State Univ (USA) DEd91. ALCD37. **d** 37 **p** 38. R Bucknall and Bagnall *Lich* 59-71; CF (TA) 66-81; Preb Lich Cathl *Lich* 67-81; V Audley 71-81; rtd 81; Chief Exec Evidence for Truth Broadcasting Assn from 83; Perm to Offic *Ches* from 83; Perm to Offic *Lich* from 83; Perm to Offic *Chich* from 83. *15 Kinnersley Avenue, Kidsgrove, Stoke-on-Trent ST7 1AP, or 13 Lismore Road, Eastbourne, E Sussex BN21 3AY* Stoke-on-Trent (01782) 773325 or Eastbourne (01323) 725231 Fax Eastbourne (01323) 649240

PEARCE, Canon Frank. b 31. St Aid Birkenhead. **d** 57 **p** 58. R W Retford *S'well* 62-70; R Kettering SS Pet and Paul *Pet* 70-94; Chapl Kettering Gen and St Mary's Hosps 70-94; Can Pet Cathl *Pet* 78-94; rtd 94. *Sherwood Lodge, 36 Queen Eleanor Road, Geddington, Kettering, Northants NN14 1AY* Kettering (01536) 742334

PEARCE, Canon Gerald Nettleton. b 25. St Jo Coll Dur BA49 DipTh51. **d** 51 **p** 52. R Wilford *S'well* 61-73; RD Bingham 73-84; P-in-c Holme Pierrepont w Adbolton 73-84; V Radcliffe-on-Trent 73-84; V Shelford 73-84; Hon Can S'well Minster 77-84; R Sigglesthorne and Rise w Nunkeeling and Bewholme *York* 84-91; RD N Holderness 86-90; rtd 91; Dioc Rtd Clergy & Widows Officer from 91. *Sutherland Bridge, Cropton, Pickering, N Yorkshire YO18 8EU* Pickering (01751) 417420

PEARCE, Mrs Janet Elizabeth. b 49. Somerville Coll Ox BA72 MA76 CertEd74. N Ord Course 85. **d** 88 **p** 94. Hon Par Dn Helsby and Dunham-on-the-Hill *Ches* 88-91; Par Dn 91-94; C from 94. *4 Fieldway, Frodsham, Warrington WA6 6RQ* Frodsham (01928) 733553

PEARCE, Preb John Frederick Dilke. b 32. Ex Coll Ox BA55 MA59. Westcott Ho Cam. **d** 57 **p** 58. C Dalston St Mark w St Bart *Lon* 57-60; C Chelsea Ch Ch 60-63; R Lower Homerton St Paul 63-81; Preb St Paul's Cathl from 70; P-in-c Clapton Park All So 72-77; V 77-84; RD Hackney 74-79; R Homerton St Barn w St Paul 81-85; TR Hackney Marsh 85; P-in-c Upper Chelsea St Simon 85-89; AD Chelsea 88-89; R Limehouse from 89. *Limehouse Rectory, 5 Newell Street, London E14 7HP*   0171-987 1502

PEARCE, Jonathan. b 55. St Jo Coll Nottm BTh85. **d** 85 **p** 86. C Gt Chesham *Ox* 85-89; C Newport Pagnell w Lathbury and Moulsoe 89-93; TV Waltham H Cross *Chelmsf* from 93. *The Vicarage, Church Road, High Beach, Loughton, Essex IG10 4AJ*   0181-508 1791

PEARCE, Kenneth Jack. b 25. CIPFA. Linc Th Coll 62. **d** 63 **p** 64. V Derby St Mark *Derby* 68-87; rtd 87. *117 Oaks Cross, Stevenage, Herts SG2 8LT*   Stevenage (01438) 317385

PEARCE, Michael Hawkins. b 29. Sarum Th Coll 61. **d** 62 **p** 63. R Jacobstow w Warbstow *Truro* 68-74; V Treneglos 68-74; V St Teath 74-94; rtd 94. *32 Trenant Road, Tywardreath, Par, Cornwall PL24 1QJ*   Par (01726) 813658

PEARCE, Neville John Lewis. b 33. CBIM88 Leeds Univ LLB53 LLM54. Trin Coll Bris 90. **d** 91 **p** 92. NSM Bath Walcot *B & W* 91-93; P-in-c Swainswick w Langridge and Woolley 93; NSM Bath St Sav w Swainswick and Woolley from 93. *Penshurst, Weston Lane, Bath BA1 4AB*   Bath (01225) 426925

PEARCE, Reginald Frederic George. b 15. St Aug Coll Cant 38. **d** 40 **p** 41. V Laneast w St Clether *Truro* 68-76; V Tresmere 70-76; V Laneast w St Clether and Tresmere 76-78; P-in-c St Erth 78-80; rtd 80. *Braehead House, Auburn Road, Kenilworth, 7700 South Africa*   Cape Town (21) 797-1917

PEARCE, Robert John. b 47. GLCM LLCM72 Birm Univ PGCE73. Ripon Coll Cuddesdon 79. **d** 82 **p** 83. C Broseley w Benthall *Heref* 82-83; C Kington w Huntington, Old Radnor, Kinnerton etc 83-85; R Westbury 85-94; R Yockleton 85-94; V Gt Wollaston 85-94; V Gwersyllt *St As* from 94. *The Vicarage, Old Mold Road, Gwersyllt, Wrexham, Clwyd LL11 4SB*   Wrexham (01978) 756391

PEARCE, Ronald Edgar John. b 21. Univ of Wales (Lamp) BA42. Lich Th Coll 42. **d** 44 **p** 45. V Warmley *Bris* 61-68; R Syston 62-68; Chapl R Wolv Sch 68-86; rtd 86. *52 Cherrington Gardens, Bramstead Avenue, Compton, Wolverhampton WV6 8AJ*   Wolverhampton (01902) 756420

PEARCE, Stephen Wilson. b 34. K Coll Lon. **d** 62 **p** 63. C Chorley St Jas *Blackb* 62-64; C Sheff St Steph w St Phil and St Ann *Sheff* 64-66; C Warton St Oswald *Blackb* 66-69; V Skerton St Chad 69-77 and 78-80; Canada 77-78; C Fleetwood *Blackb* 80-81; TV Raveningham *Nor* 81-85; P-in-c Martin w Thornton *Linc* 85-92; P-in-c Scrivelsby w Dalderby 85-92; P-in-c Roughton w Haltham 85-92; P-in-c Kirkby-on-Bain 85-92; P-in-c Thimbleby 85-92; RD Horncastle from 89; R Thornton Gp from 92. *The Vicarage, Main Road, Thornton, Horncastle, Lincs LN9 5JU*   Horncastle (01507) 526456

PEARCE, Trevor John. b 27. FSR57. Roch Th Coll 65. **d** 67 **p** 68. C Willesborough w Hinxhill *Cant* 69-73; V Devonport St Barn *Ex* 73-79; Chapl n Devon Distr Hosp Barnstaple 79-83; V Derby St Andr w St Osmund *Derby* 83-84; Chapl Derbyshire R Infirmary 83-92; Lic to Offic *Derby* from 84; rtd 92. *4 Morrell Wood Drive, Westfields, Belper, Derbyshire DE56 0JD*   Belper (01773) 828450

PEARCEY, Paul Alan Cyril. b 37. St Jo Coll Dur BA59. Cranmer Hall Dur DipTh61. **d** 61 **p** 62. C Deane *Man* 61-65; Chapl Red Bank Schs 65-67; C-in-c Blackley White Moss St Mark CD *Man* 67-73; R Cwmbach Llechryd and Llanelwedd w Llanafaredd *S & B* 73-79; V Llanelwedd w Llanfaredd w Llansantffraed etc from 79; RD Builth from 84. *The Rectory, Llanelwedd, Builth Wells, Powys LD2 3TY*   Builth Wells (01982) 553701

PEARCY, Vernon Charles. b 23. K Coll Lon BD56 AKC56. **d** 56 **p** 57. C Belmont *S'wark* 68-70; C Wimbledon 70-76; C S w N Hayling *Portsm* 76-77; R Warbleton and Bodle Street Green *Chich* 78-83; C Cleethorpes *Linc* 83-86; rtd 86. *20 Springfield Crescent, Poole, Dorset BH14 0LL*   Poole (01202) 743782

PEARE, Canon Oliver Arthur Patrick. b 17. TCD BA43 MA55. CITC 46. **d** 46 **p** 47. I Kinsale Union *C, C & R* 66-87; Treas Cork Cathl 84-87; Preb Tymothan St Patr Cathl Dub 84-87; rtd 87. *High Copse, Compass Hill, Kinsale, Co Cork, Irish Republic*   Cork (21) 774191

PEARKES, Nicholas Robin Clement. b 49. Ex Univ BA. Linc Th Coll. **d** 82 **p** 83. C Plymstock *Ex* 82-85; P-in-c Weston Mill 85-86; TV Devonport St Boniface and St Phil from 86. *The Vicarage, Bridwell Lane North, Plymouth PL5 1AN*   Plymouth (01752) 362060

PEARMAIN, Andrew Neil. b 55. K Coll Lon BD79 AKC79. Ridley Hall Cam 79. **d** 81 **p** 82. C Cranleigh *Guildf* 81-84; P-in-c Frimley 85-86; C 86-87; Chapl Frimley Park Hosp 87. *35 Cavendish Road, Bournemouth BH1 1QZ*   Bournemouth (01202) 553395

PEARMAIN, Canon Brian Albert John. b 34. Lon Univ BD68. Roch Th Coll 63. **d** 66 **p** 67. C Shirley St Jo *Cant* 66-69; C Selsdon St Jo w St Fran 69-73; P-in-c Louth H Trin *Linc* 73-75; TV Louth 75-79; R Scartho from 79; RD Grimsby and Cleethorpes 89-94; Hon Can Linc Cathl from 94. *44 Waltham Road, Grimsby, S Humberside DN33 2LX*   Grimsby (01472) 872728

PEARS, John Barbour. b 10. Sarum Th Coll 46. **d** 48 **p** 49. Chapl N Gen Hosp Sheff 56-73; Dioc Chapl *Sheff* 73-78; Lic to Offic 78-79; rtd 79; Hon C Sheff St Cuth *Sheff* 79-86. *Dulverton Hall, St Martin's Square, Scarborough, N Yorkshire YO11 2DB*   Scarborough (01723) 368225

PEARSE, Andrew George. b 46. Wycliffe Hall Ox 71. **d** 74 **p** 75. C Homerton St Luke *Lon* 74-77; C Chadderton Em *Man* 77-81; R Collyhurst 81-89; Area Sec (NE and E Midl) SAMS from 89. *9 Troutsdale Avenue, Rawcliffe, York YO3 6TR*   York (01904) 655881

PEARSE, Percy George Hedley. b 13. Univ Coll Dur LTh35 BA36 MA39. ALCD35. **d** 36 **p** 37. R Doddinghurst *Chelmsf* 59-72; R Stondon Massey 59-72; R Debden 72-77; RD Saffron Walden 74-78; rtd 78; Perm to Offic *Win* 78-92. *3 Chalfont Avenue, Christchurch, Dorset BH23 2SB*   Christchurch (01202) 482914

PEARSE, Ronald Thomas Hennessy. b 26. AKC52. **d** 53 **p** 54. R Asfordby *Leic* 58-84; P-in-c Scalford w Wycombe and Chadwell 75-76; R Thurcaston 84-89; rtd 89; Perm to Offic *Leic* from 89. *15 Burton Street, Loughborough, Leics LE11 2DT*   Loughborough (01509) 215478

PEARSON, Andrew George Campbell. b 41. Qu Coll Ox BA63 BA66. Wycliffe Hall Ox 63. **d** 71 **p** 72. C Gillingham St Mark *Roch* 71-72; C Billingshurst *Chich* 72-77; C Ches Square St Mich w St Phil *Lon* 77-82; Co-ord Busoga Trust from 82; P-in-c St Marg Pattens *Lon* from 90. *15 Chadwin Road, London E13 8ND, or 2 Elizabeth Street, London SW1W 9RB*   0171-476 6730 or 623 6630

PEARSON, Andrew John. b 59. Humberside Coll of Educn HND83. Westcott Ho Cam 86. **d** 89 **p** 90. C Knaresborough *Ripon* 89-92; C Wetherby 92-94; P-in-c Hunslet Moor St Pet and St Cuth from 94. *St Peter's Vicarage, 139 Dewsbury Road, Leeds LS11 5NW*   Leeds (0113) 277 2464

PEARSON, Brian. b 29. LTCL53 Lon Inst of Educn CertEd54. Sarum & Wells Th Coll 71. **d** 73 **p** 74. C Rainham *Roch* 73-77; Chapl Asst Pembury Hosp Tunbridge Wells 77-80; C Pembury *Roch* 77-80; V Gravesend St Aid from 80; Chapl Gravesend and N Kent Hosp 81-83. *The Vicarage, St Gregory's Crescent, Gravesend, Kent DA12 4JL*   Gravesend (01474) 352500

PEARSON, Canon Brian Robert. b 35. Leeds Univ BA59. Coll of Resurr Mirfield 59. **d** 61 **p** 62. C Chesterfield All SS *Derby* 61-66; P-in-c Derby St Jo 66-72; P-in-c Derby St Anne 66-72; R Thorpe *Nor* 72-90; Hon Can Nor Cathl 85-90; RD Nor E 86-90; V Harrogate St Wilfrid and St Luke *Ripon* from 90. *St Wilfrid's Vicarage, 51B Kent Road, Harrogate, N Yorkshire HG1 2EU*   Harrogate (01423) 503259

PEARSON, Canon Brian William. b 49. CEng MBCS FHSM Brighton Poly BSc71 City Univ MSc80. S'wark Ord Course and Clapham Ord Scheme 76. **d** 79 **p** 80. Hon C Plumstead All SS *S'wark* 79-81; Perm to Offic *Chich* 81-83; Hon C Broadwater St Mary 83-88; Bp's Research and Dioc Communications Officer *B & W* 88-90; Dioc Missr 91; Abp's Officer for Miss and Evang and Tait Missr *Cant* from 91; Abp's Dioc Chapl from 91; Hon Can Cant Cathl from 92. *20 Pilgrim's Way, Canterbury, Kent CT1 1XU, or Lambeth Palace, London SE1 7JU*   Canterbury (01227) 459781 or 459401 or 0171-928 8282   Fax 762703 or 0171-261 9836

PEARSON, Christian David John (Brother Christian). b 42. Open Univ BA76 CCC Cam BA79 MA83. AKC65. **d** 66 **p** 67. C Pallion *Dur* 66-68; C Peterlee 68-71; SSF from 71; Lic to Offic *Sarum* 71-73; Tanzania 74-75; Lic to Offic *Ely* 75-90; Asst Chapl Keble Coll Ox 82-83; Chapl St Cath Coll Cam 83-86; Chapl Down Coll Cam 86-90; Lic to Offic *Lon* from 90; Dep Warden and Chapl Lon Ho Trust 90-93; Dep Warden and Chapl Lon Goodenough Trust from 93. *William Goodenough House, Mecklenburgh Square, London WC1N 2AN*   0171-837 8888

PEARSON, Christopher Ian. b 65. Coll of Resurr Mirfield CPS93. **d** 93 **p** 94. C Newington St Mary *S'wark* 93-95; C Streatham St Pet from 95. *21 Ivymount Road, London SE27 0NB*   0181-766 7508

PEARSON, Christopher John. b 49. GRSM LRAM ARCM. Oak Hill NSM Course 81. **d** 84 **p** 85. NSM Barton Seagrave w Warkton *Pet* 84-86; C Kettering St Andr 86-88; V Nassington w Yarwell and Woodnewton 88-91; V Pet St Mark from 91. *St Mark's Vicarage, 82 Lincoln Road, Peterborough PE1 2SN*   Peterborough (01733) 54516

PEARSON, David. b 57. Man Poly BA78. Trin Coll Bris 85. **d** 88 **p** 89. C Shawbury *Lich* 88-91; C Morton 88-91; C Stanton on Hine Heath 88-91; R Mattishall w Mattishall Burgh,

PEARSON, Welborne etc *Nor* from 91. *The Vicarage, Back Lane, Mattishall, Dereham, Norfolk NR20 3PU* Dereham (01362) 850243

PEARSON, Edgar. b 13. Tyndale Hall Bris 37. **d** 41 **p** 42. C Handforth *Ches* 41; R Dallinghoo and Pettistree *St E* 65-83; P-in-c Bredfield w Boulge 74-86; rtd 83; P-in-c Dallinghoo and Pettistree *St E* 83-86. *Maendy House, Penrhos, Raglan, Gwent NP5 2LQ* Llantilio (0160085) 398

PEARSON, Fergus Tom. b 58. Middx Poly BA81. Oak Hill Th Coll DipHE92. **d** 92 **p** 93. C Mildmay Grove St Jude and St Paul *Lon* from 92. *94 Mildmay Grove, London N1 4PJ* 0171-249 6233

PEARSON, Geoffrey Charles (Geoff). b 49. ARCS BSc. Oak Hill Th Coll. **d** 82 **p** 83. C Foord St Jo *Cant* 82-86; V Ramsgate St Luke 86-93; Chapl to People at Work in Cam *Ely* from 93. *31 Thornton Close, Girton, Cambridge CB3 0NF* Cambridge (01223) 276657

PEARSON, Geoffrey Seagrave. b 51. St Jo Coll Dur BA72 DipTh73. Cranmer Hall Dur 72. **d** 74 **p** 75. C Kirkheaton *Wakef* 74-77; C-in-c Blackb Redeemer *Blackb* 77-82; V 82-85; Asst Home Sec Gen Syn Bd for Miss and Unity 85-89; Hon C Forty Hill Jes Ch *Lon* 85-89; Exec Sec BCC Evang Cttee 86-89; V Roby *Liv* from 89. *The Vicarage, 11 Church Road, Liverpool L36 9TL* 0151-489 1438

PEARSON, George Michael. b 31. FCA FBCS MIMC. Coll of Resurr Mirfield 89 Qu Coll Birm 86. **d** 88 **p** 90. NSM Solihull *Birm* from 88. *The Parsonage, 67A Hampton Lane, Solihull, W Midlands B91 2QD* 0121-705 0288

PEARSON, Harold (Brother Geoffrey). b 21. Ch Coll Cam BA43 MA46. Chich Th Coll 43. **d** 45 **p** 46. SSF from 48; Papua New Guinea 59-70; Min Gen SSF 70-85; Australia 67-70; Hon Can Win Cathl *Win* 81-86; Zimbabwe from 86; rtd 91. *St Augustine's Mission, PO Penhalonga, Zimbabwe*

PEARSON, Harry MacGregor. b 02. MICE ACGI Lon Univ BSc. **d** 64 **p** 65. C Canvey Is *Chelmsf* 64-69; P-in-c Overbury w Alstone, Teddington and Lt Washbourne *Worc* 69-71; rtd 71; Perm to Offic *St As* from 71; Perm to Offic *Lich* from 81. *17 Park Drive, Oswestry, Shropshire SY11 1BN* Oswestry (01691) 655783

PEARSON, Henry Gervis. b 47. Mansf Coll Ox BA72 MA76. St Jo Coll Nottm 72. **d** 74 **p** 75. C Southgate *Chich* 74-76; TV 76-82; V Debenham w Aspall and Kenton *St E* 82-91; Chapl to Suffolk Fire Service 88-91; RD Loes 89-91; TR Marlborough *Sarum* from 91; Chapl Savernake Hosp Marlborough from 91; RD Marlborough from 94. *The Rectory, 1 Rawlingswell Lane, Marlborough, Wilts SN8 1AU* Marlborough (01672) 512357

PEARSON, Ian. b 49. Liv Univ BA71 DAA72. S'wark Ord Course 79. **d** 82 **p** 83. Hon C Lavender Hill Ascension *S'wark* 82-84; Archivist USPG 82-85; Archivist Nat Soc 85-91; Lic to Offic *Lon* 84-86 and 88-90; Hon C Westmr St Matt 86-88; Perm to Offic *S'wark* 85-90; Perm to Offic *St Alb* 90-91; C Chesterfield All SS *Derby* 91-95; R Bengeo *St Alb* from 95. *The Rectory, Byde Street, Hertford SG14 3BS* Hertford (01992) 584537

PEARSON, Canon James Stuart. b 28. St Jo Coll Dur BA57. Cranmer Hall Dur 57. **d** 58 **p** 59. C Alverthorpe *Wakef* 63-70; V Knottingley 70-78; Dioc Soc Resp Adv 78-87; V Woolley 78-94; Chapl Bretton Hall Coll of Educn 87-94; Hon Can Wakef Cathl 89-94; RD Chevet 93-94; rtd 94. *21 Orrin Close, York YO2 2RA* York (01904)708521

PEARSON, James William (Jim). b 20. FCA59. Qu Coll Birm 75. **d** 78 **p** 79. NSM Beoley *Worc* 78-90; Perm to Offic from 90. *Ringwood, Rowney Green, Alvechurch, Birmingham B48 7QE* Redditch (01527) 66952

PEARSON, John Nigel. b 45. CA Tr Coll IDC75 E Midl Min Tr Course 78. **d** 81 **p** 82. C Stapenhill w Cauldwell *Derby* 81-83; V Measham *Leic* from 83. *The Vicarage, High Street, Measham, Swadlincote, Derbyshire DE12 7HZ* Measham (01530) 270354

PEARSON, Kevin. b 54. Leeds Univ BA75 Edin Univ BD79. Edin Th Coll 76. **d** 79 **p** 80. C Horden *Dur* 79-81; Chapl Leeds Univ *Ripon* 81-87; R Edin St Salvador *Edin* 87-93; Chapl Napier Poly 88-92; Chapl Napier Univ 92-94; Dioc Dir of Ords 90-95; Prov Dir of Ords from 91; Assoc R Edin Old St Paul 93-94; P-in-c Linlithgow 94-95; R Edin St Mich and All SS from 95. *7 Ainslie Place, Edinburgh EH3 6AS* 0131-225 6198

PEARSON, Mrs Lindsey Carole. b 61. Cov Poly BA85 CQSW85. Westcott Ho Cam 86. **d** 89 **p** 94. Par Dn High Harrogate St Pet *Ripon* 89-93; Par Dn Moor Allerton 93-94; C from 94. *St Peter's Vicarage, 139 Dewsbury Road, Leeds LS11 5NW* Leeds (0113) 277 2464

PEARSON, Michael John. b 53. Southn Univ BTh78. Sarum Th Coll 74. **d** 78 **p** 79. C Paignton St Jo *Ex* 78-82; TV Ilfracombe, Lee, W Down, Woolacombe and Bittadon 82-85; TV Ilfracombe, Lee, Woolacombe, and Bittadon etc 85-86; TV Barnstaple from 86; Chapl N Devon Distr Hosp Barnstaple from 86. *The Rectory, Sowden Lane, Barnstaple, Devon EX32 8BU* Barnstaple (01271) 73837

PEARSON, Peter. b 09. Tyndale Hall Bris 32. **d** 35 **p** 36. V Fremington *Ex* 45-74; rtd 75; P-in-c Nymet Rowland w Coldridge *Ex* 75-77; P-in-c Chawleigh w Cheldon 77-78; Lic to Offic from 78. *41 Barum Court, Litchdon Street, Barnstaple, Devon EX32 8QL* Barnstaple (01271) 73525

PEARSON, Mrs Priscilla Dawn. b 45. Oak Hill Th Coll BA90. **d** 90 **p** 94. Par Dn Stanford-le-Hope w Mucking *Chelmsf* 90-94; C 94; C Colchester St Jo from 94. *3 Northfield Gardens, Colchester CO4 4TL*

PEARSON, Raymond Joseph. b 44. AKC71. St Aug Coll Cant 71. **d** 72 **p** 73. C Wetherby *Ripon* 72-75; C Goring-by-Sea *Chich* 75-77; C Bramley *Ripon* 77-82; V Patrick Brompton and Hunton 82-94; V Crakehall 82-94; V Hornby 82-94; World Miss Officer from 88; RD Wensley 92-94; V Bardsey from 94. *The Vicarage, Wood Acre Lane, Bardsey, Leeds LS17 9DG* Collingham Bridge (01937) 572243

PEARSON, Robert James Stephen. b 52. Cov Poly BA74. St Steph Ho Ox 85. **d** 87 **p** 88. C Stoke Newington St Mary *Lon* 87-90; C Haggerston All SS from 90. *All Saint's Vicarage, Livermere Road, London E8 4EZ* 0171-254 0436

PEARSON, Robert Lyon (Bob). b 57. St Jo Coll Nottm DCM92. **d** 92 **p** 93. C Netherton *Liv* from 92. *57 Park Lane West, Bootle, Merseyside L30 1QA* 0151-521 5977

PEARSON, Roderick Percy. b 21. Linc Th Coll 74. **d** 75 **p** 76. C Darlington St Cuth w St Hilda *Dur* 75-80; V Bishop Middleham 80-91; rtd 91. *The Lever Flat, Christ's Hospital in Sherburn, Sherburn House, Durham DH1 2SE* 0191-372 1753

PEARSON, Roy Barthram. b 35. K Coll Lon 56. **d** 60 **p** 61. C Brookfield St Mary *Lon* 60-64; C St Marylebone St Cypr 64-70; V Tottenham All Hallows from 70; AD E Haringey from 95. *The Priory, Church Lane, London N17 7AA* 0181-808 2470

PEARSON, Stephen. **d** 43 **p** 44. P-in-c Clapton *Pet* 69-77; R Luddington w Hemington and Thurning 69-77; rtd 77. *Address achieved by request*

PEARSON-MILES, David. b 37. St Jo Coll Nottm 74. **d** 76 **p** 77. C Hazlemere *Ox* 76-79; R Waddesdon w Over Winchendon and Fleet Marston 79-82; CF 82-92; P-in-c Barcombe *Chich* 92-94; R from 94. *The Rectory, The Grange, Barcombe, Lewes, E Sussex BN8 5AT* Barcombe (01273) 400260

PEART, John Graham. b 36. Bps' Coll Cheshunt 65. **d** 68 **p** 69. C Cheshunt *St Alb* 68-70; C St Alb St Pet 70-73; R Hunsdon 73-76; R Widford 73-76; Ind Chapl 76-82; Chapl St Geo Hosp and Distr Gen Hosp Stafford 82-87; Qu Eliz Hosp and Bensham Hosp Gateshead 87-89; Garlands Hosp 89-94; P-in-c Cotehill and Cumwhinton *Carl* 89-94; V Irthington, Crosby-on-Eden and Scaleby from 94. *The New Vicarage, Irthington, Carlisle CA6 4NJ* Brampton (016977) 2379

PEASE, John Alfred. b 29. St Aid Birkenhead 58. **d** 60 **p** 61. C Bolton-upon-Dearne *Sheff* 65-70; V S Kirkby *Wakef* 70-81; V Bovey Tracey St Jo *Ex* 81-84; RD Moreton 83-86; P-in-c Chudleigh Knighton 83-84; V Bovey Tracey St John, Chudleigh Knighton etc 84-94; rtd 94. *220 Barton Hill Road, Barton, Torquay TQ2 8LX* Torquay (01803) 329073

PEASTON, Canon Monroe. b 14. BNC Ox BA36 MA43 Lon Univ BD48. Union Th Sem (NY) PhD64 Montreal Dioc Th Coll Hon DD75 Wycliffe Hall Ox 36. **d** 38 **p** 39. Canada 64-84; Hon Can Montreal from 66; rtd 84; USA from 84. *Address temp unknown*

PEAT, David James. b 62. Leeds Univ BA84. Cranmer Hall Dur 86. **d** 89 **p** 90. C Wetherby *Ripon* 89-92; C Beeston from 92. *St David's House, Waincliffe Drive, Leeds LS11 8ET* Leeds (0113) 270 2829

PEAT, Dr David William. b 37. Clare Coll Cam BA59 PhD63. Westcott Ho Cam 72. **d** 75 **p** 76. C Chesterton St Andr *Ely* 75-77; Chapl Univ Coll of Ripon & York St Jo 77-83; V E Ardsley *Wakef* 83-87; Prin Willesden Min Tr Scheme 87-94; NSM Headingley *Ripon* from 94; Research Lect Leeds Univ from 94. *12 North Grange Mews, Headingley, Leeds LS6 2EW* Leeds (0113) 275 3179

PEAT, Ven Lawrence Joseph (Lawrie). b 28. Linc Th Coll 55. **d** 58 **p** 59. C Bramley *Ripon* 58-61; V 65-73; R Heaton Norris All SS *Man* 61-65; P-in-c Southend St Erkenwald *Chelmsf* 73-74; TR Southend St Jo w St Mark, All SS w St Fran etc 74-79; R Skelsmergh w Selside and Longsleddale *Carl* 79-86; RD Kendal 84-89; TV Kirkby Lonsdale 86-89; Hon Can Carl Cathl from 88; Adn Westmorland and Furness from 89. *Woodcroft, Levens, Kendal, Cumbria LA8 8NQ* Sedgwick (015395) 61281 Fax 61217

PEATFIELD, Canon Alfred Charles Henry. b 22. New Coll Ox BA48 MA48. Ripon Hall Ox 48. **d** 51 **p** 52. Malaysia 63-70; Adn N Malaya 64-70; V Hornchurch St Andr *Chelmsf* 70-92; RD Havering 76-80; Hon Can Chelmsf Cathl 80-92; rtd 92. *10 Tyne Close, Upminster, Essex RM14 1QB* Upminster (01708) 220598

PEATMAN (nee HUGHES), Mrs Debbie Ann. b 62. SS Hild & Bede Coll Dur BA83 St Jo Coll Dur BA89. Cranmer Hall Dur 87. **d** 90 **p** 94. C Edin Old St Paul *Edin* 90-91; NSM Greasley *S'well* 92-94; NSM Whitley *Cov* from 94. *St James's Vicarage, 171 Abbey Road, Coventry CV3 4BG* Coventry (01203) 301617

PEATMAN, Michael Robert. b 61. Keble Coll Ox BA85 MA89 St Jo Coll Dur BA89. Cranmer Hall Dur 87. **d** 90 **p** 91. C Greasley *S'well* 90-94; P-in-c Whitley *Cov* from 94; Dio Stewardship Adv from 94. *St James's Vicarage, 171 Abbey Road, Coventry CV3 4BG* Coventry (01203) 301617

PECK, David George. b 11. Jes Coll Cam BA32 MA48 Linc Coll Ox MA51. St Steph Ho Ox 32. **d** 34 **p** 35. R Shellingford *Ox* 63-83; rtd 83. *The Barn House, Chapel Road, Stanford in the Vale, Faringdon, Oxon SN7 8LE* Stanford in the Vale (01367) 710511

PECK, David Warner. b 66. BA88 Selw Coll Cam BA94. Westcott Ho Cam CTM95. **d** 95. C Weybridge *Guildf* from 95. *St James's Church Hall, Church Street, Weybridge, Surrey KT13 3DE* Weybridge (01932) 846398

PECK, Trevor Paul Owen. b 47. Lich Th Coll 69. **d** 72 **p** 73. C Hatf *Sheff* 72-74; C Swinton 75-77; TV Gt Grimsby St Mary and St Jas *Linc* 77-81; P-in-c Glentworth 81-86; P-in-c Hemswell w Harpswell 81-86; V Burgh le Marsh 86-87; R Bratoft w Irby-in-the-Marsh 86-87. *Address temp unknown*

PECK, William Gerard. b 18. AKC40. Lich Th Coll 40. **d** 41 **p** 42. Hon CF from 49; R Fornham All SS *St E* 63-82; rtd 83; Perm to Offic *St E* from 83. *14 Suffolk Place, Woodbridge, Suffolk IP12 1XB* Woodbridge (01394) 386479

PECKETT, Desmonde Claude Brown. b 19. Ex & Truro NSM Scheme. **d** 77 **p** 78. NSM Charlestown *Truro* from 77. *Smugglers, Porthpean, St Austell, Cornwall PL26 6AY* St Austell (01726) 72768

PECKETT, John Freeman. b 20. Clifton Th Coll. **d** 74 **p** 76. Kenya 74-77; Hon C Harringay St Paul *Lon* 77-79; Hon C Palmers Green St Jo 80-85; rtd 85. *30A Finchley Road, Westcliff-on-Sea, Essex SS0 8AF* Southend-on-Sea (01702) 433644

PECKHAM, Richard Graham. b 51. Sarum & Wells Th Coll 84. **d** 86 **p** 87. C Bishop's Cleeve *Glouc* 86-89; TV Ilfracombe, Lee, Woolacombe, Bittadon etc *Ex* from 89. *The Vicarage, Springhill, Woolacombe, Devon EX34 7BX* Woolacombe (01271) 870467

PEDDER, Brian. b 38. Carl Dioc Tr Inst 88. **d** 91 **p** 92. NSM Wigton *Carl* 91-93; C Cleator Moor w Cleator from 93. *20 John Colligan Drive, Cleator Moor, Cumbria CA25 5JX* Cleator Moor (01946) 815784

PEDLAR, John Glanville. b 43. Ex Univ BA68. St Steph Ho Ox 68. **d** 70 **p** 71. C Tavistock and Gulworthy *Ex* 70-73; Prec Portsm Cathl *Portsm* 74-77; Prec St Alb Abbey *St Alb* 77-81; V Redbourn from 81; PV Westmr Abbey from 87. *The Vicarage, Church End, Redbourn, St Albans, Herts AL3 7DU* Redbourn (01582) 793122

PEDLEY, Miss Betty. b 49. ALCM78 Leeds Univ BEd71 Ripon Coll of Educn CertEd70 Coll of Preceptors DSpEd81. N Ord Course 85. **d** 88. Par Dn Sowerby *Wakef* 88-92; Par Educn Adv from 92; Youth Chapl from 92. *27 Pye Nest Grove, Halifax, W Yorkshire HX2 7JY* Halifax (01422) 346007

PEDLEY, Canon Geoffrey Stephen. b 40. Qu Coll Cam BA64 MA67. Cuddesdon Coll 64. **d** 66 **p** 67. C Liv Our Lady and St Nic *Liv* 66-69; C Cov H Trin *Cov* 69-71; Zambia 71-77; P-in-c Stockton H Trin *Dur* 77-83; V Stockton St Pet 77-88; Chapl to The Queen from 84; R Whickham *Dur* 88-93; Can Res Dur Cathl from 93. *6A The College, Durham DH1 3EQ* 0191-384 5489

PEDLEY, Nicholas Charles (Nick). b 48. DipSocWork75 CQSW75. Qu Coll Birm 88. **d** 90 **p** 91. C Stafford St Jo and Tixall w Ingestre *Lich* 90-93; C Kingswinford St Mary 93; C Kingswinford St Mary *Worc* from 93. *28 Foundry Road, Kingswinford, W Midlands DY6 9BD* Kingswinford (01384) 273961

PEDLOW, Henry Noel. b 37. QUB BA59. **d** 61 **p** 62. C Belf St Phil *Conn* 61-66; C Belf St Nic 66-70; I Eglantine 70-82; I Kilkeel *D & D* 82-89; I Belf St Donard from 89. *St Donard's Rectory, 421 Beersbridge Road, Belfast BT5 5DU* Belfast (01232) 652321

PEEBLES, Alexander Paterson. b 21. Westcott Ho Cam 62. **d** 63 **p** 64. P-in-c Grendon Underwood w Edgcott *Ox* 67-73; P-in-c Twyford (Bucks) 67-73; P-in-c Marsh Gibbon 67-73; P-in-c Preston Bissett, Chetwode and Barton Hartshorn 67-73; RD Claydon 71-73; R Glenrothes *St And* 73-81; Can St Ninian's Cathl Perth 78-82; Dioc Supernumerary 81-82; P-in-c Bathgate *Edin* 82-87; P-in-c Linlithgow 82-87; rtd 86; NSM Newburgh *St And* from 88. *The Studio, 5 Hillside Place, Newport-on-Tay, Fife DD6 8DH* Newport-on-Tay (01382) 542530

PEEBLES, David Thomas. b 64. Bris Univ BA85 Dur Univ PGCE86. Coll of Resurr Mirfield 88. **d** 90 **p** 91. C Crewe St

Andr *Ches* 90-93; Lect and Asst Dir Studies Mirfield 93-95; Chapl Qu Mary Coll *Lon* from 95; Chapl Westf Coll from 95. *24 Sidney Square, London E1 2EY* 0171-791 1971 or 980 1204

PEEK, John Richard. b 51. Bris Univ BSc72 Nottm Univ BA75. St Jo Coll Nottm DPS76. **d** 76 **p** 77. C Hebburn St Jo *Dur* 76-78; C Dunston 78-81; R Armthorpe *Sheff* 81-86; RE Teacher K Edw VI Sch Southn 87-88; Chapl and Hd RE Casterton Sch Cumbria 89; Teacher Furze Platt Comp Sch Berks 89-90; Perm to Offic *Portsm* from 90. *St Lawrence House, 59 Albert Street, Ventnor, Isle of Wight PO38 1EU* Isle of Wight (01983) 853328

PEEK, Roland Denys. b 17. Sarum Th Coll 69. **d** 70 **p** 71. C Ex St Matt *Ex* 70-74; R Moretonhampstead 74-78; R Moretonhampstead, N Bovey and Manaton 78-84; rtd 84. *6 The Oaks, St Mary's Park, Bovey Tracey, Newton Abbott, Devon TQ13 9XQ* Newton Abbott (01626) 834565

PEEL, Basil Headley. b 26. TCD BA52 MA55. Wells Th Coll 52. **d** 54 **p** 55. V Willenhall H Trin *Lich* 68-79; V Longsdon 79-92; P-in-c Rushton 84-92; P-in-c Horton 84-92; rtd 92. *Tyn-y-ddol, Penybontfawr, Oswestry, Shropshire SY10 0PB* Pennant (0169174) 551

PEEL, Mrs Christine Mary (Chris). CertEd. Portsm Dioc Tr Course. **d** 90. NSM Sheet *Portsm* from 90. *7 Crundles, Herne Farm, Petersfield, Hants GU31 4PJ* Petersfield (01730) 266926

PEEL, David Charles. b 41. AKC75. St Aug Coll Cant 75. **d** 76 **p** 77. C Tynemouth Cullercoats St Paul *Newc* 76-79; C Tynemouth St Jo 79-84; Ldr Cedarwood Project 84-88 and from 91; Warden Communicare Ho 89-91; Min Killingworth 89-91. *3 Elmfield Grove, Gosforth, Newcastle upon Tyne NE3 4XA* 0191-285 1484

PEEL, Derek. b 46. Chich Th Coll 69. **d** 72 **p** 73. C Ealing St Pet Mt Park *Lon* 72-74; C Westmr St Matt 75-79; V Bournemouth St Fran *Win* 79-82; R Lon Docks St Pet w Wapping St Jo *Lon* from 82. *St Peter's Clergy House, Wapping Lane, London E1 9RW* 0171-481 2985

PEEL, Derrick. b 50. Open Univ BA82. Linc Th Coll 75. **d** 78 **p** 79. C Otley *Bradf* 78-82; V Shelf 82-94; P-in-c Buttershaw St Aid 89-94; TR Shelf St Mich w Buttershaw St Aid from 94. *The Vicarage, 80 Carr House Road, Shelf, Halifax, W Yorkshire HX3 7RJ* Bradford (01274) 677413

PEEL, John Bruce. b 30. TCD BA54 MA68. Wells Th Coll 69. **d** 70 **p** 71. C Wilmslow *Ches* 70-75; V Weston 75-83; V Henbury from 83; Chapl Parkside Hosp Ches from 83. *The Vicarage, Henbury, Macclesfield, Cheshire SK11 9NN* Macclesfield (01625) 424113

PEEL, Dr Michael Jerome. b 31. Bris Univ BA55 MLitt73 St Cath Soc Ox DipTh59 Man Univ BD65 K Coll Lon PhD88. Wycliffe Hall Ox 57. **d** 59 **p** 60. C Stretford St Matt *Man* 59-61; C Chorlton upon Medlock 61-62; Chapl Man Univ 61-62; C Chorlton-cum-Hardy St Clem 62-65; V Chirbury *Heref* 65-68; P-in-c Marton 65-68; R Iver Heath *Ox* 68-87; V Linslade from 87. *The Vicarage, Vicarage Road, Linslade, Leighton Buzzard, Beds LU7 7LP* Leighton Buzzard (01525) 372149

PEELING, Mrs Pamela Mary Alberta. b 44. Oak Hill Th Coll 83. **dss** 86 **d** 87 **p** 94. Moulsham St Luke *Chelmsf* 86-87; Hon Par Dn 87-88; NSM N Springfield from 88. *129 Waterhouse Lane, Chelmsford CM1 2RY* Chelmsford (01245) 259285

PEERS, John Edward. b 39. Bps' Coll Cheshunt 60. **d** 63 **p** 64. C Crayford *Roch* 63-67; C Beckenham St Jas 67-69; C Winlaton *Dur* 69-72; P-in-c Silksworth 72-81; R Lt Bowden St Nic *Leic* 81-86; P-in-c Lt Bowden St Hugh 83-86; RD Gartree I (Harborough) 84-88; R Market Harborough Transfiguration 86-88; V Skipton Ch Ch *Bradf* from 88. *Christ Church Vicarage, Carleton Road, Skipton, N Yorkshire BD23 2BE* Skipton (01756) 793612

PEERS, Michael John. b 65. SS Paul & Mary Coll Cheltenham BA86. Ripon Coll Cuddesdon 88. **d** 91 **p** 92. C Birstall and Wanlip *Leic* 91-94; C Leic St Marg and All SS from 94. *St Margaret's Vicarage, 46 Brading Road, Leicester LE3 9BG* Leicester (0116) 262 7362

PEERS, Richard Charles. b 65. K Alfred's Coll Win BEd88. Chich Th Coll BTh93. **d** 93 **p** 94. C Grangetown *York* 93-95; C Portsea St Mary *Portsm* from 95. *2 Glebe Flats, Wutfield Place, Portsmouth PO1 4JF*

PEET, Derek Edwin. b 26. Sheff Univ BA51 DipEd Lon Univ DipTh57. Qu Coll Birm 66. **d** 67 **p** 68. C Hebden Bridge *Wakef* 67-70; V Darton 70-79; TR Gleadless Valley *Sheff* 79-85; V Kirk Hallam *Derby* from 85. *The Vicarage, 71 Ladywood Road, Ilkeston, Derbyshire DE7 4NF* Nottingham (0115) 932 2402

PEET, John Michael. b 44. AKC67. **d** 68 **p** 72. C Battersea St Pet *S'wark* 68-69; C Sutton St Nic 69-74; C Perry Hill St Geo 74-78; TV Stepney St Dunstan and All SS *Lon* 78-81; P-in-c Stamford Hill St Bart 81-86; V 87-89; P-in-c Mile End Old

Town H Trin 89-90; P-in-c Bromley All Hallows 89-90; TR Bow H Trin and All Hallows from 90. *Holy Trinity Vicarage, 28 Coborn Street, London E3 2AB* 0181-980 2074

PEET, John Christopher. b 56. Or Coll Ox BA80 MA83 Clare Coll Cam BA82 MA87. Ridley Hall Cam 80. **d** 83 **p** 84. C Menston w Woodhead *Bradf* 83-86; C Prenton *Ches* 86-89; V Harden and Wilsden *Bradf* from 89. *The Vicarage, Wilsden Old Road, Harden, Bingley, W Yorkshire BD16 1JD* Cullingworth (01535) 272344

PEGG, Brian Peter Richard (Bill). b 30. Sarum & Wells Th Coll 82. **d** 83 **p** 84. C Furze Platt *Ox* 83-85; V Ashbury, Compton Beauchamp and Longcot w Fernham 85-94; Chapl Malaga *Eur* from 94. *Paseo de Reding 21-2D, 29016 Malaga, Spain* Malaga (52) 219396

PEGG, Gerald Francis. b 37. FCII69 Birkb Coll Lon DipRS91. S'wark Ord Course 88. **d** 91 **p** 92. NSM Belmont *S'wark* 91-95; NSM Winchelsea and Icklesham *Chich* from 95. *Pilgrim's End, Manor Close, Icklesham, Winchelsea, E Sussex TN36 4BT* Hastings (01424) 814735

PEGLER, Frederic Arthur. b 19. Selw Coll Cam BA46 MA48. Qu Coll Birm 46. **d** 47 **p** 48. Canada 63-84; rtd 84; Perm to Offic *St Alb* 84-85. *206-1149 Rockland Avenue, Victoria, British Columbia, Canada, V8V 4T5*

PEIRCE, John. b 35. Worc Coll Ox BA59 MA64. Wycliffe Hall Ox 59. **d** 61 **p** 62. V Sturminster Newton and Hinton St Mary *Sarum* 68-74; V Kingswood *Bris* 74-79; Dir Coun Chr Care *Ex* 79-89; Public Preacher 89-92; NSM Hackney *Lon* 90-94; NSM St Botolph Aldgate w H Trin Minories 94-95; Co-ord Ch Action on Disability 90-95; Perm to Offic *Ex* from 92; rtd 95. *Rushford Forge, Narrowbridge, Chagford, Newton Abbot, Devon TQ13 8DA* Chagford (01647) 433650

PEIRCE, Canon John Martin. b 36. Jes Coll Cam BA59 MA65. Westcott Ho Cam 65. **d** 66 **p** 67. C Croydon *Cant* 66-70; C Fareham H Trin *Portsm* 70-71; TV 71-76; TR Langley Marish *Ox* 76-85; RD Burnham 78-82; Dir of Ords from 85; Dir of Post-Ord Tr from 85; Can Res Ch Ch from 87. *70 Yarnells Hill, Oxford OX2 9BG* Oxford (01865) 721330

PELHAM, John. b 36. New Coll Ox BA61 MA65. **d** 79 **p** 80. NSM Balerno *Edin* 79-91; Hon C W Linton from 91; Hon C Penicuik from 91. *2 Horsburgh Bank, Balerno, Midlothian EH14 7DA* 0131-449 3934

PELL, Charles Andrew. b 54. Leeds Univ CertEd77. Aston Tr Scheme 87 St Jo Coll Nottm 87. **d** 89 **p** 90. C Mottram in Longdendale w Woodhead *Ches* 89-90; C Handforth 90-93; P-in-c Walton Breck *Liv* 93-94; V from 94. *Holy Trinity Vicarage, Richmond Park, Liverpool L6 5AD* 0151-263 1538

PELLANT, Walter Reginald Guy. b 14. OBE79. AKC42. Cuddesdon Coll 42. **d** 43 **p** 44. Chapl RAF 48-69; Asst Chapl-in-Chief RAF 69-71; QHC from 70; Chapl Geneva *Eur* 71-80; rtd 80. *3 Fountain Court, 13 The Avenue, Poole, Dorset BH13 6EZ* Poole (01202) 768521

PELLEY, John Lawless. b 34. Oak Hill Th Coll 67. **d** 69 **p** 70. C Fareham St Jo *Portsm* 69-72; C Frogmore H Trin *St Alb* 72-76; V Standon from 76; RD Bishop's Stortford from 91. *The Vicarage, Kents Lane, Standon, Ware, Herts SG11 1PJ* Ware (01920) 821390

PELLY, Raymond Blake. b 38. Worc Coll Ox BA61 MA69 Geneva Univ DTh71. Linc Th Coll. **d** 63 **p** 64. C Gosforth All SS *Newc* 63-65. *28 Collingwood Street, Freeman's Bay, Auckland 1, New Zealand* Auckland (9) 764923

PELTON, Ian Simpson. b 30. Keble Coll Ox 50. Sarum Th Coll 55. **d** 57 **p** 58. V Coxhoe *Dur* 65-95; rtd 95. *49 Buckinghamshire Road, Belmont, Durham DH1 2AB* 0191-386 2273

PELTOR, Lawrence Frank. b 08. Keble Coll Ox BA33 MA37. Linc Th Coll 33. **d** 34 **p** 35. Hon CF from 45; R Willey w Barrow *Heref* 60-72; C Wybunbury *Ches* 72-73; rtd 73; Perm to Offic *Heref* from 73. *5 Cliff Gardens, Cliff Road, Bridgnorth, Shropshire WV16 4EZ* Bridgnorth (01746) 763173

PELZ, Werner. b 21. Lon Univ BA49. Linc Th Coll 50. **d** 51 **p** 52. C-in-c Lostock CD *Man* 54-63; rtd 86. *Warrina Lot 7, Mount Riddell Road, Healesville, Victoria, Australia 3777*

PEMBERTON, Anthony Thomas Christie (Chris). b 57. BA. Cranmer Hall Dur 82. **d** 84 **p** 85. C Maidstone St Luke *Cant* 84-88; Chapl Ox Pastorate from 88. *14 Walton Street, Oxford OX1 2HG* Oxford (01865) 244713

PEMBERTON, Mrs Carolyn Mary (Carrie). b 55. St Hilda's Coll Ox BA78 Cam Univ PGCE81 Leeds Univ MA92. Cranmer Hall Dur 83 NE Ord Course 84. **dss** 86 **d** 87 **p** 94. NSM Leeds St Geo *Ripon* 86-87; Miss Partner CMS 87-91; Dir Women's Studies Angl Th Inst Zaire 87-91; Perm to Offic *Pet* 92-94; NSM Bourn and Kingston w Caxton and Longstowe *Ely* from 94. *The Rectory, 2 Short Street, Bourn, Cambridge CB3 7SG* Caxton (01954) 719728

PEMBERTON, Crispin Mark Rugman. b 59. St Andr Univ MTh83. St Steph Ho Ox 84. **d** 86 **p** 87. C Acton St Alb w All SS *Lon* 86-88; C Acton Green 88-90; C Leckhampton SS Phil and

Jas w Cheltenham St Jas *Glouc* 90-93; V Tuffley from 93. *St Barnabas' Vicarage, Tuffley, Gloucester GL4 9SB* Gloucester (01452) 306535

PEMBERTON, David Charles. b 35. K Coll Lon 57. **d** 61 **p** 62. C Pokesdown St Jas *Win* 61-65; C W Derby St Mary *Liv* 65-67; C-in-c Cantril Farm St Jude CD 67-71; V Cantril Farm 71-74; V Devonport St Boniface *Ex* 75-83; V Stanwell *Lon* from 83; AD Spelthorne from 92. *The Vicarage, 1 Lord Knyvett Close, Staines, Middx TW19 7PQ* Ashford (01784) 252044

PEMBERTON, Jeremy Charles Baring. b 56. Mert Coll Ox MA77 Fitzw Ho Cam BA80 Leeds Univ MA92. Ridley Hall Cam 78. **d** 81 **p** 82. C Stranton *Dur* 81-84; C Leeds St Geo *Ripon* 84-87; CMS Miss Partner and Dir Angl Th Inst Zaire 87-91; V Irchester *Pet* 92-94; P-in-c Bourn and Kingston w Caxton and Longstowe *Ely* 94; R from 94. *The Rectory, 2 Short Street, Bourn, Cambridge CB3 7SG* Caxton (01954) 719728

PEMBERTON, Canon Wilfred Austin. b 14. Lon Univ BA39 AKC41 BD42 Nottm Univ PhD52. **d** 41 **p** 42. R Wilne and Draycott w Breaston *Derby* 61-91; Chapl Draycott Hosp Derby 62-72; Hon Can Derby Cathl *Derby* 80-91; rtd 91. *19 Cordwell Close, Castle Donnington, Derby DE74 2JL* Derby (01332) 853392

PEMBERY, Gerald Marcus. b 29. Glouc Sch of Min 89. **d** 90 **p** 91. NSM Bream *Glouc* from 90. *Kings Wood, The Tufts, Bream, Lydney, Glos GL15 6HW* Dean (01594) 562750

PENBERTHY (formerly LEGG), Ms Joanna Susan. b 60. Newnham Coll Cam BA81 MA85. St Jo Coll Nottm DipTh82 MTh84 St Jo Coll Dur 83. **dss** 84 **d** 87. Haughton le Skerne *Dur* 84-85; Llanishen and Lisvane *Llan* 85-87; NSM 87-89; NSM Llanwddyn and Llanfihangel and Llwydiarth *St As* 89-93; NSM Llansadwrn w Llanwrda and Manordeilo *St D* 93-95; Officer Div for Par Development Ch in Wales from 95. *The Church in Wales Centre, Woodland Place, Penarth, S Glam CF64 2EX* Cardiff (01222) 708234

PENDLEBURY, Stephen Thomas. b 50. ACA78 Southn Univ BSc73. Ridley Hall Cam 86. **d** 88 **p** 89. C Birkenhead St Jas w St Bede *Ches* 88-91; V from 91. *St James Vicarage, 56 Tollemache Road, Birkenhead, Merseyside L43 8SZ* 0151-652 1016

PENDLETON, David Julian. b 24. K Coll Lon BD54 AKC54. **d** 54 **p** 55. C-in-c Shenley Green CD *Birm* 65-70; V Shenley Green 70-89; rtd 89. *258 Mulberry Road, Birmingham B30 1ST* 0121-475 4874

PENDLETON, John Thomas. b 12. Dorchester Miss Coll 39. **d** 41 **p** 42. V Cleckheaton St Luke *Wakef* 62-77; rtd 77; Perm to Offic *Wakef* from 77. *25 Meadow Close, Robertown, Liversedge, W Yorkshire WF15 7QE* Heckmondwike (01924) 405255

PENDLETON, Mervyn Boulton. b 13. SS Coll Cam BA35 MA42. Chich Th Coll 35. **d** 37 **p** 38. R Kimpton w Thruxton w Fyfield *Win* 71-78; rtd 78. *20 Owers Way, West Wittering, Chichester, W Sussex PO20 8HA*

PENDORF, Canon James Gordon. b 45. Drew Univ New Jersey BA67. Episc Th Sch Cam Mass BD71. **d** 71 **p** 71. USA 71-76; V Colne H Trin *Blackb* 76-80; Sen Dioc Stewardship Adv *Chelmsf* 80-83; Dioc Sec *Birm* from 83; Hon Can Birm Cathl from 90. *St Luke's House, 10 St Luke's Road, Birmingham B5 7DA, or 175 Harborne Park Road, Birmingham B17 0BH* 0121-622 6258 or 427 5141 Fax 428 1114

PENFOLD, Brian Robert. b 54. Lon Univ BSc75 Bris Univ PGCE77. Oak Hill Th Coll BA84. **d** 84 **p** 85. C Norwood *S'wark* 84-87; C Rayleigh *Chelmsf* 88-92; V New Barnet St Jas *St Alb* from 92. *The Vicarage, 11 Park Road, Barnet, Herts EN4 9QA* 0181-449 4043

PENFOLD, Colin Richard. b 52. St Pet Coll Ox BA74 MA78. Ridley Hall Cam 81. **d** 84 **p** 85. C Buckhurst Hill *Chelmsf* 84-87; C Greenside *Dur* 87-90; V Cononley w Bradley *Bradf* from 90. *The Vicarage, 3 Meadow Close, Cononley, Keighley, W Yorkshire BD20 8LZ* Cross Hills (01535) 634369

PENFOLD, Dr Susan Irene. b 52. York Univ BA73 Bris Univ PhD77 Selw Coll Cam BA83 MA87. Ridley Hall Cam 81. **dss** 84 **d** 87 **p** 94. Buckhurst Hill *Chelmsf* 84-87; Hon Par Dn Greenside *Dur* 87-90; Hon C Cononley w Bradley *Bradf* from 90. *The Vicarage, 3 Meadow Close, Cononley, Keighley, W Yorkshire BD20 8LZ* Cross Hills (01535) 634369

PENGELLEY, Peter John. b 22. Sarum & Wells Th Coll 72. **d** 74 **p** 75. C Midsomer Norton *B & W* 74-78; R Stogursey w Fiddington 78-88; Ind Chapl 80-88; rtd 88; Perm to Offic *B & W* from 89. *Rosslyn Cottage, Roadwater, Watchet, Somerset TA23 0RB* Washford (01984) 40798

PENGELLY, Geoffrey. b 50. Oak Hill Th Coll 86. **d** 88 **p** 89. C Redruth w Lanner and Treleigh *Truro* 88-91; TV Bolventor 91-92; V Egloskerry, N Petherwin, Tremaine and Tresmere from 92. *The Vicarage, Egloskerry, Launceston, Cornwall PL25 8RX* North Petherwin (01566) 85365

PENMAN, John Bain. b 67. Aber Univ BD89 New Coll Edin MTh93. Edin Th Coll CECM93. **d** 93 **p** 94. C Glas St Ninian *Glas* from 93. *110 Victoria Road, Glasgow G42 7JD*   0141-424 0917

PENMAN, Miss Margaret Heather. b 50. St Martin's Coll Lanc CertEd71 Lanc Univ DipEd82 DipRE87 FRSA95. Carl Dioc Tr Inst 90. **d** 93 **p** 94. Headteacher Hesketh w Becconsall All SS C of E Sch from 85; NSM Lostock Hall *Blackb* 93-95; NSM Leyland St Jas from 95. *9 Oakfield Drive, Leyland, Preston PR5 3XE*   Leyland (01772) 435927 or 813284   Fax 814721

PENMAN, Robert George (Bob). b 42. St Jo Coll Auckland LTh66. **d** 65 **p** 66. New Zealand 65-73; C Alverstoke *Portsm* 73-74; CF 74-77; C Bridgwater St Mary w Chilton Trinity *B & W* 77-80; P-in-c Haselbury Plucknett w N Perrott 80-81; P-in-c Misterton 80-81; V Haselbury Plucknett, Misterton and N Perrott 81-89; P-in-c Appleton *Ox* from 89; P-in-c Besselsleigh w Dry Sandford from 89. *The Rectory, Oaksmere, Appleton, Abingdon, Oxon OX13 5JS*   Oxford (01865) 862458

PENN, Canon Arthur William. b 22. Man Univ BA49. Wycliffe Hall Ox 49. **d** 51 **p** 52. V Brampton *Carl* 67-83; RD Brampton 74-83; P-in-c Gilsland w Nether Denton 75-81; Hon Can Carl Cathl 78-88; P-in-c Gilsland 81-83; V Rockcliffe and Blackford 83-88; rtd 88. *1 Well Lane, Warton, Carnforth, Lancs LA5 9QZ*   Carnforth (01524) 733079

PENN, Barry Edwin. b 46. Univ of Wales (Swansea) BA72. St Jo Coll Nottm 77. **d** 79 **p** 80. C New Barnet St Jas *St Alb* 79-83; TV Preston St Jo *Blackb* 83-92; V Patchway *Bris* from 92. *St Chad's Vicarage, Southsea Road, Patchway, Bristol BS12 5DP*   Bristol (0117) 969 2935 or 979 3978

PENN, Christopher Francis. b 34. ACII63. Wells Th Coll 68. **d** 70 **p** 71. C Andover w Foxcott *Win* 70-72; C Odiham w S Warnborough 72-75; C Keynsham w Queen Charlton *B & W* 75; C Keynsham 75-76; TV 76-82; R Chilcompton w Downside and Stratton on the Fosse 82-87; RD Midsomer Norton 84-86; V Bathford 87-90; V Avonmouth St Andr *Bris* from 90; Ind Chapl from 90. *St Andrew's Vicarage, St Andrew's Road, Bristol BS11 9ES*   Bristol (0117) 982 2302

PENN, Clive Llewellyn. b 12. Oak Hill Th Coll 47. **d** 48 **p** 49. V Jersey Gouray St Martin *Win* 66-71; Lic to Offic 71-86; rtd 77. *Unit 21, 4 Gorge Road, Campbell Town, Adelaide, S Australia 5074*

PENNAL, David Bernard. b 37. Ripon Hall Ox 64. **d** 67 **p** 68. C Moseley St Mary *Birm* 67-71; C Bridgwater St Mary w Chilton Trinity *B & W* 71-73; P-in-c Hilton w Cheselbourne and Melcombe Horsey *Sarum* 73-76; R Milton Abbas, Hilton w Cheselbourne etc 76-78; P-in-c Spetisbury w Charlton Marshall 78-88; R Spetisbury w Charlton Marshall and Blandford St Mary from 89. *The Rectory, Spetisbury, Blandford Forum, Dorset DT11 9DF*   Blandford (01258) 453153

PENNANT, Dr David Falconer. b 51. Trin Coll Cam MA73. Trin Coll Bris BD84 PhD88. **d** 86 **p** 87. C Bramcote *S'well* 86-88; C Woking St Jo *Guildf* 88-93; Dir of Music St Andr Prep Sch Woking from 93. *30 Oriental Road, Woking, Surrey GU22 7AW*   Woking (01483) 768005

PENNANT, Philip Vivian Rogers. b 14. TD69. Trin Coll Cam BA47 MA48. St Mich Coll Llan 48. **d** 49 **p** 50. R Sutton Bonington *S'well* 65-79; P-in-c Adisham *Cant* 79-84; P-in-c Goodnestone H Cross w Chillenden and Knowlton 79-84; rtd 84. *2 Manor Close, Bradford Abbas, Sherborne, Dorset DT9 6RN*   Yeovil (01935) 23059

PENNELL, Canon James Henry Leslie. b 06. TD50. Edin Th Coll 29. **d** 29 **p** 30. R Pentlow, Foxearth, Liston and Borley *Chelmsf* 65-72; Hon Can St Andr Cathl Inverness *Mor* from 66; rtd 72; Perm to Offic *St E* from 73. *The Croft, Church Street, Hundon, Sudbury, Suffolk CO10 8EW*   Hundon (0144086) 221

PENNEY, David Richard John. b 39. Dur Univ BA63 DipTh65. Cranmer Hall Dur 63. **d** 67 **p** 68. C Chilvers Coton w Astley *Cov* 67-70; C Styvechale 70-72; P-in-c Shilton w Ansty 72-77; P-in-c Withybrook 74-77; R Easington w Liverton *York* 77-85; Soc Resp Adv *Sarum* 85-93; Perm to Offic *Blackb* from 93. *8 William Street, Colne, Lancs BB8 0HH*   Colne (01282) 870076   Fax as telephone

PENNEY, John Edward. b 12. St Jo Coll Dur LTh33 BA34 MA37. Clifton Th Coll 30. **d** 35 **p** 36. V Wisborough Green *Chich* 51-77; rtd 77; Perm to Offic *Ex* from 77. *28 Oakleigh Road, Exmouth, Devon EX8 2LN*   Exmouth (01395) 264863

PENNEY, William Affleck. b 41. MBIM75 FRSA91. K Coll Lon BD63 AKC63 St Boniface Warminster 65. **d** 66 **p** 67. C Chatham St Steph *Roch* 66-70; Ind Chapl 70-77; P-in-c Bredhurst 70-72; Hon C S Gillingham 72-74; Hon C Eynsford w Farningham and Lullingstone 74-77; Bp's Dom Chapl 74-88; Hon Ind Chapl 77-88; Hon C Balham St Mary and St Jo *S'wark* 89-91; Perm to Offic *St Alb* 91-94; Hon C Bushey from 94. *Michael Hall House, Aldenham Road, Elstree, Borehamwood, Herts WD6 3BT*   0181-207 5745

PENNIE, Canon Gibb Niven. b 09. Aber Univ MA30 BD44. Edin Th Coll 34. **d** 36 **p** 37. R Greenock *Glas* 57-77; Can St Mary's Cathl 61-77; rtd 77; Hon Can St Mary's Cathl *Glas* from 77. *111 Earlbank Avenue, Glasgow G14 9DY*   0141-954 6397

PENNINGTON, Frederick William. b 11. K Coll Lon. **d** 55 **p** 56. V N Molton w Twitchen *Ex* 66-77; P-in-c Molland 68-77; rtd 77; Lic to Offic *Ex* from 77. *Sunset Cottage, 103 West Street, Hartland, Bideford, Devon EX39 6BQ*   Bideford (01237) 441206

PENNINGTON, John Michael. b 32. IEng AMIEE MIHospE Em Coll Cam BA54 MA58. Wells Th Coll 58. **d** 60 **p** 61. C Stockport St Geo *Ches* 60-64; V Congleton St Steph 64-68; Chapl Nor Sch 68-70; V Hattersley *Ches* 70-72; C-in-c Upton Priory CD 72-75; V Upton Priory 75-79; Perm to Offic *Newc* 83-87; V Tynemouth St Jo 87-94; P-in-c Cambois from 94; Chapl Northumberland HA from 94; Wansbeck and Ashington Hosps from 94. *7 Wansbeck Mews, Ashington, Northd NE63 8QH*   Ashington (01670) 813526

PENNINGTON, John Kenneth. b 27. Man Univ LLB48. Linc Th Coll 51. **d** 52 **p** 53. Area Sec USPG (Dios Derby, Leic and S'well) 66-71; (Dios Derby and Sheff) 71-75; C Nottm St Mary *S'well* 75-78; C Nottm St Mary and St Cath 78-92; rtd 93. *3 St Jude's Avenue, Nottingham NG3 5FG*   Nottingham (0115) 962 3420

PENNOCK, John Harding Lovell. b 16. Ripon Hall Ox 63. **d** 65 **p** 66. V Hill *Birm* 68-78; P-in-c Sculthorpe w Dunton and Doughton *Nor* 78-82; rtd 82. *12 Swallow Croft, Lichfield, Staffs WS13 7HE*   Lichfield (01543) 264002

PENNY, Diana Eleanor. b 51. Open Univ BA87. Nor Ord Course 87. **d** 89 **p** 94. Hon C Gillingham w Geldeston, Stockton, Ellingham etc *Nor* 89-93; NSM Upton St Leonards *Glouc* from 93. *The Rectory, Bond End Road, Upton St Leonards, Gloucester GL4 8AG*   Gloucester (01452) 617443   Fax as telephone

PENNY, Edwin John. b 43. Leeds Univ BA64. Coll of Resurr Mirfield 64. **d** 66 **p** 67. C Acocks Green *Birm* 66-69; C Wombourne *Lich* 69-71; C Wednesbury St Paul Wood Green 71-74; V Kingshurst *Birm* 74-79; Chapl All Hallows Convent Norfolk 79-82; Hon Chapl Overgate Hospice Yorkshire 82-84; Hon C Raveningham *Nor* 84-90; All Hallows Hosp Nor Past Team 90-93; P-in-c Upton St Leonards *Glouc* from 93; Dioc Communications Officer from 93. *The Rectory, Bond End Road, Upton St Leonards, Gloucester GL4 8AG*   Gloucester (01452) 617443   Fax as telephone or 308324

PENNY, Michael John. b 36. Linc Th Coll 78. **d** 80 **p** 81. C Knighton St Mary Magd *Leic* 80-83; TV Leic Resurr 83-85; V Blackfordby from 85; RD Akeley W (Ashby) 88-93. *11 Vicarage Close, Blackfordby, Swadlincote, Derbyshire DE11 8AZ*   Burton (01524) 219445

PENNY, Wilfred Joseph. b 05. St Aid Birkenhead. **d** 32 **p** 33. R Winford *B & W* 62-73; rtd 73. *Dunloe Residential Home, 17 Jesmond Road, Clevedon, Avon BS21 7RZ*   Clevedon (01275) 873744

PENRITH, Suffragan Bishop of. See GARRARD, Rt Rev Richard

PENTLAND, Raymond Jackson. b 57. Open Univ BA90. St Jo Coll Nottm DPS88. **d** 88 **p** 89. C Nottm St Jude *S'well* 88-90; Chapl RAF Coll Cranwell from 90. *Chaplaincy Services (RAF), HQ, Personnel and Training Command, RAF Innsworth, Gloucester GL3 1EZ*   Gloucester (01452) 712612 Ext 5164   Fax 510828

PENTREATH, Canon Harvey. b 29. Wells Th Coll 54. **d** 57 **p** 58. R Elstead *Guildf* 65-72; V Cuddington 73-80; Hon Can Guildf Cathl 80; V Helston *Truro* 80-85; RD Kerrier 84-86; TR Helston and Wendron 85-92; Hon Can Truro Cathl 88-92; rtd 93. *Penmarr, 15 Penarwyn Crescent, Heamoor, Penzance, Cornwall TR18 3JU*   Penzance (01736) 60133

PEOPLES, James Scott. b 59. TCD BA DipTh HDipEd90. **d** 85 **p** 86. C Carlow w Urglin and Staplestown *C & O* 85-90; Chapl Kilkenny Coll 90-91; I Portarlington w Cloneyhurke and Lea *M & K* from 91; Dioc Youth Officer (Kildare) from 92. *The Rectory, Portarlington, Co Laois, Irish Republic*   Portarlington (502) 43063

PEPPER, David Reginald. b 50. Lon Bible Coll DipCK86. St Alb Minl Tr Scheme 89. **d** 92 **p** 93. NSM Cheshunt *St Alb* from 92. *93 Rowan Drive, Broxbourne, Herts EN10 6HQ*   Hoddesdon (01992) 463735

PEPPER, Leonard Edwin. b 44. Ex Univ BA71. Ripon Hall Ox 71. **d** 73 **p** 74. C Cottingham *York* 73-76; C Kingshurst *Birm* 76-79; Dir Past Studies St Steph Ho Ox 80-89; TV Aylesbury w Bierton and Hulcott *Ox* 89-91; TV High Wycombe from 91. *The Vicarage, Rutland Avenue, High Wycombe, Bucks HP12 3XA*   High Wycombe (01494) 471545

PEPPIATT, Martin Guy. b 33. Trin Coll Ox BA57 MA60. Wycliffe Hall Ox 57. **d** 59 **p** 60. C St Marylebone All So w SS

541

Pet and Jo *Lon* 59-63; Kenya 65-69; V E Twickenham St Steph *Lon* from 69. *St Stephen's Vicarage, 21 Cambridge Park, Twickenham TW1 2JE* 0181-892 5258

PEPPIATT, Quintin Brian Duncombe. b 63. Ex Univ BSc85 St Luke's Coll Ex PGCE86. Ripon Coll Cuddesdon 89 Ch Div Sch of the Pacific (USA) 90. **d** 92 **p** 93. C Gt Ilford SS Clem and Marg *Chelmsf* from 92. *99 Quebec Road, Ilford, Essex IG2 6AW* 0181-554 6190

PERCIVAL, Brian Sydney. b 37. Univ of Wales (Ban) BA61. N Ord Course 81. **d** 84 **p** 85. NSM Norbury *Ches* 84-88; P-in-c Werneth from 88. *The Vicarage, Compstall, Stockport, Cheshire SK6 5HU* 0161-427 1259

PERCIVAL, Geoffrey. b 46. Ridley Hall Cam 73. **d** 76 **p** 77. C Eccleshill *Bradf* 76-79; C Otley 79-82; V Windhill from 82. *The Vicarage, 300 Leeds Road, Windhill, Shipley, W Yorkshire BD18 1EZ* Bradford (01274) 581502

PERCIVAL, James Edward Charles. b 50. C&G69. N Ord Course 92. **d** 95. C Broughton *Blackb* from 95. *25 Northway, Fulwood, Preston PR2 9TP* Preston (01772) 713880

PERCIVAL, Martin Eric. b 45. Lon Univ BSc66 Linacre Coll Ox BA70 MA74. Wycliffe Hall Ox 67. **d** 70 **p** 71. C Anfield St Marg *Liv* 70-73; C Witney *Ox* 73-74; TV Bottesford w Ashby *Linc* 74-76; TV Grantham 76-80; R Coningsby w Tattershall 80-82; P-in-c Coleford w Holcombe *B & W* 82-83; V 83-84; Chapl Rossall Sch Fleetwood 84-88; Chapl Woodbridge Sch Suffolk from 88. *27 Haughgate Close, Woodbridge, Suffolk IP12 1LQ* Woodbridge (01394) 383997

PERCIVAL, Robert Standring. b 27. Sheff Univ BA55 Aston Univ DCouns83. Qu Coll Birm 57. **d** 59 **p** 60. V Pendlebury St Aug *Man* 63-68; Lect Glos Coll of Arts and Tech 68-93; NSM Glouc St Mary de Crypt w St Jo and Ch Ch *Glouc* 68-82; Perm to Offic from 82; rtd 92. *5 Firwood Drive, Gloucester GL4 0AB* Gloucester (01452) 522739

PERCY, Brian. b 34. Local NSM Course 91. **d** 93 **p** 94. NSM Walton *St E* from 93. *16 Lynwood Avenue, Felixstowe, Suffolk IP11 9HS* Felixstowe (01394) 286782

PERCY, Donald. b 45. Kelham Th Coll 66. **d** 71 **p** 72. C Hendon St Ignatius *Dur* 71-75; C Gorton Our Lady and St Thos *Man* 75-77; C Middlesb St Thos *York* 77-82; Guyana 82-86; P-in-c S Moor *Dur* 86-90; V 90-95. *8 Ritson Street, Stanley, Co Durham DH9 0NH*

PERCY, Mrs Emma Margaret. b 63. Jes Coll Cam BA85 MA89 St Jo Coll Dur BA89. Cranmer Hall Dur 87. **d** 90 **p** 94. C Bedf St Andr *St Alb* 90-91; Par Dn 91-94; C 94; Chapl Anglia Poly Univ *Ely* from 94. *32 Montague Road, Cambridge CB4 1BX* Cambridge (01223) 64582

PERCY, Gordon Reid. b 46. St Jo Coll Dur BA68 DipTh70. Cranmer Hall Dur 69. **d** 71 **p** 72. C Flixton St Jo *Man* 71-76; C Charlesworth *Derby* 76-77; P-in-c 77-87; P-in-c Dinting Vale 80-87; V Long Eaton St Jo from 87; RD Ilkeston from 92. *St John's Vicarage, 59 Trowell Grove, Long Eaton, Nottingham NG10 4AY* Nottingham (0115) 973 4819

PERCY, Dr Martyn William. b 62. Bris Univ BA84 K Coll Lon PhD93. Cranmer Hall Dur 88. **d** 90 **p** 91. C Bedf St Andr *St Alb* 90-94; Chapl Ch Coll Cam from 94; Dir Th and Relig Studies from 94; Lic to Offic *Ely* from 94. *Christ's College, Cambridge CB2 3BU* Cambridge (01223) 334900 Fax 334904

PERDUE, Very Rev Ernon Cope Todd. b 30. TCD BA52 BD56 MEd73 UCD DipPsych76 MPsychSc80. TCD Div Sch 53. **d** 54 **p** 55. C Dub Drumcondra w N Strand *D & G* 54-58; C Dub Booterstown w Carysfort 58-60; Dean of Residence TCD 60-68; C-in-c Dub St Mark *D & G* 66-68; C-in-c Dub St Steph 68-69; I Rathmichael 69-76; Careers Counsellor Wicklow Voc Sch 76-82; I Limerick *L & K* 82-87; Can Limerick Cathl 82-87; Dean Killaloe, Kilfenora and Clonfert from 87; I Killaloe w Stradbally from 87. *The Deanery, Killaloe, Co Clare, Irish Republic* Killaloe (61) 376687 Fax as telephone

✠**PERDUE, Rt Rev Richard Gordon.** b 10. TCD BA31 MA38 BD38. **d** 33 **p** 34 **c** 54. C Dub Drumcondra w N Strand *D & G* 33-36; C Dub Rathmines 36-40; I Castledermot w Kinneagh 40-43; I Roscrea *L & K* 43-54; Adn Killaloe and Kilfenora 51-54; Bp Killaloe, Kilfenora, Clonfert and Kilmacduagh 54-57; Bp C, C & R 57-78; rtd 78. *Hadlow 4RD, Timaru, South Island, New Zealand* Timaru (68) 60250

PERERA, George Anthony. b 51. Edin Univ BD74. Linc Th Coll 74. **d** 76 **p** 77. Chapl Mabel Fletcher Tech Coll Liv 76-79; C Wavertree H Trin *Liv* 76-79; TV Maghull 79-94; Chapl Park Lane Hosp Maghull 79-89; Asst Chapl Ashworth Hosp from 89; V Hunts Cross *Liv* from 94. *The Vicarage, 7 Kingsmead Drive, Liverpool L25 0NG* 0151-486 1220

PERFECT, Leslie Charles. b 12. Keble Coll Ox BA35 MA39. Wells Th Coll 35. **d** 36 **p** 37. V Effingham w Lt Bookham *Guildf* 71-80; rtd 81; USA 81-90. *21 Oakfield Avenue, Golborne, Warrington WA3 3QT* Ashton-in-Makerfield (01942) 727407

PERHAM, Canon Michael Francis. b 47. Keble Coll Ox BA74 MA78. Cuddesdon Coll 74. **d** 76 **p** 77. C Addington *Cant* 76-81; Sec C of E Doctrine Commn 79-84; Bp's Dom Chapl *Win* 81-84; TR Oakdale St Geo *Sarum* 84-92; Prec and Can

Res Nor Cathl *Nor* from 92. *27 The Close, Norwich NR1 4DZ* Norwich (01603) 619169 Fax 766032

PERKES, Brian Robert Keith. b 46. St Andr Univ BSc68 Liv Univ DipOR72. Nor Ord Course 91. **d** 94 **p** 95. NSM Witton *Ches* from 94. *20 Broad Acre, Comberbach, Northwich, Cheshire CW9 6QD* Comberbach (01606) 891784

PERKIN, David Arthur. b 30. Pemb Coll Ox BA54 MA58. Linc Th Coll 54. **d** 56 **p** 57. Chapl Loughb Univ *Leic* 61-84; V Paddington St Jas *Lon* 84-92; rtd 92. *14 Englewood Road, London SW12 9NZ*

PERKIN, Jonathan Guy. b 52. Westmr Coll Ox BEd76. Trin Coll Bris 89. **d** 91 **p** 92. C Cullompton *Ex* from 91. *19 Exeter Road, Cullompton, Devon EX15 1DX* Cullompton (01884) 33494

PERKIN, Paul John Stanley. b 50. Ch Ch Ox BA71 MA75 CertEd. Wycliffe Hall Ox 78. **d** 80 **p** 81. C Gillingham St Mark *Roch* 80-84; C Brompton H Trin w Onslow Square St Paul *Lon* 84-87; P-in-c Battersea Rise St Mark *S'wark* 87-92; V from 92. *St Mark's Vicarage, 7 Elsynge Road, London SW18 2HW* 0181-874 6023

PERKINS, Alban Leslie Tate. b 08. Kelham Th Coll 28. **d** 34 **p** 35. SSM from 33; C Nottm St Geo w St Jo *S'well* 34-37 and 68-72; S Africa 37-67 and 76-80; Can Bloemfontein Cathl 52-67; Lesotho 72-76; Perm to Offic *Man* 81-86; Perm to Offic *Blackb* from 86. *Willen Priory, Milton Keynes MK15 9AA* Milton Keynes (01908) 663749

PERKINS, Colin Blackmore. b 35. FCII65. Lon Coll of Div 68. **d** 70 **p** 71. C Hyson Green *S'well* 70-73; V Clarborough w Hayton 73-79; C Cropwell Bishop 79-84; P-in-c Colston Bassett 79-84; P-in-c Granby w Elton 79-84; P-in-c Langar 79-84; V Tithby w Cropwell Butler 79-84; V Cropwell Bishop w Colston Bassett, Granby etc 84-94; P-in-c Sutton Bonington w Normanton-on-Soar from 94. *19A Park Lane, Sutton Bonington, Loughborough, Leics LE12 5NQ* Kegworth (01509) 672236

PERKINS, David. b 51. Sarum & Wells Th Coll. **d** 87 **p** 88. C New Mills *Derby* 87-90; V Marlpool from 90. *The Vicarage, Marlpool, Heanor, Derbyshire DE75 7BP* Langley Mill (01773) 712097

PERKINS, David John Elmslie. b 45. ATII75 Dur Univ BA66 DipTh68. Cranmer Hall Dur. **d** 69 **p** 70. C Wadsley *Sheff* 69-71; C Shortlands *Roch* 71-73; Perm to Offic *Lon* 76-78; Perm to Offic *B & W* 78-80; Lic to Offic from 80. *Rainbow's End, Montacute Road, Stoke-sub-Hamdon, Somerset TA14 6UQ* Martock (01935) 823314

PERKINS, Douglas Brian. b 32. Or Coll Ox BA56 MA63 DipEd67. St Steph Ho Ox 56. **d** 58 **p** 60. C Burnley St Cath *Blackb* 58-59; C Teddington St Alb *Lon* 59-60; Hon C Ox St Barn *Ox* 63-64; Chapl Beechwood Park Sch St Alb 64-66; Lic to Offic *St Alb* 64-66; Lic to Offic *Lon* 66-68; C Holborn St Alb w Saffron Hill St Pet 69-79; V Streatham Ch Ch *S'wark* 79-87; TV Swinton and Pendlebury *Man* 87-90; C Notting Dale St Clem w St Mark and St Jas *Lon* 90-94. *14 Great College Street, Brighton BN2 1HL* Brighton (01273) 694619

PERKINS, Canon Eric William. b 08. Leeds Univ BA29. Coll of Resurr Mirfield 26. **d** 31 **p** 32. R Upton cum Chalvey *Ox* 56-76; Hon Can Ch Ch 62-79; Sub Warden Community St Jo Bapt Clewer from 70; rtd 76; C Burnham w Dropmore, Hitcham and Taplow *Ox* 83-84; C Farnham Royal w Hedgerley 84-85. *Flat 22, Stuart Court, High Street, Kibworth, Leicester LE8 0LE* Leicester (0116) 279 6349

PERKINS, Miss Julia Margaret. b 49. Linc Th Coll 85. **d** 87 **p** 94. Par Dn Owton Manor *Dur* 87-89; Par Dn Leam Lane 89-94; C 94; P-in-c Stockton St Chad from 94. *The Vicarage, Ragpath Lane, Stockton-on-Tees, Cleveland TS19 9JN* Stockton-on-Tees (01642) 614737

PERKINS, Malcolm Bryan. b 20. SS Coll Cam BA41 MA45. Wycliffe Hall Ox 41. **d** 43 **p** 44. Chapl St Bart Hosp Roch 59-74; R Wouldham *Roch* 65-73; Chapl Medway Hosp Gillingham 65-67; Toc H Staff Padre (SE Region) 73-85; Hon C Roch 74-85; rtd 85; Perm to Offic *Roch* from 85. *Roke Cottage, 3 Belgrave Terrace, Laddingford, Maidstone, Kent ME18 6BP* East Peckham (01622) 871774

PERKINS, Sister Patricia Doris. b 29. Gilmore Ho 60. **dss** 73 **d** 87. CSA from 71; Sherston Magna w Easton Grey *Bris* 73-75; Cant St Martin and St Paul *Cant* 76-78; Kilburn St Aug w St Jo *Lon* 80-84; Abbey Ho Malmesbury 84-87; Hon Par Dn Bayswater 87-94; Chapl St Mary's Hosp Praed Street Lon 88-89; Chapl St Chas Hosp Ladbroke Grove 88-89; rtd 89; Dean of Women's Min *Lon* from 89; Dioc Dir of Ords 90-94; Hon Par Dn St Olave Hart Street w All Hallows Staining etc from 94. *St Andrew's House, 2 Tavistock Road, London W11 1BA* 0171-229 2662

PERKINSON, Neil Donald. b 46. Wycliffe Hall Ox 84. **d** 85 **p** 86. C Workington St Jo *Carl* 85-88; TV Cockermouth w Embleton and Wythop 88-93; TV St Laurence in the Isle of Thanet *Cant* from 93. *St Mary's House, 1 Sandwich Road, Cliffsend, Ramsgate, Kent CT12 5HX* Thanet (01843) 597123

PERKINTON, Keith Glyn. b 61. Humberside Poly BA83 Leeds Univ BA92. Coll of Resurr Mirfield CPT93. **d** 93 **p** 94. C Knowle H Nativity *Bris* from 93. *12 Woodridge Road, Bristol BS4 2EU* Bristol (0117) 977 2918

PERKS, David Leonard Irving. b 38. Sussex Univ MA75. S Dios Minl Tr Scheme 84. **d** 87 **p** 88. NSM Lewes All SS, St Anne, St Mich and St Thos *Chich* 87-91; Chapl HM Pris Lewes 91-94; NSM Lewes & Seaford RD from 94. *45 Fitzjohns Road, Lewes, E Sussex BN7 1PR* Lewes (01273) 475781

PERKS, Edgar Harold Martin. b 31. Open Univ BA87. Glouc Sch of Min 85. **d** 88 **p** 89. NSM Bromfield *Heref* 88-89; NSM Culmington w Onibury 88-89; NSM Stanton Lacy 88-89; NSM Culmington w Onibury, Bromfield etc from 90. *The Oaklands, Bromfield Road, Ludlow, Shropshire SY8 1DW* Ludlow (01584) 875525

PERMAN, George Hayward. b 01. Tyndale Hall Bris 31. **d** 34 **p** 35. V Ealing St Mary *Lon* 53-68; rtd 68; Perm to Offic *Chich* from 80. *2 Wakehurst Court, St George's Road, Worthing, W Sussex BN11 2DJ* Worthing (01903) 238540

PERRENS, Eric George. b 16. Sheff Univ BA38. Lich Th Coll 38. **d** 40 **p** 41. V Rawcliffe *Sheff* 69-77; R Bradfield 77-82; rtd 82. *32 Bracken Close, Whitby, N Yorkshire YO22 4HP* Whitby (01947) 600847

PERRENS, Everard George. b 15. St Cath Coll Cam BA37 MA42. Linc Th Coll 40. **d** 42 **p** 43. Chapl St Marg Sch Bushey 65-74; Hon C Earlsdon *Cov* 75-79; C Allesley Park 79-80; rtd 80; Hon C Earlsdon *Cov* 80-83; Perm to Offic from 83. *4 Regency Drive, Kenilworth, Warks CV8 1JE* Kenilworth (01926) 55779

PERRETT, David Thomas. b 48. Cranmer Hall Dur 80. **d** 82 **p** 83. C Stapleford *S'well* 82-86; V Ollerton 86-87; P-in-c Boughton 86-87; V Ollerton w Boughton 87-93; V Winklebury *Win* from 93. *The Vicarage, Willoughby Way, Basingstoke, Hants RG23 8BD* Basingstoke (01256) 23941

PERRETT-JONES, Reginald James Archibald. b 04. Univ of Wales BA34. Dorchester Miss Coll 34. **d** 37 **p** 38. R Cliddesden and Winslade *Win* 61-77; R Cliddesden 77-82; rtd 82; Perm to Offic *B & W* 83-91. *Clydach, 26 Bridges Mead, Dunster, Minehead, Somerset TA24 6PN* Dunster (01643) 821764

PERRINS, Harold. b 21. Kelham Th Coll 38. **d** 44 **p** 45. V Edingale *Lich* 69-77; R Harlaston 69-77; V Shobnall 77-86; rtd 86; Perm to Offic *Lich* from 86. *20 Meadow Rise, Barton under Needwood, Burton-on-Trent DE13 8DT* Barton under Needwood (01283) 713515

PERRINS, Lesley. b 53. St Hugh's Coll Ox BA74 S Bank Poly DCG75. S Dios Minl Tr Scheme CECM93. **d** 93 **p** 95. NSM Stoneleigh *Guildf* 93-94; NSM Haxby w Wigginton *York* from 94. *Galtres Cottage, 21 The Village, Wigginton, York YO3 3PL* York (01904) 762809

PERRIS, Anthony. b 48. Univ of Wales (Abth) BSc69 Selw Coll Cam BA76 MA79. Ridley Hall Cam 74. **d** 77 **p** 78. C Sandal St Helen *Wakef* 77-80; C Plymouth St Andr w St Paul and St Geo *Ex* 80-87; TV Yeovil *B & W* 87-88; V Preston Plucknett from 88. *St James Vicarage, 1 Old School House, Yeovil, Somerset BA21 3TW* Yeovil (01935) 29398

PERRIS, John Martin. b 44. Liv Univ BSc66 Bris Univ DipTh70. Trin Coll Bris 69. **d** 72 **p** 73. C Sevenoaks St Nic *Roch* 72-76; C Bebington *Ches* 76-79; V Redland *Bris* from 79; RD Horfield from 91. *Redland Vicarage, 151 Redland Road, Bristol BS6 6YE* Bristol (0117) 923 8202

PERROTT, John Alastair Croome. b 36. Univ of NZ LLB60. Clifton Th Coll 62. **d** 64 **p** 65. C Tunbridge Wells St Pet *Roch* 64-67; C Stanford-le-Hope *Chelmsf* 67-78; R Elmswell *St E* from 78. *The Rectory, Elmswell, Bury St Edmunds, Suffolk IP30 9DY* Elmswell (01359) 40512

PERROTT, Canon Joseph John. b 19. **d** 64 **p** 65. C Dub St Geo *D & G* 64-71; C Dub Drumcondra 71-72; I Drimoleague Union *C, C & R* 72-75; RD Cork City 74-80; I Mallow Union 75-78; I Ballydehob w Aghadown 78-93; Can Cloyne Cathl 85-93; Preb Cork Cathl 85-93; rtd 93. *6 Kingston College, Mitchelstown, Co Cork, Irish Republic* Mitchelstown (25) 84882

PERRY, Andrew Nicholas. b 62. Westmr Coll Ox BA86. Trin Coll Bris MA91. **d** 91 **p** 92. C Bath Weston All SS w N Stoke *B & W* 91-93; C Bath Weston All SS w N Stoke and Langridge 93-95; P-in-c Longfleet *Sarum* from 95. *The Vicarage, 32 Alverton Avenue, Poole, Dorset BH15 2QG* Poole (01202) 723359

PERRY, Andrew William. b 44. R Agric Coll Cirencester NDA65 MRAC65 ADFM66. W Midl Minl Tr Course 91. **d** 94. NSM Redmarley D'Abitot, Bromesberrow w Pauntley etc *Glouc* from 94. *Rye Cottage, Broomsgreen, Dymock, Glos GL18 2DP* Dymock (01531) 890489 Fax 632552

PERRY, Anthony Henry. b 54. Leic Univ BA76. Aston Tr Scheme 89 Linc Th Coll CMinlStuds93. **d** 93 **p** 94. C Bartley Green *Birm* from 93. *19 Elmcroft Avenue, Birmingham B32 4LZ* 0121-422 1436

PERRY, Anthony Robert. b 21. Kelham Th Coll 48. **d** 52 **p** 53. SSM 52-91; S Africa 56-59 and 70-88; Lesotho 59-70; Chapl Chich Th Coll 88-90; Willen Priory 90-92; rtd 91. *St Anthony's Priory, Claypath, Durham DH1 1QT* 0191-384 3747

PERRY, Canon Colin Charles. b 16. K Coll Cam BA38 MA42. Westcott Ho Cam 39. **d** 40 **p** 41. PC Salisbury St Fran Sarum 64-69; V 69-71; V Preston *Sarum* 71-81; RD Weymouth 75-79; Can and Preb Sarum Cathl 77-82; TR Preston w Sutton Poyntz and Osmington w Poxwell 81-82; rtd 82. *6 The Ridgeway, Corfe Mullen, Wimborne, Dorset BH21 3HS* Broadstone (01202) 697298

PERRY, David William. b 42. St Chad's Coll Dur BA64 DipTh66. **d** 66 **p** 67. C Middleton St Mary *Ripon* 66-69; C Bedale 69-71; C Marton-in-Cleveland *York* 71-75; V Skirlaugh w Long Riston from 75; N Humberside Ecum Officer from 75. *The Vicarage, Skirlaugh, Hull HU11 5HE* Hornsea (01964) 562259

PERRY, Edward John. b 35. AKC62. **d** 63 **p** 64. C Honicknowle *Ex* 63-65; C Ashburton w Buckland-in-the-Moor 65-70; V Cornwood 70-92; Asst Dir of Educn from 71; I Ermington and Ugborough from 92; Chapl Moorhaven Hosp from 92. *The Vicarage, Lutterburn Street, Ugborough, Ivybridge, Devon PL21 0NG* Plymouth (01752) 896957

PERRY, Geoffrey. b 33. K Coll Lon BD57 AKC57. **d** 58 **p** 59. R St Ive *Truro* 66-75; RD W Wivelshire 73-76; R St Ive w Quethiock 75-84; R St Dennis 84-92; rtd 92. *23 Moresk Close, Truro, Cornwall TR1 1DL* Truro (01872) 72015

PERRY, John. b 09. TD60. PhD50. **d** 32 **p** 33. Can St Ninian's Cathl Perth *St And* 61-77; R Comrie 65-77; rtd 77. *29 Balhousie Street, Perth PH1 5HJ* Perth (01738) 26594

✠**PERRY, Rt Rev John Freeman.** b 35. Lon Coll of Div ALCD59 LTh74 MPhil86. **d** 59 **p** 60 **c** 89. C Woking Ch Ch *Guildf* 59-62; C Chorleywood Ch Ch *St Alb* 62; Min Chorleywood St Andr CD 63-66; V Chorleywood St Andr 66-77; RD Rickmansworth 72-77; Warden Lee Abbey 77-89; RD Shirwell *Ex* 80-84; Hon Can Win Cathl *Win* from 89; Suff Bp Southn from 89. *Ham House, The Crescent, Romsey, Hants SO51 7NG* Romsey (01794) 516005 Fax 830242

PERRY, John Neville. b 20. Leeds Univ BA41. Coll of Resurr Mirfield 41. **d** 43 **p** 44. V Feltham *Lon* 63-75; RD Hounslow 67-75; Adn Middx 75-82; R Orlestone w Snave and Ruckinge w Warehorne *Cant* 82-86; rtd 86. *73 Elizabeth Crescent, East Grinstead, W Sussex RH19 3JG* East Grinstead (01342) 315446

PERRY, John Walton Beauchamp. b 43. Ex Coll Ox BA64 Sussex Univ MA67. E Anglian Minl Tr Course 82 Westcott Ho Cam 84. **d** 85 **p** 86. C Shrewsbury St Chad w St Mary *Lich* 85-89; V Batheaston w St Cath *B & W* from 89. *The Vicarage, 34 Northend, Batheaston, Bath BA1 7ES* Bath (01225) 858192

PERRY, Jonathan Robert. b 55. St Jo Coll Nottm DipTh. **d** 82 **p** 83. C Filey *York* 82-84; C Rayleigh *Chelmsf* 84-88; Asst Chapl St Geo Hosp Linc 88-90; Chapl Qu Eliz Hosp Gateshead from 90. *The Chaplain's Office, Queen Elizabeth Hospital, Gateshead, Tyne & Wear NE9 4SX* 0191-487 8989

PERRY, Mrs Lynne Janice. b 48. **d** 90. NSM Llanfair Mathafarn Eithaf w Llanbedrgoch *Ban* from 90. *Bryn Haul, Benllech, Anglesey, Gwynedd LL74 8SR* Tyn-y-Gongl (01248) 853125

PERRY, Martin Herbert. b 43. Cranmer Hall Dur 66. **d** 70 **p** 71. C Millfield St Mark *Dur* 70-74; C Haughton le Skerne 74-77; V Darlington St Matt 77-79; V Darlington St Matt and St Luke 79-84; TR Oldland *Bris* 84-91; V from 91. *Oldland Vicarage, 39 Sunnyvale Drive, Longwell Green, Bristol BS15 6YQ* Bristol (0117) 932 7178

PERRY, Martyn. b 57. S Wales Bapt Coll DipTh85 DPS86 Coll of Resurr Mirfield 89. **d** 90 **p** 91. In Bapt Ch 85-93; C Hornsey St Mary w St Geo *Lon* 90-93; V Pontlottyn w Fochriw *Llan* from 93. *St Tyfaelog's Vicarage, 9 Picton Street, Pontlottyn, Bargoed, M Glam CF8 9PS* Rhymney (01685) 841322

PERRY, Michael Arnold. b 54. Lon Univ BD64 Southn Univ MPhil74. Oak Hill Th Coll 62 Ridley Hall Cam 63. **d** 65 **p** 66. C St Helens St Helen *Liv* 65-68; C Bitterne *Win* 68-72; V 72-81; R Eversley 81-89; V Tonbridge SS Pet and Paul *Roch* from 89; P-in-c Shipbourne from 91. *The Vicarage, Church Street, Tonbridge, Kent TN9 1HD* Tonbridge (01732) 770962

PERRY, Canon Michael Charles. b 33. Trin Coll Cam BA55 MA59. Westcott Ho Cam 56. **d** 58 **p** 59. C Baswich (or Berkswich) *Lich* 58-60; Chapl Ripon Hall Ox 61-63; Chief Asst Home Publishing SPCK 63-70; Can Res Dur Cathl *Dur* from 70; Adn Dur 70-93; Bp's Sen Chapl from 93. *7 The College, Durham DH1 3EQ* 0191-386 1891 Fax Bishop Auckland (01388) 605264

PERRY, Very Rev Robert Anthony. b 21. Leeds Univ BA47. Coll of Resurr Mirfield 47. **d** 49 **p** 50. Sarawak 54-63; Malaysia 63-66 and 75-80; Chapl HM Pris Gartree 70-73; P-in-c Mottingham St Edw *S'wark* 73-75; P-in-c Presteigne w Discoed *Heref* 80-83; R Presteigne w Discoed, Kinsham and Lingen 83-86; rtd 86; Perm to Offic *Heref* 87-93; Chapl Laslitt's *Worc* 91-92; P-in-c Ryhall w Essendine *Pet* from 94.

15 Northwick Road, Ketton, Stamford, Lincs PE9 3SB Stamford (01780) 721827

PERRY, Roy John. b 28. Chich Th Coll 71. **d** 72 **p** 73. Hon C Yeovil H Trin *B & W* 72-76; C 76-77; Perm to Offic from 77; TV Withycombe Raleigh *Ex* 77-84; TR Ex St Thos and Em 84; TV Sampford Peverell, Uplowman, Holcombe Rogus etc 86-93; P-in-c Halberton 87-88; rtd 93. *Tri-Stones, West End, Kingsbury Episcopi, Martock, Somerset TA12 6AY* Martock (01935) 823064

PERRY, Timothy Richard (Tim). b 64. Trin Coll Bris BA93. **d** 93 **p** 95. C Abingdon *Ox* from 93. *33 Mattock Way, Abingdon, Oxon OX14 2PQ* Abingdon (01235) 555083

PERRY, Valerie Evelyn. b 39. Southn Univ CertEd59 Lon Univ DipRS85. S'wark Ord Course 82. **dss** 85 **d** 87 **p** 94. Romford St Edw *Chelmsf* 85-87; NSM 87-89; Par Dn 89-91; Asst Chapl Middx Hosp Lon 92-94; Chapl S Kent Hosps NHS Trust from 94; Chapl Wm Harvey Hosp Ashford from 94; Chapl Ashford Hosp from 94; Chapl R Victoria Hosp Folkestone from 94. *William Harvey Hospital, Kennington Road, Willesborough, Ashford, Kent TN24 0LY* Ashford (01233) 633331

PERRY-GORE, Canon Walter Keith. b 34. Univ of Wales (Lamp) BA59. Westcott Ho Cam 60. **d** 61 **p** 62. C St Austell *Truro* 61-64; Barbados 64-70; Canada from 70. *1115 Rue Massawippi, North Hatley, Quebec, Canada, J0B 2C0*

PERRYMAN, David Francis. b 42. Brunel Univ BSc64. Oak Hill Th Coll 74. **d** 76 **p** 77. C Margate H Trin *Cant* 76-80; R Ardingly *Chich* 80-90; V Bath St Luke *B & W* from 90. *St Luke's Vicarage, Hatfield Road, Bath BA2 2BD* Bath (01225) 311904

PERRYMAN, Graham Frederick. b 56. Southn Univ BA78 Reading Univ PGCE80. Aston Tr Scheme 90 Trin Coll Bris DipHE94. **d** 94 **p** 95. C Hamworthy *Sarum* from 94. *35 Inglesham Way, Hamworthy, Poole, Dorset BH15 4PA* Poole (01202) 678702

PERRYMAN, James Edward (Jim). b 56. Lon Bible Coll BA85 Oak Hill Th Coll 86. **d** 88 **p** 89. C Gidea Park *Chelmsf* 88-91; C Becontree St Mary 91-94; Chapl Lyon *Eur* from 94. *38 Chemin de Taffignon, 69110 Ste-Foy-les-Lyon, France* France (33) 78 59 67 06 Fax 72 39 09 31

PERRYMAN, John Frederick Charles. b 49. Mert Coll Ox BA71 MA74. Ridley Hall Cam 72. **d** 74 **p** 75. C Shortlands *Roch* 74-78; Asst Chapl St Geo Hosp Lon 78-82; Chapl Withington Hosp Man from 83. *Withington Hospital, Nell Lane, Manchester M20 8LR, or 24 Alan Road, Withington, Manchester M20 9WG* 0161-445 8111 or 445 4769

PERSSON, Matthew Stephen. b 60. Dundee Univ BSc82. Wycliffe Hall Ox 88. **d** 91 **p** 92. C Bath Twerton-on-Avon *B & W* 91-94; C Shepton Mallet w Doulting from 94; Asst Chapl HM Pris Shepton Mallet from 94. *Ham Manor, Bowlish, Shepton Mallet, Somerset BA4 5JR*

✠**PERSSON, Rt Rev William Michael Dermot.** b 27. Or Coll Ox BA51 MA55. Wycliffe Hall Ox 51. **d** 53 **p** 54 **c** 82. C S Croydon Em *Cant* 53-55; C Tunbridge Wells St Jo *Roch* 55-58; V S Mimms Ch Ch *Lon* 58-67; R Bebington *Ches* 67-79; V Knutsford St Jo and Toft 79-82; Suff Bp Doncaster *Sheff* 82-92; rtd 93. *Ryalls Cottage, Burton Street, Marnhull, Sturminster Newton, Dorset DT10 1PS* Marnhull (01258) 820452

PERTH, Provost of. See FRANZ, Very Rev Kevin Gerhard

PESCOD, John Gordon. b 44. Leeds Univ BSc70. Qu Coll Birm DipTh71. **d** 72 **p** 73. C Camberwell St Geo *S'wark* 72-75; Chapl R Philanthropic Soc Sch Redhill 75-80; P-in-c Nunney w Wanstrow and Cloford *B & W* 80-84; R Nunney and Witham Friary, Marston Bigot etc 84-87; R Milverton w Halse and Fitzhead 87-93; V Frome St Jo and St Mary from 93; V Woodlands from 93. *The Vicarage, Vicarage Street, Frome, Somerset BA11 1PU* Frome (01373) 462325

PESKETT, Canon Osmond Fletcher. b 12. Dur Univ LTh44. Tyndale Hall Bris. **d** 37 **p** 38. V St Keverne *Truro* 68-77; rtd 77; Perm to Offic *Ex* from 91. *Gairloch, Hensleigh Drive, St Leonards, Exeter EX2 4NZ* Exeter (01392) 214387

PESKETT, Richard Howard. b 42. Selw Coll Cam BA64 MA67. Ridley Hall Cam 64. **d** 68 **p** 69. C Jesmond H Trin *Newc* 68-71; Singapore 71-91; Lect Trin Coll Bris from 91. *Trinity College, Stoke Hill, Bristol BS9 1JP* Bristol (0117) 968 2803

PESKETT, Timothy Lewis (Tim). b 64. St Kath Coll Liv BA86. Chich Th Coll BTh90. **d** 90 **p** 91. C Verwood *Sarum* 90-91; C Southsea H Spirit *Portsm* from 91. *219 Fawcett Road, Southsea, Hants PO4 0DH* Portsmouth (01705) 812128

PESTELL, Robert Carlyle. b 54. Aston Tr Scheme 89 Linc Th Coll 91. **d** 93 **p** 94. C Matson *Glouc* from 93. *58 Haycroft Drive, Gloucester GL4 9XX* Gloucester (01452) 502150

PETER, Brother. See ROUNDHILL, Stanley

PETER DOUGLAS, Brother. See NEEDHAM, Brother Peter Douglas

PETERBOROUGH, Bishop of. See WESTWOOD, Rt Rev William John

PETERBOROUGH, Dean of. See BUNKER, Very Rev Michael

PETERKEN, Canon Peter Donald. b 28. K Coll Lon BD51 AKC51. **d** 52 **p** 53. C Swanley St Mary *Roch* 52-55 and 62-65; C Is of Dogs Ch Ch and St Jo w St Luke *Lon* 55-57; R S Perrott w Mosterton and Chedington *Sarum* 57-59; Br Guiana 59-62; R Killamarsh *Derby* 65-70; V Derby St Luke 70-90; RD Derby N 79-90; Hon Can Derby Cathl from 85; R Matlock from 90. *The Rectory, Church Street, Matlock, Derbyshire DE4 3BZ* Matlock (01629) 582199

PETERS, Christopher Lind. b 56. Oak Hill Th Coll. **d** 82 **p** 83. C Knockbreda *D & D* 82-84; C Lisburn Ch Ch Cathl *Conn* 84-87; I Kilmocomogue Union *C, C & R* 87-93; P-in-c Beara 92-93; I Killiney H Trin *D & G* from 93. *Killiney Rectory, 21 Killiney Avenue, Killiney, Co Dublin, Irish Republic* Dublin (1) 285-6180

PETERS, Canon Cyril John (Bill). b 19. Fitzw Ho Cam BA42 MA45. Chich Th Coll 40. **d** 42 **p** 43. C Brighton St Mich *Chich* 42-45 and 47-50; CF (EC) 45-47; Hon CF from 47; Chapl Brighton Coll 50-69; R Uckfield *Chich* from 69; R Isfield from 69; R Lt Horsted from 69; RD Uckfield from 73; Can and Preb Chich Cathl 81-89. *The Rectory, Belmont Road, Uckfield, E Sussex TN22 1BP* Uckfield (01825) 762251

PETERS, David Lewis. b 38. Ch Ch Ox BA62 MA66. Westcott Ho Cam 63. **d** 65 **p** 66. C Stand *Man* 70-74; P-in-c Hillock 70-74; V 74-82; V Haslingden w Haslingden Grane *Blackb* 82-88; rtd 88. *15 Ambleside Avenue, Rawtenstall, Rossendale, Lancs BB4 6RY* Rossendale (01706) 228913

PETERS, Geoffrey John. b 51. MInstC(Glas) BCom BSc MDiv. Gujranwala Th Sem 90 Oak Hill Th Coll 85. **d** 87 **p** 88. C Forest Gate St Sav w W Ham St Matt *Chelmsf* 87-90; C Wembley St Jo *Lon* 90-92; TV Manningham *Bradf* from 92. *St Luke's Vicarage, 1 Selborne Grove, Manningham, Bradford, W Yorkshire BD9 4NL* Bradford (01274) 541110

PETERS, Canon Kenneth (Ken). b 54. Univ of Wales (Cardiff) DipTh77 Tokyo Univ MBA88. St Mich Coll Llan 74. **d** 77 **p** 78. C Mountain Ash *Llan* 77-80; Asst Chapl Mersey Miss to Seamen 80-82; Perm to Offic *Ches* 80-82; Chapl Miss to Seamen from 82; Japan 82-89; Hon Can Kobe from 85; Chapl Supt Mersey Miss to Seamen 89-93; Justice and Welfare Sec from 94. *St Michael Paternoster Royal, College Hill, London EC4R 2RL* 0171-248 5202 Fax 248 4761

PETERS, Michael. b 41. Chich Th Coll 75. **d** 77 **p** 78. C Redruth *Truro* 77-79; TV 79-80; TV Redruth w Lanner 80-82; R St Mawgan w St Ervan and St Eval 82-86; Chapl HM Pris Liv 86-87; Chapl HM Pris Bris from 87. *The Chaplain's Office, HM Prison, Cambridge Road, Bristol BS7 8PS* Bristol (0117) 942 6661 Fax 244228

PETERS, Richard Paul. b 13. Univ Coll Ox BA35 MA39. Cuddesdon Coll 37. **d** 38 **p** 39. Warden Home of Divine Healing Crowhurst 69-78; rtd 78; Perm to Offic *Chich* 79-92. *Stuart Court, High Street, Kibworth, Leicester LE8 0LE* Leicester (0116) 279 6347

PETERS, Robert David. b 54. BA76. Oak Hill Th Coll 78. **d** 79 **p** 80. C Hyde St Geo *Ches* 79-83; C Hartford 83-86; V Lindow from 86. *St John's Vicarage, 137 Knutsford Road, Wilmslow, Cheshire SK9 6EL* Alderley Edge (01625) 583251

PETERS, Stephen Eric. b 45. Westcott Ho Cam 74. **d** 77 **p** 78. C Wanstead St Mary *Chelmsf* 77-79; C Leigh-on-Sea St Marg 79-81; P-in-c Purleigh 81-82; P-in-c Cold Norton w Stow Maries 81-82; R Purleigh, Cold Norton and Stow Maries 83-84; V Bedf Park *Lon* 84-87; Perm to Offic *Ex* 87-88; TR Totnes and Berry Pomeroy 88-90; Chapl Ex Sch 91-93; Chapl St Marg Sch Ex 91-93; Lic to Offic *Ex* from 91. *20 South Street, Totnes, Devon TQ9 5DZ* Totnes (01803) 867199

PETERSEN, Miss Jennifer Elizabeth (Jenny). b 55. Aus Nat Univ BA78. Moore Th Coll Sydney BTh82 Wycliffe Hall Ox 92. **dss** 85 **d** 94. Australia 85-94; C Elloughton and Brough w Brantingham *York* from 94. *78 Hunter Road, Elloughton, Brough, N Humberside HU15 1LG* Hull (01482) 667054

PETERSON, Dennis. b 25. Oak Hill Th Coll 51. **d** 54 **p** 55. V E Brixton St Jude *S'wark* 58-91; rtd 91. *79 Cavendish Gardens, Westcliff-on-Sea, Essex SS0 9XP* Southend-on-Sea (01702) 334400

PETFIELD, Bruce le Gay. b 34. FHA. NE Ord Course 76. **d** 79 **p** 80. NSM Morpeth *Newc* 79-86; C Knaresborough *Ripon* 86-87; V Flamborough *York* 87-94; V Bempton 87-94; rtd 94. *36 Maple Road, Bridlington, N Humberside YO16 5TE*

PETIT, Andrew Michael. b 53. Solicitor Cam Univ MA. Trin Coll Bris DipHE82. **d** 83 **p** 84. C Stoughton *Guildf* 83-87; C Shirley *Win* 87-92; V Cholsey *Ox* from 92. *The Vicarage, Church Road, Cholsey, Wallingford, Oxon OX10 9PP* Cholsey (01491) 651216

PETITT, Michael David. b 53. BCombStuds. Linc Th Coll 79. **d** 82 **p** 83. C Arnold *S'well* 82-86; Asst Chapl HM Youth Cust Cen Glen Parva 86-87; V Blaby *Leic* 87-94; V Leagrave *St Alb* from 94. *St Luke's Vicarage, High Street, Leagrave, Luton LU4 9JY* Luton (01582) 572737

PETRICHER, Georges Herbert Philippe. b 53. St Paul's Coll Mauritius. **d** 84 **p** 85. Mauritius 83-85; Hon C Tooting All SS *S'wark* 85-87; C Kings Heath *Birm* 87-90; C Hamstead St Paul 90-93; C Stechford from 93. *221 Flaxley Road, Birmingham B33 9HE* 0121-784 0516

PETRIE, Alistair Philip. b 50. Lon Univ DipTh76. Fuller Th Sem California DMin90 Oak Hill Th Coll 73. **d** 76 **p** 77. C Eston *York* 76-79; P-in-c Prestwick *Glas* 79-81; R 81-82; Canada from 82. *Brentwood Memorial Chapel, 792 Sea Drive, Brentwood Bay, British Columbia, Canada, V8M 1B1* Brentwood Bay (604) 652-3860

PETRIE, Ian Robert (Eric). b 53. Avery Hill Coll PGCE84. Oak Hill Th Coll BA83 Qu Coll Birm 93. **d** 95. C Sedgley All SS *Worc* from 95. *13 The Priory, Sedgley, Dudley, W Midlands DY3 3UB* Sedgley (01902) 664625

PETT, Douglas Ellory. b 24. Lon Univ BD46 BD48 AKC48 PhD74. K Coll Lon 48. **d** 49 **p** 50. Chapl St Mary's Hosp Praed Street Lon 66-83; rtd 83. *23 Polsue Way, Tresillian, Truro, Cornwall TR2 4BE* Tresillian (0187252) 573

PETTENGELL, Ernest Terence. b 43. K Coll Lon. **d** 69 **p** 70. C Chesham St Mary *Ox* 69-72; C Farnborough *Guildf* 72-75; Asst Master K Alfred Sch Burnham-on-Sea 75-78; C Bishop's Cleeve *Glouc* 78-80; Chapl Westonbirt Sch 80-85; P-in-c Shipton Moyne w Westonbirt and Lasborough *Glouc* 80-85; V Berkeley w Wick, Breadstone and Newport 85-92; TV Weston-super-Mare Cen Par *B & W* from 92. *Emmanuel Vicarage, 5 Walliscote Road, Weston-super-Mare, Avon BS23 1XE* Weston-super-Mare (01934) 621046

PETTERSEN, Dr Alvyn Lorang. b 51. TCD BA73 Dur Univ BA75 PhD81. Sarum & Wells Th Coll 78. **d** 81 **p** 82. Chapl Clare Coll Cam 81-85; Lic to Offic *Ely* 81-85; Fell and Chapl Ex Coll Ox 85-92; Research Fell Linc Coll Ox 92-93; Lic to Offic *Ox* 85-93; V Frensham *Guildf* from 93. *The Vicarage, Frensham, Farnham, Surrey GU10 3DT* Frensham (01252) 792137

PETTET, Christopher Farley (Chris). b 54. Ox Univ BEd78. St Jo Coll Nottm 87. **d** 90 **p** 91. C Luton St Mary *St Alb* 90-93; C Fawley *Win* from 93. *15 Long Lane Close, Holbury, Southampton SO4 1LE* Southampton (01703) 891809

PETTIFER, Canon Bryan George Ernest. b 32. Qu Coll Cam BA55 MA59 MEd. Wm Temple Coll Rugby 56 Ridley Hall Cam 57. **d** 59 **p** 60. C Attercliffe w Carbrook *Sheff* 59-61; C Ecclesall 61-65; Chapl City of Bath Tech Coll 65-74; Adult Educn Officer *Bris* 75-80; Dir Past Th Sarum & Wells Th Coll 80-85; Can Res St Alb 85-92; Prin St Alb Minl Tr Scheme 85-92; Prin Ox Area Chr Tr Scheme *Ox* 92-94; Perm to Offic from 94; Min and Deployment Officer/Selection Sec ABM from 94. *23 Botley Road, Oxford OX2 0BL* Oxford (01865) 727444

PETTIFER, John Barrie. b 38. Linc Th Coll 63. **d** 65 **p** 66. C Stretford St Matt *Man* 65-67; C Stand 67-71; V Littleborough from 71. *The Vicarage, Deardon Street, Littleborough, Lancs OL15 9DZ* Littleborough (01706) 378334

PETTIFOR, David Thomas. b 42. Ripon Coll Cuddesdon 78. **d** 81 **p** 82. C Binley *Cov* 81-84; P-in-c Wood End 84-88; V 88-92; V Finham from 92. *St Martin's Vicarage, 136 Green Lane South, Coventry CV3 6EA* Coventry (01203) 418330

PETTIGREW, Miss Claire Gabrielle. b 23. St Mich Ho Ox 55. dss 77 **d** 87 **p** 95. Nor Heartsease St Fran *Nor* 77-81; Heigham H Trin 81-87; Dioc Lay Min Adv 83-87; Assoc Dioc Dir of Ords 87-89; rtd 89; Lic to Offic *Nor* from 89. *41 Home Colne House, London Road, Cromer, Norfolk NR27 9EF* Cromer (01263) 515215

PETTIGREW, Canon Stanley. b 27. TCD BA49 MA62. **d** 50 **p** 51. Miss to Seamen 62-92; I Wicklow w Killiskey *D & G* 62-92; RD Delgany 85-92; Can Ch Ch Cathl Dub 87-92; rtd 92. *Corr Riase, Ballarney South, Wicklow, Irish Republic* Wicklow (404) 69755

PETTIT, Arthur George Lifton. b 08. Jes Coll Ox BA31 MA35. St D Coll Lamp BA29 St Steph Ho Ox 32. **d** 32 **p** 33. R Remenham *Ox* 50-73; rtd 73. *324 Cowley Mansions, Mortlake High Street, London SW14* 0181-876 8671

PETTITT, Donald. b 09. Bps' Coll Cheshunt 57. **d** 57 **p** 58. C Worstead w Westwick and Sloley *Nor* 69-78; rtd 78; Perm to Offic *Nor* from 79. *15 Arbor Road, Cromer, Norfolk NR27 9DW* Cromer (01263) 512539

PETTITT, Maurice. b 13. Clare Coll Cam BA35 MA57 MusBac37. Lich Th Coll 56. **d** 57 **p** 58. V Riccall *York* 69-78; RD Escrick 73-78; rtd 78. *Holbeck House, Lastingham, York YO6 6TJ* Lastingham (017515) 517

PETTITT, Mervyn Francis. b 39. Qu Coll Birm DipTh66. **d** 66 **p** 67. C Loughton St Jo *Chelmsf* 69-72; R Downham w S Hanningfield 72-82; P-in-c W w S Hanningfield 77-78; C Leigh-on-Sea St Marg 82-85; rtd 85. *60 Suffolk Avenue, Leigh-on-Sea, Essex SS9 3HF* Southend-on-Sea (01702) 72202

PETTITT, Robin Adrian. b 50. MRTPI79 Newc Univ BA77. St Steph Ho Ox 81. **d** 83 **p** 84. C Warrington St Elphin *Liv* 83-87; C Torrisholme *Blackb* 87-93; P-in-c Charnock Richard from 93; Dioc Par Development Officer from 93. *The Vicarage, Church Lane, Charnock Richard, Chorley, Lancs PR7 5NA* Coppull (01257) 791385

PETTITT, Canon Simon. b 50. Nottm Univ BTh74 CertEd. Kelham Th Coll 70. **d** 75 **p** 76. C Penistone *Wakef* 75-78; Dioc Youth Officer 78-80; Dioc Schs Officer *St E* 80-86; P-in-c Hintlesham w Chattisham 80-86; V Bury St Edmunds St Jo 86-93; RD Thingoe 88-92; Dioc Communications Officer from 93; Hon Can St E Cathl from 93. *3 Crown Street, Bury St Edmunds, Suffolk IP33 1QX* Bury St Edmunds (01284) 753866 Fax as telephone

PETTY, Brian. b 34. Man Univ BA90 Melbourne Univ DipRE. St Aid Birkenhead 59. **d** 62 **p** 63. C Meole Brace *Lich* 62-65; Chapl RAF 65-69; Australia 70-75; P-in-c Kimbolton w Middleton-on-the-Hill *Heref* 76-79; P-in-c Pudleston-cum-Whyle w Hatfield, Docklow etc 76-79; P-in-c Haddenham *Ely* 79-80; V 80-84; V Fairfield *Derby* 84-90; Chapl St Geo Sch Ascot 90-93; TR Sampford Peverell, Uplowman, Holcombe Rogus etc *Ex* from 93; RD Cullompton from 95. *The Rectory, Blackdown View, Sampford Peverell, Tiverton, Devon EX16 7BP* Tiverton (01884) 821879

PETTY, Very Rev John Fitzmaurice. b 35. Trin Hall Cam BA59 MA65. Cuddesdon Coll 64. **d** 66 **p** 67. C Sheff St Cuth *Sheff* 66-69; C St Helier *S'wark* 69-75; V Hurst *Man* 75-88; AD Ashton-under-Lyne 83-87; Hon Can Man Cathl 86-88; Provost Cov from 88. *Provost's Lodge, Priory Row, Coventry CV1 5ES* Coventry (01203) 227597 Fax 631448

PETTY, Stuart. b 56. Wilson Carlile Coll DipEvang85 Chich Th Coll 91. **d** 93 **p** 94. CA from 88; C W Bromwich St Andr w Ch Ch *Lich* from 93. *23 Rowley View, West Bromwich, W Midlands B70 8QR* 0121-553 3538

PETZSCH, Hugo Max David. b 57. Edin Univ MA79 BD83. Edin Th Coll 80. **d** 83 **p** 84. C Dollar *St And* 83-86; New Zealand 86-90; R Alyth *St And* 90-91; R Blairgowrie 90-91; R Coupar Angus 90-91; Chapl Glenalmond Coll from 91. *Glenalmond College, Glenalmond, Perth PH1 3RY* Glenalmond (0173888) 205 or 268

PEVERELL, Paul Harrison. b 57. Ripon Coll Cuddesdon. **d** 82 **p** 83. C Cottingham *York* 82-85; V Middlesb St Martin 85-93; V Gt Ayton w Easby and Newton in Cleveland from 93. *The Vicarage, Low Green, Great Ayton, Middlesbrough, Cleveland TS9 6NN* Middlesbrough (01642) 722333

PEYTON, Nigel. b 51. JP. Edin Univ MA73 BD76. Union Th Sem (NY) STM77 Edin Th Coll 73. **d** 76 **p** 77. Chapl St Paul's Cathl Dundee *Bre* 76-82; Dioc Youth Chapl 76-85; Chapl Invergowrie 79-82; P-in-c 82-85; P-in-c Nottm All SS *S'well* 85; V 86-91; Chapl Bluecoat Sch Nottm 90-92; P-in-c Lambley from 91; Dioc Min Development Adv from 91. *The Rectory, Lambley, Nottingham NG4 4QP* Nottingham (0115) 931 3531 or Newark (01636) 814331 Fax Newark (01636) 815084

PEYTON JONES, Donald Lewis. b 14. DSC42. K Coll Lon 59. **d** 61 **p** 62. V Salcombe Regis *Ex* 62-72; C-in-c Lundy Is 73-78; V Appledore 73-78; rtd 79; Chapl Miss to Seamen from 79; Lic to Offic *Ex* from 79. *Fort Cottage, Cawsand, Torpoint, Cornwall PL10 1PA* Plymouth (01752) 822382 or 223865

PEYTON JONES, Mrs Dorothy Helen. b 58. LMH Ox BA79 MPhil80. Trin Coll Bris DipTh86. dss 86 **d** 87 **p** 94. W Holl St Luke *Lon* 86-87; Par Dn 87-89; C Glas St Oswald *Glas* 89-92; NSM Knightswood H Cross Miss from 92. *144 Garscadden Road, Glasgow G15 6PR* 0141-944 8491

PHAIR, Henry Lloyd. b 17. MBE64. TCD BA42 MA49. **d** 42 **p** 43. Chapl RAF 55-72; V Ercall Magna *Lich* 76-81; V Rowton 76-81; rtd 82; Perm to Offic *Chich* from 82. *43 Ashleigh Road, Horsham, W Sussex RH12 2LE* Horsham (01403) 251161

PHALO, Arthur. b 25. St Bede's Coll Umtata. **d** 52 **p** 54. S Africa 53-76; SSJE from 60. *St Edward's House, 22 Great College Street, London SW1P 3QA* 0171-222 9234

PHARAOH, Douglas William. b 18. MSHA456. Worc Ord Coll 68. **d** 69 **p** 70. C Gt Malvern Ch Ch *Worc* 69-71; Area Sec Leprosy Miss 71-72; P-in-c Gateshead St Cuth *Dur* 72-73; V New Seaham 73-76; P-in-c Wymeswold *Leic* 76-78; V Wymeswold and Prestwold w Hoton 78-80; P-in-c Grandborough w Willoughby and Flecknoe *Cov* 80-81; V 81-83; rtd 83; Perm to Offic *Cov* from 83. *5 Margetts Close, Kenilworth, Warks CV8 1EN* Kenilworth (01926) 53807

PHAROAH, Donald James. b 05. AKC27. **d** 28 **p** 29. V Headcorn *Cant* 57-71; rtd 71; Perm to Offic *Roch* from 71. *5 Springshaw Close, Sevenoaks, Kent TN13 2QE* Sevenoaks (01732) 456542

PHEELY, William Rattray. b 35. EN(M)88. Edin Th Coll 57. **d** 60 **p** 61. C Glas St Mary *Glas* 60-63; C Salisbury St Martin *Sarum* 63-66; Guyana 66-82; V Bordesley St Oswald *Birm* 82-86; Perm to Offic from 86. *Flat 23, Frogmoor House, 571 Hob Moor Road, Birmingham B25 8XD* 0121-783 1970

PHEIFFER, John Leslie. b 18. Wells Th Coll. **d** 67 **p** 68. Chapl Twickenham Prep Sch 69-71; C Chobham w Valley End *Guildf* 71-76; C Highcliffe w Hinton Admiral *Win* 79-79; V

Portswood St Denys 79-85; rtd 86. *4 Haywards Close, Felpham, Bognor Regis, W Sussex PO22 8HF* Bognor Regis (01243) 828985

PHELAN, Thomas Sylvester Patrick. b 36. Leic Univ DSocStuds62 Southn Univ DASS79 CQSW79. Chich Th Coll DipTh94. **d** 94 **p** 95. C Somers Town St Mary *Lon* from 94. *2A Camden Terrace, London NW1 9BP* 0171-267 8704

PHELPS, Canon Arthur Charles. b 26. St Cath Coll Cam BA50 MA55. Ridley Hall Cam 51. **d** 53 **p** 54. V Collier Row St Jas *Chelmsf* 65-75; R Thorpe Morieux w Preston and Brettenham *St E* 75-84; R Rattlesden w Thorpe Morieux and Brettenham 84-90; Hon Can St E Cathl 89-90; rtd 90. *Newland, Sandy Lane, Harlyn Bay, Padstow, Cornwall PL28 8SD* Padstow (01841) 520697

PHELPS, Ian James. b 29. Oak Hill Th Coll 53. **d** 56 **p** 57. CF (R of O) 67-84; Youth Chapl *Leic* 67-85; Dioc Adult Educn Officer 85-91; Past Asst to Adn Leic 91-94; rtd 94. *Farrier's Cottage, 1 Weir Lane, Houghton on the Hill, Leicester LE7 9GR* Leicester (0116) 241 6599

PHELPS, Ian Ronald. b 28. FLS58 Lon Univ BSc53 PhD57. Chich Th Coll 57. **d** 59 **p** 60. V Brighton St Luke *Chich* 68-74; TV Brighton Resurr 74-76; V Peacehaven 76-94; rtd 94. *2 Kingston Green, Seaford, E Sussex BN25 4NB* Seaford (01323) 899511

PHILBRICK, Gary James. b 57. Southn Univ BA78 K Alfred's Coll Win CertEd79 ACertCM84 Edin Univ BD86. Edin Th Coll 83. **d** 86 **p** 87. C Southn Maybush St Pet *Win* 86-90; R Fawley from 90. *The Rectory, 1 Sheringham Close, Southampton SO4 1SQ* Southampton (01703) 893552

PHILIP, Peter Wells. b 35. Ridley Hall Cam 64. **d** 67 **p** 68. C Tollington Park St Mark w St Anne *Lon* 67-70; C Battersea St Pet *S'wark* 70-72; Hon C Kennington St Mark 72-73; New Zealand 73-92 and from 94; C Finchley Ch Ch *Lon* 92-93. *Address temp unknown*

PHILIPSON, John Wharton. b 05. St Jo Coll York 24. St Deiniol's Hawarden 66. **d** 66 **p** 67. Asst Dioc Dir of Educn *Newc* from 66; Hon C Gosforth St Nic 66-79. *Scarborough Court, Alexandra Way, Cramlington, Northd NE23 6ED* Cramlington (01670) 713633

PHILLIPS, Andrew Graham. b 58. Ex Univ BSc79. Chich Th Coll 84. **d** 87 **p** 88. C Frankby w Greasby *Ches* 87-89; C Liv St Chris Norris Green *Liv* 89-92; CF from 92. *clo MOD (Army), Bagshot Park, Bagshot, Surrey GU19 5PL* Bagshot (01276) 471717 Fax 412834

PHILLIPS, Canon Dr Anthony Charles Julian. b 36. Lon Univ BD63 AKC63 G&C Coll Cam PhD67 St Jo Coll Ox MA75 DPhil80. Coll of Resurr Mirfield 66. **d** 66 **p** 67. C-in-c Chesterton Gd Shep CD *Ely* 66-69; Fell Dean and Chapl Trin Hall Cam 69-74; Chapl St Jo Coll Ox 75-85; Hd Master K Sch Cant from 85; Hon Can Cant Cathl *Cant* from 86; Can Th Truro Cathl *Truro* from 86. *The King's School, Canterbury, Kent CT1 2ES* Canterbury (01227) 475501

PHILLIPS, Mrs Audrey Katherine. b 32. Lorain Coll Ohio BS73. Ox Min Course 88. **d** 91 **p** 94. NSM Princes Risborough w Ilmer *Ox* from 91. *1 The Chestnuts, Kirtlington, Kidlington, Oxon OX5 3UB* Bicester (01869) 50194

PHILLIPS, Benjamin Lambert Meyrick (Ben). b 64. K Coll Cam BA86 MA90. Ridley Hall Cam 87. **d** 90 **p** 91. C Wareham *Sarum* 90-94; C Chipping Barnet w Arkley *St Alb* from 94. *13 Cedar Lawn Avenue, Barnet, Herts EN5 2LW* 0181-449 4797

PHILLIPS, Brian Edward Dorian William. b 36. Bris Univ BA58. Ripon Hall Ox 58. **d** 60 **p** 61. C Ross *Heref* 60-64; Chapl RAF 64-68; Hon C Fringford w Hethe and Newton Purcell *Ox* 68-73; Chapl Howell's Sch Denbigh 73-76; C Cleobury Mortimer w Hopton Wafers *Heref* 76-80; V Dixton from 80. *The Vicarage, 38 Hillcrest Road, Wyesham, Monmouth, Gwent NP5 3LH* Monmouth (01600) 712565

PHILLIPS, Canon Brian Robert. b 31. Clare Coll Cam BA53 MA57. Linc Th Coll 54. **d** 56 **p** 57. V Highworth w Sevenhampton and Inglesham etc *Bris* 69-84; Hon Can Bris Cathl 84-90; P-in-c Long Newnton 84-87; P-in-c Crudwell w Ashley 84-87; R Ashley, Crudwell, Hankerton, Long Newnton etc 87-90; rtd 90. *Hannington, Hospital Road, Shirrell Heath, Southampton SO3 2JR* Wickham (01329) 834547

PHILLIPS, Very Rev Christopher John. b 46. **d** 79 **p** 80. Hong Kong from 79; Chapl Hong Kong Cathl 83-87; Dean Hong Kong from 88. *clo St John's Cathedral, Garden Road, Hong Kong* Hong Kong (852) 523-4157 Fax 521-7830

PHILLIPS, David Elwyn. b 17. St D Coll Lamp 62. **d** 64 **p** 65. C Port Talbot St Theodore *Llan* 68-70; V Abercanaid 70-87; rtd 87; Perm to Offic *Llan* from 87. *Carmel, 13 Tyleri Gardens, Abertillery, Gwent NP3 1EZ*

PHILLIPS, David Arthur. b 36. S Dios Minl Tr Scheme 90. **d** 94 **p** 95. NSM Canford Magna *Sarum* from 94. *32 Lynwood Drive, Merley, Wimborne, Dorset BH21 1UG* Bournemouth (01202) 880262

PHILLIPS, David Keith. b 61. New Coll Ox MA90. St Jo Coll Dur BA90. **d** 91 **p** 92. C Denton Holme *Carl* 91-94; C Chadderton Ch Ch *Man* from 94. *23 Lindale Avenue, Chadderton, Oldham OL9 9DW* 0161-624 0278

PHILLIPS, Duncan Laybourne. b 08. Wycliffe Hall Ox 45. **d** 47 **p** 48. P-in-c Eye, Croft w Yarpole and Lucton *Heref* 69-73; R 73-81; rtd 81; Perm to Offic *Heref* from 81. *The Old Parsonage, Eye, Leominster, Herefordshire HR6 0DP* Leominster (01568) 613513

PHILLIPS, Edward Leigh. b 12. St Edm Hall Ox BA34 MA47. Wycliffe Hall Ox 33. **d** 35 **p** 36. V Kingston w Iford *Chich* 52-75; V Iford w Kingston and Rodmell 75-78; RD Lewes 65-77; rtd 78; Perm to Offic *Glouc* from 78. *35 Woodland Green, Upton St Leonards, Gloucester GL4 8BD* Gloucester (01452) 619894

PHILLIPS, Mrs Elizabeth Beryl. b 34. **d** 94. C Farnborough Guildf from 94. *19 Fleming Close, Farnborough, Hants GU14 8BT* Farnborough (01252) 546093

PHILLIPS, Canon Frederick Wallace (Ferdie). b 12. MC43. Univ of Wales BA34. St Mich Coll Llan 34. **d** 36 **p** 37. V Margate St Jo *Cant* 64-74; Hon Can Cant Cathl 66-84; R Smarden 74-82; R Biddenden 80-82; rtd 82; Perm to Offic *Cant* from 84. *6 South Close, The Precincts, Canterbury, Kent CT1 2EJ* Canterbury (01227) 450891

PHILLIPS, Canon Geoffrey John. b 23. BNC Ox BA47 MA56. Ridley Hall Cam 54. **d** 56 **p** 57. R Gillingham w Geldeston and Stockton *Nor* 65-70; V Eaton 70-81; RD Nor S 71-81; Hon Can Nor Cathl 78-81; Chapl Vienna w Budapest and Prague *Eur* 81-87; rtd 87; Perm to Offic *Nor* from 87. *Mere Farmhouse, White Heath Road, Bergh Apton, Norwich NR15 1AY* Thurton (01508) 480656

PHILLIPS, Gwilym Caswallon Howell. b 07. Brothers of St Paul Barfield 30. **d** 32 **p** 33. V Evenley *Pet* 61-72; rtd 72. *1 The Glebe, Flore, Northampton NN7 4LX* Weedon (01327) 40423

PHILLIPS, Horace George. b 38. Man Univ BA60 Birm Univ DipTh62 MEd84. Qu Coll Birm 60. **d** 62 **p** 63. C Wotton St Mary *Glouc* 62-65; C Standish w Hardwicke and Haresfield 65-68; C-in-c Watermoor Holy Trin 68-74; V Churchdown St Jo 74-79; P-in-c Beckford w Ashton under Hill 79-85; P-in-c Overbury w Alstone, Teddington and Lt Washbourne *Worc* 84-85; V Overbury w Teddington, Alstone etc 85-88; P-in-c Peopleton and White Ladies Aston etc 88-94; Dioc Sch Officer from 88; R Peopleton and White Ladies Aston w Churchill etc from 94. *The Rectory, Peopleton, Pershore, Worcs WR10 2EE* Worcester (01905) 840243 Fax 612302

PHILLIPS, Ivor Lynn. b 44. Leeds Univ BA70. Cuddesdon Coll 69. **d** 71 **p** 72. C Bedlinog *Llan* 71-73; C Roath St Marg 73-77; TV Wolv All SS *Lich* 77-78; TV Wolv 78-81; Chapl Charing Cross Hosp Lon 81-91; Chapl Milan w Genoa and Lugano *Eur* 91-94; C Hampstead St Jo *Lon* from 95. *3 Holly Bush Vale, London NW3 6TX* 0171-433 1115

PHILLIPS, Ven Ivor Lloyd. b 04. MC45. Univ of Wales (Abth) BSc25. St Mich Coll Llan 30. **d** 31 **p** 32. Hon CF from 46; Can St Woolos Cathl *Mon* 62-73; Warden of Ords 62-73; Adn Newport 64-73; R Tredunnoc w Kemeys Inferior etc 65-73; rtd 73; Perm to Offic *St D* from 73. *2 Connaught House, 10 The Esplanade, Tenby, Dyfed SA70 7DU* Tenby (01834) 843505

PHILLIPS, Mrs Janet Elizabeth. b 37. Bp Grosseteste Coll CertEd57. E Midl Min Tr Course 81. **dss** 84 **d** 87 **p** 94. Wisbech St Aug *Ely* 84-86; Cam St Jas 86-87; Par Dn 87-91; Par Dn Wisbech SS Pet and Paul 91-94; C from 94. *St Peters Lodge, Love Lane, Wisbech, Cambs PE13 1HP* Wisbech (01945) 476149

PHILLIPS, Jeffery Llewellyn. b 32. Sarum & Wells Th Coll. **d** 87 **p** 88. C Ringwood *Win* 87-90; V Somborne w Ashley 90-93; rtd 93. *Queen's Acre, 3 Solent Avenue, Lymington, Hants SO41 9SD* Lymington (01590) 673955

PHILLIPS, John David. b 29. G&C Coll Cam BA50 MA54 CertEd69. SW Minl Tr Course 85. **d** 87 **p** 88. NSM St Martin w E and W Looe *Truro* 87-88; NSM St Merryn 88-94; rtd 94. *The Vicarage, St Merryn, Padstow, Cornwall PL28 8ND* Padstow (01841) 520379

PHILLIPS, John Eldon. b 50. Univ of Wales (Cardiff) BEd85. St Mich Coll Llan. **d** 90 **p** 91. NSM Merthyr Cynog and Dyffryn Honddu etc *S & B* 90-94; NSM Ystradgynlais from 95. *Heddfan, 105 Tawe Park, Ystradgynlais, Swansea SA9 1GU* Glantawe (01639) 849237

PHILLIPS, John William Burbridge. b 39. Dur Univ BSc60 Lon Univ BD68. Tyndale Hall Bris 65. **d** 68 **p** 69. C Barton Seagrave *Pet* 68-71; C Northn All SS w St Kath 71-75; R Irthlingborough 75-88; V Weedon Lois w Plumpton and Moreton Pinkney etc from 88. *3 Meeting Lane, Towcester, Northants NN12 6JX* Towcester (01327) 359317

PHILLIPS, Joseph Benedict. b 11. **d** 37 **p** 38. V Bradf St Andr *Bradf* 59-66; rtd 76. *100 Ruskin Avenue, Lincoln LN2 4BT* Lincoln (01522) 534411

PHILLIPS, Judith Mary. **d** 95. NSM Clydach *S & B* from 95. *Gwalia, Felindre, Swansea SA5 7PQ*

PHILLIPS, Canon Kenneth John. b 37. Coll of Resurr Mirfield 67. **d** 67 **p** 68. C Blackb St Jas *Blackb* 67-69; C-in-c Lea CD 70-80; V Lea 80-84; P-in-c Priors Hardwick, Priors Marston and Wormleighton *Cov* from 85; RD Southam 89-95; Hon Can Cov Cathl from 94. *The Vicarage, Priors Marston, Rugby, Warks CV23 8RT* Byfield (01327) 60053

PHILLIPS, Lamont Wellington Sanderson. b 33. S'wark Ord Course 73. **d** 76 **p** 78. NSM Tottenham St Paul *Lon* 76-83; P-in-c Upper Clapton St Matt 83-88; V from 88. *St Matthew's Vicarage, 20 Moresby Road, London E5 9LF* 0181-806 2430

PHILLIPS, Canon Martin Nicholas. b 32. Em Coll Cam BA57 MA61. Linc Th Coll 57. **d** 59 **p** 60. C Stocking Farm CD *Leic* 59-63; V Sheff Gillcar St Silas *Sheff* 63-71; V Birstall *Leic* 72-82; R Wanlip 72-82; V Birstall and Wanlip 82-88; R Loughb Em from 88; Hon Can Leic Cathl from 90. *The Rectory, 14 Forest Road, Loughborough, Leics LE11 3NW* Loughborough (01509) 263264

PHILLIPS, Michael John. b 54. Trent Poly BA77. Sarum & Wells Th Coll 78. **d** 81 **p** 82. C Killay *S & B* 81-83; C Treboeth 83-85; Hong Kong 85-89; Japan 89-91; TR Scilly Is *Truro* from 91. *The Chaplaincy, St Mary's, Isles of Scilly TR21 0NA* Scillonia (01720) 423128

PHILLIPS, Michael Thomas. b 46. CQSW81. Linc Th Coll 89. **d** 90 **p** 91. C Hyson Green *S'well* 90-91; C Basford w Hyson Green 91-93; Chapl HM Pris Gartree from 93. *HM Prison Gartree, Gallow Field Road, Market Harborough, Leics LE16 7RP* Market Harborough (01858) 410234 Fax 410808

PHILLIPS, Mrs Patricia. b 45. Glouc Sch of Min 83. dss 86 **d** 87 **p** 94. Newent and Gorsley w Cliffords Mesne *Glouc* 86-87; C from 87. *30 Knights Way, Newent, Glos GL18 1QL* Newent (01531) 820865

PHILLIPS, Patrick Noble Stowell. b 22. Edin Univ MA50. ALCD52. **d** 52 **p** 53. Canada 66-71; R Arthuret *Carl* 71-88; rtd 88. *14 Gipsy Lane, Reading RG6 2HB* Reading (01734) 264654

PHILLIPS, Percy Graham. b 26. St Aid Birkenhead 46. **d** 51 **p** 52. V Stonebridge St Mich *Lon* 65-70; R Vernham Dean w Linkenholt *Win* 70-78; C Farnham *Guildf* 78-82; TV Cove St Jo 82-89; rtd 89. *22 Charts Close, Cranleigh, Surrey GU6 8BH*

PHILLIPS, Peter. b 26. Oak Hill Th Coll 63. **d** 65 **p** 66. C St Alb St Paul *St Alb* 69-73; V Riseley w Bletsoe 73-84; R Arley *Cov* 84-91; rtd 91; Perm to Offic *B & W* from 91. *Milford House, 10 Albert Road, Clevedon, Avon BS21 7RP* Clevedon (01275) 875801

PHILLIPS, Peter Miles Lucas. b 44. Reading Univ BA66 QUB DipEd69 Univ of Wales (Cardiff) MEd89. St Mich Coll Llan 89. **d** 92 **p** 93. Dep Hd Teacher Dynevor Sch from 82; NSM Llangyfelach *S & B* from 92. *Gwalia, Felindre, Swansea SA5 7PQ* Swansea (01792) 772523

PHILLIPS, Raymond Arthur. b 29. K Coll Lon 49. **d** 53 **p** 54. V Stoke Newington St Faith, St Matthias and All SS *Lon* 68-73; Trinidad and Tobago 73-80; V Hillingdon All SS *Lon* 80-93; AD Hillingdon 93-94; Chapl St Cross Hosp Win from 94; rtd 94. *The Chaplain's Lodge, Hospital of St Cross, St Cross, Winchester, Hants SO23 9SD* Winchester (01962) 853525

PHILLIPS, Robin Michael. b 33. AKC58. **d** 59 **p** 60. C Hanwell St Mellitus *Lon* 59-61; C St Margarets on Thames 61-64; C Hangleton *Chich* 64-68; V Mellor *Derby* from 68; RD Glossop 89-93. *The Vicarage, Mellor, Stockport, Cheshire SK6 5LX* 0161-427 1203

PHILLIPS, Stephen. b 38. QUB BA60. Linc Th Coll 60. **d** 62 **p** 63. C Waddington *Linc* 62-65; C Gt Grimsby St Jas 65-72; V Kirmington from 72; V Gt Limber w Brocklesby from 73; R Croxton from 82; RD Yarborough from 92. *The Vicarage, Great Limber, Grimsby, S Humberside DN37 8JN* Roxton (01469) 560641

PHILLIPS, Thomas Wynford. b 15. Univ of Wales BA37 BD40. St Mich Coll Llan. **d** 43 **p** 44. R Upton Magna *Lich* 68-73; V Withington 68-73; R Roche *Truro* 73-80; R Withiel 73-80; RD St Austell 76-80; rtd 80. *Brynawelon, Wheal Quoit Avenue, St Agnes, Cornwall TR5 0SJ* St Agnes (01872) 552862

PHILLIPS, William Ufelgwyn Maundy. b 11. St D Coll Lamp BA. **d** 34 **p** 35. V Roath St Sav *Llan* 51-73; V Margam 73-80; P-in-c Llanharry 81-83; rtd 83; Perm to Offic *Llan* from 83. *1 St Paul's Court, Heol Fair, Llandaff, Cardiff CF5 2ES* Cardiff (01222) 553146

PHILLIPS-SMITH, Edward Charles. b 50. AKC71. **d** 73 **p** 74. C Wolv *Lich* 73-76; Chapl St Pet Colleg Sch Wolv 77-87; Hon C Wolv *Lich* 78-87; V Stevenage St Pet Broadwater *St Alb* 87-89; Chapl Millfield Jun Sch Somerset from 89. *1 Edgarley Cottages, Cinnamon Lane, Glastonbury, Somerset BA6 8LB* Glastonbury (01458) 834833

PHILLIPSON, Christopher Quintin. b 14. Ch Coll Cam BA36 MA40. Ridley Hall Cam 36. **d** 38 **p** 39. V Aldingbourne *Chich* 70-81; rtd 81; Perm to Offic *Chich* from 82. *91 Little Breach, Chichester, W Sussex PO19 4TZ* Chichester (01243) 785557

PHILLIPSON-MASTERS, Miss Susan Patricia. b 52. FIST76 ACP80 Sussex Univ CertEd73 K Alfred's Coll Win BEd81.

Trin Coll Bris DipHE88. **d** 89. C Saltford w Corston and Newton St Loe *B & W* 89-94; C Uphill from 94. *6 Ellesmere Road, Weston-super-Mare, Avon BS23 4UT* Weston-super-Mare (01934) 415802

PHILLPOT, Donald John. b 27. St Jo Coll Dur BA53 DipTh55. **d** 55 **p** 56. P-in-c Astley Abbotts *Heref* 68-78; R Bridgnorth w Tasley 68-78; V Lillington *Cov* 78-92; rtd 92. *22 William Orchard, Highnam, Gloucester GL2 8EL* Gloucester (01452) 386844

PHILPOTT, Barbara May. See WILKINSON, Mrs Barbara May

PHILPOTT, Canon John David. b 43. Leic Univ BA64. Trin Coll Bris 69. **d** 72 **p** 73. C Knutsford St Jo *Ches* 72-75; C Toft 72-75; C Bickenhill w Elmdon *Birm* 75-79; V Birm St Luke 79-91; RD Birm City 83-88; Hon Can Birm Cathl 89-91; V Chilvers Coton w Astley *Cov* from 91. *Chilvers Coton Vicarage, Coventry Road, Nuneaton, Warks CV11 4NJ* Nuneaton (01203) 383010

PHILPOTT, John Wilfred. b 44. K Coll Lon BD67 AKC67. **d** 68 **p** 69. C Norbury St Steph *Cant* 68-71; C Addiscombe St Mildred 71-75; V Whitfield w Guston from 75. *The Vicarage, 45 Bewsbury Cross Lane, Whitfield, Dover CT16 3EZ* Dover (01304) 820314

PHILPOTT, Ronald (Ron). b 38. IPFA69. Cranmer Hall Dur 88. **d** 89 **p** 90. NSM S Ossett *Wakef* 89-93; R Clitheroe St Jas *Blackb* from 93. *The Rectory, Woone Lane, Clitheroe, Lancs BB7 1BJ* Clitheroe (01200) 23608

PHILPOTT, Preb Samuel. b 41. Kelham Th Coll 60. **d** 65 **p** 66. C Swindon New Town *Bris* 65-70; C Torquay St Martin Barton *Ex* 70-73; TV Withycombe Raleigh 73-76; V Shaldon 76-78; P-in-c Plymouth St Pet 78-80; V from 80; RD Plymouth Devonport 86-93; Preb Ex Cathl from 91. *St Peter's Vicarage, 23 Wyndham Square, Plymouth PL1 5EG* Plymouth (01752) 662110

PHILPS, Mark Seymour. b 51. Worc Coll Ox BA73 MA78 Lon Univ MA75 Nottm Univ BA79. St Jo Coll Nottm 77. **d** 80 **p** 81. C Chadwell Heath *Chelmsf* 80-83; C Woodford Wells 83-87; V Tipton St Matt *Lich* from 87. *St Matthew's Vicarage, Dudley Road, Tipton, W Midlands DY4 8DJ* 0121-557 1929

PHILSON, James Alexander Summers (Hamish). b 20. Edin Th Coll 48. **d** 51 **p** 52. R Dunblane *St And* 53-62; Australia from 62; rtd 85. *38 Allenswood Road, Greenwood, W Australia 6024* Perth (9) 447-9523

PHIPPS, David John. b 46. Bris Univ BSc68. Trin Coll Bris 75. **d** 78 **p** 79. C Madron w Morvah *Truro* 78-80; C Kenilworth St Jo *Cov* 80-83; TV Barnstaple, Goodleigh and Landkey *Ex* 83-84; TV Barnstaple from 85. *The Vicarage, Tanners Road, Landkey, Barnstaple, Devon EX32 0NQ* Swimbridge (01271) 830083

PHIPPS, John Maclean. b 14. Em Coll Cam BA38 MA50. Cuddesdon Coll 38. **d** 39 **p** 40. V Speenhamland *Ox* 53-71; V Buckland 72-79; V Littleworth 72-79; R Pusey 72-79; rtd 79; Perm to Offic *Chich* 84-93. *10 The Limes, Linden Road, Bedford MK40 2UX* Bedford (01234) 365137

✠**PHIPPS, Rt Rev Simon Wilton.** b 21. MC45. Trin Coll Cam BA48 MA53. Westcott Ho Cam 48. **d** 50 **p** 51 **c** 68. C Huddersfield St Pet *Wakef* 50-53; Chapl Trin Coll Cam 53-58; Ind Chapl *Cov* 58-68; C Cov Cathl 58-68; Hon Can Cov Cathl 65-68; Suff Bp Horsham *Chich* 68-75; Bp Linc 75-86; rtd 86; Asst Bp Chich from 86; Asst Bp S'wark from 86. *Sarsens, Shipley, Horsham, W Sussex RH13 8PX* Coolham (01403) 741354

PHIZACKERLEY, Ven Gerald Robert. b 29. Univ Coll Ox BA52 MA56. Wells Th Coll 52. **d** 54 **p** 55. C Carl St Barn *Carl* 54-57; Chapl Abingdon Sch 57-64; R Gaywood, Bawsey and Mintlyn *Nor* 64-78; RD Lynn 68-78; Hon Can Nor Cathl 75-78; Hon Can Derby Cathl *Derby* from 78; P-in-c Ashford w Sheldon 78-91; Adn Chesterfield from 78. *The Old Parsonage, Taddington, Buxton, Derbyshire SK17 9TW* Taddington (01298) 85607 Fax 85583

PHYPERS, David John. b 39. Leic Univ BA60 CertEd61 Lon Univ BD65. Linc Th Coll 76. **d** 78 **p** 79. NSM Normanton *Derby* 78-80; NSM Sinfin 80-87; Lic to Offic 87-88; P-in-c Denby from 88; P-in-c Horsley Woodhouse from 88. *103 Church Street, Denby Village, Ripley, Derbyshire DE5 8PH* Derby (01332) 780730

PIACHAUD, Preb Francois Allen. b 12. Lon Univ BA32 BD35 Selw Coll Cam BA37 MA41. Westcott Ho Cam 37. **d** 37 **p** 38. V Chelsea Ch Ch *Lon* 51-86; Preb St Paul's Cathl 61-86; RD Chelsea 74-77; rtd 86; Perm to Offic *Ox* from 86. *8 Linden Avenue, Maidenhead, Berks SL6 6HB* Maidenhead (01628) 20866

PIBWORTH, John David. b 23. OBE79. Ripon Hall Ox 59. **d** 61 **p** 62. V Pennington *Win* 66-94; Chapl RNVR 67-79; rtd 94. *Toad Hall, 13A School Lane, Petersfield, Hants GU32 2AS* Petersfield (01730) 233011

PICK, David. b 44. Linc Th Coll 85. **d** 87 **p** 88. C Howden TM *York* 87-90; P-in-c Sledmere and Cowlam w Fridaythorpe,

Fimer etc 90-91; V from 91. *The Vicarage, Sledmere, Driffield, N Humberside YO25 0XQ* Driffield (01377) 226220

PICK, William Harry. b 23. Open Univ BA77. St Aid Birkenhead 51. **d** 54 **p** 55. V Stoneycroft All SS *Liv* 67-79; R N Meols 79-88; rtd 88. *8 Morley Road, Southport, Merseyside PR9 9JS* Southport (01704) 541428

PICKARD, Canon Frank Eustace. b 31. Lon Univ BSc52 St Cath Soc Ox BA56 MA63. St Steph Ho Ox. **d** 57 **p** 58. C Haydock St Jas *Liv* 57-59; C Davenham *Ches* 59-60; Asst Master St Dunstan's Sch Lon 60-63; Min Can Pet Cathl *Pet* 63-72; P-in-c Newborough 67-68; V 68-72; R Isham w Pytchley 72-76; R Abington from 76; Can Pet Cathl from 86. *The Rectory, 5 Abington Park Crescent, Northampton NN3 3AD* Northampton (01604) 31041

PICKARD, Ronald William. b 16. ALCD39. **d** 39 **p** 40. Chapl Br Emb Ankara *Eur* 70-71; rtd 81. *23 Tower Gardens, Deep Lane, Crediton, Devon EX17 2BQ* Crediton (01363) 774234

PICKARD, William Priestley. b 31. MIPM72. Clifton Th Coll 56. **d** 59 **p** 60. C Upper Tulse Hill St Matthias *S'wark* 59-63; Asst Warden Shaftesbury Crusade Bris from 64. *2 Edingworth Mansions, 2 Atlantic Road South, Weston-super-Mare, Avon BS23 2DE* Weston-super-Mare (01934) 628994

PICKEN, David Anthony. b 63. Lon Univ BA84 Kent Univ PGCE85. Linc Th Coll 87. **d** 90 **p** 91. C Worth *Chich* 90-93; TV Wordsley *Worc* from 93. *1 Denleigh Road, Kingswinford, W Midlands DY6 8QB* Kingswinford (01384) 278692

PICKEN, James Hugh (Brother James). b 51. Victoria Univ (BC) BMus75. Ripon Coll Cuddesdon BA79. **d** 80 **p** 81. C Jarrow *Dur* 80-83; SSF from 83; Perm to Offic *Sarum* 87-92; Guardian Alnmouth Friary from 92; Lic to Offic *Newc* from 92. *The Friary, Alnmouth, Alnwick, Northd NE66 3NJ* Alnmouth (01665) 830213

PICKEN, William Middlewood Martin. b 06. SS Coll Cam BA28 MA32. Westcott Ho Cam 29. **d** 30 **p** 31. Hon PV Truro Cathl *Truro* from 37; R St Martin by Looe 37-71; rtd 71. *2 Stratton Terrace, Falmouth, Cornwall TR11 2SY*

PICKERING, David Colville. b 41. Kelham Th Coll 61. **d** 66 **p** 67. C Chaddesden St Phil *Derby* 66-70; C New Mills 70-72; C Buxton 72-74; V Chesterfield St Aug 74-90; R Whittington from 90. *The Rectory, 84 Church Street North, Chesterfield, Derbyshire S41 9QW* Chesterfield (01246) 450651

PICKERING, Ven Fred. b 19. St Pet Hall Ox BA41 MA45. St Aid Birkenhead 41. **d** 43 **p** 44. V Chitts Hill St Cuth *Lon* 68-74; Adn Hampstead 74-84; rtd 84; Perm to Offic *Pet* 84-93; Perm to Offic *Ex* from 94. *11 Gracey Court, Woodland Road, Broadclyst, Exeter EX5 3LP* Exeter (01392) 460988

PICKERING, Geoffrey Craig (Geoff). b 40. Newc Coll of Arts NDD61 Leic Coll of Art and Design ATD62 Leic Univ CertEd62. S Dios Minl Tr Scheme 90. **d** 93 **p** 94. C Horsham *Chich* from 93. *St Leonard's Vicarage, Cambridge Road, Horsham, W Sussex RH13 5ED* Horsham (01403) 266903

PICKERING, John Alexander. b 41. TCD BA63 MA66. CITC 65. **d** 65 **p** 66. C Magherafelt *D & D* 65-67; C-in-c Outeragh *K, E & A* 67-68; I 68-71; Deputation Sec Hibernian Bible Soc 71-74; C-in-c Drumgoon and Ashfield 74-80; I Keady w Armaghbreague and Derrynoose *Arm* 80-83; I Drumcree from 83. *Drumcree Rectory, 78 Drumcree Road, Portadown, Craigavon, Co Armagh BT62 1PE* Portadown (01762) 333711

PICKERING, John David. b 38. **d** 86 **p** 86. NSM Ellon *Ab* 86-88; NSM Cruden Bay 86-88; Ind Chapl *Dur* from 88; TV Jarrow from 91. *St Andrew's House, Borough Road, Jarrow, Tyne & Wear NE32 5BL* 0191-489 3279

PICKERING, John Michael Staunton. b 34. Sarum & Wells Th Coll 71. **d** 72 **p** 73. C Gaywood, Bawsey and Mintlyn *Nor* 72-77; P-in-c Foulsham 77-81; R Foulsham w Hindolveston and Guestwick 81-88. *The Vicarage, Church Road, Bacton, Norwich NR12 0JP* Walcott (01692) 650375

PICKERING, John Roger. b 28. Fitzw Ho Cam BA52 MA56. Linc Th Coll 62. **d** 63 **p** 66. C Folkestone H Trin w Ch Ch *Cant* 71-73; P-in-c Buckland Newton *Sarum* 73-77; P-in-c Wootton Glanville and Holnest 73-77; P-in-c Osmington w Poxwell 77-80; C Eston w Normanby *York* 83-84; P-in-c Swine 84-90; rtd 90. *The Bull Pens, Treworder Farm, Ruan Minor, Helston, Cornwall TR12 7JL* The Lizard (01326) 290908

PICKERING, Malcolm. b 37. Sarum Th Coll 65. **d** 68 **p** 69. C Milton *Portsm* 68-70; C Stanmer w Falmer and Moulsecoomb *Chich* 70-75; Chapl Brighton Coll of Educn 71-75; V Hooe *Chich* 75-80; R Ninfield 75-80; V Ventnor H Trin *Portsm* 80-88; V Ventnor St Cath 80-88; Chapl St Cath Sch Ventnor 87-88; V Marton *Blackb* from 88. *St Paul's Vicarage, 55 Vicarage Lane, Blackpool FY4 4EF* Blackpool (01253) 762679

PICKERING, Mark Penrhyn. b 36. Liv Univ BA59 St Cath Coll Ox BA62 MA67. Wycliffe Hall Ox 60. **d** 63 **p** 64. C Claughton cum Grange *Ches* 63-67; C Newland St Jo *York* 67-72; TV Marfleet 72-76; V Kingston upon Hull St Nic 76-85; V Elloughton and Brough w Brantingham 85-88; Chapl R Hull

Hosps NHS Trust from 88. *Hull Royal Infirmary, Anlaby Road, Hull HU3 2JZ, or 8 The Pickerings, North Ferriby, N Humberside HU14 3DW* Hull (01482) 328541 or 634892

PICKERING, Stephen Philip. b 52. St Jo Coll York CertEd75. Coll of Resurr Mirfield 77. **d** 79 **p** 80. C Wallsend St Luke *Newc* 79-82; Chapl RN 82-92; C-in-c Ryecroft St Nic CD *Sheff* from 92. *St Nicolas' House, Kilnhurst Road, Rawmarsh, Rotherham, S Yorkshire S62 5NG* Rotherham (01709) 522596

PICKERING, Thomas. b 07. Ch Coll Cam BA28 MA32. Ely Th Coll 30. **d** 30 **p** 31. C Leic St Mary *Leic* 30-35; C Leic St Geo 35-46; Lic to Offic 46-81; Perm to Offic from 81. *10 Park Hill Drive, Leicester LE2 8HR* Leicester (0116) 283 1242

PICKERING, William Stuart Frederick. b 22. K Coll Lon BD49 AKC49 PhD58 Manitoba Univ Hon DCL81. **d** 50 **p** 51. Canada 56-66; Lic to Offic *Newc* 66-87; rtd 87. *37 Gough Way, Cambridge CB3 9LN* Cambridge (01223) 312537

PICKETT, Brian Laurence. b 48. Reading Univ BA70. Qu Coll Birm BA73 MA77 Ripon Coll Cuddesdon. **d** 88 **p** 88. C Highcliffe w Hinton Admiral *Win* 88-91; P-in-c Colbury from 91; Chapl Southn HA from 91. *The Vicarage, Deerleap Lane, Southampton SO4 2EH* Ashurst (01703) 292132

PICKETT, Mrs Joanna Elizabeth. b 53. Leic Univ BA74 MA80. Wycliffe Hall Ox 87. **d** 89 **p** 94. Chapl Southn Univ *Win* 89-94; C N Stoneham from 94. *The Vicarage, Deerleap Lane, Southampton SO4 2EH* Ashurst (01703) 292132

PICKETT, Mark William Leslie. b 60. Westhill Coll Birm BEd84. Trin Coll Bris DipHE95. **d** 95. C Hellesdon *Nor* from 95. *7 Chapel Court, Norwich NR6 5NU* Norwich (01603) 405360

PICKETT, Peter Leslie. b 28. MRCS Lon Univ LDS. S Dios Minl Tr Scheme 83. **d** 86 **p** 87. NSM Eastbourne H Trin *Chich* 86-88; P-in-c Danehill 88-93; rtd 93; Perm to Offic *Chich* from 93. *33 Pashley Road, Eastbourne, E Sussex BN20 8DY* Eastbourne (01323) 731709

PICKLES, Harold. b 13. Sarum Th Coll 34. **d** 36 **p** 37. V Edwinstowe w Carburton *S'well* 57-78; rtd 78; Perm to Offic *St Alb* 78-84; Perm to Offic *Ripon* 84-93. *3 Old Deanery Close, Minster Road, Ripon, N Yorkshire HG4 1LZ* Ripon (01765) 604375

PICKLES, Mark Andrew. b 62. Edin Univ BA83. Cranmer Hall Dur 85. **d** 88 **p** 89. C Rock Ferry *Ches* 88-91; C Hartford 91-93; V Wharton from 93. *The Vicarage, 165 Crook Lane, Winsford, Cheshire CW7 3DR* Winsford (01606) 593215

PICKSTONE, Charles Faulkner. b 55. BNC Ox BA77 MA81 Leeds Univ BA80. Coll of Resurr Mirfield 78. **d** 81 **p** 82. C Birkenhead Priory *Ches* 81-84; Chapl Paris St Geo *Eur* 84; C Camberwell St Giles w St Matt *S'wark* 84-89; V Catford St Laur from 89; Asst RD E Lewisham from 92. *St Laurence's Vicarage, 31 Bromley Road, London SE6 2TS* 0181-698 9706

PICKTHORN, Canon Charles Howard. b 25. Linc Coll Ox BA48 MA52. Sarum Th Coll 48. **d** 50 **p** 51. R Bourton-on-the-Water w Clapton *Glouc* 60-91; Chapl RAF 60-76; RD Stow *Glouc* 67-90; P-in-c Gt Rissington 68-81; Hon Can Glouc Cathl from 77; rtd 90. *267 Prestbury Road, Prestbury, Cheltenham, Glos GL52 2EX* Cheltenham (01242) 521447

PICKUP, Harold. b 17. St Pet Hall Ox BA39 MA46. Ridley Hall Cam 46. **d** 47 **p** 48. C Middleton *Man* 47-50; V Gravesend St Mary *Roch* 51-57; Australia from 57. *69 Haig Street, Mowbray Heights, Tasmania, Australia 7248* Launceston (3) 262820

PICTON, Arthur David. b 39. Ch Ch Ox BA62 MA67. Chich Th Coll. **d** 65 **p** 66. C Hulme St Phil *Man* 65-67; C Swinton St Pet 67-71; R Stretford St Pet 71-79; P-in-c Knights Enham *Win* 79-86; R 86-89; V Basing from 89; RD Basingstoke from 93. *The Vicarage, Church Lane, Old Basing, Basingstoke, Hants RG24 0DJ* Basingstoke (01256) 473762

PIDOUX, Ian George. b 32. Univ Coll Ox BA55 MA60. Coll of Resurr Mirfield 54. **d** 57 **p** 58. C Middlesb All SS *York* 57-60; C Haggerston St Aug w St Steph *Lon* 60-62; C Aylesford *Roch* 80-81; TV Rye *Chich* 81-84; P-in-c Bridgwater St Jo *B & W* 84-86; V from 86; Chapl Bridgwater Hosp from 91. *St John's Vicarage, Blake Place, Bridgwater, Somerset TA6 5AU* Bridgwater (01278) 422540

PIDSLEY, Preb Christopher Thomas. b 36. ALCD61. **d** 61 **p** 62. C Enfield Ch Ch Trent Park *Lon* 61-66; C Rainham *Chelmsf* 66-70; V Chudleigh *Ex* from 70; RD Moreton 86-91; Preb Ex Cathl from 92. *The Vicarage, Chudleigh, Newton Abbot, Devon TQ13 0JF* Chudleigh (01626) 853241

PIERCE, Alan. b 46. St Mark & St Jo Coll Lon TCert68 Southlands Coll Lon BEd75 K Coll Lon MA85. Lon Bible Coll DipTh72 N Ord Course 89. **d** 92 **p** 93. NSM Bolton St Thos *Man* from 92. *3 Astley Road, Bolton BL2 4BR* Bolton (01204) 300071

PIERCE, Ven Anthony Edward. b 41. Univ of Wales (Swansea) BA63 Linacre Coll Ox BA65 MA71. Ripon Hall Ox 63. **d** 65 **p** 66. C Swansea St Pet *S & B* 65-67; C Swansea St Mary and H Trin 67-74; Chapl Univ of Wales (Swansea) 71-74; V Llwynderw 74-92; P-in-c Swansea St Barn from 92; Dioc Dir of Educn from 93; Can Brecon Cathl from 93; Adn Gower from 95. *St Barnabas' Vicarage, 57 Sketty Road, Swansea SA2 0EN* Swansea (01792) 298601

PIERCE, Brian William. b 42. St Steph Ho Ox 86. **d** 88 **p** 89. C Cudworth *Wakef* 88-93; TV Manningham *Bradf* from 93. *The Vicarage, 16 Wood Street, Bradford, W Yorkshire BD8 8HY* Bradford (01274) 730726

PIERCE, Bruce Andrew. b 58. TCD BBS80 BTh89. CITC 86. **d** 89 **p** 90. C Raheny w Coolock *D & G* 89-92; C Taney 92-93; I Lucan w Leixlip from 93. *The Rectory, 5 Uppercross, Ballyowen Lane, Ballydowd, Lucan, Co Dublin, Irish Republic* Dublin (1) 624-9147

PIERCE, Canon Claude Anthony (Tony). b 19. OBE46. Magd Coll Cam BA47 MA49 BD53. Ely Th Coll 47. **d** 48 **p** 49. Australia from 56; Can Perth 66-85; rtd 85. *61 Hawkestone Street, Cottesloe, W Australia 6011* Perth (9) 383-2719

PIERCE, Jeffrey Hyam. b 29. FBIM80 Chelsea Coll Lon BSc51. Ox NSM Course 86. **d** 88 **p** 89. NSM Gt Missenden w Ballinger and Lt Hampden *Ox* 88-93; NSM Penn from 93. *The Well House, Lee Common, Great Missenden, Bucks HP16 9JX* The Lee (01494) 837477

PIERCE, Stephen Barry. b 60. Birm Univ BA81 MA82. Cranmer Hall Dur. **d** 85 **p** 86. C Huyton St Mich *Liv* 85-89; V Walton Breck Ch Ch from 89. *Christ Church Vicarage, 157 Hartnup Street, Liverpool L5 1UW* 0151-263 2518

PIERCE, Thomas David Benjamin. b 67. Ulster Univ BA88. Oak Hill Th Coll DipHE92 BA94. **d** 94. C Cromer *Nor* from 94. *18 Vicarage Road, Cromer, Norfolk NR27 9DQ* Cromer (01263) 514352

PIERCE, William Johnston. b 32. N Ord Course. **d** 89 **p** 90. NSM Gt Crosby St Luke *Liv* from 89. *60 Kingswood Drive, Crosby, Liverpool L23 3DF* 0151-924 2400

PIERCY, Henry Graham. b 05. Armstrong Coll Dur BSc27. Ridley Hall Cam 27. **d** 29 **p** 30. V Newc St Geo *Newc* 50-68; rtd 68; Perm to Offic *Newc* from 68. *24 Whitebridge Park Way, Newcastle-upon-Tyne NE3 5LU* 0191-284 7999

PIERPOINT, Canon David. **d** 86 **p** 87. NSM Athboy w Ballivor and Killallon *M & K* 86-89; NSM Narraghmore w Timolin, Castledermot and Kinneagh *D & G* 89-91; Dean V St Patr Cathl Dub 90-91; NSM Dub St Patr Cathl Gp *D & G* 92-95; I Ch Ch Cathl Dub from 95; Can Ch Ch Cathl Dub from 95. *All Saints' Vicarage, 30 Phibsborough Road, Dublin 7, Irish Republic* Dublin (1) 830-4601 or 872-4154

PIERSSENE, Jeremy Anthony Rupert. b 31. CCC Cam BA55 MA. Ridley Hall Cam 56. **d** 58 **p** 59. C Enfield Ch Ch Trent Park *Lon* 58-61; Travelling Sec Scripture Union 61-69; Chapl Rugby Sch Warks 69-76; R Windlesham *Guildf* from 76; RD Surrey Heath 84-90. *The Rectory, Windlesham, Surrey GU20 6AA* Bagshot (01276) 472363

PIGGOTT, Andrew John. b 51. Qu Mary Coll Lon BSc(Econ)72. St Jo Coll Nottm 83. **d** 86 **p** 87. C Dorridge *Birm* 86-89; TV Kidderminster St Geo *Worc* 89-94; V Biddulph *Lich* from 94. *The Vicarage, Congleton Road, Biddulph, Stoke-on-Trent ST8 7RG* Stoke-on-Trent (01782) 513247

PIGGOTT, Raymond George. b 16. Leeds Univ BA38. Coll of Resurr Mirfield 38. **d** 40 **p** 41. V Roughey (or Roffey) *Chich* 65-80; P-in-c Iping Marsh 80-83; rtd 83; Perm to Offic *Chich* from 85. *Flat 3, Bramwell Lodge, Terry's Cross, Woodmancote, Henfield, W Sussex BN5 9SX* Henfield (01273) 493749

PIGOTT, Graham John. b 44. Kingston Coll of Art NDD64 Lon Univ DipTh71 BD73 Nottm Univ MPhil84. St Jo Coll Nottm DPS81. **d** 81 **p** 82. C Beeston *S'well* 81-84; P-in-c W Bridgford 84-88; V Wilford Hill from 88. *The Parsonage, Boundary Road, West Bridgford, Notts NG2 7BD* Nottingham (0115) 923 3492

PIGOTT, Canon John Drummond. b 26. TCD Div Test50 BA50 MA56. **d** 51 **p** 52. C Belf St Phil *Conn* 51-54; C Jordanstown 54-56; Chapl RAF 56-59; R Upper Clatford w Goodworth Clatford *Win* 59-65; V Warley Woods *Birm* 65-74; RD Warley 72-74; V Boldmere from 74; Hon Can Birm Cathl from 81; RD Sutton Coldfield 88-93. *The Vicarage, Church Road, Sutton Coldfield, W Midlands B73 5RX* 0121-373 0207

PIGOTT, Nicholas John Capel. b 48. Qu Coll Birm 75. **d** 78 **p** 79. C Belmont *Dur* 78-79; C Folkestone St Sav *Cant* 79-82; C Birm St Geo *Birm* 82-85; V Stevenage SS Hugh and Jo Chells *St Alb* 85-91; TV Totnes and Berry Pomeroy *Ex* 91; TV Totnes, Bridgetown & Berry Pomeroy & Dartington from 91. *St John's Vicarage, Crosspark, Totnes, Devon TQ9 5BQ* Totnes (01803) 867961

PIGREM, Terence John (Tim). b 39. Oak Hill Th Coll 66. **d** 69 **p** 70. C Islington St Andr w St Thos and St Matthias *Lon* 69-73; C Barking St Marg w St Patr *Chelmsf* 73-75; TV 75-76; C W Holl St Luke *Lon* 76-79; V from 79. *St Luke's Vicarage, Penn Road, London N7 9RE* 0171-607 1504

PIKE, David Frank. b 35. CEng MIMechE BA Lon Univ TCert. S Dios Minl Tr Scheme 82. **d** 85 **p** 86. NSM Lancing w Coombes *Chich* 85-88; R Albourne w Sayers Common and

Twineham 88-94; V Wisborough Green from 94. *The Vicarage, Wisborough Green, Billingshurst, W Sussex RH14 0DZ* Wisborough Green (01403) 700339

PIKE, Eric Sydney. b 13. Lon Univ BSc52 Lon Inst of Educn DipRE67. S'wark Ord Course 78. **d** 79 **p** 80. NSM Wimbledon Em Ridgway Prop Chpl *S'wark* 79-84; NSM Iford *Win* 84-85; Perm to Offic from 85. *31 Seaward Avenue, Bournemouth BH6 3SJ* Bournemouth (01202) 432398

PIKE, George Richard. b 38. BSc. W Midl Minl Tr Course 79. **d** 82 **p** 83. NSM Edgbaston St Bart *Birm* 82-89; NSM S Yardley St Mich from 89. *9 Star Hill, Birmingham B15 2LT* 0121-440 2843

PIKE, Horace Douglas. b 13. AKC48. **d** 48 **p** 49. V Baildon *Bradf* 59-71; R Burnsall 72-78; rtd 78; P-in-c Birdsall w Langton *York* 81-86. *18 Southfield Close, Rufforth, York YO2 3RE* Rufforth (01904) 738418

PIKE, Canon James. b 22. TCD. **d** 68 **p** 69. C Clooney *D & R* 68-72; I Ardstraw 72-76; I Ardstraw w Baronscourt 76-86; I Ardstraw w Baronscourt, Badoney Lower etc 76-92; Can Derry Cathl 90-92; rtd 92. *19 Knockgreenan Avenue, Omagh, Co Tyrone BT79 0EB* Omagh (01662) 249007 Fax 251382

PIKE, Paul Alfred. b 38. Wycliffe Hall Ox. **d** 84 **p** 85. C Penn Fields *Lich* 84-89; OMF from 89; Japan from 89. *c/o OMF, Belmont, The Vine, Sevenoaks, Kent TN13 3TZ* Sevenoaks (01732) 450747 Fax 456164

PIKE, Peter John. b 53. Southn Univ BTh. Sarum & Wells Th Coll 81. **d** 84 **p** 85. C Broughton *Blackb* 84-88; V Woodplumpton 88-93; Asst Dir of Ords and Voc Adv 89-93; P-in-c Barnacre w Calder Vale from 93; Carl Dioc Tr Course from 93. *The Vicarage, Delph Lane, Barnacre, Garstang, Preston PR3 1GL* Garstang (01995) 602117

PIKE, Robert James. b 47. Kelham Th Coll 66. **d** 70 **p** 71. C Cov St Pet *Cov* 70-74; C Bilton 74-76; P-in-c Southall St Geo *Lon* 76-81; V S Harrow St Paul 81-86; C Hillingdon St Jo 86-88; Chapl Hillingdon Hosp & Mt Vernon Hosp Uxbridge 88-90; Perm to Offic from 91. *6 Salt Hill Close, Uxbridge, Middx UB8 1PZ* Uxbridge (01895) 235212

PIKE, Canon Roger Walter. b 31. Roch Th Coll 65. **d** 67 **p** 68. C Wokingham St Paul *Ox* 67-70; C Whitley Ch Ch 70-76; C-in-c California CD 76-80; V Cowes St Faith *Portsm* 80-94; Hon Can Portsm Cathl 92-94; rtd 94. *45 Conway Road, Falmouth, Cornwall TR11 4LA* Falmouth (01326) 315901

PIKE, Timothy David. b 68. Collingwood Coll Dur BA90 Leeds Univ BA94. Coll of Resurr Mirfield 92. **d** 95. C Owton Manor *Dur* from 95. *40 Wisbech Close, Hartlepool, Cleveland TS25 2LW* Hartlepool (01429) 871522

PILDITCH, Miss Patricia Desiree. b 21. dss 82 **d** 87 **p** 94. Barnstaple *Ex* 82-87; Hon Par Dn 87-94; Hon C from 94; Chapl Asst N Devon Distr Hosp Barnstaple from 82. *4 The Mews, Swimbridge, Barnstaple, Devon EX32 0QB* Swimbridge (01271) 830770

PILGRIM, Colin Mark. b 56. BA77 Geneva Univ CES84. Westcott Ho Cam 81. **d** 84 **p** 85. C Chorlton-cum-Hardy St Clem *Man* 84-87; C Whitchurch *Bris* 87-89; V Bedminster Down from 89. *St Oswald's Vicarage, Cheddar Grove, Bristol BS13 7EN* Bristol (0117) 964 2649

PILGRIM, Ms Judith Mary. b 44. Westcott Ho Cam 88. **d** 90 **p** 94. C Probus, Ladock and Grampound w Creed and St Erme *Truro* 90-94; Par Dn Nottm All SS *S'well* 94; C from 94; Asst Chapl to the Deaf from 94. *4 Birkland Avenue, Peel Street, Nottingham NG1 4GT* Nottingham (0115) 941 0369

PILKINGTON, Miss Anne. b 57. Aston Tr Scheme 88 N Ord Course 90. **d** 93 **p** 94. C Wythenshawe Wm Temple Ch *Man* from 93. *7 Thorngreen Road, Woodhouse Park, Manchester M22 6GB* 0161-436 2981

PILKINGTON, Charles George Willink. b 21. Trin Coll Cam BA42 MA64. Westcott Ho Cam. **d** 63 **p** 64. R Withington *Man* 68-88; rtd 88; Perm to Offic *Man* from 88. *32 Rathen Road, Withington, Manchester M20 9GH* 0161-434 5365

PILKINGTON, Canon Christopher Frost. b 23. Trin Coll Cam BA50 MA60. Ridley Hall Cam 50. **d** 52 **p** 53. R Bris St Steph w St Nic and St Leon *Bris* 68-81; P-in-c 81-82; Hon Can Bris Cathl 79-82; Hon Chapl Cancer Help Cen Bris 82-89; Lic to Offic from 82; rtd 89. *North Lawn, Ston Easton, Bath BA3 4DG* Chewton Mendip (01761) 241472

PILKINGTON, Edward Russell. b 39. ALCD65. **d** 65 **p** 66. C Eccleshill *Bradf* 65-68; C Billericay St Mary *Chelmsf* 68-72; V New Thundersley 72-78; R Theydon Garnon 78-82; V Gidea Park from 82. *St Michael's Vicarage, Main Road, Romford RM2 5EL* Romford (01708) 741084

PILKINGTON, John Rowan. b 32. Magd Coll Cam BA55 MA59. Ridley Hall Cam 57. **d** 59 **p** 60. C Ashtead *Guildf* 59-61; C Wimbledon *S'wark* 62-65; R Newhaven *Chich* 65-75; R Farlington *Portsm* 75-89; V Darlington St Mark w St Paul *Dur* from 89. *St Mark's Vicarage, 394 North Road, Darlington, Co Durham DL1 3BH* Darlington (01325) 382400

PILKINGTON, Canon Peter. b 33. Jes Coll Cam BA55 MA59. Westcott Ho Cam 58. **d** 59 **p** 60. C Bakewell *Derby* 59-62;

Chapl Eton Coll Windsor 62-75; Hd Master K Sch Cant 75-85; Hon Can Cant Cathl *Cant* 75-90; High Master St Paul's Sch Barnes 86-92; Chmn Broadcasting Complaints Commn from 92; Hon C Pimlico St Mary Graham Terrace *Lon* from 92. *St Mary's Presbytery, 30 Bourne Street, London SW1W 8JJ* 0171-730 4883 or 630 1966

PILKINGTON, Timothy William. b 54. Nottm Univ BA85. Linc Th Coll 82. **d** 85 **p** 86. C Newquay *Truro* 85-88; C Cockington *Ex* 88-91; R St John w Millbrook *Truro* from 91. *The Vicarage, Millbrook, Torpoint, Cornwall PL10 1BW* Plymouth (01752) 822264

PILL, Hugh Godfrey Reginald. d 89 **p** 90. NSM Hugglescote w Donington, Ellistown and Snibston *Leic* 89-91; NSM Malborough w S Huish, W Alvington and Churchstow *Ex* 91-92. *12 Hilary Crescent, Whitwick, Coalville, Leicester LE67 5PL* Coalville (01530) 836726

✠**PILLAR, Rt Rev Kenneth Harold.** b 24. Qu Coll Cam BA48 MA53. Ridley Hall Cam 48. **d** 50 **p** 51 **c** 82. C Childwall All SS *Liv* 50-53; Chapl Lee Abbey 53-57; V New Beckenham St Paul *Roch* 57-62; V Cant St Mary Bredin *Cant* 62-65; Warden Lee Abbey 65-70; V Waltham Abbey *Chelmsf* 70-82; RD Chigwell 76-78; RD Epping Forest 78-82; Suff Bp Hertf *St Alb* 82-89; rtd 89; Asst Bp Sheff from 89. *75 Dobcroft Road, Sheffield S7 2LS* Sheffield (0114) 236 7902

PILLAR, Kenneth James. b 50. St Jo Coll Nottm 70. **d** 74 **p** 75. C Wilmington *Roch* 74-79; CF 79-87 and from 89; R Curry Rivel w Fivehead and Swell *B & W* 87-89. *clo MOD (Army), Bagshot Park, Bagshot, Surrey GU19 5PL* Bagshot (01276) 471717 Fax 412834

PILLING, Neville. b 32. ACMA60 FCCA81 CertEd71. Is of Man Tr Inst 88. **d** 92 **p** 93. NSM Douglas St Matt *S & M* from 92. *Morwenna, Athol Park, Port Erin, Isle of Man IM9 6ES* Douglas (01624) 832382

PIMENTEL, Peter Eric. b 55. BA. Ridley Hall Cam. **d** 82 **p** 83. C Gt Ilford St Andr *Chelmsf* 82-85; Chapl Basingstoke Distr Hosp 85-88; TV Grays Thurrock from 88. *St Mary's Vicarage, 147 Rectory Road, Grays, Essex RM17 6AG* Grays Thurrock (01375) 373685

PIMM, Robert John. b 57. ACIB82 Bris Univ BA78. Trin Coll Bris ADMT94. **d** 94. C Long Benton *Newc* from 94. *5 Ravenswood Close, Forest Hall, Newcastle upon Tyne NE12 9LU* 0191-270 2011

PIMPERTON, Raymond Swindale. b 12. Linc Th Coll 77. **d** 77 **p** 78. Hon C Holbeach *Linc* 77-83; rtd 83; Perm to Offic *Linc* from 83. *6 Chestnut Avenue, Holbeach, Spalding, Lincs PE12 7NE* Holbeach (01406) 22458

PINCHES, Donald Antony. b 32. Pemb Coll Cam BA55 MA60 Linacre Coll Ox BA67. Wycliffe Hall Ox 64. **d** 67 **p** 68. C Aylesbury *Ox* 67-71; C Compton Gifford *Ex* 71-74; TV Lydford, Brent Tor, Bridestowe and Sourton 74-77; V Shiphay Collaton from 77. *St John's Vicarage, 83 Cadewell Lane, Torquay TQ2 7HP* Torquay (01803) 613361

PINDER, Ven Charles. b 21. AKC49. **d** 50 **p** 51. V Catford St Laur *S'wark* 60-73; Sub-Dean S Lewisham 68-73; Boro Dean Lambeth 73-86; Adn Lambeth 86-88; rtd 88. *22 Somerstown, Chichester, W Sussex PO19 4AG* Chichester (01243) 779708

PINDER, John Ridout. b 43. Peterho Cam BA65 MA69. Cuddesdon Coll 65. **d** 73 **p** 74. C Leavesden All SS *St Alb* 73-76; Gen Sec Melanesian Miss 77-89; P-in-c Harpsden w Bolney *Ox* 82-89; R Farlington *Portsm* from 89. *27 Farlington Avenue, Farlington, Portsmouth PO6 1DF* Cosham (01705) 375145

PINDER-PACKARD, John. b 47. Lon Univ BSc. N Ord Course 81. **d** 84 **p** 85. NSM Mosborough *Sheff* 84-85; C Norton 85-88; V New Whittington *Derby* from 88. *The Vicarage, 121 Handley Road, New Whittington, Chesterfield, Derbyshire S43 2EF* Chesterfield (01246) 455830

PINE, David Michael. b 41. Lich Th Coll 68. **d** 71 **p** 72. C Northam *Ex* 71-74; R Toft w Caldecote and Childerley *Ely* 74-80; R Hardwick 74-80; V Ipswich St Andr *St E* 80-84; P-in-c Hazelbury Bryan w Stoke Wake etc *Sarum* 84-91; R Hazelbury Bryan and the Hillside Par 91-93; V Steep and Froxfield w Privett *Portsm* from 93. *The Vicarage, Steep, Petersfield, Hants GU32 2DB* Petersfield (01730) 264282

PINES, Dr Christopher Derek (Chris). b 65. Lon Univ MB, BS89. Oak Hill Th Coll DipHE93 BA93. **d** 93 **p** 94. C Heref St Pet w St Owen and St Jas *Heref* from 93. *6 Ledbury Road, Hereford HR1 2SY* Hereford (01432) 354197

PINFIELD, Leslie Arthur. b 57. Birm Univ BMus79 Univ Coll Lon DipLib90. St Steph Ho Ox DipMin94. **d** 94. C Bath Bathwick *B & W* from 94. *64 St Johns Road, Bath BA2 6PT* Bath (01225) 466375

PINK, Canon David. b 34. Qu Coll Cam BA58 MA62. Linc Th Coll 58. **d** 60 **p** 61. V Kirton in Holland *Linc* 65-71; V Spittlegate 71-77; Ecum Officer Lincs and S Humberside 77-85; Can and Preb Linc Cathl from 77; P-in-c Canwick 77-87; R Washingborough w Heighington 87-88;

R Washingborough w Heighington and Canwick 88-90; rtd 90. *The Old School, Swarby, Sleaford, Lincs NG34 8TG* Sleaford (01529) 5403

PINKERTON, Ms Patricia Edith. b 38. California Univ BA72 MA75 BTh80. Ch Div Sch of the Pacific (USA). **d** 81 **p** 82. USA 81-88; C Coleford w Staunton *Glouc* 88-92; D-in-c St Briavels w Hewelsfield 92-94; P-in-c from 94. *The Vicarage, St Anne's Close, St Briavels, Lydney, Glos GL15 6UE* Dean (01594) 530345

PINNER, John Philip. b 37. K Coll Lon BA59. Westcott Ho Cam 69. **d** 71 **p** 72. C Dover St Mary *Cant* 71-74; Chapl Felsted Sch Essex 74-83; New Zealand from 81. *clo Rathkeale College, Masterton, New Zealand* Masterton (59) 88060

PINNER, Canon Terence Malcolm William (Terry). b 35. Southn Univ MA89. AKC59. **d** 60 **p** 61. C Eltham St Barn *S'wark* 60-64; S Africa 64-67 and 69-74; USPG 67-69; Sec for Home Affairs Conf of Br Miss Socs 74-76; P-in-c Hinstock *Lich* 76-79; Adult Educn Officer 76-79; Adult RE Officer 79-83; Chapl Southn Univ *Win* 83-88; Tutor S Dios Minl Tr Scheme 88-92; Dioc Dir of Ords *Win* from 88; Hon Can Win Cathl from 92; P-in-c Old Alresford and Bighton from 93. *The Rectory, Kiln Lane, Old Alresford, Alresford, Hants SO24 9DY* Alresford (01962) 732780

PINNOCK, Geoffrey Gilbert. b 16. K Coll Lon 47. **d** 50 **p** 51. USA 66-72; Perm to Offic *Lon* 72-73; Perm to Offic *S'wark* 73-74; C Battersea St Phil w St Bart 74-75; P-in-c Boconnoc w Bradoc *Truro* 75-81; rtd 81. *11 Drove Acre Road, Oxford OX4 3DF* Oxford (01865) 247355

PINNOCK, Martyn Elliott. b 47. Dartmouth RN Coll 65. Linc Th Coll CMinlStuds93. **d** 93 **p** 94. C Fordingbridge *Win* from 93. *Hale Rectory, Woodgreen, Fordingbridge, Hants SP6 2AN* Fordingbridge (01725) 512307

PINSENT, Ewen Macpherson. b 30. Edin Th Coll 67. **d** 69 **p** 70. C Holt *Nor* 69-72; R Kelso *Edin* 72-82; R Blendworth w Chalton w Idsworth etc *Portsm* 82-90; R Blendworth w Chalton w Idsworth 90-92; rtd 92. *The Cross House, Child Okeford, Blandford Forum, Dorset DT11 8ED* Child Okeford (01258) 860803

PIPE-WOLFERSTAN, Clare Rachel. b 54. Bris Univ BA75. Bris Sch of Min 84. **d** 88 **p** 94. NSM Bris St Mary Redcliffe w Temple etc *Bris* from 88. *14 Acramans Road, Bristol BS3 1DQ* Bristol (0117) 966 3430

PIPER, Andrew. b 58. Magd Coll Ox BA79 MA83. Chich Th Coll 80. **d** 83 **p** 84. C Eastbourne St Mary *Chich* 83-88; TV Lewes All SS, St Anne, St Mich and St Thos 88-93; TR Worth from 93. *The Rectory, Church Road, Worth, Crawley, W Sussex RH10 4RT* Crawley (01293) 882229

PIPER, Clifford John. b 53. Aber Univ CSS88. Moray Ord Course 91. **d** 93 **p** 94. C Invergordon *Mor* from 93. *Hill Cottage, Hermitage Street, Evanton, Dingwall, Ross-shire IV16 9YJ* Dingwall (01349) 830377

PIPER, Gary Quentin David. b 42. Nottm Coll of Educn TCert65 Maria Grey Coll Lon DipEd71. Oak Hill Th Coll 75. **d** 78 **p** 79. Hon C Fulham St Matt *Lon* 78-85; V from 85; AD Hammersmith 86-92. *St Matthew's Vicarage, 2 Clancarty Road, London SW6 3AB* 0171-731 3272

PIPER, Graham. b 58. Chich Th Coll BTh91. **d** 91 **p** 92. C Horsham *Chich* 91-94; TV Haywards Heath St Wilfrid from 94. *The Vicarage, 1 Sandy Vale, Haywards Heath, W Sussex RH16 4JH* Haywards Heath (01444) 450173

PIPER, John Howard. b 09. St Chad's Coll Dur BA31. **d** 32 **p** 34. R Rearsby w Ratcliffe on the Wreake *Leic* 68-78; P-in-c Thrussington 77-78; R Rearsby w Ratcliffe-on-the-Wreake etc 78-82; rtd 82; Perm to Offic *Leic* from 82. *52 Avenue Road, Quenibororough, Leicester LE7 3FA* Leicester (0116) 260 6605

PIPER, Kenneth John. b 29. St Luke's Coll Ex TCert53 Leeds Univ DipEd67. S Dios Minl Tr Scheme 79. **d** 82 **p** 83. NSM Bradf w Oake, Hillfarrance and Heathfield *B & W* 82-87; Chapl to Norway and Scandinavia Lay Tr Officer *Eur* 87-89; R Durrington *Sarum* 90-94; rtd 94; NSM Antony w Sheviock *Truro* from 94. *The Rectory, Sheviock, Torpoint, Cornwall PL11 3EH* St Germans (01503) 30477

PIPER, Canon Leonard Arthur. b 08. Clifton Th Coll 32. **d** 35 **p** 36. R Hurworth *Dur* 39-73; Offg Chapl RAF 40-87; R Dinsdale w Sockburn *Dur* 61-73; Hon Can Dur Cathl 70-73; rtd 73. *Bridge Cottage, Over Dinsdale, Darlington, Co Durham DL2 1PW* Dinsdale (01325) 332864

PIPPEN, Brian Roy. b 50. St D Coll Lamp DipTh73. **d** 73 **p** 74. C Newport Maindee St Jo Ev *Mon* 73-77; TV Cwmbran 77-84; V Newport Ch Ch 84-90; R Pontypool from 90. *The Vicarage, Trevethin, Pontypool, Gwent NP4 8JF* Pontypool (01495) 762228

PIRET, Dr Michael John. b 57. NY State Univ BA79 Michigan Univ MA80 PhD91 Mert Coll Ox MLitt91. Edin Th Coll 90. **d** 92 **p** 93. C St Andr Cathl Inverness *Mor* 92-94; Dean of Div Magd Coll Ox from 94. *Magdalen College, Oxford OX1 4AU* Oxford (01865) 276027

PIRIE, John Henry. b 07. Leeds Univ BA29. Coll of Resurr Mirfield 26. **d** 32 **p** 33. V Walworth St Jo *S'wark* 56-72; rtd 72; Lic to Offic *S'wark* 72-84; Perm to Offic from 84. *42 Walter's Close, Brandon Street, London SE17 1NE* 0171-708 1509

PITCHER, Canon David John. b 33. Ely Th Coll 55. **d** 58 **p** 59. C Kingswinford St Mary *Lich* 58-61; C Kirkby *Liv* 61-66; R Ingham w Sutton *Nor* 66-72; V Lakenham St Jo 72-76; R Framlingham w Saxtead *St E* 76-91; RD Loes 82-89; Hon Can St E Cathl from 85; R Woodbridge St Mary from 91. *St Mary's Rectory, Church Street, Woodbridge, Suffolk IP12 1DR* Woodbridge (01394) 382155

PITCHER, Robert Philip (Bob). b 47. Westhill Coll Birm DipEd70. Trin Coll Bris DipHE92. **d** 92 **p** 93. C Llansamlet *S & B* from 92. *The Parsonage, 456 Birchgrove Road, Swansea SA7 9NR* Swansea (01792) 817300

PITCHER, Ronald Charles Frederick. b 21. AKC50. **d** 51 **p** 52. V Newall Green *Man* 61-73; Chapl Wythenshawe Hosp Man 64-73; C-in-c Danesholme CD *Pet* 73-81; V Estover *Ex* 81-91; rtd 91. *18 East Wyld Road, Weymouth, Dorset DT4 0RP* Weymouth (01305) 771916

PITCHFORD, Herbert John. b 34. Dur Univ BA60. Ridley Hall Cam 60. **d** 62 **p** 63. C Heref St Martin *Heref* 62-68; R Much Birch w Lt Birch 68-78; P-in-c Much Dewchurch w Llanwarne and Llandinabo 73-78; R Much Birch w Lt Birch, Much Dewchurch etc 78-80; V Grange Park St Pet *Lon* 80-91; V Wylde Green *Birm* from 91. *Emmanuel Vicarage, 17 Greenhill Road, Sutton Coldfield, W Midlands B72 1DS* 0121-373 8348

PITE, Miss Sheila Reinhardt. b 60. St Jo Coll Dur BA82. Oak Hill Th Coll 85. **d** 88 **p** 94. Par Dn Derby St Aug *Derby* 88-92; C Brampton St Thos from 92. *1 Rhodesia Road, Chesterfield, Derbyshire S40 3AL* Chesterfield (01246) 231089

PITHERS, Brian Hoyle. b 34. Chich Th Coll 63. **d** 66 **p** 67. C Wisbech SS Pet and Paul *Ely* 66-70; V Fenstanton 70-75; V Hilton 70-75; V Habergham Eaves St Matt *Blackb* 75-85; P-in-c Habergham Eaves H Trin 78-85; V Burnley (Habergham Eaves) St Matt w H Trin 85-86; TR Ribbleton 86-92; V Torrisholme from 92. *The Ascension Vicarage, 63 Michaelson Avenue, Morecambe, Lancs LA4 6SF* Morecambe (01524) 413144

PITMAN, Clifford George. b 19. St D Coll Lamp BA48. **d** 49 **p** 50. V Tonna *Llan* 60-85; rtd 85; Perm to Offic *Llan* from 85. *7 Mackworth Drive, Neath, W Glam SA11 2BR* Neath (01639) 630262

PITT, Beatrice Anne. b 50. CertEd DipHE. Trin Coll Bris 80. **d** 82. C Rhyl w St Ann *St As* 82-85; CMS 87-92; Zaire 88-92; NSM Penycae *St As* from 92. *St Thomas's Vicarage, Church Street, Penycae, Wrexham, Clwyd LL14 2RL* Rhosllanerchrugog (01978) 840878

PITT, George. b 52. QUB BD79. CITC 81. **d** 81 **p** 82. C Belf St Mary *Conn* 81-86; C Hawarden *St As* 86-87; CMS 87-92; Zaire 88-92; V Penycae *St As* from 92. *St Thomas's Vicarage, Church Street, Penycae, Wrexham, Clwyd LL14 2RL* Rhosllanerchrugog (01978) 840878

PITT, Miss Karen Lesley Finella. b 62. Lon Univ BA84. Chich Th Coll BTh94. **d** 94 **p** 95. C Walton-on-the-Hill *Liv* from 94. *The Rectory Flat, Walton Rectory, Walton, Liverpool L4 6TJ* 0151-523 0683

PITT, Mervyn George Mottram. b 10. Qu Coll Cam BA32 MA36. Wells Th Coll 32. **d** 34 **p** 35. R Over Wallop w Nether Wallop *Win* 62-78; rtd 78; Perm to Offic *Win* from 78. *2 Luzborough View, Highwood Lane, Romsey, Hants SO51 9AG* Romsey (01794) 522500

PITT, Robert Edgar. b 37. Chich Th Coll 70. **d** 73 **p** 74. C Knowle *Bris* 73-77; C Wells St Cuth w Coxley and Wookey Hole *B & W* 77-81; TV Wellington and Distr 81-94; V Burnham from 94. *The Vicarage, Rectory Road, Burnham-on-Sea, Somerset TA8 2BZ* Burnham-on-Sea (01278) 782991

PITT, Canon Trevor. b 45. Hull Univ BA66 MA69 Open Univ DipEd91. Linc Th Coll 68 Union Th Sem (NY) STM70. **d** 70 **p** 71. C Sheff St Geo *Sheff* 70-74; TV Gleadless Valley 74-78; TR 78-79; P-in-c Elham *Cant* 79-82; V Elham w Denton and Wootton 82-91; Vice-Prin Cant Sch of Min 81-91; Six Preacher Cant Cathl *Cant* 85-91; Prin NE Ord Course *Newc* from 91; Hon Can Newc Cathl from 91. *Rose Cottage, The Causeway, Wolsingham, Bishop Auckland, Co Durham DL13 3AZ, or Carter House, Pelaw Leaze Lane, Durham DH1 1TB* Bishop Auckland (01388) 527467 or 0191-384 8317 Fax 0191-384 7529

PITTIS, Stephen Charles. b 52. Oak Hill Th Coll DipTh75. **d** 76 **p** 77. C Win Ch Ch *Win* 76-79; Chapl Bournemouth and Poole Colls *Sarum* 79-84; V Woking St Paul *Guildf* from 84. *St Paul's Vicarage, Pembroke Road, Woking, Surrey GU22 7ED* Woking (01483) 772081

PITTS, Miss Evadne Ione (Eve). b 50. Qu Coll Birm. **d** 89 **p** 94. C Bartley Green *Birm* 89-93; TD Kings Norton 93-94; TV from 94. *195 Monyhull Hall Road, Birmingham B30 3QN* 0121-458 3483

PITTS, Very Rev Michael James. b 44. Worc Coll Ox BA67. Qu Coll Birm 67. **d** 69 **p** 70. C-in-c Pennywell St Thos and Grindon St Oswald CD *Dur* 69-72; C Darlington H Trin 72-74; Chapl Dunkerque w Lille Arras etc Miss to Seamen *Eur* 74-79; V Tudhoe *Dur* 79-81; Chapl Helsinki w Moscow *Eur* 81-85; Chapl Stockholm 85-88; Hon Can Brussels Cathl 87-88; Canada from 88; Hon Chapl Miss to Seamen from 88; Dean and R Ch Ch Cathl Montreal from 91. *414 Rosyln Avenue, Westmount, PQ, Canada, H3Y 2T5*

PITYANA, Nyameko Barney. b 45. BA BD. Ripon Coll Cuddesdon. **d** 82 **p** 83. C Woughton *Ox* 82-85; V Highters Heath *Birm* 85-88; Dir Progr to Combat Racism WCC 89-92; Perm to Offic *Ox* from 92. *51 Derwent Avenue, Gladstone Park, Didcot, Oxon OX11 7RF*

PIX, Stephen James. b 42. Ex Coll Ox BA64 DipTh65 MA68. Clifton Th Coll 66. **d** 68 **p** 69. C St Helens St Helen *Liv* 68-71; Lic to Offic *S'wark* 71-76; Hon C Wallington H Trin 76-84; V Osmotherley w E Harlsey and Ingleby Arncliffe *York* 84-89; V Ox St Mich w St Martin and All SS *Ox* from 89. *The Vicarage, 24 St Michael's Street, Oxford OX1 2EB* Oxford (01865) 242444 or 240940

PIZZEY, Lawrence Roger. b 42. Dur Univ BA64. Westcott Ho Cam 65. **d** 67 **p** 68. C Bramford *St E* 67-71; Tutor Woodbridge Abbey 71-77; Asst Chapl Woodbridge Sch Suffolk 71-77; P-in-c Flempton w Hengrave and Lackford *St E* 77-85; R Culford, W Stow and Wordwell 77-85; P-in-c Acton w Gt Waldingfield 85-89; V 89-95; P-in-c Sudbury and Chilton from 95. *The Rectory, Gainsborough Street, Sudbury, Suffolk CO10 6EU* Sudbury (01787) 372611

PLACE, Donald Lee. b 37. **d** 74. C Stainton-in-Cleveland *York* 79-81; TV Loughton St Jo *Chelmsf* 81-83; Chapl Worc R Infirmary and Hosps 83-85; rtd 95. *265 15th Street# A, Marathon, Florida 33050, USA*

PLACE, Rodger Goodson. b 37. St Chad's Coll Dur BA60 DipTh62. **d** 62 **p** 63. C Pontesbury I and II *Heref* 62-65; C Heref St Martin 65-68; V Ditton Priors 68-75; R Neenton 68-75; P-in-c Aston Botterell w Wheathill and Loughton 69-75; P-in-c Burwarton w N Cleobury 69-75; P-in-c Dacre *Ripon* 75; P-in-c Dacre w Hartwith 75-76; V 76-82; V Wyther Ven Bede 82-92; P-in-c Roundhay St Jo from 92. *2A Ryder Gardens, Roundhay, Leeds LS8 1JS* Leeds (0113) 266 7959

PLACE, Thomas Richard (Tom). b 59. Ridley Hall Cam CTMin93. **d** 93 **p** 94. C Huyton St Geo *Liv* from 93. *31 Endmoor Road, Liverpool L36 3UH* 0151-489 4086

PLAISTER, Keith Robin. b 43. K Coll Lon BD65 AKC65. **d** 66 **p** 67. C Laindon w Basildon *Chelmsf* 66-71; V Gt Wakering 71-78; P-in-c Foulness 78; V Gt Wakering w Foulness 78-90; C Witham from 91. *57 Powers Hall End, Witham, Essex CM8 2NH* Witham (01376) 519017

PLAISTOWE, Ven Ronald Percy Frank. b 11. St Jo Coll Dur LTh34 BA35. Clifton Th Coll. **d** 35 **p** 36. C Bris St Ambrose Whitehall *Bris* 35-39; C St Alb Westbury Park Clifton 39-42; V Cleeve *B & W* 42-48; New Zealand from 48; Adn Timaru 53-63; Adn Sumner 63-68; Adn Christchurch 68-71. *165 Waimea Road, Christchurch 8, New Zealand* Christchurch (3) 849632

PLANT, Mrs Edith Winifred Irene (Ewith). b 31. Liv Univ BEd71. Cranmer Hall Dur 81. **dss** 83 **d** 87. Countesthorpe w Foston *Leic* 83-86; Loughb All SS and H Trin 86-87; Par Dn 87-90; Par Dn Thurnby Lodge 90-91; rtd 91; Perm to Offic *Leic* from 91. *21 Pochin Drive, Market Harborough, Leics LE16 7LP* Market Harborough (01858) 467321

PLANT, John Frederick. b 61. Man Univ BA82 Birm Univ DPS. Qu Coll Birm 83. **d** 85 **p** 86. C Kersal Moor *Man* 85-88; Chapl Aston Univ *Birm* 88-94; TR Market Bosworth, Cadeby w Sutton Cheney etc *Leic* from 94. *The Rectory, Park Street, Market Bosworth, Nuneaton, Warks CV13 0LL* Market Bosworth (01455) 290239

PLANT, Richard. b 41. Qu Coll Birm 88. **d** 90 **p** 91. C Skelmersdale St Paul *Liv* 90-93; R Golborne from 93. *The Rectory, Golborne, Warrington WA3 3TH* Ashton-in-Makerfield (01942) 728305

PLANT, Richard George Nicholas. b 45. Man Univ BA67. Coll of Resurr Mirfield 68. **d** 71 **p** 72. C Cleckheaton St Jo *Wakef* 71-74; P-in-c Adel *Ripon* 74-78; V Ireland Wood 78-82; V St Bart Armley w St Mary New Wortley 82-92; R Garforth from 92. *The Rectory, Church Lane, Garforth, Leeds LS25 1NR* Leeds (0113) 286 3737

PLANT, Robert David. b 28. Birm Univ BSc49. St Deiniol's Hawarden 74. **d** 76 **p** 80. NSM Llandrillo-yn-Rhos *St As* 76-79; NSM St Nicholas at Wade w Sarre and Chislet w Hoath *Cant* from 79. *4 Sandalwood Drive, St Nicholas-at-Wade, Birchington, Kent CT7 0PE* Thanet (01843) 41276

PLASTOW, Graham Henry George. b 40. St Jo Coll Nottm 68. **d** 71 **p** 72. C St Marylebone w H Trin *Lon* 71-74; C Marlborough *Sarum* 74-77; P-in-c N Shoebury *Chelmsf* 77-83; Chapl St Jo Hosp Chelmsf 83-88; P-in-c E Hanningfield *Chelmsf* 83-91; P-in-c W Hanningfield 87-89; V Enfield St Mich *Lon* from 91. *The Vicarage, Gordon Hill, Enfield, Middx EN2 0QP* 0181-363 2483

PLATT, Andrew Martin Robert. b 41. Oak Hill Th Coll 74. **d** 76 **p** 77. C St Alb St Paul *St Alb* 76-79; V Gazeley w Dalham and Moulton *St E* 79-85; RD Mildenhall 84-86; V Gazeley w Dalham, Moulton and Kentford 85-86; P-in-c Saxmundham 86-89; R from 89. *The Rectory, Manor Gardens, Saxmundham, Suffolk IP17 1ET*   Saxmundham (01728) 604234

PLATT, Harold Geoffrey. b 27. Down Coll Cam BA50 MA52. Ridley Hall Cam 51. **d** 53 **p** 54. R Lower Broughton St Clem *Man* 57-66; P-in-c Salford St Matthias w St Simon 62-66; Lic to Offic 66-76; Lic to Offic *Worc* 76-82; Hon C Belbroughton 83-86; Hon C Belbroughton w Fairfield and Clent 86-90; NSM Hagley 87-90; rtd 90; Co-ord for Decade of Evang 90-95; Perm to Offic *Nor* from 95. *Brecklands Cottage, Brecklands Green, North Pickenham, Swaffham, Norfolk PE37 8LG*   Swaffham (01760) 441581

PLATT, John Dendy. b 24. Magd Coll Cam BA49 MA55. Wells Th Coll 50. **d** 52 **p** 53. R Skelton w Hutton-in-the-Forest *Carl* 59-71; rtd 89. *17 Primula Drive, Norwich NR4 7LZ*   Norwich (01603) 504272

PLATT, Dr John Emerson. b 36. Pemb Coll Ox BA59 MA65 DPhil77 Hull Univ MTh72. Cuddesdon Coll 59. **d** 61 **p** 62. C Adlington *Blackb* 61-64; C Sutton St Mich *York* 64-68; C Ox St Giles *Ox* 68-71; Asst Chapl Pemb Coll Ox 68-69; Chapl from 69. *Pembroke College, Oxford OX1 1DW*   Oxford (01865) 276426

PLATT, Mrs Katherine Mary (Kitty). b 29. ARIBA51 Sheff Univ BA51. Westcott Ho Cam 76. **dss** 79 **d** 87. Chesterton Gd Shep *Ely* 78-84; Whitton St Aug *Lon* 84-86; Dean of Women's Min 86-94; Hampton St Mary 86-94; Par Dn 87-94; rtd 94. *56 Mereheath Park, Knutsford, Cheshire WA16 6AU*   Knutsford (01656) 651192

PLATT, Michael Robert. b 39. SS Coll Cam MA60 Nottm Univ PGCE61. Cuddesdon Coll 62. **d** 64. C Far Headingley St Chad *Ripon* 64-65; Asst Teacher Belmont Coll Barnstaple 65-68; Qu Coll Taunton from 68; Ho Master 72-83. *8 Court Hill, Taunton, Somerset TA1 4SX*   Taunton (01823) 270687

PLATT, William David. b 31. St Chad's Coll Dur BA54. Coll of Resurr Mirfield 54. **d** 56 **p** 57. C Bethnal Green St Jo w St Simon *Lon* 56-60; C Pinner 60-65; V N Hammersmith St Kath 65-72; V Woodham *Guildf* 72-88; Chapl Community of St Mary V Wantage from 88. *10 Denchworth Road, Wantage, Oxon OX12 9AU*   Wantage (01235) 762289

PLATTEN, Very Rev Stephen George. b 47. Lon Univ BEd72 Trin Coll Ox DipTh74. Cuddesdon Coll 72. **d** 75 **p** 76. C Headington *Ox* 75-78; Linc Th Coll 78-83; Tutor 78-83; Perm to Offic *Linc* 78-83; Can Res Portsm Cathl *Portsm* 83-89; Dir of Ords 83-89; Abp's Sec for Ecum Affairs *Cant* 90-95; Hon Can Cant Cathl from 90; Lic to Offic *S'wark* from 90; Perm to Offic *Newc* from 91; Dean Nor from 95. *The Deanery, Cathedral Close, Norwich NR1 4EG*   Norwich (01603) 666835 or 760140

PLATTS, Mrs Hilary Anne Norrie. b 60. SRN81 K Coll Lon BD85 AKC85. Ripon Coll Cuddesdon 86. **d** 88 **p** 94. C Moulsham St Jo *Chelmsf* 88-90; Chapl Reading Univ *Ox* from 90; C Calcot 90-92. *St Nicholas's Vicarage, 53 Sutcliffe Avenue, Reading RG6 7JN*   Reading (01734) 663563

PLATTS, Timothy Caradoc (Tim). b 61. LMH Ox BA83 MA88 St Cross Coll Ox DPhil88. Ripon Coll Cuddesdon 87. **d** 89 **p** 90. C Whitley Ch Ch *Ox* 89-95; P-in-c Earley St Nic from 95. *St Nicolas' Vicarage, 53 Sutcliffe Avenue, Reading RG6 7JN*   Reading (01734) 663563

PLAXTON, Edmund John Swithun. b 36. AKC60. **d** 61 **p** 62. C Crofton Park St Hilda w St Cypr *S'wark* 61-65; C Coulsdon St Jo 65-69; V Forest Hill St Paul 69-80; V Belmont 80-93; V Lingfield and Crowhurst from 93. *The Vicarage, Vicarage Road, Lingfield, Surrey RH7 6HA*   Lingfield (01342) 832021

PLAYER, Leslie Mark. b 65. Ridley Hall Cam CTM95. **d** 95. C Belper *Derby* from 95. *St Swithun's House, Holbrook Road, Belper, Derbyshire DE56 1PA*   Belper (01773) 825026

PLEDGER, Miss Alison Frances. b 56. Univ of Wales (Cardiff) BA79 PGCE80. Linc Th Coll 89. **d** 91 **p** 94. Par Dn Soham *Ely* 91-94; C 94; C Ely from 94; C Prickwillow from 94; C Chettisham from 94. *25 John Amner Close, Ely, Cambs CB6 1DT*   Ely (01353) 667568

PLIMLEY, Canon William (Bill). b 17. St Aid Birkenhead 50. **d** 52 **p** 53. V Laisterdyke *Bradf* 55-83; Hon Can Bradf Cathl 67-83; rtd 83; Perm to Offic *Bradf* from 83. *465 Bradford Road, Pudsey, W Yorkshire LS28 8ED*   Bradford (01274) 664862

PLIMMER, Wayne Robert. b 64. St Chad's Coll Dur BA85. St Steph Ho Ox 86. **d** 88 **p** 89. C Cockerton *Dur* 88-91; C Poulton-le-Fylde *Blackb* 91-93; V Darton *Wakef* from 93. *The Vicarage, 17 Beaumont Road, Kexborough, Darton, Barnsley, S Yorkshire S75 5JL*   Barnsley (01226) 384596

PLOWMAN, Richard Robert Bindon. b 38. Solicitor 61. Ridley Hall Cam 76. **d** 78 **p** 79. C Combe Down w Monkton Combe *B & W* 78-81; C Combe Down w Monkton Combe and S Stoke 81-83; V Coxley, Henton and Wookey from 83. *The Vicarage, Vicarage Lane, Wookey, Wells, Somerset BA5 1JT*   Wells (01749) 677244

PLUCK, Richard. b 60. Southn Univ BTh90. Aston Tr Scheme 84 Sarum & Wells Th Coll 86. **d** 90 **p** 91. C Harpenden St Nic *St Alb* 90-94; CF from 94. *c/o MOD (Army), Bagshot Park, Bagshot, Surrey GU19 5PL*   Bagshot (01276) 471717   Fax 412834

PLUMB, Gordon Alan. b 42. Leeds Univ BA. Sarum & Wells Th Coll. **d** 82 **p** 83. C Biggleswade *St Alb* 82-86; TV Grantham *Linc* from 86. *The Vicarage, Edinburgh Road, Harrowby, Grantham, Lincs NG31 9QR*   Grantham (01476) 64781

PLUMLEY, Jack Martin. b 10. St Jo Coll Dur BA32 MLitt39 K Coll Cam MA50. **d** 33 **p** 34. R Milton *Ely* 47-57; Perm to Offic 67-80 and from 80; rtd 77; P-in-c Longstowe *Ely* 80; Chapl Pemb Coll Cam 81-82; Acting Dean 81-82. *13 Lyndewode Road, Cambridge CB1 2HL*   Cambridge (01223) 350328

PLUMLEY, Paul Jonathan. b 42. St Jo Coll Nottm 71. **d** 74 **p** 75. C Mile Cross *Nor* 74-77; P-in-c Wickham Skeith *St E* 77-79; P-in-c Stoke Ash, Thwaite and Wetheringsett 77-79; Assoc Min Woodbridge St Jo 80-81; Chapl RAF 81-86; Perm to Offic *Roch* 86-95; R Hever, Four Elms and Mark Beech from 95. *The Rectory, Hever, Edenbridge, Kent TN8 7LH*   Edenbridge (01732) 862249

PLUMMER, Canon Charles Henry. b 06. St Aid Birkenhead 40. **d** 40 **p** 41. RD Hingham and Mitford *Nor* 66-86; R E Dereham w Hoe 66-73; P-in-c Mattishall 70-73; P-in-c Hockering w Mattishall Burgh 70-73; P-in-c N Tuddenham 70-73; P-in-c Welborne 70-73; P-in-c Yaxham 70-73; rtd 73; Perm to Offic *Glouc* 86-88. *c/o The Priest's House, 1 St Scholastica's Abbey, Teignmouth, Devon TQ14 8FF*   Teignmouth (01626) 777469

PLUMMER, Mrs Deborah Ann. b 49. St Hugh's Coll Ox BA71 MA75. St Alb Minl Tr Scheme 82. **dss** 85 **d** 87 **p** 94. Ickenham *Lon* 85-87; Par Dn 87-88; C Northolt St Mary 88-92; Chapl Lee Abbey 92-95; Lic to Offic *Ex* 92-95; P-in-c Kintbury w Avington *Ox* from 95. *The Vicarage, 3 Elizabeth Gardens, Kintbury, Newbury, Berks RG17 9TB*   Kintbury (01488) 658243

PLUMMER, Frances. b 36. **dss** 82 **d** 87 **p** 94. NSM Salfords *S'wark* from 87. *50 Park View Road, Salfords, Redhill RH6 7HU*   Crawley (01293) 785852

PLUMMER, Miss June Alice. b 29. Bris Univ BA50 CertEd51. Sarum & Wells Th Coll 89. **d** 89 **p** 94. NSM Hanham *Bris* from 89. *11 Glenwood Drive, Oldland Common, Bristol BS15 6RZ*   Bristol (0117) 949 8667

PLUMPTON, Paul. b 50. Keble Coll Ox BA72 MA76. St Steph Ho Ox 72. **d** 74 **p** 75. C Tonge Moor *Man* 74-76; C Atherton 76-79; V Oldham St Jas from 79. *The Vicarage, Yates Street, Oldham OL1 4AR*   0161-633 4441

PLUMPTRE, John Basil. b 25. Pemb Coll Cam BA49 MA54 CertEd52. Launde Abbey 79. **d** 75 **p** 76. C Leic St Pet *Leic* 75-80; C Stanford on Soar *S'well* 81-90; C Rempstone 81-90; C Costock 81-90; C E Leake 81-90; rtd 91. *14 Outwoods Road, Loughborough, Leics LE11 3LT*   Loughborough (01509) 215452

PLUNKETT, Michael Edward. b 38. Leeds Univ BSc61. Ely Th Coll 61. **d** 63 **p** 64. C Kirkby *Liv* 63-68; Lect Stockton-on-Tees 68-72; Lic to Offic *Dur* 72-73; TV Stockton 73-75; V Cantril Farm *Liv* 75-81; Soc Resp Officer 81-89; V Melling 81-91; TR Speke St Aid from 91. *The Rectory, Parade Crescent, Speke, Liverpool L24 2SH*   0151-486 1521

PLUNKETT, Pelham Stanley. b 12. TCD BA36 MA39. **d** 59 **p** 59. V Mile Cross *Nor* 69-81; rtd 81; Hon C Hordle *Win* 81-86; Hon C Eastbourne All SS *Chich* from 86. *Flat 3, 11 Grassington Road, Eastbourne, E Sussex BN20 7BJ*   Eastbourne (01323) 648193

PLUNKETT, Peter William. b 30. Oak Hill Th Coll. **d** 61 **p** 62. C Fazakerley *Liv* 61-64; C St Helens St Mark 64-68; V Kirkdale St Paul N Shore 68-79; P-in-c Bootle St Mary w St Jo 77-79; V Bootle St Mary w St Paul 79-81; V Goose Green 81-89; V W Derby St Jas from 89. *St James's Vicarage, Mill Lane, Liverpool L12 7LQ*   0151-256 8693

PLYMOUTH, Archdeacon of. See ELLIS, Ven Robin Gareth

PLYMOUTH, Suffragan Bishop of. See HAWKINS, Rt Rev Richard Stephen

PNEMATICATOS, Nicholas Peter Anthony. b 59. N Lon Univ BA92 Lon Univ MA93. Ripon Coll Cuddesdon DipMin95. **d** 95. C Yeovil St Mich *B & W* from 95. *220 Goldcroft, Yeovil, Somerset BA21 4DA*   Yeovil (01935) 25621

POARCH, Canon John Chilton. b 30. Bris Univ BA54. Ridley Hall Cam 54. **d** 56 **p** 57. C Swindon Ch Ch *Bris* 56-59; C Corsham 59-61; Seychelles 61-63; V Brislington St Cuth *Bris* 63-69; adn Seychelles 69-72; V Warmley *Bris* 72-86; R Syston 72-86; RD Bitton 79-85; P-in-c Bitton 80-86; Hon Can Bris Cathl from 82; P-in-c Langley Fitzurse 86-94; Dioc Dir of Ords 86-94; Dir Ord Tr from 94; P-in-c Draycot Cerne 87-94. *The Vicarage, Kington Langley, Chippenham, Wilts SN15 5NJ*   Kington Langley (01249) 750231

POCKLINGTON, Canon Eric Charles. b 12. Kelham Th Coll 28. **d** 35 **p** 36. V St Oswald in Lee w Bingfield *Newc* 70-78; RD

Hexham 71-78; Hon Can Newc Cathl 74-78; rtd 78; P-in-c Eyemouth *Edin* 78-82; Perm to Offic *Heref* 82-93. *7 Upperhall Close, Church Street, Ledbury, Herefordshire HR8 1SZ* Ledbury (01531) 633617

POCOCK, Frank Lovell. b 08. OBE59. Em Coll Cam BA32 MA36. Ridley Hall Cam 33. **d** 33 **p** 34. R Ringwould w Oxney *Cant* 67-77; P-in-c Kingsdown 74-77; rtd 77; Perm to Offic *Cant* from 79. *55 Balfour Road, Deal, Kent CT14 7HY* Deal (01304) 372314

POCOCK, Mrs Gillian Margaret. b 35. Nottm Univ BA57. Cranmer Hall Dur 82. **dss** 83 **d** 87 **p** 94. Bearpark *Dur* 83-88; Hon Par Dn 87-88; Par Dn S Hetton w Haswell 88; Chapl St Aid Coll Dur 89-92; Par Dn Esh *Dur* 90-92; P-in-c from 92. *11 Cooke's Wood, Broompark, Durham DH7 7RL* 0191-386 1140 or 386 5011

POCOCK, Lynn Elizabeth. b 48. Coll of Wooster Ohio BA69 CertEd71 Birm Univ DipTh75. Qu Coll Birm 73. **dss** 82 **d** 87 **p** 94. Gleadless *Sheff* 82-85; Thorpe Hesley 85-87; Par Dn 87-92; NSM Ribbesford w Bewdley and Dowles *Worc* from 92. *The Rectory, 57 Park Lane, Bewdley, Worcs DY12 2HA* Bewdley (01299) 402275

POCOCK, Canon Nigel John. b 47. Lon Univ BSc68 Birm Univ MA83. Lambeth STh78 Oak Hill Th Coll 69. **d** 72 **p** 73. C Tunbridge Wells St Jas *Roch* 72-75; C Heatherlands St Jo *Sarum* 75-78; V Leic St Chris *Leic* 78-83; R Camborne *Truro* from 83; RD Carnmarth N from 91; Hon Can Truro Cathl from 92. *The Rectory, Rectory Gardens, Camborne, Cornwall TR14 7DN* Camborne (01209) 613020

PODGER, Richard Philip Champeney. b 38. K Coll Cam BA61 MA66. Cuddesdon Coll 62. **d** 64 **p** 65. C Doncaster St Geo *Sheff* 64-68; C Orpington All SS *Roch* 68-74; W Germany 76-88; Chapl Kassel *Eur* 83-88; TV Whitstable *Cant* 88-94. *St Martin's Glebe House, North Holmes Road, Canterbury, Kent CT1 1QT* Chestfield (01227) 766719

POGMORE, Edward Clement. b 52. Sarum & Wells Th Coll 76. **d** 79 **p** 80. C Calne and Blackland *Sarum* 79-82; TV Oakdale St Geo 82-89; Min Creekmoor LEP 82-89; Chapl Geo Eliot Hosp Nuneaton from 89; Chapl Nuneaton Hosps from 89; Perm to Offic *Leic* from 91. *The George Eliot Hospital, College Street, Nuneaton, Warks CV19 7DJ* Nuneaton (01203) 865281 or 351351

POIL, Canon Ronald Wickens (Ron). b 30. AKC56. **d** 57 **p** 58. C Willesborough *Cant* 57-60; Chapl RAF 60-76; P-in-c Edith Weston w Normanton *Pet* 65-67; V Southbourne *Chich* 76-80; P-in-c W Thorney 76-80; RD Westbourne 78-91; V Southbourne w W Thorney from 80; Can and Preb Chich Cathl from 90. *The Vicarage, 273 Main Road, Southbourne, Emsworth, Hants PO10 8JE* Emsworth (01243) 372436

POINTS, John David. b 43. Qu Coll Birm 78. **d** 80 **p** 81. C Wednesbury St Paul Wood Green *Lich* 80-85; V from 93; V Sedgley St Mary 85-93. *The Vicarage, Wood Green Road, Wednesbury, W Midlands WS10 9QT* 0121-556 0687

POLE, David John. b 46. Bath Academy of Art BA72. Trin Coll Bris 84. **d** 86 **p** 87. C Bris St Mary Redcliffe w Temple etc *Bris* 86-90; V Alveston from 90. *The Vicarage, Gloucester Road, Alveston, Bristol BS12 2QT* Thornbury (01454) 414810

POLE, Francis John Michael. b 42. FRSA MBIM CQSW AMInstTA. St Jo Sem Wonersh 62. **d** 67 **p** 68. In RC Ch 67-75; C Walthamstow St Pet *Chelmsf* 75; C Penge Lane H Trin *Roch* 76-77; C Shirley St Jo *Cant* 77-79; Assoc Chapl The Hague *Eur* 80-83; V Norbury St Steph and Thornton Heath *Cant* 83-84; V Norbury St Steph and Thornton Heath *S'wark* from 85. *St Stephen's Vicarage, Warwick Road, Thornton Heath, Surrey CR7 7NH* 0181-684 3820

POLHILL, Arthur John Henry. b 20. Sarum Th Coll 65. **d** 67 **p** 68. C Tormohun *Ex* 67-71; V Tipton w Venn Ottery 71-87; rtd 87. *First Floor Flat, 44 Castle Road, Salisbury SP1 3RJ* Salisbury (01722) 333888

POLHILL, Mrs Christine. b 46. Nottm Coll of Educn CertEd67. St Alb Minl Tr Scheme 81. **dss** 84 **d** 87 **p** 94. St Alb St Mary Marshalswick *St Alb* 84-87; Hon Par Dn 87-94; NSM Cottered w Broadfield and Throcking from 94. *The Rectory, Cottered, Buntingford, Herts SG9 9QA* Cottered (01763) 281218

POLITT, Robert William. b 47. ARCM LGSM68. Oak Hill Th Coll 73. **d** 76 **p** 77. C Bexleyheath St Pet *Roch* 76-82; TV Southgate *Chich* 82-90; Chapl N Foreland Lodge Sch Basingstoke from 90. *Cottage, North Foreland Lodge School, Sherfield-on-Loddon, Basingstoke, Hants RG27 0HU* Basingstoke (01256) 880051

POLKINGHORNE, Canon Dr John Charlton. b 30. FRS74 Trin Coll Cam MA56 PhD55 ScD74. Westcott Ho Cam 79. **d** 81 **p** 82. Hon Chatterton St Andr *Ely* 81-82; C Bedminster St Mich *Bris* 82-84; V Blean *Cant* 84-86; Dean Trin Hall Cam 86-89; Pres Qu Coll Cam from 89; Hon Can Liv Cathl *Liv* from 94. *The President's Lodge, Queen's College, Cambridge CB3 9ET* Cambridge (01223) 335532

POLL, Martin George. b 61. Kent Univ BA83. Ripon Coll Cuddesdon 84. **d** 87 **p** 88. C Mill Hill Jo Keble Ch *Lon* 87-90; Chapl RN from 90. *Directorate Gen, RN Chapl Services, Room 203, Victory Building, HM Naval Base, Portsmouth PO1 3LS* Portsmouth (01705) 727903 Fax 727112

POLLAK, Canon Peter Henry. b 18. Worc Ord Coll 67. **d** 69 **p** 70. C Claines St Jo *Worc* 69-73; R Grimley w Holt 73-88; RD Martley and Worc W 84-88; Hon Can Worc Cathl 85-88; rtd 88. *2 Tweenways, Main Road, Kempsey, Worcester WR5 3JY* Worcester (01905) 820351

POLLARD, Mrs Christine Beryl. b 45. DCR DNM. N Ord Course 86. **d** 89 **p** 94. Par Dn Ingrow cum Hainworth *Bradf* 89-94; C Nuneaton St Nic *Cov* from 94. *113 St Nicolas Park Drive, Nuneaton, Warks CV11 6EF* Nuneaton (01203) 375830

POLLARD, Canon Clifford Francis. b 20. AKC49. **d** 50 **p** 51. Dir of Educn *Cant* 69-87; Hon Can Cant Cathl 72-87; rtd 87. *6 Lady Wootton's Green, Canterbury, Kent CT1 1NG* Canterbury (01227) 761674

POLLARD, David. b 55. LSE BSc77. Trin Coll Bris DipHE80. **d** 80 **p** 81. Canada 81-84; C-in-c Hillsfield and Monkspath LEP *Birm* 85-89; BCMS 89-93; Crosslinks 93-95; Spain 89-94; V Doncaster St Jas *Sheff* from 95. *The Vicarage, 54 Littlemoor Lane, Doncaster, S Yorkshire DN4 0LB* Doncaster (01302) 365544

POLLARD, David John Athey. b 44. ACP74 Culham Coll Ox CertEd69. St Jo Coll Nottm LTh88. **d** 88 **p** 89. C Illogan *Truro* 88-91; R Roche and Withiel from 91. *The Rectory, Fore Street, Roche, St Austell, Cornwall PL26 8EP* St Austell (01726) 890301

POLLARD, David Stanley. b 49. Lon Univ BD80 AKC80 Bradf Univ MA. **d** 80 **p** 81. CGA 78-89; C Manningham St Mary and Bradf St Mich *Bradf* 80-83; P-in-c 83-84; TV Manningham 84-85; C 86-87; Lic to Offic 85-89; P-in-c Sidlesham *Chich* 89-94; Chapl Chich Coll of Tech 90-94; R Petworth *Chich* from 94; RD Petworth from 95. *The Rectory, Petworth, W Sussex GU28 0DB* Petworth (01798) 342505 Fax as telephone

POLLARD, Eric John. b 43. Chich Th Coll 83. **d** 85 **p** 86. C Brighton St Matthias *Chich* 85-90; C E Grinstead St Swithun from 90. *St Luke's House, Holtye Avenue, East Grinstead, W Sussex RH19 3EG* East Grinstead (01342) 323800

POLLARD, James Adrian Hunter. b 48. St Jo Coll Nottm BTh78. **d** 78 **p** 79. C Much Woolton *Liv* 78-81; CMS 81-84; V Toxteth Park Ch Ch *Liv* 85-90; CF from 90; Perm to Offic *S'wark* 92-94. *c/o MOD (Army), Bagshot Park, Bagshot, Surrey GU19 5PL* Bagshot (01276) 471717 Fax 412834

POLLARD, John Edward Ralph. b 40. ALCD68. **d** 67 **p** 68. C Ollerton *S'well* 67-71; C Walton H Trin *Ox* 71-74; P-in-c Cuddington w Dinton 74-77; V Haddenham 74-77; V Kingsey 75-77; V Haddenham w Cuddington and Kingsey 77-85; RD Aylesbury 80-85; V Haddenham w Cuddington, Kingsey etc 85-87; V Furze Platt from 87. *St Peter's Vicarage, 259 Courthouse Road, Maidenhead, Berks SL6 6HF* Maidenhead (01628) 21961

POLLARD, Noel Stewart. b 28. Sydney Univ BA51 BD56 Ch Ch Ox BA58 MA63. **d** 53 **p** 53. Australia 61-72; Lect St Jo Coll Nottm 72-88; Lect Nottm Univ 72-88; Vice-Prin Ridley Hall Cam 88-93; rtd 93. *193 Huntingdon Road, Cambridge CB3 0DL* Cambridge (01223) 276328

POLLARD, Roger Frederick. b 32. Sheff Univ BSc52 K Coll Lon PGCE55 Lanc Univ MA79. Linc Th Coll 56. **d** 58 **p** 59. S Craven Sch Cross Hills 69-91; rtd 91; Perm to Offic *Bradf* 70-94; Perm to Offic *B & W* from 94. *Orchard Corner, Sheepway, Shepton Beauchamp, Ilminster, Somerset TA19 0JT* South Petherton (01460) 241979

POLLARD, Vaughan. b 59. Aston Tr Scheme 90 Trin Coll Bris DipHE92. **d** 92 **p** 93. C Nailsea H Trin *B & W* from 92. *26 St Mary's Grove, Nailsea, Bristol BS19 2NQ* Nailsea (01275) 858837

POLLINGER, Mrs Judith. b 41. Ex Univ TCert78 BEd79. SW Minl Tr Course 92. **d** 95. NSM St Endellion w Port Isaac and St Kew *Truro* from 95. *Hillows House, St Teath, Bodmin, Cornwall PL30 3JJ* Camelford (01840) 212604

POLLITT, Preb Michael. b 30. Worc Coll Ox BA54 MA58. Wells Th Coll 54. **d** 56 **p** 57. C Cannock *Lich* 56-59; C Codsall 59-62; V W Bromwich St Pet 62-67; R Norton in the Moors 67-76; RD Leek 72-76; V Shrewsbury St Chad 76-87; V Shrewsbury St Chad w St Mary from 87; Preb Lich Cathl from 81; P-in-c Shrewsbury St Alkmund from 91. *St Chad's Vicarage, Claremont Hill, Shrewsbury SY1 1RD* Shrewsbury (01743) 343761

POLLIT, Ruth Mary. *See* LILLINGTON, Mrs Ruth Mary

POLLITT, Graham Anthony. b 48. BA79. Oak Hill Th Coll 76. **d** 79 **p** 80. C Rusholme *Man* 79-82; TV Southgate *Chich* 82-83; C Burgess Hill St Andr 83-86; Chapl St Martin's Coll of Educn *Blackb* 86-90; Chapl Cheltenham and Glouc Coll of HE from 90; Chapl Cheltenham Coll from 90. *3 The Lanes,*

Leckhampton, Cheltenham, Glos GL53 0PU   Cheltenham (01242) 260291

POLLOCK, Christopher John. b 62. TCD BTh89. CITC 86. **d** 89 **p** 90. C Agherton *Conn* 89-91; C Ballymoney w Finvoy and Rasharkin 91-93; I Derryvolgie from 93. *53 Kennedy Drive, Belsize Road, Lisburn, Co Antrim BT27 4JA*   Lisburn (01846) 663707

POLLOCK, Duncan James Morrison. b 54. QGM. Linc Th Coll BCombStuds. **d** 83 **p** 84. C Folkestone St Mary and St Eanswythe *Cant* 83-85; CF from 85. *c/o MOD (Army), Bagshot Park, Bagshot, Surrey GU19 5PL*   Bagshot (01276) 471717   Fax 412834

POLLOCK, Hugh Gillespie. b 36. Oak Hill Th Coll 61. **d** 64 **p** 65. C Maidstone St Luke *Cant* 64-68; C Washfield *Ex* 68-71; C Washfield, Stoodleigh, Withleigh etc 71-73; Chapl Lee Abbey 73-76; V Dersingham *Nor* 76-80; P-in-c Anmer 79-80; P-in-c Shernbourne 79-80; R Dersingham w Anmer and Shernborne 80-89; RD Heacham and Rising 87-89; C Barnstaple *Ex* 89-94; P-in-c Atherington and High Bickington from 94; P-in-c Burrington from 94. *The Rectory, High Bickington, Umberleigh, Devon EX37 9BB*   High Bickington (01769) 60283

POLLOCK, James Colin Graeme. b 53. St Chad's Coll Dur BA76. Ripon Coll Cuddesdon 77. **d** 78 **p** 79. C Hartlepool St Oswald *Dur* 78-81; C Hartlepool St Aid 81-84; V Dawdon from 84. *The Vicarage, Melbury Street, Seaham, Co Durham SR7 7NF*   0191-581 2317

POLLOCK, Jennifer Susan. b 51. Liv Univ BA72 CertEd73. Glouc Sch of Min 89. **d** 92 **p** 94. NSM Leominster *Heref* from 92. *1 Laurels Court, Westfield Walk, Leominster, Herefordshire HR6 8TT*   Leominster (01568) 611536

POLLOCK, John Charles. b 23. Trin Coll Cam BA46 MA48. Ridley Hall Cam 49. **d** 51 **p** 52. Ed The Churchman 53-58; R Horsington *B & W* 53-58; Perm to Offic *Ex* from 61; rtd 88. *Rose Ash House, South Molton, Devon EX36 4RB*   Bishops Nympton (01769) 550403

POLLOCK, Neil Thomas. b 38. Lon Univ DipTh68. Bernard Gilpin Soc Dur 63 Lich Th Coll 64. **d** 67 **p** 68. C Lt Stanmore St Lawr *Lon* 67-72; C-in-c Uxbridge St Marg 72-81; R Norwood St Mary 81-86; TR Ridgeway *Sarum* from 86. *The Rectory, 3 Butts Road, Chiseldon, Swindon SN4 0NN*   Swindon (01793) 740369

POLOMSKI, Elias. b 42. **d** 85 **p** 86. C Headington Quarry *Ox* 91-94; Chapl St Alb Abbey *St Alb* from 94; Chapl St Alb Sch from 94. *The Deanery Barn, Sumpter Yard, St Albans, Herts AL1 1BY*   St Albans (01727) 854950

POMEROY, Michael James. b 26. Sarum Th Coll 64. **d** 66 **p** 67. Co Chapl ACF 69-89; Hon CF from 89; P-in-c Ibberton w Belchalwell and Woolland *Sarum* 69-72; R 72-73; R Okeford Fitzpaine, Ibberton, Belchalwell etc 73-90; rtd 90. *Brandon, Wavering Lane, Gillingham, Dorset SP8 4NR*   Gillingham (01747) 822498

POMERY, David John. b 45. SS Mark & Jo Coll Chelsea CertEd67. Chich Th Coll 75. **d** 77 **p** 78. C Coseley Ch Ch *Lich* 77-79; C Stocksbridge *Sheff* 79-81; V Bentley 81-87; Radlett Prep Sch from 87. *Radlett Preparatory School, Kendall Hall, Radlett, Herts WD7 9HW*   Radlett (01923) 856812

POMFRET, Albert. b 23. Univ of Wales (Cardiff) BSc57 Lon Univ MA69. Oak Hill NSM Course 72. **d** 75 **p** 76. NSM Dartford Ch Ch *Roch* 75-80; Perm to Offic 80-92; Perm to Offic *Ex* from 92. *9 St Margaret's Court, Exe Street, Topsham, Exeter EX3 0JA*   Topsham (01392) 873404

POND, Nigel Peter Hamilton. b 40. AKC65. **d** 66 **p** 67. C E Dereham w Hoe *Nor* 66-69; C Chapl RN 69-85; TR Woughton *Ox* 85-93; Chapl Milton Keynes Gen Hosp from 85; RD Milton Keynes *Ox* 90-93; R Olney w Emberton from 93. *Olney Rectory, 9 Orchard Rise, Olney, Bucks MK46 5HB*   Bedford (01234) 713308

✠PONNIAH, Rt Rev Jacob Samuel. b 22. Bihar Univ MA59. Western Th Sem Michigan MTh64 Madras Chr Coll BA48 United Th Coll Bangalore 48. **d** 52 **p** 53 **c** 78. India 53-90; Bp Vellore 78-87; Dioc Missr *Linc* 90-91; P-in-c Fulletby w Greetham and Ashby Puerorum 90-91; P-in-c Hameringham w Scrafield and Winceby 90-91; P-in-c High Toynton 90-91; P-in-c Mareham on the Hill 90-91; P-in-c Belchford 90-91; Miss Partner CMS from 91. *c/o Rydall Hall, Ambleside, Cumbria LA22 9LX*   Ambleside (015394) 32050

PONSONBY, Simon Charles Reuben. b 66. Trin Coll Bris BA94. **d** 95. C Thorpe Edge *Bradf* from 95. *146 Rowantree Drive, Bradford, W Yorkshire BD10 8DH*   Bradford (01274) 619154

PONT, Gordon John Harper. b 35. Glas Univ BSc56 BD65. Edin Th Coll 56. **d** 59 **p** 60. C Dunfermline *St And* 59-62; C Motherwell *Glas* 62-65; R Largs 65-68; Dioc Supernumerary *Bre* 68-71; Chapl Dundee Univ 68-73; R Dundee St Luke 71-74; NSM Dundee St Paul from 74; Hon Chapl St Paul's Cathl Dundee from 74. *5 Westpark Road, Dundee DD2 1NU*   Dundee (01382) 69883

PONTEFRACT, Archdeacon of. *See* FLACK, Ven John Robert

PONTEFRACT, Suffragan Bishop of. *See* FINNEY, Rt Rev John Thornley

PONTER, Dr John Arthur. b 37. Univ of Wales (Abth) BA61 Linacre Coll Ox BA63 MA68 UEA PhD81. Wycliffe Hall Ox 61. **d** 63 **p** 64. C Gidea Park *Chelmsf* 63-67; C-in-c Colchester St Anne CD 67-69; V Colchester St Anne 69-72; Chapl UEA *Nor* 72-78; Chapl Chelmsf Cathl *Chelmsf* 78-79; Chapl Chelmsf Cathl Cen 78-84; V Moulsham St Jo 79-85; Lic to Offic *Man* 85-92; Dir Man Chr Inst and Chr Leadership Course 85-92; Educn Officer N Federation for Tr in Min 85-92; TR Stantonbury and Willen *Ox* from 92. *The Rectory, The Green, Great Linford, Milton Keynes MK14 5BD*   Milton Keynes (01908) 605892

PONTIN, Colin Henry. b 37. Trin Coll Bris. **d** 83 **p** 84. C Downend *Bris* 83-86; C Riverside *Ox* 86-88; V Eton w Eton Wick and Boveney 88-90; TV Riverside 91-95; V Churt *Guildf* from 95. *The Vicarage, Old Kiln Lane, Churt, Farnham, Surrey GU10 2HX*   Headley Down (01428) 713368

POOBALAN, Isaac Munuswamy. b 62. Chr Med Coll RN84 New Coll Edin BD94. Edin Th Coll 91. **d** 94. C Edin St Pet *Edin* from 94. *10 Hope Park Crescent, Edinburgh EH8 9NA*   0131-668 1541

POODHUN, Canon Lambert David. b 30. Natal Univ BA53. Edin Th Coll 54. **d** 56 **p** 57. S Africa 56-76; Adn Durban 75-76; C Upton cum Chalvey *Ox* 77-80; Chapl Kingston Hosp Surrey 80-81; Chapl Tooting Bec Hosp Lon 81-84; Chapl Hurstwood Park Hosp Haywards Heath from 84; Chapl St Fran Hosp Haywards Heath 84-94; Chapl Mid Sussex NHS Trust from 94; Chapl Princess R Hosp Haywards Heath from 94; Can and Preb Chich Cathl *Chich* from 93. *8 Nursery Close, Haywards Heath, W Sussex RH16 1HP, or The Princess Royal Hospital, Lewes Road, Haywards Heath, W Sussex RH16 4EX*   Haywards Heath (01444) 452571 or 441881

POOLE, Clifford George. b 36. Keble Coll Ox BA61 MA65. S'wark Ord Course 83. **d** 86 **p** 87. C W Dulwich All SS and Em S'wark 86-90; Chapl Luxembourg *Eur* from 90. *11 rue Ernest Beres, L-1232 Howald, Luxembourg*   Luxembourg (352) 485397

POOLE, Denis Tom. b 19. St Jo Coll Dur 39. St Aid Birkenhead 41. **d** 43 **p** 44. V Biddulph *Lich* 64-85; Chapl Biddulph Grange Hosp Staffs 64-85; rtd 85; Perm to Offic *Win* from 85. *14 Curlew Drive, Hythe, Southampton SO4 6GA*   Hythe (01703) 846497

POOLE, Mrs Denise June. b 49. Leic Univ BSc70 Bradf and Ilkley Coll DipAE85. N Ord Course 90. **d** 93 **p** 94. C Horton *Bradf* from 93; C Bradf St Oswald Chapel Green from 93. *St Paul's Rectory, 47 Kirkgate, Shipley, W Yorkshire BD18 3EH*   Bradford (01274) 583652

POOLE, Edward John. b 53. Hull Univ BA81. St Steph Ho Ox 81. **d** 83 **p** 84. C Stevenage St Andr and St Geo *St Alb* 83-86; Madagascar 86-88; V Weston *St Alb* from 88; P-in-c Ardeley from 88; P-in-c Cottered w Broadfield and Throcking from 94. *The Vicarage, 14 Munts Meadow, Weston, Hitchin, Herts SG4 7AE*   Weston (01462) 790330

POOLE, Frederick Harold. b 14. Clifton Th Coll 54. **d** 56 **p** 56. R Chorlton on Medlock St Steph *Man* 60-68; rtd 79. *43 Albion Street, Wallasey, Merseyside L45 9LE*   0151-638 8952

POOLE, Helen Margaret. b 39. **d** 94 **p** 95. NSM Ludgvan Truro from 94. *Underhill Farmhouse, St Levan, Penzance, Cornwall TR19 6JS*   St Buryan (01736) 810842

POOLE, Miss Joan Wendy. b 37. Sarum Dioc Teacher Tr Coll CertEd57 Dalton Ho Bris DipTh66 Trin Coll Bris 86. **d** 87 **p** 94. Par Dn Longfleet *Sarum* 87-89; Par Dn Hamworthy 89-94; C from 94. *The Parsonage, 56 Keysworth Road, Hamworthy, Poole, Dorset BH16 5BH*   Poole (01202) 674366

POOLE, John. b 19. Peterho Cam MA44. St Alb Minl Tr Scheme 77. **d** 80 **p** 81. NSM Bedf St Andr *St Alb* 80-87; NSM Elstow 87-92; Perm to Offic from 92. *35 Falcon Avenue, Bedford MK41 7DY*   Bedford (01234) 262208

POOLE, John Denys Barlow. b 33. Qu Coll Cam BA57 MA61. Cuddesdon Coll 57. **d** 59 **p** 60. CF 57-72; C Leagrave *St Alb* 59-62; C Raynes Park St Sav *S'wark* 62-65; C Apsley End *St Alb* 65-72; R W Wickham St Jo *Cant* 73-84; V Wickham St Jo *S'wark* from 85. *The Rectory, 30 Coney Hill Road, West Wickham, Kent BR4 9BX*   0181-462 4001

POOLE, John Robert. b 46. Lon Univ BSc69 Bris Univ DipTh71. Clifton Th Coll 69. **d** 72 **p** 73. C Horton *Bradf* 72-75; C Otley 76-79; V Bankfoot 79-92; TR Shipley St Paul and Frizinghall from 92. *The Rectory, 47 Kirkgate, Shipley, W Yorkshire BD18 3EH*   Bradford (01274) 583652

POOLE, Martin Bryce. b 59. Reading Univ BSc80 Nottm Univ DipTh82 DipAct85. St Jo Coll Nottm DPS84. **d** 87 **p** 88. NSM Tulse Hill H Trin and St Matthias *S'wark* from 87. *117 Casewick Road, London SE27 0UP*   0181-761 3190

POOLE, Martin Ronald. b 59. Aston Univ BSc81 Leeds Univ BA86. Coll of Resurr Mirfield 84. **d** 87 **p** 88. C Sheff St Cath Richmond Road *Sheff* 87-90; C W Hampstead St Jas *Lon*

90-94; V Colindale St Matthias from 94. *St Matthias' Vicarage, Rushgrove Avenue, London NW9 6QY* 0181-205 8783

POOLE, Peter William. b 35. St Pet Hall Ox BA59 MA63. Wells Th Coll 59. **d** 61 **p** 62. C Cheriton Street *Cant* 61-64; C Birchington w Acol 64-67; V Newington 67-73; P-in-c Lower Halstow 72-73; V Bearsted 73-76; V Lane End w Cadmore End *Ox* 84-89; R Chalfont St Giles from 89. *The Rectory, 2 Deanway, Chalfont St Giles, Bucks HP8 4JH* Chalfont St Giles (01494) 872097

POOLE, Ronald John Ajax. b 10. Selw Coll Cam BA32 MA36. Wells Th Coll 32. **d** 33 **p** 35. V Tondu *Llan* 60-73; rtd 73; Perm to Offic *Llan* from 73. *20 Park Place, Canola, Bryncethin, Bridgend, M Glam CF32 9UA* Aberkenfig (01656) 720232

POOLE, Roy John. b 26. Lon Univ BD54. St Jo Coll Lon LTh54. **d** 54 **p** 55. Regional Supervisor (S and E England) Chr Aid 68-74; Australia from 74; rtd 91. *Unit 8, 131 Hastings Street, Scarborough, W Australia 6019*

POOLE, Stanley Burke-Roche. b 09. K Coll Lon BA31 MA34. Qu Coll Birm 36. **d** 38 **p** 39. V Littlebourne *Cant* 48-70; rtd 74. *13 Chaucer Court, New Dover Road, Canterbury, Kent CT1 3AU* Canterbury (01227) 451586

POOLE, Stuart. b 33. CEng65 FIEE85 Loughb Coll of Educn DLC55 Lon Univ BScEng55 Man Univ MSc76. **d** 91 **p** 92. NSM Cheadle *Ches* from 91. *1 Dene House, Green Pastures, Stockport, Cheshire SK4 3RB* 0161-432 6426

POOLEY, Peter Owen. b 32. Kelham Th Coll 54. **d** 58 **p** 59. C Paddington St Mary Magd *Lon* 58-62; R Rockland St Mary w Hellington *Nor* 62-67; Asst Master Thos Lethaby Sch 67-70; St Phil Gr Sch Edgbaston 70-74; Lordswood Gr Sch 74-80; Hon C Edgbaston St Geo *Birm* 77-80; R Elton *Ely* from 80; P-in-c Stibbington from 80; P-in-c Water Newton from 80. *The Rectory, Elton, Peterborough PE8 6SA* Oundle (01832) 280222

POOLMAN, Alfred John. b 46. K Coll Lon BD69 AKC69 Sheff Univ DipPs83. St Aug Coll Cant 69. **d** 70 **p** 71. C Headingley *Ripon* 70-74; C Moor Allerton 75-78; C Monk Bretton *Wakef* 78-80; C Athersley 80; V Copley 80-90; Chapl Halifax Gen Hosp 80-90; R Llanfynydd *St As* from 90. *The Rectory, Llanfynydd, Wrexham, Clwyd LL11 5HH* Caergwrle (01978) 762304

POPE, Charles Guy. b 48. AKC70. St Aug Coll Cant 70. **d** 71 **p** 72. C Southgate Ch Ch *Lon* 71-74; C N St Pancras All Hallows 74-77; C Hampstead St Steph 74-77; V New Southgate St Paul 77-86; V Brookfield St Mary from 86; P-in-c Brookfield St Anne, Highgate Rise from 88; AD S Camden (Holborn and St Pancras) from 95. *St Mary's Vicarage, 85 Dartmouth Park Road, London NW5 1SL* 0171-267 5941

POPE, Colin. b 51. Brasted Place Coll 74. Linc Th Coll 75. **d** 78 **p** 79. C Wrington Gd Shep *Liv* 78-81; C-in-c Westbrook St Phil CD 81-82; V Westbrook St Phil 82-87; V Orrell from 87; Chapl Billinge Hosp Wigan from 87. *St Luke's Vicarage, 10 Lodge Road, Orrell, Wigan, Lancs WN5 7AT* Up Holland (01695) 623410

POPE, Daniel Legh (Dan). b 23. Cuddesdon Coll 67. **d** 68 **p** 69. C Llanelli *St D* 68-71; V Radley *Ox* 71-88; Miss to Seamen 88-92; Cyprus 88-92; rtd 92; P-in-c Shipley *Chich* from 92. *Shipley Vicarage, Horsham, W Sussex RH13 8PH* Horsham (01403) 741238

POPE, David Allan. b 20. Or Coll Ox BA45 MA72. Ely Th Coll 45. **d** 47 **p** 48. R Broadstairs *Cant* 65-73; P-in-c Berwick *Chich* 73-76; P-in-c Arlington 73-75; P-in-c Selmeston w Alciston 74-76; R Berwick w Selmeston and Alciston 76; P-in-c Rusper 76-79; R Colsterworth *Linc* 79-81; P-in-c Ingworth 81-85; P-in-c Alby w Thwaite *Nor* 81-85; P-in-c Erpingham w Calthorpe 81-85; P-in-c Aldborough w Thurgarton 83-85; rtd 85; Perm to Offic *Nor* from 85. *Brickfield Farm, Stibbard, Fakenham, Norfolk NR21 0EE* Great Ryburgh (0132878) 294

POPE, Donald Keith. b 35. Sarum & Wells Th Coll 81. **d** 76 **p** 77. Hon C Caerleon *Mon* 76-82; C 82-83; V Pontypool 83-86; R Grosmont and Skenfrith and Llangattock etc from 86; RD Abergavenny from 93. *The Rectory, Grosmont, Abergavenny, Gwent NP7 8LW* Golden Valley (01981) 240587

POPE, Michael John. b 37. Sarum Th Coll 62. **d** 65 **p** 66. C Broseley w Benthall *Heref* 65-68; C Shrewsbury St Giles *Lich* 68-71; P-in-c Shrewsbury St Geo 71-75; V 75-79; V Gnosall from 79; RD Eccleshall from 92. *The Vicarage, Gnosall, Stafford ST20 0ER* Stafford (01785) 822213

POPE, Michael Ronald. b 41. Bps' Coll Cheshunt 65. **d** 68 **p** 69. C Lyonsdown H Trin *St Alb* 68-72; C Seaford w Sutton *Chich* 72-76; R Hurstpierpoint 76-80. *Isle of Wight Timeshare Home, Popham Road, Shanklin, Isle of Wight PO37 6RG* Isle of Wight (01983) 862193

POPE, Very Rev Robert William. b 16. OBE70. Dur Univ LTh40. St Aug Coll Cant 35. **d** 39 **p** 40. Chapl RN 44-71; V Whitchurch w Tufton and Litchfield *Win* 71-77; Dean Gib *Eur*

77-82; rtd 82; Min Prov Third Order Soc of St Fran 85-87; Min Gen 87-90. *5 Wreath Green, Tatworth, Chard, Somerset TA20 2SN* Chard (01460) 20987

POPE, Rodney John. b 22. St D Coll Lamp BA48 BD67 MA71. **d** 49 **p** 50. V Eastham *Ches* 62-72; V Gt w Lt Saling *Chelmsf* 72-87; rtd 87; Perm to Offic *B & W* from 89. *4 Abbey Close, Curry Rivel, Langport, Somerset TA10 0EL* Langport (01458) 250808

POPEJOY, Wilfred. b 28. St Jo Coll Nottm 88. **d** 88. Hon C Donisthorpe and Moira w Stretton-en-le-Field *Leic* from 88. *79 Donisthorpe Lane, Moira, Swadlincote, Derbyshire DE12 6BB* Burton-on-Trent (01283) 760476

POPP, Miss Julia Alice Gisela. b 45. Univ of BC BA71. St Jo Coll Nottm 78. **dss** 81 **d** 87 **p** 94. Woking St Mary *Guildf* 81-83; Hornsey Rise St Mary w St Steph *Lon* 83-87; Par Dn Hornsey Rise Whitehall Park Team 87-91; Par Dn Sutton St Nic *S'wark* 91-94; C from 94; Missr Sutton Town Cen from 91. *14 Strathearn Road, Sutton, Surrey SM1 2RS* 0181-643 6712

POPPLE, Ven Dennis. b 31. Vancouver Sch of Th LTh72 San Francisco Th Sem DMin89 St Aid Birkenhead 59. **d** 62 **p** 63. C Walkden Moor *Man* 62-65; Canada from 65; Admin Adn from 87. *8580 General Currie Road, Suite 113, Richmond, British Columbia, Canada, V6Y 3V5*

POPPLEWELL, Andrew Frederick. b 53. St Jo Coll Dur BA75. Wycliffe Hall Ox 76. **d** 78 **p** 79. C Clifton *York* 78-81; C Lich St Chad *Lich* 82-84; V Laisterdyke *Bradf* from 84. *The Vicarage, Parsonage Road, Laisterdyke, Bradford, W Yorkshire BD4 8PY* Bradford (01274) 664565

PORTEOUS, Canon Eric John. b 34. AKC58. **d** 59 **p** 60. C Wandsworth St Paul *S'wark* 59-62; C Leeds St Pet *Ripon* 62-66; V Wortley de Leeds 66-72; RD Armley 70-72; R Woolwich St Mary w H Trin *S'wark* 72-77; Sub-Dean Woolwich 74-77; P-in-c Woolwich St Mich 75-77; R Woolwich St Mary w St Mich 77-79; Chapl Whipps Cross Hosp Lon from 79; Lic to Offic *Chelmsf* 79-86; Hon Can Chelmsf Cathl from 86. *Whipps Cross Hospital, Whipps Cross Road, London E11 1NR, or 128 Grove Hill, London E18 2HZ* 0181-539 5522 or 530 5660

PORTEOUS, Michael Stanley. b 35. S'wark Ord Course 70. **d** 73 **p** 74. C Barnes St Mich *S'wark* 73-76; Chapl Greycoat Hosp Sch 76-78; C Brighton Annunciation *Chich* 78-80; Chapl Ch Hosp Horsham 80-85; TV Moulsecoomb *Chich* 85-88; R W Blatchington from 88. *St Peter's Rectory, 23 Windmill Close, Hove, E Sussex BN3 7LJ* Brighton (01273) 732459

PORTER, Anthony. b 52. Hertf Coll Ox BA74 MA78 Fitzw Ho Cam BA76 MA80. Ridley Hall Cam 74. **d** 77 **p** 78. C Edgware *Lon* 77-80; C Haughton St Mary *Man* 80-83; P-in-c Bacup Ch Ch 83-87; V 87-91; R Rusholme from 91. *Holy Trinity Rectory, Platt Lane, Manchester M14 5NF* 0161-224 1123 or 248 8005

PORTER, Arthur William. b 29. St Deiniol's Hawarden 70. **d** 70 **p** 71. C Ruislip St Martin *Lon* 70-80; V Kingsbury H Innocents 80-94; rtd 94. *24 Belle Vue Road, Salisbury SP1 3YG* Salisbury (01722) 331314

PORTER, Barbara Judith. *See* JEAPES, Mrs Barbara Judith

PORTER, Brian John Henry. b 33. SW Minl Tr Course 78. **d** 81 **p** 82. NSM Plymouth St Andr w St Paul and St Geo *Ex* 81-85; NSM Perm to Offic 85-87; NSM Devonport St Barn 87-90; C Brampton St Thos *Derby* from 90. *32 Brookside Glen, Chesterfield, Derbyshire S40 3PF* Chesterfield (01246) 566346

PORTER, Damian Michael. b 66. Linc Th Coll BTh92. **d** 92 **p** 93. C Pelsall *Lich* from 92. *35 Hillside Crescent, Pelsall, Walsall WS3 4JL* Pelsall (01922) 694688

PORTER, David Anthony (Tony). b 34. Wycliffe Hall Ox 73. **d** 75 **p** 76. C Watford St Luke *St Alb* 75-78; C Worting *Win* 78-81; V Snettisham *Nor* 81-82; P-in-c Ingoldisthorpe 81-82; C Fring 81-82; R Snettisham w Ingoldisthorpe and Fring 82-84; Chapl Asst Colchester Gen Hosp 87-88; Chapl Maidstone Hosp from 88. *Maidstone Hospital, Hermitage Lane, Maidstone, Kent ME16 9QQ* Maidstone (01622) 729000 or 720851

PORTER, David Michael. b 37. Coll of Ripon & York St Jo BA88. Ely Th Coll 61. **d** 64 **p** 65. C Clun w Chapel Lawn *Heref* 64-67; C Scarborough St Mary w Ch Ch, St Paul and St Thos *York* 67-69; C Fulford 69-71; V Strensall 71-78; Chapl Claypenny and St Monica's Hosps 78-91; V Easingwold w Raskelfe *York* 78-91; TR York All SS Pavement w St Crux and St Martin etc from 91. *All Saints' Rectory, 52 St Andrewgate, York YO1 2BZ* York (01904) 631116

PORTER, Dennis Percy. b 26. K Coll Lon BSc47 AKC49 Birm Univ DipTh58. **d** 72 **p** 73. NSM Ecclesall *Sheff* 72-79; Perm to Offic from 79; Chapl Whirlow Grange Conf Cen Sheff from 79. *75 Marsh House Road, Sheffield S11 9SQ* Sheffield (0114) 236 2058

PORTER, Geoffrey Ernest. b 14. AKC48. **d** 48 **p** 49. R Ingrave *Chelmsf* 53-78; rtd 79. *Beecham's View, 25 Station Road, Mursley, Milton Keynes MK17 0SA* Mursley (01296) 720460

PORTER, John Dudley Dowell. b 33. St Edm Hall Ox BA60 MA61. Qu Coll Birm 57. **d** 59 **p** 60. C Londonderry *Birm* 59-62; C Tettenhall Regis *Lich* 62-65; Chapl RAF 65-69; V Wombourne *Lich* 69-75; V Rickerscote 75-81; P-in-c Chapel Chorlton 81-85; P-in-c Maer 81-85; P-in-c Whitmore 81-85; R Chapel Chorlton, Maer and Whitmore 85-92; TR Wednesfield from 92. *The Rectory, 9 Vicarage Road, Wednesfield, Wolverhampton WV11 1SB* Wolverhampton (01902) 731462

PORTER, Canon Prof Joshua Roy. b 21. Mert Coll Ox BA42 MA47. St Steph Ho Ox 42. **d** 45 **p** 46. Prof Th Ex Univ 62-86; Can and Preb Chich Cathl *Chich* 65-88; Wiccamical Preb Chich Cathl from 88; rtd 86; Lic to Offic *Lon* from 87. *36 Theberton Street, London N1 0QX* 0171-354 5861

PORTER, Miss Joy Dove. b 50. Lon Univ PGCE83 Ex Univ CPS86. Lon Bible Coll BA81 Wycliffe Hall Ox 89. **d** 91 **p** 94. Par Dn Chalgrove w Berrick Salome *Ox* 91-92; Par Dn Chipping Norton 92-94; C from 94. *137 Cornish Road, Chipping Norton, Oxon OX7 5LA* Chipping Norton (01608) 641005

PORTER, Kenneth Wilfred. b 27. St Aid Birkenhead 58. **d** 61 **p** 62. V Wardle *Man* 65-91; Chapl Birch Hill Hosp 84-91; rtd 91. *27 Polegate Drive, Leigh, Lancs WN7 5TB* Leigh (01942) 526184

PORTER, Michael Edward. b 44. Trin Coll Bris 75. **d** 77 **p** 78. C Corby St Columba *Pet* 77-81; C Rainham *Chelmsf* 81-82; TV 82-92; TV Rainham w Wennington 92; P-in-c S Hornchurch St Jo and St Matt from 92. *St John's Parsonage, South End Road, Rainham, Essex RM13 7XT* Rainham (01708) 555260

PORTER, William Albert. b 28. Univ of NZ BA51 MA52. Coll of Resurr Mirfield 53. **d** 55 **p** 56. Asst Chapl HM Pris Liv 69-70; Chapl 79-87; Chapl HM Pris Brixton 70-74; Chapl HM Pris Long Lartin 74-79; Chapl HM Pris Nottm 87-90; P-in-c Sneinton St Matthias *S'well* 90-93; rtd 94. *33 Valley Road, Banbury, Oxon OX16 9BH* Banbury (01295) 261892

PORTER, William George Ernest. b 17. Ripon Hall Ox 60. **d** 60 **p** 61. V Brinsley w Underwood *S'well* 67-82; rtd 82; Perm to Offic *S'well* from 82. *6 Ringwood Avenue, Mansfield, Notts NG18 4DA* Mansfield (01623) 21656

PORTEUS, Canon Alan Cruddas. b 12. St Chad's Coll Dur BA32 DipTh34. **d** 35 **p** 36. V Ponteland *Newc* 60-77; Hon Can Newc Cathl 72-79; P-in-c Blanchland w Hunstanworth 77-79; rtd 79. *14 Wembley Avenue, Whitley Bay, Tyne & Wear NE25 8TE* 0191-251 1895

PORTEUS, James Michael. b 31. Worc Coll Ox BA55 MA58. Cuddesdon Coll. **d** 57 **p** 58. C Fleetwood *Blackb* 57-60; C Ox St Mary V *Ox* 60-62; USA 62-69 and 86-91; Chapl Lon Univ *Lon* 69-74; V Hampstead Garden Suburb 74-86; Min Livingston LEP *Edin* from 91. *27 Heatherbank, Livingston, West Lothian EH54 6EE* Livingston (01506) 32326

PORTEUS, Matthew Thomas. b 10. TCD BA32. **d** 33 **p** 34. V W Haddon w Winwick *Pet* 56-73; rtd 75. *12 North Hill Way, Bridport, Dorset DT6 4JX* Bridport (01308) 24551

PORTEUS, Robert John Norman. b 50. TCD BA72. CITC 75. **d** 75 **p** 76. C Portadown St Mark *Arm* 75-79; I Ardtrea w Desertcreat 79-83; I Annaghmore from 83. *54 Moss Road, Portadown, Co Armagh BT62 1NB* Annaghmore (01762) 851555

PORTHOUSE, John Clive. b 32. Lon Univ BD58. Tyndale Hall Bris 55 Oak Hill Th Coll 58. **d** 60 **p** 61. C Leyton All SS *Chelmsf* 60-62; C Kendal St Thos *Carl* 62-64; V Flimby 64-68; V Sidcup St Andr *Roch* 68-74; V Beckenham St Jo 74-86; RD Beckenham 80-86; V Southborough St Pet w Ch Ch and St Matt from 86. *The Vicarage, 86 Prospect Road, Southborough, Tunbridge Wells, Kent TN4 0EG* Tunbridge Wells (01892) 528534

PORTHOUSE, Roger Gordon Hargreaves. b 39. Tyndale Hall Bris 66. **d** 69 **p** 70. C Wellington w Eyton *Lich* 69-71; C Cheadle *Ches* 71-75; R Frettenham w Stanninghall *Nor* 75-81; R Spixworth w Crostwick 75-81; V Hailsham *Chich* from 81. *St Mary's Vicarage, Vicarage Road, Hailsham, E Sussex BN27 1BL* Hailsham (01323) 842381

PORTSMOUTH, Archdeacon of. *See* KNOWLES, Ven Graeme Paul

PORTSMOUTH, Bishop of. *See* STEVENSON, Rt Rev Kenneth William

PORTSMOUTH, Provost of. *See* YORKE, Very Rev Michael Leslie

PORTWOOD, Derek. b 31. Keele Univ MA70. ALCD58. **d** 57 **p** 58. C Laisterdyke *Bradf* 57-60; C-in-c Westlands St Andr CD *Lich* 60-66; V Westlands St Andr 66-69. *51 River Lane, Cambridge CB5 8HP* Cambridge (01223) 311044

POST, David Charles William. b 39. Jes Coll Cam BA61 MA65. Oak Hill Th Coll 61. **d** 63 **p** 64. C Orpington Ch Ch *Roch* 63-66; C Fulwood *Sheff* 66-68; V Lathom *Liv* 68-75; V Poughill *Truro* 75-78; V Braddan *S & M* 78-79; Dioc Missr 78-79; P-in-c Santan 78; V 78-79; V Sherburn in Elmet *York* 79-91; P-in-c Kirk Fenton 84-85; V Thornthwaite cum Braithwaite and Newlands *Carl* 91-93; R Wheldrake w Thorganby *York* from 93. *The Rectory, Church Lane, Wheldrake, York YO4 6AW* Wheldrake (01904) 448230

POST, Oswald Julian. b 48. Derby Lonsdale Coll BEd79. E Midl Min Tr Course. **d** 84 **p** 85. Travelling Sec Rwanda Miss 79-89; Hon C Hulland, Atlow, Bradley and Hognaston *Derby* 84-89; V Wormhill, Peak Forest w Peak Dale and Dove Holes from 89. *The Parsonage, The Hallsteads, Dove Holes, Buxton, Derbyshire SK17 8BJ* Chapel-en-le-Frith (01298) 813344

POSTILL, John Edward. b 35. Oak Hill Th Coll 64. **d** 67 **p** 68. C Southgate *Chich* 67-70; C Bowling St Jo *Bradf* 70-74; TV Winfarthing w Shelfanger *Nor* 74-79; R Slaugham *Chich* from 79. *The Rectory, Handcross, Haywards Heath, W Sussex RH17 6BU* Handcross (01444) 400221

POSTILL, Richard Halliday. b 37. Hull Univ BSc59. Westcott Ho Cam 66. **d** 68 **p** 69. C Wylde Green *Birm* 68-72; C Kingswinford St Mary *Lich* 72-76; V Yardley Wood *Birm* 76-86; V Acocks Green from 86; RD Yardley from 93. *The Vicarage, 34 Dudley Park Road, Acocks Green, Birmingham B27 6QR* 0121-706 9764

POSTLES, Donald. b 29. MPS51 Birm Univ DipTh59 MA65. Qu Coll Birm 56. **d** 59 **p** 60. V Wigan St Steph *Liv* 63-71; V Farnworth 71-84; V Mossley Hill St Barn 84-92; rtd 93. *43 The Broadway, Abergele, Clwyd LL22 7DD* Abergele (01745) 826165

POSTLETHWAITE, Alan James. b 38. Dur Univ BA60. Linc Th Coll 60. **d** 62 **p** 63. C Cottingham *York* 62-65; C Cockermouth All SS w Ch Ch *Carl* 65-68; V Seascale 68-77; P-in-c Irton w Drigg 75-77; P-in-c Whitehaven Ch Ch w H Trin 77; V Whitehaven 77-84; TR Kidderminster St Mary and All SS etc *Worc* 84-90; P-in-c Upper Arley 86-90; TR Kidderminster St Mary and All SS w Trimpley etc from 90; RD Kidderminster from 91. *The Vicarage, 22 Roden Avenue, Kidderminster, Worcs DY10 2RF* Kidderminster (01562) 823265

POTHEN, Simon John. b 60. Westmr Coll Ox BA86. Ripon Coll Cuddesdon 86. **d** 88 **p** 89. C Southgate Ch Ch *Lon* 88-91; C Tottenham St Mary 91-93; TV Gt Grimsby St Mary and St Jas *Linc* from 93. *St Mark's Vicarage, 2A Winchester Avenue, Grimsby, S Humberside DN33 1EW* Grimsby (01472) 277781

POTIPHER, John Malcolm Barry. b 42. St Alb Minl Tr Scheme 79. **d** 82 **p** 83. Chapl Herts Fire Brigade 82-91; NSM Chambersbury (Hemel Hempstead) *St Alb* 82-84; NSM Hemel Hempstead 84-86; NSM Digswell and Panshanger 86-92; P-in-c Pirton from 92. *The Vicarage, Crabtree Lane, Pirton, Hitchin, Herts SG5 3QE* Hitchin (01462) 712230

POTTER, Charles Elmer. b 42. Georgetown Univ (USA) BS65 Valparaiso Univ JD73. Wycliffe Coll Toronto MDiv81. **d** 81 **p** 82. C Southport Ch Ch *Liv* 81-84; Chapl Lee Abbey 84-87; Australia 87-93; P-in-c Aldingham and Dendron and Rampside *Carl* from 93. *The New Rectory, Aldingham, Ulverston, Cumbria LA12 9RT* Bardsea (01229) 869305

POTTER, Christopher Nicholas Lynden. b 49. Leeds Univ BA71. St As Minl Tr Course 90. **d** 93 **p** 94. C Flint *St As* from 93. *273 Chester Road, Oakenholt, Flint, Clwyd CH6 5SE* Flint (01352) 730712

POTTER, Clive Geoffrey. b 55. Aston Tr Scheme 88 Sarum & Wells Th Coll 90. **d** 92 **p** 93. C Epsom Common Ch Ch *Guildf* from 92. *278 The Greenway, Epsom, Surrey KT18 7JF* Epsom (01372) 722698

POTTER, Colin Michael. b 53. Lanc Univ BA74 Birm Univ DipTh82. Qu Coll Birm 80. **d** 83 **p** 84. C Middlewich w Byley *Ches* 83-87; TV Ches Team from 87. *St Thomas of Canterbury Vicarage, 33 Abbott's Grange, Liverpool Road, Chester CH2 1AJ* Chester (01244) 371612

POTTER, Frank Higton. b 23. CEng MICE55 FIWSc70 Man Univ BScTech49 AMCT49. Sarum & Wells Th Coll 89. **d** 89 **p** 90. Lic to Offic *St E* 89-92; R Badwell Ash w Gt Ashfield, Stowlangtoft etc 92-94; rtd 94; P-in-c Badwell Ash w Gt Ashfield, Stowlangtoft etc *St E* from 94. *The Rectory, Badwell Ash, Bury St Edmunds, Suffolk IP31 3DH* Walsham-le-Willows (01359) 259575

POTTER, George Koszelski St John (John). b 22. ARCM45 Em Coll Cam BA43 MA47 St Cath Coll Ox DipTh53. Wycliffe Hall Ox 51. **d** 53 **p** 54. Hd of RE Harris C of E High Sch Rugby 68-76; Hd of RE Rock Valley Sch Rochdale 76-77; V Langcliffe w Stainforth *Bradf* 77-84; P-in-c Horton-in-Ribblesdale 80-84; V Langcliffe w Stainforth and Horton 85-87; rtd 87. *Bridge Cottage, Station Road, Clapham, Lancaster LA2 8DP* Clapham (015242) 51628

POTTER, Guy Anthony. b 18. St Jo Coll Cam BA40 MA44. Cuddesdon Coll 40. **d** 41 **p** 42. R Heene *Chich* 65-75; R Black Notley *Chelmsf* 75-83; rtd 83; Perm to Offic *Cov* from 83. *4 Manor Court Avenue Road, Leamington Spa, Warks CV31 3NL* Leamington Spa (01926) 35236

POTTER, Harry Drummond. b 54. Em Coll Cam BA76 MA79 MPhil81. Westcott Ho Cam 79. **d** 81 **p** 82. C Deptford St Paul *S'wark* 81-84; Chapl Selw Coll Cam 84-87; Chapl Newnham

Coll Cam 84-87; Chapl HM Pris Wormwood Scrubs 87-88; Chapl HM Young Offender Inst Aylesbury 88-93; NSM Camberwell St Giles w St Matt *S'wark* from 93. *Flat C, St Giles Centre, 81 Camberwell Church Street, London SE5 8RB*

POTTER, James David. b 35. AKC66. **d** 67 **p** 68. C Longbridge *Birm* 67-70; Lic to Offic 71-73; V N Harborne 73-78; V Smethwick H Trin w St Alb 78-83; V Blurton *Lich* 83-90; V Dordon *Birm* from 90; RD Polesworth from 91. *St Leonard's Vicarage, Watling Street, Dordon, Tamworth, Staffs B78 1TE* Tamworth (01827) 892294

POTTER, John Dennis. b 39. Ealing Tech Coll. S Dios Minl Tr Scheme 92. **d** 94 **p** 95. NSM Box w Hazlebury and Ditteridge *Bris* from 94. *6 Fuller Road, Bath BA1 7BB* Bath (01225) 316656

POTTER, John Ellis. b 45. Sarum & Wells Th Coll 82. **d** 84 **p** 85. C Wootton Bassett *Sarum* 84-88; TV Swindon New Town *Bris* from 88. *St Luke's Vicarage, 3 Briar Fields, Swindon SN1 2QN* Swindon (01793) 536679

POTTER, Canon John Henry. b 26. Lon Univ BA50. Oak Hill Th Coll 50. **d** 52 **p** 53. P-in-c Ilfracombe SS Phil and Jas *Ex* 69-72; V 72-76; R Poole *Sarum* 76-87; RD Poole 80-85; Can and Preb Sarum Cathl 83-91; P-in-c Charmouth and Catherston Leweston 87-91; rtd 91. *3 Millhams Close, Bournemouth BH10 7LW* Bournemouth (01202) 580269

POTTER, John Michael. b 28. ALCD56. **d** 56 **p** 57. V Kettlewell w Conistone *Bradf* 60-79; P-in-c Arncliffe w Halton Gill 75-78; P-in-c Hubberholme 78-79; V Kettlewell w Conistone and Hubberholme 79-82; R Somersham w Flowton and Offton w Willisham *St E* 82-93; rtd 93. *61 Hurrs Road, Skipton, N Yorkshire BD23 2JX* Skipton (01756) 797009

POTTER, Keith Clement. b 39. Leeds Univ CSocStuds78 Bradf Univ MA81. Chich Th Coll 62. **d** 64 **p** 65. C Doncaster Ch Ch *Sheff* 64-68; C Tong *Bradf* 68-70; V Bradf St Columba w St Andr 70-79; V Yeadon St Andr from 79. *St Andrew's Vicarage, Haw Lane, Yeadon, Leeds LS19 7XQ* Leeds (0113) 250 3989

POTTER, Kenneth Benjamin. Lon Univ BA. NE Ord Course. **d** 87 **p** 88. NSM Ryton w Hedgefield *Dur* from 87. *Ellesmere, Peth Lane, Ryton, Tyne & Wear NE40 3PB*

POTTER, Mrs Linda. b 47. Cranmer Hall Dur 92. **d** 94 **p** 95. C Shildon w Eldon *Dur* from 94. *4 Eldon Bank, Eldon, Bishop Auckland, Co Durham DL14 8DX* Bishop Auckland (01388) 772397

POTTER, Malcolm Emmerson. b 48. Bedf Coll Lon BSc70. St Jo Coll Nottm DPS75. **d** 75 **p** 76. C Upton (or Overchurch) *Ches* 76-78; CPAS Staff 78-84; Development Officer St Jo Coll Nottm 84-86; P-in-c Wellington, All SS w Eyton *Lich* 86-95; V from 95. *All Saints' Vicarage, 35 Crescent Road, Wellington, Telford, Shropshire TF1 3DW* Telford (01952) 641251

POTTER, Peter Maxwell. b 46. Univ of Wales (Swansea) BA69 Univ of BC MA71. Sarum & Wells Th Coll 83. **d** 85 **p** 86. C Bradford-on-Avon *Sarum* 85-88; C Harnham 88-91; P-in-c N Bradley, Southwick and Heywood from 91. *The Vicarage, 62 Church Lane, North Bradley, Trowbridge, Wilts BA14 0TA* Trowbridge (01225) 752635

POTTER, Phillip. b 54. Stirling Univ BA75. Trin Coll Bris 82. **d** 84 **p** 85. C Yateley *Win* 84-88; V Haydock St Mark *Liv* from 88. *St Mark's Vicarage, 2 Stanley Bank Road, Haydock, St Helens, Merseyside WA11 0UW* St Helens (01744) 23957

POTTER, Richard Antony. b 36. K Coll Cam BA60 MA64. Ridley Hall Cam 60. **d** 62 **p** 63. C Luton w E Hyde *St Alb* 62-72; V Lyonsdown H Trin 72-85; R Broxbourne w Wormley from 85. *The Vicarage, Churchfields, Broxbourne, Herts EN10 7AU* Hoddesdon (01992) 462382

POTTER, Stephen Michael. b 55. Oak Hill Th Coll 93. **d** 95. C Chesterfield H Trin and Ch Ch *Derby* from 95. *31 Newbold Road, Chesterfield, Derbyshire S41 7PG* Chesterfield (01246) 232048

POTTER, Timothy John (Tim). b 49. Bris Univ BSc71. Oak Hill Th Coll 73. **d** 76 **p** 77. C Wallington H Trin *S'wark* 76-79; C Hampreston *Sarum* 79-81; TV Stratton St Margaret w S Marston etc *Bris* 81-87; P-in-c Hatf Heath *Chelmsf* 87-89; P-in-c Sheering 87-89; R Hatf Heath and Sheering from 90. *The Vicarage, Broomfields, Hatfield Heath, Bishop's Stortford, Herts CM22 7EA* Bishop's Stortford (01279) 730288

POTTIER, Ronald William. b 36. S'wark Ord Course 73. **d** 76 **p** 77. NSM Lower Sydenham St Mich *S'wark* from 76. *12 Neiderwald Road, London SE26 4AD* 0181-699 4375

POTTS, Canon Hugh Cuthbert Miller. b 07. Linc Coll Ox BA29 MA41. St Steph Ho Ox 37. **d** 37 **p** 38. V Glouc St Cath *Glouc* 61-80; Hon Can Glouc Cathl 69-90; rtd 80. *5 Hilton Close, Hempsted, Gloucester GL2 6LQ* Gloucester (01452) 305188

POTTS, James. b 30. K Coll Lon BD56 AKC56. **d** 57 **p** 58. Tanzania 64-71; C-in-c Athersley and New Lodge CD *Wakef* 71-73; V Athersley 73-77; V Madeley *Lich* 77-85; V Baswich (or Berkswich) 85-93; RD Stafford from 88; rtd 93. *2 Chebsey Drive, Stafford ST16 1ST*

POTTS, William Gilbert. b 17. Bps' Coll Cheshunt 46. **d** 49 **p** 50. V Winshill *Derby* 64-82; rtd 82; Perm to Offic *Derby* from 82. *28 Roydon Close, Mickleover, Derby DE3 5PN* Derby (01332) 516328

POULARD, Christopher. b 39. FCA. Ridley Hall Cam 82. **d** 84 **p** 85. C N Walsham w Antingham *Nor* 84-86; C Oulton Broad 86-90; TV Raveningham 90-94; R The Raveningham Gp from 94. *The Rectory, Rectory Road, Haddiscoe, Norwich NR14 6PG* Aldeby (01502) 677774

POULTER, Alan John. b 39. St Aid Birkenhead 64. **d** 67 **p** 68. C Heswall *Ches* 67-72; V Bredbury St Mark 72-78; V Oxton from 78; RD Birkenhead from 93. *8 Wexford Road, Birkenhead, Merseyside L43 9TB* 0151-652 1194

POULTER, Joseph William. b 40. Dur Univ BA61 BA66 DipTh67. Cranmer Hall Dur 66. **d** 67 **p** 68. C Harlow New Town w Lt Parndon *Chelmsf* 67-71; C Washington *Dur* 71-77; Producer Metro Radio from 75; C-in-c Town End Farm CD 77-83; V Sunderland Town End Farm from 83. *Town End Farm House, Bootle Street, Sunderland SR5 4EY* 0191-536 3823

POULTNEY, Wilfred Howard. b 25. Qu Coll Birm 71. **d** 73 **p** 74. NSM S Leamington St Jo *Cov* 73-85; NSM Holbrooks 85-95; NSM Walsall St Gabr Fulbrook *Lich* from 95. *28 Walstead Road, Walsall WS5 4LX* Walsall (01922) 21673

POULTON, Arthur Leslie. b 28. K Coll Lon BA53 AKC53 BD60 Leic Univ MA85. Tyndale Hall Bris 53. **d** 55 **p** 56. Ches Coll of FE 64-87; Chapl 64-84; Sen Lect 66-87; P-in-c Gt Canfield *Chelmsf* 87-94; Dir of Studies Course in Chr Studies 87-94; rtd 94. *Peverey House North, Yeaton Peverey, Bomere Heath, Shrewsbury SY4 3AT*

POULTON, Ian Peter. b 60. Lon Univ BSc(Econ)83 TCD DipTh86 Open Univ BA94. **d** 86 **p** 87. C Newtownards *D & D* 86-89; I Bright w Ballee and Killough from 89; Relig Adv Downtown Commercial Radio from 91. *Bright Rectory, 126 Killough Road, Downpatrick, Co Down BT30 8LL* Ardglass (01396) 842041

POULTON, Katharine Margaret. b 61. Man Univ BA83 TCD DipTh87. **d** 87. C Ban St Comgall *D & D* 87-91; C Seagoe from 91. *Bright Rectory, 126 Killough Road, Downpatrick, Co Down BT30 8LL* Ardglass (01396) 842041

POUNCE, Alan Gerald. b 34. Lon Univ BSc55. Wycliffe Hall Ox 57. **d** 59 **p** 60. C Wednesfield Heath *Lich* 59-61; C Heref St Pet w St Owen *Heref* 61-63; R Gt w Lt Dunham *Nor* 63-69; Perm to Offic *Ox* 69-93; Hon C Wokingham St Sebastian from 95. *38 Longdown Road, Little Sandhurst, Camberley, Surrey GU17 8QG* Crowthorne (01344) 772870

POUNCEY, Canon Cosmo Gabriel Rivers. b 11. Qu Coll Cam BA32 MA36. Cuddesdon Coll 33. **d** 34 **p** 35. V Tewkesbury w Walton Cardiff *Glouc* 63-81; P-in-c Tredington w Stoke Orchard and Hardwicke 63-81; RD Tewkesbury 68-81; Hon Can Glouc Cathl 72-81; P-in-c Deerhurst w Apperley 74-80; rtd 81; Perm to Offic *Worc* 81-93. *Church Walk, Littlebredy, Dorchester, Dorset DT2 9HG* Long Bredy (01308) 482356

POUND, Canon Keith Salisbury. b 33. St Cath Coll Cam BA54 MA58. Cuddesdon Coll 55. **d** 57 **p** 58. C St Helier *S'wark* 57-61; Tr Officer Hollowford Tr & Conf Cen Sheff 61-64; Warden 64-67; V S'wark H Trin 68-74; P-in-c Newington St Matt 68-74; V S'wark H Trin w St Matt 74-78; RD S'wark and Newington 73-78; TR Thamesmead 78-86; Sub-Dean Woolwich 84-86; RD Greenwich 85-86; Hon Can S'wark Cathl 85-86; Chapl Gen of Pris 86-93; Chapl to The Queen from 88; Chapl HM Pris Grendon and Spring Hill from 93. *1 Park Road, Grendon Underwood, Aylesbury, Bucks HP18 0TD* Grendon Underwood (01296) 770494 Fax 770756

POUNDE, Nigel. b 46. Edin Univ MA69. Cranmer Hall Dur DipTh71. **d** 72 **p** 73. C Southsea St Simon *Portsm* 72-75; C Clayton w Keymer *Chich* 75-79; Malaysia 80-86; TV Wolv *Lich* from 87. *St Chad's Vicarage, Manlove Street, Wolverhampton WV3 0HG* Wolverhampton (01902) 26580

POUNTAIN, Eric Gordon. b 24. Sarum Th Coll 65. **d** 66 **p** 67. C New Bury *Man* 66-76; Lic to Offic *Blackb* 76-80; Chapl Lancs (Preston) Poly 80-81; P-in-c Preston St Mark 80-81; V Salesbury 81-86; rtd 86. *116 Harewood Road, Rishton, Blackburn BB1 4DZ* Blackburn (01254) 888091

POVALL, Charles Herbert. b 18. Man Univ MEd71. St Deiniol's Hawarden 75. **d** 76 **p** 77. C Norbury *Ches* 76-83; rtd 83; Perm to Offic *Ches* from 83. *3 Magda Road, Stockport, Cheshire SK2 7LX* 0161-483 6713

POVEY, John Michael. b 44. St Jo Coll Nottm BTh76. **d** 76 **p** 77. USA from 76. *67 East, Pittsfield, Massachusetts 01201, USA*

POVEY, Canon Kenneth Vincent. b 40. AKC62. **d** 63 **p** 64. C Crewe Ch Ch *Ches* 63-66; C Neston 66-69; C Kensington St Mary Abbots w St Geo *Lon* 69-72; R Ches H Trin 72-81; Chapl Copenhagen w Aarhus *Eur* 81-86; R Gawsworth *Ches* from 86; Hon Can Ches Cathl from 92. *The Rectory, Gawsworth, Macclesfield, Cheshire SK11 9RJ* North Rode (01260) 223201

POVEY, Dr William Peter. b 36. JP85. MRCS61 LRCP61 FFPHM79 FRIPHH DObstRCOG HonFChS Liv Univ DPH68 Man Univ MSc82. N Ord Course 90. **d** 93 **p** 94. NSM Latchford Ch Ch *Ches* from 93; Dioc HIV/AIDS Adv and Drug Liaison Officer from 93. *The Gables, 153 Chester Road, Grappenhall, Warrington WA4 2SB* Warrington (01925) 265530

POW, Miss Joyce. b 29. RGN55 SCM57 RSCN60 RNT73. St Jo Coll Nottm CertCS88. **d** 88 **p** 94. Hon Par Dn Largs *Glas* 88-94; Hon C from 94. *15 Shuma Court, Skelmorlie, Ayrshire PA17 5EJ* Wemyss Bay (01475) 520289

POWE, David James Hector. b 50. Brighton Poly CertMS86. Wycliffe Hall Ox 88. **d** 90 **p** 91. C Ventnor St Cath *Portsm* 90-92; Chapl HM Pris Belmarsh 93-94; Chapl HM Pris Lewes from 94. *HM Prison Lewes, Brighton Road, Lewes, E Sussex BN7 1EA* Lewes (01273) 477331 Fax 483042

POWE, Eric James. b 23. Univ of Wales (Lamp) BA50 BD61. St Steph Ho Ox 50. **d** 52 **p** 53. CF 57-73; R Broadstairs *Cant* 73-94; rtd 94; Perm to Offic *Cant* from 94. *15 Northumberland Avenue, Margate, Kent CT9 3BP* Thanet (01843) 294673

POWE, Roger Wayne. b 46. Lon Univ BEd70 MA78. S'wark Ord Course 73. **d** 76 **p** 77. NSM Surbiton St Andr *S'wark* 76-77; NSM Surbiton St Andr and St Mark 77-79; Asst Chapl Giggleswick Sch 79-80; C St Marylebone All SS *Lon* 80-81; Asst Chapl Hurstpierpoint Coll Hassocks 81-90. *Address temp unknown*

POWELL, Anthony James. b 51. Sarum & Wells Th Coll 78. **d** 79 **p** 80. C Larkfield *Roch* 79-83; C Leybourne 79-83; V Boro Green from 83. *The Vicarage, 24 Maidstone Road, Borough Green, Sevenoaks, Kent TN15 8BD* Borough Green (01732) 882447

POWELL, Colin Arthur. b 32. Hatf Coll Dur BA53. Oak Hill Th Coll 56. **d** 58 **p** 59. C Leyland St Andr *Blackb* 58-61; C Lanc St Thos 61-64; C Tranmere St Cath *Ches* 64-65; R Cheetham Hill *Man* 65-81; TV Oldham 81-86; TV Rochdale from 86; Chapl Birch Hill Hosp from 94. *Good Shepherd Vicarage, 160 Entwisle Road, Rochdale, Lancs OL16 2JJ* Rochdale (01706) 40130

POWELL, Mrs Diane. b 41. SW Minl Tr Course 85. **d** 88 **p** 94. Hon C St Merryn *Truro* 88-92; D-in-c Gerrans w St Antony in Roseland 92-94; P-in-c from 94. *The Rectory, Gerrans, Portscatho, Truro, Cornwall TR2 5EB* Truro (01872) 580277

POWELL, Dudley John. b 44. Tyndale Hall Bris 65. **d** 69 **p** 70. C Blackb Sav *Blackb* 69-71; C Rodbourne Cheney *Bris* 71-74; P-in-c Kingsdown 74-79; V 79-80; V Stoke Gifford 80-90; TR 90-91; Albania 91-94. *20 Queens Field, Stratton, Swindon SN2 6SX*

POWELL, Canon Eleanor Ann. b 55. Gwent Coll Newport CertEd76 Univ of Wales BA82. Qu Coll Birm 82. **d** 83 **p** 94. C Caereithin *S & B* 83-86; C Bishopston 86-88; Dioc Children's Officer *Glouc* 88-94; Hon Can Glouc Cathl from 94; P-in-c The Edge, Pitchcombe, Harescombe and Brookthorpe from 94; Dioc Adv for Women's Min from 94. *The Rectory, Edge, Stroud, Glos GL6 6PF* Painswick (01452) 812319

POWELL, Francis David Claude. b 09. Leeds Univ BA31. Coll of Resurr Mirfield 31. **d** 33 **p** 34. V Hammersmith St Matt *Lon* 70-75; rtd 75; Perm to Offic *Ox* 75-88; Perm to Offic *St Alb* from 75. *St Martha's Lodge, Park Road, Tring, Herts HP23 6BP* Tring (01442) 823041

POWELL, Preb Frank. b 29. AKC52. **d** 53 **p** 54. V Bilston St Leon *Lich* 69-76; P-in-c Hanbury 76-82; V Hanbury w Newborough 83-86; V Basford 86-92; Preb Lich Cathl 87-92; rtd 92. *17 Thorley Grove, Wistaston, Crewe CW2 8BA* Crewe (01270) 650513

POWELL, Geoffrey Peter. b 25. Chich Th Coll 54. **d** 56 **p** 57. V Wanborough *Bris* 62-75; R Lyddington w Wanborough 75-80; V St Cleer *Truro* 80-90; rtd 91. *The Old Bakery, Oare, Marlborough, Wilts SN8 4JQ* Marlborough (01672) 62627

POWELL, John. b 44. St Luke's Coll Ex CertEd66. Glouc Sch of Min 81. **d** 84 **p** 85. NSM Stroud and Uplands w Slad *Glouc* 84-89; Chapl Eliz Coll Guernsey 89-92; C Llandudno *Ban* 92-93; TV from 94. *The Parsonage, Morfa Road, Llandudno, Gwynedd LL49 9PA* Llandudno (01492) 860070

POWELL, John Keith Lytton. b 52. Warden Worshipful Company of Cooks. E Sussex Agric Coll OND. S Dios Minl Tr Scheme 91. **d** 94. NSM Bridgwater H Trin *B & W* from 94. *Postridge Farm, Spaxton, Bridgwater, Somerset TA5 1BN* Bridgwater (01278) 671328

POWELL, John Reginald. b 36. Nottm Univ BA59 PGCE71 St Cath Coll Ox DipPSA60. Ripon Hall Ox 59. **d** 61 **p** 62. C Thornhill *Wakef* 61-64; C Hebden Bridge 61-64; P-in-c Halifax St Aug 64-67; Hon C Lanc Ch Ch *Blackb* 67-69; V Holland Fen *Linc* 69-73; Perm to Offic *York* 73-84; Chapl K Sch Ely 77-84; V Skerton St Chad *Blackb* 84-89; V Ashton-on-Ribble St Andr from 89; RD Preston from 92. *The Vicarage, 240 Tulketh Road, Ashton-on-Ribble, Preston PR2 1ES* Preston (01772) 726848

POWELL, Miss Katherine (Kate). b 56. Sydney Univ BSocStuds79. Wycliffe Hall Ox 84. **dss** 86 **d** 87 **p** 94. Broadwater St Mary *Chich* 86-87; Par Dn 87-91; Asst Chapl Ch Hosp Horsham from 91. *7 King Edward Road, Christ's Hospital, Horsham, W Sussex RH13 7ND* Horsham (01403) 262738

POWELL, Kelvin. b 49. Wycliffe Hall Ox 71. **d** 74 **p** 75. C Prescot *Liv* 74-77; C Ainsdale 77-79; V Bickershaw 79-85; R Hesketh w Becconsall *Blackb* from 85. *All Saints' Rectory, Silverdale, Hesketh Bank, Preston PR4 6RZ* Preston (01772) 814798

POWELL, Llewellyn. b 28. Glouc Th Course 67. **d** 70 **p** 71. C Quinton *Glouc* 70-73; P-in-c 74-76; V Church Honeybourne w Cow Honeybourne 76-83; R Pebworth w Dorsington and Honeybourne 83-87; rtd 87. *Bodathro Bungalow, Llangynin, St Clears, Carmarthen, Dyfed SA33 4LD* Llanboidy (01994) 448301

POWELL, Dr Mark. b 57. Bath Univ BSc78 PhD81. Ripon Coll Cuddesdon BA84 MA88. **d** 85 **p** 86. C Evesham *Worc* 85-88; V Exhall *Cov* from 88. *Exhall Vicarage, Ash Green, Coventry CV7 9AA* Coventry (01203) 362997

POWELL, Ralph Dover. b 49. ARMCM70. Chich Th Coll 71. **d** 74 **p** 75. C Coppenhall *Ches* 74-77; C Heref H Trin *Heref* 77-80; V Crewe St Barn *Ches* from 80. *St Barnabas' Vicarage, West Street, Crewe CW1 3AX* Crewe (01270) 212418

POWELL, Raymond Leslie. b 35. AKC61. **d** 62 **p** 63. C Hendon St Mary *Lon* 62-67; C Huntingdon All SS w St Jo *Ely* 67-75; V Huntingdon St Barn 75-79; P-in-c Sawston 79-81; V from 81; P-in-c Babraham from 85; RD Shelford 89-94. *The Vicarage, Church Lane, Sawston, Cambridge CB2 4JR* Cambridge (01223) 832248

POWELL, Richard Michael Wheler. b 19. St Edm Hall Ox BA45. Wells Th Coll 47. **d** 49 **p** 50. R Tarporley *Ches* 62-72; P-in-c Lt Budworth 69-70; R Overton w Laverstoke and Freefolk *Win* 73-81; P-in-c Damerham *Sarum* 81-84; P-in-c Martin 81-84; rtd 84; Perm to Offic *B & W* 85-94; Perm to Offic *Ex* from 94. *38 Pine Park Road, Honiton, Devon EX14 8HR* Honiton (01404) 43429

POWELL, Richard Penry. b 15. Dur Univ LTh38. St Aid Birkenhead 34. **d** 38 **p** 39. V Wrockwardine *Lich* 64-80; V Uppington 64-80; rtd 80; Perm to Offic *Lich* from 80. *34 Herbert Avenue, Wellington, Telford, Shropshire TF1 2BS* Telford (01952) 242528

POWELL, Robert John (Rob). b 65. Trin Coll Bris DipHE91 BA92. **d** 92 **p** 93. C Biggin Hill *Roch* from 92. *22 Foxearth Close, Biggin Hill, Westerham, Kent TN16 3HQ* Biggin Hill (01959) 575900

POWELL, Roger Roy. b 68. Thames Poly BSc91. Ripon Coll Cuddesdon BTh94. **d** 94 **p** 95. C Leic St Jas *Leic* from 94. *Ashman House, 1 Dixon Drive, Leicester LE2 1RA* Leicester (0116) 270 0340

POWELL, Samuel John. b 21. Qu Coll Ox BA53 MA57. **d** 47 **p** 48. Lic to Offic *Ox* 47-53 and 56-58; C Pontnewynydd *Mon* 53-55; C Ashchurch *Glouc* 55-56; Brazil from 58. *Caixa Postal 161, Campos do Jordao, Sao Paulo, Brazil*

POWELL, Stuart William. b 58. K Coll Lon BD80 AKC80. Ripon Coll Cuddesdon 86. **d** 88 **p** 89. C Horden *Dur* 88-90; C Northolt Park St Barn *Lon* 90-93; R Castle Vale St Cuth *Birm* from 93. *St Cuthbert's Vicarage, Reed Square, Birmingham B35 7PS* 0121-747 4041

POWELL, William Michael. b 33. Bps' Coll Cheshunt 58. **d** 61 **p** 62. C Golders Green St Mich *Lon* 61-64; C Hatcham St Cath *S'wark* 64-67; C Woodham *Guildf* 67-72; V Guildf All SS 72-84; RD Guildf 78-84; TR Headley All SS 84-89; V Addlestone from 89. *The Vicarage, 140 Church Road, Addlestone, Surrey KT15 1SJ* Weybridge (01932) 842879

POWER, Alan Edward. b 26. Worc Coll Ox BA50 MA53. Lich Th Coll. **d** 57 **p** 58. C Summerfield *Birm* 57-60; C Oldbury 60-63; V Short Heath from 63. *St Margaret's Vicarage, Somerset Road, Birmingham B23 6NQ* 0121-373 6989

POWER, David Michael. b 56. BA81 BEd. Oak Hill Th Coll. **d** 81 **p** 82. C Warblington and Emsworth *Portsm* 81-84; C-in-c Hartplain 84-88; V Hartplain 88-91; Adv in Evang from 91. *38 Manor Close, Wickham, Fareham, Hants PO17 5BZ* Wickham (01329) 834747

POWER, Canon Ivor Jonathan. b 43. Lambeth STh87 CITC 66. **d** 69 **p** 70. C Dromore Cathl *D & D* 69-71; C Enniscorthy *C & O* 71-74; I Youghal *C, C & R* 74-78; I Youghal Union 78-81; I Athlone w Benown, Kiltoom and Forgney *M & K* from 81; RD Clonmacnoise from 86; Can Meath from 87; Dir of Ords (Meath) from 91. *The Rectory, Bonavalley, Athlone, Co Westmeath, Irish Republic* Athlone (902) 78350 Fax as telephone

POWER, James Edward. b 58. Nottm Univ BSc81 Leeds Univ BA85. Coll of Resurr Mirfield 83. **d** 86 **p** 87. C Cadoxton-juxta-Barry *Llan* 86-89; Chapl Harrow Sch Middx from 89; Perm to Offic *Lon* from 89. *35 West Street, Harrow, Middx HA1 3EG* 0181-869 1234

POWER, Mrs Jeanette. b 57. Oak Hill Th Coll BA82. **dss** 82 **d** 87 **p** 94. Warblington and Emsworth *Portsm* 82-84; Hartplain CD 84-87; Hon C Hartplain 87-91; Community Mental Health Chapl Havant and Petersfield from 91. *61 Hartplain Avenue, Cowplain, Waterlooville, Hants PO8 8RG* Waterlooville (01705) 264551

POWIS, Michael Ralph (Mike). b 63. St Jo Coll Nottm BTh95. **d** 95. C Dibden *Win* from 95. *2 Corsai Drive, Dibden Purlieu, Southampton SO45 5UF* Southampton (01703) 844376

POWLES, Charles Anthony. b 39. E Anglian Minl Tr Course. **d** 88 **p** 89. Hon C Hemsby *Nor* from 88. *Mairin, Ormesby Road, Hemsby, Great Yarmouth, Norfolk NR29 4LA* Great Yarmouth (01493) 732493

POWLES, Michael Charles. b 34. Reading Univ BSc56. Qu Coll Birm DipTh60. **d** 60 **p** 61. C Goodmayes All SS *Chelmsf* 60-65; C Surbiton St Matt *S'wark* 65-78; Lic to Offic from 79. *Spring Cottage, 3 Rushett Close, Long Ditton, Surrey KT7 0UR* 0181-398 9654

POWLEY, Robert Mallinson. b 39. Fitzw Coll Cam MA65 DPS68 DipSocWork69. Ridley Hall Cam 61. **d** 63 **p** 64. C Bermondsey St Mary w St Olave, St Jo etc *S'wark* 63-67; C Moseley St Anne *Birm* 67-69; Lic to Offic *Man* 72-77; Hon C Walshaw Ch Ch 77-88; V Prestwich St Gabr 88-94; Bp's Dom Chapl 88-94; P-in-c Hargrave *Ches* from 94; Exec Officer BSR from 94. *The Vicarage, Hargrave, Chester CH3 7RN* Huxley (01829) 781378

POWNALL, Lydia Margaret. *See* HURLE, Mrs Lydia Margaret

POWNALL, Canon Tom Basil. b 19. Jes Coll Cam BA41 MA44. Ridley Hall Cam 41. **d** 42 **p** 43. Warden Mabledon Conf Cen Tonbridge 68-74; P-in-c Fressingfield w Weybread *St E* 74-79; P-in-c Wingfield w Syleham 76-79; P-in-c Fressingfield w Weybread and Wingfield 79-86; RD Hoxne 81-86; Hon Can St E Cathl 83-86; RD Hartismere 84-85; rtd 86; Perm to Offic *Roch* from 86; Perm to Offic *Cant* from 86. *2 Abingdon Road, Maidstone, Kent ME16 9DP* Maidstone (01622) 720572

POWNE, Peter Rebbeck Lamb. b 23. Sarum & Wells Th Coll 80. **d** 83 **p** 84. C Calne and Blackland *Sarum* 83-86; V Netheravon w Fittleton and Enford 86-93; rtd 93. *2 Oak Lane, Fighelden, Salisbury SP4 8JS* Stonehenge (01980) 670326

POWNEY, Derek John. b 40. Univ Coll Ox BA62 MA66. E Anglian Minl Tr Course 90. **d** 93. C Tilbury Docks *Chelmsf* from 93. *4 Pepys Close, Tilbury, Essex RM18 8JT* Tilbury (01375) 843195

POYNER, Maurice John. b 20. St Deiniol's Hawarden. **d** 83 **p** 84. Hon C Humberstone *Leic* 83-90; Perm to Offic from 90. *127 Colchester Road, Leicester LE5 2DJ* Leicester (0116) 276 8372

POYNTING, Charles Robert Macvicar. b 23. Hertf Coll Ox BA48 MA48. Wells Th Coll 48. **d** 50 **p** 51. V Belfield *Man* 62-82; V Digby *Linc* 82-92; rtd 92. *Digby Cottage, Noke, Oxford OX3 9TX* Oxford (01865) 842794

✠POYNTZ, Rt Rev Samuel Greenfield. b 26. TCD BA48 MA51 BD53 PhD60. TCD Div Sch Div Test50. **d** 50 **p** 51 **c** 78. C Dub St Geo *D & G* 50-52; C Bray 52-55; C Dub St Michan w St Paul 55-59; Sec and Sch Insp Ch Educn Soc for Ireland 56-75; I Dub St Steph 59-67; I Dub St Ann 67-70; I Dub St Ann w St Steph 70-78; Adn Dub 74-78; Bp C, C & R 78-87; Bp Conn 87-95; rtd 95. *10 Harmony Hill, Lisburn, Co Antrim BT27 4EP* Lisburn (01846) 679013

PRAGNELL, John William. b 39. Lon Univ BD65. Lambeth STh87 LTh88. **d** 65 **p** 66. C Bitterne *Win* 65-68; C Hatf Hyde St Mary *St Alb* 68-73; Kuwait 73-75; Chapl Leavesden Hosp and Abbots Langley Hosp 75-88; Chapl Watford Gen Hosp 86-88; V St Alb St Steph *St Alb* 88-95; RD St Alb 91-95; P-in-c Copythorne and Minstead *Win* from 95; Dio Ecum Officer from 95. *The Vicarage, Pine Ridge, Romsey Road, Cadnam, Southampton SO40 2NN* Southampton (01703) 814769

PRAGNELL, Michael John. b 40. CChem MRSC FIQA81 MSOSc88 MA PhD. Ox NSM Course 81. **d** 84 **p** 85. NSM High Wycombe *Ox* from 84. *28 Carver Hill Road, High Wycombe, Bucks HP11 2UA* High Wycombe (01494) 533056

PRAILL, David William. b 57. FRGS90 York Univ BA79. Cranmer Hall Dur 81. **d** 82 **p** 83. C Digswell and Panshanger *St Alb* 82-84; CMS 84-89; Course Dir St Geo Coll Jerusalem 85-89; Dir McCabe Educn Trust 90-91; Dir St Luke's Hospice Harrow and Wembley from 91; Perm to Offic *Lon* from 94. *1A St Ann's Crescent, London SW18 2ND* 0181-870 3694

PRANCE, Robert Penrose. b 47. Southn Univ DipTh. Sarum & Wells Th Coll 69. **d** 72 **p** 73. C Gillingham and Fifehead Magdalen *Sarum* 72-76; P-in-c Edmondsham 76-80; P-in-c Woodlands 76-80; P-in-c Wimborne St Giles 76-80; P-in-c Cranborne 77-80; R Cranborne w Boveridge, Edmondsham etc 80-83; Chapl Sherborne Sch Dorset 83-93; V Stoke Gabriel and Collaton St Mary *Ex* from 93. *The Vicarage, Stoke Gabriel, Totnes, Devon TQ9 6QX* Stoke Gabriel (01803) 782358

PRASADAM, Goruganthula Samuel Narayanamurthy (Sam). b 34. Andhra Univ India BA57. Bangalore Th Coll BD65 Union Th Sem (NY) STM68. **d** 62 **p** 65. India 62-74; C Llanbeblig w Caernarfon and Betws Garmon etc *Ban* 75-76; C Norbury *Ches* 77-78; V Aberaman and Abercwmboi *Llan* 78-83; N Sec CMS 83-87; V Luton All SS w St Pet *St Alb* from 87. *All Saints' Vicarage, Shaftesbury Road, Luton LU4 8AH* Luton (01582) 20129

PRASADAM, Jemima. b 38. BD61 BA87. Cranmer Hall Dur 86. **d** 87 **p** 94. Par Dn Luton All SS w St Pet *St Alb* 87-94; Miss Partner CMS from 87; C Luton All SS w St Pet *St Alb* from 94. *All Saints' Vicarage, Shaftesbury Road, Luton LU4 8AH* Luton (01582) 20129

PRATT, Basil David. b 38. Ripon Hall Ox 64. **d** 67 **p** 68. C Lewisham St Jo Southend *S'wark* 67-68; C Caterham Valley 68-70; CF 70-93. *Address temp unknown*

PRATT, Benjamin John. b 42. TCD BA63. Cuddesdon Coll 68. **d** 70 **p** 71. C Ballymoney *Conn* 70-72; C Monaghan *Clogh* 72-74; Ind Chapl Kirkby *Liv* 74-83. *96 Parkmore, Craigavon, Co Armagh BT64 2AF*

PRATT, Christine Fiona. b 60. Reading Univ BSc81. Ox Min Course 88. **d** 91 **p** 94. NSM Reading St Luke w St Bart *Ox* from 91. *Flat 1, 59 Christchurch Road, Reading RG2 7BD* Reading (01734) 869570

PRATT, Edward Andrew (Ted). b 39. Clare Coll Cam BA61 MA65. Clifton Th Coll 63. **d** 66 **p** 67. C Southall Green St Jo *Lon* 66-69; C Drypool St Columba w St Andr and St Pet *York* 69-71; P-in-c Radbourne *Derby* 71-74; R Kirk Langley 71-78; V Mackworth All SS 71-78; V Southsea St Simon *Portsm* from 78. *St Simon's Vicarage, 6 Festing Road, Southsea, Hants PO4 0NG* Portsmouth (01705) 733068

PRATT, Eric. b 32. Open Univ BA83. Ridley Hall Cam. **d** 60 **p** 61. C Denton Holme *Carl* 60-63; C Cockermouth All SS w Ch Ch 63-65; C Bredbury St Mark *Ches* 66-69; V Eaton and Hulme Walfield 69-75; V Hollingworth from 75. *The Vicarage, Hollingworth, Hyde, Cheshire SK14 8HS* Mottram (01457) 762310

PRATT, Mrs Janet Margaret. b 40. Herts Coll BEd78. St Alb Minl Tr Scheme 78. **dss** 81 **d** 87 **p** 94. High Wych and Gilston w Eastwick *St Alb* 81-87; Hon Par Dn 87-89; Par Dn Histon *Ely* 89-94; C from 94; Par Dn Impington 89-94; C from 94. *The Vicarage, 60 Impington Lane, Impington, Cambridge CB4 4NJ* Cambridge (01223) 232826

PRATT, John Anthony. b 38. Selw Coll Cam BA61 MA65. Qu Coll Birm DipTh66. **d** 66 **p** 67. C Harrow Weald All SS *Lon* 66-69; C St Pancras w St Jas and Ch Ch 69-74; C Saffron Walden *Chelmsf* 74-75; TV Saffron Walden w Wendens Ambo and Littlebury 75-79; V St Mary-at-Latton 79-88; Chapl Princess Alexandra Hosp Harlow 82-88; RD Harlow *Chelmsf* 83-88; R Tolleshunt Knights w Tiptree and Gt Braxted from 88. *The Rectory, Rectory Road, Tiptree, Colchester CO5 0SX* Tiptree (01621) 815260

PRATT, Kenneth George. b 21. E Anglian Minl Tr Course 81. **d** 84 **p** 85. NSM March St Jo *Ely* 84-87; Chapl Doddington Hosp and Alan Conway Court from 86; P-in-c Doddington w Benwick 87-94; rtd 93. *2 Windsor Drive, March, Cambs PE15 8DF* March (01354) 58814

PRATT, Michael. *See* HARRIS, Michael

PRATT, Richard David. b 55. Linc Coll Ox BA77 MA81 Nottm Univ BCombStuds84. Linc Th Coll 81. **d** 84 **p** 85. C Wellingborough All Hallows *Pet* 84-87; TV Kingsthorpe w St Dav Northn 87-92; V Northn St Benedict from 92. *The Vicarage, 16 Sentinel Road, Northampton NN4 9UF* Northampton (01604) 768624

PRATT, Samuel Charles. b 40. Oak Hill Th Coll 69. **d** 71 **p** 72. C Upper Holloway St Jo *Lon* 71-73; C Bucknall and Bagnall *Lich* 73-76; V Liv St Mich *Liv* 76-80; Chapl R Liv Hosp from 80. *23 Caithness Road, Liverpool L8 9SJ, or Royal Liverpool Hospital, Prescot Street, Liverpool L7 8XP* 0151-427 4997 or 706 2000

PRATT, Canon William Ralph (Will). b 47. Keble Coll Ox BA69 MA73. Linc Th Coll 70. **d** 72 **p** 73. C Ifield *Chich* 72-78; TV 78; C Brighton St Pet w Chpl Royal 79-80; C Brighton St Pet w Chpl Royal and St Jo 80-83; P-in-c Hove St Jo 83-87; Dioc Communications Officer from 87; Can and Preb Chich Cathl from 90. *23 Wilbury Avenue, Hove, E Sussex BN3 6HS* Brighton (01273) 748756 Fax 821810

PREBBLE, Ven Albert Ernest. b 08. Univ of NZ BA31 MA32 St Jo Coll Auckland 32. **d** 32 **p** 33. Perm to Offic *Pet* from 59; V Greenhill St Jo *Lon* 63-72; rtd 73. *23 Glebe Rise, Kings Sutton, Banbury, Oxon OX17 3PH* Banbury (01295) 811993

PREBBLE, Frederick John. b 25. Sarum Th Coll. **d** 56 **p** 57. V Saltley *Birm* 63-75; R Capel w Lt Wenham *St E* 75-80; rtd 80. *1B Chamberlin Road, Norwich NR3 3LZ* Norwich (01603) 402067

PREECE, Barry Leslie. b 48. Lich Th Coll 68. **d** 71 **p** 72. C Ewell *Guildf* 71-74; C York Town St Mich 75-77; P-in-c Ripley 77-81; Chapl HM Det Cen Send 77-81; V Cuddington *Guildf*

81-88; V Cobham from 88. *The Vicarage, St Andrew's Walk, Cobham, Surrey KT11 3EQ* Cobham (01932) 862109

PREECE, Colin George. b 51. Bernard Gilpin Soc Dur 71 Chich Th Coll 72. **d** 75 **p** 76. C Upper Gornal *Lich* 75-78; C Wednesbury St Paul Wood Green 78-81; V Oxley 81-89; V Kennington *Cant* from 89; RD E Charing from 92. *The Vicarage, 212 Faversham Road, Kennington, Ashford, Kent TN24 9AF* Ashford (01233) 620500

PREECE, Joseph. b 23. Univ of Wales (Ban) BA50 Univ of Wales (Swansea) DipSocSc51 LSE CertCC52 Lon Univ DBRS72. NW Ord Course 73. **d** 73 **p** 74. C Claughton cum Grange *Ches* 73-74; C Barnston 74-75; R Aldford and Bruera 75-80; V Wincle and Wildboarclough 80-82; P-in-c Cleeton w Silvington *Heref* 82-86; P-in-c Farlow 82-86; V Stottesdon 82-86; R Stottesdon w Farlow, Cleeton and Silvington 86-88; rtd 88. *Lingholm, Woodhall Drive, Hanwood, Shrewsbury SY5 8JU* Shrewsbury (01743) 860946

PREECE, Mark Richard. b 61. St Paul's Cheltenham BA85. Linc Th Coll 85. **d** 87 **p** 88. C Coity w Nolton *Llan* 87-89; C Penarth w Lavernock 89-92; R Ewenny w St Brides Major from 92. *The Vicarage, Southerndown Road, St Brides Major, Bridgend, M Glam CF32 0SD* Southerndown (01656) 880108

PREECE, Ronald Alexander (Ron). b 29. Lon Univ BD56. ALCD55. **d** 56 **p** 57. Perm to Offic *Cant* 63-70; Teacher Abp's Sch Cant 64-70; OMF 70-94; SW Regional Dir 76-94; Perm to Offic *Bris* 76-94; rtd 94. *5 Tonford Lane, Canterbury CT1 3XU* Canterbury (01227) 471061

PRENTICE, Brian. b 40. St Jo Coll Nottm 81. **d** 83 **p** 84. C W Bromwich All SS *Lich* 83-86; C Tettenhall Wood 86-89; TV 89-90; V Essington from 90. *The Vicarage, Wolverhampton Road, Essington, Wolverhampton WV11 2BX* Bloxwich (01922) 478540

PRENTICE, Michael Charles. b 35. Bps' Coll Cheshunt 59. **d** 62 **p** 63. C Lon Docks St Pet w Wapping St Jo *Lon* 62-66; C Cranford 66-70; C Bethnal Green St Jas the Gt w St Jude 70-71; C Walsingham and Houghton *Nor* 71-73; C Southall Ch Redeemer *Lon* 73; V Acton Vale St Thos 73-78; P-in-c Stow Bardolph w Wimbotsham and Stow Bridge *Ely* 78-80; R Woodford *Pet* 80-94. *Doric Cottage, 1 Low Road, Wretton, King's Lynn, Norfolk PE33 9QN* Stoke Ferry (01366) 500210

PRENTICE, Walter Gordon. b 07. Nor Ord Course 73. **d** 75 **p** 76. C Swanton Morley w Worthing *Nor* 75-77; P-in-c Scarning w Wendling 77-78; rtd 78; Perm to Offic *Nor* 78-80; Perm to Offic *St E* 80-88; Hon C Cherry Hinton St Andr *Ely* from 88. *13 St Andrew's Glebe, Cherry Hinton, Cambridge CB1 3JS* Cambridge (01223) 215285

PRENTIS, Richard Hugh. b 36. Ch Coll Cam BA60 MA64. Sarum Th Coll 69. **d** 71 **p** 72. C Bath Bathwick St Mary *B & W* 71-76; Bp's Dom Chapl *Lich* 76-80; PV Lich Cathl 76-80; V Longton St Mary and St Chad 80-84; V Shifnal 84-94; P-in-c Badger 84-85; P-in-c Ryton 84-85; P-in-c Beckbury 84-85; rtd 94. *23B The Close, Lichfield, Staffs WS13 7LD* Lichfield (01543) 411234

PRESCOTT, Canon Anthony John. b 34. AKC59. **d** 60 **p** 61. V Birm St Aid Small Heath *Birm* 68-71; Hon C Washwood Heath 72-95; Asst Sec ACS 71-73; Gen Sec 73-95; Hon Can St Woolos Cathl *Mon* from 83; rtd 95. *58 rue Albert Vincon, Certe, 44570 Trignac, Loire Atlantique, France* France (33) 40 45 92 17 Fax 40 45 92 18

PRESCOTT, Thomas Robert. b 41. St Mich Coll Llan DPT95. **d** 95. C Abertillery *Mon* from 95. *St Paul's Vicarage, Cwmtillery, Abertillery, Gwent NP3 1LS* Abertillery (01495) 212364

PRESCOTT, William Allan. b 57. ACIS87. Sarum & Wells Th Coll DCM93. **d** 93 **p** 94. C Horsell *Guildf* from 93. *6 Waldens Park Road, Woking, Surrey GU21 4RN* Woking (01483) 715440

PRESS, Richard James. b 45. Southn Univ CertEd67. Sarum & Wells Th Coll CMinlStuds92. **d** 92 **p** 93. C Bradford-on-Avon *Sarum* from 92. *126 Trowbridge Road, Bradford-on-Avon, Wilts BA15 1EW* Bradford-on-Avon (01225) 862516

PRESSWELL, John Lawrence Rowley. b 28. Southn Univ BEd79. AKC51. **d** 52 **p** 53. V Battersea St Bart *S'wark* 69-71; P-in-c Newtown St Luke *Win* 71-73; C Lymington 73-79; Chapl Crookham Court Sch Newbury 79-81; Chapl Stanbridge Earls Sch Romsey 81-82; C Doncaster St Geo *Sheff* 82-85; V Edlington 85-86; C Handsworth 86-88; C Rotherham 88-90; rtd 90. *The Cottage, Todds Lane, Burton-upon-Stather, Scunthorpe, S Humberside DN15 9DG* Scunthorpe (01724) 721266

PREST, Canon Walter. b 09. St Chad's Coll Dur BA33 DipTh34 MA36. **d** 34 **p** 35. Hon Can Truro Cathl *Truro* 61-82; Preb St Endellion 70-81; R St Endellion 70-81; rtd 81. *College of St Barnabas, Blackberry Lane, Lingfield, Surrey RH7 6NJ* Dormans Park (01342) 870612

PRESTNEY, Mrs Patricia Christine Margaret (Pat). b 49. Oak Hill Th Coll 84. **d** 87 **p** 94. NSM Lawford *Chelmsf* 87-95; Perm to Offic *St E* 91-95; Chapl Benenden Sch Kent from 95.

Benenden School, Benenden, Cranbrook, Kent TN17 4AA Cranbrook (01580) 240592

PRESTON, David Francis. b 50. BNC Ox BA72 MA78. St Steph Ho Ox 72. **d** 74 **p** 75. C Beckenham St Jas *Roch* 74-79; C Hockley *Chelmsf* 81-83; C Lamorbey H Redeemer *Roch* 83-89; V Gillingham St Barn from 89. *1 St Barnabas's Close, Oxford Road, Gillingham, Kent ME7 4BU* Medway (01634) 851010

PRESTON, Donald George. b 30. St Alb Minl Tr Scheme 77. **d** 80 **p** 81. NSM Elstow *St Alb* 80-87; NSM Goldington from 87. *106 Putnoe Street, Bedford MK41 8HJ* Bedford (01234) 367313

PRESTON, Preb Frederick Arnold. MBE53. Leeds Univ BA42. Coll of Resurr Mirfield 42. **d** 44 **p** 45. C Greenford H Cross *Lon* 44-51; CF 51-61; R W Hackney St Barn *Lon* from 61; Preb St Paul's Cathl from 75. *The Rectory, 306 Amhurst Road, London N16 7UE* 0171-254 3235

PRESTON, Frederick John. b 32. MBE72. Oak Hill Th Coll 54 St Jo Coll Northwood LTh67. **d** 57 **p** 58. V Otterton *Ex* 69-71; CF 71-79; NSM 79-84; Chapl Intercon Ch Soc 84-89; rtd 89. *Elm Cottage, Craggs Lane, Tunstall, Richmond, N Yorkshire DL10 7RB* Richmond (01748) 832037

PRESTON, James Martin. b 31. Trin Coll Cam MA55 Ch Ch Ox MA57. Virginia Th Sem 57 S'wark Ord Course 87. **d** 88 **p** 88. NSM Blackheath Ascension *S'wark* from 88. *14A Church Terrace, London SE13 5BT* 0181-318 3089

PRESTON, John. b 26. St Aid Birkenhead 58. **d** 52 **p** 52. In RC Ch 50-57; C Chadderton Ch Ch *Man* 58-59; C Didsbury Ch Ch 59-63; R Cheetham St Jo from 63. *St John's Rectory, Brideoak Street, Manchester M8 7AY* 0161-205 2005

PRESTON, John Baker. b 23. Lon Univ BA49. Oak Hill Th Coll 46. **d** 51 **p** 52. V Blackheath St Jo *S'wark* 57-65; Perm to Offic *Cant* 69-91; rtd 88. *43 Wedgwood Drive, Poole, Dorset BH14 8ES*

PRESTON, Dr John Michael. b 40. K Coll Lon BD63 AKC63 Lon Univ BA81 Southn Univ PhD91. St Boniface Warminster. **d** 65 **p** 66. C Heston *Lon* 65-67; C Northolt St Mary 67-72; Trinidad and Tobago 72-74; P-in-c Aveley *Chelmsf* 74-78; V 78-82; C Eastleigh *Win* 82-84; C-in-c Boyatt Wood CD 84-87; V W End from 87. *The Vicarage, Elizabeth Close, West End, Southampton SO3 3BU* Southampton (01703) 472180

PRESTON, Joseph Arthur. b 11. Bps' Coll Cheshunt 60. **d** 61 **p** 62. Hd Master Newtown Sch Hatfield 52-72; Perm to Offic *Nor* 72-76 and 77-88; P-in-c Gt w Lt Snoring 76-77; rtd 77; Perm to Offic *Ex* from 88. *The Coach House, Powderham, Exeter EX6 8JJ* Dawlish (01626) 891353

PRESTON, Leonard Arthur. b 09. Leeds Univ BA32 DipEd48. Coll of Resurr Mirfield 34. **d** 34 **p** 35. Chapl Laleham Abbey 56-76; rtd 76; Perm to Offic *Cant* from 76. *Underhill, Mountain Street, Chilham, Canterbury, Kent CT4 8DG* Canterbury (01227) 730266

PRESTON, Maurice. b 25. Lon Univ DipTh69 BD77. St Aid Birkenhead. **d** 57 **p** 58. V Thorpe Hesley *Sheff* 62-84; V Rawcliffe 84-89; rtd 89. *19 Erw Goch, Abergele, Clwyd LL22 9AQ* Abergele (01745) 826952

PRESTON, Michael Christopher. b 47. Hatf Coll Dur BA68. Ripon Coll Cuddesdon 75. **d** 78 **p** 79. C Epsom St Martin *Guildf* 78-82; C Guildf H Trin w St Mary 82-86; V Epsom St Barn from 86. *St Barnabas' Vicarage, Hook Road, Epsom, Surrey KT19 8TU* Epsom (01372) 722874

PRESTON, Canon Percival Kenneth. b 16. Ch Ch Ox BA38 MA48. Cuddesdon Coll 38. **d** 40 **p** 45. V Horfield St Greg *Bris* 55-81; Hon Can Bris Cathl 74-82; RD Horfield 76-81; rtd 81; Perm to Offic *Bris* from 82; Perm to Offic *Glouc* from 83. *56 Gloucester Road, Rudgeway, Bristol BS12 2RT* Almondsbury (01454) 612794

PRESTON, Reuben James. b 65. York Univ BSc86 MEng87. Westcott Ho Cam 88. **d** 91 **p** 92. C Weoley Castle *Birm* 91-94; TV Malvern Link w Cowleigh *Worc* from 94. *St Peter's House, 49 Yates Hay Road, Malvern, Worcs WR14 1LH* Malvern (01684) 574041

PRESTON, Canon Prof Ronald Haydn. b 13. Lon Univ BSc(Econ)35 St Cath Soc Ox BA40 MA44 DD83. Ripon Hall Ox 38. **d** 40 **p** 41. Prof of Soc and Past Th Man Univ 70-80; Hon Can Man Cathl *Man* 71-80; rtd 80; Perm to Offic *Man* from 80. *161 Old Hall Lane, Manchester M14 6HJ* 0161-225 3291

PRESTON, Miss Rosemary Muriel. b 23. St Mich Ho Ox DipTh. **dss** 80 **d** 87. Burundi 80-85; NSM Buckland Monachorum *Ex* 87-92; Perm to Offic from 92. *Fresh Springs, 3 Buckland Court, Crapstone, Yelverton, Devon PL20 7UE* Yelverton (01822) 854037

PRESTON, Thomas Leonard. b 27. Tyndale Hall Bris. **d** 64 **p** 65. V Thornham w Gravel Hole *Man* 68-76; Chapl to the Deaf *Chich* 76-80; TV York All SS Pavement w St Crux and St

Martin etc *York* 80-93; Chapl to the Deaf 80-93; rtd 93. *31 The Green, Royle Fields, Rochdale, Lancs* Rochdale (01706) 358797

PRESTON, William. b 25. St Cath Coll Cam BA46 MA50 Reading Univ MSc79. Oak Hill Th Coll 48. **d** 50 **p** 51. Cranbrook Sch Kent 69-90; Perm to Offic *Cant* from 64; Perm to Offic *Roch* from 66; rtd 90. *29 Orchard Way, Horsmonden, Tonbridge, Kent TN12 8LA* Brenchley (01892) 722616

PRESTON-THOMAS, Canon Colin Barnabas Rashleigh. b 28. K Coll Lon 48 Edin Th Coll 51. **d** 53 **p** 54. R Inverkeithing *St And* 61-72; R Rosyth 61-72; Syn Clerk 68-93; Can St Ninian's Cathl Perth 68-93; R Forfar 72-82; Dioc Sec 80-90; R Kilmaveonaig 82-93; R Pitlochry 82-93; rtd 93; Hon Can St Ninian's Cathl Perth *St And* from 93. *14 Muirend Grove, Perth PH1 1JW* Perth (01738) 27807

PRESTWOOD, Ms Jayne Marie. b 64. Man Univ BA86. Linc Th Coll DipMin93 MA94. **d** 94 **p** 95. C Reddish *Man* from 94. *2 Rowsley Grove, Stockport, Cheshire SK5 7AH* 0161-443 1949

PREVETT, Mark Norman. b 59. Univ of Wales (Cardiff) BD88. St Mich Coll Llan 85. **d** 88 **p** 89. C Brynmawr *S & B* 88-90; C Bassaleg *Mon* 90-92; R Blaina and Nantyglo from 92. *The Rectory, Station Road, Blaina, Gwent NP3 3BW* Blaina (01495) 290079

PREVITE, Very Rev Anthony Michael Allen. b 41. TCD DipTh88. CITC 85. **d** 88 **p** 89. C Galway w Kilcummin *T, K & A* 88-91; I Omey w Ballynakill, Errislannan and Roundstone 91-93; RD Tuam from 92; Dean Tuam from 93; I Tuam w Cong and Aasleagh from 93. *Deanery Place, Cong, Co Mayo, Irish Republic* Cong (92) 46017 Fax as telephone

PREWER, Dennis. b 30. Kelham Th Coll 50. **d** 54 **p** 55. V Scarcliffe *Derby* 64-70; Org Sec CECS 70-92; Dios Liv, Ban and St As 70-78; Dio Man 78-92; Lic to Offic *Ches* from 70; Perm to Offic *Man* from 78; rtd 92. *19 Alan Drive, Marple, Stockport, Cheshire SK6 6LN* 0161-427 2827

PRICE, Alec John. b 32. Solicitor 58 Univ of Wales (Abth) LLB55. St Deiniol's Hawarden 77. **d** 79 **p** 80. Hon C St As 79-80; VC St As Cathl 79-83; Hon C St As and Tremeirchion 80-83; R Cilcain and Nannerch and Rhyd-y-mwyn 84-88; Min Can and PV Bre Cathl *S & B* 88-90; Perm to Offic *Lich* 90-91; C Shrewsbury St Chad w St Mary from 91; Chapl Shrewsbury Town Cen from 91. *St Alkmund's, 31 Belvidere Road, Shrewsbury SY2 5LS* Shrewsbury (01743) 344155

PRICE, Miss Alison Jane. b 63. NNEB84. Aston Tr Scheme 91 Wesley Ho Cam CTM95. **d** 95. C Upper Norwood All SS *S'wark* from 95. *51 Chevening Road, London SE19 3TD* 0181-768 0269

PRICE, Alun Huw. b 47. St D Coll Lamp DipTh70. **d** 70 **p** 71. C Carmarthen St Dav *St D* 70-73; V Bettws Evan 73-77; CF from 77. *c/o MOD (Army), Bagshot Park, Bagshot, Surrey GU19 5PL* Bagshot (01276) 471717 Fax 412834

PRICE, Anthony Ronald (Tony). b 49. Linc Coll Ox BA71 MA83 St Jo Coll Dur BA78. **d** 79 **p** 80. C St Alb St Paul *St Alb* 79-81; C Wootton 81-85; C Lydiard Millicent w Lydiard Tregoz *Bris* 85-86; TV The Lydiards 86-91; V Marston *Ox* 91-95; V Marston w Elsfield from 95. *The Vicarage, Marston, Oxford OX3 0PR* Oxford (01865) 247034

PRICE, Ven Cecil Johnston. b 25. ARCM TCD BA48 MA52. CITC 49. **d** 50 **p** 51. I Delgany *D & G* 69-94; Adn Glendalough 89-94; rtd 94. *31 Bellvue Park, Greystones, Co Wicklow, Irish Republic* Dublin (1) 287-6805

PRICE, Mrs Christine Janice. b 45. Sarum & Wells Th Coll 83. **dss** 86 **d** 87 **p** 94. Roxbourne St Andr *Lon* 86-87; NSM 87-90; NSM Roxeth Ch Ch and Harrow St Pet 90-93; NSM Roxeth 93-94; C from 94. *43 Yeading Avenue, Harrow, Middx HA2 9RL* 0181-866 9119

PRICE, Clive Stanley. b 42. ALCD69. **d** 69 **p** 70. C Chenies and Lt Chalfont *Ox* 69-75; R Upper Stour *Sarum* 75-79; C-in-c Panshanger CD *St Alb* 79-82; TV Digswell and Panshanger 82-86; Dioc Ecum Officer *Newc* from 86; P-in-c St Oswald in Lee w Bingfield from 86. *St Oswald's Vicarage, Wall, Hexham, Northd NE46 4DU* Hexham (01434) 681354

PRICE, David. b 27. Wycliffe Hall Ox 61. **d** 63 **p** 64. C Abingdon w Shippon *Ox* 67-76; Israel 76-84; V S Kensington St Luke *Lon* 84-92; P-in-c S Kensington St Jude 88-92; rtd 92; Hon C Hordle *Win* from 92. *Church Cottage, Sway Road, Tiptoe, Lymington, Hants SO41 6FR* New Milton (01425) 616670

PRICE, Canon David Rea. b 39. St Aid Birkenhead 61. **d** 63 **p** 64. C Green Street Green *Roch* 63-66; C Gillingham St Mary 66-69; C New Windsor St Jo *Ox* 69-72; V Winkfield 72-80; RD Bracknell 78-86; V Sunningdale 80-86; TR Wimborne Minster and Holt *Sarum* from 86; Chapl Wimborne Hosp from 86; RD Wimborne from 88; Can and Preb Sarum Cathl from 92. *The Rectory, 17 King Street, Wimborne, Dorset BH21 1DZ* Wimborne (01202) 882340

PRICE, Canon David Trevor William. b 43. Keble Coll Ox BA65 MA69 MEHS FRHistS79 FSA95. Sarum & Wells Th Coll 72. **d** 72 **p** 73. Lic to Offic *St D* 72-82; Lect Univ of Wales (Lamp)

70-87; Sen Lect from 87; Chapl 79-80; Dioc Archivist *St D* from 82; P-in-c Betws Bledrws from 86; Hon Can St D Cathl 90-92; Can from 92; Dean of Chpl 90-91. *Bodlondeb, 65 Bridge Street, Lampeter, Dyfed SA48 7AB* Lampeter (01570) 422707

PRICE, Dawson. b 31. OBE. Petcrho Cam BA52. Oak Hill NSM Course 88. **d** 91 **p** 92. NSM Harpenden St Nic *St Alb* from 91. *1 Rye Close, Harpenden, Herts AL5 4LD* Harpenden (01582) 460380

PRICE, Canon Derek William. b 27. St Pet Hall Ox BA51 MA55. Qu Coll Birm 51. **d** 53 **p** 54. R Bridgham and Roudham *Nor* 67-80; R E w W Harling 69-80; Hon Can Nor Cathl 75-92; RD Thetford and Rockland 76-86; P-in-c Kilverstone 80-87; P-in-c Croxton 80-87; TR Thetford 80-87; R Castle Acre w Newton, Rougham and Southacre 87-92; rtd 92; Perm to Offic *Nor* from 92. *Fourways, King's Road, Dereham, Norfolk NE19 2AG* Dereham (01362) 691660

PRICE, Chan Desmond. b 23. St D Coll Lamp BA50. **d** 51 **p** 52. R Dinas and Llanllawer *St D* 68-72; V Llandeilo Fawr w Llandyfeisant 72-79; V Llandeilo and Taliaris 79-91; Can St D Cathl 83-91; Chan 89-91; RD Llangadog and Llandeilo 90-91; rtd 91; Hon Can St D Cathl *St D* from 91. *24 Diana Road, Llandeilo, Dyfed SA19 6RS* Llandeilo (01558) 824039

PRICE, Canon Edward Glyn. b 35. Univ of Wales (Lamp) BA55. Ch Div Sch of the Pacific (USA) BD58. **d** 58 **p** 59. C Denbigh *St As* 58-65; V Llanasa 65-76; V Buckley 76-91; Dioc RE Adv from 77; RD Mold 86-91; Can St As Cathl from 87; Preb and Sacr from 95; V Llandrillo-yn-Rhos from 91. *Llandrillo Vicarage, 36 Llandudno Road, Colwyn Bay, Clwyd LL28 4UD* Colwyn Bay (01492) 548878

PRICE, Canon Eric. b 14. Bps' Coll Cheshunt 42. **d** 44 **p** 45. V Handsworth St Mich *Birm* 61-84; rtd 85; Perm to Offic *Birm* from 85. *11 Brosil Avenue, Birmingham B20 1LB* 0121-523 0414

PRICE, Frank Watkin. b 22. ALCM37 Univ of Wales (Lamp) BA45. St Mich Coll Llan 45. **d** 47 **p** 48. Hd Master Amman Valley Lower Sch 68-85; R St Nicholas w Bonvilston and St George-super-Ely *Llan* 85-92; rtd 92; Perm to Offic *Llan* 92-94. *105 Gwscwm Road, Burry Port, Dyfed SA16 0YU* Burry Port (01554) 834048

PRICE, Frederick Leslie. b 30. Oak Hill Th Coll 59. **d** 61 **p** 62. C Hougham in Dover Ch Ch *Cant* 61-64; R Plumbland and Gilcrux *Carl* from 64. *The Rectory, Gilcrux, Carlisle CA5 2QN* Aspatria (016973) 20255

PRICE, Geoffrey David. b 46. NDA NCA. Oak Hill Th Coll DipHE. **d** 83 **p** 84. C Gt Baddow *Chelmsf* 83-86; C Hampreston *Sarum* 86-88; TV 88-93; P-in-c Drayton in Hales *Lich* from 93; P-in-c Adderley from 93; P-in-c Moreton Say from 93. *St Mary's Vicarage, Market Drayton, Shropshire TF9 1AQ* Market Drayton (01630) 652527

PRICE, Gerald Andrew. b 31. NE Ord Course. **d** 84 **p** 85. C Monkseaton St Mary *Newc* 84-87; V Cowgate 87-94; C Beltingham w Henshaw from 94; C Haydon Bridge from 94. *24 Hallstile Bank, Hexham, Northd NE46 3PQ* Hexham (01434) 603374

PRICE, Very Rev Hilary Martin Connop. b 12. Qu Coll Cam BA33 MA37. Ridley Hall Cam 34. **d** 36 **p** 37. Provost Chelmsf 67-77; rtd 77. *98 St James's Street, Shaftesbury, Dorset SP7 8HF* Shaftesbury (01747) 52118

PRICE, John Anthony Webb. Devon Coll of Agric DipAgr60 Queensland Univ BA78. St Fran Coll Brisbane ThDip79. **d** 75 **p** 76. Australia from 75. *Avalon Road, PO Box 139, Lara, Victoria, Australia 3212* Geelong (52) 821206

PRICE, John Francis. b 32. Qu Coll Cam BA54 MA. Ridley Hall Cam 54. **d** 56 **p** 57. V Forest Gate St Mark *Chelmsf* 60-71; V Harold Hill St Geo 72-79; R Loughton St Mary 79-83; TR Loughton St Mary and St Mich 83-88; R Kirby-le-Soken w Gt Holland 88-92; rtd 92. *97 Kings Parade, Holland-on-Sea, Clacton-on-Sea, Essex CO15 5JH* Clacton-on-Sea (01255) 813202

PRICE, John Joseph. b 44. **d** 92 **p** 93. C Glenfield *Leic* from 92; Relig Affairs Adv BBC Radio Leics from 93. *47 Clovelly Road, Glenfield, Leicester LE3 8AE* Leicester (0116) 287 5488

PRICE, Canon John Lowry Augustine. b 13. Mercer Ho Melbourne TDip69. AKC39. **d** 39 **p** 40. C St Alb St Sav *St Alb* 46-48; Australia from 48; Can Ballarat from 60; rtd 65. *88 Carrington Street, Macedon, Victoria, Australia 3440* Macedon (54) 261941

PRICE, John Newman. b 32. St Alb Minl Tr Scheme 80. **d** 83 **p** 84. NSM Bedf St Pet w St Cuth *St Alb* 83-88; C Lt Berkhamsted and Bayford, Essendon etc 88-92; P-in-c Benington w Walkern from 92. *The Rectory, Bockings, Walkern, Stevenage, Herts SG2 7PB* Walkern (01438) 861322

PRICE, Canon John Richard. b 34. Mert Coll Ox BA58 MA62. Westcott Ho Cam 58. **d** 60 **p** 61. C Man St Aid *Man* 60-63; C Bramley *Ripon* 63-67; V Leeds All Hallows w St Simon 67-74; P-in-c Wrangthorn 73-74; V Claughton cum Grange *Ches*

74-78; V Mottram in Longdendale w Woodhead 78-88; RD Mottram 79-88; Hon Can Ches Cathl from 86; R Nantwich from 88. *The Rectory, Nantwich, Cheshire CW5 5RQ* Nantwich (01270) 625268

PRICE, Joseph Roderick (Rod). b 45. St Mich Coll Llan 71. **d** 75 **p** 76. C Fleur-de-Lis *Mon* 75-79; CF from 79. *c/o MOD (Army), Bagshot Park, Bagshot, Surrey GU19 5PL* Bagshot (01276) 471717 Fax 412834

PRICE, Lawrence Robert. b 43. LICeram71 N Staffs Poly CertCT66 MDCT74. St Jo Coll Dur 76. **d** 78 **p** 79. C Harlescott *Lich* 78-80; C Cheddleton 80-83; P-in-c Calton 83-84; P-in-c Cauldon 83-84; P-in-c Grindon 83-84; P-in-c Waterfall 83-84; R Calton, Cauldon, Grindon and Waterfall 85-88; rtd 88; P-in-c Kingsley *Lich* from 95. *The Rectory, Kingsley, Stoke-on-Trent ST10 2BA* Cheadle (01538) 754754

PRICE, Martin Randall Connop. b 45. Lon Univ BSc71 Fitzw Coll Cam BA75 MA79. Ridley Hall Cam 73. **d** 76 **p** 77. C Keynsham *B & W* 76-79; Ind Chapl *Sheff* 79-83; V Wortley 79-83; R Hook Norton w Gt Rollright, Swerford etc *Ox* 83-91; V Shiplake w Dunsden from 91. *The Vicarage, Shiplake, Henley-on-Thames, Oxon RG9 4BS* Wargrave (01734) 401306

PRICE, Michael Graham. b 62. Ex Coll Ox BA84. Linc Th Coll 84. **d** 86 **p** 87. C Salford St Phil w St Steph *Man* 86-90; R Man Gd Shep 90-95; V Netherton St Andr *Worc* from 95. *The Vicarage, Highbridge Road, Netherton, Dudley, W Midlands DY2 0HT* Dudley (01384) 253118

PRICE, Canon Norman Havelock. b 28. Univ of Wales (Lamp) BA52. St Mich Coll Llan 52. **d** 54 **p** 55. V Mon St Thos-over-Monnow and Wonastow *Mon* 65-71; V Overmonnow w Wonastow and Michel Troy 71-93; RD Mon 84-93; Can St Woolos Cathl 91-93; rtd 93; Hon Can St Woolos Cathl *Mon* from 93. *Escholl, Llanellen Road, Llanfoist, Abergavenny, Gwent NP7 9NF* Abergavenny (01873) 854749

PRICE, Canon Peter Bryan. b 44. Oak Hill Th Coll 72. **d** 74 **p** 75. C Portsdown *Portsm* 74-78; Chapl Scargill Ho 78-80; P-in-c Addiscombe St Mary *Cant* 80-81; V 81-84; V Addiscombe St Mary *S'wark* 85-88; Can Res and Chan S'wark Cathl 88-91; Perm to Offic from 92; Gen Sec USPG from 92. *14 Oakwood Road, London SW20 0PW or, USPG, Partnership House, 157 Waterloo Road, London SE1 8XA* 0181-946 3814 or 071-928 8681 Fax 071-928 2371

PRICE, Peter Charles. b 27. Vancouver Sch of Th DipTh61. **d** 61 **p** 62. C Bearsted *Cant* 68-74; TV Ebbw Vale *Mon* 74-77; V Llanfihangel Crucorney w Oldcastle etc 77-87; St Helena 87-90; V Llanishen w Trelleck Grange and Llanfihangel etc *Mon* 90-94; rtd 94. *1 Kynaston, Much Marcle, Ledbury, Herefordshire HR8 2PD* Ledbury (01531) 670687

PRICE, Philip. b 24. Tyndale Hall Bris 50. **d** 55 **p** 56. Kenya 55-75; R Gt Horkesley *Chelmsf* 75-89; rtd 89. *229 Meadgate Avenue, Great Baddow, Chelmsford CM2 7NJ* Chelmsford (01245) 251499

PRICE, Philip Roger. b 09. Qu Coll Birm. **d** 57 **p** 58. C Wraxall *B & W* 68-72; V Mark 72-77; P-in-c Chapel Allerton 77; R Mark w Allerton 77-79; rtd 79; Perm to Offic *B & W* 80-94. *61 Summerlands Park Avenue, Ilminster, Somerset TA19 9BU* Ilminster (01460) 53428

PRICE, Raymond Francklin. b 30. Wycliffe Hall Ox 61. **d** 62 **p** 63. C Bilston St Leon *Lich* 62-67; C Keighley *Bradf* 67-70; V Mangotsfield *Bris* 70-79; Ind Chapl *Birm* 79-86; C Birm St Martin 84-85; C Birm St Martin w Bordesley St Andr 85-86; V Edgbaston St Aug from 86. *St Augustine's Vicarage, 44 Vernon Road, Birmingham B16 9SH* 0121-454 0127

PRICE, Roy Ernest. b 13. AKC38. **d** 38 **p** 39. V S Stoke w Woodcote *Ox* 59-79; rtd 79; Perm to Offic *Win* from 82. *74A London Road, Whitchurch, Hants RG28 7LY* Whitchurch (01256) 892581

PRICE, Stanley George. b 32. FRICS69. Trin Coll Bris 84. **d** 85 **p** 86. C Newport w Longford and Chetwynd *Lich* 85-88; V Ipstones w Berkhamsytch and Onecote w Bradnop from 88. *The Vicarage, Ipstones, Stoke-on-Trent ST10 2LF* Ipstones (01538) 266313

PRICE, Timothy Fry. b 51. NE Lon Poly CQSW. St Jo Coll Nottm 85. **d** 87 **p** 88. C Church Stretton *Heref* 87-91; V Sinfin *Derby* from 91. *St Stephen's Vicarage, 311 Sinfin Lane, Sinfin, Derby DE24 9GP* Derby (01332) 760186

PRICE, Victor John. b 35. Oak Hill Th Coll 62. **d** 65 **p** 66. C Rainham *Chelmsf* 65-70; V Dover St Martin *Cant* 70-78; V Madeley *Heref* 78-90; P-in-c Derby St Pet and Ch Ch w H Trin *Derby* 90-91; V from 91. *St Peter's Vicarage, 16 Farley Road, Derby DE23 6BX* Derby (01332) 347821

PRICE, William Norman. b 52. GRNCM73. N Ord Course 86. **d** 89 **p** 90. C Lower Broughton Ascension *Man* 89-91; Succ St E Cathl *St E* from 92; Min Can from 92; Prec from 94. *Clopton Cottage, 4 The Churchyard, Bury St Edmunds, Suffolk IP33 1RS* Bury St Edmunds (01284) 755868

PRICE, William Haydn (Dai). b 20. Sarum & Wells Th Coll 77. **d** 80 **p** 81. NSM Alverstoke *Portsm* 80-85; rtd 85; Perm to Offic *Portsm* from 85. *15 Amersham Close, Alverstoke, Gosport, Hants PO12 2RU* Gosport (01705) 580965

PRICE-JONES, Haydn. b 17. MBE60. St D Coll Lamp BA38 St Mich Coll Llan 39. **d** 40 **p** 41. R Horringer cum Ickworth *St E* 65-81; rtd 81; Hon C Aberedw w Llandeilo Graban and Llanbadarn etc *S & B* 81-83; Perm to Offic *St E* from 83. *20 Boon Close, Bury St Edmunds, Suffolk IP33 2LG* Bury St Edmunds (01284) 705867

PRICE-ROBERTS, Mervyn. b 29. Trin Coll Carmarthen TCert51 Univ of Wales DipRE52 BEd79. St Mich Coll Llan 89 Ban Ord Course 84. **d** 87 **p** 88. NSM Caerhun w Llangelynnin w Llanbedr-y-Cennin *Ban* 87-89; V Llandygai w Tregarth from 89. *St Ann's Vicarage, Bethesda, Bangor, Gwynedd LL57 4AX* Bethesda (01248) 600357

PRICHARD, Canon Thomas John. b 16. FRHistS82 Keele Univ PhD81 Univ of Wales (Ban) BA38 MA72. Chich Th Coll 38. **d** 39 **p** 40. Can Llan Cathl *Llan* 66-84; R Neath w Llantwit 69-84; rtd 84. *Tros-yr-Afon, Llangwnnadl, Pwllheli, Gwynedd LL53 8NS* Tudweiliog (01758) 612832

PRIDAY, Gerald Nelson. b 35. Glouc Th Course. **d** 85 **p** 88. NSM Eardisland *Heref* 85-91; NSM Aymestrey and Leinthall Earles w Wigmore etc 85-91; NSM Kingsland 85-91; NSM Eye, Croft w Yarpole and Lucton 91-94; NSM Heref All SS from 94. *The Flat, St Barnabas Church Centre, Hereford* Hereford (01432) 264408

PRIDDIN, Mrs Maureen Anne. b 46. Leeds Univ BA67 Nottm Univ DipEd68. E Midl Min Tr Course 82. **dss** 85 **d** 87 **p** 94. Mickleover St Jo *Derby* 85-87; Hon Par Dn 87; C from 90; Dioc World Development Officer 87-90. *7 Portland Close, Mickleover, Derby DE3 5BR* Derby (01332) 513672

PRIDDIS, Anthony Martin. b 48. CCC Cam BA69 MA73 New Coll Ox DipTh71 MA75. Cuddesdon Coll 69. **d** 72 **p** 73. C New Addington *Cant* 72-75; Chapl Ch Ch Ox 75-80; Lic to Offic *Ox* 76-80; TV High Wycombe 80-86; P-in-c Amersham 86-90; R from 90; RD Amersham from 92. *The Rectory, Church Street, Amersham, Bucks HP7 0DB* Amersham (01494) 729380 Fax as telephone

PRIDEAUX, Humphrey Grevile. b 36. CCC Ox BA60 MA63 Birm Univ CertEd66 Lon Univ DipEd73 Open Univ BA87. Linc Th Coll 59. **d** 61 **p** 62. C Northn St Matt *Pet* 61-62; C Milton *Portsm* 62-65; Perm to Offic *Birm* 65-66; Hd of RE Qu Mary's Gr Sch Walsall 66-69; Lic to Offic *Lich* 66-69; Lect St Martin's Coll Lanc 69-80; Lic to Offic *Blackb* 69-80; Perm to Offic *Portsm* 80-86; Hon C Fareham H Trin 86-90; Hon C Bishops Waltham 90-94; NSM W Meon and Warnford from 94. *The Rectory, Doctors Lane, West Meon, Petersfield, Hants GU32 1LR* West Meon (01730) 829226

PRIDGEON, Paul Garth Walsingham. b 45. Sussex Univ BA69 CertEd. Glouc Sch of Min 87. **d** 87 **p** 88. NSM Cirencester *Glouc* from 87. *4 Abbey Way, Cirencester, Glos GL7 2DT* Cirencester (01285) 656860

PRIDHAM, Peter Arthur George Drake. b 16. Ely Th Coll 62. **d** 64 **p** 65. C Berwick H Trin *Newc* 67-71; V Sleekburn 71-76; P-in-c Otterburn w Elsdon and Horsley w Byrness 76-80; TV Bellingham/Otterburn Gp 80-84; rtd 84. *5 Hospital Close, Greatham, Hartlepool, Cleveland TS25 2HS* Hartlepool (01429) 870582

PRIDIE, William Raleigh (Will). b 49. ACP82 FCollP83 Bris Univ BEd72 DipMan72. **d** 93 **p** 94. C Kingstone w Clehonger, Eaton Bishop etc *Heref* from 93. *The Vicarage, Church Road, Clehonger, Hereford HR2 9SE* Hereford (01432) 277786

PRIDMORE, John Stuart. b 36. Nottm Univ BA62 MA67. Ridley Hall Cam 62. **d** 65 **p** 66. C Camborne *Truro* 65-67; Tutor Ridley Hall Cam 67-68; Chapl 68-71; Asst Chapl K Edw Sch Witley 71-75; Chapl 75-86; Tanzania 86-88; Angl Chapl Hengrave Hall Cen 88-89; C St Martin-in-the-Fields *Lon* from 89. *5 St Martin's Place, London WC2N 4JJ* 0171-930 1646/0089 or 1862

PRIEST, David. b 44. Chich Th Coll 69. **d** 73 **p** 74. C S Harrow St Paul *Lon* 73-76; C S Kensington St Steph 76-83; Perm to Offic 83-90; Hon C Pimlico St Mary Graham Terrace from 90. *78 Lupus Street, London SW1V 3EL* 0171-821 0978

PRIEST, Richard Mark. b 63. Oak Hill Th Coll BA90. **d** 90 **p** 91. C Okehampton w Inwardleigh *Ex* 90-94; C Okehampton w Inwardleigh, Bratton Clovelly etc 94; CF from 94. *c/o MOD (Army), Bagshot Park, Bagshot, Surrey GU19 5PL* Bagshot (01276) 471717 Fax 412834

PRIESTLEY, Canon Alan Charles. b 41. Lon Univ BD69. Kelham Th Coll 64 Wm Temple Coll Rugby 65. **d** 65 **p** 66. C Edgbaston St Aug *Birm* 65-68; C Chelmsley Wood 68-72; TV 72-76; V Hazelwell from 76; Dioc Communications Officer from 83; Bp's Press Officer from 85; Hon Can Birm Cathl from 87. *The Vicarage, 316 Vicarage Road, Birmingham B14 7NH* 0121-444 4469 Fax 444 8184

PRIESTLEY, John Christopher. b 39. Trin Coll Ox BA60. Wells Th Coll 61. **d** 68 **p** 69. C Habergham All SS *Blackb* 68-70; C

Padiham 70-75; V Colne Ch Ch from 75; Chapl to The Queen from 90; RD Pendle *Blackb* from 91. *The Vicarage, Keighley Road, Colne, Lancs BB8 7HF* Colne (01282) 863511

PRIESTLY, Thomas Herbert (Tom). b 67. Ulster Univ BA91. CITC BTh94. **d** 94 **p** 95. C Ballymena w Ballyclug *Conn* from 94. *6 Rockgrove Brae, Ballymena, Co Antrim BT43 5HY* Ballymena (01266) 42805

PRIESTNALL, Reginald Hayward. b 22. Jes Coll Cam BA44 MA47. Ridley Hall Cam 44. **d** 45 **p** 46. V Rockingham w Caldecote *Pet* 67-71; V Northn St Mich 71-77; V Ketton 77-89; RD Barnack 86-89; rtd 89. *56 Haverscroft Close, Taverham, Norwich NR8 6LU* Norwich (01603) 260228

PRIESTNER, Hugh. b 45. Nottm Univ BTh75. Linc Th Coll 71. **d** 75 **p** 76. C Seaton Hirst *Newc* 75-78; C Longbenton St Bart 78-81; P-in-c Glendale Gp 81-82; TV 83-88; Chapl Stafford Distr Gen Hosp from 88; Chapl Stafford Distr Infirmary from 88. *Stafford District General Hospital, Weston Road, Stafford ST16 3SA* Stafford (01785) 57731

PRIESTNER, James Arthur. b 14. Leeds Univ BA39. Coll of Resurr Mirfield 39. **d** 41 **p** 42. V Longhoughton w Howick *Newc* 70-79; rtd 79. *16 Eastfield Avenue, Monkseaton, Whitley Bay, Tyne & Wear NE25 8LT* 0191-252 9518

PRIGG, Patrick John. b 53. K Coll Lon BD82. Sarum & Wells Th Coll 89. **d** 92 **p** 93. C Wavertree St Mary *Liv* from 92; Chapl Sandown Coll from 92. *24 Orford Street, Liverpool L15 8HX* 0151-733 1989

PRIME, Geoffrey Daniel. b 12. Lich Th Coll 32. **d** 35 **p** 36. Org Sec (Dios Derby, Linc, Sheff & S'well) CECS 62-65; Perm to Offic *Derby* from 62; rtd 77. *Westside Mill Farm, Hulme End, Buxton, Derbyshire SK17 0EY* Hartington (01298) 84461

PRIMROSE, David Edward Snodgrass. b 55. Univ of Wales (Cardiff) DipSocWork78 St Jo Coll Cam MA80. Trin Coll Bris BA92. **d** 87 **p** 92. Pakistan 87-89; C Glouc St Paul *Glouc* from 92. *36 Howard Street, Gloucester GL1 4US* Gloucester (01452) 384877

PRINCE (nee GRIFFITHS), Caroline Heidi Ann. b 66. Ex Univ BA88. Linc Th Coll CMM90. **d** 90. Chapl St Woolos Cathl *Mon* 90-94; C Newport St Woolos 90-94; C Abergavenny Dnry from 94. *2 Craig View, Cross Ash, Abergavenny, Gwent NP7 8PG* Cross Ash (01873) 821320

PRINCE, Dennis Alan Ford. b 18. AKC48. **d** 48 **p** 49. R Slinfold *Chich* 60-73; R Sedlescombe w Whatlington 73-88; rtd 88. *7 Windmill Close, Clanfield, Waterlooville, Hants PO8 0NA* Horndean (01705) 596675

PRINCE, Helena. b 23. Lightfoot Ho Dur. **dss** 66 **d** 87 **p** 94. W Derby St Mary *Liv* 65-85; rtd 85; Perm to Offic *Liv* from 85. *5 Dominic Close, Liverpool L16 1JZ* 0151-722 0263

PRING, Althon Kerrigan (Kerry). b 34. AKC58. **d** 59 **p** 60. C Limehouse St Anne *Lon* 59-61; C Lt Stanmore St Lawr 61-64; C Langley Marish *Ox* 64-68; P-in-c Radnage 68-72; P-in-c Ravenstone w Weston Underwood 72-75; P-in-c Stoke Goldington w Gayhurst 72-75; R Gayhurst w Ravenstone, Stoke Goldington etc 75-85; P-in-c 85-86; RD Newport 78-80; TV Woughton 86-90; P-in-c Nash w Thornton, Beachampton and Thornborough 90-94; R from 94. *The Rectory, Chapel Lane, Thornborough, Buckingham MK18 2DJ* Buckingham (01280) 812515

PRINGLE, Ven Cecil Thomas. b 43. TCD BA65. CITC 66. **d** 66 **p** 67. C Belf St Donard *D & D* 66-69; I Cleenish *Clogh* 69-80; I Mullaghdun 78-80; I Rossory from 80; Preb Clogh Cathl 86-89; Adn Clogh from 89. *Rossory Rectory, Derryhonnelly Road, Enniskillen, Co Fermanagh BT74 7JE* Enniskillen (01365) 322874

PRINGLE, Graeme Lindsley. b 59. St Cath Coll Cam BA81 MA85. St Jo Coll Nottm DTS94. **d** 94 **p** 95. C Binley *Cov* from 94. *57 Princethorpe Way, Coventry CV3 2HG* Coventry (01203) 636335

PRINGLE, Miss Janyce Mary. b 32. ARCM53 LRAM54 Ex Univ DipAdEd70 MPhil85. SW Minl Tr Course 83. **dss** 86 **d** 87 **p** 94. Torquay St Matthias, St Mark and H Trin *Ex* 86-87; Hon Par Dn 87-94; Hon C from 94; Chapl Asst Torbay Hosp Torquay from 86. *Pendower, Wheatridge Lane, Torquay TQ2 6RA* Torquay (01803) 607136

PRINGLE, John Richard. b 55. Lon Univ AKC76 CertEd77 Open Univ BA84. Chich Th Coll 78. **d** 78 **p** 79. C Northn St Matt *Pet* 78-81; C Delaval *Newc* 81-84; V Newsham from 84; RD Bedlington from 93. *St Bede's Vicarage, Newcastle Road, Newsham, Blyth, Northd NE24 4AS* Blyth (01670) 352391

PRINGLE, Thomas Andrew (Tom). b 36. FRMetS MRIN. Cant Sch of Min 85 Edin Th Coll 89. **d** 89 **p** 91. NSM Is of Arran *Arg* from 89; Hon Chapl Miss to Seamen from 89. *8 Torr-Righe, Shiskine, Brodick, Isle of Arran KA27 8HD* Shiskine (01770) 860222

PRINS, Canon Stanley Vernon. b 30. TD76. Dur Univ BSc54 MA69. Ripon Hall Ox 56. **d** 58 **p** 59. C Benwell St Jas *Newc* 58-61; Asst Chapl Newc Univ 61-65; CF (TA) from 64; C-in-c Whorlton H Nativity Chpl Ho Estate *Newc* 65-72; TV Whorlton 73-76; V Humshaugh 76-83; P-in-c Simonburn

82-83; P-in-c Wark 82-83; RD Bellingham 83-93; R Humshaugh w Simonburn and Wark from 83; Hon Can Newc Cathl from 88. *The Vicarage, Humshaugh, Hexham, Northd NE46 4AA* Hexham (01434) 681304

PRINT, Norman George. b 38. Cuddesdon Coll 64. **d** 66 **p** 67. C Banbury *Ox* 66-69; C Whitley Ch Ch 69-75; P-in-c Shiplake 75-77; V Shiplake w Dunsden 77-90; R Balcombe *Chich* from 90. *The Rectory, Balcombe, Haywards Heath, W Sussex RH17 6PA* Balcombe (01444) 811249

PRIOR, Ven Christopher. b 12. CB68. Keble Coll Ox BA37 MA41. Cuddesdon Coll 37. **d** 38 **p** 39. Adn Portsm 69-77; rtd 77. *Ponies End, West Melbury, Shaftesbury, Dorset SP7 0LY* Fontmell Magna (01747) 811239

PRIOR, David Clement Lyndon. b 40. Trin Coll Ox BA63 MA66. Ridley Hall Cam 65. **d** 67 **p** 68. C Reigate St Mary *S'wark* 67-72; S Africa 72-79; Can Cape Town Cathl 76-79; C Ox St Aldate w H Trin *Ox* 79-82; C Ox St Aldate w St Matt 82-84; USA 84-85; V Ches Square St Mich w St Phil *Lon* 85-95; P-in-c Mayfair Ch Ch from 85; Public Preacher from 95. *21 Portman Close, London W1H 9HL* 0171-935 3477

PRIOR, Ian Graham. b 44. Lon Univ BSc(Econ)71. Oak Hill Th Coll DipHE80. **d** 80 **p** 81. C Luton Ch *Roch* 80-83; TV Southgate *Chich* 83-93; V Burgess Hill St Andr from 93. *St Andrew's Vicarage, 2 Cants Lane, Burgess Hill, W Sussex RH15 0LG* Burgess Hill (01444) 232023

PRIOR, Ian Roger Lyndon. b 46. St Jo Coll Dur BA68. Lon Coll of Div 68. **d** 70 **p** 71. C S Croydon Em *Cant* 70-73; Perm to Offic *S'wark* 73-85; Dir Overseas Personnel TEAR Fund 73-79; Dep Dir 79-83; Admin Dir CARE Trust and CARE Campaigns from 85; NSM New Malden and Coombe *S'wark* from 85. *39 Cambridge Avenue, New Malden, Surrey KT3 4LD* 0181-949 0912 or 0171-782 0013 Fax 0171-782 0014

PRIOR, James Murray. b 39. Edin Univ BCom64. St And Dioc Tr Course 85. **d** 90 **p** 91. NSM Kirriemuir *St And* from 90; NSM Forfar from 90. *Horniehaugh, Glenquiech, Forfar, Angus DD8 3UG* Cortachy (015754) 287

PRIOR, John Gilman Leathes. b 15. Qu Coll Cam BA37 MA41. Ridley Hall Cam 37. **d** 39 **p** 40. V Camberley St Paul *Guildf* 63-74; V Crondall 75-77; V Crondall and Ewshot 77-80; rtd 80; Perm to Offic *Win* from 80; Perm to Offic *Guildf* from 82; Perm to Offic *Portsm* from 84. *River Cottage, Station Road, Bentley, Farnham, Surrey GU10 5JY* Bentley (01420) 23413

PRIOR, Preb John Miskin. b 27. Lon Univ BSc(Econ)48. Westcott Ho Cam 49. **d** 51 **p** 52. V Marshfield w Cold Ashton *Bris* 66-82; P-in-c Tormarton w W Littleton 68-82; RD Bitton 73-79; R Trull w Angersleigh *B & W* 82-91; RD Taunton 84-90; Preb Wells Cathl 90-91; Chapl Huggens' Coll Northfleet from 91; rtd 92. *The Chaplain's Office, Huggens College, Northfleet, Gravesend, Kent DA11 9DL* Gravesend (01474) 352428

PRIOR, Canon Kenneth Francis William. b 26. St Jo Coll Dur BA49. Oak Hill Th Coll 46. **d** 49 **p** 50. V Hove Bp Hannington Memorial Ch *Chich* 65-70; R Sevenoaks St Nic *Roch* 70-87; Hon Can Roch Cathl 82-87; C-in-c Hampstead St Jo Downshire Hill Prop Chpl *Lon* 87-90; rtd 89. *41 Osidge Lane, London N14 5JL* 0181-368 4586

PRIOR, Canon Kenneth George William. b 17. Bris Univ BA39. Bible Churchmen's Coll 35. **d** 40 **p** 41. V Longfleet *Sarum* 55-82; RD Poole 75-80; Can and Preb Sarum Cathl 77-82; rtd 82. *Flat 5, 61 Dorchester Road, Weymouth, Dorset DT4 7JX* Weymouth (01305) 766253

PRIOR, Nigel John. b 56. Bris Univ BA78. Westcott Ho Cam 79. **d** 81 **p** 82. C Langley All SS and Martyrs *Man* 81-82; C Langley and Parkfield 82-84; C Bury St Jo w St Mark 84-87; R Man Clayton St Cross w St Paul from 87. *The Rectory, 54 Clayton Hall Road, Manchester M11 4WH* 0161-223 0766

PRIOR, Stephen Kenneth. b 55. Rhode Is Coll (USA) BA78. Wycliffe Hall Ox 79. **d** 82 **p** 83. C Aberavon *Llan* 82-85; P-in-c New Radnor and Llanfihangel Nantmelan etc *S & B* 85-86; V 86-90; V Llansamlet 90-94; P-in-c Ches le Street *Dur* from 94. *The Rectory, Lindisfarne Avenue, Chester le Street, Co Durham DH3 3PT* 0191-388 4027

PRIORY, Barry Edwin. b 44. FCIS Open Univ BA81. Qu Coll Birm 84. **d** 86 **p** 87. C Boldmere *Birm* 86-89; C Somerton w Compton Dundon, the Charltons etc *B & W* 89-93; R Porlock w Stoke Pero from 93. *The Rectory, Parsons Street, Porlock, Minehead, Somerset TA24 8QL* Porlock (01643) 863172

PRISTON, David Leslie. b 28. Lon Bible Coll 49 Oak Hill Th Coll 66. **d** 66 **p** 67. C Heref St Pet w St Owen *Heref* 66-71; R Beeby *Leic* 72-88; R Gaddesby w S Croxton 72-88; R S Croxton Gp 88-93; rtd 93. *20 Central Avenue, Chilwell, Nottingham NG9 6NG* Nottingham (0115) 922 7643

PRITCHARD, Antony Robin. b 53. Van Mildert Coll Dur BSc74 SS Paul & Mary Coll Cheltenham CertEd75. St Jo Coll Nottm DipTh82 DPS84. **d** 84 **p** 85. C Desborough *Pet* 84-87; C Rushden w Newton Bromswold 87-91; R Oulton St Mich *Nor* from 91. *The Rectory, Christmas Lane, Oulton, Lowestoft, Suffolk NR32 3JX* Lowestoft (01502) 565722

PRITCHARD, Brian James Pallister. b 27. CCC Cam BA51 MA66. Westcott Ho Cam 51. **d** 53 **p** 54. P-in-c Sheff St Swithun *Sheff* 67-72; V Welton *Linc* 72-92; RD Lawres 86-92; rtd 92. *Bridgeways, Milford Lane, Bakewell, Derbyshire DE45 1DX* Bakewell (01629) 813553

PRITCHARD, Colin Ivor. b 44. Lon Inst of Educn TCert65. Chich Th Coll 66. **d** 69 **p** 70. C Kettering St Mary *Pet* 69-72; Chapl Clayesmore Sch Blandford 72-74; Asst Chapl Ellesmere Coll Shropshire 74-77; C Duston *Pet* 77-80; V Wellingborough St Andr 80-89; R Sedlescombe w Whatlington *Chich* from 89. *The Rectory, Church Hill, Sedlescombe, Battle, E Sussex TN33 0QP* Sedlescombe (01424) 870233

PRITCHARD, Colin Wentworth. b 38. K Coll Lon St Boniface Warminster 59. **d** 63 **p** 64. C Putney St Marg *S'wark* 63-67; C Brixton St Matt 67-70; C Milton *Portsm* 70-74; V Mitcham St Mark *S'wark* 74-82; R Long Ditton 82-94; V Earlsfield St Andr from 94. *22 St Andrew's Court, Waynflete Street, London SW18 3QE* 0181-946 4214

PRITCHARD, David Paul. b 47. FRCO LTCL BA. Wycliffe Hall Ox 80. **d** 82 **p** 83. C Kidlington *Ox* 82-84; P-in-c Marcham w Garford 84-85; V from 86; RD Abingdon from 91. *The Vicarage, 24 Church Street, Marcham, Abingdon, Oxon OX13 6NP* Frilford Heath (01865) 391319

PRITCHARD, Donald Oliver. b 22. Qu Coll Birm 73. **d** 75 **p** 76. Hon C Dunchurch *Cov* 75-83; P-in-c Mells w Buckland Dinham, Elm, Whatley etc *B & W* 83-84; R 84-88; rtd 88. *Moonrakers, Pengelly, Callington, Cornwall PL17 7DZ* Liskeard (01579) 84329

PRITCHARD, John Lawrence. b 48. St Pet Coll Ox BA70 DipTh70 MA73. Dur Univ MLitt93. Ridley Hall Cam 70. **d** 72 **p** 73. C Birm St Martin *Birm* 72-76; Asst Dir RE *B & W* 76-80; Youth Chapl 76-80; P-in-c Wilton 80-88; Dir Past Studies Cranmer Hall Dur 89-93; Warden from 93. *St John's College, 3 South Bailey, Durham DH1 3RJ* 0191-374 3585 Fax 374 3573

PRITCHARD, John Richard. b 21. St D Coll Lamp. St Mich Coll Llan 46. **d** 48 **p** 49. V Lepton *Wakef* 57-69; rtd 86. *19 Church Close, Shepley, Huddersfield HD8 8ND* Huddersfield (01484) 604216

PRITCHARD, Miss Kathryn Anne. b 60. St Cath Coll Ox MA Bradf Univ DIT. St Jo Coll Dur. **d** 87. Par Dn Addiscombe St Mary *S'wark* 87-90; CPAS Staff 90-92; Perm to Offic *Cov* from 92. *16 Lindsey Crescent, Kenilworth, Warks CV8 1FL* Coventry (01203) 451160

PRITCHARD, Kenneth John. b 30. Liv Univ BEng51. NW Ord Course 72. **d** 74 **p** 75. C Ches Team *Ches* 74-78; Miss to Seamen 78-84; V Runcorn St Jo Weston *Ches* 78-84; V Gt Meols from 84. *St John's Vicarage, Birkenhead Road, Meols, South Wirral L47 0LF* 0151-632 1661

PRITCHARD, Malcolm John. b 55. Bradf Univ BA85 CQSW85. St Jo Coll Nottm 86. **d** 88 **p** 89. C Peckham St Mary Magd *S'wark* 88-93; V Luton St Matt High Town *St Alb* from 93. *St Matthew's Vicarage, Wenlock Street, Luton LU2 0NQ* Luton (01582) 32320

PRITCHARD, Michael Owen. b 49. Trin Coll Carmarthen CertEd71. St Mich Coll Llan 71. **d** 73 **p** 74. C Conwy w Gyffin *Ban* 73-76; TV Dolgellau w Llanfachreth and Brithdir etc 76-78; Dioc Children's Officer 77-86; V Bettws y Coed and Capel Curig 78-83; CF (TAVR) from 79; V Betws-y-Coed and Capel Curig w Penmachno etc *Ban* 83-86; Chapl Claybury Hosp Woodford Bridge from 86. *The Chaplain's Office, Claybury Hospital, Woodford Green, Essex IG8 8BY* 0181-504 7171

PRITCHARD, Canon Neil Lawrence. b 15. St Jo Coll Dur BA39 MA45. **d** 39 **p** 40. Hon Can Blackb Cathl *Blackb* 66-81; Dir of Ords 73-82; V Salesbury 73-80; Bp's Dom Chapl 78-83; rtd 80; Lic to Offic *Blackb* 83-93. *Sayers, Holmfield, High Street, Lyndhurst, Hants SO43 7BH* Lyndhurst (01703) 283020

PRITCHARD, Mrs Norma Kathleen. b 32. Birm Univ BA53 CertEd54. E Midl Min Tr Course 81. **dss** 84 **d** 87 **p** 94. Derby St Alkmund and St Werburgh *Derby* 84-87; Par Dn 87-90; Par Dn Derby St Andr w St Osmund 90-94; C from 94. *44 Evans Avenue, Allestree, Derby DE22 2EN* Derby (01332) 557702

PRITCHARD, Dr Peter Benson. b 30. FPhS60 LCP68 Univ of Wales (Lamp) BA51 St Cath Coll Ox DipTh57 Lon Univ PGCE68 DipEd70 Liv Univ MEd74 PhD81. Ripon Hall Ox 55. **d** 58 **p** 59. Chapl Liv Coll Boys' Sch 64-70; Hon C Wavertree St Bridget *Liv* 70-89; Lect CF Mott Coll of Educn 70-76; Sen Lect Liv Coll of HE 76-83; Liv Poly 83-87; Perm to Offic from 90; Perm to Offic *Ches* from 90; Chapl St Jo Hospice Wirral from 93; Tutor Open Univ 90-95; rtd 95. *68 Gleggside, West Kirby, Wirral, Merseyside L48 6EA* 0151-625 8093

PRITCHARD, Peter Humphrey. b 47. Univ of Wales (Ban) BA70 Liv Univ PGCE73 Birm Univ DipTh87. Qu Coll Birm 85. **d** 87 **p** 88. C Llanbeblig w Caernarfon and Betws Garmon etc *Ban* 87-90; R Llanberis w Llanrug 90-94; R Llanfaethlu w Llanfwrog and Llanrhuddlad etc from 94. *The Rectory,*

7 Tynlon Estate, Llanrhyddlad, Holyhead, Gwynedd LL65 4HT Holyhead (01407) 730251

PRITCHARD, Thomas. b 14. Ch Ch Ox BA37 MA40. Westcott Ho Cam 37. **d** 38 **p** 39. V Ex St Dav *Ex* 62-81; rtd 81; Perm to Offic *Ex* from 81. *3 Mill Cottages, Exton, Exeter EX3 0PH* Topsham (01392) 873018

PRITCHARD, Ven Thomas William. b 33. Keele Univ BA55 DipEd55. St Mich Coll Llan 55. **d** 57 **p** 58. C Holywell *St As* 57-61; C Ruabon 61-63; V 77-87; R Pontfadog 63-71; R Llanferres, Nercwys and Eryrys 71-77; Dioc Archivist from 76; Can St As Cathl from 84; RD Llangollen 86-87; Adn Montgomery from 87; V Berriew and Manafon from 87. *The Vicarage, Berriew, Welshpool, Powys SY21 8PL* Berriew (01686) 640223

PRITT, Stephen. b 06. AKC31. **d** 31 **p** 32. R Helhoughton w Raynham *Nor* 60-80; rtd 80; Perm to Offic *Glouc* 80-92. *23 Addiscombe Road, Weston-super-Mare, Avon BS23 4LT* Weston-super-Mare (01934) 622795

PRIVETT, Peter John. b 48. Qu Coll Birm 75. **d** 78 **p** 79. C Moseley St Agnes *Birm* 78-81; V Kingsbury 81-87; P-in-c Dilwyn and Stretford *Heref* 87-90; Dioc Children's Adv from 87; TV Leominster from 90. *165 Bargates, Leominster, Herefordshire HR6 8QT* Leominster (01568) 613176

PROBART, Raymond. b 21. Sarum Th Coll 49. **d** 51 **p** 52. V Douglas *Blackb* 60-88; rtd 88. *76 Waterside Way, Radstock, Bath BA3 3YQ* Radstock (01761) 433908

PROBERT, Christopher John Dixon. b 54. Univ of Wales (Cardiff) DipTh77 DPS78 BTh95. St Mich Coll Llan 74. **d** 78 **p** 79. C Aberdare St Fagan *Llan* 78-79; C Cadoxton-juxta-Barry 79-81; R Llanfynydd *St As* 81-84; V Gosberton Clough and Quadring *Linc* 84-86; TV Cov Caludon *Cov* 86-88; V Llanrhian w Llanhywel and Carnhedryn etc *St D* 88-91; V Tregaron w Ystrad Meurig and Strata Florida 91-93; V Betws-y-Coed and Capel Curig w Penmachno etc *Ban* from 93. *The Vicarage, Betws-y-Coed, Gwynedd LL24 0AD* Betws-y-Coed (01690) 710313

PROBERT, Edward Cleasby. b 58. St Cath Coll Cam BA80 MA84. Ripon Coll Cuddesdon BA84. **d** 85 **p** 86. C Esher *Guildf* 85-89; V Earlsfield St Andr *S'wark* 89-94; V Belmont from 94. *The Vicarage, Belmont Rise, Sutton, Surrey SM2 6EA* 0181-642 2363

PROBETS, Canon Desmond. b 26. AKC50. **d** 51 **p** 52. Solomon Is 62-72; Dean Honiara Cathl 69-72; V Timperley *Ches* 72-92; RD Bowdon 77-87; Hon Can Ches Cathl 82-92; rtd 92. *24 Shelley Close, Penistone, Sheffield S30 6GT* Barnsley (01226) 766402

PROCTER, Andrew David. b 52. St Jo Coll Ox BA74 MA BA86. Trin Coll Bris 74. **d** 77 **p** 78. C Barnoldswick w Bracewell *Bradf* 77-80; P-in-c Kelbrook 80-82; V 82-87; V Heaton St Barn 87-93; V Swanley St Paul *Roch* from 93. *The Vicarage, Rowhill Road, Swanley, Kent BR8 7RL* Swanley (01322) 662320

PROCTER, Robert Hendy. b 31. Trin Hall Cam BA54 MA. Edin Dioc NSM Course 88. **d** 93 **p** 94. NSM Edin Ch Ch *Edin* from 93. *2 Braid Avenue, Edinburgh EH10 6DR* 0131-447 1140

PROCTOR, Hugh Gordon. b 08. MFBA Keble Coll Ox BA30. Cuddesdon Coll 31. **d** 32 **p** 33. V Forest and Frith *Dur* 50-82; rtd 82. *4 Wrentnall Cottages, Forest in Teesdale, Barnard Castle, Co Durham DL12 0XS*

PROCTOR, Ven Jesse Heighton. b 08. Lon Univ BA29 MA32. St Andr Whittlesford 34. **d** 35 **p** 36. Adn Warw *Cov* 58-74; rtd 74; Perm to Offic *Heref* from 75. *Dilkusha, 22 Bank Crescent, Ledbury, Herefordshire HR8 1AA* Ledbury (01531) 632241

PROCTOR, Kenneth Noel. b 33. St Aid Birkenhead 61. **d** 63 **p** 64. C Oldham St Paul *Man* 63-66; C Davyhulme St Mary 66-69; V Norden w Ashworth from 69. *The Vicarage, Heap Road, Rochdale, Lancs OL12 7SN* Rochdale (01706) 41001

PROCTOR, Michael John (Mike). b 59. Longlands Coll of FE C&G78 BTEC NC81. Cranmer Hall Dur CTMin93. **d** 93 **p** 94. C Leatherhead *Guildf* from 93. *58 Kingscroft Road, Leatherhead, Surrey KT22 7BU* Leatherhead (01372) 379954

PROCTOR, Canon Michael Thomas. b 41. Ch Ch Ox BA65 MA67. Westcott Ho Cam 63. **d** 65 **p** 66. C Monkseaton St Mary *Newc* 65-69; Pakistan 69-72; C Willington *Newc* 72-77; TV Willington Team 77-79; Ed Sec Nat Soc 79-84; P-in-c Roxwell *Chelmsf* 79-84; Dir of Miss and Unity 85-94; Bp's Ecum Officer from 85; Hon Can Chelmsf Cathl from 85; P-in-c Gt Waltham w Ford End from 94. *The Vicarage, Great Waltham, Chelmsford CM3 1AR* Chelmsford (01245) 360334

PROCTOR, Canon Noel. b 30. MBE93. St Aid Birkenhead 62. **d** 64 **p** 65. C Haughton le Skerne *Dur* 64-67; R Byers Green 67-70; Chapl HM Pris Eastchurch 70-74; Chapl HM Pris Dartmoor 74-79; Chapl HM Pris Man from 79; Hon Can Man Cathl *Man* from 91. *The Chaplain's Office, HM Prison, Southall Street, Manchester M60 9AH* 0161-834 8626 or 792 1284 Fax 834 0443

PROCTOR, Mrs Susan Katherine. b 44. **d** 89 **p** 94. Par Dn Beighton *Sheff* 89-91; Par Dn Aston cum Aughton and Ulley

91-93; Par Dn Aston cum Aughton w Swallownest, Todwick & Ulley 93-94; TV from 94. *The Vicarage, 27 Skipton Road, Swallownest, Sheffield S31 0NQ* Sheffield (0114) 287 9271

PROFIT, David Hollingworth. b 17. Man Univ BA38. Cuddesdon Coll 40. **d** 41 **p** 42. C Kings Heath *Birm* 41-43; S Africa from 43. *Braehead House, Auburn Road, Kenilworth, 7700 South Africa* Cape Town (21) 762-6041

PROPHET, Canon John Roy Henderson. b 10. Dur Univ LTh48 BA49. ALCD34. **d** 34 **p** 35. Hon Can Leic Cathl *Leic* 70-80; R Church Langton w Thorpe Langton and Tur Langto 73-80; rtd 80; Perm to Offic *Leic* from 80; Perm to Offic *Pet* from 80. *29 Glebe Way, Oakham, Leics LE15 6LX* Oakham (01572) 755852

PROSSER, Canon David George. b 33. Univ of Wales (Lamp) BA55. Coll of Resurr Mirfield 55 St Mich Coll Llan 59. **d** 60 **p** 61. C Caerphilly *Llan* 60-64; C Moordown *Win* 64-65; Chapl RN 65-81; V Morecambe St Barn *Blackb* 81-85; V Lt Paxton *Ely* 85-86; V Diddington 85-86; R Southoe w Hail Weston 85-86; Chapl Hamburg w Kiel *Eur* 86-93; Miss to Seamen 86-93; Hon Can Brussels Cathl *Eur* from 91; Chapl Copenhagen w Aarhus from 93. *St Alban's House, Stigaardsvej 6, DK-2900 Hellerup, Denmark* Denmark (45) 39 62 77 36 Fax as telephone

PROSSER, Malcolm George. b 22. Univ of Wales (Lamp) BA44. St Mich Coll Llan 44. **d** 45 **p** 46. V High Littleton *B & W* 66-87; rtd 87. *141 Westway, Broadstone, Dorset BH18 9LQ* Broadstone (01202) 694280

PROSSER, Rhys. b 51. BA74. Sarum & Wells Th Coll 77. **d** 80 **p** 81. C Wimbledon *S'wark* 80-83; C St Helier 83-88; TV Gt and Lt Coates w Bradley *Linc* 88-95; P-in-c Saxilby Gp from 95. *The Rectory, 1 Westcroft Drive, Saxilby, Lincoln LN1 2PT* Lincoln (01522) 702427

PROSSER, Richard Hugh Keble. b 31. Trin Coll Cam BA53 MA57 Leeds Univ PGCE63. Cuddesdon Coll 55. **d** 57 **p** 58. C Wigan All SS *Liv* 57-60; CR 62-87; S Rhodesia 64-65; Rhodesia 65-80; Zimbabwe 80-90; TR Pocklington Team *York* 90; R Pocklington and Owsthorpe and Kilnwick Percy etc from 90. *The Vicarage, 29 The Balk, Pocklington, York YO4 2QQ* Pocklington (01759) 302133

PROTHERO, Brian Douglas. b 52. St Andr Univ MTh75 Dundee Univ CertEd77. Linc Th Coll 84. **d** 86 **p** 87. C Thornbury *Glouc* 86-89; V Goodrington *Ex* from 89. *Goodrington Vicarage, 16 Cliff Park Avenue, Paignton, Devon TQ4 6LT* Paignton (01803) 556476

PROTHERO, Cecil Charles. b 15. Lon Univ BSc(Econ)47 Bris Univ MEd74. **d** 68 **p** 69. C Ex St Mary Arches *Ex* 68-70; Chapl St Luke's Coll Ex 70-78; Dep PV Ex Cathl *Ex* from 78. *Les Gots, La Rochette, 16110 La Rochefoucauld, Charente, France* France (33) 45 63 98 55

PROTHERO, David John. b 43. St Pet Coll Ox BA66 MA70. St Steph Ho Ox 68. **d** 70 **p** 71. C Kirkby *Liv* 70-72; C St Marychurch *Ex* 72-74; V Marldon 74-83; Chapl HM Pris Channings Wood 78-83; V Torquay St Martin Barton *Ex* 83-91; P-in-c Bath Bathwick *B & W* 91-93; R from 93. *The Rectory, Sham Castle Lane, Bath BA2 6JL* Bath (01225) 460052

PROTHERO, John Martin. b 32. Oak Hill Th Coll 64. **d** 66 **p** 67. C Tipton St Martin *Lich* 66-69; C Wednesfield Heath 69-72; Distr Sec BFBS 72-85; Lic to Offic *S'well* 73-86; Hon C Gedling 73; V Willoughby-on-the-Wolds w Wysall and Widmerpool from 86. *The Rectory, Keyworth Road, Wysall, Nottingham NG12 5QQ* Wymeswold (01509) 880269

PROTHEROE, Rhys Illtyd. b 50. St D Coll Lamp DipTh74. **d** 74 **p** 75. C Pen-bre *St D* 74-76; C Carmarthen St Dav 76-78; V Llanegwad 78-79; V Llanegwad w Llanfynydd 79-82; V Gorslas 82-95; RD Dyffryn Aman from 94; V Llan-llwch w Llangain and Llangynog from 95. *The Vicarage, Llanllwch, Carmarthen, Dyfed SA31 3RN* Carmarthen (01267) 236805

PROTHEROE, Canon Robin Philip. b 33. St Chad's Coll Dur BA54 DipTh56 MA60 Nottm Univ MPhil75 Ox Univ DipEd62. **d** 57 **p** 58. C Roath St Marg *Llan* 57-60; Asst Chapl Culham Coll Abingdon 60-64; Perm to Offic *S'well* 64-66; Lic to Offic 66-84; P-in-c Barton in Fabis 70-73; P-in-c Thrumpton 70-73; Dir of Educn *Bris* from 84; Hon Can Bris Cathl from 85; Selector for ACCM 88-91; ABM from 91; Bp's Insp of Th Colls from 88. *29 Barley Croft, Bristol BS9 3TG* Bristol (0117) 968 3245 or 921 4411

PROUD, Andrew John. b 54. K Coll Lon BD79 AKC79. Linc Th Coll 79. **d** 80 **p** 81. C Stansted Mountfitchet *Chelmsf* 80-83; TV Borehamwood *St Alb* 83-90; C Hatf 90-92; R E Barnet from 92. *The Rectory, 136 Church Hill Road, Barnet, Herts EN4 8XD* 0181-368 3840 or 361 7524

PROUD, Clyde Douglas. b 09. St Aid Birkenhead 35. **d** 37 **p** 38. V Withernwick *York* 69-72; R Rise 69-72; C Bankfoot *Bradf* 72-79; rtd 74. *Beechwood Nursing Home, Esplanade Road, Scarborough, N Yorkshire YO11 2DB* Scarborough (01723) 374260

PROUD, David John. b 56. Leeds Univ BA77 Dur Univ CertEd78. Ridley Hall Cam 85. **d** 88 **p** 89. C Lindfield *Chich*

88-91; TV Horsham from 91. *St John's House, Church Road, Broadbridge Heath, Horsham, W Sussex RH12 3ND* Horsham (01403) 265238

PROUDMAN, Canon Colin Leslie John. b 34. Lon Univ BD60 MTh63. Wells Th Coll 60. **d** 61 **p** 62. C Radlett *St Alb* 61-64; Canada from 64; Dean Div Toronto Div Coll from 90. *Trinity College, 6 Hoskin Avenue, Toronto, Ontario, Canada, M5S 1H8*

PROUT, David William. b 47. FRSA Leeds Univ DipEd. St Steph Ho Ox 71. **d** 74 **p** 75. C Hanworth All SS *Lon* 74-77; Chapl Westmr City Sch 77-78; Hon C Pimlico St Pet w Westmr Ch Ch *Lon* 77-78; Chapl Roch Cathl *Roch* 78-81; C St Alb Abbey *St Alb* 81-82; Chapl St Hilda's Priory Sneaton, Whitby 82-89; P-in-c Aislaby and Ruswarp *York* from 89. *The Vicarage, Aislaby, Whitby, N Yorkshire YO21 1SU* Whitby (01947) 810350

PROUT, Hubert Douglas. b 18. St D Coll Lamp BA38. **d** 41 **p** 42. V Kirk Hallam *Derby* 58-84; rtd 84; Perm to Offic *Llan* from 85. *9 Caldy Close, Porthcawl, M Glam CF36 3QL* Porthcawl (01656) 786479

PROVOST, Ian Keith. b 47. CA Tr Coll IDC73 Ridley Hall Cam CTM93. **d** 93 **p** 94. C Verwood *Sarum* from 93. *33 Newtown Lane, Verwood, Dorset BH31 6JD* Verwood (01202) 827278

PROWSE, Mrs Barbara Bridgette Christmas. b 41. R Holloway Coll Lon BA62. **d** 91 **p** 94. C Kingsthorpe w St Dav Northn *Pet* from 91. *22 Tollgate Close, Kingsthorpe, Northampton NN2 6RP* Northampton (01604) 721016

PRUDOM, William Haigh. b 26. STh79 APhS81 Hull Univ MPhil88. St D Coll Lamp 60. **d** 62 **p** 63. V Long Preston *Bradf* 66-73; C Darlington St Cuth *Dur* 73-75; V Tichurst *Chich* 75-79; P-in-c Flimwell 78-79; V Ticehurst and Flimwell 79-81; R Spennithorne w Finghall and Hauxwell *Ripon* 81-91; rtd 91. *9 Sydall's Way, Catterick Village, Richmond, N Yorkshire DL10 7ND* Richmond (01748) 818604

PRUEN, Edward Binney. b 56. K Coll Lon BD77 AKC77. St Jo Coll Nottm 78. **d** 79 **p** 80. C Kidderminster St Mary *Worc* 79-82; C Woking St Jo *Guildf* 82-84; Chapl Asst R Marsden Hosp Lon and Surrey 84-86; C Stapleford *S'well* 86-88; Min Winklebury CD *Win* 88; V Winklebury 88-93; Chapl Ld Mayor Treloar Coll Alton from 93. *2 St Joseph's Cottage, Upper Froyle, Alton, Hants GU34 4JY* Bentley (01420) 23893

PRUEN, Hugh Barrington. b 18. AKC50. **d** 50 **p** 51. R Skegness *Linc* 64-71; V Heckington w Howell 71-79; R Ashley w Weston by Welland and Sutton Bassett *Pet* 79-83; rtd 83; Perm to Offic *Linc* from 83. *Ashleigh, Church Road, Old Bolingbroke, Spilsby, Lincs PE23 4HF* East Kirkby (01790) 504

PRUEN, Hugh George. b 30. Worc Coll Ox BA53 MA62. Ely Th Coll 55. **d** 58 **p** 59. P-in-c Selsey *Chich* 66-75; P-in-c Belbroughton *Worc* 75-82; V S w N Bersted *Chich* 82-92; rtd 92. *Ashmead, Fontwell Avenue, Eastergate, Chichester, W Sussex PO20 6RU* Eastergate (01243) 544641

PRYCE, Donald Keith. b 35. Man Univ BSc. Linc Th Coll 69. **d** 71 **p** 72. C Heywood St Jas *Man* 71-74; P-in-c 74-75; V 75-76; R Ladybarn from 86; Chapl S Man Coll from 87. *St Chad's Rectory, 1 St Chad's Road, Withington, Manchester M20 9WH* 0161-445 1185

PRYCE, Robin Mark. b 60. Sussex Univ BA82 Cam Univ MA94. Westcott Ho Cam 84 United Th Coll Bangalore 85. **d** 87 **p** 88. C W Bromwich All SS *Lich* 87-90; Chapl and Fell CCC Cam from 90; Tutor from 92. *Corpus Christi College, Cambridge CB2 1RH* Cambridge (01223) 338002 or 338000

PRYCE, William Robert. b 28. MBE91. **d** 79 **p** 80. Hon C Leverstock Green *St Alb* 79-80; Perm to Offic *Sheff* 80-84; Hon C Sheff St Barn and St Mary 84-90; NSM Alveley and Quatt *Heref* from 91. *28 Crookes Cross, Alveley, Bridgnorth, Shropshire WV15 6LS* Quatt (01746) 780588

PRYER, Miss Frances Margaret. b 24. Gilmore Ho 59. dss 69 **d** 87. Hornchurch St Andr *Chelmsf* 66-83; rtd 84; Hon Par Dn Leigh-on-Sea St Aid *Chelmsf* 87-93; Perm to Offic from 93. *131 Howard Road, Upminster, Essex RM14 2UQ* Upminster (01708) 640451

PRYKE, Dr Edward John. b 20. K Coll Lon BD51 AKC51 St Cath Coll Ox BA53 MA57 BLitt63 Lon Univ PhD71. Wycliffe Hall Ox 51. **d** 53 **p** 54. Asst Chapl & Sen Lect Coll SS Mark & Jo Chelsea 62-73; Coll of SS Mark & Jo Plymouth 74-76; P-in-c S Pool w Chivelstone *Ex* 74-75; R E Portlemouth 74-76; P-in-c Gt Paxton *Ely* 76-78; V 78-84; P-in-c 85; P-in-c Offord D'Arcy w Offord Cluny 76-78; R 78-84; P-in-c 85; rtd 85; Co-ord BRF (Dio Glos) from 90. *3 Limber Hill, Wyman's Brook, Cheltenham, Glos GL50 4RJ* Cheltenham (01242) 244629

PRYKE, Jonathan Justin Speaight. b 59. Trin Coll Cam BA80 MA85. Trin Coll Bris BD85. **d** 85 **p** 86. C Corby St Columba *Pet* 85-88; C Jesmond Clayton Memorial *Newc* from 88. *15 Lily Avenue, Jesmond, Newcastle upon Tyne NE2 2SQ* 0191-281 9854

PRYOR, Derek John. b 29. Lon Univ DipTh57 BD63 Birm Univ MEd74. Linc Th Coll 79 Chich Th Coll 79. **d** 80 **p** 81. Hon C

Youlgreave *Derby* 80-82; Hon C Stanton-in-Peak 80-82; Hon C Ingham w Cammeringham w Fillingham *Linc* 82-87 and from 92; Chapl Bp Grosseteste Coll Linc 83-84; Dioc Schs Officer *Linc* 87-92; rtd 92. *Walnut Cottage, Chapel Lane, Fillingham, Gainsborough, Lincs DN21 5BP*   Hemswell (01427) 668276

PRYOR, William Lister Archibald. b 39. Trin Coll Cam BA67 MA69. Ox NSM Course 72. **d** 75 **p** 90. NSM Summertown *Ox* 75-76; NSM Wolvercote w Summertown from 76; Perm to Offic *Nor* from 93. *Elm Tree Cottage, Summerfields Road, Oxford OX2 7EH*   Oxford (01865) 515102

PRYS, Deiniol. b 53. Univ of Wales (Ban) DipTh82 Univ of Wales (Cardiff) DPS83. St Mich Coll Llan 82. **d** 83 **p** 84. C Llanbeblig w Caernarfon and Betws Garmon etc *Ban* 83-86; TV Amlwch 86-88; V Llanerch-y-medd 89-92; R Llansadwrn w Llanddona and Llaniestyn etc from 92. *The Rectory, Llansadwrn, Porthaethwy, Ynys Mon, Gwynedd LL59 5SL*   Beaumaris (01248) 810534

PRYSOR-JONES, John Glynne. b 47. CQSW73 Liv Univ DipSocWork73 Birm Univ DPS80 Heythrop Coll Lon MA94. Westcott Ho Cam 88. **d** 90 **p** 91. C Mitcham St Mark *S'wark* 90-93; V Dudley St Fran *Worc* from 93. *The Vicarage, 50 Laurel Road, Dudley, W Midlands DY1 3EZ*   Dudley (01384) 253123

PRYTHERCH, David. b 30. Down Coll Cam BA54 MA58 Lon Univ CertEd68 DipAdEd71. Coll of Resurr Mirfield 54. **d** 56 **p** 57. Chapl St Elphin's Sch Matlock 65-85; V Thornton-le-Fylde *Blackb* 85-94; RD Poulton 91-94; rtd 94. *8A Dunraven Road, West Kirby, Wirral, Merseyside L48 4DS*

PUCKRIN, Christopher. b 47. Oak Hill Th Coll. **d** 82 **p** 83. C Heworth *York* 82-84; C Sherburn in Elmet 84-85; P-in-c Kirkby Wharfe 85-86; P-in-c Kirk Fenton 85-86; V Kirk Fenton w Kirkby Wharfe and Ulleskelfe 86-87; C York St Mich-le-Belfrey 87-94; P-in-c Barnstaple *Ex* from 94. *Holy Trinity Vicarage, Victoria Road, Barnstaple, Devon EX32 9HP*   Barnstaple (01271) 44321

PUDDEFOOT, John Charles. b 52. St Pet Coll Ox BA74 Edin Univ BD78. Edin Th Coll 76. **d** 78 **p** 79. C Darlington H Trin *Dur* 78-81; Ind Chapl *Chich* 81-84; Asst Master Eton Coll Windsor from 84; Lic to Offic *Ox* from 85. *Eton College, Windsor, Berks SL4 6DB*   Windsor (01753) 671320

PUDDY, Kenneth Wilfred. b 15. Hatf Coll Dur BA36 DipTh38. St Aug Coll Cant 37. **d** 39 **p** 39. V Kingsbury Episcopi w E Lambrook *B & W* 55-89; RD Ilminster 59-71; rtd 90. *La Rambaudie, La Chapelle Gresignac, Verteillac 24320, France*   France (33) 53 91 04 07

PUDGE, Mark Samuel. b 67. K Coll Lon BD90 AKC90. Ripon Coll Cuddesdon DipMin93. **d** 93. C Thorpe Bay *Chelmsf* from 93. *62 Bunters Avenue, Shoeburyness, Southend-on-Sea SS3 9NF*   Southend-on-Sea (01702) 290442

PUGH, Canon David. b 22. Univ of Wales (Abth) BA48. St D Coll Lamp 48. **d** 50 **p** 51. R Ban Teifi w Henllan *St D* 57-70; R Ban Teifi w Henllan and Llanfairorllwyn 70-81; RD Emlyn 73-91; R Ban Teifi w Henllan and Llanfairorllwyn etc 81-91; Can St D Cathl 88-92; rtd 92; Hon Can St D Cathl *St D* from 92. *2 Bro Dewi, Henllan, Llandyssul, Dyfed SA44 5PL*   Velindre (01559) 370619

PUGH, Ernest William. b 16. AKC41. **d** 41 **p** 42. Hd of Div Ormskirk Gr Sch 59-81; Hon C Liv St Steph w St Cath *Liv* 59-73; P-in-c 73-81; rtd 81; Hon C W Derby (or Tuebrook) St Jo *Liv* 81-89. *The Cottage, 54 Derwent Road, Liverpool L13 6QR*   0151-228 4022

PUGH, Frank William. b 19. Roch Th Coll 62. **d** 64 **p** 65. R Fordington *Sarum* 70-73; TV Dorchester 73-78; R Stalbridge 78-89; rtd 89; Perm to Offic *B & W* from 89. *3 Rose Cottages, Balsam Lane, Wincanton, Somerset BA9 9HZ*   Wincanton (01963) 34100

PUGH, Harry. b 48. K Coll Lon BD70 AKC71 Lanc Univ MA89. **d** 72 **p** 73. C Milnrow *Man* 72-75; P-in-c Rochdale Gd Shep 75-78; TV Rochdale 78-79; Perm to Offic *Liv* 79-82; C Darwen St Cuth *Blackb* 82-85; C Darwen St Cuth w Tockholes St Steph 85-86; V Burnley St Steph 86-93; R Hoole from 93. *The Rectory, 69 Liverpool Old Road, Much Hoole, Preston PR4 4GA*   Preston (01227) 612267

PUGH, Canon John. b 18. St D Coll Lamp BA40. **d** 42 **p** 43. V Bagillt *St As* 61-73; RD Holywell 71-73; V Rossett 73-83; RD Wrexham 77-82; Hon Can St As Cathl 79-83; rtd 83. *Benton Croft, Box Lane, Wrexham, Clwyd LL12 7RB*

PUGH, Ronald Keith. b 32. Jes Coll Ox BA54 MA57 DPhil57. Ripon Hall Ox 56. **d** 59 **p** 60. C Bournemouth St Mich *Win* 59-61; Asst Chapl Bryanston Sch Blandford 61-66; Chapl Cranleigh Sch Surrey 66-68; Lic to Offic *Win* from 68; Lect K Alfred Coll Winchester from 68. *6 Windermere Gardens, Alresford, Hants SO24 9NL*   Alresford (01962) 732879

PUGH, Stephen Gregory. Southn Univ BEd77. Linc Th Coll 85. **d** 87 **p** 88. C Harpenden St Nic *St Alb* 87-90; C Stevenage All

SS Pin Green 90-93; R Stotfold and Radwell from 93. *The Vicarage, Church Road, Stotfold, Hitchin, Herts SG5 4NE*   Hitchin (01462) 730218

PUGH, Miss Wendy Kathleen. b 48. Newnham Coll Cam BA69 MA75. Trin Coll Bris DipTh95. **d** 95. C Hailsham *Chich* from 95. *19 St Wilfrid's Green, Hailsham, E Sussex BN27 1DR*   Hailsham (01323) 442132

PUGH, William Bryan. b 34. Man Univ. Ridley Hall Cam 59. **d** 61 **p** 62. C Oseney Crescent St Luke w Camden Square St Paul *Lon* 61-64; C N Wembley St Cuth 64-67; CF 67-88; QHC from 85; Chapl Heathfield Sch Ascot from 88. *3 College Close, Camberley, Surrey GU15 4JU*   Camberley (01276) 28799

PUGMIRE, Alan. b 37. Lon Univ DipTh63. Tyndale Hall Bris 61. **d** 64 **p** 65. C Islington St Steph w St Bart and St Matt *Lon* 64-66; C St Helens St Mark *Liv* 66-71; R Stretford St Bride *Man* 71-82; R Burnage St Marg from 82; AD Heaton from 88. *St Margaret's Rectory, 250 Burnage Lane, Manchester M19 1FL*   0161-432 1844

PUGSLEY, Anthony John. b 39. ACIB. Oak Hill Th Coll 89. **d** 90 **p** 91. C Chadwell *Chelmsf* 90-94; P-in-c Gt Warley Ch Ch from 94. *Christ Church Vicarage, 79 Mount Crescent, Brentwood CM14 5DD*   Brentwood (01277) 220428

PULESTON, Mervyn Pedley. b 35. K Coll Lon BD60 AKC60. **d** 61 **p** 62. C Gt Marlow *Ox* 61-65; C-in-c Blackbird Leys CD 65-70; R Kidlington 70-85; TR Kidlington w Hampton Poyle 85-86; Chapl Geneva *Eur* 86-92; TV Dorchester *Ox* from 92. *The Vicarage, Clifton Hampden, Abingdon, Oxon OX14 3EE*   Clifton Hampden (01865) 407206

PULFORD, Christopher. b 59. Pemb Coll Ox BA81 MA87. Trin Coll Bris. **d** 84 **p** 85. C Parr *Liv* 84-87; Chapl Berkhamsted Sch Herts 87-92. *131 High Street, Berkhamsted, Herts HP4 2DJ*   Berkhamsted (01442) 873008

PULFORD, John Shirley Walter. b 31. Jes Coll Cam BA55 MA59. Cuddesdon Coll 55. **d** 57 **p** 58. C Blackpool St Steph *Blackb* 57-60; N Rhodesia 60-63; V Newington St Paul *S'wark* 63-68; C Seacroft *Ripon* 68-70; Asst Chapl HM Pris Liv 70-71; Chapl HM Pris Linc 71-73; Counsellor Linc Colls Art and Tech 73-79; Cam Univ Counselling Service 79-82; Dir from 82. *14 Trumpington Street, Cambridge CB2 1QA*   Cambridge (01223) 332865

PULFORD, Canon Stephen Ian. b 25. Clifton Th Coll 53. **d** 56 **p** 57. R Coberley w Cowley *Glouc* 58-94; P-in-c Colesbourne 75-94; Hon Can Glouc Cathl 84-94; RD Cirencester 88-89; rtd 94. *The Rectory, Coberley, Cheltenham, Glos GL53 9QZ*   Cheltenham (01242) 870232

PULLAN, Ben John. b 43. MSc. **d** 77 **p** 78. NSM Westbury-on-Trym St Alb *Bris* 77-91; NSM Henleaze from 91. *52 Druid Stoke Avenue, Bristol BS9 1DQ*   Bristol (0117) 968 2697

PULLAN, Lionel Stephen. b 37. ARCO58 FIST77 Keble Coll Ox BA58 MA62. Cuddesdon Coll 58. **d** 60 **p** 61. C Tranmere St Paul *Ches* 60-63; C Higher Bebington 63-64; Perm to Offic 64-70; Hon C Luton St Chris Round Green *St Alb* 70-72; Hon C Hitchin H Sav 72-73; Hon C Welwyn 73-75; Hon C Welwyn w Ayot St Peter 75-78; Hon C Kimpton w Ayot St Lawrence 78-82; Hon C Stevenage St Andr and St Geo 82-85; Deputation Appeals Org CECS 85-90; Perm to Offic *St Alb* 85-89; Public Preacher 89-90; V Sundon from 90. *St Mary's Vicarage, 1 Selina Close, Sundon, Luton LU3 3AW*   Luton (01582) 583076 or 573236

PULLAN, Mrs Pauline Margaret. b 32. N Ord Course 79. **dss** 82 **d** 87 **p** 94. Stockport St Sav *Ches* 82-83; Wilmslow 83-87; Par Dn 87-92; NSM from 92; Sub-Chapl HM Pris Styal 89-92; rtd 92. *12 Acacia Avenue, Wilmslow, Cheshire SK9 6AX*   Wilmslow (01625) 525865

PULLEN, James Stephen. b 43. Lon Univ BSc64 Linacre Coll Ox BA68. St Steph Ho Ox 66. **d** 68 **p** 69. C Chorlton-cum-Hardy St Clem *Man* 68-72; C Doncaster St Leon and St Jude *Sheff* 72-73; Chapl St Olave and St Sav Sch Orpington 73-75; Chapl Haileybury Coll Herts from 75; Perm to Offic *St Alb* from 75. *Edmonstone House, Haileybury College, Hertford SG13 7NU*   Hoddesdon (01992) 463384

PULLEN, Roger Christopher. b 43. Lon Univ BSc65 PGCE90. Wells Th Coll 65. **d** 67 **p** 68. C S w N Hayling *Portsm* 67-69; C Farlington 69-73; V Farington *Blackb* 73-80; V Chorley All SS 80-83; V Kingsley *Ches* 83-92; R Cilcain and Nannerch and Rhyd-y-mwyn *St As* from 92. *The Rectory, 9 Pen y Coed, Nannerch, Mold, Clwyd CH7 5RS*   Mold (01352) 741367

PULLIN, Andrew Eric. b 47. Linc Th Coll 71. **d** 73 **p** 74. C Pershore w Wick *Worc* 73-75; C Pershore w Pinvin, Wick and Birlingham 75-77; TV Droitwich 77-80; V Woburn Sands *St Alb* 80-85; Perm to Offic *B & W* from 85. *85 Weymouth Road, Frome, Somerset BA11 1HJ*   Frome (01373) 472170

PULLIN, Arthur. b 18. St Jo Coll Dur LTh39 BA40 MA45. ALCD39. **d** 41 **p** 42. V Midhurst *Chich* 65-85; R Woolbeding 65-85; RD Midhurst 81-85; rtd 85; Perm to Offic *Chich* from 85. *38 Carters Way, Wisborough Green, W Sussex RH14 0BY*   Wisborough Green (01403) 700566

PULLIN, Christopher. b 56. St Chad's Coll Dur BA77. Ripon Coll Cuddesdon 79. **d** 80 **p** 81. C Tooting All SS *S'wark* 80-85; V New Eltham All SS 85-92; V St Jo in Bedwardine *Worc* from 92. *St John's Vicarage, 143 Malvern Road, Worcester WR2 4LN* Worcester (01905) 422327

PULLIN, Peter.MA MSc CEng. Trin Coll Bris. **d** 88 **p** 89. NSM Rugby St Andr *Cov* 88-90; NSM Aylesbeare, Rockbeare, Farringdon etc *Ex* from 90. *Applegarth, 5 Minchin Orchard, Aylesbeare, Exeter EX5 2BY* Woodbury (01395) 232877

PULLINGER, Mrs Catherine Ann (Cathy). b 54. York Univ BA76. Oak Hill Th Coll DipHE93. **d** 93. NSM Luton St Paul *St Alb* from 93. *45 Manton Drive, Luton LU2 7DJ* Luton (01582) 38362

PULMAN, Edgar James. b 17. Selw Coll Cam BA48 MA53. ALCD50. **d** 50 **p** 51. V Finchley H Trin *Lon* 63-76; C Norton sub Hamdon, W Chinnock, Chiselborough etc *B & W* 77-78; Lic to Offic from 79; rtd 82. *5 Manor House, Norton Sub Hamdon, Stoke-sub-Hamdon, Somerset TA14 6SJ* Chiselborough (01935) 881521

PULMAN, John. b 34. Nottm Univ CTPS81. E Midl Min Tr Course 78. **d** 81 **p** 82. NSM Mansf St Pet *S'well* 81-83; C Mansf Woodhouse 83-86; V Flintham from 86; R Car Colston w Screveton from 86; Chapl HM Young Offender Inst Whatton 86-90; Chapl HM Pris Whatton from 90. *The Vicarage, Woods Lane, Flintham, Newark, Notts NG23 5LR* Newark (01636) 525750 or Whatton (01949) 50511 Fax Whatton (01949) 50124

PUMFREY, John Lawrence. b 06. Bps' Coll Cheshunt 48. **d** 49 **p** 50. V Hamstead St Paul *Birm* 62-71; rtd 71. *18 Highfield, Callow End, Worcester WR2 4TP* Worcester (01905) 830609

PUMPHREY, Norman John Albert. b 21. Nor Ord Course 76. **d** 77 **p** 78. NSM Aylsham *Nor* 77-94; Chapl St Mich Hosp Aylsham from 88; Perm to Offic *Nor* from 94. *12 Buxton Road, Aylsham, Norwich NR11 6JD* Aylsham (01263) 733207

PUNSHON, Ms Carol Mary. b 59. Liv Inst of Educn BEd83. Ridley Hall Cam CTM94. **d** 94 **p** 95. C Bushey *St Alb* from 94. *6 Farm Way, Bushey, Watford WD2 3SS* 0181-950 0114

PUNSHON, Keith. b 48. JP. Jes Coll Cam BA69 MA73 Birm Univ DipTh73 MA77. Qu Coll Birm 71. **d** 73 **p** 74. C Yardley St Edburgha *Birm* 73-76; Chapl Eton Coll Windsor 76-79; V Hill *Birm* 79-86; CF (TA) from 79; V S Yardley St Mich *Birm* from 86. *St Michael's Vicarage, 60 Yew Tree Lane, Birmingham B26 1AP* 0121-706 2563

PURCELL, Canon William Ernest. b 09. Univ of Wales BA34 Keble Coll Ox BA36 MA43. Qu Coll Birm 36. **d** 37 **p** 38. Can Res Worc Cathl *Worc* 66-76; rtd 76; Perm to Offic *Ox* 83-95. *Flat 3, Gretton Court, Girton, Cambridge CB3 0QN* Cambridge (01223) 277234

PURCHAS, Mrs Catherine Patience Ann. b 39. St Mary's Coll Dur BA61. St Alb Minl Tr Scheme 77. **dss** 80 **d** 87 **p** 94. RE Resource Cen 80-81; Relig Broadcasting Chiltern Radio 81-87; Wheathampstead *St Alb* 81-87; Hon Par Dn 87-94; Hon C from 94; Relig Broadcasting Beds Radio from 88; Bp's Officer for Women from 93; Bp's Officer for NSM and Asst Dir of Ords from 93. *The Rectory, Church Street, Wheathampstead, St Albans, Herts AL4 8LR* Wheathampstead (01582) 833144 or 834285 Fax 834285

PURCHAS, Thomas. b 35. Qu Coll Birm 59. **d** 62 **p** 63. C Hatf *St Alb* 62-71; R Blunham 71-78; P-in-c Tempsford w Lt Barford 71-78; R Blunham w Tempsford and Lt Barford 78-80; R Wheathampstead from 80; RD Wheathampstead from 92. *The Rectory, Church Street, Wheathampstead, St Albans, Herts AL4 8LR* Wheathampstead (01582) 833144 or 843285 Fax 834285

PURDIE, Dr Anthony Watson. b 08. FRCOG51 FRCSGlas65 FRCPGlas68 Glas Univ MB, ChB31 K Coll Lon BD76 AKC76. **d** 76 **p** 77. NSM Waltham Abbey *Chelmsf* 76-77; NSM Goodmayes St Paul 77-80; Perm to Offic *Ex* from 82. *Shearwater, Pope's Lane, Colyford, Colyton, Devon EX13 6QR* Colyton (01297) 553206

PURDY, John David. b 44. Leeds Univ BA65 DipTh74 MPhil76. Coll of Resurr Mirfield 72. **d** 75 **p** 76. C Marske in Cleveland *York* 75-78; C Marton-in-Cleveland 78-80; V Newby 80-87; V Kirkleatham 87-95; V Kirkbymoorside w Gillamoor, Farndale & Bransdale from 95. *The Vicarage, Kirkbymoorside, York YO6 6AZ* Kirkbymoorside (01751) 31452

PURSER, Alan Gordon. b 51. Leic Univ BSc73. Wycliffe Hall Ox 74. **d** 77 **p** 78. C Beckenham Ch Ch *Roch* 77-81; TV Barking St Marg w Ch Patr *Chelmsf* 81-84; S Africa 84-88; C Enfield Ch Ch Trent Park *Lon* from 88; Proclamation Trust from 88. *The Parsonage, 34 Crescent East, Hadley Wood, Herts EN4 0EN* 0181-449 2572

PURVEY-TYRER, Neil. b 66. Leeds Univ BA87 MA88. Westcott Ho Cam 88. **d** 90 **p** 91. C Denbigh and Nantglyn *St As* 90-92; Chapl Asst Basingstoke Distr Hosp 92-95; TV Cannock *Lich* from 95. *St Aidan's Vicarage, Albert Street, Cannock, Staffs WS11 2JD* Cannock (01543) 505674

PURVIS, Canon Colin. b 19. Kelham Th Coll 37. **d** 44 **p** 45. V Heworth St Mary *Dur* 62-76; R Egglescliffe 76-84; Hon Can Dur Cathl 83-92; rtd 84; Perm to Offic *Newc* from 84; Perm to Offic *Ripon* from 84. *15 Milbank Court, Darlington, Co Durham DL3 9PF* Darlington (01325) 355711

PURVIS, Stephen. b 48. AKC70. **d** 71 **p** 72. C Peterlee *Dur* 71-75; Dioc Recruitment Officer 75-79; V Stevenage All SS Pin Green *St Alb* 79-88; TR Borehamwood from 88; RD Aldenham from 94. *7 Furzehill Road, Borehamwood, Herts WD6 2DG* 0181-953 2554

PUSEY, Ian John. b 39. Sarum Th Coll 69. **d** 71 **p** 72. C Waltham Abbey *Chelmsf* 71-75; TV Stantonbury *Ox* 75-80; P-in-c Bletchley 80-84; R from 84. *The Rectory, 75 Church Green Road, Bletchley, Milton Keynes MK3 6BY* Milton Keynes (01908) 373357

PUSEY, Robert Guy. b 09. St Edm Hall Ox BA36 MA51. Linc Th Coll 36. **d** 38 **p** 39. V Cowleigh *Worc* 59-73; TV Malvern Link w Cowleigh 73-75; rtd 75; Perm to Offic *Worc* from 75. *Flat 2, 3 Orchard Road, Malvern, Worcs WR14 3DA* Malvern (01684) 573716

PUTMAN, Nina Maude Elaine. b 20. **dss** 75 **d** 87 **p** 94. New Malden and Coombe *S'wark* 75-87; NSM 87-92; rtd 80; Perm to Offic *S'wark* from 92. *57 Alric Avenue, New Malden, Surrey KT3 4JL* 0181-949 6042

PYATT, Noel Watson. b 34. AKC57. **d** 58 **p** 59. C Prenton *Ches* 58-61; C Cheadle Hulme All SS 61-63; P-in-c Hattersley 63-66; V 66-70; V Ches St Paul from 70. *St Paul's Vicarage, 10 Sandy Lane, Chester CH3 5UL* Chester (01244) 351377

PYBURN, Canon Alan. b 29. G&C Coll Cam BA51 MA55. Westcott Ho Cam 53. **d** 55 **p** 56. C Barnard Castle *Dur* 55-57; Chapl G&C Coll Cam 57-60; V Dallington *Pet* 60-72; V Ox St Giles *Ox* 72-79; P-in-c Remenham 79-94; R Henley 79-94; RD Henley 84-94; Hon Can Ch Ch from 90; R Henley on Thames w Remenham from 94. *The Rectory, Hart Street, Henley-on-Thames, Oxon RG9 2AU* Henley-on-Thames (01491) 577340

PYBUS, Antony Frederick. b 54. Birm Univ BA77. St Jo Coll Dur 78. **d** 81 **p** 82. C Ches H Trin *Ches* 81-84; C W Hampstead St Jas *Lon* 84-89; V Alexandra Park St Andr 89-93; V Alexandra Park from 93. *The Vicarage, 34 Alexandra Park Road, London N10 2AB* 0181-444 6898 Fax 442 1736

PYE, Alexander Frederick. b 61. St Mich Coll Llan DipPTh95. **d** 95. C Griffithstown *Mon* from 95. *82 Greenhill Road, Sebastopol, Pontypool, Gwent NP4 5BQ* Pontypool (01495) 763962

PYE, Allan Stephen. b 56. Univ of Wales (Lamp) BA78 Lanc Univ MA85 MPhil87. Westcott Ho Cam 79. **d** 81 **p** 82. C Scotforth *Blackb* 81-85; C Oswaldtwistle All SS 85-87; Chapl Wrightington Hosp 87-91; V Wrightington *Blackb* 87-91; P-in-c Hayton St Mary *Carl* 91-93; V Hayton w Cumwhitton from 93. *The Vicarage, Hayton, Carlisle CA4 9HR* Hayton (01228) 70248

PYE, James Timothy. b 58. Oak Hill Th Coll BA90. **d** 90 **p** 91. C Normanton *Derby* 90-94; R Talke *Lich* from 94. *The Rectory, Crown Bank, Talke, Stoke-on-Trent ST7 1PU* Stoke-on-Trent (01782) 782348

PYE, Joseph Terence Hardwidge. b 41. ARICS64. Trin Coll Bris 70. **d** 73 **p** 74. C Blackb Ch Ch *Blackb* 73-76; OMF 77-90; Korea 77-90; V Castle Church *Lich* from 90. *Castle Church Vicarage, Castle Bank, Stafford ST16 1DJ* Stafford (01785) 223673

PYKE, Alan. b 37. Trin Coll Bris BA87. **d** 87 **p** 88. CA 58-87; C Ipswich St Mary at Stoke w St Pet, Stoke Park *St E* 87-90; R Creeting St Mary, Creeting St Peter etc from 90. *The Rectory, Forward Green, Stowmarket, Suffolk IP14 5EF* Stowmarket (01449) 711347

PYKE, Barry John. b 62. FGS84 Qu Mary Coll Lon BSc84 Southn Univ BTh94. Sarum & Wells Th Coll BTh91. **d** 94 **p** 95. C Bengeworth *Worc* from 94. *17 Donney Brook, Evesham, Worcs WR11 6YD* Evesham (01386) 421630

PYKE, Richard Ernest. b 50. Sarum & Wells Th Coll. **d** 82 **p** 83. C Bushey *St Alb* 82-85; C Gt Berkhamsted 85-89; V St Alb St Mary Marshalswick from 89. *The Vicarage, 1 Sherwood Avenue, St Albans, Herts AL4 9QA* St Albans (01727) 851544

PYKE, Thomas Fortune (Tom). b 62. St Chad's Coll Dur BA85 Fitzw Coll Cam BA88. Ridley Hall Cam 86. **d** 89 **p** 90. C Hitchin *St Alb* 89-94; Chapl Aston Univ *Birm* from 94. *27 Worlds End Road, Handsworth Wood, Birmingham B20 2NP* 0121-507 0247

PYLE, John Alan. b 31. Qu Coll Birm. **d** 69 **p** 70. C Fenham St Jas and St Basil *Newc* 69-72; C Monkseaton St Pet 72-74; C Morpeth 74-78; R Bothal 78-83; TV Willington Team 83-91; R Chollerton w Birtley and Thockrington from 91. *The Vicarage, Chollerton, Hexham, Northd NE46 4TF* Hexham (01434) 681721

PYM, David Pitfield. b 45. Nottm Univ BA65 Ex Coll Ox DPhil68. Ripon Hall Ox 66. **d** 68 **p** 69. C Nottm St Mary *S'well* 68-72; Chapl RN 72-76 and 79-84; Chapl Worksop Coll Notts

76-79; R Avon Dassett w Farnborough and Fenny Compton *Cov* from 84. *The Rectory, Avon Dassett, Leamington Spa, Warks CV33 0AR* Farnborough (01295) 690305

PYM, Francis Victor. b 24. ARIBA52 DipArch52. St Jo Coll Dur 74. **d** 76 **p** 77. C Keighley *Bradf* 76-79; Chapl Bethany Fellowship 79-87; Dir Joshua Chr Trust from 88; Research Asst Ho of Lords from 89; Dir Gp Apologetics Initiative from 92. *Bolney House, Bolney, Haywards Heath, W Sussex RH17 5QR* Handcross (01444) 881877

PYM, Gordon Sydney. b 19. Worc Ord Coll 59. **d** 61 **p** 62. V Owston *Sheff* 69-72; V Hensall 72-75; rtd 75. *6 Grenoside Road, Swinton, Mexborough, S Yorkshire S64 8RP* Mexborough (01709) 586884

PYNE, Robert Leslie. b 51. Lanchester Poly BA72 Leeds Univ DipTh78. Coll of Resurr Mirfield 76. **d** 79 **p** 80. C Clifton All SS w St Jo *Bris* 79-81; Bp's Dom Chapl *Ox* 81-84; TV High Wycombe 84-90; Chapl RN from 90. *Directorate Gen, RN Chapl Services, Room 203, Victory Building, HM Naval Base, Portsmouth PO1 3LS* Portsmouth (01705) 727903 Fax 727112

✠**PYTCHES, Rt Rev George Edward David.** b 31. Bris Univ BA54 Nottm Univ MPhil84. Tyndale Hall Bris 51. **d** 55 **p** 56 **c** 70. C Ox St Ebbe *Ox* 55-58; C Wallington H Trin *S'wark* 58-59; Chile 59-77; Suff Bp Valparaiso 70-72; Bp Chile, Bolivia and Peru 72-77; V Chorleywood St Andr *St Alb* from 77. *St Andrew's Vicarage, 37 Quickley Lane, Chorleywood, Rickmansworth, Herts WD3 5AE* Chorleywood (01923) 282391 or 282866 Fax 284406

PYTCHES, Preb Dr Peter Norman Lambert. b 32. Lon Univ BD57 Bris Univ MLitt67 Southn Univ PhD81. Lambeth STh74 Tyndale Hall Bris 53. **d** 57 **p** 58. C Heatherlands St Jo *Sarum* 57-61; C Cromer *Nor* 61-63; V Plymouth St Jude *Ex* 63-71; V Heatherlands St Jo *Sarum* 71-76; Dir Past Tr Oak Hill Th Coll 76-81; V Finchley Ch Ch *Lon* 81-91; AD Cen Barnet 86-91; V Forty Hill Jes Ch from 91; Preb St Paul's Cathl from 92. *The Vicarage, Forty Hill, Enfield, Middx EN2 9EU* 0181-363 1935

Q

QUANCE, John David. b 42. Kelham Th Coll 61. **d** 67 **p** 68. C Southgate Ch Ch *Lon* 67-70; C Norbury St Phil *Cant* 70-73; Asst Chapl Middx Hosp Lon 73-80; R Failsworth St Jo *Man* 80-95; Australia 84-85; P-in-c Healey *Man* from 95. *Healey Vicarage, Gandy Lane, Rochdale, Lancs OL12 6EF* Rochdale (01706) 350808

QUARMBY, David John. b 43. St Jo Coll Dur BA64 Lon Univ CertEd70 Man Univ MEd89. Ridley Hall Cam 65. **d** 67 **p** 68. C Bournville *Birm* 67-71; V Erdington St Chad 71-73; Lic to Offic *Blackb* 73-83; Perm to Offic *Man* 83-90; C Oldham St Paul from 90; Counsellor Huddersfield Poly 90-92; Huddersfield Univ from 92. *30 College Avenue, Oldham OL8 4DS* 0161-626 2771

QUARRELL, John Beck. b 39. Hull Coll of Educn CertEd59. Chich Th Coll 67. **d** 70 **p** 71. C Horbury *Wakef* 70-71; C Sowerby 71-73; V Brotherton 74-80; Chapl Pontefract Gen Hosp 78-80; Staincliffe Hosp Wakef 82-88; V Staincliffe *Wakef* 80-88; R Farndon w Thorpe, Hawton and Cotham *S'well* from 89. *The Rectory, 3 Marsh Lane, Farndon, Newark, Notts NG24 3SS* Newark (01636) 705048

QUARTON, Robert Edward. b 43. E Midl Min Tr Course 84. **d** 87 **p** 88. C Gresley *Derby* 87-88; C Clay Cross 88-90; C N Wingfield, Clay Cross and Pilsley 90-91; R Darley from 91. *The Rectory, 15 Hall Rise, Darley Dale, Matlock, Derbyshire DE4 2FW* Matlock (01629) 734257

QUASH, Jonathan Ben. b 68. Peterho Cam BA90 MA94. Westcott Ho Cam 91. **d** 95. NSM Cam St Mary Less *Ely* from 95; Asst Chapl Peterho Cam from 95. *Flat 3, 28 Parkside, Cambridge CB1 1JE* Cambridge (01223) 327837

QUENNELL, Brian Michael. b 19. **d** 74 **p** 75. C Oakham w Hambleton and Egleton *Pet* 74-78; V Denford w Ringstead 78-87; rtd 87; Perm to Offic *Pet* from 87. *3 Crispin Cottages, Baker Street, Walgrave, Northampton NN6 9QL* Northampton (01604) 781022

QUIGLEY, John Molesworth. b 21. BNC Ox BA43 MA47. Wycliffe Hall Ox 43. **d** 44 **p** 45. C Wembley St Jo *Lon* 44-46; Hon C Ellesmere Port *Ches* 75; Hon C Bromborough 75-77 and 80-82; Hon C Prenton 77-80; Hon C Wallasey St Hilary 82-84; rtd 84; Perm to Offic *Bradf* from 85. *Flat 3, Ashbrook, 4 Grove Road, Ilkley, W Yorkshire LS29 9PE* Ilkley (01943) 609380

QUIGLEY, Thomas Molesworth. b 19. Lon Univ BD45. ALCD41. **d** 42 **p** 43. C Champion Hill St Sav *S'wark* 42-45; CF 45-58; C Upperby St Jo *Carl* 58-62; C Accrington St Jas *Blackb* 62-70; Australia from 70. *1/42 Hampden Road, Artarmon, Sydney, NSW, Australia 2064*

QUILL, John Stephen. b 51. Nottm Univ DipTh78. Linc Th Coll 76. **d** 79 **p** 80. C Sawbridgeworth *St Alb* 79-81; C Watford Ch Ch 81-85; Dioc Soc Services Adv *Worc* 85-90; Adv to Bd of Soc Resp 90-95. *77 Northfield Gardens, Bushey, Watford WD2 4RF* Watford (01923) 225411

QUILL, Canon Walter Paterson. b 35. **d** 60 **p** 61. C Glendermott *D & R* 60-63; I Kilbarron 63-66; I Kilcronaghan w Ballynascreen 66-81; I Derg w Termonamongan from 81; RD Strabane from 87; Can Derry Cathl from 89; RD Newtownstewart and Omagh from 90; Preb Howth St Patr Cathl Dub from 94. *13 Strabane Road, Castlederg, Co Tyrone BT81 7HZ* Castlederg (016626) 71362

QUILLIAM, Miss Anne Eleanor Scott. b 31. Bedf Coll Lon BA54 CertEd55. Dalton Ho Bris 59. **d** 87. Par Dn Toxteth St Philemon w St Gabr and St Cleopas *Liv* 87-92; rtd 92. *13 Raad ny Gabbil, Ballalough, Castletown, Isle of Man IM9 1HH* Castletown (01624) 822357

QUIN, Canon Cosslett William Charles. b 07. TCD BA30 BD. **d** 31 **p** 32. I Dungarstown w Redcross *D & G* 65-71; rtd 71. *Spruce Cottage, 2 Church Road, Carryduff, Belfast BT8 8DT* Belfast (01232) 813768

QUIN, Eric Arthur. b 22. Magd Coll Cam BA46 MA48 Lon Univ BD56. Bps' Coll Cheshunt 46. **d** 48 **p** 49. V St Ippolyts *St Alb* 58-70; RD Hitchin 68-70; V Haynes 70-87; rtd 87. *Annabel's Cottage, The Lydiate, Wirral, Merseyside L60 8PR* 0151-342 8650

QUIN, John James Neil. b 31. Ox Univ MA DipEd53. Qu Coll Birm 61. **d** 63 **p** 64. C Cannock *Lich* 63-68; V Sneyd Green 68-78; V Stafford St Paul Forebridge 78-90; TV Tettenhall Regis from 90. *Church Cottage, Church Road, Tettenhall, Wolverhampton WV6 9AJ* Wolverhampton (01902) 751941

QUIN, Ven Thomas Rothwell. b 15. OBE80. TCD BA39 MA49. **d** 39 **p** 40. Asst Chapl-in-Chief RAF 63-70; Prin RAF Chapl Sch 66-70; QHC 67-70; Chapl Zurich w St Gallen and Winterthur *Eur* 70-80; Adn Switzerland 79-80; rtd 80; Perm to Offic *Sarum* from 80. *New Rushford, Walnut Close, Sutton Veny, Warminster, Wilts BA12 7BS* Warminster (01985) 40794

QUINE, Christopher Andrew. b 38. St Aid Birkenhead 61. **d** 64 **p** 65. C Hunts Cross *Liv* 64-67; C Farnworth 67-71; C-in-c Widnes St Jo 67-71; V Clubmoor 71-78; V Formby H Trin from 78. *Holy Trinity Vicarage, 2A Brows Lane, Formby, Liverpool L37 3HZ* Formby (01704) 873642

QUINE, David Anthony. b 28. Qu Coll Cam BA52 MA59. Ridley Hall Cam 53. **d** 55 **p** 56. Lic to Offic *York* 68-71; Chapl Monkton Combe Sch Bath 71-85; rtd 85; Perm to Offic *Carl* from 85. *Stickle Cottage, Dungeon Ghyll, Great Langdale, Ambleside, Cumbria LA22 9JY* Langdale (015394) 37669

QUINE, Canon Dr Ernest Kendrick Leigh. b 21. St Jo Coll Dur BA50 MA55 DipTh51 Nottm Univ DPhil68. **d** 51 **p** 52. V Belgrave St Pet *Leic* 61-93; Hon Can Leic Cathl 67-93; rtd 93. *63 Somerset Drive, Glenfield, Leicester LE3 8QW* Leicester (0116) 232 1994

✠**QUINLAN, Rt Rev Alan Geoffrey.** b 33. Kelham Th Coll 54. **d** 58 **p** 59 **c** 88. C Bedf Leigh *Man* 58-61; S Africa from 61; Suff Bp Cen Region from 88. *Bishop's House, 79 Kildare Road, Newlands, 7700 South Africa* Cape Town (21) 642444

QUINN, Arthur Hamilton Riddel. b 37. TCD BA60 MA64 BD67. **d** 61 **p** 62. C Belf H Trin *Conn* 61-63; C Belf St Mary Magd 63-64; Chapl Hull Univ *York* 64-69; Chapl Keele Univ *Lich* 69-74; P-in-c Keele 72-74; V Shirley St Jo *Cant* 74-84; V Shirley St Jo *S'wark* from 85. *The Vicarage, 49 Shirley Church Road, Croydon CR0 5EF* 0181-654 1013

QUINN, Cecil Hugh. b 24. Oak Hill Th Coll 74. **d** 76 **p** 77. C Bedf St Jo and St Leon *St Alb* 76-79; Deputation Sec Irish Ch Miss 79-89; I Rathmullan w Tyrella *D & D* from 80; rtd 89. *Tyrella Rectory, 10 Ballydonnell Road, Downpatrick, Co Down BT30 8EN* Ballykinler (01396) 851237

QUINN, Derek John. b 55. TCD BTh88. **d** 88 **p** 89. C Mossley *Conn* 88-91; I Cappagh w Lislimnaghan *D & R* from 91. *Erganagh Rectory, 1 Erganagh Road, Cappagh, Omagh, Co Tyrone BT79 7SX* Omagh (01662) 242572

QUINN, Dr Frederick. b 94. Chapl Warsaw *Eur* 94-95; USA from 95. *Address temp unknown*

QUINN, George Bruce. b 23. **d** 82 **p** 83. NSM Douglas St Ninian *S & M* from 82. *85 Port-e-Chee Avenue, Douglas, Isle of Man IM2 5EZ* Douglas (01624) 674080

QUINN, Mrs Helen Elizabeth. b 46. Keswick Hall Coll CertEd67. E Anglian Minl Tr Course 92. **d** 95. Hon C Old Catton *Nor* from 95. *8 Shakespeare Way, Taverham, Norwich NR8 6SH* Norwich (01603) 861264

QUINN, Dr John James. b 46. TCD BA70 PhD76. St Jo Coll Nottm DipTh80. **d** 81 **p** 82. C Gorleston St Andr *Nor* 81-84; R

Belton 84-90; R Burgh Castle 84-90; R Belton and Burgh Castle from 90. *The Rectory, Belton, Great Yarmouth, Norfolk NR31 9JQ* Great Yarmouth (01493) 780210

QUINN, Kenneth Norman. b 40. QUB BSc62 CEng MICE. CITC 80. **d** 85 **p** 86. NSM Seapatrick *D & D* 85-91; Lic to Offic from 91. *4 Knollwood, Seapatrick, Banbridge, Co Down BT32 4PE* Banbridge (018206) 23515

QUINN, Marjorie. **d** 94. NSM Hawarden *St As* from 94. *21 Hawarden Way, Mancot, Deeside, Clwyd CH5 2EL* Mold (01244) 531639

QUINNELL, Peter Francis. b 48. St Steph Ho Ox DipMin95. **d** 95. C Tewkesbury w Walton Cardiff *Glouc* from 95. *83 York Road, Tewkesbury, Glos GL20 5HB* Tewkesbury (01684) 294756

QUINNEY, William Elliott. b 33. Linc Th Coll 62. **d** 64 **p** 65. C Coalville *Leic* 64-68; P-in-c Ibstock 68-69; R Nailstone w Carlton 69-79; R Nailstone and Carlton w Shackerstone from 79. *The Rectory, Rectory Lane, Nailstone, Nuneaton, Warks CV13 0QQ* Ibstock (01530) 260281

QUINT, Mrs Patricia Mary. b 51. Milton Keynes Coll of Ed CertEd76 Open Univ BA77. St Alb Minl Tr Scheme 90. **d** 93 **p** 94. C Hertf St Andr *St Alb* from 93. *8 Calton Avenue, Sele Farm, Hertford SG14 2EP* Hertford (01992) 552142

R

RABAN, Canon James Peter Caplin Priaulx. b 18. TD50. Chich Th Coll 52. **d** 54 **p** 55. V Southn Maybush St Pet *Win* 66-80; RD Southn 70-83; Hon Can Win Cathl 73-83; Chapl Countess Mountbatten Ho Southn 80-83; rtd 83; Perm to Offic *Leic* from 85. *66 Coventry Road, Market Harborough, Leics LE16 9BZ* Market Harborough (01858) 465816

RABBETTS, Reginald Douglas Cyprian. b 14. AKC38. Sarum Th Coll 38. **d** 38 **p** 39. V Woodlands *Win* 50-83; rtd 83; Perm to Offic *Win* from 83. *The Lean-To, Ship Inn, Ashford Hill, Newbury, Berks RG15 8BD* Tadley (01734) 811793

RABIN, Peter David. b 62. Southlands Coll Lon BA86. Aston Tr Scheme 88 Ripon Coll Cuddesdon BTh93. **d** 93 **p** 94. C Hornsey St Mary w St Geo *Lon* from 93. *153 Priory Road, London N8 8NA* 0181-348 5873

RABJOHNS, Alan. b 40. Leeds Univ BA62. Coll of Resurr Mirfield 62. **d** 64 **p** 65. C Ashington *Newc* 64-67; C Upton cum Chalvey *Ox* 67-76; V Roath St Sav *Llan* from 76. *St Saviour's Vicarage, 115 Splott Road, Cardiff CF2 2BY* Cardiff (01222) 461203

RABLEN, Antony Ford. b 52. St Jo Coll Nottm. **d** 82 **p** 83. C Clifton *York* 82-85; TV Marfleet 85-92; P-in-c Welton w Melton from 92. *St Helen's Vicarage, Welton, Brough, N Humberside HU15 1ND* Hull (01482) 666677

RABY, Canon Alfred Charles. b 04. St Jo Coll Ox BA27 MA30. Wells Th Coll 27. **d** 28 **p** 29. R Clapham H Trin *S'wark* 54-74; rtd 75; Perm to Offic *St E* from 75. *134B Southgate Street, Bury St Edmunds, Suffolk IP33 2AF* Bury St Edmunds (01284) 703487

RABY, Malcolm Ernest. b 47. St Jo Coll York BEd73. N Ord Course 81. **d** 84 **p** 85. NSM Chadkirk *Ches* 84-88; Consultant E England CPAS 88-94; Perm to Offic *Linc* 92-94; C Ely from 94. *44 Bentham Way, Ely, Cambs CB6 1BS* Ely (01353) 644964

RACE, Alan. b 51. Bradf Univ BTech73 Ox Univ DipTh75 Birm Univ MA82. Ripon Coll Cuddesdon 73. **d** 76 **p** 77. C Tupsley *Heref* 76-79; Asst Chapl Kent Univ *Cant* 79-84; Dir Studies S'wark Ord Course 84-94; R Aylestone St Andr w St Jas *Leic* from 94. *The Rectory, Old Church Street, Leicester LE2 8ND* Leicester (0116) 283 2458

RACE, Christopher Keith. b 43. St Paul's Grahamstown DipTh78. **d** 78 **p** 80. S Africa 78-86; V Tanworth St Patr Salter Street *Birm* from 86. *The Vicarage, Vicarage Road, Earlswood, Solihull, W Midlands B94 6DH* 0121-728 2579

RACTLIFFE, Dudley John. b 38. Man Univ BA62 Birm Univ DPS69. Ridley Hall Cam 63. **d** 66 **p** 67. C Radford *Cov* 66-68; C Haslemere *Guildf* 69-73; V Perry Beeches *Birm* 73-78; V Worle *B & W* 78-88; Dioc Ecum Officer 88-93; R Dowlishwake w Kingstone, Chillington etc 88-93; TR Swanage and Studland *Sarum* from 93. *The Rectory, 12 Church Hill, Swanage, Dorset BH19 1HU* Swanage (01929) 422916

RADCLIFFE, Henry Robert Moshe. b 30. Moore Th Coll Sydney ThL57. **d** 60 **p** 61. C St Luke in the City *Liv* 66-70; CMJ 67-80; rtd 95. *27 Melville street, Glasgow G41 2JL* 0141-423 2002

RADCLIFFE, Canon Albert Edward. b 34. Lon Univ BD63. S Aid Birkenhead Ch Div Sch of the Pacific (USA) 61. **d** 62 **p** 63.

C Knotty Ash St Jo *Liv* 62-64; C Blundellsands St Nic 64-66; Israel 66-69; V Tonge w Alkrington *Man* 69-77; R Ashton St Mich 77-91; AD Ashton-under-Lyne 87-91; Can Res Man Cathl from 91. *46 Shrewsbury Road, Prestwich, Manchester M25 8EQ* 0161-798 0459 or 833 2220 Fax 839 6226

RADCLIFFE, David Jeffrey. b 52. Linc Th Coll 77. **d** 79 **p** 80. C Poulton-le-Fylde *Blackb* 79-84; V Ingol 84-88; R Lowther and Askham *Carl* from 88. *The Rectory, Lilac House, Lowther, Penrith, Cumbria CA10 2HH* Hackthorpe (01931) 712277

RADCLIFFE, James Warner. b 23. FICE66 FRTPI66 Liv Univ BEng43 MEng46. Cranmer Hall Dur 76. **d** 78 **p** 79. C Penrith *Carl* 78-79; C Penrith w Newton Reigny 79-81; P-in-c Barton w Pooley Bridge 81-83; P-in-c Martindale 83; V Barton, Pooley Bridge and Martindale 83-86; Perm to Offic from 86; rtd 88. *Sunny Vale, Church View, Heversham, Milnthorpe, Cumbria LA7 7EN* Milnthorpe (015395) 63572

RADCLIFFE, Mrs Rosemary. b 45. SW Minl Tr Course 87. **d** 90 **p** 94. NSM Devoran *Truro* 90-93; D-in-c N Newton w St Michaelchurch, Thurloxton etc *B & W* 93-94; P-in-c from 94; Chapl to the Deaf from 93. *The Rectory, Thurloxton, Taunton, Somerset TA2 8RH* West Monkton (01823) 412479

RADFORD, Canon Andrew John (Andy). b 44. Trin Coll Bris 72. **d** 74 **p** 75. C Shirehampton *Bris* 74-78; C Henleaze 78-80; Producer Relig Progr BBC Radio Bris 74-80; V Bath St Barn w Englishcombe *B & W* 80-85; Dioc Communications Officer *Glouc* 85-93; Producer Relig Progr Severn Sound Radio 85-93; Hon Can Glouc Cathl from 91; Development and Tr Officer Ch Ho Westmr from 93. *11 Foley Rise, Hartpury, Gloucester GL19 3DW* Gloucester (01452) 700055

RADFORD, Donald George. b 16. Lich Th Coll 55. **d** 56 **p** 57. C-in-c Stoke Hill CD *Guildf* 60-69; Perm to Offic *Glouc* from 79; rtd 81. *9 Cranham Road, Cheltenham, Glos GL52 6BQ* Cheltenham (01242) 524132

RADFORD, Leslie. b 24. Lon Univ DipTh75. Local NSM Course. **d** 85 **p** 86. NSM Scotter w E Ferry *Linc* from 85. *1 Carr Villas, Laughton, Gainsborough, Lincs DN21 3QF* Laughton (01427) 628265

RADFORD, Samuel. b 17. Kelham Th Coll 40. **d** 45 **p** 46. C Barton upon Humber *Linc* 69-71; Lic to Offic *Wakef* from 71; rtd 82. *18 Caistor Road, Barton-on-Humber, S Humberside DN18 6AH* Barton-on-Humber (01652) 635006

RADLEY, Peter. b 31. Bps' Coll Cheshunt 60. **d** 62 **p** 63. C Lillington *Cov* 62-63; C Nuneaton St Nic 63-67; P-in-c Skillington *Linc* 67-68; V Waltham *Ox* from 68. *The Vicarage, Waltham St Lawrence, Reading RG10 0JD* Twyford (01734) 343249

RADLEY, Roy Taylor. b 24. Edin Th Coll 47. **d** 50 **p** 51. Miss to Seamen 53-68; Sec (Midl Region) Leprosy Miss from 68; Perm to Offic *S'well* from 82; rtd 89. *200 Broadway, Derby DE22 1BP* Derby (01332) 343109

RADLEY, Stephen Gavin. b 62. K Coll Lon BSc83 AKC83. Cranmer Hall Dur BA87 St Jo Coll Dur 85. **d** 89 **p** 90. C Darlington St Matt and St Luke *Dur* 89-92; P-in-c Chilton from 92. *1 New South View, Chilton, Co Durham DL17 0PS* Bishop Auckland (01388) 720243

RAFFAY, Julian Paul. b 60. Stirling Univ BSc84. Cranmer Hall Dur BA89. **d** 90 **p** 91. C Adel *Ripon* 90-93; C Leeds Halton St Wilfrid 93-95; Asst Chapl S Derbys Mental Health NHS Trust from 95; Asst Chapl Kingsway Hosp Derby from 95; Derby City Gen, Derby R Infirmary from 95. *Kingsway Hospital, Kingsway, Derby, DE22 3LZ, or 101 Sunnyhill Avenue, Sunnyhill, Derby DE23 7JS* Derby (01332) 362221 or 763712

RAGAN, Mrs Jennifer Mary. b 39. Linc Th Coll 71. **dss** 80 **d** 87 **p** 94. Hackney *Lon* 80-84; Hornchurch St Andr *Chelmsf* 84-87; Par Dn 87-88; Par Dn Ingrave St Steph CD 88-90; Par Dn Gt Parndon 90-94; C from 94. *14 Deer Park, Harlow, Essex CM19 4LD* Harlow (01279) 431133

RAGBOURNE, Miss Pamela Mary. b 27. CertEd47. Dalton Ho Bris 53. **dss** 76 **d** 87 **p** 94. CPAS Staff 68-79; Tottenham St Jo *Lon* 79-81; Gt Cam Road St Jo and St Jas 82-84; Camberley St Paul *Guildf* 84-86; rtd 87; Perm to Offic *Glouc* from 93; NSM Winchcombe, Gretton, Sudeley Manor etc from 93. *14 Crispin Close, Winchcombe, Cheltenham, Glos GL54 5JY* Cheltenham (01242) 603469

RAHI, Hakim Banta Singh. b 36. Union Bibl Sem Yavatmal BD71. **d** 74 **p** 74. India 74-83; In URC 83-88; Perm to Offic *Birm* 88-93; Ecum Evang Asian Community 88-93. *3 Hobson Close, Norton Street, Birmingham B18 5RH* 0121-554 2144

RAHILLY, Philip James. b 54. Univ of Wales (Cardiff) BD86. Wycliffe Hall Ox 86. **d** 88 **p** 89. C Knightwick w Doddenham, Broadwas and Cotheridge *Worc* 88; C Martley and Wichenford, Knightwick etc 89-91; C Worc St Barn w Ch Ch 91-92; TV Kidderminster St Mary and All SS w Trimpley etc from 92. *The Vicarage, 50 Nursery Grove, Kidderminster, Worcs DY11 5BG* Kidderminster (01562) 748016

RAI, Mrs Mary Anne. b 61. Southn Univ BTh83. Trin Coll Bris DipTh86. **dss** 86 **d** 87. Bury St Edmunds St Mary *St E* 86-89;

Par Dn 87-89; Perm to Offic 90-93; Perm to Offic *Cov* from 94. *18 Bolton Close, Coventry CV3 5NT*   Coventry (01203) 416244

RAIKES, Canon Myles Kenneth. b 23. New Coll Ox BA47 MA51. Wells Th Coll 47. **d** 49 **p** 50. V Bushey Heath *St Alb* 63-70; R Digswell 70-77; Hon Can St Alb 76-77; P-in-c Meare *B & W* 77-81; P-in-c W Coker 82-83; Dioc Ecum Officer 84-88; C Ilminster w Whitelackington 84-85; C S Petherton w the Seavingtons 85-87; rtd 88; Perm to Offic *B & W* from 88. *7 West Street, South Petherton, Somerset TA13 5DQ*   South Petherton (01460) 41056

RAIKES, Peter. b 37. St Mich Coll Llan 78. **d** 80 **p** 81. C Roath St Marg *Llan* 80-82; V Resolven 82-86; V Resolven w Tonna 86-92; RD Neath from 89; V Skewen from 92. *Skewen Vicarage, Hill Road, Neath Abbey, W Glam SA10 7NP*   Skewen (01792) 814116

RAIKES, Robert Laybourne. b 32. Wells Th Coll 59. **d** 61 **p** 62. C Swan *Ox* 68-71; V Whitchurch Canonicorum and Wootton Fitzpaine *Sarum* 71-75; V Whitchurch Canonicorum w Wooton Fitzpaine etc 75-81; P-in-c Branksome St Aldhelm 81-82; V 82-91; V Pitminster w Corfe *B & W* 91-92; rtd 92; Chapl Madeira *Eur* from 93. *Rua do Quebra Costas 20, 9000 Funchal, Madeira, Portugal* Madeira (91) 220674 Fax 36781

RAILTON, John Robert Henry. b 45. FCIB79 Reading Univ BSc68. S Dios Minl Tr Scheme 82. **d** 85 **p** 86. NSM Wickham *Portsm* 85-89; C Bridgemary 89-90; V from 90. *St Matthew's Vicarage, 7 Duncton Way, Gosport, Hants PO13 0FD* Fareham (01329) 235288

RAINBOW, Preb Gerald Anton Hayward. b 15. St Edm Hall Ox BA38 MA41. Linc Th Coll 38. **d** 39 **p** 40. V Leominster *Heref* 57-80; RD Leominster 60-80; Preb Heref Cathl 67-95; P-in-c Eyton 69-80; rtd 80. *65 King's Acre Road, Hereford HR4 0QL* Hereford (01432) 66718

RAINBOW, Henry David. b 10. Ripon Hall Ox 64. **d** 65 **p** 66. Chapl HM Pris Cardiff 67-71; Chapl HM Pris Pentonville 71-74; Chapl HM Pris Cant 74-78; rtd 78; Perm to Offic *Cant* 79-89; Perm to Offic *Ex* from 89. *1 Upton Hill Road, Brixham, Devon TQ5 9QR*   Brixham (01803) 854611

RAINE, Patrick John Wallace. b 21. DFC. Sarum & Wells Th Coll 72. **d** 74 **p** 75. C Chandler's Ford *Win* 74-76; R Highclere and Ashmansworth w Crux Easton 76-84; R Copythorne and Minstead 84-87; rtd 87; P-in-c Breamore *Win* 91-95. *Little Cottage, 26 Cholderton, Salisbury SP4 0DN*   Downton (01725) 513098

RAINE, Stephen James. b 49. Lanchester Poly DipAD69 Sheff Poly BA80. N Ord Course 85. **d** 86 **p** 87. C Cottingham *York* 86-90; V Dunscroft Ch Ch *Sheff* 90-92; V Dunscroft St Edwin from 92. *The Vicarage, 162 Station Road, Dunscroft, Doncaster, S Yorkshire DN7 4JR* Doncaster (01302) 841328

RAINER, John Charles. b 54. Ex Univ BA76 DipTh78 CertEd78. St Jo Coll Nottm 86. **d** 88 **p** 89. C Fletchamstead *Cov* 88-94; V Leic H Apostles *Leic* from 94. *Holy Apostles' Vicarage, 281 Fosse Road South, Leicester LE3 1AE* Leicester (0116) 282 4336

RAINES, Mrs Gisela Rolanda. b 58. Groningen Univ Kandidaats90. Lon Coll BD83. dss 84 **d** 87 **p** 94. Charlton St Luke w H Trin *S'wark* 84-87; Par Dn 87; Chapl Imp Coll *Lon* 87-91; Hon C Birch w Fallowfield *Man* 94-95; P-in-c Withington from 95. *197 Old Hall Lane, Manchester M14 6HJ* 0161-224 6643

RAINES, William Guy (Bill). b 46. Lon Univ BSc69 MSc70 Ox Univ BA80. Ripon Coll Cuddesdon 78. **d** 81 **p** 82. C W Drayton *Lon* 81-84; C Charlton St Luke w H Trin *S'wark* 84-87; Chapl K Coll Lon 87-94; Chapl Imp Coll Lon 91-94; P-in-c Birch w Fallowfield *Man* from 94. *197 Old Hall Lane, Manchester M14 6HJ* 0161-224 1310

RAINEY, Graeme Norman. b 66. Van Mildert Coll Dur BA88. Ridley Hall Cam CTMin93. **d** 93 **p** 94. C Maltby *Sheff* from 93. *86 Braithwell Road, Maltby, Rotherham, S Yorkshire S66 8JT* Rotherham (01709) 817152

RAINFORD, Robert Graham. b 55. Lanc Univ CertEd76 BEd77. St Steph Ho Ox 81. **d** 83 **p** 84. C Burnley St Cath w St Alb and St Paul *Blackb* 83-86; C-in-c Hawes Side St Chris CD 86-89; V Hawes Side from 89. *The Vicarage, Hawes Side Lane, Blackpool FY4 5AH*   Blackpool (01253) 697937

RAINSBERRY, Edward John. b 24. TCD BA48 MA58. TCD Div Sch Div Test49. **d** 49 **p** 50. C Abbeystrewry Union *C, C & R* 49-52; Chapl RAF 52-58; V Long Compton *Cov* 58-84; R Whichford 58-84; V Long Compton, Whichford and Barton-on-the-Heath from 84. *The Vicarage, Long Compton, Shipston-on-Stour, Warks CV36 5JH*   Long Compton (0160884) 207

RAINSBURY, Mark James. b 56. NE Lon Poly BA79. Oak Hill Th Coll BA87. **d** 88 **p** 89. C Tonbridge St Steph *Roch* 88-95; C Hampreston *Sarum* from 95. *57 Glenmoor Road, Ferndown, Dorset BH22 8QE*   Ferndown (01202) 876552

RAINSFORD, Peter John. b 31. FCP72. Qu Coll Birm 75. **d** 77 **p** 78. Hon C Lich St Chad *Lich* 77-81; C 82; C Coseley Ch Ch 82-84; V Wednesbury St Bart 84-91; Chapl Sandwell Distr Gen Hosp 89-91; rtd 91; Perm to Offic *Lich* from 91. *157 Broadway, Walsall, W Midlands WS1 3HD*   Walsall (01922) 24526

RAISTRICK, Dr Brian. b 38. St Paul's Cheltenham TCert60 Ex Univ ADEd68 Newc Univ MEd76 UEA PhD86. Westcott Ho Cam 92. **d** 93 **p** 94. C Haverhill w Withersfield, the Wrattings etc *St E* from 93. *12 Wratting Road, Haverhill, Suffolk CB9 0DD* Haverhill (01440) 702223

RAITH, Robert. b 31. Edin Univ MA61. Coll of Resurr Mirfield 57. **d** 59 **p** 60. C Edin St Jas *Edin* 59-61; P-in-c 76-77; Asst Prov Youth Org 61-65; C Dalmahoy 61-65; C Edin St Mark 66-76; Dioc Supernumerary 77-78; P-in-c Edin St Luke 78-79; Perm to Offic from 79; Pilsdon Community 87-90. *62 Rodwell Road, Weymouth, Dorset DT4 8QU*   Weymouth (01305) 781386

RAITT, Derek. b 41. K Coll Lon BD63 AKC63. **d** 64 **p** 65. C Blackb St Jas *Blackb* 64-67; C Burnley St Pet 67-69; V Foulridge 69-74; V Euxton 74-91; V Penwortham St Mary from 91. *St Mary's Vicarage, Cop Lane, Penwortham, Preston PR1 0SR*   Preston (01772) 743143

RAJKOVIC, Dr Michael. b 52. Sheff Univ BMet74 MMet75 PhD79. St Jo Coll Nottm MA95. **d** 95. C Harrow Weald All SS *Lon* from 95. *c/o Mr & Mrs Barker, 12 Acacia Avenue, Stanmore, Middx HA7 3JR* 0181-954 2878

RAKE, David John. b 47. Nottm Univ BA68 PhD73. Wycliffe Hall Ox DipTh73. **d** 74 **p** 75. C Radcliffe-on-Trent *S'well* 74-77; P-in-c Upwell St Pet *Ely* 77-79; P-in-c Outwell 77-79; Chapl Warw Univ *Cov* 79-86; V Kenilworth St Nic from 86. *The Vicarage, 7 Elmbank Road, Kenilworth, Warks CV8 1AL* Kenilworth (01926) 54367

RALPH, Brian Charles. b 66. St Steph Ho Ox 89. **d** 92 **p** 93. C Yeovil St Mich *B & W* 92-95. *c/o 54 St Helen's Court, Upminster Road South, Rainham, Essex RM13 9YU*

RALPH, Charles. b 15. TCD BA47 MA58. **d** 47 **p** 48. R Fordley w Middleton *St E* 64-81; R Theberton 64-81; rtd 82; Perm to Offic *St E* from 82; TV Raveningham *Nor* 82; P-in-c Rossinver *K, E & A* 85-86. *5 Gayfer Avenue, Kesgrave, Ipswich IP5 7PZ* Ipswich (01473) 622154

RALPH, Nicholas Robert (Nick). b 63. Lanc Univ BSc85. Westcott Ho Cam BA91 CTM92. **d** 92 **p** 93. C Fareham H Trin *Portsm* from 92. *61 Oak Road, Fareham, Hants PO15 5HH* Fareham (01329) 280380

RALPH, Dr Richard Gale. b 51. FRSA90 Pemb Coll Ox BA73 MA78 DPhil78. S Dios Minl Tr Scheme 84. **d** 87 **p** 88. NSM St Leonards Ch Ch and St Mary *Chich* from 87; NSM St Pancras H Cross w St Jude and St Pet *Lon* 87-94. *St Alban, The Mount, St Leonards-on-Sea, E Sussex TN38 0HR*   St Leonards-on-Sea (01424) 422722

RALPH-BOWMAN, Murray Peter. b 13. Qu Coll Cam BA35 MA45. Wells Th Coll 36. **d** 37 **p** 38. V Queen Camel *B & W* 57-78; R W Camel 57-78; rtd 78; P-in-c Bryngwyn and Newchurch and Llanbedr etc *S & B* 78-92. *30 Milton Road, Salisbury SP2 8AX*   Salisbury (01722) 335270

RALPHS, John Eric. b 26. MBAP66 St Cath Coll Ox BA52 MA56. Wycliffe Hall Ox 53. **d** 53 **p** 54. Chapl Dragon Sch Ox 55-68; Chapl St Hugh's Coll Ox 62-67; Priest-Psychotherapist from 68; Lic to Offic *Ox* from 83; rtd 91. *209 Woodstock Road, Oxford OX2 7AB*   Oxford (01865) 515550

RALPHS, Robert Brian. b 31. Qu Coll Birm 75. **d** 78 **p** 79. Hon C Wednesbury St Jo *Lich* 78-80; Hon C Wednesbury St Paul Wood Green 80-81; Perm to Offic from 81. *204 Bromford Lane, West Bromwich, W Midlands B70 7HX* 0121-553 0119

RALPHS, Sharon Ann. *See* TAPSELL, Mrs Sharon Ann

RAMELL, Arthur Lewis. b 05. Cuddesdon Coll 50. **d** 51 **p** 52. V Colerne *Bris* 56-76; P-in-c N Wraxall 68-76; rtd 76. *c/o Mrs A Johns, 17 St Leonards Court, London SW14 7NG* 0181-878 6494

RAMELL, John Edwin. b 25. Bris Univ BA55. Tyndale Hall Bris. **d** 56 **p** 57. V Wombridge *Lich* 60-70; TR Chell 70-82; V Congleton St Pet *Ches* 82-90; rtd 90. *10 Newland Close, Eynsham, Witney, Oxon OX8 1LE* Oxford (01865) 880180

RAMM, Canon Norwyn MacDonald. b 24. Linc Coll Ox BA60 MA64. St Pet Coll Jamaica 49. **d** 51 **p** 52. V Ox St Mich *Ox* 61-71; P-in-c Ox All SS w St Martin 61-71; V Ox St Mich w St Martin and All SS 71-88; Chapl HM Pris Ox 75-88; Hon Can Ch Ch *Ox* 85-88; Chapl to The Queen from 85; rtd 88. *Fairlawn, Church Lane, Harwell, Didcot, Oxon OX11 0EZ* Abingdon (01235) 835454

RAMON, Brother. *See* LLOYD, Raymond David

RAMPTON, Paul Michael. b 47. St Jo Coll Dur BA69 DipTh70 MA73 K Coll Lon PhD85. Wycliffe Hall Ox 72. **d** 73 **p** 74. C Folkestone H Trin w Ch Ch *Cant* 73-77; P-in-c Kingsdown 77-79; P-in-c Ringwould w Oxney 77-79; R Ringwould w Kingsdown 79-83; V Maidstone St Paul 83-88; V Maidstone St Martin from 88. *St Martin's Vicarage, Northumberland Road, Maidstone, Kent ME15 7LP* Maidstone (01622) 676282

RAMPTON, Mrs Valerie Edith. b 41. Nottm Univ BSc63 MSc66 BA79. Gilmore Course 78. **dss** 82 **d** 87 **p** 94. Sneinton St Chris w St Phil *S'well* 80-87; Par Dn 87-88; Par Dn Stapleford 88-93; Dioc Adv on Women in Min 90-93; D-in-c Kneesall w Laxton and Wellow 93-94; V from 94. *The Vicarage, 19 Baulk Lane, Kneesall, Newark, Notts NG22 0AA* Mansfield (01623) 835820

RAMSARAN (or COOPER), Dr Susan Mira. b 49. K Coll Lon BA70 Univ Coll Lon MA72 PhD78. Ripon Coll Cuddesdon BA92. **d** 93 **p** 94. C Selling w Throwley, Sheldwich w Badlesmere etc *Cant* from 93. *1 Hunter's Way, Sheldwich Lees, Faversham, Kent ME13 0NB* Faversham (01795) 534094

RAMSAY, Canon Alan Burnett. b 34. AKC62. **d** 63 **p** 64. C Clapham H Trin *S'wark* 63-67; C Warlingham w Chelsham and Farleigh 67-71; P-in-c Stockwell St Mich 71-78; V Lingfield 78-85; P-in-c Crowhurst 83-85; V Lingfield and Crowhurst 85-92; RD Godstone 88-92; V Mitcham St Mark from 92; Hon Can S'wark Cathl from 93. *St Mark's Vicarage, Locks Lane, Mitcham, Surrey CR4 2JX* 0181-648 2397

RAMSAY, Carl Anthoney St Aubyn. b 55. W Midl Minl Tr Course 88. **d** 90 **p** 91. C Wednesfield Heath *Lich* 90-94; V Willenhall St Anne from 94. *St Anne's Vicarage, Ann Street, Willenhall, W Midlands WV13 1EN* Willenhall (01902) 66516

RAMSAY, Eric Nicholson. b 29. **d** 94. C Forfar *St And* from 94; C Kirriemuir from 94. *4 Beechwood Place, Kirriemuir, Angus DD8 5DZ* Kirriemuir (01575) 572029

RAMSAY, James Anthony. b 52. MA. **d** 86 **p** 87. C Olney w Emberton *Ox* 86-89; V Blackbird Leys from 89. *Church House, 1 Cuddesdon Way, Oxford OX4 5JH* Oxford (01865) 778728

RAMSAY, John Leslie. b 02. LRAM. Linc Th Coll 54. **d** 56 **p** 57. V Keelby w Riby and Aylesby *Linc* 62-71; V Hogsthorpe 71-76; V Mumby 71-76; rtd 76; Perm to Offic *Linc* 76-88. *61 Clive Avenue, Lincoln LN6 7UR* Lincoln (01522) 536081

RAMSAY, Kenneth William. b 18. ALCD48. **d** 52 **p** 53. Asst Chapl Lee Abbey 57-60; Perm to Offic *Portsm* 69-80; Perm to Offic *Sarum* 77-87; rtd 87; Hon C Burstow *S'wark* from 87. *14 Woodside Crescent, Smallfield, Horley, Surrey RH6 9ND* Smallfield (01342) 843561

RAMSAY, Max Roy MacGregor. b 34. Ball Coll Ox MA58. Qu Coll Birm 82. **d** 84 **p** 85. C Hale *Ches* 84-86; C Nantwich 87; V Haslington w Crewe Green 87-91; P-in-c Dunham Massey St Marg 92-93; P-in-c Dunham Massey St Mark 92-93; P-in-c Dunham Massey St Marg and St Mark 93-95. *St Margaret's Vicarage, Dunham Road, Altrincham, Cheshire WA14 4AQ* 0161-928 1609

RAMSBOTTOM, Mrs Julie Frances. b 54. Trevelyan Coll Dur BA76. S'wark Ord Course 88. **d** 91 **p** 94. Par Dn Bray and Braywood *Ox* 91-94; C from 94. *63 Moor End, Holyport, Maidenhead, Berks SL6 2YJ* Maidenhead (01628) 778478

RAMSBURY, Area Bishop of. *See* VAUGHAN, Rt Rev Peter St George

RAMSDEN, Canon Arthur Stuart. b 34. Kelham Th Coll 56. **d** 61 **p** 62. C Featherstone *Wakef* 61-63; C Barnsley St Pet 63-67; V Charlestown 67-70; V Middlestown 70-77; V Purston cum S Featherstone from 77; Hon Can Wakef Cathl from 95. *The Vicarage, Victoria Street, Featherstone, Pontefract, W Yorkshire WF7 5EZ* Pontefract (01977) 792288

RAMSDEN, Preb Francis Samuel Lloyd. b 12. Lon Coll of Div 31. **d** 35 **p** 37. V Trentham *Lich* 58-77; C Solihull *Birm* 77-79; TV 79-80; rtd 80; Perm to Offic *Birm* from 80. *40 Orchard Croft, Barnt Green, Birmingham B45 8NJ* 0121-447 7125

RAMSDEN, Peter Stockton. b 51. Univ Coll Lon BSc74 Leeds Univ DipTh76 MA92. Coll of Resurr Mirfield 74. **d** 77 **p** 78. C Houghton le Spring *Dur* 77-80; C S Shields All SS 80-83; Papua New Guinea 83-90 and from 93; P-in-c Micklefield *York* 90-93. *PO Box 576, Goroka, EHP, Papua New Guinea* Papua New Guinea (675) 721695

RAMSDEN, Raymond Leslie. b 49. Open Univ BA86. **d** 78 **p** 79. C Greenhill St Jo *Lon* 78-85; C Staines St Mary and St Pet 85-90; V Hounslow St Steph from 90. *St Stephen's Vicarage, Parkside Road, Hounslow TW3 2BP* 0181-570 3056

RAMSEY-HARDY, Stuart John Andrew. b 46. St Jo Coll Dur BA69. Wycliffe Hall Ox 69. **d** 74 **p** 75. C Stoke Newington St Mary *Lon* 74-77; C Hersham *Guildf* 78-79; Hon C Thames Ditton 79-83. *23 New Row, London WC2N 4LA* 0171-836 2217

RANDALL, Colin Antony. b 57. SS Paul & Mary Coll Cheltenham BEd78 Bris Univ DipHE82 Lon Univ BD84. Trin Coll Bris 80. **d** 84 **p** 85. C Denton Holme *Carl* 84-87; C Brampton RD 87-90; R Hanborough and Freeland *Ox* from 90. *The Rectory, Swan Lane, Long Hanborough, Witney, Oxon OX8 8BT* Freeland (01993) 881270

RANDALL, Colin Michael Sebastian. b 50. Aston Univ BSc72. Qu Coll Birm 72. **d** 75 **p** 76. C Tonge w Alkrington *Man* 75-78; C Elton All SS 78-82; P-in-c Bridgwater H Trin *B & W* 82-86; V 86-90; V Bishops Hull from 90. *The Vicarage, Bishops Hull, Taunton, Somerset TA1 5EB* Taunton (01823) 333032

RANDALL, David William. b 47. Sarum Th Coll 68. **d** 71 **p** 72. C Poplar *Lon* 71-75; C St Botolph Aldgate w H Trin Minories 75-77; TV Notting Hill 77-82; V Notting Hill St Clem and St Mark 82-85; V Kensington St Jas Norlands 83-85; V Notting Dale St Clem w St Mark and St Jas 85-88; Dir CARA 88-94; Hon C Walham Green St Jo w St Jas *Lon* 88-89; NSM Chiswick St Nic w St Mary from 89; rtd 94. *64A Grove Park Road, London W4 3SB* 0181-742 1017 Fax as telephone

RANDALL, Canon Edmund Lawrence. b 20. CCC Cam BA40 MA47. Wells Th Coll 47. **d** 49 **p** 50. C Bournemouth St Luke *Win* 49-52; Fell and Lect Selw Coll Cam 52-57; Chapl 53-57; Prin Ely Th Coll 57-59; Can Res Ely Cathl *Ely* 57-59; Australia from 60. *44 Mackay Street, Wangaratta, Victoria, Australia 3677* Wangaratta (57) 219007

RANDALL, Gareth John. b 49. Southn Univ BA72 PGCE73 ACP80. Oak Hill NSM Course 90. **d** 93 **p** 94. Dir of Studies Dame Alice Owen's Sch Potters Bar 84-95; Dir of Personnel from 95; NSM S Mymms K Chas *St Alb* from 93. *196 Barnet Road, Potters Bar, Herts EN6 2SE* Potters Bar (01707) 651958 or 643441

RANDALL, Ian Neville. b 39. Or Coll Ox BA62 MA65. St Steph Ho Ox 62. **d** 65 **p** 66. C Perivale *Lon* 65-68; C Fulham St Jo Walham Green 68-73; C Cowley St Jas *Ox* 73-79; TV 79-82; V Didcot St Pet 82-93; P-in-c Clewer St Andr from 93. *Clewer Rectory, 16 Parsonage Lane, Windsor, Berks SL4 5EN* Windsor (01753) 865185

RANDALL, James Anthony. b 36. ACIB69 Kent Univ DipTh80. Ridley Hall Cam 68. **d** 70 **p** 71. C Rusthall *Roch* 70-74; V Shorne 74-79; V Bexleyheath Ch Ch 79-89; R Stone from 89. *The Rectory, Church Road, Stone, Greenhithe, Kent DA9 9BE* Greenhithe (01322) 842076

RANDALL, John Randall. b 28. Lon Univ BD64 LTh85. ALCD60. **d** 60 **p** 61. V Patchway *Bris* 65-73; P-in-c Olveston 73-80; Warden Roch Dioc Conf and Retreat Ho Chislehurst 80-84; TR Trunch *Nor* 84-93; rtd 93; Perm to Offic *Nor* from 93. *Ashton House, 27 Abbot Road, Horning, Norwich NR12 8PN* Horning (01692) 631416

RANDALL, Canon John Terence. b 29. St Cath Coll Cam BA52 MA59. Ely Th Coll 52. **d** 54 **p** 55. Area Sec (Dios Birm and Cov) USPG 65-76; P-in-c Avon Dassett w Farnborough *Cov* 76-78; P-in-c Fenny Compton 76-78; R Avon Dassett w Farnborough and Fenny Compton 78-84; V New Bilton 84-94; RD Rugby 89-94; Hon Can Cov Cathl 93-94; rtd 94. *52 Cymbeline Way, Rugby, Warks CV22 6LA* Rugby (01788) 816659

RANDALL, Kelvin John. b 49. JP. K Coll Lon BD71 AKC71 PGCE72. St Jo Coll Nottm DPS73. **d** 74 **p** 75. C Peckham St Mary Magd *S'wark* 74-78; C Portsdown *Portsm* 78-81; C-in-c Crookhorn Ch Cen CD 81-82; R Bedhampton 82-90; RD Havant 87-89; P-in-c Bournemouth St Jo w St Mich *Win* 90-94; V from 94; Chapl Talbot Heath Sch Bournemouth from 90. *The Vicarage, 13 Durley Chine Road South, Bournemouth BH2 5JT* Bournemouth (01202) 761962

RANDALL, Mrs Lynda Lorraine. b 44. Sarum & Wells Th Coll 89. **d** 91 **p** 94. Par Dn Chesterton St Andr *Ely* 91-94; C 94-95; C Linton from 95. *Castle and Shudy Camps Vicarage, Park Lane, Castle Camps, Cambridge CB1 6SU* Saffron Walden (01799) 584803

RANDALL, Miss Marian Sally. b 49. Trin Coll Bris 75. **dss** 80 **d** 87 **p** 94. Peckham St Mary Magd *S'wark* 80-83; Sutton Ch Ch 83-87; Par Dn 87-94; C from 94. *14A Christchurch Park, Sutton, Surrey SM2 5TN* 0181-661 7130

RANDALL, Martin Trevor. b 51. St Jo Coll Dur BA74. Trin Coll Bris 74. **d** 77 **p** 78. C Ashton on Mersey St Mary *Ches* 77-80; C Everton St Sav w St Cuth *Liv* 80-82; V W Derby Gd Shep 82-91; P-in-c Toxteth Park Ch Ch 91-94; P-in-c Toxteth Park St Bede 91-94; V Toxteth Park Ch Ch w St Bede from 95. *Christ Church Vicarage, 5 Linnet Lane, Liverpool L17 3BE* 0151-727 2827

RANDALL, Philip Joseph. b 10. K Coll Lon 57. **d** 58 **p** 59. V Eye *Pet* 61-77; rtd 77; Perm to Offic *Pet* from 85. *104 Deerleap, Bretton, Peterborough PE3 9YD* Peterborough (01733) 266782

RANDALL, Samuel Paul. b 59. Leeds Univ MA90. Ridley Hall Cam 84. **d** 87 **p** 88. C Kingston upon Hull St Nic *York* 87-89; CF 89-93; TV Bramley *Ripon* from 93. *27 Hough End Lane, Leeds LS13 4EY* Leeds (0113) 257 6202

RANDELL, David Peter. b 48. Trin Coll Bris BA88. **d** 92 **p** 93. C Wells St Cuth w Wookey Hole *B & W* 92-95; TV Wellington and Distr from 95. *22 Dyers Close, West Buckland, Wellington, Somerset TA21 9JU* Wellington (01823) 664925

RANDELL, John Harrison. b 35. Dur Univ BD62. Chich Th Coll 77. **d** 78 **p** 78. C Ribbleton *Blackb* 78-82; V Barton from 82. *St Lawrence's Vicarage, 786 Garstang Road, Barton, Preston PR3 5AA* Broughton (01772) 862020

RANDELL, Phillip John. b 45. Lon Univ DipTh68 BD73 CertEd. Linc Th Coll 67. **d** 68 **p** 69. C Henbury *Bris* 68-71; C Summertown *Ox* 71-73; C Liskeard w St Keyne *Truro* 73-75; Chapl Coll of St Mark and St Jo Plymouth *Ex* 75-79; Tanzania 80-82; R Alvescot w Black Bourton, Shilton, Holwell etc *Ox* 82-87; R St Gennys, Jacobstow w Warbstow and Treneglos *Truro* from 87. *The Rectory, Jacobstow, Bude, Cornwall EX23 0BR* St Gennys (01840) 230206

RANDLE, Canon Howard Stanley. b 12. St Jo Coll Dur LTh34 BA35. St Aid Birkenhead 30. **d** 35 **p** 36. R Mobberley *Ches* 46-80; rtd 80; Perm to Offic *Ches* from 80. *7 Carlisle Close, Mobberley, Knutsford, Cheshire WA16 7HD* Mobberley (01565) 873483

RANDOLPH, Michael Richard Spencer. b 25. FRSA62. Cant Sch of Min 88. **d** 90 **p** 91. C Biddenden and Smarden *Cant* 90-95; rtd 95. *Little Smarden House, The Street, Smarden, Ashford, Kent TN27 8NB* Smarden (01233) 770216

RANGER, Keith Brian. b 34. Down Coll Cam BA58 MA63. Glas NSM Course 58. **d** 81 **p** 82. OMF from 81; Ethnic Min Co-ord from 90; Hong Kong 81-89; Perm to Offic *Ches* from 89; Perm to Offic *Man* from 93. *28 Charter Road, Altrincham, Cheshire WA15 9RL* 0161-941 5268

RANKEN, Michael David. b 28. Man Univ BScTech49. S'wark Ord Course 76. **d** 79 **p** 80. Hon C Epsom St Martin *Guildf* from 79. *9 Alexandra Road, Epsom, Surrey KT17 4BH* Epsom (01372) 724823

RANKIN, John Cooper. b 24. Glas Univ MA44 Lon Univ BD53. Edin Th Coll 48. **d** 50 **p** 51. Prin Lect Bp Otter Coll Chich 69-84; rtd 84. *28 Worcester Road, Chichester, W Sussex PO19 4DW* Chichester (01243) 789467

RANKIN, William John Alexander. b 45. Van Mildert Coll Dur BA68 Fitzw Coll Cam BA73 MA77. Westcott Ho Cam 71. **d** 74 **p** 75. C St Jo Wood *Lon* 74-78; Chapl Clifton Coll Bris 78-86; P-in-c The Claydons *Ox* 86-91; R 91-93; R Clare w Poslingford, Cavendish etc *St E* from 93. *Durham House Vicarage, Cavendish Road, Clare, Sudbury, Suffolk CO10 8PJ* Clare (01787) 278501

RANKINE, Christopher Barry. b 66. Portsm Poly BA88. Linc Th Coll BTh93. **d** 93 **p** 95. C Farlington *Portsm* from 93. *23 Court Close, Cosham, Portsmouth PO6 2LU* Cosham (01705) 385054

RANN, Preb Harry Harvey. b 18. Sarum Th Coll 47. **d** 50 **p** 51. Dean's Chapl and PV Ex Cathl *Ex* 62-77; Sacr 65-77; Succ 73-77; V Colyton 77-84; R Colyton and Southleigh 84-86; RD Honiton 84-86; Preb Ex Cathl 84-87; TR Colyton, Southleigh, Offwell, Widworthy etc 86-87; rtd 87. *4 Scattor View, Bridford, Exeter EX6 7JF* Christow (01647) 52741

RANSOM, Nigel Lester. b 60. Leeds Univ BA81. Wycliffe Hall Ox 83 SE Asia Sch of Th MTh83. **d** 85 **p** 86. C Gidea Park *Chelmsf* 85-88; C Widford 88-91; V Eastwood from 91. *The Vicarage, Eastwoodbury Lane, Southend-on-Sea SS2 6UH* Southend-on-Sea (01702) 525272

RANSOME, Arthur. b 21. St Jo Coll Nottm 71. **d** 72 **p** 72. Israel 72-76; C Virginia Water *Guildf* 76-79; P-in-c Peper Harow 79-82; P-in-c Shackleford 79-82; P-in-c Seale 82-89; rtd 89. *St Gwendron, Rock Road, Rock, Wadebridge, Cornwall PL27 6NP* Wadebridge (01208) 862825

RANSON, Arthur Frankland. b 50. St Jo Coll Dur BA73. Wycliffe Hall Ox 73. **d** 75 **p** 76. C Bare *Blackb* 75-78; C Scotforth 78-81; V Leyland St Ambrose from 81. *St Ambrose Vicarage, 61 Moss Lane, Leyland, Preston PR5 2SH* Leyland (01772) 462204

RANSON, George Sidney. b 28. Open Univ BA78. NE Ord Course 85. **d** 86 **p** 87. NSM Acomb H Redeemer *York* 86-88; C Warton St Oswald w Yealand Conyers *Blackb* 88-90; V Pilling 90-95; rtd 95. *18 Cotswold Road, Lytham St Annes, Lancs FY8 4NN*

RANSON, Terence William James (Terry). b 42. AFAIM91 AKC64 MTh87 STM88. St Boniface Warminster 64. **d** 65 **p** 66. C Walton St Mary *Liv* 65-69; C Ipswich St Mary le Tower *St E* 69-71; Chapl Mersey Miss to Seamen 71-74; V N Keyham *Ex* 74-79; Australia 79-81; Chapl San and State Sec Fremantle Miss to Seamen 79-91; V N Mymms *St Alb* from 91. *The Vicarage, North Mymms Park, Hatfield, Herts AL9 7TN* Bowmansgreen (01727) 822062

RANYARD, Michael Taylor. b 43. Nottm Univ BTh74. Linc Th Coll 71. **d** 74 **p** 75. C Sutton in Ashfield St Mary *S'well* 74-76; Hon C Lewisham St Mary *S'wark* 76-77; C Rushmere *St E* 77-79; R Hopton, Market Weston, Barningham etc 79-83; Chr Educn and Resources Adv *Dur* 83-93; Prin Adv to Dioc Bd of Educn *Blackb* from 93. *17 Beardwood Park, Blackburn BB2 7BW* Blackburn (01254) 676281

RAPHAEL, Brother. *See* PARKER, Ramon Lewis

RAPHAEL, Ven Timothy John. b 29. Leeds Univ BA53. Coll of Resurr Mirfield. **d** 55 **p** 56. C Westmr St Steph w St Jo *Lon* 55-60; V Welling *S'wark* 60-63; New Zealand 63-72; Dean

Dunedin 65-72; V St Jo Wood *Lon* 72-83; AD Westmr St Marylebone 82-83; Adn Middx from 83. *12 St Ann's Villas, London W11 4RS* 0171-603 0856 Fax 371 1765

RAPHOE, Archdeacon of. *See* HARTE, Ven Matthew Scott

RAPHOE, Dean of. *See* WHITE, Very Rev Stephen Ross

RAPKIN, Kevern. b 39. Univ of Wales (Lamp) BA62. Lich Th Coll 63. **d** 65 **p** 66. C Hanley w Hope *Lich* 65-68; C Woodchurch *Ches* 68-70; C Abbots Langley *St Alb* 70-73; Australia from 73. *The Rectory, 195 Lesmurdie Road, Lesmurdie, W Australia 6076* Perth (9) 291-9300

RAPLEY, Frederick Arthur. b 27. Roch Th Coll 67. **d** 69 **p** 70. C Tenterden St Mildred w Smallhythe *Cant* 69-75; P-in-c Sittingbourne H Trin w Bobbing 75-85; V 85-89; rtd 89. *99 Bedford Road, Letchworth, Herts SG6 4DU* Letchworth (01462) 670626

RAPLEY, Mrs Joy Naomi. b 41. CertEd63 Open Univ BA73. Sarum & Wells Th Coll 87. **d** 89 **p** 94. Par Dn Welwyn Garden City *St Alb* 89-92; Chapl Fairfield Hosp Hitchin from 92; Chapl S Beds Community Health Care Trust from 92; C Wilbury *St Alb* from 94. *99 Bedford Road, Letchworth, Herts SG6 4DU or, Fairfield Hospital, Stotfold, Hitchin, Herts SG6 4AA* Letchworth (01462) 670626 or 730123

RAPSEY, Peter Nigel. b 46. K Coll Lon BD68 AKC68. St Boniface Warminster. **d** 69 **p** 70. C Walton-on-Thames *Guildf* 69-73; C Fleet 73-77; P-in-c The Collingbournes and Everleigh *Sarum* 77-79; TV Wexcombe 79-84; R Wokingham St Paul *Ox* 84-93; Chapl Warminster Sch Wilts from 93. *24 Vicarage Street, Warminster, Wilts BA12 8JE* Warminster (01985) 847652 or 213038 Fax 214129

RASHBROOK, Alan Victor. b 42. S'wark Ord Course. **d** 75 **p** 76. Hon C Woking St Mary *Guildf* 75-83. *Hope Cottage, Robin Hood Lane, Sutton Green, Guildford, Surrey GU4 7QG* Woking (01483) 762760

RASON, Frederick George. b 26. Qu Coll Birm 68. **d** 69 **p** 70. C Weymouth H Trin *Sarum* 69-72; P-in-c Yatesbury 72-73; P-in-c Cherhill 72-73; R Oldbury 73-76; R W Parley 76-91; rtd 91. *4 Knoll Gardens, St Ives, Ringwood, Hants BH24 2LW* Ringwood (01425) 475761

RASTALL, Preb Thomas Eric. b 19. St Aid Birkenhead 62. **d** 63 **p** 64. V Brown Edge *Lich* 67-74; P-in-c Croxden 74-78; V Denstone 74-81; P-in-c Ellastone 78-81; V Denstone w Ellastone and Stanton 81-91; RD Uttoxeter 87-91; Preb Lich Cathl 89-91; rtd 91. *21 Hammerton Way, Wellesbourne, Warwick CV35 9NS* Stratford-upon-Avon (01789) 842422

RATCHFORD, William Joseph. b 52. St Meinrad Coll (USA) BA74. St Meinrad Sch of Th (USA) MDiv79. **d** 78 **p** 79. In RC Ch 78-86; USA 78-90; NSM St Martin-in-the-Fields *Lon* from 90. *6 St Martin's Place, London WC2N 4JH* 0171-930 0089

RATCLIFF, David William. b 37. K Coll Lon DipAdEd82. Edin Th Coll 59. **d** 62 **p** 63. C Croydon St Aug *Cant* 62-65; C Selsdon St Jo w St Francis 65-69; V Milton Regis St Mary 69-75; Hon Min Can Cant Cathl 75-91; Asst Dir of Educn 75-91; Dioc Adv in Adult Educn and Lay Tr 75-91; Hon Pres Protestant Assn for Adult Educn in Eur 82-88; Chapl Frankfurt-am-Main *Eur* from 91. *Sebastian-Rinz Strasse22, D-60323 Frankfurt, Germany* Frankfurt (69) 550184 or 550186 Fax 550184

RATCLIFF, Richard Charles. b 09. Univ Coll Ox BA32. St Steph Ho Ox 33. **d** 33 **p** 34. V Boxgrove *Chich* 65-75; R Tangmere 66-75; Chapl RAF 66-75; rtd 75; P-in-c Appledram *Chich* 77-84; Perm to Offic from 84. *11 St Martin's Square, Chichester, W Sussex PO19 1LQ* Chichester (01243) 784870

RATCLIFFE, Michael David. b 43. Lon Univ BSc65 Southn Univ PGCE67 Lon Univ BA75 Dur Univ DipTh77 Lanc Univ MA84. Cranmer Hall Dur 75. **d** 77 **p** 78. C Blackpool St Thos *Blackb* 77-81; V Oswaldtwistle St Paul from 81. *St Paul's Vicarage, 71 Union Road, Oswaldtwistle, Accrington, Lancs BB5 3DD* Accrington (01254) 231038

RATCLIFFE, Peter William Lewis. b 30. Birm Univ BSc55 Lon Univ BD58. Tyndale Hall Bris 55. **d** 58 **p** 59. C Cam St Andr Less *Ely* 58-61; R Wistow 61-74; R Bury 61-74; V Rainham *Chelmsf* 74-85; R Wennington 75-85; V Heacham *Nor* 85-87; P-in-c Sedgeford w Southmere 85-87; V Heacham and Sedgeford 87-95; V Heacham from 95. *The Vicarage, Heacham, King's Lynn, Norfolk PE31 7HJ* Heacham (01485) 570268

RATHBAND, Kenneth William. b 60. Edin Univ BD86. Edin Th Coll 82. **d** 86 **p** 87. NSM Dundee St Paul *Bre* 86-88; TV Dundee St Martin 88-89; NSM Edin SS Phil and Jas *Edin* 90-91; R Alyth *St And* from 91; R Blairgowrie from 91; R Coupar Angus from 91. *Garden Cottage, Cloquhat, Bridge of Cally, Blairgowrie, Perthshire PH10 7JP* Blairgowrie (01250) 88633

RATHBONE, Paul. b 36. BNC Ox BA58 MA62. Wycliffe Hall Ox 58. **d** 60 **p** 61. C Carl St Jo *Carl* 60-63; C Heworth w Peasholme St Cuth *York* 63-68; V Thorganby w Skipwith and

N Duffield 68-83; V Acaster Malbis from 83; V Bishopthorpe from 83. *The Vicarage, 48 Church Lane, Bishopthorpe, York YO2 1QG*   York (01904) 706476

RATHBONE, Royston George (Roy). b 27. Leeds Univ CertEd78. St D Coll Lamp 58. **d** 60 **p** 61. CF (TAVR) 64-73; Chapl HM Pris Coldingley 69-73; Chapl HM Pris Linc 73-77; Chapl HM Pris Man 77-79; Chapl HM Borstal Everthorpe 79-85; Chapl HM Pris Lindholme 85-89; Chapl HM Pris Everthorpe 89-92; rtd 92. *6 Jobson's Road, South Cave, Brough, N Humberside HU15 2HN*   Howden (01430) 423254

RATINGS, John William. b 37. St Pet Coll Ox BA62 MA71. Cuddesdon Coll 62. **d** 64 **p** 65. C Langley All SS and Martyrs *Man* 64-68; C Easthampstead *Ox* 68-71; V Wargrave from 71; RD Sonning from 88. *The Vicarage, Wargrave, Reading RG10 8EU*   Wargrave (01734) 402202   Fax 401470

RATLEDGE, Canon Ernest David. b 11. Man Univ BA32 MA33 BD52. Bps' Coll Cheshunt 33. **d** 34 **p** 35. R Prestwich St Mary *Man* 67-78; RD Radcliffe and Prestwich 67-78; rtd 78. *22 Abbot's Walk, Cerne Abbas, Dorchester, Dorset DT2 7JN*   Cerne Abbas (01300) 341633

RATTENBERRY, Christopher James (Chris). b 59. Solicitor York Univ BA80. St Jo Coll Nottm DTS93. **d** 93 **p** 94. C Porchester *S'well* from 93. *127A Digby Avenue, Nottingham NG3 6DT*   Nottingham (0115) 987 7553

RATTERAY, Ven Alexander Ewen. b 42. Codrington Coll Barbados 61. **d** 65 **p** 66. C S Kirkby *Wakef* 66-68; C Sowerby St Geo 68-71; V Airedale w Fryston 71-80; Bermuda from 80; Adn Bermuda from 94. *St John's Rectory, PO Box HM 544, Hamilton HM CX, Bermuda*   Bermuda (441) 292-3261   Fax 292-5308

RATTIGAN, Paul Damian. b 61. Reading Univ BSc87 Sussex Univ PGCE88. Qu Coll Birm DipTh95. **d** 95. C Parr *Liv* from 95. *83 Malvern Road, St Helens, Merseyside WA9 2EZ*   St Helens (01744) 759803

RAVALDE, Geoffrey Paul. b 54. Barrister 78 St Cuth Soc Dur BA76 SS Coll Cam BA86 MA90 Lon Univ MTh91. Westcott Ho Cam 84. **d** 87 **p** 88. C Spalding *Linc* 87-91; P-in-c Wigton *Carl* 91-92; V from 92; RD Carl from 95. *The Vicarage, Longthwaite Road, Wigton, Cumbria CA7 9JR*   Wigton (016973) 42337

RAVEN, Barry. b 48. Sarum & Wells Th Coll 69. **d** 72 **p** 73. C Henbury *Bris* 72-76; P-in-c S Marston w Stanton Fitzwarren 76-78; TV Stratton St Margaret w S Marston etc 78-80; P-in-c Coalpit Heath 80-84; V 84-91; R Ashley, Crudwell, Hankerton, Long Newnton etc from 91. *The Rectory, 1 Days Court, Crudwell, Malmesbury, Wilts SN16 9HG*   Malmesbury (01666) 577118

RAVEN, Charles Frank. b 58. ACIB84 Magd Coll Ox BA80 MA86 St Jo Coll Dur BA87. Cranmer Hall Dur 85. **d** 88 **p** 89. C Heckmondwike *Wakef* 88-92; TV Kidderminster St Jo and H Innocents *Worc* from 92. *St John's Vicarage, 33 Lea Bank Avenue, Kidderminster, Worcs DY11 6PA*   Kidderminster (01562) 822649

RAVEN, Thomas Denys Milville. b 22. Lon Coll of Div 65. **d** 66 **p** 67. C Bradfield *Ox* 66-71; V Otterton *Ex* 71-74; V Tidebrook *Chich* 74-85; V Wadhurst 74-85; P-in-c Tasburgh *Nor* 85-87; P-in-c Tharston 85-87; P-in-c Forncett St Mary w St Pet 85-87; P-in-c Flordon 85-87; R Tasburgh w Tharston, Forncett and Flordon 87-89; rtd 89; Perm to Offic *St E* from 90. *Barfield, Church View, Holton, Halesworth, Suffolk IP19 8PB*   Halesworth (01986) 875185

RAVENS, David Arthur Stanley. b 30. Jes Coll Ox BA53 MA61 Lon Univ BD63. Wells Th Coll 61. **d** 63 **p** 64. C Seacroft *Ripon* 63-70; TV 70-73; Sir Wm Borcase's Sch Marlow 73-87; rtd 95. *44 Arthursdale Grange, Scholes, Leeds LS15 4AW*   Leeds (0113) 273 6648

RAVENSCROFT, Ven Raymond Lockwood. b 31. Leeds Univ BA53. Coll of Resurr Mirfield 54. **d** 55 **p** 56. S Africa 55-57; S Rhodesia 57-59; Bechuanaland 59-62; C St Ives *Truro* 62-64; V Falmouth All SS 64-68; V St Stephens by Launceston 68-73; P-in-c Launceston St Thos 68-73; V Launceston St Steph w St Thos 73-74; TR Probus, Ladock and Grampound w Creed and St Erme 74-88; RD Powder 77-81; Hon Can Truro Cathl 82-88; Can Lib from 88; P-in-c St Erme 84-85; Adn Cornwall from 88. *Archdeacon's House, Knights Hill, Kenwyn, Truro TR1 3UY*   Truro (01872) 72866   Fax 42102

RAVENSDALE, Jonathan Christopher (Jon). b 56. Aston Tr Scheme 90 Chich Th Coll DipTh94. **d** 94 **p** 95. C Leytonstone St Marg w St Columba *Chelmsf* from 94. *St Andrew's Vicarage, 7 Forest Glade, London E11 1LU*   0181-989 0942

RAVENSDALE, Canon Victor Andrew Joseph. b 14. OBE73. Golds Coll Lon. CMS Tr Coll Blackheath 48 Makerere Coll Kampala 64. **d** 66 **p** 67. Uganda 66-73; Chapl Basel w Angarten and Freiburg-im-Breisgau *Eur* 73; R Stilton w Denton and Caldecote *Ely* 73-77; R Folksworth w Morborne 74-77; Chapl Lisbon *Eur* 77-84; Can Gib Cathl 81-85; rtd 84; Asst Chapl Lisbon *Eur* 84-85; Perm to Offic *Cant* from 85. *96 Church Path, Deal, Kent CT14 9TJ*   Deal (01304) 360523

+RAWCLIFFE, Rt Rev Derek Alec. b 21. OBE71. Leeds Univ BA42. Coll of Resurr Mirfield 42. **d** 44 **p** 45 **c** 74. C Claines St Geo *Worc* 44-47; Solomon Is 47-58; New Hebrides 58-80; Adn S Melanesia 59-74; Asst Bp Melanesia 74-75; Bp New Hebrides 75-80; Bp Glas 81-91; rtd 91; Asst Bp Ripon from 91. *Kitkatts, Wetherby Road, Bardsey, Leeds LS17 9BB*   Collingham Bridge (01937) 572201

RAWDON-MOGG, Timothy David. b 45. St Jo Coll Dur BA76. Cuddesdon Coll 75. **d** 77 **p** 78. C Wotton St Mary *Glouc* 77-80; C Ascot Heath *Ox* 80-82; V Woodford Halse w Eydon *Pet* 82-88; V Shrivenham w Watchfield and Bourton *Ox* from 88. *St Andrew's Vicarage, Shrivenham, Swindon SN6 8AN*   Swindon (01793) 782243

RAWE, Alan Charles George. b 29. ALCD56. **d** 56 **p** 57. R Moreton *Ches* 69-80; V Coppull *Blackb* 80-83; Miss to Seamen 83-94; Felixstowe Seafarers' Cen 88-94; rtd 94. *15 Starfield Close, Lytham St Annes, Lancs FY8 4QA*   Lytham (01253) 733647

RAWLING, Miss Jane Elizabeth. b 51. Birm Univ BSc73 St Jo Coll York CertEd75. St Jo Coll Nottm LTh84. **dss** 84 **d** 87 **p** 94. Southsea St Jude *Portsm* 84-87; C 87-88; C St Paul's Cray St Barn *Roch* 88-91; Hon C from 91; SE Regional Co-ord BCMS Crosslinks from 91; Perm to Offic *S'wark* from 92. *50 Batchwood Green, Orpington, Kent BR5 2NF*   Orpington (01689) 871467

RAWLING, Stephen Charles. b 43. Man Univ BSc64 Bris Univ MSc71 DipTh73. Sarum & Wells Th Coll 71. **d** 73 **p** 74. C Bris St Andr Hartcliffe *Bris* 73-76; C Westlands St Andr *Lich* 76-78; R Darlaston St Lawr 78-90; TR Bloxwich from 90. *All Saints' Vicarage, 3 Elmore Row, Bloxwich, Walsall WS3 2HR*   Bloxwich (01922) 476598

RAWLINGS, Miss Brenda Susan. b 48. Sussex Univ CertEd69 DipHE81. Oak Hill Th Coll 85. **d** 87 **p** 94. Par Dn Green Street Green *Roch* 87-90; Par Dn Collier Row St Jas and Havering-atte-Bower *Chelmsf* 90-94; C 94; C Greenstead juxta Colchester from 94. *6 Patmore Road, Colchester CO4 3PN*   Colchester (01206) 864131

RAWLINGS, John Dunstan Richard. b 25. Oak Hill Th Coll 62. **d** 64 **p** 65. Chapl R Aircraft Establishment Farnborough 69-80; Hon C Camberley St Paul *Guildf* 76-80; C 80; P-in-c Strethall *Chelmsf* 80-81; P-in-c Elmdon and Wendon Lofts 80-81; V Elmdon w Wendon Lofts and Strethall 81-88; rtd 88. *14 Huddington Glade, Yateley, Camberley, Surrey GU17 7FG*   Yateley (01252) 875731

RAWLINGS, John Edmund Frank. b 47. AKC69. St Aug Coll Cant 69. **d** 70 **p** 71. C Rainham *Roch* 70-73; C Tattenham Corner and Burgh Heath *Guildf* 73-76; Chapl RN 76-92; V Tavistock and Gulworthy *Ex* from 92. *The Vicarage, 5A Plymouth Road, Tavistock, Devon PL19 8AU*   Tavistock (01822) 612162

RAWLINGS, Philip John. b 53. St Jo Coll Nottm BTh83. **d** 83 **p** 84. C Blackley St Andr *Man* 83-87; C Halliwell St Pet 87-93; R Stretford St Bride from 93. *St Bride's Rectory, Shrewsbury Street, Old Trafford, Manchester M16 9AP*   0161-226 6064

RAWLINS, Douglas Royston. b 17. OBE68. Univ of Wales BSc39. St Steph Ho Ox 39. **d** 41 **p** 42. Sarawak 50-63; Malaysia 63-80; rtd 80; Perm to Offic *Nor* from 81. *60 Pineheath Road, High Kelling, Holt, Norfolk NR25 6RH*   Holt (01263) 712225

RAWLINS, Geoffrey Ernest Francis. b 30. **d** 56 **p** 57. C St Marylebone All So w SS Pet and Jo *Lon* 56-66; USA from 67; rtd 95. *Flat 2, 60 Elm Park Road, London SW3 6AU*   0171-352 4076

RAWLINSON, Curwen. b 32. MBE73. Leeds Univ CertEd55 Man Univ DipEd56 Open Univ BA80. Sarum Th Coll 59. **d** 61 **p** 62. C Wigan St Mich *Liv* 61-63; CF 63-83; Dep Asst Chapl Gen 78-80; Asst Chapl Gen 80-85; QHC from 83; R Uley w Owlpen and Nympsfield *Glouc* from 85; RD Dursley from 89. *The Rectory, Uley, Dursley, Glos GL11 5SN*   Dursley (01453) 860249

RAWLINSON, Dr John. b 47. Guy's Hosp Medical Sch BSc67 MB, BS71. E Anglian Minl Tr Course 89. **d** 92 **p** 93. NSM Tilbrook *Ely* from 92; NSM Covington from 92; NSM Catworth Magna from 92; NSM Keyston and Bythorn from 92. *The Malt House, 42 Stonely, Huntingdon, Cambs PE18 0EH*   Huntingdon (01480) 860263

RAWLINSON, Rowland. b 20. Liv Univ DipAdEd68 Open Univ BA74. St Deiniol's Hawarden 79. **d** 80 **p** 81. Hon C Barnston *Ches* 80-82; C 82-85; rtd 85; Hon C Higher Bebington *Ches* from 85. *18 Winston Grove, Wirral, Merseyside L46 0PQ*   0151-677 5641

RAWSON, Michael Graeme. b 62. York Univ BA84 Ox Univ BA88. St Steph Ho Ox 86. **d** 89 **p** 90. C Brighouse St Martin *Wakef* 89-92; C Brighouse and Clifton 92-93; V Gomersal from 93. *The Vicarage, 404 Spen Lane, Gomersal, Cleckheaton, W Yorkshire BD19 4LS*   Cleckheaton (01274) 872131

RAY, Mrs Joanna Zorina. b 55. AIMLS78 K Coll Lon BSc77 Garnett Coll Lon PGCE80 Lon Inst of Educn MA92. S'wark

Ord Course 84. **d** 87 **p** 94. NSM Carshalton *S'wark* 87-91; NSM Sutton New Town St Barn 91-93; NSM Knighton St Mary Magd *Leic* 93-94; Par Dn Leic H Spirit 94; C from 94; Chapl to the Deaf from 94. *58 Kingsmead Road, Knighton, Leicester LE2 3YD* Leicester (0116) 270 5439

RAY, John Mead. b 28. OBE79. St Andr Univ MA50 DipEd51. CMS Tr Coll Chislehurst 60. **d** 70 **p** 71. Miss Partner CMS 70-95; C Sparkhill St Jo *Birm* 87-90; C Sparkbrook Em 87-90; C Sparkhill w Greet and Sparkbrook 90; Deanery Missr 90-95; rtd 95; Perm to Offic *Birm* from 95. *190 Sarehole Road, Birmingham B28 8EF* 0121-777 6143

RAY, Robin John. b 44. Sarum & Wells Th Coll 72. **d** 74 **p** 75. C Bourne Valley *Sarum* 74-78; P-in-c Dilton Marsh 78-82; V 82-87; V Taunton Lyngford *B & W* 87-93; R Exford, Exmoor, Hawkridge and Withypool from 93; Rural Affairs Officer from 93; ACORA Link Officer from 93. *The Rectory, Exford, Minehead, Somerset TA24 7LX* Exford (0164383) 586

RAYBOULD, Norman William. b 18. Lich Th Coll 51. **d** 54 **p** 55. V St Martin's *Lich* 67-76; V Sheriffhales w Woodcote 76-83; rtd 83; Perm to Offic *Lich* from 83. *Borrowdale, St Martin's Road, Gobowen, Oswestry, Shropshire SY11 3PH* Oswestry (01691) 652621

RAYFIELD, Dr Lee Stephen. b 55. Southn Univ BSc78 Lon Univ PhD81. Ridley Hall Cam CTMin93. **d** 93. C Woodford Wells *Chelmsf* from 93. *8 Firs Walk, Woodford Green, Essex IG8 0TD* 0181-505 0660

RAYMENT, Andrew David. b 45. Univ of Wales (Lamp) BA68 Univ of Wales (Abth) MA70. Ridley Hall Cam 78. **d** 80 **p** 81. C Costessey *Nor* 80-83; C Earlham St Anne 83-90; Missr from 86; V Catton 90-94; V Old Catton from 94. *St Margaret's Vicarage, 1 Parkside Drive, Norwich NR6 7DP* Norwich (01603) 425615

RAYMENT-PICKARD, Hugh Douglas John. b 61. Kent Univ BA84 Em Coll Cam BA87. Westcott Ho Cam 85. **d** 88 **p** 89. C St Jo on Bethnal Green *Lon* 88-91; C Hackney 91-92; TV 92-95; V Notting Dale St Clem w St Mark and St Jas from 95. *St Clement's House, 95 Sirdar Road, London W11 4EQ* 0171-727 5450

RAYMER, Dr Victoria Elizabeth. b 46. Wellesley Coll (USA) BA68 Harvard Univ MA69 JD78 PhD81. St Steph Ho Ox MA91 Qu Coll Birm DPS89. **d** 89 **p** 94. Par Dn Bushey St Alb 89-94; C 94; C Eaton Socon from 94. *53 Shakespeare Road, Eaton Socon, St Neots, Huntingdon, Cambs PE19 3HG* Huntingdon (01480) 214980

RAYMOND, George William. b 07. MBE55. Wycliffe Hall Ox. **d** 67 **p** 68. Hon C W Wickham St Jo *Cant* 67-84; Hon C W Wickham St Jo *S'wark* 85-87; rtd 87. *58 Gates Green Road, West Wickham, Kent BR4 9DG* 0181-462 4980

RAYNER, David. b 49. Trin Hall Cam BA72 MA75. Westcott Ho Cam 75. **d** 78 **p** 79. C Chorlton-cum-Hardy St Clem *Man* 78-81; C Cam Gt St Mary w St Mich *Ely* 81-84; Warden Trin Coll Cen Camberwell 84-88; V Camberwell St Geo *S'wark* 84-88; Warden Bp Mascall Cen *Heref* 89-90; V Smethwick H Trin w St Alb *Birm* 90-92; P-in-c W Smethwick 90-92; P-in-c Smethwick SS Steph and Mich 92-95; V Smethwick Resurrection from 92; RD Warley from 93. *The Vicarage, 69 South Road, Smethwick, Warley, W Midlands B67 7BP* 0121-558 0373

RAYNER, Canon George Charles. b 26. Bps' Coll Cheshunt 50. **d** 52 **p** 53. R Wootton *Portsm* 69-89; Hon Can Portsm Cathl 84-89; rtd 89; Perm to Offic *B & W* from 89. *Grianan, 23 Hood Close, Glastonbury, Somerset BA6 8ES* Glastonbury (01458) 833795

RAYNER, Paul Anthony. b 39. Dur Univ BA60 Lon Univ BD68 Cape Town Univ MA79. Lon Coll of Div 65. **d** 68 **p** 69. C Crookes St Thos *Sheff* 68-72; S Africa 72-79; P-in-c S Shoebury *Chelmsf* 80-84; R from 84. *The Rectory, Church Road, Shoeburyness, Southend-on-Sea SS3 9EU* Southend-on-Sea (01702) 292778

RAYNER, Richard Noel. b 24. Lon Univ BD51. Oak Hill Th Coll 50. **d** 52 **p** 53. V Slough *Ox* 71-75; V Heworth w Peasholme St Cuth *York* 72-75; V Heworth 75-81; V Okehampton w Inwardleigh *Ex* 81-89; RD Okehampton 87-89; rtd 89; Perm to Offic *Ex* from 90. *Redlands, 5 Ladymeade, Ilminster, Somerset TA19 0EA* Ilminster (01460) 52491

RAYNER, Stewart Leslie. b 39. St Jo Coll Dur BA61 DipTh66 MA73. Cranmer Hall Dur. **d** 67 **p** 68. C Whiston *Sheff* 67-70; C Doncaster St Geo 70-74; Chapl Doncaster R Infirmary 70-74; R Adwick-le-Street *Sheff* 74-85; V Totley 85-91; Asst Chapl Pastures Hosp Derby 91-94; Asst Chapl Kingsway Hosp Derby 91-94; Asst Chapl S Derby Mental Health Services 91-94; P-in-c Etwall w Egginton *Derby* from 94. *The Rectory, 1 Rectory Court, Main Street, Etwall, Derby DE65 6LP* Etwall (01283) 732349

RAYNES, Andrew. b 60. R Holloway Coll Lon BA83. Wycliffe Hall Ox DipMin95. **d** 95. C Crowborough *Chich* from 95. *2 Woodland Way, Crowborough, E Sussex TN6 3BG* Crowborough (01892) 662909

RAYNOR, Duncan Hope. b 58. Ex Coll Ox MA80 MA82 Birm Univ PGCE88. Qu Coll Birm 82. **d** 84 **p** 85. C Kings Heath *Birm* 84-87; Perm to Offic from 87; Hd of RE Alderbrook Sch Solihull 88-94; Chapl K Edw Sch Birm from 94. *134 Addison Road, Birmingham B14 7EP* 0121-443 2147

RAYNOR, Michael. b 53. Lanc Univ BA74 MSc75. Ripon Coll Cuddesdon BA84. **d** 85 **p** 86. C Gt Crosby St Faith *Liv* 85-88; V Warrington St Barn from 88. *St Barnabas' Vicarage, 73 Lovely Lane, Warrington WA5 1TY* Warrington (01925) 633556

RAYNOR, Robert Ernest. b 14. Lon Univ BA36 TCD BA49 MA55 BD55. CITC 49. **d** 49 **p** 50. I Drummaul w Duneane and Ballyscullion *Conn* 68-72; Lect and Chapl Stranmillis Coll Belf 72-79; C Belf St Bart 72-79; rtd 79. *Annadale Private Nursing Home, Annadale Avenue, Belfast BT7 3JH* Belfast (01232) 645900

RAYNOR-SMITH, Charles Alfred Walter. b 12. Sarum Th Coll. **d** 55 **p** 56. V Colehill *Sarum* 62-81; rtd 81. *19 Tatnam Road, Poole, Dorset BH15 2OW* Poole (01202) 681996

RAZEY, Miss Florence Hannah. b 12. St Andr Ho Portsm 38. **dss** 43 **d** 87. Nether Hoyland St Pet *Sheff* 69-72; rtd 72; Elson *Portsm* 72-87; Hon C 87-92. *Tamar, 10 Beech Grove, Alverstoke, Gosport, Hants PO12 2EJ* Gosport (01705) 523799

RAZZALL, Charles Humphrey. b 55. Worc Coll Ox BA76 Qu Coll Cam BA78 Worc Coll Ox MA81. Westcott Ho Cam 76. **d** 79 **p** 80. C Catford (Southend) and Downham *S'wark* 79-83; V Crofton Park St Hilda w St Cypr 83-87; UPA Field Officer from 87; TV Oldham *Man* from 87; AD Oldham from 93. *46 Godson Street, Oldham OL1 2DB* 0161-627 1640

READ, Andrew Gordon. b 40. ARICS63 Nottm Univ BA69. Cuddesdon Coll 70. **d** 70 **p** 71. C E Retford *S'well* 70-72; C Woodthorpe 72-76; P-in-c Newark St Leon 76-78; Perm to Offic *Roch* from 79. *13 Clevedon Road, London SE20 7QQ* 0181-778 9545

READ, Charles William. b 60. Man Univ BA81 Man Poly CertEd82. St Jo Coll Nottm 86. **d** 88 **p** 89. C Oldham *Man* 88-90; C Urmston 90-94; P-in-c Broughton St Jas w St Clem and St Matthias from 94. *St James's Rectory, Great Cheetham Street East, Higher Broughton, Salford M7 0UH* 0161-792 1208

READ, Christopher Holditch. b 19. Qu Coll Birm 50. **d** 53 **p** 54. R Grangemouth *Edin* 63-72; V Parwich w Alsop en le Dale *Derby* 72-87; P-in-c Fenny Bentley, Thorpe and Tissington 77; rtd 87; Perm to Offic *Mor* 88-89. *c/o 55 Power Street, Hawthorn, Victoria, Australia 3122*

READ, Geoffrey Philip. b 61. Bris Univ LLB82. Wycliffe Hall Ox 85. **d** 88 **p** 89. C Dorking St Paul *Guildf* 88-92; TV Westborough from 92. *St Clare's Vicarage, Cabell Road, Guildford, Surrey GU2 6JW* Guildford (01483) 503348

READ, Ian. b 34. Selw Coll Cam BA57. Linc Th Coll 57. **d** 59 **p** 60. C Shard End *Birm* 59-63; Mozambique 64-76; Dean Maciene 71-76; P-in-c Edgbaston St Germain *Birm* 76-80; V Worc St Wulstan *Worc* 80-92; R Stoulton w Drake's Broughton and Pirton etc from 92. *The Rectory, Worcester Road, Drakes Broughton, Pershore, Worcs WR10 2AQ* Worcester (01905) 840528

READ, Jack. b 19. Qu Coll Birm 67. **d** 68 **p** 69. C Tong *Bradf* 68-70; C Baildon 70-72; V Queensbury 72-86; rtd 86; Perm to Offic *Bradf* from 86. *7 Silver Birch Grove, Wyke, Bradford, W Yorkshire BD12 9ET* Bradford (01274) 670737

READ, James Arthur. b 51. Nottm Coll of Educn BEd74. E Midl Min Tr Course 84. **d** 87 **p** 88. C Weoley Castle *Birm* 87-91; C W Smethwick 91-92; C Smethwick Resurrection 92; TV Atherton *Man* from 92. *21 Greenfield Road, Atherton, Manchester M29 9LW* Atherton (01942) 895088

READ, John. b 33. Worc Coll Ox BA56 MA60. Chich Th Coll 56. **d** 58 **p** 59. V Ex St Matt *Ex* 69-80; P-in-c Ex St Sidwell 79-80; R Ex St Sidwell and St Matt 80-83; Chapl Warneford Hosp Leamington Spa 83-89; Chapl S Warks Hosps 83-89; Chapl Dur and Ches le Street Hosps 89-95; Chapl Dryburn Hosp 89-95; rtd 95; NSM Tamworth *Lich* from 95. *The Parsonage, Church Drive, Hopwas, Tamworth, Staffs B78 3AL* Tamworth (01827) 54599

READ, Canon John Charles. b 07. St D Coll Lamp Keble Coll Ox BA MA35. St Steph Ho Ox 29. **d** 31 **p** 32. V Canton St Luke *Llan* 43-77; Can Llan Cathl 72-77; rtd 77; Perm to Offic *Llan* from 77. *9 Granville Avenue, Cardiff CF5 1BW* Cardiff (01222) 569249

READ, John Hanson. b 17. St Jo Coll Ox BA49 MA53. Qu Coll Birm 49. **d** 50 **p** 51. R Beddington *S'wark* 60-65; RD Sutton 65-70; P-in-c Guestling *Chich* 78; P-in-c Pett 78; R Guestling and Pett 78-83; rtd 83; Perm to Offic *Chich* 84-89 and from 92; RD Rye 89-90. *6 Oast House Road, Icklesham, Winchelsea, E Sussex TN36 4BN* Hastings (01424) 814440

READ, John Samuel. b 33. Fitzw Ho Cam BA56. Clifton Th Coll 62. **d** 64 **p** 65. C Sneinton St Chris w St Phil *S'well* 64-67; C Huyton St Geo *Liv* 67-70; Lic to Offic *Blackb* 70-72; V Moldgreen *Wakef* 72-84; V Rawtenstall St Mary *Man* 84-91; Chapl Rossendale Gen Hosp 84-91; R Earsham w Alburgh and Denton *Nor* from 91; P-in-c Ditchingham, Hedenham and Broome from 94. *The Rectory, Earsham, Bungay, Suffolk NR35 2TF* Bungay (01986) 892147

READ, Robert Edgar. b 47. Kelham Th Coll 66. **d** 70 **p** 71. C Harton Colliery *Dur* 70-75; C Wilmslow *Ches* 76-80; V Gatley 80-92; V Offerton from 92. *St Alban's Vicarage, Offerton Lane, Stockport, Cheshire SK2 5AG* 0161-480 3773

READ, Victor. b 29. Lon Univ BD58. ALCD57. **d** 58 **p** 59. V Linc St Pet in Eastgate w St Marg *Linc* 67-73; V W Wimbledon Ch Ch *S'wark* 73-94; rtd 94. *27 Nightingale Drive, Towcester, Northants NN12 7RA* Towcester (01327) 352027

READE, Canon Nicholas Stewart. b 46. Leeds Univ BA70 DipTh72. Coll of Resurr Mirfield 70. **d** 73 **p** 74. C Coseley St Chad *Lich* 73-75; C Codsall 75-78; V Upper Gornal 78-82; V Mayfield *Chich* 82-88; RD Dallington 82-88; V Eastbourne St Mary from 88; RD Eastbourne from 88; Can and Preb Chich Cathl from 90; Min Hydneye CD 91-93. *The Vicarage, 2 Glebe Close, Eastbourne, E Sussex BN20 8AW* Eastbourne (01323) 720420

READE, Richard Barton. b 66. Wolv Poly BA88. Ripon Coll Cuddesdon BA91. **d** 92 **p** 93. C Wilncote *Lich* from 92. *87 Belgrave Road, Belgrave, Tamworth, Staffs B77 2LS* Tamworth (01827) 283174

READER, John. b 53. Trin Coll Ox BA75 MA79 Man Univ DSPT83 MPhil87. Ripon Coll Cuddesdon 76. **d** 78 **p** 79. C Ely 78-80; C Baguley *Man* 80-83; TV Kirkby Lonsdale *Carl* 83-86; V Lydbury N *Heref* 86-89; P-in-c Hopesay w Edgton 86-89; R Lydbury N w Hopesay and Edgton 89-90; Tutor Glouc Sch for Min 86-88; Vice-Prin 88-90; Dir Past Th Sarum & Wells Th Coll 90-92; P-in-c Elmley Lovett w Hampton Lovett and Elmbridge etc *Worc* from 92. *The Rectory, Elmley Lovett, Droitwich, Worcs WR9 0PU* Hartlebury (01299) 251798

READER, Dr Trevor Alan John. b 46. Lon Univ BSc68 MSc70 Portsm Poly PhD72. S Dios Minl Tr Scheme 83. **d** 86 **p** 87. C Alverstoke *Portsm* 86-89; P-in-c Hook w Warsash 89-95; V from 95. *The Vicarage, 112 Osborne Road, Warsash, Southampton SO3 6GH* Locks Heath (01489) 572324

READER-MOORE, Anthony. b 43. Keele Univ MA80 Hull Univ MA83. Linc Th Coll. **d** 82 **p** 83. C Addiscombe St Mildred *Cant* 82-84; C Addiscombe St Mildred *S'wark* 85-86; R N Wheatley, W Burton, Bole, Saundby, Sturton etc *S'well* 86-93; Rural Officer 89-93; P-in-c Alford w Rigsby *Linc* from 93; P-in-c Bilsby w Farlesthorpe from 93; P-in-c Hannah cum Hagnaby w Markby from 93; P-in-c Well from 93; P-in-c Maltby 93-94; P-in-c Saleby w Beesby 93-94; P-in-c Saleby w Beesby and Maltby from 95. *The Vicarage, 15 Bilsby Road, Alford, Lincs LN13 9EW* Alford (01507) 462448

READING, Canon Laurence John. b 14. DSC44. Lon Univ BD39 AKC39. **d** 39 **p** 40. Sec C of E Bd of Adult Educn Cttee 65-72; Can Heref Cathl *Heref* 72-82; rtd 82. *11 Wakelin Way, Witham, Essex CM8 2TX* Witham (01376) 513251

READING, Miss Sian Jacqueline Mary. b 64. Westcott Ho Cam CTM95. **d** 95. C Northn St Alb *Pet* from 95. *12 Oulton Rise, Northampton NN3 1EW* Northampton (01604) 492965

READING, Area Bishop of. See BONE, Rt Rev John Frank Ewan

REAGON, Darrol Franklin. b 46. Univ of Wales (Cardiff) DipTh76. St Mich Coll Llan 74. **d** 76 **p** 77. C Llandrillo-yn-Rhos *St As* 76-78; C Hawarden 78-81; V Northwich St Luke and H Trin *Ches* 81-85; V Moulton *Linc* 85-91; V Scunthorpe Resurr 91-92; P-in-c Branston 92-94; R Branston w Nocton and Potterhanworth from 94. *The Rectory, Branston, Lincoln LN4 1NN* Lincoln (01522) 791296

REAKES-WILLIAMS, Gordon Martin. b 63. St Cath Coll Cam BA86 MA89. St Jo Coll Dur BA90. **d** 91 **p** 92. C Harold Wood *Chelmsf* 91-94; Chapl Leipzig *Eur* from 95. *Scharnhorststrasse 21, 04275 Leipzig, Germany* Leipzig (341) 311254 Fax as telephone

REAKES-WILLIAMS, John Michael Reakes Andrew. b 30. St Fran Coll Brisbane 69. **d** 70 **p** 71. Australia 70-73; C Northfield *Birm* 73-74; C Penarth w Lavernock *Llan* 74-76; V Llanbradach 76-78; R Llanfabon 78-79; V Oswestry H Trin *Lich* 79-92; Miss to Seamen 92-95; Trinidad and Tobago 92-95; rtd 95. *clo G K Reakes-Williams Esq, The School House, Norbury, Bishops Castle, Shropshire SY9 5EA* Bishops Castle (01588) 650413

REALE, Mrs Kathleen. b 38. Carl Dioc Tr Course 83. dss 86 **d** 87 **p** 94. Dalston *Carl* 86-87; Par Dn 87-90; Par Dn Westward, Rosley-w-Woodside and Welton 87-90; Par Dn Thursby 89-90; D-in-c Gt Salkeld w Lazonby 90-94; P-in-c from 94. *The Rectory, Lazonby, Penrith, Cumbria CA10 1BL* Lazonby (01768) 898750

REANEY, Christopher Thomas. b 60. Univ of Wales (Lamp) BA82. St Mich Coll Llan DipTh85. **d** 85 **p** 86. C Newport Maindee St Jo Ev *Mon* 85-87; C Griffithstown 88-89; V Treherbert w Treorchy *Llan* from 89. *The Vicarage, 58 Miskin Street, Treherbert, Treorchy, M Glam CF42 5LR* Treorchy (01443) 772241

REANEY, Joseph Silvester. b 13. Selw Coll Cam BA35 MA42. Wells Th Coll 36. **d** 37 **p** 38. C Lewisham St Jo Southend *S'wark* 37-40; C Bellingham St Dunstan 40-42; Chapl RAFVR 42-46; V Gt Barr *Lich* from 47. *Great Barr Vicarage, Chapel Lane, Birmingham B43 7BD* 0121-357 1390

REARDON, Bernard Morris Garvin. b 13. Keble Coll Ox BA35 MA38. Ripon Hall Ox 35. **d** 37 **p** 38. Sen Lect, Reader, and Hd Relig Studies Newc Univ 63-78; rtd 78. *2 The Grove, Benton, Newcastle upon Tyne NE12 9PE* 0191-266 1574

REARDON, Canon Martin Alan. b 32. Selw Coll Cam BA54 MA58. Cuddesdon Coll 56. **d** 58 **p** 59. C Rugby St Andr *Cov* 58-62; C Wicker w Neepsend *Sheff* 62-65; Lic to Offic 65-71; Sub-Warden Linc Th Coll 71-78; Gen Sec Gen Syn Bd for Miss and Unity 78-89; Can and Preb Linc Cathl *Linc* 79-89; Perm to Offic *Chich* 81-89; R Plumpton w E Chiltington 89-90; Gen Sec Chs Together in England from 90; Perm to Offic *S'wark* 95. *Churches Together in England, Interchurch House, 35-41 Lower Marsh, London SE1 7RL* 0171-620 4444 Fax 928 5771

REASON, Jack. b 28. St Alb Minl Tr Scheme 77. **d** 80 **p** 81. NSM Luton Lewsey St Hugh *St Alb* 80-85; C Bideford *Ex* 85-88; R Northlew w Ashbury 88-93; R Bratton Clovelly w Germansweek 88-93; rtd 93; Perm to Offic *Ex* from 94. *5 Merryfield Road, Bideford, Devon EX39 4BX* Bideford (01237) 472150

REAST, Eileen Joan. See BANGAY, Mrs Eileen Joan

REAVIL, Michael Edward. b 51. Qu Coll Birm 89. **d** 91 **p** 92. C Cofton Hackett w Barnt Green *Birm* 91-94; C Stevenage St Mary Sheppall w Aston *St Alb* from 94. *31 Harefield, Stevenage, Herts SG2 9NG*

REAY, John. b 08. Ely Th Coll. **d** 60 **p** 61. V Crosscrake *Carl* 62-71; V Millom H Trin w Thwaites 71-75; rtd 75; Perm to Offic *Carl* from 77. *Woodlands, Drovers' Lane, Penrith, Cumbria CA11 7RB* Penrith (01768) 65226

REBERT, Nicholas Aubrey Russell. b 47. Open Univ BA88. **d** 71 **p** 72. Ceylon 71-72; Sri Lanka 72-83; C Whitehaven *Carl* 84-88; TV 88-93; Chapl W Cumberland Hosp 88-93; rtd 93. *58 Rannerdale Drive, Whitehaven, Cumbria CA28 6LA* Whitehaven (01946) 592712

RECORD, John. b 47. St Chad's Coll Dur BA71. Westcott Ho Cam 71. **d** 73 **p** 74. C Paddington St Jo w St Mich *Lon* 73-75; C Witney *Ox* 75-78; P-in-c Lt Compton and Chastleton 78-80; R Lt Compton w Chastleton, Cornwell etc 80-83; V Hawkhurst *Cant* from 83; RD W Charing from 89. *The Vicarage, Hawkhurst, Kent TN18 4QB* Hawkhurst (01580) 753397

RECORD, Sister Marion Eva. b 25. MRCS50 LRCP50 FFARCS57 Lon Univ BD79. dss 78 **d** 87 **p** 94. OHP from 72; Chapl Hull Univ *York* 72-78; Chapl York Univ 78-80; Lic to Offic from 80. *Martin House, Grove Road, Clifford, Wetherby, W Yorkshire LS23 6TX* Wetherby (01937) 843449

REDDING, Roger Charles. b 45. Chich Th Coll 87. **d** 89 **p** 90. C Yeovil *B & W* 89-90; C Yeovil St Mich 90-93; P-in-c Salisbury St Mark *Sarum* 93-94. *clo Church House, Crane Street, Salisbury SP1 2QB*

REDDINGTON, Gerald Alfred. b 34. Lon Univ DipRS79. S'wark Ord Course 76. **d** 79 **p** 79. NSM St Vedast w St Mich-le-Querne etc *Lon* 79-85; Dir Past Support Gp Scheme 83-86; Hon C St Marylebone All SS 85-90; Perm to Offic *Portsm* from 88; V Ealing St Barn *Lon* from 90. *St Barnabas' Vicarage, 66 Woodfield Road, London W5 1SH* 0181-998 0826

REDFEARN, James Jonathan. b 62. Newc Univ BA83 PGCE89. Cranmer Hall Dur CTMin95. **d** 95. C Kidsgrove *Lich* from 95. *42 Lamb Street, Kidsgrove, Stoke-on-Trent ST7 4AL* Stoke-on-Trent (01782) 782793

REDFEARN, John William Holmes. Sheff Univ BA30 MA31 DipEd31. **d** 33 **p** 34. Chapl Haberdashers' Aske's Sch Elstree 56-72; Perm to Offic *Lon* 61-76; rtd 72. *184 Cardiff Road, Llandaff, Cardiff CF5 2AD* Cardiff (01222) 567692

REDFEARN, Michael. b 42. Open Univ BA78 Hull Univ MA84 BA86. St Aid Birkenhead 64. **d** 68 **p** 69. C Bury St Pet *Man* 68-71; C Swinton St Pet 71-74; Ind Chapl *Bris* 74-81; Ind Chapl *York* 81-86; St Alb Minl Tr Scheme 93; V Southill *St Alb* 86-93; Asst Chapl HM Pris Wandsworth from 94; Lic to Offic *S'wark* from 94. *HM Prison Wandsworth, PO Box 757, Heathfield Road, London SW18 3HS* 0181-874 7292 Fax 877 0358

REDFEARN, Ms Tracy Anne. b 66. Heythrop Coll Lon BD88. Ripon Coll Cuddesdon 91. **d** 93 **p** 94. C Haslemere *Guildf* from 93. *Church Cottage, 16 Chatworth Avenue, Haslemere, Surrey GU27 1BA* Haslemere (01428) 642045

REDFERN, Canon Alastair Llewellyn John. b 48. Trin Coll Cam BA74 Ch Ch Ox MA74. Qu Coll Birm 75. **d** 76 **p** 77. C

Tettenhall Regis *Lich* 76-79; Tutor Ripon Coll Cuddesdon 79-87; Hon C Cuddesdon *Ox* 83-87; Can Res Bris Cathl *Bris* from 87; Dioc Tr Officer from 91. *Bristol Cathedral, College Green, Bristol BS1 5TJ* Bristol (0117) 942 1039

REDFERN, Paul. b 48. Ulster Univ BA88. CITC BTh94. **d** 94 **p** 95. C Belf St Aid *Conn* from 94. *50 Ashley Avenue, Lisburn Road, Belfast BT9 7BT* Belfast (01232) 669622

REDGERS, Brian. b 42. Dur Univ BA65. Westcott Ho Cam 65. **d** 67 **p** 68. C Rushmere *St E* 67-73; Lic to Offic from 73. *44 Belvedere Road, Ipswich IP4 4AB*

REDGRAVE, Cecil Goulden. b 14. Oak Hill Th Coll 37. **d** 41 **p** 42. V New Milverton *Cov* 60-76; R Tredington and Darlingscott w Newbold on Stour 76-83; rtd 83; Perm to Offic *Cov* from 83. *30 Elmdene Road, Kenilworth, Warks CV8 2BX* Kenilworth (01926) 57118

REDGRAVE, Miss Christine Howick. b 50. AIAT73. Trin Coll Bris 75. **dss** 78 **d** 87 **p** 94. Watford *St Alb* 78-83; Maidenhead St Andr and St Mary Magd *Ox* 83-85; Bracknell 85-87; Par Dn 87-94; C 94; TV from 95; Asst Dir of Ords from 95. *The Vicarage, 4 Micheldever Way, Bracknell, Berks RG12 3XX* Bracknell (01344) 50651

REDGRAVE, Ronald Oliver. b 18. Ox NSM Course. **d** 83 **p** 84. NSM Boyne Hill *Ox* 83-85; Perm to Offic *St E* 85-86; P-in-c Alderton w Ramsholt and Bawdsey 86-88; rtd 88. *16 Beaufort Drive, Wimborne, Dorset BH21 1BB* Wimborne (01202) 888457

REDGRAVE, Miss Susan Frances. b 55. CQSW75. St Deiniol's Hawarden 89. **d** 90 **p** 94. NSM Leic Resurr *Leic* 90; Par Dn De Beauvoir Town St Pet *Lon* 90-94; C 94-95; C Evington *Leic* from 95; C Leic St Phil from 95. *St Philips House, 2A Stoughton Drive North, Leicester LE5 5UB* Leicester (0116) 273 6204

REDHEAD, Edward. b 30. St Deiniol's Hawarden 60. **d** 63 **p** 64. V Rivington *Man* 67-72; V Bloxwich *Lich* 72-75; Hon C Lich St Chad 82-84; P-in-c Bromfield w Waverton *Carl* 84-85; V 85-90; P-in-c W Newton 84-85; V 85-90; R Harrington 90-93; rtd 93. *Tigh-na-Mara, 2-3 Caroy, Struan, Isle of Skye IV56 8FQ* Struan (0147072) 338

REDHOUSE, Mark David. b 67. BTEC NC86. Oak Hill Th Coll BA94. **d** 94 **p** 95. C Fulham St Mary N End *Lon* from 94. *Top Flat, 72 Edith Road, London W14 9AR* 0171-603 5909

REDKNAP, Clive Douglas. b 53. Trin Coll Bris BA95. **d** 95. C Patcham *Chich* from 95. *70 Overhill Drive, Brighton BN1 8WJ* Brighton (01273) 554791

REDMAN, Canon Arthur Thomas. b 28. Dur Univ BA52. Ridley Hall Cam 62. **d** 63 **p** 64. C Heaton St Barn *Bradf* 63-66; C Hitchin St Mary *St Alb* 66-70; PM 72-75; Perm to Offic *Nor* 70-72; V Swanwick and Pentrich *Derby* 75-80; Warden of Readers from 78; V Allestree from 80; P-in-c Morley 82-85; Hon Can Derby Cathl from 86; RD Duffield from 88. *St Edmund's Vicarage, Kings Croft, Allestree, Derby DE22 2FN* Derby (01332) 557396

REDMAN, Canon Douglas Stuart Raymond. b 35. MCIOB64. Roch Th Coll 66. **d** 68 **p** 69. C Shortlands *Roch* 68-71; V from 80; R Kingsdown 71-76; R Chatham St Mary w St Jo 76-80; RD Beckenham from 90; Hon Can Roch Cathl from 93. *The Vicarage, 37 Kingswood Road, Bromley BR2 0HG* 0181-460 4989

REDMAYNE, John. b 12. OBE44 TD46. FCA36. Qu Coll Birm DipTh49. **d** 49 **p** 50. C Esher *Guildf* 49-51; Jamaica 51-57; R Girton *Ely* 58-60; USPG 61-70; New Zealand from 70. *15 Rawene Street, Waikanae, New Zealand* Waikanae (58) 36062

REDMOND, Ernest Wilkinson. b 10. TCD BA36 MA. CITC 36. **d** 36 **p** 37. I Augher w Newtownsaville and Eskrahoole *Clogh* 65-73; RD Clogh 58-73; Preb Clogh Cathl 67-78; Chan 78-79; I Monaghan 73-79; rtd 79. *182 Orby Drive, Belfast BT5 6BD* Belfast (01232) 798198

REDPATH, Stewart Rosbotham. b 11. TCD BA39. CITC 39. **d** 39 **p** 40. I Loughgall *Arm* 62-80; rtd 80. *22 Rosemount Park, Armagh BT60 1AX* Armagh (01861) 522698

REDRUP, Robert John. b 38. Leeds Univ BA65. Oak Hill Th Coll 65. **d** 69 **p** 70. C Maidenhead St Andr and St Mary Magd *Ox* 69-74; C St Keverne *Truro* 74-78; P-in-c Kea 78-80; V from 80; P-in-c Highertown and Baldhu 80-84. *The Vicarage, Kea, Truro, Cornwall TR3 6AE* Truro (01872) 72850

REDVERS HARRIS, Jonathan Francis. b 60. Solicitor 87 Southn Univ LLB81 Univ of Wales (Cardiff) LLM94. Ridley Hall Cam 87. **d** 90 **p** 91. C Enfield St Jas *Lon* 90-93; PV Llan Cathl *Llan* from 93; PV and Succ from 94. *2 The White House, Cathedral Green, Llandaff, Cardiff CF5 2EB* Cardiff (01222) 552313

REDWOOD, Canon David Leigh. b 32. Glas Univ DipSocWork78. Edin Th Coll 57. **d** 59 **p** 60. C Stirling *Edin* 59-61; C Glas Ch Ch *Glas* 61-64; P-in-c Glas Ascension 64-66;

R 66-69; R Hamilton 69-74; R Callander *St And* 74-76; Hon C 76-78; R Lochearnhead 74-76; R Killin 74-76; Hon C Doune 76-78; Hon C Aberfoyle 78-85; R Dunfermline from 85; TR W Fife Team Min from 85; Can St Ninian's Cathl Perth from 90. *The Rectory, 17 Ardeer Place, Dunfermline, Fife KY11 4YX* Dunfermline (01383) 723901

REECE, Gp Capt Arthur. b 13. DSO44 OBE54 DFC42 AFC43. St Deiniol's Hawarden 77. **d** 79 **p** 80. Hon C Lache cum Saltney *Ches* 79-80; V Tilstone Fearnall and Wettenhall 80-90; rtd 90. *Tawelfan, Bryn Goodman, Ruthin, Clwyd LL15 1EL* Ruthin (01824) 702968

✠**REECE, Rt Rev David.** b 13. G&C Coll Cam BA34 MA38. St Mich Coll Llan 35. **d** 36 **p** 37 **c** 77. C Abth St Mich *St D* 36-41; C Llanelli 41-49; V Pemb St Mary and St Mich 49-56; V Port Talbot St Theodore *Llan* 56-71; RD Margam 66-71; Can Llan Cathl 69-71; Adn Margam 71-81; Asst Bp Llan 77-83; rtd 83. *16 Stone Hamlet, Merthyr Mawr Road, Bridgend, M Glam CF31 3NX* Bridgend (01656) 653115

REECE, Donald Malcolm Hayden. b 36. CCC Cam BA58 MA62. Cuddesdon Coll 58. **d** 60 **p** 61. C Latchford St Jas *Ches* 60-63; C Matlock and Tansley *Derby* 63-67; C-in-c Hackenthorpe Ch Ch CD 67-70; Rhodesia 70-73; V Leic St Pet *Leic* 74-82; V Putney St Marg *S'wark* 82-91; Home Sec Coun for Chr Unity from 92; Perm to Offic 93-94; Hon C Wandsworth St Anne from 94. *23 Coleford Road, London SW13 1AD* 0181-874 8432 or 0171-222 9011 Fax 0171-799 2714

REECE, Paul Michael. b 60. Southn Univ BA81. Coll of Resurr Mirfield 83. **d** 85 **p** 86. C Borehamwood *St Alb* 85-89; C Potters Bar 89-92; R Lt Stanmore St Lawr *Lon* from 92; Chapl R Nat Orthopaedic Hosp from 93. *Whitchurch Rectory, St Lawrence Close, Edgware, Middx HA8 6RB* 0181-952 0019

REED, Alan Ronald. b 44. Sarum Th Coll 66. **d** 68 **p** 70. C Ifield *Chich* 68-71; C Perivale *Lon* 71-72; C Ruislip St Martin 72-75; C Burgess Hill St Jo *Chich* 76-78; V Shoreham Beach 78-80; V Roughey (or Roffey) from 80; P-in-c Rusper 84-86. *Roffey Vicarage, 52 Shepherds Way, Horsham, W Sussex RH12 4LX* Horsham (01403) 265333

REED, Albert. b 36. Univ of Wales BA58 BD63. St Mich Coll Llan 58. **d** 61 **p** 62. C Rhymney *Mon* 61-64; Chapl St Woolos Cathl 64-66; R Blaina 66-67; Hon C Dudley St Edm *Worc* 72-94; Perm to Offic from 94. *21 Tanfield Road, Dudley, W Midlands DY2 8XF* Dudley (01384) 256118

REED, Allan Norman. b 31. Keble Coll Ox BA55 MA59 Didsbury Coll Man CertEd72. Wycliffe Hall Ox 55. **d** 57 **p** 58. R S Levenshulme *Man* 64-71; Lic Preacher 71-95; rtd 92. *21 Lyons Road, Richmond, N Yorkshire DL10 4UA* Richmond (01748) 825767

REED, Ms Annette Susan. b 54. Birm Univ BA76 Univ of Wales (Cardiff) CQSW78. Qu Coll Birm 84. **d** 87 **p** 94. C Churchover w Willey *Cov* 89-92; C Clifton upon Dunsmore and Newton 89-92; C Walsgrave on Sowe 92-95; C Cov E 92-95; C Burbage w Aston Flamville *Leic* from 95; C Hinckley St Mary from 95. *46 Salisbury Road, Burbage, Hinckley, Leics LE10 2AR* Hinckley (01455) 616226

REED, Brian. b 43. Bris Univ BSc65 Nottm Univ DipTh76. Linc Th Coll 73. **d** 76 **p** 77. C S Ashford Ch Ch *Cant* 76-78; C Spring Park 78-83; V Barming Heath from 83. *St Andrew's Vicarage, 416 Tonbridge Road, Maidstone, Kent ME16 9LW* Maidstone (01622) 726245

REED, Bruce Douglas. b 20. Fitzw Ho Cam BA52 MA56 Lambeth Hon MLitt90. Moore Th Coll Sydney LTh45. **d** 46 **p** 46. Chapl Fitzw Ho Cam 50-54; C Cam St Paul *Ely* 53-54; Chmn Grubb Inst from 69; rtd 85. *The Grubb Institute, Cloudesley Street, London N1 0HU* 0171-278 8061 Fax 278 0728

REED, Christopher John. b 42. Selw Coll Cam BA64 MA68 Dur Univ DipTh66. Cranmer Hall Dur 64. **d** 67 **p** 68. C Gt Ilford St Andr *Chelmsf* 67-70; P-in-c Bordesley St Andr *Birm* 70-72; V 72-80; V Crofton St Paul *Roch* from 80. *St Paul's Vicarage, 2 Oakwood Road, Orpington, Kent BR6 8JH* Farnborough (01689) 852939

REED, Colin Bryher. b 58. York Univ BA80 RGN86. Ridley Hall Cam CTM95. **d** 95. C Lt Thurrock St Jo *Chelmsf* from 95. *141 Southend Road, Grays, Essex RM17 5NP* Grays Thurrock (01375) 377249

REED, Colin Charles Gilmour. b 40. LCP75 FCP86 St Luke's Coll Ex TCert63 Lon Univ DipTh69. Tyndale Hall Brisbane 67. **d** 69 **p** 70. C Weston-super-Mare Ch Ch *B & W* 69-71; Kenya 71-79; Australia from 80. *St Andrew's Hall, 190 The Avenue, Parkville, Victoria, Australia 3052*

REED, Canon Douglas Victor. b 19. AKC41 Middlebury Coll (USA) Hon DD51. St Steph Ho Ox 41. **d** 42 **p** 43. V Chislehurst Annunciation *Roch* 52-85; Hon Can Roch Cathl 81-85; rtd 85; Perm to Offic *Roch* from 85. *6 Crown Lane, Chislehurst, Kent BR7 5PL* 0181-467-3360

REED, Duncan Esmond Bousfield. b 51. AKC74 Ch Ch Coll Cant PGCE75. St Aug Coll Cant 76. **d** 76 **p** 77. C Houghton le Spring *Dur* 76-79; C Stockton St Pet 79-83; V Darlington St Mark w St Paul 83-88; V Benfieldside 88-93; P-in-c Whickham from 93. *The Rectory, Church Chare, Whickham, Newcastle upon Tyne NE16 4SH* 0191-488 7397

REED, Ethel Patricia Ivy. *See* WESTBROOK, Mrs Ethel Patricia Ivy

REED, Geoffrey Martin. b 51. Univ of Wales (Cardiff) BA73. Oak Hill Th Coll 73. **d** 76 **p** 77. C Swansea St Nic *S & B* 76-78; C Sketty 78-84; V Glasbury and Llowes 84-86; V Glasbury and Llowes w Clyro and Betws from 86. *St Peter's Vicarage, Glasbury, Hereford HR3 5NU* Glasbury (01497) 847657

REED, Jack. b 23. Bris Univ BA49 Lon Univ BD51. Tyndale Hall Bris. **d** 51 **p** 52. V Drypool St Columba w St Andr and St Pet *York* 66-80; TR Drypool 80-83; P-in-c Thwing 83-85; P-in-c Rudston w Boynton and Kilham 83-85; V 85-87; rtd 88. *32 Dower Rise, Swanland, North Ferriby, N Humberside HU14 3QT* Hull (01482) 632649

REED, John Peter Cyril. b 51. BD78 AKC78. Ripon Coll Cuddesdon 78. **d** 79 **p** 80. C Croydon *Cant* 79-82; Prec St Alb Abbey *St Alb* 82-86; R Timsbury and Priston *B & W* 86-93; Chapl Rural Affairs Bath Adnry from 87; P-in-c Ilminster w Whitelackington 93-94; TR Ilminster and District from 94. *The Rectory, Court Barton, Ilminster, Somerset TA19 0DU* Ilminster (01460) 52610

REED, Matthew Colin. b 50. Edin Univ BD82. Edin Th Coll 72. **d** 84 **p** 85. C Edin St Pet *Edin* 84-87; P-in-c Linlithgow 87-94; P-in-c Bathgate 87-91; Chapl HM Pris Polmont from 91; R Motherwell *Glas* from 94; R Wishaw from 94. *14 Crawford Street, Motherwell, Lanarkshire ML1 3AD* Motherwell (01698) 262634

REED, Matthew Graham. b 68. Nottm Univ BEng89. Ripon Coll Cuddesdon BA92. **d** 93 **p** 94. C Oxton *Ches* from 93. *11 Spurstow Close, Birkenhead, Merseyside L43 2NQ* 0151-653 8811

REED, Neil Andrew. b 62. St Chad's Coll Dur BA84. Coll of Resurr Mirfield. **d** 87 **p** 88. C Bishopwearmouth Ch Ch *Dur* 87-89; C Sunderland Springwell w Thorney Close 89-93; TV E Darlington 93-94. *42 Croft Avenue, Sunderland SR4 7DP* 0191-567 0755

REED, Mrs Pamela Kathleen. b 38. E Midl Min Tr Course. **dss** 84 **d** 87 **p** 94. Cam Ascension *Ely* 84-87; Par Dn 87-88; Par Dn Cherry Hinton St Andr 88-90; C 91-95; C Teversham 91-95; V Chesterton St Geo from 95. *St George's Vicarage, 8 Chesterfield Road, Cambridge CB4 1LN* Cambridge (01223) 423374

REED, Richard David. b 32. Trin Coll Carmarthen. **d** 91 **p** 92. NSM Dale and St Brides w Marloes *St D* from 91. *Tamarisk, Glebe Lane, Marloes, Haverfordwest, Dyfed SA62 3AY* Dale (01646) 636662

REED, Robert Chase. b 47. Boston Univ BSc70 TCD HDipEd72. **d** 87 **p** 88. NSM Taney *D & G* from 87; Res Hd Master Wesley Coll Dub from 87; Succ St Patr Cathl Dub from 93. *Embury House, Wesley College, Dublin 16, Irish Republic* Dublin (1) 298-7066 or 298-7343 Fax 298-7406

REED, Roger William. b 39. Wycliffe Hall Ox 65. **d** 68 **p** 69. C Portsea St Cuth *Portsm* 68-71; C Enfield St Jas *Lon* 71-74; P-in-c Becontree St Thos *Chelmsf* 74-78; R Debden and Wimbish w Thunderley 78-93; RD Saffron Walden 82-91; P-in-c Blendworth w Chalton w Idsworth *Portsm* from 93. *The Rectory, Blendworth, Hordean, Portsmouth PO8 0AB* Horndean (01705) 592174

REED, Simon John. b 63. Trin Coll Ox BA86 MA90. Wycliffe Hall Ox BA90. **d** 91 **p** 92. C Walton H Trin *Ox* from 91. *5 Bateman Drive, Brookhurst, Aylesbury, Bucks HP21 8AF* Aylesbury (01296) 82096

REED, William Harvey. b 47. K Coll Lon BD69 AKC69. St Aug Coll Cant 69. **d** 70 **p** 71. C Stockton St Mark CD *Dur* 70-72; C Billingham St Cuth 72-76; C S Westoe 76-79; V Chilton Moor 79-87; R Hutton *Chelmsf* from 87. *The Rectory, Hutton Village, Brentwood, Essex CM13 1RX* Brentwood (01277) 210495

REEDE, Very Rev Samuel William. b 24. TCD BA48 MA52 BD55. CITC 50. **d** 50 **p** 51. Can Raphoe Cathl *D & R* 67-92; I Raphoe w Raymochy and Clonleigh 68-92; Dean Raphoe 80-92; rtd 92. *Rooskey, Newtowncunningham, Co Donegal, Irish Republic* Letterkenny (74) 56426

REES, Anthony John. b 49. St Jo Coll Dur BA72 DipTh73 MA77 Man Univ MEd89. **d** 74 **p** 75. C Smethwick St Matt w St Chad *Birm* 74-77; C Bolton St Pet *Man* 77-80; R Cheetham St Mark 80-88; V Mottram in Longdendale w Woodhead *Ches* 88-93; V Mottram in Longdendale from 93. *The Vicarage, 29 Ashworth Lane, Mottram, Hyde, Cheshire SK14 6NT* Mottram (01457) 762268

REES, Brian. b 48. McGill Univ Montreal BA74 St Andr Univ BD76 PhD80. Montreal Dioc Th Coll 76. **d** 80 **p** 81. Canada 80-85; Lic to Offic *St Alb* from 85; Chapl Bedf Sch 85-92; Hd Master Bedf Prep Sch from 92. *Pemberley House, 17 Park Avenue, Bedford MK40 2LF* Bedford (01234) 355999

REES, Brynley Mervyn. b 18. Univ of Wales BA38. Lon Coll of Div 40. **d** 41 **p** 42. V St Alb Ch Ch *St Alb* 60-84; rtd 84; C Weobley w Sarnesfield and Norton Canon *Heref* 84-91. *2 Nelson Cottage, Bridge Sollars, Hereford HR4 7JN* Bridge Sollars (0198122) 296

REES, Christopher John. b 40. Dur Univ BA62. Ridley Hall Cam 62. **d** 64 **p** 65. C Wilmslow *Ches* 64-70; C Birkenhead St Pet w St Matt 70-75; V Lostock Gralam 75-83; R Davenham from 83. *The Rectory, Church Street, Davenham, Northwich, Cheshire CW9 8NF* Northwich (01606) 42450

REES, David Aylwin. b 14. Univ of Wales (Lamp) BA46. **d** 47 **p** 48. V Spittal and Treffgarne *St D* 53-75; V Dale 75-77; V Dale and St Brides w Marloes 78-84; rtd 84. *Cartrefle, North Road, Aberystwyth, Dyfed SY23 2EE* Aberystwyth (01970) 615745

REES, David Elwyn. b 37. Univ of Wales (Swansea) BA60. Ripon Hall Ox 63. **d** 65 **p** 66. C Swansea St Thos and Kilvey *S & B* 65-69; V 81-87; C Sketty 69-73; C Clyro w Bettws, Llowes and Glasbury All SS 73-80; V Hay w Llanigon and Capel-y-Ffin from 87. *The Beeches, Newport Street, Hay-on-Wye, Hereford HR3 5BG* Hay-on-Wye (01497) 820612

REES, Canon David Frederick. b 21. SS Coll Cam BA48 MA52. Sarum Th Coll 48. **d** 50 **p** 51. V Penwortham St Mary *Blackb* 62-90; RD Leyland 70-84; Hon Can Blackb Cathl 79-90; rtd 90. *4 Queensdale Close, Walton-le-Dale, Preston PR5 4JU* Preston (01772) 259010

REES, David Grenfell. b 18. St D Coll Lamp BA40 Qu Coll Birm. **d** 43 **p** 44. V Dyffryn *Llan* 60-84; Perm to Offic from 84; rtd 84. *10 Tyn-yr-Heol Road, Bryncoch, Neath, W Glam SA10 7EA* Neath (01639) 644488

REES, Canon David Philip Dunn Hugh. b 38. Jes Coll Ox BA60 MA64 Ox Univ DipEd67. Westcott Ho Cam 62. **d** 64 **p** 65. C Salford St Phil w St Steph *Man* 64-66; Perm to Offic *St As* 66-67; Perm to Offic *Derby* 67-74; Chapl St Marg C of E High Sch Aigburth Liv 74-83; V Meliden and Gwaenysgor *St As* from 84; Dioc Adv for Schs from 85; Warden of Readers from 89; Warden of Ords from 91; Hon Can St As Cathl 93-95; Can Cursal from 95. *The Vicarage, Meliden, Prestatyn, Clwyd LL19 8HN* Prestatyn (01745) 856220

REES, David Richard. b 60. St Mich Coll Llan DipTh84. **d** 84 **p** 85. C Llanstadwel *St D* 84-86; C Carmarthen St Dav 86-91; V Llanrhian w Llanhywel and Carnhedryn etc from 91. *The Vicarage, Llanrhian, Haverfordwest, Dyfed SA62 5BG* Croesgoch (01348) 831354

REES, Eric Vernon. b 19. St Jo Coll Dur BA41 MA44. St Andr Pampisford 43. **d** 43 **p** 44. C-in-c Enfield St Giles CD *Lon* 68-80; C Edmonton All SS 80-82; C Edmonton All SS w St Mich 82-90; rtd 90. *45 Monmouth Road, London N9 0JB* 0181-807 4329

REES, Gruffydd Nicholas. b 23. Univ of Wales (Lamp) BA46. Wycliffe Hall Ox 46. **d** 48 **p** 49. V Llanbister and Llanbadarn Fynydd w Llananno *S & B* 62-75; V New Radnor and Llanfihangel Nantmelan etc 75-84; V Llangenni and Llanbedr Ystrad Yw w Patricio 84-88; rtd 88. *Trefilan, 26 Lakeside Avenue, Llandrindod Wells, Powys LD1 5NT* Llandrindod Wells (01597) 825451

REES, James Arthur. b 04. Qu Coll Newfoundland 25. **d** 28 **p** 29. R W Tarring *Chich* 58-75; rtd 75; RD Worthing *Chich* 75-80; Perm to Offic 80-84. *11 Bath Road, Worthing, W Sussex BN11 3NU* Worthing (01903) 207820

REES, John Harold. b 15. St Mich Coll Llan 53. **d** 54 **p** 55. V Llanarthne and Llanddarog *St D* 66-83; rtd 83. *Erwlon, Cwmisfael Road, Llanddarog, Carmarthen, Dyfed SA32 8NU* Llanddarog (01267) 275219

✠REES, Rt Rev John Ivor. b 26. Univ of Wales (Abth) BA50. Westcott Ho Cam 50. **d** 52 **p** 53 **c** 88. C Fishguard w Llanychar *St D* 52-55; C Llangathen w Llanfihangel Cilfargen 55-57; P-in-c Uzmaston and Boulston 57-59; V Slebech and Uzmaston w Boulston 59-65; V Llangollen and Trevor *St As* 65-74; RD Llangollen 70-74; R Wrexham 74-76; Can St As Cathl 75-76; Dean Ban 76-88; V Ban Cathl Par 79-88; Asst Bp St D 88-91; Adn St D 88-91; Bp St D 91-95; Sub-Prelate OStJ from 93; rtd 95. *Llys Dewi, 45 Clover Park, Uzmaston Road, Haverford West, Dyfed SA61 1UE* Haverfordwest (01437) 764846

REES, John Martin Rawlins Gore. b 30. St D Coll Lamp BA53. **d** 55 **p** 57. V Penycae *St As* 61-73; V Northop 73-83; V Bickerton w Bickley *Ches* 83-91; Lic to Offic from 91; rtd 95. *Hafod, 9 High Park, Gwernaffield, Mold, Clwyd CH7 5EE* Mold (01352) 740412

REES, Ven John Wynford Joshua. b 24. Univ of Wales (Lamp) BA52. **d** 53 **p** 54. V Llanyre w Llanfihangel Helygen, Llanwrthwl etc *S & B* 60-71; R Llanyre w Llanfihangel Helygen and Diserth 71-87; V Llanllyr-yn-Rhos w Llanfihangel Helygen 87-94; RD Maelienydd 74-87; Hon Can Brecon Cathl 77-79; Can Res 79-94; Treas 83-87; Adn Brecon 87-94; rtd 94. *Denebrook, Ithan Road, Llandrindod Wells, Powys LD1 6AS* Llandrindod Wells (01597) 823573

REES, Ms Judith Margaret (Judy). b 39. Southn Univ BTh89. **dss** 86 **d** 87 **p** 94. Sanderstead All SS *S'wark* 86-87; Par Dn 87; Dir Cottesloe Chr Tr Progr *Ox* from 89; Par Dn Gt Horwood 89-91; Par Dn Winslow w Gt Horwood and Addington 91-94; C from 94. *15 Weston Road, Great Horwood, Milton Keynes MK17 0QR* Winslow (01296) 713603

✠**REES, Rt Rev Leslie Lloyd.** b 19. Kelham Th Coll 36. **d** 42 **p** 43 **c** 80. C Roath St Sav *Llan* 42-45; Asst Chapl HM Pris Cardiff 42-45; Chapl HM Pris Dur 45-48; V Princetown *Ex* 48-55; Chapl HM Pris Dartmoor 48-55; Chapl HM Pris Win 55-62; Chapl Gen of Pris 62-80; Hon Can Cant Cathl *Cant* 66-80; Chapl to The Queen 71-80; Hon Can Lich Cathl *Lich* 80-86; Suff Bp Shrewsbury 80-86; rtd 86; Asst Bp Win from 87. *Kingfisher Lodge, 20 Arle Gardens, Alresford, Hants SO24 9BA* Alresford (01962) 734619

REES, Michael Lloyd. b 51. St D Coll Lamp DipTh74. **d** 74 **p** 75. C Cardigan and Mwnt and Y Ferwig *St D* 74-77; Min Can St D Cathl 77-81; TV Abth 81-83; Dioc Children's Adv from 83; V Pen-boyr 83-88; V Henfynyw w Aberaeron and Llanddewi Aberarth from 88. *The Vicarage, Panteg Road, Aberaeron, Dyfed SA46 0EP* Aberaeron (01545) 570433

REES, Percival Antony Everard. b 35. Pemb Coll Ox BA56 MA59. Clifton Th Coll 58. **d** 60 **p** 61. C Heatherlands St Jo *Sarum* 60-65 and 69-70; India 65-69; V W Hampstead St Luke *Lon* 70-82; Lect Oak Hill Th Coll 82-86; V Enfield Ch Ch Trent Park *Lon* from 87. *Christ Church Vicarage, Chalk Lane, Barnet, Herts EN4 9JQ* 0181-441 1230 or 449 0556

REES, Peter Frederick Ransom. b 18. Lon Univ BA47. Linc Th Coll 47. **d** 49 **p** 50. V Laneside *Blackb* 53-83; rtd 83; Lic to Offic *Blackb* from 84. *11 Rydal Road, Morecambe, Lancs LA3 1DT* Morecambe (01524) 424482

REES, Philip William Watkins. b 11. St D Coll Lamp BA33 St Steph Ho Ox 33. **d** 34 **p** 35. V Swansea St Mark *S & B* 53-78; rtd 78. *22 Ffynone Drive, Swansea SA1 6DP* Swansea (01792) 473776

REES, Canon Richard John Edward Williams. b 36. Univ of Wales (Lamp) BA58. St Mich Coll Llan 58. **d** 60 **p** 61. C St Issells *St D* 60-64; C Llanedy 64-67; V Whitchurch w Solva and St Elvis 67-77; RD Dewisland and Fishguard from 73; V Whitchurch w Solva and St Elvis w Brawdy etc from 77; Can St D Cathl from 87. *The Vicarage, Whitchurch, Solva, Haverfordwest, Dyfed SA62 6UP* St Davids (01437) 721281

REES, Canon Richard Michael. b 36. St Pet Hall Ox BA57 MA61. Tyndale Hall Bris 57. **d** 59 **p** 60. C Crowborough *Chich* 59-62; C Clifton Ch Ch w Em *Bris* 62-64; V Clevedon Ch Ch *B & W* 64-72; V Cam H Trin *Ely* 72-84; Lic to Offic *S'wark* 84-90; Chief Sec CA 84-90; Can Res Ches Cathl *Ches* from 90; Dioc Missr from 90. *5 Abbey Green, Chester CH1 2JH* Chester (01244) 347500

REES, Canon Sidney. b 12. St D Coll Lamp BA34 St Mich Coll Llan 35. **d** 37 **p** 38. V Whitland and Kiffig *St D* 65-79; Can St D Cathl 77-79; rtd 79. *10 Morfa Lane, Carmarthen, Dyfed SA31 3AS* Carmarthen (01267) 235757

REES, Vivian John Howard. b 51. Southn Univ LLB72 Ox Univ BA79 MA84 Leeds Univ MPhil84. Wycliffe Hall Ox 76. **d** 79 **p** 80. C Moor Allerton *Ripon* 79-82; Sierra Leone 82-86; Lic to Offic *Ox* from 86. *Oxford Diocesan Registry, 16 Beaumont Street, Oxford OX1 2LZ* Oxford (01865) 241974 Fax 726274

REES, William David Cledwyn. b 25. FRGS54 Qu Coll Cam BA49 DipEd50 MA52 Univ of Wales MA75 PhD81. St Deiniol's Hawarden 63. **d** 65 **p** 66. Hon C Rhyl w St Ann *St As* 65-72; Chapl and Lect St Mary's Coll Ban 72-77; Lic to Offic *Ban* 72-77; Lect Univ of Wales (Ban) from 77; Chapl Univ of Wales (Ban) *Ban* 77-84; Sec Dioc Schs Cttee 84-86. *Anwylfa, Fron Park Avenue, Llanfairfechan, Gwynedd LL33 0AS* Llanfairfechan (01248) 680054

REES, Canon William Elfyn. b 17. St D Coll Lamp BA37 Wycliffe Hall Ox 38. **d** 40 **p** 45. R Alverstoke *Portsm* 62-82; rtd 82. *28 Church Close, Llangynidr, Crickhowell, Powys NP8 1NY* Bwlch (01874) 730125

REESE, John David. b 49. Cuddesdon Coll 73. **d** 76 **p** 77. C Kidderminster St Mary *Worc* 76-81; Malaysia 81-85; V Bishop's Castle w Mainstone *Heref* 85-91; RD Clun Forest 87-91; V Tupsley w Hampton Bishop from 91; P-in-c Hampton Bishop and Mordiford w Dormington from 91. *The Vicarage, 107 Church Road, Hereford HR1 1RT* Hereford (01432) 274490

REEVE, Canon Brian Charles. b 36. Lon Univ BSc57 BD60. Tyndale Hall Bris 58. **d** 61 **p** 62. C Eccleston St Luke *Liv* 61-63; C Upton (or Overchurch) *Ches* 63-65; C Pemberton St Mark

Newtown *Liv* 65-68; V Macclesfield Ch Ch *Ches* 68-74; V Stone Ch Ch *Lich* 74-84; RD Trentham 77-84; V Hoole *Ches* 84-94; Chapl Ches City Hosp 84-91; P-in-c Alderley *Ches* from 94; Hon Can Ches Cathl from 94. *St Mary's Rectory, Nether Alderley, Macclesfield, Cheshire SK10 4TW* Alderley Edge (01625) 583134

REEVE, David Michael. b 44. St Cath Coll Cam BA67 MA71. Coll of Resurr Mirfield 68. **d** 70 **p** 71. C Willingdon *Chich* 70-73; C Hove All SS 73-76; C Moulsecoomb 76-80; R Singleton 80-90; V E Dean 80-90; V W Dean 80-90; R Hurstpierpoint from 90. *The Rectory, 21 Cuckfield Road, Hurstpierpoint, Hassocks, W Sussex BN6 9RP* Hurstpierpoint (01273) 832203

REEVE, Kenneth John (Ken). b 42. Sarum & Wells Th Coll DCM93. **d** 93 **p** 94. C Thorpe St Matt *Nor* from 93. *15 Stanley Avenue, Norwich NR7 0BE* Norwich (01603) 33870

REEVE, Kenneth Robert. b 23. St Cath Coll Ox BA49 MA53. Sarum Th Coll 64. **d** 68 **p** 69. Hon C Farleigh Hungerford w Tellisford *B & W* 68-71; Hon C Norton St Philip 72-74; Hon C Hinton Charterhouse 72-74; Seychelles 74-76; Perm to Offic *B & W* from 77; Perm to Offic *Chich* 78-82. *Sundial, Hill Close, Wincanton, Somerset BA9 9NF* Wincanton (01963) 33369

REEVE, Richard Malcolm. b 64. Reading Univ BSc85. Trin Coll Bris BA92. **d** 92 **p** 93. C Northolt St Mary *Lon* 92-95; C Acton Green from 95. *276 Osborne Road, London W3 8SR* 0181-993 3237

REEVE, Dr Richard Noel. b 29. MB, ChB. St Deiniol's Hawarden. **d** 84 **p** 85. Hon C Norton *Ches* 84-85; C Filey *York* 85-87; TV Brayton 87-90; rtd 90; Perm to Offic *Man* 90-93. *Kynance, Albert Street, Stone, Staffs ST15 8HQ* Stone (01785) 813796

REEVE, Preb Roger Patrick. b 42. Fitzw Coll Cam BA65 MA68. Coll of Resurr Mirfield. **d** 67 **p** 68. C Barnstaple St Pet w H Trin *Ex* 67-74; V Ernesettle 74-78; V Braunton from 78; RD Barnstaple 85-93; Preb Ex Cathl from 92. *The Vicarage, Church Street, Braunton, Devon EX33 2EL* Braunton (01271) 813367

REEVE, Canon Ronald Ernest. b 22. St Pet Hall Ox BA48 MA52 BD54 Ox Univ DPhil76. Wycliffe Hall Ox 48. **d** 50 **p** 51. Canada from 63; Prof Bp's Univ Lennoxville & Can Quebec Cathl 68-88; rtd 88. *1137 rue Vimont, Sillery, Quebec, Canada, G1S 3P9* Quebec City (418) 681-6511

REEVES, Christopher. b 30. Nottm Univ BA53. Wells Th Coll 53. **d** 55 **p** 56. C Rowbarton *B & W* 55-59; C Cant St Greg *Cant* 59-61; Chapl Schiedam Miss to Seamen *Eur* 61-67; V Barkingside H Trin *Chelmsf* from 67. *Barkingside Vicarage, Mossford Green, Ilford, Essex IG6 2BJ* 0181-550 2669

REEVES, David Eric. b 46. Sarum Th Coll 68. **d** 71 **p** 72. C Guildf H Trin w St Mary *Guildf* 71-74; C Warmsworth *Sheff* 74-78; V Herringthorpe 78-90; V Cleveleys *Blackb* from 90; RD Poulton from 94. *The Vicarage, Rough Lea Road, Thornton Cleveleys, Lancs FY5 1DP* Blackpool (01253) 852153

REEVES, Donald St John. b 34. Qu Coll Cam BA57 MA61. Cuddesdon Coll 62. **d** 63 **p** 64. C Maidstone All SS w St Phil *Cant* 63-65; Bp's Dom Chapl *S'wark* 65-68; V St Helier 69-80; R Westmr St Jas *Lon* from 80. *St James's Rectory, 197 Piccadilly, London W1V 9LF* 0171-734 4511

REEVES, Elizabeth Anne. *See* THOMAS, Mrs Elizabeth Anne

REEVES, Gillian Patricia. b 46. S'wark Ord Course 87. **d** 90 **p** 94. Par Dn Shirley St Geo *S'wark* 90-94; C from 94. *3 Malcolm Road, London SE25 5HE* 0181-654 7702

REEVES, Graham. b 65. Chich Th Coll BTh94. **d** 94 **p** 95. C Cardiff St Mary and St Steph w St Dyfrig etc *Llan* from 94. *43 Pentre Street, Cardiff CF1 7QX* Cardiff (01222) 230054

REEVES, James Lacey (Jim). b 23. FCIS58. S'wark Ord Course 60. **d** 74 **p** 75. NSM Wisborough Green *Chich* 74-81; C Horsham 81-83; R W Chiltington 83-92; rtd 93. *4 Borough House, North Street, Midhurst, W Sussex GU29 9DX* Midhurst (01730) 815122

REEVES, John Graham. b 44. Kelham Th Coll 64. **d** 69 **p** 71. C Aston cum Aughton *Sheff* 69-71; C Ribbleton *Blackb* 72-74; C Cleveleys 74-75; P-in-c Huncoat 75-77; V 77-82; V Knuzden 82-92; V Sandylands from 92. *St John's Vicarage, 2 St John's Avenue, Morecambe, Lancs LA3 1EU* Morecambe (01524) 411299

REEVES, Kenneth Gordon. b 32. K Coll Lon BD53 AKC53 CertEd54. Ripon Coll Cuddesdon 86. **d** 87 **p** 88. NSM Dorchester *Ox* 87-89; V Deddington w Barford, Clifton and Hempton from 89. *The Vicarage, Earls Lane, Deddington, Banbury, Oxon OX15 0TJ* Deddington (01869) 338329

REEVES, Kenneth William. b 38. TCD 67 NUI DipSocSc76. **d** 69 **p** 70. C Killowen *D & R* 69-70; I Ardara 70-76; TV Quidenham *Nor* 76-81; V Swaffham 81-86; Chapl Nor Coll of Educn 86-91; P-in-c Lakenham St Alb *Nor* 86-91; rtd 92; Perm to Offic *Nor* from 92. *15 Morris Close, Stoke Holy Cross, Norwich NR14 8LL* Framingham Earl (01508) 494583

REEVES, Nicholas John Harding. b 44. ALCD69. d 69 p 70. C Upton (or Overchurch) *Ches* 69-72; C Woodlands *Sheff* 72-74; C-in-c Cranham Park CD *Chelmsf* 74-79; V Cranham Park 79-88; R Aldridge *Lich* from 88. *The Rectory, 14 The Green, Aldridge, Walsall WS9 8NH* Aldridge (01922) 52414

REGAN, Brian. b 46. MBIM80. W Midl Minl Tr Course 88. d 91 p 92. C Cov St Jo *Cov* 91-94; FSJ from 93; V Tile Hill *Cov* from 94. *St Oswald's Vicarage, 228 Jardine Crescent, Coventry CV4 9PL* Coventry (01203) 465072

REGAN, Philip. b 49. Qu Mary Coll Lon BSc MSc. Wycliffe Hall Ox 81. d 83 p 84. Hon C Scotforth *Blackb* 83-89; P-in-c Combe St Nicholas w Wambrook *B & W* from 89; P-in-c Whitestaunton from 89. *The Vicarage, Combe St Nicholas, Chard, Somerset TA20 3NJ* Chard (01460) 62121

REGINALD, Brother. *See* BOX, Reginald Gilbert

REGLAR, Canon Gerald John. b 11. Melbourne Univ BA Ox Univ MA48. Kelham Th Coll 34. d 37 p 38. C Cowley St Jo *Ox* 37-40; Australia from 40. *13 Binnowie Street, Ingle Farm, S Australia 5098* Adelaide (8) 263-8473

REID, Amanda Joy. *See* MARRIOTT, Mrs Amanda Joy

REID, Andrew John. b 47. Birm Univ BEd70 Man Univ MEd76 Lon Univ DipRS88. S'wark Ord Course 88. d 88 p 89. NSM Westerham *Roch* 88-90; Chapl Abp Tenison Gr Sch Kennington from 90. *Archbishop Tenison's School, 55 Kennington Oval, London SE11 5SR* 0171-435 3771 or 435 6126

REID, Canon Colin Guthrie. b 30. d 56 p 57. R Caldbeck w Castle Sowerby *Carl* 60-76; RD Wigton 69-70; P-in-c Sebergham 75-76; R Caldbeck, Castle Sowerby and Sebergham 76-93; Hon Can Carl Cathl 88-93; rtd 93. *Mellbreak, Longthwaite Road, Wigton, Cumbria CA7 9JR* Wigton (016973) 45625

REID, Donald. b 58. Glas Univ LLB79 Pemb Coll Ox MPhil81 Edin Univ BD85. Edin Th Coll 82. d 85 p 86. C Greenock *Glas* 85-88; C Baillieston 88-91; R 91-95; C Glas St Serf 87-91; R 91-95; Chapl Glas Univ from 95. *212 Wilton Street, Glasgow G20 6BL* 0141-946 1074

REID, Very Rev Douglas William John. b 34. Edin Th Coll 60. d 63 p 64. C Ayr *Glas* 63-68; R Glas St Jas 68-73; R Glas St Ninian from 73; Syn Clerk 79-87; Can St Mary's Cathl 79-87; Dean Glas from 87. *32 Glencairn Drive, Glasgow G41 4PW* 0141-423 1247

✠REID, Rt Rev Gavin Hunter. b 34. K Coll Lon BA56. Oak Hill Th Coll 58. d 60 p 61 c 92. C E Ham St Paul *Chelmsf* 60-63; C Rainham 63-66; Publications Sec CPAS 66-71; Hon C St Paul's Cray St Barn *Roch* 68-71; Ed Sec USCL 71-74; Hon C Woking St Jo *Guildf* 72-92; Sec for Evang CPAS 74-92; Consultant Missr CPAS and BMU Adv 90-92; Suff Bp Maidstone *Cant* from 92; Six Preacher Cant Cathl from 92. *Bishop's House, Pett Lane, Charing, Ashford, Kent TN27 0DL* Charing (01233) 712950 Fax 713543

REID, Herbert Alan. b 31. AKC55. d 56 p 57. C Penwortham St Mary *Blackb* 56-59; C-in-c Penwortham St Leon CD 59-63; V Brierfield 63-72; V Warton St Paul 72-79; V Read in Whalley from 79. *The Vicarage, George Lane, Read, Burnley, Lancs BB12 7RQ* Padiham (01282) 771361

REID, Hugh Gamble. b 33. Roch Th Coll 63. d 64 p 64. Chapl HM Borstal Everthorpe 69-71; Chapl HM Pris Dur 71-74; Chapl HM Pris Wakef 74-77; V Northowram *Wakef* 77-79; Chapl HM Pris Coldingley 79-81; Chapl HM Rem Cen Risley 81-85; Chapl HM Pris Holloway 85-88; C Guilden Morden *Ely* 88-89; C Shingay Gp of Par 90; R Upwell Ch Ch 90-93; R Welney 90-93; rtd 93. *Banff, 23 Northwold, Ely, Cambs CB6 1BG* Ely (01353) 663924

REID, Canon Ian Davison. b 37. Liv Univ BA61 MA63. Clifton Th Coll 63. d 65 p 66. C Edge Hill St Cath *Liv* 65-68; C Heworth *York* 68-76; V Linthorpe from 76; Can and Preb York Minster from 90. *5 Park Road South, Middlesbrough, Cleveland TS5 6LD* Middlesbrough (01642) 817306

REID, James. b 46. Strathclyde Univ BSc69. W Midl Minl Tr Course 88. d 91 p 92. C Attleborough *Cov* 91-95; V Walsall Pleck and Bescot *Lich* from 95. *St John's Vicarage, Vicarage Terrace, Walsall WS2 9HB* Walsall (01922) 31989

REID, Peter Ivor. b 30. Qu Coll Cam BA53 MA72. St Mich Coll Llan 78. d 80 p 81. C Llantwit Major and St Donat's *Llan* 80-83; C Llantwit Major 83-84; V Laleston w Tythegston 84-88; V Laleston w Tythegston and Merthyr Mawr 84-88; V Roath St Marg from 88. *Roath Vicarage, Waterloo Road, Cardiff CF2 5AD* Cardiff (01222) 484808

REID, Stewart Thomas. b 45. Oak Hill Th Coll 66. d 70 p 71. C Normanton *Derby* 70-73; C Leyland St Andr *Blackb* 73-78; V Halliwell St Luke *Man* 78-95; V Southport Ch Ch *Liv* from 95. *The Vicarage, 12 Gloucester Road, Southport, Merseyside PR8 2AU* Southport (01704) 565120

REID, Canon William Gordon. b 43. Edin Univ MA63 Keble Coll Ox BA66 MA72. Edin Th Coll 63 Cuddesdon Coll 66. d 67 p 68. C Edin St Salvador *Edin* 67-69; Chapl and Tutor Sarum Th Coll 69-72; R Edin St Mich and All SS *Edin* 72-84; Provost St Andr Cathl Inverness *Mor* 84-87; Chapl Ankara

Eur 87-89; Chapl Stockholm w Gavle and Vasteras 89-92; V Gen to Bp Eur from 92; Can Gib Cathl from 92. *4 The Courtyard, Barnsbury Terrace, London N1 1JH* 0171-607 3834

REID, Canon William Frederick (Eric). b 22. OBE88. TCD BA45 MA53. d 46 p 47. Chapl Netherne Hosp Coulsdon 67-76; C-in-c Netherne St Luke CD *S'wark* 67-76; Lic to Offic from 76; Sec and Dir Tr Gen Syn Hosp Chapl Coun 76-87; Hon Can Newc Cathl *Newc* 79-88; rtd 88. *65 Lagham Park, South Godstone, Godstone, Surrey RH9 8EP* South Godstone (01342) 893312

REIGATE, Archdeacon of. *Vacant*

REILLY, Frederick James. b 29. CITC 70. d 73 p 74. C Agherton *Conn* 73-75; C Ballymena 75-82; I Ballyscullion *D & R* from 82. *The Rectory, 8 Ballynease Road, Bellaghy, Co Londonderry BT45 8JD* Bellaghy (0164886) 214

REILLY, Thomas Gerard. b 38. d 64 p 64. In RC Ch 64-73; Hon C Clapton Park All So *Lon* 73-76; Hon C Haggerston All SS 76-78; Hon C Walthamstow St Sav *Chelmsf* 79-85; P-in-c Forest Gate Em w Upton Cross 85-89; V 89-92; V Chaddesden St Phil *Derby* from 92. *St Philip's Vicarage, Taddington Road, Chaddesden, Derby DE21 4JU* Derby (01332) 673428

REILY, Paul Alan. b 59. UEA BA81. St Jo Coll Nottm DTS91 MA92. d 92 p 93. C Westcliff St Mich *Chelmsf* from 92. *35 Fernleigh Drive, Leigh-on-Sea, Essex SS9 1LG* Southend-on-Sea (01702) 72386

REINDORP, David Peter Edington. b 52. Trin Coll Cam BA82 MA86 CQSW DASS. Westcott Ho Cam 79. d 83 p 84. C Chesterton Gd Shep *Ely* 83-85; C Hitchin *St Alb* 85-88; V Waterbeach *Ely* from 88; R Landbeach from 88; OCF from 88; RD Quy *Ely* from 94. *The Vicarage, 3 Chapel Street, Waterbeach, Cambridge CB5 9HR* Cambridge (01223) 860353

REINDORP, Michael Christopher Julian. b 44. Trin Coll Cam BA67 MA70. Cuddesdon Coll 67 United Th Coll Bangalore 68. d 69 p 70. C Poplar *Lon* 69-74; V Chatham St Wm *Roch* 74-84; R Stantonbury *Ox* 84-87; TR Stantonbury and Willen 87-92; P-in-c Richmond St Mary w St Matthias and St Jo *S'wark* from 92. *The Vicarage, Ormond Road, Richmond, Surrey TW10 6TH* 0181-940 0362

REISS, Michael Jonathan. b 58. FIBiol90 Trin Coll Cam BA78 MA82 PhD82 PGCE83. E Anglian Minl Tr Course 87. d 90 p 91. NSM Comberton *Ely* from 90. *7 Barrons Way, Comberton, Cambridge CB3 7EQ* Cambridge (01223) 262958

REISS, Peter Henry. b 62. Hertf Coll Ox BA85 MA91 Natal Univ MA95. Trin Coll Bris DipHE90 St Jo Coll Nottm 95. d 95. C Sherwood *S'well* from 95. *56 Edwinstowe Drive, Nottingham NG5 3EP* Nottingham (0115) 962 0899

REISS, Robert Paul. b 43. Trin Coll Cam BA67 MA71. Westcott Ho Cam 67. d 69 p 70. C St Jo Wood *Lon* 69-73; Bangladesh 73; Chapl Trin Coll Cam 73-78; Selection Sec ACCM 78-85; Sen Selection Sec 83; TR Grantham *Linc* from 86; RD Grantham from 92. *The Rectory, Church Street, Grantham, Lincs NG31 6RR* Grantham (01476) 63710

REITH, Ivor Stuart Weston. b 16. Ridley Hall Cam 65. d 66 p 67. R Angmering *Chich* 69-81; rtd 81; Perm to Offic *Chich* from 84. *10 Cross Road, Southwick, Brighton BN42 4HE* Brighton (01273) 597301

REITH, Robert Michael. b 55. Oak Hill Th Coll BA83. d 83 p 84. C Kendal St Thos *Carl* 83-87; C Leyland St Andr *Blackb* 87-92; V Leyland St Jo 92-94; TR Dagenham *Chelmsf* from 94. *The Vicarage, Church Lane, Dagenham, Essex RM10 9UL* 0181-592 1339

REMPEY, Philip Roland. b 19. Glouc Th Course 74. d 76 p 76. NSM Charlton Kings St Mary *Glouc* 76-88; Perm to Offic from 88. *87 Ravensgate Road, Charlton Kings, Cheltenham, Glos GL53 8NS* Cheltenham (01242) 519313

RENDALL, Canon John Albert. b 43. Hull Univ BTh84 MA89. Ripon Hall Ox 65. d 68 p 69. C Southsea St Simon *Portsm* 68-71; C Wallington H Trin *S'wark* 71-77; P-in-c Rufforth w Moor Monkton and Hessay *York* 77-79; R from 79; P-in-c Long Marston 77-79; R from 79; RD New Ainsty from 85; Can York Minster from 94. *The Vicarage, Rufforth, York YO2 3QB* Rufforth (01904) 738262

RENDALL, Richard John. b 54. Solicitor 78 Wadh Coll Ox BA76 LLB76 MA92. Wycliffe Hall Ox 90. d 92 p 93. C Heswall *Ches* from 92. *15 Castle Drive, Heswall, Wirral, Merseyside L60 4RY* 0151-342 1598

RENDELL, Peter Vivian. b 26. K Coll Lon 48. d 52 p 53. V Felton *Newc* 74-77; V Tynemouth Cullercoats St Paul 77-89; RD Tynemouth 83-87; rtd 89. *22 Woodburn Square, Whitley Bay, Tyne & Wear NE25 3JE* 0191-252 4916

RENFREY, Edward Donald John-Baptist. b 53. DipTh. St Barn Coll Adelaide 75. d 76 p 77. Australia 76-84; Chapl RN from 84. *Directorate Gen, RN Chapl Services, Room 203, Victory Building, HM Naval Base, Portsmouth PO1 3LS* Portsmouth (01705) 727903 Fax 727112

RENISON, Gary James. b 62. SS Hild & Bede Coll Dur BA83. Ridley Hall Cam 84. **d** 86 **p** 87. C Stapenhill w Cauldwell *Derby* 86-89; C Cheadle Hulme St Andr *Ches* 89-92; Min Cheadle Hulme Em CD from 92. *198 Bruntwood Lane, Cheadle Hulme, Cheadle, Cheshire SK8 6BE* 0161-485 1154

RENNARD, Edward Lionel. b 51. Nottm Univ BTh80. Linc Th Coll 76. **d** 80 **p** 81. C Old Brumby *Linc* 80-82; C-in-c Gt Grimsby St Matt Fairfield CD 82-86; V Fairfield St Matt 86-88; V Hykeham 88-91; TR from 91. *The Rectory, Mill Lane, North Hykeham, Lincoln LN6 9PA* Lincoln (01522) 681168

RENNARD, Margaret Rose. b 49. CertEd75. Linc Th Coll 76. **d** 87 **p** 94. C Fairfield St Matt *Linc* 87-88; C Hykeham from 88; Chapl HM Pris Morton Hall from 91. *The Rectory, Mill Lane, North Hykeham, Lincoln LN6 9PA* Lincoln (01522) 681168 Fax 868068

RENNIE, Iain Hugh. b 43. Ripon Coll Cuddesdon 88. **d** 90 **p** 91. C Poulton-le-Sands w Morecambe St Laur *Blackb* 90-94; V Hornby w Claughton from 94. *The Vicarage, Main Street, Hornby, Lancaster LA2 8JY* Hornby (015242) 221238

RENNIE, Paul Antony. b 58. Heriot-Watt Univ BSc82 Edin Univ LTh. **d** 87 **p** 88. C Nairn *Mor* 87-90; C Forres 87-90; C Edin St Pet *Edin* 90-92; Dep Chapl HM Pris Leeds 92; Chapl HM Young Offender Inst Hindley 93-95; Chapl HM Pris Liv from 95. *HM Prison, 68 Hornby Road, Liverpool L9 3DF* 0151-525 5971 Fax 525 0813

RENNISON, Walter Patrick. b 18. MBE52. TCD BA40 MA45. **d** 42 **p** 43. CF 45-73; V Milland *Chich* 73-87; rtd 87. *14 Heathfield Court, Fleet, Hants GU13 8DX* Fleet (01252) 615358

RENOUF, Peter Mark. b 30. Down Coll Cam BA55 MA59 Cam Univ DipEd56. Ridley Hall Cam. **d** 58 **p** 59. C Rainham *Chelmsf* 58-61; Asst Chapl Wellington Coll Berks 61-63; Chapl 63-69; V Eastbourne All SS *Chich* 69-78; R Farnborough *Guildf* 78-84; C Welford w Wickham and Gt Shefford *Ox* 85-86; C Welford w Wickham and Gt Shefford, Boxford etc 86-89; P-in-c Beedon and Peasemore w W Ilsley and Farnborough from 89. *The Vicarage, Beedon, Newbury, Berks RG16 8SW* East Ilsley (01635) 281244

RENOWDEN, Very Rev Charles Raymond. b 23. Univ of Wales (Lamp) BA44 Selw Coll Cam BA49 MA53. Ridley Hall Cam 50. **d** 51 **p** 52. Sen Lect 67-71; Dean and Lib St As Cathl *St As* 71-92; P-in-c Cefn 71-88; V St As 71-80; V St As and Tremeirchion 80-92; rtd 92. *17 Llys Idris, St Asaph, Clwyd LL17 0AJ* St Asaph (01745) 584591

RENOWDEN, Ven Glyndwr Rhys. b 29. CB87. St D Coll Lamp BA49 LTh52. **d** 52 **p** 53. C Tenby and Gumfreston *St D* 52-55; C Chepstow *Mon* 55-58; Chapl RAF 58-75; Asst Chapl-in-Chief RAF 75-83; Chapl-in-Chief RAF 83-88; QHC from 80; Can and Preb Linc Cathl *Linc* 83-88; P-in-c Llanfallteg w Clunderwen and Castell Dwyran *St D* from 89. *Red Cedars, Kenystyle, Penally, Tenby, Dyfed SA70 7PH* Tenby (01834) 842673

RENSHAW, Anthony. b 40. McGill Univ Montreal LTh87 DipMin87. Montreal Dioc Th Coll 83. **d** 87 **p** 88. Canada 87-90; P-in-c Ainsdale *Liv* 90-91; V from 91. *The Vicarage, 708 Liverpool Road, Southport, Merseyside PR8 3QE* Southport (01704) 577760

RENSHAW, David William. b 59. Oak Hill Th Coll BA85. **d** 85 **p** 86. C Shawbury *Lich* 85-88; V Childs Ercall 88-92; R Stoke upon Tern 88-92; V Stoneleigh *Guildf* from 92; RD Epsom from 95. *The Vicarage, Stoneleigh Park Road, Stoneleigh, Surrey KT19 0QU* 0181-393 3738

RENSHAW, Peter Selwyn Kay. b 29. Keble Coll Ox BA52 MA64. St Steph Ho Ox 52. **d** 64 **p** 65. Chapl RN 66-70; Chapl Athens St Paul and Br Emb *Eur* 71-74; Gothenburg 74-75; Chapl RN Sch Haslemere 75-81; Costa Blanca *Eur* 81-82; R Ewelme *Ox* 83-85; R Ewelme, Brightwell Baldwin, Cuxham w Easington 85-92; rtd 92. *Lovedays House, Painswick, Stroud, Glos GL6 6QB* Painswick (01452) 812811

RENWICK, Colin. b 30. St Aid Birkenhead. **d** 59 **p** 60. C Drypool St Columba w St Andr and St Pet *York* 59-62; C Wigan St Cath *Liv* 62-64; Min Thornton CD 64-77; V Thornton from 77; RD Bootle 83-89. *The Vicarage, Water Street, Liverpool L23 1TB* 0151-931 4676

RENYARD, Christopher. b 52. Open Univ BA87. Coll of Resurr Mirfield 81. **d** 84 **p** 85. C Heckmondwike *Wakef* 84-88; C Harpenden St Nic *St Alb* 88-95; Asst Chapl Salisbury Gen Infirmary from 95. *Salisbury District Hospital, Salisbury SP2 8BJ* Salisbury (01722) 336262

RENYARD, Paul Holmwood. b 42. K Coll Lon BD65 AKC65. **d** 66 **p** 67. C Croydon St Aug *Cant* 66-69; C Farnham *Guildf* 69-72; V Capel 72-78; Asst Dir RE 72-78; Asst Dir RE *Roch* 78-83; Hon C Roch 78-83; V Holdenhurst *Win* 83-95; V Pennington from 95. *The Vicarage, 29 Ramley Road, Pennington, Lymington, Hants SO41 8LH* Lymington (01590) 672646

REPATH, George David. b 43. Univ of Wales (Lamp) DipTh68. **d** 68 **p** 69. C Cardiff St Jo *Llan* 68-73; C Gt Stanmore *Lon* 73-77; V Stratfield Mortimer *Ox* 77-85; RD Bradfield 82-85; P-in-c Mortimer W End w Padworth 83-85; V Bray and Braywood from 85. *The Vicarage, Bray, Maidenhead, Berks SL6 2AB* Maidenhead (01628) 21527

REPATH, John Richard. b 48. Univ of Wales (Cardiff) DipTh75. St Mich Coll Llan 72. **d** 75 **p** 76. C Canton St Jo *Llan* 75-79; C Burghclere w Newtown and Ecchinswell w Sydmonton *Win* 80-83; R Bewcastle and Stapleton *Carl* 83-88; P-in-c Kirklinton w Hethersgill and Scaleby 86-88; R Bewcastle, Stapleton and Kirklinton etc from 88. *The Rectory, Stapleton, Carlisle CA6 6LD* Roadhead (016977) 48660

REPTON, Suffragan Bishop of. *See* RICHMOND, Rt Rev Francis Henry Arthur

RESTALL, Gerald Dalton. b 22. K Coll Lon BD50 AKC50. **d** 51 **p** 52. V Becontree St Eliz *Chelmsf* 62-71; CF (R of O) 69-77; R & V Reading St Mary *Ox* 72-77; R & V Reading St Mary w St Laur 77-88; rtd 88. *20 Sudbury Avenue, Hereford HR1 1YB* Hereford (01432) 279194

RESTALL, Miss Susan Roberta (Sue). b 45. SRD. Sarum & Wells Th Coll 79. **dss** 82 **d** 87 **p** 94. Dorchester *Sarum* 82-84; Portland All SS w St Pet 84-87; Par Dn 87; TD Yate New Town *Bris* 87-94; TV 94-95; Chapl Hartland NHS Trust Hosp Birm from 95. *Hartland NHS Trust Hospital, Bordesley Green East, Birmingham B9 5SS* 0121-766 6611 Fax 773 6897

REUSS, John Christopher Edward. b 1900. Lon Coll of Div 36. **d** 38 **p** 39. C Sydenham H Trin *S'wark* 38-39; Chapl RAF 39-45; R Longhope *Glouc* 45-46; Canada 46-48 and from 52; USA 48-52. *14627 Marine Drive, White Rock, British Columbia, Canada, V4B 1B8*

REVELL, Patrick Walter Millard. b 32. Wells Th Coll 65. **d** 67 **p** 68. C Leic St Jas *Leic* 67-74; V Quorndon 74-82; TR Camelot Par *B & W* 82-90; RD Cary from 90; RD Bruton from 90; V Castle Cary w Ansford from 90. *The Vicarage, Church Street, Castle Cary, Somerset BA7 7EJ* Castle Cary (01963) 351615

REVETT, Canon Graham Francis. b 40. AKC63. **d** 64 **p** 65. C Pennywell St Thos and Grindon St Oswald CD *Dur* 64-68; C Hartlepool St Aid 68-71; V Shiney Row 71-80; V Herrington 73-80; RD Houghton 76-80; TR Cullercoats St Geo *Newc* from 80; RD Tynemouth 87-92; Hon Can Newc Cathl from 94. *The Vicarage, Beverley Gardens, North Shields, Tyne & Wear NE30 4NS* 0191-252 1817

REX, James Maxwell. b 29. TD66. CEng59 FICE73. Trin Coll Bris 88. **d** 89 **p** 90. NSM Stoke Bishop *Bris* 89-91; Hon C Ashburnham w Penhurst *Chich* 92-93; P-in-c Danehill from 93. *The Vicarage, Danehill, Haywards Heath, W Sussex RH17 7ER* Dane Hill (01825) 790269

REX, Keith Leslie Herbert. b 30. K Coll Lon 53. **d** 55 **p** 56. R Charlton Adam w Charlton Mackrell *B & W* 67-69; rtd 90. *Chestnuts, 46 High Street, Heytesbury, Warminster, Wilts BA12 0EB*

REYNISH, David Stuart. b 52. Nottm Univ BEd75. Linc Th Coll 72. **d** 77 **p** 78. C Boston *Linc* 77-80; C Chalfont St Peter *Ox* 80-84; V Thursby *Carl* 84-88; R Iver Heath *Ox* from 88. *The Rectory, 2 Pinewood Close, Iver Heath, Iver, Bucks SL0 0QS* Iver (01753) 654470

REYNOLDS, Alan Martin. b 53. Sarum & Wells Th Coll 73. **d** 77 **p** 78. C Glan Ely *Llan* 77-84; V Pontyclun w Talygarn from 84. *The Vicarage, Heol Miskin, Pontyclun, M Glam CF7 9AJ* Llantrisant (01443) 225477

REYNOLDS, Alan Thomas William. b 43. Lon Univ BSc64. Linc Th Coll 64. **d** 66 **p** 67. C Leic St Pet *Leic* 66-70; C Huntington *York* 70-72; Jamaica 72-76; V Stechford *Birm* 76-83; P-in-c Hampton in Arden 83-86; V 87-93; Chapl E Birm Hosp 86-88; Chapl Parkway Hosp Solihull 88-93; V Moseley St Anne *Birm* from 93. *The Vicarage, 15 Park Hill, Birmingham B13 8DU* 0121-449 1071

REYNOLDS, Alfred Stanley. b 18. Birm Univ BSc39 Open Univ BA88. St Deiniol's Hawarden 69. **d** 70 **p** 71. Hon C Illogan *Truro* 70-85; Hon C Trowbridge St Thos and W Ashton *Sarum* from 85. *42 Cloford Close, Trowbridge, Wilts BA14 9DH* Trowbridge (01225) 763542

REYNOLDS, David Hammerton. b 39. St Jo Coll Dur BA62. Qu Coll Birm DipTh63. **d** 65 **p** 66. C N Ormesby *York* 65-68; C Hessle 68-71; V Sherburn in Elmet 71-79; V Fulford 79-87; Resp for Clergy In-Service Tr York Area 82-87; C Egloskerry *Truro* 87; TV Bolventor 87-90; TR Brayton *York* from 90. *The Rectory, Doncaster Road, Brayton, Selby, N Yorkshire YO8 9HE* Selby (01757) 704707

REYNOLDS, David James. b 48. St Jo Coll Dur BA72 DipTh73 Lanc Univ MA85. Cranmer Hall Dur 69. **d** 73 **p** 74. C Formby H Trin *Liv* 73-77; P-in-c Widnes St Paul 77-80; V Southport St Paul 80-87; P-in-c Mawdesley *Blackb* 87-91; R from 91; Chapl Derian Ho Children's Hospice from 93. *Mawdesley Rectory, Green Lane, Ormskirk, Lancs L40 3TH* Rufford (01704) 822203

REYNOLDS, Derrick Wilfrid. b 15. St Paul's Grahamstown LTh. **d** 49 **p** 50. V Sparkwell *Ex* 62-73; V Ilsington 73-86; rtd 86; Perm to Offic *Ex* from 86. *White Gates, 7 West Buckeridge Road, Teignmouth, Devon TQ14 8NF* Teignmouth (01626) 772165

REYNOLDS, Gordon. b 42. Sarum & Wells Th Coll 71. **d** 72 **p** 73. C Tunstall *Lich* 72-74; Zambia 75-88; C Southmead *Bris* 88-90; SSF from 90. *The Friary, Hilfield, Dorchester, Dorset DT2 7BE* Cerne Abbas (01300) 341345

REYNOLDS, Canon John Lionel. b 34. JP. Chich Th Coll 58. **d** 61 **p** 62. C Whitkirk *Ripon* 61-64; C Tong *Bradf* 64-68; V Chisledon and Draycot Foliatt *Sarum* 68-74; RD Marlborough 74-76; TR Ridgeway 74-76; V Calne and Blackland 76-89; RD Calne 77-84; Can and Preb Sarum Cathl from 80; V Woodford Valley from 89. *The Vicarage, Middle Woodford, Salisbury SP4 6NR* Salisbury (01722) 782310

REYNOLDS, John Stewart. b 19. FSA81 St Edm Hall Ox BA42 MA45 BLitt50. Ridley Hall Cam 42. **d** 44 **p** 45. R Besselsleigh w Dry Sandford *Ox* 56-85; Lect Wycliffe Hall Ox 71-78; rtd 85; Perm to Offic *Ox* from 85. *Linden Lodge, 59 St Mary's Road, Oxford OX4 1PZ* Oxford (01865) 727386

REYNOLDS, Paul Andrew. b 57. BA86. Trin Coll Bris 83. **d** 86 **p** 87. C Reading St Jo *Ox* 86-90; C Dorridge *Birm* from 90. *2 Hurst Green Road, Bentley Heath, Solihull, W Midlands B93 8AE* Knowle (01564) 775494

REYNOLDS, Paul Frederick. b 56. Lon Bible Coll DRBS78 St Jo Coll Nottm DipMM92. **d** 92 **p** 93. C Hyde St Geo *Ches* from 92. *121 Dowson Road, Hyde, Cheshire SK14 5HJ* 0161-367 9353

REYNOLDS, Philip Delamere. b 53. Leeds Univ CertEd74 Nottm Univ BCombStuds82. Linc Th Coll 79. **d** 82 **p** 83. C Huddersfield St Jo *Wakef* 82-85; C Barkisland w W Scammonden 85-87; P-in-c Skelmanthorpe from 87. *St Aidan's Vicarage, Radcliffe Street, Skelmanthorpe, Huddersfield HD8 9AF* Huddersfield (01484) 863232

REYNOLDS, Raymond Ernest. b 29. Nottm Univ MPhil89. Lambeth STh84 CA Tr Coll 50 Chich Th Coll 58. **d** 60 **p** 61. R Farnley *Ripon* 64-76; R Higham-on-the-Hill w Fenny Drayton *Leic* 76-81; R Higham-on-the-Hill w Fenny Drayton and Witherley 81-90; V Sutton *Ely* 90-94; R Witcham w Mepal 90-94; rtd 94; C Nantwich *Ches* from 94. *22 Beatty Road, Nantwich, Cheshire CW5 5JP* Nantwich (01270) 623620

REYNOLDS, Richard Michael. b 42. St Steph Ho Ox 65. **d** 67 **p** 68. C Kidderminster St Mary *Worc* 67-70; Guyana 70-73; TV N Creedy *Ex* 73-80; R Holsworthy w Hollacombe 80-86; R Holsworthy w Hollacombe and Milton Dameral from 86. *The Rectory, Holsworthy, Devon EX22 6BH* Holsworthy (01409) 253435

REYNOLDS, Roderick Bredon (Rory). b 58. Man Univ BA80. Ripon Coll Cuddesdon DipMin95. **d** 95 **p** 95. C Hitchin *St Alb* from 95. *67 Whitehill Road, Hitchin, Herts SG4 9HP* Hitchin (01462) 438859

REYNOLDS, Canon Stanley Kenneth. b 14. Bps' Coll Cheshunt 47. **d** 50 **p** 51. V Chaddesden St Phil *Derby* 64-70; V Greenhill St Pet 70-74; V Greenhill *Sheff* 74-81; P-in-c Burghwallis w Skelbrooke 81-89; Hon Can Sheff Cathl 83-89; rtd 89. *4 Burton Close, Diss, Norfolk IP22 3YJ* Diss (01379) 650562

RHAM, Canon John Theodore. b 27. Magd Coll Cam BA50 MA65. Sarum Th Coll 50. **d** 52 **p** 53. V Budock *Truro* 68-93; RD Carnmarth S 77-84; Hon Can Truro Cathl 80-93; rtd 93; France from 94. *Villa Budoc, 36 Route de Bernis, Langlade, 30980 Gard, France*

RHODES, Adrian Michael. b 48. K Coll Lon BD71 AKC71 DPST76. Qu Coll Birm 71. **d** 72 **p** 73. C Bury St Jo *Man* 73-75; Chapl N Man Gen Hosp 75-77; C Crumpsall *Man* 75-77; Chapl Walsall Manor and Bloxwich Hosps 77-83; Chapl Walsall Gen Hosp 81-83; Chapl Man R Infirmary from 83; Chapl St Mary's Hosp Man from 83. *Manchester Royal Infimary, Oxford Road, Manchester M13 9WL* 0161-224 1739 or 276 4726/276 1234

RHODES, Anthony John. b 27. Mert Coll Ox BA50 MA53 DipTh53. St Steph Ho Ox 52. **d** 54 **p** 55. P-in-c S Queensferry *Edin* 60-74; V Mitcham St Olave *S'wark* 74-81; V Owston *Linc* 81-92; V W Butterwick 81-92; rtd 92. *1 Trentside, Owston Ferry, Doncaster, S Yorkshire DN9 1RS* Owston Ferry (0142772) 237

RHODES, Arthur. b 31. Dur Univ BA58. Cranmer Hall Dur 57. **d** 59 **p** 60. C Kirkdale St Lawr *Liv* 59-61; C Litherland St Phil 61-64; V St Helens St Matt Thatto Heath 64-67; V Samlesbury *Blackb* 67-79; Lic to Offic from 80. *88 Deborah Avenue, Fulwood, Preston PR2 2HU* Preston (01772) 712212

RHODES, David. b 34. St Chad's Coll Dur BA60. **d** 61 **p** 62. C Dudley St Jo *Worc* 61-64; C-in-c Stourbridge St Mich Norton CD 64-68; V Astwood Bank w Crabbs Cross 69-78; Dioc Ecum Officer 73-78; TR Hackney *Lon* 78-88; R St Giles Cripplegate w St Bart Moor Lane etc from 88. *The Rectory, 4 The Postern, Wood Street, London EC2Y 8BJ* 0171-606 3630

RHODES, David George. b 45. Univ of Wales (Abth) BA66. Trin Coll Bris 83. **d** 85 **p** 86. C Brinsworth w Catcliffe *Sheff* 85-89; V Mortomley St Sav 89-90; V Mortomley St Sav High Green from 90. *The Vicarage, Mortomley Lane, High Green, Sheffield S30 4HS* Sheffield (0114) 284 8231

RHODES, David Grant. b 43. Ex Univ BA66 Leeds Univ DipAdEd75. Sarum & Wells Th Coll 69. **d** 72 **p** 73. C Mirfield *Wakef* 72-75; V Batley St Thos 75-80; Dioc Adult Educn Officer 75-80; Hon C Huddersfield St Jo 85-86; Dir BRF 86-87; V Roberttown *Wakef* 87-94; Project Worker 'Faith in Leeds' from 94. *Address unknown*

RHODES, Duncan. b 35. Leeds Univ BSc56. Local Minl Tr Course 90. **d** 93 **p** 94. NSM Saddleworth *Man* from 93. *Folden Cottage, 21 Spurn Lane, Diggle, Oldham OL3 5QP* Saddleworth (01457) 872399

RHODES, Canon Geoffrey David. b 34. Birm Univ BSc55. Ridley Hall Cam 68. **d** 70 **p** 71. C Sedbergh *Bradf* 70-74; P-in-c Howgill w Firbank 73-76; P-in-c Killington 73-76; C Sedbergh, Cautley and Garsdale 74-76; R Carleton-in-Craven 76-78; P-in-c Lothersdale 76-78; R Carleton and Lothersdale 78-85; V Giggleswick and Rathmell w Wigglesworth from 85; Hon Can Bradf Cathl from 91. *The Vicarage, Bankwell Road, Giggleswick, Settle, N Yorkshire BD24 0AP* Settle (01729) 822425

RHODES, Heather. b 32. **d** 88. Par Dn Purley St Mark Woodcote *S'wark* 89-94; C from 94. *24 Highfield Road, Purley, Surrey CR8 2JG* 0181-660 1486

RHODES, Canon John Lovell. b 33. MBE81. Lon Univ BD59. St Aid Birkenhead 55. **d** 59 **p** 60. C Bradf St Clem *Bradf* 59-61; C Heeley *Sheff* 61-66; Ind Chapl *Linc* 66-81; Sen Ind Chapl from 81; RD Grimsby and Cleethorpes 76-83; Can and Preb Linc Cathl from 77; Chapl Franklin Coll from 92. *19 Augusta Close, Grimsby, S Humberside DN34 4TQ* Grimsby (01472) 343167

RHODES, Lois Christine. b 34. Lon Univ BSc61. Glouc Sch of Min 84. **d** 87 **p** 94. NSM Weobley w Sarnesfield and Norton Canon *Heref* 87-92; NSM Letton w Staunton, Byford, Mansel Gamage etc 87-92; Asst Chapl Heref Hosps from 93. *Bellbrook, Bell Square, Weobley, Hereford HR4 8SE* Weobley (01544) 318410

RHODES, Matthew Ivan. b 66. Bris Univ BA89. Qu Coll Birm BD93. **d** 94 **p** 95. C Willenhall H Trin *Lich* from 94. *13 Wesley Road, Willenhall, W Midlands WV12 5QT* Willenhall (01922) 405242

RHODES, Maurice Arthur. b 27. Ridley Hall Cam 67. **d** 69 **p** 70. C Skipton Ch Ch *Bradf* 69-71; C Brierley Hill *Lich* 71-74; V Walsall Wood from 74. *The Vicarage, St John's Close, Walsall Wood, Walsall WS9 9LP* Brownhills (01543) 372284

RHODES, Peter Stuart. b 26. ACP67. Coll of Resurr Mirfield 77. **d** 78 **p** 79. NSM Newbold and Dunston *Derby* from 78. *42 Westbrook Drive, Chesterfield, Derbyshire S40 3PQ* Chesterfield (01246) 566628

RHODES, Robert George (Bob). b 41. Man Univ BSc62. Ripon Hall Ox DipTh73. **d** 74 **p** 75. C Banbury *Ox* 74-77; TV Banbury 77-81; P-in-c Long Horsley *Newc* 81-86; Adult Educn Adv 81-86; R Wolverton *Ox* from 86. *The Rectory, Aylesbury Street, Wolverton, Milton Keynes MK12 5HY* Milton Keynes (01908) 312501

RHODES, Canon Trevor Martin. b 38. Kelham Th Coll 59 Qu Coll Birm 70. **d** 71 **p** 71. C Bordesley St Oswald *Birm* 71-73; Chapl St Basil's Ch Cen Birm 72-73; C Padiham *Blackb* 73-76; P-in-c Preston St Oswald 76-78; Chapl HM Borstal Hindley 78-80; V Blackhill *Dur* 80-83; V Cowgate *Newc* 83-87; Hon Can Koforidua from 86; V Wesham *Blackb* 87-90; V Danby *York* from 90. *The Vicarage, Danby, Whitby, N Yorkshire YO21 2NQ* Castleton (01287) 660388

RHODES-WRIGLEY, James. b 35. AKC59. **d** 60 **p** 61. V Hendon Ch Ch *Lon* 66-71; V Northolt Park St Barn 71-92; rtd 92. *4 Gordon Avenue, Donnington, Chichester, W Sussex PO19 2QY* Chichester (01243) 781664

RHYDDERCH, David Huw. b 48. Univ of Wales (Cardiff) DipTh73. St Mich Coll Llan 70. **d** 73 **p** 74. C Gelligaer *Llan* 73-76; C Penarth All SS 76-78; V Resolven 78-81; V Ystrad Rhondda w Ynyscynon 81-93; RD Rhondda 89-93; R St Andrew's Major and Michaelston-le-Pit from 93. *The Rectory, Lettons Way, Dinas Powys, S Glam CF64 4BY* Cardiff (01222) 512555

RHYMES, Canon Douglas Alfred. b 14. Birm Univ BA39. Ripon Hall Ox 39. **d** 40 **p** 41. V Camberwell St Giles *S'wark* 68-76; Hon Can S'wark Cathl 69-84; P-in-c Woldingham 76-84; rtd 84; Perm to Offic *Chich* from 84. *7 Duke's Road, Fontwell, Arundel, W Sussex BN18 0SP* Eastergate (01243) 543268

RHYS, Canon David Edwin. b 37. Peterho Cam BA61 MA65 Lon Univ BA74. St Steph Ho Ox. **d** 63 **p** 64. C Tividale *Lich* 63-65; C Eltham St Jo *S'wark* 65-72; Hon C 75-82; Chapl and Warden LMH Settlement 72-75; P-in-c Woolwich St Mary w St Mich 82-83; R 83-95; RD Greenwich 86-90; Sub-Dean Woolwich 86-87; Hon Can S'wark Cathl from 90; TV Catford

(Southend) and Downham from 95. *The Rectory, 43 Rectory Place, London SE18 5DA* 0181-854 2302 or 316 4338

RHYS, Trevor William. b 11. Kenyon Coll Ohio BA35. Sarum Th Coll 35. **d** 38 **p** 39. V Stogumber *B & W* 67-76; rtd 76; Perm to Offic *B & W* 76-94. *The Laurels, Westfield Lane, Draycott, Cheddar, Somerset BS27 3TN* Cheddar (01934) 742649

RICE, Brian Keith. b 32. Peterho Cam BA55 MA59. Seabury-Western Th Sem BD57 STM67 MDiv79 Linc Th Coll. **d** 57 **p** 58. C Winchmore Hill St Paul *Lon* 57-60; C Derby St Werburgh *Derby* 60-63; C Mackworth St Fran 63-66; Chapl Kingsway Hosp Derby 63-66; Educn Sec USPG 66-72; Dir of Educn *Birm* 72-84; Chapl St Chad's Hosp Birm 77-84; Soc Resp Officer *Dur* from 84. *39 Darlington Road, Hartburn, Stockton-on-Tees, Cleveland TS18 5ET* Stockton-on-Tees (01642) 582241

RICE, Brian Thomas. b 46. Univ of Wales (Cardiff) BD77. St Mich Coll Llan 75. **d** 77 **p** 78. C Llanelli *St D* 77-79; P-in-c Llandygwydd and Cenarth w Cilrhedyn 79-80; V 80-83; V Llandingat w Myddfai from 83; RD Llangadog and Llandeilo from 91. *The Vicarage, Towy Avenue, Llandovery, Dyfed SA20 0EH* Llandovery (01550) 20524

RICE, David. b 57. Nottm Univ BA79. Ripon Coll Cuddesdon 80. **d** 82 **p** 83. C Cirencester *Glouc* 82-86; R Theale and Englefield *Ox* from 86. *The Rectory, Theale, Reading RG7 5AS* Reading (01734) 302759

RICE, Franklin Arthur. b 20. FRICS49. St Alb Minl Tr Scheme 77. **d** 80 **p** 81. NSM Hoddesdon *St Alb* 80-84; Perm to Offic *Guildf* from 85. *1 Oatlands Court, St Mary's Road, Weybridge, Surrey KT13 9QE* Weybridge (01932) 846462

RICE, John Leslie Hale. b 38. FBIM GIMechE Lon Univ BScEng60 BD68. E Midl Min Tr Course 73. **d** 76 **p** 77. NSM Allestree St Nic *Derby* 76-91; NSM Ind Specialist from 90. *14 Gisborne Crescent, Allestree, Derby DE22 2FL* Derby (01332) 557222

RICE-OXLEY, John Richard. b 44. Keble Coll Ox BA66 MA69 Dur Univ MA85. Lon Coll of Div 68. **d** 70 **p** 71. C Eastwood *S'well* 70-73; Youth Adv CMS 73-78; V Mansf St Jo *S'well* 78-82; P-in-c Thornley *Dur* 82-85; P-in-c Darlington St Matt and St Luke 85-87; V from 87. *St Matthew's Vicarage, 63A Brinkburn Road, Darlington, Co Durham DL3 6DX* Darlington (01325) 463412

RICH, Christopher Robin. b 49. LSE MSc(Econ)95. Sarum & Wells Th Coll 72. **d** 74 **p** 75. C Sholing *Win* 74-76; C Southn Maybush St Pet 76-79; R Fawley 79-90; Dir Soc Resp from 90. *15 Shelley Close, Winchester, Hants SO22 5AS* Winchester (01962) 862338

RICH, Harold Reginald. b 22. Local NSM Course. **d** 79 **p** 80. NSM St Austell *Truro* 79-87; rtd 87; Perm to Offic *Truro* from 87. *106 Eastbourne Road, St Austell, Cornwall PL25 4SS* St Austell (01726) 75600

RICH, Nicholas Philip. b 49. St Cuth Soc Dur BA74 CertEd75 Coll of Ripon & York St Jo CertEd83. Linc Th Coll 86. **d** 88 **p** 89. C W Acklam *York* 88-91; Chapl St Geo Sch Harpenden from 91; Lic to Offic *St Alb* from 91. *7 Stewart Road, Harpenden, Herts AL5 4QE* Harpenden (01582) 712951 or 765477

RICH, Paul Michael. b 36. OBE87. Sarum Th Coll 62. **d** 65 **p** 66. C Woodbridge St Mary *St E* 65-68; C W Wycombe *Ox* 68-70; CF 70-88; Lic to Offic *S & B* 88-90; V Crondall and Ewshot *Guildf* from 91. *The Vicarage, Farm Lane, Crondall, Farnham, Surrey GU10 5QE* Aldershot (01252) 850379

RICH, Peter Geoffrey. b 45. Oak Hill Th Coll 74. **d** 77 **p** 78. C Blackheath St Jo *S'wark* 77-80; C Surbiton St Matt 80-87; V St Alb St Luke *St Alb* from 87. *St Luke's Vicarage, Cellbarnes Lane, St Albans, Herts AL1 5QJ* St Albans (01727) 865399

RICH, Thomas. b 52. St Jo Coll Nottm 86. **d** 88 **p** 89. C Netherton *Liv* 88-91; P-in-c Bootle Ch Ch 91-93; V from 93. *Christ Church Vicarage, 1 Breeze Hill, Bootle, Merseyside L20 9EY* 0151-525 2565

RICHARD, David Thomas. b 16. St D Coll Lamp BA39. **d** 40 **p** 41. V Darlaston St Geo *Lich* 62-70; V Mostyn *St As* 70-86; rtd 86; Perm to Offic *St D* from 86. *Ael-y-Bryn, New Quay, Dyfed SA45 9SE* New Quay (01545) 560745

RICHARDS, Alan Grenville. b 41. Kelham Th Coll 64. **d** 69 **p** 70. C Northolt St Mary *Lon* 69-75; V Fatfield *Dur* 75-84; V Beighton *Sheff* 84-91; V Endcliffe 91-94; Deputation Appeals Org Children's Soc from 94. *69 Leahurst Court, Leahurst Court Road, Brighton BN1 6UN* Brighton (01273) 507572

RICHARDS, Albert George Granston. b 06. Lon Univ BSc30. Wycliffe Hall Ox 54. **d** 55 **p** 60. V Offley w Lilley *St Alb* 69-74; RD Hurst *Chich* 75-80; P-in-c Poynings 80-82; P-in-c Edburton 80-82; rtd 82; Perm to Offic *Chich* from 82. *East Coombe, North Bank, Hassocks, W Sussex BN6 8JG* Hassocks (01273) 842203

RICHARDS, Andrew David Thomas. b 55. St Jo Coll Dur BA76. St Steph Ho Ox 76. **d** 78 **p** 79. C Shirley *Birm* 78-80; C Cowley St Jo *Ox* 80-82; Perm to Offic *Sarum* 88-92; NSM Hazelbury

Bryan and the Hillside Par 92-94; Chapl Rossall Sch Fleetwood from 94. *Rossall School, Broadway, Fleetwood, Lancs FY7 8JW* Fleetwood (01253) 774247 or 856826

RICHARDS, Anthony Francis. b 26. Edin Univ BA45 Wadh Coll Ox BA51 MA54. Ridley Hall Cam 50. **d** 52 **p** 53. V Terriers *Ox* 63-73; USA 70-71; V Cinderford St Steph w Littledean *Glouc* 73-80; V Clacton St Paul *Chelmsf* 80-93; New Zealand 88-89; rtd 93. *Mont, 58230 Ouroux en-Morvan, Montsauche, France* France (33) 86 78 24 44

RICHARDS, Mrs April Deborah. b 42. Man Univ BSc63. S Dios Minl Tr Scheme 82. **dss** 85 **d** 87 **p** 94. Catherington and Clanfield *Portsm* 85-87; C 87-89; C E Meon from 89; C Langrish from 89; Chapl St Mary's Hosp Portsm 92-93; Chapl Portsm Hosps NHS Trust from 93. *1A Hawthorn Road, Horndean, Waterlooville, Hants PO8 0ES* Horndean (01705) 594304

RICHARDS, Barbara May. b 53. Sarum & Wells Th Coll. **d** 88. Chapl Princess Marg Hosp Swindon from 88. *1 Wheeler Avenue, Swinson SN2 6HQ, or Princess Margaret Hospital, Okus Road, Swindon SN1 4JU* Swindon (01793) 611149 or 426263

RICHARDS, Basil Ernest. b 18. Lich Th Coll 51. **d** 53 **p** 54. Hon C Gt Malvern Ch Ch *Worc* 78-84; Perm to Offic from 84; Chapl Laslett's Almshouses 84-88; rtd 88. *42 Viscount Cobham Court, Pickersleigh Road, Malvern, Worcs WR14 2RJ* Malvern (01684) 565441

RICHARDS, Brian. b 39. Open Univ BA78. Nor Ord Course 65 St Deiniol's Hawarden 94. **d** 94 **p** 94. C St Mellons and Michaelston-y-Fedw *Mon* from 94. *The Rectory, Michaelston-y-Fedw, Cardiff CF3 9XS* Cardiff (01222) 680414

RICHARDS, Brian Gordon. b 21. Sarum & Wells Th Coll 71. **d** 73 **p** 74. C Milton *Win* 73-78; P-in-c Hook w Greywell 78-83; R Hook 83-88; rtd 88. *Grenville Cottage, Main Road, Bourton, Gillingham, Dorset SP8 5ES* Gillingham (01747) 840514

RICHARDS, Charles Dennis Vincent. b 37. AKC61. **d** 62 **p** 63. Chapl St Ninian's Cathl Perth *St And* 62-64; C Pimlico St Mary Graham Terrace *Lon* 64-66; C St Marylebone Ch Ch w St Barn 66-68; C Wood Green St Mich 68-69; C-in-c S Kenton Annunciation CD 69-77; P-in-c Wembley Park St Aug 70-73; Hon C Paddington St Jo w St Mich from 76. *48A Kendal Street, London W2 2BP* 0171-262 5633

RICHARDS, Charles Edmund Nicholas. b 42. Trin Coll Cam BA64 MA68. Westcott Ho Cam 64. **d** 66 **p** 67. C Rugby St Andr *Cov* 66-72; TV Basingstoke *Win* 72-77; R Rotherhithe St Mary w All SS *S'wark* from 77; RD Bermondsey 81-91. *The Rectory, 72 St Marychurch Street, London SE16 4JE* 0171-231 2465

RICHARDS, Dr Christopher Mordaunt. b 40. New Coll Ox BA63 MA72 Bris Univ MB, ChB72. Cuddesdon Coll 63. **d** 65 **p** 81. C Bris St Mary Redcliffe w Temple etc *Bris* 65-66; Perm to Offic 66-72; Hon C Keynsham *B & W* 81-90; Perm to Offic 90-93. *4 St Ronans Avenue, Bristol BS6 6EP* Bristol (0117) 974 4062

RICHARDS, Daniel James (Dan). b 40. St D Coll Lamp DipTh66. **d** 66 **p** 67. C Kingswinford H Trin *Lich* 66-69; C Banbury *Ox* 69-71; C Aylesbury 71-73; C-in-c Stoke Poges St Jo Manor Park CD 73-78; R W Slough 78-80; R Ilchester w Northover, Limington, Yeovilton etc *B & W* 80-90; RD Ilchester 81-91; RD Martock 89-91; TR Bruton and Distr from 90. *The Rectory, Plox, Bruton, Somerset BA10 0EF* Bruton (01749) 812372

RICHARDS, Canon David. b 30. Bris Univ BA52. St Mich Coll Llan 52. **d** 54 **p** 55. C Llangynwyd w Maesteg *Llan* 54-56; Iran 57-61 and 62-66; C Skewen *Llan* 61-62; V Cwmbach 66-76; Warden of Ords 71-77; R Coity w Nolton from 76; Can Llan Cathl from 88. *Nolton Rectory, 5 Merthyrmawr Road North, Bridgend, M Glam CF31 3NH* Bridgend (01656) 652247

RICHARDS, David Arnold. b 56. Wycliffe Hall Ox 76. **d** 81 **p** 82. C Skewen *Llan* 81-84; C Barking St Marg w St Patr *Chelmsf* 84-85; TV 85-90; Chapl Barking Hosp 87-88; P-in-c Stratford St Jo and Ch Ch w Forest Gate St Jas *Chelmsf* from 90. *Stratford Vicarage, Deanery Road, London E15 4LP* 0181-534 8388

RICHARDS, David Gareth. b 60. Hull Univ BA83 Birm Univ DipTh91. Qu Coll Birm 89. **d** 92 **p** 93. C Knowle *Birm* from 92. *St Anne's Cottage, 1713 High Street, Knowle, Solihull, W Midlands B93 0LN* Knowle (01564) 775672

RICHARDS, Edwin Thomas. Leeds Univ BA41. St D Coll Lamp 46. **d** 48 **p** 49. S Africa 50-86; R Llanganten, Llanafan Fawr, Llangammarch etc *S & B* 86-89; rtd 89. *PO Box 62, Fort Beaufort 5720, 5720 South Africa* Fort Beaufort (435) 32480

RICHARDS, Canon Eric. b 36. TD86. Ely Th Coll 62. **d** 63 **p** 64. C Fen Ditton *Ely* 63-65; C Swavesdon 65-68; Ceylon 68-71; Miss to Seamen 71-73; R Roos w Tunstall *York* 73-74; P-in-c Garton w Grimston and Hilston 73-74; R Roos and Garton in Holderness w Tunstall etc 74-79; CF (TAVR) 73-79; CF (TA) 79-89; Sen CF (TA) 89-92; V Wykeham and Hutton Buscel *York* from 79; RD Pickering 80-94; Abp's Adv on Rural

Affairs from 83; Can and Preb York Minster from 92. *The Vicar's House, Hutton Buscel, Scarborough, N Yorkshire YO13 9LL* Scarborough (01723) 862945 Fax 862916

RICHARDS, Harold John Thomas. b 16. St D Coll Lamp BA39 St Mich Coll Llan 45. **d** 47 **p** 48. R Goetre *Mon* 69-82; rtd 82. *48 Longhouse Barn, Goetre, Pontypool, Gwent NP4 0BD* Nantyderry (01873) 880744

RICHARDS, Canon Iorwerth. b 20. Univ of Wales (Lamp) BA41. K Coll Lon 41. **d** 43 **p** 44. R Penmaen w Nicholaston *S & B* 60-71; RD Gower 71-88; V Oxwich w Penmaen and Nicholaston 71-89; Hon Can Brecon Cathl 83-85; Can Brecon Cathl 85-89; rtd 89. *17 Carrick Avenue, Llanelli, Dyfed SA15 3JZ* Llanelli (01554) 770729

RICHARDS, Irving St Clair. b 40. Coll of Resurr Mirfield 72. **d** 74 **p** 75. C Wigston Magna *Leic* 74-78; P-in-c N Evington from 78. *The Vicarage, 214 East Park Road, Leicester LE5 5FD* Leicester (0116) 273 6752

RICHARDS, James Harcourt. b 30. Oak Hill Th Coll. **d** 63 **p** 64. P-in-c Edge Hill St Cath *Liv* 68-73; V St Helens St Matt Thatto Heath 73-87; R Feltwell *Ely* 87-92; rtd 92. Perm to Offic *Nor* from 93. *Pantiles, Church Terrace, Aylsham, Norfolk NR11 6EU* Aylsham (01263) 733468

RICHARDS, James Johnston. b 59. Solicitor 84 MLawSoc84. Lon Bible Coll BA90 Cranmer Hall Dur 90. **d** 92 **p** 93. C Trin St Mich, Harrow *Lon* 92-95; C Kendal H Trin *Carl* from 95. *7 Wattsfield Road, Kendal, Cumbria LA9 5JH* Kendal (01539) 729572

RICHARDS, Mrs Jane Valerie. b 43. Westf Coll Lon BA64 Birm Univ CertEd65. S Dios Minl Tr Scheme 84. **d** 87 **p** 94. NSM Locks Heath *Portsm* 87-90; Asst Chapl Qu Alexandra Hosp Portsm 90-92; Chapl Portsm Hosps NHS Trust 92-95; Asst to RD Fareham *Portsm* from 95. *16 Lodge Road, Locks Heath, Southampton SO31 6QY* Locks Heath (01489) 573891

RICHARDS, John. b 20. FSA70 Univ of Wales (Lamp) BA40 Keble Coll Ox BA42 MA46 BLitt48. Westcott Ho Cam 43. **d** 43 **p** 44. CF (TA) 62-86; Master Wellington Sch 67-82; V Hoylake *Ches* 67-86; rtd 86. Perm to Offic *Ches* from 86. *Ithaca, 56 Cleveley Road, Meols, South Wirral L47 8XR* 0151-632 5135

✠RICHARDS, Rt Rev John. b 33. SS Coll Cam BA55 MA59. Ely Th Coll 57. **d** 59 **p** 60 **c** 94. C Ex St Thos *Ex* 59-64; R Holsworthy w Cookbury 64-74; R Hollacombe 64-74; RD Holsworthy 70-74; V Heavitree 74-77; TR Heavitree w Ex St Paul 78-81; RD Christianity 78-81; Adn Ex and Can Res Ex Cathl 81-94; Suff Bp Ebbsfleet (PEV) *Cant* from 94. *The Rectory, Church Leigh, Stoke-on-Trent ST10 4PT* Stoke-on-Trent (01889) 502366

RICHARDS, Preb John Francis. b 37. Dur Univ BA61. Wells Th Coll 61. **d** 63 **p** 64. C Sherwood *S'well* 63-67; C Bishopwearmouth St Mich *Dur* 67-69; C Egg Buckland *Ex* 69-75; V Plymouth St Jas Ham 75-83; V Plympton St Mary from 83; RD Plymouth Moorside 88-93; Preb Ex Cathl from 91. *St Mary's Vicarage, 58 Plymbridge Road, Plympton, Plymouth PL7 4QG* Plymouth (01752) 336157

RICHARDS, John George. b 48. Qu Coll Birm 87. **d** 89 **p** 90. C Acocks Green *Birm* 89-92; TV Shirley from 92. *The Vicarage, 20 Clifton Crescent, Solihull, W Midlands B91 3LG* 0121-705 6586

RICHARDS, John Henry. b 34. CCC Cam BA57 MA75. St Mich Coll Llan BD77. **d** 77 **p** 78. C Llangynwyd w Maesteg *Llan* 77-79; C Cardiff St Jo 79-82; Asst Chapl Univ of Wales (Cardiff) 79-82; V Penmark w Porthkerry 82-83; R Stackpole Elidor w St Petrox *St D* 83-85; R St Petrox w Stackpole Elidor and Bosherston etc from 85. *The Rectory, Stackpole, Pembroke, Dyfed SA71 5BZ* Lamphey (01646) 672472

RICHARDS, John Michael. b 53. Coll of Ripon & York St Jo TCert76 Open Univ BA81. Cranmer Hall Dur CTMin93. **d** 93 **p** 94. C Wath-upon-Dearne *Sheff* from 93. *7 Coronation Road, Wath-upon-Dearne, Rotherham, S Yorkshire S63 7AP* Rotherham (01709) 878118

RICHARDS, John Stanley. b 39. St Jo Coll Dur BA60. Ridley Hall Cam 61. **d** 64 **p** 65. C Fordingbridge w Ibsley *Win* 64-67; CF (TA) 64-68; C Bitterne Park *Win* 67-68; C Pokesdown All SS 68-70; Fell Qu Coll Birm 70-71; C Chesterton St Andr *Ely* 71-73; Asst Chapl Canford Sch Wimborne 73-77; Assoc Dir Fountain Trust 77-80; Perm to Offic *Guildf* 77-81; Dir Renewal Servicing from 81; NSM New Haw *Guildf* 81-84. *Renewal Servicing, PO Box 17, Shepperton, Middx TW17 8NU*

RICHARDS, John William. b 29. Southn Univ BSc55. Sarum & Wells Th Coll 78. **d** 81 **p** 82. NSM Woking St Mary *Guildf* 81-85; C Addlestone 85-87; C S Gillingham *Roch* 87-89; Hon C W Byfleet *Guildf* 91-95; rtd 94. *16 Normandy Way, Poundbury Whitfield, Dorchester, Dorset DT1 2PP* Dorchester (01305) 251529

RICHARDS, Jonathan Berry Hillacre. b 52. DipHE86. Oak Hill Th Coll 84. **d** 86 **p** 87. C Okehampton w Inwardleigh *Ex* 86-89; C Bratton Fleming 89; TV Shirwell, Loxhore, Kentisbury,

Arlington, etc 90-92; TR from 92. *The Vicarage, 2 Barnfield, Bratton Fleming, Barnstaple, Devon EX31 4RT* Brayford (01598) 710807

RICHARDS, Julian. b 25. Wycliffe Hall Ox 71. **d** 73 **p** 74. C Hessle *York* 73-76; P-in-c Rowley 76-82; Chapl HM Pris Hull 79-82; P-in-c Boldre *Win* 82-83; P-in-c Boldre w S Baddesley 83; V 83-93; rtd 93; RD Alton *Win* from 93. *Manor End, Worldham Hill, East Worldham, Alton, Hants GU34 3AX* Alton (01420) 86894

RICHARDS, Keith David. b 50. Didsbury Coll of Educn CertEd72. S'wark Ord Course 79. **d** 82 **p** 83. NSM Walworth *S'wark* 82-85; Chapl Derbyshire Coll of HE 85-87; V Rottingdean *Chich* 87-93; TR Crawley from 93. *The Rectory, High Street, Crawley, W Sussex RH10 1BQ* Crawley (01293) 522692

RICHARDS, Kelvin. b 58. Univ of Wales (Abth) BSc80 MA88. Ripon Coll Cuddesdon BA82. **d** 83 **p** 84. C Killay *S & B* 83-86; C Morriston 86-89; V Llangattock and Llangynidr from 89. *The Rectory, Llangattock, Crickhowell, Powys NP8 1PH* Crickhowell (01873) 810270

RICHARDS, Kendrick Steven William. b 55. DMS81 Nottm Univ BTh87. St Jo Coll Nottm 84. **d** 87 **p** 88. C Belper *Derby* 87-91; V Ilkeston St Jo 91-95; rtd 95. *30 Newstead Road North, Shipley View, Ilkeston, Derbyshire DE7 8UB*

RICHARDS, Llewelyn. b 15. St Deiniol's Hawarden 73. **d** 75 **p** 76. NSM Corwen and Llangar *St As* 75-85; Past Care Gwyddelwern 78-85; rtd 85. *120 Maesyfallen, Corwen, Clwyd LL21 9AD* Corwen (01490) 412195

RICHARDS, Mrs Mary Edith. b 33. SW Minl Tr Course 85. **d** 87 **p** 94. NSM Kea *Truro* 87-88; Asst Chapl Bris Poly *Bris* 88-91; C E Clevedon and Walton w Weston w Clapton *B & W* from 91. *5 Chestnut Grove, Clevedon, Avon BS21 7LA* Clevedon (01275) 875244

RICHARDS, Norman John. b 47. BSc. Ridley Hall Cam. **d** 83 **p** 84. C Luton St Fran *St Alb* 83-86; R Aspenden and Layston w Buntingford 86-95; P-in-c Westmill 94-95; R Aspenden, Buntingford and Westmill from 95. *The Vicarage, Vicarage Road, Buntingford, Herts SG9 9BH* Royston (01763) 271552

RICHARDS, Peter Garth. b 30. Lon Univ BA51 Ex Univ PGCE72. St Chad's Coll Dur DipTh55. **d** 55 **p** 56. C Clyst St George *Ex* 66-75; TV Clyst St George, Aylesbeare, Clyst Honiton etc 75-81; rtd 92. *6 Cutlers Rough Close, Birmingham B31 1LX* 0121-477 9308

RICHARDS, Peter Lane Campling. b 26. St Cath Soc Ox BA51 MA55. Wells Th Coll 51. **d** 53 **p** 54. R Marston Morteyne *St Alb* 64-75; P-in-c Sharpness *Glouc* 75-80; R Dumbleton w Wormington and Toddington 80-91; R Dumbleton w Wormington 91-94; P-in-c Didbrook w Stanway and Hailes 82-91; P-in-c Toddington, Stanton, Didbrook w Hailes etc 91-92; rtd 94. *Bank House, New Street, Painswick, Stroud, Glos GL6 6XH* Painswick (01452) 813685

RICHARDS, Robert Graham. b 42. St Jo Coll Nottm LTh. **d** 80 **p** 81. C Radipole and Melcombe Regis *Sarum* 80-83; TV Billericay and Lt Burstead *Chelmsf* 84-91; UK Dir CMJ from 91; Lic to Offic *St Alb* from 92. *22 Dove Park, Chorleywood, Rickmansworth, Herts WD3 5NY, or 30C Clarence Road, St Albans, Herts AL1 4JJ* Chorleywood (01923) 285114 or St Albans (01727) 833114 Fax St Albans (01727) 848312

RICHARDS, Ronald Jervis. b 16. St D Coll Lamp BA37 St Mich Coll Llan 38. **d** 39 **p** 40. Chapl RAF 43-71; R Quendon w Rickling *Chelmsf* 71-75; V Dedham 75-83; rtd 83. *2 Hollies Road, St Stephens, Launceston, Cornwall PL15 8HB* Launceston (01566) 776296

RICHARDS, Simon Granston. b 47. Nottm Univ BTh72. St Jo Coll Nottm 68 ALCD72. **d** 72 **p** 73. C Waltham Abbey *Chelmsf* 72-77; TV Basildon St Martin w H Cross and Laindon etc 77-80; V Grayshott *Guildf* 80-88; V Eccleston Ch Ch *Liv* 88-92; V Berkeley w Wick, Breadstone and Newport *Glouc* from 92. *The Vicarage, Church Lane, Berkeley, Glos GL13 9BH* Dursley (01453) 810294

RICHARDS, Canon Thomas John Wynzie. b 25. St D Coll Lamp BA49. **d** 51 **p** 52. V Llandybie *St D* 71-87; Chapl Nat Nautical Sch Portishead 57-71; RD Dyffryn Aman *St D* 78-85; Can St D Cathl 83-92; Treas St D Cathl 89-92; V Pencarreg and Llanycrwys 87-92; rtd 92. *Maes Teifi, Cwmann, Lampeter, Dyfed SA48 8DT* Lampeter (01570) 423354

RICHARDS, William Antony. b 28. Ex Coll Ox BA52 MA56. St Steph Ho Ox 52. **d** 54 **p** 55. R Warmington w Shotteswell *Cov* 64-75; RD Dassett Magna 70-74; Org Sec (Dios Cov, Leic and Pet) CECS 75-81; V Bidford-on-Avon *Cov* 81-92; rtd 92. *4 Harbour Close, Bidford-on-Avon, Alcester, Warks B50 4EW* Alcester (01789) 772699

RICHARDS, Canon William Hughes. b 37. St D Coll Lamp BA58. **d** 60 **p** 61. C Llandysul *St D* 60-63; C Llanelli 63-65; V Llanddewi Brefi w Llanbadarn Odwyn 65-73; V Pen-bre 73-83; V Llangynnwr and Cwmffrwd 83-88; V Cardigan and Mwnt and Y Ferwig from 88; Can St D Cathl from 89. *The Vicarage, Napier Gardens, Cardigan, Dyfed SA43 1EG* Cardigan (01239) 612722

RICHARDS, Canon William Neal (Bill). b 38. ALCD63. **d** 63 **p** 64. C Otley *Bradf* 63-65; C Leamington Priors St Mary *Cov* 65-67; CMS 67-69; Kenya 69-74; Asst Provost and Can Res Nairobi Cathl 70-74; V Gt Malvern St Mary *Worc* 74-86; Chapl Kidderminster Health Distr 86-91; RD Kidderminster *Worc* 89-91; R Martley and Wichenford, Knightwick etc from 91. *The Rectory, Martley, Worcester WR6 6QA* Wichenford (01886) 888664

RICHARDSON, Andrew John. b 44. Ex Univ CertEd69. Trin Coll Bris. **d** 82 **p** 83. Kenya 82-87; Chapl Brentwood Sch Essex 88; Chapl Scarborough Coll from 88. *Scarborough College, Filey Road, Scarborough, N Yorkshire YO11 3BA* Scarborough (01723) 360620

RICHARDSON, Canon Charles. b 13. AKC35. Linc Th Coll 35. **d** 36 **p** 37. R Rawmarsh w Parkgate *Sheff* 54-76; Hon Can Sheff Cathl 75-80; R Harthill 76-80; rtd 80; Perm to Offic *Sheff* from 81. *41 Nether Green Road, Sheffield S11 7EH* Sheffield (0114) 230 4699

RICHARDSON, Charles Leslie. b 54. St Jo Coll Dur BA76. Coll of Resurr Mirfield 76. **d** 79 **p** 80. C Folkestone St Mary and St Eanswythe *Cant* 79-83; C Maidstone St Martin 83-86; Selection Sec and Voc Adv ACCM 86-91; PV Westmr Abbey 87-91; R Hastings St Clem and All SS *Chich* from 91; RD Hastings from 92. *Old Town Rectory, 106 High Street, Hastings, E Sussex TN34 3ES* Hastings (01424) 422023

RICHARDSON, Clive John. b 57. Trin Coll Bris BA82 Oak Hill Th Coll DipHE83. **d** 83 **p** 84. C Woking St Pet *Guildf* 83-86; C Worplesdon 86-90; V Rowledge from 90. *The Vicarage, Church Lane, Rowledge, Farnham, Surrey GU10 4EN* Frensham (01252) 792402

RICHARDSON, David Gwynne. b 39. AMIMinE. K Coll Lon 60. **d** 64 **p** 65. C Birtley *Dur* 64-67; Bp's Soc and Ind Adv 67-77; TV Brayton *York* 78-92; Ind Chapl 78-92; Chapl IMinE from 85; R Monk Fryston and S Milford from 92; RD Selby from 93. *The Rectory, Main Street, Hillam, Leeds LS25 5HH* South Milford (01977) 682357

RICHARDSON, David Anthony. b 41. Kelham Th Coll 57. **d** 66 **p** 67. C Tong *Bradf* 66-68; C Richmond St Mary *S'wark* 68-71; C Sanderstead All SS 71-74; TV 74-78; R Beddington 78-92; V Dormansland from 92; RD Godstone from 95. *The Vicarage, The Platt, Dormansland, Lingfield, Surrey RH7 6QU* Lingfield (01342) 832391

RICHARDSON, David John. b 50. MA LLB. S'wark Ord Course. **d** 85 **p** 86. NSM S Croydon Em *S'wark* from 85. *20 Hurst View Road, South Croydon, Surrey CR2 7AG* 0181-688 4947 or 688 6676

RICHARDSON, Preb Douglas Stanley. b 23. Bps' Coll Cheshunt 55. **d** 57 **p** 58. V Notting Hill St Pet *Lon* 69-78; V Staines St Pet 78-83; P-in-c Staines St Mary 81-83; V Staines St Mary and St Pet 83-92; AD Spelthorne 83-92; Preb St Paul's Cathl 92; rtd 92. *22 Rooks Down Road, Badgers Farm, Winchester, Hants SO22 4LT* Winchester (01962) 863687

RICHARDSON, Edward John. b 39. **d** 65 **p** 66. C Chessington *Guildf* 65-70; V Stoneleigh 75-79; Perm to Offic *S'wark* 92-94; Hon C Kingston All SS w St Jo from 94. *3 Westways, Stoneleigh, Epsom, Surrey KT19 0PH* 0181-393 3648

RICHARDSON, Canon Eric Hatherley Humphrey. b 12. Qu Coll Ox BA35. Westcott Ho Cam 35. **d** 36 **p** 37. C Stoke Newington St Mary *Lon* 36-39; S Africa from 39. *PO Box 2289, Kramerview, 2060 South Africa* Johannesburg (11) 787-7813

RICHARDSON, Geoffrey Stewart. b 47. St Jo Coll Ox BA69 MA73. St Steph Ho Ox 70. **d** 72 **p** 73. C Roxbourne St Andr *Lon* 72-75; C Woodford St Barn *Chelmsf* 75-80; V Goodmayes St Paul 80-87; R Stow in Lindsey *Linc* 87-92; P-in-c Coates 87-92; P-in-c Willingham 87-92; R Stow Gp from 92; RD Corringham from 93. *The Rectory, Stow in Lindsey, Lincoln LN1 2DF* Gainsborough (0427) 788251

RICHARDSON, Gerald. b 24. Chich Th Coll 54. **d** 56 **p** 57. V Smethwick St Steph *Birm* 67-72; R Aylestone Park *Leic* 72-85; Perm to Offic from 85; rtd 89. *St Eanswythe, 55 Stonesby Avenue, Leicester LE2 6TX* Leicester (0116) 283 0561

RICHARDSON, Harold. b 22. Worc Ord Coll 62. **d** 64 **p** 65. V Rockcliffe *Carl* 66-74; rtd 87. *21 St Catherine's Place, Edinburgh EH9 1NU* 0131-667 8040

RICHARDSON, Canon Jack Cyril. b 11. Leeds Univ BSc36. Coll of Resurr Mirfield 35. **d** 35 **p** 36. R Upper Clatford w Goodworth Clatford *Win* 65-77; rtd 77; Perm to Offic *St Alb* from 78. *Robin Cottage, The Street, Braughing, Ware, Herts SG11 2QR* Ware (01920) 822020

RICHARDSON, James Aidan. b 28. St Chad's Coll Dur BA51 DipThA54. **d** 54 **p** 55. V Linthwaite *Wakef* 64-79; RD Blackmoorfoot 77-79; V Clifton 79-92; P-in-c Hartshead 83-88; rtd 92. *10B Brooke Street, Cleckheaton, W Yorkshire BD19 3RY* Cleckheaton (01274) 874587

RICHARDSON, James Arthur. b 19. MC44. ARICS53 Lon Univ BSc51. Ridley Hall Cam 60. **d** 62 **p** 62. V Streatham Park St Alb *S'wark* 65-87; rtd 87. *18 Cranden Road, Eastbourne, E Sussex BN20 8LW* Eastbourne (01323) 737711

RICHARDSON, James Horner. b 19. Ch Coll Cam BA42 MA45. Ridley Hall Cam 41. **d** 43 **p** 44. Hon CF from 53; V Huyton St Mich *Liv* 59-70; V Ormskirk 70-80; V Giggleswick *Bradf* 80-82; P-in-c Rathmell 80-82; V Giggleswick and Rathmell w Wigglesworth 82-84; rtd 84; Hon Chapl Spennithorne Hall from 84; Hon C Aysgarth and Bolton cum Redmire *Ripon* from 84. *Mere Cottage, Redmire, Leyburn, N Yorkshire DL8 4ED* Wensleydale (01969) 623917

RICHARDSON, Canon James John (Jim). b 41. FRSA91 Hull Univ BA63 Sheff Univ DipEd64. Cuddesdon Coll 66. **d** 69 **p** 70. C Wolv St Pet *Lich* 69-72; P-in-c Hanley All SS 72-75; R Nantwich *Ches* 75-82; Hon Can Ripon Cathl *Ripon* 82-88; V Leeds St Pet 82-88; Exec Dir Coun of Chrs and Jews 88-92; Lic to Offic *Pet* 88-93; P-in-c Brington w Whilton and Norton from 93; P-in-c Church Brampton, Chapel Brampton, Harleston etc from 94. *The Rectory, Great Brington, Northampton NN7 4JB* Northampton (01604) 770402

RICHARDSON, John. b 41. Qu Coll Birm 69. **d** 72 **p** 73. C Ormskirk *Liv* 72-74; C Doncaster St Geo *Sheff* 74-77; R Hemsworth *Wakef* 77-79; V Penallt *Mon* 79-85; R Amotherby w Appleton and Barton-le-Street *York* 85-89; P-in-c Hovingham 86-89; C 89; P-in-c Slingsby 86-89; TR Street TM 89-90; R Skelton w Shipton and Newton on Ouse 90-93; V Alsager St Mary *Ches* from 93. *St Mary's Vicarage, 37 Eaton Road, Alsager, Stoke-on-Trent ST7 2BQ* Alsager (01270) 875748

RICHARDSON, John. b 47. Linc Th Coll 78. **d** 80 **p** 81. C Keighley St Andr *Bradf* 80-83; V Hugglescote w Donington *Leic* 83-84; V Hugglescote w Donington-le-Heath and Ellistown 84-86; TR Hugglescote w Donington, Ellistown and Snibston from 86; RD Akeley S (Coalville) from 87. *The Rectory, Grange Road, Hugglescote, Coalville, Leics LE67 2BQ* Coalville (01530) 832557

RICHARDSON, John. b 55. Lon Univ BEd BD. St Steph Ho Ox. **d** 83 **p** 84. C Thornbury *Glouc* 83-86; C Sheff Parson Cross St Cecilia *Sheff* 86-87; C Clacton St Jas *Chelmsf* 87-90; R Gt Tey and Wakes Colne w Chappel from 90. *The Rectory, Brook Road, Great Tey, Colchester CO6 1JF* Colchester (01206) 211481

RICHARDSON, John Aubrey. b 33. NE Ord Course 90. **d** 93 **p** 94. NSM Warkworth and Acklington *Newc* from 93. *Harvest Lodge, 27 Acklington Village, Morpeth, Northd NE65 9BL* Morpeth (01670) 760761

RICHARDSON, John Hedley. b 45. Leeds Univ BA72. Qu Coll Birm 72. **d** 74 **p** 75. C Chaddesden St Phil *Derby* 74-76; Perm to Offic 76-86; TV Old Brampton and Loundsley Green 86-91; R Caston w Griston, Merton, Thompson etc *Nor* from 91; RD Breckland from 94; P-in-c Hockham w Shropham Gp of Par from 94. *The Rectory, Caston, Attleborough, Norfolk NR17 1DD* Caston (01953) 483222

✠**RICHARDSON, Rt Rev John Henry.** b 37. Trin Hall Cam BA61 MA65. Cuddesdon Coll 61. **d** 63 **p** 64 **c** 94. C Stevenage *St Alb* 63-66; C Eastbourne St Mary *Chich* 66-68; V Chipperfield St Paul *St Alb* 68-75; V Rickmansworth 75-86; RD Rickmansworth 77-86; V Bishop's Stortford St Mich 86-94; Hon Can St Alb 87-94; Suff Bp Bedf from 94. *168 Kimbolton Road, Bedford MK41 8DN* Bedford (01234) 357551 Fax 218134

RICHARDSON, John Humphrey. b 33. Dur Univ BA57. Chich Th Coll 57. **d** 59 **p** 60. C Bexhill St Barn *Chich* 59-61; C Stanmer w Falmer and Moulsecoomb 61-64; C Ifield 64-70; R Earnley and E Wittering 70-79; V Stamford All SS w St Pet *Linc* 79-81; R Stamford St Jo w St Clem 79-81; RD Aveland and Ness w Stamford 80-87; V Stamford All SS w St Jo 81-92; P-in-c Metheringham w Blankney 92-94; V Metheringham w Blankney and Dunston from 94. *The Vicarage, 38 Drury Street, Metheringham, Lincoln LN4 3EZ* Metheringham (01526) 321115

RICHARDSON, Canon John Malcolm. b 39. Glas Univ MA60 BD63. Andover Newton Th Coll STM65 Edin Th Coll 84. **d** 84 **p** 85. C Edin Old St Paul *Edin* 84-86; R Leven *St And* 86-90; R Newport-on-Tay from 90; R Tayport from 90; Can St Ninian's Cathl Perth from 93. *St Mary's Rectory, 8 High Street, Newport-on-Tay, Fife DD6 8DA* Newport-on-Tay (01382) 543311

RICHARDSON, John Peter. b 50. Keele Univ BA72. St Jo Coll Nottm 73. **d** 76 **p** 77. C Birm St Paul *Birm* 76-79; C Blackheath 79-81; P-in-c Sparkbrook Ch Ch 81-83; Chapl NE Lon Poly *Chelmsf* 83-92; Chapl E Lon Univ from 92; Hon C Stratford St Jo and Ch Ch w Forest Gate St Jas from 83. *4 Matthew's Park Avenue, London E15 4AE* 0181-536 0230 or 590 7722

RICHARDSON, Very Rev John Stephen. b 50. Southn Univ BA71. St Jo Coll Nottm 72. **d** 74 **p** 75. C Bramcote *S'well* 74-77; C Radipole and Melcombe Regis *Sarum* 77-80; P-in-c Stinsford, Winterborne Came w Whitcombe etc 80-83; Asst Dioc Missr 80-83; V Nailsea Ch Ch *B & W* 83-90; Adv on

Evang 86-90; Provost Bradf from 90. *The Provost's House, Cathedral Close, Bradford BD1 4EG*   Bradford (01274) 732023   Fax 722898

RICHARDSON, Prof John Stuart. b 46. Trin Coll Ox BA68 MA71 DPhil73. **d** 79 **p** 80. NSM St Andrews *St Andr St And* 79-87; Chapl St Andr Univ 80-87; Prof Classics Edin Univ from 87; TV Edin St Columba *Edin* from 87. *29 Merchiston Avenue, Edinburgh EH10 4PH*   0131-228 3094

RICHARDSON, John William. b 56. Bp Otter Coll BA85 Chich Th Coll 85. **d** 87 **p** 88. C E Preston w Kingston *Chich* 87-89; C Goring-by-Sea 89-90; TV Aldrington 91-92; V Sompting from 92. *The Vicarage, West Street, Sompting, Lancing, W Sussex BN15 0AX*   Worthing (01903) 234511

RICHARDSON, Joseph Edmund. b 27. St Chad's Coll Dur BA49. Sarum Th Coll 51. **d** 52 **p** 53. R Davenham *Ches* 65-76; V Sale St Anne 76-84; R Delamere 84-88; rtd 88; Perm to Offic *Ex* from 94. *9 Linhey Close, Waterside Park, Kingsbridge, Devon TQ7 1LL*   Kingsbridge (01548) 853376

RICHARDSON, Maurice. b 12. **d** 66 **p** 67. V Lowdham *S'well* 69-77; rtd 77; Perm to Offic *S'well* from 77; Perm to Offic *Leic* from 82. *Old Orchard, Granby, Nottingham NG13 9PR* Whatton (01949) 50860

RICHARDSON, Neil. b 46. Southn Univ BTh83. Sarum & Wells Th Coll 71. **d** 74 **p** 75. C Oldham St Mary w St Pet *Man* 74-77; C-in-c Holts CD 77-82; R Greenford H Cross *Lon* from 82. *The Rectory, Oldfield Lane, Greenford, Middx UB6 9JS* 0181-578 1543

RICHARDSON, Paul. b 58. Univ of Wales (Cardiff) BSc80. Ridley Hall Cam 81. **d** 84 **p** 85. C Stanwix *Carl* 84-87; Ind Chapl 87-89; Staff Priest Dalton-in-Furness 87-89; V Marton Moss *Blackb* 89-95; P-in-c Prestwich St Gabr *Man* from 95; Bp's Dom Chapl from 95. *St Gabriel's Vicarage, 8 Bishops Road, Prestwich, Manchester M25 8HT*   0161-773 8839 or 792 2096

RICHARDSON, Robert Trevor. b 34. St Mich Coll Llan 58. **d** 60 **p** 61. C Cymmer and Porth *Llan* 60-62; C Worsley *Man* 62-65; V Waterfoot 65-94. *2 Lambton Gates, Rossendale, Lancs BB4 7PQ*   Rossendale (01706) 215959

RICHARDSON, Ronald Eric (Ron). b 48. York Univ CertEd Leeds Univ BEd. N Ord Course. **d** 82 **p** 83. NSM Wakef St Andr and St Mary *Wakef* 82-83; C 83-90; NSM S Ossett from 90. *37 Stanley Road, Wakefield, W Yorkshire WF1 4NA* Wakefield (01924) 381047

RICHARDSON, Simon John. b 56. Univ of Wales (Ban) BA77. Ridley Hall Cam 81. **d** 84 **p** 85. C Luton St Mary *St Alb* 84-88; C Middleton *Man* 88-91; Sweden from 91. *Address temp unknown*

RICHARDSON, Stephen. b 99. Worc Ord Coll 57. **d** 58 **p** 59. R Meysey Hampton w Marston Meysey *Glouc* 61-73; Perm to Offic 73-93; rtd 75. *The Lee, Church Street, Meysey Hampton, Cirencester, Glos GL7 5JU*   Poulton (01285) 851407

RICHARDSON, Miss Susan. b 58. Cranmer Hall Dur. **d** 87 **p** 94. Par Dn Stokesley *York* 87-91; Par Dn Beverley St Nic 91-94; P-in-c Cloughton from 94; Tr Officer E Riding Adnry from 94. *The Vicarage, Mill Lane, Cloughton, Scarborough, N Yorkshire YO13 0AB*   Scarborough (01723) 870270

RICHARDSON, Thomas Warner. b 11. St Jo Coll Dur BA38 MA44. Westcott Ho Cam 38. **d** 38 **p** 39. Hon CF 46-76; V St Austell *Truro* 65-72; P-in-c Teversal *S'well* 72-76; rtd 76. *3 Broadgait Court, Gullane, East Lothian EH31 2DL*   Gullane (01620) 822542

RICHARDSON, Canon William. b 11. Qu Coll Ox BA34 MA37 BD52. Ripon Hall Ox 35. **d** 36 **p** 37. Can and Preb York Minster *York* 70-87; TR Sutton St Jas and Wawne 71-78; rtd 78. *1 Precentor's Court, York YO1 2EJ*   York (01904) 639237

RICHBOROUGH, Suffragan Bishop of (Provincial Episcopal Visit or). *See* BARNES, Rt Rev Edwin Ronald

RICHENS, Canon Geoffrey Roger. b 23. ALCD52. **d** 52 **p** 53. V Widnes St Mary *Liv* 56-80; V Skelmersdale St Paul 80-93; Hon Can Liv Cathl 89-93; rtd 93. *43 West View, Parbold, Wigan, Lancs WN8 7NT*   Parbold (01257) 463143

RICHERBY, Glynn. b 51. K Coll Lon BD73 AKC73. St Aug Coll Cant 73. **d** 74 **p** 75. C Weston Favell *Pet* 74-78; Prec Leic Cathl *Leic* 78-81; V Glen Parva and S Wigston 81-93; Dir Post Ord Tr 86-95; V Leic St Jas from 93; Dir of Continuing Minl Educn from 95. *St James the Greater Vicarage, 216 London Road, Leicester LE2 1NE*   Leicester (0116) 254 4113

RICHES, Prof John Kenneth. b 39. CCC Cam BA61 MA65. Kirchliche Hochschule Th Coll Berlin 61 Westcott Ho Cam 62. **d** 65 **p** 66. C Costessey *Nor* 65-68; Chapl and Fell SS Coll Cam 68-72; Lect Glas Univ 72-86; Sen Lect 86-91; Prof Div and Bibl Criticism Glas Univ from 91; Chmn Balmore Trust from 90; Lic to Offic *Glas* from 85. *Viewfield, Balmore, Torrance, Glasgow G64 4AE*   Balmore (01360) 620254

✠**RICHES, Rt Rev Kenneth.** b 08. CCC Cam BA31 MA35. Gen Th Sem (NY) Hon STD56 Lambeth DD57 Cuddesdon Coll 32. **d** 32 **p** 33 **c** 52. C Portsea St Mary *Portsm* 32-35; C E Dulwich St Jo *S'wark* 35-36; Chapl SS Coll Cam 36-42; Lic

to Offic *Bradf* 36-44; R Bredfield w Boulge *St E* 42-44; Prin Cuddesdon Coll 44-52; V Cuddesdon *Ox* 44-52; Hon Can Portsm Cathl *Portsm* 50-52; Suff Bp Dorchester *Ox* 52-56; Adn Ox and Can Res Ch Ch 52-56; Bp Linc 56-74; rtd 74; Perm to Offic *St E* from 74. *Little Dingle, Dunwich, Saxmundham, Suffolk IP17 3EA*   Westleton (0172873) 316

RICHES, Malcolm Leslie. b 46. St Jo Coll Nottm DipThMin94. **d** 94 **p** 95. C Swaythling *Win* from 94. *12 Willis Road, Swaythling, Southampton SO16 2NT*   Southampton (01703) 586002

RICHEY, Canon Robert Samuel Payne. b 23. TCD BA46. **d** 48 **p** 49. C Moy *Arm* 48-50; I Killinagh w Kiltyclogher *K, E & A* 50-60; I Killinagh w Kiltyclogher and Innismagrath 60-72; I Killinagh w Kiltyclogher, Killargue etc 72-91; I Killinagh w Kiltyclogher and Innismagrath from 91; Sec Dioc Bd Educn from 64; Dioc Sec (Kilmore) from 72; Dioc Info Officer (Kilmore) from 81; Preb Kilmore Cathl from 80; Preb Mulhuddart St Patr Cathl Dub from 94. *Killinagh Rectory, Blacklion, Sligo, Irish Republic*   Manorhamilton (72) 53010   Fax as telephone

RICHMOND, Arnold. b 19. Sarum & Wells Th Coll 77. **d** 80 **p** 81. NSM Axminster *Ex* 80-83; Dep PV Ex Cathl from 83; NSM Axminster, Chardstock, Combe Pyne and Rousdon 83-86; NSM Colyton, Southleigh, Offwell, Widworthy etc from 86. *New House Farm, Combpyne Road, Musbury, Axminster, Devon EX13 6SS*   Colyton (01297) 553501

✠**RICHMOND, Rt Rev Francis Henry Arthur.** b 36. TCD BA59 MA66 Strasbourg Univ BTh60 Linacre Coll Ox MLitt64. Wycliffe Hall Ox 60. **d** 63 **p** 64 **c** 86. C Woodlands *Sheff* 63-66; Chapl Sheff Cathl 66-69; V Sheff St Geo 69-77; Chapl Sheff Univ 74-77; Warden Linc Th Coll 77-86; Can and Preb Linc Cathl *Linc* 77-86; Suff Bp Repton *Derby* from 86; Hon Can Derby Cathl from 86. *Repton House, Lea, Matlock, Derbyshire DE4 5JP*   Matlock (01629) 534644   Fax 534003

RICHMOND, Gordon Hazlewood. b 33. Launde Abbey 77. **d** 79 **p** 80. C Leic St Paul *Leic* 79-81; C Shepshed 81-84; V Ryhall w Essendine *Pet* 84-91; RD Barnack 89-91; V Gretton w Rockingham and Caldecote from 91. *The Vicarage, Station Road, Gretton, Corby, Northants NN17 3BU*   Rockingham (01536) 770237

RICHMOND, Peter James. b 54. Writtle Agric Coll HND76. St Jo Coll Nottm LTh80. **d** 80 **p** 81. C Ogley Hay *Lich* 80-83; C Trentham 83-85; P-in-c Wolv St Jo 85-89; P-in-c Loppington w Newtown 89-93; P-in-c Edstaston 89-93; Perm to Offic *Ex* from 94. *8 Shelton Place, North Street, Exeter EX1 2RE* Exeter (01392) 413762

RICHMOND, Archdeacon of. *See* GOOD, Ven Kenneth Roy

RICKETTS, Allan Fenn. b 46. Open Univ BA76. Cranmer Hall Dur 68. **d** 71 **p** 72. C Rowley Regis *Birm* 71-72; C The Quinton 72-74; C Brierley Hill *Lich* 74-77; TV Chelmsley Wood *Birm* 77-82; TV Ross w Brampton Abbotts, Bridstow and Peterstow *Heref* 82-88; R Linton w Upton Bishop and Aston Ingham from 88. *The Rectory, Linton, Ross-on-Wye, Herefordshire HR9 7RX*   Ross-on-Wye (01989) 720472

RICKETTS, Graham Victor. b 67. Leic Univ BSc89. Chich Th Coll 89. **d** 92 **p** 93. C Brighton St Geo w St Anne and St Mark *Chich* from 92. *28 Henley Road, Brighton BN2 5NA*   Brighton (01273) 696796

RICKETTS, Miss Kathleen Mary (Kate). b 39. Southlands Coll Lon TCert59 Univ of W Aus BA79. Westcott Ho Cam 81. **dss** 83 **d** 87 **p** 94. All Hallows by the Tower etc *Lon* 83-87; C 87-88; C Hall Green Ascension *Birm* 88-91; Chapl Birm Children's Hosp from 91. *28 Glaisdale Road, Birmingham B28 8PX, or Birmingham Children's Hospital, Birmingham B16 8NT*   0121-778 6233 or 454 4851

RICKETTS, Peter William. b 28. DLC53. St Alb Minl Tr Scheme 76. **d** 79 **p** 80. NSM Hertf All SS *St Alb* 79-86; R Blunham w Tempsford and Lt Barford 86-93; rtd 93. *277 Hillgrounds Road, Kempston, Bedford MK42 8TH* Bedford (01234) 841635

RIDDEL, Canon Robert John. b 37. CITC. **d** 68 **p** 69. C Derryloran *Arm* 68-74; I Keady w Armaghbreague and Derrynoose 74-80; I Mullaghdun *Clogh* 80-84; I Cleenish 80-84; I Fivemiletown from 84; RD Clogh from 85; Can Clogh Cathl from 91; Preb Donaghmore St Patr Cathl Dub from 95. *The Rectory, 160 Ballagh Road, Fivemiletown, Co Tyrone BT75 0QP*   Fivemiletown (013655) 21030

RIDDELL, Morris Stroyan. b 34. Lon Univ DipTh59 BD69. Tyndale Hall Bris 57. **d** 60 **p** 60. R Bris St Jo w St Mary-le-Port *Bris* 67-70; Dir Bris Samaritans 67-70; Chapl HM Pris Long Lartin 71-74; Brixton 74-78; Chapl Cane Hill Hosp Coulsdon 78-85; Chapl HM Rem Cen Latchmere Ho 85-89; rtd 95. *1 Orchard Way, Pinelands 7405, Cape Town, South Africa*

RIDDELSDELL, Canon John Creffield. b 23. Selw Coll Cam BA47 MA52 Lon Univ BD70. Ridley Hall Cam 47. **d** 49 **p** 50. Kenya 52-77; V Gt Ilford St Andr *Chelmsf* 77-88; rtd 88. *Waverley, Mill Lane, Walton on the Naze, Essex CO14 8PE* Clacton-on-Sea (01255) 850213

RIDDING, George. b 24. Or Coll Ox BA50 MA57. Wells Th Coll 60. **d** 61 **p** 62. Hd Master W Buckland Sch Barnstaple 68-78; USPG 78-82; P-in-c Broadhembury w Payhembury *Ex* 82-83; P-in-c Plymtree 82-83; R Broadhembury, Payhembury and Plymtree 83-89; rtd 89. *Cherwell, Higher Blandford Road, Shaftesbury, Dorset SP7 8DA* Shaftesbury (01747) 851390

RIDDING, William Thomas. b 54. Southn Univ BTh. Sarum & Wells Th Coll 80. **d** 83 **p** 84. C Verwood *Sarum* 83-86; TV Gillingham from 86. *The Vicarage, Kington Magna, Gillingham, Dorset SP8 5EW* East Stour (01747) 838494

RIDDLE, Kenneth Wilkinson. b 20. St Cath Soc Ox BA42 MA46. Ripon Hall Ox 42. **d** 43 **p** 44. R Lowestoft St Marg *Nor* 65-68; rtd 85. *The Old Post Office, East Lyng, Taunton, Somerset TA3 5AU* Burrowbridge (01823) 698427

RIDEOUT, Canon Gordon Trevor. b 38. BA87. Lon Coll of Div 58. **d** 62 **p** 63. C Southgate *Chich* 62-65; Chapl Dr Barnardo's Barkingside & Woodford Br 65-67; CF 67-73; V Nutley *Chich* 73-79; V Eastbourne All SS from 79; Chapl Moira Ho Sch E Sussex from 79; Chapl Brighton Poly *Chich* 80-92; Chapl Brighton Univ from 92; Can and Preb Chich Cathl from 90. *All Saints' Vicarage, Grange Road, Eastbourne, E Sussex BN21 4HE* Eastbourne (01323) 410033

RIDER, Andrew. b 62. RMN85 Nottm Univ BTh90. Aston Tr Scheme 85 St Jo Coll Nottm 87. **d** 90 **p** 91. C Luton Ch Ch *Roch* 90-93; C Langham Place All So *Lon* from 93. *25 Fitzroy Street, London W1P 5AF* 0171-580 3745

RIDER, Canon Dennis William Austin. b 34. Lon Univ DipTh61. St Aid Birkenhead 58. **d** 61 **p** 62. C Derby St Aug *Derby* 61-64; C Sutton *Liv* 64-67; R Stiffkey w Morston, Langham Episcopi etc *Nor* 67-71; V Buxton w Oxnead 71-79; R Lammas w Lt Hautbois 72-79; R Gaywood, Bawsey and Mintlyn 79-91; RD Lynn 89-91; Hon Can Nor Cathl from 90; R E Dereham and Scarning from 91. *The Vicarage, 1 Vicarage Meadows, Dereham, Norfolk NR19 1TW* Dereham (01362) 693143

RIDER, Geoffrey Malcolm. b 29. Selw Coll Cam BA53 MA56 Lon Inst of Educn PGCE68. Coll of Resurr Mirfield 53. **d** 55 **p** 56. V Cleckheaton St Jo *Wakef* 63-67; Public Preacher *S'wark* from 92; rtd 92; S Africa 92-95. *58 Melbury Gardens, London SW20 0DJ* 0181-946 5735

RIDER, Neil Wilding. b 35. St Jo Coll Dur BA59 DipTh61. Cranmer Hall Dur 59. **d** 62 **p** 63. C Blackb St Barn *Blackb* 62-64; C Chadderton Em *Man* 64-69; C Deane 69-72; V Coldhurst 72-75; Perm to Offic *Ely* 76-78; C Didsbury Ch Ch *Man* 78-80; Perm to Offic *St D* from 80. *Caergrawnt, Cwmann, Lampeter, Dyfed SA48 8EL* Lampeter (01570) 422921

RIDGE, Aubrey. b 25. Oak Hill Th Coll 65. **d** 68 **p** 69. C Gorleston St Andr *Nor* 68-70; C Hamworthy *Sarum* 70-75; P-in-c Pitsea *Chelmsf* 75-78; R 78-81; P-in-c Stoke Ash, Thwaite and Wetheringsett *St E* 81-85; P-in-c Bedingfield and Thorndon w Rishangles 81-85; P-in-c Thorndon w Rishangles, Stoke Ash, Thwaite etc 85-86; P-in-c Risby w Gt and Lt Saxham and Westley 86-90; rtd 90; Perm to Offic *Sarum* 90-93; Hon C Milford *Win* from 93. *65 Knowland Drive, Milford on Sea, Lymington, Hants SO41 0SF* Lymington (01590) 645694

RIDGE, Haydn Stanley. b 24. Univ of Wales (Lamp) BA51 Bris Univ CertEd52. Qu Coll Birm 56. **d** 56 **p** 57. Div Master Guernsey Gr Sch 60-75; Hon C Guernsey St Steph *Win* from 62; Dep Hd Master St Peter Port Sch 75-80; Hd Master St Sampson Sch 75-87; rtd 91. *St David, Les Cherfs, Castel, Guernsey, Channel Islands GY5 7HG* Guernsey (01481) 56209

RIDGEWAY, David. b 59. St Chad's Coll Dur BSc80 Cam Univ CertEd81. Ripon Coll Cuddesdon 84. **d** 87 **p** 88. C Kempston Transfiguration *St Alb* 87-90; C Radlett 90-95; P-in-c Heath and Reach from 95. *The Vicarage, 2 Reach Lane, Heath and Reach, Leighton Buzzard, Beds LU7 0AL* Heath and Reach (01525) 237633

RIDGEWELL, Miss Mary Jean. b 54. Dur Univ BA76 PGCE77. Ridley Hall Cam 89. **d** 91 **p** 94. Par Dn Trowbridge St Jas *Sarum* 91-94; C 94-95; Chapl Lee Abbey from 95. *Lee Abbey Fellowship, Lynton, Devon EX35 6JJ* Lynton (01598) 52621 Fax 52619

RIDGWAY, David. b 28. Trin Hall Cam BA54 MA58. Westcott Ho Cam 54. **d** 56 **p** 57. R Gosforth *Carl* 63-70; V Walney Is 70-76; P-in-c Irthington 76-78; P-in-c Crosby-on-Eden 77-78; V Irthington, Crosby-on-Eden and Scaleby 79-93; rtd 93. *11 Woodleigh, Walton, Brampton, Cumbria CA8 2DS* Brampton (016977) 3252

RIDGWAY, Mrs Janet Elizabeth Knight. b 40. St Alb Minl Tr Scheme. **dss** 86 **d** 87 **p** 94. Tring *St Alb* 86-87; Hon Par Dn 87-94; Hon C from 94. *Barleycombe, Trooper Road, Aldbury, Tring, Herts HP23 4RW* Aldbury Common (0144285) 303

RIDGWAY, Canon Maurice Hill. b 18. FSA BA. St D Coll Lamp BA40 Westcott Ho Cam 40. **d** 41 **p** 42. V Bowdon *Ches* 62-83; rtd 83; Perm to Offic *Ches* from 83; Perm to Offic *St As* from 83; Perm to Offic *Lich* from 84. *Milkwood Cottage, Rhydycroesau, Oswestry, Shropshire SY10 7PS* Oswestry (01691) 655330

RIDING, Pauline Alison. *See* BICKNELL, Mrs Pauline Alison

RIDLEY, Alfred Forbes. b 34. Bps' Coll Cheshunt 62. **d** 65 **p** 66. C Prittlewell St Mary *Chelmsf* 65-69; R Paulerspury *Pet* 69-73; P-in-c Wicken 71-73; V W Haddon w Winwick 73-83; RD Brixworth 80-83; R Guernsey St Philippe de Torteval *Win* 83-92; R Guernsey St Pierre du Bois 83-92; R Blakesley w Adstone and Maidford etc *Pet* from 92. *The Vicarage, Blakesley, Towcester, Northants NN12 8RF* Blakesley (01327) 860507

RIDLEY, Andrew Roy. b 55. St Pet Coll Ox BA77. Ripon Coll Cuddesdon 78. **d** 79 **p** 80. C Bollington St Jo *Ches* 79-83; V Runcorn St Mich 83-94; Dioc Chapl to MU from 92; RD Frodsham from 94; V Helsby and Dunham-on-the-Hill from 94; P-in-c Alvanley from 94. *St Paul's Vicarage, Vicarage Lane, Helsby, Warrington WA6 9AB* Helsby (01928) 722151

RIDLEY, David Gerhard (Vic). b 60. Southn Univ BSc82 Bath Univ PGCE83. Qu Coll Birm 91. **d** 93 **p** 94. C Faversham *Cant* from 93. *78 Cyprus Road, Faversham, Kent ME13 8HB* Faversham (01795) 538334

RIDLEY, Derek. b 40. Newc Univ BSc74. Cranmer Hall Dur 75. **d** 78 **p** 79. C Upperby St Jo *Carl* 78-81; C Penrith w Newton Reigny 81; C Penrith w Newton Reigny and Plumpton Wall 81-82; TV 82-86; V Cadishead *Man* from 86. *St Mary's Vicarage, Penry Avenue, Cadishead, Manchester M30 5AF* 0161-775 2171

RIDLEY, Jay. b 41. Birm Univ BA63. St Steph Ho Ox 63. **d** 65 **p** 66. C Woodford St Mary *Chelmsf* 65-67; C Prittlewell St Mary 67-70; C-in-c Dunscroft CD *Sheff* 70-75; Chapl HM Pris Wormwood Scrubs 75-77; Chapl HM Rem Cen Ashford 77-84; Chapl HM Young Offender Inst Feltham 84-91; Chapl HM Pris Ashwell from 91. *HM Prison Ashwell, Oakham, Leics LE15 7LS* Oakham (01572) 756075 Fax 724460

RIDLEY, John Sidney. b 15. Trin Coll Cam BA37 MA43. Chich Th Coll 37. **d** 39 **p** 40. Chapl Emscote Lawn Sch Warw 64-72; Asst Master St Dunstan's Coll Catford 72-81; Lic to Offic *S'wark* from 72; rtd 81. *4 Morden Road, London SE3 0AA*

RIDLEY, Canon Laurence Roy. b 19. St Pet Hall Ox BA41 MA45. Wycliffe Hall Ox 41. **d** 42 **p** 43. V Higher Bebington *Ches* 69-90; RD Wirral N 79-89; Hon Can Ches Cathl 80-90; rtd 90. *6 Newtons Lane, Winterley, Sandbach, Cheshire CW11 9NL* Crewe (01270) 505929

RIDLEY, Mrs Lesley. b 46. Cranmer Hall Dur 75. **dss** 78 **d** 87 **p** 94. Upperby St Jo *Carl* 78-81; Penrith w Newton Reigny and Plumpton Wall 81-86; Cadishead *Man* 86-87; Par Dn 87-94; C from 94. *St Mary's Vicarage, Penry Avenue, Cadishead, Manchester M30 5AF* 0161-775 2171

RIDLEY, Michael Edward. b 37. Ex Univ MA90. AKC62. **d** 63 **p** 64. C Chapel Allerton *Ripon* 63-67; C Epsom St Martin *Guildf* 67-70; C Claxby w Normanby-le-Wold etc *Linc* 70-72; V Leake 72-75; R Harlaxton w Wyville and Hungerton 75-80; R Stroxton 76-80; Dioc Stewardship Adv *Portsm* 80-86; P-in-c Rowlands Castle 80-82; C Blendworth w Chalton w Idsworth etc 83-86; TV N Creedy *Ex* 86-90; R W Downland *Sarum* from 90; RD Chalke from 92. *The Rectory, 97 Mill End, Damerham, Fordingbridge, Hants SP6 3HU* Rockbourne (01725) 518642

RIDLEY, Michael Laurence. b 59. BA81. Ripon Coll Cuddesdon 81. **d** 83 **p** 84. C Bollington St Jo *Ches* 83-88; V Thelwall from 88. *The Vicarage, Bell Lane, Thelwall, Warrington WA4 2SX* Warrington (01925) 661166

RIDLEY, Peter John. b 39. Keble Coll Ox BA61. Tyndale Hall Bris 61. **d** 63 **p** 64. C Clifton Ch Ch w Em *Bris* 63-67; C Lambeth St Andr w St Thos *S'wark* 67-69; V W Hampstead St Cuth *Lon* 69-77; V Eynsham *Ox* 77-85; RD Woodstock 82-84; V Nicholforest and Kirkandrews on Esk *Carl* from 85. *Nicholforest Vicarage, Penton, Carlisle CA6 5QF* Nicholforest (01228) 577221

RIDLEY, Simon. b 33. Magd Coll Ox BA54 MA58 BD66. Linc Th Coll. **d** 57 **p** 58. C St Jo Wood *Lon* 57-60; Abp's Dom Chapl *Cant* 60-61; V N Wootton *B & W* 61-66; Lect Wells Th Coll 61-65; Hong Kong 66-70; TR Basingstoke *Win* 70-73. *Prospect House, Wittersham, Tenterden, Kent TN30 7ET* Wittersham (01797) 270639

RIDLEY, Stephen James. b 57. St Pet Coll Ox MA83. Ripon Coll Cuddesdon 80. **d** 82 **p** 83. C Heald Green St Cath *Ches* 82-85; Chapl Ches Coll 85-90; Dioc Press Officer 85-90; Chapl Birkenhead Sch Merseyside from 90; Lic to Offic *Ches* from 90. *1 Kingsmead Road South, Birkenhead, Merseyside L43 6TA* 0151-652 7495

RIDLEY, Stewart Gordon. b 47. AKC72. St Aug Coll Cant 72. **d** 73 **p** 74. C St Bart Armley w St Mary New Wortley *Ripon* 73-77; C Hawksworth Wood 77-79; C Rothwell w Lofthouse 79-81; R Whitwood *Wakef* 81-87; R Ingoldmells w Addlethorpe *Linc* 87-92; RD Calcewaithe and Candleshoe 89-92; V Settle *Bradf* from 92; Dioc Chapl MU from 93. *The Vicarage, Townhead Way, Settle, N Yorkshire BD24 9JB* Settle (01729) 822288

RIDOUT, Canon Christopher John. b 33. K Coll Lon BD57 AKC57 MA92. **d** 58 **p** 59. C Roxeth Ch Ch *Lon* 58-62; CMS

62-63; Kenya 63-75; C Gt Malvern St Mary *Worc* 75-79; R Bredon w Bredon's Norton from 79; RD Pershore from 91; Hon Can Worc Cathl from 92. *The Rectory, Bredon, Tewkesbury, Glos GL20 7LT*   Bredon (01684) 772237

✝RIDSDALE, Rt Rev Philip Bullen. b 15. Trin Coll Cam BA37 MA45. Ridley Hall Cam 45. d 47 p 48 c 72. C St Helens St Helen *Liv* 47-49; Uganda 49-64; Adn Ruwenzori 61-64; Hon Can Ruwenzori from 63; R Bramfield w Stapleford *St Alb* 64-66; P-in-c Waterford 64-66; R Bramfield w Stapleford and Waterford 66-72; RD Hertf 70-72; Bp Boga-Zaire 72-80; rtd 81; Perm to Offic *Ely* from 81. *3 Pemberton Terrace, Cambridge CB2 1JA*   Cambridge (01223) 62690

RIDYARD, Preb John Gordon. b 33. St Aid Birkenhead 59. d 62 p 63. C Lanc St Mary *Blackb* 62-65; C Bushbury *Lich* 65-68; V Darlaston All SS 68-76; TV Wolv St Mark 76-78; TV Wolv 78-82; Preb Lich Cathl from 82; V Bishopswood 82-89; V Brewood 82-89; RD Penkridge 83-89; R Newc w Butterton from 89. *The Rectory, Seabridge Road, Newcastle-under-Lyme, Staffs ST5 2HS*   Newcastle-under-Lyme (01782) 616397

RIDYARD, Malcolm Charles. b 32. St D Coll Lamp BA54 Wycliffe Hall Ox 54. d 56 p 57. C Widnes St Paul *Liv* 56-59; C Ashton-in-Makerfield St Thos 59-61; India 62-71; Area Sec (Dios B & W, Bris and Sarum) CMS 71-80; P-in-c Church Coniston *Carl* 80-87; P-in-c Torver 80-87; R Bootle, Corney, Whicham and Whitbeck from 87. *The Rectory, Bootle, Millom, Cumbria LA19 5TH*   Bootle (01229) 718223

RIEM, Roland Gerardus Anthony. b 60. St Chad's Coll Dur BSc82 Kent Univ PhD86. St Jo Coll Nottm DipTh87 DPS89. d 89 p 90. C Deal St Leon and St Rich and Sholden *Cant* 89-92; Chapl Nottm Univ *S'well* from 92. *3 Wortley Close, University Park, Nottingham NG7 2RD*   Nottingham (0115) 951 3927/951 3374

RIESS, Trevor William. b 54. Down Coll Cam MA76 CertEd77. St Jo Coll Nottm 84. d 86 p 87. C Stainforth *Sheff* 86-88; Chapl St Jas Choir Sch Grimsby 89; C Lowestoft and Kirkley *Nor* 89-90; TV 90-94; TV Lowestoft St Marg 94-95; Lothingland Hosp 90-95; V Gorleston St Mary *Nor* from 95. *The Vicarage, 41 Nuffield Crescent, Gorleston, Great Yarmouth, Norfolk NR31 7LL*   Great Yarmouth (01493) 661741

RIGBY, Francis Michael. d 90 p 91. NSM Alvescot w Black Bourton, Shilton, Holwell etc *Ox* 90-92; P-in-c Gt w Lt Tew 92-95; rtd 95. *Barn Acre, Bishops Frome, Worcester WR6 5AS*   Bosbury (01531) 640768

RIGBY, Harold. b 34. Nottm Univ BA56 Man Poly DipEd77. Ripon Hall Ox BA58 MA62. d 58 p 59. C Barlow Moor Man 58-61; C Bury St Jo 61-64; C-in-c Lostock CD 64-76; C Davyhulme St Mary 76; Hon C 76-79; Lic to Offic from 79. *17 Atwood Road, Manchester M20 0TA*   0161-445 7454

RIGBY, John Basil. b 19. Sarum Th Coll 46. d 48 p 49. V Boreham Wood All SS *St Alb* 61-72; V Sandbach *Ches* 72-83; rtd 83; Perm to Offic *Ches* from 83. *6 West Way, Sandbach, Cheshire CW11 9LQ*   Crewe (01270) 763615

RIGBY, Joseph. b 37. Open Univ BA72. Ox NSM Course. d 78 p 79. NSM Earley St Pet *Ox* 78-80; C Penzance St Mary w St Paul *Truro* 80-82; V Mevagissey 82-83; P-in-c St Ewe 83; R Mevagissey and St Ewe 83-90; rtd 90. *Flat 2, Woodville, Agar Road, Truro, Cornwall TR1 1JU*

RIGBY, Michael John. b 52. MA MSc. Ridley Hall Cam. d 82 p 83. C Reading St Jo *Ox* 82-86; C Wallington H Trin *S'wark* 86-92; Pastor Foundns Chr Fellowship Trust Ch from 92. *14 Dinorben Court, Woodcote Road, Wallington, Surrey SM6 0PZ*   0181-647 8649

RIGBY, William. b 51. Leic Univ BSc(Econ) Newc Poly BSc82. Cranmer Hall Dur 86. d 88 p 89. C Morpeth *Newc* 88-92; R St Jo Lee from 92; Chapl to the Deaf from 92. *St John Lee Rectory, Hexham, Northd NE46 4PE*   Hexham (01434) 602220

RIGG, Arthur Neville. b 17. Lanc Univ MA69. St Aid Birkenhead 49. d 51 p 52. V Kirkby Stephen *Carl* 70-80; rtd 81; Perm to Offic *Carl* from 81. *Nab Barn, South Dyke, Penrith, Cumbria CA11 9LL*   Lazonby (01768) 898762

RIGGS, Marcus John Ralph. b 55. Brighton Poly BA78 Southn Univ BTh82. Chich Th Coll 79. d 82 p 83. C St Leonards Ch Ch and St Mary *Chich* 82-85; C Eastbourne St Andr 85-86; C Brighton St Mich 86-88; Asst Dir Dioc Bd of Soc Resp 88-93; Lic to Offic from 93. *32 Bennett Road, Brighton BN2 5JL*   Brighton (01273) 601016

RIGGS, Sidney James. b 39. Bps' Coll Cheshunt 62. d 63 p 64. C S'wark St Geo *S'wark* 63-66; C Plymouth Crownhill Ascension *Ex* 66-69; Asst Youth Chapl *Glouc* 69-71; Hon Min Can Glouc Cathl 71-74; Min Can Glouc Cathl 74-76; V Glouc St Mary de Lode and St Nic 76-92; R Rodborough from 92; RD Stonehouse from 94. *The Rectory, Walkley Hill, Rodborough, Stroud, Glos GL5 3TX*   Stroud (01453) 764399

RIGHTON, Sidney Lawrence. b 13. Bps' Coll Cheshunt 46. d 48 p 49. V Dewsbury Moor *Wakef* 67-76; V Darrington w Wentbridge 76-79; rtd 79. *Flat 2, Hereford Court, Hereford*

Road, Harrogate, N Yorkshire HG1 2PX   Harrogate (01423) 507128

RIGLER, Edgar Henry (Tony). b 18. St Jo Coll Dur BA50. Wycliffe Hall Ox 48. d 50 p 51. V Ealing Dean St Jo *Lon* 67-80; P-in-c Ealing St Jas 77-80; V Portsea St Luke *Portsm* 80-88; rtd 88; Hon Bp's Adv on Evang *Portsm* 88-90. *50 John Amner Close, Chevington Park, Lynn Road, Ely, Cambs CB6 1DT*   Ely (01353) 668100

RILEY, Preb Harold. b 03. Birm Univ BA24. Coll of Resurr Mirfield 25. d 27 p 28. V Kilburn St Aug w St Jo *Lon* 55-75; rtd 75; P-in-c St Mary Aldermary *Lon* 76-81; C 81-84. *49 Delaware Mansions, London W9 2LH*   0171-289 3734

RILEY, Canon John Martin. b 37. St D Coll Lamp BA62 DipTh63. d 63 p 64. C Conwy w Gyffin *Ban* 63-68; P-in-c Llanfachreth 68-70; TV Dolgellau, Llanfachreth, Brithdir etc 70-72; V Beddgelert 72-78; Dioc Youth Chapl 72-78; V Tywyn 78-82; V Tywyn w Aberdyfi 82-95; V Llanegryn w Aberdyfi w Tywyn from 95; RD Ystumaner from 87; Can Ban Cathl from 90. *The Vicarage, Tywyn, Gwynedd LL36 9DD*   Towyn (01654) 710295

RILEY, John Graeme. b 55. St Jo Coll Dur BA78. Trin Coll Bris 79. d 81 p 82. C Hensingham *Carl* 81-84; C Preston St Cuth *Blackb* 84-87; V Blackb Ch Ch w St Matt from 87; Chapl Qu Park Hosp Blackb from 87. *The Vicarage, Brandy House Brow, Blackburn BB2 3EY*   Blackburn (01254) 256292

RILEY, Very Rev Kenneth Joseph (Ken). b 40. Univ of Wales BA61 Linacre Ho Ox BA64. Wycliffe Hall Ox 61. d 64 p 65. C Fazakerley Em *Liv* 64-66; Chapl Brasted Place Coll Westerham 66-69; Chapl Oundle Sch Pet 69-74; Chapl Liv Cathl *Liv* 74-75; Chapl Liv Univ 74-93; V Mossley Hill St Matt and St Jas 75-83; RD Childwall 82-83; Can Res Liv Cathl 83-93; Treas 83-87; Prec 87-93; Dean Man from 93. *The Deanery, 44 Shrewsbury Road, Prestwich, Manchester M25 8GQ*   0161-773 2959 or 833 2220   Fax 839 6226

RILEY, Mrs Lesley Anne. b 54. Trin Coll Bris 79. dss 81 d 87. Hensingham *Carl* 81-84; Preston St Cuth *Blackb* 84-87; Hon Par Dn Blackb Ch Ch w St Matt from 87. *The Vicarage, Brandy House Brow, Blackburn BB2 3EY*   Blackburn (01254) 256292

RILEY, Martin Shaw. b 47. Selw Coll Cam BA71 Cam Univ CertEd72 MA75. Sarum & Wells Th Coll 85. d 87 p 88. C Tuffley *Glouc* 87-91; Hon Min Can Glouc Cathl from 88; P-in-c Barnwood 91-94; V from 94. *The Vicarage, 147A Barnwood Avenue, Gloucester GL4 7AD*   Gloucester (01452) 613760

RILEY, Michael Charles. b 57. Ball Coll Ox BA79 MA83 Ex Univ CertEd80. Edin Th Coll 84. d 86 p 87. C Newc St Geo *Newc* 86-89; C Chiswick St Nic w St Mary *Lon* 89-90; V Chiswick St Paul Grove Park from 90. *St Paul's Vicarage, 64 Grove Park Road, London W4 3SB*   0181-994 2163

RILEY, Patrick John. b 39. Leeds Univ BA62. Coll of Resurr Mirfield 62. d 64 p 65. C Rowbarton *B & W* 64-72; P-in-c Farleigh Hungerford w Tellisford 72-73; P-in-c Rode, Rode Hill and Woolverton 72-73; R Rode Major 73-85; RD Frome 78-85; V Glastonbury w Meare, W Pennard and Godney from 85; Preb Wells Cathl from 90. *The Vicarage, 17 Lambrook Street, Glastonbury, Somerset BA6 8BY*   Glastonbury (01458) 832362

RILEY, Peter Arthur. b 23. Kelham Th Coll 40. d 51 p 52. Jamaica 62-77; V Abertillery *Mon* 77-83; R Panteg 83-88; rtd 88; Hon C Dartmouth *Ex* from 88. *6 Church Field, Dartmouth, Devon TQ6 9HH*   Dartmouth (01803) 835309

RILEY, Reuben Cecil. b 17. St Pet Hall Ox BA39 MA43. Wycliffe Hall Ox. d 50 p 51. V Blackb St Luke *Blackb* 68-71; V Tunstall 71-90; P-in-c Leck 84-90; rtd 90. *Tunstall Vicarage, Carnforth, Lancs LA6 2RQ*   Tunstall (015242) 74228

RILEY, Sidney David. b 43. Birm Univ BA. Ridley Hall Cam 69. d 71 p 72. C Herne Bay Ch Ch *Cant* 71-74; C Croydon St Sav 74-77; C-in-c Aylesham CD 77; P-in-c Aylesham 77-78; V 78-82; V Tudeley w Capel *Roch* from 82; Asst Chapl Pembury Hosp 83-86. *The Vicarage, Sychem Lane, Five Oak Green, Tonbridge, Kent TN12 6TL*   Paddock Wood (01892) 836653

RILEY, Canon William. b 24. St Aid Birkenhead 48. d 51 p 52. C Tarleton *Blackb* 62-92; RD Leyland 84-89; Hon Can Blackb Cathl 90-92; rtd 92. *114 Liverpool Road, Hutton, Preston PR4 5SL*   Longton (01772) 614267

RIMELL, Gilbert William. b 22. Llan Dioc Tr Scheme 76. d 81 p 82. NSM Laleston w Tythegston and Merthyr Mawr *Llan* 81-94. *75 Bryntirion Hill, Bridgend, M Glam CF31 4BY*   Bridgend (01656) 658002

RIMMER, Andrew Malcolm. b 62. Magd Coll Cam BA84 MA88. Wycliffe Hall Ox 86. d 88 p 89. C Romford Gd Shep Collier Row *Chelmsf* 88-92; C Hazlemere *Ox* from 92. *Church House, George's Hill, Widmer End, High Wycombe, Bucks HP15 6BH*   High Wycombe (01494) 713848

RIMMER, Anthony Robert Walters (Tony). b 41. Hull Univ BA63. Coll of Resurr Mirfield 64. d 66 p 67. C Leeds All SS *Ripon* 66-69; C Kippax 69-72; C Preston St Jo *Blackb* 72-76;

TV 76-83; P-in-c Glasson Ch Ch 83-86; Chapl Dunkerque Miss to Seamen *Eur* from 86. *130 rue de l'Ecole Maternelle, 59140 Dunkerque, France* France (33) 28 59 04 36 Fax as telephone

RIMMER, David Henry. b 36. Ex Coll Ox BA60 MA65. Linc Th Coll 62. **d** 64 **p** 65. C Liv Our Lady and St Nic *Liv* 64-66; C Daybrook *S'well* 66-69; Chapl St Mary's Cathl *Edin* 69-71; R Kirkcaldy *St And* 71-78; R Haddington *Edin* 78-83; R Dunbar 79-83; R Edin Gd Shep from 83. *9 Upper Coltbridge Terrace, Edinburgh EH12 6AD*   0131-337 2698

RIMMER, John Clive. b 25. Oak Hill Th Coll 63. **d** 65 **p** 66. C-in-c Dallam CD *Liv* 69-74; V Southport SS Simon and Jude 74-83; V Westhead 83-90; Chapl Ormskirk Hosp *Liv* 84-90; rtd 90. *14 Hurlston Drive, Ormskirk, Lancs L39 1LD* Ormskirk (01695) 570838

RIMMER, Paul Nathanael. b 25. Jes Coll Ox BA48 MA50. Wycliffe Hall Ox 48. **d** 50 **p** 51. V Marston *Ox* 59-90; RD Cowley 69-73; rtd 90. *32 Ulfgar Road, Wolvercote, Oxford OX2 8AZ*   Kidlington (01865) 352567

RIMMER, Roy Malcolm. b 31. Fitzw Ho Cam BA58 MA62. Tyndale Hall Bris 54. **d** 59 **p** 60. The Navigators 62-70; Perm to Offic *Ox* 66-70; C Portman Square St Paul *Lon* 70-75; R Rougham *St E* 75-87; P-in-c Rushbrooke 78-87; P-in-c Beyton and Hessett 86-87; V Newmarket All SS 87-93; rtd 93. *5 Benson Street, Cambridge CB4 3QJ*   Cambridge (01223) 359063

RIMMINGTON, Dr Gerald Thorneycroft. b 30. FCP66 Lon Univ BSc56 PhD64 Leic Univ MA59 Nottm Univ MEd72 PhD75. **d** 76 **p** 78. Canada 76-79; Lic to Offic *Leic* 79-80; R Paston *Pet* 81-86; V Cosby *Leic* 86-90; Dir of Continuing Minl Educn 87-90; R Barwell w Potters Marston and Stapleton 90-95; rtd 95. *7 Beechings Close, Countesthorpe, Leicester LE8 5PA*   Leicester (0116) 277 7155

RINGER, Philip James. b 47. Ox Min Course 88. **d** 91 **p** 92. NSM Chalfont St Peter *Ox* from 91. *Hillcroft, 2 Lambscroft Way, Chalfont St Peter, Gerrards Cross, Bucks SL9 9AX*   Gerrards Cross (01753) 883269

RINGLAND, Tom Laurence. b 61. SS Hild & Bede Coll Dur BSc83. Trin Coll Bris BA89. **d** 89 **p** 90. C Southgate *Chich* 89-92; C Polegate from 92. *St Wilfrid's House, 90 Broad Road, Eastbourne, E Sussex BN20 9RA*   Eastbourne (01323) 482088

RINGROSE, Brian Sefton. b 31. Clare Coll Cam BA54 MA58. Tyndale Hall Bris 56. **d** 58 **p** 59. C Ox St Ebbe *Ox* 58-60; C Erith St Paul *Roch* 60-61; India 61-75; P-in-c Ox St Matt *Ox* 75-78; Interserve (Scotland) from 78. *12 Elm Avenue, Kirkintilloch, Glasgow G66 4HJ*   0141-776 2943   Fax 777 8146

RINGROSE, Canon Hedley Sidney. b 42. Open Univ BA79. Sarum Th Coll 65. **d** 68 **p** 69. C Bishopston *Bris* 68-71; C Easthampstead *Ox* 71-75; V Glouc St Geo w Whaddon *Glouc* 75-88; RD Glouc City 83-88; Hon Can Glouc Cathl from 86; V Cirencester from 88; RD Cirencester from 89. *Cirencester Vicarage, 1 Dollar Street, Cirencester, Glos GL7 2AJ* Cirencester (01285) 653142

RIOCH, Mrs Wenda Jean. b 35. Sarum & Wells Th Coll 84. **d** 87 **p** 94. Par Dn Basingstoke *Win* 87-91; Par Dn Catshill and Dodford *Worc* 91-94; C from 94. *27 Greendale Close, Catshill, Bromsgrove, Worcs B61 0LR*   Bromsgrove (01527) 835708

RIPLEY, Geoffrey Alan. b 39. Dur Univ BA62. St Aid Birkenhead. **d** 64 **p** 65. C E Herrington *Dur* 64-67; Hon C Hodge Hill CD *Birm* 68-70; Youth Chapl *Liv* 70-75; Chapl Liv Cathl 70-78; Bp's Dom Chapl 75-78; V Wavertree St Bridget 78-87; Lay Tr Adv *B & W* from 87; Dioc Chapl MU from 92. *35 Orchard Road, Street, Somerset BA16 0BT*   Street (01458) 46435

RIPON, Bishop of. See YOUNG, Rt Rev David Nigel de Lorentz

RIPON, Dean of. *Vacant*

RIPPINGALE, Denis Michael. b 29. Leeds Univ BA52. Coll of Resurr Mirfield 52. **d** 54 **p** 55. V Altofts *Wakef* 63-71; V S Elmsall 71-84; V Marsden 84-92; rtd 92. *61 Viking Road, Bridlington, N Humberside YO16 5PW*   Bridlington (01262) 601838

RISBY, John. b 40. Lon Univ DipTh66. Lambeth STh82 Oak Hill Th Coll 64. **d** 67 **p** 68. C Fulham Ch Ch *Lon* 67-68; C Ealing St Mary 68-70; C Chitts Hill St Cuth 70-73; C Hove Bp Hannington Memorial Ch *Chich* 73-76; V Islington St Jude Mildmay Park *Lon* 76-82; P-in-c Islington St Paul Ball's Pond 78-82; V Mildmay Grove St Jude and St Paul 82-84; R Hunsdon w Widford and Wareside *St Alb* from 84; RD Hertf from 91. *The Rectory, Acorn Street, Hunsdon, Ware, Herts SG12 8PB*   Ware (01920) 870171

RISDON, John Alexander. b 42. Lon Univ DipTh66. Clifton Th Coll 66. **d** 68 **p** 69. C Ealing Dean St Jo *Lon* 68-72; C Heref St Pet w St Owen *Heref* 72-74; Ord Cand Sec CPAS 74-77; Hon C Bromley Ch Ch *Roch* 74-77; TV Cheltenham St Mary, St Matt, St Paul and H Trin *Glouc* 77-86; R Stapleton *Bris* from 86. *The Rectory, 21 Park Road, Bristol BS16 1AZ*   Bristol (0117) 958 3858

RISING, Sidney Frederick. b 28. E Midl Min Tr Course 73. **d** 76 **p** 77. NSM W Bridgford *S'well* 76-79; C 79-82; V Whatton w Aslockton, Hawksworth, Scarrington etc 82-87; Chapl HM Det Cen Whatton 82-87; Chapl Notts Police 87-93; Rural Officer *S'well* 87-89; P-in-c Perlethorpe 88-90; P-in-c Norton Cuckney 89-90; P-in-c Staunton w Flawborough 90-93; P-in-c Kilvington 90-93; rtd 93. *3 Pelham Close, Newark, Notts NG24 4XL*   Newark (01636) 72293

RITCHIE, Brian Albert. b 34. Open Univ BA80 Birm Univ MA84. Qu Coll Birm 60. **d** 63 **p** 64. C S Leamington St Jo *Cov* 63-67; C-in-c Canley CD 67-70; Perm to Offic 71-80; Hon C Cov H Trin 82-88; R Hatton w Haseley, Rowington w Lowsonford etc from 88. *North Ferncumbe Rectory, Hatton Green, Warwick CV35 7LA*   Haseley Knob (01926) 484332

RITCHIE, David Philip. b 60. Hatf Coll Dur BA85. Wycliffe Hall Ox 85. **d** 87 **p** 88. C Chadwell *Chelmsf* 87-90; C Waltham H Cross 90-94; TV Becontree W from 94. *St Thomas' Vicarage, 187 Burnside Road, Dagenham, Essex RM8 2JN* 0181-590 6190

RITCHIE, Canon David Caldwell. b 20. Ex Coll Ox BA42 MA46. Wells Th Coll 45. **d** 47 **p** 48. V Pinner *Lon* 65-73; P-in-c Bradford-on-Avon *Sarum* 73-75; V 75-81; RD Bradf 80-84; Can and Preb Sarum Cathl 81-85; V Winsley 81-84; Custos St Jo Hosp Heytesbury 84-85; rtd 85; Hon Can Papua New Guinea from 85. *5 Berkshire Road, Salisbury SP2 8NY* Salisbury (01722) 321338

RITCHIE, David John Rose. b 48. St Jo Coll Dur BA72 DipTh74. **d** 74 **p** 75. C Harold Wood *Chelmsf* 74-79; TV Ipsley *Worc* 79-84; Chapl Vevey w Chateau d'Oex and Villars *Eur* 84-93; V Stoke Bishop *Bris* from 93. *The Vicarage, Mariner's Drive, Bristol BS9 1QJ*   Bristol (0117) 968 1858

RITCHIE, Miss Jean. b 30. Lon Univ CertEd51 DipCD71. Trin Coll Bris DipTh79. **dss** 79 **d** 87 **p** 94. Ox St Ebbe w H Trin and St Pet *Ox* 79-87; Par Dn 87-91; rtd 91; Perm to Offic *B & W* 91-94; NSM Clevedon St Andr and Ch from 94. *63 Holland Road, Clevedon, Avon BS21 7YJ*   Clevedon (01275) 871762

RITCHIE, John Young Wylie. b 45. Aber Univ MA69 Univ of Wales (Cardiff) BD76. St Mich Coll Llan 73. **d** 76 **p** 77. C Trevethin *Mon* 76-78; C Cwmbran 78-81; TV 81-82; C Ind Chapl *York* 82-91; P-in-c Micklefield 82-88; P-in-c Aislaby and Ruswarp 88-89; C Scalby w Ravenscar and Staintondale 89-91; C Shelf *Bradf* 91-94; C Shelf St Mich w Buttershaw St Aid from 94. *St Michael's House, Collinfield Rise, Bradford, W Yorkshire BD6 2SL*   Bradford (01274) 607486

RITCHIE, Samuel (Sam). b 31. Lon Coll of Div 65. **d** 67 **p** 68. C Westlands St Andr *Lich* 67-70; V Springfield H Trin *Chelmsf* 70-82; Chapl HM Pris Chelmsf 70-82; Chapl HM Pris Brixton 82-84; Chapl HM Pris Hull 84-86; Chapl HM Pris Wymott from 86. *HM Prison Wymott, Moss Lane, Leyland, Preston PR5 3LW*   Preston (01772) 421461   Fax 455960

RITCHIE, William James. b 62. TCD MA DipTh. **d** 86 **p** 87. C Enniscorthy w Clone, Clonmore, Monart etc *C & O* 86-89; Egypt 89-91; Bp's C Kells Union *C & O* 91-92; I Kells w Balrathboyne, Moynalty etc *M & K* from 92; Warden of Readers from 93. *The Rectory, Kells, Co Meath, Irish Republic* Ceanannus Mor (46) 40151   Fax as telephone

RITSON, Arthur William David. b 35. AKC58. **d** 59 **p** 60. C Bishopwearmouth St Mich *Dur* 59-63; Chapl RN 63-67; C Sudbury St Greg and St Pet *St E* 67-69; R Lt Hallingbury *Chelmsf* 69-83; P-in-c Broomfield from 83. *The Vicarage, Butlers Close, Broomfield, Chelmsford CM1 5BE*   Chelmsford (01245) 440318

RITSON, Canon Gerald Richard Stanley (Bill). b 35. CCC Cam BA59 MA63. Linc Th Coll 59. **d** 61 **p** 62. C Harpenden St Jo *St Alb* 61-65; C Goldington 65-69; R Clifton 69-76; Sec to Dioc Past Cttee 76-87; P-in-c Aldenham 76-87; Hon Can St Alb 80-87; Can Res St Alb from 87. *2 Sumpter Yard, St Albans, Herts AL1 1BY*   St Albans (01727) 861744

RIVERS, Arthur. b 20. Oak Hill Th Coll 52. **d** 53 **p** 54. V Burscough Bridge *Liv* 60-79; V Holmesfield *Derby* 79-86; rtd 86; Hon C Warton St Oswald w Yealand Conyers *Blackb* 86-88. *Holmlea, Hale, Milnthorpe, Cumbria LA7 7BL* Milnthorpe (015395) 63588

RIVERS, David John. b 51. St Jo Coll Nottm. **d** 84 **p** 85. C Woodthorpe *S'well* 84-88; C Hyson Green St Paul w St Steph 88; Asst Chapl Colchester Gen Hosp 89-91; Chapl Leeds Gen Infirmary from 91. *Leeds General Infirmary, St George Street, Leeds LS1 3EX*   Leeds (0113) 292 3527 or 292 2914

RIVERS, John Arthur. b 21. E Anglian Minl Tr Course 79. **d** 81 **p** 82. NSM Blakeney w Cley, Wiveton, Glandford etc *Nor* 81-86; Hon C Cromer 86-87; Perm to Offic from 87. *28 Compit Hills, Cromer, Norfolk NR27 9LJ*   Cromer (01263) 513051

RIVETT, Dr Andrew George. b 52. LRCP76 MRCS76 Lon Univ MB, BS76. Oak Hill Th Coll 85. **d** 87 **p** 88. C Stanford-le-Hope w Mucking *Chelmsf* 87-90; C Slough *Ox* 90-93; TV Totton *Win* from 93. *The Vicarage, Netley Marsh, Woodlands, Southampton SO4 2GX*   Southampton (01703) 862124

RIVETT, Leonard Stanley. b 23. MSSCLE82 MYPS90 St Jo Coll Dur BA47 DipTh49 York Univ CLHist88. **d** 49 **p** 50. V Norton *York* 62-74; Warden Wydale Hall 74-83; R Elvington w Sutton on Derwent and E Cottingwith 83-88; rtd 88; Offg Chapl RAF from 90. *47 Ryecroft Avenue, York YO2 2SD* York (01904) 705364

RIVETT, Peter John. b 42. St Jo Coll Dur BA71 DipTh72. Cranmer Hall Dur. **d** 72 **p** 73. C Newland St Jo *York* 72-76; TV Marfleet 76-82; V Oxhey All SS *St Alb* 82-93; TR Swanborough *Sarum* from 93. *The Rectory, Church Road, Woodborough, Pewsey, Wilts SN9 5PH* Woodborough (01672) 851746

RIVETT-CARNAC, Canon Sir Thomas Nicholas, Bt. b 27. Westcott Ho Cam. **d** 63 **p** 64. C Brompton H Trin *Lon* 68-72; P-in-c Kennington St Mark *S'wark* 72-87; V 87-89; RD Lambeth 79-83; Hon Can S'wark Cathl 80-89; rtd 89. *1 The Stable, Ashburnham Place, Battle, E Sussex TN33 9NF* Ninfield (01424) 892910

RIVIERE, Jonathan Byam Valentine. b 54. Cuddesdon Coll. **d** 83 **p** 84. C Wymondham *Nor* 83-88; TV Quidenham 88-94; P-in-c Somerleyton w Ashby, Fritton and Herringfleet 94; TV Somerleyton, Ashby, Fritton, Herringfleet etc from 95. *The Rectory, Somerleyton, Lowestoft, Suffolk NE32 5PT* Lowestoft (01502) 731885

RIVIERE, Mrs Tanagra June (Tana). b 41. S Dios Minl Tr Scheme 88. **d** 91. NSM Medstead cum Wield *Win* 91-94; NSM Bishop's Sutton and Ropley and W Tisted from 94. *The Drey, Paice Lane, Medstead, Alton, Hants GU34 5PT* Alton (01420) 563330

RIX, Patrick George. b 30. Magd Coll Ox BA54 DipEd52 MA57. Ridley Hall Cam 58. **d** 60 **p** 61. Asst Chapl Wrekin Coll Shropshire 62-70; Asst Chapl Gresham's Sch Holt 70-80; Chapl Bloxham Sch Oxon 80-86; rtd 86; P-in-c Swanton Abbott w Skeyton *Nor* 89; Perm to Offic from 89. *5 Rye Close, North Walsham, Norfolk NR28 9EY* North Walsham (01692) 402649

ROACH, Charles Alan. b 08. SS Coll Cam BA33 MA37. Westcott Ho Cam 33. **d** 35 **p** 36. St Mich Mt 66-75; Perm to Offic *Truro* from 66; rtd 75. *Trehoward, Green Lane West, Marazion, Cornwall TR17 0HH* Penzance (01736) 710514

ROACH, Kenneth Thomas. b 43. St Andr Univ BD69 Fitzw Coll Cam BA71 MA76. Westcott Ho Cam 69. **d** 71 **p** 72. C Glas St Marg *Glas* 71-73; CF 73-76; R Johnstone *Glas* 76-85; R Milngavie from 85; R Bearsden from 85; Chapl Glas Univ from 86. *34 Roman Road, Bearsden, Glasgow G61 2SQ* 0141-942 0386

ROAKE, Anthony Richard (Tony). b 52. Keble Coll Ox BA75 MA80. Wycliffe Hall Ox 75. **d** 77 **p** 78. C Clifton *S'well* 77-80; V Lapley w Wheaton Aston *Lich* 80-86; V Bournemouth St Andr *Win* from 86. *St Andrew's Vicarage, 53 Bennett Road, Bournemouth BH8 8QQ* Bournemouth (01202) 396622

ROAN, Canon William Forster. b 21. St Chad's Coll Dur BA47 DipTh49. **d** 49 **p** 50. V Workington St Jo *Carl* 70-86; Hon Can Carl Cathl 72-86; RD Solway 77-84; rtd 86; Perm to Offic *Carl* from 86. *41 Chiswick Street, Carlisle CA1 1HJ* Carlisle (01228) 21756

ROBB, Ian Archibald. b 48. K Coll Lon 68. **d** 72 **p** 73. C E Ham w Upton Park *Chelmsf* 72-74; C Leckhampton SS Phil and Jas w Cheltenham St Jas *Glouc* 74-79; P-in-c Cheltenham St Mich 79-90; V Lower Cam w Coaley from 90. *St Bartholomew's Vicarage, 99 Fairmead, Lower Cam, Dursley, Glos GL11 5JR* Dursley (01453) 542679

ROBB, Robert Hammond Neill. b 46. Queen Univ BA89 Man Univ 66. St Deiniol's Hawarden 87. **d** 87 **p** 88. C Lache cum Saltney *Ches* 87-89; V Norley and Crowton from 89; P-in-c Kingsley from 95. *The Vicarage, Crowton, Northwich, Cheshire CW8 2RQ* Kingsley (01928) 788310

ROBBINS, Angela Mary. See WEAVER, Ms Angela Mary

ROBBINS, David Ronald Walter. b 47. Sarum & Wells Th Coll 85. **d** 87 **p** 88. C Meir Heath *Lich* 87-89; C Collier Row St Jas and Havering-atte-Bower *Chelmsf* 89-93; C Tamworth *Lich* from 93. *The Parsonage, Masefield Drive, Tamworth, Staffs B79 8JB* Tamworth (01827) 64918

ROBBINS, Peter Tyndall. b 25. Magd Coll Ox BA46 DipTh47 MA51. Westcott Ho Cam 48. **d** 50 **p** 51. V Charing w Lt Chart *Cant* 63-73; V Basing *Win* 73-83; V Kingsclere 83-90; rtd 90; Perm to Offic *Birm* from 91; Asst RD Tamworth *Lich* from 91. *73 Summerfield Road, Tamworth, Staffs B77 3PJ* Tamworth (01827) 60805

ROBBINS, Richard Harry. b 14. Lon Univ BD47 Keble Coll Ox DipTh50. ALCD41. **d** 41 **p** 42. Chile 63-86; rtd 86. *61 Richmond Wood Road, Bournemouth BH8 9DQ* Bournemouth (01202) 512247

ROBBINS, Stephen. b 53. K Coll Lon BD74 AKC74. St Aug Coll Cant 75. **d** 76 **p** 77. C Tudhoe Grange *Dur* 76-80; C-in-c Harlow Green CD 80-84; V Gateshead Harlow Green 84-87; CF from 87. *clo MOD (Army), Bagshot Park, Bagshot, Surrey GU19 5PL* Bagshot (01276) 471717 Fax 412834

ROBBINS, Walter. b 35. **d** 72 **p** 73. Argentina 73-82; Adn N Argentina 80-82; C Southborough St Pet w Ch Ch and St Matt *Roch* 82-86; V Sidcup St Andr from 86. *The Vicarage, St Andrew's Road, Sidcup, Kent DA14 4SA* 0181-300 4712

ROBBINS-COLE, Adrian Peter. b 62. LSE BSc(Econ)84. Ch Div Sch of the Pacific (USA) 90 Ripon Coll Cuddesdon BA92. **d** 93 **p** 94. C S Dulwich St Steph *S'wark* from 93. *20 Drake Court, Tylney Avenue, London SE19 1LW* 0181-670 6513

ROBBINS-COLE, Ms Sarah Jane. b 68. Vermont Univ BA90. Ch Div Sch of the Pacific (USA) 92 Ripon Coll Cuddesdon BA95. **d** 95. C W Dulwich All SS *S'wark* from 95. *20 Drake Court, Tylney Avenue, London SE19 1LW* 0181-670 6513

ROBERT, Brother. See ATWELL, Brother Robert Ronald

ROBERT HUGH, Brother. See KING-SMITH, Philip Hugh

ROBERTS, Alan Moss. b 39. CEng68 MIMechE68 MIMarE68. St Jo Coll Nottm 77. **d** 79 **p** 80. C Bromsgrove St Jo *Worc* 79-83; C Edgbaston St Germain *Birm* 83-89; R Broadhembury, Payhembury and Plymtree *Ex* from 89. *The Rectory, Broadhembury, Honiton, Devon EX14 0LT* Broadhembury (01404) 841240

ROBERTS, Andrew Alexander (Andy). b 49. Open Univ BA75. Bp Otter Coll CertEd70 Sarum & Wells Th Coll 76. **d** 80 **p** 81. NSM Dorchester *Sarum* 80-85; C Swanage and Studland 85-87; TV 87-94; TR Bridgnorth, Tasley, Astley Abbotts, Oldbury etc *Heref* from 94. *The Rectory, 16 East Castle Street, Bridgnorth, Shropshire WV16 4AL* Bridgnorth (01746) 763256

ROBERTS, Anne Judith. b 44. CertEd65 DipEd78 Open Univ BA82 DCouns91. S Dios Minl Tr Scheme 86. **d** 89 **p** 94. Hon Par Dn S Kensington H Trin w All SS *Lon* 89-92; NSM Barnes St Mich *S'wark* from 92. *5 Avenue Gardens, London SW14 8PB* 0181-878 5642

ROBERTS, Arthur Frederick. b 09. K Coll Lon 38. **d** 39 **p** 40. R Shipdham *Nor* 62-75; rtd 75; Perm to Offic *Nor* from 75. *Moatside, Page's Lane, Saham Toney, Thetford, Norfolk IP25 7HJ* Watton (01953) 882405

ROBERTS, Canon Arthur Stansfield. b 06. Bp Wilson Coll 35. **d** 38 **p** 39. V Carbis Bay *Truro* 48-79; Hon Can Truro Cathl 68-79; rtd 79. *Stonehaven, North Perrott, Crewkerne, Somerset TA18 7SX* Crewkerne (01460) 77355

ROBERTS, Bernard John. b 21. Ox NSM Course 79. **d** 82 **p** 83. NSM Wendover *Ox* from 82. *19 The Paddocks, Wendover, Aylesbury, Bucks HP22 6HE* Wendover (01296) 623445

ROBERTS, Bryan Richard. b 55. Univ of Wales (Cardiff) DipTh78 BD80. St Mich Coll Llan 78. **d** 80 **p** 81. C Finham *Cov* 80-83; Asst Youth Officer *Nor* 83-86; R N and S Creake w Waterden 86-91; P-in-c E w N and W Barsham 86-91; Chapl Epsom Coll Surrey from 91. *3 Heron Court, 53 Alexandra Road, Epsom, Surrey KT17 4HU* Epsom (01372) 743016

ROBERTS, Charles Richard Meyrick. b 53. Huddersfield Poly ARCM75 BA75. St Paul's Grahamstown DipTh91. **d** 92 **p** 92. S Africa 92-94; C Bath Abbey w St Jas *B & W* from 94. *48 Devonshire Buildings, Bath BA2 4SU* Bath (01225) 422506

ROBERTS, Christopher Michael. b 39. CCSk93 Man Univ DipAE79. Qu Coll Birm 62. **d** 64 **p** 65. C Milton next Gravesend Ch Ch *Roch* 64-68; C Thirsk w S Kilvington *York* 68-69; V Castleton *Derby* 69-75; TV Buxton w Burbage and King Sterndale 75-79; Perm to Offic 86-87; NSM Marple All SS *Ches* 87-90; Asst Chapl Rainhill Hosp *Liv* 90-91; Asst Chapl St Helens Hosp Liv 90-91; Chapl Asst Whiston Co Hosp Prescot 90-91; Chapl R United Hosp Bath from 91. *The Chaplain's Office, Royal United Hospital, Combe Park, Bath BA1 3NG* Bath (01225) 428331

ROBERTS, Colin Edward. b 50. Sarum & Wells Th Coll. **d** 83 **p** 84. C Harton *Dur* 83; C S Shields All SS 83-85; C Thamesmead *S'wark* 85-87; TV 87-89; C Streatham St Pet 89-90 and 92; Zimbabwe 90-92; V Earlsfield St Jo *S'wark* from 92. *St John's Vicarage, 40 Atheldene Road, London SW18 3BW* 0181-874 2837

ROBERTS, Cyril. b 41. St Deiniol's Hawarden. **d** 84 **p** 85. C Maltby *Sheff* 84-86; TR Gt Snaith from 86. *The Rectory, Pontefract Road, Snaith, Goole, N Humberside DN14 9JS* Goole (01405) 860866

ROBERTS, David. b 44. Ex Univ BA65. St Steph Ho Ox 65. **d** 67 **p** 68. C Southwick St Columba *Dur* 67-72; C-in-c Southwick St Cuth CD 72-79; R Alyth *St And* 79-84; R Blairgowrie 79-84; R Coupar Angus 79-84; P-in-c Taunton St Jo *B & W* from 84; Chapl Somerset Coll of Arts and Tech from 84. *17 Henley Road, Taunton, Somerset TA1 5BW* Taunton (01823) 284176

ROBERTS, David Alan. b 38. Open Univ BA82. Ripon Hall Ox 71. **d** 73 **p** 74. C W Bridgford *S'well* 73-77; V Awsworth w Cossall 77-82; V Oxclose *Dur* 82-94; P-in-c New Seaham from 94. *The Vicarage, 269 Station Road, Seaham, Co Durham SR7 0BH* 0191-581 3270

ROBERTS, David Donald. b 21. TD69. Univ of Wales BA42. St Mich Coll Llan 42. **d** 44 **p** 45. CF (TA) 55-91; V Newton in Makerfield St Pet *Liv* 59-70; V Birkdale St Jas 70-91; rtd 91. *2 Fulwood Avenue, Southport, Merseyside PR8 6NW* Southport (01704) 543260

ROBERTS, Preb David Henry. b 38. St Chad's Coll Dur BA60. Qu Coll Birm DipTh62. **d** 62 **p** 63. C Stonehouse *Glouc* 62-65; C Hemsworth *Wakef* 65-69; V Newsome 69-76; R Pontesbury I and II *Heref* from 76; RD Pontesbury 83-93; Preb Heref Cathl from 85. *The Deanery, Pontesbury, Shrewsbury SY5 0PS* Shrewsbury (01743) 790316

ROBERTS, Canon David John. b 36. Man Univ BSc58. St D Coll Lamp 65. **d** 67 **p** 68. C Rhosllannerchrugog *St As* 67-70; R Cerrigydrudion w Llanfihangel G M, Llangwm etc 70-75; R Llanrwst and Llanddoget 75-77; R Llanrwst and Llanddoget and Capel Garmon 77-84; RD Llanrwst 77-84; V Abergele from 84; RD Rhos from 94; Hon Can St As Cathl from 95. *The Vicarage, Rhuddlan Road, Abergele, Clwyd LL22 7HH* Abergele (01745) 833132

ROBERTS, Dewi. b 57. LWCMD77 Cyncoed Coll CertEd78. St Mich Coll Llan DipTh84. **d** 84 **p** 85. C Clydach *S & B* 84-88; V Glantawe 88-94; V Lougher from 94. *The Rectory, 109 Glebe Road, Lougher, Swansea SA4 6SR* Gorseinon (01792) 891958

ROBERTS, Dilwyn Carey. b 38. St Deiniol's Hawarden 74. **d** 76 **p** 77. C Glanadda *Ban* 76-77; TV Amlwch, Rhosybol, Llandyfrydog etc 77-81; V Llanllechid 81-85; V Caerhun w Llangelynnin 85-87; V Caerhun w Llangelynnin w Llanbedr-y-Cennin 87-92; rtd 93. *67 St Georges Drive, Conwy, Gwynedd LL31 9PR*

ROBERTS, Donald James (Don). b 26. Sarum & Wells Th Coll 83. **d** 86 **p** 87. NSM Corfe Castle, Church Knowle, Kimmeridge etc *Sarum* 86-88; C Broadstone 88-91; rtd 91; NSM Corfe Castle, Church Knowle, Kimmeridge etc *Sarum* 91-95; Perm to Offic from 95. *14 Colletts Close, Corfe Castle, Wareham, Dorset BH20 5HG* Corfe Castle (01929) 480900

ROBERTS, Canon Edward Eric. b 11. St Aug Coll Cant 34. **d** 61 **p** 62. Can Res and Vice-Provost S'well Minster *S'well* 69-79; Bp's Dom Chapl 69-79; rtd 80; Perm to Offic *S'well* from 84. *24 Manor Close, Southwell, Notts NG25 0AP* Southwell (01636) 813246

ROBERTS, Edward Henry. b 06. Man Univ BA33 BD36. Ridley Hall Cam 64. **d** 65 **p** 66. R High Laver w Magdalen Laver *Chelmsf* 67-77; P-in-c Moreton w Lt Laver 73-77; rtd 77. *154 High Street, Ongar, Essex CM5 9JJ* Ongar (01277) 363066

✠**ROBERTS, Rt Rev Edward James Keymer.** b 08. CCC Cam BA30 MA35 Hon DD65. Cuddesdon Coll 30. **d** 31 **p** 32 **c** 56. C St Marylebone All SS *Lon* 31-35; Vice-Prin Cuddesdon Coll 35-39; Hon Can Portsm Cathl *Portsm* 47-49; R Brading w Yaverland 49-52; Adn Is of Wight 49-52; Adn Portsm 52-56; Suff Bp Malmesbury *Bris* 56-62; Suff Bp Kensington *Lon* 62-64; Bp Ely 64-77; rtd 77; Asst Bp Portsm from 77. *The House on the Marsh, Brading, Sandown, Isle of Wight PO36 0BD* Isle of Wight (01983) 407434

ROBERTS, Edward John Walford. b 31. Trin Coll Carmarthen CertEd. St D Dioc Tr Course. **d** 79 **p** 80. NSM Burry Port and Pwll *St D* from 79. *St Mary's Parsonage, Llwynygog, Cwm, Burry Port, Dyfed SA16 0YR* Burry Port (01554) 833652

ROBERTS, Canon Edward Owen (Ed). b 38. K Coll Lon BD63 AKC63. **d** 64 **p** 65. C Auckland St Andr and St Anne *Dur* 64-67; C Cheltenham St Paul *Glouc* 67-68; Asst Master Colne Valley High Sch Linthwaite 69-71; V Meltham Mills *Wakef* 71-75; R Emley 75-88; RD Kirkburton 80-88; V Huddersfield H Trin from 88; RD Huddersfield from 89; Hon Can Wakef Cathl from 92. *Holy Trinity Vicarage, 132 Trinity Street, Huddersfield HD1 4DT* Huddersfield (01484) 422998

ROBERTS, Canon Elwyn. b 25. Univ of Wales (Ban) DipTh54. St Mich Coll Llan 54. **d** 55 **p** 56. V Glanogwen *Ban* 69-88; Hon Can Ban Cathl 84-90; R Llansadwrn w Llanddona and Llaniestyn etc 88-91; rtd 91. *Llain Delyn, 10 Cae'r Delyn, Bodffordd, Anglesey, Gwynedd LL77 7EJ* Bangor (01248) 750407

ROBERTS, Ven Elwyn. b 31. Univ of Wales (Ban) BA52 Keble Coll Ox BA54 MA59. St Mich Coll Llan 54. **d** 55 **p** 56. C Glanadda *Ban* 55-57; V 66-71; Lib and Lect St Mich Coll Llan 57-66; Dir Post-Ord Tr *Ban* 70-90; R Llandudno 71-83; Can Ban Cathl 77-78; Chan Ban Cathl 78-83; Adn Meirionnydd 83-86; R Criccieth w Treflys 83-86; Adn Ban from 86. *Deiniol, 31 Trefonwys, Bangor, Gwynedd LL57 2HU* Bangor (01248) 355515

ROBERTS, Eric. b 40. Ban Ord Course 90 St Mich Coll Llan 92. **d** 93 **p** 94. Min Can Ban Cathl *Ban* from 93. *1 Alotan Crescent, Penrhosgarnedd, Bangor, Gwynedd LL57 2NG* Bangor (01248) 355911

✠**ROBERTS, Rt Rev Eric Matthias.** b 14. Univ of Wales BA35 St Edm Hall Ox BA37 MA41. St Mich Coll Llan 38. **d** 38 **p** 39 **c** 71. C Dwygyfylchi (or Penmaenmawr) *Ban* 38-40; Lic to Offic *Llan* 40-47; Chapl St Mich Coll Llan 40-45; Sub-Warden

45-47; V Port Talbot St Theodore *Llan* 47-56; V Roath St Marg 56-65; RD Cardiff 61-65; Adn Margam 65-71; Bp St D 71-81; rtd 81. *2 Tudor Close, Westbourne Road, Penarth, S Glam CF64 5BR* Penarth (01222) 708591

ROBERTS, Frederick Henry. b 22. CPsychol89 AFBPsS Univ of Wales (Ban) BA49 Lon Univ MA60 PhD68. Wycliffe Hall Ox. **d** 51 **p** 52. Chapl Maudsley Hosp Lon 64-75; Perm to Offic *Chelmsf* from 76; rtd 91. *The Green, High Street, Fowlmere, Cambs SG8 7SS* Fowlmere (01763) 208467

ROBERTS, Geoffrey Thomas. b 12. ARCM33. Worc Ord Coll 64. **d** 65 **p** 66. V Edenham *Linc* 67-79; P-in-c Witham on the Hill 76-79; rtd 79; Perm to Offic *Linc* 79-89. *West Flat, The Riding School, Grimsthorpe, Bourne, Lincs PE10 0LY* Edenham (0177832) 240

ROBERTS, George Nelson. b 24. Cranmer Hall Dur 83. **d** 84 **p** 85. C Netherton *Liv* 84-86; V Carr Mill 86-91; rtd 91. *58 Church Road, Saughall, Chester CH1 6EP* Chester (01244) 880761

ROBERTS, Gordon Branford. b 11. **d** 83 **p** 83. NSM Prestonville St Luke *Chich* from 83. *Flat 42, Tongdean Court, London Road, Brighton BN1 6YL* Brighton (01273) 558172

ROBERTS, Graham Miles. b 59. Trin Coll Bris DipHE92. **d** 92 **p** 93. C Charles w St Matthias Plymouth *Ex* from 92. *18 Dale Gardens, North Hill, Plymouth PL4 6PX* Plymouth (01752) 669087

ROBERTS, Canon Henry Edward (Ted). b 28. Oak Hill Th Coll 53. **d** 56 **p** 57. V Bethnal Green St Jas Less *Lon* 61-73; V Old Ford St Mark Victoria Park 61-73; V Bethnal Green St Jas Less w Victoria Park 73-78; RD Tower Hamlets 76-78; Can Res Bradf Cathl *Bradf* 78-82; Dioc Dir Soc Resp 78-82; V Bermondsey St Jas w Ch Ch *S'wark* 82-90; P-in-c Bermondsey St Anne 82-90; Hon Can S'wark Cathl 90-93; Gen Adv for Inner City Min 90-93; rtd 93. *12 Bromeswell Road, Ipswich IP4 3AS* Ipswich (01473) 288956

ROBERTS, Canon Hugh Godfrey Lloyd. b 09. AKC34. St Steph Ho Ox 34. **d** 34 **p** 35. R Ashley w Weston by Welland and Sutton Bassett *Pet* 69-79; rtd 79; Perm to Offic *Pet* from 79; Perm to Offic *Leic* from 81. *4 Victoria Avenue, Market Harborough, Leics LE16 7BQ* Market Harborough (01858) 463071

ROBERTS, Hughie Graham. b 28. St Mich Coll Llan 57. **d** 60 **p** 62. V Goldcliffe and Whiston and Nash *Mon* 69-73; V Garndiffaith 73-78; V Monkton *St D* 78-82; V Llansteffan and Llan-y-bri etc 82-91; rtd 91. *2 Parc-y-Ffordd, Johnstown, Carmarthen, Dyfed SA31 3HD* Carmarthen (01267) 238848

ROBERTS, James Arthur. b 34. Lon Univ BSc56. Bps' Coll Cheshunt 58. **d** 60 **p** 61. C Upper Holloway St Steph *Lon* 60-62; C March St Jo *Ely* 62-65; V Coldham 65-70; V Friday Bridge 65-70; V Ridgeway *Derby* 70-72; P-in-c Gleadless *Sheff* 72-74; TR 74-79; P-in-c Catfield *Nor* 79-82; P-in-c Ingham w Sutton 79-82; R Aldwincle w Thorpe Achurch, Pilton, Wadenhoe etc *Pet* 82-91; R Barby w Kilsby from 91; RD Daventry from 92. *The Rectory, Barby, Rugby, Warks CV23 8TY* Rugby (01788) 890252

ROBERTS, James Michael Bradley. b 18. Wycliffe Hall Ox 53. **d** 55 **p** 56. V Clerkenwell St Jas and St Jo w St Pet *Lon* 62-88; rtd 88. *42 Lavender Hill, Tonbridge, Kent TN9 2AT* Tonbridge (01732) 359756

ROBERTS, Miss Janet Lynne. b 56. Trin Coll Bris 76. dss 82 **d** 87 **p** 94. Dagenham *Chelmsf* 82-86; Huyton St Mich *Liv* 86-87; Par Dn 87-91; C Aughton Ch Ch from 91. *25 Peet Avenue, Ormskirk, Lancs L39 4SH* Ormskirk (01695) 577958

ROBERTS, Mrs Jasmine Cynthia. b 46. Cant Sch of Min 88. **d** 91. NSM Sandwich *Cant* from 91. *The Rectory, Knightride Street, Sandwich, Kent CT13 9ER* Sandwich (01304) 613138

ROBERTS, Jeffrey David. b 25. St Cath Coll Cam BA46 MA50 Lon Univ BSc58. **d** 65 **p** 66. Hd Master Adams' Gr Sch Newport Shropshire 59-73; Hd Master St Geo Sch Gravesend 74-82. *Corner House, Keyston, Huntingdon, Cambs PE18 0RD* Bythorn (018014) 254

ROBERTS, John Arthur. b 37. CEng68 MIEE68 Man Univ BScTech59. Cranmer Hall Dur DipTh71. **d** 71 **p** 72. C Wellington w Eyton *Lich* 71-75; P-in-c Newton Flowery Field *Ches* 75-80; V Dunham Massey St Marg 80-91; Chapl Countess of Ches Hosp from 91; Lic to Offic from 91; Chapl W Cheshire NHS Trust from 94. *500 Overpool Road, Whitby, South Wirral L66 2JJ* 0151-356 5458

ROBERTS, John Anthony Duckworth. b 43. K Coll Lon BD65 AKC65. St Boniface Warminster 65. **d** 66 **p** 67. C Wythenshawe Wm Temple Ch CD *Man* 66-69; C Bradford-on-Avon *Sarum* 69-72; Chapl Dauntsey's Sch Devizes 72-73; CF 73-77; P-in-c Verwood *Sarum* 77-81; V 81-86; V Clitheroe St Mary *Blackb* from 86. *St Mary's Vicarage, Church Street, Clitheroe, Lancs BB7 2DD* Clitheroe (01200) 23317

ROBERTS, John Charles. b 50. Nottm Univ BA71 Univ of the W of England, Bris DLLP93. Westcott Ho Cam BA73. **d** 73 **p** 74. C Newark St Mary *S'well* 73-77; Chapl RAF 77-93; Lic to Offic *Bris* from 93. *15 Foxbrook, Wootton Bassett, Swindon SN4 8QD* Swindon (01793) 851518

ROBERTS, John Charles Welch. b 39. UMIST BSc60. Oak Hill NSM Course 91 SW Minl Tr Course 92. **d** 94 **p** 95. NSM Washfield, Stoodleigh, Withleigh etc *Ex* from 94. *East Sidborough, Loxbeare, Tiverton, Devon EX16 8DA* Tiverton (01884) 256302 Fax as telephone

ROBERTS, John David. b 08. MBE. St D Coll Lamp BA33. **d** 33 **p** 34. Hon Chapl Miss to Seamen from 62; rtd 73. *17 Arwenack Avenue, Falmouth, Cornwall TR11 3JW* Falmouth (01326) 312415

ROBERTS, John Edward Meyrick. b 20. TD. Cam Univ CertEd73 ACP78 Keble Coll Ox BA80 MA80 Westmr Coll Ox Dip Chr Studies 95. Nor Ord Course 76. **d** 80 **p** 81. NSM Mundford w Lynford *Nor* 80-83; P-in-c W Wratting *Ely* 83-88; P-in-c Weston Colville 83-88; rtd 88; Hon C Clun w Chapel Lawn, Bettws-y-Crwyn and Newc *Heref* 89-91; Hon C Clun w Bettws-y-Crwyn and Newc from 91. *Ford House, Clun, Craven Arms, Shropshire SY7 8LD* Clun (01588) 640784

ROBERTS, Dr John Gunn. b 18. FRCS MB, ChB. Oak Hill NSM Course 82. **d** 82 **p** 82. NSM Chorleywood St Andr *St Alb* from 82. *Templar Cottage, Berks Hill, Chorleywood, Rickmansworth, Herts WD3 5AJ* Chorleywood (01923) 282061

ROBERTS, John Hugh. b 42. K Alfred's Coll Win CertEd72 Open Univ BA75. Wells Th Coll 65. **d** 67 **p** 68. C Wareham w Arne *Sarum* 67-70; C Twyford *Win* 70-72; Asst Teacher Rawlins Sch Leics 72-74; V Nassington w Yarwell *Pet* 74-77; Asst Teacher Sponne Sch Towcester 78-92; P-in-c Helmdon w Stuchbury and Radstone etc from 93; RD Brackley from 94. *Pimlico House, Pimlico, Brackley, Northants NN13 5TN* Syresham (01280) 850378

ROBERTS, John Mark Arnott. b 54. K Coll Lon AKC75 CertEd76. Chich Th Coll 77. **d** 77 **p** 78. C Ashford *Cant* 77-82; V St Mary's Bay w St Mary-in-the-Marsh etc 82-91; R Sandwich from 91. *The Rectory, Knightrider Street, Sandwich, Kent CT13 9ER* Sandwich (01304) 613138

ROBERTS, John Robert. b 15. Chich Th Coll 47. **d** 49 **p** 50. V Whiteshill *Glouc* 59-80; rtd 80; Perm to Offic *Glouc* from 81. *1 Fairby, Paganhill Lane, Stroud, Glos GL5 4JX* Stroud (01453) 750316

ROBERTS, Canon John Victor. b 34. St Edm Hall Ox BA58 MA62. Tyndale Hall Bris 58. **d** 60 **p** 61. C Southport Ch Ch *Liv* 60-62; C Pemberton St Mark Newtown 62-65; V Blackb Sav *Blackb* 65-71; Chapl Blackb and Lancs R Infirmary and Park Lee Hosp 65-71; V Parr *Liv* 71-73; TR 73-80; R Much Woolton from 80; RD Childwall 84-89; AD Liv S from 89; Hon Can Liv Cathl from 95. *The Rectory, 67 Church Road, Liverpool L25 6DA* 0151-428 1853

ROBERTS, John Victor. b 40. GIPE61. Qu Coll Birm 83. **d** 85 **p** 86. C Ludlow *Heref* 85-89 and 92-93; P-in-c Coreley w Doddington 89-92; P-in-c Knowbury 89-92; TV Ludlow, Ludford, Ashford Carbonell etc from 93. *St Giles Vicarage, Sheet Road, Ludlow, Shropshire SY8 1LR* Ludlow (01584) 876090

ROBERTS, John William. b 09. ALCD38. **d** 38 **p** 39. R Grappenhall *Ches* 60-74; rtd 74. *11 Oakley Road, Morecambe, Lancs LA3 1NR* Morecambe (01524) 414234

ROBERTS, John William Melton. b 32. St Deiniol's Hawarden. **d** 69 **p** 70. C Rhosymedre *St As* 69-72; C Wrexham 72-74; C Llanrhos 74-76; R Montgomery and Forden 76-77; R Montgomery and Forden and Llandyssil 78-89; R Llanddulas and Llysfaen from 89; Miss to Seamen from 89. *The Rectory, 2 Rhodfa Wen, Llysfaen, Colwyn Bay, Clwyd LL29 8LE* Colwyn Bay (01492) 516728

ROBERTS, Jonathan George Alfred. b 60. Lon Univ BD. Qu Coll Birm. **d** 84 **p** 85. C Shepshed *Leic* 84-86; C Braunstone 86-87; Dioc Youth Adv *Dur* 88-92; Nat Youth Officer Gen Syn Bd of Educn 92-94; P-in-c Washington *Dur* from 94. *The Rectory, The Avenue, Washington, Tyne & Wear NE38 7LE* 0191-416 3957

ROBERTS, Joseph Aelwyn. b 18. Univ of Wales (Lamp) BA40. St Mich Coll Llan 41. **d** 42 **p** 43. V Llandegai *Ban* 52-88; Dioc Dir for Soc Work 73-88; rtd 88. *The Vicarage, Llandegai, Bangor, Gwynedd LL57 4LA* Bangor (01248) 353711

ROBERTS, Keith Mervyn. b 55. LGSM78 St Pet Coll Birm CertEd76. Qu Coll Birm 89. **d** 91 **p** 92. C Hall Green St Pet *Birm* 91-95; TV Warw *Cov* from 95; Relig Affairs Correspondent BBC Radio Cov & Warw from 95. *184 Myton Road, Warwick CV34 6PS*

ROBERTS, Canon Kenneth William Alfred. b 26. Roch Th Coll 63. **d** 65 **p** 66. C Shiphay Collaton *Ex* 70-71; CF 71-74; R Bassingham *Linc* 74-75; V Carlton-le-Moorland w Stapleford 74-75; R Thurlby w Norton Disney 74-75; V Aubourn w Haddington 74-75; Chapl R Hosp Sch Holbrook 75-78; P-in-c Copdock w Washbrook and Belstead *St E* 78-79; P-in-c Brandeston w Kettleburgh 79-82; Chapl Brandeston Hall Sch 79-84; Chapl Lisbon *Eur* 84-86; Can and Chan Malta Cathl 86-89; R Wimbotsham w Stow Bardolph and Stow Bridge etc

Ely 89-91; rtd 91. *7 Borley Crescent, Tudor Mill, Elmswell, Bury St Edmunds, Suffolk IP30 9UG* Elmswell (01359) 41881

ROBERTS, Kevin Thomas. b 55. Qu Coll Cam BA78 MA82 Nottm Univ BA82. St Jo Coll Nottm 80. **d** 83 **p** 84. C Beverley Minster *York* 83-86; C Woodley St Jo the Ev *Ox* 86-91; V Meole Brace *Lich* from 91. *The Vicarage, Meole Brace, Shrewsbury SY3 9EZ* Shrewsbury (01743) 231744

ROBERTS, Laurence James. b 51. AMGAS86 Sussex Univ BEd73. Sarum & Wells Th Coll 75. **d** 78 **p** 79. C Rotherhithe St Mary w All SS *S'wark* 78-81; Ind Chapl 81-84; Hon Priest Nunhead St Silas 82-84; TV Plaistow *Chelmsf* 84-89; Chapl Newham Gen Hosp and Plaistow Hosp from 84; Tutor Community Nursing Services from 89; Tutor Westmr Past Foundn from 90; Perm to Offic *Chelmsf* from 90. *c/o 40 Boleyn Road, London E7 9QE* 0171-476 1400

ROBERTS, Malcolm Kay. b 54. Jes Coll Ox BA76 MA82. Ripon Coll Cuddesdon 84. **d** 87 **p** 88. C Frodingham *Linc* 87-91; R Fiskerton w Reepham from 91. *The Rectory, Reepham Road, Fiskerton, Lincoln LN3 4EZ* Lincoln (01522) 750577

ROBERTS, Martin Vincent. b 53. LRAM72 Birm Univ BA76 MA77 PhD82. Ripon Coll Cuddesdon 76. **d** 78 **p** 79. C Perry Barr *Birm* 78-81; Sen Chapl and Lect W Sussex Inst of HE 81-86; Leic Poly *Leic* 86-92; Sen Chapl De Montfort Univ Leic 92-95; TV Leic H Spirit 86-89; TR 89-95; V Baswich (or Berkswich) *Lich* from 95. *The Vicarage, 97 Baswich Lane, Stafford ST17 0BN* Stafford (01785) 51057

ROBERTS, Matthew Garnant. b 13. St D Coll Lamp BA37. **d** 37 **p** 38. C-in-c Hinton Ampner w Bramdean *Win* 68-70; R 70-74; R Hinton Ampner w Bramdean and Kilmeston 74-78; rtd 78; Lic to Offic *B & W* from 79. *The Granary, Quaperlake Street, Bruton, Somerset BA10 0NA* Bruton (01749) 812545

ROBERTS, Michael. b 46. Sarum Th Coll 86. **d** 88 **p** 89. C Reading St Matt *Ox* 88-91; NSM Douglas St Geo and St Barn *S & M* 91-93; V Malew from 93. *Malew Vicarage, St Mark's Road, Ballasalla, Isle of Man IM9 3FF* Castletown (01624) 822469

ROBERTS, Michael Brian. b 46. Or Coll Ox BA68 MA72 St Jo Coll Dur BA73 DipTh74. Cranmer Hall Dur 71. **d** 74 **p** 75. C St Helens St Helen *Liv* 74-76; C Goose Green 76-78; C Blundellsands St Nic 78-80; V Fazakerley St Nath 80-87; V Chirk *St As* from 87. *The Vicarage, Trevor Road, Chirk, Wrexham, Clwyd LL14 5HD* Chirk (01691) 778519

ROBERTS, Michael Graham Vernon. b 43. Keble Coll Ox BA65. Cuddesdon Coll 65 Ch Div Sch of the Pacific (USA) MDiv67. **d** 67 **p** 68. C Littleham w Exmouth *Ex* 67-70; Chapl Clare Coll Cam 70-74; V Bromley St Mark *Roch* 74-79; Tutor Qu Coll Birm 79-85; TR High Wycombe *Ox* 85-90; Vice-Prin Westcott Ho Cam 90-93; Prin from 93. *Westcott House, Jesus Lane, Cambridge CB5 8BP* Cambridge (01223) 350074 or 64680

ROBERTS, Myrfyn Wyn. b 35. Univ of Wales (Ban) BA57 BMus60 Lon Univ DipRS77. S'wark Ord Course 74. **d** 76 **p** 77. C Stepney St Dunstan and All SS *Lon* 76-79; R Crofton *Wakef* 79-85; Chapl HM Pris Dur 85-87; Chapl HM Rem Cen Ashford 87-88; Chapl HM Young Offender Inst Dover 88-92; Chapl HM Pris Albany 92-95; rtd 95. *5 Ulster Crescent, Newport, Isle of Wight PO30 5RU*

ROBERTS, Nicholas John. b 47. Lon Univ BD70 AKC70 MTh78 Surrey Univ MSc93. St Aug Coll Cant 70. **d** 71 **p** 72. C Tividale *Lich* 71-74; C St Pancras H Cross w St Jude and St Pet *Lon* 74-76; C Camberwell St Giles *S'wark* 76-78; Chapl Ch Coll Cam 78-82; V Kingstanding St Luke *Birm* 82-85; Chapl St Chas Hosp Ladbroke Grove from 85; Chapl Princess Louise Hosp Lon from 85; Chapl Paddington Community Hosp from 85. *St Charles Community Hospital, Exmoor Street, London W10 6DZ* 0181-962 4370 or 969 2488

ROBERTS, Paul Carlton. b 57. Worc Coll Ox BA78 MA86 CertEd. St Jo Coll Nottm 84. **d** 87 **p** 88. C Hazlemere *Ox* 87-91; C Woodley St Jo the Ev 91-92; TV Woodley from 92. *St James's Church House, 35 Highgate House, Reading RG5 3ND* Reading (01734) 696197

ROBERTS, Paul John. b 60. Man Univ BA82 CertEd83. St Jo Coll Nottm 83. **d** 85 **p** 86. C Burnage St Marg *Man* 85-88; Tutor Trin Coll Bris from 88. *13 Henleaze Avenue, Bristol BS9 4EU, or Trinity College, Stoke Hill, Bristol BS9 1JP* Bristol (0117) 962 3535 or 968 2803

ROBERTS, Peter. b 40. NW Ord Course 71. **d** 74 **p** 75. C Stockport St Geo *Ches* 74-77; V Bickerton 77-78; V Bickerton w Bickley 78-83; R Alderley 83-94; rtd 94. *8C Cliff Road, Bridgnorth, Shropshire WV16 4EY*

ROBERTS, Peter Francis. b 59. N Illinois Univ BSc81 Leeds Univ BA87. Coll of Resurr Mirfield 85. **d** 88 **p** 89. C Leeds All So *Ripon* 88-92; Asst Dioc Youth Chapl 91-92; USPG 92-94; Belize 92-94; V Collingham w Harewood *Ripon* from 95. *The Vicarage, Church Lane, Collingham, Wetherby, W Yorkshire LS22 5AU* Collingham Bridge (01937) 573975

ROBERTS, Peter Gwilym. b 42. N Ord Course 78. **d** 81 **p** 82. NSM Seaforth *Liv* 81-83; TV Kirkby 83-88; Dioc Adv on UPA 88-91; P-in-c Southport H Trin 91-94; S Africa from 94.

clo St Matthias Anglican Church, PO Box 231, Welkom 9460, S Africa

ROBERTS, Peter Reece. b 43. Chich Th Coll 73. **d** 75 **p** 76. C Cadoxton-juxta-Barry *Llan* 75-79; C Brixham w Churston Ferrers *Ex* 79-81; C Bexhill St Pet *Chich* 81-84; R Heene from 84; RD Worthing from 89. *Heene Rectory, 4 Lansdowne Road, Worthing, W Sussex BN11 4LY* Worthing (01903) 202312

ROBERTS, Philip Alan. b 59. Chich Th Coll 85. **d** 88 **p** 89. C Friern Barnet St Jas *Lon* 88-93; C Farnham Royal w Hedgerley *Ox* from 93. *7 Rectory Close, Farnham Royal, Slough SL2 3BG* Slough (01753) 644293

ROBERTS, Philip Anthony. b 50. St Jo Coll Dur BA73. Wycliffe Hall Ox 75. **d** 77 **p** 78. C Roby *Liv* 77-79; C Ainsdale 79-80; C Pershore w Pinvin, Wick and Birlingham *Worc* 80-83; Chapl Asst Radcliffe Infirmary Ox 83-88; John Radcliffe & Littlemore Hosps Ox 83-88; Chapl R Victoria & Bournemouth Gen Hosps 88-91; Chapl Heref Co Hosp from 91. *The County Hospital, Union Walk, Hereford HR1 2ER* Hereford (01432) 355444

ROBERTS, Philip John. b 20. **d** 74 **p** 75. NSM Downend *Bris* 74-90; Perm to Offic from 90. *Windrush, 190A Overndale Road, Bristol BS16 2RH* Bristol (0117) 956 8753

ROBERTS, Canon Phillip. b 21. Sarum Th Coll 55. **d** 57 **p** 58. V Westbury *Sarum* 63-73; TR Dorchester 73-80; Can and Preb Sarum Cathl 75-87; R Upper Chelsea H Trin w St Jude *Lon* 80-87; rtd 87; V of Close Sarum Cathl *Sarum* 89-95. *112 Harnham Road, Salisbury SP2 8JW* Salisbury (01722) 323291

ROBERTS, Ven Raymond Harcourt. b 31. CB84. St Edm Hall Ox BA54 MA58. St Mich Coll Llan 54. **d** 56 **p** 57. C Bassaleg *Mon* 56-59; Chapl RNR 58-59; Chapl RN 59-80; Chapl of the Fleet and Adn for the RN 80-84; Hon Can Gib Cathl *Eur* 80-84; QHC 80-84; Gen Sec JMECA 85-89; C Hale *Guildf* 85-89; Hon Chapl Llan Cathl *Llan* from 90. *8 Baynton Close, Llandaff, Cardiff CF5 2NZ* Cardiff (01222) 578044

ROBERTS, Richard. b 23. Univ of Wales BA48. St Mich Coll Llan 48. **d** 50 **p** 51. R Llanrwst and Llanddoget *St As* 68-75; RD Llanrwst 73-75; V Llandrillo-yn-Rhos 75-90; rtd 91. *Ardudwy, 32 Belmont Avenue, Bangor, Gwynedd LL57 2HT* Bangor (01248) 364899

ROBERTS, Canon Richard Stephanus Jacob (Steph). b 28. TCD BA51 MA57. TCD Div Sch Div Test51. **d** 51 **p** 52. Miss to Seamen 51-94; Chapl Miss to Seamen Dublin 68-72; Chapl Miss to Seamen Southn 72-94; Sen Chapl Ch on the High Seas 72-94; Hon Can Win Cathl *Win* 82-94; rtd 94. *25 Bassett Crescent West, Southampton SO1 7EB* Southampton (01703) 790734

ROBERTS, Ronald Barry. b 40. S Dios Minl Tr Scheme 80. **d** 83 **p** 85. NSM Wedmore w Theale and Blackford *B & W* 83-85; C Odd Rode *Ches* 85-87; V Eaton and Hulme Walfield from 87. *The Vicarage, Hulme Walfield, Congleton, Cheshire CW12 2JG* Congleton (01260) 279863

ROBERTS, Mrs Rosanne Elizabeth. b 51. Glouc Sch of Min 85. **d** 88 **p** 94. NSM Charlton Kings St Mary *Glouc* 88-93; C Leckhampton SS Phil and Jas w Cheltenham St Jas from 93. *32 Gratton Road, Leckhampton, Cheltenham, Glos GL50 2BU* Cheltenham (01242) 516362

ROBERTS, Stephen Bradley. b 66. K Coll Lon BD90 Wycliffe Hall Ox 89. **d** 91 **p** 92. C W Hampstead St Jas *Lon* 91-94; TV Uxbridge from 94. *St Margaret's Vicarage, 92 Harefield Road, Uxbridge, Middx UB8 1PL* Uxbridge (01895) 270759

ROBERTS, Stephen John. b 58. BD. Westcott Ho Cam. **d** 83 **p** 84. C Riverhead w Dunton Green *Roch* 83-86; C St Martin-in-the-Fields *Lon* 86-89; Warden Trin Coll Cen Camberwell from 89; V Camberwell St Geo *S'wark* from 89. *St George's Vicarage, 115 Wells Way, London SE5 7SZ* 0171-703 2895

ROBERTS, Sydney Neville Hayes. b 19. K Coll Lon 38. Cuddesdon Coll 45. **d** 47 **p** 48. R Theale w N Street *Ox* 69-76; R Theale and Englefield 76-85; rtd 85. *34 Stonebridge Road, Steventon, Abingdon, Oxon OX13 6AU* Abingdon (01235) 834777

ROBERTS, Mrs Sylvia Ann. b 40. Stockwell Coll Lon TCert60. S Dios Minl Tr Scheme 81. **dss** 84 **d** 87 **p** 94. Crookhorn *Portsm* 84-88; Hon Par Dn Bedhampton 88-89; Par Dn Southn (City Cen) *Win* 89-91; TD 91-94; TV from 94. *St Augustine's Vicarage, 27 Parsonage Road, Southampton SO14 0PQ* Southampton (01703) 493880

ROBERTS, Tegid. b 47. **d** 87 **p** 88. Lic to Offic *Ban* 87-93; NSM Llandinorwig w Penisa'r-waen from 93. *Arwel, Llanrug, Caernarfon, Gwynedd LL55 3BA* Llanberis (01286) 870760

ROBERTS, Terry Harvie. b 45. Sarum & Wells Th Coll 87. **d** 89 **p** 90. C Weymouth H Trin *Sarum* 89-93; TV Basingstoke *Win* from 93. *45 Beaconsfield Road, Basingstoke, Hants RG21 3DG* Basingstoke (01256) 464616

ROBERTS, Canon Thomas. b 21. Lon Coll of Div 61. **d** 63 **p** 64. V St Helens St Matt Thatto Heath *Liv* 68-73; Chapl Basle w Freiburg-im-Breisgau *Eur* 73-91; Can Brussels Cathl from 80; rtd 91. *27 Lancelyn Court, Spital Road, Wirral, Merseyside L63 9JJ* 0151-334 1303

ROBERTS, Canon Thomas Ewart. b 17. VRD65. Liv Univ BA41. St Aid Birkenhead 39. **d** 41 **p** 42. Hon Can Cant Cathl *Cant* 67-71; V Chesterfield All SS *Derby* 71-74; Hon Can Cant Cathl *Cant* 81-84; V Tenterden St Mildred w Smallhythe 75-82; RD W Charing 81-82; rtd 82; Asst Chapl Kent and Cant Hosp from 82; Perm to Offic *Cant* from 84. *2 Lesley Avenue, Canterbury, Kent CT1 3LF* Canterbury (01227) 451072

ROBERTS, Vaughan Edward. b 65. Selw Coll Cam BA88 MA91. Wycliffe Hall Ox 89. **d** 91 **p** 92. C Ox St Ebbe w H Trin and St Pet *Ox* from 91. *St Ebbe's Flat, 1 Roger Bacon Lane, Oxford OX1 1QE* Oxford (01865) 248365

ROBERTS, Vaughan Simon. b 59. Univ of Wales (Ban) BA80. McCormick Th Sem Chicago MA82 Westcott Ho Cam 83. **d** 85 **p** 86. C Bourne *Guildf* 85-89; Chapl Phyllis Tuckwell Hospice Farnham 88-89; Chapl Bath Univ *B & W* from 89; NSM Bath Ch Ch Prop Chpl from 90. *The Chaplain's House, The Avenue, Bath BA2 7AX* Bath (01225) 466114 or 826458 Fax 462508

ROBERTS, Vincent Akintunde. b 55. Kingston Poly BA(Econ)81. S'wark Ord Course. **d** 91 **p** 92. Hon C Brixton Rd Ch Ch *S'wark* from 91. *118 Waddon New Road, Croydon CR0 4JE* 0181-667 9322

ROBERTS, Vivian Phillip. b 35. Univ of Wales BD78. St D Coll Lamp 57. **d** 60 **p** 61. C Cwmaman *St D* 60-64; R Puncheston, Lt Newc and Castle Bythe 64-72; V Brynamman 72-77; V Brynaman w Cwmllynfell 77-83; V Pen-bre from 83. *The Vicarage, Ar-y-Bryn, Pen-bre, Burry Port, Dyfed SA16 0AJ* Burry Port (01554) 832403

ROBERTS, Wallace Lionel. b 31. Univ of Wales (Lamp) BA58. St D Coll Lamp 55. **d** 59 **p** 60. C Astley Bridge *Man* 59-61; Hon C Stand 61-66; Asst Master Stand Gr Sch 61-66; Hon CF Aden 66-67; Hon C Heaton Moor *Man* 67-70; Lect Stockport Tech Coll 67-70; Hon CF BOAR 70-76; Swaziland 76-85; Chapl Porto (or Oporto) *Eur* 86-89; Chapl Hordle Ho Sch Milford-on-Sea 89-90; C Portishead *B & W* from 91. *24 St Mary's Park Road, Portishead, Bristol BS20 8QL* Bristol (0117) 984 8934

ROBERTS, William James (Jim). b 55. Hughes Hall Cam PGCE78. Lon Bible Coll BA77 NE Ord Course 92. **d** 94. NSM York St Mich-le-Belfrey *York* from 94. *12 Bishop's Way, York YO1 5JG* York (01904) 413479

ROBERTS, Wynne. b 61. Univ of Wales (Ban) DipTh85. Ridley Hall Cam 85. **d** 87 **p** 88. C Ban Cathl Par *Ban* 87-90; Min Can Ban Cathl 87-90; V Ynyscynhaearn w Penmorfa and Porthmadog 90-94; TV Ban from 94. *St Peter's Vicarage, Penrhosgarnedd, Bangor, Gwynedd LL57 2NS* Bangor (01248) 352388

ROBERTSHAW, John Sean. b 66. Cranmer Hall Dur 90. **d** 93 **p** 94. C Morley St Pet w Churwell *Wakef* from 93. *53 Springfield Avenue, Morley, Leeds LS27 9PP* Leeds (0113) 238 1387

ROBERTSHAW, Jonathan Kempster Pickard Sykes. b 41. AKC65. **d** 66 **p** 67. C Perranzabuloe *Truro* 66-69; Miss to Seamen 69-76; Hong Kong 69-72; Namibia 73-76; TV Probus, Ladock and Grampound w Creed and St Erme *Truro* 76-79; TV N Hill w Altarnon, Bolventor and Lewannick 79-80; P-in-c Lansallos 80-84; R from 84; P-in-c Talland 80-84; V from 84. *Talland Vicarage, 3 Claremont Falls, Looe, Cornwall PL13 2JQ* Polperro (01503) 72356

ROBERTSON, Agnes Muriel Hodgson. b 20. Edin Univ MA41. Edin Th Coll. **d** 91 **p** 94. NSM Lochgelly *St And* 91-92; Par Dn Glenrothes from 92. *35 George Street, Glenrothes, Fife KY7 4HR* Glenrothes (01592) 610899

ROBERTSON, Brian Ainsley. b 50. Warw Univ BSc72. St Jo Coll Nottm DTS94. **d** 94 **p** 95. C Leic Martyrs *Leic* from 94. *62 Ashleigh Road, Leicester LE3 0FB* Leicester (0116) 254 1341

ROBERTSON, David John. b 54. Sheff Univ BA76. Ridley Hall Cam 77. **d** 79 **p** 80. C Downend *Bris* 79-83; C Yate New Town 83-85; TV 85-87; TV High Wycombe *Ox* from 87; RD Wycombe from 91. *199 Cressex Road, Booker, High Wycombe, Bucks HP12 4PZ* High Wycombe (01494) 530134

ROBERTSON, Denis Ayre. b 33. Edin Dioc NSM Course 90. **d** 92 **p** 93. NSM Dalmahoy *Edin* from 92. *13 Sommers Park, Mid Calder, Livingston, West Lothian EH53 0RZ* Mid Calder (01506) 881934

ROBERTSON, Canon Donald Keith. b 07. St D Coll Lamp BA36. **d** 36 **p** 37. Can Res Lich Cathl *Lich* 60-76; rtd 76; Perm to Offic *Carl* 77-93. *clo A M Robertson Esq, 11 Church Road, Winford, Bristol BS18 8EW* Lulsgate (01275) 475115

ROBERTSON, Edward Macallan. b 28. Aber Univ MA49 Qu Coll Ox BLitt51. Coll of Resurr Mirfield 53. **d** 55 **p** 56. R Alloa *St And* 70-73; Lic to Offic *Edin* 74-78; P-in-c Bathgate 78-82; P-in-c Linlithgow 78-82; Hon C Strathtay

St And 82-90; P-in-c Auchterarder 90-93; P-in-c Muthill 90-93; rtd 93. *65 Smithfield Crescent, Blairgowrie, Perthshire PH10 6UE* Blairgowrie (01250) 874427

ROBERTSON, Ernest Ian. b 22. Bede Coll Dur BA49. Wycliffe Hall Ox 49. **d** 51 **p** 52. Chapl Shotley Bridge Gen Hosp 60-81; V Benfieldside Dur 60-87; Chapl HM Det Cen Medomsley 61-87; rtd 87. *Flat 11, Thornley House, Sherburn House Hospital, Durham DH1 2SE* 0191-372 1992

ROBERTSON, Ian Hugh. b 44. LGSM64 ARCM65 Makerere Univ Kampala DipTh83 Lanc Univ MA91. St Mark's Dar-es-Salaam 80. **d** 83 **p** 83. SSF 73-82; Zimbabwe 83-87; TV Barrow St Geo w St Luke *Carl* 87-90; V Reigate St Mark *S'wark* from 90. *St Mark's Vicarage, 8 Alma Road, Reigate, Surrey RH2 0DA* Reigate (01737) 210639 or 210785

ROBERTSON, James Alexander. b 46. Sarum & Wells Th Coll 72. **d** 75 **p** 76. C Monkseaton St Pet *Newc* 75-78; C Prudhoe 78-79; TV Brayton *York* 79-84; V Redcar 84-93; V Selby Abbey from 93. *The Abbey Vicarage, 32A Leeds Road, Selby, N Yorkshire YO8 0HX* Selby (01757) 709218 or 703123

ROBERTSON, Canon James Smith. b 17. OBE84. Glas Univ MA38. Edin Th Coll 38. **d** 40 **p** 41. Sec for Ch Colls of Educn Gen Syn Bd of Educn 68-73; Gen Sec USPG 73-83; Chapl to The Queen 80-88; rtd 83; Perm to Offic *Lon* 83-93; Perm to Offic *S'wark* from 83. *13 Onslow Avenue Mansions, Onslow Avenue, Richmond, Surrey TW10 6QD* 0181-940 8574

ROBERTSON, John Charles. b 61. St Pet Coll Ox BA81 Trin Coll Cam BA89. Ridley Hall Cam 87. **d** 90 **p** 91. C Kenilworth St Jo *Cov* 90-94; Chapl York Univ *York* from 94. *Bede House, Heslington, York YO1 5EE* York (01904) 413925

ROBERTSON, Mrs Priscilla Biddulph. b 25. St And Dioc Tr Course 87. **d** 90 **p** 94. C St Andrews St Andr *St And* from 90. *8 Balrymonth Court, St Andrews, Fife KY16 8XT* St Andrews (01334) 74976

ROBERTSON, Scott. b 64. Edin Univ BD90. Edin Th Coll 86. **d** 90 **p** 91. C Glas Gd Shep and Ascension *Glas* from 90. *31 Westfield Drive, Cardonald, Glasgow G52 2SG* 0141-882 4996

ROBERTSON, Stephen Andrew. b 60. Strathclyde Univ BSc82. Trin Coll Bris DTS92. **d** 92 **p** 93. C Vange *Chelmsf* from 92. *26 Rivertons, Basildon, Essex SS16 4UY* Basildon (01268) 559764

ROBERTSON, Stuart Lang. b 40. Glas Univ MA63 Nottm Univ DipTh74. St Jo Coll Nottm 72. **d** 75 **p** 76. C Litherland St Jo and St Jas *Liv* 75-78; C Edin St Thos *Edin* 78-81; Chapl Edin Univ 81-83; C Edin St Pet 81-83; R Edin St Jas 83-91; Miss to Seamen 83-91; Russia from 91; BCMS 91-93; Crosslinks from 93; Chapl St Petersburg *Eur* 93-95. Crosslinks, *251 Lewisham Way, London SE4 1XF* 0181-691 6111

ROBERTSON, Thomas John. b 15. Univ of Wales BA38 Lon Univ DipTh64 DipEd66. St Steph Ho Ox 38. **d** 40 **p** 41. Hd of RE Bramhall Gr Sch 61-74; Lic to Offic *Man* 61-74; V Taddington and Chelmorton *Derby* 74-80; rtd 80; Perm to Offic *Derby* 80-87; Perm to Offic *Ches* from 80; Perm to Offic *Man* from 80. *6 Heatherdale, The Avenue, Beckenham, Kent BR3 2DH*

ROBERTSON-GLASGOW, John Nigel. b 13. Cuddesdon Coll 46. **d** 47 **p** 48. R Chipping Warden w Edgcote *Pet* 50-79; R Chipping Warden w Edgcote and Aston le Walls 79; rtd 79; Perm to Offic *Nor* from 80. *19 Hayes Lane, Fakenham, Norfolk NR21 9EP* Fakenham (01328) 863674

ROBIN, John Bryan Carteret. b 22. Trin Coll Ox BA48 MA55. Cuddesdon Coll 49. **d** 77 **p** 78. Chapl Rishworth Sch Ripponden 77-81; Australia from 82. *St George's Vicarage, 22 Hobson Street, Queencliff, Victoria, Australia 3225* Geelong (52) 521532

ROBIN, Peter Philip King. b 23. Trin Coll Cam BA48 MA81. Cuddesdon Coll 49. **d** 51 **p** 52. Papua New Guinea 54-75; R Elsing w Bylaugh *Nor* 76-85; R Lyng w Sparham 76-85; P-in-c Holme Cultram St Mary *Carl* 85-88; rtd 88; Perm to Offic *Carl* from 88. *191 Brampton Road, Carlisle CA3 9AX* Carlisle (01228) 45293

ROBINS, Christopher Charles. b 41. St Mich Coll Llan 66. **d** 68 **p** 69. C Bideford *Ex* 68-71; C Dawlish 71-74; V Laira 74-81; P-in-c E Allington 81; P-in-c Dodbrooke 81-83; P-in-c Churchstow w Kingsbridge 81-83; R Kingsbridge and Dodbrooke from 83. *The Rectory, Church Street, Kingsbridge, Devon TQ7 1NW* Kingsbridge (01548) 856231

ROBINS, Douglas Geoffrey. b 45. Open Univ BA90. Ex & Truro NSM Scheme. **d** 81 **p** 83. NSM Kenwyn *Truro* 81-84; Lic to Offic from 84. *4 Enys Road, Truro, Cornwall TR1 3TE* Truro (01872) 77469

ROBINS, Henry Temple. b 02. Qu Coll Cam BA24 MA29. Cuddesdon Coll 24. **d** 25 **p** 27. R Whimple *Ex* 55-72; rtd 72; Perm to Offic *Ex* 73-89. *Woodhayes, 36-40 St Leonard's Road, Exeter EX2 4LR* Exeter (01392) 422539

ROBINS, Ian Donald Hall. b 28. K Coll Lon BD51 AKC51 Lanc Univ MA74. **d** 52 **p** 53. Hd of RE St Chris C of E Sch Accrington 67-76; P-in-c Hugill *Carl* 76-82; Asst Adv for

Educn 76-82; Chapl St Martin's Coll of Educn *Blackb* 82-86; V St Annes St Marg 86-91; rtd 91. *20 Painter Wood, Billington, Blackburn BB7 9JD* Blackburn (01254) 824930

ROBINS, Mrs Mary Katherine. b 34. FRGS Bris Univ BSc55 CertEd56. St Alb Minl Tr Scheme. **dss** 84 **d** 87 **p** 94. N Mymms *St Alb* 84-87; Hon Par Dn 87-92; NSM Northaw from 92. *15 Bluebridge Road, Brookmans Park, Hatfield, Herts AL9 7UW* Potters Bar (01707) 656670

ROBINS, Roger Philip. b 44. AKC68. **d** 69 **p** 70. C Farncombe *Guildf* 69-73; C Aldershot St Mich 73-79; V New Haw 79-89; RD Runnymede 83-88; Chapl Merrist Wood Coll of Agric and Horticulture from 88; R Worplesdon *Guildf* from 89. *The Rectory, Perry Hill, Worplesdon, Guildford, Surrey GU3 3RB* Guildford (01483) 234616

ROBINS, Ms Wendy Sheridan. b 56. Lanc Univ BA77. E Anglian Minl Tr Course DipTh93. **d** 93 **p** 94. Dir of Communications and Resources *S'wark* from 92; NSM Walthamstow St Pet *Chelmsf* from 93. *17 Hillcrest Road, London E17 4AP, or Trinity House, 4 Chapel Court, Borough High Street, London SE1 1HW* 0181-523 0016 or 0171-403 8686 Fax 0171-403 4770

ROBINSON, Alan Booker. b 27. Keble Coll Ox BA51 MA56. Sarum Th Coll 51. **d** 53 **p** 54. V Hooe *Ex* 66-95; RD Plympton 81-82; RD Plymouth Sutton 86-91; rtd 95; Perm to Offic *Ripon* from 95. *1 Charlton Court, Knaresborough, N Yorkshire HG5 0BZ* Knaresborough (01423) 860884

ROBINSON, Albert. b 15. Roch Th Coll 60. **d** 61 **p** 62. P-in-c Roydon All SS *Nor* 64-73; V Gt w Lt Plumstead 73-81; rtd 81; Perm to Offic *Glouc* 81-91. *63 Marleyfield Way, Churchdown, Gloucester GL3 1JW* Gloucester (01452) 855178

ROBINSON, Andrew Nesbitt. b 43. AKC67. **d** 68 **p** 69. C Balsall Heath St Paul *Birm* 68-71; C Westmr St Steph w St Jo *Lon* 71-75; Chapl Sussex Univ *Chich* from 75; Chapl Brighton Poly 75-92; Chapl Brighton Univ from 92; P-in-c Stanmer w Falmer from 80. *St Laurence House, Park Street, Brighton BN1 9PG* Brighton (01273) 606928 or 606755

ROBINSON, Andrew Stephen. **d** 95. NSM Llangattock and Llangyndir *S & B* from 95. *17 Pencommin, Llangynidr, Crickhowell, Powys NP8 1LT*

ROBINSON, Canon Anthony William. b 56. CertEd. Sarum & Wells Th Coll. **d** 82 **p** 83. C Tottenham St Paul *Lon* 82-85; TV Leic Resurr *Leic* 85-89; TR Leic Resurr from 89; RD Christianity (Leic) N from 92; P-in-c Belgrave St Pet 94-95; Hon Can Leic Cathl from 94. *St Matthew's Vicarage, Taylor Road, Leicester LE4 9JN* Leicester (0116) 262 3038

ROBINSON, Arthur Robert Basil. b 32. ACP67 St Jo Coll Dur BA56 Bradf Univ MA84. Wycliffe Hall Ox 56. **d** 58 **p** 59. Chapl HM Borstal Roch 69-74; Peru 74-77; V Golcar *Wakef* 77-83; rtd 94. *Morangie, 2A Brocksfield, Skelton, York YO3 6YB* York (01904) 470558

ROBINSON, Arthur William. b 35. Dur Univ BSc60. Clifton Th Coll 60. **d** 62 **p** 63. C Ox St Clem *Ox* 62-65; Chile 65-77; V Hoxton St Jo w Ch Ch *Lon* 78-88; TV Gateacre *Liv* from 88. *Christ Church House, 44 Brownbill Bank, Liverpool L27 7AE* 0151-487 7759

ROBINSON, Brian. b 39. St Aid Birkenhead 62. **d** 64 **p** 65. C Knotty Ash St Jo *Liv* 64-68; C Sutton 68-72; V Hunts Cross 72-79; V Livesey *Blackb* 79-88; V Burscough Bridge *Liv* from 88. *St John's Vicarage, 253 Liverpool Road South, Ormskirk, Lancs L40 7TD* Burscough (01704) 893205

ROBINSON, Brian John Watson. b 33. St Cath Coll Cam BA56 MA60. Westcott Ho Cam 57. **d** 58 **p** 59. C Whitworth w Spennymoor *Dur* 58-62; India 62-66; P-in-c Preston St Steph *Blackb* 66-72; V Ashton-on-Ribble St Andr 72-79; Lic to Offic 79-82; V Preston St Jude w St Paul from 82; Chapl Preston Hosp N Shields from 83. *St Jude's Vicarage, 97 Garstang Road, Preston PR1 1LD* Preston (01772) 52987

ROBINSON, Canon Bryan. b 32. Fitzw Ho Cam BA56. Ely Th Coll 56. **d** 58 **p** 59. C Fleetwood *Blackb* 58-65; V Burnley St Andr 65-74; V Burnley St Marg 65-74; V Burnley St Andr w St Marg from 74; RD Burnley 85-91; P-in-c Burnley St Jas from 92; Hon Can Blackb Cathl from 94. *St Andrew's Vicarage, 230 Barden Lane, Burnley, Lancs BB10 1JD* Burnley (01282) 423185

ROBINSON, Cedric Henry. b 17. K Coll Lon. **d** 58 **p** 59. V Norton w Whittington *Worc* 67-79; P-in-c Hanbury 79-84; R W Bowbrook 84-87; rtd 87. *7 Mortlake Drive, Martley, Worcester WR6 6QU* Wichenford (01886) 888628

ROBINSON, Christopher Gordon. b 49. Ridley Hall Cam. **d** 82 **p** 83. C Stanton *St E* 82-85; C Lawshall 85-86; C Lawshall w Shimplingthorne and Alpheton 86; P-in-c 86-89; TV Oakdale St Geo *Sarum* from 89. *The Vicarage, 25 Nuthatch Close, Poole, Dorset BH17 7XR* Broadstone (01202) 602441

ROBINSON, Daffyd Charles. b 48. Qu Coll Birm 77. **d** 80 **p** 85. C Abington *Pet* 80-82; C Immingham *Linc* 85-90; R Willoughby from 90. *The Rectory, Station Road, Willoughby, Alford, Lincs LN13 9NA* Alford (01507) 462045

ROBINSON, David. b 42. Sarum & Wells Th Coll. **d** 82 **p** 83. C Billingham St Cuth *Dur* 82-86; V Longwood *Wakef* 86-94; C Athersley from 94. *St Helens Vicarage, 27 Laithes Lane, Barnsley, S Yorkshire S71 3AF* Barnsley (01226) 245361

ROBINSON, Canon David Hugh. b 47. Linc Th Coll 76. **d** 79 **p** 80. C Bulkington *Cov* 79-82; P-in-c Whitley 82-87; Chapl Walsgrave Hosp Cov from 87; Hon Can Cov Cathl *Cov* from 92. *Walsgrave General Hospital, Clifford Bridge Road, Walsgrave on Sowe, Coventry CV2 2DX* Coventry (01203) 538950 or 622683

ROBINSON, David Mark. b 55. Univ Coll Dur BSc76 Leic Univ MA80 CQSW80. Cranmer Hall Dur 86. **d** 88 **p** 89. C Shipley St Pet *Bradf* 88-92; P-in-c Ingrow cum Hainworth from 92. *St John's Vicarage, Keighley, W Yorkshire BD21 1BT* Keighley (01535) 604069

ROBINSON, David Michael Wood. b 28. Glas Univ BSc50 Lon Univ BD54. **d** 57 **p** 57. Japan 58-71; R Holton and Waterperry *Ox* 71-88; RD Aston and Cuddesdon 88-92; R Holton and Waterperry w Albury and Waterstock 88-94; Chapl Ox Poly 90-92; Chapl Ox Brookes Univ 92-94; rtd 94. *72 Divinity Road, Oxford OX4 1LJ* Oxford (01865) 245466

ROBINSON, David William Clough. b 40. Univ of Wales BA61 BD67 Jes Coll Ox BLitt71. St Mich Coll Llan 64. **d** 67 **p** 68. C Canton St Cath *Llan* 69-71; Lib and Lect St Mich Coll Llan 72-78; Lect Th Univ of Wales (Cardiff) 72-78; Hon C Woodside Park St Barn *Lon* 78-85. *Address temp unknown*

ROBINSON, Capt Denis Hugh. b 53. SS Mark & Jo Coll Plymouth CertEd75. Sarum & Wells Th Coll 88. **d** 91 **p** 92. NSM Bisley and W End *Guildf* from 91; Asst Chapl Gordon's Sch Woking from 91. *Ashleigh, Bagshot Road, West End, Woking, Surrey GU24 9PX* Camberley (01276) 857535 Fax Chobham (01276) 855335

ROBINSON, Denis Winston. b 42. QUB BSc68. CITC. **d** 88 **p** 89. NSM Mullavilly *Arm* 88-92; NSM Arm St Mark w Aghavilly 92-95; C Portadown St Mark from 95. *4 Killycomaine Drive, Portadown, Craigavon, Co Armagh BT63 5JJ* Portadown (01762) 335813

ROBINSON, Derek Charles. b 43. S'wark Ord Course 91. **d** 94. NSM Abbey Wood *S'wark* from 94. *19 Siverdale Road, Bexleyheath, Kent DA7 5AB* Crayford (01322) 523870

ROBINSON, Douglas. b 48. Nottm Univ BEd70 Lon Univ BD74. Trin Coll Bris 71 Union Th Sem Virginia MA75. **d** 75 **p** 76. C Southport Ch Ch *Liv* 75-78; V Clubmoor 78-85; Chapl Epsom Coll Surrey 85-88; Chapl Dauntsey's Sch Devizes from 89. *Dauntsey's School, West Lavington, Devizes, Wilts SN10 4HE* Devizes (01380) 818441

ROBINSON, Dugald Clifford. b 23. Qu Coll Birm 69. **d** 70 **p** 71. C Stratford-on-Avon w Bishopton *Cov* 71-74; V Allesley Park 74-86; rtd 86; Perm to Offic *Cov* from 86. *5 Wedgewoods, 34 Beechwood Avenue, Coventry CV5 6QG* Coventry (01203) 679617

ROBINSON, Ernest Yeomans. b 03. **d** 56 **p** 57. V Hensall *Sheff* 68-72; I Kilmoe Union *C, C & R* 76-78; rtd 78. *Ilen Lodge, Rath, Baltimore, Skibereen, Co Cork, Irish Republic* Skibbereen (28) 20152

ROBINSON, Francis George. b 08. Cranmer Hall Dur 68. **d** 69 **p** 70. C Haxby w Wigginton *York* 69-71; V Sherburn 71-75; V Kexby w Wilberfoss 75-77; rtd 77. *38 Red Lodge, New Earswick, York YO3 4ZA* York (01904) 765446

ROBINSON, Geoffrey. b 28. Hartley Victoria Coll 49 Ely Th Coll 52. **d** 53 **p** 54. V Gt Saughall *Ches* 58-95; rtd 95. *Lochaber, 20 Aspen Grove, Saughall, Chester CH1 6AL* Saughall (01244) 880485

ROBINSON, George. b 27. MIMechE HNC59. Oak Hill Th Coll 59. **d** 61 **p** 62. C Branksome St Clem *Sarum* 61-64; Australia from 64. *24 Abingdon Road, Roseville, NSW, Australia 2069* Roseville (2) 416-4330 or 332-4134

ROBINSON, Gordon Stanislaus. b 13. K Coll Lon BD37 AKC37. **d** 37 **p** 38. R Charlton Horethorne w Stowell *B & W* 53-78; rtd 78; Lic to Offic *B & W* 79-94. *18 North Street, Stoke-sub-Hamdon, Somerset TA14 6QP* Martock (01935) 823742

ROBINSON, Canon Gordon Victor Michael. b 18. Keble Coll Ox BA40 MA46. Cuddesdon Coll 40. **d** 41 **p** 42. V Ellesmere Port *Ches* 55-71; Hon Can Ches Cathl 62-83; TR Ellesmere Port 71-73; R Tarporley 73-76; TR Birkenhead Priory 76-82; Exec Officer Bd for Soc Resp 82-83; rtd 83; Perm to Offic *Ches* from 83. *69 Marian Drive, Great Boughton, Chester CH3 5RY* Chester (01244) 315828

ROBINSON, Hugh Stanley. b 21. AKC47. **d** 47 **p** 48. V Chiddingly *Chich* 67-83; V Laughton 67-76; Asst Chapl HM Pris Northeye 83-86; rtd 86; Perm to Offic *Lich* from 86. *2 Brook Drive, Wem, Shrewsbury SY4 5HQ* Wem (01939) 234683

ROBINSON, Ian. b 57. Nottm Univ BTh87. Linc Th Coll 84. **d** 87 **p** 88. C Bottesford w Ashby *Linc* 87-90; TV from 90. *Holy Spirit Vicarage, 180 Enderby Road, Scunthorpe, S Humberside DN17 2JX* Scunthorpe (01724) 842083

ROBINSON, Ian Cameron. b 19. OBE72. Em Coll Cam BA40 MA44. Linc Th Coll 71. **d** 72 **p** 73. C Ipswich St Aug *St E* 72-74; V Darsham 74-84; V Westleton w Dunwich 74-84; RD Saxmundham 79-83; rtd 84; Perm to Offic *St E* from 84. *Corner House, Rectory Street, Halesworth, Suffolk IP19 8BS* Halesworth (01986) 873573

ROBINSON, James. b 23. Ridley Hall Cam 70. **d** 72 **p** 73. C Mixenden CD *Wakef* 72-73; C Carlton-in-Lindrick *S'well* 73-74; C Tuxford 75-77; C Selston 77-85; P-in-c Shireoaks 85-93; rtd 93. *15 Walnut Avenue, Shireoaks, Worksop, Notts S81 8PQ* Worksop (01909) 483045

ROBINSON, Mrs Jane Hippisley. b 41. Somerville Coll Ox MA66 K Coll Lon PGCE. S Dios Minl Tr Scheme 88. **d** 91. NSM Ealing St Pet Mt Park *Lon* from 91. *60 Madeley Road, London W5 2LU* 0181-991 0206

ROBINSON, Mrs Janet. b 34. Milton Keynes Coll of Ed CertEd77 Open Univ BA78. W Midl Minl Tr Course 89. **d** 92 **p** 94. NSM Roade and Ashton w Hartwell *Pet* 92-94; NSM Potterspury, Furtho, Yardley Gobion and Cosgrove from 94. *73 Eastfield Crescent, Yardley Gobion, Towcester, Northants NN12 7TT* Milton Keynes (01908) 542331

ROBINSON, Ven John Kenneth. b 36. K Coll Lon BD61 AKC61. **d** 62 **p** 63. C Poulton-le-Fylde *Blackb* 62-65; C Lanc St Mary 65-66; Chapl HM Pris Lanc 65-66; Singapore 66-68; V Colne H Trin *Blackb* 68-71; USPG 71-74; Grenada 71-74; V Skerton St Luke *Blackb* 74-81; Area Sec (E Anglia) USPG 81-91; Min Can St E Cathl *St E* 82-91; Chapl Gtr Lisbon *Eur* from 91; Adn Gib from 94; Can Gib Cathl from 94. *Rua da Ginjeira, Lote 5, Alcoitao, 2765 Estoril, Portugal* Lisbon (1) 469-2303 Fax as telephone

ROBINSON, John Francis Napier (Frank). b 42. St Edm Hall Ox BA64 MA68 Lon Univ DipTh68. Clifton Th Coll 65. **d** 68 **p** 69. C Southport Ch Ch *Liv* 68-71; C Coleraine *Conn* 71-74; Deputation Sec (Ireland) BCMS 74-76; TV Marfleet *York* 76-81; V Yeadon St Jo *Bradf* from 81. *St John's Vicarage, Yeadon, Leeds LS19 7SE* Leeds (0113) 250 2272

ROBINSON, John Howard. b 52. Stockport Tech Coll C&G82 Jo Dalton Coll Man HNC84. St Jo Coll Nottm DCM92. **d** 92 **p** 93. C Meole Brace *Lich* from 92. *19 High Ridge Way, Meole Brace, Shrewsbury SY3 6DJ* Shrewsbury (01743) 367707

ROBINSON, John Leonard William. b 23. Lon Univ BA50. Bps' Coll Cheshunt 50. **d** 52 **p** 53. C Westmr St Jas *Lon* 63-81; V Compton, the Mardens, Stoughton and Racton *Chich* 81-93; V Stansted 85-93; rtd 93. *19 Greenhill Park, Barnet, Herts EN5 1HQ* 0181-449 3984

ROBINSON, John Michael. b 57. K Coll Lon BD79 AKC79. St Steph Ho Ox 81. **d** 81 **p** 82. C Plymouth St Pet *Ex* 81-84; C Sheff Parson Cross St Cecilia *Sheff* 84-87; V Thurcroft 87-88; Chapl St Jas Univ Hosp Leeds 89-91; Hon C Dalton *Sheff* 91-92; C 92-95; P-in-c Devonport St Bart *Ex* from 95; P-in-c Devonport St Mark Ford from 95. *St Bartholomew's Vicarage, 13 Outland Road, Plymouth PL2 3BZ* Plymouth (01752) 562623

ROBINSON, Jonathan William Murrell. b 42. Sarum Th Coll 65. **d** 68 **p** 69. C Tooting All SS *S'wark* 68-71; C Bourne *Guildf* 71-76; Dir Grail Trust Chr Community Cen Burtle *B & W* 78-82; Hon C Willesden Green St Gabr *Lon* 78-82; V Stoke St Gregory w Burrowbridge and Lyng *B & W* 82-90; Dir Grail Retreat Cen 90-92; NSM Aymestrey and Leinthall Earles w Wigmore etc *Heref* from 92. *The Rectory, Wigmore, Leominster, Herefordshire HR6 9UW* Wigmore (0156886) 272

ROBINSON, Canon Joseph. b 27. K Coll Lon BD51 AKC51 MTh58. **d** 52 **p** 53. C Tottenham All Hallows *Lon* 52-55; Min Can St Paul's Cathl 55-68; Lect K Coll Lon 59-68; FKC from 73; Can Res Cant Cathl *Cant* 68-80; Master of The Temple (Lon) from 81. *The Master's House, Temple, London EC4 7BB* 0171-353 8559

ROBINSON, Keith. b 48. Lon Univ BA75 BD77 AKC77. Westcott Ho Cam 77. **d** 78 **p** 79. C Bow w Bromley St Leon *Lon* 78-81; C Leighton Buzzard w Eggington, Hockliffe etc *St Alb* 81-88; PV Westmr Abbey 82-90; V Bulkington w Shilton and Ansty *Cov* 88-95; P-in-c Sarum St Martin from 95; P-in-c Laverstock St Andr from 95. *St Martin's Rectory, Tollgate Road, Salisbury SP1 2JJ* Salisbury (01722) 335895

ROBINSON, Kenneth Borwell. b 37. Lon Univ BA62. Ridley Hall Cam 68. **d** 70 **p** 71. C Walthamstow St Jo *Chelmsf* 70-74; P-in-c Becontree St Alb 74-78; P-in-c Heybridge w Langford 78-84; C Horley *S'wark* 84; TV from 84. *St Francis's House, 84 Balcombe Road, Horley, Surrey RH6 9AY* Horley (01293) 776322

ROBINSON, Leslie. b 31. St Aid Birkenhead 56. **d** 59 **p** 60. C Hugglescote w Donington *Leic* 59-61; C Greenside *Dur* 61-63; C-in-c New Cantley CD *Sheff* 63-66; VC Heref Cathl *Heref* 66-67; R Easton-on-the-Hill *Pet* 67-68; Perm to Offic Pet Cathl 68-69; C Weston-super-Mare St Jo *B & W* 69-70; V Winkleigh *Ex* 70-72; V Dishley and Thorpe Acre *Leic* 72-78; V Cloughton *York* 78-79; V Hedon w Paull 79-81; V Bywell St Pet *Newc* 81-86; V Wymeswold and Prestwold w Hoton *Leic* from 86. *The Vicarage, The Stockwell, Wymeswold, Loughborough, Leics LE12 6UF* Wymeswold (01509) 880275

ROBINSON, Miss Margaret. b 32. S'wark Ord Course 83. **dss** 86 **d** 87 **p** 94. Finsbury St Clem w St Barn and St Matt *Lon* 86-87; Par Dn St Giles Cripplegate w St Bart Moor Lane etc 87-94; C from 94. *St Luke's House, Roscoe Street, London EC1Y 8PT* 0171-253 4720

ROBINSON, Michael John. b 45. Nottm Univ BA66. Linc Th Coll 78. **d** 79 **p** 80. C Aston cum Aughton *Sheff* 79-80; C Rotherham 80-82; TV Howden TM *York* 82-86; V Heywood St Jas *Man* 86-92; V Astley 92; R Blackley St Paul from 92. *St Paul's Rectory, Erskine Road, Manchester M9 2RB* 0161-740 1518

ROBINSON, Dr Neal Sydney. b 48. Worc Coll Ox BA70 MA75 Birm Univ PhD77. Qu Coll Birm 74. **d** 76 **p** 77. C Folkestone St Sav *Cant* 76-79; Chapl Bradf Univ *Bradf* 79-87; Perm to Offic *Glouc* 87-93; Lect Coll of SS Mary and Paul Cheltenham 87-88; Sen Lect 88-90; Sen Lect Cheltenham & Glouc Coll of HE 90-92; Lect Leeds Univ from 92; C Potternewton *Ripon* from 92. *44 Sholebroke Avenue, Leeds LS7 3HB* Leeds (0113) 262 3024

ROBINSON, Ven Neil. b 29. St Jo Coll Dur BA52 DipTh54. **d** 54 **p** 55. Hon Can Leic Cathl *Leic* 68-83; RD Sparkenhoe I 69-83; R Market Bosworth w Shenton 69-83; Can Res Worc Cathl *Worc* 83-87; Adn Suffolk *St E* 87-94; rtd 94. *Skell Green, 32 Mallorie Park Drive, Ripon, N Yorkshire HG4 2QF* Ripon (01765) 603075

ROBINSON, Norman Leslie. b 50. Liv Univ BSc71. Lon Bible Coll BA78 Wycliffe Hall Ox 78. **d** 80 **p** 81. C Bebington *Ches* 80-83; C St Helens St Helen *Liv* 83-90; P-in-c Westward, Rosley-w-Woodside and Welton *Carl* from 90. *The Vicarage, Rosley, Wigton, Cumbria CA7 8AU* Wigton (016973) 43723

ROBINSON, Paul Leslie. b 46. Dur Univ BA67 Nottm Univ DipTh73. Linc Th Coll 71. **d** 74 **p** 75. C Poynton *Ches* 74-76; C Prenton 76-78; V Seacombe 78-88; V Stalybridge St Paul from 88. *St Paul's Vicarage, Huddersfield Road, Stalybridge, Cheshire SK15 2PT* 0161-338 2514

ROBINSON, Peter. b 42. Univ of Wales (Lamp) BA63 DipEd64 Univ of Wales (Cardiff) BD71. N Ord Course 78. **d** 81 **p** 82. NSM Rochdale *Man* 81-83; C Rochdale 83-86; V Shore 86-91; Chapl for Readers from 90. *St Barnabas' Vicarage, Littleborough, Lancs OL15 8EZ* Littleborough (01706) 378356

ROBINSON, Peter Charles. b 53. Open Univ BA83. Oak Hill Th Coll 85. **d** 87 **p** 88. C Nottm St Ann w Em *S'well* 87-89; C Worksop St Anne 89-92; V S Ramsey *S & M* from 92. *St Paul's Vicarage, Walpole Drive, Ramsey, Isle of Man IM8 1NA* Ramsey (01624) 812275

ROBINSON, Peter Edward Barron. b 40. Sarum & Wells Th Coll 76. **d** 78 **p** 79. C Petersfield w Sheet *Portsm* 78-82; C Bentworth and Shalden and Lasham *Win* 82-88; R W Horsley *Guildf* from 88. *The Rectory, 80 East Lane, West Horsley, Leatherhead, Surrey KT24 6LQ* East Horsley (01483) 282173

ROBINSON, Peter McCall. b 24. Worc Coll Ox BA48 MA50. Wells Th Coll 48. **d** 50 **p** 51. S Africa 57-71 and 81-82; V Payhembury *Ex* 71-79; R Cheriton w Tichborne and Beauworth *Win* 79-81; V Marystowe, Coryton, Stowford, Lewtrenchard etc *Ex* 82-85; V Blackawton and Stoke Fleming 85-88; rtd 88; Perm to Offic *Ex* from 89. *8 Malden Road, Sidmouth, Devon EX10 9LS* Sidmouth (01395) 514494

ROBINSON, Philip. b 38. JP79. MIPM74. S Dios Minl Tr Scheme 88. **d** 91 **p** 92. NSM Ickenham *Lon* from 91; P-in-c from 95. *St Giles's Rectory, 38 Swakeleys Road, Ickenham, Uxbridge, Middx UB10 8BE* Uxbridge (01895) 632803 Fax as telephone

ROBINSON, Raymonde Robin. b 43. St Jo Coll Dur BA66. Chich Th Coll 67. **d** 70 **p** 71. C Ealing St Barn *Lon* 70-72; C Pinner 72-75; C Clerkenwell H Redeemer w St Phil 75-80; TV Kingsthorpe w St Dav Northn *Pet* 80-89; R Letchworth *St Alb* 89-95; V Noel Park St Mark *Lon* from 95. *St Mark's Vicarage, Ashley Crescent, London N22 6JA* 0181-888 3442

ROBINSON, Canon Richard Malcolm. b 20. Ex Coll Ox BA42 DipTh43 MA46. Wycliffe Hall Ox 42. **d** 44 **p** 45. R Edin Ch Ch *Edin* 64-76; V Dent w Cowgill *Bradf* 76-85; RD Ewecross 80-85; Hon Can Bradf Cathl 83-85; rtd 85; Perm to Offic *Bradf* from 85. *Hollinwood, 15 Raikeswood Road, Skipton, N Yorkshire BD23 1NB* Skipton (01756) 791577

ROBINSON, Richard Hugh. b 35. St Jo Coll Cam BA58 MA62. Ridley Hall Cam 58. **d** 60 **p** 81. C Cheadle Hulme St Andr *Ches* 60-62; Hon C Alvanley 62-64; Perm to Offic *York* 64-80; Hon C Elloughton and Brough w Brantingham 80-86; C 86-87; Ext Dir CMJ 87-88; NSM Appleby *Carl* 91-93; Perm to Offic from 93. *Sledmere Cottage, The Green, North Newbald, York YO4 3SA*

ROBINSON, Canon Roger George. b 24. Qu Coll Cam BA46 MA50. Ridley Hall Cam 46. **d** 48 **p** 49. V Clifton *York* 60-70; Chapl Clifton Hosp York 61-70; V Far Headingley St Chad *Ripon* 70-81; RD Headingley 72-81; Hon Can Ripon Cathl 81;

R Drayton w Felthorpe *Nor* 81-91; rtd 91. *24 St Matthew's Walk, Leeds LS7 3PS* Leeds (0113) 269 6307

ROBINSON, Ronald Frederick (Ron). b 46. Brasted Place Coll 72. Oak Hill Th Coll 74. **d** 76 **p** 77. C Pennington *Man* 76-77; C Bedhampton *Portsm* 77-79; C Portsea N End St Mark 79-82; V 90-92; R Rowner 82-90; rtd 93. *Chez Nous, 28 Haleybridge Road, Tangmere, Chichester, W Sussex PO20 6HG* Chichester (01243) 533705

ROBINSON, Roy David. b 35. AKC59. **d** 60 **p** 61. C Acocks Green *Birm* 60-62; C Shirley 62-65; C Haslemere *Guildf* 65-70; R Headley w Box Hill 70-85; V Hinchley Wood from 85. *The Vicarage, 98 Manor Road, Esher, Surrey KT10 0AE* 0181-398 4443

ROBINSON, Simon John. b 51. Edin Univ MA72 DSA73 PhD89 Ox Univ BA77. Wycliffe Hall Ox 75. **d** 78 **p** 79. C Haughton le Skerne *Dur* 78-81; Chapl Asst N Tees Hosp Stockton-on-Tees 81-83; C Norton St Mary *Dur* 81-83; Chapl Heriot-Watt Univ *Edin* 83-90; R Dalmahoy 83-90; Chapl Leeds Univ *Ripon* from 90; P-in-c Leeds Em from 90. *14 Parkside Green, Leeds LS6 4NY* Leeds (0113) 274 6297 or 233 5070

ROBINSON, Stuart. b 39. N Ord Course. **d** 87 **p** 88. C Hull St Martin w Transfiguration *York* 87-90; P-in-c Preston and Sproatley in Holderness 90-91; R from 91. *The Rectory, Staithes Road, Preston, Hull HU12 8TB* Hull (01482) 898375

ROBINSON, Canon Thomas Fisher. b 20. St Jo Coll Dur BA49. **d** 50 **p** 51. V Garston *Liv* 57-88; Hon Can Liv Cathl 85-88; rtd 88. *208 Mather Avenue, Liverpool L18 9TG* 0151-475 7870

ROBINSON, Thomas Hugh. b 34. CBE89. TCD BA55 MA71. **d** 57 **p** 58. C Belf St Clem *D & D* 57-60; Kenya 61-64; I Youghal *C, C & R* 64-66; CF 66-89; Dep Chapl Gen 86-89; TR Cleethorpes *Linc* from 90. *The Rectory, 42 Queens Parade, Cleethorpes, S Humberside DN35 0DG* Cleethorpes (01472) 693234

ROBINSON, Thomas Irven. b 10. TCD BA34 MA45. **d** 34 **p** 35. Dhahran 69-71; P-in-c Stourpaine, Durweston and Bryanston *Sarum* 71-77; rtd 77; Perm to Offic *Ox* 77-88. *1 Avon Court, Cressex Close, Binfield, Bracknell, Berks RG12 5DR* Bracknell (01344) 51136

ROBINSON, Timothy James. b 59. Middx Poly BA84. St Steph Ho Ox 88. **d** 91 **p** 92. C W Acklam *York* 91-95; P-in-c N Ormesby from 95. *The Vicarage, James Street, North Ormesby, Middlesbrough, Cleveland TS3 6LD* Middlesbrough (01642) 225272

ROBINSON, Ven William David. b 31. Univ Coll Dur BA54 DipTh58 MA62. Cranmer Hall Dur. **d** 58 **p** 59. C Standish *Blackb* 58-61; C Lanc St Mary 61-63; V Blackb St Jas 63-73; P-in-c Shireshead 73-86; Hon Can Blackb Cathl from 75; Adn Blackb from 86; V Balderstone 86-87. *7 Billinge Close, Blackburn BB2 6SB* Blackburn (01254) 253442

ROBINSON, William Pitchford. b 50. Nottm Univ BTh75. Kelham Th Coll 71. **d** 75 **p** 76. C Bow w Bromley St Leon *Lon* 75-79; Hon C Barkingside St Geo *Chelmsf* 79-82; Chapl Claybury Hosp Woodford Bridge 79-85; Hon C Barkingside St Fran *Chelmsf* 82-85; Australia from 86. *The Rectory, 18 Walter Road, Bassendean, W Australia 6054* Perth (9) 279-1117 or 325-6644

ROBLIN, Ven Graham Henry. b 37. OBE83. AKC61. St Boniface Warminster 60. **d** 62 **p** 63. C St Helier *S'wark* 62-66; CF 66-81; Dep Asst Chapl Gen 81-83; Warden RAChD Cen Bagshot 83-85; Asst Chapl Gen (BOAR) 86-89; Dep Chapl Gen 89-93; Adn for the Army 90-93; QHC from 87; R Bere Regis and Affpuddle w Turnerspuddle *Sarum* from 93. *The Vicarage, Bere Regis, Wareham, Dorset BH20 7HQ* Bere Regis (01929) 471262

ROBOTHAM, Ven Eric William. b 07. Ex Coll Ox BA30 BTh32 MA35. Wycliffe Hall Ox 30. **d** 32 **p** 33. Australia from 53; Adn Goldfields 56-60; rtd 77. *38 North Street, Bassendean, W Australia 6054* Perth (9) 279-8393

ROBOTTOM, David Leonard Douglas. b 40. Qu Coll Birm 80 Sarum & Wells Th Coll 81. **d** 83 **p** 84. C Uppingham w Ayston and Wardley w Belton *Pet* 83-87; TV Sidmouth, Woolbrook and Salcombe Regis *Ex* 87-91; TV Sidmouth, Woolbrook, Salcombe Regis, Sidbury etc 91-95; R Bradninch and Clyst Hydon from 95. *The Rectory, 27 West End Road, Bradninch, Exeter EX5 4QS* Exeter (01392) 881264

ROBSON, Angus William. b 13. Kelham Th Coll 32. **d** 38 **p** 39. V Jersey St Jas *Win* 50-75; Chapl HM Pris Jersey 60-75; rtd 78. *Flat 1, La Petite Carriere, Wellington Road, St Helier, Jersey, Channel Islands JE2 4RJ* Jersey (01534) 31656

ROBSON, Bernard John. b 33. Ch Ch Ox BA56 MA60. Tyndale Hall Bris 57. **d** 60 **p** 61. C Walmley *Birm* 60-64; C Stapenhill w Cauldwell *Derby* 64-68; SE Area Sec CPAS 68-71; E Region Co-ord 71-84; Perm to Offic *Nor* 71-84; P-in-c Tolleshunt D'Arcy w Tolleshunt Major *Chelmsf* 84-90; C Chadwell 90-93; C Dagenham from 93. *8 Church Lane, Dagenham, Essex RM10 9UL* 0181-517 2664

ROBSON, Featherstone. b 30. Southn Univ CertEd52 Nottm Univ DipEd74. Oak Hill Th Coll 55. **d** 58 **p** 59. Teacher Larkmead Sch Abingdon 68-71; Teacher Dorking Gr Sch 71-76; Ho Master Scarisbrook Hall Sch Ormskirk 77-78; Chapl Dean Close Jr Sch Cheltenham 78-79; Asst Chapl K Edw Sch Witley 79-81; Deputation Sec for England, Irish Ch Miss 82-86; Perm to Offic *Ox* from 86; rtd 86. *71 Springfield Drive, Abingdon, Oxon OX14 1JF* Abingdon (01235) 533421

ROBSON, George. b 34. AKC58. **d** 59 **p** 60. C Chorley St Geo *Blackb* 59-62; Chapl RAF 62-87; R Raithby *Linc* from 87; R Lt Steeping from 87; V Spilsby w Hundleby from 87; R Aswardby w Sausthorpe from 87; R Langton w Sutterby from 87; R Halton Holgate from 87; R Firsby w Gt Steeping from 87. *The Vicarage, 1 Church Street, Spilsby, Lincs PE23 5DU* Spilsby (01790) 52526

ROBSON, Gilbert Alan. b 30. St Pet Hall Ox BA53 MA57. Linc Th Coll 56. **d** 57 **p** 58. Sen Lect in Div 68-72; V Shotwick *Ches* 72-74; Dir of Ords 72-74; Bp's Dom Chapl 72-74; Chapl Eton Coll Windsor 74-89; R Wrotham *Roch* 89-95; rtd 95. *3 Staden Park, Trimingham, Norwich NR11 8HX* Southrepps (01263) 834887

ROBSON, Ian Leonard. b 32. Bps' Coll Cheshunt 61. **d** 63 **p** 64. C Croxley Green All SS *St Alb* 63-65; C Harpenden St Nic 65-68; V Redbourn 68-72; V Ashford St Matt *Lon* 72-77; V Kensington St Mary Abbots w St Geo from 77; AD Kensington from 94. *St Mary Abbots Vicarage, Vicarage Gate, London W8 4HN* 0171-937 6032 or 937 9490 Fax 938 4317

ROBSON, Irwin. b 20. **d** 63 **p** 64. C-in-c Byker St Martin CD *Newc* 69-74; V Willington 74-76; TR Willington Team 76-83; V Ulgham 83-87; V Widdrington 83-87; rtd 88; Perm to Offic *Newc* from 88. *8 Brinkburn Place, Amble, Morpeth, Northd NE65 0BJ* Alnwick (01665) 710765

ROBSON, James Edward. b 65. Pemb Coll Ox BA88. Wycliffe Hall Ox 91. **d** 94. C Enfield Ch Ch Trent Park *Lon* from 94. *2 Chalk Lane, Barnet, Herts EN4 9JQ* 0181-449 4042

ROBSON, John Phillips. b 32. St Edm Hall Ox. AKC58. **d** 59 **p** 60. C Huddersfield SS Pet and Paul *Wakef* 59-62; Asst Chapl Ch Hosp Horsham 62-65; Chapl 65-80; Chapl Wellington Coll Berks 80-89; Lic to Offic *Ox* 80-89; Chapl to RVO and Qu Chpl of the Savoy from 89; Chapl to The Queen from 93. *The Queen's Chapel of the Savoy, Savoy Hill, Strand, London WC2R 0DA* 0171-836 7221 or 379 8088 Fax 836 3098

ROBSON, Mrs Margery June. b 44. Darlington Tr Coll CertEd65. St Steph Ho Ox DIM94. **d** 94. C Tuffley *Glouc* from 94. *18 Tuffley Lane, Gloucester GL4 0DT* Gloucester (01452) 423104

ROBSON, Michael Douglas. b 62. St Andr Univ MTheol85 Qu Coll Cam PGCE88 Edin Univ MTh93. Edin Th Coll CECM94. **d** 94 **p** 95. NSM Perth St Ninian *St And* from 94. *286 Balhouse Street, Perth PH1 5HJ* Perth (01738) 622140

ROBSON, Mrs Patricia Anne. b 40. CertEd60. SW Minl Tr Course 85. **d** 87 **p** 94. Dioc Youth Officer *Truro* 87-92; Hon C Paul 87-92; Hon C Kenwyn St Geo 88-92; C-in-c St Enoder 92; D-in-c 93-94; P-in-c from 94. *St Enoder Rectory, Summercourt, Newquay, Cornwall TR8 5DF* St Austell (01726) 860724 or 74242

ROBSON, Paul Coutt. b 37. Leeds Univ BA60. Coll of Resurr Mirfield 63. **d** 64 **p** 65. C Stokesay *Heref* 64-66; S Africa 66-69; Chapl HM Pris Man 70-71; Chapl HM Borstal Feltham 71-74; Chapl HM Borstal Hollesley 74-78; Chapl HM Pris Grendon and Spring Hill 79-87; Chapl HM Pris Nor 87-92; Chapl HM Pris Brinsford from 92. *Pilgrims, Henley Common, Church Stretton, Shropshire SY6 6RS* Church Stretton (01694) 781221 or Standeford (01902) 791118 Fax Standeford (01902) 790889

ROBSON, Peter Cole. b 45. Clare Coll Cam BA66 MA70 Or Coll Ox BLitt69 MLitt70. Coll of Resurr Mirfield 70. **d** 71 **p** 72. C Gt Grimsby St Mary and St Jas *Linc* 71-73; Chapl BNC Ox 73-76; R Timsbury *B & W* 76-79; P-in-c Blanchland w Hunstanworth *Newc* 80-83; rtd 87. *13 Homer Terrace, Durham DH1 4JT*

ROBSON, Stephen Thomas. b 54. Chich Th Coll 84. **d** 86 **p** 87. C Newc St Fran *Newc* 86-89; C Gateshead St Cuth w St Paul *Dur* 89-91; TV Stanley from 91. *St Stephen's House, Holly Hill Gardens East, Stanley, Co Durham DH9 6NN* Stanley (01207) 290553

ROBSON, Thomas George Harry. b 11. Jes Coll Ox BA34 MA41. Wells Th Coll 35. **d** 36 **p** 37. Rhodesia 68-79; Hon C E Grinstead St Swithun *Chich* 79-81; rtd 86. *1/2 Sackville College, East Grinstead, E Sussex RH19 3BX* East Grinstead (01342) 321835

ROBSON, William (Bill). b 34. FCIS66 FCCA80. Sarum & Wells Th Coll 77. **d** 79 **p** 80. C Lymington *Win* 79-81; CF 81-93; V Barton Stacey and Bullington etc *Win* from 93. *The Rectory, Longparish, Andover, Hants SP11 6PG* Longparish (01264) 720215

ROBUS, Keith Adrian. b 59. Chich Th Coll 85. **d** 88 **p** 89. C Greenhill St Jo *Lon* 88-92; C Willesden St Matt from 92. *St*

Matthew's Vicarage, St Mary's Road, London NW10 4AU 0181-965 3748 Fax as telephone

ROBY, Richard James (Dick). b 33. Imp Coll Lon BSc54 Lon Inst of Educn PGCE55. St Alb Minl Tr Scheme 82. **d** 85 **p** 86. NSM Bushey *St Alb* 85-92; NSM Wootton from 92. *35 Sir Malcolm Stewart Homes, Stewartby, Bedford MK43 9LS* Bedford (01234) 767979

ROCHDALE, Archdeacon of. *See* DALBY, Ven Dr John Mark Meredith

ROCHE, Barry Robert Francis. b 40. Lon Univ BD66 Dur Univ DipTh67 DipApTh92 Ox Univ MTh93. Clifton Th Coll 63. **d** 68 **p** 69. C Beckenham Ch Ch *Roch* 68-72; C Ches le Street *Dur* 72-74; C-in-c N Bletchley CD *Ox* 74-78; R Luton Ch Ch *Roch* 78-92; Chapl All SS Hosp Chatham 78-92; TR Glascote and Stonydelph *Lich* from 92. *20 Melmerby, Stonydelph, Tamworth, Staffs B77 4LP* Tamworth (01827) 331163

ROCHE, Harold John. b 24. Ripon Hall Ox 54. **d** 54 **p** 55. C Southport St Phil *Liv* 54-57; V Wigan St Steph 57-63; R Sutcombe *Ex* from 63; R W w E Putford 64-71; V Putford from 71; P-in-c Bradworthy 71-72; RD Holsworthy 80-94. *The Rectory, Sutcombe, Holsworthy, Devon EX22 7PU* Bradworthy (01409) 241298

ROCHESTER, Thomas Robson. b 33. NE Ord Course 85. **d** 90 **p** 91. NSM Glendale Gp *Newc* from 90. *Yearle House, Wooler, Northd NE71 6RB* Wooler (01668) 81314

ROCHESTER, Archdeacon of. *See* WARREN, Ven Norman Leonard

ROCHESTER, Bishop of. *See* NAZIR-ALI, Rt Rev Dr Michael James

ROCHESTER, Dean of. *See* SHOTTER, Very Rev Edward Frank

ROCK, Mrs Jean. b 37. Gilmore Course. **dss** 79 **d** 87. Douglas St Matt *S & M* 79-81; Marown 81-83; Chapl Asst Oswestry and Distr Hosp 83-90; Oswestry St Oswald *Lich* 83-87; Par Dn 87-90; C-in-c Pont Robert and Pont Dolanog *St As* from 90. *Ty'r Eglwys, Pont Robert, Meifod, Powys SY22 6HY* Meifod (0193884) 454

ROCKALL, Miss Valerie Jane. b 42. City of Cov Coll CertEd63. St Alb Minl Tr Scheme 78. **dss** 81 **d** 87 **p** 94. Asst Hd Wigginton Sch Tring 73-90; Boxmoor St Jo *St Alb* 81-87; NSM Hemel Hempstead 87-90; Par Dn Ampthill w Millbrook and Steppingley 90-93; TD Southn (City Cen) *Win* 93-94; TV from 94. *2 Merchants Walk, Southampton SO1 0AS* Southampton (01703) 211106

RODDA, William Reginald. b 09. Clifton Th Coll 35. **d** 36 **p** 37. R Leigh w Batcombe *Sarum* 71-73; rtd 74. *2 Cuthburga Road, Wimborne, Dorset BH21 1LH* Wimborne (01202) 883285

RODEN, Cyril John. b 20. E Anglian Minl Tr Course 79. **d** 81 **p** 82. NSM Clenchwarton *Ely* 81-89; rtd 89; Perm to Offic *Ely* from 89; Perm to Offic *Nor* from 89. *52 Jubilee Bank, Clenchwarton, King's Lynn, Norfolk PE34 4BW* King's Lynn (01553) 773826

RODEN, John Michael. b 37. St Jo Coll York CertEd64 Open Univ BA82. Ripon Hall Ox 71. **d** 73 **p** 74. C Saltburn-by-the-Sea *York* 73-77; Chapl St Pet Sch York 77-82; Warden Marrick Priory *Ripon* 83; Hon C Appleton Roebuck w Acaster Selby *York* 84-85; P-in-c 86; P-in-c from 86; Youth Officer from 86. *All Saints' Vicarage, Appleton Roebuck, York YO5 7DG* Appleton Roebuck (01904) 744327

RODEN, Michael Adrian Holland. b 60. Ripon Coll Cuddesdon 82. **d** 85 **p** 86. C S Lambeth St Anne and All SS *S'wark* 85-88; C Wandsworth St Paul 88-90; C Ox St Mary V w St Cross and St Pet *Ox* 90-94; Chapl Wadh Coll Ox 90-94; R Steeple Aston w N Aston and Tackley *Ox* from 94. *The Rectory, Fir Lane, Steeple Aston, Bicester, Oxon OX5 3SF* Steeple Aston (01869) 347793

RODERICK, Bertram David. b 22. S'wark Ord Course 63. **d** 66 **p** 67. C Horley *S'wark* 69-72; V Sutton New Town St Barn 73-82; R Burstow 82-89; rtd 89. *April Cottage, 2 Church Lane, Henfield, W Sussex BN5 9NY* Henfield (01273) 493797

RODERICK, John Howard. b 12. St D Coll Lamp BA33 St Mich Coll Llan 33. **d** 35 **p** 36. V Wotton St Mary *Glouc* 60-73; R Bromsberrow 73-77; rtd 78; Perm to Offic *Glouc* from 79. *24 Biddulph Way, Ledbury, Herefordshire HR8 2HN* Ledbury (01531) 634474

RODERICK, Philip David. b 49. Univ of Wales (Swansea) BA70 Univ of Wales (Abth) BD77 Lon Univ CertEd71. Linc Th Coll 79. **d** 80 **p** 81. C Llanfair-is-gaer and Llanddeiniolen *Ban* 80-82; TV Holyhead w Rhoscolyn w Llanfair-yn-Neubwll 82-84; Warden Angl Chapl Cen 84-88; Chapl and Lect Th Univ of Wales (Ban) 84-88; Dir Chiltern Chr Tr Course *Ox* 88-95; Prin Bucks Chr Tr Scheme 88-95; Dir Quiet Garden Trust from 95. *Stoke Park Farm, Park Road, Stoke Poges, Bucks SL2 4PG* Farnham Common (01753) 643050

RODFORD, Brian George. b 50. Hatf Poly BEd84. **d** 79 **p** 80. Hon C St Alb St Steph *St Alb* 79-85; Chapl St Mary's Sch 81-90; Sen Teacher 83-90; Hon C Hendon St Mary *Lon* 85-90; Hon C Golders Green 85-90; Hon C Winchmore Hill H Trin

90-95; V Ponders End St Matt from 95. *The Vicarage, Church Road, Enfield, Middx EN3 4NT* 0181-443 2255

✠**RODGER, Rt Rev Patrick Campbell.** b 20. Ch Ch Ox BA43 MA47. Westcott Ho Cam 47. **d** 49 **p** 50 **c** 70. C Edin St Jo *Edin* 49-51; Chapl Edin Univ 51-55; C Woodside Park St Barn *Lon* 55-58; Study Sec SCM 55-58; R Kilmacolm *Glas* 58-61; R Bridge of Weir 58-61; Exec Sec of Faith & Order Dept WCC 61-66; R Edin St Mary *Edin* 66-70; Vice-Provost St Mary's Cathl 66-67; Provost 67-70; Bp Man 70-78; Bp Ox 78-86; rtd 86; Asst Bp *Edin* from 86. *12 Warrender Park Terrace, Edinburgh EH9 1EG* 0131-229 5075

RODGER, Canon Raymond. b 39. Westmr Coll Ox DipApTh91 MTh93. Bps' Coll Cheshunt 62. **d** 63 **p** 64. C Frodingham *Linc* 63-66; Asst Chapl St Geo Hosp Lon 66-69; C Waltham *Linc* 69-73; V Nocton 73-86; P-in-c Potter Hanworth 74-86; P-in-c Dunston 77-86; RD Graffoe 81-92; Can and Preb Linc Cathl from 85; V Nocton w Dunston and Potterhanworth 86-92; Bp's Dom Chapl from 92. *Bishop's House, Eastgate, Lincoln LN2 1QQ* Lincoln (01522) 534701 Fax 511095

RODGERS, Canon Cyril George Hooper. b 20. Qu Coll Birm 50. **d** 52 **p** 53. CF (TA - R of O) 62-87; V Wiggenhall St Germans and Islington *Ely* 66-76; RD Lynn Marshland 68-76; R Woolpit *St E* 76-84; RD Lavenham 78-87; Hon Can St E Cathl 84-87; R Woolpit w Drinkstone 84-87; rtd 87. *Fox Farm, Wetherden, Stowmarket, Suffolk IP14 3NE* Elmswell (01359) 40364

RODGERS, David. b 26. Sarum Th Coll 63. **d** 65 **p** 66. V Leigh Woods *B & W* 68-76; R Wellow w Foxcote and Shoscombe 76-79; C Wells St Cuth w Coxley and Wookey Hole 79-82; P-in-c Wookey w Henton 79-82; V Ercall Magna *Lich* 82-89; V Rowton 82-89; RD Wrockwardine 84-88; rtd 89. *7 Bishop Crescent, Shepton Mallet, Somerset BA4 5XX*

RODGERS, Frank. b 27. Linc Th Coll 69. **d** 71 **p** 72. C Alford w Rigsby *Linc* 71-75; P-in-c Quadring 75-80; P-in-c Gosberton Clough 75-80; V Gosberton Clough and Quadring 80; R S Kelsey 80-84; P-in-c Usselby 80-84; P-in-c Kirkby w Kingerby 80-84; P-in-c N Owersby w Thornton le Moor 80-84; R S Kelsey Gp 84-86; V Cranwell 86-92; R Leasingham 86-92; rtd 92; Perm to Offic *Linc* from 92. *1 Manor Road, Quarrington, Sleaford, Lincs NG34 8UJ*

RODGERS, Frank Ernest. b 46. Tyndale Hall Bris 68. **d** 71 **p** 72. C Madeley *Heref* 71-74; C Littleover *Derby* 74-77; V Clodock and Longtown w Craswell and Llanveyno *Heref* 77-79; P-in-c St Margaret's w Michaelchurch Eskley and Newton 77-79; V Clodock and Longtown w Craswall, Llanveynoe etc from 79; RD Abbeydore from 90. *The Vicarage, Longtown, Hereford HR2 0LD* Longtown Castle (0187387) 289

RODGERS, Canon John Terence Roche. b 28. TCD BA53 MA57. Bps' Coll Cheshunt 56. **d** 57 **p** 58. I Belf St Steph *Conn* 64-79; I Dunmurry 79-94; RD Derriaghy 92-93; Can St Anne's Cathl from 92; rtd 94. *8 Aberdelghy Park, Lambeg, Lisburn, Co Antrim BT27 4QF* Lisburn (01846) 660430

RODGERS, Dr Richard Thomas Boycott. b 47. FRCS81 Lon Univ MB BS70. St Jo Coll Nottm DipTh77. **d** 77 **p** 78. C Littleover *Derby* 77-80; C Birm St Martin w Bordesley St Andr *Birm* 89-90; Lect from 89; Perm to Offic from 90. *63 Meadow Brook Road, Birmingham B31 1ND* 0121-476 0789

RODHAM, Morris. b 59. Hatf Coll Dur BA81 St Jo Coll Dur PGCE85 Bris Univ MA93. Trin Coll Bris DipHE92. **d** 93 **p** 94. C New Milverton *Cov* from 93. *9 Freeman's Close, Leamington Spa, Warks CV32 6EY* Leamington Spa (01926) 426632

RODLEY, Ian Tony. b 48. Qu Coll Birm 77. **d** 80 **p** 81. Dioc Children's Adv *Bradf* 80-85; C Baildon 80-85; V Bradf St Wilfrid Lidget Green 85-90; Chapl to the Deaf from 88; V Otley from 90. *The Vicarage, Otley, W Yorkshire LS21 3HR* Otley (01943) 462240

RODRIGUEZ-VEGLIO, Francis Bonny. b 33. Sarum Th Coll 62. **d** 64 **p** 65. C Alnwick St Paul *Newc* 64-68; V Horton w Piddington *Pet* 68-79; P-in-c Preston Deanery 68-79; Chapl ACF 75-82; TV Scilly Is *Truro* 79-82; Hon Chapl Miss to Seamen 79-82; Perm to Offic *Pet* 86-88; C Leic Ch Sav *Leic* 88-91; V Kirkwhelpington, Kirkharle, Kirkheaton and Cambo *Newc* from 91. *The Vicarage, Kirkwhelpington, Newcastle upon Tyne NE19 2RT* Otterburn (01830) 40260

RODWELL, Barry John. b 39. Birm Univ CertEd59 Cam Univ DipAdEd77. Ridley Hall Cam 67. **d** 70 **p** 71. C Sudbury St Greg and St Pet *St E* 70-73; Hd RE Hedingham Sch 73-80; R Sible Hedingham *Chelmsf* 80-85; RE Adv 85-93; V Gt Burstead from 93. *The Vicarage, 111 Church Street, Billericay, Essex CM11 2TR* Billericay (01277) 625947

RODWELL, John Stanley. b 46. Leeds Univ BSc68 Ox Univ DipTh73 Southn Univ PhD81. Cuddesdon Coll 71. **d** 74 **p** 75. Hon C Horfield H Trin *Bris* 74-75; Hon C Skerton St Luke *Blackb* 75-77; Lic to Offic from 77. *7 Derwent Road, Lancaster LA1 3ES* Lancaster (01524) 62726

ROE, Mrs Caroline Ruth. b 57. Birm Univ BA80. Wycliffe Hall Ox 81. **dss** 84 **d** 87. Olveston *Bris* 84-87; Par Dn 87; NSM

Alveley and Quatt *Heref* 87-94; Bp's Voc Officer 90-94. *4 John's Lee Close, Loughborough, Leics LE11 3LH* Loughborough (01509) 260217

ROE, Frank Ronald. b 31. Brasted Th Coll Westcott Ho Cam 55. **d** 57 **p** 58. C S w N Hayling *Portsm* 57-61; Hong Kong 61-77; Sen Chapl St Jo Cathl 61-66; Asst Chapl 77; Sen Chapl Miss to Seamen 66-69; Australia from 77; Hon Chapl Miss to Seamen from 77. *29 Andrew Street, Esperance, W Australia 6450* Kalgoorlie (90) 713661

ROE, Canon Dr Joseph Thorley. b 22. AKC49 DipAdEd Hull Univ PhD90. K Coll Lon 46. **d** 50 **p** 51. Prin Lect & Sen Couns Bretton Hall Coll Wakef 67-74; Sec for Miss and Unity *Ripon* 74-78; Dioc Missr and Bp's Dom Chapl 75-78; Can Res Carl Cathl *Carl* 78-82; Dioc Dir of Tr 78-82; Dioc Adult Educn Officer *Wakef* 82-88; Hon Can Wakef Cathl 83-88; Dir of Educn 85-88; rtd 88. *29 Milnthorpe Drive, Wakefield, W Yorkshire WF2 7HU* Wakefield (01924) 256938

ROE, Peter Harold. b 37. K Coll Lon BD62 AKC62. **d** 63 **p** 64. C Knowle St Barn *Bris* 63-65; C Leckhampton St Pet *Glouc* 65-68; V Shaw Hill *Birm* 68-73; V Hobs Moat 73-90; V Packwood w Hockley Heath from 90. *The Vicarage, Nuthurst Lane, Hockley Heath, Solihull, W Midlands B94 5RP* Knowle (01564) 783121

ROE, Robert Henry. b 22. LCP57. Westcott Ho Cam 72. **d** 74 **p** 75. Hd Master St Mary's Primary Sch Saffron Walden 74-83; NSM Saffron Walden w Wendens Ambo *Chelmsf* 74-75; NSM Saffron Walden w Wendens Ambo and Littlebury 75-87; NSM Blakeney w Cley, Wiveton, Glandford etc *Nor* from 87. *Larchmount, High Street, Cley, Holt, Norfolk NR25 7RG* Cley (01263) 740369

ROE, Robin. b 28. CBE MC68. TCD BA52 MA55. **d** 53 **p** 54. CF 55-81; QHC 77-81; R Merrow *Guildf* 81-89; rtd 89. *Lansdowne, 6 Mitchells Close, Shalford, Guildford, Surrey GU4 8HY* Guildford (01483) 63852

✠**ROE, Rt Rev William Gordon.** b 32. Jes Coll Ox BA55 MA57 DipTh57 DPhil62. St Steph Ho Ox 56. **d** 58 **p** 59 **c** 80. C Bournemouth St Pet *Win* 58-61; C Abingdon w Shippon *Ox* 61-69; Vice-Prin St Chad's Coll Dur 69-74; V Dur St Oswald *Dur* 74-80; RD Dur 74-80; Hon Can Dur Cathl 79-80; Suff Bp Huntingdon *Ely* from 80; Can Res Ely Cathl 80-89; Hon Can Ely Cathl from 89. *14 Lynn Road, Ely, Cambs CB6 1DA* Ely (01353) 662137

ROEBUCK, John William. b 11. Keble Coll Ox BA34. Cuddesdon Coll 45. **d** 47 **p** 48. R Kirkwall *Ab* 69-77; rtd 77; Perm to Offic *Derby* 77-91. *55 Stone Street, Llandovery, Dyfed SA20 0DQ* Llandovery (01550) 21132

ROEMMELE, Michael Patrick. b 49. TCD BA72 MA76. **d** 73 **p** 74. C Portadown St Columba *Arm* 73-77; C Drumachose *D & R* 77-80; Bahrain 79-83; Cyprus 79-83; Chapl RAF from 83. *Chaplaincy Services (RAF), HQ, Personnel and Training Command, RAF Innsworth, Gloucester GL3 1EZ* Gloucester (01452) 712612 Ext 5164 Fax 510828

ROESCHLAUB, Robert Friedrich. b 39. Purdue Univ BSc63. Berkeley Div Sch MDiv66. **d** 66 **p** 66. USA 66-77; Hon C Tilehurst St Cath *Ox* 78-79; Hon C Tilehurst St Mich 79-82; P-in-c Millom H Trin w Thwaites *Carl* 82-85; P-in-c Millom 85-89; R Dunstall w Rangemore and Tatenhill *Lich* 89-93; rtd 94. *The Vicarage, Church Road, Rangemore, Burton-on-Trent, Staffs DE13 9RW* Barton under Needwood (01283) 712509

ROFF, Andrew Martin. b 42. Bede Coll Dur BSc65. Westcott Ho Cam 65. **d** 70 **p** 71. C Ches St Mary *Ches* 70-73; Min Can Blackb Cathl *Blackb* 73-76; P-in-c Blackb St Jo 74-75; V Longton 76-81; Chapl Trin Coll Glenalmond 82-83; R Allendale w Whitfield *Newc* 83-92; V Gosforth St Nic from 92. *The Vicarage, 17 Rectory Road, Gosforth, Newcastle upon Tyne NE3 1XR* 0191-285 1326

ROFF, John Michael. b 47. St Chad's Coll Dur BSc69. Westcott Ho Cam 70. **d** 72 **p** 73. C Ches St Mary *Blackb* 72-75; C Dronfield *Derby* 75-76; TV 76-80; TR N Wingfield, Pilsley and Tupton 80-85; V Ilkeston St Mary 85-90; V Stockport St Geo *Ches* 90-94; Dioc Ecum Officer from 92; TR Stockport South West from 94. *St George's Vicarage, 28 Buxton Road, Stockport, Cheshire SK2 6NU* 0161-480 2453

ROGAN, Canon John. b 28. St Jo Coll Dur BA49 MA51 DipTh54 Open Univ BPhil81. **d** 54 **p** 55. V Leigh St Mary *Man* 66-78; RD Leigh 71-78; Hon Can Man Cathl 75-78; Provost St Paul's Cathl Dundee *Bre* 78-83; R Dundee St Paul 78-83; Soc Resp Adv *Bris* 83-93; Can Res Bris Cathl 83-93; rtd 93. *84 Concorde Drive, Bristol BS10 6PX* Bristol (0117) 950 5803

ROGERS, Alan Chad John. b 33. Selw Coll Cam BA56 MA60. Bps' Coll Cheshunt 58. **d** 60 **p** 61. C Sudbury St Andr *Lon* 60-62; Mauritius 62-66; C Edmonton St Alphege *Lon* 66-71; V Enfield St Geo 71-95. *Barren Cott, 25 Front Green, Hempton, Fakenham, Norfolk NR21 7LG* Fakenham (01328) 862814

ROGERS, Canon Alan David. b 24. K Coll Cam BA47 MA50. Cuddesdon Coll 50. **d** 52 **p** 53. Lect Div Weymouth Coll 67-73; Lic to Offic *Sarum* from 69; Hd of Relig and Th Depts Dorset Inst of Educn 73-82; Hon Can Antananarivo from 84; rtd 89. *4 Fossett Way, Weymouth, Dorset DT4 9HD* Weymouth (01305) 779942

✠**ROGERS, Rt Rev Alan Francis Bright.** b 07. Lambeth MA59 Bps' Coll Cheshunt 28. **d** 30 **p** 31 **c** 59. C Shepherd's Bush St Steph *Lon* 30-32; C Twickenham Common H Trin 32-34; Mauritius 34-49; Adn 46-49; Bp 59-66; Hon Can St Jas Cathl 44-59; V Twickenham St Mary *Lon* 49-54; Hon C from 85; V Hampstead St Jo 54-59; RD Hampstead 55-59; Suff Bp Fulham 66-70; Suff Bp Edmonton 70-75; rtd 75; Asst Bp Pet 75-84; P-in-c Wappenham w Abthorpe and Slapton 77-80; C Abthorpe w Slapton 81-83; Asst Bp Lon from 85. *20 River Way, Twickenham TW2 5JP* 0181-894 2031

ROGERS, Brian Robert. b 36. Open Univ BA80. St Jo Coll Nottm 70. **d** 72 **p** 73. C Ealing St Mary *Lon* 72-74; C Greenside *Dur* 74-75; Lic to Offic 75-85; Perm to Offic *Lich* from 85. *23 New Road, Uttoxeter, Staffs ST14 7DD* Uttoxeter (01889) 563515

ROGERS, Brian Victor. b 50. Trin Coll Bris 75. **d** 78 **p** 79. C Plumstead St Jo w St Jas and St Paul *S'wark* 78-83; P-in-c Gayton *Nor* 83-85; P-in-c Gayton Thorpe w E Walton 83-85; P-in-c Westacre 83-85; P-in-c Ashwicken w Leziate 83-85; R Gayton Gp of Par 85-91; R Rackheath and Salhouse from 91. *The Rectory, Stone Hill, Rackheath, Norwich NR13 6NG* Norwich (01603) 720097

ROGERS, Cecil George. b 05. St D Coll Lamp BA28. **d** 28 **p** 29. R W Horsley *Guildf* 43-53; rtd 53; Perm to Offic *Lon* 82-91. *Peasmarsh Place, Peasmarsh, Rye, E Sussex TN31 6XE* Peasmarsh (01797) 230633

ROGERS, Charles Murray. b 17. Qu Coll Cam BA38 MA40 Lon Univ DipEd43. Westcott Ho Cam 38. **d** 40 **p** 41. India 46-71; Jerusalem 71-80; Hong Kong 80-89; rtd 82; Canada from 89. *Box 683, 103 Brant Street, Deseronto, Ontario, Canada, K0K 1X0*

ROGERS, Christopher Antony. b 47. N Ord Course 79. **d** 81 **p** 82. C Chesterfield St Aug *Derby* 81-84; C Chaddesden St Phil 84-86; R Whitwell from 86. *The Rectory, Whitwell, Worksop, Notts S80 4RE* Worksop (01909) 720220

ROGERS, Christopher John. b 47. Bp Lonsdale Coll CertEd Nottm Univ DipEd. E Midl Min Tr Course. **d** 84 **p** 85. NSM Ockbrook *Derby* 84-91; P-in-c Risby w Gt and Lt Saxham and Westley *St E* 91; R from 91. *The Rectory, Risby, Bury St Edmunds, Suffolk IP28 6RQ* Bury St Edmunds (01284) 810416

ROGERS, Clive William. b 62. Selw Coll Cam BA83 MA87 MEng93 Southn Univ BTh90. Chich Th Coll 87. **d** 90 **p** 91. C Leic St Aid *Leic* 90-93; P-in-c Ryhall w Essendine *Pet* 93-94. *13 St John's Street, Duxford, Cambridge CB2 4RA*

ROGERS, Cyril David. b 55. Birm Univ BA76 BTh. Sarum & Wells Th Coll 80. **d** 83 **p** 84. C Leagrave *St Alb* 83-87; TV Langtree *Ox* from 87. *The Vicarage, Reading Road, Woodcote, Reading RG8 0QZ* Checkendon (01491) 680979

ROGERS, David. b 48. Univ of Wales (Ban) BA69. Westcott Ho Cam 70. **d** 72 **p** 73. C Rainbow Hill St Barn *Worc* 72-75; C Tolladine 72-75; C Astwood Bank w Crabbs Cross 75-79; V Cradley 79-90; V Beoley from 90. *The Vicarage, Church Hill, Beoley, Redditch, Worcs B98 9AR* Redditch (01527) 63976

ROGERS, David Alan. b 55. MCIT82 City of Lon Poly BA77. Linc Th Coll 88. **d** 90 **p** 91. C Kingston upon Hull St Nic *York* 90-93; P-in-c Kingston upon Hull St Mary from 93; Ind Chapl from 93. *1023 Anlaby Road, Hull HU4 7PN* Hull (01482) 503286

ROGERS, Ven David Arthur. b 21. Ch Coll Cam BA47 MA52. Ridley Hall Cam 47. **d** 49 **p** 50. V Sedbergh *Bradf* 59-74; RD Sedbergh 59-73; V Garsdale 60-74; V Cautley w Dowbiggin 60-74; Hon Can Bradf Cathl 67-77; P-in-c Firbank, Howgill and Killington 73-77; RD Ewecross 73-77; V Sedbergh, Cautley and Garsdale 74-79; Adn Craven 77-86; rtd 86; Perm to Offic *Bradf* from 86; Perm to Offic *Blackb* from 87; Perm to Offic *Carl* from 89. *Borrens Farm, Leck, Carnforth, Lancs LA6 2JG* Kirkby Lonsdale (015242) 71616

ROGERS, David Barrie. b 46. S Dios Minl Tr Scheme 89. **d** 93. NSM Old Alresford and Bighton *Win* from 93. *North Wing, Old Alresford Place, Alresford, Hants SO24 9DH* Winchester (01962) 732518

ROGERS, David Martyn. b 56. Univ of Wales (Lamp) BA77 K Coll Lon BD79 AKC79 St Kath Coll Liv DipEd86 Liv Univ BPhil94. Chich Th Coll 79. **d** 80 **p** 81. C Hockerill *St Alb* 80-85; Perm to Offic *St As* 85-87; C W Hampstead St Jas *Lon* 87; C Kilburn St Mary 87-90; V New Longton *Blackb* from 90; Chapl to Lancs Constabulary from 90. *All Saints' Vicarage, Station Road, New Longton, Preston PR4 4LN* Preston (01772) 613347

ROGERS, Canon Donovan Charles Edgar. b 08. Clifton Th Coll 32. **d** 35 **p** 36. C Leyton Em *Chelmsf* 35-37; C N Woolwich 37-38; Chapl RAF 38-41; CF 41-46; S Africa from 47. *The Cottage, Beach Road, Noordhoek, 7985 South Africa* Cape Town (21) 891117

ROGERS, Edward Lyon Beresford Cheselden. b 22. VRD65. Keble Coll Ox BA48 MA51. Wells Th Coll 48. **d** 49 **p** 50. Chapl RNR 58-74; R St Giles Cripplegate w St Bart Moor Lane etc *Lon* 66-87; rtd 87; Perm to Offic *Chelmsf* from 87. *Windy Ridge, Wethersfield Road, Finchingfield, Braintree, Essex CM7 4NS* Great Dunmow (01371) 810741

ROGERS, Henry Richard. b 04. Trin Coll Cam BA26 MA30. Westcott Ho Cam 25. **d** 27 **p** 28. R Liddington *Bris* 57; rtd 69. *Ellary, Achahoish, Lochgilphead, Argyll PA31 8PA* Ormsary (018803) 301

ROGERS, Very Rev John. b 34. Univ of Wales (Lamp) BA55 Or Coll Ox BA58 MA61. St Steph Ho Ox 57. **d** 59 **p** 60. C Roath St Martin *Llan* 59-63; Br Guiana 63-66; Guyana 66-71; V Caldicot *Mon* 71-77; V Mon 77-84; RD Mon 81-84; R Ebbw Vale 84-93; RD Blaenau Gwent 86-93; Can St Woolos Cathl 88-93; Dean Llan from 93; V Llan w Capel Llanilltern from 93. *The Deanery, The Cathedral Green, Llandaff, Cardiff CF5 2YF* Cardiff (01222) 561545 or 564554

ROGERS, John Robin. b 36. St Alb Minl Tr Scheme 78. **d** 81 **p** 82. NSM Digswell and Panshanger *St Alb* 81-84; C Welwyn w Ayot St Peter 85-92; R Wilden w Colmworth and Ravensden from 92. *The Rectory, Wilden, Bedford MK44 2PB* Bedford (01234) 771434

ROGERS, John Iorwerth. b 17. Univ of Wales (Lamp) BA39. Ripon Hall Ox 39. **d** 41 **p** 42. Lic to Offic *Derby* 59-86; Hd Master Normanton Sch Buxton 71-86; rtd 87. *15 Plas Hen, Llanddaniel, Gaerwen, Gwynedd LL60 6HW* Gaerwen (01248) 221812

ROGERS, John William Trevor. b 28. Qu Coll Birm. **d** 85 **p** 86. NSM Dunchurch *Cov* from 85. *15 Hillyard Road, Southam, Leamington Spa, Warks CV33 0LD* Southam (01926) 813469

ROGERS, Keith Frederick. b 10. Keble Coll Ox BA33 MA37. Chich Th Coll 34. **d** 36 **p** 37. R Chilthorne Domer, Yeovil Marsh and Thorne Coffin *B & W* 71-75; rtd 75. *54 Chandos Road, Rodborough, Stroud, Glos GL5 3QZ* Stroud (01453) 755812

ROGERS, Canon Kenneth (Ken). b 33. Cuddesdon Coll 68. **d** 69 **p** 70. C Perranzabuloe *Truro* 69-71; C Truro St Paul 71-74; P-in-c Kenwyn St Geo 74-87; RD Powder 81-88; Hon Can Truro Cathl from 87; TR Bodmin w Lanhydrock and Lanivet from 87; RD Trigg Minor and Bodmin 89-93. *The Rectory, Bodmin, Cornwall PL31 2AB* Bodmin (01208) 73867

ROGERS, Llewelyn. Univ of Wales (Lamp) BA59. St Mich Coll Llan. **d** 61 **p** 62. C Holywell *St As* 61-64; C Hawarden 64-70; R Bodfari 70-73; V Rhosymedre 73-77; V Llansantffraid-ym-Mechain 77-83; V Llansantffraid-ym-Mechain and Llanfechain from 83; RD Llanfyllin 84-88. *The Vicarage, Llansantffraid, Powys SY22 6TZ* Llansantffraid (01691) 828244

ROGERS, Malcolm Dawson. b 63. SS Hild & Bede Coll Dur BA84 Selw Coll Cam BA88. Ridley Hall Cam 86. **d** 89 **p** 90. C Ipswich St Jo *St E* 89-93; CMS from 93; Russia from 93. *The Spiritual Academy, St Petersburg, Russia*

ROGERS, Mark James. b 64. Univ of Wales (Lamp) BA. Qu Coll Birm. **d** 89 **p** 90. C Dudley Holly Hall St Aug *Worc* 89-93; C Worc St Barn w Ch Ch 93-94; TV from 94. *214 Tolladine Road, Worcester WR4 9AU* Worcester (01905) 724391

ROGERS, Martin Brian. b 53. Local NSM Course 89. **d** 92 **p** 93. NSM Collyhurst *Man* from 92. *8 Greenford Road, Crumpsall, Manchester M8 7NW* 0161-740 5637

ROGERS, Martin Stephen. b 28. St Edm Hall Ox BA50 MA54. Cuddesdon Coll 50. **d** 52 **p** 53. Lect Cuddesdon Coll 65-73; Chapl Littlemore Hosp Ox 65-74; Dept of Educn Cam Univ 73-76; Chapl Univ Coll of Ripon & York St Jo 76-93; Postgraduate Medical Educn Adv Leeds Univ 90-93; rtd 93. *Parkin, Hutton Conyers, Ripon, N Yorkshire HG4 5EB* Ripon (01765) 606218

ROGERS, Maurice George Walden. b 23. AKC51. **d** 52 **p** 53. V Gt Ilford St Luke *Chelmsf* 61-72; V Woodford St Barn 72-89; rtd 89. *The Coach House, 13 Bodorgan Road, Bournemouth BH2 6NQ* Bournemouth (01202) 291034

ROGERS, Michael Ernest. b 34. Sarum & Wells Th Coll 83. **d** 85 **p** 86. C Roehampton H Trin *S'wark* 85-88; V Ryhill *Wakef* 88-94; V S Elmsall from 94. *The Vicarage, Doncaster Road, South Elmsall, Pontefract, W Yorkshire WF9 2HS* Pontefract (01977) 642861

ROGERS, Michael Hugh Walton. b 52. K Coll Lon BD73 AKC73. St Aug Coll Cant 74. **d** 75 **p** 76. C Eastbourne St Andr *Chich* 75-78; C Uppingham w Ayston *Pet* 78-82; V Eye 82-90;

R Cottesmore and Barrow w Ashwell and Burley from 90. *The Rectory, Cottesmore, Oakham, Leics LE15 7DJ*   Oakham (01572) 812202

ROGERS, Canon Noel Desmond. b 26. TD71. Univ of Wales (Lamp) BA51. **d** 53 **p** 54. C Rhyl w St Ann *St As* 53-58; V Everton St Geo *Liv* 58-64; CF (TA) 59-75; R Newton in Makerfield Em *Liv* 64-74; V Rostherne w Bollington *Ches* from 74; CF (R of O) 75-81; RD Knutsford *Ches* from 85; Hon Can Ches Cathl from 87. *The Vicarage, Rostherne, Knutsford, Cheshire WA16 6RY*   Bucklow Hill (01565) 830595

ROGERS, Mrs Patricia Anne. b 54. Lon Univ BD. Trin Coll Bris. **d** 87 **p** 94. Hon C Gayton Gp of Par *Nor* 87-91; Hon C Rackheath and Salhouse from 91; Chapl to the Deaf from 91. *The Rectory, Stonehill, Rackheath, Norwich NR13 6NG*   Norwich (01603) 720097

ROGERS, Percival Hallewell. b 12. MBE45. St Edm Hall Ox BA35 MA46. Bps' Coll Cheshunt. **d** 46 **p** 47. Hd Master Portora R Sch Enniskillen 54-73; Chapl Gresham's Sch Holt 74-75; USA 76-80; Warden Lay Readers and Ords *Clogh* 81-84; C Sandford-on-Thames *Ox* 85-87; rtd 87; Perm to Offic from 87. *7 Eyot Place, Oxford OX4 1SA*   Oxford (01865) 244976

ROGERS, Philip John. b 52. Univ of Wales CertEd74 Nottm Univ BTh79. St Jo Coll Nottm 76. **d** 79 **p** 80. C Stretford St Bride *Man* 79-84; P-in-c Plumstead St Jo w St Jas and St Paul *S'wark* 84-85; V from 85. *St John's Vicarage, 176 Griffin Road, London SE18 7QA*   0181-855 1827

ROGERS, Richard Anthony. b 46. Ex Coll Ox BA69 Birm Univ DipTh70. Qu Coll Birm 70. **d** 71 **p** 72. C Shirley *Birm* 71-74; Chapl Solihull Sch W Midl 74-78; Hon C Cotteridge *Birm* 78-84; Hon C Hill 84-93; Head RE Kings Norton Sch from 93. *48 Jordan Road, Sutton Coldfield, W Midlands B75 5AB*   0121-308 0310

ROGERS, Richard George (Dick). b 21. **d** 88 **p** 88. NSM Eythorne and Elvington w Waldershare etc *Cant* 88-91; Perm to Offic from 91. *Maydeken, Church Road, Coldred, Dover, Kent CT15 5AQ*   Shepherdswell (01304) 830157

ROGERS, Robert. b 42. Bernard Gilpin Soc Dur 66 St Aid Birkenhead 67 Ridley Hall Cam 69. **d** 70 **p** 71. C Childwall St Dav *Liv* 70-73; C Huntington *York* 73-76; TR Brayton 76-89; RD Selby 84-89; V New Malton from 89. *The Vicarage, 17 The Mount, Malton, York YO17 0ND*   Malton (01653) 692089

ROGERS, Robert Charles. b 55. St Pet Coll Birm CertEd77. St Jo Coll Nottm 87. **d** 89 **p** 90. C Wellesbourne *Cov* 89-93; R Bourton w Frankton and Stretton on Dunsmore etc from 93. *The Rectory, Frankton, Rugby, Warks CV23 9PB*   Marton (01926) 632805

ROGERS, Ronald James. b 31. Bris Univ BA56 St Cath Soc Ox BA58 MA65. Wycliffe Hall Ox 56. **d** 58 **p** 59. C Gt Yarmouth *Nor* 58-62; C Newington St Mary *S'wark* 67-69; C Liv Our Lady and St Nic w St Anne *Liv* 78-83; C Pimlico St Pet w Westmr Ch Ch *Lon* 83-85; Chapl Westmr City Sch 85-87; P-in-c Pimlico St Sav *Lon* from 87. *59 Aylesford Street, London SW1V 3RY*   0171-821 9865 or 834 9520

ROGERS, Ms Sally Jean. b 54. Univ of Wales (Lamp) BA77 Nottm Univ BTh87. Linc Th Coll 84. **d** 87 **p** 94. Par Dn Bris St Mary Redcliffe w Temple etc *Bris* 87-90; Par Dn Greenford H Cross *Lon* 90-94; C from 94. *177 Costons Lane, Greenford, Middx UB6 9AD*   0181-578 1596

ROGERS, Thomas More Fitzgerald. b 13. **d** 62 **p** 63. Chapl to the Deaf *Guildf* 69-72; Chapl to the Deaf *Cant* 72-77; rtd 77. *15 Randolph Close, Knaphill, Woking, Surrey GU21 2NF*   Woking (01483) 480233

ROGERS, William Arthur (Bill). b 41. Lon Univ BA64 CertEd. Chich Th Coll 79. **d** 81 **p** 82. C Chandler's Ford *Win* 81-84; R Bentley and Binsted 84-94; P-in-c The Lulworths, Winfrith Newburgh and Chaldon *Sarum* from 94. *The Rectory, West Road, West Lulworth, Wareham, Dorset BH20 5RY*   Wareham (01929) 400550

✠ROGERSON, Rt Rev Barry. b 36. Leeds Univ BA60 Bris Univ Hon LLD93. Wells Th Coll 60. **d** 62 **p** 63 **c** 79. C S Shields St Hilda w St Thos *Dur* 62-65; C Bishopwearmouth St Nic 65-67; Lect Lich Th Coll 67-71; Vice-Prin 71-72; Lect Sarum & Wells Th Coll 72-74; V Wednesfield St Thos *Lich* 75-79; TR Wednesfield 79; Hon Can Lich Cathl 79-85; Suff Bp Wolv 79-85; Bp Bris from 85. *Bishop's House, Clifton Hill, Bristol BS8 1BW*   Bristol (0117) 973 0222   Fax 923 9670

ROGERSON, Colin Scott. b 30. St Andr Univ MA55. Edin Th Coll. **d** 57 **p** 58. C Byker St Ant *Newc* 57-59; C Newc St Geo 59-63; C Wooler 63-67; V Tynemouth St Aug 67-75; C Dur St Marg *Dur* 75-88; P-in-c Hebburn St Jo from 88. *St John's Vicarage, 23 St John's Avenue, Hebburn, Tyne & Wear NE31 2TZ*   0191-483 2054

ROGERSON, David George. b 38. St Chad's Coll Dur BA60 DipTh63 Newc Univ DipEd67. **d** 63 **p** 64. C Wallsend St Luke *Newc* 63-67; C Delaval 67-70; V Long Benton St Mary 70-81; V N Sunderland from 81; Warden Seahouses Dioc Hostel from 81; Miss to Seamen from 81. *The Vicarage, South Lane,*

North Sunderland, Seahouses, Northd NE68 7TU   Seahouses (01665) 720202

ROGERSON, Derek Russell. b 23. Lon Univ BA51. Sarum Th Coll 51. **d** 53 **p** 54. R Harpurhey St Steph *Man* 64-70; V Rochdale Gd Shep 70-74; Asst Chapl HM Pris Man 74-76; Chapl HM Pris Kirkham 76-83; Chapl HM Pris Haverigg 84-88; rtd 88. *26 Market Street, Millom, Cumbria LA18 4AH*   Millom (01229) 775261

ROGERSON, Ian Matthew. b 45. Bede Coll Dur CertEd67 Open Univ BA76. Oak Hill Th Coll DipHE81. **d** 83 **p** 84. C Haughton St Mary *Man* 83-86; V Ramsbottom St Andr from 86. *St Andrew's Vicarage, Henwick Hall Avenue, Ramsbottom, Bury, Lancs BL0 9YH*   Ramsbottom (01706) 826482

ROGERSON, Canon Prof John William. b 35. Man Univ BD61 DD75 Linacre Ho Ox BA63 MA67. Ripon Hall Ox 61. **d** 64 **p** 66. C Dur St Oswald *Dur* 64-67; Lect Th Dur Univ 64-75; Sen Lect 75-79; Lic to Offic *Dur* 67-79; Lic to Offic *Sheff* from 79; Prof Bibl Studies Sheff Univ from 79; Hon Can Sheff Cathl *Sheff* 82-95. *60 Marlborough Road, Sheffield S10 1DB*   Sheffield (0114) 268 1426

ROLAND, Andrew Osborne. b 45. Mert Coll Ox BA66 DPM69. Cranmer Hall Dur BA84. **d** 84 **p** 85. C Streatham St Leon *S'wark* 84-87; C Kingston All SS w St Jo 87-94; P-in-c Hackbridge and N Beddington from 94. *All Saints' Vicarage, New Road, Mitcham, Surrey CR4 4JL*   0181-648 3650

ROLAND-SHRUBB, David John. b 38. Roch Th Coll 68. **d** 70 **p** 71. C Corringham *Chelmsf* 70-72; C Burgh le Marsh *Linc* 72-74; CF 74-78; Hon Min Can Ripon Cathl *Ripon* 77-78; P-in-c Mirfield Eastthorpe St Paul *Wakef* 78-81; R Caister *Nor* 81-83; Hon Min Can Nor Cathl 81-83; Perm to Offic *Linc* from 90. *Strawberry Farm, Bicker, Boston, Lincs PE20 3BW*   Spalding (01775) 820451

ROLFE, Charles Edward. b 34. Wells Th Coll 68. **d** 70 **p** 71. C Bath Twerton-on-Avon *B & W* 70-79; TV Wellington and Distr 79-85; P-in-c Frome Ch Ch 85-89; V 89-94; Chapl Victoria Hosp Frome 85-94; Chapl St Adhelm's Hosp Frome 88-94; rtd 94; NSM Fordingbridge *Win* from 95; NSM Hale w S Charford from 95. *14 Ashford Close, Fordingbridge, Hants SP6 1DH*   Fordingbridge (01425) 652684

ROLFE, Joseph William. b 37. Qu Coll Birm 78. **d** 81 **p** 82. NSM Tredington and Darlingscott w Newbold on Stour *Cov* 81-91; NSM Brailes from 91; NSM Sutton under Brailes from 91; NSM Shipston Deanery from 91. *35 Manor Lane, Shipston-on-Stour, Warks CV36 4EF*   Shipston-on-Stour (01608) 661737

ROLFE, Paul Douglas. b 46. MIBC90. N Ord Course 90. **d** 93 **p** 94. C Urmston *Man* from 93. *157 Stretford Road, Urmston, Manchester M41 9LZ*   0161-748 8411

ROLL, Sir James William Cecil, Bt. b 12. Chich Th Coll 34. **d** 37 **p** 38. V Becontree St Jo *Chelmsf* 58-83; rtd 83. *82 Leighcliff Road, Leigh-on-Sea, Essex SS9 1DN*

ROLLETT, Robert Henry. b 39. Leeds Univ BA61 Leic Univ CertEd62. Linc Th Coll 77. **d** 79 **p** 80. C Littleport *Ely* 79-82; P-in-c Manea 82-83; V 83-85; P-in-c Wimblington 82-83; R 83-85; V Thorney Abbey 85-93; P-in-c The Ramseys and Upwood 93-94; TR from 94. *The Rectory, Hollow Lane, Ramsey, Huntingdon, Cambs PE17 1DE*   Ramsey (01487) 813271

ROLLINSON, Frederick Mark (Fred). b 24. **d** 71 **p** 72. C Bow w Bromley St Leon *Lon* 71-76; NSM Bethnal Green St Barn from 76. *11 Vivian Road, London E3 5RE*   0181-980 3568 or 981 6511

ROLLINSON, Canon John Knighton. b 14. FRCO34 Sheff Univ BMus36 AKC48. **d** 49 **p** 50. R Whittington *Derby* 64-81; P-in-c New Whittington 78-81; rtd 81; Perm to Offic *Derby* from 81. *75 Yew Tree Drive, Somersall, Chesterfield, Derbyshire S40 3NB*   Chesterfield (01246) 568647

ROLLS, Peter. b 40. HNC Leeds Inst of Educn CertEd. N Ord Course. **d** 83 **p** 84. NSM Meltham *Wakef* from 83. *14 Heather Road, Meltham, Huddersfield HD7 3EY*   Huddersfield (01484) 850389

ROLPH, Pauline Gladys. b 30. SRN51 SCM53 HVCert65. Oak Hill Th Coll 88. **d** 90 **p** 94. Hon C Chingford St Anne *Chelmsf* from 90. *150 Station Road, London E4 6AN*   0181-529 8134

ROLPH, Reginald Lewis George. b 29. Open Univ BA74. Bps' Coll Cheshunt 55. **d** 58 **p** 59. C Letchworth *St Alb* 63-78; Perm to Offic from 78; rtd 93. *22 Souberie Avenue, Letchworth, Herts SG6 3JA*   Letchworth (01462) 684596

ROLSTON, Canon Cyril Willis Matthias. b 29. CITC 66. **d** 68 **p** 69. C Portadown St Mark *Arm* 68-71; I Loughgilly w Clare 71-81; Dir of Ords from 72; I Moy w Charlemont from 81; Preb Arm Cathl from 92. *St James's Rectory, 37 The Square, Moy, Dungannon, Co Tyrone BT71 7SG*   Moy (01868) 784314

ROLSTON, Ven John Ormsby. b 28. TCD BA51 MA59 BD63. CITC 51. **d** 51 **p** 52. C Belf St Mary Magd *Conn* 51-55; C Knock *D & D* 55-59; P-in-c Gilnahirk 59-63; I 63-66; I Belf St Jas *Conn* 66-79; RD N Belf 71-88; I Belf St Jas w St Silas from 79; Can Belf Cathl from 82; Prec Belf Cathl from 88; Adn

Conn from 88. *St James's Rectory, 33 Fortwilliam Park, Belfast BT15 4AP* Belfast (01232) 779442

ROLTON, Patrick Hugh. b 49. Sarum & Wells Th Coll 72. **d** 74 **p** 75. C Roch 74-79; C Edenbridge 79-81; R N Cray w Ruxley from 81. *St James's Rectory, 2 St James Way, Sidcup, Kent DA14 5ER* 0181-300 1655

ROM, Hugh. b 22. S'wark Ord Course 77. **d** 80 **p** 81. NSM Ealing Ascension Hanger Hill *Lon* 80-82; P-in-c St Kath Cree 82-89; Perm to Offic from 90. *187 Linden Court, Brunswick Road, London W5 1AL* 0181-998 5588

ROM, Norman Charles. b 24. S'wark Ord Course 63. **d** 66 **p** 67. C Leatherhead *Guildf* 66-71; Chapl HM Pris Cant 71-74; Chapl HM Pris Pentonville 74-85; Chapl HM Pris Stocken 85-87; P-in-c Empingham *Pet* 85-87; R Empingham and Exton w Horn w Whitwell 87-94; rtd 94. *11 Dundee Drive, Stamford, Lincs PE9 2TR* Stamford (01780) 482051

ROMANES, William. b 11. Magd Coll Cam BA35 MA39. Ripon Hall Ox 35. **d** 36 **p** 37. R Ringsfield w Redisham *St E* 71-76; rtd 76; Hon C Bordesley St Benedict *Birm* 76-93; Perm to Offic from 93. *10 Shireland Close, Birmingham B20 1AN* 0121-523 7572

ROMANIS, Adam John Aidan. b 57. Pemb Coll Ox BA78 MA83. Westcott Ho Cam 81. **d** 84 **p** 85. C Northfield *Birm* 84-88; TV Seaton Hirst *Newc* 88-93; V Newc Ch Ch w St Ann from 93. *The Vicarage, 11 Gibson Street, Newcastle upon Tyne NE1 6PY* 0191-232 0516

RONAYNE, Peter Henry. b 34. FCA68. Oak Hill Th Coll 64. **d** 66 **p** 67. C Chesham St Mary *Ox* 66-69; C Worthing H Trin *Chich* 69-74; V Shoreditch St Leon w St Mich *Lon* 74-82; P-in-c Norwood *S'wark* 82-85; V 85-94; V W Norwood, St Luke from 94; RD Streatham 87-91. *The Vicarage, 6 Chatsworth Way, London SE27 9HR* 0181-670 2706 or 761 0068

RONCHETTI, Quentin Marcus. b 56. Ripon Coll Cuddesdon 79. **d** 80 **p** 81. C Eastbourne St Mary *Chich* 80-83; C Moulsecoomb 83-85; TV 85-90; V Findon Valley from 90. *The Vicarage, 29 Central Avenue, Findon, Worthing, W Sussex BN14 0DS* Findon (01903) 872900

RONE, Ven James (Jim). b 35. St Steph Ho Ox 79. **d** 80 **p** 81. C Stony Stratford *Ox* 80-82; P-in-c Fordham St Pet *Ely* 82-83; V 83-89; P-in-c Kennett 82-83; R 83-89; Can Res Ely Cathl 89-95; Treas 92-95; Adn Wisbech from 95. *Archdeacon's House, 24 Cromwell Road, Ely, Cambs CB6 1AS* Ely (01353) 662056

ROOKE, George William Emmanuel. b 12. Lon Univ BA33 BD34 AKC34. **d** 35 **p** 36. R Worc St Martin-in-the-Cornmarket *Worc* 66-77; rtd 77; Perm to Offic *Heref* from 77. *106 Church Road, Tupsley, Hereford HR1 1RT* Hereford (01432) 266915

ROOKE, Henry John Warburton. b 10. Ch Ch Ox BA32 MA45. Wycliffe Hall Ox 34. **d** 35 **p** 36. V Weobley w Sarnesfield *Heref* 51-69; rtd 69. *Flat 22, Manormead, Tilford Road, Hindhead, Surrey GU26 6RA* Hindhead (01428) 605082

ROOKE, James Templeman (Jim). b 43. Saltley Tr Coll Birm CertEd65. E Midl Min Tr Course CTPS82. **d** 84 **p** 85. NSM Bassingham *Linc* 84-94; NSM Hykeham 89-94; P-in-c Borrowdale *Carl* from 94; Chapl HM Pris Morton Hall 94; Chapl Keswick Sch from 94. *The Vicarage, Borrowdale, Keswick, Cumbria CA12 5XQ* Keswick (017687) 77238

ROOKE, John George Michael. b 47. St Jo Coll Dur BA72 DipTh74. Cranmer Hall Dur 71. **d** 74 **p** 75. C Skelmersdale St Paul *Liv* 74-78; TV Speke St Aid 78-81; Ind Chapl 81-85; V Knotty Ash St Jo from 85. *St John's Vicarage, Thomas Lane, Liverpool L14 5NR* 0151-228 2396

ROOKE, Patrick William. b 55. Open Univ BA85. Sarum & Wells Th Coll 75. **d** 78 **p** 79. C Mossley *Conn* 78-81; C Ballywillan 81-83; I Craigs w Dunaghy and Killagan 83-88; I Ballymore *Arm* 88-94; Asst Prov and Dioc Registrar 92-94; Hon VC Arm Cathl 93-94; I Agherton *Conn* from 94. *St John's Rectory, 59 Strand Road, Portstewart, Co Derry BT55 7LU* Portstewart (01265) 832538

ROOKWOOD, Colin John. b 40. TCD BA64 MA68 Lon Univ PGCE67 DipTh69. Clifton Th Coll 67. **d** 70 **p** 71. C Eccleston Ch Ch *Liv* 70-75; V Penge St Jo *Roch* 75-82; V Childwall All SS *Liv* 82-91; Chapl Bethany Sch Goudhurst from 91. *Providence Cottage, South Curtisden Green, Goudhurst, Cranbrook, Kent TN17 1LD* Goudhurst (01580) 211273

ROOM, Canon Frederick John. b 24. St Jo Coll Ox BA49 MA53. Wells Th Coll 49. **d** 51 **p** 52. C-in-c Farnham Royal S CD *Ox* 58-70; TV Thetford *Nor* 70-89; Sen Ind Missr 75-89; Hon Can Nor Cathl 77-89; rtd 89; Perm to Offic *Nor* from 89. *61 Beechwood Drive, Thorpe St Andrew, Norwich NR7 0LN* Norwich (01603) 35877

ROOMS, Nigel James. b 60. CEng86 MIChemE86 Leeds Univ BSc81. St Jo Coll Nottm DipTh89. **d** 90 **p** 91. C Chell *Lich* 90-94; Tanzania from 94. *St Margaret's Church, PO Box 306, Moshi, Tanzania*

ROONEY, James. b 31. TCD BA58. **d** 58 **p** 59. C Belf St Matt *Conn* 58-60; I 74-82; C Coleraine 60-61; I Ballintoy 61-66; P-in-c Rathlin 62-66; I Craigs w Dunaghy and Killagan 67-74; RD M Belf 80-82; I Cloughfern 82-93; Can Belf Cathl from 90; I Skerry w Rathcavan and Newtowncrommelin *Conn* from 93. *5 Rossland Park, Broughshane, Ballymena, Co Antrim BT43 7LG* Broughshane (01266) 861215

ROOSE-EVANS, James Humphrey. b 27. St Benet's Hall Ox BA52 MA56. **d** 81 **p** 81. Lic to Offic *Heref* 81-89; Perm to Offic *Lon* from 89. *71 Belsize Park Gardens, London NW3 4JP*

ROOSE FRANCIS, Leslie. *See* FRANCIS, Leslie

ROOT, Canon Howard Eugene. b 26. Univ of S California BA45 St Cath Soc Ox BA51 Magd Coll Cam MA53 Magd Coll Ox MA70. Ripon Hall Ox 49. **d** 53 **p** 54. C Trumpington *Ely* 53; Asst Lect Div Cam Univ 53-57; Lect 57-66; Fell and Chapl Em Coll Cam 54-56; Fell and Dean 56-66; Wilde Lect Ox Univ 57-60; Angl Observer Second Vatican Coun 63-65; Prof Th Southn Univ 66-81; Hon Chapl Win Cathl *Win* 66-67; Can Th 67-80; Chmn Abp's Commn on Marriage 68-71; Consultant Lambeth Confs 68 and 88; Jt Ed Journal of Th Studies 69-74; Pope Adrian VI Prof Univ of Louvain 79; St Aug Can Cant Cathl *Cant* 80-91; Dir Angl Cen Rome 81-91; Abp Cant's Counsellor on Vatican Affairs 81-91; Visiting Prof Pontifical Gregorian Univ Rome 84-91; Preceptor Malling Abbey from 93. *26 St Swithun Street, Winchester, Hants SO23 9HU* Winchester (01962) 862982

ROOT, John Brereton. b 41. Lon Univ BA64 Em Coll Cam BA66 MA. Ridley Hall Cam 64. **d** 68 **p** 69. C Harlesden St Mark *Lon* 68-73; C Lower Homerton St Paul 73-76; Chapl Ridley Hall Cam 76; Vice-Prin 76-79; V Alperton *Lon* from 79; AD Brent from 95. *The Vicarage, 34 Stanley Avenue, Wembley, Middx HA0 4JB* 0181-902 1729

ROOTES, William Brian. b 44. Edin Th Coll. **d** 91. NSM Auchterarder *St And* from 91; NSM Muthill from 91. *Belhie Aberuthven, Auchterarder, Perthshire PH3 1EH* Auchterarder (01764) 63259

ROPER, David John. b 53. St Steph Ho Ox DipMin95. **d** 95. C Hunstanton St Mary w Ringstead Parva etc *Nor* from 95. *The Rectory, Broad Lane, Brancaster, King's Lynn, Norfolk PE31 8AH* Brancaster (01485) 210268

ROPER, Canon Timothy Hamilton. b 34. Qu Coll Cam BA57 MA61. Sarum Th Coll 57. **d** 59 **p** 60. C Kingsthorpe *Pet* 59-62; C Kirkby *Liv* 62-65; Chapl Rossall Sch Fleetwood 65-84; R Arthingworth, Harrington w Oxendon and E Farndon *Pet* from 84; RD Brixworth 89-94; Can Pet Cathl from 94. *The Rectory, 35 Main Street, Great Oxendon, Market Harborough, Leics LE16 8NE* Market Harborough (01858) 462052

ROPER, Preb William Lionel. b 17. Leeds Univ BA39. Coll of Resurr Mirfield 39. **d** 41 **p** 42. R S Molton w Nymet St George *Ex* 61-71; R High Bray w Charles 61-71; V Paignton St Jo 72-82; Preb Ex Cathl 77-82; rtd 82. *12 Exeter Gate, South Molton, Devon EX36 4AN* South Molton (01769) 572147

ROSAMOND, Derek William. b 49. Linc Th Coll 87. **d** 89 **p** 90. C Cov Caludon *Cov* 89-93; Northd Ind Miss *Dur* from 93. *All Saints Vicarage, 3 Fulwell Road, Sunderland SR6 0GD* 0191-565 6606

ROSCAMP, Alan Nicholas Harrison. b 12. Dur Univ LTh37 BA39 MA42. St Aid Birkenhead 32. **d** 36 **p** 37. V Wadhurst *Chich* 51-63; V Tidebrook 52-63; Perm to Offic *Cant* from 63; rtd 78. *Horton Green, Ruckinge, Ashford, Kent TN26 2PF* Ham Street (01233) 732491

ROSCOE, David John. b 64. UEA BA87 Selw Coll Cam BA93. Aston Tr Scheme 89 Westcott Ho Cam CTM94. **d** 94 **p** 95. C Ditton St Mich *Liv* from 94. *24 Crown Avenue, Widnes, Cheshire WA8 8AT* 0151-423 5134

ROSE, Andrew David. b 45. BA81. Oak Hill Th Coll 78. **d** 81 **p** 82. C Northwood Em *Lon* 81-86; V Iver from 86. *The Vicarage, Widecroft Road, Iver, Bucks SL0 9QD* Iver (01753) 653131

ROSE, Anthony James. b 47. Trin Coll Bris BD72. **d** 73 **p** 74. C Halliwell St Pet *Man* 73-76; CF 76-94; R Colchester Ch Ch w St Mary V *Chelmsf* from 94. *The Rectory, 21 Cambridge Road, Colchester CO3 3NS* Colchester (01206) 560175

ROSE, Anthony John. b 53. Birm Univ BA79 DipHE86. Trin Coll Bris 84. **d** 86 **p** 87. C The Quinton *Birm* 86-90; R Abbas and Templecombe w Horsington *B & W* from 90. *The Rectory, 8 Church Hill, Templecombe, Somerset BA8 0HG* Templecombe (01963) 370302

ROSE, Barry Ernest. b 35. Chich Th Coll 58. **d** 61 **p** 62. C Forest Gate St Edm *Chelmsf* 61-64; Antigua 64-66; Dominica 66-69; V St Mary-at-Latton *Chelmsf* 69-79; V Stansted Mountfitchet 79-88; V Halstead St Andr w H Trin and Greenstead Green from 88; RD Halstead and Coggeshall from 91. *The Vicarage, Parsonage Street, Halstead, Essex CO9 2LD* Halstead (01787) 472171

ROSE, Bernard Frederick. b 47. Local NSM Course. **d** 91 **p** 92. NSM Ipswich St Thos *St E* from 91. *84 Chesterfield Drive, Ipswich IP1 6DN* Ipswich (01473) 462390

ROSE, Miss Geraldine Susan. b 47. Trin Coll Bris DipTh76 BD78. **dss** 78 **d** 87 **p** 94. Tonbridge St Steph *Roch* 78-80; Littleover *Derby* 80-87; Par Dn 87-90; Par Dn Wombwell *Sheff* 88-94; C from 94. *5 Church Street, Jump, Barnsley, S Yorkshire S74 0HZ*   Barnsley (01226) 749139

ROSE, Glyn Clee. b 16. Jes Coll Ox BA39 MA42. Bps' Coll Cheshunt 49. **d** 51 **p** 52. Miss to Seamen 66-73; R Millbrook *Win* 73-81; rtd 81; Perm to Offic *Win* from 81. *11 Collins Lane, Hursley, Winchester, Hants SO21 2JX*   Hursley (01962) 775403

ROSE, Canon Gordon Henry. b 23. St Cath Soc Ox BA48 MA53. Wells Th Coll 49. **d** 50 **p** 51. R Bishopstoke *Win* 55-92; Hon Can Win Cathl 82-92; rtd 92. *44 Westbury Court, Hedge End, Southampton SO3 4HN*   Botley (01489) 781309

ROSE, Ingrid Elizabeth. b 57. Univ of Wales (Abth) BA78 DipedED79. St D Coll Lamp 84. **d** 87. NSM Ysbyty Cynfyn w Llantrisant and Eglwys Newydd *St D* 87-90 and 92-94. *Ystwyth Villa, Pontrhydygroes, Ystrad Meurig, Dyfed SY25 6DF*

ROSE, John Clement Wansey. b 46. New Coll Ox BA71 MA72. Ripon Hall Ox 70. **d** 72 **p** 73. C Harborne St Pet *Birm* 72-76; TV Kings Norton 76-81; V Maney from 81. *The Vicarage, Maney Hill Road, Sutton Coldfield, W Midlands B72 1JJ*   0121-354 2426

ROSE, Dr Judith Anne. b 36. Newnham Coll Cam BA57 MA65 Ox Univ DipTh87 K Coll Lon PhD91. Ripon Coll Cuddesdon 86. **d** 87 **p** 94. Par Dn Kettering All SS *Pet* 87-92; P-in-c Aldwincle w Thorpe Achurch, Pilton, Wadenhoe etc from 92. *The Rectory, Aldwincle, Kettering, Northants NN14 3EP*   Clopton (01832) 720613

ROSE, Canon Kathleen Judith. b 37. Lon Univ DipTh66. Lon Bible Coll BD73 St Mich Ho Ox 64. **dss** 76 **d** 87 **p** 94. Leeds St Geo *Ripon* 76-81; Bradf Cathl *Bradf* 81-85; S Gillingham *Roch* 85-87; Par Dn 87-90; RD Gillingham 88-90; Bp's Dom Chapl from 90; Asst Dir of Ords from 90; Hon Can Roch Cathl from 93. *Bishopscourt Flat, 24 St Margaret's Street, Rochester, Kent ME1 1TS*   Medway (01634) 842721

ROSE, Lionel Stafford. b 38. MBE93. Wells Th Coll 69. **d** 71 **p** 72. C Minchinhampton *Glouc* 71-73; C Thornbury 73-75; R Ruardean 75-80; V Whiteshill 80-84; CF 84-93; Chapl HM Pris Kirkham from 93. *HM Prison, Kirkham, Preston PR4 2RA*   Kirkham (01772) 684343   Fax 682855

ROSE, Mrs Lynda Kathryn. b 51. Called to the Bar (Gray's Inn) 81 Ex Univ BA73 Ox Univ BA86. Wycliffe Hall Ox 86. **d** 87 **p** 94. C Highfield *Ox* 87-88; C Ox St Clem 89-93; Dir Anastasis Ministries from 93; NSM Ambrosden w Mert and Piddington from 94. *95 Staunton Road, Oxford OX3 7TR*   Oxford (01865) 68774

ROSE, Canon Paul Rosamond. b 32. Trin Hall Cam BA56 MA60. Westcott Ho Cam 57. **d** 59 **p** 60. C Wandsworth St Anne *S'wark* 59-61; C Tormohun *Ex* 61-64; S Rhodesia 64-65; Rhodesia 65-67; Min Can, Prec and Sacr Pet Cathl *Pet* 67-72; V Paddington St Jo w St Mich *Lon* 72-79; PV Westmr Abbey 74-79; Min Can and Prec Cant Cathl *Cant* 79-84; V Rothwell w Orton *Pet* 84-87; R Rothwell w Orton, Rushton w Glendon and Pipewell from 87; Can Pet Cathl from 94. *The Vicarage, Squire's Hill, Rothwell, Kettering, Northants NN14 2BQ*   Kettering (01536) 710268

ROSE, Peter Charles. b 30. St Aug Coll Cant 70. **d** 72 **p** 73. C St Martin-in-the-Fields *Lon* 72-76; C St Buryan, St Levan and Sennen *Truro* 76-78; V Feock 78-82; TV Gt Grimsby St Mary and St Jas *Linc* 82-84; rtd 84. *25 Quai du Hable, 76200 Dieppe, France*   France (33) 35 84 51 06

ROSE, Robert Alec Lewis (Bob). b 41. Man Univ BSc64. Wycliffe Hall Ox 85. **d** 87 **p** 88. C Vange *Chelmsf* 87-91; C Langdon Hills 91-94; P-in-c Bentley Common from 94; P-in-c Kelvedon Hatch from 94; P-in-c Navestock from 94. *The Vicarage, 6 Applegate, Pilgrims Hatch, Brentwood, Essex CM14 5PL*   Coxtie Green (01277) 372200

ROSE, Roy. b 11. Worc Ord Coll 63. **d** 64 **p** 65. R Hale *Linc* 68-77; V Helpringham 68-77; P-in-c Scredington 73-77; rtd 77; Perm to Offic *Linc* 77-93. *72 Lincoln Road, Ruskington, Sleaford, Lincs NG34 9AB*   Ruskington (01526) 832669

ROSE, Miss Susan Mary. b 36. Lon Univ DipTh70. Dalton Ho Bris 68 Trin Coll Bris 74. **dss** 81 **d** 87 **p** 94. Brinsworth w Catcliffe *Sheff* 75-77; Scargill Ho 77-83; Netherthorpe *Sheff* 83-87; Tutor Trin Coll Bris from 87. *Trinity College, Stoke Hill, Bristol BS9 1JP*   Bristol (0117) 968 2803

ROSE, Westmoreland Charles Edward. b 32. St Jo Coll Nottm 85. **d** 87 **p** 88. C Fairfield *Derby* 87-90; V Linton and Castle Gresley from 90. *The Vicarage, 40 Main Street, Linton, Swadlincote, Derbyshire DE12 6PZ*   Burton-on-Trent (01283) 761441

ROSE-CASEMORE, John. b 27. Chich Th Coll. **d** 55 **p** 56. R Puttenham and Wanborough *Guildf* 65-72; R Frimley 72-83; RD Surrey Heath 76-81; R Ludgershall and Faberstown *Sarum* 83-86; R Tidworth, Ludgershall and Faberstown 86-92; rtd 92; Perm to Offic *Ex* from 93. *2 Churchtown Cottages, Cornwood, Ivybridge, Devon PL21 0QJ*   Cornwood (0175537) 786

ROSE-CASEMORE, Miss Penelope Jane. b 56. Bris Univ CertEd77 BEd78. Westcott Ho Cam DipRS82. **dss** 85 **d** 87 **p** 94. Waterloo St Jo w St Andr *S'wark* 85-87; Par Dn 87-88; Asst Chapl Gt Ormond Street Hosp for Sick Children Lon 88-90; Par Dn Balham St Mary and St Jo *S'wark* 90-94; C from 94; Par Dn Upper Tooting H Trin 90-94; C from 94. *29 Avoca Road, London SW17 8SL*   0181-767 2308

ROSENTHALL, Henry David. b 08. QUB BA30 TCD 30. **d** 32 **p** 33. R Bolingbroke w Hareby *Linc* 66-72; R Ulceby w Fordington 72-76; R Willoughby w Sloothby w Claxby 72-76; rtd 76; P-in-c Salle *Nor* 78-80; Perm to Offic from 80. *Station Road, Reepham, Norwich NR10 4LJ*   Norwich (01603) 870202

ROSEWEIR, Clifford John. b 43. Glas Univ MA64 Kingston Poly DipPM81 MIPD81. S'wark Ord Course 83. **d** 84 **p** 85. NSM Redhill H Trin *S'wark* 84-89; P-in-c Croydon St Martin 89-92; Perm to Offic 92-93; Hon C Wallington H Trin 93-94; V Croydon Ch Ch from 94. *Christ Church Vicarage, 34 Longley Road, Croydon CR0 3LH*   0181-665 1277   Fax as telephone

ROSHEUVEL, Canon Siegfried Winslow Patrick. b 39. Lon Univ BA86. Codrington Coll Barbados 64. **d** 68 **p** 68. Guyana 68-75; C Worksop Priory *S'well* 75-78; Area Sec (Dios Chelmsf and St Alb) USPG 78-89; (Dio Lon) 78-92; Chapl HM Pris Wandsworth 92-93; Chapl HM Pris Rudgate from 93; Chapl HM Pris Thorp Arch from 93; Can Cape Coast from 94. *HM Prison Thorp Arch, Wetherby, W Yorkshire LS23 7KY*   Boston Spa (01937) 844241   Fax 845446

ROSKELLY, James Hereward Emmanuel. b 57. BSc ACSM80. Cranmer Hall Dur 83. **d** 86 **p** 87. C Dunster, Carhampton and Withycombe w Rodhuish *B & W* 86-90; C Ealing St Mary *Lon* 90-93; Chapl R Marsden Hosp Lon and Surrey 93-95; CF from 95. *c/o MOD (Army), Bagshot Park, Bagshot, Surrey GU19 5PL*   Bagshot (01276) 471717   Fax 412834

ROSKILLY, Dr John Noel. b 33. DRCOG60 MRCGP68 Man Univ MB, ChB58. St Deiniol's Hawarden 74. **d** 75 **p** 76. NSM Bramhall *Ches* 75-86; V Capesthorne w Siddington and Marton 86-91; Dioc Dir of Counselling 84-93; Bp's Officer for NSM 87-93; NSM Macclesfield St Paul 92-93; rtd 93. *North View, Hawkins Lane, Rainow, Macclesfield, Cheshire SK10 5TL*   Macclesfield (01625) 501014

ROSKROW, Neil. b 27. FSMC50 FBCO80. St Alb Minl Tr Scheme 82. **d** 85 **p** 86. NSM Digswell and Panshanger *St Alb* 85-90; P-in-c Gt Gaddesden from 90; P-in-c Lt Gaddesden from 92. *The Vicarage, Piper's Hill, Great Gaddesden, Hemel Hempstead, Herts HP1 3BY*   Hemel Hempstead (01442) 252672

ROSKROW, Mrs Pamela Mary. b 25. St Alb Minl Tr Scheme. **dss** 85 **d** 87 **p** 94. Digswell and Panshanger *St Alb* 85-90; Hon Par Dn 87-90; Hon Par Dn Gt Gaddesden 90-94; Hon C from 94; Hon Par Dn Lt Gaddesden 92-94; Hon C from 94. *The Vicarage, Pipers Hill, Great Gaddesden, Hemel Hempstead, Herts HP1 3BY*   Hemel Hempstead (01442) 252672

ROSOMAN, Richard John. b 59. Ripon Coll Cuddesdon 90. **d** 92 **p** 93. C Cradley *Worc* from 92. *2 Doverdale Close, Halesowen, W Midlands B63 2AT*   Dudley (01384) 567601

ROSS, Canon Alastair Alexander. b 54. CCC Ox BA75. St Jo Coll Nottm 76. **d** 79 **p** 80. C Huyton St Mich *Liv* 79-82; C-in-c Halewood St Mary CD 82-83; TV Halewood 83-87; V Netherton 87-94; Hon Can Liv Cathl 91-94; V Halifax *Wakef* from 94. *The Vicarage, Skircoat Green Road, Halifax, W Yorkshire HX3 0BQ*   Halifax (01422) 365477

ROSS, Anthony McPherson (Tony). b 38. OBE. Univ of Wales (Lamp) BA60 Lon Univ BD63. St Mich Coll Llan 60. **d** 61 **p** 62. C Gabalfa *Llan* 61-65; Chapl RN 65-93; Hon Chapl to The Queen 89-93; P-in-c Coln St Aldwyns, Hatherop, Quenington etc *Glouc* from 93. *The Vicarage, Coln St Aldwyns, Cirencester, Glos GL7 5AG*   Cirencester (01285) 750013

ROSS, David Alexander (Alex). b 46. Lon Univ DipTh73. Oak Hill Th Coll 73. **d** 75 **p** 76. C Northwood Em *Lon* 75-80; R Eastrop *Win* 80-86; V Hove Bp Hannington Memorial Ch *Chich* 86-93; V Muswell Hill St Jas w St Matt *Lon* from 93. *St James's Vicarage, 2 St James's Lane, London N10 3DB*   0181-883 6277

ROSS, Preb Duncan Gilbert. b 48. Lon Univ BSc70. Westcott Ho Cam 75. **d** 78 **p** 79. C Stepney St Dunstan and All SS *Lon* 78-84; V Hackney Wick St Mary of Eton w St Aug 84-95; Preb St Paul's Cathl from 95; P-in-c Bow Common St Paul from 95. *St Paul's Vicarage, Leopold Street, London EC3 4LA*   0171-987 4941

ROSS, Frederic Ian. b 34. Man Univ BSc56. Westcott Ho Cam 58 Episc Th Sem Mass DipTh61. **d** 62 **p** 63. C Oldham *Man* 62-65; Sec Th Colls Dept SCM 65-69; Teacher Man Gr Sch 69-84; Lic to Offic *Man* 69-84; V Shrewsbury H Cross *Lich* from 84. *131 Underdale Road, Shrewsbury SY2 5EG*   Shrewsbury (01743) 248859

ROSS, Canon Frederick. b 36. Qu Coll Birm. **d** 64 **p** 65. C Hessle *York* 64-68; V Marlpool *Derby* 68-73; P-in-c Norbury w Snelston 73-74; R 74-81; P-in-c Clifton 73-74; V 74-81; RD Ashbourne 78-81; V Melbourne from 81; RD Melbourne 81-86 and from 91; Hon Can Derby Cathl from 92. *The Vicarage, Church Square, Melbourne, Derby DE7 1EN* Melbourne (01332) 862347

ROSS, Henry Ernest. b 40. NW Ord Course 70. **d** 73 **p** 74. NSM Litherland St Phil *Liv* 73-75; C Newton-le-Willows 75-77; P-in-c Walton St Luke 77-79; V from 79; RD Walton 84-89. *St Luke's Vicarage, 136 Southport Road, Bootle, Merseyside L20 9EH* 0151-523 5460

ROSS, John. b 41. Wells Th Coll 66. **d** 69 **p** 70. C Newc St Gabr *Newc* 69-71; C Prudhoe 71-75; Hon C Shotley 75-87; Hon C Whittonstall 75-87; P-in-c Wallsend St Pet from 93. *St Peter's Rectory, Canterbury Avenue, Wallsend, Tyne & Wear NE28 6PY* 0191-262 3852

ROSS, John Colin. b 50. Oak Hill Th Coll 84. **d** 86 **p** 87. C Stowmarket *St E* 86-89; C Wakef St Andr and St Mary *Wakef* 89-91; R Gt and Lt Whelnetham w Bradfield St George *St E* 91-94; V Newmarket All SS from 94. *The Vicarage, 17 Cardigan Street, Newmarket, Suffolk CB8 8HZ* Newmarket (01638) 662514

ROSS, Malcolm Hargrave. b 37. Dur Univ BSc58. Westcott Ho Cam 63. **d** 64 **p** 65. C Armley St Bart *Ripon* 64-67; USPG 67-71; Trinidad and Tobago 67-71; V New Rossington *Sheff* 71-75; Bp's Missr in E Lon 75-82; P-in-c Haggerston All SS 75-82; V Bedf Leigh *Man* 82-85; Area Sec (Dios Bris and Glouc) USPG 85-90; Bp's Officer for Miss and Evang *Bris* 90-94; P-in-c Lacock w Bowden Hill 90-94; V Sherston Magna, Easton Grey, Luckington etc from 94. *The Vicarage, Green Lane, Sherston, Malmesbury, Wilts SN16 0NP* Malmesbury (01666) 840209

ROSS, Oliver Charles Milligan. b 58. Lon Univ BA80 St Edm Ho Cam BA85. Ridley Hall Cam 84. **d** 87 **p** 88. C Preston St Cuth *Blackb* 87-90; C Paddington St Jo w St Mich *Lon* 90-95; V Hounslow H Trin w St Paul from 95. *The Vicarage, 66 Lampton Road, Hounslow TW3 4JD* 0181-570 3066

ROSS, Canon Raymond John. b 28. Trin Coll Cam BA52 MA57. St Steph Ho Ox 52. **d** 54 **p** 55. C Clifton All SS *Bris* 54-58; C Solihull *Birm* 58-66; C-in-c Hobs Moat Cd 66-67; V Hobs Moat 67-72; R Newbold and Dunston *Derby* from 72; RD Chesterfield 78-91; Hon Can Derby Cathl from 86. *Newbold Rectory, St John's Road, Chesterfield, Derbyshire S41 8QN* Chesterfield (01246) 450374

ROSS, Vernon. b 57. RGN86 Portsm Poly BSc79. Trin Coll Bris DipHE91. **d** 91 **p** 92. C Fareham St Jo *Portsm* 91-94; P-in-c Witheridge, Thelbridge, Creacombe, Meshaw etc *Ex* from 94. *The Vicarage, Witheridge, Tiverton, Devon EX16 8AE* Tiverton (01884) 860768

ROSS, Dean of. *See* HENDERSON, Very Rev Richard Crosbie Aitken

ROSSDALE, David Douglas James. b 53. Westmr Coll Ox DipApTh90 MA91. K Coll Lon 72 Chich Th Coll 80. **d** 81 **p** 82. C Upminster *Chelmsf* 81-86; V Moulsham St Luke 86-90; V Cookham *Ox* from 90; RD Maidenhead from 94. *The Vicarage, Church Gate, Cookham, Maidenhead, Berks SL6 9SP* Maidenhead (01628) 523969 or 529661

ROSSETER, Miss Susan Mary. b 46. Man Univ BA67 Edin Univ DASS71. St Jo Coll Nottm LTh84. **d** 87 **p** 94. Par Dn Bromley Common St Aug *Roch* 87-88; C Pudsey St Lawr and St Paul *Bradf* from 88. *34 The Lanes, Pudsey, W Yorkshire LS28 7AQ* Leeds (0113) 255 1080

ROSSITER, Donald William Frank. b 30. **d** 80 **p** 81. NSM Abergavenny St Mary w Llanwenarth Citra *Mon* from 80. *10 Meadow Lane, Abergavenny, Gwent NP7 7AY* Abergavenny (01873) 855648

ROSSITER, Raymond Stephen David. b 22. St Deiniol's Hawarden 75. **d** 76 **p** 77. NSM Sale St Anne *Ches* 76-90; Perm to Offic from 90; rtd 91. *75 Temple Road, Sale, Cheshire M33 2FQ* 0161-962 3240

ROSTRON, Derek. b 34. St Mich Coll Llan 65. **d** 67 **p** 68. C Morecambe St Barn *Blackb* 67-70; C Ribbleton 70-72; V Chorley All SS 72-79; C Woodchurch *Ches* 79-80; V Audlem from 80; RD Nantwich from 88. *St James's Vicarage, 66 Heathfield Road, Audlem, Crewe CW3 0HG* Audlem (01270) 811543

ROTHERHAM, Eric. b 36. Clifton Th Coll 63. **d** 67 **p** 68. C Gt Crosby St Luke *Liv* 67-69; C Sutton 69-71; V Warrington St Paul 72-79; Lic to Offic 79-80; Perm to Offic from 80. *7 Paul Street, Warrington WA2 7LE* Warrington (01925) 633048

ROTHERY, Cecil Ivor. b 24. St Jo Coll Winnipeg 50. **d** 53 **p** 54. Canada 53-72; C Gainsborough All SS *Linc* 72-74; R Fleet 74-79; P-in-c Wrawby 79-80; C Glanford Bridge 79-80; rtd 80; Perm to Offic *S'well* 80-83; Perm to Offic *Sheff* 83-93. *129 Queen Street, Retford, Notts DN22 7DA* Retford (01777) 701551

ROTHERY, Robert Frederick (Fred). b 34. Lon Coll of Div 67. **d** 69 **p** 70. C Burscough Bridge *Liv* 69-72; C Chipping

Campden *Glouc* 72-75; P-in-c Didmarton w Oldbury-on-the-Hill and Sopworth 75-77; R Boxwell, Leighterton, Didmarton, Oldbury etc 77-83; R Stow on the Wold from 83; RD Stow from 90. *The Rectory, Stow on the Wold, Cheltenham, Glos GL54 1AA* Cotswold (01451) 830607

ROTHWELL, Bryan. b 60. St Edm Hall Ox BA81 MA85. Trin Coll Bris. **d** 85 **p** 86. C Carl St Jo *Carl* 85-88; C Ulverston St Mary w H Trin 88-90; P-in-c Preston St Mary *Blackb* from 90. *St Mary's Vicarage, St Mary's Close, Preston PR1 4XN* Preston (01772) 794222

ROTHWELL, Edwin John. b 53. Lanc Univ BA74 PhD79. Sarum & Wells Th Coll 88. **d** 90 **p** 91. C Malvern Link w Cowleigh *Worc* 90-94; R Bowbrook N from 94. *The Rectory, Droitwich Road, Hanbury, Bromsgrove, Worcs B60 4DB* Hanbury (01527) 821826

ROTHWELL, Canon Eric. b 12. Man Univ BA35. Lich Th Coll 35. **d** 37 **p** 38. Hon Can Blackb Cathl *Blackb* 61-77; R Chorley St Laur 63-77; rtd 77; Perm to Offic *Blackb* from 79; Perm to Offic *Carl* from 79. *1 Town End Meadow, Cartmel, Grange-over-Sands, Cumbria LA11 6QG* Cartmel (015395) 36574

ROTHWELL, Harold. b 34. AKC58. K Coll Lon St Boniface Warminster. **d** 59 **p** 60. V Caistor w Holton le Moor and Clixby *Linc* 67-77; Chapl Caistor Hosp 67-77; Org Sec (Dios Ex and B & W) CECS 77-81; P-in-c Deeping Fen *Linc* 78-81; C Boston 86-88; C Spilsby w Hundleby 88-91; C Bracebridge Heath 91-94; rtd 94. *47 Ridgeway, Nettleham, Lincoln LN2 2TL* Lincoln (01522) 751610

ROTHWELL, Michael John Hereward. b 46. Chich Th Coll 74. **d** 78 **p** 79. C Chelmsf All SS *Chelmsf* 78-82; C Clacton St Jas 82-85; V Thorpe *Guildf* from 85. *The Vicarage, Church Approach, Coldharbour Lane, Thorpe, Egham, Surrey TW20 8TQ* Chertsey (01932) 565986

ROTHWELL-JACKSON, Christopher Patrick. b 32. St Cath Soc Ox BA58 MA62. St Steph Ho Ox 55. **d** 59 **p** 60. C E Clevedon All SS *B & W* 59-62; C Midsomer Norton 62-65; Teacher St Pet Primary Sch Portishead 65-68; Lic to Offic 68-75; Hd Master Bp Pursglove Sch Tideswell from 75; Lic to Offic *Derby* from 76. *Hardy House, Tideswell, Buxton, Derbyshire SK17 8HL* Tideswell (01298) 871468

ROUCH, David Vaughan. b 36. Oak Hill Th Coll 67. **d** 69 **p** 70. C Denton Holme *Carl* 69-74; V Litherland St Jo and St Jas *Liv* 74-95; V Pemberton St Mark Newtown from 95. *The Vicarage, Victoria Street, Wigan, Lancs WN5 9BN* Wigan (01942) 43611

ROULSTON, Dr Joseph Ernest. b 52. MIBiol77 FRSC86 BNC Ox BA74 MA78 Lon Univ PhD81. Edin Dioc NSM Course 83. **d** 86 **p** 87. C Edin St Hilda *Edin* 86-88; C Edin St Fillan 86-88; NSM Edin St Mich and All SS from 88. *106 Gilmore Place, Edinburgh EH3 9PL* 0131-228 3862

ROUND, Keith Leonard. b 49. Sarum & Wells Th Coll 88. **d** 90 **p** 91. C Meir *Lich* 90-95; V Burslem St Werburgh from 95. *The Presbytery, Haywood Road, Stoke-on-Trent ST6 7AH* Stoke-on-Trent (01782) 87582

ROUND, Malcolm John Harrison. b 56. Lon Univ BSc77 BA81. Oak Hill Th Coll. **d** 81 **p** 82. C Guildf St Sav w Stoke-next-Guildf 81-85; C Hawkwell *Chelmsf* 85-88; R Balerno *Edin* from 88. *53 Marchbank Drive, Balerno, Midlothian EH14 7ER* 0131-449 4127

ROUNDHILL, Andrew (John). b 65. CCC Cam BA87. Ripon Coll Cuddesdon BTh93. **d** 93 **p** 94. C Lanc Ch Ch w St Jo and St Anne *Blackb* from 93. *36 Ambleside Road, Lancaster LA1 3HT* Lancaster (01524) 849186

ROUNDHILL, Canon Jack. b 22. TCD BA44 MA47 BD47. **d** 45 **p** 46. V Dorking w Ranmore *Guildf* 63-76; RD Dorking 70-75; Hon Can Guildf Cathl 76-89; R Cranleigh 76-89; rtd 89; Perm to Offic *Bris* from 89; Perm to Offic *Sarum* from 89; Perm to Offic *Ox* from 89; Chapl Hawtrey's Sch Salisbury from 93. *2 River Park, Marlborough, Wilts SN8 1NH* Marlborough (01672) 516312

ROUNDHILL, Stanley (Brother Peter). b 14. Chich Th Coll 46. **d** 49 **p** 50. OSP from 39; rtd 84. *The Abbey, Alton, Hants GU34 4AP* Alton (01420) 62145

ROUNDS, Canon Philip Rigby. b 21. Wells Th Coll 49. **d** 52 **p** 53. R Wyke Regis *Sarum* 67-89; Can and Preb Sarum Cathl 77-89; rtd 89. *8 Rodwell Lodge, Rodwell Road, Weymouth, Dorset DT4 8QT* Weymouth (01305) 781373

ROUNDTREE, Ven Samuel William. b 19. TCD BA42 MA54. CITC 43. **d** 43 **p** 44. Treas Leighlin Cathl *C & O* 62-78; RD Maryborough 62-82; Preb Ossory Cathl 62-78; I Dunleckney 62-82; Chan Ossory and Leighlin Cathls 78-80; Prec 80-82; I New w Old Ross, Whitechurch, Fethard etc 82-88; Adn Ferns 86-88; rtd 88. *7 Bellevue Cottages, Delgany, Greystones, Co Wicklow, Irish Republic* Dublin (1) 287-4428

ROUNTREE, Canon Richard Benjamin. b 52. NUI BA73. CITC 76. **d** 76 **p** 77. C Orangefield *D & D* 76-80; C Dub Zion Ch *D & G* 80-83; I Dalkey St Patr from 83; Dioc Dir Decade of

Evang from 90; Can Ch Ch Cathl Dub from 92. *The Rectory, Church Road, Dalkey, Co Dublin, Irish Republic* Dublin (1) 280-3369

ROUSE, Graham. b 58. Sheff City Coll of Educn CertEd79 Leic Univ DipEd84. Cranmer Hall Dur 90. **d** 92 **p** 93. C Longridge *Blackb* from 92. *94 Higher Road, Longridge, Preston PR3 3SY* Preston (01772) 784832

ROUTH, Mrs Eileen Rosemary. b 41. Cant Sch of Min 82. **dss** 85 **d** 87 **p** 94. Folkestone St Sav *Cant* 85-87; Par Dn 87-90; Par Dn Woodnesborough w Worth and Staple 90-91; D-in-c 91-94; V from 94. *The Vicarage, The Street, Woodnesborough, Sandwich, Kent CT13 0NQ* Sandwich (01304) 613056

ROUTH, William John. b 60. Magd Coll Ox BA81 MA92. Ripon Coll Cuddesdon 93. **d** 95. C Longton *Blackb* from 95. *66 Franklands, Longton, Preston PR4 5WD* Preston (01772) 615473

ROWBERRY, Michael James. b 46. Sussex Univ BA74. Edin Th Coll 85. **d** 87 **p** 92. C Wolvercote w Summertown *Ox* 87-88; NSM Cov St Fran N Radford *Cov* from 91. *93 Kingston Road, Coventry CV5 6LQ* Coventry (01203) 677915

ROWCROFT, Kenneth George Caulfeild. b 19. Sarum Th Coll 48. **d** 50 **p** 51. V Monkton Wyld *Sarum* 67-74; rtd 75. *Colway Rise, Colway Lane, Lyme Regis, Dorset DT7 3HE* Lyme Regis (01297) 443349

ROWE, Andrew Gidleigh Bruce. b 37. AKC62. St Boniface Warminster. **d** 63 **p** 64. C Midsomer Norton *B & W* 63-68; Chapl RN 68-84; Hon C Winkfield and Cranbourne *Ox* 84-86; Chapl Heathfield Sch 84-86; TV Wellington and Distr *B & W* 86-95; R Chewton Mendip w Ston Easton, Litton etc from 95. *The Rectory, Lower Street, Chewton Mendip, Bath BA3 4PD* Chewton Mendip (01761) 241644

ROWE, Andrew Robert (Andy). b 64. Westmr Coll Ox BA85 PGCE86. Ridley Hall Cam CTM95. **d** 95. C Broadheath *Ches* from 95. *21 Woodheys Drive, Sale, Cheshire M33 4JB* 0161-973 5274

ROWE, Canon Antony Silvester Buckingham. b 26. St Jo Coll Dur 53. **d** 55 **p** 56. V Cov St Mary *Cov* 59-83; RD Cov S 72-82; Hon Can Cov Cathl 76-92; R Harbury and Ladbroke 83-92; rtd 92; Perm to Offic *Cov* from 92; Perm to Offic *Glouc* from 92. *3 Cotswold Edge, Mickleton, Chipping Campden, Glos GL55 6TR* Mickleton (01386) 438622

ROWE, Arthur John. b 35. TCD 73. **d** 76 **p** 77. C Ban Abbey *D & D* 76-78; I Kilbarron *D & R* 78-79; I Kilbarron w Rossnowlagh 79-82; P-in-c Hockering Nor 82-85; P-in-c Honingham w E Tuddenham 82-85; P-in-c N Tuddenham 82-85; R Hockwold w Wilton *Ely* from 85; R Weeting from 85. *The Rectory, Hockwold, Thetford, Norfolk IP26 4JG* Thetford (01842) 828271

ROWE, Bryan. b 50. Carl Dioc Tr Course 87. **d** 90 **p** 91. C Kells *Carl* 90-93; P-in-c Aspatria w Hayton from 93. *The Vicarage, King Street, Aspatria, Carlisle CA5 3AL* Aspatria (016973) 20398

ROWE, Cecil Leonard. b 16. AKC48. **d** 48 **p** 49. R Girvan *Glas* 68-72; R Stratford St Mary *St E* 72-83; P-in-c Higham 72-83; rtd 83. *15 Bristol Road, Colchester CO1 2YU* Colchester (01206) 866411

ROWE, Mrs Christine Elizabeth. b 55. Southn Univ BEd77. Ripon Hall Ox 83. **dss** 86 **d** 87 **p** 94. Denham *Ox* 86-87; Par Dn 87-89; Par Dn Aylesbury 89; Par Dn Aylesbury w Bierton and Hulcott 89-93; NSM Caversham St Jo from 93. *The Vicarage, St John's Road, Caversham, Reading RG4 0AN* Reading (01734) 471814

ROWE, Cyril Ashton. b 38. AKC62. **d** 63 **p** 64. C Bethnal Green St Matt *Lon* 63-68; P-in-c 68-74; V Stoke Newington St Faith, St Matthias and All SS from 74. *St Matthias Vicarage, Wordsworth Road, London N16 8DD* 0171-254 5063

ROWE, David Brian. b 58. Trin Coll Bris DipHE82. **d** 83 **p** 84. C Radipole and Melcombe Regis *Sarum* 83-86; C Cranham Park *Chelmsf* 86-88; Assoc Min and Par Missr Eastrop *Win* 88-92; P-in-c Arborfield w Barkham *Ox* from 92. *The Rectory, Church Lane, Arborfield, Reading RG2 9HZ* Wokingham (01734) 760285

ROWE, Edward Nelson. b 05. TCD BA29 MA40. Bps' Coll Cheshunt. **d** 62 **p** 63. I Currin w Drum and Newbliss *Clogh* 66-76; RD Clones 72-76; rtd 76. *Drumclay Private Nursing Home, 15 Drumclay Road, Enniskillen, Co Fermanagh* Enniskillen (01365) 327255

ROWE, Geoffrey Lewis. b 44. Univ of Wales (Lamp) BA. Ripon Coll Cuddesdon 80. **d** 82 **p** 83. C Milber *Ex* 82-84; TV Withycombe Raleigh 84-90; R Clyst St Mary, Clyst St George etc from 90. *The Rectory, 40 Clyst Valley Road, Clyst St Mary, Exeter EX5 1DD* Exeter (01392) 874363

ROWE, Miss Joan Patricia. b 54. Trin Coll Bris BA87. **d** 88 **p** 94. C Radstock w Writhlington *B & W* 88-92; C Nailsea H Trin from 92. *16 Church Hayes Road, Nailsea, Bristol BS19 2LX* Nailsea (01275) 857910

ROWE, John Goring. b 23. McGill Univ Montreal BA48 BD51 Selw Coll Cam BA53. Montreal Dioc Th Coll LTh51. **d** 51

p 52. C Trumpington *Ely* 51-53; Hon C Bow Common *Lon* 53-84; rtd 88. *10 Cordelia Street, London E14 6DZ* 0171-515 4681

ROWE, John Nigel. b 24. Ball Coll Ox MA52 BD53 Leeds Univ PhD82. Ely Th Coll 49. **d** 54 **p** 55. V Newchurch-in-Pendle *Blackb* 60-80; V Denholme Gate *Bradf* 80-89; rtd 89. *12 Begwyns Bluff, Clyro, Hereford HR3 5SR* Hay on Wye (01497) 820086

ROWE, Peter Farquharson. b 19. Selw Coll Cam BA41. Westcott Ho Cam 41. **d** 43 **p** 44. V Eltham Park St Luke *S'wark* 65-77; V Ravensthorpe w E Haddon and Holdenby *Pet* 77-84; rtd 84; Perm to Offic *Ex* 84-93; Perm to Offic *Sarum* from 84. *28 Gordon Avenue, Winchester, Hants SO23 0QQ* Winchester (01962) 869806

ROWE, Philip William. b 57. Southn Univ BSc78. Lambeth STh86 Trin Coll Bris 82. **d** 85 **p** 86. C Tooting Graveney St Nic *S'wark* 85-89; V Abbots Leigh w Leigh Woods *Bris* from 89. *The Vicarage, Church Road, Abbots Leigh, Bristol BS8 3QU* Pill (01275) 373996

ROWE, Richard Nigel. b 41. St Pet Coll Saltley DipEd64. St Steph Ho Ox 67. **d** 70 **p** 71. C Acton Green St Pet *Lon* 70-74; C Leigh St Clem *Chelmsf* 74-80; V Leytonstone St Marg w St Columba 80-89; RD Waltham Forest 86-89; V Thaxted from 89. *The Vicarage, Watling Lane, Thaxted, Essex CM6 2QY* Thaxted (01371) 830221

ROWE, Samuel Ernest Allen. b 16. TCD BA39 MA44. **d** 40 **p** 41. I Monart w Ballycarney and Templescobin *C & O* 72-83; rtd 83. *Chestnut Lodge, Bloomfield, Enniscorthy, Co Wexford, Irish Republic* Enniscorthy (54) 33171

ROWE, Stanley Hamilton. b 18. St Pet Hall Ox BA48 MA52. ALCD50. **d** 50 **p** 51. Hd of RE Jo Hampden Sch High Wycombe 67-83; Perm to Offic *Ox* 67-84 and from 86; rtd 83; Hon C Aston Rowant w Crowell *Ox* 84-86. *37 Greenwood Avenue, Chinnor, Oxon OX9 4HW* Kingston Blount (01844) 351278

ROWE, Stephen Mark Buckingham. b 59. SS Mark & Jo Coll Plymouth BA81. Ripon Coll Cuddesdon 83. **d** 86 **p** 87. C Denham *Ox* 86-89; C Aylesbury 89; C Aylesbury w Bierton and Hulcott 89-90; TV 90-93; V Caversham St Jo from 93. *The Vicarage, St John's Road, Caversham, Reading RG4 0AN* Reading (01734) 471814

ROWE, William Alfred. b 11. Open Univ BA72. Bps' Coll Cheshunt 50. **d** 52 **p** 53. V Ermington *Ex* 62-72; R Bratton Clovelly w Germansweek 72-76; rtd 76; Lic to Offic *Ex* from 76. *Pendennis, 64 Dartmouth Road, Paignton, Devon TQ4 5AW* Paignton (01803) 556124

ROWELL, Alan. b 50. Lon Univ BSc71 AKC71. Trin Coll Bris DipTh75. **d** 75 **p** 76. C W Hampstead St Cuth *Lon* 75-78; C Camborne *Truro* 78-81; V Pendeen w Morvah from 81. *The Vicarage, Pendeen, Penzance, Cornwall TR19 7SE* Penzance (01736) 788777

✠ROWELL, Rt Rev Douglas Geoffrey. b 43. CCC Cam BA64 MA68 PhD68. Cuddesdon Coll. **d** 68 **p** 69 **c** 94. Lic to Offic *Ox* 68-94; Asst Chapl New Coll Ox 68-72; Chapl Keble Coll Ox 72-94; Wiccamical Preb Chich Cathl *Chich* 81-94; Suff Bp Basingstoke *Win* from 94. *Little Acorns, Boynes Wood Road, Medstead, Alton, Hants GU34 2EA* Alton (01420) 562925 Fax 561251

ROWELL, Frank. b 22. Chich Th Coll 50. **d** 52 **p** 53. R Otley *St E* 65-83; R Clopton 65-83; R Clopton w Otley, Swilland and Ashbocking 83-88; rtd 88; Perm to Offic *St E* from 92. *37 Riverview, Melton, Woodbridge, Suffolk IP12 1QU* Woodbridge (01394) 385449

ROWELL, William Kevin. b 51. Reading Univ BSc71. Linc Th Coll 78. **d** 80 **p** 81. C Cannock *Lich* 80-83; Ind Chapl 83-86; C Ketley and Oakengates 83-86; R Norton in the Moors 86-93; RD Leek 92-93; P-in-c Minsterley *Heref* from 93; P-in-c Habberley from 93. *The Vicarage, Minsterley, Shrewsbury SY5 0AA* Shrewsbury (01743) 791213

ROWETT, David Peter. b 55. Univ Coll Dur BA76. Ripon Coll Cuddesdon 82. **d** 84 **p** 85. C Yeovil *B & W* 84-88; C Yeovil St Mich 88-89; V Fairfield St Matt *Linc* from 89. *St Matthew's Vicarage, Thirlmere Avenue, Grimsby, S Humberside DN33 3EA* Grimsby (01472) 821183

ROWETT, Mrs Margaret Pettigrew Coupar. b 33. Sarum & Wells Th Coll 84. **dss** 86 **d** 87 **p** 95. Widley w Wymering *Portsm* 86-88; C 87-88; Par Dn Plympton St Mary *Ex* 88-91; rtd 91; NSM St Mewan *Truro* from 94. *Epiphany Cottage, 4 Handra Close, Truro, Cornwall TR1 3SL* Truro (01872) 260076

ROWETT, Brig William Berkeley. b 09. ADipR58 Lon Univ BA61. Westcott Ho Cam 62. **d** 62 **p** 63. Chapl Scilly Is and V St Mary's *Truro* 66-71; V Madron w Morvah 71-80; rtd 80; Perm to Offic *Guildf* from 80; Perm to Offic *Lon* from 81; Perm to Offic *S'wark* from 81. *Three Ducks, 30 The Island, Thames Ditton, Surrey KT7 0SQ* 0181-398 7196

ROWLAND, Barry William. b 59. St Jo Coll Nottm DipThMin95 BA95. **d** 95. C Welling *Roch* from 95. *52 Clifton Road, Welling, Kent DA16 1QD* 0181-304 4179

ROWLAND, Prof Christopher Charles. b 47. Ch Coll Cam BA69 MA73 PhD75. Ridley Hall Cam 72. **d** 75 **p** 76. Hon C Benwell St Jas *Newc* 75-78; Hon C Gosforth All SS 78-79; Dean Jes Coll Cam 79-91; Lic to Offic *Ely* from 79; Prof of Exegesis of H Scripture Ox Univ from 91. *Queen's College, Oxford OX1 4AW* Oxford (01865) 279121

ROWLAND, Ms Dawn Jeannette. b 38. RSCN61 RGN63. S'wark Ord Course. **dss** 84 **d** 87 **p** 94. Par Dn Croydon H Sav *S'wark* 84-89; NSM Riddlesdown from 89. *9 Hartley Hill, Purley, Surrey CR8 4EP* 0181-660 6270

ROWLAND, Derek John. b 47. St Jo Coll Nottm 84. **d** 86 **p** 87. C Porchester *S'well* 86-89; V Fairfield *Liv* from 89. *St John's Vicarage, 19 Lockerby Road, Liverpool L7 0HG* 0151-263 4001

ROWLAND, Derrick Edward. b 31. Univ of Wales (Lamp) BA55 St Cath Soc Ox BA57. Wycliffe Hall Ox. **d** 57 **p** 58. C Reading St Jo *Ox* 57-61; V Smethwick St Matt *Birm* 61-67; V Turnditch *Derby* 67-74; Dir of Educn 74-83; Lic to Offic 83-85; Adult Educn Officer Gen Syn Bd of Educn 85-92. *6 Royal Road, Sutton Coldfield, W Midlands B72 1SP*

ROWLAND, Eric Edward James. b 35. Leeds Univ BA62. Coll of Resurr Mirfield 61. **d** 63 **p** 64. C S Kirkby *Wakef* 63-65; C Headingley *Ripon* 65-70; V Osmondthorpe St Phil 70-79; R Sandy *St Alb* from 79; RD Biggleswade 85-94. *The Rectory, Sandy, Beds SG19 1AQ* Sandy (01767) 680512

ROWLAND, Geoffrey Watson. b 17. **d** 55 **p** 56. C Blackheath Park St Mich *S'wark* 64-89; V W Bromwich St Paul Golds Hill *Lich* 71-76; Chapl Community Relns *Lon* 77-83; C Southall Green St Jo 83; rtd 83; Perm to Offic *Lon* from 83. *3 Amber Court, Longford Avenue, Southall, Middx UB1 3QR* 0181-574 3442

ROWLAND, Henry Rees. b 03. Lon Coll of Div ALCD32 LTh74. **d** 32 **p** 33. V Bournemouth St Mich *Win* 50-69; Chapl Bournemouth and Distr Hosp 51-73; rtd 69; Perm to Offic *St Alb* from 76. *5 The Green, Welwyn, Herts AL6 9EA* Welwyn (01438) 715372

ROWLAND, Robert William. b 51. Birm Univ BA72 Univ of Wales (Cardiff) DPS73. St Mich Coll Llan 72. **d** 74 **p** 75. C Connah's Quay *St As* 74; C Shotton 74-76; C Llanrhos 76-81; V Dyserth and Trelawnyd and Cwm from 81; RD St As from 94. *The Vicarage, Dyserth, Rhyl, Clwyd LL18 6DB* Dyserth (01745) 570750

ROWLAND-SMITH, Albert. b 07. Worc Ord Coll. **d** 57 **p** 58. V Exhall *Cov* 66-71; rtd 71. *Manormead Nursing Home, Tilford Road, Hindhead, Surrey GU26 6RA* Hindhead (01428) 604780

ROWLANDS, Very Rev Daniel John. b 25. Pemb Coll Cam BA49 MA54. Bps' Coll Cheshunt 49. **d** 51 **p** 52. Miss to Seamen 53-75; Asst Gen Sec Miss to Seamen Paternoster R 69-75; R Woodbridge St Mary *St E* 75-82; Dean Gib *Eur* 82-86; Perm to Offic *St D* 86-88; P-in-c Llangrannog and Llandysiliogogo 88-92; RD Glyn Aeron 89-95; rtd 95. *Glyn Coed, Clos Dolwen, Aberporth, Cardigan SA43 2DE* Aberporth (01239) 811042 Fax as telephone

ROWLANDS, Edward. b 18. DipFL90. Kelham Th Coll 37. **d** 44 **p** 44. R Pemberton St Jo *Liv* 64-75; V Haigh 75-83; rtd 83; Perm to Offic *Liv* from 83. *24 Hallbridge Gardens, Up Holland, Skelmersdale, Lancs WN8 0ER* Up Holland (01695) 624362

ROWLANDS, Emyr Wyn. b 42. Univ of Wales (Ban) DipTh70. St Mich Coll Llan 69. **d** 70 **p** 71. C Holyhead w Rhoscolyn *Ban* 70-74; V Bodedern w Llechgynfarwy and Llechylched etc 74-88; R Machynlleth and Llanwrin from 88. *The Rectory, Machynlleth, Powys SY20 8HE* Machynlleth (01654) 702261

ROWLANDS, Forrest John. b 25. LSE BSc(Econ)51. Chich Th Coll 54. **d** 56 **p** 57. R Kingston by Sea *Chich* 62-74; rtd 90. *14 Hazel Close, Thorpe Marriott, Norwich NR8 6YE* Norwich (01603) 261704

ROWLANDS, Graeme Charles. b 53. K Coll Lon BD74 AKC74. St Aug Coll Cant 75. **d** 76 **p** 77. C Higham Ferrers w Chelveston *Pet* 76-79; C Gorton Our Lady and St Thos *Man* 79-81; C Reading H Trin *Ox* 81-89; P-in-c Kentish Town St Silas *Lon* 89-92; V from 92; P-in-c Haverstock Hill H Trin w Kentish Town St Barn from 93. *St Silas's House, 11 St Silas's Place, London NW5 3QP* 0171-485 3727

ROWLANDS, Canon John Henry Lewis. b 47. Univ of Wales (Lamp) BA68 Magd Coll Cam BA70 MA74 Dur Univ MLitt86. Westcott Ho Cam 70. **d** 72 **p** 73. C Abth *St D* 72-76; Chapl St D Coll Lamp 76-79; Youth Chapl *St D* 76-79; Lect Th Univ of Wales (Cardiff) from 79; Dean Faculty of Th Univ of Wales from 91; Dir of Academic Studies St Mich Coll Llan 79-84; Sub-Warden St Mich Coll Llan 84-88; Warden from 88; Warden of Ords *Llan* 85-88; Hon Can Llan Cathl from 90. *The Old Registry, Cardiff Road, Llandaff, Cardiff CF5 1SR* Cardiff (01222) 563116 or 563379

ROWLANDS, Canon Joseph Haydn. b 36. Univ of Wales (Lamp) BA61 DipTh63. **d** 63 **p** 64. C Llanfairisgaer *Ban* 63-68; R Maentwrog w Trawsfynydd 68-75; V Henfynyw w Aberaeron and Llanddewi Aberarth *St D* 75-80; R Trefdraeth

Ban 80-84; V Llandysul *St D* from 84; Hon Can St D Cathl 88-90; Can Res St D Cathl from 90; RD Emlyn from 92. *The Vicarage, Tan y fron, Llandyssul, Dyfed SA44 6DR* Llandyssul (01559) 362277

ROWLANDS, Kenneth Albert. b 41. MA DipAE. NW Ord Course 70. **d** 73 **p** 74. NSM Hoylake *Ches* 73-80; NSM Oxton 80-82; Perm to Offic 82-92; C Stoneycroft All SS *Liv* 92-94; V Mossley Hill St Barn from 94. *St Barnabas's Vicarage, 1 Carsdale Road, Mossley Hill, Liverpool L18 1LZ* 0151-733 1432

ROWLANDS, Mark. b 56. Cranmer Hall Dur 86. **d** 88 **p** 89. C Hattersley *Ches* 88-90; C Offerton 91-94; V Baddiley and Wrenbury w Burleydam from 94. *The Vicarage, The Green, Wrenbury, Nantwich, Cheshire CW5 8EY* Crewe (01270) 780398

ROWLANDS, Michael Huw. b 62. Birm Univ BA85 Univ of Wales (Cardiff) BD88. St Mich Coll Llan 85. **d** 88 **p** 89. C Penarth All SS Llan *St D* 88-91; V Martletwy w Lawrenny and Minwear etc *St D* from 91. *St John's Rectory, Templeton, Narberth, Dyfed SA67 8XX* Narberth (01834) 861412

ROWLANDS, Richard. b 34. St Mich Coll Llan 59. **d** 62 **p** 63. C Tywyn *Ban* 62-65; C Dwygyfylchi (or Penmaenmawr) 65-69; V Carno and Trefeglwys 69-71; CF 71-83. *Rhyd Casadog, Ty'n Lon Po, Holyhead, Gwynedd LL65 3AQ* Gwalchmai (01407) 720843

ROWLANDS, Robert. b 31. Roch Th Coll. **d** 68 **p** 69. C Hooton *Ches* 68-71; V Stretton 71-88; P-in-c Appleton Thorn and Antrobus 87-88; V Stretton and Appleton Thorn from 88. *The Vicarage, Stretton, Warrington WA4 4NT* Warrington (01925) 673276

ROWLANDSON, Gary Clyde. b 50. Lon Univ CertEd72 BA85. Oak Hill Th Coll 82. **d** 85 **p** 86. C Muswell Hill St Jas w St Matt *Lon* 85-89; C Northwood Em 89-93; R Chesham Bois *Ox* from 93. *The Rectory, Glebe Way, Chesham Bois, Amersham, Bucks HP6 5ND* Amersham (01494) 726139

ROWLEY, Christopher Francis Elmes. b 48. St Jo Coll Dur BA70 St Luke's Coll Ex PGCE71. St Steph Ho Ox 76. **d** 78 **p** 79. C Parkstone St Pet w Branksea and St Osmund *Sarum* 78-81; TV 82-85; P-in-c Chard Gd Shep Furnham *B & W* 85-89; P-in-c Dowlishwake w Chaffcombe, Knowle St Giles etc 88-89; R Chard Furnham w Chaffcombe, Knowle St Giles etc 89-91; V Stoke St Gregory w Burrowbridge and Lyng from 91. *The Vicarage, Stoke St Gregory, Taunton, Somerset TA3 6EG* North Curry (01823) 490247

ROWLEY, David Michael. b 39. N Ord Course 87. **d** 90 **p** 91. C Stainland *Wakef* 90-93; V Hayfield *Derby* from 93. *The Vicarage, 7 Station Road, Birch Vale, Stockport, Cheshire SK12 5BP* New Mills (01663) 743350

ROWLEY, Edward Patrick. b 29. Dur Univ BSc52. Coll of Resurr Mirfield 55. **d** 57 **p** 58. R Ampleforth w Oswaldkirk *York* 65-73; Chapl Yorkshire Res Sch for Deaf Doncaster 74-84; R Finningley *S'well* 84-85; P-in-c Elkesley w Bothamsall 87-91; P-in-c Gamston w Eaton and W Drayton 88-91; rtd 91. *116 Lincoln Road, Tuxford, Newark, Notts NG22 0HS* Retford (01777) 871524

ROWLING, Mrs Catherine. b 55. Man Poly BEd77. Westcott Ho Cam 83 NE Ord Course 86. **dss** 86 **d** 87 **p** 94. Gt Ayton w Easby and Newton in Cleveland *York* 86-87; Par Dn 87-89; Chapl Teesside Poly 89-92; Chapl Teesside Univ from 92. *The Vicarage, 10 Allendale Tee, New Marske, Redcar, Cleveland TS11 8HN* Redcar (01642) 484833 or 218121

ROWLING, Richard Francis. b 56. BA. Westcott Ho Cam. **d** 84 **p** 85. C Stokesley *York* 84-87; C Stainton-in-Cleveland 87-90; V New Marske from 90; V Wilton from 92. *The Vicarage, 10 Allendale Tee, New Marske, Redcar, Cleveland TS11 8HN* Redcar (01642) 484833

ROWNTREE, Peter. b 47. St D Coll Lamp BA68 Univ of Wales (Cardiff) MA70. St Steph Ho Ox 70. **d** 72 **p** 73. C Stanwell *Lon* 72-75; C Northolt St Mary 75-79; Chapl Ealing Gen Hosp 79-83 and from 87; Chapl Cherry Knowle Hosp Sunderland 83-87; Chapl Ryhope Hosp Sunderland 83-87. *Ealing Hospital, Uxbridge Road, Southall, Middx UB1 3HW* 0181-967 5130 or 574 2444

ROWSELL, Canon John Bishop. b 25. Jes Coll Cam BA49 MA55. Ely Th Coll 49. **d** 51 **p** 52. C Hackney Wick St Mary of Eton w St Aug *Lon* 51-55; C Is of Dogs Ch Ch and St Jo w St Luke 55-56; C Reading St Mary V *Ox* 56-59; V Hightown *Wakef* 59-69; R Harlton *Ely* 69-81; V Haslingfield 69-81; V Methwold from 81; RD Feltwell from 81; R Northwold from 82; Hon Can Ely Cathl from 84. *The Vicarage, Globe Street, Methwold, Thetford, Norfolk IP26 4PQ* Methwold (01366) 728892

ROWSON, Frank. b 40. CEng67 MIStructE67. Sarum & Wells Th Coll 87. **d** 90 **p** 91. NSM Ore Ch Ch *Chich* from 90. *149 Priory Road, Hastings, E Sussex TN34 3JD* Hastings (01424) 439802

ROWSTON, Geoffrey. b 34. Sarum Th Coll 59. **d** 62 **p** 63. C Ashburton w Buckland-in-the-Moor *Ex* 62-65; C Basingstoke

Win 65-68; V Netley 68-78; V W End 78-87; R Alderbury and W Grimstead *Sarum* 87-91; P-in-c Whiteparish 89-91; TR Alderbury Team from 91. *The Rectory, 5 The Copse, Alderbury, Salisbury SP5 3BL* Salisbury (01722) 710229

✠**ROWTHORN, Rt Rev Jeffery William.** b 34. Societas Liturgica MNAAL MHSA MHSGBI Ch Coll Cam BA57 MA62 Or Coll Ox BLitt72. Berkeley Div Sch DD87 Cuddesdon Coll 61 Union Th Sem (NY) BD61. d 62 p 63 c 87. C Woolwich St Mary w H Trin *S'wark* 62-65; R Garsington *Ox* 65-68; USA 68-93; Chapl and Dean Union Th Sem NY 68-73; Assoc Prof Past Th Yale and Berkeley Div Schs 73-87; Suff Bp Connecticut 87-93; American Episc Bp Eur from 93; Bp in Charge Convocation of American Chs in Eur from 94; Asst Bp Eur from 95. *clo 23 Avenue George V, 75008 Paris, France* France (33) 47 20 17 92 Fax 47 23 95 30

✠**ROXBURGH, Rt Rev James William.** b 21. St Cath Coll Cam BA42 MA46. Wycliffe Hall Ox 42. d 44 p 45 c 83. C Folkestone H Trin w Ch Ch *Cant* 44-47; C Handsworth St Mary *Birm* 47-50; V Bootle St Matt *Liv* 50-56; V Drypool St Columba w St Andr and St Pet *York* 56-65; V Barking St Marg *Chelmsf* 65-73; P-in-c Barking St Patr 65-73; Hon Can Chelmsf Cathl 72-77; V Barking St Marg w St Patr 73-75; TR 75-77; Adn Colchester 77-83; Suff Bp Barking 83-84; Area Bp Barking 84-90; rtd 90; Asst Bp Liv from 91. *53 Preston Road, Southport, Merseyside PR9 9EE* Southport (01704) 542927

ROXBY, Gordon George. b 39. Lon Univ BSc61. Coll of Resurr Mirfield 61. d 63 p 64. C Fleetwood *Blackb* 63-66; C Kirkham 66-68; V Runcorn St Jo Weston *Ches* 68-78; R Moston St Chad *Man* 78-86; V Bury St Pet from 86; AD Bury from 86. *St Peter's Vicarage, St Peter's Road, Bury, Lancs BL9 9QZ* 0161-764 1187

ROY, David Brian. b 25. MIA ARIBA Leeds Coll of Art DipArch50. d 88 p 89. Hon C Burrough Hill Pars *Leic* 88-90; Hon C Framland Deanery 88 and 90-91; TV Melton Gt Framland 91-93; TV Melton Mowbray 93-95; rtd 95. *16 Somerby Road, Pickwell, Melton Mowbray, Leics LE14 2RA* Somerby (01664) 77775

ROYALL, Preb Arthur Robert. b 19. Lambeth MA Qu Coll Birm 51. d 53 p 54. P-in-c Bromley St Mich *Lon* 64-71; R Poplar All SS w St Frideswide 64-71; P-in-c Poplar St Sav w St Gabr and St Steph 68-71; RD Tower Hamlets 68-76; R Poplar 71-73; P-in-c Mile End Old Town H Trin 73-76; P-in-c Bethnal Green St Barn 73-75; Preb St Paul's Cathl 73-86; R Bow w Bromley St Leon 73-76; Clergy Appts Adv 76-85; Perm to Offic *Nor* from 77; Perm to Offic *Ely* from 78; rtd 86; Perm to Offic *Lon* 86-91. *Carmelite House, 10 Pit Lane, Swaffham, Norfolk PE37 7DA* Swaffham (01760) 723300

ROYCROFT, James Gordon Benjamin. b 26. CITC. d 56 p 57. I Drung w Castleterra *K, E & A* 67-83; I Larah and Lavey 67-83; I Drumkeeran w Templecarne and Muckross *Clogh* 83-91; rtd 91. *Boa Island, Kesh, Enniskillen, Co Fermanagh BT93 1TE*

ROYDEN, Charles. b 60. Wycliffe Hall Ox BA86. d 87 p 88. C Bidston *Ches* 87-91; V N Brickhill and Putnoe *St Alb* 91-92; V Bedf St Mark from 93. *The Vicarage, Calder Rise, North Brickhill, Bedford MK41 7UY* Bedford (01234) 358699 or 342613

ROYDEN, Eric Ramsay. b 29. St Deiniol's Hawarden 75. d 77 p 78. Hon C Tranmere St Paul w St Luke *Ches* 77-81; C Eastham 81; V New Brighton All SS 81-95; NSM from 95; rtd 95. *14 Kinglass Road, Bebington, Wirral, Merseyside L63 9AJ*

ROYDEN, Ross Eric. b 55. Nottm Univ MTh82. Lon Bible Coll BA77 Wycliffe Hall Ox 79. d 81 p 82. C Moreton *Ches* 81-84; Chapl Bedf Coll of HE *St Alb* 84-93; R Banchory *Ab* from 93; R Kincardine O'Neil from 93. *The Rectory, High Street, Banchory, Kincardineshire AB31 3TB* Banchory (01330) 822783

ROYDS, John Caress. b 20. Qu Coll Cam BA47 MA52. d 74 p 75. C Kettering St Andr *Pet* 74-76; P-in-c Loddington w Cransley 76; R Pet 76-81; Dir of Educn 76-81; V Northn St Jas 81-85; CMS 85-86; Pakistan 85-86; rtd 87. *16B Donaldson Road, Salisbury SP1 3AD* Salisbury (01722) 332293

ROYLE, Antony Kevan. b 50. FIA76 Lon Univ BSc71. Trin Coll Bris 76. d 79 p 80. C Chell *Lich* 79-82; C Leyland St Andr *Blackb* 82-86; V Blackb Sav from 86; Chapl Blackb R Infirmary & Park Lee Hosp 86-95; Chapl E Lancs Hospice 86-95. *Walton Rectory, 42 Redwood Drive, Aylesbury, Bucks HP21 7TN* Aylesbury (01296) 394834

ROYLE, Michael Arthur. b 38. Univ of Wales (Ban) BSc61 Lon Univ DipTh63. St Jo Coll Nottm 81. d 82 p 83. C Boulton *Derby* 82-85; C Belper 85-87; P-in-c Smalley from 87; P-in-c Morley from 87; RD Heanor 89-94. *The Vicarage, 80 Main Road, Smalley, Ilkeston, Derbyshire DE7 6EF* Derby (01332) 880380

ROYLE, Canon Peter Sydney George. b 34. K Coll Lon BD57 AKC57. d 58 p 59. C St Helier *S'wark* 58-62; Australia 62-68; P-in-c Sydenham St Phil *S'wark* 69-72; V Leigh Park *Portsm* 72-85; RD Havant 77-82; V S w N Hayling from 85; Hon Can Portsm Cathl from 95. *The Vicarage, 34 Church Road, Hayling Island, Hants PO11 0NT* Hayling Island (01705) 462914

ROYLE, Canon Roger Michael. b 39. AKC61 Lambeth Hon MA90. d 62 p 63. C Portsea St Mary *Portsm* 62-65; C St Helier *S'wark* 65-68; Succ S'wark Cathl 68-71; Warden Eton Coll Dorney Par Project *Ox* 71-74; Conduct Eton Coll Windsor 74-79; Lic to Offic *S'wark* 79-90; Chapl Ld Mayor Treloar Coll Alton 90-92; Hon C Froyle and Holybourne *Win* 90-92; Hon Can and Chapl S'wark Cathl *S'wark* from 93. *clo Southwark Cathedral, Montague Close, London SE1 9DA* 0171-407 3708 Fax 430 6085

ROYLE, Canon Stanley Michael. b 43. K Coll Lon BD69 AKC69 Man Univ MA75. St Aug Coll Cant 71. d 72 p 73. C Timperley *Ches* 72-76; Perm to Offic 76-81; R Milton Abbas, Hilton w Cheselbourne etc *Sarum* 81-86; Dir of Ords from 86; Adv on Continuing Minl Educn from 86; Can and Preb Sarum Cathl from 89. *Three Firs, Blandford Road, Sturminster Marshall, Wimborne, Dorset BH21 4AF* Sturminster Marshall (01258) 857326

ROYSTON-BALL, Peter. b 38. St Mich Coll Llan 61. d 65 p 66. C Dartford St Alb *Roch* 65-67; C Chislehurst Annunciation 67-69; C St Marylebone Ch Ch w St Paul *Lon* 69-75; Hon C New Windsor *Ox* 75-78; Perm to Offic *S'wark* 75-88; C Leic St Eliz Nether Hall *Leic* 88-94; V Belvedere St Aug *Roch* from 94. *The Vicarage, St Augustine's Road, Belvedere, Kent DA17 5HH* 0181-311 6307

RUCK, John. b 47. Bris Univ BSc68. Selly Oak Coll DipRE87 All Nations Chr Coll 77. d 80 p 83. Indonesia 80-86 and 87-91; Perm to Offic *Birm* 86-87 and from 91. *94 Gristhorpe Road, Birmingham B29 7SL* 0121-472 7460

RUDD, Canon Charles Robert Jordeson. b 34. TCD BA56 MA65 BD65. d 57 p 58. C Lurgan Redeemer *D & D* 57-61; C Lisburn Ch Ch Cathl *Conn* 61-62; C Willowfield *D & D* 62-66; I Drumgooland w Kilcoo 66-75; I Moira 75-95; Can Belf Cathl 90-95; I Magheraly w Annaclone *D & D* from 95. *46 Kilmacrew Road, Banbridge, Co Down BT32 4EP* Banbridge (018206) 23655

RUDD, Colin Richard. b 41. AKC64. d 65 p 66. C N Stoneham *Win* 65-70; V Rotherwick, Hook and Greywell 70-74; R Hook w Greywell 74-78; Toc H 78-89; Lic to Offic *Ox* 83-89; V Buckland from 89; V Littleworth from 89; R Pusey from 89. *The Vicarage, Buckland, Faringdon, Oxon SN7 8QN* Buckland (0136787) 618

RUDD, Canon Julian Douglas Raymond. b 19. Leeds Univ BA40. Coll of Resurr Mirfield 40. d 42 p 43. R Old Alresford *Win* 60-70; RD Alresford 60-70; V Warw St Mary *Cov* 70-76; V Warw St Mary w St Nic 76-83; TR Warw 83-84; RD Warw 77-79; rtd 84. *East Close, Church Walk, Penny Street, Sturminster Newton, Dorset DT10 1DF* Sturminster Newton (01258) 73283

RUDD, Robert Arthur (Bob). b 33. ALCD60. d 60 p 61. V Bickersham *Liv* 65-72; Asst Chapl HM Pris Liv 72-73; Chapl HM Pris Birm 73-78; Chapl HM Pris Parkhurst 78-86; Chapl HM Pris Camp Hill 86-92; Chapl St Mary's Hosp Newport 92-95; rtd 95. *The Elms, 13 Horsebridge Hill, Newport, Isle of Wight PO30 5TJ* Isle of Wight (01983) 524415

RUDDLE, Canon Donald Arthur (Don). b 31. Linc Th Coll 64. d 66 p 67. C Kettering SS Pet and Paul *Pet* 66-70; V Earlham St Anne *Nor* 70-79; V E Malling *Roch* 79-95; RD Malling 84-93; Hon Can Roch Cathl 88-95; Chapl Boulogne w Calais *Eur* from 95. *16 rue du Calvaire, Enquin-les-Mines, 6214 Pas de Calais, France* France (33) 21 93 69 46

RUDDOCK, Brian John. b 45. Dur Univ BA66 Nottm Univ MEd91. Westcott Ho Cam 67. d 69 p 70. C Ross *Heref* 69-72; C Kettering SS Pet and Paul *Pet* 72-75; P-in-c Colchester St Steph *Chelmsf* 75-77; TR Colchester St Leon, St Mary Magd and St Steph 77-84; R March St Pet *Ely* 84-89; R March St Mary 84-89; RD March 87-89; Dioc Unemployment Officer *Sheff* 89-94. *36 Sandygate, Wath-upon-Dearne, Rotherham, S Yorkshire S63 7LW* Rotherham (01709) 873254 or 698583 Fax 698016

RUDDOCK, Canon Charles Cecil. b 28. TCD DBS. TCD Div Sch. d 57 p 58. C Newtownards *D & D* 69-72; Australia 72-83; I Mallow Union *C, C & R* 83-89; I Fenagh w Myshall, Aghade and Ardoyne *C & O* 89-95; Preb Ossory and Leighlin Cathls 92-95; rtd 95. *2 Osborne Terrace, London Road, Thrupp, Stroud, Glos GL5 2BJ* Stroud (01453) 731697

RUDDOCK, Canon Edgar Chapman. b 48. St Jo Coll Dur BA70 DipTh73 MA76. d 74 p 75. C Birm St Geo *Birm* 74-78; R 78-83; Swaziland 83-91; TR Stoke-upon-Trent *Lich* from 91. *The Rectory, St Peter's Close, Stoke-on-Trent ST4 1LP* Stoke-on-Trent (01782) 45287

RUDDOCK, Canon Kenneth Edward. b 30. TCD BA52 QUB MTh79. CITC 53 Div Test. d 53 p 54. C Ballymena *Conn* 53-56; C Belf St Thos 56-60; I Tomregan w Drumlane *K, E & A* 60-68; I Belf St Luke *Conn* 68-80; Miss to Seamen from 80; I Whitehead w Islandmagee *Conn* from 80; Can Lisburn Cathl from 90; RD Carrickfergus 90-94; Dioc Info Officer from 90. *The Rectory, 74 Cable Road, Whitehead, Carrickfergus, Co Antrim BT38 9SJ* Whitehead (01960) 373300

RUDDOCK

RUDDOCK, Leonard William. b 58. CITC 91. d 94 p 95. NSM Roscrea w Kyle, Bourney and Corbally *L & K* from 94. *Short Corville, Roscrea, Co Tipperary, Irish Republic* Roscrea (505) 22034

RUDDOCK, Canon Norman Trevor. b 35. TCD BA57 MA60 HDipEd62. TCD Div Sch 58. d 58 p 59. C Belf St Steph *Conn* 58-60; C Dub Ch Ch Leeson Park *D & G* 60-63; Perm to Offic 63-73; USA 70-72; I Killanne *C & O* 73-81; I Castlepollard and Oldcastle w Loughcrewe etc *M & K* 84-93; Can Meath 92-93; I Wexford w Ardcolm and Killurin *C & O* from 93. *The Rectory, Park, Wexford, Irish Republic* Wexford (53) 43013

RUDDOCK, Reginald Bruce. b 55. AGSM77. Chich Th Coll. d 83 p 84. C Felpham w Middleton *Chich* 83-86; C Portsea St Mary *Portsm* 86-88; P-in-c Barnes St Mich *S'wark* from 88. *St Michael's Vicarage, 39 Elm Bank Gardens, London SW13 0NX* 0181-876 5230

RUDDY, Canon Denys Henry. b 22. Jes Coll Ox BA48 MA53. Linc Th Coll 48. d 50 p 51. R Longworth and Hinton Waldrist *Ox* 58-77; RD Vale of White Horse 68-75; Warden of Readers 70-87; Chapl Abingdon St Nic 77-87; Hon Can Ch Ch 79-87; RD Abingdon 79-80; rtd 87; Perm to Offic *Ox* from 87; Perm to Offic *Pet* from 87. *32 Coberley Close, Downhead Park, Milton Keynes MK15 9BJ* Milton Keynes (01908) 604719

RUDIGER, David John. b 42. MIMgt91. Ox Min Course CBTS94. d 94. NSM Woughton *Ox* from 94. *32 Forest Rise, Eaglestone, Milton Keynes MK6 5EU* Milton Keynes (01908) 679691

RUDKIN, Simon David. b 51. Bradf Univ BA74 K Coll Lon BD77 AKC77. Coll of Resurr Mirfield 77. d 78 p 79. C Flixton St Mich *Man* 78-81; C Atherton 81-84; V Lever Bridge 84-91; P-in-c Pennington w Lindal and Marton *Carl* from 91. *The Vicarage, Main Road, Swarthmoor, Ulverston, Cumbria LA12 0SE* Ulverston (01229) 583174

RUDLAND, Patrick Ivor. b 20. ACP62 Lon Univ CertEd62. Tyndale Hall Bris 56. d 59 p 60. C Tunbridge Wells St Jas *Roch* 59-62; Lic to Offic 62-66; Hon C Sevenoaks St Nic 66-69; Hon C Tonbridge SS Pet and Paul 69-85; Hon C Shipbourne 85-88; Perm to Offic from 88. *Flat 4, 12 Dry Hill Road, Tonbridge, Kent TN9 1LX* Tonbridge (01732) 351694

RUDMAN, David Walter Thomas. b 48. Lon Univ DipTh70 BD72. Oak Hill Th Coll 68. d 72 p 73. C Plymouth St Jude *Ex* 72-75; C Radipole *Sarum* 76-77; Warden of St Geo Ho Braunton from 77; R Georgeham *Ex* from 88. *The Rectory, Newberry Road, Georgeham, Braunton, Devon EX33 1JS* Croyde (01271) 890809

RUDMAN, Thomas Peter William. b 22. Oak Hill Th Coll 60. d 62 p 63. V Lowestoft Ch Ch *Nor* 67-73; V Stapenhill w Cauldwell *Derby* 73-81; V Sutton le Marsh *Linc* 81-87; RD Calcewaithe and Candleshoe 85-87; rtd 87; Perm to Offic *Win* from 87. *1 Morley Close, Burton, Christchurch, Dorset BH23 7LA* Christchurch (01202) 476255

RUEHORN, Eric Arthur. b 33. St Aid Birkenhead 58. d 61 p 62. C Harpurhey Ch Ch *Man* 61-65; V Roughtown 65-74; V Hawkshaw Lane from 74. *St Mary's Vicarage, Bolton Road, Hawkshaw, Bury, Lancs BL8 4JN* Tottington (01204) 882955

RUFF, Brian Chisholm. b 36. FCA70 Lon Univ BD66. Oak Hill Th Coll 63. d 67 p 68. C Cheadle *Ches* 67-71; Educn and Youth Sec CPAS 72-76; V New Milverton *Cov* 76-90; Min Westbourne Ch Ch CD *Win* from 90. *43 Branksome Dene Road, Bournemouth BH4 8JW* Bournemouth (01202) 762164

RUFF, Michael Ronald. b 49. K Coll Lon BD72 AKC72. St Aug Coll Cant 72. d 73 p 74. C Old Shoreham *Chich* 73-76; Chapl Ellesmere Coll Shropshire 77-81; Chapl Grenville Coll Bideford 81-87; Chapl Stamford Sch Lincs from 87. *12 Redcot Gardens, Stamford, Lincs PE9 1DL* Stamford (01780) 66567

RUFFLE, John Leslie. b 43. ALCD66. d 66 p 67. C Eastwood *S'well* 66-70; C Keynsham w Queen Charlton *B & W* 70-75; P-in-c Weston-super-Mare Em 75; TV Weston-super-Mare Cen Par 75-84; V Yatton Moor 84-91; TR from 91. *The Rectory, 1 Well Lane, Yatton, Bristol BS19 4HT* Yatton (01934) 832184

RUFFLE, Leslie Norman. b 12. Tyndale Hall Bris 49. d 50 p 51. R Chawleigh w Cheldon *Ex* 70-77; R Eggesford 70-77; rtd 77; Perm to Offic *Ex* from 86. *16 Fairfield, Sampford Peverell, Tiverton, Devon EX16 7TD* Tiverton (01884) 821035

RUFFLE, Peter Cousins. b 19. Lon Univ BD42. ALCD42. d 42 p 43. Prin CA Wilson Carlile Coll of Evang 66-74; Can Res Blackb Cathl *Blackb* 74-78; V Meole Brace *Lich* 78-85; rtd 85; Perm to Offic *Win* from 85; Perm to Offic *Portsm* from 85. *84 Queen's Crescent, Stubbington, Fareham, Hants PO14 2QQ* Stubbington (01329) 663791

RUFLI, Alan John. b 63. TCD BA89. d 91 p 92. C Donaghcloney w Waringstown *D & D* 91-94; C Knock from 94. *3 Sandown Park South, Belfast BT5 6HE* Belfast (01232) 653370

RUGG, Andrew Philip. b 47. Kent Univ BA82. Sarum & Wells Th Coll 83. d 85 p 86. C Harlesden All So *Lon* 85-90; TV Benwell Team *Newc* from 90. *56 Dunholme Road, Newcastle upon Tyne NE4 6XE* 0191-273 5356

RUMALSHAH, Inayat. b 14. d 37 p 38. India 37-73; C Hazlemere *Ox* 74-76; C Wooburn 76-79; rtd 79. *40 Highfield Road, Bourne End, Bucks SL8 5BG* Bourne End (01628) 525186

RUMBALL, Frank Thomas. b 43. Sarum & Wells Th Coll 72. d 74 p 75. C Bromyard *Heref* 74-78; TV Ewyas Harold w Dulas 78-79; TV Ewyas Harold w Dulas, Kenderchurch etc 79-81; C Minsterley 81-82; P-in-c Eye, Croft w Yarpole and Lucton 82-91; R Condover w Frodesley, Acton Burnell etc from 91. *The Vicarage, Condover, Shrewsbury SY5 7AA* Shrewsbury (01743) 872251

RUMBALL, Dr William Michael. b 41. Surrey Univ BSc63 Birm Univ PhD66 BA75 MIM66 MINucE73. Wycliffe Hall Ox 78. d 80 p 81. C S Molton, Nymet St George, High Bray etc *Ex* 80-83; V S Hetton w Haswell *Dur* 83-90; V S Wingfield and Wessington *Derby* from 90. *The Vicarage, South Wingfield, Alfreton, Derbyshire DE55 7LJ* Alfreton (01773) 832484

RUMBLE, Miss Alison Merle. b 49. Surrey Univ BSc71. Trin Coll Bris BA89. d 89 p 94. Par Dn Willesden Green St Gabr *Lon* 89-91; Par Dn Cricklewood St Gabr and St Mich 92; Par Dn Herne Hill *S'wark* 92-94; C from 94. *1 Finsen Road, London SE5 9AX* 0171-274 3663

RUMBOLD, Bernard John. b 43. d 73 p 75. Papua New Guinea 73-76; C Gt Burstead *Chelmsf* 76-77; Chapl RAF 77-93; Chapl HM Pris Featherstone 93-95; C Wordsley *Worc* from 95. *St Paul's House, Hawbush Road, Brierley Hill, W Midlands DY5 3NL*

RUMBOLD, Graham Charles. b 44. Open Univ BA79. S Dios Minl Tr Scheme 76. d 79 p 80. NSM Widley w Wymering *Portsm* 79-82; Chapl Cynthia Spencer Unit Manfield Hosp from 82; Lic to Offic *Pet* from 82; NSM Weston Favell from 93. *3 Calstock Close, Northampton NN3 3BA* Northampton (01604) 27389

RUMENS, Canon John Henry. b 21. AKC49. d 50 p 51. R Salisbury St Edm *Sarum* 59-72; RD Salisbury 69-72; Can and Preb Sarum Cathl 72-85; R Trowbridge H Trin 72-79; P-in-c Sturminster Marshall 79-83; V 83-85; rtd 85. *20 Constable Way, Salisbury SP2 8LN* Salisbury (01722) 334716

RUMENS, Ms Katharine Mary. b 53. UEA BEd76. Westcott Ho Cam 90. d 92 p 94. Par Dn E Ham w Upton Park St Alb *Chelmsf* 92-94; C from 94. *281 Central Park Road, London E6 3AF* 0181-470 0012

RUMING, Canon Gordon William. b 27. Kelham Th Coll 45. d 52 p 53. R Calstock *Truro* 61-92; Hon Can Truro Cathl 79-92; RD E Wivelshire 85-91; rtd 92. *3 Derry Avenue, Plymouth PL4 6BH* Plymouth (01752) 661986

RUMSEY, Ian Mark. b 58. Van Mildert Coll Dur BSc79 St Jo Coll Dur BA89. Cranmer Hall Dur 87. d 90 p 91. C Dalston *Carl* 90-94; C Wreay 92-94; TV Cockermouth w Embleton and Wythop from 94. *The Vicarage, 14 Harrot Hill, Cockermouth, Cumbria CA13 0BL* Cockermouth (01900) 824383

RUMSEY, Canon Philip Charles. b 21. Bps' Coll Cheshunt 59. d 61 p 62. R Knebworth *St Alb* 66-76; V Luton Lewsey St Hugh 76-81; Hon Can St Alb 81-87; R High Wych and Gilston w Eastwick 81-87; rtd 87. *1 Folly Drive, Tupsley, Hereford HR1 1NE* Hereford (01432) 279987

RUMSEY, Thomas Philip. b 14. Selw Coll Cam BA37 MA41. St Aug Coll Cant 33. d 38 p 39. R Skelsmergh w Selside and Longsleddale *Carl* 70-79; rtd 79; Perm to Offic *Carl* from 79. *Heversham House, Heversham, Milnthorpe, Cumbria LA7 7ER* Milnthorpe (015395) 63634

✠RUNCIE of Cuddesdon, Rt Rev and Rt Hon Lord (Robert Alexander Kennedy). b 21. MC45 PC80. BNC Ox BA48 MA48 Hon DD80 Cam Univ Hon DD81 Univ of the South (USA) Hon DD81 Keele Univ Hon DLitt81 Liv Univ Hon DLitt83 Herts Univ Hon DLitt90. W Indies United Th Coll Hon DCL84 Trin Coll Toronto Hon DD86 Westcott Ho Cam 48. d 50 p 51 c 70. C Gosforth All SS *Newc* 50-52; Chapl Westcott Ho Cam 53-54; Vice-Prin 54-56; Dean Trin Hall Cam 56-60; V Cuddesdon *Ox* 60-70; Prin Cuddesdon Coll 60-70; Can and Preb Linc Cathl *Linc* 69-70; Bp St Alb 70-80; Abp Cant 80-91; Hon Fell BNC Ox from 78; FKC from 81; rtd 91; Asst Bp St Alb from 91. *26A Jennings Road, St Albans, Herts AL1 4PD* St Albans (01727) 848021

RUNCORN, David Charles. b 54. BA77 Ox Poly DipPsych88. St Jo Coll Nottm 77. d 79 p 80. C Wealdstone H Trin *Lon* 79-82; Chapl Lee Abbey 82-89; C Ealing St Steph Castle Hill *Lon* 89-90; V from 90. *St Stephens Vicarage, Sherborne Gardens, London W13 8AT* 0181-810 4929

RUNCORN, Canon Dennis Brookes. b 22. Ch Coll Cam BA47 MA52. Ridley Hall Cam 47. d 49 p 50. V Shortlands *Roch* 67-80; RD Beckenham 73-80; Hon Can Roch Cathl 78-87; V Shorne 80-87; rtd 87; Perm to Offic *Derby* from 87. *14 Hollowood Avenue, Littleover, Derby DE23 6JD* Derby (01332) 765859

RUNDLE, Mrs Beryl Rosemary. b 28. Bris Univ BA49 CertEd50. S Dios Minl Tr Scheme 83. dss 86 d 87. Tangmere *Chich* 86-87; Hon Par Dn 87-92; Boxgrove 86-87; Hon Par Dn

87-92; Hon Par Dn Eastbourne St Sav and St Pet from 92. *2 College Court, Spencer Road, Eastbourne, E Sussex BN21 4PE* Eastbourne (01323) 417433

RUNDLE, Nicholas John. b 59. Southn Univ BA80. St Steph Ho Ox. **d** 84 **p** 85. C E Preston w Kingston *Chich* 84-87; Chapl RAF 87-91; Australia from 91. *48 Arthur Street, Tranmere, Adelaide, S Australia 5073* Adelaide (8) 332-2743

RUNDLE, Penelope Anne. b 36. St Hugh's Coll Ox MA59 Lon Univ DAA64. S Dios Minl Tr Scheme 85. **d** 88 **p** 94. Hon Par Dn Mere w W Knoyle and Maiden Bradley *Sarum* 88-91; Hon Par Dn Upper Stour 91-94; Hon C from 94. *2 The Common, Kilmington, Warminster, Wilts BA12 6QY* Warminster (01985) 844610

RUPP, Ernest Walter. b 25. Westmr Coll Lon CertEd55. St Jo Coll Nottm 84. **d** 85 **p** 86. NSM Leic Ascension *Leic* 85-89; Chapl Glenfield Hosp Leic 86-89; R Barkestone w Plungar, Redmile and Stathern *Leic* 89-94; rtd 94. *13 Burgins Lane, Waltham on the Wolds, Melton Mowbray, Leics LE14 4AD* Waltham-on-the-Wolds (01664) 78824

RUSCHMEYER, Henry Cassell. b 44. Union Coll NY BA66 Bank St Coll of Ed NY MEd73 NY Univ MA88. Gen Th Sem (NY) MD78. **d** 78 **p** 79. USA 78-89; NSM Wilton Place St Paul *Lon* from 89. *Flat 7, 33 Wilton Place, London SW1X 8SH* 0171-235 3437

RUSCOE, John. b 12. Man Univ BA35. Lich Th Coll 35. **d** 37 **p** 38. R Redruth *Truro* 57-70; R Mawnan 70-84; rtd 84. *34 Tregenver Road, Falmouth, Cornwall TR11 2QW* Falmouth (01326) 315300

RUSCOE, Canon John Ernest. b 32. Dur Univ BA57. Qu Coll Birm 57. **d** 59 **p** 60. C Jarrow St Paul *Dur* 59-63; C Whitburn 63-65; V S Hylton from 65; Hon Can Dur Cathl from 85. *The Vicarage, South Hylton, Sunderland SR4 0QB* 0191-534 2325

RUSHER, James Victor Francis. b 28. RMA. Ridley Hall Cam 58. **d** 60 **p** 61. V Summerfield *Birm* 66-71; V Knowle 71-82; Perm to Offic 82-93; Chapl Parkway Hosp Solihull 85-93; rtd 93. *4 Froxmere Close, Solihull, W Midlands B91 3XG* 0121-705 4514

RUSHFORD, Harold Tilney. b 08. Qu Coll Birm 55. **d** 56 **p** 57. V Dawdon *Dur* 59-83; rtd 84. *Dalden, 18 Windsor Drive, Houghton le Spring, Tyne & Wear DH5 8JS* 0191-584 9682

RUSHFORTH, Colin Stephen. b 53. Chich Th Coll 74. **d** 77 **p** 78. C Moulsecoomb *Chich* 77-79; C Rumboldswyke 79-81; C Whyke w Rumboldswhyke and Portfield 81-82; V Friskney *Linc* 82-84; P-in-c Thorpe St Peter 82-84; TV Leic H Spirit *Leic* 84-87; Chapl Leic R Infirmary from 87. *Leicester Royal Infirmary, Infirmary Square, Leicester LE1 5WW* Leicester (0116) 254 1414/258 5487

RUSHFORTH, Richard Hamblin. b 40. Keble Coll Ox BA62 MA71. Chich Th Coll 62. **d** 64 **p** 65. C St Leonards Ch Ch *Chich* 64-79; Org Sec Fellowship of St Nic 79-81; V Portslade St Nic and St Andr from 81; Min Portslade Gd Shep Mile Oak CD 88-89. *The Vicarage, South Street, Portslade, Brighton BN41 2LE* Brighton (01273) 418090

RUSHTON, James David. b 39. Dur Univ BA61. Cranmer Hall Dur DipTh64. **d** 64 **p** 65. C Upper Armley *Ripon* 64-67; C Blackpool Ch Ch *Blackb* 67-70; V Preston St Cuth 70-79; V Denton Holme *Carl* from 79. *St James's Vicarage, Goschen Road, Carlisle CA2 5PF* Carlisle (01228) 515639 or 810616

RUSHTON, Ms Janet Maureen (Jan). b 46. Keele Univ BA68 Leic Univ PGCE69. Wycliffe Hall Ox BTh94. **d** 94. C Harrow St Mary *Lon* from 94. *The Flat, 6 Crown Street, Harrow, Middx HA2 0HR* 0181-864 7003

RUSHTON, Malcolm Leslie. b 47. Bris Univ BSc69 Birm Univ PhD72 Fitzw Coll Cam BA74. Ridley Hall Cam 72. **d** 75 **p** 76. C Cullompton *Ex* 75-79; Chapl Univ Coll *Lon* 79-87; Chapl R Veterinary Coll 87-90; Chapl R Free Medical Sch 87-90. *191A Kentish Town Road, London NW5 2AE* 0171-482 4077

RUSHTON, Philip William. b 38. Open Univ BA87. Clifton Th Coll 62. **d** 65 **p** 66. C Brixton St Paul *S'wark* 65-67; C Aldridge *Lich* 67-69; C Bushbury 69-71; Chapl Nat Nautical Sch Portishead 71-72; Chapl RAF 72-79; P-in-c Bolton on Swale *Ripon* 79-87; P-in-c The Cowtons 80-82; V 82-89; CF (TA) from 88; R Litcham, Kempston, Lexham, Mileham, Beeston etc *Nor* 89-95; P-in-c Tittleshall w Godwick 93-95; R Litcham w Kempston, E & W Lexham, Mileham etc from 95. *The Rectory, Pound Lane, Litcham, King's Lynn, Norfolk PE32 2QR* Fakenham (01328) 701223

RUSHTON, Mrs Susan Elizabeth. b 44. Univ of Wales (Cardiff) BA65. Bris Sch of Min 83. **dss** 86 **d** 87 **p** 94. Westbury-on-Trym H Trin *Bris* 86-91; Hon Par Dn 87-91; C Wotton St Mary *Glouc* 91-94; Chapl Bris Gen Hosp from 94; P-in-c Frampton Cotterell *Bris* from 94. *The Rectory, Rectory Road, Frampton Cotterell, Bristol BS17 2BP* Winterbourne (01454) 772112

RUSHTON, Mrs Valerie Elizabeth Wendy. b 40. Birm Univ BSocSc62 DPS87. W Midl Minl Tr Course 86. **d** 89 **p** 94. C Nuneaton St Nic *Cov* 89-93; C Stockingford from 93. *51 Merlin Avenue, Nuneaton, Warks CV10 9JY* Chapel End (01203) 396343

RUSK, Canon Frederick John. b 28. QUB BA50. **d** 53 **p** 54. C Ballymoney *Conn* 53-56; C Belf St Nic 56-59; I Broomhedge 59-65; RE Insp 64-66; I Belf St Simon 65-78; I Ballymena w Ballyclug 78-88; I Belf St Nic from 88; Preb Conn Cathl 84-86; Treas 86-90; Prec 90; Chan from 90. *15 Harberton Park, Belfast BT9 6TW* Belfast (01232) 667753

RUSK, Michael Frederick. b 58. Cam Univ BA MA. Westcott Ho Cam 81. **d** 84 **p** 85. C Altrincham St Geo *Ches* 84-87; Chapl Collingwood and Grey Coll Dur 87-90; C-in-c Neville's Cross St Jo CD from 90. *St John's Vicarage, The Avenue, Durham DH1 4DX* 0191-384 4260

RUSS, Timothy John (Tim). b 41. AKC64. Sarum Th Coll 66. **d** 66 **p** 67. C Walthamstow St Pet *Chelmsf* 66-70; C Epping St Jo 70-73; C Stepney St Dunstan and All SS *Lon* 73-75; Youth Officer 75-79; Tutor YMCA Nat Coll Walthamstow 79-84; Hon C St Botolph Aldgate w H Trin Minories *Lon* 82-89; Selection Sec ACCM 84-89; Dir St Marylebone Healing and Counselling Cen 89-92; Gen Sec Inst of Religion and Medicine 89-92; Hon C Hoxton St Anne w St Columba *Lon* 90-92; P-in-c St Dennis *Truro* from 92; Par Development Adv from 92. *The Rectory, Carne Hill, St Dennis, St Austell, Cornwall PL26 8AZ* St Austell (01726) 822317

RUSSELL, Adrian Camper. b 45. Chich Th Coll 79. **d** 81 **p** 82. C Marton *Blackb* 81-84; C Haslemere *Guildf* 84-85; V Hartlepool H Trin *Dur* 85-89; P-in-c Cornforth 89-94; R Auchterarder *St And* from 94; R Muthill from 94. *St Kessog's Rectory, High Street, Auchterarder, Perthshire PH3 1AD* Auchterarder (01764) 662525 Fax as telephone

✠RUSSELL, Rt Rev Anthony John. b 43. St Chad's Coll Dur BA65 Trin Coll Ox DPhil71. Cuddesdon Coll 65. **d** 70 **p** 71 c 88. C Hilborough w Bodney *Nor* 70-73; P-in-c Preston-on-Stour w Whitchurch *Cov* 73-76; P-in-c Atherstone on Stour 73-76; V Preston on Stour and Whitchurch w Atherstone 77-88; Can Th Cov Cathl 77-88; Chapl Arthur Rank Cen 73-82; Dir 83-88; Chapl to The Queen 83-88; Area Bp Dorchester *Ox* from 88. *Holmby House, Sibford Ferris, Banbury, Oxon OX15 5RG*

RUSSELL, Brian Kenneth. b 50. Trin Hall Cam BA73 MA76 Birm Univ MA77 PhD83. Cuddesdon Coll 74. **d** 76 **p** 77. C Redhill St Matt *S'wark* 76-79; Dir of Studies NE Ord Course 79-83; P-in-c Merrington *Dur* 79-83; Dir of Studies and Lect Linc Th Coll 83-86; Perm to Offic *S'wark* 86-93; Selection Sec and Sec Cttee for Th Educn ACCM 86-91; Selection Sec ABM 91-93; Bp's Dir for Min *Birm* from 93. *43 Cartland Road, Birmingham B30 2SD* 0121-444 7641 or 427 5141 Fax 428 1114

RUSSELL, Brian Robert. b 61. QUB BA TCD DipTh85. **d** 85 **p** 86. C Dub Drumcondra w N Strand *D & G* 85-87; C Carrickfergus *Conn* 87-90; I Kilmegan w Maghera *D & D* from 90. *50 Main Street, Dundrum, Newcastle, Co Down BT33 0LY* Dundrum (0139675) 225

RUSSELL, David John. b 57. Sarum & Wells Th Coll BTh94. **d** 94 **p** 95. C Glouc St Geo w Whaddon *Glouc* from 94. *3 Rylands, Gloucester GL4 0QA* Gloucester (01452) 500716

RUSSELL, David Robert. b 43. Brasted Th Coll 66 Sarum Th Coll 68. **d** 70 **p** 71. C Leintwardine *Heref* 70-73; C Bridgnorth w Tasley 73-75; Australia from 75. *125 Hampton Road, South Fremantle, W Australia 6162* Perth (9) 335-9732

RUSSELL, Canon Derek John. b 30. St Pet Hall Ox BA54 MA58. Qu Coll Birm 54. **d** 56 **p** 57. Chapl HM Pris Wormwood Scrubs 63-65 and 71-89; Chapl HM Pris Stafford 65-69; Pentonville 70; SE Regional Chapl 74-81; Chapl HM Rem Cen Latchmere Ho 74-77; Asst Chapl Gen of Pris 81-83; Dep 83-90; Hon Can Cant Cathl *Cant* 86-90; rtd 90. *25 Pier Avenue, Whitstable, Kent CT5 2HQ* Canterbury (01227) 276654

RUSSELL, Eric. b 19. Dur Univ LTh42 BA48 MA53 Man Univ BD52 Nottm Univ MPhil87. Oak Hill Th Coll 38. **d** 42 **p** 43. Hd of Relig Studies Sheff Coll of Educn 67-78; Lic to Offic *Sheff* 67-78; Lect Liv Bible Coll 78-88; rtd 88. *16A St Paul's Street, Southport, Merseyside PR8 1LZ* Southport (01704) 534797

RUSSELL, Eric Watson. b 39. FCA73. Clifton Th Coll 66. **d** 69 **p** 70. C Kinson *Sarum* 69-73; C Peckham St Mary Magd *S'wark* 73-77; TV Barking St Marg w St Patr *Chelmsf* 77-82; V Lozells St Paul and St Silas *Birm* 82-95; RD Aston 89-94; P-in-c Barston from 95. *20 Slater Road, Bentley Heath, Solihull, W Midlands B93 8AG* Knowle (01564) 776864

RUSSELL, Ven Harold Ian Lyle. b 34. Lon Coll of Div ALCD59 BD60. **d** 60 **p** 61. C Iver *Ox* 60-63; C Fulwood *Sheff* 63-67; V Chapeltown 67-75; RD Tankersley 73-75; V Nottm St Jude *S'well* 75-89; Hon Can S'well Minster 88-89; Adn Cov from 89. *9 Armorial Road, Coventry CV3 6GH* Coventry (01203) 417750

RUSSELL, Herbert Mark. b 12. Dur Univ LTh38. Trin Coll Bris 35. **d** 38 **p** 39. V Danehill *Chich* 67-77; rtd 77; Hon C Glynde, W Firle and Beddingham *Chich* 77-80; Perm to Offic from 80.

RUSSELL

Pelham House, London Road, Cuckfield, Haywards Heath, W Sussex RH17 5EU   Haywards Heath (01444) 417954

RUSSELL, Mrs Isabel. b 31. Lightfoot Ho Dur 58. **dss** 71 **d** 87 **p** 94. Gt Barr *Lich* 71-74; E Farleigh and Coxheath *Roch* 75-84; Ogwell and Denbury *Ex* 85-87; Hon Par Dn 87-91; Sub-Chapl HM Pris Dartmoor 89-91; rtd 91. *Church Cottage, Manaton Green, Newton Abbot, Devon TQ13 9UJ*

RUSSELL, Mrs Janet Mary. b 53. Univ of Wales BSc74 BArch76. Ox Min Course 91. **d** 94. C Watlington w Pyrton and Shirburn *Ox* from 94. *Timbers, Pyrton, Watlington, Oxford OX9 5AP*   Watlington (01491) 613022

RUSSELL, Canon John Arthur. b 29. AKC62. **d** 63 **p** 64. C Fareham H Trin *Portsm* 63-67; R Greatham w Empshott 67-79; V Ham St Andr *S'wark* 79-87; P-in-c Battersea St Luke 87-92; V from 92; Hon Can S'wark Cathl from 95. *52 Thurleigh Road, London SW12 8UD*   0181-673 6506

RUSSELL, John Bruce. b 56. Ripon Coll Cuddesdon DipMin95. **d** 95. C Newport Pagnell w Lathbury and Moulsoe *Ox* from 95. *3 Castle Meadow Close, Newport Pagnell, Bucks MK16 9EJ*   Newport Pagnell (01908) 613161

RUSSELL, John Graham. b 35. G&C Coll Cam BA58 MA62. Westcott Ho Cam 59. **d** 61 **p** 62. C Durleigh *B & W* 61-66; C Bridgwater St Mary w Chilton Trinity 61-66; C Far Headingley St Chad *Ripon* 66-72; P-in-c Leeds St Matt Lt Lon 72-79; V Rowley Regis *Birm* 79-84; V Hall Green Ascension from 84. *The Vicarage, 592 Fox Hollies Road, Birmingham B28 9DX*   0121-777 3689

RUSSELL, Canon Jonathan Vincent Harman. b 43. K Coll Lon 68. **d** 69 **p** 70. C Addington *Cant* 69-73; C Buckland in Dover w Buckland Valley 73-76; P-in-c Selling 76-85; P-in-c Throwley w Stalisfield and Otterden 79-85; R Selling w Throwley, Sheldwich w Badlesmere etc from 85; Hon Min Can Cant Cathl 83-94; RD Ospringe 90-95; Hon Can Cant Cathl from 94. *The Rectory, Selling, Faversham, Kent ME13 9RD*   Canterbury (01227) 752221

RUSSELL, Jonathan Wingate (Jon). b 55. BSc BA DMS DIM. St Jo Coll Nottm 81. **d** 84 **p** 85. C Southsea St Jude *Portsm* 84-87; P-in-c Shorwell w Kingston 87-92; V from 92; P-in-c Gatcombe 87-92; R from 92; P-in-c Chale 89-92; R from 92. *The Vicarage, 5 Northcourt Close, Shorwell, Newport, Isle of Wight PO30 3LD*   Chillerton (0198370) 246

RUSSELL, Lloyd George Winkler. b 19. Hatf Coll Dur LTh45 BA49. **d** 45 **p** 46. Perm to Offic *Roch* 58-81 and from 85; Jamaica 82-85; rtd 85; Perm to Offic *S'wark* from 85. *39 Pembroke Road, Bromley BR1 2RT*   0181-460 1498

RUSSELL, Martin Christopher. b 48. St Jo Coll Dur BA70. Coll of Resurr Mirfield 72. **d** 74 **p** 75. C Huddersfield SS Pet and Paul *Wakef* 74-75; C Huddersfield St Pet 75-77; Trinidad and Tobago 78-85; V S Crosland *Wakef* from 85; P-in-c Helme from 85. *The Vicarage, Church Lane, South Crosland, Huddersfield HD4 7DB*   Huddersfield (01484) 661080

RUSSELL, Michael John. b 38. Clifton Th Coll 68. **d** 68 **p** 69. C Cranham Park CD *Chelmsf* 68-70; C Bucknall and Bagnall *Lich* 70-77; P-in-c Tintwistle *Ches* 77-79; V 79-86; New Zealand from 86. *201 Cambridge Avenue, Ashurst, New Zealand*   Ashurst (63) 268543

RUSSELL, Morris Charles. b 14. AKC36. **d** 37 **p** 38. C Tottenham St Phil *Lon* 37-39; C Winchmore Hill H Trin 39-41; CF (EC) 41-46; V Thornham w Titchwell *Nor* 46-51; R Newmarket St Mary *St E* 51-59; R Ipswich St Matt 59-66; New Zealand from 67. *19 Paisley Street, Howick, New Zealand*   Auckland (9) 534-3116

RUSSELL, Neil. b 47. Nottm Univ CPS81 Ox Univ DipApTh95. E Midl Min Tr Course 78. **d** 81 **p** 82. NSM Wyberton *Linc* 81-84; C 84-85; V Frampton 85-93; Agric Chapl and Countryside Officer from 88; P-in-c Stamford All SS w St Jo from 93. *26 Hazel Grove, Stamford, Lincs PE9 2HJ*   Stamford (01780) 56942

RUSSELL, Mrs Noreen Margaret. b 39. Man Univ BA60 Lon Univ PGCE61 BD66. W Midl Minl Tr Course 90. **d** 91 **p** 94. NSM Swynnerton and Tittensor *Lich* from 91. *40 Old Road, Barlaston, Stoke-on-Trent ST12 9EQ*   Stone (01785) 817780

RUSSELL, Norman Atkinson. b 43. Chu Coll Cam BA65 MA69 Lon Univ BD70. Lon Coll of Div 67. **d** 70 **p** 71. C Clifton Ch Ch w Em *Bris* 70-74; C Enfield Ch Ch Trent Park *Lon* 74-77; R Harwell w Chilton *Ox* 77-84; P-in-c Gerrards Cross 84-88; P-in-c Fulmer 85-88; R Gerrards Cross and Fulmer from 88. *The Rectory, Oxford Road, Gerrards Cross, Bucks SL9 7DJ*   Gerrards Cross (01753) 883301   Fax 892177

RUSSELL, Miss Pamela. b 34. SRN SCM. Coll of Resurr Mirfield 85. **dss** 86 **d** 87. Barnburgh w Melton on the Hill *Sheff* 86-93; Hon Par Dn 87-93; Chapl Asst Grimsby Distr Gen Hosp from 93. *Grimsby District General Hospital, Scartho Road, Grimsby, S Humberside DN33 2BA*   Grimsby (01472) 874111

RUSSELL, Paul Selwyn. b 38. ALCD61. **d** 61 **p** 62. C Gillingham St Mark *Roch* 61-64; SAMS 64-84; Chile, Peru and Bolivia 64-84; V Brinsworth w Catcliffe *Sheff* 84-91; R Brinklow *Cov* from 91; R Harborough Magna from 91; V Monks Kirby w Pailton and Stretton-under-Fosse from 91. *The Rectory, 31 Coventry Road, Brinklow, Rugby, Warks CV23 0NE*   Rugby (01788) 832274

RUSSELL, Philip John Seymour. b 1900. Wells Th Coll 22. **d** 23 **p** 24. rtd 67; Perm to Offic *Glas* from 68. *High Portling, Dalbeattie, Kirkcudbrightshire DG5 4PZ*   Rockcliffe (0155663) 359

RUSSELL, Ralph Geoffrey Major. b 19. St Aug Coll Cant 47 Sarum Th Coll 48. **d** 50 **p** 51. V New Bradwell w Stantonbury *Ox* 62-73; P-in-c Linslade 74-75; V 75-87; rtd 87; Perm to Offic *Ox* from 87; Perm to Offic *Pet* from 89. *60 Cheneys Walk, Bletchley, Milton Keynes MK3 6JY*   Milton Keynes (01908) 641998

RUSSELL, Richard Alexander. b 44. Univ of Wales (Abth) BA65 McMaster Univ Ontario MA67 Bris Univ MA73 PGCE74 MEd76. Trin Coll Bris DipHE81. **d** 82 **p** 83. C Hartlepool St Paul *Dur* 82-85; P-in-c Bath Widcombe *B & W* 85-88; V from 88. *Widcombe Vicarage, 65 Prior Park Road, Bath BA2 4NL*   Bath (01225) 310580

RUSSELL, Roger Geoffrey. b 47. Worc Coll Ox BA69 MA73. Cuddesdon Coll 70. **d** 72 **p** 73. C Anlaby Common St Mark *York* 72-75; C Wilton Place St Paul *Lon* 75-86; R Lancing w Coombes *Chich* from 86. *The Vicarage, 63 Manor Road, Lancing, W Sussex BN15 0EY*   Lancing (01903) 753212

RUSSELL, William Douglas. b 16. LCP72 Open Univ BA73. Worc Ord Coll 57. **d** 59 **p** 60. V Stanton Drew *B & W* 61-82; rtd 82; Perm to Offic *B & W* from 82. *42 Keward Avenue, Wells, Somerset BA5 1TS*   Wells (01749) 677203

RUSSELL, William Warren. b 52. QUB BSocSc74. CITC 74. **d** 77 **p** 78. C Agherton *Conn* 77-79; C Lisburn Ch Ch Cathl 79-83; I Magheadroll *D & D* from 83; RD Dromore from 93. *18 Church Road, Ballynahinch, Co Down BT24 8LP*   Ballynahinch (01238) 562289

RUSSELL-SMITH, Miss Joy Dorothea. b 29. St Anne's Coll Ox BA52 MA55 K Coll Lon BD67. Ridley Hall Cam 83. **dss** 85 **d** 87 **p** 94. Witney *Ox* 85-87; Par Dn 87-88; NSM Saffron Walden w Wendens Ambo and Littlebury *Chelmsf* from 88; rtd 92. *1 The Meadow, Littlebury Green, Saffron Walden, Essex CB11 4XE*   Royston (01763) 838856 or Saffron Walden (01799) 525303

RUSSELL-SMITH, Mark Raymond. b 46. New Coll Edin MTh91. St Jo Coll Dur BA71 Cranmer Hall Dur DipTh72. **d** 72 **p** 73. C Upton (or Overchurch) *Ches* 72-75; C Deane *Man* 75-77; UCCF Travelling Sec 77-80; Lic to Offic *York* 78-81; BCMS 81-92; Kenya 81-92; P-in-c Slaidburn *Bradf* from 92. *The Rectory, Slaidburn, Clitheroe, Lancs BB7 3ER*   Slaidburn (01200) 446238

RUSSON, Joseph Kenneth. b 21. St Aid Birkenhead 56. **d** 59 **p** 60. V Burnley St Jas *Blackb* 65-91; Chapl Burnley Gen Hosp 65-91; rtd 91. *1 Hillingdon Road, Burnley, Lancs BB10 2EG*   Burnley (01282) 456948

✠**RUSTON, Rt Rev John Harry Gerald.** b 29. SS Coll Cam BA52 MA56. Ely Th Coll 52. **d** 54 **p** 55 **c** 83. C Leic St Andr *Leic* 54-57; OGS from 55; Tutor Cuddesdon Coll 57-61; C Cuddesdon *Ox* 57-61; S Africa 62-91; Suff Bp Pretoria 83-91; Bp St Helena from 91. *Bishopsholme, PO Box 62, St Helena*   St Helena (290) 4471

RUTHERFORD, Anthony Richard (Tony). b 37. Culham Coll Ox TCert62 Lon Univ DipAdEd68 Sussex Univ MA77. S'wark Ord Course 83. **d** 86 **p** 87. Hon C Tunbridge Wells St Luke *Roch* 86-88; C Bromley SS Pet and Paul 88-90; V Wragby *Linc* 90-94; Asst Min Officer 90-94; V Penge Lane H Trin *Roch* from 94. *Holy Trinity Vicarage, 64 Lennard Road, London SE20 7LX*   0181-778 7258

RUTHERFORD, Arthur Ernest. b 26. Saltley Tr Coll Birm CertEd53 Loughb Coll of Educn DipEd54. Sarum & Wells Th Coll 91. **d** 92 **p** 93. NSM Lilliput *Sarum* from 92. *Kirinyaga, 8 Jennings Road, Poole, Dorset BH14 8RY*   Poole (01202) 748777

RUTHERFORD, Daniel Fergus Peter. b 65. Hatf Coll Dur BA86 CertEd87. Ridley Hall Cam 88. **d** 90 **p** 91. C Harold Wood *Chelmsf* 90-94; C Hove Bp Hannington Memorial Ch *Chich* from 94. *47 Nevill Avenue, Hove, E Sussex BN3 7NB*   Brighton (01273) 739144

RUTHERFORD, David Lesslie Calderwood. b 29. Master Mariner 55 Open Univ BA76. Local NSM Course 89. **d** 91 **p** 92. Dioc Moderator for Reader Tr *St E* 90-95; NSM Acton w Gt Waldingfield from 91. *18 Gotsfield Close, Acton, Sudbury, Suffolk CO10 0AS*   Sudbury (01787) 374169

RUTHERFORD, Ian William. b 46. Univ of Wales (Lamp) BA68. Cuddesdon Coll 68. **d** 70 **p** 71. C Gosforth All SS *Newc* 70-72; C Prestbury *Glouc* 73-76; Chapl RN 76-93; TV Redruth w Lanner and Treleigh *Truro* 93-94; V Paulsgrove *Portsm* from 94. *St Michael's Vicarage, Hempsted Road, Portsmouth PO6 4AS*   Cosham (01705) 375912

RUTHERFORD, Janet Elizabeth. b 37. S'wark Ord Course 86. d 89. NSM Plaistow St Mary *Roch* 89-90; NSM Linc St Botolph by Bargate *Linc* 91-94. *Holy Trinity Vicarage, 64 Lennard Road, London SE20 7LX* 0181-778 7258

RUTHERFORD, Canon John Allarton Edge. b 10. SS Coll Cam BA32 MA36. Westcott Ho Cam 32. d 33 p 34. V Walsham le Willows *St E* 70-83; P-in-c 83-85; Hon Can St E Cathl 82-85; rtd 84; Perm to Offic *St E* from 85. *Jalla Halli, Hinderclay, Diss, Norfolk IP22 1HN* Diss (01379) 898948

RUTHERFORD, Canon John Bilton. b 23. Qu Coll Birm 49. d 52 p 53. V Walker *Newc* 66-74; V Benwell St Jas 74-81; Hon Can Newc Cathl 80-90; V Lesbury w Alnmouth 81-90; RD Alnwick 86-89; rtd 90. *68 Worcester Way, Woodlands Park, Wideopen, Newcastle upon Tyne NE5 5JE* 0191-236 4785

RUTHERFORD, Peter George. b 34. Nor Ord Course 73. d 76 p 77. NSM New Catton Ch Ch *Nor* 76-79; NSM Eaton 79-80; NSM Nor St Steph 81-93; Perm to Offic 93-95; NSM Earlham St Mary from 95. *30 The Close, Norwich NR1 4DZ* Norwich (01603) 624386

RUTHERFORD, Peter Marshall. b 57. St Andr Univ MTheol81. CITC 83. d 83 p 84. C Stormont *D & D* 83-85; CF from 85. *c/o MOD (Army), Bagshot Park, Bagshot, Surrey GU18 5PL* Bagshot (01276) 471717 Fax 412834

RUTLEDGE, Canon Christopher John Francis. b 44. Lon Univ BSc67 Clare Coll Cam PGCTh70 Lon Inst of Educn FETC80 Univ of Wales MPhil94. Sarum Th Coll 67. d 70 p 71. C Birm St Pet *Birm* 70-73; C Calne and Blackland *Sarum* 73-76; P-in-c Derry Hill 76-78; V 78-81; P-in-c Talbot Village 81-82; V from 82; Hon Can Sarum Cathl from 95. *The Vicarage, 20 Alton Road, Bournemouth BH10 4AE* Bournemouth (01202) 529349

RUTLEDGE, Francis George. b 62. DipTh Ulster Poly BA83 TCD BTh90. d 86 p 87. C Holywood *D & D* 86-89; C Willowfield 89-91; I Kilmakee *Conn* from 91. *Kilmakee Rectory, 60 Killeaton Park, Dunmurry, Belfast BT17 9HE* Belfast (01232) 610505

RUTT, Canon Denis Frederic John. b 17. Kelham Th Coll 34. d 41 p 42. R Kirkley *Nor* 61-71; RD Lothingland 65-71; R N Lynn w St Marg and St Nic 71-76; Can Res and Prec Lich Cathl *Lich* 76-83; rtd 83; Perm to Offic *Bradf* from 83. *28 St Philip's Way, Burley in Wharfedale, Ilkley, W Yorkshire LS29 7EW* Burley-in-Wharfedale (01943) 863778

RUTT-FIELD, Benjamin John. b 48. Chich Th Coll. d 90 p 91. C Wickford and Runwell *Chelmsf* 90-94; V Goodmayes St Paul from 94. *St Paul's Vicarage, 20 Eastwood Road, Ilford, Essex IG3 8XA* 0181-590 6596

RUTTER, Canon Allen Edward Henry (Claude). b 28. Qu Coll Cam BA52 Cam Univ DipAgr53 Qu Coll Cam MA56. Cranmer Hall Dur DipTh58. d 59 p 60. C Bath Abbey w St Jas *B & W* 59-60; C E Dereham w Hoe *Nor* 60-64; R Cawston 64-69; Chapl Cawston Coll 64-69; P-in-c Felthorpe w Haveringland 64-69; S Africa 69-73; P-in-c Over and Nether Compton, Trent etc *Sarum* 73-80; RD Sherborne 77-87; P-in-c Oborne w Poyntington 79-80; P-in-c Queen Thorne from 80; Can and Preb Sarum Cathl from 86. *The Rectory, Trent, Sherborne, Dorset DT9 4SL* Marston Magna (01935) 851049

RUTTER, John Edmund Charles. b 53. Qu Coll Cam MA76. All Nations Chr Coll DipMiss82 St Jo Coll Nottm MA93. d 93 p 94. C Penge St Jo *Roch* from 93. *19 Cottingham Road, London SE20 7PU* 0181-676 9992

RUTTER, Martin Charles. b 54. Wolv Poly BSc75 Southn Univ BTh81. Sarum & Wells Th Coll 76. d 79 p 80. C Cannock *Lich* 79-82; C Uttoxeter w Bramshall 82-86; V W Bromwich St Jas from 86; P-in-c W Bromwich St Paul Golds Hill from 89; RD W Bromwich from 94. *St James's Vicarage, 151A Hill Top, West Bromwich, W Midlands B70 0SB* 0121-556 0805

RYALL, John Francis Robert. b 30. New Coll Ox BA52 MA57. Westcott Ho Cam 52. d 54 p 55. R Frating w Thorrington *Chelmsf* 67-73; R Gt Yeldham 74-76; P-in-c Lt Yeldham 75-76; R Gt w Lt Yeldham 76-80; P-in-c Thorley *Portsm* 80-82; P-in-c Shalfleet 80-82; V 82-95; V Calbourne w Newtown 82-95; rtd 95. *Weald House, Main Road, Wellow, Yarmouth, Isle of Wight PO41 0SZ* Calbourne (01983) 760783

RYALL, Michael Richard. b 36. TCD BA58 MA65 HDipEd66. TCD Div Sch Div Test58. d 58 p 59. C Dub St Geo *D & G* 58-62; CF 62-65 and 68-90; CF (TAVR) 67-68; C Dub Rathmines *D & G* 65-66; Dungannon Sec Sch 66-68; R Yardley Hastings, Denton and Grendon etc *Pet* from 90. *The Rectory, Yardley Hastings, Northampton NN7 1EL* Yardley Hastings (01604) 696223

RYAN, David Peter. b 64. Aston Univ BSc86. Linc Th Coll BTh94. d 94 p 95. C Horsforth *Ripon* from 94. *7 Featherbank Walk, Horsforth, Leeds LS18 4QN* Leeds (0113) 258 9567

RYAN, Graham William Robert (Gregg). b 51. CITC 90 St Jo Coll Nottm CertCS93. d 93 p 94. NSM Clonsast w Rathangan,

Thomastown etc *M & K* from 93. *Millicent Hall, Millicent South, Sallins, Naas, Co Kildare, Irish Republic* Sallins (45) 879464 Fax as telephone

RYAN, James Francis. b 47. Surrey Univ BSc. Trin Coll Bris DipHE St Jo Coll Nottm. d 83 p 84. C Littleover *Derby* 83-86; C Chipping Sodbury and Old Sodbury *Glouc* 86-89; V Pype Hayes *Birm* from 89. *St Mary's Vicarage, 1162 Tyburn Road, Birmingham B24 0TB* 0121-373 3534

RYAN, Roger John. b 47. Lon Bible Coll BA79 Oak Hill Th Coll 79. d 80 p 81. C Luton St Fran *St Alb* 80-83; R Laceby *Linc* 83-88; V Summerstown *S'wark* from 88. *St Mary's Vicarage, 46 Wimbledon Road, London SW17 0UQ* 0181-946 9853

RYAN, Stephen John. b 49. Univ of Wales (Swansea) BA70 Bris Univ DipTh73. Sarum & Wells Th Coll 70. d 73 p 74. C Llantrisant *Llan* 73-77; V Treherbert w Treorchy 77-89; Youth Chapl 80-85; RD Rhondda 84-89; V Aberdare St Fagan from 89. *St Fagan's Vicarage, Trecynon, Aberdare, M Glam CF44 8LL* Aberdare (01685) 881435

RYCROFT, Stanley. b 30. Bris Univ MEd81 Open Univ BA84. Sarum Th Coll 56. d 59 p 60. C Earley St Bart *Ox* 59-62; Chapl Whittlebury Sch Towcester 62-63; C Christchurch *Win* 63-67; Chapl Durlston Court Sch Barton on Sea 67-71; Chapl Millfield Jun Sch Somerset 71-75; Chapl Wellington Sch Somerset 75-83; V Silksworth *Dur* from 84. *St Matthew's Vicarage, Silksworth Road, Sunderland SR3 2AA* 0191-521 1167

RYDER, Derek Michael. b 36. St Cath Coll Cam BA60 MA64. Tyndale Hall Bris 61. d 63 p 64. C Hampreston *Sarum* 63-66; Asst Chapl Brentwood Sch Essex 66-72; Chapl Ipswich Sch 72-77; Home Sec CMJ 77-87; TR Wexcombe *Sarum* from 87; RD Pewsey from 89. *The Vicarage, Shalbourne, Marlborough, Wilts SN8 3QH* Marlborough (01672) 870421

RYDER, John Merrick. b 55. Natal Univ BA75 BA77. St Pet Coll Natal 81. d 82 p 83. C Africa 84-88; St Helena 88-91; C Havant *Portsm* 91-95; P-in-c Godshill from 95. *The Vicarage, Godshill, Ventnor, Isle of Wight PO38 3HY* Isle of Wight (01983) 840272

RYDER, Canon Lisle Robert Dudley. b 43. Selw Coll Cam BA68 MA72 Birm Univ DPS76. Sarum Th Coll 69. d 71 p 72. C Lowestoft St Marg *Nor* 71-75; Chapl Asst Oxon Area HA 76-79; C Littlehampton St Jas *Chich* 79-85; C Wick 79-85; C Littlehampton St Mary 79-85; Chapl Worc R Infirmary from 85; Hon Can Worc Cathl *Worc* from 89. *1 Holywell Hill, Worcester WR2 5NZ, or Worcester Royal Infirmary, Castle Street, Worcester WR1 3AS* Worcester (01905) 763333

RYDINGS, Donald. b 33. Jes Coll Ox BA57 MA61. Linc Th Coll 57. d 59 p 60. C Poulton-le-Fylde *Blackb* 59-62; Staff Sec SCM Ox 62-66; C Ox St Mary V *Ox* 62-66; C-in-c Bourne End St Mark CD 66-74; R Hedsor and Bourne End 74-76; P-in-c Gt Missenden w Ballinger and Lt Hampden 76-93; RD Wendover 79-89; V Gt Missenden w Ballinger and Lt Hampden from 93. *The Vicarage, 2 Walnut Close, Great Missenden, Bucks HP16 9AA* Great Missenden (01494) 862447

RYE, David Ralph. b 33. AKC59. d 60 p 61. C Barnham Broom w Kimberley, Bixton etc *Nor* 64-76; TV Barnham Broom 76-82; TR 82-95; P-in-c Reymerston w Cranworth, Letton, Southburgh etc 85-95; rtd 95. *5A Yarmouth Road, Norwich NR7 0EA*

RYECART, John Reginald. b 07. AKC32. St Steph Ho Ox 32. d 33 p 34. V Gt Sampford w Hempstead *Chelmsf* 60-74; rtd 74. *100 Fronks Road, Dovercourt, Essex CO12 3RY* Harwich (01255) 507370

RYELAND, John. b 58. K Coll Lon BD80 AKC80. Linc Th Coll 80. d 81 p 82. C Enfield St Jas *Lon* 81-84; C Coulsdon St Andr *S'wark* 84-87; C-in-c Ingrave St Steph CD *Chelmsf* from 87. *St Stephen's House, St Stephen's Crescent, Ingrave, Essex CM13 2AT* Brentwood (01277) 214623

RYLAND, Colin William. b 16. TD52. MRCVS. St Steph Ho Ox 61. d 62 p 63. R Church w Chapel Brampton *Pet* 66-73; V Wellingborough St Barn 73-83; rtd 83; Chapl St Chad's Coll Dur from 94. *13 St John's Road, Durham DH1 4NU* 0191-386 9638

RYLANDS, Mrs Amanda Craig. b 52. CertEd75. All Nations Chr Coll DipMiss82 Trin Coll Bris DipHE85. dss 85 d 87 p 94. Chippenham St Andr w Tytherton Lucas *Bris* 85-87; Par Dn Stockport St Geo *Ches* 87; NSM 88-91; Par Dn Acton & Worleston, Church Minshull & Wettenhall 91-94; C from 94. *St Mary's Vicarage, Chester Road, Acton, Nantwich, Cheshire CW5 8LG* Nantwich (01270) 628864

RYLANDS, Mark James. b 61. SS Hild & Bede Coll Dur BA83. Trin Coll Bris BA87. d 87 p 88. C Stockport St Geo *Ches* 87-91; V Acton & Worleston, Church Minshull & Wettenhall from 91. *St Mary's Vicarage, Chester Road, Acton, Nantwich, Cheshire CW5 8LG* Nantwich (01270) 628864

RYLANDS, Canon Thomas Michael. b 18. CCC Cam BA39 MA46. Wells Th Coll. d 47 p 48. R Malpas and Threapwood

Ches 68-85; RD Malpas 70-84; Hon Can Ches Cathl 72-85; rtd 85; Perm to Offic *Ches* from 85. *Haughton Thorn, Tarporley, Cheshire CW6 9RN* Tarporley (01829) 260215

RYLE, Denis Maurice. b 16. OBE70. St Aid Birkenhead 35. **d** 39 **p** 40. Dep Asst Chapl Gen 65-73; P-in-c Latimer w Flaunden *Ox* 73-85; rtd 85. *5 Church Close, Wheldrake, York YO4 6DP* York (01904) 898124

RYLEY, Canon Patrick Macpherson. b 30. Pemb Coll Ox BA54 Lon Univ BD56. Clifton Th Coll 54. **d** 56 **p** 57. Kenya 68-75; V Lynn St Jo *Nor* 76-92; V King's Lynn St Jo the Ev 92-95; RD Lynn 78-83; Hon Can Nor Cathl 90-95; rtd 95. *106 Little Lane, Ilkley, W Yorkshire LS29 8JJ* Ilkley (01943) 817026

RYLEY, Timothy Patrick (Tim). b 64. Man Univ BA86. St Jo Coll Nottm DTS92 MA93. **d** 93 **p** 94. C Pendlebury St Jo *Man* from 93. *41 Danesway, Swinton, Manchester M27 1JS* 0161-736 3163

RYMER, David John Talbot. b 37. Chich Th Coll 63. **d** 66 **p** 67. C Tuffley *Glouc* 66-69; Rhodesia 69-79; P-in-c S Kensington St Jude *Lon* 79-82; V 82-88; P-in-c Ambergate *Derby* 88-91; P-in-c Heage 88-91; P-in-c Ambergate and Heage 91; R from 91. *The Vicarage, 65 Derby Road, Ambergate, Belper, Derbyshire DE56 2GD* Ambergate (01773) 852072

RYRIE, Alexander Crawford. b 30. Edin Univ MA52 BD55 Glas Univ MLitt75. Union Th Sem (NY) STM56. **d** 83 **p** 83. Hon C Edin St Mary *Edin* 83-85; R Jedburgh 85-95; rtd 95. *The Rectory, 46 Castlegate, Jedburgh, Roxburghshire TD8 6BB* Jedburgh (01835) 863892

RYRIE, Mrs Isabel. b 31. ABPsS73 CPsychol88 Edin Univ MA51 Glas Univ MEd70. Moray Ho Edin DipRE52. **d** 89 **p** 94. Bp's Dn *Edin* 89-91; NSM Edin St Mary from 91. *The Rectory, 46 Castlegate, Jedburgh, Roxburghshire TD8 6BB* Jedburgh (01835) 863892

S

SABAN, Ronald Graham Street. b 28. Bps' Coll Cheshunt 60. **d** 62 **p** 63. C Maidstone St Martin *Cant* 62-66; C Croydon St Sav 66; rtd 94. *34 Kingsway, Caversham Park Village, Reading RG4 0RA* Reading (01734) 479454

SABELL, Michael Harold. b 42. Open Univ BA78 Surrey Univ MSc. Sarum & Wells Th Coll 77. **d** 80 **p** 81. NSM Shirley *Win* 80-82; Chapl to the Deaf 81-82; NSM Finham *Cov* 82-85; Chapl to the Deaf 82-85; Chapl to the Deaf *Sheff* 85-89; Chapl to the Deaf *Lich* from 89. *55 Bustleholme Lane, West Bromwich, W Midlands B71 3BD* 0121-588 6417

SABOURIN, Robert. b 21. TCD. **d** 52 **p** 53. V Guernsey St Matt *Win* 57-60; Public Preacher 60-80; Perm to Offic 80-86; rtd 86; Chapl Rouen and Le Havre *Eur* 86-87; Chapl Menton 87-90; Lic to Offic from 90. *Anchorage, 21 rue du 11 Novembre, 27690 Léry, France*

SADDINGTON, Peter David. b 42. Cranmer Hall Dur. **d** 84 **p** 85. C Tudhoe Grange *Dur* 84-86; C Monkwearmouth St Andr 86-88; V Burnopfield 88-94; P-in-c Greenside from 94. *The Vicarage, Greenside, Ryton, Tyne & Wear NE40 4AA* 0191-413 8281

SADGROVE, Very Rev Michael. b 50. Ball Coll Ox BA71 MA75. Trin Coll Bris 72. **d** 75 **p** 76. Lic to Offic *Ox* 75-77; Tutor Sarum & Wells Th Coll 77-82; Vice-Prin 80-82; V Alnwick St Mich and St Paul *Newc* 82-87; Prec Cov Cathl *Cov* 87-95; Vice-Provost Cov Cathl 87-95; Can Res Cov Cathl 87-95; Provost Sheff from 95. *Provost's Lodge, 22 Hallam Gate Road, Sheffield S10 5BS* Sheffield (0114) 266 2373 Fax 278 0244

SADLER, Preb Anthony Graham. b 36. Qu Coll Ox BA60 MA64. Lich Th Coll 60. **d** 62 **p** 63. C Burton St Chad *Lich* 62-65; V Rangemore 65-72; V Dunstall 65-72; V Abbots Bromley 72-79; V Pelsall 79-90; RD Walsall 82-90; Preb Lich Cathl from 87; P-in-c Uttoxeter w Bramshall from 90; P-in-c Stramshall from 90; P-in-c Kingstone w Gratwich from 90; P-in-c Checkley from 90; P-in-c Marchington w Marchington Woodlands from 90; P-in-c Leigh from 93. *The Vicarage, 12 Orchard Close, Uttoxeter, Staffs ST14 7DZ* Uttoxeter (01889) 563651

SADLER, John Ernest. b 45. Nottm Univ BTh78. Linc Th Coll 74. **d** 78 **p** 79. C Brampton St Thos *Derby* 78-81; TV Cov Caludon *Cov* 81-85; P-in-c High Elswick St Phil *Newc* 85; P-in-c Newc St Aug 85; V Newc St Phil and St Aug 86-94; P-in-c Newc Epiphany from 94. *12 Shannon Court, Newcastle upon Tyne NE3 2XF* 0191-286 4050

SADLER, John Harvey. b 33. K Coll Lon AKC57 BD66 Warw Univ MEd78 Birm Univ PhD83. St Boniface Warminster 57. **d** 58 **p** 59. V Ewell *Guildf* 69-71; Hd of Relig Studies Dyson

Perrins High Sch from 78; NSM Malvern Link w Cowleigh *Worc* from 80; Perm to Offic *Heref* from 82; rtd 95. *Little Queenswood, Stone Drive, Colwall, Malvern, Worcs WR13 6QL* Colwall (01684) 40047

SADLER, Michael Stuart. b 57. Wycliffe Hall Ox 78. **d** 81 **p** 82. C Henfynyw w Aberaeron and Llanddewi Aberarth *St D* 81-88; V Llanddewi Rhydderch w Llangattock-juxta-Usk etc *Mon* 88-90; V Llanddewi Rhydderch and Llangattock etc from 90. *The Vicarage, Llanddewi Rhydderch, Abergavenny, Gwent NP7 9TS* Abergavenny (01873) 840373

SAGAR, Brian. b 39. Sarum & Wells Th Coll 78. **d** 80 **p** 81. C Radcliffe St Thos and St Jo *Man* 80-82; P-in-c Charlestown 82-85; R Gt Lever 85-89; Chapl Cov Ch Housing Assn *Cov* 89-92; V Wing w Grove *Ox* from 92. *The Vicarage, 27B Aylesbury Road, Wing, Leighton Buzzard, Beds LU7 0PD* Aylesbury (01296) 688496

SAGE, Andrew George. b 58. Chich Th Coll 83. **d** 85 **p** 86. C Rawmarsh w Parkgate *Sheff* 85-87; C Fareham SS Pet and Paul *Portsm* 87-89; C Southsea H Spirit 89-91; P-in-c Nuthurst *Chich* 91-93; R from 93. *The Rectory, The Street, Nuthurst, Horsham, W Sussex RH13 6LH* Lower Beeding (01403) 891449

SAGE, Canon Jesse. b 35. Trin Hall Cam BA61 MA65. Chich Th Coll 61. **d** 63 **p** 64. C Feltham *Lon* 63-67; S Africa 67-72; R Abbas and Temple Combe *B & W* 72-75; R Abbas and Templecombe w Horsington 76-77; Chapl Agric and Rural Soc in Kent *Cant* from 78; Hon Can Cant Cathl from 90. *The Rectory, Pluckley, Ashford, Kent TN27 0QT* Pluckley (01233) 840232

SAGE, John Arthur. b 32. MInstP Lon Univ BSc54. St Alb Minl Tr Scheme 78. **d** 81 **p** 82. NSM Stevenage St Mary Shephall *St Alb* 81-86; NSM Stevenage St Mary Sheppall w Aston 86-87; C St Peter-in-Thanet *Cant* from 87. *St Andrew's House, 29 Reading Street, Broadstairs, Kent CT10 3AZ* Thanet (01843) 868923

SAGOVSKY, Dr Nicholas. b 47. CCC Ox BA69 St Edm Ho Cam PhD81. St Jo Coll Nottm BA73. **d** 74 **p** 75. C Newc St Gabr *Newc* 74-77; C Cam Gt St Mary w St Mich *Ely* 81; Vice-Prin Edin Th Coll 82-86; Dean of Chpl Clare Coll Cam from 86. *5 St Andrews Road, Cambridge CB2 1DH* Cambridge (01223) 460115

✠SAINSBURY, Rt Rev Roger Frederick. b 36. Jes Coll Cam BA58 MA62. Clifton Th Coll. **d** 60 **p** 61 **c** 91. C Spitalfields Ch Ch w All SS *Lon* 60-63; Missr Shrewsbury Ho Everton 63-74; P-in-c Everton St Ambrose w St Tim *Liv* 67-74; Warden Mayflower Family Cen Canning Town *Chelmsf* 74-81; P-in-c Victoria Docks St Luke 78-81; V Walsall *Lich* 81-87; TR 87-88; Adn W Ham *Chelmsf* 88-91; Area Bp Barking from 91. *Barking Lodge, 110 Capel Road, London E7 0JS, or Bishop's Office, Saints Drive, London E7 0RF* 0181-478 2456 or 503 5953 Fax 0181-503 5954

SAINT, Arthur James Maxwell. b 10. St Jo Coll Ox BA31 MA35. Cuddesdon Coll 34. **d** 35 **p** 36. V Ox SS Phil and Jas *Ox* 65-76; rtd 76. *65 Ramsay Road, Oxford OX3 8AY* Oxford (01865) 61241

SAINT, David Gerald. b 45. Sarum & Wells Th Coll 72. **d** 75 **p** 76. C Wellingborough All Hallows *Pet* 75-79; R Kislingbury w Rothersthorpe 79-83; V Kings Heath 83-85; Relig Progr Producer BBC Radio Northn from 85; Perm to Offic *Pet* from 86. *49 Colwyn Road, Northampton NN1 3PZ* Northampton (01604) 239100

ST ALBANS, Archdeacon of. *See* DAVIES, Ven Philip Bertram

ST ALBANS, Bishop of. *Vacant*

ST ALBANS, Dean of. *See* LEWIS, Very Rev Christopher Andrew

ST ANDREWS, DUNKELD AND DUNBLANE, Bishop of. *See* HENLEY, Rt Rev Michael Harry George

ST ANDREWS, DUNKELD AND DUNBLANE, Dean of. *See* WATT, Very Rev Alfred Ian

ST ASAPH, Archdeacon of. *See* DAVIES, Ven John Stewart

ST ASAPH, Bishop of. *See* JONES, Most Rev Alwyn Rice

ST ASAPH, Dean of. *See* GOULSTONE, Very Rev Thomas Richard Kerry

ST DAVIDS, Archdeacon of. *See* HARVEY, Ven Cyril John

ST DAVIDS, Bishop of. *Vacant*

ST DAVIDS, Dean of. *See* EVANS, Very Rev John Wyn

ST EDMUNDSBURY AND IPSWICH, Bishop of. *See* DENNIS, Rt Rev John

ST EDMUNDSBURY AND IPSWICH, Provost of. *See* ATWELL, Very Rev James Edgar

ST GERMANS, Suffragan Bishop of. *See* JAMES, Rt Rev Graham Richard

ST JOHN-CHANNELL, Michael Alister Morrell. b 53. Bris Univ BEd76. Ripon Coll Cuddesdon 76. **d** 78 **p** 79. C Portsea St Mary *Portsm* 78-81; PV Linc Cathl *Linc* 82-85; P-in-c Linc St Mary-le-Wigford w St Benedict etc 82-85; R Cranford *Lon*

85-92; V Staines St Mary and St Pet from 92. *St Peter's Vicarage, 14 Thames Side, Staines, Middx TW18 2HA* Staines (01784) 453039 or 469155

ST JOHN NICOLLE, Michael George. b 29. St Jo Coll Dur BA52 DipEd. **d** 70 **p** 71. C Lt Bowden St Nic *Leic* 70; C Knighton St Jo 71-74; R Desford 74-81; R Tarrant Valley *Sarum* 81-85; R Jersey St Jo *Win* 85-94; rtd 94. *Lew Noyers, Les Chendles, St John, Jersey, Channel Islands JE3 4FB* Jersey (01534) 861677

SAKER, Sidney William. b 08. Dur Univ 32. ALCD35. **d** 35 **p** 36. Perm to Offic *Leic* from 46; Lic to Offic *S'wark* 64-73; Area Sec (SW Lon) Leprosy Miss 71-73; rtd 73. *397 Uppingham Road, Leicester LE5 4DP* Leicester (0116) 276 0855

SALENIUS, Richard Mark. b 57. K Coll Lon BD79 AKC79. Linc Th Coll 79. **d** 80 **p** 81. C St Marylebone w H Trin *Lon* 80-84; C Sale St Anne *Ches* 84-87; V Macclesfield St Jo from 87. *The Vicarage, Wilwick Lane, Macclesfield, Cheshire SK11 8RS*

SALES, Patrick David. b 43. K Coll Lon AKC68 BD74. **d** 69 **p** 70. C Maidstone All SS w St Phil *Cant* 69-72; C Chart next Sutton Valence 72-74; C Birchington w Acol 75-77; V Boughton under Blean w Dunkirk 77-83; Hon Min Can Cant Cathl from 83; V Herne from 83; RD Reculver 86-92. *The Vicarage, Herne, Herne Bay, Kent CT6 7HE* Herne Bay (01227) 374328

SALISBURY, Miss Anne Ruth. b 37. Bible Churchmen's Coll. **d** 87 **p** 94. C Trin St Mich, Harrow *Lon* from 87. *1A Headstone Drive, Harrow, Middx HA3 5QX* 0181-427 1129 or 863 6131

SALISBURY, George Malcolm Owen. b 11. Bp's Coll Calcutta 40. **d** 43 **p** 44. R Shenley *St Alb* 68-81; rtd 81; Chapl St Alb City Hosp 81-87. *23 Elizabeth Court, Jersey Farm, St Albans, Herts AL4 9JB* St Albans (01727) 834568

SALISBURY, Harold Gareth. b 21. St Pet Hall Ox BA42 MA46. Wycliffe Hall Ox 42. **d** 44 **p** 45. V Duddo *Newc* 63-70; V Norham 63-70; V Norham and Duddo 70-78; V Snaith *Sheff* 78-86; P-in-c Cowick 78-86; TR Gt Snaith 86; rtd 86; Perm to Offic *Pet* from 87. *33 Nightingale Drive, Towcester, Northants NN12 7RA* Towcester (01327) 53674

SALISBURY, John Forbes. b 16. St Jo Coll Dur 46. **d** 50 **p** 51. V Tosside *Bradf* 67-79; Lic to Offic 80-84; rtd 81; Perm to Offic *Bradf* from 84. *14 Victoria Mill, Belmont Wharf, Skipton, N Yorkshire BD23 1RL* Skipton (01756) 701411

SALISBURY, Peter Brian Christopher. b 58. MBCS85 UMIST BSc80. Sarum & Wells Th Coll BTh92. **d** 92 **p** 93. C Stanmore *Win* from 92. *St Mark's House, Oliver's Battery Crescent, Winchester, Hants SO22 4EU* Winchester (01962) 861970

SALISBURY, Roger John. b 44. Lon Univ BD67. Lon Coll of Div 66. **d** 68 **p** 69. C Harold Wood *Chelmsf* 68-73; V Dorking St Paul *Guildf* 73-82; R Rusholme *Man* 82-90; TR Gt Chesham *Ox* from 90. *The Rectory, Church Street, Chesham, Bucks HP5 1HY* Chesham (01494) 783629

SALISBURY, Canon Tobias (Toby). b 33. Em Coll Cam BA60. Ripon Hall Ox 60. **d** 62 **p** 63. C Putney St Mary *S'wark* 62-65; C Churchdown St Jo *Glouc* 65-67; V Urchfont w Stert *Sarum* 67-73; R Burton Bradstock w Shipton Gorge and Chilcombe 73-79; P-in-c Long Bredy w Lt Bredy and Kingston Russell 75-79; TR Bride Valley 79-86; V Gt and Lt Bedwyn and Savernake Forest from 86; Can and Preb Sarum Cathl from 92. *The Vicarage, Church Street, Great Bedwyn, Marlborough, Wilts SN8 3PF* Marlborough (01672) 870779

SALISBURY, Archdeacon of. See HOPKINSON, Ven Barnabas John (Barney)

SALISBURY, Bishop of. See STANCLIFFE, Rt Rev David Staffurth

SALISBURY, Dean of. See DICKINSON, Very Rev the Hon Hugh Geoffrey

SALMON, Andrew Ian. b 61. St Jo Coll Nottm BTh88. **d** 88 **p** 89. C Collyhurst *Man* 88-92; P-in-c Pendleton St Ambrose from 92. *St Ambrose's Vicarage, 92 Fitzwarren Street, Pendleton, Salford M6 5RS* 0161-745 7608

SALMON, Andrew Meredith Bryant. b 30. Jes Coll Cam BA54 MA58. Wells Th Coll 54. **d** 56 **p** 57. C Enfield Ch Ch Trent Park *Lon* 56-58; Chapl Monkton Combe Sch Bath 58-71; Chapl Milton Abbey Sch Dorset 71-89; TV Bride Valley *Sarum* from 89. *The Vicarage, Litton Cheney, Dorchester, Dorset DT2 9AG* Long Bredy (01308) 482302

SALMON, Anthony James Heygate. b 30. CCC Ox BA53 DipTh54 MA57. Cuddesdon Coll 54. **d** 56 **p** 57. C S Norwood St Mark *Cant* 56-59; S Africa 59-69; Chapl USPG Coll of the Ascension Selly Oak 69-74; P-in-c Frinsted 74-78; R Harrietsham *Cant* 74-85; P-in-c Ulcombe 81-85; V Chobham w Valley End *Guildf* from 85. *The Vicarage, Bagshot Road, Chobham, Woking, Surrey GU24 8BY* Chobham (01276) 858197

SALMON, Bernard Bryant. b 24. Trin Hall Cam BA50 MA54. Wells Th Coll 50. **d** 52 **p** 53. R Cramlington *Newc* 58-71; V

Winscombe *B & W* 71-91; RD Locking 78-86; rtd 91. *Scaddens House, Scaddens Lane, Rodney Stoke, Cheddar, Somerset BS27 3UR* Wells (01749) 870194

SALMON, Mrs Constance Hazel. b 25. R Holloway Coll Lon BSc46. Lon Bible Coll 66 Gilmore Course 71. **dss** 80 **d** 87. Sidcup St Andr *Roch* 80-88; NSM 87-88; Perm to Offic from 88. *43 Old Mill Close, Eynsford, Dartford DA4 0BN* Dartford (01322) 866034

SALMON, Mrs Margaret. b 37. Leeds Univ BA59 CertEd60. SW Minl Tr Course 85. **d** 88 **p** 94. NSM Yelverton, Meavy, Sheepstor and Walkhampton *Ex* from 88. *Hinnies, Leg-o-Mutton Corner, Yelverton, Devon PL20 6DJ* Yelverton (01822) 853310

SALMON, Richard Harold. b 35. Fitzw Ho Cam BA57. Clifton Th Coll 57. **d** 59 **p** 60. C Blackheath Park St Mich *S'wark* 59-62; C St Alb St Paul *St Alb* 62-64; OMF 64-66; Malaysia 66-75; P-in-c March St Wendreda *Ely* 75-76; R 76-85; V Congresbury w Puxton and Hewish St Ann *B & W* from 85. *The Vicarage, Station Road, Congresbury, Bristol BS19 5DX* Yatton (01934) 833126

SALMON, Very Rev Thomas Noel Desmond Cornwall. b 13. TCD BA35 BD42 MA49. CITC 36. **d** 37 **p** 38. Lect TCD 45-89; Dean Ch Ch Cathl Dub *D & G* 67-89; I Dub Ch Ch Cathl 76-89; rtd 89. *3 Glenageary Terrace, Dun Laoghaire, Co Dublin, Irish Republic* Dublin (1) 280-0101

SALMON, William John. b 50. Lon Univ BSc72. St Jo Coll Dur 77. **d** 79 **p** 80. C Summerstown *S'wark* 79-81; C Hampreston *Sarum* 81-86; V Sundon *St Alb* 86-90; Dep Chapl HM Young Offender Inst Glen Parva 90-91; Chapl HM Pris Whitemoor from 91. *HM Prison Whitemoor, Longhill Road, March, Cambs PE15 0PR* March (01354) 660653 Fax 50783

SALONIA, Ivan. b 38. CQSW78 Open Univ BA81 N Lon Poly MA85. Milan Th Coll (RC). **d** 63 **p** 64. In RC Ch (Hong Kong) 64-73; Hon C Woolwich St Thos *S'wark* 89-91; C Greenwich St Alfege w St Pet and St Paul 91-93; C Kidbrooke St Jas 93-95; TV from 95. *48 Crookston Road, London SE9 1YB* 0181-850 0529 or 319 3874

SALOP, Archdeacon of. See FROST, Ven George

SALSBURY, Harry. b 31. Lon Univ TCert62. **d** 60 **p** 61. In RC Ch 60-82; NSM Bexhill St Pet *Chich* 83-84; Chapl Brighton Coll Jun Sch 84-93; C Eastbourne St Mary *Chich* 93-94; Perm to Offic from 94. *39 Croxden Way, Eastbourne, E Sussex BN22 0TZ* Eastbourne (01323) 507091

SALT, Canon David Christopher. b 37. Univ of Wales (Lamp) BA59. Sarum Th Coll 59. **d** 61 **p** 62. C Kidderminster St Mary *Worc* 61-66; Ind Chapl 66-72; R Knightwick w Doddenham, Broadwas and Cotheridge 72-82; Chapl Worc Coll of HE 72-82; V Redditch St Steph from 82; P-in-c Tardebigge 84-88; RD Bromsgrove from 91; Hon Can Worc Cathl from 92. *St Stephen's Vicarage, 248 Birchfield Road, Redditch, Worcs B97 4LZ* Redditch (01527) 541738

SALT, David Thomas Whitehorn. b 32. K Coll Lon AKC56 BD57. **d** 57 **p** 58. V Shelf *Bradf* 68-73; R Checkendon *Ox* 73-81; RD Henley 78-84; TR Langtree 81-84; Chapl Hungerford Hosp 84-89; V Hungerford and Denford *Ox* 84-89; P-in-c Harpsden w Bolney 89-95; Gen Sec Melanesian Miss 89-95; rtd 95. *Willow Cottage, 239 East Grafton, Marlborough, Wilts SN8 3DP* Marlborough (01672) 810049

SALT, Very Rev John William. b 41. Kelham Th Coll 61. **d** 66 **p** 67. C Barrow St Matt *Carl* 66-70; S Africa from 70; Adn S Zululand and Dean Eshowe Cath from 89. *PO Box 207, Eshowe, 3815 South Africa* Eshowe (354) 41215

SALT, Leslie. b 29. Linc Th Coll 68. **d** 69 **p** 69. C Alford w Rigsby *Linc* 69-75; V Torksey 75-94; R Kettlethorpe 77-94; V Marton 77-94; V Newton-on-Trent 77-94; rtd 94. *2 Holdenby Close, Lincoln LN2 4TQ*

SALTER, Arthur Thomas John. b 34. TD88. AKC60. **d** 61 **p** 62. C Ealing St Pet Mt Park *Lon* 61-65; C Shepherd's Bush St Steph w St Thos 65-66; C Holborn St Alb w Saffron Hill St Pet 66-70; P-in-c Barnsbury St Clem 70-77; P-in-c Islington St Mich 70-77; V Pentonville St Silas w All SS and St Jas from 70; CF (TAVR) from 75; Gen Sec Angl and E Chs Assn from 76; Chmn from 90; P-in-c St Dunstan in the West *Lon* from 79. *The Vicarage, 87 Richmond Avenue, London N1 0LX* 0171-607 2865 or 405 1929

SALTER, Canon George Alfred. b 25. TCD BA47 MA. CITC 49. **d** 49 **p** 50. I Cork St Luke w St Ann *C, C & R* 55-73; Preb Ross Cathl 69-88; Preb Cork Cathl 69-88; Treas 88-94; I Cork St Luke Union 73-94; Preb Tymothan St Patr Cathl Dub 88-94; rtd 94. *Mount Vernon House, 66 Wellington Road, Cork, Irish Republic* Cork (21) 506844

SALTER, Mrs Janet Elizabeth (Jan). b 48. Leeds Univ CertEd69. SW Minl Tr Course 92. **d** 95. C Coleshill *Birm* from 95. *6 Brutus Drive, Coleshill, Birmingham B46 1UF* Coleshill (01675) 467705

SALTER, John Frank. b 37. Dur Univ BA62 DipTh64. Cranmer Hall Dur 62. **d** 64 **p** 65. C Bridlington Priory *York* 64-67; Travelling Sec IVF 67-70; V Stoughton *Guildf* from 70; RD

Guildf 89-94. *The Vicarage, 3 Shepherd's Lane, Guildford, Surrey GU2 6SJ* Guildford (01483) 61603

SALTER, John Leslie. b 51. AKC76. Coll of Resurr Mirfield 77. **d** 78 **p** 79. C Tottenham St Paul *Lon* 78-82; P-in-c Castle Vale *Birm* 82-83; TV Curdworth w Castle Vale 83-90; R Castle Vale St Cuth 90-92; V Wantage *Ox* from 93. *The Vicarage, The Cloisters, Wantage, Oxon OX12 8AQ* Wantage (01235) 762214

SALTER, Nigel Christopher Murray. b 46. Loughb Univ BTech. Ripon Coll Cuddesdon 79. **d** 81 **p** 82. C Glouc St Aldate *Glouc* 81-84; C Solihull *Birm* 84-88; V Highters Heath from 88. *Immanuel Vicarage, Pickenham Road, Hollywood, Birmingham B14 4TG* 0121-430 7578

SALTER, Richard. b 24. Edin Th Coll 46. **d** 48 **p** 49. C Dundee St Salvador *Bre* 48-51; C Watford St Andr *St Alb* 51-54; C Oxhey St Matt 54-58; V Robertstown *Wakef* 58-62; V Watford St Jo *St Alb* from 62. *St John's Vicarage, 9 Monmouth Road, Watford WD1 1QW* Watford (01923) 236174

SALTER, Roger John. b 45. Trin Coll Bris 75. **d** 79 **p** 80. C Bedminster St Mich *Bris* 79-82; C Swindon Ch Ch 82-84; V Bedminster Down 84-89; P-in-c Northwood *Portsm* 89-93; P-in-c W Cowes H Trin 89-92; V Cowes H Trin and St Mary 92-94; USA from 94. *St Matthew's Episcopal Church, ACA, PO Box 36026, Birmingham, Alabama, USA 35236-6026* Birmingham (205) 823-7967

SALTER, Samuel. b 22. St Edm Hall Ox BA49 MA53. St Steph Ho Ox 49. **d** 50 **p** 51. Chapl Cheltenham Coll 65-81; TV Grantham *Linc* 81-87; rtd 87; Perm to Offic *Linc* from 87. *6 Gladstone Terrace, Grantham, Lincs NG31 8BW* Grantham (01476) 60249

SALWAY, Canon Donald Macleay. b 31. St Pet Hall Ox BA54 MA59. Oak Hill Th Coll 54. **d** 56 **p** 57. C Holloway St Mary w St Jas *Lon* 56-67; V Leam St Phil *Ely* 67-81; V Mile Cross *Nor* from 81; RD Nor N 89-95; Hon Can Nor Cathl from 91. *St Catherine's Vicarage, Aylsham Road, Mile Cross, Norwich NR3 2RJ* Norwich (01603) 426767

SAMBELL, David John. b 31. St Aid Birkenhead 60. **d** 63 **p** 64. C Sutton St Geo *Ches* 63-67; C Alsager St Mary 67-71; V Crewe St Pet 71-81; V Upton Priory from 81. *The Vicarage, Church Way, Macclesfield, Cheshire SK10 3HT* Macclesfield (01625) 827761

SAMBROOK, Ernest. b 16. Kelham Th Coll 36. **d** 42 **p** 43. V Stockport St Sav *Ches* 58-76; V Brinnington w Portwood 76-82; rtd 82; Perm to Offic *Ches* from 86. *189 Overdale Road, Stockport, Cheshire SK6 3EN* 0161-494 1614

SAMMAN, Peter Bryan. b 27. TCD BA53. Coll of Resurr Mirfield 53. **d** 55 **p** 56. V Lanc Ch Ch *Blackb* 67-74; V Lostock Hall 74-85; V Morecambe St Barn 85-91; rtd 91. *14 Wentworth Crescent, Morecambe, Lancs LA3 3NX* Morecambe (01524) 425208

SAMME, Raymond Charles (Ray). b 50. Trent Poly MIBiol80. Oak Hill Th Coll 85. **d** 87 **p** 88. C Holmer w Huntington *Heref* 87-90; C Derby St Alkmund and St Werburgh *Derby* 90-93; V Romford Gd Shep Collier Row *Chelmsf* from 93. *Good Shepherd Vicarage, 97 Collier Row Lane, Romford RM5 3BA* Romford (01708) 745626

SAMMONS, John Trevor. b 22. Birm Univ BA48. Ripon Hall Ox. **d** 50 **p** 51. V Birm St Luke *Birm* 55-70; Chapl Birm Skin Hosp 56-70; P-in-c Nomans Heath *Lich* 70-82; R Newton Regis w Seckington and Shuttington *Birm* 70-86; rtd 87; Perm to Offic *Birm* from 87. *39 Kurtus, Dosthill, Tamworth, Staffs B77 1NX* Tamworth (01827) 283875

SAMPFORD, John Alfred. b 36. Lich Th Coll 58. **d** 61 **p** 62. C Lambeth St Phil *S'wark* 61-65; C Beddington 65-69; V Hampstead Ch Ch *Lon* 69-79; V Enfield Chase St Mary from 79. *St Mary Magdalene Vicarage, 30 The Ridgeway, Enfield, Middx EN2 8QH* 0181-363 1875

SAMPSON, Brian Andrew. b 39. **d** 94 **p** 95. C Glem Valley United Benefice *St E* from 94. *The Rectory, Stanstead, Sudbury, Suffolk CO10 9AT* Glemsford (01787) 280738

SAMPSON, Clive. b 38. St Jo Coll Cam BA61 MA64. Ridley Hall Cam 63. **d** 65 **p** 66. C Tunbridge Wells St Jo *Roch* 65-69; Travelling Sec Scripture Union 69-79; V Maidstone St Luke *Cant* 79-94. *25 Townsend Drive, St Albans, Herts AL3 5RF* St Albans (01727) 850282

SAMPSON, Desmond William John. b 25. FRICS60. Roch Th Coll 63. **d** 65 **p** 66. C Hythe *Cant* 65-70; V Alkham w Capel le Ferne and Hougham 70-76; V Wingham w Elmstone and Preston w Stourmouth 76-86; RD E Bridge 81-86; C Hythe 86-91; rtd 91. *25 Albert Road, Hythe, Kent CT21 6BP* Hythe (01303) 268457

SAMPSON, Preb Everard Archbold. b 12. Keble Coll Ox BA33 MA47. Linc Th Coll 33. **d** 35 **p** 36. V Holcombe Burnell *Ex* 49-77; Preb Ex Cathl 60-92; rtd 77; Sub-Dean Ex Cathl *Ex* from 84. *11 Arundel Close, Alphington, Exeter EX2 8UG* Exeter (01392) 438389

SAMPSON, Jeremy John Egerton. b 23. Dur Univ BSc45. Wells Th Coll 46. **d** 48 **p** 49. V Killingworth *Newc* 62-76; V Consett

Dur 76-90; RD Lanchester 80-85; rtd 90. *6 Kilkenny Road, Guisborough, Cleveland TS14 7LE* Guisborough (01287) 632734

SAMPSON, Canon Terence Harold Morris. b 41. ACA64 FCA75. Bps' Coll Cheshunt 64. **d** 67 **p** 68. C Penrith St Andr *Carl* 67-72; V Carl St Barn 72-80; TR Carl H Trin and St Barn 80-84; Chapl Cumberland Infirmary 83-84; R Workington St Mich *Carl* from 84; Hon Can Carl Cathl from 89; RD Solway 90-95. *St Michael's Rectory, Dora Crescent, Workington, Cumbria CA14 2EZ* Workington (01900) 602311

SAMS, David Stevenson. b 27. Hertf Coll Ox BA50 MA54 Man Univ DipAE78. Wycliffe Hall Ox 50. **d** 52 **p** 53. Lic Preacher *Man* 69-79; Welfare Officer Stockport Tech Coll 69-79; Perm to Offic *Chelmsf* 79-92; Sen Tutor Colchester Inst 79-91; rtd 91. *26 Beaconsfield Road, Clacton-on-Sea, Essex CO15 6BU* Clacton-on-Sea (01255) 432295

SAMS, Michael Charles. b 34. Ox NSM Course 81. **d** 84 **p** 85. NSM Abingdon *Ox* from 84. *13 Hound Close, Abingdon, Oxon OX14 2LU* Abingdon (01235) 529084

SAMUEL, Brother. See DOUBLE, Richard Sydney

SAMUEL, Canon James Louis (Jim). b 30. Birm Poly CQSW72 Open Univ BA77. Sarum Th Coll 59. **d** 61 **p** 62. P-in-c Dudley Holly Hall St Aug *Worc* 81-86; V 86-94; RD Dudley 87-93; Hon Can Worc Cathl 88-94; rtd 94; Perm to Offic *Worc* from 94. *6 Arrowsmith Avenue, Bartestree, Hereford HR1 4DW* Hereford (01432) 850585

SAMUEL, Stuart. b 48. AKC70. St Aug Coll Cant 70. **d** 71 **p** 72. C Golcar *Wakef* 71-77; V Brampton St Mark *Derby* 77-79; P-in-c Hathern *Leic* 79-83; R Hathern, Long Whatton and Diseworth 83-90; R Hathern, Long Whatton and Diseworth w Belton etc from 90; RD Akeley E (Loughb) from 92. *The Rectory, Church Street, Hathern, Loughborough, Leics LE12 5LA* Loughborough (01509) 842259

SAMUEL, Theophilus (Theo). b 34. BScTech59. Oak Hill Th Coll 70. **d** 72 **p** 73. C Slough *Ox* 72-73; Chapl Community Relns 73-78; Chapl Brunel Univ *Lon* 78-85; V W Drayton from 85. *The Vicarage, 191 Station Road, West Drayton, Middx UB7 7NQ* West Drayton (01895) 442194 Fax as telephone

SAMUELS, Mrs Ann Elizabeth. b 51. Birm Univ BA73 CertEd74. Trin Coll Bris 85. **d** 87 **p** 94. Par Dn Moreton *Ches* 87-91; Par Dn Halton 91-94; Adv Women's Min from 94; Bp's Adv for Women in Min from 94; C Halton from 94. *The Vicarage, Halton, Runcorn, Cheshire WA7 2BE* Runcorn (01928) 563636

SAMUELS, Christopher William John. b 42. AKC66. **d** 67 **p** 68. C Kirkholt *Man* 67-72; C-in-c Houghton Regis St Thos CD *St Alb* 72-76; R Tarporley *Ches* 76-83; R Ches St Mary from 83; RD Ches from 95. *The Rectory, St Mary-without-the-Walls, Chester CH4 7HL* Chester (01244) 671202

SAMUELS, Raymond John. b 49. Qu Mary Coll Lon BSc73 Essex Univ CertEd74. Trin Coll Bris 85. **d** 87 **p** 88. C Moreton *Ches* 87-91; V Halton from 91. *The Vicarage, Halton, Runcorn, Cheshire WA7 2BE* Runcorn (01928) 563636

SAMUELS, Mrs Sheila Mary. b 57. St Andr Univ MA79 Wolfs Coll Ox MLitt82 CertEd83. Trin Coll Bris BA89. **d** 89 **p** 94. C Skirbeck H Trin *Linc* from 89. *43 Spilsby Road, Boston, Lincs PE21 9NX* Boston (01205) 368721

SAMWAYS, Denis Robert. b 37. Leeds Univ BA62. Coll of Resurr Mirfield 62. **d** 64 **p** 65. C Clun w Chapel Lawn *Heref* 64-69; C Pocklington w Yapham-cum-Meltonby, Owsthorpe etc *York* 69-71; C Millington w Gt Givendale 69-71; R Hinderwell w Roxby 71-76; Hon C 80-91; Hon C Loftus 76-80; V Boosbeck w Moorsholm 91-95; R Kirby Misperton w Normanby, Edston and Salton from 95. *The Rectory, Normanby, Sinnington, York YO6 6RH* Kirkbymoorside (01751) 31288

SAMWAYS, John Feveral. b 44. BA DipTh. Trin Coll Bris 81. **d** 83 **p** 84. C Patcham *Chich* 83-86; C Ox St Aldate w St Matt *Ox* 86-94; R Ox St Matt from 95. *The Vicarage, Marlborough Road, Oxford OX1 4LW* Oxford (01865) 243434

SANDAY, Robert Ward. b 55. Sarum & Wells Th Coll 89. **d** 91 **p** 92. C Swindon Ch Ch *Bris* 91-94; R Lyddington and Wanborough and Bishopstone etc from 94. *The Vicarage, 19 Church Road, Wanborough, Swindon SN4 0BZ* Swindon (01793) 790242

SANDBERG, Peter John. b 37. Lon Univ LLB59. Lon Coll of Div 67. **d** 69 **p** 70. C Hailsham *Chich* 69-72; C Billericay St Mary *Chelmsf* 72-77; TV Billericay and Lt Burstead 77-83; R Thundersley from 83; RD Hadleigh from 90. *St Peter's Rectory, 390 Church Road, Thundersley, Benfleet, Essex SS7 3HG* South Benfleet (01268) 792235

SANDELLS-REES, Mrs Kathy Louise. b 68. Abth Coll of FE DipBBSS87 Univ of Wales (Cardiff) DipTh90. Qu Coll Birm DipTh92. **d** 92. C Holyhead w Rhoscolyn w Llanfair-yn-Neubwll *Ban* 92-94; C Ban from 94. *1 Fford Belmont, Bangor, Gwynedd LL57 2LL* Bangor (01248) 353405

SANDEMAN, Arthur Alastair Malcolm. b 14. Chich Th Coll 37. **d** 39 **p** 40. V Cressing *Chelmsf* 61-75; rtd 75; Perm to Offic *Ex* from 75. *20 Orient Road, Paignton, Devon TQ3 2PB* Paignton (01803) 521385

SANDERS, Allan Cameron Ebblewhite. b 34. CCC Ox MA59 Univ of E Africa MEd69. Ox NSM Course 82. **d** 85 **p** 86. Hd Master Reading Blue Coat Sch from 74; Hon C Sonning *Ox* from 85. *Headmaster's House, Reading Blue Coat School, Reading RG4 0SU* Reading (01734) 693200

SANDERS, Colin Anthony Wakefield. b 26. Wadh Coll Ox MA55. Ox NSM Course 89. **d** 90 **p** 91. NSM Eynsham and Cassington *Ox* from 90. *Little Firs, 41 Bladon Road, Woodstock, Oxon OX20 1QD* Woodstock (01993) 813357

SANDERS, Frederick Alvin Oliver. b 06. CCC Cam BA28 MA37. Coll of Resurr Mirfield. **d** 30 **p** 31. CF (TA) from 50; R Stalbridge *Sarum* 59-78; rtd 78; Lic to Offic *L & K* from 78. *Skehanagh Point, Coolbawn, Nenagh, Co Tipperary, Irish Republic* Nenagh (67) 28007

SANDERS, Graham Laughton. b 32. Kelham Th Coll 52. **d** 56 **p** 57. C Glouc St Paul *Glouc* 56-60; India 61-68; V Heaton St Martin *Bradf* 68-76; V Gt Waltham *Chelmsf* 76-79; Sec Dioc Liturg Cttee 78-87; P-in-c Ford End 79; V Gt Waltham w Ford End 79-87; TR Guiseley w Esholt *Bradf* 87-94. *4 Marlborough Road, Shipley, W Yorkshire BD18 3NX* Shipley (01274) 587896

SANDERS, Henry William. b 36. **d** 62 **p** 64. C Nottm St Ann S'well 62-65; C Dagenham *Chelmsf* 65-67; C W Thurrock 67-73; C W Ham 73-78. *20 Vale Road, London E7 8BJ*

SANDERS, Herbert. b 21. Clifton Th Coll 51. **d** 53 **p** 54. V Oxenhope *Bradf* 59-66; Lic to Offic *Linc* 66-81; rtd 81. *The Vicarage, Low Toynton, Horncastle, Lincs LN9 6JU* Horncastle (01507) 523410

SANDERS, Mrs Hilary Clare. b 57. Hull Univ BA79 UEA CertEd81. E Anglian Minl Tr Course 83. **dss** 85 **d** 87 **p** 94. Haverhill w Withersfield, the Wrattings etc *St E* 85-87; Hon Par Dn Melton 87-94; Hon C from 94; Dioc Schs Officer from 88. *The Rectory, Station Road, Woodbridge, Suffolk IP12 1PX* Woodbridge (01394) 380279

SANDERS, James Alexander. b 29. **d** 65 **p** 66. Australia 65-78; C Enfield St Jas *Lon* 78-81; rtd 94. *81 Queen Street, Woollahra, NSW 2025, Australia*

SANDERS, Mark. b 57. Hull Univ BA79 Cam Univ BA82. Westcott Ho Cam 80. **d** 83 **p** 84. C Haverhill w Withersfield, the Wrattings etc *St E* 83-87; P-in-c Melton 87-91; R from 91. *The Rectory, Station Road, Melton, Woodbridge, Suffolk IP12 1PX* Woodbridge (01394) 380279

SANDERS, Michael Barry. b 45. Fitzw Coll Cam BA67 MA71 Lon Univ BD71. St Jo Coll Nottm 68 Lon Coll of Div. **d** 71 **p** 72. C Ashtead *Guildf* 71-74; Chapl St Jo Coll Cam 75-79; V Dorridge *Birm* 79-89; TR Walsall *Lich* from 89. *The Vicarage, 48 Jesson Road, Walsall WS1 3AX* Walsall (01922) 24012

SANDERS, Nigel Wilding. b 29. Mert Coll Ox MA55. Ox Min Course 91. **d** 92 **p** 93. NSM Maidenhead St Andr and St Mary Magd *Ox* from 92. *Fieldway, Worcester Road, Cookham, Maidenhead, Berks SL6 9JG* Maidenhead (01628) 521516

SANDERS, Mrs Nora Irene. b 29. Lon Univ BA50 CertEd51. W Midl Minl Tr Course 74. **dss** 78 **d** 87 **p** 94. Dorridge *Birm* 78-87; Par Dn 87-90; rtd 90; Hon C Tanworth *Birm* from 94. *8 Cransley Grove, Solihull, W Midlands B91 3ZA* 0121-705 2391

SANDERS, Roderick David Scott. b 58. Southn Univ BA80 CertEd81. Cranmer Hall Dur 85. **d** 88 **p** 89. C Luton St Mary *St Alb* 88-93; P-in-c Clovelly *Ex* 93-94; P-in-c Woolfardisworthy and Buck Mills 93-94; TV Parkham, Alwington, Buckland Brewer etc from 94. *The Rectory, Old Market Drive, Woolsery, Bideford, Devon EX39 5QF* Hartland (01237) 431571

SANDERS, Mrs Susan Rachel (Susie). b 61. St Mary's Coll Dur BA83. Cranmer Hall Dur 85. **d** 88 **p** 94. Par Dn Luton St Mary *St Alb* 88-93; Perm to Offic *Ex* 93-94; NSM Parkham, Alwington, Buckland Brewer etc from 94. *The Rectory, Old Market Drive, Woolsery, Bideford, Devon EX39 5QF* Hartland (01237) 431571

SANDERS, Mrs Wendy Elizabeth. b 49. Carl Dioc Tr Course 87. **d** 90 **p** 94. NSM Bampton w Mardale *Carl* 90-92; C Walney Is 92-94; C Stanwix from 94. *45 Knowe Park Avenue, Carlisle CA3 9EL* Carlisle (01228) 21528 or 511430

SANDERS, William John. b 48. Liv Inst of Educn BA80. Wycliffe Hall Ox 81. **d** 83 **p** 84. C Netherton *Liv* 83-87; P-in-c Wavertree St Bridget from 87. *St Bridget's Vicarage, 93 Salisbury Road, Wavertree, Liverpool L15 2HU* 0151-733 1117

SANDERSON, Colin James. b 54. SEN SR N. St Mich Coll Llan 85. **d** 87 **p** 88. C Merthyr Dyfan *Llan* 87-90; C Cadoxton-juxta-Barry 90-91; V Llangeinor from 91. *The Vicarage, Corbett Street, Ogmore Vale, Bridgend, M Glam CF32 7AA* Bridgend (01656) 842565

SANDERSON, Daniel. b 40. AKC66. **d** 67 **p** 68. C Upperby St Jo *Carl* 67-72; V Addingham 72-75; V Ireleth w Askam from 75; RD Furness from 94. *St Peter's Vicarage, Duke Street, Askham-in-Furness, Cumbria LA16 7AD* Dalton-in-Furness (01229) 462647

SANDERSON, Canon Gillian. b 47. Cranmer Hall Dur 80. **dss** 82 **d** 87 **p** 94. Allesley *Cov* 82-86; Warw 86-87; C 87-94; TV from 94; Hon Can Cov Cathl from 94. *The Vicarage, 25 Sutherland Close, Warwick CV34 5UJ* Warwick (01926) 492097

SANDERSON, Harold. b 26. St Aid Birkenhead. **d** 61 **p** 62. V Warrington St Ann *Liv* 64-73; P-in-c Warrington St Pet 70-73; V Orrell 73-79; V Scarisbrick 79-91; rtd 91. *29 Green Lane, Ormskirk, Lancs L39 1ND* Ormskirk (01695) 571421

SANDERSON, Very Rev Peter Oliver. b 29. St Chad's Coll Dur BA52 DipTh54. **d** 54 **p** 55. V Winksley cum Grantley and Aldfield w Studley *Ripon* 68-74; V Leeds St Aid 74-84; Can St Paul's Cathl Dundee *Bre* 84-91; Provost St Paul's Cathl Dundee 84-91; R Dundee St Paul 84-91; USA from 91; rtd 94. *805 Meadow Lane, Storm Lake, Iowa 50588-2756, USA* Storm Lake (712) 732-7189

SANDERSON, Peter Richard Fallowfield. b 18. St Cath Soc Ox BA41 MA46. Chich Th Coll 41. **d** 42 **p** 44. V Poundstock *Truro* 56-74; P-in-c Hove St Patr *Chich* 74-79; P-in-c Buxted St Mary 79-82; P-in-c Hadlow Down 79-82; P-in-c Buxted and Hadlow Down 82-83; rtd 83; Perm to Offic *Chich* from 83. *Nova Scotia, 48 Parklands Road, Hassocks, W Sussex BN6 8JZ* Hassocks (01273) 843117

SANDERSON, Scott. b 42. Oak Hill Th Coll DipHE. **d** 82 **p** 83. C Galleywood Common *Chelmsf* 82-88; P-in-c Newport w Widdington 88-92; V Newport from 92. *The Vicarage, Newport, Saffron Walden, Essex CB11 2RB* Saffron Walden (01799) 540339

SANDES, Denis Lindsay. BTh. **d** 89 **p** 90. C Bandon Union *C, C & R* 89-92; I Kells Union *C & O* from 92. *The Priory, Kells, Co Kilkenny, Irish Republic* Kilkenny (56) 28367

SANDFORD, Jack. b 11. Ripon Hall Ox. **d** 60 **p** 61. V Barkingside St Laur *Chelmsf* 67-77; rtd 77. *15 Lyndhurst Road, Holland-on-Sea, Clacton-on-Sea, Essex CO15 5HT* Clacton-on-Sea (01255) 815294

SANDFORD, Nicholas Robert. b 63. Kent Univ BA84 Univ of Wales (Cardiff) BD87. St Mich Coll Llan 84. **d** 87 **p** 88. C Neath w Llantwit *Llan* 87-90; C Cardiff St Jo 90-94; R Cilybebyll from 94. *The Rectory, 7 Cwmnantllyd Road, Gellinudd, Pontardawe, Swansea SA8 3DT* Pontardawe (01792) 862118

SANDFORD, Paul Richard. b 47. Em Coll Cam BA69 MA73. Wycliffe Hall Ox 72. **d** 75 **p** 76. C Upper Holloway St Pet *Lon* 75-77; C Finchley St Paul Long Lane 77-81; Ind Chapl *Newc* 81-88; TV Cramlington 81-88; TV Dronfield *Derby* 88-90; TV Dronfield w Holmesfield from 90. *St Philip's Vicarage, 43 Firthwood Road, Dronfield, Sheffield S18 6BW* Dronfield (01246) 413893

SANDFORD of Banbury, Rev and Rt Hon Lord (John Cyril Edmondson). b 20. DSC43. Dartmouth RN Coll. Westcott Ho Cam 56. **d** 58 **p** 60. Perm to Offic *St Alb* from 63; Chapl for Miss and Ecum St Alb 63-66; Chmn Redundant Chs Cttee Ch Commrs 82-88; rtd 85. *27 Ashley Gardens, Ambrosden Avenue, London SW1P 1QD* 0171-834 5722

SANDHAM, Stephen McCourt. b 41. K Coll Lon BD65 AKC65. **d** 66 **p** 67. C Stockton St Pet *Dur* 66-69; C Bishopwearmouth Gd Shep 69-71; C Bishopwearmouth St Mich w St Hilda 71-75; V Darlington St Mark w St Paul 75-82; P-in-c Sunderland St Chad 82-87; R Shincliffe from 87. *The Rectory, Shincliffe, Durham DH1 2NJ* 0191-386 2142

SANDOM, Miss Carolyn Elizabeth (Carrie). b 63. Homerton Coll Cam BEd85. Wycliffe Hall Ox BTh93. **d** 94. C St Helen Bishopsgate w St Andr Undershaft etc *Lon* from 94. *39 Treby Street, London E3 4TE* 0181-981 6360

SANDS, Colin Robert. b 38. JP84. Chester Coll CertEd64. N Ord Course 82. **d** 85 **p** 86. Hd Master Magull Primary Sch from 80; NSM Bootle Ch Ch *Liv* 85-94; NSM Maghull from 94. *16 Strafford Drive, Bootle, Merseyside L20 9JW* 0151-525 8709

SANDS, Frederick William. b 25. St Deiniol's Hawarden 86. **d** 87 **p** 88. Chapl Asst Leic Gen Hosp 87-89; Chapl 89-95; rtd 95. *Gwendolen Road, Leicester LE5 4PW* Leicester (0116) 249 0490

SANDS, Nigel John. b 39. Dur Univ BA64 MA68. Oak Hill Th Coll 65. **d** 67 **p** 68. C Skelmersdale St Paul *Liv* 67-71; C Childwall All SS 71-72; V Wavertree St Bridget 72-78; P-in-c Welford w Wickham and Gt Shefford *Ox* 78-86; P-in-c Boxford w Stockcross and Speen 84-86; R Welford w Wickham and Gt Shefford, Boxford etc from 86. *The Rectory, Wickham, Newbury, Berks RG16 8HD* Hungerford (01488) 608244

SANDS, William James (Bill). b 55. St Jo Coll Nottm LTh83. **d** 83 **p** 84. C St Mary-at-Latton *Chelmsf* 83-86; Zimbabwe

86-87 and from 92; C-in-c Barkingside St Cedd *Chelmsf* 87-89; C Woodford St Mary w St Phil and St Jas 87-89; P-in-c Elmsett w Aldham *St E* 89-92; P-in-c Kersey w Lindsey 89-92. *The Rectory, St Mary's Church, PO Esigodini, Zimbabwe* Esigodini (88) 263

SANGER, Reginald Stephen John. b 15. Wycliffe Hall Ox. **d** 57 **p** 58. V Lee St Mildred *S'wark* 62-83; rtd 83; Perm to Offic *Chich* from 87. *62 Quantock Road, Durrington, Worthing, W Sussex BN13 2HQ* Worthing (01903) 692905

SANGSTER, Andrew. b 45. K Coll Lon BD67 AKC67 BA71 MA84 Lon Inst of Educn MPhil93. St Boniface Warminster. **d** 69 **p** 70. C Aylesford *Roch* 69-72; C Shirley *Win* 73-76; V Woolston 76-79; Prov Youth Chapl Ch in Wales 79-82; New Zealand 82-89; Chapl Eton Coll Windsor 89-92; Hd Master St Edm Sch Hindhead from 92. *St Edmund's School, Hindhead, Surrey GU26 6BH* Hindhead (01428) 604808

SANKEY, Julian. b 52. Qu Coll Ox BA74 MA79. St Jo Coll Nottm 84. **d** 86 **p** 87. C New Barnet St Jas *St Alb* 86-89; C Mansf St Pet *S'well* 89-94; Chapl St Luke's Hospice Sheff from 94. *St Lukes Hospice, Little Common Lane, Sheffield S11 9NE, or, 2 Woodvale Road, Sheffield S10 3EX* Sheffield (0114) 236 9911

SANKEY, Terence Arthur Melville (Terry). b 51. CertTS. Trin Coll Bris 87. **d** 89 **p** 90. C Chalke Valley W *Sarum* 89-93; NSM Chalke Deanery from 93. *Rookhaye Farmhouse, Bower Chalke, Salisbury SP5 5BT* Salisbury (01722) 780774

SANSBURY, Christopher John. b 34. Peterho Cam BA57 MA. Westcott Ho Cam 58. **d** 59 **p** 60. C Portsea N End St Mark *Portsm* 59-63; C Weeke *Win* 63-71; V N Eling St Mary 71-78; R Long Melford *St E* from 78. *The Rectory, Long Melford, Sudbury, Suffolk CO10 9DL* Sudbury (01787) 310845

SANSOM, John Reginald. b 40. St Jo Coll Nottm 73. **d** 75 **p** 76. C Ipswich St Marg *St E* 75-79; P-in-c Emneth *Ely* 79-85; P-in-c Hartford 85-86; TV Huntingdon 86-91; R Sawtry from 91. *The Rectory, Sawtry, Huntingdon, Cambs PE17 5TD* Ramsey (01487) 830215

SANSOM, Canon Michael Charles. b 44. Bris Univ BA66 St Jo Coll Dur PhD74. Cranmer Hall Dur 68. **d** 72 **p** 73. C Ecclesall *Sheff* 72-76; Lic to Offic *Ely* 76-88; Dir of Studies Ridley Hall Cam 76-88; Vice-Prin 79-88; Dir of Ords *St Alb* from 88; Can Res St Alb from 88. *4D Harpenden Road, St Albans, Herts AL3 5AB* St Albans (01727) 833777

SANSOM, Robert Arthur. b 29. BA. St Aid Birkenhead 60. **d** 62 **p** 63. C Sutton in Ashfield St Mary *S'well* 62-65; V Holbrooke *Derby* 65-70; Canada from 70. *2254 Amherst Avenue, Sidney, British Columbia, Canada, V8L 2G7*

SANSOME, Geoffrey Hubert. b 29. Man Univ BA53. Qu Coll Birm DipTh62. **d** 62 **p** 63. C Prenton *Ches* 62-68; P-in-c Liscard St Thos 68-72; V Kingsley 72-83; V Wybunbury w Doddington 83-91; V Marbury from 91. *The Vicarage, Marbury, Whitchurch, Shropshire SY13 4LN* Whitchurch (01948) 663758

SANSUM, David Henry. b 31. Bris Univ BA52 MA63. St Aid Birkenhead 54. **d** 56 **p** 57. C Henleaze *Bris* 56-59; C Stratton St Margaret 59-60; C Stoke Bishop 60-64; V Stechford Birm 64-76; V Ashbourne w Mapleton *Derby* from 76; V Ashbourne St Jo from 81; RD Ashbourne from 91. *The Vicarage, Belle Vue Road, Ashbourne, Derbyshire DE6 1AT* Ashbourne (01335) 343129

✠**SANTER, Rt Rev Mark.** b 36. Qu Coll Cam BA60 MA64. Westcott Ho Cam. **d** 63 **p** 64 **c** 81. Tutor Cuddesdon Coll 63-67; C Cuddesdon *Ox* 63-67; Fell and Dean Clare Coll Cam 67-72; Tutor 68-72; Prin Westcott Ho Cam 73-81; Hon Can Win Cathl *Win* 78-81; Area Bp Kensington *Lon* 81-87; Bp Birm from 87. *Bishop's Croft, Old Church Road, Birmingham B17 0BG* 0121-427 1163 Fax 426 1322

SANTRAM, Philip James. b 27. MA Delhi Univ BSc48 Serampore Univ BD53. Bp's Coll Calcutta 49. **d** 52 **p** 54. C Horton *Bradf* 68-71; C Whitley Ch Ch *Ox* 71-72; P Missr St Mary Magd Conv Tilehurst 72-76; V Tilehurst St Mary 76-78; Canada from 78; rtd 92. *3544 du Souvenir, Laval, Quebec, Canada, H7V 1X2*

SARALIS, Preb Christopher Herbert (Chris). b 34. Univ of Wales BA54 St Cath Coll Ox BA56 MA60. Wycliffe Hall Ox. **d** 57 **p** 58. C Abergavenny St Mary w Llanwenarth Citra *Mon* 57-61; C Bridgwater St Mary w Chilton Trinity *B & W* 61-65; V Berrow 65-72; RD Burnham 72-76; R Berrow and Breane 72-76; V Minehead 76-92; RD Exmoor 80-86; Preb Wells Cathl 84-92; V Bovey Tracey SS Pet, Paul and Thos w Hennock *Ex* from 92. *The Vicarage, Coombe Cross, Bovey Tracey, Newton Abbot, Devon TQ13 9EP* Bovey Tracey (01626) 833813

SARAPUK, Susan. b 59. Lon Univ BA80 Univ of Wales PGCE81. St Mich Coll Llan DPS90. **d** 90. C Morriston *S & B* 90-94; C Swansea St Pet from 94. *St Illtyd's Parsonage, 18 Ystrad Road, Forestffach, Swansea SA5 4BT* Swansea (01792) 586437

SARGAN, Miss Phyllis Elsie. b 24. TCert44 Lon Univ DSocStuds67. Gilmore Ho IDC51. **d** 88 **p** 94. Hon C Bawtry w Austerfield and Misson *S'well* from 88; rtd 90. *Pilgrim House, 1 Highfield Road, Bawtry, Doncaster, S Yorkshire DN10 6QN* Doncaster (01302) 710587

SARGANT, Canon John Raymond. b 38. CCC Cam BA61 MA70. Westcott Ho Cam 64 Harvard Div Sch 66. **d** 67 **p** 68. C Croydon *Cant* 67-72; Zambia 72-75; P-in-c Bradford-on-Avon Ch Ch *Sarum* 76-81; V 81-90; TV Marlborough from 90; Adv on Inter-Faith Relns from 90; Can and Preb Sarum Cathl from 92. *Preshute Vicarage, 7 Golding Avenue, Marlborough, Wilts SN8 1TH* Marlborough (01672) 513408

✠**SARGEANT, Rt Rev Frank Pilkington.** b 32. St Jo Coll Dur BA55 DipTh58 Nottm Univ DipAdEd73. Cranmer Hall Dur 57. **d** 58 **p** 59 **c** 84. C Gainsborough All SS *Linc* 58-62; C Gt Grimsby St Jas 62-66; V Hykeham 66-73; Dir In-Service Tr and Adult Educn *Bradf* 73-84; Can Res Bradf Cathl 73-77; Adn Bradf 77-84; Suff Bp Stockport *Ches* 84-94; Bp at Lambeth (Hd of Staff) *Cant* from 94. *2nd Floor Flat, Queen's Stairs, Lambeth Palace, London SE1 7JU* 0171-928 8282 Fax 261 9836

SARGEANT, George Henry. b 19. Bps' Coll Cheshunt 60. **d** 62 **p** 63. C-in-c Gt w Lt Wratting *St E* 69-70; R 70-77; C-in-c Barnardiston 69-70; R 71-77; rtd 84. *1 Belgrave Gardens, Dereham, Norfolk NR19 1PZ* Dereham (01362) 693020

SARGEANT, Kenneth Stanley. b 19. Lon Coll of Div 68. **d** 70 **p** 71. C E Ham St Paul *Chelmsf* 70-73; C Southborough St Pet w Ch Ch and St Matt *Roch* 73-77; Chapl Joyce Green Hosp Dartford 77-88; R Greenhithe St Mary *Roch* 77-88; rtd 88. *2 Westfield Close, Polegate, E Sussex BN26 6EF* Polegate (01323) 488153

SARGEANTSON, Kenneth William. b 30. **d** 90 **p** 91. NSM The Marshland *Sheff* 90-93; NSM Goole from 93. *St Mary's Church House, Swinefleet Road, Goole, N Humberside DN14 5TN* Goole (01405) 761749

SARGENT, John Philip Hugh. b 34. Or Coll Ox BA55 MA63. Chich Th Coll 55. **d** 57 **p** 58. C Kington w Huntington *Heref* 57-59; C Bridgnorth St Mary 59-63; C Leighton Buzzard *St Alb* 63-64; V Stonebroom *Derby* 64-73; Chapl Southn Gen Hosp 74-95. *Flat 2, 352 Winchester Road, Southampton SO16 6TW*

SARGENT, Preb Richard Henry. b 24. Man Univ BA50. Ridley Hall Cam 50. **d** 52 **p** 53. V Bushbury *Lich* 67-73; V Castle Church 73-89; RD Stafford 81-88; Preb Lich Cathl 87-89; rtd 89. *6 Kingcup Road, Stafford ST17 9JQ* Stafford (01785) 223582

SARGISSON, Conrad Ralph. b 24. Keble Coll Ox BA46 MA50. Wells Th Coll 48. **d** 50 **p** 51. V Penzance St Mary *Truro* 62-73; RD Penwith 72-73; V Westbury-on-Trym H Trin *Bris* 73-79; P-in-c Blisland w St Breward *Truro* 79-83; V Mylor w Flushing 83-91; rtd 91; P-in-c St Hilary *Truro* from 93. *The Rectory, St Hilary Churchtown, Penzance, Cornwall TR20 9DQ* Penzance (01736) 710294

SARKIES, Col John Walter Robert Courtney. b 12. MRCS36 LRCP36 DOMS48. Cuddesdon Coll 57. **d** 59 **p** 60. C Bearsted *Cant* 59-61; S Africa 61-67; Mauritius 67-69; Hon C Douglas St Matt *S & M* from 69; Perm to Offic from 94. *2 Westminster Terrace, Douglas, Isle of Man IM1 4ED* Douglas (01624) 674835

SARMEZEY, George Arpad. b 61. Qu Mary Coll Lon BA83 Golds Coll Lon PGCE86. Westcott Ho Cam CTM92. **d** 92 **p** 93. C Eastville St Anne w St Mark and St Thos *Bris* 92-94; C Stratton St Margaret w S Marston etc from 94. *54 Nythe Road, Stratton St Margaret, Swindon SN3 4AP* Swindon (01793) 822653

SASADA, Benjamin John. b 33. MA. E Anglian Minl Tr Course. **d** 82 **p** 83. NSM Dickleburgh, Langmere, Shimpling, Thelveton etc *Nor* 82-88; Perm to Offic *St E* from 84; NSM Diss *Nor* from 88. *The Grange, Walcott Green, Diss, Norfolk IP22 3SS* Diss (01379) 642174

SASSER, Howell Crawford. b 37. Maryland Univ BA72 Geo Mason Univ Virginia MA74. Washington Dioc Course 75. **d** 77 **p** 78. USA 77; W Germany 77-80; Somalia 80-92; Chapl Montreux w Gstaad *Eur* from 92. *92 ave de Chillon, 1820 Territet, Montreux, Switzerland* Montreux (21) 963-4354

SATTERFORD, Douglas Leigh. b 18. DSC42. Ripon Hall Ox 59. **d** 60 **p** 61. V Lyminster *Chich* 65-85; V Poling 65-85; rtd 85; Perm to Offic *Chich* 85-90; Perm to Offic *St E* from 90. *24 Wheatfields, Whatfield, Ipswich IP7 6RB*

SATTERLY, Gerald Albert. b 34. Lon Univ BA56 Ex Univ Hon BA. Wycliffe Hall Ox 58. **d** 60 **p** 61. C Southborough St Pet *Roch* 60-63; C S Lyncombe *B & W* 63-66; V Sheff St Barn *Sheff* 66-69; R Adwick-le-Street 69-73; V Awre and Blakeney *Glouc* 73-82; P-in-c Newnham 80-82; V Newnham w Awre and Blakeney 82-90; R Instow *Ex* from 90; V Westleigh from 90. *The Rectory, Quay Lane, Instow, Bideford, Devon EX39 4JR* Instow (01271) 860346

✠**SATTERTHWAITE, Rt Rev John Richard.** b 25. CMG91. Leeds Univ BA46. Coll of Resurr Mirfield 48. **d** 50 **p** 51 **c** 70. C Carl St Barn *Carl* 50-53; C Carl St Aid and Ch Ch 53-55; Asst Gen Sec C of E Coun on Foreign Relns 55-59; C St Mich Paternoster Royal *Lon* 55-59; P-in-c 59-65; Gen Sec C of E Coun on Foreign Relns 59-70; V St Dunstan in the West *Lon* 59-70; Hon Can Cant Cathl *Cant* 63-70; Gen Sec Abp's Commn on RC Relns 65-70; Suff Bp Fulham *Lon* 70-80; Bp Gib 70-80; Bp Eur 80-93; Dean Malta 70-93; rtd 93; Hon Ass Bp Carlisle from 93. *25 Spencer House, St Paul's Square, Carlisle CA1 1DG* Carlisle (01228) 594055

SAUL, Norman Stanley. b 30. St Aid Birkenhead 51. **d** 54 **p** 55. V Barton *Blackb* 68-72; V Foxdale *S & M* 72-77; V Maughold 77-90; CF (ACF) 80-86; rtd 90. *15 Croft Meadow, Bamber Bridge, Preston PR5 8HX* Preston (01772) 314475

SAUNDERS, Andrew Vivian. b 44. Leeds Univ BA65. Coll of Resurr Mirfield 66. **d** 68 **p** 69. C Goodmayes St Paul *Chelmsf* 68-71; C Horfield H Trin *Bris* 71-75; C Oldland 75-77; Ind Chapl *B & W* 77-80; P-in-c Buckland Dinham w Elm, Orchardleigh etc 77-78; P-in-c Buckland Dinham 78-80; V Westf 80-90; R Clutton w Cameley from 90. *The Rectory, Main Road, Temple Cloud, Bristol BS18 5DA* Temple Cloud (01761) 552296

SAUNDERS, Brian Gerald. b 28. Pemb Coll Cam BA49 MA53. Cuddesdon Coll 63. **d** 66 **p** 67. NSM Gt Berkhamsted *St Alb* 66-87; P-in-c Lt Gaddesden 87-92; rtd 92; Perm to Offic *Ox* from 92; Perm to Offic *St Alb* from 92. *73 Drayton Road, Newton Longville, Milton Keynes MK17 0BH* Milton Keynes (01908) 641876

SAUNDERS, Bruce Alexander. b 47. St Cath Coll Cam BA68 MA72 Ox Univ DipTh70. Cuddesdon Coll 68. **d** 71 **p** 72. C Westbury-on-Trym H Trin *Bris* 71-74; Hon C Clifton St Paul 74-78; Asst Chapl Bris Univ 74-78; TV Fareham H Trin *Portsm* 78-84; TR Mortlake w E Sheen *S'wark* from 84; RD Richmond and Barnes 89-94. *The Rectory, 170 Sheen Lane, London SW14 8LZ* 0181-876 4816

SAUNDERS, David. b 28. Keble Coll Ox BA50 DipTh51 MA59. Cuddesdon Coll 51. **d** 53 **p** 54. V Grimsby All SS *Linc* 67-78; V Caistor w Clixby 78-88; P-in-c Grasby 78-94; Chapl Caistor Hosp 78-94; P-in-c Searby w Owmby *Linc* 79-94; V Dunholme 88-92; P-in-c Welton and Dunholme w Scothern 92-94; rtd 94. *2 Oundle Close, Washingborough, Lincoln LN4 1DR* Lincoln (01522) 793164

SAUNDERS, David Anthony. b 48. Trin Coll Bris 76. **d** 78 **p** 79. C Bath Walcot *B & W* 78-80; Asst Dir RE 80-83; Youth Chapl 80-83; C Long Ashton 83-84; V Bath St Bart 84-90; Offg Chapl RN 84-90; V Cullompton *Ex* from 90; R Kentisbeare w Blackborough from 90. *The Vicarage, Gravel Walk, Cullompton, Devon EX15 1DA* Cullompton (01884) 33249 Fax 34747

SAUNDERS, Edward George Humphrey. b 23. St Jo Coll Cam BA48 MA50. Ridley Hall Cam. **d** 50 **p** 51. Lic to Offic *Leic* 69-71; V Ches Square St Mich w St Phil *Lon* 71-84; P-in-c Mayfair Ch Ch 80-84; Hon C Ox St Andr *Ox* from 84; rtd 88. *The Hensol, Shire Lane, Chorleywood, Rickmansworth, Herts WD3 5NH* Chorleywood (01923) 284816

SAUNDERS, George Arthur. b 18. Kelham Th Coll 35. **d** 41 **p** 42. V Plumstead Ascension *S'wark* 57-82; rtd 82. *69 Estuary Park, Combwich, Bridgwater, Somerset TA5 2RF* Combwich (01278) 653091

SAUNDERS, Graham Howard. b 53. Hatf Poly BSc77. Trin Coll Bris BA86. **d** 86 **p** 87. C Birm St Martin w Bordesley St Andr *Birm* 86-89; C Olton from 89. *35 Marsden Close, Solihull, W Midlands B92 7JR* 0121-707 3559

SAUNDERS, Guy. b 27. AKC51. **d** 52 **p** 53. P-in-c Burton w Coates *Chich* 69-81; P-in-c Up Waltham 69-81; P-in-c Duncton 69-81; P-in-c Bolney 81-83; V 83-91; rtd 91; Hon C Zeal Monachorum *Ex* from 92. *The Rectory, Zeal Monachorum, Crediton, Devon EX17 6DG* Bow (01363) 82342

SAUNDERS, John Barry. b 40. Chich Th Coll. **d** 83 **p** 84. C St Breoke *Truro* 83-84; C St Breoke and Egloshayle 84-87; V Treverbyn from 87; RD St Austell from 91. *The Vicarage, Treverbyn Road, Stenalees, St Austell, Cornwall PL26 8TL* St Austell (01726) 850335

SAUNDERS, Canon John Michael. b 40. Brasted Th Coll 66 Clifton Th Coll 68. **d** 70 **p** 71. C Homerton St Luke *Lon* 70-74; SAMS from 74; Brazil 74-91; P-in-c Horsmonden *Roch* from 91; Area Sec (SE England) SAMS from 91. *The Rectory, Goudhurst Road, Horsmonden, Tonbridge, Kent TN12 8JU* Brenchley (01892) 722521

SAUNDERS, Kenneth John. b 35. Linc Th Coll 73. **d** 75 **p** 76. C Boultham *Linc* 75-79; V Swinderby 79-87; V Cherry Willingham w Greetwell from 87. *The Vicarage, 14 Church Lane, Cherry Willingham, Lincoln LN3 4AB* Lincoln (01522) 750356

SAUNDERS, Malcolm Walter Mackenzie. b 34. Em Coll Cam BA58 MA62. Wycliffe Hall Ox 58. **d** 60 **p** 61. C Northn St

Giles *Pet* 60-63; C Northn St Alb 63-66; V Corby St Columba 66-84; Nat Dir Evang Explosion 84-91; Lic to Offic *Pet* 84-91; V Ketton 91-92; R Ketton w Tinwell from 92. *The Vicarage, 4 Edmonds Drive, Ketton, Stamford, Lincs PE9 3TH* Stamford (01780) 720228

SAUNDERS, Mrs Margaret Rose. b 49. Newnham Coll Cam BA71 St Jo Coll York CertEd72. St Alb Minl Tr Scheme 85. **d** 88 **p** 94. Hon Par Dn Gt Berkhamsted *St Alb* 88-90; Hon Chapl Asst Gt Ormond St Hosp Lon 88-90; Asst Chapl Aylesbury Vale HA Priority Care Unit 90-92; Asst Chapl Stoke Mandeville Hosp 90-92; Chapl St Jo Hosp Aylesbury 90-92; Chapl Milton Keynes Gen Hosp from 92. *Milton Keynes General Hospital, Standing Way, Milton Keynes MK6 5LD* Milton Keynes (01908) 660033/641876

SAUNDERS, Martin Paul. b 54. K Coll Lon BD76 AKC76. Westcott Ho Cam 77. **d** 78 **p** 79. C Seaton Hirst *Newc* 78-81; Hong Kong 81; C Egglescliffe *Dur* 81-82; Chapl to Arts and Recreation 81-84; C Jarrow 82-84; TV 84-88; V Southwick St Columba 88-94. *65 Deckham Terrace, Gateshead, Tyne & Wear NE5 3UY* 0191-477 2853

SAUNDERS, Michael. b 35. AKC61. **d** 61 **p** 62. V Weston *Guildf* 66-73; C St Alb Abbey *St Alb* 73-76; P-in-c Eversholt w Milton Bryan 76-79; C 79-80; P-in-c Old Alresford *Win* 80; R Old Alresford and Bighton 80-82; Perm to Offic from 82; Perm to Offic *Portsm* from 83; rtd 95. *11 Perins Close, Alresford, Hants SO24 9QL* Alresford (01962) 733496

SAUNDERS, Dr Michael. b 35. Lon Univ MB,BS FRCP FRCPEd MSOSc. NE Ord Course 82. **d** 84 **p** 85. Lic to Offic *York* 84-92; Tutor NE Ord Course 84-93; NSM Stokesley *York* 92-93; C Ripon Cathl *Ripon* 93-95; Perm to Offic *York* from 93; NSM Gt and Lt Ouseburn w Marton-cum-Grafton *Ripon* from 95; Tutor NE Ord Course from 95. *9 Park Street, Ripon, N Yorkshire HG4 2AX* Ripon (01765) 606425

SAUNDERS, Michael Walter (Mike). b 58. CChem MRSC84 Grey Coll Dur BSc79. Wycliffe Hall Ox 86. **d** 89 **p** 90. C Deane *Man* 89-93; TV Eccles from 93. *St Andrew's Vicarage, 11 Abbey Grove, Eccles, Manchester M30 9QN* 0161-707 1742

SAUNDERS, Reginald Frederick. b 15. Local NSM Course 76. **d** 79 **p** 80. NSM Perth St Ninian *St And* from 79; NSM Stanley from 79. *31 Muirend Road, Perth PH1 1JU* Perth (01738) 26217

SAUNDERS, Canon Richard Charles Hebblethwaite. b 17. Qu Coll Ox BA40 DipTh41 MA42. Westcott Ho Cam 41. **d** 42 **p** 43. V Bris St Ambrose Whitehall *Bris* 62-75; TR E Bris 75-77; P-in-c Colerne 77-82; P-in-c N Wraxall 77-82; RD Chippenham 80-82; rtd 82; Hon C Honiton, Gittisham, Combe Raleigh, Monkton etc *Ex* from 85. *St Michael's Cottage, Gittisham, Honiton, Devon EX14 0AH* Honiton (01404) 850634

SAUNDERS, Richard George (Dick). b 54. BNC Ox BA76 MA81. St Jo Coll Nottm 82. **d** 85 **p** 86. C Barrow St Mark *Carl* 85-89; C Cranham Park *Chelmsf* from 89. *226 Moor Lane, Upminster, Essex RM14 1HN* Upminster (01708) 221711

SAUNDERS, Ronald. b 37. ACP67 St Pet Coll Birm CertEd62 CertEd62 Columbia Univ MA82 PhD87. Sarum Th Coll 69. **d** 68 **p** 70. Malawi 68-72; C Kensington St Mary Abbots w St Geo *Lon* 72-73; C Bournemouth St Fran *Win* 73-75; Canada 75-81; C Gt Marlow *Ox* 81-82; Area Org Leprosy Miss 82-85; V Penycae *St As* 85-87; TV Wrexham 87-89; NSM Dio *Ox* 90-91; Chapl Morden Coll Blackheath from 91. *The Chaplain's House, Morden College, 19 St Germans Place, London SE3 0PW* 0181-858 3988

SAUNT, James Peter Robert. b 36. Chich Th Coll 73. **d** 75 **p** 76. C Portland All SS w St Pet *Sarum* 75-78; P-in-c Bratton 78-81; V 81-94; Chapl HM Young Offender Inst Erlestoke Ho from 81; P-in-c Oldbury *Sarum* from 94. *The Rectory, Heddington, Calne, Wilts SN11 0PR* Headington (01380) 850411 Fax 818663

SAUSBY, John Michael. b 39. AKC. **d** 63 **p** 64. C Crosland Moor *Wakef* 63-65; C Halifax St Jo Bapt 65-67; V Birkby 67-77; V Holmfirth 77-89; TR Upper Holme Valley from 89. *The Vicarage, 2 Rosegarth Avenue, Newmill Road, Holmfirth, Huddersfield HD7 2TE* Holmfirth (01484) 683285

SAVAGE, Christopher Marius. b 46. Bps' Coll Cheshunt Qu Coll Birm 68. **d** 70 **p** 71. C Battersea St Luke *S'wark* 70-75; TV Newbury *Ox* 75-80; R Lich St Mary w St Mich *Lich* 80-85; V Chessington *Guildf* 85-91; Ind Chapl *Win* from 91; Chapl Basingstoke Coll of Tech from 91. *15 Camwood Close, Basingstoke, Hants RG21 3BL* Basingstoke (01256) 469219

SAVAGE, Mrs Hilary Linda. b 48. RGN71 RM86. W Midl Minl Tr Course 89. **d** 92 **p** 94. C Quinton Road W St Boniface *Birm* from 92. *1 Four Acres, Birmingham B32 1RY* 0121-421 7600

SAVAGE, Leslie Walter. b 15. Cranmer Hall Dur 63. **d** 65 **p** 66. V Bolton w Cliburn *Carl* 69-74; V Holme-in-Cliviger *Blackb* 74-81; rtd 81; Perm to Offic *Chich* from 81. *42 Wilton Road, Bexhill-on-Sea, E Sussex TN40 1HX* Bexhill-on-Sea (01424) 223829

SAVAGE, Mark David John. b 55. Birm Univ BA76 Dur Univ BA82 Newc Univ MLitt83. Cranmer Hall Dur 80. **d** 83 **p** 84. C Newc St Gabr *Newc* 83-86; Adult Educn Adv 86-94; V Bedlington from 94. *The Vicarage, 21 Church Lane, Bedlington, Northd NE22 5EL* Bedlington (01670) 829220

SAVAGE, Michael Atkinson. b 33. St Pet Hall Ox BA57 MA61. Tyndale Hall Bris 57. **d** 59 **p** 60. C Rugby St Matt *Cov* 59-62; C Welling *Roch* 62-66; V Bowling St Steph *Bradf* 66-73; V Ben Rhydding 73-92; RD Otley 87-92; TR Quidenham *Nor* from 92. *The Rectory, Church Street, Banham, Norwich NR16 2HN* Quidenham (01953) 887562

SAVAGE, Paul James. b 58. Liv Univ BA81. Wycliffe Hall Ox 88. **d** 91 **p** 92. C Litherland St Phil *Liv* 91-94; CMS from 94. *Church Mission Society, Partnership House, 157 Waterloo Road, London SE1 8UU* 0171-928 8681 Fax 401 3215

SAVAGE, William Humphrey. b 15. Worc Ord Coll 63. **d** 65 **p** 66. V Thorverton *Ex* 68-73; V Cadbury 68-73; R Alphington 73-79; C Ex St Matt 79-80; C Ex St Sidwell and St Matt 80-84; rtd 84; Perm to Offic *Ex* 84-93. *1A Welsford Avenue, Wells, Somerset BA5 2HX* Wells (01749) 675659

SAVIDGE, Dr Graham John. b 47. Univ of Wales (Ban) BSc69 PhD78. CITC 89. **d** 92 **p** 94. Lic to Offic *D & D* from 92; NSM Down Cathl from 94. *7 Cedar Grove, Ardglass, Downpatrick, Co Down BT30 7UE* Ardglass (01396) 841501

SAVIGE, John Sydney. b 24. Launde Abbey. **d** 73 **p** 74. C Leic St Pet *Leic* 73-75; P-in-c Harby 76-77; P-in-c Stathern 76-77; R Harby w Stathern 77-83; RD Framland I 80-88; R Harby, Long Clawson and Hose 83-89; rtd 89. *43 Kingston Way, Seaford, E Sussex BN25 4NG* Seaford (01323) 490572

SAVIGEAR, Miss Elfrida Beatrice. b 49. Wye Coll Lon BSc71 Edin Univ DipAE72 Bath Univ MSc85. Trin Coll Bris DTS90 Ridley Hall Cam 91. **d** 93 **p** 94. C Ross w Brampton Abbotts, Bridstow, Peterstow etc *Heref* from 93. *The Little House, Sussex Avenue, Ross-on-Wye, Herefordshire HR9 5HA* Ross-on-Wye (01989) 564453

SAVILE, Canon Ian Keith Wrey. b 26. Trin Hall Cam BA50 MA54. Ridley Hall Cam 51. **d** 53 **p** 54. V Wandsworth All SS *S'wark* 64-74; RD Wandsworth 69-74; V S'well H Trin *S'well* 74-80; Bp's Adv on Evang 74-80; V Canford Magna *Sarum* 80-88; TR 88; RD Wimborne 85-88; Can and Preb Sarum Cathl 86-88; Patr Sec CPAS 88-93; Perm to Offic *Cov* 88-93; rtd 93. *Corner Cottage, West Street, Winterbourne Stickland, Blandford Forum, Dorset DT11 0NT* Milton Abbas (01258) 880459

SAVILL, David. b 27. TD69 and Bar 75. Em Coll Cam BA49 MA52. Ridley Hall Cam 50. **d** 52 **p** 53. V Heston *Lon* 67-73; Hon C Mettingham w Ilketshall St John *St E* 73-79; Hon C Mettingham 79-80; Chapl Felixstowe Coll 80-90; rtd 90. *Sancroft, 210 Park View, Crewkerne, Somerset TA18 8JL* Crewkerne (01460) 77298

SAVILLE, David James. b 39. Ch Ch Ox BA60 MA64. Clifton Th Coll 61. **d** 63 **p** 64. C Darfield *Sheff* 63-66; C St Leonards St Leon *Chich* 66-68; Cand Sec CPAS 69-74; V Taunton St Jas *B & W* 74-80; RD Taunton 78-80; V Chorleywood Ch Ch *St Alb* 80-90; RD Rickmansworth 86-90; Adv for Evang Edmonton *Lon* from 91. *9 Twyford Avenue, London N2 9NU* 0181-442 1442

SAVILLE, Edward Andrew. b 47. Leeds Univ CertEd70 Open Univ BA75. Carl Dioc Tr Inst. **d** 90 **p** 91. C Accrington St Jo w Huncoat *Blackb* 90-93; C Standish from 93. *St Wilfrid's House, 7 Rectory Lane, Standish, Wigan, Lancs WN6 0XA* Standish (01257) 425806

SAVILLE, George Edward. b 15. **d** 42 **p** 43. V Ilkeston H Trin *Derby* 56-63; rtd 80. *Fernecumbe House, Kings Coughton, Alcester, Warks B49 5QD* Alcester (01789) 762960

SAVILLE, Jeremy David. b 35. Or Coll Ox BA59 MA62. Chich Th Coll 58. **d** 60 **p** 61. C Tynemouth Cullercoats St Paul *Newc* 60-63; C Hexham 63-65; Lic to Offic *Ox* 65-68; Chapl Cuddesdon Coll 65-68; R Holt *Nor* 68-73; P-in-c Kelling w Salthouse 68-71; R Edgefield 71-73; R Hoe 73-78; R E Dereham w Hoe 73-81; V E Dereham 80-81; R Scarning w Wendling 78-81; R Beckenham St Geo *Roch* 81-89; Hon Can Roch Cathl 86-89; R Ashdon w Hadstock *Chelmsf* from 89. *The Rectory, Ashdon, Saffron Walden, Essex CB10 2HP* Ashdon (01799) 584897

SAVILLE, Mrs Margaret. b 46. SW Minl Tr Course 93. **d** 94 **p** 95. C Over St Chad *Ches* from 94. *St Chad's House, 9 Heaton Square, Winsford, Cheshire CW7 1EB* Winsford (01606) 553989

SAVILLE-DEANE, Marcus. b 58. Imp Coll Lon BSc80. Wycliffe Hall Ox 83. **d** 87 **p** 88. C Spring Grove St Mary *Lon* 87-92. *c/o The Bishop of Kensington, 19 Campden Hill Square, London W8 7JY* 0171-727 9818 Fax 229 3651

SAWARD, Canon Michael John. b 32. Bris Univ BA55. Tyndale Hall Bris. **d** 56 **p** 57. C Croydon Ch Ch Broad Green *Cant* 56-59; C Edgware *Lon* 59-64; Sec Liv Coun of Chs 64-67; Radio and TV Officer CIO 67-72; Hon C Beckenham St Jo *Roch* 70-72; V Fulham St Matt *Lon* 72-78; V Ealing St Mary 78-91; AD Ealing E 79-84; P-in-c Ealing St Paul 86-89; Preb St Paul's Cathl 85-91; Can Res and Treas St Paul's Cathl from 91. *6 Amen Court, London EC4M 7BU* 0171-248 8572 Fax as telephone

SAWLE, Martin. b 49. Solicitor 74 Dundee Univ LLB70. N Ord Course 87. **d** 90 **p** 91. NSM Longton *Blackb* 90-92; P-in-c Hoghton from 92. *The Vicarage, Chapel Lane, Hoghton, Preston PR5 0RY* Hoghton (01254) 852529

SAWLE, Ralph Burford. b 14. Lich Th Coll 34. **d** 37 **p** 38. V St Giles on the Heath w Virginstow *Truro* 68-72; V Werrington 68-72; V St Neot 72-79; rtd 79; Perm to Offic *Win* from 79. *32 Cavendish Close, Romsey, Hants SO51 7HT* Romsey (01794) 516132

SAWLE, William John. b 16. Lon Univ BD39. Tyndale Hall Bris 34. **d** 39 **p** 40. V Leyland St Andr *Blackb* 57-81; rtd 81. *8 Queensdale Close, Walton-le-Dale, Preston PR5 4JU* Preston (01772) 821213

SAWREY, Harold. b 14. Edin Th Coll 58. **d** 60 **p** 61. R Orton All SS *Carl* 63-80; P-in-c Tebay 77-80; rtd 80; Perm to Offic *Carl* from 81. *8 Atkinson Court, Newby Bridge, Ulverston, Cumbria LA12 8NW* Newby Bridge (015395) 31314

SAWYER, Andrew William. b 49. AKC71 St Aug Coll Cant 71. **d** 72 **p** 73. C Farnham *Guildf* 72-75; C Dawlish *Ex* 75-78; R Colkirk w Oxwick, Whissonsett and Horningtoft *Nor* 78-82; R Colkirk w Oxwick w Pattesley, Whissonsett etc 82-90; V Hungerford and Denford *Ox* from 90. *The Vicarage, Parsonage Lane, Hungerford, Berks RG17 0JB* Hungerford (01488) 682844

SAWYER, Derek Claude. b 33. ALCD58. **d** 58 **p** 59. C Kirby Muxloe *Leic* 58-60; C Braunstone 60-65; Mauritius 65-68; V Knighton St Mich *Leic* 68-82; Chapl Kifissia *Eur* 82; Lic to Offic *Glouc* 85-87; V Glouc St Aldate from 87. *St Aldate's Vicarage, Finlay Road, Gloucester GL4 9TN* Gloucester (01452) 523906

SAWYERS, Thomas Adam Barton. b 21. Edgehill Th Coll Belf 58. **d** 61 **p** 62. I Lissan *Arm* 69-82; rtd 82. *Lynwood, 82 Coleraine Road, Portrush, Co Antrim BT56 8HN* Portrush (01265) 823441

✝**SAXBEE, Rt Rev John Charles.** b 46. Bris Univ BA68. Cranmer Hall Dur DipTh69 PhD74. **d** 72 **p** 73 **c** 94. C Compton Gifford *Ex* 72-77; P-in-c Weston Mill 77-80; V 80-81; TV Cen Ex 81-87; Jt Dir SW Min Tr Course 81-92; Preb Ex Cathl 88-92; Adn Ludlow *Heref* from 92; Preb Heref Cathl from 92; P-in-c Wistanstow 92-94; P-in-c Acton Scott 92-94; Suff Bp Ludlow from 94. *Bishop's House, Corvedale Road, Halford, Craven Arms, Shropshire SY7 9BT* Craven Arms (01588) 673571 Fax 673585

SAXBY, Harold. b 11. St Chad's Coll Dur BA37 MA40. **d** 38 **p** 39. R Jarrow St Paul *Dur* 69-76; rtd 76; Hon C Wrington w Butcombe *B & W* 79-84. *Terrys Cross House, Woodmancote, Henfield, W Sussex BN5 9SX* Henfield (01273) 494648

SAXBY, Martin Peter. b 52. St Jo Coll Dur BA77 DipTh78. Cranmer Hall Dur 74. **d** 78 **p** 79. C Peckham St Mary Magd *S'wark* 78-81; C Ramsey *Ely* 81-84; P-in-c Yaxham *Nor* 84-89; P-in-c Welborne 84-89; P-in-c Mattishall w Mattishall Burgh 84-89; R Mattishall w Mattishall Burgh, Welborne etc 89-90; V Rugby St Matt *Cov* from 90. *St Matthew's Vicarage, 7 Vicarage Road, Rugby, Warks CV22 7AJ* Rugby (01788) 560572 or 535208

SAXON, Miss Doreen Harold Graham. b 29. Qu Coll Birm 77. dss 80 **d** 87 **p** 94. Wolv *Lich* 86-87; Par Dn 87-89; rtd 89. *20 Chequerfield Drive, Penn Fields, Wolverhampton WV3 7DH* Wolverhampton (01902) 342432

SAXON, Canon Eric. b 14. Man Univ BA35 MA80 Lon Univ BD40. ALCD40. **d** 40 **p** 41. R Salford St Matt *Man* 51-82; Chapl to The Queen 67-84; OStJ from 73; rtd 82; Perm to Offic *Ches* from 83. *27 Padstow Drive, Bramhall, Stockport, Cheshire SK7 2HU* 0161-439 7323

SAXTON, James. b 54. Lanc Univ BEd77 Hull Univ MEd85. Linc Th Coll 84. **d** 86 **p** 87. C Moor Allerton *Ripon* 86-90; C Knaresborough 90-92; TV Seacroft from 92. *St Luke's Vicarage, Stanks Lane North, Leeds LS14 5AS* Leeds (0113) 273 1302

✝**SAY, Rt Rev Richard David.** b 14. KCVO88. Ch Coll Cam BA38 MA41 Kent Univ Hon DCL87. Lambeth DD61 Ridley Hall Cam 38. **d** 39 **p** 40 **c** 61. C Croydon *Cant* 39-43; C St Martin-in-the-Fields *Lon* 43-50; Asst Sec C of E Youth Coun 42-44; Gen Sec 44-47; Gen Sec BCC 47-55; R Hatf *St Alb* 55-61; Hon Can St Alb 57-61; Bp Roch 61-88; ChStJ from 61; High Almoner 70-88; rtd 88; Asst Bp Cant from 88. *23 Chequers Park, Wye, Ashford, Kent TN25 5BB* Wye (01233) 812720

SAYER, Derek John. b 32. St Steph Ho Ox 55. **d** 58 **p** 58. C Tottenham All Hallows *Lon* 58-61; C Letchworth *St Alb* 61-63; Chapl RADD 63-64 and 66-82; C Lancing St Mich *Chich* 64-66; C Dorking w Ranmore *Guildf* 89-92; V Holmwood from 92. *The Vicarage, South Holmwood, Dorking, Surrey RH5 4JX* Dorking (01306) 889118

SAYER, Harold John. b 15. CCC Cam BA36. **d** 67 **p** 68. C Churchdown St Jo *Glouc* 67-71; C-in-c Wapley w Codrington and Dodington *Bris* 71-73; R Highnam w Lassington and Rudford *Glouc* 73-81; rtd 81; Perm to Offic *Glouc* 81-91; Perm to Offic *Ox* from 83. *27 Woolstrop Way, Quedgeley, Gloucester GL2 6NL* Gloucester (01452) 502091

SAYER, John Martin. b 35. Bris Univ BA57. Clifton Th Coll 59. **d** 61 **p** 62. C Hamworthy *Sarum* 61-64; Area Sec (N England, Glas, Edin and S & M) CMJ 64-66; Canada 66-78; USA from 78. *Address temp unknown*

SAYER, William Anthony John (Bill). b 37. St Mich Coll Llan 60. **d** 64 **p** 65. C Gorleston St Andr *Nor* 64-67; P-in-c Witton w Ridlington 67-71; P-in-c Honing w Crostwight 67-71; V Bacton w Edingthorpe 67-71; CF 71-84; Miss to Seamen from 84; R Holkham w Egmere w Warham, Wells and Wighton *Nor* from 84; RD Burnham and Walsingham 87-92. *The Rectory, Wells-next-the-Sea, Norfolk NR23 1JB* Fakenham (01328) 710107

SAYERS, Guy Anthony. b 10. Ex Coll Ox BA35 MA37. Ely Th Coll 34. **d** 36 **p** 37. R Empingham *Pet* 68-81; rtd 81; Perm to Offic *Pet* 82-93. *5 Gracey Court, Woodland Road, Broadclyst, Exeter EX5 3LP* Exeter (01392) 460721

SAYERS, Simon Philip. b 59. Cam Univ MA81. Oak Hill Th Coll 83. **d** 85 **p** 86. C Alperton *Lon* 85-89; C Hornsey Rise Whitehall Park Team 89-90; TV from 90. *43 Dresden Road, London N19 3BG* 0171-281 8775 or 281 9085

SAYLE, Philip David. b 61. St Jo Coll Nottm DipThMin94. **d** 94 **p** 95. C Helston and Wendron *Truro* from 94. *Wendron Vicarage, Wendron, Helston, Cornwall TR13 0EA* Helston (01326) 572169

SAYWELL, Philip. b 33. Linc Th Coll 57. **d** 60 **p** 61. V Lanteglos by Fowey *Truro* 66-73; Iran 73-77; R Cockley Cley w Gooderstone *Nor* 78-81; V Didlington 78-81; R Gt and Lt Cressingham w Threxton 78-81; R Hilborough w Bodney 78-81; R Oxborough w Foulden and Caldecote 78-81; UAE 81-84; Perm to Offic *Chich* 84-88; Nat Co-ord (UK) SOMA 85-88; rtd 93. *Little Ashott, Exford, Minehead, Somerset TA24 7NG* Exford (01643843) 619

SCAIFE, Andrew. b 50. Ex Coll Ox BA73 MA76. Wycliffe Hall Ox. **d** 77 **p** 78. C Everton St Geo *Liv* 77-81; P-in-c Liv St Mich 81; TV St Luke in the City 81-86; V Litherland St Phil from 86. *St Philip's Vicarage, Orrell Road, Litherland, Liverpool L21 8NG* 0151-928 3902

SCALES, Barbara Marion. b 24. S'wark Ord Course. **dss** 82 **d** 87 **p** 94. St Helier *S'wark* 82-87; Hon Par Dn 87-89; Chapl Asst St Helier Hosp Carshalton 82-88; NSM Cheam Common St Phil *S'wark* 89-95; rtd 95; Perm to Offic *S'wark* from 95. *51 Tonfield Road, Sutton, Surrey SM3 9JP* 0181-644 3712

SCAMMELL, Frank. b 56. Cam Univ MA. St Jo Coll Nottm BA83. **d** 82 **p** 83. C Stapenhill w Cauldwell *Derby* 82-86; TV Swanage and Studland *Sarum* 86-92; Min Southgate LEP *St E* from 92. *1A Mayfield Road, Bury St Edmunds, Suffolk IP33 2TJ* Bury St Edmunds (01284) 767693

SCAMMELL, Canon John James Frank. b 07. AKC32. St Paul's Coll Burgh 32. **d** 32 **p** 33. V Leighton Buzzard *St Alb* 54-80; V Eggington 54-80; P-in-c Billington 65-80; rtd 80; Perm to Offic *St Alb* from 80. *49 Heath Court, Plantation Road, Leighton Buzzard, Beds LU7 7JR* Leighton Buzzard (01525) 381380

SCAMMELL, John Richard Lyn. b 18. TD50. Bris Univ LLB45. Wycliffe Hall Ox 46. **d** 48 **p** 49. RAChD 53-73; P-in-c Bicknoller *B & W* 73-78; P-in-c Crowcombe 75-78; R Bicknoller w Crowcombe and Sampford Brett 78-81; Perm to Offic 81-93; rtd 83; Perm to Offic *Guildf* from 84. *4 Pine Ridge Drive, Lower Bourne, Farnham, Surrey GU10 3JW* Farnham (01252) 713100

SCANDINAVIA, Archdeacon of. See BROWN, Ven Gerald Arthur Charles

SCANLON, Geoffrey Edward Leyshon. b 44. Coll of Resurr Mirfield. **d** 76 **p** 77. C Beamish *Dur* 76-79; C-in-c Bishopwearmouth St Mary V w St Pet CD 79-81; USA from 81. *1226 North Vermilion, Danville, Illinois 61832, USA* Illinois (217) 442-1677

SCANTLEBURY, James Stanley. b 48. St Jo Coll Dur BA69 Heythrop Coll Lon MTh80. Westcott Ho Cam 70. **d** 72 **p** 73. C Upperby St Jo *Carl* 72-75; C Guildf H Trin w St Mary *Guildf* 75-77; Order of St Aug 77-86; Chapl Austin Friars Sch Carl 80-86; Chapl Mayfield Coll E Sussex 86-88; Chapl H Trin Sen Sch Halifax 88-90; NSM Ripponden *Wakef* 88-90; V Torpenhow *Carl* 91-94; V Allhallows 91-94; V Falmouth All SS *Truro* from 94. *All Saints' Vicarage, 72 Dracaena Avenue, Falmouth, Cornwall TR11 2EN* Falmouth (01326) 314141

SCARBOROUGH, John Richard Derek. b 32. Lon Univ BA54. Cuddesdon Coll. **d** 69 **p** 70. C Fulbeck *Linc* 69-72; C Bassingham 73-74; NSM from 93; Lic to Offic 74-76 and 78-93; R Boothby Graffoe 76-77; R Navenby 76-77; V Wellingore w Temple Bruer 76-77; V Graffoe 77-78. *Hales Cottage, 47 High Street, Navenby, Lincoln LN5 0DZ* Lincoln (01522) 811031

SCARGILL, Christopher Morris. b 57. UEA BA79 York Univ MA81 Leeds Univ CertEd81 Nottm Univ BTh89. Linc Th Coll 86. **d** 89 **p** 90. C Desborough *Pet* 89-92; C Buxton w Burbage and King Sterndale *Derby* 92-93; TV from 93. *17 Lismore Road, Buxton, Derbyshire SK17 9AN* Buxton (01298) 22433

SCARTH, John Robert. b 34. Leeds Univ BSc55 CertEd St Jo Coll Dur DipTh65. Cranmer Hall Dur 63. **d** 65 **p** 66. C Dewsbury All SS *Wakef* 65-68; V Shepley 68-72; Asst Master Kingston-upon-Hull Gr Sch 72-78; St Mary's C of E Sch Hendon 78-81; V Ossett cum Gawthorpe 81-88; R Tarrington w Stoke Edith, Aylton, Pixley etc *Heref* from 88. *The Rectory, Tarrington, Hereford HR1 4EU* Hereford (01432) 890314

SCARTH, Maurice John. b 31. MInstPS. St Deiniol's Hawarden 81. **d** 83 **p** 84. C Llandrillo-yn-Rhos *St As* 83-87; V Rhosymedre 87-91; V Kerry and Llanmerewig and Dolfor 91-93; rtd 93. *23 Penrhyn Beach East, Penrhyn Bay, Llandudno, Gwynedd LL30 3NU* Colwyn Bay (01492) 547906

SCATTERGOOD, William Henry. b 26. **d** 56 **p** 57. Australia 56-84; V Lonan *S & M* 84-92; V Laxey 84-92; rtd 92. *5 Sandgate Close, Seaford, E Sussex BN25 3LL* Seaford (01323) 492203

SCEATS, David Douglas. b 46. Ch Coll Cam BA68 MA72 Bris Univ MA71. Clifton Th Coll 68. **d** 71 **p** 72. C Cam St Paul *Ely* 71-74; Lect Trin Coll Bris 74-83; V Shenstone *Lich* 83-86; Dioc Tr Officer 86-91; P-in-c Colton 86-90; Dioc Dir of Local Min Development from 91; Warden of Readers from 91; C Lich St Chad from 94. *Diocesan Local Ministry Office, St Mary's House, The Close, Lichfield, Staffs WS13 7LD* Lichfield (01543) 414551

SCHAEFER, Carl Richard. b 67. Coll of Resurr Mirfield CPS94. **d** 94 **p** 95. C Ribbleton *Blackb* from 94. *43 Grange Place, Preston PR2 6QT* Preston (01772) 702960

SCHARF, Ulrich Eduard Erich Julian. b 35. Melbourne Univ BA59 MA67 Linacre Coll Ox BA67 MA72 Lon Univ PhD81. Ripon Hall Ox 65. **d** 67 **p** 68. C Hackney St Jo *Lon* 68-71; Lic to Offic 71-75; Bp Stepney's Chapl 71-75; P-in-c Shadwell St Paul w Ratcliffe St Jas 75-90; R St Geo-in-the-East w St Paul 79-86; P-in-c W Ham *Chelmsf* from 90. *The Vicarage, Devenay Road, London E15 4AZ* 0181-519 0955

SCHIBILD, Nigel Edmund David. b 47. Oak Hill Th Coll BA81. **d** 81 **p** 82. C Eccleston Ch Ch *Liv* 81-85; P-in-c Sydenham H Trin *S'wark* 85-87; V 87-91; Chapl Mildmay Miss Hosp from 91. *Mildmay Mission Hospital, Hackney Road, London E2 7NA* 0171-739 2331

SCHIFF, Canon Leonard Maro. b 08. Ex Coll Ox BA29 MA34. Westcott Ho Cam 32. **d** 32 **p** 33. Chapl to Overseas Peoples *Birm* 69-75; Hon Can Birm Cathl 69-75; Chapl Aston Univ 72-75; rtd 75; Perm to Offic *Carl* from 77. *9 Hoad Terrace, Ulverston, Cumbria LA12 7AS* Ulverston (01229) 587032

SCHILD, John. b 38. ALCD64. **d** 64 **p** 65. C Cheltenham Ch Ch *Glouc* 64-67; Area Sec (Dios Sheff and S'well) CMS 67-73; Area Sec (Dios Chelmsf and St Alb) CMS 73-76; V Lt Heath *St Alb* 76-88; R Bedf St Pet w St Cuth 88-94; P-in-c King's Walden and Offley w Lilley from 94. *The Vicarage, Church Road, Kings Walden, Hitchin, Herts SG4 8LX* Whitwell (01438) 871278

SCHLEGER, Ms Maria Francesca. b 57. LSE BA78 SS Coll Cam BA84 MA89. Westcott Ho Cam 82. **dss** 85 **d** 87 **p** 94. De Beauvoir Town St Pet *Lon* 85-87; Par Dn 87-90; D-in-c Bromley All Hallows 90; TD Bow H Trin and All Hallows 90-94; Dean of Women's Min (Stepney Area) 90-94; TV Bow H Trin and All Hallows 94; Perm to Offic *Birm* from 94. *The Vicarage, 69 South Road, Smethwick, Warley, W Midlands B67 7BP* 0121-558 0373

SCHOFIELD, Andrew Thomas. b 47. K Coll Lon BD70 AKC71 PGCE72. St Aug Coll Cant 70. **d** 81 **p** 82. C Whittlesey *Ely* 81-84; C Ramsey 84-87; P-in-c Ellington 87-94; P-in-c Grafham 87-94; P-in-c Spaldwick w Barham and Woolley 87-94; P-in-c Easton 87-94; P-in-c March St Jo 94; R from 94. *St John's Rectory, Station Road, March, Cambs PE15 8NG* March (01354) 53525

SCHOFIELD, David. b 43. Linc Th Coll 74. **d** 75 **p** 76. C Gainsborough All SS *Linc* 75-78; R Bolingbroke w Hareby 78-79; P-in-c Hagnaby 78-79; P-in-c Hagworthingham w Asgarby and Lusby 78-79; P-in-c Mavis Enderby w Raithby 78-79; P-in-c E Kirkby w Miningsby 78-79; R Bolingbroke 79-81; C-in-c Stamford Ch Ch CD 81-90; V Crowle from 90. *The Vicarage, Crowle, Scunthorpe, S Humberside DN17 4LE* Scunthorpe (01724) 710268

SCHOFIELD, Edward Denis. b 20. **d** 61 **p** 62. V Boughton under Blean *Cant* 66-75; P-in-c Dunkirk 73-75; V Boughton under Blean w Dunkirk 75-76; V Sandgate St Paul 76-85; rtd 85. *53 Haydons Park, Honiton, Devon EX14 8TA* Honiton (01404) 42584

SCHOFIELD, Canon John Martin. b 47. Selw Coll Cam BA69 MA73. St Steph Ho Ox 70. **d** 72 **p** 73. C Palmers Green St Jo *Lon* 72-75; C Friern Barnet St Jas 75-80; V Luton St Aug

Limbury *St Alb* 80-89; V Biddenham 89-94; Dir Continuing Minl Educn 89-94; Dir Minl Tr *Guildf* from 94; Can Res Guildf Cathl from 95. *4 Cathedral Close, Guildford, Surrey GU2 5TL* Guildford (01483) 577713 or 571826 Fax 567896

SCHOFIELD, John Verity. b 29. Jes Coll Ox BA52 DipTh53 MA56. Cuddesdon Coll 53. **d** 55 **p** 56. Asst Chapl St Paul's Sch Barnes 69-70; Chapl 71-80; Australia 81-83; Gen Sec Friends of Elderly & Gentlefolk's Help 83-94; rtd 94. *Bishops Barn, Foots Hill, Cann, Shaftesbury, Dorset SP7 0BW* Shaftesbury (01747) 853852

SCHOFIELD, Nigel Timothy. b 54. FRCO Dur Univ BA76 Nottm Univ BCombStuds83. Linc Th Coll 80. **d** 83 **p** 84. C Cheshunt *St Alb* 83-86; TV Colyton, Southleigh, Offwell, Widworthy etc *Ex* 86-94; V Seaton from 94. *The Vicarage, Colyford Road, Seaton, Devon EX12 2DF* Seaton (01297) 20391

SCHOFIELD, Richard Wyndham. b 09. Or Coll Ox BA32 MA38. Ripon Hall Ox 36. **d** 37 **p** 38. R Grundisburgh w Burgh *St E* 58-82; rtd 82; Perm to Offic *St E* from 82. *5 Constable Road, Ipswich IP4 2UN* Ipswich (01473) 256340

SCHOFIELD, Preb Rodney. b 44. St Jo Coll Cam BA64 MA67 St Pet Hall Ox BA70 MA73. St Steph Ho Ox 68. **d** 71 **p** 72. C Northn St Mary *Pet* 71-76; V Irchester 76-84; Lesotho 84-86; R W Monkton *B & W* from 86; Asst Dir of Ords 87-89; Dir of Ords from 89; Preb Wells Cathl from 90. *The Rectory, West Monkton, Taunton, Somerset TA2 8QT* West Monkton (01823) 412226

SCHOLEFIELD, John. b 27. Leeds Univ BSc50. Wells Th Coll 51. **d** 53 **p** 54. V Darton *Wakef* 64-70; V Stoke Gabriel *Ex* 70-84; P-in-c Collaton St Mary 82-84; V Stoke Gabriel and Collaton St Mary 84-92; rtd 92; Perm to Offic *Ex* from 92. *25 Droridge, Dartington, Totnes, Devon TQ9 6JQ* Totnes (01803) 863192

SCHOLER, Douglas William. b 23. Chich Th Coll 47. **d** 50 **p** 51. V W Pennard w W Bradley *B & W* 70-81; P-in-c Bleadon 81-82; R 82-87; rtd 87; Perm to Offic *B & W* from 87. *Rose Cottage, Middle Road, Cossington, Bridgwater, Somerset TA7 8LH* Bridgwater (01278) 722778

SCHOLEY, Donald. b 38. Leeds Univ CertEd60. Lich Th Coll 69. **d** 72 **p** 73. C Blaby *Leic* 72-75; TV Daventry w Norton *Pet* 75-78; R Wootton w Quinton and Preston Deanery from 78. *The Rectory, Water Lane, Wootton, Northampton NN4 0LG* Northampton (01604) 761891

SCHOLFIELD, Peter. b 35. Sarum Th Coll 64. **d** 66 **p** 67. P-in-c Carlton *Wakef* 69-90; rtd 90. *31 Springhill Avenue, Crofton, Wakefield, W Yorkshire WF1 1HA* Wakefield (01924) 863430

SCHOLLAR, Mrs Pamela Mary. b 39. Southn Univ DipEd80. S Dios Minl Tr Scheme 89. **d** 92 **p** 94. NSM Bournemouth St Andr *Win* 92-94; NSM Pokesdown St Jas from 94. *22 Bethia Road, Bournemouth BH8 9BD* Bournemouth (01202) 397925

SCHOOLING, Bruce James. b 47. Rhodes Univ BA73. St Paul's Grahamstown 76. **d** 76 **p** 77. S Africa 76-86; C Wanstead St Mary *Chelmsf* 87-90; V Leigh-on-Sea St Jas from 90. *St James's Vicarage, 103 Blenheim Chase, Leigh-on-Sea, Essex SS9 3BY* Southend-on-Sea (01702) 73603

SCHORAH, Michael James (Mike). b 63. Keble Coll Ox BA89 MA91. Trin Coll Bris BA95. **d** 95. C Cheltenham St Mary, St Matt, St Paul and H Trin *Glouc* from 95. *18 Eldon Road, Cheltenham, Glos GL52 6TU* Cheltenham (01242) 528567

SCHRAM, Dr Ralph. b 27. Down Coll Cam BA49 MA MB BChir55 St Thos Hosp Lon MD67. Oak Hill NSM Course 84. **d** 87 **p** 88. NSM Croydon Ch Ch *S'wark* 87-93; Perm to Offic Portsm from 93. *Nile Cottage, Colwell Road, Freshwater, Isle of Wight PO40 9NB* Isle of Wight (01983) 754865

SCHULD DE VERNY, Dietrich Gustave. *See* de VERNY, David Dietrich

SCHUNEMANN, Bernhard George. b 61. LRAM83 K Coll Lon BD86 AKC86. Ripon Coll Cuddesdon 88. **d** 90 **p** 91. C Kirkby *Liv* 90-93; C St Martin-in-the-Fields *Lon* from 93; Chapl British Sch of Osteopathy from 93. *6 St Martin's Place, London WC2N 4JJ* 0171-839 6067 or 930 0089/1862 Fax 839 5163

SCHWABACHER, Kurt Frederick. b 12. Chich Th Coll 36. **d** 39 **p** 40. V Forest Hill St Paul *S'wark* 63-68; Perm to Offic *Roch* from 68; rtd 77. *1 Raleigh Court, 21A The Avenue, Beckenham, Kent BR3 2DL* 0181-650 8670

SCHWIER, Peter Andrew. b 52. **d** 91 **p** 92. NSM Fressingfield, Mendham, Metfield, Weybread etc *St E* from 91. *Valley Farm, Metfield, Harleston, Norfolk IP20 0JZ* Fressingfield (01379) 384517

SCLATER, John Edward. b 46. Nottm Univ BA68 St Edm Hall Ox CertEd71. Cuddesdon Coll 69. **d** 71 **p** 72. C Bris St Mary Redcliffe w Temple etc *Bris* 71-75; Chapl Bede Ho Staplehurst 75-79; Chapl Warw Sch 79; P-in-c Offchurch *Cov* 79-80; Belgium 81-89; Willen Priory 89-91; C Linslade *Ox* 91-94; P-in-c Hedsor and Bourne End from 94. *The Rectory, 1 Wharf Lane, Bourne End, Bucks SL8 5RS* Bourne End (01628) 523046

SCOBIE, Dr Geoffrey Edward Winsor (Geoff). b 39. AFBPsS Bris Univ BSc62 MSc68 Birm Univ MA70 Glas Univ PhD78. Tyndale Hall Bris 62. **d** 65 **p** 66. C Summerfield *Birm* 65-66; C Moseley St Anne 66-67; Lect Psychology Glas Univ from 67; Hon C Glas St Silas *Glas* 70-83; P-in-c 83-84; Hon R 84-85; TR 85-86; Team Chapl 86-88; Asst Team Chapl from 88. *3 Norfolk Crescent, Bishopbriggs, Glasgow G64 3BA* 0141-722 2907

SCOONES, Roger Philip. b 48. DipTh. Trin Coll Bris. **d** 82 **p** 83. C Childwall All SS *Liv* 82-85; Bradf Cathl *Bradf* 85-90; V Congleton St Pet *Ches* from 90; P-in-c Congleton St Steph from 94. *St Peter's Vicarage, Chapel Street, Congleton, Cheshire CW12 4AB* Congleton (01260) 273212

SCORER, John Robson. b 47. Westcott Ho Cam 73. **d** 75 **p** 76. C Silksworth *Dur* 75-78; C Newton Aycliffe 78-82; V Sherburn 82-83; V Sherburn w Pittington 83-89; P-in-c Croxdale 89-93; Chapl Dur Constabulary from 89. *1 Vicarage Close, Howden le Wear, Crook, Co Durham DL15 8RB* Bishop Auckland (01388) 764938

SCOTLAND, Nigel Adrian Douglas. b 42. McGill Univ Montreal MA71 Aber Univ PhD75 CertEd75 Bris Univ MLitt. Gordon-Conwell Th Sem MDiv70 Lon Coll of Div ALCD66 LTh74. **d** 66 **p** 67. C Harold Wood *Chelmsf* 66-69; USA 69-70; Canada 70-72; Lic to Offic *Ab* 72-75; Chapl and Lect St Mary's Coll Cheltenham 75-79; Sen Lect 77-79; Chapl and Sen Lect Coll of SS Paul and Mary 79-84; NSM Cheltenham St Mark *Glouc* 85-92; Sen Lect Cheltenham and Glouc Coll of HE from 89; Perm to Offic from 92. *23 School Road, Charlton Kings, Cheltenham, Glos GL53 8BG* Cheltenham (01242) 529167

SCOTLAND, Primus of the Episcopal Church in. *See* HOLLOWAY, Most Rev Richard Frederick

SCOTT, Adam. b 47. TD78. Barrister 72 CEng81 MIEE81 Ch Ch Ox BA68 MA72 City Univ MSc79. S'wark Ord Course 73. **d** 75 **p** 76. NSM Blackheath Park St Mich *S'wark* from 75; Dean for MSE, Woolwich from 90. *19 Blackheath Park, London SE3 9RW* 0181-852 3286

SCOTT, Alfred Thomas. b 19. St Steph Ho Ox 78. **d** 81 **p** 82. NSM S Ascot *Ox* 81-85; NSM Bridport *Sarum* 85-89; Perm to Offic 89-90; rtd 90; Perm to Offic *Truro* from 90. *22 Castle Hill Court, Cross Lane, Bodmin, Cornwall PL31 2LE*

SCOTT, Preb Allan George. b 39. Man Univ BA61. Coll of Resurr Mirfield 61. **d** 63 **p** 64. C Bradf cum Beswick *Man* 63-66; P-in-c 66-72; Hon C Bramhall *Ches* 72-74; Hon C Tottenham St Jo *Lon* 74-76; Hon C Bush Hill Park St Steph 76-79; R Stoke Newington St Mary from 79; Preb St Paul's Cathl from 91; P-in-c Brownswood Park from 95. *The Rectory, Stoke Newington Church Street, London N16 9ES* 0171-254 6072

SCOTT, Andrew Charles Graham. b 28. Mert Coll Ox BA57 MA. Wells Th Coll 57. **d** 59 **p** 60. C Rugby St Andr *Cov* 59-64; Chapl RN 64-68; C Prenton *Ches* 68-71; V Tow Law *Dur* 71-81; RD Stanhope 77-81; V Bampton w Clanfield *Ox* from 81. *5 Deanery Court, Broad Street, Bampton, Oxford OX18 2LY* Bampton Castle (01993) 851222

SCOTT, Barrie. b 63. Birm Univ BA85 Golds Coll Lon PGCE86. St Steph Ho Ox 93. **d** 95. C Tilehurst St Mich *Ox* from 95. *Tilston Lodge, New Lane Hill, Reading RG3 4JN* Reading (01734) 411487

SCOTT, Basil John Morley. b 34. Qu Coll Cam BA59 Banaras Hindu Univ MA65. Ridley Hall Cam 58. **d** 60 **p** 61. C Woking St Pet *Guildf* 60-63; India 63-83; TR Kirby Muxloe *Leic* 83-89; Asian Outreach Worker (Leic Martyrs) 89-95; Derby Asian Chr Min Project *Derby* from 95. *16 Eastleigh Road, Leicester LE3 0DB* Leicester (0116) 254 2476

SCOTT, Brian. b 35. CCC Ox BA58. Coll of Resurr Mirfield 59. **d** 61 **p** 65. C Carl St Aid and Ch Ch *Carl* 61-62; Asst Master Hutton Gr Sch 63-65; Perm to Offic *Leic* 65-67; Lic to Offic 67-70; P-in-c Theddingworth 71-78; V Lubenham 71-78; Asst Chapl Oundle Sch *Pet* 78-83; R Barrowden and Wakerley w S Luffenham *Pet* from 83. *The Rectory, Barrowden, Oakham, Leics LE15 8ED* Morcott (01572) 87248

SCOTT, Charles Geoffrey. b 32. St Jo Coll Cam BA54 MA58. Cuddesdon Coll 56. **d** 58 **p** 59. C Brighouse *Wakef* 58-61; V Bathwick w Woolley *B & W* 61-64; V Frome Ch Ch 64-78; R Winchelsea *Chich* 78-93; R Winchelsea and Icklesham from 93. *The Rectory, St Thomas Street, Winchelsea, E Sussex TN36 4EB* Rye (01797) 226254

SCOTT, Christopher John Fairfax. b 45. Magd Coll Cam BA67 MA71. Westcott Ho Cam 68. **d** 70 **p** 71. C Nor St Pet Mancroft *Nor* 70-73; Chapl Magd Coll Cam 73-79; V Hampstead Ch Ch *Lon* 79-94. *87 Gough Way, Cambridge CB3 9LN* Cambridge (01223) 353477

SCOTT, Christopher Michael. b 44. SS Coll Cam BA66 MA70. Cuddesdon Coll 66. **d** 68 **p** 69. C New Addington *Cant* 68-73; C Westmr St Steph w St Jo *Lon* 73-78; V Enfield St Mich 78-81;

V Effingham w Lt Bookham *Guildf* 81-87; R Esher from 87; RD Emly from 91. *The Rectory, 4 Esher Place Avenue, Esher, Surrey KT10 8PY* Esher (01372) 462611

SCOTT, Christopher Stuart (Chris). b 48. Surrey Univ BA92. Sarum & Wells Th Coll 79. **d** 81 **p** 82. C Enfield Chase St Mary *Lon* 81-82; C Coalbrookdale, Iron-Bridge and Lt Wenlock *Heref* 82-86; P-in-c Breinton 86-89; Chapl Hickey's Almshouses Richmond from 89; Lic to Offic *S'work* from 89. *164 Sheen Road, Richmond, Surrey TW9 1XD* 0181-940 6560

SCOTT, Claude John. b 37. Qu Mary Coll Lon BSc60 PhD64 Lon Inst of Educn PGCE61. E Anglian Minl Tr Course 88. **d** 91 **p** 92. NSM Heigham H Trin *Nor* from 91. *17 Lime Tree Road, Norwich NR2 2NQ* Norwich (01603) 55686

SCOTT, Clifford Wentworth. b 04. Lon Univ BSc25. Ridley Hall Cam 25. **d** 27 **p** 28. R Sapcote *Leic* 64-72; rtd 72. *4 Egerton Road, Padstow, Cornwall PL28 8DJ* Padstow (01841) 532649

SCOTT, Colin. b 32. Dur Univ BA54. Coll of Resurr Mirfield 58. **d** 60 **p** 61. C Wallsend St Pet *Newc* 60-64; C Seaton Hirst 64-68; C Longbenton St Bart 68-70; V Benwell St Aid 70-77; V Sleekburn 77-89; P-in-c Cambois 77-88; V Longhoughton w Howick from 89. *The Vicarage, 3 South End, Longhoughton, Alnwick, Northd NE66 3AW* Longhoughton (01665) 577305

✠**SCOTT, Rt Rev Colin John Fraser.** b 33. Qu Coll Cam BA56 MA60. Ridley Hall Cam 56. **d** 58 **p** 59 **c** 84. C Clapham Common St Barn *S'work* 58-61; C Hatcham St Jas 61-64; V Kennington St Mark 64-71; RD Lambeth 68-71; Vice-Chmn Dioc Past Cttee 71-77; Hon Can S'wark Cathl 73-84; TR Sanderstead All SS 77-84; Suff Bp Hulme *Man* from 84; Chmn CCC from 94. *1 Raynham Avenue, Didsbury, Manchester M20 0BW* 0161-445 5922 Fax 448 9687

SCOTT, Cuthbert Le Messurier. b 13. Wells Th Coll 60. **d** 61 **p** 62. V Paddington St Jo w St Mich *Lon* 64-72; V Shamley Green *Guildf* 72-83; rtd 83; Perm to Offic *Chich* from 84; Chapl St Dunstans from 88. *Flat 10, 6 Sussex Square, Brighton BN2 1FJ* Brighton (01273) 689832

SCOTT, Ven David. b 24. Trin Hall Cam BA50 MA54. Cuddesdon Coll 50. **d** 52 **p** 53. V Boston *Linc* 66-75; Can and Preb Linc Cathl 71-89; RD Holland E 71-75; Adn Stow 75-89; V Hackthorn w Cold Hanworth 75-89; P-in-c N w S Carlton 78-89; Chapl to The Queen from 84; rtd 89. *4 Honing Drive, Southwell, Notts NG25 0LB* Southwell (01636) 813900

SCOTT, David. b 40. Rhodes Univ BA63. St Paul's Grahamstown LTh65. **d** 65 **p** 66. S Africa 65-91; TV Cheltenham St Mark *Glouc* from 92. *St Silas' Vicarage, Chesters Way Lane, Cheltenham, Glos GL51 0LB* Cheltenham (01242) 580496

SCOTT, David Lloyd Thomas. b 31. FCA Jes Coll Cam BA76 MA80. Ridley Hall Cam 73. **d** 76 **p** 77. C Swindon Ch Ch *Bris* 76-79; R Ripple *Worc* 79-82; V Broadheath, Crown E and Rushwick 82-88; V Lenton *S'well* 88-93; rtd 93. *6 Chandres Court, Allestree, Derby DE22 2FA* Derby (01332) 551445

SCOTT, David Victor. b 47. St Chad's Coll Dur BA69. Cuddesdon Coll 69. **d** 71 **p** 72. C St Mary-at-Latton *Chelmsf* 71-73; Chapl Haberdashers' Aske's Sch Elstree 73-80; V Torpenhow *Carl* 80-91; V Allhallows 80-91; R Win St Lawr and St Maurice w St Swithun *Win* from 91; Warden Sch of Spirituality Win from 91. *The Rectory, Colebrook Street, Winchester, Hants SO23 9LH* Winchester (01962) 868056

SCOTT, Edgar. b 12. Linc Th Coll 76. **d** 76 **p** 76. Hon C Wombwell *Sheff* 76-90; rtd 90; Perm to Offic *Sheff* 90-93. *17 Wood Walk, Wombwell, Barnsley, S Yorkshire S73 0LZ* Barnsley (01226) 753020

SCOTT, Canon Eric Walter. b 16. St Jo Coll Cam BA38 MA43. Ridley Hall Cam 38. **d** 40 **p** 41. C Reading St Jo *Ox* 40-43; C Cam H Trin *Ely* 43-45; C-in-c Tilehurst St Mary CD *Ox* 45-49; V Brimpton w Wasing 49-53; Canada 53-87 and 89-90; Perm to Offic *Nor* 87-89; Perm to Offic *Ely* from 89. *4 Allen Court, Hauxton Road, Trumpington, Cambridge CB2 2LU* Cambridge (01223) 841015

SCOTT, Gary James. b 61. Edin Univ BD87. Edin Th Coll 85. **d** 87 **p** 88. C Edin St Cuth *Edin* 87-90; R Peebles 90-92; P-in-c Innerleithen from 92. *St Peter's Rectory, 36 Wemyss Place, Peebles EH45 8JT* Peebles (01721) 720571

SCOTT, Canon Gordon. b 30. Man Univ BA51. St Jo Coll Dur 51. **d** 53 **p** 54. Chapl Dunrobin Sch Sutherland 66-72; Chapl Pocklington Sch York 72-74; V Barton w Pooley Bridge *Carl* 74-80; RD Penrith 79-82; P-in-c Lazonby 80-90; R Gt Salkeld w Lazonby 80-90; Hon Can Carl Cathl 83-94; P-in-c Patterdale 90-94; rtd 94. *48 Lakeland Park, Keswick, Cumbria CA12 4AT* Keswick (017687) 75862

SCOTT, Harold James. b 05. Dur Univ LTh30 Jes Coll Cam 61. St Aug Coll Cant 26. **d** 30 **p** 31. V Swavesey *Ely* 61-71; rtd 71. *Flat 14, Stuart Court, High Street, Kibworth, Leicester LE8 0LE* Leicester (0116) 279 6351

SCOTT, Hedley. b 36. Coll of Resurr Mirfield 68. **d** 70 **p** 71. C High Elswick St Phil *Newc* 70-73; C Sleekburn 73-76; V

Shilbottle 76-82; V Scotswood 82-92; V Weetslade from 92. *59 Kirklands, Burradon, Cramlington, Northd NE23 7LE* 0191-250 0251

SCOTT, Mrs Helen Ruth. b 59. St Thos Hosp Lon SRN81 R Shrewsbury Hosp RM85. S'wark Ord Course DipRS92. **d** 92 **p** 94. NSM Richmond St Mary w St Matthias and St Jo *S'wark* from 92. *164 Sheen Road, Richmond, Surrey TW9 1XD* 0181-940 6560

SCOTT, Ian. b 45. MBChA87 MSSCh87. Qu Coll Birm 92. **d** 94 **p** 95. C Cropthorne w Charlton *Worc* from 94. *The Vicarage, Cropthorne, Pershore, Worcs WR10 3NB* Evesham (01386) 860279

SCOTT, Ian Michael. b 25. Bris Univ BA50 Leic Univ DipEd51. Bps' Coll Cheshunt 52. **d** 53 **p** 54. V Haverstock Hill H Trin w Kentish Town St Barn *Lon* 63-93; rtd 93; Perm to Offic *Nor* from 93. *Barnsters Roost, Cromer Road, High Kelling, Holt, Norfolk NR25 6QE* Holt (01263) 711343

SCOTT, Mrs Inez Margaret Gillette. b 26. St Alb Minl Tr Scheme 76. **dss** 79 **d** 87 **p** 94. Preston w Sutton Poyntz and Osmington w Poxwell *Sarum* 83-86; Dorchester 86-87; Par Dn 87-88; NSM from 88; rtd 88. *14 Came View Road, Dorchester, Dorset DT1 2AE* Dorchester (01305) 267547

SCOTT, James Alexander Gilchrist (Jim). b 32. Linc Coll Ox BA56 DipTh57 MA60. Wycliffe Hall Ox 56. **d** 58 **p** 59. C Shipley St Paul *Bradf* 58-61; Abp's Dom Chapl *York* 61-65; Brazil 65-67; V Grassendale *Liv* 68-77; V Thorp Arch *York* 77; P-in-c Walton 77; V Thorp Arch w Walton 77-89; Chapl HM Pris Rudgate 77-82; Askham Grange 82-87; RD Tadcaster 78-86; V Kirk Ella 89-92; TR from 92. *The Vicarage, 2 School Lane, Kirk Ella, Hull HU10 7NR* Hull (01482) 653040

SCOTT, James William. b 39. S Dios Minl Tr Scheme 84. **d** 88 **p** 89. NSM Bremhill w Foxham and Hilmarton *Sarum* 88-94; NSM Derry Hill w Bremhill and Foxham from 94. *14 Bremhill, Calne, Wilts SN11 9LA* Calne (01249) 813114

SCOTT, Janice Beasant. b 44. MCSP66 Middx Hosp Physiotherapy Sch DipPh70. E Anglian Minl Tr Course 89. **d** 92 **p** 94. NSM Fakenham w Alethorpe *Nor* 94-95; C Eaton from 95. *12 Fulton Close, Eaton, Norwich NR4 6HX* Norwich (01603) 57922

SCOTT, John. b 54. QUB BD79. CITC 80. **d** 81 **p** 82. C Willowfield *D & D* 81-83; C Newtownards 83-85; I Kilskeery w Trillick *Clogh* 85-90; rtd 90; Lic to Offic *D & D* from 90. *60 Lismore Road, Ardglass, Downpatrick, Co Down BT30 7SY* Downpatrick (01396) 841958

SCOTT, John David. b 52. St Jo Coll Ox BA74 MA78 Leeds Univ BA78. Coll of Resurr Mirfield 76. **d** 78 **p** 79. C Oundle *Pet* 78-81; C Dalston H Trin w St Phil *Lon* 81-85; V Ponders End St Matt 85-91; Chapl Bede Ho Staplehurst from 91. *Bede House, Goudhurst Road, Staplehurst, Tonbridge, Kent TN12 0HQ* Staplehurst (01580) 891995

SCOTT, John Eric. b 16. FSA St Cath Coll Ox BA38 MA42. Ripon Hall Ox 39. **d** 40 **p** 41. Ho Master Forest Sch Snaresbrook 55-81; P-in-c St Mich Cornhill w St Pet le Poer etc *Lon* 81-85; rtd 85. *17 Harman Avenue, Woodford Green, Essex IG8 9DS* 0181-505 7093

SCOTT, Preb John Gilbert Mortimer. b 25. St Edm Hall Ox BA49 MA52. Bps' Coll Cheshunt. **d** 51 **p** 52. V Newton St Cyres *Ex* 66-84; RD Cadbury 81-84; Preb Ex Cathl from 84; P-in-c Bampton 84; P-in-c Clayhanger 84; P-in-c Petton 84; V Bampton, Morebath, Clayhanger and Petton 84-91; rtd 91. *Trelake, Bridgetown Hill, Totnes, Devon TQ9 5BA* Totnes (01803) 867754

SCOTT, John Harold. b 46. Univ of Wales (Cardiff) BSc69. St Steph Ho Ox 69. **d** 72 **p** 73. C Skewen *Llan* 72-74; C Port Talbot St Theodore 74-77; P-in-c Bedlinog 77-78; V 78-85; R Penderyn w Ystradfellte and Pontneathvaughan *S & B* from 85. *The Vicarage, Ystradfellte, Aberdare, M Glam CF44 9JE* Glyn Neath (01639) 720405

SCOTT, John Peter. b 47. Open Univ BA80. Lambeth STh81 K Coll Lon 69 St Aug Coll Cant 74. **d** 75 **p** 76. C Dartford St Alb *Roch* 75-78; C-in-c Goring-by-Sea *Chich* 78-81; Chapl Wells and Meare Manor Hosps 81-86; CF (TAVR) 82-90; Chapl Pangbourne Coll Berks 86-90; Min Reigate St Phil CD *S'work* 90-92; P-in-c Reigate St Phil from 92; Chapl St Bede's Ecum Sch Redhill from 90. *The Parsonage, 102A Nutley Lane, Reigate, Surrey RH2 9HA* Reigate (01737) 244542

SCOTT, Keith Brounton de Salve. b 55. QUB BD. DipTh. **d** 83 **p** 84. C Belf St Matt *Conn* 83-87; I Ardclinis and Tickmacrevan w Layde and Cushendun from 87. *76 Largy Road, Carnlough, Ballymena, Co Antrim BT44 0JJ* Carnlough (01574) 885618

SCOTT, Kenneth James (Ken). b 46. Bris Univ BA68. Trin Coll Bris 71. **d** 73 **p** 74. C Illogan *Truro* 73-76; C Camberley St Paul *Guildf* 76-81; R Bradf Peverell, Stratton, Frampton etc *Sarum* from 81; RD Dorchester from 95. *The Rectory, Church Lane, Frampton, Dorchester, Dorset DT2 9NL* Maiden Newton (01300) 320429

SCOTT, Dr Kevin Francis. b 51. GRSC Peterho Cam MA Mert Coll Ox DPhil76. Wycliffe Hall Ox. **d** 83 **p** 84. C Ox St Ebbe w

H Trin and St Pet *Ox* 83-86; P-in-c Prestonpans *Edin* 86-93; R Musselburgh 86-93; R Edin SS Phil and Jas from 93. *The Rectory, 5 Wardie Road, Edinburgh EH5 3QE* 0131-552 4300

SCOTT, Kevin Peter. b 43. Reigate Coll of Art DipAD73. Coll of Resurr Mirfield CPT93. **d** 93 **p** 94. C Rushall *Lich* from 93. *61 Daw End Lane, Walsall WS4 1JP* Walsall (01922) 35116

SCOTT, Kevin Willard. b 53. Westhill Coll Birm CYCW77. Linc Th Coll CMinlStuds92. **d** 92 **p** 93. C Walton-on-Thames *Guildf* from 92. *1 Egmont Road, Walton-on-Thames, Surrey KT12 2NW* Walton-on-Thames (01932) 229621

SCOTT, Lester Desmond Donald. NUI BA89. CITC BTh92. **d** 92 **p** 93. C Kilmore w Ballintemple, Kildallon etc *K, E & A* from 92. *Killeshandra Rectory, Killeshandra, Co Cavan, Irish Republic* Killeshandra (49) 34238 Fax 33204

SCOTT, Canon Malcolm Kenneth Merrett. b 30. ACA53 FCA64. Clifton Th Coll 56. **d** 58 **p** 59. C Highbury Ch Ch *Lon* 58-60; CMS 60-61; Uganda 61-74; V Sunnyside w Bourne End *St Alb* 74-90; V Clapham from 90. *The Vicarage, Green Lane, Clapham, Bedford MK41 6ER* Bedford (01234) 352814

SCOTT, Michael Bernard Campion. b 29. Or Coll Ox BA52 MA56 DTh. Edin Th Coll 52. **d** 54 **p** 55. C Reading St Mary V *Ox* 66-72; C-in-c Reading St Mark CD 72-76; C-in-c Orton Malborne CD *Ely* 76-91; Chapl Glouc Cen for Mentally Handicapped Orton 77-91; rtd 91. *13 Mill Street, Puddletown, Dorchester, Dorset DT2 8SQ* Puddletown (01305) 848030

SCOTT, Patrick Henry Fowlis. b 25. Jes Coll Cam BA51 MA55. Wells Th Coll 51. **d** 53 **p** 54. CF 57-70; Dep Asst Chapl Gen 70-71 and 74-80; Sen CF 72-74; P-in-c Fridaythorpe w Fimber and Thixendale *York* 80-83; P-in-c Sledmere and Wetwang w Cowlan 80-83; V Sledmere and Cowlam w Fridaythorpe, Fimer etc 84-90; rtd 90. *3 Appleby Glade, Haxby, York YO3 3YW* York (01904) 769258

SCOTT, Peter Crawford. b 35. Ch Ch Ox BA56 MA61. Cuddesdon Coll 60. **d** 62 **p** 63. C Broseley w Benthall *Heref* 62-66; P-in-c Hughenden *Ox* 66-71; C Hykeham *Linc* 71-73; P-in-c Stotteston *Heref* 73-76; Australia from 76. *St Andrew's Rectory, Alvie, Victoria, Australia 3249* Geelong (52) 348232

SCOTT, Peter James Douglas Sefton. b 59. Edin Univ BD83. Edin Th Coll 81. **d** 83 **p** 84. C Helensburgh *Glas* 83-86; C-in-c Glas St Oswald 86-89; R 89-91; Chapl RN from 91. *Directorate Gen, RN Chapl Services, Room 203, Victory Building, HM Naval Base, Portsmouth PO1 3LS* Portsmouth (01705) 727903 Fax 727112

SCOTT, Peter Lawrence. b 20. St Cath Coll Cam BA43 MA46. Ely Th Coll. **d** 47 **p** 48. R Withyham St Mich *Chich* 53-86; rtd 86. *Abbeyfield, 10 Eastfield Park, Weston-Super-Mare, Avon BS22 2PE* Weston-super-Mare (01934) 614343

SCOTT, Peter Lindsay. b 29. Keble Coll Ox BA54 MA58. Linc Th Coll 54. **d** 56 **p** 57. V Heap Bridge *Man* 63-73; V Rochdale St Geo w St Alb 73-86; R Droylsden St Andr 86-94; rtd 94. *2 Chancel Place, Rochdale, Lancs OL16 1FB* Rochdale (01706) 523270

SCOTT, Simon James. b 65. Ch Ch Ox BA87 MA91. Wycliffe Hall Ox 88. **d** 91 **p** 92. C Cheadle All Hallows *Ches* 91-95; Scripture Union from 95. *59F Lake Street, Oxford OX1 4RR* Oxford (01865) 723318 Fax as telephone

SCOTT, Terence. b 56. QUB BSc77. CITC 77. **d** 80 **p** 81. C Ballymena *Conn* 80-83; C Antrim All SS 83-85; P-in-c Conn w Antrim St Patr 85-88; I Magherafelt *Arm* from 88; Hon VC Arm Cathl from 95. *St Swithin's Rectory, 1 Churchwell Lane, Magherafelt, Co Londonderry BT45 6AL* Magherafelt (01648) 32365

SCOTT, Mrs Theresa Anne. b 53. Bris Univ BSc75 Lon Univ PGCE76. Ox Min Course 89. **d** 92 **p** 94. NSM Wickham Bishops w Lt Braxted *Chelmsf* 92-93; NSM Drayton St Pet (Berks) *Ox* from 94. *The Driftway, Sutton Wick Lane, Drayton, Oxon OX14 4HJ* Abingdon (01235) 533714

SCOTT, Timothy Charles Nairne (Tim). b 61. Ex Univ BA83. Westcott Ho Cam 84. **d** 87 **p** 88. C Romford St Edw *Chelmsf* 87-89; Community Priest 89-94; P-in-c Leytonstone H Trin Harrow Green from 94. *The Vicarage, 4 Holloway Road, London E11 4LD* 0181-539 7760

SCOTT, Vernon Malcolm. b 30. TCD BA57 MA60. TCD Div Sch Div Test56 Ridley Hall Cam 58. **d** 58 **p** 59. C Limehouse St Anne *Lon* 58-62; C N St Pancras All Hallows 62-66; V Enfield St Mich 66-77; R Tansor w Cotterstock and Fotheringhay *Pet* 77-81; R Barby w Onley 81-83; V Kilsby 81-83; R Barby w Kilsby 83-90; R Coxford Gp *Nor* 90-94; P-in-c South Raynham, E w W Raynham, Helhoughton, etc from 94; R E and W Rudham, Houghton-next-Hartley etc from 95. *The Rectory, Broomsthorpe Road, East Rudham, King's Lynn, Norfolk PE31 8RG* East Rudham (01485) 528756

SCOTT, Walter David Craig. b 22. Selw Coll Cam BA49 MA53. Sarum Th Coll 49. **d** 51 **p** 52. V Cleadon Park *Dur* 67-71; V Bulkington *Cov* 72-83; RD Bedworth 76-79; V Bulkington w Shilton and Ansty 83-87; rtd 87; Perm to Offic *Cov* from 87. *8 Osprey Close, Nuneaton, Warks CV11 6TF* Nuneaton (01203) 345561

SCOTT, William. b 20. Coll of Resurr Mirfield. **d** 60 **p** 61. C Wolborough w Newton Abbot *Ex* 60-63; Chapl St Cath Sch Bramley 63-66; Chapl SS Mary and Anne's Sch Abbots Bromley 72-76; Perm to Offic *Cant* 79-90; Chapl Boulogne-sur-Mer w Calais and Lille *Eur* 90-93; Chapl Lille from 93. *Christ Church, rue Watteau, 59000 Lille, France*

SCOTT, William John. b 46. TCD BA70. CITC. **d** 71 **p** 72. C Ban St Comgall *D & D* 71-74; C Holywood 74-80; I Carnalea 80-90; I Seapatrick from 90. *The Rectory, 63 Lurgan Road, Banbridge, Co Down BT32 4LY* Banbridge (018206) 22612

SCOTT, William Sievwright. b 46. Edin Th Coll 67. **d** 70 **p** 71. C Glas St Ninian *Glas* 70-73; C Bridgwater St Fran *B & W* 73-77; R Shepton Beauchamp w Barrington, Stocklinch etc 77-81; P-in-c Cossington 82-84; P-in-c Woolavington 82-84; Chapl Community of All Hallows Ditchingham 84-91; V Pimlico St Mary Graham Terrace *Lon* from 91. *St Mary's Presbytery, 30 Bourne Street, London SW1W 8JJ* 0171-730 2423

SCOTT-DEMPSTER, Canon Colin Thomas. b 37. Em Coll Cam BA65 MA68. Cuddesdon Coll 64. **d** 66 **p** 67. C Caversham *Ox* 66-69; Chapl Coll of SS Mark and Jo Chelsea 69-73; V Chieveley w Winterbourne and Oare *Ox* from 73; RD Newbury from 77; Hon Can Ch Ch from 90. *Chieveley Vicarage, Newbury, Berks RG16 8UT* Chieveley (01635) 248341

✠**SCOTT-JOYNT, Rt Rev Michael Charles.** b 43. K Coll Cam BA65 MA68. Cuddesdon Coll 65. **d** 67 **p** 68 **c** 87. C Cuddesdon *Ox* 67-70; Tutor Cuddesdon Coll 67-71; Chapl 71-72; TV Newbury St Nic *Ox* 72-75; P-in-c Bicester 75-79; P-in-c Caversfield 75-79; P-in-c Bucknell 76-79; TR Bicester w Bucknell, Caversfield and Launton 79-81; RD Bicester and Islip 76-81; Can Res St Alb 82-87; Dir of Ords and Post-Ord Tr 82-87; Suff Bp Stafford *Lich* 87-92; Area Bp Stafford from 92; Hon Can Lich Cathl from 87. *Ash Garth, Broughton Crescent, Barlaston, Stoke-on-Trent ST12 9DD* Barlaston (01782) 373308 Fax 373705

SCOTT-OLDFIELD, Ivor Erroll Lindsay. b 21. Univ Coll Dur BA49. Sarum Th Coll 49. **d** 51 **p** 52. Dir Gen RADD 68-87; rtd 87. *11E Prior Bolton Street, London N1 2NX*

SCOTT-THOMPSON, Ian Mackenzie. b 57. Ch Ch Ox BA78. St Jo Coll Nottm BA82. **d** 83 **p** 84. C Hartley Wintney, Elvetham, Winchfield etc *Win* 83-85; C Bitterne 85-89; V Iford from 89. *St Saviour's Vicarage, Holdenhurst Avenue, Bournemouth BH7 6RB* Bournemouth (01202) 425978

SCRACE, David Peter. b 46. Sarum & Wells Th Coll 79. **d** 81 **p** 82. C Abbots Langley *St Alb* 81-85; TV Chippenham St Paul w Hardenhuish etc *Bris* 85-91; P-in-c Harnham *Sarum* from 91; RD Salisbury from 93. *The Vicarage, Old Blandford Road, Harnham, Salisbury SP2 8DQ* Salisbury (01722) 333564

SCREECH, Prof Michael. b 26. l'Ordre national du Merite 83 l'Ordre national de la Legion d'Honneur 93. FBA81 FRSL87 Univ Coll Lon BA50 DLitt82 Birm Univ DLitt59 All So Coll Ox MA84 DLitt90 Ex Univ Hon DLitt93. Ox Min Course 92. **d** 93 **p** 94. Fell Univ Coll Lon from 82; NSM Ox St Giles and SS Phil and Jas w St Marg *Ox* from 93. *5 Swanston Field, Whitchurch, Reading RG8 7HP* Pangbourne (01734) 842513

SCREECH, Royden. b 53. K Coll Lon BD74 AKC74. St Aug Coll Cant 75. **d** 76 **p** 77. C Hatcham St Cath *S'wark* 76-80; V Nunhead St Antony 80-87; P-in-c Nunhead St Silas 82-87; RD Camberwell 83-87; V New Addington 87-94; Perm to Offic from 95; Selection Sec ABM from 94. *6 Brooklyn Grove, London SE25 4NJ, or Church House, Great Smith Street, London SW1P 3NZ* 0181-656 8965 or 0171-222 9022 Fax 799 2714

SCRINE, Ralph. b 19. Bris Univ BA40 Fitzw Ho Cam BA46 MA60 Lon Univ MPhil81. Westcott Ho Cam 45. **d** 46 **p** 47. Chapl Ch Ch Coll Cant 68-75; Sen Lect Ch Ch Coll Cant 68-84; rtd 84; Perm to Offic *Cant* from 84. *Little Henny, Stone Street, Petham, Canterbury, Kent CT4 5PP* Petham (01227) 700725

✠**SCRIVEN, Rt Rev Henry William.** b 51. Sheff Univ BA72. St Jo Coll Nottm DPS75. **d** 75 **p** 76 **c** 95. C Wealdstone H Trin *Lon* 75-79; SAMS (Argentina) 79-82; USA 82-83; SAMS (Spain) 84-90; Chapl Madrid w Bilbao *Eur* 90-95; Suff Bp Eur and Dean Brussels from 95. *c/o Diocesan Office, 14 Tufton Street, London SW1P 3QZ* 0171-976 8001 Fax 976 8002

SCRIVEN, Hugh Alexander. b 59. Trin Coll Cam BA80. Cranmer Hall Dur 81. **d** 84 **p** 85. C Pudsey St Lawr and St Paul *Bradf* 84-87; C Madeley *Heref* 87-91; TV from 91. *Sutton Hill Vicarage, 1 Spencer Drive, Sutton Hill, Telford, Shropshire TF7 4JY* Telford (01952) 680004

SCRIVEN, Paul Michael. b 51. Bris Univ BSc72 Lon Univ CertEd74. S Dios Minl Tr Scheme 84. **d** 87 **p** 88. NSM Redmarley D'Abitot, Bromesberrow w Pauntley etc *Glouc* 87-90; Lic to Offic *Heref* 90-95; Lic to Offic *Mon* 94-95; V Dingestow and Llangovan w Penyclawdd etc from 95. *The Vicarage, Dingestow, Monmouth, Gwent NP5 4DY* Dingestow (0160083) 206

SCRIVENER, Robert Allan. b 54. Nottm Univ BEd78. Linc Th Coll 79. **d** 80 **p** 81. C Sherwood *S'well* 80-83; C Burghclere w Newtown and Ecchinswell w Sydmonton *Win* 83-86; TV Hemel Hempstead *St Alb* 86-93; V Kingston upon Hull St Nic *York* from 93. *St Nicholas' Vicarage, 898 Hessle High Road, Hull HU4 6SA* Hull (01482) 507944

SCRIVENS, Ernest. b 25. Lon Univ DipTh53. Wycliffe Hall Ox. **d** 62 **p** 63. Miss to Seamen W Australia 69-79; V Yeadon St Jo *Bradf* 79-80; Australia from 81; rtd 88. *31 Carindale Village, 43 Scrub Road, Carindale, Queensland, Australia 4152*

SCRUBY, Ven Ronald Victor. b 19. Trin Hall Cam BA48 MA52. Cuddesdon Coll 48. **d** 50 **p** 51. Adn Is of Wight *Portsm* 65-77; Adn Portsm 77-85; rtd 85; Perm to Offic *Chich* from 85; Perm to Offic *Portsm* from 85. *The Dower House, Rogate, Petersfield, Hants GU31 5EG* Rogate (01730) 821325

SCUFFHAM, Canon Frank Leslie. b 30. AKC56 DSRS68. **d** 57 **p** 58. C Kettering SS Pet and Paul *Pet* 57-59; Ind Chapl *Sheff* 60-61; Ind Chapl *Pet* from 61; Can Pet Cathl from 72; RD Corby 76-79; P-in-c Stoke Albany w Wilbarston 79; R from 79. *The Rectory, Stoke Albany, Market Harborough, Leics LE16 8PZ* Dingley (01858) 535213

SCULLY, Kevin John. b 55. NIDA DipAct82. St Steph Ho Ox 91. **d** 93 **p** 94. C Stoke Newington St Mary *Lon* from 93. *The Rectory Flat, Church Street, London N16 9ES* 0171-249 6138

SCUTT, John Melville. b 07. St Edm Hall Ox BA29 DipTh30 MA33. Wycliffe Hall Ox 29. **d** 31 **p** 32. V Woodford Wells *Chelmsf* 60-72; rtd 72; C Colney Heath St Mark *St Alb* 72-73; P-in-c Elvedon *St E* 75-77; Perm to Offic *St Alb* from 77. *Trembaths Home, Talbot Way, Letchworth, Herts SG6 1UA* Letchworth (01462) 481694

SCUTTER, Canon James Edward. b 36. AKC59 St Boniface Warminster 59. **d** 60 **p** 61. C Tilbury Docks *Chelmsf* 60-63; S Rhodesia 63-65; Rhodesia 65-70; New Zealand from 80; Hon Can Wellington from 87. *67 Freyburg Street, Lyall Bay, Wellington 3, New Zealand* Wellington (4) 879269

SEABROOK, Alan Geoffrey. b 43. ALCD65. **d** 66 **p** 67. C Bethnal Green St Jas Less *Lon* 66-70; C Madeley *Heref* 70-73; V Girlington *Bradf* 74-80; P-in-c Abdon w Clee St Margaret *Heref* 80-83; R Bitterley 80-83; P-in-c Cold Weston 80-83; P-in-c Hopton Cangeford 80-83; P-in-c Stoke St Milburgh w Heath 80-83; R Bitterley w Middleton, Stoke St Milborough etc from 83. *The Rectory, Bitterley, Ludlow, Shropshire SY8 3HJ* Ludlow (01584) 890239

SEABROOK, Geoffrey Barry. b 45. Open Univ BA77 DipEd Lon Univ MA(Ed)84. Chich Th Coll 66. **d** 69 **p** 70. C Tottenham All Hallows *Lon* 69-72; C Winchmore Hill H Trin 72-74; V Hornsey St Geo 74-82; P-in-c Hornsey St Mary 80-82; R Hornsey St Mary w St Geo from 82; P-in-c Hornsey H Innocents 84-92; AD W Haringey from 95. *Hornsey Rectory, 140 Cranley Gardens, London N10 3AH* 0181-883 6846

SEABROOK, Richard Anthony. b 68. Chich Th Coll BTh92. **d** 92 **p** 93. C Cottingham *York* 92-94; C Hawley H Trin *Guildf* from 94. *295 Fernhill Road, Farnborough, Hants GU14 9EW* Blackwater (01276) 34241

SEAFORD, Very Rev John Nicholas. b 39. Dur Univ BA67 DipTh68. St Chad's Coll Dur 68. **d** 68 **p** 69. C Bush Hill Park St Mark *Lon* 68-71; C Stanmore *Win* 71-73; V N Baddesley 73-76; V Chilworth w N Baddesley 76-78; V Highcliffe w Hinton Admiral 78-93; RD Christchurch 90-93; Hon Can Win Cathl from 93; Dean Jersey from 93; R Jersey St Helier from 93. *The Deanery, St Helier, Jersey, Channel Islands JE2 4TB* Jersey (01534) 20001 Fax 617488

SEAGER, Roland Douglas. b 08. St Boniface Warminster 32. **d** 33 **p** 34. P-in-c Nottm St Cath *S'well* 71-73; rtd 74; Perm to Offic *S'well* from 74. *22 Willow Road, Nottingham NG4 3BH*

SEAL, Edward Hugh. b 10. ARCM31 Lon Univ BMus36. Wells Th Coll 46. **d** 48 **p** 49. R Poulton-le-Sands *Blackb* 63-78; rtd 78; Lic to Offic *Blackb* from 79. *3 Fern Bank, Scotforth, Lancaster LA1 4TT* Lancaster (01524) 67078

SEAL, Nicholas Peter. b 57. Ex Univ BA. Linc Th Coll 81. **d** 83 **p** 84. C Wareham *Sarum* 83-87; Chapl K Alfred Coll *Win* 87-91; V Stanmore from 91. *St Luke's Vicarage, Mildmay Street, Stanmore, Winchester, Hants SO22 4BX* Winchester (01962) 865240

SEAL, Philip Trevor. b 32. AKC55. **d** 56 **p** 57. C Godalming *Guildf* 56-60; C Tamworth *Lich* 60-61; R Lich St Chad 61-73; Chapl HM Youth Cust Cen Swinfen Hall 66-73; R Shere *Guildf* 74-88; RD Cranleigh 76-81; V Abbotsbury, Portesham and Langton Herring *Sarum* from 88. *The Vicarage, Portesham, Weymouth, Dorset DT3 4HB* Abbotsbury (01305) 871217

SEAL, Ronald Frederick. b 28. CA Tr Coll 50 Lich Th Coll 59. **d** 61 **p** 62. R N and S Kilworth *Leic* 65-71; R Barwell w Potters Marston and Stapleton 71-80; P-in-c Upper Stour *Sarum* 80-83; R Upper Stour 84-90; RD Heytesbury 87-89; Bermuda 90-92; Miss to Seamen 90-92; rtd 92. *28 Clarendon Close, Gillingham, Dorset SP8 4NL* Gillingham (01747) 824679

SEAL, William George. b 27. Lon Univ DipTh71. Oak Hill Th Coll 67. **d** 70 **p** 71. C Plumstead St Jo w St Jas and St Paul *S'wark* 70-73; C Camberwell All SS 73-80; V Luton St Matt High Town *St Alb* 80-92; rtd 93. *1A Barnfield Avenue, Luton LU2 7AS* Luton (01582) 576939

SEALE, Daisy Elaine. b 09. Gilmore Ho 55. **dss** 62 **d** 87. Clapham H Trin *S'wark* 62-69; rtd 69; W Cheshire Hosp Ches 69-75; Uffculme *Ex* 75-87; Hon Par Dn 87-90. *17 Markers, Uffculme, Cullompton, Devon EX15 3DZ* Craddock (01884) 840517

SEALE, William Arthur. b 62. NUI BA84 TCD DipTh87. **d** 87 **p** 88. C Drumragh w Mountfield *D & R* 87-90; I Drumgath w Drumgooland and Clonduff *D & D* from 90. *The Rectory, 29 Cross Road, Hilltown, Newry, Co Down BT34 5TF* Rathfriland (018206) 30304

SEALY, Daniel O'Neill. b 21. Oak Hill Th Coll 62. **d** 64 **p** 65. Chapl RN 67-73; Nigeria 73-79; Libya 79-82; Tunisia 82-86; rtd 86; I Kilgariffe Union *C, C & R* 87-92. *Homleigh, 2 Broad Street, Weobley, Hereford HR4 8SA*

SEALY, Canon Gordon William Hugh. b 27. Leeds Univ BA53 MA64. Coll of Resurr Mirfield 53. **d** 55 **p** 56. C Greenford H Cross *Lon* 55-58; Br Honduras 58-68; R Tarrant Gunville, Tarrant Hinton etc *Sarum* 68-74; V Leic St Paul *Leic* from 74; Hon Can Leic Cathl from 86. *St Paul's Vicarage, Kirby Road, Leicester LE3 6BD* Leicester (0116) 262 8062

SEALY, Stephen. b 52. K Coll Lon BD86 AKC86. Linc Th Coll 86. **d** 88 **p** 89. C Botley *Portsm* 88-91; Prec Cant Cathl *Cant* from 91. *8 Burgate House, Canterbury, Kent CT1 2HB* Canterbury (01227) 761498 or 762862

SEAMAN, Canon Arthur Roland Mostyn. b 32. TCD BA55 DipEd56 Div Test56 MA58. Westcott Ho Cam 58. **d** 58 **p** 59. C Blackley St Pet *Man* 58-61; C Sanderstead All SS *S'wark* 61-62; V Heywood St Luke *Man* 62-70; Dir of Educn 70-85; Hon Can Man Cathl from 74; R Chorlton-cum-Hardy St Werburgh from 85. *St Werburgh's Rectory, Wilbraham Road, Manchester M21 1ST* 0161-881 1642

SEAMAN, Canon Brian Edward. b 35. Dur Univ BA59. Cranmer Hall Dur. **d** 61 **p** 62. C Burnage St Marg *Man* 61-65; Chapl Mayflower Family Cen Canning Town *Chelmsf* 65-75; V High Elswick St Paul *Newc* from 75; Hon Can Newc Cathl from 82. *St Paul's Vicarage, Park Close, Newcastle upon Tyne NE4 6SB* 0191-273 4705

SEAMAN, Paul Robert. b 61. Bp Grosseteste Coll BEd82. Chich Th Coll 83. **d** 86 **p** 87. C Tilehurst St Mich *Ox* 86-91; TV Moulsecoomb *Chich* from 91. *Coldean Vicarage, Selham Drive, Coldean, Brighton BN1 9EL* Brighton (01273) 601854

SEAMAN, Robert John. b 44. ACP DipEd. E Anglian Minl Tr Course. **d** 84 **p** 85. NSM Downham Market w Bexwell *Ely* 84-90; V Southea w Murrow and Parson Drove from 90; V Guyhirn w Ring's End from 90. *Southea Vicarage, Main Road, Parson Drove, Wisbech, Cambs PE13 4JA* Wisbech (01945) 700426

SEAMER, Stephen James George. b 50. AKC73. Ridley Hall Cam 74. **d** 75 **p** 76. C Rustington *Chich* 75-78; C Bulwell St Jo *S'well* 78-79; P-in-c Camber and E Guldeford *Chich* 79-80; TV Rye 80-83; V Knowle *Birm* 83-87; Assoc Chapl Brussels Cathl *Eur* 87-88; P-in-c Tervuren from 88; P-in-c Liege from 90; Chapl Tervuren and P-in-c Liege from 94. *Smisstraat 63, 3080 Vossem Turvuren, Belgium* Brussels (2) 767-3435 or 767-3021 Fax 767 3435

SEAR, Peter Lionel. b 49. Ex Univ BA72. Linc Th Coll 72. **d** 74 **p** 75. C Sheldon *Birm* 74-77; C Caversham *Ox* 77-81; C Caversham and Mapledurham 81-85; TR Thatcham from 85. *The Rectory, 17 Church Gate, Newbury, Berks RG13 4PN* Thatcham (01635) 862616

SEAR, Terence Frank (Terry). b 39. LDSRCSEng62 Univ Coll Lon BDS63. Portsm Dioc Tr Course 88. **d** 89. NSM Ryde H Trin *Portsm* from 89; NSM Swanmore St Mich w Havenstreet 89-92; NSM Swanmore St Mich and All Angels from 92. *Glebe Cottage, Wray Street, Ryde, Isle of Wight PO33 3ED* Isle of Wight (01983) 615856

SEARIGHT, Mervyn Warren. b 26. TCD DBS. **d** 59 **p** 60. I Killermogh *C & O* 68-77; I Aughaval *T, K & A* 77-79; I Kiltegan w Hacketstown, Clonmore and Moyne *C & O* 79-86; C Dub St Geo and St Thos, Finglas and Free Ch *D & G* 86-93; rtd 93. *Railway Cottage, 2 Newgardens, Athy Road, Carlow, Irish Republic* Carlow (503) 30936

SEARLE, Charles Peter. b 20. Selw Coll Cam BA48 MA53. Ridley Hall Cam. **d** 50 **p** 51. V Weston-super-Mare Ch Ch *B & W* 60-70; V Woking Ch Ch *Guildf* 70-85; rtd 85; Perm to Offic *Ex* from 85. *Old Chimes, 14 Gravel Walk, Cullompton, Devon EX15 1DA* Cullompton (01884) 33386

SEARLE, Capt Francis Robert. b 52. IDC74. CA Tr Coll 72 St Steph Ho Ox 88. **d** 90 **p** 91. CA from 72; C Lancing w Coombes *Chich* 90-93; V Hampden Park from 93. *The Vicarage, 60 Brassey Avenue, Eastbourne, E Sussex BN22 9QH* Eastbourne (01323) 503166

SEARLE, Hugh Douglas. b 35. St Cath Coll Cam BA59 MA63 Cranfield Inst of Tech MSc85. Oak Hill Th Coll 59. **d** 61 **p** 62. C Islington H Trin Cloudesley Square *Lon* 61-64; Chapl HM Pris Lewes 64-65; Chapl HM Borstal Roch 65-69; Chapl HM Youth Cust Cen Hollesley Bay Colony 70-74; Chapl HM Pris Parkhurst 74-78; P-in-c Barton *Ely* 78-84; V from 84; P-in-c Coton 78-84; R from 84; RD Bourn 81-94. *The Vicarage, Barton, Cambridge CB3 7BG* Cambridge (01223) 262218

SEARLE, Ms Jacqueline Ann (Jackie). b 60. Whitelands Coll Lon BEd82. Trin Coll Bris DipHE92. **d** 92 **p** 94. Par Dn Roxeth Ch Ch and Harrow St Pet *Lon* 92-93; Par Dn Roxeth 93-94; C 94; C Ealing St Steph Castle Hill from 94. *St Stephens Vicarage, Sherborne Gardens, London W13 8AT* 0181-810 4929

SEARLE, Michael Stanley. b 38. HNC60. AMIQ63. N Ord Course 93. **d** 95. NSM Hoole *Ches* from 95. *48 Green Lane, Vicars Cross, Chester CH3 5LB* Chester (01244) 347828 Fax as telephone

SEARLE, Michael Westran. b 47. Leeds Univ LLB68 Nottm Univ DipTh69. Cuddesdon Coll 69. **d** 71 **p** 72. C Norton St Mary *Dur* 71-74; C Westbury-on-Trym H Trin *Bris* 74-77; V Bedminster Down 77-84; V Bris Ch the Servant Stockwood 84-88; Dir of Tr *York* from 88. *Cavalino, Back Lane, Allerthorpe, York YO4 4RP* Pocklington (01759) 302544

SEARLE, Philip Robert. b 67. Westcott Ho Cam. **d** 95. C Plymstock *Ex* from 95. *93 Holmwood Avenue, Plymstock, Plymouth PL9 9EZ* Plymouth (01752) 407788

SEARLE, Ralph Alan. b 57. Cam Univ MA. Coll of Resurr Mirfield 81. **d** 83 **p** 84. C Cockerton *Dur* 83-86; C S Shields All SS 86-88; TV from 88. *79 Chesterton Road, South Shields, Tyne & Wear NE34 9TL* 0191-536 1831

SEARLE-BARNES, Albert Victor. b 28. Sheff Univ BA48 Lon Univ BD53. ALCD53. **d** 53 **p** 54. R Wick w Doynton *Bris* 64-70; Perm to Offic 70-72; V Downend 73-78; V Market Rasen *Linc* 78-86; R Linwood 79-86; V Legsby 79-86; R Green's Norton w Bradden *Pet* 86-88; V Hambledon *Portsm* 88-92; rtd 92. *32 Oakland Avenue, Prestbury Road, Cheltenham, Glos GL52 3EP* Cheltenham (01242) 227425

SEARS, Derek Lynford. b 25. St Jo Coll Cam BA49 MA53. Wycliffe Hall Ox 49. **d** 51 **p** 52. V Freckleton *Blackb* 66-74; Jamaica 74-78; V Ashton-on-Ribble St Mich *Blackb* 78-90; P-in-c Preston St Mark 82-90; rtd 90. *61 Greencroft, Penwortham, Preston PR1 9LB* Preston (01772) 740190

SEARS, Frank. b 29. Wycliffe Hall Ox 62. **d** 64 **p** 65. C Ashtead *Guildf* 64-72; V Finchley St Luke *Lon* 72-82; P-in-c Finchley St Paul Long Lane 76-82; TR Whitton *Sarum* 82-90; P-in-c Trowbridge St Thos and W Ashton from 91; Chapl St Jo Hosp Trowbridge from 95; Chapl Trowbridge Community Hosp from 95. *St Thomas's Vicarage, York Buildings, Trowbridge, Wilts BA14 8SF* Trowbridge (01225) 754826

SEARS, Dr Jeanette. b 59. Man Univ BA80 PhD84 Lon Univ PGCE85. Wycliffe Hall Ox DPS. **d** 92 **p** 94. NSM Ox St Aldate w St Matt *Ox* 92-94; NSM Ox St Aldate from 95. *2 Fairacres Road, Oxford OX4 1TE* Oxford (01865) 249305

SEARS, Michael Antony. b 50. Birm Univ BSc71 PGCE72. Linc Th Coll 78. **d** 80 **p** 81. C Willenhall H Trin *Lich* 80-83; C Caldmore 83-84; P-in-c 84-86; V 86-89; Abp Ilsley RC Sch Birm from 89; Perm to Offic Birm from 94. *131 Lowlands Avenue, Streetley, Sutton Coldfield, W Midlands B74 3RE* 0121-353 8739

SEATON, Canon James Bradbury. b 29. Ch Coll Cam BA53 MA57. Westcott Ho Cam 53. **d** 55 **p** 56. V Preston on Tees *Dur* 64-72; TV Stockton H Trin 72-73; TV Cen Stockton 73-75; R Anstey *Leic* 75-89; RD Sparkenhoe III 81-89; Hon Can Leic Cathl 87-94; R Market Harborough Transfiguration 89-94; rtd 94. *Wayside, Sheep Street, Chipping Campden, Glos GL55 6DW* Evesham (01386) 841753

SEBER, Derek Morgan. b 43. Man Univ CertRS79 Man Poly CTUS83 MA88. Oak Hill Th Coll 71. **d** 73 **p** 74. C Collyhurst *Man* 73-76; C Radcliffe St Thos and St Jo 76-77; Ind Missr 77-89; P-in-c Hulme St Geo 77-83; Hon C Moss Side St Jas w St Clem from 83; Project Officer Linking Up from 89. *56 Alness Road, Whalley Range, Manchester M16 8HW* 0161-861 0360 or 832 5208

SECCOMBE, Marcus John. b 34. Oak Hill Th Coll 60. **d** 63 **p** 64. C Woodthorpe *S'well* 63-67; C Doncaster St Mary *Sheff* 67-72; V Owston 72-90; R Rossington from 90. *The Rectory, Sheep Bridge Lane, Rossington, Doncaster, S Yorkshire DN11 0EZ* Doncaster (01302) 867597

SECKER, Brian. b 34. Qu Coll Birm 62. **d** 65 **p** 66. C Goldthorpe *Sheff* 65-68; V New Bentley 68-75; P-in-c Pet St Barn *Pet* 75-80; V Pet St Paul from 75. *St Paul's Vicarage, Peterborough PE1 2PA* Peterborough (01733) 343746

SECOMBE, Preb Frederick Thomas. b 18. St D Coll Lamp BA40 St Mich Coll Llan 40. **d** 42 **p** 43. R Hanwell St Mary *Lon* 69-83; AD Ealing W 78-82; rtd 83. *30 Westville Road, Penylan, Cardiff CF2 5AG* Cardiff (01222) 483978

SECRETAN, Ms Jenny Ruth. b 54. St Aid Coll Dur BA76 Ex Univ PGCE77 Nottm Univ DipTh82. Linc Th Coll 81 Cranmer Hall Dur 83. **dss** 84 **d** 87 **p** 94. Asst Chapl Newc Poly *Newc* 84-86; Sunderland St Chad *Dur* 84-86; Bordesley St Oswald *Birm* 86-87; Par Dn 87-91; Assoc Soc Resp Officer *Dur* from 92. *129 King George Road, South Shields, Tyne & Wear NE34 0EU* 0191-456 7786

SECRETAN, Paul Lawrence. b 49. Linc Th Coll. **d** 83 **p** 84. C Sunderland St Chad *Dur* 83-86; V Bordesley St Oswald *Birm* 86-91; Chapl Miss to Seamen from 91. *clo The Missions to Seamen, 53 Mill Dam, South Shields, Tyne & Wear NE33 1EF* 0191-456 0878 or 455 5963 Fax 456 1658

SEDDON, Ernest Geoffrey. b 26. AR1BA51 Man Univ DipArch50 DipTh83 MA85. St Deiniol's Hawarden 80. **d** 80 **p** 81. C Dunham Massey St Marg *Ches* 80-83; P-in-c Warburton 82-87; P-in-c Dunham Massey St Mark 85-86; V 86-92; rtd 92. *10 Honiton Way, Altrincham, Cheshire WA14 4UW* 0161-929 1895

SEDDON, Philip James. b 45. Jes Coll Cam BA68 MA71. Ridley Hall Cam 67. **d** 70 **p** 71. C Tonge w Alkrington *Man* 70-74; Nigeria 74-78; Lect St Jo Coll Nottm 78-79; Lic to Offic *Ely* 79-85; Chapl Magd Coll Cam 79-85; Lect Bibl Studies Selly Oak Colls from 86; Lic to Offic *Birm* from 87. *Central House, Selly Oak Colleges, Birmingham B29 6QT* 0121-472 4231

SEDEN, Martin Roy. b 47. Man Univ MSc Salford Univ PhD. E Midl Min Tr Course. **d** 82 **p** 83. NSM Knighton St Mary Magd *Leic* from 82. *139 Shanklin Drive, Leicester LE2 3QG* Leicester (0116) 270 2128

SEDGLEY, Mrs Jean. b 41. Whitelands Coll Lon CertEd63. S Dios Minl Tr Scheme 92. **d** 95. NSM Haywards Heath St Wilfrid *Chich* from 95. *25 Pasture Hill Road, Haywards Heath, W Sussex RH16 1LY* Haywards Heath (01444) 413974

SEDGLEY, Canon Timothy John. b 42. St Jo Coll Ox BA63 DipTh64 MA68. Westcott Ho Cam 64. **d** 66 **p** 67. C Nor St Pet Mancroft *Nor* 66-70; V Costessey 70-79; RD Nor N 75-79; V Walton-on-Thames *Guildf* from 79; Hon Can Guildf Cathl from 86; RD Emly 86-91. *The Vicarage, 53 Ashley Park Avenue, Walton-on-Thames, Surrey KT12 1EV* Walton-on-Thames (01932) 227184

SEDGMORE, Evan. b 09. St D Coll Lamp 47. **d** 50 **p** 51. V Llanbradach *Llan* 71-76; rtd 76; Perm to Offic *Llan* from 76. *52 Hockland Road, Newton, Porthcawl, M Glam CF36 5SG* Porthcawl (01656) 718991

SEDGWICK, Jonathan Maurice William. b 63. BNC Ox BA85 MA89 Leeds Univ BA88. Coll of Resurr Mirfield 86. **d** 89 **p** 90. C Chich St Paul and St Pet *Chich* 89-91; Dean of Div and Chapl Magd Coll Ox from 91. *Magdalen College, Oxford OX1 4AU* Oxford (01865) 276027

SEDGWICK, Peter Humphrey. b 48. Trin Hall Cam BA70 Dur Univ PhD83. Westcott Ho Cam 71. **d** 74 **p** 75. C Stepney St Dunstan and All SS *Lon* 74-77; P-in-c Darlington *Dur* 77-79; Lect Th Birm Univ 79-82; Hon C The Lickey *Birm* 79-82; Th Consultant for NE Ecum Gp *Dur* 82-88; Abp's Adv on Ind Issues *York* 88-94; Lect Th Hull Univ 88-94; Vice-Prin Westcott Ho Cam from 94. *1 Short Street, Cambridge CB1 1LB or, Westcott House, Jesus Lane, Cambridge CB5 8BP* Cambridge (01223) 352922 or 350074

SEED, Richard Edward. b 55. UNISA BTh86. Kalk Bay Bible Inst S Africa DipTh79. **d** 80 **p** 81. S Africa 80-85 and 87-89; Zimbabwe 85-87; Asst Chapl Haigham Hill Sch 89-90; C Beckenham Ch Ch *Roch* from 90. *78 The Drive, Beckenham, Kent BR3 1EG* 0181-650 7669

SEED, Richard Murray Crosland. b 49. Leeds Univ MA91. Edin Th Coll 69. **d** 72 **p** 73. C Skipton Ch Ch *Bradf* 72-75; C Baildon 75-77; Chapl HM Det Cen Kidlington 77-80; TV Kidlington *Ox* 77-80; V Boston Spa *York* from 80; P-in-c Newton Kyme 84-85; P-in-c Clifford from 89. *The Vicarage, Boston Spa, Wetherby, W Yorkshire LS23 5EA* Boston Spa (01937) 842454

SEELEY, John Frederick. b 36. AKC61. **d** 62 **p** 63. C Lower Broughton Ascension *Man* 62-64; C Chiswick St Paul Grove Park *Lon* 64-66; C Ruislip St Mary 66-67; C Hampstead Garden Suburb 67-69; P-in-c St Jo Wood All SS 69-71; C Stamford Hill St Bart 74-80; P-in-c Harringay St Paul 80-84; V from 84. *St Paul's Vicarage, Wightman Road, London N4 1RW* 0181-340 5299

SEELEY, Martin Alan. b 54. Jes Coll Cam BA76 MA79. Ripon Coll Cuddesdon 76 Union Th Sem (NY) STM78. **d** 78 **p** 79. C Bottesford w Ashby *Linc* 78-80; USA 80-90; Selection Sec ABM from 90; Sec for Continuing Minl Educn from 90. *114 Kennington Road, London SE11 6RE* 0171-582 4424

SEFTON, Thomas Albert. b 21. Kelham Th Coll 38. **d** 45 **p** 46. C Deptford St Paul *S'wark* 45-47; C Lewisham St Jo Southend 47-48; CF 48-55; V Tottenham St Paul *Lon* 55-58; Australia from 58. *29 Ella Gladstone Drive, Eagle Bay, W Australia 6281* Dunsborough (97) 553192

SEGAL, Michael Bertram. b 20. Lon Univ BA44. Cuddesdon Coll 46. **d** 48 **p** 49. V S Wimbledon St Pet *S'wark* 61-71; V Crofton Park St Hilda w St Cypr 72-82; P-in-c Grendon w Castle Ashby *Pet* 82-85; V Gt Doddington 82-85; rtd 85; Perm to Offic *Cant* from 85. *9 Glebe Gardens, Lenham, Maidstone, Kent ME17 2QA* Maidstone (01622) 858033

SEIGNIOR, James Frederick. b 97. TD46. Univ Coll Lon ALA28. St Deiniol's Hawarden 45. **d** 46 **p** 47. V Bruera *Ches* 49-69; rtd 69; Australia 69-79; Perm to Offic *Glouc* 79-80; Perm to Offic *Guildf* from 80. *64 Roof of the World, Boxhill Road, Tadworth, Surrey KT20 7JR* Betchworth (01737) 844520

SELBY, Miss Carole Janis. b 50. Chelsea Coll Lon CertEd71 Sussex Univ BEd72. Westcott Ho Cam CTM95. **d** 95. C Worc St Barn w Ch Ch *Worc* from 95. *22 Salters Close, Worcester WR4 9XT* Worcester (01905) 456504

✠**SELBY, Rt Rev Prof Peter Stephen Maurice.** b 41. St Jo Coll Ox BA64 MA67 K Coll Lon PhD75. Episc Th Sch Cam Mass BD66 Bps' Coll Cheshunt 66. **d** 66 **p** 67 **c** 84. C Queensbury All SS *Lon* 66-69; C Limpsfield and Titsey *S'wark* 69-77; Assoc Dir of Tr 69-73; Vice-Prin S'wark Ord Course 70-72; Asst Dioc Missr *S'wark* 73-77; Dioc Missr *Newc* 77-84; Can Res Newc Cathl 77-84; Suff Bp Kingston-upon-Thames *S'wark* 84-91; Area Bp Kingston-upon-Thames 91-92; Pres Modern Churchpeople's Union from 91; Wm Leech Professorial Fell Dur Univ from 92; Asst Bp Dur from 92; Asst Bp Newc from 92. *c/o Department of Theology, Abbey House, Palace Green, Durham DH1 3RS* 0191-374 2065 Fax 374 4744

SELBY, Canon Sydney Arthur. b 17. K Coll Lon 41. **d** 48 **p** 49. V Kildwick *Bradf* 53-74; RD S Craven 73-74; Hon Can Bradf Cathl 73-82; V Gisburn 74-82; RD Bowland 80-81; rtd 82; Perm to Offic *Bradf* from 82. *Clough Cottage, Clough Lane, Simonstone, Burnley, Lancs BB12 7HW* Burnley (01282) 773108

SELBY, Suffragan Bishop of. *See* TAYLOR, Rt Rev Humphrey Vincent

SELF, David Christopher. b 41. Toronto Univ BSc62 MA64 K Coll Lon BD68 AKC68. **d** 69 **p** 70. C Tupsley *Heref* 69-73; Chapl Dur Univ *Dur* 73-78; TV Southn (City Cen) *Win* 78-84; TR Dunstable *St Alb* 84-95; RD Dunstable 90-91; TR Bris St Paul's *Bris* from 95. *St Paul's Rectory, 131 Ashley Road, Bristol BS6 5NU* Bristol (0117) 955 0150

SELF, John Andrew. b 47. Pershore Coll of Horticulture Worcs CANP68. Trin Coll Bris 74 CMS Tr Coll Crowther Hall 76. **d** 81 **p** 83. CMS 77-91; Pakistan 77-91; AV Bath Weston All SS w N Stoke *B & W* 91-92; V Sparkhill w Greet and Sparkbrook *Birm* from 92. *St John's Vicarage, 15 Phipson Road, Birmingham B11 4JE* 0121-449 2760

SELF, Peter Allen. b 41. S Dios Minl Tr Scheme 84. **d** 87 **p** 87. NSM Wilton *B & W* 87-91; NSM Taunton Lyngford from 91. *20 Dyers Close, West Buckland, Wellington, Somerset TA21 9JU* Wellington (01823) 663408

SELL, John Lewis. b 10. Univ Coll Dur LTh37 BA40 New Coll Ox BA43 MA47. St Boniface Warminster 30. **d** 35 **p** 36. R Coln St Denys w Coln Rogers *Glouc* 50-75; V Sandhurst 75-80; rtd 81; Perm to Offic *Glouc* 81-91. *79 Calton Road, Gloucester GL1 5DT* Gloucester (01452) 416906

SELL, Noel Lightfoot. b 15. St Cath Coll Cam BA38 MA44. Wycliffe Hall Ox. **d** 41 **p** 42. V Broomfield *B & W* 64-77; V Kingston St Mary 64-77; rtd 77. *32 Saxon Way, Saffron Walden, Essex CB11 4EG* Saffron Walden (01799) 526165

SELLARS, Charles Harold. b 18. Leeds Univ BA40. Coll of Resurr Mirfield 37. **d** 42 **p** 44. Chapl Qu Sch Rheindahlen Germany *Eur* 61-70; V Hampton St Mary *Lon* 70-78; R Nuthurst *Chich* 78-83; P-in-c Lynch w Iping Marsh 83-86; rtd 86; Perm to Offic *Chich* from 87. *50 Rewhams Road, Horsham, W Sussex RH12 2NZ* Horsham (01403) 260641

SELLER, James Stoddart. b 16. TD64. St Jo Coll Dur LTh45. Tyndale Hall Bris 40. **d** 44 **p** 45. R Burnby *York* 60-89; R Londesborough 60-89; R Nunburnholme 60-89; P-in-c Shiptonthorpe w Hayton 78-89; rtd 89. *7 Wilton Road, Hornsea, N Humberside HU18 1QU* Hornsea (01964) 533164

SELLER, Dr Mary Joan. b 40. Qu Mary Coll Lon BSc61 Lon Univ PhD64 DSc82. S'wark Ord Course. **d** 91 **p** 94. NSM Hurst Green *S'wark* from 91. *11 Home Park, Oxted, Surrey RH8 0JS* Oxted (01883) 715675

SELLERS, Anthony. b 48. Southn Univ BSc71 PhD76. Wycliffe Hall Ox 84. **d** 86 **p** 87. C Luton St Mary *St Alb* 86-90; V Luton St Paul from 90. *37A Arthur Street, Luton LU1 3SG* Luton (01582) 481796

SELLERS, George William. b 35. N Ord Course. **d** 89 **p** 90. NSM Rothwell *Ripon* from 89. *16 Thornegrove, Rothwell, Leeds LS26 0HP* Leeds (0113) 282 3522

SELLERS, Robert. b 58. Coll of Resurr Mirfield 90. **d** 92 **p** 93. C Wotton St Mary *Glouc* 92-95; TV Redruth w Lanner and Treleigh *Truro* from 95. *Pencoys Vicarage, Four Lanes, Redruth, Cornwall TR16 6LR* Redruth (01209) 215035

SELLERS, Warren John. b 43. K Coll Lon BD63 AKC63 W Sussex Inst of HE DipAdEd88. Bp Otter Coll TCert73

Sarum Th Coll 65. **d** 68 **p** 69. C Guildf H Trin w St Mary *Guildf* 68-72; Hon C Chich St Paul and St Pet *Chich* 72-73; C Epping St Jo *Chelmsf* 73-76; Hon C Pulborough *Chich* 76-90; Hon C Fleet *Guildf* 90-92; Teacher 73-89; Waltham Abbey St Lawr and H Cross Schs Essex 73-76; Pulborough St Mary, Easebourne & Bp Tuffnell Schs 76-89; Hd Teacher St Pet Jun Sch Farnborough 90-92; TV Upper Kennett *Sarum* from 92. *The Vicarage, Broad Hinton, Swindon SN4 9PA* Swindon (01793) 731310

SELLGREN, Eric Alfred. b 33. AKC61. **d** 62 **p** 63. C Ditton St Mich *Liv* 62-66; V Hindley Green 66-72; V Southport St Paul 72-80; Warden Barn Fellowship Winterborne Whitchurch 80-86; V The Iwernes, Sutton Waldron and Fontmell Magna *Sarum* from 86. *The Vicarage, Iwerne Minster, Blandford Forum, Dorset DT11 8NF* Fontmell Magna (01747) 811291

SELLIX, Martin Gordon. b 45. Ridley Hall Cam 74. **d** 76 **p** 77. C Crofton St Paul *Roch* 76-80; Ind Chapl *Chelmsf* 80-94; R Rayne 80-86; V Blackmore and Stondon Massey 86-94; RD Ongar 89-94; TR Liskeard, St Keyne, St Pinnock, Morval etc *Truro* from 94. *The Rectory, Church Street, Liskeard, Cornwall PL14 3AQ* Liskeard (01579) 342178

SELLORS, Michael Harry. b 36. K Coll Lon 60 St Boniface Warminster 61. **d** 61 **p** 62. C Willesden St Mary *Lon* 61-64; C Aldershot St Mich *Guildf* 64-67; V Hale 67-84; P-in-c E w W Beckham *Nor* 84-85; P-in-c Bodham 84-85; V Weybourne w Upper Sheringham 84-85; R Kelling w Salthouse 84-85; R Weybourne Gp 85-91; V Hunstanton St Edm w Ringstead from 91. *St Edmund's Vicarage, 53 Northgate, Hunstanton, Norfolk PE36 6DS* Hunstanton (01485) 532157

SELMAN, Cyril Allen. b 25. Wycliffe Hall Ox 64. **d** 65 **p** 65. V Beedon *Ox* 69-87; R Peasemore 69-87; rtd 88. *10 Griffin Terrace, Penrhyndeudraeth, Gwynedd LL48 6LR*

SELMAN, Michael Richard. b 47. Sussex Univ BA68 Bris Univ MA70. Coll of Resurr Mirfield 71. **d** 73 **p** 74. C Hove All SS *Chich* 73-74; C Horfield H Trin *Bris* 74-78; P-in-c Landkey *Ex* 78-79; C Barnstaple and Goodleigh 78-79; TV Barnstaple, Goodleigh and Landkey 79-82; TR 82-84; RD Barnstaple 83-85; P-in-c Sticklepath 83-85; TR Barnstaple 85; TR Cen Ex from 85. *The Rectory, 3 Spicer Road, Exeter EX1 1SX* Exeter (01392) 72450

SELMES, Brian. b 48. Nottm Univ BTh74. Linc Th Coll 70. **d** 74 **p** 75. C Padgate *Liv* 74-77; C Sydenham St Bart *S'wark* 77-80; Chapl Darlington Memorial Hosp from 80; Chapl Aycliffe Hosp Darlington from 80. *Memorial Hospital, Hollyhead Road, Darlington, Co Durham DL3 6HX* Darlington (01325) 359688 or 380100

SELVEY, Canon John Brian. b 33. Dur Univ BA54. Cuddesdon Coll 56. **d** 58 **p** 59. C Lanc St Mary *Blackb* 58-61; C Blackb Cathl 61-65; Cathl Chapl 64-65; V Foulridge 65-69; V Walton-le-Dale 69-82; V Cleveleys 82-89; Hon Can Bloemfontein Cathl from 88; V Slyne w Hest *Blackb* from 89; Hon Can Blackb Cathl from 93. *The Vicarage, Summerfield Drive, Slyne, Lancaster LA2 6AQ* Hest Bank (01524) 822128

SELVINI, John Claude Gaston. b 46. ESC (Paris) 68. St Steph Ho Ox 72. **d** 75 **p** 76. C Derby St Luke *Derby* 75-78; C Bordesley St Oswald *Birm* 78-80; C Shrewsbury All SS w St Mich *Lich* 80-88; V Goldenhill from 88. *St John's Vicarage, Drummond Street, Stoke-on-Trent ST6 5RF* Stoke-on-Trent (01782) 782736

SELWOOD, Michael. b 40. Oak Hill Th Coll DipHE90 BA91. **d** 91 **p** 92. Canada 91-95; P-in-c Sherborne, Windrush, the Barringtons etc *Glouc* from 95. *The New Vicarage, Windrush, Burford, Oxon OX18 4TS* Cotswold (01451) 844276

SELWOOD, Robin. b 37. ALCD61. **d** 61 **p** 62. C Lenton *S'well* 61-63; C Norbury *Ches* 63-66; V Newton Flowery Field 66-75; V Kelsall 75-89; V Sale St Paul from 89. *St Paul's Vicarage, 15 Springfield Road, Sale, Cheshire M33 1XG* 0161-973 1042

SELWOOD, Timothy John. b 45. Lon Univ LLB66. Sarum Th Coll. **d** 83 **p** 84. NSM Colbury *Win* 83-85; NSM Copythorne and Minstead 85-90. *Forest Cottage, Seamans Lane, Minstead, Lyndhurst, Hants SO43 7FT* Southampton (01703) 812873

SELWYN, David Gordon. b 38. MEHS Clare Coll Cam BA62 MA66 New Coll Ox MA66. Ripon Hall Ox 62. **d** 64 **p** 65. C Ecclesall *Sheff* 64-65; Asst Chapl New Coll Ox 65-68; Lect St D Univ Coll Lamp *St D* from 68. *19 Penbryn, Lampeter, Dyfed SA48 7EU* Lampeter (01570) 422748

SEMEONOFF, Canon Jean Mary Agnes. b 36. BSc56 Leic Univ CertEd57. E Midl Min Tr Course 84. **d** 87 **p** 94. Par Dn Leic H Spirit *Leic* 87 and 89-94; Chapl to the Deaf *Derby* 87-89; Chapl to the Deaf *Leic* 89-93; Hon Can Leic Cathl 92-94; rtd 94; Chapl Women's Min from 94; NSM Leic St Anne *Leic* from 94. *107 Letchworth Road, Leicester LE3 6FN* Leicester (0116) 285 8854

SEMEONOFF, Dr Robert. b 40. Edin Univ PhD67 BSc62. E Midl Min Tr Course 81. **d** 84 **p** 85. NSM Leic H Spirit *Leic* 84-88; Hon C from 89; NSM Loughb Gd Shep 88-89; Chapl

Leic Univ from 89; Min for Special Pastoral Duties from 94. *107 Letchworth Road, Leicester LE3 6FN*   Leicester (0116) 285 8854

SEMPER, Cecil Michael. b 29. LLCM St D Coll Lamp BA51 Fitzw Ho Cam BA53 MA57 Lanc Univ PGCE. St Mich Coll Llan 53. **d** 54 **p** 55. RD Pool *St As* 65-76; R Montgomery and Forden 66-76; V Gresford 76-87; R Claypole *Linc* 87-89; V Stoke by Nayland w Leavenheath *St E* 89-93; rtd 94. *7 Greenfield View, Cross Lanes, Marchwiel, Wrexham, Clwyd LL13 0QA*   Bangor-on-Dee (01978) 781018

SEMPER, Very Rev Colin Douglas. b 38. Keble Coll Ox BA62. Westcott Ho Cam 61. **d** 63 **p** 64. C Guildf H Trin w St Mary *Guildf* 63-66; Hon C 66-82; Sec ACCM 67-69; Producer Relig Broadcasting Dept BBC 69-75; Overseas Relig Broadcasting Org BBC 75-79; Hd of Relig Progr BBC Radio 79-82; Hon Can Guildf Cathl *Guildf* 80-82; Provost Cov 82-87; Can and Treas Westmr Abbey from 87; Steward 87-90. *8 Little Cloister, Westminster Abbey, London SW1P 3PL*   0171-222 5791 Fax 233 2072

SEMPLE, Dr Henry Michael. b 40. CMath FIMA FIMgt FRSA K Coll Lon BSc62 Birkb Coll Lon PhD67. S Dios Minl Tr Scheme. **d** 87 **p** 88. NSM Steyning *Chich* 87-91; Perm to Offic *Guildf* 87-91; Perm to Offic *Linc* 92-93; NSM Linc Cathl from 93. *15 Minster Yard, Lincoln LN2 1PW*   Lincoln (01522) 535938

SEMPLE, Patrick William. b 45. Sussex Univ BA66 Bris Univ DipTh70. Sarum & Wells Th Coll 68. **d** 72 **p** 73. C Paddington Ch Ch *Lon* 72-75; Ind Chapl *Nor* 75-79; P-in-c Woodbastwick 76-79; V Kensington St Barn *Lon* 79-83; V Coleford w Staunton *Glouc* from 83; P-in-c Forest of Dean Ch Ch w English Bicknor 84-89. *The Vicarage, 40 Boxbush Road, Coleford, Glos GL16 8DN*   Dean (01594) 833379

SEMPLE, Studdert Patrick. b 39. TCD BA66. CITC 67. **d** 67 **p** 68. C Orangefield *D & D* 67-70; I Stradbally *C & O* 71-82; Ch of Ireland Adult Educn Officer 82-88; I Donoughmore and Donard w Dunlavin *D & G* from 88. *The Rectory, Donard, Dunlavin, Co Wicklow, Irish Republic*   Naas (45) 404631 Fax 404800

SENIOR, Brian Stephen. b 55. Brighton Coll of Educn CertEd76. Oak Hill Th Coll DipHE93. **d** 93 **p** 94. C Hildenborough *Roch* from 93. *12 Fellowes Way, Hildenborough, Tonbridge, Kent TN11 9DG*   Hildenborough (01732) 832638

SENIOR, David John. b 47. Oak Hill Th Coll. **d** 82 **p** 83. C Market Harborough *Leic* 82-85; TV Marfleet *York* 85-91; R Desford and Peckleton w Tooley *Leic* from 91. *The Rectory, 27 Church Lane, Desford, Leicester LE9 9GD*   Desford (01455) 822276

SENIOR, George. b 36. Open Univ BA83. E Midl Min Tr Course 82. **d** 86 **p** 87. NSM Spratton *Pet* 86-90; NSM Cottesbrooke w Gt Creaton and Thornby 86-90; C Darwen St Pet w Hoddlesden *Blackb* 90-92; V Foulridge from 92. *The Vicarage, Skipton Road, Foulridge, Colne, Lancs BB8 7NP*   Colne (01282) 865491

SENIOR, John Peter. b 23. Lon Univ BSc48. Edin Th Coll 63. **d** 65 **p** 66. C Heysham *Blackb* 68-71; V Blackpool St Mich 71-79; V Heddon-on-the-Wall *Newc* 79-88; rtd 88. *56 Thorpe Lane, Huddersfield HD5 8TA*   Huddersfield (01484) 530466

SENIOR, Patrick Nicolas Adam. b 63. Univ of Wales (Ban) BA86. Trin Coll Bris BA94. **d** 94 **p** 95. C Derringham Bank *York* from 94. *176 Willerby Road, Hull HU5 5JW*   Hull (01482) 53299

SENTAMU, Canon Dr John Mugabi. b 47. MA DD. **d** 79 **p** 79. Chapl HM Rem Cen Latchmere Ho 79-82; C Ham St Andr *S'wark* 79-82; C Herne Hill St Paul 82-83; P-in-c Tulse Hill H Trin 83-84; V Upper Tulse Hill St Matthias 83-84; V Tulse Hill H Trin and St Matthias from 85; P-in-c Brixton Hill St Sav 87-89; Hon Can S'wark Cathl from 93. *The Vicarage, 49 Trinity Rise, London SW2 2QP*   0181-674 6721

SENTANCE, Cecil Leslie. b 23. Lon Univ BSc58. S'wark Ord Course 64. **d** 67 **p** 68. C Finchley St Mary *Lon* 67-73; V Friern Barnet St Pet le Poer 73-75; V Feltham 75-82; Bursar Chich Th Coll and Custos St Mary's Hosp 82-86; rtd 86. *Bryn Gosal, Eglwysbach, Colwyn Bay, Clwyd LL28 5UN*   Tynygroes (01492) 650768

SEPPALA, Christopher James. b 59. St Jo Coll Dur BA82. Chich Th Coll 83. **d** 85 **p** 86. C Whitstable *Cant* 85-88; C S Ashford Ch Ch 88-91. *9 Newton Road, Whitstable, Kent CT5 2JD*   Whitstable (01227) 266411

SERCOMBE, Theodore Friend. b 27. Ch Coll Cam BA47 MA51. Wycliffe Hall Ox DipTh70. **d** 70 **p** 71. C Plymouth St Andr *Ex* 70-73; New Zealand from 73. *46 Invergarry Road, Taupo, New Zealand*   Taupo (7) 378-3372

SERGEANT, John Middlemore. b 13. Wadh Coll Ox BA34 DipTh35 MA38. Wycliffe Hall Ox 34. **d** 36 **p** 37. R Fringford w Hethe and Newton Purcell *Ox* 54-78; P-in-c Cottisford 68-78; P-in-c Hardwick w Tusmore 68-78; rtd 78; Hon C Glympton

Ox 82-87. *121 Chancellors Road, Stevenage, Herts SG1 4TZ*   Stevenage (01438) 742224

SERJEANT, Frederick James. b 28. Lon Inst of Educn BEd77. AKC53 St Boniface Warminster 53. **d** 54 **p** 55. V Battersea St Pet *S'wark* 65-71; C-in-c Battersea St Paul 67-71; V W Mersea *Chelmsf* 71-73; P-in-c E Mersea 71-73; R W w E Mersea 73-75; rtd 93. *5 Bothen Drive, Bridport, Dorset DT6 4DJ*   Bridport (01308) 420573

SERJEANT, John Frederick. b 33. K Coll Lon 52. **d** 56 **p** 57. V Gatley *Ches* 69-79; TV Halesworth w Linstead and Chediston *St E* 79-80; TV Halesworth w Linstead, Chediston, Holton etc 80-82; C Chesterfield All SS *Derby* 82-88; Chapl Chesterfield R Hosp 82-88; Chapl Chesterfield and N Derbyshire R Hosp 88-95; rtd 95. *188 Queen Victoria Road, New Tupton, Chesterfield, Derbyshire S42 6DW*   Chesterfield (01246) 863395

SERJEANTSON, Eric William. b 09. St Jo Coll Dur BA32 MA40. St Boniface Warminster 30. **d** 32 **p** 33. V Leebotwood w Longnor *Heref* 54-74; P-in-c Stapleton 72-74; P-in-c Dorrington 72-74; rtd 74; Perm to Offic *Heref* 74-90. *c/o 102 Keslake Road, London NW6 6DG*

SEROCOLD, Ralph Edward Pearce. b 16. ERD54. Trin Coll Cam BA38 MA45. Bps' Coll Cheshunt 57. **d** 58 **p** 59. R N Stoneham *Win* 69-75; V Hamble le Rice 75-82; rtd 82; Perm to Offic *Portsm* from 82. *Pleasant House, West Street, Hambledon, Waterlooville, Hants PO7 4RW*   Hambledon (0170132) 626

SERTIN, John Francis. b 22. Fitzw Ho Cam BA50 MA54. Tyndale Hall Bris. **d** 45 **p** 46. P-in-c Woburn Square Ch Ch *Lon* 67-77; R Holborn St Geo w H Trin and St Bart 67-80; R Donyatt w Horton, Broadway and Ashill *B & W* 80-92; rtd 92. *9 Lower Vellow, Williton, Taunton, Somerset TA4 4LS*   Williton (01984) 561141

SERTIN, Canon Peter Frank. b 27. Fitzw Ho Cam BA50 MA55. Ridley Hall Cam 50. **d** 52 **p** 53. V Chorleywood Ch Ch *St Alb* 69-80; Chapl Paris St Mich *Eur* 80-85; Adn N France 84-85; R Hambledon *Guildf* 85-89; TR Canford Magna *Sarum* 89-94; rtd 94. *1 Kiln Field, Station Road, Liss, Hampshire GU33 7SW*   Liss (01730) 894482

SERVANT, Ms Alma Joan. b 51. Nottm Univ BA76 DipLib79. Westcott Ho Cam 83. **dss** 85 **d** 87 **p** 94. Ordsall *S'well* 85-87; Par Dn 87-88; Par Dn Man Whitworth *Man* 88-94; TV from 94; Chapl Man Metrop Univ from 94. *11 Mardale Avenue, Withington, Manchester M20 9TU*   0161-434 4071 or 228 6171

SERVANTE, Kenneth Edward. b 29. AKC55. **d** 56 **p** 57. V Derby St Paul *Derby* 63-70; V Elmton 70-81; P-in-c Winster 81-82; P-in-c Elton 81-82; R S Darley, Elton and Winster 82-94; rtd 94. *14 Ashes Avenue, Hulland Ward, Derby DE6 3FT*   Hulland Ward (01335) 370561

SESSFORD, Alan. b 34. Bps' Coll Cheshunt 65. **d** 66 **p** 67. C Highcliffe w Hinton Admiral *Win* 66-69; C Minehead *B & W* 70; C Chandler's Ford *Win* 70-73; V Burton and Sopley from 73; RD Christchurch from 93. *The Vicarage, Preston Lane, Burton, Christchurch, Dorset BH23 7JU*   Christchurch (01202) 484471

✠SESSFORD, Rt Rev George Minshull. b 28. St Andr Univ MA51. Linc Th Coll 51. **d** 53 **p** 54 **c** 70. C Glas St Mary *Glas* 53-58; Chapl Glas Univ 55-58; P-in-c Cumbernauld 58-66; R Forres *Mor* 66-70; Bp Mor 70-93; rtd 93. *Caladh Na Sith, Mellon Charles, Aultbea, Achnasheen, Ross-shire IV22 2JL*   Aultbea (01445) 731303

SETTERFIELD, Nicholas Manley. b 63. Colchester Inst of Educn BA89. St Steph Ho Ox 89. **d** 92 **p** 93. C Prestbury *Glouc* from 92. *Oak Cottage, Blacksmiths Lane, Prestbury, Cheltenham, Glos GL52 5JA*   Cheltenham (01242) 252941

SETTIMBA, John Henry. b 52. Nairobi Univ BSc78 Leeds Univ MA91. Pan Africa Chr Coll BA78. **d** 78 **p** 80. Kenya 78-81; Uganda 81-85; C Allerton *Bradf* 86-87; C W Ham *Chelmsf* 87-91; C-in-c Forest Gate All SS 91-94; P-in-c from 94. *All Saints' Vicarage, 37 Saints' Drive, London E7 0RF*   0181-472 0592

SEVILLE, Christopher John. b 57. Trin Hall Cam MA80. Coll of Resurr Mirfield 87. **d** 89 **p** 90. C Knowle *Bris* 89-93; CR from 93. *House of the Resurrection, Mirfield, W Yorkshire WF14 0BN*   Mirfield (01924) 494318

SEWARD, Jolyon Frantom. b 57. Univ of Wales (Cardiff) BA81. Chich Th Coll 83. **d** 86 **p** 87. C Llanblethian w Cowbridge and Llandough etc *Llan* 86-88; C Newton Nottage 88-93; V Penyfai w Tondu from 93. *The Vicarage, Pen y Fai, Bridgend, M Glam CF31 4LS*   Bridgend (01656) 652849

SEWELL, Andrew William. b 61. Nottm Univ BSc83. St Jo Coll Nottm DTS93. **d** 93 **p** 94. C Adel *Ripon* from 93. *16 Adel Vale, Leeds LS16 8LF*   Leeds (0113) 261 0238

SEWELL, John. b 10. MBE46. Tyndale Hall Bris 60. **d** 61 **p** 62. R Yelvertoft w Clay Coton and Lilbourne *Pet* 69-74; rtd 75. *Flat 4, 7 Chatsworth Gardens, Eastbourne, E Sussex BN20 7JP*   Eastbourne (01323) 640980

SEWELL, Dr John Barratt (Barry). b 39. DRCOG66 St Bart Hosp Medical Coll MB, BS63. Ridley Hall Cam CTM92. **d** 92 **p** 93. C Ulverston St Mary w H Trin *Carl* 92-94; Asst Chapl R Cornwall Hosp Trust Truro from 94. *Trelisk Hospital, Truro, Cornwall TR1 3LJ, or Cleswyth, Creegbrawse, St Day, Redruth, Cornwall TR16 5QR*　Truro (01872) 74242 or Redruth (01209) 821696

SEWELL, Jonathan William. b 60. Lanc Univ BA82 BTh86. Linc Th Coll 83. **d** 86 **p** 87. C Ilkeston St Mary *Derby* 86-89; C Enfield Chase St Mary *Lon* 89-92; Dioc Youth Officer *Win* from 92. *Diocesan Youth Officer, Church House, 9 The Close, Winchester, Hants SO23 9LS*　Winchester (01962) 844644 Fax 841815

SEWELL, Robin Warwick. b 42. Trin Coll Bris. **d** 82 **p** 83. C Hinckley H Trin *Leic* 82-85; C Broadwater St Mary *Chich* 85-89; Chapl Barcelona *Eur* from 89. *Calle San Juan de la Salle 41, Horacio 38, 08022 Barcelona, Spain*　Barcelona (3) 417-8867　Fax 212-8433

SEWELL, Miss Sarah Frances. b 61. Wycliffe Hall Ox 87. **d** 91 **p** 94. C Binley *Cov* 91-94; Asst Chapl Derriford Hosp Plymouth from 94. *45 St George's Avenue, Plymouth, PL2 3PW or Derriford Hospital, Derriford Road, Plymouth PL6 8DH*　Plymouth (01752) 783592 or 777111

SEXTON, Canon Michael Bowers. b 28. SS Coll Cam BA52 MA56. Wells Th Coll 52. **d** 54 **p** 55. R Filby w Thrigby w Mautby *Nor* 62-72; P-in-c Runham 67-72; P-in-c Stokesby w Herringby 68-72; R Hettersett w Canteloff 72-85; V Ketteringham 73-84; RD Humbleyard 81-86; Hon Can Nor Cathl 85-93; R Hettersett w Canteloff w Lt and Gt Melton 85-86; V Hunstanton St Mary w Ringstead Parva, Holme etc 86-93; rtd 94; Perm to Offic *Nor* from 94. *3 Forge Close, Poringland, Norwich NR14 7SZ*　Framingham Earl (01508) 493885

SEYMOUR, David. b 43. Kelham Th Coll 60. **d** 68 **p** 69. C Cowley St Jas *Ox* 68-73; TV Lynton, Brendon, Countisbury, Lynmouth etc *Ex* 73-77; C-in-c Luton (Princes Park) CD *Roch* 78-79; V Rosherville 79-90; rtd 90. *4 Swinburne Drive, Lowry Hill, Carlisle CA3 0PY*　Carlisle (01228) 818344

SEYMOUR, David Raymond Russell. b 56. Keble Coll Ox BA79 MA88. St Steph Ho Ox 79. **d** 81 **p** 82. C Tilehurst St Mich *Ox* 81-85; TV Parkstone St Pet w Branksea and St Osmund *Sarum* 85-91; V Bradford-on-Avon Ch Ch from 91. *Christ Church Vicarage, 3D Mount Pleasant, Bradford-on-Avon, Wilts BA15 1SJ*　Bradford-on-Avon (01225) 867656

SEYMOUR, Canon John Charles. b 30. Oak Hill Th Coll 51 and 55 Wycliffe Coll Toronto 54. **d** 57 **p** 58. V Thornton *Leic* 63-70; R Kirby Muxloe 70-81; TR 81-83; Hon Can Leic Cathl 82-93; RD Sparkenhoe I 83-88; R Market Bosworth w Shenton 83-87; TR Market Bosworth, Cadeby w Sutton Cheney etc 87-93; RD Sparkenhoe W (Hinkley and Bosworth) 89-92; rtd 93. *7 Merton Close, Broughton Astley, Leicester LE9 6QP* Sutton Elms (01455) 282525

SEYMOUR, Ralph. b 05. Cuddesdon Coll 73. **d** 73 **p** 73. Hon C Tring *St Alb* 73-80; Perm to Offic from 80. *6 Regal Court, Tring, Herts HP23 4PT*　Tring (01442) 822223

SEYMOUR-WHITELEY, Richard Dudley. b 59. Leic Poly BSc80. Linc Th Coll 82. **d** 85 **p** 86. C Bushey *St Alb* 85-89; C Stevenage St Mary Sheppall w Aston 89-93; P-in-c Blunham w Tempsford and Lt Barford from 93. *The Rectory, Park Lane, Blunham, Bedford MK44 3NJ*　Biggleswade (01767) 40298

SHACKELL, Kenneth Norman. b 26. S'wark Ord Course. **d** 69 **p** 70. NSM Greenwich St Alfege w St Pet and St Paul *S'wark* 69-95; Perm to Offic *Sarum* from 95. *17 Portman Drive, Child Okeford, Blandford Forum, Dorset DT11 8HU*　Child Okeford (01258) 861583

SHACKERLEY, Capt Albert Paul. b 56. Birkb Coll Lon DipRS86 DipTh89 Chich Tech Coll CCouns93. CA Tr Coll DipEvang83 Chich Th Coll DMinlTh93. **d** 93 **p** 94. C Harlesden All So *Lon* from 93. *The Hall Flat, 1 Station Road, London NW10 4UJ*　0181-961 2750

SHACKLADY, Mrs Thelma. b 38. Liv Univ BA60. St Alb Minl Tr Scheme 89. **d** 92 **p** 94. NSM Luton St Andr *St Alb* from 92. *31 Fairford Avenue, Luton LU2 7ER*　Luton (01582) 23252

SHACKLETON, Canon Alan. b 31. Sheff Univ BA53. Wells Th Coll 54. **d** 56 **p** 57. C Ladybarn *Man* 56-58; C Bolton St Pet 58-61; V Middleton Junction 61-70; V Heywood St Luke 70-84; AD Rochdale 82-92; Hon Can Man Cathl from 84; V Heywood St Luke w All So 85-86; TV Rochdale 86-91; TR from 91. *The Vicarage, Sparrow Hill, Rochdale, Lancs OL16 1QT*　Rochdale (01706) 45014

SHACKLETON, Bernard. b 35. Lon Univ BD65 St Chad's Coll Dur BA58 DipTh60. **d** 60 **p** 61. C Chislehurst Annunciation *Roch* 60-67; V Higham and Merston 67-87; V N Curry *B & W* 87-94. *5 Blackdown View, Curry Rivel, Langport, Somerset TA10 0ER*　Langport (01458) 257367

SHACKLETON, Ian Roderick. b 40. St Fran Coll Brisbane 69 ACT ThL71. **d** 72 **p** 72. Australia 72-78; C Birch St Agnes *Man* 79-80; P-in-c Newton Heath St Wilfrid and St Anne 80-87; NSM W Derby (or Tuebrook) St Jo *Liv* 87-90; C 90-94;

P-in-c Southport St Luke from 94; Asst Chapl HM Pris Liv from 94. *The Clergy House, 71 Hawkshead Street, Southport, Merseyside PR9 9BT*　Southport (01704) 538703

SHACKLOCK, David Peter Riley. b 36. CCC Cam BA60 MA64. Ridley Hall Cam 60. **d** 62 **p** 63. C Park Estate St Chris CD *Leic* 62-66; CF 66-71; R Northiam *Chich* 71-80; V Fulham St Mary N End *Lon* 80-87; V Redhill H Trin *S'wark* from 87. *Holy Trinity Vicarage, 2 Carlton Road, Redhill RH1 2BX* Redhill (01737) 766604

SHAFEE, Kenneth Harold. b 30. ALA64. Ex & Truro NSM Scheme 78. **d** 81 **p** 82. NSM Littleham w Exmouth *Ex* 81-85; Custos St Jo Hosp Heytesbury 85-89; NSM Lydford, Brent Tor, Bridestowe and Sourton *Ex* 89-90; rtd 90; Perm to Offic *Ex* from 90. *The Firs, Exeter Road, Dawlish, Devon EX7 0LX* Dawlish (01626) 888326

SHAIL, Canon William Frederick. b 15. Kelham Th Coll. **d** 41 **p** 42. V Bournemouth St Alb *Win* 68-78; V Burley Ville 78-84; rtd 84; Perm to Offic *Win* from 84. *19 Halton Close, Bransgore, Christchurch, Dorset BH23 8HZ*　Bransgore (01425) 73064

SHAKESPEARE, Daniel. b 19. E Anglian Minl Tr Course 79. **d** 81 **p** 82. NSM Hethersett w Canteloff *Nor* 81-85; NSM Hethersett w Canteloff w Lt and Gt Melton 85-89; Perm to Offic from 89. *23 Central Crescent, Hethersett, Norwich NR9 3EP*　Norwich (01603) 810727

SHALLCROSS, Canon Martin Anthony. b 37. FRICS70. Sarum & Wells Th Coll 75. **d** 78 **p** 79. NSM Landford w Plaitford *Sarum* 78-81; NSM Bramshaw 78-81; NSM Tisbury from 81; Hon Can Sarum Cathl from 93. *Wallmead Farm, Tisbury, Salisbury SP3 6RB*　Tisbury (01747) 870208

SHAMBROOK, Roger William. b 46. Sarum & Wells Th Coll 78. **d** 83 **p** 84. OSP 76-82; C Southbourne St Kath *Win* 83-86; TV Bridport *Sarum* from 86; Chapl Bridport Hosp from 86. *The Vicarage, Parsonage Road, Bridport, Dorset DT6 5ET* Bridport (01308) 423458

SHAND, Dr Brian Martin. b 53. Univ Coll Lon BA76 PhD82. St Steph Ho Ox 85. **d** 87 **p** 88. C Uxbridge St Marg *Lon* 87-88; C Uxbridge 88-90; C Worplesdon *Guildf* 90-94; Relig Affairs Producer BBC Radio Surrey 90-94; V Weston from 94. *All Saints' Vicarage, 1 Chestnut Avenue, Esher, Surrey KT10 8JL* 0181-398 1849

SHAND, John. b 06. Aber Univ MA27. Edin Th Coll 32. **d** 34 **p** 35. R Buckie *Ab* 69-71; rtd 71. *7 Albany Court, Dennyduff Road, Fraserburgh, Aberdeenshire AB43 5NG*　Fraserburgh (01346) 27948

SHANKS, Robert Andrew Gulval. b 54. Ball Coll Ox BA75 G&C Coll Cam BA79. Westcott Ho Cam 77. **d** 80 **p** 81. C Potternewton *Ripon* 80-83; C Stanningley St Thos 84-87. *52 Newton Court, Leeds LS8 2PH*　Leeds (0113) 248 5011

SHANNON, Brian James. b 35. St Chad's Coll Dur BA59 DipTh61. **d** 61 **p** 62. C Palmers Green St Jo *Lon* 61-65; C Kenton 65-70; V Roxbourne St Andr 70-81; V Thorpe-le-Soken *Chelmsf* 81-91; V Gt Wakering w Foulness from 91. *The Vicarage, 2 New Road, Great Wakering, Southend-on-Sea SS3 0AH*　Southend-on-Sea (01702) 219226

SHANNON, Canon Francis Thomas. b 16. TCD BA39 MA. CITC. **d** 39 **p** 40. I Carnew w Kilrush *C & O* 61-91; RD Wexford 68-91; Preb Ferns Cathl 71-91; Treas 80-81; Chan 81-85; Prec 85-91; rtd 91. *16 Clonattin, Gorey, Co Wexford, Irish Republic*　Gorey (55) 22284

SHANNON, Ven Malcolm James Douglas. b 49. TCD BA72 MA75. CITC 75. **d** 75 **p** 76. C Clooney *D & R* 75-78; I Kilcolman w Kiltallagh, Killorglin, Knockane etc *L & K* from 78; Adn Ardfert and Aghadoe from 88; Treas Limerick Cathl from 88; Dir of Ords from 91. *Kilcolman Rectory, Miltown, Killarney, Co Kerry, Irish Republic*　Tralee (66) 67302　Fax as telephone

SHANNON, Canon Trevor Haslam. b 33. Selw Coll Cam BA57 MA61 Lon Univ BD69. Westcott Ho Cam 57. **d** 59 **p** 60. C Moss Side Ch Ch *Man* 59-62; V Woolfold 62-66; Chapl Forest Sch Snaresbrook 66-80 and 87-88; V Gt Ilford St Marg *Chelmsf* 88-90; TR Gt Ilford SS Clem and Marg from 90; RD Redbridge from 90; Hon Can Chelmsf Cathl from 93. *The Vicarage, 70 Brisbane Road, Ilford, Essex IG1 4SL*　0181-554 7542

SHANNON, Canon William Patrick. b 09. ARCO34 Glas Univ MA31. Edin Th Coll 31. **d** 33 **p** 34. R Kington w Huntington *Heref* 65-75; RD Kington and Weobley 72-75; Preb Heref Cathl 74-75; rtd 75; Hon Can St Andr Cathl *Ab* from 76; Perm to Offic *Glouc* 76-94. *1 Abbey Cottage, Gloucester Road, Tewkesbury, Glos GL20 5SR*　Tewkesbury (01684) 295330

SHAPLAND, David Edward. b 26. Cuddesdon Coll 51. **d** 53 **p** 54. Warden Llanerchwen Trust 70-91; Lic to Offic *S & B* 70-91; Perm to Offic *Chich* 79-91; rtd 91. *Willowdown Cottage, Rodmell, Lewes, E Sussex BN7 3HF*　Lewes (01273) 483557

SHARE, David James. b 30. Sarum Th Coll 56. **d** 58 **p** 59. C Whipton *Ex* 58-63; Min Tiverton St Andr Statutory Distr 63-69; RD Tiverton 67-74; V Tiverton St Andr 69-79; P-in-c Ex St Thos 79-80; TR Ex St Thos and Em 80-83; V Woodbury from 83. *The Vicarage, Woodbury, Exeter EX5 1EF* Woodbury (01395) 232315

SHARLAND, Canon Charles Thomas. b 08. Wycliffe Hall Ox 45. **d** 45 **p** 46. R Heigham H Trin *Nor* 61-75; Hon Can Nor Cathl 73-85; rtd 75; Perm to Offic *Nor* from 75. *35 Cromwell House, Cecil Road, Norwich NR1 2QL* Norwich (01603) 626817

SHARLAND, Mrs Marilyn. b 40. City of Birm Coll CertEd61. Oak Hill Th Coll 84. **dss** 86 **d** 87 **p** 94. Barkingside St Laur *Chelmsf* 86-87; Hon Par Dn 87-88; Hon Par Dn Hucclecote *Glouc* 88-89; C Coney Hill from 89. *58 Bullfinch Road, Gloucester GL4 8LX* Gloucester (01452) 416788

SHARMAN, Herbert Leslie John. b 27. St Aid Birkenhead 60. **d** 62 **p** 63. C Brandon and Santon Downham *St E* 66-87; Perm to Offic from 87; rtd 92. *18 Princes Close, Brandon, Suffolk IP27 0LH* Thetford (01842) 811163

SHARMAN, Hilary John. b 32. Leeds Univ BA58. Coll of Resurr Mirfield 58. **d** 60 **p** 61. C Hertf St Andr *St Alb* 60-64; C Harpenden St Nic 64-72; V High Cross from 72; V Thundridge from 72. *7 Ducketts Wood, Thundridge, Ware, Herts SG12 0SR* Ware (01920) 465561

SHARP, Alfred James Frederick. b 30. Oak Hill Th Coll 62. **d** 64 **p** 65. P-in-c Leverton *Linc* 68-84; Chapl Pilgrim Hosp Boston 76-84; P-in-c Benington w Leverton *Linc* 84; V Ch Broughton w Boylestone & Sutton on the Hill *Derby* 84-89; R Ch Broughton w Barton Blount, Boylestone etc 89-94; rtd 94. *14 Edgefield, Weston, Spalding, Lincs PE12 6RQ* Spalding (01406) 370376

SHARP, Andrew Timothy. b 58. K Alfred's Coll Win BA79. Wycliffe Hall Ox 82. **d** 85 **p** 86. C Scarborough St Mary w Ch Ch and H Apostles *York* 85-89; C Luton St Fran *St Alb* 89-90; V from 90. *The Vicarage, 145 Hollybush Road, Luton LU2 9HQ* Luton (01582) 28030

SHARP, Bernard Harold. b 40. Linc Th Coll 64. **d** 67 **p** 68. C Newton Aycliffe *Dur* 67-69; C Leam Lane CD 69-71; Malawi 72-75; P-in-c Blakenall Heath *Lich* 75-77; TV Gateshead *Dur* 77-79; C Warmsworth *Sheff* 84; C Caerau w Ely *Llan* 85-92; V Cwmbach from 92. *The Vicarage, Bridge Road, Cwmbach, Aberdare, M Glam CF44 0LS* Aberdare (01685) 878674

SHARP, Brian Phillip. b 48. Cant Sch of Min 85. **d** 88 **p** 89. C S Ashford Ch Ch *Cant* 88-92; C St Laurence in the Isle of Thanet from 92. *St Christopher House, Kimberley Road, Newington, Ramsgate, Kent CT12 6HH* Thanet (01843) 594160

SHARP, Canon David Malcolm. b 33. Hertf Coll Ox BA56 MA59. Cuddesdon Coll 56. **d** 58 **p** 59. C Bris St Mary Redcliffe w Temple *Bris* 58-65; V Henleaze 65-75; V Nor St Pet Mancroft *Nor* 75-82; R Nor St Pet Mancroft w St Jo Maddermarket from 82; Hon Can Nor Cathl from 86; Dioc Eur Contact from 91. *The Chantry, Chantry Road, Norwich NR2 1QZ* Norwich (01603) 610443 or 627816

SHARP, Nicholas Leonard (Nick). b 64. Grey Coll Dur BA85. St Jo Coll Nottm DTS94 MA95. **d** 95. C Oakwood St Thos *Lon* from 95. *22 Curthwaite Gardens, Enfield, Middx EN2 7LN* 0181-363 4396

SHARP, Ralph Norman. b 96. Qu Coll Cam BA21 MA24. Ridley Hall Cam 21. **d** 22 **p** 23. Iran 24-67; rtd 67; Perm to Offic *Bris* from 68. *7 Hungerford Road, Chippenham, Wilts SN15 1QW* Chippenham (01249) 652659

SHARP, Canon Reuben Thomas George (Tom). b 27. ALCD57. **d** 57 **p** 58. C Pudsey St Lawr *Bradf* 57-60; V Cononley w Bradley 60-63; Dioc Youth Chapl 60-63; Dioc Youth Officer *Wakef* 63-68; V Dewsbury All SS 68-84; RD Dewsbury 68-90; Hon Can Wakef Cathl from 76; TR Dewsbury 84-90; V Cawthorne from 90. *The Vicarage, 5 Church Lane, Cawthorne, Barnsley, S Yorkshire S75 4DW* Barnsley (01226) 790235

SHARP, Preb Robert. b 36. FLCM58. St Aid Birkenhead 64. **d** 67 **p** 68. C Shipley St Paul *Bradf* 67-70; C-in-c Thwaites Brow CD 70-74; V Thwaites Brow 74-77; P-in-c Alberbury w Cardeston *Heref* 77-78; V 78-87; V Ford 77-87; V Claverley w Tuckhill from 87; RD Bridgnorth from 89; Preb Heref Cathl from 91. *The Vicarage, Lodge Park, Claverley, Wolverhampton WV5 7DP* Claverley (01746) 710268

SHARPE, Canon Alan Brian. b 39. Lich Th Coll 64. **d** 67 **p** 68. C Croydon Woodside *Cant* 67-70; C Portsea St Mary *Portsm* 70-75; V Sheerness H Trin w St Paul *Cant* 75-83; V Hove St Patr w Ch Ch and St Andr *Chich* 83-90; V Hove St Patr from 90; Can and Preb Chich Cathl from 93. *St Patrick's Vicarage, 30 Cambridge Road, Hove, E Sussex BN3 1DF* Brighton (01273) 733151

SHARPE, Bruce Warrington. b 41. JP88. DMS85 MIMgt85. Ely Th Coll 62 St Steph Ho Ox 64. **d** 65 **p** 66. C Streatham St Pet *S'wark* 65-67; St Lucia 67-68; Hon C Leic St Matt and St Geo *Leic* 68-69; Hon C Catford St Laur *S'wark* 69-70; Hon C Deptford St Paul 70-75; Hon C Lamorbey H Redeemer *Roch* 76-83; Perm to Offic 83-88; Hon C Sidcup St Andr from 88. *72 Faraday Avenue, Sidcup, Kent DA14 4JF* 0181-300 0695

SHARPE, Cecil Frederick. b 23. Edin Th Coll 52. **d** 54 **p** 55. V Withall *Birm* 58-80; Perm to Offic from 80; rtd 88. *35 Shirley*

Park Road, Shirley, Solihull, W Midlands B90 2BZ* 0121-745 6905

SHARPE, David Francis. b 32. Ex Coll Ox BA56 MA59. St Steph Ho Ox 57. **d** 60 **p** 61. C Hunslet St Mary and Stourton *Ripon* 60-63; C Notting Hill St Jo *Lon* 63-68; V Haggerston St Mary w St Chad 68-78; P-in-c Haggerston St Aug w St Steph 73-78; V Haggerston St Chad 78-83; V Mill Hill St Mich from 83. *St Michael's Vicarage, 9 Flower Lane, London NW7 2JA* 0181-959 1449

SHARPE, David Robert Scott. b 31. Keble Coll Ox BA54 MA66. Ely Th Coll 54. **d** 56 **p** 57. C Bethnal Green St Jo w St Simon *Lon* 56-59; C St Ives *Truro* 59-61; V Pencoys w Carnmenellis 61-65; V Penwerris 65-69; Lic to Offic *Portsm* from 73. *16 Privett Place, Gosport, Hants PO12 3SQ* Gosport (01705) 589248

SHARPE, Derek Martin Brereton (Pip). b 29. Birkb Coll Lon BA60. NE Ord Course 90. **d** 90 **p** 91. NSM Scarborough St Luke *York* 90-92; Asst Chapl Scarborough Distr Hosp 90-92; P-in-c Sherburn and W and E Heslerton w Yedingham from 92. *Low Farm House, Allerston, Pickering, N Yorkshire YO18 7PG* Scarborough (01723) 859271

SHARPE, Gerard John. b 23. Westcott Ho Cam. **d** 64 **p** 65. C Thetford St Cuth w H Trin *Nor* 64-70; V Holme *Ely* 70-76; R Conington 70-76; R Glatton 74-93; V Holme w Conington 76-93; RD Yaxley 82-88; rtd 93. *24 St Margaret's Road, Girton, Cambridge CB3 0LT* Cambridge (01223) 574246

SHARPE, Miss Joan Valerie. b 33. E Midl Min Tr Course 73. **dss** 84 **d** 88 **p** 94. Hon Par Dn Warsop *S'well* 88-94; Hon C from 94. *1 Forest Court, Eakring Road, Mansfield, Notts NG18 3DP* Mansfield (01623) 631505

SHARPE, John Brebber (Brother Mark). b 14. **d** 85. CSWG from 82; Lic to Offic *Chich* from 85. *The Monastery, 23 Cambridge Road, Hove, E Sussex BN3 1DE* Brighton (01273) 726698

SHARPE, John Edward. b 50. Dur Univ BSc72 St Jo Coll Dur DipTh75. **d** 76 **p** 77. C Woodford Wells *Chelmsf* 76-79; C Ealing St Mary *Lon* 79-83; Min Walsall St Martin *Lich* 83-87; TV Walsall from 87. *St Martin's House, 17 Daffodil Road, Walsall WS5 3DQ* Walsall (01922) 23216

SHARPE, Canon John Leslie. b 33. MInstGA89 Birm Univ DPS72 Open Univ BA75. Kelham Th Coll 54. **d** 58 **p** 59. Papua New Guinea 62-70; Adn N Distr 68-70; P-in-c Southn SS Pet and Paul w All SS *Win* 71-73; TV Southn (City Cen) 73-75; Chapl SW Hants Psychiatric Services 75-93; Chapl Knowle Hosp Fareham 75-93; Hon Can Portsm Cathl *Portsm* 86-93; rtd 93. *Clare Cottage, 23 West Dean, Salisbury SP5 1JB* Lockerley (01742) 340028

SHARPE, Canon Kenneth William (Ken). b 40. Univ of Wales (Lamp) BA61. Sarum Th Coll 61. **d** 63 **p** 64. C Hubberston *St D* 63-71; TV Cwmbran *Mon* 71-74; Dioc Children's Adv 72-82; Dioc Youth Chapl 74-82; V Dingestow and Llangovan w Penyclawdd and Tregaer 74-82; V Newport St Mark from 82; Chapl Alltyryn Hosp Gwent from 83; RD Newport *Mon* from 93; Can St Woolos Cathl from 94. *The Vicarage, 7 Goldtops, Newport, Gwent NP9 4PH* Newport (01633) 263321

SHARPE, Mrs Margaret Theresa. b 48. Man Univ BEd70 Dur Univ DipTh74. Cranmer Hall Dur 72 W Midl Minl Tr Course 90. **d** 91 **p** 94. C W Bromwich H Trin *Lich* from 91. *St Martin's House, 17 Daffodil Road, Walsall, W Midlands WS5 3DQ* Walsall (01922) 23216

SHARPE, Miss Mary. b 31. CQSW71. Dalton Ho Bris 58. **dss** 78 **d** 87 **p** 94. Upton (or Overchurch) *Ches* 78-83; Harlescott *Lich* 83-84; New Brighton All SS *Ches* 85-89; Par Dn 87-89; rtd 89. *13 Manor Close, Neston, South Wirral L64 6TE*

SHARPE, Mrs Mary Primrose. b 22. Gilmore Ho B27. Coll of St Matthias Bris CertEd. Gilmore Ho CertRK51 DC51 CMS Tr Coll Chislehurst. **dss** 81 **d** 87. Coley *Wakef* 81-87; Hon Par Dn 87-89; rtd 89. *54 Bradford Road, Menston, Ilkley, W Yorkshire LS29 6BX* Menston (01943) 877710

SHARPE, Richard Gordon. b 48. Birm Univ BA69. St Jo Coll Nottm BA74. **d** 75 **p** 76. C Hinckley H Trin *Leic* 75-78; C Kingston upon Hull H Trin *York* 78-85; Chapl Marston Green Hosp Birm 85-88; Chapl Chelmsley Hosp Birm 86-88; TV Chelmsley Wood *Birm* 85-88; P-in-c Dosthill 88-93; V from 93. *The Vicarage, Dosthill, Tamworth, Staffs B77 1LU* Tamworth (01827) 281349

SHARPE, Canon Roger. b 35. TCD BA60 MA63. Qu Coll Birm 60. **d** 62 **p** 63. C Stockton H Trin *Dur* 62-64; C Oakdale St Geo *Sarum* 64-68; V Redlynch and Morgan's Vale 68-86; RD Alderbury 82-86; V Warminster St Denys 86-88; R Upton Scudamore 86-88; V Horningsham 86-88; R Warminster St Denys, Upton Scudamore etc from 88; Can and Preb Sarum Cathl from 89; RD Heytesbury 87-92; Chmn Dioc Assn for Deaf from 91; P-in-c Corsley from 92. *The Vicarage, 5 Church Street, Warminster, Wilts BA12 8PG* Warminster (01985) 213456

SHARPE, Tony Ernest Charles. E Anglian Minl Tr Course. **d** 93. NSM Leigh-on-Sea St Jas *Chelmsf* from 93. *39 Grange Road,*

Leigh-on-Sea, Essex SS9 2HT Southend-on-Sea (01702) 79949

SHARPLES, Canon Alfred Cyril. b 09. Man Univ BA33. Linc Th Coll 33. **d** 35 **p** 36. V Hope St Jas *Man* 51-76; Hon Can Man Cathl 74-76; rtd 76; Perm to Offic *Ches* from 77; Perm to Offic *Man* from 77. *30 Greenbank Drive, Bollington, Macclesfield, Cheshire SK10 5LW* 0161-207 5073

SHARPLES, David. b 41. Linc Th Coll 71. **d** 73 **p** 74. C Reddish *Man* 73-75; C Prestwich St Mary 76-78; V Ashton St Jas 78-86; V Hope St Jas from 86. *Hope Vicarage, Vicarage Close, Pendleton, Salford M6 8EJ* 0161-789 3303

SHARPLES, David. b 58. Lon Univ BD81 AKC81. Coll of Resurr Mirfield. **d** 82 **p** 83. C Prestwich St Mary *Man* 82-87; V Royton St Anne from 87; AD Tandle from 94. *St Anne's Vicarage, St Anne's Avenue, Royton, Oldham OL2 5AD* 0161-624 2249

SHARPLES, Dr Derek. b 35. SS Paul & Mary Coll Cheltenham CertEd57 Liv Univ DipEd63 Man Univ MEd66 Bath Univ PhD72 Open Univ BA79 FCollP86. W Midl Minl Tr Course 83. **d** 86 **p** 87. NSM Malvern H Trin and St Jas *Worc* 86-90; C St Jo in Bedwardine 90-92; R Belbroughton w Fairfield and Clent from 92. *The Rectory, Bradford Lane, Belbroughton, Stourbridge, W Midlands DY9 9TF* Belbroughton (01562) 730531

SHARPLES, John Charles. b 29. St Jo Coll York TCertE48 Lon Univ BSc55. St Deiniol's Hawarden 87. **d** 87 **p** 88. Hon C Wigan St Mich *Liv* 87-89; P-in-c New Springs from 89. *New Springs Vicarage, 7 Lealholme Avenue, Wigan, Lancs WN2 1EH* Wigan (01942) 43071

SHARPLES, Ms Susan Margaret (Sue). b 58. SRN82 Worc Coll of Educn BA89. W Midl Minl Tr Course 91. **d** 94 **p** 95. NSM Worc SE *Worc* from 94. *252 Worcester Road, Malvern, Worcs WR14 1AW* Malvern (01684) 568814

SHARPLEY, Ven Roger Ernest Dion. b 28. Ch Ch Ox BA52 MA56. St Steph Ho Ox 52. **d** 54 **p** 55. V Middlesb All SS *York* 60-81; P-in-c Middlesb St Hilda w St Pet 64-72; RD Middlesbrough 70-81; Can and Preb York Minster 74-81; P-in-c Middlesb St Aid 79; V 79-81; V St Andr Holborn *Lon* 81-92; Adn Hackney 81-92; rtd 92. *2 Hill Meadows, High Shincliffe, Durham DH1 2PE* 0191-386 1908

SHARPUS-JONES, Trevor. b 20. TD66. St And Dioc Tr Course 83. **d** 87 **p** 88. NSM St Andrews St Andr *St And* 87-89; P-in-c Elie and Earlsferry 89-90; P-in-c Pittenweem 89-90; NSM Leven from 90. *Etta Bank, 40 Leven Road, Lundin Links, Leven, Fife KY8 6AH* Lundin Links (01333) 320510

SHAW, Alan. b 24. Man Univ BSc44 MSc48 PhD51. Ely Th Coll 55. **d** 57 **p** 58. Perm to Offic *Liv* 61-71; V Beckermet St Jo *Carl* 71-76; V Lt Leigh and Lower Whitley *Ches* 76-80; V Latchford Ch Ch 80-91; rtd 91. *7 Gainsborough Road, Warrington WA4 6DA* Warrington (01925) 240133

SHAW, Alan Taylor. b 52. Sarum & Wells Th Coll 88. **d** 90 **p** 91. C Beeston *Ripon* 90-93; C Stanningley St Thos from 93. *50 Lane End, Pudsey, W Yorkshire LS28 9AD* Leeds (0113) 256 6535 or 255 3830

SHAW, Alan Walter. b 41. MIEI TCD BA63 BAI63 Chu Coll Cam MSc66. **d** 94 **p** 95. NSM Drumcliffe w Kilnasoolagh *L & K* from 94. *Inismore, 40 College Park, Corbally, Limerick, Irish Republic* Limerick (61) 343959 Fax as telephone

SHAW, Canon Alexander Martin. b 44. AKC67. **d** 68 **p** 69. C Glas St Oswald *Glas* 68-70; C Edin Old St Paul *Edin* 70-75; Chapl K Coll Cam 75-77; C St Marylebone All SS *Lon* 77-78; R Dunoon *Arg* 78-81; Succ Ex Cathl *Ex* 81-83; Dioc Miss and Ecum Officer 83-89; TV Cen Ex 83-87; Can Res St E Cathl *St E* from 89. *1 Abbey Precincts, Bury St Edmunds, Suffolk IP33 1RS* Bury St Edmunds (01284) 761982

SHAW, Andrew Jonathan. b 50. Leeds Univ CertEd72 Open Univ BA81. Wycliffe Hall Ox 85. **d** 87 **p** 88. C Witton w Brundall and Braydeston *Nor* 87-89; C Postwick 87-89; C Brundall w Braydeston and Postwick 89-90; C Grayswood *Guildf* 90-91; P-in-c from 91; Chapl RN Sch Haslemere from 90. *Church House, Church Close, Grayswood, Haslemere, Surrey GU27 2DB* Haslemere (01428) 656504

SHAW, Ms Anne Lesley (Annie). b 50. Linc Th Coll 77. **dss** 80 **d** 87 **p** 94. Camberwell St Luke *S'wark* 80-85; Chapl Asst Lon Hosp (Whitechapel) 85-90; Chapl Lewisham Hosp from 90; Chapl Hither Green Hosp from 90. *The Chaplain's Office, Lewisham Hospital, High Street, London SE13 6LH* 0181-690 4311

SHAW, Dr Anne Patricia Leslie. b 39. MRCS LRCP63 MB, BS63 DA68. Qu Coll Birm 79. **dss** 81 **d** 87 **p** 94. Pinner *Lon* 81-84; Rickmansworth *St Alb* 84-87; NSM from 87. *37 Sandy Lodge Road, Moor Park, Rickmansworth, Herts WD3 1LP* Northwood (01923) 827663

SHAW, Anthony Keeble. b 36. K Alfred's Coll Win CertEd60. SW Minl Tr Course 78. **d** 81 **p** 82. NSM E Teignmouth *Ex* 81-83; NSM Highweek and Teigngrace 83-87; C Southbourne St Kath *Win* 87-89; Teaching from 89; Perm to Offic *Lon* from 93. *33 Stephenson Street, London NW10 6TX* 0181-933 1753

SHAW, Basil Earle. b 06. BNC Ox BA28 DipTh29 MA32. Wells Th Coll 29. **d** 30 **p** 31. V N Frodingham *York* 60-73; rtd 74. *21 Cranbrook Avenue, Hull HU6 7SP*

SHAW, Colin Clement Gordon. b 39. RMN60 TNC62 DPS72. Linc Th Coll 65. **d** 67 **p** 68. C Tettenhall Regis *Lich* 67-70; C Tile Cross *Birm* 70-72; V Edstaston *Lich* 72-75; V Whixall 72-75; Chapl Stoke Mandeville Hosp and St Jo Hosp 75-90; Manor Ho Hosp and Tindal Gen Hosp Aylesbury 75-90; R Bledlow w Saunderton and Horsenden *Ox* from 90. *The Rectory, Church End, Bledlow, Princes Risborough, Bucks HP27 9PD* Princes Risborough (01844) 344762

SHAW, Colin Martin. b 21. Oak Hill Th Coll 68. **d** 69 **p** 70. C Halliwell St Pet *Man* 69-72; V Tonge Fold 72-78; V Gresley *Derby* 78-82; V Gt Marsden *Blackb* 82-87; rtd 87. *Holborn Close, Huntingdon, Cambs PE17 3AJ* Ramsey (01487) 822246

SHAW, Cuthbert Charles. b 08. St Edm Hall Ox BA35 MA46. Westcott Ho Cam 30. **d** 32 **p** 33. R Aveton Gifford *Ex* 61-72; rtd 73; Perm to Offic *Guildf* 73-92. *Manormead Nursing Home, Tilford Road, Hindhead, Surrey GU26 6RP* Hindhead (01428) 604780

SHAW, David George. b 40. Lon Univ BD64. Tyndale Hall Bris 58. **d** 65 **p** 66. C Kirkdale St Lawr *Liv* 65-68; C Bebington *Ches* 68-70; V Swadlincote *Derby* 70-75; R Eyam from 75. *The Rectory, Eyam, Sheffield S30 1QH* Hope Valley (01433) 630821

SHAW, David Michael. b 61. Univ Coll Dur BA83. Trin Coll Bris DipHE93. **d** 93 **p** 94. C Wotton-under-Edge w Ozleworth and N Nibley *Glouc* from 93. *39 Parklands, Wotton-under-Edge, Glos GL12 7LT* Dursley (01453) 843945

SHAW, David Parlane. b 32. CITC. **d** 69 **p** 70. Bp's C Lower w Upper Langfield *D & R* 69-75; R Chedburgh w Depden and Rede *St E* 75-78; R Chedburgh w Depden, Rede and Hawkedon 79-82; R Desford *Leic* 82-83; R Desford and Peckleton w Tooley 84-91; P-in-c Ramsden Crays w Ramsden Bellhouse *Chelmsf* 91-95; rtd 95. *9 Hambleton Close, Leicester Forest East, Leicester LE3 3NA* Leicester (0116) 239 5591

SHAW, David Thomas. b 45. Open Univ BA78. W Midl Minl Tr Course 87. **d** 90 **p** 91. C Sheldon *Birm* 90-93; TR Chelmsley Wood from 93. *The Rectory, Pike Drive, Birmingham B37 7US* 0121-770 5155 or 770 1511

SHAW, Denis. b 26. Westcott Ho Cam. **d** 59 **p** 60. R Newton Heath St Wilfrid *Man* 63-71; R Clewer St Andr *Ox* 71-92; rtd 92. *The Coach House Cottage, Bedford Place, Bridport, Dorset DT6 3QL* Bridport (01308) 421700

SHAW, Denis Alfred Arthur. b 24. Wells Th Coll 64. **d** 65 **p** 66. C Redditch St Steph *Worc* 65-70; R Addingham *Bradf* 70-92; rtd 92. *67 Crowther Avenue, Calverley, Pudsey, W Yorkshire LS28 5SA* Bradford (01274) 611746

SHAW, Canon Denis Walter. b 16. Sarum Th Coll 65. **d** 67 **p** 68. C Bridport *Sarum* 67-70; R Tarrant Rushton, Tarrant Rawston etc 70-76; RD Milton and Blandford 77-84; P-in-c Bere Regis 76-77; R Bere Regis and Affpuddle w Turnerspuddle 78-85; Can and Preb Sarum Cathl 77-85; rtd 85. *29 Martleaves Close, Weymouth, Dorset DT4 9UT* Dorchester (01305) 774738

SHAW, Ernest Ronald. b 16. K Coll Lon BA38. Chich Th Coll 72. **d** 72 **p** 73. Chapl Cov Cathl *Cov* 72-78; Perm to Offic *Sarum* 79-80; C Semley and Sedgehill 80-85; rtd 85. *Fairmead, Church Hill, Stour Row, Shaftesbury, Dorset SP7 0QW* East Stour (01747) 838350

SHAW, Mrs Felicity Mary. b 46. UEA BSc67 MSc68 Liv Inst of Educn DipRE87. N Ord Course 88. **d** 91 **p** 94. Par Dn Benchill *Man* 91-94; C 94-95; TV E Farnworth and Kearsley from 95. *195 Harrowby Street, Farnworth, Bolton BL4 9QU* Bolton (01204) 72455

SHAW, Frederick Hugh. b 16. CChem MRSC Dur Univ BSc49 MSc66. E Midl Min Tr Course 73. **d** 76 **p** 77. Hon C Wingerworth *Derby* from 76. *1 Frances Drive, Wingerworth, Chesterfield, Derbyshire S42 6SJ* Chesterfield (01246) 278321

SHAW, Gary Robert. b 59. **d** 85 **p** 86. C Dundonald *D & D* 85-87; I Tullaniskin w Clonoe *Arm* 87-94; Bp's C Stoneyford *Conn* from 94; Chapl R Vic Hosps Belf from 94. *62 Stoneyford Road, Stoneyford, Lisburn, Co Antrim BT28 3SP* Lisburn (01846) 648300

SHAW, Canon Geoffrey Norman. b 26. Jes Coll Ox MA50. Wycliffe Hall Ox 49. **d** 51 **p** 52. Lic to Offic *Sheff* 68-72; Vice-Prin and Lect Oak Hill Th Coll 72-79; Prin Wycliffe Hall Ox 79-88; Hon Can Ch Ch *Ox* 86-88; rtd 88. Lic to Offic *Nor* 88-91. *15A West Street, Kingham, Chipping Norton, Oxon OX7 6YF* Kingham (01608) 658006

SHAW, Gerald Oliver. b 32. K Coll Lon 56. **d** 60 **p** 61. C Burnley St Cuth *Blackb* 60-62; C Heysham 62-65; C-in-c Oswaldtwistle All SS CD 65-66; V Oswaldtwistle All SS 66-69; Chapl Leavesden Hosp Abbots Langley 69-75; Chapl Broadmoor Hosp Crowthorne 75-88; C Easthampstead *Ox* 88-92; P-in-c Beech Hill, Grazeley and Spencers Wood from 92. *The Vicarage, 11 Clares Green Road, Spencers Wood, Reading RG7 1DY* Reading (01734) 883215

SHAW, Graham. b 44. Worc Coll Ox BA65. Cuddesdon Coll. **d** 69 **p** 70. C Esher *Guildf* 69-73; R Winford *B & W* 73-78; Chapl Ex Coll Ox 78-85; R Farnborough *Roch* 88-95. *7 The Barnyard, Ebbisham Lane, Tadworth, Surrey KT20 7UW* Tadworth (01737) 812398

SHAW, Grahame David. b 44. Lich Th Coll 65. **d** 68 **p** 69. C Grange St Andr *Ches* 68-73; TV E Runcorn w Halton 73-74; TV Thamesmead *S'wark* 74-79; V Newington St Paul from 79; S'wark Adnry Ecum Officer from 90. *The Vicarage, Lorrimore Square, London SE17 3QU* 0171-735 2947 or 735 8815

SHAW, Mrs Irene. b 45. Gilmore Course 80 NE Ord Course 82. dss 83 **d** 87 **p** 94. Elloughton and Brough w Brantingham *York* 83-86; Westborough *Guildf* 86-87; C 87-88; C Shottermill 88-91; C Lamorbey H Redeemer *Roch* from 91. *34 Ronaldstone Road, Sidcup, Kent DA15 8QU* 0181-859 4058

SHAW, Jack Firth. b 11. Dorchester Miss Coll 35. **d** 38 **p** 39. V Mert St Jo *S'wark* 64-76; rtd 77; Perm to Offic *Cant* 79-92. *3 Worcester Drive, Langland, Swansea SA3 4HL* Swansea (01792) 368516

SHAW, James Alan. b 20. Keble Coll Ox BA42 MA47. Linc Th Coll 42. **d** 44 **p** 45. R Flax Bourton *B & W* 65-80; V Barrow Gurney 77-80; Chapl and Lect St Deiniol's Lib Hawarden 80-81; rtd 81; Perm to Offic *Ban* 82-89; Perm to Offic *Mor* from 90. *Ceol na Mara, 25 Dalchalm, Brora, Sutherland KW9 6LP* Brora (01408) 21058

SHAW, John. b 20. K Coll Lon 57. **d** 59 **p** 60. V Burnley St Cuth *Blackb* 63-74; V Goosnargh w Whittingham 74-85; RD Garstang 79-85; rtd 85; Perm to Offic *Newc* from 85. *9 Villiers Road, Woodthorpe, Nottingham NG5 4FB* Nottingham (0115) 960 5108

SHAW, John Reginald Derek. b 32. Sarum Th Coll 57. **d** 59 **p** 60. C Thornbury *Bradf* 59-61; C Tong 62-63; C Clifford *York* 63-65; V Bramham from 65. *The Vicarage, Vicarage Lane, Bramham, Wetherby, W Yorkshire LS23 6QG* Boston Spa (01937) 843631

SHAW, John Richard Astley. b 24. St Jo Coll Dur 46. ACT ThL53. **d** 51 **p** 53. R Guernsey St Marguerite de la Foret *Win* 65-90; rtd 90. *St Antony, Clos de Cornus, St Martin's, Guernsey, Channel Islands* Guernsey (01481) 37097

SHAW, Kenneth James. b 36. St Jo Coll Nottm 85 Edin Th Coll 88. **d** 87 **p** 89. NSM Troon *Glas* 87-89; C Glas St Mary 89-90; R Lenzie from 90. *The Rectory, 1A Beech Road, Kirkintilloch, Glasgow G66 4HN* 0141-776 4149

SHAW, Michael Howard. b 38. Leeds Univ BSc61. Linc Th Coll 64. **d** 66 **p** 67. C W Hartlepool St Paul *Dur* 66-68; Asst Master Stockbridge Co Sec Sch 68; Totton Coll 69; Gravesend Boys' Gr Sch 70-72; Maidstone Gr Sch from 72; Perm to Offic *Roch* from 82. *2 Bredgar Close, Maidstone, Kent ME14 5NG* Maidstone (01622) 673415

SHAW, Neil Graham. b 61. St Jo Coll Nottm LTh89. **d** 91 **p** 92. C Leamington Priors St Paul *Cov* 91-95; TV Bestwood *S'well* from 95. *St Matthews Vicarage, Padstow Road, Bestwood, Nottingham NG5 5GH* Nottingham (0115) 927 6107

SHAW, Norman. b 33. Cranmer Hall Dur. **d** 82 **p** 83. C Beamish *Dur* 82-84; P-in-c Craghead 84-88; V Cleadon from 88. *The Vicarage, 5 Sunderland Road, Sunderland SR6 7UR* 0191-536 7147

SHAW, Peter Haslewood. b 17. Pemb Coll Cam BA39 MA65. Worc Ord Coll 65. **d** 67 **p** 68. V Alderney *Win* 69-78; V Disley *Ches* 78-82; rtd 82; Chapl Athens w Kifissia, Patras and Corfu *Eur* 82-85; Hon C Las Palmas 84-85; Hon C Breamore *Win* 85-89. *Manor Cottage, Church Road, Greatworth, Banbury, Oxon OX17 2DU* Banbury (01295) 712102

SHAW, Ralph. b 38. Man Univ MEd70. Sarum & Wells Th Coll 78. **d** 80 **p** 81. C Consett *Dur* 80-84; P-in-c Tanfield 84-88; V from 88. *The Vicarage, Tanfield, Stanley, Co Durham DH9 9PX* Stanley (01207) 232750

SHAW, Ralph Michael. b 45. DipAdEd. Lich Th Coll 68. **d** 70 **p** 71. C Dewsbury All SS *Wakef* 70-75; TV Redcar w Kirkleatham *York* 75-76; Dioc Youth Officer *St Alb* 76-91; Lic to Offic from 91; Chief Exec Jo Grooms Assn for the Disabled from 91. *Welwyn, 18 Wyton Road, Welwyn Garden City, Herts AL7 2PF* Welwyn Garden (01707) 321813 Fax 0181-809 1754

SHAW, Richard. b 46. **d** 89 **p** 90. NSM Porchester *S'well* 89-91. *95 Marshall Hill Drive, Nottingham NG3 6HX* Nottingham (0115) 962 1705

SHAW, Richard Tom. b 42. AKC69. St Aug Coll Cant 69. **d** 70 **p** 71. C Dunston St Nic *Dur* 70-73; C Maidstone All SS w St Phil and H Trin *Cant* 73-75; Chapl RN 75-79; V Barrow-on-Humber *Linc* 79-83; V Linc St Faith and St Martin w St Pet 83-91; V Clun w Bettws-y-Crwyn and Newc *Heref* from 91; RD Clun Forest from 94. *The Vicarage, Vicarage Road, Clun, Craven Arms, Shropshire SY7 8JG* Clun (01588) 640809

SHAW, Robert Christopher. b 34. Man Univ BA BD. Union Th Sem (NY) STM. **d** 82 **p** 83. C Sharlston *Wakef* 82-83; C Scissett St Aug 83-85; R Cumberworth w Denby Dale 85-90; P-in-c Denby 85-90; R Bolton w Ireby and Uldale *Carl* 90-95;

rtd 95. *Bay Tree Cottage, Paddock Close, Helmsley, York YO6 5BQ* Helmsley (01439) 770178

SHAW, Robert William. b 46. Lon Univ BD69. St Aug Coll Cant 69. **d** 70 **p** 71. C Hunslet St Mary and Stourton *Ripon* 70-71; C Hunslet St Mary 71-74; C Hawksworth Wood 74-76; R Stanningley St Thos 76-84; V Potternewton 84-94; V Manston from 94. *Manston Vicarage, Church Lane, Leeds LS15 8JB* Leeds (0113) 260 0348 or 264 5530

SHAW, Roderick Kenneth. b 37. MBIM77. Moray Ord Course 88. **d** 92. Hon C Grantown-on-Spey *Mor* from 92; Hon C Rothiemurchus from 92. *The Cottage, Balliefurth, Grantown-on-Spey, Morayshire PH26 3NH* Nethybridge (01479) 821496

SHAW, Ronald Forbes. b 16. FRICS55 RIBA47. S'wark Ord Course 67. **d** 70 **p** 71. C Belmont *S'wark* 70-73; P-in-c Lower Sydenham St Mich 73-83; rtd 83; Hon C Surbiton St Matt *S'wark* 83-88; Hon C Kingswood from 88. *6 St Andrews Close, Reigate, Surrey RH2 7JF* Reigate (01737) 246290

SHAW, Mrs Rosemary Alice. b 44. CertEd65 DipTh75 CQSW78. S'wark Ord Course 87. **d** 89 **p** 94. Par Dn Walworth *S'wark* 89-92; Par Dn E Dulwich St Jo 92-95; NSM from 95; Eileen Kerr Mental Health Fellow Maudsley Hosp from 95. *19 Scutari Road, London SE22 0NN* 0181-693 6325

SHAW-HAMILTON, Mrs Janet Elizabeth (Jan). b 43. W Midl Minl Tr Course 88. **d** 91 **p** 94. NSM Bromsgrove All SS *Worc* from 91. *76 Hanbury Road, Stoke Prior, Bromsgrove, Worcs B60 4DN* Bromsgrove (01527) 79843

SHAYLER-WEBB, Peter. b 57. Bath Univ BSc81 BArch83. Ripon Coll Cuddesdon 93. **d** 95. C Bedf St Paul *St Alb* from 95. *54 The Grove, Bedford MK40 3JN* Bedford (01234) 218563

SHAYLOR, Denis Freke. Sarum Th Coll 68. **d** 69 **p** 70. C Caversham *Ox* 69-75; Lic to Offic 76-79; Perm to Offic *Win* 80-93. *Asante, Lasham, Alton, Hants GU34 5SJ* Herriard (01256) 381351

SHEA, Guy Roland John. b 33. Trin Coll Connecticut BA55 Ch Ch Ox BA58 MA62. Coll of Resurr Mirfield 60. **d** 60 **p** 61. C Kennington St Jo *S'wark* 60-63 and 75-77; C N Audley Street St Mark Lon 63-67; C Hammersmith St Sav 67-70; P-in-c Gunnersbury St Jas 70-75; Perm to Offic 77-82; Hon C Fulham St Alb 82-92; Hon C Fulham St Alb w St Aug from 92. *c/o St Alban's Vicarage, 4 Margravine Road, London W6 8HJ* 0171-385 0724

SHEAD, John Frederick Henry. b 38. ACP74 FCP81. Westcott Ho Cam 72. **d** 74 **p** 75. Hd Master Thaxted Co Primary Sch 70-85; Hon C Thaxted *Chelmsf* 74-85; C Saffron Walden w Wendens Ambo and Littlebury 86-88; P-in-c Wethersfield w Shalford from 88; P-in-c Finchingfield and Cornish Hall End from 94; RD Braintree from 95. *The Vicarage, Finchingfield, Braintree, Essex CM7 4JR* Great Dunmow (01371) 810309

SHEARCROFT, Sister Elizabeth Marion. b 57. **d** 94 **p** 95. NSM Margate H Trin *Cant* from 94; Chapl Cant and Thanet Community Health Trust from 94. *83 Victoria Avenue, Margate, Kent CT9 2VE* Thanet (01843) 290826

SHEARD, Andrew Frank. b 60. York Univ BA81. St Jo Coll Nottm 92. **d** 94 **p** 95. C Uxbridge *Lon* from 94. *St Andrew's Vicarage, The Greenway, Uxbridge, Middx UB8 2PJ* Uxbridge (01895) 237853

SHEARD, Ernest. b 29. Linc Th Coll 73. **d** 74 **p** 75. Hon C Birstall *Leic* 74-82; Hon C Birstall and Wanlip 82-84; Asst Chapl Loughb Univ and Colls 75-90; Lic to Offic *Leic* from 90. *21 Orchard Road, Birstall, Leicester LE4 4GD* Leicester (0116) 267 3901

SHEARD, Gillian Freda. *See* COOKE, Ms Gillian Freda

SHEARD, Dr Michael Rowland. b 42. K Coll Lon BA Man Univ PhD. **d** 95 **p** 95. *68 Sneyd Lane, Essington, Wolverhampton WV11 2DH* Bloxwich (01922) 475915

SHEARD, Neil Jeremy. b 58. Chich Th Coll. **d** 84 **p** 85. C Gelligaer *Llan* 84-86; C Caerphilly 86-90; V Treboeth *S & B* from 90. *St Alban's Vicarage, Heol Fach, Treboeth, Swansea SA5 9DE* Swansea (01792) 771332

SHEARER, Very Rev John. b 26. OBE94. TCD BA48 MA53 BD53. **d** 50 **p** 51. C Magheralin w Dollingstown *D & D* 50-52; C Ballymacarrett St Patr 52-59; I Magheradroll 59-64; I Seagoe 64-85; Adn Dromore 70-85; I Belf St Anne *Conn* from 85; Dean Belf from 85. *The Deanery, 5 Deramore Drive, Belfast BT9 5JQ* Belfast (01232) 660980 or 328332 Fax 238855

SHEARER, John Frank. b 35. Ex Univ BSc60. Tyndale Hall Bris 62. **d** 63 **p** 64. C Blackheath St Jo *S'wark* 63-67; R Nuff *Ox* from 67. *The Rectory, Nuffield, Henley-on-Thames, Oxon RG9 5SN* Nettlebed (01491) 641305

SHEARING, Michael James. b 39. Lanc Univ BA71. Linc Th Coll. **d** 66 **p** 67. Hon C Hartlepool St Paul *Dur* 66-76; Asst Master Dyke Ho Comp Sch Hartlepool 76-87; C Houghton le Spring 87; P-in-c Wheatley Hill from 87. *The Vicarage, Wheatley Hill, Co Durham DH6 3RA* Wellfield (01429) 820496

SHEARLOCK, Very Rev David John. b 32. FRSA91 Birm Univ BA55. Westcott Ho Cam 56. **d** 57 **p** 58. C Guisborough *York* 57-60; C Christchurch *Win* 60-64; V Kingsclere 64-71; V Romsey 71-82; Dioc Dir of Ords 77-82; Hon Can Win Cathl 78-82; Dean Truro from 82; R Truro St Mary from 82; Chapl Cornwall Fire Brigade from 91. *The Deanery, Lemon Street, Truro, Cornwall TR1 2PE* Truro (01872) 72661 or 76782 Fax 77788

SHEARMAN, Michael Alan. b 22. Down Coll Cam BA44 MA48. Coll of Resurr Mirfield 46. **d** 48 **p** 49. V Enfield St Luke *Lon* 58-87; rtd 87; Perm to Offic *Nor* from 87. *18 Thompson Avenue, Holt, Norfolk NR25 6EN* Holt (01263) 713072

SHEARS, Michael George Frederick. b 33. Pemb Coll Cam BA57 MA68. St Steph Ho Ox 57. **d** 59 **p** 60. C Grantham St Wulfram *Linc* 59-68; R Waltham 68-80; R Barnoldby le Beck 74-80; RD Haverstoe 78-80; V Soham *Ely* from 80; RD Fordham from 83. *The Vicarage, Soham, Ely, Cambs CB7 5DU* Ely (01353) 720423

SHEARWOOD, Alexander George Dobbie. b 21. New Coll Ox BA48. Wells Th Coll 49. **d** 50 **p** 51. R Wickenby w Friesthorpe *Linc* 59-81; R Lissington w Holton cum Beckering 60-81; R Snelland w Snarford 63-81; R Wickenby Gp 82; Perm to Offic *Truro* from 82; rtd 86. *Trelowen, 3 Old Road, Boscastle, Cornwall PL35 0AJ* Boscastle (01840) 250663

SHEASBY, Adrian. b 29. Open Univ BA89. St Aid Birkenhead 54. **d** 57 **p** 58. V Maxey w Northborough *Pet* 65-94; rtd 94. *26 Beech Close, Market Deeping, Peterborough PE6 8LL* Market Deeping (01778) 343329

SHEDDEN, Mrs Valerie. b 56. Ripon Coll of Educn CertEd77. Cranmer Hall Dur 81. **dss** 84 **d** 87 **p** 94. Tudhoe Grange *Dur* 84-85; Whitworth w Spennymoor 85-87; Par Dn 87-91; Par Dn E Darlington 91-94; TV 94; P-in-c Bishop Middleham from 94; Dioc RE Adv from 94. *1 Broad Oaks, Bishop Middleham, Ferryhill, Co Durham DL17 9BW* Ferryhill (01740) 654591

SHEEHY, Jeremy Patrick. b 56. Magd Coll Ox BA78 MA81 New Coll Ox DPhil90. St Steph Ho Ox 78. **d** 81 **p** 82. C Erdington St Barn *Birm* 81-83; C Small Heath St Greg 83-84; Dean Div, Fell and Chapl New Coll Ox 84-90; V Leytonstone St Marg w St Columba *Chelmsf* from 90; P-in-c Leytonstone St Andr from 93. *St Margaret's Vicarage, 15 Woodhouse Road, London E11 3NG* 0181-519 0813

SHEEKEY, Raymond Arthur. b 23. Chich Th Coll 51. **d** 53 **p** 54. V Brabourne w Smeeth *Cant* 61-79; RD N Lympne 75-78; Chapl Lenham Hosp 79-88; R Lenham w Boughton Malherbe 79-88; rtd 88. *Rosewell Cottage, Leighterton, Tetbury, Glos GL8 8UJ* Leighterton (01666) 890268

SHEEN, Canon John Harold. b 32. Qu Coll Cam BA54 MA58. Cuddesdon Coll 56. **d** 58 **p** 59. C Stepney St Dunstan and All SS *Lon* 58-62; V Tottenham St Jo 62-68; V Wood Green St Mich 68-78; P-in-c Southgate St Mich 77-78; R Bride *S & M* from 78; Chapl Ramsey Cottage Hosp from 80; V Lezayre St Olave Ramsey from 80; RD Ramsey from 88; Can St German's Cathl from 91. *The Rectory, Kirk Bride, Ramsey, Isle of Man IM7 4AT* Ramsey (01624) 880351

SHEEN, Canon Victor Alfred. b 17. Tyndale Hall Bris 47. **d** 49 **p** 50. V Clapham St Jas *S'wark* 65-86; RD Clapham and Brixton 78-82 and 85-86; Hon Can S'wark Cathl 80-86; rtd 86; Perm to Offic *Chich* from 86. *10 Porters Way, Polegate, E Sussex BN26 6AP* Polegate (01323) 487487

SHEERAN, Canon Ernest William. b 17. St Aid Birkenhead 47. **d** 50 **p** 51. V Edwalton *S'well* 55-86; RD Bingham S 68-86; Hon Can S'well Minster 72-86; rtd 86; Perm to Offic *S'well* from 86. *Brodick, 20 Taunton Road, Nottingham NG2 6EW* Nottingham (0115) 923 1895

SHEFFIELD, Michael Julian (Mike). b 53. Brentwood Coll of Educn CertEd. Sarum & Wells Th Coll 76. **d** 79 **p** 80. C Locks Heath *Portsm* 79-83; C Waterlooville 83; C Ryde All SS 83-86; P-in-c Ryde H Trin 86-92; V from 92; P-in-c Swanmore St Mich w Havenstreet 86-92; V Swanmore St Mich and All Angels from 92. *The Vicarage, Wray Street, Ryde, Isle of Wight PO33 3ED* Isle of Wight (01983) 562984

SHEFFIELD, Archdeacon of. *See* LOWE, Ven Stephen Richard

SHEFFIELD, Bishop of. *See* LUNN, Rt Rev David Ramsay

SHEFFIELD, Provost of. *See* SADGROVE, Very Rev Michael

SHEGOG, Eric Marshall. b 37. Lon Univ DipTh60 City Univ MA88. Lich Th Coll 64. **d** 65 **p** 66. C Benhilton *S'wark* 65-68; Asst Youth Adv 68-70; V Abbey Wood 70-76; Chapl Sunderland Town Cen 76-83; C Bishopwearmouth St Mich w St Hilda *Dur* 76-83; Hd Relig Broadcasting IBA 84-90; Perm to Offic *Lon* 85-90; Perm to Offic *St Alb* 85-89; Hon C Harpenden St Nic from 89; Dir Communications for C of E from 90. *Church House, Great Smith Street, London SW1P 3NZ, or 3 The Pleasance, Harpenden, Herts AL5 3NA* 0171-222 9011 or Harpenden (01582) 460406 Fax 0171-222 6672

SHEILD, Canon Edward Oscar. b 10. Univ of NZ LLB33 Qu Coll Ox BA36 MA40 BD82. **d** 36 **p** 37. V Chapel Allerton

Ripon 64-75; rtd 75; Perm to Offic *Carl* from 75; P-in-c Coldstream *Edin* 77-79. *Midtown Cottage, Askham, Penrith, Cumbria CA10 2PF* Hackthorpe (01931) 712427

SHELDON, John Gordon. b 22. Trin Coll Cam BA43 MA44. Ridley Hall Cam 43. **d** 45 **p** 46. V Lindfield *Chich* 62-80; P-in-c Cowden *Roch* 80-81; R Cowden w Hammerwood *Chich* 81-87; rtd 87. *Portland Cottage, Thornhill, Stalbridge, Sturminster Newton, Dorset DT10 2SJ* Stalbridge (01963) 362469

SHELDON, Jonathan Mark Robin. b 59. Cam Univ MA83. Ridley Hall Cam 81. **d** 83 **p** 84. C Dulwich St Barn *S'wark* 83-86; C Worle *B & W* 86-88; V Chesterton St Andr *Ely* from 88. *10 Lynfield Lane, Chesterton, Cambridge CB4 1DR*

SHELLEY, Derrick Sydney David. b 38. Lon Univ LLB60 AKC65. Linc Th Coll. **d** 68 **p** 69. C Weybridge *Guildf* 68-72; Chapl Red Bank Schs 72-77; Lic to Offic *Blackb* from 80. *21 Agnew Street, Lytham St Annes, Lancs FY8 5NJ*

SHELLEY, George. b 18. Qu Coll Birm 56. **d** 57 **p** 58. Miss to Seamen 67-71; R Gt Ringstead *Nor* 71-77; P-in-c Sedgeford w Southmere 71-77; P-in-c Gateshead St Jas *Dur* 77-78; R 78-82; rtd 82; Perm to Offic *Nor* from 82. *18 Burnt Hills, Cromer, Norfolk NR27 9LW* Cromer (01263) 512957

SHELLEY, Robin Arthur. b 34. CEng MIMechE. St Jo Coll Nottm 85. **d** 87 **p** 88. C Countesthorpe w Foston *Leic* 87-90; V Enderby w Lubbesthorpe and Thurlaston from 90. *The Rectory, 16A Desford Road, Thurlaston, Leicester LE9 7TE* Desford (01455) 888488

SHELLOCK, Norman Stanley. b 15. ATCL53 Dur Univ LTh38. St Aug Coll Cant 34. **d** 38 **p** 39. Area Sec (Dios Ely and St E) USPG 59-80; rtd 80; Perm to Offic *Nor* from 80; Perm to Offic *St E* from 81. *24 Runnymede Green, Bury St Edmunds, Suffolk IP33 2LH* Bury St Edmunds (01284) 703506

SHELLS, Canon Charles Harry. b 15. St Chad's Coll Dur BA38 MA43. **d** 39 **p** 40. R Trunch w Swafield *Nor* 65-71; R Bradfield 65-71; C-in-c Gimingham 65-71; C-in-c Trimingham 65-71; C-in-c Antingham w Thorpe Market 65-71; C-in-c Gunton St Pet 65-71; Can Res Bris Cathl *Bris* 71-81; rtd 81; Lic to Offic *B & W* from 81; Lic to Offic *Sarum* from 81; Perm to Offic *Bris* from 81. *13 Dod Lane, Glastonbury, Somerset BA6 8BZ* Glastonbury (01458) 832052

SHELTON, Ian Robert. b 52. BEd74 Lon Univ MA79. Ripon Coll Cuddesdon BA81 MA90. **d** 82 **p** 83. C Wath-upon-Dearne w Adwick-upon-Dearne *Sheff* 82-86; TV Grantham *Linc* 86-93; P-in-c Waltham from 93; P-in-c Barnoldby le Beck from 93. *The Rectory, 95 High Street, Waltham, Grimsby, S Humberside DN37 0PN* Grimsby (01472) 822172

SHENTON, Brian. b 43. Chich Th Coll 73. **d** 75 **p** 76. C Mill Hill Jo Keble Ch *Lon* 75-78; C New Windsor *Ox* 78-81; TV 81-82; P-in-c Cherbury 82-83; V Calcot 83-89; R Reading St Mary w St Laur from 89; RD Reading from 95. *39 Downshire Square, Reading RG1 6NH* Reading (01734) 551738 or 571057

SHENTON, David. b 57. Aston Tr Scheme 91 Ripon Coll Cuddesdon DipMin95. **d** 95. C Thurmaston *Leic* from 95. *118 Dovedale Road, Thurmaston, Leicester LE4 8ND* Leicester (0116) 269 5440

SHEPHARD, Brian Edward. b 34. Magd Coll Cam BA56 MA60 Ox Univ DipPSA60 CertEd71 HDipRE71. Wycliffe Hall Ox 58. **d** 60 **p** 61. C Wigan St Cath *Liv* 60-62; C Kidderminster St Geo *Worc* 62-65; Lect CA Tr Coll Blackheath 65-70; Lect Hamilton Coll of Educn 70-77; Perm to Offic *Glas* 70-77; Chapl Buchan Sch Castletown 77-88; Lic to Offic *S & M* 77-88; Lic to Offic *S'wark* 88-89; Tutor CA Wilson Carlile Coll of Evang 88-89; C Andreas St Jude *S & M* 89-91; C Jurby 89-91; V Lezayre from 91. *The Vicarage, Lezayre, Ramsey, Isle of Man IM7 2AN* Ramsey (01624) 812500

SHEPHEARD-WALWYN, John. b 16. Or Coll Ox BA38 MA44. Wells Th Coll 38. **d** 40 **p** 42. R Horwood *Ex* 61-78; V Westleigh 61-78; P-in-c Harberton w Harbertonford 78-82; rtd 82; Perm to Offic *Bris* from 82. *12 Luccombe Hill, Bristol BS6 6SN* Bristol (0117) 973 1261

SHEPHERD, Anthony Michael. b 50. Em Coll Cam BA72 MA76. Westcott Ho Cam 72. **d** 74 **p** 75. C Folkestone St Mary and St Eanswythe *Cant* 74-79; Bp's Dom Chapl *Ripon* 79-87; Dioc Communications Officer 79-87; V High Harrogate St Pet from 87. *St Peter's Vicarage, 13 Beech Grove, Harrogate, N Yorkshire HG2 0ET* Harrogate (01423) 500901

SHEPHERD, Christopher Francis Pleydell. b 44. St Steph Ho Ox 68. **d** 69 **p** 70. C Milber *Ex* 69-72; C Ex St Thos 72-74; TV Ilfracombe, Lee and W Down 74-78; TV Ilfracombe, Lee, W Down, Woolacombe and Bittadon 78-80; P-in-c Tregony w St Cuby and Cornelly *Truro* 80-83; R from 83. *The Rectory, Tregony, Truro, Cornwall TR2 5SE* Tregony (01872) 530507

SHEPHERD, David. b 42. St Jo Coll Dur BA65 MA68 MLitt76. Edin Th Coll 66. **d** 68 **p** 69. Chapl St Paul's Cathl Dundee *Bre* 68-79; Chapl Dundee Univ 73-79; R Dundee St Mary Magd from 79. *14 Albany Terrace, Dundee DD3 6HR* Dundee (01382) 23510

SHEPHERD, David Mark. b 59. Reading Univ BA81 Nottm Univ BTh86. Linc Th Coll 83. **d** 86 **p** 87. C Wilmslow *Ches*

86-89; C Bromborough 89-92; V Leasowe from 92. *St Chad's Vicarage, 123 Reeds Lane, Wirral, Merseyside L46 1QT* 0151-677 6550

SHEPHERD, Canon Ernest John Heatley. b 27. TCD BA48 BD53. **d** 50 **p** 51. C Belf St Mary Magd *Conn* 50-54; I Whitehouse from 54; Can Conn Cathl 86-90; Co-ord Aux Min from 87; Treas Conn Cathl 90; Prec Conn Cathl from 90. *283 Shore Road, Newtownabbey, Co Antrim BT37 9SR* Belfast (01232) 851622

SHEPHERD, Miss Jayne Elizabeth. b 57. Reading Univ BA78. Cranmer Hall Dur 79. **dss** 82 **d** 87 **p** 94. Wombourne *Lich* 82-85; Harlescott 85-87; Par Dn 87-90; Chapl Asst Univ Hosp Nottm from 90. *Queen's Medical Centre, Nottingham, NG7 2UH, or 54 William Road, Stapleford, Nottingham NG9 8ES* Nottingham (0115) 924 9924

SHEPHERD, Mrs Joan Francis Fleming. b 45. RGN66. **dss** 84 **d** 86 **p** 94. NSM Ellon *Ab* from 84; NSM Cruden Bay from 84; Bp's Chapl for Tr and Educn from 95. *8 Ythan Court, Ellon, Aberdeenshire AB41 9BL* Ellon (01358) 723241

SHEPHERD, John Donald. b 33. Cranmer Hall Dur BA59 DipTh61. **d** 61 **p** 62. C Dewsbury All SS *Wakef* 61-63; C Chapelthorpe 63-66; V Stainland 66-70; Dioc Youth Chapl *Truro* 70-74; V Newquay 74-84; RD Pydar 81-84; Chapl Borocourt Mental Handicap Hosp 84-95; TR Langtree *Ox* 84-95. *The Rectory, Checkendon, Reading RG8 0QS* Checkendon (01491) 680252

SHEPHERD, John Michael. b 42. BNC Ox BA63 MA72. Coll of Resurr Mirfield 64. **d** 66 **p** 67. C Clapham H Spirit *S'wark* 66-69; C Kingston All SS 69-72; V Upper Tooting H Trin 73-80; V Wandsworth St Paul 80-90; P-in-c Mitcham SS Pet and Paul 90-92; V from 92. *21 Church Road, Mitcham, Surrey CR4 3BE* 0181-648 1566

SHEPHERD, John William. b 20. S'wark Ord Course 67. **d** 70 **p** 71. C Leighton Buzzard St Alb 70-77; P-in-c Studham w Whipsnade 77-80; V 80-82; P-in-c Kensworth 82; V Kensworth, Studham and Whipsnade 82-86; rtd 86; Asst Chapl Costa Blanca *Eur* 86-89. *24 Church Road, Studham, Dunstable, Beds LU6 2QA* Whipsnade (01582) 872298

SHEPHERD, Keith Frederick. b 42. E Midl Min Tr Course 86. **d** 89 **p** 90. Hon C Stocking Farm *Leic* 89-94; P-in-c Church Langton w Tur Langton, Thorpe Langton etc from 94. *The Rectory, Stonton Road, Church Langton, Market Harborough, Leics LE16 7SZ* Market Harborough (01858) 545740

SHEPHERD, Peter James. b 38. Dur Univ BA64. Ridley Hall Cam 64. **d** 66 **p** 67. C Luton Ch Ch *Roch* 66-70; C Belvedere All SS 70-71; C Wisley w Pyrford *Guildf* 71-75; V Thorney Abbey *Ely* 75-85; V Yaxley 85-93; RD Yaxley 88-92; P-in-c Feltwell from 93. *The Rectory, 7 Oak Street, Feltwell, Thetford, Norfolk IP26 4DB* Thetford (01842) 828631

SHEPHERD, Peter William. b 48. DASE Reading Univ BA71 Lon Univ BD80 Brighton Poly MPhil87 Lanc Univ MA94. Chich Th Coll 77. **d** 80 **p** 81. NSM Eastbourne St Sav and St Pet *Chich* 80-83; Hd Master Wm Temple Sch Preston 83-88; NSM Clitheroe St Mary *Blackb* from 83; Hd Master Canon Slade Sch Bolton from 89. *Homestead, Eastham Street, Clitheroe, Lancs BB7 2HY* Clitheroe (01200) 25053

SHEPHERD, Philip Reginald. b 07. Keble Coll Ox BA29 MA36. Cuddesdon Coll 29. **d** 30 **p** 31. R Shepton Beauchamp *B & W* 64-72; rtd 72; Perm to Offic *B & W* 72-94. *3 Coles Lane, South Petherton, Somerset TA13 5AF* South Petherton (01460) 40809

✠**SHEPHERD, Rt Rev Ronald Francis.** b 26. Univ of BC BA48. AKC52 St Jo Coll Winnipeg Hon DD89. **d** 52 **p** 53 **c** 85. C Westmr St Steph w St Jo *Lon* 52-57; Canada from 57; Dean All Saints' Cathl Edmonton 65-70; Dean Ch Ch Cathl Montreal 70-82; Bp BC 85-92; rtd 92. *1256 Beach Drive, Victoria, British Columbia, Canada, V8S 2N3* Victoria (604) 598-7882

SHEPHERD, Timothy Roy. b 34. Selw Coll Cam BA58. Linc Th Coll 62. **d** 64 **p** 65. C Selly Oak St Mary *Birm* 64-67; C Stockland Green 67-72; V Perry Common 72-76; V Holton-le-Clay *Linc* 76-84; V Habrough Gp 84-93; P-in-c Uffington 93-95; R Uffington Gp from 95. *The Rectory, 67 Main Road, Uffington, Stamford, Lincs PE9 4SN* Stamford (01780) 481786

✠**SHEPPARD, Rt Rev David Stuart.** b 29. Trin Hall Cam BA53 MA56. Ridley Hall Cam 53. **d** 55 **p** 56 **c** 69. C Islington St Mary *Lon* 55-58; Chapl & Warden Mayflower Family Cen Canning Town *Chelmsf* 58-69; Suff Bp Woolwich *S'wark* from 75. *Bishop's Lodge, Woolton Park, Liverpool L25 6DT, or Diocesan Church House, 1 Hanover Street, Liverpool L1 3DW* 0151-708 9480 Fax 709 2885

SHEPPARD, Ian Arthur Lough. b 33. Sarum & Wells Th Coll 71. **d** 74 **p** 75. C Bishop's Cleeve *Glouc* 74-77; Chapl RAF 77-81; V Gosberton *Linc* 81-87; V Leven Valley *Carl* 87-90; Deputation and Gen Appeals Org Children's Soc from 90. *57 Seymour Grove, Eaglescliffe, Stockton-on-Tees, Cleveland TS16 0LE* Eaglescliffe (01642) 790777

SHEPPARD, Martin. b 37. Hertf Coll Ox BA61 MA65. Chich Th Coll 63. **d** 65 **p** 66. C N Hull St Mich *York* 65-68; C Hove St

Jo *Chich* 68-71; V Heathfield St Rich 71-77; V New Shoreham 77-94; V Old Shoreham 77-94; TR Rye from 94; RD Rye from 95. *St Mary's Rectory, Gungarden, Rye, E Sussex TN31 7HH* Rye (01797) 222430

SHEPPARD, Norman George. b 32. Wolv Teacher Tr Coll CertEd73. St D Coll Lamp 57. **d** 59 **p** 60. Asst Master Madeley Court Sch 73-75; Gilbert Inglefield Sch Leighton Buzzard 75-80; USPG 80-81; Argentina from 80; rtd 95. *Santa Rosa 1650, Vincente Lopez, Province of Buenos Aires, Argentina* Buenos Aires (1) 797-9748

SHEPPARD, Stanley Gorton. b 18. St Jo Coll Dur 46. **d** 62 **p** 63. R Cole Orton *Leic* 65-75; V Ashby Folville and Twyford w Thorpe Satchville 75-88; rtd 88; Perm to Offic *Ex* from 89. *1 Peak Coach House, Cotmaton Road, Sidmouth, Devon EX10 8SY* Sidmouth (01395) 516124

SHEPTON, Robert Leonard McIntyre (Bob). b 35. Jes Coll Cam BA58 MA61. Oak Hill Th Coll 59. **d** 61 **p** 62. C Weymouth St Jo *Sarum* 61-63; Boys' Ldr Cam Univ Miss Bermondsey 63-66; Warden Ox-Kilburn Club 66-69; Chapl St D Coll Llandudno 69-77; Chief Instructor Carnoch Outdoor Cen 77-80; Chapl Kingham Hill Sch Ox from 80. *Swansea House, Kingham Hill School, Kingham, Chipping Norton, Oxon OX7 6TH* Kingham (01608) 658999

SHERBORNE, Archdeacon of. See WHEATLEY, Ven Paul Charles

SHERBORNE, Area Bishop of. See KIRKHAM, Rt Rev John Dudley Galtrey

SHERGOLD, William Frank. b 19. St Chad's Coll Dur BA40 MA47. Coll of Resurr Mirfield 40. **d** 42 **p** 43. V Charlton-by-Dover St Bart *Cant* 69-72; P-in-c Charlton-by-Dover SS Pet and Paul 70-72; R Charlton-in-Dover 72-78; R Tunstall 78-83; rtd 84; TV Poplar *Lon* 84; Hon C 84-92; Perm to Offic *Chich* from 92. *6 College Gardens, Brighton BN2 1HP* Brighton (01273) 696174

SHERIDAN, Mrs Deborah Jane. b 47. ALA73 Kent Univ BA69. W Midl Minl Tr Course 90. **d** 93 **p** 94. NSM Lich St Chad *Lich* from 93. *45 High Grange, Lichfield, Staffs WS13 7DU* Lichfield (01543) 264363

SHERIDAN, Peter. b 37. Saltley Tr Coll Birm CertEd59 Leic Poly BEd82. N Ord Course 89. **d** 92 **p** 93. NSM Braunstone *Leic* 92-95; NSM Ratby w Groby from 95. *24 Flaxfield Close, Groby, Leicester LE6 0EZ* Leicester (0116) 232 1178

SHERLEY-PRICE, Lionel Digby (Leo). b 11. SS Coll Cam BA32 MA36. Chich Th Coll 33. **d** 34 **p** 35. V Dawlish *Ex* 69-74; R Manaton 74-78; R N Bovey 74-78; rtd 78; RD Moreton *Ex* 80-83; Lic to Offic from 83. *7 High Close, Bovey Tracey, Newton Abbot, Devon TQ13 9EX* Bovey Tracey (01626) 833448

SHERLOCK, Charles Patrick. b 51. New Coll Ox BA73 MA76. Ripon Coll Cuddesdon 75. **d** 77 **p** 78. C Ashtead *Guildf* 77-81; Ethiopia 81-82; Chapl Belgrade w Zagreb *Eur* 82-84; USPG (Ethiopia) 84-91; R Dollar *St And* from 91. *St James Rectory, 12 Harvieston Road, Dollar, Clackmannanshire FK14 7HF* Dollar (01259) 742494

SHERLOCK, Canon Desmond. b 31. K Coll Lon BD60 AKC60. **d** 61 **p** 62. C Mitcham Ascension *S'wark* 61-64; C Reigate St Luke S Park 64-67; V Aldersbrook *Chelmsf* 67-77; RD Redbridge 74-77; TR Witham from 77; Can Chelmsf Cathl from 93. *The Vicarage, 7 Chipping Dell, Witham, Essex CM8 2JX* Witham (01376) 512056

SHERLOCK, Ewart Templeman. b 03. AKC31. **d** 30 **p** 31. V Dorney *Ox* 60-70; rtd 71. *11 Fairview Road, Taplow, Maidenhead, Berks SL6 0NQ* Burnham (01628) 604226

SHERLOCK, Thomas Alfred. **d** 90 **p** 91. NSM Kilmallock w Kilflynn, Kilfinane, Knockaney etc *L & K* 90-94; C Templemore w Thurles and Kilfithmone *C & O* from 95. *The Rectory, Roscrea Road, Templemore, Co Tipperary, Irish Republic* Templemore (504) 31175

SHERRATT, Allan Dennis. b 48. Chich Th Coll 78. **d** 79 **p** 80. C Seaford w Sutton *Chich* 79-81; Chapl Eliz Coll Guernsey 81-84; C Guernsey Ste Marie du Castel *Win* 84-85; P-in-c 85-87; C Guernsey St Matt 84-85; P-in-c 85-87; Lic to Offic 88-89; Lic to Offic *York* 89-90; P-in-c Barmby on the Moor w Fangfoss 90; R Barmby Moor w Allerthorpe, Fangfoss and Yapham 90-94. *Westerfield, 2 Norse Way, Stamford Bridge, York YO4 1DR*

SHERRATT, David Arthur. b 60. Univ of Wales (Lamp) BA82 Leeds Univ BA91. Coll of Resurr Mirfield CPT92. **d** 92 **p** 93. C St Jo on Bethnal Green *Lon* from 92. *Flat 24, Mary McArthur House, Warley Street, London E2 0QD* 0181-981 0118

SHERSBY, Brian Alfred. b 41. Clifton Th Coll 68. **d** 71 **p** 72. C Stoughton *Guildf* 71-74; C Heref St Pet w St Owen *Heref* 75-79; V Earlham St Mary *Nor* 79-91; R Murston w Bapchild and Tonge *Cant* from 91. *Bapchild Rectory, School Lane, Sittingbourne, Kent ME9 9NL* Sittingbourne (01795) 472929

SHERWIN, David Royston. b 56. HNC. St Jo Coll Nottm 84. **d** 89 **p** 90. C Conisbrough *Sheff* from 89. *130 Old Road,*

Conisbrough, Doncaster, S Yorkshire DN12 3LR   Rotherham (01709) 863525

SHERWIN, Miss Margaret Miriam. b 32. dss 83 d 87 p 94. Holborn St Alb w Saffron Hill St Pet *Lon* 83-87; Par Dn 87-88; Par Dn Highgate St Mich 88-93; rtd 93; NSM Purbrook *Portsm* from 93. *16 Lombard Court, Lombard Street, Portsmouth PO1 2HU*   Portsmouth (01705) 838429

SHERWOOD, David James. b 45. St Steph Ho Ox 81. d 83 p 84. C Westbury-on-Trym H Trin *Bris* 83-85; C Corringham *Chelmsf* 85-87; V Hullbridge 87-94; V Kenton *Lon* from 94. *St Mary's Vicarage, 3 St Leonard's Avenue, Harrow, Middx HA3 8EJ*   0181-907 2914

SHERWOOD, Denys Charles. b 20. Lon Univ BA49. Oak Hill Th Coll. d 51 p 52. V Lenton Abbey *S'well* 67-77; V Basford *Lich* 77-85; rtd 85; Perm to Offic *S'well* from 85. *5 Larch Crescent, Eastwood, Nottingham NG16 3RB*   Langley Mill (01773) 760922

SHERWOOD, Gordon Frederick. b 29. Sarum & Wells Th Coll 77. d 80 p 81. Hon C Weeke *Win* 80-82; C Kirk Ella *York* 82-85; P-in-c Burstwick w Thorngumbald 85-87; V 87-90; R Kirby Misperton w Normanby, Edston and Salton 90-94; rtd 94. *76 Bysing Wood Road, Faversham, Kent ME13 7RH*   Faversham (01795) 535934

SHERWOOD, Ian Walter Lawrence. b 57. TCD BA80 DipTh82. d 82 p 84. C Dub St Patr Cathl Gp *D & G* 82-83; Chapl Billinge Hosp Wigan 83-86; C Orrell *Liv* 83-86; Chapl Bucharest w Sofia *Eur* 86-89; Chapl Istanbul w Moda from 89. *c/o British Consulate General, Tepebasi, Bevoglu 80072, Istanbul, Turkey*   Istanbul (1) 244-4228

SHERWOOD, Kenneth Henry. b 37. CITC 90. d 93 p 94. NSM Malahide w Balgriffin *D & G* from 93. *23 Foxfield Park, Raheny, Dublin 5, Irish Republic*   Dublin (1) 832-4920

SHERWOOD, Nigel John Wesley. b 58. DipTh. CITC 86. d 86 p 87. C Kilmore w Ballintemple, Kildallon etc *K, E & A* 86-88; I Tullow w Shillelagh, Aghold and Mullinacuff *C & O* 88-95; I Arklow w Inch and Kilbride *D & G* from 95. *The Rectory, Arklow, Co Wicklow, Irish Republic*   Arklow (402) 32439

SHERWOOD, Suffragan Bishop of. See MORGAN, Rt Rev Alan Wyndham

SHEWAN, Alistair Boyd. b 44. Open Univ BA83. Edin Th Coll 63. d 67 p 68. Prec St Andr Cathl Inverness *Mor* 67-69; C Shepherd's Bush St Steph w St Thos *Lon* 70-72; Hon C Edin St Mich and All SS *Edin* 73-75; Perm to Offic 75-81; Hon C Edin Old St Paul 81-86; NSM Edin St Columba 87-91; Asst Dioc Supernumerary from 91. *3 Castle Wynd North, Edinburgh EH1 2NQ*   0131-225 6537

SHEWAN, James William. b 36. Sarum Th Coll 61. d 63 p 64. C Rainbow Hill St Barn *Worc* 63-64; C Newton Aycliffe *Dur* 64-66; C Harton 66-69; V S Moor 69-72; CF 72-77 and from 81; P-in-c Benwell St Aid *Newc* 77-79; V Longhoughton w Howick 79-88; V Spittal from 88; V Scremerston from 88. *St John's Vicarage, 129 Main Street, Spittal, Berwick-upon-Tweed TD15 1RP*   Berwick-upon-Tweed (01289) 307342

SHEWELL, Edward Charles Beaudon. b 12. St Pet Hall Ox BA36 MA46. Ridley Hall Cam 36. d 37 p 38. V Berry Pomeroy *Ex* 54-77; R Lt Hempston 69-77; rtd 77; Hon C Tetcott w Luffincott *Ex* 77-81; Hon C Clawton 77-81. *3 Dreva Road, Broughton, Biggar, Lanarkshire ML12 6HG*   Broughton (018994) 219

SHIELD, Ian Thomas. b 32. Hertf Coll Ox BA56 MA60 BLitt60. Westcott Ho Cam 59. d 61 p 62. Tutor Lich Th Coll 64-71; Chapl 67-71; V Dunston w Coppenhall *Lich* 71-79; TV Wolv 79-86; rtd 87; Perm to Offic *Lich* from 87. *13 Duke Street, Penn Fields, Wolverhampton WV3 7DT*   Wolverhampton (01902) 337037

SHIELDS, Canon Michael Penton. b 30. Bps' Coll Cheshunt. d 64 p 65. C Kingsbury St Andr *Lon* 64-67; C Friern Barnet All SS 67-69; V Colindale St Matthias 69-76; Chapl Sevenoaks Hosp 76-94; V Sevenoaks St Jo *Roch* 76-95; RD Sevenoaks 84-95; Chapl St Mich Sch Otford 84-95; Hon Can Roch Cathl 94-95; rtd 95. *Flat 14, Bromley College, London Road, Bromley BR1 1PE*   0181-464 7906

SHIELS, Donald Allan Patterson. b 15. Selw Coll Cam BA38 MA42. Wycliffe Hall Ox 38. d 39 p 40. V Stoke Gifford *Bris* 62-80; rtd 80; Perm to Offic *Glouc* from 80. *5 Down Hatherley Lane, Gloucester GL2 9PT*   Gloucester (01452) 730367

SHILL, Kenneth Leslie. b 49. Leic Univ BA70 Lon Univ BD73 Cam Univ DipTh77. Ridley Hall Cam 75. d 77 p 78. C Harborne Heath *Birm* 77-83; V Mansf St Jo *S'well* 83-93; Bp's Adv on Healing 89-93; Chapl Amsterdam w Heiloo *Eur* 93-95; TR Bath Twerton-on-Avon *B & W* from 95. *The Rectory, Watery Lane, Bath BA2 1RL*   Bath (01225) 421438

SHILLAKER, Mrs Christine Frances. b 39. Lon Univ DipTh61. Gilmore Ho 74. dss 86 d 87 p 94. Colchester St Leon, St Mary Magd and St Steph *Chelmsf* 86-87; Par Dn 87-89; Par Dn Colchester, New Town and The Hythe 89-94; C from 94. *The Rectory, 24 New Town Road, Colchester CO1 2EF*   Colchester (01206) 570442

SHILLAKER, John. b 34. K Coll Lon BD60 AKC60. d 61 p 62. C Bush Hill Park St Mark *Lon* 61-65; C Milton *Win* 65-69; C-in-c Moulsham St Luke CD *Chelmsf* 69-78; V Moulsham St Luke 78-85; P-in-c Colchester St Leon, St Mary Magd and St Steph 85-86; R 86-89; R Colchester, New Town and The Hythe from 89. *The Rectory, 24 New Town Road, Colchester CO1 2EF*   Colchester (01206) 570442

SHILLING, Ms Audrey Violet. b 26. Dur Univ BA69. CA Tr Coll 51 Cranmer Hall Dur 66. d 87 p 94. CA from 53; NSM Gillingham H Trin *Roch* 87-93; NSM Rainham from 94. *13 Motney Hill Road, Gillingham, Kent ME8 7TZ*   Medway (01634) 233654

SHILLINGFORD, Brian. b 39. Lich Th Coll 65. d 68 p 69. C Lewisham St Swithun *S'wark* 68-71; C Godstone 71-75; TV Croydon *Cant* 75-81; TV N Creedy *Ex* 81-93; TR from 93. *The Rectory, Morchard Bishop, Crediton, Devon EX17 6PJ*   Cheriton Fitzpaine (01363) 877221

SHILSON-THOMAS, Mrs Annabel Margaret. b 60. Jes Coll Ox BA82. Westcott Ho Cam 87. d 89. Par Dn Sydenham St Bart *S'wark* 89-93; Journalist CAFOD from 95. *21 Burney Avenue, Surbiton, Surrey KT5 8DF*   0181-339 9479

SHILSON-THOMAS, Hugh David. b 64. Ex Coll Ox BA86. Westcott Ho Cam 87. d 89 p 90. C Sydenham All SS *S'wark* 89-92; C Lower Sydenham St Mich 89-92; Chapl Kingston Univ from 93. *21 Burney Avenue, Surbiton, Surrey KT5 8DF*   0181-339 9479

SHILVOCK, Geoffrey. b 47. Univ of Wales (Lamp) BA69. Sarum Th Coll 70. d 72 p 73. C Kidderminster St Mary *Worc* 72-78; P-in-c Gt Malvern Ch Ch 78-85; V Wolverley and Cookley from 85. *The Vicarage, Wolverley, Kidderminster, Worcs DY11 5XD*   Kidderminster (01562) 851133

SHILVOCK, Kelvin David. b 50. MHCIMA71 Birm Coll of Food OND69. Qu Coll Birm 91. d 93 p 94. C Kidderminster St Jo and H Innocents *Worc* from 93. *59 Stretton Road, Kidderminster, Worcs DY11 6LE*   Kidderminster (01562) 754194

SHIMWELL, Robert John. b 46. ARCM65. Lon Bible Coll DipTh68 Trin Coll Bris 75. d 78 p 79. C Richmond H Trin *S'wark* 78-79; C Cullompton *Ex* 79-81; C Kentisbeare w Blackborough 79-81; V S Cave and Ellerker w Broomfleet *York* 81-87; Chapl Lee Abbey 87-88; R Glas St Silas *Glas* 88-94; V Upton (or Overchurch) *Ches* from 94. *The Vicarage, 20 Church Road, Upton, Wirral, Merseyside L49 6JZ*   0151-677 4810 or 677 1186   Fax 606 1935

SHINER, Michael Joseph. b 21. Chich Th Coll 51. d 53 p 54. V Powerstock w W Milton, Witherstone and N Poorton *Sarum* 67-73; V Knutsford St Cross *Ches* 73-75; Area Sec Age Concern Cornwall 75-86; Co-Org W Sussex 80-86; rtd 86. *1 Clay Lane, Puncknowle, Dorchester, Dorset DT2 9BJ*   Burton Bradstock (01308) 897007

SHINN, William Raymond. b 22. Sarum & Wells Th Coll 71. d 73 p 74. C Letchworth St Paul *St Alb* 73-75; C Dunstable 76-78; TV 78-80; V Luton St Chris Round Green 80-88; rtd 88. *31 Coleridge Close, Hitchin, Herts SG4 0QX*   Hitchin (01462) 450899

SHIPLEY, Christopher John. b 44. Leeds Univ BSc65 MSc70 BA72. Coll of Resurr Mirfield 70. d 73 p 74. C Preston St Jo *Blackb* 73-77; Chapl Lancs (Preston) Poly 75-77; V Blackb St Mich w St Jo 77-81; P-in-c Blackb H Trin 78-81; V Blackb St Mich w St Jo and H Trin 81-82; V Walthamstow St Pet *Chelmsf* 82-85; Gen Sec Mary Feilding Guild Lon 85-86; Org Waltham Forest Coun for Voluntary Service 86-89; Gen Sec Hull 89-91; Dir Grimsby & Cleethorpes 91-93; Perm to Offic *York* 90-93. *Address temp unknown*

SHIPLEY, Miss Marjorie. b 17. Gilmore Ho 67. dss 72 d 87 p 94. Acomb St Steph *York* 72-78; rtd 78; Perm to Offic *York* 78-84; NSM Scarborough St Martin from 84. *Flat 25, Normanton Rise, Belvedere Place South, Scarborough, N Yorkshire YO11 2XD*   Scarborough (01723) 353150

SHIPLEY, Stephen Edwin Burnham. b 52. Univ Coll Dur BA74. Westcott Ho Cam 85. d 87 p 88. C Ipswich St Marg *St E* 87-90; P-in-c Stuntney *Ely* 90-95; Min Can, Prec and Sacr Ely Cathl 90-95; Producer Worship Progr BBC Relig Broadcasting from 95. *BBC, PO Box 27, Manchester M60 1SJ*   0161-244 3292

SHIPP, Mrs Patricia Susan. b 54. Univ of Wales BA76. St Paul's Grahamstown 77 Linc Th Coll 81. d 83 p 94. C Cyncoed *Mon* 83-87; Par Dn Lawrence Weston *Bris* 89-91; Par Dn Henbury 91-94; D-in-c Longwell Green 94; P-in-c from 94. *The Vicarage, 85 Bath Road, Longwell Green, Bristol BS15 6DF*   Bristol (0117) 983 3713

SHIPSIDES, Brian Kenneth. b 56. Reading Univ BA. Westcott Ho Cam 79. d 82 p 83. C Bramley *Ripon* 82-85; C Notting Dale St Clem w St Mark and St Jas *Lon* 85-90; Chapl N Lon Poly 90-92; Chapl N Lon Univ from 92. *123 Calabria Road, London N5 1HS*   0171-704 9914 or 753 7038

SHIPTON, Andrew James. b 60. Leeds Univ BA82. Cranmer Hall Dur 83. d 85 p 86. C Fishponds St Jo *Bris* 85-88; C Gosforth All SS *Newc* 88-91; V Long Benton St Mary from 91.

St Mary's House, Blackfriars Way, Newcastle upon Tyne NE12 8ST   0191-266 2326

SHIPTON, Miss Linda Anne. b 60. Avery Hill Coll DipHE84. Westcott Ho Cam 84. **dss** 86 **d** 87 **p** 94. Borehamwood *St Alb* 86-87; Par Dn 87-89; Par Dn Sheff St Cuth *Sheff* 89-90; Chapl Asst N Gen Hosp Sheff 89-90; Chapl from 90. *Northern General Hospital, Herries Road, Sheffield S5 7AU* Sheffield (0114) 286 9264/243 4343

SHIPTON (nee WILSON), Mrs Marjorie Jayne. b 59. Hull Univ BA80 K Alfred's Coll Win PGCE81. St Jo Coll Dur 85. **dss** 86 **d** 87 **p** 94. Ormesby *York* 86-87; Par Dn 87-89; Chapl Asst Newc Gen Hosp 89-91; Chapl from 91; NSM Whorlton Newc from 94. *Newcastle General Hospital, Westgate Road, Newcastle upon Tyne NE4 6BE* 0191-273 8811

SHIRE, William Stanley. b 17. TCD BA39 MA43. **d** 40 **p** 41. R Aldwincle w Thorpe Achurch, Pilton, Wadenhoe etc *Pet* 70-82; rtd 82; Lic to Offic *Pet* 82-85; Perm to Offic from 85. *96 Glapthorne Road, Oundle, Peterborough PE8 4PS* Oundle (01832) 272125

SHIRES, Alan William. b 36. Lon Univ BA60. Oak Hill Th Coll 57. **d** 61 **p** 62. C York St Paul *York* 61-64; C Southgate *Chich* 64-67; V Doncaster St Mary *Sheff* 67-75; Student Counsellor Portsm Poly 75-88; Hd Student Services Portsm Poly from 88. *18 Salisbury Road, Cosham, Portsmouth PO6 2PN* Portsmouth (01705) 843170

SHIRESS, Canon David Henry Faithfull. b 27. St Cath Coll Cam BA49 MA53. Ridley Hall Cam 51. **d** 53 **p** 54. V Blackheath Park St Mich *S'wark* 67-93; Sub-Dean Greenwich 81-90; RD Greenwich 90-91; Hon Can S'wark Cathl 89-93; rtd 93. *35 Rempstone Road, Wimborne, Dorset BH21 1SS* Wimborne (01202) 887845

SHIRLEY, Timothy Francis. b 25. Univ Coll Ox BA49 MA49. Qu Coll Birm 49. **d** 51 **p** 52. V Fulham St Etheldreda w St Clem *Lon* 68-90; rtd 90. *70 St Dunstan's Cresent, Worcester WR5 2AQ* Worcester (01905) 353930

SHIRRAS, Ven Edward Scott (Eddie). b 37. St Andr Univ BSc61. Clifton Th Coll 61. **d** 63 **p** 64. C Surbiton Hill Ch Ch *S'wark* 63-66; C Jesmond Clayton Memorial *Newc* 66-68; Youth Sec CPAS 68-71; Publications Sec 71-74; Asst Gen Sec 74-75; Hon C Wallington H Trin *S'wark* 69-75; V Roxeth Ch Ch *Lon* 75-82; V Roxeth Ch Ch and Harrow St Pet 82-85; AD Harrow 82-85; Adn Northolt 85-92; V Win Ch Ch *Win* from 92. *Christ Church Vicarage, Sleepers Hill, Winchester, Hants SO22 4ND* Winchester (01962) 862414

SHIRRAS, Ms Rachel Joan. b 66. Univ of Wales (Abth) BSc88. St Jo Coll Nottm 88. **d** 91 **p** 94. Par Dn Ockbrook *Derby* 91-94; C 94; C Bris St Matt and St Nath *Bris* from 94. *Bishopston Vicarage, 25 Morley Square, Bristol BS7 9DW* Bristol (0117) 942 4359

SHOLL, Preb Ernest Redfern. b 09. AKC33. **d** 33 **p** 34. V Stogursey *B & W* 53-74; Preb Wells Cathl 57-74; R Fiddington 64-74; rtd 74. *Langdale, Kirtlebridge, Lockerbie, Dumfriesshire DG11 3LT* Kirtlebridge (014615) 659

SHONE, John Terence. b 35. Selw Coll Cam BA58 MA64 Newc Univ MA92. Linc Th Coll 58. **d** 60 **p** 61. C St Pancras w St Jas and Ch Ch *Lon* 60-62; Chapl Aber Univ *Ab* 62-68; Chapl St Andr Cathl 62-65; V Gt Grimsby St Andr and St Luke *Linc* 68-69; Chapl Stirling Univ *St And* 69-80; R Bridge of Allan 69-86; P-in-c Alloa 77-85; Can St Ninian's Cathl Perth 80-89; P-in-c Dollar 81-86; Dean St Andr 82-89; Research and Development Officer 86-89; Dioc Supernumerary 86-89; TV Cullercoats St Geo *Newc* from 89. *St Hilda's Vicarage, Preston Gate, North Shields, Tyne & Wear NE29 9QB* 0191-257 6595

SHONE, Raymond. b 21. St Jo Coll Dur BA47 MA54 Brighton Poly DCouns81. Linc Th Coll 48. **d** 48 **p** 49. Perm to Offic *Chich* from 66; Sen Lect Eastbourne Coll of Educn 66-76; E Sussex Coll of HE 76-79; Brighton Poly 79-80; Counsellor W Sussex Inst of HE 83-87; rtd 87. *28 Hawthorn Close, Chichester, W Sussex PO19 3DZ* Chichester (01243) 774543

SHONE, Robert Alan. b 16. Qu Coll Cam BA38 MA42. St Steph Ho Ox 39. **d** 39 **p** 40. V Wardleworth St Mary *Man* 63-73; V Wardleworth St Mary w St Jas 73-81; rtd 81; Perm to Offic *Man* from 81. *172 Bar Terrace, Market Street, Whitworth, Rochdale, Lancs OL12 8TB* Rochdale (01706) 344405

SHONE, Miss Ursula Ruth. b 34. Lon Univ DBRS59 Stirling Univ BA75 Open Univ BPhil88. **dss** 81 **d** 86 **p** 94. Bridge of Allan *St And* 81-85; Lochgelly 85-87; Chapl Cov Cathl *Cov* 87-90; Ind Chapl 87-90; Par Dn Ainsdale *Liv* 90-94; Dioc Science Adv from 90; C Ainsdale from 94. *St John's House, 25 Pinfold Lane, Southport PR8 3QH* Southport (01704) 576098

SHORROCK, John Musgrave. b 29. TCD BA54 MA58. Bps' Coll Cheshunt 54. **d** 56 **p** 57. Min Can and Sacr Cant Cathl *Cant* 67-70; V Chorley St Geo *Blackb* 71-78; P-in-c Bredgar w Bicknor and Huckinge *Cant* 78-82; P-in-c Frinsted w Wormshill and Milstead 78-82; R Bredgar w Bicknor and

Frinsted w Wormshill etc 82-92; rtd 92; Perm to Offic *Cant* from 92. *3 Bradgate, School Lane, Bekesbourne, Canterbury, Kent CT4 5ER* Canterbury (01227) 832133

SHORT, Brian Frederick. b 29. St Jo Coll Nottm 70. **d** 72 **p** 73. C Walton *St E* 72-75; P-in-c Barking w Darmsden and Gt Bricett 75-78; P-in-c Ringshall w Battisford and Lt Finborough 75-78; TV Nor St Pet Parmentergate w St Jo *Nor* 78-88; R Winfarthing w Shelfanger w Burston w Gissing etc 88-90; rtd 90; Perm to Offic *Nor* from 92. *31 Nursery Gardens, Blofield, Norwich NR13 4JE* Norwich (01603) 712396

SHORT, Ms Clare. b 50. Leic Univ BA72 St Mary's Coll Twickenham PGCE73. All Nations Chr Coll CDRS81 S Dios Minl Tr Scheme 89. **d** 92 **p** 94. NSM Horsham *Chich* from 92. *19 York Close, Southwater, Horsham, W Sussex RH13 7XJ* Horsham (01403) 730880

SHORT, John Timothy. b 43. Lon Univ DipTh67. Kelham Th Coll 63. **d** 68 **p** 69. C St Marylebone Ch Ch w St Barn *Lon* 68-70; C Southgate Ch Ch 70-72; P-in-c Mosser *Carl* 72-78; Dioc Youth Officer 72-78; R Heyford w Stowe Nine Churches *Pet* 78-87; V Northn St Jas from 87; RD Wootton from 88. *St James's Vicarage, Vicarage Road, Northampton NN5 7AX* Northampton (01604) 751164

SHORT, Canon John Sinclair. b 33. Oak Hill Th Coll 64. **d** 66 **p** 67. C Islington St Mary *Lon* 66-70; V Becontree St Mary *Chelmsf* 70-76; V New Malden and Coombe *S'wark* 76-90; RD Kingston 79-84; Hon Can S'wark Cathl 83-90; P-in-c Peldon w Gt and Lt Wigborough *Chelmsf* 90-93; rtd 93; Perm to Offic *S'wark* from 93. *22 Chart Lane, Reigate, Surrey RH1 7BP* Reigate (01737) 245244

SHORT, Kenneth Arthur. b 33. Tyndale Hall Bris 64. **d** 67 **p** 68. C E Twickenham St Steph *Lon* 67-71; C Paddock Wood *Roch* 71-74; SE Area Sec BCMS 74-82; Hon C Sidcup Ch Ch 74-82; V Tollington Park St Mark w St Anne *Lon* 82-86; V Holloway St Mark w Em 86-89; R Alfold and Loxwood *Guildf* from 89. *The Rectory, Loxwood, Billingshurst, W Sussex RH14 0RG* Loxwood (01403) 752320

SHORT, Martin Peter. b 54. Peterho Cam BA77 MA81. Wycliffe Hall Ox 77. **d** 79 **p** 80. C Shipley St Pet *Bradf* 79-82; C Becontree St Mary *Chelmsf* 82-86; V Bolton St Jas w St Chrys *Bradf* 86-92; Dioc Communications Officer from 92; C Otley from 92. *30 Newall Hall Park, Otley, W Yorkshire LS21 2RD* Otley (01943) 465071 Fax 467269

SHORT, Martin Ronald. b 57. Crewe & Alsager Coll CertEd78 Leic Univ BEd85. St Jo Coll Nottm DTS93. **d** 93 **p** 94. C Frankby w Greasby *Ches* from 93. *5 Flail Close, Greasby, South Wirral L49 2RN* 0151-605 0735

SHORT, Canon Michael John. b 38. Univ of Wales (Lamp) BA59. Sarum Th Coll 59. **d** 61 **p** 62. C Swansea St Nic *S & B* 61-64; C Oystermouth 64-69; V Merthyr Vale w Aberfan *Llan* 69-82; RD Merthyr Tydfil 76-82; R Caerphilly from 82; RD Caerphilly from 83; Can Llan Cathl from 89. *The Rectory, 2 St Martin's Road, Caerphilly, M Glam CF8 1EJ* Caerphilly (01222) 882992

SHORT, Neil Robert. b 58. Loughb Univ BSc81 St Jo Coll Dur BA86. Cranmer Hall Dur 83. **d** 86 **p** 87. C Whitfield *Derby* 86-90; C Bradf St Aug Undercliffe *Bradf* from 90. *96 Sydenham Place, Bradford BD3 0LA* Bradford (01274) 630545

SHORT, Robert Leslie. b 48. Em Coll Cam BA70 MA76. Wycliffe Hall Ox 87. **d** 92 **p** 92. Mexico 92-93; Chapl Repton Sch Derby from 93. *Repton School, Repton, Derby DE65 6FH* Burton-on-Trent (01283) 813640

SHORT, Terence. b 32. AKC63. **d** 64 **p** 65. P-in-c Sutton in Ashfield St Mich *S'well* 69-75; V Carlton 75-85; R Etwall w Egginton *Derby* 85-91; rtd 91. *19 Monk Street, Tutbury, Staffs DE13 9NA* Burton-on-Trent (01283) 813640

SHORTEN, Richard Deering. b 08. Qu Coll Cam BA30 MA48. Westcott Ho Cam 30. **d** 32 **p** 33. V Preshute *Sarum* 56-75; Asst Chapl Marlborough Coll Wilts 56-75; rtd 75. *Throg Cottage, Preshute Lane, Marlborough, Wilts SN8 4HQ* Marlborough (01672) 512447

SHORTER, Robert Edward. b 48. Ripon Coll Cuddesdon 89. **d** 91 **p** 92. C Braunton *Ex* 91-94; C Bishopsnympton, Rose Ash, Mariansleigh etc from 94. *The Vicarage, Molland, South Molton, Devon EX36 3NG* South Molton (01769) 550551

SHORTHOUSE, Raymond Trevor. b 34. DipAdEd. Ridley Hall Cam 68. **d** 70 **p** 71. C Gt Ilford St Andr *Chelmsf* 70-73; C Ludlow *Heref* 73-75; P-in-c Cressage w Sheinton 76-80; P-in-c Harley w Kenley 76-80; P-in-c Denby *Derby* 80-84; Adult Educn Officer 80-85; RD Heanor 83-84; V Chellaston 84-88; P-in-c Breadsall from 88; Dioc Dir of Studies from 88. *Breadsall Rectory, Derby DE21 5LL* Derby (01332) 831352

SHORTHOUSE, Canon Stephen Arthur. b 20. Trin Coll Cam BA41 MA45. Westcott Ho Cam 41. **d** 43 **p** 44. V Yardley Wood *Birm* 57-75; V Bartley Green 75-85; Hon Can Birm Cathl 76-85; rtd 85; Perm to Offic *Birm* from 85; Perm to Offic *Worc* from 86. *15 Lansdowne Terrace, Malvern, Worcs WR14 2AR* Malvern (01684) 569033

SHORTLAND, Thomas (Tom). b 26. Ox Min Course 89. **d** 91 **p** 92. NSM Welford w Wickham and Gt Shefford, Boxford etc *Ox* from 91. *Tregenna, 45 Orchard Park Close, Hungerford, Berks RG17 0BS* Hungerford (01488) 682031

SHORTT, Noel Christopher. b 36. Open Univ BA76 Ulster Univ MA DipContEd DPhil91. Bps' Coll Cheshunt 63. **d** 63 **p** 64. C Belf St Mary *Conn* 63-66; C Agherton 66-68; Chapl RAF 68-69; I Duneane w Ballyscullion *Conn* 69-79; I Belf St Steph w St Luke 79-89; RD M Belf 82-86 and 88-89; I Ballyrashane w Kildollagh from 89. *9 Sandelwood Avenue, Coleraine, Co Londonderry BT52 1JW* Coleraine (01265) 43061

SHOTLANDER, Lionel George. b 27. Cant Univ (NZ) BA49 MA51. **d** 51 **p** 52. New Zealand 60-74; V Curdridge *Portsm* 74-85; R Durley 79-85; V Twyford and Owslebury and Morestead *Win* 85-91; rtd 91. *Cambria, High Street, Shirrell Heath, Southampton SO3 2JN* Wickham (01329) 832353

SHOTTER, Very Rev Edward Frank. b 33. Univ of Wales (Lamp) BA58. St Steph Ho Ox 58. **d** 60 **p** 61. C Plymouth St Pet *Ex* 60-62; Inter-Colleg Sec SCM (Lon) 62-66; Perm to Offic *Lon* 62-69; Dir Lon Medical Gp 63-89; Chapl Lon Univ Medical Students *Lon* 69-89; Dir Inst of Medical Ethics 74-89; Preb St Paul's Cathl *Lon* 77-89; Dean Roch from 89. *The Deanery, Rochester, Kent ME1 1TG* Medway (01634) 844023 or 843366

SHOULER, Simon Frederic. b 54. ARICS77 Pemb Coll Cam MA79. E Midl Min Tr Course 82. **d** 85 **p** 86. NSM Asfordby *Leic* 85-92; Perm to Offic from 92. *Tower Cottage, Wartnaby, Melton Mowbray, Leics LE14 3HU* Melton Mowbray (01664) 822698

SHREEVE, Ven David Herbert. b 34. St Pet Hall Ox BA57 MA61. Ridley Hall Cam 57. **d** 59 **p** 60. C Plymouth St Andr *Ex* 59-64; V Bermondsey St Anne *S'wark* 64-71; V Eccleshill *Bradf* 71-84; RD Calverley 78-84; Hon Can Bradf Cathl 83-84; Adn Bradf from 84. *11 The Rowans, Baildon, Shipley, W Yorkshire BD17 5DB* Bradford (01274) 583735 Fax 586184

SHREWSBURY, Preb Michael Buller. b 30. St Jo Coll Dur BA54. Linc Th Coll 54. **d** 56 **p** 57. Bermuda 67-70; V Dalston H Trin w St Phil *Lon* 70-86; AD Hackney 79-84; Preb St Paul's Cathl 86-92; R Stepney St Dunstan and All SS 86-92; rtd 92; Perm to Offic *Lon* from 92. *Flat 1, 150 Wapping High Street, London E1 9XG* 0171-480 5479

SHREWSBURY, Area Bishop of. See HALLATT, Rt Rev David Marrison

SHRIMPTON, Canon Aner Clive. b 14. Lon Univ BD39. ALCD39. **d** 39 **p** 40. V Ruddington *S'well* 52-84; Hon Can S'well Minster 78-84; rtd 84; Perm to Offic *S'well* from 84. *36 Brookview Drive, Keyworth, Nottingham NG12 5JN* Nottingham (0115) 937 2795

SHRIMPTON, George Roderick. b 33. Selw Coll Cam BA56 MA60. Linc Th Coll 56. **d** 58 **p** 59. C Bilston St Leon *Lich* 58-63; C High Wycombe All SS *Ox* 63-67; V Dalton *Sheff* 67-74; V Milborne Port w Goathill *B & W* 74-90; P-in-c Barkston and Hough Gp *Linc* 90; R from 90; RD Loveden from 93. *The Parsonage, The Drift, Syston, Grantham, Lincs NG32 2BY* Loveden (01400) 50381

SHRIMPTON, Mrs Sheila Nan. b 32. Qu Mary Coll Lon BA54 LSE CSocStuds55. St Chris Coll Blackheath 57. **dss** 83 **d** 87 **p** 94. Lic to Offic *B & W* 83-90; NSM Barkston and Hough Gp *Linc* from 90; Asst Local Min Officer from 90. *The Parsonage, The Drift, Syston, Grantham, Lincs NG32 2BY* Loveden (01400) 50381

SHRISUNDER, David Shripat. b 29. Osmania Univ Hyderabad BA52 Serampore Univ BD59 Shivaji Univ Kolhapur MA69. Bp's Coll Calcutta 54. **d** 57 **p** 58. India 57-71, 72-75, 77-79 and 88-90; C Batley All SS *Wakef* 71-72; C Skegness *Linc* 75-77; C Derringham Bank *York* 80-81; TV Grays Thurrock *Chelmsf* 81-85; R Uddingston *Glas* 85-88; R Cambuslang 85-88; P-in-c Sinfin Moor *Derby* 90-94; rtd 94. *225 Chanterlands Avenue, Hull HU5 3TP* Hull (01482) 447290

SHRIVES, Austen Geoffrey. b 28. Lon Univ BD68 MTh77. S'wark Ord Course. **d** 69 **p** 69. Miss to Seamen 68-74; V Epsom St Martin *Guildf* 74-84; V York Town St Mich 84-87; R Churchstanton, Buckland St Mary and Otterford *B & W* 87-93; rtd 93. *1 Jacqueline House, Ticklemore Street, Totnes, Devon TQ9 5EJ* Totnes (01803) 863576

SHUCKSMITH, John Barry. b 37. Lon Univ DipTh68 Hull Univ DipTh84 FRSA87. Oak Hill Th Coll. **d** 68 **p** 69. C Tooting Graveney St Nic *S'wark* 68-70; S Africa 74-76; P-in-c Liv Ch Ch Norris Green *Liv* 82-86; Chapl RN 86-91; R Broughton *Linc* 91-94. *3 Fourth Avenue, Portsmouth PO6 3HX* Portsmouth (01705) 375100

SHUFFLEBOTHAM, Alastair Vincent. b 32. Nottm Univ CSocSc57. Lich Th Coll 63. **d** 65 **p** 66. C W Kirby St Bridget *Ches* 65-69; V Tranmere St Paul 69-71; V Tranmere St Paul w St Luke 71-78; V Neston from 78. *The Vicarage, Neston, South Wirral L64 9TZ* 0151-336 4544

SHUKMAN, Dr Ann Margaret. b 31. Girton Coll Cam BA53 MA58 LMH Ox DPhil74. W Midl Minl Tr Course 80. **dss** 84 **d** 92 **p** 94. Steeple Aston w N Aston and Tackley *Ox* 84-92; NSM from 92. *Old School House, Tackley, Kidlington, Oxon OX5 3AH* Tackley (01869) 331761

SHUTT, Anthony John. b 57. Brunel Univ BSc79 DipHE89. Trin Coll Bris 87. **d** 89 **p** 90. C Epsom St Martin *Guildf* from 89. *12 Worple Road, Epsom, Surrey KT18 5EE* Epsom (01372) 720088

SHUTT, Laurence John. b 42. MPS64 MRPharmS88. St Steph Ho Ox 87 Llan Dioc Tr Scheme 80. **d** 84 **p** 85. NSM Whitchurch *Llan* 84-87; C Llanishen and Lisvane 88-90; Chapl RNR from 89; V Middlestown *Wakef* from 90. *The Vicarage, 19 Wood Mount, Overton, Wakefield, W Yorkshire WF4 4SB* Wakefield (01924) 276159

SHUTT, Nicholas Stephen. b 58. Qu Mary Coll Lon LLB80 Solicitor 83. SW Minl Tr Course 91. **d** 94 **p** 95. NSM Yelverton, Meavy, Sheepstor and Walkhampton *Ex* from 94. *12 Blackbrook Close, Walkhampton, Yelverton, Devon PL20 6JF* Yelverton (01822) 854653

SHUTT, Rowland James Heath. b 11. St Chad's Coll Dur BA33 PhD36 MA36. **d** 35 **p** 36. Warden Worc Ord Coll 64-69; rtd 77. *7 Greenhill, Bath Road, Worcester WR5 2AT* Worcester (01905) 355410

SHUTTLEWORTH, Claude Tone. b 16. Solicitor 48 St Cath Coll Cam BA38 MA54. Edin Th Coll 55. **d** 57 **p** 58. R Lamplugh w Ennerdale *Carl* 61-65; rtd 81. *31 Thorntrees Drive, Thornhill, Egremont, Cumbria CA22 2SU* Egremont (01946) 820014

SIBBALD, Miss Olwyn Eileen. b 57. Linc Th Coll 87. **d** 89 **p** 94. Par Dn Wythenshawe St Martin *Man* 89-93; Par Dn Baguley 93-94; C from 94. *28 Arcadia Avenue, Sale, Cheshire M33 3SA*

SIBLEY, Jonathan Paul Eddolls. b 55. Newc Univ BA77. Westcott Ho Cam 78 Ripon Coll Cuddesdon 85. **d** 87 **p** 88. C Waltham Cross *St Alb* 87-90; C Chalfont St Peter *Ox* from 90. *All Saints' Parsonage, Oval Way, Chalfont St Peter, Gerrards Cross, Bucks SL9 8PZ* Gerrards Cross (01753) 883839

SIBLEY, Peter Linsey. b 40. Selw Coll Cam BA61 MA63 DipHE. Oak Hill Th Coll 79. **d** 81 **p** 82. C Crofton *Portsm* 81-84; TV Cheltenham St Mark *Glouc* 84-93; P-in-c Tewkesbury H Trin from 93. *Holy Trinity Vicarage, 49 Barton Street, Tewkesbury, Glos GL20 5PU* Tewkesbury (01684) 293233

SIBSON, Edward John. b 39. Brasted Th Coll 61 St Aid Birkenhead 63. **d** 65 **p** 66. C Gt Parndon *Chelmsf* 65-69; C Saffron Walden 69-72; P-in-c Colchester St Leon 72-77; Ind Chapl 72-80; TV Colchester St Leon, St Mary Magd and St Steph 77-80; V Layer-de-la-Haye 80-90; R Chipping Ongar w Shelley from 90; RD Ongar from 94. *The Rectory, Shakletons, Ongar, Essex CM5 9AT* Ongar (01277) 362173

SIBSON, Robert Francis. b 46. Leeds Univ CertEd68. Sarum & Wells Th Coll 78. **d** 80 **p** 81. C Watford St Mich *St Alb* 80-83; TV Digswell and Panshanger 83-90; V Biggleswade from 90. *The Vicarage, Shortmead Street, Biggleswade, Beds SG18 0AT* Biggleswade (01767) 312243

SICHEL, Stephen Mackenzie. b 59. RGN85 RMN87 UEA BA80. Ripon Coll Cuddesdon 87. **d** 90 **p** 91. C Tettenhall Regis *Lich* 90-95; C Camberwell St Giles w St Matt *S'wark* from 95. *St Matthew's House, 77 Coldharbour Lane, London SE5 9NS* 0171-274 3778

SIDAWAY, Canon Geoffrey Harold. b 42. Kelham Th Coll 61. **d** 66 **p** 67. C Beighton *Derby* 66-70; C Chesterfield All SS 70-72; P-in-c Derby St Bart 72-74; V 74-77; V Maidstone St Martin *Cant* 77-86; V Bearsted w Thurnham from 86; RD Sutton from 92; Hon Can Cant Cathl from 94. *The Vicarage, Church Lane, Bearsted, Maidstone, Kent ME14 4EF* Maidstone (01622) 737135

SIDDALL, Arthur. b 43. Lanc Univ MA81 DMS90 Surrey Univ PGCE94. Lon Coll of Div ALCD67 LTh74. **d** 67 **p** 68. C Formby H Trin *Liv* 67-70; C Childwall All SS 70-72; CMS 72-77; Bangladesh 74-77; V Clitheroe St Paul Low Moor *Blackb* 77-82; V Blackb St Gabr 82-90; Dep Gen Sec Miss to Seamen 90-93; Perm to Offic *Lon* 90-93; Hon C Leatherhead *Guildf* 90-94; Perm to Offic from 94. *2 Homefield Close, Leatherhead, Surrey KT22 8RW* Leatherhead (01372) 372282

SIDDLE, Michael Edward. b 33. Dur Univ BA54. St Aid Birkenhead 55. **d** 57 **p** 58. C Fazakerley Em *Liv* 57-59; C Farnworth 59-62; V Swadlincote *Derby* 62-70; Distr Sec (Northd and Dur) BFBS 70-72; Yorkshire 72-82; V Bamber Bridge St Aid *Blackb* 82-87; V Horsforth *Ripon* from 87. *St Margaret's Vicarage, Church Lane, Horsforth, Leeds LS18 5LA* Leeds (0113) 258 2481

SIDEBOTHAM, Canon Stephen Francis. b 35. Qu Coll Cam BA58 MA80. Linc Th Coll 58. **d** 60 **p** 61. C Bitterne Park *Win* 60-64; Hong Kong 64-83; Dean Hong Kong 76-83; Chapl Gravesend and N Kent Hosp 83-94; R Gravesend St Geo

SIDEBOTTOM

Roch 83-94; RD Gravesend 91-94; P-in-c Rosherville 91-94; Acorn Chr Healing Trust from 94. *Whitehill Chase, High Street, Bordon, Hants GU35 0AP* Bordon (01420) 472779

SIDEBOTTOM, Andrew John. b 54. FRCO75 FTCL76 LRAM75 Univ of Wales (Abth) BMus76 St Martin's Coll Lanc PGCE78. Sarum & Wells Th Coll 79. **d** 81 **p** 82. C Tenby w Gumfreston *St D* 81-84; C Llanelli 84-86; V Monkton 86-91; V Fairfield *Derby* from 91. *The Vicarage, Fairfield, Buxton, Derbyshire SK17 7EB* Buxton (01298) 23629

SIDEBOTTOM, George. b 16. TCD 43. **d** 49 **p** 50. V Felmersham *St Alb* 62-81; rtd 81; Perm to Offic *St Alb* from 81. *11 Cody Road, Clapham, Bedford MK41 6ED* Bedford (01234) 356189

SIDES, Canon James Robert. b 37. TCD BA66. CITC 68. **d** 67 **p** 68. C Belf St Clem *D & D* 67-70; C Antrim All SS *Conn* 70-73; I Tomregan w Drumlane *K, E & A* 73-80; I Killesher from 80; Preb Kilmore Cathl from 89. *Killesher Rectory, Tully, Florencecourt, Enniskillen, Co Fermanagh BT92 1FN* Florencecourt (01365) 348235

SILCOCK, Donald John. b 30. AKC59. **d** 60 **p** 61. C Felpham w Middleton *Chich* 68-74; R Ightham *Roch* 74-84; R Cliffe at Hoo w Cooling 84-92; RD Strood 85-91; rtd 92. *Puck's House, 26 Ancton Way, Elmer Sands, Middleton-on-Sea, Bognor Regis, W Sussex PO22 6JN* Bognor Regis (01243) 582589

SILK, Ian Geoffrey. b 60. Pemb Coll Cam BA81 MA85. Trin Coll Bris BA89. **d** 89 **p** 90. C Linc St Giles *Linc* 89-93; P-in-c Linc St Geo Swallowbeck from 93. *St George's Vicarage, Eastbrook Road, Lincoln LN6 7EW* Lincoln (01522) 683394

SILK, John Arthur. b 52. Selw Coll Cam BA73 MA77 K Coll Lon MTh80. Westcott Ho Cam 75. **d** 77 **p** 78. C Banstead *Guildf* 77-80; C Dorking w Ranmore 80-84; R Ringwould w Kingsdown *Cant* from 84. *The Rectory, Upper Street, Kingsdown, Deal, Kent CT14 8BJ* Deal (01304) 373951

✠**SILK, Rt Rev Robert David.** b 36. Ex Univ BA58. St Steph Ho Ox 58. **d** 59 **p** 60 **c** 94. C Gillingham St Barn *Roch* 59-62; C Lamorbey H Redeemer 63-69; R Swanscombe SS Pet and Paul 69-71; P-in-c Swanscombe All SS 69-71; R Swanscombe 71-75; R Beckenham St Geo 75-80; Adn Leic 80-94; TR Leic H Spirit 82-88; Australia from 94; Bp Ballarat from 94. *The Bishop's Registry, PO Box 89, Ballarat, Victoria, Australia 3353* Ballarat (53) 311183 or 392370 Fax 382782

SILKSTONE, Harry William James. b 21. St D Coll Lamp BA48. **d** 49 **p** 50. R Debden *Chelmsf* 63-72; V Bocking St Pet 72-78; R Gt Hallingbury 78-86; rtd 86; Perm to Offic *B & W* 86-93. *Trevarah, 13 Lye Mead, Winford, Bristol BS18 8AU* Bristol (0117) 987 2836

SILKSTONE, Thomas William. b 27. St Edm Hall Ox BA51 MA55 BD67. Wycliffe Hall Ox 51. **d** 53 **p** 54. Lect K Alfred's Coll Win 62-65; Sen Lect 65-75; Prin Lect 75-85; Lic to Offic *Win* 62-85; Perm to Offic *Truro* from 82; rtd 92. *Trevalyon, Lansallos, Looe, Cornwall PL13 2PX* Polperro (01503) 72110

SILLER, James Robert William. b 44. Pemb Coll Ox BA65 MA70 Qu Coll Cam 69. Westcott Ho Cam 67. **d** 70 **p** 71. C Spring Grove St Mary *Lon* 70-73; C Leeds St Pet *Ripon* 73-77; P-in-c Quarry Hill 73-77; V Gilling and Kirkby Ravensworth 77-82; P-in-c Melsonby 77-82; R Farnley 82-94; V Potternewton from 94. *St Martin's Vicarage, 2A St Martin's View, Leeds LS7 3LB* Leeds (0113) 262 4271

SILLETT, Angela Veronica Isabel. See BERNERS-WILSON, Mrs Angela Veronica Isabel

SILLEY, Michael John. b 48. Ripon Coll Cuddesdon 82. **d** 84 **p** 85. C Frodingham *Linc* 84-87; V Ingham w Cammeringham w Fillingham from 87; R Aisthorpe w Scampton w Thorpe le Fallows etc from 87; RD Lawres from 92; P-in-c N w S Carlton from 93. *The Vicarage, Ingham, Lincoln LN1 2YW* Lincoln (01522) 730519

SILLIS, Eric Keith. b 41. NW Ord Course 75. **d** 78 **p** 79. C Blackpool St Steph *Blackb* 78-82; V Huncoat 82-86; V Blackpool St Wilfrid 86-95; V Fleetwood St Dav from 95. *St David's Vicarage, 211 Broadway, Fleetwood, Lancs FY7 8AZ* Blackpool (01253) 779725

SILLIS, Graham William. b 46. S'wark Ord Course 73. **d** 76 **p** 77. C Palmers Green St Jo *Lon* 76-79; C Dawlish *Ex* 79-81; V Ipswich St Thos *St E* 81-87; V Babbacombe *Ex* 87-95. *8 Waterloo Road, Torquay TQ1 3AY* Torquay (01803) 291005

SILLITOE, Pauline Ann. b 42. ACP71 FCP82 CertEd69 Birm Poly DipEd80. Qu Coll Birm 82. **dss** 85 **d** 87 **p** 94. Kingshurst *Birm* 85-86; Castle Bromwich St Clem 86-87; NSM from 87; Chapl Chelmsley Hosp Birm from 92. *The Vicarage, Lanchester Way, Birmingham B36 9JG* 0121-747 4460

SILLITOE, William John. b 37. Lich Th Coll 67. **d** 69 **p** 70. C Ettingshall *Lich* 69-71; C March St Jo *Ely* 72-74; P-in-c Kennett 74-77; V Fordham St Pet 74-77; V Castle Bromwich St Clem *Birm* from 77. *The Vicarage, Lanchester Way, Birmingham B36 9JG* 0121-747 4460

SILLS, Peter Michael. b 41. Barrister 76 Nottm Univ BA63 LLM68. S'wark Ord Course 78. **d** 81 **p** 82. C W Wimbledon Ch

Ch *S'wark* 81-85; P-in-c Barnes H Trin 85-93; Wandsworth Adnry Ecum Officer 90-93; V Purley St Mark Woodcote from 93. *St Mark's Vicarage, 22 Peaks Hill, Purley, Surrey CR8 3JE* 0181-660 7204

SILVERSIDES, Mark. b 51. Lon Univ BD73. St Jo Coll Nottm 74. **d** 76 **p** 77. C Hornchurch St Andr *Chelmsf* 76-80; P-in-c Becontree St Thos 80-85; TR Becontree W 85-86; CPAS Staff 86-92; Freelance Chr Video and Resources Producer from 92. *13 Cedar Crescent, Low Fell, Gateshead, Tyne & Wear NE9 6ER* 0191-482 6358

SILVERTHORN, Alan. b 37. St Mich Coll Llan 62. **d** 65 **p** 66. C Machen and Rudry *Mon* 65-71; V New Tredegar 71-83; V Llanfrechfa and Llanddewi Fach w Llandegveth from 83. *The Vicarage, Llanfrechfa, Cwmbran, Gwent NP44 8DQ* Cwmbran (01633) 482343

SILVESTER, David. b 59. Qu Mary Coll Lon BSc80 Nottm Univ BCombStuds85. Linc Th Coll 82. **d** 85 **p** 86. C Walthamstow St Mary w St Steph *Chelmsf* 85-90; TV Barking St Marg w St Patr from 90. *The Vicarage, Bastable Avenue, Barking, Essex IG11 0NG* 0181-594 1976

SILVESTER, Stephen David. b 59. Chu Coll Cam BA80 MA83 Man Univ PGCE82. St Jo Coll Nottm 88. **d** 91 **p** 92. C Nottm St Jude *S'well* from 91. *19 Kent Road, Nottingham NG3 6BE* Nottingham (0115) 962 0281

SIM, David Hayward. b 29. Qu Coll Birm 57. **d** 59 **p** 60. V Frampton *Linc* 69-74; V Gainsborough St Geo 74-82; V Sturminster Newton and Hinton St Mary *Sarum* 82-89; R Stock and Lydlinch 82-89; Dorchester 89-94; Chapl HM Pris Dorchester 89-94; rtd 95. *12 Eldridge Close, Dorchester, Dorset DT1 2JS* Dorchester (01305) 269262

SIMCOCK, Canon Michael Pennington. b 27. Qu Coll Cam BA50 MA52. Bps' Coll Cheshunt 50. **d** 52 **p** 53. V Altarnon and Bolventor *Truro* 67-70; V Treleigh 70-87; RD Carnmarth N 75-91; Hon Can Truro Cathl 82-92; R Redruth w Lanner 87-88; TR Redruth w Lanner and Treleigh 88-92; rtd 92. *1C Straton Place, Falmouth, Cornwall TR11 2ST*

SIMISTER, Charles Arnold. b 19. MM44. Edin Th Coll 49. **d** 52 **p** 53. CF 63-84; R Kircudbright *Glas* 63-84; R Gatehouse of Fleet 63-84; rtd 84; Perm to Offic *Glas* from 84. *98 High Street, Kirkcudbright DG6 4JQ* Kirkcudbright (01557) 330747

SIMISTER, Norman Harold. b 39. Bris Univ BSc60. Local NSM Course 91. **d** 93 **p** 94. NSM Wainford *St E* from 93. *Romaine, 1 School Road, Ringsfield, Beccles, Suffolk NR34 8NZ* Beccles (01502) 715549

SIMISTER, Thomas Brocklehurst. b 19. Keble Coll Ox BA48 MA53. St Steph Ho Ox 48. **d** 50 **p** 51. V Rushall *Lich* 55-88; rtd 88; Perm to Offic *Nor* 88-94. *61 Loddon Road, Ditchingham, Bungay, Suffolk NR35 2RA* Bungay (01986) 894668

SIMMONDS, David Brian. b 38. Selw Coll Cam BA62 MA66. Ridley Hall Cam. **d** 65 **p** 66. C Newc w Butterton *Lich* 65-69; V Branston from 69; RD Tutbury from 95. *The Vicarage, Branston, Burton-on-Trent, Staffs DE14 3EX* Burton-on-Trent (01283) 68926

SIMMONDS, Edward Alan. b 32. St Edm Hall Ox MA60. Ripon Coll Cuddesdon 88. **d** 89 **p** 90. NSM Ox St Mich w St Martin and All SS *Ox* 89-92; NSM Ox St Mary V w St Cross and St Pet 92-94; Chapl Lugano *Eur* from 94. *13 via al Nido, 6900 Lugano-Besso, Switzerland* Lugano (91) 581038

SIMMONDS, John. b 24. Sheff Univ BA50. Ridley Hall Cam 50. **d** 52 **p** 53. V W Streatham St Jas *S'wark* 65-73; V Congresbury *B & W* 73-75; P-in-c Puxton w Hewish St Ann and Wick St Lawrence 73-75; V Congresbury w Puxton and Hewish St Ann 75-84; Warden Home of Divine Healing Crowhurst 84-89; rtd 89. *Beach Villa, 14 The Beach, Clevedon, Avon BS21 7QU* Clevedon (01275) 342295

SIMMONDS, Paul Andrew Howard. b 50. Nottm Univ BSc73 Lon Univ DipTh78. Trin Coll Bris 75. **d** 78 **p** 79. C Leic H Trin w St Jo *Leic* 78-82; SW Regional Co-ord CPAS 83-86; Hd Adult Tr and Resources CPAS 86-95; Perm to Offic *B & W* 83-89; Lic to Offic *Bris* 83-89; Hon C Wolston and Church Lawford *Cov* 89-94; C from 95; Dioc Miss Adv from 95. *31 John Simpson Close, Wolston, Coventry CV8 2HX* Wolston (01203) 543188

SIMMONDS, Paul Richard. b 38. AKC63. **d** 64 **p** 65. C Newington St Mary *S'wark* 64-67; C Cheam 68-73; P-in-c Stockwell Green St Andr 73-87; V from 87. *St Andrew's Vicarage, Moat Place, London SW9 0TA* 0171-274 7531

SIMMONDS, Robert William (Bob). b 52. Nottm Univ BTh77 Birm Poly DCG79. Linc Th Coll 72. **d** 80 **p** 81. C Roehampton H Trin *S'wark* 80-83; TV Hemel Hempstead *St Alb* 83-90; V S Woodham Ferrers *Chelmsf* 90-94; rtd 94. *14 Hardy Street, Maidstone, Kent ME14 2SH* Maidstone (01622) 681129

SIMMONDS, William Hugh Cyril. b 08. Lon Univ DipOAS47. St Jo Hall Highbury. **d** 37 **p** 38. V S Malling *Chich* 67-78; rtd 78; Perm to Offic *Chich* from 82. *79 Grange Close, Horam, Heathfield, E Sussex TN21 0EG* Horam Road (014353) 2743

SIMMONS, Barry Jeremy. b 52. London Univ BA54 MA62. Ridley Hall Cam 61. **d** 63 **p** 64. C Buttershaw St Aid *Bradf* 63-65; Jamaica 65-68; V Earby *Bradf* 68-73; Hong Kong

634

73-74; Bahrain 75-79; Chapl Luxembourg *Eur* 80-91; V Shoreham *Roch* from 91. *The Vicarage, Shoreham, Sevenoaks, Kent TN14 7SA* Otford (01959) 522363

SIMMONS, Bernard Peter. b 26. CA Tr Coll 48 S'wark Ord Course 86. **d** 88 **p** 88. C Chatham St Wm *Roch* 88-91; rtd 91; P-in-c Underriver *Roch* from 91; P-in-c Seal St Lawr from 91. *St Lawrence Vicarage, Stone Street, Seal, Sevenoaks, Kent TN15 0LQ* Sevenoaks (01732) 761766

SIMMONS, Canon Brian Dudley. b 35. Master Mariner. St Steph Ho Ox 62. **d** 64 **p** 65. C Bournemouth St Pet *Win* 64-67; Miss to Seamen 67-71; Hon C Milton next Gravesend w Denton *Roch* 67-70; Hon C Gravesend St Geo 70-71; V Lamorbey H Trin 71-90; R Hever w Mark Beech 90-93; P-in-c Four Elms 90-93; R Hever, Four Elms and Mark Beech 93-94; Hon Can Roch Cathl from 91; V Langton Green from 94. *The Vicarage, The Green, Langton Green, Tunbridge Wells, Kent TN3 0JB* Langton (01892) 862072

SIMMONS, Christopher John. b 49. Mert Coll Ox MA77. NE Ord Course 88. **d** 90 **p** 91. C Kirkleatham *York* 90-93; P-in-c Barlby 93-95; V Barlby w Riccall from 95. *The Vicarage, York Road, Barlby, Selby, N Yorkshire YO8 7JP* Selby (01757) 702384

SIMMONS, Eric. b 30. Leeds Univ BA51. Coll of Resurr Mirfield 51. **d** 53 **p** 54. C Chesterton St Luke *Ely* 53-57; Chapl Keele Univ *Lich* 57-61; Lic to Offic *Wakef* 63-65 and from 67; CR from 63; Lic to Offic *Ripon* 65-67; Warden Hostel of the Resurr Leeds 66-67; Superior CR 74-87. *Royal Foundation of St Katharine, 2 Butcher Row, London E14 8DS* 0171-790 3540

SIMMONS, Gary David. b 59. Trin Coll Bris BA86. **d** 87 **p** 88. C Ecclesfield *Sheff* 87-90; Min Stapenhill Immanuel CD *Derby* from 90. *Immanuel Vicarage, 150 Hawthorn Crescent, Burton-on-Trent, Staffs DE15 9QW* Burton-on-Trent (01283) 563959

SIMMONS, Godfrey John. b 39. Open Univ BA77. Edin Th Coll 77. **d** 74 **p** 74. Dioc Supernumerary *St And* 74-75 and 80-81; C Strathtay 75-77; C Dunkeld 75-77; C Bridge of Allan 77-80; C Alloa 77-80; Chapl Stirling Univ 79-80; Chapl HM Pris Perth 80-85; Min Crieff *St And* 80-81; R 81-85; Min Muthill 80-81; R 81-85; Min Comrie 80-81; R 81-85; R Stromness 85-89; R Kirkwall 85-91; Miss to Seamen from 85; Hon Chapl (Scotland) 85-90; Hon Area Chapl (Scotland) 90-94; R Longside *Ab* 91-94; R Old Deer 91-94; R Peterhead 91-92; R Strichen 91-94; Chapl HM Pris Peterhead 91-94; Chapl Supt Mersey Miss to Seamen from 94. *Colonsay House, 20 Crosby Road South, Liverpool L22 1RQ* 0151-920 3253 Fax 928 0244

SIMMONS, Miss Joan Yvonne. b 14. Gilmore Ho 57. **dss** 61 **d** 87. Adult Educn Officer *Lon* 69-78; rtd 78; Perm to Offic *Chich* from 87. *12 Whittington College, London Road, East Grinstead, W Sussex RH19 2QU* East Grinstead (01342) 312781

SIMMONS, John. b 53. Carl Dioc Tr Course 82. **d** 85 **p** 86. C Wotton St Mary *Glouc* 85-88; P-in-c Amberley 88-92; R Burton Latimer *Pet* from 92; RD Kettering from 94. *The Rectory, Preston Court, Burton Latimer, Kettering, Northants NN15 5LR* Burton Latimer (01536) 722959 Fax as telephone

SIMMONS, John Graham. b 54. Westf Coll Lon BSc75 Man Univ PGCE76 CertRE81. N Ord Course 89. **d** 92 **p** 93. C Thame w Towersey *Ox* from 92. *8 Victoria Mead, Thame, Oxon OX9 3HY* Thame (01844) 218832

SIMMONS, John Harold. b 46. FCCA. Sarum & Wells Th Coll 86. **d** 89 **p** 90. NSM The Iwernes, Sutton Waldron and Fontmell Magna *Sarum* from 89. *Fourways, Iwerne Courteney, Blandford Forum, Dorset DT11 8QL* Blandford (01258) 860515

SIMMONS, Canon Maurice Samuel. b 27. St Chad's Coll Dur BA50 DipTh52. **d** 52 **p** 53. R Croxdale *Dur* 58-81; Soc and Ind Adv to Bp Dur 61-70; Gen Sec Soc Resp Gp 70-75; Hon Can Dur Cathl 71-92; Sec Dioc Bd for Miss and Unity 75-82; V Norton St Mary 81-92; RD Stockton 85-92; rtd 92. *11 Roecliffe Grove, Stockton-on-Tees, Cleveland TS19 8JU* Stockton-on-Tees (01642) 618880

SIMMONS, Norman. b 11. Wycliffe Hall Ox 49. **d** 49 **p** 50. V Doncaster St Leon and St Jude *Sheff* 53-74; R Burghwallis w Skelbrooke 74-81; rtd 81. *21 Norseway, Stamford Bridge, York YO4 1DR* Stamford Bridge (01759) 371498

SIMMONS, Raymond Agar. b 35. Linc Th Coll 69. **d** 71 **p** 72. C Hartlepool St Luke *Dur* 71-74; P-in-c Purleigh *Chelmsf* 74-81; Ind Chapl 74-81; P-in-c old Norton w Stow Maries 81; Chapl Rampton Hosp Retford from 81. *4 Galen Avenue, Woodbeck, Retford, Notts DN22 0PD, or Rampton Hospital, Retford, Notts DN22 0PD* Retford (01777) 84531 or 247524

SIMMONS, Richard Andrew Cartwright. b 46. Trin Coll Bris 73. **d** 75 **p** 76. C Worting *Win* 75-80; R Six Pilgrims *B & W* 80-92; R Bincombe w Broadwey, Upwey and Buckland Ripers *Sarum* from 92. *The Rectory, 526 Littlemoor Road, Weymouth, Dorset DT3 5PA* Upwey (01305) 812542

SIMMS, Ernest Desmond Ross. b 25. TCD BA48 MA51 BD51. **d** 51 **p** 52. CF 62-81; R Cheriton w Tichborne and Beauworth *Win* 81-90; RD Alresford 84-90; rtd 90. *11 Buttermere Gardens, Alresford, Hants SO24 9NN* Alresford (01962) 735526

SIMMS, William Michael (Bill). b 41. DMA66 ACIS70 MIPM75 Open Univ BA87. NE Ord Course 84. **d** 87 **p** 88. NSM Croft *Ripon* 87; C 88; NSM Middleton Tyas and Melsonby 87; C 88; C Headingley 88-90; C Richmond w Hudswell 90-93; C-in-c Downholme and Marske 90-93; V Hawes and Hardraw from 93. *The Vicarage, Hawes, N Yorkshire DL8 3NP* Wensleydale (01969) 667553

SIMON, Brother. See BROOK, Peter Geoffrey

SIMON, David Sidney. b 49. CDipAF76 Univ of Wales (Abth) BSc(Econ)70 Hull Univ MA83. NE Ord Course 84. **d** 87 **p** 88. NSM Beverley St Mary *York* from 87; Chapl Humberside Poly 87-92; Chapl Humberside Univ from 92. *8 Melrose Park, Beverley, N Humberside HU17 8JL* Hull (01482) 862855

SIMON, Frederick Fairbanks. b 42. Ripon Coll Cuddesdon 75. **d** 77 **p** 78. C Cheddleton *Lich* 77-79; C Woodley St Jo the Ev *Ox* 79-82; V Spencer's Wood 82-85; P-in-c Steventon w Milton 85-87; Chapl Grenville Coll Bideford from 87; Lic to Offic *Ex* from 88. *Bracken Brae, Belvoir Road, Bideford, Devon EX39 3JR* Bideford (01237) 476380

SIMON, Oliver. b 45. Dur Univ BA67 Sussex Univ MA68 Ox Univ DipTh71 Man Univ CertRS89. Cuddesdon Coll 69. **d** 71 **p** 72. C Kidlington *Ox* 71-74; C Bracknell 74-78; V Frodsham *Ches* 78-85; R Easthampstead *Ox* from 88. *The Rectory, Easthampstead, Bracknell, Berks RG12 7ER* Bracknell (01344) 425205 or 423253 Fax 425205

SIMON, Prof Ulrich Ernst. b 13. K Coll Lon BD38 AKC38 MTh43 DD59. Linc Th Coll 38. **d** 38 **p** 39. C St Helier *S'wark* 38-42; C Upton cum Chalvey *Ox* 42-45; Lect Hebrew and OT K Coll Lon 45-59; FKC from 57; Hon C Bletchingley *S'wark* 50-52; P-in-c Millbrook *St Alb* 52-55; Lic to Offic 55-72; Prof Chr Lit Lon Univ 71-80; Dean K Coll Lon 78-80; Lic to Offic *Lon* from 85. *22 Collingwood Avenue, London N10 3ED* 0181-883 4852

SIMONS, Miss Christine. b 40. RGN62 RM64 RHV69. St Jo Coll Nottm 82. **dss** 84 **d** 87 **p** 94. Claygate *Guildf* 84-87; C Camberley St Paul 87-93; NSM from 93. *70 Inglewood Avenue, Camberley, Surrey GU15 1RS* Camberley (01276) 684702

SIMONS, Preb John Trevor. b 34. Lon Univ BD67. ALCD66. **d** 67 **p** 68. C Becontree St Mary *Chelmsf* 67-71; V Cranham Park 71-78; P-in-c Nailsea H Trin *B & W* 78-83; R from 83; Preb Wells Cathl from 90. *The Rectory, 2 Church Lane, Nailsea, Bristol BS19 2NG* Nailsea (01275) 853227

SIMONS, Mark Anselm. b 38. ARCM62. Oak Hill Th Coll 62. **d** 65 **p** 66. C Nottm St Ann *S'well* 65-68; C N Ferriby *York* 68-75; P-in-c Sherburn 75-78; V Gt and Lt Driffield 78-93. *Address temp unknown*

SIMONS, William Angus. b 18. Keble Coll Ox BA39 MA47. Cuddesdon Coll 40. **d** 41 **p** 42. Chapl Hammersmith Hosp Lon 65-68; St Edm Hosp 68-88; Northn Gen Hosp 68-72; Lic to Offic *Pet* 68-72 and from 81; P-in-c Northn St Lawr 72-76; C Northn H Sepulchre w St Andr and St Lawr 76-81; Northants Past Coun Service 76-81; rtd 83. *54 Park Avenue North, Northampton NN3 2JE* Northampton (01604) 713767

SIMONSON, Canon Juergen Werner Dietrich. b 24. Lon Univ BD52. ALCD52. **d** 52 **p** 53. V Putney St Marg *S'wark* 69-81; RD Wandsworth 74-81; Hon Can S'wark Cathl 75-90; R Barnes St Mary 81-90; rtd 90. *Elm Cottage, Horseshoe Lane, Ibthorpe, Andover, Hants SP11 0BY* Hurstbourne Tarrant (01264) 76381

SIMPER, Miss Rachel Dawn. b 67. K Coll Lon BD89. Westcott Ho Cam CTM92. **d** 92 **p** 94. Par Dn Clitheroe St Mary *Blackb* 92-94; C 94-95; C Nor St Pet Mancroft w St Jo Maddermarket *Nor* from 95. *63 Recreation Road, Norwich NR2 3PA* Norwich (01603) 51878

SIMPER, Terence Ernest. b 27. Qu Coll Birm 53. **d** 56 **p** 57. Australia 69-75; P-in-c Bris Lockleaze St Mary Magd w St Fran *Bris* 76-79; P-in-c Brislington St Anne 79-84; P-in-c St Dominic *Truro* 84-87; P-in-c St Mellion w Pillaton 84-87; P-in-c Landulph 84-87; R St Dominic, Landulph and St Mellion w Pillaton 87-90; rtd 90. *21 St Anne's Drive, Oldland Common, Bristol BS15 6RD* Bristol (0117) 932 2514

SIMPKIN, Mrs Doris Lily. b 30. E Midl Min Tr Course 79. **dss** 82 **d** 87 **p** 94. Mugginton and Kedleston *Derby* 82-87; NSM 87-94; Perm to Offic from 94. *71 Wheeldon Avenue, Derby DE22 1HP* Derby (01332) 343830

SIMPKIN, Paul. b 29. E Midl Min Tr Course. **d** 92 **p** 83. NSM Mugginton and Kedleston *Derby* 92-92; Lic to Offic from 92. *71 Wheeldon Avenue, Derby DE22 1HP* Derby (01332) 343830

SIMPKINS, Frank Charles. b 19. Oak Hill Th Coll 72. **d** 75 **p** 76. C Harrow Weald St Mich *Lon* 75-78; Hon C 81-84; P-in-c Dollis Hill St Paul 78-80; Chapl Northwick Park Hosp Harrow 81-83; Hon C Trin St Mich, Harrow Lon 84-94; Perm to Offic from 94. *7 Milne Field, Pinner, Middx HA5 4DP* 0181-428 2477

SIMPKINS, Canon Lionel Frank. b 46. UEA BSc68. Lambeth STh77 St Jo Coll Nottm ALCD72 LTh74. **d** 73 **p** 74. C Leic H Apostles *Leic* 73-77; C Bushbury *Lich* 77-80; V Sudbury w Ballingdon and Brundon *St E* from 80; Chapl Sudbury Hosps from 80; RD Sudbury from 88; Hon Can St E Cathl from 94. *All Saints' Vicarage, Church Street, Sudbury, Suffolk CO10 6BL* Sudbury (01787) 372400

SIMPSON, Alexander (Alex). b 31. Oak Hill Th Coll 74. **d** 76 **p** 77. Hon C Lower Homerton St Paul *Lon* 76-81; Hon C Homerton St Barn w St Paul 81-85; TV Hackney Marsh 85-87; V Kensington St Helen w H Trin from 87. *St Helen's Vicarage, St Helen's Gardens, London W10 6LP* 0181-969 1520

SIMPSON, Andrew. b 48. Liv Univ BEng69. Sarum Th Coll 83. **d** 86 **p** 87. NSM Canford Magna *Sarum* from 86. *17 Sopwith Crescent, Wimborne, Dorset BH21 1SH* Wimborne (01202) 883996

SIMPSON, Athol. b 20. Lich Th Coll 41. **d** 44 **p** 45. V Amble *Newc* 63-90; rtd 90. *63 Briardene Crescent, Gosforth, Newcastle upon Tyne NE3 4RX*

SIMPSON, Canon Brian Shepherd Tinley. b 12. Linc Th Coll 38. **d** 40 **p** 41. R Portnacrois *Arg* 70-80; R Duror 70-80; Can St Jo Cathl Oban 78-80; rtd 80; Hon Can St Jo Cathl Oban *Arg* from 80. *Tigh-na-Crois, Appin, Argyll PA38 4BL* Appin (0163173) 297

SIMPSON, Dr Charles Michael. b 38. St Cath Coll Cam MA64 Campion Hall Ox MA65 K Coll Lon PhD71 Heythrop Coll Lon STL69. **d** 68 **p** 69. Lect Th Lon Univ 72-84; Chapl Prince of Peace Community Greenwich 85-87; Retreat Dir St Beuno's Clwyd 87-91; P-in-c Selkirk *Edin* 91-94; P-in-c Offchurch *Cov* from 94; Warden Offa Retreat Ho from 94. *The Vicarage, Offchurch, Leamington Spa, Warks CV33 9AL* Leamington Spa (01926) 424401 Fax 330350

SIMPSON, Clarence. b 13. Bps' Coll Cheshunt 39. **d** 40 **p** 41. P-in-c Bicknoller *B & W* 66-74; P-in-c Port Isaac *Truro* 74-77; P-in-c Welsh Newton w Llanrothal *Heref* 77-78; C 78-80; rtd 78; Perm to Offic *Glouc* 80-88; Sen Chapl Glouc City Mental Hosp 86-89; Chapl Beauchamp Community 88-90. *12 Handbury Road, Malvern, Worcs WR14 1NN* Malvern (01684) 569388

SIMPSON, David John. b 61. Univ Coll Dur BA85. Sarum & Wells Th Coll 89. **d** 91 **p** 92. C Selby Abbey *York* 91-94; C Romsey *Win* from 94. *15 Mount Temple, Romsey, Hants SO51 8UW* Romsey (01794) 523840

SIMPSON, Derek John. b 59. Oak Hill Th Coll BA89. **d** 89 **p** 90. C Alperton *Lon* from 89. *19 Bowrons Avenue, Wembley, Middx HA0 4QS* 0181-997 0083

SIMPSON, Derrick. b 27. NW Ord Course 72. **d** 75 **p** 76. C Disley *Ches* 75-79; C Stockport St Geo 79-81; R Wistaston 81-90; Chapl Barony Hosp Nantwich 81-89; V Newton in Mottram *Ches* 90-93; rtd 93. *60 Dane Bank Avenue, Crewe CW2 8AD*

SIMPSON, Dr Geoffrey Sedgwick. b 32. Hamilton Coll (NY) BA54 Wisconsin Univ MA Pemb Coll Cam PhD70. Gen Th Sem (NY) STB57. **d** 57 **p** 57. USA 57-77; Chapl Birm Univ *Birm* 77-80; V Shoreham *Roch* 80-90; TR Street TM *York* from 90. *The Rectory, Barton-le-Street, Malton, N Yorkshire YO17 0PL* Malton (01653) 628376

SIMPSON, George William. b 18. Ox NSM Course. **d** 76 **p** 77. NSM Didcot Ox 76-87; C Swan 87-89; rtd 89; Perm to Offic *Ex* from 90. *21 Crescent Gardens, Ivybridge, Plymouth PL21 0BS* Plymouth (01752) 894425

SIMPSON, Godfrey Lionel. b 42. Sarum Th Coll 63. **d** 66 **p** 67. C Leintwardine *Heref* 66-70; C Leominster 70-73; P-in-c Whitbourne 73-79; V Barlaston *Lich* from 79; RD Trentham from 85. *The Vicarage, Barlaston, Stoke-on-Trent ST12 9AB* Barlaston (01782) 372452

SIMPSON, Herbert. b 20. Carl Dioc Tr Course. **d** 82 **p** 83. NSM Barrow St Aid *Carl* 82; NSM Barrow St Jo 82-90; rtd 90; Perm to Offic *Carl* from 90. *3 Glenridding Drive, Barrow-in-Furness, Cumbria LA14 4PE* Barrow-in-Furness (01229) 823707

SIMPSON, Very Rev John Arthur. b 33. Keble Coll Ox BA56 MA60. Clifton Th Coll 56. **d** 58 **p** 59. C Low Leyton *Chelmsf* 58-59; C Orpington Ch Ch *Roch* 59-62; Tutor Oak Hill Th Coll 62-72; V Ridge *St Alb* 72-79; P-in-c 79-81; Dir of Ords and Post-Ord Tr 75-81; Hon Can St Alb 77-79; Can Res St Alb 79-81; Adn Cant and Can Res Cant Cathl *Cant* 81-86; Dean Cant from 86. *The Deanery, The Precincts, Canterbury, Kent CT1 2EH* Canterbury (01227) 765983 or 762862

SIMPSON, John Bernard. b 40. ACP66 St Paul's Cheltenham CertEd62. **d** 93 **p** 93. In URC 63-93; Asst to RD Lothingland *Nor* 93-94; C Hopton w Corton 93-94; P-in-c from 94. *The Vicarage, 51 The Street, Corton, Lowestoft, Suffolk NR32 5HT* Lowestoft (01502) 730977 Fax 731272

SIMPSON, Canon John Lawrence. b 33. ARCM60 SS Coll Cam BA55 MA59. Wells Th Coll 63. **d** 65 **p** 66. Chapl Win Cathl *Win* 65-66; C Win St Bart 65-69; Chapl Repton Sch Derby 69-71; Hd of RE Helston Sch 71-78; Lic to Offic *Truro* 71-78; P-in-c Curry Rivel *B & W* 79-80; R Curry Rivel w Fivehead

and Swell 80-86; V Tunbridge Wells K Chas *Roch* 86-89; Can Res Bris Cathl *Bris* from 89. *55 Salisbury Road, Bristol BS6 7AS* Bristol (0117) 942 1452

SIMPSON, John Peter. b 39. ALCD66. **d** 66 **p** 67. C Woodside *Ripon* 66-69; C Burnage St Marg *Man* 69-72; V Rochdale Deeplish St Luke 72-80; R Lamplugh w Ennerdale *Carl* from 80. *The Rectory, Vicarage Lane, Ennerdale, Cleator, Cumbria CA23 3BE* Lamplugh (01946) 861310

SIMPSON, John Raymond. b 41. MASCH87 NSW Sch of Hypnotic Sciences DipCH87 Univ of S Aus GradDipEd92. Chich Th Coll 65. **d** 67 **p** 68. C Scarborough St Martin *York* 67-71; C Grangetown 71-72; Bermuda 72-75; C Lewisham St Mary *S'wark* 76; Australia from 76. *Chaplaincy House, 306 ABW, RAAF Base Pearce, Bullsbrook, W Australia 6084* Bullsbrook (15) 033651

SIMPSON, John Raymond. b 55. Oak Hill Th Coll 88. **d** 90 **p** 91. C Immingham *Linc* 90-94; TV The Ramseys and Upwood *Ely* from 94. *The Vicarage, Thatchers Close, Upwood, Huntingdon, Cambs PE17 1PN* Ramsey (01487) 814473

SIMPSON, Mrs June Hall. b 31. LRAM59 Sheff Univ BEd74. E Midl Min Tr Course 83. **dss** 86 **d** 87 **p** 94. Hon Par Dn Carlton-in-Lindrick *S'well* 87-94; Hon C from 94. *57 Arundel Drive, Carlton-in-Lindrick, Worksop, Notts S81 9DL* Worksop (01909) 730665

SIMPSON, Miss Margery Patricia. b 36. SRN57 SCM59. Oak Hill Th Coll BA86. **dss** 86 **d** 87 **p** 94. Rodbourne Cheney *Bris* 86-87; Par Dn 87-90; Par Dn Warmley 90-94; C Warmley, Syston and Bitton from 94. *25 Poplar Road, Warmley, Bristol BS15 5JX* Bristol (0117) 960 9969

SIMPSON, Patrick Verrent. b 26. Fitzw Ho Cam BA49 MA54 Lon Univ PGCE70. Ridley Hall Cam 49. **d** 51 **p** 52. W Germany 67-71; Chapl Northfleet Girl's Sch 71-81; Hon C Meopham w Nurstead *Roch* 72-81; P-in-c Weare Giffard w Landcross *Ex* 81-82; P-in-c Littleham 81-82; P-in-c Monkleigh 81-82; R Landcross, Littleham, Monkleigh etc 82-86; P-in-c Bovey Tracey SS Pet and Paul 86-91; Chapl Bovey Tracey Hosp 86-91; Chapl Hawkmoor Hosp 86-87; rtd 91. *10 Vicarage Close, Burton-in-Kendal, Carnforth, Lancs LA6 1NP* Burton (01524) 782386

SIMPSON, Peter. b 28. Trin Hall Cam BA56 MA60. **d** 57 **p** 58. C Kemp Town St Mark *Chich* 57-60; C Walthamstow St Pet *Chelmsf* 60-64; V Chingford St Anne 64-75; P-in-c Widdington 75; Perm to Offic *Win* 76-79; Chapl Princess Eliz Hosp Guernsey 77-79; R Guernsey St Michel du Valle *Win* 79-91; V Sark from 91. *The Vicarage, Sark, Guernsey, Channel Islands GY9 0SF* Sark (01481) 832040

SIMPSON, Canon Peter Wynn. b 32. Birm Univ BA53. Ripon Hall Ox 55. **d** 57 **p** 58. V Foleshill St Laur *Cov* 63-70; V Radford 70-79; RD Cov N 76-79; V Finham 79-91; RD Cov S 82-88; Hon Can Cov Cathl 83-91; rtd 91. *Faith Cottage, 118 Main Street, Wolston, Coventry CV8 3HP* Coventry (01203) 418330

SIMPSON, Philip Alexander. b 54. Keele Univ BA79 CQSW79. CMS Tr Coll Selly Oak 85. **d** 89. CMS from 85; Pakistan from 85. *42 H/6 Pechs, Karachi 75400, Pakistan* Karachi (21) 438332 or 515180 Fax 455-4278 or 568-0236

SIMPSON, Raymond James. b 40. Lon Coll of Div ALCD63 LTh74. **d** 64 **p** 65. C Longton St Jas *Lich* 64-68; C Upper Tooting H Trin *S'wark* 68-71; BFBS Distr Sec E Anglia 71-77; C-in-c Bowthorpe CD *Nor* 78-84; V Bowthorpe from 84. *Church Community House, Bowthorpe Hall Road, Bowthorpe, Norwich NR5 9AA* Norwich (01603) 745698

SIMPSON, Ven Rennie. b 20. LVO74. Lambeth MA70 Kelham Th Coll 39. **d** 45 **p** 46. Prec Westmr Abbey 63-74; P in O 67-74; Sub-Prelate OStJ from 73; Can Res Ches Cathl Ches 74-78; Vice-Dean Ches 75-78; Adn Macclesfield 78-85; R Gawsworth 78-85; Chapl to The Queen 82-90; rtd 86. *18 Roseberry Green, North Stainley, Ripon, N Yorkshire HG4 3HZ* Ripon (01765) 689286

SIMPSON, Richard Lee (Rick). b 66. Keble Coll Ox BA88 MPhil91 Westmr Coll Ox PGCE89. Wycliffe Hall Ox DipMin93. **d** 93 **p** 94. C Newc St Gabr *Newc* from 93. *33 Swindon Terrace, Newcastle upon Tyne NE6 5RB* 0191-224 1596

SIMPSON, Robert Charles. b 46. Ridley Hall Cam. **d** 85 **p** 86. C Eastwood *S'well* 85-88; V Yardley St Cypr Hay Mill *Birm* 88-93; P-in-c Newent and Gorsley w Cliffords Mesne *Glouc* from 93. *The Rectory, 43 Court Road, Newent, Glos GL18 1SD* Newent (01531) 820248

SIMPSON, Robert David. b 61. Fitzw Coll Cam BA83 MA87. Trin Coll Bris DipHE87. **d** 87 **p** 88. C Beckenham Ch Ch *Roch* 87-90; C Heydon w Gt and Lt Chishill *Chelmsf* 90; C Chrishall 90; C Elmdon w Wendon Lofts and Strethall 90; C Heydon, Gt and Lt Chishill, Chrishall etc 91-93; TV Shirwell, Loxhore, Kentisbury, Arlington, etc *Ex* from 93. *The Rectory, Shirwell, Barnstaple, Devon EX31 4JR* Barnstaple (01271) 850436

SIMPSON, Robert Theodore (Theo). b 34. Linc Coll Ox BA58 MA61 K Coll Lon PhD71 UNISA DTEd83 MEd85. Chich

Th Coll 58. **d** 60 **p** 61. C Ellesmere Port *Ches* 60-63; CR 63-66; S Africa 68-88; Prin St Pet Coll 72-75; Pres Federal Th Sem 73-75; Sen Lect Th Swaziland Univ 83-87; Assoc Prof Th 87-88; Chapl and Lect Coll of SS Mark and Jo Plymouth 88-90; Tutor Simon of Cyrene Th Inst 90-92; Perm to Offic *S'wark* 91-92; P-in-c Shadwell St Paul w Ratcliffe St Jas *Lon* from 92. *The Vicarage, 298 The Highway, London E1 9DH* 0171-488 4633

SIMPSON, Roger Westgarth. b 51. Lon Univ BSc72. St Jo Coll Nottm 77. **d** 79 **p** 80. C St Marylebone All So w SS Pet and Jo *Lon* 79-85; R Edin St Paul and St Geo *Edin* 85-95; Canada from 95. *1440 W 12th Avenue, Vancouver, Canada, V6H 1M8*

SIMPSON, Ven Samuel. b 26. TCD BA55 MA69 Div Test56. **d** 56 **p** 57. C Coleraine *Conn* 56-60; I Donagh w Cloncha and Clonmany *D & R* 60-64; I Ballyscullion 64-81; RD Maghera and Kilrea 75-89; Can Derry Cathl from 78; I Errigal w Garvagh from 81; Adn Derry from 89. *St Paul's Rectory, 58 Station Road, Garvagh, Co Londonderry BT51 5LA* Garvagh (012665) 58226

SIMPSON (nee RALPHS), Mrs Sharon Ann. b 55. St Mary's Coll Dur BA77. Cranmer Hall Dur 81. **dss** 83 **d** 87 **p** 94. Caverswall *Lich* 83-87; Par Dn 87-89; Asst Dioc Officer for Minl Tr *St As* 90-91; NSM Selkirk *Edin* 91-94; C Offchurch *Cov* from 94; Warden Offa Retreat Ho from 94. *The Vicarage, Offchurch, Leamington Spa, Warks CV33 9AL* Leamington Spa (01926) 424401 Fax 330350

SIMPSON, Thomas Eric. b 31. St Chad's Coll Dur BA55. Ely Th Coll 55. **d** 57 **p** 58. V Chopwell *Dur* 63-92; Chapl Norman Riding Hosp Tyne & Wear 79-83; Chapl Shotley Bridge Gen Hosp 83-90; rtd 92. *58 Tanmeads, Nettlesworth, Chester le Street, Co Durham DH2 3PY* 0191-371 9814

SIMPSON, William Michael. b 45. Leeds Univ BA66. St Jo Coll Nottm 75. **d** 77 **p** 78. C Desborough *Pet* 77-80; P-in-c Arthingworth w Kelmarsh and Harrington 79-80; Hong Kong 80-85 and from 92; P-in-c Beetham and Milnthorpe *Carl* 85-92. *Christ Church Vicarage, 2 Derby Road, Kowloon Tong, Kowloon, Hong Kong* Hong Kong (852) 338 4433 Fax 338 8422

SIMPSON, William Thomas. b 10. St Chad's Coll Dur BA35 DipTh36 MA38. **d** 36 **p** 37. R Week St Mary *Truro* 59-81; R Whitstone 62-81; rtd 81. *Waverley, Under Road, Gunnislake, Cornwall PL18 9JL* Tavistock (01822) 833396

SIMPSON, William Vaughan. b 16. Worc Ord Coll 55. **d** 57 **p** 58. R Willersey w Saintbury *Glouc* 60-73; RD Campden 70-73; P-in-c Cherington 74-76; V Clearwell 76-79; Perm to Offic 79-91; rtd 81. *62 Fruitlands, Malvern, Worcs WR14 4XA* Malvern (01684) 567009

SIMS, Bernard David. b 40. LRSC65 MIWEM68 Bris Coll DipTech Chem63 Bath Univ BSc66. Ox Min Course 91. **d** 94. NSM Beedon and Peasemore w W Ilsley and Farnborough *Ox* from 94. *Dove Cottage, 9 Prospect Place, Newbury, Berks RG14 7PZ* Newbury (01635) 46877

SIMS, Canon Christopher Sidney. b 49. Wycliffe Hall Ox 74. **d** 77 **p** 78. C Walmley *Birm* 77-80; V Yardley St Cypr Hay Mill 80-88; V Stanwix *Carl* from 88; RD Carl 89-95; Hon Can Carl Cathl from 91. *Stanwix Vicarage, Dykes Terrace, Carlisle CA3 9AS* Carlisle (01228) 514600 or 511430

SIMS, David John. b 18. Handsworth Coll Birm 44 St Aug Coll Cant 59. **d** 56 **p** 56. In Meth Ch 47-56; W Indies 47-63; V Haxey *Linc* 63-73; USA 73-83; rtd 83; Perm to Offic *Chich* from 87. *Bungalow 6, Terry's Cross, Brighton Road, Henfield, W Sussex BN5 9SX* Henfield (01273) 493487

SIMS, James Henry. b 35. St Jo Coll Nottm. **d** 89 **p** 91. NSM Ban Abbey *D & D* 89-93; C Holywood 93; Bp's C Kilbroney from 93. *The Vicarage, 15 Kilbroney Road, Rostrevor, Newry, Co Down BT34 3BH* Rostrevor (016937) 38293

SIMS, Peter George Russell. b 36. Univ of Wales (Swansea) BA57. St Mich Coll Llan 63. **d** 65 **p** 66. C Brecon w Battle *S & B* 65-72; Min Can Brecon Cathl 65-72; V Llanfrynach and Cantref w Llanhamlach from 72. *The Rectory, Llanfrynach, Brecon, Powys LD3 7AJ* Llanfrynach (0187486) 667

SIMS, Sidney. b 20. Wycliffe Hall Ox. **d** 64 **p** 65. V Ramsey St Mary's w Ponds Bridge *Ely* 67-70; V Cam St Matt 70-85; Algeria 85-86; rtd 86; Perm to Offic *Nor* from 86. *66 Morston Road, Blakeney, Norfolk NR25 7BE* Cley (01263) 740184

SINCLAIR, Andrew John McTaggart. b 58. Ex Univ BA80. Westcott Ho Cam 81. **d** 84 **p** 85. C Aston cum Aughton and Ulley *Sheff* 84-87; C Rotherham 87-88; TV Edin Old St Paul *Edin* 88-93; Hon Angl Chapl Edin Univ and Moray Ho Coll 89-93; TV Dunstable *St Alb* from 93. *The Priory Vicarage, 20 Friars Walk, Dunstable, Beds LU6 3JA* Dunstable (01582) 600972 or 696725

SINCLAIR, Arthur Alfred. b 46. **d** 87 **p** 89. Hon C St Andr Cathl Inverness *Mor* 87-92; C from 93; Chapl Asst Inverness Hosp 87-89; Dioc Chapl 87-89; NSM Culloden St Mary-in-the-Fields 89-92; P-in-c from 93; Edin Th Coll 92-93; P-in-c

Inverness St Jo *Mor* from 93; Chapl Raigmore Hosp Inverness from 93. *St John's Rectory, Southside Road, Inverness IV2 3BG* Inverness (01463) 716288

SINCLAIR, Charles Horace. b 19. Keble Coll Ox BA40 MA44. Linc Th Coll 41. **d** 42 **p** 43. Hd Master St Aid Sch Denby Dale 57-64; rtd 84. *Oakstead, 94 Harbour Way, Folkestone, Kent CT20 1NB* Folkestone (01303) 250882

SINCLAIR, Colin. b 30. **d** 84 **p** 85. NSM Ramoan w Ballycastle and Culfeightrin *Conn* 84-92. *4 Bushfoot Cottages, Portballintrae, Bushmills, Co Antrim BT57 8RN* Bushmills (012657) 31551

SINCLAIR, Gordon Keith. b 52. MA. Cranmer Hall Dur. **d** 84 **p** 85. C Summerfield *Birm* 84-88; V Aston SS Pet and Paul from 88. *Aston Vicarage, Sycamore Road, Birmingham B6 5UH* 0121-327 5856

SINCLAIR, Canon Jane Elizabeth Margaret. b 56. St Hugh's Coll Ox BA78 MA80 Nottm Univ BA82. St Jo Coll Nottm 80. **dss** 83 **d** 87 **p** 94. Herne Hill St Paul *S'wark* 83-86; Chapl and Lect St Jo Coll Nottm 86-93; Can Res Sheff Cathl *Sheff* from 93. *62 Kingfield Road, Sheffield S11 9AU* Sheffield (0114) 255 7782/275 3434

SINCLAIR, John Robert. b 58. Oak Hill Th Coll DipHE92. **d** 92 **p** 93. C Ponteland *Newc* from 92. *2 Grange Road, Ponteland, Newcastle upon Tyne NE20 9UL* Ponteland (01661) 821895

✠**SINCLAIR, Most Rev Maurice Walter.** b 37. Nottm Univ BSc59 Leic Univ PGCE60. Tyndale Hall Bris 62. **d** 64 **p** 65 **c** 90. C Boscombe St Jo *Win* 64-67; SAMS from 67; Personnel Sec 79-83; Asst Gen Sec 83-84; Prin Crowther Hall CMS Tr Coll Selly Oak 84-90; Perm to Offic *Birm* 84-90; Bp N Argentina from 90; Primate of S Cone from 95. *Iglesia Anglicana, Casilla 187, 4400 Salta, Argentina* Salta (87) 310167

SINCLAIR, Nigel Craig. b 65. Teesside Poly BA87. St Jo Coll Dur BA93. **d** 94 **p** 95. C Marton-in-Cleveland *York* from 94. *37 Lambourne Drive, Marton-in-Cleveland, Middlesbrough, Cleveland TS7 8QF* Middlesbrough (01642) 314504

SINCLAIR, Peter. b 44. Oak Hill Th Coll 86. **d** 88 **p** 89. C Darlington H Trin *Dur* 88-91; C-in-c Bishop Auckland Woodhouse Close CD from 91. *18 Watling Road, Bishop Auckland, Co Durham DL14 6RP* Bishop Auckland (01388) 604086

SINCLAIR, Robert Charles. b 28. Liv Univ LLB49 QUB LLM69 PhD82. Ely Th Coll 58. **d** 60 **p** 61. C Glenavy *Conn* 60-63; Chapl RN 63-67; C Cregagh *D & D* 67-68; Perm to Offic *Conn* from 69. *Juniper Cottage, 11A Glen Road, Glenavy, Crumlin, Co Antrim BT29 4LT* Crumlin (01849) 453126

SINCLAIR, Robert Michael. b 41. CQSW81. Edin Th Coll 63. **d** 66 **p** 67. C Dunfermline *St And* 66-68; C Edin Old St Paul *Edin* 68-72; P-in-c Edin St Dav 72-77; Hon Dioc Supernumerary from 77. *121/19 Comiston Drive, Edinburgh EH10 5QU* 0131-447 5068

SINDALL, Mrs Christine Ann. b 42. ALA69. E Anglian Minl Tr Course 84. **d** 87 **p** 94. NSM Sutton *Ely* 87-89; C Cam Ascension 89-94; TV from 94. *The Vicarage, 2 Stretten Avenue, Cambridge CB4 3EP* Cambridge (01223) 315320

SINFIELD, George Edward. b 16. E Midl Min Tr Course 73. **d** 76 **p** 77. NSM Radcliffe-on-Trent *S'well* 76-79; NSM St Oswald in Lee w Bingfield *Newc* 79-86; rtd 86; Perm to Offic *S'well* from 86; Perm to Offic *Linc* from 89. *62 Station Road, Collingham, Newark, Notts NG23 7RA* Newark (01636) 892766

SINGH, Balwant. b 32. BA60. Saharanpur Th Coll 50. **d** 53 **p** 58. India 53-67 and 71-73; Hon C Handsworth St Jas *Birm* 67-71; Hon C N Hinksey *Ox* 73-80; Lic to Offic 80-81; Hon C S Hinksey from 82. *9 Jersey Road, Oxford OX4 4RT* Oxford (01865) 717277

SINGH, Vivian Soorat. b 30. Trin Coll Cam BA MA53. Westcott Ho Cam 54. **d** 55 **p** 56. Asst Master Framlingham Coll Suffolk 59-72; Chapl 60-72; Chapl Wymondham Coll 72-75; Dep Hd Litcham High Sch 75-88; rtd 88. *Manor Cottage, Wendling Road, Longham, Dereham, Norfolk NR12 2RD* Wendling (01362) 687382

SINGLETON, Mrs Editha Mary. b 27. W Midl Minl Tr Course 85. **dss** 84 **d** 87 **p** 94. Lich St Chad *Lich* 84-90; Hon Par Dn 87-90; Hon Par Dn Beaulieu and Exbury and E Boldre *Win* 90-94; Hon C from 94. *The Peregrine, The Lane, Fawley, Southampton SO4 1EY* Southampton (01703) 894364

SINGLETON, Ernest George (Brother Paul). b 15. St Aug Coll Cant 38. **d** 41 **p** 42. Prior St Teilo's Priory Cardiff 61-68; rtd 80; Hon C Twickenham St Mary *Lon* 91-93; Perm to Offic from 93. *4 Eyot Lodge, Cross Deep, Twickenham TW1 4QH* 0181-892 5496

SINGLETON, James Richard. b 56. CEng85 RN Eng Coll Plymouth BSc79 RN Coll Greenwich DipNuc81. Ripon Coll Cuddesdon 90. **d** 92 **p** 93. C Bourne *Guildf* from 92. *Heavitree, 5 Dene Lane, Lower Bourne, Farnham, Surrey GU10 3PN* Farnham (01252) 725879

SINGLETON, Kenneth Miller (Ken). b 58. Oak Hill Th Coll DipHE91. **d** 91 **p** 92. C Grove *Ox* from 91. *21 Albermarle Drive, Grove, Wantage, Oxon OX12 0NB* Wantage (01235) 769722

SINNAMON, Canon William Desmond. b 43. TCD BA65. CITC 66. **d** 66 **p** 67. C Seapatrick *D & D* 66-70; C Arm St Mark *Arm* 70-74; VC Arm Cathl 73-74; I Ballinderry 75-80; I Dub St Patr Cathl Gp *D & G* 80-83; Preb Tipperkevin St Patr Cathl Dub 80-83; I Taney *D & G* from 83; RD Taney from 91; Can Ch Ch Cathl Dub from 91; Treas St Patr Cathl Dub from 91. *Taney Rectory, Stoney Road, Dundrum, Dublin 14, Irish Republic* Dublin (1) 298-4497 or 298-5491

SINNICKSON, Charles. b 21. Princeton Univ BA44. Cuddesdon Coll 60. **d** 63 **p** 64. C Chelsea St Luke *Lon* 67-72; Hon C S Kensington St Jude 72-81; NSM Upper Chelsea St Simon 81-86; NSM S Kensington St Aug 86-90; rtd 90; Perm to Offic *Lon* from 90. *4 Cranley Mansion, 160 Gloucester Road, London SW7 4QF* 0171-373 2767

SINTON, Bernard. b 43. Leic Univ BSc66. Sarum & Wells Th Coll 87. **d** 90 **p** 91. NSM Horsham *Chich* from 90. *Kinsale, 28 Kennedy Road, Horsham, W Sussex RH13 5DA* Horsham (01403) 262991

SINTON, Vera May. b 43. Somerville Coll Ox BA65 MA Bris Univ CertEd66. Trin Coll Bris DipHE81. **dss** 81 **d** 87 **p** 94. Broxbourne w Wormley *St Alb* 81-87; Hon Par Dn 87; Tutor All Nations Chr Coll 81-87; Chapl St Hilda's Coll Ox 87-90; Tutor Wycliffe Hall Ox from 87. *22 Norham Gardens, Oxford OX2 6QD* Oxford (01865) 274212 (work)

SIRMAN, Allan George. b 34. Lon Univ BA58. Oak Hill Th Coll 55. **d** 59 **p** 60. C Uphill *B & W* 59-61; C Morden *S'wark* 61-65; R Chadwell *Chelmsf* 65-75; V Wandsworth All SS *S'wark* from 75. *Wandsworth Vicarage, 11 Rusholme Road, London SW15 3JX* 0181-788 7400

SIRR, Very Rev John Maurice Glover. b 42. TCD BA63. CITC 65. **d** 65 **p** 66. C Belf St Mary *Conn* 65-68; C Finaghy 68-69; I Drumcliffe w Lissadell and Munninane *K, E & A* 69-87; RD S Elphin 75-87; Preb Elphin Cathl 81-87; Dean Limerick and Ardfert *L & K* from 87; I Limerick City from 87; Chapl Limerick Pris from 87. *The Deanery, 7 Kilbane, Castletroy, Co Limerick, Irish Republic* Limerick (61) 338697 Fax as telephone

SISSON, Trevor. b 54. St Jo Coll Dur 76. **d** 79 **p** 80. C Rainworth *S'well* 79-83; C Worksop Priory 83-85; R Bilborough w Strelley 85-94; P-in-c Keyworth from 94; P-in-c Stanton-on-the-Wolds from 94; RD Bingham S from 95. *The Rectory, Keyworth, Nottingham NG12 5ED* Nottingham (0115) 937 2017

SITCH, Keith Frank. b 40. Ex Univ BA63. S'wark Ord Course 72. **d** 75 **p** 76. NSM Romford St Edw *Chelmsf* 75-78; NSM Kidbrooke St Jas *S'wark* from 78. *92 Kidbrooke Park Road, London SE3 0DX* 0181-856 3843

SIVITER, Cecil Isaac Hill. b 11. Tyndale Hall Bris 36. **d** 41 **p** 42. V Pott Shrigley *Ches* 60-74; V Alsager Ch *Ch* 74-79; rtd 79; Perm to Offic *Ches* from 79. *193 South Parade, West Kirby, Wirral, Merseyside L48 3HX* 0151-625 6676

SIVITER, Hugh Basil. b 21. St Pet Hall Ox MA47. Wycliffe Hall Ox 46. **d** 48 **p** 49. V Knotty Ash St Jo *Liv* 66-84; rtd 85. *2 Heol Bodran, Abergele, Clwyd LL22 7UW* Abergele (01745) 824860

SIZER, Stephen Robert. b 53. Sussex Univ BA DipHE Ox Univ MTh94. Trin Coll Bris 80. **d** 83 **p** 84. C St Leonards St Leon *Chich* 83-86; C Guildf St Sav w Stoke-next-Guildf 86-89; R Stoke-next-Guildf from 89. *Stoke Rectory, 2 Joseph's Road, Guildford, Surrey GU1 1DW* Guildford (01483) 32397

SKEET, Edward Kenneth Walter (Ted). b 27. Southn Univ BEd70. Chich Th Coll 79. **d** 81 **p** 82. Hon C Denmead *Portsm* 81-85. *76 Whichers Gate Road, Rowland's Castle, Hants PO9 6BB* Rowland's Castle (01705) 412084

SKEET, Hedley Ernest Burt. b 24. Lon Univ DipRE. Sarum & Wells Th Coll. **d** 84 **p** 85. Hon C Frimley *Guildf* from 84. *42 Denton Way, Frimley, Camberley, Surrey GU16 5UQ* Camberley (01276) 27742

SKELDING, Donald Brian. b 23. Trin Coll Cam BA47 MA52. Cuddesdon Coll. **d** 50 **p** 51. V Southport St Paul *Liv* 65-72; R Norton Canes *Lich* 72-81; R Hinstock and Sambrook 81-84; rtd 84; P-in-c Whiteparish *Sarum* 91-92; C Alderbury Team 91-94; Perm to Offic from 94. *The New Vicarage, Common Road, Whiteparish, Salisbury SP5 5SU* Whiteparish (01794) 884315

SKELDING, Mrs Hazel Betty. b 25. LGSM66 CertEd45. Gilmore Course 80. **dss** 83 **d** 87 **p** 94. Hinstock and Sambrook *Lich* 83-84; Asst Children's Adv *Lich* 86-91; Hon Par Dn Alderbury Team *Sarum* 91-94; C from 94. *The New Vicarage, Common Road, Whiteparish, Salisbury SP5 5SU* Whiteparish (01794) 884315

SKELTON, Beresford. b 52. St Chad's Coll Dur BA74. Chich Th Coll 74. **d** 76 **p** 77. C Byker St Ant *Newc* 76-80; Chapl Asst Newc Gen Hosp 80-81; C Newc St Jo *Newc* 80-82; Chapl Asst

Freeman Hosp Newc 81-82; V Cresswell and Lynemouth *Newc* 82-88; P-in-c Millfield St Mary *Dur* 88-93; V from 93. *St Mary Magdalene's Vicarage, Sunderland SR4 6HJ* 0191-565 6318

SKELTON, Dennis Michael. b 33. K Coll Lon BSc55. NE Ord Course 76. **d** 79 **p** 80. NSM Pennywell St Thos and Grindon St Oswald CD *Dur* 79-84; V Heatherycleugh from 84; V St John in Weardale from 84; V Westgate from 84. *Heatherycleugh Vicarage, Cowshill, Bishop Auckland, Co Durham DL13 1DA* Bishop Auckland (01388) 537260

SKELTON, Frank Seymour. b 20. DFC and Bar 44 DSO and Bar 45. Trin Hall Cam BA48 MA52. Ridley Hall Cam 48. **d** 50 **p** 51. Dir Lambeth Endowed Charities 69-85; Lic to Offic *S'wark* 69-85; rtd 85. *Flat B, 36 Champion Hill, London SE5 8AP* 0171-737 2187

SKELTON, Canon Henry John Nugent. b 13. Linc Th Coll 37. **d** 40 **p** 41. V Holbeach *Linc* 56-73; Can and Preb Linc Cathl 70-73; rtd 78. *Upton Castle, Cosheston, Pembroke Dock, Dyfed SA72 4SE* Pembroke (01646) 682435

✠**SKELTON, Rt Rev Kenneth John Fraser.** b 18. CBE72. CCC Cam BA40 MA44. Wells Th Coll 40. **d** 41 **p** 42 c 62. C Normanton *Derby* 41-43; C Bakewell 43-45; C Bolsover 45-46; PV Wells Cathl *B & W* 46-50; Lect Wells Th Coll 46-50; V Howe Bridge *Man* 50-55; R Walton St Mary *Liv* 55-62; Bp Matabeleland 62-70; Asst Bp Dur 70-75; R Bishopwearmouth St Mich w St Hilda 70-75; RD Wearmouth 70-75; Bp Lich 75-84; rtd 84; Asst Bp Derby from 84; Asst Bp Sheff from 84. *65 Crescent Road, Sheffield S7 1HN* Sheffield (0114) 255 1260

SKELTON, Melvyn Nicholas. b 38. St Pet Coll Ox BA61 MA65 Selw Coll Cam BA63 MA68. Ridley Hall Cam 62. **d** 64 **p** 65. C St Marychurch *Ex* 64-66; C Bury St Edmunds St Mary *St E* 66-69; Hon C 69-78; Lic to Offic from 78. *Address temp unknown*

SKELTON, Pamela Dora. b 38. Hull Coll of Educn DipEd58. Edin Th Coll 80. **dss** 78 **d** 86 **p** 94. Edin St Barn *Edin* 78-86; D-in-c 86-90; Dioc Youth Chapl 83-90; Min Edin Ch Ch from 91. *112 St Alban's Road, Edinburgh EH9 2PG* 0131-667 1280

SKEMP, Canon Stephen Rowland. b 12. Wadh Coll Ox BA34 MA62. Cuddesdon Coll 34. **d** 35 **p** 36. Adn Aegean *Eur* 71-77; Chapl Athens St Paul 74-77; rtd 77; Perm to Offic *Ox* from 83. *Orchard Bank, Goose Green, Deddington, Oxford OX15 0SZ* Deddington (01869) 38487

SKEOCH, Canon David Windsor. b 37. Ch Ch Ox BA58 MA62. Westcott Ho Cam 73. **d** 74 **p** 75. NSM Pimlico St Mary Graham Terrace *Lon* 74-79; Bp's Dom Chapl *Truro* 79-81; Bp's Dom Chapl *Lon* 81-83; V Pimlico St Gabr from 83; Can The Murray from 92. *St Gabriel's Vicarage, 30 Warwick Square, London SW1V 2AD* 0171-834 7520 or 834 2136

SKEPPER, Robert. b 25. **d** 67 **p** 68. C Loughb All SS *Leic* 67-71; R Shelthorpe Gd Shep 71-80; V Loughb Gd Shep 80-82; rtd 90. *c/o Black Bull Caravan Park, Malton Road, Pickering, N Yorkshire YO18 8EA*

SKETCHLEY, Edward Sydney. b 20. Qu Coll Birm. **d** 49 **p** 50. V Walsgrave on Sowe *Cov* 65-73; V Hound *Win* 73-90; rtd 90. *55 Terminus Terrace, Southampton SO14 3FE* Southampton (01703) 233249

SKIDMORE, Mrs Sheila Ivy. b 36. **d** 87 **p** 94. Hon Par Dn Leic Resurr *Leic* 87-91; Par Dn Clarendon Park St Jo w Knighton St Mich 91-94; TV from 94. *St Michael and All Angels Vicarage, 12 Scott Street, Leicester LE2 6DW* Leicester (0116) 270 0964

SKIDMORE, Walton Sudbury. b 09. Leeds Univ BA32. Coll of Resurr Mirfield 28. **d** 34 **p** 35. C Long Eaton St Jo *Derby* 34-37; Chapl RN 37-64; Perm to Offic *Sarum* 64-71; Perm to Offic *Glouc* 73-75; Perm to Offic *Ex* 75-79. *7 Poplar Drive, South Wootton, King's Lynn, Norfolk PE30 3JS*

SKILLEN, John Clifford Tainish. b 50. NUU BA72 MA82 QUB DipEd73 TCD BTh89. CITC 86. **d** 89 **p** 90. C Ban Abbey *D & D* 89-92; I Kilwarlin Upper w Kilwarlin Lower from 92. *Kilwarlin Rectory, 9 St John's Road, Hillsborough, Co Down BT26 6ED* Hillsborough (01846) 683299

SKILLINGS, Martyn Paul. b 46. St Chad's Coll Dur BA68. Linc Th Coll 68. **d** 70 **p** 71. C Stanley *Liv* 70-72; C Warrington St Elphin 72-75; Ind Chapl 75-76; V Surfleet *Linc* 88-92; V Burton St Chad *Lich* from 92. *The Vicarage, 113 Hunter Street, Burton-on-Trent, Staffs DE14 2SS* Burton-on-Trent (01283) 64044

SKILTON, Christopher John (Chris). b 55. Magd Coll Cam BA76 MA80. Wycliffe Hall Ox 77. **d** 80 **p** 81. C Ealing St Mary *Lon* 80-84; C New Boro and Leigh *Sarum* 84-88; TV Gt Baddow *Chelmsf* 88-95; TR Sanderstead All SS *S'wark* from 95. *The Rectory, 1 Addington Road, South Croydon, Surrey CR2 8RE* 0181-657 1366

SKILTON, Joseph Laurence. b 41. Univ of Wales TCert64 Univ of Wales (Cardiff) DipTh70 Murdoch Univ Aus BA89. St Mich Coll Llan. **d** 70 **p** 71. C Bicester *Ox* 71-73; C Shrewsbury

St Chad *Lich* 73-76; V W Bromwich St Phil 76-80; Australia from 80. *52 Pangbourne Street, Wembley, W Australia 6014* Perth (9) 387-2287 or 387-2487

✠**SKINNER, Rt Rev Brian Antony.** b 39. Reading Univ BSc60. Tyndale Hall Bris 66. **d** 67 **p** 68 **c** 77. C Woking St Pet *Guildf* 67-70; Chile 70-86; Adn Valparaiso 76-77; Suff Bp Valparaiso 77-86; C Chorleywood St Andr *St Alb* from 87. *Dell View, Quickley Lane, Chorleywood, Rickmansworth, Herts WD3 5AF* Chorleywood (01923) 282238

SKINNER, Graeme John. b 57. Southn Univ BSc79. Trin Coll Bris BA. **d** 86 **p** 87. C Bebington *Ches* 86-90; V Ashton on Mersey St Mary from 90. *St Mary's Vicarage, 20 Beeston Road, Sale, Cheshire M33 5AG* 0161-973 5118

SKINNER, Mrs Jane Mary. b 59. Leeds Univ BA81. Cranmer Hall Dur 82. **dss** 84 **d** 87 **p** 94. Chatham St Phil and St Jas *Roch* 84-87; Hon Par Dn 87; Hon Par Dn Torver *Carl* 87-91; Hon Par Dn Church Coniston 87-91; NSM Dalton-in-Furness from 91; Chapl HM Pris Haverigg from 92. *The Vicarage, Market Place, Dalton-in-Furness, Cumbria LR15 8RZ* Dalton-in-Furness (01229) 462526

SKINNER, Preb John Cedric. b 30. Bris Univ BA55 Lon Univ DipTh57. Tyndale Hall Bris 55. **d** 57 **p** 58. C St Leonard *Ex* 57-62; Univ Sec IVF 62-68; V Guildf St Sav *Guildf* 68-76; R Stoke next Guildf St Jav 74-76; R Guildf St Sav w Stoke-next-Guildf 76-84; R Ex St Leon w H Trin *Ex* from 84; Preb Ex Cathl from 92. *St Leonard's Rectory, 27 St Leonard's Road, Exeter EX2 4LA* Exeter (01392) 55681

SKINNER, John Richard. b 45. N Ord Course 84. **d** 87 **p** 88. C Allerton *Liv* 87-90; C Huyton St Mich from 90. *1 The Cross, Stanley Road, Liverpool L36 9XL* 0151-449 3800

SKINNER, John Timothy. b 55. Linc Th Coll 79. **d** 81 **p** 82. C Newton Aycliffe *Dur* 81-82; Perm to Offic *Newc* from 95. *Northumbrian Community, Nether Springs, Hetton Hall, Chatton, Alnwick, Northd NE66 5SD*

SKINNER, Leonard Harold. b 36. K Coll Lon BD62 AKC62. **d** 63 **p** 64. C Hackney Wick St Mary of Eton w St Aug *Lon* 63-66; C Palmers Green St Jo 66-70; V Grange Park St Pet 70-80; TV Hanley H Ev *Lich* 80-86; Chapl Sunderland Poly *Dur* 86-92; Chapl Sunderland Univ 92-93; P-in-c Hebburn St Oswald from 93. *St Oswald's Vicarage, St Oswald's Road, Hebburn, Tyne & Wear NE31 1HR* 0191-483 2082

SKINNER, Maurice Wainwright. b 30. FRSC70 St Jo Coll Ox BA53 MA59. Ox NSM Course. **d** 86 **p** 87. NSM Furze Platt *Ox* from 86; NSM Hurley and Stubbings from 94. *5 Clarefield Close, Maidenhead, Berks SL6 5DR* Maidenhead (01628) 24875

SKINNER, Michael Thomas. b 39. Open Univ BA88 MA90. S'wark Ord Course 73. **d** 78 **p** 79. NSM Orpington St Andr *Roch* 78-82; NSM Orpington All SS from 82; Asst Bps Officer for Hon Clergy from 91. *80 Spur Road, Orpington, Kent BR6 0QN* Orpington (01689) 825322

SKINNER, Raymond Frederick (Ray). b 45. St Jo Coll Dur BA67 Dur Univ MA93. Cranmer Hall Dur. **d** 70 **p** 71. C High Elswick St Paul *Newc* 70-76; V Newbottle *Dur* 76-87; Ind Chapl 81-87; RD Houghton 84-87; Oman 87-90; TR Morden *S'wark* from 90; Asst RD Merton from 91. *The Rectory, London Road, Morden, Surrey SM4 5QT* 0181-648 3920 or 658 0012

SKINNER, Stephen John. b 52. AIA Bris Univ BSc St Jo Coll Dur BA Dur Univ MLitt. Cranmer Hall Dur. **d** 83 **p** 84. C Chatham St Phil and St Jas *Roch* 83-87; P-in-c Torver *Carl* 87-90; P-in-c Church Coniston 87-90; V 90-91; R Torver 90-91; V Dalton-in-Furness from 91. *The Vicarage, Market Place, Dalton-in-Furness, Cumbria LR15 8RZ* Dalton-in-Furness (01229) 462526

SKIPPER, Joseph Allen. b 17. Selly Oak Coll 45 Lich Th Coll 58. **d** 59 **p** 60. R Bishopstrow and Boreham *Sarum* 64-72; R Fleet *Linc* 72-74; V Sutterton 74-78; P-in-c Wigtoft 77-78; V Sutterton and Wigtoft 78-83; rtd 83; P-in-c Tidworth *Sarum* 83-86; C Tidworth, Ludgershall and Faberstown 86-88. *68 Wellington Court, Weymouth, Dorset DT4 8UE* Weymouth (01305) 777449

SKIPPER, Mrs Joyce Evelyn. b 27. Cam Univ CertEd71. Gilmore Ho 73. **dss** 75 **d** 87 **p** 94. Cranham *Chelmsf* 75-87; Hon Par Dn 87-90; NSM Upminster 90-94; NSM N Ockendon from 94. *53 Tawny Avenue, Upminster, Essex RM14 2EP* Upminster (01708) 225703

SKIPPER, Kenneth Graham. b 34. St Aid Birkenhead 65. **d** 68 **p** 69. C Newland St Aug *York* 68-71; C Newby 71-74; V Dormanstown 74-78; C-in-c Mappleton w Goxhill 78; C-in-c Withernwick 78; V Aldbrough w Cowden Parva 78; V Aldbrough, Mappleton w Goxhill and Withernwick 79-89; R Londesborough from 89; R Burnby from 90; R Nunburnholme and Warter from 90; V Shiptonthorpe w Hayton from 90. *The Rectory, 3 Fairview, Town Street, Shiptonthorpe, York YO4 3PE* Market Weighton (01430) 872513

SKIPPER, Canon Lawrence Rainald. b 17. St Pet Hall Ox BA39 MA43. Wycliffe Hall Ox 39. **d** 41 **p** 41. RD Ches 69-78; R Eccleston and Pulford 72-82; Hon Can Ches Cathl 74-82; rtd 82; Perm to Offic *Ches* from 82. *Stud Farmhouse, Churton, Chester CH3 6LL* Farndon (01829) 270296

SKIPPON, Kevin John. b 54. St Steph Ho Ox 78. **d** 81 **p** 82. C Gt Yarmouth *Nor* 81-84; C Kingstanding St Luke *Birm* 84-86; V Smethwick SS Steph and Mich 86-92; Chapl Derbyshire R Infirmary from 92. *The Royal Infirmary, London Road, Derby DE1 2QY* Derby (01332) 347141

SKIPWITH, Osmund Humberston. b 06. New Coll Ox BA28 MA33. Cuddesdon Coll 29. **d** 30 **p** 31. C Worle *B & W* 71-74; rtd 74. *16 Kingswood Court, Southcote Road, Reading RG3 2AU* Reading (01734) 571246

SKLIROS, Michael Peter. b 33. Clare Coll Cam BA57 MA62. Ridley Hall Cam 57. **d** 59 **p** 60. C Hornchurch St Andr *Chelmsf* 59-61; Asst Chapl Denstone Coll Uttoxeter 61-65; Chapl RAF 65-77; P-in-c Stowmarket *St E* 77-78; Lic to Offic 78-85; C Gt Finborough w Onehouse and Harleston 85-91; P-in-c 91; R Gt and Lt Bealings w Playford and Culpho from 91. *The Rectory, Hill Farm Road, Playford, Ipswich IP16 9DT* Ipswich (01473) 623884

SKUCE, David. b 56. NUU BSc79 QUB PGCE80 TCD BTh89. CITC 87. **d** 89 **p** 90. C Templemore *D & R* 89-92; I Kilbarron w Rossnowlagh and Drumholm from 92; Bp's Dom Chapl from 94. *The Rectory, Ballintra, Co Donegal, Irish Republic* Ballintra (73) 34025

SLACK, Canon Ellis Edward. b 23. Birm Univ BA51 MA53. Qu Coll Birm 51. **d** 53 **p** 53. V N Dulwich St Faith *S'wark* 64-72; V Bethnal Green St Jo w St Simon *Lon* 72-78; V Bethnal Green St Jo w St Bart 78-79; Can Res Portsm Cathl *Portsm* 79-83; V Woodplumpton *Blackb* 83-88; Dir of Post-Ord Tr 83-88; rtd 88; Perm to Offic *York* from 88. *6 Parkfield, Stillington, York YO6 1JW* Easingwold (01347) 810104

SLACK, Michael. b 53. RGN83 St Jo Coll Dur BA74 Lon Univ PGCE79 Newc Poly DPSN86. St Steph Ho Ox 74. **d** 76 **p** 77. C Wolv St Steph *Lich* 76-77; NSM Bywell St Pet *Newc* 89-93; TV Cullercoats St Geo from 93. *St Aidan's Vicarage, 29 Billy Mill Lane, North Shields, Tyne & Wear NE29 8BZ* 0191-257 3616

SLADDEN, Duncan Julius Edward. b 25. K Coll Cam BA50 MA51. Cuddesdon Coll 51. **d** 53 **p** 54. P-in-c Stevenage *St Alb* 65-70; R Johnstone *Glas* 70-76; Prayer Gp Adv Scottish Chs Renewal 76-81; Sec Scottish Episc Renewal Fellowship 81-84; R E Kilbride 85-90; rtd 90. *17 Bruce Avenue, Dunblane, Perthshire FK15 9JB* Dunblane (01786) 825520

SLADDEN, John David. b 49. RN Eng Coll Plymouth BSc74 St Edm Coll Cam MA86. Ridley Hall Cam. **d** 83 **p** 84. C St Bees *Carl* 83-85; Perm to Offic *Lich* 85-87; Miss Co-ord Down to Earth Evangelistic Trust 85-87; V Doncaster St Jas *Sheff* 87-94. *30 Curlew Avenue, Chatteris, Cambs PE16 6PL* Chatteris (01354) 694097

SLADDEN, Canon John Cyril. b 20. Mert Coll Ox BA42 MA46 BD66. Wycliffe Hall Ox 46. **d** 48 **p** 49. V Nether Peover *Ches* 59-86; RD Knutsford 80-85; Hon Can Ches Cathl 80-86; rtd 86. *Rossa, Penmon, Beaumaris, Gwynedd LL58 8SN* Llangoed (01248) 490207

SLADE, Canon Adrian Barrie. b 47. K Alfred's Coll Win DipEd68. St Jo Coll Nottm BTh73 ALCD72. **d** 73 **p** 74. C Streatham Immanuel w St Anselm *S'wark* 73-76; C Chipping Barnet *St Alb* 76-78; C Chipping Barnet w Arkley 78-80; V Sundon 80-85; Soc Resp Officer *Glouc* from 86; Hon Can Glouc Cathl from 91. *38 Sydenham Villas Road, Cheltenham, Glos GL52 6DZ* Cheltenham (01242) 242672

SLADE, Alfred Laurence. b 12. ACII. Roch Th Coll 67. **d** 69 **p** 70. Hon C Cliftonville *Cant* 69-71; Hon C Westgate St Jas 71-75; Perm to Offic *Sarum* 75-81; Perm to Offic *Cant* 81-93. *21 McKinlay Court, The Parade, Minnis Bay, Birchington, Kent CT7 9QG* Thanet (01843) 46882

SLADE, Harold Godfrey Rex. b 87 **d** 88. NSM Patrick *S & M* from 87; NSM German St Jo from 87; NSM Foxdale from 87. *2 Hamilton Close, Lower Foxdale, Douglas, Isle of Man* St Johns (0162471) 431

SLADE, Herbert Edwin William. b 12. Lon Univ BA33. Dorchester Miss Coll 34. **d** 35 **p** 36. C Tuffley *Glouc* 35-39; SSJE from 39; Lic to Offic *Chich* 71-82; rtd 82. *The Anchorhold, 35 Paddockhall Road, Haywards Heath, W Sussex RH16 1HN* Haywards Heath (01444) 452468

SLADE, Canon William Clifford. b 24. St Jo Coll Dur BA47 DipTh49 MA53. **d** 49 **p** 50. R Stokesley *York* 67-71; V Felixkirk w Boltby 71-82; V Kirby Knowle 71-82; Can and Preb York Minster 79-86; C Topcliffe w Dalton and Dishforth 82-86; Abp's Adv for Spiritual Direction 82-86; rtd 86. *Bede House, Back Lane, South Kilvington, Thirsk, N Yorkshire YO7 3RU* Thirsk (01845) 522915

SLADEN, Philip. b 50. Fitzw Coll Cam BA71 MA75 DipTh. Ripon Hall Ox 72. **d** 75 **p** 76. C Bushey Heath *St Alb* 75-78;

Chapl RAF from 78. *Chaplaincy Services (RAF), HQ, Personnel and Training Command, RAF Innsworth, Gloucester GL3 1EZ* Gloucester (01452) 712612 Ext 5164 Fax 510828

SLADER, William Basil. b 16. Sarum Th Coll 55. **d** 57 **p** 58. R Copythorne and Minstead *Win* 60-70; V St Mary Bourne and Woodcott 70-81; rtd 81; Perm to Offic *Win* 81-88; Perm to Offic *Ely* from 81. *103 Lisle Close, Ely, Cambs CB7 4AD* Ely (01353) 666410

SLATER, Mrs Ann. b 46. Somerville Coll Ox BA67 MA71. W Midl Minl Tr Course 92. **d** 95. C Northn St Benedict *Pet* from 95. *44 Barn Owl Close, Northampton NN4 0AU* Northampton (01604) 761878

SLATER, Edward Ian. b 31. E Midl Min Tr Course 81. **d** 84 **p** 85. NSM Cherry Willingham w Greetwell *Linc* 84-86; C Cleethorpes 86-88; TV 88-92; P-in-c Bassingham from 92; P-in-c Aubourn w Haddington from 92; P-in-c Thurlby w Norton Disney from 92; P-in-c Carlton-le-Moorland w Stapleford from 92. *The Rectory, Torgate Lane, Bassingham, Lincoln LN5 9HF* Bassingham (01522) 788383

SLATER, Gilbert Leonard. b 09. Selw Coll Cam BA31 MA35. Wells Th Coll 31. **d** 32 **p** 34. V Gt and Lt Dalby *Leic* 60-87; rtd 88. *99 Main Street, Asfordby, Melton Mowbray, Leics LE14 3RZ* Melton Mowbray (01664) 813456

SLATER, James Richard David. b 61. BA83 TCD BTh89. CITC 86. **d** 89 **p** 90. C Clooney w Strathfoyle *D & R* 89-93; I Aghadowey w Kilrea from 93. *Kilrea Rectory, 2 Moneygran Road, Kilrea, Co Londonderry BT51 5SJ* Kilrea (012665) 40257

SLATER, John. b 45. K Coll Lon BA67 AKC67 Fitzw Coll Cam BA69 MA73. Westcott Ho Cam 67 Union Th Sem (NY) STM70. **d** 70 **p** 71. C St Marylebone All SS *Lon* 70-77; V Paddington St Sav 77-83; Dir Post-Ord Tr from 82; V St Jo Wood from 83; AD Westmr St Marylebone from 92. *St John's House, St John's Wood High Street, London NW8 7NE* 0171-722 4378

SLATER, John Albert. b 25. Lon Univ BA52. Oak Hill Th Coll 47. **d** 52 **p** 53. V Bacup St Sav *Man* 61-70; V Blackpool St Thos *Blackb* 70-84; rtd 84; Lic to Offic *Blackb* from 84. *18 Church Road, Thornton Cleveleys, Lancs FY5 2TZ* Cleveleys (01253) 853330

SLATER, John Allen. b 20. St Aid Birkenhead 60. **d** 62 **p** 63. V Welton w Melton *York* 65-82; P-in-c Burstwick w Thorngumbald 82-84; rtd 85. *103 Burden Road, Beverley, N Humberside HU17 9LN* Hull (01482) 867416

SLATER, John Ralph. b 38. Kent Univ BA90. Linc Th Coll 71. **d** 73 **p** 74. C S Hackney St Mich w Haggerston St Paul *Lon* 73-74; C Leytonstone St Marg w St Columba *Chelmsf* 74-77; C Whitstable All SS w St Pet *Cant* 77-80; V Gt Ilford St Alb *Chelmsf* 80-83; V Clipstone *S'well* 83-87; rtd 87. *8 Edgar Close, Whitstable, Kent CT5 2SA* Whitstable (01227) 792154

SLATER, Mark Andrew. b 56. ARCS79 Imp Coll Lon BSc79. Ridley Hall Cam 87. **d** 89 **p** 90. C Northn St Giles *Pet* 89-92; C Stopsley *St Alb* 92-93; C-in-c Bushmead CD from 93. *73 Hawkfields, Bushmead, Luton LU2 7NW* Luton (01582) 487327

SLATER, Paul John. b 58. CCC Ox MA83 Dur Univ BA83. Cranmer Hall Dur 81. **d** 84 **p** 85. C Keighley St Andr *Bradf* 84-88; Dir Dioc Foundn Course 88-93; P-in-c Cullingworth 88-93; Bp's Personal Exec Asst from 93. *48 Toller Grove, Heaton, Bradford, W Yorkshire BD9 5NP* Bradford (01274) 482059 or 545414 Fax 544831

SLATER, Canon Philip David. b 27. K Coll Lon 58. **d** 60 **p** 61. C Havant *Portsm* 60-67; C Leigh Park 68-69; Hants Co RE Adv 69-74; Gosport and Fareham RE Adv 74-82; Hon C Bishops Waltham 76-82; V Bulford, Figheldean and Milston *Sarum* 82-93; RD Avon 85-95; Can and Preb Sarum Cathl from 91; V Avon Valley 93-95; V of Close Sarum Cathl from 95. *102 Coombe Road, Salisbury SP2 8BD* Salisbury (01722) 332529

SLATER, Robert Adrian. b 48. St Jo Coll Nottm 76. **d** 79 **p** 80. C Bedworth *Cov* 79-82; TV Billericay and Lt Burstead *Chelmsf* 82-88; V Rounds Green *Birm* 88-94. *11 Lewis Road, Birmingham B30 2SU* 0121-443 3646

SLATER, Ronald Spencer. b 13. Man Univ BA36. Lich Th Coll 36. **d** 38 **p** 39. V Mabe *Truro* 71-76; rtd 76. *1 Col-Moor Close, Hayle, Cornwall TR27 4PT* Hayle (01736) 754057

SLATER, Thomas Ernest (Tom). b 37. Chelsea Coll Lon TCert60 Lon Univ BD71 NE Lon Poly DipG&C88. ALCD66. **d** 67 **p** 68. C Bootle Ch Ch *Liv* 67-72; C Stapleford *S'well* 72-75; Supt Tower Hamlets Miss 75-77; Hon C Stepney St Pet w St Benet *Lon* 78-79; Asst Chapl The Lon Hosp (Whitechapel) 79-83; Chapl 83-89; NSM Poplar *Lon* 89-92; Perm to Offic from 92. *11 Elgin House, Cordelia Street, London E14 6EG* 0171-987 4504

SLATER, Victoria Ruth. b 59. Hertf Coll Ox BA82 MA87 Selw Coll Cam BA89. Westcott Ho Cam 86. **d** 89 **p** 94. Chapl Asst Man R Infirmary 89-94; Chapl Chu Hosp Ox from 94; Chapl St Michael Sobell Ho Hospice from 94. *Churchill Hospital,*

Old Road, Headington, Oxford OX3 7LJ Oxford (01865) 741841 or 226090

SLATER, William Edward. b 51. Bolton Inst of Tech HNC77. Aston Tr Scheme 85 Oak Hill Th Coll 87. **d** 89 **p** 90. C Balderstone *Man* 89-94; V Newchapel *Lich* from 94. *The Vicarage, 32 Pennyfield Road, Newchapel, Stoke-on-Trent ST7 4PN* Stoke-on-Trent (01782) 782837

SLATOR, Edward Douglas Humphreys. b 18. TCD BA41 MA47 Hull Univ BPhil75. **d** 43 **p** 44. I Killea *C & O* 60-73; C Taney *D & G* 74-80; P-in-c Rathmolyon w Castlerickard, Rathcore and Agher *M & K* 80-87; rtd 87. *31 St John's, Park Avenue, Dublin 4, Irish Republic* Dublin (1) 283-9395

SLATOR, Canon William Thompson Howard. b 09. TCD BA31 MA34. **d** 33 **p** 34. Preb Elphin Cathl *K, E & A* 66-81; I Kiltoghart 66-81; RD Fenagh 67-81; rtd 81. *Bayside, 5 Haddington Terrace, Dun Laoghaire, Dublin, Irish Republic*

SLATTERY, Maurice Michael. b 43. Southlands Coll Lon TCert73 BEd74. S'wark Ord Course 91. **d** 94. NSM Malden St Jas *S'wark* from 94. *7 Windsor Avenue, New Malden, Surrey KT3 5EY* 0181-942 1259

SLAUGHTER, Clive Patrick. b 36. St Paul's Grahamstown DipTh78. **d** 77 **p** 78. S Africa 77-87; R Thorley w Bishop's Stortford H Trin *St Alb* 87-90; R Thorley from 90. *The Rectory, Viceron's Place, Thorley, Bishop's Stortford, Herts CM23 4EL* Bishop's Stortford (01279) 654955

SLAUGHTER, Canon Maurice Basil. b 20. Leeds Univ BA42. Coll of Resurr Mirfield 42. **d** 44 **p** 45. V Skipton Ch Ch *Bradf* 63-78; Hon Can Bradf Cathl 67-85; RD Skipton 73-82; P-in-c Bolton Abbey 78-85; P-in-c Rylstone 78-85; P-in-c Arncliffe w Halton Gill 79-82; rtd 85; Perm to Offic *Bradf* from 85; Perm to Offic *Wakef* from 85. *Hewitt Gate, Threshfield, Skipton, N Yorkshire BD23 5HB* Grassington (01756) 752158

SLEDGE, Ven Richard Kitson. b 30. Peterho Cam BA52 MA57. Ridley Hall Cam 52. **d** 54 **p** 55. C Compton Gifford *Ex* 54-57; C Ex St Martin, St Steph, St Laur etc 57-63; V Dronfield *Derby* 63-76; TR 76-78; RD Chesterfield 72-78; Adn Huntingdon *Ely* from 78; R Hemingford Abbots 78-89; Hon Can Ely Cathl from 78. *The Rectory, Hemingford Abbots, Huntingdon, Cambs PE18 9AN* St Ives (01480) 469856

SLEDGE, Timothy Charles Kitson. b 64. Coll of Ripon & York St Jo BA87 York Univ MA88. Trin Coll Bris DipHE95 ADUT95. **d** 95. C Huddersfield St Thos *Wakef* from 95. *8 Longroyd Place, Huddersfield HD1 4RP* Huddersfield (01484) 430681

SLEE, Very Rev Colin Bruce. b 45. K Coll Lon BD69 AKC69. St Aug Coll Cant 69. **d** 70 **p** 71. C Nor Heartsease St Fran *Nor* 70-73; C Cam Gt St Mary w St Mich *Ely* 73-76; Chapl Girton Coll Cam 73-76; Tutor and Chapl K Coll Lon 76-82; Sub-Dean from 82; Can Res St Alb 82-94; Provost S'wark from 94. *The Provost's Lodging, 51 Bankside, London SE1 9JE* 0171-928 6414

SLEE, John Graham. b 51. Brunel Univ BTech73. Oak Hill Th Coll 85. **d** 87 **p** 88. C St Columb Minor and St Colan *Truro* 87-91; R St Mawgan w St Ervan and St Eval from 91; RD Pydar from 93. *The Rectory, St Mawgan, Newquay, Cornwall TR8 4EZ* St Mawgan (01637) 860358

SLEGG, John Edward. b 36. St Pet Coll Ox BA62 MA66. Ridley Hall Cam 62. **d** 64 **p** 65. C Perranzabuloe *Truro* 64-66; CF 66-86; P-in-c Poling *Chich* 86-89; V from 89; P-in-c Lyminster 86-89; V from 89. *The Vicarage, 3 Middle Paddock, Lyminster, Littlehampton, W Sussex BN17 7QH* Arundel (01903) 882152

SLEIGHT, Gordon Frederick. b 47. AKC69. St Aug Coll Cant 69. **d** 70 **p** 71. C Boston *Linc* 70-74; P-in-c Louth St Mich 74-75; P-in-c Stewton 75; TV Louth 75-81; V Crosby 81-95; P-in-c Nettleham from 95. *The Vicarage, 2 Vicarage Lane, Nettleham, Lincoln LN2 2RH* Lincoln (01522) 754732

SLIM, David Albert. b 49. Westhill Coll Birm CertEd72. Linc Th Coll CMinlStuds90. **d** 90 **p** 91. C Walmley *Birm* 90-93; P Marchwiel and Isycoed *St As* from 93. *Marchwiel Rectory, Overton Road, Marchwiel, Wrexham, Clwyd LL13 0TE* Bangor-on-Dee (01978) 780640

SLIPPER, Dr Charles Callan. b 55. Lanc Univ BA77 PhD84. S Dios Minl Tr Scheme 91. **d** 93 **p** 94. NSM N Acton St Gabr *Lon* from 93. *57 Twyford Avenue, London W3 9PZ* 0181-992 7666 Fax 993 6944

SLIPPER, Robert James. b 64. St Jo Coll Cam BA87 MA91. Wycliffe Hall Ox BA92. **d** 92 **p** 93. C Southgate *Chich* from 92. *20 Chandler Close, Crawley, W Sussex RH10 6DF* Crawley (01293) 551217

SLOANE, Isaac Reuben. b 16. TCD BA41 MA60. **d** 42 **p** 43. I Ardstraw w Baronscourt, Badoney Lower etc *D & R* 54-76; I Drumclamph w Lower and Upper Langfield 76-78; rtd 78. *40 Rawdon Place, Moira, Craigavon, Co Armagh BT67 0NX* Moira (01846) 611547

SLOGGETT, Donald George. b 49. Trin Coll Bris 81. **d** 83 **p** 84. C Horfield H Trin *Bris* 83-86; C Highworth w Sevenhampton and Inglesham etc 86-88; P-in-c Upavon w Rushall *Sarum* 88-90; R Uphavon w Rushall and Charlton from 90. *The*

Vicarage, 5A Vicarage Lane, Upavon, Pewsey, Wilts SN9 6AA Stonehenge (01980) 630248

SLOUGH, Colin Richard. b 40. AKC66. Ripon Hall Ox. **d** 68 **p** 69. P-in-c Portsea St Geo *Portsm* 70-72; Hon Chapl Portsm Cathl 70-72; RE Adv *Ox* 72-75; Lect Cudham Coll 72-75; Dep Hd Master St Luke's Sch Southsea 75-80; P-in-c Sandown Ch Ch *Portsm* 80; V 80-87; P-in-c Lower Sandown St Jo 80; V 80-87; Chapl Birm Poly *Birm* 87-91; Perm to Offic 91-92; rtd 91. *2 South Hill, Godalming, Surrey GU7 1JT* Godalming (01483) 416539

SLOW, Leslie John. b 47. Liv Univ BSc68 MSc69. N Ord Course 77. **d** 80 **p** 81. NSM Gt Horton *Bradf* from 80. *25 Grasleigh Way, Bradford, W Yorkshire BD15 9BE* Bradford (01274) 491808

SLUMAN, Richard Geoffrey Davies. b 34. St Jo Coll Ox BA68 MA68. Sarum Th Coll 68. **d** 70 **p** 71. C Gt Yarmouth *Nor* 70-73; V Churchdown *Glouc* 73-82; P-in-c Blockley w Aston Magna 82-83; V Blockley w Aston Magna and Bourton on the Hill 83-94; rtd 94. *21 Manor Farm Road, Tredington, Shipston-on-Stour, Warks CV36 4NZ* Shipston-on-Stour (01608) 662317

SLY, Canon Christopher John. b 34. Selw Coll Cam BA58 MA62. Wycliffe Hall Ox. **d** 60 **p** 61. C Buckhurst Hill *Chelmsf* 60-64; V Berechurch 64-75; V Southend St Sav Westcliff 75-87; R Wickham Bishops w Lt Braxted from 87; RD Witham from 87; Hon Can Chelmsf Cathl from 93. *The Rectory, 1 Church Road, Wickham Bishops, Witham, Essex CM8 3LA* Maldon (01621) 891360

SLY, Canon Harold Kenneth. b 15. Kelham Th Coll 34. **d** 38 **p** 39. V Hampton in Arden *Birm* 57-83; rtd 83; Perm to Offic *Worc* 83-91; Chapl Convent of the H Name Malvern 83-90; Perm to Offic *Birm* from 95. *28 Holifast Road, Sutton Coldfield, W Midlands B72 1AP* 0121-384 6570

SLYFIELD, John David. b 32. TD67. Roch Th Coll 66. **d** 68 **p** 69. C St Mary in the Marsh *Cant* 68-71; P-in-c Steeple Claydon *Ox* 71-76; P-in-c Middle w E Claydon 71-76; RD Claydon 73-78; R The Claydons 76-78; V S Westoe *Dur* 78-82; V Tideswell *Derby* 82-92; RD Buxton 84-91; rtd 92. *Stile Close, Taddington, Buxton, Derbyshire SK17 9TP* Buxton (01298) 85507

SMAIL, Richard Charles. b 57. CCC Ox BA80 MA83. Ox Min Course 90. **d** 93 **p** 95. NSM Keble Coll Ox from 93. *Keble College, Oxford OX1 3PG* Oxford (01865) 272727

SMAIL, Canon Thomas Allan. b 28. Glas Univ MA49 Edin Univ BD52. **d** 79 **p** 79. Hon C E Twickenham St Steph *Lon* 79; Vice-Prin St Jo Coll Nottm 80-85; TR Sanderstead All SS *S'wark* 85-94; Hon Can S'wark Cathl 91-94; rtd 94. *36B Alexandra Road, Croydon CR0 6EU* 0181-656 9683

SMAILES, Robert Anthony. b 44. Linc Th Coll 79 DipMin88. **d** 81 **p** 82. C Stokesley *York* 81-83; V Lythe 83-85; P-in-c Ugthorpe 83-85; V Lythe w Ugthorpe 85-88; V Saltburn-by-the-Sea 88-92; V Ormesby from 92. *The Vicarage, 54 Church Lane, Ormesby, Middlesbrough, Cleveland TS7 9AU* Middlesbrough (01642) 314445

SMALE, Frederick Ronald (Fred). b 37. K Coll Lon BD60 AKC60. **d** 61 **p** 62. C Bearsted *Cant* 61-64; C Fishponds St Mary *Bris* 64-69; V Hartlip *Cant* 69-71; P-in-c Stockbury w Bicknor and Huckinge 69-71; V Hartlip w Stockbury 71-75; R River 75-85; V Birchington w Acol and Minnis Bay from 85. *All Saints' Vicarage, 15 Minnis Road, Birchington, Kent CT7 9SE* Thanet (01843) 41117

SMALL, David Binney. b 39. Brasted Th Coll 61 Westcott Ho Cam 63. **d** 65 **p** 66. C Milton *Portsm* 65-69; CF 69-92; R Wickwar w Rangeworthy *Glouc* from 92; RD Hawkesbury from 94. *The Rectory, High Street, Wickwar, Wotton-under-Edge, Glos GL12 8NP* Chipping Sodbury (01454) 294267

SMALL, Gordon Frederick. b 41. St Jo Coll Nottm 77. **d** 79 **p** 80. C Belper *Derby* 79-84; NSM Matlock Bath 90-91; C Ripley 91-93; TV Bucknall and Bagnall *Lich* from 93. *The Vicarage, Dawlish Drive, Stoke-on-Trent ST2 0ET* Stoke-on-Trent (01782) 260876

SMALLDON, Keith. b 48. Open Univ BA76 Newc Univ MA94. St Mich Coll Llan DipTh71. **d** 71 **p** 72. C Cwmbran *Mon* 71-73; C Chepstow 73-75; Dioc Youth Adv *Bradf* 75-79; P-in-c Woolfold *Man* 82-85; Dioc Youth and Community Officer 82-90; P-in-c Thursby *Carl* 90-94; Dir of Clergy Tr 90-94; TR Daventry, Ashby St Ledgers, Braunston etc *Pet* from 94. *The Rectory, Golding Close, Daventry, Northants NN11 5PN* Daventry (01327) 702638

SMALLEY, Mrs Kathleen. b 23. Linc Th Coll 81. dss 84 **d** 87 **p** 94. Leominster *Heref* 84-85; Bridgnorth, Tasley, Astley Abbotts, Oldbury etc 85-87; Hon C from 87. *8A Cliff Road, Bridgnorth, Shropshire WV16 4EY* Bridgnorth (01746) 766202

SMALLEY, Very Rev Stephen Stewart. b 31. Jes Coll Cam BA55 MA58 PhD79. Eden Th Sem (USA) BD57 Ridley Hall Cam. **d** 58 **p** 59. C Portman Square St Paul *Lon* 58-60; Chapl Peterho Cam 60-63; Dean 62-63; Nigeria 63-69; Lect Th Man Univ

70-77; Prec Cov Cathl *Cov* 77-87; Can Res Cov Cathl 77-87; Vice-Provost Cov Cathl 86-87; Dean Ches from 87. *The Deanery, 7 Abbey Street, Chester CH1 2JF* Chester (01244) 351380 or 324756

SMALLMAN, Miss Margaret Anne. b 43. Hull Univ BSc64 Bris Univ CertEd65. St Jo Coll Nottm DipTh82. dss 83 **d** 87 **p** 94. Bromsgrove St John *Worc* 83-87; Par Dn 87-88; Par Dn Stoke Prior, Wychbold and Upton Warren 88-90; TD Tettenhall Wood *Lich* 91-94; TV from 94. *21 Tintagel Close, Perton, Wolverhampton WV6 7RG* Wolverhampton (01902) 750232

SMALLWOOD, Canon Graham Marten. b 19. St Pet Hall Ox BA48 MA52. Cuddesdon Coll 48. **d** 50 **p** 51. R Cannock *Lich* 69-76; TR 76-78; RD Rugeley 72-78; P-in-c Hatherton 76-78; Can Res Lich Cathl 78-88; rtd 88. *Brook House, The Cross, Childswickham, Broadway, Worcester WR12 7HJ* Broadway (01386) 853173

SMALLWOOD, Simon Laurence. b 58. St Jo Coll Dur BSc80. Cranmer Hall Dur 89. **d** 92 **p** 93. C Stapenhill w Cauldwell *Derby* from 92. *3 Stapenhill Road, Burton-on-Trent, Staffs DE15 9AF* Burton-on-Trent (01283) 64589

SMART, Barry. b 57. Lanc Univ BEd79. St Steph Ho Ox 85. **d** 88 **p** 89. C Wantage *Ox* 88-91; C Abingdon 91-93; TV 93-95; C Princes Risborough w Ilmer from 95. *23 Crossfield Road, Princes Risborough, Aylesbury, Bucks HP27 9AR* Princes Risborough (01844) 347437

SMART, Mrs Carol. b 45. SSF SRN67. S Dios Minl Tr Scheme 89. **d** 92 **p** 94. Chapl St Mary's Hosp Newport from 92. *20 Sydney Close, Shide, Newport, Isle of Wight PO30 1YG* Isle of Wight (01983) 526242

SMART, Clifford Edward James. b 28. Kelham Th Coll 48. **d** 53 **p** 54. Korea 66-93; rtd 93. *6430 Telegraph Road, St Louis, MO 63129-4934, USA* St Louis (314) 846-5927

SMART, Harry Gavin. b 67. St D Coll Lamp BA90 Selw Coll Cam DipTh92. Westcott Ho Cam CTM94. **d** 94 **p** 95. C Thirsk *York* from 94. *73 Hambleton Avenue, Thirsk, N Yorkshire YO7 1EG* Thirsk (01845) 523767

SMART, Canon Haydn Christopher. b 38. Wells Th Coll 66. **d** 69 **p** 70. C Hillmorton *Cov* 69-72; C Duston *Pet* 72-75; V Woodford Halse 75-79; V Woodford Halse w Eydon 79-82; V Wellingborough All SS 82-92; RD Wellingborough 87-92; V Longthorpe from 92; Can Pet Cathl from 92. *The Vicarage, 315 Thorpe Road, Longthorpe, Peterborough PE3 6LU* Peterborough (01733) 263016

SMART, Mrs Hilary Jean. b 42. SOAS Lon BA63 CSocSc64 DASS67. E Midl Min Tr Course 85. **d** 88 **p** 94. Par Dn Walsall Pleck and Bescot *Lich* 88-94; C 94; TV Sheff Manor *Sheff* from 94; Bp's Ecum Officer from 94. *William Temple Vicarage, 195 Harborough Avenue, Sheffield S2 1QT* Sheffield (0114) 239 8202

SMART, John Francis. b 36. Keble Coll Ox BA59 MA69. Cuddesdon Coll 59. **d** 61 **p** 66. C Cannock *Lich* 61-63; Hon C Gt Wyrley 63-66; C Wednesfield St Thos 66-70; V Brereton 70-85; R E Clevedon and Walton w Weston w Clapton *B & W* from 85. *The Rectory, All Saints' Lane, Clevedon, Avon BS21 6AU* Clevedon (01275) 873257

SMART, Richard Henry. b 22. St Jo Coll Dur 46 Clifton Th Coll 48. **d** 52 **p** 53. BFBS Distr Sec E Anglia 63-70; Bp's Ecum Adv *Ely* 70-81; Dioc Missr 70-74; P-in-c Dry Drayton 74-81; Min Bar Hill LEP 74-81; P-in-c Madingley 80-81; V Sandylands *Blackb* 81-92; rtd 92. *35 St Oswald Street, Bowerham, Lancaster LA1 3AS* Lancaster (01524) 65335

SMART, Richard Henry. b 23. Lon Univ BA51. Oak Hill Th Coll. **d** 53 **p** 54. V Hanley Road St Sav w St Paul *Lon* 59-71; V Plumstead All SS *S'wark* 71-88; rtd 88. *2 Annington Road, Eastbourne, E Sussex BN22 8NG* Eastbourne (01323) 726850

SMART, Canon Sydney. b 15. TCD BA37 MA43. **d** 39 **p** 40. I Belf All SS *Conn* 60-83; Can Belf Cathl 76-83; rtd 83. *43 Norwood Avenue, Belfast BT4 2EF* Belfast (01232) 653932

SMEATON, Malcolm John. b 56. BSc(Econ). Coll of Resurr Mirfield 79. **d** 83 **p** 84. C Tynemouth Ch Ch w H Trin *Newc* 83-84; C Long Benton 85-90; V Byker St Martin 90-95; Chapl HM Young Offender Inst Hindley from 95. *HM Prison Hindley, Gibson Street, Bickershaw, Wigan, Lancs WN2 5TH* Wigan (01942) 866255 Fax 867442

SMEATON, Canon William Brian Alexander. b 37. CITC 69. **d** 71 **p** 72. C Belf St Luke *Conn* 71-81; I Tullyaughnish w Kilmacrennan and Killygarvan *D & R* from 81; Bp's Dom Chapl from 87; Can Raphoe Cathl from 88; RD Kilmacrenan E and W from 90; Dioc Radio Officer from 90. *The Rectory, Ramelton, Letterkenny, Co Donegal, Irish Republic* Ramelton (74) 51013

SMEDLEY, Paul Mark. b 59. Bris Univ BA80 Lanc Univ MA81. S Dios Minl Tr Scheme 89. **d** 92 **p** 93. NSM Acton St Mary *Lon* from 92. *12 Baldwyn Gardens, London W3 6HH* 0181-993 5527

SMERDON, Stanley William. b 19. Oak Hill Th Coll 72. **d** 74 **p** 75. C Bournemouth St Paul *Win* 74-81; P-in-c Luccombe *B & W* 81; Perm to Offic from 85; Chapl Sandhill Park Hosp

Taunton from 87; rtd 89. *Heather Cottage, The Ball, Minehead, Somerset TA24 5JJ* Minehead (01643) 702933

SMETHURST, David Alan. b 36. Lon Univ BD60 Man Univ MPhil84. Tyndale Hall Bris 57. **d** 61 **p** 62. C Burnage St Marg *Man* 61-63; P-in-c Whalley Range St Marg 63-65; R Haughton St Mary 65-74; R Ulverston St Mary w H Trin *Carl* 74-87; Dean Hong Kong 87; Dir Acorn Chr Healing Trust Resource Cen 88-93; V Epsom St Martin *Guildf* from 93. *The Vicarage, 35 Burgh Heath Road, Epsom, Surrey KT17 4LP* Epsom (01372) 743336

SMETHURST, Gordon James. b 33. CEng FIStructE. N Ord Course 79. **d** 82 **p** 83. NSM Halliwell St Marg *Man* 82-87; NSM Bradshaw 87-88; Asst Chapl Bolton R Infirmary 88-95; Asst Chapl Bolton Gen Hosp 88-95; Hon C Westhoughton from 95. *91 Albert Road West, Bolton BL1 5ED* Bolton (01204) 842561

SMETHURST, Gordon McIntyre. b 40. Man Univ BA62 BD69. **d** 70 **p** 71. C Sandal St Helen *Wakef* 70-72; P-in-c Smawthorpe St Mich 72-75; P-in-c Whitwood 74-75; Asst Master Goole Gr Sch 75-84; Hon C Howden *York* 77-79; Hon C Howden TM 80-84; Perm to Offic from 94. *20 Broadacre Park, Brough, N Humberside HU15 1LT* Hull (01482) 665525

SMETHURST, John Michael Benedict. b 44. St Pet Coll Ox BA66 MA70. St Steph Ho Ox 66. **d** 68 **p** 69. C Gladstone Park St Fran *Lon* 68-71; C St Pancras H Cross w St Jude and St Pet 71-73; C Hendon St Mary 73-76; Chapl S Devon Tech Coll Torbay 76-79; V N Keyham *Ex* from 80; RD Plymouth Devonport 83-86. *St Thomas's Presbytery, 90 Royal Navy Avenue, Plymouth PL2 2AJ* Plymouth (01752) 561102

SMETHURST, Leslie Beckett. b 22. CEng. NW Ord Course 72. **d** 75 **p** 76. C Baguley *Man* 75-78; TV Droylsden St Mary 78-81; V Droylsden St Martin 81-86; rtd 87; Perm to Offic *Blackb* from 87. *27 Calf Croft Place, Lytham St Annes, Lancs FY8 4PU* Lytham (01253) 733159

SMILLIE, Linda Barbara. b 46. Oak Hill Th Coll DipHE87. **d** 87 **p** 94. Par Dn Holloway St Mary w St Jas *Lon* 87-88; Par Dn Holloway St Mary Magd 88-90; Chapl W End Stores 90-91; C Holloway St Mark w Em 90-91; Hon C Islington St Mary 92-94; C-in-c Southall Em CD from 95. *37 Dormers Wells Lane, Southall, Middx UB1 3HX* 0181-843 9556

SMITH, Alan. b 38. Tyndale Hall Bris 63. **d** 65 **p** 66. C New Milverton *Cov* 65-68; C Cheadle *Ches* 68-71; V Handforth 71-78; Asst Chapl HM Pris Styal 75-78; Chapl HM Pris Wormwood Scrubs 78-79; Chapl HM Borstal Wellingborough 79-83; R Rushden w Newton Bromswold *Pet* from 83; Chapl Rushden Sanatorium from 83. *The Rectory, Rectory Road, Rushden, Northants NN10 0HA* Rushden (01933) 312554 or 412235

SMITH, Alan Gregory Clayton. b 57. Birm Univ BA78 MA79. Wycliffe Hall Ox 79. **d** 81 **p** 82. C Pudsey St Lawr *Bradf* 81-82; C Pudsey St Lawr and St Paul 82-84; Chapl Lee Abbey 84-90; TV Walsall *Lich* from 90; Dioc Missr from 90. *14 Gorway Gardens, Walsall WS1 3BJ* Walsall (01922) 26010

SMITH, Alan Leonard. b 51. Madeley Coll of Educn CertEd72. Trin Coll Bris DipTh95. **d** 95. C Taunton St Mary *B & W* from 95. *3 Woodrush Close, Taunton, Somerset TA1 3XB* Taunton (01823) 289185

SMITH, Alan Pearce Carlton. b 20. Trin Hall Cam BA40 MA45 LLB46. Westcott Ho Cam 55. **d** 78 **p** 79. Hon C Cherry Hinton St Jo *Ely* 78-82; P-in-c Madingley 82-83; P-in-c Dry Drayton 82-83; P-in-c Swaffham Bulbeck 84-88; Perm to Offic from 88. *38 Alpha Road, Cambridge CB4 3DG* Cambridge (01223) 358124

SMITH, Alan Thomas. b 35. BA DipEd. Ridley Hall Cam 82. **d** 84 **p** 85. C Bedworth *Cov* 84-89; R Carlton Colville w Mutford and Rushmere *Nor* from 89. *The Rectory, Carlton Colville, Lowestoft, Suffolk NR33 8BB* Lowestoft (01502) 565217

SMITH, Alec John. b 29. AKC53. **d** 54 **p** 55. CF 69-88; V Douglas St Thos *S & M* 88-92; rtd 92; Perm to Offic *S & M* from 92. *Church Barn, Church Road, Lonan, Isle of Man IM4 7JX* Laxey (01624) 861325

SMITH, Alexander Montgomery. b 36. TCD BA59 MA64 BD65. TCD Div Sch Div Test60. **d** 61 **p** 62. C Knock *D & D* 61-64; C Belf St Thos *Conn* 64-66; Lect St Kath Coll Liv 66-69; Sen Lect from 69; Asst Chapl St Kath Coll *Liv* 66-69; Chapl 69-80; NSM Allerton from 80. *15 Glenathol Road, Liverpool L18 3JS* 0151-475 3310

SMITH, Alfred Lawrence. b 23. FCP84 Open Univ BA72 Birm Univ DipEd73. E Midl Min Tr Course 82. **d** 85 **p** 86. NSM Ashover *Derby* 85-86; NSM Ashover and Brackenfield from 86. *Cotton House Farm, Amber Lane, Ashover, Chesterfield, Derbyshire S45 0DZ* Chesterfield (01246) 590265

SMITH, Andrew John. b 37. Leeds Univ BA61. Coll of Resurr Mirfield 61. **d** 63 **p** 64. C W Hackney St Barn *Lon* 63-65; Dir and Chapl Northorpe Hall Trust Yorkshire 65-72; Warden Ox Ho Bethnal Green 72-78; Dir and Chapl The Target Trust 78-86; P-in-c Gt Staughton *Ely* 86-88; Norfolk DTI Educn

Adv 88-91; Perm to Offic *Ex* from 92. *6 Beacon Cottages, Buckland-in-the-Moor, Ashburton, Newton Abbot, Devon TQ13 7HL* Ashburton (01364) 652654

SMITH, Andrew John. b 46. ACGI Lon Univ BScEng67 DIC PhD71 Trin Coll Ox DipTh74 Bath Univ MEd88. Coll of Resurr Mirfield 74. **d** 76 **p** 77. C Swindon New Town *Bris* 76-78; C Southmead 78-79; Perm to Offic from 79. *15 Dyrham Close, Bristol BS9 4TF* Bristol (0117) 942 8594

SMITH, Andrew John. b 59. Birm Univ BSc80 PhD81. W Midl Minl Tr Course 89. **d** 91 **p** 92. C Lower Mitton *Worc* 91-92; C Stourport-on-Severn and Wilden 92-95; TV Redditch, The Ridge from 95. *The Vicarage, St George's Road, Redditch, Worcs B98 8EE* Redditch (01527) 63017

SMITH, Andrew Perry Langton. b 56. Sheff City Poly BSc79 Imp Coll Lon MSc80. Trin Coll Bris 89. **d** 91 **p** 92. C Littleover *Derby* from 91. *4 Merridale Road, Littleover, Derby DE23 7DJ* Derby (01332) 766060

SMITH, Mrs Anita Elisabeth. b 57. Westhill Coll Birm BEd79. Trin Coll Bris DipHE88 ADPS88. **d** 88 **p** 94. Par Dn Bermondsey St Anne *S'wark* 88-92; Par Dn Brockley Hill St Sav 92-94; C from 94. *St Saviour's Vicarage, 5 Lowther Hill, London SE23 1PZ* 0181-690 2499

SMITH, Ann Veronica. b 38. Doncaster Coll of Educn DipEd. Edin Dioc NSM Course 88. **d** 95. NSM S Queensferry *Edin* from 95. *16 Mannerston, Linlithgow, W Lothian EH49 7ND* Linlithgow (01506) 834361

SMITH, Anthony Adam Dalziel. b 42. Qu Coll Birm 65. **d** 68 **p** 69. C Peterlee *Dur* 68-71; C Tilehurst St Mich *Ox* 71-76; V Wootton (Boars Hill) 76-88; R Brightwalton w Catmore, Leckhampstead etc from 88. *The Rectory, Chaddleworth, Newbury, Berks RG16 0EW* Chaddleworth (01488) 638566

SMITH, Anthony Charles. b 43. Sarum & Wells Th Coll 90. **d** 92 **p** 93. C Dartford H Trin *Roch* 92-95; V Northfleet from 95. *The Vicarage, The Hill, Northfleet, Gravesend, Kent DA11 9EU* Gravesend (01474) 566400

SMITH, Anthony Cyril (Tony). b 40. K Coll Lon 65. **d** 69 **p** 70. C Crewkerne *B & W* 69-74; TV Hemel Hempstead *St Alb* 74-76; Asst Chapl K Coll Taunton 76-80; Chapl from 80. *40 South Road, Taunton, Somerset TA1 3DY* Taunton (01823) 272251

SMITH, Anthony Grahame (Tony). b 29. ALCD54. **d** 54 **p** 55. R Mistley w Manningtree *Chelmsf* 69-81; RD Harwich 75-81; R Fordham 81-92; rtd 92. *10 Glebe Way, Frinton-on-Sea, Essex CO13 9HR*

SMITH, Anthony James. b 57. ACA Sheff Univ BA. Ridley Hall Cam 83. **d** 86 **p** 87. C Woking St Pet *Guildf* 86-90; C Reigate St Mary *S'wark* 90-94; CMS from 94; Kenya from 94. *PO Box 40360, Nairobi, Kenya*

SMITH, Ven Anthony Michael Percival. b 24. G&C Coll Cam BA48 MA53. Westcott Ho Cam 48. **d** 50 **p** 51. V Yeovil St Jo w Preston Plucknett *B & W* 66-72; RD Merston 68-72; Preb Wells Cathl 70-72; V Addiscombe St Mildred *Cant* 72-79; Adn Maidstone 79-89; Dir of Ords 80-89; Hon Can Cant Cathl 80-89; rtd 89; Perm to Offic *Cant* from 89; Perm to Offic *Chich* 89-91 and from 93; RD Rye 91-93. *The Garden House, Horseshoe Lane, Beckley, Rye, E Sussex TN31 6RZ* Beckley (01797) 260514

SMITH, Ven Arthur Cyril. b 09. VRD55. Sheff Univ BA34 MA50. St Jo Coll Manitoba 29 Westcott Ho Cam 33. **d** 34 **p** 35. Adn Linc 60-76; Can and Preb Linc Cathl 60-77; R Algarkirk 60-76; rtd 77. *28 London Court, London Road, Headington, Oxford OX3 7SL* Oxford (01865) 744788

SMITH, Miss Audrey. b 47. S'wark Ord Course 89. **d** 92 **p** 94. NSM Croydon St Aug *S'wark* from 92. *19 Queen Street, Croydon CR0 1SY* 0181-681 7005

SMITH, Mrs Audrey Isabel. b 20. Lon Univ. Qu Coll Birm IDC79. **dss** 84 **d** 87 **p** 94. NSM Kingston All SS w St Jo *S'wark* from 87. *49 St Winifred's Road, Teddington, Middx TW11 9JT* 0181-977 2928

SMITH, Austin John Denyer. b 40. Worc Coll Ox BA62. Cuddesdon Coll 64. **d** 66 **p** 67. C Shepherd's Bush St Steph w St Thos *Lon* 66-69; C W Drayton 69-72; Chapl Sussex Univ *Chich* 72-79; V Caddington *St Alb* from 79. *The Vicarage, Collings Wells Close, Caddington, Luton LU1 4BG* Luton (01582) 31692

SMITH, Mrs Barbara Jean. b 39. Bris Univ BA62. S'wark Ord Course 83. **dss** 86 **d** 87 **p** 94. Chislehurst St Nic *Roch* 86-87; Hon Par Dn 87-90; Hon C Wrecclesham *Guildf* 90-94; NSM Herriard w Winslade and Long Sutton etc *Win* from 94. *The Parsonage, Gaston Lane, South Warnborough, Hants RG25 1RH* Basingstoke (01256) 862843

SMITH, Miss Barbara Mary. b 47. Doncaster Coll of Educn TCert68. Cranmer Hall Dur 82. **dss** 85 **d** 87 **p** 94. Beverley St Nic *York* 85-87; Par Dn 87; NSM S'wark H Trin w St Matt *S'wark* 89-90; Ind Chapl Teesside *York* from 91. *12 Fox Howe, Middlesbrough, Cleveland TS8 0RU* Middlesbrough (01642) 597745

SMITH, Chan Barry. b 41. Univ of Wales (Lamp) BA62 Fitzw Ho Cam BA64 MA68. Ridley Hall Cam. **d** 65 **p** 66. C Rhyl w

St Ann *St As* 65-70; Chapl Scargill Ho 70-72; C Flint *St As* 72-74; V Broughton 74-86; Dioc Ecum Officer from 82; RD Wrexham 82-86; R Wrexham from 86; Can Cursal St As Cathl from 86; Chan St As Cathl from 95. *The Rectory, 7 Westminster Drive, Wrexham, Clwyd LL12 7AT* Wrexham (01978) 263905 or 355808

SMITH, Brian. b 44. Westmr Coll Ox MTh95. Sarum & Wells Th Coll 71. **d** 74 **p** 75. C Pennywell St Thos and Grindon St Oswald CD *Dur* 74-77; Chapl RAF 77-95; P-in-c Keswick St Jo *Carl* from 95. *St John's Vicarage, Ambleside Road, Keswick, Cumbria CA12 4DD* Keswick (017687) 72130

✠SMITH, Rt Rev Brian Arthur. b 43. Edin Univ MA66 Fitzw Coll Cam BA68 MA72 Jes Coll Cam MLitt73. Westcott Ho Cam 66. **d** 72 **p** 73 **c** 93. Tutor and Lib Cuddesdon Coll 72-75; Dir of Studies 75-78; C Cuddesdon *Ox* 76-79; Sen Tutor Ripon Coll Cuddesdon 78-79; Dir Tr *Wakef* 79-87; P-in-c Halifax St Jo Cragg Vale 79-85; Hon Can Wakef Cathl 81-87; Adn Craven *Bradf* 87-93; Suff Bp Tonbridge *Roch* from 93. *Bishop's Lodge, 48 St Botolph's Road, Sevenoaks, Kent TN13 3AG* Sevenoaks (01732) 456070 Fax 741449

SMITH, Brian Godfrey. b 24. Chich Th Coll 63. **d** 65 **p** 66. C Redcar *York* 68-72; C Kirkleatham 68-72; V Wortley de Leeds *Ripon* 72-76; Chapl Costa del Sol E *Eur* 76-82; Chapl Estoril 82-84; V Worfield *Heref* 84-89; rtd 89. *2 Pineway, Lodge Farm, Bridgnorth, Shropshire WV15 5DT* Bridgnorth (01746) 764088

SMITH, Ven Brian John. b 33. Sarum Th Coll 62. **d** 65 **p** 66. C Whitstable All SS *Cant* 65-69; V Woodford w Wilsford *Sarum* 69-74; P-in-c Durnford 74; V Woodford Valley 74-76; V Mere w W Knoyle and Maiden Bradley 76-80; RD Heytesbury 78-80; Adn Wilts from 80; Can and Preb Sarum Cathl from 80; V Bishop's Cannings, All Cannings etc 80-83; Adv Chr Giving 83-90; TV Redhorn from 90. *The Vicarage, 57 The Street, Chirton, Devizes, Wilts SN10 3QS* Devizes (01380) 840271

SMITH, Brian Michael. b 42. Kelham Th Coll 69. **d** 69 **p** 70. C Somers Town St Mary *Lon* 70-74; C Stamford Hill St Jo 74-75; C Stamford Hill St Bart 75-84; P-in-c Edmonton St Pet w St Martin 84-92; V from 92. *The Vicarage, St Peter's Road, London N9 8JP* 0181-807 2974 Fax 345 6110

SMITH, Mrs Bridget Mary. b 46. Bp Otter Coll CertEd67 S Dios Minl Tr Scheme 88. **d** 91 **p** 94. C Pet H Spirit Bretton *Pet* 91-95; P-in-c Silverstone and Abthorpe w Slapton from 95. *St Michael's Vicarage, High Street, Silverstone, Towcester, Northants NN12 8US* Silverstone (01327) 857996

SMITH, Canon Charles. b 11. St Jo Coll Dur BA39 MA42. **d** 39 **p** 40. V Heatherycleugh *Dur* 48-83; V St John in Weardale 57-83; V Westgate 57-83; Hon Can Dur Cathl 79-83; rtd 83. *Rutson House, Nunnington, York YO6 5UR* Nunnington (014395) 204

SMITH, Charles Frederick. b 18. St Aid Birkenhead 54. **d** 56 **p** 58. R Everleigh *Sarum* 60-74; V Burneside *Carl* 74-79; Perm to Offic *Chich* from 80; rtd 83. *7 Manor Road, Seaford, E Sussex BN25 4NL* Seaford (01323) 890433

SMITH, Charles Henry Neville. b 31. Nottm Univ BA52 MA65. Sarum Th Coll 55. **d** 57 **p** 58. C Thirsk w S Kilvington *York* 57-60; C Linthorpe 60-61; V Danby 61-66; Chapl United Cam Hosps 66-76; Chapl Lanc Moor Hosp 76-84; Hon Can Blackb Cathl *Blackb* 81-84; Asst Sec Gen Syn Hosp Chapl Coun 84-88; Hon C Lee St Marg *S'wark* 84-88; Chapl Guy's Hosp *Lon* from 88. *Guy's Hospital, St Thomas Street, London SE1 9RT* 0171-955 4591 or 955 5000

SMITH, Charles Rycroft (Ryc). b 46. Sarum & Wells Th Coll 76. **d** 78 **p** 79. C Heref St Martin *Heref* 78-81; C Southn Maybush St Pet *Win* 81-83; R The Candover Valley from 83; RD Alresford from 90. *The Rectory, Alresford Road, Preston Candover, Basingstoke, Hants RG25 2EE* Preston Candover (01256) 389245

SMITH, Charles Septimus. b 23. Bris & Glouc Tr Course. **d** 79 **p** 80. NSM Bris St Agnes and St Simon w St Werburgh *Bris* 79-86; C 86-87; C Bris St Paul's 87-89; rtd 89. *353 Queen Street South, Mississauga, Ontario, Canada, L5M1 M3*

SMITH, Christine Lydia. See CARTER, Mrs Christine Lydia

SMITH, Christopher Blake Walters. b 63. Univ of Wales (Cardiff) BMus84 BD88 LLM95. St Mich Coll Llan 85. **d** 88 **p** 89. C Aberdare St Jo *Llan* 88-93; V Tongwynlais from 93. *The Vicarage, 1 Merthyr Road, Tongwynlais, Cardiff CF4 7LE* Cardiff (01222) 810437

SMITH, Christopher Francis. b 46. K Coll Lon BD68 AKC68. St Aug Coll Cant 69. **d** 70 **p** 71. C Norwood All SS *Cant* 70-72; Asst Chapl Marlborough Coll Wilts 72-76; C Deal St Leon w Sholden *Cant* 77-81; P-in-c Benenden 81-83; V from 83. *The Vicarage, Benenden, Cranbrook, Kent TN17 4DL* Cranbrook (01580) 240658

SMITH, Christopher Matthew. b 67. New Coll Ox BA89 MA93 Homerton Coll Cam PGCE90. St Steph Ho Ox BA94. **d** 95. C Wantage *Ox* from 95. *5 Barnards Way, Wantage, Oxon OX12 7EA* Wantage (01235) 763309

SMITH, Canon Christopher Milne. b 44. Selw Coll Cam BA66. Cuddesdon Coll 67. **d** 69 **p** 70. C Liv Our Lady and St Nic *Liv*

69-74; TV Kirkby 74-81; R Walton St Mary 81-91; Can Res Sheff Cathl *Sheff* from 91. *9 Stumperlowe Hall Road, Sheffield S10 3QR* Sheffield (0114) 230 4181/ 275 3434

SMITH, Clarice Mary. b 25. St Mich Coll Llan 76. **dss** 77 **d** 80. Llangiwg *S & B* 77-80; C Llwynderw 80-84; C Newton St Pet 84-88; rtd 88. *33 Sherringham Drive, Newton, Swansea SA3 4UG* Swansea (01792) 367984

SMITH, Clifford. b 31. Lon Univ DipTh60. St Aid Birkenhead 59. **d** 61 **p** 62. C Limehouse St Anne *Lon* 61-63; C Ashtead *Guildf* 63-66; R Bromley All Hallows *Lon* 66-76; V Hillsborough and Wadsley Bridge *Sheff* 76-89; V Stainforth from 89. *The Vicarage, Field Road, Stainforth, Doncaster, S Yorkshire DN7 5AQ* Doncaster (01302) 841295

SMITH, Clive Leslie. b 50. Leeds Univ BA72 Ch Coll Liv PGCE. Coll of Resurr Mirfield 75. **d** 77 **p** 78. C Goldington *St Alb* 77-81; C Cheshunt 81-84; V Watford St Pet 84-89; Chapl Leavesden Hosp Abbots Langley 89-94; Chapl Hemel Hempstead Gen Hosp from 94; Chapl Cell Barnes Hosp St Alb from 94. *Hemel Hempstead General Hospital, Hillfield Road, Hemel Hempstead, Herts HP2 4AD* Hemel Hempstead (01442) 213141

SMITH, Colin Graham. b 59. Hatf Poly BA82 CQSW82. Trin Coll Bris BA88. **d** 88 **p** 89. C Bermondsey St Jas w Ch Ch *S'wark* 88-92; V Brockley Hill St Sav from 92. *St Saviour's Vicarage, 5 Lowther Hill, London SE23 1PZ* 0181-690 2499

SMITH, Colin Ian McNaughton. b 28. St Jo Coll Dur BA53. **d** 55 **p** 56. V Weaverthorpe w Helperthorpe and Luttons *York* 67-76; P-in-c Kirby Grindalythe 74-76; RD Buckrose 75-76; V Weaverthorpe w Helperthorpe, Luttons Ambo etc 76-91; rtd 91. *Aynsley House, East Lutton, Malton, N Yorkshire YO17 8TG* West Lutton (01944) 738539

SMITH, Colin Richard. b 53. Liv Poly BA80 Liv Univ MTD83. Oak Hill Th Coll 84. **d** 86 **p** 87. C Ormskirk *Liv* 86-89; V Wigan St Cath 89-94; C St Helens St Helen from 94. *211A Dentons Green Lane, St Helens, Merseyside WA10 6RU* Merseyside (01744) 453681

SMITH, Craig Philip. b 61. Huddersfield Poly HND82 Sheff City Poly BA86. St Jo Coll Nottm DTS92 DipMM93. **d** 93 **p** 94. C Bramley and Ravenfield *Sheff* 93-95; C Bramley and Ravenfield w Hooton Roberts etc from 95. *28 Ferndale Drive, Bramley, Rotherham, S Yorkshire S66 0YD* Rotherham (01709) 703415

SMITH, Darren John Anthony. b 62. Nottm Univ BCombStuds84. Linc Th Coll 84. **d** 86 **p** 87. C Leic Ascension *Leic* 86-90; C Curdworth w Castle Vale *Birm* 90; C Castle Vale St Cuth 90-91; C Kingstanding St Luke 91-92; P-in-c 92-93; V from 93. *The Vicarage, 49 Caversham Road, Birmingham B44 0LW* 0121-354 3281

SMITH, David Earling. b 35. AKC60. **d** 61 **p** 62. R Claxby w Normanby-le-Wold *Linc* 69-74; R Nettleton 69-74; R S Kelsey 69-74; R N Owersby w Thornton le Moor 69-74; R Stainton-le-Vale w Kirmond le Mire 69-74; V Ancaster 74-79; Warden and Chapl St Anne Bedehouses Linc 79-89; C Linc Minster Gp 79-89; rtd 89; Perm to Offic *Linc* from 90. *17 Egerton Road, Lincoln LN2 4PJ* Lincoln (01522) 510336

SMITH, David Geoffrey Stuart. b 62. RGN88 K Coll Lon BD83 AKC83. St Steph Ho Ox 88. **d** 92 **p** 93. C Somers Town St Mary *Lon* 92-95. *The Vicarage, Camden Square, London NW1 9XG* 0171-485 3147

SMITH, David Graham. b 08. MBE46. Wadh Coll Ox BA31 MA34. Cuddesdon Coll 31. **d** 32 **p** 33. V Woldingham *S'wark* 59-76; rtd 76; Perm to Offic *B & W* from 86. *St Mary's, Whitegate Road, Minehead, Somerset TA24 5SP* Minehead (01643) 702336

✠SMITH, Rt Rev David James. b 35. AKC58. **d** 59 **p** 60 **c** 87. C Gosforth All SS *Newc* 59-62; C Newc St Fran 62-64; C Longbenton St Bart 64-68; V Longhirst 68-75; V Monkseaton St Mary 75-82; RD Tynemouth 80-82; Hon Can Newc Cathl 81-87; Adn Lindisfarne 81-87; V Felton 82-83; Suff Bp Maidstone *Cant* 87-92; Bp HM Forces 90-92; Bp Bradf from 92. *Bishopscroft, Ashwell Road, Heaton, Bradford, W Yorkshire BD9 4AU* Bradford (01274) 545414 Fax 544831

SMITH, David John. b 32. Lon Univ BA76 MSc79. Lon Coll of Div 68. **d** 70 **p** 71. C Clerkenwell St Jas and St Jo w St Pet *Lon* 70-73; P-in-c Penge St Paul *Roch* 74-78; V 78-89; RD Beckenham 86-89; Chapl Bromley and Sheppard's Colls from 90; Dioc Clergy Widows and Retirement Officer from 90. *The Chaplain's House, Bromley College, London Road, Bromley BR1 1PE* 0181-460 4712

SMITH, David John. b 42. Oak Hill Th Coll 75. **d** 77 **p** 78. C New Milverton *Cov* 77-81; V Hartshill 81-86; V Attleborough 86-95. *Attleborough Vicarage, 5 Fifield Close, Nuneaton, Warks CV11 4TS* Nuneaton (01203) 382926

SMITH, David John Parker (Brother Victor). See EVANS, David

SMITH, David Leonard. b 37. St Alb Minl Tr Scheme 84. **d** 91 **p** 92. NSM Potton w Sutton and Cockayne Hatley *St Alb* from

91. *11 Judith Gardens, Potton, Sandy, Beds SG19 2RJ* Potton (01767) 260583

SMITH, David Roland Mark. b 46. ACP78 FRSA87 SSC88 Dur Univ BA68. Edin Th Coll 68. **d** 70 **p** 71. C Southwick St Columba *Dur* 70-74 and 81-82; Asst Chapl Univ of Wales (Cardiff) *Llan* 74-76; Hon C E Bris 76-78; Hon C Filton 78-79; Min Leam Lane CD *Dur* 80-81; V Leam Lane 81; Chapl Sunderland Poly 81-86; Co-ord Chapl Service 81-86; Chapl Birm Univ *Birm* 86-95; Perm to Offic *Cov* 88-95; Chapl Heathrow Airport *Lon* from 95; Perm to Offic *Ox* from 95. *12 Cherry Orchard, West Drayton, Middx UB7 7JR* West Drayton (01895) 447904 Fax 0181-745 4261 Mobile 037-887 6695

SMITH, David Sidney Mark. b 54. Bris Univ BEd76. Ripon Coll Cuddesdon 77. **d** 79 **p** 80. C Wotton-under-Edge w Ozleworth and N Nibley *Glouc* 79-83; TV Malvern Link w Cowleigh *Worc* 83-93; Relig Affairs Producer BBC Heref and Worc 90-93; V Clevedon St Jo *B & W* from 93. *St John's Vicarage, 1 St John's Road, Clevedon, Avon BS21 7TG* Clevedon (01275) 872410

SMITH, David Stanley. b 41. Ox NSM Course. **d** 84 **p** 85. NSM Burghfield *Ox* 84-86; NSM Stratfield Mortimer 86-88; NSM Mortimer W End w Padworth 86-88; C St Breoke and Egloshayle *Truro* 88-93; V Penwerris from 93. *Penwerris Vicarage, 12 Stratton Terrace, Falmouth, Cornwall TR11 2SY* Falmouth (01326) 314263

SMITH, David Watson. b 31. Sarum Th Coll 63. **d** 65 **p** 66. C W Wimbledon Ch Ch *S'wark* 65-69; C Cheam 69-74; V Haslington *Ches* 74-83; V Haslington w Crewe Green 83-87; V Daresbury from 87. *The Vicarage, Daresbury, Warrington WA4 4AE* Moore (01925) 740348

SMITH, David William. b 46. Sarum Th Coll 70. **d** 72 **p** 73. C Stokesley *York* 72-75; C Edin St Mich and All SS *Edin* 75-77; R Galashiels 77-85; R Yarm *York* from 85. *The Rectory, 6 Westgate, Yarm, Cleveland TS15 9BU* Middlesbrough (01642) 781115

SMITH, Mrs Decia Jane. b 47. ALAM66. W Midl Minl Tr Course 92. **d** 95. C Edgbaston St Germain *Birm* from 95. *74 Lordswood Road, Birmingham B17 9BY* 0121-427 5526

SMITH, Denis Richard. b 53. St Jo Coll Nottm 83. **d** 85 **p** 86. C Hersham *Guildf* 85-88; C Thatcham *Ox* 88-91; V Shefford *St Alb* from 91. *The Vicarage, 9 The Hollies, Shefford, Beds SG17 5BX* Hitchin (01462) 811100

SMITH, Dennis Austin. b 50. Lanc Univ BA71 Liv Univ PGCE72. NW Ord Course 74. **d** 77 **p** 78. NSM Gt Crosby St Faith *Liv* 77-83; Hon C from 83; NSM Seaforth 77-83; Asst Chapl Merchant Taylors' Sch Crosby 79-83; Chapl from 83. *16 Fir Road, Liverpool L22 4QL* 0151-928 5065

SMITH, Dennis Peter. b 35. Qu Coll Birm 83. **d** 85 **p** 86. C Sedgley All SS *Lich* 85-89; C Penkridge w Stretton 89-90; TV Penkridge Team 90-93; V Ketley and Oakengates from 93. *Holy Trinity Vicarage, Holyhead Road, Oakengates, Telford, Shropshire TF2 6BN* Telford (01952) 612004

SMITH, Derek Arthur. b 38. Chich Th Coll 63. **d** 66 **p** 67. C Cheadle *Lich* 66-70; C Blakenall Heath 70-72; P-in-c 76-77; TR 77-86; V Knutton 72-76; R Lich St Mary w St Mich from 86; P-in-c Wall from 90. *St Michael's Rectory, St Michael Road, Lichfield, Staffs WS13 6SN* Lichfield (01543) 262420

SMITH, Derek Arthur Byott. b 26. Hull Univ MA89. S Dios Minl Tr Scheme 78. **d** 81 **p** 82. NSM Wimborne Minster and Holt *Sarum* 81-83; C Northn St Alb *Pet* 83-85; Ind Chapl *York* 85-89; P-in-c Kingston upon Hull St Mary 88-89; P-in-c Newington w Dairycoates 89-93; rtd 93. *107 Cardigan Road, Bridlington, N Humberside YO15 3LP* Bridlington (01262) 678852

SMITH, Derek Arthur Douglas. b 26. Dur Univ BA51. Qu Coll Birm 58. **d** 60 **p** 61. V Thelwall *Ches* 68-78; V Whitegate w Lt Budworth 78-92; rtd 92. *10 Newtons Crescent, Winterley, Sandbach, Cheshire CW11 9NS* Crewe (01270) 589130

SMITH, Derek Graham. b 52. St Cath Coll Cam BA74 MA77. Westcott Ho Cam 74. **d** 76 **p** 77. C Weymouth H Trin *Sarum* 76-79; P-in-c Bradpole 79; TV Bridport 79-84; R Monkton Farleigh, S Wraxall and Winsley from 84. *The Rectory, 6 Millbourn Close, Winsley, Bradford-on-Avon, Wilts BA15 2NN* Limpley Stoke (01225) 722230

SMITH, Donald Edgar. b 56. Oak Hill Th Coll 89. **d** 91 **p** 92. C Holloway St Mark w Em *Lon* 91-92; C Tollington from 92. *127 Coldershaw Road, London W13 9DU* 0181-566 3459

SMITH, Ven Donald John. b 26. Clifton Th Coll 50. **d** 53 **p** 54. R Whitton and Thurleston w Akenham *St E* 62-75; Hon Can St E Cathl 73-91; R Rickinghall 75-76; P-in-c Redgrave w Botesdale and Wortham 75-76; Adn Suffolk 75-84; R Redgrave cum Botesdale w Rickinghall 76-78; Adn Sudbury 84-91; rtd 91. *St Peter's Cottage, Stretton-on-Fosse, Moreton-in-Marsh, Glos GL56 9SE* Shipston-on-Stour (01608) 662751

✠**SMITH, Rt Rev Donald Westwood.** b 28. Edin Th Coll 54. **d** 54 **p** 55 **c** 90. Asst Dioc Supernumerary *Ab* 54-55; Chapl St Andr Cathl 55-56; Canada 56-57; R Longside *Ab* 57-65; Mauritius 65-85; P-in-c St Geo-in-the-East St Mary *Lon* 85-86;

Madagascar from 86; Bp Toamasina from 90. *BP 531, Toamasina 501, Madagascar*

SMITH, Douglas David Frederick. b 28. Lon Univ BD53. ALCD53. **d** 53 **p** 54. R Higher Openshaw *Man* 69-80; R Church w Chapel Brampton *Pet* 80-81; R Church and Chapel Brampton w Harlestone 81-86; Perm to Offic *Ox* from 86; rtd 89. *1 Maybush Walk, Olney, Bucks MK46 5NA* Bedford (01234) 712256

SMITH, Edward Leonard Richard. b 27. Lon Univ DipRS77. S'wark Ord Course 74. **d** 77 **p** 78. NSM N Wembley St Cuth *Lon* 77-83; C Broxbourne w Wormley *St Alb* 83-89; R Therfield w Kelshall 89-94; rtd 94. *32 The Tanyard, Bassingbourn, Royston, Herts SG8 5NH* Royston (01763) 242731

SMITH, Miss Elizabeth. b 46. Liv Inst of Educn CertEd67 Heythrop Coll Lon BD76 Lon Univ MPhil84. Westcott Ho Cam CTM92. **d** 92 **p** 94. Par Dn Moulsham St Jo *Chelmsf* 92-94; C from 94. *Glebe House, 19 Vicarage Road, Moulsham, Chelmsford CM2 9PH* Chelmsford (01245) 359040

SMITH (nee HOWSE), Mrs Elizabeth Ann (Beth). b 39. Bath Academy of Art CertEd60 Warw Univ BEd85 Westhill Coll Birm DipRE88. W Midl Minl Tr Course 91. **d** 94. C Fletchamstead *Cov* from 94. *20 Hathaway Road, Coventry CV4 9HW* Coventry (01203) 473197

SMITH, Miss Elizabeth Jane (Liz). b 50. Birm Univ BA72 DCG73. Trin Coll Bris 88. **d** 90 **p** 95. C Lowestoft and Kirkley *Nor* 90-94; TV Rugby St Andr *Cov* from 94. *63A Lower Hillmorton Road, Rugby, Warks CV21 3TQ*

SMITH, Elizabeth Marion. b 52. ACA76 FCA82. Carl Dioc Tr Inst 91. **d** 94. C Appleby *Carl* from 94. *10 Castle View Road, Appleby-in-Westmorland, Cumbria CA16 6HH* Appleby (017683) 52786

SMITH, Elvyn Garston. b 09. St Pet Hall Ox BA36 MA40. Wycliffe Hall Ox 36. **d** 37 **p** 38. V Patcham *Chich* 55-75; RD Preston 73-75; rtd 75; Perm to Offic *Chich* from 75. *45 Sheridan Road, Worthing, W Sussex BN14 8EU* Worthing (01903) 208611

SMITH, Eric Alfred Norman. b 25. St D Coll Lamp BA51 LTh53. **d** 53 **p** 54. J H Whitley Sch Halifax 70-81; C Stocksbridge *Sheff* 81-83; V Deepcar 83-84; R Caister *Nor* 84-93; rtd 93. *31 Mulberry Lane, Goring-by-Sea, Worthing, W Sussex BN12 4QU*

SMITH, Eric Frederick. b 19. Lon Univ BA40 BD42. ALCD42. **d** 42 **p** 43. R Long Ditton *S'wark* 67-81; V Deal St Geo *Cant* 81-85; RD Sandwich 82-85; rtd 85; Perm to Offic *Cant* 85-88; Chapl Cant Sch of Min from 88. *Beach Cottage, 179 Beach Street, Deal, Kent CT14 6LE* Deal (01304) 367648

SMITH, Ernest John. b 24. ARICS49. Oak Hill Th Coll 59. **d** 61 **p** 62. C Hove Bp Hannington Memorial Ch *Chich* 64-72; V W Hampstead Trin *Lon* 72-89; rtd 90. *11 Oziers, Elsenham, Bishop's Stortford, Herts CM22 6LS* Bishop's Stortford (01279) 816872

SMITH, Esmond Ernest Carrington. b 22. Mert Coll Ox BA43 MA47. Westcott Ho Cam 46. **d** 46 **p** 47. V Aston SS Pet and Paul *Birm* 65-75; RD Aston 71-75; Asst Master Stainiforth Sch Thetford 75-78; Perm to Offic *St E* from 78; rtd 87. *The Saltings, Broad Street, Orford, Suffolk IP12 2NQ* Orford (01394) 405234

SMITH, Eustace. b 20. St Pet Hall Ox BA43 MA46. Wycliffe Hall Ox 43. **d** 46 **p** 46. V Buckminster w Sewstern *Leic* 59-74; V Buckminster w Sewstern, Sproxton and Coston 74-82; R Algarkirk *Linc* 82-88; V Fosdyke 82-88; rtd 89. *32 Wordsworth Way, Measham, Swadlincote, Derbyshire DE12 7ER* Measham (01530) 273765

SMITH, Dr Felicity Ann. b 40. Bris Univ MB, ChB63. Qu Coll Birm. **dss** 86 **d** 87 **p** 94. NSM Dioc Bd for Soc Resp *Cov* from 86. *14 Oakwood Grove, Warwick CV34 5TD* Warwick (01926) 492452

SMITH, Francis Armand. b 10. Sarum Th Coll 59. **d** 61 **p** 62. V Upavon w Rushall *Sarum* 63-76; rtd 76; Perm to Offic *S'wark* from 76; Perm to Offic *Roch* from 77; Perm to Offic *Chich* from 78. *15 High Street, Cowden, Edenbridge, Kent TN8 5AB* Cowden (01342) 850484

SMITH, Francis James Prall. b 22. Nor Ord Course 73. **d** 76 **p** 77. NSM Gunthorpe w Bale *Nor* 76-82; NSM Friston *St E* 82-86; NSM Knodishall w Buxlow 82-86; NSM Aldringham w Thorpe, Knodishall w Buxlow etc 86-89; rtd 89; Perm to Offic *St E* from 90. *6 Bluebell Way, Worlingham, Beccles, Suffolk NR34 7BT* Beccles (01502) 711528

SMITH, Francis Malcolm (Frank). b 44. FBIM AIB69 Open Univ BA82. E Anglian Minl Tr Course 90. **d** 93. NSM Prittlewell *Chelmsf* from 93. *43 Burlescoombe Road, Southend-on-Sea SS1 3QE* Southend-on-Sea (01702) 586680 Fax 586293

SMITH, Frank. b 39. Nottm Univ CertEd65 Open Univ BA76. Paton Congr Coll Nottm 61 Cuddesdon Coll 69. **d** 69 **p** 70. In Congr Ch 65-69; C Davyhulme St Mary *Man* 69-72; V Peak Forest and Wormhill *Derby* 72-78; R W Hallam and

Mapperley 78-85; V Henleaze *Bris* from 85; RD Clifton from 93. *St Peter's Vicarage, 17 The Drive, Bristol BS9 4LD* Bristol (0117) 962 0636 or 962 3196

SMITH, Frank John. b 55. SS Mark & Jo Coll Chelsea BA85. Chich Th Coll CMT93. **d** 93 **p** 94. C Solihull *Birm* from 93. *17 Church Hill Close, Solihull, W Midlands B91 3JB* 0121-705 8923

SMITH, Geoffrey. b 45. Bernard Gilpin Soc Dur 65 Sarum Th Coll 66. **d** 69 **p** 70. C Hatf *Sheff* 69-71; C Bolton St Pet *Man* 71-74; V Lt Hulton 74-78; P-in-c Newc St Andr *Newc* 78-87; Soc Resp Adv 78-87; Hon Can Newc Cathl 84-87; Public Preacher *Birm* 87-93; Dir Cen for Applied Chr Studies 87-91; Team Ldr Home Office Birm Drug Prevention Unit 91-93; C Brampton and Farlam and Castle Carrock w Cumrew *Carl* from 93; Dioc Link Officer for ACUPA *Sarum* from 94. *The Rectory, Castle Carrock, Carlisle CA4 9LZ* Hayton (01228) 70120

SMITH, Canon Geoffrey Cobley. b 30. Bps' Coll Cheshunt 63. **d** 65 **p** 66. C Hockerill *St Alb* 65-68; C Evesham *Worc* 68-72; V Walberswick w Blythburgh *St E* 72-85; RD Halesworth 81-85; R Newmarket St Mary w Exning St Agnes from 85; RD Mildenhall from 86; Hon Can St E Cathl from 87. *The Rectory, 5A Fitzroy Street, Newmarket, Suffolk CB8 0JW* Newmarket (01638) 662448

SMITH, Geoffrey Keith. b 37. Lon Coll of Div 57. **d** 60 **p** 61. C Leek St Luke *Lich* 60-63; C Trentham 63-66; V Lilleshall 66-84; P-in-c Sheriffhales w Woodcote 83-84; V Lilleshall and Sheriffhales 84-87; P-in-c Haughton 83-91; R Derrington, Haughton and Ranton from 91. *The Rectory, Haughton, Stafford ST18 9HU* Stafford (01785) 780181

SMITH, Geoffrey Raymond. b 49. AKC71. St Aug Coll Cant 71. **d** 72 **p** 73. C Hendon St Alphage *Lon* 72-75; C Notting Hill St Mich and Ch Ch 75-78; P-in-c Isleworth St Fran 78-83; P-in-c Chipping Ongar *Chelmsf* 83-84; R 84-86; R Shelley 84-86; R Chipping Ongar w Shelley 86-89; RD Ongar 88-89; P-in-c Harlow St Mary Magd 89-90; V from 90. *The Vicarage, Harlow, Essex CM17 9ND* Harlow (01279) 422681

SMITH, George Ælbert. b 15. Sarum & Wells Th Coll 77. **d** 80 **p** 81. NSM Milton Abbot w Dunterton *Ex* 80-81; Hon C 80-81; NSM Milton Abbot, Dunterton, Lamerton etc 81-83; Perm to Offic 83-86; NSM Colyton, Southleigh, Offwell, Widworthy etc from 86. *St Mary's, Church Street, Colyton, Devon EX13 6JY* Colyton (01297) 552089

SMITH, George Frederic. b 35. AKC59. **d** 60 **p** 61. V Burton Dassett *Cov* 67-71; CF 71-74; V Lapley w Wheaton Aston *Lich* 74-80; V Gt Wyrley 80-90; V Shareshill 90-95; rtd 95. *16 Dan Yr Eppynt, Tirabad, Llangammarch Wells, Powys LD4 4DR*

SMITH, Canon George Robert Henry. b 24. Chich Th Coll 49. **d** 52 **p** 53. V Tuffley *Glouc* 65-82; Hon Can Glouc Cathl 81-94; R Leckhampton St Pet 82-94; rtd 94; NSM Westcote w Icomb and Bledington *Glouc* from 95. *The Vicarage, Chapel Street, Bledington, Chipping Norton, Oxon OX7 6UR* Kingham (01608) 658102

SMITH, Gerald. b 36. Sarum Th Coll 61. **d** 63 **p** 64. C Menston w Woodhead *Bradf* 63-66; Chapl RAF 66-70; C Hoylake *Ches* 70-72; R Inverurie *Ab* 72-74; R Kemnay 72-74; TV Hucknall Torkard *S'well* 74-75; Falkland Is 75-78; V Luddenden w Luddenden Foot *Wakef* 79-86; V Scopwick Gp *Linc* 86-94; P-in-c Leasingham from 94. *The Rectory, 3 Moor Lane, Leasingham, Sleaford, Lincs NG34 8JN* Sleaford (01529) 306756

SMITH, Preb Gilbert. b 14. Lon Univ BD64. Lambeth STh57 K Coll Lon 39. **d** 40 **p** 41. V Codsall *Lich* 58-83; RD Penkridge 72-82; Preb Lich Cathl 82-88; rtd 83; P-in-c Blymhill w Weston-under-Lizard *Lich* 83-88. *14 Malthouse Lane, Bradley, Stafford ST18 9DU* Stafford (01785) 780365

SMITH, Gill. **d** 94 **p** 95. NSM Haydock St Mark *Liv* from 94. *63 Arlington Drive, Leigh, Lancs WN7 3QP* Leigh (01942) 680402

SMITH, Mrs Gillian Angela (Gill). b 39. RGN60 RM62. All Nations Chr Coll IDC65. **d** 94 **p** 95. NSM Haydock St Mark *Liv* from 94. *63 Arlington Drive, Lowton, Leigh, Lancs WN7 3QP* Leigh (01942) 680402

SMITH, Godfrey Declan Burfield. b 42. TCD BA64 MA67 PGCE65. Irish Sch of Ecum DipEcum82 Sarum Th Coll. **d** 69 **p** 70. Zambia 70-75; Perm to Offic *D & G* from 81; S Regional Sec (Ireland) CMS from 81; Overseas Sec from 87. *Overseas House, 3 Belgrave Road, Rathmines, Dublin 6, Irish Republic* Dublin (1) 497-0931 or 280-7452 Fax 497-0939 or 280-7452

SMITH, Graeme Richard. b 65. Leeds Univ BA87. Qu Coll Birm 87. **d** 89 **p** 90. C Daventry *Pet* 90-92; C Daventry, Ashby St Ledgers, Braunston etc 92; Perm to Offic *Birm* from 92. *51 Weoley Avenue, Birmingham B29 6PP* 0121-472 4178

SMITH, Graham Charles Morell. b 47. St Chad's Coll Dur BA74. Westcott Ho Cam 74. **d** 76 **p** 77. C Tooting All SS *S'wark* 76-80; C Thamesmead 80-87; TR Kidlington w

Hampton Poyle *Ox* from 87; RD Ox 89-95. *St Mary's Rectory, 19 Mill Street, Kidlington, Oxon OX5 2EE* Kidlington (01865) 372230 Fax 378014

SMITH, Graham David Noel. b 37. Oak Hill Th Coll 72. **d** 73 **p** 74. C Southborough St Pet w Ch Ch and St Matt *Roch* 73-76; C Bedworth *Cov* 76-79; C Cov Caludon 79; R Treeton *Sheff* 79-84; V Riddlesden *Bradf* from 84; RD S Craven from 91. *The Vicarage, Riddlesden, Keighley, W Yorkshire BD20 5PA* Keighley (01535) 603419

SMITH, Canon Graham Francis. b 27. Leic Univ DSocStuds51 Lon Univ BD57. Wells Th Coll 51. **d** 54 **p** 55. V Angell Town St Jo *S'wark* 63-73; V Wandsworth St Anne 73-85; P-in-c Wandsworth St Faith 75-78; RD Wandsworth 81-85; Hon Can S'wark Cathl 82-92; Mert Deanery Missr 85-92; rtd 92. *The Haven, 9 High Street, Syresham, Brackley, Northants NN13 5HL* Syresham (01280) 850421

SMITH, Graham John. b 31. SSC. **d** 75 **p** 76. Hon C Devonport St Mark Ford *Ex* 75-81; Hon C Plympton St Maurice 81-90; V Ernesettle from 90. *St Aidan's Vicarage, 122 Rochford Crescent, Plymouth PL5 2QD* Plymouth (01752) 364374

SMITH, Graham John. b 60. BScEng84. Trin Coll Bris BA90. **d** 90 **p** 91. C Herne *Cant* 90-93; Chapl RN from 93. *Directorate Gen, RN Chapl Services, Room 203, Victory Building, HM Naval Base, Portsmouth PO1 3LS* Portsmouth (01705) 727903 Fax 727112

SMITH, Grahame Clarence. b 32. Lich Th Coll 58. **d** 60 **p** 61. R Tydd *Linc* 63-76; V Barholm w Stowe 76-81; V Tallington 76-81; R Uffington 76-81; P-in-c W Deeping 76-77; R 77-81; R Uffington 81-92; rtd 92. *Keeper's Cottage, Careby Road, Aunby, Stamford, Lincs PE9 4EG* Stamford (01780) 66386

SMITH, Gregory James. See CLIFTON-SMITH, Gregory James

SMITH, Canon Guy Howard. b 33. Man Univ BA54. Coll of Resurr Mirfield 60. **d** 62 **p** 63. C Oswestry H Trin *Lich* 62-66; Malaysia 66-69; V Willenhall St Anne *Lich* 69-79; P-in-c Willenhall St Steph 75-79; Malawi 79-82; Adn Lilongwe Lake Malawi 80-82; V Tettenhall Wood *Lich* 82-89; TR 89-91; TR Kidderminster St Jo and H Innocents *Worc* from 91. *The Vicarage, 9 Sutton Park Road, Kidderminster, Worcs DY11 6LE* Kidderminster (01562) 822186 Fax as telephone

SMITH, Harold. b 20. Qu Coll Birm 77. **d** 80 **p** 81. NSM Gravelly Hill *Birm* 80-85; NSM Duddeston w Nechells 85-93; Perm to Offic from 93. *37 Dovey Tower, Duddeston Manor Road, Birmingham B7 4LE* 0121-359 0568

SMITH, Harvey Jefferson. b 19. AMCT39 FIEE38 FIMechE52 FIPlantE67 ACIArb78. St Alb Minl Tr Scheme 81. **d** 88. Hon C Hemel Hempstead *St Alb* 88-92; Perm to Offic from 92. *43 Garland Close, Hemel Hempstead, Herts HP2 5HU* Hemel Hempstead (01442) 66377

SMITH, Sister Hazel Ferguson Waide. b 33. Univ Coll Lon BA55. **dss** 64 **d** 87. CSA 58-77; St Etheldreda's Children's Home Bedf 64-85; Bedf St Paul *St Alb* 85-92; Par Dn 87-92; rtd 92; Perm to Offic *St Alb* 92-95; Perm to Offic *Ox* 93-95. *Paddock House, 6 Linford Lane, Willen, Milton Keynes MK15 9DL* (01908) 661554 or (0589) 654881

SMITH, Henry Neville. b 25. Chich Th Coll 53. **d** 54 **p** 55. V Ivinghoe w Pitstone *Ox* 63-73; Chapl Qu Anne's Sch Caversham 73-90; rtd 90. *12 Poulner Close, Bognor Regis, W Sussex PO22 8HN* Bognor Regis (01243) 822716

SMITH, Henry Robert. b 41. Lanchester Poly BSc66. Qu Coll Birm 75. **d** 78 **p** 79. Hon C Hillmorton *Cov* 78-81; Lic to Offic *S'well* 81-85; Hon C Radcliffe-on-Trent and Shelford etc 85-89; C Sutton in Ashfield St Mary 89-92; P-in-c Forest Town from 92. *The Vicarage, Old Mill Lane, Forest Town, Mansfield, Notts NG19 0EP* Mansfield (01623) 21120

SMITH, Howard Alan. b 46. DCouns81 St Jo Coll Dur BA73 DipTh74. **d** 74 **p** 75. C Brighton St Matthias *Chich* 74-77; C Henfield 77-78; C Henfield w Shermanbury and Woodmancote 78-80; R Northiam 80-87; Chapl St Ebba's Hosp Epsom 87-94; Chapl Qu Mary's Hosp Carshalton 87-94; Chapl Merton and Sutton Community Trust from 94. *Merton and Sutton Community Trust, Damson Way, Orchard Hill, Carshalton, Surrey SM5 4NR* 0181-770 8000

SMITH, Howard Gilbert. b 48. Leeds Univ BA69. St Steph Ho Ox BA71 MA75 Ridley Hall Cam 72. **d** 73 **p** 74. C Wallsend St Luke *Newc* 73-76; C Farnworth and Kearsley *Man* 76-77; P-in-c Farnworth All SS 77-78; TV E Farnworth and Kearsley 78-82; V Belfield 82-93; V Leesfield from 93. *St Thomas's Vicarage, Wild Street, Lees, Oldham OL4 5AD* 0161-624 3731

SMITH, Ian. b 62. Hull Univ BA83. Oak Hill Th Coll DipHE87 BA88. **d** 88 **p** 89. C W Hampstead St Luke *Lon* 88-90; C Woking St Pet *Guildf* 90-95; V Leyland St Jo *Blackb* from 95. *St John's Vicarage, Leyland Lane, Leyland, Preston PR5 3HB* Leyland (01772) 621646

SMITH, Ian Charles. b 39. Lich Th Coll 65. **d** 68 **p** 69. C Kingshurst *Birm* 68-72; Chapl RAF 72-83; Chapl Winterton Hosp Sedgefield 83-91; Asst Chapl HM Pris Wakef 91-92; Chapl HM Pris Haverigg from 92. *HM Prison, Haverigg,*

Millom, Cumbria LA18 4NA Millom (01229) 772131 Fax 772561

SMITH, Canon Ian Walker. b 29. Leeds Univ BA52. Coll of Resurr Mirfield 52. **d** 54 **p** 55. C Crawley *Chich* 62-79; TV 79-81; R Clenchwarton *Ely* 81-94; RD Lynn Marshland 84-94; Hon Can Ely Cathl 88-94; Perm to Offic *Nor* from 88; rtd 94. *27 Jubilee Drive, Dersingham, King's Lynn, Norfolk PE31 6YA* Dersingham (01485) 540203

SMITH, James. b 26. NE Ord Course 76. **d** 79 **p** 80. NSM Seaton Hirst *Newc* 79-82; NSM Cresswell and Lynemouth 82-88; NSM Cambois 88-93; rtd 93. *140 Pont Street, Ashington, Northd NE63 0PX* Ashington (01670) 816557

SMITH, James Edward. b 30. Chich Th Coll 57. **d** 58 **p** 59. V Walton St Jo *Liv* 65-71; V Anfield St Columba 71-79; V Altcar 79-92; rtd 92; Perm to Offic *Linc* from 93. *272 Skellingthorpe Road, Lincoln LN6 0EU* Lincoln (01522) 696865

SMITH, James Harold (Jim). b 31. Ch Coll Tasmania ThL61. **d** 61 **p** 61. Australia 61-63 and 65-84 and 92-94; Canada 64-65; Chapl St Chris Hospice Lon 86-87; Asst Chapl Brook Gen Hosp Lon 87-92; Asst Chapl Greenwich Distr Hosp Lon 87-92; Perm to Offic *S'wark* from 94. *15 Couthurst Road, London SE3 8TN* 0181-858 4692

SMITH, James Henry. b 32. St Aid Birkenhead. **d** 65 **p** 66. C Wigan St Cath *Liv* 65-68; V Parkfield in Middleton *Man* 68-77; V Bolton Breightmet St Jas from 77. *St James's Vicarage, Roscow Avenue, Bolton BL2 6HU* Bolton (01204) 25640

SMITH, James William. b 47. RGN RMN MRIPHH Lambeth STh90. Chich Th Coll 78. **d** 80 **p** 80. C Kenwyn *Truro* 80-82; C Haslemere *Guildf* 82-84; TV Honiton, Gittisham, Combe Raleigh, Monkton etc *Ex* 84-91; Chapl R Marsden Hosp Lon and Surrey from 91; Perm to Offic *S'wark* from 91. *The Chaplain's Office, Royal Marsden Hospital, Sutton, Surrey SM2 5PT* 0181-642 6011

SMITH, Jeffery Donald Morris. b 23. **d** 53 **p** 54. S Africa 68-73; P-in-c Bintree w Themelthorpe *Nor* 73-76; V Twyford w Guist 73-76; R Twyford w Guist and Bintry w Themelthorpe 76-80; RD Sparham 79-81; R Twyford w Guist w Bintry w Themelthorpe etc 81; TR Hempnall 81-84; R Catfield 84-89; R Ingham w Sutton 84-89; rtd 89; Perm to Offic *Nor* from 89. *27 Dale Road, East Dereham, Norfolk NR19 2DD* Dereham (01362) 697022

SMITH, Jeffry Bradford. b 56. BA82. Ch Div Sch of the Pacific (USA) MDiv85 Ripon Coll Cuddesdon. **d** 86 **p** 87. C Frimley *Guildf* 87-91; R E and W Clandon from 91. *The Rectory, The Street, West Clandon, Guildford, Surrey GU4 7RG* Guildford (01483) 222573

SMITH, Mrs Jennifer Pamela (Jenny). b 63. Girton Coll Cam BA85 MA88. Oak Hill Th Coll BA91. **d** 91 **p** 94. C Rawdon *Bradf* 91-93; Chapl Bradf Cathl from 93. *Cathedral Cottage, 5 Cathedral Close, Bradford, W Yorkshire BD1 4EG* Bradford (01274) 390893

SMITH, Jeremy Victor. b 60. Keble Coll Ox BA82. Chich Th Coll 83. **d** 85 **p** 86. C Alton St Lawr *Win* 85-88; C W Hampstead St Jas *Lon* 88-93; V St Geo-in-the-East St Mary from 93. *St Mary's Vicarage, Johnson Street, London E1 0AQ* 0171-790 0973

SMITH, John Alec. b 37. Lon Coll of Div ALCD62 BD63. **d** 63 **p** 64. C Cromer *Nor* 63-66; C Barking St Marg *Chelmsf* 66-69; V Attercliffe *Sheff* 69-75; P-in-c Sheff St Barn 76-78; V Sheff St Barn and St Mary 78-89; Ind Chapl 78-89; RD Ecclesall 80-85; TR Chippenham St Paul w Hardenhuish etc *Bris* from 89. *St Paul's Rectory, 9 Greenway Park, Chippenham, Wilts SN15 1QG* Chippenham (01249) 653839

SMITH, John Bartlett. b 50. AIPM St Chad's Coll Dur BA73 Lanchester Poly DipIR80. Cuddesdon Coll 73. **d** 76 **p** 77. C Heref St Martin *Heref* 76-86; NSM Isleworth St Mary *Lon* 86-89; NSM Millom *Carl* 89-92; NSM Balham St Mary and St Jo *S'wark* from 92. *101 Gosberton Road, London SW12 8LG* 0181-675 1743

SMITH, John David Elliott. b 39. Dur Univ BA61. Cranmer Hall Dur 61. **d** 64 **p** 65. C Stratford-on-Avon w Bishopton *Cov* 64-70; P-in-c Tredington 70-76; P-in-c Newbold on Avon 76-81; V 81-89; P-in-c Arlington, Folkington and Wilmington *Chich* from 89. *The Vicarage, The Street, Wilmington, Polegate, E Sussex BN26 5SW* Alfriston (01323) 870268

SMITH, Dr John Denmead. b 44. Ox Univ BA65 MA69 DPhil71. Coll of Resurr Mirfield 72. **d** 75 **p** 76. Asst Chapl Win Coll from 75. *11 Kingsgate Street, Winchester, Hants SO23 9PD* Winchester (01962) 861820

SMITH, Canon John Douglas. b 20. Roch Th Coll 63. **d** 65 **p** 66. C Hersham *Guildf* 69-72; V Churt 72-80; V Cobham 80-88; RD Leatherhead 83-88; Hon Can Guildf Cathl 85-88; rtd 88. *77 Home Park, Oxted, Surrey RH8 0JT* Oxted (01883) 714861

SMITH, John Eckersley. b 26. Univ of Wales (Lamp). St Aug Coll Cant Wycliffe Hall Ox 53. **d** 55 **p** 56. C Northenden *Man* 73-75; V Charlestown 75-82; Perm to Offic from 85; rtd 91.

19 Arthur Street, Swinton, Manchester M27 3HP 0161-793 7707

SMITH, John Edward Allin. b 29. K Coll Lon BA52 Brunel Univ MPhil81. St Aug Coll Cant 49 Ridley Hall Cam 52. **d** 54 **p** 55. V Lewisham St Swithun *S'wark* 65-71; R Wexham *Ox* 71-83; P-in-c Princes Risborough w Ilmer 83-84; R 84-91; rtd 91. *8 Goldsmith Close, Bicester, Oxon OX6 8XT* Deddington (01869) 248019

SMITH, John Ernest. b 52. St Andr Univ MTh77. Wycliffe Hall Ox 78. **d** 79 **p** 80. C Bermondsey St Mary w St Olave, St Jo etc *S'wark* 79-87; P-in-c Whyteleafe from 87. *8 Whyteleafe Road, Whyteleafe, Surrey CR3 5EE*

SMITH, John Graham. b 32. **d** 78 **p** 79. NSM Hordle *Win* from 78. *3 Marryat Road, New Milton, Hants BH25 5LW* New Milton (01425) 615701

SMITH, John Lawrence. b 43. Birm Univ BSc65. Linc Th Coll 67. **d** 70 **p** 71. C Frodingham *Linc* 70-75; TV Gt Grimsby St Mary and St Jas 75-83; V Wolv St Andr *Lich* from 83. *St Andrew's Vicarage, 66 Albert Road, Wolverhampton WV6 0AF* Wolverhampton (01902) 712935

SMITH, John Leslie. b 44. Trin Coll Cam BA65 MA71. Ripon Coll Cuddesdon 79. **d** 81 **p** 82. C Ollerton *S'well* 81-84; P-in-c Farndon 84-88; P-in-c Thorpe 84-88; P-in-c Langford w Holme from 88; P-in-c Winthorpe from 88; Dioc Chief Insp Ch Schs from 88. *The Rectory, The Spinney, Winthorpe, Newark, Notts NG24 2NT* Newark (01636) 704985

SMITH, John Macdonald. b 29. Ch Coll Cam BA52 MA56. Wells Th Coll 56. **d** 58 **p** 59. V Kidmore End *Ox* 63-82; rtd 82. *38 Main Road, Norton, Evesham, Worcs WR11 4TL* Evesham (01386) 870918

SMITH, John Malcolm. b 36. ACIB60. N Ord Course 81. **d** 84 **p** 85. NSM Bury St Pet *Man* from 84. *46 Ajax Drive, Bury, Lancs BL9 8EF* 0161-766 8378

SMITH, John Oswald Salkeld. b 32. Oak Hill Th Coll 57. **d** 60 **p** 61. C Peckham St Mary Magd *S'wark* 61-63; C Rodbourne Cheney *Bris* 63-67; V Bradf St Aug Undercliffe *Bradf* 67-74; P-in-c Hammersmith St Simon *Lon* 74-76; V Chelsea St Jo w St Andr from 76. *St Andrew's Vicarage, 43 Park Walk, London SW10 0AU* 0171-352 1675

SMITH, Canon John Reginald. b 15. TCD BA39 MA42. Wycliffe Hall Ox 40. **d** 41 **p** 42. C Heaton Norris Ch Ch *Man* 41-44; C Stretford St Matt 44-47; R Stretford All SS 47-49; V Radcliffe St Thos 49-59; R Sutton *Liv* 59-66; RD Bury Man 66-86; R Bury St Mary from 66; Hon Can Man Cathl from 72. *St Mary's Rectory, Bury, Lancs BL9 0JR* 0161-764 2452

SMITH, John Roger. b 36. Dur Univ BA59. Tyndale Hall Bris 59. **d** 61 **p** 62. C Chaddesden St Mary *Derby* 61-63; C Gresley 63-66; V Burton Ch Ch *Lich* 66-76; V Doncaster St Mary *Sheff* 76-92; R Barnburgh w Melton on the Hill 92-94; R Barnburgh w Melton on the Hill etc from 94. *The Rectory, Barnburgh, Doncaster, S Yorkshire DN5 7ET* Rotherham (01709) 892598

SMITH, Canon John Stewart. b 18. St Cath Soc Ox BA42 MA46. Ripon Hall Ox 42. **d** 43 **p** 44. V Shirehampton *Bris* 58-72; V Westbury-on-Trym St Alb 72-83; RD Clifton 73-79; Hon Can Bris Cathl 77-84; rtd 83; Perm to Offic *Bris* from 84. *48A Downs Park West, Bristol BS6 7QL* Bristol (0117) 962 9208

SMITH, John Thomas. b 29. Shuttleworth Agric Coll NDA55 Keele Univ DASE72 Wolv Poly MPhil81 PhD87. W Midl Minl Tr Course 87. **d** 91 **p** 92. NSM Drayton in Hales *Lich* from 91. *Red Bank House, Market Drayton, Shropshire TF9 1AY* Market Drayton (01630) 652302

SMITH, John Thompson. b 30. Wycliffe Hall Ox 64. **d** 66 **p** 67. V Stoke Prior *Worc* 69-75; Asst Gen Sec Red Triangle Club 75-85; R Tendring and Lt Bentley w Beaumont cum Moze *Chelmsf* 85-89; R Fairstead w Terling and White Notley etc 89-92; Chapl Heath Hosp Tendring 85-92; rtd 92. *1 Harvey Close, Weston-super-Mare, Avon BS22 0DW* Weston-super-Mare (01934) 514256

SMITH, John Trevor. b 47. GGSM. Coll of Resurr Mirfield 74. **d** 77 **p** 78. C Loughton St Jo *Chelmsf* 77-80; C Ruislip St Martin *Lon* 80-84; P-in-c Southall Ch Redeemer 84-91; V Kingsbury St Andr from 91. *St Andrew's Vicarage, 28 Old Church Lane, London NW9 8RZ* 0181-205 7447

SMITH, Jonathan Paul. b 60. Univ of Wales (Lamp) BA81. Wycliffe Hall Ox 82. **d** 84 **p** 85. C Baglan *Llan* 84-88; C Gabalfa 88-90; V Llanganten and Llangammarch and Llanfechan etc *S & B* from 90. *The Rectory, Maes Glas, Llangammarch Wells, Powys LD4 4EE* Llangammarch Wells (015912) 482

SMITH, Jonathan Peter. b 55. K Coll Lon BD77 AKC77 Cam Univ PGCE78. Westcott Ho Cam 79. **d** 80 **p** 81. C Gosforth All SS *Newc* 80-82; C Waltham Abbey *Chelmsf* 82-85; Chapl City Univ Lon 85-88; R Harrold and Carlton w Chellington *St Alb* from 88; Chapl Beds Police from 90. *The Rectory, 3 The Moor, Carlton, Bedford MK43 7JR* Bedford (01234) 720262

SMITH, Julian. b 48. K Coll Lon 70. Linc Th Coll 71. **d** 73 **p** 74. C Taunton Lyngford *B & W* 73-76; TV Wellington and Distr 76-81; R Axbridge w Shipham and Rowberrow from 81; Chapl St Jo Hosp Axbridge from 84. *The Rectory, Cheddar Road, Axbridge, Somerset BS26 2DL* Axbridge (01934) 732261

SMITH, Julian William. b 64. Liv Univ BSc85. Trin Coll Carmarthen BA93. **d** 93 **p** 94. C Henfynyw w Aberaeron and Llanddewi Aberarth *St D* from 93. *Hillcrest, Vicarage Hill, Aberaeron, Dyfed SA46 0DY* Aberaeron (01545) 570792

SMITH, Keith. b 46. ACIB. S Dios Minl Tr Scheme. **d** 87 **p** 88. NSM W Worthing St Jo *Chich* 87-94; NSM Maybridge from 94. *20 Trent Road, Worthing, W Sussex BN12 4EL* Worthing (01903) 505850

SMITH, Kenneth Robert. b 48. K Coll Lon BD75 AKC75. St Aug Coll Cant 75. **d** 76 **p** 77. C Birtley *Dur* 76-80; V Lamesley 80-90; R Whitburn from 90. *The Rectory, 51 Front Street, Whitburn, Sunderland SR6 7JD* 0191-529 2232

SMITH, Kenneth Victor George. b 37. Lon Univ BD62. ALCD61. **d** 62 **p** 63. Hon C Bromley Common St Aug *Roch* 62-66; Hon C Streatham Immanuel w St Anselm *S'wark* 66-68; Perm to Offic 68-78; Hon C Sanderstead All SS 78-91; Chapl Whitgift Sch and Ho Croydon from 78; Hon C Croydon St Jo from 91. *Bridle Ways, Haling Grove, Croydon CR2 6DQ* 0181-680 4460

SMITH, Kevin. b 66. Westmr Coll Ox BA89. Chich Th Coll 90. **d** 92 **p** 93. C Worksop Priory *S'well* from 92. *268 Kilton Road, Worksop, Notts S80 2DZ* Worksop (01909) 485642

SMITH, Canon Laurence Kenneth Powell. b 17. Lon Coll of Div ALCD41 LTh74. **d** 41 **p** 42. V Iford *Win* 57-72; R Stockbridge and Houghton 72-85; RD Romsey 79-85; Hon Can Win Cathl 82-85; rtd 85; Perm to Offic *Win* from 85. *8 Riverside Gardens, Romsey, Hants SO51 8HN* Romsey (01794) 518262

SMITH, Laurence Sidney. b 37. Sarum & Wells Th Coll 70. **d** 73 **p** 74. C Surbiton St Matt *S'wark* 73-76; C Horley 76-81; V W Ewell *Guildf* 81-90; V W Byfleet from 90. *The Vicarage, 5 Dartnell Avenue, West Byfleet, Surrey KT14 6PJ* Weybridge (01932) 345270

SMITH, Lawrence Paul. b 51. Southn Univ BTh81. Chich Th Coll 76. **d** 79 **p** 80. C Margate St Jo *Cant* 79-84; R Eythorne w Waldershare 84-87; P-in-c Sibertswold w Coldred 85-87; R Eythorne and Elvington w Waldershare etc from 87. *The Rectory, Barfreystone Road, Eythorne, Dover, Kent CT15 4AH* Shepherdswell (01304) 830241

SMITH, Canon Lewis Shand. b 52. Aber Univ MA74 Edin Univ BD78. Edin Th Coll 74. **d** 77 **p** 78. C Wishaw *Glas* 77-79; P-in-c 79-80; C Motherwell 77-79; P-in-c 79-80; R Lerwick *Ab* from 80; R Burravoe from 80; Miss to Seamen from 80; Can St Andr Cathl *Ab* from 93. *1 Greenrig, Lerwick, Isle of Shetland ZE1 0AW* Lerwick (01595) 3862

SMITH, Miss Lorna Cassandra. b 43. Open Univ BA76. Cant Sch of Min 82. **dss** 86 **d** 87 **p** 94. Birchington w Acol and Minnis Bay *Cant* 86-87; Par Dn 87-92; C Addlestone *Guildf* from 92. *St Augustine's House, Albert Road, Addlestone, Surrey KT15 2PX* Weybridge (01932) 821176

SMITH, Mrs Lorna Rosalind. b 53. Oak Hill NSM Course 89. **d** 92 **p** 94. NSM Squirrels Heath *Chelmsf* 92-94; NSM Stanford-le-Hope w Mucking from 94. *24 Martin's Close, Stanford-le-Hope, Essex SS17 8AB* Grays Thurrock (01375) 642439/672271

SMITH, Mrs Margaret Elizabeth. b 46. Bretton Hall Coll CertEd67. N Ord Course 85. **d** 88 **p** 94. Hon Par Dn Battyeford *Wakef* 88-91; Hon C Mirfield 89-91; Chapl HM Pris New Hall from 90; D-in-c Flockton cum Denby Grange *Wakef* 91-94; P-in-c from 94. *The Vicarage, 23 Hardcastle Lane, Flockton, Wakefield, W Yorkshire WF4 4AR* Wakefield (01924) 848349 Fax 840692

SMITH, Mark Gordon Robert Davenport. b 56. St Jo Coll Dur BA77. Ridley Hall Cam 78. **d** 80 **p** 81. C Sheff St Jo *Sheff* 80-83; C Brightside w Wincobank 83-86; V Kimberworth Park 86-91; Perm to Offic from 91; Consultant NE England CPAS from 91. *78 Storrs Hill Road, Ossett, Wakefield, W Yorkshire WF5 0DA* Wakefield (01924) 270497

SMITH, Mark Graham. b 63. Ex Univ BA86 Qu Coll Cam DipTh89. Westcott Ho Cam 87. **d** 90 **p** 91. C Cottingham *York* 90-92; C Guisborough 92-94; Chapl St Martin's Coll of Educn *Blackb* from 94. *St Martin's College, Bowerham Road, Lancaster LA1 3JD* Lancaster (01524) 63446

SMITH, Mark Richard Samuel. b 63. UMIST BSc84. Cranmer Hall Dur 89. **d** 92 **p** 93. C Kersal Moor *Man* 89-93; C Halliwell St Pet from 93. *St Andrew's House, 29 Tattersall Avenue, Bolton BL1 5TE* Bolton (01204) 849432

SMITH, Martin David. b 52. LTCL Hull Univ BA75. Cuddesdon Coll 75. **d** 78 **p** 79. C Brentwood St Thos *Chelmsf* 78-80; C Reading St Giles *Ox* 80-91; R Colkirk w Oxwick w Pattesley, Whissonsett etc *Nor* 91-95; P-in-c Gt and Lt Ryburgh w Gateley and Testerton 94-95; P-in-c Hempton and

Pudding Norton 94-95; P-in-c Nor St Pet Parmentergate w St Jo from 95. *The Rectory, 10 Stepping Lane, Norwich NR1 1PE* Norwich (01603) 622509

SMITH, Martin John. b 59. Qu Coll Birm 86. **d** 89 **p** 90. C Grays Thurrock *Chelmsf* 89-92; C Warley Woods *Birm* 92-94; V Stocking Farm *Leic* from 94. *The Vicarage, 97 Halifax Drive, Stocking Farm, Leicester LE4 2DP* Leicester (0116) 235 3206

SMITH, Martin Lee. b 47. Worc Coll Ox BA68. Cuddesdon Coll 68. **d** 70 **p** 71. C Digswell *St Alb* 70-71; C Cheshunt 71-73; Perm to Offic *Ox* 74-80; USA from 81. *Address temporarily unknown*

SMITH, Canon Martin William. b 40. K Coll Lon BD63 AKC63. **d** 64 **p** 65. C Ashford St Hilda CD *Lon* 64-67; Malaysia 67-71; V Lakenham St Mark *Nor* 72-85; V N Walsham w Antingham from 85; RD Tunstead from 91; Hon Can Nor Cathl from 93; P-in-c Neatishead, Barton Turf and Irstead from 94. *The Vicarage, 28A Yarmouth Road, North Walsham, Norfolk NR28 9AT* North Walsham (01692) 406380

SMITH, Martyn. b 52. CertEd73. Oak Hill Th Coll BA81. **d** 81 **p** 82. C Halliwell St Pet *Man* 81-86; V Cam St Martin *Ely* 86-89; Vineyard Chr Fellowship from 89. *6 Lambeth Close, Horwich, Bolton BL6 6DQ* Horwich (01204) 669529

SMITH, Maurice Jeffrey. b 18. Bps' Coll Cheshunt 56. **d** 56 **p** 57. V Springfield H Trin *Chelmsf* 58-70; Chapl HM Pris Chelmsf 65-70; R Wickham Bishops *Chelmsf* 70-86; RD Witham 76-86; rtd 86; Perm to Offic *Ex* from 88. *88 Valley Way, Exmouth, Devon EX8 4RL* Exmouth (01395) 278524

SMITH, Merrick Thomas Jack. b 37. CEng65 MCIBSE65 Glos Coll of Arts & Tech ONC57. Oak Hill NSM Course 90. **d** 92 **p** 93. NSM Isleworth St Mary *Lon* 92-94; Perm to Offic *Birm* from 94. *10A Mulroy Road, Sutton Coldfield, W Midlands B74 2PY*

SMITH, Mervyn Gilbert Morris. b 18. Ripon Hall Ox 56. **d** 58 **p** 59. V Rosherville *Roch* 67-79; R Horsmonden 79-86; Chapl HM Det Cen Blantyre Ho 82-86; rtd 86; Perm to Offic *Portsm* from 86. *9 Golden Ridge, Freshwater, Isle of Wight PO40 9LE* Isle of Wight (01983) 754857

SMITH, Michael. b 54. Matlock Coll of Educn CertEd76 Nottm Univ BEd77. Ridley Hall Cam 87. **d** 89 **p** 90. C Ilkeston St Mary *Derby* 89-92; TV Wirksworth from 92. *58 Yokecliffe Drive, Wirksworth, Matlock, Derbyshire DE4 4EX* Matlock (01629) 822896

SMITH, Michael Anthony. b 47. Univ of Wales (Abth) MA73. **d** 78 **p** 79. NSM Llandingat w Llanfair and Myddfai 78-82; Chapl Llandovery Coll 81-82; Chapl Pocklington Sch York from 82. *Hosmer Lodge, 35 Percy Road, Pocklington, York YO4 2LZ* Pocklington (01759) 304543 or 303125

SMITH, Michael David. b 57. BA80. St Steph Ho Ox 81. **d** 83 **p** 84. C Beaconsfield *Ox* 83-87; V Wing w Grove 87-92; R Farnham Royal w Hedgerley from 92. *The Rectory, Victoria Road, Farnham Royal, Slough SL2 3NJ* Farnham Common (01753) 643233

SMITH, Michael George. b 33. Univ Coll Ox BA57 MA61 BD65. St Steph Ho Ox 57. **d** 60 **p** 61. C Ex St Thos *Ex* 60-63; C Ox St Mary V *Ox* 63-65; USA 65-70; Chapl Qu Marg Sch Escrick Park 70-74; Chapl Pocklington Sch York 74-82; V Ex St Dav *Ex* 82-91; R Silverton 91-95; R Butterleigh 91-95. *1 Station Road, Ide, Exeter EX2 9RP* Exeter (01392) 496523

SMITH, Michael Ian Antony. b 69. Warw Univ BSc91. Oak Hill Th Coll BA95. **d** 95. C Cheadle *Ches* from 95. *1 Warren Avenue, Cheadle, Cheshire SK8 1NB* 0161-428 3001

SMITH, Michael James. b 47. AKC69. St Aug Coll Cant 70. **d** 71 **p** 72. C Corby St Columba *Pet* 71-78; V Collierley *Dur* 78-80; CPAS Evang from 83. *6 Blind Lane, Chester le Street, Co Durham DH3 4AG* 0191-388 1977

SMITH, Michael John. b 47. Lon Univ DipTh71. Kelham Th Coll 65. **d** 71 **p** 72. C Cov St Mary *Cov* 71-75; Chapl RN 75-90; CF 90-95; V Lynch w Iping Marsh and Milland *Chich* from 95. *The Rectory, Fernhurst Road, Milland, Liphook, Hants GU30 7LU* Milland (01428) 741285

SMITH, Michael Keith John (Mike). b 66. Thames Poly BSc88. Linc Th Coll BTh95. **d** 95. C Birch St Agnes *Man* from 95; C Longsight St Jo w St Cypr from 95. *St John's Rectory, St John's Road, Longsight, Manchester M13 0WU* 0161-224 2744

SMITH, Michael Raymond. b 36. ARCM56 ARCO56 Qu Coll Cam BA59 MA63. Cuddesdon Coll 64. **d** 65 **p** 66. C Redcar *York* 65-70; V Dormanstown 70-73; Prec Worc Cathl *Worc* 73-77; TR Worc St Barn w Ch Ch 77-83; RD Worc E 79-83; V Eskdale, Irton, Muncaster and Waberthwaite *Carl* 83-87; Chapl Uppingham Sch Leics 87-93; Lic to Offic *Pet* 88-93; P-in-c Stoke Lacy, Moreton Jeffries w Much Cowarne etc *Heref* from 93; Dioc Schs Officer from 93. *The Rectory, Stoke Lacy, Bromyard, Herefordshire HR7 4HH* Munderfield (01885) 490257

SMITH, Michael Richard Guy. b 55. Man Univ BA77. Ripon Coll Cuddesdon 88. **d** 90 **p** 91. C Wallasey St Hilary *Ches* 90-93; C Howden TM *York* 93-94; TV from 94. *The Vicarage, Pontington Road, Eastrington, Goole, N Humberside DN14 7QE* Howden (01430) 410282

SMITH, Michael Robin. b 34. ACIB58. Sarum Th Coll. **d** 62 **p** 63. C Perry Hill St Geo *S'wark* 62-65; C Streatham St Leon 65-68; NSM E Brixton St Jude 68-70; Brixton Chr Counselling Min 70-79; Wandsworth Ch Inst 80-91. *8 Turret House, Limmer Lane, Felpham, Bognor Regis, W Sussex PO22 7EN* Bognor Regis (01243) 864339

SMITH, Neil Reginald. b 47. Qu Coll Birm 70. **d** 72 **p** 73. C Horton *Bradf* 72-75; C New Mills *Derby* 76-79; Perm to Offic *Ches* from 79; Lic to Offic *Derby* from 79; Chapl Community of the K of Love Whaley Bridge from 79. *Whaley Hall, Reservoir Road, Whaley Bridge, Stockport, Cheshire SK12 7BL* Whaley Bridge (01663) 32495

SMITH, Nicholas Victor. b 54. St Jo Coll Dur BA76. St Steph Ho Ox 76. **d** 78 **p** 85. C Saltley *Birm* 78-79; C St Marylebone Ch Ch *Lon* 84-87; C Barnsley St Mary *Wakef* 87-90; Perm to Offic *Birm* from 93. *16 Maple Road, Sutton Coldfield, W Midlands B72 1JP* 0121-355 1744

SMITH, Norman. b 22. Coll of Resurr Mirfield 85. **d** 85 **p** 86. Hon C Greenhill *Sheff* 85-89; rtd 89; Hon C Blackpool St Mary *Blackb* from 89. *21 Cairn Court, Squires Gate Lane, Blackpool FY4 2QQ* Blackpool (01253) 401498

SMITH, Norman George. b 27. K Coll Lon BD52 AKC52. **d** 53 **p** 54. R Bedhampton *Portsm* 63-81; V Win St Bart *Win* 81-92; RD Win 84-89; rtd 92. *40 Goring Field, Winchester, Hants SO22 5NH* Winchester (01962) 852882

SMITH, Norman Jordan. b 30. Sarum Th Coll 57. **d** 60 **p** 61. V Chidham *Chich* 68-94; rtd 95. *Potters Paradise, 82 Church Road, Hayling Island, Hants PO11 0NX*

SMITH, Mrs Olwen. b 44. Birm Univ BA66 DPS68. Selly Oak Coll 67. **d** 87 **p** 94. Ind Chapl Black Country Urban Ind Miss *Lich* from 84. *16 Albert Road, Wolverhampton WV6 0AF* Wolverhampton (01902) 712935

SMITH, Miss Pamela Frances (Pam). b 44. St Mary's Cheltenham TCert65. W of England Minl Tr Course 91. **d** 94. NSM Badgeworth w Shurdington *Glouc* from 94. *The Tynings, 38 Andsell Drive, Gloucester GL3 4BU* Gloucester (01452) 610805

SMITH, Paul Aidan. b 59. Birm Univ BA82. Wycliffe Hall Ox 82. **d** 85 **p** 86. C Selly Park St Steph and St Wulstan *Birm* 85-88; C Kensal Rise St Mark and St Martin *Lon* 88-91; V Water Eaton *Ox* from 91. *The Vicarage, 38 Mill Road, Bletchley, Milton Keynes MK2 2LD* Milton Keynes (01908) 374585

SMITH, Paul Andrew. b 55. St Chad's Coll Dur BA76. Chich Th Coll 78. **d** 80 **p** 81. C Habergham Eaves St Matt *Blackb* 80-83; C Ribbleton 83-86; V Rishton from 86; RD Whalley from 95. *The Vicarage, Somerset Road, Rishton, Blackburn BB1 4BP* Great Harwood (01254) 886191

SMITH, Preb Paul Gregory. b 39. Ex Univ BA61. St Steph Ho Ox 61. **d** 63 **p** 64. C Walthamstow St Mich *Chelmsf* 63-66; C Devonport St Mark Ford *Ex* 66-69; C Hemel Hempstead *St Alb* 69-71; TV 71-83; R Bideford *Ex* from 83; Chapl Bideford and Torridge Hosps from 83; Preb Ex Cathl *Ex* from 95. *The Rectory, Abbotsham Road, Bideford, Devon EX39 3AB* Bideford (01237) 470228

SMITH, Paul Raymond. b 60. Sheff Univ BA81. Qu Coll Birm 82. **d** 85 **p** 86. C Frecheville and Hackenthorpe *Sheff* 85-88; C Rawmarsh w Parkgate 88-89; TV Staveley and Barrow Hill *Derby* 89-93. *55 Ladbrooke Crescent, Basford, Nottingham NG6 0GL*

SMITH, Mrs Pauline Frances. b 37. Bris Univ BA58 Lon Univ CertEd59. Sarum & Wells Th Coll 87. **d** 90 **p** 94. C Cobham *Guildf* from 90. *18 Daymerslea Ridge, Leatherhead, Surrey KT22 8TF* Leatherhead (01372) 376284

SMITH, Peter. b 36. Keele Univ BA60. Cuddesdon Coll 73. **d** 75 **p** 76. C Shrewsbury St Chad *Lich* 75-80; V Burton St Chad 80-90; P-in-c Berwick w Selmeston and Alciston *Chich* 90-91; R from 91. *The Parsonage, Berwick, Polegate, E Sussex BN26 6SR* Alfriston (01323) 870512

SMITH, Peter. b 49. Ex Univ BSc69 PGCE73. Carl Dioc Tr Course. **d** 82 **p** 83. NSM Kendal H Trin *Carl* from 82. *55 Empson Road, Kendal, Cumbria LA9 5PR* Kendal (01539) 721467

SMITH, Peter Albert. b 26. Keble Coll Ox BA51 MA55. Wells Th Coll 51. **d** 53 **p** 54. Bp's Chapl to Students *Bradf* 67-73; V Madeley *Lich* 73-77; rtd 81; Lic to Offic *Glouc* 81-89. *8 Newport Road, Whitchurch, Shropshire SY13 1QE*

SMITH, Peter Alexander. *See* GRAYSMITH, Peter Alexander

SMITH, Peter Anson Stewart. b 16. AKC37. **d** 39 **p** 40. V Leavesden All SS *St Alb* 49-73; V Greenhill St Jo *Lon* 73-81; Selection Sec ACCM 75-81; rtd 81; Perm to Offic *Chich* 81-83; P-in-c Brighton St Matthias 83-84; P-in-c Brighton St Pet w Chpl Royal and St Jo 85; P-in-c Brighton St Mich 85-86; P-in-c Moulsecoomb 86-87; TV 88-89; P-in-c Preston 87-88; P-in-c

Brighton St Aug and St Sav 89-91; P-in-c Hove St Andr Old Ch 92. *3 West Drive, Brighton BN2 2GD* Brighton (01273) 605042

SMITH, Peter Denis Frank. b 52. Local Minl Tr Course. **d** 81 **p** 83. NSM Camberwell St Mich w All So w Em *S'wark* 81-94; NSM Croydon St Jo from 95. *57 Alton Road, Croydon CR0 4LZ* 0181-760 9656

SMITH, Peter Francis Chasen. b 28. Leeds Univ BA54. Coll of Resurr Mirfield 54. **d** 56 **p** 57. Chapl St Aid Sch Harrogate 68-85; P-in-c Lower Nidderdale *Ripon* 85-93; rtd 93. *Clematis Cottage, Main Street, Kilburn, York YO6 4AH* Coxwold (01347) 868394

SMITH, Peter Howard. b 55. St Andr Univ MTh78. Trin Coll Bris 78. **d** 79 **p** 80. C Handforth *Ches* 79-82; C Eccleston St Luke *Liv* 82-85; V Leyton St Paul *Chelmsf* 85-91; V Darwen St Barn *Blackb* from 91. *St Barnabas' Vicarage, 68 Park Road, Darwen, Lancs BB3 2LD* Darwen (01254) 702732

SMITH, Peter Howard. b 57. St Jo Coll Dur BSc78 Selw Coll Cam BA82 MA85. Ridley Hall Cam 80. **d** 83 **p** 84. C Welling *Roch* 83-87; C Hubberston w Herbrandston and Hasguard etc *St D* 87-89; C Hubberston 89-91; V Canley *Cov* from 91. *St Stephen's Vicarage, 47 Glebe Close, Coventry CV4 8DJ* Coventry (01203) 421685

SMITH, Peter James. b 23. K Coll Lon 49. **d** 53 **p** 54. Chapl Highcroft Hosp Birm 62-71; C Wolborough w Newton Abbot *Ex* 71-74; C Furze Platt *Ox* 74-78; Travelling Sec Ch Coun for Health and Healing 78-81; P-in-c Bisham *Ox* 82-90; rtd 90; NSM Hindhead *Guildf* from 90. *Church Cottage, Tilford Road, Hindhead, Surrey GU26 6RB* Hindhead (01428) 606782

SMITH, Peter Michael. b 28. Open Univ BA75. K Coll Lon 52. **d** 56 **p** 57. V Barrow St Aid *Carl* 69-72; V Preston Patrick 72-93; rtd 93; Chapl to the Deaf and Hard of Hearing *Carl* from 93. *7 Green Road, Kendal, Cumbria LA9 4QR* Kendal (01539) 726741 or (0973) 224289

SMITH, Peter William. b 31. Glouc Th Course 74. **d** 77 **p** 77. C Coleford w Staunton *Glouc* 77; Hon C 77-87; P-in-c Alderton w Gt Washbourne 87-94; R Alderton, Gt Washbourne, Dumbleton etc from 94. *The Rectory, Alderton, Tewkesbury, Glos GL20 8NR* Cheltenham (01242) 620238

SMITH, Philip James. b 32. St Alb Minl Tr Scheme. **d** 82 **p** 83. NSM Radlett *St Alb* 82-85; C 85-89; V Codicote from 89; RD Hatf from 95. *The Vicarage, 4 Bury Lane, Codicote, Hitchin, Herts SG4 8XT* Stevenage (01438) 820266

SMITH, Philip Hathway. b 66. St Andr Univ MTh88. Coll of Resurr Mirfield 90. **d** 92 **p** 93. C Shrewsbury St Giles w Sutton and Atcham *Lich* 92-94; C Clayton from 94. *Church House, 285 Clayton Road, Newcastle, Staffs ST5 3EU*

SMITH, Philip James. b 60. ACGI82 Imp Coll Lon BScEng82 Fitzw Coll Cam BA94. Ridley Hall Cam CTM95. **d** 95. C Aldborough w Boroughbridge and Roecliffe *Ripon* from 95. *Rollinson House, Ladywell Road, Boroughbridge, York YO5 9AX* Boroughbridge (01423) 324747

SMITH, Philip Lloyd Cyril. b 22. Ch Coll Cam BA47 MA49. Wycliffe Hall Ox 47. **d** 49 **p** 50. R Burslem St Jo *Lich* 56-83; P-in-c Burslem St Paul 82-83; R Burslem 83-86; rtd 86; Perm to Offic *Sheff* from 86. *7 Melfort Glen, Sheffield S10 5SU* Sheffield (0114) 230 4238

SMITH, Canon Philip Morell. b 10. Wadh Coll Ox BA33 MA36. Wells Th Coll 33. **d** 34 **p** 35. R Streatham St Leon *S'wark* 64-72; Hon Can S'wark Cathl 68-72; RD Streatham 68-72; R Puttenham and Wanborough *Guildf* 72-78; rtd 78; Perm to Offic *Win* 78-95. *The Doreys, Edge, Stroud, Glos GL6 6NF* Painswick (01452) 813580

SMITH, Philip Sydney Bellman (Luke). b 11. St Cath Soc Ox BA35 DipTh36 MA46. St Steph Ho Ox 35. **d** 37 **p** 38. C Storrington *Chich* 39-42; CR from 51; rtd 81. *House of the Resurrection, Mirfield, W Yorkshire WF14 0BN* Mirfield (01924) 494318

SMITH, Raymond Charles William (Ray). b 56. K Coll Lon BD78 AKC78. Coll of Resurr Mirfield 79. **d** 80 **p** 81. C Iffley *Ox* 80-83; C Wallingford w Crowmarsh Gifford etc 83-86; V Tilehurst St Mary from 86. *St Mary Magdalen's Vicarage, 270 Kentwood Hill, Reading RG3 6DR* Reading (01734) 427234

SMITH, Canon Raymond Douglas. b 31. TCD BA53 MA56 BD56. **d** 54 **p** 55. C Belf St Mich *Conn* 54-56; C Ballymacarrett St Patr *D & D* 56-58; CMS Tr Coll Chislehurst 58-60; Kenya (CMS) 60-71; Asst Gen Sec (Hibernian) CMS 71-74; Gen Sec CMS 74-86; CMS Ireland 76-86; Hon Can N Maseno from 78; I Powerscourt w Kilbride and Annacrevy *D & G* from 86; Can Ch Ch Cathl Dub from 94. *Powerscourt Rectory, Enniskerry, Bray, Co Wicklow, Irish Republic* Dublin (1) 286-3534

SMITH, Raymond Frederick. b 28. Lon Univ BSc51 Leeds Univ MA65. Oak Hill Th Coll 51. **d** 53 **p** 54. V Normanton *Wakef* 66-81; RD Chevet 73-81; R Moreton *Ches* 81-90; rtd 90. *Peniarth Uchaf, Meifod, Powys SY22 6DS* Meifod (0193884) 366

SMITH, Raymond George Richard. b 38. Univ of Wales (Ban) BSc61 MSc65. W Midl Minl Tr Course 91. **d** 94 **p** 95. NSM Edgmond w Kynnersley and Preston Wealdmoors *Lich* from 94; Chapl Princess R Hosp Telford from 95. *10 Chetwynd Road, Edgmond, Newport, Shropshire TF10 8HJ* Newport (01952) 813346

SMITH, Raymond Horace David (Ray). b 30. Sir John Cass Coll Lon FIBMS61. Lon Coll of Div 64. **d** 67 **p** 68. C Shoreditch St Leon *Lon* 67-70; SAMS 71-73; Chile 71-80; P-in-c Castle Hedingham *Chelmsf* 80-83; P-in-c Cam St Phil *Ely* 83-86; V 86-91; Chapl Ibiza *Eur* 91-94; C Lowton St Mary *Liv* from 94. *63 Arlington Drive, Leigh, Lancs WN7 3QP* Leigh (01942) 680402

SMITH, Richard. b 47. St D Coll Lamp DipTh75. **d** 75 **p** 76. C Aberavon *Llan* 75-78; Ind Chapl 78-81; TV Bournemouth St Pet w St Swithun, St Steph etc *Win* 81-85; Chapl Colchester Gen Hosp from 85; Chapl Severalls Hosp Colchester from 85. *Colchester General Hospital, Turner Road, Colchester CO4 3JL* Colchester (01206) 832513

SMITH, Richard Geoffrey. b 46. St Jo Coll Dur BA68 MA69. St Steph Ho Ox BA74 MA78. **d** 75 **p** 76. C Brentwood St Thos *Chelmsf* 75-78; C Corringham 78-81; R Shepton Beauchamp w Barrington, Stocklinch etc *B & W* 81-83; TV Redditch, The Ridge *Worc* 85-89; R Teme Valley S from 89. *The Rectory, Lindridge, Tenbury Wells, Worcs WR15 8JQ* Eardiston (01584) 881331

SMITH, Richard Harwood. b 34. Sarum Th Coll 57. **d** 59 **p** 60. C Kington w Huntington *Heref* 59-62; Br Guiana 62-66; Guyana 66-69; C Broseley w Benthall *Heref* 69-70; Lic to Offic 70-76; USPG Area Sec (Dios Heref and Worc) 70-76; R Wigmore Abbey 76-84; V Eye w Braiseworth and Yaxley *St E* from 84; P-in-c Bedingfield from 84; P-in-c Occold from 84. *The Vicarage, Eye, Suffolk IP23 7AW* Eye (01379) 870277

SMITH, Richard Ian. b 46. Jes Coll Ox BA69 MA80. Ripon Hall Ox 69. **d** 70 **p** 71. C Eston *York* 70-76; TV E Ham w Upton Park St Alb *Chelmsf* 76-80; R Crook *Dur* 80-86; V Stanley 80-86; V Billingham St Cuth from 86; RD Stockton from 92. *St Cuthbert's Vicarage, Church Road, Billingham, Cleveland TS23 1BW* Stockton-on-Tees (01642) 553236

SMITH, Richard Keith. b 44. Harper Adams Agric Coll NDA69. St Jo Coll Nottm. **d** 84 **p** 85. C Wirksworth w Alderwasley, Carsington etc *Derby* 84-87; R Hulland, Atlow, Bradley and Hognaston from 87. *The Vicarage, 16 Eaton Close, Hulland Ward, Ashbourne, Derbyshire DE6 3EX* Ashbourne (01335) 370605

SMITH, Richard Michael. b 52. Lon Univ BA74. E Anglian Minl Tr Course 79. **d** 82 **p** 83. NSM Cam Ascension *Ely* 82-84; C Rainham *Roch* 84-88; V Southborough St Thos from 88. *The Vicarage, 28 Pennington Road, Southborough, Tunbridge Wells TN4 0SL* Tunbridge Wells (01892) 529624

SMITH, Robert Harold. b 23. Lon Univ BA49. Oak Hill Th Coll 46. **d** 50 **p** 51. R Upton *Ex* 67-80; P-in-c Fersfield *Nor* 80-81; P-in-c N w S Lopham 80-81; R Bressingham 80-81; R Bressingham w N and S Lopham and Fersfield 81-87; rtd 87; Perm to Offic *Nor* from 87. *22 St Walstan's Road, Taverham, Norwich NR8 6NG* Norwich (01603) 861285

✠**SMITH, Rt Rev Robin Jonathan Norman.** b 36. Worc Coll Ox BA60 MA64. Ridley Hall Cam 60. **d** 62 **p** 63. C Barking St Marg *Chelmsf* 62-67; Chapl Lee Abbey 67-72; V Chesham St Mary *Ox* 72-80; RD Amersham 79-82; TR Gt Chesham 80-90; Hon Can Ch Ch 88-90; Suff Bp Hertf *St Alb* from 90. *Hertford House, Abbey Mill Lane, St Albans, Herts AL3 4HE* St Albans (01727) 866420 Fax 811426

SMITH, Rodney Frederic Brittain. b 38. Jes Coll Cam BA61 MA64. St Steph Ho Ox 87. **d** 88 **p** 89. NSM Rainworth *S'well* 88-89; C Basford St Aid 89-91; C Sneinton St Cypr 91-94; P-in-c Sneinton St Matthias from 94. *St Matthias Vicarage, Woodhouse Street, Sneinton, Nottingham NG3 2FG* Nottingham (0115) 950 2750

SMITH, Rodney John Boughton. b 19. AKC41. Sarum Th Coll 41. **d** 42 **p** 43. V E Meon *Portsm* 68-84; V Langrish 76-84; rtd 84; Perm to Offic *Ex* from 84. *3 Barton Orchard, Tipton St John, Sidmouth, Devon EX10 0AN* Ottery St Mary (01404) 814673

SMITH, Roger Douglas St John. b 12. TD56. Selw Coll Cam BA37 MA41. Jes Coll Ox BA39 MA43 Man Univ BD51. Ripon Hall Ox 37. **d** 39 **p** 40. R Darley w S Darley *Derby* 63-77; rtd 77. *28 Ffordd Penrhwylfa, Prestatyn, Clwyd LL19 8AG* Prestatyn (01745) 857307

SMITH, Roger Owen. b 50. FRGS Univ of Wales (Abth) BA72 St Chad's Coll Dur CertEd73. S'wark Ord Course 84. **d** 87 **p** 88. NSM Nunhead St Antony w St Silas *S'wark* 87-91; NSM Forest Hill St Aug from 91; NSM Crofton Park St Hilda w St Cypr from 91; NSM Brockley Hill St Sav from 91. *32 Mundania Road, London SE22 0NW* 0181-693 4882

SMITH, Roger Stuart. b 41. Chich Th Coll 65. **d** 66 **p** 67. C Garforth *Ripon* 66-70; C Cockley Cley w Gooderstone *Nor* 70-73; C Gt and Lt Cressingham w Threxton 70-73; C Didlington 70-73; C Hilborough w Bodney 70-73; C

Oxborough w Foulden and Caldecote 70-73; TV 73-78; V Mendham w Metfield and Withersdale *St E* 78-89; P-in-c Fressingfield w Weybread 86-89; R Fressingfield, Mendham, Metfield, Weybread etc 90-91; RD Hoxne 86-91; R Kelsale-cum-Carlton, Middleton-cum-Fordley etc from 91. *The Rectory, Middleton, Saxmundham, Suffolk IP17 3NR* Westleton (0172873) 421

SMITH, Ronald. b 26. ALCD56. **d** 56 **p** 57. C-in-c Istead Rise CD *Roch* 59-79; V Istead Rise 79-93; rtd 93. *114 Maidstone Road, Rochester, Kent ME1 3DT* Medway (01634) 829183

SMITH, Ronald Deric. b 21. Lon Univ BA46. Bps' Coll Cheshunt 59. **d** 61 **p** 62. C W Malling w Offham *Roch* 68-71; V Slade Green 71-78; V Bromley Common St Luke 78-91; rtd 91. *5 Bromley College, London Road, Bromley BR1 1PE* 0181-464 0212

SMITH, Ronald Eric (Ron). b 43. E Midl Min Tr Course CTPS93. **d** 93 **p** 94. NSM Wingerworth *Derby* from 93. *21 Windsor Drive, Wingerworth, Chesterfield, Derbyshire S42 6TG* Chesterfield (01246) 279004

SMITH, Ronald George (Ron). b 34. St Jo Coll Dur BA56 Bede Coll Dur PGCE73. Cranmer Hall Dur DipTh58. **d** 58 **p** 59. C Shirley *Win* 58-60; C Basingstoke 60-63; R Wolviston *Dur* 63-74; Teacher Hartlepool 74-78; Lic to Offic 74-78; Hd of Relig Studies Loughton Co High Sch 78-80; Perm to Offic *Chelmsf* 78-80; V Harold Hill St Geo 80-86; V Elmstead from 86. *The Vicarage, Church Road, Elmstead, Colchester CO7 7AW* Wivenhoe (01206) 822431

SMITH, Ronald James. b 36. Linc Th Coll 73. **d** 75 **p** 76. C Bilborough St Jo *S'well* 75-78; P-in-c Colwick 78-81; R 81-85; P-in-c Netherfield 78-81; V 81-85; C Worksop Priory 85-90; TV Langley and Parkfield *Man* from 90. *316 Windermere Road, Middleton, Manchester M24 4LA* 0161-654 8562

SMITH, Ronald William. b 16. ACIS40 FCIS61 Open Univ BA85. Worc Ord Coll 63. **d** 65 **p** 66. V Stretton Grandison and Ashperton w Canon Frome *Heref* 68-71; P-in-c Yarkhill w Weston Beggard 68-71; V Stretton Grandison w Ashperton, Canon Frome etc 71-81; rtd 82; Perm to Offic *Heref* from 82. *17 Knapp Close, Ledbury, Herefordshire HR8 1AW* Ledbury (01531) 634620

SMITH, Ronald William. b 45. St Jo Coll York CertEd67. Chich Th Coll 70. **d** 73 **p** 74. C Scarborough St Martin *York* 73-76; C Stainton-in-Cleveland 76-80; V Coatham 80-89; V Brookfield from 89. *Brookfield Vicarage, 89 Low Lane, Brookfield, Middlesbrough, Cleveland TS5 8EF* Middlesbrough (01642) 592136

SMITH, Roy Leonard. b 36. Clifton Th Coll 63. **d** 66 **p** 67. C Clapham St Jas *S'wark* 66-70; C Kennington St Mark 70-74; C-in-c Southall Em CD *Lon* 74-83; V Stonebridge St Mich from 83. *St Michael's Vicarage, Hillside, London NW10 8LB* 0181-965 7443

SMITH, Royston. b 55. E Midl Min Tr Course 87. **d** 90 **p** 91. NSM Shirland *Derby* 90-94; NSM Ashover and Brackenfield from 95. *Kirkdale Cottage, Greenfield Lane, Milltown, Ashover, Chesterfield, Derbyshire S45 0HA* Ashover (01246) 590975

SMITH, Royston Burleigh. b 26. St Deiniol's Hawarden 76. **d** 79 **p** 80. C Prestatyn *St As* 79-83; V Kerry and Llanmerewig 83-90; C Rhyl w St Ann 90-91; rtd 91. *18 Garth Clarendon, Kinmel Bay, Rhyl, Clwyd LL18 5DZ*

SMITH, Mrs Shirley Ann. b 46. RSCN68 RM82 RGN84 RHV86 Univ of Wales PGDipPastTh94. Sarum & Wells Th Coll 89. **d** 93 **p** 94. Par Dn Totton *Win* 93-94; C from 94. *7 Briardene Court, Totton, Southampton SO4 3WD* Southampton (01703) 663267

SMITH, Canon Stanley. b 10. St D Coll Lamp BA35 LTh. **d** 35 **p** 36. C Beamish *Dur* 35-37; Miss to Seamen 37-38 and 49-54; S Africa 38-49; Canada from 54. *Apartment 304, 2710 Lonsdale Avenue, Vancouver, Canada, V7N 3J1*

SMITH, Stephen. b 53. Leeds Poly CQSW78. Sarum & Wells Th Coll 87. **d** 89 **p** 90. C Redcar *York* 89-92; C Leeds St Aid *Ripon* from 92. *67 Morritt Drive, Leeds LS15 7HZ* Leeds (0113) 260 9498

SMITH, Stephen John. b 46. Kelham Th Coll 65. **d** 69 **p** 70. C Warsop *S'well* 69-73; C Heaton Ch Ch *Man* 73-75; V Bolton St Bede 75-78; R Bilborough w Strelley *S'well* 78-84; R E Leake 84-92; P-in-c Costock 84-92; P-in-c Rempstone 84-92; P-in-c Stanford on Soar 84-92; R E and W Leake, Stanford-on-Soar, Rempstone etc from 92; RD Bingham W from 92. *The Rectory, 3 Bateman Road, East Leake, Loughborough, Leics LE12 6LN* East Leake (01509) 852228

SMITH, Stephen John. b 55. Lon Univ BD80. Trin Coll Bris 77. **d** 81 **p** 82. C Fulham St Matt *Lon* 81-86; C Stoke Gifford *Bris* 86-90; TV from 90. *The Vicarage, Mautravers Close, Bradley Stoke, Bristol BS12 8ED* Bristol (0117) 931 2222

SMITH, Steven Barnes. b 60. Cov Poly BA83 Leeds Univ BA86. Coll of Resurr Mirfield 84. **d** 87 **p** 88. C Darlington St Mark w

St Paul *Dur* 87-89; C Prescot *Liv* 89-91; V Hindley Green from 91. *The Vicarage, 848 Atherton Road, Hindley, Wigan, Lancs WN2 4SA* Wigan (01942) 59032

SMITH, Steven Gerald Crosland. b 48. Linc Th Coll 82. **d** 84 **p** 85. Chapl St Jo Sch Tiffield Northants 84-87; C Towcester w Easton Neston *Pet* 84-87; P-in-c Kings Heath 87-89; V 89-93; TV N Creedy *Ex* from 93. *The Vicarage, Cheriton Fitzpaine, Crediton, Devon EX17 4JB* Crediton (01363) 866352

SMITH, Sydney John. b 21. Univ of Wales (Lamp) BA48. **d** 49 **p** 50. V Scarborough St Luke *York* 59-86; rtd 86. *309 Scalby Road, Scarborough, N Yorkshire YO12 6TF* Scarborough (01723) 378736

SMITH, Sydney Robert. b 17. St Jo Coll Dur LTh39 BA40 ALCD39. **d** 40 **p** 41. V Fazakerley St Nath *Liv* 64-75; V Westhead 75-82; rtd 82; Perm to Offic *Liv* from 82. *59 Crosshall Brow, Ormskirk, Lancs L40 6JD* Ormskirk (01695) 575285

SMITH, Terence. b 38. Lon Univ DipTh69. Tyndale Hall Bris 67. **d** 69 **p** 70. C Cheylesmore *Cov* 69-71; C Leamington Priors St Paul 71-74; V Halliwell St Paul *Man* 74-75; Lect Brunel Univ 75-86; R Medstead cum Wield *Win* from 86. *The Rectory, Trinity Hill, Medstead, Alton, Hants GU34 5LT* Alton (01420) 562050

SMITH, Terrence Gordon. b 34. TD83. MCSP58 SRN60. St Mich Coll Llan 68. **d** 70 **p** 71. C Gelligaer *Llan* 70-73; CF (TA) from 72; C Aberavon *Llan* 73-75; V Pontlottyn w Fochriw 75-77; V Kenfig Hill 77-84; V Dyffryn from 84. *The Vicarage, Dyffryn, Bryncoch, Neath, W Glam SA10 7AZ* Skewen (01792) 814237

SMITH, Thomas Robert Selwyn. b 12. Bps' Coll Cheshunt 35. **d** 37 **p** 38. V Box *Bris* 55-92; rtd 93. *Woodland View, Devizes Road, Box, Corsham, Wilts SN14 9EB* Bath (01225) 742405

SMITH, Thomas Roger. b 48. Cant Sch of Min 77. **d** 80 **p** 81. NSM Folkestone St Sav *Cant* 80-82; NSM Lyminge w Paddlesworth, Stanford w Postling etc 82-85; Chapl Cant Sch of Min 82-91; R Biddenden and Smarden *Cant* 86-91; TR Totnes, Bridgetown & Berry Pomeroy & Dartington *Ex* from 91. *The Rectory, Northgate, Totnes, Devon TQ9 5NX* Totnes (01803) 862104

SMITH, Timothy Brian. b 62. Brisbane Coll BA(Theol)92. **d** 92 **p** 92. Australia 92-94; C Heald Green St Cath *Ches* from 94. *103 Baslow Drive, Cheadle, Cheshire SK8 3HW*

SMITH, Tony. b 23. Roch Th Coll 62. **d** 64 **p** 65. V Hadlow *Roch* 67-78; R Wrotham 78-89; RD Shoreham 80-89; rtd 89. *25 Wye Road, Borough Green, Sevenoaks, Kent TN15 8DX* Borough Green (01732) 885884

SMITH, Trevor Andrew. b 60. St Jo Coll Dur BA86. Cranmer Hall Dur 83. **d** 87 **p** 88. C Guisborough *York* 87-90; C Northallerton w Kirby Sigston 90-95; P-in-c Middleton w Newton, Levisham and Lockton from 95. *St Andrew's House, 15 Carr Lane, Middleton, Pickering, N Yorkshire YO18 8PU* Pickering (01751) 74858

SMITH, Trevor Bernard. b 33. Oak Hill Th Coll 61. **d** 64 **p** 65. C Bispham *Blackb* 64-66; C Chesham St Mary *Ox* 66-68; Perm to Offic 90-94. *235 Whitecross, Wootton, Abingdon, Oxon OX13 6BW* Abingdon (01235) 521692

SMITH, Vernon Hemingway. b 33. St Alb Minl Tr Scheme 83. **d** 86 **p** 87. NSM Leighton Buzzard w Eggington, Hockliffe etc *St Alb* from 86. *41 Orion Way, Leighton Buzzard, Beds LU7 8XJ* Leighton Buzzard (01525) 377391

SMITH, Walter. b 37. Westcott Ho Cam 67. **d** 69 **p** 70. C N Hull St Mich *York* 69-72; C Whitby 72-74; V Newington w Dairycoates 74-77; P-in-c Skipton Bridge 77-78; P-in-c Baldersby 77-78; TV Thirsk 77-88; P-in-c Topcliffe w Dalton and Dishforth 82-87; V Lythe w Ugthorpe from 88. *The Vicarage, Lythe, Whitby, N Yorkshire YO21 3RL* Whitby (01947) 893479

SMITH, Miss Wendy Hamlyn. b 41. ALA70 Open Univ BA85. Ridley Hall Cam 85. **d** 87 **p** 94. C Stroud H Trin *Glouc* 87-90 and 91-92; Australia 90-91; TD Stoke-upon-Trent *Lich* 92-94; TV from 94. *St Paul's House, 235 Wheildon Road, Fenton, Stoke-on-Trent ST4 4JT* Stoke-on-Trent (01782) 44800

SMITH, William Carrington. b 16. Selw Coll Cam BA40 MA44. S'wark Ord Course 63. **d** 66 **p** 67. NSM Nunhead St Antony S'wark 66-83; rtd 83; Perm to Offic *Roch* from 83. *5 Reed Street, Cliffe, Rochester, Kent ME3 7UN* Medway (01634) 221898

SMITH, William Joseph Thomas. b 20. Chich Th Coll 54. **d** 55 **p** 56. V Boreham *Chelmsf* 65-90; rtd 90. *7 Trelawn, Church Road, Boreham, Chelmsford CM3 3EF* Chelmsford (01245) 466930

SMITH, William Manton. b 64. Univ of Wales (Abth) LLB85 St Jo Coll Dur PGCE90. United Th Coll Abth BD89 St Jo Coll Nottm 91. **d** 93 **p** 94. C Cov Caludon *Cov* from 93. *111 Momus Boulevard, Coventry CV2 5NB* Coventry (01203) 457727

SMITH, William Melvyn. b 47. K Coll Lon BD69 AKC69 PGCE70. St Aug Coll Cant 71. **d** 71 **p** 72. C Kingswinford H Trin *Lich* 71-73; Hon C Coseley Ch Ch 73-74; C Wednesbury St Paul Wood Green 75-78; V Coseley St Chad 78-91; RD Himley 83-93; RD Himley *Worc* from 93; TR Wordsley *Lich* 91-93; TR Wordsley *Worc* from 93. *The Rectory, 13 Dunsley Drive, Wordsley, Stourbridge, W Midlands DY8 5RA* Kingswinford (01384) 277215

SMITH-CAMERON, Canon Ivor Gill. b 29. Madras Univ BA50 MA52. Coll of Resurr Mirfield. **d** 54 **p** 55. Chapl Imp Coll *Lon* 58-72; Dioc Missr S'wark 72-92; Can Res S'wark Cathl 72-94; C Battersea Park All SS 92-94; Hon C from 94; Co-ord All Asian Chr Consultation 92-93; rtd 94; Chapl to The Queen from 95. *100 Prince of Wales Drive, London SW11 4BN* 0171-622 3809

SMITHIES, Edwin Henry. b 23. Leeds Univ DBS47. **d** 60 **p** 61. Hd Master Highfields Gr Sch Ossett 62-73; Lic to Offic *Wakef* 68-73; C Beeston *Ripon* 73-79; Perm to Offic 79-81; Lic to Offic 81-83; Hon C Leeds St Pet 83-90; rtd 88; Hon C Leeds City *Ripon* 90-94; Perm to Offic *Wakef* from 94. *8 Noster View, Leeds LS11 8QQ* Leeds (0113) 277 0154

✠**SMITHSON, Rt Rev Alan.** b 36. Qu Coll Ox BA62 MA68. Qu Coll Birm DipTh64. **d** 64 **p** 65 **c** 90. C Skipton Ch Ch *Bradf* 64-68; C Ox St Mary V w St Cross and St Pet *Ox* 68-72; Chapl Qu Coll Ox 69-72; Chapl Reading Univ *Ox* 72-77; V Bracknell 77-83; TR 83-84; Can Res Carl Cathl *Carl* 84-90; Dir of Tr Inst 84-90; Dioc Dir of Tr 85-90; Suff Bp Jarrow *Dur* from 90. *The Old Vicarage, Hallgarth, Pittington, Co Durham DH6 1AB* 0191-372 0225 Fax 372 2326

SMITHSON, Michael John. b 47. FRGS Newc Univ BA68 Lon Univ BD79 Dur Univ PGCE. Trin Coll Bris 76. **d** 79 **p** 80. C S Mimms Ch Ch *Lon* 79-81; Support and Public Relations Sec UCCF 82-84; R Frating w Thorrington *Chelmsf* 84-88; V Portsea St Luke *Portsm* from 88. *St Luke's Vicarage, Greetham Street, Southsea, Hants PO5 4LH* Portsmouth (01705) 826073

SMITHURST, Jonathan Peter. b 54. E Midl Min Tr Course DTPS94. **d** 94 **p** 95. NSM Bramcote S'well from 94. *46 Sandy Lane, Beeston, Nottingham NG9 3GS* Nottingham (0115) 925 7302

SMITS, Eric. b 29. **d** 61 **p** 62. C Thornaby on Tees St Paul *York* 61-66; R Brotton Parva from 66. *The Rectory, Brotton, Saltburn-by-the-Sea, Cleveland TS12 2PJ* Guisborough (01287) 676275

SMOUT, Canon Michael John. b 37. St Pet Coll Ox BA61 MA75 DipTh62 Lon Univ BD64. Lon Coll of Div 62. **d** 64 **p** 65. C Toxteth Park St Philemon w St Silas *Liv* 64-69; C Everton St Sav 69-70; Missr E Everton Gp of Chs 70-74; V Everton St Sav w St Cuth 74-79; R Aughton St Mich from 79; RD Ormskirk 82-89; AD from 89; Hon Can Liv Cathl from 92. *The Rectory, 10 Church Lane, Ormskirk, Lancs L39 6SB* Aughton Green (01695) 423204

SMURTHWAITE, William. b 25. Edin Th Coll 54. **d** 57 **p** 58. Miss to Seamen 59-72; Lic to Offic *Linc* 65-72; R Ladybank *St And* 73-90; R Cupar 73-90; rtd 90. *10 Park View, Balmullo, St Andrews, Fife KY16 0DN* St Andrews (01334) 870639

SMYTH, Anthony Irwin. b 40. TCD BA63 MA66. Clifton Th Coll 64. **d** 66 **p** 67. C Worthing St Geo *Chich* 66-69; Chile 70-75; C Woodley St Jo the Ev *Ox* 76-80; V St Leonards St Ethelburga *Chich* 80-93; R Stopham and Fittleworth from 93. *The Rectory, Fittleworth, Pulborough, W Sussex RH20 1JG* Fittleworth (01798) 865455

SMYTH, Francis George. b 20. Ridley Hall Cam 64. **d** 65 **p** 66. C Ormskirk *Liv* 65-70; V Bicton *Lich* 70-90; Chapl HM Pris Shrewsbury 71-90; rtd 90. *41 Sutton Road, Shrewsbury SY8 6DL* Shrewsbury (01743) 360030

SMYTH, Gordon William. b 47. Open Univ BA. St Jo Coll Nottm 81. **d** 83 **p** 84. C St Keverne *Truro* 83-86; V Landrake w St Erney and Botus Fleming from 86; RD E Wivelshire 94-95. *All Saints Vicarage, Highertown, Truro, Cornwall TR1 3LF* Truro (01872) 76688

SMYTH, James Desmond. b 12. TCD BA36 MA39. **d** 36 **p** 37. R Wappenham w Abthorpe and Slapton *Pet* 58-77; rtd 77; Perm to Offic *Glouc* from 79. *The Ferns, Vicarage Lane, Frampton on Severn, Gloucester GL2 7EE* Gloucester (01452) 740744

SMYTH, Canon Kenneth James. b 44. TCD BA67 MA72. **d** 68 **p** 69. C Ban Abbey *D & D* 68-71; C Holywood 71-74; I Gilnahirk 74-82; I Newtownards w Movilla Abbey 82-89; I Newtownards from 89; Preb Wicklow St Patr Cathl Dub from 93. *36 Belfast Road, Newtownards, Co Down BT23 4TT* Newtownards (01247) 812527

SMYTH, Lucinda Elizabeth Jane (Liz). b 67. New Hall Cam BA88 MA92. Wycliffe Hall Ox BTh93. **d** 93 **p** 94. C Cam St Barn *Ely* from 93. *80 St Barnabas Road, Cambridge CB1 2DE* Cambridge (01223) 67578

SMYTH, Robert Andrew Laine (Brother Anselm). b 30. Trin Coll Cam BA53 MA59 Lon Univ PGCE60 DipEd65. **d** 79 **p** 80. SSF from 53; Min Prov Eur Prov SSF 79-91; Lic to Offic *Linc*

84-92; P-in-c Cam St Benedict *Ely* 92-93; V from 93. *St Francis House, 15 Botolph Lane, Cambridge CB2 3RD* Cambridge (01223) 321576

SMYTH, Trevor Cecil. b 45. Chich Th Coll 66. **d** 69 **p** 70. C Cookridge H Trin *Ripon* 69-73; C Middleton St Mary 73-75; C Felpham w Middleton *Chich* 75-78; P-in-c Wellington Ch Ch *Lich* 78-80; V 80-86; P-in-c W Wittering *Chich* 86; R W Wittering and Birdham w Itchenor 86-94. *clo 3 Sunderton Road, Birmingham B14 6JQ*

SMYTHE, Mrs Angela Mary. b 53. St Jo Coll Nottm 85. **d** 87 **p** 94. Par Dn Forest Town *S'well* 87-90; D-in-c Pleasley Hill 90-94; V from 94. *The Vicarage, Pleasley Hill, Mansfield, Notts NG19 7SZ*

SMYTHE, Harry Reynolds. b 23. Sydney Univ BA45 St Pet Hall Ox BA48 MA51 Ch Ch Ox DPhil51. Moore Th Coll Sydney 43 ACT ThL45. **d** 51 **p** 53. Australia 54-70 and 81-83; Dir Angl Cen Rome 70-81; Lib Pusey Ho 83-91; Dir of Studies 91-94; Lic to Offic *Ox* 83-94; rtd 91. *57A Palace Street, Canterbury, Kent CT1 2DY* Canterbury (01227) 450685

SMYTHE, Paul Rodney. b 05. Mert Coll Ox BA28 MA31 BD37. Ripon Hall Ox 34. **d** 35 **p** 36. V Horningsea *Ely* 45-83; rtd 83. *82 High Street, Horningsea, Cambridge CB5 9SH* Cambridge (01223) 860392

SMYTHE, Canon Ronald Ingoldsby Meade. b 25. Qu Coll Ox BA46 MA48. Ely Th Coll 51. **d** 54 **p** 55. V Hatf Heath *Chelmsf* 62-78; Hon C Writtle 78-81; Hon C Writtle w Highwood 81-85; P-in-c Whatfield w Semer, Nedging and Naughton *St E* 85-89; Dir Ipswich Concern Counselling Cen from 85; Dioc Adv for Counselling 85-89; Dioc Adv for Counselling and Past Care from 89; rtd 90; Hon Can St E Cathl *St E* from 93. *94 Wangford Road, Reydon, Southwold, Suffolk IP18 6NY* Southwold (01502) 723413

SNAITH, Bryan Charles. b 33. Univ of Wales BSc55. St Mich Coll Llan 61. **d** 61 **p** 62. C Bargoed w Brithdir *Llan* 61-62; C Llanishen and Lisvane 62-71; Ind Chapl *Dur* 71-76; Ind Chapl *Worc* 76-81; P-in-c Stone 76-81; C Chaddesley Corbett 77-81; Ind Chapl *Chelmsf* from 81; TV Colchester St Leon, St Mary Magd and St Steph 81-86. *2 Colvin Close, Colchester CO3 4BS* Colchester (01206) 767793

SNAPE, Sqn Ldr Bernard Reginald Roy. b 08. OBE56. Sarum Th Coll 69. **d** 69 **p** 70. C W Leigh *Portsm* 69-71; V Arreton 71-75; rtd 75. *23 Shady Bower Close, Salisbury SP1 2RQ* Salisbury (01722) 328645

SNAPE, Harry. b 21. Qu Coll Birm 76. **d** 78 **p** 79. NSM Highters Heath *Birm* 78-82; NSM Stirchley 82-84; TV Corby SS Pet and Andr w Gt and Lt Oakley *Pet* 84-89; rtd 89. *9 Church Vale Road, Bexhill-on-Sea, E Sussex TN40 2ED* Bexhill-on-Sea (01424) 216925

SNASDELL, Antony John. b 39. St Chad's Coll Dur BA63 DipTh65. **d** 65 **p** 66. C Boston *Linc* 65-70; Hon C Worksop Priory *S'well* 71-82; P-in-c Gt Massingham *Nor* 82-84; P-in-c Harpley 82-84; P-in-c Lt Massingham 82-84; R Gt and Lt Massingham and Harpley 84-91; R Thorpe from 91. *The Rectory, 56A Thunder Lane, Norwich NR7 0JW* Norwich (01603) 33578

SNEARY, Michael William. b 38. Brentwood Coll of Educn CertEd71 Open Univ BA79. Ely Th Coll 61. **d** 64 **p** 65. C Loughton St Jo *Chelmsf* 64-67; Youth Chapl 67-70; Hon C Ingrave 70-71; Teacher Harold Hill Gr Sch Essex 71-74; Ivybridge Sch 74-76; Coombe Dean Sch Plymouth from 76. *The Lodge, Lower Port View, Saltash, Cornwall PL12 4BY*

SNEATH, Canon Sidney Dennis. b 23. Leeds Univ BA50. Bps' Coll Cheshunt 50. **d** 52 **p** 53. C Nuneaton St Mary *Cov* 52-59; C-in-c Galley Common Stockingford CD 59-68; V Camp Hill w Galley Common from 68; Hon Can Cov Cathl from 80. *The Vicarage, Cedar Road, Nuneaton, Warks CV10 9DL* Chapel End (01203) 392523

SNEDKER, Walter Frank. b 22. MBE. Bp Sumiu Takatsu Th Coll Brazil 78. **d** 80 **p** 81. Brazil from 80; rtd 93. *Caixa Postal 25, 11001 970, Santos SP, Brazil* Santos (132) 372325

SNELGAR, Canon Douglas John. b 17. DSC45. Trin Hall Cam BA48 MA53. Westcott Ho Cam 48. **d** 50 **p** 51. V Steep *Portsm* 57-92; P-in-c Froxfield w Privett 88-92; Hon Can Portsm Cathl 85-92; rtd 92. *37 South Acre, South Harting, Petersfield, Hants GU31 5LL* Petersfield (01730) 825142

✠**SNELGROVE, Rt Rev Donald George.** b 25. TD72. Qu Coll Cam BA48 MA53. Ridley Hall Cam. **d** 50 **p** 51 **c** 81. C Oakwood St Thos *Lon* 50-53; C Hatch End St Anselm 53-56; V Dronfield *Derby* 56-62; CF (TA) 60-73; V Hessle *York* 63-70; RD Hull 67-70 and 81-90; Can and Preb York Minster 69-81; Adn E Riding 70-81; R Cherry Burton 70-78; Suff Bp Hull 81-94; rtd 94. *Kingston House, 8 Park View, Barton-upon-Humber, S Humberside DN18 6AX*

SNELL, Mrs Brigitte. b 43. BA85. E Anglian Minl Tr Course 86. **d** 89 **p** 94. NSM Cam Gt St Mary w St Mich *Ely* 89-91; Par Dn Cam St Jas 91-94; C from 94. *130 Hulatt Road, Cambridge CB1 4TH* Cambridge (01223) 210602

SNELL, James Osborne. b 13. Selw Coll Cam BA35 MA39. Ely Th Coll 35. **d** 36 **p** 37. R Ramsgate H Trin *Cant* 69-78; rtd 79; Perm to Offic *Cant* from 79. *3 Glebe Close, St Margarets-at-Cliffe, Dover, Kent CT15 6AF* Dover (01304) 852210

SNELL, William Graham Brooking. b 14. Lon Coll of Div 36. **d** 39 **p** 40. R Ashby w Oby, Thurne and Clippesby *Nor* 57-79; rtd 79; Perm to Offic *Nor* from 79. *17 Park Home, Burgh Hall, Fleggburgh, Great Yarmouth, Norfolk NR29 3AF* Fleggburgh (01493) 369776

SNELLGROVE, Frederic Mortimer. b 06. Lon Univ BSc28. Ridley Hall Cam 28. **d** 29 **p** 30. R Bergh Apton w Yelverton *Nor* 60-72; rtd 72; Perm to Offic *Chich* from 74. *64 Rugby Road, Worthing, W Sussex BN11 5NB* Worthing (01903) 505120

SNELLGROVE, Martin Kenneth. b 54. City Univ BSc77 CEng80 MICE84. Aston Tr Scheme 85 Ridley Hall Cam 87. **d** 89 **p** 90. C Four Oaks *Birm* 89-92; TV Wrexham *St As* from 92. *The Vicarage, 160 Borras Road, Wrexham, Clwyd LL13 9ER* Wrexham (01978) 350202

SNELLING, Brian. b 40. Oak Hill Th Coll DipTh68. **d** 69 **p** 70. C Slough *Ox* 69-72; C Hoole *Ches* 72-76; V Millbrook 76-80; V Homerton St Luke *Lon* 80-90; R Marks Tey w Aldham and Lt Tey *Chelmsf* from 90. *The Rectory, Church Lane, Marks Tey, Colchester CO6 1LW* Colchester (01206) 210396

SNELLING, Stanley Alfred. b 03. Lich Th Coll 54. **d** 55 **p** 56. V Furneux Pelham w Stocking Pelham *St Alb* 62-76; rtd 77; Perm to Offic *St Alb* from 77. *7 Elms Road, Ware, Herts SG12 7HT* Ware (01920) 460176

SNELSON, William Thomas (Bill). b 45. Ex Coll Ox BA67 Fitzw Coll Cam BA69 MA75. Westcott Ho Cam 67. **d** 69 **p** 70. C Godalming *Guildf* 69-72; C Leeds St Pet *Ripon* 72-75; V Chapel Allerton 75-81; V Bardsey 81-93; Dioc Ecum Officer 86-93; W Yorkshire Ecum Officer *Bradf* from 93. *17 Falcon Close, Otley, W Yorkshire LS21 3EG* Otley (01943) 466820

SNOOK, Mrs Margaret Ann. b 41. S Dios Minl Tr Scheme. **d** 91 **p** 94. NSM Keynsham *B & W* from 91. *32 Hurn Lane, Keynsham, Bristol BS18 1RS* Bristol (0117) 986 3439

SNOOK, Walter Currie. b 39. Lon Univ DipTh66. Tyndale Hall Bris 64. **d** 67 **p** 68. C Cromer *Nor* 67-70; C Macclesfield St Mich *Ches* 70-74; R Postwick *Nor* 74-87; Chapl Jas Paget Hosp Gorleston from 87. *The James Paget Hospital, Lowestoft Road, Gorleston, Great Yarmouth, Norfolk NR31 6LA* Great Yarmouth (01493) 452408/452452

SNOW, Campbell Martin Spencer. b 35. JP. Roch Th Coll 65. **d** 67 **p** 68. C Dover St Mary *Cant* 67-72; C Birchington w Acol 72-74; V Reculver 74-80; P-in-c New Addington 80-81; V 81-84; V New Addington *S'wark* 85-87; CF (ACF) 84-87; CF (TA) 87-92; P-in-c Caterham Valley *S'wark* from 87. *Caterham Valley Vicarage, 51 Crescent Road, Caterham, Surrey CR3 6LH* Caterham (01883) 343188

SNOW, Canon Edward Brian. b 22. CITC. **d** 65 **p** 66. C Dun Laoghaire *D & G* 67-72; Hon CV Ch Ch Cathl Dub 69-72; I Rathkeale *L & K* 72-77; I Kilmallock w Kilflynn, Kilfinane, Knockaney etc 77-94; Adn Limerick 81-92; Chapter Clerk Limerick, Killaloe and Clonfert 92-94; RD Limerick 92-94; rtd 94. *Balladik, 9 St Catherines Road, Glenageary, Co Dublin* Dublin (1) 284-6004

SNOW, Frank. b 31. Lon Univ BD57. **d** 83 **p** 84. Hon C Tweedmouth *Newc* 83-86; Hon C Berwick H Trin 86-89; Hon C Berwick St Mary 86-89; Hon C Berwick H Trin and St Mary 89-90; R Gt Smeaton w Appleton Wiske and Birkby etc *Ripon* from 90. *The Rectory, Great Smeaton, Northallerton, N Yorkshire DL6 2EP* Great Smeaton (01609) 881205

SNOW, Glyn Francis. b 53. Dur Univ BA74 CertEd. St Steph Ho Ox 76. **d** 78 **p** 79. C Pontnewynydd *Mon* 78-82; TV Ebbw Vale 82-91. *25 William Street, Cwmfelinfach, Ynysddu, Newport, Gwent NP1 7GY* Ynysddu (01495) 201354

SNOW, Martyn James. b 68. Sheff Univ BSc89. Wycliffe Hall Ox BTh95. **d** 95. C Brinsworth w Catcliffe and Treeton *Sheff* from 95. *18 St George's Drive, Brinsworth, Rotherham, S Yorkshire S60 5NG* Rotherham (01709) 261677

SNOW, Miss Patricia Margaret. b 21. TCD 45. St Mich Ho Ox 51. **dss** 72 **d** 87. W Ham *Chelmsf* 72-78; Acomb St Steph *York* 78-83; rtd 83. *29 Huggens' College, College Road, Northfleet, Gravesend, Kent DA11 9DL* Gravesend (01474) 352963

SNOW, Peter David. b 37. St Jo Coll Cam BA62 MA66. Ridley Hall Cam 62. **d** 64 **p** 65. C Kingshurst *Birm* 64-66; USA from 67. *927 36th Avenue, Seattle, Washington 98122, USA*

SNOW, Peter Normington. b 23. St Jo Coll Ox BA48 MA52. Ely Th Coll 48. **d** 50 **p** 51. V Emscote *Cov* 56-89; RD Warw 67-77; rtd 89. *3 Park Lane, Harbury, Leamington Spa, Warks CV33 9HX* Harbury (01926) 612410

SNOW, Richard John. b 57. Bris Univ BSc80. **d** 90 **p** 91. C Preston Plucknett *B & W* 90-95; TV Stratton St Margaret w S Marston etc *Bris* from 95. *The Vicarage, South Marston, Swindon SN3 4SR* Swindon (01793) 827021

SNOW, William George Sinclair. b 08. Edin Univ MA31 PhD40. Edin Th Coll 32. **d** 33 **p** 34. V Bognor *Chich* 52-76; rtd 76; Perm to Offic *Chich* from 76. *25 Merton Avenue, Rustington, Littlehampton, W Sussex BN16 2EQ*   Rustington (01903) 771610

SNOWBALL, Michael Sydney. b 44. Dur Univ BA70 MA72 St Jo Coll Dur DipTh72. **d** 72 **p** 73. C Stockton St Pet *Dur* 72-75; C Dunston St Nic 75-77; C Dunston 77-78; C Darlington St Jo 78-81; V Chilton 81-91; V Brompton w Deighton *York* from 91. *The Vicarage, Brompton, Northallerton, N Yorkshire DL6 2QA*   Northallerton (01609) 772436

SNOWDEN, Miss Alice Isabel Glass. b 55. Lanc Univ BA77 Humberside Coll of Educn PGCE84. Ripon Coll Cuddesdon 91. **d** 94 **p** 95. C Mirfield *Wakef* from 94. *16 Towngate Grove, Mirfield, W Yorkshire WF14 9JF*   Mirfield (01924) 495288

SNOWSELL, Raymond Ernest Elijah. b 15. Wycliffe Hall Ox 67. **d** 68 **p** 69. V Oaks (Charnwood Forest) *Leic* 71-79; V Oaks in Charnwood and Copt Oak 79-80; rtd 80; Perm to Offic *B & W* from 81. *Charnwood, Castle Street, Keinton Mandeville, Somerton, Somerset TA11 6DX*   Somerton (01458) 223225

SNUGGS, David Sidney. b 49. Keble Coll Ox BA71 PGCE72 MA75. S Dios Minl Tr Scheme 89. **d** 92 **p** 93. C Bitterne *Win* from 92. *4 Aberdour Close, Southampton SO2 5PF*   Southampton (01703) 473436

SOAR, Arthur Leslie. b 20. ACII. Linc Th Coll 82. **d** 83 **p** 84. NSM Chilham *Cant* 83-86; NSM Crundale w Godmersham 86-90; NSM Elmsted w Hastingleigh 86-90; rtd 90; Perm to Offic *Cant* from 90. *9 Northdowns Close, Old Wives Lees, Canterbury, Kent CT4 8BP*   Canterbury (01227) 730205

SOAR, Martin William. b 54. Wye Coll Lon BSc78. Wycliffe Hall Ox 86. **d** 88 **p** 89. C Henfynyw w Aberaeron and Llanddewi Aberarth *St D* 88-91; C Hubbertson 91-93; P-in-c Low Harrogate St Mary *Ripon* 93-95; V from 95. *St Mary's Vicarage, 22 Harlow Oval, Harrogate, N Yorkshire HG2 0DS*   Harrogate (01423) 502614

SODOR AND MAN, Bishop of. See JONES, Rt Rev Noel Debroy

SOGA, Hector Ian. b 47. Glas Univ MA70 BMus78 Selw Coll Cam BA72 MA76. St And NSM Tr Scheme 87. **d** 88 **p** 89. NSM Dollar *St And* from 88. *2 Harviestoun Road, Dollar, Clackmannanshire FK14 7HF*   Dollar (01259) 743169

SOKOLOWSKI (nee MAHON), Mrs Stephanie Mary. b 56. Liv Univ BSc80 SRN80. S'wark Ord Course 91. **d** 94. C Warlingham w Chelsham and Farleigh *S'wark* from 94. *12 Marston Drive, Warlingham, Surrey CR6 9SY*   Caterham (01883) 565896

SOLOMON, Arthur Creagh. b 33. ACT LTh Ch Coll Hobart. **d** 62 **p** 63. Australia 62-67; C Addiscombe St Mildred *Cant* 67-68; Chapl Pierrepont Sch Frensham 69-72; R Clifton Campville w Chilcote *Lich* 72-95; P-in-c Thorpe Constantine 83-95; R Clifton Campville w Edingale from 95. *The Rectory, Clifton Campville, Tamworth, Staffs B79 0AP*   Clifton Campville (0182786) 257

SOLOMON, Gerald Tankerville Norris. b 12. Lon Univ BA36. Sarum Th Coll 37. **d** 39 **p** 40. R Corsley *Sarum* 63-78; rtd 78. *The Old Forge, Hindon, Salisbury SP3 6DR*   Hindon (01747) 89255

SOMERVELL, Mrs Katherine Mary. b 30. Edin Univ CQSW51. W Midl Minl Tr Course 86. **d** 88 **p** 94. Par Dn Caldmore *Lich* 88-92; Par Dn Wilnecote 92-94; C 94-95; NSM Loppington w Newtown from 95; rtd 95. *The Vicarage, Loppington, Shrewsbury SY4 5ST*   Wem (01939) 233388

SOMERVILLE, John William Kenneth. b 38. St D Coll Lamp 60. **d** 63 **p** 64. C Rhosllannerchrugog *St As* 63-67; C Llangystennin 67-70; V Gorsedd 70-77; V Gorsedd w Brynford and Ysgeifiog from 77. *The Vicarage, Gorsedd, Holywell, Clwyd CH8 8QZ*   Holywell (01352) 711675

SONG, James. b 32. Lon Coll of Div 57. **d** 60 **p** 61. V Matlock Bath *Derby* 66-76; V Woking St Jo *Guildf* 76-94; RD Woking 87-92; rtd 94. *Ash House, Churt, Farnham, Surrey GU10 2NU*   Headley Down (01428) 714493

SOOSAINAYAGAM, Xavier. b 50. S'wark Ord Course 89 St Paul's Sem Trichy BTh77 Sri Lanka Nat Sem BPh73. **d** 76 **p** 77. In RC Ch 76-89; C Streatham St Leon *S'wark* 89-94; C Mert St Jas from 94. *7 Westcroft Gardens, Morden, Surrey SM4 4DS*   0181-540 2217

SOPER, Brian Malcolm. b 31. Lon Univ BSc53 Mansf Coll Ox DipTh56. Ripon Hall Ox 63. **d** 63 **p** 64. C Platt *Roch* 63-64; Chapl K Sch Roch 64-72; Chapl Repton Sch Derby 72-75; Chapl Bennett Memorial Sch Tunbridge Wells 75-84; Perm to Offic *Cant* 70-87; Perm to Offic *Chich* from 87. *The Croft, Point Hill, Rye, E Sussex TN31 7NP*   Rye (01797) 222897

SORENSEN, Ms Anna Katrine Elizabeth. b 58. Man Univ BA82. Ripon Coll Cuddesdon 83. **d** 87 **p** 94. Par Dn Ashton H Trin *Man* 87-88; Asst Chapl St Felix Sch Southwold 89-90; Chapl from 90; Hon Par Dn Reydon *St E* 89-92; Hon Par Dn Blythburgh w Reydon 92-94; Hon C from 94. *The Rectory, Moll's Lane, Brampton, Beccles, Suffolk NR34 8DB*   Brampton (01502) 575859

SORENSEN, Arthur Frank. b 28. S'wark Ord Course 66. **d** 69 **p** 70. C Broadwater Down *Chich* 69-71; P-in-c Shenley *Ox* 72-75; R Loughton and Bradwell 72-73; R Loughton 73-75; P-in-c Thornborough 75-77; P-in-c Beachampton w Thornton and Nash 75-77; R Nash w Thornton, Beachampton and Thornborough 77-83; P-in-c Gt Milton 83-86; P-in-c Lt Milton 83-86; rtd 86. *Shambala, 54 Beaufort Road, Morecambe, Lancs LA4 6UA*   Morecambe (01524) 419741

SOULSBY, Michael. b 36. Dur Univ BSc57. Westcott Ho Cam 61. **d** 62 **p** 63. C Selly Oak St Mary *Birm* 62-66; C Kings Norton 66-72; TV 73-76; TR Sutton *Liv* 76-88; RD Prescot 84-88; P-in-c Orton Longueville *Ely* from 88; RD Yaxley from 92. *The Rectory, Orton Longueville, Peterborough PE2 7DN*   Peterborough (01733) 371071

SOUPER, Patrick Charles. b 57. AKC55. **d** 57 **p** 58. Chapl St Paul's Sch Barnes 65-70; Lect in Educn Southn Univ 70-93; Lic to Offic *Win* 70-93; rtd 93. *Villa Galini, Prines, 74100 Rethymnon, Crete, Greece*   Rethymnon (831) 31521

SOURBUT, Philip John. b 57. Cam Univ BA MA. Cranmer Hall Dur BA. **d** 85 **p** 86. C Springfield All SS *Chelmsf* 85-88; C Roxeth Ch Ch and Harrow St Pet *Lon* 88-91; P-in-c Bath St Sav *B & W* 91-93; R Bath St Sav w Swainswick and Woolley from 93. *St Saviour's Rectory, Claremont Road, Bath BA1 6LX*   Bath (01225) 311637

SOUTH, Mrs Gillian. b 51. NE Ord Course 87. **d** 90 **p** 94. C Rothbury *Newc* 90-93; C Morpeth from 93. *23 Green Acres, Morpeth, Northd NE61 2AD*   Morpeth (01670) 511662

SOUTH, Canon Thomas Horsman (Tom). b 06. Qu Coll Ox BA31 MA35. Cuddesdon Coll 31. **d** 32 **p** 33. V Latimer w Flaunden *Ox* 62-73; Hon Can Ch Ch 65-73; rtd 73. *clo The Red House, 34 Alexandra Road, Hemel Hempstead, Hertfordshire HP2 5BS*   Hemel Hempstead (01442) 246665

SOUTHALL, Colin Edward. b 36. Lich Th Coll 63. **d** 65 **p** 82. C Wylde Green *Birm* 65-67; Perm to Offic 68-73; Perm to Offic *Pet* 73-81; Hon C Linc St Faith and St Martin w St Pet *Linc* 82-85; Hon C Gt Glen, Stretton Magna and Wistow etc *Leic* 85-93; Chapl Asst Leic R Infirmary from 93. *Leicester Royal Infirmary, Infirmary Square, Leicester LE1 5WW*   Leicester (0116) 259 2959 or 258 5487

SOUTHAMPTON, Suffragan Bishop of. See PERRY, Rt Rev John Freeman

SOUTHEND, Archdeacon of. See JENNINGS, Ven David Willfred Michael

SOUTHERN, Humphrey Ivo John. b 60. Ch Ch Ox BA82 MA86. Ripon Coll Cuddesdon 83. **d** 86 **p** 87. C Rainham *Roch* 86-90; C Walton St Mary *Liv* 90-92; C Walton-on-the-Hill 92; V Hale *Guildf* from 92; Dioc Ecum Officer from 92. *The Vicarage, 25 Upper Hale Road, Farnham, Surrey GU9 0NX*   Farnham (01252) 716469

SOUTHERN, John Abbott. b 27. Leeds Univ BA47. Coll of Resurr Mirfield. **d** 51 **p** 52. C Leigh St Mary *Man* 51-55; C Gt Grimsby St Jas *Linc* 55-58; V Oldham St Jas *Man* 58-60; V Haigh *Liv* 60-75; R Pemberton St Jo from 75. *The Vicarage, 148 Orrell Road, Orrell, Wigan, Lancs WN5 8HJ*   Wigan (01942) 222237

SOUTHERN, Paul Ralph. b 48. Oak Hill Th Coll DipHE. **d** 87 **p** 88. C Chadwell Heath *Chelmsf* 87-91; P-in-c Tolleshunt D'Arcy w Tolleshunt Major from 91. *8 Vicarage Close, Tolleshunt D'Arcy, Maldon, Essex CM9 8UG*   Maldon (01621) 860521

SOUTHERTON, Miss Kathryn Ruth. b 66. Univ of Wales (Lamp) BA88. Sarum & Wells Th Coll 90. **d** 92. C Connah's Quay *St As* from 92. *Ty'r Llan, 3 Firbrook Avenue, Connah's Quay, Deeside, Clwyd CH5 4PF*   Deeside (01244) 836474

SOUTHERTON, Peter Clive. b 38. Univ of Wales (Lamp) BA59. Qu Coll Birm DipTh60. **d** 61 **p** 62. C Llandrillo-yn-Rhos *St As* 61-68; Bermuda 68-71; V Esclusham *St As* 72-82; V Prestatyn from 82. *The Vicarage, 109 High Street, Prestatyn, Clwyd LL19 9AR*   Prestatyn (01745) 853780

SOUTHEY, George Rubidge. b 34. St Mich Coll Llan 84. **d** 86 **p** 87. C Hessle *York* 86-89; P-in-c Scarborough St Columba 89-92; V from 92. *160 Dean Road, Scarborough, N Yorkshire YO12 7JH*   Scarborough (01723) 375070

SOUTHGATE, Geoffrey Trevor Stanley. b 28. AKC56. **d** 57 **p** 58. C Tonge Moor *Man* 57-60; C Lon Docks St Pet w Wapping St Jo *Lon* 60-62; V Upper Clapton St Matt 62-67; V Fleetwood *Blackb* 68-85; R Cov St Jo *Cov* from 85. *St John's Rectory, 9 Davenport Road, Coventry CV5 6QA*   Coventry (01203) 673203

SOUTHGATE, Dr Graham. b 63. GIBiol85 Bris Poly HDipABiol83 NE Surrey Coll of Tech PhD89. Ripon Coll Cuddesdon BTh93. **d** 93 **p** 94. C Tisbury *Sarum* from 93. *7 Church Street Close, Tisbury, Salisbury SP3 6QY*   Tisbury (01747) 870790

SOUTHGATE, Very Rev John Eliot. b 26. St Jo Coll Dur BA53 DipTh55. **d** 55 **p** 56. R Old Charlton *S'wark* 66-72; Boro Dean Greenwich 69-72; Hon Can S'wark Cathl 70-72; Can and Preb York Minster *York* 72-84; V Harome 72-77; Adn Cleveland

74-84; Dean York 84-94; Chmn Assn of English Cathls 90-94; rtd 94; Perm to Offic *Nor* from 94. *39 Churchfields, Hethersett, Norfolk NR9 3PH* Norwich (01603) 812116

SOUTHWARD, Canon Douglas Ambrose. b 32. St Jo Coll Nottm LTh74 ALCD57. **d** 57 **p** 58. C Otley *Bradf* 57-61; C Sedbergh 61-63; C Cautley w Dowbiggin 61-63; C Garsdale 61-63; PV Lich Cathl *Lich* 63-65; V Hope *Derby* 65-72; V Crosby Ravensworth *Carl* 72-82; V Bolton 74-82; Sec Dioc Past and Redundant Chs Uses Cttees 78-82; RD Appleby 78-82; Hon Can Carl Cathl from 81; R Asby 81-82; V Hawkshead and Low Wray w Sawrey from 82; P-in-c Windermere St Jo 84-89; RD Windermere 84-89; P-in-c Colton w Satterthwaite and Rusland from 94. *The Vicarage, Hawkshead, Ambleside, Cumbria LA22 0PD* Hawkshead (015394) 36301

SOUTHWARD, James Fisher. b 57. St Martin's Coll Lanc BEd80. Chich Th Coll 83. **d** 86 **p** 87. C Woodford St Barn *Chelmsf* 86-89; TV Crawley *Chich* 89-95; V Higham and Merston *Roch* from 95. *The Vicarage, Hermitage Road, Higham, Rochester, Kent ME3 7NE* Medway (01634) 717360

SOUTHWARK, Archdeacon of. See BARTLES-SMITH, Ven Douglas Leslie

SOUTHWARK, Bishop of. See WILLIAMSON, Rt Rev Robert Kerr (Roy)

SOUTHWARK, Provost of. See SLEE, Very Rev Colin Bruce

SOUTHWELL, Peter John Mackenzie. b 43. New Coll Ox BA64 MA68. Wycliffe Hall Ox 66. **d** 67 **p** 68. Lect Sheff Univ 67-70; C Crookes St Thos *Sheff* 67-70; Sen Tutor Wycliffe Hall Ox from 70; Chapl Qu Coll Ox from 82. *Queen's College, Oxford OX1 4AW* Oxford (01865) 279143 or 53829 Fax 274215

SOUTHWELL, Ven Roy. b 14. AKC42. **d** 42 **p** 43. V Hendon Ch Ch *Lon* 68-71; Adn Northolt 70-80; rtd 80; Warden Community of All Hallows Ditchingham 83-89; Lic to Offic *Nor* 83-89; Perm to Offic from 89. *397 Sprowton Road, Norwich NR3 4HY* Norwich (01603) 405977

SOUTHWELL-SANDER, Canon Peter George. b 41. G&C Coll Cam BA64 MA67. Westcott Ho Cam 63. **d** 65 **p** 66. C Maidstone All SS w St Phil *Cant* 65-68; C Cam Gt St Mary w St Mich *Ely* 68-71; Chapl Girton Coll Cam 69-73; V Clapham St Paul *S'wark* 73-77; V Mert St Mary 77-84; P-in-c Mert St Jo 77-79; Dir of Min *Chelmsf* 85-94; Can Res Chelmsf Cathl 85-94. *North House, Church Road, Boreham, Chelmsford CM3 3EJ, or Guy Harlings, 53 New Street, Chelmsford CM1 1NG* Chelmsford (01245) 465946 or 266731 Fax 492786

SOUTHWELL, Bishop of. See HARRIS, Rt Rev Patrick Burnet

SOUTHWELL, Provost of. See LEANING, Very Rev David

SOUTHWOOD, Robert Alfred. b 31. Sarum & Wells Th Coll 72. **d** 74 **p** 75. C Christchurch *Win* 74-76; C Fordingbridge w Ibsley 76-79; P-in-c Ernesettle *Ex* 79-80; V 80-83; R Stoke-in-Teignhead w Combe-in-Teignhead etc from 83. *The Rectory, Stoke-in-Teignhead, Newton Abbot, Devon TQ12 4QB* Shaldon (01626) 873493

SOUTTAR, Preb Edward Herbert. b 16. Bps' Coll Cheshunt 38. **d** 46 **p** 47. V Sidmouth St Nic *Ex* 65-73; TR Sidmouth, Woolbrook, Salcombe Regis etc 73-81; Preb Ex Cathl 72-85; rtd 81; Perm to Offic *Ex* from 85. *20 Fosseway Close, Axminster, Devon EX13 5LW* Axminster (01297) 34382

SOWDON, Henry Lewis Malcolm. b 37. TCD BA. Bps' Coll Cheshunt. **d** 64 **p** 65. C Newport w Longford *Lich* 64-66; C Caverswall 66-69; Chapl Clayesmore Sch Blandford 69-72; Hon C Hornsey Ch Ch *Lon* 72-80; Chapl Gordon's Sch Woking 80-86; TV Hodge Hill *Birm* 86-91; Perm to Offic from 91. *157 Heathfield Road, Birmingham B19 1JD* 0121-515 3557

SOWERBUTTS, Alan. b 49. Sheff Univ BSc70 PhD73 Qu Coll Cam BA75 MA79. Westcott Ho Cam 74. **d** 76 **p** 77. C Salesbury *Blackb* 76-80; V Lower Darwen St Jas 80-84; V Musbury 84-93; P-in-c Brindle from 93; Sec Dioc Adv Cttee for the Care of Chs from 93. *The Rectory, Sandy Lane, Brindle, Chorley, Lancs PR6 8JN* Hoghton (01254) 854130

SOWERBY, Geoffrey Nigel Rake. b 35. St Aid Birkenhead 56. **d** 60 **p** 61. V Leeds All SS *Ripon* 69-73; V Leyburn w Bellerby 73-81; R Edin Old St Paul *Edin* 81-86; V Hawes and Hardraw *Ripon* 86-92; Dioc Adv in Deliverance Min 91-92; rtd 92. *6 Wycar Terrace, Bedale, N Yorkshire DL8 2AG* Bedale (01677) 425860

SOWERBY, Mark Crispin Rake. b 63. K Coll Lon BD85 AKC85. Coll of Resurr Mirfield 85. **d** 87 **p** 88. C Knaresborough *Ripon* 87-90; C Darwen St Cuth w Tockholes St Steph *Blackb* 90-92; V Accrington St Mary from 92. *St Mary Magdalen's Vicarage, 5 Queens Road, Accrington, Lancs BB5 6AR* Accrington (01254) 233173

SOWTER, Dr Colin Victor. b 35. Ball Coll Ox MA59 DPhil60. Oak Hill NSM Course 88. **d** 91 **p** 92. NSM Cranleigh *Guildf* 91-93; NSM Wonersh from 93. *Hollycroft, Grantley Avenue, Wonersh Park, Guildford, Surrey GU5 0QN* Guildford (01483) 892094

SOX, Harold David. b 36. N Carolina Univ BA58. NY Th Sem MDiv61. **d** 61 **p** 61. USA 61-74; Hon C Richmond St Mary *S'wark* 74-79; Hon C Richmond St Mary w St Matthias and St Jo 79-82; Hon C Kensington St Mary Abbots w St Geo *Lon* 82-84 and 89-93; Perm to Offic 84-89; Hon C Beedon and Peasemore w W Ilsley and Farnborough *Ox* 93-94; Perm to Offic from 94. *Bramble Cottage, Peasemore, Newbury, Berks RG16 0JJ* Chieveley (01635) 248042

SPACKMAN, Ven Peter John. b 37. Southn Univ BSc60. Westcott Ho Cam 65. **d** 66 **p** 67. C Boxmoor St Jo *St Alb* 66-69; C Alnwick St Paul *Newc* 69-72; Jamaica 72-74; Canada 74-95; Adn Gaspe 88-95; Perm to Offic *Ex* from 95. *4 Underwood Close, Dawlish, Devon EX7 9RY* Dawlish (01626) 862695

SPAFFORD, Very Rev Christopher Garnett Howsin. b 24. St Jo Coll Ox BA48 MA54. Wells Th Coll 48. **d** 50 **p** 51. V Shrewsbury St Chad *Lich* 69-76; V Newc St Nic *Newc* 76-89; Provost Newc 76-89; rtd 89. *Low Moor, Elm Close, Leominster, Herefordshire HR6 8JX* Leominster (01568) 614395

SPAIGHT, Robert George. b 45. Ridley Hall Cam. **d** 84 **p** 85. C St Columb Minor and St Colan *Truro* 84-87; C Worksop St Jo *S'well* 87-89; V Barlings *Linc* from 89. *The Vicarage, Station Road, Langworth, Lincoln LN3 5BB* Lincoln (01522) 754233

SPALDING, Wilfrid Frank. b 20. Sarum Th Coll. **d** 57 **p** 58. R Hoole *Blackb* 69-85; rtd 85. *5 Park Walk, Fulwood, Preston PR2 4PA* Preston (01772) 774663

SPANNER, Douglas Clement. b 16. Lon Univ BSc46 PhD51 DSc72. Local NSM Course. **d** 73 **p** 75. Hon C Ealing St Mary *Lon* 73-78; Hon C Eynsham *Ox* 79-83; Hon C Grove 83-86; Lic to Offic from 86. *Ivy Cottage, Main Street, Grove, Wantage, Oxon OX12 7JY* Wantage (01235) 766845

SPANNER, Handley James. b 51. Lanchester Poly BSc73 BA. Oak Hill Th Coll 82. **d** 85 **p** 86. C Cov H Trin *Cov* 85-89; V Rye Park St Cuth *St Alb* from 89. *St Cuthbert's Vicarage, Ogard Road, Hoddesdon, Herts EN11 0NU* Hoddesdon (01992) 463168

SPARHAM, Canon Anthony George. b 41. St Jo Coll Dur BA69 DipTh. Cranmer Hall Dur 66. **d** 71 **p** 72. C Bourne *Linc* 71-74; TV Tong *Bradf* 74-76; V Windhill 76-81; Dir of Educn *St E* 82-85; V Goostrey *Ches* from 85; Dir Lay Tr 85-90; Jt Dir Lay Tr from 90; Hon Can Ches Cathl from 94. *The Vicarage, Goostrey, Crewe CW4 8PG* Holmes Chapel (01477) 532109

SPARKES, Colin Anthony. b 37. MIEE Surrey Univ MSc68 Bath Univ MEd83. Ox NSM Course 78. **d** 81 **p** 82. NSM Shrivenham w Watchfield and Bourton *Ox* 81-84; NSM Shellingford 84-91; R Hawkinge w Acrise and Swingfield *Cant* from 91. *The Rectory, 78 Canterbury Road, Hawkinge, Folkestone, Kent CT18 7BP* Hawkinge (01303) 892369

SPARKES, Donald James Henry. b 33. Oak Hill Th Coll DipTh59. **d** 59 **p** 60. C Southall Green St Jo *Lon* 59-63; P-in-c Pitsmoor *Sheff* 63-70; V 70-73; P-in-c Wicker w Neepsend 70-73; V Pitsmoor w Wicker 73-79; V Pitsmoor w Ellesmere 79-86; V Pitsmoor Ch Ch from 86. *The Vicarage, 257 Pitsmoor Road, Sheffield S3 9AQ* Sheffield (0114) 272 7756

SPARKES, Richard Graham Brabant. b 21. St Jo Coll Ox BA42 MA47. Westcott Ho Cam 54. **d** 55 **p** 56. V Oulton *Ripon* 69-75; rtd 86. *Ty Newydd, Bethel, Llanfyllin, Powys SY22 5HJ* Llanfyllin (01691) 648783

SPARKS, Christopher Thomas. b 29. Lanc Univ PGCE69 Birm Univ 81. St D Coll Lamp BA53 Lich Th Coll 53. **d** 55 **p** 56. Lic to Offic *Blackb* 68-79; C Lanc St Mary 79-83; Chapl HM Pris Lanc 83-84; Perm to Offic *Blackb* from 84; rtd 94. *The Hollies, Littlefell Lane, Lancaster LA2 0RG* Lancaster (01524) 60292

SPARKS, Hedley Frederick Davis. b 08. ATCL27 FBA59 BNC Ox BA30 MA34 BD37 DD49 Birm Univ MA47 Hon DD83 St Andr Univ Hon DD63. Ripon Hall Ox 30. **d** 33 **p** 34. Oriel Prof Interpr of H Scripture Ox 52-76; R Wytham *Ox* 61-68; Lic to Offic *Cant* from 69; rtd 76-91. *14 Longport, Canterbury, Kent CT1 1PE* Canterbury (01227) 766265

SPARKS, Herbert Francis. b 23. AKC49. **d** 50 **p** 51. Chapl HM Pris Leic 69-74; Chapl HM Pris Kirkham 74-76; Chapl HM Pris Liv 76-79; Chapl HM Pris Long Lartin 79-84; rtd 84; Perm to Offic *York* from 84. *21 Chestnut Avenue, Withernsea, N Humberside HU19 2PG* Withernsea (01964) 614183

SPARLING, Harold William. b 19. ARCM53 Lon Univ BD40 AKC40. Bps' Coll Cheshunt 40. **d** 41 **p** 43. R Upper Hardres w Stelling *Cant* 67-70; Teacher Ashford Sch Kent 75-80; Perm to Offic *St E* from 81; rtd 84. *89 Langton Green, Eye, Suffolk IP23 7SH* Eye (01379) 870073

SPARROW, Michael Kenneth. St Jo Coll Dur BA74. Coll of Resurr Mirfield 74. **d** 75 **p** 76. C N Hinksey *Ox* 75-78; C Portsea St Mary *Portsm* 78-85; V Midsomer Norton w Clandown *B & W* 85-93; Chapl Schiedam Miss to Seamen *Eur* from 93. *Jan Steenstraat 69, 3117 TC Schiedam, The Netherlands* Schiedam (10) 427-0063

SPEAK, Geoffrey Lowrey. b 24. OBE70. Selw Coll Cam BA49 MA53. Ridley Hall Cam 49. **d** 51 **p** 52. Hong Kong 54-85; rtd 91. *Murren, Watery Lane, Donhead St Mary, Shaftesbury, Dorset SP7 9DP* Donhead (01747) 828613

SPEAKMAN, Joseph Frederick. b 26. NW Ord Course 75. **d** 78 **p** 79. NSM Wallasey St Hilary *Ches* 78; C 79-82; V Marthall w Over Peover 82-91; rtd 91. *10 Aberford Avenue, Wallasey, Merseyside L45 8PX* 0151-637 0109

SPEAR, Andrew James Michael. b 60. Dur Univ BA81. Ridley Hall Cam 83. **d** 86 **p** 87. C Haughton le Skerne *Dur* 86-90; C Eastbourne H Trin *Chich* 90-95; C Patcham from 95. *32 Fairview Rise, Brighton BN1 5GL* Brighton (01273) 503926

SPEAR, Miss Jennifer Jane. b 53. Westhill Coll Birm BEd76. Trin Coll Bris DipHE84. **dss** 84 **d** 87. Reading St Jo *Ox* 84-90; Par Dn 87-90; Hon Par Dn Devonport St Barn *Ex* 90-91; Hon Par Dn Devonport St Mich 90-91; Par Dn Plymstock 91-94; C from 94. *63 Plymstock Road, Plymstock, Plymouth PL9 7NX* Plymouth (01752) 405202

SPEAR, John Cory. b 33. Open Univ BA87. Ridley Hall Cam 68. **d** 70 **p** 71. C Gerrards Cross *Ox* 70-73; TV Washfield, Stoodleigh, Withleigh etc *Ex* 73-79; R Instow 79-90; V Westleigh 79-90; RD Hartland 82-89; V Pilton w Ashford from 90. *The Vicarage, 4 Northfield Lane, Pilton West, Barnstaple, Devon EX31 1QB* Barnstaple (01271) 45958

SPEAR, Sylvia Grace. b 36. St Chris Coll Blackheath 60. **dss** 76 **d** 87 **p** 94. S Wimbledon H Trin and St Pet *S'wark* 76-80; Lee Gd Shep w St Pet 80-87; Par Dn 87-94; C from 94. *56 Weigall Road, London SE12 8HF* 0181-318 2363

SPEARS, Reginald Robert Derek. b 48. Trin Coll Ox BA72 MA75. Cuddesdon Coll 72. **d** 75 **p** 76. C Hampton All SS *Lon* 75-79; C Caversham *Ox* 79-81; C Caversham and Mapledurham 81-84; V Reading St Matt 84-94; V Earley St Pet from 94. *St Peter's Vicarage, 129 Whiteknights Road, Reading RG6 2BB* Reading (01734) 262009

SPECK, Preb Peter William. b 42. Univ of Wales BSc64 Birm Univ BA66 DPS67 MA71. Qu Coll Birm 64. **d** 67 **p** 68. C Rhosddu *St As* 67-71; C Wrexham 71-72; Asst Chapl United Sheff Hosps 72-73; Chapl N Gen Hosp Sheff 73-79; Chapl R Free Hosp Lon 79-95; Hon Sen Lect Sch of Med 87-95; Preb St Paul's Cathl *Lon* 92-95; Chapl Southn Univ Hosp NHS Trust from 95. *The Chaplain's Office, Southampton General Hospital, Tremona Road, Southampton SO16 6YD* Southampton (01703) 796745 or 777222

SPECK, Raymond George. b 39. Oak Hill Th Coll 64. **d** 67 **p** 68. C Stretford St Bride *Man* 67-70; C Roxeth Ch Ch *Lon* 70-74; V Woodbridge St Jo *St E* 74-85; R Jersey St Ouen w St Geo *Win* from 85. *The Rectory, St Ouen, Jersey, Channel Islands JE3 2GG* Jersey (01534) 481800

SPEDDING, Geoffrey Osmond. b 46. Hull Univ BA67 Fitzw Coll Cam BA69 MA BD. **d** 70 **p** 71. C Bradf Cathl *Bradf* 70-73; C Sutton St Jas and Wawne *York* 73-76; TV Preston St Jo *Blackb* 76-82; TV Yate New Town *Bris* 82-87; TR Bestwood *S'well* 87-94; V Ravenshead from 94. *The Vicarage, 55 Sheepwalk Lane, Ravenshead, Nottingham NG15 9FD* Mansfield (01636) 892317

SPEDDING, William Granville. b 39. Lon Univ BD60. Tyndale Hall Bris 57. **d** 62 **p** 63. C Man Albert Memorial Ch *Man* 62-65; Co-ord Humanities Hayward Sch Bolton 65-93; Perm to Offic 65-67; Hon C New Bury 67-79; Hon C Bolton St Paul w Em 79-86; NSM Pennington from 86. *26 Milverton Close, Lostock, Bolton BL6 4RR* Bolton (01204) 842148

SPEEDY, Darrel Craven. b 35. St Chad's Coll Dur BA57. Wells Th Coll 57. **d** 59 **p** 60. C Frodingham *Linc* 59-63; V Heckington w Howell 63-71; V Barton upon Humber 71-79; R Tain *Mor* 79-85; Dioc Sec 82-85; Can St Andr Cathl Inverness 83-85; Syn Clerk 83-85; R Whaley Bridge *Ches* from 85; RD Chadkirk from 88. *St James's Rectory, Taxal Road, Whaley Bridge, Stockport, Cheshire SK12 7DY* Whaley Bridge (01663) 732696

SPEERS, Canon Albert Edward. b 10. Wycliffe Hall Ox. **d** 44 **p** 44. V Barnehurst *Roch* 67-87; Hon Can Roch Cathl 75-87; rtd 87. *48 Birch Grove, Hempstead, Gillingham, Kent ME7 3RB* Medway (01634) 379464

SPEERS, Canon Samuel Hall. b 46. TCD BA70 MA75. Cuddesdon Coll 70. **d** 73 **p** 74. C Boreham Wood All SS *St Alb* 73-76; Madagascar 76-88; Hon Can Antananarivo from 85; R S Lafford *Linc* from 88. *The Rectory, West Street, Folkingham, Sleaford, Lincs NG34 0SN* Folkingham (01529) 497391

SPENCE, Brian Robin. b 39. St Chad's Coll Dur BA61 DipTh63. **d** 63 **p** 64. C Weston *Guildf* 63-67; Lesotho 67-68; C Chobham w Valley End *Guildf* 68-71; C Gt Yarmouth *Nor* 71-74; V Warnham *Chich* 74-81; V E Grinstead St Mary 81-86; V Crowthorne *Ox* from 86. *The Vicarage, 56 Duke's Ride, Crowthorne, Berks RG11 6NY* Crowthorne (01344) 772413

SPENCE, James Knox (Jim). b 30. Worc Coll Ox BA55 MA58. Ridley Hall Cam. **d** 57 **p** 58. C W Hampstead Trin *Lon* 57-60; C Ox St Ebbe w St Pet *Ox* 61-64; Cand Sec CPAS 64-68;

V Reading Greyfriars *Ox* 68-78; C St Helen Bishopsgate w St Martin Outwich *Lon* 78-80; C St Helen Bishopsgate w St Andr Undershaft etc 80-82; P-in-c Gt Baddow *Chelmsf* 82-86; V 86-88; TR 88-95; rtd 95. *15 High Street, Wallingford, Oxon OX10 0BP* Wallingford (01491) 826814

SPENCE, James Timothy. b 35. St Jo Coll Cam BA59 MA63. Wycliffe Hall Ox 59. **d** 61 **p** 62. C Stoke *Cov* 61-64; C Cam H Trin *Ely* 64-67; R Tarrington w Stoke Edith *Heref* 67-72; Dioc Youth Officer 67-72; Lic to Offic *Win* 72-75; R Falstone *Newc* 75-80; TV Bellingham/Otterburn Gp 80-82; Dioc Ecum Adv 82-87; V Dinnington 82-87; V Shap w Swindale *Carl* 87-93; P-in-c Bowness from 93; P-in-c Kirkbride w Newton Arlosh from 93. *The Rectory, Church Road, Kirkbride, Carlisle CA5 5HY* Kirkbride (016973) 51256

SPENCE, Canon John Edis. b 24. St Edm Hall Ox BA46 MA48. Westcott Ho Cam 47. **d** 48 **p** 49. Chapl RNR from 65; V St Germans *Truro* 65-73; V Tideford 65-73; P-in-c Sheviock 69-70; Perm to Offic 73-76; Dioc Chapl to Bp 76-78; C Newlyn St Newlyn 76-78; Chapl for Maintenance of the Min 78-87; Stewardship Adv 80-87; Hon Can Truro Cathl 84-89; Bp's Dom Chapl 87-89; P-in-c St Allen 87-89; rtd 89; Lic to Offic *Truro* from 89; Perm to Offic *Ex* from 91. *26 Kerries Road, South Brent, Devon TQ10 9DA* South Brent (01364) 72578

SPENCE, Philip Arthur. b 39. Lon Univ BD71 Open Univ BA76. Hartley Victoria Coll DipTh67 Westcott Ho Cam 78. **d** 78 **p** 79. In Meth Ch 67-78; C Walthamstow St Pet *Chelmsf* 78-80; Dioc Adv on Evang 80-87; Dep Dir Dept of Miss (Evang Division) 80-85; P-in-c Greensted 80-86; Bp's Adv on Tourism 81-87; Asst Dir of Miss and Unity 85-87; R Greensted-juxta-Ongar w Stanford Rivers 86-87; V Cam St Mark *Ely* from 87; Chapl Wolfs Coll Cam from 87; Relig Adv Anglia TV from 91. *St Mark's Vicarage, Barton Road, Cambridge CB3 9JZ* Cambridge (01223) 63339

SPENCE, Very Rev Walter Cyril. b 19. TCD BA40 MA43 BD43. **d** 42 **p** 43. Dean Tuam *T, K & A* 66-81; I Tuam 66-81; Dioc Registrar 66-85; Preb Kilmactalway St Patr Cathl Dub 67-85; I Kilmoremoy w Castleconnor, Easkey, Kilglass etc *T, K & A* 81-85; rtd 85. *Beth Shalom, 1 Gracefield Avenue, Dublin 5, Irish Republic*

SPENCELEY, Malcolm. b 40. St Jo Coll Dur 78. **d** 80 **p** 81. C Redcar *York* 80-85; V Middlesb Ascension 85-93; V Newby from 93. *The Vicarage, 77 Green Lane, Scarborough, N Yorkshire YO12 6HT* Scarborough (01723) 363205

SPENCER, Anthony Wade. b 50. AIQS78 Birm Poly HNC74 Wolv Poly MCIOB76. Ridley Hall Cam CTM94. **d** 94 **p** 95. C Bury St Edmunds St Geo *St E* from 94. *165 Tollgate Lane, Bury St Edmunds, Suffolk IP32 6DF* Bury St Edmunds (01284) 768970

SPENCER, Christopher Graham (Chris). b 61. Magd Coll Cam BA83 MA87 Bath Univ MSc84. St Jo Coll Nottm DTS93. **d** 93 **p** 94. C Ore *Chich* from 93. *Church House, 311 The Ridge, Hastings, E Sussex TN34 2RA* Hastings (01424) 754501

SPENCER, David William. b 43. E Anglian Minl Tr Course 80. **d** 81 **p** 82. NSM Wisbech St Aug *Ely* 81-84; C Whittlesey 84-86; R Upwell Ch Ch 86-90; R March St Pet from 90; R March St Mary from 90. *St Peter's Rectory, High Street, March, Cambs PE15 9JR* March (01354) 52297

SPENCER, Geoffrey. b 50. ALCM76 Nottm Univ CertEd78 ACertCM79 Open Univ BA84. Linc Th Coll 85. **d** 87 **p** 88. C Skegness and Winthorpe *Linc* 87-90; V Heckington 90-93; P-in-c Bottesford and Muston *Leic* from 93; P-in-c Harby, Long Clawson and Hose from 94; P-in-c Barkestone w Plungar, Redmile and Stathern from 94. *The Rectory, 4 Rutland Lane, Bottesford, Nottingham NG13 0BX* Bottesford (01949) 42335

SPENCER, George. b 56. Cam Univ BA77 MA83. Coll of Resurr Mirfield 80. **d** 83 **p** 84. C Edin Old St Paul *Edin* 83-85; P-in-c Edin St Ninian 85-92; Chapl Asst Whiston Hosp from 92; Chapl Asst St Helen's and Knowsley Hosps Trust from 92. *Chapel House, Whiston Hospital, Warrington Road, Prescot, Merseyside L35 5DR* 0151-430 1657 or 426 1600

SPENCER, Gilbert Hugh. b 43. Lon Univ BD67. ALCD66. **d** 67 **p** 68. C Bexleyheath Ch Ch *Roch* 67-73; C Bexley St Jo 73-76; P-in-c Bromley St Jo 76-78; V 78-81; R Chatham St Mary w St Jo 81-91; V Minster in Sheppey *Cant* from 91; Chapl Sheppey Gen Hosp from 91; RD Sittingbourne *Cant* from 94. *The Vicarage, Vicarage Road, Minster-in-Sheppey, Sheerness, Kent ME12 2HE* Minster (01795) 873185

SPENCER, Gordon Charles Craig. b 13. Oak Hill Th Coll 35. **d** 38 **p** 39. V Bathampton *B & W* 66-81; rtd 81; P-in-c Ditteridge *Bris* 81-86; Perm to Offic from 86; Perm to Offic *B & W* from 86. *26 Elm Grove, Bath BA1 7AZ* Bath (01225) 316570

SPENCER, Graham Lewis. b 48. St Jo Coll Nottm 80. **d** 82 **p** 83. C Leic St Anne *Leic* 82-85; P-in-c Frisby-on-the-Wreake w

654

Kirby Bellars 85-86; TV Melton Gt Framland 86-93; V Upper Wreake from 93. *The Vicarage, 2 Carrfields Lane, Frisby on the Wreake, Melton Mowbray, Leics LE14 2NT* Melton Mowbray (01664) 434878

SPENCER, John Edward. b 36. Bris Univ BA60. Tyndale Hall Bris 57. **d** 61 **p** 62. C St Helens St Mark *Liv* 61-64; Japan 65-70; Area Sec (Dios Leic and Pet) CMS 70-71; Lic to Offic *Leic* 70-71; Perm to Offic *Guildf* 71-73; Warden and Chapl Rikkyo Japanese Sch Rudgwick 71-73; Hd Master Pennthorpe Sch Rudgwick from 73; Perm to Offic *Chich* from 73. *Pennthorpe School, Rudgwick, Horsham, W Sussex RH12 3HJ* Rudgwick (01403) 822391

SPENCER, John Leslie. b 09. St Cath Soc Ox BA30 MA34. St Aid Birkenhead 31. **d** 32 **p** 33. V Bramfield and Walpole *St E* 69-74; rtd 74; Perm to Offic *Chich* 80-91. *Flat 7, Capel Court, The Burgage, Prestbury, Cheltenham, Glos GL52 3EL* Cheltenham (01242) 577516

SPENCER, Norman Ernest. b 07. FCIS70. **d** 74 **p** 75. NSM Olveston *Bris* 74-82; Perm to Offic from 82. *26 Park Crescent, Bristol BS16 1NZ* Bristol (0117) 956 8873

SPENCER, Peter Cecil. b 30. Lich Th Coll 58. **d** 61 **p** 62. C Alton St Lawr *Win* 61-63; C Bournemouth St Luke 63-66; C W End 67-70; C Reading St Mary V *Ox* 70-72; C-in-c Reading St Matt CD 72-76; V Reading St Matt 76-78; TV Sidmouth, Woolbrook and Salcombe Regis *Ex* 78-86; R Birch w Layer Breton and Layer Marney *Chelmsf* from 86. *The Rectory, Birch, Colchester CO2 0NA* Colchester (01206) 330241

SPENCER, Peter Roy. b 40. CertEd. Sarum & Wells Th Coll 72. **d** 74 **p** 75. C Northn St Alb *Pet* 74-77; TV Cov E *Cov* 77-90; V Erdington St Barn *Birm* from 90. *The Vicarage, 26 Church Road, Birmingham B24 9AX* 0121-373 0884 or 350 9945

SPENCER, Richard Hugh. b 62. Univ of Wales (Cardiff) LLB84 BD88. St Mich Coll Llan 85. **d** 88 **p** 89. C Barry All SS *Llan* 88-90; Asst Chapl Univ of Wales (Cardiff) 90-92; Lect from 92; Tutor St Mich Coll Llan from 92. *St Michael's College, 54 Cardiff Road, Llandaff, Cardiff CF5 2YF* Cardiff (01222) 563379

SPENCER, Richard William Edward. b 33. W Midl Minl Tr Course 78. **d** 81 **p** 82. NSM The Lickey *Birm* 81-83; Area Sec (Warks and W Midl) Chr Aid 83-93; Perm to Offic *Birm* 84-91; Lic to Offic from 91; Perm to Offic *Cov* from 85. *104 Witherford Way, Birmingham B29 4AW* 0121-624 5344

SPENCER, Canon Robert. b 27. FRSA. St Aid Birkenhead 48. **d** 51 **p** 52. V Stockport St Alb Hall Street *Ches* 62-71; V Crewe All SS and St Paul 71-81; V Over St Chad 81-89; Hon Can Ches Cathl 89-93; V Baddiley and Wrenbury w Burleydam 89-93; rtd 93. *25 Coleridge Way, Crewe CW1 1JW*

SPENCER, Robert. b 48. St Jo Coll Nottm CertCS93. **d** 93 **p** 94. NSM Ellon *Ab* from 93; NSM Cruden Bay from 93. *12 Riverview Place, Ellon, Aberdeenshire AB41 9NW* Ellon (01358) 723193

SPENCER, Roy Primett. b 26. Oak Hill Th Coll 50. **d** 53 **p** 54. V Accrington St Paul *Blackb* 69-78; V Woodplumpton 78-83; Chapl Preston Hosp N Shields 83-91; P-in-c Preston St Luke *Blackb* 83-89; P-in-c Preston St Luke and St Oswald 89-90; rtd 91. *5 Hollywood Avenue, Penwortham, Preston PR1 9AS* Preston (01772) 743783

SPENCER, Stanley. b 11. Clifton Th Coll 32. **d** 36 **p** 37. R Monken Hadley *Lon* 67-77; rtd 77. *27 Chestnut Avenue, Holbeach, Spalding, Lincs PE12 7NE* Holbeach (01406) 22894

SPENCER, Dr Stephen Christopher. b 60. Ball Coll Ox BA82 DPhil90. Edin Th Coll 88. **d** 90 **p** 91. C Harlesden All So *Lon* 90-93; Zimbabwe from 93. *St James's Mission, PO Box 23, Nyamandhlovu, Zimbabwe* Nyamandhlovu (87) 23419

SPENCER, Stephen Nigel Howard. b 53. Pemb Coll Ox BA75 Jes Coll Cam PGCE76. Trin Coll Bris 80. **d** 82 **p** 83. C Partington and Carrington *Ches* 82-85; C Brunswick *Man* 85-88; Chapl UEA *Nor* 88-92; rtd 92; Perm to Offic *Nor* from 92. *43 College Lane, Norwich NR4 6TW* Norwich (01603) 506815

SPENCER, Mrs Susan. b 47. E Midl Min Tr Course 87. **d** 90 **p** 94. Par Dn Cotgrave *S'well* 90-94; C from 94. *Church House, 35 East Acres, Cotgrave, Notts NG12 3JP* Nottingham (0115) 989 3478 or 0850-469354 (mobile)

SPENCER, Canon William Lowbridge. b 16. Keble Coll Ox BA38 MA46. Wells Th Coll 46. **d** 47 **p** 48. C Swindon New Town *Bris* 50-51; Tanganyika 52-64; Tanzania from 64; Can Masasi from 75; rtd 86. *St Cyprian's College, PO Box 212, Lindi, Tanzania*

SPENCER-THOMAS, Owen Robert. b 40. Lon Univ BSc(Soc)70. Westcott Ho Cam 70. **d** 72 **p** 73. C S Kensington St Luke *Lon* 72-76; Lect Relig Studies S Kensington Inst 74-76; Dir Lon Chs Radio Workshop & Relig Producer BBC 76-78; Relig Producer Anglia TV 78-95; Lic to Offic *Lon* 76-86; Perm to Offic *Ely* 85-87; Perm to Offic *Lon* 86-87; Perm to

Offic *Pet* from 86; NSM Cam Ascension *Ely* from 87; Chapl St Jo Coll Sch Cam from 93. *52 Windsor Road, Cambridge CB4 3JN* Cambridge (01223) 358446

SPENDLOVE, Mrs Lindsay Kate. b 55. Man Univ LLB77 Essex Univ BA88. E Anglian Minl Tr Course 89. **d** 92 **p** 94. NSM Lexden *Chelmsf* 92-94; NSM Colchester Ch Ch w St Mary V from 94. *Stables, 4 Lexden Road, Colchester CO3 3NE* Colchester (01206) 560495

SPERRING, Clive Michael. b 43. Oak Hill Th Coll 71. **d** 75 **p** 76. C Hawkwell *Chelmsf* 75-78; C-in-c Gt Baddow 78-82; New Zealand from 82. *49 Te Arawa Street, Orakei, Auckland 5, New Zealand 1105* Auckland (9) 521-0296

SPICER, David John. b 49. Lon Univ BEd71. Linc Th Coll 76. **d** 78 **p** 79. C Upminster *Chelmsf* 78-80; C Mosborough *Sheff* 80-82; V Frisby-on-the-Wreake w Kirby Bellars *Leic* 82-84; Hon C Gt Ilford St Luke *Chelmsf* 85-88; C Cleethorpes *Linc* 88-90; C-in-c Stamford Ch Ch CD 90-92; V Stamford Ch Ch from 92. *Christ Church Vicarage, 14 Queen Street, Stamford, Lincs PE9 1QS* Stamford (01780) 62990

SPICER, David John. b 52. Sussex Univ BA76 Lon Univ MTh78. Westcott Ho Cam 77. **d** 79 **p** 80. C E Dulwich St Jo *S'wark* 79-82; C Richmond St Mary w St Matthias and St Jo 82-87; V Lewisham St Swithun 87-91; Chapl Community of All Hallows Ditchingham from 91. *St Edmund's House, All Hallows Convent, Ditchingham, Bungay, Suffolk NR35 2DZ* Bungay (01986) 892139

SPICER, Leigh Edwin. b 56. Sarum & Wells Th Coll 78. **d** 81 **p** 82. C Harborne St Pet *Birm* 81-83; C Bloxwich *Lich* 83-87; Chapl RAF from 87. *Chaplaincy Services (RAF), HQ, Personnel and Training Command, RAF Innsworth, Gloucester GL3 1EZ* Gloucester (01452) 712612 Ext 5164 Fax 510828

SPICER, Nicolas. b 61. Univ of Wales (Lamp) BA84. Coll of Resurr Mirfield 84. **d** 86 **p** 87. C Westbury-on-Trym H Trin *Bris* 86-89; C Willesden Green St Andr and St Fran of Assisi *Lon* 89-93; Chapl Asst Charing Cross Hosp Lon from 93. *The Chaplaincy, Charing Cross Hospital, Fulham Palace Road, London W6 8RF* 0181-846 1041 Fax 846 1111

SPIERS, Ven Graeme Hendry Gordon. b 25. ALCD52. **d** 52 **p** 53. V Aigburth *Liv* 66-80; RD Childwall 75-79; Hon Can Liv Cathl 77-91; Adn Liv 80-91; rtd 91. *19 Barkfield Lane, Formby, Merseyside L37 1LY* Formby (01704) 872902

SPIERS, Peter Hendry. b 61. St Jo Coll Dur BA82. Ridley Hall Cam 83. **d** 86 **p** 87. C W Derby St Luke *Liv* 86-90; TV Everton St Pet 90-95; V Everton St Geo from 95. *St George's Vicarage, Northumberland Terrace, Liverpool L5 3QG* 0151-263 1945

SPIKIN, Simon John Overington. b 48. Linc Th Coll 70. **d** 75 **p** 76. C Sawbridgeworth *St Alb* 75-79; C Odiham w S Warnborough and Long Sutton *Win* 79-81; P-in-c Rushall 81-82; R Dickleburgh w Thelveton w Frenze and Shimpling *Nor* 81-82; R Dickleburgh, Langmere, Shimpling, Thelveton etc from 82. *The Rectory, Burston Road, Dickleburgh, Diss, Norfolk IP21 4NN* Diss (01379) 741313

SPILLER, David Roger. b 44. St Jo Coll Dur BA70 Fitzw Coll Cam BA72 MA76 Nottm Univ DipAdEd80. Ridley Hall Cam 70. **d** 73 **p** 74. C Bradf Cathl *Bradf* 73-77; C Stratford-on-Avon w Bishopton *Cov* 77-80; Chapl Geo Eliot Hosp Nuneaton 80-90; V Chilvers Coton w Astley *Cov* 80-90; RD Nuneaton 84-90; Prin Aston Tr Scheme from 90; Lic to Offic *Birm* from 90. *148 Court Oak Road, Birmingham B17 9AB* 0121-472 4247 or 427 5225 Fax 427 8345

SPILLER, Edward William. b 32. Cranmer Hall Dur. **d** 82 **p** 83. C Kirkleatham *York* 82-85; R The Thorntons and The Otteringtons from 85. *The Vicarage, Thornton le Moor, Northallerton, N Yorkshire DL7 9DT* Northallerton (01609) 774232

SPILMAN, Derrick Geoffrey. b 27. Roch Th Coll. **d** 63 **p** 64. C Dover St Mary *Cant* 63-67; CF 67-71; Canada from 71. *Apt 607, 2190 Bellevue Avenue, West Vancouver, British Columbia, Canada, V7V 1C4*

SPILSBURY, Stephen Ronald Paul. b 39. Nottm Univ BSc69 MPhil72. Linc Th Coll 71. **d** 64 **p** 65. In RC Ch 64-71; C Cricklade w Latton *Bris* 72-75; P-in-c Swindon All SS 76-81; V Lawrence Weston from 81; RD Westbury and Severnside 89-91. *The Vicarage, 335 Long Cross, Bristol BS11 0NN* Bristol (0117) 982 5863

SPINDLER, Miss Jane Diana. b 54. Southn Univ BA75 CertEd76. Wycliffe Hall Ox 87. **d** 89 **p** 94. Par Dn Bishopsworth *Bris* 89-93; Par Dn Brislington St Luke 93-94; C 94; rtd 95; Perm to Offic *Bris* from 95. *16 Elvaston Road, Bedminster, Bristol BS3 4QJ* Bristol (0117) 966 7099

SPINK, Canon George Arthur Peter. b 26. Oak Hill Th Coll 54. **d** 56 **p** 57. Chapl Cov Cathl *Cov* 68-70; Can Res Cov Cathl 70-77; Warden The Dorothy Kerin Trust Burrswood 77-81; Prior Omega Order from 80; Lic to Offic *Roch* 80-86; Lic to Offic *B & W* from 86; rtd 89. *The Priory, Winford Manor, Winford, Bristol BS18 8DW* Lulsgate (01275) 472262 Fax 472065

SPINKS, Dr Bryan Douglas. b 48. FRHistS85 St Chad's Coll Dur BA70 DipTh71 BD79 K Coll Lon MTh72 Dur Univ DD88. **d** 75 **p** 76. C Witham *Chelmsf* 75-78; C Clacton St Jas 78-79; Lic to Offic *Ely* from 80; Chapl Chu Coll Cam from 80; Perm to Offic *St Alb* from 84. *25 Peer Road, Eaton Socon, St Neots, Huntingdon, Cambs PE19 3JR* Huntingdon (01480) 476790

SPINKS, Christopher George. b 53. Brighton Poly HND80. Oak Hill Th Coll BA88. **d** 88 **p** 89. C Hove Bp Hannington Memorial Ch *Chich* 88-92; Travelling Sec UCCF from 92; Lic to Offic *Chich* from 92. *35 St Heliers Avenue, Hove, E Sussex BN3 5RE* Brighton (01273) 724920

SPINKS, John Frederick. b 40. Oak Hill Th Coll 79. **d** 82 **p** 83. NSM Roxbourne St Andr *Lon* 82-89; C Northwood H Trin 89-93; P-in-c Greenhill St Jo from 93. *St John's Vicarage, 11 Flambard Road, Harrow, Middx HA1 2NB* 0181-907 7956 or 863 3690

SPINNEY, Giles Martin. b 16. Ch Coll Cam BA39 MA43. Wycliffe Hall Ox 39. **d** 41 **p** 42. R Brixton Deverill *Sarum* 54-72; R Kingston Deverill w Monkton Deverill 55-72; R The Deverills 72-81; rtd 81. *17 Chancery Lane, Warminster, Wilts BA12 9JS* Warminster (01985) 214813

SPITTLE, Robin. b 57. St Jo Coll Nottm 84. **d** 86 **p** 87. C Ipswich St Fran *St E* 86-91; Min Shotley St Mary CD 91-92; R Shotley from 92. *The Vicarage, 2 Gate Farm Road, Shotley, Ipswich IP9 1QH* Shotley (01473) 788166

SPIVEY, Colin. b 35. ACII61 Ex Univ DSA68. Oak Hill Th Coll 74. **d** 76 **p** 77. C Egham *Guildf* 76-79; C Edgware *Lon* 79-83; R Haworth *Bradf* 83-95; V Thorpe Edge from 95. *The Vicarage, Northwood Crescent, Bradford, W Yorkshire BD10 9HX* Bradford (01274) 613246

SPIVEY, Canon Peter. b 19. Edin Th Coll 46. **d** 48 **p** 49. V Meltham *Wakef* 61-85; RD Blackmoorfoot 79-85; Hon Can Wakef Cathl 81-85; rtd 85; Perm to Offic *Wakef* from 85. *3 Follett Avenue, Huddersfield HD4 5LW* Huddersfield (01484) 654674

SPIVEY, Ronald. b 28. ACMA MInstAM. E Midl Min Tr Course 83. **d** 86 **p** 87. NSM Sutton St Mary *Linc* from 86. *5 Lancaster Drive, Long Sutton, Spalding, Lincs PE12 9BD* Holbeach (01406) 362084

SPOKES, Keith John. b 29. E Anglian Minl Tr Course. **d** 84 **p** 85. NSM Bury St Edmunds St Mary *St E* 84-89; P-in-c Helmingham w Framsden and Pettaugh w Winston 89-92; rtd 93. *16 Croft Rise, Bury St Edmunds, Suffolk IP33 2PY* Bury St Edmunds (01284) 706742

SPONG, Terence John. b 32. CLJ. Roch Th Coll 63. **d** 66 **p** 67. Rhodesia 68-80; Zimbabwe 80-84; R Christow, Ashton, Trusham and Bridford *Ex* 84-86; Chapl Puerto de la Cruz Tenerife *Eur* 86-93; Miss to Seamen 86-93; rtd 93; Perm to Offic *Win* from 93. *14B Stuart Road, Highcliffe, Christchurch, Dorset BH23 5JS* Highcliffe (01425) 277833

SPOONER, Anthony Patrick David (Tony). b 45. Univ Coll of Rhodesia Univ Coll of Nyasaland BA68 Nottm Univ DipTh72. Linc Th Coll 71. **d** 74 **p** 75. C Glynde, W Firle and Beddingham *Chich* 74-77; Rhodesia 77-80; Zimbabwe 80-86; P-in-c Clacton St Jas *Chelmsf* 86-90; V from 90. *St James's Vicarage, 44 Wash Lane, Clacton-on-Sea, Essex CO15 1DA* Clacton-on-Sea (01255) 422007

SPOOR, Norman Leslie. b 15. BSc PhD DipTh. Ripon Coll Cuddesdon. **d** 83 **p** 83. NSM Steventon w Milton *Ox* 88-90; NSM Abingdon 90-92; Perm to Offic from 92. *4 Ladygrove Paddock, Drayton Road, Abingdon, Oxon OX14 5HT* Abingdon (01235) 528750

SPOTTISWOODE, Anthony Derek. b 25. Solicitor 50 Pemb Coll Cam BA47 MA86. Sarum & Wells Th Coll 85. **d** 86 **p** 87. C Hampstead St Jo *Lon* 86-94; rtd 95. *Flat 2, 26 Belsize Lane, London NW3 5AB* 0171-435 6756

SPRACKLING, Frederick Phillips. b 16. Bible Churchmen's Coll 37. **d** 40 **p** 41. V Stamford Brook *Lon* 57-81; rtd 81. *1 Tyrrell Square, Mitcham, Surrey CR4 3SD* 0181-687 1614

SPRATLEY, Deryck Edward. b 30. BSc. Oak Hill Th Coll 62. **d** 64 **p** 65. C W Holl St Dav *Lon* 67-73; V Upper Holloway St Pet 73-79; V Upper Holloway St Pet w St Jo 79-82; P-in-c Dagenham *Chelmsf* 82-88; P-in-c Becontree St Geo 84-88; TR Dagenham 88-93; rtd 93. *35 Upper Second Avenue, Frinton-on-Sea, Essex CO13 9LP* Frinton-on-Sea (01255) 851216

SPRATT, Laurence Herbert. b 28. Linc Th Coll 76. **d** 78 **p** 79. C Mexborough *Sheff* 78-80; R Wrentham w Benacre, Covehithe, Frostenden etc *St E* 80-88; Perm to Offic *Arg* 89-90; P-in-c Inveraray 90-91; Perm to Offic from 91; rtd 93. *Inver, Minard, Inveraray, Argyll PA32 8YB* Minard (01546) 86276

SPRATT, Robert Percival (Bob). b 31. MRSH83. Carl Dioc Tr Inst 84. **d** 87 **p** 88. NSM Kendal St Thos *Carl* 87-89; Chapl HM Pris Preston from 89. *The Chaplain's Office, HM Prison, 2 Ribbleton Lane, Preston PR1 5AB* Preston (01772) 57734 Fax 556643

SPRAY, Canon Charles Alan Francis Thomas. b 27. ARSM51 Lon Univ BScEng51. Ridley Hall Cam 57. **d** 59 **p** 60. R Ore *Chich* 70-85; V Burgess Hill St Andr 85-93; Can and Preb Chich Cathl 88-93; rtd 93. *6 Silverdale Road, Burgess Hill, W Sussex RH15 0EF* Burgess Hill (01444) 232149

SPRAY, John William. b 29. Sarum & Wells Th Coll 71. **d** 73 **p** 74. C Clayton *Lich* 73-77; V Hartshill 77-82; P-in-c Aston 82-83; P-in-c Stone St Mich 82-83; P-in-c Stone St Mich w Aston St Sav 83-84; R 84-90; rtd 90. *2 Belvoir Avenue, Trentham, Stoke-on-Trent ST4 8SY* Stoke-on-Trent (01782) 644959

SPRAY, Richard Alan. b 43. **d** 88 **p** 89. NSM Cotgrave *S'well* from 88. *Church Lodge, 10 Miller Hives Close, Cotgrave, Nottingham NG12 3QY* Nottingham (0115) 989 3562

SPREAD, John Henry Seymour. b 14. MC46. Lon Univ BA37. Chich Th Coll 38. **d** 39 **p** 41. V Sundon w Streatley *St Alb* 53-79; rtd 79; Hon C Gt w Lt Hormead, Anstey, Brent Pelham etc *St Alb* 79-89; Hon C Much Hadham 89-91; Perm to Offic from 91. *1 Old Red Lion, Much Hadham, Herts SG10 6DD* Much Hadham (01279) 843140

SPRENT, Michael Francis (Brother Giles). b 34. Ex Coll Ox BA58 MA62. Kelham Th Coll 58. **d** 61 **p** 62. C Plaistow St Andr *Chelmsf* 61-63; SSF from 61; Papua New Guinea 65-69; Hilfield Friary 69-74 and 77-78; Alnmouth Friary 74-76; Harbledown Friary 78-82; Sweden 76-77; TV High Stoy *Sarum* 77-78; Solomon Is from 83. *La Verna Friary, Hautambu, PO Box 519, Honiara, Solomon Islands*

SPRIGGS, Harold. b 99. Dorchester Miss Coll 29. **d** 31 **p** 32. V Mountfield *Chich* 60-85; V Netherfield 60-85; rtd 85; Perm to Offic *Chich* from 85. *2 Church Cottages, Mountfield, Robertsbridge, E Sussex TN32 5JS* Robertsbridge (01580) 880261

SPRIGGS, John David Robert. b 36. BNC Ox BA58 MA63. S'wark Ord Course 73. **d** 75 **p** 76. Lic to Offic *Ox* from 75; Chapl Pangbourne Coll from 95. *St Vincent, Bere Court Road, Pangbourne, Reading RG8 8JY* Pangbourne (01734) 844933

SPRINGATE, Paul Albert Edward. b 48. Oak Hill Th Coll 81. **d** 83 **p** 84. C Pennycross *Ex* 83-87; P-in-c Cossington and Seagrave *Leic* 87; TV Sileby, Cossington and Seagrave from 87. *The Vicarage, Main Street, Cossington, Leicester LE7 4UU* Sileby (01509) 813455

SPRINGBETT, John Howard. b 47. Pemb Coll Cam BA70 MA74. Ridley Hall Cam 70. **d** 72 **p** 73. C Ulverston St Mary w H Trin *Carl* 72-76; V Dewsbury Moor *Wakef* 76-84; V Hoddesdon *St Alb* from 84; RD Cheshunt from 94. *The Vicarage, 11 Amwell Street, Hoddesdon, Herts EN11 8TS* Hoddesdon (01992) 462127

SPRINGETT, Robert Wilfred. b 62. Nottm Univ BTh89. Linc Th Coll 86. **d** 89 **p** 90. C Colchester St Jas, All SS, St Nic and St Runwald *Chelmsf* 89-92; C Basildon, St Martin of Tours w Nevendon 92-94; P-in-c Belhus Park from 94; P-in-c S Ockendon from 94. *The Vicarage, 121 Foyle Drive, South Ockendon, Essex RM15 5HF* South Ockendon (01708) 853246

SPRINGETT, Simon Paul. b 56. Warw Univ LLB78. Wycliffe Hall Ox 78. **d** 81 **p** 82. C Harlow St Mary and St Hugh w St Jo the Bapt *Chelmsf* 81-84; C Gt Clacton 84-86; R Rayne 86-91; Chapl RN from 91. *Directorate Gen, RN Chapl Services, Room 203, Victory Building, HM Naval Base, Portsmouth PO1 3LS* Portsmouth (01705) 727903 Fax 727112

SPRINGFORD, Patrick Francis Alexander. b 45. Wycliffe Hall Ox 71. **d** 74 **p** 75. C Finchley Ch Ch *Lon* 74-79; CF from 79. *c/o MOD (Army), Bagshot Park, Bagshot, Surrey GU19 5PL* Bagshot (01276) 471717 Fax 412834

SPRINGHAM, Desmond John. b 32. Bris Univ BA56. Oak Hill Th Coll 56. **d** 58 **p** 59. C St Alb St Paul *St Alb* 58-61; C Reading St Jo *Ox* 61-66; R Worting *Win* 66-80; V Jersey St Andr from 80. *St Andrew's Vicarage, First Tower, Jersey, Channel Islands* Jersey (01534) 34975

SPRINGTHORPE, David Frederick. b 47. Open Univ BA. AKC72. **d** 73 **p** 74. C Dartford St Alb *Roch* 73-77; C Biggin Hill 77-80; R Ash 80-89; R Ridley 80-89; R Eynsford w Farningham and Lullingstone 89-94; V Barnehurst from 94. *The Vicarage, 93 Pelham Road, Barnehurst, Bexleyheath, Kent DA7 4LY* Crayford (01322) 523344

SPROSTON, Bernard Melvin. b 37. St Jo Coll Dur 77. **d** 79 **p** 80. C Westlands St Andr *Lich* 79-82; P-in-c Heage *Derby* 82-87; V Heath from 87. *The Vicarage, Main Street, Heath, Chesterfield, Derbyshire S44 5RX* Chesterfield (01246) 850339

SPROULE, Gerald Norman. b 26. TCD DBS60. **d** 60 **p** 61. I Magheracross *Clogh* 68-73; Admin Sec (Ireland) BCMS 73-79; I Belf St Aid *Conn* 79-86; I Magherally w Annaclone *D & D* 86-94; rtd 94. *4 Hilden Park, Lisburn, Co Antrim BT27 4UT* Lisburn (01846) 601528

SPURGEON, Michael Paul. b 53. MIEx. Linc Th Coll 83. **d** 85 **p** 86. C Lillington *Cov* 85-89; C Min Can Ripon Cathl *Ripon* from 89. *The School House, Berrygate Road, Sharow, Ripon, N Yorkshire HG4 5BJ* Ripon (01765) 607017

SPURIN, Canon Richard Mark. b 28. Peterho Cam BA52 MA60. Wycliffe Hall Ox 54. **d** 55 **p** 56. Kenya 61-73; C-in-c Ewell St Paul Howell Hill CD *Guildf* 73-82; V Netherton *Liv* 82-86; V Brandwood *Birm* 86-91; C Padiham *Blackb* 91-93; Hon Can Nambale Cathl Kenya from 92; rtd 93. *93 Westbourne Avenue South, Burnley, Lancs BB11 4QZ* Burnley (01282) 421402

SPURR, Andrew. b 58. St Jo Coll Dur BA80. Ripon Coll Cuddesdon 80 Roch Div Sch (USA) 84 Qu Coll Birm 92. **d** 93 **p** 94. C Rainham *Roch* from 93. *70 Elmstone Road, Gillingham, Kent ME8 9BE* Medway (01634) 233786

SPURR, Roger Colin. b 29. Linc Th Coll. **d** 82 **p** 83. C Street w Walton *B & W* 82-85; R Stogumber w Nettlecombe and Monksilver 85-95; rtd 95. *The Rectory, Yellow Road, Stogumber, Taunton, Somerset TA4 3TL* Stogumber (01984) 56221

SPURRELL, John Mark. b 34. FSA87 CCC Ox BA57 DipTh58 MA61. Linc Th Coll 58. **d** 60 **p** 61. C Tilbury Docks *Chelmsf* 60-65; C Boston *Linc* 65-76; R Stow in Lindsey 76-85; P-in-c Willingham 76-85; P-in-c Coates 76-85; P-in-c Brightwell w Sotwell *Ox* from 85. *The Rectory, Brightwell, Wallingford, Oxon OX10 0RX* Wallingford (01491) 837110

SPURRIER, Richard Patrick Montague. b 25. Bris Univ BA59. Wycliffe Hall Ox 59. **d** 61 **p** 62. C Weston St Jo *B & W* 63-64; rtd 90. *48 Longford Road, Melksham, Wilts SN12 6AU* Melksham (01225) 707419

SQUAREY, Canon Gerald Stephen Miles. b 36. Lich Th Coll 59. **d** 62 **p** 63. C Poplar All SS w St Frideswide *Lon* 62-64; C Heston 64-67; V Bradf Abbas w Clifton Maybank *Sarum* 67-74; P-in-c Corfe Castle 74-79; R 79-84; R Steeple w Tyneham, Church Knowle and Kimmeridge 79-84; R Corfe Castle, Church Knowle, Kimmeridge etc 84-90; P-in-c Pimperne 90-91; P-in-c Stourpaine, Durweston and Bryanston 90-91; R Pimperne, Stourpaine, Durweston and Bryanston from 91; RD Milton and Blandford from 91; Can and Preb Sarum Cathl from 92. *The Vicarage, Shaston Road, Stourpaine, Blandford Forum, Dorset DT11 8TA* Blandford (01258) 480580

SQUIRE, Clenyg. b 31. TCert53. Cuddesdon Coll 89. **d** 90 **p** 91. NSM Hale and Ashley *Ches* 90-93; P-in-c Kingsley 93-95; C from 95. *St John's Vicarage, Pike Lane, Kingsley, Warrington WA6 8EH* Kingsley (01928) 788386

SQUIRE, David George Mitchell. b 31. Worc Coll Ox BA54 MA58. Qu Coll Birm DipTh66. **d** 67 **p** 68. C Dursley *Glouc* 67-70; V Cam 71-77; Org Sec (Dios Birm, Heref, Lich and Worc) CECS 77-88; Perm to Offic *Heref* from 81; rtd 88. *Ty Gwyn, Diheuyd, Lampeter, Dyfed SA48 7PP* Lampeter (01570) 470260

SQUIRE, Geoffrey Frank. b 36. Ex & Truro NSM Scheme. **d** 83 **p** 84. NSM Barnstaple, Goodleigh and Landkey *Ex* 83-85; NSM Barnstaple from 85. *Little Cross, Northleigh Hill, Goodleigh, Barnstaple, Devon EX32 7NR* Barnstaple (01271) 44935

SQUIRE, Humphrey Edward. b 29. St Chad's Coll Dur BA55. Coll of Resurr Mirfield. **d** 57 **p** 58. R Drayton *Nor* 64-75; Chapl Dover Coll Kent 75-83; TV Wareham *Sarum* 83-94; rtd 94. *La Retraite, Burbidge Close, Lytchett Matravers, Poole, Dorset BH16 6EG* Wareham (01929) 552501

SQUIRE, Preb John Brinsmead. b 16. St Edm Hall Ox BA38 MA43. Linc Th Coll 38. **d** 40 **p** 40. V Taunton St Andr *B & W* 57-81; Preb Wells Cathl from 77; rtd 81. *Xanadu, 1 St Mary Street, Nether Stowey, Bridgwater, Somerset TA5 1LJ* Nether Stowey (01278) 732957

SQUIRES, Malcolm. b 46. St Chad's Coll Dur BA72. Cuddesdon Coll 72. **d** 74 **p** 75. C Headingley *Ripon* 74-77; C Stanningley St Thos 77-80; V Bradshaw *Wakef* 80-85; V Ripponden 85-89; V Barkisland w W Scammonden 85-89; V Mirfield from 89. *The Vicarage, Vicarage Meadow, Mirfield, W Yorkshire WF14 9JL* Mirfield (01924) 492188

SSEMAKULA, James. **d** 94. Asst Chapl Stockholm w Gavle and Vasteras *Eur* from 94. *c/o Styrmansgatan 1, 11454 Stockholm, Sweden*

SSERUNKUMA, Michael Wilberforce. b 54. Trin Coll Bris DipHE88 BA90 Bp Tucker Coll Mukono 77. **d** 77 **p** 78. Uganda 77-87; C Gabalfa *Llan* 90-94; TV Cyncoed *Mon* from 94. *62 Hollybush Road, Cyncoed, Cardiff CF2 6TA* Cardiff (01222) 755306

STABLES, Courtley Greenwood. b 13. Keble Coll Ox BA49 MA54. St Steph Ho Ox 48. **d** 50 **p** 51. Sen Lect Coll of All SS Tottenham 63-72; Chmn Coun of Ch Schs Co 68-87; C St Andr Undershaft w St Mary Axe *Lon* 64-72; Hon C Uckfield *Chich* from 72; rtd 78. *Abotslare, Pound Green, Buxted, E Sussex TN22 4JZ* Buxted (01825) 732467

STABLES, Miss Katharine Ruth. b 45. DipInstHSM70 R Holloway Coll *Lon* BA67. W Midl Minl Tr Course 90. **d** 93 **p** 94. NSM Knutton *Lich* from 93; NSM Silverdale and

Alsagers Bank from 93. *19 Kennet Close, Newcastle, Staffs ST5 4ER*

STACEY, Dr Helen Norman. Edin Univ MB, ChB45 PhD49. S'wark Ord Course 82. **dss** 83 **d** 87 **p** 94. Notting Hill St Jo and St Pet *Lon* 83-85; Upper Kennett *Sarum* 85-87; Hon Par Dn 87-93; Perm to Offic from 93. *Greystones House, Green Street, Avebury, Marlborough, Wilts SN8 1RE* Avebury (01672) 539289

STACEY, John Roderick (Jack). b 33. Bris Univ BA54. St D Coll Lamp LTh56. **d** 56 **p** 57. C Bedwellty *Mon* 56-58; C Mon 58-62; V New Tredegar 62-66; CF 66-69; TV Ebbw Vale *Mon* 69-73; CF (TA) from 70; V Mamhilad and Llanfihangel Pontymoile *Mon* 73-77; V Pontnewynydd 77-85; R Bettws Newydd w Trostrey etc from 85. *The Rectory, Bettws Newydd, Usk, Gwent NP5 1JN* Nantyderry (01873) 880258

STACEY, Nicolas David. b 27. St Edm Hall Ox BA51 MA55. Cuddesdon Coll 51. **d** 53 **p** 54. Dep Dir Oxfam 68-70; Perm to Offic *Ox* 68-71; P-in-c Selling *Cant* 76-78; Perm to Offic 79-84 and from 90; Six Preacher Cant Cathl 84-90; rtd 92. *The Old Vicarage, Selling, Faversham, Kent ME13 9RD* Canterbury (01227) 752833

STACEY (nee O'BRIEN), Mrs Shelagh Ann. b 55. RGN83 Bedf Coll *Lon* BSc77. N Ord Course 89. **d** 92 **p** 94. Par Dn S Elmsall *Wakef* 92-94; C from 94. *40A Beech Street, South Elmsall, Pontefract, W Yorkshire WF9 2LS* Pontefract (01977) 640967

STACEY, Timothy Andrew (Tim). b 58. Imp Coll Lon BSc79 York Univ PGCE83. St Jo Coll Nottm DTS94. **d** 94 **p** 95. C Chorleywood Ch Ch *St Alb* from 94. *19 Highfield Way, Rickmansworth, Herts WD3 2PP* Rickmansworth (01923) 777966

STACEY, Victor George. b 44. NUI BA69 QUB MTh. CITC 72. **d** 72 **p** 73. C Derriaghy *Conn* 72-76; C Knock *D & D* 76-79; I Ballymacarrett St Martin 79-86; I Dub Santry w Glasnevin *D & G* 86-95; Bp's Dom Chapl from 90; RD Fingal 90-95; I Dun Laoghaire from 95; Prov and Dioc Registrar from 95. *Christ Church Vicarage, 2 Park Road, Dun Laoghaire, Co Dublin, Irish Republic* Dublin (1) 280-9537

STACKPOLE, Robert Aaron. b 59. Williams Coll Mass BA82 Or Coll Ox MLitt88. St Steph Ho Ox 88. **d** 90 **p** 91. C Kettering SS Pet and Paul *Pet* 90-93; Canada from 93. *c/o Mrs Alice Stackpole, 378 Syasset-Woodbury Road, Woodbury, New York 11797, USA*

STAFF, Mrs Jean. b 44. CertEd64. E Midl Min Tr Course 81. **dss** 84 **d** 87 **p** 94. Old Brumby *Linc* 84-87; C 87-88; C Gainsborough St Geo 88-91; D-in-c 91-94; P-in-c from 94. *St George's Vicarage, Heapham Road, Gainsborough, Lincs DN21 1QU* Gainsborough (01427) 612717

STAFF, Miss Susan. b 59. Leeds Univ BA82. Ridley Hall Cam 88. **d** 90 **p** 94. Par Dn Mickleover All SS *Derby* 90-93; Par Dn Chatham St Wm *Roch* 93-94; C from 94. *26 Ballens Road, Chatham, Kent ME5 8NT* Medway (01634) 862787

STAFFORD, David George. b 45. Qu Coll Birm 75. **d** 77 **p** 78. C Chesterfield St Aug *Derby* 77-80; C Ranmoor *Sheff* 80-83; V Bolton-upon-Dearne from 83. *The Vicarage, 41 Station Road, Bolton-on-Dearne, Rotherham, S Yorkshire S63 8AA* Rotherham (01709) 893163

STAFFORD, Canon John Ingham Henry. b 31. TCD BA52 MA58. **d** 53 **p** 55. C Clonallon *D & D* 53-56; C Belf Malone St Jo *Conn* 56-59; Australia 59-64; Min Can Down Cathl *D & D* 64-68; Hd of S Ch Miss Ballymacarrett 68-73; I Bright w Killough 73-83; CF Ban Primacy 83-92; Can Down Cathl 90-92; I Urney w Sion Mills *D & R* from 92. *112 Melmount Road, Sion Mills, Strabane, Co Tyrone BT82 9PY* Sion Mills (016626) 58020

STAFFORD, John James. b 31. Linc Th Coll 69. **d** 71 **p** 72. C Ordsall *S'well* 71-73; V Worksop St Paul 74-78; R Nuthall 78-85; R Plumtree 85-95; RD Bingham S 93-95; rtd 95. *11 Ridgeway Close, Farnsfield, Newark, Notts NG2 6HL* Newark (01623) 883486

STAFFORD-WHITTAKER, William Paul. b 69. Chich Th Coll DipTh94. **d** 94 **p** 95. C Brighton Resurr *Chich* from 94. *St Martin's House, 6 Edinburgh Road, Brighton BN2 3HY* Brighton (01273) 620232

STAFFORD, Area Bishop of. See SCOTT-JOYNT, Rt Rev Michael Charles

STAGG, Charles Roy. b 18. G&C Coll Cam BA45 MA47. Ripon Hall Ox 47. **d** 48 **p** 49. Chapl Dur Sch 48-54; C The Lickey *Birm* 54-55; Uganda 55-58; Chapl Aldenham Sch Herts 59-64; Kenya 64-80; Perm to Offic *Glouc* from 81. *Wyck Cottage, Childswickham, Broadway, Worcs WR12 7HF* Broadway (01386) 853229

STAGG, Jeremy Michael. b 47. Leeds Univ BSc69 Fontainebleau MBA77. Sarum & Wells Th Coll 90. **d** 92 **p** 93. C Basing *Win* from 92. *35 Feld Way, Lychpit, Basingstoke, Hants RG24 8UW* Basingstoke (01256) 59077

STAGG, Michael Hubert. b 39. St Chad's Coll Dur 58. **d** 63 **p** 64. C Weston-super-Mare St Sav *B & W* 63-66; P-in-c Fosdyke *Linc* 66-71; R Brompton Regis w Upton and Skilgate *B & W*

71-78; P-in-c Kidderminster St Jo *Worc* 78-80; P-in-c Cannington *B & W* 80-84; R Cannington, Otterhampton, Combwich and Stockland 84-87; Dioc Communications Officer *Nor* 88-93; Bp's Chapl 88-93; R Sprowston w Beeston from 93; RD Nor N from 95. *The Vicarage, 2 Wroxham Road, Norwich NR7 8TZ* Norwich (01603) 426492

STAINER, Richard Bruce. b 62. Linc Th Coll 92. **d** 94 **p** 95. C N Walsham w Antingham *Nor* from 94. *35 Kimberley Road, North Walsham, Norfolk NR28 9DZ* North Walsham (01692) 404755

STAINES, Edward Noel. b 26. Trin Coll Ox MA52 MSc85. Chich Th Coll 51 57. **d** 57 **p** 58. V Amberley w N Stoke *Chich* 61-70; V Forest Row 70-75; R Ashurst 70-75; V Bexhill St Aug 75-79; TR Ovingdean w Rottingdean and Woodingdean 79-85; V Rottingdean 85-86; Perm to Offic *Worc* from 86; Perm to Offic *Glouc* 86-88; Chapl Gtr Lisbon *Eur* 88-90; Chapl Marseille 90; rtd 90. *White House, Harpley Road, Defford, Worcester WR8 9BL* Evesham (01386) 750817

STAINES, Michael John. b 28. Trin Coll Ox BA52 MA56. Wells Th Coll 62. **d** 64 **p** 65. TV Harling Gp *Nor* 67-73; PM S Chilterns Gp *Ox* 74-75; R W Wycombe w Bledlow Ridge, Bradenham and Radnage 76-93; RD Wycombe 83-87; rtd 93. *Upper Town Cottage, Berrington, Tenbury Wells, Worcs WR15 8TH* Tenbury Wells (01584) 811533

STALEY, John Colin George. b 44. Hull Univ MA83. Wycliffe Hall Ox 68. **d** 71 **p** 72. C Tinsley *Sheff* 71-73; C Slaithwaite w E Scammonden *Wakef* 73-75; V Wakef St Andr and St Mary 75-80; Warden Scargill Ho 80-82; P-in-c Macclesfield St Pet *Ches* 82-85; TV Macclesfield Team Par from 85; Dioc Ind Missr from 87; Sen Ind Chapl from 91. *261 Oxford Road, Macclesfield, Cheshire SK11 8JY* Macclesfield (01625) 423851

STALKER, William John. b 49. N Ord Course 89. **d** 91 **p** 92. C Formby H Trin *Liv* 91-94; V Stoneycroft All SS from 94. *All Saints' Vicarage, West Oak Hill Park, Liverpool L13 4BW* 0151-228 3581

STALLARD, Canon Frederick Hugh. b 11. Pemb Coll Cam BA33 MA37. Cuddesdon Coll 33. **d** 34 **p** 35. V Pet All SS *Pet* 46-81; Can Pet Cathl 57-81; rtd 81. *3 Friday Bridge Road, Elm, Wisbech, Cambs PE14 0AR* Wisbech (01945) 860812

STALLARD, John Charles. b 34. Selw Coll Cam BA58 MA62. Ripon Hall Ox 62. **d** 64 **p** 65. C Hall Green Ascension *Birm* 64-66; C Sutton Coldfield H Trin 66-68; C-in-c Brandwood CD 68-71; Chapl Dame Allan's Schs Newc 71-74; V Warley Woods *Birm* 75-84; TR Droitwich *Worc* 84-87; P-in-c Dodderhill 84-87; TR Droitwich Spa 87-94; V Pennsett from 94. *The Vicarage, Vicarage Lane, Pensnett, Brierley Hill, W Midlands DY5 4JH* Brierley Hill (01384) 262666

STALLARD, Ms Mary Kathleen Rose. b 67. Selw Coll Cam BA88 Lon Inst of Educn PGCE90. Qu Coll Birm 91. **d** 93. C Newport St Matt *Mon* from 93. *16 Kensington Place, Newport, Gwent NP9 8GL* Newport (01633) 281053

STALLEY, Brian Anthony. b 38. Oak Hill Th Coll 60. **d** 63 **p** 64. C Summerstown *S'wark* 63-70; Surrey BFBS Sec 70-73; Manager Action Cen BFBS 73-76; R Branston *Linc* 76-91; rtd 91. *2 Carlton Mews, Washingborough, Lincoln LN4 1RB* Lincoln (01522) 794164

STAMFORD, Brian. b 37. **d** 91 **p** 92. CMS 88-95; Uganda 88-95; P-in-c North Hill and Lewannick *Truro* from 95. *The Rectory, North Hill, Launceston, Cornwall PL15 7PQ* Launceston (01566) 782806

STAMFORD, Dean of. *See* IND, Rt Rev William

STAMP, Andrew Nicholas. b 44. Ex Univ BA67. Sarum Th Coll 67. **d** 69 **p** 70. C S Beddington St Mich *S'wark* 69-73; Tutor Sarum & Wells Th Coll 73-76; Chapl RN 76-81; C-in-c W Leigh CD *Portsm* 81-82; V W Leigh 82-87; R Botley from 87; V Curdridge from 94; R Durley from 94. *All Saints' Rectory, Brook Lane, Botley, Southampton SO3 2ER* Botley (01489) 781534

STAMP, Harold William Tremlett. b 08. St Aug Coll Cant 30. **d** 35 **p** 36. R Farway w Northleigh and Southleigh *Ex* 69-72; V Branscombe 72-76; rtd 76; Hon C Nymet Rowland w Coldridge *Ex* 77-81; Lic to Offic from 81. *9 Clampitt Road, Ipplepen, Newton Abbot, Devon TQ12 5RJ* Ipplepen (01803) 813332

STAMP, Ian Jack. b 47. Aston Tr Scheme 82 N Ord Course 83. **d** 86 **p** 87. C Tonge w Alkrington *Man* 86-89; V Heywood St Marg from 89. *St Margaret's Vicarage, Heys Lane, Heywood, Lancs OL10 3RD* Heywood (01706) 368053

STAMP, Philip Andrew. b 53. Linc Th Coll 86. **d** 88 **p** 89. C Barton w Peel Green *Man* 88-91; R Blackley H Trin from 91. *Holy Trinity Rectory, Goodman Street, Manchester M9 1FE* 0161-205 2879

STAMP, Richard Mark. b 36. St Chad's Coll Dur BA60 DipTh62. **d** 62 **p** 63. Australia 62-69 and from 72; C Greenhill St Jo *Lon* 69-72. *69 Sullivan Street, Inglewood, Australia 3517* Inglewood (54) 383055

STAMPS, Dennis Lee. b 55. MSBiblLit88 MAAR88 Biola Univ(USA) BA78. Trin Evang Div Sch(USA) MDiv83 MA87 Westcott Ho Cam 90. **d** 92 **p** 93. C Moseley St Mary *Birm* from 92. *4 Woodrough Drive, Birmingham B13 9EP* 0121-449 1336

✠**STANAGE, Rt Rev Thomas Shaun.** b 32. Pemb Coll Ox BA56 MA60 Nashotah Ho Wisconsin Hon DD86. Cuddesdon Coll 56. **d** 58 **p** 59 **c** 78. C Gt Crosby St Faith *Liv* 58-61; Min Orford St Andr CD 61-63; V Orford St Andr 63-70; S Africa from 70; Dean Kimberley 75-78; Suff Bp Johannesburg 78-82; Bp Bloemfontein from 82. *Bishop's House, 16 York Road, Bloemfontein, 9301 South Africa* Bloemfontein (51) 314351 or 476053 Fax 475874

STANBRIDGE, Ven Leslie Cyril. b 20. St Jo Coll Dur BA47 DipTh49 MA54. **d** 49 **p** 50. R Cottingham *York* 64-72; Can and Preb York Minster 68-88; Succ Canonicorum from 88; RD Hull 70-72; Adn York 72-88; rtd 88. *1 Deangate, York YO1 2JB* York (01904) 621174

✠**STANCLIFFE, Rt Rev David Staffurth.** b 42. Trin Coll Ox BA65 MA68. Cuddesdon Coll 65. **d** 67 **p** 68 **c** 93. C Armley St Bart *Ripon* 67-70; Chapl Clifton Coll Bris 70-77; Dir of Ords *Portsm* 77-82; Can Res Portsm Cathl 77-82; Provost Portsm 82-93; Bp Sarum from 93. *South Canonry, 71 The Close, Salisbury SP1 2ER* Salisbury (01722) 334031 Fax 413112

STANDEN, Mark Jonathan. b 63. LMH Ox BA85 Barrister 86. Ridley Hall Cam BA94 CTM95. **d** 95. C Sevenoaks St Nic *Roch* from 95. *40 South Park, Sevenoaks, Kent TN13 1EJ* Sevenoaks (01732) 454331

STANDEN McDOUGAL, Canon John Anthony Phelps. b 33. AKC58. **d** 59 **p** 60. C Wadhurst *Chich* 65-70; C Tidebrook 65-70; R Tollard Royal w Farnham *Sarum* 70-81; P-in-c Gussage St Michael and Gussage All Saints 71-76; R 76-81; RD Milton and Blandford 81-86; R Tollard Royal w Farnham, Gussage St Michael etc 82-86; Can and Preb Sarum Cathl 86-94; TR Bride Valley 86-94; rtd 94. *Silverbridge Cottage, North Chideock, Bridport, Dorset DT6 6LG* Chideock (01297) 489408

STANDING, Victor Denis. b 44. FRCO67 Lon Univ BMus66 Ox Univ DipTh77 Clare Coll Cam CertEd68. Ripon Coll Cuddesdon 75. **d** 78 **p** 79. C Wimborne Minster *Sarum* 78-80; TV Wimborne Minster and Holt 80-83; R Ex St Sidwell and St Matt *Ex* 83-94; Dep PV Ex Cathl from 83; Chapl R Devon and Ex Hosp 83-93; Chapl W of England Eye Infirmary Ex 83-93; P-in-c Tedburn St Mary, Whitestone, Oldridge etc *Ex* from 94. *The Rectory, Church Lane, Whitestone, Exeter EX4 2JT* Longdown (01392) 811406

STANDISH, Derrick Edgar. b 41. Univ of Wales (Lamp) BA67. Wycliffe Hall Ox 68. **d** 68 **p** 69. C Brynmawr *S & B* 68-69; C Morriston 69-74; V Merthyr Cynog and Dyffryn Honddu 74-76; R Llanwenarth Ultra *Mon* 76-83; V Abersychen and Garndiffaith 83-91. *7 Intermediate Road, Brynmawr, Gwent NP3 4SF* Brynmawr (01495) 312183

STANDLEY, Leslie Gordon. b 19. St Chad's Coll Dur BA42 DipTh43 MA45. **d** 43 **p** 44. V Ulceby *Linc* 67-70; V Wootton 67-70; R Croxton 67-70; V Forest Town *S'well* 70-76; V Swineshead *Linc* 76-84; RD Holland W 79-84; rtd 84; Perm to Offic *Linc* from 86. *28 Highfields, Nettleham, Lincoln LN2 2SZ* Lincoln (01522) 754731

STANDLEY, Robert Henry. b 21. Lon Univ BD42. Linc Th Coll 42. **d** 44 **p** 45. V Coleby *Linc* 65-74; V Harmston 65-74; V Skirbeck Quarter 74-86; RD Holland E 80-85; rtd 86; Perm to Offic *Linc* from 86. *9 Grammar School Road, Brigg, S Humberside DN20 8AA* Brigg (01652) 652020

STANDRING, Rupert Benjamin Charles. b 68. Pemb Coll Ox BA90. Ridley Hall Cam BA94 CTM95. **d** 95. C Bromley Ch Ch *Roch* from 95. *68 Warren Road, Bromley BR1 4BS* 0181-460 1174

STANES, Ven Ian Thomas. b 39. Sheff Univ BSc62 Linacre Coll Ox BA65 MA69. Wycliffe Hall Ox 63. **d** 65 **p** 66. C Leic H Apostles *Leic* 65-69; V Broom Leys 69-76; Warden Marrick Priory *Ripon* 76-82; Officer Miss, Min & Evang (Willesden Episc Area) *Lon* 82-92; Continuing Minl Educn Officer 82-92; Preb St Paul's Cathl 89-92; Adn Loughb *Leic* from 92. *The Archdeaconry, 21 Church Road, Glenfield, Leicester LE3 8DP* Leicester (0116) 231 1632 Fax 232 1593

STANESBY, Canon Derek Malcolm. b 31. Leeds Univ BA56 Man Univ MEd75 PhD84. Coll of Resurr Mirfield 56. **d** 58 **p** 59. C Lakenham St Jo *Nor* 58-60; C Welling *S'wark* 60-62; V Bury St Mark *Man* 62-67; R Ladybarn 67-85; Can and Steward Windsor from 85. *4 The Cloisters, Windsor Castle, Windsor, Berks SL4 1NJ* Windsor (01753) 864142

STANIFORD, Mrs Doris Gwendoline. b 43. Gilmore Course IDC79. **dss** 80 **d** 87 **p** 94. Hangleton *Chich* 80-82; Durrington 82-87; Par Dn 87-89; Chich Th Coll 83-89; C Crawley from 89; Chapl Crawley Gen Hosp from 89; Chapl St Cath Hospice Crawley from 92; Dioc Voc Adv *Chich* from 92. *10 Borrowdale Close, Crawley, W Sussex RH11 8SH* Crawley (01293) 611807

STANLEY, Arthur Patrick. b 32. TCD BA54 Div Test55 MA64. d 55 p 56. C Waterford H Trin *C & O* 55-57; CF 58-74; Dep Asst Chapl Gen 74-83; USA from 84. *1205 South Center Street, Shenandoah, Iowa 51061, USA* Shenandoah (712) 246-1647

STANLEY, Baden Thomas. b 68. TCD BA91. CITC BTh94. d 94 p 95. C Seapatrick *D & D* from 94. *16 Bannview Heights, Banbridge, Co Down BT32 4LZ* Banbridge (018206) 28303

STANLEY, Bernard Leslie. b 32. Ox Poly ONC63. Ox NSM Course 75. d 76 p 77. NSM Thame w Towersey *Ox* 76-84; Asst Chapl Jo Radcliffe Hosp Ox 91-93; NSM Long Crendon w Chearsley and Nether Winchendon 92-93; Perm to Offic *Ex* from 94. *Christmas Cottage, 24 Church Street, Kingsteignton, Newton Abbot, Devon TQ12 3BQ* Newton Abbot (01626) 51043

STANLEY, Eric William. b 22. TCD BA45 MA58. d 45 p 46. Can Killaloe Cathl *L & K* 65-89; I Nenagh 66-89; Chan Killaloe Cathl 72-79; Adn Killaloe, Kilfenora, Clonfert etc 79-89; Preb Taney St Patr Cathl Dub 81-89; rtd 89. *Cuanbeg, Ballycotton, Midleton, Co Cork, Irish Republic* Midleton (21) 646076

STANLEY, Canon John Alexander. b 31. Tyndale Hall Bris DipTh56. d 56 p 57. C Preston All SS *Blackb* 56-60; C St Helens St Mark *Liv* 60-63; V Everton St Cuth 63-70; P-in-c Everton St Sav 69-70; V Everton St Sav w St Cuth 70-74; V Huyton St Mich from 74; Hon Can Liv Cathl from 87; AD Huyton from 89; Chapl to The Queen from 93. *The Vicarage, Huyton, Liverpool L36 7SA* 0151-449 3900 Fax 480 6002

STANLEY, Joseph. b 12. Chich Th Coll 37. d 39 p 40. V Swaffham *Nor* 51-60; rtd 77. *Alveston Nursing Home, 14 Warwick New Road, Leamington Spa, Warks CV32 5JG* Leamington Spa (01926) 426753

STANLEY, Robert John. b 27. TCD BA50 MA54. d 50 p 51. CF 63-79; V Prittlewell St Steph *Chelmsf* 79-92; rtd 92. *281 Prittlewell Chase, Westcliff-on-Sea, Essex SS0 0PL* Southend-on-Sea (01702) 344204

STANLEY, Simon Richard. b 44. Wells Th Coll 66. d 69 p 70. C Foleshill St Laur *Cov* 69-71; C Hessle *York* 71-75; P-in-c Flamborough 75-80; R Dunnington 80-92; P-in-c York St Barn from 92. *St Barnabas's Vicarage, Jubilee Terrace, Leeman Road, York YO2 4YZ* York (01904) 654214

STANLEY-SMITH, James (Jim). b 29. Hatf Coll Dur BA54 DipEd55. S Dios Minl Tr Scheme 81. d 84 p 85. C Bournemouth St Jo w St Mich *Win* 84-87; R Hale w S Charford 87-94; rtd 94. *10 Rownhams Way, Rownhams, Southampton SO16 8AE* Southampton (01703) 732529

STANNARD, Miss Beryl Elizabeth. b 36. SRN62 SCM64. Oak Hill Th Coll BA92. d 92 p 94. Par Dn Streatham Park St Alb *S'wark* 92-94; C from 94. *51 Aldrington Road, London SW16 1TV* 0181-769 5663

STANNARD, Brian. b 46. MICE71 MIStructE71. Cranmer Hall Dur 86. d 88 p 89. C Burnage St Marg *Man* 88-91; V Walmersley from 91. *The Vicarage, 14 Springside Road, Bury, Lancs BL9 5JE* 0161-797 9273

STANNARD, Ven Colin Percy. b 24. TD66. Selw Coll Cam BA47 MA49. Linc Th Coll 47. d 49 p 50. V Upperby St Jo *Carl* 64-70; R Gosforth 70-75; RD Calder 70-75; P-in-c Natland 75-76; V 76-84; RD Kendal 75-84; Hon Can Carl Cathl 75-84; Can Res Carl Cathl 84-93; Adn Carl 84-93; rtd 93. *51 Longlands Road, Carlisle CA3 9AE* Carlisle (01228) 38584

STANNARD, Harold Frederick David. b 12. AKC37. d 37 p 38. V W Quantoxhead *B & W* 48-77; rtd 77. *Little Orchard, Bosinver Lane, Polgooth, St Austell, Cornwall PL26 7BA* St Austell (01726) 68712

STANNARD, Canon Peter Graville. b 59. Univ of Wales (Abth) BSc81 Ox Univ BA85. St Steph Ho Ox 83. d 86 p 87. C Worksop Priory *S'well* 86-89; Ghana from 89; Hon Can Koforidua from 93. *St Nicholas's Theological College, Cape Coast, Ghana*

STANSBURY, Alan David. b 29. Ridley Hall Cam 59. d 61 p 62. C Kennington St Mark *S'wark* 61-63; S Africa from 63. *PO Box 15, Aliwal North, 5530 South Africa* Aliwal North (551) 2281

STANTON, Miss Barbara. b 51. DipNCTD77 Whitelands Coll Lon TCert72 Lon Univ BD86. W Midl Minl Tr Course 89. d 92 p 94. NSM Hinckley St Mary *Leic* from 92. *25 Atterton Lane, Witherlel, Atherstone, Warks CV9 3LP* Atherstone (01827) 717875

STANTON, David John. b 60. FSAScot89 St Andr Univ MTheol82. Ripon Coll Cuddesdon 83. d 85 p 86. C Beckenham St Geo *Roch* 85-88; Asst Chapl Shrewsbury Sch 88-90; Hon C Shrewsbury All SS w St Mich *Lich* 88-90; P-in-c Abbotskerswell *Ex* 90-94; Chapl Plymouth Univ from 92; P-in-c Bovey Tracey St John, Chudleigh Knighton etc from 94. *St John's Vicarage, Newton Road, Bovey Tracey, Newton Abbot, Devon TQ13 9BD* Bovey Tracey (01626) 833451

STANTON, Gregory John. b 47. Sarum & Wells Th Coll 84. d 86 p 87. C Willenhall H Trin *Lich* 86-89; C Plympton St Mary *Ex*

89-91; V Milton Abbot, Dunterton, Lamerton etc from 91. *The Vicarage, Milton Abbot, Tavistock, Devon PL19 0NZ* Milton Abbot (01822) 87384

STANTON, John Maurice. b 18. Univ Coll Ox BA45 MA45. Wycliffe Hall Ox 51. d 52 p 53. Hd Master Blundell's Sch 59-71; Public Preacher *Ex* 71-72; C Ex St Matt 72-73; R Chesham Bois *Ox* 73-83; rtd 83; Perm to Offic *Ox* from 83. *37A St Andrew's Road, Oxford OX3 9DL* Oxford (01865) 65206

STANTON, Ronald Geoffrey. b 14. Leeds Univ BA48. Wells Th Coll. d 50 p 51. R Walton D'Eiville *Cov* 61-72; V Finham 72-79; rtd 79; Perm to Offic *Cov* from 79. *8 Margetts Close, Kenilworth, Warks CV8 1EN* Kenilworth (01926) 511036

STANTON, Thomas Hugh (Timothy). b 17. Trin Coll Cam BA38 MA45. Coll of Resurr Mirfield 46. d 47 p 48. CR from 52; S Africa 54-87; rtd 87. *Community of the Resurrection, Mirfield, W Yorkshire WF14 0BN* Mirfield (01924) 494318

STANTON-HYDE, Mrs Marjorie Elizabeth. b 37. TCert58. Cranmer Hall Dur 86. d 88 p 94. Par Dn Elmley Lovett w Hampton Lovett and Elmbridge etc *Worc* 88-91; Par Dn Wilden 88-91; Par Dn Hartlebury 88-91; D-in-c 91-94; R 94; P-in-c from 94. *The Rectory, Hartlebury, Kidderminster, Worcs DY11 7TB* Hartlebury (01299) 250292

STANTON-SARINGER, Maurice Charles. b 49. Bris Univ BSc71 PGCE72 Fitzw Coll Cam BA77 MA81. Ridley Hall Cam 75. d 78 p 79. C Gerrards Cross *Ox* 78-80; C Bletchley 80-83; Lic to Offic 83-91; Chapl Stowe Sch Bucks 83-91; R Sherington w Chicheley, N Crawley, Astwood etc *Ox* from 91. *The Rectory, School Lane, Sherington, Newport Pagnell, Bucks MK16 9NF* Milton Keynes (01908) 610521

STANWAY, Peter David. b 48. K Coll Lon BD71. St Aug Coll Cant 72. d 73 p 74. C Maidstone All SS w St Phil and H Trin *Cant* 73-77; Canada 77-84; C Waterlooville *Portsm* 84-87; R Laughton w Ripe and Chalvington *Chich* 87-90; Chapl Witney Community Hosp 90-91; C Wheatley w Forest Hill and Stanton St John *Ox* 91-92; C Cowley St Jas from 93. *Benson Cottage, Beauchamp Lane, Cowley, Oxford OX4 3LF* Oxford (01865) 778821

STAPLES, David. b 35. Jes Coll Ox BA59 MA63 BD75. Linc Th Coll 59. d 61 p 62. C Kettering St Andr *Pet* 61-64; C Doncaster St Geo *Sheff* 64-66; Youth Chapl 66-71; V Mexborough 71-83; RD Wath 77-83; Hon Can Sheff Cathl 80-83; V W Haddon w Winwick *Pet* 83-88; RD Brixworth 83-89; V W Haddon w Winwick and Ravensthorpe from 88. *The Vicarage, 4 West End, West Haddon, Northampton NN6 7AY* West Haddon (01788) 510207

STAPLES, Canon Edward Eric. b 10. OBE73 CBE77. Chich Th Coll 46. d 48 p 49. Chapl Helsinki w Moscow *Eur* 66-80; Chapl to The Queen 73-80; rtd 80; Perm to Offic *Bris* 81-88; Perm to Offic *B & W* 81-86. *The Old Farmhouse, 13 Oxford Street, Ramsbury, Marlborough, Wilts SN8 2PG* Marlborough (01672) 21118

STAPLES, John Wedgwood. b 42. Hertf Coll Ox BA64 MA. Wycliffe Hall Ox 64. d 66 p 67. C Yardley St Edburgha *Birm* 66-69; C Knowle 69-74; R Barcombe *Chich* 74-81; V Old Windsor *Ox* from 81. *The Vicarage, Church Road, Old Windsor, Windsor, Berks SL4 2PQ* Windsor (01753) 865778

STAPLES, Peter. b 35. Jes Coll Ox BA59. Ripon Hall Ox 59. d 62 p 63. C Fairfield *Derby* 62-63; C Dore 63-66; C Wilne and Draycott w Breaston 66-71; The Netherlands from 72; Asst Chapl Utrecht w Arnhem, Zwolle, Amersfoort etc *Eur* from 94. *Doldersweg 39C, 3712 BR Huis Ter Heide, Utrecht, The Netherlands* Utrecht (3404) 31928

STAPLES, Peter Brian. b 38. Bps' Coll Cheshunt 66. d 68 p 69. C Birkdale St Jas *Liv* 68-71; C Sevenoaks St Jo *Roch* 71-74; V Treslothan *Truro* 74-80; V Truro St Paul and St Clem from 80. *The Vicarage, 41 Tregolls Road, Truro, Cornwall TR1 1LE* Truro (01872) 72576

STAPLES, Terence Malcolm. b 43. Trin Coll Bris BA95. d 95. C Bath St Sav w Swainswick and Woolley *B & W* from 95. *40 Fairfield Avenue, Bath BA1 6NH* Bath (01225) 311598

STAPLETON, Very Rev Henry Edward Champneys. b 32. FSA74 Pemb Coll Cam BA54 MA58. Ely Th Coll 54. d 56 p 57. C York St Olave w St Giles *York* 56-59; C Pocklington w Yapham-cum-Meltonby, Owsthorpe etc 59-61; R Seaton Ross w Everingham and Bielby and Harswell 61-67; RD Weighton 66-67; R Skelton by York 67-75; V Wroxham w Hoveton *Nor* 75-81; P-in-c Belaugh 76-81; Can Res and Prec Roch Cathl *Roch* 81-88; Dean Carl from 88. *The Deanery, Carlisle CA3 8TZ* Carlisle (01228) 23335

STAPLETON, Canon Kenneth Hargrave. b 11. St Pet Hall Ox BA38 MA42. Wells Th Coll 38. d 39 p 40. V Leeds Halton St Wilfrid *Ripon* 62-78; Hon Can Ripon Cathl 74-78; rtd 78; Perm to Offic *Ripon* 78-93; Perm to Offic *Wakef* from 90. *29 St Paul's Road, Mirfield, W Yorkshire WF14 8AY* Mirfield (01924) 491746

STAPLETON, Leonard Charles. b 37. Chich Th Coll 75. d 77 p 78. C Crayford *Roch* 77-81; C Lamorbey H Redeemer 81-83; V Belvedere St Aug 83-89; V Beckenham St Jas from 89. *The*

Vicarage, St James Avenue, Beckenham, Kent BR3 4HF 0181-650 0420

STAPLETON, Robert Michael Vorley (Bob). b 25. ALCD51. **d** 51 **p** 52. R Chenies and Lt Chalfont *Ox* 64-87; P-in-c Latimer w Flaunden 86-87; R Chenies and Lt Chalfont, Latimer and Flaunden 87-92; rtd 92. *Woodside, Swannaton Road, Dartmouth, Devon TQ6 9RL* Dartmouth (01803) 832972

STAPLETON, Robert Vauvelle. b 47. Dur Univ BA70. Cranmer Hall Dur DipTh71. **d** 71 **p** 72. C Moreton *Ches* 71-73; C Monkwearmouth All SS *Dur* 73-76; C Stranton 76-79; P-in-c Kelloe 79-86; V New Shildon from 86. *All Saints' Vicarage, Shildon, Co Durham DL4 2JT* Bishop Auckland (01388) 772785

STARBUCK, Francis Tony. b 36. Kelham Th Coll 57. **d** 61 **p** 62. C Mansf St Mark *S'well* 61-64; C Didcot *Ox* 67-71; C-in-c California CD 71-75; R Barkham 74-75; V Hagbourne 75-82; V Maidenhead St Luke 82-87; New Zealand from 87. *St John's Vicarage, PO Box 67, Te Tuke, New Zealand* Tauranga (7) 573-7970

STARES, Brian Maurice William. b 44. St Deiniol's Hawarden 74. **d** 74 **p** 75. C Risca *Mon* 74-77; V Newport St Steph and H Trin 77-87; V Fleur-de-Lis 87-92; Asst Chapl HM Pris Belmarsh 92-93; Chapl HM Young Offender Inst Dover from 93. *HM Young Offender Institution, The Citadel, Western Heights, Dover, Kent CT17 9DR* Dover (01304) 203848 Fax 215165

STARES, Mrs Olive Beryl. b 33. Sarum Th Coll 83. **dss** 86 **d** 87 **p** 94. Crofton *Portsm* 86-87; Hon C from 87. *62 Mancroft Avenue, Hill Head, Fareham, Hants PO14 2DD* Stubbington (01329) 668540

STARK, Mrs Beverley Ann. b 52. Bp Otter Coll CertEd73 E Midl Min Tr Course CTPS92. **d** 92 **p** 94. Par Dn Bulwell St Jo *S'well* 92-94; C from 94. *45 Howick Drive, Nottingham NG6 7FQ* Nottingham (0115) 976 0475

STARK, Preb Edwin George John. b 20. Ex Coll Ox BA48 MA52. Wells Th Coll. **d** 49 **p** 50. V Hackney Wick St Mary of Eton w St Aug *Lon* 64-77; P-in-c Falmouth All SS *Truro* 77; V 77-80; V Mylor w Flushing 80-83; Preb St Endellion from 81; P-in-c Blisland w St Breward 83-84; R 84-88; rtd 88. *Marnays, Polzeath, Wadebridge, Cornwall PL27 6TN* Trebetherick (01208) 862888

STARK, John Jordan. b 40. Hull Univ BA62 St Chad's Coll Dur DipTh64. **d** 64 **p** 65. C Buxton *Derby* 64-67; C Wolborough w Newton Abbot *Ex* 67-74; R Belstone 74-79; P-in-c Plymouth St Gabr 79-80; V from 80. *The Vicarage, 1 Peverell Terrace, Plymouth PL3 4JJ* Plymouth (01752) 663938

STARK, Margaret Alison. b 46. Univ of Wales BA70 BA71. St Mich Coll Llan DPS90. **d** 90. C Llanishen and Lisvane Llan 90-93; C Llanishen 93-94; C Aberavon from 94. *77 Victoria Road, Port Talbot, M Glam SA12 6QQ* Port Talbot (01639) 892306

STARK, Michael. b 35. Dur Univ BSc56. Chich Th Coll 58. **d** 60 **p** 61. C Middlesb St Paul *York* 60-64; C S Bank 64-66; R Skelton in Cleveland 66-74; P-in-c Upleatham 66-67; R 67-74; Asst Chapl HM Pris Wormwood Scrubs 74-77; Chapl HM Pris Featherstone 77-84; Chapl HM Pris Ex 84-89; Chapl HM Pris Leic from 89. *HM Prison, 116 Welford Road, Leicester LE2 7AJ* Leicester (0116) 254 0911 Fax 247 1753

STARKEY, Gerald Dennis. b 34. Qu Coll Birm 79. **d** 82 **p** 83. C Wilncote *Lich* 82-86; Min Stoke-upon-Trent 86-90; P-in-c W Bromwich St Pet from 90. *The Vicarage, Oldbury Road, West Bromwich, W Midlands B70 9DP* 0121-525 5147

STARKEY, John Douglas. b 23. St Chad's Coll Dur BA47 DipTh48. **d** 48 **p** 49. V Freehay *Lich* 66-84; P-in-c Oakamoor w Cotton 78-84; R Dunstall w Rangemore and Tatenhill 84-88; rtd 88; Perm to Offic *Lich* from 88; Perm to Offic *Derby* from 88. *34 Park Crescent, Doveridge, Ashbourne, Derbyshire DE6 5NE* Uttoxeter (01889) 566384

STARKEY, Michael Stuart (Mike). b 63. LMH Ox BA85 Nottm Univ BTh92 MA93. St Jo Coll Nottm 90. **d** 93 **p** 94. C Ealing St Mary *Lon* from 93. *38 Airedale Road, London W5 4SD* 0181-567 6926

STARKEY, Simon Mark. b 36. Liv Univ BA78. Clifton Th Coll. **d** 66 **p** 67. C Ox St Ebbe w St Pet *Ox* 66-72; Community Chapl CPAS Kirkdale 72-77; TV Toxteth Park St Bede *Liv* 77-78; P-in-c 78-80; V 80-90; RD Toxteth 81-89; Chapl Ches Coll *Ches* from 90. *61 Parkgate Road, Chester CH1 4AQ* Chester (01244) 372003 or 375444

STARNES, Peter Henry. b 19. LTCL74 St Jo Coll Cam BA42 MA47 Ch Ch Coll Cant PGCE72. Linc Th Coll 42. **d** 44 **p** 45. V Westwell *Cant* 56-65; R Eastwell w Boughton Aluph 60-65; rtd 84. *Whitebeams, High Halden, Ashford, Kent TN26 3LY* Ashford (01233) 850245

STARNS, Helen Edna. *See* PATTEN, Mrs Helen Edna

STARR, John Michael. b 50. Southn Univ. Sarum & Wells Th Coll 71. **d** 74 **p** 75. C Basingstoke *Win* 74-78; C Southn

---

Maybush St Pet 78-79; C Milton 79-83; V Lupset *Wakef* 83-90; V Kennington St Mark *S'wark* from 90. *St Mark's Vicarage, Kennington Oval, London SE11 5SW* 0171-735 1801

STARR, Dr Michael Reginald. b 41. MICE71 Bris Univ BSc63 PhD66. Ox NSM Course 83. **d** 86 **p** 87. NSM Gt Faringdon w Lt Coxwell *Ox* from 86. *23 Gloucester Street, Faringdon, Oxon SN7 7JA* Faringdon (01367) 240686

STARR, Michael Richard. b 43. Sarum Th Coll 65. **d** 68 **p** 69. C Plymouth St Pet *Ex* 68-72; C Blackpool St Paul *Blackb* 72-74; V Burnley St Cuth 74-79; C Eastbourne St Mary *Chich* 79-84; P-in-c Eastbourne Ch Ch 84-87; V 87-88; R Guernsey Ste Marie du Castel *Win* from 88; V Guernsey St Matt from 94. *The Rectory, Ste Marie du Castel, Guernsey, Channel Islands GY5 7NA* Guernsey (01481) 56793

STARTIN, Geoffrey Neil. b 56. Essex Univ BA81 Ch Ch Ox MSc84 Westmr Coll Ox CertEd85. St Steph Ho Ox 86. **d** 88 **p** 89. C Coseley Ch Ch *Lich* 88-90; C Wellingborough All Hallows *Pet* 90-92; Asst Chapl HM Pris Wormwood Scrubs 92-93; C Newton Nottage *Llan* from 93. *5B Belle View Court, West End Avenue, Porthcawl, M Glam CF36 3NE* Porthcawl (01656) 783762

STARTIN, Nicola Gail. b 57. K Coll Lon LLB79. St Steph Ho Ox 88. **d** 90. C Wellingborough All SS *Pet* 90-92; NSM Pyle w Kenfig *Llan* 94-95; Chapl Mid-Kent Healthcare Trust from 95; Asst Chapl Maidstone Hosp from 95. *Chaplain's Office, Maidstone Hospital, Hermitage Lane, Maidstone, Kent ME19 9QQ* Maidstone (01622) 729000

STARTUP, Stephen Paul. b 53. CEng MIMechE MBIM Nottm Univ BSc76. Oak Hill Th Coll DTPS92. **d** 92 **p** 93. C Oakwood St Thos *Lon* 92-95; V Grange Park St Pet from 95. *St Peter's Vicarage, Langham Gardens, London N21 1DJ* 0181-360 2294

STATHAM, Brian Edward (Brother Brian Edward). b 55. K Coll Lon MA AKC76. St Steph Ho Ox 77. **d** 78 **p** 79. C Ches H Trin *Ches* 78-81; C Birkenhead Priory 81-82; TV 82-86; V Newton 86-91; SSF from 91; TV Horsham *Chich* from 95; Chapl Horsham Gen Hosp from 95. *Trinity House, Blunts Way, Horsham, W Sussex RH12 2BL* Horsham (01403) 265401

STATHAM, John Francis. b 31. Kelham Th Coll 51. **d** 56 **p** 57. V New Mills *Derby* 69-81; RD Glossop 78-81; R Matlock 81-89; R Killamarsh 89-93; rtd 93. *33 Ackford Drive, The Meadows, Worksop, Notts S80 1YG* Worksop (01909) 476031

STATON, Preb Geoffrey. b 40. Wells Th Coll 64. **d** 66 **p** 67. C Wednesfield St Thos *Lich* 66-69; C Cannock 69-72; V Cheddleton 72-82; RD Leek 77-82; V Harlescott 82-90; Preb Lich Cathl from 87; TR Penkridge Team from 90. *The Rectory, Penkridge, Stafford ST19 5DN* Penkridge (01785) 712378

STAUNTON, Richard Steedman. b 25. Wadh Coll Ox BA49 MA50 BSc51. Cuddesdon Coll 63. **d** 64 **p** 65. V Tile Hill *Cov* 68-76; V Hillmorton 76-90; rtd 90. *2 Tan-y-fron, Corris Uchaf, Machynlleth, Powys SY20 9BN* Corris (01654) 761466

STAVELEY, Dennis Frank. b 21. Open Univ BA75. S'wark Ord Course 77. **d** 80 **p** 81. C Danbury *Chelmsf* 80-84; P-in-c Lt Hallingbury 84-91; P-in-c Gt Hallingbury 86-91; R Gt Hallingbury and Lt Hallingbury 91; rtd 91. *99 Mumford Road, West Bergholt, Colchester CO6 3BN* Colchester (01206) 240965

STAVELEY-WADHAM, Robert Andrew. b 43. Ridley Hall Cam 79. **d** 81 **p** 82. C Saffron Walden w Wendens Ambo and Littlebury *Chelmsf* 81-84; P-in-c Austrey *Birm* 84-87; P-in-c Warton 84-87; Perm to Offic *Ely* from 88. *Address temp unknown*

STEAD, Andrew Michael. b 63. BA84. Coll of Resurr Mirfield 84. **d** 87 **p** 88. C Wellingborough All Hallows *Pet* 87-90; Chapl St Alb Abbey *St Alb* 90-94; Chapl Aldenham Sch Herts from 94. *Chaplain's Lodge, Aldenham School, Aldenham Road, Elstree, Borehamwood, Herts WD6 3AJ* Radlett (01923) 853360 Fax 854410

STEAD, Canon George Christopher. b 13. FBA80 K Coll Cam BA35 MA38 LittD78 New Coll Ox BA35 Keble Coll Ox MA49. Cuddesdon Coll 38. **d** 38 **p** 41. Ely Prof Div Cam Univ 71-80; Can Res Ely Cathl *Ely* 71-80; rtd 80. *13 Station Road, Haddenham, Ely, Cambs CB6 3XD* Ely (01353) 740575

STEAD, Leslie Cawthorn. b 11. Oak Hill Th Coll 58. **d** 59 **p** 60. V Collier Street *Roch* 62-71; Hon C Ashburnham w Penhurst *Chich* 71-84; rtd 79; Perm to Offic *Chich* from 84. *5 Cornford Court, Cornford Lane, Pembury, Tunbridge Wells TN2 4QS* Pembury (01892) 824635

STEAD, Philip John. b 60. Sheff Univ LLB82 City of Lon Poly ACII85. Linc Th Coll CMinlStuds95. **d** 95. C Warsop *S'well* from 95. *Churchside Cottage, Church Warsop, Mansfield, Notts NG20 0SF* Mansfield (01623) 847687

STEAD, Timothy James (Tim). b 60. Ex Univ BSc82. St Steph Ho Ox DipMin95. **d** 95. C Broseley w Benthall, Jackfield, Linley etc *Heref* from 95. *3 Blakeway Close, Broseley, Shropshire TF12 5SS* Broseley (01952) 882153

STEADMAN, Fred. b 11. Univ Coll Ox BA34 MA65. **d** 65 **p** 66. C Timperley *Ches* 65-69; V Willaston 69-79; P-in-c

Capenhurst 71-79; Perm to Offic from 79. *24 Glan Aber Park, Chester CH4 8LF*   Chester (01244) 682989

STEADMAN, Norman Neil. b 39. QUB BSc61 TCD Div Test63. **d** 63 **p** 64. C Newtownards *D & D* 63-65; C Belf Whiterock *Conn* 65-67; Asst Dean of Residences QUB 67-71; Perm to Offic *St Alb* 71-73; Dioc Youth Officer 73-76; P-in-c Hitchin H Sav 76; TV Hitchin 77-84; V Brampton *Carl* 84-93; R Brampton and Farlam and Castle Carrock w Cumrew from 93. *St Martin's Vicarage, Main Street, Brampton, Cumbria CA8 1SH*   Brampton (016977) 2486

STEADMAN-ALLEN, Miss Barbara. b 53. ARCM83 Trent Park Coll of Educn CertEd74 Birm Univ BMus77. Cranmer Hall Dur 88. **d** 90 **p** 94. C Chessington *Guildf* from 90. *4 North Grove, Chertsey, Surrey KT16 9DU*   Chertsey (01932) 567944

STEADY, Miss Vilda May. b 51. Linc Th Coll 87. **d** 89 **p** 94. Par Dn Cannock *Lich* 89-91; Par Dn Hammerwich 91-94; C from 94. *Hammerwich Vicarage, Hammerwich, Walsall WS7 0JT*   Burntwood (01543) 677708

STEAR, Michael Peter Hutchinson (Mike). b 47. Golds Coll Lon TCert68. Wycliffe Hall Ox 71. **d** 74 **p** 75. C Streatham Vale H Redeemer *S'wark* 74-77; C Ramsgate St Luke *Cant* 77-82; V Ramsgate St Mark 82-83; Min Jersey St Paul Prop Chpl *Win* 83-94; TR Radipole and Melcombe Regis *Sarum* from 94; Chapl Weymouth Coll from 94. *The Rectory, 27 Carlton Avenue South, Weymouth, Dorset DT4 7PL*   Weymouth (01305) 785553

STEARE, Peter Douglas. b 27. S Dios Minl Tr Scheme. **d** 84 **p** 85. NSM Upton cum Chalvey *Ox* 84-86; Perm to Offic *Bris* 86-88; Hon C Kington 88-90; NSM Tetbury w Beverston *Glouc* from 94. *Kensell, Hayes Road, Nailsworth, Glos GL6 0EB*   Stroud (01453) 833776

STEARN, Peter Reginald. b 38. ARCM. Linc Th Coll 75. **d** 77 **p** 78. C St Alb St Pet *St Alb* 77-79; C Bushey 79-82; V Kings Langley from 82. *The Vicarage, The Glebe, Kings Langley, Herts WD4 9HY*   Kings Langley (01923) 262939

STEBBING, Michael Langdale (Nicolas). b 46. Univ of Zimbabwe BA68 Univ of S Africa MTh86. Coll of Resurr Mirfield. **d** 74 **p** 75. C Borrowdale *Carl* 74-76; Rhodesia 76-79; S Africa 79-86; CR from 80. *House of the Resurrection, Mirfield, W Yorkshire WF14 0BN*   Mirfield (01924) 494318

STEDMAN, Preb Michael Sydney. b 34. ARICS58. Clifton Th Coll 62. **d** 65 **p** 66. C Lindfield *Chich* 65-68; C Gt Baddow *Chelmsf* 68-73; TV Ashby w Thurton, Claxton and Carleton *Nor* 73-75; P-in-c 75-85; TV Rockland St Mary w Hellington 73-75; P-in-c 75-85; TV Framingham Pigot 73-75; P-in-c 75-85; TV Bramerton w Surlingham 73-75; P-in-c 75-85; TV Bergh Apton w Yelverton 73-75; P-in-c 75-85; RD Loddon 78-85; R Church Stretton *Heref* from 85; RD Condover from 88; Preb Heref Cathl from 94. *The Rectory, Carding Mill Valley, Church Stretton, Shropshire SY6 6JF*   Church Stretton (01694) 722585

STEDMAN, Robert Alfred. b 24. Qu Coll Birm 50. **d** 52 **p** 53. V Salehurst *Chich* 61-76; R Newhaven 76-90; rtd 90. *14 Gorham Court, Gorham Way, Telscombe Cliffs, Peacehaven, E Sussex BN10 7BB*   Peacehaven (01273) 584254

STEED, Herbert Edward. b 23. St Jo Coll Dur BA51 DipTh52. **d** 52 **p** 53. R E Barnet *St Alb* 65-91; rtd 91. *1 Harrier Close, Cranleigh, Surrey GU6 7BS*   Cranleigh (01483) 278151

STEEL, David Pitcaithley. b 42. St Andr Univ MA70 Dundee Univ DipEd DipRE71 Jordan Hill Coll Glas HDipRE74 Harley Univ DD82. **d** 83. NSM Laurencekirk *Bre* from 83; NSM Drumtochty from 84; NSM Fasque 84-91; NSM Drumlithie 84-91. *Churchlands, 29 Arduthie Road, Stonehaven, Kincardineshire AB3 2EH*   Stonehaven (01569) 65341

STEEL, Graham Reginald. b 51. Cam Univ MA. Trin Coll Bris 80. **d** 83 **p** 84. C Gt Parndon *Chelmsf* 83-86; C Barking St Marg w St Patr 86-89; P-in-c Westcliff St Cedd from 89; Chapl Southend Health Care NHS Trust from 89; P-in-c Prittlewell St Pet *Chelmsf* from 91. *122 Mendip Crescent, Westcliff-on-Sea, Essex SS0 0HN*   Southend-on-Sea (01702) 525126

STEEL, Leslie Frederick. Univ of NZ LTh65. St Jo Coll Auckland 57. **d** 59 **p** 60. New Zealand 59-91; Chapl Lausanne *Eur* from 91. *Fief-de-Chapitre 8, CH1213 Petit Lancy, Lausanne, Switzerland*   Geneva (22) 793-5633

STEEL, Norman William. b 53. Sarum & Wells Th Coll 85. **d** 87 **p** 88. C S Woodham Ferrers *Chelmsf* 87-91; V Woolavington w Cossington and Bawdrip *B & W* from 91. *The Rectory, Woolavington, Bridgwater, Somerset TA7 8DX*   Puriton (01278) 683448

STEEL, Richard John. b 57. Dur Univ BA79 Cam Univ MA86. Ridley Hall Cam 81. **d** 84 **p** 85. C Hull Newland St Jo *York* 84-87; Relig Broadcasting Officer *Derby* 88-92; Dioc Communications Officer *Blackb* from 92. *155 Sharoe Green Lane North, Fulwood, Preston PR2 4HE*   Preston (01772) 718012   Fax as telephone

STEEL, Thomas Molyneux. b 39. Man Univ BA61 Ox Univ DipPSA62. Ripon Hall Ox 61. **d** 63 **p** 64. C Newc H Cross

Newc 63-66; P-in-c Man St Aid *Man* 66-71; R Failsworth St Jo 71-79; P-in-c Farnham Royal *Ox* 79-81; P-in-c Hedgerley 80-81; R Farnham Royal w Hedgerley 81-91; V Prescot *Liv* from 91. *The Vicarage, Prescot, Merseyside L34 1LA*   0151-426 6719

STEELE, Charles Edward Ernest. b 24. Cuddesdon Coll 72. **d** 74 **p** 75. C Rubery *Birm* 74-77; P-in-c Shaw Hill 77-79; V 79-82; C Curdworth 82-83; C Curdworth w Castle Vale 83-85; rtd 85; Perm to Offic *Birm* from 85. *3 Dominic Drive, Middleton Hall Road, Birmingham B30 1DW*   0121-451 3372

STEELE, David Robert. b 29. Peterho Cam BA53 MA57. Oak Hill Th Coll 53. **d** 56 **p** 57. Lic to Offic *Lon* 65-83; Chapl Steward's Trust Lon 65-72; Jt Gen Sec Intercon Ch Soc 72-81; Dir 2 Tim 2 Trust from 82; Perm to Offic *Lon* 83-91; Perm to Offic *Win* from 83; rtd 94. *Worthy Park Grove, Abbots Worthy, Winchester, Hants SO21 1AN*   Winchester (01962) 882082

STEELE, Gerald Robert. b 25. St D Coll Lamp BA49. **d** 51 **p** 52. V Llangeinor *Llan* 63-73; R Cadoxton-juxta-Barry 73-91; Chapl Barry Community Hosp 73-91; Miss to Seamen 73-91; rtd 91; Perm to Offic *Llan* from 91. *74 Redbrink Crescent, Barry, S Glam CF62 5TU*   Barry (01446) 373554

STEELE, Gordon John. b 55. Kent Univ BA76 Worc Coll Ox BA82 MA87. Coll of Resurr Mirfield 82. **d** 84 **p** 85. C Greenhill St Jo *Lon* 84-88; C Uxbridge St Andr w St Jo 88; C Uxbridge 88; TV 88-94; V Northn St Alb *Pet* from 94. *St Alban's Vicarage, Broadmead Avenue, Northampton NN3 2RA*   Northampton (01604) 407074

STEELE, John Thomas Robson. b 02. Qu Coll Ox BA24. **d** 32 **p** 33. R Kirkandrews-on-Esk *Carl* 53-70; rtd 70; Lic to Offic *Carl* from 70. *Croftfield Residential Home, Croftfield Annexe, Cotehill, Carlisle CA4 9TB*   Wetheral (01228) 560316

STEELE, Keith Atkinson. b 28. CEng MIMechE. Oak Hill Th Coll 80. **d** 81 **p** 82. Hon C Westoning w Tingrith *St Alb* 81-87; Hon C Chalgrave 87-88; P-in-c from 88; RD Dunstable from 91. *Mariner's Lodge, Church Road, Westoning, Bedford MK45 5JW*   Flitwick (01525) 714111

STEELE, Peter Gerald (Pete). b 44. Bournemouth Tech Coll BSc67 Essex Univ MSc69. Sarum & Wells Th Coll DipTh93. **d** 93 **p** 94. C Beaminster Area *Sarum* from 93. *25A Clay Lane, Beaminster, Dorset DT8 3BX*   Beaminster (01308) 863156

STEELE, Terence. b 54. Linc Th Coll 85. **d** 87 **p** 88. C New Sleaford *Linc* 87-90; V Cowbit 90-95; P-in-c Burgh le Marsh from 95; P-in-c Orby from 95; P-in-c Bratoft w Irby-in-the-Marsh from 95; P-in-c Welton-le-Marsh w Gunby from 95. *The Vicarage, 41 Chapman Avenue, Burgh, Skegness, Lincs PE24 5LY*   Skegness (01754) 810216

STEELE-PERKINS, Richard De Courcy. b 36. Clifton Th Coll 61. **d** 64 **p** 65. C Stoke Damerel *Ex* 64-65; C Washfield 65-68; P-in-c Wimbledon *S'wark* 68-70; Chapl Lambeth Hosp 70-74; Asst Chapl St Thos Hosp Lon 70-74; P-in-c Tawstock *Ex* 74-75; R 75-81; P-in-c Sticklepath 74-75; R 75-81; V Buckfastleigh w Dean Prior 81-91; TR Camelot Par *B & W* 91-94; Asst Chapl R Surrey Co Hosp Guildf from 94. *Royal Surrey County Hospital, Egerton Road, Guildford, Surrey GU2 5XX*   Guildford (01483) 571122

STEER, Martin Leslie. b 41. Dur Univ BA65. Oak Hill Th Coll 65. **d** 67 **p** 68. C Rayleigh *Chelmsf* 67-70; CF 70-76; Past Care, Guidance & Counselling Univ of Wales 76-77; Teacher and Lib Intake High Sch Leeds 77-88; NSM Roundhay St Edm *Ripon* 83-85; NSM Moor Allerton 85-88; Chapl HM Young Offender Inst Portland from 88. *HM Young Offender Institution, Easton, Portland, Dorset DT5 1DL*   Portland (01305) 820301   Fax 823718

STEINBERG, Eric Reed (Joseph). b 65. Trin Coll Bris BA94. **d** 94 **p** 95. C Chigwell and Chigwell Row *Chelmsf* from 94. *St Winifred's Vicarage, Manor Road, Chigwell, Essex IG7 5PS*   0181-500 4608   Fax 500 2805

STELL, Peter Donald. b 50. MInstM MBAC MAPCC Leeds Univ 74. Sarum & Wells Th Coll 78. **d** 81 **p** 82. C Rothwell w Lofthouse *Ripon* 81-85; TV Brayton *York* 85-87; Chapl Asst Leybourne Grange Hosp W Malling 87-88; Chapl Asst Kent, Sussex and Pembury Hosps Tunbridge Wells 87-88; C Spalding St Jo w Deeping St Nicholas *Linc* 88-93; Chapl S Lincs HA Mental Handicap Unit 90-93; Chapl HM Pris Liv 93-94; Chapl HM Pris Wayland from 94. *HM Prison, Wayland, Griston, Thetford, Norfolk IP25 6RL*   Watton (01953) 884103   Fax 885775

STEPHEN, Canon Kenneth George. b 47. Strathclyde Univ BA69 Edin Univ BD72. Edin Th Coll 69. **d** 72 **p** 73. C Ayr *Glas* 72-75; R Renfrew 75-80; R Motherwell 80-93; R Wishaw 80-93; Can St Mary's Cathl from 87; R Kilmarnock from 93. *The Parsonage, 1 Dundonald Road, Kilmarnock, Ayrshire KA1 1EQ*   Kilmarnock (01563) 23577

STEPHENI, Frederick William. b 28. TD73. FSAScot81 FRSA82 Cranfield Inst of Tech MSc82. Lambeth STh83 Qu Coll Birm 84. **d** 55 **p** 56. CF (TA) 60-88; R Cotgrave *S'well* 63-76; V Owthorpe 63-76; Chapl Addenbrooke's Hosp Cam 76-88; Lic to Offic *Ely* from 76; rtd 88. *Thatchers, 13 Tunwells Lane, Great Shelford, Cambridge CB2 5LJ*   Cambridge (01223) 842914

STEPHENS, Canon Archibald John. b 15. Selw Coll Cam BA37 MA44. Wells Th Coll 46. **d** 47 **p** 48. Nigeria 70-72; V Ash Vale *Guildf* 72-77; P-in-c Thursley 77-82; rtd 82; Perm to Offic *Guildf* from 85. *Fernhill, 12 Vicarage Lane, Farnham, Surrey GU9 8HN* Farnham (01252) 722514

STEPHENS, Charles Herbert. b 18. Lon Univ BA41 AKC42. **d** 42 **p** 43. Asst Master Nottm High Sch 45-78; Perm to Offic *S'well* from 73; rtd 83. *96 Grassington Road, Nottingham NG8 3PE* Nottingham (0115) 929 1586

STEPHENS, Francis William. b 21. ARCA50. S'wark Ord Course 68. **d** 70 **p** 71. C Primrose Hill St Mary w Avenue Road St Paul *Lon* 70-92; Perm to Offic from 92; Ed Ch Pulpit Year Book from 81. *14 St Edmund's Close, London NW8 7QS* 0171-722 7931

STEPHENS, Geoffrey Elford. b 19. St Jo Coll Dur BA41 MA58. Ripon Hall Ox 41. **d** 43 **p** 44. R Mawdesley *Blackb* 60-86; CF (R of O) 68-74; rtd 86; Perm to Offic *Liv* from 86; Perm to Offic *Blackb* from 86. *19 Cambridge Avenue, Southport, Merseyside PR9 9SA* Southport (01704) 212385

STEPHENS, Harold William Barrow. b 47. Lon Univ BEd. S Dios Minl Tr Scheme 80. **d** 82 **p** 83. NSM Heytesbury and Sutton Veny *Sarum* 82-83; NSM Bishopstrow and Boreham 83-91; Lic to Offic Heytesbury Deanery from 91; Dep Hd Master Westwood St Thos Sch Salisbury from 91. *14 Prestbury Drive, Warminster, Wilts BA12 9LB* Warminster (01985) 217776

STEPHENS, Horace Alfred Patrick. b 14. MRCVS49. **d** 77 **p** 78. NSM Dingle w Killiney and Kilgobbin *L & K* 77-94; NSM Tralee w Ballymacelligott, Kilnaughtin etc from 94. *Magharabeg, Castlegregory, Tralee, Co Kerry, Irish Republic* Tralee (66) 39159 Fax as telephone

STEPHENS, James Charles. b 62. DipAnChem. **d** 91 **p** 92. C Kilcolman w Kiltallagh, Killorglin, Knockane etc *L & K* from 91. *Kilderry, Miltown, Co Kerry, Irish Republic* Tralee (66) 67735

STEPHENS, Mrs Jean. b 46. St As Minl Tr Course. **d** 89. NSM Gwernaffield and Llanferres *St As* from 89. *Noddfa, Pen-y-Fron Road, Pantymwyn, Mold, Clwyd CH7 5EF* Mold (01352) 740037

STEPHENS, John Michael. b 29. ARICS52. Lich Th Coll 62. **d** 64 **p** 65. C Birchington w Acol *Cant* 64-70; V Tovil 70-79; V Brabourne w Smeeth 79-94; RD N Lympne 87-94; rtd 94. *Southacre, Kirby Mills, Kirkbymoorside, York YO6 6NR* Kirkbymoorside (01751) 432766

STEPHENS, John James Frederick. b 10. QUB BA34. Lon Coll of Div 34. **d** 37 **p** 38. V Broadheath *Worc* 51-82; rtd 82; Perm to Offic *Worc* from 82. *Jerred Cottage, Church Lane, Lower Broadheath, Worcester WR2 6QY* Worcester (01905) 640224

STEPHENS, Miss Mary. b 26. Reading Univ BA50 BEd51. Linc Th Coll. **d** 87 **p** 94. NSM Gt Grimsby St Mary and St Jas *Linc* 86-91; C 91-92; TD 92-94; TV from 94. *33 Amesbury Avenue, Grimsby, S Humberside DN33 3HT*

STEPHENS, Paul. b 53. AGSM73 Newton Park Coll Bath PGCE74. Trin Coll Bris DipHE93. **d** 93 **p** 94. C S Molton w Nymet St George, High Bray etc *Ex* from 93. *2 North Road, South Molton, Devon EX36 3AZ* South Molton (01769) 573919

STEPHENS, Peter John. b 42. Or Coll Ox BA64 MA67. Clifton Th Coll 63. **d** 68 **p** 68. C Lenton *S'well* 68-71; C Brixton Hill St Sav *S'wark* 71-73; P-in-c 73-82; TV Barnham Broom *Nor* 82-89; V Gorleston St Mary 89-94; RD Flegg (Gt Yarmouth) 92-94; P-in-c High Oak from 94; RD Humbleyard from 95. *The Rectory, Deopham Road, Morley St Botolph, Wymondham, Norfolk NR18 9DA* Wymondham (01953) 606332

STEPHENS, Preb Peter Stanley. b 33. ALCD59. **d** 59 **p** 60. C Paignton St Paul Preston *Ex* 59-64; V Buckland Monachorum 64-74; RD Tavistock 70-74; V Compton Gifford 74-85; RD Plymouth Sutton 83-86; Preb Ex Cathl from 84; TR Plymouth Em w Efford 85-86; R Thurlestone w S Milton from 86. *The Rectory, Thurlestone, Kingsbridge, Devon TQ7 3NJ* Kingsbridge (01548) 560232

STEPHENS, Richard William. b 37. Dur Univ BSc62 DipTh64. Cranmer Hall Dur 62. **d** 64 **p** 65. C Hensingham *Carl* 64-67; C Norbury *Ches* 67-71; R Elworth and Warmingham 71-79; V Bootle St Matt *Liv* 79-89; P-in-c Litherland St Andr 79-83; P-in-c Failsworth H Trin *Man* 89-93; R from 93. *Holy Trinity Rectory, 103 Oldham Road, Failsworth, Manchester M35 0BH* 0161-682 7901

STEPHENS, Ronald John. b 13. Sarum Th Coll 56. **d** 57 **p** 58. V Stanstead Abbots *St Alb* 61-82; rtd 82; Perm to Offic *Nor* from 82. *63 Beechlands Park, Southrepps, Norwich NR11 8NT* Southrepps (01263) 834893

STEPHENS, Simon Edward. b 41. Qu Coll Birm DPS68 PhD80 Bps' Coll Cheshunt 63. **d** 67 **p** 68. C Cov St Mark *Cov* 67-71; C Lillington 71-76; C-in-c Canley CD 76-79; V Canley 79-80; Chapl RN from 80. *Directorate Gen, RN Chapl Services, Room 203, Victory Building, HM Naval Base, Portsmouth PO1 3LS* Portsmouth (01705) 727903 Fax 727112

STEPHENS, Simon James. b 66. Univ of Wales (Lamp) BD89 Univ of Wales (Cardiff) MTh93. St Mich Coll Llan 89. **d** 91 **p** 92. C Caldicot *Mon* 91-94; C Paignton St Jo *Ex* from 94. *6 Tower Road, Paignton, Devon TQ3 3EP* Paignton (01803) 521859

STEPHENS-HODGE, Lionel Edmund Howard. b 14. Selw Coll Cam BA36 MA40. Ridley Hall Cam 36. **d** 38 **p** 39. R Brindle *Blackb* 64-74; rtd 74; Perm to Offic *Ex* from 79. *26 Gracey Court, Woodland Road, Broadclyst, Exeter EX5 3LP* Exeter (01392) 460442

STEPHENS-WILKINSON, Patricia Ann. b 45. Univ of Wales (Cardiff) BA66 CQSW80 MSc(Econ)91. Bp Burgess Hall Lamp CPS69. **dss** 69 **d** 89. Abth *St D* 69-71; Lic to Offic *Carl* 71-74; Perm to Offic *Mon* 74-89; NSM Machen 89-93. *Address temp unknown*

STEPHENSON, David John. b 65. Bris Univ BSc(Soc)87 Dur Univ BA91. Cranmer Hall Dur DMinlStuds92. **d** 92 **p** 93. C Whickham *Dur* 92-94; C Sunderland Pennywell St Thos from 94. *72 Sevenoaks Drive, Sunderland SR4 9NU* 0191-534 3009

STEPHENSON, Canon Eric George. b 41. Bede Coll Dur CertEd63. Qu Coll Birm DipTh65. **d** 66 **p** 67. C Wakef St Jo *Wakef* 66-69; C Seaham w Seaham Harbour *Dur* 69-73; C Cockerton 73-75; Lic to Offic 75-85; V E Boldon from 85; RD Jarrow from 92; Hon Can Dur Cathl from 93. *The Vicarage, 2 Ashleigh Villas, East Boldon, Tyne & Wear NE36 0LA* 0191-536 2557

STEPHENSON, Ian Clarke. b 24. Lon Univ DipTh69. Tyndale Hall Bris 52. **d** 56 **p** 57. R Biddulph Moor *Lich* 65-70; Hon C Biddulph 70-88; Hon C Burslem 85-88; New Zealand from 87; rtd 89. *5 Arthur Terrace, Balclutha, Otago, New Zealand* Christchurch (3) 417-8244

STEPHENSON, John Joseph. b 35. St Jo Coll Dur BA74. Qu Coll Birm 75. **d** 76 **p** 77. C Whitworth w Spennymoor *Dur* 76-79; V Eppleton from 79. *The Vicarage, Church Road, Eppleton, Houghton le Spring, Tyne & Wear DH5 9AJ* 0191-526 7412

STEPHENSON, Martin Woodard. b 55. St Cath Coll Cam BA77 MA82. Westcott Ho Cam 78. **d** 81 **p** 82. C Eastleigh *Win* 81-85; C Ferryhill *Dur* 85-87; Asst Dir of Ords 87-89; Chapl St Chad's Coll Dur 87-89; TR Clarendon Park St Jo w Knighton St Mich *Leic* from 89. *The Rectory, 9 Springfield Road, Leicester LE2 3BB* Leicester (0116) 270 6097

STEPHENSON, Nicolas William. b 22. Ely Th Coll 60. **d** 62 **p** 63. CR from 68; Hon C Westgate Common *Wakef* 74-75; Lic to Offic 75-87; Asst Chapl HM Pris Wakef 84-87; rtd 87. *24 Nicholson Court, 25 Fitzroy Drive, Leeds LS8 4AB* Leeds (0113) 248 5166

STEPHENSON, Robert. b 36. St Chad's Coll Dur BA58 DipTh60. **d** 60 **p** 61. C Whickham *Dur* 60-63; C Gateshead St Mary 63-65; V Low Team 65-67; R Stella 67-74; V Comberton *Ely* from 74; RD Bourn from 94. *The Vicarage, Comberton, Cambridge CB3 7ED* Cambridge (01223) 262793

STEPHENSON, Canon Robert Ommanney. b 09. St Cath Coll Cam BA32 MA36. Cuddesdon Coll 32. **d** 33 **p** 34. V Bitterne Park *Win* 47-70; Hon Can Win Cathl 67-79; R E Woodhay and Woolton Hill 70-79; RD Whitchurch 72-79; rtd 79; Perm to Offic *B & W* from 79. *Fairlawn, Witcombe Lane, Ash, Martock, Somerset TA12 6AH* Martock (01935) 824330

STEPHENSON, Simon George. b 44. St Jo Coll Dur BA67. Trin Coll Bris 74. **d** 76 **p** 77. C Hildenborough *Roch* 76-82; C Bishopsworth *Bris* 82-85; C-in-c Withywood CD 85-90; TV Wreningham *Nor* from 90; P-in-c Tasburgh w Tharston, Forncett and Flordon from 94. *The Vicarage, 16 The Fields, Tacolneston, Norwich NR16 1DG* Bunwell (01953) 788227

STEPNEY, Area Bishop of. See CHARTRES, Rt Rev Richard John Carew

STERLING, Anne. See HASLEHURST, Mrs Anne

STERLING, John Haddon. b 40. Pemb Coll Cam BA62 MA66. Cuddesdon Coll 63. **d** 65 **p** 66. S Africa 65-70; Chapl Bris Cathl *Bris* 71-74; Member Dioc Soc & Ind Team *C* 71-74; Ind Chapl *Linc* 74-87; Ind Chapl *Ripon* 87-92; TV Hanley H Ev *Lich* from 92; Min in Ind from 92. *The Vicarage, 10 Emery Street, Cobridge, Stoke on Trent ST6 2JJ* Stoke-on-Trent (01782) 212639

STERRY, Christopher. b 54. K Coll Lon BD77 AKC77. Episc Sem Austin Texas CSpST78 St Jo Coll Nottm DPS80. **d** 80 **p** 81. C Huddersfield St Jo *Wakef* 80-84; V Middlestown 84-89; Chapl and Tutor N Ord Course 89-94; Lect Ches Coll 93-94; Lic to Offic *Man* 89-92; NSM Padgate *Liv* 92-94; Chapl Whalley Abbey from 94; Bp's Dom Chapl *Blackb* from 94. *Whaley Lodge, Whalley Abbey, Whalley, Blackburn BB7 9SS* Whalley (01254) 824679 or 248234

STERRY, Timothy John (Tim). b 34. Or Coll Ox BA58 MA62 DipTh60. Wycliffe Hall Ox 58. **d** 60 **p** 61. C Cromer *Nor* 60-64; Chapl Oundle Sch Pet 64-72; Chapl Cheam Sch Newbury 72-75; Hd Master Temple Grove Sch E Sussex 75-80; Team

Ldr Scripture Union Independent Schs from 81. *1 The Close, Chart Lane, Reigate, Surrey RH2 7BN* Reigate (01737) 244370 Fax 0171-782 0014

STEVEN, David Bowring. b 38. AKC64. **d** 64 **p** 65. C Grantham St Wulfram *Linc* 64-68; S Africa 68-75; C Bramley *Ripon* 76-77; V Sutton Valence w E Sutton and Chart Sutton *Cant* 77-82; P-in-c Littlebourne 82-86; V Mansf Woodhouse *S'well* from 86. *The Vicarage, 7 Butt Lane, Mansfield Woodhouse, Mansfield, Notts NG19 9JS* Mansfield (01623) 21875

STEVEN, James Henry Stevenson. b 62. CCC Cam MA87 St Jo Coll Dur BA87. Cranmer Hall Dur 84. **d** 87 **p** 88. C Welling *Roch* 87-91; C Bournemouth St Jo w St Mich *Win* 91-94; TV Bournemouth St Pet w St Swithun, St Steph etc from 94; Chapl Bournemouth and Poole Colls *Sarum* from 94. *1 Gervis Road, Bournemouth BH1 3ED* Bournemouth (01202) 554355

STEVENETTE, John Maclachlan. b 30. St Pet Coll Ox MA60. Ripon Hall Ox 60. **d** 61 **p** 62. C Newhaven *Chich* 61-66; V Lynch w Iping Marsh 66-74; R Birdham w W Itchenor 74-78; R Byfleet *Guildf* 78-86; V Whittlesey *Ely* 86-90; TR Whittlesey and Pondersbridge 91; R Itchen Valley *Win* from 91. *Itchen Valley Rectory, Chillandham Lane, Martyr Worthy, Winchester, Hants SO21 1AS* Itchen Abbas (01962) 779832

STEVENETTE, Simon Melville. b 62. Hull Univ BA83. Wycliffe Hall Ox 84. **d** 87 **p** 88. C Carterton *Ox* 87-90; C Keynsham *B & W* 90-91; TV from 91; Chapl Keynsham Hosp Bris from 92. *9 Chelmer Grove, Keynsham, Bristol BS18 1QA* Bristol (0117) 986 6390

STEVENS, Alan Robert. b 55. Warw Univ BA77. St Jo Coll Nottm 87. **d** 89 **p** 90. C Ex St Leon w H Trin *Ex* 89-92; TV Rugby St Andr *Cov* from 92. *St Michael's House, 43 Bowfell, Brownsover, Rugby, Warks CV21 1JF* Rugby (01788) 573696

STEVENS, Andrew Graham. b 54. BEd MA. Coll of Resurr Mirfield. **d** 83 **p** 84. C Leigh Park *Portsm* 83-87; TV Brighton Resurr *Chich* 87-94; V Plumstead St Nic *S'wark* from 94. *St Nicholas's Vicarage, 64 Purrett Road, London SE18 1JP* 0181-854 0461

STEVENS, Anne Helen. b 61. Warw Univ BA82 Fitzw Coll Cam BA90 MA94. Ridley Hall Cam 88. **d** 91 **p** 94. Par Dn E Greenwich Ch Ch w St Andr and St Mich *S'wark* 91-94; Chapl Trin Coll Cam from 94. *7 Green Street, Cambridge CB2 3JU* Cambridge (01223) 32810 or 338400 Fax 338564

STEVENS, Anthony Harold. b 46. CEng72 MIStructE71 FIStructE87 MICE75 FICE92 S Bank Univ ONC65 HNC67. St Mich Coll Llan DipPTh95. **d** 95. C Cardiff St Jo *Llan* from 95. *41 Colum Road, Cardiff CF1 3EE* (01222) 224036 or (0589) 819025

STEVENS, Arthur Edward Geary. b 14. Lon Coll of Div 34. **d** 37 **p** 38. V Bitterne *Win* 67-72; V Duffield *Derby* 72-94; rtd 94. *Flat 2, 3 Avenue Road, Duffield, Belper, Derbyshire DE56 4DW* Derby (01332) 842924

STEVENS, Brian Henry. b 28. Oak Hill Th Coll. **d** 69 **p** 70. C Chadwell *Chelmsf* 69-75; V Penge Ch Ch w H Trin *Roch* 75-85; V St Mary Cray and St Paul's Cray 85-93; rtd 93; Perm to Offic *Cant* from 93. *53 Middle Deal Road, Deal, Kent CT14 9RG*

STEVENS, Brian Henry. b 45. Open Univ BA80. S Dios Minl Tr Scheme 81. **d** 84 **p** 85. NSM S Malling *Chich* 84-86; C Langney 86-87; TV Wolverton *Ox* 87-88; V Welford w Sibbertoft and Marston Trussell *Pet* 88-91; V Hardingstone and Horton and Piddington from 91. *The Vicarage, 29 Back Lane, Hardingstone, Northants NN4 0BY* Northampton (01604) 760110

STEVENS, Cyril David Richard. b 25. NZ Bd of Th Studies LTh66. **d** 59 **p** 60. R Rendham w Swefling and Cransford *St E* 69-73; RD Saxmundham 72-74; R Rendham w Swefling 73-95; rtd 95. *Meadow Cottage, Low Road, Marlesford, Woodbridge, Suffolk IP13 0AW* Wickham Market (01728) 746013

STEVENS, Canon David Charles. b 31. Keble Coll Ox BA55 DipTh56 MA59. Wycliffe Hall Ox 55. **d** 57 **p** 58. Asst Chapl Bryanston Sch Blandford 66-70; Chapl 70-73; P-in-c Shilling Okeford *Sarum* 73-76; Lic to Offic *Chelmsf* 76-86; R Tarrant Valley *Sarum* 86-94; rtd 94. *Bumble Cottage, 3 Yondover, Loders, Bridport, Dorset DT6 4NW* Bridport (01308) 421025

STEVENS, David John. b 45. Bris Univ BA67 Lon Univ DipTh69. Clifton Th Coll. **d** 70 **p** 71. C Ex St Leon w H Trin *Ex* 70-75; P-in-c Lt Burstead *Chelmsf* 75-77; TV Billericay and Lt Burstead 77-81; P-in-c Illogan *Truro* 81-83; R from 83. *The Rectory, Illogan, Redruth, Cornwall TR16 4RX* Portreath (01209) 842233

STEVENS, Canon David Johnson (Brother David Stephen). b 13. St Cath Soc Ox BA51 MA55. Wycliffe Hall Ox 49. **d** 52 **p** 53. Ind Chapl *Liv* 57-67; V Warrington St Paul 61-70; Guardian of Franciscan Ho Liv 70-77; SSF from 77; Lic to Offic *Newc* from 79; rtd 83. *The Friary, Alnmouth, Alnwick, Northd NE66 3NJ* Alnwick (01665) 830213

STEVENS, David Leonard. b 28. St Edm Hall Ox BA51 MA57. Cuddesdon Coll 60. **d** 62 **p** 63. Chapl St Alb Sch Chorley 67-71;

V Linc St Faith and St Martin w St Pet *Linc* 72-83; C Wolborough w Newton Abbot *Ex* 83-87; P-in-c 87-94; rtd 94. *Yew Tree Cottage, Sticklepath, Okehampton, Devon EX20 2NW* Okehampton (01837) 840098

STEVENS, Douglas George. b 47. Lon Univ BA69. Westcott Ho Cam 69. **d** 72 **p** 73. C Portsea St Geo CD *Portsm* 72-75; C Portsea N End St Mark 75-79; Chapl NE Lon Poly *Chelmsf* 79-83; C-in-c Orton Goldhay CD *Ely* 83-87; V Elm 87-91; V Coldham 87-91; V Friday Bridge 87-91; R Woodston from 91; P-in-c Fletton from 94. *The Rectory, 183A London Road, Peterborough PE2 9DS* Peterborough (01733) 62786

STEVENS, Frank Hayman. b 11. Univ Coll Ox BA32 MA38. Linc Th Coll 64. **d** 65 **p** 66. R Kenn w Kingston Seymour *B & W* 68-74; P-in-c Cossington 74-76; rtd 76; Perm to Offic *B & W* 76-93. *14 Eastgate Gardens, Taunton, Somerset TA1 1RD* Taunton (01823) 270436

STEVENS, Frederick Crichton (Fred). b 42. K Coll Lon BD78 AKC78. St Steph Ho Ox 78. **d** 79 **p** 80. C Newquay *Truro* 79-81; C St Martin-in-the-Fields *Lon* 81-85; P-in-c Soho St Anne w St Thos and St Pet from 85. *57 Dean Street, London W1V 5HH* 0171-437 5006

STEVENS, James Anthony. b 47. Worc Coll Ox MA69. Trin Coll Bris 78. **d** 80 **p** 81. C Heref St Pet w St Owen and St Jas *Heref* 80-84; C Lowestoft and Kirkley *Nor* 84-85; TV 85-89; V Dorridge *Birm* from 89. *The Vicarage, 6 Manor Road, Dorridge, Solihull, W Midlands B93 8DX* Wythall (01564) 772472 or 775652

STEVENS, John David Andrew. b 44. Wycliffe Hall Ox. **d** 68 **p** 69. C Standish *Blackb* 68-71; C Stonehouse *Glouc* 71-76; P-in-c Closworth *B & W* 76-77; P-in-c Barwick 76-77; TV Yeovil 77-80; R Chewton Mendip w Ston Easton, Litton etc 80-94; R Quantokhead from 94; RD Quantock from 95. *The New Rectory, Kilve, Bridgwater, Somerset TA5 1DZ* Holford (01278) 741501

STEVENS, Martin Leonard. b 35. St Jo Coll Dur BA60 MA72. Oak Hill Th Coll 60. **d** 62 **p** 63. C Low Elswick *Newc* 62-65; C S Croydon Em *Cant* 65-69; Hon C 70-74; S England Dep Sec Irish Ch Miss 69-74; V Felling *Dur* 74-86; NSM Ches Square St Mich w St Phil *Lon* from 92. *Flat B, 8 Carleton Gardens, Brecknock Road, London N19 5AQ* 0171-485 4305

STEVENS, Michael John. b 37. St Cath Coll Cam BA63. Coll of Resurr Mirfield 63. **d** 65 **p** 66. C Poplar All SS w St Frideswide *Lon* 65-71; Asst Chapl The Lon Hosp (Whitechapel) 71-74; Chapl St Thos Hosp Lon from 75. *St Thomas's Hospital, Lambeth Palace Road, London SE1 7EH, or 2 Walcot Square, London SE11 4TZ* 0171-928 9292 or 735 7362

STEVENS, Neville. b 21. Clare Coll Cam BA52 MA54 Or Coll Ox DipTh54. Wycliffe Hall Ox 52. **d** 54 **p** 55. C Bishopsworth *Bris* 54-56; Chapl Leeds Gr Sch 56-84; Perm to Offic *Wakef* from 71; Perm to Offic *Ripon* from 85. *6 Hill Top Green, West Ardsley, Tingley, Wakefield, W Yorkshire WF3 1HS* Leeds (0113) 253 8038

STEVENS, Peter David. b 36. ARICS. Oak Hill Th Coll DipHE81. **d** 81 **p** 82. C Branksome St Clem *Sarum* 81-87; R Moreton and Woodsford w Tincleton from 87. *The Rectory, Moreton, Dorchester, Dorset DT2 8RH* Bindon Abbey (01929) 462466

STEVENS, Philip Terence. b 55. MBIM Man Univ BSc76 Lon Univ BD81 St Jo Coll Dur MA86. Cranmer Hall Dur 81. **d** 83 **p** 84. C Withington St Paul *Man* 83-86; C Middleton 86-88; V Saddleworth 88-92; V Sheff St Paul Wordsworth Avenue *Sheff* from 93. *St Paul's Vicarage, Wheata Road, Sheffield S5 9FP* Sheffield (0114) 246 8137

STEVENS, Canon Ralph. b 11. Selw Coll Cam BA36 MA40. Qu Coll Birm 36. **d** 38 **p** 39. R Colchester Ch Ch w St Mary V *Chelmsf* 65-79; Hon Can Chelmsf Cathl 71-79; rtd 79; Perm to Offic *St E* from 79. *9 York Road, Southwold, Suffolk IP18 6AN* Southwold (01502) 723705

STEVENS, Canon Ralph Samuel Osborn. b 13. Birm Univ BSc34 St Cath Soc Ox BA36 MA41. Ripon Hall Ox 34. **d** 36 **p** 37. V Birm St Paul *Birm* 50-83; Hon Can Birm Cathl 52-83; RD Birm City 58-73; Chapl to The Queen 67-83; rtd 83; Perm to Offic *Birm* from 84. *10 Harrison's Green, Birmingham B15 3LH* 0121-454 3089

STEVENS, Richard William. b 36. AKC59. **d** 60 **p** 61. Chapl RAF 63-79; CF from 79; rtd 91. *The Old Vicarage, Stockbury, Sittingbourne, Kent ME9 7UN* Sittingbourne (01795) 844891

STEVENS, Robin George. b 43. Leic Univ BA65. Cuddesdon Coll 74. **d** 74 **p** 75. C Hemel Hempstead *St Alb* 74-77; Chapl K Coll Sch Wimbledon from 77. *329 Wimbledon Park Road, London SW19 6NS* 0181-788 1501 or 947 9311

STEVENS, Miss Sylvia Joyce. b 41. Qu Mary Coll Lon BA63 Bris Univ CertEd64 St Jo Coll Dur BA77 DipTh78. Cranmer Hall Dur 75. **dss** 78 **d** 87 **p** 94. Chapl Trent (Nottm) Poly *S'well* 78-92; Chapl Nottm Trent Univ 92-93; Continuing Minl

Educn Officer *Bris* from 93; Tutor Trin Coll Bris from 93; Hon C Chippenham St Pet *Bris* from 93. *11 Aintree Drive, Chippenham, Wilts SN14 0FA* Chippenham (01249) 657737 Fax 448087

STEVENS, Thomas Walter. b 33. Bps' Coll Cheshunt. **d** 65 **p** 66. C Wallsend St Luke *Newc* 69-70; C Cranford *Lon* 70-87; C Fulwell St Mich and St Geo 87-90; C Teddington SS Pet and Paul and Fulwell 90-91; rtd 92. *23A Samos Road, London SE20 7UQ*

✠**STEVENS, Rt Rev Timothy John.** b 46. Selw Coll Cam BA68 MA72 DipTh. Ripon Coll Cuddesdon 75. **d** 76 **p** 77 **c** 95. C E Ham w Upton Park St Alb *Chelmsf* 76-80; TR Canvey Is 80-88; Dep Dir Cathl Cen for Research and Tr 82-84; Bp's Urban Officer 87-91; Hon Can Chelmsf Cathl 87-91; Adn W Ham 91-95; Suff Bp Dunwich *St E* from 95. *The Old Vicarage, Church Road, Stowupland, Stowmarket, Suffolk IP14 4BQ* Stowmarket (01449) 678234 Fax 771148

STEVENSEN, Albert. b 24. Wycliffe Hall Ox 61. **d** 62 **p** 63. Chapl HM Pris Brixton 64-70; C Wandsworth All SS *S'wark* 70-71; V Wandsworth St Steph 71-88; rtd 88. *33 Durnsford Avenue, London SW19 8BH* 0181-946 3650

STEVENSON, Alastair Rice. b 42. Open Univ BA78. Ripon Coll Cuddesdon 78. **d** 80 **p** 81. C Bexhill St Pet *Chich* 80-82; C Brighton St Matthias 82-84; C Swindon Ch Ch *Bris* 84-87; Bp's Soc and Ind Adv from 87. *23 Sedgebrook, Swindon SN3 6EY* Swindon (01793) 612385 Fax as telephone

STEVENSON, Bernard Norman. b 57. Kent Univ BA78 Fitzw Coll Cam BA81 MA86. Ridley Hall Cam. **d** 82 **p** 83. C Mortlake w E Sheen *S'wark* 82-84; C Kensal Rise St Martin *Lon* 84-88; C Headstone St Geo 88-90; V Worfield *Heref* 90-95; R Hutton *B & W* from 95. *The Rectory, Church Lane, Hutton, Weston-super-Mare, Avon BS24 9SL* Bleadon (01934) 812366

STEVENSON, Brian. b 34. JP66. NW Ord Course 76. **d** 79 **p** 80. C Padiham *Blackb* 79-82; V Clitheroe St Paul Low Moor 82-89; V Blackb St Silas from 89. *St Silas' Vicarage, Preston New Road, Blackburn BB2 6PS* Blackburn (01254) 671293

STEVENSON, Christopher James. b 43. TCD BA65 MA73 Em Coll Cam BA69 MA73. Westcott Ho Cam 68. **d** 70 **p** 71. C Newc H Cross *Newc* 70-72; C Arm St Mark *Arm* 72-73; C Dub Crumlin *D & G* 73-76; Hon CV Ch Ch Cathl Dub 75-76; C-in-c Appley Bridge All SS CD *Blackb* 76-82; P-in-c Appley Bridge 82-91; Bp's C Cloonclare w Killasnett, Lurganboy and Drumlease *K, E & A* from 92. *The Rectory, Manorhamilton, Co Leitrim, Irish Republic* Manorhamilton (72) 55041

STEVENSON, David Andrew. b 60. Trin Coll Bris BA92. **d** 92 **p** 93. C Nottm St Sav *S'well* from 92. *2 St Saviour's Vicarage, Arkwright Walk, Nottingham NG2 2JU* Nottingham (0115) 985 0931

STEVENSON, Derick Neville. b 36. Open Univ BA76. Ridley Hall Cam 79. **d** 80 **p** 81. C Bonchurch *Portsm* 80-84; C-in-c Crookhorn Ch Cen CD 84-87; R Norton Fitzwarren *B & W* from 87. *The Rectory, Rectory Road, Norton Fitzwarren, Taunton, Somerset TA2 6SE* Taunton (01823) 272570

STEVENSON, Donald Macdonald (Don). b 48. Lon Univ BSc(Econ)70 Leeds Univ MA72 Univ of Wales (Abth) CertEd73 Warw Univ MEd78. Oak Hill Th Coll BA88. **d** 88 **p** 89. C Gt Malvern St Mary *Worc* 88-92; Chapl Bedf Sch from 92. *Bedford School, Burnaby Road, Bedford MK40 2TU* Bedford (01234) 353493

STEVENSON, Frank Beaumont. b 39. MInstGA(Lon) Duke Univ (USA) BA61. Episc Th Sch Harvard MDiv64. **d** 64 **p** 64. USA 64-66; Zambia 66-68; Lect Th Ox Univ from 68; Bp's Tr Officer *Ox* 69-70; Chapl Keble Coll Ox 71-72; Chapl Isis Gp Hosps 73-75; Chapl Littlemore Hosp Ox from 75; Officer for Continuing Minl Educn from 90. *Littlemore Hospital, Littlemore, Oxford OX4 4XN, or The School House, Stanton St John, Oxford OX33 1ET* Oxford (01865) 778911 or 351635

STEVENSON, Gerald Ernest. b 35. S'wark Ord Course 80. **d** 83 **p** 84. NSM Eltham Park St Luke *S'wark* 83-88; Asst Chapl HM Pris Wormwood Scrubs from 88. *106 Grangehill Road, London SE9 1SE* 0181-850 2748 Fax 749 5655

STEVENSON, John. b 39. Glas Univ MA64 Jordan Hill Coll Glas TCert65. St Jo Coll Nottm 87. **d** 87 **p** 88. NSM Moffat *Glas* 87-92; P-in-c Eastriggs from 92; P-in-c Gretna from 92; P-in-c Langholm from 92. *4 Kingfisher Lane, Gretna, Dumfriesshire DG16 5JS* Gretna (01461) 338176

STEVENSON, John Charles. b 22. St Jo Coll Dur LTh48. Oak Hill Th Coll 45. **d** 49 **p** 50. V Bolton St Bede *Man* 64-75; Asst Chapl HM Pris Wandsworth 75-77; Chapl HM Pris Linc 77-80; R Fiskerton *Linc* 80-87; rtd 87. *15 The Coppice, Redwood Park, Beaufort Road, Morecambe, Lancs LA4 6TY* Morecambe (01524) 423653

STEVENSON, John William. b 44. Salford Univ BSc66 E Warks Coll DipMan73 Univ of S Africa BTh89. St Paul's Grahamstown DipTh86. **d** 87 **p** 87. S Africa 87-93; V Broom Leys *Leic* from 93. *St David's Vicarage, 7 Greenhill Road, Coalville, Leics LE67 4RL* Coalville (01530) 836262

✠**STEVENSON, Rt Rev Kenneth William.** b 49. FRHistS90 Edin Univ MA70 Southn Univ PhD75 Man Univ DD87.

Sarum & Wells Th Coll 70. **d** 73 **p** 74 **c** 95. C Grantham w Manthorpe *Linc* 73-76; C Boston 76-80; Chapl Man Univ *Man* 80-86; TV Man Whitworth 80-82; TR 82-86; Lect Man Univ 80-86; R Guildf H Trin w St Mary *Guildf* 86-95; Bp Portsm from 95. *Bishopswood, The Avenue, Fareham, Hants PO14 1NT* Fareham (01329) 280247 Fax 231538

STEVENSON, Leslie Thomas Clayton. b 59. TCD BA DipTh MPhil. **d** 83 **p** 84. C Dundela *D & D* 83-87; I Kilmore w Inch 87-92; I Donaghadee from 92. *3 The Trees, New Road, Donaghadee, Co Down BT21 0EJ* Donaghadee (01247) 882594

STEVENSON, Lorna. b 43. Moray Ho Edin DipEd65. dss 85 **d** 86. NSM Dundee St Luke *Bre* from 85. *39 Charleston Drive, Dundee DD2 2HF* Dundee (01382) 66631

STEVENSON, Michael Richard Nevin. b 52. Univ Coll Lon MA77. CITC DipTh86. **d** 86 **p** 87. C Clooney w Strathfoyle *D & R* 86-89; CF from 89. *c/o MOD (Army), Bagshot Park, Bagshot, Surrey GU19 5PL* Bagshot (01276) 471717 Fax 412834

STEVENSON, Ven Richard Clayton. b 22. TCD BA48 MA56. CITC 48. **d** 48 **p** 49. I Belf St Barn *Conn* 60-70; I Belf St Nic 70-88; Adn Conn 79-88; rtd 88. *42 Malone Heights, Belfast BT9 5PG* Belfast (01232) 615006

STEVENSON, Robert Brian. b 40. QUB BA61 Qu Coll Cam BA67 MA71 Pemb Coll Ox BA69 BD76 MA76 Birm Univ PhD70. Cuddesdon Coll 69. **d** 70 **p** 71. C Lewisham St Jo Southend *S'wark* 70-73; C Catford (Southend) and Downham 73-74; Lect and Dir Past Studies Chich Th Coll 74-81; Acting Vice-Prin 80-81; V W Malling w Offham *Roch* from 81; RD Malling from 93. *The Vicarage, 138 High Street, West Malling, Kent ME19 6NE* West Malling (01732) 842245

STEVENSON, Canon Ronald. b 17. Leeds Univ BA38. Coll of Resurr Mirfield 38. **d** 40 **p** 41. C Pontefract All SS *Wakef* 40-44; C-in-c Lundwood CD 44-47; Area Sec Miss to Seamen 47-49; Perm to Offic Linc, Ches, Man, Blackb, Carl 49-65; Leic, Derby and Pet 49-65; Chapl Lanc Moor Hosp 49-65; Chapl N Lancs and S Westmorland Hosps 65-75; Hon Can Blackb Cathl *Blackb* 71-75. *28 Slyne Road, Torrisholme, Morecambe, Lancs LA4 6PA* Morecambe (01524) 410957

STEVENSON, Trevor Donald. b 59. TCD Div Sch BTh. **d** 91 **p** 92. C Magheralin w Dollingstown *D & D* 91-95; CMS from 95; Uganda from 95. *Church Mission Society, Partnership House, 157 Waterloo Road, London SE1 8UU* 0171-928 8681 Fax 401 3215

STEVENTON, Mrs June Lesley. b 61. Aston Tr Scheme 86 Sarum & Wells Th Coll BTh91. **d** 91 **p** 94. Par Dn Chatham St Steph *Roch* 91-94; C from 94. *59 Greenway, Chatham, Kent ME5 9UX* Medway (01634) 861045

STEVINSON, Harold John Hardy. b 34. Selw Coll Cam BA57 MA61. Qu Coll Birm. **d** 59 **p** 60. C Bris St Mary Redcliffe w Temple *Bris* 59-63; C Caversham Ox 63-73; Soc Resp Officer *Dur* 74-82; Sec Dioc Bd for Miss and Unity 82-88; P-in-c Croxdale 82-88; P-in-c Leamington Hastings and Birdingbury *Cov* from 88. *The Vicarage, Leamington Hastings, Rugby, Warks CV23 8DY* Marton (01926) 632455

STEVINSON, Josephine Mary. STh55. Cranmer Hall Dur 86. dss 86 **d** 87 **p** 94. Croxdale *Dur* 86-87; Hon Par Dn 87-88; Lic to Offic *Cov* from 88; NSM Leamington Hastings and Birdingbury from 94. *The Vicarage, Leamington Hastings, Rugby, Warks CV23 8DY* Marton (01926) 632455

STEWARD, Mrs Linda Christine. b 46. NE Lon Poly CQSW82. S'wark Ord Course 85. **d** 88 **p** 94. NSM E Ham w Upton Park St Alb *Chelmsf* 88-90; Chapl Newham Gen Hosp from 90; NSM Plaistow *Chelmsf* from 94. *Newham General Hospital, Glen Road, London E13 8RU, or 131 Windsor Road, London E7 0RA* 0171-363 8053 or 0181-552 8877

STEWARDSON, Ian Joseph. b 28. Ex Coll Ox BA52 DipTh54 MA56. Wycliffe Hall Ox 52. **d** 54 **p** 55. V New Barnet St Jas *St Alb* 60-72; R Potton w Sutton and Cockayne Hatley 72-82; R Cottered w Broadfield and Throcking 82-94; rtd 94. *77 Burford Road, Witney, Oxon OX8 5DR* Witney (01993) 704076

STEWART, Miss Betty. b 25. S'wark Ord Course 91. **d** 93 **p** 94. NSM Wandsworth Common St Mary *S'wark* from 93. *71 Ormond Drive, Hampton, Middx TW12 2TL* 0181-979 6047

STEWART, Brian. b 59. BTh. **d** 91 **p** 92. C Ballywillan *Conn* 91-94; I Belf St Geo from 94; Bp's Dom Chapl from 94. *St George's Rectory, 28 Myrtlefield Park, Belfast BT9 6NF* Belfast (01232) 667134 or 231275

STEWART, Canon Alexander Butler. b 25. **d** 58 **p** 59. I Helen's Bay *D & D* 65-72; I Donegal w Killymard, Lough Eske and Laghey *D & R* 72-90; Can Raphoe Cathl 81-90; rtd 90; Lic to Offic *D & D* from 90. *31 Upper Ballygelagh Road, Ardkeen, Newtownards, Co Down BT22 1JG* Kircubbin (012477) 38601

STEWART, Canon Charles. b 55. St Jo Coll Cam BA77 CertEd79 MA81. Wycliffe Hall Ox 85. **d** 87 **p** 88. C Bowdon *Ches* 87-90; C Bath Abbey w St Jas *B & W* 90-94; Can Res,

Prec and Sacr Win Cathl *Win* from 94. *5 The Close, Winchester, Hants SO23 9LS* Winchester (01962) 856236

STEWART, Ian Guild. b 43. Edin Th Coll 89. **d** 84 **p** 85. NSM Dundee St Mary Magd *Bre* 84-87; NSM Dundee St Jo 87-90; C 90-92; NSM Dundee St Martin 87-90; C 90-92; R Montrose from 92; P-in-c Inverbervie from 92. *The Rectory, 17 Panmure Place, Montrose, Angus DD10 8ER* Montrose (01674) 672652

STEWART, James. b 32. **d** 69 **p** 70. C Belf St Donard *D & D* 69-72; C Dundonald 72-74; I Rathmullan w Tyrella 74-80; I Belf St Clem from 80. *St Clement's Rectory, 80A Sandown Road, Belfast BT5 6GU* Belfast (01232) 657345

STEWART, James Patrick. b 55. Keele Univ BA77 Birm Univ MA78. Ridley Hall Cam 86. **d** 88 **p** 89. C Boulton *Derby* 88-91; C Cove St Jo *Guildf* 91-92; TV from 92. *Fircroft, 21 St John's Road, Farnborough, Hants GU14 9RL* Farnborough (01252) 543502

STEWART, Mrs Janet Margaret. b 41. CertEd62 DipRK70. Cranmer Hall Dur 67. **d** 87 **p** 94. Hon Par Dn Oulton Broad *Nor* 87-94; Hon C from 94; Asst Chapl Lowestoft Hosp from 94. *St Mark's Vicarage, 212 Bridge Road, Oulton Broad, Lowestoft, Suffolk NR33 9JX* Lowestoft (01502) 572563

STEWART, John. b 09. St Cath Coll Cam BA31 MA35. Cuddesdon Coll 31. **d** 32 **p** 33. V Appleton-le-Moors *York* 57-74; V Lastingham 57-74; rtd 74; Chapl Qu Mary's Sch Helmsley 75-85. *Bodney Cottage, Buckingham Square, Helmsley, York YO6 5DZ* Helmsley (01439) 70517

STEWART, John. b 39. Oak Hill Th Coll 75. **d** 77 **p** 78. C Accrington Ch Ch *Blackb* 77-79; TV Darwen St Pet w Hoddlesden 79-86; R Coppull St Jo from 86. *St John's Vicarage, Darlington Street, Coppull, Chorley, Lancs PR7 5AB* Coppull (01257) 791258

STEWART, Canon John Roberton. b 29. Sarum Th Coll 63. **d** 65 **p** 66. C Gillingham *Sarum* 65-70; R Langton Matravers 70-84; RD Purbeck 82-89; Can and Preb Sarum Cathl 83-90; R Kingston, Langton Matravers and Worth Matravers 84-90; Can Res Sarum Cathl 90-95; Treas 90-95. *23 The Close, Salisbury SP1 2EH* Salisbury (01722) 322172

STEWART, John Vernon. b 36. BNC Ox BA57 MA66. Coll of Ressur Halki 59. **d** 61 **p** 62. R Sibford *Ox* 70-75; R Northolt St Mary *Lon* 75-82; rtd 82. *Rua Jo Arco, Cerdeira 6345, Portugal*

STEWART, John Wesley. b 52. QUB BD76 TCD 76. **d** 77 **p** 78. C Seagoe *D & D* 77-79; C Lisburn Ch Ch *Conn* 79-85; I Ballybay w Mucknoe and Clontibret *Clogh* 85-90; I Derryvullen S w Garvary from 90; RD Enniskillen 91-95; Bp Dom Chapl from 95. *The Rectory, Tullyharney, Enniskillen, Co Fermanagh BT74 4PR* Lisbellaw (01365) 387236 Fax as telephone

STEWART, Kim Deborah. *See* MATHERS, Mrs Kim Deborah

STEWART, Malcolm James. b 44. TD78. Solicitor 79 York Univ BA66 K Coll Lon MA68 Lon Inst of Educn PGCE69. NE Ord Course 89. **d** 93 **p** 94. NSM Upper Nidderdale *Ripon* 93-95; C Fountains Gp from 95. *Hazel Close, Grewelthorpe, Ripon, N Yorkshire HG4 3BL*

STEWART, Very Rev Maurice Evan. b 29. TCD BA50 MA53 BD67 QUB PhD75. **d** 52 **p** 53. C Belf St Jas *Conn* 52-55; Chapl Bps' Coll Cheshunt 55-58; Hd of Trin Coll Miss Belf 58-61; I Newc *D & D* 61-69; Lect CITC 69-91; Vice-Prin 80-91; Lect in Div TCD 72-91; Chan St Patr Cathl Dub 80-89; Prec 89-91; Dean St Patr Cathl Dub from 91; I Dub St Patr Cathl Gp *D & G* from 91. *The Deanery, Upper Kevin Street, Dublin 8, Irish Republic* Dublin (1) 454-3428 or 453-9472 Fax 454-6374

STEWART, Maxwell Neville Gabriel. b 33. Hertf Coll Ox BA58. Wycliffe Hall Ox DipTh59. **d** 60 **p** 61. C Perry Beeches *Birm* 60-62; Chapl Rosenberg Coll St Gallen 62-64; Perm to Offic *Chelmsf* 64-70; Warden Leics Poly 70-92; De Montfort Univ Leic 92-93; Perm to Offic St Mary *Leic* from 74. *25 Sidney Court, Norwich Road, Leicester LE4 0LR*

STEWART, Michael. b 65. St Jo Coll Nottm LTh89. **d** 89 **p** 90. C Ealing St Paul *Lon* 89-93; P-in-c N Wembley St Cuth from 93. *St Cuthbert's Vicarage, 214 Carlton Avenue West, Wembley, Middx HA0 3QY* 0181-904 7657

STEWART, Norman Andrew. b 42. Edin Th Coll 54. **d** 58 **p** 59. C Glas Ch Ch *Glas* 58-59; C Paisley H Trin 59-60; C Glas St Marg 60-62; C Kingsthorpe *Pet* 62-64; Belize from 70. *St Mary's Rectory, PO Box 246, Belize City, Belize*

STEWART, Raymond John. b 55. TCD BA79 MA82. CITC 74 Div Test77. **d** 79 **p** 80. C Clooney *D & R* 79-82; I Dunfanaghy 82-87; I Gweedore 85-87; Dioc Youth Adv 83-87; I Castledawson from 87; RD Maghera and Kilrea from 89; Ed D & R Dioc News 89-93. *12 Station Road, Castledawson, Magherafelt, Co Londonderry BT45 8AZ* Castledawson (01648) 468235

STEWART, Canon Robert Stevenson. b 15. TCD BA38. **d** 39 **p** 40. I Ballymoney *Conn* 59-82; Can Conn Cathl 78-82; rtd 82. *7 Willan Drive, Portrush, Co Antrim BT56 8PU* Portrush (01265) 824336

STEWART, Canon William Allen. b 43. Trin Coll Cam BA65 MA69. Cranmer Hall Dur DipTh68. **d** 68 **p** 69. C Ecclesall

Sheff 68-72; C Cheltenham St Mary *Glouc* 72-74; V Glouc St Jas 74-80; P-in-c Glouc All SS 78-80; R Upton *Ex* 80-85; V Oulton Broad *Nor* from 85; RD Lothingland from 92; RD Hon Can Nor Cathl from 94. *St Mark's Vicarage, 212 Bridge Road, Oulton Broad, Lowestoft, Suffolk NR33 9JX* Lowestoft (01502) 572563

STEWART, William James. BA DipTh. **d** 83 **p** 84. C Glenageary *D & G* 83-86; Rostrevor Renewal Cen 86-87; I Naas w Kill and Rathmore *M & K* 87-93; Min Dub Ch Ch Cathl Gp *D & G* from 93; CORE (St Werburgh Ch) from 93; Chapl Rotunda Hosp from 94; Chapl Dub Coll of Catering from 94. *96 Lower Drumcondra Road, Dublin 9, Irish Republic* Dublin (1) 830-0935

STEWART, William Jones. b 32. Trin Hall Cam BA55 MA59 Cam Univ CertEd56. Edin Th Coll 67. **d** 69 **p** 69. Chapl St Ninian's Cathl Perth *St And* 69-71; Bp's Dom Chapl *Ox* 71-75; V Lambourn 75-90; V Lambourn from 90; P-in-c Lambourne Woodlands 83-90; P-in-c Eastbury and E Garston from 83. *Lambourn Vicarage, Newbury, Berks RG16 7PD* Lambourn (01488) 71546

STEWART-DARLING, Dr Fiona Lesley. b 58. Kingston Poly GRSC79 Lon Univ PhD82. Trin Coll Bris BA91. **d** 91 **p** 94. C Cirencester *Glouc* 91-94; Chapl Cheltenham and Glouc Coll of HE from 94. *30 Rothmere Close, Cheltenham, Glos GL51 5UU* Cheltenham (01242) 863135 or 513836

STEWART ELLENS, Gordon Frederick. *See* ELLENS, Dr Gordon Frederick Stewart

STEWART-SMITH, Canon David Cree. b 13. K Coll Cam BA39 MA42. Cuddesdon Coll 40. **d** 41 **p** 42. Can Res Roch Cathl *Roch* 69-76; Adn Roch 69-76; Home Sec JMECA 76-78; rtd 78; Perm to Offic *Glouc* from 86. *16 Capel Court, Prestbury, Cheltenham, Glos GL52 3EL* Cheltenham (01242) 510972

STEWART-SYKES, Alistair Charles. b 60. St Andr Univ MA83 Birm Univ PhD92. Qu Coll Birm 86. **d** 89 **p** 90. C Stevenage St Andr and St Geo *St Alb* 89-92; C Castle Vale St Cuth *Birm* 92-93; Barbados from 93. *Codrington College, St John, JO6, Barbados* Barbados (1 809) 423-1577 Fax as telephone

STEWART-SYKES, Teresa Melanie. b 64. Bris Univ BA85. Qu Coll Birm 87. **d** 89. Par Dn Stevenage St Andr and St Geo *St Alb* 89-92; NSM Castle Vale St Cuth *Birm* 92-93; Barbados from 93. *Codrington College, St John, JO6, Barbados* Barbados (1 809) 423-1577 Fax as telephone

STEYNOR, Victor Albert. b 15. Southn Univ DipEd62. S'wark Ord Course 68. **d** 71 **p** 72. C Bognor *Chich* 71-75; P-in-c Kenton and Ashfield w Thorpe *St E* 75-81; P-in-c Aspall 75-81; V Debenham 75-81; V Debenham w Aspall and Kenton 81-82; rtd 82; Perm to Offic *St E* from 82. *74 Elmhurst Drive, Ipswich IP3 0PB* Ipswich (01473) 728922

STIBBE, Dr Mark William Godfrey. b 60. Trin Coll Cam BA83 MA86 Nottm Univ PhD88. St Jo Coll Nottm 83. **d** 86 **p** 87. C Stapleford *S'well* 86-90; C Crookes St Thos *Sheff* 90-93; Lect Sheff Univ from 90; V Grenoside from 93. *St Mark's Vicarage, 19 Graven Close, Grenoside, Sheffield S30 3QT* Sheffield (0114) 246 7513

STICKLAND, Geoffrey John Brett. b 42. St D Coll Lamp DipTh66. **d** 66 **p** 67. C Aberavon H Trin *Llan* 66-69; C Llanrumney *Mon* 69-72; C Tetbury w Beverston *Glouc* 72-75; V Hardwicke 75-82; R Hardwicke, Quedgeley and Elmore w Longney from 82. *The Rectory, School Lane, Quedgeley, Gloucester GL2 6PN* Gloucester (01452) 720411

STIDOLPH, Robert Anthony. b 54. GRSM ARCM. St Steph Ho Ox 77. **d** 80 **p** 80. C Hove All SS *Chich* 80-84; TV Brighton Resurr 84-87; Chapl Cheltenham Coll from 87. *1 Waterfield Close, Cheltenham, Glos GL53 7NL* Cheltenham (01242) 230800

STIEVENARD, Alphonse Etienne Arthur. b 13. Selw Coll Cam BA36 MA40. Lon Coll of Div 36. **d** 37 **p** 38. V Jersey Millbrook St Matt *Win* 51-78; rtd 78. *Le Ruisselet, Mont Rossignol, St Ouen, Jersey, Channel Islands JE3 2LN* Jersey (01534) 481215

STIFF, Derrick Malcolm. b 40. Lich Th Coll 69. **d** 72 **p** 73. C Cov St Geo *Cov* 72-75; R Benhall w Sternfield *St E* 75-79; P-in-c Snape w Friston 75-79; V Cartmel *Carl* 79-87; R Sudbury and Chilton *St E* 87-94; Min Can St E Cathl from 90; P-in-c Lavenham from 94; P-in-c Preston from 94. *The Rectory, Lavenham, Sudbury, Suffolk CO10 9SA* Lavenham (01787) 247244

STILEMAN, William Mark Charles. b 63. Selw Coll Cam BA85 MA89 PGCE86. Wycliffe Hall Ox DipTh89. **d** 91 **p** 92. C Ox St Andr *Ox* 91-95; C Gt Chesham from 95. *14A Manor Way, Chesham, Bucks HP5 3BG* Chesham (01494) 784372

STILL, Colin Charles. b 35. Selw Coll Cam BA67 MA71. Cranmer Hall Dur DipTh68 United Th Sem Dayton STM69. **d** 69 **p** 70. C Drypool St Columba w St Andr and St Pet *York* 69-72; Abp's Dom Chapl 72-75; Recruitment Sec ACCM 76-80; P-in-c Ockham w Hatchford *Guildf* 76-80; R 80-90; Can

665

Missr and Ecum Officer 80-90; Perm to Offic *Chich* from 92. *Flat 9, 16 Lewes Crescent, Brighton BN2 1GB* Brighton (01273) 686014

STILL, Jonathan Trevor Lloyd. b 59. Ex Univ BA81 Qu Coll Cam BA84 MA88. Westcott Ho Cam 82. **d** 85 **p** 86. C Weymouth H Trin *Sarum* 85-88; Chapl for Agric *Heref* 88-93; V N Petherton w Northmoor Green *B & W* from 93. *The Dower House, North Petherton, Bridgwater, Somerset TA6 6SE* North Petherton (01278) 662429

STILLMAN, Roger John. b 47. St Steph Ho Ox 81. **d** 83 **p** 84. C St Helier *S'wark* 83-88; P-in-c Falinge *Man* 88; TV Rochdale 88-94; P-in-c Wokingham St Paul *Ox* from 94. *St Paul's Rectory, Holt Lane, Wokingham, Berks RG11 1ED* Wokingham (01734) 780629

STILWELL, Malcolm Thomas. b 54. Coll of Resurr Mirfield 83. **d** 86 **p** 87. C Workington St Mich *Carl* 86-90; P-in-c Flimby 90-93; Perm to Offic from 93. *18 Moorfield Avenue, Workington, Cumbria CA14 4HJ* Workington (01900) 66757

STIMPSON, Graham George. b 40. Lon Univ MB BS65 DPM. Cuddesdon Coll 69. **d** 70 **p** 71. NSM Bris St Mary Redcliffe w Temple etc *Bris* from 70. *12 Challoner Court, Bristol BS1 4RG* Bristol (0117) 926 0802

STIMPSON, Nigel Leslie. b 60. St Martin's Coll Lanc BA92. Coll of Resurr Mirfield CPT94. **d** 94 **p** 95. C Heyhouses on Sea *Blackb* from 94. *2 Vicarage Close, St Annes, Lytham St Annes, Lancs FY8 3BQ* St Annes (01253) 780262

STINSON, William Gordon. b 29. Lon Univ BSc50. Ely Th Coll 51. **d** 52 **p** 53. V New Cleethorpes *Linc* 67-76; RD Grimsby and Cleethorpes 73-76; P-in-c Dovercourt *Chelmsf* 76-83; TR Dovercourt and Parkeston 83-91; RD Harwich 87-91; V Gosfield 91-95; rtd 95. *1 Cluanie Orchard, Melford Road, Cavendish, Sudbury, Suffolk CO10 8AA* Sudbury (01787) 281969

STIRK, Peter Francis. b 24. Linc Coll Ox BA49 MA53. Qu Coll Birm 49. **d** 50 **p** 51. P-in-c Kirby-on-the-Moor *Ripon* 68-71; V 71-81; P-in-c Cundall 73-81; V Kirby-on-the-Moor, Cundall w Norton-le-Clay etc 81-90; rtd 90. *Devonshire Cottage, Marton le Moor, Ripon, N Yorkshire HG4 5AT* Harrogate (01423) 322330

STIRLING, Mrs Christina Dorita (Tina). b 48. Lon Univ BEd73. Wycliffe Hall Ox 87. **d** 89 **p** 94. Par Dn Thame w Towersey *Ox* 89-94; C from 94. *29 Chalgrove Road, Thame, Oxon OX9 3TF* Thame (01844) 216508

STIRRUP, Roger. b 34. St Cath Coll Cam BA58 MA62. Linc Th Coll 58. **d** 60 **p** 61. C Selly Oak St Mary *Birm* 60-63; C Battersea St Mary *S'wark* 63-65; Chapl St Andr Univ *St And* 65-68; Chapl Nottm High Sch 68-80; Asst Chapl Rugby Sch Warks 80-85; V Fordingbridge *Win* 85-92; TR Ross w Brampton Abbotts, Bridstow and Peterstow *Heref* 92-93; TR Ross w Brampton Abbotts, Bridstow, Peterstow etc from 93. *The Rectory, Church Street, Ross-on-Wye, Herefordshire HR9 5HN* Ross-on-Wye (01989) 562175

STOBART, Mrs Judith Audrey. b 43. St Hugh's Coll Ox BA65 MA71 Lon Univ CertEd71 DipEd72. St Alb Minl Tr Scheme 82. **dss** 85 **d** 87 **p** 94. Hatf *St Alb* 85-87; Par Dn Hatf Hyde St Mary 87-91; NSM Welwyn Garden City 91-92; Par Dn 92-94; C from 94. *23 Park Meadow, Hatfield, Herts AL9 5HA* Hatfield (01707) 264251

STOCK, Lionel Crispian. b 58. ACMA85 ACIS94. Linc Th Coll BTh94. **d** 94 **p** 95. C Preston w Sutton Poyntz and Osmington w Poxwell *Sarum* from 94. *7 Wyke Oliver Close, Preston, Weymouth, Dorset DT3 6DR* Weymouth (01305) 835018

STOCK, Miss Ruth Vaughan. b 51. Birkb Coll Lon BA79 MA85. Wycliffe Hall Ox 91. **d** 93 **p** 94. Par Dn Toxteth St Philemon w St Gabr and St Cleopas *Liv* 93-94; C from 94. *40 Madryn Street, Liverpool L8 3TT* 0151-727 5899

STOCK, Victor Andrew. b 44. AKC68. **d** 69 **p** 70. C Pinner *Lon* 69-73; Chapl Lon Univ 73-79; R Friern Barnet St Jas 79-86; R St Mary le Bow w St Pancras Soper Lane etc from 86; P-in-c St Mary Aldermary from 87. *The Rector's Lodgings, Cheapside, London EC2V 6AU* 0171-248 5139

STOCK, William Nigel. b 50. Dur Univ BA72 Ox Univ DipTh75. Ripon Coll Cuddesdon 75. **d** 76 **p** 77. C Stockton St Pet *Dur* 76-79; Papua New Guinea 79-84; V Shiremoor *Newc* 85-91; TR N Shields from 91; RD Tynemouth from 92. *The Vicarage, 26 Cleveland Road, North Shields, Tyne & Wear NE29 0NG* 0191-257 1721

STOCK-HESKETH, Jonathan Philip. b 49. St Chad's Coll Dur BA Cam Univ CertEd Nottm Univ MTh PhD93. St Steph Ho Ox. **d** 83 **p** 84. C Leic St Phil *Leic* 83-86; C Loughb Em 86-89; Lect Nottm Univ from 95. *Theology Department, Nottingham University, Nottingham NG7 2RD* Nottingham (0115) 951 5886

STOCKBRIDGE, Alan Carmichael. b 33. MBE89. Keble Coll Ox BA55 MA62. Wycliffe Hall Ox 66. **d** 68 **p** 69. CF 68-78 and 82-92; Chapl Reading Sch 78-82; R Harrietsham w Ulcombe *Cant* from 92. *The Rectory, Church Road, Harrietsham, Maidstone, Kent ME17 1AP* Maidstone (01622) 859466

STOCKBRIDGE, Nelson William. b 35. Trin Th Coll Auckland 61. **d** 84 **p** 85. New Zealand 85-86; C Shildon w Eldon *Dur* 87; C Norton St Mary 87-88; C Cottingham *York* 88-91; V Aldbrough, Mappleton w Goxhill and Withernwick from 91. *The Vicarage, Carlton Drive, Aldbrough, Hull HU11 4SF* Hornsea (01964) 527364

STOCKER, David William George. b 37. Bris Univ BA58 CertEd. Qu Coll Birm 59. **d** 60 **p** 61. C Sparkhill St Jo *Birm* 60-64; C Keighley *Bradf* 64-66; V Grenoside *Sheff* 66-83; V Sandbach *Ches* from 83. *The Vicarage, 15 Offley Road, Sandbach, Cheshire CW11 9AY* Crewe (01270) 762379

STOCKER, Rachael Ann. *See* KNAPP, Mrs Rachael Ann

STOCKLEY, Mrs Alexandra Madeleine Reuss. b 43. Cranmer Hall Dur 80 Carl Dioc Tr Inst. **dss** 84 **d** 87 **p** 94. Upperby St Jo *Carl* 84-87; Par Dn 87-89; D-in-c Grayrigg, Old Hutton and New Hutton 90-94; P-in-c from 94. *The Vicarage, Grayrigg, Kendal, Cumbria LA8 9BU* Grayrigg (01539) 824272

STOCKLEY, Michael Ian. b 41. Lon Coll of Div 66. **d** 69 **p** 70. C St Helens St Mark *Liv* 69-74; C Fazakerley Em 74; TV 74-82; V Ince Ch Ch 82-92; V Birkdale St Pet from 92. *St Peter's Vicarage, 2 St Peter's Road, Southport, Merseyside PR8 4BY* Southport (01704) 68448

STOCKLEY, Roland. b 23. St Jo Coll Dur BA47 DipTh49. **d** 49 **p** 50. R Pedmore *Worc* 68-88; rtd 88. *64 Hyperion Road, Stourbridge, W Midlands DY7 6SB* Stourbridge (01384) 393463

STOCKPORT, Suffragan Bishop of. *See* TURNER, Rt Rev Geoffrey Martin

STOCKS, John Cedric Hawkesworth. b 13. Em Coll Cam BA37 MA40. Westcott Ho Cam 39. **d** 40 **p** 41. V Sheriff Hutton *York* 65-80; rtd 80. *8 Dale Close, Hampsthwaite, Harrogate, N Yorkshire HG3 2EQ* Harrogate (01423) 770834

STOCKTON, Dr Ian George. b 49. Selw Coll Cam BA72 MA76 Hull Univ PhD90. St Jo Coll Nottm CertEd74. **d** 75 **p** 76. C Chell *Lich* 75-78; C Trentham 78-80; R Dalbeattie *Glas* 80-84; P-in-c Scotton w Northorpe *Linc* 84-88; Asst Local Min Officer 84-88; Local Min Officer from 88. *105 Nettleham Road, Lincoln LN2 1RU* Lincoln (01522) 524428 or 542121

STOCKTON, Wilfred. b 32. Roch Th Coll 63. **d** 65 **p** 66. C Shirebrook *Derby* 65-67; C Boulton 67-69; V Ault Hucknall 69-73; R Pinxton 73-83; P-in-c Riddings 83-85; P-in-c Ironville 83-85; V Ladybrook *S'well* from 85. *St Mary's Vicarage, Bancroft Lane, Mansfield, Notts NG18 5LZ* Mansfield (01623) 21709

STOCKWELL, John Nicholas. b 49. Trin Coll Bris 80. **d** 82 **p** 83. C Flixton St Jo *Man* 82-86; V Accrington Ch Ch *Blackb* 86-90; R Chulmleigh *Ex* 90-93; R Chawleigh w Cheldon 90-93; R Wembworthy w Eggesford 90-93; P-in-c Burwash Weald *Chich* from 93. *The Vicarage, Burwash Common, Etchingham, E Sussex TN17 7NA* Burwash (01435) 883287

STOKE-ON-TRENT, Archdeacon of. *See* EDE, Ven Dennis

STOKER, Andrew. b 64. Coll of Ripon & York St Jo BA86. Coll of Resurr Mirfield 87. **d** 90 **p** 91. C Horton *Newc* 90-92; C Clifford *York* from 92. *8 Lea Croft, Clifford, Wetherby, W Yorkshire LS23 6EY* Wetherby (01937) 541173

STOKER, Howard Charles. b 62. Linc Th Coll BTh93. **d** 93 **p** 94. C Hessle *York* from 93. *60 Beverley Road, Hessle, N Humberside HU13 9BL* Hull (01482) 648349

STOKER, Mrs Joanna Mary (Jo). b 57. Leic Univ BA79 Nottm Univ BCombStuds83. Linc Th Coll 80. **dss** 83 **d** 87 **p** 94. Greenford H Cross *Lon* 83-87; Par Dn 87-89; Par Dn Farnham Royal w Hedgerley *Ox* 89-92; Par Dn Seer Green and Jordans 92-94; D-in-c 94; P-in-c from 94. *The Vicarage, 43 Long Grove, Seer Green, Beaconsfield, Bucks HP9 2YN* Beaconsfield (01494) 675013

STOKES, Canon Albert Edward. b 21. TCD BA43 MA46 BD46. CITC 43. **d** 46 **p** 47. Lect Ch of Ireland Coll of Educn Dub 49-79; I Powerscourt w Kilbride and Annacrevy *D & G* 56-69; Ch Ch Cathl Dub 70-86; rtd 86. *Cotehele, The Riverwalk, Ashford, Wicklow, Irish Republic* Wicklow (404) 40360

STOKES, Canon Andrew John. b 38. G&C Coll Cam BA60 MA64. Ripon Hall Ox 60. **d** 62 **p** 63. C Northn All SS w St Kath *Pet* 62-65; C Endcliffe *Sheff* 65-68; Ind Missr 65-68; Sen Ind Chapl 69-74; P-in-c Bridport *Sarum* 75-79; TR Bridport 79-80; V Holbeach Marsh *Linc* 82-88; Bp's Dom Chapl from 88; Can Res and Prec Linc Cathl from 92. *The Precentory, 16 Minster Yard, Lincoln LN2 1PX* Lincoln (01522) 523644

STOKES, Donald Roy (Don). b 30. K Coll Lon BD79 AKC79. **d** 80 **p** 81. C St Geo-in-the-East w St Paul *Lon* 80-84; Ind Chapl 84-95; rtd 95. *12 The Orchard, London N21 2DH* 0181-360 1205

STOKES, George Smithson Garbutt. b 13. Leeds Univ BA35. Coll of Resurr Mirfield 35. **d** 37 **p** 38. V Amport, Grateley and Quarley *Win* 69-74; V Sonning *Ox* 74-85; rtd 85; Perm to Offic *Ox* from 85. *Myrtle Cottage, Sheep Street, Charlbury, Chipping Norton, Oxon OX7 3RR* Charlbury (01608) 811207

STOKES, Godfrey Julian Fenwick. b 04. SS Coll Cam BA26 MA31. Westcott Ho Cam 29. **d** 30 **p** 31. C Staveley *Derby* 30-34 and 40-42; India 34-40; OSB from 42; Lic to Offic *Ox* from 42; Abbot Nashdom Abbey 84-88; Elmore Abbey from 87. *Elmore Abbey, Church Lane, Speen, Newbury, Berks RG13 1SA* Newbury (01635) 33080

STOKES, Leonard Peter Norton. b 21. Jes Coll Cam BA43 MA47. Westcott Ho Cam 44. **d** 45 **p** 46. Chapl Newton Abbot Hosp 59-86; Chapl Forde Park Sch 59-86; R Wolborough w Newton Abbot *Ex* 59-86; rtd 86. *67 Conway Road, Paignton, Devon TQ4 5LH* Paignton (01803) 529764

STOKES, Miss Mary Patricia. b 39. St Hilda's Coll Ox BA62 MA66 Lanc Univ MA80 Bris Univ CertEd63. E Midl Min Tr Course 78. **d** 87 **p** 94. Par Dn Pheasey *Lich* 87-93; C Walton-on-Thames *Guildf* from 93. *50 Misty's Field, Walton-on-Thames, Surrey KT12 2BG* Walton-on-Thames (01932) 248945

STOKES, Michael John. b 34. Lich Th Coll 63. **d** 65 **p** 66. C Worplesdon *Guildf* 65-68; Chapl RAF 68-84; Asst Chapl-in-Chief RAF 84-89; QHC 88-95; V Chesterton w Middleton Stoney and Wendlebury *Ox* 89-95; RD Bicester and Islip 92-95; Cyprus from 95. *PO Box 171, Girne, Mersin, Turkey* Kyrenia (357-8) 54329

STOKES, Peter. b 31. Qu Coll Birm 68. **d** 69 **p** 70. C Norton *St Alb* 69-77; V Harlington 77-85; P-in-c Chalgrave 80-85; V Luton St Andr 85-94; Asst RD Luton 89-94; rtd 94. *Chinook, 27 Croft Road, Ipplepen, Newton Abbot, Devon TQ12 5ST* Ipplepen (01803) 813664

STOKES, Canon Richard Spencer. b 29. TCD 66. **d** 68 **p** 69. C Lisburn Ch Ch Cathl *Conn* 68-71; C Dub St Geo and St Thos *D & G* 71-75; C Dub Rathfarnham 75-79; I Blessington w Kilbride, Ballymore Eustace etc 79-94; RD Ballymore and Salmon Leap 87-94; Can Ch Ch Cathl Dub 92-94; rtd 94. *Camlagh, Church Road, Greystones, Co Wicklow, Irish Republic* Dublin (1) 287-4147

STOKES, Roger Sidney. b 47. Clare Coll Cam BA68 MA72. Sarum & Wells Th Coll 69. **d** 72 **p** 73. C Keighley *Bradf* 72-74; C Bolton St Jas w St Chrys 74-78; V Harmyn w *Wakef* 78-85; Dep Chapl HM Pris Wakef 85-87; Chapl HM Pris Full Sutton 87-89; Perm to Offic *Wakef* from 92. *36 Newlands Drive, Stanley, Wakefield, W Yorkshire WF3 4DU* Wakefield (01924) 829918

STOKES, Simon Colin. b 62. Nene Coll Northampton BSc83. Ridley Hall Cam CTM92. **d** 92 **p** 93. C New Catton Ch Ch *Nor* from 92. *171 Beaconsfield Road, Norwich NR3 4AB* Norwich (01603) 621300 Fax as telephone

STOKES, Terence Harold. b 46. Man Univ DSPT84 Open Univ BA89. Sarum & Wells Th Coll 71. **d** 73 **p** 74. C Blakenall Heath *Lich* 73-75; C Walsall Wood 75-78; C Northn St Alb *Pet* 78-81; TV Swinton St Pet *Man* 81-85; V Daisy Hill 85-92. *8 Westbury Close, Westhoughton, Bolton BL5 3UL* Westhoughton (01942) 819057

STOKES, Terence Ronald. b 35. Linc Th Coll. **d** 69 **p** 70. C Bramley *Ripon* 69-72; C Osbournby w Scott Willoughby *Linc* 72-74; C Hykeham 74-77; V Birchwood 77-94; P-in-c Scopwick Gp from 94. *The Vicarage, Scopwick, Lincoln LN4 3NT* Metheringham (01526) 321047

STOKES, Preb Terence Walter (Terry). b 34. Bps' Coll Cheshunt 62. **d** 64 **p** 65. C Wanstead St Mary *Chelmsf* 64-67; C St Alb Abbey *St Alb* 67-70; Asst Dir RE *B & W* 70-75; Youth Chapl 70-75; P-in-c Yeovil 75-77; TV 77-82; R Wellington and Distr from 82; RD Tone from 89; Preb Wells Cathl from 90. *The Rectory, 72 High Street, Wellington, Somerset TA21 8RF* Wellington (01823) 662248

STOKOE, Rodney James Robert. b 20. Dur Univ BSc46 BA48 DipTh49. Crozer Th Sem Penn ThM67 Atlantic Sch of Th Halifax (NS) Hon DD87. **d** 49 **p** 50. C W Hartlepool St Paul *Dur* 49-53; R Edin Ch Ch *Edin* 53-57; P-in-c Bishopwearmouth St Gabr *Dur* 57-60; Canada from 60; Prof Div K Coll NS 60-71; Prof Past Th Atlantic Sch Th NS 71-85. *403 Prince Street, Ste 206, Truro, Nova Scotia, Canada, B2N 1E6* Halifax (902) 895-0047

STONE, Albert John. b 44. Loughb Univ BTech67 BSc. Sarum & Wells Th Coll 83. **d** 85 **p** 86. C Plymstock *Ex* 85-88; P-in-c Whitestone 88-92; P-in-c Oldridge 88-92; P-in-c Holcombe Burnell 88-92; P-in-c Tedburn St Mary 92; R Tedburn St Mary, Whitestone, Oldridge etc 93-94; P-in-c Yarcombe w Membury and Upottery 94; P-in-c Cotleigh 94; V Yarcombe, Membury, Upottery and Cotleigh from 95. *The Vicarage, Yarcombe, Honiton, Devon EX14 9BD* Upottery (01404) 86561

STONE, Andrew Francis. b 43. AKC65. **d** 66 **p** 67. C Walthamstow St Mich *Chelmsf* 66-67; C Ealing St Barn *Lon* 67-70; C E Grinstead St Mary *Chich* 70-74; C-in-c Hydneye CD 74-81; R Denton w S Heighton and Tarring Neville 81-93; V Eastbourne St Andr from 93. *St Andrew's Vicarage, 425 Seaside, Eastbourne, E Sussex BN22 7RT* Eastbourne (01323) 723739

STONE, Christopher John. b 49. Lanc Univ MA89 Keele Univ MA92. Lambeth STh84 Linc Th Coll 78. **d** 81 **p** 82. C Bromley St Mark *Roch* 81-84; R Burgh-by-Sands and Kirkbampton w Kirkandrews etc *Carl* 84-89; Chapl N Staffs R Infirmary Stoke-on-Trent 89-93; Co-ord Staff Support Services N Staffs Hosp from 93. *4 Brackenberry, Newcastle, Staffs ST5 9PS* Newcastle-under-Lyme (01782) 625134

STONE, Dr David Adrian. b 56. Or Coll Ox BA78 MA83 BM BCh83. Wycliffe Hall Ox 85. **d** 88 **p** 89. C Holborn St Geo w H Trin and St Bart *Lon* 88-91; C S Kensington St Jude 91-93; V from 93. *St Jude's Vicarage, 20 Collingham Road, London SW5 0LX* 0171-373 1693 or 370 1360 Fax 373 1693

STONE, Ernest Arthur. b 09. VRD60. AKC34 Open Univ BA81 MPhil91. **d** 34 **p** 35. V Bexhill St Aug *Chich* 54-74; Dioc RE Adv 54-80; rtd 74; Lic to Offic *Chich* 80-86 and from 89; RD Worthing 86-89. *56 Manor Road, Worthing, W Sussex BN11 4SQ* Worthing (01903) 235120

STONE, Godfrey Owen. b 49. Ex Coll Ox BA71 MA75 W Midl Coll of Educn PGCE72. Wycliffe Hall Ox BA78. **d** 81 **p** 82. C Rushden w Newton Bromswold *Pet* 81-87; Dir Past Studies Wycliffe Hall Ox 87-92; TR Bucknall and Bagnall *Lich* from 92. *The Rectory, Werrington Road, Bucknall, Stoke-on-Trent ST2 9AQ* Stoke-on-Trent (01782) 214455

STONE, Jeffrey Peter. b 34. Nottm Univ TCert72 BEd73. Lich Th Coll 58. **d** 61 **p** 62. C Newark St Mary *S'well* 61-65; C Sutton in Ashfield St Mich 65-69; Robert Smyth Sch Market Harborough 72-89; Perm to Offic *Leic* 88-90; R Waltham on the Wolds, Stonesby, Saxby etc from 90. *The Rectory, Melton Road, Waltham on the Wolds, Melton Mowbray, Leics LE14 4AJ* Waltham-on-the-Wolds (01664) 78774

STONE, John Christopher. b 53. MSTSD74 MESB74 LGSM72 Newc Univ BA74 Birkb Coll Lon MA77. Oak Hill NSM Course 89. **d** 92 **p** 93. NSM Southfleet *Roch* from 92. *Clearbrook, 37 The Old Yews, New Barn, Longfield, Kent DA3 7JS* Longfield (01474) 707511 Fax 0171-323 5060

STONE, John Geoffrey Elliot. b 20. Ch Coll Cam BA41 MA45. Ridley Hall Cam 47. **d** 49 **p** 50. V Southwater *Chich* 59-70; V Thornham w Titchwell *Nor* 70-74; R Copdock w Washbrook and Belstead *St E* 74-77; P-in-c Therfield *St Alb* 77-82; P-in-c Kelshall 77-82; C Littlehampton St Jas *Chich* 82-85; C Littlehampton St Mary 82-85; C Wick 82-85; TV Littlehampton and Wick 86; rtd 86; C Compton, the Mardens, Stoughton and Racton *Chich* 86-92; Perm to Offic *Nor* from 92. *Stella Cottage, Shepherd's Pightle, Thornham, Hunstanton, Norfolk PE36 6NA* Thornham (0148526) 395

STONE, John Anthony. b 46. St Chad's Coll Dur BA68 DipTh69. **d** 69 **p** 70. C New Addington *Cant* 69-72; C Tewkesbury w Walton Cardiff *Glouc* 72-76; C-in-c Dedworth CD *Ox* 76-82; V Dedworth 82-86; TV Chipping Barnet w Arkley *St Alb* from 86. *St Stephen's Vicarage, 1 Spring Close, Bells Hill, Barnet, Herts EN5 2UR* 0181-449 7758

STONE, Michael Graham (Mike). b 33. FBCS. S Dios Minl Tr Scheme. **d** 83 **p** 84. NSM Chich St Paul and St Pet *Chich* from 83. *125 Cedar Drive, Chichester, W Sussex PO19 3EL* Chichester (01243) 784484

STONE, Michael John. b 33. Trin Hall Cam MA56 LLB57. E Anglian Minl Tr Course 78. **d** 80 **p** 81. NSM Whitton and Thurleston w Akenham *St E* 80-84; NSM Westerfield and Tuddenham St Martin w Witnesham from 84; Dioc Chr Stewardship Adv 93-95; from Dioc Voc Adv from 95. *13 Tower Street, Ipswich IP1 3BG, or 4 The Granaries, Tuddenham, Ipswich IP6 9BW* Ipswich (01473) 211028 or 785363 Fax 232407

STONE, Nigel John. b 57. Bedf Coll Lon BSc82 Lon Bible Coll MA95. St Jo Coll Nottm 82. **d** 85 **p** 86. C Battersea Park St Sav *S'wark* 85-87; C Battersea St Sav and St Geo w St Andr 87-89; P-in-c Brixton St Paul 89-92; V from 92. *St Paul's Vicarage, 73 Baytree Road, London SW2 5UA* 0171-274 6907

STONE, Noel Alfred William. b 33. St Jo Coll Morpeth 58. **d** 62 **p** 63. Australia 62-74; C The Quinton *Birm* 74-75; Hong Kong 75-78; New Zealand 78-85; P-in-c Witham Gp *Linc* 85; R 85-93; RD Beltisloe 90-93; rtd 93. *Allt & Bhruie, St Catherine's, Cairndow, Argyll PA25 8BA* Strachur (0136986) 628

STONE, Peter James. b 54. Leic Univ BA75 Qu Coll Cam BA77 MA81. Westcott Ho Cam 76. **d** 78 **p** 79. C Bradford-on-Avon *Sarum* 78-81; R Corsley 81-83; Chapl Dauntsey's Sch Devizes 83-88; V Studley *Sarum* 89-94; Chapl Cheltenham Coll from 94. *4 Waterfield Close, Cheltenham, Glos GL53 7NL* Cheltenham (01242) 230800

STONE, Philip William. b 58. Ridley Hall Cam 85. **d** 88 **p** 89. C Hackney Marsh *Lon* from 88. *105 Mayola Road, London E5 0RG* 0181-533 4034

STONE, Reginald Peter. b 32. Ex Coll Ox BA56 MA61 DipEd64. St Steph Ho Ox 56. **d** 58 **p** 59. Chapl and Hd of RE Abp Tenison's Gr Sch Lon 63-75; Highgate Sch Lon 75-92; Perm to Offic *Truro* from 65; Lic to Offic *S'wark* 67-75; Lic to

Offic *Lon* 75-92; rtd 92. *3 Trescobeas Road, Falmouth, Cornwall TR11 2JB* Falmouth (01326) 313156

STONE, Richard Anthony. b 46. Hatf Coll Dur BA68 Nottm Univ DipTh71. Linc Th Coll 70. **d** 73 **p** 74. C Marske in Cleveland *York* 73-78; TV Haxby w Wigginton 78-87; V Osbaldwick w Murton from 87. *The Vicarage, 80 Osbaldwick Lane, York YO1 3AX* York (01904) 416763

STONE, Rodney Cameron. b 32. Sarum Th Coll 67. **d** 69 **p** 70. C Milton *Portsm* 69-74; CF (TA) from 72; R Rowlands Castle *Portsm* 74-80; V Tividale *Lich* 80-81; C Weeke *Win* 81-88; V Win St Barn from 89. *St Barnabas' Vicarage, Fromond Road, Winchester, Hants SO22 6DY* Winchester (01962) 882728

STONE, Rodney Milton Robertson. b 25. Ely Th Coll 51. **d** 53 **p** 54. R Gunthorpe w Bale *Nor* 57-70; P-in-c Sharrington 62-70; R Tayport *St And* 70-90; R Newport-on-Tay 70-90; Can St Ninian's Cathl Perth 87-90; rtd 90; Lic to Offic *Newc* from 90. *12 Well Square, Tweedmouth, Berwick-upon-Tweed TD15 2AL* Berwick-upon-Tweed (01289) 307791

STONEBANKS, David Arthur. b 34. Louvain Univ Belgium MA70. Coll of Resurr Mirfield 64. **d** 66 **p** 67. C Burgess Hill St Jo *Chich* 66-68; Chapl City Univ *Lon* 70-73; Chapl Strasbourg w Stuttgart and Heidelberg *Eur* 73-80; Chapl Geneva 80-86; Chapl Zurich w St Gallen and Winterthur 86-89; R Horsted Keynes *Chich* from 89. *The Rectory, Horsted Keynes, Haywards Heath, W Sussex RH17 7ED* Dane Hill (01825) 790317

STONEHOUSE, Joseph Christopher. b 48. Chich Th Coll 68. **d** 71 **p** 72. C Beamish *Dur* 71-76; C Doncaster St Leon and St Jude *Sheff* 76-80; V Copmanthorpe *York* from 80. *The Vicarage, 17 Sutor Close, Copmanthorpe, York YO2 3TX* York (01904) 706280

STONES, John Graham. b 49. Southn Univ BSc72. SW Minl Tr Course 91. **d** 94. C Okehampton w Inwardleigh, Bratton Clovelly etc *Ex* from 94. *19 Fern Meadow, Okehampton, Devon EX20 1PB* Okehampton (01837) 54263

STONESTREET, George Malcolm. b 38. AKC61. **d** 62 **p** 63. C Leeds St Pet *Ripon* 62-64; C Far Headingley St Chad 64-67; V Askrigg w Stallingbusk 67-82; V Bramley 82-85; TR 85-94; V Eskdale, Irton, Muncaster and Waberthwaite *Carl* from 94. *Eskdale Vicarage, Boot, Holmrook, Cumbria CA19 1TF* Eskdale (01946) 723242 Fax 723142

STONEY, Ven Thomas Vesey. b 34. Or Coll Ox BA56 MA60. CITC 58. **d** 58 **p** 59. I Skerry w Rathcavan and Newtowncrommelin *Conn* 66-92; Adn Dalriada 85-92; rtd 93. *Ardagh Lodge, Carrowbeg, Westport, Co Mayo, Irish Republic* Westport (98) 41150

STOODLEY, Peter Bindon. b 47. Linc Th Coll 89. **d** 91 **p** 92. C Holbeck *Ripon* 91-94; P-in-c Osmondthorpe St Phil from 94. *St Philip's Vicarage, 68 Osmondthorpe Lane, Leeds LS9 9EF* Leeds (0113) 249 7371

STOPFORD, Eric. b 08. Tyndale Hall Bris 31. **d** 34 **p** 35. R Whitmore *Lich* 48-79; rtd 79. *Flat 7, Manor Court, Swan Road, Pewsey, Wilts SN9 5DW* Marlborough (01672) 64028

STOPPARD, Henry. b 16. Worc Ord Coll 60. **d** 61 **p** 62. V Blackwell *Derby* 63-83; rtd 83; Perm to Offic *Bris* from 83. *White Horse Cottage, 3 Church Hill, Olveston, Bristol BS12 3BX* Almondsbury (01454) 615108

STOREY, Mrs Elizabeth Mary. b 37. Cam Univ DipRS80 Man Univ BA84. Local Minl Tr Course 81. **dss** 84 **d** 87 **p** 94. Liv All So Springwood *Liv* 84-87; Par Dn 87-91; C St Helens St Helen 91-94; Par Dn Garston 94; Asst Chapl Liv Univ from 94; C Garston from 94. *24 Mentmore Road, Mossley Hill, Liverpool L18 4PU* 0151-724 2075

STOREY, Gerard Charles Alfred. b 57. GRSC80 Thames Poly BSc80 Lon Univ PhD84. Wycliffe Hall Ox 84. **d** 87 **p** 88. C Broadwater St Mary *Chich* 87-92; TV from 92; Chapl Northbrook Coll of Design and Tech 90-95. *28 Loxwood Avenue, Worthing, W Sussex BN14 7QY* Worthing (01903) 238288

STOREY, Michael. b 36. Chich Th Coll 73. **d** 75 **p** 76. C Illingworth *Wakef* 75-78; V Rastrick St Jo 78-87; V Crosland Moor from 87. *The Vicarage, Church Avenue, Crosland Moor, Huddersfield HD4 5DF* Huddersfield (01484) 422381

STOREY, Timothy (Tim). b 60. Trin Coll Bris DipHE94. **d** 94 **p** 95. C Bath Weston St Jo w Kelston *B & W* from 94. *3 Rosslyn Road, Bath BA1 3LQ* Bath (01225) 482757

STOREY, William Earl Cosbey. b 58. Kent Univ BA. CITC DipTh86. **d** 82 **p** 83. C Drumglass w Moygashel *Arm* 82-86; I Crinken *D & G* from 86. *Crinken Parsonage, Bray, Co Wicklow, Irish Republic* Dublin (1) 282-2048

STOREY, William Leslie Maurice. b 31. Oak Hill Th Coll 67. **d** 69 **p** 70. C Wembley St Jo *Lon* 69-71; C Ealing Dean St Jo 71-75; V W Derby St Luke *Liv* 75-80; V Hunts Cross 80-83; Hon C Brixton St Paul *S'wark* 83-86; P-in-c 87-88; P-in-c Brixton Hill St Sav 83-86; rtd 88. *124 Surbiton Hill Park, Surbiton, Surrey KT5 8EP* 0181-390 2821

STORR VENTER, Phillip. b 52. Called to the Bar (Gray's Inn) 74. S'wark Ord Course 90. **d** 93. NSM Bethnal Green St

Barn *Lon* from 93. *Bearsden, Tredegar Place, 109 Bow Road, London E3 2AN* 0181-981 6195 Fax as telephone

STORY, Victor Leonard. b 45. BSc. Ripon Coll Cuddesdon. **d** 81 **p** 82. C Evesham *Worc* 81-85; P-in-c Ilmington w Stretton on Fosse and Ditchford *Cov* 85-90; P-in-c Ilmington w Stretton-on-Fosse etc from 90. *The Rectory, Ilmington, Shipston-on-Stour, Warks CV36 4LB* Ilmington (01608) 682210

STOTE-BLANDY, Canon Gordon Blandy. b 12. G&C Coll Cam BA33 MA38. Westcott Ho Cam 33. **d** 35 **p** 36. C Epsom St Martin *Guildf* 35-38; New Zealand from 38; Hon Can St Paul's Cathl Wellington 65-78. *16 Wren Street, Waikanae, New Zealand* Waikanae (58) 34831

STOTER, David John. b 43. AKC66. **d** 67 **p** 68. C Reading St Giles *Ox* 67-71; C Luton Lewsey St Hugh *St Alb* 71-73; Chapl Westmr Hosp Lon 73-79; Convenor of Chapls Notts Distr HA from 79; Chapl Univ Hosp Nottm from 79; Chapl Nottm Gen Hosp from 79. *Queen's Medical Centre, Nottingham NG7 2HU* Nottingham (0115) 924 9924

STOTT, Antony. b 21. Bps' Coll Cheshunt 53. **d** 55 **p** 56. V Bratton *Sarum* 66-74; R Marnhull 74-81; P-in-c Broad Chalke and Bower Chalke 81; P-in-c Ebbesbourne Wake w Fifield Bavant and Alvediston 81; P-in-c Berwick St John 81; V Chalke Valley W 81-87; rtd 87; Perm to Offic *Ex* from 87. *11 Luscombe Close, Ivybridge, Devon PL21 9TT* Plymouth (01752) 896142

STOTT, Christopher John (Chris). b 45. Lon Univ BD68. Tyndale Hall Bris. **d** 69 **p** 70. C Croydon Ch Ch Broad Green *Cant* 69-72; Ethiopia 73-76; Area Sec (SW) BCMS 76-78; Tanzania 78-85; R Harwell w Chilton *Ox* from 85; RD Wallingford from 91. *The Rectory, Harwell, Didcot, Oxon OX11 0EW* Abingdon (01235) 835365

STOTT, Eric. b 36. ALCD62. **d** 62 **p** 63. C Penn Fields *Lich* 62-65; C Normanton *Derby* 65-71; R Lower Broughton St Clem w St Matthias *Man* 71-79; V Chadderton Em from 79. *Emmanuel Vicarage, 15 Chestnut Street, Chadderton, Oldham OL9 8HB* 0161-681 1310

STOTT, Frederick. b 23. Bris Univ DipFE75 Univ of Wales (Cardiff) CQSW71. Sarum & Wells Th Coll 83. **d** 85 **p** 86. Hon C Sholing *Win* 85-90; Perm to Offic from 90; Perm to Offic *Portsm* from 89. *35 Broadwater Road, Southampton SO2 2DW* Southampton (01703) 557193

STOTT, Dr John Robert Walmsley. b 21. Trin Coll Cam BA45 MA50. Lambeth DD83 Ridley Hall Cam 44. **d** 45 **p** 46. R St Marylebone All So w SS Pet and Jo *Lon* 50-75; Hon C 75-88; Hon C Langham Place All So from 88; Chapl to The Queen 59-91; Extra Chapl to The Queen from 91; Dir Lon Inst of Contemporary Christianity 82-86; Pres from 86; rtd 91. *12 Weymouth Street, London W1N 3FB* 0171-580 1867

STOTT, Miss Teresa (Terrie). b 57. Linc Th Coll CMinlStuds94. **d** 94 **p** 95. C Lee-on-the-Solent *Portsm* from 94. *85 Seymour Road, Lee-on-the-Solent, Hants PO13 9EQ* Lee-on-the-Solent (01705) 552108

STOTT, Wilfrid. b 04. Lon Univ BA26 BD27 Linc Coll Ox BLitt62 DPhil66. Lon Coll of Div 26. **d** 27 **p** 28. Kenya 66-71; rtd 71; P-in-c Croxton and Eltisley *Ely* 71-85. *12 Westfield, Harwell, Didcot, Oxon OX11 0LG* Didcot (01235) 832791

STOW, John Mark. b 51. Selw Coll Cam BA73 MA77. Linc Th Coll 76. **d** 78 **p** 79. C Harpenden St Jo *St Alb* 78-82; TV Beaminster Area *Sarum* 82-87; P-in-c Hawkchurch 87-90; P-in-c Marshwood Vale 87-88; TR Marshwood Vale TM 88-91; Past Co-ord Millfield Jun Sch from 93. *Chestnut House, Edgarley Hall, Glastonbury, Somerset BA6 8LL* Glastonbury (01458) 832245

STOW, Peter John. b 50. Oak Hill Th Coll. **d** 89 **p** 90. C Forest Gate St Mark *Chelmsf* 89-94; V from 94. *St Mark's Vicarage, Tylney Road, London E7 0LS* 0181-555 2988

STOW, Archdeacon of. See WELLS, Ven Roderick John

STOWE, Brian. b 32. Trin Coll Cam BA55 BA56 MA59. Ridley Hall Cam 55. **d** 57 **p** 58. Chapl R Masonic Sch Bushey 59-70; Tutor Rickmansworth Sch Herts 70-71; Chapl Alleyn's Foundn Dulwich 71-75; Hon C Dulwich St Barn *S'wark* 71-75; Chapl Ellerslie Sch Malvern 75-92; Chapl Malvern Coll Worcs 92-93; TV Malvern Link w Cowleigh *Worc* 93-94; rtd 95. *31 Park View, Grange Road, Malvern, Worcs WR14 3HG* Malvern (01684) 568134

STOWE, Nigel James. b 36. Bris Univ BSc57. Clifton Th Coll 59. **d** 61 **p** 62. C Ware Ch Ch *St Alb* 61-64; C Reigate St Mary *S'wark* 64-67; V Islington St Jude Mildmay Park *Lon* 67-75; V Penn Street *Ox* from 75. *The Vicarage, Penn Street, Amersham, Bucks HP7 0PX* High Wycombe (01494) 712194

STOWE, Canon Rachel Lilian. b 33. Qu Coll Birm 79. **dss** 83 **d** 87 **p** 94. Hon Deac w Yelden, Melchbourne and Shelton *St Alb* 82-87; Pertenhall w Swineshead 82-87; Bp's Officer for NSM and Asst Dir of Ords 87-93; NSM The Stodden Churches from 87; Hon Can St Alb from 92; rtd 93. *Kirkhill, 63 Wood End Lane, Pertenhall, Bedford MK44 2AS* Huntingdon (01480) 860514 or 0860-618600 Fax as telephone

STRACHAN, Donald Philip Michael. b 37. St D Coll Lamp 60. **d** 62 **p** 63. C Aber St Mary *Ab* 62-64; P-in-c Aber St Paul 64-66; Chapl St Andr Cathl 65-68; Itinerant Priest *Mor* 68-73; R Coatbridge *Glas* 73-85; Chapl HM Pris Glas (Barlinnie) 84-87; Dioc Supernumerary *Glas* from 85. *50 Monkland View Crescent, Bargeddie, Baillieston, Glasgow G69 7RX* 0141-771 4122

✠**STRADLING, Rt Rev Leslie Edward.** b 08. Qu Coll Ox BA30 MA31 Bp's Univ Lennoxville Hon DCL68. Wycliffe Hall Ox 32. **d** 33 **p** 34 **c** 45. C Stoke Newington St Andr *Lon* 33-38; V Camberwell St Luke *S'wark* 38-43; Chapl Camberwell Ho 38-43; V Wandsworth St Anne 43-45; S Africa from 45; Bp Masasi 45-52; Bp SW Tang 52-61; Bp Johannesburg 61-74; rtd 74. *Braehead House, Auburn Road, Kenilworth, 7700 South Africa* Parow (21) 761-6251

STRAFFORD, Nigel Thomas Bevan. b 53. Univ of Wales (Lamp) BA80. Sarum & Wells Th Coll 80. **d** 82 **p** 94. C Kidderminster St Mary *Worc* 82; C Kidderminster St Mary and All SS etc 82-83; Hon C Stockton St Mark *Dur* 84-86; NSM Longwood *Wakef* 86-94; V Athersley from 94. *The Vicarage, 27 Laithes Lane, Athersley, Barnsley, S Yorkshire S71 3AF* Barnsley (01226) 245361

STRAIN, Christopher Malcolm (Chris). b 56. MLawSoc Southn Univ LLB77. Wycliffe Hall Ox 83. **d** 86 **p** 87. C Werrington *Pet* 86-89; C Broadwater St Mary *Chich* 89-94; TV Hampreston *Sarum* from 94. *The Vicarage, 19 Canford Bottom, Wimborne, Dorset BH21 2HA* Wimborne (01202) 884796

STRANACK, Canon David Arthur Claude. b 43. Chich Th Coll 65. **d** 68 **p** 69. C Forest Gate St Edm *Chelmsf* 68-69; C Colchester St Jas, All SS, St Nic and St Runwald 69-74; V Brentwood St Geo 74-82; V Nayland w Wiston *St E* from 82; Hon Can St E Cathl from 94. *The Vicarage, Bear Street, Nayland, Colchester CO6 4LA* Nayland (01206) 262316

STRANACK, Dr Fay Rosemary. b 30. Lon Univ BSc55 PhD60. Westcott Ho Cam 88. **d** 89 **p** 94. NSM Denmead *Portsm* from 89. *35 Yew Tree Gardens, Denmead, Waterlooville, Hants PO7 6LH* Portsmouth (01705) 256785

STRANACK, Richard Nevill. b 40. Leeds Univ BA63. Coll of Resurr Mirfield 63. **d** 65 **p** 66. C Bush Hill Park St Mark *Lon* 65-68; C Brighton St Martin *Chich* 68-72; P-in-c Toftrees w Shereford *Nor* 72-74; V 74-81; P-in-c Pensthorpe 72-74; R 74-81; V Hempton and Pudding Norton 72-81; RD Burnham and Walsingham 78-81; V Par *Truro* 81-94; P-in-c St Blazey 87-91; Hon Chapl Miss to Seamen from 81; V Stratton and Launcells *Truro* from 94. *The Vicarage, Diddies Road, Stratton, Bude, Cornwall EX23 9DW* Bude (01288) 352254

STRANEX, Douglas. b 07. **d** 40 **p** 41. I Stoneyford *Conn* 53-78; rtd 78. *25 Bann View Heights, Banbridge, Co Down BT32 4LZ* Banbridge (018206) 23967

STRANGE, Alan Michael. b 57. Pemb Coll Ox BA79 MA83. Wycliffe Hall Ox 81. **d** 84 **p** 85. C York St Paul *York* 84-87; Assoc Chapl Brussels Cathl *Eur* 87-95; Assoc Chapl Brussels w Charleroi 87-95; P-in-c Heigham H Trin *Nor* from 95. *The Rectory, Essex Street, Norwich NR2 2BL* Norwich (01603) 621120

STRANGE, Bryan. b 26. Sarum & Wells Th Coll 73. **d** 75 **p** 76. C King's Worthy *Win* 75-78; C Wilton *B & W* 78-80; V Kewstoke w Wick St Lawrence 80-89; rtd 89; Hon C Tiverton St Andr *Ex* from 90. *29 Bluebell Avenue, Tiverton, Devon EX16 6SX*

STRANGE, Edward Stanley. b 24. Ab Dioc Tr Course 82 Moray Ord Course 88. **d** 90 **p** 91. Hon C Inverness St Jo *Mor* from 90. *1 Burn Brae Crescent, Westhill, Inverness IV1 2HD* Inverness (01463) 792017

STRANGE, Malcolm. b 58. Sarum & Wells Th Coll 82. **d** 85 **p** 86. C Seaton Hirst *Newc* 85-88; C Ridgeway *Sarum* 88-89; TV 89-91; TV Newbury *Ox* from 91. *St George's Vicarage, 206 Andover Road, Newbury, Berks RG14 6NU* Newbury (01635) 582911

STRANGE, Mark Jeremy. b 61. Aber Univ LTh82. Linc Th Coll 87. **d** 89 **p** 90. C Worc St Barn w Ch Ch *Worc* 89-92; V Worc St Wulstan from 92. *St Wulstan's Vicarage, Cranham Drive, Warndon, Worcester WR4 9PA* Worcester (01905) 57806

STRANGE, Mrs Mary McKellar. b 53. FCA75 ATII77. St Jo Coll Nottm BTh93 Westcott Ho Cam 93. **d** 94 **p** 95. C Weston Favell *Pet* from 94. *66 Weston Avenue, Weston Fabell, Northampton NN3 3JQ* Northampton (01604) 415719

STRANGE, Canon Peter Robert. b 48. Univ Coll Lon BA69 Ex Coll Ox BA71 MA76. Cuddesdon Coll 71. **d** 72 **p** 73. C Denton *Newc* 72-74; C Newc St Jo 74-79; Chapl for Arts and Recreation 79-90; R Wallsend St Pet 79-86; Can Res Newc Cathl from 86; Angl Adv Tyne Tees TV from 90. *55 Queen's Terrace, Jesmond, Newcastle upon Tyne NE2 2PL* 0191-281 0181

STRANGE, Preb Robert Lewis. b 45. Sarum & Wells Th Coll 72. **d** 74 **p** 75. C Walthamstow St Barn and St Jas *Gt Chelmsf* 74-77; C Wickford 77-80; P-in-c Treverbyn *Truro* 80-83; V 83-86; Asst Stewardship Adv from 82; V Newlyn St Pet from 86; Miss to Seamen from 86; Preb St Endellion *Truro* from 95. *St Peter's Vicarage, Newlyn, Penzance, Cornwall TR18 5HT* Penzance (01736) 62678

STRANGE, Dr William Anthony. b 53. Qu Coll Cam BA76 MA80 Win Coll CertEd77 Ox Univ DPhil89. Wycliffe Hall Ox. **d** 82 **p** 83. Tutor Wycliffe Hall Ox 82-87; Lic to Offic *Ox* 82-87; C Abth *St D* 87; TV 87-91; V Llandeilo and Taliaris from 91. *The Vicarage, 10 Carmarthen Road, Llandeilo, Dyfed SA19 6RS* Llandeilo (01558) 822421

STRANGEWAYS, Canon David Inderwick. b 12. DSO43 OBE44. Trin Hall Cam BA33 MA36. Wells Th Coll 58. **d** 59 **p** 60. V Bradford-on-Avon Ch Ch *Sarum* 65-73; Chapl Stockholm *Eur* 73-77; Chan Malta Cathl 77-81; rtd 81; Perm to Offic *St E* from 81; Perm to Offic *Nor* from 81. *10 Dowes Hill Close, Beccles, Suffolk NR34 9XL* Beccles (01502) 716086

STRANRAER-MULL, Very Rev Gerald Hugh. b 42. AKC69. St Aug Coll Cant 69. **d** 70 **p** 71. C Hexham *Newc* 70-72; C Corbridge w Halton 72; R Cruden Bay *Ab* from 72; R Ellon from 72; Can St Andr Cathl from 81; Dean Ab from 88. *The Rectory, Ellon, Aberdeenshire AB41 9NP* Ellon (01358) 720366

STRAPPS, Canon Robert David. b 28. St Edm Hall Ox BA52 MA56. Wycliffe Hall Ox 52. **d** 54 **p** 55. V Sandal St Helen *Wakef* 60-94; RD Chevet 81-93; Hon Can Wakef Cathl 92-94; rtd 94. *Brookside, Hill Road, Kemerton, Tewkesbury, Glos GL20 7JN* Overbury (01386) 725515

STRASZAK, Edmund Norman. b 57. Coll of Resurr Mirfield 88. **d** 90 **p** 91. C Adlington *Blackb* 90-93; C Harrogate St Wilfrid and St Luke *Ripon* 93-95; V Chorley All SS *Blackb* from 95. *All Saints' Vicarage, Moor Road, Chorley, Lancs PR7 2LR* Chorley (01257) 265665

STRATFORD, Mrs Anne Barbara. Southn Univ CertEd58. W Midl Minl Tr Course. **d** 91 **p** 94. Asst Dio Bd of Soc Resp (Family Care) *Lich* from 85; NSM Kinnerley w Melverley and Knockin w Maesbrook 91-95; Chapl Robert Jones and Agnes Hunt Orthopaedic Hosp from 95; NSM Oswestry *Lich* from 95. *Pentre Cleddar, Lower Hengoed, Oswestry, Shropshire SY10 7AB* Oswestry (01691) 655469

STRATFORD, Ven Ralph Montgomery. b 30. TCD BA53 MA67. CITC 53. **d** 54 **p** 54. C Droz Curate *C & O* 54-55; C Waterford Ch Ch 55-56; I Ballisodare w Collooney and Emlaghfad *T, K & A* from 56; RD Straid 61-66 and from 88; Adn Killala and Achonry from 69; Preb Kilmactalway St Patr Cathl Dub from 85. *The Rectory, Ballysadare, Co Sligo, Irish Republic* Sligo (71) 67260

STRATFORD, Terence Stephen (Terry). b 45. Chich Th Coll 67. **d** 69 **p** 70. C Old Shoreham *Chich* 69-73; C New Shoreham 69-73; C Uckfield 73-75; C Lt Horsted 73-75; C Isfield 73-75; P-in-c Waldron 76-80; R 80-82; V Blacklands Hastings Ch Ch and St Andr 82-89; P-in-c Ovingdean from 89; Dioc Ecum Officer from 89. *St Wulfran's Rectory, 43 Ainsworth Avenue, Brighton BN2 7BQ* Brighton (01273) 303633

STRATFORD, Timothy Richard (Tim). b 61. York Univ BSc82. Wycliffe Hall Ox 83. **d** 86 **p** 87. C Mossley Hill St Matt and St Jas *Liv* 86-89; C St Helens St Helen 89-91; Bp's Dom Chapl 91-94; V W Derby Gd Shep from 94. *The Vicarage, 136 Carr Lane East, Liverpool L11 4SL* 0151-546 7527

STRATFORD, William Anthony. b 23. Roch Th Coll 64. **d** 66 **p** 67. C Doncaster St Geo *Sheff* 68-71; V Arksey 71-75; R Armthorpe 75-80; R Harthill 80-82; R Harthill and Thorpe Salvin 82-85; rtd 85; Perm to Offic *Sheff* from 85. *Dulverton Hall, St Martin's Square, Scarborough, N Yorkshire YO11 2DQ* Scarborough (01723) 366550

STRATTA, Antony Charles (Tony). b 36. ACIS. S'wark Ord Course 82. **d** 85 **p** 86. C Southborough St Pet w Ch Ch and St Matt *Roch* 85-88; R Gt Mongeham w Ripple and Sutton by Dover *Cant* from 88. *The Rectory, Northbourne Road, Great Mongeham, Deal, Kent CT14 0HB* Deal (01304) 360170

STRATTON, Ven Basil. b 06. Hatf Coll Dur BA29 MA32. **d** 30 **p** 31. Adn Stafford *Lich* 59-74; Can Res and Treas Lich Cathl 60-74; Chapl to The Queen 65-76; rtd 74. *The Ridge, Pettridge Lane, Mere, Warminster, Wilts BA12 6DG* Mere (01747) 860235

STRATTON, Geoffrey Frederick. b 25. ARICS52. Oak Hill Th Coll 78. **d** 81 **p** 82. NSM Chipping Barnet w Arkley *St Alb* 81-85; TV 85-90; rtd 90; Perm to Offic *Linc* from 90. *Witsend, 8 Thornton Crescent, Horncastle, Lincs LN9 6JP* Horncastle (01507) 525508

STRATTON, Henry William. b 39. Bris Univ CertEd74 BEd75. Glouc Sch of Min 80. **d** 83 **p** 84. NSM Cainscross w Selsley *Glouc* 83-87; C Odd Rode *Ches* 87-92; V Runcorn H Trin from 92. *Holy Trinity Vicarage, Grange Park Avenue, Runcorn, Cheshire WA7 5UT* Runcorn (01928) 572299

STRATTON, Ian Herbert Shearing. b 27. St Jo Coll Dur BA52 DipTh53 MA78. **d** 53 **p** 54. P-in-c Chettle *Sarum* 69-72; C

Salisbury St Fran 72-80; C Harnham 81-87; rtd 88. *20 Bradley Road, Warminster, Wilts BA12 8BP* Warminster (01985) 212785

STRATTON, John Jefferies. b 27. Bps' Coll Cheshunt 53. **d** 55 **p** 56. R Cottered w Broadfield and Throcking *St Alb* 65-82; RD Buntingford 75-82; V S Mimms St Mary and Potters Bar *Lon* 82-84; V Potters Bar *St Alb* 85-94; NSM Flamstead from 94; rtd 94. *The Vicarage, 50 Trowley Hill Road, Flamstead, St Albans, Herts AL3 8EE* Luton (0182) 840271

STRATTON, Canon Leslie Verdun. b 16. Edin Th Coll 36. **d** 39 **p** 40. P-in-c Dundee St Jo *Bre* 50-81; Syn Clerk 71-81; Can St Paul's Cathl Dundee 71-81; rtd 81; Hon Can St Paul's Cathl Dundee *Bre* from 81. *16 Argyle Street, Dundee DD4 7AL* Dundee (01382) 462413

STREATER, David Arthur. b 33. Oak Hill Th Coll 67. **d** 68 **p** 69. C Lindfield *Chich* 68-71; S Africa 71-86; R Kingham w Churchill, Daylesford and Sarsden *Ox* 86-91; Dir Ch Soc and Sec Ch Soc Trust from 91; Lic to Offic *St Alb* from 91. *Dean Wace House, 16 Rosslyn Road, Watford WD1 7EY* Watford (01923) 213370

STREATFEILD, Francis Richard Champion. b 22. Qu Coll Cam BA48 MA59. Cuddesdon Coll 48. **d** 50 **p** 51. India 53-70; V Sacriston *Dur* 70-79; Lic to Offic *Carl* 79-85; Area Sec (Dio Carl) USPG 79-85; C Carl St Aid and Ch Ch *Carl* 85-88; rtd 88; Perm to Offic *Carl* from 88. *Fenton Lane Head, How Mill, Carlisle CA4 9LD* Carlisle (01228) 70470

STREEK, Stanley James. b 11. Man Univ BD42. Wycliffe Hall Ox. **d** 42 **p** 43. V Holmebridge *Wakef* 51-76; rtd 76. *Bridgend, Laurieston, Castle Douglas, Kirkcudbrightshire DG7 2PW*

STREET, Anthony James. b 57. Trin Coll Bris DipHE81. **d** 85 **p** 87. SAMS from 85; Chile from 85. *Casilla 26-D, Temuco, Chile* Temuco (45) 251557

STREET, David Grover. b 24. St Aid Birkenhead 49. **d** 54 **p** 55. Warden Rugby Clubs Notting Hill 68-70; Chapl Milton Abbey Sch Dorset 70; Chapl St Lawr Coll Ramsgate 71; Community Cen Strabane Co Tyrone 73-74; Boys' Welfare Club Hartlepool 74-84; rtd 89. *80 Woodside, Barnard Castle, Co Durham DL12 8AP* Teesdale (01833) 37351

STREET, Peter Ernest. b 17. Oak Hill Th Coll 37. **d** 40 **p** 42. V Cheadle Hulme St Andr *Ches* 68-73; CPAS Evang 74-78; rtd 78; Perm to Offic *Nor* from 78. *49 Eckling Grange, Dereham, Norfolk NR20 3BB* Dereham (0162) 698896

STREET, Peter Jarman. b 29. K Coll Lon BD59 AKC59. **d** 59 **p** 60. St Pet Coll of Educn Birm 66-70; RE Adv Essex Co Coun 70-92; Hon C Gt Dunmow *Chelmsf* 71-85; Sen Insp RE and Humanities 74-92; R Gt w Lt Yeldham 85-92; RD Belchamp from 90; rtd 92. *18 Jubilee Court, Great Dunmow, Essex CM6 1DY* Great Dunmow (01371) 876811

STREET, Philip. b 47. Lon Univ BPharm68. NW Ord Course 75. **d** 78 **p** 79. C Heaton St Barn *Bradf* 78-81; C Evington *Leic* 82-84; P-in-c Wymondham w Edmondthorpe 84; P-in-c Buckminster w Sewstern, Sproxton and Coston 84; R Wymondham w Edmondthorpe, Buckminster etc 84-88; V Gosberton Clough and Quadring *Linc* 88-95; Asst Local Min Officer 88-95; V Buttershaw St Paul *Bradf* from 95. *The Vicarage, Wibsey Park Avenue, Bradford, W Yorkshire BD6 3QA* Bradford (01274) 676735

STREETER, Christine Mary. *See* HADDON-REECE, Mrs Christine Mary

STREETER, David James. b 42. Pemb Coll Cam BA64 MA68. Qu Coll Birm 65. **d** 67 **p** 68. C Saffron Walden *Chelmsf* 67-71; C Shrub End 71-73; R Rayne 73-79; V Highams Park All SS 79-82; P-in-c Stradbroke w Horham and Athelington *St E* 82-87; R Stradbroke, Horham, Athelington and Redlingfield from 87; RD Hoxne from 91. *The Rectory, Doctors Lane, Stradbroke, Eye, Suffolk IP21 5HU* Stradbroke (01379) 384363

STREETING, John William. b 52. ACertCM89 Cam Inst of Educn CertEd74 Birm Univ BEd77. St Steph Ho Ox 90. **d** 92 **p** 93. C Upminster *Chelmsf* 92-95; C Chingford SS Pet and Paul from 95. *Old Church House, Priory Avenue, London E4 8AA* 0181-529 0110

STREETING, Laurence Storey. b 14. VRD65. St Jo Coll Dur BA39 DipTh40 MA42. **d** 40 **p** 41. Chapl RNVR 42-90; R Guernsey St Sampson *Win* 65-71; Windward Is 71-76; Chapl Madeira *Eur* 76-80; Perm to Offic *Win* from 79; rtd 80. *L'Amarrage, La Marette, St Sampson, Guernsey, Channel Islands* Guernsey (01481) 47320

STRETCH, Richard Mark. b 53. Local NSM Course 91. **d** 93 **p** 94. NSM Stowmarket *St E* from 93. *91 Kipling Way, Stowmarket, Suffolk IP14 1TS* Stowmarket (01449) 676219

STRETTON, George Peter. b 22. MBE. **d** 70 **p** 71. Malaysia 70-78; V Shireoaks *S'well* 79-85; Perm to Offic *B & W* from 86; rtd 87. *9 The Lerburne, Wedmore, Somerset BS28 4ED* Wedmore (01934) 713244

STRETTON, Reginald John. b 37. MRPharmS63 CBiol70 MIBiol70 Man Univ BSc62 Nottm Univ PhD65 SOSc. E Midl Min Tr Course 88. **d** 91 **p** 92. NSM Loughb Gd Shep *Leic*

91-94; P-in-c Burrough Hill Pars from 94. *The Rectory, 1 High Street, Somerby, Melton Mowbray, Leics LE14 2PZ* Somerby (01664) 454318

STRETTON, Robert John. b 45. **d** 69 **p** 70. C Hendon St Ignatius *Dur* 69-73; C Middlesb St Thos *York* 73-77; OSB 77-78; V Brandon *Dur* 78-85; Lic to Offic 85-91; SSM from 85; Tr in Evang Ch in Wales 91-94. *The Society of the Sacred Mission, 96 Vassall Road, London SW9 6IA* 0171-582 2162

STREVENS, Brian Lloyd. b 49. St Jo Coll Dur BA70. Ripon Hall Ox 70. **d** 73 **p** 74. C Old Trafford St Jo *Man* 73-76; C Bolton St Pet 76-78; Org Sec Southn Coun of Community Service from 78; Perm to Offic *Win* 82-86; NSM Bitterne Park from 86. *186 Hill Lane, Southampton SO1 5DB* Southampton (01703) 333301

STREVENS, Richard Ernest Noel. b 34. Nottm Univ BA60. Linc Th Coll 60. **d** 62 **p** 63. C St Botolph Aldgate w H Trin Minories *Lon* 62-66; C Ealing St Steph Castle Hill 66-68; Hon C St Botolph without Bishopgate 68-76; V Clent *Worc* 76-86; V Pirbright *Guildf* from 86. *The Vicarage, The Green, Pirbright, Woking, Surrey GU24 0JE* Brookwood (01483) 473332

STRIBLEY, William Charles Harold. b 29. SW Minl Tr Course. **d** 87 **p** 88. NSM Kenwyn St Geo *Truro* 87-92; NSM Truro St Paul and St Clem from 92. *54 Chirgwin Road, Truro, Cornwall TR1 1TT* Truro (01872) 72958

STRICKLAND, Derek. b 26. Bps' Coll Cheshunt 64. **d** 66 **p** 66. C Hall Green Ascension *Birm* 67-70; V Hamstead St Bernard 70-76; Ind Chapl *St Alb* 76-93; rtd 93. *9 Dove House Crescent, Farnham Royal, Slough SL2 2PZ* Slough (01753) 521701

STRICKLAND (nee CUTTS), Mrs Elizabeth Joan Gabrielle. b 61. St Jo Coll Dur BA83. Westcott Ho Cam 87. **d** 90 **p** 94. Par Dn Cayton w Eastfield *York* 90-92; NSM Biggin Hill *Roch* from 93. *Oak Tree House, Arthur Road, Biggin Hill, Westerham, Kent TN16 3DD* Biggin Hill (01959) 576539

STRICKLAND, Canon Ernest Armitage. b 24. Ch Coll Cam BA49 MA54. Wycliffe Hall Ox 49. **d** 51 **p** 52. V Southport St Phil *Liv* 64-76; R Broughton *Linc* 76-90; RD Yarborough 81-86; Can and Preb Linc Cathl from 85; rtd 90; Perm to Offic *Linc* from 90. *143 Grimsby Road, Waltham, Grimsby, S Humberside DN37 0PU* Grimsby (01472) 821126

STRICKLAND, Canon Paul Lowndes. b 21. Linc Th Coll 46. **d** 49 **p** 50. V Debenham *St E* 61-75; V Lakenheath 75-83; rtd 83. *4 Albany Gardens East, Clacton-on-Sea, Essex CO15 6HW* Clacton-on-Sea (01255) 426303

STRIDE, Clifford Stephen. b 21. Ex & Truro NSM Scheme. **d** 81 **p** 82. NSM Chulmleigh *Ex* 81-83; NSM Hardham *Chich* 87-93; NSM Coldwaltham and Hardham from 93. *Ambleside, Sandy Lane, Watersfield, Pulborough, W Sussex RH20 1NF* Bury (01798) 831851

STRIDE, Desmond William Adair. b 15. Ch Coll Cam BA37 MA41. Ridley Hall Cam 38. **d** 39 **p** 40. Chapl Heathfield Sch Ascot 67-80; rtd 80; Perm to Offic *Lon* from 90; Perm to Offic *Chich* from 90. *5 Oakmede Way, Ringmer, Lewes, E Sussex BN8 5JL* Lewes (01273) 813561

STRIDE, Edgar George. b 23. Tyndale Hall Bris 47. **d** 51 **p** 52. V Becontree St Mary *Chelmsf* 61-70; R Spitalfields Ch Ch w All SS *Lon* 70-89; rtd 89; Perm to Offic *Linc* from 89; Perm to Offic *Pet* from 89. *23 Pembroke Road, Stamford, Lincs PE9 1BS* Stamford (01780) 56325

STRIDE, John David. b 46. Ex Univ BSc68. Oak Hill Th Coll DipHE88. **d** 88 **p** 89. C Ashtead *Guildf* from 88. *1 Oakfield Road, Ashtead, Surrey KT21 2RE* Ashtead (01372) 274578

STRIDE, John Michael. b 48. BA. Oak Hill Th Coll 77. **d** 80 **p** 81. C Edmonton All SS *Lon* 80-82; C Edmonton All SS w St Mich 82-83; C Wembley St Jo 83-85; P-in-c Hockering *Nor* 85-89; R Hockering, Honingham, E and N Tuddenham 89-91; V Tuckswood 91-93; Chapl HM Pris Leeds from 93. *HM Prison, Armley, Leeds LS12 2JT* Leeds (0113) 263 6411 Fax 790151

STRIKE, Maurice Arthur. b 44. FRSA66 NDD66. Sarum & Wells Th Coll 85. **d** 87 **p** 88. C Chippenham St Andr w Tytherton Lucas *Bris* 87-91; R Corfe Castle, Church Knowle, Kimmeridge etc *Sarum* from 91. *The Rectory, Corfe Castle, Wareham, Dorset BH20 5EE* Corfe Castle (01929) 480257

STRINGER, Adrian Nigel. b 60. Univ of Wales (Cardiff) BD82 Lanc Univ PGCE83. Sarum & Wells Th Coll 86. **d** 88 **p** 89. C Barrow St Matt *Carl* 88-92; TV Westhoughton *Man* 92-94; I Inver w Mountcharles, Killaghtee and Killybegs *D & R* from 94. *The Rectory, Inver, Co Donegal, Irish Republic* Donegal (73) 36013

STRINGER, Harold John. b 36. Peterho Cam BA58. Ripon Hall Ox 62. **d** 64 **p** 65. C Hackney St Jo *Lon* 64-68; C Roehampton H Trin *S'wark* 68-71; P-in-c Southn St Mich w H Rood, St Lawr etc *Win* 71-73; TV Southn (City Cen) 73-82; Ind Chapl 77-82; V Notting Hill St Jo *Lon* 82-87; V Notting Hill St Pet 82-87; V Notting Hill St Jo and St Pet from 87. *25 Ladbroke Road, London W11 3PD* 0171-727 3439

STRINGER, Canon John Roden. b 33. AKC61. **d** 62 **p** 63. C Auckland St Helen *Dur* 62-63; C Hebburn St Cuth 63-67; V

Cassop cum Quarrington 67-88; RD Sedgefield 84-88; V Lumley from 88; Hon Can Dur Cathl from 88. *The Vicarage, Great Lumley, Chester le Street, Co Durham DH3 4ER* 0191-388 2228

STRINGER, Leonard Gordon. b 14. Westcott Ho Cam 64. **d** 66 **p** 67. C Bath Abbey w St Jas *B & W* 66-80; rtd 80; Perm to Offic *B & W* from 82. *8 Hockley Court, Weston Park West, Bath BA1 4AR* Bath (01225) 318286

STRINGER, Ralph Stuart. b 47. Chich Th Coll 82. **d** 84 **p** 85. C Hadleigh w Layham and Shelley *St E* 84-87; P-in-c Needham Market w Badley 87-89; V from 89; P-in-c Ringshall w Battisford, Barking w Darmsden etc from 94; RD Bosmere from 94. *The Vicarage, 3 Stowmarket Road, Needham Market, Ipswich IP6 8DR* Needham Market (01449) 720316

STRONG, Christopher Patteson. b 43. Ridley Hall Cam. **d** 83 **p** 84. C Dalton-in-Furness *Carl* 83-87; V Wootton *St Alb* from 87; RD Elstow from 94. *The Vicarage, Wootton, Bedford MK43 9HF* Bedford (01234) 768391

STRONG, Donald Frederick. b 18. Oak Hill Th Coll 46. **d** 50 **p** 51. R Bedf St Jo *St Alb* 61-75; R Bedf St Jo and St Leon 75-81; rtd 81; Perm to Offic *St Alb* from 81. *Flat 9, Roedean Court, 82B Kimbolton Road, Bedford MK40 2PS* Bedford (01234) 327986

STRONG, Canon George Noel. b 97. St Chad's Coll Dur BA21 DipTh22 MA24. **d** 22 **p** 23. Master St Jo Hosp Lich 64-81; rtd 81. *4 Fecknam Way, Lichfield, Staffs WS13 6BY* Lichfield (01543) 264976

STRONG, Jack. b 16. St Aid Birkenhead 52. **d** 54 **p** 55. V Burgh-by-Sands w Kirkbampton *Carl* 66-83; R Burgh-by-Sands and Kirkbampton w Kirkandrews etc 83; rtd 83; Perm to Offic *Glouc* from 84. *Aballava, 18 Wincel Road, Winchcombe, Cheltenham, Glos GL54 5YE* Cheltenham (01242) 603347

STRONG, Canon John David. b 34. Cuddesdon Coll 59. **d** 61 **p** 62. C Gosforth All SS *Newc* 61-65; Chapl Malvern Coll Worcs 65-71; R Welford w Weston on Avon *Glouc* 72-79; V Nailsworth from 79; RD Tetbury from 83; Hon Can Glouc Cathl from 91. *The Vicarage, Avening Road, Nailsworth, Stroud, Glos GL6 0PJ* Stroud (01453) 832181

STRONG, Matthew John. b 60. Lon Univ BA81 Cam Univ BA84 MA89. Ridley Hall Cam 82. **d** 85 **p** 86. C Houghton *Carl* 85-89; C Hirwaun *Llan* 89-91; V Troedyrhiw w Merthyr Vale 91-95; Tutor Llan Ord Course 91-95. *92 Manor Abbey Road, Halesowen, W Midlands B62 0AA* 0121-422 0970

STRONG, Neil. b 34. Bps' Coll Cheshunt 57. **d** 61 **p** 62. C Ludlow *Heref* 69-71; P-in-c Withern *Linc* 71-74; P-in-c N and S Reston w Castle Carlton 71-74; P-in-c Strubby 71-74; P-in-c Gayton le Marsh 71-74; P-in-c Authorpe w Tothill 71-74; P-in-c Swaby w S Thoresby 73-74; R Belleau w Aby and Claythorpe 73-74; R Stanningley St Thos *Ripon* 74-76; P-in-c Bishop Wilton *York* 76-78; P-in-c Full Sutton w Skirpenbeck 76-78; P-in-c Bishop Wilton w Full Sutton 78-80; V Holme-on-Spalding Moor 80-82; V Nunthorpe 82-85; rtd 85. *51 Reeth Road, Linthorpe, Middlesbrough, Cleveland TS5 5JU* Middlesbrough (01642) 821433

STRONG, Rowan Gordon William. b 53. Victoria Univ Wellington BA76. St Jo Coll (NZ) LTh80 Melbourne Coll of Div ThM88. **d** 77 **p** 78. New Zealand 77-83; Australia 83-89; NSM Edin Old St Paul *Edin* from 89. *4 New Street, Edinburgh EH8 8BH* 0131-557 3493

STRONG, Preb Stephen Charles. b 16. Em Coll Cam BA38 MA43. Lon Coll of Div 38. **d** 40 **p** 41. V Heref St Pet w St Owen *Heref* 66-79; Preb Heref Cathl 78-85; V Heref St Pet w St Owen and St Jas 79-82; rtd 82; Perm to Offic *Heref* from 83. *162 Buckfield Road, Leominster, Herefordshire HR6 8UF* Leominster (01568) 615534

STRONG, Capt William John Leonard. b 44. CA Tr Coll 64 Chich Th Coll 87. **d** 89 **p** 90. CA from 66; C Mayfield *Chich* 89-92; C Seaford w Sutton 92-94; V Crawley Down All SS from 94. *The Vicarage, Vicarage Road, Crawley Down, Crawley, W Sussex RH10 4JJ* Copthorne (01342) 713246

STROUD, Ven Ernest Charles Frederick. b 31. St Chad's Coll Dur BA59 DipTh60. **d** 60 **p** 61. C S Kirkby *Wakef* 60-63; C Whitby *York* 63-66; C-in-c Chelmsf All SS CD *Chelmsf* 66-69; V Chelmsf All SS 69-75; V Leigh-on-Sea St Marg 75-83; Asst RD Southend 76-79; RD Hadleigh 79-83; Hon Can Chelmsf Cathl 82-83; Adn Colchester from 83. *Archdeacon's House, 63 Powers Hall End, Witham, Essex CM8 1NH* Witham (01376) 513130 Fax 500789

STROUD, Canon Robert Owen. b 29. AKC56. **d** 57 **p** 58. V High Elswick St Phil *Newc* 66-72; V Tynemouth Cullercoats St Paul 72-77; R Orlestone w Ruckinge w Warehorne *Cant* 77-81; RD N Lympne 79-81; V Folkestone H Trin w Ch Ch 81-83; TR Folkestone H Trin and St Geo w Ch Ch 83-90; R Folkestone H Trin w Ch Ch 90-93; RD Elham 90-93; Hon Can Cant Cathl 92-93; rtd 93; Perm to Offic *Ex* from 94. *The Old Barn, 8 Dares Orchard, Colyton, Devon EX13 6RN* Colyton (01297) 553761

STROYAN, John Ronald Angus. b 55. MTh. Qu Coll Birm 81 Bossey Ecum Inst Geneva 82. **d** 83 **p** 84. C Cov E *Cov* 83-87;

V Smethwick St Matt w St Chad *Birm* 87-94; V Bloxham w Milcombe and S Newington *Ox* from 94. *The Vicarage, Church Street, Bloxham, Banbury, Oxon OX15 4ET* Banbury (01295) 720252

STRUDWICK, Canon Donald Frank. b 12. Leeds Univ BA33. Coll of Resurr Mirfield 33. **d** 35 **p** 37. V E Dulwich St Clem *S'wark* 49-85; Hon Can S'wark Cathl 73-85; rtd 85; Perm to Offic *Roch* from 85. *8 Mount Avenue, Yalding, Maidstone, Kent ME18 6JG* Maidstone (01622) 814514

STRUDWICK, Canon Vincent Noel Harold. b 32. Nottm Univ BA59 DipEd. Kelham Th Coll 52. **d** 59 **p** 60. Tutor Kelham Th Coll 59-63; Sub-Warden 63-70; C Crawley *Chich* 70-73; Adult Educn Adv 73-77; R Fittleworth 73-77; Planning Officer for Educn Milton Keynes 77-80; Dir of Educn *Ox* 80-89; Hon Can Ch Ch from 82; Continuing Minl Educn Adv 85-89; Dir Dioc Inst for Th Educn from 89; Prin Ox Min Course 89-94; Prin St Alb and Ox Min Course from 94; Fell and Tutor Kellogg Coll Ox from 94. *35 Windmill Street, Brill, Aylesbury, Bucks HP18 9TG* (01844) 237748 or (01865) 790084 Fax (01865) 790470

STRUGNELL, Dr John Richard. b 30. Lon Univ BA52 Leeds Univ MA61 Queensland Univ PhD77. Wells Th Coll 54. **d** 56 **p** 57. C Leeds Halton St Wilfrid *Ripon* 56-59; C Moor Allerton 59-62; Australia from 62. *231 Grandview Road, Pullenvale, Queensland, Australia 4069* Brisbane (7) 374-1776

STRUTT, Mrs Susan. b 45. Glouc Sch of Min 87. **d** 90 **p** 94. NSM Eye, Croft w Yarpole and Lucton *Heref* 90-94; NSM Leominster 94; C from 94. *8 Radnor View, Leominster, Herefordshire HR6 8TF* Leominster (01568) 612124

STUART, Dr Angus Fraser. b 61. Bedf Coll Lon BA83 K Coll Lon PhD91. Cranmer Hall Dur BA92. **d** 93 **p** 94. C Twickenham St Mary *Lon* from 93. *27 Strafford Road, Twickenham TW1 3AD* 0181-891 1709

STUART, Brother. See BURNS, Brother Stuart Maitland

STUART, Francis David. b 32. Barrister-at-Law Lon Univ BA54 AKC57. Ridley Hall Cam 62. **d** 64 **p** 65. C Addiscombe St Mildred *Cant* 64-67; Chapl RN 67-71; Lic to Offic *Liv* 76-80; TV Oldham *Man* 84-89; Chapl Oldham and Distr Gen Hosp 84-89; Chapl Oldham R Infirmary 86-89; Chapl R Oldham Hosp from 89. *Royal Oldham Hospital, Rochdale Road, Oldham OL1 2JH, or Pine House, Barton Street, Oldham OL1 2NR* 0161-624 0420 or 626 6804

STUART, Canon Herbert James. b 26. CB83. TCD BA48 MA55. **d** 49 **p** 50. Chapl RAF 55-73; Asst Chapl-in-Chief RAF 73-80; Chapl-in-Chief and Archdeacon for the RAF 80-83; Can and Preb Linc Cathl *Linc* 81-83; R Cherbury *Ox* 83-87; Perm to Offic *Glouc* from 87; Perm to Offic *Ox* from 87; rtd 91. *1 Abbot's Walk, Lechlade, Glos GL7 3DB* Faringdon (01367) 253299

STUART-BLACK, Veronica. See BRADSHAW, Mrs Veronica

STUART-FOX, Ven Desmond. b 11. Selw Coll Cam BA33 MA37. Bps' Coll Cheshunt 33. **d** 34 **p** 35. C Leic St Pet *Leic* 34-37; C Lich St Mich *Lich* 37-40; Sacr Lich Cathl 37-40; CF (EC) 40-46; V W Bromwich St Andr *Lich* 46-49; Australia from 49. *5/24 Church Street, Goulburn, NSW, Australia 2580* Goulburn (48) 211339

STUART-LEE, Nicholas (Nick). b 54. Wycliffe Hall Ox. **d** 83 **p** 84. C Costessey *Nor* 83-85; TV Dewsbury *Wakef* 85-90; R Rowlands Castle *Portsm* from 90. *The Rectory, 9 College Road, Rowland's Castle, Portsmouth PO9 6AJ* Rowland's Castle (01705) 412605

STUART-SMITH, David. b 36. St Pet Coll Ox BA61 MA65. Tyndale Hall Bris. **d** 63 **p** 64. C Tooting Graveney St Nic *S'wark* 63-67; C Richmond H Trin 67-70; Lic to Offic 70-74; NSM Canonbury St Steph *Lon* 70-74; Travelling Sec IVF 70-74; Bangladesh 74-79; V Clapham Park St Steph *S'wark* 79-95; RD Streatham 83-87; P-in-c Wye w Brook *Cant* from 95; Chapl Wye Coll Kent from 95. *The Vicarage, Wye, Ashford, Kent TN25 5AS* Wye (01233) 812450

STUART-WHITE, William Robert. b 59. Ox Univ BA. Trin Coll Bris BA. **d** 86 **p** 87. C Upper Armley *Ripon* 86-91; P-in-c Austrey *Birm* 91-92; P-in-c Warton 91-92; V Austrey and Warton from 92. *The Vicarage, Austrey, Atherstone, Warks CV9 3EB* Tamworth (01827) 830572

STUBBINGS, Frank Edward. b 20. Fitzw Coll Cam BA48 MA53. Worc Ord Coll 60. **d** 61 **p** 62. V Catcott *B & W* 64-74; V Burtle 64-74; Chapl St Cath Sch Bramley 74-83; P-in-c Barkestone w Plungar, Redmile and Stathern *Leic* 83-87; rtd 87; Perm to Offic *B & W* 88-91; Hon C Lostwithiel, St Winnow w St Nectan's Chpl etc *Truro* from 91. *Goosey Down, Park Road, Lostwithiel, Cornwall PL22 0VU* Bodmin (01208) 872762

STUBBS, Anthony Richard Peter (Ælred). b 23. Ball Coll Ox BA49. Coll of Resurr Mirfield 51. **d** 54 **p** 54. Lic to Offic *Wakef* from 82; CR from 54; S Africa 60-77; Lesotho 77-81; rtd 94. *House of the Resurrection, Mirfield, W Yorkshire WF14 0BN* Mirfield (01924) 494318

STUBBS, Ian Kirtley. b 47. Man Univ DipAE90. Kelham Th Coll. **d** 70 **p** 71. C Chandler's Ford *Win* 70-75; C Farnham Royal *Ox* 75-80; Ind Chapl 75-80; Ind Chapl *Man* 81-86; TV Oldham 81-86; TR Langley and Parkfield 86-88; Lic to Offic from 88; Dir Laity Development from 90. *91 Werneth Hall Road, Oldham OL8 4BS*   0161-624 4144

STUBBS, Stanley Peter Handley. b 23. Lon Univ BD52 Lille Univ LesL82. Ely Th Coll 55. **d** 55 **p** 56. CF (TA) 59-78; V Northn St Alb *Pet* 63-76; R Brondesbury Ch Ch and St Laur *Lon* 76-93; rtd 93. *3 Westbury Lodge Close, Pinner, Middx HA5 3FG*   0181-868 8296

STUBBS, Trevor Noel. b 48. AKC70. St Aug Coll Cant 73. **d** 74 **p** 75. C Heckmondwike *Wakef* 74-77; Australia 77-80; V Middleton St Cross *Ripon* 80-89; R Wool and E Stoke *Sarum* 89-95; TR Bridport from 95. *The Rectory, 84 South Street, Bridport, Dorset DT6 3NW*   Bridport (01308) 422138

STUBENBORD, Jess William. b 48. BA72. Trin Coll Bris 75. **d** 78 **p** 79. C Cromer *Nor* 78-82; C Gorleston St Mary 82-85; P-in-c Saxthorpe and Corpusty 85-89; P-in-c Blickling 86-89; R Saxthorpe w Corpusty, Blickling, Oulton etc 89-93; P-in-c Mulbarton w Kenningham from 93; PinC Flordon from 94; P-in-c Wreningham from 95. *The Rectory, The Common, Mulbarton, Norwich NR14 8JS*   Mulbarton (01508) 570296

STUBLEY, Dr Peter Derek. b 28. AKC57 Dur Univ MA79 PhD91. **d** 58 **p** 59. C Stockton St Chad *Dur* 58-61; V W Hartlepool St Oswald 61-66; Ind Chapl 66-76; Ind Chapl *York* from 76; V Gt Totham *Chelmsf* 83; P-in-c Kingston upon Hull St Mary *York* 83-88. *223 Cottingham Road, Hull HU5 4AU*   Hull (01482) 43182

STUDD, Christopher Sidney. b 25. S'wark Ord Course. **d** 68 **p** 69. C Shenfield *Chelmsf* 68-73; R Stifford 73-83; P-in-c Bowers Gifford w N Benfleet 83-86; R 83-92; rtd 92. *9 Stonehill Road, Roxwell, Chelmsford CM1 4PF*   Chelmsford (01245) 248824

STUDD, John Eric. b 34. Clare Coll Cam BA58 MA62. Coll of Resurr Mirfield 58. **d** 60 **p** 61. C Westmr St Steph w St Jo *Lon* 60-65; Australia 65-69; Hon C Kensington St Mary Abbots w St Geo *Lon* 70-71; P-in-c Monks Risborough *Ox* 72-77; P-in-c Gt and Lt Kimble 72-77; C Aylesbury 78; Chapl to the Deaf 78-82; Chapl Hants, Is of Wight and Channel Is Assn for Deaf 82-91; Perm to Offic *Guildf* from 82; Perm to Offic *Portsm* from 82; Chapl to the Deaf *Win* from 91. *Albion Lodge, Halterworth Lane, Romsey, Hants SO51 9AE*   Romsey (01794) 512575

STUDDERT, Michael John de Clare. b 39. Trin Coll Cam BA64 MA67. Cuddesdon Coll 64. **d** 66 **p** 67. C Langley All SS and Martyrs *Man* 66-69; C Fleet *Guildf* 69-73; Perm to Offic 73-77; Chapl Eagle Ho Sch Sandhurst 77-88. *Southlands, Churt Road, Hindhead, Surrey GU26 6PS*   Hindhead (01428) 604620

STUDDERT, Canon Richard Charles Guy. b 03. Lon Coll of Div 26. **d** 28 **p** 30. I Tullow *C & O* 34-78; Prec Leighlin Cathl 62-78; rtd 78. *Station House, Tullow, Co Carlow, Irish Republic*   Carlow (503) 51246

STUDDERT-KENNEDY, Andrew Geoffrey. b 59. Ch Ch Ox BA80 MA86. Ripon Coll Cuddesdon BA88. **d** 89 **p** 90. C Wimbledon *S'wark* 89-94; V Norbury St Oswald from 94. *220 Norbury Avenue, Thornton Heath, Surrey CR7 8AJ*   0181-764 2853

STUDDERT-KENNEDY, Canon Christopher John. b 22. BNC Ox BA49 MA53. Wells Th Coll 49. **d** 51 **p** 52. R Godstone *S'wark* 66-91; RD Godstone 76-88; Hon Can S'wark Cathl 80-91; rtd 91; Perm to Offic *Chich* from 91. *Orchard House, The Street, Washington, Pulborough, W Sussex RH20 4AS*   Ashington (01903) 892774

STURCH, Richard Lyman. b 36. Ch Ch Ox BA58 MA61 DPhil70. Ely Th Coll. **d** 62 **p** 63. C Hove All SS *Chich* 62-65; C Burgess Hill St Jo 65-66; C Ox St Mich w St Martin and All SS *Ox* 67-68; Tutor Ripon Hall Ox 67-71; Nigeria 71-74; Lect Lon Bible Coll 75-80; Lic to Offic *Lon* 75-80; TV Wolverton *Ox* 80-86; R Islip w Charlton on Otmoor, Oddington, Noke etc from 86. *The Rectory, 3 The Rise, Islip, Kidlington, Oxon OX5 2TG*   Kidlington (01865) 372163

STURDY, John Vivian Mortland. b 33. Ch Ch Ox BA54 MA57 Trin Coll Cam BA58 MA62. Westcott Ho Cam 56. **d** 58 **p** 59. C Hitchin St Mary *St Alb* 58-62; V Ampthill w Millbrook and Steppingley 62-63; Tutor Wells Th Coll 63-65; Lic to Offic *Ely* from 65; Dean G&C Coll Cam from 65. *Gonville and Caius College, Cambridge CB1 2EZ*   Cambridge (01223) 332488

STURDY, William David Mark. b 28. Ch Coll Cam BA52 MA56. Qu Coll Birm. **d** 55 **p** 56. V Dishley and Thorpe Acre *Leic* 61-72; R Kegworth 72-82; V Cringleford *Nor* 82-85; R Colney 82-85; R Cringleford w Colney and Bawburgh 85-93; RD Humbleyard 87-93; rtd 94; Perm to Offic *Nor* from 94. *20 Valley Rise, Dersingham, Kings Lynn, Norfolk PE31 6PT*   Dersingham (01485) 543762

STURMAN, Robert George. b 50. Nottm Univ BTh79. Linc Th Coll 75. **d** 79 **p** 80. C Cainscross w Selsley *Glouc* 79-83; TV Bottesford w Ashby *Linc* 83-88; V Prescot *Liv* 88-91; P-in-c

Abenhall w Mitcheldean *Glouc* from 93. *St Michael's Rectory, Hawker Hill, Mitcheldean, Glos GL17 0BS*   Dean (01594) 542434

STURT, Rock Andre Daniel. b 56. Liv Univ BSc79 Lon Univ CertEd80. Oak Hill Th Coll DipTh88 BA88. **d** 88 **p** 89. Chapl St Bede's Sch Cam 88-90; Par Dn Cam St Martin *Ely* 89-90; C 90-91; P-in-c Alwalton and Chesterton from 91. *Alwalton Rectory, Peterborough PE7 3UU*   Peterborough (01733) 236205

STUTZ, Clifford Peter. b 25. **d** 83 **p** 84. NSM Cusop w Clifford, Hardwicke, Bredwardine etc *Heref* from 83. *Burnt House, Middlewood, Clifford, Hereford HR3 5SX*   Clifford (01497) 831472

STYLER, Geoffrey Marsh. b 15. CCC Ox BA37 MA40 Cam Univ MA44. Union Th Sem (NY) STM39 Cuddesdon Coll 40. **d** 41 **p** 42. Lect Th Cam Univ 53-82; rtd 82. *Middleton Cottage, Sidgwick Avenue, Cambridge CB3 9DA*   Cambridge (01223) 358420

STYLER, Jamie Cuming. b 36. Sarum & Wells Th Coll 70. **d** 72 **p** 73. C Whipton *Ex* 72-75; C Paignton St Jo 76-78; V Topsham 78-88; V Plymouth St Simon from 88; Chapl Mt Gould Hosp Plymouth from 94. *St Simon's Vicarage, 86 Edith Avenue, Plymouth PL4 8TL*   Plymouth (01752) 660654

STYLES, Clive William John. b 48. W Midl Minl Tr Course 87. **d** 90 **p** 91. C Burslem *Lich* 90-94; TV Wednesfield from 94. *157 Stubby Lane, Wednesfield, Wolverhampton WV11 3NE*   Wolverhampton (01902) 732763

STYLES, Canon Lawrence Edgar. b 19. AM88. Pemb Coll Cam BA48 MA52. Ridley Hall Cam. **d** 50 **p** 51. V Tyldesley w Shakerley *Man* 53-60; Australia from 60; Can Melbourne from 82; rtd 86. *25 Carson Street, Kew, Victoria, Australia 3101*   Melbourne (3) 861-9749

STYLES, Nigel Charles. b 57. Keele Univ BA79 Rob Coll Cam BA92. Ridley Hall Cam CTM93. **d** 95. C Bedf Ch Ch *St Alb* from 95. *9 Rothsay Road, Bedford MK40 3PP*   Bedford (01234) 720564

SUART, Geoffrey Hugh. b 49. Man Univ BSc70 Nottm Univ CertEd71. Oak Hill Th Coll DipHE83. **d** 83 **p** 84. C Ogley Hay *Lich* 83-86; TV Wenlock *Heref* 86-90; TR Kirby Muxloe *Leic* from 90. *The Rectory, 6 Station Road, Kirby Muxloe, Leicester LE9 2EJ*   Leicester (0116) 238 6822

SUCH, Canon Howard Ingram James. b 52. Southn Univ BTh81. Sarum & Wells Th Coll 77. **d** 81 **p** 82. C Cheam *S'wark* 81-84; Prec Cant Cathl *Cant* 84-91; Hon Min Can Cant Cathl from 91; V Borden from 91. *The Vicarage, Borden, Sittingbourne, Kent ME9 8JS*   Sittingbourne (01795) 472986

SUCH, Paul Nigel. b 52. FGA72 BTh84. Chich Th Coll 79. **d** 84 **p** 85. C Handsworth St Andr *Birm* 84-87; C Rugeley *Lich* 87-88; TV 88-91; R Longton from 91. *The Rectory, Rutland Road, Longton, Stoke-on-Trent ST3 1EH*   Stoke-on-Trent (01782) 595098

SUCH, Royston Jeffery. b 46. Solicitor Univ Coll Lon LLB67. Sarum & Wells Th Coll 83. **d** 83 **p** 84. NSM Ringwood *Win* 83-90; R Bishop's Sutton and Ropley and W Tisted from 90. *The Vicarage, Lyeway Lane, Ropley, Alresford, Hants SO24 0DW*   Winchester (01962) 772205

SUCKLING, Keith Edward. b 47. CChem FRSC Darw Coll Cam PhD71 Liv Univ BSc87 DSc89. Oak Hill NSM Course 91. **d** 94 **p** 95. NSM Digswell and Panshanger *St Alb* from 94. *291 Knightsfield, Welwyn Garden City, Herts AL8 7NH*   Welwyn Garden (01707) 330022

SUDBURY, Peter John. b 41. Southn Univ BA80 Westmr Coll Ox MTh94. Sarum & Wells Th Coll 78. **d** 79 **p** 80. C Leckhampton SS Phil and Jas w Cheltenham St Jas *Glouc* 79-82; CF (R of O) from 81; R Siddington w Preston *Glouc* 82-86; P-in-c Rendcomb from 86; Chapl Rendcomb Coll Cirencester from 86; Asst ChStJ from 90. *The Rectory, Rendcomb, Cirencester, Glos GL7 7EX*   Cirencester (01285) 831319 or 831213

SUDBURY, Archdeacon of. See COX, Ven John Stuart

SUDDARDS, John Martin. b 52. Barrister-at-Law 75 Trin Hall Cam BA74 MA77 Birm Univ DipTh89. Qu Coll Birm 86. **d** 89 **p** 90. C Halstead St Andr w H Trin and Greenstead Green *Chelmsf* 89-93; P-in-c Gt w Lt Yeldham from 93; P-in-c Toppesfield and Stambourne from 93. *The Rectory, Church Road, Great Yeldham, Halstead, Essex CO9 4PT*   Great Yeldham (01787) 237358

SUDELL, Philip Henry. b 61. Thames Poly BScEng84 Lon Univ PGCE85. Wycliffe Hall Ox 89. **d** 92 **p** 93. C Worthing Ch the King *Chich* from 92. *80 King Edward Avenue, Worthing, W Sussex BN14 8DQ*   Worthing (01903) 204317

SUDWORTH, Frank. b 43. DipHE. Oak Hill Th Coll 76. **d** 78 **p** 79. C Deane *Man* 78-81; C Worksop St Jo *S'well* 82-85; V Wollaton Park 85-90; P-in-c Lenton Abbey 85-86; V 86-90; V Upper Armley *Ripon* from 90; RD Armley from 92. *Christ Church Vicarage, Armley Ridge Road, Leeds LS12 3LE*   Leeds (0113) 263 8788

SUFFERN, Richard William Sefton. b 57. Reading Univ BSc79. Trin Coll Bris DipHE90. **d** 90 **p** 91. C Radipole and Melcombe

Regis *Sarum* 90-94; TV Cheltenham St Mark *Glouc* from 94. *St Barnabas' Rectory, 152 Alstone Lane, Cheltenham, Glos GL51 8HL* Cheltenham (01242) 255568

SUFFOLK, Archdeacon of. *See* ARRAND, Ven Geoffrey William

SUFFRIN, Canon Arthur Charles Emmanuel. b 09. Selw Coll Cam BA30 MA34. Qu Coll Birm 34. **d** 35 **p** 36. V Pirton *St Alb* 68-74; rtd 74. *32 St Michael's Road, Melksham, Wilts SN12 6HN* Melksham (01225) 708041

SUGDEN, Andrew Neville Burn. b 14. ERD54 TD60. St Pet Hall Ox BA37 MA41. Wycliffe Hall Ox 37. **d** 46 **p** 47. V High Harrogate St Pet *Ripon* 67-87; CF(ACF) 68-70; rtd 87. *Crosskeys, 11 Park Chase, Harrogate, N Yorkshire HG1 5AL* Harrogate (01423) 503758

SUGDEN, Charles Edward. b 59. Magd Coll Cam MA81 PGCE82. Trin Coll Bris DipHE91. **d** 91 **p** 92. C Gidea Park *Chelmsf* 91-94; TV Melksham *Sarum* from 94. *St Andrew's Vicarage, 33 Church Lane, Melksham, Wilts SN12 7EF* Melksham (01225) 702310

SUGDEN, Christopher Michael Neville. b 48. St Pet Coll Ox BA70 MA74 Nottm Univ MPhil74 PhD88. St Jo Coll Nottm 72. **d** 74 **p** 75. C Leeds St Geo *Ripon* 74-77; India 77-83; Lic to Offic *Ox* from 83. *Oxford Centre for Missionary Studies, PO Box 70, Oxford OX2 6HB* Oxford (01865) 56071 Fax 510823

SUGDEN, Mrs Kerstin. b 58. Man Univ BSc81 W Midl Coll of Educn PGCE82. Trin Coll Bris BA91. **d** 91. NSM Gidea Park *Chelmsf* 91-94; NSM Melksham *Sarum* from 95. *St Andrew's Vicarage, 33 Church Lane, Melksham, Wilts SN12 7EF* Melksham (01225) 702310

SULLIVAN, Adrian Michael. b 55. Sarum & Wells Th Coll 85. **d** 87 **p** 88. C Louth *Linc* 87-90; P-in-c E and W Keal 90; P-in-c Marden Hill Gp 90-92; R from 92. *The Rectory, West Keal, Spilsby, Lincs PE23 4BJ* Spilsby (01790) 53534

SULLIVAN, Bernard George. b 24. St Jo Coll Dur BA50. **d** 51 **p** 52. Chapl St Mary's Hosp Stannington 62-91; V Stannington *Newc* 63-91; rtd 91. *1 St Aidan's Crescent, Stobhill, Morpeth, Northd NE61 2UP*

SULLIVAN, Julian Charles. b 49. Lon Univ BSc74 CertEd75. Wycliffe Hall Ox 80. **d** 83 **p** 84. C Southall Green St Jo *Lon* 83-87; C Wells St Cuth w Wookey Hole *B & W* 87-90; V Sheff St Barn and St Mary *Sheff* 90-91; V Sheff St Mary w Highfield Trin 91-95; V Sheff St Mary Bramhall Lane from 95. *St Mary's Vicarage, 42 Charlotte Road, Sheffield S1 4TL* Sheffield (0114) 272 4987

SULLIVAN, Miss Nicola Ann. b 58. SRN81 RM84. Wycliffe Hall Ox BTh95. **d** 95. C Earlham St Anne *Nor* from 95. *8 Corie Road, Norwich NR4 7JB* Norwich (01603) 454509

SULLIVAN, Canon Trevor Arnold. b 40. CITC 69. **d** 70 **p** 71. C Lurgan Ch Ch *D & D* 71-72; C Tralee *L & K* 72-75; Irish Sch of Ecum 75-77; Ind Chapl *D & G* 77-80; I Ematris *Clogh* 80-84; I Aughrim w Ballinasloe etc *L & K* from 84; Can Limerick and Killaloe Cathls from 89. *The Rectory, Aughrim, Ballinasloe, Co Galway, Irish Republic* Ballinasloe (905) 73735

SULLY, Andrew Charles. b 67. Southn Univ BA88. Qu Coll Birm DPS91. **d** 93 **p** 94. C Newport Maindee St Jo Ev *Mon* from 93. *16 Kensington Place, Newport, Gwent NP9 8GL* Newport (01633) 281053

SULLY, Martin John. b 44. AIAS. St Jo Coll Nottm 80. **d** 82 **p** 83. C Lindfield *Chich* 82-86; V Walberton w Binsted from 86. *St Mary's Vicarage, The Street, Walberton, Arundel, W Sussex BN18 0PQ* Yapton (01243) 551488

SUMMERS, John Ewart. b 35. MIMechE66. ALCD69. **d** 69 **p** 70. C Fulham St Matt *Lon* 69-72; Chapl RN 72-81; V Devonport St Barn *Ex* from 81. *St Barnabas' Vicarage, 10 De La Hay Avenue, Plymouth PL3 4HU* Plymouth (01752) 666544

SUMMERS, Paul Anthony. b 53. Coll of Resurr Mirfield 77. **d** 80 **p** 81. C Manston *Ripon* 80-83; Prec 83-88; Min Can Ripon Cathl 83-88; Chapl Univ Coll of Ripon & York St Jo 84-88; V Whitkirk *Ripon* 88-95; R Kirkby Overblow from 95. *The Rectory, Kirkby Overblow, Harrogate, N Yorkshire HG3 1HD* Harrogate (01423) 872314

SUMMERS, Raymond John (Ray). b 41. Univ of Wales TCert63 DPS88 Open Univ BA75. St Mich Coll Llan 77. **d** 77 **p** 78. NSM Mynyddislwyn *Mon* 77-81; NSM Abercarn 81-82; P-in-c 82-89; V 89-91; V Mynyddislwyn 91-95; TR Mynyddislwyn from 95; RD Bedwellty from 93. *The Vicarage, Tom-y-Moch Road, Pontllanfraith, Blackwood, Gwent NP2 2DP* Blackwood (01495) 224240

SUMMERS, Thomas Gresley. b 25. Worc Coll Ox BA53 MA57. Cuddesdon Coll 53. **d** 55 **p** 56. OGS from 61; V Chesterton St Luke *Ely* 63-81; V Brownswood Park *Lon* 81-95; rtd 95. *Flat 1, Lichport Court, 1 Portland Rise, London N4 2PN*

SUMMERS, Ms Ursula Jeanne. b 35. Birm Univ BA56 Liv Univ CertEd57. Glouc Sch of Min. **dss** 85 **d** 87 **p** 94. Fownhope *Heref* 85-87; Hon C 87; Brockhampton w Fawley 85-87; Hon C 87; C Marden w Amberley and Wisteston 88-94; P-in-c

from 94; RD Heref Rural from 93. *99 Walkers Green, Marden, Hereford HR1 3EA* Sutton St Nicholas (01432) 880497

SUMNER, Canon Gillian Mansell (Gill). b 39. St Anne's Coll Ox BA61 MA65 MLitt76. Wycliffe Hall Ox 83. **dss** 86 **d** 87 **p** 94. Ox St Andr *Ox* 86-91; Hon C 87-91; Tutor Wycliffe Hall Ox 86-89; Vice-Prin Ox Min Course 89-91; Assoc Prin 91-94; Prin Ox Adnry Chr Tr Scheme *Ox* 89-94; Hon C Kirtlington w Bletchingdon, Weston etc 91-95; Hon Can Ch Ch from 94; Local Min Officer *Heref* from 95; P-in-c Wistanstow from 95. *The Parsonage, Wistanstow, Craven Arms, Shropshire SY7 8DG* Craven Arms (01588) 672067

SUMNER, John Gordon. b 46. CCC Cam BA68 MA72. Ridley Hall Cam 69. **d** 72 **p** 73. C Liskeard w St Keyne *Truro* 72-75; C Caversham *Ox* 75-81; V Swallowfield 81-93; Asst Chapl Reading Univ 81-93; C Glastonbury w Meare, W Pennard and Godney *B & W* from 93; Ldr Quest Community from 93. *The White Cottage, 15 Bere Lane, Glastonbury, Somerset BA6 8BD* Glastonbury (01458) 832377

SUMNERS, Ms Cristina Jordan. b 47. Vassar Coll (NY) BA73 BNC Ox MPhil85. Princeton Th Sem 73 Gen Th Sem (NY) MDiv76. **d** 78 **p** 82. USA 79-91; Asst Chapl K Edw Sch Witley from 93. *South Haven, Woolmer Hill, Haslemere, Surrey GU27 1LT* Haslemere (01428) 641575

SUMPTER, Timothy Mark (Tim). b 62. St Jo Coll Nottm BTh95. **d** 95. C Ockbrook *Derby* from 95. *34 Rutland Avenue, Borrowash, Derby DE7 3JF* Derby (01332) 674252

SUNDERLAND, Christopher Allen. b 52. BA75 St Pet Coll Ox MA80 DPhil80 DipTh86. Trin Coll Bris 84. **d** 86 **p** 87. C Stratton St Margaret w S Marston etc *Bris* 86-90; V Barton Hill St Luke w Ch Ch from 90; RD Bris City from 94. *St Luke's Vicarage, 60 Barton Hill Road, Bristol BS5 0AW* Bristol (0117) 955 5947

SUNDERLAND, Preb Geoffrey. b 21. St Edm Hall Ox BA43 MA47 DipTh47. St Steph Ho Ox 46. **d** 48 **p** 49. V Plymstock *Ex* 68-86; RD Plympton 76-81; Preb Ex Cathl 82-86; rtd 86; Perm to Offic *B & W* from 86; Perm to Offic *Ex* from 86. *22 Blackdown View, Sampford Peverell, Tiverton, Devon EX16 7BE* Tiverton (01884) 821688

SURMAN, Malcolm Colin. b 48. Birm Univ CertEd72 Southn Univ BTh88. Sarum & Wells Th Coll 76. **d** 78 **p** 79. C Basingstoke *Win* 78-81; P-in-c Alton All SS 81-85; V from 85; Chapl Lord Mayor Treloar Hosp Alton from 84. *All Saints' Vicarage, Queen's Road, Alton, Hants GU34 1HU* Alton (01420) 83458

SURREY, Archdeacon of. *Vacant*

SURRIDGE, Mrs Faith Thomas. b 45. Open Univ BA75 DipRD83 Lon Univ PGCE76 Ex Univ DipMathEd87. SW Minl Tr Course 83. **dss** 85 **d** 87 **p** 94. St Breoke and Egloshayle *Truro* 85-87; Hon C St Mawgan w St Ervan and St Eval from 91. *Lanvean Orchard, St Mawgan, Newquay, Cornwall TR8 4EY* St Mawgan (01637) 860806

SURTEES, Geoffrey. b 06. St Chad's Coll Dur BA33 DipTh34 MA36. **d** 34 **p** 35. Chapl Community St Laur Belper 57-75; V Bridge Hill *Derby* 57-75; rtd 75; Perm to Offic *Derby* from 75. *28 Penn Lane, Melbourne, Ashbourne, Derbyshire DE6 5NE* Melbourne (01332) 862381

SURTEES, Timothy John de Leybourne. b 31. G&C Coll Cam BA54 MA58. Westcott Ho Cam 54. **d** 56 **p** 57. C Guisborough *York* 56-59; C Grantham St Wulfram *Linc* 59-61; V Cayton w Eastfield *York* 61-72; R Cheam *S'wark* from 72. *Cheam Rectory, 15 Malden Road, Sutton, Surrey SM3 8QD* 0181-644 9110

SUSTINS, Nigel. b 46. Lon Univ BEd70. S'wark Ord Course 86. **d** 88 **p** 90. Hon C Mitcham St Mark *S'wark* 89-93. *19 Frensham Court, Phipps Bridge Road, Mitcham, Surrey CR4 3PG* 0181-685 9603

SUTCH, Christopher David. b 47. AKC69. St Aug Coll Cant 69. **d** 70 **p** 71. C Bris St Andr Hartcliffe *Bris* 70-75; C Swindon Dorcan 75-78; TV 78-79; P-in-c Alveston 79-83; V 83-89; RD Westbury and Severnside 86-89; TR Yate New Town from 89. *The Rectory, Canterbury Close, Yate, Bristol BS17 5TU* Chipping Sodbury (01454) 311483

SUTCH, Canon Christopher Lang. b 21. Or Coll Ox BA47 MA47. Cuddesdon Coll 47. **d** 49 **p** 50. V Hanham *Bris* 58-74; R Brinkworth w Dauntsey 74-86; RD Malmesbury 79-85; Hon Can Bris Cathl 82-86; rtd 86; Hon C E Bris from 86. *42 Henleaze Park Drive, Bristol BS9 4LL* Bristol (0117) 962 1952

SUTCLIFFE, Crispin Francis Henry. b 48. Keble Coll Ox BA69. Sarum & Wells Th Coll 73. **d** 74 **p** 75. C Truro St Paul *Truro* 74-77; S Africa 77-80; P-in-c Treslothan *Truro* 80-85; V 85-91; R Ilchester w Northover, Limington, Yeovilton etc *B & W* from 91. *The Rectory, Ilchester, Yeovil, Somerset BA22 8LJ* Ilchester (01935) 840296

SUTCLIFFE, Canon David. b 29. Lon Univ BD57. ALCD56. **d** 57 **p** 58. V Eccleshill *Bradf* 65-71; Lic to Offic 71-74; V Manningham St Luke 74-79; V Bolton St Jas w St Chrys 79-85;

V Calverley 85-94; RD Calverley 88-93; Hon Can Bradf Cathl 89-94; rtd 94. *49 Galloway Lane, Pudsey, W Yorkshire LS28 7UG* Leeds (0113) 257 4053

SUTCLIFFE, Howard Guest. b 44. Fitzw Coll Cam BA66 MA70 Birm Univ MA75 Man Univ CertRS88. Westcott Ho Cam 73. **d** 74 **p** 75. C Chorlton-cum-Hardy St Clem *Man* 74-77; Chapl Chetham's Sch of Music 77-80; V Oldham St Paul *Man* 80-94; Lic to Offic from 94; Co-ord Werneth and Freehold Community Development Project from 94. *34 Lynn Street, Oldham OL9 7DW, or 155 Windsor Road, Oldham OL8 1RG* 0161-628 2235

SUTCLIFFE, John Leslie. b 35. Liv Univ BA56. Sarum Th Coll 58. **d** 60 **p** 61. C Lytham St Cuth *Blackb* 60-62; C Altham w Clayton le Moors 62-65; C-in-c Penwortham St Leon CD 65-71; Ind Chapl *Liv* 71-74; V Orford St Andr 74-79; V Burnley St Cuth *Blackb* 79-88; Bp's Adv on UPA *Ripon* 88-94; Hon C Leeds Gipton Epiphany 88-94; I Carrickmacross w Magheracloone *Clogh* from 94. *The Rectory, Drumconrath Road, Carrickmacross, Co Monaghan, Irish Republic* Carrickmacross (42) 61931

SUTCLIFFE, Maurice. b 13. St Aug Coll Cant 39. **d** 42 **p** 43. V Barnacre *Blackb* 58-89; rtd 89. *Dean House, Bypass Road, Catterall, Preston PR3 0HL* Garstang (01995) 603643

SUTCLIFFE, Peter John. b 58. BA. Linc Th Coll. **d** 82 **p** 83. C Skipton Ch Ch *Bradf* 82-85; C Tettenhall Regis *Lich* 85-86; TV 86-89; TV Warw *Cov* 89-93; Relig Producer BBC Radio Cov & Warks 89-93; V Burley in Wharfedale *Bradf* from 93. *The Vicarage, Burley-in-Wharfedale, Ilkley, W Yorkshire LS29 7DR* Burley-in-Wharfedale (01943) 863216

SUTCLIFFE, Canon Thomas Henry. b 07. Qu Coll Cam BA30 MA34. Westcott Ho Cam 30. **d** 31 **p** 32. Org Sec C of E Coun for Deaf 52-74; Hon Can Cant Cathl *Cant* 66-85; rtd 75; Perm to Offic *Ox* 85-90; Perm to Offic *S'wark* 85-90; Perm to Offic *Cant* 85-88; Perm to Offic *B & W* 88-93. *12 Parsonage Court, Bishops Hull, Taunton, Somerset TA1 5HR* Taunton (01823) 332715

SUTCLIFFE, William Norman. b 09. Lich Th Coll 56. **d** 57 **p** 58. V Northmoor Green *B & W* 60-69; V Burrow Bridge 60-69; Perm to Offic *Sarum* 69-72; Lic to Offic 72-89; rtd 74. *The Bungalow, Hollis Hill, Broadwindsor, Beaminster, Dorset DT8 3QS* Broadwindsor (01308) 868476

SUTER, Richard Alan. b 48. Rhodes Univ BA72 St Jo Coll Dur BA74. Cranmer Hall Dur 72. **d** 75 **p** 76. C Darlington H Trin *Dur* 75-77; C Wrexham *St As* 77-82; R Llansantffraid Glan Conway and Eglwysfach 82-87; V Broughton 87-92; RD Wrexham from 90; V Rossett from 92. *The Vicarage, Rossett, Wrexham, Clwyd LL12 0HE* Rossett (01244) 570498

SUTHERLAND, Alan. b 55. Sarum & Wells Th Coll. **d** 80 **p** 81. C Hessle *York* 80-83; USA from 83. *501 South Phoenix, Russellville, Arkansas 72801, USA*

SUTHERLAND, Alistair Campbell. b 31. MIEE CEng Lon Univ BSc50 Ex Univ BA77. Wycliffe Hall Ox 77. **d** 78 **p** 79. C Nottm St Jude *S'well* 78-81; R Barton in Fabis from 81; P-in-c Thrumpton 81; V from 81; RD Bingham W 87-92; Dioc Adv on Ind Society from 92; NSM Gotham from 93; NSM Kingston and Ratcliffe-on-Soar from 93. *The Rectory, Church Lane, Barton, Nottingham NG11 0AG* Nottingham (0115) 983 0252

SUTHERLAND, Eric. b 54. AKC76. Sarum & Wells Th Coll 76. **d** 77 **p** 78. C Roehampton H Trin *S'wark* 77-80; C Tattenham Corner and Burgh Heath *Guildf* 80-84; V Guildf All SS 84-91; Dep Chapl HM Pris Wandsworth 91-92; Chapl HM Young Offender Inst Huntercombe and Finnamore from 92. *HM Young Offender Institution, Huntercombe Place, Nuffield, Henley-on-Thames, Oxon RG9 5SB* Nettlebed (01491) 641711 or 641715   Fax 641902

SUTHERLAND, Mark Robert. b 55. Univ of NZ LLB77 Lon Univ DAC89. Ripon Coll Cuddesdon 82. **d** 85 **p** 86. C Pinner *Lon* 85-88; C Sudbury St Andr 88-91; Chapl Maudsley Hosp Lon from 91; Chapl Bethlem N Pris Beckenham from 91; Perm to Offic *S'wark* 91-92. *The Maudsley Hospital, Denmark Hill, London SE5 8AZ* 0171-919 2815

SUTTERS, Herbert John. b 15. St Jo Coll Ox BA37 MA40. St Steph Ho Ox 37. **d** 39 **p** 40. V Highbridge *B & W* 61-73; V St Margarets on Thames *Lon* 73-80; rtd 80; Perm to Offic *Ox* from 81. *22 Alexandra Road, Oxford OX2 0DB* Oxford (01865) 723549

SUTTLE, Dr Neville Frank. b 38. Reading Univ BSc61 Aber Univ PhD64. **d** 76 **p** 77. NSM Penicuik *Edin* from 76. *44 St James's Gardens, Penicuik, Midlothian EH26 9DU* Penicuik (01968) 673819

SUTTON, Brian Ralph. b 33. Trin Coll Bris DPS81 Sarum & Wells Th Coll. **d** 83 **p** 84. NSM Timsbury *B & W* 83-84; NSM Timsbury and Priston 85-88; V Thorncombe w Winsham and Cricket St Thomas from 89. *The Vicarage, Chard Street, Thorncombe, Chard, Somerset TA20 4NE* Winsham (01460) 30479

SUTTON, Charles Edwin. b 53. Bris Univ BEd77 Ox Univ. Ripon Coll Cuddesdon 77. **d** 80 **p** 81. C Stanwix *Carl* 80-84; Warden Marrick Priory *Ripon* 84-88. *7 Beech Close, Baldersby, Thirsk, N Yorkshire YO7 4QB* Melmerby (01765) 640616

SUTTON, Christopher Peter. b 06. St Edm Hall Ox BA31 DipTh32 MA43. Wycliffe Hall Ox 27 and 31. **d** 32 **p** 33. R Aldbury *St Alb* 63-78; rtd 78; Perm to Offic *Chich* from 78. *1 The Twitten, Southwick, Brighton BN42 4DB* Brighton (01273) 593574

SUTTON, Colin Phillip. b 51. Birm Univ BA73. Chich Th Coll 73. **d** 75 **p** 76. C Penarth All SS *Llan* 75-77; C Roath St Marg 77-80; C Caerau w Ely 80-84; V Rhydyfelin from 84. *St Luke's House, 6 Fairfield Lane, Hawthorn, Pontypridd, M Glam CF37 5LN* Pontypridd (01443) 852298

SUTTON, David Robert. b 49. Birm Univ BA69 Ox Univ CertEd72. St Steph Ho Ox 70. **d** 72 **p** 73. C Clitheroe St Mary *Blackb* 72-75; C Fleetwood 75-78; V Calderbrook *Man* 78-88; V Winton from 88; Chapl Salford Mental Health Services (NHS Trust) from 92. *The Vicarage, Albany Road, Eccles, Manchester M30 8DE* 0161-788 8991

SUTTON, James William. b 41. Oak Hill Th Coll 81. **d** 84 **p** 85. NSM Chorleywood St Andr *St Alb* from 84. *Belmount, 7 Hillside Road, Chorleywood, Rickmansworth, Herts WD3 5AP* Chorleywood (01923) 282806

SUTTON, Jeremy John Ernest. b 60. Ridley Hall Cam 83. **d** 86 **p** 87. C Seacombe *Ches* 86-88; C Northwich St Luke and H Trin 88-90; TV Birkenhead Priory 90-94; V Over St Chad from 94. *The Vicarage, 1 Over Hall Drive, Over, Winsford, Cheshire CW7 1EY* Winsford (01606) 593222

SUTTON, John. b 47. St Jo Coll Dur BA70. Ridley Hall Cam 70. **d** 72 **p** 73. C Denton St Lawr *Man* 72-77; R 77-82; V High Lane *Ches* 82-88; V Sale St Anne from 88. *St Anne's Vicarage, Church Road, Sale, Cheshire M33 3HB* 0161-973 4145

SUTTON, John Stephen. b 33. Em Coll Cam BA57 MA61. Wycliffe Hall Ox 57. **d** 59 **p** 60. C Dagenham *Chelmsf* 59-62; C Bishopwearmouth St Gabr *Dur* 62-63; V Over Kellet *Blackb* 63-67; V Darwen St Barn 67-74; V Walthamstow St Jo *Chelmsf* 74-84; V Stebbing w Lindsell from 84; RD Dunmow from 94. *The Vicarage, High Street, Stebbing, Dunmow, Essex CM6 3SF* Stebbing (01371) 865468

SUTTON, Canon John Wesley. b 48. Rolle Coll CertEd71. All Nations Chr Coll DipMiss75. **d** 76 **p** 77. Chile 76-77; Peru 79-84; Area Sec SAMS 84-88; Youth Sec SAMS 88-91; Personnel Sec SAMS from 91; Asst Gen Sec SAMS from 91; Perm to Offic *Chelmsf* from 84; Perm to Offic *Ox* from 85; Perm to Offic *St Alb* from 85; Hon Can Peru from 93. *88 Horn Lane, Woodford Green, Essex IG8 9AH* 0181-505 7888   Fax Tunbridge Wells (01892) 525797

✠**SUTTON, Rt Rev Keith Norman.** b 34. Jes Coll Cam BA58 MA62. Ridley Hall Cam. **d** 59 **p** 60 **c** 78. C Plymouth St Andr *Ex* 59-61; Chapl St Jo Coll Cam 62-67; Uganda 68-72; Prin Ridley Hall Cam 73-78; Suff Bp Kingston-upon-Thames *S'wark* 78-84; Bp Lich from 84. *Bishop's House, 22 The Close, Lichfield, Staffs WS13 7LG* Lichfield (01543) 262251   Fax 415801

SUTTON, Canon Malcolm David. b 26. Selw Coll Cam BA47 MA52. Ridley Hall Cam 48. **d** 50 **p** 51. R Beccles St Mich *St E* 63-82; TR 82-94; RD Beccles 65-73; Hon Can St E Cathl 70-94; rtd 94; Perm to Offic Nor from 95. *10 Merville, Carlton Colville, Lowestoft, Suffolk NR33 8JN*

SUTTON, Peter. b 20. Ely Th Coll 60. **d** 62 **p** 63. R Hamerton *Ely* 64-77; V Winwick 64-77; V Upton and Copmanford 70-77; V Bradworthy *Ex* 77-90; rtd 90. *Mowhay Villa, Chilsworthy, Holsworthy, Devon EX22 7BQ* Holsworthy (01409) 254900

SUTTON, Peter Allerton. b 59. Ex Univ BA85. Linc Th Coll 85. **d** 87 **p** 88. C Fareham H Trin *Portsm* 87-90; C Alverstoke 90-93; Chapl HM Pris Haslar from 90; V Lee-on-the-Solent *Portsm* from 93. *St Faith's Vicarage, Victoria Square, Lee-on-the-Solent, Hants PO13 9NF* Lee-on-the-Solent (01705) 550269

SUTTON, Richard Alan. b 39. Reading Univ BSc61. Wycliffe Hall Ox 70. **d** 72 **p** 73. C Galleywood Common *Chelmsf* 72-76; Pakistan 76-79; C Walsall St Martin *Lich* 79-83; V Barton Hill St Luke w Ch Ch *Bris* 83-89; V Sidcup Ch Ch *Roch* 89-95; rtd 95. *117 Wren Road, Sidcup, Kent DA14 4NQ* 0181-302 9233

SUTTON, Richard John. b 45. Lon Inst of Educn CertEd68. St Alb Minl Tr Scheme 77 Linc Th Coll 81. **d** 82 **p** 83. C Royston *St Alb* 82-87; C Hatf from 87. *St Michael's House, 31 Homestead Road, Hatfield, Herts AL10 0QJ* Hatfield (01707) 262897

SUTTON, Ronald. b 27. FSCA. NW Ord Course 76. **d** 79 **p** 80. C Helsby and Dunham-on-the-Hill *Ches* 79-81; R Church Lawton 81-92; RD Congleton 91-92. *79 Thornton Avenue, Macclesfield, Cheshire SK11 7XL* Macclesfield (01625) 430212

SWABEY, Brian Frank. b 44. BA. Oak Hill Th Coll 79. **d** 82 **p** 83. C Clapham St Jas *S'wark* 82-84; C Wallington H Trin 84-88;

Chapl Mt Gould Hosp Plymouth 88-89; V Plymouth St Jude *Ex* 88-92; Chapl RN from 92. *Directorate Gen, RN Chapl Services, Room 203, Victory Building, HM Naval Base, Portsmouth PO1 3LS* Portsmouth (01705) 727903 Fax 727112

SWABEY, Henry Sandys. b 16. Univ Coll Dur BA37 MA40 BD50. Chich Th Coll 37. **d** 39 **p** 40. V Deeping Fen *Linc* 58-78; R Rippingale 78-82; R Dunsby w Dowsby 78-82; rtd 82; Perm to Offic *Pet* from 82. *29 High Street, Maxey, Peterborough PE6 9EB* Market Deeping (01778) 342800

SWABY, Canon John Edwin. b 11. St Jo Coll Dur BA32 DipTh34 MA35 Leic Univ PhD83. **d** 34 **p** 35. Can and Preb Linc Cathl *Linc* 69-77; V Barholm w Stowe 71-76; R Uffington 71-76; V Tallington 71-76; rtd 76; Perm to Offic *Pet* from 76. *6 Willoughby Drive, Empingham, Oakham, Leics LE15 8PZ* Empingham (0178086) 719

SWABY, Keith Graham. b 48. Southn Univ BA75. St Steph Ho Ox 75. **d** 77 **p** 78. C Lt Stanmore St Lawr *Lon* 77-80; C Hove All SS *Chich* 80-83; C Haywards Heath St Wilfrid 83; TV from 83. *69 William Allen Lane, Lindfield, Haywards Heath, W Sussex RH16 2ST* Haywards Heath (01444) 454417

SWABY, Leward Anthony Woodrow. b 60. Trin Coll Bris 86 Ripon Coll Cuddesdon 89. **d** 92 **p** 93. C Wembley St Jo *Lon* 92-95; C Northn St Matt *Pet* from 95. *5 Brookland Crescent, Northampton NN1 4SS* Northampton (01604) 711467

SWAIN, David Noel. b 36. Wellington Univ (NZ) BA63 MA66. Coll of Resurr Mirfield 65. **d** 67 **p** 68. C Clapham H Trin *S'wark* 67-70; New Zealand 70-75; P-in-c Hermitage *Ox* 75-76; P-in-c Hampstead Norris 75-76; V Hermitage w Hampstead Norreys 76-80; TR Hermitage and Hampstead Norreys, Cold Ash etc 80-82; R Bingham *S'well* 82-94; rtd 94. *20 Thorold Road, Barrowby, Grantham, Lincs NG32 1TD* Grantham (01476) 60823

SWAIN, John Edgar. b 44. Lich Th Coll 67. **d** 69 **p** 70. C E Dereham w Hoe *Nor* 69-73; V Haugh *Linc* 73-74; R S Ormsby w Ketsby, Calceby and Driby 73-74; R Harrington w Brinkhill 73-74; R Oxcombe 73-74; R Ruckland w Farforth and Maidenwell 73-74; R Somersby w Bag Enderby 73-74; R Tetford and Salmonby 73-74; R Belchford 73-74; V W Ashby 73-74; C Attleborough *Nor* 74-78; Canada 78-90; P-in-c Kirton w Falkenham *St E* from 90; Chapl Suffolk Constabulary from 90. *The Rectory, Kirton, Ipswich IP10 0PT* Kirton (01394) 448226

SWAIN, Canon John Roger. b 29. Fitzw Ho Cam BA55 MA59. Bps' Coll Cheshunt 55. **d** 57 **p** 58. V Wyther Ven Bede *Ripon* 65-75; V Horsforth 75-86; P-in-c Roundhay St Edm 86-88; V 88-95; RD Allerton 89-94; Hon Can Ripon Cathl 89-95; rtd 95. *3 Harlow Court, Park Avenue, Leeds LS8 2JH*

SWAIN, Peter John. b 44. NCA63. Sarum & Wells Th Coll 86. **d** 88 **p** 89. C Beaminster Area *Sarum* 88-92; P-in-c Bromfield w Waverton *Carl* from 92; P-in-c W Newton from 92; Member Rural Life and Agric Team from 93; RD Solway from 95. *The Vicarage, Langrigg, Aspatria, Carlisle CA5 3NB* Aspatria (016973) 20261

SWAIN, Raymond Thomas. b 60. Oak Hill Th Coll BA89. **d** 89 **p** 90. C New Clee *Linc* 89-93; TV Cheltenham St Mark *Glouc* from 93. *St Aidan's Vicarage, 21 Brooklyn Road, Cheltenham, Glos GL51 8DT* Cheltenham (01242) 574179

SWAIN, Ronald Charles Herbert. b 08. Dur Univ LTh32 BA42 MA50. St Aug Coll Cant 29. **d** 32 **p** 33. V Shipley *Chich* 70-74; rtd 74; Perm to Offic *St E* from 74. *81 Westley Road, Bury St Edmunds, Suffolk IP33 3RU* Bury St Edmunds (01284) 761655

SWAIN, Mrs Sharon Juanita. b 46. Sussex Univ BA75 CertEd76. Glouc Sch of Min 84 Qu Coll Birm. **dss** 84 **d** 87 **p** 94. Upton St Leonards *Glouc* 84-87; C 87-88; Children's Officer *Worc* 88-95; Min Can Worc Cathl from 94; V Hanley Castle, Hanley Swan and Welland from 95. *The Vicarage, 5 Westmere, Hanley Swan, Worcester WR8 0DL* Hanley Swan (01684) 310321

SWAIN, William Allan. b 38. Kelham Th Coll 63. **d** 68 **p** 69. C Welwyn Garden City *St Alb* 68-72; C Romsey *Win* 72-74; C Weeke 74-78; V Bournemouth H Epiphany 78-91; P-in-c Moordown 91-94; V from 94. *St John's Vicarage, 2 Vicarage Road, Bournemouth BH9 2SA* Bournemouth (01202) 546400

SWAINE, John Arthur. b 45. St Steph Ho Ox 68. **d** 71 **p** 72. C Kilburn St Aug *Lon* 71-74; C Lavender Hill Ascension *S'wark* 74-77; C Deptford St Paul 77-78; Hon C 78-80; Warden St Mark's Youth & Community Cen Deptford 78-80; V Leic St Chad *Leic* 80-86; V Leytonstone H Trin Harrow Green *Chelmsf* 86-94; rtd 94. *7 rue des Goelands, 17120 Mortagne-sur-Gironde, France* France (33) 46 90 50 06

SWAINSON, Norman. b 38. Salford Univ MSc75. St Jo Coll Nottm 77. **d** 79 **p** 80. C Levenshulme St Pet *Man* 79-84; R Jarrow Grange *Dur* from 84. *Christ Church Rectory, Clayton Street, Jarrow, Tyne & Wear NE32 3JR* 0191-489 4682

SWALES, David James. b 58. Warw Univ BA. Cranmer Hall Dur. **d** 84 **p** 85. C Eccleshill *Bradf* 84-88; C Prenton *Ches* 88-92;

V Oakworth *Bradf* from 92. *The Vicarage, 18 Sunhurst Drive, Oakworth, Keighley, W Yorkshire BD22 7RG* Haworth (01535) 647335

SWALES, Peter. b 52. ACIB78. Ridley Hall Cam 85. **d** 87 **p** 88. C Allestree *Derby* 87-91; P-in-c Horsley from 91. *The Vicarage, Horsley, Derby DE21 5BR* Derby (01332) 880284

SWALLOW, Mrs Alice Gillian. b 51. Birm Univ BA72 CertEd73. NE Ord Course 82. **dss** 84 **d** 87 **p** 94. Morpeth *Newc* 84-86; Uttoxeter w Bramshall *Lich* 86-87; Par Dn 87-88; Par Dn Rocester 88; Chapl to the Deaf *Man* 88-90; Par Dn Goodshaw and Crawshawbooth 88-93; C Barkisland w W Scammonden *Wakef* 93-95; V Ripponden from 95. *Christ Church Vicarage, Stainland Road, Barkisland, Halifax, W Yorkshire HX4 0AQ* Halifax (01422) 822339

SWALLOW, Arnold Robert. b 04. SS Coll Cam BA27 MA30. Westcott Ho Cam 37. **d** 38 **p** 39. R Fulbourn *Ely* 57-76; rtd 76. *40 Pierce Lane, Fulbourn, Cambridge CB1 5DL* Cambridge (01223) 880358

SWALLOW, John Brian. b 36. Trent Poly 78. **d** 84 **p** 85. C Cleveleys *Blackb* 84-87; V Blackpool St Mich 87-93; P-in-c Burnley St Steph from 93. *St Stephen's Vicarage, 154 Todmorden Road, Burnley, Lancs BB11 3ER* Burnley (01282) 424733

SWALLOW, John Allen George. b 28. St Jo Coll Dur BA53 DipTh54. **d** 54 **p** 55. V S Weald *Chelmsf* 64-81; R W w E Mersea 81-93; rtd 93. *72 Rembrandt Way, Bury St Edmunds, Suffolk IP33 2LT* Bury St Edmunds (01284) 725136

SWALLOW, Robert Andrew (Bob). b 52. Leeds Univ BA73 Sheff Univ PGCE74 Keele Univ MA76. Linc Th Coll 76. **d** 78 **p** 79. C Gt Wyrley *Lich* 78-81; C Blakenall Heath 81-83; TV 83-90; TV Fareham H Trin *Portsm* 90-92. *Address temp unknown*

SWAN, Duncan James. b 65. Imp Coll Lon BSc88 SS Coll Cam BA91. Ridley Hall Cam CTM92. **d** 92 **p** 93. C Stevenage St Andr and St Geo *St Alb* from 92. *46 Crossgates, Stevenage, Herts SG1 1LS* Stevenage (01438) 367654

SWAN, Owen. b 28. ACP71. Edin Th Coll 56. **d** 59 **p** 60. C Lewisham St Jo Southend *S'wark* 59-64; CF (TA) from 60; V Richmond St Luke *S'wark* 64-82; C-in-c Darlington St Hilda and St Columba CD *Dur* 82-84; R Feltwell *Ely* 84-87; R Holywell w Needingworth from 87. *The Rectory, Holywell, St Ives, Huntingdon, Cambs PE17 3TQ* St Ives (01480) 494287

SWAN, Philip Douglas. b 56. Wye Coll Lon BSc78 Qu Coll Cam MA81 CertEd81 Nottm Univ DipTh87. St Jo Coll Nottm 86. **d** 88 **p** 89. C Birm St Martin w Bordesley St Andr *Birm* 88-92; C Selly Park St Steph and St Wulstan from 92. *927 Pershore Road, Selly Park, Birmingham B29 7PS* 0121-472 2514

SWAN, Preb Ronald Frederick. b 35. St Cath Coll Cam BA59 MA. Coll of Resurr Mirfield. **d** 61 **p** 62. C Staveley *Derby* 61-66; Chapl Lon Univ *Lon* 66-72; C St Martin-in-the-Fields 72-77; V Ealing St Barn 77-88; V Ealing St Steph Castle Hill 81-88; AD Ealing E 84-87; V Harrow St Mary from 88; AD Harrow 89-94; Preb St Paul's Cathl from 91. *St Mary's Vicarage, Church Hill, Harrow, Middx HA1 3HL* 0181-422 2652

SWAN, Thomas Hugh Winfield. b 26. New Coll Ox BA50 MA62 Barrister 51. Ridley Hall Cam 63. **d** 65 **p** 66. R Sawtry *Ely* 69-79; P-in-c Fordham St Mary 79-82; V 82-87; P-in-c Hilgay 79-82; R 82-87; P-in-c Southery 79-82; R 82-87; rtd 91. *24 Chiefs Street, Ely, Cambs CB6 1AT* Ely (01353) 668452

SWANBOROUGH, Alan William. b 38. Southn Univ BEd75. Sarum & Wells Th Coll 77. **d** 80 **p** 81. NSM Ventnor H Trin *Portsm* 80-85; NSM Ventnor St Cath 80-85; Chapl Upper Chine Sch Shanklin from 85; NSM Shanklin St Blasius *Portsm* 91-93; P-in-c from 93. *The Rectory, Rectory Road, Shanklin, Isle of Wight PO37 6NS* Isle of Wight (01983) 862407

SWANBOROUGH, Robert Charles. b 28. Sarum & Wells Th Coll 75. **d** 77 **p** 78. C Woodley St Jo the Ev *Ox* 77-78; C Bray and Braywood 79-80; V Gt Coxwell w Buscot, Coleshill & Eaton Hastings from 80. *The Vicarage, Great Coxwell, Faringdon, Oxon SN7 7NG* Faringdon (01367) 240665

SWANEPOEL, David John. b 41. Rhodes Univ BA62 UNISA BA64 DipHE80 BTh84. **d** 75 **p** 76. S Africa 75-94; Dean George 85-89; NSM Hellingly and Upper Dicker *Chich* from 94. *Providence House, Upper Dicker, Hailsham, E Sussex BN27 3QE* Hailsham (01323) 843887

SWANN, Antony Keith. b 34. Lon Univ DipTh60. St Aid Birkenhead 58. **d** 61 **p** 62. C Bilston St Leon *Lich* 61-66; Sierra Leone 66-70; V W Bromwich St Phil *Lich* 70-75; Nigeria 76-78; R Church Lench w Rous Lench and Abbots Morton *Worc* 78-88; Chapl HM Pris Coldingley 88-91; Chapl HM Pris Leyhill from 91. *HM Prison Leyhill, Wotton-under-Edge, Glos GL12 8BT* Falfield (01454) 260681 Fax 261398

SWANN, Ven Edgar John. b 42. TCD BA66 MA70 BD77. CITC 68. **d** 68 **p** 69. C Crumlin *Conn* 68-70; C Howth *D & G* 70-73; I Greystones from 73; Can Ch Ch Cathl Dub from 90; Adn Glendalough from 93. *The Rectory, Greystones, Co Wicklow, Irish Republic* Dublin (1) 287-4077 Fax (1) 287-3766

SWANN, Frederick David. b 38. d 69 p 70. C Lurgan Ch Ch *D & D* 69-77; I Ardmore w Craigavon 77-79; I Comber 79-85; I Drumglass w Moygashel *Arm* from 85. *The Rectory, 24 Circular Road, Dungannon, Co Tyrone BT71 6BE* Dungannon (01868) 722614

SWANN, Paul David James. b 59. Ch Ch Ox BA81 MA88. St Jo Coll Nottm DTS89 DPS90. d 90 p 91. C Old Hill H Trin *Worc* 90-94; V from 94. *The Vicarage, 58 Wrights Lane, Cradley Heath, Warley, West Midlands B64 6RD* 0121-559 7407

SWANN, Robert Edgar. b 50. Salford Univ BSc72 Leeds Univ DipTh79. Coll of Resurr Mirfield 77. d 80 p 81. C Southport H Trin *Liv* 80-84; R Rufford *Blackb* from 84. *St Mary's Rectory, 17 Church Road, Rufford, Ormskirk, Lancs L40 1TA* Rufford (01704) 821261

SWANNELL, George Alfred Roderick. b 20. St Edm Hall Ox BA47 MA51. Ridley Hall Cam 47. d 49 p 50. V Hildenborough *Roch* 68-80; Lic to Offic from 80; Chapl Kent and Sussex Hosp Tunbridge Wells 80-86; rtd 85; Chapl Sevenoaks Hosp from 86; Chapl Sevenoaks Sch Kent from 86; Chapl W Heath Sch Sevenoaks from 86. *68 Mount Ephraim, Tunbridge Wells, Kent TN4 8BG* Tunbridge Wells (01892) 529674

SWANSEA AND BRECON, Bishop of. *See* BRIDGES, Rt Rev Dewi Morris

SWARBRIGG, David Cecil. b 42. TCD BA64 MA67. d 65 p 66. C Lisburn Ch Ch *Conn* 65-67; C Thames Ditton *Guildf* 72-76; Chapl Hampton Sch Middx from 76. *The Chaplain's Office, Hampton School, Hampton, Middx TW12 3HD* 0181-979 5526

SWART-RUSSELL, Dr Phoebe. b 58. Cape Town Univ BA79 MA82 DPhil88. Ox NSM Course 89. d 90 p 94. C Riverside *Ox* from 90. *3 Leigh Park, Datchet, Slough SL3 9JP* Slough (01753) 540395

SWEATMAN, John. b 44. Open Univ BA89. Oak Hill Th Coll 68. d 71 p 72. C Rayleigh *Chelmsf* 71-73; C Seaford w Sutton *Chich* 73-77; Chapl RN 77-82; CF 82-85; V Hellingly and Upper Dicker *Chich* 85-90. *3 Porters Way, Polegate, E Sussex BN26 6AP* Polegate (01323) 485523

SWEED, John William. b 35. Bernard Gilpin Soc Dur 58 Clifton Th Coll 59. d 62 p 63. C Shrewsbury St Julian *Lich* 62-64; C Sheff St Jo *Sheff* 64-70; V Doncaster St Jas 70-79; V Hatf from 79; RD Snaith and Hatf from 84. *The Vicarage, Hatfield, Doncaster, S Yorkshire DN7 6RS* Doncaster (01302) 840280

SWEENEY, Robert Maxwell. b 48. QUB BA63 MA66 Birm Univ MA78. Cuddesdon Coll 63. d 65 p 66. C Prestbury *Glouc* 65-68; C Handsworth St Andr *Birm* 68-70; Asst Chapl Lancing Coll W Sussex 70-73; Perm to Offic *Chich* 70-73; V Wotton St Mary *Glouc* 74-79; V Ox St Thos w St Frideswide and Binsey *Ox* from 79; Chapl Magd Coll Ox 82-88. *19 Botley Road, Oxford OX2 0BL* Oxford (01865) 251403

SWEET, Canon John Philip McMurdo. b 27. New Coll Ox BA49 MA52 Lambeth DD94. Westcott Ho Cam 53 Yale Div Sch 54. d 55 p 56. Chapl Selw Coll Cam 58-83; Lic to Offic *Ely* from 58; Wiccamical Preb Chich Cathl *Chich* from 62; Asst Lect Div Cam Univ 60-63; Lect 64-94; Dean of Chapl Selw Coll Cam 83-94; rtd 94. *97 Barton Road, Cambridge CB3 9LL* Cambridge (01223) 353186

SWEET, Reginald Charles. b 36. Open Univ BA74. Ripon Hall Ox 61. d 62 p 63. C Styvechale *Cov* 62-65; Chapl RN 65-69 and 74-93; R Riddlesworth w Gasthorpe and Knettishall *Nor* 69-74; R Brettenham w Rushford 69-74; Perm to Offic from 93. *Walnut Tree Cottage, Rushford, Thetford, Norfolk IP24 2SB* Thetford (01842) 753346

SWEET, Vaughan Carroll. b 46. Aston Univ BSc69 MSc70. Linc Th Coll 89. d 91 p 92. C Uttoxeter w Bramshall *Lich* 91-95; P-in-c Hadley from 95. *The Vicarage, 19 Manor Road, Hadley, Telford, Shropshire TF1 4PN* Telford (01952) 254251

SWEET-ESCOTT, Richard Mark. b 28. Hertf Coll Ox BA51 MA53. Westcott Ho Cam 56. d 58 p 59. C Seaford w Sutton *Chich* 65-72; P-in-c Burpham 72-75; V Easebourne 75-79; V Crawley Down All SS 79-93; rtd 93. *8 Buttsfield Lane, East Hoathly, Lewes, E Sussex BN8 6EF* Halland (01825) 841052

SWEETMAN, Denis Harold. b 22. Roch Th Coll 61. d 63 p 64. C Riverhead *Roch* 63-70; C Dunton Green 67-70; Chapl Sevenoaks Hosp 70-72; R Eynsford w Lullingstone *Roch* 71-73; R Eynsford w Farningham and Lullingstone 73-89; rtd 89; Perm to Offic *Newc* from 89. *31 Gloster Park, Amble, Morpeth, Northd NE65 0JQ* Alnwick (01665) 711863

SWENARTON, Canon John Creighton. b 19. TCD BA41 MA45. d 42 p 43. I Donaghadee *D & D* 60-84; rtd 84. *The Court, Culverhay, Wotton-under-Edge, Glos GL12 7LS* Dursley (01453) 842038

SWENSSON, Sister Gerd Inger. b 51. Lon Univ MPhil Uppsala Univ 70. dss 74 d 87. In Ch of Sweden 74-75; Notting Hill *Lon* 75-77; CSA from 75; Abbey Ho Malmesbury 77-79; R Foundn of St Kath 79-81; Notting Hill All SS w St Columb *Lon* 81-84; Kensington St Mary Abbots w St Geo 85-89; C Bedf Park from 91. *2 Old Forge Mews, London W12 9JP* 0181-740 0173

SWIDENBANK, Stephen. b 37. Lich Th Coll 58. d 61 p 62. V Kells *Carl* 67-76; V Staveley w Kentmere 76-85; rtd 85; Perm to Offic *Carl* from 86. *Flat 1, Engadine, New Road, Windermere, Cumbria LA23 2LA* Windermere (015394) 46507

SWIFT, Ainsley. b 56. Liv Univ BEd80. Ripon Coll Cuddesdon DipMin94. d 94 p 95. C Prescot *Liv* from 94. *St Mary's House, West Street, Prescot, Merseyside L34 1LQ* 0151-426 0716

SWIFT, Christopher James. b 65. Hull Univ BA86. Westcott Ho Cam 89. d 91 p 92. C Longton *Blackb* 91-94; TV Chipping Barnet w Arkley *St Alb* from 94. *St Peter's Vicarage, Barnet Road, Barnet, Herts EN5 3JF* 0181-440 2046

SWIFT, Christopher John. b 54. Linc Coll Ox BA76 MA Selw Coll Cam BA80. Westcott Ho Cam 79. d 81 p 82. C Portsea N End St Mark *Portsm* 81-84; C Alverstoke 84-87; V Whitton SS Phil and Jas *Lon* 87-94; R Shepperton from 94. *The Rectory, Church Square, Shepperton, Middx TW17 9JY* Walton-on-Thames (01932) 220511

SWIFT, Francis Bernard. b 06. Dur Univ LTh32. Lich Th Coll 28. d 31 p 32. V Ireby w Uldale *Carl* 58-72; rtd 72; Lic to Offic *Carl* 72-77; Perm to Offic from 77. *5 Westhaven, Thursby, Carlisle CA5 6PH* Dalston (01228) 710099

SWIFT, Ms Pamela Joan. b 47. Liv Univ BSc68. NE Ord Course 85. d 88 p 94. Par Dn Bermondsey St Jas w Ch Ch *S'wark* 88-91; Par Dn Middleton St Cross *Ripon* 91-92; Dioc Stewardship Adv from 92. *33 Lovell Park Hill, Leeds LS10 4NW* Leeds (0113) 245 8678 or 248 7487

SWIFT, Richard Barrie. b 33. Selw Coll Cam BA58 MA64. Ripon Hall Ox. d 60 p 61. C Sidmouth St Nic *Ex* 64-72; P-in-c W Hyde St Thos *St Alb* 72-77; V Mill End 72-77; V Mill End and Heronsgate w W Hyde 77-82; V Axminster *Ex* 82-83; P-in-c Chardstock 82-83; P-in-c Combe Pyne w Rousdon 82-83; TR Axminster, Chardstock, Combe Pyne and Rousdon 83-94; rtd 94. *Wheel Cottage, Exmouth Road, Colaton Raleigh, Sidmouth, Devon EX10 0LE*

SWIFT, Selwyn. b 41. Trin Coll Bris 73. d 76 p 77. C Melksham *Sarum* 76-79; TV 79-81; TV Whitton 81-84; V Derry Hill 84-89; R Bunwell, Carleton Rode, Tibenham, Gt Moulton etc *Nor* from 89. *The Rectory, Carleton Rode, Norwich NR16 1RN* Bunwell (01953) 789218

SWIFT, Stanley (Stan). b 47. ACIS71 Nottm Univ DipTh73 Open Univ BA86. Linc Th Coll 71. d 74 p 75. C Heaton St Barn *Bradf* 74-77; C Bexhill St Pet *Chich* 77-81; R Crowland *Linc* 81-86; RD Elloe W 82-86; R Upminster *Chelmsf* 86-95; P-in-c N Ockendon 94-95; V Rush Green from 95. *St Augustine's Vicarage, Birkbeck Road, Romford RM7 0QP* Romford (01708) 741460

SWINBURNE, Harold Noel. b 27. Univ Coll Lon BA49 St Chad's Coll Dur DipTh. d 53 p 54. V Chilton Moor *Dur* 59-71; Lect Relig Studies New Coll Dur 71-93; Lic to Offic *Dur* 71-85; V Bishopwearmouth St Nic 85-93; rtd 93. *39 Durham Moor Crescent, Durham DH1 5AS* 0191-386 2603

SWINDELL, Anthony Charles. b 50. Selw Coll Cam BA73 MA77 Leeds Univ MPhil77. Ripon Hall Ox 73. d 75 p 76. C Hessle *York* 75-78; P-in-c Litlington w W Dean *Chich* 78-80; Adult Educn Adv E Sussex 78-80; TV Heslington *York* 80-81; Chapl York Univ 80-81; R Harlaxton *Linc* 81-91; RD Grantham 85-90; R Jersey St Sav *Win* from 91; Perm to Offic *Nor* from 93. *The Rectory, St Saviour, Jersey, Channel Islands JE2 7NP* Jersey (01534) 36679

SWINDELL, Brian. b 35. St Jo Coll Nottm 86. d 88 p 89. C Wombwell *Sheff* 88-91; V Brinsworth w Catcliffe 91-93; TR Brinsworth w Catcliffe and Treeton from 93. *The Vicarage, 61 Whitehill Lane, Brinsworth, Rotherham, S Yorkshire S60 5JR* Rotherham (01709) 363850

SWINDELL, Richard Carl. b 45. FCollP87 Didsbury Coll Man CertEd67 Open Univ BA73 Leeds Univ MEd86. N Ord Course 79 Qu Coll Birm. d 82 p 83. Hd Teacher Moorside Jun Sch from 78; NSM Halifax St Aug *Wakef* 82-92; NSM Huddersfield H Trin from 92. *38 The Gardens, Heath Road, Halifax, W Yorkshire HX1 2PL* Halifax (01422) 361972

SWINDELLS, Andrew Wallis (Andy). b 65. Peterho Cam BA88 MA92. Ridley Hall Cam 89. d 92 p 93. C Walworth *S'wark* 92-94; Asst Chapl Tonbridge Sch Kent from 94. *Tonbridge School, High Street, Tonbridge, Kent TN9 1JP* Tonbridge (01732) 365555

SWINDELLS, Philip John. b 34. St Edm Hall Ox BA56 MA60. Ely Th Coll 56. d 58 p 59. C Upton cum Chalvey *Ox* 58-62; C Bishops Hull St Jo *B & W* 62-66; C Stevenage St Geo *St Alb* 66-71; V Stevenage All SS Pin Green 71-78; R Clophill from 78; P-in-c Upper w Lower Gravenhurst from 83. *The Rectory, Great Lane, Clophill, Bedford MK45 4BQ* Silsoe (01525) 860792

SWINDLEHURST, Canon Michael Robert Carol. b 29. Worc Coll Ox BA52 MA56. Cuddesdon Coll 61. d 63 p 64. V Brightlingsea *Chelmsf* 69-95; Miss to Seamen 69-95; RD St

Osyth *Chelmsf* 84-94; Hon Can Chelmsf Cathl 89-95; rtd 95. *9 Radwinter Road, Saffron Walden, Essex CB11 3HU* Saffron Walden (01799) 513788

SWINDLEY, Canon Geoffrey. b 25. St Mich Coll Llan 59. **d** 61 **p** 62. V Buttington and Pool Quay *St As* 68-77; R Welshpool w Castle Caereinion 77-92; RD Pool 77-92; Hon Can St As Cathl 83-93; rtd 93. *2 Cobden Street, Welshpool, Powys SY21 7EH* Welshpool (01938) 555942

SWINDON, Archdeacon of. See MIDDLETON, Ven Michael John

SWINDON, Suffragan Bishop of. See DOE, Rt Rev Michael David

SWINGLER, Preb Jack Howell. b 19. St Jo Coll Cam BA41 MA47. Ridley Hall Cam 46. **d** 48 **p** 49. V Henstridge *B & W* 53-79; RD Merston 74-84; P-in-c Charlton Horethorne w Stowell 78-79; Preb Wells Cathl from 79; R Henstridge and Charlton Horethorne w Stowell 79-85; rtd 85. *St Andrew's, March Lane, Galhampton, Yeovil, Somerset BA22 7AN* North Cadbury (01963) 40842

SWINHOE, Terence Leslie (Terry). b 49. Man Univ BA71 PGCE72. N Ord Course. **d** 84 **p** 85. C Harborne St Pet *Birm* 84-87; V Warley *Wakef* from 87. *The Vicarage, 466 Burnley Road, Warley, Halifax, W Yorkshire HX2 7LW* Halifax (01422) 363623

SWINN, Gerald Robert. b 40. Leeds Univ BSc60 Lon Univ BD70. Oak Hill Th Coll 63. **d** 66 **p** 67. C Weston-super-Mare Ch Ch *B & W* 66-69; C Harefield *Lon* 70-72; Lic to Offic *Sarum* from 72. *16 Heddington Drive, Blandford Forum, Dorset DT11 7TP* Blandford (01258) 451637

SWINNERTON, Edward. b 26. St Aid Birkenhead 62. **d** 64 **p** 65. V Hambleton *Blackb* 69-88; P-in-c Out Rawcliffe 84-88; V Hambleton w Out Rawcliffe 88-89; V Barnacre w Calder Vale 89-92; rtd 92. *136 Prince Rupert Drive, Tockwith, York YO5 8PU* Boroughbridge (01423) 358203

SWINNERTON, Ernest George Francis. b 33. Clare Coll Cam BA54 MA57. Linc Th Coll 56. **d** 58 **p** 59. C Kirkholt *Man* 58-61; C Swindon Ch Ch *Bris* 61-67; C-in-c Walcot St Andr CD 67-75; P-in-c Chilton Foliat *Sarum* 76; TV Whitton 76-85; V Bolton St Matt w St Barn *Man* from 85. *St Matthew's Vicarage, Stowell Street, Bolton BL1 3RQ* Bolton (01204) 22810

SWINNEY, Thomas. b 14. Kelham Th Coll 32. **d** 38 **p** 39. V Witton le Wear *Dur* 59-79; V Fir Tree 77-79; rtd 79. *6 Wesley Grove, Bishop Auckland, Co Durham DL14 7TG* Bishop Auckland (01388) 603739

SWINTON, Garry Dunlop. b 59. SS Mark & Jo Coll Plymouth BA81 CertEd82. Ripon Coll Cuddesdon 85. **d** 88 **p** 89. C Surbiton St Andr and St Mark *S'wark* 88-92; Succ S'wark Cathl from 92. *St Paul's Vicarage, Kipling Street, London SE1 3RU* 0171-407 8290

SWITHINBANK, Kim Stafford. b 53. SS Coll Cam BA77 MA80. Cranmer Hall Dur 78. **d** 80 **p** 81. C Heigham H Trin *Nor* 80-83; Chapl Monkton Combe Sch Bath 83-85; C St Marylebone All So w SS Pet and Jo *Lon* 85-88; C Langham Place All So 88-89; R Stamford St Geo w St Paul *Linc* from 90. *St George's Rectory, Stamford, Lincs PE9 2BN* Stamford (01780) 63351

SWITZERLAND, Archdeacon of. See HAWKER, Ven Peter John

SWYER, David Martin. b 64. Univ of Wales (Abth) BA87 PGCE89. St Mich Coll Llan DipTh91. **d** 91 **p** 92. C Killay *S & B* 91-93; C Newton St Pet 93-95; R Albourne w Sayers Common and Twineham *Chich* from 95. *The Rectory, 5 The Twitten, Albourne, Hassocks, W Sussex BN6 9DF* Hassocks (01273) 832129

SWYER (nee HARRIS), Mrs Rebecca Jane. b 67. **d** 91. C Sketty *S & B* 91-95. *The Rectory, 5 The Twitten, Albourne, Hassocks, W Sussex BN6 9DF* Hassocks (01273) 832129

SWYNNERTON, Brian Thomas. b 31. JP77. Ox Univ Inst of Educn 56 NY Univ BA74 PhD75 FRGS62 LCP62. Lich Th Coll 67. **d** 69 **p** 70. C Swynnerton *Lich* 69-71; CF (TAVR) 70-80; C Eccleshall *Lich* 71-74; C Croxton w Broughton 74-80; Chapl and Lect Stafford Coll 80-84; Chapl Naples w Sorrento, Capri and Bari *Eur* 84-85; Perm to Offic *Lich* 85-88; Perm to Offic *Wakef* 85-88; Chapl Rishworth Sch Ripponden 85-88; Chapl Acton Reynald Sch Shrewsbury from 88. *Hales Farm, Market Drayton, Shropshire TF9 2PP* Market Drayton (01630) 657156

SYER, Canon George Vivian. b 11. AKC39. ACT ThL56. **d** 39 **p** 42. V Whitchurch Canonicorum and Stanton *Sarum* 59-71; R Wootton Fitzpaine 66-71; RD Lyme Bay 62-71; Can Sarum Cathl 70-71; R Chagford *Ex* 71-76; rtd 76; Perm to Offic *Ex* 76-90. *48 Newtown, Milborne Port, Sherborne, Dorset DT9 5BJ* Milborne Port (01963) 250375

SYKES, Albert. b 08. Man Egerton Hall 33. **d** 35 **p** 36. V Pelynt *Truro* 67-73; R Lanreath 67-73; rtd 73; Hon C St Austell *Truro* from 78. *32 Biscovey Road, Par, Cornwall PL24 2HW* Par (01726) 814139

SYKES, Frederick Drummond. b 11. CCC Cam BA33 MA37. Ely Th Coll 33. **d** 34 **p** 35. V Hepworth *Wakef* 71-76; rtd 76; Perm to Offic *Wakef* from 85. *4 West Lodge Crescent, Huddersfield HD2 2EH* Halifax (01422) 372223

SYKES, Graham Timothy Gordon. b 59. ACIB89. St Jo Coll Nottm BTh92. **d** 92 **p** 93. C Kington w Huntington, Old Radnor, Kinnerton etc *Heref* from 92. *5 Gravel Hill Drive, Kington, Herefordshire HR5 3BS* Kington (01544) 231403

SYKES, Ian. b 44. Lon Univ DipTh Leic Univ DipEd. Bris Bapt Coll 64 Ripon Coll Cuddesdon 84. **d** 85 **p** 86. In Bapt Ch 64-84; C Headington *Ox* 85-88; TV Bourne Valley *Sarum* from 88. *The Rectory, High Street, Porton, Salisbury SP4 0LH* Idmiston (01980) 610305

SYKES, James Clement. b 42. Keble Coll Ox BA64 MA71. Westcott Ho Cam 65. **d** 67 **p** 68. C Bishop's Stortford St Mich *St Alb* 67-71; Chapl St Jo Sch Leatherhead 71-73; Bermuda 74-79; V Northaw *St Alb* 79-87; Chapl St Marg Sch Bushey from 87. *The Chaplain's House, St Margaret's School, Bushey, Herts WD2 1DT* 0181-950 4616

SYKES, Miss Jean. b 45. Leeds Univ BA66 Bris Univ CertEd67. Ripon Coll Cuddesdon 86. **d** 88 **p** 94. C N Huddersfield *Wakef* 88-91; TD 91-93; TV Kippax w Allerton Bywater *Ripon* from 94. *The Vicarage, 134 Leeds Road, Allerton Bywater, Castleford, W Yorkshire WF10 2HB* Leeds (0113) 286 9415

SYKES, Jeremy Jonathan Nicholas. b 61. Wycliffe Hall Ox. **d** 89 **p** 90. C Knowle *Birm* 89-92; Asst Chapl Oakham Sch Leics from 92. *8 Ashwell Road, Oakham, Leics LE15 6QG* Oakham (01572) 724540

SYKES, Canon John. b 39. Man Univ BA62. Ripon Hall Ox 61. **d** 63 **p** 64. C Heywood St Luke *Man* 63-67; Chapl Bolton Colls of FE 67-71; C Bolton H Trin *Man* 67-71; R Reddish 71-78; V Saddleworth 78-87; TR Oldham from 87; Hon Can Man Cathl from 91; Chapl to The Queen from 95. *The Vicarage, 15 Grotton Hollow, Oldham OL4 4LN* 0161-678 6767 or 624 4866

SYKES, John Trevor. b 35. Lich Th Coll 60. **d** 62 **p** 63. C Lillington *Cov* 62-65; C Cov St Marg 65-68; P-in-c Bubbenhall 68-77; V Ryton on Dunsmore 68-77; V Ryton on Dunsmore w Bubbenhall from 77. *The Vicarage, Ryton on Dunsmore, Coventry CV8 3ET* Coventry (01203) 303570

✠SYKES, Rt Rev Stephen Whitefield. b 39. St Jo Coll Cam BA61 MA65. Ripon Hall Ox 63. **d** 64 **p** 65 **c** 90. Fell and Dean St Jo Coll Cam 64-74; Asst Lect Div Cam Univ 64-68; Lect 68-74; Can Res Dur Cathl *Dur* 74-85; Van Mildert Prof Div Dur Univ 74-85; Regius Prof Div Cam Univ 85-90; Hon Can Ely Cathl *Ely* 85-90; Bp Ely from 90. *Bishop's House, Ely, Cambs CB7 4DW* Ely (01353) 662749 Fax 669477

SYKES, William George David (Bill). b 39. Ball Coll Ox BA63 MA68. Wycliffe Hall Ox 63. **d** 65 **p** 66. Chapl Bradf Cathl *Bradf* 65-69; Chapl Univ Coll Lon 69-78; Chapl Univ Coll Ox from 78. *The Senior Common Room, University College, Oxford OX1 4BH* Oxford (01865) 276602

SYLVIA, Keith Lawrence Wilfred. b 63. Chich Th Coll 85. **d** 88 **p** 89. C Newbold and Dunston *Derby* 88-91; C Heston *Lon* 91-95; V Brighton St Matthias *Chich* from 95. *St Matthias's Vicarage, 45 Hollington Park Avenue, Brighton BN1 7JQ* Brighton (01273) 508178

SYMES, Collin. b 20. Birm Univ BA47 MA48. Bps' Coll Cheshunt 56. **d** 58 **p** 59. Hon C Rusthall *Roch* 68-85; Chapl W Kent Coll of FE 68-73; Chapl Chapl R N Sch Haslemere 81-84; rtd 84; Chapl St Elphin's Sch Matlock 85-86. *3 Eden Walk, Tunbridge Wells, Kent TN1 1TT* Tunbridge Wells (01892) 532283

SYMES, Percy Peter. b 24. Leeds Univ BA50. Coll of Resurr Mirfield 50. **d** 52 **p** 53. V Reading St Luke *Ox* 61-81; V Drayton St Pet (Berks) 81-89; rtd 89; Hon C Lower Windrush *Ox* from 94. *107 Abingdon Road, Standlake, Witney, Oxon OX8 7QN*

SYMES-THOMPSON, Hugh Kynard. b 54. Peterho Cam BA76 MA81 St Jo Coll Dur DipTh79. **d** 79 **p** 80. C Summerfield *Birm* 79-82; C Harlow New Town w Lt Parndon *Chelmsf* 82-83; Australia 84-89; TV Dagenham *Chelmsf* from 89. *St George's Vicarage, 86 Rogers Road, Dagenham, Essex RM10 8JX* 0181-593 2760

SYMINGTON, Patricia Ann. See TURNER, Mrs Patricia Ann

SYMMONS, Roderic Paul (Rod). b 56. Chu Coll Cam MA77. Oak Hill Th Coll BA83. **d** 83 **p** 84. C Ox St Aldate w St Matt *Ox* 83-88; USA 89-90; R Ardingly *Chich* from 90. *The Rectory, Church Lane, Ardingly, Haywards Heath, W Sussex RH17 6UR* Ardingly (01444) 892332

SYMON, Canon John Francis Walker. b 26. Edin Univ MA50. Edin Th Coll 50. **d** 52 **p** 53. R Dunblane *St And* 68-85; Can St Ninian's Cathl Perth 74-91; Chapl Trin Coll Glenalmond 85-91; rtd 91. *Westgarth, Tom-na-croich, Fortingall, Aberfeldy, Perthshire PH15 2LJ* Kenmore (01887) 830287

SYMON, Canon Roger Hugh Crispin. b 34. St Jo Coll Cam BA59. Coll of Resurr Mirfield 59. **d** 61 **p** 62. C Westmr St Steph w St Jo *Lon* 61-66; P-in-c Hascombe *Guildf* 66-68; Chapl Surrey Univ 66-74; V Paddington Ch Ch *Lon* 74-78; V

Paddington St Jas 78-79; USPG 80-87; Abp Cant's Acting Sec for Angl Communion Affairs 87-94; Can Res Cant Cathl *Cant* from 94. *19 The Precincts, Canterbury CT1 2EP* Canterbury (01227) 459918 Fax as telephone

SYMONDS, Alan Jeffrey. b 56. Ridley Hall Cam CTM95. **d** 95. C Bath St Luke *B & W* from 95. *59 Longfellow Avenue, Bath BA2 4SH* Bath (01225) 480189

SYMONDS, Edward George. b 03. Launde Abbey 58. **d** 59 **p** 60. V Leic All SS *Leic* 64-74; rtd 74; Perm to Offic *Llan* from 74. *19 Victoria Square, Penarth, S Glam CF64 3EJ* Penarth (01222) 705546

SYMONDS, James Henry. b 31. Ripon Hall Ox 67. **d** 69 **p** 70. C Southn (City Cen) *Win* 69-71; CF 71-78; CF from 79; P-in-c Arrington *Ely* 78-79; P-in-c Orwell 78-79; P-in-c Wimpole 78-79; P-in-c Croydon w Clopton 78-79; rtd 91. *clo MOD (Army), Bagshot Park, Bagshot, Surrey GU19 5PL* Bagshot (01276) 471717 Fax 412834

SYMONDS, James Robert Pinder. b 10. CCC Cam BA32 MA37. Linc Th Coll 32. **d** 34 **p** 35. OGS from 44; V Leic St Mary *Leic* 56-74; Subwarden St Deiniol's Lib Hawarden 74-78; rtd 75; Chapl Trin Hosp Retford 78-87; Perm to Offic *Chich* 87-94. *Flat 10, Stuart Court, High Street, Kibworth, Leicester LE8 0LE* Leicester (0116) 279 6380

SYMONS, Fernley Rundle. b 39. Peterho Cam BA61 MA71. St Steph Ho Ox 61. **d** 64 **p** 65. C Chesterton St Geo *Ely* 64-67; C Henleaze *Bris* 67-72; V Shirehampton from 72. *St Mary's Vicarage, 8 Priory Gardens, Bristol BS11 0BZ* Bristol (0117) 982 2737

SYMONS, James Edward. b 28. AKC57. **d** 58 **p** 59. C Benwell St Jas *Newc* 58-62; C Alnwick St Mich 62-65; C Prudhoe 65-67; V Mickley from 67. *The Vicarage, Mickley, Stocksfield, Northd NE43 7LS* Stocksfield (01661) 843342

SYMONS, Peter Henry. b 25. AKC51. **d** 52 **p** 53. V Woolacombe *Ex* 61-75; V Kingsteignton 75-89; rtd 89. *13 Harbour Court, Penzance, Cornwall TR18 2LS*

SYMONS, Stewart Burlace. b 31. Keble Coll Ox BA55 MA59. Clifton Th Coll 55. **d** 57 **p** 58. C Hornsey Rise St Mary *Lon* 57-60; C Gateshead St Geo *Dur* 60-61; C Patcham *Chich* 61-64; R Stretford St Bride *Man* 64-71; V Waterloo St Jo *Liv* 71-83; R Ardrossan *Glas* from 83; C-in-c Irvine St Andr from 83; Miss to Seamen from 83. *31 Milgarholm Avenue, Irvine, Ayrshire KA12 0EL* Irvine (01294) 278341

SYMS, Richard Arthur. b 43. Ch Coll Cam BA66 MA71. Wycliffe Hall Ox 66. **d** 68 **p** 69. C New Eltham All SS *S'wark* 68-72; Chapl to Arts and Recreation *Dur* 72-73; C Hitchin St Mary *St Alb* 73-76; TV Hitchin 77-78; Perm to Offic from 78. *94 Pondcroft Road, Knebworth, Herts SG3 6DE* Stevenage (01438) 811933

SYNNETT, Alan Patrick Sutherland. b 59. **d** 85 **p** 86. C Lisburn Ch Ch *Conn* 85-88; CF 88-95; I Galloon w Drummully *Clogh* from 95. *The Rectory, Newtownbutler, Enniskillen, Co Fermanagh BT92 8JD* Newtownbutler (013657) 245

SYNNOTT, Canon Patrick Joseph. b 18. **d** 52 **p** 54. I Magheralin *D & D* 63-74; RD Shankill 70-74; I Belf St Donard 74-89; Can Down Cathl 80-89; Chan Down Cathl 87-89; rtd 89; Lic to Offic *D & D* from 90. *7 Norwood Drive, Belfast BT4 2EA* Belfast (01232) 652365

T

TABERN, James. b 23. St Aid Birkenhead 57. **d** 59 **p** 60. V Litherland St Paul Hatton Hill *Liv* 61-72; V Gillingham St Mark *Roch* 72-79; V Lindow *Ches* 79-85; rtd 85; Perm to Offic *Liv* 86-91. *12 Dickinson Road, Formby, Merseyside L37 4BX* Formby (01704) 831131

TABERNACLE, Peter Aufrere. b 22. S'wark Ord Course 72. **d** 74 **p** 75. NSM Enfield St Geo *Lon* 74-80; C Corby Epiphany w St Jo *Pet* 80-83; V Wellingborough St Mark 83-88; P-in-c Wilby 83-88; rtd 88; Perm to Offic *Pet* from 88. *15 Archfield Court, Oxford Street, Wellingborough, Northants NN8 4HH* Wellingborough (01933) 228570

TABOR, John Tranham. b 30. Ball Coll Ox BA56 MA58. Ridley Hall Cam 55. **d** 58 **p** 59. C Lindfield *Chich* 58-62; Tutor Ridley Hall Cam 62-63; Chapl 63-68; Warden Scargill Ho 68-75; R Berkhamsted St Mary *St Alb* from 75. *The Rectory, 80 High Street, Northchurch, Berkhamsted, Herts HP4 3QW* Berkhamsted (01442) 865312

TABOR, Leonard Frank. b 15. St Steph Ho Ox 47. **d** 50 **p** 51. V Margate All SS *Cant* 66-86; rtd 86; Perm to Offic *Cant* from 86.

Appleshaw, 18B Whitehall Gardens, Canterbury, Kent CT2 8BD Canterbury (01227) 464342

TABRAHAM, Canon Albert John. b 14. Birm Univ DipTh71. Coll of Resurr Mirfield 55. **d** 56 **p** 57. V Stockland Green *Birm* 59-70; RD Aston 68-70; V Acocks Green 70-80; RD Yardley 74-77; Hon Can Birm Cathl 78-80; rtd 80; Hon C Duns *Edin* from 80. *10 Gourlays Wynd, Duns, Berwickshire TD11 3AZ* Duns (01361) 82483

TADMAN, John Christopher. b 33. Lon Coll of Div 54. **d** 58 **p** 59. C Blackheath St Jo *S'wark* 58-61; C Surbiton Hill Ch Ch 61-64; R Cratfield w Heveningham and Ubbeston *St E* 65-70; R Kelsale w Carlton 70-74; R Ashurst *Roch* 74-76; V Fordcombe 74-77; P-in-c Penshurst 76-77; R Penshurst and Fordcombe 77-85; V Felsted *Chelmsf* 85-93; Resource Min Brentwood from 93; Chapl Warley Hosp Brentwood from 93. *The Rectory, 2 Church Road, Kelvedon Common, Brentwood, Essex CM14 5TJ*

TADMAN-ROBINS, Christopher Rodney (Chris). b 47. JP82. LRAM68 ARCM68 GNSM68 Lon Inst of Educn PGCE69 Westmr Coll Ox BA91 DipApTh93 Ox Univ MTh94. Ox NSM Course 86. **d** 89 **p** 90. NSM Burford w Fulbrook and Taynton *Ox* 89-94; NSM Burford w Fulbrook, Taynton, Asthall etc from 94. *Rest Harrow, Meadow Lane, Fulbrook, Burford, Oxon OX18 4BS* Burford (01993) 823551

TAGGART, Canon Justin Paul. b 11. Linc Th Coll 32. **d** 34 **p** 35. V Woodhall Spa and Kirkstead *Linc* 52-76; R Langton w Woodhall 52-76; Can and Preb Linc Cathl 68-76; rtd 76. *Reedsbeck, Droghadfayle Road, Port Erin, Isle of Man IM9 6EE* Port Erin (01624) 834204

TAGGART, William Joseph. b 54. DipFD. DipTh. **d** 85 **p** 86. C Belf St Mich *Conn* 85-90; Chmn Dioc Youth Coun from 90; I Belf St Kath from 90. *St Katharine's Rectory, 24 Lansdowne Road, Belfast BT15 4DB* Belfast (01232) 777647

TAGUE, Russell. b 59. Aston Tr Scheme 90 Linc Th Coll 92. **d** 94 **p** 95. C Astley *Man* from 94. *42 Manor Road, Astley, Tyldesley, Manchester M29 7HT* Atherton (01942) 878622

TAILBY, Mark Kevan. b 36. K Coll Lon 60. **d** 64 **p** 65. C Newbold on Avon *Cov* 64-67; C Stratford-on-Avon w Bishopton 67-70; CF 70-76; P-in-c S Shoebury *Chelmsf* 76-79; P-in-c Stambridge 79-89; Chapl Rochford Gen Hosp 79-89; TV Dovercourt and Parkeston *Chelmsf* 89-93; P-in-c Colchester St Botolph w H Trin and St Giles from 93; OCF from 93. *St Botolph's Vicarage, 50B Priory Street, Colchester CO1 2QB* Colchester (01206) 868043

TAILBY, Peter Alan. b 49. Chich Th Coll 83. **d** 85 **p** 86. C Stocking Farm *Leic* 85-88; C Knighton St Mary Magd 88-90; P-in-c Thurnby Lodge from 90. *Christ Church Vicarage, 73 Nursery Road, Leicester LE5 2HQ* Leicester (0116) 241 3848

TAIT, Henry Alexander. b 29. Chester Coll CertEd55 Dur Univ DipTh63 Newc Univ MA95. St Chad's Coll Dur 65. **d** 66 **p** 67. Dioc Educn Officer *St E* 69-74; R Elmsett w Aldham 69-75; P-in-c Kersey w Lindsey 74-75; R Sandiacre *Derby* 75-81; V E Dereham *Nor* 81-88; P-in-c Scarning 81-88; R E Dereham and Scarning 89-90; RD Hingham and Mitford 86-90; V Gilling and Kirkby Ravensworth *Ripon* 90-94; Asst RD Richmond 91-94; rtd 94. *31 Dotland Close, Hexham, Northd NE46 1UF* Hexham (01434) 607626

TAIT, James Laurence Jamieson. b 47. St Jo Coll Dur 78. **d** 80 **p** 81. C Heyside *Man* 80-81; C Westhoughton 81-84; R Aldingham and Dendron and Rampside *Carl* 84-88; V Flookburgh 88-92; New Zealand from 92. *St Peter's Vicarage, 229 Ruahine Street, Palmerston North, New Zealand* Levin (6) 358-5403 or 358-9134

TAIT, Philip (Leslie). b 52. Ex Univ BA73 Hull Univ PGCE74. NE Ord Course 87. **d** 90 **p** 91. NSM Osbaldwick w Murton *York* 90-92; Chapl Burnholme Sch York 90-92; Chapl and Hd Relig Studies Berkhamsted Sch Herts from 93. *Adelbert House, Mill Street, Berkhamsted, Herts HP4 2BA* Berkhamsted (01442) 878190

TAIT, Ruth Elizabeth. Moray Ord Course 88. **dss** 90 **d** 94. Elgin w Lossiemouth *Mor* 90-94; C from 94. *30 Mayne Road, Elgin, Morayshire IV30 1PB* Elgin (01343) 542919

TAIT, Thomas William. b 07. St Cath Soc Ox BA30 MA33. Clifton Th Coll 40 Edin Th Coll 42. **d** 43 **p** 44. R Church Lawton *Ches* 64-67; rtd 72. *43 Hanover Gardens, Cuckoofield Lane, Mulbarton, Norwich NR14 8DA* Mulbarton (01508) 70598

TALBOT, Alan John. b 23. BNC Ox BA49 MA55. Coll of Resurr Mirfield 49. **d** 51 **p** 52. V Stepney St Aug w St Phil *Lon* 69-78; V Twickenham All Hallows 78-86; rtd 88. *46 Brandon Street, London SE17 1NL* 0171-703 0719

TALBOT, Derek Michael. b 55. St Jo Coll Dur BSc77 Nottm Univ DipTh85. St Jo Coll Nottm 84. **d** 87 **p** 88. C Rushden w Newton Bromswold *Pet* 87-90; C Barton Seagrave w Warkton from 90. *9 Churchill Way, Kettering, Northants NN15 5DP* Kettering (01536) 517553

TALBOT, George Brian. b 37. Qu Coll Birm 78. **d** 80 **p** 81. C Heref St Martin *Heref* 80-83; R Bishop's Frome w Castle Frome and Fromes Hill 83-90; P-in-c Acton Beauchamp and Evesbatch w Stanford Bishop 83-90; R Burstow *S'wark* from 90. *The Rectory, Church Road, Burstow, Horley, Surrey RH6 9RG* Smallfield (01342) 842224

TALBOT, John Herbert Boyle. b 30. TCD BA51 MA57. CITC 52. **d** 53 **p** 54. C Dub St Pet *D & G* 53-57; Chan Vicar St Patrick's Cathl Dub 56-61; C Dub Zion Ch 57-61; Chapl Asst St Thos Hosp Lon 61-64; Min Can and Sacr Cant Cathl *Cant* 64-67; R Brasted *Roch* 67-84; R Ightham from 84; P-in-c Shipbourne 87-91; RD Shoreham 89-95. *The Rectory, Tonbridge Road, Ightham, Sevenoaks, Kent TN15 9BG* Borough Green (01732) 884176

TALBOT, John Frederick Maurice. b 12. Chich Th Coll 47. **d** 50 **p** 51. R Wednesbury St Jo *Lich* 57-73; R W Felton 73-87; rtd 87. *8 Rose Hill Close, Whittington, Shropshire SY11 4DY* Oswestry (01691) 657962

TALBOT, Dr John Michael. b 23. FRSM FRCPath68 Lon Univ MD52. S'wark Ord Course 75. **d** 78 **p** 79. NSM S Croydon Em *Cant* 78-81; Perm to Offic *Nor* 82-85; NSM Hethersett w Canteloff w Lt and Gt Melton from 85. *3 White Gates Close, Hethersett, Norwich NR9 3JG* Norwich (01603) 811709

TALBOT, June Phyllis. b 46. Ripon Coll of Educn CertEd67. NE Ord Course 88. **d** 91 **p** 94. NSM Cleadon *Dur* from 91. *66 Wheatall Drive, Whitburn, Sunderland SR6 7HQ* 0191-529 2265

TALBOT (nee KINGHAM), Mrs Mair Josephine. b 59. Univ Coll Lon BA84. Ridley Hall Cam 85. **d** 88 **p** 94. C Gt Yarmouth *Nor* 88-94; Raveningham 94; The Raveningham Gp from 94. *The Rectory, Church Road, Thurlton, Norwich NR14 6RN* Norwich (01508) 548648

TALBOT, Mrs Marian. b 25. Qu Coll Birm 76. **dss** 78 **d** 87 **p** 94. Droitwich *Worc* 78-87; Chapl Droitwich Hosps 83-88; Par Dn Droitwich Spa 87-88; Perm to Offic from 88; Asst Chapl Alexandra Hosp Redditch from 88. *Talbot House, Foredraught Lane, Tibberton, Droitwich, Worcs WR9 7NH* Spetchley (01905) 345404

TALBOT, Very Rev Maurice John. b 12. TCD BA35 MA43. **d** 35 **p** 36. Dean Limerick *L & K* 54-71; Preb St Patr Cathl Dub 59-73; C Kilmallock *L & K* 71-73; Lic to Offic 75-80; I Drumcliffe 80-84; Bp's C Banagher *M & K* 85-86; rtd 86. *Woodbrook, Lower Main Street, Abbeyleix, Co Laois, Irish Republic* Abbeyleix (502) 31721

TALBOT, Stephen Richard. b 52. BSc. Trin Coll Bris DipHE. **d** 84 **p** 85. C Tonbridge SS Pet and Paul *Roch* 84-89; P-in-c Hemingford Grey *Ely* from 89; P-in-c Hemingford Abbots from 89. *The Vicarage, Braggs Lane, Hemingford Grey, Huntingdon, Cambs PE18 9BW* St Ives (01480) 467305

TALBOT, Ms Susan Gabriel. b 46. Leeds Univ BA69 Man Poly CertEd70 Lon Univ DipTh72. N Ord Course 91. **d** 94. C Wythenshawe St Martin *Man* from 94. *45 Amberwood Drive, Baguley, Manchester M23 9NZ* 0161-998 3220

TALBOT-PONSONBY, Preb Andrew. b 44. Leeds Univ DipTh66. Coll of Resurr Mirfield 66. **d** 68 **p** 70. C Radlett *St Alb* 68-70; C Salisbury St Martin *Sarum* 70-73; P-in-c Acton Burnell w Pitchford *Heref* 73-80; P-in-c Frodesley 73-80; P-in-c Cound 73-80; Asst Youth Officer 73-80; P-in-c Bockleton w Leysters 80-81; V 81-92; P-in-c Kimbolton w Middleton-on-the-Hill 80-81; V Kimbolton w Hamnish and Middleton-on-the-Hill 81-92; P-in-c Wigmore Abbey from 92; Preb Heref Cathl from 87. *The Rectory, Leintwardine, Craven Arms, Shropshire SY7 0LL* Leintwardine (01547) 540235

TALBOT-PONSONBY, Mrs Gillian (Jill). b 50. Sarum & Wells Th Coll 89. **d** 91 **p** 94. C Leominster *Heref* 91-92; NSM Wigmore Abbey from 92. *The Rectory, Leintwardine, Craven Arms, Shropshire SY7 0LL* Leintwardine (01547) 540235

TALBOTT, Brian Hugh. b 34. RD78. St Pet Hall Ox BA57 MA64. Westcott Ho Cam. **d** 59 **p** 60. C Newc H Cross *Newc* 59-61; C Newc St Jo 61-64; Chapl RNR 63-77; Sen Chapl RNR from 77; Chapl Barnard Castle Sch 64-71; Chapl Bishop's Stortford Coll Herts from 71; Hon C Bishop's Stortford St Mich *St Alb* from 71. *The Chaplain's House, Lower Green, Bishop's Stortford College, Bishop's Stortford, Herts CM23 2QZ* Bishop's Stortford (01279) 651845

TALBOTT, Simon John. b 57. Pontifical Univ Maynooth BD81. **d** 81 **p** 82. In RC Ch 81-87; C Headingley *Ripon* 88-91; V Gt and Lt Ouseburn w Marton-cum-Grafton from 91; Chapl Qu Ethelburga's Coll York from 91. *The Vicarage, Great Ouseburn, York YO5 9RQ* Boroughbridge (01423) 330928

TALENT, Canon Jack. b 23. AKC49. **d** 50 **p** 51. C Grantham St Wulfram *Linc* 50-59; R Corsley *Sarum* 59-62; S Africa from 62; Hon Can Kimberley and Kuruman from 81. *27 Armenia Crescent, Plattekloof Glen, Monta Vista, 7460 South Africa* Cape Town (21) 559-1431

TALLANT, John. b 45. Edin Th Coll 86. **d** 88 **p** 89. C Cayton w Eastfield *York* 88-90; C N Hull St Mich 90-91; V Scarborough St Sav w All SS 91-93; V Fleetwood St Nic *Blackb* from 93. *St Nicholas's Vicarage, Highbury Avenue, Fleetwood, Lancs FY7 7DJ* Fleetwood (01253) 874402

TAMBLING, Peter Francis. b 20. St Pet Hall Ox BA47. Westcott Ho Cam. **d** 49 **p** 50. R Zeals and Stourton *Sarum* 64-73; P-in-c Bourton w Silton 71-73; R Upper Stour 73-74; R Glenfield *Leic* 74-85; RD Sparkenhoe III 76-81; rtd 85; Perm to Offic *B & W* 86-94. *20 Balsam Fields, Wincanton, Somerset BA9 9HF* Wincanton (01963) 34237

TAMPLIN, Peter Harry. b 44. Sarum & Wells Th Coll 71. **d** 73 **p** 74. C Digswell *St Alb* 73-76; C Chesterton St Luke *Ely* 76-82; V Chesterton St Geo 82-95; R Durrington *Sarum* from 95. *The Rectory, Church Street, Durrington, Salisbury SP4 8AL* Stonehenge (01980) 652229

TAMS, Gordon Thomas Carl. b 37. LLCM76 Leeds Univ BMus60 Reading Univ CertEd61 Newc Univ MLitt84. Edin Dioc NSM Course 83. **d** 90 **p** 91. NSM Kelso *Edin* 90-92; P-in-c Coldstream from 92. *St Mary's Parsonage, 47 Lennel Mount, Coldstream, Berwickshire TD12 4NS* Coldstream (01890) 882479

TAMS, Paul William. b 56. Huddersfield Poly CertEd77. E Anglian Minl Tr Course 87. **d** 90 **p** 91. NSM Mildenhall *St E* from 90. *28 Raven Close, Mildenhall, Bury St Edmunds, Suffolk IP28 7LF* Mildenhall (01638) 715475

TANKARD, Reginald Douglas Alan. b 37. Sarum Th Coll 60. **d** 62 **p** 63. C Howden *York* 62-65; C Heckmondwike *Wakef* 65-67; CF 67-70; C Thornbury *Bradf* 82-88; P-in-c Rockcliffe and Blackford *Carl* 88-90; V from 90. *The Vicarage, Rockcliffe, Carlisle CA6 4AA* Rockcliffe (0122874) 209

TANN, Canon David John. b 31. K Coll Lon BD57 AKC57. **d** 58 **p** 59. Hon C Fulham All SS *Lon* 72-82; Lic to Offic 68-72; Teacher Godolphin and Latymer Sch Hammersmith 68-73; Ealing Boys Gr Sch 69-73; Hd of RE Green Sch Isleworth 73-82; V Dudley St Jas *Worc* 82-95; Chapl Burton Rd Hosp Dudley 83-95; Hon Can Worc Cathl *Worc* 90-95; RD Dudley 93-95; rtd 95. *75 Parkview Court, Fulham High Street, London SW6 3LL* 0171-736 6018

TANNER, Preb Alan John. b 25. Linc Coll Ox BA52 MA65. Coll of Resurr Mirfield 52. **d** 54 **p** 55. C Hendon St Mary *Lon* 54-58; V S Harrow St Paul 58-60; Dir Coun for Chr Stewardship 60-65; Dir Lay Tr 65-71; Sec Coun for Miss and Unity 65-80; V St Nic Cole Abbey 66-78; Preacher of the Charterhouse from 73; Sec Gtr Lon Chs' Coun 76-83; P-in-c St Ethelburga Bishopgate *Lon* 78-85; R St Botolph without Bishopgate from 78; P-in-c All Hallows Lon Wall from 80; Bp's Ecum Officer from 81; AD The City from 90; Preb St Paul's Cathl from 91. *9 Sunningfields Road, London NW4 4QR* 0171-588 3388 or 588 1053 Fax 638 1256

TANNER, Canon Frank Hubert. b 38. St Aid Birkenhead. **d** 66 **p** 67. C Ipswich St Marg *St E* 66-69; C Mansf St Pet *S'well* 69-72; V Huthwaite 72-79; Chapl to the Deaf 79-92; Hon Can S'well Minster from 90; Chapl Northn and Rutland Miss to the Deaf from 92. *11 The Avenue, Spinney Hill, Northampton NN3 1BA* Northampton (01604) 494366 or 250922

TANNER, Frederick James. b 24. **d** 64 **p** 65. Uganda 64-69; Hd Master Summerhill Jun Mixed Sch Bris from 69; Perm to Offic *Bris* from 69; Hon C Chew Magna w Dundry *B & W* 81-86; Perm to Offic 86-94. *The Byre, Eastfields, Charlton, Horethorne, Sherborne, Dorset DT9 4PB* Corton Denham (01963) 220641

TANNER, Canon Laurence Ernest. b 17. St Cath Coll Cam BA39 MA43. St Mich Coll Llan. **d** 40 **p** 41. V Shamley Green *Guildf* 64-71; RD Cranleigh 68-71; Can Res Guildf Cathl 71-82; Sub-Dean 72-82; Dir of Ords 71-82; rtd 82; Perm to Offic *St E* from 82. *Homestead Cottage, South Green, Southwold, Suffolk IP18 6EU* Southwold (01502) 722602

TANNER, Mark Stuart. b 59. Nottm Univ BA81. Sarum & Wells Th Coll. **d** 85 **p** 86. C Radcliffe-on-Trent *S'well* 85; C Radcliffe-on-Trent and Shelford etc 85-88; C Bestwood 88-89; TV 89-93; P-in-c S'well H Trin from 93; Bp's Research Officer from 93. *Holy Trinity Vicarage, Westthorpe, Southwell, Notts NG25 0NB* Southwell (01636) 813243

TANNER, Martin Philip. b 54. Univ Coll Lon BSc(Econ)75. Ridley Hall Cam 79. **d** 82 **p** 83. C Bitterne *Win* 82-85; C Weeke 85-88; V Long Buckby w Watford *Pet* from 88. *The Vicarage, 10 Hall Drive, Long Buckby, Northampton NN6 7QU* Long Buckby (01327) 842909

TANSILL, Canon Derek Ernest Edward. b 36. Univ of Wales (Lamp) BA61. Ripon Hall Ox 61. **d** 63 **p** 64. C Chelsea St Luke *Lon* 63-67; C-in-c Saltdean CD *Chich* 67-69; V Saltdean 69-73; V Billingshurst 73-82; RD Horsham 77-82 and 85-93; Can and Preb Chich Cathl from 81; R Bexhill St Pet 82-85; RD Battle and Bexhill 84-86; V Horsham 85-86; TR from 86. *The Vicarage, The Causeway, Horsham, W Sussex RH12 1HE* Horsham (01403) 272919 or 253762

TAPLIN, John. b 35. St Alb Minl Tr Scheme 78. **d** 81 **p** 82. NSM Knebworth *St Alb* 81-88; C Braughing, Lt Hadham, Albury,

Furneux Pelham etc 88; R Lt Hadham w Albury from 88. *The Vicarage, Parsonage Lane, Albury, Ware, Herts SG11 2HU* Albury (01279) 771361

TAPLIN, Kim. b 58. Lon Bible Coll BA79 Homerton Coll Cam PGCE84. S Dios Minl Tr Scheme 94. **d** 94 **p** 95. C Sholing *Win* from 94. *St Francis House, 75 Montague Avenue, Southampton SO19 0QB* Southampton (01703) 443733

TAPPER, John A'Court. b 42. FCA64. Sarum & Wells Th Coll 89. **d** 91 **p** 92. C Ashford *Cant* 91-94; P-in-c Folkestone H Trin w Ch Ch from 94. *Holy Trinity Vicarage, 21 Manor Road, Folkestone, Kent CT20 2SA* Folkestone (01303) 253831

TARGETT, Kenneth. b 28. Qu Coll Birm 54. **d** 57 **p** 58. Perm to Offic *Bradf* 65-82; Australia 82-87; V Old Leake w Wrangle *Linc* 87-94; rtd 94. *The Sloop, Sea Lane, Old Leake, Boston, Lincs PE22 9JA*

TARLETON, Denis Reginald. b 12. TCD BA35 MA45. CITC 36. **d** 36 **p** 37. I Devenish w Boho *Clogh* 59-63; rtd 63; Perm to Offic *D & D* from 67. *33 Drumkeen Court, Belfast BT8 4TU* Belfast (01232) 691003

TARLETON, Peter. b 46. TCD BA72 Div Test73 HDipEd77 MA80. **d** 73 **p** 74. C Cork St Luke w St Ann *C, C & R* 73-75; C Dub Drumcondra *D & G* 75-78; I Limerick City *L & K* 78-82; I Drumgoon w Dernakesh, Ashfield etc *K, E & A* 82-85; Chapl HM Young Offender Inst Hindley 85-89; Chapl HM Pris Lindholme from 89. *HM Prison, Bawtry Road, Hatfield Woodhouse, Doncaster, S Yorkshire DN7 6EE* Doncaster (01302) 846600 Fax 843352

TARLING, Paul. b 53. Oak Hill Th Coll BA. **d** 85 **p** 86. C Old Hill H Trin *Worc* 85-89; V Walford w Bishopswood *Heref* 89-90; P-in-c Goodrich w Welsh Bicknor and Marstow 89-90; R Walford and Saint John, w Bishopswood etc from 90; RD Ross and Archenfield from 95. *The Vicarage, Walford, Ross-on-Wye, Herefordshire HR9 5QP* Ross-on-Wye (01989) 562703

TARPER, Ms Ann Jennifer. b 47. SRN71 Nottm Univ BCombStuds82. Linc Th Coll 79. **dss** 83 **d** 87. Stamford All SS w St Jo *Linc* 82-85; Witham *Chelmsf* 85-90; Par Dn 87-90; Min and Educn Adv to Newmarch Gp Min *Heref* 90-93; Perm to Offic 93-95; Dep Chapl HM Pris Dur from 95. *Chaplain's Office, HM Prison Durham, Old Elvet, Durham DH1 3HU* 0191-386 2621

TARR, James Robert. b 39. Bps' Coll Cheshunt 64. **d** 67 **p** 68. C Wortley de Leeds *Ripon* 67-69; C Hunslet St Mary and Stourton St Andr 70-73; V Moorends *Sheff* 73-77; V Cross Stone *Wakef* 77-83; V Chilworth w N Baddesley *Win* 83-90; V Andover St Mich 90-93; V W Andover from 93. *St Michael's Vicarage, 13 The Avenue, Andover, Hants SP10 3EW* Andover (01264) 352553

TARRANT, Ian Denis. b 57. Cam Univ BA MA Nottm Univ DipTh. St Jo Coll Nottm 81. **d** 84 **p** 85. CMS from 79; C Ealing St Mary *Lon* 84-87; Zaire from 88. *CAZ Arua, PO Box 21285, Nairobi, Kenya*

TARRANT, John Michael. b 38. St Jo Coll Cam BA59 MA63 Ball Coll Ox BA62 MA76. Ripon Hall Ox 60. **d** 62 **p** 63. C Chelsea All SS *Lon* 62-65; Chapl and Lect St Pet Coll Saltley 66-70; Br Honduras 70-73; Belize 73-74; V Forest Row *Chich* 75-87; Perm to Offic *Heref* from 93. *The Vicarage, Bridstow, Ross-on-Wye, Herefordshire HR9 6QE* Ross-on-Wye (01989) 65805

TARRANT, Paul John. b 57. Chich Th Coll. **d** 82 **p** 83. C Southgate Ch Ch *Lon* 82-85; C Hornsey St Mary w St Geo 85-90; USA from 90. *50 Thomas's Rectory, 115 High Street, Taunton, Massachusetts 02780, USA*

TARRIS, Canon Geoffrey John. b 27. Em Coll Cam BA50 MA55. Westcott Ho Cam 51. **d** 53 **p** 54. V Bungay H Trin w St Mary *St E* 59-72; RD S Elmham 65-72; V Ipswich St Mary le Tower 72-78; Hon Can St E Cathl 74-82; V Ipswich St Mary le Tower w St Lawr and St Steph 78-82; Can Res St E Cathl 82-93; Dioc Dir of Lay Min and Warden of Readers 82-87; Dioc Dir of Ords 87-93; rtd 93; Perm to Offic *Nor* from 93. *53 The Close, Norwich NR1 4EG* Norwich (01603) 622136

TARRY, Gordon Malcolm. b 54. Leeds Univ BSc75. Lon Bible Coll BA83 Ridley Hall Cam. **d** 85 **p** 86. C Gt Ilford St Andr *Chelmsf* 85-89; C Rainham 89-92; C Rainham w Wennington 92-93; V Gt Ilford St Jo from 93. *St John's Vicarage, 2 Regent Gardens, Ilford, Essex IG3 8UL* 0181-590 5884

TASH, Stephen Ronald. b 56. Warw Univ BEd79. W Midl Minl Tr Course 88. **d** 91 **p** 92. C Studley *Cov* 91-95; P-in-c Salford Priors from 95. *The Vicarage, Salford Priors, Evesham, Worcs WR11 5UX* Bidford-on-Avon (01789) 772445

TASKER, Harry Beverley. b 41. BA76. Wycliffe Hall Ox 64. **d** 67 **p** 68. C Withington St Paul *Man* 67-71; C Bingley All SS *Bradf* 71-72; Chapl RAF 72-76; R Publow w Pensford, Compton Dando and Chelwood *B & W* 76-84; V Long Ashton from 84; RD Portishead 86-91. *The Vicarage, 7 Church Lane, Long Ashton, Bristol BS18 9LU* Bristol (0117) 939 3109

TASSELL, Douglas Rene. b 15. St Edm Hall Ox BA37 MA52. Wycliffe Hall Ox 37. **d** 39 **p** 40. R Delamere *Ches* 69-74; RD

Middlewich 69-74; P-in-c Welland *Worc* 75-79; Chapl St Jas Sch Malvern 77-81; AP Hanley Castle, Hanley Swan & Welland 79; rtd 80; Lic to Offic *Worc* 80-85; Perm to Offic from 85. *12 Gardens Walk, Upton-upon-Severn, Worcester WR8 0LL* Upton-upon-Severn (01684) 592205

TASSELL, Canon Dudley Arnold. b 16. K Coll Lon BD49 AKC49. **d** 49 **p** 50. R Rotherhithe St Mary w All SS *S'wark* 63-77; RD Bermondsey 69-76; Hon Can S'wark Cathl 72-76; V Spring Park *Cant* 76-84; RD Croydon Addington 81-84; V Spring Park All SS *S'wark* 85-86; rtd 86; Perm to Offic *Guildf* from 86. *80 Sandy Lane, Woking, Surrey GU22 8BH* Woking (01483) 766154

TATE, Harold Richard. b 24. St Jo Coll Dur BA50. **d** 51 **p** 52. R Blackley St Pet *Man* 60-79; V Alsager Ch Ch *Ches* 79-89; rtd 89. *57 Neville Road, Gargrave, Skipton, N Yorkshire BD23 3RE* Skipton (01756) 748315

TATE, Henry Charles Osmond. b 13. K Coll Lon 64. **d** 65 **p** 66. R Winfrith Newburgh w Chaldon Herring *Sarum* 68-78; V Chardstock *Ex* 78-82; rtd 82. *Manormead Residential Home, Tilford Road, Hindhead, Surrey GU26 6RA* Hindhead (01428) 604780

TATE, James (Jim). b 56. DipAD80. Oak Hill Th Coll DipHE95. **d** 95. C Hammersmith St Simon *Lon* from 95. *4 Mackenzie Trench House, 363 Lillie Road, London SW6 7PA* 0171-381 9241

TATE, John Robert. b 38. Dur Univ BA61 MA71. Cranmer Hall Dur DipTh69. **d** 70 **p** 71. C Bare *Blackb* 70-73; V Over Darwen St Jas 73-81; V Caton w Littledale from 81. *The Vicarage, 153 Brookhouse Road, Brookhouse, Lancaster LA2 9NX* Caton (01524) 770300

TATE, Robert John Ward. b 24. St Jo Coll Morpeth ThL48. **d** 49 **p** 50. Australia from 49; Chapl RN 53-79; QHC 76-79. *58 Sky Point Road, Carey Bay, NSW, Australia 2283* Maitland (49) 592921

TATHAM, Dr Andrew Francis. b 49. MSUC73 MSBC73 MICA86 Grey Coll Dur BA71 Southlands Coll Lon DAM80 K Coll Lon PhD84. S'wark Ord Course DipRS92. **d** 92 **p** 93. Hon C Headley w Box Hill *Guildf* from 92. *27 Newton Wood Road, Ashtead, Surrey KT21 1NN* Ashtead (01372) 274484

TATNALL, Alec James. b 09. Codrington Coll Barbados 51. **d** 52 **p** 53. Belize 69-75; C Hale *Guildf* 75-79; rtd 79; Perm to Offic *Ex* 79-90. *15 Ashdown Close, Ashdown Road, Reigate, Surrey RH2 7QS* Reigate (01737) 224964

TATTERSALL, Canon George Neville. b 10. Em Coll Cam BA32 MA36. Ridley Hall Cam 32. **d** 33 **p** 34. V Batley All SS *Wakef* 50-85; Hon Can Wakef Cathl 68-85; rtd 85; Perm to Offic *Wakef* 85-86; Perm to Offic *Ely* from 86. *22 Beach Road, Grafham, Huntingdon, Cambs PE18 0BA* Huntingdon (01480) 811013

TATTERSALL, James. b 31. Sheff Univ BSc53 DipEd54. Linc Th Coll 81. **d** 82 **p** 83. C Boston *Linc* 82-84; C Tyldesley w Shakerley *Man* 84-85; TV Sutton *Liv* 89-94; rtd 94. *111 Croston Road, Garstang, Preston PR3 1HQ* Garstang (01995) 600083

TATTON-BROWN, Simon Charles. b 48. Qu Coll Cam BA70 MA78 Man Univ CQSW72. Coll of Resurr Mirfield 78. **d** 79 **p** 80. C Ashton St Mich *Man* 79-82; P-in-c Prestwich St Gabr 82-87; V 87-88; Bp's Dom Chapl 82-88; TR Westhoughton from 88. *St Bartholomew's Rectory, Market Street, Westhoughton, Bolton BL5 3AZ* Westhoughton (01942) 813280

TATTUM, Ian Stuart. b 58. N Lon Poly BA79 Lanc Univ DipRS86 Fitzw Coll Cam BA89. Westcott Ho Cam 87. **d** 90 **p** 91. C Beaconsfield *Ox* 90-94; C Bushey *St Alb* from 94. *Trinity House, Bushey Mill Lane, Bushey, Watford WD2 2AS* Watford (01923) 220565

TAUNTON, Archdeacon of. See FRITH, Ven Richard Michael Cokayne

TAUNTON, Suffragan Bishop of. See LEWIS, Rt Rev John Hubert Richard

TAVERNOR, James Edward. b 23. Lich Th Coll 41 St D Coll Lamp BA49. **d** 50 **p** 51. C Buxton *Derby* 67-69; Perm to Offic 70-75; Perm to Offic *Heref* 75-83; Perm to Offic *St D* 83-91; rtd 88. *Trenova, Aberarth, Aberaeron, Dyfed SA46 0LT* Aberaeron (01545) 570930

TAVERNOR, William Noel. b 16. Lich Th Coll 37. **d** 40 **p** 41. V Canon Pyon w Kings Pyon and Birley *Heref* 65-88; rtd 88. *Vine Cottage, Kingsland, Leominster, Herefordshire HR6 9QS* Kingsland (01568) 708817

TAVINOR, Michael Edward. b 53. ARCO77 Univ Coll Dur BA75 Em Coll Cam CertEd76 K Coll Lon MMus77 AKC77 Ox Univ BA81 MA86. Ripon Coll Cuddesdon 79. **d** 82 **p** 83. C Ealing St Pet Mt Park *Lon* 82-85; Prec Ely Cathl *Ely* 85-90; Min Can and Sacr 85-90; P-in-c Stuntney 87-90; V Tewkesbury w Walton Cardiff *Glouc* from 90. *The Abbey House, Abbey Precinct, Tewkesbury, Glos GL20 5SR* Tewkesbury (01684) 293333

TAWN, Andrew. b 61. Trin Coll Cam BA83 Ox Univ BA88. Ripon Coll Cuddesdon 86. **d** 89 **p** 90. C Dovecot *Liv* 89-93; TV Dorchester *Ox* from 93; Student Supervisor Cuddesdon Coll from 93. *The Vicarage, Cherwell Road, Berinsfield, Oxford OX10 7PB* Oxford (01865) 340460

TAYLOR, Alan Cecil. b 34. Keble Coll Ox BA57 MA63. Cuddesdon Coll 58. **d** 60 **p** 61. C Blackpool St Steph *Blackb* 60-63; C Chorley St Laur 63-65; V Burnley St Mark from 65. *St Mark's Vicarage, 9 Rossendale Road, Burnley, Lancs BB11 5DQ* Burnley (01282) 428178

TAYLOR, Alan Clive. b 48. Southn Univ BTh79. Sarum Th Coll 69. **d** 74 **p** 75. C Watford St Pet *St Alb* 74-78; C Broxbourne w Wormley 78-83; Chapl to the Deaf 83-91; V Shefford 83-91; R Portishead *B & W* from 91. *The Rectory, Church Road South, Portishead, Bristol BS20 9PU* Portishead (01275) 842284

TAYLOR, Alan Gerald. b 33. Roch Th Coll 61 St Aid Birkenhead 61. **d** 63 **p** 64. C W Bridgford *S'well* 63-66; C E w W Barkwith *Linc* 66-69; V E Stockwith 69-76; V Morton 69-76; Countryside Officer 69-88; R Ulceby w Fordington 76-88; R Willoughby w Sloothby w Claxby 76-88; R Woolpit w Drinkstone *St E* from 88; Rural Min Adv from 88. *The Rectory, Woolpit, Bury St Edmunds, Suffolk IP30 9QP* Elmswell (01359) 42244

TAYLOR, Alan Leonard. b 43. Chich Th Coll 67. **d** 69 **p** 70. C Walton St Mary *Liv* 69-73; C Toxteth St Marg 73-75; V Stanley 75-83; V Leeds St Aid *Ripon* from 84. *The Vicarage, Elford Place West, Leeds LS8 5QD* Leeds (0113) 248 6992

TAYLOR, Alfred Harry Bryant. b 17. St Deiniol's Hawarden 77. **d** 79 **p** 80. Hon C Woodchurch *Ches* 79-85; C 85-87; Hon C 87-92; Perm to Offic from 92. *111 New Hey Road, Birkenhead, Merseyside L49 7NE* 0151-677 4933

TAYLOR, Andrew David. b 58. Ox Univ BA81 MA86 Toronto Univ MDiv92. Westcott Ho Cam 85. **d** 87 **p** 89. C Leckhampton SS Phil and Jas w Cheltenham St Jas *Glouc* 87-91; C Cheltenham St Pet 91; C Highgate St Mich *Lon* from 94. *17 Bisham Gardens, London N6 6DJ* 0181-340 7363

TAYLOR, Ms Anne Elizabeth. b 68. Ulster Univ BSc91. CITC BTh94. **d** 94 **p** 95. C Dub Rathfarnham *D & G* from 94. *9 Main Street, Rathfarnham, Dublin 14, Irish Republic* Dublin (1) 492-4936

TAYLOR, Arthur Alfred. b 32. MA. Ox NSM Course. **d** 83 **p** 84. NSM Monks Risborough *Ox* from 83. *9 Place Farm Way, Monks Risborough, Princes Risborough, Bucks HP27 9JJ* Princes Risborough (01844) 347197

TAYLOR, Arthur Harry. b 17. **d** 48 **p** 49. C Kilburn St Aug *Lon* 50-55; rtd 82. *Buckfast Abbey, Buckfastleigh, Devon TQ11 0EE* Buckfastleigh (01364) 43301

TAYLOR, Arthur John. b 17. Lon Univ BD39 BA52. ALCD39. **d** 40 **p** 41. Asst Master K Sch Ely 56-80; Perm to Offic *Ely* 56-85; rtd 80; Perm to Offic *Mon* from 86. *44 Homeforge House, Goldwire Lane, Monmouth, Gwent NP5 3HA* Monmouth (01600) 716269

TAYLOR, Arthur Robert. b 26. ACIS59. Oak Hill Th Coll 67. **d** 68 **p** 69. C Wilmington *Roch* 68-71; C Polegate *Chich* 71-73; R Chesterton w Haddon *Ely* 73-80; P-in-c Alwalton 73-75; R 75-80; R Sawtry 80-91; rtd 91. *10 Faraday Ride, Tonbridge, Kent TN10 4RL* Tonbridge (01732) 358694

TAYLOR, Bernard Richmond Hartley. b 30. Reading Univ MEd. S Dios Minl Tr Scheme 82. **d** 85 **p** 86. NSM Englefield Green *Guildf* 85-90; NSM Lyddington w Stoke Dry and Seaton *Pet* from 90. *4 Windmill Way, Lyddington, Oakham, Leics LE15 9LY* Uppingham (01572) 822717

TAYLOR, Brian. b 29. FSA83 FRHistS84 Keble Coll Ox BA52 MA56. Linc Th Coll 54. **d** 57 **p** 58. V Leic St Gabr *Leic* 69-75; R Guildf St Nic *Guildf* 75-93; rtd 93. *252 Worplesdon Road, Guildford, Surrey GU2 6XH* Guildford (01483) 576351

TAYLOR, Brian. b 38. MBIM Bris Univ BA60 Liv Univ BA70 Southn Univ MA90. Ridley Hall Cam 60. **d** 66 **p** 66. Nigeria 66-72; Perm to Offic *Derby* 74-78; Chapl Newbury Coll 76-94; P-in-c Shaw cum Donnington *Ox* 89-90; R from 90. *The Rectory, Well Meadow, Shaw, Newbury, Berks RG13 2DR* Newbury (01635) 40450 or 41155

TAYLOR, Brian. b 42. St Deiniol's Hawarden 78. **d** 80 **p** 81. C Mold *St As* 80-84; V Bagillt from 84. *The Vicarage, Bagillt, Clwyd CH6 6BZ* Flint (01352) 732732

TAYLOR, Brian. b 61. St Mich Coll Llan DipTh91. **d** 94 **p** 95. C Aberdare St Jo *Llan* from 94. *9 College Street, Abernant, Aberdare, M Glam CF44 0RN* Aberdare (01685) 882641

TAYLOR, Brian Valentine. b 34. St Deiniol's Hawarden 69. **d** 71 **p** 72. C Workington St Mich *Carl* 71-72; C Carl St Aid and Ch Ch 73-74; Chapl Rotterdam Miss to Seamen *Eur* 74-75; Asst Chapl Madrid 75-76; Chapl Marseille w St Raphael Aix-en-Provence etc 77-78; Chapl Alassio w Genoa and Rapallo 78-81; C Higher Broughton *Man* 82-83; P-in-c Cheetwood St Alb 83-84; Lic to Offic 84-85; rtd 85; Perm to Offic *Man*

from 85. *5 Kimberley Street, Higher Broughton, Salford M7 0AF* 0161-792 2442

TAYLOR, Charles Derek. b 36. Trin Hall Cam BA59 MA62. Ripon Hall Ox 59. **d** 61 **p** 62. C Nottm All SS *S'well* 61-64; C Binley *Cov* 64-67; C Stoke 67-70; R Purley *Ox* 70-74; V Milton *B & W* 74-93; RD Locking 86-87 and 90-93; V Wells St Cuth w Wookey Hole from 93. *The Vicarage, 1 St Cuthbert Street, Wells, Somerset BA5 2AW* Wells (01749) 673136

TAYLOR, Canon Charles William. b 53. Selw Coll Cam BA74 MA78. Cuddesdon Coll 74. **d** 76 **p** 77. C Wolv *Lich* 76-79; Chapl Westmr Abbey 79-84; V Stanmore *Win* 84-90; R N Stoneham 90-95; Can Res and Prec Lich Cathl *Lich* from 95. *23 The Close, Lichfield, Staffs WS13 7LD* Lichfield (01543) 263337

TAYLOR, Preb Clive Cavanagh. b 28. MBE91. Cranmer Hall Dur 61. **d** 63 **p** 64. V Tottenham St Jo *Lon* 69-76; RD E Haringey 73-76; Dir of Ords 76-85; Chapl Metrop Police Coll Hendon 76-93; Sen Chapl Metrop Police 78-93; V Temple Fortune St Barn 79-93; Preb St Paul's Cathl 78-93; AD W Barnet 79-85; rtd 93. *26 Wenthill Close, East Dean, Eastbourne, E Sussex BN20 0HT* East Dean (01323) 422346

TAYLOR, David. b 53. St Jo Coll Dur BA74 PGCE75. Sarum & Wells Th Coll DCM93. **d** 93 **p** 94. C Cheadle Hulme All SS *Ches* from 93. *3 Hulme Hall Crescent, Cheadle Hulme, Cheadle, Cheshire SK8 6LG* 0161-485 8935

TAYLOR, Dr David Christopher Morgan. b 56. Leeds Univ BSc77 Univ Coll Lon PhD80. Nor Ord Course 91. **d** 94 **p** 95. NSM Waterloo Ch Ch and St Mary *Liv* from 94. *20 Liverpool Road, Formby, Liverpool L37 4BW* Formby (01704) 873304 Fax 0151-794 5337

TAYLOR, Dennis James. b 31. ACIS62. Ripon Hall Ox 63. **d** 68 **p** 69. C Baswich (or Berkswich) *Lich* 68-77; P-in-c Hastings H Trin *Chich* 77-81; V 81-86; R Catsfield and Crowhurst from 86. *The Rectory, Church Lane, Catsfield, Battle, E Sussex TN33 9DR* Ninfield (01424) 892319

TAYLOR, Very Rev Derek John. b 31. Univ of Wales (Lamp) BA52 Fitzw Ho Cam BA54 MA58 Ex Univ CertEd70 Birm Univ ACertEd92. St Mich Coll Llan 54. **d** 55 **p** 56. V Exminster *Ex* 64-70; Hd of RE Heathcote Sch Tiverton 70-71; W Germany 71-75; Chapl R Russell Sch Croydon 75-79; Chapl St Andr Sch Croydon 79-84; P-in-c Croydon St Andr *Cant* 79-81; V 81-84; Chapl Bromsgrove Sch Worcs 84-89; Provost St Chris Cathl Bahrain from 90; Hon Chapl Miss to Seamen from 90; rtd 92. *St Christopher's Cathedral, PO Box 36, Manama, Bahrain* Bahrain (973) 246436 or 253866 Fax 253866

TAYLOR, Donald Alastair. b 26. Lon Univ BD Linc Coll Ox DPhil77. St Paul's Coll Mauritius. **d** 65 **p** 65. Seychelles 66-78; SSJE from 68; Lect Relig Studies Middx Poly 78-92; rtd 91. *50 St Bartholomew's Road, Reading RG1 3QA* Reading (01734) 661247

TAYLOR, Edward Frank. b 23. Lon Univ BSc44. Chich Th Coll 50. **d** 52 **p** 53. V Hangleton *Chich* 63-73; V Wivelsfield 73-88; rtd 88; Perm to Offic *Bradf* from 88. *4 Clarendon Street, Haworth, Keighley, W Yorkshire BD22 8PT* Haworth (01535) 642493

TAYLOR, Eric Hargreaves. b 21. Oak Hill Th Coll 47. **d** 51 **p** 52. V Camerton H Trin W Seaton *Carl* 62-71; V Ramsgate Ch Ch *Cant* 71-85; Chapl Ramsgate Gen Hosp 71-85; rtd 85; Perm to Offic *Cant* 85-90; Perm to Offic *Blackb* from 89. *27 Pilling Lane, Preesall, Poulton-le-Fylde, Lancs FY6 0EX* Knott End (01253) 810146

TAYLOR, Frank. b 02. Kelham Th Coll 22. **d** 28 **p** 29. V Lambourn *Ox* 61-70; Perm to Offic *Ox* 74-91. *18 Bertie Road, Cumnor, Oxford OX2 9PS* Oxford (01865) 863239

TAYLOR, Frank Hampton. b 49. St Jo Coll Nottm 80. **d** 82 **p** 83. C Hoole *Ches* 82-85; C Timperley 85-89; V Birkenhead Ch Ch 89-95. *9 Peckswood Road, Todmorden, Lancs OL14 7JR* Todmorden (01706) 817214

TAYLOR, Frank Leslie. b 05. St Jo Coll Ox BA27 DipTh28 MA30. Wycliffe Hall Ox 27. **d** 29 **p** 30. R E Hoathly *Chich* 62-72; rtd 72. *c/o Burley and Geach, 2 West Street, Haslemere, Surrey GU27 2AG* Haslemere (01428) 656011

TAYLOR, George Davidson. b 27. St Aid Birkenhead 60. **d** 62 **p** 63. V Shuttleworth *Man* 65-71; V Litherland St Phil *Liv* 71-85; rtd 85. *34 Beckwith Crescent, Harrogate, N Yorkshire HG2 0BQ* Harrogate (01423) 560023

TAYLOR, George James Trueman. b 36. Ripon Hall Ox 66. **d** 69 **p** 70. C Wavertree H Trin *Liv* 69-73; V Newton-le-Willows 73-79; V Stoneycroft All SS 79-83; V Haigh from 83. *The Vicarage, Copperas Lane, Haigh, Wigan, Lancs WN2 1PA* Wigan (01942) 831255

TAYLOR, Godfrey Alan. b 36. Oak Hill Th Coll DipTh60. **d** 61 **p** 62. C Herne Bay Ch Ch *Cant* 61-64; C Tunbridge Wells St Jas *Roch* 64-68; V Guernsey H Trin *Win* 68-81; V Boscombe

St Jo from 81. *St John's Vicarage, 17 Browning Avenue, Bournemouth BH5 1NR* Bournemouth (01202) 396667

TAYLOR, Canon Gordon. b 46. AKC68. St Aug Coll Cant 69. **d** 70 **p** 71. C Rotherham *Sheff* 70-74; P-in-c Brightside St Thos 74-79; P-in-c Brightside St Marg 77-79; V Brightside St Thos and St Marg 79-82; R Kirk Sandall and Edenthorpe 82-91; V Beighton from 91; Hon Can Sheff Cathl from 93. *The Vicarage, 27 Tynker Avenue, Beighton, Sheffield S19 6DX* Sheffield (0114) 248 7635

TAYLOR, Gordon Clifford. b 15. VRD56 and Bars 66. FSA Ch Coll Cam BA37 MA41. Ripon Hall Ox 37. **d** 38 **p** 39. C Ealing St Steph Castle Hill *Lon* 38-40; Chapl RNVR 40-58; Asst Master Eton Coll 46-49; R St Giles-in-the-Fields *Lon* from 49; RD Finsbury and Holborn 54-67; Chapl RNR 58-70. *St Giles's Rectory, 15A Gower Street, London WC1E 6HG* 0171-636 4646

TAYLOR, Graham Peter. b 58. NE Ord Course DipHE95. **d** 95. NSM Pickering *York* from 95. *3 The Mount, Thornton Dale, Pickering, N Yorkshire YO18 7TF* Pickering (01751) 473462

TAYLOR, Henry. b 46. St Cath Coll Ox BA69 MA73. Liturg Inst Trier DipLit Cuddesdon Coll 70. **d** 73 **p** 74. C Tettenhall Regis *Lich* 73-76; C Walsall 76-80; V Witton le Wear and Firtree *Dur* 80-92; rtd 92. *Briarside, 79 Queens Road, Consett, Co Durham DH8 0BW* Consett (01207) 583160

TAYLOR, Canon Herbert Cyril. b 06. Em Coll Cam BA29 MA34. Ridley Hall Cam 29. **d** 31 **p** 32. V Orpington Ch Ch *Roch* 42-73; Hon Can Roch Cathl 64-73; rtd 73. *Rogers House, Drewery Drive, Wigmore, Gillingham, Kent ME8 0NX* Medway (01634) 261810

✠**TAYLOR, Rt Rev Humphrey Vincent.** b 38. Pemb Coll Cam BA61 MA66 Lon Univ MA70. Coll of Resurr Mirfield 61. **d** 63 **p** 64 **c** 91. C N Hammersmith St Kath *Lon* 63-64; C Notting Hill St Mark 64-66; USPG 67-71; Malawi 67-71; Chapl Bp Grosseteste Coll Linc 72-74; Sec Chapls in HE Gen Syn Bd of Educn 75-80; Gen Sec USPG 80-91; Sec Miss Progr 80-84; Hon Can Bris Cathl *Bris* 86-91; Lic to Offic *S'wark* 89-91; Suff Bp Selby *York* from 91. *10 Precentor's Court, York YO1 2EJ* York (01904) 656592 Fax 655671

TAYLOR, Ian. b 53. Saltley Tr Coll Birm CertEd75. Local NSM Course 92. **d** 95. NSM Heywood St Luke w All So *Man* from 95. *818A Edenfield Road, Rochdale, Lancs OL12 7RB* Rochdale (01706) 355738

TAYLOR, James McMurray. b 16. TCD BA38 MA. **d** 39 **p** 40. I Castle Archdale and Killadeas *Clogh* 57-80; rtd 80. *Inan, Farnamullan Road, Lisbellaw, Co Fermanagh BT94 5ER* Lisbellaw (01365) 87259

TAYLOR, Jan William Karel. b 59. QUB BD82 MSocSc89 TCD DipTh84. **d** 84 **p** 85. C Belf St Simon w St Phil *Conn* 84-87; I Belf St Paul 87-92; Chapl RAF from 92. *Chaplaincy Services (RAF), HQ, Personnel and Training Command, RAF Innsworth, Gloucester GL3 1EZ* Gloucester (01452) 712612 Ext 5164 Fax 510828

TAYLOR, Mrs Janette Elizabeth (Jan). b 44. Glouc Sch of Min 89. **d** 92 **p** 94. C Glouc St Geo w Whaddon *Glouc* from 92. *3 St George's Close, Gloucester GL4 0PE* Gloucester (01452) 422519

TAYLOR (nee PATTERSON), Sister Jennifer Mary. b 41. CA Tr Coll IDC65. **dss** 77 **d** 87. CA from 65; Chapl Asst HM Pris Holloway 75-79; Ho Mistress Ch Hosp Sch Hertf 78-79; Chapl Asst RAChD 80-90; Germany from 91. *Wentworth Barracks, BFPO 15*

TAYLOR, John Alexander. b 54. S Dios Minl Tr Scheme 89. **d** 92 **p** 93. NSM Abbotts Ann and Upper and Goodworth Clatford *Win* from 92. *21 Sainsbury Close, Andover, Hants SP10 2LE* Andover (01264) 353339

TAYLOR, Canon John Ambrose. b 19. K Coll Lon 45. Coll of Resurr Mirfield 49. **d** 50 **p** 51. V Ches St Oswald w Lt St Jo *Ches* 63-72; TV Ches 72-74; Hon Can Gib Cathl *Eur* 74-91; V Withyham St Jo *Chich* 74-88; RD Rotherfield 77-87; P-in-c Withyham St Mich 87; rtd 88. *11 Park View, Buxted, Uckfield, E Sussex TN22 4LS* Uckfield (01825) 813475

TAYLOR, John Andrew. b 53. Linc Th Coll 86. **d** 88 **p** 89. C Stanley *Liv* 88-91; V Wigan St Jas w St Thos from 91. *St James' Vicarage, Poolstock Lane, Wigan, Lancs WN3 5HL* Wigan (01942) 43896

TAYLOR, John Andrew Wemyss. b 27. RCS LDS51 PhD62. Sarum & Wells Th Coll 70. **d** 72 **p** 73. C Ashburton w Buckland-in-the-Moor *Ex* 72-76; P-in-c E Portlemouth 76-79; P-in-c S Pool w Chivelstone 76-79; R E Portlemouth, S Pool and Chivelstone 79-81; Miss to Seamen from 81; V Salcombe *Ex* 81-88; RD Woodleigh 83-88; Perm to Offic from 88; rtd 92. *Waverley, Grand View Road, Hope Cove, Kingsbridge, Devon TQ7 3HF* Kingsbridge (01548) 561332

✠**TAYLOR, Rt Rev John Bernard.** b 29. Ch Coll Cam BA50 MA54 Jes Coll Cam 52 Hebrew Univ Jerusalem 54. Ridley Hall Cam 55. **d** 56 **p** 57 **c** 80. C Morden *S'wark* 56-59; V Henham *Chelmsf* 59-64; V Elsenham 59-64; Sen Tutor Oak

Hill Th Coll 64-65; Vice-Prin 65-72; V Woodford Wells 72-75; Dioc Dir of Ords 72-80; Adn W Ham 75-80; Bp St Alb 80-95; High Almoner from 88; rtd 95. *22 Conduit Head Road, Cambridge CB3 0EY* Cambridge (01223) 313783

TAYLOR, John Charles Browne. b 23. CEng58 MIEE58. Oak Hill Th Coll 81. **d** 82 **p** 83. NSM Havering-atte-Bower *Chelmsf* 82-85; NSM Collier Row St Jas and Havering-atte-Bower 86-89; rtd 89; Lic to Offic *Chelmsf* from 89. *Giffords, North Road, Havering-atte-Bower, Romford RM4 1PX* Romford (01708) 742072

TAYLOR, John Denys. b 20. Leeds Univ BA49. Coll of Resurr Mirfield. **d** 51 **p** 52. C Leeds St Marg *Ripon* 51-54; India 54-59; C Gt Grimsby St Jas *Linc* 59-66; New Zealand from 66. *155 Queen Street, Northcote, Auckland 9, New Zealand* Auckland (9) 480-5968

TAYLOR, Canon John Frederick. b 20. St Chad's Coll Dur 39. Ely Th Coll 59. **d** 61 **p** 62. V Middlesb St Cuth *York* 64-71; V Skipsea w Ulrome 71-79; P-in-c Barmston w Fraisthorpe 77-79; Can and Preb York Minster 79-85; R Skipsea w Ulrome and Barmston w Fraisthorpe 79-82; V Hemingbrough 82-85; rtd 85. *19 Willow Garth, Eastrington, Goole, N Humberside DN14 7QP* Howden (01430) 410647

TAYLOR, Canon John Michael. b 30. St Aid Birkenhead 56. **d** 59 **p** 60. C Chorley St Jas *Blackb* 59-62; C Broughton 62-64; Chapl St Boniface Coll Warminster 64-68; V Altham w Clayton le Moors *Blackb* 68-76; RD Accrington 71-76; Can Res Blackb Cathl from 76. *22 Billinge Avenue, Blackburn BB2 6SD* Blackburn (01254) 261152

✠**TAYLOR, Rt Rev John Mitchell.** b 32. Aber Univ MA54. Edin Th Coll 54. **d** 56 **p** 57 **c** 91. C Aber St Marg *Ab* 56-58; R Glas H Cross *Glas* 58-64; R Glas St Ninian 64-73; R Dumfries 73-91; Chapl Dumfries and Galloway R Infirmary 73-91; Can St Mary's Cathl *Glas* 79-91; Bp Glas from 91. *Bishop's House, 25 Quadrant Road, Glasgow G43 2QP* 0141-633 5877 or 637 5659 Fax 633 5877

TAYLOR, John Porter. b 48. Ex Univ BA71 MA76. Cranmer Hall Dur CTMin93. **d** 93 **p** 94. C Ossett cum Gawthorpe *Wakef* from 93. *18 Headlands Park, Ossett, W Yorkshire WF5 8RB* Wakefield (01924) 273622

TAYLOR, John Ralph. b 48. St Jo Coll Nottm BTh74. **d** 74 **p** 75. C Clitheroe St Jas *Blackb* 74-77; C Kidsgrove *Lich* 77-79; C Hawkwell *Chelmsf* 79-82; V Linc St Geo Swallowbeck *Linc* 82-92; rtd 92. *The Gables, Beck Lane, South Hykeham, Lincoln LN6 9PQ* Lincoln (01522) 692043

TAYLOR, Canon John Rowland. b 29. OBE74. St Mich Coll Llan 57. **d** 58 **p** 59. C Caerau St Cynfelin *Llan* 58-59; C Aberdare St Jo 59-61; Miss to Seamen 61-88; Tanganyika 61-64; Tanzania 64-73; Adn Dar-es-Salaam 65-73; V-Gen 67-73; Thailand 73-84; Chapl Rotterdam w Schiedam *Eur* 84-88; V Warnham *Chich* from 88. *The Vicarage, Church Street, Warnham, Horsham, W Sussex RH12 3QW* Horsham (01403) 265041

✠**TAYLOR, Rt Rev John Vernon.** b 14. Trin Coll Cam BA36 St Cath Soc Ox BA38 MA41. Wycliffe Coll Toronto Hon DD64 Wycliffe Hall Ox 36. **d** 38 **p** 39 **c** 75. C St Marylebone All So w SS Pet and Jo *Lon* 38-40; C St Helens St Helen *Liv* 40-43; CMS 45-63; Gen Sec CMS 63-74; Bp Win 75-85; rtd 85; Perm to Offic *Ox* from 86. *Camleigh, 65 Aston Street, Oxford OX4 1EW* Oxford (01865) 248502

TAYLOR, Joseph Robin Christopher. b 34. St Aid Birkenhead 58. **d** 61 **p** 62. C Aldershot St Mich *Guildf* 61-64; C Fleet 64-68; R Manaton *Ex* 69-74; R N Bovey 69-74; V Dawlish 74-87; P-in-c Christow, Ashton, Trusham and Bridford 87-88; R from 88. *The Rectory, Dry Lane, Christow, Exeter EX6 7PE* Christow (01647) 52845

TAYLOR, Justin Wray Lindsay. b 39. Moray Ord Course 77. **d** 84 **p** 87. Hon C Nairn *Mor* 84-87; Hon C Inverness St Andr from 87. *68 High Street, Ardersier, Inverness IV1 2QF* Ardersier (01667) 462509

TAYLOR, Kenneth Charles (Ken). b 24. St Deiniol's Hawarden 76. **d** 76 **p** 77. C Wilmslow *Ches* 76-79; V Willaston 79-93; Chapl Clatterbridge Hosp Wirral 86-93; rtd 93. *9 Windsor Drive, Whitby, South Wirral L65 6SH* 0151-356 2477

TAYLOR, Kenneth Gordon. b 30. Selw Coll Cam BA54 MA58. Chich Th Coll 54. **d** 56 **p** 57. C Moor Allerton *Ripon* 62-71; R Northwold *Ely* 71-81; P-in-c Harlton 81-87; R 87-89; P-in-c Haslingfield 81-87; V 87-89; P-in-c Thornage w Brinton w Hunworth and Stody *Nor* 89-92; P-in-c Briningham 89-92; P-in-c Melton Constable w Swanton Novers 89-92; R Brinton, Briningham, Hunworth, Stody etc 92-95; rtd 95. *1 Pereers Close, Holt, Norfolk NR25 6JF* Holt (01263) 713146

TAYLOR, Kingsley Graham. b 55. Univ of Wales (Cardiff) BD93. St Mich Coll Llan 90. **d** 93 **p** 94. C Llanelli *St D* from 93. *44 Coldstream Street, Llanelli, Dyfed SA15 3BH* Llanelli (01554) 752056

TAYLOR, Lyndon John. b 95. NSM Swansea St Nic *S & B* from 95. *27 Gelli Gwyn Road, Morriston, Swansea SA6 7PP*

TAYLOR, Canon Marcus Beresford. b 13. TCD BA35 MA43. CITC 36. **d** 36 **p** 37. I Stillorgan *D & G* 47-78; Can Ch Ch Cathl Dub 71-86; I Stillorgan w Blackrock 78-86; rtd 86. *78 Beech Trees, Galloping Green Lane, Stillorgan, Dublin, Irish Republic* Dublin (1) 288-4196

TAYLOR, Marcus Iles. b 16. Ely Th Coll 48. **d** 49 **p** 50. V Cookham Dean *Ox* 56-71; rtd 81. *Kimbers, Budnick, Perranporth, Cornwall TR6 0AA* Truro (01872) 572143

TAYLOR, Mrs Marian Alexandra. b 62. Newc Univ BA85. Qu Coll Birm 89. **d** 91. C Earls Barton *Pet* 91-93; NSM Wellingborough St Barn from 95. *The Methodist Manse, 96A Kingsway, Wellingborough, Northants NN8 2PD* Wellingborough (01933) 222357

TAYLOR, Mark Frederick. b 62. N Ireland Poly BA84 TCD DipTh87. **d** 87 **p** 88. C Ballymacarrett St Patr *D & D* 87-90; C Dundela 90-93; Hon Chapl Miss to Seamen from 90; I Kilmore w Inch *D & D* from 93. *8A Kilmore Village, Crossgar, Downpatrick, Co Down BT30 9HP* Downpatrick (01396) 830371

TAYLOR, Michael Alan. b 47. Bris Univ CertEd70 Lon Univ BD85. Trin Coll Bris 72. **d** 76 **p** 77. C Chilwell *S'well* 76-79; Chapl RAF 79-87; New Zealand from 87. *1 Merton Place, Bryndwr, Christchurch 5, New Zealand* Christchurch (3) 352-4788

TAYLOR, Michael Allan. b 50. Nottm Univ BTh80. St Jo Coll Nottm 76. **d** 80 **p** 81. C Bowling St Jo *Bradf* 80-82; C Otley 82-85; P-in-c Low Moor St Mark 85-92; P-in-c Bris St Andr w St Bart *Bris* from 92. *The Vicarage, Walsingham Road, Bristol BS6 5BT* Bristol (0117) 924 8683

TAYLOR, Michael Barry. b 38. Bps' Coll Cheshunt 63. **d** 65 **p** 66. C Leeds St Cypr Harehills *Ripon* 65-68; C Stanningley St Thos 68-70; V Hunslet Moor St Pet and St Cuth 70-78; V Starbeck from 78. *The Vicarage, 78 High Street, Harrogate, N Yorkshire HG2 7LW* Harrogate (01423) 883036 or 889856

TAYLOR, Michael Frank Chatterton. b 30. St Aid Birkenhead 59. **d** 61 **p** 62. C Knighton St Jo *Leic* 61-65; V Briningham *Nor* 65-86; R Melton Constable w Swanton Novers 65-86; P-in-c Thornage w Brinton w Hunworth and Stody 85-86; R Lyng w Sparham 86-90; R Elsing w Bylaugh 86-90; R Lyng, Sparham, Elsing and Bylaugh from 90; RD Sparham from 92. *The Rectory, Lyng, Norwich NR9 5RA* Norwich (01603) 872381

TAYLOR, Michael John. b 63. Lanc Univ BA85. Linc Th Coll 86. **d** 88 **p** 89. C Carl St Aid and Ch Ch *Carl* 88-91; C Loughton St Jo *Chelmsf* 91-93; V Eastwood St Dav from 93. *St David's Vicarage, 400 Rayleigh Road, Leigh-on-Sea, Essex SS9 5PT* Southend-on-Sea (01702) 523126

TAYLOR, Michael Joseph. b 49. Gregorian Univ Rome STB72 PhL74 Birm Univ MA81. English Coll Rome 67. **d** 72 **p** 73. In RC Ch 72-83; Hon C Newport Pagnell w Lathbury *Ox* 83-86; TV Langley Marish 86-90; Vice Prin E Midl Min Tr Course *S'well* from 90. *52 Parkside Gardens, Wollaton, Nottingham NG8 2PQ* Nottingham (0115) 928 3111 or 484848

TAYLOR, Michael Laurence. b 43. ARCM68 Ch Coll Cam BA66 MA70 CertEd72 MPhil88. Cuddesdon Coll 66. **d** 68 **p** 69. C Westbury-on-Trym H Trin *Bris* 68-72; Asst Chapl Wellington Coll Berks 72-76; C St Helier *S'wark* 76-78; TV Bedminster *Bris* 78-82; P-in-c Chippenham St Andr w Tytherton Lucas 82-88; V 88-89; Dioc Ecum Officer *B & W* 89-90; P-in-c Rodney Stoke w Draycott 89-90. *21 Bath Road, Wells, Somerset BA5 2DJ* Wells (01749) 670348

TAYLOR, Michael Stewart. b 58. St Mich Coll Llan BTh. **d** 91 **p** 92. C Llangynnwr and Cwmffrwd *St D* 91-94; V Llansantffraed and Llanbadarn Trefeglwys etc from 94. *Windycott, Stryd yr Eglwys, Llanon, Dyfed SY23 5HW* Llanon (01974) 202339

TAYLOR, Nancy. b 49. SRN70 SCM72. Ox Min Course 88. **d** 91 **p** 94. Chapl Asst Stoke Mandeville Hosp Aylesbury from 91; NSM Weston Turville *Ox* from 91. *Elmhurst, 23 School Lane, Weston Turville, Aylesbury, Bucks HP22 5SG* Aylesbury (01296) 613384 or 316677

TAYLOR, Neil Hamish. b 48. Open Univ BA87. Linc Th Coll 72. **d** 75 **p** 76. C Rotherham *Sheff* 75-78; C Doncaster St Geo 78-82; P-in-c Knaresdale 82-87; V Alston cum Garrigill w Nenthead and Kirkhaugh *Newc* 82-87; TR Alston Team 87-88; V Maidstone St Paul *Cant* from 88; OCF 88-94. *St Paul's Vicarage, 130 Boxley Road, Maidstone, Kent ME14 2AH* Maidstone (01622) 691926

TAYLOR, Neville Patrick. b 40. Trin Coll Bris DipTh82. **d** 82 **p** 83. C Old Trafford St Jo *Man* 82-84; C Hurst 84-87; R Levenshulme St March from 87. *St Mark's Rectory, 331 Mount Road, Levenshulme, Manchester M19 3HW* 0161-224 9551

TAYLOR, Nicholas James. b 46. St Chad's Coll Dur BA67 DipTh68. **d** 69 **p** 70. C Beamish *Dur* 69-74; C Styvechale *Cov* 74-77; P-in-c Wilmcote w Billesley 77-79; P-in-c Aston Cantlow 77-79; V Aston Cantlow and Wilmcote w Billesley 79-87; V Cov St Fran N Radford from 87; RD Cov N from 93. *St Francis's Vicarage, Treherne Road, Coventry CV6 3DY* Coventry (01203) 595178

TAYLOR, Nigel Thomas Wentworth. b 60. Bris Univ BA82 Ox Univ BA86. Wycliffe Hall Ox 84. **d** 87 **p** 88. C Ches Square St Mich w St Phil *Lon* 87-91; C Roxeth Ch Ch and Harrow St Pet 91-93; TV Roxeth from 93. *48 Whitmore Road, Harrow, Middx HA1 4AD* 0181-423 3168

TAYLOR, Norman. b 26. CCC Cam BA49 MA52. Cuddesdon Coll 49. **d** 51 **p** 52. R Lt Wilbraham *Ely* 55-71; Chapl St Faith's Sch Cam 71-86; Lic to Offic *Ely* 72-87; Hon C Chesterton St Andr 87-91; rtd 91; Hon C Lyme Regis *Sarum* from 91. *Shire End West, Cobb Road, Lyme Regis, Dorset DT7 3JP* Lyme Regis (01297) 442922

TAYLOR, Norman Adrian. b 48. St D Coll Lamp DipTh73. **d** 73 **p** 74. C Fleur-de-Lis *Mon* 73-75; C W Drayton *Lon* 75-79; C-in-c Hayes St Edm CD 79-85; V Hayes St Edm 85-87; V Pilton w Ashford *Ex* 87-89; V Sidley *Chich* from 89. *All Saints Vicarage, All Saints Lane, Bexhill-on-Sea, E Sussex TN39 5HA* Bexhill-on-Sea (01424) 221071

TAYLOR, Norman Wyatt. b 23. Wells Th Coll 58. **d** 60 **p** 61. V Bishop's Cannings *Sarum* 69-77; V Bishop's Cannings, All Cannings etc 77-80; V W Moors 80-87; rtd 88; Perm to Offic *Ex* from 89. *3 Kits Close, Chudleigh, Newton Abbot, Devon TQ13 0LG* Newton Abbot (01626) 852733

TAYLOR, Paul. b 63. RGN85. Sarum & Wells Th Coll 92 Linc Th Coll BTh95. **d** 95. C Boultham *Linc* from 95. *7 Earls Park, Boultham Park Road, Lincoln LN6* Lincoln (01522) 533644

TAYLOR, Paul Frank David. b 60. ARICS87 Leic Poly BSc84. Trin Coll Bris BA91. **d** 91 **p** 92. C Edin St Thos *Edin* 91-94; C Kempshott *Win* from 94. *12 Maplehurst Chase, Meadowcroft, Hatch Warren, Basingstoke, Hants RG22 4XQ* Basingstoke (01256) 472632

TAYLOR, Paul Latham. b 11. **d** 49 **p** 50. Chapl Milford Chest Hosp 70-72; Warden Coll of St Barn Lingfield 72-77; rtd 77; Perm to Offic *Win* from 83. *22 Halton Close, Bransgore, Christchurch, Dorset BH23 8HZ* Bransgore (01425) 72137

TAYLOR, Paul Stanley. b 53. Ox Univ BEd. Westcott Ho Cam. **d** 84 **p** 85. C Bush Hill Park St Steph *Lon* 84-88; Asst Dir Post Ord Tr Edmonton Episc Area 87-94; Dir Post Ord Tr from 94; V Southgate St Andr from 88. *St Andrew's Vicarage, 184 Chase Side, London N14 5HN* 0181-886 7523

TAYLOR, Peter David. b 38. FCA. N Ord Course 77. **d** 80 **p** 81. C Penwortham St Mary *Blackb* 80-84; V Farington 84-92; V Euxton from 92. *The Vicarage, Wigan Road, Euxton, Chorley, Lancs PR7 6JH* Chorley (01257) 262102

TAYLOR, Peter David. b 47. Liv Univ BEd74 Man Univ MEd78 Lanc Univ MA88. N Ord Course 78. **d** 81 **p** 82. C Formby H Trin *Liv* 81-84; V Stoneycroft All SS 84-91; Chapl St Kath Coll from 91; Dioc RE Field Officer from 91. *55 Woolacombe Road, Liverpool L16 9LG* 0151-737 2090

TAYLOR, Peter Flint. b 44. Qu Coll Cam BA65 MA69. Lon Coll of Div BD70. **d** 70 **p** 71. C Highbury New Park St Aug *Lon* 70-73; C Plymouth St Andr w St Paul and St Geo *Ex* 73-77; V Ironville *Derby* 77-83; P-in-c Riddings 82-83; R Rayleigh *Chelmsf* from 83; Chapl HM Young Offender Inst Bullwood Hall 85-90; RD Rochford *Chelmsf* from 89. *The Rectory, Hockley Road, Rayleigh, Essex SS6 8BA* Rayleigh (01268) 742151

TAYLOR, Peter Graham. b 45. Liv Univ 86 TCert69 CQSW69. Local Minl Tr Course 91. **d** 94 **p** 95. NSM Holywell *St As* from 94. *22 Nant Eos, Holway, Holywell, Clwyd CH8 7DA* Holywell (01352) 712413

TAYLOR, Peter John. b 40. Oak Hill Th Coll 62. **d** 65 **p** 66. C St Paul's Cray St Barn *Roch* 65-69; C Woking St Jo *Guildf* 69-77; R Necton w Holme Hale *Nor* 77-94; P-in-c N Pickenham w S Pickenham etc 94; I Necton, Holme Hale w N and S Pickenham from 95; RD Breckland 86-94. *The Rectory, Necton, Swaffham, Norfolk PE37 8HT* Swaffham (01760) 722021

TAYLOR, Peter John. b 46. Trin Coll Bris 71. **d** 73 **p** 74. C Walshaw Ch Ch *Man* 73-75; C Rodbourne Cheney *Bris* 75-78; Asst Chapl HM Pris Pentonville 78-79; Chapl HM Borstal Roch 79-84; Chapl HM Pris Highpoint 84-90; Asst Chapl Gen of Pris from 90. *c/o Home Office, Calthorpe House, Hagley Road, Birmingham B16 8QR* 0121-455 9855 Fax 454 6738

TAYLOR, Peter John. b 60. New Coll Edin LTh87. Edin Th Coll 83. **d** 87 **p** 88. C Edin SS Phil and Jas *Edin* 87-90; USA 90-92; R Glas St Oswald *Glas* from 92. *The Rectory, 1 King's Park Avenue, Glasgow G44 4UW* 0141-632 1852

TAYLOR, Peter Joseph. b 41. Bps' Coll Cheshunt 66. **d** 68 **p** 69. C Wollaton *S'well* 68-71; C Cockington *Ex* 71-74; V Broadhembury 74-79; V Broadhembury w Payhembury 79-81; V Gt Staughton *Ely* 81-86; Chapl HM Young Offender Inst Gaynes Hall 81-91; R Offord D'Arcy w Offord Cluny *Ely* from 86; V Gt Paxton from 86. *The Rectory, Offord D'Arcy, Huntingdon, Cambs PE18 9RH* Huntingdon (01480) 810588

TAYLOR (or URMSON-TAYLOR), Ralph Urmson. b 28. Tulsa Univ MA72 Man Coll of Educn DipEd74 TCert82. Kelham Th Coll DipTh56 BD56. **d** 56 **p** 57. C Bridlington Quay H Trin *York* 59-62; C Sewerby w Marton 60-62; USA from 62; rtd 93.

TAYLOR

2136 East, 22nd Place, Tulsa, Oklahoma 74114, USA   Tulsa (918) 747-3876

TAYLOR, Raymond. b 34. Lon Coll of Div 62. **d** 65 **p** 66. C Pennington *Man* 65-70; P-in-c Wombridge *Lich* 70-80; R S Normanton *Derby* 80-88; RD Alfreton 86-88; V Youlgreave, Middleton, Stanton-in-Peak etc from 88. *The Vicarage, Youlgreave, Bakewell, Derbyshire DE45 1WL*   Bakewell (01629) 636285

TAYLOR, Raymond Montgomery. b 43. Oak Hill Th Coll 77. **d** 80 **p** 81. Hon C Cricklewood St Pet *Lon* 80-85; Hon C Golders Green 85-87; V New Southgate St Paul from 87. *St Paul's Vicarage, 11 Woodland Road, London N11 1PN*   0181-361 1946

TAYLOR, Richard. b 46. Reading Univ BA68. Sarum & Wells Th Coll 70. **d** 73 **p** 74. C Swindon Ch Ch *Bris* 73-76; P-in-c Charlton w Brokenborough and Hankerton 76-79; P-in-c Croydon St Matt *Cant* 79-81; V 81-84; V Croydon St Matt *S'wark* from 85; RD Croydon Cen 92-95. *The Vicarage, 7 Brownlow Road, Croydon CR0 5JT*   0181-688 5055

TAYLOR, Richard David. b 44. Worc Coll Ox BA67 MA70. Coll of Resurr Mirfield 67. **d** 69 **p** 70. C Barrow St Geo w St Luke *Carl* 69-73; C Gosforth All SS *Newc* 73-80; V Tynemouth Priory 83-91; TR Benwell Team from 91. *Benwell Rectory, Benwell Lane, Newcastle upon Tyne NE15 6RS*   0191-273 5021

TAYLOR, Preb Richard John. b 21. Kelham Th Coll 38. **d** 45 **p** 46. R Edgmond *Lich* 68-77; V Streetly 77-87; Preb Lich Cathl 78-87; rtd 87; Perm to Offic *Lich* from 87. *15 Covey Close, Lichfield, Staffs WS13 6BS*   Lichfield (01543) 268558

TAYLOR, Richard John. b 46. Ripon Coll Cuddesdon 85. **d** 85 **p** 86. C Moseley St Mary *Birm* 85-87; V Kingsbury 87-91; TR Hodge Hill from 91. *The Rectory, Hodge Hill Common, Birmingham B36 8AG*   0121-747 2094 or 747 9262

TAYLOR, Roger. b 21. Birkb Coll Lon BA50 Leeds Univ MA59. Oak Hill Th Coll 47. **d** 51 **p** 52. V Felixstowe SS Pet and Paul *St E* 68-81; P-in-c Gt and Lt Thurlow w Lt Bradley 81-82; TV Haverhill w Withersfield, the Wrattings etc 82-84; R Hopton, Market Weston, Barningham etc 84-86; rtd 86; Perm to Offic *St E* from 87. *Chapel House, Lindsey, Ipswich IP7 6QA*   Boxford (01787) 211120

TAYLOR, Canon Roland Haydn (Roly). b 29. St Chad's Coll Dur BA53 DipTh55. **d** 55 **p** 56. C N Gosforth *Newc* 55-58; C Barnsley St Mary *Wakef* 58-61; V Brotherton 61-68; V Purston cum S Featherstone 68-76; RD Pontefract 74-94; R Badsworth from 76; Hon Can Wakef Cathl from 81. *The Rectory, Main Street, Badsworth, Pontefract, W Yorkshire WF9 1AF*   Pontefract (01977) 643642

TAYLOR, Roy William. b 37. Ch Coll Cam BA61 MA64. Clifton Th Coll 61. **d** 63 **p** 64. C Blackb Sav *Blackb* 63-66; C Hensingham *Carl* 66-68; CMS 69-79; Taiwan 69-79; TV Bushbury *Lich* 79-85; OMF 85-93; Perm to Offic *Lich* 85-93; Hon C Wolv St Jude 93-94; P-in-c Torquay St Jo and Ellacombe *Ex* from 94. *Christ Church Vicarage, 1A Lower Ellacombe Church Road, Torquay TQ1 1JH*   Torquay (01803) 293441

TAYLOR, Mrs Stella Isabelle. b 31. S Dios Minl Tr Scheme 86. **d** 89 **p** 94. NSM Haworth *Bradf* 89-91; Par Dn Keighley St Andr 92-94; C from 94. *Home Cottage, 4 Clarendon Street, Haworth, Keighley, W Yorkshire BD22 8PT*   Haworth (01535) 642493

TAYLOR, Stephen Gordon. b 35. Bris Univ BA60. Ridley Hall Cam 60. **d** 62 **p** 63. C Gt Baddow *Chelmsf* 62-65; C Portsdown *Portsm* 65-69; P-in-c Elvedon *St E* 69-70; R 70-75; P-in-c Eriswell 69-70; R 70-75; P-in-c Icklingham 69-70; R 70-75; Chapl St Felix Sch Southwold 75-77; R Lt Shelford w Newton *Ely* from 77. *The Rectory, Manor Road, Little Shelford, Cambridge CB2 5HF*   Cambridge (01223) 843710

TAYLOR, Stephen James. b 48. Chich Th Coll 70. **d** 73 **p** 74. C Tottenham St Paul *Lon* 73-76; St Vincent 78-85; Grenada 85-88; C-in-c Hammersmith SS Mich and Geo White City Estate CD *Lon* from 88; AD Hammersmith from 92; P-in-c Hammersmith St Luke from 94. *The Parsonage, 1 Commonwealth Avenue, London W12 7QR*   0181-743 7100

TAYLOR, Stephen Ronald. b 55. Cranmer Hall Dur 80. **d** 83 **p** 84. C Ches le Street *Dur* 83-87; V Newbottle 87-92; V Stranton from 92. *The Vicarage, Westbourne Road, Hartlepool, Cleveland TS25 5RE*   Hartlepool (01429) 263190

TAYLOR, Stewart. b 51. St Jo Coll Dur 74. **d** 77 **p** 78. C Norwood *S'wark* 77-81; C Surbiton Hill Ch Ch 81-91; V Cam St Phil *Ely* from 91. *St Philip's Vicarage, 252 Mill Road, Cambridge CB1 3NF*   Cambridge (01223) 247652

TAYLOR, Stuart Bryan. b 40. St Chad's Coll Dur BA64 DipTh66. **d** 66 **p** 67. C Portsea N End St Mark *Portsm* 66-70; C Epsom St Martin *Guildf* 70-76; Perm to Offic *Bris* 76-93; Chapl Clifton Coll Bris 76-88; Perm to Offic *Bris* 88-93; Dir Bloxham Project 88-93; Chapl Giggleswick Sch from 93; Tr Officer for Sch Chapls from 93. *Huntsman's Cottage, Giggleswick, Settle, N Yorkshire BD24 0DE*   Settle (01729) 822637

TAYLOR, Mrs Susan Mary. b 48. Univ of Wales (Swansea) BA69 Univ of Wales (Lamp) LTh72. St D Coll Lamp 70. **dss** 72 **d** 87. Chepstow *Mon* 72-73; Mynyddislwyn 73-75; Perm to Offic *Lon* 75-79; Hayes St Edm 79-87; NSM Pilton w Ashford *Ex* 87-89; NSM Sidley *Chich* from 89. *All Saints' Vicarage, All Saints Lane, Sidley, Bexhill-on-Sea, Sussex TN39 5HA*   Bexhill-on-Sea (01424) 221071

TAYLOR, Thomas. b 42. St Jo Coll Dur BA64. Linc Th Coll 64. **d** 66 **p** 67. C Clitheroe St Mary *Blackb* 66-69; C Skerton St Luke 69-71; C-in-c Penwortham St Leon CD 71-72; V Penwortham St Leon 72-78; R Poulton-le-Sands 78-81; P-in-c Morecambe St Lawr 78-81; R Poulton-le-Sands w Morecambe St Laur 81-85; Chapl Ld Wandsworth Coll Long Sutton 85-92; V Walton-le-Dale *Blackb* 92-94; P-in-c Samlesbury 92-94; V Walton-le-Dale St Leon w Samlesbury St Leon from 95; RD Leyland from 94. *The Vicarage, Church Brow, Walton-le-Dale, Preston PR5 4BH*   Preston (01772) 880233

TAYLOR, Thomas (Tom). b 33. Sarum & Wells Th Coll 77. **d** 80 **p** 81. NSM Heatherlands St Jo *Sarum* 80-82; TV Kinson 82-88; TV Shaston from 88; Chapl Westmr Memorial Hosp Shaftesbury from 88. *The Vicarage, Motcombe, Shaftesbury, Dorset SP7 9NX*   Shaftesbury (01747) 851442

TAYLOR, Thomas Fish. b 13. Glas Univ MA46. Kelham Th Coll 30. **d** 36 **p** 37. P-in-c Rattery *Ex* 69-79; rtd 79; Perm to Offic *Ex* 79-92. *Digby House, 40 Avenue Road, Wimborne, Dorset BH21 1BT*   Wimborne (01202) 841596

TAYLOR, Thomas Ronald Bennett. b 23. TCD BA46 MA54. Div Test. **d** 47 **p** 48. I Tynan w Middletown *Arm* 68-85; rtd 85. *34 Kernan Park, Portadown, Co Armagh BT63 5QX*   Portadown (01762) 337230

TAYLOR, William Austin. b 36. Linc Th Coll 65. **d** 67 **p** 68. C Tyldesley w Shakerley *Man* 67-71; R Cheetham St Mark 71-79; V Peel 79-90; AD Farnworth 83-90; V Pelton *Dur* from 90. *The Vicarage, Church Road, Pelton, Chester le Street, Co Durham DH2 1XB*   0191-370 2204

TAYLOR, William David. b 60. Southn Univ BTh90. Sarum & Wells Th Coll 87. **d** 90 **p** 91. C Washington *Dur* 90-94; P-in-c Heworth St Mary from 94. *The Vicarage, High Heworth Lane, Heworth, Gateshead, Tyne & Wear NE10 0PB*   0191-469 2111

TAYLOR, William Henry. b 56. FRAS MA MTh PhD88. Westcott Ho Cam. **d** 83 **p** 84. C Maidstone All SS and St Phil w Tovil *Cant* 83-86; Abp's Adv on Orthodox Affairs 86-88; C St Marylebone All SS *Lon* 86-88; Chapl Guy's Hosp Lon 88; CMS 88-91; Jordan 88-91; V Ealing St Pet Mt Park *Lon* from 91; AD Ealing from 93. *St Peter's Vicarage, Mount Park Road, London W5 2RU*   0181-997 1620

TAYLOR, William Richard de Carteret Martin (Bill). b 33. CCC Cam MA57. Westcott Ho Cam 58. **d** 59 **p** 60. C Eastney *Portsm* 59-63; Chapl RN 63-67 and 70-87; V Childe Okeford *Sarum* 67-70; V Manston w Hamoon 67-70; QHC from 83; TR Tisbury *Sarum* 87-89; Chapl Hatf Poly *St Alb* 89-92; Chapl Herts Univ from 92. *University of Hertfordshire, College Lane, Hatfield, Herts AL10 9AB*   Hatfield (01707) 279000 or 279456

TAYLOR, Capt William Thomas. b 61. Rob Coll Cam BA83 BA90. Ridley Hall Cam 88. **d** 91 **p** 92. C Bromley Ch Ch *Roch* 91-95; C St Helen Bishopsgate w St Andr Undershaft etc *Lon* from 95. *16 Ravensden Street, London SE11 4AR*   0171-283 2231

TEAGUE, Dr Gaythorne Derrick. b 24. MRCGP53 Bris Univ MB, ChB49 DPH. **d** 74 **p** 75. NSM Bris St Andr Hartcliffe *Bris* 74-86; Perm to Offic *B & W* 79-86; NSM Blagdon w Compton Martin and Ubley from 86. *Innisfree, Bell Square, Blagdon, Bristol BS18 6UB*   Blagdon (01761) 462671

TEAGUE, Robert Hayden. b 15. Univ of Wales (Ban). Dorchester Miss Coll 36 St Deiniol's Hawarden. **d** 63 **p** 64. V Llangernyw, Gwytherin and Llanddewi *St As* 66-77; V Meliden and Gwaenysgor 77-83; rtd 83. *4 Ffordd Tanrallt, Melidan, Prestatyn, Clwyd LL19 8PR*   Prestatyn (01745) 857419

TEAL, Andrew Robert. b 64. Birm Univ BA85. Ripon Coll Cuddesdon 86. **d** 88 **p** 89. C Wednesbury St Paul Wood Green *Lich* 88-92; TV Sheff Manor *Sheff* from 92; Tutor Ripon Coll Cuddesdon from 92; Asst Dioc Post Ord Tr Offic from 93. *The Vicarage, 2 Manor Lane, Sheffield S2 1UF*   Sheffield (0114) 272 4676

TEALE, Adrian. b 53. Univ of Wales (Abth) BA74 CertEd77 MA80 Univ of Wales (Cardiff) MTh89. Wycliffe Hall Ox 78. **d** 80 **p** 81. C Betws St Dav w Ammanford *St D* 80-84; V Brynaman w Cwmllynfell from 84. *The Vicarage, 23 Llandeilo Road, Brynaman, Dyfed SA18 1BA*   Amman Valley (01269) 822275

TEALE, Ernest Burdett. b 20. Keble Coll Ox BA42 MA46. Westcott Ho Cam 42. **d** 43 **p** 45. P-in-c Radbourne *Derby* 69-70; Adv for Primary and Middle Schs *Lon* 70-85; rtd 85; Lic to Offic *Lon* from 85. *103 Sandringham Gardens, London N12 0PA*   0181-445 2037

684

TEARE, Canon Robert John Hugh. b 39. Bris Univ BSc62 Leeds Univ DipTh69. Coll of Resurr Mirfield 67. **d** 70 **p** 71. C Fareham SS Pet and Paul *Portsm* 70-73; Chapl K Alfred Coll *Win* 73-78; V Pokesdown St Jas 78-82; R Winnall from 82; RD Win from 89; Hon Can Win Cathl from 92. *The Rectory, 22 St John's Street, Winchester, Hants SO23 0HF* Winchester (01962) 863891

TEARNAN, John Herman Janson. b 37. Bris Univ BSc59. Kelham Th Coll 62. **d** 66 **p** 67. C Kettering SS Pet and Paul *Pet* 66-71; Lic to Offic 71-85; Perm to Offic *St Alb* from 82; Perm to Offic *Pet* from 85; Sub-Chapl HM Young Offender Inst Wellingborough from 89; Chapl HM Young Offender Inst Glen Parva from 90. *HM Young Offender Institution, Glen Parva, Tigers Road, Wigston, Leics LE18 2TN* Leicester (0116) 277 2022 Fax 477679

TEASDALE, Keith. b 56. Cranmer Hall Dur 86. **d** 88 **p** 89. C Crook *Dur* 88-92; V Dunston from 92. *St Nicholas' Vicarage, Willow Avenue, Dunston, Gateshead, Tyne & Wear NE11 9UN* 0191-460 0509

TEBBOTH, Alfred Thomas Henderson. b 09. Qu Coll Birm 51. **d** 52 **p** 53. R Kelshall *St Alb* 69-76; R Therfield 69-76; rtd 77. *c/o R J W Tebboth Esq, Lulworth, 10 Meadowside Gardens, Rushmere, Ipswich IP4 5RD* Ipswich (01473) 623137

TEBBS, Richard Henry. b 52. Southn Univ BTh. Sarum & Wells Th Coll 75. **d** 78 **p** 79. C Cinderhill *S'well* 78-82; C Nor St Pet Mancroft *Nor* 82; C Nor St Pet Mancroft w St Jo Maddermarket 82-85; TV Bridport *Sarum* 85-94; TR Yelverton, Meavy, Sheepstor and Walkhampton *Ex* from 94. *The Rectory, Meavy Lane, Yelverton, Devon PL20 6AE* Yelverton (01822) 832362

TEBBUTT, Simon Albert. b 27. Qu Coll Birm 88. **d** 89 **p** 90. NSM Northn St Matt *Pet* 89-92; TV Duston Team 92-94; rtd 94; NSM Gt and Lt Houghton w Brafield on the Green *Pet* from 94. *Tanners, Moulton Lane, Boughton, Northampton NN2 8RF* Northampton (01604) 843240

TEDMAN, Alfred. b 33. AKC59. **d** 60 **p** 61. C Newington St Mary *S'wark* 60-64; C Milton *Portsm* 64-68; R Bonchurch from 68; RD E Wight 78-83; P-in-c Whitwell 79-82; P-in-c St Lawrence 82-84; V Wroxall from 84. *The Rectory, Bonchurch, Ventnor, Isle of Wight PO38 1NU* Isle of Wight (01983) 852357

TEE, John. b 59. **d** 82 **p** 83. C Walworth *S'wark* 82-85; Chapl RAF 85-89; CF from 89. *c/o MOD, Army, Bagshot Park, Bagshot, Surrey GU19 5PL* Bagshot (01276) 471717

TEGGIN, John. b 26. **d** 83 **p** 84. NSM Dub Sandford w Milltown *D & G* 84-93; Leprosy Miss from 86. *4 Temple Hill, Blackrock, Co Dublin, Irish Republic* Dublin (1) 280-4008

TELFER, Canon Frank Somerville. b 30. Trin Hall Cam BA53 MA58. Ely Th Coll 53. **d** 55 **p** 56. C Liv Our Lady and St Nic *Liv* 55-58; Chapl Down Coll Cam 58-62; Bp's Chapl *Nor* 62-65; Chapl Kent Univ *Cant* 65-73; Can Res Guildf Cathl *Guildf* from 73. *2 Cathedral Close, Guildford, Surrey GU2 5TL* Guildford (01483) 60329

TELFORD, Alan. b 46. St Jo Coll Nottm. **d** 83 **p** 84. C Normanton *Derby* 83-86; TV N Wingfield, Pilsley and Tupton 86-90; TV N Wingfield, Clay Cross and Pilsley 90-92; P-in-c Oakwood 92-94; V Leic St Chris *Leic* from 94. *The Vicarage, 84A Marriott Road, Leicester LE2 6NU* Leicester (0116) 283 2679

TELFORD, Cyril Harry. b 22. S Dios Minl Tr Scheme. **d** 54 **p** 55. V Lt Lever *Man* 60-94; rtd 94. *1 Aintree Road, Little Lever, Bolton BL3 1EZ* Bolton (01204) 72392

TELFORD, Canon Edward Cecil. b 17. Selw Coll Cam BA47 MA52. Linc Th Coll 47. **d** 49 **p** 50. R Langdon Hills *Chelmsf* 59-70; R Shenfield 70-85; Hon Can Chelmsf Cathl 75-85; RD Brentwood 76-84; rtd 85; Perm to Offic *Ely* from 86. *13 Harlestones Road, Cottenham, Cambridge CB4 4TR* Cottenham (01954) 51184

TELFORD, John Edward. b 16. TCD BA40 MA46. CITC 40. **d** 41 **p** 42. I Dub Irishtown *D & G* 44-60; rtd 60. *12 Woodbine Avenue, Blackrock, Co Dublin, Irish Republic* Dublin (1) 269-1187

TELFORD, Richard Francis. b 46. K Coll Lon. **d** 69 **p** 70. C Barkingside H Trin *Chelmsf* 69-72; C Wickford 72-77; P-in-c Romford St Jo 77-80; V 80-82; Perm to Offic from 93. *59 Hartswood Road, Brentwood, Essex CM14 5AG* Brentwood (01277) 214911

TELLINI, Canon Dr Gianfranco. b 36. Gregorian Univ Rome DTh65. Franciscan Sem Trent 57. **d** 61 **p** 61. In RC Ch 61-66; C Mill Hill Jo Keble Ch *Lon* 66; C Roxbourne St Andr 66-67; Lect Sarum Th Coll 67-69; Sen Tutor 69-74; Vice-Prin Edin Th Coll 74-82; Lect Th Edin Univ from 74; R Pittenweem *St And* 82-85; R Elie and Earlsferry 82-85; R Dunblane from 85; Can St Ninian's Cathl Perth from 90. *The Rectory, Smithy Loan, Dunblane, Perthshire FK15 0HQ* Dunblane (01786) 824225

TEMPERLEY, Robert Noble. b 29. JP. ACP52 St Jo Coll York CertEd50 Dur Univ DAES62. NE Ord Course 85. **d** 88 **p** 88.

NSM Ryhope *Dur* from 88. *18 Withernsea Grove, Ryhope, Sunderland SR2 0BU* 0191-521 1813

✠**TEMPLE, Rt Rev Frederick Stephen.** b 16. Ball Coll Ox BA39 MA45 Trin Hall Cam BA47 MA52. Westcott Ho Cam 45. **d** 47 **p** 48 **c** 73. C Arnold *S'well* 47-49; C Newark w Coddington 49-51; R Birch St Agnes *Man* 51-53; Dean Hong Kong 53-59; Abp's Sen Chapl *Cant* 59-61; V Portsea St Mary *Portsm* 61-70; Hon Can Portsm Cathl 65-69; Adn Swindon *Bris* 70-73; Hon Can Bris Cathl 70-83; Suff Bp Malmesbury 73-83; rtd 83; Asst Bp Bris from 83; Asst Bp Sarum from 83. *7 The Barton, Wood Street, Wootton Bassett, Swindon SN4 7BG* Swindon (01793) 851227

TEMPLE, Ven George Frederick. b 33. Wells Th Coll 66. **d** 68 **p** 69. C Gt Bookham *Guildf* 68-70; C Penzance St Mary *Truro* 70-72; V St Just in Penwith 72-74; V Sancreed 72-74; V St Gluvias 74-81; Adn Bodmin 81-89; Hon Can Truro Cathl 81-89; V Saltash St Nich and St Faith 82-85; Dioc Dir of Ords 85-89; rtd 89. *50 Athelstan Park, Bodmin, Cornwall PL31 1DT* Bodmin (01208) 77568

TEMPLE, Mrs Sylvia Mary. b 48. Ex Univ BA70 Univ of Wales (Abth) PGCE71. St D Dioc Tr Course 93. **d** 94. NSM Tenby *St D* from 94. *Llwyn Onn, Trafalgar Road, Tenby, Dyfed SA70 7DW* Tenby (01834) 842104

TEMPLEMAN, Peter Morton. b 49. Ch Ch Ox BA71 MA75 BTh75. Wycliffe Hall Ox 73. **d** 76 **p** 77. C Cheltenham St Mary, St Matt, St Paul and H Trin *Glouc* 76-79; Chapl St Jo Coll Cam 79-84; P-in-c Finchley St Paul Long Lane *Lon* 84-85; P-in-c Finchley St Luke 84-85; V Finchley St Paul and St Luke from 85. *St Paul's Vicarage, 50 Long Lane, London N3 2PU* 0181-346 8729

TEMPLETON (nee McCUTCHEON), Irene. b 41. QUB BEd. Dalton Ho Bris 65. **d** 89 **p** 90. Lic to Offic *Conn* 89; Hon Par Dn Kilmakee 89-90; C 90-91; NSM Jordanstown from 91. *15 Cairnshill Avenue, Belfast BT8 4NR* Belfast (01232) 701686

TENNANT, Charles Roger. b 19. Open Univ PhD75. Linc Th Coll 49. **d** 51 **p** 52. V Bitteswell *Leic* 62-88; P-in-c Misterton w Walcote 80-88; rtd 88. *Middle House, Station Road, Ullesthorpe, Lutterworth, Leics LE17 5BS* Hinckley (01455) 209703

TENNANT, Cyril Edwin George. b 37. Keble Coll Ox BA59 MA63 Lon Univ BD61. Clifton Th Coll 59. **d** 62 **p** 63. C Stapleford *S'well* 62-65; C Felixstowe SS Pet and Paul *St E* 65-69; V Gipsy Hill Ch Ch *S'wark* 69-84; V Lee St Mildred 84-90; V Ilfracombe SS Phil and Jas w W Down *Ex* from 90. *St James's Vicarage, Kingsley Avenue, Ilfracombe, Devon EX34 8ET* Ilfracombe (01271) 863519

TENNANT, Osmond Roy. b 21. Worc Ord Coll 62. **d** 63 **p** 64. V Escot *Ex* 67-89; R Talaton 67-89; P-in-c Clyst Hydon and Clyst St Lawrence 74-87; rtd 89; Perm to Offic *Ex* from 89. *Rockleigh, 29 West Clyst, Exeter EX1 3TL* Exeter (01392) 65515

TENNICK, Edward. b 10. St Aid Birkenhead 38. **d** 40 **p** 41. V Southborough St Thos *Roch* 62-75; rtd 75; Perm to Offic *Chich* from 87. *Flat 3, 7 Chatsworth Gardens, Eastbourne, E Sussex BN20 7JP* Eastbourne (01323) 648490

TER BLANCHE, Harold Daniel. b 35. S Africa 63-82; Miss to Seamen 82-84; Chapl Grimsby Distr Gen Hosp from 84. *Grimsby District General Hospital, Scartho Road, Grimsby, S Humberside DN33 2BA* Grimsby (01472) 875204

TERESA, Sister. *See* WHITE, Sister Teresa Joan

TERRANOVA, Jonathan Rossano. b 62. Sheff Poly BA85. Oak Hill Th Coll BA88. **d** 88 **p** 89. C Carl St Jo *Carl* 88-91; C Stoughton *Guildf* 91-94; R Ditton *Roch* from 94. *The Rectory, 2 The Stream, Ditton, Maidstone, Kent ME20 6AG* West Malling (01732) 842027

TERRELL, Richard Charles Patridge. b 43. Wells Th Coll 69. **d** 71 **p** 72. C Shepton Mallet *B & W* 71-76; P-in-c Drayton 76-78; P-in-c Muchelney 76-78; TV Langport Area Chs 78-82; P-in-c Tatworth 82-89; V from 89. *The Vicarage, Tatworth, Chard, Somerset TA20 2PD* South Chard (01460) 220404

TERRETT, Mervyn Douglas. b 43. AKC65. **d** 66 **p** 67. C Pet St Mary *Pet* 66-69; C Sawbridgeworth *St Alb* 69-74; V Stevenage H Trin 74-85; Perm to Offic from 86. *Red Roofs, 20 Woodfield Road, Stevenage, Herts SG1 4BP* Stevenage (01438) 720152

TERRY, Christopher Laurence. b 51. FCA80. St Alb Minl Tr Scheme. **d** 83 **p** 84. Hon C Dunstable *St Alb* 83-89; C Abbots Langley 89-92; TV Chambersbury (Hemel Hempstead) from 92. *St Mary's Vicarage, 31 Chipperfield Road, Apsley, Hemel Hempstead, Herts HP3 0AJ* Hemel Hempstead (01442) 61610

TERRY, Ian Andrew. b 53. St Jo Coll Dur BA74 St Jo Coll York PGCE75. Coll of Resurr Mirfield 78. **d** 80 **p** 81. C Beaconsfield *Ox* 80-83; C N Lynn w St Marg and St Nic *Nor* 83-84; Chapl & Head RE Eliz Coll Guernsey 84-89; Chapl St Jo Sch Leatherhead 89-92; R Bisley and W End *Guildf* from 92. *The Rectory, Clews Lane, Bisley, Woking, Surrey GU24 9DY* Brookwood (01483) 473377

TERRY, John Arthur. b 32. S'wark Ord Course. **d** 66 **p** 67. C Plumstead All SS *S'wark* 66-69; C Peckham St Mary Magd 69-72; V Streatham Vale H Redeemer 72-80; R Sternfield w Benhall and Snape *St E* 80-84; V Stevenage St Mary Shephall *St Alb* 84-86; V Stevenage St Mary Sheppall w Aston 86-90; V Cople w Willington from 90; Chapl Shuttleworth Agric Coll from 90. *The Vicarage, Cople, Bedford MK44 3TT* Bedford (01234) 838431

TERRY, Justyn Charles. b 65. Keble Coll Ox BA86 St Jo Coll Dur BA95. Cranmer Hall Dur 92. **d** 95. C Paddington St Jo w St Mich *Lon* from 95. *12 Connaught Street, London W2 2AF* 0171-706 4099   Fax 262 1732

TERRY, Stephen John. b 49. K Coll Lon BD72 AKC74. **d** 75 **p** 76. C Tokyngton St Mich *Lon* 75-78; C Hampstead St Steph w All Hallows 78-81; V Whetstone St Jo 81-89; TR Aldrington *Chich* from 89; OStJ from 89. *The Rectory, 77 New Church Road, Hove, E Sussex BN3 4BB* Brighton (01273) 737915

TESTA, Luigi Richard Frederick. b 30. Nottm Univ CTPS85. **d** 85 **p** 86. NSM Castle Donington and Lockington cum Hemington *Leic* from 85. *40 Hillside, Castle Donington, Derby DE74 2NH* Derby (01332) 810823

TESTER, Clarence Albert. b 20. Qu Coll Birm 47. **d** 50 **p** 51. Chapl Ham Green Hosp Bris 55-70; V Halberton *Ex* 70-85; rtd 85; Perm to Offic *B & W* from 86. *Brays Batch, Chewton Mendip, Bath BA3 4LH* Chewton Mendip (01761) 241218

TESTER, Canon Francis Edward. b 24. Leeds Univ BA46. Coll of Resurr Mirfield 45. **d** 47 **p** 48. V Hockerill *St Alb* 64-71; Chapl Highwood and St Faith's Hosps Brentwood 71-89; V Brentwood St Thos *Chelmsf* 71-89; RD Brentwood 84-89; Hon Can Chelmsf Cathl 87-89; rtd 89; Perm to Offic *Chelmsf* from 89; Perm to Offic *Nor* 89-91 and from 94; P-in-c Toftrees w Shereford 91-94; P-in-c Hempton and Pudding Norton 91-94. *Wythe, Burnt Street, Wells-next-the-Sea, Norfolk NR23 1HW* Fakenham (01328) 711306

TETLEY, Brian. b 38. FCA BA. Cranmer Hall Dur 80. **d** 83 **p** 84. C Chipping Sodbury and Old Sodbury *Glouc* 83-86; Chapl and Succ Roch Cath *Roch* 86-89; R Gravesend H Family w Ifield 89-93. *201A Milton Road, Cambridge CB4 1XG* Cambridge (01223) 423633

TETLEY, Canon Joy Dawn. b 46. St Mary's Coll Dur BA68 Leeds Univ CertEd69 St Hugh's Coll Ox BA75 MA80 Dur Univ PhD88. NW Ord Course 77. **dss** 77 **d** 87 **p** 94. Bentley *Sheff* 77-79; Buttershaw St Aid *Bradf* 79-80; Dur Cathl *Dur* 80-83; Lect Trin Coll Bris 83-86; Chipping Sodbury and Old Sodbury *Glouc* 83-86; Dn Roch Cathl *Roch* 87-89; Hon Can Roch Cathl 90-93; Assoc Dir of Post Ord Tr 87-88; Dir Post Ord Tr 88-93; Hon Par Dn Gravesend H Family w Ifield 89-93; Prin E Anglian Minl Tr Course *Ely* from 93. *201A Milton Road, Cambridge CB4 1XG* Cambridge (01223) 423633 or 322633

TETLEY, Matthew David. b 61. Bucks Coll of Educn BSc83. Sarum & Wells Th Coll BTh89. **d** 87 **p** 88. C Kirkby *Liv* 87-90; C Hindley St Pet 90-93; TV Whorlton *Newc* from 93. *St Wilfrid's House, Trevelyan Drive, Newbiggen Hall, Newcastle upon Tyne NE5 4DA* 0191-286 0345

TETLOW, John. b 46. St Steph Ho Ox 73. **d** 76 **p** 77. C Stanwell *Lon* 76-77; C Hanworth All SS 77-80; C Somers Town St Mary 80-83; TV Wickford and Runwell *Chelmsf* 83-90; P-in-c Walthamstow St Mich from 90. *St Michael's Vicarage, Palmerston Road, London E17 6PQ* 0181-520 6328

TETLOW, Richard Jeremy. b 42. Trin Coll Cam MA66 Golds Coll Lon CQSW74. Qu Coll Birm 81. **d** 83 **p** 84. C Birm St Martin *Birm* 83-85; C Birm St Martin w Bordesley St Andr 85-88; V Birm St Jo Ladywood from 89. *St John's Vicarage, Darnley Road, Birmingham B16 8TF* 0121-454 0973

TEWKESBURY, Alec. b 13. Dur Univ LTh38. ALCD36. **d** 36 **p** 37. V Loxwood *Chich* 70-78; rtd 78; Perm to Offic *Chich* from 78. *1 Stonefield Close, Crawley, W Sussex RH10 6AU* Crawley (01293) 534420

TEWKESBURY, Noel. b 44. Hull Univ BA67. Wycliffe Hall Ox 70. **d** 72 **p** 73. C Bishops Waltham *Portsm* 72-76; C Havant 76-77; C Filey *York* 77-79; V Monk Fryston 79-84; V Hambleton 79-84; TV Bolventor *Truro* 84-86; TR 86-91; R N Elmham w Billingford and Worthing *Nor* from 91. *The Vicarage, Holt Road, North Elmham, Dereham, Norfolk NR20 5JQ* Dereham (01362) 668244

TEWKESBURY, Suffragan Bishop of. *Vacant*

THACKER, Charles Kent. b 09. K Coll Cam BA31 MA35. Ely Th Coll 31. **d** 32 **p** 34. Chapl Victoria Coll Jersey 63-74; C Jersey St Clem *Win* 73-74; rtd 74. *Sea Court, Bel Royal, Jersey, Channel Islands JE3 1JU* Jersey (01534) 20019

THACKER, Ian David. b 59. DCR DRI. Oak Hill Th Coll BA91. **d** 91 **p** 92. C Illogan *Truro* 91-94; C Eglwysilan *Llan* from 94. *1 Caerphilly Road, Senghenydd, Caerphilly, M Glam CF8 2FR* Cardiff (01222) 830392

THACKER, James Robert. b 40. Cath Univ of America BA63 MDiv66 MSW76. Nashotah Ho. **d** 66 **p** 66. USA 66-90; Bermuda from 90. *PO Box FL 239, Smith's FL BX, Bermuda* Bermuda (1-809) 236-8360   Fax 236-7148

THACKER, Jonathan William. b 53. Lon Univ BA74 Nottm Univ DipTh78. Linc Th Coll 76. **d** 79 **p** 80. C Bromyard *Heref* 79-82; C Penkridge w Stretton *Lich* 82-87; V Brothertoft Gp *Linc* from 87; RD Holland W from 92. *The Vicarage, Main Road, Brothertoft, Boston, Lincs PE20 3SW* Langrick (01205) 280267

THACKER, Kenneth Ray. b 31. Open Univ BA73. Tyndale Hall Bris 56. **d** 59 **p** 60. V Moxley *Lich* 64-71; R Leigh 71-91; rtd 92. *24 Rugby Close, Newcastle-under-Lyme ST5 3JN* Newcastle-under-Lyme (01782) 617812

THACKER, Roger Ailwyn Mackintosh. b 46. CCC Cam BA68 MA73. Westcott Ho Cam 68. **d** 70 **p** 71. C St Jo Wood *Lon* 70-74; P-in-c Hammersmith St Paul 74-79; V from 79. *21 Lower Mall, Hammersmith Road, London W6 9DJ* 0171-603 4303 or 748 3855

THACKRAY, John Adrian. b 55. ACIB84 Southn Univ BSc76. Coll of Resurr Mirfield 81. **d** 84 **p** 85. C Loughton St Jo *Chelmsf* 84-87; Chapl Bancroft's Sch Woodford Green 87-92; Sen Chapl K Sch Cant from 92. *14 Monastery Street, Canterbury, Kent CT1 1NJ* Canterbury (01227) 455320 or 475561

THACKRAY, Peter Michael. b 29. Coll of Resurr Mirfield BA52. **d** 54 **p** 55. W Germany 67-73; CF 73-78; Lic to Offic *Eur* 78-84; Hon C Sellindge w Monks Horton and Stowting *Cant* 84-86; Hon C Lympne w W Hythe 84-86; Hon C Sellindge w Monks Horton and Stowting etc 86-91; Perm to Offic 91-95; rtd 94; Hon C Brabourne w Smeeth *Cant* 95. *The Rectory, Church Road, Smeeth, Ashford, Kent TN25 6SA* Sellindge (01303) 812126

THACKRAY, William Harry. b 44. Leeds Univ CertEd66. Chich Th Coll 70. **d** 73 **p** 74. C Sheff St Cuth *Sheff* 73-76; C Stocksbridge 76-78; P-in-c Newark St Leon *S'well* 79-80; TV Newark w Hawton, Cotham and Shelton 80-82; VC S'well Minster 82-85; V Bawtry w Austerfield 85; P-in-c Misson 85; V Bawtry w Austerfield and Misson 86-93; RD Bawtry 90-93; P-in-c Balderton from 93. *The Vicarage, Main Street, Balderton, Newark, Notts NG24 3NN* Newark (01636) 704811

THADDEUS, Brother. *See* BURGOYNE-JOHNSON, Philip Simon

THAKE, Preb Terence (Terry). b 41. ALCD65. **d** 66 **p** 67. C Gt Faringdon w Lt Coxwell *Ox* 66-70; C Aldridge *Lich* 70-73; V Werrington 73-82; Chapl HM Det Cen Werrington Ho 73-82; TR Chell *Lich* 82-94; Chapl Westcliffe Hosp 82-94; RD Stoke N 91-94; Preb Lich Cathl from 94; V Colwich w Gt Haywood from 94; P-in-c Colton from 95. *The Vicarage, Little Haywood, Stafford ST18 0TS* Little Haywood (01889) 881262

THAME, Miss Margaret Eve. b 31. SRN54 SCM55. Glouc Sch of Min 85. **d** 88 **p** 94. NSM Cheltenham All SS *Glouc* 88-94; NSM Cheltenham St Mich from 94. *13 Brighton Road, Cheltenham, Glos GL52 6BA* Cheltenham (01242) 241228

THATCHER, Barbara Mary. b 25. Lon Univ BCom. **d** 90 **p** 94. NSM Helensburgh *Glas* from 90. *228 West Princes Street, Helensburgh, Dunbartonshire G84 8HA* Helensburgh (01436) 672003

THATCHER, Rodney David (Rod). b 38. Sarum & Wells Th Coll 83. **d** 86 **p** 87. NSM Wilton *B & W* 86-89; C Bridgwater St Mary, Chilton Trinity and Durleigh 89-91; P-in-c Charlton Musgrove, Cucklington and Stoke Trister from 91; Chapl Rural Affairs Wells Adnry from 92. *The Rectory, Charlton Musgrove, Wincanton, Somerset BA9 8HN* Wincanton (01963) 33233

THATCHER, Stephen Bert. b 58. St Jo Coll Nottm LTh87. **d** 87 **p** 88. C Bargoed and Deri w Brithdir *Llan* 87-89; C Llanishen and Lisvane 89-91; V Llanwnda, Goodwick, w Manorowen and Llanstinan *St D* from 91. *The Vicarage, Goodwick, Dyfed SA64 0AN* Fishguard (01348) 873758

THAWLEY, Very Rev David Laurie. b 24. St Edm Hall Ox BA47 MA49. Cuddesdon Coll 49. **d** 51 **p** 52. C Bitterne Park *Win* 51-56; C-in-c Andover St Mich CD 56-60; Australia from 60; Can Res Brisbane 64-72; Dean Wangaratta 72-89. *Lavender Cottage, 2 Bond Street, North Caulfield, Victoria, Australia 3161* Melbourne (3) 571-0513

THAYER, Michael David. b 52. Sarum & Wells Th Coll 77. **d** 80 **p** 81. C Minehead *B & W* 80-85; Chapl RN 85-89; TV Lowestoft and Kirkley *Nor* 89-92; Chapl St Helena's Hospice Colchester from 92. *St Helena's Hospice, Eastwood Drive, Highwoods, Colchester CO4 4JU* Colchester (01206) 845566

THEAKSTON, Ms Sally Margaret. b 62. UEA BSc84 Ox Univ BA89. Ripon Coll Cuddesdon 86. **d** 89 **p** 94. C Hackney *Lon* 89-93; Par Dn Putney St Mary *S'wark* 93-94; C from 94. *54 Clarendon Drive, London SW15 1AH* 0181-785 2257

THELWELL, Canon John Berry. b 49. Univ of Wales (Ban) BD72. Qu Coll Birm 73. **d** 73 **p** 74. C Minera *St As* 73-80; Dioc Youth Chapl 78-86; V Gwernaffield and Llanferres 80-93;

Chapl Clwyd Fire Service from 88; RD Mold 91-95; R Hawarden from 93; Can Cursal St As Cathl from 95. *The Rectory, 2 Birch Rise, Hawarden, Deeside, Clwyd CH5 3DD* Hawarden (01244) 531103 or 535816

THEOBALD, Graham Fitzroy. b 43. ALCD67. **d** 67 **p** 68. C Crookham *Guildf* 67-71; C York Town St Mich 71-74; V Wrecclesham 74-83; R Frimley 83-85; Perm to Offic *Ox* 90-92; C Easthampstead from 92. *The Vicarage, 4 Qualitas, Roman Hill, Bracknell, Berks RG12 7QG* Bracknell (01344) 487248

THEOBALD, Henry Charles. b 32. Lon Univ DBS63 DRBS63. S'wark Ord Course 60. **d** 63 **p** 64. C Reigate St Luke S Park *S'wark* 68-73; Chapl S Lon Hosp for Women & St Jas Hosp Balham 73-83; Chapl St Mary's Hosp Portsm 83-93; rtd 93. *141 Warren Avenue, Southsea, Hants PO4 8PP* Portsmouth (01705) 817443

THEOBALD, John Walter. b 33. St Aid Birkenhead. **d** 65 **p** 66. C Hindley All SS *Liv* 65-68; C Beverley Minster *York* 68-71; R Loftus 71-86; P-in-c Carlin How w Skinningrove 73-86; Asst Chapl HM Pris Leeds 86-89; Chapl HM Pris Rudgate 89-93; Chapl HM Pris Thorp Arch 89-93; Chapl HM Pris Leeds from 93. *HM Prison, Armley, Leeds LS12 2TJ* Leeds (0113) 263 6411 Fax 790151

THEODOSIUS, Hugh John. b 32. Trin Coll Cam BA56 MA60. Cuddesdon Coll 56. **d** 58 **p** 59. C Milton *Win* 58-62; C Romsey 62-64; C Southn Maybush St Pet 64-70; V Malden St Jo *S'wark* 70-81; V Billingborough *Linc* 81-94; V Horbling 81-94; V Sempringham w Pointon and Birthorpe 81-94; RD Aveland and Ness w Stamford 87-93. *The Cottage, Gosberton Bank, Spalding, Lincs PE11 4PB* Spalding (01775) 841129

THEODOSIUS, Richard Francis. b 35. Fitzw Coll Cam BA59. Lich Th Coll 69. **d** 71 **p** 72. C Bloxwich *Lich* 71-73; Chapl Blue Coat Comp Sch Walsall 71-73; Lic to Offic *S'well* from 73; Chapl Ranby Ho Sch Retford from 73. *Downlea, 51 Town Street, Lound, Retford, Notts DN22 8RT* Retford (01777) 818744

THETFORD, Suffragan Bishop of. *See* de WAAL, Rt Rev Hugo Ferdinand

THEWLIS, Andrew James. b 64. Man Univ BSc86. Cranmer Hall Dur 87. **d** 90 **p** 91. C Walshaw Ch Ch *Man* 90-95; P-in-c Jersey St Jo *Win* from 95. *The Rectory, La Rue des Landes, St John, Jersey, Channel Islands JE3 4AF* Jersey (01534) 861677

THEWLIS, Dr John Charles. b 49. Van Mildert Coll Dur BA70 PhD75. N Ord Course 78. **d** 81 **p** 82. NSM Hull Sculcoates St Mary *York* 81-83; C Spring Park *Cant* 83-84; C Spring Park All SS *S'wark* 85-86; V Eltham Park St Luke from 86. *St Luke's Vicarage, 107 Westmount Road, London SE9 1XX* 0181-850 3030

THICKE, James Balliston. b 43. Sarum & Wells Th Coll 74. **d** 77 **p** 78. C Wareham *Sarum* 77-80; TV 80-83; Dioc Youth Adv *Dur* 83-87; C Portishead *B & W* 87-90; V Westf from 90. *Westfield Vicarage, Midsomer Norton, Bath BA3 4BJ* Midsomer Norton (01761) 412105

✠**THIRD, Rt Rev Richard Henry McPhail.** b 27. Em Coll Cam BA50 MA55 Kent Univ Hon DCL90. Linc Th Coll 50. **d** 52 **p** 53 **c** 76. C Mottingham St Andr *S'wark* 52-55; C Sanderstead All SS 55-59; V Sheerness H Trin w St Paul *Cant* 59-67; V Orpington All SS *Roch* 67-76; RD Orpington 73-76; Hon Can Roch Cathl 74-76; Suff Bp Maidstone *Cant* 76-80; Suff Bp Dover 80-92; rtd 92; Asst Bp *B & W* from 92. *25 Church Close, Martock, Somerset TA12 6DS* Martock (01935) 825519

THISELTON, Canon Prof Anthony Charles. b 37. Novi Testamenti Societas 75 Lon Univ BD59 K Coll Lon MTh64 Sheff Univ PhD77 Dur Univ DD93. Oak Hill Th Coll 58. **d** 60 **p** 61. C Sydenham H Trin *S'wark* 60-63; Tutor Tyndale Hall Bris 63-67; Sen Tutor 67-70; Lect Bibl Studies Sheff Univ 70-79; Sen Lect 79-85; Prof Calvin Coll Grand Rapids 82-83; Special Lect Th Nottm Univ 86-88; Prin St Jo Coll Nottm 86-88; Prin St Jo Coll w Cranmer Hall Dur 88-92; Prof Chr Th Nottm Univ from 93; Can Th Leic Cathl *Leic* from 94. *Department of Theology, Nottingham University, University Park, Nottingham NG7 2RD* Nottingham (0115) 951 5852 Fax 951 5887

THISTLETHWAITE, Dr Nicholas John. b 51. Selw Coll Cam BA73 MA77 PhD80 Ox Univ BA78 MA83. Ripon Coll Cuddesdon BA78. **d** 79 **p** 80. C Newc St Gabr *Newc* 79-82; Lic to Offic *Ely* 82-90; Chapl G&C Coll Cam 82-90; V Trumpington *Ely* from 90. *The Vicarage, Trumpington, Cambridge CB2 2LH* Cambridge (01223) 841262

THISTLEWOOD, Michael John. b 31. Ch Coll Cam BA53 MA57. Linc Th Coll 54. **d** 56 **p** 57. V Newland St Aug *York* 67-72; Asst Master Bemrose Sch Derby 72-80; V Derby St Andr w St Osmund *Derby* 80-82; Lic to Offic *Ox* from 84; rtd 88; Perm to Offic *Carl* from 88. *9 Lightburn Road, Ulverston, Cumbria LA12 0AU* Ulverston (01229) 584687

THODY, Charles Michael Jackson. b 62. Linc Th Coll BTh94. **d** 94 **p** 95. C Immingham *Linc* from 94. *95 Pilgrim Avenue, Immingham, Grimsby, S Humberside DN40 1DJ* Immingham (01469) 573518

THOM, Alastair George. b 60. ACA86 G&C Coll Cam BA81 MA84. Ridley Hall Cam 88. **d** 91 **p** 92. C Lindfield *Chich* 91-94; C Finchley St Paul and St Luke *Lon* from 94. *Church House, Howes Close, Mountfield Road, London N3 3BX* 0181-346 0563

THOM, James. b 31. St Chad's Coll Dur BA53 DipTh57. **d** 57 **p** 58. V Copmanthorpe *York* 63-75; V Coxwold 75-77; RD Easingwold 77-82; V Coxwold and Husthwaite 77-87; Abp's Adv for Spiritual Direction 86-93; P-in-c Topcliffe 87-93; rtd 93. *34 Hellwath Grove, Ripon, N Yorkshire HG4 2JT* Ripon (01765) 605083

THOM, Thomas Kennedy Dalziel. b 29. Pemb Coll Cam BA53 MA57. St Steph Ho Ox 60. **d** 61 **p** 62. USPG 65-70; Ghana 65-70; SSJE 71-72; Chapl Essex Univ *Chelmsf* 73-80; Sec Chapls in HE Gen Syn Bd of Educn 81-87; Partnership Sec and Dep Gen Sec USPG 87-92; Chapl Burrswood Chr Cen *Roch* 93-94; rtd 95. *24 South Island Place, London SW9 0DX* 0171-582 2798

THOMAS, Adrian Leighton. b 37. St D Coll Lamp BA62 DipTh. **d** 63 **p** 64. C Port Talbot St Theodore *Llan* 63-70; V Troedrhiwgarth 70-73; C Sandhurst *Ox* 73-77; V Streatley 77-84; P-in-c Moulsford 81-84; V Streatley w Moulsford 84-90; P-in-c Sutton Courtenay w Appleford from 90. *The Vicarage, 3 Tullis Close, Sutton Courtenay, Abingdon, Oxon OX14 4BD* Abingdon (01235) 848297

THOMAS, Canon Alan. b 42. Univ of Wales (Cardiff) BA65. St Mich Coll Llan 65. **d** 67 **p** 68. C Fairwater *Llan* 67-69; C Llanishen and Lisvane 69-73; V Troedyrhiw w Merthyr Vale 73-77; V Pemb Dock *St D* 77-93; P-in-c Cosheston w Nash and Upton 85-93; R 93; V Pemb Dock w Cosheston w Nash and Upton from 93; Chapl S Pemb Hosp from 77; RD Castlemartin *St D* from 83; Can St D Cathl from 89. *The Vicarage, Church Street, Pembroke Dock, Dyfed SA72 6AR* Pembroke (01646) 682943

THOMAS, Alan William Charles. b 19. Liv Univ BA41. St Aid Birkenhead 42. **d** 43 **p** 44. V Wolv St Jude *Lich* 67-87; rtd 87; Perm to Offic *Lich* 87-89; Perm to Offic *Ex* from 89. *Gable Cottage, Radway, Sidmouth, Devon EX10 8TW* Sidmouth (01395) 513302

THOMAS, Albert Kenneth. b 18. St D Coll Lamp BA40 St Mich Coll Llan 40. **d** 42 **p** 43. R Charlton Musgrove *B & W* 67-80; R Charlton Musgrove, Cucklington and Stoke Trister 80-83; rtd 83; Perm to Offic *B & W* 84-86. *Chelwood, 32 Shreen Way, Gillingham, Dorset SP8 4EL* Gillingham (01747) 822093

THOMAS, Aled Huw. b 59. Univ of Wales (Abth) BD81 DPS83. St Mich Coll Llan 84. **d** 85 **p** 86. C Llandeilo and Taliaris *St D* 85-86; P-in-c Llangrannog and Llandysiliogogo 86-88; Chapl RAF 88-92; R Ystradgynlais *S & B* 92-94; CF from 94. *c/o MOD (Army), Bagshot Park, Bagshot, Surrey GU19 5PL* Bagshot (01276) 71717 Fax 412834

THOMAS, Alfred James Randolph. b 48. St D Coll Lamp DipTh71. **d** 71 **p** 72. C Cydweli and Llandyfaelog *St D* 71-74; C Carmarthen St Dav 74-76; TV Abth 76-81; V Betws St Dav w Ammanford 81-93; RD Dyffryn Aman 90-93; V Carmarthen St Pet from 93. *The Vicarage, Carmarthen, Dyfed SA31 1LJ* Carmarthen (01267) 237117

THOMAS, Andrew Herbert Redding. b 41. Lon Coll of Div 66. **d** 69 **p** 70. C Cromer *Nor* 69-72; Holiday Chapl 72-76; R Grimston w Congham 76-83; R Roydon All SS 76-83; C-in-c Ewell St Paul Howell Hill CD *Guildf* 83-89; V Howell Hill 89-95; RD Epsom 93-95; TR Beccles St Mich *St E* from 95. *The Rectory, 53 Cromwell Avenue, Beccles, Suffolk NR34 9XF* Beccles (01502) 716017

THOMAS, Arthur George. b 19. Univ of Wales (Swansea) BA40. St Mich Coll Llan 40. **d** 42 **p** 43. R Llanganten w Llanafan Fawr, Maesmynis etc *S & B* 69-79; R Llanganten, Llanafan Fawr, Llangammarch etc 79-84; rtd 84. *Fritham House Rest Home, 36 Shirley Park Road, Southampton SO16 4FU* Southampton (01703) 777588

THOMAS, Arthur Norman. b 17. St Aid Birkenhead 54. **d** 56 **p** 57. R Seacroft *Ripon* 65-70; TR 70-76; R Thornton Watlass w Thornton Steward and E Witton 76-86; rtd 86. *Christmas Cottage, Emmerdale Garth, Kirkby Malzeard, Ripon, N Yorkshire HG4 3SH* Kirkby Malzeard (01765) 658884

THOMAS, Canon Arthur Roy. b 25. St Steph Ho Ox 55. **d** 58 **p** 59. C St Mary Aldermary *Lon* 66-72; Regional Officer SPCK 67-72; V Canning Town St Cedd *Chelmsf* 72-80; P-in-c Victoria Docks Ascension 78-79; P-in-c Runwell 80-81; P-in-c Wickford 80-81; TR Wickford and Runwell 81-85; V Gosfield 85-91; RD Halstead and Coggeshall 87-91; Hon Can Chelmsf Cathl 90-91; rtd 91; Perm to Offic *St E* from 91. *1 Beech Cottage, Stoke by Nayland, Colchester CO6 4QH* Colchester (01206) 262110

THOMAS, Austin George. b 23. Open Univ BA75. Wells Th Coll 65. **d** 67 **p** 68. C Brislington St Luke *Bris* 67-73; P-in-c Bris St Geo 73-74; P-in-c Bris St Leon Redfield 74-75; TV E Bris

THOMAS

75-80; R Lyddington w Wanborough 80-88; rtd 88; Perm to Offic *Bris* from 88. *11 College Road, Bristol BS16 2HN* Bristol (0117) 958 3511

THOMAS, Canon Barry Wilfred. b 41. Univ of Wales (Cardiff) BD75. St Mich Coll Llan 72. **d** 75 **p** 76. C Porthmadog *Ban* 75-78; V Llanegryn and Llanfihangel-y-Pennant etc 78-82; Sec Dioc Coun for Miss and Unity 81-94; R Llanbeblig w Caernarfon and Betws Garmon etc 82-94; Can Ban Cathl 89-94; Chapl Monte Carlo *Eur* from 95. *St Paul's Church House, Avenue de Grande Bretagne, Monte-Carlo, MC 98000* Monaco (3393) 30 71 06

THOMAS, Bryan. b 36. Univ of Wales (Abth) BA59. St Deiniol's Hawarden 68. **d** 70 **p** 71. C Llangynwyd w Maesteg *Llan* 70-72; V Cwmllynfell *St D* 72-76; V Gors-las 76-82; R Yarnbury *Sarum* from 82; RD Wylye and Wilton from 94. *The Rectory, Steeple Langford, Salisbury SP3 4NH* Salisbury (01722) 790337

THOMAS, Charles Moray Stewart Reid. b 53. BNC Ox BA74 MA79. Wycliffe Hall Ox 75. **d** 78 **p** 79. C Bradf Cathl *Bradf* 78-81; C Barnsbury St Andr and H Trin w All SS *Lon* 81-90; TV Barnsbury from 90. *10 Thornhill Square, London N1 1BQ* 0171-837 0720 or 609 5525

THOMAS, Ven Charles Edward (Ted). b 27. Univ of Wales (Lamp) BA51. Coll of Resurr Mirfield 51. **d** 53 **p** 54. R Monksilver w Brompton Ralph and Nettlecombe *B & W* 66-74; R S Petherton w the Seavingtons 74-83; RD Crewkerne 77-83; Adn Wells, Can Res and Preb Wells Cathl 83-93; rtd 93. *Geryfelin, Pentre, Tregaron, Dyfed SY25 6JG* Tregaron (01974) 298102

THOMAS, Colin Norman. b 41. Open Univ BA78. Trin Coll Bris 72. **d** 74 **p** 75. C Handforth *Ches* 74-77; C Bucknall and Bagnall *Lich* 77-80; TV 80-86; V Ogley Hay from 86. *St James's Vicarage, 37 New Road, Brownhills, Walsall WS8 6AT* Brownhills (01543) 372187

THOMAS, Canon David. b 42. Keble Coll Ox BA64 BA66 MA67. St Steph Ho Ox 64. **d** 67 **p** 68. C Hawarden *St As* 67-69; Lect St Mich Coll Llan 69-70; Chapl 70-75; Sec Ch in Wales Liturg Commn 70-75; Vice-Prin St Steph Ho Ox 75-79; Prin 82-87; V Chepstow *Mon* 79-82; Lic to Offic *Ox* 82-87; V Newton St Pet *S & B* from 87; Can Brecon Cathl from 94. *The Vicarage, Mary Twill Lane, Newton, Swansea SA3 4RB* Swansea (01792) 368348

THOMAS, David Brian. b 45. MIEEE. St D Dioc Tr Course 82. **d** 85 **p** 86. NSM Llandysul *St D* 85-87; NSM Lamp Pont Steffan w Silian 88-92; NSM Lamp and Ultra-Aeron Deanery from 92. *Dwyfor, Maesyllan, Lampeter, Dyfed SA48 7EN* Lampeter (01570) 422706

THOMAS, David Edward. b 60. Univ of Wales (Lamp) BA83 LTh85. St Mich Coll Llan DPS86. **d** 86 **p** 87. C Killay *S & B* 86-89; P-in-c Newbridge-on-Wye and Llanfihangel Brynpabuan 89-90; V 90-91; V Brecon St David w Llanspyddid and Llanilltyd from 91. *The Vicarage, 26 St David's Crescent, Ffrwdgrech Road, Brecon, Powys LD3 8DP*

THOMAS, Canon David Geoffrey. b 24. AKC48. **d** 49 **p** 50. Miss to Seamen 52-53 and 68-81; V Milford Haven *St D* 68-89; Can St D Cathl 77-89; Treas 85-89; rtd 89. *49 Pill Lane, Milford Haven, Dyfed SA73 2LD* Milford Haven (01646) 695792

THOMAS, David Geoffrey. b 37. Univ of Wales (Cardiff) BA58. Launde Abbey 70 Qu Coll Birm 71. **d** 71 **p** 72. Hon C Fenny Drayton *Leic* 71-75; Chapl Community of the H Family Baldslow Chich 75-77; Perm to Offic *Chich* 77-79; P-in-c Mill End and Heronsgate w W Hyde *St Alb* 79-81; Perm to Offic 82-91; Sen Lect Watford Coll 82-91; R Walgrave w Hannington and Wold and Scaldwell *Pet* from 91. *The Rectory, Lower Green, Walgrave, Northampton NN6 9QB* Northampton (01604) 781974

THOMAS, Canon David Glynne. b 41. Dur Univ BSc63. Westcott Ho Cam 64. **d** 67 **p** 68. C St Jo Wood *Lon* 67-70; Min Can St Alb 70-72; Chapl Wadh Coll Ox 72-75; C Ox St Mary V w St Cross and St Pet *Ox* 72-75; Bp's Dom Chapl 75-78; P-in-c Burnham 78-82; TR Burnham w Dropmore, Hitcham and Taplow 82-83; Australia 83-87; Can Res Worc Cathl *Worc* from 87. *The Chaplain's House, St Oswald's Close, The Tything, Worcester WR1 1HR* Worcester (01905) 616619

THOMAS, David Godfrey. b 50. St Chad's Coll Dur BA71 Fitzw Coll Cam BA74 MA78. Westcott Ho Cam 72. **d** 75 **p** 76. C Kirkby *Liv* 75-78; TV Cov E *Cov* 78-88; TR Canvey Is *Chelmsf* 88-92; R Wivenhoe from 92. *The Rectory, 44 Belle Vue Road, Wivenhoe, Colchester CO7 9LD* Wivenhoe (01206) 825174

THOMAS, David John. b 34. Univ of Wales (Swansea) St D Coll Lamp. St D Dioc Tr Course 85. **d** 88 **p** 89. NSM Cwmaman *St D* from 88. *9 New School Road, Garnant, Ammanford, Dyfed SA18 1LL* Amman Valley (01269) 823936

THOMAS, Dr David Richard. b 48. BNC Ox BA71 MA74 Fitzw Coll Cam BA75 MA80 Lanc Univ PhD83. Ridley Hall Cam 73 Qu Coll Birm 79. **d** 80 **p** 81. C Anfield St Columba *Liv* 80-83; C Liv Our Lady and St Nic w St Anne 83-90; Chapl CCC Cam 85-90; V Witton *Blackb* 90-93; Bp's Adv on Inter-

Faith Relns 90-93; Lect Cen for Study of Islam and Chr-Muslim Relns from 93; Perm to Offic *Birm* from 94. *15 Appletree Close, Birmingham B31 2YP* 0121-472 4231

THOMAS, David Ronald Holt. b 28. Lich Th Coll 55. **d** 58 **p** 59. C Uttoxeter w Bramshall *Lich* 58-61; C Hednesford 61-66; R Armitage from 66; RD Rugeley 88-94. *The Rectory, Hood Lane, Armitage, Rugeley, Staffs WS15 4AG* Armitage (01543) 490278

THOMAS, David Thomas. b 44. St Cath Coll Cam BA66 MA70 St Jo Coll Dur DipTh68. **d** 71 **p** 72. C Chorlton-cum-Hardy St Clem *Man* 71-74; Chapl Salford Tech Coll 74-79; P-in-c Pendleton St Thos *Man* 75-77; V 77-80; TR Gleadless *Sheff* 80-90; RD Attercliffe 86-90; V Benchill *Man* from 90. *St Luke's Vicarage, Brownley Road, Benchill, Manchester M22 4PT* 0161-998 2071

THOMAS, Canon David William. b 17. Univ of Wales BA63 MA67. St D Coll Lamp BA38 St Mich Coll Llan 39. **d** 41 **p** 43. V Pontyberem *St D* 67-76; V Llanilar w Rhostie and Llangwyryfon etc 76-83; Hon Can St D Cathl 78-83; rtd 83. *12 Stryd Margred, Ammaford, Dyfed SA18 2NN* Ammanford (01269) 594986

THOMAS, David William Wallace. b 51. St Chad's Coll Dur BA72. St Mich Coll Llan 72. **d** 75 **p** 76. C Bargoed and Deri w Brithdir *Llan* 75-79; Hon C 79-81; V Nantymoel w Wyndham 81-84; Chapl RN from 84. *Directorate Gen, RN Chapl Services, Room 203, Victory Building, HM Naval Base, Portsmouth PO1 3LS* Portsmouth (01705) 727903 Fax 727112

THOMAS, David Wynford. b 48. Univ of Wales (Abth) LLB70. Qu Coll Birm 76. **d** 79 **p** 80. C Swansea St Mary w H Trin and St Mark *S & B* 79-83; P-in-c Swansea St Mark 83-89; Lic to Offic 90. *74 Terrace Road, Swansea SA1 6HU*

THOMAS, Canon Dillwyn Morgan. b 26. Univ of Wales (Lamp) BA50. Qu Coll Birm 50. **d** 52 **p** 53. V Bargoed w Brithdir *Llan* 68-74; V Bargoed and Deri w Brithdir 74-75; V Penarth All SS 75-88; Can Llan Cathl 86-88; rtd 88; Perm to Offic *Llan* from 88. *11 Baroness Place, Penarth, S Glam CF64 3UL* Penarth (01222) 704090

THOMAS, Canon Donald George. b 22. DFC44. Qu Coll Cam BA47 MA52. Ridley Hall Cam 47. **d** 49 **p** 50. V Runcorn All SS *Ches* 61-88; RD Frodsham 82-88; Hon Can Ches Cathl 84-88; rtd 88. *11 Parc Capel, Lixwm, Holywell, Clwyd CH8 8NA* Holywell (01352) 780163

THOMAS, Edward Bernard Meredith. b 21. Leeds Univ BA44 Queensland Univ BEd68 BD72. Coll of Resurr Mirfield 47. **d** 49 **p** 50. C St Mary-at-Lambeth *S'wark* 49-54; C Portsea N End St Mark *Portsm* 54-56; V Portsea All SS 56-64; Australia from 64. *33 Highfield Street, Durack, Queensland, Australia 4077* Brisbane (7) 372-3517

THOMAS, Canon Edward Maldwyn. b 12. Univ of Wales BA34. St Mich Coll Llan 37. **d** 38 **p** 39. V Duddeston *Birm* 51-83; Hon Can Birm Cathl 72-83; rtd 83; Perm to Offic *Birm* from 83. *3 Birchtree Grove, Solihull, W Midlands B91 1HD* 0121-705 3706

THOMAS, Edward Walter Dennis. b 32. St Mich Coll Llan 61. **d** 63 **p** 64. C Lougher *S & B* 63-69; V Ystradfellte 69-74; V Dukinfield St Mark and St Luke *Ches* from 74; Chapl Gtr Man Police from 77; OCF from 88. *The Vicarage, 2 Church Square, Dukinfield, Cheshire SK16 4PX* 0161-330 2783

THOMAS, Miss Eileen Anne Harwood. b 35. Univ of Wales (Swansea) BA59 Kent Univ MA80. Cant Sch of Min 80. **dss** 83 **d** 87 **p** 94. Mill Hill Jo Keble Ch *Lon* 83-86; The Lydiards *Bris* 86-87; Par Dn 87-92; C-in-c Woodgate Valley CD *Birm* from 92. *34 Simcox Gardens, Birmingham B32 3RX* 0121-427 3514

THOMAS, Eirwyn Wheldon. b 35. St Mich Coll Llan 58. **d** 61 **p** 62. C Glanadda *Ban* 61-67; R Llantrisant and Llandeusant 67-75; V Nefyn w Pistyll w Tudweiliog w Llandudwen etc from 75. *The Vicarage, Nefyn, Pwllheli, Gwynedd LL53 6BS* Nefyn (01758) 720494

THOMAS (nee REEVES), Mrs Elizabeth Anne. b 45. Sheff Univ BA67 PGCE75. SW Minl Tr Course 87. **d** 90 **p** 94. Par Dn Stoke Damerel *Ex* 90-93; Par Dn Baildon *Bradf* 93-94; Dioc Children's Adv 93-94; C Baildon from 94. *93 Hoyle Court Road, Baildon, Shipley, W Yorkshire BD17 6EL* Bradford (01274) 594790

THOMAS, Elwyn Bernard. b 45. Univ of Wales (Swansea) BSc68. St Mich Coll Llan BD71. **d** 71 **p** 72. C Aberdare St Fagan *Llan* 71-74; C Merthyr Dyfan 74-76; R Dowlais 76-86; V Llangynwyd w Maesteg from 86. *The Vicarage, 33 Brynmawr Place, Maesteg, M Glam CF34 9PB* Maesteg (01656) 733194

THOMAS, Canon Ernest Keith. b 49. Univ of Wales (Cardiff) DipTh76. St Mich Coll Llan 73. **d** 76 **p** 77. C Swansea St Gabr *S & B* 76-79; S Africa 80-93; V Aberdare St Jo *Llan* from 93. *Ingledene, 26 Abernant Road, Aberdare, M Glam CF44 0PY* Aberdare (01685) 884769

✠**THOMAS, Rt Rev Eryl Stephen.** b 10. St Jo Coll Ox BA32 MA38. Wells Th Coll 32. **d** 33 **p** 34 **c** 68. C Colwyn Bay *St As*

33-38; C Hawarden 38-43; V Risca *Mon* 43-48; Warden St Mich Coll Llan 48-54; Dean Llan 54-68; Bp Mon 68-71; Bp Llan 71-75; rtd 75; Asst Bp S & B from 88. *17 Orchard Close, Gilwern, Abergavenny, Gwent NP7 0EN* Gilwern (01873) 831050

THOMAS, Euros Lloyd. b 53. Bris Poly LLB75. St Mich Coll Llan DipTh79. **d** 79 **p** 80. C Llanelli *St D* 79-84; R Cilgerran w Bridell and Llantwyd from 84; RD Cemais and Sub-Aeron from 93. *The Rectory, Cilgerran, Cardigan, Dyfed SA43 2RZ* Cardigan (01239) 614500

THOMAS, Frank Lowth. b 22. Lon Coll of Div 64. **d** 66 **p** 67. C Bickenhill w Elmdon *Birm* 68-71; R Carlton Colville *Nor* 71-81; R Smallburgh w Dilham w Honing and Crostwight 81-85; rtd 85; Perm to Offic *Nor* from 86. *7 Mill Close, Salhouse, Norwich NR13 6QB* Norwich (01603) 720376

THOMAS, Geler Harries. b 28. St D Coll Lamp BA55. **d** 57 **p** 58. V Llanedy *St D* 69-79; V Llangennech and Hendy 79-88; V Llanegwad w Llanfynydd 88-92; RD Llangadog and Llandeilo 89-90; rtd 92. *14 Llys-y-Ferin, Pont-ar-Gothi, Nantgaredig, Carmarthen, Dyfed SA32 7NF* Nantgaredig (01267) 290516

THOMAS, Geoffrey Brynmor. b 34. K Coll Lon BA56 AKC56. Ridley Hall Cam 58. **d** 60 **p** 61. C Harlow New Town w Lt Parndon *Chelmsf* 60-65; V Leyton All SS 65-74; V Halifax All So *Wakef* 74-82; R The Winterbournes and Compton Valence *Sarum* 82-89; TV Cheltenham St Mark *Glouc* 89-92; P-in-c Dowdeswell and Andoversford w the Shiptons etc from 92; RD Northleach from 92. *The Rectory, Shipton Oliffe, Cheltenham, Glos GL54 4HU* Cheltenham (01242) 820230

THOMAS, Geoffrey Charles. b 30. St Jo Coll Nottm LTh ALCD64. **d** 64 **p** 65. C Cheltenham Ch Ch *Glouc* 67-70; V Whitgift w Adlingfleet *Sheff* 70-74; P-in-c Eastoft 72-74; V Mortomley St Sav 74-88; R Middleton Cheney w Chacombe *Pet* 88-93; rtd 94. *77 Penyghent Avenue, York YO3 0QH* York (01904) 414082

THOMAS, Canon Geoffrey Heale. b 29. St Mich Coll Llan 58. **d** 60 **p** 61. C Llansamlet *S & B* 60-63; Nigeria 63-67; V Swansea St Nic *S & B* 67-80; CF (TA) 72; V Oystermouth *S & B* from 80; Hon Can Brecon Cathl from 92. *The Vicarage, 9 Western Close, Mumbles, Swansea SA3 4HF* Swansea (01792) 369971 or 361684

THOMAS, George. b 46. Leeds Univ BEd69. St Jo Coll Dur 75 Cranmer Hall Dur DipTh77. **d** 78 **p** 79. C Highfield *Liv* 78-83; V Chorley St Jas *Blackb* from 83. *St James's Vicarage, St James's Place, Chorley, Lancs PR6 0NA* Chorley (01257) 263153

THOMAS, Glyn. b 36. Lon Univ BPharm61. St Deiniol's Hawarden 80. **d** 82 **p** 83. C Rhyl w St Ann *St As* 83-85; R Llanycil w Bala and Frongoch and Llangower etc from 85. *The Rectory, Heol-y-Castell, Bala, Gwynedd LL23 7YA* Bala (01678) 521047

THOMAS, Gwilym Ivor. b 20. St D Coll Lamp BA41 Univ of Wales MPhil95. **d** 43 **p** 44. V Llansantffraed *St D* 62-70; V Llansantffraed and Llanbadarn Trefeglwys 70-80; V Llansantffraed and Llanbadarn Trefeglwys etc 80-85; RD Glyn Aeron 78-85; rtd 85. *Stanley House, 9 Hill Street, New Quay, Dyfed SA45 9QD* New Quay (01545) 560167

THOMAS, Gwynfor. b 13. St D Coll Lamp BA40. **d** 46 **p** 47. V Wookey *B & W* 69-74; V Wookey w Henton 74-78; rtd 78; Lic to Offic *B & W* from 79. *10 Fairfield, Somerton, Somerset TA11 7PE* Somerton (01458) 72549

THOMAS, Harold Heath. b 08. Man Univ BA32 AKC47. Linc Th Coll 47. **d** 47 **p** 48. V Low Marple *Ches* 53-75; rtd 75; Perm to Offic *Ches* from 75. *102 Hollins Lane, Marple Bridge, Stockport, Cheshire SK6 5DA* 0161-449 8176

THOMAS, Herbert John. b 13. AKC42. **d** 42 **p** 43. R Bridgwater St Jo w Chedzoy *B & W* 62-73; R Compton Martin w Ubley 73-79; rtd 79; Perm to Offic *B & W* 79-90. *25 Delmore Road, Frome, Somerset BA11 4EG* Frome (01373) 463762

THOMAS, Miss Hilary Faith. b 43. Ex Univ BA65 Southn Univ PGCE66. Trin Coll Bris DipHE92 DPS94. **d** 94 **p** 95. C Yeovil w Kingston Pitney *B & W* from 94. *67 Preston Grove, Yeovil, Somerset BA20 2BJ* Yeovil (01935) 25452

THOMAS, Howard Donald Lewis. b 19. Chich Th Coll 46. **d** 49 **p** 50. R Hanborough *Ox* 67-84; rtd 84; Chapl Soc of All SS Sisters of the Poor 84-87; Perm to Offic *Ox* from 84. *7 Marlborough Crescent, Long Hanborough, Witney, Oxon OX8 8JP* Freeland (01993) 881805

THOMAS, Hugh. b 14. St D Coll Lamp BA36. **d** 37 **p** 38. R Clocaenog and Gyffylliog *St As* 55-79; rtd 79. *2 Hafan Deg, Clawdd Newydd, Ruthin, Clwyd LL15 2ND* Clawdd Newydd (018245) 716

THOMAS, Hugh. b 25. St D Coll Lamp BA50. **d** 51 **p** 52. V Llanfynydd *St D* 63-74; V Pontyates 74-80; V Pontyates and Llangyndeyrn 80-90; rtd 91. *90 Priory Street, Cydweli, Dyfed SA17 4TY* Cydweli (01554) 890114

THOMAS, Hugh Meredith. b 39. Univ of Wales (Lamp) BA61. St Mich Coll Llan 61. **d** 63 **p** 64. C Llandeilo Fawr and

Llandefeisant *St D* 63-70; V Gwynfe and Llanddeusant 70-74; V Llanpumsaint 74-80; V Llanpumsaint w Llanllawddog 80-85; R Newport w Cilgwyn and Dinas w Llanllawer 85-91; V Llanarthne and Llanddarog from 91. *The Vicarage, Llanddarog, Carmarthen, Dyfed SA38 8PA* Llanddarog (01267) 275268

THOMAS, Canon Huw Glyn. b 42. Univ of Wales (Lamp) BA62 Linacre Coll Ox BA65 MA69. Wycliffe Hall Ox 62. **d** 65 **p** 66. C Oystermouth *S & B* 65-68; Asst Chapl Solihull Sch Warks 68-69; Chapl Solihull Sch W Midl 69-73; Selection Sec ACCM 73-78; C Loughton St Jo *Chelmsf* 74-77; V Bury St Jo *Man* 78-83; Dir of Ords 82-87; V Bury St Jo w St Mark 83-86; Can Res and Treas Liv Cathl *Liv* from 87. *2 Cathedral Close, Liverpool L1 7BR* 0151-708 0932

THOMAS, Ian Melville. b 50. Jes Coll Ox BA71 MA75. St Steph Ho Ox 71. **d** 73 **p** 74. PV St D Cathl *St D* 73-77; Chapl RAF from 77; Asst Chapl-in-Chief RAF from 95. *Chaplaincy Services (RAF), HQ, Personnel and Training Command, RAF Innsworth, Gloucester GL3 1EZ* Gloucester (01452) 712612 Ext 5164 Fax 510828

THOMAS, Ian William. b 53. Bedf Coll of Educn CertEd74. Ox Min Course 89. **d** 92 **p** 93. NSM Fenny Stratford *Ox* from 92. *5 Laburnum Grove, Bletchley, Milton Keynes MK2 2JW* Milton Keynes (01908) 644457

THOMAS, Idris. b 48. St D Coll Lamp DipTh71. **d** 71 **p** 72. C Llanbeblig w Caernarfon and Betws Garmon etc *Ban* 71-75; P-in-c Llanaelhaiarn 75-77; R Llanaelhaearn w Clynnog Fawr from 77; RD Arfon from 93. *The Rectory, Trefor, Caernarfon, Gwynedd LL54 5HN* Clynnogfawr (01286) 660547

THOMAS, Ven Ilar Roy Luther. b 30. St D Coll Lamp BA51. St Mich Coll Llan 51. **d** 53 **p** 54. CF (ACF) 62-90; Children's Adv *S & B* 63-77; RD Knighton 66-79; V Knighton and Norton 66-79; V Sketty 79-89; Can Brecon Cathl from 75; Treas 87-88; Chan 88-90; Adn Gower 90-95; rtd 95. *2 Druids Close, Mumbles, Swansea SA3 5TY*

THOMAS, Iris. b 18. Univ of Wales (Abth) BA39 DipEd40. **d** 80. Hon C Tylorstown *Llan* 80-84; Hon C Ferndale w Maerdy 84-85; rtd 85; Perm to Offic *Llan* from 86. *18 Richard Street, Maerdy, Ferndale, M Glam CF43 4AU* Ferndale (01443) 755235

THOMAS, James Morris. b 02. **d** 37 **p** 38. R Tintern Parva w Chapel Hill *Mon* 57-73; rtd 73; Perm to Offic Mon 73-90; Perm to Offic *Heref* 74-90. *c/o 23 Dundee Court, Duncraig, Australia 6023*

THOMAS, Jennifer Monica (Jenny). b 58. Wilson Carlile Coll DipEvang82 Sarum & Wells Th Coll DipMin93. **d** 93 **p** 94. Par Dn Wandsworth St Paul *S'wark* 93-94; C from 94. *90 Augustus Road, London SW19 6ER* 0181-785 7943

THOMAS, John Arun. b 47. Bombay Univ BA69 MA72 Nottm Univ CertEd80. Oak Hill Th Coll 84. **d** 88 **p** 89. C Liv Ch Ch Norris Green *Liv* 88-89; C Wavertree St Mary 89-93; V St Mary Cray and St Paul's Cray *Roch* from 93. *The Vicarage, Main Road, Orpington, Kent BR5 3EN* Orpington (01689) 827697

THOMAS, John Bryn. b 37. Lich Th Coll 63. **d** 66 **p** 67. C Stoke upon Trent *Lich* 66-71; R Wotton *Guildf* 71-79; P-in-c Holmbury St Mary 78-79; R Wotton and Holmbury St Mary 79-86; C Easthampstead *Ox* 86-88; TV Chambersbury (Hemel Hempstead) *St Alb* from 88. *The Vicarage, Peascroft Road, Hemel Hempstead, Herts HP3 8EP* Hemel Hempstead (01442) 243934

THOMAS, Canon John Degwel. b 11. Univ of Wales BSc33. St Steph Ho Ox 34. **d** 36 **p** 37. V Chesterton St Geo *Ely* 51-74; R Rampton 74-81; Press and Communications Officer 74-86; Hon Can Ely Cathl 77-81; rtd 81. *17 King Street, Over, Cambridge CB4 5PS* Swavesey (01954) 731198

THOMAS, Canon John Elwern. b 14. Univ of Wales BA35. Coll of Resurr Mirfield 35. **d** 37 **p** 38. Can Cursal Ban Cathl 68-70; Warden Ruthin w Llanrhydd *St As* 70-79; Can Cursal St As Cathl 77-79; rtd 79. *33 The Park, Ruthin, Clwyd LL15 1PN* Ruthin (01824) 703384

THOMAS, John Herbert Samuel. b 34. Pemb Coll Cam BA57 MA64. St Mich Coll Llan 57. **d** 58 **p** 59. C Port Talbot St Theodore *Llan* 58-60; C Llantwit Major and St Donat's 60-67; P-in-c Barry All SS 67-74; V Dinas w Penygraig 74-85; V Pontypridd St Cath 85-90; V Pontypridd St Cath w St Matt from 90; RD Pontypridd from 90. *St Catherine's Vicarage, Gelliwastad Grove, Pontypridd, M Glam CF37 2BS* Pontypridd (01443) 402021

THOMAS, Dr John Thurston. b 28. CChem FRSC65 Univ of Wales (Swansea) BSc48 DipEd49 Leeds Univ PhD58. Glouc Sch of Min 88. **d** 90 **p** 91. NSM S Cerney w Cerney Wick and Down Ampney *Glouc* from 90. *Samantha, Silver Street, South Cerney, Cirencester, Glos GL7 5TP* Cirencester (01285) 860382

THOMAS, Joseph Neville. b 33. Univ of Wales (Lamp) BA57. St Mich Coll Llan. **d** 59 **p** 60. C Porthmadog *Ban* 59-62; C Cardiff St Jo *Llan* 62-65; CF 65-88; R Sherfield-on-Loddon and

THOMAS

Stratfield Saye etc *Win* from 88. *The Rectory, Breach Lane, Sherfield-on-Loddon, Basingstoke, Hants RG27 0EU* Basingstoke (01256) 882209

THOMAS, June Marion. b 31. Univ of Wales BA53 DipEd54. NE Ord Course 83. **dss** 86 **d** 87 **p** 94. Stockton St Pet *Dur* 86-87; Hon Par Dn 87-89; NSM Stockton St Mark from 89. *50 Brisbane Grove, Stockton-on-Tees, Cleveland TS18 5BP* Stockton-on-Tees (01642) 582408

THOMAS, Keith. b 55. Southlands Coll Lon TCert80. N Ord Course 92. **d** 95. NSM Knuzden *Blackb* from 95; Moorbrook Sch Preston from 95. *20 Duxbury Street, Darwen, Lancs BB3 2LA* Darwen (01254) 776484

THOMAS, Leslie Richard. b 45. Lon Coll of Div 65. **d** 69 **p** 70. C Knotty Ash St Jo *Liv* 69-72; C Sutton 72-74; TV 74-77; V Banks 77-82; V Gt Crosby All SS 82-92; P-in-c Marthall *Ches* from 92; Chapl Dav Lewis Cen for Epilepsy from 92. *The Vicarage, Sandlebridge Lane, Marthall, Knutsford, Cheshire WA16 7SB* Chelford (01625) 861642

THOMAS, Lewis Llewellyn. b 21. Univ of Wales (Lamp) BA41 Selw Coll Cam BA44 MA48. Westcott Ho Cam 44. **d** 45 **p** 46. V Bilston St Mary *Lich* 55-75; Perm to Offic 75-80 and 82-89; Hon C Wolv St Jo 80-82; rtd 86; Perm to Offic *Glouc* from 86. *Flat 14, Capel Court, The Burgage, Prestbury, Cheltenham, Glos GL52 3EL* Cheltenham (01242) 576384

THOMAS, Ms Margaret. b 41. Bris Univ BSc63 Leeds Univ CertEd64 Ex Univ ADC70. Cranmer Hall Dur 81. **dss** 83 **d** 87 **p** 94. Maghull *Liv* 83-86; Asst Chapl Liv Univ from 86; St Luke in the City 86-87; Par Dn 87-89; Chapl Whiston Hosp from 89; Chapl St Helen's and Knowsley HA 89-92; Chapl St Helen's and Knowsley Hosps Trust from 92. *Chapel House, Whiston Hospital, Warrington Road, Prescot, Merseyside L35 5DR* 0151-430 1657 or 426 1600

THOMAS, Mark Wilson. b 51. Dur Univ BA72 Hull Univ MA89. Ripon Coll Cuddesdon 76. **d** 78 **p** 79. C Chapelthorpe *Wakef* 78-81; C Seaford w Sutton *Chich* 81-84; V Gomersal *Wakef* 84-92; TR Almondbury w Farnley Tyas from 92; RD Almondbury from 93. *The Vicarage, 2 Westgate, Almondbury, Huddersfield HD5 8XE* Huddersfield (01484) 421753

THOMAS, Sister Mary Josephine. b 30. Ripon Dioc Tr Coll TCert50 Carl Dioc Tr Course 88. **d** 90 **p** 94. NSM Hawes Side *Blackb* 90-93; NSM St Annes St Marg from 93. *112 St Andrew's Road North, Lytham St Annes, Lancs FY8 2JQ* St Annes (01253) 728016

THOMAS, Michael Longdon Sanby. b 34. Trin Hall Cam BA55 MA60. Wells Th Coll 56. **d** 58 **p** 59. C Sandal St Helen *Wakef* 58-60; Chapl Portsm Cathl *Portsm* 60-64; V Shedfield 64-69; V Portchester from 69. *The Vicarage, 164 Castle Street, Portchester, Fareham, Hants PO16 9QH* Cosham (01705) 376289

THOMAS, Preb Owen. b 17. Selw Coll Cam BA40 MA58. St Mich Coll Llan 40. **d** 41 **p** 42. R Welshpool w Castle Caereinion *St As* 65-77; RD Pool 76-77; Adn Montgomery 77-87; Preb St As Cathl 77-87; V Berriew and Manafon 80-87; rtd 87. *Oaklands, Fron, Montgomery, Powys SY15 6RZ* Berriew (01686) 640675

THOMAS, Owen James. b 17. Univ of Wales BA38. Tyndale Hall Bris 38. **d** 40 **p** 41. Chapl and Lect Lon Bible Coll 62-76; Hon C Northwood Em *Lon* 70-76; V Canonbury St Steph 76-85; rtd 85; Perm to Offic *Chich* from 85. *22 Woodland Way, Fairlight, Hastings, E Sussex TN35 4AU* Hastings (01424) 813613

THOMAS, Ms Pamela Sybil (Pam). b 38. Ripon Coll Cuddesdon 88. **d** 90 **p** 94. C Preston w Sutton Poyntz and Osmington w Poxwell *Sarum* 90; C from 94; Par Dn 91-94. *228 Preston Road, Preston, Weymouth, Dorset DT3 6BJ* Preston (01305) 835018

THOMAS, Mrs Patricia Margaret. b 44. Hockerill Coll Cam TCert65. Sarum & Wells Th Coll 79. **dss** 82 **d** 87 **p** 94. Verwood *Sarum* 82-87; Hon Par Dn 87-88; Chapl Asst Friern Hosp Lon 88-90; Par Dn Upton cum Chalvey *Ox* 90-94; C from 94. *11 Cooper Way, Windsor Meadows, Slough SL1 9JA* Slough (01753) 538714

THOMAS, Dr Patrick Hungerford Bryan. b 52. St Cath Coll Cam BA73 MA77 Leeds Univ BA78 Univ of Wales PhD82. Coll of Resurr Mirfield 76. **d** 79 **p** 80. C Abth *St D* 79-81; C Carmarthen St Pet 81-82; R Llangeitho and Blaenpennal w Betws Leucu etc 82-84; Warden of Ords 83-86; R Brechfa w Abergorlech etc from 84. *The Rectory, Brechfa, Carmarthen, Dyfed SA32 7RA* Brechfa (01267) 202389

THOMAS, Paul Robert. b 42. N Ord Course. **d** 82 **p** 83. C Hull Newland St Jo *York* 82-84; P-in-c Rowley 84-87; Soc Resp Officer Hull 84-87; R Rowley w Skidby 87-88; TR Barking St Marg w St Patr *Chelmsf* 88-93; Gen Sec & Admin St Luke's Hosp for the Clergy from 93. *St Luke's Hospital for the Clergy, 14 Fitzroy Square, London W1P 6AH* 0171-388 4954

THOMAS, Paul Wyndham. b 55. Or Coll Ox BA76 BTh78 MA80. Wycliffe Hall Ox 77. **d** 79 **p** 80. C Llangynwyd w Maesteg *Llan* 79-85; TV Langport Area Chs *B & W* 85-90;

P-in-c Thorp Arch w Walton *York* 90-93; Clergy Tr Officer from 90; V Nether w Upper Poppleton from 93. *The Vicarage, 15 Nether Way, Upper Poppleton, York YO2 6JQ* York (01904) 794744

THOMAS, Peter Rhys. b 37. MInstPkg MIPM TCD BA59 MA72. **d** 72 **p** 73. C Cong *T, K & A* 73-75; I 75-77; C Bingley All SS *Bradf* 77-79; V Shelf 79-81; Producer Relig Broadcasting Viking Radio 81-84; P-in-c Croxton *Linc* 81-82; P-in-c Ulceby 81-82; P-in-c Wootton 81-82; P-in-c Ulceby Gp 82; V Ulceby Gp 82-84; R E and W Tilbury and Linford *Chelmsf* 84-89; I Celbridge w Straffan and Newcastle-Lyons *D & G* 89-93; I Youghal Union *C, C & R* from 93; Dio Info Officer (Cork) from 95. *The Rectory, Upper Strand, Youghal, Co Cork, Irish Republic* Youghal (24) 92350 Fax as telephone

THOMAS, Peter George Hartley. b 38. AKC63. **d** 64 **p** 65. C Leigh Park St Fran CD *Portsm* 64-69; V Cosham 69-77; R Hayes *Roch* from 77. *The Rectory, Hayes Street, Bromley BR2 7LH* 0181-462 1373

THOMAS, Peter James. b 53. Lon Univ BSc75. Trin Coll Bris 77. **d** 80 **p** 81. C Hucclecote *Glouc* 80-84; C Loughb Em *Leic* 84-85; TV Parr *Liv* 85-92; V Eckington *Worc* from 92; V Defford w Besford from 92. *The Vicarage, Drakes Bridge Road, Eckington, Pershore, Worcs WR10 3BN* Evesham (01386) 750203

THOMAS, Peter Wilson. b 58. BD AKC. Ripon Coll Cuddesdon. **d** 82 **p** 83. C Stockton St Pet *Dur* 82-85; TV Solihull *Birm* 85-90; V Rednal from 90. *St Stephen's Vicarage, Edgewood Road, Rednal, Birmingham B45 8SG* 0121-453 3347

THOMAS, Philip Harold Emlyn. b 41. Cant Univ (NZ) BA64 MA77 Dur Univ PhD82. Melbourne Coll of Div BD68. **d** 68 **p** 69. Australia 68-71; New Zealand 71-77; Fell and Chapl Univ Coll Dur 77-83; V Heighington *Dur* from 84; RD Darlington from 94. *The Vicarage, Heighington, Co Durham DL5 6PP* Aycliffe (01325) 312134

THOMAS, Philip Sewell. b 09. Linc Coll Ox BA32 MA38. Ely Th Coll 32. **d** 33 **p** 34. V Barton St David w Kingweston *B & W* 49-91; rtd 91. *20 Brookside Close, Batheaston, Bath BA1 7HP* Bath (01225) 859588

THOMAS, Ralph Pilling. b 23. Univ of Wales (Lamp) BA49. Wycliffe Hall Ox 49. **d** 51 **p** 52. Chapl HM Pris Leeds 69-74; R Kirklington w Burneston and Wath *Ripon* 74-88; RD Wensley 85-88; rtd 88. *20 The Maltings, Staithe Road, Bungay, Suffolk NR35 1EJ* Bungay (01986) 895118

THOMAS, Richard. b 45. St D Coll Lamp 68. **d** 71 **p** 72. C Llanelli St Paul *St D* 71-74; Chapl RN 74-90; V St Ishmael's w Llan-saint and Ferryside *St D* 90-93; V Newport Maindee St Jo Ev *Mon* 93-95; V St Clears w Llangynin and Llanddowror etc *St D* from 95. *The Vicarage, High Street, St Clears, Carmarthen, Dyfed SA33 4EE* St Clears (01994) 230266

THOMAS, Richard Frederick. b 24. Qu Coll Cam BA45 MA49. Ridley Hall Cam 47. **d** 49 **p** 50. Jerusalem 67-73; Ho Master Bp Luffa Sch Chich 74-80; Lic to Offic *Chich* 75-77; Hon C Chich St Pancras and St Jo 78-80; R N Mundham w Hunston and Merston 80-89; rtd 89. *16 Brent Court, Emsworth, Hants PO10 7JA* Emsworth (01243) 378974

THOMAS, Richard Paul. b 50. MIPR. Wycliffe Hall Ox 74. **d** 76 **p** 77. C Abingdon w Shippon *Ox* 76-80; R Win All SS w Chilcomb and Chesil *Win* 80-88; Dioc Communications Officer 83-89; Dioc Communications Officer *Ox* from 89. *18 Eason Drive, Abingdon, Oxon OX14 3YD* Abingdon (01235) 553360 or Oxford (01865) 244566 Fax Oxford (01865) 790470

THOMAS, Robert Stanley. b 31. Lon Univ BD65 Man Univ MEd78. Sarum Th Coll 66. **d** 67 **p** 68. C Maltby *Sheff* 67-70; Lic to Offic *St Alb* 70-72; Lic to Offic *Man* 72-79; Lic to Offic *St As* 80-82; Dioc RE Adv from 82; V Glyndyfrdwy and Llansantfraid Glyn Dyfrdwy from 82; RD Edeyrnion from 88. *The Vicarage, Glyndyfrdwy, Corwen, Clwyd LL21 9HG* Glyndwr (0149083) 201

THOMAS, Robin. b 27. Cen Sch of Art Lon NDD50. St Steph Ho Ox 89. **d** 89 **p** 90. NSM Clifton All SS w St Jo *Bris* 89-94; P-in-c Tintagel *Truro* from 94. *The Vicarage, Tintagel, Cornwall PL34 0DJ* Camelford (01840) 770315

THOMAS, Roderick Charles Howell (Rod). b 54. LSE BSc75. Wycliffe Hall Ox 91. **d** 93 **p** 94. C Plymouth St Andr w St Paul and St Geo *Ex* 93-95; C Plymouth St Andr and St Paul Stonehouse from 95. *117 Lipson Road, Plymouth PL4 7NQ* Plymouth (01752) 661334

THOMAS, Roger James. b 37. Bris Univ BA59. Wells Th Coll 59. **d** 61 **p** 62. C Henbury *Bris* 61-64; C Stapleton 64-69; P-in-c Hardenhuish 69-71; R 71-75; P-in-c Kington 69-71; V 71-75; V Bris St Andr Hartcliffe 75-81; RD Bedminster 79-81; P-in-c Frenchay 81-86; P-in-c Winterbourne Down 81-86; R Frenchay and Winterbourne Down from 86. *The Rectory, Frenchay Common, Frenchay, Bristol BS16 1NB* Bristol (0117) 956 7616

THOMAS, Ronald Stuart. b 13. Univ of Wales BA35. St Mich Coll Llan 35. d 36 p 37. R Aberdaron and Bodferin w Rhiw w Llanfaelrhys *Ban* 72-78; rtd 78. *Cefn du Ganol, Llanfairynghornwy, Holyhead, Gwynedd LL65 4LG* Llanfaethlu (01407) 730943

THOMAS, Russen William. b 30. Univ of Wales (Lamp) BA55. St Mich Coll Llan 55. d 57 p 58. V Newport St Julian *Mon* 69-79; V Stratton *Truro* 79-88; RD Stratton 83-88; V Lanteglos by Fowey 88-91; Miss to Seamen from 88; rtd 92; Chapl Puerto de la Cruz Tenerife *Eur* 93-95; Chapl Playa de Las Americas Tenerife from 95. *Capellania Anglicana, Apartado de Correos 215, Los Cristianos 38650, Tenerife, Canary Islands* Tenerife (22) 793143

THOMAS, Simon Jonathan Francklin. b 51. Sheff Univ BA72. St Jo Coll Nottm BA78. d 80 p 80. SAMS from 80; Bolivia from 80. *Casilla 3048, Santa Cruz, Bolivia* Casilla (3) 328875

THOMAS, Preb Stephen Blayney. b 35. St D Coll Lamp BA62. Bp Burgess Hall Lamp DipTh63. d 63 p 64. C Ledbury *Heref* 63-67; C Bridgnorth w Tasley 67-68; C Clun w Chapel Lawn, Bettws-y-Crwyn and Newc 68-73; C Clungunford w Clunbury and Clunton, Bedstone etc 68-73; V Worfield 73-84; RD Bridgnorth 81-83; R Kingsland from 84; P-in-c Aymestrey and Leinthall Earles w Wigmore etc from 84; P-in-c Eardisland from 84; Preb Heref Cathl from 85. *Kingsland Rectory, Leominster, Herefordshire HR6 9QW* Kingsland (01568) 708255

THOMAS, Stuart Grahame. b 54. Pemb Coll Cam BA77 MA81. Ridley Hall Cam 85. d 87 p 88. C Guildf H Trin w St Mary *Guildf* 87-91; V Churt 91-94; V Ewell St Fran from 94. *St Francis's Vicarage, 61 Ruxley Lane, Ewell, Surrey KT19 0JG* 0181-393 5616

THOMAS, Canon Sydney Robert. b 44. Univ of Wales (Swansea) BA65 MA83. St D Coll Lamp LTh67. d 67 p 68. C Llanelli *St D* 67-77; V Pontyberem from 77; RD Cydweli from 94; Hon Can St D Cathl from 94. *The Vicarage, 56 Llannon Road, Pontyberem, Llanelli, Dyfed SA15 5LY* Pontyberem (01269) 870345

THOMAS, Telford Ifano. b 17. Univ of Wales BA38. St D Coll Lamp 38. d 40 p 41. V Llangennech and Hendy *St D* 61-79; V Llansteffan and Llan-y-bri etc 79-82; rtd 82. *33 Ty Rees, The Parade, Carmarthen, Dyfed SA31 1LY* Carmarthen (01267) 221942

THOMAS, Theodore Eilir. b 36. Univ of Wales (Lamp) BA58. Sarum Th Coll 58. d 60 p 61. C Fenton *Lich* 60-63; C Stourport All SS and St Mich CD *Worc* 63-67; V Worc H Trin 67-74; P-in-c Dudley St Fran 74-79; V 79-83; R Plympton St Maurice *Ex* from 83. *St Maurice's Rectory, 31 Wain Park, Plympton, Plymouth PL7 3HX* Plymouth (01752) 346114

THOMAS, Thomas (Tom). b 48. Selw Coll Cam BA90. Wycliffe Hall Ox 91. d 93 p 94. C Much Woolton *Liv* from 93. *46 Linkstor Road, Liverpool L25 6DH* 0151-428 3339

THOMAS, Thomas Alan. b 37. K Coll Lon BD60 AKC60. St Boniface Warminster 60. d 61 p 62. C Washington *Dur* 61-65; C Bishopwearmouth St Mary V w St Pet CD 65-70; V Ruishton w Thornfalcon *B & W* 70-82; R Hutton 82-94; V Frome Ch Ch from 94. *Christ Church Vicarage, 73 Weymouth Road, Frome, Somerset BA11 1HJ* Frome (01373) 473249

THOMAS, Thomas Hugh. b 25. Open Univ BA77 Westmr Coll Ox MTh94. St D Coll Lamp 59. d 60 p 61. V Martletwy and Lawrenny w Minwear *St D* 63-78; V Martletwy w Lawrenny and Minwear and Yerbeston 78-79; P-in-c Nolton w Roberston Wathen and Crinow 79-95; RD Narberth 82-94; rtd 95. *27 Haven Road, Haverfordwest, Dyfed SA61 1DU* Haverfordwest (01437) 767182

THOMAS, Thomas John. b 15. St D Coll Lamp BA37 St Mich Coll Llan 37. d 38 p 39. V St Benet Paul's Wharf *Lon* 64-82; C-in-c Paddington St Dav Welsh Ch 64-82; Perm to Offic *S'wark* from 74; Chapl R Hosp and Home Putney from 74; rtd 82. *5 Amberley Drive, Twyford, Reading RG10 9BX* Twyford (01734) 345018

THOMAS, Thomas John Samuel. b 21. St D Coll Lamp BA48. d 49 p 50. Chapl RAF 52-77; QHC 73-85; V Horsham *Chich* 77-85; rtd 85; Perm to Offic *St D* from 85. *1 Glynhir Road, Llandybie, Ammanford, Dyfed SA18 2TA* Llandybie (01269) 850726

THOMAS, Canon Thomas Vernon. b 21. St D Coll Lamp BA42 Selw Coll Cam BA44 MA48. St Mich Coll Llan 44. d 45 p 46. V Beeston *Ripon* 55-77; Hon Can Ripon Cathl 75-89; R Spofforth w Kirk Deighton 77-89; rtd 89. *The Lodge, Main Street, East Keswick, Leeds LS17 9DB* Collingham Bridge (01937) 573033

THOMAS, Trevor Wilson. b 17. Adelaide Univ BA39. St Barn Coll Adelaide 40 ACT ThL41. d 41 p 42. V Littlehampton St Jas *Chich* 65-76; R W Blatchington 76-82; rtd 82; Hon C Westbourne *Chich* 82-86; Hon C Stansted 82-86; Perm to Offic from 86. *10 Andrew Avenue, Felpham, Bognor Regis, W Sussex PO22 7QS* Bognor Regis (01243) 584212

THOMAS, Tristan Emmanuel Douglas. b 38. Mysore Univ BA60. Bp's Coll Calcutta DipTh65. d 65 p 66. India 65-70; Miss to Seamen 70-72; Chapl Rotterdam w Schiedam etc *Eur* 70-71; C Gt Clacton *Chelmsf* 72-74; Chapl Hamburg w Kiel *Eur* 74-85; V Halliwell St Marg *Man* 85-93; V Brompton-by-Sawdon w Snainton, Ebberston etc *York* from 93. *The Vicarage, Pudding Lane, Snainton, Scarborough, N Yorkshire YO13 9AS* Scarborough (01723) 859805

THOMAS, Wallis Huw Wallis. b 06. Univ of Wales BA27. St Mich Coll Llan 30. d 31 p 32. R Llanelltud *Ban* 66-76; rtd 76. *The Vicarage, Llanelltyd, Dolgellau, Gwynedd LL40 2SU* Dolgellau (01341) 422517

THOMAS, William Alwyn. b 11. St D Coll Lamp BA33 St Mich Coll Llan 33. d 34 p 35. R Weyhill cum Penton Newsey *Win* 66-78; rtd 78. *The Brow, Ferryside, Dyfed SA17 5RS* Ferryside (01267) 267369

THOMAS, William Brynmor. b 11. St D Coll Lamp BA33 BD41 Wycliffe Hall Ox 34. d 35 p 36. V Belper *Derby* 53-76; rtd 76. *42 Eastfield Avenue, Haxby, York YO3 3EY* York (01904) 760110

THOMAS, William George. b 29. JP. FRSA Birm Univ BA50 CertEd51. E Anglian Minl Tr Course 82. d 85 p 86. NSM Brampton *Ely* 85-87; NSM Bluntisham w Earith 87-89; P-in-c Foxton from 89. *The Vicarage, 7 West Hill Road, Foxton, Cambridge CB2 6SZ* Cambridge (01223) 870375

THOMAS, William John. b 11. St D Coll Lamp BA48. d 49 p 50. V Formby St Pet *Liv* 53-76; rtd 76. *Bro Gain, 49 Pen-y-Cefn Road, Caerwys, Mold, Clwyd CH7 5BH* Mold (01352) 720811

THOMAS, William John Charles. b 17. St D Coll Lamp BA50. d 51 p 52. Chapl Springfield Hosp Lon 64-82; rtd 82; Perm to Offic *S'wark* 82-93. *101 Heybridge Avenue, London SW16 3DS*

THOMAS, Ven William Jordison. b 27. K Coll Cam BA50 MA55. Cuddesdon Coll 51. d 53 p 54. V Alwinton w Holystone and Alnham *Newc* 59-70; V Alston cum Garrigill w Nenthead and Kirkhaugh 70-80; P-in-c Lambley w Knaresdale 72-80; RD Bamburgh and Glendale 81-83; TR Glendale Gp 80-83; Adn Northd and Can Res Newc Cathl 83-92; rtd 92. *Wark Cottage, Whittingham, Alnwick, Northd NE66 4RB* Whittingham (0166574) 300

THOMAS, Canon William Kenneth. b 19. Mert Coll Ox BA40 MA44. Westcott Ho Cam 40. d 42 p 43. V Minety w Oaksey *Bris* 71-82; P-in-c 82-84; RD Malmesbury 73-79; Hon Can Bris Cathl 77-84; P-in-c Crudwell w Ashley 82-84; rtd 84; Perm to Offic *Bris* from 84. *27 Hamilton Road, Bristol BS3 4EN* Bristol (0117) 963 2198

THOMAS, William Phillip. b 43. Lich Th Coll 68. d 70 p 71. C Llanilid w Pencoed *Llan* 70-74; C Pontypridd St Cath 74-76; V Tonyrefail 76-84; Youth Chapl 78-80; RD Rhondda 81-84; R Neath w Llantwit from 84. *The Rectory, London Road, Neath, W Glam SA11 1LE* Neath (01639) 644612

THOMAS, William Rhys Ithel Phillips. b 16. St Jo Coll Dur BA38 DipTh41 MA42. d 41 p 42. Lic to Offic *Ely* 68-78; Chapl Asst Addenbrooke's Hosp Cam 78-81; rtd 81; Perm to Offic *Ely* from 85. *19 Brooklyn Court, Cherry Hinton Road, Cambridge CB1 4HF* Cambridge (01223) 246348

THOMAS ANTHONY, Brother. See DE HOOP, Thomas Anthony

THOMPSON, Anthony Edward. b 38. Bris Univ BA61. Ridley Hall Cam 61. d 63 p 64. C Peckham St Mary Magd *S'wark* 63-66; Paraguay 67-72; C Otley *Bradf* 72-75; TV Woughton Ox 75-82; P-in-c Lower Nutfield *S'wark* from 82; RD Reigate 91-93; Local Min Adv Croydon Episc Area from 93. *136 Mid Street, South Nutfield, Redhill RH1 5RP* Nutfield Ridge (01737) 822211

THOMPSON, Athol James Patrick. b 34. St Paul's Grahamstown 72. d 74 p 75. S Africa 74-83; P-in-c Dewsbury St Matt and St Jo *Wakef* 84; TV Dewsbury 84-93; Chapl Staincliffe & Dewsbury Gen Hosps Wakef 84-90; Chapl Dewsbury Distr Hosp 90-93; V Shiregreen St Jas and St Chris *Sheff* from 93. *The Vicarage, 510 Bellhouse Road, Sheffield S5 0RG* Sheffield (0114) 245 6526

THOMPSON, Barry (Brother Aidan). b 33. St Jo Coll Lusaka. d 69 p 70. SSF from 59; Zambia 69-76; Miss to Seamen from 76; Tanzania 76-81; Korea 81-82; Australia 83-85; Chapl Vlissingen (Flushing) Miss to Seamen etc *Eur* 85-95. *The Friary, Hilfield, Dorchester, Dorset DT2 7BE* Cerne Abbas (01300) 341345

THOMPSON, Canon Barry Pearce. b 40. St Andr Univ BSc63 Ball Coll Ox PhD66 Hull Univ MA82. NW Ord Course 76. d 79 p 80. C Cottingham *York* 79-82; V Swine 82-83; Lect Th Hull Univ 83-88; Ind Chapl *York* 83-85; Abp's Adv on Ind Issues 85-88; Can Res Chelmsf Cathl *Chelmsf* from 88. *2 Harlings Grove, Waterloo Lane, Chelmsford CM1 1YQ* Chelmsford (01245) 355041

THOMPSON, Brian. b 34. BSc. St Jo Coll Nottm. d 84 p 85. C Bletchley *Ox* 84-87; V Sneyd Green *Lich* from 87. *St Andrew's Vicarage, 42 Granville Avenue, Sneyd Green, Stoke-on-Trent ST1 6BH* Stoke-on-Trent (01782) 215139

THOMPSON, David Arthur. b 37. Clifton Th Coll. **d** 69 **p** 70. C Finchley Ch Ch *Lon* 69-72; C Barking St Marg w St Patr *Chelmsf* 72-75; TV 75-81; V Toxteth Park St Clem *Liv* 81-91; TR Parr from 91. *The Rectory, Delta Road, St Helens, Merseyside WA9 2DZ* St Helens (01744) 23726

THOMPSON, David Frank. b 44. Hull Univ BA65 MA69. St Steph Ho Ox 73. **d** 75 **p** 76. C Sidmouth, Woolbrook and Salcombe Regis *Ex* 75-78; C Lamorbey H Redeemer *Roch* 78-80; Chapl R Masonic Sch for Girls Rickmansworth from 81. *Royal Masonic School for Girls, Rickmansworth Park, Rickmansworth, Herts WD3 4HF* Rickmansworth (01923) 73168

THOMPSON, David John. b 17. Selw Coll Cam BA48 MA52. Ridley Hall Cam 48. **d** 50 **p** 51. V Wallington H Trin *S'wark* 62-74; R Hambledon *Guildf* 74-84; rtd 84; Perm to Offic *Chich* from 85. *1 Pond Willow, North Trade Road, Battle, E Sussex TN33 0HU* Battle (01424) 773000

THOMPSON, David John (Dave). b 64. Cranmer Hall Dur CTM95. **d** 95. C Poulton-le-Sands w Morecambe St Laur *Blackb* from 95. *31 Dallam Avenue, Morecambe, Lancs LA4 5BB* Morecambe (01524) 422974

THOMPSON, Miss Denise. b 50. Chich Th Coll 88. **d** 90. Par Dn Eighton Banks *Dur* 90-94. *1 Radlett Road, Sunderland SR5 5QZ* 0191-549 0952

THOMPSON, Canon Donald Frazer. b 20. St Cath Coll Cam BA46 MA49. Coll of Resurr Mirfield 46. **d** 48 **p** 49. V Leeds St Aid *Ripon* 62-73; RD Allerton 70-73; R Adel 73-87; Hon Can Ripon Cathl 75-87; RD Headingley 85-87; rtd 87. *75 Cubbington Road, Leamington Spa, Warks CV32 7AQ* Leamington Spa (01926) 332935

THOMPSON, Edward Ronald Charles. b 25. AKC51. **d** 52 **p** 53. P-in-c St Mary-le-Strand w St Clem Danes *Lon* 67-74; R 74-93; rtd 93; Perm to Offic *S'wark* from 95. *3 Woodsyre, London SE26 6SS* 0181-670 8289

THOMPSON, Eric John. b 41. Chich Th Coll 83. **d** 85 **p** 86. C Newbold and Dunston *Derby* 85-88; P-in-c Taddington and Chelmorton 88-90; P-in-c Earl Sterndale and Monyash 88-90; V Taddington, Chelmorton and Flagg, and Monyash 90-92; V Blackwell 92-95; P-in-c Walton-on-Trent w Croxall etc from 95. *The Rectory, Walton-on-Trent, Swadlincote, Derbyshire DE12 8NA* Barton under Needwood (01283) 712442

THOMPSON, Frederick Robert. b 15. Dur Univ LTh40. St Aug Coll Cant 37. **d** 40 **p** 41. V Tutbury *Lich* 64-80; rtd 80. *1 Panorama Road, Poole, Dorset BH13 7RA* Canford Cliffs (01202) 700735

✠**THOMPSON, Rt Rev Geoffrey Hewlett.** b 29. Trin Hall Cam BA52 MA56. Cuddesdon Coll 52. **d** 54 **p** 55 **c** 74. C Northn St Matt *Pet* 54-59; V Wisbech St Aug *Ely* 59-66; V Folkestone St Sav *Cant* 66-74; Suff Bp Willesden *Lon* 74-79; Area Bp Willesden 79-85; Bp Ex from 85. *The Palace, Exeter EX1 1HY* Exeter (01392) 72362 Fax 430923

THOMPSON, George Harry Packwood. b 22. Qu Coll Ox BA48 MA48 BTh49. Qu Coll Birm 50. **d** 51 **p** 52. V Combe *Ox* 64-85; Perm to Offic from 85; rtd 87. *12 Briar Thicket, Woodstock, Oxon OX20 1NT* Woodstock (01993) 811915

THOMPSON, Gordon George. b 37. Brasted Place Coll 64. Edin Th Coll 66. **d** 68 **p** 69. C Ches St Jo *Ches* 68-72; C Hackney *Lon* 72-76; P-in-c Craghead *Dur* 76-77; V 77-79; Warden Pemb Coll Miss Walworth *S'wark* 79-82; TV Walworth 79-82; V Mitcham St Olave 82-94. *10 Woodland Court, 77 Grove Road, Sutton, Surrey SM1 2DB* 0181-643 7200

THOMPSON, Preb Gordon Henry Moorhouse. b 41. Univ of Wales LLM95. K Coll Lon 63 St Boniface Warminster 66. **d** 67 **p** 68. C Leominster *Heref* 67-70; C Burford II w Greete and Hope Bagot 70-74; TV 74-89; C Burford III w Lt Heref 70-74; TV 74-89; C Tenbury 70-74; TV 74-89; TV Burford I 74-89; RD Ludlow 83-89; Preb Heref Cathl from 85; rtd 89. *The Poplars, Bitterley, Ludlow, Shropshire SY8 3HQ* Ludlow (01584) 891093

THOMPSON, Harold Anthony. b 41. N Ord Course 84. **d** 87 **p** 88. C Leeds Belle Is St Jo and St Barn *Ripon* 87-90; V Leeds St Cypr Harehills from 90. *St Cyprian's Vicarage, 43A Coldcotes Avenue, Leeds LS9 6ND* Leeds (0113) 249 3746

THOMPSON, Ian Charles. b 58. Wycliffe Hall Ox 80. **d** 83 **p** 84. C Knutsford St Jo and Toft *Ches* 83-86; C Birkenhead Ch Ch 86-88; V Balderstone *Man* from 88. *The Sett, Badger Lane, Craiglands, Rochdale, Lancs OL16 4RD* Rochdale (01706) 49886

THOMPSON, Ian Malcolm. b 59. Wm Booth Memorial Coll CertEd79. Edin Th Coll 93. **d** 94 **p** 95. C Old Deer *Ab* from 94; C Longside from 94; C Strichen from 94. *12 Bain Terrace, Mintlaw, Peterhead, Aberdeen AB42 8EW* Mintlaw (01771) 622553

THOMPSON, Father James. b 30. MNACH90 DipHyp84 Nottm Univ DipEd65 DipTh65. Paton Congr Coll Nottm 61 Wycliffe Hall Ox 66. **d** 66 **p** 67. R Firbeck w Letwell *Sheff* 69-71; V Milnsbridge *Wakef* 71-80; Chapl St Luke's Hosp Huddersfield 71-80; NSM Dewsbury 80-84; Lect Huddersfield

Coll FE 80-84; Dioc Chapl Aber Hosps 84-89; Dioc Supernumerary *Ab* 84-89; R Buckie 89-94; R Portsoy 89-94; rtd 95. *Ty Coch, Fron Park Road, Holywell, Clwyd CH8 7UY* Holywell (01352) 713268

THOMPSON, James. b 37. Coll of Resurr Mirfield 64. **d** 67 **p** 68. C Shieldfield Ch Ch *Newc* 67-69; C Hendon *Dur* 69-74; V Gateshead St Chad Bensham 74-85; R Easington 85-90; Chapl Thorpe Hosp Easington from 85; V Cassop cum Quarrington *Dur* from 90. *The Vicarage, Bowburn, Co Durham DH6 5DL* 0191-377 0347

✠**THOMPSON, Rt Rev James Lawton.** b 36. ACA59 FCA70 Em Coll Cam BA64 MA71 Hon DLitt89 Ex Univ Hon DD95. Cuddesdon Coll 64. **d** 66 **p** 67 **c** 78. C E Ham St Geo *Chelmsf* 66-68; Chapl Cuddesdon Coll 68-71; Lic to Offic *S'wark* 71-72; TR Thamesmead 72-78; Suff Bp Stepney *Lon* 78-79; Area Bp Stepney 79-91; Bp B&W from 91. *The Palace, Wells, Somerset BA5 2PD* Wells (01749) 672341 Fax 679355

THOMPSON, John David. b 40. Lon Univ BD65 Ch Ch Ox DPhil69. St Steph Ho Ox 65. **d** 67 **p** 68. C Solihull *Birm* 67-71; C Biddestone w Slaughterford *Bris* 71-73; Lect Wells Th Coll 71-72; C Yatton Keynell *Bris* 71-73; C Castle Combe 71-73; V Braughing *St Alb* 74-77; R Digswell 77-82; TR Digswell and Panshanger from 82. *The Rectory, 354 Knightsfield, Welwyn Garden City, Herts AL8 7NG* Welwyn Garden (01707) 326677

THOMPSON, John Michael. b 47. Nottm Univ BTh77 Cam Univ BA84 Hull Univ CLRHist90. Linc Th Coll 73. **d** 77 **p** 78. C Old Brumby *Linc* 77-80; C Grantham 80-81; TV 81-84; V Holton-le-Clay 84-94; V Holton-le-Clay and Tetney from 94. *The Vicarage, Church Walk, Holton-le-Clay, Grimsby, Humberside DN36 5AN* Grimsby (01472) 824082

THOMPSON, John Miller. b 26. St Deiniol's Hawarden. **d** 63 **p** 64. V Askern *Sheff* 67-72; P-in-c Moss 69-72; Ind Chapl 72-85; P-in-c Brightside St Marg 72-77; P-in-c Sheff Gillcar St Silas 77-88; Chapl Weston Park Hosp Sheff 85-93; C Ranmoor *Sheff* 88-93; Chapl to Homes for the Aged 88-93; rtd 93. *2 Knab Close, Sheffield S7 2ER* Sheffield (0114) 258 6790

THOMPSON, John Turrell. b 57. Sheff Univ BA(Econ)79 Southn Univ BTh88. Sarum & Wells Th Coll 83. **d** 86 **p** 87. C Tavistock and Gulworthy *Ex* 86-90; TV Pinhoe and Broadclyst 90-95; P-in-c Northam w Westward Ho! and Appledore from 95. *The Rectory, Northam, Bideford, Devon EX35 1AW* Bideford (01237) 474379

THOMPSON, John Wilfred. b 44. CA Tr Coll 66 St Deiniol's Hawarden 85-86. **d** 85 **p** 86. C Rhyl w St Ann *St As* 85-87; R Fritwell w Souldern and Ardley w Fewcott *Ox* from 87. *The Vicarage, 44 Forge Place, Fritwell, Bicester, Oxon OX6 9QQ* Fritwell (01869) 346739

THOMPSON (nee LILLIE), Mrs Judith Virginia. b 44. LMH Ox BA66 Univ of E Africa DipEd67 Essex Univ MA73 Bris Univ DCouns92. Gilmore Course IDC82. **dss** 82 **d** 87 **p** 94. Asst Chapl Bris Univ *Bris* 76-80; Lawrence Weston 82-85; E Bris 85-87; Hon Par Dn 87-95; Chapl HM Rem Cen Pucklechurch 87-91; Chapl Asst Southmead Hosp Bris 91-94; Asst Chapl Bris NHS Trust 94-95; C Knowle St Barn *Bris* from 95. *St Barnabas Vicarage, Daventry Road, Bristol BS4 1DQ* Bristol (0117) 966 4139

THOMPSON, Kenneth. b 31. St Deiniol's Hawarden. **d** 87 **p** 88. Hon Par Dn Upton (or Overchurch) *Ches* 87-90; NSM Tranmere St Cath from 90. *33 Meadway, Upton, Wirral, Merseyside L49 6JQ* 0151-677 6433

THOMPSON, Kevin. b 55. Sheff Univ BEd77. Oak Hill Th Coll DipHE89. **d** 89 **p** 90. C Brinsworth w Catcliffe *Sheff* 89-92; V Kimberworth Park from 92. *The Vicarage, 21 Birks Road, Rotherham, S Yorkshire S61 3JX* Rotherham (01709) 552268

THOMPSON, Mark William. b 52. St Jo Coll Nottm 77. **d** 81 **p** 82. C Barnsbury St Andr and H Trin w All SS *Lon* 81-84; C Addiscombe St Mary *Cant* 84; C Addiscombe St Mary *S'wark* 85-87; V Thorpe Edge *Bradf* 87-94; Chapl Colchester Gen Hosp from 94. *Colchester General Hospital, Turner Road, Colchester CO4 5JL* Colchester (01206) 853535

THOMPSON, Matthew. b 68. CCC Cam BA90 MA94 MPhil94. Ridley Hall Cam 91. **d** 94 **p** 95. C Hulme Ascension *Man* from 94. *The Arnott Centre, 2 Tarnbrook Walk, Manchester M15 6NL* 0161-226 4694

THOMPSON, Mervyn Patrick. b 59. Wilson Carlile Coll 84 Coll of Resurr Mirfield 90. **d** 92 **p** 93. C Sheff St Cath Richmond Road *Sheff* 92-95; V Thurnscoe St Hilda from 95. *The Vicarage, Hanover Street, Thurnscoe, Rotherham, S Yorkshire S63 0HJ* Rotherham (01709) 893259

THOMPSON, Michael. b 49. NE Ord Course 83. **d** 86 **p** 87. C Ashington *Newc* 86-88; C Ponteland 88-91; TV New Epiphany from 91. *7 Fawdon Lane, Newcastle upon Tyne NE3 2RR* 0191-285 5403

THOMPSON, Dr Michael Bruce. b 53. N Carolina Univ BA75 Ch Coll Cam PhD88. Dallas Th Sem ThM79 Virginia Th Sem

79. **d** 80 **p** 81. USA 80-83; Lect St Jo Coll Nottm 88-95; Dir of Studies Ridley Hall Cam from 95. *Dashwood House, Sidgwick Avenue, Cambridge CB3 9HG* Cambridge (01223) 65984

THOMPSON, Nathanael (Brother Nathanael). b 29. St Deiniol's Hawarden 76. **d** 78 **p** 79. SSF from 62; C Llanbeblig w Caernarfon *Ban* 78-80; C Swansea St Gabr *S & B* 84-87; C Swansea St Mary w H Trin 87. *The Monastery, Shrawley, Worcester WR6 6TQ* Great Witley (01299) 896345

THOMPSON, Neil Hamilton. b 48. SS Hild & Bede Coll Dur BEd72 Leic Univ MA75. S'wark Ord Course 77. **d** 80 **p** 81. C Mert St Mary *S'wark* 80-82; C Dulwich St Barn 82-84; V Shooters Hill Ch Ch 84-87; V S Dulwich St Steph from 87. *St Stephen's Vicarage, College Road, London SE21 7HN* 0181-693 3797

THOMPSON, Patrick Arthur. b 36. Dur Univ BA59. Qu Coll Birm DipTh61. **d** 61 **p** 62. C W Wickham St Fran *Cant* 61-65; C Portchester *Portsm* 65-68; C Birchington w Acol *Cant* 68-71; V S Norwood St Mark 71-77; P-in-c Norbury St Oswald 77-81; V Norbury St Oswald *S'wark* 81-93; V Sutton New Town St Barn from 93. *St Barnabas' Vicarage, 37 St Barnabas' Road, Sutton, Surrey SM1 4NS* 0181-661 9619

THOMPSON, Paul. b 58. Ox Univ BA. Ripon Coll Cuddesdon 80. **d** 83 **p** 84. Chapl Fazakerley Hosp 83-86; C Kirkby *Liv* 83-86; TV 86-89; Ind Chapl 86-89; Chapl Kirkby Coll of FE 86-89; CF from 89. *c/o MOD (Army), Bagshot Park, Bagshot, Surrey GU19 5PL* Bagshot (01276) 471717 Fax 412834

THOMPSON, Paul. b 65. TCD BA87. CITC 87. **d** 89 **p** 90. C Orangefield w Moneyreagh *D & D* 89-91; I Dromara w Garvaghy from 91. *58 Banbridge Road, Dromara, Dromore, Co Down BT25 2NE* Dromara (01238) 532234

THOMPSON, Paul Noble. b 54. Univ of Wales (Cardiff) BMus77. Coll of Resurr Mirfield DipTh79. **d** 80 **p** 81. C Bargoed and Deri w Brithdir *Llan* 80-83; C Whitchurch 83-84; V Porth w Trealaw 84-89; V Llanharan w Peterston-super-Montem from 89. *The Vicarage, Brynna Road, Llanharan, Pontyclun, M Glam CF7 9QE* Newtown Llantwit (01443) 226307

THOMPSON, Mrs Pauline. b 44. E Midl Min Tr Course 81. **dss** 84 **d** 87 **p** 94. Derby St Aug *Derby* 84-87; Par Dn 87-88; Par Dn Boulton 88-90; Par Dn Allestree 91-94; C from 94; Sub-Chapl HM Pris Sudbury from 92. *33 Portreath Drive, Allestree, Derby DE22 2BJ*

THOMPSON, Peter Homer. b 17. Chich Th Coll 39. **d** 41 **p** 42. V Ruislip St Mary *Lon* 59-81; V Mullion *Truro* 81-87; rtd 87. *22 Parkside Drive, Exmouth, Devon EX8 4LB* Exmouth (01395) 266359

THOMPSON, Peter Kerr. b 32. Kelham Th Coll. **d** 56 **p** 57. Solomon Is 56-76; Adn Malaita and Outer E Solomon 62-68; Adn N Melanesia 68-70; Australia from 76. *28 Saunders Street, Point Vernon, Queensland, Australia 4655* Brisbane (71) 243645

THOMPSON, Canon Dr Peter Ross. b 26. St Jo Coll Cam BA47 MB50 BChir50. Tyndale Hall Bris. **d** 60 **p** 61. R Slaugham *Chich* 66-72; V Polegate 72-92; Can and Preb Chich Cathl 91-92; rtd 92. *Tregenna, Barley Mow Lane, Knaphill, Woking, Surrey GU21 2HX* Woking (01483) 480595

THOMPSON, Randolph. b 25. Lich Th Coll 63. **d** 65 **p** 66. P-in-c Cornholme *Wakef* 69-71; V 71-72; Chapl Barnsley Hall & Lea Hosps Bromsgrove 72-84; V Hanley Castle, Hanley Swan and Welland *Worc* 84-89; rtd 89. *37 Hampton Fields, Oswestry, Shropshire SY11 1TL* Oswestry (01691) 658484

THOMPSON, Raymond Craigmile. b 42. **d** 84 **p** 85. C Clooney *D & R* 84-86; I Urney w Sion Mills 86-92; I Derryvullen N w Castlearchdale *Clogh* from 92. *The Rectory, Enniskillen Road, Irvinestown, Co Fermanagh BT94 1GW* Irvinestown (013656) 21225 Fax as telephone

THOMPSON, Richard Brian. b 60. Sheff Poly BSc83. Ripon Coll Cuddesdon 86. **d** 89 **p** 90. C Thorpe Bay *Chelmsf* 89-92; V Rushmere *St E* from 92. *The Vicarage, 253 Colchester Road, Rushmere, Ipswich IP4 4SH* Ipswich (01473) 270976

THOMPSON, Robert. b 36. AKC61. **d** 62 **p** 63. C Cockerton *Dur* 62-65; C Dur St Marg 65-70; V Wallsend St Jo *Newc* 70-78; V Norham and Duddo from 78. *The Vicarage, Norham, Berwick-upon-Tweed TD15 2LF* Berwick-upon-Tweed (01289) 382325

THOMPSON, Ronald. b 08. DFC43. Linc Th Coll. **d** 60 **p** 61. R Saham Toney *Nor* 65-78; rtd 78; Perm to Offic *Nor* from 79. *4 Oval Avenue, Norwich NR5 0DP* Norwich (01603) 744139

THOMPSON, Dr Ross Keith Arnold. b 53. Sussex Univ BA75 Bris Univ PhD82. Coll of Resurr Mirfield 80. **d** 82 **p** 83. C Knowle *Bris* 82-85; TV E Bris 85-94; V Bristol St Aid w St Geo 94-95; P-in-c Knowle St Barn from 95. *St Barnabas' Vicarage, Daventry Road, Bristol BS4 1DQ* Bristol (0117) 966 4139

THOMPSON, Miss Ruth Jean. b 47. St Alb Minl Tr Scheme 85. **d** 90 **p** 94. Par Dn Stonebridge St Mich *Lon* 90-94; C 94; C Ealing St Paul from 94. *23 Littleway Close, London W13 9XH* 0181-567 7834

THOMPSON, Thomas. b 25. NE Ord Course. **d** 85 **p** 86. NSM Ford *Newc* 85-86; NSM Tweedmouth 86-93; rtd 93. *35 Magdalene Drive, Berwick-upon-Tweed TD15 1PX* Berwick-upon-Tweed (01289) 305725

THOMPSON, Thomas Oliver. b 27. TCD 61. **d** 63 **p** 64. Chapl to Ch of Ireland Miss to Deaf and Dumb 68-76; I Glenavy w Tunny and Crumlin *Conn* 77-92; rtd 92. *34 Strandview Avenue, Portstewart, Co Londonderry BT55 7LL* Portstewart (01265) 833267

THOMPSON, Canon Timothy. b 34. Fitzw Ho Cam BA59 MA64. Cuddesdon Coll 59. **d** 61 **p** 62. C Noel Park St Mark *Lon* 61-64; C Shrub End *Chelmsf* 64-67; New Zealand 67-70; R Tolleshunt Knights w Tiptree *Chelmsf* 70-81; R Colchester St Jas, All SS, St Nic and St Runwald 81-88; RD Colchester 84-88; Hon Can Chelmsf Cathl 85-88; Vice-Provost Chelmsf from 88; Can Res Chelmsf Cathl from 88. *115 Rainsford Road, Chelmsford CM1 2PH* Chelmsford (01245) 267773

THOMPSON, Timothy Charles. b 51. Lon Univ BSc73 AKC. Westcott Ho Cam 75. **d** 78 **p** 79. C Ipswich St Mary at Stoke w St Pet & St Mary Quay *St E* 78-81; Ind Chapl *Nor* 81-88; C Lowestoft and Kirkley 81-83; TV 83-88; V Coney Hill *Glouc* 88-94; P-in-c Caister *Nor* from 94. *The Rectory, Caister-on-Sea, Great Yarmouth, Norfolk NR30 5EH* Great Yarmouth (01493) 720287

THOMPSON, Timothy William. b 48. Bris Univ CertEd70 Open Univ BA78. E Midl Min Tr Course. **d** 88 **p** 89. C Scartho *Linc* 88-91; V Haxey from 91. *The Vicarage, Haxey, Doncaster DN9 2HY* Haxey (01427) 752351

THOMPSON, Tom Malcolm. b 38. Dur Univ BA60. Bps' Coll Cheshunt 60. **d** 62 **p** 63. C Standish *Blackb* 62-65; C Lanc St Mary 65-67; V Chorley All SS 67-72; V Barrowford 72-78; RD Pendle 75-78; R Northfield *Birm* 78-82; RD Kings Norton 79-82; V Longton *Blackb* 82-94; RD Leyland 89-94; V Nunthorpe *York* from 94. *The Vicarage, Nunthorpe, Middlesbrough, Cleveland TS7 0PD* Middlesbrough (01642) 346570

THOMPSON-McCAUSLAND, Marcus Perronet. b 31. Trin Coll Cam BA54 MA60. Coll of Resurr Mirfield 57. **d** 59 **p** 60. V Rubery *Birm* 65-72; R Cradley *Heref* 72-82; P-in-c Storridge 72-82; P-in-c Mathon 72-82; P-in-c Castle Frome 72-82; Hon C Camberwell St Giles *S'wark* 82-87; Hon C Lydbury N *Heref* 88-89; Hon C Lydbury N w Hopesay and Edgton 89-94; rtd 93. *18 Watling Street, Leintwardine, Craven Arms, Shropshire SY7 0LW* Leintwardine (015473) 228

THOMPSTONE, John Deaville. b 39. BNC Ox BA63 MA67. Ridley Hall Cam 63. **d** 65 **p** 66. C Hoole *Ches* 65-68; C Fulwood *Sheff* 68-71; V Skirbeck H Trin *Linc* 71-77; V Shipley St Pet *Bradf* 77-91; RD Airedale 82-88; V Poynton *Ches* from 91. *The Vicarage, 41 London Road North, Poynton, Cheshire SK12 1AF* Poynton (01625) 872711

THOMSETT, Murray Richard. b 32. MBKSTS Kingston Tech Coll HND54. Oak Hill Th Coll 91. **d** 92 **p** 93. NSM Whitton SS Phil and Jas *Lon* from 92. *27 Coombe Road, Hampton, Middx TW12 3PB* 0181-949 7549

THOMSON, Alexander Keith. b 38. Cranmer Hall Dur BA63. **d** 64 **p** 65. C Middleton *Man* 64-68; Chapl Rannoch Sch Perthshire 68-72; P-in-c Kinloch Rannoch *St And* 68-72; Asst Chapl Oundle Sch Pet from 72; Lic to Offic *Pet* from 73; Chapl Laxton Sch Oundle from 88. *34 Kings Road, Oundle, Peterborough PE8 4AY* Oundle (0832) 273416

THOMSON, Andrew Maitland. b 43. CA(Z)67 Univ Coll of Rhodesia and Nyasaland DipApEc65. Westcott Ho Cam 78. **d** 80 **p** 81. Zimbabwe 80-92; P-in-c E w N and W Barsham *Nor* from 92; P-in-c N and S Creake w Waterden 92-94; P-in-c Sculthorpe w Dunton and Doughton 92-94; R N and S Creake w Waterden, Syderstone etc from 95. *The Rectory, 18 Front Street, South Creake, Fakenham, Norfolk NR21 9PE* South Creake (01328) 823433

THOMSON, Miss Celia Stephana Margaret. b 55. LMH Ox MA83 Birkb Coll Lon MA87 K Coll Lon MA94. Sarum & Wells Th Coll 89. **d** 91 **p** 94. Par Dn Southfields St Barn *S'wark* 91-94; C 94-95; V W Wimbledon Ch Ch from 95. *Christ Church Vicarage, Copse Hill, London SW20 0HG* 0181-946 4491

THOMSON, Preb Clarke Edward Leighton. b 19. TD65. Pemb Coll Ox BA41 MA45. Wycliffe Hall Ox 44. **d** 45 **p** 46. V Chelsea All SS *Lon* 51-92; CF (TA) 52-69; Preb St Paul's Cathl *Lon* 86-92; rtd 92. *15 Redburn Street, London SW3 4DA* 0171-351 5371

THOMSON, Colin Hugh. b 21. **d** 91 **p** 92. C Galway w Kilcummin *T, K & A* 91-94; NSM Tuam from 94. *The Rectory, Luimnagh West, Corrandulla, Co Galway, Irish Republic* Galway (91) 91482 Fax 91386

THOMSON, Dr David. b 52. Keble Coll Ox MA78 DPhil78 Selw Coll Cam BA80 MA84. Westcott Ho Cam 78. **d** 81 **p** 82. C Maltby *Sheff* 81-84; Sec Par and People 84-94; TV Banbury *Ox* 84-94; TR Cockermouth w Embleton and Wythop *Carl* from 94. *The Rectory, Lorton Road, Cockermouth, Cumbria CA13 9DU* Cockermouth (01900) 823269

THOMSON, George Miller McMillan. b 33. Edin Th Coll 59. **d** 62 **p** 63. C Brookfield St Mary *Lon* 68-72; V Noel Park St Mark 72-81; RD E Haringey 77-81; Chapl Newark Hosp 81-87; TR Newark w Hawton, Cotham and Shelton *S'well* 81-87; R Glas St Bride *Glas* from 87; rtd 94. *St Bride's Rectory, 25 Queensborough Gardens, Glasgow G12 9QP* 0141-334 1401

THOMSON, John Bromilow. b 59. York Univ BA81. Wycliffe Hall Ox BA84 MA91. **d** 85 **p** 86. C Ecclesall *Sheff* 85-89; S Africa 89-92; V Doncaster St Mary *Sheff* from 93. *St Mary's Vicarage, 59 St Mary's Road, Doncaster, S Yorkshire DN1 2NR* Doncaster (01302) 342565

THOMSON, Julian Harley. b 43. AKC70. St Aug Coll Cant 70. **d** 71 **p** 72. C Wellingborough All Hallows *Pet* 71-74; Min Can, Prec and Sacr Ely Cathl *Ely* 74-80; P-in-c Stuntney 76-80; V Arrington 80-91; R Croydon w Clopton 80-91; R Orwell 80-91; R Wimpole 80-91; V Linton from 91; R Bartlow from 91; P-in-c Castle Camps from 91. *The Vicarage, Church Lane, Linton, Cambridge CB1 6JX* Cambridge (01223) 891291

THOMSON, (Ban), Matthew James. b 63. Nottm Univ BA92 Univ of Wales (Ban). St Jo Coll Nottm 92. **d** 95. C Cosham *Portsm* from 95. *211 Hawthorn Crescent, Cosham, Portsmouth PO6 2TL* Portsmouth (01705) 349609

THOMSON, Oliver Miles. b 38. Magd Coll Cam BA61 MA65. Wycliffe Hall Ox 61. **d** 63 **p** 64. C St Marylebone All So w SS Pet and Jo *Lon* 63-67; C Fulwood *Sheff* 67-70; R Wick w Doynton *Bris* 70-74; V Harold Wood *Chelmsf* 74-87; R Sevenoaks St Nic *Roch* from 87. *The Rectory, Rectory Lane, Sevenoaks, Kent TN13 1JA* Sevenoaks (01732) 740340 Fax 742810

THOMSON, Peter Malcolm. b 44. Trin Coll Bris 75. **d** 78 **p** 79. C Tonbridge St Steph *Roch* 78-82; R Cobham w Luddesdowne and Dode 82-90; V Withall *Birm* 90-92; V Wythall from 92. *St Mary's Vicarage, 27 Lea Green Lane, Wythall, Birmingham B47 6HE* Wythall (01564) 823381

THOMSON, Canon Richard Irving. b 32. Oak Hill Th Coll 57. **d** 60 **p** 61. C Kingston upon Hull H Trin *York* 60-63; C S Croydon Em *Cant* 63-66; V Shoreditch St Leon *Lon* 66-73; Chapl Vevey w Chateau d'Oex and Villars *Eur* 73-78; V Reigate St Mary *S'wark* from 78; Hon Can S'wark Cathl from 90. *St Mary's Vicarage, 76 Church Street, Reigate, Surrey RH2 0SP* Reigate (01737) 242973

THOMSON, Richard William Byars. b 60. Birm Univ BA86. Ripon Coll Cuddesdon 86. **d** 88 **p** 89. C Moulsecoomb *Chich* 88-90; P-in-c Kirriemuir *St And* 90-94; P-in-c Piddletrenthide w Plush, Alton Pancras etc *Sarum* from 94. *The Vicarage, Piddletrenthide, Dorchester, Dorset DT2 7QX* Piddletrenthide (01300) 348763 Fax as telephone

THOMSON, Robert Douglass. b 37. Dur Univ BEd75. Cranmer Hall Dur 76. **d** 79 **p** 80. NSM Shincliffe *Dur* from 79; Chapl St Aid Coll Dur from 95. *11 Hill Meadows, High Shincliffe, Durham DH1 2PE* 0191-386 3358

THOMSON, Canon Ronald. b 24. Leeds Univ BA49. Coll of Resurr Mirfield 49. **d** 51 **p** 52. V Shiregreen St Hilda *Sheff* 57-73; RD Ecclesfield 72-73; V Worsbrough 73-88; RD Tankersley 75-85; Hon Can Sheff Cathl 77-88; rtd 88. *34 Kingwell Road, Worsbrough, Barnsley, S Yorkshire S70 4HF* Barnsley (01226) 203553

THOMSON, Ronald Arthur. b 29. G&C Coll Cam BA53 MA57. Ripon Hall Ox. **d** 57 **p** 58. R Watton at Stone *St Alb* 68-94; rtd 94. *Ashby, 65 Edmonds Drive, Aston Brook, Stevenage, Herts SG2 9TJ*

THOMSON, Russell. b 39. AKC62. **d** 63 **p** 64. C Hackney *Lon* 63-66; C Plumstead Wm Temple Ch Abbey Wood CD *S'wark* 66-69; TV Strood *Roch* 69-75; V Gillingham St Mary 75-89; V Roch from 89; Chapl St Bart Hosp Roch from 89; Chapl Wisdom Hospice from 89. *The Vicarage, 138 Delce Road, Rochester, Kent ME1 2EH* Medway (01634) 845122 or 848900

THOMSON, Preb Sidney Seward Chartres. b 01. OBE44. St Geo Windsor. **d** 54 **p** 55. V Worfield *Heref* 56-72; Preb Heref Cathl 70-72; rtd 72; Perm to Offic *Heref* from 72. *Bradney House, Worfield, Bridgnorth, Shropshire WV15 5NT* Bridgnorth (01746) 765974

THOMSON, Mrs Winifred Mary. b 35. St Mary's Coll Dur BA57 MA58 Lon Univ 86. Qu Coll Birm 79. dss 82 **d** 87 **p** 94. Leic H Spirit *Leic* 82-86; Oadby 86-87; Par Dn 87-92; rtd 93. *140 Knighton Church Road, Leicester LE2 3JJ* Leicester (0116) 270 5863

THOMSON GIBSON, Thomas. *See* GIBSON, Thomas Thomson

THOMSON-GLOVER, Canon William Hugh. b 28. Trin Hall Cam BA52 MA56. Cuddesdon Coll 52. **d** 54 **p** 55. V Bris Lockleaze St Mary Magd w St Fran *Bris* 70-76; P-in-c Sherston Magna w Easton Grey 76-81; P-in-c Luckington w Alderton 76-81; V Sherston Magna, Easton Grey, Luckington etc 81-93; P-in-c Foxley w Bremilham 84-86; RD Malmesbury

THOMSON 88-93; Hon Can Bris Cathl 91-93; rtd 93. *Woodgate Farm House, Woodgate, Culmstock, Cullompton, Devon EX15 3HW* Cullompton (01884) 841465

THORBURN, Austin Noel. b 13. Trin Coll Cam BA36 MA40. Bps' Coll Cheshunt 36. **d** 38 **p** 39. C Langley Marish *Ox* 71-76; TV 76-79; rtd 79; Perm to Offic *Carl* 79-88; Perm to Offic *Ox* from 88. *28 Blacklands Road, Benson, Wallingford, Oxon OX10 6NW* Wallingford (01491) 832365

THORBURN, Guy Douglas Anderson. b 50. Ridley Hall Cam. **d** 83 **p** 84. C Putney St Marg *S'wark* 83-87; R Moresby *Carl* from 87. *The Rectory, Low Moresby, Whitehaven, Cumbria CA28 6RR* Whitehaven (01946) 693970

THORBURN, Peter Hugh. b 17. Worc Coll Ox BA41 MA43. Wells Th Coll 46. **d** 47 **p** 48. V Chipping Sodbury and Old Sodbury *Glouc* 68-72; Chapl Withington Hosp Man 72-82; rtd 82; Perm to Offic *B & W* from 83; Perm to Offic *Bris* from 85; Warden Servants of Ch the K from 89. *8 Stoberry Crescent, Wells, Somerset BA5 2TG* Wells (01749) 672919

THORBURN, Simon Godfrey. b 51. Newc Univ BSc73 Fitzw Coll Cam BA77 MA81. Westcott Ho Cam 75. **d** 78 **p** 79. C Stafford St Mary and St Chad *Lich* 78-79; C Stafford 79-82; C Tettenhall Regis 82-83; TV 83-90; Soc Resp Officer *S'wark* from 90. *104 Queens Road, London SW19 8LS* 0181-543 8874

THORLEY-PAICE, Alan. b 26. AKC53. **d** 55 **p** 56. C Eton w Boveney *Ox* 63-74; P-in-c Hawridge w Cholesbury 74-83; P-in-c Lee 74-83; V 83-86; P-in-c Aston Clinton St Leon 79-83; R Hawridge w Cholesbury and St Leonard 83-86; rtd 86. *Glaston, Kingstone, Hereford HR2 9ES* Golden Valley (01981) 250195

THORN, Peter. b 50. Man Poly BEd79. Ridley Hall Cam 82. **d** 84 **p** 85. C Aughton Ch Ch *Liv* 84-87; C Skelmersdale St Paul 87-90; Dioc Children's Officer 87-92; P-in-c Croft w Southworth 90-92; C Streatley *St Alb* from 92. *66 Marsom Grove, Luton LU3 4BQ* Luton (01582) 575153

THORN, Robert Anthony D'Venning (Bob). b 54. AKC76. Chich Th Coll 75. **d** 77 **p** 78. C Bodmin *Truro* 77-80; TV N Hill w Altarnon, Bolventor and Lewannick 80-83; V Feock 83-90; Dioc Ecum Officer 83-90; Broadcasting Officer *Linc* 90-93; V Whitchurch *Bris* from 93. *The Vicarage, 780 Whitchurch Lane, Bristol BS14 0EU* Whitchurch (01275) 832380

THORNBURGH, Richard Hugh Perceval. b 52. Sarum & Wells Th Coll. **d** 84 **p** 85. C Broadstone *Sarum* 84-87; TV Beaminster Area from 87. *The Vicarage, Orchard Mead, Broadwindsor, Beaminster, Dorset DT8 3RA* Broadwindsor (01308) 868805

THORNBURY, Peter Dawson. b 43. Open Univ BA84 TCD BTh93. CITC 90. **d** 93 **p** 94. C Annagh w Drumgoon, Ashfield etc *K, E & A* from 93. *The Rectory, Cootehill, Co Cavan, Irish Republic* Cavan (49) 52004

THORNE, Mrs Anita Dawn. b 46. Trin Coll Bris 84. dss 86 **d** 87 **p** 94. Chapl Bris Poly *Bris* 86-88; Par Dn Olveston 88-94; P-in-c from 94. *The Vicarage, The Street, Olveston, Bristol BS12 3DA* Almondsbury (01454) 612296

THORNE, Clifford Graham. b 16. St Jo Coll Cam BA38 MA50. Westcott Ho Cam 78. **d** 78 **p** 79. Hon C Ponteland *Newc* from 78. *Dissington Old Hall, Dalton, Newcastle upon Tyne NE18 0BN* Ponteland (01661) 825258

THORNE, Mrs Marie Elizabeth. b 47. E Midl Min Tr Course 83. dss 86 **d** 87 **p** 94. Cleethorpes *Linc* 86-87; C 87-90; C Brigg from 90. *The Vicarage, Vicarage Road, Wrawby, Brigg, S Humberside DN20 8RR* Brigg (01652) 657605

THORNE, Canon Ralph Frederick. b 14. ALCD36 St Jo Coll Dur LTh36 BA37. **d** 37 **p** 38. R Heaton Reddish *Man* 62-80; Hon Can Man Cathl 74-80; rtd 80; Perm to Offic *Man* from 80. *9 Greenfield Road, Atherton, Manchester M46 9LW* Atherton (01942) 873894

THORNETT, Frederick Charles. b 34. Harris Coll CQSW68. Local Minl Course. **d** 85 **p** 86. NSM Skegness and Winthorpe *Linc* 85-90; C New Sleaford 90-92; P-in-c Harlaxton from 92. *The Rectory, Harlaxton, Grantham, Lincs NG32 1HD* Grantham (01476) 75019

THORNEWILL, Canon Mark Lyon. b 25. ALCD56. **d** 56 **p** 58. R Lifton *Ex* 62-66; R Kelly w Bradstone 62-66; USA from 66; Hon Can Louisville Cathl from 70; rtd 90. *9709 Covered Bridge Road, Prospect, Kentucky 40059, USA*

THORNEYCROFT, Mrs Pippa Hazel Jeanetta. b 44. Ex Univ BA65. Qu Coll Birm 85 W Midl Minl Tr Course. **d** 88 **p** 94. NSM Albrighton *Lich* 88-90; NSM Beckbury 90-93; NSM Badger 90-93; NSM Kemberton, Sutton Maddock and Stockton 90-93; NSM Ryton 90-93; NSM Beckbury, Badger, Kemberton, Ryton, Stockton etc from 93. *Kemberton Hall, Shifnal, Shropshire TF11 9LH* Telford (01952) 580588

THORNLEY, Arthur Richard. b 15. Selw Coll Cam BA38. Westcott Ho Cam 38. **d** 39 **p** 40. Chapl Lon Ho 70-75; PV Truro Cathl *Truro* 75-80; Chapl Truro Cathl Sch 75-80; rtd 80; Hon PV Truro Cathl *Truro* from 80. *54 Linkswood, Compton Place Road, Eastbourne, E Sussex BN21 1EF* Eastbourne (01323) 647686

THORNLEY, David Howe. b 43. Wycliffe Hall Ox 77. **d** 79 **p** 80. C Burgess Hill St Andr *Chich* 79-83; P-in-c Amberley w N Stoke 83-84; P-in-c Parham and Wiggonholt w Greatham 83-84; V Amberley w N Stoke and Parham, Wiggonholt etc 84-92; P-in-c S w N Bersted from 92. *121 Victoria Drive, Bognor Regis, W Sussex PO21 2EH* Bognor Regis (01243) 862018

THORNLEY, Geoffrey Pearson. b 23. Pemb Coll Cam BA47 MA52. Cuddesdon Coll. **d** 50 **p** 51. Chapl RN 53-73; Bp's Dom Chapl *Linc* 73-75; P-in-c Riseholme 73-78; P-in-c Scothern w Sudbrooke 77-78; V Dunholme 75-85; Hon PV Linc Cathl 75-85; rtd 85; Chapl Allnutt's Hosp Goring Heath from 85. *The Chaplaincy, Allnutt's Hospital, Goring Heath, Reading RG8 7RR* Checkendon (01491) 680261

THORNLEY, Nicholas Andrew. b 56. St Jo Coll Nottm BTh81. **d** 81 **p** 84. C Frodingham *Linc* 81-84; P-in-c Belton All SS 84-85; V 85-90; V Horncastle w Low Toynton from 90; RD Horncastle from 94. *The Vicarage, 9 Langton Drive, Horncastle, Lincs LN9 5AJ* Horncastle (01507) 525564

THORNTON, Canon Cecil. b 26. Lon Univ BD PhD. Tyndale Hall Bris 47. **d** 50 **p** 51. I Fahan Lower and Upper *D & R* 65-88; RD Innishowen 67-88; Can Raphoe Cathl 79-88; rtd 88; Perm to Offic *Conn* from 91. *Cluain-Fois, 38 Ballywillan Road, Portrush, Co Antrim BT56 8JN* Portrush (01265) 824270

THORNTON, David John Dennis. b 32. Kelham Th Coll 52. **d** 56 **p** 57. C New Eltham All SS *S'wark* 56-58; C Stockwell Green St Andr 58-62; V Tollesbury *Chelmsf* 62-74; P-in-c Salcot Virley 72-74; V Kelvedon from 74. *The Vicarage, Church Street, Kelvedon, Colchester CO5 9AL* Kelvedon (01376) 570373

THORNTON, John. b 26. St Edm Hall Ox BA53 MA57. Westcott Ho Cam 53. **d** 55 **p** 56. R Gt Witcombe *Glouc* 63-91; Chapl HM Pris Glouc 82-91; rtd 91. *24 Spencer Close, Hucclecote, Gloucester GL3 3EA* Gloucester (01452) 619775

THORNTON, Canon Kenneth. b 27. Open Univ BA77. ALCD55. **d** 55 **p** 56. V Childwall All SS *Liv* 69-82; RD Childwall 79-82; V Ormskirk 82-92; Hon Can Liv Cathl 87-92; rtd 92. *Weavers, 1 Old Row, Stainton, Kendal, Cumbria LA8 0LQ* Sedgwick (015395) 61348

THORNTON, Peter Stuart. b 36. St Pet Hall Ox BA59 MA67. Cuddesdon Coll 59. **d** 61 **p** 62. C Coatham *York* 61-64; C Scarborough St Martin 64-67; R Seaton Ross w Everingham and Bielby and Harswell 67-81; RD Weighton 75-85; P-in-c Thornton w Allerthorpe 80-81; R Seaton Ross Gp of Par 81-85; V York St Lawr w St Nic from 85. *St Lawrence's Vicarage, 11 Newland Park Close, York YO1 3HW* York (01904) 411916

THORNTON, Timothy Charles Gordon. b 35. Ch Ch Ox BA58 MA61. Linc Th Coll 60. **d** 62 **p** 63. C Kirkholt CD *Man* 62-64; Tutor Linc Th Coll 64-68; Chapl 66-68; Fiji 69-73; Chapl Brasted Place Coll Westerham 73-74; Can Missr *Guildf* 74-79; P-in-c Hascombe 74-79; V Chobham w Valley End 79-84; V Spelsbury and Chadlington *Ox* 84-87; V Chadlington and Spelsbury, Ascott under Wychwood from 87. *The Vicarage, Church Road, Chadlington, Chipping Norton, Oxon OX7 3LY* Chipping Norton (01608) 676572

THORNTON, Timothy Martin (Tim). b 57. Southn Univ BA78. St Steph Ho Ox 78. **d** 80 **p** 81. C Todmorden *Wakef* 80-82; P-in-c Walsden 82-85; Lect Univ of Wales (Cardiff) 85-87; Chapl 85-86; Sen Chapl 86-87; Bp's Chapl *Wakef* 87-91; Dir of Ords 88-91; Bp's Dom Chapl *Lon* 91-94; Lic to Offic from 94; Dep P in O 91-94; N Thames Minl Tr Course from 94. *4 Midhurst Avenue, London N10 3EN or, N Thames Ministerial Training Course, Chase Side, London N14 4PS* 0181-444 3552 or 364 9442 Fax 0171-799 2629

THOROGOOD, John Martin. b 45. Birm Univ BA68 PGCE69. Ox NSM Course 82. **d** 85 **p** 86. NSM Sunningdale *Ox* 85-90; Chapl St Geo Sch Ascot 88-90; TV Camelot Par *B & W* from 90. *The Rectory, Holton, Wincanton, Somerset BA9 8AN* Wincanton (01963) 32163

THOROLD, Henry Croyland. b 21. Ch Ch Ox 40. Cuddesdon Coll 42. **d** 44 **p** 45. Chapl Summer Fields Sch Ox 68-75; Lic to Offic *Ox* 69-81; rtd 81. *Marston Hall, Grantham, Lincs NG32 2HY* Loveden (01400) 50225

THOROLD, John Robert Hayford. b 16. K Coll Cam BA43 MA45. Cuddesdon Coll 42. **d** 42 **p** 43. V Mitcham SS Pet and Paul *S'wark* 52-86; OGS from 53; rtd 87; Perm to Offic *Blackb* from 87. *St Deiniol's Library, Hawarden, Deeside, Clwyd CH5 3DF* Hawarden (01244) 531256

THOROLD, John Stephen. b 35. Bps' Coll Cheshunt 61. **d** 63 **p** 64. C Cleethorpes *Linc* 63-70; V Cherry Willingham w Greetwell 70-77; P-in-c Firsby w St Swithin Spilsby 77-79; R 79-86; R Aswardby w Sausthorpe 77-86; R Halton Holgate 77-86; R Langton w Sutterby 77-86; V Spilsby w Hundleby 77-86;

R Lt Steeping 79-86; R Raithby 79-86; V New Sleaford from 86; RD Lafford from 87. *The Vicarage, Sleaford, Lincs NG34 7SH* Sleaford (01529) 302117

THOROLD, Trevor Neil. b 63. Hull Univ BA87. Ripon Coll Cuddesdon 87. **d** 89 **p** 90. C W Bromwich St Andr w Ch Ch *Lich* 89-93; C Oswestry H Trin 93-94; C Oswestry from 94. *Holy Trinity Vicarage, 29 Balmoral Crescent, Oswestry, Shropshire SY11 2XQ* Oswestry (01691) 652540

THORP, Adrian. b 55. Clare Coll Cam BA77 MA80 Lon Univ BD80. Trin Coll Bris 77. **d** 80 **p** 81. C Kendal St Thos *Carl* 80-83; C Handforth *Ches* 83-86; V Siddal *Wakef* 86-91; V Bishopwearmouth St Gabr *Dur* from 91. *The Vicarage, 1 St Gabriel's Avenue, Sunderland SR4 7TF* 0191-567 5200

THORP, Mrs Helen Mary. b 54. Bris Univ BA75 MA77 DipHE. Trin Coll Bris 78. **d** 87. NSM Siddal *Wakef* 87-91; NSM Bishopwearmouth St Gabr *Dur* from 91; Voc Adv from 93. *The Vicarage, 1 St Gabriel's Avenue, Sunderland SR4 7TF* 0191-567 5200

THORP, Mrs Maureen Sandra. b 47. Local NSM Course 92. **d** 95. NSM Heywood St Marg *Man* from 95. *4 Lyn Grove, Heywood, Lancs OL10 4SS* Heywood (01706) 366714

THORP, Norman Arthur. b 29. DMA63. Tyndale Hall Bris 63. **d** 65 **p** 66. C Southsea St Jude *Portsm* 65-68; C Braintree *Chelmsf* 68-73; P-in-c Tolleshunt D'Arcy w Tolleshunt Major 73-75; V 75-83; R N Buckm *Ox* from 83; RD Buckm 90-95. *The Rectory, Maids Moreton, Buckingham MK18 1QD* Buckingham (01280) 813246

THORP, Roderick Cheyne. b 44. Ch Ch Ox BA65 MA69. Ridley Hall Cam 66. **d** 69 **p** 70. C Reading Greyfriars *Ox* 69-73; C Kingston upon Hull St Martin *York* 73-76; C Heworth 76-79; C-in-c N Bletchley CD *Ox* 79-86; TV Washfield, Stoodleigh, Withleigh etc *Ex* from 86; RD Tiverton from 91. *The Vicarage, 3 Court Gardens, Stoodleigh, Tiverton, Devon EX16 9PL* Oakford (013985) 373

THORP, Stephen Linton. b 62. Lon Bible Coll CertRS88 Trin Coll Bris BA92. **d** 92 **p** 93. C Knutsford St Jo and Toft *Ches* from 92. *92 Grove Park, Knutsford, Cheshire WA16 8QB* Knutsford (01565) 632894

THORP, Thomas Malcolm (Tom). b 49. AKC. St Aug Coll Cant 71. **d** 72 **p** 73. C Derby St Bart *Derby* 72-76; C Newport Pagnell *Ox* 76-79; C Newport Pagnell w Lathbury 79; Dioc Youth and Community Officer 79-82; TV Schorne 82-92; TR from 92. *The Vicarage, White Horse Lane, Whitchurch, Aylesbury, Bucks HP22 4JZ* Aylesbury (01296) 641768

THORPE, Christopher David Charles. b 60. Cov Poly BA83. Ripon Coll Cuddesdon 85. **d** 88 **p** 89. C Norton *St Alb* 88-92; TV Blakenall Heath *Lich* from 92. *St Aidan's Vicarage, 78A Chestnut Road, Leamore, Walsall WS3 1AP* Walsall (01922) 407768

THORPE, Donald Henry. b 34. St Aid Birkenhead 57. **d** 60 **p** 61. V Doncaster Intake *Sheff* 67-74; V Millhouses H Trin 74-85; Prec Leic Cathl *Leic* 85-89; TR Melton Gt Framland 89-93; rtd 93. *18 All Hallows Drive, Tickhill, Doncaster, S Yorkshire DN11 9PP* Doncaster (01302) 743129

THORPE, Miss Eileen. **d** 95. NSM Daventry, Ashby St Ledgers, Braunston etc *Pet* from 95. *Waterside, Dark Lane, Braunston, Daventry, Northants NN11 7HJ*

THORPE, Canon Harry Fletcher Cyprian. b 12. Kelham Th Coll 30. **d** 36 **p** 37. S Africa 36-73; R Ecton *Pet* 73-81; rtd 78; Perm to Offic *Portsm* from 81. *9 Borough Hill, Petersfield, Hants GU32 3LQ* Petersfield (01730) 261413

THORPE, John Wellburn. b 31. Lich Th Coll 55. **d** 58 **p** 59. R Gt w Lt Witley *Worc* 65-70; C Tuffley *Glouc* 70-72; P-in-c Blaisdon w Flaxley 73-76; C Westbury-on-Severn w Flaxley and Blaisdon 76-77; V 77-84; P-in-c Walton on Trent w Croxall etc *Derby* 84-94; rtd 94. *3 Standing Butts Close, Walton-on-Trent, Swadlincote, Derbyshire DE12 8NJ*

THORPE, Kerry Michael. b 51. Lon Univ BD78. Oak Hill Th Coll DipTh76. **d** 78 **p** 79. C Upton (or Overchurch) *Ches* 78-81; C Ches le Street *Dur* 81-84; V Fatfield 84-93; V Margate H Trin *Cant* from 93. *The Vicarage, 5 Offley Close, Northdown Park Road, Margate, Kent CT9 3UT* Thanet (01843) 230318 or 230317

THORPE, Martin Xavier. b 66. Collingwood Coll Dur BSc87 GRSC87. Trin Coll Bris BA94. **d** 94 **p** 95. C Ravenhead *Liv* from 94. *8 Dawn Close, Thatto Heath, St Helens, Merseyside WA9 5JB* St Helens (01744) 815128

THORPE, Michael William. b 42. Lich Th Coll 67. **d** 70 **p** 71. C Walthamstow St Mich *Chelmsf* 70-71; C Plaistow St Andr 71; P-in-c Plaistow St Mary 72-74; TV Gt Grimsby St Mary and St Jas *Linc* 74-78; Chapl Grimsby Distr Hosps 78-83; Chapl Roxbourne, Northwick Park and Harrow Hosps 83-87; Chapl St Geo Linc and Linc Co Hosps 87-92; Chapl Ipswich Hosp from 92. *339 Colchester Road, Ipswich IP4 4SE, or Ipswich Hospital, Heath Road, Ipswich IP4 5PD* Ipswich (01473) 713095 or 704100

THORPE, Trevor Cecil. b 21. Em Coll Cam BA47 MA52. Ridley Hall Cam 48. **d** 50 **p** 51. C Farnborough *Guildf* 50-53; C W Ham All SS *Chelmsf* 53-57; V N Weald Bassett from 57. *The Vicarage, Vicarage Lane, North Weald, Epping, Essex CM16 6AL* North Weald (01992) 522246

THRALL, Canon Margaret Eleanor. b 28. Girton Coll Cam BA50 MA54 PhD60. **d** 82. Asst Chapl Univ of Wales (Ban) *Ban* 82-88; Lect Th Univ of Wales (Ban) from 83; Hon Can Ban Cathl *Ban* from 94. *25 Y Rhos, Bangor, Gwynedd LL57 2LT* Bangor (01248) 364957

THREADGILL, Alan Roy. b 31. St Alb Minl Tr Scheme 77. **d** 80 **p** 81. NSM Bedf St Andr *St Alb* 80-83; Chapl RAD 83-86; C Melton Gt Framland *Leic* 86-89; R Wymondham w Edmondthorpe, Buckminster etc from 89. *The Rectory, Sycamore Lane, Wymondham, Melton Mowbray, Leics LE14 2AZ* Wymondham (0157284) 238

THROSSELL, John Julian. b 30. Nottm Univ BSc53 Syracuse Univ PhD56. Oak Hill Th Coll 72. **d** 75 **p** 76. NSM Wheathampstead *St Alb* 75-82; V Codicote 82-88; rtd 91. *20 Dakings Drift, Halesworth, Suffolk IP19 8TQ* Halesworth (01986) 874602

THROWER, Clive Alan. b 41. CEng90 Sheff Univ BSc62. E Midl Min Tr Course 76. **d** 79 **p** 80. C Derby Cathl *Derby* 79-86; C Spondon 86-91; Soc Resp Officer 86-91; Faith in the City Link Officer 88-91; Dioc Rural Officer 91; P-in-c Ashford w Sheldon 91; V Ashford w Sheldon and Gt Longstone 92-93; V Ashford w Sheldon and Longstone from 93. *The Vicarage, Ashford in the Water, Bakewell, Derbyshire DE45 1QN* Bakewell (01629) 812298 Fax 815402

THROWER, Philip Edward. b 41. Kelham Th Coll 61. **d** 66 **p** 67. C Hayes St Mary *Lon* 66-69; C Yeovil *B & W* 69-71; C Shirley St Jo *Cant* 71-77; P-in-c S Norwood St Mark 77-81; V 81-84; V S Norwood St Mark *S'wark* from 85. *St Mark's Vicarage, 101 Albert Road, London SE25 4JE* 0181-656 9462

THUBRON, Thomas William. b 33. Edin Th Coll 62. **d** 65 **p** 66. C Gateshead St Mary *Dur* 65-66; C Shildon 66-67; E Pakistan 68-71; Bangladesh 71-80; V Wheatley Hill *Dur* 80-87; V Dur St Giles from 87. *St Giles's Vicarage, Durham DH1 1QH* 0191-386 4241

THURBURN-HUELIN, David Richard. b 47. St Chad's Coll Dur BA69. Westcott Ho Cam 69. **d** 71 **p** 72. C Poplar *Lon* 71-76; Chapl Liddon Ho Lon 76-80; R Harrold and Carlton w Chellington *St Alb* 81-88; V Goldington 88-95; Dir LNSM *Truro* from 95. *The Vicarage, Mount Hawke, Truro, Cornwall TR4 8DE* Porthtowan (01209) 890926

THURMER, Canon John Alfred. b 25. Or Coll Ox BA50 MA55 Ex Univ Hon DD91. Linc Th Coll 50. **d** 52 **p** 53. Chapl Ex Univ Ex 54-73; Lect 64-85; Can Res and Chan Ex Cathl 73-91; rtd 91. *38 Velwell Road, Exeter EX4 4LD* Exeter (01392) 72277

THURNELL, David Christopher. b 37. Open Univ BA83. Sarum & Wells Th Coll 88. **d** 90 **p** 94. NSM Chippenham St Pet *Bris* from 90. *81 Westcroft, Chippenham, Wilts SN14 0LZ* Chippenham (01249) 654828

THURSFIELD, John Anthony. b 21. Magd Coll Ox BA47 MA51. Cuddesdon Coll 47. **d** 49 **p** 50. V Basing *Win* 60-72; Chapl Bonn w Cologne *Eur* 72-75; R W Clandon *Guildf* 75-79; R W Clandon 75-79; V Reydon *St E* 79-83; Perm to Offic *Heref* 84-93; rtd 86. *Little Homend, The Homend, Ledbury, Herefordshire HR8 1AR* Ledbury (01531) 632935

THURSFIELD, John Richard. b 22. ALAM64. Roch Th Coll 60. **d** 62 **p** 63. C Battersea St Luke *S'wark* 69-71; C Wandsworth St Mich 71-72; Chapl St Ebba's Hosp Epsom 72-86; Qu Mary's Carshalton & Henderson Sutton 73-86; rtd 87. *St David's Care Home, 39 Winchester Road, Worthing, W Sussex BN11 4DH* Worthing (01903) 239751

THURSTON, Colin Benedict. b 47. Chich Th Coll 88. **d** 90 **p** 91. C Up Hatherley *Glouc* from 90. *St James's House, Reddings Road, The Reddings, Cheltenham, Glos GL51 6PA* Gloucester (01452) 856980

THURSTON, Ian Charles. b 54. SS Hild & Bede Coll Dur CertEd78. S Dios Minl Tr Scheme 87. **d** 89 **p** 90. C St Chris Cathl Bahrain 89-91; C All Hallows by the Tower etc *Lon* from 91. *14 Codling Close, London E1 9UX* 0171-709 0609 or 488 4772 Fax 488 3333

THURSTON-SMITH, Trevor. b 59. Chich Th Coll 83. **d** 86 **p** 87. C Rawmarsh w Parkgate *Sheff* 86-87; C Horninglow *Lich* 87-91. *Address temp unknown*

TIBBO, George Kenneth. b 29. Reading Univ BA50 MA54. Coll of Resurr Mirfield 55. **d** 57 **p** 58. C W Hartlepool St Aid *Dur* 57-61; V Darlington St Mark 61-74; V Darlington St Mark w St Paul 74-75; R Crook 75-80; V Stanley 76-80; V Oldham St Chad Limeside *Man* 80-87; V Hipswell *Ripon* from 87; OCF from 90. *The Vicarage, Piper Hill, Catterick Garrison, N Yorkshire DL9 4PN* Richmond (01748) 833320

TIBBOTT, Joseph Edwards. b 14. K Coll Lon. **d** 55 **p** 56. V Stockwell St Mich *S'wark* 59-71; V Llangiwg *S & B* 76-77; R Llangammarch w Garth, Llanlleonfel etc 77-80; rtd 80. *Pellingbridge Farm House, Scaynes Hill, Haywards Heath, W Sussex RH17 7NG* Scaynes Hill (01444) 831381

TIBBS, Canon Howard Abraham Llewellyn Thomas. b 13. Univ of Wales BA39. Coll of Resurr Mirfield 39. **d** 41 **p** 42. V Northn H Sepulchre w St Andr *Pet* 66-76; RD Northn 70-79; Can Pet Cathl 75-85; V Northn H Sepulchre w St Andr and St Lawr 76-85; rtd 85; Perm to Offic *Pet* from 85. *30 Fairway, Northampton NN2 7JZ* Northampton (01604) 716863

TIBBS, Canon John Andrew. b 29. AKC53. **d** 54 **p** 55. V Sompting *Chich* 69-73; R Ifield 73-78; TR 78-83; V Elstow *St Alb* 83-89; rtd 90; Chapl Bedf Gen Hosp 90-95; Hon Can St Alb from 91. *19 Adelaide Square, Bedford MK40 2RN* Bedford (01234) 359579

TICE, Richard Ian (Rico). b 66. Bris Univ BA88. Wycliffe Hall Ox BTh94. **d** 94 **p** 95. C Langham Place All So *Lon* from 94. *20 Holcroft Court, Clipstone Street, London W1P 7DL* 0171-580 1033

TICEHURST, David. b 29. K Coll Lon 50. **d** 55 **p** 56. Hd Master Hawley Place Camberley 67-76; P-in-c Bury and Houghton *Chich* 76-81; V 81-89; P-in-c Sutton w Bignor 78; P-in-c Barlavington 78; rtd 89. *34 Outerwyke Road, Felpham, Bognor Regis, W Sussex PO22 8HX* Bognor Regis (01243) 863985

TICKLE, Robert Peter. b 51. St Chad's Coll Dur BA74. St Steph Ho Ox 74. **d** 76 **p** 77. *5 Bramley Court, Orchard Lane, Harrold, Bedford MK43 7BG* Bedford (01234) 721417

TICKNER, Colin de Fraine. b 37. Chich Th Coll. **d** 66 **p** 67. C Huddersfield SS Pet and Paul *Wakef* 66-68; C Dorking w Ranmore *Guildf* 68-74; V Shottermill 74-91; RD Godalming 89-91; R Ockley, Okewood and Forest Green from 91. *The Rectory, Stane Street, Ockley, Dorking, Surrey RH5 5SY* Dorking (01306) 711550

TICKNER, David Arthur. b 44. MBE89. AKC67. **d** 69 **p** 70. C Thornhill Lees *Wakef* 69-71; C Billingham St Aid *Dur* 71-74; TV 74-78; CF from 78. *c/o MOD (Army), Bagshot Park, Bagshot, Surrey GU19 5PL* Bagshot (01276) 471717 Fax 412834

TICKNER, Geoffrey John. b 55. BD. St Mich Coll Llan. **d** 82 **p** 83. C Bourne *Guildf* 82-85; C Grayswood 85-90; V New Haw from 90. *The Vicarage, 149 Woodham Lane, New Haw, Addlestone, Surrey KT15 3NJ* Byfleet (01932) 343187

TICQUET, Cyril Edward. b 11. Dip.Th. Ripon Hall Ox 63. **d** 64 **p** 65. V Castle Bromwich St Clem *Birm* 68-76; rtd 76; Hon C Stokenham w Sherford *Ex* 77-92; Perm to Offic from 92. *Bay Trees, Slapton, Kingsbridge, Devon TQ7 2PN* Kingsbridge (01548) 580564

TIDMARSH, Canon Peter Edwin. b 29. Keble Coll Ox BA52 MA56 DipEd. St Steph Ho Ox 52. **d** 54 **p** 55. C Stepney St Dunstan and All SS *Lon* 54-58; C Streatham St Pet *S'wark* 58-62; Chapl Shiplake Coll Henley 62-64; Hd Master All SS Choir Sch 64-68; C St Marylebone All SS *Lon* 64-68; V Cubert *Truro* from 68; Dir of Educn 69-85; Hon Can Truro Cathl from 73. *The Vicarage, St Cubert, Newquay, Cornwall TR8 5HA* Crantock (01637) 830301

TIDMARSH, Philip Reginald Wilton. b 14. G&C Coll Cam BA36 MA40. Ridley Hall Cam 46. **d** 48 **p** 49. V Odiham w S Warnborough *Win* 66-76; P-in-c Abbotts Ann 76-79; Perm to Offic *Heref* from 79; rtd 86. *The Gravel Pit Bungalow, Broadheath, Presteigne, Powys LD8 2HG* Presteigne (01544) 267275

TIDY, Very Rev John Hylton. b 48. AKC72 St Aug Coll Cant 72. **d** 73 **p** 74. C Newton Aycliffe *Dur* 73-78; V Auckland St Pet 78-84; V Burley in Wharfedale *Bradf* 84-92; Dean Jerusalem from 93. *The Dean's Flat, Cathedral Close, PO Box 19018, Jerusalem, Israel* Jerusalem (2) 283261 Fax 276401

TIERNAN, Paul Wilson. b 54. Man Univ BA76. Coll of Resurr Mirfield 77. **d** 79 **p** 80. C Lewisham St Mary *S'wark* 79-83; V Sydenham St Phil from 83. *St Philip's Vicarage, 122 Wells Park Road, London SE26 6AS* 0181-699 4930

TIGWELL, Brian Arthur. b 36. S'wark Ord Course 74. **d** 77 **p** 78. C Purley St Mark Woodcote *S'wark* 77-80; TV Upper Kennett *Sarum* 80-85; V Devizes St Pet from 85; Wilts Adnry Ecum Officer from 88; RD Devizes from 92. *The Vicarage, Bath Road, Devizes, Wilts SN10 2AP* Devizes (01380) 722621

TILL, Barry Dorn. b 23. Jes Coll Cam BA49 MA49. Westcott Ho Cam 48. **d** 50 **p** 51. Prin Morley Coll Lon 66-87; Dir Baring Foundn 87-92; rtd 92. *44 Canonbury Square, London N1 2AW* 0171-359 0708

TILL, Ven Michael Stanley. b 35. Linc Coll Ox BA60 MA67. Westcott Ho Cam. **d** 64 **p** 65. C St Jo Wood *Lon* 64-67; Chapl K Coll Cam 67-70; Dean 70-80; AD Hammersmith *Lon* 81-86; V Fulham All SS 81-86; Adn Cant and Can Res Cant Cathl *Cant* from 86. *29 The Precincts, Canterbury, Kent CT1 2EP* Canterbury (01227) 463036 Fax 785209

TILLER, Charles Edgar Gregory. b 61. St Mich Coll Llan BD. d 89 p 90. C Ex St Thos and Em *Ex* 89-93; C Crediton and Shobrooke 93-95. *Church House, Park Road, Crediton, Devon EX17 3ET* Crediton (01363) 773749

TILLER, Edgar Henry. b 22. ACP71 Open Univ BA78. Wells Th Coll 57. d 59 p 60. V Stoke Lane *B & W* 62-67; V Leigh upon Mendip 62-67; Perm to Offic *Ex* from 67; rtd 91. *3 Byron Close, Pilton, Barnstaple, Devon EX31 1QH* Barnstaple (01271) 72483

TILLER, Canon John. b 38. Ch Ch Ox BA60 MA64 Bris Univ MLitt72. Tyndale Hall Bris 60. d 62 p 63. C Bedf St Cuth *St Alb* 62-65; C Widcombe *B & W* 65-67; Tutor Tyndale Hall Bris 67-71; Chapl 67-71; Lect Trin Coll Bris 71-73; P-in-c Bedf Ch Ch *St Alb* 73-78; Chief Sec ACCM 78-84; Hon Can St Alb 79-84; Can Res and Chan Heref Cathl *Heref* from 84; Dioc Dir of Tr from 91. *The Canon's House, 3 St John Street, Hereford HR1 2NB* Hereford (01432) 265659

TILLETT, Leslie Selwyn. b 54. Peterho Cam BA75 MA79 Leeds Univ BA80. Coll of Resurr Mirfield 78. d 81 p 82. C W Dulwich All SS and Em *S'wark* 81-85; R Purleigh, Cold Norton and Stow Maries *Chelmsf* 85-93; R Beddington *S'wark* from 93. *The Rectory, 18 Bloxworth Close, Wallington, Surrey SM6 7NL* 0181-647 1973

TILLEY, David Robert. b 38. Kelham Th Coll 58. d 63 p 64. C Bournemouth St Fran *Win* 63-67; C Moulsecoomb *Chich* 67-70; C Ifield 70-75; C Warw St Mary *Cov* 76; TV 76; TV Warw 76-85; P-in-c Alderminster 85-89; P-in-c Halford 85-89; Dioc Min Tr Adv from 85; P-in-c Alderminster and Halford from 90; Minl Educn Adv from 90. *The Vicarage, Alderminster, Stratford-upon-Avon, Warks CV37 8PE* Alderminster (01789) 450208

TILLEY, Derise Ralph. b 21. Sarum Th Coll 55. d 57 p 58. V Millbrook *Truro* 64-80; P-in-c Antony w St Jo 76-80; R St John w Millbrook 80-90; rtd 90. *25 York Road, Torpoint, Cornwall PL11 2LG* Plymouth (01752) 815450

TILLEY, James Stephen (Steve). b 55. St Jo Coll Nottm BTh84. d 84 p 85. C Nottm St Jude *S'well* 84-88; C Ches le Street *Dur* 88-92; Tr and Ed CYFA (CPAS) from 92; Perm to Offic *Cov* from 93. *c/o CPAS, Athena Drive, Tachbrook Drive, Warwick CV34 6NG* Warwick (01926) 334242 Fax 337613

TILLEY, Peter Robert. b 41. Bris Univ BA62. Sarum & Wells Th Coll 77. d 79 p 80. C Wandsworth St Paul *S'wark* 79-82; V Mitcham St Mark 82-91; RD Merton 89-91; R Walton St Mary *Liv* 91-92; TR Walton-on-the-Hill from 92. *The Rectory, Walton Village, Liverpool L4 6TJ* 0151-525 3130

TILLIER, Dr Jane Yvonne. b 59. New Hall Cam BA81 PhD85. Ripon Coll Cuddesdon BA90. d 91 p 94. Par Dn Sheff St Mark Broomhall *Sheff* 91-92; Par Dn Sheff St Mark Broomhill 92-94; C 94-95; Chapl Glouc Cathl *Glouc* from 95. *10 College Green, Gloucester GL1 2LX* Gloucester (01452) 300655

TILLMAN, Miss Mary Elizabeth. b 43. S Dios Minl Tr Scheme 86. d 89 p 95. NSM Bridgemary *Portsm* 89-93; NSM Portsea All SS from 93; Adv in Min to People w Disabilities from 93. *391 Fareham Road, Gosport, Hants PO13 0AD* Fareham (01329) 232589

TILLOTSON, Simon Christopher. b 67. Lon Univ BA90 Trin Coll Cam BA93. Ridley Hall Cam 91. d 94. C Paddock Wood *Roch* from 94. *3 Ashcroft Road, Paddock Wood, Tonbridge, Kent TN12 6LG* Paddock Wood (01892) 833194

TILLYARD, James Donald. b 16. St D Coll Lamp BA38 Ripon Hall Ox 38. d 39 p 40. CF 42-71; V Uffington w Woolstone and Baulking *Ox* 71-81; rtd 81; Perm to Offic *Ox* 82-87. *Wingleting, Chapel Lane, Uffington, Faringdon, Oxon SN7 7RY* Faringdon (01367) 820513

TILLYER, Desmond Benjamin. b 40. Ch Coll Cam BA63 MA67. Coll of Resurr Mirfield 64. d 66 p 67. C Hanworth All SS *Lon* 66-70; Chapl Liddon Ho Lon 70-74; V Pimlico St Pet w Westmr Ch Ch *Lon* from 74; AD Westmr St Marg 85-92. *1 St Peter's House, 119 Eaton Square, London SW1W 9AL* 0171-235 4242

TILSON, Alan Ernest. b 46. TCD. d 70 p 71. C Londonderry Ch Ch *D & R* 70-73; I Inver, Mountcharles and Killaghtee 73-79; I Leckpatrick w Dunnalong 79-89; Bermuda from 89. *Holy Trinity Rectory, PO Box CR 186, Hamilton Parish CR BX, Bermuda* Bermuda (1-809) 293-1710 Fax 293-4363

TILSTON, Derek Reginald. b 27. NW Ord Course. d 73 p 74. NSM Bury St Mark *Man* 73-77; NSM Holcombe 77-82; NSM Bury St Jo 82-83; NSM Bury St Jo w St Mark 83-84; C Bramley *Ripon* 85-87; TV 87-90; R Tendring and Lt Bentley w Beaumont cum Moze *Chelmsf* 90-92; rtd 93. *Cobbler's Croft, 19 The Street, Wissett, Halesworth, Suffolk IP19 0JE* Halesworth (01986) 874693

TILTMAN, Alan Michael. b 48. Selw Coll Cam BA70 MA74. Cuddesdon Coll 71. d 73 p 74. C Chesterton Gd Shep *Ely* 73-77; C Preston St Jo *Blackb* 77-79; Chapl Lancs (Preston) Poly 77-79; TV Man Whitworth *Man* 79-86; Chapl Man Univ

(UMIST) 79-86; V Urmston from 86. *St Clement's Vicarage, Manor Avenue, Urmston, Manchester M31 1HH* 0161-748 3972 Fax as telephone

TIMBERLAKE, Neil Christopher. b 26. Kelham Th Coll 47. d 51 p 52. Australia 68-70; C Leyland St Ambrose *Blackb* 70-72; C Bilborough w Strelley *S'well* 72-74; V Langold 74-86; rtd 86. *7 Thirlmere Avenue, Colne, Lancs BB8 7DD* Colne (01282) 863879

TIMBRELL, Keith Stewart. b 48. Edin Th Coll 72. d 74 p 75. C Chorley St Pet *Blackb* 74-77; C Altham w Clayton le Moors 77-79; Chapl Whittingham Hosp Preston 79-95; Chapl St Ann's Hosp Poole from 95. *St Ann's Hospital, 69 Haven Road, Poole, Dorset BH13 7LN* Poole (01202) 708881

TIMBRELL, Maxwell Keith. b 28. St Jo Coll Morpeth ThL51. d 51 p 52. Australia 51-58 and 64-82; C Hanworth All SS *Lon* 59-63; P-in-c Kildale *York* 83-85; V Ingleby Greenhow w Bilsdale Priory 83-85; V Ingleby Greenhow w Bilsdale Priory, Kildale etc from 85. *The Vicarage, Ingleby Greenhow, Middlesbrough, Cleveland TS9 6LL* Great Ayton (01642) 723947

TIMINS, John Francis Holmer. b 03. Clare Coll Cam MA29. Ely Th Coll 33. d 34 p 35. R Horringer cum Ickworth *St E* 59-65; Lic to Offic 67-75; rtd 68. *56 Forest Road, Worthing, W Sussex BN14 9LY* Worthing (01903) 234059

TIMMS, Ven George Boorne. b 10. St Edm Hall Ox BA33 MA45. Coll of Resurr Mirfield 33. d 35 p 36. Dir of Ords *Lon* 64-81; V St Andr Holborn 65-81; Adn Hackney 71-81; Perm to Offic *Cant* from 78; rtd 81. *Cleve Lodge, Minster-in-Thanet, Ramsgate, Kent CT12 4BA* Thanet (01843) 821777

TIMMS, Robert Newell. b 13. Dur Univ LTh36. Dorchester Miss Coll 33. d 36 p 37. R Watton at Stone *St Alb* 64-68; rtd 69; Perm to Offic *Glouc* 76-84; Perm to Offic *Worc* from 85. *76 Red Hall Road, Gornall Wood, Dudley, W Midlands DY3 2NL* Dudley (01384) 241383

TIMPERLEY, Patrick. b 65. St D Coll Lamp BA86. St Jo Coll Dur 86. d 88 p 89. C Pemb St Mary and St Mich *St D* 88-91; C Higher Bebington *Ches* 91-93. *23 All Saints Road, Thurcaston, Leicester LE7 7JD* Leicester (0116) 236 3252

TINDALL, Canon Frederick Cryer. b 1900. Lon Univ AKC22 BD23. Ely Th Coll 23. d 24 p 25. Prin Sarum Th Coll 50-65; Can and Preb Sarum Cathl *Sarum* 50-81; rtd 70. *16 The Close, Salisbury SP1 2EB* Salisbury (01722) 322373

TINGAY, Kevin Gilbert Xavier. b 43. Sussex Univ BA79. Chich Th Coll 79. d 80 p 81. C W Tarring *Chich* 80-83; TV Worth 83-90; R Bradf w Oake, Hillfarrance and Heathfield *B & W* from 90. *The Rectory, Bradford on Tone, Taunton, Somerset TA4 1HG* Bradford-on-Tone (01823) 461423

TINGLE, Michael Barton. b 31. Bps' Coll Cheshunt 65. d 67 p 68. C Totteridge *St Alb* 67-70; C Hitchin St Mary 70-73; V Gt Gaddesden 73-78; V Belmont *Lon* 78-86; V Burford w Fulbrook and Taynton *Ox* from 86. *The Vicarage, Burford, Oxon OX18 4SE* Burford (01993) 822275

TINKER, Preb Eric Franklin. b 20. OBE89. Ex Coll Ox BA42 MA46 Lon Univ Hon DD89. Linc Th Coll 42. d 44 p 45. Preb St Paul's Cathl *Lon* 69-90; Sen Chapl Lon Univs and Polys 69-90; Dir of Educn (Dios Lon and S'wark) 72-80; Gen Sec Lon Dioc Bd of Educn 80-82; rtd 90; Hon C St Giles Cripplegate w St Bart Moor Lane etc *Lon* from 95. *35 Theberton Street, London N1 0QY* 0171-359 4750

TINKER, Melvin. b 55. Hull Univ BSc Ox Univ MA. Wycliffe Hall Ox 80. d 83 p 84. C Wetherby *Ripon* 83-85; Chapl Keele Univ *Lich* 85-90; V Cheadle All Hallows *Ches* 90-94; V Hull Newland St Jo *York* from 94. *St John's Vicarage, Clough Road, Hull HU6 7PA* Hull (01482) 43658

TINKER, Michael Jonathan Russell. b 50. York Univ BA72. Qu Coll Birm DipTh74. d 75 p 76. C Castle Vale *Birm* 75-78; Bp's Dom Chapl 78-80; R Stretford All SS *Man* 80-88; V Stalybridge from 88; AD Ashton-under-Lyne from 94. *The Vicarage, 2 Tintagel Court, Astley Road, Stalybridge, Cheshire SK15 1RA* 0161-338 2368

TINKLER, Ian Henry. b 32. Selw Coll Cam BA57 MA61. Westcott Ho Cam. d 60 p 61. C Gosforth All SS *Newc* 60-65; Asst Chapl Brussels *Eur* 65-68; R S Ferriby *Linc* 68-85; V Horkstow 68-85; R Saxby All Saints 72-85; V Humberston from 85. *The Vicarage, 34 Tetney Road, Humberstone, Grimsby, S Humberside DN36 4JF* Grimsby (01472) 813158

TINSLEY, Bernard Murray. b 26. Nottm Univ BA51 Birm Univ DPS. Westcott Ho Cam 51. d 53 p 54. R Alverdiscott w Huntshaw *Ex* 61-78; R Newton Tracey 61-78; R Beaford and Roborough 67-78; V St Giles in the Wood 67-78; V Yarnscombe 67-78; R Newton Tracey, Alverdiscott, Huntshaw etc 78-88; RD Torrington 81-86; rtd 88; Perm to Offic *Ex* from 88. *The Grange, Orange Road, Bideford, Devon EX39 4AS* Bideford (01237) 471414

TINSLEY, Derek. b 31. ALCM65. NW Ord Course 73. d 76 p 77. C Gt Crosby St Faith *Liv* 76-80; V Wigan St Anne 80-85; V Colton w Satterthwaite and Rusland *Carl* 85-93; rtd 93. *Lyndale, 43 Renacres Lane, Ormskirk, Lancs L39 8SG*

TINSLEY

TINSLEY, Preb Derek Michael. b 35. Lon Coll of Div ALCD66 LTh. **d** 66 **p** 67. C Rainhill *Liv* 66-68; C Chalfont St Peter *Ox* 68-74; R N Buckm 74-82; RD Buckm 78-82; P-in-c Alstonfield *Lich* 82-84; P-in-c Butterton 82-84; P-in-c Warslow and Elkstones 82-84; P-in-c Wetton 82-84; RD Alstonfield 85-95; V Alstonfield, Butterton, Warslow w Elkstone etc 85-95; V Cheddleton from 95. *The Vicarage, Hollow Lane, Cheddleton, Leek, Staffs ST13 7HP* Churnet Side (01538) 360226

TINSLEY, Canon John. b 17. AKC49. **d** 49 **p** 50. V Wandsworth St Paul *S'wark* 56-70; RD Wandsworth 69-70; V Redhill St Jo 70-80; RD Reigate 76-80; Hon Can S'wark Cathl 80-81; P-in-c Othery *B & W* 80; P-in-c Middlezoy 80; P-in-c Moorlinch w Stawell and Sutton Mallet 80; V Middlezoy and Othery and Moorlinch 81-85; rtd 85. *Cedar House, 1 Quantock Rise, Kingston St Mary, Taunton, Somerset TA2 8HJ* Taunton (01823) 451317

TIPLADY, Dr Peter. b 42. MRCGP72 FFPHM86 Dur Univ MB, BS65. Carl Dioc Tr Course 86. **d** 89 **p** 90. NSM Wetheral w Warw *Carl* from 89. *The Arches, The Green, Wetheral, Carlisle CA4 8ET* Wetheral (01228) 561611

TIPP, James Edward. b 45. Oak Hill Th Coll 73. **d** 75 **p** 76. C St Mary Cray and St Paul's Cray *Roch* 75-78; C Southborough St Pet w Ch Ch and St Matt 78-82; R Snodland All SS w Ch Ch from 82. *The Vicarage, 11 St Katherine's Lane, Snodland, Kent ME6 5EH* Snodland (01634) 240232

TIPPER, Michael William. b 38. Hull Univ BSc59 MSc61. Em Coll Saskatoon 72. **d** 73 **p** 74. Canada 73-77, 79-80, 83-88 and from 91; R Amcotts *Linc* 77-79; V Aycliffe *Dur* 80-83; V Kneesall w Laxton and Wellow *S'well* 88-91. *Box 302, Cardston, Alberta, Canada, T0K 0K0* Cardston (403) 653-1225

TIPPING, John Henry. b 27. St Mich Coll Llan 63. **d** 65 **p** 66. C Clydach *S & B* 65-68; C Oystermouth 68-70; R Llangynllo and Bleddfa 70-79; V Cwmddauddwr w St Harmon's and Llanwrthwl 79-80; R Ashton Gifford *Sarum* from 80. *The Rectory, Green Lane, Codford, Warminster, Wilts BA12 0NY* Warminster (01985) 850320

TIPPING, John Woodman. b 42. AKC65. **d** 66 **p** 67. C Croydon St Sav *Cant* 66-70; C Plaistow St Mary *Roch* 70-72; V Brockley Hill St Sav *S'wark* 72-83; P-in-c Sittingbourne St Mary *Cant* 83-86; V 86-94; P-in-c Mersham w Hinxhill from 94; P-in-c Sevington from 94; P-in-c Brabourne w Smeeth from 95. *The Rectory, Bower Road, Mersham, Ashford, Kent TN25 6NN* Ashford (01233) 502138

TITCOMBE, Peter Charles. *See* JONES, Peter Charles

TITFORD, Richard Kimber. b 45. UEA BA67. Ripon Coll Cuddesdon 78. **d** 80 **p** 80. C Middleton *Man* 80-83; P-in-c Edwardstone w Groton and Lt Waldingfield *St E* 83-90; R from 90. *The Rectory, Willow Corner, Edwardstone, Sudbury, Suffolk CO10 5PG* Boxford (01787) 210026

TITLEY, David Joseph. b 47. Ex Univ BSc Surrey Univ PhD. Wycliffe Hall Ox. **d** 82 **p** 83. C Stowmarket *St E* 82-85; C Bloxwich *Lich* 85-90; TV 90-95; V Prees from 95; V Fauls from 95. *The Vicarage, Church Street, Prees, Whitchurch, Shropshire SY13 2EE* Whitchurch (01948) 840243

TITLEY, Robert John. b 56. Ch Coll Cam BA78 MA82. Westcott Ho Cam DipTh83. **d** 85 **p** 86. C Lower Sydenham St Mich *S'wark* 85-88; C Sydenham All SS 85-88; Chapl Whitelands Coll of HE 88-94; V W Dulwich All SS from 94. *The Vicarage, 165 Rosendale Road, London SE21 8LN* 0181-670 0826

TITTERINGTON, Canon John Milne. b 23. St Cath Soc Ox BA49 MA53. Linc Th Coll 49. **d** 51 **p** 52. V Langley All SS and Martyrs *Man* 68-72; RD Rossendale 72-80; R Newchurch St Nic 72-73; R Newchurch 73-80; Hon Can Cathl 77-80; Papua New Guinea 80-92; rtd 90. *52 Bradford Court, Whitstable Road, Moston, Manchester M40 0DT* 0161-682 8135

TITTLEY, Donald Frank. b 22. ACP70 LCP74. NE Ord Course 78. **d** 80 **p** 81. NSM Tynemouth Cullercoats St Paul *Newc* from 80. *22 Selwyn Avenue, Whitley Bay, Tyne & Wear NE25 9DH* 0191-252 6655

TIVEY, Nicholas. b 65. Liv Poly BSc89. Ridley Hall Cam CTM94. **d** 94 **p** 95. C Bromborough *Ches* from 94. *193 Allport Road, Wirral, Merseyside L62 6BA* 0151-334 4181

TIZZARD, Canon David John. b 40. LRAM. Sarum Th Coll 65. **d** 68 **p** 69. C Foley Park *Worc* 68-70; Hon C Gravesend St Geo *Roch* 70-73; Miss to Seamen 70-72; PV Truro Cathl *Truro* 73-75; TV Bemerton *Sarum* 75-79; Soc Resp Adv 79-85; Chapl to the Deaf 79-85; Can and Preb Sarum Cathl 84-85; R S Hill w Callington *Truro* 85-87; P-in-c Linkinhorne 86-87; Relig Affairs Producer BBC Radio Solent 87-94; V Portswood St Denys *Win* 87-94; P-in-c Distington *Carl* from 94; Soc Resp Officer from 94; Hon Can Carl Cathl from 94. *The Rectory, Church Road, Distington, Workington, Cumbria CA14 5TE* Harrington (01946) 830384 Fax 832020

TIZZARD, Dudley Frank. b 19. Roch Th Coll 63. **d** 65 **p** 66. C Cant St Martin w St Paul *Cant* 68-71; Chapl HM Pris Cant 68-71; V Petham w Waltham *Cant* 71-75; C Sevenoaks St Jo *Roch* 75-78; Perm to Offic *Cant* 78-84; rtd 84; Lic to Offic *Cant* from 84. *62 Knaves Acre, Headcorn, Ashford, Kent TN27 9TJ* Headcorn (01622) 891498

TIZZARD, Peter Francis. b 53. Oak Hill Th Coll DipHE88. **d** 90 **p** 91. C Letchworth St Paul w Willian *St Alb* 90-95; I Drumkeeran w Templecarne and Muckross *Clogh* from 95. *Drumkeeran Rectory, Tubrid, Kesh, Enniskillen, Co Fermanagh BT93 1BE* Kesh (013656) 31210

TOAN, Robert Charles. b 50. Oak Hill Th Coll. **d** 84 **p** 85. C Upton (or Overchurch) *Ches* 84-87; V Rock Ferry from 87. *The Vicarage, St Peter's Road, Birkenhead, Merseyside L42 1PY* 0151-645 1622

TOBIAS, Edwin John Rupert. b 16. TCD BA40 MA59. **d** 40 **p** 41. RD Loughscudy and Mullingar *M & K* 68-82; I Killucan 77-82; rtd 82. *Sue Ryder House, Chalet 7, Ballyroan, Co Laois, Irish Republic* Portlaoise (502) 31906

TOBIAS, William Trevor. b 10. St Steph Ho Ox 62. **d** 63 **p** 64. P-in-c Hanwell St Mark *Lon* 69-80; rtd 80; Perm to Offic *Lon* from 81. *58 Claremont Road, London W13 0DG* 0181-997 6023

TOBIN, Richard Francis. b 44. CertEd. Chich Th Coll 76. **d** 78 **p** 79. C W Leigh CD *Portsm* 78-79; C Halstead St Andr *Chelmsf* 79; C Halstead St Andr w H Trin 79; C Halstead St Andr w H Trin and Greenstead Green 79-87; Youth Chapl 82-87; V S Shields St Simon *Dur* from 87. *St Simon's Vicarage, Wenlock Road, South Shields, Tyne & Wear NE34 9AL* 0191-455 3164

TODD, Alastair. b 20. CMG71. CCC Ox BA45 Lon Univ DipTh65. Sarum & Wells Th Coll 71. **d** 73 **p** 74. C Willingdon *Chich* 73-77; P-in-c Brighton St Aug 77-78; V Brighton St Aug and St Sav 78-86; rtd 86; Perm to Offic *Chich* from 86. *59 Park Avenue, Eastbourne, E Sussex BN21 2XH* Eastbourne (01323) 505843

TODD, Andrew John. b 61. Keble Coll Ox Univ Coll Dur BA84. Coll of Resurr Mirfield 85. **d** 87 **p** 88. C Thorpe *Nor* 87-91; Chapl K Alfred Coll *Win* 91-94; Sen Asst Priest E Dereham and Scarning *Nor* from 94; Dir Studies EAMTC from 94. *Acacia House, Commercial Road, Dereham, Norwich NR19 1AE* Dereham (01362) 697043

TODD, Clive. b 57. Linc Th Coll 89. **d** 91 **p** 92. C Consett *Dur* 91-93; C Bensham 93-95; P-in-c S Hetton w Haswell from 95. *The Vicarage, South Hetton, Durham DH6 2SW* 0191-526 1157

TODD, Edward Peter. b 44. Cranmer Hall Dur 86. **d** 88 **p** 89. C Hindley All SS *Liv* 88-91; P-in-c Wigan St Steph from 91. *St Stephen's Vicarage, 141 Whelley, Wigan, Lancs WN2 1BL* Wigan (01942) 42579

TODD, George Robert. b 21. Sarum & Wells Th Coll 74. **d** 76 **p** 77. Hon C Wellington and Distr *B & W* 76-86; Perm to Offic from 86. *15 John Grinter Way, Wellington, Somerset TA21 9AR* Wellington (01823) 662828

TODD, John Lindsay. b 22. Univ of Wales (Ban) BA49. St Mich Coll Llan 49. **d** 51 **p** 52. R Guilsfield *St As* 58-92; rtd 92. *25 Acrefield Avenue, Guilsfield, Welshpool, Powys SY21 9PN* Welshpool (01938) 555742

TODD, Joy Gertrude. b 28. Local NSM Course. **d** 90 **p** 94. NSM Guildf H Trin w St Mary *Guildf* from 90. *165 Stoke Road, Guildford, Surrey GU1 1EY* Guildford (01483) 67500

TODD, Leslie Alwill. b 15. St Aid Birkenhead 46. **d** 48 **p** 49. Bahamas 70-73; C Clerkenwell H Redeemer w St Phil *Lon* 73-74; Chapl Nat Hosp for Nervous Diseases Lon 74-80; rtd 80; P-in-c Ipswich St Mary at the Elms *St E* 80-85; Perm to Offic *Man* 86-88; Perm to Offic *Wakef* 88-92; Perm to Offic *Nor* from 95. *3 Swan Entry, Walsingham, Norfolk NR22 6DH* Walsingham (01328) 820732

TODD, Canon Dr Norman Henry. b 19. PhC Lon Univ BPharm42 Fitzw Ho Cam BA50 MA55 Nottm Univ PhD78. Westcott Ho Cam 50. **d** 52 **p** 53. R Elston w Elston Chapelry *S'well* 71-76; R E Stoke w Syerston 72-76; V Sibthorpe 72-76; Bp's Adv on Tr 76-83; C Averham w Kelham 76-80; V Rolleston w Morton 80-83; P-in-c Upton 80-83; V Rolleston w Fiskerton, Morton and Upton 83-88; Hon Can S'well Minster 82-88; rtd 88; Abps' Adv for Bps' Min *Cant* 88-94. *70 Park Road, Nottingham NG7 1JG* Nottingham (0115) 941 8345

TODD, William Colquhoun Duncan. b 26. AKC53 St Boniface Warminster 53. **d** 54 **p** 55. C Westmr St Steph w St Jo *Lon* 54-59; C-in-c Leigh Park CD *Portsm* 59-69; V Leigh Park 69-72; Win Coll Missr 60-72; Angl Adv Southern TV 62-72; Thames TV 72-92; Carlton TV from 93; R Hatf *St Alb* from 72. *The Rectory, 1 Fore Street, Hatfield, Herts AL9 5AN* Hatfield (01707) 262072

TODD, Canon William Moorhouse. b 26. Lich Th Coll 54. **d** 57 **p** 58. C W Derby St Mary *Liv* 57-61; V Liv St Chris Norris Green from 61; Hon Can Liv Cathl from 92. *St Christopher's Vicarage, Lorenzo Drive, Norris Green, Liverpool L11 1BQ* 0151-226 1637

698

TOFTS, Jack. b 31. Roch Th Coll 66. **d** 68 **p** 69. C Richmond *Ripon* 68-71; C Croydon *Cant* 71-74; P-in-c Welney *Ely* 74-78; P-in-c Upwell Ch Ch 74-79; V Gorefield 78-94; R Newton 78-94; R Tydd St Giles 78-94. *The Birches, Church Road, Walpole St Peter, Wisbech, Cambs PE14 7NU* Wisbech (01945) 780455

TOLL, Brian Arthur. b 35. Ely Th Coll 62 Linc Th Coll 64. **d** 65 **p** 66. C Cleethorpes *Linc* 65-68; C Hadleigh w Layham and Shelley *St E* 69-72; R Claydon and Barham 72-86; P-in-c Capel w Lt Wenham 86-94; P-in-c Holton St Mary w Gt Wenham 87-91; R Capel St Mary w Lt and Gt Wenham from 94; Bp's Adv on Deliverance and Exorcism from 89. *The Rectory, Days Road, Capel St Mary, Ipswich IP9 2LE* Great Wenham (01473) 310236

TOLLER, Elizabeth Margery. b 53. Leeds Univ BA75. Ripon Coll Cuddesdon 84. **d** 87. Perm to Offic *Nor* from 87; Chapl Lt Plumstead Hosp 92-93; Asst Chapl HM Pris Nor from 93. *The Rectory, Coltishall, Norwich NR12 7HL* Norwich (01603) 737255 or 737531 Fax 300867

TOLLER, Heinz Dieter. b 52. Bonn Univ DipTh77. NE Ord Course 86. **d** 87 **p** 88. C Leeds Gipton Epiphany *Ripon* 87-90; R Coltishall w Gt Hautbois and Horstead *Nor* from 90. *The Rectory, Coltishall, Norwich NR12 7HL* Norwich (01603) 737255

TOLLEY, Canon George. b 25. FRSC CBIM Lon Univ BSc45 MSc48 PhD52 Sheff Univ Hon DSc83. Linc Th Coll 65. **d** 67 **p** 68. C Sheff Sharrow *Sheff* 67-90; Hon Can Sheff Cathl from 76. *74 Furniss Avenue, Sheffield S17 3QP* Sheffield (0114) 236 0538

TOLWORTHY, Colin. b 37. Chich Th Coll 64. **d** 67 **p** 68. C Hulme St Phil *Man* 67-70; C Lawton Moor 70-71; C Hangleton *Chich* 72-76; V Eastbourne St Phil 76-87; V Hastings H Trin from 87. *Holy Trinity Vicarage, 72 Priory Avenue, Hastings, E Sussex TN34 1UG* Hastings (01424) 441766

TOMBLING, Canon Arthur John. b 32. St Jo Coll Cam BA54 MA58. Ridley Hall Cam 55. **d** 57 **p** 58. V Battersea Park St Sav *S'wark* 66-74; P-in-c Battersea St Geo w St Andr 74-87; RD Battersea 85-90; V Battersea St Sav and St Geo w St Andr 87-95; P-in-c Battersea Park All SS 89-95; Hon Can S'wark Cathl 89-95; rtd 95. *5 William Steele Way, Higham Ferrers, Rushden, Northants NN10 8LS* Wellingborough (01933) 418072

TOMBS, Kenneth Roberts. b 42. Open Univ BA84. S Dios Minl Tr Scheme 92. **d** 95. Dep Hd Twyford C of E High Sch Acton from 86; NSM Ickenham *Lon* from 95. *91 Burns Avenue, Southall, Middx UB1 2LT* 0181-574 3738

TOMKINS, Clive Anthony. b 47. Cant Sch of Min 85. **d** 88 **p** 89. C Eastry and Northbourne w Tilmanstone etc *Cant* 88-91; R from 91; Chapl Eastry Hosp from 91. *The Vicarage, Brook Street, Eastry, Sandwich, Kent CT13 0HR* Sandwich (01304) 611323

TOMKINSON, Raymond David. b 47. RGN MSSCh. E Anglian Minl Tr Course 86. **d** 89 **p** 90. NSM Chesterton St Geo *Ely* 89-91; C Sawston 91-93; C Babraham 91-93; P-in-c Wimbotsham w Stow Bardolph and Stow Bridge etc 93-94; R from 94; RD Fincham from 94. *The Rectory, Wimbotsham, King's Lynn, Norfolk PE34 3QG* Downham Market (01366) 384279

TOMLIN, Graham Stuart. b 58. Linc Coll Ox MA80. Wycliffe Hall Ox BA85. **d** 86 **p** 87. C Ex St Leon w H Trin *Ex* 86-89; Tutor Wycliffe Hall Ox from 89; Chapl Jes Coll Ox 89-94. *Wycliffe Hall, Oxford OX2 6PW* Oxford (01865) 274205

TOMLIN, Keith Michael. b 53. Imp Coll Lon BSc75. Ridley Hall Cam 77. **d** 80 **p** 81. C Heywood St Jas *Man* 80-83; C Rochdale 83-84; TV 84-85; Chapl Rochdale Tech Coll 83-85; R Benington w Leverton *Linc* from 85. *The Rectory, Main Road, Benington, Boston, Lincs PE22 0BT* Boston (01205) 760962

TOMLINE, Stephen Harrald. b 35. Dur Univ BA57. Cranmer Hall Dur DipTh61. **d** 61 **p** 62. C Blackley St Pet *Man* 61-66; V Audenshaw St Steph 66-90; V Newhey from 90. *St Thomas's Vicarage, Newhey, Rochdale, Lancs OL16 3QS* Shaw (01706) 845159

TOMLINSON, Dr Anne Lovat. b 56. Edin Univ MA78 PhD85. St Jo Coll Nottm CertCS87. **d** 93. Tutor Edin Dioc Tr for Min Course from 93; Lic to Offic *Edin* from 93. *8 Buckstone Drive, Edinburgh EH10 6PD* 0131-445 2942

TOMLINSON, Arthur John Faulkner. b 20. Clare Coll Cam BA41 MA45. Ridley Hall Cam 46. **d** 48 **p** 49. R Sarratt *St Alb* 62-85; rtd 85; Perm to Offic *Nor* from 85. *The Retreat, The Heath, Buxton, Norwich NR10 5JA* Buxton (01603) 279470

TOMLINSON, Barry William. b 47. Reading Univ DipTh. Clifton Th Coll 72. **d** 72 **p** 73. C Pennington *Man* 72-76; SAMS 76-80; Chile 77-80; C-in-c Gorleston St Mary CD *Nor* 80; Chapl Jas Paget Hosp Gorleston 81-87; V Gorleston St Mary *Nor* 80-88; P-in-c Gt w Lt Plumstead 88-89; R Gt w Lt Plumstead and Witton 89-93; R Gt and Lt Plumstead w

Thorpe End and Witton from 93; Chapl Lt Plumstead Hosp from 88. *The Rectory, 9 Lawn Crescent, Thorpe End, Norwich NR13 5BP* Norwich (01603) 34778

TOMLINSON, David Robert. b 60. Kent Univ BSc82 Chelsea Coll Lon PGCE83 Jes Coll Cam BA92. Ridley Hall Cam CTM93. **d** 93 **p** 94. C Godalming *Guildf* from 93. *St Mark's House, 29 Franklyn Road, Godalming, Surrey GU7 2LD* Godalming (01483) 424710

TOMLINSON, Eric Joseph. b 45. Qu Coll Birm 70. **d** 73 **p** 74. C Cheadle *Lich* 73-76; C Sedgley All SS 77-79; V Ettingshall 79-94; P-in-c Longsdon 94; P-in-c Rushton 94; P-in-c Horton 94; V Horton, Lonsdon and Rushton Spencer from 94. *The Vicarage, Longsdon, Stoke-on-Trent ST9 9QF* Leek (01538) 385318

TOMLINSON, Frederick William (Fred). b 58. Glas Univ MA80 Edin Univ BD83. Edin Th Coll 80. **d** 83 **p** 84. C Cumbernauld *Glas* 83-86; C Glas St Mary 86-88; R Edin St Hilda *Edin* from 88; R Edin St Fillan from 88. *8 Buckstone Drive, Edinburgh EH10 6PD* 0131-445 2942

TOMLINSON, Canon Geoffrey. b 15. Linc Coll Ox BA37 MA47. Westcott Ho Cam 37. **d** 39 **p** 40. V Lanc St Mary *Blackb* 66-81; Hon Can Blackb Cathl 67-86; RD Lanc 71-82; V Overton 81-86; rtd 86; Perm to Offic *Bradf* from 86; Perm to Offic *Blackb* from 87. *3 Kirk Beck Close, Brookhouse, Lancaster LA2 9JN* Caton (01524) 770051

TOMLINSON, Ian James. b 50. K Coll Lon AKC72 MA90. St Aug Coll Cant 72. **d** 73 **p** 74. C Thirsk w S Kilvington and Carlton Miniott etc *York* 73-76; C Harrogate St Wilfrid *Ripon* 76-79; R Appleshaw, Kimpton, Thruxton and Fyfield *Win* from 79. *The Rectory, Ragged Appleshaw, Andover, Hants SP11 9HX* Weyhill (01264) 772414

TOMLINSON, Mrs Jean Mary. b 32. K Coll Lon CertRK53 BEd75. S Dios Minl Tr Scheme 84. **d** 87 **p** 94. Hon Par Dn Spring Park All SS *S'wark* 87-92; Chapl HM Young Offender Inst Hatf from 92. *HM Young Offender Institution, Thorne Road, Hatfield, Doncaster DN7 6EL* Thorne (01405) 812336 Fax 813325

TOMLINSON (nee MILLS), Mrs Jennifer Clare. b 61. Trin Hall Cam BA82 MA86. Ridley Hall Cam 88. **d** 91 **p** 94. C Busbridge *Guildf* 91-95; C Godalming from 95. *St Mark's House, 29 Franklyn Road, Godalming, Surrey GU7 2LD* Godalming (01483) 424710

TOMLINSON, Canon John Coombes. b 34. Nottm Univ DipEd76. Lich Th Coll 60. **d** 62 **p** 63. C Cheadle *Lich* 62-66; Warden Lich Dioc Tr Cen 66-73; C Alstonfield 66-68; P-in-c Ilam w Blore Ray and Okeover 68-73; Dioc Youth Tr Officer 68-73; Bp's Youth Chapl *Derby* 73-84; Dep Dir of Educn 78-79; Dir 79-84; TR Buxton w Burbage and King Sterndale from 84; Dioc Adv Past Care and Counselling from 85; RD Buxton from 91; Hon Can Derby Cathl from 91. *The Rectory, Lismore Park, Buxton, Derbyshire SK17 9AU* Buxton (01298) 22151

TOMLINSON, John Howard. b 54. MICE83 Newc Univ BSc76. Chich Th Coll 91. **d** 93 **p** 94. C Blewbury, Hagbourne and Upton *Ox* from 93. *1 Saxons Way, Didcot, Oxon OX11 9RA* Didcot (01235) 814729

TOMLINSON, John William Bruce. b 60. Univ of Wales (Abth) BA82 Man Univ MA(Theol)90. Hartley Victoria Coll 87 Linc Th Coll 91. **d** 92 **p** 93. C Sawley *Derby* from 92. *The Curate's Flat, 681 Tamworth Road, Long Eaton, Nottingham NG10 3AB* Nottingham (0115) 972 0241

TOMLINSON, Matthew Robert Edward. b 61. St Chad's Coll Dur BA83. St Mich Coll Llan BD94. **d** 94 **p** 95. C Abergavenny St Mary w Llanwenarth Citra *Mon* from 94. *12A Park Court, Abergavenny, Gwent NP7 5SR* Abergavenny (01873) 852407

TOMLINSON, Peter Robert Willis. b 19. CertEd49. Linc Th Coll 53. **d** 55 **p** 56. V Barrow Gurney *B & W* 70-77; Asst Chapl and Lect Coll of St Matthias Bris 70-77; TV Langport Area Chs 78-80; R Flax Bourton 80-84; V Barrow Gurney 80-84; rtd 84. *Flat 2, Vernon Lodge, 87 Hampton Park, Bristol BS6 6LQ* Bristol (0117) 946 6011

TOMLINSON, Miss Thelma Marcelle. b 20. K Coll Lon 46. dss 67 **d** 87 **p** 94. Liv Cathl *Liv* 69-81; Liv Univ 69-75; Dioc Lay Min Adv 75-81; rtd 81; Hon C Worle *B & W* 81-87; Perm to Offic from 87. *Cranbrook, 16 Greenwood Road, Worle, Weston-super-Mare, Avon BS22 0EX* Weston-super-Mare (01934) 515112

TOMPKINS, David John. b 32. Oak Hill Th Coll 55. **d** 58 **p** 59. C Northn St Giles *Pet* 58-61; C Heatherlands St Jo *Sarum* 61-63; V Selby St Jas *York* 63-73; V Wistow 63-73; V Retford *S'well* 73-87; P-in-c Clarborough w Hayton 84-87; V Kidsgrove *Lich* 87-90; V Tockwith and Bilton w Bickerton *York* from 90. *The Vicarage, Westfield Road, Tockwith, York YO5 8PY* Boroughbridge (01423) 358338

TOMPKINS, Francis Alfred Howard. b 26. St Jo Coll Dur BA50 DipTh52. **d** 52 **p** 53. V Donington *Linc* 65-79; RD Holland W

69-78; V Silloth *Carl* 79-91; rtd 91; Perm to Offic *Linc* from 91. *22 Silver Street, Branston, Lincoln LN4 1LR* Lincoln (01522) 791689

TOMPKINS, Michael John Gordon. b 35. JP76. Man Univ BSc58 MPS59. N Ord Course 82. **d** 85 **p** 86. C Abington *Pet* 85-87; TV Daventry 87-92; P-in-c Braunston 87-92; TV Daventry, Ashby St Ledgers, Braunston etc 92-93; R Paston from 93. *The Rectory, 236 Fulbridge Road, Peterborough PE4 6SN* Peterborough (01733) 571943

TOMS, Sheila Patricia. b 33. **d** 94. NSM Peterston-super-Ely w St Brides-super-Ely *Llan* from 94. *East Wing, Dingestow Court, Dingestow, Monmouth, Gwent NP5 4YD* Dingestow (01600) 83262

TONBRIDGE, Archdeacon of. *See* MASON, Ven Richard John

TONBRIDGE, Suffragan Bishop of. *See* SMITH, Rt Rev Brian Arthur

TONES, Kevin Edward. b 64. Hertf Coll Ox BA85. Ridley Hall Cam 88. **d** 91 **p** 92. C Warmsworth *Sheff* 91-92; C Thorne from 92. *154 Grampion Way, Thorne, Doncaster, S Yorkshire DN8 5YW* Thorne (01405) 815415

TONG, Canon Peter Laurence. b 29. Lon Univ BA50. Oak Hill Th Coll 52. **d** 54 **p** 55. V Islington St Andr w St Thos and St Matthias *Lon* 65-75; V Welling *Roch* 75-82; TR Bedworth *Cov* 82-94; Hon Can Cov Cathl 88-94; Hon Can Chile from 89; rtd 94. *46 Bladington Drive, Bexley, Kent DA5 3BP* 0181-303 0085

TONGE, Brian. b 36. Dur Univ BA58. Ely Th Coll 59. **d** 61 **p** 62. C Fleetwood *Blackb* 61-65; Chapl Ranby Ho Sch Retford 65-69; Hon C Burnley St Andr w St Marg *Blackb* from 69. *230 Barden Lane, Burnley, Lancs BB10 1TD* Burnley (01282) 423185

TONGE, Lister. b 51. K Coll Lon AKC74 Man Univ DCouns92 Loyola Univ Chicago MPS95. St Aug Coll Cant 74. **d** 75 **p** 76. C Liv Our Lady and St Nic w St Anne *Liv* 75-78; S Africa 78-79; CR 79-91; Lic to Offic *Wakef* 83-91; Perm to Offic *Man* 89-94; USA 93-95; Perm to Offic *Liv* 95; Chapl Community of St Jo Bapt Windsor from 96. *The Cottage, Convent of St John the Baptist, Hatchley Lane, Windsor, Berks SL4 3QR* Windsor (01753) 860449

TONGUE, Denis Harold. b 15. Em Coll Cam BA37 MA41. Tyndale Hall Bris 37. **d** 38 **p** 39. Lect NT Tyndale Hall Bris 46-72; Trin Coll Bris 72-77; rtd 80. *c/o The Social Services Director, Devon County Council, Cranmere Court, Lustleigh Close, Exeter EX2 8PW* Exeter (01392) 382000

TONGUE, Canon Paul. b 41. St Chad's Coll Dur BA63 DipTh64. **d** 64 **p** 65. C Dudley St Edm *Worc* 64-69; C Sedgley All SS *Lich* 69-70; V Amblecote *Worc* from 70; Hon Can Worc Cathl from 93. *The Vicarage, 4 The Holloway, Amblecote, Stourbridge, W Midlands DY8 4DL* Stourbridge (01384) 394057

TONKIN, Canon Richard John. b 28. Lon Coll of Div ALCD59 BD60. **d** 60 **p** 61. V Hinckley H Trin *Leic* 66-74; RD Sparkenhoe II 71-74; R Oadby 74-84; Hon Can Leic Cathl 83-93; V Leic H Apostles 84-93; rtd 93. *39 Shackerdale Road, Wigston, Leicester LE8 1BQ* Leicester (0116) 281 2517

TONKINSON, David Boyes. b 47. K Coll Lon BD71 AKC71. St Aug Coll Cant 71. **d** 72 **p** 73. C Surbiton St Andr *S'wark* 72-74; C Selsdon St Jo w St Fran *Cant* 75-81; V Croydon St Aug 81-84; V Croydon St Aug *S'wark* 85-89; Easthampstead *Ox* from 89; Ind Chapl from 89; Chapl Bracknell Coll from 93. *17 Squirrel Close, Sandhurst, Camberley, Surrey GU17 8DL* Camberley (01252) 861722

TOOBY, Anthony Albert. b 58. Sarum & Wells Th Coll 89. **d** 91 **p** 92. C Warsop *S'well* 91-95; C Ollerton w Boughton from 95. *The Glebe House, Church Road, Broughton, Newark, Notts NG22 9RJ* Mansfield (01623) 836013

TOOGOOD, Noel Hare. b 32. Birm Univ BSc54. Wells Th Coll 59. **d** 61 **p** 62. C Rotherham *Sheff* 61-65; C Darlington St Jo *Dur* 65-70; V Burnopfield 70-81; P-in-c Roche *Truro* 81-84; P-in-c Withiel 81-84; R Roche and Withiel 84-91; RD St Austell 88-91; V Madron from 91. *The Vicarage, Madron, Penzance, Cornwall TR20 8SW* Penzance (01736) 60992

TOOGOOD, Robert Charles. b 45. AKC70. St Aug Coll Cant 70. **d** 71 **p** 72. C Shepperton *Lon* 71-74; C Kirk Ella *York* 74-76; P-in-c Levisham w Lockton 76-81; P-in-c Ebberston w Allerston 76-81; R Kempsey and Severn Stoke w Croome d'Abitot *Worc* 81-92; V Bramley *Win* from 92. *The Vicarage, Bramley, Basingstoke, Hants RG26 5DQ* Basingstoke (01256) 881373

TOOGOOD, Robert Frederick (Bob). b 43. St Paul's Cheltenham CertEd65 DipPE65 Open Univ BA74. Trin Coll Bris DipHE95. **d** 95. C Southbroom *Sarum* from 95. *33 Brickley Lane, Devizes, Wilts SN10 3BH* Devizes (01380) 729386

TOOKE, Mrs Sheila. b 44. E Anglian Minl Tr Course 88. **d** 91 **p** 94. NSM March St Wendreda *Ely* 91-95; P-in-c Upwell Ch

Ch from 95; P-in-c Welney from 95; P-in-c Manea from 95. *The Rectory, Church Road, Christchurch, Wisbech, Cambs PE14 9PQ* Cambridge (01354) 638379

TOOKEY, Preb Christopher Tom. b 41. AKC67. **d** 68 **p** 69. C Stockton St Pet *Dur* 68-71; C Burnham *B & W* 71-77; R Clutton w Cameley 77-81; V Wells St Thos w Horrington from 81; RD Shepton Mallet 86-95; Preb Wells Cathl from 90. *St Thomas's Vicarage, St Thomas's Street, Wells, Somerset BA5 2UZ* Wells (01749) 672193

TOOLEY, Geoffrey Arnold. b 27. Lon Coll of Div 55. **d** 58 **p** 59. C Chalk *Roch* 58-60; C Meopham 60-62; P-in-c Snodland and Paddlesworth 62-68; P-in-c Burham 68-76; C Riverhead w Dunton Green 76-79; C S w N Bersted *Chich* 79-83; C-in-c N Bersted CD from 83. *Church House, 330 Chichester Road, North Bersted, Bognor Regis, W Sussex PO21 5AU* Bognor Regis (01243) 823800

TOOLEY, Norman Oliver. b 27. Roch Th Coll. **d** 65 **p** 66. C Ormskirk *Liv* 68-73; Chapl Merseyside Cen for the Deaf 73-78; C Bootle Ch Ch 78-80; C W Ham *Chelmsf* 80-86; Chapl RAD 86-92; rtd 92. *42 Richford Road, London E15 3PQ* 0181-534 4538

TOOMBS, Alan Trevor. b 33. Man Univ BA54. Ripon Hall Ox 54. **d** 56 **p** 57. C Hope St Jas *Man* 56-61; R Moston St Mary 61-74; V Weaste 74-81; R Newchurch 81-85; R Newchurch from 85. *The Rectory, 539 Newchurch Road, Newchurch, Rossendale, Lancs BB4 9HH* Rossendale (01706) 215098

TOON, John Samuel. b 30. Bps' Coll Cheshunt 64. **d** 65 **p** 66. Canada 70, 73-76 and from 78; R Osgathorpe *Leic* 70-72; C Maidstone All SS w St Phil and H Trin *Cant* 76-78; rtd 95. *804, 10th Street N W, Portage la Prairie, Manitoba, Canada, R1N 3K2* Brandon (204) 857-4213

TOON, Dr Peter. b 39. K Coll Lon BD65 MTh67 Liv Univ MA72 Ch Ch Ox DPhil77 DD. Lambeth STh65 NW Ord Course 72. **d** 73 **p** 74. C Skelmersdale St Paul *Liv* 73-74; Lib Latimer Ho Ox 74-76; C Ox St Ebbe w St Pet *Ox* 74-76; Hon Lect St Giles-in-the-Fields *Lon* 76-82; Tutor Oak Hill Th Coll 76-82; Dir of Post-Ord Tr *St E* 82-87; P-in-c Boxford 82-88; V Staindrop *Dur* 88-91; USA from 91. *Nashotah Episcopal Seminary, 2777 Mission Road, Nashotah, Wisconsin 53058, USA*

TOONE, Canon Lawrence Raymond. b 32. Open Univ BA79. Roch Th Coll 60 St Aid Birkenhead 61. **d** 63 **p** 64. C Birch St Agnes *Man* 63-66; C Didsbury Ch Ch 66-69; V Oldham St Paul 69-79; V Greenfield from 79; AD Oldham 80-93; Hon Can Man Cathl from 82; P-in-c Oldham St Chad Limeside 92; AD Saddleworth from 94. *St Mary's Vicarage, 1 Park Lane, Greenfield, Oldham OL3 7DX* Saddleworth (01457) 872346

TOOP, Alan Neil. b 49. St Alb Minl Tr Scheme 79 Linc Th Coll 82. **d** 83 **p** 84. C Kempston Transfiguration *St Alb* 83-87; C Ludlow *Heref* 87-92; P-in-c Stokesay from 92. *The Vicarage, Clun Road, Stokesay, Craven Arms, Shropshire SY7 9QW* Craven Arms (01588) 672797

TOOP, William John. b 07. Lon Univ BSc27 K Coll Cam BA38 MA42. **d** 41 **p** 42. R Torwood St Mark *Ex* 52-79; P-in-c Torquay H Trin 74-79; R Torwood St Mark w H Trin 79; rtd 79; Lic to Offic *Ex* from 79. *Ardmore, Asheldon Road, Torquay TQ1 2QN* Torquay (01803) 201387

TOOTH, Nigel David. b 47. Sarum & Wells Th Coll 71. **d** 74 **p** 75. C S Beddington St Mich *S'wark* 74-77; C Whitchurch *Bris* 77-83; TV Bedminster 83-87; Chapl Dorchester Hosps 87-94; Chapl Herrison Hosp Dorchester 87-94; Chapl W Dorset Hosp Dorchester from 94. *West Dorset Hospital, Damers Road, Dorchester, Dorset DT1 2JY* Dorchester (01305) 251150

TOOVEY, Preb Kenneth Frank. b 26. K Coll Lon BD51 AKC51. **d** 52 **p** 53. V Upper Teddington SS Pet and Paul *Lon* 60-70; V Ruislip St Martin 70-81; RD Hillingdon 75-81; V Greenhill St Jo 81-91; Preb St Paul's Cathl 83-91; rtd 91. *10 Fort Road, Northolt, Middx UB5 5HH* 0181-842 2812

TOOZE, Margaret Elizabeth. b 27. St Mich Ho Ox 54. **dss** 83 **d** 89 **p** 94. Miss Bible Churchmen's Soc (Kenya) 61-88; Par Dn Bath Walcot *B & W* 89-94; C 94-95; Perm to Offic from 95. *38 The Paragon, Bath BA1 5LY* Bath (01225) 465642

TOPHAM, Paul Raby. b 31. MI66 Columbia Pacific Univ LTh80 MA81. **d** 85 **p** 86. Chapl St Paul's Prep Sch Barnes 85-91; Chapl Toulouse w Biarritz, Cahors and Pau *Eur* 91-94; Perm to Offic *Lon* from 94; Perm to Offic *Eur* from 94. *58 Gloucester Road, Hampton, Middx TW12 2UH* 0181-979 4277

TOPPING, Kenneth Bryan Baldwin. b 27. Bps' Coll Cheshunt 58. **d** 59 **p** 60. V Ringley *Man* 63-70; V Cleator Moor w Cleator *Carl* 70-91; rtd 92. *22 Sunningdale Avenue, Hest Bank, Lancaster LA2 6DF* Lancaster (01524) 822197

TOPPING, Norman. b 32. NW Ord Course 73. **d** 76 **p** 77. NSM Prenton *Ches* 76-79; C E Runcorn w Halton 79-80; C Halton 80; P-in-c Newton Flowery Field 80-81; V 81-86; V Bredbury St Mark from 86. *St Mark's Vicarage, George Lane, Bredbury, Stockport, Cheshire SK6 1AT* 0161-406 6552

TOPPING, Roy William. b 37. MBE92. S Dios Minl Tr Scheme 91. **d** 92 **p** 93. Bahrain 89-94; Chapl Miss to Seamen Milford Haven from 94. *7A Castle Pill Road, Steynton, Milford Haven, Dyfed SA73 1HE* Milford Haven (01646) 697572

TORDOFF, Donald William. b 45. Nottm Univ BA69. Qu Coll Birm 69. **d** 71 **p** 72. C High Harrogate Ch Ch *Ripon* 71-75; C Moor Allerton 75-80; V Bilton 80-92; R Spennithorne w Finghall and Hauxwell from 92. *The Rectory, Spennithorne, Leyburn, N Yorkshire DL8 5PR* Wensleydale (01969) 623010

TORDOFF (nee PARKER), Mrs Margaret Grace. b 40. SRN65 SCM67. Cranmer Hall Dur 81. **dss** 83 **d** 87 **p** 94. Bilton *Ripon* 83-87; C 87-92; Chapl Spennithorne Hall from 92; NSM Spennithorne w Finghall and Hauxwell from 92. *The Rectory, Spennithorne, Leyburn, N Yorkshire DL8 5PR* Wensleydale (01969) 623010

TORLACH, Ven Charles Emil. b 1900. Kelham Th Coll 23. **d** 27 **p** 28. Australia from 29; Hon Can Rockhampton 56-65; Adn 65-69; rtd 69. *Sinnamon Retirement Village, 17 Mile Rocks Road, Sinnamon Park, Queensland, Australia 4073* Jamboree Heights (7) 376-4053

TORODE, Brian Edward. b 41. FCollP93 St Paul's Cheltenham TCert63 Poitiers Univ DFStuds62. W of England Minl Tr Course 90. **d** 93 **p** 94. Hd Master Elmfield Sch Cheltenham from 82; NSM Up Hatherley *Glouc* 93-94; NSM Cheltenham St Steph from 93; NSM Cheltenham Em from 94. *23 Arden Road, Leckhampton, Cheltenham, Glos GL53 0HG* Cheltenham (01242) 231212

TORRENS, Robert Harrington. b 33. Trin Coll Cam BA56 MA61. Ridley Hall Cam 56. **d** 58 **p** 59. V Eaton Socon *St Alb* 63-73; Lic to Offic 73-75; V Cheltenham All SS *Glouc* 75-84; Chapl Frenchay Hosp Bris 84-94; Chapl Manor Park Hosp Bris 84-94; rtd 94; Chapl St Pet Hospice Bris from 94. *21 Church Road, Winterbourne Down, Bristol BS17 1BX* Winterbourne (01454) 775445

TORRY, Alan Kendall. b 33. Ex & Truro NSM Scheme. **d** 77 **p** 79. NSM Truro St Paul *Truro* 77-80; TV Probus, Ladock and Grampound w Creed and St Erme 80-84; P-in-c Gulval 84-88; V from 88; P-in-c Marazion 85-88; V from 88. *The Vicarage, Gulval, Penzance, Cornwall TR18 3BG* Penzance (01736) 62699

TORRY, Malcolm Norman Alfred. b 55. St Jo Coll Cam BA76 MA80 Lon Univ BD78 K Coll Lon MTh79 PhD90. Cranmer Hall Dur 79. **d** 80 **p** 81. C S'wark H Trin w St Matt *S'wark* 80-83; C S'wark Ch Ch 83-88; Ind Chapl 83-88; V Hatcham St Cath from 88. *St Catherine's Vicarage, 102 Pepys Road, London SE14 5SG* 0171-639 1050

TOSTEVIN, Alan Edwin John. b 41. BA. Trin Coll Bris 83. **d** 86 **p** 87. C Hildenborough *Roch* 86-89; TV Ipsley *Worc* from 89. *29 Sheldon Road, Redditch, Worcs B98 7QS* Redditch (01527) 501092

TOSTEVIN, Ronald Edwin. b 26. Selw Coll Cam BA51 MA56. Ely Th Coll 51. **d** 53 **p** 54. V Coppenhall St Paul *Ches* 57-71; R Woodchurch 71-85; RD Birkenhead 74-85; Hon Can Ches Cathl 78-85; R Somerton w Compton Dundon, the Charltons etc *B & W* 85-91; rtd 91. *The Court House, 3 Princess Avenue, Christchurch, Dorset TA11 7NQ* Bournemouth (01202) 480153

TOTNES, Archdeacon of. *Vacant*

TOTTEN, Andrew James. b 64. QUB BA87 TCD BTh90. CITC. **d** 90 **p** 91. C Newtownards *D & D* 90-94; CF from 94. *c/o MoD (Army), Bagshot Park, Bagshot, Surrey GU19 5PL* Bagshot (01276) 471717 Fax 412834

TOTTERDELL, Mrs Rebecca Helen. b 57. Lon Bible Coll BA80. Oak Hill Th Coll 88. **d** 91 **p** 94. Par Dn Broxbourne w Wormley *St Alb* 91-94; C from 94. *15 Trafalgar Avenue, Broxbourne, Herts EN10 7DJ* Hoddesdon (01992) 441524

TOTTY, Canon Lawrence Harold. b 07. Tyndale Hall Bris 46. **d** 46 **p** 47. R Kingswood *Glouc* 65-72; rtd 72; Perm to Offic *Glouc* from 72. *10 Kingscote Close, Cheltenham, Glos GL51 6JU* Cheltenham (01242) 522809

TOUCHSTONE, Grady Russell. b 32. Univ of S California 51. Wells Th Coll 63. **d** 65 **p** 66. C Maidstone St Mich *Cant* 65-70; USA from 70; rtd 95. *1069 South Gramercy Place, Los Angeles, California 90019-3634, USA* Los Angeles (213) 731-5822

TOURNAY, Ms Corinne Marie Elaine Ghislaine. b 57. Louvain Univ Belgium STB90 MA90. Cuddesdon Coll DipMin94. **d** 94 **p** 95. C Redhill St Jo *S'wark* from 94. *15 Earlsbrook Road, Redhill RH1 6DR* Reigate (01737) 778834

TOVAR, Miss Gillian Elaine. b 48. Sussex Univ CertEd69. Trin Coll Bris BA86. **dss** 86 **d** 87 **p** 94. Tonbridge SS Pet and Paul *Roch* 86-87; Par Dn 87-94; C from 94. *2 Larch Crescent, Tonbridge, Kent TN10 3NN* Tonbridge (01732) 361204

TOVEY, Phillip Noel. b 56. Societas Liturgica MSLS Lon Univ BA77 Nottm Univ MPhil88. Lon Bible Coll BA83 St Jo Coll Nottm 85 Lambeth STh95. **d** 87 **p** 88. C Beaconsfield *Ox*

87-90; C Banbury 90-91; TV from 91; SSF from 90. *St Francis House, Highlands, Banbury, Oxon OX16 7FA* Banbury (01295) 275449

TOVEY, Canon Ronald. b 27. AKC51. **d** 52 **p** 53. Lesotho 69-85; Adn S Lesotho 77-85; Hon Can Lesotho Cathl 85-92; R Reddish *Man* 85-92; rtd 92. *86 Kings Road, Oakham, Leics LE15 6PD* Oakham (01572) 770628

TOWARD, Stanley. b 25. Cranmer Hall Dur 65. **d** 66 **p** 67. V Swalwell *Dur* 69-74; R Ryton 74-86; R Ryton w Hedgefield 86-91; rtd 91. *3 Orchard Close, Rowlands Gill, Tyne & Wear NE39 1EQ* Rowlands Gill (01207) 542092

TOWELL, Alan. b 37. Sarum & Wells Th Coll 86 W Midl Minl Tr Course 87. **d** 89 **p** 90. C Boultham *Linc* 89-93; P-in-c Scunthorpe Resurr from 93. *The Vicarage, Mirfield Road, Scunthorpe, S Humberside DN15 8AN* Scunthorpe (01724) 842196

TOWELL, Geoffrey Leonard. b 37. K Coll Lon BA59. Linc Th Coll 59. **d** 61 **p** 62. V Alkborough w Whitton *Linc* 67-80; R W Halton 68-80; P-in-c Winteringham 75-80; V Alkborough 81-85; Dioc Ecum Officer 85-91; rtd 91. *40 Lady Frances Drive, Market Rasen, Lincoln LN8 3JJ* Market Rasen (01673) 843983

TOWELL, Canon John William. b 16. St Jo Coll Dur BA38 DipTh39 MA41. **d** 39 **p** 40. Can Res Bradf Cathl *Bradf* 67-77; rtd 77; Perm to Offic *Bradf* 77-94; Perm to Offic *S'wark* from 94. *22 Dobell Road, London SE9 1HE* 0181-850 2408

TOWERS, Canon David Francis. b 32. G&C Coll Cam BA56 MA60. Clifton Th Coll 56. **d** 58 **p** 59. C Gresley *Derby* 58-63; V Brixton St Paul *S'wark* 63-75; V Chatteris *Ely* 75-87; RD March 82-87; Hon Can Ely Cathl 85-87; R Burnley St Pet *Blackb* from 87. *The Rectory, 42 Pasturegate, Burnley, Lancs BB11 4DE* Burnley (01282) 413599

TOWERS, John Keble. b 19. Keble Coll Ox BA41 MA57. Edin Th Coll 41. **d** 43 **p** 44. V Bradf St Oswald Chapel Green *Bradf* 71-78; P-in-c Holme Cultram St Mary *Carl* 78-80; V 80-85; rtd 85; Perm to Offic *Glas* 85-92; Hon C Moffat from 92. *Achnacarry, Harthope Place, Moffat, Dumfriesshire DG10 9RS* Moffat (01683) 21232

TOWERS, Patrick Leo. b 43. AKC68 Hull Univ CertEd69. **d** 74 **p** 75. Japan 74-81; TV Bourne Valley *Sarum* 81-83; Dioc Youth Officer 81-83; Chapl Oundle Sch Pet 83-86; I Rathkeale w Askeaton and Kilcornan *L & K* 86-89; RD Limerick 88-89; I Nenagh from 89. *St Mary's Rectory, Church Road, Nenagh, Co Tipperary, Irish Republic* Nenagh (67) 32598 Fax as telephone

TOWERS, Terence John. b 33. AKC60. **d** 61 **p** 62. V Ushaw Moor *Dur* 67-93; rtd 93. *8 Beech Court, Langley Park, Durham DH7 9XL* 0191-373 0210

TOWLER, David George. b 42. Cranmer Hall Dur 73. **d** 76 **p** 77. C Newbarns w Hawcoat *Carl* 76-80; V Huyton St Geo *Liv* from 80. *St George's Vicarage, 1 St George's Road, Huyton, Liverpool L36 8BE* 0151-489 1997

TOWLSON, Arthur Stanley. b 20. St Jo Coll Dur LTh48 BA49 ALCD48. **d** 50 **p** 51. R Blithfield *Lich* 57-70; R Colton 57-70; R Longton St Jas 70-71; Lic to Offic 71-78; P-in-c Checkley 78-84; P-in-c Croxden 78-84; rtd 85; Perm to Offic *Lich* from 85. *4 The Close, Lichfield, Staffs WS13 7LD* Lichfield (01543) 258608

TOWLSON, George Eric. b 40. N Ord Course 80. **d** 83 **p** 84. NSM Wakef St Andr and St Mary *Wakef* 83-84; NSM Ox St Mich w St Martin and All SS *Ox* 84-86; Perm to Offic 86-87; NSM Hoar Cross w Newchurch *Lich* 87-93; C Wednesbury St Paul Wood Green from 93. *St Luke's House, 33 Oldbury Street, Wednesbury, W Midlands WS10 0QJ* 0121-556 0443

TOWNDROW, Ven Frank Noel. b 11. K Coll Cam BA34 MA38. Coll of Resurr Mirfield 35. **d** 37 **p** 38. Can Res Pet Cathl *Pet* 66-77; Adn Oakham 67-77; Chapl to The Queen 75-81; rtd 77; Perm to Offic *Pet* from 77. *17 Croake Hill, Swinstead, Grantham, Lincs NG33 4PE* Corby Glen (01476) 550478

TOWNE, David William. b 34. St Jo Coll Dur BA58. Cranmer Hall Dur DipTh60. **d** 60 **p** 61. C Bromley St Jo *Roch* 60-63; Lect Watford St Mary *St Alb* 63-66; V Prestonville St Luke *Chich* 66-73; R Slaugham 73-79; V Wilmington *Roch* 79-85; V Otford from 85. *The Vicarage, The Green, Otford, Sevenoaks, Kent TN14 5PD* Otford (01959) 523185

TOWNEND, John Philip. b 52. Southn Univ BTh95. Sarum & Wells Th Coll 89. **d** 91 **p** 92. C Sherborne w Castleton and Lillington *Sarum* 91-95; P-in-c Wool and E Stoke from 95. *The Vicarage, Wool, Wareham, Dorset BH20 6EB* Bindon Abbey (01929) 462215

TOWNEND, Noel Alexander Fortescue. b 06. Selw Coll Cam BA28 MA32. Cuddesdon Coll 29. **d** 30 **p** 32. V Port Isaac *Truro* 68-73; rtd 73; Hon C N Petherton w Northmoor Green *B & W* from 73. *4 Tappers Lane, North Petherton, Bridgwater, Somerset TA6 6SH* Bridgewater (01278) 663279

TOWNER, Paul. b 51. Bris Univ BSc72 BTh81. Oak Hill Th Coll 78. **d** 81 **p** 82. C Aspley *S'well* 81-84; R Gt Hanwood *Heref*

TOWNLEY

from 84; RD Pontesbury from 93. *The Rectory, Hanwood, Shrewsbury SY5 8LJ* Shrewsbury (01743) 860074

TOWNLEY, Peter Kenneth. b 55. Sheff Univ BA78 Man Univ DSPT87. Ridley Hall Cam 78. **d** 80 **p** 81. C Ashton Ch Ch *Man* 80-83; C-in-c Holts CD 83-88; R Stretford All SS from 88. *The Rectory, 233 Barton Road, Stretford, Manchester M32 9RB* 0161-865 1350

TOWNLEY, Very Rev Robert Keith. b 44. St Jo Coll Auckland LTh67. **d** 67 **p** 68. New Zealand 67-70; C Lisburn Ch Ch *Conn* 71-74; C Portman Square St Paul *Lon* 75-80; Chan Cork Cathl *C, C & R* 82-94; Dean Ross 82-94; I Ross Union 82-94; Dean Kildare *M & K* from 95; Hon CF from 95; I Kildare, Edenderry, Naas and Newbridge *M & K* from 95. *Dean's House, Curragh Camp, Co Kildare, Irish Republic* Kildare (45) 441654

TOWNLEY, Roger. b 46. Man Univ BSc York Univ MSc. St Deiniol's Hawarden 82. **d** 84 **p** 85. C Longton *Blackb* 84-88; V Penwortham St Leon 88-92; V Wrightington from 92; Chapl Wrightington Hosp from 92. *The Vicarage, Church Lane, Wrightington, Wigan, Lancs WN6 9SL* Eccleston (01257) 451332

TOWNROE, Canon Edward John. b 20. St Jo Coll Ox BA42 MA48. Linc Th Coll 42. **d** 43 **p** 44. Warden St Boniface Coll Warminster 56-69; Can and Preb Sarum Cathl *Sarum* 69-93; rtd 85. *St Boniface Lodge, Church Street, Warminster, Wilts BA12 8PG* Warminster (01985) 212355

TOWNROE, Canon Michael Dakeyne. b 15. Linc Th Coll 35. **d** 38 **p** 39. R Bexhill St Pet *Chich* 59-82; RD Battle and Bexhill 64-77; Can and Preb Chich Cathl 69-82; rtd 82. *Pax, Pett Road, Pett, Hastings, E Sussex TN35 4HE* Hastings (01424) 813381

TOWNSEND, Allan Harvey. b 43. W Midl Minl Tr Course 89. **d** 92 **p** 93. NSM Fenton *Lich* from 92. *3 Daintry Street, Oakhill, Stoke-on-Trent ST4 5NN* Stoke-on-Trent (01782) 410604

TOWNSEND, Dr Anne Jennifer. b 38. MRCS60 LRCP60 Lon Univ MB, BS60. S'wark Ord Course 88. **d** 91 **p** 94. NSM Wandsworth St Paul *S'wark* from 91; Chapl Asst St Geo Hosp Tooting 91-92; Dean MSE from 93. *89E Victoria Drive, London SW19 6PT* 0181-785 7675

TOWNSEND, Christopher Robin. b 47. St Jo Coll Nottm LTh74. **d** 74 **p** 75. C Gt Horton *Bradf* 74-77; C Heaton St Barn 77-78; C Wollaton *S'well* 78-80; V Slaithwaite w E Scammonden *Wakef* from 80. *The Vicarage, Station Road, Slaithwaite, Huddersfield HD7 5AW* Huddersfield (01484) 842748

TOWNSEND, Dr Derek William (Bill). b 52. Fitzw Coll Cam BA74 Man Univ PhD89. St Jo Coll Nottm DTS91. **d** 91 **p** 92. C Hazlemere *Ox* 91-95; C Banbury from 95. *Saint Paul's House, Prescott Avenue, Banbury, Oxon OX16 0LR* Banbury (01295) 264003

TOWNSEND, Canon John Clifford. b 24. St Edm Hall Ox BA48 MA49. Wells Th Coll. **d** 50 **p** 51. Chapl RNR 58-75; V Branksome St Aldhelm *Sarum* 60-70; R Melksham 70-73; TR 73-80; Can and Preb Sarum Cathl 72-90; RD Bradf 73-80; P-in-c Harnham 80-81; V St Paul's 80-85; rtd 90. *19 Wyke Oliver Close, Preston, Weymouth, Dorset DT3 6DR* Weymouth (01305) 833641

TOWNSEND, John Elliott. b 39. ALCD63. **d** 64 **p** 65. C Harold Wood *Chelmsf* 64-68; C Walton *St E* 68-72; V Kensal Rise St Martin *Lon* 72-83; V Hornsey Ch Ch from 83. *Christ Church Vicarage, 32 Crescent Road, London N8 8AX* 0181-340 1566

TOWNSEND, John Errington. b 20. St Aug Coll Cant 64. **d** 65 **p** 66. R Droxford *Portsm* 69-74; Soc Work Org Sec 74-78; Perm to Offic from 82; rtd 85. *Greytiles, Frogmore, East Meon, Petersfield, Hants GU32 1QQ* East Meon (01730) 823374

TOWNSEND, Peter. b 35. AKC63. **d** 64 **p** 65. C Norbury St Oswald *Cant* 64-67; C New Romney w Hope 67-69; C Westborough *Guildf* 69-74; P-in-c Wicken *Pet* 74-87; R Paulerspury 74-84; P-in-c Whittlebury w Silverstone 82-84; V Whittlebury w Paulerspury 84-87; V Greetham and Thistleton w Stretton and Clipsham from 87. *The Vicarage, Greetham, Oakham, Leics LE15 7NF* Oakham (01572) 812015

TOWNSEND, Peter. b 37. Open Univ BA87. Wells Th Coll 67. **d** 69 **p** 70. C Desborough *Pet* 69-72; C Bramley *Ripon* 72-75; C-in-c Newton Hall LEP *Dur* 75-80; P-in-c Newton Hall 80-81; V Hartlepool St Luke from 81. *St Luke's Vicarage, 5 Tunstall Avenue, Hartlepool TS26 8NF* Hartlepool (01429) 272893

TOWNSEND, Philip Roger. b 51. Sheff Univ BA78. Trin Coll Bris 78. **d** 80 **p** 81. C W Streatham St Jas *S'wark* 80-85; C Ardsley *Sheff* 85-88; V Crookes St Tim from 88. *St Timothy's Vicarage, 152 Slinn Street, Sheffield S10 1NZ* Sheffield (0114) 266 1745

TOWNSEND, Robert William. b 68. Univ of Wales (Ban) BA90. St Mich Coll Llan BTh93. **d** 93 **p** 95. C Dolgellau w Llanfachreth and Brithdir etc *Ban* 93-94; Min Can Ban Cathl from 94. *Caplandy, Glanrafon, Bangor, Gwynedd LL57 1LH* Bangor (01248) 352466

TOWNSHEND, Charles Hume. b 41. St Pet Coll Ox BA64 MA69. Westcott Ho Cam 64. **d** 66 **p** 67. C Warlingham w Chelsham and Farleigh *S'wark* 66-75; R Old Cleeve, Leighland and Treborough *B & W* 75-85; R Bishops Lydeard w Bagborough and Cothelstone 85-95; V N Curry from 95. *The Vicarage, North Curry, Taunton, Somerset TA3 6JZ* North Curry (01823) 490255

TOWNSHEND, David William. b 57. Lon Univ PGCE80 Ox Univ MA85. Cranmer Hall Dur 81. **d** 84 **p** 85. C Barking St Marg w St Patr *Chelmsf* 84-87; Canada from 87. *PO Box 116, 15 Carleton Street, Newboro, Ontario, Canada, K0G 1P0* Kingston (613) 272-2664

TOWNSHEND, Edward George Hume. b 43. Pemb Coll Cam BA66 MA70. Westcott Ho Cam 68. **d** 70 **p** 71. C Hellesdon *Nor* 70-74; Ind Chapl 74-81; TV Lowestoft St Marg 74-79; TV Lowestoft and Kirkley 79-81; V Stafford St Jo *Lich* 81-85; P-in-c Tixall w Ingestre 81-85; V Stafford St Jo and Tixall w Ingestre 85-87; R Lich St Chad from 87; RD Lich from 94; P-in-c Hammerwich from 94. *St Chad's Rectory, The Windings, Lichfield, Staffs WS13 7EX* Lichfield (01543) 262254

TOWNSON, Eric James. b 34. St Aid Birkenhead 60. **d** 62 **p** 63. Rwanda 69-74; C Burley *Ripon* 74-85; V 85-87; P-in-c Kelbrook *Bradf* 87-94; Dioc Adv in Evang 87-94; rtd 94. *10 Nelson Street, Lytham, Lytham St Annes, Lancs FY8 4AB* Lytham (01253) 731640

TOWSE, Anthony Norman Beresford. b 21. Linc Coll Ox BA48 MA72. Westcott Ho Cam 48. **d** 50 **p** 51. V Appledore *Cant* 64-72; V Appledore w Stone in Oxney and Ebony 72-75; V Appledore w Stone in Oxney and Ebony etc 75-82; RD S Lympne 81-90; V Appledore w Brookland, Fairfield, Brenzett etc 82-90; rtd 90. *3 Oaks Road, Tenterden, Kent TN30 6RD* Tenterden (01580) 766402

TOY, Elizabeth Margaret. b 37. NDAD59 CQSW77. Oak Hill NSM Course 85. **d** 88 **p** 94. NSM Hildenborough *Roch* from 88. *2 Francis Cottages, London Road, Hildenborough, Tonbridge, Kent TN11 8NQ* Hildenborough (01732) 833886

TOY, Canon John. b 30. Hatf Coll Dur BA53 MA62 Leeds Univ PhD82. Wells Th Coll 53. **d** 55 **p** 56. C Newington St Paul *S'wark* 55-58; S Sec SCM 58-60; Chapl Ely Th Coll 60-64; Chapl Gothenburg w Halmstad and Jonkoping *Eur* 65-69; Asst Chapl St Jo Coll York 69-72; Sen Lect 72-79; Prin Lect 79-83; Can Res and Chan York Minster *York* from 83. *4 Minster Yard, York YO1 2JF* York (01904) 620877

TOZE, Stephen James. b 51. Birm Univ BA79. Qu Coll Birm 76 Westcott Ho Cam 93. **d** 93 **p** 94. C Leominster *Heref* 93-94; R Gt Brickhill w Bow Brickhill and Lt Brickhill *Ox* from 94. *The Rectory, 6 Rushmere Close, Bow Brickhill, Milton Keynes MK17 9JB* Milton Keynes (01908) 642086

TOZER, Frank William. b 21. Wells Th Coll 61. **d** 63 **p** 64. C Crawley *Chich* 65-73; V Heathfield 73-87; rtd 87. *30 Orchid Close, Eastbourne, E Sussex BN23 8DE* Eastbourne (01323) 768270

TOZER, Reginald Ernest. b 25. St Aid Birkenhead 57. **d** 59 **p** 60. V E Ham w Upton Park *Chelmsf* 69-75; V Hatf Peverel w Ulting 75-91; rtd 91. *Basil's Place, 4 Church Road, Snape, Saxmundham, Suffolk IP17 1SZ* Snape (01728) 688895

TRACEY, Thomas Patrick. b 14. Sarum Th Coll 54. **d** 56 **p** 57. R Rotherfield Peppard *Ox* 71-75; P-in-c Stadhampton w Chislehampton 75-77; P-in-c Warborough 75-77; TV Dorchester 78-81; rtd 81; Perm to Offic *Ox* from 85. *The Abbeyfield Society, 57 Corn Street, Witney, Oxon OX8 7DQ*

TRAFFORD, Mrs Joyce. b 35. N Ord Course 84. **d** 87 **p** 94. Par Dn Chapelthorpe *Wakef* 87-94; C from 94. *1 Gillion Crescent, Durkar, Wakefield, W Yorkshire WF4 6PP* Wakefield (01924) 252033

TRAFFORD, Peter. b 39. Chich Th Coll. **d** 83 **p** 84. C Bath Bathwick *B & W* 83-86; Chapl RN 86-90; P-in-c Donnington *Chich* from 90. *The Vicarage, 65 Stockbridge Road, Donnington, Chichester, W Sussex PO20 2QE* Chichester (01243) 776395

TRAFFORD-ROBERTS, Rosamond Jane (Ros). b 40. Qu Coll Birm 93. **d** 95. C Ledbury w Eastnor *Heref* from 95. *Old Colwall House, Malvern, Worcs WR13 6HF* Colwall (01684) 540618 Fax as telephone

TRAPNELL, Canon Stephen Hallam. b 30. G&C Coll Cam BA53 MA57. Ridley Hall Cam 53 Virginia Th Sem BD56 MDiv70. **d** 56 **p** 57. C Upper Tulse Hill St Matthias *S'wark* 56-59; C Reigate St Mary 59-61; V Richmond Ch Ch 61-72; P-in-c Sydenham H Trin 72-80; R Worting *Win* 80-92; Field Officer Decade of Evang from 92; Can Shyogwe (Rwanda) from 93. *Downs Cottage, Rivar Road, Shalbourne, Marlborough, Wilts SN8 3QE* Marlborough (01672) 870514

TRASLER, Graham Charles George. b 44. Ch Ch Ox BA65 MA69. Cuddesdon Coll 66. d 68 p 69. C Gateshead St Mary *Dur* 68-71; P-in-c Monkwearmouth St Pet 71-79; P-in-c Bentley *Guildf* 79; P-in-c Binsted *Win* 79; R Bentley and Binsted 80-84; R New Alresford w Ovington and Itchen Stoke from 84. *The Rectory, 37 Jacklyns Lane, Alresford, Hants SO24 9LF* Alresford (01962) 732105

TRAVERS, Colin James. b 49. St Pet Coll Ox BA70 MA74. Ridley Hall Cam 70. d 72 p 73. C Hornchurch St Andr *Chelmsf* 72-75; Youth Chapl 75-77; C Aldersbrook 75-77; V Barkingside St Laur 77-82; V Waltham Abbey 82-88; V S Weald 88-95; Co-ord N Thames Minl Tr Course from 95; NSM Gt Warley w Childerditch and Ingrave from 95. *The Vicarage, Thorndon Gate, Ingrave, Brentwood, Essex CM13 3RG* Brentwood (01277) 810238

TRAVERS, John William. b 48. Open Univ BA84 Hull Univ MA86. Linc Th Coll 75. d 78 p 79. C Headingley *Ripon* 78-81; TV Louth *Linc* 81-89; P-in-c Shingay Gp of Par *Ely* 89; V 90-95; V Hamble le Rice *Win* from 95. *The Vicarage, Hamble, Southampton SO3 5JF* Southampton (01703) 452148

TRAVERSE, Ernest. b 28. Oak Hill Th Coll 73. d 75 p 76. C Roby *Liv* 75-76; C Rainhill 76-78; V Manor St Barn Marsh Green 78-80; TV Bemerton *Sarum* 80-83; C Hednesford *Lich* 83-86; rtd 86; Perm to Offic *Liv* from 86. *20 Ashgrove Crescent, Billinge, Wigan, Lancs WN5 7NH* Billinge (01744) 894257

TRAVIS, Robert Leonard. b 15. Sarum Th Coll 55. d 56 p 57. V Sevenoaks Weald *Roch* 61-66; rtd 66. *131 Dodson Valley Road, Atawhai, Nelson, New Zealand* Nelson (54) 545-0221

TREADGOLD, Very Rev John David. b 31. LVO90. Nottm Univ BA58. Wells Th Coll 58. d 59 p 60. VC S'well Minster *S'well* 59-64; CF (TA) 62-67 and 74-78; R Wollaton *S'well* 64-74; V Darlington St Cuth w St Hilda *Dur* 74-81; Chapl in the Gt Park 81-89; Can Windsor 81-89; Chapl to The Queen 81-89; Dean Chich from 89. *The Deanery, Chichester, W Sussex PO19 1PX* Chichester (01243) 783286 or 787337

TREADWELL, Albert Frederick. K Coll Lon. St Boniface Warminster 55. d 57 p 58. V Barnes St Mich *S'wark* 65-85; rtd 85; Hon C Wexham *Ox* 87; Perm to Offic *S'wark* from 85; Perm to Offic Lon 87-91; Perm to Offic *Ox* from 87. *11 Misbourne Court, High Street, Langley, Slough SL3 8LG* Slough (01753) 581672

TREANOR, Canon Desmond Victor. b 28. St Jo Coll Dur BA53 DipTh54 MA59. d 54 p 55. V Leic St Anne *Leic* 68-75; V Humberstone 75-86; Hon Can Leic Cathl 78-93; P-in-c Leic St Eliz Nether Hall 81-86; RD Christianity (Leic) N 82-86; R Gt Bowden w Welham, Glooston and Cranoe 86-93; RD Gartree I (Harborough) 88-93; rtd 93. *5 Brookfield Way, Kibworth, Leicester LE8 0SA* Leicester (0116) 279 2750

TREANOR, Terence Gerald. b 29. St Jo Coll Ox BA52 MA56. Wycliffe Hall Ox 52. d 54 p 55. Chapl Oakham Sch Leics 66-94; Lic to Offic *Pet* 66-94; rtd 94; Perm to Offic *Leic* from 94; Perm to Offic *Linc* from 94; Perm to Offic *Pet* from 94. *35 Glebe Way, Oakham, Leics LE15 6LX* Oakham (01572) 757495

TREASURE, Andrew Stephen. b 51. Or Coll Ox BA73 MA77. St Jo Coll Nottm BA76. d 77 p 78. C Beverley Minster *York* 77-81; C Cam H Trin *Ely* 81-84; C Cam H Trin w St Andr Gt 84-85; V Eccleshill *Bradf* from 85. *The Vicarage, Fagley Lane, Eccleshill, Bradford, W Yorkshire BD2 3NS* Bradford (01274) 636403

TREASURE, Geoffrey. b 39. Hatf Coll Dur BA61 Univ of Wales (Cardiff) DipEd62. Oak Hill NSM Course 90. d 93 p 94. NSM Forty Hill Jes Ch *Lon* 93-94. *11 Caversham Avenue, London N13 4LL* 0181-882 5523

TREASURE, Mrs Joy Elvira. b 23. St Anne's Coll Ox MA50 CertEd. S Dios Minl Tr Scheme 80. dss 82 d 87 p 94. Tisbury *Sarum* 82-87; Hon Par Dn 87-91; rtd 92; Perm to Offic *Sarum* from 92. *Friars Lodge, The Friary, Salisbury SP1 2HU* Salisbury (01722) 333741

TREASURE, Ronald Charles. b 24. Or Coll Ox BA48 MA52. Cuddesdon Coll. d 50 p 51. V New Malton *York* 62-89; RD Malton 63-75; rtd 89. *Castle Walls, Castlegate, Kirkbymoorside, York YO6 6BW* Kirkbymoorside (01751) 32916

TREBLE, Harry. b 06. Lon Univ BD55 BA61. AKC32. d 32 p 33. V Barkingside St Cedd *Chelmsf* 61-83; rtd 83. *8 Fairlight Avenue, Woodford Green, Essex IG8 9JP*

TREBY, David Alan. b 47. FIMLS72 Bris Poly MSc90. St Jo Coll Nottm DTS94 MA95. d 95. C Camborne *Truro* from 95. *6 St Meriadoc Road, Camborne, Cornwall TR14 7HL* Camborne (01209) 613160

TREDENNICK, Angela Nicolette (Nicky). b 38. SRN62 SCM63 Lon Inst of Educn HVCert66. S'wark Ord Course 87. d 90 p 94. NSM Charlwood *S'wark* 90-92; Par Dn Roehampton H Trin 92-94; C from 94; RD Wandsworth from 95. *The Manse, Minstead Gardens, London SW15 4EB* 0181-878 7682

TREE, Robin Leslie. b 46. S Dios Minl Tr Scheme 89. d 92 p 93. NSM St Leonards Ch Ch and St Mary *Chich* from 92. *30 The Links, St Leonards-on-Sea, E Sussex TN38 0UW* Hastings (01424) 433289

TREEBY, Stephen Frank. b 46. Man Univ LLB67 Nottm Univ DipTh69. Cuddesdon Coll 69. d 71 p 72. C Ashbourne w Mapleton *Derby* 71-74; C Boulton 74-76; Chapl Trowbridge Coll *Sarum* 76-79; TV Melksham 79-87; V Dilton Marsh from 87; Chapl Westbury Hosp from 87. *The Vicarage, The Hollows, Dilton Marsh, Westbury, Wilts BA13 4BU* Westbury (01373) 822560

TREEN, Anthony Robert. b 37. Chich Th Coll 72. d 74 p 75. C Haywards Heath St Rich *Chich* 74-77; Ind Chapl 77-80; V Burgess Hill St Jo 80-85; P-in-c Walpole St Andrew *Ely* 85-86; P-in-c Walpole St Peter 85-86; R Walpole St Peter w St Andr from 86; P-in-c W Walton from 87; P-in-c Marshland St James from 94; RD Lynn Marshland from 94. *The Rectory, Walpole St Peter, Wisbech, Cambs PE14 7NS* Wisbech (01945) 780252

TREEN, Preb Robert Hayes Mortlock. b 19. New Coll Ox BA46 MA46. Westcott Ho Cam 45. d 47 p 48. R Bath St Sav *B & W* 61-76; Preb Wells Cathl 74-84; V Bishops Hull 76-84; RD Taunton S 77-81; RD Taunton 81-84; rtd 84; Perm to Offic *B & W* from 84. *13 The Leat, Bishops Lydeard, Taunton, Somerset TA4 3NY* Bishops Lydeard (01823) 433437

TREETOPS, Ms Jacqueline. b 47. NE Ord Course 83. dss 86 d 87 p 94. Low Harrogate St Mary *Ripon* 86-87; C Roundhay St Edm 87-95; C Potternewton from 95. *43 Lincombe Bank, Leeds LS8 1QP* Leeds (0113) 266 7223

TREFUSIS, Charles Rodolph. b 61. Hull Univ BA83. Wycliffe Hall Ox 85. d 90 p 91. C Blackheath St Jo *S'wark* 90-94; V Purley Ch Ch from 94. *The Vicarage, 38 Woodcote Valley Road, Purley, Surrey CR8 3AJ* 0181-660 1790

TREHERNE, Canon Alan Thomas Evans. b 30. Univ of Wales (Lamp) BA53. Wycliffe Hall Ox. d 55 p 56. C Heref St Pet w St Owen *Heref* 55-57; India 57-72; C-in-c Netherley Ch Ch CD *Liv* 72-74; R Gateacre 74-75; TR from 75; RD Farnworth 81-89; Hon Can Liv Cathl from 94. *St Stephen's Rectory, Belle Vale Road, Liverpool L25 2PQ* 0151-487 9338

TRELLIS, Very Rev Oswald Fitz-Burnell (Ossie). b 35. Chich Th Coll 73. d 74 p 75. C Chelmsf All SS *Chelmsf* 74-78; C-in-c N Springfield CD 79-85; V Heybridge w Langford 85-94; Dean Georgetown from 94. *The Deanery, 79 Carmichael Street, Georgetown,*

TREMBATH, Martyn Anthony. b 65. Leeds Univ BA86. Ripon Coll Cuddesdon. d 90 p 91. C Bodmin w Lanhydrock and Lanivet *Truro* 90-91; C St Erth from 92; C Phillack w Gwithian and Gwinear from 94; C Hayle from 94. *The Vicarage, 43 School Lane, St Erth, Hayle, Cornwall TR27 6HN* Hayle (01736) 754194

TREMLETT, Andrew. b 64. Pemb Coll Cam BA86 Qu Coll Ox BA88. Wycliffe Hall Ox 86. d 89 p 90. C Torquay St Matthias, St Mark and H Trin *Ex* 89-92; Miss to Seamen 92-94; Asst Chapl Rotterdam *Eur* 92-94; Chapl 94-95; TV Fareham H Trin *Portsm* from 95. *St Columba Vicarage, Hillson Drive, Fareham, Hants PO15 6PF* Fareham (01329) 843705

TREMLETT, Ven Anthony Frank (Tony). b 37. Ex & Truro NSM Scheme 78. d 81 p 82. C Southway *Ex* 81-82; P-in-c 82-84; V 84-88; RD Plymouth Moorside 86-88; Adn Totnes 88-94; Adn Ex and Can Res Ex Cathl from 94. *St Matthew's House, Spicer Road, Exeter EX1 1TA* Exeter (01392) 425432 Fax as telephone

TRENCHARD, Hubert John. b 26. S Dios Minl Tr Scheme. d 83 p 84. NSM Sturminster Marshall *Sarum* 83-87; NSM Blandford Forum and Langton Long from 87. *20 Chapel Gardens, Blandford Forum, Dorset DT11 7UY* Blandford (01258) 459576

TRENCHARD, Hugh. b 50. St Mich Coll Llan BD75. d 75 p 76. C Caerleon *Mon* 75-80; Dioc Chapl GFS 78-86; Asst Chapl Mon Sch 80-84; R Llanarth w Clytha, Llansantffraed and Bryngwyn *Mon* 80-84; TV Cyncoed 84-93; Prov Officer for Soc Resp from 94. *The Church in Wales Centre, Woodland Place, Penarth, S Glam CF64 2EX* Penarth (01222) 705278

TRENCHARD, Paul Charles Herbert Anstiss. b 53. Liv Univ LLB76. St Steph Ho Ox 77. d 80 p 81. C Torquay St Martin Barton *Ex* 80-84; R Ashprington, Cornworthy and Dittisham 84-92; R Barnwell w Tichmarsh, Thurning and Clapton *Pet* from 92. *The Rectory, Barnwell, Peterborough PE8 5PG* Oundle (01832) 272374

TRENDALL, Peter John. b 43. Oak Hill Th Coll 66. d 69 p 70. C Beckenham Ch Ch *Roch* 69-73; C Bedworth *Cov* 73-76; V Hornsey Rise St Mary *Lon* 76-82; P-in-c Upper Holloway St Steph 80-82; V Hornsey Rise St Mary w St Steph 82-84; V Walthamstow St Mary w St Steph *Chelmsf* 84-85; TR 85-93; P-in-c Chigwell 93-94; TR Chigwell and Chigwell Row from 94. *The Rectory, 66 High Road, Chigwell, Essex IG7 6QB* 0181-500 3510

TRENDER, Lawrence. b 37. Bps' Coll Cheshunt 64. d 66 p 67. C Petersham *S'wark* 66-71; C Malden St Jo 71-73; R Thornham

Magna w Thornham Parva *St E* 73-81; P-in-c Mellis 73-81; P-in-c Gislingham 73-81; R Thornhams Magna and Parva, Gislingham and Mellis 81-87; RD Hartismere 85-87; R Skipsea w Ulrome and Barmston w Fraisthorpe *York* from 92. *The Rectory, Barmston, Driffield, N Humberside YO25 8PG* Skipsea (01262) 468188

TRENEER, Cyril George Howard. b 14. Leeds Univ BA36. Coll of Resurr Mirfield 36. **d** 38 **p** 39. V Plymouth St Gabr *Ex* 60-79; rtd 79; Lic to Offic *Ex* from 79. *2 Headborough Road, Ashburton, Newton Abbot, Devon TQ13 7QP* Ashburton (01364) 652159

TRESIDDER, Alistair Charles. b 65. Qu Coll Ox BA88. Cranmer Hall Dur DMinlStuds93. **d** 93 **p** 94. C Limehouse *Lon* from 93. *31 Kildare Walk, London E14 7DB* 0171-515 9082

TRETHEWEY, Frederick Martyn. b 49. Lon Univ BA70 DipTh77. Lambeth STh79 Oak Hill Th Coll 75. **d** 78 **p** 79. C Tollington Park St Mark w St Anne *Lon* 78-82; C Whitehall Park St Andr Hornsey Lane 82-87; TV Hornsey Rise Whitehall Park Team 87-88; V Brockmoor *Lich* 88-93; V Brockmoor *Worc* from 93; Chapl Russells Hall Hosp Dudley from 88. *5 Leys Road, Brockmoor, Brierley Hill, W Midlands DY5 3UR* Brierley Hill (01384) 263327

TREVELYAN, Preb James William Irvine. b 37. Selw Coll Cam BA64 MA67. Cuddesdon Coll 62. **d** 65 **p** 66. C Heston *Lon* 65-68; C Folkestone St Sav *Cant* 68-72; R Lenham w Boughton Malherbe 72-78; P-in-c Honiton, Gittisham and Combe Raleigh *Ex* 78-79; R Honiton, Gittisham, Combe Raleigh and Monkton 79-83; TR Honiton, Gittisham, Combe Raleigh, Monkton etc from 83; P-in-c Farway w Northleigh and Southleigh 84-86; Preb Ex Cathl from 95. *The Rectory, Exeter Road, Honiton, Devon EX14 8AN* Honiton (01404) 42925

TREVOR, Canon Charles Frederic. b 27. Sarum Th Coll 54. **d** 56 **p** 57. V Thornton in Lonsdale w Burton in Lonsdale *Bradf* 66-74; V Kirkby Malham 74-85; P-in-c Coniston Cold 81-85; Hon Can Bradf Cathl 85-92; V Sutton 85-92; RD S Craven 86-91; C Embsay w Eastby 92; rtd 92. *5 Brooklyn, Threshfield, Skipton, W Yorkshire BD23 5ER* Skipton (01756) 752640

TREVOR-MORGAN, Canon Basil Henry. b 27. Univ of Wales (Lamp) BA51. Wells Th Coll 51. **d** 53 **p** 54. CF (TA) 59-92; V Stourbridge St Thos *Worc* 59-76; Chapl Christchurch Hosp 76-92; V Christchurch *Win* 76-92; Hon Can Win Cathl 84-92; rtd 93. *31 West Walk, West Bay, Bridport, Dorset DT6 4HT* Bridport (01308) 56461

TREW, Alen Robert. b 30. St Mich Coll Llan BD77. **d** 77 **p** 78. C Abergavenny St Mary w Llanwenarth Citra *Mon* 77-79; Hon C Broughty Ferry *Bre* from 81. *4 Bridge Lane, Broughty Ferry, Dundee DD5 2SZ* Dundee (01382) 78537

TREW, Robin Nicholas. b 52. UWIST BSc74. St Jo Coll Nottm 87. **d** 89 **p** 90. C Cov H Trin *Cov* 89-93; V Snitterfield w Bearley from 93. *The Vicarage, Church Road, Snitterfield, Stratford-upon-Avon, Warks CV37 0LN* Stratford-upon-Avon (01789) 731263

TREWEEKS, Mrs Angela Elizabeth. b 35. Gilmore Ho IDC59. **dss** 59 **d** 87 **p** 94. Chapl Asst St Nic Hosp Newc 85-87; Chapl 87; Hon C Newc St Geo *Newc* 87-89; Chapl St Mary's Hosp Stannington 92-95; Hon C Rothbury *Newc* from 94; rtd 95. *The Nook, Pondicherry, Rothbury, Morpeth, Northd NE65 7YS* Rothbury (01669) 620393

TRIBE, Arthur Wilfrid Newton (Pip). b 03. Trin Coll Ox BA25 MA31. Ridley Hall Cam 25. **d** 27 **p** 28. R High Ongar w Norton Mandeville *Chelmsf* 61-76; rtd 76. *19 Longfields, Ongar, Essex CM5 9BZ* Ongar (01277) 364211

TRICKETT, Judith. b 50. St Jo Coll Nottm 89. **d** 91 **p** 94. Par Dn Kimberworth *Sheff* 91-93; D-in-c Worsbrough Common 93-94; V from 94. *The Vicarage, 9 Mount Close, Barnsley, S Yorkshire S70 4EE* Barnsley (01226) 282619

TRICKETT, Stanley Mervyn Wood. b 27. Lich Th Coll 64. **d** 66 **p** 67. C Kington w Huntington *Heref* 66-70; P-in-c Old Radnor 70-81; P-in-c Knill 70-81; V Shrewton *Sarum* from 81; P-in-c Winterbourne Stoke 81-92; RD Wylye and Wilton 85-89. *The Vicarage, Chapel Lane, Shrewton, Salisbury SP3 4BX* Shrewton (01980) 620580

TRICKETT, Mrs Susan. b 42. JP89. S Dios Minl Tr Scheme 91. **d** 94. NSM Combe Down w Monkton Combe and S Stoke *B & W* from 94. *Granville House, Tyning Road, Combe Down, Bath BA2 5ER* Bath (01225) 833007

TRICKEY, Frederick Marc. b 35. Dur Univ BA62. Cranmer Hall Dur DipTh64. **d** 64 **p** 65. C Alton St Lawr *Win* 64-68; V Win St Jo cum Winnall 68-77; R Guernsey St Martin from 77; Angl Adv Channel TV from 77. *The Rectory, Grande Rue, St Martin, Guernsey, Channel Islands GY4 6RR* Guernsey (01481) 38303

TRICKEY, Jolyon. b 57. Barrister-at-Law 80 Jes Coll Cam BA79 MA83. Trin Coll Bris BA90. **d** 90 **p** 91. C Chesham Bois

Ox 90-94; R Busbridge *Guildf* from 94. *Busbridge Rectory, Brighton Road, Godalming, Surrey GU7 1XA* Godalming (01483) 421267

TRICKLEBANK, Steven. b 56. Nottm Univ BTh88. Linc Th Coll 85. **d** 88 **p** 89. C Ditton St Mich *Liv* 88-91; C Wigan All SS 91-93; Chapl Aintree NHS Hosps Trust from 93; Chapl Fazakerley Hosp Liv from 93. *Fazakerley Hospital, Lower Lane, Liverpool L9 7AL, or 23 Newbury Way, West Derby, Liverpool L12 9JZ* 0151-525 5980 or 228 0914

TRIGG, Jeremy Michael. b 51. Open Univ BA88. Ripon Coll Cuddesdon 80. **d** 81 **p** 82. C Roundhay St Edm *Ripon* 81-84; C Harrogate St Wilfrid and St Luke 84-87; TV Pocklington Team *York* 87-90; R Rowley w Skidby from 90; Perm to Offic *Linc* from 91. *The Rectory, Southwold, Little Weighton, Hull HU20 3UQ* Hull (01482) 843317

TRIGG, John Alfred. b 29. Keble Coll Ox BA64 MA64. Ripon Hall Ox 64. **d** 65 **p** 66. C Swan *Ox* 68-72; P-in-c Stokenchurch and Cadmore End 72-76; V Stokenchurch and Ibstone 76-94; rtd 94. *Medbury, Tisbury Row, Tisbury, Salisbury SP3 6RZ* Shaftesbury (01747) 870707

TRIGG, Jonathan David. b 49. Ex Coll Ox BA71 MA75 Dur Univ PhD92. Cranmer Hall Dur BA82. **d** 83 **p** 84. C Enfield St Andr *Lon* 83-87; V Oakwood St Thos from 87; AD Enfield from 92. *St Thomas's Vicarage, 2 Sheringham Avenue, London N14 4UE* 0181-360 1749

TRILL, Barry. b 42. Chich Th Coll 65. **d** 68 **p** 69. C W Hackney St Barn *Lon* 68-73; TV Is of Dogs Ch Ch and St Jo w St Luke 73-78; P-in-c Hastings All So *Chich* 78-79; V from 79. *All Souls' Vicarage, 16 Berlin Road, Hastings, E Sussex TN35 5JD* Hastings (01424) 421445

TRILL, Victor Alfred Mansfield. b 21. St Deiniol's Hawarden. **d** 81 **p** 82. Hon C Prestbury *Ches* 81-83; Hon C Church Hulme 83-85; V Marbury 85-90; rtd 90. *5 Maisterson Court, Nantwich, Cheshire CW5 5TZ* Nantwich (01270) 628948

TRIMBLE, Mrs Anne Inman. b 40. Kenton Lodge Tr Coll CertEd60 New Coll Dur DipRS84. NE Ord Course 89. **d** 92 **p** 94. NSM Longnewton w Elton *Dur* from 92. *3 Queen Anne Terrace, Stockton-on-Tees, Cleveland TS18 5HS* Stockton-on-Tees (01642) 581141

TRIMBLE, Canon John Alexander. b 33. Lon Univ BD65. Edin Th Coll 55. **d** 58 **p** 59. CF from 87; C Glas St Mary *Glas* 58-60; C Edin St Jo *Edin* 60-65; R Baillieston *Glas* 65-69; R Falkirk *Edin* 69-86; R Troon *Glas* from 86; Can St Mary's Cathl from 91. *The Rectory, 70 Bentinck Drive, Troon, Ayrshire KA10 6HZ* Troon (01292) 313731

TRIMBLE, Canon Thomas Henry. b 36. TCD DipTh82 BTh90. CITC 79. **d** 82 **p** 83. C Seapatrick *D & D* 82-85; I Magheracross *Clogh* 85-90; Bp's Appeal Sec 89-90; I Donegal w Killymard, Lough Eske and Laghey *D & R* from 90; RD S Donegal from 91; Can Raphoe Cathl from 93. *The Rectory, Ballyshannon Road, Donegal, Co Donegal, Irish Republic* Donegal (73) 21075

TRIMBY, George Henry. b 44. DipTh. Trin Coll Bris 84. **d** 86 **p** 87. C Newtown w Llanllwchaiarn w Aberhafesp *St As* 86-88; P-in-c Llanfair, Derwen, Llanelidan and Efenechtyd 88-90; V from 90. *The Vicarage, Llanfair Dyffryn Clwyd, Ruthin, Clwyd LL15 2SA* Ruthin (01824) 704551

TRINDER, John Derek. b 28. Glouc Th Course 74. **d** 77 **p** 78. C Forest of Dean Ch Ch w English Bicknor *Glouc* 77; Hon C 77-79; Hon C Chepstow *Mon* 79-81; C Newport St Paul 81-82; V Dingestow and Llangovan w Penyclawdd and Tregaer 82-87; V Kirton in Holland *Linc* 87-93; rtd 93; Perm to Offic *Linc* from 93. *96 Little London, Long Sutton, Spalding, Lincs PE12 9LF* Holbeach (01406) 363045

TRIPLOW, Keith John. b 44. Selw Coll Cam BA66 MA70. Chich Th Coll 70. **d** 72 **p** 73. C Ipswich All Hallows *St E* 72-76; C Dartford H Trin *Roch* 76-78; V Fyfield w Tubney and Kingston Bagpuize *Ox* from 78. *The Vicarage, Fyfield, Abingdon, Oxon OX13 5LR* Frilford Heath (01865) 390803

TRISTRAM, Canon Catherine Elizabeth (Kate). b 31. Somerville Coll Ox BA53 MA57. **dss** 83 **d** 87 **p** 94. Holy Is *Newc* 84-87; Hon C from 87; Hon Can Newc Cathl from 94. *Marygate House, Holy Island, Berwick-upon-Tweed TD15 2SD*

TRISTRAM, Geoffrey Robert. b 53. K Coll Lon BA76 Pemb Coll Cam BA78 MA80. Westcott Ho Cam 77. **d** 79 **p** 80. C Weymouth H Trin *Sarum* 79-82; C Gt Berkhamsted *St Alb* 83-85; OSB from 85; Lic to Offic *Pet* 86-91; Asst Chapl Oundle Sch Pet 86-88; Sen Chapl 88-91; R Welwyn w Ayot St Peter *St Alb* from 91; Chapl Qu Victoria Hosp & Danesbury Home from 91. *The Rectory, 6 Hobbs Hill, Welwyn, Herts AL6 9DF* Welwyn (01438) 714150

TRISTRAM, Michael Anthony. b 50. Solicitor 76 Ch Coll Cam BA72 MA76. Ripon Coll Cuddesdon 79. **d** 82 **p** 83. C Stanmore *Win* 82-85; R Abbotts Ann and Upper and Goodworth Clatford 85-92; V Pershore w Pinvin, Wick and Birlingham *Worc* from 92. *The Vicarage, Church Street, Pershore, Worcs WR10 1DT* Pershore (01386) 552071

TRIVASSE, Keith Malcolm. b 59. Man Univ BA81 CertEd82 MPhil90 Birm Univ DipTh86. Qu Coll Birm 84. **d** 86 **p** 87. C Prestwich St Marg *Man* 86-88; C Orford St Marg *Liv* 88-90; TV Sunderland *Dur* 90-91; P-in-c N Hylton St Marg Castletown 91-95; R Bothal and Pegswood w Longhirst *Newc* from 95. *Bothal Rectory, Longhirst Road, Pegswood, Morpeth, Northd NE61 6XF* Morpeth (01670) 510793

TRNKA, Oldrich. b 15. Inst of Th Olomouc 32. **d** 37 **p** 38. V Penton Street St Silas w All SS *Lon* 66-68; rtd 68. *2 Carlton Court, Bosanquet Close, Cowley, Middx UB8 3PF* Uxbridge (01895) 254390

TRODDEN, Michael John. b 54. K Coll Lon BD77 AKC77 CertEd. Wycliffe Hall Ox 79. **d** 80 **p** 81. C Woodford St Mary w St Phil and St Jas *Chelmsf* 80-87; V Aldborough Hatch from 87. *The Vicarage, St Peter's Close, Oaks Lane, Ilford, Essex IG2 7QN* 0181-599 0524

TROLLOPE, David Harvey. b 41. BSc63. Lon Coll of Div 66. **d** 68 **p** 69. C Bermondsey St Jas w Ch Ch *S'wark* 68-71; Uganda 71-77; Kenya 77-82; V Gt Crosby St Luke *Liv* from 82. *St Luke's Vicarage, 71 Liverpool Road, Crosby, Liverpool L23 5SE* 0151-924 1737

TROMANS, Kevin Stanley. b 57. St Martin's Coll Lanc BEd79. Aston Tr Scheme 90 Coll of Resurr Mirfield 92. **d** 94 **p** 95. C Rawdon *Bradf* from 94. *69 Leeds Road, Rawdon, Leeds LS19 6NT* Leeds (0113) 250 8088

TROOP, John Richard. b 37. Ely Th Coll 61. **d** 64 **p** 65. C Linc St Andr *Linc* 64-66; C Linc St Swithin 64-66; C Gt Grimsby St Andr and St Luke 66-70; V Wrangle 70-78; V S Moor *Dur* 78-85; Chapl Dur and Northd ATC from 82; V Darlington St Hilda and St Columba 85-95; P-in-c Southwick St Columba from 95. *St Columba's Vicarage, Cornhill Road, Southwick, Sunderland SR5 1RU* 0191-516 0244

TROSS, Canon Julian Chamings. b 14. AKC35. Bps' Coll Cheshunt 37. **d** 37 **p** 38. R Datchworth *St Alb* 55-77; Hon Can St Alb 72-79; P-in-c Tewin 76-77; R Datchworth w Tewin 77-79; rtd 79; Perm to Offic *St Alb* from 79. *63 Colestrete, Stevenage, Herts SG1 1RE* Stevenage (01438) 354150

TROTMAN, Anthony Edward Fiennes. b 11. Ex Coll Ox BA33 MA56. Wycliffe Hall Ox 46. **d** 48 **p** 49. R Chilmark *Sarum* 59-76; rtd 76. *17 Estcourt Road, Salisbury SP1 3AP* Salisbury (01722) 324857

TROTT, Stephen John. b 57. FRSA86 Hull Univ BA79 Fitzw Coll Cam BA83 MA87. Westcott Ho Cam 81. **d** 84 **p** 85. C Hessle *York* 84-87; C Kingston upon Hull St Alb 87-88; R Pitsford w Boughton *Pet* from 88; Sec Continuing Minl Educn 88-93; Chapl Northants Gr Sch from 91; Adjunct Asst Prof American Univ of Lon from 93. *The Rectory, Humfrey Lane, Boughton, Northampton NN2 8RQ* Northampton (01604) 821387 Fax 820637

TROTTER, Harold Barrington (Barry). b 33. Sarum Th Coll 64. **d** 66 **p** 67. C Salisbury St Fran *Sarum* 66-69; Dioc Youth Officer 69-72; V Horton and Chalbury 69-73; R Frenchay *Bris* 73-81; V Henbury from 81. *St Mary's Vicarage, Station Road, Bristol BS10 7QQ* Bristol (0117) 950 0536

TROUNSON, Ronald Charles. b 26. Em Coll Cam BA48 MA52. Ripon Hall Ox 54. **d** 56 **p** 57. Chapl Denstone Coll Uttoxeter 58-76; Bursar 76-78; Prin St Chad's Coll Dur 78-88; R Easton on the Hill, Collyweston w Duddington etc *Pet* 89-94; NSM from 94; RD Barnack 91-94; rtd 94. *The Rectory, 38 West Street, Easton On The Hill, Stamford, Lincs PE9 3LS* Stamford (01780) 62616

TROUT, Keith. b 49. Trin Coll Bris DipHE92. **d** 92 **p** 93. C Pudsey St Lawr and St Paul *Bradf* from 92. *18 West Park, Pudsey, W Yorkshire LS28 7SN* Leeds (0113) 257 4582

TRUBRIDGE, George Ernest Samuel. b 11. ALCD35. **d** 35 **p** 36. R Broughton *Linc* 52-76; rtd 76. *27 Clarendon Road, Broadstone, Dorset BH18 9HT* Broadstone (01202) 695808

TRUBY, David Charles. b 57. BA79 Nottm Univ DipTh80. Linc Th Coll 79. **d** 82 **p** 83. C Stanley *Liv* 82-85; C Hindley St Pet 85-90; R Brimington *Derby* from 90. *The Rectory, Brimington, Chesterfield, Derbyshire S43 1JG* Chesterfield (01246) 273103

TRUDGILL, Harry Keith. b 25. LCP54 Leeds Univ DipEd49 Lon Univ BD61. St Deiniol's Hawarden 76. **d** 76 **p** 76. C Glas St Marg *Glas* 76-78; R Lenzie 78-86; rtd 86; Perm to Offic *Bradf* from 86. *4 High Bank, Grassington, Skipton, N Yorkshire BD23 5BU* Grassington (01756) 752371

TRUEMAN, Reginald. b 24. K Coll Cam BA47 MA49 Man Univ BD53. St Jo Coll Winnipeg Hon DD58 Ely Th Coll 48 Union Th Sem (NY) STM50. **d** 50 **p** 51. Lect K Coll Lon 61-74; Sen Lect N Co Coll of Educn 75-78; Teacher Manor Park Sch Newc 78-82; Lesotho 84-86; rtd 92. *17 Burnt Ash Cottages, Steep Marsh, Petersfield, Hants GU32 2BB* Petersfield (01730) 261341

TRUMAN, John Malcolm. b 33. Cuddesdon Coll 61. **d** 63 **p** 64. C Billingham St Aid *Dur* 63-65; C Alnwick St Mich *Newc* 65-68; R Ford 68-75; V Fenham St Jas and St Basil 75-84; V Chevington 84-87; Lic to Offic from 87; Chapl HM Young Offender Inst Castington 84-92; Chapl HM Pris Acklington from 92. *HM Prison Acklington, Morpeth, Northd NE65 9XF* Morpeth (01670) 760411 Fax 761362

TRUMPER, Roger David. b 52. Ex Univ BSc74 K Coll Lon MSc75 Ox Univ BA80 MA85. Wycliffe Hall Ox 78. **d** 81 **p** 82. C Tunbridge Wells St Jo *Roch* 81-84; C Slough *Ox* 84-87; TV Shenley and Loughton 87-88; TV Watling Valley 88-93; R Byfleet *Guildf* from 93. *The Rectory, 81 Rectory Lane, West Byfleet, Surrey KT14 7LX* Byfleet (01932) 342374

TRUNDLE, Herbert Edward. b 11. Lich Th Coll 33. **d** 36 **p** 37. V Cheam Common St Phil *S'wark* 52-76; rtd 76. *Westlands, Mappowder, Sturminster Newton, Dorset DT10 2EH* Sturminster Newton (01258) 817694

TRURO, Bishop of. See BALL, Rt Rev Michael Thomas

TRURO, Dean of. See SHEARLOCK, Very Rev David John

TRUSS, Charles Richard. b 42. Reading Univ BA63 K Coll Lon MPhil79 Linacre Coll Ox BA66 MA69. Wycliffe Hall Ox 64. **d** 66 **p** 67. C Leic H Apostles *Leic* 66-69; C Hampstead St Jo *Lon* 69-72; V Belsize Park 72-79; V Wood Green St Mich 79-82; TR Wood Green St Mich w Bounds Green St Gabr etc 82-85; R Shepperton 85-94; V Waterloo St Jo w St Andr *S'wark* from 94; RD Lambeth from 95. *St John's Vicarage, 1 Secker Street, London SE1 8UF* 0171-928 2003

TRUSTRAM, David Geoffrey. b 49. Pemb Coll Ox BA71 MA76 Qu Coll Cam BA73 MA77. Westcott Ho Cam 74. **d** 75 **p** 76. C Surbiton St Mark *S'wark* 75-77; C Surbiton St Andr and St Mark 77-78; C Richmond St Mary 78-79; C Richmond St Mary w St Matthias and St Jo 79-82; P-in-c Eastry *Cant* 82-88; R Eastry and Northbourne w Tilmanstone etc 88-90; Chapl Eastry Hosp 82-90; V Tenterden St Mildred w Smallhythe *Cant* from 90. *The Vicarage, Church Road, Tenterden, Kent TN30 6AT* Tenterden (01580) 763118

TSIPOURAS, John George. b 38. Trin Coll Bris 76. **d** 78 **p** 79. C Cheadle Hulme St Andr *Ches* 78-82; V Hurdsfield from 82. *197A Hurdsfield Road, Macclesfield, Cheshire SK10 2PY* Macclesfield (01625) 424587

TUAM, Archdeacon of. *Vacant*

TUAM, Dean of. See PREVITE, Very Rev Anthony Michael Allen

TUAM, KILLALA AND ACHONRY, Bishop of. See NEILL, Rt Rev John Robert Winder

TUAM, Provost of. See MacCARTHY, Very Rev Robert Brian

TUBBS, Preb Brian Ralph. b 44. AKC66. **d** 67 **p** 68. C Ex St Thos *Ex* 67-72; TV Sidmouth, Woolbrook and Salcombe Regis 72-77; R Ex St Jas from 77; RD Christianity from 89; Preb Ex Cathl from 95. *St James's Rectory, 4 Rosebank Crescent, Exeter EX4 6EJ* Exeter (01392) 55871

TUBBS, Canon Christopher Norman. b 25. G&C Coll Cam BA51 MA54. Wycliffe Hall Ox. **d** 52 **p** 53. C Neston *Ches* 52-55; C Nor St Pet Mancroft *Nor* 55-59; V Scalby *York* 59-68; V Scalby w Ravenscar and Staintondale from 68; RD Scarborough 76-82; Can and Preb York Minster from 85. *The Vicarage, Scalby, Scarborough, N Yorkshire YO13 0PS* Scarborough (01723) 362740

TUBBS, Peter Alfred. b 22. G&C Coll Cam BA48 MA53. Linc Th Coll 55. **d** 57 **p** 58. V Cardington *St Alb* 69-85; RD Elstow 77-82; C Sandy 85-89; rtd 89; Perm to Offic *St Alb* from 89. *1 Foster Grove, Sandy, Beds SG19 1HP* Sandy (01767) 682803

TUCK, Andrew Kenneth. b 42. Kelham Th Coll 63. **d** 68 **p** 69. C Poplar *Lon* 68-74; TV 74-76; V Walsgrave on Sowe *Cov* 76-90; R Farnham *Guildf* from 90. *The Rectory, Upper Church Lane, Farnham, Surrey GU9 7PW* Farnham (01252) 715412

TUCK, David John. b 36. St Cath Coll Cam BA61 MA65. Cuddesdon Coll 61. **d** 63 **p** 64. C Kelling w Salthouse *Nor* 63-69; C Holt 63-69; Zambia 69-73; V Sprowston *Nor* 73-84; R Beeston St Andr 73-84; RD Nor N 81-84; V Pinner *Lon* from 84. *The Vicarage, 2 Church Lane, Pinner, Middx HA5 3AA* 0181-866 3869 or 866 2676

TUCK, Nigel Graham. b 57. Chich Th Coll 82. **d** 85 **p** 86. C Port Talbot St Theodore *Llan* 85-87; C Llantrisant 87-90; TV Duston Team *Pet* from 90. *St Francis House, Eastfield Road, Duston, Northampton NN5 6TQ* Northampton (01604) 753679

TUCK, Ralph Thomas. b 42. Worc Coll Ox BA64 Bris Univ CertEd66 Leeds Univ DipFE81. N Ord Course 87. **d** 90 **p** 91. NSM S Crosland *Wakef* from 90; NSM Helme from 90. *5 Nields Road, Slaithwaite, W Yorkshire HD7 5HT* Huddersfield (01484) 843583

TUCK, Ronald James. b 47. S'wark Ord Course 75. **d** 78 **p** 79. C Upper Holloway St Pet *Lon* 78-79; C Upper Holloway St Pet w St Jo 79-81; P-in-c Scottow *Nor* 81-88; P-in-c Swanton Abbott w Skeyton 81-88; R Bradwell from 88. *The Rectory, Church Walk, Bradwell, Great Yarmouth, Norfolk NR31 8QQ* Great Yarmouth (01493) 663219

TUCKER, Andrew Michael. b 64. K Coll Lon BD87. Wycliffe Hall Ox DipMin95. **d** 95. C Moreton *Ches* from 95. *441 Hoylake Road, Moreton, Wirral, Merseyside L46 6DQ* 0151-678 1646

TUCKER, Anthony Ian. b 50. CYCW78. CA Tr Coll 73 S'wark Ord Course 81. **d** 85 **p** 86. NSM E Ham w Upton Park St Alb *Chelmsf* 85-86; NSM S'well Minster *S'well* 86-90; C Rolleston w Fiskerton, Morton and Upton 90-93; P-in-c Teversal from 93; Chapl Sutton Cen from 93. *The Parsonage, Fackley Road, Sutton-in-Ashfield, Notts NG17 3JA*   Mansfield (01623) 550730 or 554554

TUCKER, Desmond Robert. b 29. Bris Sch of Min 83. **d** 86 **p** 87. C Bris St Mich *Bris* 86-88; P-in-c 88-94; rtd 94. *94 Fremantle House, Dove Street, Bristol BS2 8LH* Bristol (0117) 924 6803

TUCKER, Douglas Greening. b 17. Lon Univ DipTh53. St Aid Birkenhead 49. **d** 52 **p** 53. V Elsham *Linc* 62-85; V Worlaby 62-85; V Bonby 73-85; rtd 85. *Balintore, Main Street, Bowsden, Northd TD15 2TW* Berwick-upon-Tweed (01289) 88630

TUCKER, Harold George. b 21. St Aug Coll Cant 48 Sarum Th Coll 50. **d** 51 **p** 52. R Bratton Fleming *Ex* 64-73; P-in-c Goodleigh 67-73; P-in-c Stoke Rivers 67-73; P-in-c Parracombe 69-73; P-in-c Martinhoe 69-73; R Whimple 73-86; rtd 86. *Lansdowne, The Crescent, Widemouth Bay, Bude, Cornwall EX23 0AE* Bude (01288) 361396

TUCKER, Ian Malcolm. b 46. Bris Coll HND69 ONC66. S Dios Minl Tr Scheme 86. **d** 89 **p** 90. NSM Pill w Easton in Gordano and Portbury *B & W* 89-95; C Frome St Jo and St Mary from 95. *St Mary's House, Innox Hill, Frome, Somerset BA11 2LN* Frome (01373) 463525

TUCKER, John Yorke Raffles. b 24. Magd Coll Cam BA49 MA56. Westcott Ho Cam 49. **d** 51 **p** 52. V Belmont *Lon* 67-78; V Sunbury 78-89; rtd 89; Perm to Offic *Ex* 89-93. *Tudor Cottage, Fivehead, Taunton, Somerset TA3 6PJ* South Chard (01460) 281330

TUCKER, Michael. b 33. MA. **d** 84 **p** 85. NSM Sawston *Ely* 84-87; C Ely 87-90; P-in-c Barton Bendish w Beachamwell and Shingham from 90; P-in-c Wereham from 90. *The Rectory, Barton Bendish, King's Lynn, Norfolk PE33 9DP* Fincham (013664) 363

TUCKER, Dr Michael Owen. b 42. Lon Univ BSc66 Surrey Univ PhD69. Glouc Sch of Min 81. **d** 84 **p** 85. NSM C Uley w Owlpen and Nympsfield *Glouc* 84-92; P-in-c Amberley from 92; Dioc NSM Officer from 94. *The Rectory, Amberley, Stroud, Glos GL5 5JG* Stroud (01453) 878515

TUCKER, Nicholas Harold (Nick). b 41. Reading Univ BSc66. N Ord Course 90. **d** 93 **p** 94. NSM Ilkley All SS *Bradf* from 93. *Waddington House, 2 Margerison Road, Ilkley, W Yorkshire LS29 8QU* Ilkley (01943) 609472 Fax 609829

TUCKER, Richard Parish. b 51. Cam Univ BA72 MA76 Lon Univ BD83. Wycliffe Hall Ox 80. **d** 83 **p** 84. C Wellington w Eyton *Lich* 83-84; C Walsall 84-88; TV Dronfield *Derby* 88-90; TV Dronfield w Holmesfield from 90. *11 Rothay Close, Dronfield Woodhouse, Sheffield S18 5PR* Dronfield (01246) 416893

TUCKER, Stephen Reid. b 51. New Coll Ox MA76 DipTh76. Ripon Coll Cuddesdon 75. **d** 77 **p** 78. C Hove All SS *Chich* 77-80; Lect Chich Th Coll 80-86; V Portsea St Alb *Portsm* 86-90; Chapl and Dean of Div New Coll Ox from 90; Lic to Offic *Ox* from 90. *New College, Oxford OX1 3BN* Oxford (01865) 279541

TUCKETT, Prof Christopher Mark. b 48. Qu Coll Cam MA71 Lanc Univ PhD79. Westcott Ho Cam 71. **d** 75 **p** 76. C Lanc St Mary *Blackb* 75-77; Chapl and Fell Qu Coll Cam 77-79; Lect NT Man Univ 79-89; Sen Lect 89-91; Prof Bibl Studies from 91. *Kidd Road Farm, Charlesworth, Glossop, Derbyshire SK13 9PN* Glossop (01457) 860150

TUCKEY, John William Townsend. b 19. TCD BA41 MA. **d** 43 **p** 44. V Milton *B & W* 65-74; P-in-c E Brent 74-75; R E Brent w Lympsham 75-81; rtd 84; Perm to Offic *B & W* from 85. *7 Parkfields, Butleigh, Glastonbury, Somerset BA6 8SZ* Glastonbury (01458) 51107

TUCKWELL, Paul. b 12. Magd Coll Ox BA35 MA38. Westcott Ho Cam 36. **d** 38 **p** 39. R Appleton *Ox* 66-79; rtd 79; Perm to Offic *Glouc* from 79. *18 Canonbury Street, Berkeley, Glos GL13 9BG* Dursley (01453) 810120

TUDBALL, Arthur James. b 28. AKC54. **d** 54 **p** 55. Malaysia 63-73 and 75-79; Brunei 73-75; Singapore from 79; rtd 89. *Orchard Point, PO Box 160, Singapore 9123* Singapore (65) 259-4298

TUDGE, Paul Quartus. b 55. Leeds Univ BEd78. Cranmer Hall Dur 84. **d** 87 **p** 88. C Roundhay St Edm *Ripon* 87-90; C Leeds St Pet 90; C Leeds City 91; V Woodside from 91. *St James's Vicarage, 1 Scotland Close, Horsforth, Leeds LS18 5SG* Leeds (0113) 258 2433

TUDGEY, Stephen John. b 51. St Jo Coll Nottm BTh81 LTh. **d** 81 **p** 82. C Grays Thurrock *Chelmsf* 81-83; C Grays SS Pet and Paul, S Stifford and W Thurrock 83-84; C Grays Thurrock 84; C Madeley *Heref* 84-87; R Chilcompton w Downside and Stratton on the Fosse *B & W* from 87. *The Rectory, The Street, Chilcompton, Bath BA3 4HN* Stratton-on-the-Fosse (01761) 232219

TUDOR, David Charles Frederick. b 42. Sarum & Wells Th Coll 70. **d** 73 **p** 74. C Plymouth St Pet *Ex* 73-75; C Reddish *Man* 75-78; P-in-c Hamer 78-80; V Goldenhill *Lich* 80-87; V Meir 87-91; Chapl Asst Nottm City Hosp 91-94; Chapl Cen Sheff Univ Hosps NHS Trust from 94. *The Royal Hallamshire Hospital, Glossop Road, Sheffield S10 2JF* Sheffield (0114) 276 6222

TUDOR, David St Clair. b 55. K Coll Lon BD77 AKC77 K Coll Lon MTh89. Ripon Coll Cuddesdon 77. **d** 78 **p** 79. C Plumstead St Nic *S'wark* 78-80; C Redhill St Matt 80-83; C-in-c Reigate St Phil CD 83-87; Asst Sec Gen Syn Bd for Miss and Unity 87-88; Perm to Offic *S'wark* from 94. *68 Venner Road, London SE26 5EL* 0181-676 9582

TUDOR, Malcolm George Henry Booth. b 36. Nottm Univ BA71. Linc Th Coll 72. **d** 60 **p** 61. In RC Ch 60-71; C Cinderhill *S'well* 72-74; P-in-c Broxtowe 74-78; P-in-c E Drayton w Stokeham 78-86; R E Markham and Askham 78-86; P-in-c Headon w Upton 78-86; V Llandinam w Trefeglwys w Penstrowed *Ban* from 86. *The Vicarage, Llandinam, Powys SY17 5BS* Caersws (01686) 688341

TUFFEL, Kennedy Joseph. b 20. Worc Ord Coll 64. **d** 66 **p** 67. C Goring-by-Sea *Chich* 68-72 and 81-89; NSM from 89; V Barnham 72-78; Hon C W Worthing St Jo 78-81; rtd 89. *15 Mill House Gardens, Mill Road, Worthing, W Sussex BN11 4NE* Worthing (01903) 700671

TUFFIELD, Canon Basil Thomas. b 23. Fitzw Ho Cam BA49 MA54. Wells Th Coll 50. **d** 52 **p** 53. V Carshalton Beeches *S'wark* 65-79; P-in-c Crosscanonby *Carl* 79-82; V 82-90; P-in-c Allonby w W Newton 81-82; V Allonby 82-90; RD Solway 84-90; Hon Can Carl Cathl 87-90; rtd 90. *Hafod y Cwm, Nannerch, Mold, Clwyd CH7 5RP* Mold (01352) 741234

TUFFIN, Mrs Gillian Patricia. b 43. S Dios Minl Tr Scheme 91. **d** 94 **p** 95. C Gidea Park *Chelmsf* from 94. *109 Carlton Road, Romford RM2 5AU* Romford (01708) 769669

TUFFNELL, Nigel Owen. b 65. Teesside Poly BSc90. St Jo Coll Nottm 91. **d** 94 **p** 95. C Guisborough *York* from 94. *16 Lealholm Way, Guisborough, Cleveland TS14 8LN* Guisborough (01287) 635873

TUFNELL, Edward Nicholas Pember. b 45. Chu Coll Cam MA68. St Jo Coll Nottm BA73. **d** 73 **p** 74. C Ealing St Mary *Lon* 73-76; BCMS 76-88; Tanzania 76-88; P-in-c Lt Thurrock St Jo *Chelmsf* 89-91; V from 91; Chapl Thurrock Hosp from 89. *St John's Vicarage, Victoria Avenue, Grays, Essex RM16 2RP* Grays Thurrock (01375) 372101

TUFT, Preb Patrick Anthony. b 31. Selw Coll Cam BA56 MA60. Edin Th Coll 56. **d** 58 **p** 59. C Keighley *Bradf* 58-63; PV Chich Cathl *Chich* 63-68; Min Can St Paul's Cathl *Lon* 68-74; Hon Min Can St Paul's Cathl from 74; V Chiswick St Nic w St Mary from 74; PV Westmr Abbey 74-79; AD Hounslow *Lon* 87-93; P-in-c Chiswick St Paul Grove Park 88-90; Preb St Paul's Cathl from 95. *Chiswick Vicarage, The Mall, London W4 2PJ* 0181-995 4717

TUGWELL, Elizabeth Ann. b 36. **d** 94. NSM Carbis Bay w Lelant *Truro* from 94. *Buslasson, Close, Carbis Bay, St Ives, Cornwall TR26 2SD* St Ives (01736) 798551

TULL, Preb Christopher Stuart. b 36. Hertf Coll Ox BA60 MA64. Oak Hill Th Coll 60. **d** 62 **p** 63. C Stoodleigh *Ex* 62-71; C Washfield 62-71; TV Washfield, Stoodleigh, Withleigh etc 71-74; RD Tiverton 74-75; R Bishops Nympton w Rose Ash 75-77; V Mariansleigh 75-77; TR Bishopsnympton, Rose Ash, Mariansleigh etc from 77; RD S Molton 80-87; Preb Ex Cathl from 84. *The Rectory, Bishops Nympton, South Molton, Devon EX36 4NY* Bishops Nympton (01769) 550427

TULLETT, Peter Watts. b 46. Qu Coll Birm 92. **d** 94 **p** 95. C Worle *B & W* from 94. *6 Rookery Close, Worle, Weston-super-Mare, Avon BS22 9LN* Weston-super-Mare (01934) 512467

TULLOCH, Richard James Anthony. b 52. Wadh Coll Ox BA74 Selw Coll Cam BA79. Ridley Hall Cam 76. **d** 79 **p** 80. C Morden *S'wark* 79-83; C Jesmond Clayton Memorial *Newc* 83-94; V New Boro and Leigh *Sarum* from 94. *The Vicarage, 15 St John's Hill, Wimborne, Dorset BH21 1BX* Wimborne (01202) 883490

TULLOCH, Walter Harold. b 16. AIMLS53 MRSH62. St Deiniol's Hawarden 79. **d** 79 **p** 80. NSM Maghull *Liv* 79-86; Hon C from 88; rtd 86; Perm to Offic *Liv* 86-88. *8 Tailor's Lane, Maghull, Liverpool L31 3HD* 0151-526 1936

TULLY, David John. b 56. St Jo Coll Dur BA77 Nottm Univ PGCE78. Ridley Hall Cam 81. **d** 84 **p** 85. C Gosforth St Nic *Newc* 84-86; C Newburn 86-90; TV Whorlton from 90. *St John's Vicarage, Whorlton, Newcastle upon Tyne NE5 1NN* 0191-286 9648

TULLY, Ross. b 22. Clare Coll Cam BA44 MA48. Ridley Hall Cam 47. **d** 49 **p** 50. Pakistan 53-73; Chapl St Bernard's Hosp Southall 74-80; C Eastbourne H Trin *Chich* 80-86; rtd 87. *Venn House, 17 Boyne Park, Tunbridge Wells, Kent TN4 8EL* Tunbridge Wells (01892) 534729

TUNBRIDGE, John Stephen. b 31. Keble Coll Ox BA54 MA59. Ely Th Coll 54. **d** 56 **p** 57. C Upper Norwood All SS w St Marg

Cant 56-57; C Ramsgate St Geo 57-60; P-in-c 76-84; C Folkestone St Mary and St Eanswythe 60-62; R Gt Chart 62-67; V Womenswold 67-76; C-in-c Aylesham CD 67-76; R Harbledown 84-94; Perm to Offic *St D* from 94. *Ashdown, 11 Castle Road, St Ishmaels, Haverfordwest, Dyfed SA62 3SF* Dale (01646) 636584

TUNLEY, Timothy Mark (Tim). b 61. Oak Hill Th Coll DipHE84 Ridley Hall Cam CTM92. **d** 92 **p** 93. C Aldborough w Boroughbridge and Roecliffe *Ripon* 92-95; C Knaresborough from 95. *39 Birkdale Avenue, Knaresborough, N Yorkshire HG5 0LS* Boroughbridge (01423) 864484

TUNNICLIFFE, Mrs Jean Sarah. b 36. RGN69. Glouc Sch of Min 89. **d** 92 **p** 94. NSM Dixton *Heref* from 92. *Bryn Awelon, 21 Ridgeway, Wyesham, Monmouth, Gwent NP5 3JX* Monmouth (01600) 714115

TUNNICLIFFE, Canon Martin Wyndham. b 31. Keele Univ BA56. Qu Coll Birm 59. **d** 60 **p** 61. C Castle Bromwich SS Mary and Marg *Birm* 60-65; V Shard End 65-73; R Over Whitacre w Shustoke 73-78; V Tanworth from 78; RD Solihull 89-94; Hon Can Birm Cathl from 91. *The Vicarage, Tanworth-in-Arden, Solihull, W Midlands B94 5EB* Tanworth-in-Arden (01564) 742565

TUNSTALL, Barry Anthony. b 29. Sarum Th Coll 53. **d** 55 **p** 56. V N Mymms *St Alb* 63-81; P-in-c Kirkby Overblow *Ripon* 81; R Kirkby Overblow 81-94; rtd 94. *22 Roman Row, Whichford, Shipston-on-Stour, Warks CV36 5PJ* Shipston-on-Stour (01608) 684362

TUPPER, Michael Heathfield. b 20. St Edm Hall Ox BA41 MA46. Ridley Hall Cam 41. **d** 43 **p** 44. C Win Ch Ch *Win* 43-45; Chapl Monkton Combe Sch Bath 45-48; Asst Chapl Shrewsbury Sch 48-59 and 60-79; Kenya 59-60; Hon C Bayston Hill *Lich* from 80. *9 Eric Lock Road, Bayston Hill, Shrewsbury SY3 0HQ* Shrewsbury (01743) 722674

TURAY, Prince Eddie Solomon. b 60. Sierra Leone Th Hall 82. **d** 85 **p** 87. Sierra Leone 85-91; Hon C Gt Cam Road St Jo and St Jas *Lon* from 94. *73 Haselbury Road, London N18 1PZ* 0181-372 5161

✠**TURNBULL, Rt Rev Anthony Michael Arnold.** b 35. Keble Coll Ox BA58 MA62. Cranmer Hall Dur DipTh60. **d** 60 **p** 61 **c** 88. C Middleton *Man* 60-61; C Luton w E Hyde *St Alb* 61-65; Dir of Ords *York* 65-69; Abp's Dom Chapl 65-69; Chapl York Univ 69-76; V Heslington 69-76; Chief Sec CA 76-84; Can Res Roch Cathl *Roch* 84-88; Adn Roch 84-88; Bp Roch 88-94; Bp Dur from 94. *Auckland Castle, Bishop Auckland, Co Durham DL14 7NR* Bishop Auckland (01388) 602576 Fax 605264

TURNBULL, Brian Robert. b 43. Chich Th Coll 71. **d** 74 **p** 75. C Norbury St Phil *Cant* 74-76; C Folkestone St Sav 76-77; Hon C Tong *Lich* 83-88; C Jarrow *Dur* 88-89; TV 89-94; P-in-c Hartlepool St Oswald from 94. *St Oswald's Clergy House, Brougham Terrace, Hartlepool, Cleveland TS24 8EU* Hartlepool (01429) 273201

TURNBULL, Charles Philip. b 13. Ely Th Coll 37. **d** 38 **p** 39. V Hornsey St Pet *Lon* 64-76; Chapl Laleham Abbey 76-79; rtd 79; Perm to Offic *Chich* from 79. *White Lodge, South Strand, East Preston, Littlehampton, W Sussex BN16 1PN* Littlehampton (01903) 784415

TURNBULL, Ven David Charles. b 44. Leeds Univ BA65. Chich Th Coll 67. **d** 69 **p** 70. C Jarrow St Paul *Dur* 69-74; V Carlinghow *Wakef* 74-83; V Penistone 83-86; TR Penistone and Thurlstone 86-93; RD Barnsley 88-93; Hon Can Wakef Cathl 92-93; Adn Carl from 93. *2 The Abbey, Carlisle CA3 8TZ* Carlisle (01228) 23026 Fax 594899

TURNBULL, James. b 19. St Aug Coll Cant 57. **d** 58 **p** 59. R Twineham *Chich* 61-75; P-in-c Kingston Buci 75-80; Perm to Offic *B & W* from 80; rtd 84. *34 Hood Close, Glastonbury, Somerset BA6 8ES* Glastonbury (01458) 833796

TURNBULL, James Awty. b 28. Solicitor. Cranmer Hall Dur 89. **d** 89 **p** 90. NSM Bolton Abbey *Bradf* from 89. *Deerstones Cottage, Deerstones, Skipton, N Yorkshire BD23 6JB*

TURNBULL, Canon John Smith Gardiner. b 13. Kelham Th Coll 30. **d** 36 **p** 37. V Auckland St Helen *Dur* 53-78; Hon Can Dur Cathl 58-78; rtd 79. *32 The Ridgeway, Mount Park Drive, Lanchester, Durham DH7 0PT* Lanchester (01207) 520541

TURNBULL, Peter Frederick. b 64. SS Mark & Jo Coll Plymouth BA85. Sarum & Wells Th Coll 89. **d** 91 **p** 92. C Upper Norwood All SS *S'wark* 91-95; Chapl HM Pris Dorchester from 95; Dorchester *Sarum* from 95. *The Vicarage, Maiden Newton, Dorchester, Dorset DT2 0AT* Dorchester (01305) 320284

TURNBULL, Richard Duncan. b 60. Reading Univ BA82 MICAS85. Cranmer Hall Dur BA92. **d** 94 **p** 95. C Portswood Ch Ch *Win* from 94. *6 Royston Close, Southampton SO17 1TB* Southampton (01703) 595015

TURNBULL, Stephen. b 40. Nottm Univ BTh74. Linc Th Coll 70. **d** 74 **p** 75. C Kirkstall *Ripon* 74-76; C Fairfield *Derby* 76-79; TV Seacroft *Ripon* 79-84; Lic to Offic *Derby* from 84; Chapl

Derby City Hosp from 84; Chapl Derbyshire Children's Hosp from 84. *Derby City General Hospital, Uttoxeter Road, Derby DE22 3NE* Derby (01332) 340131

TURNBULL, William George. b 25. Lich Th Coll 63. **d** 65 **p** 66. C Portishead *B & W* 69-73; C Holsworthy w Cookbury *Ex* 73-76; P-in-c Bridgerule 76-79; P-in-c Pyworthy w Pancraswyke 77-79; P-in-c Pyworthy, Pancrasweek and Bridgerule 79-80; R 80-81; V Otterton and Colaton Raleigh 81-90; rtd 90; Chapl Convent Companions Jes Gd Shep W Ogwell 90-94; Lic to Offic *Ex* 90-94. *College of St Barnabas, Blackberry Lane, Lingfield, Surrey RH7 6NJ* Dormans Park (01342) 870260

TURNER, Alan James. b 40. Oak Hill Th Coll BA81. **d** 81 **p** 82. C Bradley *Wakef* 81-84; C Sandal St Helen 84-86; P-in-c Sileby *Leic* 86-87; TR Sileby, Cossington and Seagrave 87-94; R Hollington St Leon *Chich* from 94. *The Rectory, Tile Barn Road, St Leonards-on-Sea, E Sussex TN38 9PA* Hastings (01424) 852257

TURNER, Albert Edward. b 41. Glouc Sch of Min 83. **d** 89 **p** 90. C Woodford St Mary w St Phil and St Jas *Chelmsf* 89-91; R Greatworth and Marston St Lawrence etc *Pet* from 91. *The Rectory, Marston St Lawrence, Banbury, Oxon OX17 2DA* Banbury (01295) 712279

TURNER, Andrew John. b 52. St Jo Coll Nottm LTh. **d** 83 **p** 84. C Framlingham w Saxtead *St E* 83-86; P-in-c Badingham w Bruisyard and Cransford 86-88; P-in-c Dennington 86-88; R Badingham w Bruisyard, Cransford and Dennington 88-91; Chapl RAF from 91. *Chaplaincy Services (RAF), HQ, Personnel and Training Command, RAF Innsworth, Gloucester GL3 1EZ* Gloucester (01452) 712612 Ext 5164 Fax 510828

TURNER, Mrs Ann Elizabeth Hamer. b 58. Ex Univ BA59 PGCE60. Trin Coll Bris 84. **dss** 86 **d** 87 **p** 94. Bath St Luke *B & W* 86-87; Hon C 87-91; Chapl Dorothy Ho Foundn 89-91; C Bath Twerton-on-Avon 91-94; TV from 94. *24 Edgeworth Road, Bath BA2 2LY* Bath (01225) 424234

TURNER, Anthony John. b 49. St Mich Coll Llan 89. **d** 91 **p** 92. C Coity w Nolton *Llan* 91-95; R Castlemartin w Warren and Angle etc *St D* from 95. *The Rectory, Angle, Pembroke, Dyfed SA71 5AN* Angle (01646) 641368

TURNER, Ven Antony Hubert Michael (Tony). b 30. FCA63 Lon Univ DipTh56. Tyndale Hall Bris 54. **d** 56 **p** 57. C Nottm St Ann *S'well* 56-58; C Cheadle *Ches* 58-62; V Macclesfield Ch Ch 62-68; Lic to Offic *S'wark* 68-74; Home Sec BCMS 68-74; V Southsea St Jude *Portsm* 74-86; P-in-c Portsea St Luke 75-80; RD Portsm 79-84; Hon Can Portsm Cathl 85-86; Adn Is of Wight from 86. *3 Beech Grove, Ryde, Isle of Wight PO33 3AN* Isle of Wight (01983) 565522 Fax as telephone

TURNER, Benjamin John. b 45. Bolton Inst of Tech CEng MICE. N Ord Course 82. **d** 85 **p** 86. C Worsley *Man* 85-88; V Elton St Steph from 88. *St Stephen's Vicarage, 44 Peers Street, Bury, Lancs BL9 2QF* 0161-764 1775

TURNER, Mrs Beryl Rose. b 31. Nottm Univ CertEd75 BEd76. **dss** 84 **d** 87 **p** 94. Mortomley St Sav *Sheff* 84-86; Whitgift w Adlingfleet and Eastoft 86; The Marshland 86-87; Par Dn Goole 87-94; C 94; rtd 95. *49 Colonel's Walk, Goole, N Humberside DN14 6HJ* Goole (01405) 769193

TURNER, Carl Francis. b 60. St Chad's Coll Dur BA81. St Steph Ho Ox 83. **d** 85 **p** 86. C Leigh-on-Sea St Marg *Chelmsf* 85-88; C Brentwood St Thos 88-90; TV Plaistow from 90. *St Martin's Vicarage, 34 St Martin's Avenue, London E6 3DX* 0181-470 3262

TURNER, Charles Maurice Joseph. b 13. **d** 79 **p** 80. Hon C Brislington St Luke *Bris* 79-83; Hon C Bris Ch Ch w St Ewen and All SS 83-84; Hon C Bris St Steph w St Nic and St Leon 83-84; Hon C City of Bris 84-89; Perm to Offic from 89. *31 Eagle Road, Bristol BS4 3LQ* Bristol (0117) 977 6329

TURNER, Mrs Christine. E Midl Min Tr Course. **d** 94 **p** 95. Chapl Qu Medical Cen Nottm from 94. *Bridge Farm, Hickling, Melton Mowbray, Leics LE14 3AH* Kinoulton (01949) 81304

TURNER, Christopher Gilbert. b 29. New Coll Ox BA52 MA55. Ox Min Course 91. **d** 92 **p** 93. Hon C Hook Norton w Gt Rollright, Swerford etc *Ox* from 92. *Rosemullion, High Street, Great Rollright, Chipping Norton, Oxon OX7 5RQ* Hook Norton (01608) 737359

TURNER, Christopher James Shepherd. b 48. Ch Ch Ox BA70 MA74. Wycliffe Hall Ox 71. **d** 74 **p** 75. C Rusholme *Man* 74-78; C Chadderton Ch Ch 78-80; V 80-89; V Selly Park St Steph and St Wulstan *Birm* from 89. *St Stephen's Vicarage, 20 Elmdon Road, Birmingham B29 7LF* 0121-472 0050

TURNER, Colin Peter John. b 42. Clifton Th Coll 63. **d** 66 **p** 67. C Kinson *Sarum* 66-68; C York St Paul *York* 68-72; Org Sec (SE Area) CPAS 73-78; TV Weymouth St Jo *Sarum* 78-87; TV Radipole and Melcombe Regis 78-87; R Radstock w Writhlington *B & W* from 90; R Kilmersdon w Babington from 90. *The Rectory, 1 Bristol Road, Radstock, Bath BA3 3EF* Radstock (01761) 433182

TURNER

TURNER, David. b 40. St Andr Univ BSc63. Ridley Hall Cam 63. **d** 65 **p** 66. C Bootle St Matt *Liv* 65-68; C Wigan St Barn Marsh Green 68-73; V Huyton St Geo 73-79; V Meltham Mills *Wakef* 79-89; V Wilshaw 79-89; P-in-c Helme 81-85; P-in-c Meltham 85-89; V Gawber from 89. *The Vicarage, Church Street, Gawber, Barnsley, S Yorkshire S75 2RL* Barnsley (01226) 207140

TURNER, David Stanley. b 35. MISM69 MISE69 Lon Univ CertRK69 Westmr Coll Ox BA84. W Midl Minl Tr Course 86. **d** 87 **p** 88. In Free Ch of England 75-77; NSM Worc St Mich *Worc* 87-90; Min Shelfield St Mark CD *Lich* 90-95; C Walsall Wood 90-95; Chapl St Woolos Cathl *Mon* from 95. *Hebron, 9 Clifton Road, Newport, Gwent NP9 4EW* Newport (01633) 267191

TURNER, Derek John. b 54. Univ of Wales (Ban) BSc81 PhD86. St Jo Coll Nottm. **d** 87 **p** 88. C Pelsall *Lich* 87-91; C Stratford-on-Avon w Bishopton *Cov* from 91. *6 Verney Drive, Stratford-upon-Avon, Warks CV37 0DX* Stratford-upon-Avon (01789) 269874

TURNER, Donald. b 29. S'wark Ord Course. **d** 71 **p** 72. C Hounslow St Steph *Lon* 71-76; Hon C Isleworth St Jo 76-78; C Brighton St Pet w Chpl Royal *Chich* 78-80; C Brighton St Pet w Chpl Royal and St Jo 80-85; P-in-c St Leonards SS Pet and Paul 85-87; V 87-91; rtd 91. *The Vicarage, West Alvington, Kingsbridge, Devon TQ7 3PZ* Kingsbridge (01548) 857658

TURNER, Douglas John. b 15. Ely Th Coll 45. **d** 47 **p** 48. V Ventnor H Trin *Portsm* 66-72; V Ventnor St Cath 66-72; V Ryde All SS 72-81; rtd 81; Perm to Offic *Chich* 81-94; Perm to Offic *Nor* from 94. *29 Primrose Avenue, Mulbarton, Norwich NR14 8BJ* Mulbarton (01508) 570185

TURNER, Canon Edward Robert. b 37. Em Coll Cam BA62 BTh66 MA67. Westcott Ho Cam 64. **d** 66 **p** 67. C Salford St Phil w St Steph *Man* 66-69; Chapl Tonbridge Sch Kent 69-81; Adv for In-Service Tr *Roch* 81-89; Dir of Educn from 81; Can Res Roch Cathl from 81; Vice-Dean Roch Cathl from 88. *1 King's Orchard, The Precinct, Rochester, Kent ME1 1TG* Medway (01634) 842756 or 830333

TURNER, Mrs Eileen Margaret. b 45. Golds Coll Lon TCert66. N Ord Course 90. **d** 93 **p** 94. Par Dn Sandal St Cath *Wakef* 93-94; C from 94. *6 Kensington Road, Wakefield, W Yorkshire WF1 3JX* Wakefield (01924) 374213

TURNER, Canon Eric Gurney Hammond. b 11. St Edm Hall Ox BA40 MA44. Cuddesdon Coll 40. **d** 41 **p** 42. R Colchester St Jas, All SS, St Nic and St Runwald *Chelmsf* 69-81; Hon Can Chelmsf Cathl 74-81; RD Colchester 75-81; rtd 81. *D'Arcy Cottage, South Street, Tolleshunt D'Arcy, Maldon, Essex CM9 8TR* Maldon (01621) 860232

TURNER, Canon Francis Edwin. b 29. Sarum Th Coll 54. **d** 57 **p** 58. R Northbourne w Betteshanger and Ham *Cant* 64-70; R Northbourne, Tilmanstone w Betteshanger and Ham 70-74; V Sittingbourne St Mich 74-94; RD Sittingbourne 78-84; Hon Can Cant Cathl 84-94; rtd 94. *6 Cherry Grove, Hungerford, Berks RG17 0HP* Hungerford (01488) 682683

TURNER, Frederick Charles Jesse. b 07. St Boniface Warminster 31. **d** 36 **p** 37. V Hooe *Chich* 65-74; R Ninfield 65-74; rtd 74. *1 Birchwood Road, Malvern, Worcs WR14 1LD* Leigh Sinton (01886) 832453

TURNER, Canon Frederick Glynne. b 30. Univ of Wales (Lamp) BA52. St Mich Coll Llan 52. **d** 54 **p** 55. C Aberaman *Llan* 54-60; C Oystermouth *S & B* 60-64; V Abercynon *Llan* 64-71; V Ton Pentre 71-73; V Ystradyfodwg 73-77; R Caerphilly 77-82; V Whitchurch from 82; Can Llan Cathl from 84. *The Vicarage, 6 Penlline Road, Whitchurch, Cardiff CF4 2AD* Cardiff (01222) 626072

TURNER, Geoffrey. b 46. St Deiniol's Hawarden 86. **d** 87 **p** 88. C Lougher *S & B* 87-89; C Swansea St Pet 89-90; V New Radnor and Llanfihangel Nantmelan etc from 90. *The Rectory, New Radnor, Presteigne, Powys LD8 2SS* New Radnor (0154421) 258

TURNER, Geoffrey. b 51. Selw Coll Cam BA75 PGCE75 MA78. N Ord Course 90. **d** 93 **p** 94. C E Crompton *Man* from 93. *15 Oak Street, Shaw, Oldham OL2 8EJ* Shaw (01706) 844934

TURNER, Dr Geoffrey Edwin. b 45. Aston Univ BSc68 Newc Univ MSc69 PhD72. Cranmer Hall Dur BA74 DipTh75. **d** 75 **p** 76. C Wood End *Cov* 75-79; V Huyton Quarry *Liv* 79-86; Press and Communications Officer *Ely* 86-94; P-in-c Gt w Lt Abington 86-94; P-in-c Hildersham 86-94; V Letchworth St Paul w Willian *St Alb* from 94. *St Paul's Vicarage, 177 Pixmore Way, Letchworth, Herts SG6 1QT* Letchworth (01462) 683083 Fax 894172

✠**TURNER, Rt Rev Geoffrey Martin.** b 34. Oak Hill Th Coll 60. **d** 63 **p** 64 **c** 94. C Tonbridge St Steph *Roch* 63-66; C Heatherlands St Jo *Sarum* 66-69; V Derby St Pet *Derby* 69-73; V Chadderton Ch Ch *Man* 73-79; R Bebington *Ches* 79-93; Hon Can Ches Cathl 89-93; RD Wirral N 89-93; Adn Ches

93-94; Suff Bp Stockport from 94. *Bishop's Lodge, Back Lane, Dunham Town, Altrincham, Cheshire WA14 4SG* 0161-928 5611 Fax 929 0692

TURNER, Canon Gerald Garth. b 38. Univ of Wales (Lamp) BA61 St Edm Hall Ox BA63 MA67. St Steph Ho Ox 63. **d** 65 **p** 66. C Drayton in Hales *Lich* 65-68; Chapl Prebendal Sch Chich 68-70; PV Chich Cathl *Chich* 68-70; C Forest Row 70-72; V Hope *Derby* 72-78; Prec Man Cathl *Man* 78-86; Can Res 78-86; R Tattenhall and Handley *Ches* from 86. *The Rectory, Tattenhall, Chester CH3 9QE* Tattenhall (01829) 70328

TURNER, Graham Colin. b 55. Bradf Univ BTech. Oak Hill Th Coll BA81. **d** 81 **p** 82. C Upper Armley *Ripon* 81-86; V Bordesley Green *Birm* from 86. *The Vicarage, 405 Belcher's Lane, Bordesley Green, Birmingham B9 5SY* 0121-772 0418 Fax 766 5401

TURNER, Mrs Heather Winifred. b 43. SRN65. Cant Sch of Min 89. **d** 90 **p** 94. Par Dn Orpington All SS *Roch* 90-93; Dioc and RAD Chapl amongst the Deaf from 93. *24 Wallace Road, Rochester, Kent ME1 2TA* Medway (01634) 845091

TURNER, Henry John Mansfield. b 24. Magd Coll Cam BA45 MA48 Man Univ PhD85. Westcott Ho Cam 48. **d** 50 **p** 51. C Crosby *Linc* 50-52; C Chorlton upon Medlock *Man* 52-55; Inter-Colleg Sec SCM (Man) 52-55; C Leigh St Mary *Man* 55-57; V Rochdale Gd Shep 57-62; India 63-67; V Becontree St Geo *Chelmsf* 67-71; R Weeley 71-79; Chapl St Deiniol's Lib Hawarden 79-80; Sub-Warden 80-86; Perm to Offic *St As* 86-87; Perm to Offic *Chelmsf* from 86; Hon C St Botolph without Bishopgate *Lon* from 87. *Merrywood, 25 Fourth Avenue, Frinton-on-Sea, Essex CO13 9DU* Frinton-on-Sea (01255) 677554

TURNER, Canon Prof Henry Ernest William. b 07. St Jo Coll Ox BA39 MA33 Linc Coll Ox BD40 DD55. Wycliffe Hall Ox 31. **d** 31 **p** 32. Can Res Dur Cathl *Dur* 51-73; Prof Div Dur Univ 58-74; rtd 74; Perm to Offic *Carl* from 77. *Realands, Eskdale Green, Holmrook, Cumbria CA19 1TW* Eskdale (01946) 723321

TURNER, James Alfred (Jim). b 34. Ox Coll FE MCIPS76. Ox Min Course 91. **d** 94. NSM Kidlington w Hampton Poyle *Ox* from 94. *11 St Mary's Close, Kidlington, Oxford OX5 2AY* Oxford (01865) 375562

TURNER, Miss Jessica Mary. b 60. SS Coll Cam BA81 PGCE82. Trin Coll Bris 88. **d** 91 **p** 94. Par Dn Preston Em *Blackb* 91-94; Par Dn Bamber Bridge St Aid 94; C from 94. *17 Station Road, Bamber Bridge, Preston PR5 6QR* Preston (01772) 312663

TURNER, Miss Jessie Irene. b 06. Qu Mary Coll Lon BSc29 DipEd30. dss 60 **d** 87. Coleford w Staunton *Glouc* 60-69; Chingford St Edm *Chelmsf* 69-87; Hon Par Dn 87-93; Perm to Offic from 93. *57 Normanshire Drive, London E4 9HE* 0181-524 4108

TURNER, John David Maurice. b 22. Keble Coll Ox BA45 MA48. Ripon Hall Ox 69. **d** 70 **p** 71. C Crowthorne *Ox* 70-73; V Cropredy w Gt Bourton 73-79; V Cropredy w Gt Bourton and Wardington 80-83; Perm to Offic from 83; Perm to Offic *Pet* from 83; rtd 87. *Appletree Cottage, The Close, Greatworth, Banbury, Oxon OX17 2EB* Banbury (01295) 711326

TURNER, John Edward. b 19. S Dios Minl Tr Scheme. **d** 82 **p** 83. NSM Radipole and Melcombe Regis *Sarum* 82-91; Perm to Offic from 91. *95 Weymouth Bay Avenue, Weymouth, Dorset DT3 5AD* Weymouth (01305) 771024

TURNER, John Gilbert. b 06. Cranmer Hall Dur. **d** 66 **p** 67. C Tithby w Cropwell Butler *S'well* 71-77; C Colston Bassett 71-77; C Cropwell Bishop 71-77; C Langar 71-77; C Granby w Elton 71-77; rtd 77; Perm to Offic *S'well* from 79. *Landyke, Iythby Road, Cropwell Butler, Nottingham NG12 7AR* Nottingham (0115) 933 3166

TURNER, John Girvan. b 54. Glas Univ MA79 Dur Univ BA82. **d** 82 **p** 83. C Kippax *Ripon* 82-85; C Kippax w Allerton Bywater 85; Chapl Glas and Strathclyde Univs 86-94; Chapl Berlin St Geo *Eur* from 94. *Karolinger Platz 2, App 12, 14052 Berlin, Germany* Berlin (30) 301-4646

TURNER, John William. b 43. Sheff Univ BSc73. Wycliffe Hall Ox 86. **d** 88 **p** 89. C Clayton *Bradf* 88-91; C Horton 91-92; V Bankfoot from 92. *The Vicarage, Carbottom Road, Bankfoot, Bradford, W Yorkshire BD5 9AA* Bradford (01274) 726529

TURNER, Keith Howard. b 50. Southn Univ BA71. Wycliffe Hall Ox 72. **d** 75 **p** 76. C Enfield Ch Ch Trent Park *Lon* 75-79; C Chilwell *S'well* 79-83; P-in-c Linby w Papplewick 83-90; R from 90. *The Rectory, Main Street, Linby, Nottingham NG15 8AE* Nottingham (0115) 963 2346

TURNER, Lawrence John. b 43. Kelham Th Coll 65. **d** 70 **p** 71. C Lower Gornal *Lich* 70-73; C Wednesbury St Paul Wood Green 73-74; C Porthill 75-77; C Wilton *York* 77-80; P-in-c 80-82; R Jersey St Martin *Win* from 82; Chmn Jersey Miss to Seamen from 82. *St Martin's Rectory, Jersey, Channel Islands JE3 6HW* Jersey (01534) 854294

708

TURNER, Leslie. b 29. NE Lon Poly BSc87. St Jo Coll Dur 50 St Aid Birkenhead 51. **d** 54 **p** 55. Chapl Belmont and Henderson Hosps Sutton 65-71; St Ebba's Hosp Epsom 65-71; Qu Mary's Carshalton 67-71; Lic to Offic *Pet* 71-94; Chapl Princess Marina & St Crispin's Hosps 71-87; Chapl Northn Gen Hosp 87-94; Chapl Manfield Hosp Northn 87-94; Chapl St Edm Hosp Northn 87-94; rtd 94. *20 Banbury Close, Northampton NN4 9UA* Northampton (01604) 769233

TURNER, Mark. b 60. Aston Tr Scheme 87 Sarum & Wells Th Coll BTh92. **d** 92 **p** 93. C New Sleaford *Linc* 92-94; C Bottesford and Muston *Leic* from 94; C Harby, Long Clawson and Hose from 94; C Barkestone w Plungar, Redmile and Stathern from 94. *The Rectory, 1 Boyers Orchard, Harby, Melton Mowbray, Leics LE14 4BA*

TURNER, Mark Richard Haythornthwaite. b 41. TCD MA67 Linc Coll Ox BA68. Wycliffe Hall Ox 65. **d** 68 **p** 69. C Birtley *Newc* 68-71; C Cam Gt St Mary w St Mich *Ely* 71-74; Chapl Loughb Univ *Leic* 74-79; P-in-c Keele *Lich* 80-85; Chapl Keele Univ 80-85; P-in-c Ashley from 85; P-in-c Mucklestone from 86. *The Rectory, Ashley, Market Drayton, Shropshire TF9 4LQ* Ashley (01630) 872210

TURNER, Martin John. b 34. Trin Hall Cam BA55 MA59. Cuddesdon Coll 58. **d** 60 **p** 61. C Rugby St Andr *Cov* 60-65; C Cov Cathl 65-68; USA 68-70; V Rushmere *St E* 70-82; V Monkwearmouth St Pet *Dur* 82-90; V Bathford *B & W* from 90. *Bathford Vicarage, Ostlings Lane, Bath BA1 7RW* Bath (01225) 858325

TURNER, Mrs Maureen. b 55. Leeds Univ BA78. St Jo Coll Nottm 84. **d** 87 **p** 94. Par Dn Darlaston St Lawr *Lich* 87-91; C Stratford-on-Avon w Bishopton *Cov* from 91. *6 Verney Drive, Stratford-upon-Avon, Warks CV37 0DX* Stratford-upon-Avon (01789) 269874

TURNER, Maurice William. b 27. Sarum Th Coll 53. **d** 56 **p** 57. V Gawber *Wakef* 60-71; V Alverthorpe 71-74; V Oxon and Shelton *Lich* 74-81; P-in-c Battlefield w Albrighton 81-82; V Leaton 81-82; V Leaton and Albrighton w Battlefield 82-92; rtd 92. *10 Melbourne Rise, Bicton Heath, Shrewsbury SY3 5DA* Shrewsbury (01743) 352667

TURNER, Michael Andrew. b 34. K Coll Cam BA59 MA62. Cuddesdon Coll 59. **d** 61 **p** 62. C Luton St Andr *St Alb* 61-64; V 70-77; C-in-c Northolt St Mary *Lon* 64-70; Perm to Offic *St Alb* 77-93; Dep Hd and Chapl Greycoat Hosp Sch 86-93; Perm to Offic *Lon* 86-93; P-in-c Shilling Okeford *Sarum* from 93; Chapl Croft Ho Sch Shillingstone from 93. *The Rectory, Shillingstone, Blandford Forum, Dorset DT11 0SL* Child Okeford (01258) 860261

TURNER, Michael John Royce. b 43. St Jo Coll Dur BA65. Chich Th Coll 65. **d** 67 **p** 68. C Hodge Hill *Birm* 67-71; C Eling, Testwood and Marchwood *Win* 71-72; TV 72-77; R Kirkwall *Ab* 77-85; R Laurencekirk *Bre* from 85; R Drumtochty from 85; R Fasque from 85; R Drumlithie from 85. *Beattie Lodge, Laurencekirk, Kincardineshire AB30 1HJ* Laurencekirk (01561) 377380

TURNER, Canon Nicholas Anthony. b 51. Clare Coll Cam BA73 MA77 Keble Coll Ox BA77 MA81. Ripon Coll Cuddesdon 76. **d** 78 **p** 79. C Stretford St Matt *Man* 78-80; Tutor St Steph Ho Ox 80-84; V Leeds Richmond Hill *Ripon* 84-91; Ascension Is from 91; Offg Chapl RAF from 91; Can Th St Helena Cathl from 94. *St Mary's Vicarage, Georgetown, Ascension Island, South Atlantic Ocean* Ascension Island (247) 6431 Fax 6431

TURNER, Noel Macdonald Muncaster. b 08. Ch Coll Cam BA31. Ely Th Coll 32. **d** 32 **p** 33. R Gonalston *S'well* 41-73; V Epperstone 41-73; Chapl HM Youth Cust Cen Lowdham Grange 45-73; P-in-c Oxton *S'well* 67-73; rtd 73; Perm to Offic *Chich* from 73; Perm to Offic *Portsm* from 73. *27 West Close, Fernhurst, Haslemere, Surrey GU27 3JR* Haslemere (01428) 653542

TURNER (nee SYMINGTON), Mrs Patricia Ann. b 46. SRN68 RMN71 SCM72 Cam Univ DipRS82. St Steph Ho Ox 82. **dss** 84 **d** 87. Buttershaw St Aid *Bradf* 84-87; TD Manningham 87-91; Ascension Is from 91. *St Mary's Vicarage, Georgetown, Ascension Island, South Atlantic Ocean* Ascension Island (247) 6431 Fax 6431

TURNER, Peter Carpenter. b 39. Oak Hill Th Coll 63. **d** 66 **p** 67. C Chadwell *Chelmsf* 66-69; C Braintree 69-73; R Fyfield 73-87; P-in-c Moreton 77-87; C-in-c Bobbingworth 82-87; P-in-c Willingale w Shellow and Berners Roding 84-87; P-in-c E Ham St Geo from 87. *The Vicarage, Buxton Road, London E6 3NB* 0181-472 2111

TURNER, Peter Robin. b 42. Open Univ BA79. AKC65. **d** 66 **p** 67. C Crediton *Ex* 66-69; Chapl RAF 70-88; Asst Chapl-in-Chief RAF 88-95; QHC from 92; Chapl-in-Chief RAF from 95. *Chaplaincy Services (RAF), HQ, Personnel and Training Command, RAF Innsworth, Gloucester GL3 1EZ* Gloucester (01452) 712612 Ext 5164 Fax 510828

TURNER, Philip William. b 25. CM65. Worc Coll Ox BA50 MA62. Chich Th Coll 49. **d** 51 **p** 52. Relig Broadcasting Org BBC Midl Region 66-71; Asst Master Brian Mill Sch

Droitwich 71-73; Chapl Eton Coll Windsor 73-75; Chapl Malvern Coll Worcs 75-84; Chapl St Jas & Abbey Schs Malvern 84-86; rtd 90. *181 West Malvern Road, Malvern, Worcs WR14 4AY* Malvern (01684) 563852

TURNER, Canon Robert Edgar. b 20. TCD BA42 MA51. Linc Th Coll 44. **d** 45 **p** 46. I Belf St Geo *Conn* 58-90; Can Belf Cathl 71-76; Preb Clonmethan St Patr Cathl Dub 76-90; Dioc Registrar *Conn* from 82; rtd 90. *19 Cricklewood Park, Belfast BT9 5GU* Belfast (01232) 663214

TURNER, Robin Edward. b 35. Selw Coll Cam BA57 MA63. Qu Coll Birm DipTh63. **d** 63 **p** 64. C Aveley *Chelmsf* 63-67; C Upminster 67-71; R Goldhanger w Lt Totham 71-80; R Lt Baddow from 80; Chapl New Hall Sch Essex from 80. *The Rectory, Colam Lane, Little Baddow, Chelmsford CM3 4SY* Danbury (01245) 223488

TURNER, Roger Dyke. b 39. Trin Coll Bris 79. **d** 81 **p** 82. C Clevedon St Andr *B & W* 81-82; C Clevedon St Andr and Ch Ch 83-85; R Freshford, Limpley Stoke and Hinton Charterhouse 85-88; V Kenilworth St Jo *Cov* from 88; RD Kenilworth from 90. *St John's Vicarage, Clarke's Avenue, Kenilworth, Warks CV8 1HX* Kenilworth (01926) 53203

TURNER, St John Alwin. b 31. Dur Univ BA57 MA61. Cranmer Hall Dur DipTh58. **d** 59 **p** 60. C W Hartlepool St Paul *Dur* 59-62; C S Shore H Trin *Blackb* 62-65; V Huncoat 65-67; Org Sec (Dios Ripon and York) CMS 67-72; V Harrogate St Mark *Ripon* 72-94. *2 The Tilney, Whaplode, Spalding, Lincs PE12 6UW* Holbeach (01406) 371390

TURNER, Susan. b 58. Man Univ BA89. N Ord Course 89. **d** 92 **p** 93. NSM Balderstone *Man* 92-93; NSM E Crompton 93-94; Hon C from 94; Chapl Man Coll of Arts and Tech from 93. *15 Oak Street, Shaw, Oldham OL2 8EJ*

TURNER (formerly BENBOW), Mrs Susan Catherine (Sue). b 47. Birm Univ BEd70. St Alb Minl Tr Scheme 82. **dss** 85 **d** 87 **p** 94. Gt Wyrley *Lich* 85-87; Par Dn 87-88; Par Dn Whitstable *Cant* 88-92; Par Dn Eastry and Northbourne w Tilmanstone etc 92-94; C from 94. *The Rectory, The Street, Northbourne, Deal, Kent CT14 0LG* Deal (01304) 374967

TURNER, Sylvia Jean. b 46. Lon Univ 72 Open Univ BA77. Westcott Ho Cam CTM95. **d** 95. C Whitstable *Cant* from 95. *64 Cromwell Road, Whitstable, Kent CT5 1NN* Whitstable (01227) 262590

TURNER, Walter. b 21. Lich Th Coll 51. **d** 53 **p** 54. V Frizington *Carl* 65-70; V Underbarrow w Helsington and Crook 70-77; V Allithwaite 77-79; TV Kirkby Lonsdale 79-82; TV Penrith w Newton Reigny and Plumpton Wall 82-86; rtd 86; Perm to Offic *Carl* from 86. *69 Lansdowne Crescent, Carlisle CA3 9ES* Carlisle (01228) 401177

TURNER, Canon Walter John. b 29. Bris Univ BA53. Clifton Th Coll 49. **d** 54 **p** 55. V Wednesfield St Thos *Lich* 65-74; RD Shifnal 75-83; V Boningale 75-83; V Shifnal 75-83; Preb Lich Cathl 80-83; Can Res and Prec Lich Cathl 83-94; rtd 94. *9 Kestrel Close, Newport, Shropshire TF10 8QE* Newport (01952) 820758

TURNER, William Edward (Bill). b 41. Keble Coll Ox BA63 MA73. Linc Th Coll 76. **d** 78 **p** 79. C Lich St Chad *Lich* 78-80; Chapl Trent (Nottm) Poly *S'well* 80-89; Chapl Lancs (Preston) Poly *Blackb* 89-92; Chapl Cen Lancs Univ from 92. *10 Queens Road, Fulwood, Preston PR2 3EA* Preston (01772) 717791 or 892615 Fax 202073

TURNOCK, Geoffrey. MSOSc Leeds Univ BSc61 PhD64. E Midl Min Tr Course 84. **d** 87 **p** 88. NSM Oadby *Leic* from 87; Chapl Leic Univ from 93. *51 Brambling Way, Oadby, Leicester LE2 5PB* Leicester (0116) 271 4115

TURP, Paul Robert. b 48. Oak Hill Th Coll BA79. **d** 79 **p** 80. C Southall Green St Jo *Lon* 79-83; V Shoreditch St Leon w St Mich 83-88; TR Shoreditch St Leon and Hoxton St Jo from 88. *The Vicarage, 36 Hoxton Square, London N1 6NN* 0171-739 2063

TURPIN, John Richard. b 41. St D Coll Lamp BA63 Magd Coll Cam BA65 MA70. Cuddesdon Coll 65. **d** 66 **p** 67. C Tadley St Pet *Win* 66-71; V Southn Thornhill St Chris 71-85; V Ringwood from 85. *The Vicarage, 65 Southampton Road, Ringwood, Hants BH24 1HE* Ringwood (01425) 473219

TURRALL, Albert Thomas George. b 19. Linc Th Coll 64. **d** 66 **p** 67. R Astley *Worc* 69-74; V Montford w Shrawardine *Lich* 74-77; R Montford w Shrawardine and Fitz 77-84; rtd 84; Perm to Offic *Heref* from 86; Perm to Offic *Lich* from 86. *15 Highbury Close, Shrewsbury SY2 6SN* Shrewsbury (01743) 249831

TURRELL, Stephen John. b 35. S'wark Ord Course. **d** 83 **p** 84. NSM W Wickham St Jo *Cant* 83-84; NSM Addington *S'wark* 85-92. *Address temp unknown*

TURTON, Arthur Bickerstaffe. b 19. Oak Hill Th Coll 46. **d** 48 **p** 49. V Southborough St Pet w Ch Ch and St Matt *Roch* 68-76; V Histon *Ely* 76-82; rtd 84; Perm to Offic *Chich* 82-88; Perm to Offic *Ely* from 88. *20 St Peter's Drive, Chatteris, Cambs PE16 6BY* Chatteris (01354) 695551

TURTON, Douglas Walter. b 38. Kent Univ BA77 Surrey Univ MSc90. Oak Hill Th Coll 77. **d** 78 **p** 79. C Cant St Mary Bredin *Cant* 78-80; P-in-c Thornton Heath St Paul 80-81; V 81-84; V Thornton Heath St Paul *S'wark* 85-91; R Eastling w Ospringe and Stalisfield w Otterden *Cant* from 91. *The Rectory, Newnham Lane, Eastling, Faversham, Kent ME13 0AS* Eastling (01795) 890487

TURTON, Neil Christopher. b 45. Wycliffe Hall Ox 77. **d** 79 **p** 80. C Guildf Ch Ch *Guildf* 79-83; C Godalming 83-86; V Wyke 86-92; R Frimley from 92. *The Rectory, Parsonage Way, Frimley, Camberley, Surrey GU16 5AG* Camberley (01276) 23309

TURTON, Paul Edward. b 26. St Pet Hall Ox BA50 MA55. Qu Coll Birm 50. **d** 52 **p** 53. Perm to Offic *S'wark* 68-70; Dir of Educn *Nor* 70-75; Dep Dir Nat Soc Cen Camberwell 75-77; Dir Nat Soc RE Cen Kensington 78-84; C Eastbourne St Mary *Chich* 84-86; rtd 86; Perm to Offic *Chich* from 87. *32 Churchill Close, Eastbourne, E Sussex BN20 8AJ* Eastbourne (01323) 638089

✠**TUSTIN, Rt Rev David.** b 35. Magd Coll Cam BA57 MA61. Cuddesdon Coll 58. **d** 60 **p** 61 c 79. C Stafford St Mary *Lich* 60-63; C St Dunstan in the West *Lon* 63-67; Asst Gen Sec C of E Coun on Foreign Relns 63-67; V Wednesbury St Paul Wood Green *Lich* 67-71; V Tettenhall Regis 71-79; RD Trysull 76-79; Suff Bp Grimsby *Linc* from 79; Can and Preb Linc Cathl from 79. *Bishop's House, Church Lane, Irby-upon-Humber, Grimsby, S Humberside DN37 7JR* Grimsby (01472) 371715 Fax 371716

TUTTON, Canon John Knight. b 30. Man Univ BSc51. Ripon Hall Ox 53. **d** 55 **p** 56. C Tonge w Alkrington *Man* 55-57; C Bushbury *Lich* 57-59; R Blackley St Andr *Man* 59-67; R Denton Ch Ch from 67; Hon Can Man Cathl from 90. *Christ Church Rectory, 1 Windmill Lane, Denton, Manchester M34 3RN* 0161-336 2126

TWADDELL, Canon William Reginald. b 33. TCD 61. **d** 62 **p** 63. C Belf Whiterock *Conn* 62-65; I Loughgilly w Clare *Arm* 65-71; I Milltown 71-84; I Portadown St Mark from 84; RD Kilmore from 86; Preb Arm Cathl from 88. *The Rectory, Brownstown Road, Portadown, Co Armagh BT62 3QA* Portadown (01762) 332368

TWEDDLE, David William Joseph. b 28. ATCL56 Dur Univ BSc50. Wycliffe Hall Ox 54. **d** 56 **p** 57. C Pet St Jo *Pet* 65-71; Hon Min Can Pet Cathl 68-93; V Southwick w Glapthorn 71-83; P-in-c Benefield 80-83; R Benefield and Southwick w Glapthorn 83-93; RD Oundle 84-89; rtd 94. *6 Barton Square, Ely, Cambs CB7 4DF* Ely (01353) 668020

TWEED, Andrew. b 48. Univ of Wales (Cardiff) BA69. St Deiniol's Hawarden. **d** 81 **p** 84. NSM Llandrindod w Cefnllys S & B 81-87; NSM Llandrindod w Cefnllys and Disserth from 87. *Gwenallt, Wellington Road, Llandrindod Wells, Powys LD1 5NB* Llandrindod Wells (01597) 823671

TWEEDIE-SMITH, Ian David. b 60. Newc Univ BA83. Wycliffe Hall Ox 83. **d** 85 **p** 86. C Hatcham St Jas *S'wark* 85-89; C Bury St Edmunds St Mary *St E* from 89. *St Mary's House, 18 Vinery Road, Bury St Edmunds, Suffolk IP33 2JR* Bury St Edmunds (01284) 705035

TWENTYMAN, Trevor Lawrence Holme. b 35. Chich Th Coll 67. **d** 70 **p** 71. C N Holmwood *Guildf* 70; C Sheff Parson Cross St Cecilia *Sheff* 71; C S Kensington St Aug *Lon* 76-83; Colombia from 87; Vicar General from 88. *Sotwell Manor, Wallingford, Oxon OX10 0PX* Wallingford (01491) 838854

TWIDELL, William James. b 30. St Mich Coll Llan 58. **d** 60 **p** 61. C Tonge w Alkrington *Man* 60-63; C High Wycombe All SS *Ox* 63-65; P-in-c Elkesley w Bothamsall *S'well* 65-66; V Bury St Thos *Man* 66-72; V Daisy Hill 72-84; R Flixton St Mich from 84; AD Stretford from 88. *The Rectory, 348 Church Road, Flixton, Urmston, Manchester M31 3HR* 0161-748 2884

TWISLETON, Dr John Fiennes. b 48. St Jo Coll Ox MA73 DPhil73. Coll of Resurr Mirfield DipTh75. **d** 76 **p** 77. C New Bentley *Sheff* 76-79; P-in-c Moorends 79-80; V 80-86; USPG 86-90; Coll of the Ascension Selly Oak 86-87; Guyana 87-90; V Holbrooks *Cov* from 90. *St Luke's Vicarage, Rotherham Road, Coventry CV6 4FE* Coventry (01203) 688604

TWISLETON, Peter. b 50. Linc Th Coll. **d** 84 **p** 85. C Bodmin w Lanhydrock and Lanivet *Truro* 84-87; C Par 87-90; R St Breoke and Egloshayle 90-93; R Bude Haven and Marhamchurch from 93. *The Rectory, 8 Falcon Terrace, Bude, Cornwall EX23 8LJ* Bude (01288) 352318

TWISLETON-WYKEHAM-FIENNES, Oliver William. *See* FIENNES, Very Rev the Hon Oliver William

TWISS, Dorothy Elizabeth. Gilmore Ho 68 Linc Th Coll 70. **d** 87 **p** 94. Chapl Asst RAF 78-91; TV Pewsey TM *Sarum* from 91. *The Vicarage, Crossroads, Easton Royal, Pewsey, Wilts SN9 5LS* Marlborough (01672) 810970

TWITTY, Miss Rosamond Jane. b 54. Univ of Wales (Ban) BSc75 CertEd76. Trin Coll Bris BA89. **d** 90 **p** 94. Par Dn Lt Thurrock St Jo *Chelmsf* 90-94; C 94-95; C Upper Armley

Ripon from 95. *115A Heights Drive, Leeds LS12 3TG* Leeds (0113) 263 7240

TWOHIG, Dr Brian Robert. b 48. La Trobe Univ Victoria BA77 PhD86. St Mich Th Coll Crafers 70. **d** 72 **p** 73. Australia 72-78 and 80-82; C Leatherhead *Guildf* 78-80; TV New Windsor *Ox* 82-92; V Sheff St Cuth *Sheff* from 92. *St Cuthbert's Vicarage, 7 Horndean Road, Sheffield S5 6UJ* Sheffield (0114) 243 6506

TWOMEY, Jeremiah Francis (Derry). b 50. Man Poly BA83 Univ of Wales (Ban) PGCE85 Real Colegio de Escoceses Valladolid Spain. NE Ord Course 92. **d** 94. C Beverley St Nic *York* from 94. *11 Cherry Garth, Beverley, N Humberside HU17 0EP* Hull (01482) 868298

TWOMEY, Jeremiah Thomas Paul. b 46. CITC 87. **d** 87 **p** 88. C Derryloran *Arm* 87-90; I Brackaville w Donaghendry and Ballyclog from 90. *82 Dungannon Road, Coalisland, Co Tyrone BT71 4HT* Coalisland (018687) 40243

TWYCROSS, Christopher John. St Pet Coll Ox BA59 MA63. Wycliffe Hall Ox 60. **d** 64 **p** 65. C Blaby *Leic* 64-66; C Loughb Em 66-69; R Shelthorpe Gd Shep 69-71; R Holbrook and Stutton *St E* 71-73; Asst Master & Hon Chapl Wellesley Ho Broadstairs 73-78; Perm to Offic 77-90; Asst Master Chantry High Sch Ipswich 78-90; P-in-c Shenley *St Alb* from 90; Chapl Shenley Hosp Radlett Herts from 90. *The Rectory, 63 London Road, Shenley, Radlett, Herts WD7 9BW* Radlett (01923) 855383

TWYCROSS, Stephen Jervis. b 33. Nottm Univ BEd73 Leic Univ MA85. Lambeth STh88 Kalk Bay Bible Inst S Africa 56 Wycliffe Hall Ox 58. **d** 60 **p** 61. C Hinckley H Trin *Leic* 60-64; V Barlestone 64-71; NSM Dio Leic 71-87; P-in-c Stokesay *Heref* 87-91; P-in-c Sibdon Carwood w Halford 87-91; Chapl Utrecht w Amersfoort, Harderwijk & Zwolle *Eur* 91-94; V Llanwddyn and Llanfihangel and Llwydiarth *St As* from 94. *The Vicarage, Llanwddyn, Oswestry, Shropshire SY10 0LY* Llanwddyn (01691) 870663

TWYFORD, Canon Arthur Russell. b 36. ALCD60. **d** 60 **p** 61. Asst Dioc Youth Officer *Ox* 64-70; R Maids Moreton w Foxcote 64-72; P-in-c Lillingstone Dayrell w Lillingstone Lovell 70-72; V Desborough *Pet* 72-88; P-in-c Braybrook 73-77; P-in-c Brampton Ash w Dingley 73-77; R Brampton Ash w Dingley and Braybrooke 77-88; RD Kettering 79-87; Can Pet Cathl 81-95; R Stanwick w Hargrave 88-95; rtd 95. *1 Laws Lane, Finedon, Wellingborough, Northants NN9 5LU* Wellingborough (01933) 682116

TYDEMAN, Canon Richard. b 16. St Jo Coll Ox BA39 MA43. Ripon Hall Ox 38. **d** 39 **p** 40. R St Sepulchre w Ch Greyfriars etc *Lon* 63-81; Dep Min Can St Paul's Cathl 63-81; Preacher Lincoln's Inn 72-81; rtd 81; Perm to Offic *St E* from 82. *10 Colneis Road, Felixstowe, Suffolk IP11 9HP* Felixstowe (01394) 283214

TYE, Eric John. b 37. St Alb Minl Tr Scheme. **d** 81 **p** 82. NSM Rushden w Newton Bromswold *Pet* from 81. *31 Morris Avenue, Rushden, Northants NN10 9PB* Rushden (01933) 53274

TYE, John Raymond. b 31. Lambeth STh64 Linc Th Coll 66. **d** 68 **p** 69. C Crewe St Mich *Ches* 68-71; C Wednesfield St Thos *Lich* 71-76; P-in-c Petton w Cockshutt 76-79; P-in-c Hordley 79; P-in-c Weston Lullingfield 79; R Petton w Cockshutt and Weston Lullingfield etc 79-81; V Hadley 81-84; R Ightfield w Calverhall 84-89; V Ash 84-89; R Calton, Cauldon, Grindon and Waterfall from 89. *The Vicarage, Waterfall Lane, Waterhouses, Stoke-on-Trent ST10 3HT* Waterhouses (01538) 308506

TYE, Leslie Bernard. b 14. AKC40. **d** 40 **p** 41. V Ambergate *Derby* 69-79; rtd 79; Perm to Offic *Derby* from 79. *31 Cromwell Drive, Swanwick, Derby DE55 1DB* Leabrooks (01773) 602895

TYERS, Canon Gerald Seymour. b 22. St Pet Hall Ox BA46 MA49. Linc Th Coll 47. **d** 49 **p** 50. V Erith Ch Ch *Roch* 67-82; Chapl Erith and Distr Hosp 67-82; RD Erith 79-82; R Foots Cray *Roch* 82-91; Hon Can Roch Cathl 82-91; rtd 91. *Yew Tree Cottage, Castle Hill, Hartley, Dartford DA3 7BH* Longfield (01474) 707923

TYERS, Canon John Haydn. b 31. Lon Univ BSc51. Ridley Hall Cam 53. **d** 55 **p** 56. C Nuneaton St Nic *Cov* 55-58; C Rugby St Andr 58-62; V Cov St Anne 62-63; C Keresley and Coundon 71-78; V Atherstone 78-85; P-in-c Pleshey *Chelmsf* 85-91; Warden Pleshey Retreat Ho 85-91; Hon Can Chelmsf Cathl *Chelmsf* 86-91; P-in-c Ash *Lich* from 91; P-in-c Ightfield w Calverhall from 91. *The Rectory, Ightfield, Whitchurch, Shropshire SY13 4NU* Calverhall (0194876) 610

TYERS, Philip Nicolas. b 56. Nottm Univ BTh84. St Jo Coll Nottm 80. **d** 84 **p** 85. C Rugby St Matt *Cov* 84-88; TV Cov E 88-95; P-in-c Preston St Matt *Blackb* from 95. *St Matthew's Vicarage, 20 Fishwick View, Preston PR1 4YA* Preston (01772) 794312

TYLDESLEY, Douglas Wilfred. b 31. CCC Cam BA54 MA58. Oak Hill Th Coll 54. **d** 56 **p** 57. C Skellingthorpe *Linc* 56-58; C Doddington 57-58; C Beckenham St Jo *Roch* 58-61; V

Walthamstow St Luke *Chelmsf* 61-66; V Prestwold w Hoton *Leic* 66-72; R Sapcote 72-83; R Sapcote and Sharnford w Wigston Parva from 83. *The Rectory, 4 Sharnford Road, Sapcote, Leicester LE9 4JN* Sapcote (01455) 272215

TYLER, Alan William. b 60. Univ of Wales (Ban) DipTh84. Ridley Hall Cam 84. **d** 86 **p** 87. C Bedwellty *Mon* 86-89; C St Mellons and Michaelston-y-Fedw 89-92; V Abersychen and Garndiffaith from 92. *The Vicarage, Abersychan, Pontypool, Gwent NP4 8PL* Talywain (01495) 772213

TYLER, Andrew. b 57. Univ of Wales (Lamp) BA79 Warw Univ MA80 Man Univ BD86. Coll of Resurr Mirfield 83. **d** 87 **p** 88. C Glen Parva and S Wigston *Leic* 87-90; C Didcot All SS *Ox* 90-92; Asst Chapl Chu Hosp *Ox*; NSM Caversham St Andr from 93. *55 Albert Road, Reading RG4 7AW* Reading (01734) 462447

TYLER, Brian Sidney. b 32. MIPI79. Chich Th Coll 62. **d** 64 **p** 65. C Brighton St Mich *Chich* 64-69; C-in-c Southwick St Pet 69-75; Perm to Offic 80; NSM Brighton Resurr 93-94; Chapl St Dunstan's Hosp Brighton 93-95; C Brighton St Matthias *Chich* from 95. *318 Ditchling Road, Brighton BN1 6JG* Brighton (01273) 559292

TYLER (nee FOSTER), Mrs Frances Elizabeth. b 55. Linc Th Coll 81. **dss** 84 **d** 87 **p** 94. Hampton All SS *Lon* 84-87; Par Dn Brentford 87-91; NSM Walsgrave on Sowe *Cov* from 91. *The Vicarage, 4 Farber Road, Coventry CV2 2BG* Coventry (01203) 615152 or 618845

TYLER, Mrs Gaynor. b 46. Univ of Wales (Abth) BA68. S'wark Ord Course 87. **d** 90 **p** 94. NSM Reigate St Luke S Park *S'wark* from 90. *2 Sheep Walk Cottage, The Clears, Reigate, Surrey RH2 9JQ* Reigate (01737) 247160

TYLER, John Arthur Preston. b 19. Em Coll Cam BA42 MA46. Wycliffe Hall Ox 42. **d** 44 **p** 45. R Ickham w Wickhambreaux and Stodmarsh *Cant* 65-85; rtd 85; Perm to Offic *Ox* 86-89; Perm to Offic *Cant* from 89. *Church Orchard, Church Lane, Kingston, Canterbury, Kent CT4 6HY* Canterbury (01227) 830193

TYLER, John Thorne. b 46. Selw Coll Cam BA68 MA71 Ex Univ DipAd70. Sarum & Wells Th Coll 70. **d** 72 **p** 73. C Frome St Jo *B & W* 72-74; Chapl Huish Coll Taunton 74-93; Hon C Stoke St Gregory w Burrowbridge and Lyng *B & W* 77-93; P-in-c Shepton Beauchamp w Barrington, Stocklinch etc 93-94; TV Ilminster and District from 94. *The Rectory, Church Street, Shepton Beauchamp, Ilminster, Somerset TA19 0LQ* South Petherton (01460) 240338

TYLER, Ven Leonard George. b 20. Liv Univ BA41 Ch Coll Cam BA46 MA50. Westcott Ho Cam. **d** 43 **p** 44. Prin Wm Temple Coll 66-73; R Easthampstead *Ox* 73-85; rtd 85; Perm to Offic *Ox* from 85. *11 Ashton Place, Kintbury, Newbury, Berks RG15 0XS* Kintbury (01488) 58510

TYLER, Malcolm. b 56. Kent Univ BSc77 Cam Univ BA84. Ridley Hall Cam 82. **d** 85 **p** 86. C Twickenham St Mary *Lon* 85-88; C Acton St Mary 88-91; V Walsgrave on Sowe *Cov* from 91. *The Vicarage, 4 Farber Road, Coventry CV2 2BG* Coventry (01203) 615152 or 618845

TYLER, Paul Graham Edward. b 58. Cranmer Hall Dur. **d** 83 **p** 84. C Stranton *Dur* 83-86; C Collierley w Annfield Plain 86-89; V Esh 89-92; V Hamsteels 89-92. *Address temp unknown*

TYLER, Samuel John. b 32. Lon Univ BD57. Oak Hill Th Coll 57. **d** 58 **p** 59. R Aythorpe w High and Leaden Roding *Chelmsf* 64-72; Perm to Offic 73-74; P-in-c Gt Ilford St Jo 74-76; V 76-92; rtd 92. *21 Ash Green, Canewdon, Rochford, Essex SS4 3QN* Southend-on-Sea (01702) 258526

TYLER (nee WAITE), Mrs Sheila Margaret. b 25. SRN47 Lon Univ DipTh73. Trin Coll Bris. **dss** 79 **d** 87 **p** 94. Easton H Trin w St Gabr and St Lawr *Bris* 79-80; Westbury-on-Trym St Alb 81-85; rtd 85; Hon Par Dn Henleaze *Bris* 87-94; Hon C from 94; Chapl Stoke Park and Purdown Hosps Stapleton 88-90. *7 Ramenham Drive, Bristol BS9 4HY* Bristol (0117) 962 8394

TYLER, William Stanley. b 12. Ripon Hall Ox 54. **d** 55 **p** 56. R Woodleigh and Loddiswell *Ex* 68-76; rtd 76. *258 Hillbury Road, Warlingham, Surrey CR6 9TP*

TYMMS, Canon Wilfrid Widdas. b 18. Ch Coll Cam BA40 MA44. Linc Th Coll 40. **d** 41 **p** 42. R Middleton St Geo *Dur* 70-78; Can Res Dur Cathl 78-83; rtd 83. *4 Piggy Lane, Gainford, Darlington, Co Durham DL2 3DJ* Darlington (01325) 730086

TYNDALE-BISCOE, John Annesley. b 08. Cam Univ BA33 MA61. Westcott Ho Cam 34. **d** 34 **p** 35. R Gilston w Eastwick *St Alb* 60-76; rtd 76; Perm to Offic *Chelmsf* from 76. *33 Hadleigh Road, Frinton-on-Sea, Essex CO13 9HQ* Frinton-on-Sea (01255) 671520

TYNDALE-BISCOE, William Francis. b 04. Trin Coll Ox BA25 MA29. Westcott Ho Cam 27. **d** 28 **p** 29. SSF from 37; Cen Africa 62-74; Australia 74-77 and from 86; Melanesia 77-86; rtd 86. *Hermitage of St Bernadine, Stroud, NSW, Australia 2425*

TYNDALL, Daniel Frank. b 61. Aston Tr Scheme 90 Sarum & Wells Th Coll BTh93. **d** 93 **p** 94. C Wolv *Lich* from 93. *3 Westland Gardens, Wolverhampton WV3 9NU* Wolverhampton (01902) 23739

TYNDALL, Mrs Elizabeth Mary. b 30. St Andr Univ MA51 Hughes Hall Cam CertEd52 Birm Univ DPS81. Qu Coll Birm 81. **dss** 83 **d** 87 **p** 94. Rugby St Andr *Cov* 83-87; Par Dn Feltham *Lon* 87-91; rtd 92; NSM Vale of White Horse Deanery *Ox* from 93. *The Cobbler's Cottage, 18 Stanford Road, Faringdon, Oxon SN7 7AQ* Faringdon (01367) 240977

TYNDALL, Jeremy Hamilton. b 55. St Jo Coll Nottm BTh81 LTh81. **d** 81 **p** 82. C Oakwood St Thos *Lon* 81-84; C Upper Holloway St Pet w St Jo 84-87; TV Halewood *Liv* from 87. *The Rectory, 3 Rectory Drive, Halewood, Liverpool L26 6LJ* 0151-487 5610

TYNDALL, Simon James. b 54. Lon Univ BSc(Econ)77 PGCE82. St Jo Coll Nottm 88. **d** 90 **p** 91. C Yeovil w Kingston Pitney *B & W* 90-94; V Rastrick St Jo *Wakef* from 94. *St John's Vicarage, 2 St John Street, Brighouse, W Yorkshire HD6 1HN* Brighouse (01484) 715889

TYNDALL, Canon Timothy Gardner. b 25. Jes Coll Cam BA50. Wells Th Coll 50. **d** 51 **p** 52. V Sherwood *S'well* 60-75; P-in-c Bishopwearmouth St Mich w St Hilda *Dur* 75-85; RD Wearmouth 75-85; Hon Can Dur Cathl 83-90; Chief Sec ACCM 85-90; rtd 90; Perm to Offic *Lon* from 90. *29 Kingswood Road, London W4 5EU* 0181-994 4516

TYNEY, Canon James Derrick. b 33. TCD. **d** 62 **p** 63. C Ballynafeigh St Jude *D & D* 62-64; C Ban St Comgall 64-69; I Clonallon w Warrenpoint 69-75; I Groomsport from 75; RD Ban from 91; Can St Anne's Cathl *Conn* from 93. *32 Bangor Road, Groomsport, Bangor, Co Down BT19 2JF* Bangor (01247) 464476

TYRER, Ms Jayne Linda. b 59. Golds Coll Lon BA81 CertEd82. Sarum & Wells Th Coll 85. **d** 87. C Rochdale *Man* 87-88; Par Dn Heywood St Luke w All So 88-91; Hon Par Dn Burneside *Carl* from 91; Chapl Kendal Hosps from 91. *St Oswald's Vicarage, Burneside, Kendal, Cumbria LA9 6QX* Kendal (01539) 722015

TYRREL, John Cockett. b 16. Qu Coll Cam BA38 MA42. Ridley Hall Cam 38. **d** 40 **p** 41. S Africa 46-50; Australia from 50; rtd 81. *23 Mawson Drive, Mawson, NSW, Australia 2607* Canberra (6) 286-1317

TYRRELL, Canon Charles Robert. b 51. SRN73 Open Univ BA80. Oak Hill Th Coll 74. **d** 77 **p** 78. C Halewood *Liv* 77-80; C St Helens St Helen 80-83; V Banks 83-88; New Zealand from 88; Can Wellington from 88. *9 Williamson Way, Karori, Wellington, New Zealand* Wellington (4) 763511

TYRRELL, Frank Englefield. b 20. DSC44 VRD. Qu Coll Birm 70. **d** 72 **p** 73. C S Gillingham *Roch* 72-76; Chapl N Staffs R Infirmary Stoke-on-Trent 76-78; Chapl Stoke-on-Trent City Gen Hosp 76-78; rtd 86. *Daneway, 2 Minford, Tyn-y-Gongl, Gwynedd LL74 8QG* Tyn-y-Gongl (01248) 853104

TYRRELL, John Patrick Hammond. b 42. Cranmer Hall Dur 62. **d** 65 **p** 66. C Edin St Jo *Edin* 65-68; Chapl RN 68-72; Hong Kong 72-74 and 79-82; R Westborough *Guildf* 74-78; C Yateley *Win* 82-83; C-in-c Darby Green CD 83-88; V Darby Green from 88. *St Barnabas House, Green Lane, Blackwater, Camberley, Surrey GU17 0NU* Yateley (01252) 877817

TYRRELL, Stephen Jonathan. b 39. Sheff Univ BA62. Clifton Th Coll. **d** 65 **p** 66. C Rodbourne Cheney *Bris* 65-68; C Lillington *Cov* 68-72; P-in-c Bishop's Itchington 73-78; V 78-86; V Kingston upon Hull St Nic *York* 86-92; TV Cheltenham St Mary, St Matt, St Paul and H Trin *Glouc* from 92. *85 Brunswick Street, St Paul's, Cheltenham, Glos GL50 4HA* Cheltenham (01242) 524572

TYSOE, James Raymond. b 19. Qu Coll Birm 70. **d** 75 **p** 76. NSM Cov E *Cov* 75-85; NSM Cov Cathl 85-87; Perm to Offic *Glouc* from 87. *Wisma Mulia, Bridge Road, Frampton on Severn, Gloucester GL2 7HE* Gloucester (01452) 740890

TYSON, John Wood Worsley. b 22. ACII50. Ripon Hall Ox 54. **d** 56 **p** 57. V Sneinton St Steph w St Alb *S'well* 59-87; rtd 87. *5 St Peter's Court, 398 Woodborough Road, Nottingham NG3 4JF* Nottingham (0115) 985 6177

TYSON, Canon William Edward Porter. b 25. St Cath Coll Cam BA49 MA52. Ridley Hall Cam 49. **d** 51 **p** 52. V Over Tabley *Ches* 62-70; V High Legh 62-70; (CF (TA) 64-91; V Church Hulme *Ches* 70-91; Chapl Cranage Hall Hosp 70-91; Hon Can Ches Cathl *Ches* 82-91; RD Congleton 85-90; rtd 91. *59 Kirkhead Road, Allithwaite, Grange-over-Sands, Cumbria LA11 7DD* Grange-over-Sands (015395) 35291

TYTE, Ven Keith Arthur Graham. b 31. St D Coll Lamp BA55. **d** 57 **p** 58. C Mynyddislwyn *Mon* 57-61; C Llanfrechfa All SS 61-64; V Bettws 64-71; V Griffithstown 71-77; RD Pontypool 74-77; Can St Woolos Cathl 77-86; V Malpas 77-87; Adn Mon 86-93; R Llanmartin 87-93; Adn Newport from 93. *The Archdeaconry, 93 Stow Hill, Newport, Gwent NP9 4EA* Llanwern (01633) 215012

TYZACK, Canon Leonard George. b 37. BA DipTh. Chich Th Coll. **d** 63 **p** 64. C Folkestone St Mary and St Eanswythe *Cant* 63-67; Abp's Dom Chapl 67-69; C-in-c Buckland Valley CD 69-72; R Buckland in Dover w Buckland Valley from 72; RD Dover 81-86; Hon Can Cant Cathl from 83; Dir of Ords *Eur* 86-94. *St Andrew's Rectory, London Road, Dover, Kent CT17 0TF* Dover (01304) 201324

U

UCHIDA, Job Minoru. b 28. St Paul's Univ Tokyo BA51. **d** 54 **p** 55. Japan 54-56 and 59-89; SSM 56-58; Chapl to Japanese in UK from 89; Hon C W Acton St Martin *Lon* from 95. *St Martin's Cottage, Hale Gardens, London W3 9SQ* 0181-993 4227

✠**ud-DIN, Rt Rev Khair.** b 21. Punjab Univ BA70. K Coll (NS) 59 Coll of Ascension 72 Gujranwala Th Sem Hon DD87 N India Clergy Tr Cen DipTh48. **d** 48 **p** 49 **c** 82. Pakistan 48-90; V Lahore Cathl 68-77; Adn and Dean Lahore Cathl 77-82; Bp Peshawar 82-90; Miss Partner CMS 90-92; rtd 92; Min Ox St Clem *Ox* 92-93. *60 St Leonard's Road, Headington, Oxford OX3 8AB* Oxford (01865) 62053

UDY, John Francis. b 24. E Midl Min Tr Course 78. **d** 81 **p** 82. NSM Kirton in Holland *Linc* 81-89; NSM Sutterton w Fosdyke and Algarkirk from 89. *26 Grosvenor Road, Frampton, Boston, Lincs PE20 1DB* Boston (01205) 722043

UFFINDELL, David Wilfred George. b 37. Qu Coll Birm 72. **d** 75 **p** 76. NSM Harlescott *Lich* from 75. *13 Kenley Avenue, Heath Farm, Shrewsbury SY1 3HA* Shrewsbury (01743) 352029

UFFINDELL, Harold David. b 61. Down Coll Cam MA87. Wycliffe Hall Ox BA86 MA91 Oak Hill Th Coll 86. **d** 87 **p** 88. C Kingston Hill St Paul *S'wark* 87-91; C Surbiton St Matt from 91. *127 Hamilton Avenue, Surbiton, Surrey KT6 7QA* 0181-397 4294

ULLMANN, Clair. *See* FILBERT-ULLMANN, Mrs Clair

UNDERDOWN, Steven. Hull Univ BSc75 CertEd76. **d** 88. CSWG from 82; Lic to Offic *Chich* from 88. *The Monastery, Crawley Down, Crawley, W Sussex RH10 4LH* Copthorne (01342) 712074

UNDERHILL, Edward Mark Thomas. b 24. Univ Coll Dur BA50. St Aid Birkenhead 50. **d** 52 **p** 53. C Meopham *Roch* 52-54; Kenya 55-57; PC Gateshead St Geo *Dur* 57-68; V Gateshead St Geo from 68. *St George's Vicarage, 327 Durham Road, Gateshead, Tyne & Wear NE9 5AJ* 0191-487 5587

UNDERHILL, Very Rev Michael Leeke. b 10. CBE. Qu Coll Ox BA34 MA38. Westcott Ho Cam 34. **d** 35 **p** 36. C Millom H Trin *Carl* 35-38; New Zealand from 38; Dean Christchurch 66-81. *95 Church Street, Rangiora, New Zealand* Rangiora (502) 313-5261

UNDERHILL, Stanley Robert. b 27. Cant Sch of Min. **d** 82 **p** 83. C New Addington *Cant* 82-84; C Cannock *Lich* 84-86; TV 86-88; R Dymchurch w Burmarsh and Newchurch *Cant* 88-92; rtd 92; Chapl Menorca *Eur* 92-94. *Casa Pequena Es Barranc, Officina de Correos, 07710 San Luis, Menorca, Spain* Mahon (71) 150889

UNDERWOOD, Brian. b 35. Dur Univ BA57 Keble Coll Ox PGCE76 Dur Univ MA72. Clifton Th Coll 57. **d** 59 **p** 60. C Blackpool Ch Ch *Blackb* 59-61; C New Malden and Coombe *S'wark* 61-64; Travel Sec Pathfinders 64-68; Chapl Chantilly *Eur* 68-69; Home Sec CCCS 69-71; P-in-c Gatten St Paul *Portsm* 71-72; Chapl Lyon w Grenoble and Aix-les-Bains *Eur* 72-75; Asst Chapl Trent Coll Nottm 76-80; Lic to Offic *Derby* 76-80; Chapl Qu Eliz Gr Sch Blackb 80-85; Lic to Offic *Blackb* 80-85; R Bentham St Jo *Bradf* 85-92; V St Alb Ch Ch *St Alb* from 92. *Christ Church Vicarage, 5 High Oaks, St Albans, Herts AL3 6DJ* St Albans (01727) 857592

UNDERWOOD, Charles Brian. b 23. Leeds Univ BA48 CertEd. Coll of Resurr Mirfield 48. **d** 50 **p** 51. Dioc Youth Chapl *Bradf* 63-72; R Carleton-in-Craven 63-76; V Twyning *Glouc* 76-88; RD Tewkesbury 81-88; rtd 88. *9 Ellendene Drive, Pamington, Tewkesbury, Glos GL20 8LU* Bredon (01684) 72504

UNDERWOOD, David Richard. b 47. AKC69 St Osyth Coll of Educn PGCE72. St Aug Coll Cant 69. **d** 70 **p** 92. C Witham *Chelmsf* 70-71; Teacher 71-82; Hd Teacher Gt Heath Sch Mildenhall 82-91; NSM Chevington w Hargrave and Whepstead w Brockley *St E* 82-91; Par Dn Haverhill w Withersfield, the Wrattings etc 91-92; TV 92-94; P-in-c Bury St Edmunds St Jo from 94. *The Vicarage, 37 Well Street, Bury St Edmunds, Suffolk IP33 1EQ* Bury St Edmunds (01284) 754335

UNDERWOOD, Jack Maurice. b 13. Leeds Univ BA36 Lon Univ BD41. Coll of Resurr Mirfield 36. **d** 38 **p** 39. Prin Stroud Court Ox 60-71; Perm to Offic *Eur* 73-78; rtd 78. *Willow Lea, Hatford, Faringdon, Oxon SN7 8JF* Stanford in the Vale (01367) 710364

UNDERWOOD, Luke William. b 21. SW Minl Tr Course. **d** 85 **p** 86. NSM Duloe w Herodsfoot *Truro* 85-87; P-in-c 87-89; rtd 89. *Harewold, Tredinnick, Duloe, Liskeard, Cornwall PL14 4PJ* Looe (01503) 263541

UNGOED-THOMAS, Peter. b 27. Pemb Coll Ox BA51 MA67. St Mich Coll Llan. **d** 60 **p** 61. RAChD 67-70; Chapl Leigh C of

---

E Schs 70-74; C Leigh St Mary *Man* 70-74; Lect Warley Coll 74-86; Perm to Offic *Birm* from 75; Perm to Offic *St D* from 75; Lect Sandwell Coll of F&HE from 86; rtd 94. *93 Heol Felin-Foel, Llanelli, Dyfed SA15 3JQ*

UNSWORTH, Thomas Foster. b 28. Lon Univ BA56. Lich Th Coll 60. **d** 62 **p** 63. V Leyburn *Ripon* 68-73; V Bellerby 68-73; Chapl Whittingham Hosp Preston 73-79; V Freckleton *Blackb* 79-83; V S Yardley St Mich *Birm* 83-86; V Sutton w Carlton and Normanton upon Trent etc *S'well* 86-90; rtd 90; Chapl St Raphael *Eur* from 90. *16 rue Emile Zola, Lou Roucas, 85520 Roquebrune-sur-Argens, France* France (33) 94 44 05 67

UNWIN, Christopher Michael Fairclough. b 31. Dur Univ BA57. Linc Th Coll 65. **d** 67 **p** 68. C S Shields St Hilda w St Thos *Dur* 67-73; R Tatsfield *S'wark* 73-81; RE Adv to Ch Secondary Schs 73-81; V Newc St Gabr *Newc* from 81. *St Gabriel's Vicarage, 9 Holderness Road, Heaton, Newcastle upon Tyne NE6 5RH* 0191-276 3957

UNWIN, Christopher Philip. b 17. TD63. Magd Coll Cam BA39 MA63. Qu Coll Birm 39. **d** 40 **p** 41. V Adn Northd and Can Res Newc Cathl *Newc* 63-82; rtd 82. *60 Sandringham Avenue, Benton, Newcastle upon Tyne NE12 8JX* 0191-270 0418

UNWIN, Ven Kenneth. b 26. St Edm Hall Ox BA48 MA52. Ely Th Coll 49. **d** 51 **p** 52. V Royston *Wakef* 69-73; V Wakef St Jo 73-82; Hon Can Wakef Cathl 80-82; RD Wakef 80-81; Adn Pontefract 82-92; rtd 92. *2 Rockwood Close, Skipton, N Yorkshire BD23 1UG* Skipton (01756) 791323

UPCOTT, Derek Jarvis. b 26. CEng FIMechE FBIM. S'wark Ord Course 81. **d** 84 **p** 85. NSM Gt Chesham *Ox* from 84; Perm to Offic *St Alb* from 90. *Bluff Cottage, Blackthorne Lane, Ballinger, Great Missenden, Bucks HP16 9LN* The Lee (01494) 837505

UPHILL, Keith Ivan. b 35. Keble Coll Ox BA70 MA74. Wycliffe Hall Ox 67. **d** 70 **p** 71. C Maghull *Liv* 70-73; V Wroxall *Portsm* 73-77; TV Fareham H Trin 77-82; C Havant 82-84; P-in-c Mert St Jo *S'wark* 84-85; V from 85. *St John's Vicarage, High Path, London SW19 2JY* 0181-542 3283

UPRICHARD, Jervis. b 17. **d** 42 **p** 43. V Edgeside *Man* 60-66; rtd 82; Perm to Offic *Man* from 82. *14 Chestnut Drive, Rawtenstall, Rossendale, Lancs BB4 6DP* Rossendale (01706) 211502

UPTON, Anthony Arthur. b 30. Wells Th Coll 61. **d** 63 **p** 64. Chapl RN 67-83; V Foleshill St Laur *Cov* 83-91; rtd 91. *Redlands Bungalow, Banbury Road, Lighthorne, Warwick CV35 0AH*

UPTON, Ms Caroline Tracey (Carrie). b 67. Lon Univ BMus90 Edin Univ BD94. Edin Th Coll 91. **d** 94. C Edin St Martin *Edin* from 94. *6 Cadzow Place, Edinburgh EH7 5SN* 0131-661 9346

UPTON, Clement Maurice. b 49. Linc Th Coll 88. **d** 90 **p** 91. C Northn St Alb *Pet* 90-93; V Laxey *S & M* from 93; V Lonan from 93. *The New Vicarage, South Cape, Laxey, Isle of Man IM4 7HX* Laxey (01624) 862050

UPTON, Donald George Stanley. b 16. Peterho Cam BA38 MA44. Westcott Ho Cam 39. **d** 40 **p** 41. Lic to Offic *St Alb* from 69; Chapl St Alb High Sch for Girls 69-73; Ch Hosp Sch Hertf 73-80; rtd 81. *The Pump House, Braughing, Ware, Herts SG11 2QS*

UPTON, Miss Julie. b 61. Ripon Coll Cuddesdon 87. **d** 88 **p** 94. C Kirkstall *Ripon* 88-91; Par Dn E Greenwich Ch Ch w St Andr and St Mich *S'wark* 91-94; C 94. *3 Presswood House, Drummond Road, London SE16 4BX*

UPTON, Kenneth Roy. b 19. K Coll Cam BA40 MA48. Oak Hill Th Coll 46. **d** 48 **p** 49. V Derby St Chad *Derby* 65-86; rtd 86; Perm to Offic *Derby* from 86. *31 Stone Hill Road, Derby DE23 6TJ* Derby (01332) 343765

UPTON, Michael Gawthorne. b 29. AKC53. **d** 54 **p** 55. Hon C Riverhead *Roch* 63-70; Youth Chapl 63-70; Lic to Offic *Ex* from 70; Chr Aid Area Sec (Devon and Cornwall) 70-94; Chr Aid SW Region Co-ord 73-89; rtd 94. *Otter Dell, Harpford, Sidmouth, Devon EX10 0NH* Colaton Raleigh (01395) 568448

UPTON-JONES, Peter John. b 38. Selw Coll Cam BA63 MA67 Liv Univ CertEd64. N Ord Course 90. **d** 92 **p** 93. NSM Formby H Trin *Liv* from 92. *25 Greenloons Drive, Formby, Liverpool L37 2LX* Formby (01704) 874510

UREN, Malcolm Lawrence. b 37. AKC63. **d** 64 **p** 65. C Cant St Martin w St Paul *Cant* 64-67; C Falmouth K Chas *Truro* 67-71; V St Blazey 71-79; P-in-c Tuckingmill 79-83; V 83-89; V Launceston St Steph w St Thos 89-92; V St Steph by Launceston from 92. *St Stephen's Vicarage, Launceston, Cornwall PL15 8HH* Launceston (01566) 772974

URMSON-TAYLOR, Ralph. *See* TAYLOR, Ralph Urmson

URQUHART, David Andrew. b 52. BA77. Wycliffe Hall Ox 82. **d** 84 **p** 85. C Kingston upon Hull St Nic *York* 84-87; TV Drypool 87-92; V Cov H Trin *Cov* from 92. *The Vicarage, 6 Davenport Road, Coventry CV5 6PY* Coventry (01203) 674996 or 220418

URQUHART, Edmund Ross. b 39. Univ Coll Ox BA62 DipTh63 MA68. St Steph Ho Ox 62. **d** 64 **p** 65. C Milton *Win* 64-69; C Norton *Derby* 69-73; V Bakewell from 73. *The Vicarage, Bakewell, Derbyshire DE45 1FD* Bakewell (01629) 812256

URSELL, Philip Elliott. b 42. Univ of Wales BA66 Ox Univ MA82. St Steph Ho Ox 66. **d** 68 **p** 69. C Newton Nottage *Llan* 68-71; Asst Chapl Univ of Wales (Cardiff) 71-77; Chapl Wales Poly 74-77; Lic to Offic *Llan* 77-82; Chapl Em Coll Cam 77-82; Prin Pusey Ho Ox from 82; Lic to Offic *Ox* from 82. *Pusey House, Oxford OX1 3LZ* Oxford (01865) 278415 Fax 270708

URWIN, John Hope. b 09. Lich Th Coll 29. **d** 32 **p** 33. V Trysull *Lich* 60-74; rtd 74. *77 Fountain Fold, Gnosall, Stafford ST20 0DR* Stafford (01785) 822601

✛URWIN, Rt Rev Lindsay Goodall. b 55. Ripon Coll Cuddesdon 77. **d** 80 **p** 81 **c** 93. C Walworth *S'wark* 80-83; V N Dulwich St Faith 83-88; Dioc Missr *Chich* 88-93; OGS from 91; Area Bp Horsham *Chich* from 94. *Bishop's House, 21 Guildford Road, Horsham, W Sussex RH12 1LU* Horsham (01403) 211139 Fax 217349

URWIN, Preb Roger Talbot. b 22. Ex Coll Ox BA43 MA47. Sarum Th Coll 48. **d** 50 **p** 50. CF (R of O) 56-77; R Littleham w Exmouth *Ex* 66-72; TR 72-87; RD Aylesbeare 69-73; P-in-c Withycombe Raleigh 72-74; Preb Ex Cathl 82-87; rtd 87. *Bishop's Lodge, Kelly Park, St Mabyn, Bodmin, Cornwall PL30 3RL* St Mabyn (0120884) 606

USHER, George. b 30. Univ of Wales (Swansea) BSc51. St Deiniol's Hawarden 73. **d** 75 **p** 76. NSM Clun w Chapel Lawn *Heref* 75-78; NSM Clun w Chapel Lawn, Bettws-y-Crwyn and Newc 79-80; C Shrewsbury St Giles *Lich* 80-83; C Shrewsbury St Giles w Sutton and Atcham 83-84; R Credenhill w Brinsop, Mansel Lacey, Yazor etc *Heref* from 84; P-in-c Bishopstone from 86; P-in-c Kenchester and Bridge Sollers from 86. *St Mary's Rectory, Credenhill, Hereford HR4 7DL* Hereford (01432) 760687

USHER, Robin Reginald. b 50. AKC74. St Aug Coll Cant 75. **d** 76 **p** 77. C Hulme Ascension *Man* 76-80; P-in-c Newall Green 80-85; C Atherton 85-87; TV 87-90; V Leigh St Jo from 90; Chapl Leigh Infirmary Lancs from 93. *The Vicarage, Gordon Street, Leigh, Lancs WN7 1RT* Leigh (01942) 672868

UTLEY, Canon Edward Jacob. b 24. AKC52. **d** 53 **p** 54. Chapl Dudley Road Hosp Birm 60-89; RD Birm City *Birm* 75-82; Hon Can Birm Cathl 80-89; rtd 89; Perm to Offic *Birm* from 89. *St Raphael, 50 Wheatsheaf Road, Birmingham B16 0RY* 0121-454 2666

UTTLEY, Mrs Valerie Gail. b 43. Man Univ BA64. N Ord Course 80. **dss** 83 **d** 87 **p** 94. Otley *Bradf* 83-87; Hon Par Dn 87-89; Par Dn Calverley 89-92; Ind Chapl *Ripon* from 92. *11 St Richard's Road, Otley, N Yorkshire LS21 2AL* Otley (01943) 463722

V

VAIL, David William. b 30. Dur Univ BA56 Sheff Univ DipEd71. Oak Hill Th Coll 56. **d** 58 **p** 59. C Toxteth Park St Bede *Liv* 58-61; Kenya 61-77; Chapl Versailles *Eur* 77-82; Gen Sec Rwanda Miss 82-88; V Virginia Water *Guildf* from 88. *Christ Church Vicarage, Christ Church Road, Virginia Water, Surrey GU25 4LD* Wentworth (01344) 842374

VAIZEY, Martin John. b 37. AKC64. **d** 65 **p** 66. C Bishopwearmouth Gd Shep *Dur* 65-69; C Darlington H Trin 69-72; V Easington Colliery 72-80; C-in-c Bishopwearmouth St Mary V w St Pet CD 80-85; V Sunderland Springwell w Thorney Close 85-88; R Witton Gilbert from 88. *The Rectory, Witton Gilbert, Durham DH7 6ST* 0191-371 0376

VALE, David Phipps. b 37. Lon Univ BSc64. St Steph Ho Ox 64. **d** 66 **p** 67. C Chiswick St Nic w St Mary *Lon* 66-70; Trinidad and Tobago 70-72; Ind Chapl *Wakef* 72-73; V Huddersfield St Andr 72-73; Asst Chapl St Olave and St Sav Sch Orpington 73-75; Perm to Offic *St E* 76-78; Hon C Ipswich St Clem w H Trin 78-80; TV Wolstanton *Lich* 80-89; V Ramsbottom St Jo and St Paul *Man* 89-92; rtd 92. *9 Regent Street, Bury, Lancs BL9 5AT* 0161-764 7742

VALE, Thomas Stanley George. b 52. Chich Th Coll 85. **d** 87 **p** 88. C Leic St Phil *Leic* 87-90; C Knighton St Mary Magd 90-93; P-in-c Leic St Chad from 93. *St Chad's Clergy House, 145 Coleman Road, Leicester LE5 4LH* Leicester (0116) 276 6062

VALENTINE, Derek William. b 24. S'wark Ord Course 65. **d** 68 **p** 69. NSM Battersea St Luke *S'wark* 68-77; NSM Fenstanton *Ely* 77-88; Perm to Offic *Bradf* from 88. *4 Woodland Drive, Skipton, N Yorkshire BD23 1QU* Skipton (01756) 799399

VALENTINE, Hugh William James. b 56. Bradf Univ BA83 CQSW. S'wark Ord Course 86. **d** 89 **p** 90. NSM Stoke Newington Common St Mich *Lon* 89-92; NSM Westmr St Jas from 92. *4 Leigh House, 1 Halcrow Street, London E1 2HF* 0171-377 7500

VALENTINE, Jeremy Wilfred. b 38. NW Ord Course 76. **d** 79 **p** 80. C Cundall *Ripon* 79-82; TV Huntington *York* 82-87; V Sand Hutton from 87. *The Vicarage, Sand Hutton, York YO4 1LB* Flaxton Moor (01904) 468443 Fax 468670

VALENTINE, John Harvey. b 63. Ch Ch Ox BA85 MA85. Ridley Hall Cam BA92. **d** 93 **p** 94. C Heigham H Trin *Nor* from 93. *14 Trinity Street, Norwich NR2 2BQ* Norwich (01603) 614231

VALLINS, Christopher. b 43. Lich Th Coll 63. **d** 66 **p** 67. C Cuddington *Guildf* 66-70; C Aldershot St Mich 70-73; V W Ewell 73-81; R Worplesdon 81-89; Chapl Merrist Wood Coll of Agric 81-89; RD Guildf 86-89; Chapl Epsom Healthcare NHS Trust from 89; Chapl Horton Hosp Epsom from 95. *The Chaplain's Office, Epsom General Hospital, Dorking Road, Epsom, Surrey KT18 7EG* Epsom (01372) 735322 Fax 745026

VAN CARRAPIETT, Timothy Michael James. b 39. Chich Th Coll 60. **d** 63 **p** 64. C Sugley *Newc* 63-65; C Newc St Fran 65-69; P-in-c Wrangbrook w N Elmsall CD *Wakef* 69-74; P-in-c Flushing *Truro* 74-75; P-in-c Mylor w Flushing 75-76; P-in-c St Day 76-82; R Aldrington *Chich* 82-87; V Bexhill St Barn from 87. *The Vicarage, Cantelupe Road, Bexhill-on-Sea, E Sussex TN40 1JG* Bexhill-on-Sea (01424) 212036

VAN CULIN, Canon Samuel. b 30. Princeton Univ AB52. Virginia Th Sem DB55 Hon DD. **d** 55 **p** 56. USA 55-83; Hon Can Cant Cathl *Cant* from 83; Sec Gen ACC from 83; Hon C All Hallows by the Tower etc *Lon* from 89. *ACC, Partnership House, 157 Waterloo Road, London SE1 8UT* 0171-620 1110 Fax 620 1070

VAN DE KASTEELE, Peter John. b 39. Magd Coll Cam BA61 MA65. Clifton Th Coll 61. **d** 63 **p** 64. C Eastbourne H Trin *Chich* 63-66; C N Pickenham w S Pickenham etc *Nor* 66-70; R Mursley w Swanbourne and Lt Horwood *Ox* 70-80; Perm to Offic *Glouc* 83-88; Admin Sec Clinical Th Assn from 83; Gen Dir from 88; Hon C Westcote w Icomb and Bledington 88-92; Perm to Offic from 92. *St Mary's House, Church Westcote, Chipping Norton, Oxon OX7 6SF* Shipton-under-Wychwood (01993) 830209

van de WEYER, Robert William Bates. b 50. Lanc Univ BA76. S'wark Ord Course 78. **d** 81 **p** 82. Warden Lt Gidding Community from 77; Hon C Gt w Lt Gidding and Steeple Gidding *Ely* 81-83; P-in-c 83-93; P-in-c Winwick 83-93; P-in-c Hamerton 83-93; P-in-c Upton and Copmanford 83-93; Perm to Offic from 93. *Castle House, Leighton, Leighton Bromswold, Huntingdon, Cambs PE18 0SJ* Huntingdon (01480) 890333

VAN DEN BERG, Jan Jacob. b 56. Sarum & Wells Th Coll 86. **d** 88 **p** 89. C Glouc St Aldate *Glouc* 88-91; C Ollerton w Boughton *S'well* 91-95; P-in-c Scrooby from 95. *The Vicarage, 7 Arundel Drive, Ranskill, Retford, Notts DN22 8PG* Retford (01777) 818470

van der LINDE, Herbert John. b 43. Rhodes Univ BA66. Coll of Resurr Mirfield. **d** 68 **p** 69. C Kingston St Luke *S'wark* 68-75; C Chipping Campden w Ebrington *Glouc* 75-78; V Cheltenham St Pet 78-84; V Bussage from 84. *St Michael's Vicarage, Bussage, Stroud, Glos GL6 8BB* Brimscombe (01453) 883556

VAN DER PUMP, Charles Lyndon. b 25. FRCM. S'wark Ord Course 86. **d** 88 **p** 89. NSM Primrose Hill St Mary w Avenue Road St Paul *Lon* from 88. *48 Canfield Gardens, London NW6 3EB* 0171-624 4517

van der VALK, Jesse. b 59. Nottm Univ BTh84 Avery Hill Coll PGCE85 Birm Univ MPhil88. St Jo Coll Nottm 81. **d** 88 **p** 89. C Droitwich Spa *Worc* 88-92; V Hartshead and Hightown *Wakef* from 92. *The Vicarage, Church Street, Hightown, Liversedge, W Yorkshire WF15 8HR* Cleckheaton (01274) 873786

VAN GORDER, Lloyd Franklin. b 11. **d** 73 **p** 74. V Hartley Wintney and Elvetham *Win* 74-76; Perm to Offic *Chich* 76-78; Perm to Offic *Portsm* from 79. *Address temp unknown*

VAN LEEUWEN, Dirk Willem. b 45. Utrecht Univ LLD71. Th Faculty Brussels 71 S'wark Ord Course 80. **d** 82 **p** 83. Asst Chapl Brussels Cathl *Eur* 82-84; Chapl Haarlem 84-93; Chapl Antwerp St Boniface from 94; Charleroi from 94. *Gretrystraat 39, 2018 Antwerp, Belgium* Antwerp (3) 239-3339 Fax 281-3946

VAN STRAATEN, Christopher Jan (Chris). b 55. Bris Univ BA77 Natal Univ HDipEd78. Oak Hill Th Coll DipHE92. **d** 92 **p** 93. C Woodley *Ox* from 92. *8 Caldbeck Drive, Woodley, Reading RG5 4LA* Reading (01734) 440690

VANDERSTOCK, Alan. b 31. St Jo Coll Dur BA57. Cranmer Hall Dur DipTh59. **d** 59 **p** 60. Lic Preacher *Cant* from 67; Sen Tutor Heath Clark High Sch Croydon 73-83; Dep Hd Teacher Norbury Manor High Sch Croydon 83-86; Sen Master Shirley

High Sch Croydon 86-92; rtd 92. *11 State Farm Avenue, Orpington, Kent BR6 7TN* Farnborough (01689) 862643

VANE, Walter Brian. b 21. Liv Univ BSc46 MA50. Coll of Resurr Mirfield 51. **d** 53 **p** 54. Hon C Heaton Norris Ch Ch *Man* 66-70; Lic to Offic 71-84; Lic to Offic *Ches* 71-84; Chapl Costa del Sol W *Eur* 84-88; rtd 88. *6 The Mead, Cirencester, Glos GL7 2BB* Cirencester (01285) 653235

VANN, Ms Cherry Elizabeth. b 58. ARCM78 GRSM80. Westcott Ho Cam 86. **d** 89 **p** 94. Par Dn Flixton St Mich *Man* 89-92; Chapl Bolton Coll of F&HE from 92; Par Dn Bolton St Pet 92-94; C from 94. *1 Bramcote Avenue, Bolton BL2 1LF* Bolton (01204) 35279 or 28851

VANN, Paul. b 41. St D Coll Lamp DipTh65. **d** 65 **p** 66. C Griffithstown *Mon* 65-67; C Llanfrechfa All SS 67-71; Dioc Youth Chapl 69-74; Chapl St Woolos Cathl 71-72; P-in-c Llanrumney 72-76; V from 76; Asst Chapl HM Pris Cardiff 75-78; RD Bassaleg *Mon* from 90. *The Vicarage, Countisbury Avenue, Cardiff CF3 9RN* Cardiff (01222) 792761

VANNOZZI, Peter. b 62. Lon Univ BA83 Ox Univ BA86. Ripon Coll Cuddesdon 84. **d** 87 **p** 88. C Kenton *Lon* 87-90; C Fleet *Guildf* 90-93; V Northwood Hills St Edm *Lon* from 93; AD Harrow from 95. *St Edmund's Vicarage, 2 Pinner Road, Northwood, Middx HA6 1QS* 0181-866 9230

VANSTON, Ven William Francis Harley. b 24. TCD BA48 MA52. **d** 48 **p** 49. I Arklow w Inch *D & G* 67-73; I Arklow w Inch and Kilbride 73-89; RD Rathdrum 77-89; Adn Glendalough 83-89; rtd 89. *11 Seabank Court, Sandycove, Dun Laoghaire, Co Dublin, Irish Republic* Dublin (1) 280-4575

VANSTONE, Walford David Frederick. b 38. Open Univ BA81. AKC69. **d** 70 **p** 71. C Feltham *Lon* 70-75; TV E Runcorn w Halton *Ches* 75-80; V Grange St Andr 80-82; V Hampton All SS *Lon* from 82. *All Saints' Vicarage, 40 The Avenue, Hampton, Middx TW12 3RS* 0181-979 2102

VANSTONE, Canon William Hubert. b 23. Ball Coll Ox BA48 MA St Jo Coll Cam BA50 MA. Lambeth DD88 Westcott Ho Cam 48 Union Th Sem (NY) STM50. **d** 50 **p** 51. V Kirkholt *Man* 64-76; Hon Can Man Cathl 68-76; V Hattersley *Ches* 77-78; Can Res Ches Cathl 78-90; Six Preacher Cant Cathl *Cant* from 83; rtd 91. *6 Hodges Close, Tetbury, Glos GL8 8HL* Tetbury (01666) 502689

VARAH, Preb Edward Chad. b 11. OBE69 CBE95. Keble Coll Ox BA33 MA46 Leic Univ Hon LLD79 St Andr Univ Hon LLD93 City Univ Hon DSc93. Linc Th Coll 34. **d** 35 **p** 36. C Linc St Giles *Linc* 35-38; C Putney St Mary *S'wark* 38-40; C Barrow St Jo *Carl* 40-42; V Blackb H Trin *Blackb* 42-49; V Battersea St Paul *S'wark* 49-53; P-in-c St Steph Walbrook and St Swithun etc *Lon* 53-54; R from 54; Founder The Samaritans 53; Dir 53-74; Preb St Paul's Cathl *Lon* from 75. *St Stephen's Vestry, 39 Walbrook, London EC4N 8BP* 0171-283 4444 or 626 8242

VARAH, Paul Hugh. b 46. St Deiniol's Hawarden 83. **d** 85 **p** 86. C Prestatyn *St As* 85-87; P-in-c Hawarden 87-88; TV 88-89; V Esclusham from 89. *The Vicarage, Vicarage Hill, Rhostyllen, Wrexham, Clwyd LL14 4AR* Wrexham (01978) 354438

VARGAS, Eric Arthur Dudley. b 27. BD. S Dios Minl Tr Scheme 81. **d** 83 **p** 84. C Farncombe *Guildf* 83-86; R Ockley, Okewood and Forest Green 86-90; V Kirdford *Chich* 90-93; rtd 93. *5 Bath Road, Emsworth, Hants PO10 7EP* Emsworth (01243) 376284

VARGESON, Peter Andrew. b 53. Wycliffe Hall Ox 85. **d** 87 **p** 88. C Yateley *Win* 87-92; V Bursledon from 92. *The Vicarage, School Road, Bursledon, Southampton SO3 8BW* Bursledon (01703) 402821

VARLEY, Robert. b 36. St Jo Coll Cam BA57 MA64. NW Ord Course 71. **d** 74 **p** 75. C Wallasey St Hilary *Ches* 74-77; V Rock Ferry 77-81; Perm to Offic *Man* 82-83; Hon C E Farnworth and Kearsley 83-86; Hon C Walkden Moor 86-87; C 87-89; V Lt Hulton 89-90. *66 Normanby Road, Worsley, Manchester M28 5TS* 0161-790 8420

VARNEY, Donald James (Don). b 35. Chich Th Coll 84. **d** 86. Hon C Liss *Portsm* from 86. *12 Birch Close, Liss, Petersfield, Hants GU33 7HS* Liss (01730) 893945

VARNEY, Peter David. b 38. Dur Univ BA61 MA64 Birm Univ DipTh63. Qu Coll Birm 61. **d** 64 **p** 65. C Newington St Paul *S'wark* 64-66; C Camberwell St Mich w All So w Em 66-67; Malaysia 67-68; Hon C Croxley Green All SS *St Alb* 69; Perm to Offic *Roch* 69-72 and 74-84; Asst Chapl Chapl Community St Jo Bapt Clewer 72-73; Asst Sec Chrs Abroad 74-79; Dir Bloxham Project 84-86; Perm to Offic *Cant* 84-85; Perm to Offic *S'wark* 85-86; P-in-c Thornage w Brinton w Hunworth and Stody *Nor* 87; P-in-c Briningham 87; P-in-c Melton Constable w Swanton Novers 87; Perm to Offic from 89; Chapl Yare and Norvic Clinics and St Andr Hosp Nor from 90. *8 High Green, Norwich NR1 4AP* Norwich (01603) 34855

VARNEY, Stephen Clive. b 59. Qu Mary Coll Lon BSc80 Sussex Univ MSc82 Southn Univ BTh88. Sarum & Wells Th Coll 84.

d 86 **p** 87. C Riverhead w Dunton Green *Roch* 86-91; V Bostall Heath from 91. *St Andrew's Parsonage, 276 Brampton Road, Bexleyheath, Kent DA7 5SF* 0181-303 9332

VARNEY, Wilfred Davies. b 10. Sarum & Wells Th Coll 71. **d** 71 **p** 72. C Glouc St Paul *Glouc* 71-74; V Lydbrook 74-77; rtd 77; Hon C Felpham w Middleton *Chich* 77-80; Hon C Overbury w Alstone, Teddington and Lt Washbourne *Worc* 80-82; P-in-c Nor St Andr *Nor* 87-91; Perm to Offic 82-87 and 91-93. *11 Manormead, Tilford Road, Hindhead, Surrey GU26 6RA* Hindhead (01428) 606652

VARNEY, William James Granville. b 22. St D Coll Lamp 62. **d** 65 **p** 66. V Strata Florida *St D* 68-71; V Llandyfriog, Llanfair Trelygen, Troedyraur etc 71-78; OCF 78; R Aber-porth w Tre-main and Blaen-porth *St D* 78-87; P-in-c Penbryn and Betws Ifan w Bryngwyn 88-92; rtd 92. *Alma, Tan y Groes, Cardigan, Dyfed SA43 2JT* Aberporth (01239) 810217

VARNHAM, Gerald Stanley. b 29. Sarum & Wells Th Coll 74. **d** 77 **p** 78. Hon C Portchester *Portsm* from 77. *15 Southampton Road, Fareham, Hants PO16 7DZ* Fareham (01329) 234182

VARNON, Nicholas Charles Harbord. b 45. Ex Univ BEd71 MPhil87. St Mich Coll Llan DipTh93. **d** 93 **p** 94. C Pontypridd St Cath w St Matt *Llan* from 93. *St Matthew's House, 26 East Street, Pontypridd, M Glam CF37 4PL* Pontypridd (01443) 406101

VARTY, John Eric. b 44. Tyndale Hall Bris 68. **d** 71 **p** 72. C Barrow St Mark *Carl* 71-74; C Cheadle *Ches* 74-82; V Cheadle All Hallows 82-89; V Alsager Ch Ch from 89. *Christ Church Vicarage, 43 Church Road, Alsager, Stoke-on-Trent ST7 2HS* Alsager (01270) 873727

VARTY, Robert. b 46. LRAM. Sarum & Wells Th Coll 84. **d** 86 **p** 87. C Plympton St Mary *Ex* 86-89; TV Northam w Westward Ho! and Appledore from 89. *The Vicarage, Meeting Street, Appledore, Bideford, Devon EX39 1RJ* Bideford (01237) 470469

VASEY, David. b 26. St Aid Birkenhead 55. **d** 58 **p** 59. V Leeds St Cypr Harehills *Ripon* 68-78; V Scarborough St Columba *York* 78-87; rtd 87. *45 Newlands Park Grove, Scarborough, N Yorkshire YO12 6PU* Scarborough (01723) 352122

VASEY, Michael Richard. b 46. Ball Coll Ox BA68 MA71. Wycliffe Hall Ox 68. **d** 71 **p** 72. C Tonbridge SS Pet and Paul *Roch* 71-75; Lic to Offic *Dur* 75-92; Tutor St Jo Coll Dur from 75; Sec Praxis from 92. *St John's College, 3 South Bailey, Durham DH1 3RJ* 0191-374 3584 or 384 0593 Fax 374 3573

VASS, Robert James Templeton. b 28. Lon Coll of Div 62. **d** 64 **p** 68. C Horsell *Guildf* 64-65; Kenya from 72. *PO Box 11860, Nairobi, Kenya*

VAUGHAN, Andrew Christopher James. b 61. Univ of Wales (Lamp) BA82. Linc Th Coll CMM84. **d** 84 **p** 85. C Caerleon *Mon* 84-86; C Magor w Redwick and Undy 86-88; Ind Chapl 84-94; Linc Ind Miss *Linc* from 94. *4 Grange Close, Canwick, Lincoln LN4 2RH* Lincoln (01522) 528266

✠**VAUGHAN, Rt Rev Benjamin Noel Young.** b 17. Univ of Wales (Lamp) BA40 St Edm Hall Ox BA42 MA46. Westcott Ho Cam 42. **d** 43 **p** 44 **c** 61. C Llan-non *St D* 43-45; C Carmarthen St Dav 45-48; Barbados 48-52; Lect St D Coll Lamp 52-55; Trinidad and Tobago 55-61; Dean Port of Spain 55-61; Jamaica 61-67; Suff Bp Mandeville 61-67; Adn S Middx 61-64; Bp Br Honduras 67-71; Dean Ban 71-76; Asst Bp Ban 71-76; Bp S & B 76-87; Pres Coun of Ch for Wales 79-82; rtd 87. *4 Caswell Drive, Newton, Swansea SA3 4RJ* Swansea (01792) 360646

VAUGHAN, Brian John. b 38. Lich Th Coll 65. **d** 68 **p** 69. C Fisherton Anger *Sarum* 68-70; C Wareham w Arne 70-73; Australia from 73. *The Rectory, PO Box 33, Murray Street, Pinjarra, W Australia 6208* Perth (9) 531-1248

VAUGHAN, Charles Jeremy Marshall. b 52. Man Univ BSc75 LTh. St Jo Coll Nottm 83. **d** 85 **p** 86. C Epsom Common Ch Ch *Guildf* 85-88; C Woking Ch Ch 88-93; R Worting *Win* from 93. *The Rectory, Glebe Lane, Basingstoke, Hants RG23 8QA* Basingstoke (01256) 331531

VAUGHAN, Idris Samuel. b 46. Sarum Th Coll 70. **d** 72 **p** 73. C Workington St Jo *Carl* 72-76; C Foley Park *Worc* 76-79; P-in-c Hayton St Mary *Carl* 79; V 79-85; Chapl Asst Univ Hosp Nottm 85-90; Chapl Asst Nottm Gen Hosp 85-90; Chapl Stafford Distr Gen Hosp from 90. *The Chaplain's Office, Stafford District General Hospital, Weston Road, Stafford ST16 3RS* Stafford (01785) 57731

VAUGHAN, Jeffrey Charles. b 45. S'wark Ord Course 85. **d** 88 **p** 89. NSM Tottenham St Paul *Lon* 88-91; C Hendon St Alphage 91-95; V Enfield SS Pet and Paul from 95. *The Vicarage, 177 Ordnance Road, Enfield, Middx EN3 6AB* Lea Valley (01992) 719770 Fax 0181-292 8456

VAUGHAN, John. b 30. Sarum Th Coll 53. **d** 56 **p** 57. C Wigan St Andr *Liv* 56-59; Australia 59-64; P-in-c Riddings *Derby* 64-71; R Hasland 71-80; V Temple Normanton 71-80; TV Dronfield 80-86; V Bradwell from 86. *The Vicarage, Bradwell, Sheffield S30 2HJ* Hope Valley (01433) 620485

VAUGHAN, Canon Dr Patrick Handley. b 38. TCD BA60 BD65 Selw Coll Cam BA62 MA66 Nottm Univ PhD88. Ridley Hall Cam 61. **d** 63 **p** 64. Min Can Bradf Cathl *Bradf* 63-66; Uganda 67-73; P-in-c Slingsby *York* 74-77; Tutor NW Ord Course 74-77; P-in-c Hovingham *York* 74-77; Prin E Midl Min Tr Course *S'well* 77-90; Hon Can Leic Cathl *Leic* 87-90. *50 Crescent Road, Sheffield S7 1HN* Sheffield (0114) 258 2110

✠**VAUGHAN, Rt Rev Peter St George.** b 30. Selw Coll Cam BA55 MA59 BNC Ox MA63. Ridley Hall Cam. **d** 57 **p** 58 **c** 89. C Birm St Martin *Birm* 57-63; Chapl Ox Pastorate 63-67; Asst Chapl BNC Ox 63-67; Ceylon 67-72; New Zealand 72-75; Prin Crowther Hall CMS Tr Coll Selly Oak 75-83; Lic to Offic *Birm* 75-83; Adn Westmorland and Furness *Carl* 83-89; Hon Can Carl Cathl 83-89; Area Bp Ramsbury *Sarum* from 89; Can and Preb Sarum Cathl from 89. *Bishop's House, High Street, Urchfont, Devizes, Wilts SN10 4QH* Devizes (01380) 840373 Fax 848247

VAUGHAN, Richard John. b 09. MC45. St Edm Hall Ox BA34 DipTh35 MA38. Wycliffe Hall Ox 34. **d** 35 **p** 36. V Headstone St Geo *Lon* 55-81; rtd 81; Perm to Offic *Lon* from 83. *3 Brookshill Avenue, Harrow, Middx HA3 6RZ* 0181-954 7855

VAUGHAN, Roger Maxwell. b 39. AKC62. **d** 63 **p** 64. C W Bromwich All SS *Lich* 63-65; C Wolv 65-70; V Tunstall Ch Ch 70-79; V Tunstall 79; V Abbots Bromley 79-86; P-in-c Blithfield 85-86; V Abbots Bromley w Blithfield 86-93; V Stafford St Jo and Tixall w Ingestre from 93. *St John's Vicarage, Westhead Avenue, Stafford ST16 3RP* Stafford (01785) 53493

VAUGHAN, Ronald Alfred (Ron). b 38. S'wark Ord Course 78. **d** 81 **p** 82. NSM Stepney St Pet w St Benet *Lon* 81-86; NSM St Jo on Bethnal Green from 87. *St Bartholomew's Vicarage, Buckhurst Street, London E1 5QT* 0171-247 8013

VAUGHAN, Trevor. b 41. Linc Th Coll 66. **d** 69 **p** 70. C Wyken *Cov* 69-72; C Stratford-on-Avon w Bishopton 72-73; P-in-c Monks Kirby w Withybrook and Copston Magna 73-75; P-in-c Wolvey, Burton Hastings and Stretton Baskerville 73-77; P-in-c Withybrook w Copston Magna 73-77; V Heyhouses *Blackb* 77-80; V Chorley St Geo 80-83; R Bolton by Bowland w Grindleton *Bradf* 83-89; V Settle 89-91; R Broughton, Marton and Thornton from 91. *The Rectory, Broughton, Skipton, N Yorkshire BD23 3AN* Earby (01282) 842332

VAUGHAN-JONES, Canon Frederick Edward Cecil. b 19. Selw Coll Cam BA40 MA44. Cuddesdon Coll 40. **d** 42 **p** 43. C Leigh-on-Sea St Marg *Chelmsf* 42-46; S Africa 46-62 and from 65; R Gt w Lt Gransden *Ely* 63-65; Can Grahamstown 70-73; Adn Johannesburg 82-86. *PO Box 225, Ramsgate, 4285 South Africa* Ramsgate (3931) 44113

VAUGHAN-JONES, Canon Geraint James. b 29. JP77. St D Coll Lamp 50 St Deiniol's Hawarden 68. **d** 70 **p** 71. C Llanaber w Caerdeon *Ban* 70-73; TV Dolgellau w Llanfachreth and Brithdir etc 73-76; R Mallywd w Cemais and Llanymawddwy from 76; RD Cyfeiliog and Mawddwy from 85; Can Ban Cathl from 86; Prec Ban Cathl from 89. *The Rectory, Mallwyd, Machynlleth, Powys SY20 9HJ* Dinas Mawddwy (01650) 531217

VAUGHAN-JONES, Canon John Paschal. b 18. Keble Coll Ox BA39 MA43. St Steph Ho Ox 39. **d** 41 **p** 42. R Chipping Ongar *Chelmsf* 49-83; R Shelley 49-83; RD Ongar 72-82; Hon Can Chelmsf Cathl 78-83; rtd 83. *Ryecroft, Old Harwich Road, Little Bentley, Colchester CO7 8SX* Colchester (01206) 250238

VAUGHAN-WILSON, Jane Elizabeth. b 61. Magd Coll Ox MA87. Cranmer Hall Dur. **d** 89 **p** 94. Par Dn Ormesby *York* 89-93; D-in-c Middlesb St Agnes 93-94; P-in-c from 94. *St Agnes Vicarage, 1 Broughton Avenue, Middlesbrough, Cleveland TS4 3PX* Middlesbrough (01642) 316144

VAYRO, Mark Shaun. b 66. Aston Tr Scheme 88 Linc Th Coll BTh93. **d** 93 **p** 94. C Northn St Mich w St Edm *Pet* from 93. *56 King Edward Road, Northampton NN1 5LU* Northampton (01604) 21268

VEAR, Frank Henry. b 12. K Coll Lon 67. **d** 68 **p** 69. C N Stoneham *Win* 68-75; V Southbourne St Chris 75-86; rtd 86; Perm to Offic *Win* from 86. *St Boniface, 2 Glenroyd Gardens, Bournemouth BH6 3JN* Bournemouth (01202) 427021

VEAZEY, Harry Christopher Hurford. b 11. Westcott Ho Cam 33. **d** 35 **p** 36. V Doddington w Wychling *Cant* 57-80; V Newnham 57-80; RD Ospringe 78-80; rtd 80; Perm to Offic *Cant* from 80. *Five Oaks, Pluckley Road, Charing, Ashford, Kent TN27 0AJ* Charing (01233) 712300

VELLACOTT, John Patrick Millner. b 29. Ox NSM Course 86. **d** 89 **p** 90. NSM Cholsey *Ox* 89-93; Chapl Nerja *Eur* from 93. *13 Calle de Jilguera, Almijara 2, 29780 Nerja, Spain* Malaga (52) 525406

VELLACOTT, Peter Graham. b 37. Seale-Hayne Agric Coll NDA59. E Midl Min Tr Course 90. **d** 93 **p** 94. NSM Framlingham w Saxtead *St E* 93-95; NSM Brandeston w Kettleburgh from 95. *Soham House, Brandeston, Woodbridge, Suffolk IP13 7AX* Snape (01728) 685423

VENABLES, Arthur Peter. b 20. Vancouver Sch of Th LTh47. **d** 49 **p** 50. V Kensington St Phil Earl's Court *Lon* 69-74; P-in-c Uxbridge Moor 74-82; rtd 82; Perm to Offic *Lon* from 82. *4 Wharf Court, Iver Lane, Cowley, Middx UB8 2JD*

VENABLES, Dudley James. b 17. Cant Sch of Min 77. **d** 80 **p** 81. NSM Ramsgate H Trin *Cant* 80-82; Chapl Asst St Aug Hosp Cant 83-88; NSM Wye w Brook 83-88; Perm to Offic from 88. *48 Abbots Walk, Wye, Ashford, Kent TN25 5ES* Wye (01233) 813000

✠**VENABLES, Rt Rev Gregory James (Greg).** b 49. Lon Univ CertEd74. **d** 84 **p** 84 **c** 93. SAMS from 77; Paraguay 78-90; C Rainham *Chelmsf* 90-92; C Rainham w Wennington 92-93; Aux Bp Peru and Bolivia 93-95; Bp Bolivia from 95; Asst Primate of S Cone from 95. *Iglesia Anglicana de Bolivia, Casilla 9574, La Paz, Bolivia* La Paz (2) 371414 Fax as telephone

VENABLES, Mrs Margaret Joy. b 37. ADB. Bp Otter Coll CertEd57 S Dios Minl Tr Scheme 86. **d** 89 **p** 94. NSM Wilton *B & W* 89-91; NSM Taunton St Andr 91-92; C from 92. *11 Henley Road, Taunton, Somerset TA1 5BN* Taunton (01823) 335023

VENABLES, Philip Richard Meredith. b 58. Magd Coll Ox BA79 CertEd80. Wycliffe Hall Ox 85. **d** 88 **p** 89. C Gillingham St Mark *Roch* 88-93; V Penge St Jo from 93. *The Vicarage, St John's Road, London SE20 7EQ* 0181-778 6176

VENESS, David Roger. b 48. Brunel Univ BTech70. St Jo Coll Nottm 73. **d** 75 **p** 76. C Selly Hill St Steph *Birm* 75-80; V Colney Heath St Mark *St Alb* from 80; RD Hatf 88-93. *St Mark's Vicarage, Colney Heath, St Albans, Herts AL4 0NQ* Bowmansgreen (01727) 822040

✠**VENNER, Rt Rev Stephen Squires.** b 44. Birm Univ BA65 Linacre Coll Ox BA67 MA71 Lon Univ PGCE72. St Steph Ho Ox 65. **d** 68 **p** 69 **c** 94. C Streatham St Pet *S'wark* 68-71; C Streatham Hill St Marg 71-72; C Balham Hill Ascension 72-74; Bp's Chapl to Overseas Students 74-76; V Clapham St Pet 74-76; P-in-c Studley *Sarum* 76; V Weymouth H Trin 82-94; RD Weymouth 88-93; Can and Preb Sarum Cathl 89-94; Suff Bp Middleton *Man* from 94. *The Hollies, Manchester Road, Rochdale, Lancs OL11 3QY* Rochdale (01706) 358550 Fax 354851

VENNING, Nigel Christopher. b 50. K Coll Lon BD75 AKC75. St Aug Coll Cant 75. **d** 76 **p** 77. C Minehead *B & W* 76-80; C Fawley *Win* 80-83; P-in-c Combe St Nicholas w Wambrook *B & W* 83-89; P-in-c Whitestaunton 83-89; R Staplegrove from 89. *The Rectory, Rectory Drive, Staplegrove, Taunton, Somerset TA2 6AP* Taunton (01823) 272787

VENUS, John Charles. b 29. AKC53. **d** 54 **p** 55. Chapl RN 66-70 and 78-83; Chapl Trin Coll Glenalmond 70-78; R Abinger cum Coldharbour *Guildf* 83-93; rtd 93. *Dora Cottage, Beech Hill, Hambledon, Godalming, Surrey GU8 4HL* Haslemere (01428) 682087

VERE HODGE, Preb Francis. b 19. MC43. Worc Coll Ox BA46 MA46. Cuddesdon Coll 46. **d** 48 **p** 49. V Moorlinch w Stawell and Sutton Mallet *B & W* 65-79; R Greinton 68-79; RD Glastonbury 75-79; Preb Wells Cathl 79-85; P-in-c Lydeard St Lawrence w Combe Florey and Tolland 79-84; rtd 84; Perm to Offic *B & W* 84-94. *Rose Cottage, Ham Street, Baltonsborough, Glastonbury, Somerset BA6 8PN* Baltonsborough (01458) 50032

✠**VERNEY, Rt Rev Stephen Edmund.** b 19. MBE45. Ball Coll Ox BA48 MA48. **d** 50 **p** 51 **c** 77. C Gedling *S'well* 50-52; C-in-c Clifton CD 52-57; V Clifton St Fran 57-58; Dioc Missr *Cov* 58-64; V Leamington Hastings 64-70; Can Res Cov Cathl 64-70; Can Windsor 70-77; Suff Bp Repton *Derby* 77-85; Hon Can Derby Cathl 77-85; Dioc Dir of Post-Ord Tr 83-85; rtd 86; Perm to Offic *Ox* 86-91. *Charity School House, Church Road, Blewbury, Didcot, Oxon OX11 9PY* Didcot (01235) 850004

VERNON, Bryan Graham. b 50. Qu Coll Cam BA72 MA76. Qu Coll Birm DipTh74. **d** 75 **p** 76. C Newc St Gabr *Newc* 75-79; Chapl Newc Univ 79-91; Chmn Newc Mental Health Trust from 91. *34 Queens Road, Newcastle upon Tyne NE2 2PQ* 0191-281 3861

VERNON, John Christie. b 40. Lon Univ BSc62. Linc Th Coll 63. **d** 65 **p** 66. C Barnard Castle *Dur* 65-69; CF 69-92; Chapl Ellesmere Coll Shropshire from 92. *Ellesmere College, Ellesmere, Shropshire SY12 9AB* Ellesmere (01691) 622321

VERNON, Mark Nicolas. b 66. St Jo Coll Dur BSc89 Ox Univ BTh93. St Steph Ho Ox 90. **d** 93 **p** 94. C Billingham St Cuth *Dur* from 93. *St Agnes Cottage, Church Road, Billingham, Cleveland TS23 1BW* Stockton-on-Tees (01642) 533103

VERNON, Reginald Joseph (Reg). b 08. Lon Coll of Div 49. **d** 51 **p** 52. V Steeple Claydon *Ox* 59-71; rtd 71. *Bethany,*

46 Blenheim Place, Aylesbury, Bucks HP21 8AQ   Aylesbury (01296) 84516

VERNON, Robert Leslie. b 47. Sarum & Wells Th Coll 73. **d** 76 **p** 77. C Hartlepool St Luke *Dur* 76-79; C Birm St Geo *Birm* 79-82; V Bordesley Green 82-86; Dioc Youth Officer *Carl* 86-89; P-in-c Holme 86-89; Dioc Youth Adv *Newc* from 89. *9 Winsford Avenue, North Shields, Tyne & Wear NE29 9EE* 0191-258 1183

VERNON, William Bradney. b 05. St Jo Coll Ox BA28 MA32. Wells Th Coll 28. **d** 29 **p** 30. R Winterslow *Sarum* 65-70; rtd 70. *9 Brooke Court, Parkleys, Ham, Richmond, Surrey TW10 5LX* 0181-546 8495

VESSEY, Andrew John. b 45. Bp Otter Coll CertEd67 Sarum & Wells Th Coll 84. **d** 86 **p** 87. C Framlingham w Saxtead *St E* 86-89; V Catshill and Dodford *Worc* 89-94; P-in-c Areley Kings from 94. *The Rectory, Areley Kings, Stourport-on-Severn, Worcs DY13 0TH*   Stourport (01299) 822868

VESSEY, Peter Allan Beaumont. b 36. Lon Coll of Div ALCD65 LTh74. **d** 64 **p** 65. C Rayleigh *Chelmsf* 64-67; C Cam H Trin *Ely* 67-71; V Kingston upon Hull Southcoates St Aid *York* 71-80; V Swanwick and Pentrich *Derby* 80-94; Perm to Offic from 94. *Hillview Cottage, 30 Chapel Hill, Cromford, Matlock, Derbyshire DE4 3QG*   Matlock (01629) 825572

VETTERS, Miss Shirley Jacqueline Margaret. b 34. S'wark Ord Course 85. **d** 88 **p** 94. NSM E Ham w Upton Park St Alb *Chelmsf* 88-91; C Birm St Martin w Bordesley St Andr *Birm* from 91. *341 George Road, Erdington, Birmingham B23 7RY* 0121-382 4109

VEVAR, Canon John Harvard. b 14. Univ of Wales BA36. St Mich Coll Llan 37. **d** 38 **p** 40. R Mellteyrn w Botwnnog and Llandygwnnin etc *Ban* 51-84; Can Ban Cathl 78-84; rtd 84; Perm to Offic *Ban* from 84. *Gwynant, Tudweiliog, Pwllheli, Gwynedd LL53 8AJ*   Tudweiliog (0175887) 270

VEVERS, Eric. b 22. Oak Hill Th Coll 54. **d** 56 **p** 57. V Ealing St Mary *Lon* 68-78; V Sidmouth All SS *Ex* 78-88; rtd 88. *16 Clayton Drive, Guildford, Surrey GU2 6TZ*   Guildford (01483) 506269

VEVERS, Geoffrey Martin. b 51. Oak Hill Th Coll. **d** 82 **p** 83. C Wealdstone H Trin *Lon* 82-84; C Trin St Mich, Harrow 84-88; V Wandsworth St Steph *S'wark* from 88. *St Stephen's Vicarage, 2A Oakhill Road, London SW15 2QU*   0181-874 5610

VEYSEY, John Norris. b 14. **d** 47 **p** 48. Chapl to the Deaf *B & W* 50-79; rtd 79; Perm to Offic *B & W* from 80. *8 Richmond Place, Lansdown, Bath BA1 5PZ*   Bath (01225) 313965

VIBERT, Simon David Newman. b 63. Oak Hill Th Coll BA89. **d** 89 **p** 90. C Houghton *Carl* 89-92; C-in-c Buxton Trin Prop Chpl *Derby* from 92. *37 Temple Road, Buxton, Derbyshire SK17 9BA*   Buxton (01298) 23461

VICARS, David. b 22. Leeds Univ BA48. Coll of Resurr Mirfield 48. **d** 50 **p** 51. Area Sec (Llan, Mon, St D and S & B) USPG 67-77; R Coychurch w Llangan and St Mary Hill *Llan* 77-90; rtd 90; Perm to Offic *Llan* from 90. *43 Bryn Rhedyn, Pencoed, Bridgend, M Glam CF35 6TL*   Bridgend (01656) 860920

VICARY, Canon Douglas Reginald. b 16. Trin Coll Ox BA38 BSc39 DipTh40 MA42. Wycliffe Hall Ox 39. **d** 40 **p** 41. Hd Master K Sch Roch 57-75; Hon Can Roch Cathl *Roch* 57-75; Can Res and Prec Wells Cathl *B & W* 75-88; Chapl to The Queen 77-87; rtd 88. *8 Tor Street, Wells, Somerset BA5 2US* Wells (01749) 679137

VICK, Samuel Kenneth Lloyd. b 31. Univ of Wales (Lamp) BA53. Linc Th Coll. **d** 55 **p** 56. C Shotton *St As* 55-56; C Wrexham 56-61; C Knowle H Nativity *Bris* 61-67; V Mirfield Eastthorpe St Paul *Wakef* 67-78; V Altofts from 78. *The Vicarage, Altofts, Normanton, W Yorkshire WF6 2QG* Wakefield (01924) 892299

VICKERMAN, John. b 42. Chich Th Coll 69. **d** 72 **p** 73. C Horbury *Wakef* 72-76; C Elland 76-78; V Glasshoughton 78-89; V Bruntcliffe from 89. *St Andrew's Vicarage, 4 Lewisham Street, Morley, Leeds LS27 0LA*   Leeds (0113) 252 3783

VICKERS, Allan Frederick. b 24. St Jo Coll Dur BA50 DipTh52. **d** 52 **p** 53. Chapl RAF 57-77; Asst Chapl HM Pris Wandsworth 78-79; Chapl HM Pris Ford 79-87; rtd 87. *23 Ashurst Close, Bognor Regis, W Sussex PO21 5UJ*

VICKERS, Dennis William George. b 30. RIBA72 York Univ MA91. Glouc Th Course 83. **d** 86 **p** 87. NSM Stokesay *Heref* 86-88; NSM Bucknell w Chapel Lawn, Llanfair Waterdine etc 88-92; NSM Wigmore Abbey from 93. *Reeves Holding, Reeves Lane, Stanage, Knighton, Powys LD7 1NA*   Bucknell (015474) 530577

VICKERS, Mrs Mary Janet. b 57. St Jo Coll Nottm BTh85. **dss** 85 **d** 87. Worc City St Paul and Old St Martin etc *Worc* 85-89; Par Dn 87-89; World Miss Officer *Worc* 89-92; USPG from 92; Lic to Offic *Eur* from 95. *Angelsachsenweg 20, 48167 Munster, Germany*   Munster (251) 626507

✠**VICKERS, Rt Rev Michael Edwin.** b 29. Worc Coll Ox BA56 MA56 Dur Univ DipTh59. **d** 59 **p** 60 **c** 88. C Bexleyheath Ch Ch *Roch* 59-62; Chapl Lee Abbey 62-67; V Hull Newland St Jo *York* 67-81; AD W Hull 72-81; Can and Preb York Minster 81-88; Adn E Riding 81-88; Area Bp Colchester *Chelmsf* 88-94; rtd 94. *2 Collingham Park, Lancaster LA1 4PD* Lancaster (01524) 848492

VICKERS, Peter. b 56. St Jo Coll Nottm LTh85. **d** 85 **p** 86. C Worc St Barn w Ch Ch *Worc* 85-88; TV Kidderminster St Mary and All SS etc 88-90; TV Kidderminster St Mary and All SS w Trimpley etc 90-92; Ind Chapl 88-92; CF from 92. *c/o MOD (Army), Bagshot Park, Bagshot, Surrey GU19 5PL* Bagshot (01276) 471717   Fax 412834

VICKERS, Peter George. b 41. Local Minl Tr Course 90. **d** 93 **p** 94. Hon C Cobham *Guildf* from 93. *24 Station Road, Stoke D'Abernon, Cobham, Surrey KT11 3BN*   Cobham (01932) 862497

VICKERS, Randolph. b 36. MCIM65 FInstD Newc Univ MA93. St Alb Minl Tr Scheme 77. **d** 80 **p** 82. NSM Hitchin *St Alb* 80-87; NSM Luton Lewsey St Hugh 87-89; NSM Shotley *Newc* from 89. *Beggar's Roost, 26 Painshawfield Road, Stocksfield, Northd NE43 7PF*   Stocksfield (01661) 842364

VICKERY, Charles William Bryan. b 38. Lich Th Coll 63. **d** 65 **p** 66. C Hove St Barn *Chich* 65-73; Chapl Hostel of God Clapham 73-76; P-in-c Kingston St Luke *S'wark* 76-82; V 82-94. *63 Connaught Road, Teddington, Middx TW11 0QF* 0181-977 8628

VICKERY, Jonathan Laurie. b 58. Bretton Hall Coll CertEd79 Leeds Univ BEd80. Wycliffe Hall Ox 81. **d** 84 **p** 85. C Gorseinon *S & B* 84-86; P-in-c Whitton and Pilleth and Cascob etc 86-87; V 87-91; V Crickhowell w Cwmdu and Tretower from 91. *The Rectory, Crickhowell, Powys NP8 1DW*   Crickhowell (01873) 811224

VICKERY, Robin Francis. b 48. K Coll Lon BD73 AKC73. **d** 74 **p** 75. C Clapham St Jo *S'wark* 74-77; C Clapham Ch Ch and St Jo 75-77; C Reigate St Luke S Park 77-79; Hon C Clapham H Spirit 80-87; Hon C Clapham TM from 87. *Norfolk House, 13 Chelsham Road, London SW4 6NR*   0171-622 4792

VICKERY, Trevor Hopkin. b 17. Univ of Wales BA39. St Mich Coll Llan 39. **d** 40 **p** 41. R Staplehurst *Cant* 51-91; Chapl HM Det Cen Blantyre Ho 54-80; rtd 91. *Park View, Cranbrook Road, Staplehurst, Kent TN12 0EJ*   Staplehurst (01580) 891091

VIDAL-HALL, Roderic Mark. b 37. Sheff Univ BSc60 Birm Univ DPS70. Lich Th Coll 62. **d** 64 **p** 65. C Ilkeston St Mary *Derby* 64-67; C Nether and Over Seale 67-70; V Chellaston 70-84; C Marchington w Marchington Woodlands *Lich* from 84; C Kingstone w Gratwich from 85. *13 Moisty Lane, Marchington, Uttoxeter, Staffs ST14 8JY*   Burton-on-Trent (01283) 820030

VIGAR, Gilbert Leonard. b 12. Lon Univ BD46 BA50 MA52 Nottm Univ MPhil72. Kelham Th Coll 32. **d** 38 **p** 39. Prin Lect Bp Grosseteste Coll Linc 61-77; Lic to Offic *Linc* 61-77; rtd 77; Hon C Win H Trin *Win* 79-85; Hon C Eastbourne St Sav and St Pet *Chich* 85-88. *5 Chatsworth Gardens, Eastbourne, E Sussex BN20 7JP*   Eastbourne (01323) 644121

VIGARS, Anthony Roy (Tony). b 54. St Jo Coll Dur BA75. Trin Coll Bris 77. **d** 78 **p** 79. C Barking St Marg w St Patr *Chelmsf* 78-81; C Littleover *Derby* 81-84; C-in-c Stapenhill Immanuel CD 84-90; V Meltham *Wakef* from 90. *The Vicarage, 150 Huddersfield Road, Meltham, Huddersfield HD7 3AL* Huddersfield (01484) 850050

VIGEON, Canon Owen George. b 28. Peterho Cam BA52 MA57. Ely Th Coll 52. **d** 54 **p** 55. V Bilsborrow *Blackb* 69-73; Asst Dir RE 69-73; V St Annes 74-85; RD Fylde 80-85; R Halton w Aughton 85-93; Hon Can Blackb Cathl 92-93; rtd 93. *19 Lynden Close, Bromsgrove, Worcs B61 8PD* Bromsgrove (01527) 574520

VIGERS, Neil Simon. b 62. K Coll Lon BD84 MTh87. Linc Th Coll 88. **d** 90 **p** 91. C Chelsea St Luke and Ch Ch *Lon* 90-93; C Staines St Mary and St Pet from 93. *Peter House, St Peter's Close, Staines, Middx TW18 2ED*   Staines (01784) 450861

VIGOR, Ms Margaret Ann. b 45. Ripon Coll Cuddesdon 85. **d** 87. Chapl Asst All SS Convent Ox 87-89; Par Dn Basildon, St Martin of Tours w Nevendon *Chelmsf* 89-91; Bp's Ho Iona 91. *15 Mitchell Street, Hartlepool, Cleveland TS26 9EZ* Hartlepool (01429) 867458

VILE, John Frederick. b 48. Univ of Wales (Cardiff) DipTh74. St Mich Coll Llan 71. **d** 74 **p** 75. C Roath St German *Llan* 74-78; C Newton Nottage 78-80; V Landore *S & B* 80-84; SSF 85-86; Hon C Clifton All SS w St Jo *Bris* 88-91; C Tile Hill *Cov* 91-94. *7 Hanbury Road, Clifton, Bristol BS8 2EW*   Bristol (0117) 973 8700

VILLAGE, Dr Andrew. b 54. Collingwood Coll Dur BSc75 Edin Univ PhD80. Trin Coll Bris BA92. **d** 92 **p** 93. C Northn St Giles *Pet* 92-95; R Middleton Cheney w Chacombe from 95. *The Rectory, 3 High Street, Middleton Cheney, Banbury, Oxon OX17 2PB*   Banbury (01295) 710254

VILLER, Allan George Frederick. b 38. E Anglian Minl Tr Course 78. **d** 81 **p** 82. NSM Ely 81-85; V Emneth 85-92; V

Littleport from 92. *St George's Vicarage, 30 Church Lane, Littleport, Ely, Cambs CB6 1PS* Ely (01353) 860207

VILLIERS, Preb Tony. b 35. Lich Th Coll 59. **d** 62 **p** 63. C Shifnal *Lich* 62-65; C Wednesbury St Paul Wood Green 65-67; R Llanymynech from 67; V Morton from 72; RD Oswestry 82-87; Preb Lich Cathl from 89. *Llanymynech Rectory, Pant, Oswestry, Shropshire SY10 9RA* Oswestry (01691) 830446

VINCE, Mrs Barbara Mary Tudor. b 29. St Alb Minl Tr Scheme 79. **dss** 82 **d** 87 **p** 94. Northwood H Trin *Lon* 82-86; Belmont 86-87; Par Dn 87-89; rtd 90; Perm to Offic *Lon* from 90. *22 St Mary's Avenue, Northwood, Middx HA6 3AZ* Northwood (01923) 825730

VINCE, David Eric. b 59. Birm Univ BA81 Nottm Univ BCombStuds85 Golds Coll Lon PGCE90. Linc Th Coll 82. **d** 85 **p** 86. C Gt Malvern St Mary *Worc* 85-88; C All Hallows by the Tower etc *Lon* 88-90; Min St Giles Cripplegate w St Bart Moor Lane etc 90-92; R Salwarpe and Hindlip w Martin Hussingtree *Worc* from 92. *The Rectory, Salwarpe, Droitwich, Worcs WR9 0AH* Droitwich (01905) 778757

VINCE, Edwin George. b 13. Leeds Univ BA36. Coll of Resurr Mirfield 36. **d** 39 **p** 40. C Glouc St Aldate *Glouc* 66-73; Chapl Convent Companions Jes Gd Shep W Ogwell 74-77; rtd 77. *The Grey House, Church Street, Chiseldon, Swindon SN4 0NJ* Swindon (01793) 740240

VINCE, Raymond Michael. b 45. Lon Univ BD69 Bris Univ MA72 K Coll Lon MTh80 LSE MSc83. Tyndale Hall Bris 66. **d** 71 **p** 72. C Southsea St Jude *Portsm* 71-75; Hon C Islington St Mary *Lon* 75-83; Chapl N Lon Poly 75-83; USA from 83. *906 South Orleans Drive, Tampa, Florida 33606, USA*

VINCENT, Preb Alfred James. b 30. Bris Univ BA54 Lon Univ BD56. Tyndale Hall Bris 50. **d** 54 **p** 55. Lect Qu Coll Birm 68-70; Lic to Offic *Birm* 68-70; V Bordesley St Oswald 70-76; V S Shields St Hilda w St Thos *Dur* 76-84; Miss to Seamen 84-92; V Bude Haven *Truro* 84-89; R Bude Haven and Marhamchurch 89-92; RD Stratton 88-92; Preb St Endellion from 90; rtd 92. P-in-c Chacewater *Truro* 92-95. *5 Raymond Road, Redruth, Cornwall TR15 2HD* Truro (01209) 209263

VINCENT, Bruce Matthews. b 24. Univ of Wales (Swansea) DipYW50 Open Univ BA76 Surrey Univ MPhil83. **d** 88 **p** 88. Hon C Sidcup St Jo *Roch* from 88. *497 Footscray Road, London SE9 3UH* 0181-850 5450

VINCENT, Christopher Robin. b 30. Sarum Th Coll 57. **d** 60 **p** 61. V Puxton w Hewish St Ann and Wick St Lawrence *B & W* 64-70; V Buckland Dinham w Elm 70-71; V Buckland Dinham w Elm, Orchardleigh etc 71-77; P-in-c Frome H Trin 77-90; Chapl St Adhelm's Hosp Frome 77-88; RD Frome *B & W* 85-89; V Kewstoke w Wick St Lawrence 90-94; rtd 94; Perm to Offic *B & W* from 94. *Willows Edge, 2 Westwood Close, Weston-super-Mare, Avon BS22 0JU* Weston-super-Mare (01934) 517425

VINCENT, David Cyril. b 37. Selw Coll Cam BA60 MA64. Coll of Resurr Mirfield 60. **d** 62 **p** 63. C Cheetwood St Alb *Man* 62-65; C Lawton Moor 65-67; V Wandsworth Common St Mary *S'wark* 67-84; RD Tooting 75-80; R Stoke D'Abernon *Guildf* from 84. *The Rectory, Blundell Lane, Stoke D'Abernon, Cobham, Surrey KT11 2SE* Cobham (01932) 862502

VINCENT, George William Walter. b 13. ALCD40. **d** 40 **p** 41. R Alderton w Ramsholt and Bawdsey *St E* 55-86; rtd 86; Perm to Offic *St E* from 86. *c/o B Vincent Esq, Rectory House, Alderton, Woodbridge, Suffolk IP12 3BL* Shottisham (01394) 411306

VINCENT, Henry William Gordon. b 16. Leeds Univ BA42. Coll of Resurr Mirfield 42. **d** 44 **p** 45. V Whitton St Aug *Lon* 64-81; rtd 81. *20 West Mills Road, Dorchester, Dorset DT1 1SR* Dorchester (01305) 263933

VINCENT, John Leonard. b 61. Univ of Wales (Lamp) BA83 Southn Univ BTh87. Chich Th Coll 84. **d** 87 **p** 88. C Hampton All SS *Lon* 87-90; C Shepperton 90-95; V Whitton SS Phil and Jas from 95. *The Vicarage, 205 Kneller Road, Twickenham TW2 7DY* 0181-894 1932

VINCENT, Michael Francis. b 48. CertEd70 Open Univ BA83. Sarum & Wells Th Coll 85. **d** 87 **p** 88. C Nuneaton St Mary *Cov* 87-90; C Stockingford 90-91; P-in-c from 91. *The Vicarage, Church Road, Stockingford, Nuneaton, Warks CV10 8LG* Nuneaton (01203) 383024

VINCENT, Canon Noel Thomas. b 36. Fitzw Ho Cam BA60 MA64. Ridley Hall Cam 61. **d** 63 **p** 64. C Fenham St Jas and St Basil *Newc* 63-67; C Prudhoe 67-70; V Holbrooke *Derby* 70-74; P-in-c Lt Eaton 72-74; P-in-c Osmaston w Edlaston 74-78; Hon C 78-85; Dioc Info Officer 74-78; Sen Producer Relig Progr BBC Man 82-91; Hon C Brailsford w Shirley and Osmaston w Edlaston *Derby* 85-86; Hon Can Derby Cathl from 85; Perm to Offic *Ches* 86-92; Chief Producer BBC Relig Progr Lon 91-93; Hon C Twickenham St Mary *Lon* from 92; Chief Asst to Hd BBC Relig Broadcasting from 93. *St Mary's Flat, Riverside, Twickenham TW1 3DT* 0181-891 5144

VINCENT, Roy David. b 37. Univ of Wales (Swansea) DipYW. Chich Th Coll 81. **d** 83 **p** 84. C Atherton *Man* 83-86; V E Crompton 86-95; P-in-c Burwash *Chich* from 95. *The Rectory, Burwash, Etchingham, E Sussex TN19 7BH* Burwash (01435) 882301

VINCENT, Canon William Alfred Leslie. b 11. Bris Univ BA33 St Edm Hall Ox BLitt44 DPhil68. **d** 39 **p** 40. Chapl R Wanstead Sch 39-41; C S Woodford H Trin CD *Chelmsf* 39-41; Lic to Offic *Mon* from 42; Chapl Ch Ch Ox 45-51; Chapl Dioc Tr Coll Ches 51-64; Lic to Offic *Ches* from 52; Can Res Bris Cathl *Bris* 74-77; Lic to Offic from 77. *80 College Road, Bristol BS16 2HP*

VINCER, Michael (Mike). b 41. Sarum & Wells Th Coll 77. **d** 80 **p** 81. Hon C Littleham w Exmouth *Ex* 80-92; Miss to Seamen 80-92; Area Sec (Dios Ex and Truro) USPG 86-92; Ind Chapl Gtr Man Ind Miss *Man* from 92; Chapl Man Airport from 92. *10 Highfield Crescent, Wilmslow, Cheshire SK9 2JL* Wilmslow (01625) 525982

VINE, John. b 24. Keble Coll Ox BA45 MA50. St Steph Ho Ox 45. **d** 48 **p** 49. C Hackney Wick St Mary of Eton w St Aug *Lon* 48-50; C Holborn St Alb w Saffron Hill St Pet 50-53; Chapl Ely Th Coll 53-56; Vice-Prin Ely Th Coll 56-60; Hon C St Leonards Ch Ch *Chich* 60-62; Chapl Lich Th Coll 62-67; R Wrington *B & W* 67-69; V Earl's Court St Cuth w St Matthias *Lon* from 69. *St Cuthbert's Clergy House, 50 Philbeach Gardens, London SW5 9EB* 0171-370 3263

VINE, Michael Charles. b 51. Worc Coll Ox BA73 MA80. Cuddesdon Coll 73. **d** 76 **p** 77. C Wallsend St Luke *Newc* 76-79; C Denton 79-81; V Sugley 81-91; V Shiremoor from 91. *St Mark's Vicarage, Brenkley Avenue, Shiremoor, Newcastle upon Tyne NE27 0PP* 0191-253 3291

VINE, Michael Derek. b 35. Ch Ch Ox BA58 MA63. Ely Th Coll 58. **d** 60 **p** 61. C Syston *Leic* 60-63; C S Ascot *Ox* 63-66; Chapl RN 66-70; Perm to Offic *Portsm* 71-74; Perm to Offic *Lon* 74-91; C Chepstow *Mon* 91-94; V Llantillio Pertholey w Bettws Chpl etc from 94. *St Teilo's Vicarage, Llantillio Pertholey, Abergavenny, Gwent NP7 6NY* Abergavenny (01873) 854323

VINE, Neville Peter. b 54. K Coll Lon BD80 AKC80. Linc Th Coll 80. **d** 81 **p** 82. C Peterlee *Dur* 81-86; Chapl Peterlee Coll 84-86; V Auckland St Pet *Dur* 86-89; Perm to Offic 89-91; R Easington from 91. *The Rectory, 5 Tudor Grange, Easington, Peterlee, Co Durham SR8 3DF* 0191-527 0287

VINER, Canon Leonard Edwin. b 20. Univ Coll Dur LTh41 BA43. St Aug Coll Cant 38. **d** 43 **p** 44. Malawi 64-71; R Honing w Crostwight *Nor* 71-75; P-in-c E Ruston 71-73; V 73-75; P-in-c Witton w Ridlington 71-73; V 73-75; C Corby Epiphany w St Jo *Pet* 75-79; V Brigstock w Stanion 79-86; rtd 86; Asst Chapl Lisbon *Eur* 86-87; Chapl Tangier 87-89. *8 Clive Close, Kettering, Northants NN15 5BQ* Kettering (01536) 519734

VINEY, Arthur William. b 32. BEd. S Dios Minl Tr Scheme. **d** 82 **p** 83. NSM Clayton w Keymer *Chich* 82-86; NSM Streat w Westmeston 86-94; rtd 94. *48 Friars Avenue, Peacehaven, Newhaven, E Sussex BN10 8SB* Plumpton (01273) 582353

VINEY, Peter. b 43. Ox NSM Course. **d** 76 **p** 77. NSM High Wycombe *Ox* from 76. *5 Avery Avenue, Downley, High Wycombe, Bucks HP13 5UE* High Wycombe (01494) 436065

VIPERS, Christopher James. b 63. Man Univ BA84. St Steph Ho Ox 87. **d** 89 **p** 90. C Wood Green St Mich w Bounds Green St Gabr etc *Lon* 89-93; TV from 93. *27 Collings Close, London N22 4RL* 0181-881 9836

VIPOND, Canon John. b 17. Lon Univ BD48. ALCD48. **d** 48 **p** 49. V Pudsey St Lawr and St Paul *Bradf* 56-73; V St Austell *Truro* 73-83; rtd 83. *Wisteria, 15 Coffeelake Meadow, Lostwithiel, Cornwall PL22 0LT* Bodmin (01208) 873141

VIRGO, Canon Leslie Gordon. b 25. Linc Th Coll 56. **d** 58 **p** 59. C Hatcham Park All SS *S'wark* 58-61; C Selsdon St Jo *Cant* 61-65; Chapl Warlingham Park Hosp Croydon 65-73; Dioc Adv on Past Care and Counselling from 74; R Chelsfield *Roch* from 74; Hon Can Roch Cathl from 83. *The Rectory, Skibbs Lane, Orpington, Kent BR6 7RH* Orpington (01689) 825749

VIRTUE, Thomas James. b 32. QUB BA56 TCD 58 Liv Univ DipRS80. **d** 58 **p** 59. C Belf St Mich *Conn* 58-61; C Belf St Bart 61-63; I Tempo *Clogh* 63-66; P-in-c Glynn w Raloo and Templecorran *Conn* 66-70; TV Ellesmere Port *Ches* 70-74; TV Ches Team 74-83; V Gt Sutton from 83. *St John's Vicarage, 1 Church Lane, Great Sutton, South Wirral L66 4RE* 0151-339 9916

VITTLE, Cyril Wilfred. b 13. **d** 55 **p** 56. V Brislington St Cuth *Bris* 69-76; C Thornbury *Glouc* 76-79; rtd 79; Perm to Offic *Glouc* 80-90. *39 Hyde Avenue, Thornbury, Avon BS12 1HZ* Thornbury (01454) 415561

VIVASH, Peter Henry. b 57. Hockerill Coll of Educn CertEd78 Chelmer Inst of HE CQSW85. Cranmer Hall Dur 90. **d** 92 **p** 93. C Malpas *Mon* 92-95; V Bettws from 95. *St David's Rectory, Bettws Hill, Bettws, Newport, Gwent NP9 6AD* Newport (01633) 855193

VIVIAN, Adrian John. b 42. K Coll Lon BD65 AKC66. **d** 66 **p** 67. C Bromley St Andr *Roch* 66-69; C Egg Buckland *Ex* 69-73; Perm to Offic 73-84; P-in-c Newton Ferrers w Revelstoke 84-87. *The Parsonage Farm, Parsonage Road, Newton Ferrers, Plymouth PL8 1AT*

VIVIAN, Thomas Keith. b 27. St Jo Coll Cam BA48 MA52. St Deiniol's Hawarden 76. **d** 80 **p** 81. Hd Master Lucton Sch Leominster 62-85; Lic to Offic *Heref* 80-85; P-in-c Chew Stoke w Nempnett Thrubwell *B & W* 85-88; R from 88; P-in-c Norton Malreward 85-88; R from 88; RD Chew Magna from 92. *The Rectory, Chew Stoke, Bristol BS18 8TU* Chew Magna (01275) 332554

VIVIAN, Victor Ivan. b 38. Nottm Poly LLB87. E Midl Min Tr Course DTPS94. **d** 94 **p** 95. NSM Bestwood *S'well* from 94. *12 Deepdale Road, Nottingham NG8 2FU* Nottingham (0115) 928 3954

VOAKE, Andrew James Frederick. b 28. Dur Univ BA55. Oak Hill Th Coll 51. **d** 55 **p** 56. Chapl Millfield Sch Somerset 63-71; R Bp Latimer Memorial Ch *Birm* 71-73; R Birm Bishop Latimer w All SS 73-80; V Crondall and Ewshot *Guildf* 80-90; rtd 90; Perm to Offic *B & W* from 90. *1 St Aubyns Avenue, Uphill, Weston-super-Mare, Avon BS23 4UJ* Weston-super-Mare (01934) 620587

VOCKINS, Michael David. b 44. Univ of Wales (Abth) BSc69. Glouc Sch of Min 85. **d** 88 **p** 89. NSM Cradley w Mathon and Storridge *Heref* from 88; Perm to Offic *Worc* from 88. *Birchwood Lodge, Birchwood, Storridge, Malvern, Worcs WR13 5EZ* Suckley (01886) 884366

✠**VOCKLER, Rt Rev John Charles (Brother John-Charles).** b 24. Queensland Univ BA53. ACT ThL48 ThD61 Gen Th Sem (NY) STB54 STM56 Hon STD61 St Jo Coll Morpeth 48. **d** 48 **p** 48 **c** 59. Australia 48-53 and 56-62 and 75-81; USA 54-56 and from 81; Bp Coadjutor Adelaide 59-62; Adn Eyre Peninsula 59-62; Bp Polynesia 62-68; SSF from 69; Perm to Offic *Sarum* 69-72; Asst Bp Worc 71-72; Perm to Offic *Lon* 72-75; Asst Bp Chelmsf 72-73; Asst Bp S'wark 73-75; Hon Can S'wark Cathl 75; rtd 90; Asst Bp Quincy from 90; Superior Franciscan Order Divine Compassion from 90. *Holyrood Seminary, PO Box 111, Liberty, New York 12754-0111, USA*

VODEN, Capt Raymond William Lang. b 35. CQSW74. SW Minl Tr Course 85. **d** 88 **p** 89. CA from 60; NSM Bideford *Ex* 88-94; C Northlew w Ashbury 94; C Bratton Clovelly w Germansweek 94; TV Okehampton w Inwardleigh, Bratton Clovelly etc from 94. *The Vicarage, Northlew, Okehampton, Devon EX20 3NJ* Beaworthy (01409) 221714

VOGEL, Charles Edward. b 06. Trin Coll Ox BA28 MA31. Cuddesdon Coll 64. **d** 65 **p** 65. C-in-c Childrey *Ox* 69-75; P-in-c Sparsholt w Kingston Lisle 73-75; rtd 75. *Flat 12, Ellesborough Manor, Butlers Cross, Aylesbury, Bucks HP17 0XF* Aylesbury (01296) 696125

VOGT, Charles William Derek. b 36. Portsm Poly DipSocWork76 Sheff Sch of Counselling & Psychology CertAnPsych85. E Midl Min Tr Course 83. **d** 86 **p** 87. NSM Ilkeston H Trin *Derby* 86-87; C Derby St Anne and St Jo 87-90; TV Staveley and Barrow Hill 90-95; P-in-c Hasland from 95. *The Rectory, 49 Churchside, Hasland, Chesterfield, Derbyshire S41 0JX* Chesterfield (01246) 232486

VOGT, Robert Anthony. b 25. Jes Coll Cam BA50 MA54. S'wark Ord Course 60. **d** 63 **p** 64. C Kidbrooke St Jas *S'wark* 67-72; V Wood End *Cov* 72-80; RD Cov E 77-80; R Kidbrooke St Jas *S'wark* 80-85; TR 85-90; rtd 90. *16 Tristan Square, London SE3 9UB* 0181-297 2361

VOKES, Prof Frederick Ercolo. b 10. FTCD74 St Jo Coll Cam BA33 MA46 BD53 TCD MA67. Westcott Ho Cam 33. **d** 34 **p** 35. Prof of Div TCD 57-80; rtd 80. *Flat 24, The Hastings, Greaves Road, Lancaster LA1 4TF* Lancaster (01524) 69428

VOKES-DUDGEON, Preb Thomas Pierre. b 09. Univ of NZ BA32 St Jo Coll Auckland 29. **d** 32 **p** 33. V St Marychurch *Ex* 51-75; Preb Ex Cathl 72-75; rtd 75; Perm to Offic *Ex* from 75. *Flat 3, Petroc House, Falkland Road, Torquay TQ2 5JP* Torquay (01803) 293968

VON BENZON, Charles Nicholas. b 54. Solicitor 79 Kent Univ BA78. S'wark Ord Course 82. **d** 85 **p** 86. NSM Bromley SS Pet and Paul *Roch* 85-87; Ed Newsletter among Ministers at Work 89-93; Perm to Offic *Chich* 87-93; Asst to RD Dallington Chich 93-95; C The Deverills *Sarum* from 95. *The Rectory, 6 Homefield Close, Longbridge Deverill, Warminster, Wilts BA12 7DQ* Warminster (01985) 840278

VON MALAISE, Nicolas Christoph Axel. b 62. Univ Coll Ox BA84. Ripon Coll Cuddesdon BA86. **d** 87 **p** 88. C Oxhey St Matt *St Alb* 87-90; C Northfield *Birm* 90-92; Asst Chapl Win Coll from 92. *Winchester College, Winchester, Hants SO23 9LX* Winchester (01962) 884056

VONBERG, Canon Michael. b 27. Lon Univ BA51. Wells Th Coll 58. **d** 59 **p** 60. V Camberwell St Geo *S'wark* 64-74; V Kenley 75-94; RD Croydon S 85-93; Hon Can S'wark Cathl 89-94; rtd 94. *81 Christchurch Mount, Epsom, Surrey KT19 8LP*

VOOGHT, Canon Michael George Peter. b 38. St Pet Hall Ox BA61 MA65. Chich Th Coll 61. **d** 63 **p** 64. C E Dulwich St Jo *S'wark* 63-66; C Prestbury *Glouc* 66-72; R Minchinhampton 72-85; RD Stonehouse 79-85; V Thornbury from 85; Hon Can Glouc Cathl from 86. *The Vicarage, Castle Street, Thornbury, Bristol BS12 1HQ* Thornbury (01454) 413209

VORLEY, Kenneth Arthur. b 27. Sarum Th Coll 65. **d** 67 **p** 68. C Ashbourne w Mapleton and Clifton *Derby* 67-71; R W Hallam and Mapperley 71-77; V Hemingford Grey *Ely* 78-88; rtd 88. *The Old Manor, Little Braithwaite, Keswick, Cumbria CA12 5SR* Braithwaite (01768) 782535

VOSS, Mrs Philomena Ann. **d** 90. NSM Nazeing *Chelmsf* from 90. *21 Queen's Road, Hertford SG13 8AZ* Hertford (01992) 554676

VOUSDEN, Alan Thomas. b 48. K Coll Lon BSc69. Qu Coll Birm DipTh71. **d** 72 **p** 73. C Orpington All SS *Roch* 72-76; C Belvedere All SS 76-80; R Cuxton and Halling 80-86; V Bromley St Mark from 86; Chapl Bromley Hosp from 86. *St Mark's Vicarage, 51 Hayes Road, Bromley BR2 9AE* 0181-460 6220

VOUT, Victor Alan. b 25. Lon Univ BA53 Hull Univ BA56. Ripon Hall Ox 63. **d** 65 **p** 66. C Norton Woodseats St Paul *Sheff* 65-70; V Clifton St Jas 70-92; rtd 92. *87 Spinneyfield, Moorgate, Rotherham, S Yorkshire S60 3LZ* Rotherham (01709) 839258

VOWLES, Miss Patricia. b 50. S'wark Ord Course 84. **d** 87 **p** 94. USPG 70-91; NSM Nunhead St Antony w St Silas *S'wark* 87-91; Par Dn Newington St Mary 91; D-in-c Camberwell St Mich w All So w Em 91; Par Dn 91-94; V from 94. *163A John Ruskin Street, London SE5 0PQ* 0171-703 8686

VOWLES, Canon Peter John Henry. b 25. Magd Coll Ox BA50 MA55. Westcott Ho Cam 50. **d** 52 **p** 53. V 64-72; R Cottingham *York* 72-83; R Man St Ann *Man* 83-91; Hon Can Man Cathl 83-91; rtd 91. *10 Redshaw Close, Fallowfield, Manchester M14 6JB* 0161-257 2065

VYSE, Canon Jack Walter Miller. b 15. CCC Cam BA37 MA41. Westcott Ho Cam 38. **d** 39 **p** 40. V St Mary Abchurch *Lon* 61-70; Vice-Prin S'wark Ord Course 66-70; P-in-c Alby w Thwaite *Nor* 70-81; V Aylsham 70-88; Chapl St Mich Hosp Aylsham 70-88; RD Ingworth *Nor* 74-88; Hon Can Nor Cathl 81-88; rtd 88; Perm to Offic *Linc* 88-89; RD Louthesk 89-94. *The Old Post Office, Ludford, Lincoln LN3 6AD* Burgh-on-Bain (01507) 313740

VYVYAN, John Philip. b 28. New Coll Ox BA51 MA59. Cuddesdon Coll 57. **d** 59 **p** 60. V Adderbury w Milton *Ox* 64-93; rtd 93. *25 Tremayne Close, Devoran, Truro, Cornwall TR3 6QE* Truro (01872) 870153

W

WADDINGTON, Very Rev Robert Murray. b 27. Selw Coll Cam BA51 MA55. Ely Th Coll 51. **d** 53 **p** 54. Australia 61-71; OGS from 60; Can Res Carl Cathl *Carl* 72-77; Bp's Adv for Educn 72-77; Hon Can Carl Cathl 77-84; Gen Sec Gen Syn Bd of Educn 77-84; Gen Sec Nat Soc 77-84; Dean Man 84-93; rtd 93. *6 Waverley Street, York YO3 7QZ* York (01904) 670200

WADDINGTON-FEATHER, John Joseph. b 33. FRSA89 Leeds Univ BA54. St Deiniol's Hawarden 75. **d** 77 **p** 78. Hon C Longden and Annscroft w Pulverbatch *Heref* from 77; Sub-Chapl HM Pris Shrewsbury from 77; Chapl Prestfelde Sch Shrewsbury from 86. *Fair View, Old Coppice, Lyth Bank, Shrewsbury SY3 0BW* Shrewsbury (01743) 722177

WADDLE, William. b 31. Linc Th Coll 64. **d** 66 **p** 67. C Longbenton St Bart *Newc* 69-75; V Denton 75-81; V Beadnell 81; V Beadnell w Ellingham 81-93; RD Bamburgh and Glendale 83-92; rtd 93. *Kilmartin, 58J Church Street, Berwick-upon-Tweed TD15 1DU* Berwick-upon-Tweed (01289) 305908

WADDLETON, Edwin Henry. b 12. Clifton Th Coll 37. **d** 39 **p** 40. R Chippenham St Paul w Langley Burrell *Bris* 65-77; rtd 77; Perm to Offic *Bris* from 77. *66 Sadler's Mead, Chippenham, Wilts SN15 3PL* Chippenham (01249) 653721

WADDY, Richard Patteson Stacy. b 04. Ball Coll Ox BA26 MA30. Cuddesdon Coll 26. **d** 27 **p** 28. Chapl Qu Anne's Sch Caversham 67-72; rtd 72. *Manormead, Tilford Road, Hindhead, Surrey GU26 6RA* Hindhead (01428) 604780

WADE, Andrew John. b 50. Trin Coll Bris. **d** 86 **p** 87. C St Keverne *Truro* 86-89; TV Probus, Ladock and Grampound w

Creed and St Erme 89-92; V Constantine from 92. *The Vicarage, Charlbury Heights, Constantine, Falmouth, Cornwall TR11 5AN* Falmouth (01326) 40259

WADE, Anthony Austen. b 14. Leeds Univ BA36 MA38. Coll of Resurr Mirfield 36. **d** 38 **p** 39. V Sudbury St Andr *Lon* 68-79; rtd 79; Perm to Offic *Bris* 88-92. *15 Stuart Court, High Street, Kibworth, Leicester LE8 0LE* Leicester (0116) 279 6369

WADE, Christopher John. b 54. ARICS82 ACIArb88 Basford Coll Nottm ONC76 Trent Poly BSc81. Aston Tr Scheme 88 Trin Coll Bris DipHE92. **d** 92 **p** 93. C Barnsley St Geo *Wakef* from 92. *54 Vernon Way, Gawber, Barnsley, S Yorkshire S75 2NN* Barnsley (01226) 202631

WADE, David Peter (Dave). b 65. St Jo Coll Nottm LTh92 DCM92. **d** 92 **p** 93. C Victoria Docks Ascension *Chelmsf* 92-95; P-in-c Victoria Docks St Luke from 95. *St Luke's Vicarage, 105 Tarling Road, London E16 1HN* 0171-476 2076

WADE, Canon John Martin. b 22. Wells Th Coll. **d** 54 **p** 55. V Nayland w Wiston *St E* 60-74; Chapl Jane Walker Hosp Nayland 62-74; V Shrivenham w Watchfield and Bourton *Ox* 74-88; RD Vale of White Horse 83-87; Hon Can Ch Ch 86-88; rtd 88; Perm to Offic *Ox* from 88; Perm to Offic *Glouc* from 90. *Cranham, 13 Besbury Park, Minchinhampton, Stroud, Glos GL6 9EN* Stroud (01453) 885449

WADE, Walter. b 29. Oak Hill Th Coll 64. **d** 66 **p** 67. V Jesmond H Trin *Newc* 69-78; R Moresby *Carl* 78-87; P-in-c Langdale 87-94; Member Rural Life and Agric Team 93-94; rtd 94. *Manor Cottage, Fellside, Caldbeck, Wigton, Cumbria CA7 8HA* Caldbeck (016974) 78214

WADE-STUBBS, Edward Pomery Flood. b 17. St Jo Coll Dur LTh39 BA40. Tyndale Hall Bris 36. **d** 40 **p** 41. V Norton Bavant *Sarum* 63-66; R Sutton Veny 63-66; rtd 69; Perm to Offic *Sarum* 90-95. *44 All Saints Road, Hawkhurst, Cranbrook, Kent TN18 4HT*

WADGE, Alan. b 46. Grey Coll Dur BA68 MA72 St Chad's Coll Dur DipTh69. **d** 70 **p** 71. C Cockerton *Dur* 70-74; C Whitworth w Spennymoor 74-75; P-in-c Shipton Moyne w Westonbirt and Lasborough *Glouc* 75-80; Chapl Westonbirt Sch 75-80; V Dean Forest H Trin *Glouc* 80-83; Chapl Gresham's Sch Holt 83-91; R Ridgeway *Ox* from 91; RD Wantage from 95. *The Rectory, Letcombe Regis, Wantage, Oxon OX12 9LD* Wantage (01235) 763805

WADHAM, Philip Andrew. b 41. Vancouver Sch of Th BTh80. **d** 79 **p** 80. Canada 80-82 and 85-88; Ecuador 82-85; Area Sec (Dios Wakef and Bradf) USPG 88-92; Perm to Offic *Bradf* from 88. *6 Glenhurst Road, Shipley, W Yorkshire BD18 4DZ* Bradford (01274) 588935

WADLAND, Douglas Bryan. b 33. CQSW62 K Coll Dur BA61 Liv Univ DSA62. Oak Hill Th Coll 90. **d** 91 **p** 92. NSM Cowley *Lon* 91-93; Asst Chapl Hillingdon Hosp Uxbridge from 91; P-in-c Wembley St Jo from 93. *The Vicarage, 3 Crawford Avenue, Wembley, Middx HA0 2HX* 0181-902 0273

WADSWORTH, Andrew James. b 56. St Jo Coll Dur BA79 Cam Univ CertEd80. Sarum & Wells Th Coll 84 Chich Th Coll 86 Lambeth STh95. **d** 87 **p** 88. NSM Forest Row *Chich* 87-89; NSM E Grinstead St Swithun 87-89; C Shrewsbury St Chad w St Mary *Lich* 89-91; TV Honiton, Gittisham, Combe Raleigh, Monkton etc *Ex* from 91. *The Vicarage, Awliscombe, Honiton, Devon EX14 0PJ* Honiton (01404) 42983

WADSWORTH, Jean. b 44. Cranmer Hall Dur BA71 St Jo Coll Dur. **d** 87 **p** 94. Par Dn Thamesmead *S'wark* 87-92; Par Dn Rotherhithe H Trin 92-94; C from 94. *7 Howland Way, London SE16 1HN* 0171-252 2995

WADSWORTH, Michael Philip. b 43. Qu Coll Ox BA65 MA68 DPhil75 Cam Univ PhD78. Ripon Hall Ox 67. **d** 70 **p** 71. C Sutton St Mich *York* 70-73; Lect Sussex Univ 73-78; Fell 78-81; Hon C Hove St Jo *Chich* 75-78; Chapl SS Coll Cam 78-81; Dir Th Studies 79-81; CF (TA) from 80; C Ditton St Mich *Liv* 81; TV 82-84; Dioc Lay Tr Officer 83-89; V Orford St Marg 84-89; V Haddenham *Ely* from 89; V Wilburton from 89; RD Ely from 94. *The Vicarage, Haddenham, Ely, Cambs CB6 3TB* Ely (01353) 740309

WADSWORTH, Norman Charles. b 26. Bps' Coll Cheshunt 62. **d** 64 **p** 65. P-in-c Wing *Ox* 69-73; P-in-c Grove St Mic 69-73; P-in-c Wingrave 69-74; V Wing w Grove 73-79; R Didcot All SS 79-91; rtd 91. *25 Snipewood, Eccleston, Chorley, Lancs PR7 5RQ* Eccleston (01257) 450162

WADSWORTH, Peter Richard. b 52. Qu Coll Ox BA73 MA77. Cuddesdon Coll 74 English Coll Rome 76. **d** 77 **p** 78. C High Wycombe *Ox* 77-81; C Farnham Royal w Hedgerley 81-84; Dioc Ecum Officer *Portsm* 84-90; V E Meon from 84; V Langrish from 84. *The Vicarage, East Meon, Petersfield, Hants GU32 1NH* East Meon (01730) 823221

WADSWORTH, Roy. b 37. NE Ord Course 89. **d** 89 **p** 90. NSM Alne *York* from 89; Ind Chapl from 94. *The Rosery, Tollerton, York YO6 2DX* Tollerton (01347) 838212

WAGGETT, Geoffrey James. b 49. Sarum & Wells Th Coll 83. **d** 85 **p** 86. C Newton Nottage *Llan* 85-88; TV Glyncorrwg w Afan Vale and Cymmer Afan 88-89; R from 89. *The Vicarage,*

Church Street, Glyncorrwg, Port Talbot, W Glam SA13 3BW Cymmer (01639) 851301

WAGHORN, Geoffrey Brian. b 28. St Aid Birkenhead 62. **d** 64 **p** 65. C Lenton w Ingoldsby *Linc* 68-70; V Messingham 70-77; R Fishtoft 77-85; R Durley *Portsm* 85-93; V Curdridge 85-93; rtd 93. *17 Waters Edge, Hedge End, Southampton SO3 4AE* Botley (01489) 782795

WAGHORNE, Frederick Charles. b 07. St Jo Coll Dur BA32 MA35 DipTh35. **d** 33 **p** 34. V Bearsted *Cant* 63-73; rtd 73; Perm to Offic *Cant* 73-93. *Townfield, Burleigh Road, Charing, Ashford, Kent TN27 0JB* Charing (01233) 713130

WAGNER, Canon Peter Frederick. b 33. Lon Univ BSc56. Westcott Ho Cam. **d** 60 **p** 61. C Longbridge *Birm* 60-64; V Nechells 64-70; Rhodesia 70-80; Zimbabwe from 80; Dean Gweru 84-87. *PO Box 75, Kwekwe, Zimbabwe* Kwekwe (55) 2535

WAGSTAFF, Alan Robert Joseph. b 21. Lon Univ DipTh69. S'wark Ord Course 67. **d** 70 **p** 71. C St Paul's Cray St Barn *Roch* 70-76; V Southborough St Pet w Ch Ch and St Matt 76-86; RD Tunbridge Wells 83-86; rtd 86; Perm to Offic *Chich* from 86; Perm to Offic *Roch* from 86. *27A The Green, St Leonards-on-Sea, E Sussex TN38 0SX* Hastings (01424) 425895

WAGSTAFF, Andrew Robert. b 56. K Coll Lon BD79 AKC79. Coll of Resurr Mirfield 81. **d** 83 **p** 84. C Newark w Hawton, Cotham and Shelton *S'well* 83-86; C Dub St Bart w Ch Ch Leeson Park *D & G* 86-89; V Nottm St Geo w St Jo *S'well* 89-95; V Worksop Priory from 95. *The Vicarage, Cheapside, Worksop, Notts S80 2HX* Worksop (01909) 472180

WAGSTAFF, Ven Christopher John Harold. b 36. St D Coll Lamp BA62 DipTh63. **d** 63 **p** 64. C Queensbury All SS *Lon* 63-68; V Tokyngton St Mich 68-73; V Coleford w Staunton *Glouc* 73-83; RD Forest S 76-82; Adn Glouc from 83; Hon Can St Andr Cathl Njombe (Tanzania) from 93. *Christ Church Vicarage, 6 Spa Villas, Gloucester GL1 1LB* Gloucester (01452) 528500 Fax 318528

WAGSTAFF, Miss Joan. b 33. Gilmore Ho. dss 75 **d** 87 **p** 94. Ellesmere Port *Ches* 86-87; Par Dn 87-93; rtd 93. *41 Heywood Road, Great Sutton, South Wirral L66 3PS* 0151-348 0884

WAGSTAFF, Michael. b 59. R Holloway Coll Lon BA81. Coll of Resurr Mirfield 86. **d** 89 **p** 90. C Worksop Priory *S'well* 89-92; C Ab Kettleby Gp *Leic* 92-94; TV Leic Resurr from 94. *St Alban's House, Weymouth Street, Leicester LE4 6FN* Leicester (0116) 266 1002

WAGSTAFF, Robert William. b 36. Edin Th Coll 61. **d** 63 **p** 64. C Harringay St Paul *Lon* 63-64; C Mill Hill Jo Keble Ch 64-69; Perm to Offic *S'wark* 76-81; Lic to Offic *Worc* from 81; NSM Ombersley w Doverdale from 94. *The Red House, Quarry Bank, Hartlebury, Kidderminster, Worcs DY11 7TE* Hartlebury (01299) 250883

WAGSTAFFE, Eric Herbert. b 25. St Aid Birkenhead 55. **d** 57 **p** 58. V Pendlebury St Jo *Man* 69-84; V Hoghton *Blackb* 84-91; rtd 91. *3 Chelwood Close, Bolton BL1 7LN* Bolton (01204) 596048

WAIN, Frank. b 13. Leeds Univ BA35. Coll of Resurr Mirfield 35. **d** 37 **p** 38. R Kinwarton w Gt Alne and Haselor *Cov* 55-83; rtd 83; Perm to Offic *Cov* from 83. *21 Queensway, Bidford-on-Avon, Alcester, Warks B50 4BA* Bidford-on-Avon (01789) 778586

WAIN, Phillip. b 54. Aston Tr Scheme 89 Linc Th Coll CMinlStuds93. **d** 93 **p** 94. C Witton *Ches* from 93. *The Curate's House, 162 Middlewich Road, Rudheath, Northwich, Cheshire CW9 7DX* Northwich (01606) 41965

WAINAINA, Francis Samson Kamoko. b 51. BA84 Dur Univ MA89. Oak Hill Th Coll 81. **d** 84 **p** 85. Kenya 84-88; C Upton (or Overchurch) *Ches* 89-92; V Ellesmere St Pet *Sheff* from 92. *The Vicarage, 85 Malton Street, Sheffield S4 7EA* Sheffield (0114) 276 2555

✠**WAINE, Rt Rev John.** b 30. Man Univ BA51. Ridley Hall Cam 53. **d** 55 **p** 56 **c** 75. C W Derby St Mary *Liv* 55-58; C Sutton 58-60; V Ditton St Mich 60-64; V Southport H Trin 64-69; V Kirkby 69-71; TR 71-75; Suff Bp Stafford *Lich* 75-78; Preb Lich Cathl 75-78; Bp St E 78-86; Bp Chelmsf from 86; Clerk of the Closet from 89. *Bishopscourt, Margaretting, Ingatestone, Essex CM4 0HD* Ingatestone (01277) 352001 Fax 355374

WAINE, Stephen John. b 59. Westcott Ho Cam 81. **d** 84 **p** 85. C Wolv *Lich* 84-88; Min Can and Succ St Paul's Cathl *Lon* 88-93; V Romford St Edw *Chelmsf* from 93. *St Edward's Vicarage, 15 Oaklands Avenue, Romford RM1 4DB* Romford (01708) 740385

WAINWRIGHT, David Bernard Pictor. b 25. St Jo Coll Dur BA50 MA53. Chich Th Coll 50. **d** 51 **p** 52. Sen Soc Worker Bd for Soc Resp Man 69-73; V Scouthead *Man* 69-72; Asst Sec Gen Syn Bd for Soc Resp 74-78; Dep Sec 78-79; P-in-c Charlton on Otmoor and Oddington *Ox* 79-85; Soc Resp Officer 79-88; RD Bicester and Islip 82-85; Sec Ox Dioc Bd for Soc Resp 85-88; rtd 88. *8 St Robert's Gardens, Knaresborough, N Yorkshire HG5 8EH* Harrogate (01423) 865236

WAINWRIGHT, Frank Alan. b 18. Leeds Univ BA39. Coll of Resurr Mirfield 39. **d** 41 **p** 42. V Woodham *Guildf* 64-72; rtd 83. *Menhay, Pendoggett, St Kew, Bodmin, Cornwall PL30 3HH* Bodmin (01208) 880528

WAINWRIGHT, John Pounsberry. b 42. St Steph Ho Ox 64. **d** 66 **p** 67. C Palmers Green St Jo *Lon* 66-70; C Primrose Hill St Mary w Avenue Road St Paul 70-71; P-in-c St Jo Wood All SS 71-73; V Hendon All SS Childs Hill from 73. *All Saints' Vicarage, Church Walk, London NW2 2JT* 0171-435 3182

WAINWRIGHT, Joseph Allan. b 21. K Coll Lon BD50 AKC50 Columbia Pacific Univ PhD82 Sussex Univ DPhil85. **d** 50 **p** 51. Lect Moray Ho Coll of Educn Edin 66-78; Perm to Offic *Chich* from 79; rtd 86. *Beggar's Roost, Lewes, E Sussex BN7 1LX* Lewes (01273) 477453

WAINWRIGHT, Kevin Frank. b 46. Linc Th Coll 73. **d** 75 **p** 76. C Stand *Man* 75-78; C Radcliffe St Thos and St Jo 78-80; V Kearsley Moor from 80. *St Stephen's Vicarage, Blair Street, Kearsley, Bolton BL4 8QP* Farnworth (01204) 72535

WAINWRIGHT, Maurice Sidney. b 30. Lon Univ BSc54. Bps' Coll Cheshunt 54. **d** 56 **p** 57. C Caversham *Ox* 59-61; Public Preacher *Chelmsf* 61-95; rtd 95. *60 Eastwood Road, London E18 1BU* 0181-989 1529

WAINWRIGHT, Miss Pauline Barbara. b 40. St Deiniol's Hawarden 83. **dss** 84 **d** 87 **p** 94. New Ferry *Ches* 84-87; Par Dn 87-90; Par Dn Hallwood 90-94; C from 94. *39 Badger Close, Palace Fields, Runcorn, Cheshire WA7 2QW* Runcorn (01928) 715688

WAINWRIGHT, Raymond Laycock. b 25. Lon Univ BD60. Ho of Resurr Mirfield 55. **d** 56 **p** 57. V Gawthorpe and Chickenley Heath *Wakef* 60-74; V New Mill 74-89; V Thurstonland 74-89; TV Upper Holme Valley 89-91; rtd 91. *7 Greenlaws Close, Holmfirth, Huddersfield HD7 2GB* Huddersfield (01484) 683779

WAIT, Alan Clifford. b 33. St Cath Soc Ox BA58 MA70. Coll of Resurr Mirfield. **d** 60 **p** 61. C Old Charlton *S'wark* 60-67; C Caterham 67-72; V N Dulwich St Faith 72-83; RD Dulwich 78-83; V Purley St Barn from 83; RD Croydon S from 93. *St Barnabas's Vicarage, 84 Higher Drive, Purley, Surrey CR8 2HJ* 0181-660 3251

WAITE, John Langton (Tony). b 10. Solicitor 34 ACP37 Man Univ 30. Wycliffe Hall Ox 37. **d** 39 **p** 40. V Woking St Jo *Guildf* 58-76; rtd 76; Perm to Offic *Portsm* from 82. *11 The Crescent, Alverstoke, Gosport, Hants PO12 2DH* Gosport (01705) 521458

WAITE, Julian Henry. b 47. Brasted Th Coll 68 Ridley Hall Cam 70. **d** 72 **p** 73. C Wollaton *S'well* 72-76; C Herne Bay Ch Ch *Cant* 76-79; P-in-c Mersham 79-87; P-in-c Sevington 79-87; R Mersham w Hinxhill 87; V Marden 87-93; Chapl HM Pris Blantyre Ho from 90. *Address temp unknown*

WAITE, Sheila Margaret. *See* TYLER, Mrs Sheila Margaret

WAIYAKI, Henry. b 34. MBE88. ALA64. NE Ord Course 89. **d** 92 **p** 94. NSM Ulgham *Newc* from 92; NSM Widdrington from 92. *6 Woodburn Street, Stobswood, Morpeth, Northd NE61 5QD* Morpeth (01670) 791066

WAKE, Colin Walter. b 50. Or Coll Ox BA72 MA. Cuddesdon Coll 74. **d** 75 **p** 76. C Sandhurst *Ox* 75-78; C Faversham *Cant* 79-80; TV High Wycombe *Ox* 80-89; R Weston Favell *Pet* from 89; Chapl St Jo Hosp Weston Favell from 89. *The Rectory, Churchway, Weston Favell, Northampton NN3 3BX* Northampton (01604) 784679 or 787117

WAKEFIELD, Allan. b 31. Qu Coll Birm 72. **d** 74 **p** 75. C Kingsthorpe w St Dav Northn *Pet* 74-77; TV Clifton *S'well* 77-81; V Bilborough St Jo 81-85; R Bere Ferrers *Ex* 85-91; R Mevagissey and St Ewe *Truro* from 91. *The Rectory, School Hill, Mevagissey, St Austell, Cornwall PL26 6TQ* Mevagissey (01726) 842488

WAKEFIELD, Andrew Desmond. b 55. K Coll Lon BD77 AKC77. Coll of Resurr Mirfield 77. **d** 78 **p** 79. C Mitcham Ascension *S'wark* 78-81; C Putney St Mary 81-86; TV Wimbledon 86-91; Ind Chapl from 90; Dioc Urban Missr from 91; P-in-c S Wimbledon St Andr from 91. *St Andrew's Vicarage, 47 Wilton Grove, London SW19 3QU* 0181-542 1794

WAKEFIELD, David Geoffrey. b 43. AMIC90. S'wark Ord Course 84. **d** 87 **p** 88. C Addiscombe St Mildred *S'wark* 87-89; C Reigate St Luke S Park 89-93; Chapl HM Pris Bullingdon from 93. *HM Prison Bullingdon, PO Box 50, Bicester, Oxon OX6 0PR* Bicester (01869) 322111 Fax 243383

WAKEFIELD, Gavin Tracy. b 57. Van Mildert Coll Dur BSc Sheff Univ CertEd Nottm Univ DipTh. St Jo Coll Nottm 83. **d** 86 **p** 87. C Anston *Sheff* 86-89; C Aston cum Aughton and Ulley 89-91; TV Billericay and Lt Burstead *Chelmsf* from 91. *10 Chestwood Close, Billericay, Essex CM12 0PB* Billericay (01277) 652659

WAKEFIELD, Kenneth (Ken). b 54. St Jo Coll Dur BA95. **d** 95. C E and W Leake, Stanford-on-Soar, Rempstone etc *S'well* from 95. *The Rectory, Stanford on Soar, Loughborough, Leics LE12 5PY* Loughborough (01509) 266794

WAKEFIELD, Canon Kenneth Eyles. b 25. St Jo Coll Dur BA50 DipTh51 MA56. **d** 51 **p** 52. Chapl Bartlet Hosp Felixstowe 59-89; V Walton *St E* 59-88; Hon Chapl Miss to Seamen 64-88; RD Colneys *St E* 73-86; Hon Can St E Cathl 75-88; rtd 89. *14 Fleetwood Road, Felixstowe, Suffolk IP11 7EQ* Felixstowe (01394) 672113

WAKEFIELD, Peter. b 48. Nottm Univ BTh72 DipAdEd85. St Jo Coll Nottm 68 ALCD72. **d** 72 **p** 73. C Hinckley H Trin *Leic* 72-75; C Kirby Muxloe 75-78; V Barlestone 78-85; TV Padgate *Liv* 85-88; V Quinton w Marston Sicca *Glouc* from 91. *The Vicarage, Lower Quinton, Stratford-upon-Avon, Warks CV37 8SG* Stratford-upon-Avon (01789) 720707

WAKEFIELD, Bishop of. *See* McCULLOCH, Rt Rev Nigel Simeon

WAKEFIELD, Provost of. *See* ALLEN, Very Rev John Edward

WAKELIN, Alan Frank. b 32. Univ of Wales (Lamp) BA58. Coll of Resurr Mirfield 58. **d** 60 **p** 61. C Northn St Matt *Pet* 60-63; C Pet All SS 63-65; C Spalding *Linc* 65-68; R Skirbeck St Nic from 68. *The Rectory, Skirbeck, Boston, Lincs PE21 0DJ* Boston (01205) 362734

WAKELIN, Paul Edward. b 60. St Steph Ho Ox 90. **d** 92 **p** 93. C Sevenoaks St Jo *Roch* from 92. *14 Quakers Hall Lane, Sevenoaks, Kent TN13 3TR* Sevenoaks (01732) 740652

WAKELING, Bruce. b 50. Lon Univ BA74. Westcott Ho Cam 74. **d** 77 **p** 78. C Weymouth H Trin *Sarum* 77-82; TV Oakdale St Geo 82-89; R Clopton w Otley, Swilland and Ashbocking *St E* from 89. *The Rectory, Clopton, Woodbridge, Suffolk IP13 6SE* Grundisburgh (01473) 735765

WAKELING, Hugh Michael. b 42. CEng MIMechE82 Cape Town Univ BSc63. Wycliffe Hall Ox 71. **d** 74 **p** 75. C Kennington St Mark *S'wark* 74-78; C Surbiton Hill Ch Ch 78-80; Hon C Richmond H Trin and Ch Ch 80-84; Hon C California *Ox* 85-89; Hon C Arborfield w Barkham from 89. *Pine Lodge, 52 Pine Drive, Wokingham, Berks RG11 3LE* Eversley (01734) 734078

WAKELING, Joan. b 44. Hockerill Coll Cam CertEd65 Lon Univ DipTh79. S'wark Ord Course 76. **dss** 79 **d** 90 **p** 94. Surbiton Hill Ch Ch *S'wark* 79-80; Richmond H Trin and Ch Ch 80-84; California *Ox* 84-89; Arborfield w Barkham 89-90; NSM from 90; Chapl Luckley Oakfield Sch Wokingham from 90. *Pine Lodge, 52 Pine Drive, Wokingham, Berks RG11 3LE* Eversley (01734) 734078

✠**WAKELING, Rt Rev John Denis.** b 18. MC45. St Cath Coll Cam BA40 MA44 Nottm Univ Hon DD84. Ridley Hall Cam 46. **d** 47 **p** 48 **c** 70. C Barwell w Potters Marston and Stapleton *Leic* 47-50; Chapl Clare Coll Cam 50-52; Lic to Offic *Ely* 50-52; V Plymouth Em *Ex* 52-59; Preb Ex Cathl 57-59; V Barking St Marg *Chelmsf* 59-65; P-in-c Barking St Patr 60-65; Adn W Ham 65-70; Bp S'well 70-85; rtd 85. *50 St Anne Place, Salisbury SP1 2SU* Salisbury (01722) 322016

WAKELING, Stanley George. b 11. St Cath Coll Cam BA35 MA39. Wycliffe Hall Ox 35. **d** 37 **p** 38. V Tulse Hill H Trin *S'wark* 69-73; V Lower Nutfield 73-76; rtd 76; Hon C Nether Stowey w Over Stowey *B & W* 77-80; Perm to Offic 86-93. *3 Suffolk Crescent, Taunton, Somerset TA1 4JL* Taunton (01823) 271007

WAKELY, Marcus. b 40. Solicitor 62 FRSA88. E Midl Min Tr Course 84. **d** 87 **p** 88. NSM Carrington *S'well* 87-91; C Worksop Priory 91-95; V Sheff St Matt *Sheff* from 95. *29 Winchester Road, Sheffield S10 4EE* Sheffield (0114) 230 5641

WAKELY, Roger. b 42. St Paul's Cheltenham CertEd. S'wark Ord Course 67. **d** 70 **p** 71. C Ealing St Mary *Lon* 70-76; Chapl Bp Wand's Sch Sunbury-on-Thames 76-82; R Gaulby *Leic* 82-87; V Galleywood Common *Chelmsf* from 87; Warden of Ords from 89. *Galleywood Vicarage, 450 Beehive Lane, Chelmsford CM2 8RN* Chelmsford (01245) 353922

WAKELY, Simon Nicolas. b 66. K Alfred's Coll Win BA88. St Jo Coll Nottm DTS91 DipMM92. **d** 92 **p** 93. C Wymondham *Nor* from 92. *76A Norwich Road, Wymondham, Norfolk NR18 0SZ* Wymondham (01953) 604342

WAKEMAN, Canon Hilary Margaret. b 38. E Anglian Minl Tr Course. **dss** 85 **d** 87 **p** 94. Heigham St Thos *Nor* 85-87; C 87-90; C Nor St Mary Magd w St Jas 90-91; D-in-c Nor-over-the-Water Colegate St Geo 90-91; TD Nor Over-the-Water 91-94; TV from 94; Hon Can Nor Cathl from 94. *32 Grosvenor Road, Norwich NR2 2PZ* Norwich (01603) 666455

WAKER, Anthony Francis. b 30. St Chad's Coll Dur BA56 DipTh57. **d** 57 **p** 58. C Stokenchurch *Ox* 57-60; C Summertown 60-65; R Iron Acton *Bris* from 65. *The Rectory, High Street, Iron Acton, Bristol BS17 1UQ* Rangeworthy (01454) 228412

WAKERELL, Richard Hinton. b 55. Qu Coll Birm. **d** 84 **p** 85. C Gillingham St Mary *Roch* 84-87; C Kingswinford St Mary *Lich* 87-93; V Rickerscote 93. *Address temp unknown*

WALDEN, John Edward Frank. b 38. FInstSMM. Oak Hill Th Coll 67. **d** 69 **p** 70. C Rainham *Chelmsf* 69-73; P-in-c Bris H Cross Inns Court *Bris* 73-78; Conf and Publicity Sec SAMS

78-81; Hon C Southborough St Pet w Ch Ch and St Matt *Roch* 78-81; Exec Sec Spanish and Portuguese Ch Aid Soc 80-81; Hon C Tonbridge St Steph 81-84; R Earsham w Alburgh and Denton *Nor* 84-89. *clo Michael Hall & Co, Garsett House, Norwich NR3 1AU* Norwich (01603) 617772

WALDEN, Samuel (Sam). b 15. Richmond Th Coll 45. **d** 57 **p** 58. USA 57-71; R Blackley H Trin *Man* 71-74; Chapl Prestwich Hosp Man 74-80; rtd 80. *5 Castlegate, New Brook Street, Ilkley, W Yorkshire LS29 8DF* Ilkley (01943) 601860

WALDRON, Geoffrey Robert. b 15. Selw Coll Cam BA37 MA41. Ely Th Coll 37. **d** 38 **p** 39. R Barwick *B & W* 63-76; R Closworth 63-76; P-in-c Charlton Adam w Charlton Mackrell 76-78; R Charlton Adam w Charlton Mackrell and Kingsdon 78-80; rtd 80; Perm to Offic *B & W* 81-93. *Roseland, Castle Street, Keinton Mandeville, Somerton, Somerset TA11 6DX* Charlton Mackrell (01458) 223224

WALDRON, Laurence Charles. b 22. Bps' Coll Cheshunt 58. **d** 59 **p** 60. V Lea Hall *Birm* 66-77; V Wiggenhall St Mary Magd *Ely* 77-87; V Wiggenhall St Germans and Islington 77-87; rtd 87. *16 Heath Gardens, Stone, Staffs ST15 0AW* Stone (01785) 818237

WALES, David Neville. b 55. Rhodes Univ BA78. Coll of Resurr Mirfield 80. **d** 82 **p** 83. Zimbabwe 82-88; C Linslade *Ox* 89-91; P-in-c Weston Turville from 91. *The Rectory, Church Walk, Weston Turville, Aylesbury, Bucks HP22 5SH* Aylesbury (01296) 613212

WALES, Archbishop of. *See* JONES, Most Rev Alwyn Rice

WALFORD, Mrs Angela. b 44. Whitelands Coll Lon CertEd76. S Dios Minl Tr Scheme 85. **d** 92 **p** 94. NSM Boyatt Wood *Win* from 92. *St Peter's Church House, 53 Sovereign Way, Eastleigh, Hants SO5 4SA* Southampton (01703) 642188

WALFORD, David. b 45. S'wark Ord Course 75. **d** 78 **p** 79. NSM Hackbridge and N Beddington S'wark 78-83; C Fawley *Win* 83-87; C-in-c Boyatt Wood CD 87-90; V Boyatt Wood from 90. *St Peter's Church House, 53 Sovereign Way, Eastleigh, Hants SO5 4SA* Eastleigh (01703) 642188

WALFORD, David John. b 47. St Luke's Coll Ex CertEd68 AKC71. St Aug Coll Cant. **d** 72 **p** 73. C Oxton *Ches* 72-77; C Neston 77-80; Youth Chapl 80-81; V Backford 80-81; C Woodchurch 81; Chapl Fulbourn Hosp and Ida Darw Hosp Cam 82-83; Chapl N Man Gen Hosp 83-86; Chapl Distr Chapl in Mental Health Ex HA from 86; Chapl R Devon and Ex Hosp (Wonford) from 86; Lic to Offic *Ex* from 86. *Royal Devon and Exeter Hospital, Exeter EX2 5DW, or Dean Clarke House, Southernhay East, Exeter EX1 1PQ* Exeter (01392) 402024 or 411222

WALFORD, David Sanderson. b 23. BEM49. Chich Th Coll 78. **d** 79 **p** 80. Hon C Chich St Pet *Chich* 79-81; C Chich St Paul and St Pet 81-83; P-in-c Wisbech St Aug *Ely* 83-86; rtd 88. *Sibford, Church Hill, Marnhull, Sturminster Newton, Dorset DT10 1PU* Marnhull (01258) 820201

WALFORD, Dr Frank Roy. b 35. Birm Univ MB, ChB58. Qu Coll Birm 78. **d** 80 **p** 81. Hon C Walsall Pleck and Bescot *Lich* 80-85; Chr Healing Cen Bordon 85-88; Dep Medical Dir St Wilfrid's Hospice Chich from 88; Perm to Offic *Chich* from 88. *15 Grove Road, Chichester, W Sussex PO19 2AR* Chichester (01243) 533947

WALFORD, Robin Peter. b 46. Qu Coll Birm 75. **d** 78 **p** 79. C Radcliffe-on-Trent *S'well* 78-81; TV Newark w Hawton, Cotham and Shelton 81-84; P-in-c Forest Town 84-92; Chapl Leeds Community and Mental Health Services from 92; Chapl Leeds Gen Infirmary from 92. *St Mary's Hospital, Greenhill Road, Leeds LS12 3QE* Leeds (0113) 279 0121

WALKER, Alan David. b 44. Bretton Hall Coll CertEd65. E Anglian Minl Tr Course 92. **d** 95. NSM Ashill w Saham Toney *Nor* from 95. *4 Orchard Close, Ashill, Thetford, Norfolk IP25 7AP* Holme Hale (01760) 441554

WALKER, Alan Robert Glaister. b 52. K Coll Cam BA76 MA79 New Coll Ox BA76 MA84 Cen Lon Poly LLB91 Heythrop Coll Lon MTh93. St Steph Ho Ox 82. **d** 84 **p** 85. C St Jo Wood *Lon* 84-86; Chapl Poly Cen Lon 87-92; Chapl Univ Westmr 92-94; Chapl Univ Ch Ch the K 87-94; V Hampstead Garden Suburb from 94. *St Jude's Vicarage, 1 Central Square, London NW11 7AH* 0181-455 7206 Fax as telephone

WALKER, Albert William John. b 14. Linc Th Coll 43. **d** 45 **p** 46. V Kingston St Luke *S'wark* 67-74; V Mickleton *Glouc* 74-79; rtd 79; Chapl Convent of St Mary at the Cross Edgware 79-87; Lic to Offic *Lon* 79-87; Perm to Offic *Carl* from 87. *Shepherd's Fold, 4 Fairview Cottages, Ambleside, Cumbria LA22 9EE* Ambleside (015394) 32418

WALKER, Allen Ross. b 46. Chich Th Coll 86. **d** 88. C Cosham *Portsm* 88-91; Chapl Portsm Mental Health Community from 91; Dn Portsm Deanery from 91. *39 Magdala Road, Cosham, Portsmouth PO6 2QG* Cosham (01705) 325121

WALKER, Andrew Stephen. b 58. St Chad's Coll Dur BA80. St Steph Ho Ox 83. **d** 85 **p** 86. C Fareham SS Pet and Paul *Portsm*

85-87; C St Jo Wood *Lon* 87-93; V Streatham St Pet *S'wark* from 93. *St Peter's Vicarage, 113 Leigham Court Road, London SW16 2NX* 0181-769 2922

WALKER, Anthony Charles St John (Tony). b 55. Trin Coll Ox MA80. Wycliffe Hall Ox 78. **d** 81 **p** 82. C Bradf Cathl *Bradf* 81-84; C Nottm St Ann w Em *S'well* 84-88; V Retford from 88. *St Saviour's Vicarage, 31 Richmond Road, Retford, Notts DN22 6SJ* Retford (01777) 703800

WALKER, Canon Arthur Keith. b 33. Dur Univ BSc57 Fitzw Ho Cam BA60 MA64 Leeds Univ PhD68. Lich Th Coll 62. **d** 63 **p** 64. C Slaithwaite w E Scammonden *Wakef* 63-66; Lect Wells Th Coll 66-71; V N Wootton *B & W* 66-71; Can Res and Prec Chich Cathl *Chich* 71-80; TV Basingstoke *Win* 81-87; Can Res Win Cathl from 87. *5 The Close, Winchester, Hants SO23 9LS* Winchester (01962) 864923

WALKER, Barry Donovan. b 28. Linc Coll Ox BA52 MA56. Linc Th Coll 52. **d** 54 **p** 55. V Kensal Rise St Martin *Lon* 61-71; V Palmers Green St Jo 71-83; R Takeley w Lt Canfield *Chelmsf* 83-88; rtd 88. *122 Waterfall Road, London N14 7JN* 0181-886 1695

WALKER, Miss Bethany Helen. b 58. RGN80 DON80 Lon Univ DN83. Cranmer Hall Dur 86. **d** 89 **p** 94. C Newark-upon-Trent *S'well* 89-93; rtd 93. *Julian House, 76 Peveril Road, Beeston, Nottingham NG9 2HU* Nottingham (0115) 922 8806

WALKER, Brian Cecil. b 28. FCA62. Cranmer Hall Dur 68. **d** 70 **p** 71. C Heworth w Peasholme St Cuth *York* 70-73; C Attenborough w Chilwell *S'well* 73-75; C Chilwell 75-78; R Trowell 78-89; rtd 89. *1 Kendal Close, Bromsgrove, Worcs B60 2HW* Bromsgrove (01527) 579382

WALKER, Charles Edward Cornwall. b 18. Selw Coll Cam BA39 MA43. Cuddesdon Coll 40. **d** 41 **p** 42. V Gt Amwell *St Alb* 48-81; P-in-c Stanstead St Marg 74-81; V Gt Amwell w St Marg 81-94; rtd 94. *Great Amwell Vicarage, Ware, Herts SG14 1AE* Ware (01902) 484605

WALKER, Christopher James Anthony. b 43. Sarum & Wells Th Coll 85. **d** 87 **p** 88. Hon C Durrington *Sarum* 87-89; CF from 87. *clo MOD (Army), Bagshot Park, Bagshot, Surrey GU19 5PL* Bagshot (01276) 471717 Fax 412834

WALKER, Christopher John. b 52. ALA74. Chich Th Coll 75. **d** 78 **p** 79. C Reading All SS *Ox* 78-82; C Stony Stratford 82-84; C Wokingham All SS 84-90; V Headington St Mary from 90. *St Mary's Vicarage, Bayswater Road, Oxford OX3 9EY* Oxford (01865) 61886

WALKER, Christopher John Deville. b 42. St Jo Coll Dur BA69. Westcott Ho Cam 69. **d** 71 **p** 72. C Portsea St Mary *Portsm* 71-75; C Saffron Walden w Wendens Ambo and Littlebury *Chelmsf* 75-77; C St Martin-in-the-Fields *Lon* 77-80; V Riverhead w Dunton Green *Roch* 80-89; V Chatham St Steph from 89. *St Stephen's Vicarage, 55 Pattens Lane, Chatham, Kent ME4 6JR* Medway (01634) 849791

WALKER, David. b 48. Linc Th Coll 71. **d** 74 **p** 75. C Arnold *S'well* 74-77; C Crosby *Linc* 77-79; V Scrooby *S'well* 79-86; V Sutton in Ashfield St Mary 86-94; P-in-c Sutton in Ashfield St Mich 89-94; TR Birkenhead Priory *Ches* from 94. *St Anne's Vicarage, 29 Park Road West, Birkenhead, Merseyside L43 1UR* 0151-652 1309

WALKER, David Andrew. b 52. St Andr Univ MTh75 MA. Linc Th Coll 79. **d** 81 **p** 82. C Hessle *York* 81-84; C N Hull St Mich 84-86; V from 86. *St Michael's Vicarage, 214 Orchard Park Road, Hull HU6 9BX* Hull (01482) 803375

WALKER, Canon David Grant. b 23. FSA60 FRHistS62 Bris Univ BA49 Ball Coll Ox DPhil54. **d** 62 **p** 62. Hon C Swansea St Mary w H Trin *S & B* 62-86; Chapl and Lect Univ of Wales (Swansea) 62; Sen Lect 63-82; Dir of Post-Ord Tr 65-93; Can Brecon Cathl from 72; Prec 79-90; Chan 90-93; Chapl Univ of Wales (Swansea) 75-76; Dir of In-Service Tr from 77; P-in-c Caereithin 86-87. *52 Eaton Crescent, Swansea SA1 4QN* Swansea (01792) 472624

WALKER, David Ian. b 41. DipCMus. Bernard Gilpin Soc Dur 64 Bps' Coll Cheshunt 65. **d** 68 **p** 69. C Todmorden *Wakef* 68-72; V Rastrick St Jo 72-77; V Crossland Moor 77-86; V Kirton in Lindsey *Linc* from 86; R Grayingham from 86; R Manton from 86; OCF from 88. *The Vicarage, 28 Southcliffe Road, Kirton-in-Lindsey, Gainsborough, Lincs DN21 4NR* Kirton Lindsey (01652) 648009

WALKER, David John. b 47. St Jo Coll Nottm 88. **d** 90 **p** 91. C Strood St Fran *Roch* 90-94; V Larkfield from 94. *The Vicarage, 206 New Hythe Lane, Larkfield, Maidstone, Kent ME20 6PT* West Malling (01732) 843349

WALKER, David Stuart. b 57. Cam Univ MA. Qu Coll Birm DipTh. **d** 83 **p** 84. C Handsworth *Sheff* 83-86; TV Maltby 86-91; Ind Chapl 86-91; V Bramley and Ravenfield 91-95; R Bramley and Ravenfield w Hooton Roberts etc from 95. *The Vicarage, 88 Main Street, Bramley, Rotherham, S Yorkshire S66 0SQ* Rotherham (01709) 542028

WALKER, Dennis Richard. b 25. Bp Gray Coll Cape Town LTh57. **d** 57 **p** 58. S Africa 57-73; V Catterick *Ripon* 73-78;

V Manston 78-86; rtd 86. *Micklegarth, Cliff Road, Sewerby, Bridlington, N Humberside YO15 1EW*   Bridlington (01262) 678417

WALKER, Derek Fred. b 46. Trin Coll Bris 71. **d** 74 **p** 75. C St Paul's Cray St Barn *Roch* 74-78; C Rushden w Newton Bromswold *Pet* 78-80; R Kirkby Thore w Temple Sowerby and Newbiggin *Carl* 80-83; V Coppull *Blackb* 83-87; V New Ferry *Ches* from 87. *St Mark's Vicarage, New Chester Road, New Ferry, Wirral, Merseyside L62 1DG*   0151-645 2638

WALKER, Douglas. b 36. Lich Th Coll 61. **d** 63 **p** 64. C Bris St Ambrose Whitehall *Bris* 63-68; P-in-c Easton All Hallows 68-71; V Penhill 71-79; P-in-c Crundale w Godmersham *Cant* 79-83; P-in-c Elmsted w Hastingleigh 79-83; V Sheerness H Trin w St Paul from 83. *The Vicarage, 241 High Street, Sheerness, Kent ME12 1UR*   Sheerness (01795) 662589

WALKER, Duncan Andrew. b 59. **d** 90 **p** 91. C Gorseinon *S & B* 90-91; C Morriston 92-94; V Llanelli Ch Ch *St D* from 94. *Christ Church Vicarage, New Dock Road, Llanelli, Dyfed SA15 2HE*   Llanelli (01554) 774264

WALKER, Mrs Edna Bilbie. b 20. Nottm Univ BEd76. **d** 88 **p** 94. NSM Oakham, Hambleton, Egleton, Braunston and Brooke *Pet* from 88. *Chestnut Cottage, Braunston, Oakham, Leics LE15 8QZ*   Oakham (01572) 722365

WALKER, Canon Edward William Murray (Dominic). b 48. AKC73. **d** 72 **p** 72. CGA 67-83; C Wandsworth St Faith *S'wark* 72-73; Bp's Dom Chapl 73-76; R Newington St Mary 76-85; RD S'wark and Newington 80-85; OGS from 83; Superior from 90; V Brighton St Pet w Chpl Royal and St Jo *Chich* 85-86; P-in-c Brighton St Nic 85-86; TR Brighton St Pet and St Nic w Chpl Royal from 86; RD Brighton from 85; Can and Preb Chich Cathl from 85. *Brighton Vicarage, 87 London Road, Brighton BN1 4JF*   Brighton (01273) 682960 or 676051 Fax 600466

WALKER, Mrs Elizabeth. b 42. Sunderland Poly CQSW85. NE Ord Course 91. **d** 94. NSM Stockton St Chad *Dur* from 94. *29 Bramble Road, Stockton-on-Tees, Cleveland TS19 0NQ*   Stockton (01642) 615332

WALKER, Mrs Elizabeth Margaret Rea. b 49. Ch Ch Coll Cant TCert70. S'wark Ord Course 89. **d** 92 **p** 94. NSM Ash *Roch* from 92; NSM Ridley from 92; Asst Chapl St Geo Sch Gravesend from 92. *1 Capelands, New Ash Green, Dartford DA3 8LG*   Ash Green (01474) 872550

WALKER, Eric Henry. b 15. Lon Univ BD54. AKC39. **d** 39 **p** 40. V Rotherhithe St Kath w St Barn *S'wark* 56-81; RD Bermondsey 78-81; rtd 81. *10 Barton Road, Ely, Cambs CB7 4DE*   Ely (01353) 665927

WALKER, Ernest Alwyn. b 18. Clifton Th Coll 54. **d** 56 **p** 57. V Kingston upon Hull St Barn *York* 59-70; V Shiptonthorpe w Hayton 70-77; V Daubhill *Man* 77-84; rtd 84; Perm to Offic *Bradf* from 84. *1 Hillside View, Pudsey, W Yorkshire LS28 9DH*   Leeds (0113) 257 8468

WALKER, Gavin Russell. b 43. FCA78. Coll of Resurr Mirfield 76. **d** 78 **p** 79. C Wakef St Jo *Wakef* 78-81; C Northallerton w Kirby Sigston *York* 81-83; V Whorlton w Carlton and Faceby 83-85; Chapl Pontefract Gen Infirmary 85-89; P-in-c Brotherton *Wakef* 85-89; V Earlsheaton from 89. *45 Chatsworth Terrace, Dewsbury, W Yorkshire WF12 8BH*   Dewsbury (01924) 461490

WALKER, Canon George Percival John. b 13. Dur Univ LTh38. St Boniface Warminster 35. **d** 38 **p** 39. At St Kitts-Nevis 52-78; Hon Can Antigua 55-78; Adn St Kitts 64-78; rtd 78. *St Peter's Cottage, Monkey Hill, St Kitts*   St Kitts (1809) 461-4091

WALKER, Gerald Roger. b 41. K Coll Lon BD67 AKC67. **d** 68 **p** 69. C High Elswick St Phil *Newc* 68-70; C Goring-by-Sea *Chich* 70-75; R Selsey 75-81; V Howe St Andr Old Ch 81-91; V Copthorne 91-95; rtd 95; NSM Streat w Westmeston *Chich* from 95. *Rectory Bungalow, Streat, Hassocks, W Sussex BN6 8RX*   Hassocks (01273) 890607

WALKER, Canon Graham. b 35. Ex Coll Ox BA58 BTh60 MA62 Leeds Univ MPhil80. Sarum Th Coll 60. **d** 61 **p** 62. C Guiseley *Bradf* 61-64; C Ingrow cum Hainworth 64-68; Lic to Offic 68-80; V Hellifield from 80; RD Bowland from 86; Hon Can Bradf Cathl from 89; P-in-c Gisburn from 94. *The Vicarage, Hellifield, Skipton, N Yorkshire BD23 4HY*   Hellifield (01729) 850243

WALKER, Canon Harvey William. b 26. Edin Univ MA52. St Steph Ho Ox 58. **d** 60 **p** 61. V Newc St Matt w St Mary *Newc* 64-94; Hon Can Newc Cathl 80-94; rtd 95. *21 Grosvenor Drive, Whitley Bay, Tyne & Wear NE26 2JP*   0191-252 1858

WALKER, Helen Margaret. *See* WALKER, Miss Bethany Helen

WALKER, Ian Richard Stevenson. b 51. Univ of Wales (Lamp) BA73. Qu Coll Birm DipTh75. **d** 76 **p** 77. C Stainton-in-Cleveland *York* 76-79; C Fulford 79-81; C Kidderminster St Mary *Worc* 81-82; TV Kidderminster St Mary and All SS etc 82-86; R Keyingham w Ottringham, Halsham and Sunk Is *York* from 86; RD S Holderness from 94. *The Rectory, Keyingham, Hull HU12 9RX*   Withernsea (01964) 622171

WALKER, Jack. b 21. Kelham Th Coll 37. **d** 45 **p** 46. C Tynemouth Ch Ch *Newc* 45-49; C Wallsend St Luke 49-51; C Linthorpe *York* 51-55; V Newbald from 55; V Sancton from 55. *The Vicarage, North Newbald, York YO4 3SY*   Market Weighton (01430) 827284

WALKER, John. b 49. Sheff Univ BSc74. Qu Coll Birm DipTh77. **d** 78 **p** 79. C Loughb Em *Leic* 78-81; C Nottm All SS S'well 81-84; V Radford St Pet from 84. *St Peter's Vicarage, Hartley Road, Nottingham NG7 3DW*   Nottingham (0115) 978 4450

WALKER, John. b 51. Aber Univ MA74. Edin Th Coll BD78. **d** 78 **p** 79. C Broughty Ferry *Bre* 78-81; P-in-c Dundee St Jo 81-85; Ind Chapl 83-88; R Dundee St Luke 85-95; R Alford *Ab* from 95. *The Rectory, 4 St Luke's Road, Dundee DD3 0LD*   Dundee (01382) 825165

WALKER, John Anthony Patrick. b 58. Trin Coll Bris BA86. **d** 86 **p** 87. C Canford Magna *Sarum* 86-90; TV Glyncorrwg w Afan Vale and Cymmer Afan *Llan* from 90. *The Vicarage, 17 School Road, Cymmer, Port Talbot, W Glam SA13 3EG*   Cymmer (01639) 851058

WALKER, Canon John Cameron. b 31. St Andr Univ MA52. Edin Th Coll 63. **d** 65 **p** 66. C Edin H Cross *Edin* 65-67; C Perth St Jo *St And* 67-70; Chapl Angl Students Glas 70-74; Youth Chapl Warks Educn Cttee 75-77; Officer Gen Syn Bd of Educn 78-82; C W Hendon St Jo *Lon* 79-82; PV Westmr Abbey 82-84; Chapl Ghent w Ypres *Eur* 84-92; Chapl Ghent from 92; Miss to Seamen from 84; Can Brussels Cathl *Eur* from 93. *Blankenbergestraat 39, B-9000 Ghent, Belgium*   Ghent (9) 222-3659 Fax 220-8004

WALKER, John David. b 44. St Jo Coll Dur BA76 DipTh77. **d** 77 **p** 78. C Heworth *York* 77-81; P-in-c Barmby on the Moor w Fangfoss 81-83; P-in-c Allerthorpe 81-83; TV Pocklington Team 84-89; P-in-c Hovingham 89; TV Street TM 89-92; R Dunnington from 92. *The Rectory, Church Street, Dunnington, York YO1 5PW*   York (01904) 489349

WALKER, John Frank. b 53. Leeds Univ BEd76 Ripon Coll of Educn CertEd75. NW Ord Course 78. **d** 81 **p** 82. NSM Whitkirk *Ripon* 81-82; C 82-85; V Sutton Courtenay w Appleford *Ox* 85-90; Dioc Children's Adv *S'wark* 90-94; V Walworth St Jo from 94; Youth and Children's Officer Woolwich Episc Area from 95. *St John's Vicarage, 18 Larcom Street, London SE17 1NQ*   0171-703 4375

WALKER, John Frederick. b 21. St Jo Coll Dur BA47 DipTh49 MA51. **d** 49 **p** 50. V Halifax All So *Wakef* 59-74; V Hampsthwaite *Ripon* 74-86; P-in-c Killinghall 76-86; rtd 86. *36 Rockwood Drive, Skipton, N Yorkshire BD23 1UW*   Skipton (01756) 799835

WALKER, John Howard. b 47. Brasted Th Coll 67 Clifton Th Coll 69. **d** 72 **p** 73. C Upton (or Overchurch) *Ches* 72-76; Asst Chapl Liv Univ *Liv* 76-79; V Everton St Chrys 79-82; C Parr Mt 83-86; SAMS 86-94; Area Sec (NE and E Midl) SAMS 86-89; Paraguay 89-94; V Calverley *Bradf* from 95. *The Vicarage, Town Gate, Calverley, Pudsey, W Yorkshire LS28 5NF*   Leeds (0113) 257 7968

WALKER, John Hugh. b 34. K Coll Lon BD57 AKC57 K Coll Lon MTh75 MA85 Lon Inst of Educn PGCE68. St Boniface Warminster 57. **d** 58 **p** 59. Hon C Forest Gate St Edm *Chelmsf* 68-74; Perm to Offic *Cant* 75-82 and from 87; R Dymchurch w Burmarsh and Newchurch 82-87; rtd 94. *Aberfeldy, Covet Lane, Kingston, Canterbury, Kent CT4 6HU*   Canterbury (01227) 830818

WALKER, John Michael. b 32. Qu Coll Birm. **d** 57 **p** 58. C Ruddington *S'well* 57-60; C Horsham *Chich* 60-64; C Sullington 64-70; C Storrington 64-70; V Peasmarsh 70-73; V Washington 73-77; R Ashington, Washington and Wiston with Buncton from 77. *The Rectory, Ashington, Pulborough, W Sussex RH20 3BH*   Ashington (01903) 892304

WALKER, John Percival. b 45. CITC 68. **d** 71 **p** 72. C Belf St Clem *D & D* 71-74; C Magheraculmoney *Clogh* 74-78; C Lisburn St Paul *Conn* 78-81; I Belf St Ninian 81-88; I Belf St Mary 88-89; I Belf St Mary w H Redeemer from 89. *558 Crumlin Road, Belfast BT14 7GL*   Belfast (01232) 391120 or 748423

WALKER, Keith. b 48. Linc Th Coll 82. **d** 84 **p** 85. C Whickham *Dur* 84-87; C Trimdon Station 87; P-in-c 87-89; V 89-90; R Penshaw from 90; P-in-c Shiney Row from 92; P-in-c Herrington from 93. *All Saints' Rectory, Penshaw, Houghton le Spring, Tyne & Wear DH4 7ER*   0191-584 2531

WALKER, Ven Kingsley. b 17. St Chad's Coll Dur MA46. St Paul's Grahamstown LTh47. **d** 47 **p** 48. V Preston-on-Stour w Whitchurch *Cov* 68-73; S Africa 73-91; rtd 91; Perm to Offic *Chich* from 92. *17 Uplands Park, Broad Oak, Heathfield, E Sussex TN21 8SJ*   Heathfield (01435) 882270

WALKER, Mrs Lesley Ann. b 53. S Dios Minl Tr Scheme 85. **d** 88 **p** 94. Par Dn Oakdale St Geo *Sarum* 88-92; TD Bridgnorth, Tasley, Astley Abbotts, Oldbury etc *Heref* 92-94; TV from 94. *32 Goodwood Avenue, Bridgnorth, Shropshire WV15 5BD*   Bridgnorth (01746) 765874

WALKER, Mrs Margaret Joy (Margi). b 44. Avery Hill Coll DipHE80 Newc Univ MA93. CA Tr Coll 80. **dss** 86 **d** 87 **p** 94. Scargill Ho 86-87; Hon Par Dn Monkwearmouth St Andr *Dur* 87; Hon Par Dn Ches le Street 87-93; NSM Wells Cathl *B & W* from 94. *6 The Liberty, Wells, Somerset BA5 2SU* Wells (01749) 672224

WALKER, Mark Robert Joseph George. b 66. Nottm Univ BA88. CITC 90. **d** 92 **p** 93. C Larne and Inver *Conn* from 92. *57 Sallagh Park Central, Larne, Co Antrim BT40 1NU* Larne (01574) 275196

WALKER, Martin Frank. b 39. St Jo Coll Nottm 71. **d** 73 **p** 74. C Penn *Lich* 73-78; V Bentley 78-82; V Kinver 82-88; R Kinver and Enville 88-91; V Harlescott from 91. *Harlescott Vicarage, Meadow Farm Drive, Shrewsbury SY1 4NG* Shrewsbury (01743) 362883

WALKER, Martin John. b 52. Linc Coll Ox BA73 PGCE74 Chateau de Bossey Geneva DipEcum78. Cranmer Hall Dur BA78. **d** 79 **p** 80. C Harlow New Town w Lt Parndon *Chelmsf* 79-81; C Dorchester *Ox* 81-83; Chapl Bath Coll of FE 83-89; TV Southn (City Cen) *Win* 89-91; Adv in RE and Resources *Sarum* 91-92; NSM Northolt St Mary *Lon* from 92; Chapl Bancroft's Sch Woodford Green from 92. *St Mary's Rectory, Ealing Road, Northolt, Middx UB5 6AA* 0181-841 5691

WALKER, Michael John. b 39. Univ of Wales (Lamp) BA61. St Aid Birkenhead 61. **d** 63 **p** 64. C Clifton *York* 63-66; C Marfleet 66-69; V Salterhebble St Jude *Wakef* 69-83; V Llangollen w Trevor and Llantysilio *St As* 83-93; RD Llangollen 87-93; V Kerry and Llanmerewig and Dolfor from 93. *The Vicarage, Kerry, Newtown, Powys SY16 4NY* Kerry (01806) 670466

WALKER, Canon Michael John Maynard. b 32. BNC Ox BA55 MA59. Clifton Th Coll 55. **d** 57 **p** 58. R Saxmundham *St E* 66-71; V New Beckenham St Paul *Roch* 71-78; V Bury St Edmunds St Mary *St E* 78-92; Hon Can St E Cathl 86-94; V Debenham w Aspall and Kenton 92-94; rtd 94. *Martletts, 3 Rembrandt Gardens, Bury St Edmunds, Suffolk IP33 2LX* Bury St Edmunds (01284) 724236

WALKER, Michael Sykes. b 10. TD. Trin Hall Cam BA33 MA40. Wycliffe Hall Ox. **d** 49 **p** 50. R Escrick *York* 61-75; rtd 75; Hon C Ryther *York* 75-80. *2 Rawcliffe Grove, Clifton Lane, York YO3 6NR* York (01904) 636453

WALKER, Canon Nigel Maynard. b 39. ALCD66. **d** 67 **p** 68. C Southsea St Jude *Portsm* 67-70; S Africa 70-76; C Abingdon w Shippon *Ox* 76-80; V Upton (or Overchurch) *Ches* 80-94; Chan Brussels Cathl *Eur* from 94; Chapl Brussels from 94. *7 Venelle Bleue, 1150 Woluwe St Pierre, Brussels, Belgium* Brussels (2) 511-7183 Fax 511-1028

WALKER, Mrs Pamela Sarah. b 52. Somerville Coll Ox BA73 MA77 St Jo Coll Dur BA78. Cranmer Hall Dur 76. **dss** 79 **d** 87 **p** 94. Harlow New Town w Lt Parndon *Chelmsf* 79-81; Dorchester *Sarum* 82-83; Bath St Bart *B & W* 85-87; Hon C 87-88; Par Dn Warmley *Bris* 88-89; Par Dn Bitton 88-89; Par Dn Southn (City Cen) *Win* 89-92; Par Dn Northolt St Mary *Lon* 92-94; C 94; R from 94. *The Rectory, Ealing Road, Northolt, Middx UB5 6AA* 0181-841 5691

WALKER, Paul Gary. b 59. Lon Univ BD. St Jo Coll Nottm 82. **d** 84 **p** 85. C Bowling St Steph *Bradf* 84-87; C Tong 87-90; P-in-c Oakenshaw cum Woodlands from 90. *589 Bradford Road, Oakenshaw, Bradford, W Yorkshire BD12 7ES* Bradford (01274) 676410

WALKER, Paul Laurence. b 63. St Chad's Coll Dur BA84. Chich Th Coll BTh90. **d** 88 **p** 89. C Shildon w Eldon *Dur* 88-91; C Barnard Castle w Whorlton 91-93; C Silksworth from 93. *24 Midhurst Close, Sunderland SR3 2QD* 0191-528 8845

WALKER, Pauline Ann. b 51. Open Univ BA87. St As Minl Tr Course 88. **d** 93. NSM Bistre *St As* from 93. *Mountain Farm, Foxes Lane, Alltami, Mold, Clwyd CH7 6RT* Buckley (01244) 550638

WALKER, Peter Anthony. b 57. Pemb Coll Cam BA79 MA83 St Jo Coll Dur BA86. Cranmer Hall Dur 84. **d** 87 **p** 88. C Chesham Bois *Ox* 87-90; Chapl Bradf Cathl *Bradf* 90-93; TV The Lydiards *Bris* from 93. *6 Springhill Close, Westlea, Swindon SN5 7BG* Swindon (01793) 872932

WALKER, Peter Anthony Ashley. b 46. Chich Th Coll 67. **d** 70 **p** 71. C Stamford Hill St Thos *Lon* 70-74; C Bethnal Green St Matt 74-77; V Hackney Wick St Mary of Eton w St Aug 77-84; Warden Rydal Hall *Carl* 84-95; P-in-c Rydal 84-95; P-in-c Porthleven w Sithney *Truro* from 95. *The Vicarage, Breageside, Porthleven, Helston, Cornwall TR13 9JS* Helston (01326) 562419

WALKER, Peter Jeffrey. b 46. Kelham Th Coll 65. **d** 70 **p** 71. C Middlesb All SS *York* 70-75 and 77-78; SSF 75-77; C-in-c Wrangbrook w N Elmsall CD *Wakef* 78-82; V Athersley 82-86; Perm to Offic *Blackb* 86-87; Perm to Offic *Dur* 87-89; V Hartlepool H Trin 89-95; OGS from 95; Dep Chapl HM Pris Birm from 95. *HM Prison Birmingham, Winson Green Road, Birmingham B18 4AS* 0121-554 3838

✠**WALKER, Rt Rev Peter Knight.** b 19. Qu Coll Ox BA47 MA47 Cam Univ Hon DD78. Westcott Ho Cam 53. **d** 54 **p** 55 **c** 72. Asst Master Merchant Taylors' Sch Lon 50-56; C Hemel Hempstead St Mary *St Alb* 56-58; Fell Dean and Lect Th CCC Cam 58-62; Asst Tutor 59-62; Prin Westcott Ho Cam 62-72; Hon Can Ely Cathl *Ely* 66-72; Suff Bp Dorchester *Ox* 72-77; Can Res Ch Ch 72-77; Bp Ely 77-89; rtd 89; Asst Bp Ox from 89. *Anchorage House, The Lanes, Bampton, Oxon OX8 2LA* Bampton Castle (01993) 850943

WALKER, Peter Sidney Caleb. b 50. DipMin80. St Mich Th Coll Crafers 76. **d** 80 **p** 81. Australia 80-88; R Swallow *Linc* 88-94; R Selworthy and Timberscombe and Wootton Courtenay *B & W* 94-95; R Luccombe 94-95; R Selworthy, Timberscombe, Wootton Courtenay etc from 95. *The Rectory, Selworthy, Minehead, Somerset TA24 8TL* Porlock (01643) 862445

WALKER, Peter Stanley. b 56. SRN RMN Nottm Univ BCombStuds. Linc Th Coll 80. **d** 83 **p** 84. C Woodford St Barn *Chelmsf* 83-86; C Brentwood St Thos 86-88; V Colchester St Barn 88-94; P-in-c Colchester St Jas, All SS, St Nic and St Runwald from 94. *The Rectory, 76 East Hill, Colchester CO1 2QW* Colchester (01206) 866802

WALKER, Peter William Leyland. b 61. CCC Cam BA82 MA86 PhD87. Wycliffe Hall Ox 87. **d** 89 **p** 90. C Tonbridge SS Pet and Paul *Roch* 89-93; Fell Tyndale Ho Cam from 93; Lic to Offic *Ely* from 93. *202 Histon Road, Cambridge CB4 3HJ* Cambridge (01223) 573930

WALKER, Canon Philip Geoffrey. b 47. St Jo Coll Dur BA70 Or Coll Ox BA72 MA76 Newc Univ MA93. Ripon Hall Ox 70. **d** 74 **p** 75. C Sheff St Geo *Sheff* 74-77; C Cam Gt St Mary w St Mich *Ely* 77-81; V Monkwearmouth St Andr *Dur* 81-87; R Ches le Street 87-93; RD Ches le Street 89-93; Dioc Missr *B & W* from 93; Can Res Wells Cathl from 94. *6 The Liberty, Wells, Somerset BA5 2SU* Wells (01749) 672224

WALKER, Philip Kingsley. b 47. Ox Univ BA70 Univ of Wales DPS90. St Mich Coll Llan. **d** 90 **p** 91. C Newport Maindee St Jo Ev *Mon* 90-92; C Llanmartin 92-94; R Bishton from 94. *The Vicarage, Station Road, Llanwern, Newport, Gwent NP6 2DW* Llanwern (01633) 413457

WALKER, Raymond. b 28. Carl Dioc Tr Inst 83. **d** 86 **p** 87. NSM Gt Salkeld w Lazonby *Carl* 86-91; C Greystoke, Matterdale, Mungrisdale, etc 91-92; TV from 92. *Matterdale Vicarage, Penrith, Cumbria CA11 0LD* Glenridding (017684) 82301

WALKER, Richard David. Hull Univ BSc. S Dios Minl Tr Scheme. **d** 95. Hon C Horfield St Greg *Bris* from 95. *10 Saxon Way, Bradley Stoke, Bristol BS12 9AS* Almondsbury (01454) 202139

WALKER, Richard Mainprize. b 43. Keele Univ BA DipEd. Wycliffe Hall Ox 84. **d** 86 **p** 87. C Guildf Ch Ch *Guildf* 86-90; V Bradley St Martin *Lich* from 90. *St Martin's Vicarage, King Street, Bradley, Bilston, W Midlands WV14 8PQ* Bilston (01902) 493109

WALKER, Robert Edward Lea. b 23. Qu Coll Ox MA49. Wycliffe Hall Ox 49. **d** 51 **p** 52. V Wroxton w Balscott *Ox* 61-80; P-in-c Shenington and Alkerton w Shutford 79-80; R Wroxton w Balscote and Shenington w Alkerton 80-88; rtd 88. *11 Tanners Court, Charlbury, Chipping Norton, Oxon OX7 3RP* Charlbury (01608) 810461

WALKER, Mrs Ruth Elizabeth. b 58. St Jo Coll Dur BA79 Cam Univ CertEd81. St Jo Coll Nottm 86. **d** 88 **p** 94. Par Dn Princes Risborough w Ilmer *Ox* 88-90; Chapl Bradf Cathl *Bradf* 90-93; Par Dn The Lydiards *Bris* 93-94; Hon C from 94. *6 Springhill Close, Westlea, Swindon SN5 7BG* Swindon (01793) 872932

WALKER, Stanley Frederick. b 48. St Jo Coll Nottm. **d** 84 **p** 85. C Ellesmere Port *Ches* 84-89; V Seacombe from 89. *The Vicarage, 5 Brougham Road, Wallasey, Merseyside L44 6PN* 0151-638 3677

WALKER, Canon Stephen. b 09. St Jo Coll Dur BA30 DipTh31 MA33. **d** 32 **p** 33. V Beverley St Mary *York* 58-77; RD Beverley 63-73; Can and Preb York Minster 64-77; rtd 77. *Dulverton Hall, St Martin's Square, Scarborough, N Yorkshire YO11 2DQ* Scarborough (01723) 373082

WALKER, Stephen Michael Maynard. b 62. St Jo Coll Dur BA84. Trin Coll Bris 86. **d** 88 **p** 89. C Eastwood *S'well* 88-92; CF from 92. *c/o MOD (Army), Bagshot Park, Bagshot, Surrey GU19 5PL* Bagshot (01276) 471717 Fax 412834

WALKER, Stephen Patrick. b 62. York Univ BSc83 PGCE84. St Jo Coll Nottm DipTh89 DPS90. **d** 90 **p** 91. C Hull Newland St Jo *York* 90-94; Min Grove Green LEP *Cant* from 94. *7 Samphire Close, Weavering, Maidstone, Kent ME14 5UD* Maidstone (01622) 739294

WALKER, Mrs Susan Joy. b 52. Univ of Wales (Lamp) BA73 Hull Univ MA91. Qu Coll Birm 75. **dss** 83 **d** 87 **p** 94. Kidderminster St Mary and All SS etc *Worc* 83-86; Keyingham w Ottringham, Halsham and Sunk Is *York* 86-87; Hon Par Dn 87-94; Hon C from 94; Chapl Hull Coll of FE from 89. *The Rectory, Keyingham, Hull HU12 9RX* Withernsea (01964) 622171

WALKER, Thomas. b 18. St Aid Birkenhead 58. **d** 60 **p** 61. V Wrightington *Blackb* 69-87; rtd 87. *6 Cranford Close, Eastham, South Wirral L62 9DH* 0151-327 1380

WALKER, Ven Thomas Overington (Tom). b 33. Keble Coll Ox BA58 MA61. Oak Hill Th Coll 58. **d** 60 **p** 61. C Woking St Paul *Guildf* 60-62; C St Leonards St Leon *Chich* 62-64; Travelling Sec IVF 64-67; Succ Birm Cathl *Birm* 67-70; Hon Can Birm Cathl 80-91; V Harborne Heath 70-91; P-in-c Edgbaston St Germain *Birm* 80; RD Edgbaston 89-91; Adn Nottm *S'well* from 91. *16 Woodthorpe Avenue, Woodthorpe, Nottingham NG5 4FD* Nottingham (0115) 926 7349 Fax Southwell (01636) 815882

WALKER, Trevor John. b 51. Southn Univ BTh80. Sarum & Wells Th Coll 75. **d** 78 **p** 79. C Standish *Blackb* 78-81; P-in-c N Somercotes *Linc* 81-82; P-in-c S Somercotes 81-82; V Somercotes 82-85; R Binbrook Gp from 85. *The Rectory, Binbrook, Lincoln LN3 6BJ* Binbrook (01472) 398227

WALKER, Canon Walter Stanley. b 21. AKC42. Cuddesdon Coll 42. **d** 44 **p** 45. R Bromborough *Ches* 66-77; R Wallasey St Hilary 77-86; RD Wallasey 77-86; Hon Can Ches Cathl 80-86; rtd 86; Perm to Offic *Ches* from 86. *39 Lyndhurst Road, Wallasey, Merseyside L45 6XB* 0151-630 4237

WALKER, William. b 10. FCIM48. **d** 51 **p** 52. Chapl, Lect and Tutor Stanford Hall Loughb 52-70; V Daybrook *S'well* 70-80; rtd 80; Perm to Offic *S'well* from 80. *278 Rutland Road, Nottingham NG2 5EB* Nottingham (0115) 986 9353

WALKER, Canon William George Leslie. b 10. TCD BA39 MA42. **d** 39 **p** 40. I Knockbreda *D & D* 59-78; Can Down Cathl 70-78; rtd 78. *Larch House, 160 Ballylesson Road, Belfast BT8 8JU* Drumbo (01232) 826578

WALKEY, Malcolm Gregory Taylor. b 44. Lon Univ DipTh68. Kelham Th Coll 63. **d** 68 **p** 69. C Oadby *Leic* 68-72; TV Corby SS Pet and Andr w Gt and Lt Oakley *Pet* 72-79; R Ashton w Hartwell 79-86; TR Halesworth w Linstead, Chediston, Holton etc *St E* 86-91; 91-93; P-in-c Laxfield from 93. *The Vicarage, 15 Noyes Avenue, Laxfield, Woodbridge, Suffolk IP13 8EB* Ubbeston (01986) 798218

WALL, Charles William. b 20. Kelham Th Coll 39. **d** 44 **p** 45. P-in-c Sidlow Bridge *S'work* 71-76; R Feltwell *Ely* 76-78; rtd 78; Perm to Offic *Chich* from 80. *56 Barrack Road, Bexhill-on-Sea, E Sussex TN40 2AZ* Bexhill-on-Sea (01424) 219711

WALL, David Oliver. b 39. TD JP. OStJ. Bps' Coll Cheshunt 62. **d** 65 **p** 66. C Lt Ilford St Mich *Chelmsf* 65-68; CF 68-73; R Sudbourne w Orford *St E* 73-76; R Orford w Sudbourne and Chillesford w Butley 76-79; P-in-c Iken 76-79; P-in-c Ipswich St Bart 77-79; R Drinkstone 79-82; R Rattlesden 79-82; R Chedburgh w Depden, Rede and Hawkedon from 82; Chapl to Suffolk Fire Service from 91. *The Rectory, Rede, Bury St Edmunds, Suffolk IP29 4BE* Hawkedon (0128489) 342

✠**WALL, Rt Rev Eric St Quintin.** b 15. BNC Ox BA37 MA46. Wells Th Coll 37. **d** 38 **p** 39 **c** 72. C Boston *Linc* 38-41; Chapl RAFVR 41-45; V Sherston Magna w Easton Grey *Bris* 44-53; RD Malmesbury 51-53; V Cricklade w Latton 53-60; Bp's Chapl 60-66; Dioc Adv in Chr Stewardship 60-66; Hon Can Bris Cathl 60-72; V Westbury-on-Trym St Alb 66-72; RD Clifton 67-72; Suff Bp Huntingdon *Ely* 72-80; Can Res Ely Cathl 72-80; rtd 80; Perm to Offic *Nor* from 80; Perm to Offic *St E* from 81; Perm to Offic *Ely* from 86. *7 Peregrine Close, Diss, Norfolk IP22 3PG* Diss (01379) 644331

WALL, James Leach. b 19. Leeds Univ BA40. **d** 64 **p** 65. C Prenton *Ches* 66-71; C Auckland St Andr and St Anne *Dur* 71-74; V Hart w Elwick Hall 74-80; rtd 81. *191 Park Road, Hartlepool, Cleveland TS26 9LP* Hartlepool (01429) 275105

WALL, John Caswallen. b 60. York Univ BA83 MA85 Ox Univ BA89. St Steph Ho Ox 86. **d** 89 **p** 90. C Ifield *Chich* 89-94; C Brighton St Pet and St Nic w Chpl Royal from 94. *40 Kemp Street, Brighton, E Sussex BN1 4EF* Brighton (01273) 675684

WALL, Martyn Philip Lucas. b 17. Hertf Coll Ox BA38 MA43. Wells Th Coll 69. **d** 71 **p** 72. C Highworth w Sevenhampton and Inglesham etc *Bris* 71-74; R Wick w Doynton 74-85; rtd 85. *9 Woburn Close, Trowbridge, Wilts BA14 9TJ* Trowbridge (01225) 754323

WALL, Nicholas John. b 46. Brasted Th Coll 69 Trin Coll Bris 71. **d** 73 **p** 74. C Morden *S'work* 73-78; V Dunkeswell and Dunkeswell Abbey *Ex* 78-83; V Sheldon 78-83; P-in-c Luppitt 81-83; V Dunkeswell, Sheldon and Luppitt from 83. *The Rectory, Dunkeswell, Honiton, Devon EX14 0RE* Luppitt (01404) 891243

WALL, Mrs Pauline Ann. b 39. Bris Sch of Min 87. **dss** 85 **d** 87 **p** 94. Bris Ch the Servant Stockwood *Bris* 85-87; Hon Par Dn 87-94; Hon C from 94; Chapl St Brendan's Sixth Form Coll from 90. *41 Ladman Road, Bristol BS14 8QD* Whitchurch (01275) 833083

WALL, Philip John. b 12. St Chad's Coll Dur BA34 DipTh35 MA37. **d** 35 **p** 36. R Norwood St Mary *Lon* 69-81; rtd 81; Perm to Offic *Lon* 82-91; Perm to Offic *Ox* from 89. *9 Hervines Court, Amersham, Bucks HP6 5HH* Amersham (01494) 728124

WALL, Robert William. b 52. Ex Coll Ox MA Ex Univ BPhil77. Trin Coll Bris 80. **d** 83 **p** 84. C Blackb Sav *Blackb* 83-86; C Edgware *Lon* 86-89; C Barnsbury 89-90; TV from 90. *43 Matilda Street, London N1 0LA* 0171-278 5208 or 607 4552

WALLACE, Alastair Robert. b 50. St Cath Coll Cam BA71 MA75 Lon Univ BD75. Trin Coll Bris 72. **d** 75 **p** 76. C Ex St Leon w H Trin *Ex* 75-79; Chapl Ridley Hall Cam 79-80; R Bath St Mich w St Paul *B & W* from 83; RD Bath from 90. *71 Priory Close, Combe Down, Bath BA2 5AP* Bath (01225) 835490

WALLACE, Mrs Brenda Claire. b 52. Linc Th Coll 73 S'wark Ord Course 78. **dss** 80 **d** 87 **p** 94. Sutton at Hone *Roch* 80-83; Borstal 83-87; Hon Par Dn 87-89; HM Pris Cookham Wood 83-89; Asst Chapl HM Pris Cookham Wood 83-89; NSM Stansted Mountfitchet *Chelmsf* from 89. *The Vicarage, 5 St John's Road, Stansted, Essex CM24 8JP* Bishop's Stortford (01279) 812203

WALLACE, Derek George. b 33. Glas Univ MA55. **d** 57 **p** 58. V Oldham St Jo *Man* 67-70; R Burravoe *Ab* 70-78; R Lerwick 70-78; R Port Glas 78-94; Miss to Seamen 78-94; rtd 94. *39 Coronation Crescent, Margate, Kent CT9 5PN* Margate (01843) 223869

WALLACE, Edgar Walker. b 17. St D Coll Lamp BA40. **d** 42 **p** 43. Ind Chapl *Chelmsf* 65-84; rtd 84. *18 Gotts Park Road, Southgate, Crawley, W Sussex RH11 8AX* Crawley (01293) 522713

WALLACE, Godfrey Everingham. b 32. Tyndale Hall Bris BA57. **d** 58 **p** 59. C Broadwater St Mary *Chich* 58-61; V Shipton Bellinger w S Tidworth *Win* 61-70; V Bournemouth St Paul 70-84; V Throop from 84. *St Paul's Vicarage, Chesildene Avenue, Bournemouth BH8 0AZ* Bournemouth (01202) 531064

WALLACE, Hugo. b 31. Trin Coll Cam BA54 MA59. Ridley Hall Cam 54. **d** 56 **p** 57. C Hornchurch St Andr *Chelmsf* 56-58; Uganda 58-60; C Bermondsey St Mary w St Olave and St Jo *S'wark* 61; S Africa from 61. *Shalom, 7 Ixia Avenue, Kommetjie Cape, 7976 South Africa* Cape Town (21) 831466

WALLACE, Julie Michele. b 58. Cam Univ DipRS82 Lon Univ DCouns88 PgDipTh92 CCouns92 Ox Univ MTh93. CA Tr Coll 77. **d** 88 **p** 94. Chapl Middx Poly *Lon* 86-90; Voc Adv CA 90-92; Member CA Counselling Service from 92; NSM Bellingham St Dunstan *S'wark* from 91. *293 Torridon Road, London SE6 1RE* 0181-461 1106

WALLACE, Canon Martin William. b 48. K Coll Lon BD70 AKC70. St Aug Coll Cant 70. **d** 71 **p** 72. C Attercliffe *Sheff* 71-74; C New Malden and Coombe *S'wark* 74-77; V Forest Gate St Mark *Chelmsf* 77-93; RD Newham 82-91; P-in-c Forest Gate Em w Upton Cross 85-89; Hon Can Chelmsf Cathl from 89; P-in-c Forest Gate All SS 91-93; Dioc ACUPA Link Officer from 91; P-in-c Bradwell on Sea from 93; Ind Chapl Maldon and Dengie Deanery from 93. *The Rectory, East End Road, Bradwell-on-Sea, Southminster, Essex CM0 7PX* Maldon (01621) 776203

WALLACE, Nicholas Robert. b 56. Trin Coll Bris DipHE95. **d** 95. C Fishponds St Jo *Bris* from 95. *5 Lodgeside Gardens, Bristol BS15 1NY* Bristol (0117) 961 5707

WALLACE, Raymond Sherwood. b 28. Selw Coll Dunedin (NZ). **d** 52 **p** 54. V Stroud Green H Trin *Lon* 67-79; V Penwerris *Truro* 79-84; R Wymington w Podington *St Alb* 84-87; rtd 87; Perm to Offic *St Alb* from 87. *141 Dunsmore Road, Luton LU1 5JX* Luton (01582) 455882

WALLACE, Richard Colin. b 39. Mert Coll Ox BA61 MA64. St Chad's Coll Dur 69. **d** 71 **p** 72. Tutor St Chad's Coll Dur 71-72; P-in-c Kimblesworth *Dur* 72-74; Chapl Bradf Univ *Bradf* 74-79; C Bingley All SS 79-80; TV 80-89; V Earby from 89. *The Vicarage, Earby, Colne, Lancs BB8 6JL* Earby (01282) 842291

WALLACE, Richard John. b 56. Coll of Resurr Mirfield. **d** 82 **p** 83. C Catford St Laur *S'wark* 82-85; C Bellingham St Dunstan 85-87; V 87-95; TR Stanley *Dur* from 95. *St Andrew's Rectory, Churchbank, Stanley, Co Durham DH9 0DU* Stanley (01207) 233936

WALLACE, Richard Samuel. b 17. TCD BA39 MA53. **d** 41 **p** 42. V Teddington St Mark *Lon* 60-83; rtd 83; Perm to Offic *Ex* from 83. *St Christopher, 17 Hartley Road, Exmouth, Devon EX8 2SG* Exmouth (01395) 279595

WALLACE, Robert (Bob). b 52. Sussex Univ BSc73 Nottm Univ DipTh75. Linc Th Coll 73. **d** 76 **p** 77. C Plaistow St Mary *Roch* 76-79; C Dartford H Trin 79-83; Chapl The Foord Almshouses 83-89; V Borstal *Roch* 83-89; Chapl HM Pris Cookham Wood 83-89; V Stansted Mountfitchet *Chelmsf* from 89; P-in-c Farnham from 89. *The Vicarage, 5 St John's Road, Stansted, Essex CM24 8JP* Bishop's Stortford (01279) 812203

WALLACE-HADRILL, David Sutherland. b 20. CCC Ox BA41 MA45 Man Univ BD44 DD60. **d** 43 **p** 44. V Eston *York* 55-62; Lic to Offic *St Alb* from 62; rtd 85. *1 The Almshouse, High Street, Elstree, Borehamwood, Herts WD6 3EY* 0181-207 2919

WALLBANK, Preb Newell Eddius. b 14. Qu Coll Cam BA34 MusB34 MA40 TCD MusD36 Lon Univ BA40 PhD56. Ripon Hall Ox 35. **d** 37 **p** 38. R Smithfield St Bart Gt *Lon* 45-79; Preb St Paul's Cathl 64-79; Select Preacher Ox Univ 68; rtd 79; Perm to Offic *Lon* 80-91. *Meldrum, Boveney Road, Dorney, Windsor, Berks SL4 6QD* Burnham (01628) 602399

WALLER, David Arthur. b 61. Leeds Univ BA83. Chich Th Coll 89. **d** 91 **p** 92. C Aldwick *Chich* from 91. *59 Westminster Drive, Aldwick, Bognor Regis, W Sussex PO21 3RE* Bognor Regis (01243) 830124

WALLER, David James. b 58. Whitelands Coll Lon BA85. Ripon Coll Cuddesdon 85. **d** 88 **p** 89. C Tettenhall Regis *Lich* 88-91; Chapl Greenwich Univ *S'wark* from 92. *35 Elmdene Road, London SE18 6TZ* 0181-855 6858 or 316 8150

WALLER, Derek James Keith. b 54. Em Coll Cam BA75 PGCE76. Trin Coll Bris 88. **d** 91 **p** 92. C Church Stretton *Heref* 91-95; R The Appleby Gp *Leic* from 95. *The Rectory, Rectory Lane, Appleby Magna, Swadlincote, Derbyshire DE12 7BQ* Measham (01530) 270482

WALLER, Miss Elizabeth Jean (Liz). b 58. Keswick Hall Coll BEd BTh. Linc Th Coll 84. **d** 87 **p** 94. Par Dn Mile End Old Town H Trin *Lon* 87-90; Manna Chr Cen 90-91; Chapl LSE *Lon* from 91. *Flat 3, 80A Southampton Row, London WC1B 4BA* 0171-831 9288 or 955 7965

WALLER, Canon Gordon Hamilton. b 18. AKC49. **d** 49 **p** 50. V Biscot *St Alb* 62-71; R Meppershall 71-86; R Upper Stondon 71-86; Hon Can St Alb 82-86; R Campton 82-86; rtd 86; Perm to Offic *St Alb* from 86. *102 High Street, Meppershall, Shefford, Beds SG17 5LZ* Hitchin (01462) 816368

WALLER, John. b 60. Man Univ BA84. St Jo Coll Nottm 85. **d** 87 **p** 88. C Chorlton-cum-Hardy St Clem *Man* 87-90; R Openshaw from 90; Chapl Ancoats Hosp Man from 93. *St Barnabas' Rectory, South Street, Openshaw, Manchester M11 2EW* 0161-231 4365

WALLER, John Pretyman. b 41. Sarum Th Coll 68. **d** 71 **p** 72. C Ipswich St Jo *St E* 71-74; R Waldringfield w Hemley 74-78; P-in-c Newbourn 74-78; R Waldringfield w Hemley and Newbourn from 78. *The Rectory, Mill Road, Waldringfield, Woodbridge, Suffolk IP12 4PY* Waldringfield (0147336) 247

✠**WALLER, Rt Rev John Stevens.** b 24. Peterho Cam BA48 MA53. Wells Th Coll 48. **d** 50 **p** 51 **c** 79. C Hillingdon St Jo *Lon* 50-52; C Twerton *B & W* 52-55; C-in-c Weston-super-Mare St Andr Bournville CD 55-59; V Weston-super-Mare St Andr Bournville 59-60; R Yarlington 60-63; Youth Chapl 60-63; Tr Officer C of E Youth Coun 63-67; V Frindsbury w Upnor *Roch* 67-72; P-in-c Strood St Fran 67-72; P-in-c Strood St Mary 67-72; P-in-c Strood St Nic 67-72; TR Strood 72-73; RD Strood 67-73; R Harpenden St Nic *St Alb* 73-79; Hon Can Lich Cathl *Lich* 79-87; Suff Bp Stafford 79-87; Asst Bp B & W from 87; P-in-c Long Sutton w Long Load 87-88; TV Langport Area Chs 88-89; rtd 89. *102 Harnham Road, Salisbury SP2 8JW* Salisbury (01722) 329739

WALLER, Canon John Watson. b 35. Qu Mary Coll Lon BSc57 St Cath Soc Ox DipTh60. Wycliffe Hall Ox 59. **d** 61 **p** 62. C Pudsey St Lawr *Bradf* 61-65; V 74-82; V Mortomley St Saw *Sheff* 65-74; V Pudsey St Lawr and St Paul *Bradf* 82-88; Hon Can Bradf Cathl 84-88; RD Calverley 84-88; V Kingston upon Hull H Trin *York* from 88; AD Cen & N Hull from 94; Can York Minster from 95. *Holy Trinity Vicarage, 66 Pearson Park, Hull HU5 2TQ* Hull (01482) 42292

WALLER, Orlando Alfred. b 12. St Aid Birkenhead 39. **d** 41 **p** 42. V Bearpark *Dur* 71-76; rtd 77. *22 Thornley Close, Broom Park, Durham DH7 7NN*

WALLER, Philip Thomas. b 56. Ex Coll Ox BA78 MA88. St Jo Coll Dur BA87. **d** 88 **p** 89. C Enfield St Andr *Lon* 88-91; C Belper *Derby* from 91. *St Mark's House, Openwoodgate, Belper, Derbyshire DE56 0FD* Belper (01773) 825727

WALLER, Canon Trevor. b 04. Selw Coll Cam BA27 MA31. Ridley Hall Cam 27. **d** 29 **p** 30. R Waldringfield w Hemley *St E* 48-74; R Newbourn 50-74; Hon Can St E Cathl 65-74; rtd 74; Perm to Offic *St E* 74-90. *White Hall Cottage, Mill Road, Waldringfield, Woodbridge, Suffolk IP12 4PY* Waldringfield (0147336) 348

WALLES, Bruce Andrew. b 54. Coll of Resurr Mirfield 90. **d** 92 **p** 93. C Maidstone St Martin *Cant* from 92. *78 Plains Avenue, Maidstone, Kent ME15 7AU* Maidstone (01622) 764019

WALLING, Mrs Caroline. b 47. **d** 86 **p** 87. Saudi Arabia 89 and from 94; Par Dn Mottingham St Andr *S'wark* 90; Par Dn Battersea St Mary 91-94. *Address temp unknown*

WALLINGTON, Paul. b 62. Birm Univ BCom83 ACA86. Trin Coll Bris BA94. **d** 94 **p** 95. C Chorley St Laur *Blackb* from 94. *57 Park Road, Chorley, Lancs PR7 1QZ* Chorley (01257) 274170

WALLIS, Benjamin John. b 55. Wimbledon Sch of Art BA79. Chich Th Coll 92. **d** 94 **p** 95. C Battersea Ch Ch and St Steph *S'wark* from 94. *Christ Church Flat, Cabul Road, London SW11 2PN* 0171-350 0851

WALLIS, Dr Ian George. b 57. Sheff Univ BA79 PhD92 St Edm Ho Cam MLitt87. Ridley Hall Cam 88. **d** 90 **p** 91. C Armthorpe *Sheff* 90-92; Chapl SS Coll Cam 92-95; R Houghton le Spring *Dur* from 95. *The Rectory, Dairy Lane, Houghton le Spring, Tyne & Wear DH4 5PR* 0191-584 2198

WALLIS, Canon John. b 13. Pemb Coll Ox BA36 MA40. Wells Th Coll 36. **d** 37 **p** 38. RD Birstall *Wakef* 59-79; Hon Can Wakef Cathl 65-79; V Hartshead 69-79; rtd 79; Perm to Offic *Wakef* from 79. *Dulverton Hall, St Martin's Square, Scarborough, N Yorkshire YO11 2DB* Scarborough (01723) 370088

WALLIS, John Anthony. b 36. St Pet Coll Ox BA60 MA64. Clifton Th Coll 60. **d** 62 **p** 63. C Blackpool St Mark *Blackb* 62-65; C Leeds St Geo *Ripon* 65-69; Korea 69-74; Nat Sec (Scotland) OMF 75-78; Home Dir OMF 78-89; Hon C Sevenoaks St Nic *Roch* 82-89; Chapl The Hague *Eur* 89-95; V Northwood Em *Lon* from 95. *Emmanuel Vicarage, 3 Gatehill Road, Northwood, Middx HA6 3QB* Northwood (01923) 821598

WALLIS, Paul Justin. b 65. St Jo Coll Nottm BTh90. **d** 90 **p** 91. C Somers Town St Mary *Lon* 90-93; P-in-c Southsea St Pet *Portsm* 93-94. *Address temp unknown*

WALLIS, Raymond Christopher. b 38. Moor Park Coll Farnham 61. Sarum Th Coll 63. **d** 66 **p** 67. C Allerton *Bradf* 66-68; C Langley Marish *Ox* 68-69; C Caister *Nor* 69-73; P-in-c E w W Bradenham 73-80; R Outwell *Ely* 80-84; V Upwell St Pet 80-84; V Bishopstone *Chich* from 84. *The Vicarage, Bishopstone Road, Bishopstone-Seaford, E Sussex BN25 2UD* Seaford (01323) 892972

WALLIS, Roderick Vaughan. b 37. Leic Univ BA79 Warw Univ MA80 Leeds Univ CertEd82 E Lon Poly DCouns90. Lich Th Coll 64. **d** 66 **p** 67. C Cookham *Ox* 66-70; C Daventry *Pet* 70-72; TV Northn Em 72-76; Hon C 81-89; Hon C Northn St Matt 76-81; Perm to Offic from 89. *28 Lingswood Park, Northampton NN3 4TA* Northampton (01604) 401578

WALLIS, Roland Seabon. b 17. MBE44. Lon Univ BSc38 Ex Univ BSc57. St Aug Coll Cant 75. **d** 77 **p** 78. Hon C Whitstable All SS w St Pet *Cant* 77-84; Hon C Whitstable 84-87; Perm to Offic from 87. *22 Mickleburgh Avenue, Herne Bay, Kent CT6 6HA* Canterbury (01227) 372263

WALLMAN, Jane Elizabeth. b 61. Homerton Coll Cam BEd83 Bell Educational Trust CertTESOL85 Open Univ ADEd88 Drama Studio Lon DipThe88. St Steph Ho Ox 89 Sarum & Wells Th Coll BTh92. **d** 93 **p** 94. C Woodbridge St Mary *St E* from 93. *40 Old Barrack Road, Woodbridge, Suffolk IP12 4ET* Woodbridge (01394) 384929

WALLS, Canon Michael Peter. b 38. Cape Town Univ BA57 Lon Univ DipTh61. Wells Th Coll 59. **d** 61 **p** 62. C Morecambe St Barn *Blackb* 61-64; C Birm St Paul *Birm* 64-66; Ind Chapl 64-74; V Temple Balsall 66-74; Chapl Wroxall Abbey Sch 72-74; V Kings Heath *Birm* 74-76; Hon C Small Heath St Greg 76-78; Chapl Oakham Sch Leics 78-83; P-in-c Leic St Sav *Leic* 83-85; P-in-c Knossington and Cold Overton 85-87; P-in-c Owston and Withcote 85-87; V Tilton w Lowesby 85-87; P-in-c 87; V Whatborough Gp of Par 87-90; Bp's Adv Relns w People of Other Faiths 89-93; Hon Can Leic Cathl 89-93; V Leic St Mary 90-93. *358 Aylestone Road, Leicester LE2 8BL*

WALLS, Canon Raymond William. b 10. AKC35. **d** 35 **p** 36. R Ufford *St E* 59-77; Hon Can St E Cathl 65-77; rtd 77. *4 St Florence Cottages, St Florence, Tenby, Dyfed SA70 8NQ* Tenby (01834) 871064

WALLS, Simon Conor. b 67. Dur Univ BA89 TCD MPhil90. **d** 91 **p** 92. C Castleknock and Mulhuddart, w Clonsilla *D & G* 91-93; Chapl Asst Maidstone Hosp 93-95; Chapl R Sussex Co Hosp Brighton from 95. *Royal Sussex County Hospital, Eastern Road, Brighton BN2 5BE* Brighton (01273) 696955

WALMSLEY, Andrew John. b 55. Ex Univ BA75. Ridley Hall Cam 76. **d** 78 **p** 79. C W Brompton St Mary w St Pet *Lon* 78-81; USA from 81. *Trinity School, 101 West 91st Street, New York City, New York 10024, USA*

WALMSLEY, Alexander David. b 07. Qu Coll Ox BA30 DipTh34 MA35. Wycliffe Hall Ox 33. **d** 34 **p** 35. R Whitchurch St Mary *Ox* 64-74; rtd 74; Perm to Offic *Glouc* 74-90. *Mon Choisy, 128 Kennington Road, Kennington, Oxford OX1 5PE* Oxford (01865) 326310

WALMSLEY, Derek. b 57. Oak Hill Th Coll DipHE91. **d** 91 **p** 92. C Bletchley *Ox* 91-95; C Utley *Bradf* from 95. *194 Skipton Road, Keighley, W Yorkshire BD21 2SY* Keighley (01535) 681448

WALMSLEY, George Bernard. b 07. Leeds Univ BA29. Coll of Resurr Mirfield 25. **d** 31 **p** 32. V Meerbrook *Lich* 59-72; P-in-c Quarnford 65-72; rtd 72. *46 Parker Street, Leek, Staffs ST13 6LB* Leek (01538) 373927

WALMSLEY, John William. b 37. Hull Univ BA71 MA73 PhD81. Wycliffe Hall Ox 71. **d** 72 **p** 73. C Clifton *York* 72-74; C Acomb St Steph 74-76; P-in-c Newton upon Ouse 76-81; P-in-c Shipton w Overton 76-81; V York St Thos w St Maurice

81-89; V Barkingside St Laur *Chelmsf* 89-92; Dir Romanian Children's Aid from 92. *St Laurence's Vicarage, Donnington Avenue, Ilford, Essex IG6 1AJ* 0181-554 2003

WALMSLEY-McLEOD, Paul Albert. b 56. St Cuth Soc Dur BA82 Cam Univ CertEd83. Westcott Ho Cam 85. **d** 87 **p** 88. C Gt Bookham *Guildf* 87-90; Asst Chapl St Chris Hospice Sydenham 90-93; Soc Care Team Member Phoenix Ho Fountain Project from 93; Perm to Offic *S'wark* from 93. *5 Lawrence Court, 77 Lawrie Park Road, London SE26 6ED* 0181-676 9994

WALNE, John Clifford. b 29. Wycliffe Hall Ox. **d** 87 **p** 88. NSM Hedsor and Bourne End *Ox* 87-88; Hon C Lezayre St Olave Ramsey *S & M* 88-92; Hon C Bride 88-92; P-in-c Berrington and Betton Strange *Heref* from 92. *49 Severn Way, Cressage, Shrewsbury SY5 6DS* Cressage (01952) 510571

WALROND-SKINNER, Susan Mary. b 42. Bris Univ BA63 CertEd68 Univ of Wales DASS70. Bris Minl Tr Scheme 82 Ripon Coll Cuddesdon. **dss** 84 **d** 87 **p** 94. Assoc Dir of Ords *Bris* 84-86; Continuing Minl Educn Officer 87-91; Dir Past Care and Counselling *S'wark* from 91. *St Michael's Vicarage, 78 Stockwell Park Road, London SW9 0DA* 0171-733 867

WALSER, Emil Jonathan. b 16. St Jo Coll Dur LTh38 BA39 MA43. Oak Hill Th Coll 35. **d** 39 **p** 40. V Baslow *Derby* 65-82; RD Bakewell and Eyam 78-81; rtd 82. *2 Almond Grove, Filey, N Yorkshire YO14 9EH* Scarborough (01723) 515582

WALSER (nee SHIELS), Mrs Rosalinde Cameron. b 47. Edin Univ MA68 Moray Ho Coll of Educn PGCE69. N Ord Course 92. **d** 95. NSM Scarborough St Mary w Ch Ch and H Apostles *York* from 95. *29 Sea Cliff Road, Scarborough, N Yorkshire YO11 2XU* Scarborough (01723) 372382

WALSH, Bertram William Nicholas. b 21. TCD BA44. CITC 46. **d** 46 **p** 47. Chapl St Columba's Coll Dub 60-87; rtd 87. *130 Grange Road, Rathfarnham, Dublin 14, Irish Republic* Dublin (1) 493-1229

✠**WALSH, Rt Rev Geoffrey David Jeremy.** b 29. Pemb Coll Cam BA53 MA58. Linc Th Coll 53. **d** 55 **p** 56 **c** 86. C Southgate Ch Ch *Lon* 55-58; SCM Sec Cam 58-61; C Cam Gt St Mary w St Mich *Ely* 58-61; V Moorfields *Bris* 61-66; R Marlborough *Sarum* 66-76; Can and Preb Sarum Cathl 73-76; Adn Ipswich *St E* 76-86; R Elmsett w Aldham 76-80; Suff Bp Tewkesbury *Glouc* 86-95; rtd 95. *6 Warren Lane, Martlesham Heath, Ipswich IP5 7SH* Ipswich (01473) 620797

WALSH, Geoffrey Malcolm. b 46. Sarum & Wells Th Coll 82. **d** 84 **p** 85. C Wellington and Distr *B & W* 84-87; TV Axminster, Chardstock, Combe Pyne and Rousdon *Ex* 87-90; Chapl R N 90-94; R Huntspill *B & W* from 94. *The Rectory, Church Road, West Huntspill, Highbridge, Somerset TA9 3RN* Burnham-on-Sea (01278) 793950

WALSH, John Alan. b 37. Chich Th Coll 63. **d** 66 **p** 67. C Wigan St Anne *Liv* 66-69; C Newport w Longford *Lich* 69-73; V Dunstall 73-83; V Rangemore 73-83; P-in-c Tatenhill 77-83; R Dunstall w Rangemore and Tatenhill 83; V Hartshill from 83. *Holy Trinity Vicarage, Hartshill, Stoke-on-Trent ST4 7NJ* Newcastle-under-Lyme (01782) 616965

WALSH, Julia Christine (Sister Julian). b 20. K Coll Lon DipTh49. Gilmore Ho 46. **dss** 56 **d** 87 **p** 94. CSA from 53. *St Andrew's House, 2 Tavistock Road, London W11 1BA* 0171-229 2662

WALSH, Peter. b 64. Liv Univ BA86 Nottm Univ BTh90. Linc Th Coll 87. **d** 90 **p** 91. C Cantley *Sheff* 90-93; C Poulton-le-Fylde *Blackb* 93-95; V Blackpool St Steph from 95. *The Vicarage, St Stephen's Avenue, Blackpool FY2 9RB* Blackpool (01253) 51484

WALSH, Canon William Arthur. b 12. St Jo Coll Dur BA34 MA41 DipTh41. **d** 35 **p** 36. V Dartford Ch Ch *Roch* 44-77; Hon Can Roch Cathl 71-77; rtd 77. *33 Correnden Road, Tonbridge, Kent TN10 3AU*

WALSHE, Canon Brian. b 28. AKC49. St Boniface Warminster. **d** 54 **p** 55. R Langley Marish *Ox* 68-76; Chapl Manfield Hosp Northn 76-88; V Northn St Alb *Pet* 76-88; Dir Mountbatten Community Trust from 76; Chief Exec Lon Youth Trust from 87; rtd 88; Perm to Offic *Pet* 88-93. *9/10 Warrior Court, 16 Warrior Way, St Leonards-on-Sea, E Sussex*

WALT, Trevor. RMN74 RNT79. Ox NSM Course 83. **d** 86 **p** 87. NSM Crowthorne *Ox* from 86; Chapl Asst Broadmoor Hosp Crowthorne 86-89; Chapl from 89. *Broadmoor Hospital, Crowthorne, Berks RG11 7EG* Crowthorne (01344) 773111 or 773999

WALTER, Canon Arthur Reginald. b 13. Keble Coll Ox BA34 MA38. St Mich Coll Llan 35. **d** 36 **p** 37. R Swanton Morley w Worthing *Nor* 60-78; Hon Can Nor Cathl 75-78; rtd 78; Chapl Madeira *Eur* 80-90; Perm to Offic *Nor* from 90. *4 Southern Reach, Mulbarton, Norfolk NR14 8BU* Mulbarton (01508) 78107

WALTER, Christopher Stuart Radclyffe (Chris). b 47. Sarum & Wells Th Coll DipTh93. **d** 93 **p** 94. C Fakenham w Alethorpe *Nor* from 93. *58 Whitelands, Fakenham, Norfolk NR21 8EN* Fakenham (01328) 855707

WALTER, Donald Alex. b 34. Ripon Hall Ox 57. **d** 60 **p** 61. C Ealing St Steph Castle Hill *Lon* 60-63; Jamaica 63-80; V Twickenham Common H Trin *Lon* from 81. *Holy Trinity Vicarage, 1 Vicarage Road, Twickenham TW2 5TS* 0181-898 1168

WALTER, Giles Robert. b 54. Cam Univ MA76. Cranmer Hall Dur 78. **d** 82 **p** 83. C Finchley Ch Ch *Lon* 82-86; C Cam H Sepulchre w All SS *Ely* 86-92; C Cam H Sepulchre 92-93; P-in-c Tunbridge Wells St Jo *Roch* 93-95; V from 95. *St John's Vicarage, 1 Amherst Road, Tunbridge Wells, Kent TN4 9LG* Tunbridge Wells (01892) 521183

WALTER, Ian Edward. b 47. Edin Univ MA69 Keble Coll Ox BA71 MA78. Cuddesdon Coll 71. **d** 73 **p** 74. C Greenock *Glas* 73-76; C Glas St Mary 76-79; Chapl Angl Students Glas 76-79; R Paisley St Barn 79-84; P-in-c Bolton St Phil *Man* 84-86; V 86-91; Bp's Ecum Adv from 89; V Elton All SS from 91. *All Saints' Vicarage, 90 Tottington Road, Bury, Lancs BL8 1LR* 0161-764 1431

WALTER, Michael. b 36. AKC62. **d** 63 **p** 64. C Middlesb St Jo the Ev *York* 63-65; C Sherborne *Win* 65-68; C Bournemouth St Fran 68-69; Prec Newc Cathl *Newc* 69-71; C Dur St Marg *Dur* 72-74; P-in-c Deaf Hill cum Langdale 74-77; V Newington w Dairycoates *York* 77-88; Perm to Offic 88-92; C Feltham *Lon* from 92. *39A St Dunstan's Road, Feltham, Middx TW13 4JY* 0181-751 4075

WALTER, Noel. b 41. St D Coll Lamp DipTh66. **d** 66 **p** 67. C Mitcham Ascension *S'wark* 66-71; C Caterham 71-74; V Welling 74-82; C Warlingham w Chelsham and Farleigh 82-88; Chapl R Earlswood Hosp Redhill from 88; Chapl Redhill Gen Hosp from 88; Chapl E Surrey Hosp Redhill from 88. *11 Ringwood Avenue, Redhill RH1 2DY, or East Surrey Hospital, Three Arch Road, Redhill RH1 5RH* Redhill (01737) 765043 or 768511

WALTER, Peter John. b 44. CEng MIGasE. Chich Th Coll 80. **d** 82 **p** 83. C Leominster *Heref* 82-85; P-in-c Brimfield 85-90; P-in-c Orleton 85-90; R Orleton w Brimfield 91-95. *12 Rainbow Street, Leominster, Herefordshire HR6 8DQ*

WALTER, Robin. b 37. Univ Coll Dur BA63 MA90 Linacre Coll Ox BA65 MA69. St Steph Ho Ox 63. **d** 66 **p** 68. C Peckham St Jo *S'wark* 66-69; Chapl Lon Univ *Lon* 69-70; C Dur St Marg *Dur* 70-74; R Burnmoor 74-79; Asst Master Barnard Castle Sch from 79; Lic to Offic 79-82; Hon C Whorlton 82-88; NSM Barnard Castle Deanery from 88. *4 Montalbo Road, Barnard Castle, Co Durham DL12 8BP* Teesdale (01833) 31741

WALTERS, Andrew Farrar. b 42. ACP67 St Luke's Coll Ex CertEd71. **d** 81 **p** 82. Hd Master and Warden St Mich Coll Tenbury 77-85; Chapl Ex Cathl Sch 85-87; Hd Master Homefield Sch Sutton 87-92; Hd Master Lich Cathl Sch from 92; Hon C Sutton St Nic *S'wark* 87-92. *Lichfield Cathedral School, The Palace, Lichfield, Staffs WS13 7LH* Lichfield (01543) 263326

WALTERS, Christopher John Linley. b 24. St Pet Hall Ox BA47 MA49. Linc Th Coll 48. **d** 50 **p** 51. V Newc St Paul *Lich* 61-70; V Pattingham 70-85; P-in-c Patshull 77-85; V Pattingham w Patshull 85-89; rtd 89. *Old School House, 19 Cardington, Church Stretton, Shropshire SY6 7JZ* Longville (01694) 771528

WALTERS, David Michael Trenham. b 46. Open Univ BA86. St D Coll Lamp DipTh69. **d** 69 **p** 70. C Killay *S & B* 69-72; CF 72-89 and from 91; Chapl Eagle Ho Prep Sch Crowthorne 89-91. *clo MOD (Army), Bagshot Park, Bagshot, Surrey GU19 5PL* Bagshot (01276) 471717 Fax 412834

WALTERS, Canon David Miles Ivor. b 12. Qu Coll Cam BA34 MA38. Wells Th Coll 34. **d** 35 **p** 36. V Rottingdean *Chich* 55-74; Chapl Butlin's Ocean Hotel 55-72; Can and Preb Chich Cathl 72-80; TR Ovingdean w Rottingdean and Woodingdean 74-78; rtd 78; Perm to Offic *Chich* from 80. *8 Elmstead Gardens, West Wittering, Chichester, W Sussex PO20 8NG* Birdham (01243) 513644

WALTERS, David Trevor. b 37. Ex Coll Ox BA58 MA62. St Steph Ho Ox 62. **d** 64 **p** 65. C Cardiff St Mary *Llan* 64-69; C Brecon w Battle *S & B* 69-73; Min Can Brecon Cathl 69-73; V Llanddew and Talachddu 73-78; V Cefncoed and Capel Nantddu 78-80; V Cefn Coed and Capel Nantddu w Vaynor etc 80-87; V Talgarth and Llanelieu from 87. *The Vicarage, 10 Bronant, Talgarth, Brecon, Powys LD3 0HF* Talgarth (01874) 711249

WALTERS, Canon Douglas Lewis. b 20. Univ of Wales BA41. St Mich Coll Llan 41. **d** 43 **p** 44. V Kidwelly *St D* 58-80; RD Cydweli 77-85; Can St D Cathl 78-86; V Cydweli and Llandyfaelog 80-86; rtd 86. *83 Ashburnham Road, Burry Port, Dyfed SA16 0TW* Burry Port (01554) 834139

WALTERS, Canon Francis Raymond. b 24. Ball Coll Ox BA49 MA54. Wycliffe Hall Ox 51. **d** 53 **p** 54. V Leic St Nic *Leic*

64-74; Chapl Leic Univ 64-74; R Appleby 74-77; Dir of Educn 77-89; Hon Can Leic Cathl 77-91; P-in-c Swithland 77-91; rtd 91; Perm to Offic *Nor* from 91. *2 Beeston Common, Sheringham, Norfolk NR26 8ES* Sheringham (01263) 824414

WALTERS, Ian Robert. b 51. ACA75 FCA81. Local NSM Course 80. **d** 85 **p** 86. NSM Ingoldsby *Linc* from 85. *Dairy Farmhouse, Westby, Grantham, Lincs NG33 4EA* Ingoldsby (0147685) 542

WALTERS, John Morgan. b 09. **d** 34 **p** 35. V High Wych *St Alb* 52-74; rtd 74; Perm to Offic *St E* from 75. *5 Cannonfields, Bury St Edmunds, Suffolk IP33 1JX* Bury St Edmunds (01284) 761010

WALTERS, John Philip Hewitt. b 50. Coll of Resurr Mirfield 72. **d** 73 **p** 74. C Llangiwg *S & B* 73-76; Min Can Brecon Cathl 76-79; C Brecon w Battle 76-79; V Merthyr Cynog w Dyffryn Honddu etc 79-83; V Llandeilo Tal-y-bont from 83. *The Vicarage, 28 Bolgoed Road, Pontardulais, Swansea SA4 1JE* Pontardulais (01792) 882468

WALTERS, Leslie Ernest Ward. b 27. Wadh Coll Ox BA51 MA55. Ridley Hall Cam 55. **d** 57 **p** 58. V Streatham Immanuel w St Anselm *S'wark* 68-81; V Cotmanhay *Derby* 81-92; Chapl Ilkeston Gen Hosp 81-88; Chapl Ilkeston Community Hosp 88-92; rtd 92; Perm to Offic *Nor* from 93. *Rokeby, Taverham Road, Felthorpe, Norwich NR10 4DR* Hevingham (0160548) 5134

WALTERS, Canon Michael William. b 39. Dur Univ BSc61. Clifton Th Coll 61. **d** 63 **p** 64. C Aldershot H Trin *Guildf* 63-66; C Upper Armley *Ripon* 66-69; NE Area Sec CPAS 69-75; V Hyde St Geo *Ches* 75-82; V Knutsford St Jo and Toft from 82; Hon Can Ches Cathl from 94. *The Vicarage, 11 Gough's Lane, Knutsford, Cheshire WA16 8QL* Knutsford (01565) 632834

WALTERS, Nicholas Humphrey. b 45. K Coll Lon BD67 AKC67. **d** 68 **p** 69. C Weston *Guildf* 68-71; Chapl and Lect NE Surrey Coll of Tech Ewell 71-77; Hon C Ewell 71-77; Warden Moor Park Coll Farnham 77-80; Tutor Surrey Univ *Guildf* from 80; Dir of Studies Guildf Inst from 82; Lic to Offic from 84. *9 Valley View, Godalming, Surrey GU7 1RD* Godalming (01483) 415106

WALTERS, Peter. b 27. Leeds Univ BSc48 Univ of Wales (Abth) MSc52. Ripon Coll Cuddesdon 78. **d** 79 **p** 80. C Kingswood *Bris* 79-82; R Stanton St Quintin, Hullavington, Grittleton etc 82-88; rtd 88. *Newcombes End, Elkstone, Cheltenham, Glos GL53 9PD* Cheltenham (01242) 870258

WALTERS, Peter Shane. b 54. SS Paul & Mary Coll Cheltenham DipRS83 Univ of Wales (Cardiff) BD87. St Mich Coll Llan 84. **d** 87 **p** 88. C Newport St Julian *Mon* 87-90; Asst Admin of Shrine of Our Lady of Walsingham from 91; Lic to Offic *Nor* from 91. *The College, Walsingham, Norfolk NR2 6EF* Walsingham (01328) 821073

WALTERS, Very Rev Rhys Derrick Chamberlain. b 32. OBE94. LSE BSc55. Ripon Hall Ox. **d** 57 **p** 58. C Manselton *S & B* 57-58; C Swansea St Mary and H Trin 58-62; Chapl Univ of Wales (Swansea) 58-62; V Totley *Sheff* 62-67; V Boulton *Derby* 67-74; Dioc Missr *Sarum* 74-83; P-in-c Burcombe 74-79; Can and Preb Sarum Cathl 77-79; Can Res and Treas Sarum Cathl 79-83; Dean Liv from 83. *The Deanery, 1 Cathedral Close, Liverpool L1 7BR* 0151-708 0924

WALTERS, Mrs Sheila Ann Beatrice. b 37. Bris Univ DipEd58. E Midl Min Tr Course 85. **d** 89 **p** 94. NSM Ashby-de-la-Zouch St Helen w Coleorton *Leic* from 89. *115 Loughborough Road, Coleorton, Coalville, Leics LE67 8HH* Coalville (01530) 832267

WALTERS, Thomas. b 24. St Deiniol's Hawarden. **d** 79 **p** 80. NSM Bardsley *Man* 79-94; rtd 90. *49 Fir Tree Avenue, Oldham, Lancs OL8 2QS* 0161-652 4108

WALTHEW, Mrs Nancy Jennifer. b 39. Leeds Inst of Educn CertEd59 Ripon Coll of Educn RTC59. N Ord Course 92. **d** 95. NSM Wilmslow *Ches* from 95. *Ashburn, 13 Priory Road, Wilmslow, Cheshire SK9 5PS* Wilmslow (01625) 525462

WALTON, Mrs Alison Claire. b 59. Homerton Coll Cam BEd82. Lon Bible Coll DPS87 Oak Hill Th Coll DipHE89 BA90 MPhil92. **d** 92. C Bedf Ch Ch *St Alb* 92-94; Perm to Offic 94-95. *1 Peache Way, Chilwell Lane, Beeston, Nottingham NG9 3DX* Nottingham (0115) 922 9499

WALTON, Brian. b 53. Sarum & Wells Th Coll 83. **d** 85 **p** 86. C Silksworth *Dur* 85-86; C Bishopwearmouth St Mich w St Hilda 86-88; Chapl RN 88-92; V Sugley *Newc* from 92; Chapl Lemington Hosp from 92. *Sugley Vicarage, Lemington, Newcastle upon Tyne NE15 8RD* 0191-267 4633

WALTON, Ven Geoffrey Elmer. b 34. Dur Univ BA59. Qu Coll Birm DipTh61. **d** 61 **p** 62. C Warsop *S'well* 61-65; Dioc Youth Chapl 65-69; V Norwell 65-69; Recruitment Sec ACCM 69-75; V Weymouth H Trin *Sarum* 75-82; RD Weymouth 79-82; Can and Preb Sarum Cathl from 81; Adn Dorset from 82; P-in-c Witchampton and Hinton Parva, Long Crichel etc from 82. *The Vicarage, Witchampton, Wimborne, Dorset BH21 5AP* Witchampton (01258) 840422

WALTON, John Victor. b 45. Lon Univ BSc67. Linc Th Coll 79. **d** 81 **p** 82. C Stevenage St Mary Shephall *St Alb* 81-85; TV Bourne Valley *Sarum* 85-95; P-in-c Puddletown and Tolpuddle from 95. *The Vicarage, The Square, Puddletown, Dorchester, Dorset DT2 8SL* Puddletown (01305) 848216

WALTON, Kevin Anthony. b 64. St Chad's Coll Dur BA87. Trin Coll Bris BA91. **d** 92 **p** 93. C Stranton *Dur* 92-95; C Hartlepool H Trin from 95. *43 Alderwood Close, Hartlepool, Cleveland TS27 3QR*

WALTON, Maurice James. b 31. RIBA54 MRTPI55 Liv Univ BArch53 MCD54. Wycliffe Hall Ox 93. **d** 94 **p** 95. NSM Gt w Lt Billing *Pet* from 94. *Caldecote, Garrick Road, Northampton NN1 5ND* Northampton (01604) 20760

WALTON, Philip William. b 28. Dur Univ BScAgr52. Tyndale Hall Bris 54. **d** 56 **p** 58. Chapl Maisons-Laffitte w Versailles and Caen *Eur* 69-74; V Worthing Ch Ch *Chich* 74-85; R Wigmore Abbey *Heref* 85-92; rtd 92. *Larkey Lodge, The Cwm, Knighton, Powys LD7 1HF*

WALTON, Reginald Arthur. b 40. St Jo Coll Nottm 80. **d** 81 **p** 82. C Woodthorpe *S'well* 81-84; P-in-c Nottm St Andr 84-85; V 85-91; R Moreton *Ches* from 91. *The Rectory, Dawpool Drive, Moreton, South Wirral L46 0PH* 0151-677 3540

WALTON, Stephen John (Steve). b 55. Birm Univ BSc76 Fitzw Coll Cam BA79 MA82. Ridley Hall Cam 77. **d** 83 **p** 84. C Bebington *Ches* 83-86; Voc and Min Adv CPAS 86-92; Lic to Offic *St Alb* 86-94; Bp's Dom Chapl 94-95; Lect St Jo Coll Nottm from 95. *St John's College, Chilwell Lane, Beeston, Nottingham NG9 3DS* Nottingham (0115) 925 1114 or 922 9499 Fax 943 6438

WALTON, Wilfred James. b 14. St Jo Coll Dur BA39 MA51. **d** 39 **p** 40. Lic to Offic *Sheff* from 68; rtd 79; Perm to Offic *Derby* from 79. *25 Main Avenue, Totley, Sheffield S17 4FH* Sheffield (0114) 236 7183

WANDSWORTH, Archdeacon of. *See* GERRARD, Ven David Keith Robin

WANJIE, Lukas Macharia. b 50. Fitzw Coll Cam BA79 MA83. St Paul's Coll Limuru 72 Ridley Hall Cam 76. **d** 75 **p** 76. Kenya 75-76 and 80-91; Prin Trin Bib Coll Nairobi 85-91; C Mill End and Heronsgate w W Hyde *St Alb* 79; C St Alb St Steph 91-94; Perm to Offic from 94. *59 Manor Road, London Colney, St Albans, Herts AL2 1PP* St Albans (01727) 824340

WANN, Canon Denis Francis. b 27. TCD BA55 MA77. Div Test. **d** 56 **p** 57. C Belf St Donard *D & D* 56-58; Tanzania 58-65; The Philippines 65-72; Hon Can Moro from 72; C Lurgan Ch the Redeemer *D & D* 72-73; Australia 73-91 and from 95; Adn Wollongong and Camden 82-84; I Bailieborough w Knockbride, Shercock and Mullagh *K, E & A* 91-95. *Address temp unknown*

WANSTALL, Noelle Margaret. *See* HALL, Mrs Noelle Margaret

WARBRICK, Quentin David. b 66. Jes Coll Ox BA88. Cranmer Hall Dur 89. **d** 92 **p** 93. C Birm St Martin w Bordesley St Andr *Birm* from 92. *90 Durley Dean Road, Birmingham B29 6RX* 0121-471 3027

WARBURTON, Andrew James. b 44. Oak Hill Th Coll 64. **d** 69 **p** 70. C New Milverton *Cov* 69-72; C Fulham St Matt *Lon* 72-76; C Chesham St Mary *Ox* 76-80; TV Gt Chesham 80-94; Chapl Paris St Mich *Eur* from 94. *5 rue d'Aguesseau, 75008 Paris, France* France (1) 47 42 70 88 Fax 47 42 70 11

WARBURTON, John Bryce. b 33. St Aid Birkenhead 64. **d** 66 **p** 67. C Padiham *Blackb* 66-69; C Burnley St Pet 69-70; V Tideswell *Derby* 70-81; V Bollington St Jo *Ches* 81-91; V Capesthorne w Siddington and Marton from 91. *The Vicarage, School Lane, Marton, Macclesfield, Cheshire SK11 9HD* Marton Heath (01260) 224447

WARBURTON, Piers Eliot de Dutton. b 30. Cranmer Hall Dur BA65. **d** 65 **p** 66. C Grassendale *Liv* 65-68; Bermuda 68-71; R Sherborne *Win* 71-76; V Yateley 76-82; R Guernsey St Andr 82-89; V Hartley Wintney, Elvetham, Winchfield etc from 89. *The Vicarage, Church Lane, Hartley Wintney, Basingstoke, Hants RG27 8DZ* Hartley Wintney (01252) 842670

WARBURTON, Canon Robert Tinsley. b 23. MBE66 TD69. Jes Coll Cam BA47 MA52. Oak Hill Th Coll 47. **d** 47 **p** 48. C Ipswich St Marg *St E* 47-50; R Dallinghoo and Pettistree 50-54; P-in-c Playford w Culpho and Tuddenham St Martin 52-54; V Attenborough w Bramcote *S'well* 54-67; RD Beeston 60-67; CF (TA) from 55; V Mansf St Pet *S'well* from 67; Chapl Mansf Gen Hosp from 67; RD Mansf *S'well* 67-92; P-in-c Teversal 68-72; Hon Can S'well Minster from 72. *The Vicarage, Lindhurst Lane, Mansfield, Notts NG18 4JE* Mansfield (01623) 21600

WARBURTON, Walter George. b 16. Bede Coll Dur BA40 DipTh42 MA43. **d** 41 **p** 42. V Gt Marsden *Blackb* 60-81; rtd 81; Lic to Offic *Blackb* from 81. *145 Halifax Road, Nelson, Lancs BB9 0EL* Nelson (01282) 697589

WARCHUS, Michael Edward George. b 37. Lon Univ DipTh67. Roch Th Coll 65. **d** 68 **p** 69. C Buckhurst Hill *Chelms* 68-71; C Stainton-in-Cleveland *York* 71-76; V Carlton and Drax 76-86; V Acomb St Steph from 86. *The Vicarage, 32 Carr Lane, Acomb, York YO2 5HX* York (01904) 798106

WARD, Alan William. b 56. Trin Coll Bris 80. **d** 81 **p** 82. C New Ferry *Ches* 81-86; Dioc Youth Officer 86-91; C Charlesworth and Dinting Vale *Derby* from 91. *7 Burwell Close, Glossop, Derbyshire SK13 9PG* Glossop (01457) 856831

WARD, Albert George. b 27. K Coll Lon BD54 AKC54. **d** 55 **p** 56. TR Usworth *Dur* 69-78; V S Shields St Simon 78-86; C Darlington St Cuth 86-88; rtd 88. *25 West Crescent, Darlington, Co Durham DL3 7PS* Darlington (01325) 351572

WARD, Alfred John. b 37. Coll of Resurr Mirfield. **d** 93 **p** 94. C Hendon St Mary *Lon* from 93. *St Mary's Cottage, 48 Church End, London NW4 4JX* 0181-203 4673

WARD, Anthony Colin. b 55. Wycliffe Hall Ox 78. **d** 80 **p** 81. Zimbabwe 80-85; S Africa 85-90; C Leic H Trin w St Jo *Leic* from 90. *15 Northcote Road, Knighton, Leicester LE2 3FH* Leicester (0116) 270 3135

WARD, Anthony Peter. b 46. Bris Univ BSc67 Ox Univ DipEd68. St Jo Coll Nottm. **d** 82 **p** 83. C Hellesdon *Nor* 82-85; P-in-c Nor St Aug w St Mary 85-91; P-in-c Nor-over-the-Water Colegate St Geo 85-90; Norfolk Churches' Radio Officer from 85; TV Nor Over-the-Water from 91. *St Paul's Vicarage, 1 Mill Lane, Norwich NR3 4LD* Norwich (01603) 622240

WARD, Arthur John. b 32. Lon Univ BD57. St Aid Birkenhead 57. **d** 57 **p** 58. C Ecclesfield *Sheff* 57-60; C Fulwood 60-63; Tutor St Aid Birkenhead 63-66; R Denton St Lawr *Man* 66-74; CMS 74-82; TV Wolv *Lich* 82-90; V Edgbaston SS Mary and Ambrose *Birm* from 90. *St Ambrose Vicarage, 15 Raglan Road, Birmingham B5 7RA* 0121-440 2196

WARD, Ven Arthur Frederick. b 12. Armstrong Coll Dur BA33. Ridley Hall Cam 33. **d** 35 **p** 36. Preb Ex Cathl *Ex* 70-89; Adn Ex and Can Res Ex Cathl 70-81; Prec 72-81; rtd 81. *Melrose, Christow, Exeter EX6 7LY* Christow (01647) 52498

WARD, Canon Calvin. b 34. Univ of Wales BA57 DipEd60 Fitzw Ho Cam BA63 MA67. Westcott Ho Cam 61. **d** 64 **p** 65. C Handsworth St Mich *Birm* 64-66; C Shaw Hill 66-69; V Windhill *Bradf* 69-76; V Esholt 76-81; V Oakworth 81-91; V Allerton from 91; Hon Can Bradf Cathl from 94. *The Vicarage, Leytop Lane, Allerton, Bradford, W Yorkshire BD15 7LT* Bradford (01274) 541948

WARD, Christopher John William. b 36. Bps' Coll Cheshunt 66 Qu Coll Birm 68. **d** 69 **p** 70. C Wednesbury St Bart *Lich* 69-73; CF 73-94; Perm to Offic *Sarum* from 94. *6 Meadow View, Blandford Forum, Dorset DT11 7JB* Blandford (01258) 455140

WARD, David. b 40. St Jo Coll Nottm 83. **d** 85 **p** 86. C Aspley *S'well* 85-89; V from 89. *St Margaret's Vicarage, 319 Aspley Lane, Nottingham NG8 5GA* Nottingham (0115) 929 2920

WARD, David Conisbee. b 33. St Jo Coll Cam BA54 MA59. S'wark Ord Course 77. **d** 80 **p** 81. NSM Surbiton St Matt S'wark 80-83; C Streatham Immanuel w St Anselm 83-84; P-in-c 84-87; V Hook 87-93; rtd 93. Perm to Offic *S'wark* from 94. *50 Elgar Avenue, Surbiton, Surrey KT9 9JN* 0181-399 9679

WARD, David Robert. b 51. Oak Hill Th Coll 74. **d** 77 **p** 78. C Kirkheaton *Wakef* 77-81; V Earlsheaton 81-88; V Bradley from 88. *The Vicarage, 87 Bradley Road, Huddersfield HD2 1RA* Huddersfield (01484) 427838

WARD, David Towle Greenfield. b 22. Ch Coll Cam BA47 MA49. Linc Th Coll 47. **d** 49 **p** 50. V Potter Heigham *Nor* 64-77; V Repps 64-77; R Ditchingham w Pirnough 77-87; R Broome 77-87; R Hedenham 77-87; rtd 87; Perm to Offic *Nor* from 87. *Manor Cottage, 58 Mount Street, Diss, Norfolk IP22 3QQ* Diss (01379) 651328

WARD, Ven Edwin James Greenfield. b 19. LVO63. Ch Coll Cam BA46 MA48. Ridley Hall Cam 46. **d** 48 **p** 49. Chapl to The Queen 55-90; Extra Chapl to The Queen from 90; R W Stafford w Frome Billet *Sarum* 67-84; Can and Preb Sarum Cathl 67-84; Adn Sherborne 67-84; rtd 85. *14 Arle Close, Alresford, Hants SO24 9BG* Alresford (01962) 735501

WARD, Ms Frances Elizabeth Fearn. b 59. St Andr Univ MTh83 Jes Coll Cam DipTh89. Westcott Ho Cam 87. **d** 89 **p** 94. Par Dn Westhoughton *Man* 89-93; Tutor Practical Th N Coll Man from 93; Hon C Bury St Pet from 94. *142 Manchester Road, Bury, Lancs BL9 0TL* 0161-761 4541

WARD, Frank Neal. b 16. E Anglian Minl Tr Course 78. **d** 80 **p** 81. NSM Weybourne w Upper Sheringham *Nor* 80-84; NSM Kelling w Salthouse 80-84; NSM Briningham 84-92; NSM Brinton, Briningham, Hunworth, Stody etc from 92. *The Street, Sharrington, Melton Constable, Norfolk NR24 2AB* Melton Constable (01263) 860337

WARD, Frank Wyatt. b 30. Oak Hill NSM Course 84. **d** 92 **p** 94. NSM Paddington St Pet *Lon* from 92. *82 Hill Rise, Greenford, Middx UB6 8PE* 0181-575 5515

WARD, Geoffrey. b 35. Cranmer Hall Dur 77. **d** 79 **p** 80. C Garforth *Ripon* 79-81; V Holmfield *Wakef* 81-85; TV

Thornaby on Tees *York* 85-91; V Linc St Jo *Linc* from 91. *St John's Vicarage, Sudbrooke Drive, Lincoln LN2 2EF* Lincoln (01522) 525621

WARD, Geoffrey Edward. b 30. Linc Th Coll 62. **d** 64 **p** 65. C Weston Favell *Pet* 68-70; TV 70-72; R Cottingham w E Carlton 72-95; rtd 95. *4 Sovereigns Court, Saxonfields, Kettering, Northants NN16 9SS* Kettering (01536) 520498

WARD, Graham John. b 55. Fitzw Coll Cam BA80 Selw Coll Cam MA83. Westcott Ho Cam 87. **d** 90 **p** 91. C Bris St Mary Redcliffe w Temple etc *Bris* 90-92; Chapl Ex Coll Ox 92-94; Dean Peterho Cam from 95. *Peterhouse, Cambridge CB2 1RD* Cambridge (01223) 338200

WARD, Ian Stanley. b 62. K Coll Lon BD83. Cranmer Hall Dur 84. **d** 86 **p** 87. C Moreton *Ches* 86-89; Chapl RAF from 89. *Chaplaincy Services (RAF), HQ, Personnel and Training Command, RAF Innsworth, Gloucester GL3 1EZ* Gloucester (01452) 712612 Ext 5164 Fax 510828

WARD, Jack. b 08. Tyndale Hall Bris. **d** 57 **p** 58. V Mow Cop *Lich* 61-79; rtd 79. *9 Wentworth Drive, Rookery, Stoke-on-Trent ST7 4SU* Stoke-on-Trent (01782) 773316

WARD, John Frederick. b 55. St Mich Coll Llan 81. **d** 84 **p** 85. C Pemb Dock *St D* 84-86; PV Llan Cathl *Llan* 86-89; R St Brides Minor w Bettws from 89. *St Bride's Rectory, Sarn, Bridgend, M Glam CF32 9RH* Bridgend (01656) 720274

WARD, John Raymond. b 31. St Jo Coll Dur BA54 DipTh56. **d** 56 **p** 57. C Leeds St Pet *Ripon* 56-60; C Seacroft 60-63; V Kirkstall 63-75; V Bramhope from 75. *The Vicarage, 26 Leeds Road, Bramhope, Leeds LS16 9BQ* Leeds (0113) 284 2543

WARD, Prof John Stephen Keith. b 38. Univ of Wales (Cardiff) BA62 Linacre Coll Ox BLitt68 Trin Hall Cam MA72. Westcott Ho Cam 72. **d** 72 **p** 73. Hon C Hampstead St Jo *Lon* 72-75; Fell and Dean Trin Hall Cam 75-82; Prof Moral and Soc Th K Coll Lon 82-85; Prof Hist and Philosophy of Religion 85-91; Regius Prof Th Ch Ch Ox from 91. *Christ Church, Oxford OX1 1DP* Oxford (01865) 276246 or 722208

WARD, John Stewart. b 43. St Jo Coll Dur BA66. Ripon Coll Cuddesdon 77. **d** 79 **p** 80. C High Harrogate Ch Ch *Ripon* 79-82; V Ireland Wood 82-86; Chapl Wells Cathl Sch 86-88; V Menston w Woodhead *Bradf* from 88. *The Vicarage, 12 Fairfax Gardens, Menston, Ilkley, W Yorkshire LS29 6ET* Menston (01943) 872818

WARD, Keith Raymond. b 37. Dur Univ BSc60. Chich Th Coll 63. **d** 65 **p** 66. C Wallsend St Luke *Newc* 65-68; C Wooler 68-74; V Dinnington 74-81; V Bedlington 81-93; V Stannington from 93. *The Vicarage, Stannington, Morpeth, Northd NE61 6HL* Morpeth (01670) 789222

WARD, Kenneth Arthur. b 22. St D Coll Lamp BA50 Chich Th Coll 50. **d** 52 **p** 53. R Daventry *Pet* 58-72; RD Daventry 68-76; R Daventry w Norton 73-79; R Daventry 79-82; V Pattishall w Cold Higham 82-88; rtd 88; Perm to Offic *Pet* from 89. *43 Inlands Rise, Daventry, Northants NN11 4DQ*

WARD, Dr Kevin. b 47. Edin Univ MA69 Trin Coll Cam PhD76. **d** 78 **p** 79. CMS 75-92; Uganda 76-90; Qu Coll Birm 91; Perm to Offic *Birm* 91; C Halifax *Wakef* 91-92; P-in-c Charlestown from 92. *St Thomas's Vicarage, Bell Street, Claremount, Halifax, W Yorkshire HX3 6AP* Halifax (01422) 348188

WARD, Canon Leslie Alan James. b 38. AKC61. **d** 62 **p** 63. C Earlham St Anne *Nor* 62-65; C Gt Yarmouth 65-70; R Belton 70-83; R Burgh Castle 71-83; Chapl Norfolk and Nor Hosp from 83; Chapl W Norwich and Colman Hosp from 83; Hon Can Nor Cathl *Nor* from 86. *Norfolk & Norwich Hospital, Brunswick Road, Norwich NR1 3SR, or 24 Carnoustie, Norwich NR4 6AY* Norwich (01603) 286286 or 58245

WARD, Lionel Owen. b 37. Univ of Wales (Cardiff) BA58 Univ of Wales (Swansea) DipEd59 MA65 Lon Univ PhD70. St Mich Coll Llan 83. **d** 85 **p** 86. NSM Swansea St Mary w H Trin *S & B* 85-89; P-in-c Swansea St Matt w Greenhill from 89; Asst Dir of Educn from 92. *96 Glanbrydan Avenue, Uplands, Swansea SA2 0JH* Swansea (01792) 208081

WARD, Louis Arthur. b 13. Ripon Hall Ox 72. **d** 73 **p** 74. C Corsham *Bris* 73-77; Bp's Chapl for the Arts 76-80; V Bitton 78-80; rtd 80; Perm to Offic *Bris* from 80; Perm to Offic *Glouc* from 86. *10 Orchard Close, Westbury-on-Trym, Bristol BS9 1AS* Bristol (0117) 962 8332

WARD, Mrs Marjorie. b 38. Univ of Wales (Abth) BA59 DipEd60. N Ord Course 83. **dss** 86 **d** 87 **p** 94. Keighley St Andr *Bradf* 86-87; Hon Par Dn 87-88; Hon Par Dn Oakworth 88-90; C Allerton from 91. *The Vicarage, Leytop Lane, Allerton, Bradford, W Yorkshire BD15 7LT* Bradford (01274) 541948

WARD, Mark. b 62. ACGI84 Imp Coll Lon BScEng84. Wycliffe Hall Ox BTh93. **d** 93 **p** 94. C Parkham, Alwington, Buckland Brewer etc from 93. *5 Manor Court, Parkham, Bideford, Devon EX39 5PG* Horns Cross (01237) 451800

WARD, Canon Michael Anthony. b 42. Sarum Th Coll 67. **d** 70 **p** 71. C Bridport *Sarum* 70-74; TV Swanborough 74-77; P-in-c Chute w Chute Forest 77-79; P-in-c Shalbourne w Ham 77-79; TR Wexcombe 79-86; V Southbroom from 86; Hon Can

Sarum Cathl from 95. *Southbroom Vicarage, London Road, Devizes, Wilts SN10 1LT* Devizes (01380) 723891

WARD, Michael Reginald. b 31. BNC Ox BA54 MA58. Tyndale Hall Bris 54. **d** 56 **p** 57. C Ealing St Mary *Lon* 56-59; C Morden *S'wark* 59-61; Area Sec (Midl and E Anglia) CCCS 61-66; V Chelsea St Jo *Lon* 66-73; P-in-c Chelsea St Andr 72-73; V Chelsea St Jo w St Andr 73-76; P-in-c Hawkesbury *Glouc* 76-80; P-in-c Alderley w Hillesley 79-80; P-in-c Bibury w Winson and Barnsley 80-85; V Bagendon and Queniborough *Leic* 85-90; R Gunthorpe w Bale w Field Dalling, Saxlingham etc *Nor* from 90. *The Rectory, Bale, Fakenham, Norfolk NR21 0QJ* Fakenham (01328) 878292

WARD, Nigel Andrew. b 50. Peterho Cam BA72 MA76. Oak Hill NSM Course 89. **d** 92 **p** 93. NSM Frogmore H Trin *St Alb* from 92. *15 Park Street, St Albans, Herts AL2 2PE* St Albans (01727) 872667

WARD, Patricia. b 43. **d** 91. NSM Swansea St Mary w H Trin *S & B* from 91. *96 Glanbrydan Avenue, Uplands, Swansea SA2 0JH* Swansea (01792) 208081

WARD, Peter Garnet. b 28. GRSM51 LRAM. Ridley Hall Cam 59. **d** 61 **p** 62. Kenya 64-73; Master St Leon Mayfield Sch Sussex 73-83; Perm to Offic *Chich* 74-75; P-in-c Coleman's Hatch 75-77; Lic to Offic 77-83; P-in-c Herstmonceux 83-84; P-in-c Wartling 83-84; R Herstmonceux and Wartling 84-94; rtd 94. *Old Jesolo, Cross Lane, Ticehurst, Wadhurst, E Sussex TN5 7HQ* Ticehurst (01580) 201340

WARD, Canon Philip Paul Ben. b 35. Toronto Univ BA61. ALCD66. **d** 66 **p** 67. C Chenies and Lt Chalfont *Ox* 66-68; C Ardsley *Sheff* 68-70; C Finham *Cov* 70-73; V Terrington St Clement *Ely* 73-81; Canada from 81. *369 Main Street, Saint John, New Brunswick, Canada, E2K 1J1*

WARD, Philip Percival Ford. b 33. City Univ BSc61. Wells Th Coll 67. **d** 69 **p** 70. C Clifton All SS *Bris* 69-72; P-in-c Bedminster Down 72-76; V 76-77; P-in-c Fishponds All SS 77-80; V Fishponds St Jo 77-83; V Walney Is *Carl* 83-90; V Hambleton w Out Rawcliffe *Blackb* from 90. *The Vicarage, Church Lane, Hambleton, Poulton-le-Fylde, Lancs FY6 9BZ* Blackpool (01253) 700231

WARD, Richard. b 09. St Aug Coll Cant 63. **d** 64 **p** 65. V Hoar Cross *Lich* 69-78; P-in-c Newborough w Ch Ch on Needwood 76-78; rtd 78. *Hoar Cross Nursing Home, Hoar Cross, Burton-on-Trent, Staffs DE13 8QS* Hoar Cross (0128375) 210

WARD, Robert. b 60. Em Coll Cam BA81 MA85. Chich Th Coll. **d** 86 **p** 87. C Horfield H Trin *Bris* 86-90; C Stantonbury and Willen *Ox* 90; TV from 90. *The Vicarage, Bradwell Road, Bradville, Milton Keynes MK13 7AX* Milton Keynes (01908) 314224

WARD, Robert Arthur Philip. b 53. Lon Univ BD82 Open Univ BA88. Qu Coll Birm 77. **d** 79 **p** 80. C Balsall Heath St Paul *Birm* 79-82; Chapl RAF from 82. *Chaplaincy Services (RAF), HQ, Personnel and Training Command, RAF Innsworth, Gloucester GL3 1EZ* Gloucester (01452) 712612 Ext 5164 Fax 510828

WARD, Robert Charles Irwin. b 48. Leic Univ LLB70. St Jo Coll Dur 78. **d** 80 **p** 81. C Byker St Mich w St Lawr *Newc* 80-85; Perm to Offic from 86. *1 Hawthorn Villas, The Green, Wallsend, Tyne & Wear NE28 7NT* 0191-234 3969

WARD, Robin. b 66. Magd Coll Ox BA87 MA91. St Steph Ho Ox 88. **d** 91 **p** 92. C Romford St Andr *Chelmsf* 91-94; C Willesden Green St Andr and St Fran of Assisi *Lon* from 94. *150 Ellesmere Road, London NW10 1JT* 0181-452 3999

WARD, Stanley. b 34. NE Ord Course. **d** 84 **p** 85. NSM Jarrow *Dur* 84-90; P-in-c Thornley from 90. *The Vicarage, 10 Church Walk, Thornley, Durham DH6 3EN* Hartlepool (01429) 820363 or 821766

WARD, Stanley Gordon. b 21. Qu Coll Cam BA43 MA47. E Midl Min Tr Course 76. **d** 79 **p** 80. NSM Wollaton *S'well* 79-83; NSM Plympton St Mary *Ex* 84-88; Perm to Offic from 88. *60 Wain Park, Plympton, Plymouth PL7 3HX* Plymouth (01752) 344042

WARD, Mrs Susan Elizabeth. b 50. N Ord Course 92. **d** 95. NSM Heyside *Man* from 95. *45 Fold Green, Chadderton, Oldham OL9 9DX* 0161-620 2839

WARD, Timothy John Conisbee (Tim). b 62. New Coll Ox BA85 PGCE86. Wycliffe Hall Ox BA91. **d** 92 **p** 93. C Dorking St Paul *Guildf* from 92. *6 Falkland Road, Dorking, Surrey RH4 3AB* Dorking (01306) 889513

WARD, Timothy William. b 49. Open Univ BA74. St Deiniol's Hawarden 78. **d** 79 **p** 80. Hon C Handsworth St Mary *Birm* from 79. *3 Dale Close, Birmingham B43 6AS* 0121-358 1880

WARD, William. b 13. Wycliffe Hall Ox 63. **d** 64 **p** 65. V Stillington w Marton and Farlington *York* 68-73; V Langtoft w Foxholes, Butterwick and Cottam 73-78; rtd 78. *14 Park Close, Easingwold, York YO6 3BR* Easingwold (01347) 823009

WARD, William Edward. b 48. FSAScot71. AKC71. **d** 72 **p** 73. C Heref St Martin *Heref* 72-77; C Blakenall Heath *Lich* 77-78; TV 78-82; V Astley, Clive, Grinshill and Hadnall 82-91; R

Edgmond w Kynnersley and Preston Wealdmoors from 91. *The Rectory, Edgmond, Newport, Shropshire TF10 8JR* Newport (01952) 820217

WARD, William Francis. b 35. Ely Th Coll 61 Coll of Resurr Mirfield 64. **d** 64 **p** 65. C Byker St Ant *Newc* 64-67; C Glas St Marg *Glas* 67-69; R Glas Ascension 69-74; Chapl RNR 72-74; Chapl RN 74-78; R Arbroath *Bre* from 78; Hon Chapl Miss to Seamen from 78; P-in-c Auchmithie *Bre* 79-90. *The Rectory, 2 Springfield Terrace, Arbroath DD11 1EL* Arbroath (01241) 73392

WARD-ANDREWS, Canon Lewes. b 12. Kelham Th Coll 29. **d** 36 **p** 37. SSM from 36; P-in-c Nottm St Geo w St Jo *S'well* 60-82; Hon Can S'well Minster 66-82; rtd 82; Perm to Offic *Blackb* 82-90. *Woodlands Nursing Home, Sleights, Whitby, N Yorkshire YO21 1RY* Whitby (01947) 810879

WARD-BODDINGTON, Canon Douglas. b 20. S'wark Ord Course 69. **d** 72 **p** 73. C S'wark Ch Ch *S'wark* 72-77; Admin S Lon Ind Miss 72-77; Chapl Algarve *Eur* 77-80 and 83-89; V Gen to Bp Eur 80-83; Can Gib Cathl from 80; rtd 89; Chapl Porto (or Oporto) *Eur* from 89. *Rua do Campo Alegre 640-5 D, 4100 Porto, Portugal* Porto (2) 609-1006 or 606-4989

WARDALE, Dr Harold William (Harry). b 40. BSc PhD. Wycliffe Hall Ox 83. **d** 85 **p** 86. C Bedminster St Mich *Bris* 85-89; C Bishopston 89; TV from 89. *89 King's Drive, Bristol BS7 8JQ* Bristol (0117) 924 3424

WARDALE, Robert Christopher. b 46. Newc Univ BA69. Coll of Resurr Mirfield 77. **d** 79 **p** 80. C Cockerton *Dur* 79-84; P-in-c Hedworth 84-87; V 87-92; V Darlington H Trin from 92. *Holy Trinity Vicarage, 45 Milbank Road, Darlington, Co Durham DL3 9NL* Darlington (01325) 480444

WARDEN, John Michael. b 41. Univ Coll Lon BA63 Trin Coll Ox BA65 MA. NE Ord Course 80. **d** 82 **p** 83. NSM Osmotherley w E Harlsey and Ingleby Arncliffe *York* 82-86; V Kirkdale from 86. *Kirkdale Vicarage, Nawton, York YO6 5ST* Helmsley (01439) 71206

WARDEN, Richard James. b 57. BA MTh. Wycliffe Hall Ox 81. **d** 83 **p** 84. C Fulham St Mary N End *Lon* 83-85; CF 85-89; Chapl Wycombe Abbey Sch High Wycombe from 89. *Wycombe Abbey School, High Wycombe, Bucks HP11 1PE* High Wycombe (01494) 520381

WARDLE, Edward Christian. b 13. **d** 62 **p** 63. C Farnley *Ripon* 62-64; C Wortley de Leeds 64-66; V Llanwyddelan w Manafon *St As* 66-79; P-in-c Stottesdon *Heref* 79-82; Perm to Offic *Ripon* 82-92. *The Gables Nursing Home, Swinnow Road, Pudsey, Leeds LS28 9AP* Leeds (0113) 257 0123

WARDLE, Canon John Alexander (Jack). b 30. TD73. Lon Univ BA59 Man Univ MA81. Oak Hill Th Coll 53. **d** 57 **p** 58. C Blackpool St Mark *Blackb* 57-60; C Tunbridge Wells St Jo *Roch* 60-62; V Maidstone St Luke *Cant* 62-69; CF (TA) 62-73; V Hartford *Ches* 69-79; R Barton Seagrave w Warkton *Pet* from 79; Can Pet Cathl from 94. *The Rectory, Barton Seagrave, Kettering, Northants NN15 6SR* Kettering (01536) 513629 or 414052

WARDLE, John Argyle. b 47. ARCM67 St Jo Coll Dur BA71 CertEd73. Cranmer Hall Dur DipTh72. **d** 73 **p** 74. C Mansf St Pet *S'well* 73-77; Chapl St Felix Sch Southwold 77-87; TV Haverhill w Withersfield, the Wrattings etc *St E* 87-90; VC S'well Minster *S'well* from 90; Bp's Adv on Healing from 94. *3 Vicars' Court, Southwell, Notts NG25 0HP* Southwell (01636) 813767

WARDLE-HARPUR, Canon Charles Noel. b 03. St Edm Hall Ox BA25 MA29. Wycliffe Hall Ox 26. **d** 26 **p** 27. TR Stockton *Dur* 58-71; Hon Can Dur Cathl 59-71; RD Stockton 59-71; rtd 71. *19 Elm Crescent, The Paddocks, Charlbury, Chipping Norton, Oxon OX7 3PZ* Charlbury (01608) 810600

WARDLE-HARPUR, Canon James. b 31. St Jo Coll Dur BA55. Wells Th Coll 55. **d** 56 **p** 57. C Sheff Parson Cross St Cecilia *Sheff* 56-59; C Maltby 59-61; V Doncaster St Jude 61-64; Pakistan 64-68; R Man Victoria Park *Man* 68-75; V Foxton w Gumley and Laughton *Leic* 75-79; V Foxton w Gumley and Laughton and Lubenham 79-82; TR Leic Resurr 82-88; V Burrough Hill Pars 88-94; Hon Can Leic Cathl 88-94. *Laburnum Cottage, 1 Coates Lane, Starbotton, Skipton, N Yorkshire BD23 5HZ* Skipton (01756) 760401

WARDMAN, Carol Joy. b 56. Lon Univ BA79. Nor Ord Course 91. **d** 94 **p** 95. NSM Hebden Bridge *Wakef* from 94. *3 The Pond, Triangle, Sowerby Bridge, W Yorkshire HX6 3NM* Halifax (01422) 835464

WARDROBE, Bevan. b 26. Hatf Coll Dur BA53. Cuddesdon Coll 53. **d** 54 **p** 55. Hd Master York Minster Song Sch 67-85; VC York Minster *York* 67-85; Chapl Rome *Eur* 85-91; rtd 91; Chapl San Remo *Eur* from 91. *via Fratelli Asquasciati, 68/1, 18038 San Remo (Imperia), Italy* San Remo (184) 577200

WARDROP, David John. b 34. ALCD59. **d** 59 **p** 60. Chapl RNR from 61; Asst Gen Sec Ind Chr Fellowship 67-76; P-in-c Pertenhall w Swineshead *St Alb* 76-80; R Wymington w Podington 80-83; R Cavendish *St E* 83-89; P-in-c Clare w Poslingford 86-89; P-in-c Stoke by Clare w Wixoe 86-89;

R Clare w Poslingford, Cavendish etc 89-91; RD Clare 87-91; Chapl Aquitaine *Eur* 91-95; rtd 95. *Cotswold, 6 Shreen Way, Gillingham, Dorset SP8 4EL* Gillingham (01747) 822189

WARE, Austin Neville. b 14. St D Coll Lamp BA37 St Mich Coll Llan 37. **d** 39 **p** 41. V Knapton *York* 58-75; R W and E Heslerton w Knapton 75-79; rtd 79. *Craigsmoor, Lon Crecrist, Trearddur Bay, Holyhead, Gwynedd LL65 2BQ* Trearddur Bay (01407) 860106

WARE, John Franklin Jones. b 07. Univ of Wales BA30 Keble Coll Ox BA33 MA36. **d** 32 **p** 33. V Hove St Phil *Chich* 65-79; rtd 79; Perm to Offic *B & W* 80-93. *Tegfan, 3 Windsor Way, Haverfordwest, Dyfed SA61 1TT* Haverfordwest (01437) 765578

WARE, Canon John Lawrence. b 37. Nottm Univ BA59. Ridley Hall Cam 62. **d** 62 **p** 63. C Attercliffe *Sheff* 62-66; C Ranmoor 66-68; R Liddington *Bris* 68-74; Soc and Ind Adv 74-79; P-in-c City of Bris 74-79; Hon Can Bris Cathl from 76; V Kingswood 79-88; RD Bitton 85-87; P-in-c Broad Blunsdon 88-94; RD Cricklade 88-94; R Broad Blunsdon 94; P-in-c Blunsdon 94; R The Blunsdons from 94. *The Rectory, Burytown Lane, Blunsdon, Bristol SN2 4DQ* Swindon (01793) 729592

WARE, Stephen John. b 55. Univ of Wales (Lamp) BA76. Ripon Coll Cuddesdon 77. **d** 79 **p** 80. C Lighthorne *Cov* 79-82; Chapl RAF from 82. *Chaplaincy Services (RAF), HQ, Personnel and Training Command, RAF Innsworth, Gloucester GL3 1EZ* Gloucester (01452) 712612 Ext 5164 Fax 510828

WAREHAM, Mrs Caroline. b 32. Lightfoot Ho Dur 55. **dss** 80 **d** 87 **p** 94. Stanwell *Lon* 80-87; Par Dn 87-88; C Epsom St Barn *Guildf* 88-95; C Aldershot St Mich from 95. *Ascension Church House, Ayling Hill, Aldershot, Hants GU11 3LL* Aldershot (01252) 330224

WAREHAM, Mrs Sheila. b 36. CertEd56. N Ord Course 85. **d** 88 **p** 94. NSM Lostock Hall *Blackb* 88-90; NSM Allithwaite Carl 90-91; NSM Windermere RD 91-94; NSM Colton w Satterthwaite and Rusland from 94. *Lyng Nook, Church Road, Allithwaite, Grange-over-Sands, Cumbria LA11 7RD* Grange-over-Sands (015395) 35237

WARING, Graham George Albert. b 37. ACII62. Portsm Dioc Tr Course 86. **d** 87. Chapl Asst Qu Alexandra Hosp Portsm 87-92; NSM Portsea All SS *Portsm* 92-94; NSM Widley w Wymering 94-95; NSM Wisbech St Aug *Ely* from 95. *1 Ivesdyke Close, Leverington, Wisbech, Cambs PE13 5EQ*

WARING, Jeffery Edwin. b 53. Trin Coll Bris 80. **d** 83 **p** 84. C Harpurhey Ch Ch *Man* 83-86; TV Eccles 86-92; P-in-c Hamworthy *Sarum* from 92. *The Rectory, 323 Blandford Road, Hamworthy, Poole, Dorset BH15 4HP* Poole (01202) 674878

WARING, John Valentine. b 29. St Deiniol's Hawarden 65. **d** 67 **p** 68. C Bistre *St As* 67-71; C Blackpool St Thos *Blackb* 71-72; R Levenshulme St Pet *Man* 72-87; R Caerwys and Bodfari *St As* 87-94; rtd 94. *13 St Mellors Road, Southdown Park, Buckley, Clwyd CH7 2ND* Buckley (01244) 547290

WARING, Roger. b 32. ACP66 CertEd56 Open Univ BA74. SW Minl Tr Course 83. **d** 86 **p** 87. NSM Ex St Sidwell and St Matt *Ex* 86-90; NSM Tavistock and Gulworthy from 90. *St Eustace, 32 Plym Crescent, Tavistock, Devon PL19 9HX* Tavistock (01822) 615501

WARING, Mrs Ruth. b 44. Keele Univ CertEd65. SW Minl Tr Course 86. **d** 90 **p** 94. Par Dn Tavistock and Gulworthy *Ex* 90-94; C from 94. *St Eustace, 32 Plym Crescent, Tavistock, Devon PL19 9HX* Tavistock (01822) 615501

WARING, Mrs Sheila May. b 29. SS Paul & Mary Coll Cheltenham CertEd49. Oak Hill Th Coll 85. **dss** 86 **d** 87 **p** 94. Eastwood *Chelmsf* 86-87; NSM 87-92; Chapl Rochford Hosp from 87; NSM Prittlewell St Pet *Chelmsf* from 92. *42 Manchester Drive, Leigh-on-Sea, Essex SS9 3HR* Southend-on-Sea (01702) 711046

WARING, Wilfrid Harold. b 11. TD46. Jes Coll Cam BA33 MA37. Ripon Hall Ox 33. **d** 34 **p** 35. V Saddleworth *Man* 67-77; rtd 77. *Trinity Close, 8A Kirkby Road, Ripon, N Yorkshire HG4 2ET* Ripon (01765) 605880

WARKE, Alistair Samuel John. b 66. CITC BTh92. **d** 92 **p** 93. C Arm St Mark w Aghavilly *Arm* 92-95; I Killyman from 95; Hon VC Arm Cathl from 95. *St Andrew's Rectory, 85 Dungorman Road, Killyman, Dungannon, Co Tyrone BT71 6SE* Dungannon (01868) 722500

✠**WARKE, Rt Rev Robert Alexander.** b 30. TCD BA52 BD60. Union Th Sem (NY) DipEcum60. **d** 53 **p** 54 **c** 88. C Newtownards *D & D* 53-56; C Dub St Cath w St Victor *D & G* 56-58; C Dub Rathfarnham 58-64; Min Can St Patr Cathl Dub 59-64; I Dunlavin w Ballymore Eustace and Hollywood *D & G* 64-67; I Dub Drumcondra w N Strand 67-71; I Dub St Barn 67-71; I Dub Zion Ch 71-88; RD Taney 77-80; Adn Dub 80-88; Bp C, C & R from 88. *The Palace, Bishop Street, Cork, Irish Republic* Cork (21) 316114 Fax 273437

WARLAND, Preb Cyril John. b 21. St Cath Soc Ox BA43 MA56. Cuddesdon Coll. **d** 44 **p** 45. R Marytavy *Ex* 56-88; RD Tavistock 77-88; P-in-c Walkhampton 80-83; Preb Ex Cathl

82-88; R Peter Tavy 82-88; rtd 88; Lic to Offic *Ex* from 88. *2 Rowantree Road, Newton Abbot, Devon TQ1 4LL* Newton Abbot (01626) 55369

WARLAND, Peter William. b 35. K Coll Lon 56. **d** 60 **p** 61. C Pemberton St Jo *Liv* 60-64; C Warrington St Elphin 64-66; V Farnworth All SS *Man* 66-71; Chapl RN 71-92; Hon Chapl to The Queen 88-92; Chapl Greenbank and Freedom Fields Hosps Ex from 92; Perm to Offic *Ex* from 94. *122 Wingfield Road, Plymouth PL3 4ER* Plymouth (01752) 561381

WARMAN, Canon Cyril Aidan Oswald. b 08. Pemb Coll Ox BA30 MA35. Ridley Hall Cam 30. **d** 31 **p** 32. Hon Can Wakef Cathl *Wakef* 62-74; V Kellington w Whitley 66-74; rtd 74; Perm to Offic *York* from 74. *Dulverton Hall, St Martin's Square, Scarborough, N Yorkshire YO11 2BD* Scarborough (01723) 371040

WARMAN, Canon John Richard. b 37. Pemb Coll Ox BA61 MA. Ridley Hall Cam 61. **d** 63 **p** 64. C Huyton St Mich *Liv* 63-67; Asst Chapl Liv Univ 67-68; Chapl 68-74; P-in-c Holbrooke *Derby* 74-80; P-in-c Lt Eaton 74-80; R Sawley from 80; RD Ilkeston 82-92; Hon Can Derby Cathl from 91. *The Rectory, Tamworth Road, Long Eaton, Nottingham NG10 3AB* Nottingham (0115) 973 4900

WARMAN, Miss Marion Alice. b 20. Newnham Coll Cam BA43 MA50. S'wark Ord Course 58. **dss** 79 **d** 87 **p** 94. Spring Grove St Mary *Lon* 79-87; Hon Par Dn 87-93; Chapl Asst W Middx Hosp Isleworth from 80; Perm to Offic from 93. *43 Thornbury Road, Isleworth, Middx TW7 4LE* 0181-560 5905

WARNER, Alan Winston. b 51. Lon Univ BSc73 Leeds Univ DipTh75. Coll of Resurr Mirfield 73. **d** 76 **p** 77. C Willenhall St Anne *Lich* 76-78; C Baswich (or Berkswich) 78-81; V Wednesfield St Greg 81-87; Chapl Frimley Park Hosp from 87. *14 The Cloisters, Frimley, Camberley, Surrey GU16 5JR* Camberley (01276) 64685 or 692777

WARNER, Andrew Compton. b 35. Fitzw Ho Cam BA58 MA62. Westcott Ho Cam 59. **d** 60 **p** 61. C Addlestone *Guildf* 60-64; C-in-c Ash Vale CD 64-71; V Hinchley Wood 71-80; R Gt Bookham from 80; RD Leatherhead 88-93. *The Rectory, 2A Fife Way, Leatherhead, Surrey KT23 3PH* Bookham (01372) 452405

WARNER, Clifford Chorley. b 38. Hull Univ MA88. E Midl Min Tr Course 76. **d** 79 **p** 80. NSM Swanwick and Pentrich *Derby* 79-88; NSM Allestree from 88. *17 Amber Heights, Ripley, Derbyshire DE5 3SP* Ripley (01773) 745089

WARNER, David. b 40. AKC63. **d** 64 **p** 65. C Castleford All SS *Wakef* 64-68; Warden Hollowford Tr and Conf Cen Sheff 68-72; R Wombwell *Sheff* 72-83; V Wortley 83-84; V Wortley w Thurgoland from 84; RD Tankersley 88-93. *The Vicarage, Park Avenue, Wortley, Sheffield S30 7DR* Sheffield (0114) 288 2238

WARNER, David Leonard John. b 24. Kelham Th Coll 47. **d** 51 **p** 52. V Bournemouth H Epiphany *Win* 68-78; V Whitchurch w Tufton and Litchfield 78-89; RD Whitchurch 79-89; rtd 89. *9 Sparkford Close, Winchester, Hants SO22 4NH* Winchester (01962) 867343

WARNER, Dennis Vernon. b 46. Lon Univ BA68 K Coll Lon BD71. **d** 72 **p** 73. C W Bromwich All SS *Lich* 72-75; C Uttoxeter w Bramshall 75-79; Lic to Offic from 79. *17 Shrewsbury Road, Stretton, Swadlincote, Derbyshire DE13 0JF* Burton-on-Trent (01283) 48058

WARNER, Canon George Francis. b 36. Trin Coll Ox BA60 MA64 Qu Coll Cam BA63. Westcott Ho Cam 61. **d** 63 **p** 64. C Birm St Geo *Birm* 63-66; C Maidstone All SS w St Phil and H Trin *Cant* 66-69; Chapl Wellington Coll Berks 69-78; TR Cov Caludon *Cov* 78-95; Hon Can Cov Cathl from 85; RD Cov E 89-95; P-in-c Leamington Priors All SS from 95; P-in-c Leamington Spa and Old Milverton from 95. *Holy Trinity Vicarage, Clive House, Kenilworth Road, Leamington Spa, Warks CV32 5TL* Leamington Spa (01926) 424016

WARNER, James Morley (Jim). b 32. S'wark Ord Course 66. **d** 69 **p** 70. C S Mymms K Chas *Lon* 69-72; C Bush Hill Park St Steph 72-75; V W Hendon St Jo from 75. *St John's Vicarage, Vicarage Road, London NW4 3PX* 0181-202 8606

WARNER, John Philip. b 59. Keble Coll Ox BA80 MA85. St Steph Ho Ox. **d** 83 **p** 84. C Brighton Resurr *Chich* 83-87; C Paddington St Mary *Lon* 87-90; V Teddington St Mark and Hampton Wick St Jo from 90. *The Vicarage, 23 St Mark's Road, Teddington, Middx TW11 9DE* 0181-977 4067

WARNER, Martin Clive. b 58. St Chad's Coll Dur BA80 MA85. St Steph Ho Ox. **d** 84 **p** 85. C Plymouth St Pet *Ex* 84-88; TV Leic Resurr *Leic* 88-93; Admin of Shrine of Our Lady of Walsingham from 93; Lic to Offic *Nor* from 92. *The College, Walsingham, Norfolk NR22 6EF* Fakenham (01328) 820266

WARNER, Dr Mary. b 52. Univ of Wales (Swansea) BSc73 Aber Univ PhD77. NE Ord Course 90. **d** 93 **p** 94. C Bensham *Dur* from 93. *The Vicarage, Lamesley, Gateshead, Tyne & Wear NE11 0EU* 0191-487 6490

WARNER, Michael John William. b 41. Sarum Th Coll 68. **d** 71 **p** 72. C Plympton St Mary *Ex* 71-75; V St Goran w St Mich

Caerhays *Truro* 75-78; V Bishops Tawton *Ex* 78-79; V Newport 78-79; Perm to Offic *Truro* 79-83; V St Stythians w Perranarworthal and Gwennap 83-93; P-in-c Budock from 93; Sec Dioc Adv Cttee from 93. *The Vicarage, School Lane, Budock Water, Falmouth, Cornwall TR11 5DJ*   Falmouth (01326) 372227   Fax 376955

WARNER, Nigel Bruce. b 51. ALCM67 St Jo Coll Cam BA72 DipTh73 MA76. Wycliffe Hall Ox 75. **d** 77 **p** 78. C Luton St Mary *St Alb* 77-80; Prec Dur Cathl *Dur* 80-84; R St Jo Lee *Newc* 84-91; V Lamesley *Dur* from 91. *The Vicarage, Lamesley, Gateshead, Tyne & Wear NE11 0EU*   0191-487 6490

WARNER, Canon Robert William. b 32. TCD BA54 MA65 BD65. TCD Div Sch Div Test56. **d** 56 **p** 57. C Wythenshawe St Martin CD *Man* 56-60; R Hulme St Steph w St Mark 60-66; R Droylsden St Mary 66-76; R Stand from 76; AD Radcliffe and Prestwich from 85; Hon Can Man Cathl from 87. *Stand Rectory, Church Lane, Whitefield, Manchester M25 7NF*   0161-766 2619

WARNER, Canon Samuel John. b 10. TCD BA34 MA50. **d** 34 **p** 35. I Laghey *D & R* 64-79; Can Raphoe Cathl 72-79; rtd 79. *Coolkelure, Laghey, Donegal, Irish Republic*   Laghey (73) 21808

WARNER, Terence. b 36. Local NSM Course. **d** 92 **p** 93. NSM Leek and Meerbrook *Lich* from 92. *5 School Close, Leek, Staffs ST13 8HS*   Leek (01538) 387336

WARNER, Dr Thomas Edward. b 06. TCD BA28 BD32 MA39 MLitt60 Lon Univ BD49 PhD54. **d** 30 **p** 30. C Rathkeale w Nantenan *L & K* 30-33; India 33-34; I Corbally *L & K* 34-36; Chapl Pannal Ash Coll 36-37; C Gt and Lt Driffield *York* 37-40; Chapl RAF 41-61; Chapl Wycliffe Coll Stonehouse Glos 61-75. *West End, Pearcroft Road, Stonehouse, Glos GL10 2JY*   Stonehouse (01453) 822065

WARNES, Brian Leslie Stephen. b 40. Natal Univ BSocSc76. Kelham Th Coll 59. **d** 67 **p** 68. C Tonge Moor *Man* 67-71; S Africa 71-87; V Blean *Cant* 87-94; New Zealand from 94. *St John's Vicarage, 47 George Street, Te Awamutu, New Zealand*   Te Awamutu (7) 871-4627

WARNES, Miss Marjorie. b 32. Leeds Inst of Educn CertEd53. St Jo Coll Nottm 85. **d** 87 **p** 94. C Leamington Priors St Mary *Cov* from 87. *78 Lewis Road, Radford Semele, Leamington Spa, Warks CV31 1UQ*   Leamington Spa (01926) 420811

WARNES, Warren Hugh. b 23. St Barn Coll Adelaide ThL49. **d** 50 **p** 50. V Kings Heath *Pet* 64-71; V Rockingham w Caldecote 71-73; V Gretton w Rockingham and Caldecote 73-83; V Marston St Lawrence w Warkworth and Thenford 83-89; rtd 89; Perm to Offic *Pet* from 89. *17 Thorpe Road, Earls Barton, Northampton NN6 0PJ*   Northampton (01604) 812935

WARR, Timothy Gerald (Tim). b 59. Trin Coll Bris BA86. **d** 88 **p** 89. C Yateley *Win* 88-91; C Chapel Allerton *Ripon* 91-93; V Wortley de Leeds from 93. *The Vicarage, Dixon Lane Road, Leeds LS12 4RU*   Leeds (0113) 263 8867

WARREN, Very Rev Alan Christopher. b 32. CCC Cam BA56 MA60. Ridley Hall Cam 56. **d** 57 **p** 58. V Leic H Apostles *Leic* 64-72; Hon Can Cov Cathl *Cov* 72-78; Dioc Missr 72-78; Provost Leic 78-92; rtd 92; Perm to Offic *Nor* from 92. *9 Queen's Drive, Hunstanton, Norfolk PE36 6EY*   Hunstanton (01485) 534533

WARREN, Canon Christopher Bruce. TCD BA58 MA61. **d** 62 **p** 63. C Waterford H Trin *C & O* 62-64; I Askeaton w Shanagolden and Loghill *L & K* 64-66; I Kilcolman 66-73; I Dub St Werburgh *D & G* 73-74; I Kilrossanty *C & O* 74-80; I Fenagh w Myshall, Aghade and Ardoyne 80-86; Preb Ossory Cathl 85-88; I Castlecomer w Colliery Ch, Mothel and Bilbo 86-88; Finland 88-94; I Omey w Ballynakill, Errislannan and Roundstone *T, K & A* from 94. *The Rectory, Church Hill, Clifden, Co Galway, Irish Republic*   Clifden (95) 21147

WARREN, Clifford Frederick. b 32. Univ of Wales (Lamp) BA53. St Mich Coll Llan 54. **d** 56 **p** 57. C Whitchurch *Llan* 56-68; Lic to Offic 68-70; C Llanedeyrn *Mon* 70-76; R Machen from 76. *The Rectory, Machen, Newport, Gwent NP1 8SA*   Machen (01633) 440321

WARREN, David. b 39. S'wark Ord Course. **d** 87 **p** 88. NSM Mottingham St Andr *S'wark* from 87. *26 Longcroft, London SE9 3BQ*   0181-851 4824

WARREN, Desmond Benjamin Moore. b 22. TCD BA44 MA49. Bps' Coll Cheshunt 46. **d** 48 **p** 49. R Sandy *St Alb* 63-78; P-in-c Gt Munden 78-79; P-in-c Westmill 78-79; R Westmill w Gt Munden 79-84; rtd 84; Lic to Offic (Lismore) *C & O* 84-90; Lic to Offic *C, C & R* from 91. *Dysert, Ardmore, Youghal, Co Cork, Irish Republic*   Youghal (24) 94110

WARREN, Eric Anthony. b 28. MBE. Ex & Truro NSM Scheme. **d** 83 **p** 84. NSM Chudleigh *Ex* 83-88; Perm to Offic from 88. *Lower Radway House, Bishopsteignton, Teignmouth, Devon TQ14 9SS*   Teignmouth (01626) 772135 or 779277

WARREN, Ernest Bruce. b 24. K Coll Lon BD54 AKC54. **d** 54 **p** 55. V Lostwithiel *Truro* 67-77; V Perranzabuloe 77-89; rtd

WARREN, Canon Frederick Noel. b 30. TCD BA52 MA58 BD66 QUB PhD72. **d** 53 **p** 54. C Belf St Matt *Conn* 53-56; C Belf St Geo 56-59; I Castlewellan *D & D* 59-65; I Clonallon w Warrenpoint 65-69; I Newc 69-87; Can Belf Cathl 73-76; Preb Wicklow St Patr Cathl Dub 76-88; I Dunfanaghy, Raymunterdoney and Tullaghbegley *D & R* from 87; Preb Swords St Patr Cathl Dub from 89. *The Rectory, Dunfanaghy, Letterkenny, Co Donegal, Irish Republic*   Letterkenny (74) 36187

WARREN, Geoffrey Richard. b 44. Middx Poly MA91. Bps' Coll Cheshunt 66 Qu Coll Birm 68. **d** 69 **p** 70. C Waltham Cross *St Alb* 69-73; C Radlett 73-78; C Tring 78-80; TV Tring 80-95; V Watford St Andr from 95. *St Andrew's Vicarage, 18 Park Road, Watford WD1 3QN*   Watford (01923) 224858

WARREN, Mrs Gillian (Jill). b 53. Sheff Univ BA74 PGCE75. W Midl Minl Tr Course 89. **d** 92 **p** 94. Par Dn Tettenhall Regis *Lich* 92-94; C 94-95; TV Bilston from 95. *43 Willenhall Road, Bilston, W Midlands WV14 6NW*   Bilston (01902) 490255

WARREN, Gordon Lenham (Bunny). b 45. Wycliffe Hall Ox DipMin93. **d** 93 **p** 94. C Sunbury *Lon* from 93. *22 Sunmead Road, Sunbury-on-Thames, Middx TW16 6PE*   Sunbury-on-Thames (01932) 772882

WARREN, Preb Henry Fiennes. b 21. Keble Coll Ox BA42 MA47. Cuddesdon Coll 42. **d** 48 **p** 49. R Exford *B & W* 53-75; RD Wiveliscombe 65-73; Preb Wells Cathl from 73; R W Monkton 75-86; rtd 86. *6 Brookside, Broadway, Ilminster, Somerset TA19 9RT*   Ilminster (01460) 57922

WARREN, James Randolph. b 54. St Paul's Cheltenham CertEd75 Bris Univ BEd76 Birm Univ MEd84. Ridley Hall Cam CTM92. **d** 92 **p** 93. C Boldmere *Birm* from 92. *St Michael's House, 46 Redacre Road, Sutton Coldfield, W Midlands B73 5AE*   0121-354 8432

WARREN, Malcolm Clive. b 46. St D Coll Lamp DipTh74. **d** 74 **p** 75. C Newport St Andr *Mon* 74-78; C Risca 78-79; V St Hilary Greenway 79-84; TV Grantham *Linc* 84-90; Ind Chapl 87-90; Ind Chapl *Worc* from 90; P-in-c Dudley Holly Hall St Aug from 95. *St Augustine's Vicarage, 1 Hallchurch Road, Dudley, W Midlands DY2 0TG*   Brierley Hill (01384) 261026

WARREN, Martin John. b 59. Ch Coll Cam BA81 MA85 LTh DPS. St Jo Coll Nottm 83. **d** 86 **p** 87. C Littleover *Derby* 86-90; C Hermitage and Hampstead Norreys, Cold Ash etc *Ox* 90-91; TV from 91. *The Rectory, Yattendon, Newbury, Berks RG16 0UR*   Newbury (01635) 201213

WARREN, Michael John. b 40. Kelham Th Coll 59. **d** 64 **p** 65. C Withington *Man* 64-67; C Worsley 67-69; C Witney *Ox* 69-72; V S Hinksey 72-80; Canada from 80. *Box 1117, Fort McLeod, Alberta, Canada, T0L 0Z0*

WARREN, Michael Philip. b 62. Nottm Univ DipPhys87. Oak Hill Th Coll BA91. **d** 94 **p** 95. C Tunbridge Wells St Jo *Roch* from 94. *112 Stephens Road, Tunbridge Wells, Kent TN4 9QA*   Tunbridge Wells (01892) 521767

WARREN, Ven Norman Leonard. b 34. CCC Cam BA58 MA62. Ridley Hall Cam 58. **d** 60 **p** 61. C Bedworth *Cov* 60-63; V Leamington Priors St Paul 63-77; R Morden *S'wark* 77-88; TR 88-89; RD Merton 86-89; Adn Roch from 89; Can Res Roch Cathl from 89. *The Archdeaconry, Rochester, Kent ME1 1SX*   Medway (01634) 842527

WARREN, Canon Paul Kenneth. b 41. Selw Coll Cam BA63 MA67. Cuddesdon Coll 64. **d** 67 **p** 68. C Lanc St Mary *Blackb* 67-70; Chapl Lanc Univ 70-78; V Langho Billington 78-83; Bp's Dom Chapl 83-88; Chapl Whalley Abbey 83-88; R Standish from 88; Hon Can Blackb Cathl from 91; RD Chorley from 92. *The Rectory, 13 Rectory Lane, Standish, Wigan, Lancs WN6 0XA*   Standish (01257) 421396

WARREN, Peter. b 40. FCA64. Oak Hill Th Coll 77. **d** 79 **p** 80. C Newc w Butterton *Lich* 79-82; TV Sutton St Jas and Wawne *York* 82-87; V Ledsham w Fairburn from 87. *The Vicarage, 11 Main Street, Ledston, Castleford, W Yorkshire WF10 2AA*   Castleford (01977) 556946

WARREN, Peter John. b 55. CertEd76 BA86. Trin Coll Bris 83. **d** 86 **p** 87. C W Streatham St Jas *S'wark* 86-91; P-in-c Edin Clermiston Em *Edin* from 91. *127 Clermiston Road, Edinburgh EH12 6UR*   0131-316 4706

WARREN, Canon Robert. b 54. TCD BA78 MA81. CITC 76. **d** 78 **p** 79. C Limerick City *L & K* 78-81; Dioc Youth Adv (Limerick) 79-86; I Adare w Kilpeacon and Croom 81-88; Bp's Dom Chapl 81-95; Dioc Registrar (Limerick etc) from 81; Dioc Registrar (Killaloe etc) from 86; I Tralee w Ballymacelligott, Kilnaughtin etc from 88; RD Tralee from 89; Can Limerick, Killaloe and Clonfert Cathls from 95. *St John's Rectory, Ashe Street, Tralee, Co Kerry, Irish Republic*   Tralee (66) 22245   Fax 29004

WARREN, Robert Geoffrey. b 51. DipHE. Trin Coll Bris 79. **d** 82 **p** 83. C Felixstowe SS Pet and Paul *St E* 82-86; V Gazeley w Dalham, Moulton and Kentford 86-90; P-in-c Ipswich St Clem w St Luke and H Trin from 90. *42 Clapgate Lane, Ipswich IP3 0RD* Ipswich (01473) 723467

WARREN, Robert Irving. b 38. Univ of BC BA58 Ox Univ MA73. Angl Th Coll (BC) LTh61. **d** 61 **p** 63. Canada 61-89; R Northfield *Birm* from 89. *The Rectory, Rectory Road, Birmingham B31 2NA* 0121-477 3111 or 475 1518

WARREN, Canon Robert Peter Resker. b 39. Jes Coll Cam BA63 MA. ALCD65. **d** 65 **p** 66. C Rusholme *Man* 65-68; C Bushbury *Lich* 68-71; V Crookes St Thos *Sheff* 71-90; TR 90-93; RD Hallam 78-83; Hon Can Sheff Cathl 82-93; Can Th Sheff Cathl from 93; Nat Officer for Evang from 93. *9 Healey Wood Gardens, Brighouse, W Yorkshire HD6 3SQ* Brighouse (01484) 710920

WARREN, William Frederick. b 55. Sarum & Wells Th Coll 83. **d** 86 **p** 87. C E Greenwich Ch Ch w St Andr and St Mich *S'wark* 86-91; C Richmond St Mary w St Matthias and St Jo from 91. *22A Cambrian Road, Richmond, Surrey TW10 6JQ* 0181-948 7217

WARRICK, Mark. b 54. Aston Univ BSc76 Nottm Univ BCombStuds83. Linc Th Coll 80. **d** 83 **p** 84. C Grantham *Linc* 83-87; C Cirencester *Glouc* 87-91; V Over *Ely* from 91. *The Vicarage, Over, Cambridge CB4 5NX* Swavesey (01954) 30329

WARRILLOW, Brian Ellis. b 39. Linc Th Coll 81. **d** 83 **p** 84. C Tunstall Ch Ch *Lich* 83; C Tunstall 83-85; C Shrewsbury H Cross 86-87; P-in-c Tilstock 88; P-in-c Whixall 88; V Tilstock and Whixall 89-92; TV Hanley H Ev 92-94; rtd 94. *19 Widecombe Road, Stoke-on-Trent ST1 6SL* Stoke-on-Trent (01782) 267243

WARRILOW, Mrs Christine. b 42. Lanc Univ BA86. N Ord Course 86. **d** 89 **p** 94. C Netherton *Liv* 89-92; C Cantril Farm 92-94; V from 94. *St Jude's Vicarage, 168 Round Hey, Liverpool L28 1RQ* 0151-220 4524

WARRINER, Leonard. b 15. Ox NSM Course. **d** 79 **p** 80. NSM Chalfont St Peter *Ox* from 79. *Briar Rose, Winkers Lane, Chalfont St Peter, Gerrards Cross, Bucks SL9 0AJ* Gerrards Cross (01753) 884443

WARRINGTON, Gwynfa Lewis Jones. b 44. St D Coll Lamp 64. **d** 67 **p** 68. C Gorseinon *S & B* 67-70; C Pemb Dock St D 70-74; V Rosemarket and Freystrop 74-78; R Llangwm and Freystrop 78-79; V Ystradfellte *S & B* 79-84; V Abercynon *Llan* 84-87; V Beguildy and Heyope *S & B* from 87. *The Vicarage, Beguildy, Knighton, Powys LD7 1YE* Beguildy (015477) 252

WARRINGTON, Katherine Irene. **d** 95. NSM Knighton and Norton *S & B* from 95. *The Vicarage, Knighton, Powys LD7 1AG*

WARRINGTON, Archdeacon of. See WOODHOUSE, Ven Charles David Stewart

WARRINGTON, Suffragan Bishop of. See HENSHALL, Rt Rev Michael

WARWICK, Gordon Melvin. b 31. N Ord Course 79. **d** 80 **p** 81. NSM Darrington w Wentbridge *Wakef* 80-87; TV Almondbury w Farnley Tyas 87-95; rtd 95. *Andante, Christon Bank, Alnwick, Northd NE66 3EZ* Alnwick (01665) 576742

WARWICK, Canon John Michael. b 37. Fitzw Ho Cam BA58 MA62. Ely Th Coll 58. **d** 60 **p** 61. C Towcester w Easton Neston *Pet* 60-63; C Leighton Buzzard *St Alb* 63-64; C Boston *Linc* 64-66; P-in-c Sutterton 66-72; V 72-74; V Sutton St Mary 74-84; V Bourne from 84; Chapl Bourne Hosps Lincs from 84; Hon Can Linc Cathl *Linc* from 89; RD Aveland and Ness w Stamford from 93. *The Vicarage, Bourne, Lincs PE10 9LX* Bourne (01778) 422412

WARWICK, Archdeacon of. See PAGET-WILKES, Ven Michael Jocelyn James

WARWICK, Suffragan Bishop of. See HANDFORD, Rt Rev George Clive

WASH, John. **d** 81 **p** 83. Hon C Newington St Mary *S'wark* from 81. *15 Canterbury Place, London SE17 3AD* 0171-582 9280

WASHINGTON, Patrick Leonard. b 44. Nottm Univ BSc66. St Steph Ho Ox 65. **d** 68 **p** 69. C Fleet *Guildf* 68-71; C Farnham 71-74; TV Staveley and Barrow Hill *Derby* 74-83; V Norbury St Phil *Cant* 83-84; V Norbury St Phil *S'wark* from 85; RD Croydon N from 90. *St Philip's Vicarage, 66 Pollards Hill North, London SW16 4NY* 0181-764 1812

WASSALL, Keith Leonard. b 45. Bede Coll Dur TCert67. Chich Th Coll 68. **d** 71 **p** 72. C Upper Gornal *Lich* 71-74; C Codsall 74-75; C Shelton 75-76; TV Hanley All SS 76-79; Bermuda 79-81; V Rickerscote *Lich* 81-92; P-in-c Coven from 92; Asst Chapl HM Pris Featherstone from 92. *St Paul's New Vicarage, Church Lane, Coven, Wolverhampton WV9 5DD* Standeford (01902) 790230 or 790991

WASSELL, Miss Leonora Jane. b 55. La Sainte Union Coll CertEd76. N Ord Course 91. **d** 94 **p** 95. NSM High Harrogate St Pet *Ripon* from 94. *7 Rydal Road, Harrogate, N Yorkshire HG1 4SQ* Harrogate (01423) 886570

WASTELL, Canon Eric Morse. b 33. St Mich Coll Llan DipTh62. **d** 62 **p** 63. C Oystermouth *S & B* 62-65; Antigua 65-74; Hon Can Antigua 71-74; V Swansea St Gabr *S & B* from 74; RD Clyne from 88; Can Brecon Cathl from 90. *St Gabriel's Vicarage, Bryn Road, Brynmill, Swansea SA2 0AP* Swansea (01792) 464011

WASTIE, Canon David Vernon. b 37. BA84. Chich Th Coll 79. **d** 81 **p** 82. C Bitterne Park *Win* 81-83; TV Chambersbury (Hemel Hempstead) *St Alb* 83-87; V Jersey St Luke *Win* from 87; P-in-c Jersey St Jas 87-93; V from 93. *The Vicarage, Longueville Farm, Longueville Road, St Saviour, Jersey, Channel Islands JE2 7SA* Jersey (01534) 81445 or 33957 Fax 89442

WATCHORN, Canon Brian. b 39. Em Coll Cam BA61 MA65 Ex Coll Ox BA62. Ripon Hall Ox 61. **d** 63 **p** 64. C Bolton St Pet *Man* 63-66; Chapl G&C Coll Cam 66-74; V Chesterton St Geo *Ely* 75-82; Fell Dean and Chapl Pemb Coll Cam from 82; Lic to Offic *Ely* from 82; Hon Can Ely Cathl from 94. *Pembroke College, Cambridge CB2 1RF* Cambridge (01223) 338100

WATERER, Anthony Tatham. b 14. ARCA38. Cuddesdon Coll 45. **d** 47 **p** 48. V Staveley w Copgrove *Ripon* 53-72; R Rawreth w Rettendon *Chelmsf* 73-82; rtd 82; Perm to Offic *Chich* from 83. *3 Stafford Way, Hassocks, W Sussex BN6 8QG* Hassocks (01273) 844341

WATERFORD, Dean of. See NEILL, Very Rev William Benjamin Alan

WATERHOUSE, Eric Thomas Benjamin. b 24. Lon Univ DipTh60. Qu Coll Birm 50. **d** 51 **p** 52. R Worc St Clem *Worc* 64-77; P-in-c Abberton, Naunton Beauchamp and Bishampton etc 77-80; R 80-92; rtd 92. *7 Hazel Avenue, Evesham, Worcs WR11 6XT* Evesham (01386) 421312

WATERHOUSE, Peter. b 46. Leeds Univ DipTh68. Linc Th Coll 68. **d** 70 **p** 71. C Consett *Dur* 70-73; C Heworth St Mary 73-76; V Stockton St Chad 76-83; V Lanchester from 83; RD Lanchester from 90. *The Vicarage, 1 Lee Hill Court, Lanchester, Durham DH7 0QE* Lanchester (01207) 521170

WATERMAN, Albert Thomas. b 33. Roch Th Coll 61. **d** 64 **p** 65. C Dartford St Alb *Roch* 64-67; V from 79; V Ilkeston St Jo *Derby* 67-75; V Mackworth St Fran 75-79; RD Dartford *Roch* from 84. *St Alban's Vicarage, 51 Watling Street, Dartford DA1 1RW* Dartford (01322) 224052

WATERMAN, Mrs Jacqueline Mahalah. b 45. ALCM71. Cant Sch of Min 82. **dss** 85 **d** 87 **p** 94. Wavertree H Trin *Liv* 85-87; Par Dn 87-90; Par Dn Anfield St Columba 90-94; C 94; TV Speke St Aid from 94. *All Saints Vicarage, Speke Church Road, Speke, Liverpool L24 3TA* 0151-486 2922

WATERS, Arthur Brian. b 34. St Deiniol's Hawarden 71. **d** 73 **p** 74. C Pembroke *Mon* 73-76; P-in-c Newport All SS 76-81; V Mynyddislwyn 81-91; C-in-c Maesglas Newport CD 91-95; I Maesglas and Duffryn from 95. *The Vicarage, Old Cardiff Road, Newport, Gwent NP9 3AT*

WATERS, Charles Eric. b 14. Hatf Coll Dur LTh37 BA38. St Aug Coll Cant 34. **d** 38 **p** 39. R Bromham *Sarum* 62-79; V Chittoe 73-79; rtd 79. *3 St Mary's Court, Silver Street, Bridgwater, Somerset TA6 3EG* Bridgwater (01278) 453675

WATERS, David Keith. b 46. S Wales Bapt Coll DipTh73 DPS73 St Mich Coll Llan 83. **d** 93 **p** 94. In Bapt Ch 73-90; C Caerphilly *Llan* from 93. *St Andrew's House, Troed-y-Bryn, Penyrheol, Caerphilly, M Glam CF8 2PX* Caerphilly (01222) 884103

WATERS, Miss Jill Christine. b 43. CertEd64. Cranmer Hall Dur 82. **dss** 82 **d** 87 **p** 94. New Milverton *Cov* 82-86; Draycott-le-Moors w Forsbrook *Lich* 86-87; Par Dn 87-94; C from 94. *366 Uttoxeter Road, Blythe Bridge, Stoke-on-Trent ST11 9LY* Blythe Bridge (01782) 392707

WATERS, John Michael. b 30. Qu Coll Cam BA53 MA58. Ridley Hall Cam 53. **d** 55 **p** 56. V Blackb H Trin *Blackb* 63-70; Sec Birm Coun Chr Chs 70-77; Chapl Birm Cathl *Birm* 70-74; Dioc Ecum Officer 74-77; V Hednesford *Lich* 77-93; RD Rugeley 78-88; rtd 93; NSM Etton w Dalton Holme *York* from 93. *The Rectory, Etton, Beverley, N Humberside HU17 7PQ* Market Weighton (01430) 810735

WATERS, Mark. b 51. Sarum & Wells Th Coll. **d** 82 **p** 83. C Clifton All SS w St Jo *Bris* 82-85; P-in-c Brislington St Anne 85-91; Dioc Soc Resp Officer *Sheff* 91-94; Community Org Citizen Organisation Foundn from 94; NSM Rotherham from 94. *9 The Copse, Bramley, Rotherham, S Yorkshire S66 0TB* Rotherham (01709) 548967

WATERS, Nicholas Marshall Stephenson. b 35. Selw Coll Cam BA59 MA63. Wells Th Coll 59. **d** 61 **p** 62. C Eastbourne St Mary *Chich* 61-64; Asst Chapl Ardingly Coll Haywards Heath 64-93; P-in-c Slindon, Eartham and Madehurst *Chich* from 94. *The Rectory, Dyers Lane, Slindon, Arundel, W Sussex BN18 0RE* Slindon (01243) 814275

WATERS, Stephen. b 49. Chich Th Coll 83. **d** 85 **p** 86. C Baildon *Bradf* 85-87; C Altrincham St Geo *Ches* 87-89; TV Ellesmere

Port 89-91; P-in-c Crewe St Jo 91-93; V Mossley from 93. *The Vicarage, 79 Leek Road, Congleton, Cheshire CW12 3HX* Congleton (01260) 273182

WATERS, William Paul. b 52. Aston Tr Scheme 84 Chich Th Coll 86. **d** 88 **p** 89. C Tottenham St Paul *Lon* 88-91; C Stroud Green H Trin from 91. *30 Tregaron Avenue, London N8 9EY* 0181-348 1109

WATERSON, John Hayden Lionel. b 13. K Coll Cam BA35 MA39. Cuddesdon Coll 35. **d** 36 **p** 37. R Stoke D'Abernon *Guildf* 49-83; rtd 83. *Duck End, The Street, Corpusty, Norwich NR11 6QP* Saxthorpe (0126387) 703

WATERSON, Raymond Arthur. b 25. Wells Th Coll 69. **d** 70 **p** 71. C Wotton St Mary *Glouc* 70-74; C Cirencester 74-79; P-in-c Falfield w Rockhampton 79-90; P-in-c Oldbury-on-Severn 85-90; rtd 90. *91 Brampton Way, Portishead, Bristol BS20 9YT* Bristol (0117) 984 5134

WATERSTONE, Canon Albert Thomas. b 23. TCD BA45 BD67. CITC 46. **d** 46 **p** 47. I Tullamore w Lynally and Rahan *M & K* 64-73; I Tullamore w Durrow, Newtownfertullagh, Rahan etc 73-90; Can Meath 81-90; rtd 90. *Lynally House, Mocklagh, Blue Ball, Tullamore, Co Offaly, Irish Republic* Tullamore (506) 21367

WATERSTREET, Canon John Donald. b 34. Trin Hall Cam BA58 MA62. Lich Th Coll 58. **d** 60 **p** 61. C Blackheath *Birm* 60-64; C Aston SS Pet and Paul 64-67; R Sheldon 67-77; RD Coleshill 75-77; V Selly Oak St Mary 77-89; RD Edgbaston 84-89; Hon Can Birm Cathl from 86; R The Whitacres and Shustoke from 89. *The Rectory, Dog Lane, Coleshill, Birmingham B46 2DU* Furnace End (01675) 481252

WATHEN, Mark William Gerard. b 12. TD45. ACIB. K Coll Lon 31. **d** 82 **p** 82. Hon C Broadford *Arg* 82-91; Hon C Fort William 82-91; Hon C Portree 82-92; rtd 92. *Talisker House, Carbost, Isle of Skye IV47 8SF* Carbost (01478) 640245

WATHEN, Sydney Gordon. Open Univ BA. E Midl Min Tr Course. **d** 86 **p** 87. NSM W Hallam and Mapperley *Derby* from 86. *40 Station Road, West Hallam, Ilkeston, Derbyshire DE7 6GW* Nottingham (0115) 932 9255

WATHERSTON, Peter David. b 42. FCA76 Lon Univ BSc69. Ridley Hall Cam 75. **d** 77 **p** 78. C Barnsbury St Andr *Lon* 77-78; C Barnsbury St Andr w H Trin 79-80; C Barnsbury St Andr and H Trin w All SS 81; Chapl Mayflower Family Cen Canning Town *Chelmsf* from 81. *Mayflower Family Centre, Vincent Street, London E16 1LZ* 0171-476 9890

WATKIN, David William. b 42. FCA70. Qu Coll Birm 84. **d** 86 **p** 87. C Tunstall *Lich* 86-89; Camberwell Deanery Missr *S'wark* 89-95; V Trent Vale *Lich* from 95. *The Vicarage, Crosby Road, Stoke-on-Trent ST4 6JY* Stoke-on-Trent (01782) 747669

WATKIN, Stephen Roy. b 23. DFC. BSc. Worc Ord Coll 66. **d** 68 **p** 69. C Sutton St Geo *Ches* 68-73; V Aston by Sutton 73-76; P-in-c Eaton and Hulme Walfield 76-77; V 77-80; P-in-c Ipstones *Lich* 80-83; P-in-c Onecote cum Bradnop 80-83; V Ipstones w Berkhamsytch and Onecote w Bradnop 83-87; rtd 87. *2 Hawthorne Close, Tean, Stoke-on-Trent ST10 4NL* Tean (01538) 723475

WATKIN, Thomas Glyn. b 52. Barrister-at-Law (Middle Temple) 76 Pemb Coll Ox BA74 BCL75 MA77. Llan Dioc Tr Scheme 89. **d** 92 **p** 94. NSM Roath St Martin *Llan* from 92. *49 Cyncoed Road, Penylan, Cardiff CF2 6AB* Cardiff (01222) 495662

WATKINS, Alfred Felix Maceroni. b 20. Glouc Th Course 70. **d** 72 **p** 73. C Yate *Glouc* 72-75; V Dean Forest St Paul 75-90; rtd 90. *Leylines, 26 Southbank Road, Hereford HR1 2TJ* Hereford (01432) 341014

WATKINS, Anthony John. b 42. St D Coll Lamp BA64 St Steph Ho Ox 64. **d** 66 **p** 67. C E Dulwich St Jo *S'wark* 66-71; C Tewkesbury w Walton Cardiff *Glouc* 71-75; Prec 75-81; Chapl Choral Ches Cathl *Ches* 75-81; V Brixworth w Holcot *Pet* from 81. *The Vicarage, Station Road, Brixworth, Northampton NN6 9DF* Northampton (01604) 880286

WATKINS, Christopher. b 43. Sarum & Wells Th Coll 88. **d** 90 **p** 91. C Abergavenny St Mary w Llanwenarth Citra *Mon* 90-94; TV Cwmbran from 94. *St Mary's Vicarage, 87 Bryn Eglwys, Croesceiliog, Cwmbran, Gwent NP44 2LF* Cwmbran (01633) 483425

WATKINS, David James Hier. b 39. Trin Coll Carmarthen CertEd60 Univ of Wales DipEd67 BEd76. **d** 90 **p** 91. NSM Oystermouth *S & B* from 90. *10 Lambswell Close, Langland, Swansea SA3 4HJ* Swansea (01792) 369742

WATKINS, Gordon Derek. b 29. **d** 53 **p** 54. V Gt and Lt Bentley *Chelmsf* 67-73; R Gt Canfield 73-78; Dioc Past Sec *Lon* 78-84; Sec Dioc Adv Cttee 84-94; PV Westmr Abbey 84-89; P-in-c St Martin Ludgate *Lon* 84-89; P in O 84-94; rtd 94. *6 Orchard Ground, Fifield, Chipping Norton, Oxon OX7 6HG* Shipton-under-W'wood (01993) 831473

WATKINS, Mrs Gwyneth. b 35. Univ of Wales (Swansea) BA MEd. St Mich Coll Llan. **d** 91. NSM Llanbadarn Fawr w Capel Bangor and Goginan *St D* 91-94; P-in-c Maenordeifi

and Capel Colman w Llanfihangel etc from 94. *The Rectory, Manordeifi, Cardigan, Dyfed SA43 2PN* Llechryd (01239) 682568

WATKINS, Herbert Ernest. b 22. Clifton Th Coll 39 Oak Hill Th Coll 43. **d** 46 **p** 47. V Rodbourne Cheney *Bris* 58-73; V Bilton St Helen *York* 73-77; V Tockwith 73-77; V Hurdsfield *Ches* 77-82; V Pott Shrigley 82-87; rtd 87; Perm to Offic *Cov* 87-88; Chapl to the Deaf *Bradf* from 88. *41 Hawkcliffe View, Silsden, Keighley, W Yorkshire BD20 0BS* Steeton (01535) 656284

WATKINS, Jonathan. b 58. Padgate Coll of Educn BEd79. Trin Coll Bris DipHE92. **d** 92 **p** 93. C Wallington H Trin *S'wark* from 92. *14 Harcourt Field, Wallington, Surrey SM6 8BA* 0181-647 0132

WATKINS, Miss Lorna Ann Frances Charles. b 59. Trin Coll Carmarthen BEd82. St Steph Ho Ox 82. **d** 84. C Tenby and Gumfreston *St D* 84-89; C Pemb Dock 89-91; D-in-c Cosheston w Nash and Upton 91-92; C Bassaleg *Mon* 92-94; C Mynyddislwyn 94-95; TV Mynyddislwyn from 95. *Church House, 12 Orchard Court, Pontllanfraith, Blackwood, Gwent NP2 2NG* Blackwood (01495) 221409

WATKINS, Dr Michael Morris. b 32. MRCS60 LRCP60. St Jo Coll Nottm DPS78. **d** 81 **p** 81. C Hornchurch St Andr *Chelmsf* 81-84; P-in-c Snitterfield w Bearley *Cov* 84-90; V 90-92; rtd 93; Perm to Offic *Cov* from 93. *Orchard Cottage, Church Road, Snitterfield, Stratford-upon-Avon, Warks CV37 0LW* Stratford-upon-Avon (01789) 731538

WATKINS, Peter. b 51. Oak Hill Th Coll BA. **d** 82 **p** 83. C Whitnash *Cov* 82-86; V Wolston and Church Lawford from 86; RD Rugby from 94. *The Vicarage, Brook Street, Wolston, Coventry CV8 3HD* Coventry (01203) 542722

WATKINS, Peter Gordon. b 34. St Pet Coll Ox BA57 MA61. Wycliffe Hall Ox 58. **d** 59 **p** 60. C Wolv St Geo *Lich* 59-60; C Burton St Chad 60-61; C Westmr St Jas *Lon* 61-63; USA 63-65; V Ealing Common St Matt *Lon* from 65. *St Matthew's Vicarage, 7 North Common Road, London W5 2QA* 0181-567 3820

WATKINS, Robert Henry. b 30. New Coll Ox BA54 MA60. Westcott Ho Cam 59. **d** 60 **p** 61. V Delaval *Newc* 67-80; V Lanercost w Kirkcambeck and Walton *Carl* 80-90; rtd 90. *Lowpark, Loweswater, Cockermouth, Cumbria CA13 0RU* Lorton (01900) 85242

WATKINS, Walter. b 27. St Deiniol's Hawarden 80. **d** 81 **p** 82. C Lache cum Saltney *Ches* 81-84; P-in-c Over Tabley and High Legh 84-93; rtd 93. *30 St Matthew's Drive, Derrington, Stafford ST18 9LU* Stafford (01785) 46349

WATKINS, Canon William Hywel. b 36. St D Coll Lamp BA58. Wycliffe Hall Ox 58. **d** 61 **p** 62. C Llanelli *St D* 61-68; V Llwynhendy 68-78; V Slebech and Uzmaston w Boulston from 78; Asst Chapl OStJ 82-87; Sub-Chapl from 87; RD Daugleddau *St D* from 87; Hon Can *St D* Cathl from 91. *The Vicarage, Uzmaston, Haverfordwest, Dyfed SA62 4AE* Haverfordwest (01437) 762325

WATKINS-JONES, Arthur Basil. b 24. Sarum Th Coll 67. **d** 69 **p** 70. C Broadstone *Sarum* 69-73; P-in-c Winterbourne Stickland and Turnworth etc 73-76; R 76-78; P-in-c Lilliput 78-82; V 82-89; rtd 89. *Oak Cottage, 31 Danecourt Road, Poole, Dorset BH14 0PG* Parkstone (01202) 746074

WATKINS-WRIGHT, Richard Kenneth David. b 39. Westcott Ho Cam 66. **d** 70 **p** 71. C Bilton *Cov* 70-74; Asst Chapl St Geo Hosp Lon 74-75; Chapl Oakwood Hosp Maidstone 76-78; R Gt w Lt Gransden *Ely* from 78. *The Vicarage, Webb's Meadow, Great Gransden, Sandy, Beds SG19 3BL* Great Gransden (01767) 677227

WATLING, Arthur Edward. b 28. St Chad's Coll Dur BA57. Linc Th Coll 57. **d** 59 **p** 60. V Eastwood *Sheff* 64-88; R Easington w Skeffling, Kilnsea and Holmpton *York* 88-93; rtd 93. *23 Chestnut Avenue, Withernsea, N Humberside HU19 2PG* Withernsea (01964) 613571

WATLING, His Honour Judge David Brian. b 35. QC79. Barrister-at-Law (Middle Temple) 57 K Coll Lon LLB56 LLM90. E Anglian Minl Tr Course 84. **d** 87 **p** 88. Hon C Lavenham *St E* 87-90; Hon C Nayland w Wiston from 90. *The Manse, Bear Street, Nayland, Colchester CO6 4HK* Nayland (01206) 263494

WATLING, Sister Rosemary Dawn. b 32. Newnham Coll Cam BA70 MA73. Gilmore Course 70. dss 85 **d** 87 **p** 94. CSA 79-90; Paddington St Mary *Lon* 85-86; E Bris 86-87; Hon Par Dn 87; Par Dn Clifton H Trin, St Andr and St Pet 87-94; C 94-95; rtd 95. *St Leonard's Vicarage, Parkfield Avenue, Bristol BS5 8DP* Bristol (0117) 955 6286

WATSON, Canon Alan. b 34. Lon Univ LLB58. Linc Th Coll 58. **d** 60 **p** 61. C Spring Park *Cant* 60-63; C Sheerness H Trin w St Paul 63-68; R Allington 68-73; P-in-c Maidstone St Pet 73; R Allington and Maidstone St Pet from 73; Hon Can Cant Cathl from 85; RD Sutton 86-92. *The Rectory, 35 Poplar Grove, Allington, Maidstone, Kent ME16 0DE* Maidstone (01622) 758704

WATSON, Albert Victor. b 44. Ridley Hall Cam 85. **d** 87 **p** 88. C Hornchurch St Andr *Chelmsf* 87-94; P-in-c Tye Green w Netteswell from 94. *The Rectory, Tawneys Road, Harlow, Essex CM18 6QR* Harlow (01279) 425138

WATSON, Andrew John. b 61. CCC Cam BA82 MA90. Ridley Hall Cam 84. **d** 87 **p** 88. C Ipsley *Worc* 87-91; C Notting Hill St Jo and St Pet *Lon* from 91. *48 Ladbroke Road, London W11 3NW* 0171-229 7275

WATSON, Basil Alderson. b 16. OBE65. Selw Coll Cam BA38 MA44. Westcott Ho Cam 39. **d** 40 **p** 41. Chapl RN 46-70; V St Lawr Jewry *Lon* 70-86; RD The City 76-79; rtd 86. *19 Straightsmouth, London SE10 9LB* 0181-853 0643

WATSON, Canon Cecil Henry Barrett. b 14. Jes Coll Ox BA35 MA39. Bps' Coll Cheshunt 35. **d** 37 **p** 38. RD Gedling *S'well* 58-85; R Gedling 58-85; Hon Can S'well Minster 61-85; rtd 85; Perm to Offic *S'well* from 85. *65 Lambley Lane, Burton Joyce, Nottingham NG14 5BL* Nottingham (0115) 931 2490

WATSON, Derek Richard. b 38. Selw Coll Cam BA61 MA65. Cuddesdon Coll 62. **d** 64 **p** 65. C New Eltham All SS *S'wark* 64-66; Chapl Ch Coll Cam 66-70; Bp's Dom Chapl *S'wark* 70-73; V Surbiton St Mark 73-77; V Surbiton St Andr and St Mark 77-78; Can Res and Treas S'wark Cathl 78-82; Dioc Dir of Ords 78-82; P-in-c Chelsea St Luke *Lon* 82-85; R 85-87; P-in-c Chelsea Ch 86-87; R Chelsea St Luke and Ch Ch from 87; AD Chelsea from 94. *The Rectory, 64A Flood Street, London SW3 5TE* 0171-352 6331 or 351 7365

WATSON, Derek Stanley. b 54. NE Ord Course DipHE95. **d** 95. C W Acklam *York* from 95. *41 Ambleside Grove, Middlesborough, Cleveland TS5 7DQ* Middlesborough (01642) 816997

WATSON, Mrs Diane Elsie. b 44. **d** 95. C Grange St Andr *Ches* from 95. *8 Fenwick Lane, Runcorn, Cheshire WA7 5YY* Runcorn (01928) 576661

WATSON, Preb Donald Wace. b 17. Qu Coll Cam BA39 MA43. Lich Th Coll 39. **d** 41 **p** 42. V Kinver *Lich* 55-82; Preb Lich Cathl 78-82; rtd 82. *Criddon Cottage, Upton Cressett, Bridgnorth, Shropshire WV16 6UJ* Middleton Scriven (0174635) 661

WATSON, Douglas John Muirhead. b 29. Keble Coll Ox BA52 MA56 DipEd. Ely Th Coll 58. **d** 60 **p** 61. V W Wickham St Fran *Cant* 66-72; V Headcorn 72-94; rtd 94; Perm to Offic *Cant* from 95. *4 Hastings Place, Sandwich, Kent CT2 0RE* Sandwich (01304) 614841

WATSON, Edward John. b 48. Chu Coll Cam BA70 MA74. Chich Th Coll 79. **d** 81 **p** 82. C Liv Our Lady and St Nic w St Anne *Liv* 81-84; C Clayton w Keymer *Chich* 84-87; V Frizington and Arlecdon *Carl* 87-94. *Tiraghoil Cottage, Bunessan, Isle of Mull PA67 6DU* Fionnphort (01681) 700581

WATSON, Mrs Elsada Beatrice (Elsie). b 30. Westhill Coll Birm CPS86. W Midl Minl Tr Course. **d** 89 **p** 94. NSM Birm St Pet *Birm* 89-90; NSM Lozells St Paul and St Silas 90-93; Par Dn 93-94; C from 94. *4 Maidstone Road, Birmingham B20 3EH* 0121-356 0626

WATSON, Geoffrey. b 48. Liv Univ BEd71. Linc Th Coll 81. **d** 83 **p** 84. C Hartlepool St Luke *Dur* 83-87; P-in-c Shadforth 87-94; Soc Resp Officer 87-94; Dioc Rural Development Adv 90-94; V Staveley, Ings and Kentmere *Carl* from 94. *The Vicarage, Kentmere Road, Staveley, Kendal, Cumbria LA8 9PA* Staveley (01539) 821267

WATSON, George. b 11. New Coll Ox BA32 MA43. St Steph Ho Ox 32. **d** 34 **p** 35. V Southend St Alb *Chelmsf* 65-76; rtd 76. *Terrys Cross House, Brighton Road, Woodmancote, Henfield, W Sussex BN5 9SX* Henfield (01273) 495263

WATSON, Gordon Mark Stewart. b 67. Wolv Poly BA90 DipEd. CITC BTh95. **d** 95. C Ballymoney w Finvoy and Rasharkin *Conn* from 95. *14 Queen's Avenue, Ballymoney, Co Antrim BT53 6DF* Ballymoney (012656) 64329

WATSON, Graeme Campbell Hubert. b 35. Ch Ch Ox BA58 MA61. Coll of Resurr Mirfield 59. **d** 61 **p** 62. C Edin St Mary *Edin* 61-63; C Carrington *S'well* 63-67; Tanzania 67-77; P-in-c Kingston St Mary w Broomfield *B & W* 77-80; V 80-81; R Kingston St Mary w Broomfield etc from 81. *The Vicarage, Kingston St Mary, Taunton, Somerset TA2 8HW* Kingston St Mary (01823) 451257

WATSON, Hartley Roger. b 40. K Coll Lon. **d** 64 **p** 65. C Noel Park St Mark *Lon* 64-67; C Munster Square St Mary Magd 67-68; C Stamford Hill St Jo 68-70; Chapl RAF 70-76; R St Breoke *Truro* 76-84; P-in-c Egloshayle 82-84; R Wittering w Thornhaugh and Wansford *Pet* from 84. *The Rectory, Wittering, Peterborough PE8 6AQ* Stamford (01780) 782428

WATSON, Henry Stanley. b 36. **d** 72 **p** 74. Hon C Bethnal Green St Jas Less *Lon* 72-83; Hon C Old Ford St Paul w St Steph and St Mark 83-88; Hon C Bethnal Green St Jas Less 89-93; Hon C Scarborough St Mary w Ch Ch and H Apostles *York* from 93. *36 Ashville Avenue, Scarborough, N Yorkshire YO12 7NF* Scarborough (01723) 375852

WATSON, Ian Leslie Stewart. b 50. Wycliffe Hall Ox 79. **d** 81 **p** 82. C Plymouth St Andr w St Paul and St Geo *Ex* 81-85; TV

Ipsley *Worc* 85-90; V Woodley St Jo the Ev *Ox* 90-92; TR Woodley 92-95; Chapl Amsterdam w Den Helder and Heiloo *Eur* from 95. *Bouwmeester 2, 1188 DT, Amstelveen, The Netherlands* Amsterdam (20) 441-0355 or 624-8877

WATSON, James Valentine John Giles. b 65. Newc Univ BA87. Ripon Coll Cuddesdon BA91. **d** 92 **p** 93. C Newc St Geo *Newc* from 92. *Tower House, St George's Close, Jesmond, Newcastle upon Tyne NE2 2TF* 0191-281 3871

WATSON, Ven Jeffrey John Seagrief (Jeff). b 39. Em Coll Cam BA61 MA65. Clifton Th Coll 62. **d** 65 **p** 66. C Beckenham Ch Ch *Roch* 65-69; C Southsea St Jude *Portsm* 69-71; V Win Ch Ch *Win* 71-81; V Bitterne 81-93; RD Southn 83-93; Hon Can Win Cathl 91-93; Adn Ely from 93. *St Botolph's Rectory, 1A Summerfield, Cambridge CB3 9HE* Cambridge (01223) 350684

WATSON, John. b 16. Oak Hill Th Coll 76. **d** 78 **p** 79. Hon C Lexden *Chelmsf* 78-81; Perm to Offic *Ches* 81-85; Hon C Alsager St Mary from 85. *9 Woolaston Drive, Alsager, Stoke-on-Trent ST7 2PL* Alsager (01270) 874565

WATSON, John Davidson. b 25. Kelham Th Coll. **d** 58 **p** 59. C Brixham *Ex* 61-70; V Treverbyn *Truro* 70-73; V S Shields St Jude *Dur* 73-78; V Rekendyke 78-84; V Coleford w Holcombe *B & W* 84-91; rtd 91. *La Ribouilliere, 53510 Chatillon sur Colmont, France*

WATSON, Canon John Derrick. b 35. K Coll Lon 56. Edin Th Coll 60. **d** 61 **p** 62. C Fulham St Etheldreda *Lon* 61-64; P-in-c Stevenage H Trin *St Alb* 64-71; V 71-74; V Leagrave 74-84; RD Luton 80-82; V Eaton Socon from 84; Hon Can St Alb from 93; RD Biggleswade from 94. *St Mary's Vicarage, 34 Drake Road, Eaton Socon, St Neots, Huntingdon, Cambs PE19 3HS* Huntingdon (01480) 212219

WATSON, Preb John Francis Wentworth. b 28. St Jo Coll Nottm LTh59. **d** 59 **p** 60. R Ashtead *Guildf* 66-72; V Plymouth St Andr w St Paul and St Geo *Ex* 72-94; Angl Adv TV SW 83-93; Westcountry TV 93-94; Preb Ex Cathl 84-94; rtd 94. *Woodland House, Western Road, Ivybridge, Devon PL21 9AL* Plymouth (01752) 893735

WATSON, John Lionel. b 39. G&C Coll Cam BA61 MA65. Ridley Hall Cam 62. **d** 64 **p** 65. C Toxteth Park St Philemon w St Silas *Liv* 64-69; C Morden *S'wark* 69-73; C Cam St Phil *Ely* 73-74; Chapl Elstree Sch Woolhampton 74-77; R Woolhampton w Midgham *Ox* 77-81; R Woolhampton w Midgham and Beenham Valance 81-95. *The Rectory, New Road Hill, Midgham, Reading RG7 5RY* Woolhampton (01734) 712264

WATSON, Canon John Robertson Thomas. b 27. CITC 68. **d** 70 **p** 71. C Belf St Steph *Conn* 71-73; Bp's C Swanlinbar w Templeport *K, E & A* 73-82; I Arvagh w Carrigallen, Gowna and Columbkille from 82; Preb Kilmore Cathl from 88. *The Rectory, Arva, Cavan, Irish Republic* Cavan (49) 35233

WATSON, Jonathan Ramsay George. b 38. Or Coll Ox BA61 MA65 DipEd62. Ridley Hall Cam 88. **d** 90 **p** 91. C Locks Heath *Portsm* 90-94; V Erith St Paul *Roch* from 94. *The Vicarage, 44A Colyers Lane, Erith, Kent DA8 3NP* Dartford (01322) 332809

WATSON, Kenneth Roy. b 27. CEng68 MIMechE68. E Midl Min Tr Course 83. **d** 86 **p** 87. NSM Ashby-de-la-Zouch St Helen w Coleorton *Leic* 86-90; R Breedon cum Isley Walton and Worthington 90-93; rtd 93. *2 Meadow Gardens, Atherstone Road, Measham, Swadlincote, Derbyshire DE12 7EG* Measham (01530) 273263

WATSON, Laurence Leslie. b 31. Keble Coll Ox BA55 MA59. Ely Th Coll. **d** 57 **p** 58. V Billesley Common *Birm* 67-95; rtd 95. *10 Redwing Close, Bishopton, Stratford-upon-Avon, Warks CV37 9EX* Stratford-upon-Avon (01789) 294569

WATSON, Leonard Alexander David. b 37. Man Univ BSc59. Coll of Resurr Mirfield 62. **d** 64 **p** 65. C Rawmarsh w Parkgate *Sheff* 64-68; S Africa 69-74; TV E Runcorn w Halton *Ches* 74-79; TV Sanderstead All SS *S'wark* 79-86; TR Selsdon St Jo w St Fran from 86; RD Croydon Addington from 90. *The Rectory, Upper Selsdon Road, South Croydon, Surrey CR2 8DD* 0181-657 2343

WATSON, Michael Paul (Mike). b 58. Trin Coll Bris DipHE93. **d** 93 **p** 94. C Derby St Alkmund and St Werburgh *Derby* from 93. *54 Park Grove, Derby DE22 1HF* Derby (01332) 372408

WATSON, Nicholas Edgar (Nick). b 67. St Cath Coll Cam BA88 MA92. Wycliffe Hall Ox BA91. **d** 92 **p** 93. C Benfieldside *Dur* 92-95; C-in-c Stockton Green Vale H Trin CD from 95; Chapl Ian Ramsey Sch Stockton from 95. *4 Greymouth Close, Stockton-on-Tees, Cleveland TS18 5LF* Stockton-on-Tees (01642) 585749

WATSON, Paul Frederick. b 44. MRCVS69 RVC(Lon) BSc66 BVetMed69 Sydney Univ PhD73. Oak Hill NSM Course 86. **d** 88 **p** 89. Hon C Muswell Hill St Jas w St Matt *Lon* from 88. *43 Grasmere Road, London N10 2DH* 0181-444 7158

WATSON, Paul William. b 55. Huddersfield Poly BA. St Jo Coll Nottm. **d** 86 **p** 87. C Meltham Mills *Wakef* 86-89; C Meltham 89-90; TV Borehamwood *St Alb* from 90. *The Vicarage,*

142 Brook Road, Borehamwood, Herts WD6 5EQ 0181-953 2362

WATSON, Philip. b 60. RGN83. Qu Coll Birm 86. **d** 89 **p** 90. C Ordsall *S'well* 89-93; TV Benwell Team *Newc* from 93. *14 Bentinck Road, Newcastle upon Tyne NE4 6UU* 0191-273 2055

✠**WATSON, Rt Rev Richard Charles Challinor (Dick).** b 23. New Coll Ox BA48 MA48. Westcott Ho Cam 50. **d** 51 **p** 52 **c** 70. C Stratford St Jo *Chelmsf* 51-53; Tutor and Chapl Wycliffe Hall Ox 54-57; Chapl to Ox Pastorate 57-61; Chapl Wadh Coll Ox 57-62; V Hornchurch St Andr *Chelmsf* 62-70; R Burnley St Pet *Blackb* 70-77; Suff Bp Burnley 70-87; Hon Can Blackb Cathl 70-88; Asst Bp Ox from 87; rtd 88. *6 Church Road, Thame, Oxon OX9 3AJ* Thame (01844) 213853

WATSON, Richard Frederick. b 66. Avery Hill Coll BA87. Trin Coll Bris ADMT93. **d** 93 **p** 94. C Kempston Transfiguration *St Alb* from 93. *16 Rosedale Way, Kempston, Bedford MK42 8JE* Bedford (01234) 854881

WATSON, Richard Rydill. b 47. Sarum & Wells Th Coll 74. **d** 77 **p** 78. C Cayton w Eastfield *York* 77-80; C Howden TM 80-82; P-in-c Burton Pidsea and Humbleton w Elsternwick 82-83; V Dormanstown 83-87; V Cotehill and Cumwhinton *Carl* 87-89; Chapl Harrogate Distr and Gen Hosp from 89. *Harrogate General Hospital, Knaresborough Road, Harrogate, N Yorkshire HG2 7ND* Harrogate (01423) 885959 or 864816

WATSON, Robert Bewley. b 34. Bris Univ BA59. Clifton Th Coll 56. **d** 61 **p** 62. C Bebington *Ches* 61-65; C Woking St Jo *Guildf* 65-68; V Knaphill from 68. *Trinity House, Trinity Road, Knaphill, Woking, Surrey GU21 2SY* Brookwood (01483) 473489

WATSON, Mrs Sheila Anne. b 53. St Andr Univ MA75 MPhil80. Edin Th Coll 79. **dss** 79 **d** 87 **p** 94. Bridge of Allan *St And* 79-80; Alloa 79-80; Monkseaton St Mary *Newc* 80-84; Adult Educn Officer *Lon* 84-87; Hon C Chelsea St Luke and Ch Ch from 87; Selection Sec ABM 92-93; Sen Selection Sec ABM from 93. *29 Burnstall Street, London SW3 3SR, or Church House, Great Smith Street, London SW1P 3NZ* 0171-352 6331 or 222 9011 Fax 799 2714

WATSON, Miss Stephanie Abigail. b 61. Heriot-Watt Univ BA84 Dur Univ CCSk90. Cranmer Hall Dur 86. **d** 90 **p** 94. C Bishop's Castle w Mainstone *Heref* 90-93; Dep Chapl HM Pris Dur 93-95; Chapl HM Rem Cen Low Newton from 95. *The Chaplaincy, HM Remand Centre, Low Newton, Durham DH1 5SD* 0191-386 1141 Fax 386 2620

WATSON, Terence David. b 38. Jes Coll Ox BA61 MA67. Chich Th Coll 73. **d** 74 **p** 75. C Sidley *Chich* 74-78; C Woodham *Guildf* 78-86; C Willesborough w Hinxhill *Cant* 86-87; C Willesborough 87-93; C Maidstone St Mich 93-94; C Clacton St Jas *Chelmsf* from 94. *8 Trafalgar Road, Clacton-on-Sea, Essex CO15 1LR* Clacton-on-Sea (01255) 434763

WATSON, Thomas Anthony. b 23. Chich Th Coll 50. **d** 52 **p** 53. V Honicknowle *Ex* 65-72; R Butterleigh 72-90; R Silverton 72-90; rtd 90; Chapl Palermo w Taormina *Eur* 90-93. *13A Lower North Street, Exeter EX4 3ET* Exeter (01392) 424423

WATSON, Timothy Patrick. b 38. ALCD66. **d** 66 **p** 67. C Northwood Em *Lon* 66-70; TV High Wycombe *Ox* 70-76; Gen Sec Intercon Ch Soc 76-82; R Bath Weston All SS w N Stoke *B & W* 82-93; R Bath Weston All SS w N Stoke and Langridge 93-94; TR Cheltenham St Mary, St Matt, St Paul and H Trin *Glouc* from 94. *The Rectory, 18 Park Place, Cheltenham, Glos GL50 2QT* Cheltenham (01242) 512208

WATSON, Miss Violet Hazel. b 29. SRN52 SCM54 RSCN59. Linc Th Coll 83. **dss** 85 **d** 87. Hammersmith SS Mich and Geo White City Estate CD *Lon* 85-86; Sunbury 86; Fulham St Dionis Parson's Green 86-87; Par Dn 87; Perm to Offic *St Alb* 88-90. *4 Hayes Terrace, Crown Lane, Shorne, Gravesend, Kent DA12 3DZ*

WATSON, William. b 36. Ripon Hall Ox 64. **d** 66 **p** 67. C Leamington Priors H Trin *Cov* 66-69; V Salford Priors 69-74; V Malin Bridge *Sheff* 74-79; Chapl Shrewsbury R Hosps 79-89; Chapl R Hallamshire Hosp Sheff 89-92; Chapl Cen Sheff Univ Hosps NHS Trust 92-93; P-in-c Alveley and Quatt *Heref* from 93. *The Vicarage, Alveley, Bridgnorth, Shropshire WV15 6ND* Bridgnorth (01746) 780326

WATSON, William Lysander Rowan. b 26. TCD BA47 MA50 Clare Coll Cam MA52 St Pet Hall Ox MA57. **d** 49 **p** 50. Chapl St Pet Coll Ox 57-93; Fell and Tutor 59-93; Sen Tutor 77-81; Vice Master 83-85; Lect Th Ox Univ 60-93; rtd 93. *19 Cobden Crescent, Oxford OX1 4LJ* Oxford (01865) 721895

WATSON-PEGMAN, John Basil. b 24. **d** 58 **p** 59. Miss to Seamen 68-87; E Regional Dir 74-87; Lic to Offic *Chelmsf* 69-74; Lic to Offic *Linc* 74-87; R Skelsmergh w Selside and Longsleddale *Carl* 87-90; rtd 90. *Little Owl Cottage, Brook Lane, Thornton Dale, Pickering, N Yorkshire YO18 7RZ* Pickering (01751) 76238

WATSON WILLIAMS, Richard Hamilton Patrick. b 31. SS Coll Cam BA57 MA62. St Aug Coll Cant. **d** 59 **p** 60. C Dorking St Paul *Guildf* 59-63; C Portsea St Mary *Portsm* 63-66; V Culgaith *Carl* 66-71; V Kirkland 66-71; V Wigton

72-79; Warden Dioc Conf Ho Crawshawbooth *Man* 79-82; P-in-c Crawshawbooth 79-82; Master Lady Kath Leveson Hosp from 82; P-in-c Temple Balsall *Birm* 82-84; V from 84. *The Master's House, Knowle, Solihull, W Midlands B93 0AL* Knowle (01564) 772415

WATT, Very Rev Alfred Ian. b 34. Edin Th Coll 57. **d** 60 **p** 61. Chapl St Paul's Cathl Dundee *Bre* 60-63; Prec 63-66; P-in-c Dundee H Cross 64-66; R Arbroath 66-69; R Perth St Ninian *St And* 69-82; Provost St Ninian's Cathl Perth 69-82; Can St Ninian's Cathl Perth from 82; R Kinross from 82; Dean St Andr from 89. *St Paul's Rectory, 55 Muirs, Kinross KY13 7AU* Kinross (01577) 862271

WATT, Prof William Montgomery. b 09. Edin Univ MA30 PhD44 Ball Coll Ox BA32 BLitt36 MA36 Aber Univ Hon DD66. Cuddesdon Coll 38. **d** 39 **p** 40. Prof Arabic and Islamic Studies 64-91; Hon C Dalkeith *Edin* 80-93; Hon C Lasswade 80-93; rtd 93. *The Neuk, 2 Bridgend, Dalkeith, Midlothian EH22 1JT* 0131-663 3197

WATT-WYNESS, Gordon. b 25. Cranmer Hall Dur 70 St Jo Coll Dur 70. **d** 72 **p** 73. C Scarborough St Mary w Ch Ch, St Paul and St Thos *York* 72-76; R Rossington *Sheff* 76-90; rtd 90. *29 Church Street, Filey, N Yorkshire YO14 9ED* Scarborough (01723) 516608

WATTERSON, Mrs Susan Mary.d 87 **p** 94. NSM Rushen *S & M* 87-90; Dioc Youth Officer from 88; C Castletown from 90. *46 Ballahane Close, Port Erin, Isle of Man IM9 6EQ* Port Erin (01624) 832835

WATTERSON, William Howard. b 16. Dur Univ LTh39 BA47 MA58. St Aid Birkenhead 36. **d** 39 **p** 40. Hd of RE Waterloo Gr Sch 53-72; Lic to Offic *Liv* 70-81; Hd of RE Aylesbury High Sch Bucks 72-77; Perm to Offic *Ox* 72-77; rtd 81; Perm to Offic *Liv* from 81. *10 Dinorwic Road, Southport, Merseyside PR8 4DL* Southport (01704) 65682

WATTHEY, Arthur Edward. b 20. St Cath Coll Cam BA45 MA48. St Aug Coll Cant 73. **d** 73 **p** 74. NSM Glen Magna w Stretton Magna *Leic* 73-76; NSM Carlton Curlieu, Illston on the Hill etc 76-81; Perm to Offic from 81; Perm to Offic *Pet* from 85; Bp's Insp of Par Registers and Records *Leic* from 90. *2 The Chase, Great Glen, Leicester LE8 9EQ* Leicester (0116) 259 2603

WATTLEY, Jeffery Richard. b 57. Univ of Wales (Abth) BSc(Econ)79. Trin Coll Bris BA92. **d** 92 **p** 93. C Reading Greyfriars *Ox* from 92. *26 Prospect Street, Reading RG1 7YG* Reading (01734) 599930 Fax 573016

WATTON, Robert Newman Kingsley. b 45. Qu Coll Birm 72. **d** 74 **p** 75. C Madron w Morvah *Truro* 74-78; Dioc Adv in RE 78-81; P-in-c Lostwithiel 78-83; P-in-c Lanhydrock 81-83; P-in-c Lanivet 81-82; V Launceston 83-91; RD Trigg Major 89-91; R Kingston, Langton Matravers and Worth Matravers *Sarum* from 91. *The Rectory, St George's Close, Langton Matravers, Swanage, Dorset BH19 3HZ* Swanage (01929) 422559

WATTS, Anthony George (Tony). b 46. K Coll Lon BD69 AKC69 Lon Univ CertEd70. Sarum & Wells Th Coll 82. **d** 84 **p** 85. C Wimborne Minster and Holt *Sarum* 84-87; P-in-c Shilling Okeford 87-92; Chapl Croft Ho Sch Shillingstone 87-92; R W Parley *Sarum* from 92. *The Rectory, 250 New Road, West Parley, Ferndown, Dorset BH22 8EW* Ferndown (01202) 873561

WATTS, Anthony John. b 30. AKC59. **d** 60 **p** 61. C Whitburn *Dur* 60-63; C Croxdale 63-65; V Warrington St Pet *Liv* 65-70; V Peel *Man* 70-78; P-in-c Bury St Mark 78-81; V Davyhulme Ch Ch from 81. *Christ Church Vicarage, 14 Welbeck Avenue, Urmston, Manchester M31 1GJ* 0161-748 2018

WATTS, Canon Arthur James. b 08. Hatf Coll Dur BA30 MA47. **d** 32 **p** 33. R Harpsden w Bolney *Ox* 51-77; Hon Can Ch Ch 59-77; rtd 77. *clo C J F Watts Esq, 18 Meadow Road, Salisbury SP2 7BN* Salisbury (01722) 330965

WATTS, David Henry. b 27. Ex Coll Ox BA50 MA55. Wells Th Coll 57. **d** 53 **p** 54. Educn Officer Essex Educn Cttee 62-70; HMI of Schs 70-87; Hon C Wetherby *Ripon* 83-87; P-in-c Healaugh w Wighill, Bilbrough and Askham Richard *York* 87-89; Chapl HM Pris Askham Grange from 87; rtd 89. *3 Westwood Way, Boston Spa, Wetherby, W Yorkshire LS23 6DX* Boston Spa (01937) 845005 Fax York (01904) 702931

WATTS, Canon Frank Walter. b 30. St Boniface Warminster 53 AKC54. **d** 54 **p** 55. V Brize Norton and Carterton *Ox* 63-69; Australia from 69; Hon Can Perth from 78; rtd 95. *1 Allambi Way, South Yunderup, W Australia 6208* Perth (9) 537-8178 Fax as telephone

WATTS, Dr Fraser Norman. b 46. FBPsS80 CPsychol89 Magd Coll Ox BA68 MA74 Lon Univ MSc70 PhD75 Magd Coll Cam DipTh90. Westcott Ho Cam 88. **d** 90 **p** 91. NSM Harston w Hauxton *Ely* 90-95; P-in-c 91-95; Lect Cam Univ from 94; Fell Qu Coll Cam from 94; Chapl Cam St Edw Prop Chpl *Ely* from 95. *81 Church Road, Hauxton, Cambridge CB2 5HS* Cambridge (01223) 871810

WATTS, Gordon Sidney Stewart. b 40. CITC 63. **d** 66 **p** 67. C Belf St Steph *Conn* 66-69; CF 69-94; V Boldre w S Baddesley *Win* from 94. *The Vicarage, Boldre, Lymington, Hants SO41 5QF* Lymington (01590) 673484

WATTS, Canon Horace Gordon. b 20. TCD BA42 MA52. **d** 43 **p** 44. I Fanlobbus Union *C & R* 56-76; Preb Cork Cathl 67-88; Treas Cloyne Cathl 68-88; I Douglas w Frankfield 76-86; I Douglas Union w Frankfield 86-88; rtd 88. *St Anton, 29 Carrigcourt, Carrigaline, Co Cork, Irish Republic* Cork (21) 373406

WATTS, Ian Charles. b 63. Hull Univ BA85. Linc Th Coll 86. **d** 88 **p** 89. C W Kirby St Bridget *Ches* 88-93; V High Lane from 93. *The Vicarage, 85 Buxton Road, High Lane, Stockport, Cheshire SK6 8DX* Disley (01663) 762627

WATTS, Ian Harold. b 15. St Pet Coll Ox BA39 MA47. Wycliffe Hall Ox. **d** 65 **p** 66. Chapl Uppingham Sch *Leics* 68-73; Hon C Mirfield *Wakef* 73-79; Chapl Cannes *Eur* 80-87; rtd 87. *67 Arden Street, Edinburgh EH9 1BT* 0131-447 6760

WATTS, John Robert. b 39. Leeds Univ BSc60 MSc63 DipEd63. Oak Hill Th Coll 88. **d** 90 **p** 91. C Partington and Carrington *Ches* 90-93; P-in-c Tintwistle from 93. *The Vicarage, Tintwistle, Hadfield, Hyde, Cheshire SK14 7JR* Glossop (01457) 852575

WATTS, John Harry. b 24. St Aid Birkenhead 57. **d** 59 **p** 60. V S Wingfield *Derby* 65-86; C-in-c Wessington CD 77-86; V S Wingfield and Wessington 86-89; rtd 89. *57 Abbotts Road, Alfreton, Derbyshire DE55 7HD* Alfreton (01773) 521063

WATTS, John Stanley. b 28. LCP62 Birm Univ DipEd65 MEd72 Nottm Univ MPhil83. Qu Coll Birm 83. **d** 86 **p** 87. Hon C Dudley St Fran *Worc* 86-91; Hon C Sedgley St Mary *Lich* 91-93; Hon C Sedgley St Mary *Worc* from 93. *5 Warren Drive, Sedgley, Dudley, W Midlands DY3 3RQ* Sedgley (01902) 661265

WATTS, Mrs Mary Kathleen. b 31. Lon Univ DipRS73 BA86. Gilmore Ho 73. **dss** 77 **d** 87 **p** 94. Lower Streatham St Andr *S'wark* 77-88; C 87-88; C Streatham Immanuel w St Anselm 87-88; C Streatham Immanuel and St Andr 90-91; rtd 91; Perm to Offic *S'wark* 91-94; Hon C Norbury St Oswald from 94. *25 Hilldown Road, London SW16 3DZ* 0181-764 6165

WATTS, Michael. b 24. NE Ord Course. **d** 82 **p** 83. NSM Stockton St Pet *Dur* from 82. *59 Richmond Road, Stockton-on-Tees, Cleveland TS18 4DT* Stockton-on-Tees (01642) 675602

WATTS, Michael. b 32. St Cath Soc Ox BA57 MA61. St Steph Ho Ox 57. **d** 58 **p** 59. C Ox St Mich *Ox* 58-60; Chapl New Coll Ox 60-72; Chapl Ch Ch *Ox* 60-81; Prec Ch Ch 64-81; C Ox St Mary Magd 63-73; R Sulhamstead Abbots and Bannister w Ufton Nervet from 81; PV Westmr Abbey 82-88. *The Rectory, Ufton Nervet, Reading RG7 4DH* Burghfield Common (01734) 832328

WATTS, Paul George. b 43. Nottm Univ BA67. Wells Th Coll 67. **d** 69 **p** 70. C Sherwood *S'well* 69-74; Chapl Trent (Nottm) Poly 74-80; V Nottm All SS 80-84; Lic to Offic from 84. *16 Grosvenor Avenue, Nottingham NG5 3DX* Nottingham (0115) 960 9964

WATTS, Canon Peter Alan Witney. b 37. Dur Univ BA59 Birm Univ MSocSc83. Qu Coll Birm DipTh61. **d** 61 **p** 62. C Hamstead St Paul *Birm* 61-65; C Ward End 65-66; V Burney Lane 66-73; V Sutton Coldfield St Chad from 73; Hon Can Birm Cathl from 89. *The Vicarage, 41 Hollyfield Road, Sutton Coldfield, W Midlands B75 7SN* 0121-329 2995

WATTS, Raymond Ivor. b 31. DIM. Local NSM Course. **d** 85 **p** 86. NSM Scotter w E Ferry *Linc* from 85. *5 St Peter's Road, Scotter, Gainsborough, Lincs DN21 3SG* Scunthorpe (01724) 762691

WATTS, Miss Rebecca Harriet. b 61. St Cath Coll Cam BA83 MA. Wycliffe Hall Ox 87. **d** 90 **p** 94. C Goldsworth Park *Guildf* 90-94; Chapl Wadh Coll Ox from 94; C Ox St Mary V w St Cross and St Pet *Ox* from 94. *156 Kingston Road, Oxford OX2 6RP* Oxford (01865) 513803 or 277905

WATTS, Roger Edward. b 39. S'wark Ord Course 85. **d** 88 **p** 89. C Belmont *S'wark* 88-92; R Godstone from 92. *The Rectory, 17 Ivy Mill Lane, Godstone, Surrey RH9 8NK* Godstone (01883) 742354

WATTS, Roger Mansfield. b 41. CEng76 MIEE76 Univ of Wales (Cardiff) BSc63 Southn Univ. Chich Th Coll 89. **d** 91 **p** 92. C Chippenham St Andr w Tytherton Lucas *Bris* 91-93; C Henfield w Shermanbury and Woodmancote *Chich* from 93. *41 Furners Mead, Henfield, W Sussex BN5 9JA* Henfield (01273) 494421

WATTS, Ronald Horace (Ron). b 57. CITC DTh92. **d** 92 **p** 93. C Sligo *K, E & A* 92-93; C Limerick City *L & K* 94-95; I Holmpatrick w Balbriggan and Kenure *D & G* from 95. *Holmpatrick Rectory, Miller's Lane, Skerries, Co Dublin, Irish Republic* Dublin (1) 849-2247

WATTS, Mrs Valerie Anne. b 44. UEA BEd79. E Anglian Minl Tr Course 90. **d** 93 **p** 94. NSM N Walsham w Antingham *Nor* from 93. *15 Millfield Road, North Walsham, Norfolk NR28 0EB* North Walsham (01692) 405119

WATTS, Wilfred Richard James. b 11. St Mich Coll Llan 64. **d** 66 **p** 66. V Viney Hill *Glouc* 69-82; rtd 82; Perm to Offic *Glouc* from 82. *5 Lambert Drive, Shurdington, Cheltenham, Glos GL51 5SP* Cheltenham (01242) 862377

WATTS, William Henry Norbury. b 51. CertEd. St Jo Coll Nottm 87. **d** 89 **p** 90. C S Molton w Nymet St George, High Bray etc *Ex* 89-93; TV Swanage and Studland *Sarum* from 93. *The Vicarage, School Lane, Studland, Swanage, Dorset BH19 3AJ* Swanage (01929) 450441

WATTS-JONES, William Vyvyan Francis Kynaston. b 22. Em Coll Cam BA43 MA47 CertEd72. Ridley Hall Cam 47. **d** 49 **p** 50. V Bilton *Ripon* 60-70; Asst Master St Pet Colleg Ch Sch Wolv 72-74; R Brampton St Thos *Derby* 74-84; rtd 84; Perm to Offic *Derby* from 84. *9 Kerwin Road, Sheffield S17 3DH* Sheffield (0114) 236 6733

WAUD, John David. b 31. N Ord Course 82. **d** 85 **p** 86. C Cayton w Eastfield *York* 85-88; R Brandesburton 88-93; R Beeford w Frodingham and Foston from 93. *The Rectory, Rectory Lane, Beeford, Driffield, N Humberside YO25 8BA* Beeford (01262) 488042

WAUDBY, Miss Christine. b 45. TCert66. Trin Coll Bris DipHE. **d** 90 **p** 94. C Weston-super-Mare Ch Ch *B & W* 90-94; C Blackheath *Birm* from 94. *25 Garland Crescent, Halesowen, W Midlands B62 9NJ* 0121-421 4821

WAUGH, Mrs Jane Leitch. b 38. DMusEd60 CertEd61 Toronto Univ MDiv83. Trin Coll Toronto 80. **d** 84 **p** 94. Canada 84-87; Par Dn Dunnington *York* 88-90; Perm to Offic 90-93; NSM York St Olave w St Giles from 93. *Moonrakers, Rectory Corner, Brandsby, York YO6 4RJ* Brandsby (01347) 888637

WAUGH, Canon Nigel John William. b 56. TCD BA78 MA81. CITC 76. **d** 79 **p** 80. C Ballymena *Conn* 79-82; C Ballyholme *D & D* 82-84; I Bunclody w Kildavin *C & O* 84-86; I Bunclody w Kildavin and Clonegal 86-91; I Bunclody w Kildavin, Clonegal and Kilrush from 91; RD New Ross from 86; Preb Ferns Cathl 88-91; Treas from 91; Radio Officer (Cashel) 90-91; (Ferns) from 92; Dioc Info Officer (Ferns) from 91. *St Mary's Rectory, Bunclody, Enniscorthy, Co Wexford, Irish Republic* Enniscorthy (54) 77652 Fax 76151

WAXHAM, Derek Frank. b 33. Oak Hill Th Coll 76. **d** 79 **p** 80. Hon C Old Ford St Paul w St Steph *Lon* 79-82; Hon C Old Ford St Paul w St Steph and St Mark 82-89; NSM Bow w Bromley St Leon from 89. *39 Hewlett Road, London E3 5NA* 0181-980 1748

WAY, Albert James. b 27. St D Coll Lamp BA61 DipTh63. **d** 63 **p** 64. C Neath w Llantwit *Llan* 63-68; C Watford St Jo *St Alb* 68; R Clayhidon *Ex* 68-76; V Llanbadog and Llanllowell *Mon* 76-83; V Llanhilleth from 83. *The Rectory, Aberbeeg, Abertillery, Gwent NP3 2DA* Abertillery (01495) 214236

WAY, Andrew Lindsay. b 43. Linc Th Coll 76. **d** 78 **p** 79. C Shenfield *Chelmsf* 78-82; C Waltham *Linc* 82-84; V New Waltham 84-89; R Duxford *Ely* 89-94; V Hinxton 89-94; V Ickleton 89-94; P-in-c Doddington w Benwick from 94; P-in-c Wimblington from 94. *The Rectory, Ingle's Lane, Doddington, March, Cambs PE15 0TE* March (01354) 740692

WAY, Anthony Hilton (Tony). b 21. ARIBA. Chich Th Coll 57. **d** 59 **p** 60. V Horam *Chich* 63-70; V Ditchling 70-77; Asst Dioc Sec 77-83; Chapl Dioc Ch Ho 79-83; V Linchmere 83-91; rtd 91. *59 Finches Garden, Lindfield, Haywards Heath, W Sussex RH16 2PB* Haywards Heath (01444) 484584

WAY, Mrs Barbara Elizabeth. b 47. Open Univ BA82 Hull Univ PGCE86. Linc Th Coll IDC78. **dss** 78 **d** 87 **p** 94. Shenfield *Chelmsf* 78-82; Adult Educn Adv *Linc* 82-85; Dioc Lay Min Adv 85; New Waltham 82-87; Min 87-89; Tetney 86-87; Min 87-89; NSM Duxford *Ely* 89-94; NSM Ickleton 89-94; NSM Hinxton 89-94; Dir of Past Studies E Anglian Min Tr Course 91-94; Min Pampisford 92-94; P-in-c Coates from 94. *The Rectory, North Green, Coates, Whittlesey, Peterborough PE7 2BQ* Peterborough (01733) 840254

WAY, Colin George. b 31. St Cath Coll Cam BA55 MA59 Lon Inst of Educn PGCE58. E Anglian Minl Tr Course. **d** 84 **p** 85. NSM Hempnall *Nor* 84-87; C Gaywood, Bawsey and Mintlyn 87-90; R Acle w Fishley and N Burlingham from 90; RD Blofield from 95. *The Rectory, Acle, Norwich NR13 3BU* Great Yarmouth (01493) 750393

WAY, David Victor. b 54. Pemb Coll Ox MA DPhil. Cranmer Hall Dur BA Cuddesdon Coll 83. **d** 85 **p** 86. C Chenies and Lt Chalfont *Ox* 85-87; C Chenies and Lt Chalfont, Latimer and Flaunden 87-88; Tutor and Dir of Studies Sarum & Wells Th Coll 88-93; Selection Sec ABM from 94; Sec Minl Educn Cttee from 94. *Church House, Great Smith Street, London SW1P 3NZ* 0171-222 9011 Fax 799 2714

WAY, Lawrence William. b 32. St Mich Coll Llan 77. **d** 79 **p** 80. C Merthyr Dyfan *Llan* 79-82; V Abercynon 82-84; TV Cwmbran *Mon* 84-86; V Caerwent w Dinham and Llanfair Discoed etc 86-90; V Pontnewydd 90-93; rtd 93. *8 Ceredig Court, Llanyrafon, Cwmbran, Gwent NP44 8SA* Cwmbran (01633) 865309

WAY, Michael David. b 57. K Coll Lon BD78 AKC78. St Steph Ho Ox 79. **d** 80 **p** 83. C Bideford *Ex* 80-81; Hon C Wembley Park St Aug *Lon* 81-84; C Kilburn St Aug w St Jo 84-89; V Earlsfield St Jo *S'wark* 89-92; Project Co-ord CARA from 92. *13 Sparkford House, Sunbury Lane, London SW11 3NQ* 0171-792 8299

WAYNE, Kenneth Hammond. b 31. Bps' Coll Cheshunt 58. **d** 61 **p** 62. C Eyres Monsell CD *Leic* 61-62; C Loughb Em 62-65; C-in-c Staunton Harold 65-73; R Breedon w Isley Walton 65-73; V Leic St Phil 73-85; V Ault Hucknall *Derby* from 85. *The Vicarage, 59 The Hill, Glapwell, Chesterfield, Derbyshire S44 5LX* Chesterfield (01246) 850371

WAYTE, Alleyn Robert. b 33. Trin Coll Ox BA56 MA60. Westcott Ho Cam 60. **d** 61 **p** 62. P-in-c Dawley *Lich* 66-75; V Stretton w Claymills 75-92; rtd 92. *2 Church Close, Willington, Derby DE65 6EN* Burton-on-Trent (01283) 701815

WAYTE, Christopher John. b 28. Lon Univ BSc54. Wells Th Coll 54. **d** 56 **p** 57. R Biddenden *Cant* 58-64; P-in-c Boughton Monchelsea 80-85; V St Margarets-at-Cliffe w Westcliffe etc 85-91; rtd 92. *9 St John's Road, Hythe, Kent CT21 4BE* Hythe (01303) 263060

WEALE, Colin Alexander. b 26. Univ of Wales (Lamp) BA49 Lon Univ DipRS77 Open Univ MPhil87. Lambeth STh81 Sarum Th Coll 49. **d** 51 **p** 52. R Bengeo *St Alb* 69-93; rtd 93; Perm to Offic *Nor* from 93. *1 Diana Way, Caister-on-Sea, Great Yarmouth, Norfolk NR30 5TP* Great Yarmouth (01493) 377946

WEARE, Sydney Vincent. b 17. Solicitor 39 Linc Coll Ox BA48 MA52 Univ of W Aus MA57. Westcott Ho Cam 48. **d** 50 **p** 51. Australia from 55; P-in-c Lolworth *Ely* 80-81; P-in-c Fen Drayton w Conington 80-81; rtd 81; Perm to Offic *Ely* from 81. *42 Rosalie Street, Shenton Park, W Australia 6008, or 63 Cedars Road, Beckenham, Kent BR3 4JG* Perth (9) 381-2696 or 0181-650 8856

WEARMOUTH, Alan Wilfred. b 54. St Paul's Cheltenham CertEd75 Bris Univ BEd76. Glouc Sch of Min 85. **d** 88 **p** 89. Hon C Coleford w Staunton *Glouc* from 88. *22 Forest Patch, Christchurch, Coleford, Glos GL16 8RB* Dean (01594) 832660

WEARMOUTH, Paul Frederick. b 37. Wells Th Coll 60. **d** 62 **p** 63. Ho Master Castleview Sch Sunderland 68-84; rtd 84; Perm to Offic *Dur* from 84. *9 Withernsea Grove, Ryhope, Sunderland SR2 0BU* 0191-521 0174

WEARN, William Frederick. b 51. S Dios Minl Tr Scheme. **d** 85 **p** 86. NSM Hythe *Win* 85-94; Asst Chapl HM Pris Liv from 94. *HM Prison, 68 Hornby Road, Liverpool L9 3DF* 0151-525 5971 Fax 525 0831

WEATHERBY, Peter John James. b 58. Keble Coll Ox BA80 MA91. St Steph Ho Ox 81. **d** 83 **p** 84. C Latchford St Jas *Ches* 83-85; C Calcot *Ox* 85-88; Asst Chapl HM Pris Reading 85-88; TV Cowley St Jas *Ox* 88-92; V Burslem St Werburgh *Lich* 92-94. *16 Earlswood Road, Stoke-on-Trent ST1 6UF* Stoke-on-Trent (01782) 202093

WEATHERHEAD, Very Rev Thomas Leslie. b 13. Hatf Coll Dur BA37 LTh37. St Aug Coll Cant 32. **d** 37 **p** 38. Dean and V-Gen Nassau 65-72; R Felmingham *Nor* 72-79; R Colby w Banningham and Tuttington 74-79; R Suffield 74-79; RD Tunstead 76-79; rtd 79. *St Nicholas's Lodge, 25 Bishopton Lane, Ripon, N Yorkshire HG4 2QN* Ripon (01765) 600413

WEATHERLEY, Miss Mary Kathleen. b 36. SRN57 SCM59 MTD72. SW Minl Tr Course 78. **dss** 82 **d** 87 **p** 94. Littleham w Exmouth *Ex* 82-84; Heavitree w Ex St Paul 85-87; Hon Par Dn 87-88; Chapl Asst R Devon and Ex Hosp 85-93; Lic to Offic *Ex* 88-94; NSM Littleham w Exmouth from 94. *Flat 5, 36 Douglas Avenue, Exmouth, Devon EX8 2HB* Exmouth (01395) 265528

WEATHRALL, Ian Charles. b 22. OBE75. AKC47. **d** 47 **p** 48. India from 51; Brotherhood of Ascension from 51; Hd 70-88; rtd 92. *7 Court Lane, Delhi 110 054, India* Delhi (11) 251-8515

WEAVER, Alan William. b 63. Brighton Poly HNC88. Linc Th Coll CMinlStuds95. **d** 95. C Seaford w Sutton *Chich* from 95. *29 Stafford Road, Seaford, E Sussex BN25 1UE* Seaford (01323) 891831

WEAVER (nee ROBBINS), Ms Angela Mary. b 48. W Midl Minl Tr Course 92. **d** 95. C Hill *Birm* from 95. *3 Dower Road, Sutton Coldfield, W Midlands B75 1SH* 0121-308 0759

WEAVER, Prof Arthur Kenneth (Ken). b 17. MRAeS Trin Coll Cam MA. Wycliffe Hall Ox 81 Ox NSM Course 81. **d** 81 **p** 82. NSM Ashbury, Compton Beauchamp and Longcot w Fernham *Ox* from 81. *White Lodge, King's Lane, Longcot, Faringdon, Oxon SN7 7SS* Swindon (01793) 782364

WEAVER, Brian John. b 34. Oak Hill Th Coll 82. **d** 84 **p** 85. C Nailsea H Trin *B & W* 84-88; R Nettlebed w Bix and Highmore *Ox* from 88. *The Rectory, Nettlebed, Henley-on-Thames, Oxon RG9 5DD* Nettlebed (01491) 641575

WEAVER, David Anthony. b 43. Hatf Coll Dur BSc65. Lich Th Coll 68. **d** 71 **p** 72. C Walsall Wood *Lich* 71-75; C Much Wenlock w Bourton *Heref* 75-76; Canada 76-79 and 82; V Mow Cop *Lich* 79-82; P-in-c Burntwood from 82; Chapl

St Matt Hosp Burntwood 83-85. *The Vicarage, Church Road, Burntwood, Walsall WS7 9EA* Burntwood (01543) 675014

WEAVER, Duncan Charles. b 60. St Jo Coll Nottm DipTh94. **d** 94. C Watford *St Alb* from 94. *8A Lammas Road, Watford WD1 8BA* Watford (01923) 232979

WEAVER, George Edward. b 1900. **d** 53 **p** 54. R Drayton Bassett *Lich* 64-71; P-in-c Canwell CD 64-71; rtd 71. *42 Park Road West, Wollaston, Stourbridge, W Midlands DY8 3NQ*

WEAVER, Ven John. b 28. Ex Coll Ox BA51 MA55. St Steph Ho Ox 52. **d** 55 **p** 56. C Ex St Dav *Ex* 55-58; S Africa from 58; Adn Midl from 84. *PO Box 21, Himeville, 4585 South Africa* Himeville (33722) 13

WEAVER, Canon Michael Howard. b 39. Leeds Univ DipArch63 DipTh66 DipL&A69 Southn Univ MPhil95. Chich Th Coll 63. **d** 66 **p** 67. C Kidderminster St Jo *Worc* 66-69; Br Honduras 69-71; TV Droitwich *Worc* 71-76; V Arundel w Tortington and S Stoke *Chich* from 76; Sub-Chapl HM Pris Ford from 77; P-in-c Clymping 84-87; RD Arundel and Bognor 88-93; Hon Can Enugu from 94. *The Vicarage, 26 Maltravers Street, Arundel, W Sussex BN18 9BU* Arundel (01903) 882573 or 882262

WEAVER, Raymond Alexander (Ray). Bris Univ BA. Sarum Th Coll. **d** 86 **p** 87. NSM Weymouth H Trin *Sarum* from 86. *1 Fairclose, Weymouth, Dorset DT4 0DF* Weymouth (01305) 783681

WEAVER, Canon Thomas James. b 04. **d** 53 **p** 54. V Liv Ch Ch Kensington *Liv* 60-74; RD Toxteth 72-77; P-in-c Edge Hill St Cypr 74-75; V Toxteth St Cypr w Ch Ch 75-77; rtd 77. *24 Wirral View, Connah's Quay, Deeside, Clwyd CH5 4TE* Deeside (01244) 818564

WEAVER, William. b 40. Man Univ BA63 BD65. **d** 74 **p** 75. Lect Th Leeds Univ 67-91; Hon C Clifford *York* 82-86; Chapl K Edw Sch Birm 91-94; Provost Woodard Schs (Midl Division) from 94. *2 Nidd View, Cattal, York YO5 8DZ* Boroughbridge (01423) 358512

WEBB, Canon Albert (Bertie). b 22. AKC49. **d** 50 **p** 51. V Evesham *Worc* 66-87; RD Evesham 73-79; Hon Can Worc Cathl 75-87; rtd 87. *2 Dolphin Close, Worcester WR2 6BG* Worcester (01905) 422230

WEBB, Andrew David. b 60. St Chad's Coll Dur BA81. Coll of Resurr Mirfield 82. **d** 84 **p** 85. C Hemsworth *Wakef* 84-87; C Leytonstone H Trin Harrow Green *Chelmsf* 87-89; OSB 89-90; C Willesden Green St Andr and St Fran of Assisi *Lon* 90-94. *Flat C, 143 Fordwych Road, London NW2 3NG* 0181-452 1876

WEBB, Anthony John. b 24. Sarum & Wells Th Coll 79. **d** 81 **p** 82. C Yeovil *B & W* 81-84; P-in-c Cossington 84-87; P-in-c Woolavington 84-87; V Woolavington w Cossington and Bawdrip 87-91; rtd 91; Perm to Offic *B & W* from 91. *4 Brue Crescent, Burnham-on-Sea, Somerset TA8 1LR* Burnham-on-Sea (01278) 787483

WEBB, Arthur Robert. b 33. FRSA LCP67 Lanc Univ MA82. Wells Th Coll 69. **d** 70 **p** 70. C W Drayton *Lon* 70-72; Hd Master St Jas Cathl Sch Bury St Edmunds 72-86; Min Can St E Cathl *St E* 72-87; Succ St E Cathl 81-87; P-in-c Seend and Bulkington *Sarum* 87-88; V 88-91; R Heytesbury and Sutton Veny from 91. *Water Meadow Barn, Parsonage Farm, Tytherington Road, Heytesbury, Warminster, Wilts BA12 0EG* Warminster (01985) 840608

WEBB, Cyril George. b 19. Roch Th Coll 64. **d** 66 **p** 67. C Bournemouth St Andr *Win* 66-71; V Micheldever 71-72; V Micheldever and E Stratton, Woodmancote etc 72-79; V Bubwith w Ellerton and Aughton *York* 79-83; I Tomregan w Drumlane *K, E & A* 83-86; rtd 86. *62 Columbia Avenue, Whitstable, Kent CT5 4EH* Whitstable (01227) 264687

WEBB, David Basil. b 30. Ch Coll Cam BA54 MA58. Ripon Hall Ox 54. **d** 55 **p** 56. C Wimbledon *S'wark* 55-57; Chapl Em Coll Cam 57-60; V Langley Mill *Derby* 60-64; R Farnborough *Roch* 64-73; R Dunstable *St Alb* 73-78; TR 78-84; RD Dunstable 81-84; TR Bemerton *Sarum* 84-90; V Haslingden w Grane and Stonefold *Blackb* from 90; RD Accrington 92-95. *St James's Vicarage, Church Lane, Haslingden, Rossendale, Lancs BB4 5QZ* Rossendale (01706) 215533

WEBB, David William. b 30. MRINA Kent Univ DipTh84. Cant Sch of Min 86. **d** 89 **p** 90. NSM Sittingbourne St Mary *Cant* from 89. *5 Windermere Grove, Sittingbourne, Kent ME10 1UU* Sittingbourne (01795) 424502

WEBB, Mrs Diane. b 45. Local NSM Course 91. **d** 93 **p** 94. NSM Stowmarket *St E* from 93. *36 Wordsworth Road, Stowmarket, Suffolk IP14 1TT* Stowmarket (01449) 677880

WEBB, Frances Mary. See BATTIN, Mrs Frances Mary

WEBB, Mrs Gillian Anne. b 49. Whitelands Coll Lon CertEd71. St Alb Minl Tr Scheme 83. **dss** 86 **d** 87 **p** 94. Kempston Transfiguration *St Alb* 86-87; NSM from 87. *2 Hillson Close, Marston Moreteyne, Bedford MK43 0QN* Bedford (01234) 767256

WEBB, Gregory John. b 55. Man Univ LLB77. Oak Hill Th Coll 89. d 91 p 92. C Bury St Edmunds St Geo *St E* 91-94; P-in-c Bury St Edmunds All SS from 94. *All Saints Vicarage, 59 Bennett Avenue, Bury St Edmunds, Suffolk IP33 3JJ* Bury St Edmunds (01284) 701063

WEBB, Harold William. b 37. Dur Univ BA59. St Steph Ho Ox 59. d 61 p 62. C Plumstead St Nic *S'wark* 61-65; S Africa 65-70; Sacr Wakef Cathl *Wakef* 71-72; P-in-c Lane End *Ox* 72-76; V Lane End w Cadmore End 76-84; Chapl to the Deaf *Guildf* from 84. *1 Lindfield Gardens, London Road, Guildford, Surrey GU1 1TP* Guildford (01483) 573228

WEBB (nee EDWARDS), Mrs Helen Glynne. b 57. SRN79 RMN81. Wycliffe Hall Ox 88. d 90 p 94. Par Dn Clapham St Jas *S'wark* 90-94; Asst Chapl Southmead Hosp Bris from 94. *157 Ratcliffe Drive, Stoke Gifford, Bristol BS12 6TZ* Bristol (0117) 931 1847

WEBB, Jason Stephen. b 72. Southlands Coll Lon BA93. St Steph Ho Ox DipMin95. d 95. C Leeds St Aid *Ripon* from 95. *St Aidan's House, 84 Copgrove Road, Leeds LS8 2ST* Leeds (0113) 248 0050

WEBB, John Christopher Richard. b 38. ACA63 FCA74. Wycliffe Hall Ox 64. d 67 p 68. C Hendon St Paul Mill Hill *Lon* 67-71; CF 71-93; R Bentworth and Shalden and Lasham *Win* from 93. *The Rectory, Bentworth, Alton, Hants GU34 5RB* Alton (01420) 563218

WEBB, Dr Kenneth Gordon Webb (Ken). b 47. DRCOG73 Lon Univ MB, BS71. Trin Coll Bris BA92 ADPS93. d 93 p 94. C Cheltenham St Mark *Glouc* from 93. *305 Gloucester Road, Cheltenham, Glos GL51 7AR* Cheltenham (01242) 227928

WEBB, Marjorie Valentine (Sister Elizabeth). b 31. Bedf Coll Lon. d 88 p 94. CSF from 55; New Mother 71-86; Lic to Bp Heref 86-90; Perm to Offic *Lon* 88-90; Lic to Offic *Lich* 90-91. *Compton Durville Manor House, South Petherton, Somerset TA13 5ES* South Petherton (01460) 40473

WEBB, Michael David. b 59. K Coll Lon BD82 PGCE83. Ripon Coll Cuddesdon 88. d 90 p 91. C Broughton Astley *Leic* 90-93; C Hugglescote w Donington, Ellistown and Snibston from 93. *St James Vicarage, Highfield Street, Coalville, Leicester LE67 3BN* Coalville (01530) 832679

WEBB, Michael John. b 49. Linc Coll Ox BA70 MA74. Linc Th Coll 70. d 72 p 73. C Chipping St Alb 72-75; C Chipping Barnet 75-78; C Chipping Barnet w Arkley 78-82; TV Cullercoats St Geo *Newc* 82-89; V Newc H Cross from 89. *Holy Cross Vicarage, 16 Whittington Grove, Newcastle upon Tyne NE5 2QP* 0191-274 4476

WEBB, Mrs Pauline Nikola. b 49. W Midl Minl Tr Course. d 87 p 94. C Walsgrave on Sowe *Cov* 87-91; TD Grantham *Linc* 91-94; Ind Chapl from 91; TV Grantham from 94. *St John's Vicarage, 4 Station Road, Grantham, Lincs NG31 6JY* Grantham (01476) 592432

WEBB, Peter Henry. b 55. Nottm Univ BA77. St Steph Ho Ox 77. d 79 p 80. C Lancing w Coombes *Chich* 79-82; C Hydneye CD 82-84; C-in-c 84-86; Chapl Sunderland Distr Gen Hosp from 86. *The Chaplain's Office, Sunderland District General Hospital, Kayll Road, Sunderland SR4 7TP* 0191-565 6256

WEBB, Richard. b 38. Oak Hill NSM Course 91. d 94 p 95. NSM Hanwell St Mary w St Chris *Lon* from 94. *46 Graham Avenue, London W13 9TQ* 0181-579 9798

WEBB, Richard Frederick. b 42. Cant Sch of Min. d 84 p 85. C Ipswich St Clem w H Trin *St E* 84-87; R Rougham and Beyton w Hessett 87-91; R Rougham, Beyton w Hessett and Rushbrooke 91-92; P-in-c Woodbridge St Jo from 92. *St John's Vicarage, St John's Hill, Woodbridge, Suffolk IP12 1HS* Woodbridge (01394) 382083

WEBB, Richard Lacey. b 09. ALCD30. d 32 p 33. V Lakenham St Alb *Nor* 66-77; rtd 77; Hon C Nor St Andr *Nor* 83-86; Perm to Offic from 86. *32 Ipswich Road, Norwich NR4 6QR* Norwich (01603) 51348

WEBB, Rowland James. b 33. Roch Th Coll 64. d 67 p 68. C Tavistock and Gulworthy *Ex* 67-70; Chapl RN 70-86; R Mundford w Lynford *Nor* 86-90; V Burnham *Chelmsf* from 90. *The Vicarage, 2A Church Road, Burnham-on-Crouch, Essex CM0 8DA* Maldon (01621) 782071

WEBB, William John. b 43. Cuddesdon Coll 68. d 71 p 72. C Weston Favell *Pet* 71-73; C Newport w Longford *Lich* 74-77; C Baswich (or Berkswich) 77-79; P-in-c Stonnall 79-83; P-in-c Wall 79-83; V Fauls 83-95; V Prees 83-95; V St Martin's from 95. *The Vicarage, St Martins, Oswestry, Shropshire SY11 3AP* Oswestry (01691) 772295

WEBBER, David Price. b 39. Chich Th Coll 90. d 91 p 92. NSM Shoreham Beach *Chich* 91-93; NSM Hove St Patr from 93. *69 Grinstead Lane, Lancing, W Sussex BN15 9DT* Lancing (01903) 753950

WEBBER, Eric Michael. b 16. Lon Univ BD54 ATh(SA)55 Univ of Tasmania MEd77 MHums85. AKC43. d 43 p 44. C Clapham H Spirit *S'wark* 43-47; C Wimbledon 47-50; S Africa 50-58; Australia from 58; Sen Lect Relig Studies Tasmanian Coll Adv Educn 71-81. *1 Hean Street, Hobart, Tasmania, Australia 7004* Hobart (2) 236413

WEBBER, John Arthur. b 45. Keble Coll Ox BA67 MA71. Gen Th Sem (NY) STM85 Cuddesdon Coll 70. d 71 p 72. C Penarth All SS *Llan* 71-74; USPG 75-91; Bangladesh 75-91; C Stepney St Dunstan and All SS *Lon* from 91; Bp's Adv on Inter-Faith Relns from 91. *6 Arbour Square, London E1 0SH* 0171-791 0330

WEBBER, Canon Lionel Frank. b 35. Kelham Th Coll St Mich Coll Llan. d 60 p 61. C Bolton Sav *Man* 60-63; C Aberavon *Llan* 63-65; R Salford Stowell Memorial *Man* 65-69; V Aberavon H Trin *Llan* 69-74; TV Stantonbury *Ox* 74-76; TR Basildon St Martin w H Cross and Laindon *Chelmsf* 76-79; P-in-c Nevendon 77-79; RD Basildon 79-89; R Basildon, St Martin of Tours w Nevendon 79-95; R Basildon, St Martin of Tours from 95; Hon Can Chelmsf Cathl from 84; Chapl to The Queen from 94. *The Rectory, Pagel Mead, Basildon, Essex SS14 1DX* Basildon (01268) 280039

WEBBER, Michael Champneys Wilfred. b 48. Man Univ BA71 MA(Theol)78. Cuddesdon Coll 73. d 75 p 76. C Caterham *S'wark* 75-79; P-in-c Kidbrooke St Jas 79-84; TV 84-85; V Earls Barton *Pet* from 87. *The Vicarage, 7 High Street, Earls Barton, Northampton NN6 0JG* Northampton (01604) 810447

WEBBER, Peter Cecil. b 21. Lon Coll of Div ALCD55 LTh. d 55 p 56. V Foord St Jo *Cant* 67-86; R/D Elham 80-83; rtd 86; Perm to Offic *Chich* from 86. *15 Goodwin Close, Hailsham, E Sussex BN27 3DE* Hailsham (01323) 848668

WEBBER, Raymond John. b 40. Lon Univ DipTh65. Linc Th Coll 84. d 85 p 86. C Helston *Truro* 85; C Helston and Wendron 85-90; TV 90-93; R Kenton, Mamhead, Powderham, Cofton and Starcross *Ex* from 93. *The Vicarage, 1 Staplake Rise, Starcross, Exeter EX6 8SJ* Starcross (01626) 890331

WEBER, Douglas John Craig. b 20. Ex Coll Ox BA46 MA46. Sarum Th Coll. d 49 p 50. V Hook w Warsash *Portsm* 55-88; rtd 88; Perm to Offic *Portsm* from 88. *1 Trevose Way, Titchfield, Fareham, Hants PO14 4NG* Locks Heath (01489) 583065

WEBLEY, Robin Bowen. b 32. Univ of Wales (Cardiff) DPS. St Mich Coll Llan 87. d 89 p 90. C St D Cathl *St D* 89-91; Min Can St D Cathl 89-91; R Castlemartin w Warren and Angle etc 91-94; Min Can St D Cathl from 94; Succ St D Cathl from 94. *The Archdeaconry, St Davids, Haverfordwest, Dyfed SA62 6PE* St Davids (01437) 720456

WEBSTER, Very Rev Alan Brunskill. b 18. KCVO88. Qu Coll Ox BA39 MA43 BD54 City Univ Hon DD. Westcott Ho Cam 41. d 42 p 43. Warden Linc Th Coll 59-70; Can and Preb Linc Cathl *Linc* 64-70; Dean Nor 70-78; Dean St Paul's *Lon* 78-87; rtd 88. *20 Beechbank, Norwich NR2 2AL* Norwich (01603) 55833

WEBSTER, David Edward. b 39. K Coll Lon 60 Edin Th Coll 62. d 64 p 65. C Maghull *Liv* 64-69; R Wavertree St Mary 69-76; TV Greystoke, Matterdale and Mungrisdale *Carl* 76-81; R Lowton St Luke *Liv* 81-88; Chapl Nat Agric Cen from 88; R Stoneleigh w Ashow and Baginton *Cov* from 88. *The Rectory, Church Lane, Stoneleigh, Coventry CV8 3DN* Coventry (01203) 415506

WEBSTER, David Robert. b 32. Selw Coll Cam BA56 MA60. Linc Th Coll 56. d 58 p 59. V Lumley *Dur* 64-76; V Belmont 76-93; rtd 93. *25 Eldon Grove, Hartlepool, Cleveland TS26 9LY* Hartlepool (01429) 275698

WEBSTER, Dennis Eric. b 39. Fitzw Ho Cam BA60 MA64 Linacre Coll Ox MA70 Lon Univ CertEd61. Wycliffe Hall Ox 62. d 65 p 66. C Herne Bay Ch Ch *Cant* 65-68; C Tulse Hill H Trin *S'wark* 68-69; Kenya 70-75; Chapl Pierrepont Sch Frensham 75-91; R Chiddingfold *Guildf* from 91. *The Rectory, Coxcombe Lane, Chiddingfold, Godalming, Surrey GU8 4QA* Wormley (01428) 682008

WEBSTER, Derek Herbert. b 34. FRSA82 Hull Univ BA55 Lon Univ BD55 Leic Univ MEd68 PhD73. Lambeth STh67 Linc Th Coll 76. d 76 p 77. Lect Hull Univ from 72; Hon C Cleethorpes *Linc* from 76. *60 Queen's Parade, Cleethorpes, S Humberside DN35 0DG* Cleethorpes (01472) 693786

WEBSTER, Mrs Diane Margaret. b 43. Oak Hill NSM Course 91. d 94. NSM Welwyn Garden City *St Alb* from 94. *26 Dellcott Close, Welwyn Garden City, Herts AL8 7BD* Welwyn Garden (01707) 323103

WEBSTER, Geoffrey William. b 36. St Alb Minl Tr Scheme 77. d 80 p 81. NSM Harlington *St Alb* 80-82; C Belmont *Dur* 82-86; R Gateshead Fell 86-94; P-in-c Hamsterley 94-95; P-in-c Hamsterley and Witton-le-Wear from 95. *The Vicarage, Hamsterley, Bishop Auckland, Co Durham DL13 3PP* Witton-le-Wear (01388) 488418

WEBSTER, Canon Glyn Hamilton. b 51. SRN73. Cranmer Hall Dur 74 St Jo Coll Dur 74. d 77 p 78. C Huntington *York* 77-81; V York St Luke 81-92; Chapl York Distr Hosp from 81;

Sen Chapl York Health Services NHS Trust from 92; Hon Can York Minster *York* from 94. *York District Hospital, Wiggington Road, York YO3 7HE, or 22 Markham Crescent, York YO3 7NS* York (01904) 631313 or 632380

WEBSTER, Prof John Bainbridge. b 55. Clare Coll Cam MA81 PhD82. **d** 83 **p** 84. Chapl and Dep Sen Tutor St Jo Coll Dur 83-86; Hon C Bearpark *Dur* 83-86; Assoc Prof Systematic Th Wycliffe Coll Tor Univ from 86. *Wycliffe College, 5 Hoskin Avenue, Toronto, Ontario, Canada, M5S 1H7* Toronto (416) 979-2870

WEBSTER, John Maurice. b 34. Sarum & Wells Th Coll 73. **d** 76 **p** 77. Hon C Hythe *Win* from 76. *Avery Lodge, Long Lane, Marchwood, Southampton SO4 4WR* Southampton (01703) 862388

WEBSTER, Martin Duncan. b 52. Nottm Univ BSc74 DipTh76. Linc Th Coll 75. **d** 78 **p** 79. C Thundersley *Chelmsf* 78-81; C Canvey Is 81-82; TV 82-86; V Nazeing from 86; RD Harlow from 88. *The Vicarage, Betts Lane, Nazeing, Waltham Abbey, Essex EN9 2DB* Nazeing (01992) 893167

WEBSTER, Mrs Patricia Eileen. b 34. St Gabr Coll Lon TCert54. Gilmore Ho 56. **d** 87 **p** 94. Par Dn Belmont *Dur* 87-93; rtd 93. *25 Eldon Grove, Hartlepool, Cleveland TS26 9LY* Hartlepool (01429) 275698

WEBSTER, Peter. b 26. FASI. Cranmer Hall Dur 68. **d** 70 **p** 71. C Tickhill w Stainton *Sheff* 70-72; C Conisbrough 72-73; V Walkley 73-77; V Rawcliffe 77-84; V Barrow-on-Humber *Linc* 84; P-in-c Goxhill 84; V Barrow and Goxhill 84-91; rtd 91. *17 Kirkham Court, Goole, N Humberside DN14 6JU* Goole (01405) 766513

WEBSTER, Sarah Vernoy (Sally). b 38. Univ of Georgia BSc61. S'wark Ord Course 87. **d** 90 **p** 94. NSM Primrose Hill St Mary w Avenue Road St Paul *Lon* from 90. *15 Elsworthy Rise, London NW3 3QY* 0171-722 5756

WEBSTER, Mrs Sheila Mary. b 22. Bedf Coll Lon CSocStuds43. Gilmore Ho 69. **dss** 81 **d** 87. Patcham *Chich* 77-83; Hove All SS 84-90; Hon Par Dn 87-90; rtd 90. *108 Surrenden Road, Brighton BN1 6WB* Brighton (01273) 561222

WEBSTER-SMITH, Preb Alfred William. b 10. St Chad's Coll Dur BA32 DipTh33 MA35. **d** 33 **p** 34. R Pontesbury I and II *Heref* 66-76; Preb Heref Cathl 73-81; rtd 76; Perm to Offic *S'wark* from 80. *6 Frederick Gardens, Cheam, Surrey SM1 2HX* 0181-641 0226

WEDDERBURN, John Alroy. b 07. St Aid Birkenhead 46. **d** 47 **p** 48. V Hornby w Claughton *Blackb* 54-82; rtd 72. *Flat 3, Manormead, Tilford Road, Hindhead, Surrey GU26 6RA* Hindhead (01428) 605428

WEDDERSPOON, Very Rev Alexander Gillan. b 31. Jes Coll Ox BA54 MA61 Lon Univ BD62. Cuddesdon Coll. **d** 61 **p** 62. C Kingston All SS *S'wark* 61-63; Lect RE Lon Univ 63-66; Educn Adv C of E Sch Coun 66-70; Can Res Win Cathl *Win* 70-87; Vice-Dean 80-87; Treas 80-85; Dean Guildf from 87. *1 Cathedral Close, Guildford, Surrey GU2 5TL* Guildford (01483) 60328 or 65287 Fax 303350

WEDGBURY, John William. b 53. RMCS BSc78. St Jo Coll Nottm 84. **d** 87 **p** 88. C Foord St Jo *Cant* 87-91; V Mangotsfield *Bris* 91-92. *138 Wessex Oval, Wareham, Dorset BH20 4ET* Wareham (01929) 552880

WEDGEWORTH, Michael John. b 40. Nottm Univ BSc62. Wesley Ho Cam MA66. **d** 93 **p** 94. In Meth Ch 66-93; NSM Feniscowles *Blackb* from 93. *46 Preston New Road, Blackburn BB2 6AH* Blackburn (01254) 260078 Fax 392597

WEDGWOOD, Preb Charles Mervyn. b 16. Selw Coll Cam BA38 MA46. Wycliffe Hall Ox 38. **d** 40 **p** 41. Preb Wells Cathl *B & W* 63-81; V Combe Down w Monkton Combe 73-81; RD Bath 76-81; V Combe Down w Monkton Combe and S Stoke 81; rtd 81; Perm to Offic *Ex* 86-93. *17 High Street, High Littleton, Bristol BS18 5HU* Mendip (01761) 472896

WEDGWOOD, George Peter. b 26. St Jo Coll Dur BA51 DipTh52 MA56. **d** 52 **p** 53. Prin Lect St Kath Coll 69-83; Lic to Offic *Bradf* 83-86; Hd of Div Liv Coll of HE 84-86; P-in-c Kirkoswald, Renwick and Ainstable *Carl* 86-88; rtd 88; Perm to Offic *Carl* 88-92. *Chameutre, 71250 Bergesserin, Saone-et-Loire, France*

WEDGWOOD, Keith. b 20. Hertf Coll Ox BA42 MA46. Wycliffe Hall Ox 42. **d** 43 **p** 44. Canada 68-72; P-in-c Osmington w Poxwell *Sarum* 72-77; TV The Iwernes and Sutton Waldron 77-78; P-in-c 78-81; V The Iwernes, Sutton Waldron and Fontmell Magna 81-85; rtd 85. *18 Walton Road, Bournemouth BH10 4BJ* Bournemouth (01202) 532116

WEDGWOOD, Peter John. b 20. Worc Ord Coll. **d** 66 **p** 67. C Claines St Jo *Worc* 66-90; Chapl Alice Ottley Sch Upper Tything from 73; rtd 90. *28 Cornmeadow Lane, Worcester WR3 7NY* Worcester (01905) 453730

WEDGWOOD GREENHOW, Stephen John Francis. b 57. Man Univ BA82. Edin Th Coll MTh84. **d** 84 **p** 85. C Wythenshawe Wm Temple Ch *Man* 84-87; USA from 87. *Address temp unknown*

WEEDEN, Simon Andrew. b 55. York Univ BA79. Wycliffe Hall Ox 88. **d** 90 **p** 91. C Gt Chesham *Ox* 90-94; P-in-c Haversham w Lt Linford, Tyringham w Filgrave from 94. *The Rectory, Haversham, Milton Keynes MK19 7DT* Milton Keynes (01908) 312136

WEEDING, Paul Stephen. b 62. Leic Poly BSc. Ripon Coll Cuddesdon. **d** 90 **p** 91. C Llanishen and Lisvane *Llan* 90-93; C Merthyr Tydfil Ch Ch from 93. *1 Andrews Close, Merthyr Tydfil, M Glam CF48 1SS* Merthyr Tydfil (01685) 387379

✠**WEEKES, Rt Rev Ambrose Walter Marcus.** b 19. CB70. AKC41 Linc Th Coll 41. **d** 42 **p** 43 **c** 77. C New Brompton St Luke *Roch* 42-44; Chapl RNVR 44-46; Chapl RN 46-69; Chapl of the Fleet and Adn for the RN 69-72; QHC from 69; Can Gib Cathl *Eur* 71-73; Chapl Tangier 72-73; Dean Gib 73-77; Aux Bp Eur 77-80 and from 89; Suff Bp Eur 80-86; Dean Brussels 81-86; rtd 86; Asst Bp Roch 86-88; Chapl Montreux w Gstaad *Eur* 89-92. *c/o All Saints' Vicarage, 7 Margaret Street, London W1N 8JQ* 0171-580 6467

WEEKES, Very Rev Cecil William. b 31. CITC. **d** 78 **p** 79. NSM Glenageary *D & G* 78-80; Bp's V Kilkenny Cathl *C & O* 80-83; I Carlow w Urglin and Staplestown 83-90; Preb Leighlin Cathl from 88; Preb Ossory Cathl from 88; I Lismore w Cappoquin, Kilwatermoy, Dungarvan etc from 90; Dean Lismore from 90; Chan Cashel Cathl from 90; Prec Waterford Cathl from 90. *The Deanery, The Mall, Lismore, Co Waterford, Irish Republic* Lismore (58) 54137 Fax as telephone

WEEKES, David John. b 34. Magd Coll Cam BA59 MA68 Lon Univ CertEd68 Aber Univ MTh79. Clifton Th Coll 62. **d** 64 **p** 65. C Cheadle *Ches* 64-68; Uganda 69-73; Perm to Offic *St And* 73-74; Chapl and Hd of RE Fettes Coll Edin 74-94; Lic to Offic *Edin* 74-94; Lee Abbey International Students' Club Kensington from 94; Perm to Offic *Lon* from 94. *Lee Abbey International Students' Club, 57-67 Lexham Gardens, London W8 6JJ* 0171-373 7242 or 244 8758 Fax 244 8702

WEETMAN, John Charles. b 66. Qu Coll Ox BA87. Trin Coll Bris BA91. **d** 91 **p** 92. C Hull Newland St Jo *York* from 91. *St Faith's House, Dunswell Lane, Hull HU6 0AS* Hull (01482) 854526

WEIR, David Alexander. b 69. City Univ BSc91 Fitzw Coll Cam BA94. Westcott Ho Cam CTM. **d** 95. NSM Locks Heath *Portsm* from 95. *11 Laurel Road, Locks Heath, Southampton SO31 6QG*

WEIR, Graham Francis. b 52. GSM LASI. N Ord Course 88. **d** 91 **p** 92. NSM High Crompton *Man* 91-92; NSM Heyside from 92; Asst Chapl Bolton Gen Hosp from 94. *Bolton General Hospital, Minerva Road, Farnworth, Bolton BL4 0JR* Bolton (01204) 390770 or 390390

WEIR, John Michael Vavasour. b 48. K Coll Lon BD72 AKC72. **d** 73 **p** 74. C Hatf Hyde St Mary *St Alb* 73-76; C Watford St Mich 76-79; Asst Chapl Oslo St Edm *Eur* 80-81; V Bethnal Green St Pet w St Thos *Lon* from 81; Chapl Qu Eliz Hosp for Children Lon from 81. *St Peter's Vicarage, St Peter's Close, London E2 7AE* 0171-739 2717

WEIR, John William Moon. b 36. St Luke's Coll Ex CertEd69 Ex Univ BEd76. SW Minl Tr Course 82. **d** 85 **p** 86. NSM Meavy, Sheepstor and Walkhampton *Ex* 85-87; NSM Yelverton, Meavy, Sheepstor and Walkhampton from 87; Hd Master Princetown Primary Sch from 87; Sub-Chapl HM Pris Dartmoor from 87. *Goblin's Green, Dousland, Yelverton, Devon PL20 6ND* Yelverton (01822) 852671

WEIR, William Daniel Niall. b 57. BA. Ripon Coll Cuddesdon. **d** 83 **p** 84. C Chelsea St Luke *Lon* 83-87; PV Westmr Abbey 85-89; C Poplar *Lon* 87-88; TV 88-93; P-in-c Forest Gate Em w Upton Cross *Chelmsf* from 93. *Emmanuel Vicarage, 2B Margery Park Road, London E7 9JY* 0181-536 0244

WELANDER, Canon David Charles St Vincent. b 25. FSA. Lon Coll of Div BD47 ALCD47. **d** 48 **p** 49. V Cheltenham Ch Ch *Glouc* 63-75; RD Cheltenham 73-75; Can Res Glouc Cathl 75-91; rtd 91; Perm to Offic *Bris* from 91. *Willow Cottage, 1 Sandpits Lane, Sherston Magna, Malmesbury, Wilts SN16 0NN* Malmesbury (01666) 840180

WELBOURN, David Anthony. b 41. K Coll Lon BD63 AKC63 DMS. **d** 64 **p** 65. C Stockton St Chad *Dur* 64-67; C S Westoe 69-74; Ind Chapl 69-80; Ind Chapl *Nor* 80-90; Ind and Commerce Officer Guildf from 90. *81 Collingwood Crescent, Guildford, Surrey GU1 2NU* Guildford (01483) 570600

WELBY, Justin Portal. b 56. MACT84 Trin Coll Cam BA78 MA90. Cranmer Hall Dur BA91 DMinlStuds92. **d** 92 **p** 93. C Chilvers Coton w Astley *Cov* from 92. *126 Coventry Road, Nuneaton, Warks CV10 7AD* Nuneaton (01203) 383086

WELBY, Peter Edlin Brown. b 34. Open Univ BA75. St Jo Coll Dur 75. **d** 77 **p** 78. C Auckland St Andr and St Anne *Dur* 77-79; C S Westoe 79-81; V Tudhoe 81-93; R Croxdale and Tudhoe from 93. *21 York Villas, Tudhoe Village, Spennymoor, Co Durham DL16 6LP* Spennymoor (01388) 818418

WELBY, Richard Alexander Lyon (Alex). b 58. St Jo Coll Nottm BTh81 LTh Ridley Hall Cam 83. **d** 84 **p** 85. C Stoke Bishop *Bris* 84-88; V Bowling St Steph *Bradf* 88-95; P-in-c

Hatherleigh, Meeth, Exbourne and Jacobstowe *Ex* from 95. *The Rectory, Hatherleigh, Okehampton, Devon EX20 3JY* Okehampton (01837) 810314

WELCH, Miss Alice. b 41. Trin Coll Bris 77. dss 85 **d** 87 **p** 94. Chesterfield H Trin *Derby* 85-87; Par Dn 87-89; Chapl to the Deaf 89-95; D-in-c Rowsley 89-94; P-in-c 94-95; rtd 95. *The Vicarage, Rowsley, Matlock, Derbyshire DE4 2EA* Matlock (01629) 733296

WELCH, Derek. b 27. Keble Coll Ox BA51 MA57. Coll of Resurr Mirfield 51. **d** 53 **p** 54. V Salesbury *Blackb* 66-72; V Heyhouses on Sea 73-92; rtd 92. *76 St Thomas's Road, Lytham St Annes, Lancs FY8 1JR* St Annes (01253) 781469

WELCH, Francis Hughan. b 16. Lon Univ BD67. S'wark Ord Course 67. **d** 70 **p** 71. C St Alb St Steph *St Alb* 71-75; P-in-c 75-80; Chapl St Alb City Hosp 80-90; Perm to Offic *Lon* 80-90; rtd 81; Perm to Offic *St Alb* 80-81 and 90-93; Hon C St Alb St Pet 81-89; Hon C St Alb St Mich 89-90. *Bryntelor, Sanau, Llandysul, Dyfed SA44 6QN* Aberporth (01239) 654573

WELCH, Frederick George. b 23. St Cath Coll Cam BA44 MA48 Lon Univ BD59. St Aug Coll Cant 63. **d** 74 **p** 75. Kenya 74-87; rtd 87; Asst Chapl Tenerife *Eur* 87-88; Hon C Tamworth *Lich* 88-89; Hon C Hordle *Win* 89-92; Perm to Offic from 92. *8 Cruse Close, Sway, Lymington, Hants SO41 6AY* Lymington (01590) 682134

WELCH, Gordon Joseph. b 47. Man Univ BSc68 PhD72. N Ord Course 84. **d** 87 **p** 88. NSM Upton Ascension *Ches* from 87. *6 St James Avenue, Chester CH2 1NA* Chester (01244) 382196

WELCH, Canon Grant Keith. b 40. AKC63. **d** 64 **p** 65. C Nottm St Mary *S'well* 64-68; V Cinderhill 68-73; Master St Jo Hosp Weston Favell 73-88; R Weston Favell *Pet* 73-88; Can Pet Cathl 83-88; P-in-c Gt Houghton 84-85; V Wymondham *Nor* 88; C Loughton St Jo *Chelmsf* 89-92; TR from 92. *The Rectory, Church Lane, Loughton, Essex IG10 1PD* 0181-508 1224

WELCH, Harold Gerald. b 16. St Cath Soc Ox BA48 MA53. Wycliffe Hall Ox 48. **d** 50 **p** 51. V Austrey *Birm* 66-83; V Warton 66-83; rtd 83; Perm to Offic *Birm* from 88; Perm to Offic *Lich* from 88. *2 Clifford Close, Tamworth, Staffs B77 2DD* Tamworth (01827) 53678

WELCH, John Harry. b 52. Oak Hill Th Coll 85. **d** 87 **p** 88. C Parr *Liv* 87-90; V W Derby St Luke from 90. *St Luke's Vicarage, Princess Drive, West Derby, Liverpool L14 8XG* 0151-228 6025

WELCH, Canon Michael Robin. b 33. MBE81. St Chad's Coll Dur BSc55. Wells Th Coll 57. **d** 59 **p** 60. C S Shields St Hilda *Dur* 59-63; CF (R of O) 61-88; Warden and Tr Officer Dioc Youth Cen *Newc* 63-68; Soc and Ind Adv *Portsm* from 68; V Portsea All SS 72-85; V Swanmore St Barn from 85; RD Bishops Waltham 88-93; Hon Can Portsm Cathl from 92. *The Vicarage, Swanmore, Southampton SO3 2PA* Bishops Waltham (01489) 892105

WELCH, Paul Baxter. b 47. Lanc Univ BEd74 MA75. St Alb Minl Tr Scheme 80. **d** 83 **p** 84. NSM Heath and Reach *St Alb* 83-84; Bp's Sch Adv *Win* 84-89; P-in-c Clungunford w Clunbury and Clunton, Bedstone etc *Heref* 89-93; V Wellingborough All SS *Pet* from 93. *The Vicarage, 154 Midland Road, Wellingborough, Northants NN8 1NF* Wellingborough (01933) 227101

WELCH, Stephan John. b 50. Hull Univ BA74. Qu Coll Birm DipTh76. **d** 77 **p** 78. C Waltham Cross *St Alb* 77-80; P-in-c Reculver *Cant* 80-86; P-in-c Herne Bay St Bart 82-86; V Reculver and Herne Bay St Bart 86-92; V Hurley and Stubbings *Ox* from 92. *St Mary's Vicarage, High Street, Hurley, Maidenhead, Berks SL6 6AB* Maidenhead (01628) 829032

✠**WELCH, Rt Rev William Neville.** b 06. Keble Coll Ox BA27 MA32. Wycliffe Hall Ox 27. **d** 29 **p** 30 **c** 68. C Kidderminster *Worc* 29-32; C St Alb St Mich *St Alb* 32-34; Miss to Seamen 34-39; V Grays Thurrock *Chelmsf* 39-43; V Gt Ilford St Clem 43-53; RD Barking 46-53; Hon Can Chelmsf Cathl 51-53; V Gt Burstead 53-56; Adn Southend 53-73; Suff Bp Bradwell 68-73; rtd 73; Perm to Offic *Nor* from 73. *112 Earlham Road, Norwich NR2 3HE* Norwich (01603) 618192

WELCHMAN, Richard Neville de Beaufort. b 11. St Pet Hall Ox BA33 DipTh34 MA37. Wycliffe Hall Ox 33. **d** 34 **p** 35. V Pinhoe *Ex* 62-76; rtd 77; Lic to Offic *Ex* from 77. *8 Culvert Road, Stoke Canon, Exeter EX5 4BD* Exeter (01392) 841503

WELDON, William Ernest. b 41. TCD BA62 MA66. **d** 64 **p** 65. C Belf Trin Coll Miss *Conn* 64-67; C Carnmoney 67-71; Chapl RN from 71. *Directorate Gen, RN Chapl Services, Room 203, Victory Building, HM Naval Base, Portsmouth PO1 3LS* Portsmouth (01705) 727903 Fax 727112

WELFORD, Alan Traviss. b 14. St Jo Coll Cam BA35 MA39 ScD64. **d** 37 **p** 38. Australia 68-79; rtd 79; Perm to Offic *Win* 87-90. *187A High Street, Aldeburgh, Suffolk IP15 5AL* Felixstowe (01394) 278536

WELHAM, Clive Richard. b 54. **d** 80 **p** 81. C Bellingham St Dunstan *S'wark* 80-84; Chapl Golds Coll Lon 84-95; V

Plumstead Ascension from 95. *The Ascension Vicarage, Thornhill Avenue, London SE18 2HS* 0181-854 3395

WELLER, John Beresford. b 15. Lon Univ BD52. Tyndale Hall Bris 39. **d** 42 **p** 43. V Harlow St Mary and St Hugh w St Jo the Bapt *Chelmsf* 60-77; RD Harlow 73-80; V Hatf Broad Oak 77-80; rtd 80; Hon C Duffield *Derby* from 81. *8 Chadfield Road, Duffield, Belper, Derbyshire DE56 4DU* Derby (01332) 842271

WELLER, Canon John Christopher. b 25. St Pet Hall Ox BA49 MA52 Nottm Univ BD57. Qu Coll Birm 50. **d** 51 **p** 52. Zambia 64-71; V W Heath *Birm* 71-81; Warden and Chapl Resthaven Home Stroud 81-84; P-in-c Duddeston 84-85; Zimbabwe 85-90; Can Harare 87-90; rtd 90. *42 Mallard Close, Acocks Green, Birmingham B27 6BN* 0121-706 7535

WELLER, Richard Morton. b 33. Selw Coll Cam BA57 MA61. Wells Th Coll 61. **d** 63 **p** 64. C Stockingford *Cov* 63-66; C Pontefract St Giles *Wakef* 66-68; C-in-c Stockton St Jas *CD Dur* 68-74; V E Ardsley *Wakef* 74-83; V Heckmondwike 83-91; V Birstall from 92. *The Vicarage, Kings Drive, Birstall, Batley, W Yorkshire WF17 9JJ* Batley (01924) 473715

WELLER, Ronald Howden. b 18. Wycliffe Hall Ox. **d** 60 **p** 61. V Broxbourne *St Alb* 63-70; Singapore 70-74; New Zealand from 74; rtd 83. *4 Rydal Street, Hoon Hay, Christchurch 2, New Zealand*

WELLER, William John France. b 12. MBE58. Ridley Hall Cam 60. **d** 61 **p** 62. R Stratfield Saye *Win* 65-73; R Stratfield Saye w Hartley Wespall 73-74; C-in-c Hartley Wespall w Stratfield Turgis 65-74; RD Odiham 69-74; P-in-c Southwick w Boarhunt *Portsm* 75-77; rtd 77; Perm to Offic *Ex* 78-94. *10 Kingsley Terrace, Portreath, Redruth, Cornwall TR16 4LX*

WELLING, Anthony Wyndham. b 29. Ely Th Coll 55. **d** 58 **p** 83. C Coppenhall St Paul *Ches* 58-60; Lic to Offic *Ox* 82; Hon C Cookham from 83. *Broadway Barn, High Street, Ripley, Woking, Surrey GU23 6AQ* Guildford (01483) 225384

WELLINGTON, Canon James Frederick. b 51. Leic Univ LLB72 Fitzw Coll Cam BA76. Ridley Hall Cam 74. **d** 77 **p** 78. C Mill Hill Jo Keble Ch *Lon* 77-80; C Wood Green St Mich 80-82; C Wood Green St Mich w Bounds Green St Gabr etc 82-83; V Stocking Farm *Leic* 83-90; V Gt Glen, Stretton Magna and Wistow etc from 90; Warden of Readers from 91; Hon Can Leic Cathl from 94. *St Cuthbert's Vicarage, Church Road, Great Glen, Leicester LE8 9FE* Leicester (0116) 259 2238

WELLS, Andrew Stuart. b 48. St Jo Coll Dur BA71. Cranmer Hall Dur DipTh73. **d** 74 **p** 75. C Walmsley *Man* 74-77; C Failsworth H Family 77-79; R Openshaw 79-90; V Hindsford from 90. *St Anne's Vicarage, Powys Street, Atherton, Manchester M29 9AR* Atherton (01942) 883902

WELLS, Anthony Martin Giffard. b 42. St Jo Coll Nottm 72. **d** 74 **p** 75. C Orpington Ch Ch *Roch* 74-78; P-in-c Odell *St Alb* 78-82; R 82-86; P-in-c Pavenham 78-82; V 82-86; RD Sharnbrook 81-86; R Angmering *Chich* from 86; RD Arundel and Bognor from 93. *The Rectory, Rectory Lane, Angmering, Littlehampton, W Sussex BN16 4JU* Rustington (01903) 784979

WELLS, Antony Ernest (Tony). b 36. Oak Hill Th Coll 58. **d** 61 **p** 62. C Bethnal Green St Jas Less *Lon* 61-64; SAMS 64-69; Paraguay 64-69; V Kirkdale St Athanasius *Liv* 69-73; SAMS 73-75; Argentina 73-75; V Warfield *Ox* 75-81; V Fairfield *Liv* 81-83; C Rainhill 83-85; TV Cheltenham St Mark *Glouc* 85-89; P-in-c Forest of Dean Ch Ch w English Bicknor from 89. *Christ Church Vicarage, Ross Road, Coleford, Glos GL16 7NS* Dean (01594) 832334

WELLS, Bryan Arthur. b 47. Golds Coll Lon BMus72 DipEd83 MA85. Coll of Resurr Mirfield 77. **d** 79 **p** 82. C Leigh-on-Sea St Marg *Chelmsf* 79-80; Hon C Limpsfield and Titsey *S'wark* 81-85; C Weymouth St Paul *Sarum* 86-89; TV Selsdon St Jo w St Fran *S'wark* from 89. *St Francis's Vicarage, Tedder Road, South Croydon, Surrey CR2 8AH* 0181-657 7864

WELLS, Miss Cecilia Isabel. b 24. Bedf Coll Lon BA45. St Mich Ho Ox 46. dss 62 **d** 87. Ches le Street *Dur* 74-84; rtd 84; Perm to Offic *Ches* from 84. *12 Rectory Close, Nantwich, Cheshire CW5 5SW* Nantwich (01270) 627258

WELLS, Canon Charles. b 07. Cu Coll Cam BA28 MA32. Westcott Ho Cam 28. **d** 30 **p** 31. V Win St Bart *Win* 55-73; Hon Can Win Cathl 70-73; rtd 73; Perm to Offic *Win* from 73; Perm to Offic *Portsm* from 83. *7 Park Court, Park Road, Winchester, Hants SO23 7BE* Winchester (01962) 869015

WELLS, Charles Francis (Charlie). b 39. Oak Hill Th Coll DipHE. **d** 85 **p** 86. C Southend St Sav Westcliff *Chelmsf* 85-89; P-in-c E and W Horndon w Lt Warley from 89. *The Rectory, Thorndon Avenue, Brentwood, Essex CM13 3TR* Brentwood (01277) 811223

WELLS, David Henry Nugent. b 20. St Chad's Coll Dur BA42 MA46 DipTh47. **d** 47 **p** 48. V Alrewas *Lich* 64-73; V Wychnor 64-73; R Upton Magna 73-81; V Withington 73-81; P-in-c Uffington 81; R Uffington, Upton Magna and Withington

81-85; rtd 85; Perm to Offic *Lich* from 85. *13 Belvidere Avenue, Shrewsbury SY2 5PF* Shrewsbury (01743) 365822

WELLS, Canon Edward Arthur. b 23. SRN. Oak Hill Th Coll. **d** 57 **p** 58. R Sproughton w Burstall *St E* 62-74; V Ipswich St Nic 74-80; Hon Can St E Cathl 80-88; Chapl Ipswich Hosp 80-90; rtd 88. *74 Christchurch Street, Ipswich IP4 2DH* Ipswich (01473) 254046

WELLS, George Reginald. b 11. K Coll Cam BA33. Cuddesdon Coll 33. **d** 34 **p** 35. V Hagbourne *Ox* 61-74; P-in-c Gt Coxwell 74-80; P-in-c Buscot 74-80; P-in-c Coleshill 74-80; P-in-c Eaton Hastings 74-80; P-in-c Gt Coxwell w Buscot, Coleshill & Eaton Hastings 80; rtd 80; Perm to Offic *Glas* from 80. *8 Greystone Avenue, Dumfries DG1 1PE* Dumfries (01387) 68294

WELLS, Jeremy Stephen. b 47. Nottm Univ BA69 Univ of Wales DPS87. Chich Th Coll 72. **d** 73 **p** 74. C S Yardley St Mich *Birm* 73-76; C St Marychurch *Ex* 76-78; P-in-c Bridgwater H Trin *B & W* 78-82; P-in-c Brent Knoll 82-84; P-in-c E Brent w Lympsham 82-84; R Brent Knoll, E Brent and Lympsham from 84. *The Rectory, Church Road, East Brent, Highbridge, Somerset TA9 4HZ* Brent Knoll (01278) 760271

WELLS, John Michael. b 35. Mert Coll Ox BA58 MA61. Westcott Ho Cam 60. **d** 62 **p** 63. C Hornchurch St Andr *Chelmsf* 62-64; C Barking St Marg 64-66; C Wanstead H Trin Hermon Hill 66-69; V Elm Park St Nic Hornchurch 69-76; Offg Chapl RAF 69-76; R Wakes Colne w Chappel *Chelmsf* 76-79; Project Officer Cathl Cen for Research and Tr 79-81; Hon Chapl Chelmsf Cathl 79-81; Area Sec (Dios Chelmsf and Ely) CMS 81-88; E Cen Co-ord 85-91; Area Sec (Dios Chelmsf and St E) 88-91; Public Preacher *Chelmsf* 82-91; V Hanging Heaton *Wakef* from 92. *The Vicarage, 150 High Street, Hanging Heaton, Batley, W Yorkshire WF17 6DW* Dewsbury (01924) 461917

WELLS, Ven John Rowse David. b 27. Kelham Th Coll 53. **d** 57 **p** 58. SSM from 57; Lic to Offic *S'well* 57-59; Australia 59-65; Basutoland 65-66; Lesotho from 66; Can SS Mary and Jas Cathl Maseru from 77; Adn Cen Lesotho from 85. *PO Box 1579, Maseru, Lesotho 100* Lesotho (266) 315979

WELLS, Mark Wynne-Eyton. b 20. Peterho Cam BA48 MA54. Westcott Ho Cam 48. **d** 50 **p** 51. V Stoke by Nayland w Leavenheath *St E* 62-88; RD Hadleigh 71-76 and 85-86; rtd 88; Perm to Offic *Nor* from 88. *Red House, The Street, Great Snoring, Fakenham, Norfolk NR21 0AH* Fakenham (01328) 820641

WELLS, Michael John. b 46. Solicitor 74 Univ Coll Ox BA68 MA73. S Dios Minl Tr Scheme 92. **d** 95. NSM Brighton St Pet and St Nic w Chpl Royal *Chich* from 95. *35 Park Crescent, Brighton BN2 3HB* Brighton (01273) 600735

WELLS, Nicholas Anthony. b 60. Cranmer Hall Dur 88. **d** 91 **p** 92. C Accrington St Jo w Huncoat *Blackb* 91-94; C Douglas St Geo and St Barn *S & M* from 94. *62 Ballabrooie Way, Douglas, Isle of Man IM1 4HB* Douglas (01624) 621547

WELLS, Norman Charles. b 18. Keble Coll Ox BA40 MA44. St Steph Ho Ox 40. **d** 42 **p** 43. V St Margarets on Thames *Lon* 62-73; V Highbridge *B & W* 73-84; RD Burnham 76-82; rtd 84; Perm to Offic *B & W* from 85. *40 Mount Road, Nether Stowey, Bridgwater, Somerset TA5 1LU* Nether Stowey (01278) 732609

WELLS, Oswald Bertie (Bert). b 18. Linc Th Coll. **d** 48 **p** 49. C Loughton St Jo *Chelmsf* 81-84; Hon C from 84; rtd 84. *2 Baldwins Hill, Loughton, Essex IG10 1SD* 0181-508 4602

WELLS, Peter Robert. b 59. Wilson Carlile Coll 78 Sarum & Wells Th Coll 87. **d** 89 **p** 90. CA from 81; C Mortlake w E Sheen *S'wark* 89-93; Dir St Marylebone Healing and Counselling Cen from 93. *17 Marylebone Road, London NW1 5LT* 0171-935 6374

WELLS, Philip Anthony. b 57. BA MPhil. Coll of Resurr Mirfield. **d** 84 **p** 85. C Wylde Green *Birm* 84-87; Chapl and Succ Birm Cathl 87-91; Bp's Dom Chapl from 91. *East Wing, Bishop's Croft, Old Church Road, Birmingham B17 0BE* 0121-427 1163 or 427 2295 Fax 426 1322

WELLS, Richard John. b 46. St Mich Coll Llan DipTh70 Cuddesdon Coll 70. **d** 71 **p** 72. C Kingston upon Hull St Alb *York* 71-75; C Addlestone *Guildf* 75-80; V Weston 80-88; V Milford from 88; Chapl Milford Hosp Surrey from 88. *The Vicarage, Milford, Godalming, Surrey GU8 5BX* Godalming (01483) 414710

WELLS, Robert Crosby. b 28. St Jo Coll Dur BA52. **d** 54 **p** 55. V Ribby w Wrea *Blackb* 69-93; rtd 93. *4 Myra Road, Fairhaven, Lytham St Annes, Lancs FY8 1EB* Lytham (01253) 739851

WELLS, Ven Roderick John. b 36. Dur Univ BA63 Hull Univ MA85. Cuddesdon Coll 63. **d** 65 **p** 66. C Lambeth St Mary the Less *S'wark* 65-68; P-in-c 68-71; R Skegness *Linc* 71-77; P-in-c Winthorpe 77; R Skegness and Winthorpe 77-78; TR Gt and Lt Coates w Bradley 78-89; RD Grimsby and Cleethorpes 83-89; Hon Can Linc Cathl from 86; Adn Stow from 89; V Hackthorn w Cold Hanworth 89-93; P-in-c N w S Carlton

89-93. *The Vicarage, Hackthorn, Lincoln LN2 3PF* Welton (01673) 860382

WELLS, Ronald Charles (Ron). b 20. AKC50. **d** 51 **p** 52. R Springfield All SS *Chelmsf* 65-80; Chapl Southend Gen Hosp 80-91; V Prittlewell St Pet *Chelmsf* 80-90; P-in-c 91; rtd 91. *61 Byrne Drive, Southend-on-Sea SS2 6SA* Southend-on-Sea (01702) 338006

WELLS, Samuel Martin Bailey. b 65. Mert Coll Ox BA87. Edin Th Coll 88. **d** 91 **p** 92. C Wallsend St Luke *Newc* from 91. *St Luke's Church House, Hugh Street, Wallsend, Tyne & Wear NE28 6RL* 0191-262 3631

WELLS, Stephen Glossop. b 22. CCC Ox BA48 MA48. Westcott Ho Cam 48. **d** 50 **p** 51. R Saltford *B & W* 56-80; P-in-c Corston w Newton St Loe 76-80; RD Chew Magna 80-85; R Saltford w Corston and Newton St Loe 80-87; Preb Wells Cathl 84-90; TV Wellington and Distr 87-90; rtd 90. *57 Meadow Road, Berkhamsted, Herts HP4 1JL* Berkhamsted (01442) 870981

WELLS, Terry Roy John. b 45. E Anglian Minl Tr Course 89. **d** 92 **p** 93. C Martlesham w Brightwell *St E* 92-95; R Higham, Holton St Mary, Raydon and Stratford from 95. *The Rectory, Stratford St Mary, Colchester CO7 6LZ* Colchester (01206) 322128

WELLS, Canon William David Sandford. b 41. JP. Or Coll Ox BA64 MA66. Ridley Hall Cam 63. **d** 65 **p** 66. C Gt Malvern St Mary *Worc* 65-70; V Crowle 70-84; P-in-c Himbleton w Huddington 78-84; V E Bowbrook 84-89; Hon Can Worc Cathl from 84; RD Droitwich from 84; R Bowbrook S from 89. *The Vicarage, Crowle, Worcester WR7 4AT* Upton Snodsbury (01905) 381617

WELLS, Canon William Alan John. St Fran Coll Brisbane ThL51. **d** 52 **p** 53. Bahamas 68-70; C Penton Street St Silas w All SS *Lon* 71; Grenada 72-73; St Vincent 73-75; Belize 74-79; Can Belize Cathl from 77; Asst Chapl HM Pris Liv 79-82; Chapl HM Pris Rudgate and HM Rem Cen Thorp Arch 82-87; V Middlesb St Thos *York* 87-94; rtd 94; Perm to Offic *Nor* from 94. *35 Cleaves Drive, Wells Road, Walsingham, Norfolk NR22 6EQ* Walsingham (01328) 820598

WELLS, Archdeacon of. *See* ACWORTH, Ven Richard Foote

WELLS, Dean of. *See* LEWIS, Very Rev Richard

WELSBY, Canon Paul Antony. b 20. Univ Coll Dur BA42 MA45 Sheff Univ PhD58. Linc Th Coll 42. **d** 44 **p** 45. Can Res Roch Cathl *Roch* 68-88; Dir Post Ord Tr 66-88; Chapl to The Queen 80-90; rtd 88; Bp's Dom Chapl *Roch* 88-90. *20 Knights Ridge, Pembury, Tunbridge Wells, Kent TN2 4HP* Pembury (01892) 823053

WELSH, Angus Alexander. b 30. Trin Coll Cam BA54 MA59 St Jo Coll Dur DipTh56. **d** 56 **p** 57. C Jesmond Clayton Memorial *Newc* 56-60; C Fenham St Jas and St Basil 60-62; V Bacup St Jo *Man* 62-68; Tristan da Cunha 68-71; St Vincent 72-78; R Heysham *Blackb* 78-88; V Blackb St Steph from 88. *St Stephen's Vicarage, 285 Whalley Old Road, Blackburn BB1 5RS* Blackburn (01254) 255546

WELSH, Jennifer Ann. b 48. Univ Coll Lon BA. **d** 81. NSM Newport St Matt *Mon* 81-85; NSM Risca from 85. *470 Caerleon Road, Newport, Gwent NP9 7LW* Newport (01633) 258287

WELSH, Jennifer Lee (Jenny). b 59. Calgary Univ BSc81. Cam Episc Div Sch (USA) MDiv87. **d** 87 **p** 88. Canada 87-89; Asst Chapl HM Pris Linc from 89. *46 Yarborough Crescent, Lincoln LN1 3LU* Lincoln (01522) 512650 or 533633 Fax 532116

WELSH, Miss Mary Elizabeth. b 22. St Hilda's Coll Ox BA44 MA48 Lon Univ DipEd45 BD50. Lambeth STh64. **dss** 68 **d** 87 **p** 94. Ex St Mark *Ex* 70-82; Lic to Offic 82-85; Yatton Moor *B & W* 85-87; Perm to Offic from 87. *26 Rectory Way, Yatton, Bristol BS19 4JF* Yatton (01934) 833329

WELSH, Maxwell Wilfred. b 29. Bp's Coll Calcutta 55. **d** 58 **p** 59. India 58-72; C Cannock *Lich* 73-76; C Wednesfield 76-79; V Milton 79-86; V Croxton w Broughton and Adbaston from 86. *The Vicarage, Croxton, Stafford ST21 6PF* Wetwood (0163082) 231

WELSH, Philip Peter. b 48. Keble Coll Ox BA69 MA73 Selw Coll Cam BA72 MA76. Westcott Ho Cam 71. **d** 73 **p** 74. C W Dulwich All SS and Em *S'wark* 73-76; C Surbiton St Andr 76-77; C Surbiton St Andr and St Mark 77-79; India 79-81; V Malden St Jo *S'wark* 81-87; Min Officer *Linc* 87-94; TR Basingstoke *Win* from 94. *The Rectory, Church Street, Basingstoke, Hants RG21 1QT* Basingstoke (01256) 26654

WELSH, Robert Leslie. b 32. Sheff Univ BA54 St Jo Coll Dur DipTh58. **d** 58 **p** 59. C S Westoe *Dur* 58-62; C Darlington St Cuth 62-66; CF (TA) 64-67; V E Rainton *Dur* 66-85; R W Rainton 66-85; R Wolsingham and Thornley from 85. *The Rectory, 14 Rectory Lane, Wolsingham, Bishop Auckland, Co Durham DL13 3AJ* Bishop Auckland (01388) 527344

WELTON, Peter Abercrombie. b 62. Ball Coll Ox BA84. Qu Coll Birm 84. **d** 86 **p** 87. C Walthamstow St Pet *Chelmsf* 86-89; Community Priest 89-93. *c/o Citizens, PO Box 459, Wolverhampton WV10 0YY*

WEMYSS, Gary. b 52. St Jo Coll Dur 79. **d** 80 **p** 81. C Blackb St Jas *Blackb* 80-83; C Padiham 83-86; V Stalmine 86-90; P-in-c Egton-cum-Newland and Lowick *Carl* from 90. *The Vicarage, Penny Bridge, Ulverston, Cumbria LA12 7RQ* Ulverston (01229) 861285

WENHAM, David. b 45. MA PhD. Ridley Hall Cam. **d** 84 **p** 85. Lic to Offic *Ox* from 84; Tutor Wycliffe Hall Ox from 84. *Wycliffe Hall, 54 Banbury Road, Oxford OX2 6PW* Oxford (01865) 274200/5/8 Fax 274215

WENHAM, John William. b 13. Pemb Coll Cam BA35 MA39 Lon Univ BD43. **d** 38 **p** 39. Warden Latimer Ho Ox 70-73; Lic to Offic *Ox* 70-73; C Cottisford 73-75; C Hardwick w Tusmore 73-75; Perm to Offic *Sarum* 75-78; rtd 78. *55 Bainton Road, Oxford OX2 7AG* Oxford (01865) 58820

WENHAM, Michael Timothy. b 49. Pemb Coll Cam MA75. Wycliffe Hall Ox DipTh85. **d** 86 **p** 87. C Norbury *Ches* 86-89; V Stanford in the Vale w Goosey and Hatford *Ox* from 89. *The Vicarage, Stanford in the Vale, Faringdon, Oxon SN7 8HU* Stanford in the Vale (01367) 710267

WENSLEY, Mrs Beryl Kathleen. b 29. CertRK55. Selly Oak Coll 53. **dss** 76 **d** 87 **p** 94. Raynes Park St Sav *S'wark* 76-83; Chapl Asst St Geo Hosp Lon 83-89; rtd 89; Chapl R Hants Co Hosp Win 89-94; Chapl Win HA 89-94. *Flat 6, Normans, Norman Road, Winchester, Hants SO23 9BX* Winchester (01962) 863992

WENSLEY, John Ettery. b 29. AKC53. **d** 54 **p** 55. C Atherton *Man* 54-57; C St Pancras w St Jas and Ch Ch *Lon* 57-60; C Portsea St Mary *Portsm* 60-61; C Portsea All SS 61-62; C Battersea St Pet *S'wark* 68-69. *3 Bulls Row, Mantle Street, Wellington, Somerset TA21 8BQ* Wellington (01823) 665221

WENT, Ven John Stewart. b 44. CCC Cam BA66 MA70. Oak Hill Th Coll 67. **d** 69 **p** 70. C Northwood Em *Lon* 69-75; V Margate H Trin *Cant* 75-83; Vice-Prin Wycliffe Hall Ox 83-89; Adn Surrey *Guildf* from 89; Chmn Dioc Coun for Unity and Miss from 90. *Tarawera, 71 Boundstone Road, Rowledge, Farnham, Surrey GU10 4AT* Frensham (01252) 793987

WENZEL, Peggy Sylvia. STh. Gilmore Ho. **d** 88 **p** 94. Perm to Offic *Sarum* from 88; rtd 92. *Church Cottage, Church Street, Pewsey, Wilts SN9 5DL* Marlborough (01672) 63834

WERNER, David Robert Edmund. b 33. Clifton Th Coll 61. **d** 63 **p** 64. C Holywell *St As* 63-68; C Llanrhos 68-70; R Tedburn St Mary *Ex* 71-91; RD Kenn 80-83; Perm to Offic from 92. *The Old Rectory, Tedburn St Mary, Exeter EX6 6EN* Tedburn St Mary (01647) 61253

WERNER, Donald Kilgour. b 39. Univ of Wales BA61 Linacre Coll Ox BA64 MA67. Wycliffe Hall Ox 61. **d** 64 **p** 65. C Wrexham *St As* 64-69; Chapl Brasted Place Coll Westerham 69-73; Chapl Bris Univ *Bris* 73-76; Hon C Clifton St Paul 73-76; Chapl Keele Univ *Lich* 77-79; P-in-c Keele 77-79; C York St Mich-le-Belfrey *York* 79-83; Dir of Evang 79-83; R Holborn St Geo w H Trin and St Bart *Lon* from 83. *13 Doughty Street, London WC1N 2PL* 0171-831 0588

WERRELL, Ralph Sidney. b 29. Tyndale Hall Bris 54. **d** 56 **p** 57. R Combs *St E* 65-75; V Bootle Ch Ch *Liv* 75-80; R Scole w Billingford and Thorpe Parva *Nor* 80; P-in-c Brockdish w Thorpe Abbots 80; R Scole, Brockdish, Billingford, Thorpe Abbots etc 80-83; R Southam w Stockton *Cov* 83-89; R Southam 89-94; rtd 95; Perm to Offic *Birm* from 95; Perm to Offic *Cov* from 95. *2A Queens Road, Kenilworth, Warks CV8 1JQ* Kenilworth (01926) 58677

WERWATH, Wolfgang Albert Richard Kurt. b 22. Ripon Hall Ox 54. **d** 56 **p** 57. V Whitfield *Derby* 67-75; V Bretby w Newton Solney 75-88; rtd 88; Perm to Offic *Derby* from 88. *28 D'Ayncourt Walk, Farnsfield, Newark, Notts NG22 8DP* Mansfield (01623) 882635

WESSON, Basil. b 24. **d** 83 **p** 84. NSM Belper Ch Ch and Milford *Derby* from 83. *Wescot, Belper Lane End, Belper, Derbyshire DE56 2DL* Belper (01773) 827566

WESSON, Canon John Graham. b 38. St Pet Coll Ox BA62 DipTh63 MA68. Clifton Th Coll 63. **d** 65 **p** 66. C Southport Ch Ch w St Andr *Liv* 65-68; C Ox St Ebbe w St Pet *Ox* 68-71; Chapl Poly Cen Lon 71-76; C-in-c Edin St Thos *Edin* 76-82; Dir Past Studies Trin Coll Bris 82-86; R Birm St Martin w Bordesley St Andr *Birm* from 86; RD Birm City 88-95; Hon Can Birm Cathl from 91. *The Rectory, 37 Barlows Road, Birmingham B15 2PN* 0121-454 0119

WEST, Alan David. b 61. Southn Univ BTh92. Aston Tr Scheme 87 Sarum & Wells Th Coll 89. **d** 92 **p** 93. C S'wark St Geo the Martyr w St Jude *S'wark* 92-94; C S'wark St Geo the Martyr w St Alphege & St Jude from 95. *2 St Alphege House, Pocock Street, London SE1 0BJ* 0171-928 7163

WEST, Andrew Victor. b 59. Wycliffe Hall Ox 87. **d** 90 **p** 91. C Leyland St Andr *Blackb* 90-94; C Blackpool St Jo from 94. *52 Leeds Road, Blackpool FY1 4HJ* Blackpool (01253) 24036

WEST, Arthur. b 20. Linc Th Coll 59. **d** 60 **p** 61. V Nether w Upper Poppleton *York* 68-85; RD Ainsty 77-85; rtd 85. *8 River View, Linton on Ouse, York YO6 2BJ* Linton-on-Ouse (01347) 848463

WEST, Bryan Edward. b 39. Avery Hill Coll CertEd69 BEd80 Kent Univ MA86. Cant Sch of Min 85. **d** 88 **p** 89. NSM Gravesend H Family w Ifield *Roch* 88-92; C Gravesend St Geo 92-95; NSM Hatcham Park All SS *S'wark* from 95. *Flat 6, 76 Wickham Road, London SE4 1LS* 0181-692 8897

WEST, Mrs Christine Cecily. TCD BA60 MA63 HDipEd61. CITC 91. **d** 94 **p** 95. NSM Bray *D & G* from 94. *55 Beech Park Road, Foxrock, Dublin 18, Irish Republic* Dublin (1) 289-6374

WEST, Canon Clive. QUB BD75. CITC. **d** 64 **p** 65. C Lisburn Ch Ch Cathl *Conn* 64-68; Asst Master Lisnagarvey Sec Sch Lisburn 68-70; C Belf All SS 70-75; I from 84; Can Belf Cathl from 95; I Mullabrack w Kilcluney *Arm* 76-84. *All Saints Rectory, 25 Rugby Road, Belfast BT7 1PT* Belfast (01232) 323327

WEST, David Marshall. b 48. St Jo Coll Dur BA70. Qu Coll Birm DipTh72. **d** 73 **p** 74. C Wylde Green *Birm* 73-76; C Wokingham St Paul *Ox* 76-79; V Hurst 79-88; V Maidenhead St Luke 88-95; C Whitley Ch Ch from 95. *32 Bourne Avenue, Reading RG2 7AJ* Reading (01734) 872935

WEST, Derek Elvin. b 47. Hull Univ BA69. Westcott Ho Cam 71. **d** 73 **p** 74. C Walthamstow St Pet *Chelmsf* 73-77; C Chingford SS Pet and Paul 77-80; TV W Slough *Ox* 80-88; Slough Community Chapl from 88. *16 Buckland Avenue, Slough SL3 7PH* Slough (01753) 524293

WEST, Eric Edward. b 32. Leeds Univ BA60. Bps' Coll Cheshunt 63. **d** 64 **p** 65. C Biscot *St Alb* 64-71; V from 71. *The Vicarage, 161 Bishopscote Road, Luton LU3 1PD* Luton (01582) 573421

WEST, Eric Robert Glenn. b 55. QUB BA79 Man Univ DipEd80. CITC BTh92. **d** 92 **p** 93. C Enniskillen *Clogh* 92-95; I Lisbellaw from 95. *The Rectory, Lisbellaw, Enniskillen, Co Fermanagh BT94 5BS* Enniskillen (01365) 87219

✠**WEST, Rt Rev Francis Horner.** b 09. Magd Coll Cam BA31 MA35. Ridley Hall Cam 31. **d** 33 **p** 34 c 62. C Burmantofts St Steph and St Agnes *Ripon* 33-36; C Cam H Trin *Ely* 36; Chapl and Tutor Ridley Hall Cam 36-38; V Starbeck *Ripon* 38-42; CF (R of O) 39-46; V Upton *S'well* 46-51; Can Newark 47-62; V E Retford 51-54; RD Retford 51-53; R Dinder *B & W* 62-71; Preb Wells Cathl 62-77; Suff Bp Taunton 62-77; rtd 77. *11 Castle Street, Aldbourne, Marlborough, Wilts SN8 2DA* Marlborough (01672) 40630

WEST, Gerald Eric. b 18. ACII48. St Deiniol's Hawarden. **d** 80 **p** 81. Hon C Bramhall *Ches* 80-82; C 82-87; rtd 87; Perm to Offic *Ches* from 87. *255 Bramhall Moor Lane, Hazel Grove, Stockport, Cheshire SK7 5JL* 0161-439 3029

WEST, Harold Reginald. b 15. Dur Univ BA43 MA46. Coll of Resurr Mirfield 43. **d** 45 **p** 46. V Newc St Luke *Newc* 61-82; rtd 82. *42 Linden Road, Gosforth, Newcastle upon Tyne NE3 4HB* 0191-284 4291

WEST, Henry Cyrano. b 28. K Coll Lon. **d** 51 **p** 52. V Sculcoates *York* 63-71; P-in-c Kingston upon Hull St Jude w St Steph 67-71; Lic to Offic *Cov* 71-75; Lic to Offic *Man* 75-87; Hon C Hulme Ascension from 87; rtd 91. *6 King's Drive, Middleton, Manchester M24 4PB* 0161-643 4410

WEST, Keith. b 63. Sunderland Poly BSc86. Chich Th Coll 92 Coll of Resurr Mirfield BTh95. **d** 95. C Rawmarsh w Parkgate *Sheff* from 95. *117 Hague Avenue, Rawmarsh, Rotherham, S Yorkshire S62 7PT* Rotherham (01709) 710056

WEST, Canon Michael Brian. b 39. Bris Univ BSc60. Linc Th Coll 64. **d** 66 **p** 67. C Hatf *St Alb* 66-69; Ind Chapl 69-81; Hon Can St Alb 78-81; Sen Ind Chapl *Sheff* from 81; Hon Can Sheff Cathl from 81. *21 Endcliffe Rise Road, Sheffield S11 8RU* Sheffield (0114) 266 1921

WEST, Michael Frederick. b 50. Trin Coll Ox BA72 MA76. Westcott Ho Cam 72. **d** 74 **p** 75. C Wolv *Lich* 74-78; C Wolv 78; C Hanley H Ev 78-79; TV 79-82; Dioc Youth Officer *St E* 83-88; V Ipswich St Thos from 88. *St Thomas's Vicarage, 102 Cromer Road, Ipswich IP1 5EP* Ipswich (01473) 741215

WEST, Michael John. b 33. ARSM54 CEng60 FIMM68 FEng89 Imp Coll Lon BScEng54. S'wark Ord Course 85. **d** 88 **p** 89. Hon C Caterham *S'wark* from 88. *1 Church Road, Kenley, Surrey CR8 5DW* 0181-668 1548

WEST, Michael Oakley. b 31. Wells Th Coll 62. **d** 63 **p** 64. C Swindon Ch Ch *Bris* 63-66; Libya 66-68; R Lydiard Millicent w Lydiard Tregoz *Bris* 68-75; V Breage w Germoe *Truro* 75-82; CMS 82-91; Israel 82-91; Chapl Shiplake Coll Henley 91-94; Asst Chapl Bryanston Sch Blandford from 94. *Bryanston School, Blandford Forum, Dorset DT11 0PX* Blandford (01258) 452411 or 456863

WEST, Miss Penelope Anne Margaret (Penny). b 44. City of Birm Coll CertEd68. Glouc Sch of Min 74 Ridley Hall Cam 85. **dss** 86 **d** 87 **p** 94. Portishead *B & W* 86-87; C 87-92; C Bath Abbey w St Jas 92-95; Chapl Bath Gp Hosps 92-95; V Kewstoke w Wick St Lawrence *B & W* from 95. *The Vicarage, 35 Kewstoke Road, Kewstoke, Weston-super-Mare, Avon BS22 9YE* Weston-super-Mare (01934) 416162

WEST, Peter Harcourt. b 29. **d** 59 **p** 60. C Braintree *Chelmsf* 61-63; Perm to Offic from 72; rtd 94. *Westgates, 139 Witham*

Road, Black Notley, Braintree, Essex CM7 8LR   Braintree (01376) 323048

WEST, Philip William. b 48. Magd Coll Ox BA70 MA78. St Jo Coll Nottm BA74 DPS75. **d** 75 **p** 76. C Rushden w Newton Bromswold *Pet* 75-79; C Pitsmoor w Ellesmere *Sheff* 79-83; V Attercliffe 83-89; Ind Chapl 85-90; P-in-c Darnall H Trin 86-89; V Stannington from 89. *The Vicarage, 334 Oldfield Road, Stannington, Sheffield S6 6EA*   Sheffield (0114) 234 5586/ 232 4490

WEST, Reginald George. b 14. ACA39 FCA57. Worc Ord Coll 66. **d** 68 **p** 69. C Oundle *Pet* 68-73; V Weedon Lois w Plumpton and Moreton Pinkney 73-79; rtd 79. *57 Greenacres Way, Newport, Shropshire TF10 7PH*   Newport (01952) 812645

WEST, Reginald Roy. b 28. St Deiniol's Hawarden 74. **d** 74 **p** 75. C Abergavenny St Mary w Llanwenarth Citra *Mon* 74-77; V Tredegar St Jas from 77. *St James's Vicarage, Poplar Road, Tredegar, Gwent NP2 4LH*   Tredegar (01495) 252510

WEST, Richard Wilfrid Anthony. b 20. Magd Coll Cam BA41 MA45. Wells Th Coll 41. **d** 43 **p** 44. V Brockham Green *S'wark* 50-86; P-in-c Betchworth 81-86; rtd 86. *2 Abbotts Walk, Cerne Abbas, Dorchester, Dorset DT2 7JN*   Cerne Abbas (01300) 341567

WEST, Canon Ronald Cameron. b 06. AKC33. **d** 33 **p** 34. V Freeland *Ox* 53-76; RD Woodstock 76-80; Hon Can Ch Ch 79-80; rtd 80; Perm to Offic *Truro* from 80. *Flat 22, Chynance, Alexandra Road, Penzance, Cornwall TR18 4LY*   Penzance (01736) 66612

WEST, Stephen Peter. b 52. Liv Univ CertEd74. Oak Hill Th Coll 87. **d** 89 **p** 90. C Gateacre *Liv* 89-92; V Liv All So Springwood from 92. *Springwood Vicarage, Mather Avenue, Liverpool L19 4TF*   0151-427 5699

WEST, Timothy Ralph (Tim). b 53. Bath Univ BSc75. Ridley Hall Cam 82. **d** 85 **p** 86. C Mildenhall *St E* 85-88; TV Melbury *Sarum* 88-92; TR from 92. *The Rectory, Summer Lane, Evershot, Dorchester, Dorset DT2 0JP*   Evershot (01935) 83238

WEST, Thomas Roderic. b 55. DipTh BTh90. TCD Div Sch. **d** 86 **p** 87. C Dromore Cathl *D & D* 86-89; I Carrowdore w Millisle 89-95; I Moira from 95. *The Rectory, 1 Main Street, Moira, Craigavon, Co Armagh BT67 0LE*   Moira (01846) 611268

WEST CUMBERLAND, Archdeacon of. *See* PACKER, Ven John Richard

WEST HAM, Archdeacon of. *Vacant*

WEST-LINDELL, Stein Eric. b 54. BA. Linc Th Coll 82. **d** 84 **p** 85. C Allington and Maidstone St Pet *Cant* 84-87; R Orlestone w Snave and Ruckinge w Warehorne 87-93; R Byfield w Boddington and Aston le Walls *Pet* from 93. *The Rectory, Church Street, Byfield, Daventry, Northants NN11 6XN*   Byfield (01327) 60204

WESTALL, Canon Michael Robert. b 39. Qu Coll Cam BA62 MA66. Cuddesdon Coll 63 Harvard Div Sch 65. **d** 66 **p** 67. C Heref St Martin *Heref* 66-70; India 70-83; Vice Prin Bp's Coll Calcutta 76-79; Prin 79-83; Tanzania 84-92; Prin St Mark's Th Coll Dar-es-Salaam 84-92; R Alfrick, Lulsley, Suckley, Leigh and Bransford *Worc* from 93. *The Rectory, Leigh, Worcester WR6 5LE*   Leigh Sinton (01886) 832355

WESTBROOK, Canon Colin David. b 36. Or Coll Ox BA59. St Steph Ho Ox DipTh60 MA63. **d** 61 **p** 62. C Roath St Martin *Llan* 61-66; C Roath St Marg 66-74; V Llantarnam *Mon* 74-79; V Newport St Jo Bapt from 79; Hon Can St Woolos Cathl 88-91; Can St Woolos Cathl from 91; Warden of Ords from 91. *St John's Vicarage, Oakfield Road, Newport, Gwent NP9 4LP*   Newport (01633) 265581

WESTBROOK (nee REED), Mrs Ethel Patricia Ivy. b 42. Bris Univ CertEd63. Cant Sch of Min 82. **dss** 84 **d** 87 **p** 94. Fawkham and Hartley *Roch* 84-85; Asst Dir of Educn 84-86; Cliffe at Hoo w Cooling 85-86; Corby SS Pet and Andr w Gt and Lt Oakley *Pet* 86-87; Par Dn 87-90; Par Dn *Roch* 90-94; C 94; C Rainham from 94. *60 Childscroft Road, Rainham, Gillingham, Kent ME8 7SN*   Medway (01634) 363631

WESTBROOK, Richard Henry. b 09. **d** 67 **p** 68. R Carlton Curlieu and Illston on the Hill etc *Leic* 70-76; R Carlton Curlieu, Illston on the Hill etc 76-81; rtd 81; Perm to Offic *Roch* from 90. *Providence House, 60 Childscroft Road, Gillingham, Kent ME8 7SN*   Medway (01634) 363631

WESTCOTT, Cuthbert Philip Brooke. b 09. Magd Coll Ox BA32 MA36. Westcott Ho Cam 36. **d** 36 **p** 37. Chapl San Remo *Eur* 71-74; Chapl Palermo w Taormina 75-77; rtd 77; Chapl St Jean-de-Luz w Pau and Biarritz *Eur* 77-80; Perm to Offic *Birm* 81-86; Perm to Offic *Linc* from 87; Perm to Offic *Pet* from 87. *Karnak House, Second Drift, Wothorpe, Stamford, Lincs PE9 3JH*   Stamford (01780) 56174

WESTCOTT, Donald Ralph. b 27. Bris Univ BA51. Ridley Hall Cam 51. **d** 53 **p** 54. V Benchill *Man* 63-70; R Islip *Ox* 70-86; R

Noke 70-86; P-in-c Woodeaton 70-86; R Roydon St Remigius *Nor* 86-90; rtd 90. *54 Arosa Drive, Malvern, Worcs WR14 3QF*   Malvern (01684) 568653

WESTCOTT, James John. b 55. St Jo RC Sem Surrey 76. **d** 81 **p** 82. In RC Ch 81-93; C Westmr St Steph w St Jo *Lon* from 93. *Flat C, Napier Hall, Hide Place, London SW1P 4NJ*   0171-821 6195

WESTERN, Canon Robert Geoffrey. b 37. Man Univ BSc60. Qu Coll Birm DipTh62. **d** 62 **p** 63. C Sedbergh *Bradf* 62-65; PV Linc Cathl *Linc* 65-73; Hd Master Linc Cathl Sch from 74; Can and Preb Linc Cathl *Linc* from 74. *Headmaster's House, 8 Eastgate, Lincoln LN2 1QG*   Lincoln (01522) 528489 or 523769

WESTLAKE, Michael Paul. b 34. Ex Coll Ox BA56 MA64. Wells Th Coll 59. **d** 61 **p** 62. C Southmead *Bris* 61-67; V Eastville St Thos 67-74; V Eastville St Thos w St Anne 74-83; P-in-c Easton St Mark 79-83; V Marshfield w Cold Ashton and Tormarton etc from 83. *The Vicarage, Church Lane, Marshfield, Chippenham, Wilts SN14 8NT*   Bath (01225) 891850

WESTLAKE, Peter Alan Grant. b 19. CMG72 MC43. FRAS CCC Ox MA48 Univ of Wales (Ban) BD81 MSc81. **d** 81 **p** 82. Hon C Llandegfan w Llandysilio *Ban* from 81. *53 Church Street, Beaumaris, Gwynedd LL58 8AB*   Beaumaris (01248) 810114

WESTLAND, Richard Theodore. b 27. Local NSM Course. **d** 87 **p** 88. NSM Freiston w Butterwick *Linc* from 87. *76 Brand End Road, Butterwick, Boston, Lincs PE22 0JD*   Boston (01205) 760572

WESTLEY, Stuart. b 24. Em Coll Cam BA48 MA52 Man Univ DASE84. Wells Th Coll 49. **d** 50 **p** 51. Lic to Offic *Blackb* 58-70; Asst Chapl Denstone Coll Uttoxeter 70-73; Chapl Ermysted's Gr Sch Skipton 73-85; Hon C Blackpool St Mich *Blackb* 75-77; Perm to Offic *Bradf* 77-78; Lic to Offic 78-85; C Padiham *Blackb* 85-89; rtd 89. *Ad Viam, Side Gate Lane, Lothersdale, Keighley, W Yorkshire BD20 8EU*   Keighley (01535) 635646

WESTMACOTT, Preb Ian Field. b 19. Wells Th Coll 60. **d** 60 **p** 61. V Long Ashton *B & W* 63-84; RD Portishead 72-82; Preb Wells Cathl 77-84; rtd 84; Perm to Offic *Bris* from 85; Perm to Offic *B & W* from 85. *8A York Place, Bristol B58 1AH*   Bristol (0117) 973 6057

WESTMINSTER, Archdeacon of. *See* HARVEY, Ven Anthony Ernest

WESTMINSTER, Dean of. *See* MAYNE, Very Rev Michael Clement Otway

WESTMORLAND AND FURNESS, Archdeacon of. *See* PEAT, Ven Lawrence Joseph

WESTNEY, Michael Edward William. b 29. Lich Th Coll 64. **d** 65 **p** 66. C Banbury *Ox* 68-71; TV Trunch *Nor* 71-78; V Reading St Matt *Ox* 78-83; TV W Slough 83-88; TR 88-94; rtd 94. *59 Portland Close, Burnham, Slough SL2 2LT*   Slough (01628) 660052

WESTON, Christopher James. b 20. G&C Coll Cam BA46 MA49. Ridley Hall Cam 47. **d** 49 **p** 50. V Clifton St Jas *Sheff* 63-70; P-in-c Stevenage St Nic *St Alb* 70-71; V 71-87; rtd 87. *15 Coltsfoot Close, Cherry Hinton, Cambridge CB1 4YH*   Cambridge (01223) 242604

WESTON, Canon Dr David Wilfrid Valentine. b 37. Lanc Univ PhD93. **d** 67 **p** 68. OSB 60-84; Lic to Offic *Ox* 67-84; Prior Nashdom Abbey 71-74; Abbot 74-84; C Chorley St Pet *Blackb* 84-85; V Pilling 85-89; Bp's Dom Chapl *Carl* 89-94; Can Res Carl Cathl from 94. *3 The Abbey, Carlisle CA3 8TZ*   Carlisle (01228) 21834

WESTON, Ven Frank Valentine. b 35. Qu Coll Ox BA60 MA64. Lich Th Coll 60. **d** 61 **p** 62. C Atherton *Man* 61-65; Chapl USPG Coll of the Ascension Selly Oak 65-69; Prin 69-76; Prin Edin Th Coll 76-82; Can St Mary's Cathl *Edin* 76-82; Adn Ox and Can Res Ch Ch *Ox* from 82. *Archdeacon's Lodging, Christ Church, Oxford OX1 1DP*   Oxford (01865) 276185   Fax 276276

WESTON, Frederick Victor Henry. b 41. Qu Coll Cam BA63 MA67. St D Coll Lamp LTh65. **d** 65 **p** 66. C Grangetown *Llan* 65-67; C Cwmmer w Abercregan CD 67-69; C Haverhill *St E* 69-74; R Gt and Lt Whelnetham 74-79; Perm to Offic from 84. *154 Southgate Street, Bury St Edmunds, Suffolk IP33 2AF*

WESTON, Harold John. b 24. Worc Ord Coll 65. **d** 67 **p** 68. C Northn St Mich *Pet* 67-71; C Pet St Jo 71-74; R Peakirk w Glinton 75-89; rtd 89. *8 Delph Court, Delph Street, Whittlesey, Peterborough PE7 1QQ*   Peterborough (01733) 205516

WESTON, Ivan John. b 45. MBE88. Chich Th Coll 71. **d** 74 **p** 75. C Harlow St Mary Magd *Chelmsf* 74-77; Chapl RAF from 77; Perm to Offic *Nor* from 93. *Chaplaincy Services (RAF), HQ, Personnel and Training Command, RAF Innsworth, Gloucester GL3 1EZ*   Gloucester (01452) 712612 Ext 5164   Fax 510828

WESTON, John Oglivy. b 30. St Pet Coll Ox BA66 MA70. Linc Th Coll 71. **d** 71 **p** 72. Lect Trent (Nottm) Poly 66-82; Hon C Long Clawson and Hose *Leic* 71-82; Hon C Bingham *S'well*

82-85; Lic to Offic 85-91; rtd 91; Perm to Offic *Heref* from 91. *The Cliffords Farm House, Nash, Ludlow, Shropshire SY8 3DE* Tenbury Wells (01584) 811491

WESTON, Mrs Judith. b 36. MSR56 Open Univ BA75. St Jo Coll Nottm 84. **dss** 85 **d** 87 **p** 94. Huddersfield H Trin *Wakef* 85-87; Par Dn 87-91; Par Dn Wakef St Andr and St Mary 91-94; C 94-95; Chapl Huddersfield NHS Trust from 95. *The Vicarage, Johnston Street, Wakefield, W Yorkshire WF1 4DZ* Wakefield (01924) 200573

WESTON, Canon Keith Aitken Astley. b 26. Trin Hall Cam BA51 MA55. Ridley Hall Cam 51. **d** 53 **p** 54. R Ox St Ebbe w H Trin and St Pet *Ox* 64-85; RD Ox 71-76; Hon Can Ch Ch 81-85; Dir of Post-Ord Tr *Nor* 85-90; Dioc Dir of Ords 85-91; P-in-c Nor St Steph 85-91; Hon Brigade Chapl to Norfolk Co Fire Service from 90; rtd 91. *18 Moor End Lane, Thame, Oxon OX9 3BQ* Thame (01844) 215441

WESTON, Neil. b 51. Jes Coll Ox BA73 MA78. Ridley Hall Cam 74. **d** 76 **p** 77. C Ealing St Mary *Lon* 76-80; P-in-c Pertenhall w Swineshead *St Alb* 80-89; P-in-c Dean w Yelden, Melchbourne and Shelton 80-89; R The Stodden Churches 89-91; R Newhaven *Chich* from 91; Miss to Seamen from 91. *The Rectory, 36 Second Avenue, Newhaven, E Sussex BN9 9HN* Newhaven (01273) 515251

WESTON, Paul David Astley. b 57. Trin Hall Cam BA80 MA83 Westmr Coll Ox MPhil92. Wycliffe Hall Ox 83. **d** 85 **p** 86. C New Malden and Coombe *S'wark* 85-89; Lect Oak Hill Th Coll from 89. *Oak Hill College, Chase Side, London N14 4PS* 0181-449 0467 Fax 441 5996

WESTON, Ralph Edward Norman. b 30. Worc Ord Coll 67. **d** 69 **p** 70. C Harborne St Pet *Birm* 69-71; CF 71-75; Chapl Oswestry Sch 75-85; Chapl Rotherham Distr Gen Hosp 85-95; CF (ACF) from 87; TV Thorverton, Cadbury, Upton Pyne etc *Ex* from 95. *The Vicarage, Newton St Cyres, Exeter EX5 5BN*

WESTON, Stephen. b 48. St Steph Ho Ox 74. **d** 77 **p** 78. C Wigston Magna *Leic* 77-82; C Corringham *Chelmsf* 82-84; V Southtown *Nor* 84-89; R Catfield 90-92; R Sutton w Ingham and Catfield from 92. *The Rectory, Fenside, Catfield, Great Yarmouth, Norfolk NR29 5DB* Stalham (01692) 582290

WESTON, Stephen John Astley. b 55. Aston Univ BSc77. Ridley Hall Cam 78. **d** 81 **p** 82. C Gt Chesham *Ox* 81-85; C Southport Ch Ch *Liv* 85-87; P-in-c Gayhurst w Ravenstone, Stoke Goldington etc *Ox* 87-91; R from 91; RD Newport from 92. *The Rectory, Stoke Goldington, Newport Pagnell, Bucks MK16 8LL* Stoke Goldington (0190855) 221

WESTON, Mrs Virginia Anne. b 58. UEA BSc79. Wycliffe Hall Ox 84. **d** 87. Par Dn New Malden and Coombe *S'wark* 87-89; Lic to Offic *Lon* from 89. *Oak Hill College, Chase Side, London N14 4PS* 0181-449 0467 Fax 441 5996

WESTRUP, Wilfrid Allan. b 08. Ch Coll Cam BA30 MA34. Westcott Ho Cam 30. **d** 32 **p** 33. Chapl Cranbrook Sch Kent 52-64; rtd 73. *Sharon, Hartley Hill, Cranbrook, Kent TN17 3QD* Cranbrook (01580) 712595

WESTWELL, Ven George Leslie Cedric. b 31. Lich Th Coll 59. **d** 61 **p** 63. V Maidstone St Martin *Cant* 72-77; R Otham 68-72; V Bethersden w High Halden 77-79; R Lichborough w Maidford and Farthingstone *Pet* 79-80; Perm to Offic *Chich* 80-81; Perm to Offic *Cant* 80-81; Perm to Offic *Llan* 81-83; Chapl Florence w Siena *Eur* 83-92; Adn Italy 85-92; rtd 92. *Hazeldene, Bexhill Road, Ninfield, Battle, E Sussex TN33 9EE* Ninfield (01424) 892754

WESTWOOD, John Richard. b 55. Clare Coll Cam BA77 MA81. Lambeth DipTh93 Ripon Coll Cuddesdon 77. **d** 79 **p** 80. C Oakham w Hambleton and Egleton *Pet* 79-81; C Oakham, Hambleton, Egleton, Braunston and Brooke 81-83; V Gt w Lt Harrowden and Orlingbury 83-90; V Wellingborough St Andr from 90; RD Wellingborough from 92. *The Vicarage, Berrymoor Road, Wellingborough, Northants NN8 2HU* Wellingborough (01933) 222692

WESTWOOD, Peter. b 38. Open Univ BA76. AKC64. **d** 65 **p** 66. C Acomb St Steph *York* 65-68; Chapl HM Youth Cust Cen Onley 69-73; Chapl HM Pris Leic 73-77; Chapl HM Pris Maidstone 77-81; Chapl HM Pris Dur 81-87; Chapl HM Pris Brixton 87-93; Chapl HM Pris Wormwood Scrubs from 93. *HM Prison Wormwood Scrubs, PO Box 757, Du Cane Road, London W12 0AE* 0181-743 0311 Fax 749 5655

✠**WESTWOOD, Rt Rev William John.** b 25. Em Coll Cam BA50 MA55 Leic Univ Hon LLD91. Westcott Ho Cam 50. **d** 52 **p** 53 **c** 75. C Kingston upon Hull H Trin *York* 52-57; R Lowestoft St Marg *Nor* 57-65; RD Lothingland 59-65; V Nor St Pet Mancroft 65-75; RD Nor 66-71; Hon Can Nor Cathl 68-75; Suff Bp Edmonton *Lon* 75-79; Area Bp Edmonton 79-84; Bp Pet from 84. *The Palace, Peterborough PE1 1YA* Peterborough (01733) 62492 Fax 890077

WETHERALL, Canon Cecil Edward (Ted). b 29. St Jo Coll Dur 49. **d** 56 **p** 57. R Hitcham *St E* 59-79; P-in-c Kettlebaston 71-91; R Hitcham w Lt Finborough 79-91; Hon Can St E Cathl 83-93; P-in-c Preston 85-91; rtd 92; Asst Chapl Athens w Kifissia, Patras, Thessaloniki & Voula *Eur* from 92. *40 Kokinaki/Markou Botsari 63, GR 14651, Kifissia, Athens, Greece* Athens (1) 807-5335

WETHERALL, Nicholas Guy. b 52. Lon Univ BMus73 Ox Univ CertEd75. Chich Th Coll 82. **d** 84 **p** 85. C Cleobury Mortimer w Hopton Wafers *Heref* 84-87; TV Leominster 87-92; V Cuckfield *Chich* from 92. *The Vicarage, Broad Street, Cuckfield, Haywards Heath, W Sussex RH17 5LL* Haywards Heath (01444) 454007

WETHERELL, Ms Eileen Joyce. b 44. Westf Coll Lon BSc66. S Dios Minl Tr Scheme 89. **d** 92 **p** 94. Par Dn Southn Maybush St Pet *Win* 92-94; C from 94. *60 Brookwood Road, Southampton SO1 9AJ* Southampton (01703) 781228

WETHERELL, Philip Anthony. b 45. Leic Univ MPhil87. AKC72. **d** 73 **p** 74. C Walthamstow St Sav *Chelmsf* 73-75; Chapl Bp Namibia and Tutor Namibia Internat Peace Cen 75-76; C Knighton St Mary Magd *Leic* 76-80; TV Southn (City Cen) *Win* 80-84; Miss Personnel Sec USPG from 84. *19 Bassett Green Road, Southampton SO2 3DJ* Southampton (01703) 552783 Fax 0171-928 2371

WETZ, Peter Joseph Patrick. b 37. **d** 62 **p** 62. C Hatf Hyde St Mary *St Alb* 85; C Stevenage St Pet Broadwater 85-87; V Irlam Man from 87. *The Vicarage, Vicarage Road, Irlam, Manchester M44 6WA* 0161-775 2461

WEYMAN, John Derek Henry. b 31. Wells Th Coll 69. **d** 70 **p** 71. C Headley All SS *Guildf* 70-76; V Westcott from 76; RD Dorking 84-89. *The Vicarage, Guildford Road, Westcott, Dorking, Surrey RH4 3QB* Dorking (01306) 885309

WEYMAN, Richard Darrell George. b 46. Lon Univ BA Bris Univ PhD. Sarum & Wells Th Coll. **d** 84 **p** 85. C Sherborne w Castleton and Lillington *Sarum* 84-88; V Marlden St Jo *S'wark* 88-92; P-in-c Marnhull *Sarum* from 92; Dir Post Ord Tr from 92. *The Rectory, Conyers Place, Marnhull, Sturminster Newton, Dorset DT10 1PZ* Marnhull (01258) 821130

WEYMONT, Miss Gillian. b 41. SRN67. Trin Coll Bris 88. **d** 90 **p** 94. C Wincanton *B & W* 90-94; P-in-c Middlezoy and Othery and Moorlinch from 94. *The Vicarage, North Lane, Othery, Bridgwater, Somerset TA7 0QG* Burrowbridge (01823) 698073

WEYMONT, Martin Eric. b 48. St Jo Coll Dur BA69 MA74 CertEd73 Lon Univ PhD88. Westcott Ho Cam 71. **d** 73 **p** 74. C Blackheath *Birm* 73-76; Hon C Willesden St Matt *Lon* 76-77; Hon C Belmont 76-79; P-in-c W Twyford 79-85; P-in-c Cricklewood St Mich 85-88; Chapl St Pet Colleg Sch Wolv 88-91; Hon C Wolv *Lich* 88-91; NSM Bickershaw *Liv* from 91. *Bickershaw Vicarage, 582 Bickershaw Lane, Bickershaw, Wigan, Lancs WN2 4AE* Wigan (01942) 866139

WHALE, Desmond Victor. b 35. Bris Sch of Min 81. **d** 84 **p** 85. Lic to Offic *Bris* 84-88; C Parr *Liv* 88-91; R Winfarthing w Shelfanger w Burston w Gissing etc *Nor* from 91. *The Rectory, Winfarthing, Diss, Norfolk IP22 2EA* Diss (01379) 642543

WHALE, Canon Jeffery Walter George. b 33. Lon Univ BSc60. Cuddesdon Coll 60. **d** 62 **p** 63. C Rugby St Andr *Cov* 62-68; C-in-c Britwell St Geo CD *Ox* 68-77; P-in-c Datchet 77-78; TR Riverside 78-88; RD Burnham 83-87; Hon Can Ch Ch from 85; TR New Windsor from 88. *The Rectory, Park Street, Windsor, Berks SL4 1LU* Windsor (01753) 864572

WHALE, Dr Peter Richard. b 49. Down Coll Cam BA74 MA78 Auckland Univ BSc71 MA72 Otago Univ BD78 Ex Univ PhD89. St Jo Coll Auckland 75. **d** 77 **p** 78. New Zealand 77-85; TV Saltash *Truro* 85-90; Jt Dir SW Min Tr Course Truro 86-90; Preb St Endellion 89-90; Prin W Midl Minl Tr Course 90-92. *83 Chaddesley Court, Coventry CV5 7JP*

WHALER, Herbert Riggall. b 13. St Andr Pampisford 47. **d** 49 **p** 50. R Bucknall w Tupholme *Linc* 52-82; R Horsington w Stixwould 52-82; R Kirkby-on-Bain 61-82; V Martin w Thornton 61-82; R Roughton w Haltham 61-82; R Scrivelsby w Dalderby 66-82; P-in-c Thimbleby 80-82; rtd 82. *Stocks Hill Lodge, Stixwould, Lincoln LN3 5HP* Woodhall Spa (01526) 352064

WHALES, Jeremy Michael. b 31. Bris Univ MA82. Lambeth STh72 Wycliffe Hall Ox 59. **d** 61 **p** 62. Asst Chapl and Sen Lect 67-74; Chapl 74-78; Assoc Chapl & Sen Lect Coll of St Mary & St Paul 78-84; V Cheltenham St Luke and St Jo *Glouc* 85-92; rtd 92. *5 Robert Burns Avenue, Benhall, Cheltenham, Glos GL52 6NU*

WHALEY, Stephen John. b 57. York Univ BA79. Cranmer Hall Dur BA85. **d** 86 **p** 87. C Selby Abbey *York* 86-90; V Derringham Bank from 90. *110 Calvert Road, Hull HU5 5DH* Hull (01482) 52175

WHALLEY, Anthony Allen (Tony). b 41. Linc Th Coll 77. **d** 79 **p** 80. C Upton cum Chalvey *Ox* 79-83; R Newton Longville w Stoke Hammond and Whaddon from 83. *The Rectory, Drayton Road, Newton Longville, Milton Keynes MK17 0BH* Milton Keynes (01908) 377847

WHALLEY, George Peter. b 40. Local NSM Course 82. **d** 86 **p** 86. NSM Ellon *Ab* from 86; NSM Cruden Bay from 86. *128 Braehead Drive, Cruden Bay, Aberdeenshire AB42 7NW* Cruden Bay (01779) 812511

744

WHALLEY, Michael Thomas. b 30. AKC55. d 56 p 57. Lic to Offic *Linc* 70-75; Chapl HM Pris Aylesbury 75-79; C Aylesbury *Ox* 79-83; P-in-c Bierton w Hulcott 83-89; TV Aylesbury w Bierton and Hulcott 89-95; rtd 95. *17 Willowfield Avenue, Nettleham, Lincoln LN2 2TH* Lincoln (01522) 595372

WHARTON, Christopher Joseph. b 33. Keble Coll Ox BA57 MA61. d 79 p 80. NSM Harpenden St Nic *St Alb* 79-93; R Kimpton w Ayot St Lawrence from 93. *The Vicarage, 11 High Street, Kimpton, Hitchin, Herts SG4 8RA* Kimpton (01438) 833419

WHARTON, Miss Gillian Vera. b 66. TCD BTh93. CITC 90. d 93 p 94. C Glenageary *D & G* from 93. *10 Silchester Park, Glenageary, Co Dublin, Irish Republic* Dublin (1) 280-7543

✠**WHARTON, Rt Rev John Martin.** b 44. Van Mildert Coll Dur BA69 Linacre Coll Ox BTh71 MA76. Ripon Hall Ox 69. d 72 p 73 c 92. C Birm St Pet *Birm* 72-75; C Croydon *Cant* 76-77; Dir Past Studies Ripon Coll Cuddesdon 77-83; C Cuddesdon *Ox* 79-83; Sec to Bd of Min and Tr *Bradf* 83-92; Dir Post-Ord Tr 84-92; Hon Can Bradf Cathl 84-92; Can Res Bradf Cathl 92; Bp's Officer for Min and Tr 92; Area Bp Kingston-upon-Thames *S'wark* from 92. *24 Albert Drive, London SW19 6LS* 0181-789 3218 or 780 2308 Fax 789 3985

WHARTON, Thomas Anthony. b 21. Bps' Coll Cheshunt 49. d 52 p 53. V Chipping Norton *Ox* 53-86; Chapl Berne *Eur* 86-89; rtd 89. *4 Bowling Green Crescent, Cirencester, Glos GL7 2HA* Cirencester (01285) 659043

WHATLEY, Preb Henry Lawson. b 16. Worc Coll Ox BA38. Wells Th Coll 38. d 39 p 40. R Colwall *Heref* 63-82; Preb Heref Cathl 76-82; rtd 82; Perm to Offic *Heref* 84-90. *Manormead Nursing Home, Tilford Road, Hindhead, Surrey GU26 6RA* Hindhead (01428) 604780

WHATMORE, Michael John. b 30. Bris Univ BA51 St Cath Soc Ox BA53 MA54. Wycliffe Hall Ox 56. d 56 p 58. V Speke All SS *Liv* 67-70; Teacher & Sen Tutor Barton Peveril Coll 70-92; rtd 92. *26 Grebe Close, Milford on Sea, Lymington, Hants SO41 0XA* Lymington (01590) 644892

WHATMORE, Terence James Brian. b 38. St Mich Coll Llan 64. d 66 p 67. C Sevenoaks St Jo *Roch* 66-70; C Newport St Julian *Mon* 70-72; V Bordesley St Benedict *Birm* 72-81; Chapl Florence w Siena *Eur* 81-83; V Hove St Thos *Chich* 83-89; V Tipton St Jo *Lich* 89-94. *26 Knightley Way, Gnosall, Stafford ST20 0HX* Stafford (01785) 823726

WHATMOUGH, Michael Anthony (Tony). b 50. ARCO71 Ex Univ BA72. Edin Th Coll BD81. d 81 p 82. C Edin St Hilda *Edin* 81-84; C Edin St Fillan 81-84; C Salisbury St Thos and St Edm *Sarum* 84-86; R 86-93; RD Salisbury 90-93; V Bris St Mary Redcliffe w Temple etc *Bris* from 93. *The Vicarage, 10 Redcliffe Parade West, Bristol BS1 6SP* Bristol (0117) 929 1487

WHATSON, Mark Edwin Chadwick. b 57. CEng83 MIMechE83 Southn Univ BSc79. N Ord Course 86. d 88 p 91. NSM Church Hulme *Ches* 88-95; NSM Hardwicke, Quedgeley and Elmore w Longney *Glouc* from 95. *2 Carters Orchard, Quedgeley, Gloucester GL2 6WB*

WHAWELL, Arthur Michael. b 38. Sarum & Wells Th Coll 74. d 76 p 77. C Cottingham *York* 76-79; P-in-c Bessingby 79-84; P-in-c Carnaby 79-84; V Birchencliffe *Wakef* 84-87; Chapl St Bart Hosp Lon 87-95; V St Bart Less *Lon* from 87. *The Vicar's Office, St Bartholomew's Hospital, London EC1A 7BE* 0171-601 8888

WHEALE, Alan Leon. b 43. HNC65 AKC69. St Aug Coll Cant 69 DipMin89. d 70 p 71. C Tamworth *Lich* 70-73; C Cheddleton 73-75; V Garretts Green *Birm* 75-78; V Perry Beeches 78-83; V Winshill *Derby* 83-84; Deputation Appeals Org (E Midl) CECS 84-86; C Arnold *S'well* 86-88; V Daybrook from 88. *St Paul's Vicarage, 241 Oxclose Lane, Nottingham NG5 6FB* Nottingham (0115) 926 2686

WHEALE, Canon Gerald Arnold. b 32. MBE93. St Jo Coll Dur BA56 Man Univ MEd74 PhD79. Ridley Hall Cam 56. d 58 p 59. C Tonge w Alkrington *Man* 58-60; Nigeria 60-62; R Moss Side St Jas *Man* 62-73; R Moss Side St Jas w St Clem from 73; AD Hulme from 82; Hon Can Man Cathl from 84. *The Rectory, 68 Dudley Road, Whalley Range, Manchester M16 8DE* 0161-226 1684 or 226 4211

WHEALE, Sarah Ruth. *See* BULLOCK, Mrs Sarah Ruth

WHEAT, Charles Donald Edmund. b 37. Nottm Univ BA70 Sheff Univ MA76. Kelham Th Coll 58. d 62 p 63. C Sheff Arbourthorne *Sheff* 62-67; Lic to Offic *S'well* 67-69; SSM from 69; Chapl St Martin's Coll Lanc 70-73; Prior SSM Priory Sheff 73-75; Lic to Offic *Sheff* from 73; C Ranmoor 75-77; Asst Chapl Sheff Univ 75-77; Chapl 77-80; Prov SSM in England from 81; Dir 82-89; Lic to Offic *Blackb* 81-88; V Middlesb All SS *York* from 88. *All Saints' Vicarage, Grange Road, Middlesborough, Cleveland TS1 2LR* Middlesbrough (01642) 245035

WHEATLEY, Canon Arthur. b 31. Edin Th Coll 68. d 70 p 70. C Dundee St Salvador *Bre* 70-71; C Dundee St Martin 70-71;

P-in-c Dundee St Ninian 71-76; R Elgin H Trin *Mor* 76-80; R Lossiemouth 76-80; Can St Andr Cathl Inverness 78-80 and from 83; Provost 80-83; R Inverness St Andr 80-83; Chapl HM Pris Inverness from 80; P-in-c Grantown-on-Spey *Mor* from 83; P-in-c Rothiemurchus from 83. *West Carr Cottage, Dulnain Bridge, Grantown-on-Spey, Morayshire PH26 3LX* Grantown-on-Spey (01479) 851273

WHEATLEY, Gordon Howard. b 29. Trin Coll Cam MA52. Lon Bible Coll DipTh58. d 90 p 91. C Cockley Cley w Gooderstone *Nor* 90-94; C Didlington 90-94; C Gt and Lt Cressingham w Threxton 90-94; C Hilborough w Bodney 90-94; C Oxborough w Foulden and Caldecote 90-94; P-in-c Mundford w Lynford from 94; P-in-c Ickburgh w Langford from 94; P-in-c Cranwich from 94. *The Rectory, St Leonard's Street, Mundford, Thetford, Norfolk IP26 5HG* Thetford (01842) 878220

WHEATLEY, Ian James. b 62. Chich Th Coll BTh94. d 94 p 95. C Braunton *Ex* from 94. *11 Hazel Avenue, Braunton, Devon EX33 2EZ* Braunton (01271) 814735

WHEATLEY, John. b 14. d 77 p 78. NSM Cambois *Newc* 77-87; rtd 87; Perm to Offic *Newc* from 87. *20 Cypress Gardens, Blyth, Northd NE24 2LP* Blyth (01670) 353353

WHEATLEY, Canon Maurice Samuel. b 13. AKC36. Chich Th Coll 36. d 37 p 38. Bermuda 72-80; Hon Can N Queensland from 62; rtd 80. *30 Barnes Close, Sturminster Newton, Dorset DT10 1BN* Sturminster Newton (01258) 473066

WHEATLEY, Ven Paul Charles. b 38. Dur Univ BA61. Linc Th Coll 61. d 63 p 64. C Bishopston *Bris* 63-68; Youth Chapl 68-73; V Swindon St Paul 73-77; TR Swindon Dorcan 77-79; R Ross *Heref* 79-81; P-in-c Brampton Abbotts 79-81; RD Ross and Archenfield 79-91; TR Ross w Brampton Abbotts, Bridstow and Peterstow 81-91; Preb Heref Cathl 87-91; Adn Sherborne *Sarum* from 91; P-in-c W Stafford w Frome Billet from 91. *The Rectory, West Stafford, Dorchester, Dorset DT2 8AB* Dorchester (01305) 264637

WHEATLEY, Ven Peter William. b 47. Qu Coll Ox BA69 MA73 Pemb Coll Cam BA71 MA75. Ripon Hall Ox 72. d 73 p 74. C Fulham All SS *Lon* 73-78; V St Pancras H Cross w St Jude and St Pet 78-82; P-in-c Hampstead All So 82-90; P-in-c Kilburn St Mary 82-90; P-in-c Kilburn St Mary w All So 90-95; V W Hampstead St Jas 82-95; Dir Post-Ord Tr from 85; AD N Camden (Hampstead) 88-93; Adn Hampstead from 95. *27 Thurlow Road, London NW3 5PP* 0171-435 5890

WHEATLEY PRICE, Canon John. b 31. Em Coll Cam BA54 MA58. Ridley Hall Cam 54. d 56 p 57. C Drypool St Andr and St Pet *York* 56-59; CMS 59-74; Uganda 60-74; Adn Soroti 72-74; Hon Can Soroti from 78; Kenya 74-76; Adn N Maseno 74-76; V Clevedon St Andr *B & W* 76-82; V Clevedon St Andr and Ch Ch 82-87; Chapl Amsterdam *Eur* 87-92; P-in-c Cromford *Derby* 92-95; P-in-c Matlock Bath 92-95; V Matlock Bath and Cromford from 95. *Holy Trinity Vicarage, 8 Derby Road, Matlock, Derbyshire DE4 3PU* Matlock (01629) 582947

WHEATON, Christopher. b 49. St Jo Coll Nottm BTh80 LTh80. d 80 p 81. C Hatcham St Jas *S'wark* 80-83; C Warlingham w Chelsham and Farleigh 83-87; V Carshalton Beeches from 87. *The Vicarage, 38 Beeches Avenue, Carshalton, Surrey SM5 3LW* 0181-647 6056

WHEATON, Canon David Harry. b 30. St Jo Coll Ox BA53 MA56 Lon Univ BD55. Oak Hill Th Coll 58. d 59 p 60. Tutor Oak Hill Th Coll 59-62; Prin 71-86; C Enfield Ch Ch Trent Park *Lon* 59-62; R Ludgershall *Ox* 62-66; V Onslow Square St Paul *Lon* 66-71; Chapl Brompton Hosp 69-71; Hon Can St Alb from 76; V Ware Ch Ch from 86; RD Hertf 88-91; Chapl to The Queen from 90. *The Vicarage, 15 Hanbury Close, Ware, Herts SG12 7BZ* Ware (01920) 463165 or 487267

WHEATON, Canon Ralph Ernest. b 32. St Jo Coll Dur BA54. Cranmer Hall Dur DipTh58. d 58 p 59. C Evington *Leic* 58-63; V Bardon Hill 63-71; V Whitwick St Jo the Bapt 71-81; RD Akeley S (Coalville) 79-81; V Blyth *S'well* from 81; P-in-c Scofton w Osberton 83-86; V from 86; RD Worksop 83-93; Hon Can S'well Minster from 86; P-in-c Langold 86-91. *The Vicarage, Blyth, Worksop, Notts S81 8EQ* Blyth (01909) 591229

WHEBLE, Eric Clement. b 23. S'wark Ord Course 68. d 71 p 72. C Croydon H Trin *Cant* 71-78; Hon C Croydon St Sav 78-80; Hon C Norbury St Oswald 80-81; TV Selsdon St Jo w St Fran 81-84; TV Selsdon St Jo w St Fran *S'wark* 85-88; rtd 88. *20 Michael's Way, Fair Oak, Eastleigh, Hants S05 7NT* Southampton (01703) 693239

WHEELDON, John Graham. b 32. Sarum & Wells Th Coll 86. d 87 p 88. C Winchcombe, Gretton, Sudeley Manor etc *Glouc* 87-90; R Huntley and Longhope 90-91; rtd 91. *17 Mitton Way, Mitton, Tewkesbury, Glos GL20 8AW*

WHEELDON, William Dennis. b 25. Leeds Univ BA51. Coll of Resurr Mirfield 52. d 54 p 56. CR 55-76; Prin Coll of Resurr Mirfield 66-75; P-in-c New Whittington *Derby* 83-87; P-in-c

Belper Ch Ch and Milford 87-90; rtd 90. *10 Brooklyn, Threshfield, Skipton, N Yorkshire BD23 5ER*   Grassington (01756) 753187

WHEELER, Alban Massy. b 19. Dur Univ 40. Bps' Coll Cheshunt 40. **d** 43 **p** 44. C Leckhampton SS Phil and Jas *Glouc* 66-67; Perm to Offic 68-81; Perm to Offic *Ex* 81-84; rtd 84. *Terry's Cross House, Woodmancote, Henfield, W Sussex BN5 9SX*

WHEELER, Alexander Quintin Henry (Alastair). b 51. Lon Univ BA73 Nottm Univ DipTh75. St Jo Coll Nottm 74. **d** 77 **p** 78. C Kenilworth St Jo *Cov* 77-80; C Madeley *Heref* 80-83; P-in-c Draycott-le-Moors *Lich* 83-84; P-in-c Forsbrook 83-84; R Draycott-le-Moors w Forsbrook 84-91; V Nailsea Ch Ch *B & W* from 91; RD Portishead from 95. *The Vicarage, Christ Church Close, Nailsea, Bristol BS19 2DL*   Nailsea (01275) 853187

WHEELER, Andrew Charles. b 48. CCC Cam MA69 Makerere Univ Kampala MA72 Leeds Univ CertEd72. Trin Coll Bris BA88. **d** 88 **p** 88. CMS from 76; C Whitton *Sarum* 88-89; Egypt 89-90; Sudan from 90. *PO Box 52802, Nairobi, Kenya*

WHEELER, Anthony William (Tony). b 28. **d** 76 **p** 77. NSM Shirehampton *Bris* from 76; Chmn Avonmouth Miss to Seamen from 76. *Flat 3, The Priory, Priory Gardens, Bristol BS11 0BZ*   Bristol (0117) 982 2261

WHEELER (nee MILLAR), Mrs Christine. b 55. City of Lon Poly BSc76 DipCOT81. S Dios Minl Tr Scheme 84. **d** 87 **p** 94. NSM Kingston Buci *Chich* 87-89; Par Dn Merstham and Gatton *S'wark* 89-94; C from 94. *Epiphany House, Mansfield Drive, Merstham, Redhill RH1 3JP*   Merstham (01737) 642628

WHEELER, Dr David Ian. b 49. Southn Univ BSc70 PhD78. N Ord Course 87. **d** 90 **p** 91. C Blackpool St Jo *Blackb* 90-94; R Old Trafford St Jo *Man* from 94. *St John's Rectory, Lindum Avenue, Old Trafford, Manchester M16 9NQ*   0161-872 0500

WHEELER, David James. b 49. S Dios Minl Tr Scheme 87. **d** 90 **p** 91. C Hythe *Cant* 90-92; C Knaresborough *Ripon* from 92. *9 Castle Yard, Knaresborough, N Yorkshire HG5 0LS*   Harrogate (01423) 864484

WHEELER, David Robert. b 62. Birm Univ BSc84. Oak Hill Th Coll BA95. **d** 95. C Lanc St Thos *Blackb* from 95. *30 Connaught Road, Lancaster LA1 4BQ*   Lancaster (01524) 381837

WHEELER, Desmond Reginald Sessel. b 18. Rhodes Univ BA49. St Paul's Grahamstown LTh51. **d** 50 **p** 51. V Sutton on Plym *Ex* 63-70; V Bishopsteignton 71-85; rtd 85; Perm to Offic *Ex* from 85. *30 Odlehill Grove, Abbotskerswell, Newton Abbot, Devon TQ12 5NJ*   Newton Abbot (01626) 51162

WHEELER, Sister Eileen Violet. b 28. TCert48 Newnham Coll Cam MA52. Chich Th Coll 85. **dss** 86 **d** 87 **p** 95. Bexhill St Pet *Chich* 86-87; Hon Par Dn 87-90; Par Dn 90-94; NSM 94-95; rtd 94; Hon C Bexhill St Mark *Chich* from 95. *1 The Briary, St Peter's Crescent, Bexhill-on-Sea, E Sussex TN40 2EG*   Bexhill-on-Sea (01424) 215115

WHEELER, Graham John. b 39. St Mich Coll Llan DipTh66 BD78. **d** 66 **p** 67. C Roath St Martin *Llan* 66-71; C Cadoxton-juxta-Barry 71-75; Perm to Offic 75-79; C Highcliffe w Hinton Admiral *Win* 79-83; C Milton 83-90; P-in-c Bournemouth St Ambrose from 90. *St Ambrose Vicarage, 72 West Cliff Road, Bournemouth BH4 8BE*   Bournemouth (01202) 764957

WHEELER, James Albert. b 49. Sarum & Wells Th Coll 74. **d** 76 **p** 77. C Orpington All SS *Roch* 76-79; C Roch 79-81; C Bexley St Jo 81-84; V Penge Lane H Trin 84-93; P-in-c Tunbridge Wells St Luke from 93. *St Luke's Vicarage, 158 Upper Grosvenor Road, Tunbridge Wells, Kent TN1 2EQ*   Tunbridge Wells (01892) 521374

WHEELER, John David. b 31. Selw Coll Cam BA54 MA58. Ely Th Coll 54. **d** 56 **p** 57. C Old Charlton *S'wark* 56-60; C Northolt St Mary Lon 61-63; V Bush Hill Park St Mark 64-71; V Ealing St Pet Mt Park 71-74; V Truro St Paul *Truro* 74-79; V Truro St Paul and St Clem 79-80; P-in-c Hammersmith St Sav *Lon* 80-83; V Cobbold Road St Sav w St Mary from 83. *St Saviour's Vicarage, Cobbold Road, London W12 9LQ*   0181-743 4769

WHEELER, Julian Aldous. b 48. Nottm Univ BTh74. Kelham Th Coll 70. **d** 75 **p** 76. C Bideford *Ex* 75-79; Lic to Offic 79-86; Hon C Parkham, Alwington, Buckland Brewer etc from 86. *Forge Cottage, Pump Lane, Abbotsham, Bideford, Devon EX39 5AY*   Bideford (01237) 473948

WHEELER, Preb Madeleine. b 42. Gilmore Course 76. **dss** 78 **d** 87 **p** 94. Ruislip Manor St Paul *Lon* 78-87; Par Dn 87-91; Chapl for Women's Min (Willesden Episc Area) from 86; TD Ruislip Manor St Paul 91-92; P-in-c N Greenford All Hallows from 94; Preb St Paul's Cathl from 95. *All Hallows' Vicarage, 72 Horsenden Lane North, Greenford, Middx UB6 0PD*   0181-422 3183

WHEELER, Michael. b 26. Qu Coll Cam MA54 Lon Univ PGCE53. Sarum & Wells Th Coll 93. **d** 94 **p** 95. NSM Redhorn

Sarum from 94. *Dominie's, Wilsford, Pewsey, Wilts SN9 6HB*   Pewsey (01672) 851373

WHEELER, Nicholas Gordon Timothy. b 59. BCombStuds84. Linc Th Coll. **d** 84 **p** 85. C Hendon St Alphage *Lon* 84-87; C Wood Green St Mich w Bounds Green St Gabr etc 87-89; TV 89-93; R Cranford from 93. *The Rectory, 34 High Street, Cranford, Hounslow TW5 9RG*   0181-897 8836

WHEELER, Nicholas Paul. b 60. Ox Univ BA86 MA91. Wycliffe Hall Ox 83. **d** 87 **p** 88. C Wood Green St Mich w Bounds Green St Gabr etc *Lon* 87-91; Chapl to Bp Edmonton from 91. *4 Silsoe House, Park Village East, London NW1 7QH*   0171-388 2166 or 267 4455   Fax 267 4404

WHEELER, Richard Anthony. b 23. St Chad's Coll Dur BA46 MA48 DipTh48. **d** 48 **p** 49. R Dorchester H Trin w Frome Whitfield *Sarum* 64-73; TV Dorchester 73-87; rtd 87. *25 Victoria Road, Dorchester, Dorset DT1 1SB*   Dorchester (01305) 262803

WHEELER, Canon Richard Roy. b 44. K Coll Lon BD72. St Aug Coll Cant. **d** 74 **p** 74. C Brixton St Matt *S'wark* 74-78; Dir St Matt Meeting Place Brixton 78-79; Sec BCC Community Work Resource Unit 79-82; TV Southn (City Cen) *Win* 83-88; TR from 88; Hon Can Win Cathl from 94. *St Michael's Vicarage, 55 Bugle Street, Southampton SO1 0AG*   Southampton (01703) 224242

WHEELOCK, Canon John Richard. b 18. TCD BA41 MA51. CITC 42. **d** 42 **p** 43. I Annagh Union *K, E & A* 56-83; Preb Kilmore Cathl 72-83; rtd 83. *c/o Mrs J Elliott, Tomkin Road, Belturbet, Co Cavan, Irish Republic*   Cavan (49) 22865

WHEELWRIGHT, Michael Harvey. b 39. Bps' Coll Cheshunt 64. **d** 67 **p** 68. C Glen Parva and S Wigston *Leic* 67-70; C Evington 70-74; V Leic St Eliz Nether Hall 74-79; Chapl Prudhoe Hosp Northd from 79. *Prudhoe Hospital, Prudhoe, Northd NE42 5NT, or 61 Dene Road, Wylam, Northd NE41 8HB*   Prudhoe (01661) 32501 or 852508

WHELAN, Canon John Bernard. b 17. Dur Univ LTh41. Oak Hill Th Coll 38. **d** 47 **p** 48. C Bury St Mary *Man* 68-71; Asst Chapl Crumpsall Hosp Man 71-73; Chapl N Man Gen Hosp 73-82; rtd 82; Chapl Las Palmas *Eur* 82-84; Asst Chapl Valletta w Sliema 84-93; Can Malta Cathl 87-93. *146 Rudolphe Street, Sliema SLM02, Malta*   Malta (356) 330214

WHELAN, Miss Patricia Jean (Pat). b 33. ACA55 FCA82. Dalton Ho Bris 58. **dss** 64 **d** 87 **p** 94. Aylesbury *Ox* 69-75; Bushbury *Lich* 75-77; Patchway *Bris* 77-81; Trin Coll Bris 81-82; W Swindon LEP 82-86; High Wycombe *Ox* 86-87; Par Dn 87-91; Par Dn Ox St Ebbe w H Trin and St Pet 91-93; rtd 93. *81 Cogges Hill Road, Witney, Oxon OX8 6XU*   Witney (01993) 779099

WHELAN, Peter Warwick Armstrong. b 34. Southn Univ BTh80 Open Univ BA80. Sarum Th Coll 69. **d** 71 **p** 72. C Salisbury St Mark *Sarum* 71-73; C Solihull *Birm* 73-77; TR Shirley 77-86; Chapl Whittington Hosp NHS Trust from 86; Chapl Camden & Islington Community & Health NHS Trust from 86. *51 Tytherton Road, London N19 4PZ*   0171-272 5309 or 288 5337

WHELAN, Raymond Keith (Ray). b 40. Cant Sch of Min 85. **d** 88 **p** 91. C Eastbourne St Andr *Chich* 88-93; C-in-c Parklands St Wilfrid CD from 93. *St Wilfrid's House, 7 Durnford Close, Chichester, W Sussex PO19 3AG*   Chichester (01243) 783853

WHERRY, Anthony Michael (Tony). b 44. Nottm Univ BA65 Univ Coll Lon DAA66. W Midl Minl Tr Course 88. **d** 91 **p** 92. NSM Worc City St Paul and Old St Martin etc *Worc* from 91. *2 Redfern Avenue, Worcester WR5 1PZ*   Worcester (01905) 358532

WHETTEM, Canon John Curtiss. b 27. Peterho Cam BA50 MA55. Wycliffe Hall Ox 50. **d** 52 **p** 53. R N Mundham w Hunston *Chich* 68-80; P-in-c Oving w Merston 75-80; TR Swanborough *Sarum* 80-92; RD Pewsey 84-89; rtd 92. *32 Hogshill Street, Beaminster, Dorset DT8 3AA*   Beaminster (01308) 863050

WHETTER, Michael Arnold. b 30. Bris Univ BA51. Wells Th Coll 53. **d** 55 **p** 56. C Dursley *Glouc* 55-58; C Coppenhall *Ches* 58-61; R Ches H Trin 61-71; V Stockport St Alb Hall Street 72-90; V Offerton 90-91; Chapl Cherry Tree Hosp Stockport 72-91; Chapl Offerton Hosp Stockport 72-91; V Bollington St Jo *Ches* from 91. *The Vicarage, Shrigley Road, Bollington, Macclesfield, Cheshire SK10 5RD*   Bollington (01625) 573162

WHETTINGSTEEL, Raymond Edward. b 44. S Dios Minl Tr Scheme 79. **d** 82 **p** 83. NSM Sholing *Win* 82-84; C Southn Maybush St Pet 84-89; V Hatherden w Tangley, Weyhill and Penton Mewsey from 89. *The Rectory, Penton Mewsey, Andover, Hants SP11 0RD*   Weyhill (01264) 773554

WHETTON, Nicholas John. b 56. St Jo Coll Nottm 83. **d** 86 **p** 87. C Hatf *Sheff* 86-90; V Cornholme *Wakef* from 90. *Cornholme Vicarage, 30 Cross Lee Road, Todmorden, Lancs OL14 8EH*   Todmorden (01706) 813604

WHIFFEN, Canon William Timothy (Bill). b 25. SS Coll Cam BA50 MA54. Linc Th Coll. **d** 52 **p** 53. V Clay Cross *Derby* 69-74; Sec (Overseas Division) USPG 74-79; TR Woughton

Ox 79-85; P-in-c Seer Green and Jordans 85-91; Hon Can Ch Ch 91-92; rtd 91. *90 Booker Avenue, Bradwell Common, Milton Keynes MK13 8EF* Milton Keynes (01908) 677466

WHILD, Canon James Edward. b 24. Bris Univ BA52. Tyndale Hall Bris 48. **d** 53 **p** 54. Australia from 56; Hon Can Sydney 73-77; Can from 77; rtd 89. *7 Casuarina Drive, Cherrybrook, NSW, Australia 2126*

✠**WHINNEY, Rt Rev Michael Humphrey Dickens.** b 30. Pemb Coll Cam BA55 MA59. Gen Th Sem (NY) STM90 Ridley Hall Cam 55. **d** 57 **p** 58 **c** 82. C Rainham *Chelmsf* 57-60; Hd Cam Univ Miss Bermondsey 60-67; Chapl 67-73; V Bermondsey St Jas w Ch Ch *S'wark* 67-73; Adn S'wark 73-82; Suff Bp Aston *Birm* 82-85; Bp S'well 85-88; Asst Bp Birm from 88; Can Res Birm Cathl from 92. *3 Moor Green Lane, Birmingham B13 8NE, or Diocesan Office, Birmingham B17 0BH* 0121-449 2856 or 428 2228 Fax 428 1114

WHINTON, William Francis Ivan. b 35. N Ord Course 77. **d** 80 **p** 81. NSM Stockport St Mary *Ches* 80-82; NSM Disley 82-87; V Birtles from 87; Dioc Officer for Disabled from 89. *The Vicarage, Birtles, Macclesfield, Cheshire SK10 4RX* Chelford (01625) 861238

WHIPP, Anthony Douglas (Tony). b 46. Leeds Univ BSc68. Ripon Coll Cuddesdon 84. **d** 86 **p** 87. C Dalston *Carl* 86-89; V Holme Cultram St Mary from 89; V Holme Cultram St Cuth from 89. *The Vicarage, Abbey Town, Carlisle CA5 4SP* Abbeytown (016973) 61246

WHIPP, Dr Margaret Jane. b 55. MRCP82 FRCR86 LMH Ox BA76 Sheff Univ MB, ChB79. N Ord Course 87. **d** 90 **p** 94. NSM Wickersley *Sheff* from 90. *7 Scholey Road, Wickersley, Rotherham, S Yorkshire S66 0HU* Rotherham (01709) 548661

WHITAKER, David Arthur Edward. b 27. New Coll Ox BA50 MA55. Wells Th Coll 51. **d** 53 **p** 54. R Buckerell *Ex* 69-76; R Feniton 69-76; P-in-c Tiverton St Pet 76-79; R 79-92; rtd 92. *The Cottage, Hereford Road, Weobley, Hereford HR48 8SW* Weobley (01544) 318669

WHITAKER, Michael Benjamin (Ben). b 60. Nottm Univ BA83. Sarum & Wells Th Coll 85. **d** 87 **p** 88. C Gt Grimsby St Mary and St Jas *Linc* 87-91; C Abingdon *Ox* 91-95; Chapl to the Deaf *Sarum* from 95. *2 Orchard Mews, Gillingham, Dorset SP8 4TQ* Gillingham (01747) 825375

WHITBY, Suffragan Bishop of. *See* BATES, Rt Rev Gordon

WHITCOMBE, Michael George Stanley. b 34. Keble Coll Ox BA58 MA62. Wycliffe Hall Ox DipTh59. **d** 60 **p** 61. C Nuneaton St Nic *Cov* 60-63; Malaysia 63-67; V Warw St Paul *Cov* 67-68; Hong Kong 68-72; V Lightcliffe *Wakef* 72-79; R Largs *Glas* 79-81; P-in-c Ipswich St Fran *St E* 81-82; TR 82-93; TV Mildenhall from 93. *The Vicarage, Worlington, Bury St Edmunds, Suffolk IP28 8RU* Mildenhall (01638) 713510

WHITCOMBE, Stanley Edward Cuthbert. b 07. K Coll Lon 42. **d** 42 **p** 42. R Bourton w Frankton *Cov* 65-72; rtd 72; Perm to Offic *Wakef* 73-79 and from 81; Perm to Offic *Glas* 79-81. *10 Cricketers Close, Ackworth, Pontefract, W Yorkshire WF7 7PW* Hemsworth (01977) 616477

WHITCROFT, Graham Frederick. b 42. Oak Hill Th Coll 64. **d** 66 **p** 67. C Cromer *Nor* 66-69; C Attercliffe *Sheff* 69-72; V Kimberworth Park 72-85; V Lepton *Wakef* from 85. *The Vicarage, 138 Wakefield Road, Lepton, Huddersfield HD8 0EJ* Huddersfield (01484) 602172

WHITE, Alan. b 18. Man Univ BSc39 MSc40 St Cath Soc Ox BA42 MA46 Leeds Univ MEd52. Ripon Hall Ox 40. **d** 42 **p** 43. Lic to Offic *Worc* 56-89; Chapl Bromsgrove Sch Worcs 72-83; rtd 83; P-in-c Tardebigge *Worc* from 89. *25 Leadbetter Drive, Bromsgrove, Worcs B61 7JG* Bromsgrove (01527) 877955

WHITE, Alan. b 43. Ex Univ BA65. Chich Th Coll 65. **d** 68 **p** 69. C Upper Clapton St Matt *Lon* 68-72; C Southgate Ch Ch 72-76; P-in-c Friern Barnet St Pet le Poer 76-79; V 79-85; TR Ex St Thos and Em *Ex* from 85. *St Thomas's Vicarage, 57 Cowick Street, Exeter EX4 1HR* Exeter (01392) 55219

WHITE, Mrs Alison Mary. b 56. St Aid Coll Dur BA78. Cranmer Hall Dur 83. **d** 86 **p** 94. NSM Ches le Street *Dur* 86-89; Hon Par Dn Birtley 89-93; Adv in Local Miss 89-93; Dir Past Studies Cranmer Hall Dur from 93. *St John's Vicarage, 6 Ruskin Road, Birtley, Chester le Street, Co Durham DH3 1AD* 0191-410 2115 or 374 3500 Fax 374 3573

WHITE, Andrew Paul Bartholomew. b 64. MIOT85 ABIST85 St Thos Hosp Lon DipSurg84 DA84 CertMBiol84. Ridley Hall Cam 86. **d** 90 **p** 91. C Battersea Rise St Mark *S'wark* 90-93; P-in-c Balham Hill Ascension from 93. *Ascension Vicarage, 22 Malwood Road, London SW12 8EN* 0181-673 7666

WHITE, Andrew Peter. b 65. Lon Univ BA87. Sarum & Wells Th Coll BTh94. **d** 94 **p** 95. C Croydon St Matt *S'wark* from 94. *3 Chichester Road, Croydon CR0 5NQ* 0181-688 8675

WHITE, Charles William Langston. b 13. Lon Coll of Div 52. **d** 54 **p** 55. R St Leonards St Leon *Chich* 68-76; Jerusalem 76-78; rtd 78. *Shalom, Church Knowle, Wareham, Dorset BH20 5NQ* Wareham (01929) 480728

WHITE, Canon Christopher Norman Hessler. b 32. TD76. St Cath Coll Cam BA56 MA60. Cuddesdon Coll 57. **d** 59 **p** 60. C Solihull *Birm* 59-62; C Leeds St Aid *Ripon* 62-65; CF (TA) 64-85; V Aysgarth *Ripon* 65-74; R Richmond 74-76; P-in-c Hudswell w Downholme and Marske 75-76; R Richmond w Hudswell from 76; RD Richmond 75-80 and from 93; Hon Can Ripon Cathl from 89; Chapl St Fran Xavier Sch Richmond from 89. *The Rectory, Church Wynd, Richmond, N Yorkshire DL10 7AQ* Richmond (01748) 823398

WHITE, Clement. b 25. AKC50. **d** 51 **p** 52. V Monkseaton St Pet *Newc* 69-89; rtd 89. *18 Beach Road, Tynemouth, Tyne & Wear NE30 2NS* 0191-258 7505

WHITE, Colin Davidson. b 44. St And Dioc Tr Course 85. **d** 88 **p** 89. NSM Glenrothes *St And* 88-91; R Leven from 92. *The Rectory, Victoria Road, Leven, Fife KY8 4EX* Leven (01333) 426488

WHITE, Crispin Michael. b 42. Bps' Coll Cheshunt 62. **d** 65 **p** 66. C S Harrow St Paul *Lon* 65-67; C Mill Hill St Mich 67-68; Canada 68-71; Toc H Padre (W Region) 71-75; (E Midl Region) 75-82; Ind Chapl *Portsm* from 82. *11 Burnham Wood, Fareham, Hants PO16 7UD* Fareham (01329) 239390

WHITE, David Christopher. b 51. Lon Univ LLB73. St Jo Coll Nottm 86. **d** 88 **p** 89. C Bulwell St Mary *S'well* 88-92; V Nottm All SS from 92. *The Vicarage, 16 All Saints' Street, Nottingham NG7 4DP* Nottingham (0115) 970 4197 or 786362

WHITE, David John. b 26. Leeds Univ BA53. Coll of Resurr Mirfield 53. **d** 55 **p** 56. In RC Ch 62-73; Perm to Offic *Nor* from 73; Lect Whitelands Coll Lon 72-75; R Tregony w St Cuby and Cornelly *Truro* 75-79; R Castle Bromwich SS Mary and Marg *Birm* 79-83; V Plymouth St Simon *Ex* 83-88; R Lapford, Nymet Rowland and Coldridge 88-93; RD Chulmleigh 93; rtd 93; Perm to Offic *Ex* from 94. *The Belvedere, Peak Hill Road, Sidmouth, Devon EX10 8RZ* Sidmouth (01395) 513365

WHITE, David Martin. b 50. St Jo Coll Dur BA72. Cranmer Hall Dur DipTh73. **d** 74 **p** 75. C Ripley *Derby* 74-78; C Normanton 78-80; C-in-c Sinfin 78-80; P-in-c 80; V 80-88; P-in-c Belper 88-91; V from 91. *St Peter's Vicarage, Chesterfield Road, Belper, Derbyshire DE56 1FD* Belper (01773) 822148

WHITE, David Paul. b 58. Oak Hill Th Coll. **d** 84 **p** 85. C Toxteth Park St Clem *Liv* 84-87; C Woodford Wells *Chelmsf* 87-89; C Woodside Park St Barn *Lon* 89-90; TV Canford Magna *Sarum* 90-93; V York St Mich-le-Belfrey *York* from 93. *Half, The Avenue, Clifton, York YO3 6AS* York (01904) 628539

WHITE, Derek. b 35. **d** 84 **p** 85. Hon C St Marylebone St Cypr *Lon* 84-87; C from 87; Bp's Chapl for the Homeless from 87. *80 Coleraine Road, London SE3 7BE, or 17 Homer Row, London W1H 1HU* 0181-858 3622 or 0171-723 3501

WHITE, Derek James. K CT93. Birm Univ BA56. Chich Th Coll 56. **d** 58 **p** 59. C Stanmer w Falmer and Moulsecoomb *Chich* 58-61; Asst Chapl Ardingly Coll Haywards Heath 61-63; Chapl 63-72; C Glynde, W Firle and Beddingham *Chich* 72-73; R Bramber w Botolphs 73-87; V Upper Beeding 73-87; R Beeding and Bramber w Botolphs from 87. *The Rectory, Church Lane, Beeding, Steyning, W Sussex BN44 3HP* Steyning (01903) 815474

WHITE, Douglas Richard Leon (Rick). b 49. Linc Th Coll. **d** 83 **p** 84. C Warsop *S'well* 83-88; R Kirkby in Ashfield St Thos 88-93; Asst Chapl Univ Hosp Nottm from 93. *University Hospital, Queen's Medical Centre, Nottingham NG7 2UH* Nottingham (0115) 942 9924

WHITE, Dudley William. b 33. Univ of Wales (Ban) BSc53. St Mich Coll Llan BD69. **d** 59 **p** 60. C Sketty *S & B* 59-66; R New Radnor and Llanfihangel Nantmelan 66-70; V Penyfai w Tondu *Llan* 70-77; V Swansea St Jude *S & B* from 77. *St Jude's Vicarage, Hillside Crescent, Swansea SA2 0RD* Swansea (01792) 473154

WHITE, Egbert Douglas. b 06. Keble Coll Ox BA28 MA32. Wycliffe Hall Ox 28. **d** 34 **p** 35. C Weston-super-Mare St Paul *B & W* 34-36; P-in-c Locking 40-42; C Kewstoke 44-49; V Mudford 49-87; R Chilton Cantelo w Ashington 67-87; R Chilton Cantelo, Ashington, Mudford, Rimpton etc from 87. *The Vicarage, Mudford, Yeovil, Somerset BA21 5TJ* Marston Magna (01935) 850381

WHITE, Francis (Frank). b 49. Univ of Wales (Cardiff) BSc(Econ)70 DSocStuds71. St Jo Coll Nottm DipTh78. **d** 80 **p** 81. C Dur St Nic *Dur* 80-84; C Ches le Street 84-87; Chapl Dur and Ches le Street Hosps 87-89; V Birtley Dur from 89; RD Ches le Street from 93. *The Vicarage, 6 Ruskin Road, Birtley, Chester le Street, Co Durham DH3 1AD* 0191-410 2115

WHITE, Frederick William Hartland. b 22. MBE62. Kelham Th Coll 39. **d** 45 **p** 46. CF 50-70; Asst Chapl Gen 70-74; QHC from 73; V Harrow St Mary *Lon* 74-87; rtd 87. *Whitesfield House, 5 Seend Cleeve, Melksham, Wilts SN12 6PS*

WHITE, Canon Gavin Donald. b 27. Toronto Univ BA49 Lon Univ PhD70. Trin Coll Toronto BD61 Gen Th Sem (NY)

WHITE

STM68 St Steph Ho Ox 51. **d** 53 **p** 54. C Hampstead St Steph *Lon* 68-70; Lect Glas Univ 71-92; Lic to Offic *Glas* 71-90; rtd 92; Hon Can St Mary's Cathl *Glas* from 92; Hon C St Andrews St Andr *St And* from 94. *85D Market Street, St Andrews, Fife KY16 9NX* St Andrews (01334) 477338

WHITE, Geoffrey Brian. b 54. Jes Coll Ox BA76 MA80. St Steph Ho Ox 76. **d** 79 **p** 80. C Huddersfield St Pet *Wakef* 79-82; C Flixton St Mich *Man* 82-84; TV Westhoughton 84-91; V Stevenage St Mary Sheppall w Aston *St Alb* from 91. *St Mary's Vicarage, 148 Hydean Way, Sheppall, Stevenage, Herts SG2 9YA* Stevenage (01438) 351963

WHITE, Canon Geoffrey Gordon. b 28. Selw Coll Cam BA50 MA54. Cuddesdon Coll 51. **d** 53 **p** 54. V Aldwick *Chich* 66-76; V Brighton Gd Shep Preston 76-93; Can and Preb Chich Cathl 90-93; rtd 93; Hon C Stepney St Dunstan and All SS *Lon* from 94. *Flat 65, Telfords Yard, 6/8 The Highway, London E1 9BQ* 0171-480 6585

WHITE, Gordon Benjamin James. b 13. Worc Ord Coll 60. **d** 62 **p** 63. V Leonard Stanley *Glouc* 65-83; RD Stonehouse 67-79; rtd 83. *The Old Vicarage, Honeyhill, Wootton Bassett, Swindon SN4 7DY* Swindon (01793) 851363

WHITE, Harold Kent. b 05. St Cath Soc Ox BA27 MA37. St Steph Ho Ox 28. **d** 28 **p** 29. V St Mary Aldermary *Lon* 62-75; rtd 75; Chapl Venice w Trieste *Eur* 75-76. *3 Pickwick Road, London SE21 7JN* 0171-274 1006

WHITE, Howard Christopher Graham. b 43. Leeds Univ BA65. Coll of Resurr Mirfield 67. **d** 67 **p** 68. C Friern Barnet St Jas *Lon* 67-71; P-in-c Uxbridge Moor 71-73; Asst Chapl RADD 73-77; Hon C Corringham *Chelmsf* 73-77; Team Ldr St Sav Cen for the Deaf Acton 77-84; Perm to Offic *Guildf* 86-94. *Drake Cottage, Hook Hill Lane, Woking, Surrey GU22 0PS*

WHITE, Ian Terence. b 56. CertEd. Ripon Coll Cuddesdon 83. **d** 86 **p** 87. C Maidstone St Martin *Cant* 86-89; C Earley St Pet *Ox* 89-91; TV Schorne from 91. *The Rectory, Church Street, Quainton, Aylesbury, Bucks HP22 4AP* Aylesbury (01296) 655237

WHITE, Dr Jack Chapman. b 27. BSc49 PhD82. **d** 54 **p** 55. USA 54-94; Chapl Izmir (Smyrna) w Bornova *Eur* from 95. *PK 1005, Arzu Apartment, 1404 Sokat 6, No 7, Izmir, 35214 Turkey* Izmir (232) 463-6608 or 463-5151 Fax 421-2914

WHITE, Miss Janice. b 49. Trin Coll Bris IDC76. **d** 91 **p** 94. C Claygate *Guildf* from 91. *The Church Flat, Church Road, Claygate, Esher, Surrey KT10 0JP* Esher (01372) 464894

WHITE, Jeremy Spencer. b 54. St Luke's Coll Ex BEd78. Wycliffe Hall Ox 81. **d** 84 **p** 85. C S Molton w Nymet St George, High Bray etc *Ex* 84-87; TV 87-95; V Sway *Win* from 95. *The Vicarage, Station Road, Sway, Lymington, Hants SO41 6BA* Lymington (01590) 682358

WHITE, Canon John Austin. b 42. Hull Univ BA64. Coll of Resurr Mirfield 64. **d** 66 **p** 67. C Leeds St Aid *Ripon* 66-69; Asst Chapl Leeds Univ 69-73; Chapl N Ord Course 73-82; Can and Prec Windsor from 82. *8 The Cloisters, Windsor Castle, Windsor, Berks SL4 1NJ* Windsor (01753) 860409

WHITE, John Christopher. b 62. Keble Coll Ox BA84. Wycliffe Hall Ox 86. **d** 89 **p** 90. C Southway *Ex* 89-93; TV Plymouth Em, Efford and Laira from 93. *St Paul's Vicarage, 1 Yeo Close, Blandford Park, Plymouth PL3 6ER* Plymouth (01752) 785576

WHITE, John Cooper. b 58. LTCL79 FRSA K Alfred's Coll Win BEd82 Lon Univ MA92. St Steph Ho Ox 86. **d** 89 **p** 90. C Christchurch *Win* 89-93; P-in-c Bournemouth St Alb from 93. *St Alban's Vicarage, 17 Linwood Road, Bournemouth BH9 1DW* Bournemouth (01202) 534193

WHITE, John Francis. b 47. Qu Coll Cam BA69 MA73. Cuddesdon Coll 72. **d** 72 **p** 73. Sacr Wakef Cathl *Wakef* 72-73; Prec 73-76; V Thurlstone 76-82; P-in-c Hoyland Swaine 81-82; V Chapelthorpe from 82. *The Vicarage, Church Lane, Chapelthorpe, Wakefield, W Yorkshire WF4 3JB* Wakefield (01924) 255360

WHITE, John Malcolm. b 54. Aston Univ BSc77. Trin Coll Bris BA87. **d** 87 **p** 88. C Harborne Heath *Birm* 87-91; C S Harrow St Paul *Lon* 91-93; TV Roxeth from 93. *St Paul's Vicarage, Corbins Lane, Harrow, Middx HA2 8NJ* 0181-422 2991

WHITE, John McKelvey. b 57. QUB BA TCD DipTh82. **d** 82 **p** 83. C Clooney *D & R* 82-84; C Belf H Trin *Conn* 84-86; I Kilcronaghan w Draperstown and Sixtowns *D & R* 86-94; I Ballybeen *D & D* from 94. *1 Grahamsbridge Road, Dundonald, Belfast BT16 0DB* Belfast (01232) 489297

WHITE, John Neville. b 41. Edin Univ MA63. Cranmer Hall Dur DipTh65. **d** 65 **p** 66. C Sedgefield *Dur* 65-68; C Stoke *Cov* 68-72; V Wrose *Bradf* 72-90; V Farsley from 90; RD Calverley from 93. *The Vicarage, 9 St John's Avenue, Farsley, Pudsey, W Yorkshire LS28 5DJ* Leeds (0113) 257 4009

WHITE, Jonathan Roger. b 36. Lon Univ BSc61. Cuddesdon Coll 63. **d** 65 **p** 66. C Swinton St Pet *Man* 65-67; C Prestwich St Mary 67-70; R Salford Stowell Memorial 70-74; TV Swan *Ox* 74-78; P-in-c Monks Risborough 78-84; P-in-c Gt and Lt

Kimble 78-84; P-in-c Prestwood 84-87; P-in-c Gt w Lt Hampden 85-87; P-in-c Prestwood and Gt Hampden 87-93; R from 93; RD Wendover 89-94. *The Rectory, 140 Wycombe Road, Prestwood, Great Missenden, Bucks HP16 0HJ* Great Missenden (01494) 862130

WHITE, Canon Joseph George. b 19. Liv Univ DPA50 Leeds Univ CertEd57. St Deiniol's Hawarden 61. **d** 61 **p** 62. V Rainow w Saltersford *Ches* 65-72; P-in-c Macclesfield Forest w Wildboarclough 66-72; TV Ches 72-75; Dir of Educn 74-88; Hon Can Ches Cathl 79-88; P-in-c Capenhurst 79-87; rtd 88. *17 Endsleigh Close, Chester CH2 1LX* Chester (01244) 382376

WHITE, Julian Edward Llewellyn. b 53. St D Coll Lamp BA79 Chich Th Coll 79. **d** 79 **p** 80. C Newport St Mark *Mon* 79-83; TV Llanmartin 83-86; R Llandogo and Tintern from 86. *The Rectory, Llandogo, Monmouth, Gwent NP5 4TW* Dean (01594) 530887

WHITE, Keith. b 54. Liv Poly BA78 Lon Univ BD82. Wycliffe Hall Ox 78. **d** 81 **p** 82. C Edin St Thos *Edin* 81-84; C Fulwood *Sheff* 84-87; R Heigham H Trin *Nor* 87-95; Zimbabwe from 95. *City Church, Bulawayo, Zimbabwe*

WHITE, Keith Robert. b 48. St Jo Coll Nottm. **d** 84 **p** 85. C Erith St Paul *Roch* 84-88; Chapl Salisbury Coll of Tech *Sarum* 88. *22 Chapel Hill, Dartford DA1 4BY* Crayford (01322) 523779

WHITE, Kenneth Charles. b 15. TD. FCIS FHSM. St Deiniol's Hawarden 76. **d** 77 **p** 78. Hon C Upton Ascension *Ches* 77-79; R Warburton 79-82; rtd 82; Perm to Offic *Ches* from 82; Chapl Asst Countess of Ches Hosp from 84. *13 Queen's Park House, Queen's Park View, Handbridge, Chester CH4 7DB* Chester (01244) 680348

WHITE, Kenneth Charles. b 26. Tyndale Hall Bris 48. **d** 54 **p** 56. V Leyton Ch Ch *Chelmsf* 66-81; V Totland Bay *Portsm* 81-91; rtd 91; Perm to Offic *Llan* from 91. *30 Pendwyallt Road, Whitchurch, Cardiff CF4 7EG* Cardiff (01222) 611529

WHITE, Malcolm Robert. b 46. Man Univ BSc68. St Jo Coll Dur 74. **d** 77 **p** 78. C Linthorpe *York* 77-81; C Sutton St Jas and Wawne 81-83; V Upper Holloway St Pet w St Jo *Lon* 83-95; TV Burnham w Dropmore, Hitcham and Taplow *Ox* from 95. *12 Hatchgate Gardens, Burnham, Slough SL1 8DD* Burnham (01628) 662739

WHITE, Marilyn. **d** 88 **p** 94. NSM Westbury-on-Severn w Flaxley and Blaisdon *Glouc* from 88. *Beacon View, Northwood Green, Westbury-on-Severn, Glos GL14 1NA* Gloucester (01452) 760419

WHITE, Mrs Maureen Barbara. b 42. Bris Univ BA63 Ox Univ DipEd64. Oak Hill Th Coll 87. **d** 89. NSM Wallington H Trin *S'wark* 89-91. *20 Woodcote Avenue, Wallington, Surrey SM6 0QY* 0181-647 1639

WHITE, Nicolas John. b 54. BEd. Wycliffe Hall Ox. **d** 83 **p** 84. C Islington St Mary *Lon* 83-87; Chapl Univ Coll 87-89. *3 Carleton Villas, Leighton Grove, London NW5 2TU* 0171-482 2133

WHITE, Noel Louis. b 11. TCD BA45 MA58. CITC 46. **d** 46 **p** 47. I Belf St Silas *Conn* 62-74; Asst Gen Sec CMS Ireland 74-81; Lic to Offic *D & D* 75-82; rtd 82; Hon C Newtownards *D & D* from 82. *Achlon, 90 Hamilton Road, Bangor, Co Down BT20 4LG* Bangor (01247) 450121

WHITE, Paul Raymond. b 49. Canberra Coll BTh86 DipMin87 Heythrop Coll Lon MTh89. **d** 85 **p** 86. Australia 85-87 and 89-92; P-in-c Reigate St Phil *S'wark* 87-89; V Redhill St Matt from 92. *St Matthew's Vicarage, 23 Ridgeway Road, Redhill RH1 6PQ* Redhill (01737) 761568

WHITE, Peter Francis. b 27. St Edm Hall Ox BA51 MA55. Ridley Hall Cam 51. **d** 53 **p** 54. CF 62-78; R Barming *Roch* 78-89; rtd 89. *Middleton House Cottage, Middleton on the Hill, Ludlow, Shropshire SY8 4BE* Leysters (01568) 750454

WHITE, Canon Peter John. b 23. Hertf Coll Ox BA45 MA49. Wycliffe Hall Ox 45. **d** 47 **p** 48. V Chipping Campden *Glouc* 69-75; P-in-c Ebrington 69-75; RD Campden 73-88; V Chipping Campden w Ebrington 75-88; Hon Can Glouc Cathl 86-88; rtd 88. *70 Northmoor Way, Wareham, Dorset BH20 4EG* Wareham (01929) 553502

WHITE, Peter John. b 26. St Aid Birkenhead 57. **d** 60 **p** 61. C Keighley *Bradf* 68-71; C Newington w Dairycoates *York* 71-75; C Frodingham *Linc* 75-80; R Mareham-le-Fen and Revesby 80-86; V Wrawby 86-91; V Melton Ross w New Barnetby 86-91; rtd 91; Perm to Offic *Linc* from 91. *91 Emfield Road, Scartho, Grimsby, S Humberside DN33 3BY* Grimsby (01472) 823097

WHITE, Philip William. b 53. Bede Coll Dur CertEd75. St Jo Coll Nottm DCM91. **d** 91 **p** 92. C Clifton *York* 91-95; TV Heworth from 95. *St Wulstans Vicarage, 8 Abbotsway, York YO3 9LD* York (01904) 425188

WHITE, Canon Phillip George. b 33. Univ of Wales (Lamp) BA54. St Mich Coll Llan 54. **d** 56 **p** 57. C Tongwynlais *Llan* 56-58; C Mountain Ash 58-60; C Aberavon 60-62; Area Sec (Middx) CMS 62-64; V Treherbert *Llan* 64-76; P-in-c Treorchy 75-76; V Treherbert w Treorchy 76-77; V Pyle w

Kenfig from 77; RD Margam from 86; Can Llan Cathl from 91. *The Vicarage, Pyle, Bridgend, M Glam CF33 6PG* Bridgend (01656) 740500

WHITE, Mrs Priscilla Audrey. b 62. St Hugh's Coll Ox BA84. Wycliffe Hall Ox 87. **d** 89 **p** 94. Par Dn Southway *Ex* 89-93; NSM Plymouth Em, Efford and Laira from 93. *St Paul's Vicarage, 1 Yeo Close, Blandford Road, Plymouth PL3 6ER* Plymouth (01752) 785576

WHITE, Richard Alfred. b 49. DipSocWork CQSW. St Jo Coll Nottm. **d** 90 **p** 91. C Leic St Phil *Leic* 90-95; C Old Dalby and Nether Broughton from 95. *The Vicarage, Old Dalby, Melton Mowbray, Leics LE14 3LB* Leicester (0116) 482 2878

WHITE, Richard Allen. b 25. Open Univ BA78 Southn Univ MPhil88. Sarum & Wells Th Coll 78. **d** 81 **p** 82. NSM Bursledon *Win* 81-85; C W End 85-90; C Fareham SS Pet and Paul *Portsm* from 90. *Manor Cottage, Church Path, Osborn Road, Fareham, Hants PO16 7DT* Fareham (01329) 280226

WHITE, Robert Bruce (Bob). b 42. Sarum & Wells Th Coll 71. **d** 73 **p** 74. C Woodford St Barn *Chelmsf* 73-75; Youth Chapl 75-79; C-in-c Sutton 75-78; P-in-c 78-79; C-in-c Shopland 75-78; P-in-c 78-79; TR Southend St Jo w St Mark, All SS w St Fran etc 79-82; P-in-c Southend St Alb 80-82; TR Southend 82-89; P-in-c Brentwood St Thos from 89; RD Brentwood from 93. *The Vicarage, 91 Queen's Road, Brentwood, Essex CM14 4EY* Brentwood (01277) 225700

WHITE, Robert Charles (Bob). b 61. Mansf Coll Ox BA83. St Steph Ho Ox 83. **d** 85 **p** 86. C Forton *Portsm* 85-88; C Portsea N End St Mark 88-92; V Warren Park St Clare from 92; P-in-c Leigh Park from 94. *St Clare's House, Strouden Court, Havant, Hants PO9 4JX* Havant (01705) 451762

WHITE, Ven Robin Edward Bantry. b 47. TCD BA70 BD79. CITC 72. **d** 72 **p** 73. C Dub Zion Ch *D & G* 72-76; Min Can St Patr Cathl Dub 76-79; C Taney Ch Ch *D & G* 76-79; I Abbeystrewry Union *C, C & R* 79-89; RD Mid W Cork 87-89; I Douglas Union w Frankfield from 89; Preb Ross Cathl 89-93; Preb Cork Cathl 89-93; RD Cork City from 89; Adn Cork, Cloyne and Ross 93. *The Rectory, Carrigaline Road, Douglas, Cork, Irish Republic* Cork (21) 891539 Fax as telephone

WHITE, Roderick Harry. b 55. Trin Coll Bris BA86. **d** 86 **p** 87. C Northn St Giles *Pet* 86-89; C Godley cum Newton Green *Ches* 89-93; P-in-c from 93. *The Vicarage, 43 Sheffield Road, Hyde, Cheshire SK14 2PR* 0161-368 2159

WHITE, Roger Charles. b 37. St Alb Minl Tr Scheme 77. **d** 80 **p** 81. NSM Wilshamstead and Houghton Conquest *St Alb* from 80. *30 Wood End Road, Wood End, Kempston, Bedford MK43 9BB* Bedford (01234) 852472

WHITE, Roger David. b 36. St Mich Coll Llan DipTh66. **d** 66 **p** 67. C Mountain Ash *Llan* 66-71; C Port Talbot St Theodore 71-74; V Caerhun w Llangelynnin *Ban* 74-85; R Llanbedrog w Llannor w Llanfihangel etc 85-88; V Llangeinor *Llan* 88-90; V Spittal w Trefgarn and Ambleston w St Dogwells *St D* from 90. *The Vicarage, West Gate, Spittal, Haverfordwest, Dyfed SA26 5QP* Treffgarne (01437) 741505

WHITE, Roger Ian Scott. b 41. Leeds Univ BA62 Culham Coll Ox PGCE70. Coll of Resurr Mirfield 62. **d** 64 **p** 65. C Wootton-under-Edge *Glouc* 64-69; NSM Rugby St Andr *Cov* 71-80; W Germany 80-82; P-in-c Brinklow *Cov* 82-86; R 86-90; P-in-c Harborough Magna 82-86; R 86-90; P-in-c Monks Kirby w Pailton and Stretton-under-Fosse 82-86; V 86-90; Germany 90-92; V St Anne Lydgate w Ch Ch Friezland *Man* from 92. *The Vicarage, Stockport Road, Lydgate, Oldham OL4 4JJ* Saddleworth (01457) 872117

✠**WHITE, Rt Rev Roger John.** b 41. Kelham Th Coll. **d** 66 **p** 67 **c** 84. C Manston *Ripon* 66-69; USA from 69; Bp Milwaukee from 85. *804 East Juneau Avenue, Milwaukee, Wisconsin 53202, USA*

WHITE, Ronald Henry. b 36. Bris Univ BSc58 Ox Univ DipEd59 Lon Univ DipTh64. SW Minl Tr Course 82. **d** 85 **p** 86. C Ivybridge *Ex* 85-87; C Ivybridge w Harford 87-88; V Blackawton and Stoke Fleming from 88. *The Vicarage, Stoke Flemming, Dartmouth, Devon TQ6 0QB* Stoke Fleming (01803) 770361

WHITE, Canon Roy Sidney. b 34. Sarum Th Coll 62. **d** 65 **p** 66. C Selsdon St Jo *Cant* 65-68; C Ranmoor *Sheff* 68-72; V Croydon St Andr *Cant* 72-78; Dir Abp Coggan Tr Cen 78-85; Dir of Chr Stewardship *S'wark* 85-91; Hon Can S'wark Cathl 85-91; Can Res S'wark Cathl from 91; Vice Provost S'wark from 91. *73 St George's Road, London SE1 6EQ* 0171-735 8322 or 407 3708 Fax 357 7389

WHITE, Simon Inigo Dexter. b 58. York Univ BA80 Nottm Univ PGCE81. St Jo Coll Nottm 87. **d** 90 **p** 91. C Chadkirk *Ches* 90-94; C Stockport St Geo 94; Chapl Stockport Grammar Sch from 94; TV Stockport South West from 94. *19 Frewland Avenue, Stockport, Cheshire SK3 8TZ* 0161-456 2691

WHITE, Very Rev Stephen Ross. b 58. Hull Univ BA Ox Univ BA QUB DPhil93. Ripon Coll Cuddesdon 82. **d** 85 **p** 86. C

Redcar *York* 85-88; P-in-c Gweedore, Carrickfin and Templecrone *D & R* 88-92; Bp's Dom Chapl 91-92; Dean Raphoe from 92; I Raphoe w Raymochy and Clonleigh from 93. *The Deanery, Raphoe, Lifford, Co Donegal, Irish Republic* Raphoe (74) 45226

WHITE, Sister Teresa Joan. b 36. Wellesley Coll (USA) BA58 Harvard Univ STB61 Lon Univ CertEd74 Hon DD86. **dss** 75 **d** 87 **p** 94. CSA from 72; Teacher Burlington-Danes Sch 74-76; Lect Inst of Chr Studies *Lon* 76-78; Gen Sec World Congress of Faiths 77-81; Lect Dioc Readers' Course *S'wark* 81-89; Asst Abp's Sec for Ecum Affairs 81-82; Ed Distinctive Diaconate from 81; Ed DIAKONIA News from 87. *St Andrew's House, 2 Tavistock Road, London W11 1BA* 0171-229 2662

WHITE, Trevor John. b 37. St Pet Coll Ox BA61 MA65. Wycliffe Hall Ox. **d** 63 **p** 64. C Walsall *Lich* 63-67; V Greasbrough *Sheff* 67-73; Chapl Nat Nautical Sch Portishead 73-82; Chapl Bris Cathl Sch from 82; Perm to Offic *B & W* from 82. *4 Gardner Road, Portishead, Bristol BS20 9ER* Whitchurch (01275) 847855

WHITE, Canon Vernon Philip. b 53. Clare Coll Cam BA75 MA79 Or Coll Ox MLitt80. Wycliffe Hall Ox DipTh76. **d** 77 **p** 78. Tutor Wycliffe Hall Ox 77-83; Chapl and Lect Ex Univ 83-87; R Wotton and Holmbury St Mary *Guildf* 87-93; Dir of Ords 87-93; Can Res and Chan Linc Cathl *Linc* from 93. *The Chancery, 11 Minster Yard, Lincoln LN2 1PJ* Lincoln (01522) 525610

WHITE, William John. b 54. BSc. Wycliffe Hall Ox. **d** 84 **p** 85. C Bowdon *Ches* 84-87; C Chadkirk 87-90; R Wistaston from 90. *The Rectory, 44 Church Lane, Wistaston, Crewe CW2 8HA* Crewe (01270) 67119

WHITE SPUNNER, Mrs Jessie Janet. b 37. SRN59 SCM61. CITC 91. **d** 94 **p** 95. NSM Shinrone w Aghancon etc *L & K* from 94. *Milltown Park, Shinrone, Birr, Co Offaly, Irish Republic* Birr (505) 47143

WHITE-THOMSON, Very Rev Ian Hugh. b 04. BNC Ox BA27 MA37 Kent Univ Hon DCL71. Cuddesdon Coll 28. **d** 29 **p** 30. Dean Cant 63-76; rtd 76; Perm to Offic *Cant* from 76. *Camphill, Harville Road, Wye, Ashford, Kent TN25 5EY* Wye (01233) 812210

WHITEFIELD, Dr Keith Russell. b 60. Aber Univ MA83 PhD91 Edin Univ BD91. Edin Th Coll 88. **d** 91 **p** 93. C Haddington *Edin* 91-94; C Dunbar 91-94; Miss Priest Wester Hailes St Luke from 94. *24/3 Wester Hailes Park, Edinburgh EH14 3AF* 0131-453 4265

WHITEHEAD, Barry. b 30. Or Coll Ox BA53 MA62. St Steph Ho Ox 53. **d** 55 **p** 56. C Edge Hill St Dunstan *Liv* 55-58; C Upholland 58-61; Ind Chapl 61-90; CF (TA) 64-78; V Aspull *Liv* from 77. *St Elizabeth's Vicarage, Bolton Road, Aspull, Wigan, Lancs WN2 1PR* Wigan (01942) 831236

WHITEHEAD, Brian. b 36. DipTh SRN. S'wark Ord Course 74. **d** 75 **p** 77. C Croydon St Aug *Cant* 75-78; C St Marychurch *Ex* 78-80; V Devonport St Mark Ford 80-87; V Castle Donington and Lockington cum Hemington *Leic* from 87. *The Vicarage, 6 Delven Lane, Castle Donington, Derby DE74 2LJ* Derby (01332) 810364

WHITEHEAD, Christopher Martin Field. b 36. ALCD62. **d** 62 **p** 63. C Higher Openshaw *Man* 62-63; C Halliwell St Pet 64-66; V Owlerton *Sheff* 66-75; V Hunmanby w Muston *York* 75-95; RD Scarborough 91-94; R Lockington and Lund and Scorborough w Leconfield from 95. *The Rectory, Lockington, Driffield, N Humberside YO25 9SU* Market Weighton (01430) 810604

WHITEHEAD, Canon Denys Gordon. b 22. Pemb Coll Ox BA50 MA55. Linc Th Coll 49. **d** 52 **p** 53. Zambia from 60; Adn S Zambia 80-89; rtd 89; Hon Can Zambia from 93. *PO Box 60648, Livingstone, Zambia* Livingstone (3) 323565

WHITEHEAD, Canon Dr Derek. b 27. St Jo Coll Cam BA50 MA55 Lon Univ BD60 Lanc Univ PhD73. Wells Th Coll 55. **d** 56 **p** 57. Lect Div Preston Poly 65-79; Dir of Educn *Chich* 79-94; Can and Preb Chich Cathl 82-94; NSM Fletching 93-94; rtd 94. *The Rectory, Fletching, Uckfield, E Sussex TN22 3SR* Newick (01825) 722498

WHITEHEAD, Frederick Keith. b 35. K Coll Lon BD58 AKC58. St Boniface Warminster 58. **d** 59 **p** 60. C S Shore H Trin *Blackb* 59-63; C Whitfield *Derby* 63-66; Lic to Offic 66-93; V Glossop from 93. *The Vicarage, Church Street South, Glossop, Derbyshire SK13 9RU* Glossop (01457) 852146

WHITEHEAD, Gordon James. b 42. Clifton Th Coll 66. **d** 73 **p** 74. Chile 73-87; C Coleraine *Conn* 87-94; I Errigle Keerogue w Ballygawley and Killeshil *Arm* from 94. *Richmond Rectory, 24 Old Omagh Road, Ballygawley, Co Tyrone BT70 2AA* Ballygawley (016625) 68670

WHITEHEAD, Mrs Hazel. b 54. K Coll Lon AKC76 BD76 Lon Univ CertTESOL89. Oak Hill Th Coll 93. **d** 94 **p** 95. NSM Oatlands *Guildf* 94; C from 95; Tutor Guildf Dio Min Course from 94. *The Vicarage, 5 Burwood Road, Walton-on-Thames, Surrey KT12 4AA* Walton-on-Thames (01932) 227445 Fax as telephone

WHITEHEAD, Ian Richard. b 63. St Jo Coll Nottm BA95. d 95. C Hillmorton *Cov* from 95. *24 Deane Road, Hillmorton, Rugby, Warks CV21 4NZ* Rugby (01788) 547091

WHITEHEAD, John Stanley. b 38. Jes Coll Cam BA63 MA67 MPhil. Westcott Ho Cam 63. d 64 p 65. C Batley All SS *Wakef* 64-67; C Mitcham St Mark *S'wark* 67-70; C Frindsbury w Upnor *Roch* 70-72; TV Strood 72-75; R Halstead 75-82; V Betley *Lich* 82-85; Asst Chapl Keele Univ from 82; V Betley and Keele from 85. *The Vicarage, Betley, Crewe CW3 9AX* Crewe (01270) 820245

WHITEHEAD, Matthew Alexander. b 44. Leeds Univ BA65 St Chad's Coll Dur DipEd66 Birm Univ MA75. Qu Coll Birm DipTh68. d 69 p 70. C Bingley All SS *Bradf* 69-72; C Keele *Lich* 72-74; Asst Chapl Keele Univ 72-74; Bp's Dom Chapl *Dur* 74-80; V Escomb 74-80; V Witton Park 74-80; V Birtley 80-89; RD Ches le Street 84-89; V Stockton St Pet from 89. *The Vicarage, 77 Yarm Road, Stockton-on-Tees, Cleveland TS18 3PJ* Stockton-on-Tees (01642) 676625

WHITEHEAD, Canon Michael Hutton. b 33. St Chad's Coll Dur 54. d 58 p 59. C Southwick St Columba *Dur* 58-64; V Hendon St Ignatius 64-70; P-in-c Sunderland 67-80; V Hendon 70-80; V Hendon and Sunderland 80-87; Hon Can Dur Cathl from 84; V Hartlepool St Aid from 87; RD Hartlepool from 91. *The Vicarage, St Aidan's Street, Hartlepool, Cleveland TS25 1SN* Hartlepool (01429) 273539

WHITEHEAD, Nicholas James. b 53. AIB. Ridley Hall Cam 86. d 88 p 89. C Bourne *Guildf* 88-92; V Hersham from 92. *The Vicarage, 5 Burwood Road, Hersham, Walton-on-Thames, Surrey KT12 4AA* Walton-on-Thames (01932) 227445

WHITEHEAD, Paul Conrad. b 60. St Jo Coll Nottm LTh92. d 92 p 93. C Mansf Woodhouse *S'well* from 92. *68 Ley Lane, Mansfield Woodhouse, Mansfield, Notts NG19 8JX* Mansfield (01623) 650093

WHITEHEAD, Philip. b 34. Kelham Th Coll 55. d 59 p 60. C Sugley *Newc* 59-62; C Alnwick St Paul 62-63; C Newc St Gabr 63-66; C Gosforth All SS 66-67; V Kenton Ascension 67-75; V Spittal 75-88; P-in-c Scremerston 81-88; V Cresswell and Lynemouth from 88. *The Vicarage, 33 Till Grove, Ellington, Morpeth, Northd NE61 5ER* Morpeth (01670) 860242

WHITEHEAD, Roger Milton. b 25. Pemb Coll Ox BA50 MA54. Ely Th Coll 50. d 52 p 53. V Gosfield St Jo *Portsm* 64-72; V Albrighton *Lich* 72-80; R Euston w Barnham and Fakenham *St E* 80-85; R Euston w Barnham, Elvedon and Fakenham Magna 85-89; rtd 89. *Groveways, Spur Road, Barnham Broom, Norwich NR9 4BY* Barnham Broom (0160545) 779

WHITEHORN, Arthur Basil. b 24. W Midl Minl Tr Course. d 84 p 85. Asst Chapl Bromsgrove & Redditch Health Auth 84-89; NSM Bromsgrove St Jo *Worc* 84-94; Perm to Offic from 94. *15 Perry Lane, Bromsgrove, Worcs B61 7JL* Bromsgrove (01527) 74857

WHITEHORN, Jean Margaret. b 28. Lon Univ DipSocSc49 Cam Univ TCert70 Lon Univ DipRS85. S'wark Ord Course 87. d 89 p 94. NSM Orsett *Chelmsf* 89-90; NSM Orsett and Bulphan 90-93; NSM Orsett and Bulphan and Horndon on the Hill from 93. *46 Monks Haven, Stanford-le-Hope, Essex SS17 7EF* Stanford-le-Hope (01375) 676074

WHITEHOUSE, Alan Edward. b 35. Glouc Sch of Min 89. d 92 p 93. NSM Evesham *Worc* from 92. *99 Greenhill, Evesham, Worcs WR11 4NB* Evesham (01386) 442427

WHITEHOUSE, Nigel Andrew. b 57. St Mary's RC Sem Birm 75. d 80 p 81. In RC Ch 81-87; C Whittlesey and Pondersbridge *Ely* 92-94; P-in-c Newton from 94; P-in-c Gorefield from 94; P-in-c Tydd St Giles from 94. *The Rectory, Newton, Wisbech, Cambs PE13 5EX* Wisbech (01945) 870205

WHITEHOUSE, Robert Edward. b 64. Oak Hill Th Coll BA. d 91 p 92. C Sheff Norwood St Leon *Sheff* 91-94; P-in-c Birchencliffe *Wakef* from 94; Dioc Youth Officer from 94; Bp's Chapl for Youth from 94. *The Vicarage, 191 Birkby Road, Huddersfield HD2 2BX*

WHITEHOUSE, Miss Susan Clara. b 48. R Holloway Coll Lon BA70. Westcott Ho Cam 87. d 89 p 94. Par Dn Farnley *Ripon* 89-93; Dioc Development Rep from 92; C Bedale from 93; C Thornton Watlass w Thornton Steward from 93. *The Rectory, Thornton Watlass, Ripon, N Yorkshire HG4 4AH* Ripon (01677) 422737

WHITELEY, Alan. b 42. ACII. Lich Th Coll 68. d 71 p 72. C Wales *Sheff* 71-75; TV Frecheville and Hackenthorpe 75-79; V Malin Bridge from 79. *St Polycarp's Vicarage, 33 Wisewood Lane, Sheffield S6 4WA* Sheffield (0114) 234 3450

WHITELEY, Donal Royston. b 27. Qu Coll Birm 54. d 57 p 58. C Handsworth St Mary *Birm* 57-60; C Kingswinford St Mary *Lich* 60-63; R Norton Canes 63-71; V Wetley Rocks from 71. *St John's Vicarage, Wetley Rocks, Stoke-on-Trent ST9 0AP* Wetley Rocks (01782) 550251

WHITELEY, Robert. b 36. Dur Univ BA67. Cranmer Hall Dur 62. d 67 p 68. C Maidstone All SS w St Phil and H Trin *Cant*

67-70; Asst Chapl K Sch Roch 70-71; Chapl 71-82. *c/o Mrs L E Walton, 10 Greenway, Wilmslow, Cheshire SK9 1LU* Wilmslow (01625) 524019

WHITELEY, Canon Robert Louis. b 28. Leeds Univ BA48. Coll of Resurr Mirfield 50. d 52 p 53. V Westgate Common *Wakef* 68-75; Can Res Wakef Cathl 75-80; Hon Can Wakef Cathl 80-93; V Almondbury 80-82; TR Almondbury w Farnley Tyas 82-92; RD Almondbury 81-93; rtd 93. *12 Woodland Avenue, Lepton, Huddersfield HD8 0HZ* Huddersfield (01484) 608050

WHITEMAN, Canon Cedric Henry. b 28. Lich Th Coll 59. d 61 p 62. V Kettering St Andr *Pet* 64-79; RD Kettering 73-79; Can Pet Cathl 77-79; V Rotherham *Sheff* 79-87; RD Rotherham 79-86; Hon Can Sheff Cathl from 85; Bp's Dom Chapl from 86; V Wentworth 87-91; rtd 91. *11 Thornbrook Close, Chapeltown, Sheffield S30 4BB* Sheffield (0114) 245 7479

WHITEMAN, Christopher Henry Raymond. b 51. Portsm Poly BA73 Worc Coll of Educn PGCE74. St Jo Coll Nottm DipTh90. d 90 p 91. C Rockland St Mary w Hellington, Bramerton etc *Nor* 90-93; P-in-c Gillingham w Geldeston, Stockton, Ellingham etc 93-94; R from 94. *The Rectory, The Street, Geldeston, Beccles, Suffolk NR34 0LN* Beccles (01502) 712255

WHITEMAN, Ven Rodney David Carter. b 40. Ely Th Coll 61. d 64 p 65. C Kings Heath *Birm* 64-70; V Rednal 70-79; V Erdington St Barn 79-89; RD Aston 81-86 and 88-89; Hon Can Birm Cathl 85-89; Adn Bodmin *Truro* from 89; P-in-c Cardynham from 89; P-in-c Helland from 89; Hon Can Truro Cathl from 89. *The Rectory, Cardinham, Bodmin, Cornwall PL30 4BL* Cardinham (01208) 821614 Fax 821602

WHITESIDE, Canon Peter George. b 30. St Cath Coll Cam BA55 MA61. Cuddesdon Coll 55. d 57 p 58. C Westmr St Steph w St Jo *Lon* 57-61; Chapl Clifton Coll Bris 61-70; Hd Master Linc Cathl Sch 71-73; Australia 74-92; TV Brentford *Lon* from 92. *St Faith's Vicarage, 122 Windmill Road, Brentford, Middx TW8 9NA* 0181-560 3782

WHITFIELD, Canon Benjamin Owen. b 17. Saskatchewan Univ BA43. Em Coll Saskatoon LTh43 BD53. d 43 p 44. V Clee *Linc* 62-70; Can and Preb Linc Cathl 70-85; V Gainsborough All SS 70-81; RD Corringham 72-78; V Morton 76-81; V Melton Ross w New Barnetby 81-85; V Wrawby 81-85; rtd 85. *6 The Copse, Bigby High Road, Brigg, S Humberside DN20 9HY* Brigg (01652) 652695

WHITFIELD, Charles. b 25. St Pet Hall Ox BA49 MA53. Ridley Hall Cam 49. d 51 p 52. V Egg Buckland *Ex* 68-90; rtd 90. *23 Chapel Meadow, Buckland Monachorum, Yelverton, Devon PL20 7LR*

WHITFIELD, George Joshua Newbold. b 09. Lon Univ AKC30 MA35. Bps' Coll Cheshunt. d 62 p 63. Hon C Hampton St Mary *Lon* 62-74; Gen Sec Gen Syn Bd of Educn 69-74; rtd 74; Lic to Offic *Ex* from 78. *Bede Lodge, 31A Rolle Road, Exmouth, Devon EX8 2AW* Exmouth (01395) 274162

WHITFIELD, Joy Verity. *See* CHAPMAN, Mrs Joy Verity

WHITFIELD, Kenneth. b 18. Lich Th Coll 54. d 56 p 57. V Leeds St Marg *Ripon* 64-73; Chapl Community of St Pet Horbury 73-84; rtd 83; Perm to Offic *Nor* from 84. *47 Charles Road, Holt, Norfolk NR25 6DA* Holt (01263) 712004

WHITFIELD, Trevor. b 48. Bedf Coll Lon BSc71 Bris Univ PGCE73 Fitzw Coll Cam BA78 MA88. Ridley Hall Cam 76. d 79 p 80. C Battersea St Pet and St Paul *S'wark* 79-82; Chapl Stockholm w Uppsala *Eur* 82-83; C-in-c Roundshaw CD *S'wark* 83-89; Asst Chapl R Victoria Infirmary Newc 89-92; Asst Chapl Berne w Neuchatel *Eur* 92-95; Chapl Utrecht w Amersfoort, Harderwijk & Zwolle from 95. *V Hogendorpstraat 26, 3581 KE Utrecht, The Netherlands* Utrecht (30) 513424

WHITFORD, William Laurence. b 56. Open Univ BA92. N Ord Course 92. d 95. C Hindley All SS *Liv* from 95. *45 Woodland Avenue, Wigan, Lancs WN2 4PP* Wigan (01942) 254824

WHITING, Antony Gerald Stroud. b 26. CITC 81. d 86 p 87. NSM Clonmel Union *C, C & R* 86-87; Cork St Fin Barre's Union 87-88; Lic to Offic 88-92; Bp's C Mallow Union from 92. *The Rectory, Lower Bearforest, Mallow, Co Cork, Irish Republic* Mallow (22) 21473 Fax as telephone

WHITING, Graham James. b 58. Bris Univ BSc81. Chich Th Coll 83. d 86 p 88. C Portslade St Nic and St Andr *Chich* 86-87; C W Tarring 87-91; C Seaford w Sutton 91-94; P-in-c Bournemouth St Clem *Win* from 94. *The Vicarage, St Clement's Road, Bournemouth BH1 4DZ* Bournemouth (01202) 392851

WHITING, Joseph Alfred. b 41. Oak Hill Th Coll 82. d 85 p 86. Hon C Sidcup St Andr *Roch* 85-88; C Southborough St Pet w Ch Ch and St Matt 88-92; C Aldridge *Lich* from 92. *14 St Thomas' Close, Aldridge, Walsall WS9 8SL* Walsall (01922) 53942

WHITLEY, Prof Charles Francis. TCD BA42 MA45 BD45 PhD49 Ox Univ MA66 MLitt82. d 43 p 44. C Dundalk *Arm* 43-45; C Dub Zion Ch *D & G* 45-49; Lect OT Dur Univ 49-52; Tutor St Jo Coll Dur 49-52; V Bolton St Barn *Man* 52-53; Lect

Hebrew and OT Univ of Wales (Ban) 53-67; Sen Lect 67-84; Prof Bibl Studies from 84. *Elmbank, Llandegfan, Menai Bridge, Gwynedd LL59 5YE*

WHITLEY, Eric Keir. b 47. Salford Univ BSc68. Trin Coll Bris 77. **d** 79 **p** 80. C Nottm St Ann w Em *S'well* 79-83; V Donisthorpe and Moira w Stretton-en-le-Field *Leic* 83-91; V Dishley and Thorpe Acre from 91. *The Vicarage, Knightthorpe Road, Loughborough, Leics LE11 0LF*   Loughborough (01509) 214553

WHITLEY, John Duncan Rooke. b 29. Trin Coll Cam BA51 MA55. Coll of Resurr Mirfield 52. **d** 54 **p** 55. C Ashington *Newc* 54-59; C Chiswick St Nic w St Mary *Lon* 59-61; V Ware St Mary *St Alb* 61-71; Can Missr St Mary's Cathl Edin 71-74; Dioc Educn Officer 71-74; Lic to Offic from 74. *114 Viewforth, Edinburgh EH10 4LN*   0131-229 0130

WHITLEY, John William. b 46. TCD BA68. Cranmer Hall Dur BA71. **d** 71 **p** 72. C Belf St Mary Magd *Conn* 71-73; C Toxteth St Philemon w St Gabr *Liv* 73-78; P-in-c Toxteth Park St Cleopas 78-88; TV Toxteth St Philemon w St Gabr and St Cleopas 89-95; P-in-c Litherland St Paul Hatton Hill from 95. *St Paul's Vicarage, Watling Avenue, Liverpool L21 9NU*   0151-928 2705

WHITLOCK, James Frederick. b 44. Ch Coll Cam BA75 MA78. Westcott Ho Cam 73. **d** 76 **p** 77. C Newquay *Truro* 76-79; P-in-c St Mawgan w St Ervan and St Eval 79-81; R 81; Bp's Dom Chapl 82-85; Dioc Dir of Ords 82-85; V Leagrave *St Alb* 85-89; TR Probus, Ladock and Grampound w Creed and St Erme *Truro* 89-95; V Penzance St Mary w St Paul from 95. *St Mary's Vicarage, Chapel Street, Penzance, Cornwall TR18 4AP*   Penzance (01736) 63079

WHITLOW, Very Rev Brian William. b 14. St Edm Hall Ox BA36 DipTh37 Bp's Univ Lennoxville MEd52 BD59 DD67. Westcott Ho Cam 37. **d** 38 **p** 39. C Leeds St Aid *Ripon* 38-41; Chapl RAFVR 41-46; Canada from 46; Dean Ch Ch Cathl Victoria 55-80. *1347 Craigdarroch Road, Victoria, British Columbia, Canada, V8S 2A6*   Victoria (604) 592-6109

WHITMORE, Benjamin Nicholas. b 66. Imp Coll Lon BEng88. Cranmer Hall Dur 89. **d** 92 **p** 93. C Gt Wyrley *Lich* 92-95; C Hednesford from 95. *554 Littleworth Road, Rawnsley, Cannock, Staffs WS12 5JD*   Cannock (01543) 879686

WHITMORE, Mrs Dorothy Mary. b 28. Sheff Univ BA49 DipEd50. Gilmore Course 79. **dss** 81 **d** 87 **p** 94. Marston Green *Birm* 81-87; NSM from 87. *116 Elmdon Lane, Birmingham B37 7DN*   0121-779 2695

WHITMORE, Edward James. b 36. Lon Univ BD66. Tyndale Hall Bris. **d** 68 **p** 69. Tanzania 68-76; Lic to Offic *Blackb* from 77. *74 Greencroft, Penwortham, Preston PR1 9LB*   Preston (01772) 746522

WHITMORE, Miss Jane Frances. b 30. **dss** 79 **d** 87 **p** 94. Elloughton and Brough w Brantingham *York* 79-83; Foley Park *Worc* 83-87; C Frimley *Guildf* from 87. *20 Winterbourne Walk, Frimley, Camberley, Surrey GU16 5YB*   Camberley (01276) 837425

WHITMORE, Stephen Andrew. b 53. Sheff Univ BSc74. St Jo Coll Nottm DTS89. **d** 91 **p** 92. C Newbury *Ox* from 91. *10 Braunfels Walk, Newbury, Berks RG14 5NQ*   Newbury (01635) 582006

WHITNALL, Robert Edward (Dominic). b 14. Magd Coll Ox BA37. Cuddesdon Coll 37. **d** 38 **p** 39. S Africa 47-66; CR from 47; Hon C Battyeford *Wakef* from 68; rtd 84. *House of the Resurrection, Mirfield, W Yorkshire WF14 0BN*   Mirfield (01924) 494318

WHITROW, Capt Henry Thomas. b 32. RMA 50. Oak Hill Th Coll 61. **d** 63 **p** 64. C Reading St Jo *Ox* 68-69; rtd 94. *Grenfell, Ellesborough Manor, Aylesbury, Bucks HP17 0XF*

WHITTA, Rex Alfred Rought. b 28. Leeds Inst of Educn CertEd52 Lon Univ BA88 Lon Univ CertTESOL89. Qu Coll Birm DipTh63. **d** 63 **p** 64. V Elloughton and Brough w Brantingham *York* 68-74; TR Redcar w Kirkleatham 74-78; V Redcar 78-84; V Bassenthwaite, Isel and Setmurthy *Carl* 84-86; P-in-c Cloughton *York* 86-88; P-in-c Hackness w Harwood Dale 86-88; rtd 89. *14 Candler Street, Scarborough, N Yorkshire YO12 7DF*   Scarborough (01723) 375740

WHITTAKER, Arthur. b 30. Oak Hill Th Coll. **d** 60 **p** 61. C Bispham *Blackb* 60-64; V Edge Hill St Cypr *Liv* 64-73; Area Sec (Dios Ban, St As, Ches and S & M) CMS 73-74; C Maghull *Liv* 74; V Bilsborrow *Blackb* from 74. *The Vicarage, Church Lane, Bilsborrow, Preston PR3 0RL*   Brock (01995) 640269

WHITTAKER, Arthur George. b 14. MRIPHH38 LTCL57 Man Univ 48. **d** 60 **p** 61. V Hadfield *Derby* 63-72; V Coldham *Ely* 72-81; V Friday Bridge 72-81; rtd 81; Perm to Offic *Glouc* from 81. *27 Mosley Crescent, Cashes Green, Stroud, Glos GL5 4LT*   Stroud (01453) 763622

WHITTAKER, Brian Lawrence. b 39. Clifton Th Coll. **d** 66 **p** 67. C Whitton and Thurleston w Akenham *St E* 66-69; C Normanton *Wakef* 69-74; P-in-c Castle Hall *Ches* 74-77; P-in-c Dukinfield Ch Ch 74-77; P-in-c Stalybridge H Trin and Ch Ch 74-77; V 77-83; TR Bucknall and Bagnall *Lich* 83-91; R

Draycott-le-Moors w Forsbrook from 91. *The Rectory, 7 Cheadle Road, Blythe Bridge, Stoke-on-Trent ST11 9PW*   Blythe Bridge (01782) 392259

WHITTAKER, Bryan. b 58. Southn Univ BTh82. Chich Th Coll 82. **d** 84 **p** 85. C Whitleigh *Ex* 84-88; C Corringham *Chelmsf* 88-92; V Rush Green 92-94. *361 Dagenham Road, Romford RM7 0XX*

WHITTAKER, Garry. b 59. St Jo Coll Nottm DCM91. **d** 91 **p** 92. C Denton Ch Ch *Man* from 91. *65 Hulme Road, Denton, Manchester M34 2WX*   0161-336 3455

WHITTAKER, Ivan Harrison. b 08. Westcott Ho Cam 44. **d** 46 **p** 47. Chapl St Mich Sch Otford 65-73; rtd 73; Perm to Offic *Chich* from 73. *1 Manor Close, North Lancing, W Sussex BN15 0QY*   Lancing (01903) 752387

WHITTAKER, James Rawstron. b 14. Worc Coll Ox BA38 MA46. Wells Th Coll 38. **d** 40 **p** 41. V Almeley *Heref* 70-80; P-in-c Kinnersley w Norton Canon 74-80; rtd 81; Perm to Offic *Heref* from 82. *Eign Gate House, 142 Eign Street, Hereford HR4 0AP*   Hereford (01432) 268961

WHITTAKER, Jeremy Paul. b 59. Ox Univ MA. Ripon Coll Cuddesdon 82. **d** 84 **p** 85. C Crowthorne *Ox* 84-87; C Westborough *Guildf* 87-88; TV 88-91; Chapl Pierrepont Sch Frensham from 91. *6 Springhaven Close, Guildford, Surrey GU1 2JP*

WHITTAKER, Canon John. b 20. Ch Coll Cam BA47 MA49. Ridley Hall Cam 46. **d** 48 **p** 49. V New Bury *Man* 66-75; Hon Can Man Cathl 71-87; R Middleton 75-87; rtd 87. *5 Farnborough Road, Bolton BL1 7HJ*   Bolton (01204) 595499

WHITTAKER, John. b 27. Oak Hill Th Coll 53. **d** 55 **p** 56. V Skelmersdale St Paul *Liv* 67-77; V Gt Faringdon w Lt Coxwell *Ox* 77-83; RD Vale of White Horse 80-83; rtd 83; Perm to Offic *Ox* 83-88; C Broughton Poggs w Filkins, Broadwell etc from 88. *26 The Pines, Faringdon, Oxon SN7 8AU*   Faringdon (01367) 241009

WHITTAKER, Karl Paul. b 55. CITC BTh95. **d** 95. C Killowen *D & R* from 95. *27 Ballycranny Drive, Coleraine, Co Londonderry BT51 3JX*   Coleraine (01265) 52006

WHITTAKER, Canon Peter Harold. b 39. AKC62. **d** 63 **p** 64. C Walton St Mary *Liv* 63-67; C Ross *Heref* 67-70; R Bridgnorth St Mary 70-78; P-in-c Oldbury 70-78; TR Bridgnorth, Tasley, Astley Abbotts and Oldbury 78-81; RD Bridgnorth 78-81; Preb Heref Cathl 80-81; V Leighton Buzzard w Eggington, Hockliffe etc *St Alb* 81-92; RD Dunstable 84-85; R Barton-le-Cley w Higham Gobion and Hexton from 92; Hon Can St Alb from 92. *The Rectory, Barton-le-Clay, Bedford LU7 7AB*   Luton (01582) 881226

WHITTAKER, Robert Andrew. b 49. DipEd Open Univ BA75 Nottm Univ MA83. Linc Th Coll 85. **d** 87 **p** 88. C Mansf Woodhouse *S'well* 87-90; V Norwell w Ossington, Cromwell and Caunton from 90. *The Vicarage, Norwell, Newark, Notts NG23 6JT*   Caunton (0163686) 329

WHITTAKER, William Paul. *See* STAFFORD-WHITTAKER, William Paul

WHITTAM, Canon Kenneth Michael. b 26. Ball Coll Ox BA50 MA54. Cuddesdon Coll 50. **d** 52 **p** 53. Chapl Highgate Sch Lon 66-75; V Shotwick *Ches* 75-89; Can Res Ches Cathl and Dioc Missr 75-85; Hon Can Ches Cathl 85-90; Clergy Study Officer 85-91; rtd 91. *22 Warwick Close, Little Neston, South Wirral L64 0SR*

WHITTINGHAM, Peter. b 58. Sheff Univ BA79. St Jo Coll Nottm 88. **d** 90 **p** 91. C Northowram *Wakef* 90-93; C Airedale w Fryston from 93. *31 Redhill Road, Castleford, W Yorkshire WF10 3AD*   Castleford (01977) 553122

WHITTINGHAM, Ronald Norman. b 43. Linc Coll Ox BA65 MA68. Coll of Resurr Mirfield 65. **d** 67 **p** 68. C Horninglow *Lich* 67-69; C Drayton in Hales 69-70; C Uttoxeter w Bramshall 71-75; P-in-c Burton St Paul 75-80; V Shareshill 80-83; V Silverdale and Knutton Heath 83-89; P-in-c Alsagers Bank 83-89; V Silverdale and Alsagers Bank 89-92; V Honley *Wakef* from 92. *The Vicarage, St Mary's Road, Honley, Huddersfield HD7 2AZ*   Huddersfield (01484) 661178

WHITTINGTON, Canon David John. b 45. Qu Coll Ox BA67 MA71. Coll of Resurr Mirfield 69. **d** 71 **p** 72. Chapl St Woolos Cathl *Mon* 71-72; C Ox St Mary V w St Cross and St Pet *Ox* 72-76; Chapl Qu Coll Ox 72-76; V Stockton *Dur* from 77; Hon Can Dur Cathl from 93. *61 Bishopton Road, Stockton-on-Tees, Cleveland TS18 4PD*   Stockton-on-Tees (01642) 617420

WHITTINGTON, Peter Graham. b 68. Ox Poly BA90. Trin Coll Bris BA95. **d** 95. C Gateacre *Liv* from 95. *14 Egremont Lawn, Liverpool L27 5RB*   0151-487 3391

WHITTINGTON, Richard Hugh (Dick). b 47. MBE74. Sarum & Wells Th Coll DipTh93. **d** 93 **p** 94. C Enfield St Jas *Lon* from 93. *Glebe House, 146 Hertford Road, Enfield, Middx EN3 5AY*   0181-804 3100

WHITTLE, Alan. b 29. K Coll Lon BD52 AKC52. **d** 53 **p** 54. Lic to Offic *S'wark* 69-72; V Mitcham Ch Ch 72-92; rtd 92. *117 May Cross Avenue, Morden, Surrey SM4 4DF*

WHITTLE, Fred. b 17. Keble Coll Ox BA40 MA44. Cuddesdon Coll 40. **d** 41 **p** 42. R Gt w Lt Addington *Pet* 71-82; rtd 82; Lic to Offic *Pet* 82-85; Perm to Offic from 85. *6 Coleman Street, Raunds, Wellingborough, Northants NN9 6NJ* Wellingborough (01933) 624989

WHITTLE, Ian Christopher. b 60. Univ Coll Dur BA81 Fitzw Coll Cam BA87. Ridley Hall Cam. **d** 88 **p** 89. C S Petherton w the Seavingtons *B & W* 88-91; Asst Chapl The Hague *Eur* from 91. *Kijkdionsestraat 858, 2554 AB The Hague, The Netherlands* The Hague (70) 356-1653

WHITTLE, John William. b 46. Qu Mary Coll Lon BA68. Sarum & Wells Th Coll 84. **d** 86 **p** 87. C Blandford Forum and Langton Long etc *Sarum* 86-88. *Leslie House, The Tabernacle, Blandford Forum, Dorset DT11 7DW* Blandford (01258) 451943

WHITTLE, Robin Jeffrey. b 51. Bris Univ BA72 Leic Univ CQSW75. Sarum & Wells Th Coll 85. **d** 87 **p** 88. C Henbury *Bris* 87-91; V Capel *Guildf* from 91. *The Vicarage, Capel, Dorking, Surrey RH5 5LN* Dorking (01306) 711260

WHITTOCK, Michael Graham. b 47. Hull Univ BA69 Fitzw Ho Cam BA71 MA76. Westcott Ho Cam 69 Union Th Sem Richmond 71. **d** 72 **p** 73. C Kirkby *Liv* 72-76; C Prescot 76-79; R Methley w Mickletown *Ripon* 79-92; RD Whitkirk 88-92; V Morley St Pet w Churwell *Wakef* from 92. *St Peter's Vicarage, Rooms Lane, Morley, Leeds LS27 9PA* Leeds (0113) 253 2052

WHITTOME, Donald Marshall. b 26. Cam Univ BA50 MA53. S Dios Minl Tr Scheme. **d** 84 **p** 85. NSM Henfield w Shermanbury and Woodmancote *Chich* 84-93; P-in-c Poynings w Edburton, Newtimber and Pyecombe from 93. *The Rectory, Poynings, Brighton BN45 7AQ* Poynings (01273) 857375

WHITTON, Eric. b 33. N Lon Poly 78. Lon Coll of Div ALCD59 Western Th Sem Michigan 60. **d** 60 **p** 61. Youth Officer *Lon* 66-72; Tr Officer Gen Syn Bd of Educn 73-78; Visiting Lect Roehampton Inst of HE from 80; rtd 94. *31 Ovington Street, London SW3 2JA* 0171-584 8819

WHITTON, Norman. b 17. Edin Th Coll 65. **d** 67 **p** 68. V Brough w Stainmore *Carl* 70-76; P-in-c Harraby 76-80; rtd 80; Perm to Offic *Carl* from 83. *Hartley Fold Cottage, Hartley, Kirkby Stephen, Cumbria CA17 4JH* Kirkby Stephen (017683) 71047

WHITTON, Robert Archibald. b 17. Edin Univ MA37. Moray Ho Edin TCert60 Edin Th Coll 38. **d** 40 **p** 41. C Ayr *Glas* 40-43; R Stromness *Ab* 43-51; R Kirkwall 45-51; Adn Orkney 47-51; R Helensburgh *Glas* 51-59; Chapl Fettes Coll Edin 59-60; Perm to Offic *Edin* from 60. *36 Bryce Road, Currie, Midlothian EH14 5LW* 0131-449 4303

WHITTY, Gordon William. b 46. S Midl Minl Tr Course. **d** 82 **p** 83. NSM Willenhall St Giles *Lich* 82-84; NSM Coseley Ch Ch 84-85; C 85-87; TV Hanley H Ev 87-91; P-in-c Meir from 91. *The Vicarage, 715 Uttoxeter Road, Meir, Stoke-on-Trent ST3 5PY* Stoke-on-Trent (01782) 313347

WHITTY, Harold George. b 41. TCD BA64 MA67. CITC Div Test65. **d** 65 **p** 66. C Willowfield *D & D* 65-68; C Lisburn Ch Ch *Conn* 68-71; Bp's Dom Chapl 70-71; Asst Dir Exhibitions CMJ 71-72; C Enfield Ch Ch Trent Park *Lon* 72-75; TV Washfield, Stoodleigh, Withleigh etc *Ex* 75-83; R Washfield, Stoodleigh, Withleigh etc 83-84; TR 84-93; RD Tiverton 82-84; P-in-c Allithwaite *Carl* from 93. *The Vicarage, Boarbank Lane, Allithwaite, Grange-over-Sands, Cumbria LA11 7QR* Cartmel (015395) 32437

WHITWAM, Miss Diana Morgan. b 28. MCSP54 Brighton Poly DCouns82. Local Minl Tr Course 88. **d** 93 **p** 94. NSM Stoke-next-Guildford *Guildf* from 93. *2 Acacia Road, Guildford, Surrey GU1 1HL* Guildford (01483) 36443

WHITWELL, John Peter. b 36. Qu Coll Birm 62. **d** 65 **p** 66. C Stepney St Dunstan and All SS *Lon* 65-68; C Chingford SS Pet and Paul *Chelmsf* 68-71; V Walthamstow St Sav 71-78; P-in-c Lt Ilford St Mich 78-88; R from 88; RD Newham from 91. *The Rectory, Church Road, London E12 6HA* 0181-478 2182

WHITWELL, Martin Corbett. b 32. Pemb Coll Ox BA55 MA59. Clifton Th Coll 55. **d** 57 **p** 58. Chapl Sandbach Co Secondary Sch 68-74; C Chipping Campden *Glouc* 70-71; Perm to Offic *Chich* 74-75; Perm to Offic *Bris* 75-76; C Tranmere St Cath *Ches* 76-80; V Lt Leigh and Lower Whitley 80-90; rtd 90. *11 Hollies Drive, Bayston Hill, Shrewsbury SY3 0HN* Bayston Hill (01743) 874241

WHITWORTH, Benjamin Charles Battams (Ben). b 49. CCC Ox BA71 MA85. Linc Th Coll 83. **d** 85 **p** 86. C Swanborough *Sarum* 85-88; C Sherborne w Castleton and Lillington 88-91; V Milborne Port w Goathill *B & W* from 91. *The Vicarage, Bathwell Lane, Milborne Port, Sherborne, Dorset DT9 5AN* Milborne Port (01963) 250248

WHITWORTH, Duncan. b 47. K Coll Lon BD69 AKC69. **d** 70 **p** 71. C Tonge Moor *Man* 70-73; C Upper Norwood St Jo *Cant* 73-78; Asst Chapl Madrid *Eur* 78-82; Chapl Br Emb Ankara

82-83; V Douglas St Matt *S & M* from 84; RD Douglas from 91. *St Matthew's Vicarage, Alexander Drive, Douglas, Isle of Man IM2 3QN* Douglas (01624) 676310

WHITWORTH, Canon Patrick John. b 51. Ch Ch Ox BA72 MA76 St Jo Coll Dur DipTh75 MA78. **d** 76 **p** 77. C York St Mich-le-Belfrey *York* 76-79; C Brompton H Trin w Onslow Square St Paul *Lon* 79-84; V Gipsy Hill Ch Ch *S'wark* 84-95; Hon Can Bauchi from 95; R Bath Weston All SS w N Stoke and Langridge *B & W* from 95. *The Vicarage, Weston, Bath BA1 4BU* Bath (01225) 421159

WHITWORTH-HARRISON, Bernard. b 05. St Cath Coll Ox BA36 MA38. St Chad's Coll Dur 28 K Coll Lon 28. **d** 34 **p** 36. R Langham *Chelmsf* 62-75; rtd 75. *19 Trinity Close, Balsham, Cambridge CB1 6DW* Cambridge (01223) 893921

WHYBORN, Robert. b 42. Loughb Coll of Educn CSD69. N Ord Course 87. **d** 90 **p** 91. NSM Milnrow *Man* from 90. *5 Delamere Avenue, Shaw, Oldham OL2 8HN* Shaw (01706) 843644

WHYBRAY, Prof Roger Norman. b 23. Keble Coll Ox BA44 MA48 DPhil62 BD81 DD81. Linc Th Coll 44. **d** 46 **p** 47. Lect Th Hull Univ 65-71; Reader 71-78; Prof Hebrew and OT 78-82; rtd 88. *45 Hills Lane, Ely, Cambs CB6 1AY* Ely (01353) 663897

WHYMAN, Oliver. b 27. ALCM52 LCP57. S'wark Ord Course 60. **d** 63 **p** 64. C Streatham Ch Ch *S'wark* 63-68; Lic to Offic 68-87; NSM Sutton New Town St Barn 87-92; rtd 92. *37 Jubilee Court, London Road, Thornton Heath, Surrey CR7 6JL* 0181-684 5320

WHYTE, Alastair John. b 61. Coll of Ripon & York St Jo BA83. Sarum & Wells Th Coll 83. **d** 85 **p** 86. C Chorley St Geo *Blackb* 85-88; C Poulton-le-Fylde 88-91; V Wesham from 91; Chapl Wesham Park Hosp Blackb from 91. *The Vicarage, Mowbreck Lane, Wesham, Preston PR4 3HA* Kirkham (01772) 682206

WHYTE, Duncan Macmillan. b 25. St Jo Coll Dur BA49 St Cath Soc Ox BA51 MA57. Wycliffe Hall Ox 49. **d** 51 **p** 53. Gen Sec Lon City Miss 66-92; Hon C Blackheath St Jo *S'wark* 66-92; rtd 92. *1 The Meadows, Salisbury SP1 2SS* Salisbury (01722) 330528

WHYTE, Henry Lewis. b 38. Lon Coll of Div ALCD70 LTh74. **d** 70 **p** 71. C Crawley *Chich* 70-74; V Bermondsey St Jas w Ch Ch *S'wark* 74-82; V Kingston Hill St Paul 82-94; V Blackheath Park St Mich from 94. *St Michael's Vicarage, 2 Pond Road, London SE3 9JL* 0181-852 5287

WHYTE, Canon Herbert Blayney. b 21. TCD BA43 MA53. **d** 44 **p** 45. CV Ch Ch Cathl Dub *D & G* 68-91; I Dub Crumlin 68-91; Can Ch Ch Cathl Dub 80-86; Chan 86-91; rtd 91. *238 Redford Park, Greystones, Co Wicklow, Irish Republic* Dublin (1) 287-7264

WHYTE, Canon Malcolm Dorrance. b 29. Man Univ BA50 BD53. Wycliffe Hall Ox 57. **d** 57 **p** 58. C Roch St Pet w St Marg *Roch* 57-60; V Ravenhead *Liv* 60-67; V Southport Em from 67; RD N Meols 78-89; AD 89-95; Hon Can Liv Cathl from 91. *Emmanuel Vicarage, 12 Allerton Road, Southport, Merseyside PR9 9NJ* Southport (01704) 532743

WHYTE, Robert Euan. b 44. St Pet Coll Ox BA67. Cuddesdon Coll 67. **d** 69 **p** 70. C Blackheath Ascension *S'wark* 69-73; NSM Lewisham St Swithun 73-76; NSM Heston *Lon* 76-77; NSM Rusthall *Roch* 77-87; C 87-88; V from 88; RD Tunbridge Wells from 91. *The Vicarage, Bretland Road, Rusthall, Tunbridge Wells, Kent TN4 8PB* Tunbridge Wells (01892) 521357

WHYTE, Thomas Arthur. b 15. Man Univ BA48. Wycliffe Hall Ox 56. **d** 56 **p** 57. V Hunts Cross *Liv* 59-71; V Roby 71-83; rtd 83; Perm to Offic *Liv* from 83; Perm to Offic *Ches* 83-90; NSM Aston by Sutton from 90. *11 Acres Crescent, Westbrook Park, Kingsley, Warrington WA6 3DZ* Kingsley (01928) 788194

WIBBERLEY, Anthony Norman. b 36. K Coll Lon BSc58 AKC58. Sarum & Wells Th Coll 76. **d** 79 **p** 80. Hon C Tavistock and Gulworthy *Ex* 79-86; R Hoby cum Rotherby w Brooksby, Ragdale & Thru'ton *Leic* 86-90; V Ingol *Blackb* from 90. *St Margaret's Vicarage, 299 Tag Lane, Ingol, Preston PR2 3XA* Preston (01772) 727208

WIBREW, Mrs Janet Anne (Jan). b 48. Win Sch of Arts NDAD89. S Dios Minl Tr Scheme 89. **d** 92 **p** 94. NSM Basingstoke Win from 92. *High Meadows, Green Lane, Ellisfield, Basingstoke, Hants RG25 2QW* Basingstoke (01256) 381387

WIBROE, Andrew Peter. b 56. K Coll Lon BD83 AKC83 Thames Poly PGCE91. Ripon Coll Cuddesdon 83. **d** 86 **p** 87. C Purley St Mark Woodcote *S'wark* 86-88; C Boyne Hill *Ox* 89-90; Hon C Milton next Gravesend Ch Ch *Roch* from 90. *15 Pinnocks Avenue, Gravesend, Kent DA11 7QD* Gravesend (01474) 354321

WICK, Patricia Anne. b 54. Lon Bible Coll BA80 Oak Hill Th Coll DipHE86. **dss** 86 **d** 87 **p** 94. Halliwell St Luke *Man* 86-87;

Par Dn 87-91; Par Dn Drypool *York* 91-94; C 94-95; TV from 95. *3 Caledonia Park, Hull HU9 1TE* Hull (01482) 589786

WICKENS, Andrew St Lawrence John. b 63. Mert Coll Ox BA85. Qu Coll Birm 89. **d** 92 **p** 93. C Birchfield *Birm* from 92. *9 Leonard Avenue, Birmingham B19 1LX* 0121-554 9150

WICKENS, John Philip. b 33. Open Univ BA76. K Coll Lon 57. **d** 61 **p** 62. USA 64-66; Tutor Richmond Fellowship Coll from 66; Hon C Sutton Ch Ch *S'wark* 68-83; Hon C Benhilton from 83; rtd 95. *8 Orchard Road, Sutton, Surrey SM1 2QA* 0181-642 8071

WICKENS, Moira. b 56. S Dios Minl Tr Scheme 91. **d** 94. NSM Ifield *Chich* from 94. *55 Warren Drive, Ifield, Crawley, W Sussex RH11 0DT* Crawley (01293) 546634

WICKHAM, Lionel Ralph. b 32. LRAM St Cath Coll Cam BA57 MA61 PhD. Westcott Ho Cam 57. **d** 59 **p** 60. C Boston *Linc* 59-63; Tutor Cuddesdon Coll 61-63; V Cross Stone *Wakef* 63-67; Lect Th Southn Univ 67-78; Sen Lect 78-81; V Honley 81-87; Lect Cam Univ from 87; NSM W Wratting *Ely* from 89; NSM Weston Colville from 89. *The Vicarage, The Causeway, West Wratting, Cambridge CB1 5NA* Cambridge (01223) 290001

WICKHAM, Nicholas John. b 27. Trin Coll Cam BA51 MA56. Coll of Resurr Mirfield 54 Ox NSM Course 85. **d** 87 **p** 88. NSM Banbury *Ox* 87-92; rtd 92. *19 Britannia Wharf, Britannia Road, Banbury, Oxon OX16 8DS* Banbury (01295) 256537

WICKHAM, Canon Norman George. b 25. Kelham Th Coll 42. **d** 51 **p** 52. TP Edin St Jo *Edin* 69-79; Can and Vice-Provost St Mary's Cathl Edin 74-79; R Edin Ch Ch 79-88; Can St Mary's Cathl 86-91; rtd 88; Hon Can St Mary's Cathl *Edin* from 91. *Linton Mill, Mill Wynd, East Linton, East Lothian EH40 3AE* East Linton (01620) 860142

WICKINGS, Luke Iden. b 59. Sheff Poly BA81. Oak Hill Th Coll BA90. **d** 90 **p** 91. C Fulham St Mary N End *Lon* 90-94; C Bletchley *Ox* from 94. *1 Ashburnam Place, Bletchley, Milton Keynes MK3 7TR* Milton Keynes (01908) 371373

WICKS, Christopher Blair. b 59. BA. Oak Hill Th Coll 85. **d** 88 **p** 89. C Edmonton All SS w St Mich *Lon* 88-92; C Southborough St Pet w Ch Ch and St Matt *Roch* from 92. *72 Powdermill Lane, High Brooms, Southborough, Kent TN4 9EJ* Tunbridge Wells (01892) 529098

WICKSTEAD, Gavin John. b 46. St Chad's Coll Dur BA67. Linc Th Coll 82. **d** 84 **p** 85. C Louth *Linc* 84-87; P-in-c E Markham and Askham *S'well* 87-89; P-in-c Headon w Upton 87-89; P-in-c Grove 87-89; R E Markham w Askham, Headon w Upton and Grove 90-92; P-in-c Skegness and Winthorpe *Linc* from 92. *The Rectory, 31 Lumley Avenue, Skegness, Lincs PE25 2AT* Skegness (01754) 760566

WIDDAS, Preb John Anderson. b 38. Kelham Th Coll 58. **d** 63 **p** 64. C Willenhall H Trin *Lich* 63-66; C Tamworth 66-69; V from 86; V Chesterton 69-74; R Lich St Chad 74-86; RD Lich 77-86; Preb Lich Cathl from 80; P-in-c Gentleshaw 80-82; P-in-c Farewell 80-82; RD Tamworth from 91. *The Vicarage, Hospital Street, Tamworth, Staffs B79 7EE* Tamworth (01827) 62446 or 52598

WIDDECOMBE, Canon Malcolm Murray. b 37. Tyndale Hall Bris 57. **d** 62 **p** 63. C Bris H Trin *Bris* 62-65; C Barton Hill St Luke w Ch Ch 65-67; P-in-c Barton Hill St Jacob w Em 67-74; V from 74; RD Bris City 79-85; Hon Can Bris Cathl from 86. *The Vicarage, 7 King's Drive, Bristol BS7 8JW* Bristol (0117) 924 3169

WIDDICOMBE, Alexander Charles Ernest. b 11. Jes Coll Cam BA32 MA36. Wells Th Coll 33. **d** 34 **p** 35. R Chedburgh w Depden and Rede *St E* 66-71; S Africa from 72; rtd 79. *PO Box 20, Saldanha, 7395 South Africa* Vredenburg (2281) 42662

WIDDOWS, David Charles Roland. b 52. Hertf Coll Ox BA75 MA79. St Jo Coll Nottm BA77. **d** 79 **p** 80. C Blackley St Andr *Man* 79-83; P-in-c Rochdale Deeplish St Luke 83-84; V 84-92; TR Stoke Gifford *Bris* from 92. *The Vicarage, 24 North Road, Stoke Gifford, Bristol BS12 6PB* Bristol (0117) 923 6395 or 969 2486

WIDDOWS, Edward John. b 45. Lon Coll of Div 66. **d** 70 **p** 71. C Formby St Pet *Liv* 70-72; C Uckfield *Chich* 72-73; C Isfield 72-73; C Lt Horsted 72-73; C Babbacombe *Ex* 73-76; V Sithney *Truro* 76-78; RD Kerrier 77-78; V Bude Haven 78-84; P-in-c Laneast w St Clether and Tresmere 84-85; P-in-c N Hill w Altarnon, Bolventor and Lewannick 84-85; P-in-c Boyton w N Tamerton 84-85; P-in-c N Petherwin 84-85; R Collingham w S Scarle and Besthorpe and Girton *S'well* 85-92; R Guernsey St Michel du Valle *Win* from 92. *The Rectory, L'Abbaye, Vale, Guernsey, Channel Islands GY3 5SF* Guernsey (01481) 44088

WIDDOWS, John Christopher (Kit). b 46. Trin Coll Cam BA69 MA72. Cuddesdon Coll 69. **d** 71 **p** 72. C Herrington *Dur* 71-76; Chapl Nat Exhibition Cen 76-80; TV Chelmsley Wood *Birm* 76-80; V Halifax St Hilda *Wakef* from 80; RD Halifax from 92. *St Hilda's Vicarage, Gibralter Road, Halifax, W Yorkshire HX1 4HE* Halifax (01422) 354448

WIDDOWSON, Charles Leonard. b 28. ALCD62. **d** 62 **p** 63. R Newark Ch Ch *S'well* 66-69; Australia from 69; rtd 93. *241 Tooronga Road, Malvern, Victoria, Australia 3144* Melbourne (3) 824-7086

WIDDOWSON, Robert William. b 47. Linc Th Coll 83. **d** 85 **p** 86. C Syston *Leic* 85-88; R Husbands Bosworth w Mowsley and Knaptoft etc 88-93; R Asfordby from 93; P-in-c Ab Kettleby Gp from 93; P-in-c Old Dalby and Nether Broughton from 95. *The Rectory, Church Lane, Asfordby, Melton Mowbray, Leics LE14 3RU* Melton Mowbray (01664) 812327

WIERSUM, Timothy Peter. b 55. Cranmer Hall Dur. **d** 83 **p** 84. C Boldmere *Birm* 83-86; C Ashton St Mich *Man* 86-88; CMS from 89; Guinea from 90. *Cathedrale Toussaint, BP 1187, Conakry, Republic de Guinea*

WIFFEN, Richard Austin. b 58. St Pet Coll Ox BA80. Trin Coll Bris BA90. **d** 90 **p** 91. C Bowdon *Ches* 90-93; C Ellesmere Port 93-94; TV from 94. *4 Deeside Close, Ellesmere Port, South Wirral L65 6TH* 0151-355 5661

WIGFIELD, Thomas Henry Paul. b 26. Edin Th Coll 46. **d** 49 **p** 50. Asst Dir Chr TV Cen 63-79; Perm to Offic *Lon* 63-91; Perm to Offic *St Alb* from 66; Hd of Services Foundn for Chr Communication 79-84; Chs' Liaison Officer 84-91; rtd 91. *16 Fishers Field, Buckingham MK18 1SF* Buckingham (01280) 817893

WIGGEN, Richard Martin. b 42. Open Univ BA78 Hull Univ MA86. Qu Coll Birm 64. **d** 67 **p** 68. C Penistone w Midhope *Wakef* 67-70; C Leeds St Pet *Ripon* 70-73; Asst Youth Chapl *Glouc* 73-76; Youth Officer *Liv* 76-80; V Kirkstall *Ripon* 80-90; V Meanwood from 90. *Meanwood Vicarage, 9 Parkside Green, Leeds LS6 4NY* Leeds (0113) 275 7885

WIGGINS, Karl Patrick. b 38. FRICS64 Lon Univ BD72. Trin Coll Bris 71. **d** 72 **p** 73. C Hildenborough *Roch* 72-76; Hon C Reading St Barn *Ox* 76-78; Lic to Offic 78-83; NSM Beech Hill, Grazeley and Spencers Wood from 83. *93 Crescent Road, Reading RG1 5SC* Reading (01734) 663832

WIGGINTON, Canon Peter Walpole. b 20. Dur Univ LTh44. Edin Th Coll 40. **d** 43 **p** 44. R W Keal *Linc* 56-83; R E Keal 57-83; RD Bolingbroke 66-88; Can and Preb Linc Cathl 77-88; R E and W Keal 83-88; R Bolingbroke 83-88; R Toynton All Saints w Toynton St Peter 83-88; rtd 88; Chapl Trin Hosp Retford from 88. *The Rectory Farm, Rectory Road, Retford, Notts DN22 7AY* Retford (01777) 860352

WIGGLESWORTH, Mark. b 60. Clare Coll Cam BA82. St Jo Coll Nottm DTS91 DipMM92. **d** 92 **p** 93. C Brinsworth w Catcliffe *Sheff* 92-93; C Brinsworth w Catcliffe and Treeton 93-95; C Goole from 95. *8 Bournville, Goole, N Humberside DN14 6LA* Goole (01405) 722333

WIGGS, Robert James. b 50. Pemb Coll Cam BA72 MA CertEd. Qu Coll Birm 78. **d** 80 **p** 81. C Stratford St Jo and Ch Ch w Forest Gate St Jas *Chelmsf* 80-83; C E Ham w Upton Park St Alb 83-86; TV 86-91; TR Grays Thurrock from 91. *The Rectory, 10 High View Avenue, Grays, Essex RM17 6RU* Grays Thurrock (01375) 373215

WIGHT, Dennis Marley. b 53. Southn Univ BTh87. Sarum & Wells Th Coll 82. **d** 85 **p** 86. C Gillingham *Sarum* 85-87; Appeals Org CECS from 87; Perm to Offic *Birm* from 89; V Coseley Ch Ch *Lich* 90-93; V Coseley Ch Ch *Worc* 93-94; R Stoke Prior, Wychbold and Upton Warren from 94. *The Rectory, Fish House Lane, Stoke Prior, Bromsgrove, Worcs B60 4JT* Bromsgrove (01527) 832501

WIGHT (nee JONES), Mrs Sian Hilary. b 54. CertEd75 Birm Univ BEd76 Southn Univ BTh87. Sarum & Wells Th Coll 82. **dss** 85 **d** 87 **p** 94. Ex St Sidwell and St Matt *Ex* 85-87; Par Dn 87-88; Perm to Offic *Lich* 89-90 and from 93; Hon Par Dn Coseley Ch Ch 90-93; Hon Par Dn Coseley Ch Ch *Worc* 93-94; NSM Stoke Prior, Wychbold and Upton Warren from 94. *The Rectory, Fish House Lane, Stoke Prior, Bromsgrove, Worcs B60 4JT* Bromsgrove (01527) 832501

WIGHTMAN, Very Rev William David. b 39. Birm Univ BA61. Wells Th Coll 61. **d** 63 **p** 64. C Rotherham *Sheff* 63-67; C Castle Church 67-70; V Buttershaw St Aid *Bradf* 70-76; V Cullingworth 76-83; R Peterhead *Ab* 83-91; R Strichen 90-91; R Old Deer 90-91; R Longside 90-91; Provost St Andr Cathl from 91; R Aber St Andr from 91; P-in-c Aber St Ninian from 91; Hon Can Ch Ch Cathl Connecticut from 91. *15 Morningfield Road, Aberdeen AB2 4AP* Aberdeen (01224) 314765 or 640119

WIGLEY, Brian Arthur. b 31. Qu Coll Birm. **d** 82 **p** 83. C Houghton le Spring *Dur* 82-85; C Louth *Linc* 85-86; TV 86-89; Chapl City Hosp NHS Trust 89-95; rtd 95. *27 Buffery Road, Dudley, W Midlands DY2 8EB* Dudley (01384) 254824

WIGLEY, Canon Harry Maxwell (Max). b 38. Oak Hill Th Coll 61. **d** 64 **p** 65. C Upton (or Overchurch) *Ches* 64-67; C Gateacre *Liv* 67-69; C Chadderton Ch Ch *Man* 67; V Gt Horton *Bradf* 69-88; Hon Can Bradf Cathl from 85; V Pudsey St Lawr and St Paul from 88. *The Vicarage, Vicarage Drive, Pudsey, W Yorkshire LS28 7RL* Leeds (0113) 257 7843

WIGLEY, Ms Jennifer. b 53. Bris Univ BA74 Birm Univ MA75 Ox Univ CertEd76. Qu Coll Birm 86. **d** 87. C Llangollen w Trevor and Llantysilio *St As* 87-89; C Swansea St Jas *S & B* 89-94; NSM Abth *St D* from 95. *39 Maesceinion, Waunfawr, Aberystwyth, Dyfed SY23 3QQ* Aberystwyth (01970) 617296

WIGRAM, Andrew Oswald. b 39. Lon Univ BD64. Bps' Coll Cheshunt 61. **d** 64 **p** 65. C Marton-in-Cleveland *York* 64-69; Kenya 69-82; V Westcliff St Mich *Chelmsf* 82-95; RD Southend-on-Sea 89-94; V Cropwell Bishop w Colston Bassett, Granby etc *S'well* from 95. *The Vicarage, 2 Dobbin Close, Cropwell Bishop, Nottingham NG12 3GR* Nottingham (0115) 989 3172

WIGRAM, Canon Sir Clifford Woolmore, Bt. b 11. Trin Coll Cam BA32 MA36. Ely Th Coll 33. **d** 34 **p** 35. V Marston w Warkworth *Pet* 45-75; V Marston St Lawrence w Warkworth and Thenford 75-83; Can Pet Cathl 73-83; rtd 83; Perm to Offic *B & W* 84-94. *2 Mold Cottages, Marston St Lawrence, Banbury, Oxon OX17 2DB* Banbury (01295) 711779

WIGRAM, Miss Ruth Margaret. b 41. CertEd63. Cranmer Hall Dur 83. **dss** 84 **d** 87 **p** 94. Shipley St Paul and Frizinghall *Bradf* 84-87; Par Dn 87-90; Asst Dioc Dir of Ords from 90; C Skipton H Trin from 90. *7 Princes Drive, Skipton, N Yorkshire BD23 1HN* Skipton (01756) 701063

WIGSTON, Kenneth Edmund. b 28. Lich Th Coll 55. **d** 58 **p** 59. R Airdrie *Glas* 68-78; R Gartcosh 68-78; R Glas St Oswald 78-85; R Onich *Arg* 85-94; R Glencoe 85-94; R Ballachulish 85-94; rtd 94. *Old Croft Cottage, 18 Tighphuirt, Glencoe, Argyll PA39 4HN*

WIKELEY, Canon John Roger Ian. b 41. AKC64. **d** 65 **p** 66. C Southport H Trin *Liv* 65-69; C Padgate Ch Ch 69-71; TV Padgate 71-73; R 73-74; TR 74-85; TV W Derby St Mary from 85; AD W Derby from 89; Hon Can Liv Cathl from 94. *The Rectory, West Derby, Liverpool L12 5EA* 0151-256 6600

WIKNER, Richard Hugh. b 46. MSI. St Alb Minl Tr Scheme 79. **d** 94 **p** 95. NSM Lt Heath *St Alb* from 94. *Koinonia, 5 The Avenue, Potters Bar, Herts EN6 1EG* Potters Bar (01707) 650437

WILBOURNE, David Jeffrey. b 55. Jes Coll Cam BA78 MA82. Westcott Ho Cam 79. **d** 81 **p** 82. C Stainton-in-Cleveland *York* 81-85; Chapl Asst Hemlington Hosp 81-85; R Monk Fryston and S Milford *York* 85-91; Abp's Dom Chapl from 91; Dir of Ords from 91. *Brew House Cottage, Bishopthorpe, York YO2 1QE, or Bishopthorpe Palace, Bishopthorpe, York YO2 1QE* York (01904) 706822 or 707021 Fax 709204

WILBOURNE, Geoffrey Owen. b 29. Lich Th Coll 60. **d** 62 **p** 63. V Ellerton Priory w Aughton and E Cottingwith *York* 65-70; TV Scalby w Ravenscar and Staintondale 70-73; V Kingston upon Hull St Nic 73-76; V Keyingham 76-85; V Hemingbrough 85-91; rtd 91. *4 Eastleigh Court, Hasland, Chesterfield, Derbyshire S41 0BH* Chesterfield (01246) 239939

WILBRAHAM, David. b 59. Oak Hill Th Coll BA88. **d** 88 **p** 89. C Ince Ch Ch *Liv* 88-91; C St Helens St Helen 91-93. *Address temp unknown*

WILBY, Mrs Jean Davina (Sister Jean Davina). b 38. Open Univ BA82. Wycliffe Hall Ox 83. **dss** 85 **d** 87 **p** 94. Maidenhead St Andr and St Mary Magd *Ox* 85-87; C 87; TD Hermitage and Hampstead Norreys, Cold Ash etc 87-91; Lic to Offic from 91; All SS Convent Ox from 91. *All Saints Convent, Saint Mary's Road, Oxford OX4 1RU* Oxford (01865) 249127

WILBY, Timothy David. b 59. Univ Coll Dur BA80 MA87. Ripon Coll Cuddesdon 81. **d** 83 **p** 84. C Standish *Blackb* 83-86; CF 86-89; V Chorley All SS *Blackb* 89-95; V Penwortham St Leon from 95. *St Leonard's Vicarage, Marshall's Brow, Penwortham, Preston PR1 9HY* Preston (01772) 742367

WILBY, Mrs Wendy Ann. b 49. ARCM69 LRAM72 St Hugh's Coll Ox BA71. NE Ord Course. **d** 90 **p** 94. Par Dn Barwick in Elmet *Ripon* 90-93; C High Harrogate St Pet 93-94; V Birstwith 94; P-in-c from 94; Chapl St Aid Sch Harrogate from 94. *The Vicarage, Wreaks Road, Birstwith, Harrogate, N Yorkshire HG3 3AN* Harrogate (01423) 772315

WILCOCK, Michael Jarvis. b 32. Dur Univ BA54. Tyndale Hall Bris 60. **d** 62 **p** 63. C Southport Ch Ch *Liv* 62-65; C St Marylebone All So w SS Pet and Jo *Lon* 65-69; V Maidstone St Faith *Cant* 69-77; Dir Past Studies Trin Coll Bris 77-82; V Dur St Nic *Dur* from 82. *St Nicholas' Vicarage, Kepier Rise, Durham DH1 1JP* 0191-384 6066

WILCOCK, Paul Trevor. b 59. Bris Univ BA. Trin Coll Bris 83. **d** 87 **p** 88. C Kirkheaton *Wakef* 87-90; Chapl Huddersfield Poly 90-92; Chapl Huddersfield Univ 92-93; Dir Student Services from 93; NSM Huddersfield H Trin from 92. *Huddersfield University, Queensgate, Huddersfield HD1 3DH* Huddersfield (01484) 422288

WILCOCKSON, Stephen Anthony. b 51. Nottm Univ BA73 Ox Univ BA75 MA81. Wycliffe Hall Ox 73. **d** 76 **p** 77. C Pudsey St Lawr *Bradf* 76-78; C Wandsworth All SS *S'wark* 78-81;

V Rock Ferry *Ches* 81-86; V Lache cum Saltney from 86. *St Mark's Vicarage, 5 Cliveden Road, Chester CH4 8DR* Chester (01244) 671702

WILCOX, Anthony Gordon (Tony). b 41. Lon Coll of Div LTh67 ALCD67. **d** 67 **p** 68. C Cheltenham Ch Ch *Glouc* 67-72; C Beccles St Mich *St E* 72-74; TV 74-81; V Ipswich All SS from 81. *All Saints' Vicarage, 264 Norwich Road, Ipswich IP1 4BT* Ipswich (01473) 252975

WILCOX, Brian Howard. b 46. Westcott Ho Cam 71. **d** 73 **p** 74. C Kettering SS Pet and Paul *Pet* 73-78; V Eye 78-82; R Clipston w Naseby and Haselbech w Kelmarsh 82-90; V Hornsea w Atwick *York* from 90. *The Vicarage, 9 Newbeggin, Hornsea, N Humberside HU18 1AB* Hornsea (01964) 532531

WILCOX, Colin John. b 43. St Mich Coll Llan 84. **d** 86 **p** 87. C Newport St Andr *Mon* 86-88; C Llanmartin 88-90; TV 90-92; V Griffithstown from 92. *St Hilda's Vicarage, 2 Sunnybank Road, Griffithstown, Pontypool, Gwent NP4 5LT* Pontypool (01495) 763641

✠**WILCOX, Rt Rev David Peter.** b 30. St Jo Coll Ox BA52 MA56. Linc Th Coll 52. **d** 54 **p** 55 **c** 86. C St Helier *S'wark* 54-56; C Ox St Mary V *Ox* 56-59; Tutor Linc Th Coll 59-60; Chapl 60-61; Sub-Warden 61-63; India 64-70; R Gt w Lt Gransden *Ely* 70-72; Can Res Derby Cathl *Derby* 72-77; Warden E Midl Min Tr Course 73-77; Prin Ripon Coll Cuddesdon 77-85; V Cuddesdon *Ox* 77-85; Suff Bp Dorking *Guildf* 85-95; rtd 95. *4 The Court, Hoo Gardens, Willingdon, Eastbourne, E Sussex BN20 9AX*

WILCOX, Graham James. b 43. Qu Coll Ox BA64 MA75. Ridley Hall Cam 64. **d** 66 **p** 67. C Edgbaston St Aug *Birm* 66-69; C Sheldon 69-72; Asst Chapl Wrekin Coll Shropshire 72-74; C Asterby w Goulceby *Linc* 74-77; P-in-c 77; R 77-81; R Benniworth w Market Stainton and Ranby 77-81; R Donington on Bain 77-81; R Stenigot 77-81; R Gayton le Wold w Biscathorpe 77-81; V Scamblesby w Cawkwell 77-81; R Asterby Gp 81-88; V Sutton le Marsh 88-90; R Sutton, Huttoft and Anderby from 90. *The Vicarage, Huttoft Road, Mablethorpe, Lincs LN12 2RU* Mablethorpe (01507) 441169

WILCOX, Haydon Howard. b 56. Sarum & Wells Th Coll. **d** 82 **p** 83. C Fishponds St Jo *Bris* 82-85; TV Hucknall Torkard *S'well* 85-91; R Bilsthorpe from 91; R Eakring from 91; V Maplebeck from 91; P-in-c Winkburn from 91. *The Rectory, Church Hill, Bilsthorpe, Newark, Notts NG22 8RU* Mansfield (01623) 870256

WILCOX, Hugh Edwin. b 37. St Edm Hall Ox BA62 MA66. St Steph Ho Ox 62. **d** 64 **p** 65. C Colchester St Jas, All SS, St Nic and St Runwald *Chelmsf* 64-66; Hon C Clifton St Paul *Bris* 66-68; SCM 66-68; Sec Internat Dept BCC 68-76; Asst Gen Sec 74-76; V Ware St Mary *St Alb* from 76. *The Vicarage, 31 Thunder Court, Milton Road, Ware, Herts SG12 0PT* Ware (01920) 464817

WILCOX, Jeffry Reed. b 40. K Coll Lon AKC65 BA78. **d** 66 **p** 67. C Ryhope *Dur* 66-69; C Cockerton 69-71; P-in-c Pallion 71-82; R Streatham St Leon *S'wark* from 82; RD Streatham from 92. *The Rectory, 1 Becmead Avenue, London SW16 1UH* 0181-769 4366 or 769 1216

WILCOX, Joe. b 21. ACT LTh62 Lich Th Coll. **d** 62 **p** 63. V Leek St Luke *Lich* 67-75; P-in-c Ellington *Ely* 75-80; P-in-c Spaldwick w Barham and Woolley 75-80; P-in-c Easton 75-80; P-in-c Grafham 75-80; R Holywell w Needingworth 80-86; rtd 86; Perm to Offic *Ely* from 87. *16 Silver Birch Avenue, St Ives, Huntingdon, Cambs PE17 4TS* St Ives (01480) 496846

WILCOX, John Bower. b 28. AKC55. **d** 58 **p** 59. Ind Chapl *Linc* 63-74; R Aisthorpe w W Thorpe and Scampton 63-74; R Brattleby 64-74; Ind Chapl *York* 74-89; P-in-c Middlesb St Cuth 89-93; Urban Development Officer 89-93; rtd 93. *5 Duncan Avenue, Redcar, Cleveland TS10 5BX* Redcar (01642) 489683

WILCOX, Peter Jonathan. b 61. St Jo Coll Dur BA84 MA91 St Jo Coll Ox DPhil93. Ridley Hall Cam BA86. **d** 87 **p** 88. C Preston on Tees *Dur* 87-90; NSM Ox St Giles and SS Phil and Jas w St Marg *Ox* 90-93; TV Gateshead *Dur* from 93; Dir Urban Miss Cen Cranmer Hall from 93. *St Columba House, Peterborough Close, Gateshead, Tyne & Wear NE8 1RB* 0191-478 5116

WILCOX, Raymond Trevor. b 22. St D Coll Lamp BA47. **d** 48 **p** 49. V Bentley *Lich* 58-78; P-in-c Blithfield 78-84; P-in-c Colton 78-84; V Llanddewi Rhydderch w Llangattock-juxta-Usk etc *Mon* 84-87; rtd 87. *8 Orchard Close, Uttoxeter, Staffs ST14 7QZ* Uttoxeter (01889) 566308

WILD, Hilda Jean. b 48. Linc Th Coll CMinlStuds95. **d** 95. C Newark-upon-Trent *S'well* from 95. *28 Harewood Avenue, Newark, Notts NG24 4AN* Newark (01636) 700396

WILD, Robert David Fergusson. b 10. MC45 MBE46 TD50. Ex Coll Ox BA33 MA36. Westcott Ho Cam 34. **d** 35 **p** 36. C Eastleigh *Win* 35-36; Bp's Dom Chapl 36-37; Lic to Offic 37;

Chapl Eton Coll Windsor 37-69; CF (TA) 39-50; Select Preacher Cam Univ 52; P-in-c Staplegrove *B & W* 70-71; P-in-c Bicknoller 73-74; Perm to Offic 74-93. *Yard End, Carters Lane, Crowcombe, Taunton, Somerset TA4 4AA* Crowcombe (019848) 640

WILD, Roger Bedingham Barratt. b 40. Hull Univ MA94. ALCD64. **d** 65 **p** 66. C Shipley St Pet *Bradf* 65-68; C Pudsey St Lawr 68-71; P-in-c Rawthorpe *Wakef* 71-73; V 73-78; V Ripon H Trin *Ripon* 78-93; RD Ripon 86-93; R Barwick in Elmet from 93. *The Rectory, Main Street, Barwick in Elmet, Leeds LS15 4JR* Leeds (0113) 281 2218

WILDE, David Wilson. b 37. Lon Coll of Div ALCD61 BD62. **d** 62 **p** 63. C Kirkheaton *Wakef* 62-66; C Attenborough w Chilwell *S'well* 66-72; P-in-c Bestwood Park 72-83; R Kimberley from 83. *The Rectory, Kimberley, Nottingham NG16 2LL* Nottingham (0115) 938 3565

WILDEY, Ian Edward. b 51. St Chad's Coll Dur BA72. Coll of Resurr Mirfield 72. **d** 74 **p** 75. C Westgate Common *Wakef* 74-77; C Barnsley St Mary 77-81; V Ravensthorpe 81-95; R Barnsley St Mary from 95. *The Rectory, 30 Victoria Road, Barnsley, S Yorkshire S70 2BU* Barnsley (01226) 282270

WILDING, Miss Anita Pamela. b 38. Blackpool and Fylde Coll of Further Tech TCert61. CMS Tr Coll Chislehurst 65. **dss** 89 **d** 92 **p** 93. CMS from 87; Kenya from 87. *St Andrew's College, PO Box 6, Kerugoya, Kenya* Kerugoya (163) 21025

WILDING, David. b 43. K Coll Lon BD67 AKC67. **d** 68 **p** 69. C Thornhill *Wakef* 68-70; C Halifax St Jo Bapt 70-72; V Scholes 72-79; V Lightcliffe from 79. *The Vicarage, Wakefield Road, Lightcliffe, Halifax, W Yorkshire HX3 8TH* Halifax (01422) 202424

WILDING, Joseph. b 14. Edin Th Coll 50. **d** 52 **p** 53. R Alexandria *Glas* 56-80; P-in-c 80-84; rtd 84. *Ash House Farm, Ulnes Walton, Preston PR5 3LU*

WILDING, Michael Paul. b 57. Chich Th Coll 82. **d** 85 **p** 86. C Treboeth *S & B* 85-87; C Llangiwg 87-88; V Defynnog w Rhydybriw and Llandilo'r-fan from 88. *The Vicarage, Sennybank, Sennybridge, Brecon, Powys LD3 8PP* Sennybridge (01874) 638927

WILDRIDGE, Peter. b 24. Univ of Wales (Lamp) BA51. St D Coll Lamp BA51. **d** 52 **p** 53. V Islington St Pet *Lon* 60-80; rtd 89. *66 Queensborough Terrace, London W2 3SH* 0171-221 0022

WILDS, Canon Anthony Ronald (Tony). b 43. Dur Univ BA64. Bps' Coll Cheshunt 64. **d** 66 **p** 67. C Newport Pagnell *Ox* 66-72; Zambia 72-75; V Chandler's Ford *Win* 75-85; V Andover w Foxcott from 85; RD Andover 89-94; Hon Can Win Cathl from 91. *St Mary's Vicarage, Church Close, Andover, Hants SP10 1DP* Andover (01264) 352729

WILES, David James. b 50. Univ Coll Lon BSc72 K Coll Lon CertEd73. St Jo Coll Nottm 85. **d** 88 **p** 89. C Clapham Park St Steph *S'wark* 88-92; V Wimbledon St Luke from 92. *St Luke's Vicarage, 28 Farquhar Road, London SW19 8DA* 0181-946 3396

WILES, Canon Prof Maurice Frank. b 23. FBA Ch Coll Cam BA47 MA52 DD. Ridley Hall Cam 48. **d** 50 **p** 51. Prof Chr Doctrine K Coll Lon 67-70; Can Res Ch Ch *Ox* 70-91; Regius Prof Div Ox Univ 70-91; rtd 91. *11 Baytree Close, Oxford OX4 4DT* Oxford (01865) 777091

WILKES, Canon Eric. b 22. Dur Univ BA51. St Steph Ho Ox 50. **d** 53 **p** 54. V Toxteth Park St Marg *Liv* 63-71; V Orford St Marg 71-83; Hon Can Liv Cathl 76-83; R Shepton Beauchamp w Barrington, Stocklinch etc *B & W* 83-92; RD Ilminster 87-92; rtd 92. *4 Lodwells Orchard, North Curry, Taunton, Somerset TA3 6DX* Taunton (01823) 491093

WILKES, Canon Keith Reid. b 30. FBIM75 Pemb Coll Cam BA53 MA60 Bris Univ MA71 Bris Poly DipEdMan74. Linc Th Coll 53. **d** 55 **p** 56. Dir of Educn *Bris* 70-80; Chapl Bris Cathl 70-74; Hon Can Bris Cathl 74-80; R Bris Ch Ch w St Ewen 70-74; R Bris Ch Ch w St Ewen and All SS 74-80; Hon Chapl Bp Bris 73-76; Provost Woodard Schs (Midl Division) 80-94; Perm to Offic *S'well* 80-94; Perm to Offic *Derby* 80-94; Lic to Offic *Lich* 80-94; rtd 94. *The Mount, St John's Hill, Ellesmere, Shropshire SY12 0EY* Ellesmere (01691) 622466

WILKES, Robert Anthony (Bob). b 48. Trin Coll Ox BA70 MA73. Wycliffe Hall Ox 71. **d** 74 **p** 75. C Netherton *Liv* 74-77; V 77-81; Bp's Dom Chapl 81-85; CMS from 85; Pakistan 85-86; Regional Sec Middle E and Pakistan from 87; Perm to Offic *S'wark* from 90; Perm to Offic *Ox* from 90. *28 Lonsdale Road, Oxford OX2 7EW* (01865) 59362 or 0171-928 8681 Fax 0171-401 3215

WILKIE, James. b 17. Chich Th Coll 39. **d** 42 **p** 43. V Lindale *Carl* 69-71; P-in-c Field Broughton 71; V Lindale w Field Broughton 71-85; rtd 85; Perm to Offic *Carl* from 85. *Fernlea, Beckermet, Cumbria CA21 2YF* Beckermet (01946) 841284

WILKIN, Kenneth. b 54. S'wark Ord Course 86 Wilson Carlile Coll. **d** 88 **p** 89. C Wolv *Lich* 88-92; V W Bromwich St Andr w Ch Ch from 92. *St Andrew's Vicarage, Oakwood Street, West Bromwich, W Midlands B70 9SN* 0121-553 1871

WILKIN, Paul John. b 56. Linc Th Coll 88. **d** 90 **p** 91. C Leavesden All SS *St Alb* 90-93; C Jersey St Brelade *Win* from 93. *The Parsonage, High Street, St Aubin, Jersey, Channel Islands JE3 8BR* Jersey (01534) 44009

WILKIN, Rose Josephine. *See* HUDSON-WILKIN, Mrs Rose Josephine

WILKINS, Mrs Janice Joy. b 49. St D Coll Lamp 90. **d** 93. NSM Tredegar St Jas *Mon* from 93. *Ty-Heddwch, Fflorens Road, Newbridge, Newport, Gwent NP1 4DU* Newbridge (01495) 245199

WILKINS, Ralph Herbert. b 29. Lon Univ BD61. St Aug Coll Cant 72. **d** 73 **p** 74. C Epsom Common Ch Ch *Guildf* 73-76; C Haslemere 77-79; P-in-c Market Lavington and Easterton *Sarum* 79-82; V 82-90; P-in-c Puddletown and Tolpuddle 90-94; P-in-c Milborne St Andrew w Dewlish 92-94; P-in-c Piddletrenthide w Plush, Alton Pancras etc 92-94; rtd 94. *Spiggie Lodge, Scousburgh, Dunrossness, Shetland ZE2 9JE* Sumburgh (01950) 60563

WILKINS, Miss Susan Stafford (Sue). b 47. Dur Univ BA. Sarum Th Coll. **dss** 82 **d** 87 **p** 94. Redlynch and Morgan's Vale *Sarum* 82-87; Hon Par Dn 87-88; Hon Par Dn Bemerton 88-90; Par Dn Hilperton w Whaddon and Staverton etc 90-94; C 94; TV Worle *B & W* from 94. *The Vicarage, 6 Gannet Road, Worle, Weston-super-Mare, Avon BS22 8UR* Weston-super-Mare (01934) 521765

WILKINS, Vernon Gregory. b 53. Trin Coll Cam MA74 Ox Univ BA88. Wycliffe Hall Ox 86. **d** 89 **p** 90. C Boscombe St Jo *Win* 89-91; C Bursledon 91-94; V Ramsgate St Luke *Cant* from 94. *St Luke's Vicarage, St Luke's Avenue, Ramsgate, Kent CT11 7JX* Thanet (01843) 592562

WILKINSON, Adrian Mark. b 68. TCD BA90 NUI HDipEd91. CITC BTh94. **d** 94 **p** 95. C Douglas Union w Frankfield *C, C & R* from 94. *64 Willow Bank, Church Road, Blackrock, Cork, Irish Republic* Cork (21) 358226

WILKINSON, Canon Alan Bassindale. b 31. St Cath Coll Cam BA54 MA58 PhD59. Coll of Resurr Mirfield 57. **d** 59 **p** 60. C Kilburn St Aug w St Jo *Lon* 59-61; Chapl St Cath Coll Cam 61-67; V Barrow Gurney *B & W* 67-70; Asst Chapl St Matthias's Coll Bris 67-70; Prin Chich Th Coll 70-74; Can and Preb Chich Cathl *Chich* 70-74; Warden Verulam Ho 74-75; Dir of Aux Min Tr *St Alb* 74-75; Sen Lect Crewe & Alsager Coll 75-78; Dioc Dir of Tr *Ripon* 78-84; P-in-c Thornthwaite w Thruscross and Darley 84-88; Hon Can Ripon Cathl 84-88; Hon C Portsm Cathl *Portsm* from 88. *Hope Cottage, 27 Great Southsea Street, Portsmouth PO5 3BY* Portsmouth (01705) 825788

WILKINSON, Alice Margaret Marion. *See* BISHOP, Mrs Alice Margaret Marion

WILKINSON (nee PHILPOTT), Mrs Barbara May. b 48. Leeds Univ BA70 CertEd71 MA90. N Ord Course 90. **d** 93 **p** 94. NSM Carleton and Lothersdale *Bradf* from 93. *37 Aire Valley Drive, Bradley, Keighley, W Yorkshire BD20 9HY* Cross Hills (01535) 636339

WILKINSON, David Andrew. b 62. Edge Hill Coll of HE BA83. Oak Hill Th Coll BA85. **d** 88 **p** 89. C Upton (or Overchurch) *Ches* 88-91; C Fulham St Matt *Lon* 91-94; V Duffield *Derby* from 94. *St Alkmund's Vicarage, Vicarage Lane, Duffield, Belper, Derbyshire DE56 4EB* Derby (01332) 841168

WILKINSON, David Edward Paul. b 36. Univ of Wales (Swansea) BSc57. St Mich Coll Llan 57. **d** 59 **p** 60. C Brecon w Battle *S & B* 59-60; Min Can Brecon Cathl 60-66; R Llanelwedd w Llanfaredd, Cwmbach Llechryd etc 66-72; V Tycoch 72-74; Asst Master Churchmead Sch Datchet 75-82; Perm to Offic *Ox* 80-82; TV Seacroft *Ripon* from 82. *St Paul's Vicarage, 58 Whinmoor Crescent, Leeds LS14 1EW* Leeds (0113) 265 5649

WILKINSON, David James. b 45. St D Coll Lamp 65 Wycliffe Hall Ox 68. **d** 69 **p** 70. C Swansea St Thos and Kilvey *S & B* 69-73; C Clydach 73-76; R Llanbadarn Fawr, Llandegley and Llanfihangel etc 76-81; V Swansea St Nic 81-88; V Killay 88-94; V Ilston w Pennard from 94. *The Vicarage, 88 Pennard Road, Pennard, Swansea SA3 2AD* Swansea (01792) 232928

WILKINSON, Edward. b 55. Cranmer Hall Dur 86. **d** 88 **p** 89. C Bishopwearmouth St Nic *Dur* 88-92; P-in-c Newbottle from 92. *The Vicarage, Newbottle, Houghton le Spring, Tyne & Wear DH4 4EP* 0191-584 3244

WILKINSON, Edwin. b 29. Oak Hill Th Coll 53. **d** 56 **p** 57. V Rye Harbour *Chich* 66-73; V Camber and E Guldeford 73-79; V Westf 79-87; V Bexhill St Steph 87-93; rtd 93. *51 Anderida Road, Eastbourne, E Sussex BN22 0PZ* Eastbourne (01323) 503083

WILKINSON, Guy Alexander. b 48. Magd Coll Cam BA69. Ripon Coll Cuddesdon 85. **d** 87 **p** 88. C Cov Caludon *Cov* 87-90; P-in-c Ockham w Hatchford *Guildf* 90-91; R 91-94;

WILKINSON

Bp's Dom Chapl 90-94; V Small Heath St Aid w St Greg and St Oswald *Birm* from 94. *St Aidan's Clergy House, 172 Herbert Road, Birmingham B10 0PR* 0121-772 0318

WILKINSON, Canon James Noel Batthews. b 30. LRAM66 TCD BA53 MA65 BD65. CITC 55. **d** 55 **p** 56. C Antrim All SS *Conn* 66-70; I Belf Ardoyne 70-79; Min Can Belf Cathl 72-88; RD M Belf *Conn* 78-79; I Derryvolgie 79-93; Can Belf Cathl 88-93; rtd 93. *68 Orangefield Road, Belfast BT5 6DD* Belfast (01232) 654075

WILKINSON, John Andrew. b 59. Pemb Coll Ox BA83 MA87 St Jo Coll Dur BA86. Cranmer Hall Dur 84. **d** 87 **p** 88. C Broadheath *Ches* 87-91; TV Worthing Ch the King *Chich* from 91. *5 Christchurch Road, Worthing, W Sussex BN11 1JH* Worthing (01903) 202433

WILKINSON, John David. b 36. AKC59. **d** 60 **p** 61. C Wythenshawe Wm Temple Ch CD *Man* 60-63; C Stockport St Pet w Churwell *Wakef* 63-65; V Robertttown 65-75; V Battyeford 75-88; V Airedale w Fryston from 88. *The Vicarage, The Mount, Airedale, Castleford, W Yorkshire WF10 3JL* Castleford (01977) 553157

WILKINSON, Canon John Donald. b 29. Mert Coll Ox BA53 MA56 Louvain Univ Belgium LTh59 Lon Univ PhD82. Gen Th Sem (NY) Hon STD70 Cuddesdon Coll 54. **d** 56 **p** 57. Dean St Geo Coll Jerusalem 69-75; Can Jerusalem 73-75; P-in-c S Kensington H Trin w All SS *Lon* 75-78; Bp's Dir of Clergy Tr 75-79; Dir Br Sch of Archaeology Jerusalem 79-85; USA 85-90 and 91; NSM Kensington St Mary Abbots w St Geo *Lon* 90-91 and 92; rtd 94; Perm to Offic *Lon* from 94. *7 Tenniel Close, London W2 3LE* 0171-229 9205

WILKINSON, John Lawrence. b 43. Ch Coll Cam BA65 MA69 Birm Univ DipTh68 Gen Th Sem (NY) STB69. **d** 69 **p** 70. C Braunstone *Leic* 69-71; C Hodge Hill *Birm* 71-74; P-in-c Aston St Jas 75-84; Tutor Qu Coll Birm 85-95; Hon C Birm St Geo *Birm* 86-95; P-in-c Kings Heath from 95. *All Saints' Vicarage, 2 Vicarage Road, Birmingham B14 7RA* 0121-444 1207

WILKINSON, John Stoddart. b 47. Univ of Wales (Cardiff) CQSW83. St D Coll Lamp DipTh70. **d** 70 **p** 71. C Kells *Carl* 70-72; C Barrow St Geo w St Luke 72-74; Perm to Offic *Mon* 74-89; Sub-Chapl HM Young Offender Inst Hewell Grange from 89; Sub-Chapl HM Rem Cen Brockhill from 89. *HM Young Offender Institution, Hewell Grange, Redditch, Worcs B97 6QQ* Redditch (01527) 550843

WILKINSON, Jonathan Charles. b 61. Leeds Univ BA83. Wycliffe Hall Ox 85. **d** 87 **p** 88. C Plymouth St Andr w St Paul and St Geo *Ex* 87-90; C Oulton Broad *Nor* 90-93; V Hallwood *Ches* from 93. *The Vicarage, 6 Kirkstone Crescent, Runcorn, Cheshire WA7 3JQ* Runcorn (01928) 713101

WILKINSON, Miss Julia Mary. b 52. Cam Inst of Educn CertEd73 Open Univ BA85 Univ of Wales (Ban) BD89. Linc Th Coll CMM92. **d** 92 **p** 94. Par Dn High Wycombe *Ox* 92-94; C from 94. *162 Hicks Farm Rise, High Wycombe, Bucks HP13 7SG* High Wycombe (01494) 437567

WILKINSON, Keith Howard. b 48. Hull Univ BA70 Em Coll Cam MA74. Westcott Ho Cam 74. **d** 76 **p** 77. C Pet St Jude *Pet* 76-79; Chapl Eton Coll Windsor 79-84; Perm to Offic *Pet* from 82; Chapl Malvern Coll Worcs 84-89; Hd Master Berkhamsted Sch Herts from 89; Lic to Offic *St Alb* from 89. *Wilson House, Castle Street, Berkhamsted, Herts HP4 2BE* Berkhamsted (01442) 863236 Fax 877657

WILKINSON, Ven Kenneth Samuel. b 31. TCD BA60 MA69. CITC 60. **d** 60 **p** 61. C Dub St Michan w St Paul *D & G* 60-63; Min Can St Patr Cathl Dub 62-67; C Dub Ch Ch Leeson Park *D & G* 63-67; I Killegney *C & O* 67-70; I Enniscorthy w Clone, Clonmore, Monart etc from 70; Preb Ferns Cathl 83-88; Adn Ferns from 88; Dio Dir Ords from 94. *The Rectory, Enniscorthy, Co Wexford, Irish Republic* Enniscorthy (54) 33249

WILKINSON, Miss Marlene Sandra. b 45. SRN71 Huddersfield Poly NDN86 Leeds Univ DipTh91 Sheff Univ DBS93. Trin Coll Bris IDC78. **dss** 78 **d** 93 **p** 94. Wrose *Bradf* 78-82; Chapl St Luke's Hosp Bradf 78-82; Past Tutor Aston Tr Sch 79-81; W Yorkshire CECS 82-84; Westgate Common *Wakef* 84-86; E Ardsley 86-92; Wakef St Jo 92-94; NSM 93-94; C Barrow St Geo w St Luke *Carl* 94; TV from 94. *The Vicarage, 98A Roose Road, Barrow-in-Furness, Cumbria LA13 9RL* Barrow-in-Furness (01229) 821258

WILKINSON, Michael Alan. b 27. Selw Coll Cam BA51. Westcott Ho Cam 52. **d** 53 **p** 54. C Swindon Ch Ch *Bris* 53-57; C Knowle St Barn 57-59; C Eltham St Jo *S'wark* 59-65; C Sydenham St Bart 65-77; Perm to Offic *Ex* 77-84; P-in-c Yealmpton 84-91; P-in-c Brixton 87-91; V Yealmpton and Brixton from 91; RD Ivybridge 91-93. *The Vicarage, Bowden Hill, Yealmpton, Plymouth PL8 2JX* Plymouth (01752) 880229

WILKINSON, Norman Ellis. b 10. Peterho Cam BA31 MA35. Sarum Th Coll 32. **d** 33 **p** 34. V Broadhempston and

Woodland *Ex* 59-75; rtd 75. *Manor Farmhouse, Walditch, Bridport, Dorset DT6 4LQ* Bridport (01308) 56025

WILKINSON, Paul. b 51. Sarum & Wells Th Coll 75. **d** 78 **p** 79. C Allerton *Bradf* 78-80; C Baildon 80-83; V Hengoed w Gobowen *Lich* 83-90; V Potterne w Worton and Marston *Sarum* from 90; Chapl Roundway Hosp Devizes from 92. *The Vicarage, 4 Rookes Lane, Potterne, Devizes, Wilts SN10 5NF* Devizes (01380) 723189

WILKINSON, Paul Martin. b 56. Brunel Univ BSc. Wycliffe Hall Ox 83. **d** 86 **p** 87. C Hinckley H Trin *Leic* 86-90; V Newbold on Avon *Cov* from 90. *The Vicarage, Main Street, Newbold, Rugby, Warks CV21 1HH* Rugby (01788) 543055

WILKINSON, Peter David Lloyd. b 67. Trin Coll Ox BA89 MA93. Ridley Hall Cam BA94 CTM95. **d** 95. C Brampton St Thos *Derby* from 95. *1 Rhodesia Road, Chesterfield, Derbyshire S40 3AL* Chesterfield (01246) 231089

WILKINSON, Peter Francis. b 20. Cuddesdon Coll 63. **d** 65 **p** 66. C Chobham w Valley End *Guildf* 65-78; V Yalding *Roch* 68-72; V Yalding w Collier Street 72-87; rtd 87. *Chartfield, Flimwell, Wadhurst, E Sussex TN5 7PA* Flimwell (01580) 87372

WILKINSON, Peter Howarth. b 32. St Pet Hall Ox BA54 MA58. Ridley Hall Cam 56. **d** 58 **p** 59. V Nettlebed *Ox* 62-68; rtd 68; Hon C Cheadle *Ches* 69-82. *10 Norbreck Avenue, Cheadle, Cheshire SK8 2ET* 0161-428 7699

WILKINSON, Canon Raymond Stewart. b 19. AKC42. Bps' Coll Cheshunt 42. **d** 43 **p** 44. R Woodchurch *Ches* 61-71; R Solihull *Birm* 71-79; TR 79-87; Hon Can Birm Cathl 76-87; Chapl to The Queen 83-87; rtd 87; Perm to Offic *Cov* from 87. *42 Coten End, Warwick CV34 4NP* Warwick (01926) 493510

WILKINSON, Robert Ian (Bob). b 43. MIMunE73 MICE84 CEng73. Oak Hill NSM Course. **d** 88 **p** 89. NSM Hawkwell *Chelmsf* 88-89; NSM Thundersley 89-91; C New Thundersley 91-94; V Berechurch St Marg w St Mich from 94. *The Vicarage, 348 Mersea Road, Colchester CO2 8RA* Colchester (01206) 576859

WILKINSON, Canon Robert Matthew. b 21. TCD BA46. CITC 47. **d** 47 **p** 48. I Derryloran *Arm* 55-73; Can Arm Cathl 67-73; I Ballymore 73-87; Treas Arm Cathl 73-75; Chan 75-83; Prec 83-87; rtd 87. *60 Coleraine Road, Portrush, Co Antrim BT56 8HN* Portrush (01265) 822758

WILKINSON, Robert Samuel (Rob). b 52. Wycliffe Hall Ox DipMin94. **d** 94 **p** 95. C Boughton Monchelsea *Cant* from 94. *29 Lewis Court Drive, Boughton Monchelsea, Maidstone, Kent ME17 4LG* Maidstone (01622) 747082

WILKINSON, Roger. b 46. K Coll Lon BA68 AKC68 AKC72. St Aug Coll Cant 72. **d** 73 **p** 74. C Lt Stanmore St Lawr *Lon* 73-76; Asst Chapl St Geo Hosp Lon 76-78; Chapl Hounslow and Spelthorne HA 78-88; TV Langley and Parkfield *Man* 88-89; C Shelf and C Butttershaw St Aid *Bradf* 89-90; Chapl Asst Ipswich Hosp 90-94; Perm to Offic *St E* 90-94; C Fingringhoe w E Donyland and Abberton etc *Chelmsf* from 94. *St Lawrence House, Rectory Road, Rowhedge, Colchester CO5 7HR* Colchester (01206) 728071

WILKINSON, Roy Geoffrey. b 42. Sarum Th Coll 67. **d** 70 **p** 71. C Belsize Park *Lon* 70-73; C Heston 73-75; C Hythe *Cant* 75-79; P-in-c Croydon Woodside 79-81; V 81-84; V Croydon Woodside *S'wark* 85-86. *Sundown, Church Lane, Skegness, Lincs PE25 1EG* Skegness (01754) 766727

WILKINSON, Simon Evelyn. b 49. Nottm Univ BA74. Cuddesdon Coll 74. **d** 76 **p** 77. C Cheam *S'wark* 76-78; P-in-c Warlingham w Chelsham and Farleigh 78-83; Radley Coll Abingdon 83-89; R Bishops Waltham *Portsm* from 89; R Upham from 89. *The Rectory, Bishops Waltham, Southampton SO3 1EE* Bishops Waltham (01489) 892618

WILKINSON, Walter Edward Robert. b 38. St Andr Univ MA60. Lon Coll of Div BD63 ALCD63. **d** 63 **p** 64. C High Wycombe *Ox* 63-70; PV, Succ and Sacr Roch Cathl *Roch* 70-73; P-in-c Asby w Ormside *Carl* 73-80; R Cherry Burton *York* 80-95; RD Beverley 88-94; P-in-c Grasmere *Carl* from 95. *The Rectory, Grasmere, Ambleside, Cumbria LA22 9SW* Grasmere (015394) 35326

WILKINSON, Canon Wilfred Badger. b 21. K Coll Lon BD50 AKC50. **d** 50 **p** 51. R Clifton w Glapton *S'well* 65-71; TR Clifton 71-86; Hon Can S'well Minster 83-86; rtd 86; Perm to Offic *S'well* from 86. *13 Farthingate Close, Southwell, Notts NG25 0HU* Southwell (01636) 814047

WILKS, Eric Percival. b 32. Wells Th Coll 67. **d** 68 **p** 69. C Fladbury w Throckmorton, Wyre Piddle and Moor *Worc* 68-70; Perm to Offic from 70. *4 Catherine Cottages, Droitwich Road, Hartlebury, Kidderminster, Worcs DY10 4EL* Hartlebury (01299) 251580

WILKS, Ernest Howard. b 26. Oak Hill Th Coll 64. **d** 66 **p** 67. R Gressenhall w Longham and Bittering Parva *Nor* 69-77; Area Sec (Dios St E & I and Nor) CMS 77-83; P-in-c Deopham w Hackford *Nor* 83-84; P-in-c Morley 83-84; P-in-c Wicklewood and Crownthorpe 83-84; R Morley w Deopham, Hackford, Wicklewood etc 84-88; CMS 89-91; Nigeria 89-91; rtd 91;

756

Perm to Offic *Nor* from 91. *Corner Cottage, Carbrooke Road, Griston, Thetford, Norfolk IP25 6QE* Watton (01953) 881413

WILL, Nicholas James. b 53. Birm Univ LLB75. Qu Coll Birm 93. **d** 95. C Bridgnorth, Tasley, Astley Abbotts, Oldbury etc *Heref* from 95. *c/o The Rectory, 16 East Castle Street, Brignorth, Shropshire WV16 4AZ* Bridgnorth (01746) 763256

WILLANS, Jonathan Michael Arthur. b 60. QUB BD. CITC 83. **d** 85 **p** 86. C Larne and Inver *Conn* 85-88; R Hawick *Edin* 88-91; P-in-c Brockham Green *S'wark* from 91; P-in-c Leigh from 91. *The Vicarage, Clayhill Road, Leigh, Reigate, Surrey RH2 8PD* Dawes Green (01306) 611224

WILLARD, John Fordham. b 38. K Coll Lon BD62 AKC62. **d** 63 **p** 64. C Balham Hill Ascension *S'wark* 63-67; C Leigh Park *Portsm* 67-73; C-in-c Leigh Park St Clare CD 73-75; R Bishops Waltham 75-87; P-in-c Upham 78-79; R 79-87; V Dalston H Trin w St Phil *Lon* from 87; P-in-c Haggerston All SS from 90. *Holy Trinity Vicarage, 89 Forest Road, London E8 3BL* 0171-254 5062

WILLCOCK, Albert. b 13. St D Coll Lamp BA41. **d** 41 **p** 42. V Long Clawson and Hose *Leic* 61-74; R Stonton Wyville w Glooston, Slawston and Cranoe 74-78; rtd 78; Perm to Offic *Linc* from 78; Perm to Offic *Leic* from 78. *19 Teesdale Road, Grantham, Lincs NG31 8ES* Grantham (01476) 73774

WILLCOCK, Donald Thomas. b 07. Chich Th Coll 52. **d** 54 **p** 55. V Gt Totham *Chelmsf* 58-81; rtd 81. *7 Hawkes Road, Coggeshall, Colchester CO6 1QP* Coggeshall (01376) 561803

WILLCOCK, Richard William. b 39. Hertf Coll Ox BA62 MA66. Ripon Hall Ox 62. **d** 64 **p** 65. C Ashton St Mich *Man* 64-68; Bp's Dom Chapl 68-72; V Charlestown 72-73; V Charlestown 73-75; Chapl Casterton Sch 75-80; V Bamford *Man* 80-92; R Framlingham w Saxtead *St E* from 92. *The Rectory, Framlingham, Woodbridge, Suffolk IP13 9BJ* Framlingham (01728) 621082

WILLCOX, Canon Frederick John (Fred). b 29. Kelham Th Coll 49. **d** 54 **p** 55. S Africa 60-70; P-in-c Derby St Andr w St Osmund *Derby* 70-74; V 74-80; V Netherton St Andr *Worc* 80-94; Hon Can Worc Cathl 91-94; rtd 94. *48 Meadow Croft, West Hagley, Stourbridge, W Midlands DY9 0LJ* Hagley (01562) 887255

WILLCOX, Ralph Arthur. b 32. Westhill Coll Birm CertYS59 Cranfield Inst of Tech MSc80. St Alb Minl Tr Scheme 86. **d** 89 **p** 90. NSM Aspley Guise w Husborne Crawley and Ridgmont *St Alb* 89-92; Chapl HM Pris Bedf from 92. *HM Prison, St Loyes, Bedford MK40 1HG* Bedford (01234) 358671 Fax 273568

WILLCOX, Dr Richard John Michael. b 39. Birm Univ BSc62 PhD67. Qu Coll Birm 78. **d** 80 **p** 81. C Boldmere *Birm* 80-83; V Edgbaston SS Mary and Ambrose 83-89; V Evercreech w Chesterblade and Milton Clevedon *B & W* from 89; Dioc Development Rep from 90. *The Vicarage, Church Lane, Evercreech, Shepton Mallet, Somerset BA4 6HU* Evercreech (01749) 830322

WILLCOX, Canon Sydney Harold. b 36. Univ of Wales (Lamp) BA58. St Mich Coll Llan. **d** 60 **p** 61. C Pwllheli *Ban* 60-62; C Llandegfan w Beaumaris and Llanfaes 62-65; R Llanenddwyn 65-70; R Dolgellau, Llanfachreth, Brithdir etc 70-76; TR Ridgeway *Sarum* 76-86; RD Marlborough 81-86; TR Cockermouth w Embleton and Wythop *Carl* 86-94; RD Derwent 89-94; Hon Can Carl Cathl 91-94; V Chalke Valley W *Sarum* from 94. *The Vicarage, Broad Chalke, Salisbury SP5 5DS* Salisbury (01722) 780262

WILLENBROCK, Dr Philip Charles. b 42. Ox Univ MA BM BCh. Ex & Truro NSM Scheme. **d** 82 **p** 83. NSM Treslothan *Truro* 82-87; NSM Redruth w Lanner and Treleigh 87-89; Perm to Offic *Sarum* 89-90; Perm to Offic *Chelmsf* from 90. *18 The Dale, Wivenhoe, Colchester CO7 9NL* Colchester (01206) 823812

WILLESDEN, Area Bishop of. See DOW, Rt Rev Geoffrey Graham

WILLETT, Canon Allen Gardiner. b 20. Bris Univ BA51 Lon Univ BD54. Clifton Th Coll 47. **d** 54 **p** 55. V Galleywood Common *Chelmsf* 68-87; RD Chelmsf 81-86; Hon Can Chelmsf Cathl 85-87; rtd 87; Perm to Offic *Pet* from 87; Perm to Offic *Ely* from 90; Perm to Offic *Linc* from 90. *4 Abbotts Grove, Werrington, Peterborough PE4 5BT* Peterborough (01733) 77532

WILLETT, Frank Edwin. b 45. Lon Univ DipTh68. Kelham Th Coll 64. **d** 68 **p** 69. C Oswestry H Trin *Lich* 68-71; C Bilston St Leon 71-74; USPG Coll of the Ascension Selly Oak 74-75; USPG 74-80; Zambia 75-80; V Curbar and Stoney Middleton *Derby* 80-88; Area Sec (Dios Derby and Leic) USPG 88-91; V Chesterfield St Aug *Derby* from 91. *St Augustine's Vicarage, 1 Whitecotes Lane, Chesterfield, Derbyshire S40 3HJ* Chesterfield (01246) 273942

WILLETT, Canon Geoffrey Thomas. b 38. Dur Univ BA59 MA82. Cranmer Hall Dur DipTh61. **d** 62 **p** 63. C Widnes St Paul *Liv* 62-65; C Harborne Heath *Birm* 65-68; V Wakef St Andr and St Mary *Wakef* 68-75; V Hinckley H Trin *Leic* 75-89; TR 89; RD Sparkenhoe II 84-87; RD Sparkenhoe W (Hinkley and Bosworth) 87-89; Hon Can Leic Cathl from 87; P-in-c Markfield 89-90; R from 90; RD Sparkenhoe E from 91. *The Rectory, The Nook, Markfield, Leics LE67 9WE* Markfield (01530) 242844

WILLETT, John Ivon. b 40. Ch Ch Ox BA63 MA65. Chich Th Coll 61. **d** 63 **p** 64. C Leic St Andr *Leic* 63-66; C Bordesley St Alb *Birm* 66-72; Min Can, Prec and Sacr Pet Cathl *Pet* 72-82; R Uppingham w Ayston and Wardley w Belton from 82. *The Rectory, Uppingham, Oakham, Leics LE15 9TJ* Uppingham (01572) 823381

WILLETT, Michael John Farquhar. b 32. St Mich Coll Llan DMinlStuds92. **d** 92 **p** 93. NSM Llangorse, Cathedine, Llanfihangel Talyllyn etc *S & B* from 92. *Beaufort House, Llangynidr, Crickhowell, Powys NP8 1NT* Bwlch (01874) 730449

WILLETT, Stephen John. b 54. Ridley Hall Cam 88. **d** 90 **p** 91. C Chapeltown *Sheff* 90-94; V Hackenthorpe from 94. *The Vicarage, 63 Sheffield Road, Sheffield S12 4LR* Sheffield (0114) 248 4486

WILLETTS, Alfred. b 15. **d** 62 **p** 63. R Man St Phil w St Mark *Man* 67-75; R Man Apostles 75-84; rtd 85; Perm to Offic *Ches* from 85; Perm to Offic *Man* from 85. *22 Larne Drive, Broughton, Chester CH4 0QF* Chester (01244) 533485

WILLEY, David Geoffrey. b 53. Imp Coll Lon BSc74 BA66. Oak Hill Th Coll 83. **d** 86 **p** 87. C Cromer *Nor* 86-90; R High Halstow w All Hallows and Hoo St Mary *Roch* 90-94; R Gravesend St Geo from 94; P-in-c Rosherville from 94. *St George's Rectory, Gravesend, Kent DA11 0DJ* Gravesend (01474) 534965

WILLEY, Graham John. b 38. Moray Ord Course 91. **d** 93 **p** 94. Hon C W Coast Jt Congregations Moray *Mor* from 93. *Harbour View, Badachro, Gairloch, Ross-shire IV21 2AA* Badachro (01445) 741316

WILLIAMS, Alan Ronald Norman. b 60. RMN85. Linc Th Coll CMinlStuds95. **d** 95. C Malvern Link w Cowleigh *Worc* from 95. *17 Bosbury Road, Malvern, Worcs WR14 1TR* Malvern (01684) 569890

WILLIAMS, Aled Jones. b 56. Univ of Wales (Ban) BA77 Univ of Wales (Cardiff) DipTh79. St Mich Coll Llan 77. **d** 79 **p** 80. C Conwy w Gyffin *Ban* 79-82; R Llanrug 82-86; R Machynlleth and Llanwrin 86-87; Member L'Arche Community 88-95; V Ynyscynhaearn w Penmorfa and Porthmadog from 95. *The Vicarage, Llety'r Llan, Porthmadoc, Gwynedd LL49 9PA* Porthmadoc (01766) 512167

WILLIAMS, Aled Wyn. b 47. Univ of Wales (Abth) BA69. St Mich Coll Llan 69. **d** 71 **p** 72. C Llanelli *St D* 71-73; P-in-c Capel Colman w Llanfihangel Penbedw etc 73-74; V 74-81; V Llanddewi Brefi w Llanbadarn Odwyn 81-84; V Llanddewi Brefi w Llanbadarn Odwyn and Cellan etc from 84. *The Vicarage, Llanddewi Brefi, Tregaron, Dyfed SY25 6PE* Tregaron (01974) 298937

WILLIAMS, Alexander Ernest. b 14. Fitzw Ho Cam BA35 MA46 Regent's Park Coll Ox 35. Coll of Resurr Mirfield 79. **d** 79 **p** 80. Hon C Carshalton Beeches *S'wark* 79-87; rtd 87. *88 Grosvenor Avenue, Carshalton, Surrey SM5 3EP* 0181-647 8446

WILLIAMS, Alfred Donald. b 26. St Aid Birkenhead 57. **d** 59 **p** 60. V Ladybrook *S'well* 62-70; P-in-c Newark Ch Ch 70-71; R Gotham 72-88; P-in-c W Leake w Kingston-on-Soar etc 72-81; rtd 88; Perm to Offic *Bradf* from 88. *20 Grassington Road, Skipton, N Yorkshire BD23 1LL* Skipton (01756) 794496

WILLIAMS, Alfred George. b 21. St D Coll Lamp BA42. **d** 46 **p** 47. V Rock Ferry *Ches* 64-77; V Lache cum Saltney 77-86; rtd 86; Perm to Offic *Ches* from 86. *7 Lache Park Avenue, Chester CH4 8HR* Chester (01244) 678768

WILLIAMS, Allen Philpin. b 10. St D Coll Lamp BA32 St Mich Coll Llan. **d** 34 **p** 35. V Manordeilo and Taliaris *St D* 70-78; rtd 78. *7 Diana Road, Llandeilo, Dyfed SA19 6RR* Llandeilo (01558) 822376

WILLIAMS, Miss Amanda Clare (Mandy). b 69. Univ of Wales (Ban) BD90. Westcott Ho Cam CTM92. **d** 92. C Carmarthen St Dav *St D* 92-94; Chapl Trin Coll Carmarthen from 94. *Llwynon, College Road, Carmarthen, Dyfed SA31 3EQ* Carmarthen (01267) 238175

WILLIAMS, Andrew David. b 67. Univ of Wales (Lamp) BA91. Linc Th Coll CMM93. **d** 93 **p** 94. C Perry Street *Roch* from 93. *6 Dene Holm Road, Gravesend, Kent DA11 8LE* Gravesend (01474) 332652

WILLIAMS, Andrew Gibson. b 31. Edin Univ MA57. Edin Th Coll 56. **d** 59 **p** 60. CF 65-71; R Winterslow *Sarum* 71-84; P-in-c Condover *Heref* 84-88; P-in-c Acton Burnell w Pitchford 84-88; P-in-c Frodesley 84-88; R Condover w Frodesley, Acton Burnell etc 88-90; R Whimple, Talaton and Clyst St Lawr *Ex* 90-94; rtd 94. *6 Culvery Close, Woodbury, Exeter EX5 1LZ* Exeter (01395) 233079

WILLIAMS, Andrew Joseph. b 55. St Jo Coll Nottm BTh81. **d** 81 **p** 82. C Hollington St Leon *Chich* 81-84; C Sutton Coldfield H Trin *Birm* 84-87; Perm to Offic from 87; Chapl Blue Coat Comp Sch Walsall from 91. *139 Rectory Road, Sutton Coldfield, W Midlands B75 7RV* 0121-378 2962

WILLIAMS, Mrs Anthea Elizabeth. b 50. Trevelyan Coll Dur BA71. Linc Th Coll 72. **dss** 79 **d** 87 **p** 94. St Marylebone Ch Ch *Lon* 79-84; Maidstone St Martin *Cant* 84-87; Par Dn 87-91; Par Dn Rolvenden 91; D-in-c 91-94; P-in-c from 94. *The Vicarage, Rolvenden, Cranbrook, Kent TN17 4ND* Cranbrook (01580) 241235

WILLIAMS, Dr Anthony David. b 38. MRCGP68 LRCP62 MRCS62 DRCOG65 FPACert65. S Dios Minl Tr Scheme 87. **d** 90 **p** 91. Hon C Jersey St Pet *Win* 90-92; NSM Jersey St Helier from 92. *Beau Vallon, Mont de la Rosiere, St Saviour, Jersey, Channel Islands JE2 7HF* Jersey (01534) 863859

WILLIAMS, Anthony Francis. b 21. Trin Coll Ox BA49 MA53. Coll of Resurr Mirfield 49. **d** 51 **p** 52. V Lindridge *Worc* 67-77; P-in-c Bluntisham w Earith *Ely* 77-79; R 79-88; rtd 88. *21 Kings Hedges, St Ives, Huntingdon, Cambs PE17 6XU* St Ives (01480) 467686

WILLIAMS, Canon Anthony Riley. b 36. Univ of Wales BA60. Chich Th Coll 57. **d** 59 **p** 60. C Llandinworric *Ban* 59-61; C Llandegfan w Beaumaris and Llanfaes 61-64; R Ludchurch and Templeton *St D* 64-72; V Lamphey w Hodgeston 72-83; RD Castlemartin 75-83; V Llanelli from 83; Can St D Cathl from 86; Chapl Bryntirion Hosp Llanelli from 90; Chan St D Cathl *St D* from 93. *The Vicarage, 11 Old Road, Llanelli, Dyfed SA15 3HW* Llanelli (01554) 772072

WILLIAMS, Arfon. b 58. Univ of Wales (Abth) BD83 Univ of Wales (Ban) MA84. Wycliffe Hall Ox 83. **d** 84 **p** 85. C Carmarthen St Dav *St D* 84-86; TV Abth 86-88; V Glanogwen *Ban* 88-94; Dir Oast Ho Retreat Cen *Chich* from 95; Asst to RD Rye from 95; C Ewhurst from 95. *6 Weald View, Staplecross, Robertsbridge, E Sussex TN32 5QW* Robertsbridge (01580) 830653

WILLIAMS, Preb Arthur Edwin. b 33. Leeds Univ BA57. Coll of Resurr Mirfield 57. **d** 59 **p** 60. C Wednesfield St Thos *Lich* 59-62; C Codsall 62-65; V from 83; V Coseley St Chad 65-73; R Kingswinford H Trin 73-81; TR Wordsley 81-83; RD Himley 77-83; Preb Lich Cathl from 82; RD Penkridge 89-94. *The Vicarage, Church Road, Codsall, Wolverhampton WV8 1EH* Codsall (01902) 842168

WILLIAMS, Canon Arthur James Daniel. b 24. Univ of Wales (Lamp) BA49. St Mich Coll Llan 49. **d** 51 **p** 52. V Llantwit Fadre *Llan* 66-89; RD Pontypridd 84-88; Can Llan Cathl 86-89; rtd 89; Perm to Offic *Llan* from 89. *Ty Pica, Efail Isaf, Church Village, Pontypridd, M Glam CF38 1BA* Pontypridd (01443) 480423

WILLIAMS, Barrie. b 33. Em Coll Cam BA54 MA58 Bris Univ MLitt71. Lambeth STh75 Ripon Hall Ox 62. **d** 63 **p** 64. C Penwortham St Mary *Blackb* 63-65; Hon C Salisbury St Martin *Sarum* 65-77; Chapl St Edw K and Martyr Cam *Ely* 77-84; Asst Chapl Trin Hall Cam 77-84; R Ashley w Weston by Welland and Sutton Bassett *Pet* 84-85; Asst Chapl St Hilda's Sch Whitby from 85. *Flat 5, Crinkle Court, 9 Chubb Hill, Whitby, N Yorkshire YO21 1JU* Whitby (01947) 600766

WILLIAMS, Benjamin Clive. b 24. Lon Univ BD59. Westcott Ho Cam 59. **d** 61 **p** 62. R Denton w S Heighton and Tarring Neville *Chich* 66-74; Dioc Stewardship Adv 74-81; P-in-c Clapham w Patching 76-81; V Ticehurst and Flimwell 81-89; rtd 89. *14 Lindfield Avenue, Seaford, E Sussex BN25 4DY* Seaford (01323) 491019

WILLIAMS, Brian. b 48. W Midl Minl Tr Course. **d** 83 **p** 84. NSM Lich St Chad *Lich* from 83. *82 Walsall Road, Lichfield, Staffs WS13 8AF* Lichfield (01543) 253120

WILLIAMS, Brian Luke. b 54. AKC75. St Steph Ho Ox 76. **d** 77 **p** 78. C Kettering St Mary *Pet* 77-80; C Walsall St Gabr Fulbrook *Lich* 80-83; P-in-c Sneyd 83-85; V from 85; RD Stoke N from 94. *Sneyd Vicarage, Hamil Road, Stoke-on-Trent ST6 1AP* Stoke-on-Trent (01782) 825841

WILLIAMS, Brian Thomas. b 48. GSM69. Linc Th Coll 89. **d** 91 **p** 92. C Liss *Portsm* 91-95; C Portsea N End St Mark from 95. *St Nicholas' House, 90A Compton Road, Portsmouth PO2 0SR* Portsmouth (01705) 660657

WILLIAMS, Mrs Carol Jean. b 45. FIPM89. Ox NSM Course 86. **d** 89 **p** 94. NSM High Wycombe *Ox* from 89. *3 Pimms Close, High Wycombe, Bucks HP13 7EG* High Wycombe (01494) 814571

WILLIAMS, Dr Cecil Peter. b 41. TCD BA63 MA67 Lon Univ BD67 PhD86 Bris Univ MLitt77. Clifton Th Coll 64. **d** 67 **p** 68. C Maghull *Liv* 67-70; Lic to Offic *Bris* 70-91; Tutor Clifton Th Coll 70-72; Tutor Trin Coll Bris 72-91; Lib 73-81; Course Ldr 81-85; Vice-Prin 85-91; V Ecclesall *Sheff* from 91. *Ecclesall Vicarage, Ringinglow Road, Sheffield S11 7PQ* Sheffield (0114) 236 0084 Fax as telephone

WILLIAMS, Cecil Augustus Baldwin. b 09. TCD BA31 MA39. CITC 32. **d** 32 **p** 33. I Crinken *D & G* 71-81; rtd 81. *3 St John's Close, Portstewart, Co Londonderry BT55 7HJ* Portstewart (01265) 834249

WILLIAMS, Clifford Smith. b 48. Univ of Wales (Ban) BD79. St Deiniol's Hawarden 79. **d** 80 **p** 81. C Llanbeblig w Caernarfon and Betws Garmon etc *Ban* 80-82; R Llanfair Mathafarn Eithaf w Llanbedrgoch from 82. *The Rectory, Bay View Road, Tyn-y-Gongl, Gwynedd LL74 8TT* Tyn-y-Gongl (01248) 852348

WILLIAMS, Clive Gregory. b 45. Trin Coll Bris 83. **d** 85 **p** 86. C Bedhampton *Portsm* 85-88; V Highley *Heref* from 88. *The Vicarage, Church Street, Highley, Bridgnorth, Shropshire WV16 6NA* Highley (01746) 861612

WILLIAMS, Colin Henry. b 52. Pemb Coll Ox BA73 MA78. St Steph Ho Ox BA80. **d** 81 **p** 82. C Liv St Paul Stoneycroft *Liv* 81-84; TV Walton St Mary 84-89; Chapl Walton Hosp Liv 86-89; Bp's Dom Chapl *Blackb* 89-94; Chapl Whalley Abbey 89-94; V Poulton-le-Fylde from 94. *The Vicarage, 7 Vicarage Road, Poulton-le-Fylde, Blackpool FY6 7BE* Poulton-le-Fylde (01253) 883086

WILLIAMS, Creswell. b 13. Univ of Wales BA36. St D Coll Lamp 37. **d** 38 **p** 39. V Eglwysfach and Llangynfelin *St D* 67-78; rtd 78; Lic to Offic *Ban* from 78. *4 Londonderry Terrace, Machynlleth, Powys SY20 8BG* Machynlleth (01654) 702349

WILLIAMS, Cyril. b 06. Univ of Wales BA34. St Mich Coll Llan 34. **d** 35 **p** 36. R Denbigh *St As* 61-77; rtd 77. *Bryniog, 13 Nant y Patrick, St Asaph, Clwyd LL17 0BN* Trefnant (01745) 730264

WILLIAMS, David. b 19. **d** 66 **p** 67. Hon C Dean Forest St Paul *Glouc* 66-78; Hon C Coleford w Staunton 78-83; Perm to Offic from 83. *The Nook, Parkend Road, Bream, Lydney, Glos GL15 6JZ* Dean (01594) 562240

WILLIAMS, David. b 33. Ch Coll Cam BA56 MA60 Cranfield Inst of Tech MSc72. Sarum & Wells Th Coll 71. **d** 73 **p** 74. C Ex St Jas *Ex* 73-75; Lic to Offic 75-84; Teacher St Wilfrid Sch Ex 75-76; Teacher Hele's Sch Ex 76-84; TV Thorverton, Cadbury, Upton Pyne etc 84-92; TR 92-93; rtd 93. *1 Wrefords Close, Exeter EX4 5AY* Exeter (01392) 435759

WILLIAMS, David. b 43. ACA65 K Coll Lon AKC69 BD70. St Aug Coll Cant 69. **d** 70 **p** 71. C Walkden Moor *Man* 70-72; C Deane 72-75; V Horwich St Cath 75-81; Hon C Chorley All SS *Blackb* 84-86; P-in-c Weeton 86-87; V Singleton w Weeton from 87. *St Michael's Vicarage, Church Road, Weeton, Preston PR4 3WD* Weeton (01253) 836249

WILLIAMS, Canon David. b 49. BTh DTechM. **d** 88 **p** 89. C Lurgan etc w Ballymachugh, Kildrumferton etc *K, E & A* 88-91; I Kinsale Union *C, C & R* from 91; Miss to Seamen from 91; Can Cork and Cloyne Cathls *C, C & R* from 95. *St Multose Rectory, Abbey Court, Kinsale, Co Cork, Irish Republic* Cork (21) 772220

WILLIAMS, David Albert. b 15. St D Coll Lamp BA35 St Mich Coll Llan 36. **d** 38 **p** 39. Lic to Offic *Heref* 69-80; rtd 80; Perm to Offic *St D* 81-94; P-in-c Cilycwm and Ystrad-ffin w Rhandir-mwyn etc 94-95; P-in-c Llanegwad w Llanfynydd 94-95. *London House, Llanwrda, Dyfed SA19 8AA* Llangadog (01550) 777671

WILLIAMS, Dr David Alun. b 65. St Thos Hosp Lon MB, BS88. Wycliffe Hall Ox BTh94. **d** 94 **p** 95. C Ware Ch Ch *St Alb* from 94. *10 Cromwell Road, Ware, Herts SG12 7JZ* Ware (01920) 467918

WILLIAMS, David Frank. b 48. S Dios Minl Tr Scheme 91. **d** 94 **p** 95. NSM Romsey *Win* from 94. *24 Feltham Close, Romsey, Hants SO51 8PB* Romsey (01794) 524050

WILLIAMS, David Gareth. b 58. Lon Univ BD81. Ripon Coll Cuddesdon 82. **d** 84 **p** 85. C Chandler's Ford *Win* 84-88; C Alton St Lawr 88-90; R Crawley and Littleton and Sparsholt w Lainston from 90. *The Rectory, Church Lane, Littleton, Winchester, Hants SO22 6QY* Winchester (01962) 881898

WILLIAMS, Canon David Gerald Powell. b 35. St Mich Coll Llan DipTh62. **d** 62 **p** 63. C Canton St Jo *Llan* 62-64; Field Tr Officer Ch in Wales Prov Youth Coun 63-70; Prov Youth Chapl 65-70; V Treharris *Llan* 70-75; R Flemingston w Gileston and St Hilary 75-78; Warden of Ords 77-80; Dir Past Studies and Chapl St Mich Coll Llan 78-80; Sub-Warden 79-80; Dir Ch in Wales Publications and Communications 80-85; Prov Dir of Educn Ch in Wales 80-85; Dir of Miss Ch in Wales 85-87; Hon Can Llan Cathl *Llan* 84-93; V Pendoylan and Welsh St Donats 87-93; R Llandudno *Ban* 93-95; Press Officer to Abp of Wales from 93. *39 Cathedral Road, Cardiff CF1 9XF*

WILLIAMS, David Gordon. b 43. Selw Coll Cam BA65 MA69. Oak Hill Th Coll 66. **d** 68 **p** 69. C Maidstone St Luke *Cant* 68-71; C Rugby St Matt *Cov* 71-73; P-in-c Budbrooke 73-74; V 74-81; V Lenton *S'well* 81-87; TR Cheltenham St Mark *Glouc* from 87. *St Mark's Rectory, Fairmount Road, Cheltenham, Glos GL51 7AQ* Cheltenham (01242) 255110

WILLIAMS, David Grant. b 61. Bris Univ BSocSc83. Wycliffe Hall Ox 86. **d** 89 **p** 90. C Ecclesall *Sheff* 89-92; V Dore from 92. *The Vicarage, 51 Vicarage Lane, Dore, Sheffield S17 3GY* Sheffield (0114) 236 3335

WILLIAMS, David Henry. b 33. Trin Coll Cam BA56 MA60 PhD77. St D Coll Lamp 67. **d** 69 **p** 70. C Mon 69-70; Chapl St Woolos Cathl 70-71; P-in-c Six Bells 71-76; Libya 76-79; P-in-c Crumlin *Mon* 79-80; R Llanddewi Skirrid w Llanvetherine etc 80-83; Perm to Offic 83-87; Guest Master Caldey Abbey 83-87; V Buttington and Pool Quay *St As* from 87. *The Vicarage, Buttington, Welshpool, Powys SY21 8HD* Welshpool (01938) 553351

WILLIAMS, Canon David Humphrey. b 23. Em Coll Cam BA49 MA54. St Steph Ho Ox 49. **d** 51 **p** 52. RD Bulwell *S'well* 70-88; P-in-c Bestwood Park 71-78; R Hucknall Torkard 63-71; TR 71-88; Hon Can S'well Minster 75-88; rtd 88. *12 Wollaton Paddocks, Trowell Road, Nottingham NG8 2ED* Nottingham (0115) 928 0639

WILLIAMS, David James. b 42. Chich Th Coll 67. **d** 70 **p** 71. C Charlton-by-Dover St Bart *Cant* 70-74; C Dorking w Ranmore *Guildf* 74-77; C Guildf H Trin w St Mary 77-78; P-in-c E Molesey St Paul 78-88; V Burpham 88-94; rtd 95. *Hilclare, Stag Leys, Ashtead, Surrey KT21 2TQ*

WILLIAMS, David John. b 30. Open Univ BA79. St D Coll Lamp 64. **d** 66 **p** 67. C Mold *St As* 66-69; C Llanrhos 69-71; R Llangynhafal and Llanbedr Dyffryn Clwyd 71-86; P-in-c Llanynys w Llanychan from 77; RD Dyffryn Clwyd from 86; R Ruthin w Llanrhydd from 86. *The Cloisters, Ruthin, Clwyd LL15 1BL* Ruthin (01824) 22068

WILLIAMS, David John. b 38. AKC62. **d** 63 **p** 64. C Benchill *Man* 63-66; C Heywood St Jas 66-69; V Leesfield 69-73; Chapl TS Arethusa 73-74; TV Southend St Jo w St Mark, All SS w St Fran etc *Chelmsf* 74-80; V Horndon on the Hill 80-93; RD Thurrock 83-92; P-in-c Rochford from 93. *The Rectory, 36 Millview Meadows, Rochford, Essex SS4 1EF* Southend-on-Sea (01702) 530621

WILLIAMS, David John. b 43. Wadh Coll Ox BA64. St Jo Coll Nottm 73. **d** 75 **p** 76. C Newc w Butterton *Lich* 75-79; P-in-c Oulton 79-89; P-in-c Stone Ch Ch 84-89; V Stone Ch Ch and Oulton from 89. *Christ Church Vicarage, Bromfield Court, Stone, Staffs ST15 8DA* Stone (01785) 812669

WILLIAMS, David John. b 52. N Ord Course 92. **d** 95. C Gt Crosby St Luke *Liv* from 95. *20 Ascot Park, Crosby, Liverpool L23 2HX* 0151-931 4907

WILLIAMS, David Leslie. b 35. ALCD63. **d** 63 **p** 64. C Bexleyheath Ch Ch *Roch* 63-64; C Gt Faringdon w Lt Coxwell *Ox* 64-66; CMS 67-76; Uganda 67-73; C Shortlands *Roch* 73-74; Fiji 74-76; V Bromley H Trin *Roch* 77-86; R Meopham w Nurstead from 86; RD Cobham from 86. *The Rectory, Shipley Hills Road, Meopham, Gravesend, Kent DA13 0AD* Meopham (01474) 815259 or 813106

WILLIAMS, David Michael Rochfort. b 40. Hull Univ DipTh81. St Mich Coll Llan DipTh65. **d** 65 **p** 66. C Pemb Dock *St D* 65-68; Miss to Seamen 68-71; Ind Chapl *St D* 68-71; P-in-c Walwyn's Castle w Robeston W 68-70; R 70-71; Ind Chapl *Mon* 71-74; Hon Chapl St Woolos Cathl 71-74; V Blaenavon w Capel Newydd 74-77; Ind Chapl *St As* 77-88; V Whitford 81-87; V Ruabon 87-92; TR Cen Telford *Lich* from 92. *The Rectory, Church Road, Dawley, Telford, Shropshire TF4 2AS* Telford (01952) 501655

WILLIAMS, David Norman. b 54. Lanc Univ BSc Leeds Univ BA. Coll of Resurr Mirfield. **d** 84 **p** 85. C Ireland Wood *Ripon* 84-87; C Beeston 87-91; V Cross Roads cum Lees *Bradf* from 91. *The Vicarage, Cross Roads, Keighley, W Yorkshire BD22 9DL* Haworth (01535) 642210

WILLIAMS, David Paul. See HOWELL, David Paul

WILLIAMS, David Roger. b 49. St D Coll Lamp DipTh73. **d** 73 **p** 74. C Llansamlet *S & B* 73-76; C Oystermouth 76-79; V Aberedw w Llandeilo Graban and Llanbadarn etc 79-81; V Brynmawr 81-89; V Newport St Julian *Mon* from 89. *St Julian's Vicarage, 41 St Julian's Avenue, Newport, Gwent NP9 7JT* Newport (01633) 258046

WILLIAMS, Derek. b 27. Man Univ BSc49. St Deiniol's Hawarden 76. **d** 78 **p** 79. NSM Abergele *St As* from 78. *48 Eldon Drive, Abergele, Clwyd LL22 7DA* Abergele (01745) 833479

WILLIAMS, Derek Howard. b 24. Leeds Univ BSc49. Coll of Resurr Mirfield 49. **d** 51 **p** 52. Rhodesia 65-80; Zimbabwe from 80; Dean Mutare 84-86; rtd 95. *Box 530, Mutare, Zimbabwe* Mutare (20) 62682

WILLIAMS, Derek Lawrence. b 45. Lon Univ DipTh68. Tyndale Hall Bris 65. **d** 69 **p** 70. C Cant St Mary Bredin *Cant* 69-71; Gen Sec Inter-Coll Chr Fellowship 71-75; Lic to Offic *St Alb* 78-84; Lic to Offic *Bris* 85-92; Perm to Offic *Pet* from 92. *58 Clarence Avenue, Northampton NN2 6NZ* Northampton (01604) 710404

WILLIAMS, Derwyn Gavin. b 69. Trin Coll Cam BA89 MA93. Ripon Coll Cuddesdon DipMin94. **d** 94 **p** 95. C Harpenden St Nic *St Alb* from 94. *37 St James Road, Harpenden, Herts AL5 4PB* Luton (01582) 761657

WILLIAMS, Diana Mary (Di). b 36. Bris Univ CertEd56 Leeds Univ BSc57. Oak Hill Th Coll 86. **d** 87 **p** 94. NSM S Mymms K Chas *St Alb* 87-93; Par Dn 93-94; C 94-95; V from 95. *The Vicarage, 40 Dugdale Hill Lane, Potters Bar, Herts EN6 2DW* Potters Bar (01707) 654219

WILLIAMS, Ms Diane Patricia. b 53. Dur Univ CertEd74 Liv Univ DipRE83 Lanc Univ MA84. Cranmer Hall Dur 84. **dss** 86 **d** 87 **p** 94. Clubmoor *Liv* 86-87; Par Dn 87-90; Par Dn Everton St Geo 90-94; Dioc Lay Tr Officer from 90; C Everton St Geo from 94. *2 Stanfield Avenue, Liverpool L5 4TA* 0151-264 8835

WILLIAMS, Diane Ruth. b 52. Hull Univ BA80. Linc Th Coll. **d** 94 **p** 95. Par Dn Stokesley *York* 94; C from 94. *25 Riversdene, Stokesley, Middlesbrough, Cleveland TS9 5DD* Middlesbrough (01642) 710911

WILLIAMS, Doiran George. b 26. Barrister-at-Law (Gray's Inn) 52. W of England Minl Tr Course 91. **d** 93 **p** 94. NSM Edvin Loach w Tedstone Delamere etc *Heref* from 93. *Howberry, Whitbourne, Worcester WR6 5RZ* Knightwick (01886) 21189

WILLIAMS, Ven Edward Bryan. b 36. Univ of Wales (Lamp) BA58. St Mich Coll Llan 58. **d** 60 **p** 61. C Rhyl w St Ann *St As* 60-68; Dioc Youth Chapl 66-78; V Dyserth and Trelawnyd and Cwm 68-77; R Denbigh 77-82; Can St As Cathl 81-87; R Denbigh and Nantglyn 82-87; Adn Wrexham from 87; V Bwlchgwyn from 87. *The Vicarage, 8 Whiteoaks, Bwlchgwyn, Wrexham, Clwyd LL11 5UB* Wrexham (01978) 752627

WILLIAMS, Edward Ffoulkes (Peter). b 34. ALA65. Chich Th Coll 71. **d** 73 **p** 74. C Kidderminster St Geo *Worc* 73-78; TV Worc St Barn w Ch Ch 78-82; V Exhall w Wixford *Cov* from 82; V Temple Grafton w Binton from 82. *The Vicarage, Temple Grafton, Alcester, Warks B49 6PA* Bidford-on-Avon (01789) 772314

WILLIAMS, Edward Heaton. b 18. St Aid Birkenhead 56. **d** 58 **p** 59. R Wistaston *Ches* 66-81; V Burton 81-85; rtd 85; Perm to Offic *Ox* from 85; Perm to Offic *Pet* from 85. *4 Bowmens Lea, Aynho, Banbury, Oxon OX17 3AG* Croughton (01869) 810533

WILLIAMS, Prof Edward Sydney. b 23. FRCP FRCR K Coll Lon BSc PhD MB, BS MD AKC. Sarum & Wells Th Coll 84. **d** 87 **p** 88. NSM Bramley and Grafham *Guildf* 87-89; Hon C Shamley Green 89-94; Perm to Offic from 94. *Bisney Cottage, Shamley Green, Guildford, Surrey GU5 0TB* Guildford (01483) 892591

WILLIAMS, Elfed Owain. b 24. Newc Univ DipAdEd74. St Deiniol's Hawarden 79. **d** 81 **p** 82. Hon C Whorlton *Newc* 81-82; Hon C Elham w Denton and Wootton *Cant* 82-86; R Barham w Bishopsbourne and Kingston 86-91; rtd 91. *Chusan, 31 Ryecroft Way, Wooler, Northd NE71 6DY* Wooler (01668) 81253

WILLIAMS, Eric Rees. b 30. Roch Th Coll 60 St Deiniol's Hawarden 71. **d** 72 **p** 73. C Llanelli *St D* 72-75; P-in-c Tregaron 75-76; V 76-82; RD Lamp and Ultra-Aeron 82-87; V Tregaron w Ystrad Meurig and Strata Florida 82-87; V St Dogmael's w Moylgrove and Monington from 87. *The Vicarage, St Dogmaels, Cardigan, Dyfed SA43 3DX* Cardigan (01239) 612030

WILLIAMS, Evelyn Joyce. b 37. Cant Sch of Min 86. **d** 89 **p** 94. NSM Sittingbourne H Trin w Bobbing *Cant* from 89. *32 Rock Road, Sittingbourne, Kent ME10 1JF* Sittingbourne (01795) 470372

WILLIAMS, Frederick Errol. b 41. MBIM80. Sarum & Wells Th Coll 86. **d** 88 **p** 89. C Milton *Win* 88-91; P-in-c Chilbolton cum Wherwell 91-94; R from 94. *The Rectory, Chilbolton, Stockbridge, Hants SO20 6BA* Chilbolton (01264) 860258

WILLIAMS, Frederick Vivian. b 08. St Andr Pampisford 47. **d** 48 **p** 49. V Croydon St Martin *Cant* 60-73; rtd 73. *1 St Augustine's Close, Cooden Drive, Bexhill-on-Sea, E Sussex TN39 3AZ* Bexhill-on-Sea (01424) 221370

WILLIAMS, Fredric Barry. b 41. Man Univ BSc62 CertEd63 Man Poly DMEd87. N Ord Course 79. **d** 82 **p** 83. NSM Darwen St Cuth *Blackb* 82-85; NSM Darwen St Cuth w Tockholes St Steph 85-88; V Rillington w Scampston, Wintringham etc *York* from 88; RD Buckrose from 90. *The Vicarage, 2 High Street, Rillington, Malton, N Yorkshire YO17 8LA* Rillington (01944) 758891

WILLIAMS, Gareth Wynn. b 67. St D Coll Lamp BA88 Hull Univ MA89. Westcott Ho Cam 89. **d** 91 **p** 92. C Mold *St As* 91-93; TV Hawarden 93-95; Ecum Chapl Glam Univ *Llan* from 95. *University of Glamorgan, Treforest, Pontypridd, M Glam* Pontypridd (01443) 480480

WILLIAMS, Gavin John. b 61. Barrister-at-Law 85 Down Coll Cam BA84. Wycliffe Hall Ox BA88. **d** 89 **p** 90. C Muswell Hill St Jas w St Matt *Lon* 89-92; Asst Chapl Shrewsbury Sch from 92. *Flat B, Lindisfarne, 6 Kennedy Road, Shrewsbury SY3 7AD* Shrewsbury (01743) 364393

WILLIAMS, Canon Geoffrey Ainsworth. b 16. Univ Coll Dur BA38 MA41. **d** 39 **p** 40. Can Res and Chan Blackb Cathl *Blackb* 65-90; Warden of Readers 65-89; Warden Whalley Abbey from 77; rtd 90. *22 Buncer Lane, Blackburn BB2 6SE* Blackburn (01254) 256706

WILLIAMS, Geoffrey Thomas. b 35. Ox NSM Course 77. **d** 80 **p** 81. NSM Earley St Bart *Ox* 80-82; NSM Reading St Luke 82-85; C Wembley Park St Aug *Lon* 85-86; C-in-c S Kenton Annunciation CD 86-90; V Streatham Hill St Marg *S'wark* from 90. *St Margaret's Vicarage, 165 Barcombe Avenue, London SW2 3BH* 0181-674 7348

WILLIAMS, George Harold. b 20. Lon Univ BSc49. **d** 67 **p** 68. C Bishopsworth *Bris* 67-70; V Weston-super-Mare Ch Ch *B & W* 70-85; rtd 85; Perm to Offic *B & W* from 86. *15 Elmhurst Road, Hutton, Weston-super-Mare, Avon BS24 9RJ* Weston-super-Mare (01934) 813342

WILLIAMS, George Maxwell Frazer. b 42. TCD BA65 MA69. Cuddesdon Coll 65. **d** 67 **p** 68. C Bolton St Jas w St Chrys *Bradf* 67-70; C Lich St Chad *Lich* 70-73; V Shawbury 73-79; P-in-c Moreton Corbet 73-79; V Willenhall H Trin 79-86; TR 86-88; V Penn from 88. *St Bartholemew's Vicarage, 68 Church Hill, Penn, Wolverhampton WV4 5JD* Wolverhampton (01902) 341399

WILLIAMS, George Melvin (Kim). b 24. Worc Ord Coll 64. **d** 66 **p** 67. C Holdenhurst *Win* 66-70; V Yateley 70-75; V St Leonards and St Ives 75-90; rtd 90. *Amen Cottage, 23 Edifred Road, Bournemouth BH9 3PB* Bournemouth (01202) 521763

WILLIAMS, Canon Giles Peter. b 54. Lon Univ BA77 MA78. Trin Coll Bris 80. **d** 82 **p** 83. C Reading Greyfriars *Ox* 82-85; Rwanda Miss 85-90; Mid-Africa Min (CMS) 90-94; Can Kigali Cathl Rwanda from 90; V Woking St Jo *Guildf* from 95. *The Vicarage, St John's Hill Road, Woking, Surrey GU21 1RQ* Woking (01483) 761253

WILLIAMS, Glyn. b 54. K Coll Lon BD77 AKC77. Ripon Coll Cuddesdon 77. **d** 78 **p** 79. C Coppenhall *Ches* 78-81; C Northn St Alb *Pet* 81-82; TV Birkenhead Priory *Ches* 82-85; Chapl RAF 85-90; Dep Chapl HM Pris Wandsworth 90-91; Chapl HM Pris Elmley from 91. *HM Prison Elmley, Eastchurch, Sheerness, Kent ME12 4DZ* Eastchurch (01795) 880808

WILLIAMS, Glyn Alun. b 17. St D Coll Lamp BA40. **d** 41 **p** 42. V Pencarreg and Llanycrwys *St D* 71-73; rtd 73. *11 Tirwaun, Pwll, Llanelli, Dyfed SA15 4AY* Llanelli (01554) 759850

WILLIAMS, Graham Ivor. b 23. Jes Coll Ox BA48 MA48. Cuddesdon Coll 48. **d** 49 **p** 50. C Swansea St Mary and H Trin *S & B* 49-53; C Edgbaston St Bart *Birm* 53-55; R Nutfield *S'wark* from 55. *The Rectory, Blechingley Road, Nutfield, Redhill RH1 4HN* Nutfield Ridge (01737) 822286

WILLIAMS, Graham Parry. b 46. Bp Burgess Hall Lamp 67 St D Coll Lamp DipTh70. **d** 70 **p** 71. C Ebbw Vale *Mon* 70-73; C Trevethin 73-74; V Nantyglo 74-76; Chapl RN 76-85; R Northlew w Ashbury *Ex* 85-87; R Bratton Clovelly w Germansweek 85-87; TV Pontypool *Mon* 88-90; C Skegness and Winthorpe *Linc* 90-91; V Sutton Bridge 91-94; P-in-c Witham Gp from 94. *The Rectory, 15 Hill View Road, High Street, South Witham, Grantham, Lincs NG33 5QB* Thistleton (01572) 767240

WILLIAMS, Gwenllian. *See* GILES, Mrs Gwenllian

WILLIAMS, Gwilym Elfed. b 33. Univ of Wales (Lamp) BA53. St Mich Coll Llan 53. **d** 56 **p** 57. C Llandudno *Ban* 56-59; C Aberdare St Jo *Llan* 59-63; C Penarth All SS 63-65; R Eglwysilan 65-70; V Mountain Ash 70-81; V Llanblethian w Cowbridge and Llandough etc 81-93; P-in-c St Hilary 87-91; V Lisvane from 93. *The Vicarage, 2 Llwynpia Road, Lisvane, Cardiff CF4 5SY* Cardiff (01222) 753338

WILLIAMS, Canon Gwilym Kenneth. b 12. Univ of Wales BA34. St Mich Coll Llan 34. **d** 35 **p** 36. RD Llanbadarn Fawr *St D* 71-80; Can St D Cathl 75-80; V Borth and Eglwys-fach w Llangynfelyn 79-80; rtd 80. *2 Clos-y-Drindod, Buarth Road, Aberystwyth, Dyfed SY23 1NB* Aberystwyth (01970) 615756

WILLIAMS, Ven Harold Edgar. b 17. Univ of Wales (Lamp) BA39. AKC42. **d** 42 **p** 43. Dir of Ords *S & B* 55-79; V Brynmawr 67-76; Can Brecon Cathl 72-83; Sec Prov Selection Bd for Ords 73-76; V Newton St Pet 76-87; Chan Brecon Cathl 79-83; Adn Gower 83-87; rtd 87. *10 Budehaven Terrace, Mumbles, Swansea SA3 5PY* Swansea (01792) 404728

WILLIAMS, Harry Abbott. b 19. Trin Coll Cam BA41 MA45. Cuddesdon Coll 41. **d** 43 **p** 44. Fell and Lect Trin Coll Cam 51-69; Dean of Chpl and Tutor 58-69; CR from 72; Lic to Offic *Wakef* from 80; rtd 89. *House of the Resurrection, Mirfield, W Yorkshire WF14 0BN* Mirfield (01924) 493272

WILLIAMS, Mrs Heather Marilyn. b 42. Oak Hill Th Coll 82. **dss** 85 **d** 87 **p** 94. Taunton Lyngford *B & W* 85-87; Hon C

87-89; C Worle 89-94; V Weston-super-Mare St Andr Bournville from 94. *St Andrew's Vicarage, Coniston Crescent, Weston-super-Mare, Avon BS23 3RX* Weston-super-Mare (01934) 627818

WILLIAMS, Helena Maria Alija. b 43. **d** 88 **p** 95. NSM Roath St Marg *Llan* 88-91; Westcott Ho Cam 91-92; Asst Chapl Univ Hosp of Wales Cardiff 92-95; Chapl Bris R Hosp for Sick Children from 95. *Bristol Royal Hospital for Sick Children, St Michael's Hill, Bristol BS2 8BJ* Bristol (0117) 921 5411

WILLIAMS, Henry Gordon. b 33. JP83. St Aid Birkenhead 57. **d** 60 **p** 61. C Radcliffe St Mary *Man* 60-63; Australia from 63; OStJ from 78. *PO Box 157, Northampton, W Australia 6530* Northampton (99) 341259

WILLIAMS, Ven Henry Leslie. b 19. Univ of Wales (Lamp) BA41. St Mich Coll Llan 41. **d** 43 **p** 44. V Barnston *Ches* 53-84; RD Wirral N 67-75; Hon Can Ches Cathl 72-75; Adn Ches 75-88; rtd 88. *1 Bartholomew Way, Westminster Park, Chester CH4 7RJ* Chester (01244) 675296

WILLIAMS, Herbert Brian. b 18. BNC Ox BA39 MA48. Linc Th Coll 80. **d** 81 **p** 82. NSM Asterby Gp *Linc* 81-94; rtd 88; Lic to Offic *Linc* from 94. *55 Upgate, Louth, Lincs LN11 9HD* Louth (01507) 608093

WILLIAMS, Canon Howard. b 08. Univ of Wales BA29 MA32 St Jo Coll Cam MLitt45. St Steph Ho Ox 30. **d** 31 **p** 32. Chapl Llanelli Gen Hosp 57-75; V Llanelli *St D* 57-75; Can St D Cathl 60-75; Treas 73-75; rtd 75. *Cwm Eithin, 53 Maes Hendre, Waunfawr, Aberystwyth, Dyfed SY23 3PS* Aberystwyth (01970) 615311

WILLIAMS, Howard Graham (Brother Anthony). b 04. **d** 52 **p** 53. OSB from 48; Perm to Offic *Ox* from 52. *Elmore Abbey, Church Lane, Speen, Newbury, Berks RG13 1SA* Newbury (01635) 33080

WILLIAMS, Howell Mark. b 56. Univ of Wales (Cardiff) BD87. St Mich Coll Llan 84. **d** 87 **p** 88. C Swansea St Thos and Kilvey *S & B* 87-89; TV Abth *St D* 89-93; V Hirwaun *Llan* from 93. *The Vicarage, High Street, Hirwaun, Aberdare, M Glam CF44 9SL* Hirwaun (01685) 811316

WILLIAMS, Canon Hugh. b 27. MRIPHH ACP48. AKC53. **d** 54 **p** 55. V Over Darwen H Trin *Blackb* 65-74; P-in-c Hoddlesden 65-74; P-in-c Over Darwen St Jo 68-74; P-in-c Darwen St Geo 69-74; TR Darwen St Pet w Hoddlesden 74-77; RD Darwen 75-77; R Burnley St Pet 77-85; RD Burnley 78-85; Hon Can Blackb Cathl 78-92; V Bolton le Sands 85-92; rtd 92. Bp's Officer for Rtd Clergy (Blackb Adnry) *Blackb* from 92. *37 Albert Street, Brierfield, Nelson, Lancs BB9 5JF* Nelson (01282) 614891

WILLIAMS, Hugh Martin. b 45. AKC73. St Aug Coll Cant 73. **d** 74 **p** 75. C Heston *Lon* 74-78; Chapl City Univ 78-84; PV Westmr Abbey 82-84; V Newquay *Truro* 84-93; V Christchurch *Win* from 93. *The Priory Vicarage, Quay Road, Christchurch, Dorset BH23 1BU* Christchurch (01202) 483102

WILLIAMS, Hugh Wynford. b 16. Selw Coll Cam BA40 MA44. St D Coll Lamp BA38 St Mich Coll Llan 40. **d** 41 **p** 42. Perm to Offic *Pet* 51-74; Chapl Oundle Sch 54-74; R Tichmarsh *Pet* 74-88; P-in-c Clapton 77-88; rtd 88. *28 Church Street, Tichmarsh, Kettering, Northants NN14 3DB* Thrapston (01832) 734529

WILLIAMS, Ian Geoffrey. b 50. Lon Univ BD71 AKC71 CertEd. St Jo Coll Nottm 72. **d** 74 **p** 75. C Harborne Heath *Birm* 74-76; C Hazlemere *Ox* 77-84; V Littleover *Derby* 84-90; Hd of RE Woodlands Sch Derby from 90. *30 Redshaw Street, Derby DE1 3SG* Derby (01332) 343987 or 551921

WILLIAMS, Ian Kenneth. b 44. MMS83 MBIM87. E Midl Min Tr Course 84. **d** 87 **p** 88. NSM Corby Glen *Linc* from 87. *6 Market Place, Corby Glen, Grantham, Lincs NG33 4NH* Corby Glen (01476) 550595

WILLIAMS, Ian Withers. b 43. Linc Th Coll 68. **d** 69 **p** 70. C Burney Lane *Birm* 69-72; C Cleobury Mortimer w Hopton Wafers *Heref* 72-75; P-in-c Coreley w Doddington 75-79; V Knowbury 75-79; V Lich Ch Ch *Lich* from 79. *Christ Church Vicarage, Lichfield, Staffs WS13 8AL* Lichfield (01543) 264431 Fax 262039

WILLIAMS, Ieuan Merchant. b 13. St D Coll Lamp BA36. **d** 39 **p** 40. R Brightwell Baldwin *Ox* 71-80; R Cuxham w Easington 72-80; P-in-c Britwell Salome 76-80; P-in-c Ewelme 76-80; rtd 80; Perm to Offic *Ox* from 80. *5 The Cloisters, Ewelme, Oxford OX10 6HS* Oxford (01865) 38897

WILLIAMS, Ifan. b 24. St D Coll Lamp 54. **d** 56 **p** 57. Area Sec (Merioneth) USPG 63-89; V Ffestiniog w Blaenau Ffestiniog *Ban* 67-89; RD Ardudwy 80-89; rtd 89. *Cil y Coed, 6 Penrallt, Llanystumdwy, Criccieth, Gwynedd LL52 0SR* Criccieth (01766) 522978

WILLIAMS, Jack. b 26. Univ of Wales (Ban) BSc50. St Mich Coll Llan 50. **d** 52 **p** 53. Hd Master Rishworth Sch Ripponden 68-86; V Halifax St Jo Cragg Vale *Wakef* 86-89; rtd 89. *36 Tros-yr-Afon, Llangoed, Beaumaris, Gwynedd LL58 8AT* Llangoed (01248) 490839

WILLIAMS, James Einon. b 18. St Mary's Univ (NS) BEd63. St D Coll Lamp BA39. **d** 46 **p** 47. Chapl RCN 52-70; V Mydroilyn and Llanarth w Llanina *St D* 73-80; rtd 80. *244 Hartland Avenue, Victoria, British Columbia, Canada, U8X 4M6*

WILLIAMS, James Llanfair Warren. b 48. St Mich Coll Llan DMinlStuds92. **d** 92 **p** 93. C Pemb Dock *St D* 92-93; C Pemb Dock w Cosheston w Nash and Upton 93-95; V Cwmaman from 95. *Cwmaman Vicarage, Vicarage Road, Garnant, Ammanford, Dyfed SA18 1JQ* Amman Valley (01269) 822107

WILLIAMS, James Nicholas Owen (Nick). b 39. MBE. CEng DipTh. S'wark Ord Course. **d** 82 **p** 83. C Petersfield w Sheet *Portsm* 82-86; TV Droitwich *Worc* 86-87; TV Droitwich Spa 87-88; R Church Lench w Rous Lench and Abbots Morton 88-94; V Milton *B & W* from 94. *Milton Vicarage, 475 Locking Road, Weston-super-Mare, Avon BS22 8QW* Weston-super-Mare (01934) 419294

WILLIAMS, Preb John. b 31. AKC56. **d** 57 **p** 58. C Cockerton *Dur* 57-60; C Camberwell St Geo *S'wark* 60-62; C Stockton St Chad *Dur* 62-65; V 65-68; R Longnewton 68-75; Soc Resp Officer 68-83; Hon Can Dur Cathl 80-83; Bp's Officer for Min *Lich* from 83; Preb Lich Cathl from 83. *200E Upper St John Street, Lichfield, Staffs WS14 9EF* Lichfield (01543) 253480

WILLIAMS, Dr John Anthony. b 53. G&C Coll Cam BA75 MA79 St Jo Coll Dur BA83 PhD86. Cranmer Hall Dur 81. **d** 86 **p** 87. C Beverley Minster *York* 86-89; C Cloughton 89-90; P-in-c 90-93; Clergy Tr Officer E Riding 89-93; P-in-c Emley *Wakef* from 93; Dioc Minl Tr Officer from 93. *The Rectory, 14 Grange Drive, Emley, Huddersfield HD8 9SF* Wakefield (01924) 848301

WILLIAMS, John Barrie. b 38. Lon Univ DSocStuds68 Univ of Wales (Cardiff) MSc77 DipEd80. St Mich Coll Llan 89. **d** 87 **p** 88. NSM Newc *Llan* 87-89; C Port Talbot St Theodore 89; Perm to Offic from 89. *Shorncliffe, 11 Priory Oak, Bridgend, M Glam CF31 2HY* Bridgend (01656) 660369

WILLIAMS, John Beattie. b 42. Univ of Wales BA66. Cuddesdon Coll 67. **d** 69 **p** 69. C St Helier *S'wark* 69-70; C Yeovil H Trin *B & W* 70-76; P-in-c Ebbesbourne Wake w Fifield Bavant and Alvediston *Sarum* 76-78; Chapl to the Deaf 76-78; Chapl to the Deaf *B & W* 78-83; TV Fareham H Trin *Portsm* 83-94; R W Wittering and Birdham w Itchenor *Chich* from 94. *The Rectory, Cakeham Road, West Wittering, Chichester, W Sussex PO20 8AD* Birdham (01243) 514057

WILLIAMS, Ven John Charles. b 12. Univ Coll Ox 34 St D Coll Lamp BA34. Qu Coll Birm 36. **d** 37 **p** 38. R Halesowen *Worc* 59-70; Hon Can Worc Cathl 65-75; Adn Dudley 68-75; V Dodderhill 70-75; Add Worc and Can Res Worc Cathl 75-80; Dir of Ords 75-79; rtd 80; Lic to Offic *Worc* from 80; Perm to Offic *Cov* from 80; Asst Chapl HM Pris Long Lartin 82-87. *The Old Vicarage, Church Lane, Norton, Evesham, Worcs WR11 4TL* Evesham (01386) 870213

WILLIAMS, John David Anthony. b 55. St Steph Ho Ox 85. **d** 87 **p** 88. C Paignton St Jo *Ex* 87-90; C Heavitree w Ex St Paul 90-91; TV from 91. *St Lawrence Vicarage, Lower Hill Barton Road, Exeter EX1 3EH* Exeter (01392) 466302

WILLIAMS, John Edward. b 31. Univ of Wales (Abth) DipTh55. St Deiniol's Hawarden 76. **d** 76 **p** 77. C Llansamlet *S & B* 76-78; V Aberffraw and Llangwyfan w Llangadwaladr *Ban* 78-83; rtd 83. *17 Pontwillim Estate, Brecon, Powys LD3 9BT*

WILLIAMS, John Elwyn Askew. b 09. St Jo Coll Cam BA32 MA36. Ridley Hall Cam 32. **d** 34 **p** 35. V Whitchurch w Creslow *Ox* 61-81; R Hardwick St Mary 76-81; R Quainton 76-81; R Schorne 76-81; rtd 81; Perm to Offic *Ox* from 81. *15 Manor Park, Maids Moreton, Buckingham MK18 1OY* Buckingham (01280) 814101

WILLIAMS, John Francis Meyler. b 34. St Jo Coll Cam BA56 MA60. Sarum & Wells Th Coll 79. **d** 81 **p** 82. C Hadleigh w Layham and Shelley *St E* 81-84; P-in-c Parham w Hacheston 84-87; P-in-c Campsey Ashe and Marlesford 84-87; R Campsea Ashe w Marlesford, Parham and Hacheston 87-95; P-in-c Kedington from 95. *The Rectory, Kedington, Haverhill, Suffolk CB9 7NN* Haverhill (01440) 712052

WILLIAMS, Canon John Francis Oliver. b 15. TCD BA40 MA43. **d** 40 **p** 41. I Dalkey St Patr *D & G* 73-82; Can Ch Ch Cathl Dub 81-82; rtd 82. *Wayside, Church Road, Greystones, Co Wicklow, Irish Republic* Dublin (1) 287-4953

WILLIAMS, Dr John Frederick Arthur. b 26. Lon Univ BSc50 Southn Univ PhD53. Ridley Hall Cam 63. **d** 65 **p** 66. C Cam H Sepulchre w All SS *Ely* 65-66; P-in-c Cam St Mark 66-67; C Portswood Ch Ch *Win* 67-90; AV 90-93; C Win Ch Ch from 93. *Carlyon, Kingsgate Road, Winchester, Hants SO23 9QQ* Winchester (01962) 865851

WILLIAMS, John Gilbert. b 36. St Aid Birkenhead 64. **d** 67 **p** 68. C Bollington St Jo *Ches* 67-69; C Oxton 69-72; P-in-c Acton Beauchamp and Evesbatch 72-76; P-in-c Castle Frome *Heref* 72-76; P-in-c Bishop's Frome 72-76; R Kingsland 76-83; P-in-c Eardisland 77-83; P-in-c Aymestry and Leinthall Earls 82-83;

R Cradley w Mathon and Storridge 83-94; R Norton St Philip w Hemington, Hardington etc *B & W* from 94. *The Rectory, Vicarage Lane, Norton St Philip, Bath BA3 6LY* Frome (01373) 834447

WILLIAMS, John Glyn. b 18. Lon Univ BA47. St Mich Coll Llan 46. **d** 49 **p** 50. Clerical Org Sec (S Wales) CECS 59-83; P-in-c Llanharry *Llan* from 83; rtd 88; Perm to Offic *St D* from 88. *St Caron's, 40 Parkfields Road, Bridgend, M Glam CF31 4BJ* Bridgend (01656) 654110

WILLIAMS, John Gordon. b 06. Lon Univ BA27. Ridley Hall Cam 30. **d** 32 **p** 33. Chapl and Educn Officer SPCK 57-72; rtd 72. *2 Sunnybank Place, Borrage Lane, Ripon, N Yorkshire HG4 2PZ* Ripon (01765) 603352

WILLIAMS, Canon John Heard. b 35. Bris Univ BA58. Clifton Th Coll 59. **d** 59 **p** 60. C Tunbridge Wells Ch Ch *Roch* 59-65; V Forest Gate St Sav *Chelmsf* 65-75; P-in-c W Ham St Matt 72-75; TR Forest Gate St Sav w W Ham St Matt from 75; Hon Can Chelmsf Cathl from 82. *St Saviour's Rectory, Sidney Road, London E7 0EF* 0181-534 6109

WILLIAMS, John Herbert. b 19. LVO89. St D Coll Lamp BA41 Sarum & Wells Th Coll 41. **d** 43 **p** 44. Chapl HM Pris Wormwood Scrubs 64-71; SE Regional Chapl 71-74; Chapl HM Remand Cen Latchmere Ho 71-74; Dep Chapl Gen of Pris 74-83; P in O 79-83; Chapl RVO 83-89; Chapl to RVO and Qu Chpl of the Savoy 83-89; Chapl to The Queen 87-89; rtd 89. *75 Monks Drive, London W3 0ED* 0181-992 5206

WILLIAMS, John James. b 08. Qu Coll Cam BA31 MA35. Ely Th Coll 31. **d** 32 **p** 33. R Wokingham St Paul *Ox* 62-73; P-in-c N w S Moreton 73-77; rtd 77; Perm to Offic *Ox* from 77. *Iona, Coopers Lane, Wantage, Oxon OX12 8HQ* Wantage (01235) 767904

WILLIAMS, Canon John James. b 20. TD61. Linc Coll Ox BA42 MA46. St Mich Coll Llan 42. **d** 44 **p** 45. V Powyke *Worc* 64-85; Hon Can Worc Cathl 77-85; rtd 85; Perm to Offic *Worc* from 85. *9 St Nicholas's Road, Peopleton, Pershore, Worcs WR10 2EN* Worcester (01905) 840032

WILLIAMS, John Mark Gruffydd. MA MSc DPhil. **d** 89 **p** 90. NSM Girton *Ely* 89-91; Perm to Offic *Ban* from 91. *Department of Psychology, University of Wales (Bangor), Gwynedd LL57 2DG* Bangor (01248) 351151

WILLIAMS, John Michael. b 44. MBASW Univ of Wales (Cardiff) CQSW74. St Deiniol's Hawarden 80. **d** 83 **p** 84. NSM Llanrhos *St As* 83-94; P-in-c Brynymaen w Trofarth from 94. *The Vicarage, Brynymaen, Colwyn Bay, Clwyd LL28 5EW* Colwyn Bay (01492) 532567

WILLIAMS, John Peter Philip. b 49. Univ of Wales (Ban) DipTh70 Open Univ BA84. Chich Th Coll 71. **d** 72 **p** 73. C Abergele *St As* 72-77; R Henllan and Llannefydd 77-82; R Henllan and Llannefydd and Bylchau from 82. *The Rectory, Henllan, Denbigh, Clwyd LL16 5BB* Denbigh (01745) 812628

WILLIAMS, John Richard. b 48. Rhodes Univ BA68 K Coll Lon BD72 AKC72. **d** 73 **p** 74. S Africa 73-76; C Addington *Cant* 77-80; C Minster in Sheppey 80-86; R Temple Ewell w Lydden 86-90; V Hound *Win* 90-94; V Highcliffe w Hinton Admiral from 94. *The Vicarage, 33 Nea Road, Christchurch, Dorset BH23 4NB* Highcliffe (01425) 272761

WILLIAMS, John Roger. b 31. Bris Univ BA55 Lon Univ BD57. Tyndale Hall Bris 57. **d** 57 **p** 58. V Selly Hill St Steph *Birm* 64-74; P-in-c Chilwell *S'well* 74-75; V 75-90; Dioc Tourism Chapl 90-95; P-in-c Perlethorpe 90-95; P-in-c Norton Cuckney 90-95; rtd 95. *Derwent Lights, 4 Wyntor Avenue, Winster, Matlock, Derbyshire DE4 2DU*

WILLIAMS, Canon John Roger. b 37. Lich Th Coll 60. **d** 63 **p** 64. C Wem *Lich* 63-66; C Wolv St Pet 66-69; R Pudleston w Hatf *Heref* 69-74; P-in-c Stoke Prior and Ford w Humber 69-74; P-in-c Docklow 69-74; V Fenton *Lich* 74-81; P-in-c Honington w Idlicote *Cov* 81; P-in-c Shipston-on-Stour w Tidmington 81; R Shipston-on-Stour w Honington and Idlicote 81-92; RD Shipston 83-90; Hon Can Cov Cathl from 90; R Lighthorne from 92; V Chesterton from 92; V Newbold Pacey w Moreton Morrell from 92. *The Rectory, Church Lane, Lighthorne, Warwick CV35 0AR* Warwick (01926) 651279

WILLIAMS, John Strettle. b 44. DipEd73 BA84. N Ord Course 77. **d** 80 **p** 81. NSM Liv St Paul Stoneycroft *Liv* 80-83; Chapl Cen Liv Coll of FE from 80; Hon C Liv Our Lady and St Nic w St Anne from 83; Chapl RNR 84-90; Chapl City Coll of FE Liv from 85. *28 Brook Street, Whiston, Prescot, Merseyside L35 5AP* 0151-426 9598

WILLIAMS, John Trefor. b 23. Worc Ord Coll 65. **d** 67 **p** 68. C Paignton St Jo *Ex* 67-72; V Winkleigh 72-80; P-in-c Ashreigney 73-79; R 79-80; P-in-c Brushford 75-79; V 79-80; R Broadwoodkelly 79-80; P-in-c Berrynarbor 80-81; P-in-c Combe Martin 80-81; R Combe Martin and Berrynarbor 81-92; rtd 92. *97 Littleham Road, Exmouth, Devon EX8 2RA* Exmouth (01395) 264460

WILLIAMS, Jonathan Simon. b 60. Univ of Wales (Cardiff) BSc81. Coll of Resurr Mirfield 83. **d** 86 **p** 87. C Gelligaer *Llan*

86-89; C Cwmbran *Mon* 89-90; TV from 90. *The Vicarage, Llantarnam, Cwmbran, Gwent NP44 3BW* Cwmbran (01633) 483532

WILLIAMS, Miss Joy Margaret. b 30. Lon Univ BD69. Linc Th Coll 82. **dss** 83 **d** 87 **p** 94. Pershore w Pinvin, Wick and Birlingham *Worc* 83-87; Par Dn 87-88; Par Dn Dudley St Jo 88-90; rtd 90. *Pixie Cottage, 40 Ridge Street, Pershore, Worcs WR10 1AT* Pershore (01386) 556867

WILLIAMS, Julian Thomas. b 65. Clare Coll Cam BA87. Wycliffe Hall Ox BA90. **d** 91 **p** 92. Min Can St D Cathl *St D* 91-94; C St D Cathl 91-94; V Cilycwm and Ystrad-ffin w Rhandir-mwyn etc from 94. *The Vicarage, Cil-y-Cwm, Llandovery, Dyfed SA20 0SP* Llandovery (01550) 21109

WILLIAMS, Keith. b 37. St Jo Coll Nottm 83. **d** 85 **p** 86. C Holbeck *Ripon* 85-88; R Swillington 88-95; V Batley All SS *Wakef* from 95; P-in-c Purlwell from 95. *The Vicarage, Churchfield Street, Batley, W Yorkshire WF17 5DL* Batley (01924) 473049

WILLIAMS, Keith Douglas. b 41. E Midl Min Tr Course 86. **d** 89 **p** 90. Hon C Netherfield w Colwick *S'well* from 89; Chapl Nottm Healthcare NHS Trust from 93. *15 Mile End Road, Nottingham NG4 2DW* Nottingham (0115) 961 4850

WILLIAMS, Keith Graham. b 38. ARICS62 Reading Univ MSc70 St Jo Coll Dur DipTh77. **d** 77 **p** 78. C Almondbury *Wakef* 77-81; C Chapelthorpe 81-82; V Ryhill 82-88; V E Ardsley from 88. *The Vicarage, Church Lane, East Ardsley, Wakefield, W Yorkshire WF3 2LJ* Wakefield (01924) 822184

WILLIAMS, Kelvin George John. b 36. ALCD62. **d** 62 **p** 63. C Bath Abbey w St Jas *B & W* 62-65; CF (TA) 64-65 and 70-79; Chapl R Nat Hosp for Rheumatic Diseases Bath 64-65; CF 65-68; C Clevedon St Andr *B & W* 68-70; V Ston Easton w Farrington Gurney 70-74; P-in-c Bradf 74-75; R Bradf w Oake, Hillfarrance and Heathfield 75-76; NSM Puriton and Pawlett 89-91; V from 92; NSM Bridgwater Deanery 91-92. *The Vicarage, 1 The Rye, Puriton, Bridgwater, Somerset TA7 8BZ* Puriton (01278) 683500

WILLIAMS, Ven Leslie Arthur. b 09. Down Coll Cam BA40 MA45. Clifton Th Coll 34. **d** 34 **p** 35. Hon Can Bris Cathl *Bris* 58-79; Adn Bris 67-79; rtd 79. *St Monica's Rest Home, Cote Lane, Bristol BS9 3UN* Bristol (0117) 949 4316

WILLIAMS, Lloyd. b 43. Oak Hill Th Coll 71. **d** 74 **p** 75. C Laisterdyke *Bradf* 74-77; C Hoole *Ches* 77-80; V Rawthorpe *Wakef* 80-84; HM Pris Leeds 84-85; Chapl HM Pris Cardiff 85-88; R Aldington w Bonnington and Bilsington *Cant* from 88; Chapl HM Pris Aldington from 88; RD N Lympne *Cant* from 94. *The Rectory, Aldington, Ashford, Kent TN25 7ES* Ashford (01233) 720898 Fax 720886

WILLIAMS, Mrs Louise Margaret. b 66. Lanc Univ BA87. St Jo Coll Nottm DPS91. **d** 91 **p** 94. Par Dn W Ham *Chelmsf* 91-94; C Harold Hill St Geo 94-95. *45 Mafeking Road, London E16 4NS* 0171-511 7848

WILLIAMS, Malcolm Kendra. b 34. Oak Hill NSM Course. **d** 85 **p** 86. NSM Margate H Trin *Cant* 85-87; P-in-c Austrey *Birm* 87-90; V Wonersh *Guildf* from 90. *The Vicarage, Wonersh, Guildford, Surrey GU5 0PF* Guildford (01483) 893131

WILLIAMS, Mark Naylor. b 28. CCC Cam BA52 MA56 CertEd. Ripon Hall Ox 58. **d** 59 **p** 60. C Dorchester *Ox* 59-65; R Gt and Lt Braxted *Chelmsf* 65-70; R E Kilbride *Glas* 70-74; R Norton *Sheff* 74-89; R Lt w Gt Ellingham w Rockland *Nor* from 89. *The Rectory, Great Ellingham, Attleborough, Norfolk NR17 1LD* Attleborough (01953) 453200

WILLIAMS, Ven Martin Inffeld. b 37. SS Coll Cam BA62. Chich Th Coll 62. **d** 64 **p** 65. C Greenford H Cross *Lon* 64-70; Tutor Chich Th Coll 70-75; Vice-Prin 75-77; V Roath St German *Llan* 77-92; Adn Margam from 92; V Penydarren from 92. *The Vicarage, Church Street, Penydarren, Merthyr Tydfil, M Glam CF47 9HS* Merthyr Tydfil (01685) 385559

WILLIAMS, Maxwell Holman Bentley. b 24. Reading Univ BA50. Cuddesdon Coll 56. **d** 58 **p** 59. R Bemerton *Sarum* 67-75; rtd 89. *1 Three Yards Close, Portland, Dorset DT5 1JN* Weymouth (01305) 821055

WILLIAMS, Mervyn Rees. b 28. Univ of Wales (Swansea) BA49 Lon Univ PGCE54. St Deiniol's Hawarden 68. **d** 72 **p** 73. NSM Llangollen w Trevor and Llantysilio *St As* 72-94; rtd 94. *12 Wern Road, Llangollen, Clwyd LL20 8DU* Llangollen (01978) 860369

WILLIAMS, Meurig Llwyd. b 61. Univ of Wales (Abth) BA83 PGCE84 Univ of Wales (Cardiff) BD90. Westcott Ho Cam 90. **d** 92 **p** 93. C Holyhead w Rhoscolyn w Llanfair-yn-Neubwll *Ban* 92-95; P-in-c Denio w Aber-erch from 95. *The Rectory, Yr Ala, Pwllheli, Gwynedd LL53 5BL* Pwllheli (01758) 612305

WILLIAMS, Michael Dermot Andrew. b 57. Ex Univ BA86. Ripon Coll Cuddesdon 90. **d** 92 **p** 93. C Leominster *Heref* 92; NSM Christow, Ashton, Trusham and Bridford *Ex* from 92. *25 Smithay Meadow, Exeter EX6 7LU* Cristow (01647) 52766

WILLIAMS, Michael John. b 31. St Edm Hall Ox BA53 MA57. Wells Th Coll 53. **d** 55 **p** 56. C Thatcham *Ox* 66-70; Perm to

Offic *Ex* 70-81; C Rainhill *Liv* 81-86; Chapl Whiston Hosp 83-86; rtd 86; Perm to Offic *Ex* from 86. *1 Bramble Lane, Crediton, Devon EX17 1DA* Crediton (01363) 774005

WILLIAMS, Michael John. b 48. Ox NSM Course. **d** 84 **p** 85. NSM Prestwood *Ox* 84-87; NSM Terriers from 87. *Chiltern Cottage, 87 Amersham Road, High Wycombe, Bucks HP13 5AA* High Wycombe (01494) 529257

WILLIAMS, Canon Michael Joseph. b 42. Cranmer Hall Dur BA68. **d** 70 **p** 71. C Toxteth Park St Philemon *Liv* 70-75; TV Toxteth St Philemon w St Gabr 75-78; Dir Past Studies St Jo Coll Dur 78-89; Prin N Ord Course from 89; Hon Can Liv Cathl *Liv* from 92. *75 Framingham Road, Brooklands, Sale, Cheshire M33 3RH* 0161-962 7513 or 225 6668 Fax 248 9201

WILLIAMS, Michael Robert John. b 41. Cranmer Hall Dur 67. **d** 70 **p** 71. C Middleton *Man* 70-73; C-in-c Blackley White Moss St Mark CD 73-79; R Blackley White Moss St Mark 79-86; R Gorton Em from 86. *Emmanuel Rectory, 35 Blackwin Street, Manchester M12 5LS* 0161-223 3510

WILLIAMS, Nigel Howard. b 63. Llys Fasi Agric Coll NCA81. St Mich Coll Llan DipTh95. **d** 95. C Denbigh and Nantglyn *St As* from 95. *34 Trewen, Denbigh, Clwyd LL16 3HF* Denbigh (01745) 812262

WILLIAMS, Norman Ernest. b 23. IEng FIEEE AMIEE Cardiff Coll of Tech HNC. Llan Dioc Tr Scheme 78. **d** 82 **p** 83. NSM Llanblethian w Cowbridge and Llandough etc *Llan* 82-93. *The Poplars, Cowbridge, S Glam CF7 7BD* Cowbridge (01446) 772107

WILLIAMS, Norman Henry. b 17. Bris Univ BA43. Qu Coll Birm 77. **d** 77 **p** 78. NSM Cov Cathl *Cov* from 77. *63 Daventry Road, Coventry CV3 5DH* Coventry (01203) 502448

WILLIAMS, Norman Leigh. b 26. Open Univ BA86 Trin Coll Carmarthen 83. **d** 85 **p** 86. NSM Lougher *S & B* from 85; NSM Adnry Gower from 87. *Gorwydd Villa, 13 The Woodlands, Gowerton, Swansea SA4 3DP* Gowerton (01792) 874853

WILLIAMS, Ogwen Lloyd. b 20. Univ of Wales (Ban) BA42. St Mich Coll Llan 42. **d** 44 **p** 45. V Bistre *St As* 65-80; V Llansantffraid and Llanarmon and Pontfadog 80-85; rtd 85; Perm to Offic *St D* from 85. *Gwendraeth, 3 Heol y Gof, Newcastle Emlyn, Dyfed SA38 9HW* Newcastle Emlyn (01239) 710295

WILLIAMS, Owen David. b 38. S'wark Ord Course 72. **d** 75 **p** 76. NSM Tatsfield *S'wark* 75-80; C Maidstone All SS w St Phil and H Trin *Cant* 80-81; C Maidstone All SS w St Phil w Tovil 81-82; V St Nicholas at Wade w Sarre and Chislet w Hoath 82-92; TV Bruton and Distr *B & W* from 92. *The Parsonage, Gold Hill, Batcombe, Shepton Mallet, Somerset BA4 6HF* Shepton Mallet (01749) 850671

WILLIAMS, Paul Andrew. b 62. Oak Hill Th Coll BA91. **d** 91 **p** 92. C Ware Ch Ch *St Alb* 91-94; C Harold Wood *Chelmsf* from 94. *48 Harold Court Road, Harold Wood, Romford RM3 0YX*

WILLIAMS, Paul Gavin. b 68. Grey Coll Dur BA89. Wycliffe Hall Ox MPhil93. **d** 92. C Muswell Hill St Jas w St Matt *Lon* from 92. *67 St James Lane, London N10 3QY* 0181-883 7417

WILLIAMS, Paul Rhys. b 58. St Andr Univ MTh82. Westcott Ho Cam 83. **d** 86 **p** 87. Asst Chapl Selw Coll Cam 86-87; C Chatham St Steph *Roch* 87-90; V Gillingham St Aug from 90. *St Augustine's Vicarage, Rock Avenue, Gillingham, Kent ME7 5PW* Medway (01634) 850288

WILLIAMS, Peris Llewelyn. b 39. Univ of Wales (Lamp) BA59. Qu Coll Birm 59. **d** 62 **p** 63. C Upton (or Overchurch) *Ches* 62-65; C Davenham 65-68; C Grange St Andr 68-73; TV E Runcorn w Halton 73-74; V Backford 74-80; Youth Chapl 74-80; V Witton 80-86; V Hoylake 86-93; R Ches H Trin from 93. *Holy Trinity Rectory, Norris Road, Chester CH1 5DZ* Chester (01244) 372721

WILLIAMS, Peter David. b 32. K Coll Lon BSc56 AKC56 PhD62 St Jo Coll Cam PGCE69 Lon Univ BD70. Clifton Th Coll 62. **d** 64 **p** 65. C Southport St Phil *Liv* 64-70; Chapl St Ninian's Sch Dumfriesshire 70-74; Chapl Crawfordton Sch Dumfriesshire 74-75; CMS 75-93; Kenya 76-88; Tanzania 88-92; rtd 93; NSM Kirriemuir *St And* from 93. *3/4 Lilybank, Brechin Road, Kirriemuir, Angus DD8 4BW* Kirriemuir (01575) 74025

WILLIAMS, Peter Hurrell. b 34. Keble Coll Ox BA58 MA61. Tyndale Hall Bris 62. **d** 64 **p** 65. C Sparkbrook Ch Ch *Birm* 64-67; C Rushden St Pet 67-70; P-in-c Clapham Park All SS *S'wark* 70-78; R Stanford-le-Hope w Mucking *Chelmsf* 78-92; P-in-c Gt Oakley w Wix from 92. *The Rectory, Wix Road, Great Oakley, Harwich, Essex CO12 5BJ* Ramsey (01255) 880230

WILLIAMS, Peter John. b 55. Southn Univ BTh80 Univ of Wales (Swansea) DSocStuds90. Chich Th Coll 76. **d** 80 **p** 81. C Chepstow *Mon* 80-84; C Morriston *S & B* 84-85; V Glantawe 85-88; R Reynoldston w Penrice and Llangennith from 88; Dioc Soc Resp Officer from 88. *The Vicarage, Llangennith, Swansea SA3 1HU* Swansea (01792) 386391

WILLIAMS, Peter Rodney. b 22. Chich Th Coll 60. **d** 62 **p** 63. P-in-c Wivelsfield *Chich* 65-72; V Eastbourne St Jo 72-87; rtd 87. *Sussex Cottage, 14 Michel Dene Road, East Dean, Eastbourne, E Sussex BN20 0JN* Eastbourne (01323) 422417

WILLIAMS, Philip Allan. b 48. Bris Univ BSc69 CertEd74. Trin Coll Bris 86. **d** 88 **p** 89. C Heref St Pet w St Owen and St Jas *Heref* 88-93; R Peterchurch w Vowchurch, Turnastone and Dorstone from 93. *The Rectory, 29 Lewis Way, Peterchurch, Hereford HR2 0SE* Golden Valley (01981) 550084

WILLIAMS, Philip Andrew. b 64. Sheff Univ BA86. St Jo Coll Dur 88. **d** 90 **p** 91. C Hillsborough and Wadsley Bridge *Sheff* 90-94; C Lenton Abbey *S'well* from 94; C Wollaton Park from 94. *St Barnabas Vicarage, Derby Road, Beeston, Nottingham NG9 2SN* Nottingham (0115) 925 4995

WILLIAMS, Philip James. b 52. St Chad's Coll Dur BA73. Coll of Resurr Mirfield 74. **d** 76 **p** 77. C Stoke upon Trent *Lich* 76-80; TV 80; Chapl N Staffs Poly 80-84; TV Stoke-upon-Trent 80-84; R Shrewsbury St Giles w Sutton and Atcham from 84. *St Giles's Rectory, 127 Abbey Foregate, Shrewsbury SY2 6LY* Shrewsbury (01743) 356426

WILLIAMS, Ray. b 23. Birm City Tech Coll DipMechEng41 Lon Univ DipEd46. St Aid Birkenhead 56. **d** 58 **p** 59. C Sparkhill St Jo *Birm* 58-60; Area Sec (Dios St Alb and Chelmsf) CMS 60-65; V Shenstone *Lich* 65-73; New Zealand from 73. *178 St Vincent Street, Nelson, New Zealand* Christchurch (3) 546-9078

WILLIAMS, Raymond Howel (Ray). b 27. St Jo Coll Cam BA49 MA51 Ball Coll Ox BLitt63. St Jo Coll Nottm 72 NW Ord Course 73. **d** 73 **p** 74. C Derby St Pet *Derby* 73-76; C Enfield Ch Ch Trent Park *Lon* 75-81; V S Mymms K Chas *St Alb* 81-94; NSM 94-95; rtd 94. *The Vicarage, 40 Dugdale Hill Lane, Potters Bar, Herts EN6 2DW* Potters Bar (01707) 654219

WILLIAMS, Richard Dennis. b 57. LTCL79. Coll of Resurr Mirfield 79. **d** 82 **p** 83. C Roath St Marg *Llan* 82-85; C Penarth w Lavernock 85-88; V Abertillery *Mon* 88-95; V Tredunnoc and Llantrisant w Llanhennock etc from 95. *The Rectory, Tredunnock, Usk, Gwent NP3 1LY* Tredunnock (0163349) 231

WILLIAMS, Richard Elwyn. b 57. Hull Univ BA79. Coll of Resurr Mirfield 79. **d** 81 **p** 82. C Altrincham St Geo *Ches* 81-84; C Stockport St Thos 84-85; C Stockport St Thos w St Pet 86; R Withington St Crispin *Man* 86-95; V Alveston *Cov* from 95. *The Vicarage, Alveston, Stratford-upon-Avon, Warks CV37 7QB* Stratford-upon-Avon (01789) 292777

WILLIAMS, Canon Richard Glyndwr. b 37. St D Coll Lamp BA39 BD50. **d** 41 **p** 42. Warden Ch Hostel Ban 62-70; Chapl Univ of Wales (Ban) *Ban* 62-70; Dir of Ords 62-70 and 84-86; Prec Ban Cathl 68-88; Can from 68; R Llanbeblig w Caernarfon 70-71; R Llanbeblig w Caernarfon and Betws Garmon etc 71-81; V Llandysilio and Llandegfan 81-88; RD Tindaethwy 82-88; rtd 88. *Borth, 9 Cae Cil Melyn, Penrhos, Bangor, Gwynedd LL57 2HD* Bangor (01248) 362883

WILLIAMS, Canon Richard Henry Lowe. b 31. Liv Univ BA52. K Coll (NS) BD64 Ridley Hall Cam 54. **d** 56 **p** 57. C Drypool St Andr and St Pet *York* 56-59; Canada 59-64; V Kirkdale St Athanasius *Liv* 64-68; R Much Woolton 68-79; R Croft w Southworth 79-89; Dioc Communications Officer from 79; Hon Can Liv Cathl from 88; R Wavertree St Mary from 89. *St Mary's Rectory, 1 South Drive, Wavertree, Liverpool L15 8JJ* 0151-734 3103

WILLIAMS, Richard Huw (Rick). b 63. Bradf and Ilkley Coll BA85. St Jo Coll Nottm LTh88 DPS89. **d** 89 **p** 90. C Forest Gate St Edm *Chelmsf* 89-90; C Plaistow 90-92; C Canning Town St Matthias from 92. *45 Mafeking Road, London E16 4NS* 0171-511 7848

WILLIAMS, Richard Pierce. b 09. Univ of Wales BSc31. St Mich Coll Llan 32. **d** 35 **p** 36. V Bettws-yn-Rhos *St As* 62-73; rtd 73. *c/o 64 Luton Road, Harpenden, Herts AL5 2UR*

WILLIAMS, Canon Robert. b 20. OBE90. Univ of Wales (Ban) BA43. St Mich Coll Llan 43. **d** 45 **p** 46. R Llangwnnadl w Penllech and Bryncroes *Ban* 55-90; RD Llyn 76-90; Hon Can Ban Cathl 84-90; R Aberdaron and Bodferin w Rhiw w Llanfaelrhys 89-90; rtd 90. *Hendre Bach, Aberdaron, Pwllheli, Gwynedd LL53 8BL* Aberdaron (0175886) 624

WILLIAMS, Robert David. b 05. St D Coll Lamp BA32. **d** 33 **p** 34. V Llandysilio (or Menai Bridge) *Ban* 62-75; rtd 75. *31 Parc Henblas, Llanfairfechan, Gwynedd LL33 0RW* Llanfairfechan (01248) 680102

WILLIAMS, Canon Robert Edward. b 17. St Mich Coll Llan 45. **d** 47 **p** 48. V Llanwnda w Llanfaglan *Ban* 55-87; Hon Can Ban Cathl 86-87; rtd 87. *Bodfryn, 49 Llwyn Beuno, Bontnewydd, Caernarfon, Gwynedd LL49 2UH* Caernarfon (01286) 673877

WILLIAMS, Robert Edward. b 42. Ex Univ BA63. Lich Th Coll. **d** 65 **p** 66. C Wednesbury St Paul Wood Green *Lich* 65-67; C Whitchurch 67-69; P-in-c Whixall 69-72; P-in-c Edstaston 69-72; CF 72-91; R Cheriton w Tichborne and Beauworth *Win* from 91. *The Rectory, Cheriton, Alresford, Hants SO24 0QH* Bramdean (01962) 771226

WILLIAMS, Robert Edward. b 50. Univ of Wales (Ban) DipTh71. St Mich Coll Llan BD74 CertEd79. **d** 74 **p** 75. C Flint *St As* 74-77; Asst Chapl Sandbach Sch Cheshire 79-80; Chapl and Hd RE 80-88; Perm to Offic *Ches* 86-88; Perm to Offic *St As* 87-88; CF from 88. *c/o MOD (Army), Bagshot Park, Bagshot, Surrey GU19 5PL* Bagshot (01276) 471717 Fax 412834

WILLIAMS, Robert Ellis Greenleaf. b 12. St D Coll Lamp BA34 Lich Th Coll 34. **d** 36 **p** 37. V Rochdale St Aid *Man* 66-75; TV Weston-super-Mare Cen Par *B & W* 75-78; P-in-c Castleton All So *Man* 78-80; rtd 80; Perm to Offic *Man* from 81. *18 Barrowdale Drive, Rochdale, Lancs OL11 3JZ* Rochdale (01706) 356582

WILLIAMS, Robert George Dibdin. b 20. St Mich Coll Llan 56. **d** 58 **p** 59. V Cilcain and Nannerch *St As* 68-75; V Gwersyllt 75-85; rtd 85. *30 Ffordd y Gaer, Bradley, Wrexham, Clwyd LL11 4BW* Wrexham (01978) 754007

WILLIAMS, Robert Gwynne. b 15. St D Coll Lamp BA38. **d** 41 **p** 42. R Goodrich w Welsh Bicknor and Marstow *Heref* 51-81; rtd 81. *The Arch Bungalow, Goodrich, Ross-on-Wye, Herefordshire HR9 6HY* Symonds Yat (01600) 890285

WILLIAMS, Robert Jeffrey Hopkin. b 62. ALAM Univ of Wales (Abth) BA84. Chich Th Coll BTh90. **d** 90 **p** 91. C Eastbourne St Mary *Chich* 90-94; R Upper St Leonards St Jo from 94. *53 Brittany Road, St Leonards-on-Sea, E Sussex TN38 0RD* Hastings (01424) 423367

WILLIAMS, Robert John. b 51. Cartrefle Coll of Educn CertEd73 Univ of Wales (Ban) BEd. St Mich Coll Llan BD76. **d** 76 **p** 77. C Swansea St Mary and H Trin *S & B* 76-78; Chapl Univ of Wales (Swansea) 78-84; Children's Adv 81-88; Asst Dir of Educn 81-88; Bp's Chapl for Th Educn 83-88; R Reynoldston w Penrice and Llangennith 84-88; R Denbigh and Nantglyn *St As* 88-94; V Sketty *S & B* from 94; Dir of Ords from 94. *The Vicarage, De la Beche Road, Sketty, Swansea SA2 9AR* Swansea (01792) 202767

WILLIAMS, Robert Wilfred Callard. b 16. St D Coll Lamp BA37 Chich Th Coll 37. **d** 39 **p** 40. V Manorbier *St D* 63-83; rtd 83. *17 The Green, Lydstep, Tenby, Dyfed SA70 8EY* Manorbier (01834) 871247

WILLIAMS, Roger Anthony. b 54. Univ of Wales (Lamp) BA76. Bp Burgess Hall Lamp 72 Qu Coll Birm 76. **d** 78 **p** 79. C Llanelli *St D* 78-82; V Monkton 82-86; Chapl to the Deaf *B & W* 86-90; Chapl to the Deaf *Ox* from 90. *Denchworth House, Denchworth, Wantage, Oxon OX12 0DX* Didcot (01235) 868248

WILLIAMS, Roger Arthur. b 15. St Pet Hall Ox BA37 MA45. Wycliffe Hall Ox 37. **d** 38 **p** 39. R Hartley *Roch* 58-76; Chapl Bromley Coll Kent 76-80; rtd 80; Perm to Offic *Ex* from 85. *3 Gracey Court, Woodland Road, Broadclyst, Exeter EX5 3LP* Exeter (01392) 462732

WILLIAMS, Roger Stewart. b 54. Qu Coll Cam BA75 MA79. Wycliffe Hall Ox BA78 MA82. **d** 79 **p** 80. C Hamstead St Paul *Birm* 79-82; C Barking St Marg w St Patr *Chelmsf* 82-85; V Mildmay Grove St Jude and St Paul *Lon* 85-95; P-in-c Charles w St Matthias Plymouth *Ex* from 95; Chapl Plymouth Univ from 95. *The Vicarage, 6 St Lawrence Road, Plymouth PL4 6HN* Plymouth (01752) 665640

WILLIAMS, Ronald Hywel. b 35. St D Coll Lamp BA62. **d** 63 **p** 64. C Machynlleth and Llanwrin *Ban* 63-66; C Llanaber 66-69; C Hawarden *St As* 69-73; R Llansantffraid Glan Conway and Eglwysfach 73-77; V Rhosllannerchrugog 77-88; R Cilcain and Nannerch and Rhyd-y-mwyn 88-92; V Llanbadarn Fawr w Capel Bangor and Goginan *St D* from 92; RD Llanbadarn Fawr from 94. *The Vicarage, Llanbadarn Fawr, Aberystwyth, Dyfed SY23 3QU* Aberystwyth (01970) 623368

✠**WILLIAMS, Rt Rev Rowan Douglas.** b 50. FBA90 Ch Coll Cam BA71 MA75 Wadh Coll Ox DPhil75 DD89. Coll of Resurr Mirfield 75. **d** 77 **p** 78 **c** 92. Tutor Westcott Ho Cam 77-80; Hon C Chesterton St Geo *Ely* 80-83; Lect Div Cam Univ 80-86; Dean Clare Coll Cam 84-86; Can Th Leic Cathl *Leic* 81-92; Can Res Ch Ch *Ox* 86-92; Lady Marg Prof of Div Ox Univ 86-92; Bp Mon from 92. *Bishopscourt, Newport, Gwent NP9 4EA* Newport (01633) 263510

WILLIAMS, Canon Roy. b 28. Lon Univ DipTh60. Ely Th Coll 58. **d** 60 **p** 61. V Bilborough St Jo *S'well* 63-73; V Arnold 73-92; Hon Can S'well Minster 85-92; rtd 92. *10 Maris Drive, Burton Joyce, Nottingham NG14 5AJ* Nottingham (0115) 931 2030

WILLIAMS, Royce. b 35. Leeds Univ BA56 Lanc Univ MA82. St Steph Ho Ox 58. **d** 60 **p** 61. C Ardwick St Benedict *Man* 60-62; C Bedf Leigh 62-64; V Blackb St Pet *Blackb* 64-68; Perm to Offic 70-78; Chapl W R Tuson Coll Preston 75-78; V Burnley St Cath 78-81; P-in-c Burnley St Alb w St Paul 78-81; V Burnley St Cath w St Alb and St Paul from 81. *St Catherine's Vicarage, 156 Todmorden Road, Burnley, Lancs BB11 3ER* Burnley (01282) 423351

WILLIAMS, Shamus Frank Charles. b 57. St Cath Coll Cam BA79 MA83. Ripon Coll Cuddesdon 81. **d** 84 **p** 85. C Swanage and Studland *Sarum* 84-87; C St Alb St Pet *St Alb* 87-90; TV Saffron Walden w Wendens Ambo and Littlebury *Chelmsf* from 90. *The Vicarage, Church Walk, Littlebury, Saffron Walden, Essex CB11 4TT* Saffron Walden (01799) 521004

WILLIAMS, Preb Sidney Austen. b 12. CVO79. St Cath Coll Cam BA36 MA56. Westcott Ho Cam 36. **d** 37 **p** 38. V St Martin-in-the-Fields *Lon* 56-84; Chapl to The Queen 61-82; Extra Chapl to The Queen from 82; Preb St Paul's Cathl *Lon* 73-84; rtd 84. *37 Tulsemere Road, London SE27 9EH* 0181-670 7945

WILLIAMS, Stephen Clark (**Steve**). b 47. Univ of Wales (Cardiff) BSc(Econ)69 Warw Univ MSc70. Wycliffe Hall Ox DipMin93. **d** 93 **p** 94. C High Wycombe *Ox* from 93. *60 Shelley Road, High Wycombe, Bucks HP11 2UW* High Wycombe (01494) 439420

WILLIAMS, Stephen Geoffrey. b 54. St Jo Coll Nottm BTh79 LTh79. **d** 79 **p** 80. C Skelmersdale St Paul *Liv* 79-81; C Burley *Ripon* 81-86. *24 Coronation Drive, Penketh, Warrington WA5 2DD* Penketh (01925) 723599

WILLIAMS, Stephen Grant. b 51. K Coll Lon BD73 AKC73. **d** 75 **p** 76. C Paddington Ch Ch *Lon* 75-78; C Paddington St Jas 78-80; Chapl LSE 80-91; Sen Chapl Lon Univs and Polys 91-93; Sen Chapl Lon Univs from 93. *15 Wilmington Square, London WC1X 0ER* 0171-837 1782 or 387 0670

WILLIAMS, Stephen James. b 52. Lon Univ BSc73. Ridley Hall Cam 73. **d** 78 **p** 79. C Waltham Abbey *Chelmsf* 78-82; C Bedf St Paul *St Alb* 82-86; P-in-c Chalgrave 86-88; V Harlington from 86. *The Vicarage, Church Road, Harlington, Dunstable, Beds LU5 6LE* Toddington (01525) 872413

WILLIAMS, Stephen Stuart. b 60. Magd Coll Ox BA82 Dur Univ BA88. Cranmer Hall Dur 86. **d** 89 **p** 90. C W Derby Gd Shep *Liv* 89-93; TV Liv Our Lady and St Nic w St Anne from 93. *43 Bisphan House, Lace Street, Liverpool L3 2BP* 0151-236 3420

WILLIAMS, Terence. b 36. Univ of Wales (Abth) BSc57 Univ of Wales (Cardiff) MA67 Aston Univ PhD71. Glouc Sch of Min 78. **d** 81 **p** 81. NSM Deerhurst, Apperley w Forthampton and Chaceley *Glouc* 81-87; NSM Tarrington w Stoke Edith, Aylton, Pixley etc *Heref* 87-88; P-in-c Upper and Lower Slaughter w Eyford and Naunton *Glouc* 88-91; P-in-c Redmarley D'Abitot, Bromesberrow w Pauntley etc from 91; RD Forest N from 95. *The Rectory, Redmarley, Gloucester GL19 3HS* Newent (01531) 650630

WILLIAMS, Terence John. b 36. Univ of Wales BSc62. St Deiniol's Hawarden 85. **d** 86 **p** 87. C Llangyfelach *S & B* 86-88; C Morriston 88-89; V Llanwrtyd w Llanddulas in Tir Abad etc 89-91; V Llanedi w Tycroes and Saron *St D* from 91. *The Vicarage, 37 Hendre Road, Tycroes, Ammanford, Dyfed SA18 3LF* Ammanford (01269) 592384

WILLIAMS, Thomas Bruce. b 41. Oak Hill Th Coll 74. **d** 76 **p** 77. C Liskeard w St Keyne and St Pinnock *Truro* 76-79; Australia from 79. *213 Thompson Street, (PO Box 165), Tennant Creek, NT, Australia 0861*

WILLIAMS, Canon Thomas Gerald. b 14. Ex Coll Ox BA35 MA39. Chich Th Coll 35. **d** 37 **p** 38. R Willesborough w Hinxhill *Cant* 62-80; Hon Can Cant Cathl 73-81; rtd 80; Perm to Offic *Cant* from 81. *2 Heathfield Court, Heathfield Road, Ashford, Kent TN24 8QD* Ashford (01233) 639328

WILLIAMS, Timothy John. b 54. BEd83. Trin Coll Carmarthen. **d** 89 **p** 90. NSM Llansamlet *S & B* from 89. *32 Midland Place, Llansamlet, Swansea SA7 9QU* Swansea (01792) 774452

WILLIAMS, Timothy John. b 64. Kent Univ BA86. St Mich Coll Llan BD89. **d** 89 **p** 90. C Killay *S & B* 89-91; C Llwynderw 91-94; V Knighton and Norton from 94. *The Vicarage, Knighton, Powys LD7 1AG* Knighton (01547) 528566

WILLIAMS, Tom David. b 19. St D Coll Lamp BA41 St Mich Coll Llan 41. **d** 43 **p** 45. V Llanidloes w Llangurig *Ban* 60-75; RD Arwystli 73-75; R Criccieth w Treflys 75-82; V Llanfihangel Ysgeifiog and Llanffinan etc 82-84; rtd 84; Perm to Offic *Ban* from 84. *Trefri Fach, Llangaffo, Gaerwen, Gwynedd LL60 6LT* Newborough (0124879) 687

WILLIAMS, Trevor Russell. b 48. TCD BA71. St Jo Coll Nottm BA73. **d** 74 **p** 75. C Maidenhead St Andr and St Mary Magd *Ox* 74-77; Asst Chapl QUB 78-80; Relig Broadcasting Producer BBC 81-88; Lic to Offic *Conn* 81-88; I Newc *D & D* 88-93; Leader Corrymeela Community from 93. *54 North Parade, Ormeau Road, Belfast BT7 2GG* Belfast (01232) 694206 or 325008 Fax Ballycastle (012657) 62626

WILLIAMS, Trevor Stanley Morlais. b 38. Jes Coll Ox BA63 Univ of E Africa MA67. Westcott Ho Cam BA67. **d** 67 **p** 68. C Clifton St Paul *Bris* 67-70; Asst Chapl Bris Univ 67-70; Chapl and Fell Trin Coll Ox from 70. *Trinity College, Oxford OX1 3BH* Oxford (01865) 279886

WILLIAMS, Vincent Handley. b 24. LRAM LLCM ARCM CertEd. St Deiniol's Hawarden 76. **d** 78 **p** 79. Hon C Barrow

Ches 78-81; C Dodleston 81-83; V Lostock Gralam 83-90; rtd 90. *2 Springfield Close, Higher Kinnerton, Chester CH4 9BU* Chester (01244) 660983

WILLIAMS, Walter Haydn. b 31. Univ of Wales (Lamp) BA53 Selw Coll Cam BA55 MA60. St Mich Coll Llan 55. **d** 56 **p** 57. V Northop *St As* 68-73; V Mold 73-86; RD Mold 79-86; Can St As Cathl 77-82; Prec 81-82; Preb and Chan 82-86; R Overton and Erbistock and Penley 86-94; Chmn Ch of Wales Liturg Cttee 86-94; rtd 94. *2 Park Lane, Craig y Don, Llandudno, Clwyd LL30 1PQ* Llandudno (01492) 877294

WILLIAMS, William Arwyn. b 15. Univ of Wales (Abth) BA37. Clifton Th Coll 38. **d** 40 **p** 41. CF 48-72; Hon Chapl to The Queen from 69; Chapl Salisbury Hosps 72-80; rtd 80; Perm to Offic *B & W* 84-94; Perm to Offic *Bris* from 85. *The Coach House, Entry Hill Drive, Bath BA2 5NJ* Bath (01225) 312658

WILLIAMS, William David Brynmor. b 48. Univ of Wales (Swansea) DipTh71 Open Univ BA89. St D Coll Lamp 71. **d** 72 **p** 73. C Killay *S & B* 72-74; C Wokingham All SS *Ox* 74-75; CF 75-77; C Spilsby w Hundleby *Linc* 83-87; R Meppershall w Campton and Stondon *St Alb* 87-90; V Hemsby *Nor* from 90; P-in-c Winterton w E and W Somerton and Horsey from 94. *The Vicarage, Hemsby, Great Yarmouth, Norfolk NR29 4EU* Great Yarmouth (01493) 730308

WILLIAMS, William John. b 23. Fitzw Ho Cam BA50 MA55. Wycliffe Hall Ox. **d** 54 **p** 55. V Cholsey *Ox* 69-73; rtd 88. *38 Hordley Road, Wellington, Telford, Shropshire TF1 3NR* Telford (01952) 242210

WILLIAMS-HUNTER, Ian Roy. b 44. Trin Coll Bris 71. **d** 73 **p** 74. C Redhill H Trin *S'wark* 73-75; C Deane *Man* 76-80; R Hartshorne *Derby* from 80. *The Rectory, 74 Woodville Road, Hartshorne, Swadlincote, Derbyshire DE11 7ET* Burton-on-Trent (01283) 217866

WILLIAMSON, Alfred Michael. b 28. Kelham Th Coll 53. **d** 58 **p** 59. V Kenwyn St Geo *Truro* 64-73; V St Agnes 73-87; Australia from 87; rtd 93. *PO Box 76, Pacific Palms, NSW, 2428 Australia*

WILLIAMSON, Andrew John. b 39. MRPharmS. St Alb Minl Tr Scheme 82. **d** 85 **p** 86. NSM Oxhey All SS *St Alb* 85-88; NSM Bricket Wood from 88. *148 Penrose Avenue, Watford WD1 5AH* 0181-421 0623

WILLIAMSON, Canon Anthony William (**Tony**). b 33. OBE77. Trin Coll Ox BA56 MA60. Cuddesdon Coll 56. **d** 60 **p** 61. Hon C Cowley St Jas *Ox* 60-79; TV 79-89; Dir of Educn (Schs) from 89; Hon Can Ch Ch from 94. *9 The Goggs, Watlington, Oxon OX9 5JX* Watlington (01491) 612143

WILLIAMSON, David Barry. b 56. St Jo Coll Nottm. **d** 83 **p** 84. C N Mymms *St Alb* 83-86; C Burley *Ripon* 86-92; Perm to Offic from 92; Perm to Offic *Bradf* from 92. *45 The Turnways, Leeds LS5 3DT* Leeds (0113) 278 1920

WILLIAMSON, Edward McDonald. b 42. CITC 67. **d** 69 **p** 70. CF 70-73; C Penzance St Mary w St Paul *Truro* 73-76; V Mullion 76-81; rtd 81. *Hazelmere, The Commons, Mullion, Helston, Cornwall TR12 7HZ* Mullion (01326) 240865

WILLIAMSON, Gavin Leslie. b 59. FRSA Hull Univ BA82 TCD DipTh85. **d** 85 **p** 86. C Stillorgan w Blackrock *D & G* 85-87; Min Can St Patr Cathl Dub from 86; Warden Guild of Lay Readers from 86; I Dunboyne w Kilcock, Maynooth, Moyglare etc *M & K* from 87; Treas St Patr Cathl Dub from 90; Dioc Tutor for Tr of Aux Min (Meath) *M & K* from 93. *The Rectory, Lismahon, Batterstown, Co Meath, Irish Republic* Dublin (1) 825-0020

WILLIAMSON, Ivan Alister. TCD BTh. **d** 90 **p** 91. C Lisburn St Paul *Conn* 90-95. *19 Dunrod Walk, Lisburn, Co Antrim BT28 1PU* Lisburn (01846) 604955

WILLIAMSON, Mrs Jennifer Irene. b 44. Glas Univ MA66 Sunderland Poly DipT79. NE Ord Course 89. **d** 92 **p** 94. NSM Easby w Brompton on Swale and Bolton on Swale *Ripon* 92-95; P-in-c Gilling and Kirkby Ravensworth from 95. *The Vicarage, Gilling West, Richmond, N Yorkshire DL10 5JG* Richmond (01748) 824466

WILLIAMSON, John. b 33. Bede Coll Dur. NE Ord Course 81. **d** 84 **p** 85. NSM Beamish *Dur* 84-85; C Sedgefield 85-88; P-in-c Trimdon 88-89; V 89-94; rtd 94. *9 Beamish View, Stanley, Co Durham DH9 0XB* Stanley (01207) 237380

WILLIAMSON, Dr John Brian Peter. b 30. CEng FIMechE FIEE FInstP FWeldI Selw Coll Cam PhD55. W Midl Minl Tr Course. **d** 84 **p** 87. NSM Malvern H Trin and St Jas *Worc* 84-94; Perm to Offic from 94. *Monkfield House, Newland, Malvern, Worcs WR13 5BB* Worcester (01905) 830522

WILLIAMSON, John Mark. b 43. FCP87 Birm Univ BA65 Univ of Wales (Cardiff) MEd75 MA82. St D Coll Lamp LTh67. **d** 67 **p** 68. C Shepton Mallet *B & W* 67-70; Hon C Dinder 70-71; Chapl Clifton Coll Bris 71-75; Lect All SS Bris 75-78; Chapl Bris Cathl *Bris* 77-78; Perm to Offic *Pet* 78-84; Perm to Offic *B & W* from 84. *6 Upper Lansdown Mews, Bath BA1 5HG* Bath (01225) 429938

WILLIAMSON, Michael John. b 39. ALCD63. **d** 64 **p** 65. C Pennington *Man* 64-67; C Higher Openshaw 67-69; P-in-c

Man St Jerome w Ardwick St Silas 69-72; C-in-c Holts CD 72-77; R Droylsden St Mary from 77. *The Rectory, Dunkirk Street, Droylsden, Manchester M35 7FB* 0161-370 1569

WILLIAMSON, Nigel. b 65. Qu Coll Ox BA87. Cranmer Hall Dur CTMin93. **d** 93 **p** 94. C Stannington *Sheff* from 93. *50 Goodison Crescent, Stannington, Sheffield S6 5HU* Sheffield (0114) 234 2136

WILLIAMSON, Paul Stewart. b 48. K Coll Lon BD71 AKC71. **d** 72 **p** 73. C Deptford St Paul *S'wark* 72-75; Hon C Kennington St Jo 76-77; C Hoxton H Trin w St Mary *Lon* 78-83; C St Marylebone All SS 83-84; C Willesden St Mary 84-85; Perm to Offic 86-89; C Hanworth St Geo 89-92; P-in-c from 92. *The Rectory, 7 Blakewood Close, Feltham, Middx TW13 7NL* 0181-844 0457

WILLIAMSON, Peter Barry Martin. b 21. Wycliffe Hall Ox 61. **d** 62 **p** 63. V Bentley Common *Chelmsf* 68-77; V Lt Thurrock St Jo 77-86; rtd 86; Perm to Offic *St E* from 86. *Corner Cottage, The Street, Kelsale, Saxmundham, Suffolk IP17 2PB* Saxmundham (01728) 602963

WILLIAMSON, Ralph James. b 62. LSE BSc(Econ)84. Ripon Coll Cuddesdon BA89. **d** 90 **p** 91. C Southgate St Andr *Lon* 90-93; TV Ross w Brampton Abbotts, Bridstow, Peterstow etc *Heref* from 93. *The Rectory, Brampton Abbotts, Ross-on-Wye, Herefordshire HR9 7JD* Ross-on-Wye (01989) 564876

WILLIAMSON, Robert John. b 55. K Coll Lon BA77. Coll of Resurr Mirfield 78. **d** 79 **p** 80. C Kirkby *Liv* 79-82; C Warrington St Elphin 82-84; P-in-c Burneside *Carl* 84-90; V Walney Is from 90. *The Vicarage, Promenade, Walney, Barrow-in-Furness, Cumbria LA14 3QU* Barrow-in-Furness (01229) 471268

✠**WILLIAMSON, Rt Rev Robert Kerr (Roy).** b 32. Oak Hill Th Coll 61. **d** 63 **p** 64 **c** 84. C Crowborough *Chich* 63-66; V Hyson Green *S'well* 66-72; V Nottm St Ann w Em 72-76; V Bramcote 76-79; Adn Nottm 78-84; Bp Bradf 84-91; Bp S'wark from 91. *Bishop's House, 38 Tooting Bec Gardens, London SW16 1QZ* 0181-769 3256 Fax 769 4126

WILLIAMSON, Canon Thomas George. b 33. AKC57. **d** 58 **p** 59. C Winshill *Derby* 58-61; C Hykeham *Linc* 61-64; V Brauncewell w Dunsby 64-78; R S w N Leasingham 64-78; RD Lafford 78-87; V Cranwell 78-80; R Leasingham 78-80; V Billinghay 80-87; V Gosberton from 87; Hon Can Linc Cathl from 94. *The Vicarage, Wargate Way, Gosberton, Spalding, Lincs PE11 4NH* Spalding (01775) 840694

WILLIE, Andrew Robert. b 43. Bris Univ BA65 Fitzw Coll Cam BA73 MA77. Ridley Hall Cam 71. **d** 74 **p** 75. Chapl St Woolos Cathl *Mon* 74-79; Chapl St Woolos Hosp Newport 75-79; V Newbridge *Mon* 79-85; V Mathern and Mounton w St Pierre from 85; Post-Ord Tr Officer from 85; Warden of Readers from 91. *St Tewdric's Vicarage, Mathern, Chepstow, Gwent NP6 6JA* Chepstow (01291) 622317

WILLIMENT, Paul. b 47. Leeds Univ BSc68. St Steph Ho Ox 70. **d** 73 **p** 74. C Guiseley *Bradf* 73-76; C Northn St Mary *Pet* 76-79; Malaysia from 80. *Box 347, Kuching, Sarawak, Malaysia*

WILLINK, Simon Wakefield. b 29. Magd Coll Cam BA52 MA55. Cuddesdon Coll 52. **d** 54 **p** 55. New Zealand 65-71; Perm to Offic *Ex* 90-92; NSM Sidmouth, Woolbrook, Salcombe Regis, Sidbury etc from 92; rtd 95. *Willows, 6 Ridgeway Close, Sidbury, Sidmouth, Devon EX10 0SN* Sidmouth (01395) 597545

WILLIS, Andrew Lyn. b 48. Univ of Wales (Lamp) BA73. **d** 74 **p** 75. C Swansea St Mary w H Trin and St Mark *S & B* 74-81; V Glasbury and Llowes 81-83; Chapl RAF from 83. *Chaplaincy Services (RAF), HQ, Personnel and Training Command, RAF Innsworth, Gloucester GL3 1EZ* Gloucester (01452) 712612 Ext 5164 Fax 510828

WILLIS, Anthony John. b 38. Univ of Wales (Lamp) BA62. Qu Coll Birm DipTh74. **d** 64 **p** 65. C Kidderminster St Jo *Worc* 64-68; C Dunstable *St Alb* 68-72; V Rubery *Birm* 72-80; R Salwarpe and Hindlip w Martin Hussingtree *Worc* 80-92; Chapl of Agric and Rural Life from 85. *Glebe House, Grafton Flyford, Worcester WR7 4PG* Droitwich (01905) 381460

WILLIS, Anthony David (Tony). b 40. Sarum & Wells Th Coll 87. **d** 89 **p** 90. C Ivybridge w Harford *Ex* 89-92; C Catherington and Clanfield *Portsm* 92-94; R Ellesborough, The Kimbles and Stoke Mandeville *Ox* from 94. *The Rectory, Ellesborough, Butlers Cross, Aylesbury, Bucks HP17 0XA* Wendover (01296) 622110

WILLIS, Christopher Charles Billopp (Chris). b 32. MITD. Bps' Coll Cheshunt 57. **d** 59 **p** 60. C Golders Green St Alb *Lon* 59-61; C N Harrow St Alb 61-64; V Shaw and Whitley *Sarum* 64-69; Ind Chapl *Ex* 69-77; C Swimbridge 70-77; Lic to Offic from 77; Chapl W Buckland Sch Barnstaple 77-92. *Lower Upcott, Chittlehampton, Umberleigh, Devon EX37 9RX* Chittlehamholt (01769) 540289

WILLIS, David George. b 45. Oak Hill Th Coll BA79. **d** 79 **p** 80. C Wallington H Trin *S'wark* 79-84; V Ramsgate St Mark *Cant* 84-89; Hon C Woodnesborough w Worth and Staple from 94. *75 Poulders Gardens, Sandwich, Kent CT13 0AJ* Sandwich (01304) 611959

WILLIS, Geoffrey Stephen Murrell. b 58. Sussex Univ BA80. Wycliffe Hall Ox 83. **d** 86 **p** 87. C Ashtead *Guildf* 86-89; Chapl Lee Abbey 89-94; Lic to Offic *Ex* 89-94; R Dunsfold *Guildf* from 94. *The Rectory, Church Green, Dunsfold, Godalming, Surrey GU8 4LT* Guildford (01483) 200207

WILLIS, Preb George Arnold. b 16. Liv Univ BVSc46. Ely Th Coll 52. **d** 53 **p** 53. R Ex St Martin, St Steph, St Laur etc *Ex* 64-74; Preb Ex Cathl 73-81; TV Cen Ex 74-78; TR 78-81; rtd 81; Perm to Offic *Ox* 90-94; Hon C Binfield from 94. *11 Knox Green, Binfield, Bracknell, Berks RG12 5NZ* Bracknell (01344) 428522

WILLIS, Joyce Muriel. b 42. CQSW73 Open Univ BA86. E Anglian Minl Tr Course 86. **d** 89 **p** 94. NSM Hadleigh w Layham and Shelley *St E* from 89. *26 Ramsey Road, Hadleigh, Ipswich IP7 6AN* Hadleigh (01473) 823165

WILLIS, Peter Ambrose Duncan. b 34. Kelham Th Coll 55 Lich Th Coll 58. **d** 59 **p** 60. C Sevenoaks St Jo *Roch* 59-63; Trinidad and Tobago 63-68; P-in-c Diptford *Ex* 68-69; R 69-85; P-in-c N Huish 68-69; R 69-85; R Diptford, N Huish, Harberton and Harbertonford from 85. *The Rectory, Diptford, Totnes, Devon TQ9 7NY* Gara Bridge (01548) 821392

WILLIS, Very Rev Robert Andrew. b 47. Warw Univ BA68 Worc Coll Ox DipTh71. Cuddesdon Coll 70. **d** 72 **p** 73. C Shrewsbury St Chad *Lich* 72-75; VC Sarum Cathl *Sarum* 75-78; TR Tisbury 78-87; Chapl Cranborne Chase Sch Wilts 78-92; RD Chalke *Sarum* 82-87; V Sherborne w Castleton and Lillington 87-92; Can and Preb Sarum Cathl 88-92; RD Sherborne 91-92; Dean Heref from 92; P-in-c Heref St Jo from 92. *The Deanery, The Cloisters, Hereford HR1 2NG* Hereford (01432) 272525

WILLIS, Mrs Rosemary Ann. b 39. Local NSM Course 89. **d** 93. NSM Fressingfield, Mendham, Metfield, Weybread etc *St E* from 93. *Priory House, Fressingfield, Eye, Suffolk IP21 5PH* Fressingfield (0137986) 254

WILLIS, Stephen Anthony. b 65. Univ of Wales BA86. Chich Th Coll 87. **d** 90 **p** 91. C Bethnal Green St Matt w St Jas the Gt *Lon* from 90. *The Rectory Flat, Hereford Street, London E2 6EX* 0171-729 0878

WILLIS, Thomas Charles (Tom). b 30. Bps' Coll Cheshunt 55. **d** 58 **p** 59. C Anlaby Common St Mark *York* 58-61; C Middlesb St Martin 61-63; V Kingston upon Hull St Paul w Sculcoates Ch Ch 63-69; P-in-c Sculcoates St Silas 67-69; V Sculcoates St Paul w Ch Ch and St Silas 69-80; V Bridlington H Trin and Sewerby w Marton from 80. *The Vicarage, Sewerby, Cloverley Road, Bridlington, N Humberside YO16 5TX* Bridlington (01262) 675725

WILLMINGTON, Canon John Henry William. b 14. AKC37. St Steph Ho Ox 35. **d** 37 **p** 38. V Selsdon St Jo w St Fran *Cant* 63-79; Hon Can Cant Cathl 74-79; rtd 79; Perm to Offic *Cant* from 79; Perm to Offic *S'wark* from 82. *22 Barrow Green Road, Oxted, Surrey RH8 0NL* Oxted (01883) 715669

WILLMINGTON, John Martin Vanderlure. b 45. St D Coll Lamp BA69. St Steph Ho Ox 69. **d** 71 **p** 72. C Upper Teddington SS Pet and Paul *Lon* 71-75; C Kensington St Mary Abbots w St Geo 75-83; R Perivale 83-91; V Acton Green from 91. *206 St Alban's Avenue, London W4 5JU* 0181-994 5735

WILLMONT, Anthony Vernon. b 45. Lich Th Coll 62. **d** 63 **p** 64. C Yardley St Edburgha *Birm* 63-65; C Smethwick H Trin w St Alb 65-68; V Ropley w W Tisted *Win* 68-77; V Ipswich St Aug *St E* 77-84; R King's Worthy *Win* 84-90; R Headbourne Worthy 84-90; R Lapworth *Birm* from 90; R Baddesley Clinton from 90. *The Rectory, Church Lane, Lapworth, Solihull, W Midlands B94 5NX* Lapworth (01564) 782098

WILLMOTT, Philip Boulton. b 15. St Pet Hall Ox BA36 MA41. Westcott Ho Cam 38. **d** 38 **p** 39. Chapl Win Coll 50-77; Lic to Offic *Win* 60-84; Chapl St Jo and St Mary Magd Hosps Win 79-80; rtd 80; Perm to Offic *Win* from 84. *34 Hatherley Road, Winchester, Hants SO22 6RT* Winchester (01962) 852360

WILLMOTT, Oliver Leonard. b 10. Lon Univ DipTh41. Kelham Th Coll 31. **d** 38 **p** 39. V Loders *Sarum* 47-82; R Askerswell 52-82; rtd 82. *Bell Cottage, West Milton, Bridport, Dorset DT6 3SW* Bridport (01308) 424291

WILLMOTT, Robert Owen Noel (Bob). b 41. Lich Th Coll 65. **d** 68 **p** 69. C Perry Hill St Geo *S'wark* 68-71; C Denham *Ox* 71-76; P-in-c Tingewick w Water Stratford 76-77; P-in-c Radclive 76-77; R Tingewick w Water Stratford, Radclive etc 77-89; R Wingrave w Rowsham, Aston Abbotts and Cublington from 89. *The Rectory, Leighton Road, Wingrave, Aylesbury, Bucks HP22 4PA* Aylesbury (01296) 681623

WILLMOTT, Canon Trevor. b 50. St Pet Coll Ox BA71 MA74. Westcott Ho Cam DipTh73. **d** 74 **p** 75. C Norton *St Alb* 74-77; Asst Chapl Chapl Italy w Bergen, Trondheim and Stavanger *Eur* 78-79; Chapl Naples w Sorrento, Capri and Bari 79-83;

Warden Ecton Ho 83-89; R Ecton *Pet* 83-89; Dir of Post-Ord Tr from 86; Dir of Ords from 86; Can Res, Prec and Sacr Pet Cathl from 89. *The Precentor's Lodging, Minster Precincts, Peterborough PE1 1XX* Peterborough (01733) 343389

WILLOUGHBY, Canon Bernard Digby. b. 96. Bps' Coll Cheshunt 39. **d** 42 **p** 43. I Cong *T, K & A* 50-73; I Ballinrobe w Kilcommon and Ballyovie 50-73; rtd 73. *Maneys, Salruck, Renvyle, Co Galway, Irish Republic* Lettergesh (95) 43498

WILLOUGHBY, Ven David Albert. b 31. St Jo Coll Dur BA53 DipTh57. **d** 57 **p** 58. C Shipley St Pet *Bradf* 57-61; C Barnoldswick w Bracewell 61-62; R Moston St Chad *Man* 62-72; V Marown *S & M* 72-80; Dioc Stewardship Adv from 76; V Douglas St Geo and St Barn from 80; RD Douglas 80-82; Adn Man from 82. *St George's Vicarage, 16 Devonshire Road, Douglas, Isle of Man 1M2 3RB* Douglas (01624) 675430

WILLOUGHBY, Francis Edward John. b 38. St Jo Coll Nottm. **d** 83 **p** 84. C Tonbridge SS Pet and Paul *Roch* 83-87; V Sutton at Hone from 87. *The Vicarage, Main Road, Sutton at Hone, Dartford DA4 9HQ* Farningham (01322) 862253

WILLOUGHBY, Ven George Charles. b 20. TCD BA43 MA46. CITC 44. **d** 44 **p** 45. I Clooney *D & R* 59-85; Dioc Dir of Ords 62-72; Adn Derry 79-85; rtd 85. *21 Tyler Avenue, Limavady, Co Londonderry BT49 0DT* Limavady (015047) 65382

✠**WILLOUGHBY, Rt Rev Noel Vincent.** b 26. TCD BA48 MA52. TCD Div Sch Div Test48. **d** 50 **p** 51 **c** 80. C Drumglass *Arm* 50-53; C Dub St Cath *D & G* 53-55; C Bray Ch Ch 55-59; I Delgany 59-69; I Glenageary 69-80; Treas St Patr Cathl Dub 77-80; Adn Dub 78-80; Bp C & O from 80. *The Palace, Kilkenny, Irish Republic* Kilkenny (56) 21560 Fax 64399

WILLOUGHBY, Paul Moore. b 60. DipTh BA. **d** 86 **p** 87. C Dub St Patr Cathl Gp *D & G* 86-90; C Glenageary 90-92; I Dub Booterstown 92-94; I Kilmocomogue Union *C, C & R* from 94. *The Rectory, Durrus, Bantry, Co Cork, Irish Republic* Bantry (27) 61011

WILLOWS, David Keith. b. 70. St Jo Coll Dur BA90 K Coll Lon MA94. Wycliffe Hall Ox DipMin94. **d** 95. C Ox St Mary V w St Cross and St Pet *Ox* from 95. *Flat 4, 31 Banbury Road, Kidlington, Oxon OX5 1AQ* Oxford (01865) 374181

WILLOWS, Michael John. b 35. Sarum & Wells Th Coll 70. **d** 72 **p** 73. C Pershore w Wick *Worc* 72-75; P-in-c Astley 75-81; Ind Chapl from 75; P-in-c Hallow 81-85; V 85-88; V Wollaston from 88. *The Vicarage, 46 Vicarage Road, Wollaston, Stourbridge, W Midlands DY8 4NP* Stourbridge (01384) 395674

WILLOX, Peter. b 63. Sunderland Poly BSc85. St Jo Coll Dur 86. **d** 89 **p** 90. C Bradley *Wakef* 89-92; C Utley *Bradf* 92-95; TV Bingley All SS from 95. *The Vicarage, Winston Grange, Eldwick, Bingley, W Yorkshire BD16 3EQ* Bradford (01274) 568266

WILLS, David (Dave). b 58. Oak Hill Th Coll DipHE94. **d** 94 **p** 95. C Chadwell *Chelmsf* from 94. *7 Cedar Road, Grays, Essex RM16 4ST* Tilbury (01375) 850877

WILLS, David Ernest. b 58. St Jo Coll Cam BA58 MA62. Ridley Hall Cam 58. **d** 60 **p** 61. C Kenilworth St Jo *Cov* 60-63; C Northwood Em *Lon* 63-66; V Huyton St Geo *Liv* 66-73; V Littleover *Derby* 73-84; V Mossley Hill St Matt and St Jas *Liv* from 84. *The Vicarage, Rose Lane, Mossley Hill, Liverpool L18 8DB* 0151-724 2650

WILLS, David Stuart Ralph. b 36. Chich Th Coll 64. **d** 66 **p** 67. C Bodmin *Truro* 66-70; V Bude Haven 70-78; TV Banbury *Ox* 78-83; Accredited Counsellor from 81; V Launceston St Steph w St Thos *Truro* 83-88; P-in-c Kenwyn St Geo 88-93; V Truro St Geo and St Jo from 93. *St George's Vicarage, St George's Road, Truro, Cornwall TR1 3NW* Truro (01872) 72630

WILLS, Herbert Ashton Peter. b 24. St Edm Hall Ox BA46 MA50. Qu Coll Birm 60. **d** 60 **p** 61. Chapl St Matthias's Coll Bris 69-78; Asst Chapl Sheff Univ *Sheff* 78-80; Chapl 80-84; R Flax Bourton *B & W* 84-92; V Barrow Gurney 84-92; rtd 92. *2 The Pavilions, Sansford Road, Cheltenham, Glos GL53 7AV* Cheltenham (01242) 263748

WILLS, Ian Leslie. b 49. Wycliffe Hall Ox 77. **d** 80 **p** 81. C Henbury *Bris* 80; C Gtr Corsham 80-83; C Whitchurch 83-86; Chapl HM Rem Cen Pucklechurch from 86; P-in-c Pucklechurch and Abson w Dyrham *Bris* 86-87; V Pucklechurch and Abson from 87. *The Vicarage, Westerleigh Road, Pucklechurch, Bristol BS17 3RD* Bristol (0117) 937 2260 Fax 372729

WILLS, Canon Kenneth Charles Austen. b 21. Cuddesdon Coll 68. **d** 70 **p** 71. C Petersfield w Sheet *Portsm* 70-73; R W Meon and Warnford 73-74; RD Petersfield 85-90; Hon Can Portsm Cathl 89-94; rtd 94. *Old Hunt Farm, Galhampton, Yeovil, Somerset BA22 7BA* Yeovil (01963) 440001

WILLS, Morley. b. 35. Ex & Truro NSM Scheme. **d** 80 **p** 81. NSM St Enoder *Truro* 80-82; NSM Kenwyn St Geo 82-85; NSM Truro St Paul and St Clem 85-88; NSM Crantock from 89. *The Vicarage, Beach Road, Crantock, Newquay, Cornwall TR8 5RE* Crantock (01637) 830174

WILLSON, Andrew William. b. 64. Or Coll Ox BA85 Nottm Univ BTh90. Linc Th Coll 87. **d** 90 **p** 91. C Northn St Mary *Pet* 90-93; C Cov E *Cov* from 93. *St Catherine's House, 7 St Catherine's Close, Coventry CV3 1EH* Coventry (01203) 635737

WILLSON, Stephen Geoffrey. b. 63. Nottm Univ BTh90. St Jo Coll Nottm. **d** 90 **p** 91. C Newport St Andr *Mon* 90-92; C Risca 92-94; TV Cyncoed from 94. *13 Clos Alyn, Cardiff CF2 7LB* Cardiff (01222) 540071

WILLSON, Stuart Leslie. b 61. Nottm Univ BA83. Sarum & Wells Th Coll 83. **d** 84 **p** 85. C Llandrindod w Cefnllys *S & B* 84-85; Asst Chapl Angl Students Univ of Wales (Swansea) 85-88; C Llwynderw 85-88; Chapl Gatwick Airport *Chich* from 88. *18 Aldingbourne Close, Ifield, Crawley, W Sussex RH11 0QJ* Crawley (01293) 541139 or 503857

WILMAN, Arthur Garth. b. 37. E Anglian Minl Tr Course 84. **d** 87 **p** 88. NSM Swavesey *Ely* 87-90; NSM Fen Drayton w Conington 87-90; NSM Hardwick from 90; NSM Toft w Caldecote and Childerley from 90. *37 Prentice Close, Longstanton, Cambridge CB4 5DY* Crafts Hill (01954) 781400

WILMAN, Mrs Dorothy Ann Jane. b 38. Reading Univ BSc60 Lon Univ DipTh67. Westcott Ho Cam 89. **d** 90 **p** 94. NSM Toft w Caldecote and Childerley *Ely* from 90; Chapl Trin Hall Cam from 93. *37 Prentice Close, Longstanton, Cambridge CB4 5DY* Crafts Hill (01954) 781400

WILMAN, Leslie Alan. b 37. Selw Coll Cam BA61 MA65. Ridley Hall Cam 61. **d** 63 **p** 64. C Skipton H Trin *Bradf* 63-67; C Guiseley 67-69; V Morton St Luke 69-79; R Swanton Morley w Worthing *Nor* 79-82; P-in-c E Bilney w Beetley 79-82; P-in-c Hoe 80-82; R Swanton Morley w Worthing, E Bilney, Beetley etc 82-89; R Swanton Morley w Beetley w E Bilney and Hoe from 89; RD Brisley and Elmham 87-93. *The Rectory, Beetley, Dereham, Norfolk NR20 4AB* Dereham (01362) 860328

WILMER, John Watts. b 26. Lich Th Coll 56. **d** 58 **p** 59. V Dresden *Lich* 63-76; TV Sutton St Jas and Wawne *York* 76-80; R Bishop Wilton w Full Sutton 80; P-in-c Kirby Underdale w Bugthorpe 80; R Bishop Wilton w Full Sutton, Kirby Underdale etc 80-87; V York St Hilda 87-91; rtd 92. *27 Hunters Way, Dringhouses, York YO2 2JL* York (01904) 709591

WILMOT, David Mark Baty. b 60. Liv Univ BA82. Sarum & Wells Th Coll 84. **d** 87 **p** 88. C Penrith w Newton Reigny and Plumpton Wall *Carl* 87-91; C St Alb St Pet *St Alb* 91-93; Chapl City Coll St Alb 92-93; V Milton *Lich* from 93. *The Vicarage, Baddeley Green Lane, Stoke-on-Trent ST2 7EY* Stoke-on-Trent (01782) 534062

WILMOT, Jonathan Anthony de Burgh. b 48. St Jo Coll Nottm LTh73 BTh74. **d** 74 **p** 75. C Cam St Martin *Ely* 74-77; Chapl Chantilly *Eur* 77-82; Asst Chapl Chapl Paris St Mich 80-82; Chapl Versailles 82-87; V Blackheath St Jo *S'wark* from 88. *146 Langton Way, London SE3 7JS* 0181-293 0023

WILMOT, Stuart Leslie. b 42. Oak Hill Th Coll. **d** 68 **p** 69. C Spitalfields Ch Ch w All SS *Lon* 68-71; C Islington St Mary 71-74; P-in-c Brixton St Paul *S'wark* 75-81; R Mursley w Swanbourne and Lt Horwood *Ox* 81-91; P-in-c Bermondsey St Jas w Ch Ch *S'wark* from 91; P-in-c Bermondsey St Anne 91-93; P-in-c Bermondsey St Anne and St Aug from 93. *St Anne's Vicarage, Thorburn Street, London SE1 5QH* 0171-237 3950

WILSON, Dr Alan Thomas Lawrence. b 55. St Jo Coll Cam BA77 MA81 Ball Coll Ox DPhil89. Wycliffe Hall Ox 77. **d** 79 **p** 80. Hon C Eynsham *Ox* 79-81; C 81-82; C Caversham and Mapledurham 82-89; V Caversham St Jo 89-92; R Sandhurst from 92. *The Rectory, 155 High Street, Sandhurst, Camberley, Surrey GU17 8HR* Yateley (01252) 872168

WILSON, Canon Alfred Michael Sykes. b 32. Jes Coll Cam BA56 MA61. Ridley Hall Cam 56. **d** 58 **p** 59. C Fulwood *Sheff* 58-63; V Gt Horton *Bradf* 63-69; R Rushden w Newton Bromswold *Pet* 69-76; RD Higham 75-83; P-in-c Rushden St Pet 75-77; R Rushden w Newton Bromswold 77-83; Can Pet Cathl from 77; R Preston and Ridlington w Wing and Pilton from 83; RD Rutland from 85. *The Rectory, Preston, Oakham, Leics LE15 9NN* Manton (01572) 737287

WILSON, Canon Allen. b. 22. TCD BA44. TCD Div Sch BD47. **d** 45 **p** 46. I Dub Santry w Glasnevin *D & G* 64-73; I Dub Rathfarnham 73-92; Preb Rathmichael St Patr Cathl Dub 85-92; rtd 92. *21 Glenview Court, Blessington, Co Wicklow, Irish Republic* Blessington (45) 865920

WILSON, Andrew Alan. b 47. Nottm Univ BA68. St Steph Ho Ox 68. **d** 71 **p** 72. C Streatham St Paul *S'wark* 71-75; TV Catford (Southend) and Downham 75-80; V Malden St Jas 80-89; Chapl Croydon Community Mental Health Unit from 89; Chapl Warlingham Park Hosp Croydon from 89. *Warlingham Park Hospital, Croydon CR6 9YR, or 7 Leas Road, Warlingham, Surrey CR6 9LN* Upper Warlingham (01883) 622101

WILSON, Andrew Kenneth. b 62. CertJourn. Oak Hill Th Coll BA91. d 91 p 92. C Springfield H Trin *Chelmsf* from 91. *15 Shelley Road, Chelmsford CM2 6ER*   Chelmsford (01245) 351813

WILSON, Andrew Marcus William. b 69. Ex Coll Ox BA91 CCC Cam BA93. Westcott Ho Cam CTM94. d 94 p 95. C Forest Gate Em w Upton Cross *Chelmsf* from 94. *52 Bolton Road, London E15 4JY*   0181-522 0425

WILSON, Arthur. b 20. Worc Ord Coll 62. d 64 p 65. V Altofts *Wakef* 71-78; V Staincross 78-84; rtd 84. *Flat 1, Hastings House, South Milford, Leeds LS25 5LL*   South Milford (01977) 684591

WILSON, Arthur Guy Ross. b 28. St Aid Birkenhead 58. d 59 p 60. C Bexley St Mary *Roch* 59-63; C Gravesend St Geo 63-66; C Belvedere All SS 66-70; V Brighton St Matthias *Chich* 70-77; V Bradf St Clem *Bradf* 77-84; Lic to Offic 84-87; C Baildon 87-88; V Skirwith, Ousby and Melmerby w Kirkland *Carl* 88-93; C Menston w Woodhead *Bradf* from 93; Chapl High Royds Hosp Menston from 93. *Menston Lodge, Menston Drive, Menston, Ilkley, W Yorkshire LS29 6AG*   Ilkley (01943) 877522

WILSON, Arthur Neville. b 43. ACGI Lon Univ BScEng65 Linacre Coll Ox BA70 MA74. St Steph Ho Ox 68. d 71 p 72. C Whitton St Aug *Lon* 71-73; C Chiswick St Nic w St Mary 73-76; C Littlehampton St Jas *Chich* 76-81; C Littlehampton St Mary 76-81; C Wick 76-81; V Whitworth *Man* 81-88; V Shaw from 88. *The Vicarage, 13 Church Road, Shaw, Oldham OL2 7AT*   Shaw (01706) 847369

WILSON, Barry Richard. b 46. W Midl Minl Tr Course 88. d 91 p 92. NSM Leek and Meerbrook *Lich* 91-93; C Styvechale *Cov* from 93. *55 Watercall Avenue, Coventry CV3 5AX*   Coventry (01203) 417920

WILSON, Bernard Martin. b 40. St Jo Coll Cam BA63 MA68 Lon Univ CertEd67. Ripon Hall Ox 72. d 73 p 74. C Bilton *Cov* 73-77; Dioc Development Officer *Birm* 78-83; Soc Resp Officer *Derby* 83-90; V Darley Abbey 83-90; Chapl Derbyshire R Infirmary 88-90; Educn Unit Dir Traidcraft Exchange 91; V Mickleover St Jo *Derby* from 92. *St John's Vicarage, 7 Onslow Road, Mickleover, Derby DE3 5JJ*   Derby (01332) 516545

WILSON, Brian Arthur. b 37. Portsm Dioc Tr Course 84 Chich Th Coll. d 85. NSM S w N Hayling *Portsm* 85-88; Chapl Asst RN from 88. *Directorate Gen, RN Chapl Sevices, Room 203, Victory Building, HM Naval Base, Portsmouth PO1 3LS*   Portsmouth (01705) 727903   Fax 727112

WILSON, Cecil Henry. b 40. CITC 67. d 69 p 70. C Lurgan St Jo *D & D* 69-72; Min Can Dromore Cathl 72-75; Youth Sec CMS Ireland 75-80; N Regional Sec 80-87; Gen Sec from 87. *20 Knockbreda Road, Belfast BT6 0JA*   Belfast (01232) 644011 or 324581   Fax 321756

WILSON, Canon Cecil Moffat. b 26. TCD BA51. d 52 p 53. I Mountmellick *M & K* 64-76; Can Kildare Cathl 72-75; Adn Kildare 75-76; I Raheny w Coolock *D & G* 76-91; Preb Dunlavin St Patr Cathl Dub 88-91; rtd 91. *3A Galway Mews, Comber Road, Dundonald, Belfast BT16 0AU*   Belfast (01232) 484967

WILSON, Charles Michael. b 39. Magd Coll Ox BA63 MA66. NE Ord Course 76. d 79 p 80. NSM Darlington St Jas *Dur* from 79. *29 Prescott Street, Darlington, Co Durham DL1 2ND*   Darlington (01325) 460442

WILSON, Charles Roy. b 30. Brasted Place Coll 56. St Aid Birkenhead 57. d 59 p 60. C Kirkdale St Paul N Shore *Liv* 59-62; C St Helens St Mark 62-66; V Wolv St Matt *Lich* 66-74; V Ripley *Derby* 74-88; V Willington from 88; V Findern from 88. *The Vicarage, 66 The Castle Way, Willington, Derby DE65 6BU*   Burton-on-Trent (01283) 702203

WILSON, Christopher Harry. b 59. Man Univ MusB80. Wycliffe Hall Ox 88. d 91 p 92. C S Lafford *Linc* 91-95; P-in-c Billingborough from 95; P-in-c Sempringham w Pointon and Birthorpe from 95; P-in-c Horbling from 95. *The Vicarage, 13 High Street, Billingborough, Sleaford, Lincs NG34 0QG*   Sleaford (01529) 240750

WILSON, Mrs Claire Frances. b 43. Hull Univ BA65. SW Minl Tr Course 85. d 87 p 94. Par Dn Belsize Park *Lon* 87-94; C from 94. *26 Frognal Lane, London NW3 7DT*   0171-794 9408

WILSON, Colin Edward. b 63. Ripon Coll Cuddesdon BTh94. d 94 p 95. C High Wycombe Ox from 94. *7 Totteridge Road, High Wycombe, Bucks HP13 6DR*   High Wycombe (01494) 452953

WILSON, Colin Myles. b 40. St Aid Birkenhead 64. d 66 p 67. C Frodsham *Ches* 66-68; C Heald Green St Cath 68-70; C Kirkby *Liv* 70-73; CF from 73. *c/o MOD (Army), Bagshot Park, Bagshot, Surrey GU19 5PL*   Bagshot (01276) 471717   Fax 412834

WILSON, David Brian. b 47. QUB BA68. CITC 71. d 71 p 72. C Ballyholme *D & D* 71-74; C Guildf Ch Ch *Guildf* 74-78; I Arvagh w Carrigallen, Gowna and Columbkille *K, E & A* 78-81; I Clogherney w Seskinore and Drumnakilly *Arm* 81-95; I Caledon w Brantry from 95. *The Rectory, 36 Church Hill Road, Caledon, Co Tyrone BT68 4UY*   Caledon (01861) 568205

WILSON, David Gordon. b 40. Man Univ BSc61 Clare Coll Cam BA63 MA68. Ridley Hall Cam 63. d 65 p 66. C Clapham Common St Barn *S'wark* 65-69; C Onslow Square St Paul *Lon* 69-73; V Leic H Apostles *Leic* 73-84; V Spring Grove St Mary *Lon* from 84. *St Mary's Vicarage, Osterley Road, Isleworth, Middx TW7 4PW*   0181-560 3555

WILSON, David Mark. b 53. Lon Univ BSc75. Wycliffe Hall Ox BA77 MA82. d 78 p 79. C Romford Gd Shep Collier Row *Chelmsf* 78-81; C Cheadle Hulme St Andr *Ches* 81-85; V Huntington from 85. *St Luke's Vicarage, 14 Celandine Close, Huntington, Chester CH3 6DT*   Chester (01244) 347345

WILSON, David Merritt. b 26. S'wark Ord Course 61. d 64 p 65. C Brixton St Paul *S'wark* 64-69; Perm to Offic from 69. *18 Calais Street, London SE5 9LP*   0171-274 5707

WILSON, Derrick. b 33. Oak Hill Th Coll 69. d 71 p 72. C Lurgan Ch the Redeemer *D & D* 71-74; C Willowfield 74-75; I 83-88; I Knocknamuckley 75-83; I Tullylish from 88. *Tullylish Rectory, 100 Banbridge Road, Gilford, Craigavon, Co Armagh BT63 6DL*   Gilford (01762) 831298

WILSON, Mrs Dorothy Jean. b 35. St Mary's Coll Dur BA57 DipEd58 Newc Poly LLB78. NE Ord Course 86. d 88. NSM Dur St Giles *Dur* from 88; Perm to Offic *Newc* from 88; Chapl Univ of Northumbria at Newc from 94. *86 Gilesgate, Durham DH1 1HY*   0191-386 5016

WILSON, Edward Thomas. b 48. Southn Univ BTh82. Chich Th Coll 78. d 82 p 83. C Cardiff St Jo *Llan* 82-86; V Aberavon H Trin 86-92; R St Nicholas w Bonvilston and St George-super-Ely from 92. *The Rectory, 8 Ger-y-Llan, St Nicholas, Cardiff CF5 6SY*   Peterston-super-Ely (01446) 760728

WILSON, Erik. b 51. Lanc Univ BA72. Trin Coll Bris 83. d 85 p 86. C Linthorpe *York* 85-89; V Hull St Martin w Transfiguration from 89. *St Martin's Vicarage, 942 Anlaby Road, Hull HU4 6AH*   Hull (01482) 52995

WILSON, Francis. b 34. ACP67. Cuddesdon Coll 71. d 73 p 74. C Newc St Fran *Newc* 73-79; V Wallsend St Jo from 79. *St John's Vicarage, Station Road, Wallsend, Tyne & Wear NE28 8DT*   0191-262 3944

WILSON, Frederick John. b 25. Lon Univ BScEng45. Oak Hill Th Coll 68. d 70 p 71. C Wandsworth All SS *S'wark* 70-75; P-in-c Garsdon w Lea and Cleverton *Bris* 75-84; P-in-c Charlton w Brokenborough and Hankerton 80-84; Chapl Barn Fellowship Whatcombe Ho 84-87; C Corby Epiphany w St Jo *Pet* 87-92; rtd 92; Perm to Offic *Linc* from 93. *2 Thorseby Close, Netherton, Peterborough PE3 9QS*   Peterborough (01733) 263386

WILSON, Canon Harold (Harry). b 29. St Jo Coll Ox BA53 MA57. Ridley Hall Cam 57. d 59 p 60. Chapl Barcelona *Eur* 67-73; V Burslendon *Win* 73-83; RD Eastleigh 75-83; V Yateley 83-94; RD Odiham 85-88; Hon Can Win Cathl 87-94; rtd 94. *11 Hill Meadow, Overton, Basingstoke, Hants RG25 3JD*   Overton (01256) 771825

WILSON, Harold Marcus. b 32. St Jo Coll Dur BA55 DipTh57. d 57 p 58. C Adlington *Blackb* 57-60; Miss to Seamen 60-81; Iraq 60-63; Japan 63-67; P-in-c Crowfield w Stonham Aspal and Mickfield *St E* from 81. *The Rectory, Stonham Aspal, Stowmarket, Suffolk IP14 6AQ*   Stowmarket (01449) 711409

WILSON, Ian Andrew. b 57. Nottm Univ BTh89. Linc Th Coll 86. d 89 p 90. C Whitton and Thurleston w Akenham *St E* 89-93; P-in-c Elmsett w Aldham from 93. *The Rectory, Hadleigh Road, Elmsett, Ipswich IP7 6ND*   Offton (01473) 658219

WILSON, James Andrew Christopher. b 48. Ex & Truro NSM Scheme. d 82 p 83. NSM Plymouth Crownhill Ascension *Ex* 82-83; NSM Yelverton 83-85; C Plymstock 85-87; R Lifton 87-92; R Kelly w Bradstone 87-92; V Broadwoodwidger 87-92; R Calstock *Truro* from 92. *The Rectory, Sand Lane, Calstock, Cornwall PL18 9QX*   Tavistock (01822) 832518

WILSON, James Charles. b 58. TCD BA82 MA84 DipTh85. d 85 p 86. C Ban Abbey *D & D* 85-88; C Dub Rathfarnham *D & G* 88-91; I Ardtrea w Desertcreat *Arm* 91-94; C Derryloran from 94. *Address temp unknown*

WILSON, James Kenneth. b 47. d 88 p 89. C Holyhead w Rhoscolyn w Llanfair-yn-Neubwll *Ban* 88-91; Chapl RAF from 91. *Chaplaincy Services (RAF), HQ, Personnel and Training Command, RAF Innsworth, Gloucester GL3 1EZ*   Gloucester (01452) 712612 Ext 5164   Fax 510828

WILSON, James Lewis. b 39. TCD BA62 HDipEd63 MA65 BD71. TCD Div Sch Div Test74. d 74 p 75. C Enniskillen *Clogh* 74-76; C Belf St Matt *Conn* 76-79; I Killeshandra w Killegar *K, E & A* 79-81; I Derrylane 79-81; I Loughgilly w Clare *Arm* from 81. *The Rectory, 124 Gosford Road, Loughgilly, Armagh BT60 2DE*   Glenanne (01861) 507265

WILSON, James Phillip Maclean. b 31. RMA 52 MBIM75. Glouc Sch of Min 89. d 91 p 92. NSM Quinton w Marston Sicca *Glouc* from 91. *The Old Bakery, Upper Quinton,*

Stratford-upon-Avon, Warks CV37 8SX   Stratford-upon-Avon (01789) 720224

WILSON, James Robert. b 36. CITC. **d** 66 **p** 67. C Ballywillan *Conn* 67-73; I Drummaul 73-79; I Drummaul w Duneane and Ballyscullion from 79; RD Antrim from 93. *The Vicarage, 1A Glenkeen, Randalstown, Antrim BT41 3JX*   Randalstown (01849) 472561

WILSON, Miss Jane Jennifer. b 43. Ch Ch Coll Cant TCert65 Open Univ BA84. Wycliffe Hall Ox 89. **d** 91 **p** 94. Par Dn Northwood *Em Lon* 91-94; C from 94. *27 Foxfield Close, Northwood, Middx HA6 3NU*   Northwood (01923) 825390

WILSON, John Anthony. b 34. Linc Th Coll. **d** 83 **p** 84. C Nunthorpe *York* 83-85; V Whorlton w Carlton and Faceby 85-94; V Coatham from 94. *The Vicarage, 9 Blenheim Terrace, Redcar, Cleveland TS10 1QP*   Redcar (01642) 482870

WILSON, Canon John Christopher Heathcote. b 13. Qu Coll Ox BA39 MA41. Cuddesdon Coll 40. **d** 41 **p** 42. V Kirk Ella *York* 59-88; AD W Hull 72-79; Can and Preb York Minster from 79; rtd 88. *14 Tremayne Avenue, Brough, N Humberside HU15 1BL*   Hull (01482) 668481

WILSON, John Clifford. b 32. AKC58. **d** 57 **p** 58. C Bordesley St Andr *Birm* 57-59; C Kings Norton 59-61; Somalia and Aden 61-63; V Lydbrook *Glouc* 64-67; TV Bow w Bromley St Leon *Lon* 69-73; P-in-c Stepney St Pet w St Benet 73-80; P-in-c Long Marton w Dufton and w Milburn *Carl* 80-81; R 81-87; V Annesley Our Lady and All SS *S'well* from 87. *The Vicarage, Annesley Cutting, Annesley, Nottingham NG15 0AJ*   Mansfield (01623) 759666

WILSON, John Frederick. b 33. Qu Coll Birm 58. **d** 61 **p** 62. C Jarrow St Paul *Dur* 61-65; C Monkwearmouth All SS 65-68; Br Honduras 68-71; V Scunthorpe Resurr *Linc* 71-90; Chapl Divine Healing Miss Crowhurst 90-91; V Terrington St Clement *Ely* from 91. *The Vicarage, 27 Sutton Road, Terrington St Clement, King's Lynn, Norfolk PE34 4RQ*   King's Lynn (01553) 828430

WILSON, Canon John Hamilton. b 29. St Chad's Coll Dur BA53. Sarum Th Coll 53. **d** 55 **p** 56. C W End *Win* 55-59; C Fishponds St Mary *Bris* 59-64; V Bedminster St Fran 64-73; RD Bedminster 68-73; R Horfield H Trin from 73; Hon Can Bris Cathl from 77. *The Rectory, Wellington Hill, Bristol BS7 8ST*   Bristol (0117) 924 6185

WILSON, Canon John Hewitt. b 24. CB77. TCD BA46 Div Test47 MA61. **d** 47 **p** 48. Chapl RAF 50-73; Chapl-in-Chief RAF 73-80; QHC 73-80; Can and Preb Linc Cathl *Linc* 74-80; R The Heyfords w Rousham and Somerton *Ox* 81-93; rtd 93. *Glencree, Philcote Street, Deddington, Oxford OX15 0TB*   Deddington (01869) 38903

WILSON, John Lake. b 34. Linc Th Coll 74. **d** 76 **p** 77. C N Lynn w St Marg and St Nic *Nor* 76-80; V Narborough w Narford 80-85; V Pentney St Mary Magd w W Bilney 80-85; V Lakenham St Mark 85-93; P-in-c Trowse 92-93; V Lakenham St Mark w Trowse from 93; Chapl Whitlingham Hosp from 93. *The Vicarage, 2 Conesford Drive, Bracondale, Norwich NR1 2BB*   Norwich (01603) 622579

WILSON, Dr John Michael. b 16. MRCP48 Lon Univ MB, BS42 MD48. **d** 53 **p** 56. Birm Univ Research Fell 67-71; Lect 71-78; Sen 78-81; rtd 81. *4 Eastern Road, Birmingham B29 7JP*   0121-472 1051

WILSON, John Stafford. b 21. Bible Churchmen's Coll 49. **d** 51 **p** 52. V Packington w Normanton-le-Heath *Leic* 68-72; V Worthing St Geo *Chich* 72-84; P-in-c Ashby w Fenby and Brigsley *Linc* 84; P-in-c Beelsby 84; P-in-c E and W Ravendale w Hatcliffe 84; R Ravendale Gp 84-87; rtd 88. *88 Bruce Avenue, Worthing, W Sussex BN11 5LA*   Worthing (01903) 245844

WILSON, Canon John Walter. b 25. St Jo Coll Dur BA67 Hatf Coll Dur MSc74. Cranmer Hall Dur. **d** 67 **p** 68. V S Hetton *Dur* 69-75; Lect Sunderland Poly 75-82; V Ormesby w Scratby *Nor* 82-92; RD Flegg (Gt Yarmouth) 89-92; Hon Can Nor Cathl 91-92; rtd 92; Perm to Offic *Nor* from 92. *4 Rectory Lane, Chedgrave, Norwich NR14 6NE*   Loddon (01508) 20259

WILSON, Joseph William Sidney. b 22. St Aid Birkenhead 62. **d** 64 **p** 65. C Birkdale St Jo *Liv* 68-71; V Eppleton *Dur* 71-78; V Riccall *York* 78-84; V Freckleton *Blackb* 84-87; rtd 87. *27 Sandy Lane, Wallasey, Merseyside L45 3JY*   0151-639 9083

WILSON, Miss Judith Anne. b 48. Keele Univ BA71 Leic Univ PGCE72. S Dios Minl Tr Scheme 92. **d** 95. NSM Slaugham *Chich* from 95; Perm to Offic *S'wark* from 95; Sub Chapl HM Pris Wandsworth from 95. *7 The Street, Warninglid, Haywards Heath, W Sussex RH17 5TR*   Warninglid (01444) 461380

WILSON, Keith. b 38. UEA BA87 MA90. Chich Th Coll 60. **d** 63 **p** 64. C W Bromwich St Fran *Lich* 63-66; C Kirkley *Nor* 66-70; R Swainsthorpe w Newton Flotman 70-75; R Acle 75-89; R Fishley 77-89; RD Blofield 79-87; P-in-c Burlingham St Andr w St Pet 85-89; R Acle w Fishley and N Burlingham

89; TV Thetford from 89; Ind Chapl from 89; Dioc Rep for Abp's Commn on UPA from 91. *44 Monksgate, Thetford, Norfolk IP24 1BY*   Thetford (01842) 766074

WILSON, Kenneth. b 59. ARICS84 Selw Coll Cam MA82 DipRS88. S'wark Ord Course 86. **d** 89 **p** 90. C Walthamstow St Pet *Chelmsf* 89-92; TV Wolv *Lich* from 92. *All Saints Vicarage, Vicarage Road, Wolverhampton WV2 1DT*   Sedgley (01902) 883255

WILSON, Malcolm Richard Milburn. b 30. Edin Th Coll 57. **d** 59 **p** 60. R Newport-on-Tay *St And* 65-70; R Tayport 65-70; R Baillieston *Glas* 70-74; R Milngavie 74-84; R Bearsden 74-84; R Dalbeattie 84-88; R Gourock 88-94; rtd 94. *20 Dougalston Gardens North, Milngavie, Glasgow G62 6HN*   0141-956 4138

WILSON, Marjorie Jayne. *See* SHIPTON, Mrs Marjorie Jayne

WILSON, Mark Anthony John. b 56. TCD BA80. CITC 75. **d** 80 **p** 81. C Dub Rathfarnham *D & G* 80-83; Bp's C Dub Finglas 83-85; I Celbridge w Straffan and Newcastle-Lyons 85-88; CF 88-93; I Dundalk w Heynestown *Arm* from 93. *The Rectory, Old Golf Links Road, Blackrock, Co Louth, Irish Republic*   Dundalk (42) 21402

WILSON, Mark John Crichton. b 46. Clare Coll Cam BA67 MA70. Ridley Hall Cam 67. **d** 69 **p** 70. C Luton w E Hyde *St Alb* 69-72; C Ashtead *Guildf* 72-77; Chapl Epsom Coll Surrey 77-81; V Epsom Common Ch Ch *Guildf* from 81; RD Epsom 87-91. *Christ Church Vicarage, 20 Christ Church Road, Epsom, Surrey KT19 8NE*   Epsom (01372) 720302

WILSON, Canon Mavis Kirby. b 42. Cam Univ CertEd71 Ex Univ BA64. S Dios Minl Tr Scheme 82. **dss** 84 **d** 87 **p** 94. Chessington *Guildf* 84-85; Epsom St Martin 85-86; Epsom Common Ch Ch 86-87; C from 87; Dioc Adv in Miss and Evang from 90; Hon Can Guildf Cathl from 94. *Christ Church Vicarage, 20 Christ Church Road, Epsom, Surrey KT19 8NE*   Epsom (01372) 720302

WILSON, Mervyn Raynold Alwyn. b 33. Qu Coll Cam BA57 MA61. Ripon Hall Ox 57. **d** 59 **p** 60. C Rubery *Birm* 59-62; C Kings Norton 62-63; V Hamstead St Bernard 63-69; R Bermondsey St Mary w St Olave, St Jo etc *S'wark* 69-78; R Bulwick, Blatherwycke w Harringworth and Laxton *Pet* from 78. *The Rectory, Church Lane, Bulwick, Corby, Northants NN17 3DY*   Bulwick (01780) 285249

WILSON, Very Rev Mervyn Robert. b 22. Bris Univ BA51 Lon Univ BD58. Tyndale Hall Bris 52. **d** 52 **p** 53. I Ballyphilip w Ardquin *D & D* 61-70; I Newry St Patr 70-92; RD Newry and Mourne 77-83; RD Kilbroney 77-83; Preb Dromore Cathl 83-85; Can St Anne's Cathl *Conn* 85-89; Dean Dromore *D & D* 90-92; rtd 92. *31 Manor Drive, Lisburn, Co Antrim BT28 1JH*   Lisburn (01846) 666361

WILSON, Michael. b 13. Trin Coll Cam BA35 MA39. Westcott Ho Cam 37. **d** 38 **p** 39. C Bournemouth St Clem w St Mary *Win* 68-73; V Appleshaw 73-78; rtd 78. *The Friary, 19 St Cross Road, Winchester, Hants SO23 9JA*   Winchester (01962) 860172

WILSON, Canon Michael. b 44. Liv Univ BA66 Fitzw Coll Cam BA68 MA73. Westcott Ho Cam. **d** 69 **p** 70. C Worksop Priory *S'well* 69-71; C Gt Malvern St Mary *Worc* 71-75; V Leic St Anne *Leic* 75-85; TR Leic Ascension 85-88; Hon Can Leic Cathl 85-88; Can Res and Treas from 88. *7 St Martins East, Leicester LE1 5FX*   Leicester (0116) 253 0580

WILSON, Neil. b 61. Newc Univ BA83. Ripon Coll Cuddesdon 85. **d** 88 **p** 89. C Wallsend St Luke *Newc* 88-91; C Monkseaton St Pet 91-93; V Earsdon and Backworth from 93. *Earsdon Vicarage, 5 Front Street, Whitley Bay, Tyne & Wear NE25 9JU*   0191-252 9393

WILSON, Paul Edward. b 43. Ridley Hall Cam 81. **d** 83 **p** 84. C Brighstone and Brooke w Mottistone *Portsm* 83-86; C Shorwell w Kingston 83-86; TV Tring *St Alb* 86-90; P-in-c Renhold 90-91; Chapl HM Pris Bedf 90-91; V Buckfastleigh w Dean Prior *Ex* from 91. *The Vicarage, Glebelands, Buckfastleigh, Devon TQ11 0BH*   Buckfastleigh (01364) 44228

WILSON, Paul Hugh. b 26. Glouc Sch of Min 80. **d** 83 **p** 84. NSM Much Birch w Lt Birch, Much Dewchurch etc *Heref* 83-86; C 86-92; rtd 92; Perm to Offic *Heref* from 92. *Cherry Lyn, Staunton-on-Wye, Hereford HR4 7LR*   Golden Valley (01981) 500231

WILSON, Paul Thomas Wardley. b 43. AKC67. St Aug Coll Cant. **d** 70 **p** 71. C Tokyngton St Mich *Lon* 70-74; Soc Community Worker *Roch* 74-81; Perm to Offic from 81; Lic to Offic *Cant* 83-88; Sen Adv Coun for Soc Resp from 83; Chief Exec Carr Gomm Soc from 88. *Carr Gomm Society, Telegraph Hill Centre, Kitto Road, London SE14 5TY*   0171-277 5050

WILSON, Peter James. b 65. Natal Univ BA85 Cape Town Univ HDipEd86 BA87. **d** 89 **p** 89. S Africa 89-91; C Newton Aycliffe *Dur* 91-94; OGS from 91; C Tottenham St Paul *Lon* from 94. *The Curate's Flat, St Paul's Vicarage, 60 Park Lane, London N17 0JR*   0181-885 1395

WILSON, Peter John. b 43. CertEd76 BEd84. Linc Th Coll. **d** 71 **p** 72. C Stretford St Matt *Man* 71-73; C Rugby St Andr *Cov* 73-76; TV 86-92; Hon C Bilton 76-79; Asst Dir of Educn

Blackb 79-81; P-in-c Accrington St Paul 79-81; Dioc Officer for Stewardship *Carl* from 92; P-in-c Dacre from 95. *Dacre Vicarage, Stainton, Penrith, Cumbria CA11 0ES* Penrith (01768) 63179

WILSON, Peter Sheppard. b 39. TCD BA61. CITC 62. **d** 62 **p** 63. C Killowen *D & R* 62-68; C Portadown St Columba *Arm* 68-70; I Convoy w Monellan and Donaghmore *D & R* 70-78; P-in-c Castletown *S & M* 78; V 78-83; R Kilmacolm *Glas* 83-84; R Bridge of Weir 83-84; I Camus-juxta-Bann *D & R* 85-92; Bp's Dom Chapl 90-92; I Maguiresbridge w Derrybrusk *Clogh* from 92; RD Enniskillen from 95. *9 Drumgoon Road, Maguiresbridge, Co Fermanagh BT94 4PJ* Lisnaskea (013657) 21250

WILSON, Quentin Harcourt. b 45. FTCL75 K Coll Lon AKC68 BD76. St Aug Coll Cant 69. **d** 70 **p** 71. C Is of Dogs Ch Ch and St Jo w St Luke *Lon* 70-72; C Muswell Hill St Jas 72-77; Succ and Sacr Ex Cathl *Ex* 77-81; Min Can Windsor 81-84; V Langho Billington *Blackb* from 84; Chapl Brockhall Hosp Blackb from 85; RD Whalley *Blackb* 89-95. *St Leonard's Vicarage, Whalley Road, Billington, Clitheroe, Lancs BB7 9NA* Whalley (01254) 822246

WILSON, Robert Brian. b 29. AKC55. **d** 56 **p** 57. V Hunslet Moor St Pet and St Cuth *Ripon* 63-70; V Bilton 70-80; V Gt and Lt Ouseburn w Marton-cum-Grafton 80-90; rtd 90. *56 Church Avenue, Harrogate, N Yorkshire HG1 4HG* Harrogate (01423) 504398

WILSON, Canon Robert Malcolm (Robin). b 35. St Andr Univ MA59. ALCD62. **d** 62 **p** 63. C Wallington H Trin *S'wark* 62-66; C Dur St Nic *Dur* 66-70; V Colchester St Pet *Chelmsf* from 70; RD Colchester from 93; Hon Can Chelmsf Cathl from 94. *The Vicarage, Balkerne Close, Colchester CO1 1NZ* Colchester (01206) 572641

WILSON, Robert Michael. b 33. Linc Th Coll 73. **d** 75 **p** 76. C Knottingley *Wakef* 75-78; P-in-c Cleckheaton St Luke 78-84; Ind Chapl 78-94; P-in-c Cleckheaton St Luke and Whitechapel 84; V Batley All SS 86-94; RD Dewsbury 90-93; rtd 94. *1 White Lee Side, Heckmondwike, W Yorkshire WF16 9PD* Batley (01924) 411778

WILSON, Robert Stoker. b 39. Dur Univ BSc62. Oak Hill Th Coll 62. **d** 64 **p** 65. C High Elswick St Paul *Newc* 64-68; C Kirkheaton 68-70; Youth Chapl *Liv* 70-73; P-in-c S Shields St Steph *Dur* 73-78; R 78-83; Youth Chapl 73-77; P-in-c S Shields St Aid 81-83; V Greenside 83-94; P-in-c Fatfield from 94. *49 Larchwood, Harraton, Washington, Tyne & Wear NE38 9BT* 0191-416 3134

✠**WILSON, Rt Rev Roger Plumpton.** b 05. KCVO74. Keble Coll Ox BA28 MA34. Lambeth DD49 Westcott Ho Cam 35. **d** 35 **p** 36 **c** 49. C Prince's Park St Paul *Liv* 35-38; C Westmr St Jo 38-39; V S Shore H Trin *Blackb* 39-44; V Radcliffe-on-Trent *S'well* 44-49; Adn Nottm 44-49; V Shelford 46-49; Bp Wakef 49-58; Bp Chich 58-74; Clerk of the Closet 63-74; rtd 74; Asst Bp B & W from 74. *Kingsett, Wrington, Bristol BS18 7NH* Wrington (01934) 862464

WILSON, Canon Ronald. b 11. St Aid Birkenhead. **d** 51 **p** 52. V Pinchbeck *Linc* 63-78; Can and Preb Linc Cathl 72-78; rtd 78. *14 Windermere Gardens, Linslade, Leighton Buzzard, Beds LU7 7QP* Leighton Buzzard (01525) 379676

WILSON, Canon Spencer William. b 08. AKC35. **d** 35 **p** 36. V Haydock St Jas *Liv* 42-82; Hon Can Liv Cathl 71-82; rtd 82; Perm to Offic *Chich* from 83. *College of St Barnabas, Blackberry Lane, Lingfield, Surrey RH7 6NJ* Dormans Park (01342) 870260

WILSON, Stanley. b 24. TCD BA45 MA50. **d** 46 **p** 47. Chapl Worc Hosps 67-77; V The Guitings, Cutsdean and Farmcote *Glouc* 77-92; rtd 92. *St Columb, 10 Haslette Way, Up Hatherley, Cheltenham, Glos GL51 5RQ* Cheltenham (01242) 578937

WILSON, Stephen Charles. b 51. Newc Univ BA73 Cam Univ MA82. Westcott Ho Cam BA78. **d** 79 **p** 80. C Fulham All SS *Lon* 79-82; C W Hampstead St Jas 82-85; P-in-c Alexandra Park St Sav 85-93; V Preston next Faversham, Goodnestone and Graveney *Cant* from 93. *The Vicarage, Preston Lane, Faversham, Kent ME13 8LG* Faversham (01795) 536801

WILSON, Stephen John. b 45. Bradf Univ BTech69. Trin Coll Bris DipHE92. **d** 92 **p** 93. C Marple All SS *Ches* from 92. *125 Church Lane, Marple, Stockport, Cheshire SK6 7LD* 0161-427 1467

WILSON, Stuart Michael. b 47. Surrey Univ BSc71. St Steph Ho Ox BA73 MA78. **d** 74 **p** 75. C Tottenham St Paul *Lon* 74-78; C-in-c S Kenton Annunciation CD 78-82; V Hoxton H Trin w St Mary from 82. *Holy Trinity Vicarage, 3 Bletchley Street, London N1 7QG* 0171-253 4796

WILSON, Thomas Irven. b 30. TCD BA51 MA58. **d** 53 **p** 54. Chapl RAF 56-75; QHC from 80; rtd 80. *Rathclaren House, Kilbrittain, Co Cork, Irish Republic* Clonakilty (23) 49689

WILSON, Canon Thomas Roderick. b 26. St Pet Hall Ox BA50 MA55. Sarum Th Coll 50. **d** 52 **p** 53. V Habergham Eaves H Trin *Blackb* 58-78; RD Burnley 70-78; Hon Can Blackb Cathl

75-89; V Bare 78-81; P-in-c Accrington St Jas 81-82; P-in-c Accrington St Paul 81-82; V Accrington St Jas w St Paul 82-89; rtd 89. *33 Nook Terrace, Cherry Tree, Blackburn BB2 4SW* Blackburn (01254) 209390

WILSON, Timothy Charles. b 62. Oak Hill Th Coll BA90. **d** 90 **p** 91. C Highley *Heref* 90-94; C Margate H Trin *Cant* from 94. *4 Sandhurst Road, Margate, Kent CT9 3HR* Thanet (01843) 221178

WILSON, Timothy John (Tim). b 58. St Pet Coll Ox MA80. Trin Coll Bris 81. **d** 83 **p** 84. C Gt Horton *Bradf* 83-86; C Handforth *Ches* 86-90; V Salterhebble All SS *Wakef* from 90. *All Saints' Vicarage, Greenroyd Avenue, Halifax, W Yorkshire HX3 0LP* Halifax (01422) 365805

WILSON, Victor Isaac. b 23. St Deiniol's Hawarden 69. **d** 71 **p** 72. C Davenham *Ches* 71-75; V Latchford Ch Ch 75-80; V Stalybridge St Paul 80-88; rtd 88. *215 Huddersfield Road, Stalybridge, Cheshire SK15 3DY* 0161-38 2386

WILSON, Walter. b 33. **d** 60 **p** 61. C Sheff St Swithun *Sheff* 60-64; Ind Chapl 64-66; C Attercliffe 66-69; R Swallow w Cabourn *Linc* 69-72; Dioc Youth Officer *Heref* 72-77; Chapl Ipswich Sch from 77. *37 Henley Road, Ipswich IP1 3SJ* Ipswich (01473) 255561 or 255313

WILSON, William Adam (Bill). b 53. Sheff Univ BA74 St Jo Coll Dur BA84. Cranmer Hall Dur 82. **d** 85 **p** 86. C S Croydon Em *S'wark* 85-89; C Wandsworth All SS 89-93; Chapl Fontainebleau *Eur* from 93. *21 Quai Franklin Roosevelt, 77920 Samois sur Seine, France* France (33) 64 24 81 57 Fax as telephone

WILSON, William Bell. b 04. AKC28. **d** 27 **p** 28. V Cov St Geo *Cov* 39-71; rtd 71. *c/o E H Whitehead Esq, 7 Warwick Road, Stratford-upon-Avon, Warks CV37 6YW* Stratford-upon-Avon (01789) 294867

WILSON, William Gerard (Bill). b 42. St Chad's Coll Dur BA65 DipTh67. **d** 67 **p** 68. C Hollinwood *Man* 67-71; V Oldham St Jas 71-79; R Birch w Fallowfield 79-93; V Paddington St Jas *Lon* from 93. *The Vicarage, 6 Gloucester Terrace, London W2 3DD* 0171-723 8119

✠**WILSON, Rt Rev William Gilbert.** b 18. TCD BA39 MA44 BD44 PhD49. TCD Div Sch Div Test40. **d** 41 **p** 42 **c** 81. C Belf St Mary Magd *Conn* 41-44; C Ban St Comgall *D & D* 44-47; I Armoy w Loughguile *Conn* 47-76; Preb Conn Cathl 64-76; I Lisburn Ch Ch 76-81; Dean Conn 76-81; Bp K, E & A 81-93; rtd 93. *24 Pennington Park, Cairnshill Road, Belfast BT8 4GJ* Belfast (01232) 701742

WILSON, William Hubert. b 08. Clare Coll Cam BA31 MA34. Westcott Ho Cam 31. **d** 32 **p** 33. R Church Stretton *Heref* 64-72; Israel 72-76; rtd 76. *Anchorage Cottage, Denhead, St Andrews, Fife KY16 8PB* Strathkinness (0133485) 589

WILSON, William John (Bill). b 25. CEng MIEE MRTS. S Dios Minl Tr Scheme 79. **d** 82 **p** 83. NSM Weeke *Win* 82-88; NSM Win St Barn from 89. *23 Buriton Road, Winchester, Hants SO22 6JE* Winchester (01962) 881904

WILTON, Albert Edward. b 10. St Paul's Grahamstown 69. **d** 67 **p** 68. S Africa 69-77; rtd 77; Perm to Offic *St E* 77-86; Perm to Offic *Chich* from 92. *College of St Barnabas, Blackberry Lane, Lingfield, Surrey RH7 6NJ* Dormans Park (01342) 870609

WILTON, Gary Ian. b 60. Bath Univ BSc83. Trin Coll Bris MA93 Wycliffe Hall Ox 85. **d** 88 **p** 89. C Clevedon St Andr and Ch Ch *B & W* 88-92; Lect Univ of the W of England, Bris 92-93; TV Bath Twerton-on-Avon *B & W* from 93. *The Ascension Vicarage, 35A Claude Avenue, Bath BA2 1AF* Bath (01225) 421971

WILTON (nee ADAMS), Mrs Gillian Linda. b 57. SRN79 SCM81. Trin Coll Bris DipHE84 DPS85. **dss** 85 **d** 87 **p** 94. Easton H Trin w St Gabr and St Lawr and St Jude *Bris* 85-87; Par Dn 87-91; Regional Adv (Dios B & W and Bris) CMJ from 91; Perm to Offic *B & W* 92-93; NSM Bath Twerton-on-Avon from 93. *The Ascension Vicarage, 35A Claude Avenue, Bath BA2 1AF* Bath (01225) 421971

WILTON, Glenn Warner Paul. b 33. Miami Univ BSc55 Washington Univ MSocWork76. Ch Div Sch of the Pacific (USA) 77. **d** 65 **p** 66. In RC Ch 65-72; USA 77-81; Chapl Pastures Hosp Derby 82-88; Chapl St Aug Hosp Cant 89-94; Chapl St Martin's Hosp Cant from 94. *St Martin's Hospital, Littlebourne Road, Canterbury, Kent CT1 1TD* Canterbury (01227) 454230 or 459584

WILTON, Harry Owens (Hal). b 22. St Aid Birkenhead 43. **d** 46 **p** 47. C Edge Hill St Cypr *Liv* 46-49; C Kingston upon Hull H Trin *York* 49-51; Area Sec (NW England) CCCS 51-53; V Southport All So *Liv* 53-56. *Crantock, 34 Prenton Lane, Birkenhead, Merseyside L42 8LB* 0151-608 4540 Fax 609 0529

WILTSE, Joseph August Jean Paul. b 41. Leeds Univ BA64. Coll of Resurr Mirfield 64. **d** 66 **p** 67. C Airedale w Fryston *Wakef* 66-70; Canada from 70. *6983 Richmond Street, Powell River, British Columbia, Canada, V8A 1H7*

WILTSHIRE, Albert. b 19. Qu Coll Birm 49. **d** 51 **p** 52. V Woodhorn w Newbiggin *Newc* 63-71; V Chatton w

Chillingham 71-75; Chapl OHP 75-77; P-in-c Felton *Newc* 77-80; V Cornhill w Carham 80-85; V Branxton 80-85; rtd 85. *The Levers, Yeavering, Wooler, Northd NE71 6HG* Milfield (016686) 427

WILTSHIRE, John Herbert Arthur. b 27. S'wark Ord Course 63. **d** 66 **p** 67. Min W Dulwich Em CD *S'wark* 69-79; R Coulsdon St Jo 79-93; rtd 93. *66 Meadow Lane, Willaston, South Wirral L64 2TZ* 0151-327 6668

WILTSHIRE, Robert Michael (Bob). b 50. W Midl Minl Tr Course. **d** 89 **p** 90. NSM Droitwich Spa *Worc* from 89. *Address temp unknown*

WILTSHIRE, Archdeacon of. *See* SMITH, Ven Brian John

WIMBUSH, Timothy. b 44. JP. St Steph Ho Ox. **d** 68 **p** 69. C Hobs Moat *Birm* 68-71; C W Wycombe *Ox* 71-76; R Epwell w Sibford, Swalcliffe and Tadmarton from 76; RD Deddington from 86. *The Rectory, Sibford Gower, Banbury, Oxon OX15 5RW* Swalcliffe (01295) 780555

WIMMER, Michael John. b 41. Natal Univ BA64. Coll of Resurr Mirfield 65. **d** 67 **p** 68. S Africa 67-86; Canada from 86; Miss to Seamen from 86. *c/o Missions to Seamen, 50 North Dunlevy Avenue, Vancouver, BC, Canada, V6A 3R1*

WIMSETT, Paul. b 58. Univ of Wales (Abth) BSc(Econ)79 Hull Univ MA86. St Jo Coll Nottm DipTh83. **d** 85 **p** 86. C Nuneaton St Nic *Cov* 85-89; C Loughb Em *Leic* 89-92; TV Totnes, Bridgetown & Berry Pomeroy & Dartington *Ex* from 92. *The Vicarage, Week, Dartington, Totnes, Devon TQ9 6JL* Totnes (01803) 868304

WIMSHURST, Michael Alexander. b 33. St Jo Coll Ox BA58. Westcott Ho Cam 59. **d** 60 **p** 61. C Lewisham St Mary *S'wark* 60-65; India 66-70; V Battersea St Pet *S'wark* 71-73; V Battersea St Pet and St Paul from 73. *St Peter's Vicarage, Plough Road, London SW11 2DE* 0171-228 8027

WINBOLT LEWIS, Martin John. b 46. Fitzw Coll Cam BA69 MA72. St Jo Coll Nottm LTh75. **d** 75 **p** 76. C Highbury Ch Ch *Lon* 75-78; C Nottm St Nic *S'well* 79-82; R Carlton Colville *Nor* 82-83; R Carlton Colville w Mutford and Rushmere 83-88; V Burley *Ripon* from 88. *The Vicarage, 271 Burley Road, Leeds LS4 2EL* Leeds (0113) 278 5872 or 230 4408

WINCH, Victor Edward. b 17. AIB41 Selw Coll Cam BA47 MA52. Ridley Hall Cam. **d** 48 **p** 49. V Kirdford *Chich* 69-82; rtd 82; Perm to Offic *Heref* from 83. *16 Whitehouse Drive, Kingstone, Hereford HR2 9ER* Golden Valley (01981) 250796

WINCHESTER, Gordon Law. b 50. LTCL LRAM ARCM. Trin Coll Bris. **d** 82 **p** 83. C Cheadle *Ches* 82-84; Asst Chapl Amsterdam *Eur* 84-88; C Hove Bp Hannington Memorial Ch *Chich* from 88. *43 Hogarth Road, Hove, E Sussex BN3 5RH* Brighton (01273) 725642

WINCHESTER, Paul. b 44. St Pet Coll Ox BA66 MA70. Ridley Hall Cam 67. **d** 69 **p** 70. C Wednesfield Heath *Lich* 69-72; Perm to Offic *Sarum* 73-84; R Tushingham and Whitewell *Ches* from 84. *The Vicarage, Tushingham, Whitchurch, Shropshire SY13 4QS* Hampton Heath (0194885) 328

WINCHESTER, Paul Marc. b 53. Univ of Wales (Lamp) BA80 DipTh. St Mich Coll Llan 82. **d** 84 **p** 85. C Bedwellty *Mon* 84-86; C Chepstow 86-89; V Cwmcarn 89-93; V Fleur-de-Lis from 93. *The Vicarage, Commercial Street, Fleur-de-Lis, Blackwood, Gwent NP2 1TX* Bargoed (01443) 830467

WINCHESTER, Archdeacon of. *See* CLARKSON, Ven Alan Geoffrey

WINCHESTER, Bishop of. *Vacant*

WINCHESTER, Dean of. *See* BEESON, Very Rev Trevor Randall

WINDEBANK, Clive Leonard. b 41. New Coll Ox BA62 MA85. Ox NSM Course 75. **d** 78 **p** 79. Kuwait 78-83; NSM Brompton H Trin w Onslow Square St Paul *Lon* 83-84; NSM Basildon w Aldworth and Ashampstead *Ox* 85-88; NSM Streatley w Moulsford from 88. *The Coombe House, The Coombe, Streatley, Reading RG8 9QL* Goring-on-Thames (01491) 872174

WINDER, John William. b 15. SS Coll Cam BA37 MA41. Ridley Hall Cam 37. **d** 39 **p** 40. R Bolton by Bowland *Bradf* 66-81; rtd 81; Perm to Offic *Bradf* from 81. *2 Croft Rise, Menston, Ilkley, W Yorkshire LS29 6LU* Menston (01943) 872084

WINDIATE, Mrs Mary Elizabeth. b 49. Linc Th Coll CMinlStuds94. **d** 94 **p** 95. C Loughton St Jo *Chelmsf* from 94. *2 Doubleday Road, Loughton, Essex IG10 2LG*

WINDLE, Christopher Rodney. b 45. Univ of Wales (Lamp) BA66. Qu Coll Birm DipTh68. **d** 70 **p** 71. C Lache cum Saltney *Ches* 70-73; C Stockton Heath 73-76; P-in-c Bredbury St Barn 76-83; V from 83. *St Barnabas' Vicarage, Osborne Street, Stockport, Cheshire SK6 2DA* 0161-494 1191

WINDMILL, Roy Stanley. b 17. Sarum Th Coll. **d** 54 **p** 55. C-in-c Kineton *Cov* 70-75; C-in-c Combroke w Compton Verney 70-75; C Wraxall *B & W* 76-78; P-in-c Holton 78-82; rtd 82; Perm to Offic *B & W* from 82. *The Garden Flat, 38B Berrow Road, Burnham-on-Sea, Somerset TA8 2EX* Burnham-on-Sea (01278) 782715

WINDRIDGE, Michael Harry. b 47. Sarum & Wells Th Coll DCM93. **d** 93 **p** 94. C Hempnall *Nor* from 93. *Ferndene, Broaden Lane, Hempnall, Norwich NR15 2LU* Hempnall (01508) 499043

WINDRIDGE, Peter William Roland. b 23. ACGI MIMechE BScEng. Sarum & Wells Th Coll 82. **d** 84 **p** 85. NSM Shirley St Jo *Cant* 84; NSM Shirley St Jo *S'wark* 85-86; NSM New Addington 86-95; rtd 95. *83 Orchard Avenue, Croydon CR0 7NF* 0181-655 0872

WINDROSS, Andrew (Andy). b 49. Univ of Wales (Ban) BA71. Cuddesdon Coll 71. **d** 74 **p** 75. C Wakef St Jo *Wakef* 74-78; C Bromley All Hallows *Lon* 78-83; V De Beauvoir Town St Pet from 83; AD Hackney 89-94. *St Peter's Vicarage, 86 De Beauvoir Road, London N1 5AT* 0171-254 5670

WINDROSS, Anthony Michael (Tony). b 50. CCC Cam BA72 MA75 Birm Univ PGCE73. S Dios Minl Tr Scheme 90. **d** 93 **p** 94. NSM Eastbourne St Mary *Chich* from 93. *15 Peppercombe Road, Eastbourne, E Sussex BN20 8JH* Eastbourne (01323) 643917

WINDSLOW, Miss Kathryn Alison. b 62. Southn Univ BTh83. Linc Th Coll 84. **dss** 86 **d** 87 **p** 94. Littlehampton and Wick *Chich* 86-87; Par Dn 87-89; D-in-c Scotton w Northorpe *Linc* 89-94; Asst Local Min Officer from 89; P-in-c Scotton w Northorpe from 94. *The Rectory, Scotton, Gainsborough, Lincs DN21 3QP* Scunthorpe (01724) 764020

WINDSOR, Dean of. *See* MITCHELL, Very Rev Patrick Reynolds

WINFIELD, Ms Flora Jane Louise. b 64. Univ of Wales (Lamp) BA85. Ripon Coll Cuddesdon 87. **d** 89 **p** 94. Par Dn Stantonbury and Willen *Ox* 89-92; Glos Ecum Coun Co Officer *Glouc* 92-94; Chapl Mansf Coll Ox from 94. *1 Laburnam Avenue, Abingdon, Oxon OX13 6EN* Abingdon (01235) 550772

WINFIELD, Miss June Mary. b 29. Gilmore Ho 57. **dss** 66 **d** 87 **p** 94. Bracknell *Ox* 68-74; Dean of Women's Min 74-80; St Marylebone w H Trin *Lon* 80-82; Ind Chapl 82-89; rtd 89; NSM Ealing St Steph Castle Hill *Lon* from 89; Asst Dio Dir Ord Willesden Area from 94. *Kaire, 3 Clementine Close, London W13 9UB* 0181-840 5696

WING, Miss Myra Susan. b 45. Cranmer Hall Dur 92. **d** 94 **p** 95. C Appledore w Brookland, Fairfield, Brenzett etc *Cant* from 94; Hon C Wittersham w Stone-in-Oxney and Ebony from 95. *Puddleglum, Rhee Wall, Brenzett, Romney Marsh, Kent TN29 9VB* Brookland (01797) 344125

WINGATE, Andrew David Carlile. b 44. Worc Coll Ox BA66 MPhil68 MA71. Linc Th Coll 70. **d** 72 **p** 73. C Halesowen *Worc* 72-75; India 76-82; Prin W Midl Minl Tr Course 82-90; Prin Coll of Ascension Selly Oak from 90. *The College of the Ascension, Weoley Park Road, Birmingham B29 6RD* 0121-472 1667 Fax 472 4320

WINGATE, Canon David Hugh. b 22. Qu Coll Cam BA48 MA53. Qu Coll Birm 47. **d** 49 **p** 50. Chapl United Leeds Hosp 66-71; Chapl Garlands Cumberland and Westmoreland Hosps 71-86; V Cotehill and Cumwhinton *Carl* 72-86; Hon Can Carl Cathl 85-86; rtd 87; Perm to Offic *Carl* from 87. *26 Beechwood Avenue, Carlisle CA3 9BW* Carlisle (01228) 38061

WINGFIELD, Christoper Laurence (Chris). b 57. Ripon Coll Cuddesdon DipMin95. **d** 95. C Hadleigh w Layham and Shelley *St E* from 95. *74 Ann Beaumont Way, Hadleigh, Ipswich IP7 6SB* Ipswich (01473) 823135

WINGFIELD, Eric John. b 16. Queensland Univ BA51. ACT ThL43 St Fran Coll Brisbane. **d** 44 **p** 44. R Wadingham w Snitterby *Linc* 59-77; V Cowbit 77-78; P-in-c Moulton St Jas 77-78; P-in-c Weston 78; V Cowbit 78-81; rtd 81. *1A Fallowfield, Luton LU3 1UL* Luton (01582) 592208

WINGFIELD-DIGBY, Andrew Richard. b 50. Keble Coll Ox BA72. Wycliffe Hall Ox 74. **d** 77 **p** 78. C Cockfosters Ch Ch CD *Lon* 77-80; C Enfield Ch Ch Trent Park 80-84; Dir Chrs in Sport from 84; Hon C Ox St Aldate w St Matt *Ox* 84-94; Hon C Ox St Aldate from 95. *Christians in Sport, PO Box 93, Oxford OX2 7YP* Oxford (01865) 311211

WINGFIELD DIGBY, Very Rev Richard Shuttleworth. b 11. Ch Coll Cam BA35 MA39. Westcott Ho Cam 35. **d** 36 **p** 37. Dean Pet 66-80; rtd 80; Perm to Offic *B & W* from 81. *Byways, Higher Holton, Wincanton, Somerset BA9 8AP* Wincanton (01963) 32137

WINGFIELD-DIGBY, Ven Stephen Basil. b 10. MBE. Ox Univ MA. Wycliffe Hall Ox. **d** 36 **p** 37. Can Res Sarum Cathl *Sarum* 68-79; Adn Sarum 68-79; rtd 79. *Eastbury House, Long Street, Sherborne, Dorset DT9 3BZ* Sherborne (01935) 812876

WINKETT, Miss Lucy Clare. b 68. ARCM92 Selw Coll Cam BA90 MA94. Qu Coll Birm BD94. **d** 95. C Lt Ilford St Mich *Chelmsf* from 95. *3 Toronto Avenue, London E12 5JF* 0181-553 4627

WINKS, Paul David. b 45. Ex Univ BA67. Cuddesdon Coll 68. **d** 70 **p** 71. C Rickerscote *Lich* 70-73; Chapl RAF 73-75; C Yate *Bris* 76-77; TV Yate New Town 77-83; P-in-c Leigh upon

Mendip w Stoke St Michael *B & W* 83-84; V from 84. *The Vicarage, Leigh Street, Leigh upon Mendip, Bath BA3 5QP* Mells (01373) 812559

WINLO, Ronald. b 14. Open Univ BA74. AKC41. **d** 41 **p** 42. V Kirkby Malzeard w Dallow Gill *Ripon* 66-81; rtd 81. *12 Roslyn Road, Harrogate, N Yorkshire HG2 7SB* Harrogate (01423) 884442

WINN, Mrs Jean Elizabeth. b 58. Man Univ BSc80. Wycliffe Hall Ox 85. **d** 88. C W Derby St Luke *Liv* 88-89. *St Thomas's Vicarage, Elm Road, Liverpool L21 1BH* 0151-928 1889

WINN, Paul William James. b 44. Liv Univ BSc66. E Midl Min Tr Course 86. **d** 89 **p** 90. NSM Spalding St Paul *Linc* 89-94. *10 Holland Road, Spalding, Lincs PE11 1UL* Spalding (01775) 722802

WINN, Peter Anthony. b 60. Worc Coll Ox BA82 MA86. Wycliffe Hall Ox 83. **d** 86 **p** 87. C W Derby Gd Shep *Liv* 86-89; V Seaforth from 89. *St Thomas's Vicarage, Elm Road, Liverpool L21 1BH* 0151-928 1889

WINNARD, Jack. b 30. Oak Hill Th Coll 79. **d** 81 **p** 82. C Skelmersdale St Paul *Liv* 81-84; C Goose Green 84-85; V Wigan St Barn Marsh Green from 85. *St Barnabas' Vicarage, Lancaster Road, Wigan, Lancs WN5 0PT* Wigan (01942) 222092

WINNINGTON-INGRAM, David Robert. b 59. Hertf Coll Ox BA82 MA85 K Coll Cam BA89. Westcott Ho Cam 87. **d** 90 **p** 91. C Bishop's Cleeve *Glouc* 90-94; TV Walton, Southleigh, Offwell, Widworthy etc *Ex* from 94. *The Rectory, Offwell, Honiton, Devon EX14 9SB* Honiton (01404) 831480

WINSOR, Anthony Geoffrey. b 56. Univ of Wales (Abth) BA. BTh87. Linc Th Coll 84. **d** 87 **p** 88. C Cobbold Road St Sav w St Mary *Lon* 87-88; Barnardo's CANDL Project 88-89. *Address temp unknown*

WINSPER, Arthur William (Brother Benedict). b 46. Glas NSM Course 89. **d** 91 **p** 92. SSF from 70; NSM Barrowfield *Glas* from 91. *16 Dalserf Street, Barrowfield, Glasgow G31 4AS* 0141-550 1202

✠WINSTANLEY, Rt Rev Alan Leslie. b 49. Nottm Univ BTh72. St Jo Coll Nottm 68 ALCD72. **d** 72 **p** 73 **c** 88. C Livesey *Blackb* 72-75; C Gt Sankey *Liv* 75-77; P-in-c Penketh 75-77; V 78-81; SAMS 81-93; Peru 88-93; Bp Bolivia and Peru 88-93; V Eastham *Ches* from 94; Asst Bp Ches from 94. *The Vicarage, Ferry Road, Eastham, Wirral, Merseyside L62 0AJ* 0151-327 2182

WINSTANLEY, Canon Cyril Henry. b 04. Liv Univ BA26 MA30. Ridley Hall Cam 30. **d** 32 **p** 33. V Liv Ch Ch Norris Green *Liv* 41-72; Hon Can Liv Cathl 66-72; rtd 72; Perm to Offic *Liv* from 83. *49 Menlove Gardens West, Liverpool L18 2ET* 0151-722 9177

WINSTANLEY, John Graham. b 47. K Coll Lon 67. **d** 71 **p** 72. C Wandsworth St Paul *S'wark* 71-74; Chapl Salford Univ *Man* 75-79; R Kersal Moor 79-87. *14 Lyndhurst Avenue, Prestwich, Manchester M25 8DF* 0161-740 2715

WINSTON, Jeremy Hugh. b 54. Univ of Wales BEd76. St Steph Ho Ox BA78. **d** 79 **p** 80. C Bassaleg *Mon* 79-83; Dioc Children's Adv from 79; V Itton and St Arvans w Penterry and Kilgwrrwg etc 83-93; V Abergavenny St Mary w Llanwenarth Citra from 93. *St Mary's Vicarage, Monk Street, Abergavenny, Gwent NP7 5ND* Abergavenny (01873) 853168

WINSTONE, Canon Peter John. b 30. Jes Coll Ox BA52 MA56. Ridley Hall Cam 53. **d** 55 **p** 56. V Clapham *Bradf* 67-84; R Leathley w Farnley, Fewston and Blubberhouses 84-95; Hon Can Bradf Cathl 89-95; rtd 95. *7 Kingfisher Close, Worcester WR5 3RY* Worcester (01905) 763114

WINTER, Anthony Cathcart. b 28. FCA. Ridley Hall Cam 54. **d** 56 **p** 57. V Newmarket All SS *St E* 63-73; Lic to Offic 74-81; Perm to Offic *Lon* 78-81; Hon C St Andr-by-the-Wardrobe w St Ann, Blackfriars 81-86; Hon C Smithfield St Bart Gt from 86. *246 Crescent House, London EC1Y 0SL* 0171-250 0741

WINTER, Canon David Brian. b 29. K Coll Lon BA53 CertEd54. Oak Hill NSM Course. **d** 87 **p** 88. Hon C Finchley St Paul and St Luke *Lon* 87-89; Hd Relig Broadcasting BBC 87-89; Bp's Officer for Evang *Ox* 89-95; P-in-c Ducklington 89-95; Hon Can Ch Ch from 95; rtd 95; NSM Hermitage and Hampstead Norreys, Cold Ash etc *Ox* from 95. *The Vicarage, Cold Ash Hill, Cold Ash, Newbury, Berks RG16 9PT* Newbury (01635) 864395

WINTER, Canon Dennis Graham St Leger. b 33. K Coll Lon BSc54 AKC54. Tyndale Hall Bris BD62. **d** 61 **p** 62. C Pennycross *Ex* 61-64; C Maidstone St Faith *Cant* 64-66; V Paddock Wood *Roch* from 66; RD Tonbridge from 89; Hon Can Roch Cathl from 90. *The Vicarage, 116 Maidstone Road, Paddock Wood, Tonbridge, Kent TN12 6DZ* Paddock Wood (01892) 833917

WINTER, Ernest Philip. b 18. Bris Univ BA49 St Cath Coll Ox BLitt54 MA56. Worc Ord Coll 57. **d** 58 **p** 59. V Reddal Hill St Luke *Worc* 61-79; P-in-c Upper Arley 79-86; P-in-c Wribbenhall 81-83; rtd 86; Perm to Offic *Worc* from 86; Perm

to Offic *Heref* from 87. *4 Summit Road, Clows Top, Kidderminster, Worcs DY14 9HN* Clows Top (01299) 832342

WINTER, Henry David. b 24. Sarum Th Coll 51. **d** 53 **p** 54. C Hope St Jas *Man* 53-55; C Heywood St Luke 55-58; R Hulme St Mich 58-63; Chapl Essex Co Hosp Colchester 63-85; V Colchester St Paul *Chelmsf* from 63. *The Vicarage, 141 North Station Road, Colchester CO1 1UX* Colchester (01206) 578383

WINTER, Jonathan Gay. b 37. AKC64. **d** 65 **p** 66. C W Dulwich All SS and Em *S'wark* 65-69; Asst Master Kidbrooke Sch 69-77; Norwood Sch from 77; Hon C Dulwich St Barn from 90. *160 Turney Road, London SE21 7JJ* 0171-274 3060

WINTER, Norman Gladwyn. b 50. Ch Ch Ox BA72 MA76. Wycliffe Hall Ox 72. **d** 76 **p** 77. C Huyton St Mich *Liv* 76-80; C-in-c Skelmersdale Ecum Cen 80-82; V Skelmersdale Ch at Cen 82-87; Producer BBC Relig Broadcasting Unit Man from 87. *43 Falstone Close, Birchwood, Warrington WA3 6SU* Padgate (01925) 831953 Fax 0161-236 1005 or 200 2496

WINTER, Raymond McMahon. b 23. FSA73 Selw Coll Cam BA52 MA60. Wycliffe Hall Ox 59. **d** 61 **p** 62. P-in-c Horstead w Frettenham w Stanninghall *Nor* 64-71; Youth Chapl 64-71; Warden Dioc Conf Ho 64-71; Chapl Loretto Sch Musselburgh 71-74; P-in-c Latchingdon w Mundon and N Fambridge *Chelmsf* 74-75; P-in-c Brettenham w Rushford *Nor* 75-83; P-in-c Riddlesworth w Gasthorpe and Knettishall 76-83; P-in-c Garboldisham w Blo' Norton 77-83; Chapl Bedgebury Sch Kent 83-91; Hon C Kilndown *Cant* 83-87; Hon C Goudhurst w Kilndown 87-91; Warden Coll of St Barn Lingfield 88-94; rtd 91; Perm to Offic *Nor* from 94. *27 Breydon Road, Norwich NR7 8EF* Norwich (01602) 484889

WINTER, Stephen Christopher. b 55. Southn Univ BA76. Trin Coll Bris 85. **d** 88 **p** 89. C Birm St Luke *Birm* 88-92; TV Kings Norton from 92. *93 Westhill Road, Birmingham B38 8SX* 0121-459 3098

WINTER, Thomas Andrew. b 24. Wadh Coll Ox BA51 MA63. Ely Th Coll 51. **d** 53 **p** 54. S Africa 56-83; R Woodston *Ely* 83-90; rtd 90. *6 The Close, Shoreham-by-Sea, W Sussex BN43 5AH* Shoreham-by-Sea (01273) 452606

WINTERBOTHAM, Canon Anthony James Marshall (Tony). b 27. Magd Coll Cam BA51 MA55. Wells Th Coll 55. **d** 57 **p** 58. Hon Chapl Portsm Cathl *Portsm* from 67; Hon Can 90-91; Chapl and Hd of RE Portsm Gr Sch 67-91; rtd 92. *4 Poynings Place, St Nicholas Street, Portsmouth PO1 2PB* Portsmouth (01705) 825068

WINTERBOTTOM, Ian Edmund. b 42. St Andr Univ MA66 Nottm Univ DipTh68. Linc Th Coll 66. **d** 68 **p** 69. C Blackb St Steph *Blackb* 68-71; C Wingerworth *Derby* 71-73; P-in-c Brimington 73-77; R 77-89; RD Bolsover and Staveley 86-93; R Pleasley 89-94; P-in-c Shirebrook 92-94; TR E Scarsdale from 94. *The Vicarage, Main Street, Shirebrook, Notts NG20 8DN* Mansfield (01623) 742395

WINTERBOURNE, George. b 20. S'wark Ord Course 64. **d** 67 **p** 68. C Cove St Jo *Guildf* 67-71; Perm to Offic 72; Hon C Aldershot St Mich 73-78; Perm to Offic *B & W* 79-80; Lic to Offic 80-87; rtd 87; Perm to Offic *Glouc* from 87. *4 Lawn Crescent, Shurdington, Cheltenham, Glos GL51 5UR* Cheltenham (01242) 862671

WINTERBURN, Derek Neil. b 60. Bris Univ BSc82 Ox Univ BA85. Wycliffe Hall Ox 83. **d** 86 **p** 87. C Mildmay Grove St Jude and St Paul *Lon* 86-89; C Hackney Marsh 89-91; TV from 91. *The Vicarage, Overbury Street, London E5 0AJ* 0181-986 5076

WINTERBURN, Ieuan Thomas. b 16. Univ of Wales BA37 Univ of S Africa BA48 Witwatersrand Univ MA52. K Coll Lon 37. **d** 39 **p** 40. S Africa 70-72; Rhodesia 72-80; Zimbabwe 80-81; V Borth and Eglwys-fach w Llangynfelyn *St D* 81-85; rtd 85. *209 Wilsborough Mansions, Seaview Street, Durban 4000, South Africa*

WINTERBURN, Maurice. b 14. Oak Hill Th Coll 61. **d** 62 **p** 63. V Stambermill *Worc* 68-79; P-in-c The Lye 74-79; rtd 79; Perm to Offic *Worc* from 79. *36 Whittingham Road, Halesowen, W Midlands B63 3TF* 0121-550 0434

WINTERSGILL, Allan Vernon. b 19. St Jo Coll Dur BA49. Ely Th Coll 49. **d** 50 **p** 51. V Pet St Barn *Pet* 57-70; V Northn St Jas 70-81; V Staverton w Helidon and Catesby 81-89; rtd 89; Perm to Offic *Pet* from 89. *20 Church Lane, Nether Heyford, Northampton NN7 3LQ* Weedon (01327) 40796

WINTLE, Anthony Robert. b 44. K Coll Lon 64. St Mich Coll Llan DipTh68. **d** 68 **p** 69. C Llan N *Llan* 68-70; C Baglan 70-75; V Treharris 75-86; V Treharris w Bedlinog 86-90; R St Fagans w Michaelston-super-Ely from 90. *The Rectory, Greenwood Lane, St Fagans, Cardiff CF5 6EL* Cardiff (01222) 565869

WINTLE, David Robert. b 56. Open Univ BA84. Qu Coll Birm 93. **d** 95. C Cov St Mary *Cov* from 95. *193 Allesley Old Road, Coventry CV5 8FL* Coventry (01203) 691392

WINTLE, Graham. b 52. Bris Univ BSc73. Oak Hill Th Coll BA86. **d** 86 **p** 87. C Southgate *Chich* 86-89; C New Malden and

Coombe *S'wark* 89-92; V Surbiton Hill Ch Ch from 92. *Christ Church Vicarage, 7 Christ Church Road, Surbiton, Surrey KT5 8JJ* 0181-399 3444

WINTLE, Canon Ruth Elizabeth. b 31. Westf Coll Lon BA53 St Hugh's Coll Ox BA67 MA74. St Mich Ho Ox 63. **dss** 72 **d** 87 **p** 94. Tutor St Jo Coll Dur 72-74; Selection Sec ACCM 74-83; St Jo in Bedwardine *Worc* 83-87; Par Dn 87-94; Dir of Ords 84-92; Hon Can Worc Cathl 87-94; rtd 95. Bp's Adv on Women's Min *Worc* from 95. *72 Henwick Road, Worcester WR2 5NT* Worcester (01905) 422841 Fax 612302

WINTON, Alan Peter. b 58. Sheff Univ BA83 PhD87. Linc Th Coll CMM91. **d** 91 **p** 92. C Southgate Ch Ch *Lon* 91-95; P-in-c St Paul's Walden *St Alb* from 95; Dir Continuing Minl Educn from 95. *The Vicarage, Bendish Lane, Whitwell, Hitchin, Herts SG4 8HX* Whitwell (01438) 871658

WINTON, Ms Philippa Mary (Pippa). b 56. Nottm Univ BA78. Trin Coll Bris DipHE82. **dss** 83 **d** 87 **p** 94. Sheff St Jo *Sheff* 83-86; Sheff Gillcar St Silas 86-87; Hon Par Dn 87-90; Chapl Asst R Hallamshire Hosp Sheff 87; Hon Par Dn Linc St Faith and St Martin w St Pet *Linc* 90-92; Chapl Asst W Middx Univ Hosp Isleworth 92-93; Perm to Offic *Lon* from 93. *62 Oakfield Road, London N14 6LX* 0181-886 3346

WINTON, Stanley Wootton. b 30. Sarum & Wells Th Coll 70. **d** 72 **p** 73. C Birkenhead St Jas w St Bede *Ches* 72-75; V 75-79; TR Ellesmere Port 79-88; Chapl Ellesmere Port and Manor Hosps 79-95; R Delamere *Ches* 88-95; rtd 95. *26 Wimborne Avenue, Thingwall, Wirral, Merseyside L61 7UL* 0151-648 0176

WINWARD, Stuart James. b 36. Open Univ BA85. Lich Th Coll 65. **d** 68 **p** 69. C Lytham St Cuth *Blackb* 68-71; C Padiham 71-73; V Musbury 73-84; R Old Trafford St Hilda *Man* 84-89; V Davyhulme St Mary from 89. *St Mary's Vicarage, Vicarage Road, Davyhulme, Manchester M31 3TP* 0161-748 2210

WIPPELL, David Stanley. b 46. Queensland Univ BSc67. Westcott Ho Cam BA77 MA. **d** 78 **p** 79. C Wolvercote w Summertown *Ox* 78; Hon C from 78; Asst Chapl St Edw Sch Ox from 78; Chapl St Hugh's Coll Ox from 80. *Segar's House, St Edward's School, Woodstock Road, Oxford OX2 7NN* Oxford (01865) 58239

WISBECH, Archdeacon of. *See* RONE, Ven James (Jim)

WISE, David Reginald. b 46. Glas Univ BSc68 QUB PhD74. Edin Th Coll 72. **d** 74 **p** 75. Chapl St Andr Cathl *Ab* 74-75; C Ayr *Glas* 75-78; R Airdrie 78-81; P-in-c Gartcosh 78-81; P-in-c Leic St Nic *Leic* 81-82; Chapl Leic Univ 81-89; TV Leic H Spirit 82-89; Chapl St Hilda's Priory and Sch Whitby from 89. *56 Ruswarp Lane, Whitby, N Yorkshire YO21 1ND* Whitby (01947) 603619

WISE, Geoffrey John. b 23. Qu Coll Birm 61. **d** 63 **p** 64. S Rhodesia 63-65; Rhodesia 65-76; P-in-c Cottesmore *Pet* 76; R 76-79; P-in-c Ashwell w Burley 76; R Cottesmore and Barrow w Ashwell and Burley 79-89; rtd 89. *14 Butterslade Grove, Ynysforgan, Swansea SA6 6QU* Swansea (01792) 774734

WISE, Ms Pamela Margaret. b 51. CertEd73 BA79. Ripon Coll Cuddesdon 89. **d** 91 **p** 94. Par Dn Tokyngton St Mich *Lon* 91-94; C N Greenford All Hallows 94; C Bedf All SS *St Alb* from 94. *9 Wingfield Close, Bedford MK40 4PD* Bedford (01234) 354631

WISE, Very Rev Randolph George. b 25. VRD64. MBIM Qu Coll Ox BA49 MA55. Linc Th Coll 49. **d** 51 **p** 52. Ind Chapl *Lon* 66-76; V St Botolph without Aldersgate 72-76; TR Notting Hill 76-81; Dean Pet 81-92; rtd 92; Perm to Offic *Pet* from 92. *2 Derwent Drive, Oakham, Leics LE15 6SA* Oakham (01572) 756263

WISEMAN, David John. b 51. Lon Univ BD80 Birm Univ DipIslam87. Cranmer Hall Dur 77. **d** 80 **p** 81. C Bilston *Lich* 80-84; P-in-c W Bromwich St Phil 84-86; V 86-89; P-in-c Cheetham St Mark *Man* 89-94; Dioc Community Relns Officer from 89; P-in-c Ashton H Trin from 94. *Holy Trinity Vicarage, Dean Street, Ashton-under-Lyne, Lancs OL6 7HD* 0161-344 0075

WISEMAN, John. b 56. Sarum & Wells Th Coll 80. **d** 83 **p** 84. C Swinton St Pet *Man* 83-87; C Swinton and Pendlebury 87-88; TV Atherton 88-93; V Bedf Leigh from 93. *St Thomas's Vicarage, 121 Green Lane, Leigh, Lancs WN7 2TW* Leigh (01942) 673519

WISHART, Michael Leslie. b 45. St Mich Coll Llan DipTh73. **d** 73 **p** 74. C Llangyfelach *S & B* 73-76; Chapl RN 77-80 and from 85; Chapl RNR 80-85; V Beguildy and Heyope *S & B* 80-84; V Gowerton 84-85. *Directorate Gen, RN Chapl Services, Room 203, Victory Building, HM Naval Base, Portsmouth PO1 3LS* Portsmouth (01705) 727903 Fax 727112

WISKEN, Canon Brian Leonard. b 34. Dur Univ BA58. Linc Th Coll 58. **d** 60 **p** 61. C Lobley Hill *Dur* 60-63; C Ipswich All Hallows *St E* 63-65; P-in-c Scunthorpe All SS *Linc* 65-69; V 69-71; Dioc Stewardship Adv 70-75; R Panton w Wragby 71-75; V Langton by Wragby 71-75; R Cleethorpes 75-77; TR Cleethorpes 77-89; Hon Can Linc Cathl from 88; V Linc St Nic

w St Jo Newport from 89. *St Nicholas Vicarage, 103 Newport, Lincoln LN1 3EE* Lincoln (01522) 525653

WISKER, George Richard. b 35. S'wark Ord Course 69. **d** 72 **p** 73. C Croydon Ch Ch Broad Green *Cant* 72-76; C Barking St Erkenwald *Chelmsf* 76-77; P-in-c 77-82; V from 82. *St Erkenwald's Vicarage, Levett Road, Barking, Essex IG11 9JZ* 0181-594 2271

WITCHELL, David William. b 47. St Jo Coll Nottm BTh75 LTh75. **d** 75 **p** 76. C Northn St Mary *Pet* 75-78; C Oakham w Hambleton and Egleton 78-81; C Oakham, Hambleton, Egleton, Braunston and Brooke 81-82; V Weedon Bec w Everdon 82-90; V Wellingborough St Barn from 90. *St Barnabas's Vicarage, St Barnabas Street, Wellingborough, Northants NN8 3HB* Wellingborough (01933) 226337

WITCOMBE, John Julian. b 59. Cam Univ MA84. St Jo Coll Nottm BA83 DPS84. **d** 84 **p** 85. C Birtley *Dur* 84-87; C Chilwell *S'well* 87-91; V Lodge Moor St Luke *Sheff* 91-95; Chapl Lodge Moor Hosp 91-95; TR Uxbridge *Lon* from 95. *The Rectory, Nursery Waye, Uxbridge, Middx UB8 2BJ* Uxbridge (01895) 239055

WITCOMBE, Mrs Maureen Dorothy (Mo). b 56. CertEd77 Nottm Univ BTh83. St Jo Coll Nottm 80. **dss** 84 **d** 87 **p** 94. Birtley *Dur* 84-85; Hon Par Dn Chilwell *S'well* 87-91; Par Dn Lodge Moor St Luke *Sheff* 91-94; C 94-95; Asst Chapl R Hallamshire Hosp Sheff 91-92; Asst Chapl Cen Sheff Univ Hosps NHS Trust 92-94. *The Rectory, Nursery Way, Uxbridge, Middx UB8 2BJ* Uxbridge (01895) 239055

WITCOMBE, Michael David. b 53. Univ of Wales (Lamp) BA76. Qu Coll Birm 76. **d** 78 **p** 79. C Neath w Llantwit *Llan* 78-80; C Whitchurch 80-83; V Newc from 83; P-in-c Ewenny 84-86. *The Vicarage, 1 Walters Road, Bridgend, M Glam CF31 4HE* Bridgend (01656) 655999

WITCOMBE, Simon Christopher. b 61. Dundee Univ MA83 PGCE84 Dur Univ BA90. St Jo Coll Dur 88. **d** 91 **p** 92. C Earlham St Anne *Nor* 91-95; C Skegness and Winthorpe *Linc* from 95. *St Clement's Parsonage, 134 Lincoln Road, Skegness, Lincs PE25 2DN* Skegness (01750) 761966

WITHERIDGE, John Stephen. b 53. Kent Univ BA76 Ch Coll Cam BA78 MA82. Ridley Hall Cam 78. **d** 79 **p** 80. C Luton St Mary *St Alb* 79-82; Asst Chapl Marlborough Coll Wilts 82-84; Abp's Chapl *Cant* 84-87; Conduct Eton Coll Windsor from 87. *3 Savile House, Westons Yard, Eton College, Windsor, Berks SL4 6DW* Windsor (01753) 65411

WITHERS, Mrs Christine Mary. b 37. ALA60. Qu Coll Birm DipRS81. **dss** 81 **d** 87 **p** 94. Chorleywood Ch Ch *St Alb* 81-86; Darley *Derby* 86-87; C 87-92; Chapl HM Pris Drake Hall from 92. *The Chaplain's Office, HM Prison Drake Hall, Eccleshall, Stafford ST21 6LQ* Eccleshall (01785) 850621 Fax 851931

WITHERS, Geoffrey Edward. b 68. QUB BSc90 TCD BTh93. CITC 90. **d** 93 **p** 94. C Ballymena w Ballyclug *Conn* from 93. *38 Ballee Road East, Ballymena, Co Antrim BT42 3DH* Ballymena (01266) 47038

WITHERS, John Geoffrey. b 39. St Jo Coll Dur BA61 Birm Univ CertEd63 Reading Univ DipEdG70 CQSW72. SW Minl Tr Course 84. **d** 87 **p** 88. NSM Drewsteignton *Ex* from 87. *Broomhill, Chagford, Newton Abbot, Devon TQ13 8DD* Chagford (01647) 432340

WITHERS, Michael. b 41. TCD BA66 Edin Univ BD70 QUB MTh83. Union Th Sem (NY) STM71. **d** 71 **p** 73. C Seagoe *D & D* 71-77; C Seapatrick 77-80; I Belf St Chris 80-89; I Movilla from 89. *34 Hollymount Road, Newtownards, Co Down BT23 3DL* Newtownards (01247) 810787

WITHERS GREEN, Timothy. b 30. K Coll Lon 51. **d** 55 **p** 56. C Greenhill St Jo *Lon* 55-58; C St Helier *S'wark* 58-61; V Belmont 61-79; CF (TA) 71-79; R Hexham *Newc* 79-84; R Weldon w Deene *Pet* from 84. *The Rectory, 13 School Lane, Weldon, Corby, Northants NN17 3JN* Corby (01536) 203671

WITHEY, Michael John. b 45. Open Univ BA80 Westmr Coll Ox DipApTh95. Oak Hill Th Coll 71. **d** 74 **p** 75. C St Alb St Paul *St Alb* 74-76; C Luton St Mary 77; C Luton St Fran 77-80; V Woodside w E Hyde 80-87; CF (TA) 83-87; Dioc Stewardship Adv *Ox* 87-89; Chapl HM Young Offender Inst Onley 89-91; V Hengoed w Gobowen *Lich* 91-95; Chapl Robert Jones and Agnes Hunt Orthopaedic Hosp 91-95; P-in-c Chasetown *Lich* from 95. *The Vicarage, 158A High Street, Chase Town, Walsall WS7 8XG* Burntwood (01543) 686276

WITHINGTON, George Kenneth. b 37. Birm Univ BA59. Wells Th Coll 59. **d** 61 **p** 62. C Hartcliffe St Andr CD *Bris* 61-65; V Swindon St Jo 65-73; V Cricklade w Latton from 73; RD Cricklade from 94. *The Vicarage, High Street, Cricklade, Swindon SN6 6DA* Swindon (01793) 750300

WITHINGTON, Canon Keith. b 32. Univ of Wales (Lamp) BA55. Qu Coll Birm 55. **d** 57 **p** 58. C Bournville *Birm* 57-61; V from 61; RD Moseley 81-91; Hon Can Birm Cathl from 83. *The Vicarage, 61 Linden Road, Birmingham B30 1JT* 0121-472 1209 or 472 7215

WITHNELL, Roderick David. b 55. Leic Univ CTPS89. E Midl Min Tr Course 86 Ridley Hall Cam 89. **d** 90 **p** 91. C Shenfield

Chelmsf 90-94; C Woodleigh and Loddiswell *Ex* from 94. *Wyseland Barn, Well Street, Loddiswell, Kingsbridge, Devon TQ7 4QH* Kingsbridge (01548) 550841

WITHY, John Daniel Forster. b 38. Bible Tr Inst Glas CertRK61 ALCD64. **d** 64 **p** 65. C Belf St Aid *Conn* 64-68; Dir Chr Conf Cen Sion Mills from 68. *Zion House, 120 Melmont Road, Strabane, Co Tyrone BT82 9ET* Sion Mills (016626) 58672

WITT, Bryan Douglas. b 52. St Mich Coll Llan BD84. **d** 84 **p** 85. C Betws St Dav w Ammanford *St D* 84-87; V Llanllwni 87-91; V Llangennech and Hendy from 91. *The Vicarage, Mwrwg Road, Llangennech, Llanelli, Dyfed SA14 8UA* Llangennech (01554) 820324

✠**WITT, Rt Rev Howell Arthur John.** b 20. Leeds Univ BA42. Coll of Resurr Mirfield 42. **d** 44 **p** 45 **c** 65. C Usk and Monkswood w Glascoed Chpl and Gwehelog *Mon* 44-48; C Camberwell St Geo *S'wark* 48-49; Australia from 49; Bp NW Aus 65-81; Bp Bathurst 81-89; rtd 89. *U20 DGV, 99 McCabe Street, Mosman Park, W Australia 6012* Perth (9) 383-3301

WITTER, Mrs Tania Judy Ingram. b 37. Girton Coll Cam BA58 MA63. St Jo Coll Nottm DipPC95 Oak Hill Th Coll 94. **d** 95. NSM Highbury Ch Ch w St Jo and St Sav Lon from 95. *27 Arvon Road, London N5 1PL* 0171-607 3156 Fax as telephone

WITTEY, William Francis George. b 05. AKC31. **d** 31 **p** 32. V Torpenhow *Carl* 63-72; rtd 72; Perm to Offic *Carl* from 72. *14 High Croft Drive, Allithwaite, Grange-over-Sands, Cumbria LA11 7QL* Grange-over-Sands (015395) 33979

WITTS, Cyril Charles. b 14. Sarum Th Coll 47. **d** 49 **p** 50. V Enfield Chase St Mary *Lon* 67-78; rtd 78; Perm to Offic *Win* from 81. *18 Southlea Avenue, Bournemouth BH6 3AB* Bournemouth (01202) 431633

WITTS, Donald Roger. b 47. Cranmer Hall Dur 86. **d** 88 **p** 89. C Leyland St Ambrose *Blackb* 88-90; C Staines St Mary and St Pet *Lon* 90-93; Ind Missr *Man* 93-95; P-in-c Blean *Cant* from 95; Dioc Communications Officer from 95. *The Vicarage, 24 Tyler Hill Road, Blean, Canterbury, Kent CT2 9HT* Canterbury (01227) 471261

WITTS, Graham Robert. b 53. Newc Univ BEd. Linc Th Coll 79. **d** 82 **p** 83. C Horncastle w Low Toynton *Linc* 82-85; TV Gt Grimsby St Mary and St Jas 85-89; TR Yelverton, Meavy, Sheepstor and Walkhampton *Ex* 89-93; C Glastonbury w Meare, W Pennard and Godney *B & W* from 93. *The Parsonage, St Mary's Road, Meare, Glastonbury, Somerset BA5 9SR* Meare Heath (01458) 860276

WIXON, Jack. b 44. Lich Th Coll 68. **d** 71 **p** 72. C Adlington *Blackb* 71-74; C St Annes 74-76; V Chorley St Jas 76-82; V Preston Em 82-94; V Ribby w Wrea from 94. *The Vicarage, 1 Vicarage Close, Wrea Green, Preston PR4 2PQ* Kirkham (01772) 687644

WOADDEN, Christopher Martyn. b 56. St Jo Coll Nottm LTh. **d** 87 **p** 88. C Mickleover All SS *Derby* 87-90; C Wirksworth w Alderwasley, Carsington etc 90-92; C Wirksworth 92; TV Gt and Lt Coates w Bradley *Linc* from 92. *The Vicarage, Wingate Road, Grimsby DN37 9EL* Grimsby (01472) 885709

WODEHOUSE, Armine Boyle. b 24. Oak Hill Th Coll 83. **d** 86 **p** 86. NSM Gt Parndon *Chelmsf* 86-92; Perm to Offic *Eur* 89-92; Chapl Menton from 92. *103 Orient Place, 1 rue de la Republique, 06500 Menton, France* France (33) 93 35 77 41 Fax as telephone

WODEHOUSE, Lady Carol Lylie. b 51. St Hugh's Coll Ox BA73 CertEd74 MA77. Ripon Coll Cuddesdon 87. **d** 89 **p** 94. NSM Hambleden Valley *Ox* from 89. *Glendalough, Innings Lane, Little Freith, Henley-on-Thames, Oxon RG9 6NU* High Wycombe (01494) 881087

WODEMAN, Cyril Peter Guy. b 28. ARCO54 LRAM58 ARCM58 Qu Coll Cam BA50 MA55. Cranmer Hall Dur 72. **d** 73 **p** 74. C Penwortham St Mary *Blackb* 73-77; V Burnley St Steph 77-85; V Hornby w Claughton 85-93; rtd 93. *5 Harling Bank, Kirkby Lonsdale, Carnforth, Lancs LA6 2DJ* Carnforth (01524) 272474

WOLFE, Dr Kenneth Wesley. b 19. QUB MB42. Linc Th Coll 52. **d** 57 **p** 61. C Branksome St Aldhelm *Sarum* 68-76; C Rugby St Matt *Cov* 76-80; Hon C Northn St Alb *Pet* 80-84; rtd 84; Perm to Offic *Pet* from 84. *40 Greenfield Avenue, Northampton NN3 2AF* Northampton (01604) 406369

WOLFE, Canon Michael Matheson. b 29. Pemb Coll Ox BA49 MA53. Cuddesdon Coll 51. **d** 53 **p** 54. C Moorfields *Bris* 53-57; P-in-c Fochabers *Mor* 57-58; Sub-Warden Aberlour Orphanage 58-59; V Southport St Paul *Liv* 59-65; V Upholland 65-73; TR 73-82; RD Ormskirk 78-82; Hon Can Liv Cathl 78-82; Can Res Liv Cathl from 82; Merseyside Ecum Officer from 82; AD Toxteth and Wavertree from 89. *23 Hunters Lane, Liverpool L15 8HL* 0151-733 1541

WOLFENDEN, Peter Graham. b 40. St Pet Coll Ox BA63 MA66. Linc Th Coll 62. **d** 64 **p** 65. C Adlington *Blackb* 64-66; Asst Master Barton Peveril Gr Sch 66-69; Chapl Bp Wordsworth Sch Salisbury 69-72; Hon C Ponteland *Newc*

from 72; Hd Master Coates Middle Sch Ponteland from 78. *16 Fern Avenue, Jesmond, Newcastle upon Tyne NE2 2QT* 0191-281 9346

WOLLASTON, Canon Barbara Kathleen. b 30. LSE BSc(Soc)64. Gilmore Ho 51. **d** 87 **p** 94. Dir Past Studies Qu Coll Birm 80-89; Dioc Dir of Ords *S'wark* 89-94; rtd 94. *6 Chapel Street, Wem, Shropshire SY4 5ER* Wem (01939) 232229

WOLLEY, John. BSc. **d** 85 **p** 86. Hon C Croydon St Aug *S'wark* 85-89; Perm to Offic *Linc* from 89. *7 Royal Oak Court, Upgate, Louth, Lincs LN11 9JA* Louth (01507) 601614

WOLLEY, Richard. b 33. Ox Univ MA. S Dios Minl Tr Scheme 82. **d** 85 **p** 86. NSM Brighton Resurr *Chich* 85-88; C Brighton St Geo w St Anne and St Mark 89-91; R Buxted and Hadlow Down from 91. *St Mary's Vicarage, Buxted, Uckfield, E Sussex TN22 4LP* Buxted (01825) 733103

WOLSTENCROFT, Canon Alan. b 37. Cuddesdon Coll. **d** 69 **p** 70. C Halliwell St Thos *Man* 69-71; C Stand 71-73; V Wythenshawe St Martin 73-80; AD Withington 78-91; Chapl Wythenshawe Hosp Man 80-89; V Baguley *Man* 80-91; Hon Can Man Cathl from 86; V Bolton St Pet from 91. *St Peter's Vicarage, Churchgate, Bolton BL1 1PS* Bolton (01204) 33847

WOLSTENHULME, Arthur James. b 20. Leeds Univ BA42. Coll of Resurr Mirfield 42. **d** 44 **p** 46. R Kingsthorpe *Pet* 66-73; TR Kingsthorpe w St Dav Northn 73-86; rtd 86; Perm to Offic *Pet* from 86. *2 Springbanks Way, Northampton NN4 0QA* Northampton (01604) 766405 Fax as telephone

WOLVERHAMPTON, Area Bishop of. See BOURKE, Rt Rev Michael Gay

WOMERSLEY, Walter John. b 28. AKC52. **d** 53 **p** 54. S Africa 70-86; C E and W Keal *Linc* 87-90; Chapl St Jas Choir Sch Grimsby 90-92; rtd 92. *6 Abbey Park Road, Grimsby, S Humberside DN32 0HR* Grimsby (01472) 354289

WONNACOTT, Charles Edward. b 14. Wycliffe Hall Ox 62. **d** 63 **p** 64. C Sidley *Chich* 70-73; P-in-c Peasmarsh 73-76; R Beckley and Peasmarsh 76-81; rtd 81; Perm to Offic *Win* from 81. *The Grove, 3 Cedar Avenue, St Leonards, Ringwood, Hants BH24 2QF* Ferndown (01202) 895457

WOOD, Mrs Ann Rene. b 49. St Deiniol's Hawarden 87. **d** 90 **p** 94. Par Dn Bamber Bridge St Aid *Blackb* 90-93; Par Dn W Burnley 93-94; C from 94. *23 Brantfell Drive, Burnley, Lancs BB12 8AW* Burnley (01282) 455170

WOOD, Anthony James. b 38. Kelham Th Coll 58. **d** 63 **p** 64. C Shrewsbury St Alkmund *Lich* 63; C Harlescott 63-66; C Porthill 66-70; P-in-c Priorslee 70-76; Chapl Telford Town Cen 73-74; V Barton under Needwood from 76. *The Vicarage, Barton under Needwood, Burton-on-Trent DE13 8HU* Barton under Needwood (01283) 712359

WOOD, Ven Arnold. b 18. Clifton Th Coll 66. **d** 65 **p** 66. V Mt Pellon *Wakef* 67-73; R Lanreath *Truro* 73-81; V Pelynt 73-81; RD W Wivelshire 76-81; Lib Truro Cathl 81-88; Can Res Truro Cathl 81-88; Adn Cornwall 81-88; Warden Community of the Epiphany Truro from 85; rtd 88. *Cobblers, Quethiock, Liskeard, Cornwall PL14 3SQ* Liskeard (01579) 344788

WOOD, Barry. b 56. CQSW81 CYCW81 Open Univ BA87. St Steph Ho Ox 87. **d** 89 **p** 90. C Tranmere St Paul w St Luke *Ches* 89-92; TV Ches Team 92-94; P-in-c S Tawton and Belstone *Ex* from 94. *The Vicarage, South Tawton, Okehampton, Devon EX20 2LQ* Okehampton (01837) 840337

WOOD, Beresford Donald Richard. b 32. Leeds Univ BA58. Cant Sch of Min 91. **d** 94. C Folkestone St Mary and St Eanswythe *Cant* from 94. *St Katherine's Cottage, Pound Lane, Elham, Canterbury, Kent CT4 6TS* Folkestone (01303) 840817

WOOD, Miss Beryl Jean. b 54. Linc Th Coll 85. **d** 87 **p** 94. C Gaywood, Bawsey and Mintlyn *Nor* 87-92; C Gaywood St Faith 92-93; Chapl Asst Univ Hosp Nottm from 93. *University Hospital, Queen's Medical Centre, Nottingham NG7 2UH* Nottingham (0115) 924 9924

WOOD, Canon Brian Frederick. b 31. Leeds Univ BA52. Coll of Resurr Mirfield 55. **d** 57 **p** 58. V Carlinghow *Wakef* 63-73; V Drighlington 73-94; RD Birstall 83-92; Hon Can Wakef Cathl 89-94; rtd 94. *10 Grove Road, Menston, Ilkley, Yorks LS29 6JD* Guiseley (01943) 872820

WOOD, Charles Laver. b 14. Wells Th Coll 66. **d** 68 **p** 69. C Stoke *Cov* 68-71; V Ramsey w Lt Oakley *Chelmsf* 71-85; P-in-c Wrabness w Wix 82-85; V Ramsey w Lt Oakley and Wrabness 85-88; RD Harwich 81-87; rtd 88. *9 Richards Way, Salisbury SP2 8NT*

WOOD, Christoper William. b 44. Rhodes Univ BA66 Univ of S Africa BTh82. St Bede's Coll Umtata 79. **d** 80 **p** 82. S Africa 80-87; C Houghton Regis *St Alb* from 87. *The New Clergy House, Lowry Drive, Houghton Regis, Dunstable, Beds LU5 5SJ* Dunstable (01582) 863292

WOOD, Colin Arthur. b 41. CEng MICE68 MIStructE68. S'wark Ord Course 86. **d** 89 **p** 90. C Tadworth *S'wark* 89-93; TV Morden from 93. *49 Cambourne Road, Morden, Surrey SM4 4JL* 0181-542 2966

WOOD, Canon David Abell. b 25. Qu Coll Cam BA50 MA54. Wells Th Coll 50. **d** 50 **p** 51. Perm to Offic *Heref* 67-70; Warden Communicare Ho *Newc* 70-88; V Mitford 88-93; Chapl Northgate Mental Handicap Unit Morpeth 88-93; Hon Can Newc Cathl *Newc* 88-93; rtd 93. *3 Fontburn Cottages, Ewesley, Morpeth, Northd NE61 4PL*

WOOD, David Arthur. b 30. Man Univ BA51 DSA55. Lich Th Coll 59. **d** 61 **p** 62. Dioc Youth Adv *Newc* 68-72; R Cramlington 72-73; TR 73-83; V Wylam 83-86; TV Egremont and Haile *Carl* 86-94; rtd 94. *6 John Street, Maryport, Cumbria CA15 6JT* Maryport (01900) 816706

WOOD, David Christopher. b 52. Oak Hill Th Coll DipHE91. **d** 91 **p** 92. C Kendal St Thos *Carl* 91-95; P-in-c Crosby Ravensworth from 95; P-in-c Asby from 95; P-in-c Bolton from 95. *The Vicarage, Crosby Ravensworth, Penrith, Cumbria CA10 3JA* Penrith (01768) 890177

WOOD, David Michael. b 39. Chich Th Coll. **d** 82 **p** 83. C Epping St Jo *Chelmsf* 82-85; C Totton *Win* 85-88; V Southway *Ex* from 88. *The Vicarage, 70 Inchkeith Road, Plymouth PL6 6EJ* Plymouth (01752) 771938

WOOD, Dennis William. b 28. Qu Mary Coll Lon BSc53 Glas Univ PhD57. NE Ord Course 82. **d** 85 **p** 85. NSM Stanhope *Dur* 85-86; NSM Stanhope w Frosterley 86-94; NSM Eastgate w Rookhope 86-94; NSM Melrose *Edin* from 94. *Gordonlee, Ormiston Terrace, Melrose, Roxburghshire TD6 9SP* Melrose (01896) 823835

WOOD, Edward Francis. b 28. Chich Th Coll 56. **d** 58 **p** 59. Dioc Broadcasting Adv *Newc* 68-78; V Shiremoor 68-78; C Newc St Geo 78-82; C Newc Epiphany 82-93; rtd 93. *52 Albemarle Avenue, Jesmond, Newcastle upon Tyne NE2 3NQ* 0191-284 5338

WOOD, Edward Berryman. b 33. Ely Th Coll 54. **d** 57 **p** 58. C Aldershot St Mich *Guildf* 57-60; C Worplesdon 60-62; V Littleport St Matt *Ely* 62-64; V Balham St Jo Bedf Hill *S'wark* 64-71; V New Eltham All SS 71-84; RD Eltham (Sub-Deanery) 79-82; P-in-c Woldingham from 84. *The Rectory, Woldingham, Caterham, Surrey CR3 7DB* Caterham (01883) 652192

WOOD, Elizabeth Lucy. b 35. W Midl Minl Tr Course 89. **d** 92 **p** 94. NSM Wellingborough St Mark *Pet* 92-95; P-in-c Stanwick w Hargrave from 95. *46 Finedon Road, Wellingborough, Northants NN8 4AA* Wellingborough (01933) 223143

WOOD, Eric Basil. b 25. St Edm Hall Ox BA50 MA50. Cuddesdon Coll 50. **d** 51 **p** 52. P-in-c Drayton St Pet (Berks) *Ox* 68-72; V 72-81; P-in-c Buckland 81-84; V 84-88; P-in-c Littleworth 81-84; V 84-88; P-in-c Pusey 81-84; R 84-88; Master Hugh Sexey's Hosp Bruton 88-95; rtd 89. *2 Bedwardine House, Henwick Road, Worcester WR2 5NT* Worcester (01905) 748207

WOOD, Eric Stanley. b 16. AKC40. **d** 40 **p** 41. R Lowton St Luke *Liv* 64-81; rtd 81. *12 Cranham Avenue, Lowton, Warrington WA3 2PQ* Leigh (01942) 674045

WOOD, Ernest Charles Anthony. b 06. RMA 25. Wycliffe Hall Ox 52. **d** 53 **p** 54. R Nurstead w Ifield *Roch* 55-78; rtd 78. *14 Maryland Drive, Barming, Maidstone, Kent ME16 9EW* Maidstone (01622) 727120

WOOD, Frederick Leonard. b 19. BEM59. Worc Ord Coll. **d** 64 **p** 65. V Charles w St Matthias Plymouth *Ex* 68-81; rtd 82; Perm to Offic *B & W* 85-92. *Oaklands, 1 Windrush Heights, Sandhurst, Camberley, Surrey GU17 8ET* Crowthorne (01344) 762368

WOOD, Geoffrey. b 33. Tyndale Hall Bris 56. **d** 61 **p** 62. C Tranmere St Cath *Ches* 61-64; C Newburn *Newc* 64-68; R Gt Smeaton w Appleton upon Wiske *Ripon* 69-79; P-in-c Cowton w Birkby 73-79; P-in-c Danby Wiske w Yafforth and Hutton Bonville 76-79; R Gt Smeaton w Appleton Wiske and Birkby etc 79-89; P-in-c Bishop Monkton and Burton Leonard 89; R Fressingfield, Mendham, Metfield, Weybread etc *St E* from 92. *The Vicarage, Metfield, Harleston, Norfolk IP20 0JY* Fressingfield (01379) 853442

WOOD, Geoffrey James. b 47. N Ord Course 88. **d** 91 **p** 92. C Stainton-in-Cleveland *York* 91-94; V Middlesb St Oswald from 94. *St Oswald's Vicarage, Lambton Road, Middlesbrough, Cleveland TS4 2RG* Middlesbrough (01642) 816156

WOOD, George Albert. b 22. St Paul's Grahamstown. **d** 54 **p** 55. S Africa 63-77; Area Sec (Dio Chich) USPG from 78; TV Littlehampton and Wick *Chich* 86-88; rtd 88. *3 Orchard Gardens, Rustington, Littlehampton, W Sussex BN16 3HS* Rustington (01903) 787746

WOOD, George John Edmund. b 09. ACP50. Roch Th Coll 69. **d** 70 **p** 71. C Thornton Heath St Jude *Cant* 70-72; C W Wickham St Mary 72-76; rtd 76; Perm to Offic *Chich* from 76. *91 Cross Road, Southwick, Brighton BN42 4HH* Brighton (01273) 591755

WOOD, George Robert. b 26. Em Coll Cam BA52. Oak Hill Th Coll 52. **d** 53 **p** 54. R Watermillock *Carl* 61-74; V Holme Eden

74-76; Chapl Lindley Lodge 76-78; C Kingston upon Hull H Trin *York* 78-80; V Chipping *Blackb* 80-81; P-in-c Whitewell 80-81; V Chipping and Whitewell 82-83; R Bunwell w Carleton Rode and Tibenham *Nor* 83-88; P-in-c Wray w Tatham Fells *Blackb* 88-89; rtd 89. *5 Rimington Way, Penrith, Cumbria CA11 8TG* Penrith (01768) 890177

WOOD, Gordon Cooper. b 20. St Pet Hall Ox BA43 MA46. Wycliffe Hall Ox. **d** 44 **p** 45. V Roundhay St Jo *Ripon* 65-90; rtd 90. *Flat 55, Moorland Drive, Leeds LS17 6JP* Leeds (0113) 266 6994

WOOD, Lt-Col Gordon Edward. b 12. Ely Th Coll 63. **d** 64 **p** 65. R Houghton *Ely* 66-74; R Wyton 66-74; V Billingborough *Linc* 74-80; V Horbling 75-80; V Sempringham w Pointon and Birthorpe 75-80; rtd 80; C Broughton *Ely* 81-91. *4 Kings Hedges, St Ives, Huntingdon, Cambs PE17 4XR* St Ives (01480) 461806

WOOD, Miss Helen Ruth. b 54. Bedf Coll Lon BA75 Ex Univ PGCE77. Glouc Sch of Min 87. **d** 91 **p** 94. NSM Up Hatherley *Glouc* from 91; Chapl Cheltenham Ladies' Coll from 91. *17 Naunton Terrace, Cheltenham, Glos GL53 7NU* Cheltenham (01242) 242793

WOOD, Jack Barrington. b 24. St Aug Coll Cant 56. **d** 57 **p** 58. V Bradpole *Sarum* 64-73; rtd 89. *41 Vernons Court, Bridport, Dorset DT6 3QF*

WOOD, Miss Jane. b 38. Wye Coll Lon BSc59. St Jo Coll Nottm LTh89. **d** 89. NSM Newtown w Llanllwchaiarn w Aberhafesp *St As* 89-93; C Mochdre from 93. *The Rectory Close, Old Kerry Road, Newtown, Powys SY22 6RN* Newtown (01686) 622309

WOOD, Mrs Jennifer Sarah. b 40. Sarum Dioc Tr Coll CertEd60. Oak Hill Th Coll DipHE94. **d** 94 **p** 95. C Illogan *Truro* from 94. *46 Bosmeor Park, Illogan, Redruth, Cornwall TR15 3JN* Redruth (01209) 219268

WOOD, John. b 37. Local NSM Course 75. **d** 77 **p** 79. NSM Dunbar *Edin* from 77; NSM Haddington from 77. *7 Herdmanflatt, Haddington, East Lothian EH41 3LN* Haddington (01620) 822838

WOOD, John Anthony Scriven. b 48. Leeds Univ BSc70. St Jo Coll Nottm 76. **d** 79 **p** 80. C Colwich *Lich* 79-82; C W Bridgford *S'well* 82-90; R Gamston and Bridgford from 90; Chapl Kings Mill Cen NHS Trust Nottm from 95. *64 Henry Road, Nottingham NG2 7ND* Nottingham (0115) 982 0969

WOOD, John Arthur. b 23. Roch Th Coll 68. **d** 70 **p** 71. C Wetherby *Ripon* 70-71; P-in-c Sheff Arbourthorne *Sheff* 71-75; TV Sheff Manor 75-81; R Rodney Stoke w Draycott *B & W* 81-88; rtd 88. *Flat 36, The Glen, Endcliffe Vale Road, Sheffield S10 3FN* Sheffield (0114) 266 5173

WOOD, John Maurice. b 58. Qu Coll Cam BA80 MA83. Wycliffe Hall Ox BA87. **d** 87 **p** 88. C Northwood Em *Lon* 87-91; C Muswell Hill St Jas w St Matt 91-94; P-in-c Tottenham St Ann from 94. *St Ann's Vicarage, South Grove, London N15 5QG* 0181-800 3506

WOOD, John Samuel. b 47. Lanchester Poly BSc69 Sheff Univ DipEd. Westcott Ho Cam 72. **d** 81 **p** 82. NSM Haverhill *St E* 81-83; C Haverhill w Withersfield, the Wrattings etc 83; C Whitton and Thurleston w Akenham 83-86; P-in-c Walsham le Willows 86-88; P-in-c Finningham w Westhorpe 86-88; R Walsham le Willows and Finningham w Westhorpe 88-94; Min Can St E Cathl 89-94; TR Whitstable *Cant* from 94. *The Vicarage, Church Street, Whitstable, Kent CT5 1PG* Canterbury (01227) 272308

WOOD, Keith. b 49. St Steph Ho Ox 76. **d** 78 **p** 79. C Bognor *Chich* 78-81; C Hangleton 81-83; R W Blatchington 83-87; V W Worthing St Jo from 87. *St John's Vicarage, 15 Reigate Road, Worthing, W Sussex BN11 5NF* Worthing (01903) 247340

WOOD, Canon Keith Ernest. b 33. Qu Coll Ox BA55 BCL56 DipTh57 MA70. Wycliffe Hall Ox 56. **d** 58 **p** 59. C Barking St Marg *Chelmsf* 58-61; Min Basildon St Andr ED 61-70; V Brampton Bierlow *Sheff* 70-82; R Grasmere *Carl* 82-94; RD Windermere 89-94; Hon Can Carl Cathl from 91; Bp's Dom Chapl from 94. *The Chaplain's House, Rose Castle, Dalston, Carlisle CA5 7BZ* Raughton Head (016974) 76274 Fax 76550

WOOD, Laurence Henry. b 27. Kelham Th Coll 47. **d** 52 **p** 53. R Bonsall *Derby* 64-70; V Cromford 64-70; V Longwood *Wakef* 70-76; V Liversedge 76-92; rtd 92. *203 The Rock, Gillroyd Lane, Linthwaite, Huddersfield HD7 5SR* Huddersfield (01484) 843499

WOOD, Mrs Lorna. b 43. E Anglian Minl Tr Course 85. **d** 88 **p** 94. Hon C Sprowston *Nor* 88-90; Hon C Sprowston w Beeston 90-95; Chapl The Gt Hosp Bishopgate Nor from 95; P-in-c Nor St Helen *Nor* from 95. *39 Inman Road, Norwich NR7 8JT* Norwich (01603) 408710

✠**WOOD, Rt Rev Maurice Arthur Ponsonby.** b 16. DSC44. Qu Coll Cam BA38 MA42. Ridley Hall Cam 40. **d** 40 **p** 41 **c** 71. C Portman Square St Paul *Lon* 40-43; Chapl RNVR 43-46; R Ox St Ebbe *Ox* 47-52; V Islington St Mary *Lon* 52-61; RD

Islington 52-61; Prin Oak Hill Th Coll 61-71; Preb St Paul's Cathl *Lon* 69-71; Bp Nor 71-85; Chapl RNR from 71; rtd 85; Asst Bp Lon from 85; Res P Theale and Englefield 87-94; Asst Bp Ox from 89. *41 Fir Tree Walk, Enfield, Middx EN1 3TZ* 0181-363 4491

WOOD, Michael Frank. b 55. Nottm Univ BCombStuds. Linc Th Coll. **d** 84 **p** 85. C Marton *Blackb* 84-88; TV Ribbleton 88-93; V Blackpool St Mary from 93. *St Mary's Vicarage, 59 Stony Hill Avenue, Blackpool FY4 1PR* Blackpool (01253) 342713

WOOD, Nicholas Martin. b 51. AKC74. **d** 75 **p** 76. C E Ham w Upton Park St Alb *Chelmsf* 75-78; C Leyton St Luke 78-81; V Rush Green 81-91; Chapl Barking Tech Coll 81-91; TR Elland *Wakef* from 91. *Elland Rectory, 50 Victoria Road, Elland, W Yorkshire HX5 0QA* Elland (01422) 372133

WOOD, Paul Dominic. b 52. R Agric Coll Cirencester DipAgr74 Tasmania Coll of Advanced Educn DipEd80. Ridley Coll Melbourne BTh87. **d** 87 **p** 88. Australia 87-92; TV Ifield *Chich* from 92. *St Leonard's House, 10 Martyrs Avenue, Langley Green, Crawley, W Sussex RH11 7RZ* Crawley (01293) 518419

WOOD, Peter Palmer. b 36. Nottm Univ BA58. Bps' Coll Cheshunt 58. **d** 60 **p** 61. C Lewes St Anne *Chich* 67-70; C The Quinton *Birm* 70-72; V Kirkby Wharfe *York* 72-85; V Riccall 85-94; rtd 94. *28 Hallcroft Lane, Copmanthorpe, York YO2 3UQ* York (01904) 703457

WOOD, Preb Peter Thomas. b 31. Clifton Th Coll 57. **d** 60 **p** 61. C Woodford Wells *Chelmsf* 60-63; SAMS 63-72; Chile 63-72; V Clevedon Ch Ch *B & W* 72-82; Chapl St Brandon's Sch Clevedon 72-82; Chapl Heref Gen Hosp from 82; V Heref St Pet w St Owen and St Jas *Heref* from 82; Police Chapl from 86; RD Heref City from 90; Preb Heref Cathl from 91. *St James's Vicarage, 102 Green Street, Hereford HR1 2QW* Hereford (01432) 273676

WOOD, Philip Hervey. b 42. Sarum & Wells Th Coll 73. **d** 74 **p** 75. C Cov H Trin *Cov* 74-75; C Finham 75-77; C Wandsworth Common St Mary *S'wark* 78-81; R Bodiam *Chich* 81-87; R Ewhurst 81-87; Dep Chapl HM Pris Wandsworth 88-90; Chapl HM Rem Cen Latchmere Ho 88-90; Lic to Offic *Chich* from 90. *24 Knebworth Road, Bexhill-on-Sea, E Sussex TN39 4JJ* Bexhill-on-Sea (01424) 730031

WOOD, Canon Philip James. b 48. Bris Univ BSc69. Oak Hill Th Coll 71. **d** 74 **p** 75. C Islington St Mary *Lon* 74-77; C Stapenhill w Cauldwell *Derby* 77-80; V Walthamstow St Luke *Chelmsf* 80-94; RD Waltham Forest 89-94; Can Chelmsf Cathl 93-94. *c/o 86 Aldersbrook Road, London E12 5DH*

WOOD, Raymond John Lee. b 28. ACII55 ACIArb. Linc Th Coll 66. **d** 68 **p** 69. C Beaconsfield *Ox* 68-72; CF 70-72; V Wath-upon-Dearne w Adwick-upon-Dearne *Sheff* 72-77; R St Tudy w Michaelstow *Truro* 77-86; P-in-c St Mabyn 82-86; R St Tudy w St Mabyn and Michaelstow from 86; Chapl Bodmin Fire Brigade from 91. *The Rectory, St Tudy, Bodmin, Cornwall PL30 3NH* Bodmin (01208) 850374

WOOD, Reginald John. b 16. Worc Ord Coll 61. **d** 63 **p** 64. V The Seavingtons w Lopen *B & W* 68-80; rtd 81; Perm to Offic *Ex* from 82. *Downside, 11 Station Road, Budleigh Salterton, Devon EX9 6RW* Budleigh Salterton (01395) 442389

✠**WOOD, Rt Rev Richard James.** b 20. Wells Th Coll 51. **d** 52 **p** 53 **c** 73. C Calne *Sarum* 52-55; S Africa 55-73; Namibia 73-77; Suff Bp Damaraland 73-77; V Kingston upon Hull St Mary *York* 77-79; Chapl Hull Coll of HE 77-79; Tanzania 79-85; rtd 85; Asst Bp York 79 and from 85. *90 Park Lane, Cottingham, N Humberside HU16 5RX* Hull (01482) 843928

WOOD, Richard Olivier Ronald. b 19. TCD BA42 MA51. **d** 43 **p** 44. CF 47-74; V Kemble w Poole Keynes *Glouc* 74-77; V Kemble, Poole Keynes, Somerford Keynes etc 77-81; rtd 81. *73 Newbarn Lane, Prestbury, Cheltenham, Glos GL52 3LB* Cheltenham (01242) 577552

WOOD, Roger Graham. b 49. K Coll Lon BD. Chich Th Coll 74. **d** 76 **p** 77. C Skipton H Trin *Bradf* 76-79; Dioc Youth Chapl 79-87; V Queensbury from 87. *7 Russell Hall Lane, Queensbury, Bradford, W Yorkshire BD13 2AJ* Bradford (01274) 880573

WOOD, Roger William. b 43. Leeds Univ BA65 MA67 Fitzw Coll Cam BA69 MA75. Westcott Ho Cam 67. **d** 70 **p** 71. C Bishop's Stortford St Mich *St Alb* 70-74; C Sundon w Streatley 74-79; V Streatley from 80. *17 Sundon Road, Streatley, Luton LU3 3PL* Luton (01582) 882780

WOOD, Ronald Ernest (Ron). b 49. Sarum & Wells Th Coll 79. **d** 81 **p** 82. C Weston-super-Mare Cen Par *B & W* 81-84; C Forest of Dean Ch Ch w English Bicknor *Glouc* 84-88; R Handley w Gussage St Andrew and Pentridge *Sarum* from 88. *The Vicarage, 60 High Street, Sixpenny Handley, Salisbury SP5 5ND* Handley (01725) 552608

WOOD, Stanley Charles. b 26. Glouc Th Course. **d** 83 **p** 84. NSM Lower Cam w Coaley *Glouc* 83-87; P-in-c Shipton

Moyne w Westonbirt and Lasborough 87-91; rtd 92; Perm to Offic *Glouc* from 92. *8 The Vennings, Cam, Dursley, Glos GL11 5NQ* Dursley (01453) 544873

✠**WOOD, Rt Rev Stanley Mark.** b 19. Univ of Wales BA40. Coll of Resurr Mirfield 40. **d** 42 **p** 43 **c** 71. C Cardiff St Mary *Llan* 42-45; S Africa 45-55; S Rhodesia 55-65; Rhodesia 65-77; Can Mashonaland 61-65; Dean Salisbury 65-71; Bp Matabeleland 71-77; Asst Bp Heref 77-81; Preb Heref Cathl 77-87; Suff Bp Ludlow 81-87; Adn Ludlow 82-83; rtd 87. *13 Bruton Place, Llandaff, Cardiff CF5 2ER* Cardiff (01222) 560632

WOOD, Mrs Sylvia Marian. b 40. Gilmore Ho 77. dss 80 **d** 87 **p** 94. Tolleshunt Knights w Tiptree *Chelmsf* 80-83; Leigh-on-Sea St Jas 83-86; Canvey Is 86-87; Par Dn 87-92; Miss to Seamen 87-92; Warden of Ords *Chelmsf* 89-92; Par Dn Hutton 92-94; Continuing Minl Educn Officer 92-94; C Hutton from 94. *156C Rayleigh Road, Hutton, Brentwood, Essex CM13 1PH* Brentwood (01277) 216544

WOOD, Thomas Henry. Glassboro Coll (USA) BEcon84. St D Coll Lamp 57. **d** 60 **p** 61. C Pontnewynydd *Mon* 60-62; C Middlesb All SS *York* 64-69; C Fleetwood *Blackb* 69-73; V Ferndale *Llan* 73-77; C Sheff Parson Cross St Cecilia *Sheff* 88-93; V St Hilary Greenway *Mon* from 93. *St Hilary's Vicarage, 38 Rhyl Road, Cardiff CF3 8PA* Cardiff (01222) 793460

✠**WOOD, Rt Rev Dr Wilfred Denniston.** b 36. Lambeth DipTh62 Gen Th Sem (NY) Hon DD86 Codrington Coll Barbados 57. **d** 61 **p** 62 **c** 85. C Hammersmith St Steph *Lon* 62-63; V Shepherd's Bush St Steph w St Thos 63-74; Bp's Chapl for Community Relns 67-74; V Catford St Laur *S'wark* 74-82; Hon Can S'wark Cathl 77-82; RD E Lewisham 77-82; Boro Dean S'wark 82-85; Adn S'wark 82-85; Suff Bp Croydon 85-91; Area Bp Croydon from 91. *53 Stanhope Road, Croydon CR0 5NS* 0181-686 1822 or 681 5496 Fax 686 2074

WOOD, William. b 03. St Jo Coll Morpeth 28 ACT ThL31. **d** 31 **p** 32. Brotherhood of the Gd Shep (NSW) from 28; Chapl and Trustee Lon Healing Miss 68-71; rtd 71; Perm to Offic *Ox* from 83; Perm to Offic *S'wark* 83-91. *32 The Maltings, Kennet Road, Newbury, Berks RG14 5HZ* Newbury (01635) 523447

WOOD, William George. b 31. Oak Hill Th Coll 61. **d** 63 **p** 64. C Woking St Jo *Guildf* 63-69; V Camberwell All SS *S'wark* 69-88; R Horne from 88; P-in-c Outwood from 88. *The Rectory, Church Road, Horne, Horley, Surrey RH6 9LA* Smallfield (01342) 842054

WOODALL, Hugh Gregory. b 11. Keble Coll Ox BA33 MA37. Cuddesdon Coll 33. **d** 34 **p** 35. V Boston Spa *York* 55-80; RD Tadcaster 72-78; rtd 80. *Kirklea, Gracious Street, Huby, York YO6 1HR* York (01904) 810705

WOODALL, Reginald Homer. b 38. Univ of Wales DipTh59. St Mich Coll Llan 59. **d** 61 **p** 62. C Hawarden *St As* 66-70; CF 70-74; C Thornton Heath St Jude *Cant* 74-77; TV Cannock *Lich* 77-79; TV Basildon St Martin w H Cross and Laindon etc *Chelmsf* 79-84; P-in-c Canning Town St Cedd 84-93; rtd 93. *64 Stephens Road, London E15 3JL*

WOODBRIDGE, Trevor Geoffrey. b 31. Lon Univ BSc52. ALCD57. **d** 58 **p** 59. Area Sec (Dios Ex and Truro) CMS 65-81; SW Regional Sec 70-81; TV Clyst St George, Aylesbeare, Clyst Honiton etc *Ex* 82-84; V Aylesbeare, Rockbeare, Farringdon etc 85-95; rtd 95. *19 Marlborough Road, Exeter EX2 4TJ*

WOODCOCK, John Charles Gerard. b 31. Kelham Th Coll 52. **d** 56 **p** 57. SSM 56-88; S Africa 56-62 and 76-83; Lesotho 62-76; Chapl Bede Ho Staplehurst 83-87; C Auckland St Andr and St Anne *Dur* 87-88. *3 Helena Terrace, Cockton Hill, Bishop Auckland, Co Durham DL14 6BP* Bishop Auckland (01388) 604956

WOODCOCK, Nicholas Ethelbert (Nick). b 46. FRSA90. Cant Sch of Min 80. **d** 90 **p** 91. Chief Exec and Co Sec Keston Coll Kent 89-92; NSM Clerkenwell H Redeemer w St Phil *Lon* 90-92; NSM Clerkenwell H Redeemer and St Mark 92-93; Chapl RN from 93. *Directorate Gen, RN Chapl Services, Room 203, Victory Building, HM Naval Base, Portsmouth PO1 3LS* Portsmouth (01705) 727903 Fax 727112

WOODD, Basil John. b 07. Jes Coll Cam BA31 MA35. Westcott Ho Cam 31. **d** 32 **p** 33. R Gt Gonerby *Linc* 59-68; rtd 68. *College of St Barnabas, Blackberry Lane, Lingfield, Surrey RH7 6NJ* Dormans Park (01342) 870260

WOODERSON, Mrs Marguerite Ann. b 44. RGN SCM. Qu Coll Birm 86. **d** 89 **p** 94. Par Dn Stoneydelph St Martin CD *Lich* 89-90; Par Dn Glascote and Stonydelph 90-91; Par Dn Chasetown 91-94; C 94. *15 Spring Gardens, Sallins Road, Naas, Co Kildare, Irish Republic* Naas (45) 897206

WOODERSON, Preb Michael George. b 39. Southn Univ BA61. Lon Coll of Div BD69. **d** 69 **p** 70. C Morden *S'wark* 69-73; C Aldridge *Lich* 73-81; V Chasetown 81-94; RD Lich 86-94; Preb Lich Cathl 89-94; P-in-c Hammerwich 91-94; I Naas w Kill and Rathmore *M & K* from 94. *15 Spring Gardens, Sallins Road, Naas, Co Kildare, Irish Republic* Naas (45) 897206 Fax as telephone

WOODERSON, Timothy George Arthur. b 39. St Chad's Coll Dur BA61 DipTh63. **d** 63 **p** 64. C S w N Hayling *Portsm* 63-66; Papua New Guinea 66-70; C Rowner *Portsm* 71-77; R Bermondsey St Mary w St Olave, St Jo etc *S'wark* 78-89; V Redhill St Jo from 89. *St John's Vicarage, Church Road, Redhill RH1 6QA* Redhill (01737) 766562

WOODFIELD, Robert Ronald. b 13. Ch Coll Cam BA35 MA49. Ridley Hall Cam 35. **d** 37 **p** 38. R Shaw cum Donnington *Ox* 53-71; R Leadenham *Linc* 71-78; R Welbourn 73-78; rtd 78. *Upper Treasurer's House, 42 Bromley College, London Road, Bromley BR1 1PE* 0181-290 1544

WOODGATE, Douglas Digby. b 09. Bris Univ BA32. Wells Th Coll 33. **d** 34 **p** 35. V Elkesley w Bothamsall *S'well* 45-80; rtd 80; Perm to Offic *S'well* from 80. *4 Elm Tree Court, Potter Street, Worksop, Notts S80 2HL* Worksop (01909) 484740

WOODGATE, Michael James. b 35. Dur Univ BA60. St Steph Ho *Ox* 60. **d** 62 **p** 63. C Streatham St Pet *S'wark* 62-69; V 69-84; RD Streatham 78-84; R St Magnus the Martyr w St Marg New Fish Street *Lon* from 84; P-in-c St Clem Eastcheap w St Martin Orgar from 89. *St Magnus' Vestry House, Lower Thames Street, London EC3R 6DN* 0171-626 4481

WOODGER, John McRae. b 36. Tyndale Hall Bris 60. **d** 63 **p** 64. C Heref St Pet w St Owen *Heref* 63-66; C Macclesfield St Mich *Ches* 66-69; V Llangarron w Llangrove *Heref* 69-74; P-in-c Garway 70-74; R Church Stretton 74-84; Preb Heref Cathl 82-84; V Watford *St Alb* from 84. *St Mary's Vicarage, 14 Cassiobury Drive, Watford WD1 3AB* Watford (01923) 254005 or 225189

WOODGER, John Page. b 30. Master Mariner 56 Lon Univ DipTh58. St Aid Birkenhead 56. **d** 59 **p** 60. Chapl HM Borstal Pollington 62-70; V Balne *Sheff* 63-70; C Halesowen *Worc* 70-74; V Cookley 74-81; TV Droitwich 81-85; TV Bedminster *Bris* 85-93; rtd 93. *4 Cambridge Crescent, Bristol BS9 3QG*

WOODGER, Richard William. b 50. Sarum & Wells Th Coll 76. **d** 79 **p** 80. C Chessington *Guildf* 79-82; C Frimley 82-85; C Frimley Green 82-85; V N Holmwood 85-90; TR Headley All SS from 90. *All Saints Rectory, High Street, Headley, Bordon, Hants GU35 8PP* Headley Down (01428) 717321

WOODHALL, Peter. b 32. Edin Th Coll 57. **d** 60 **p** 61. C Carl St Barn *Carl* 60-63; Hon Chapl Estoril St Paul *Eur* 63-65; Chapl RN 66-82; TR Scilly Is *Truro* 82-90; V Mithian w Mt Hawke 90-95. *Tregarth, 4 Peverell Road, Porthleven, Helston, Cornwall TR13 9DH*

WOODHAM, Richard Medley Swift. b 43. Master Mariner 70 DipTh. S'wark Ord Course 71. **d** 73 **p** 74. C Gravesend St Aid *Roch* 73-75; C Chessington *Guildf* 75-78; Warden Dioc Conf Ho Horstead *Nor* 78-87; R Horstead 87-91; Youth Chapl from 78; V Nor St Mary Magd w St Jas 87-91; TR Nor Over-the-Water from 91. *The Vicarage, Crome Road, Norwich NR3 4RQ* Norwich (01603) 625699 or 661381

WOODHAMS, Roy Owen. b 57. GRSM78 ARCM86 Lon Inst of Educn TCert79. Ripon Coll Cuddesdon DipMin93. **d** 93 **p** 94. C Deal St Leon and St Rich and Sholden *Cant* from 93. *327 London Road, Deal, Kent CT14 9PR* Deal (01304) 372597

WOODHAMS, Mrs Sophie Harriet. b 27. Cranmer Hall Dur 66. **dss** 80 **d** 87. Raveningham *Nor* 80-81; Henleaze *Bris* 81-87; rtd 87. *31 Hanover Close, Shaftgate Avenue, Shepton Mallet, Somerset BA4 5YQ* Shepton Mallet (01749) 344124

WOODHEAD, Alan Howard. b 37. Open Univ BA73. St Aid Birkenhead 62. **d** 65 **p** 66. C Kirkstall *Ripon* 65-68; C Marfleet *York* 68-71; V Barmby on the Moor w Fangfoss 71-80; Chapl R Russell Sch Croydon from 81. *Old Ballard's Cottage, Hollingsworth Road, Croydon CR0 5RP* 0181-651 2756 or 657 4433

WOODHEAD, Christopher Godfrey. b 26. Pemb Coll Cam BA50 MA55. Ely Th Coll 50. **d** 52 **p** 53. R Earl Stonham *St E* 66-72; V Hoo St Werburgh *Roch* 72-88; C Cheam *S'wark* 88-91; rtd 91. *4 Eastgate Close, Herne Bay, Kent CT6 7ER* Herne Bay (01227) 374137

WOODHEAD, Miss Helen Mary. b 35. Bedf Coll Lon BA57. Westcott Ho Cam 86. **d** 87 **p** 94. Par Dn Daventry *Pet* 87-90; C Godalming *Guildf* 90-95; Asst Dioc Dir of Ords from 90; C Worplesdon from 95. *St Albans House, 96 Oak Hill, Wood Street Village, Guildford, Surrey GU3 3ES* Guildford (01483) 235136

WOODHEAD, Canon Henry Hamilton (Harry). b 22. TCD BA45. **d** 47 **p** 48. I Killowen *D & R* 65-91; Can Derry Cathl 81-91; rtd 91; Miss to Seamen from 91. *7 Woodland Park, Coleraine, Co Londonderry BT52 1JG* Coleraine (01265) 51382

WOODHEAD, Michael. b 51. St Jo Coll Nottm 88. **d** 90 **p** 91. C Stannington *Sheff* 90-93; V Deepcar from 93. *St John's Vicarage, 27 Carr Road, Deepcar, Sheffield S30 5PQ* Sheffield (0114) 288 5138

WOODHEAD, Mrs Sandra Buchanan. b 42. Man Poly BA82 Man Univ BD85. St Deiniol's Hawarden. **dss** 86 **d** 87 **p** 94.

High Lane *Ches* 86-87; Hon Par Dn 87-90; C Brinnington w Portwood 91-94; V from 94. *St Luke's Vicarage, Brinnington Road, Stockport, Cheshire SK5 8BS* 0161-430 4164

WOODHEAD-KEITH-DIXON, James Addison. b 25. St Aid Birkenhead 44. **d** 48 **p** 49. V Lorton *Carl* 59-80; Chapl Puerto de la Cruz Tenerife *Eur* 80-82; TV Bellingham/Otterburn Gp *Newc* 82-83; TR 83-91; TR N Tyne and Redesdale Team 91-92; rtd 92. *Cree Grange, Cree Bridge, Newton Stewart, Wigtownshire DG8 6NR*

WOODHOUSE, Miss Alison Ruth. b 43. Bedf Coll of Educn CertEd64 Lon Univ DipTh70. Dalton Ho Bris 68. **dss** 79 **d** 87 **p** 94. Bayston Hill *Lich* 79-81; W Derby St Luke *Liv* 81-86; Burscough Bridge 86-87; Par Dn 87-94; C from 94. *32 Manor Avenue, Burscough, Ormskirk, Lancs L40 7TT* Burscough (01704) 894731

WOODHOUSE, Ven Andrew Henry. b 23. DSC45. Qu Coll Ox BA48 MA49. Linc Th Coll 48. **d** 50 **p** 51. V W Drayton *Lon* 56-70; RD Hillingdon 67-70; Adn Ludlow *Heref* 70-82; R Wistanstow 70-82; P-in-c Acton Scott 70-73; Can Res Heref Cathl 82-91; Treas 82-85; Adn Heref 82-91; rtd 91. *Orchard Cottage, Bracken Close, Woking, Surrey GU22 7HD* Woking (01483) 760671

WOODHOUSE, Andrew Laurence. b 40. NW Ord Course. **d** 82 **p** 83. NSM Bedale *Ripon* from 82. *86 South End, Bedale, N Yorkshire DL8 2DS* Bedale (01677) 423573

WOODHOUSE, Ven Charles David Stewart. b 34. Kelham Th Coll 55. **d** 59 **p** 60. C Leeds Halton St Wilfrid *Ripon* 59-63; Youth Chapl *Liv* 63-66; Bermuda 66-69; Asst Gen Sec CEMS 69-70; Gen Sec 70-76; Bp's Dom Chapl *Ex* 76-81; R Ideford, Luton and Ashcombe 76-81; V Hindley St Pet *Liv* 81-92; Adn Warrington from 81; Hon Can Liv Cathl from 83. *22 Rob Lane, Newton-le-Willows, Merseyside WA12 0DR* Warrington (01925) 229247

WOODHOUSE, Canon David. b 36. FRSA FCollP Selw Coll Cam BA60 MA64. St Steph Ho Ox 60. **d** 62 **p** 63. C Boston *Linc* 62-64; C Pimlico St Gabr *Lon* 64-66; Chapl Woodbridge Sch Suffolk 66-73; V Heap Bridge *Man* 73-75; Can Res Wakef Cathl *Wakef* 76-85; Dir of Educn 76-85; Hon Can Liv Cathl *Liv* from 85; Dir of Educn from 85. *5 Cathedral Close, Liverpool L1 7BR* 0151-708 0942

WOODHOUSE, David Edwin. b 45. Lon Univ BSc68. Cuddesdon Coll 68. **d** 71 **p** 72. C E Dulwich St Jo *S'wark* 71-74; Lic to Offic 74-77; Perm to Offic *Bris* 77-79; Lic to Offic from 79. *St Augustine's Vicarage, Morris Street, Swindon SN2 2HT* Swindon (01793) 522741

WOODHOUSE, David Maurice. b 40. Lon Univ BA62. Clifton Th Coll 63. **d** 65 **p** 66. C Wellington w Eyton *Lich* 65-69; C Meole Brace 69-71; V Colwich 71-82; Chapl St Gt Haywood 78-82; R Clitheroe St Jas *Blackb* 82-88; Ellel Grange Chr Healing Cen 88-91; V The Lye and Stambermill *Worc* from 91. *The Vicarage, High Street, Lye, Stourbridge, W Midlands DY9 8LF* Lye (01384) 423142

WOODHOUSE, Hugh Frederic. b 12. TCD BA34 BD37 DD52. **d** 37 **p** 38. Regius Prof Div TCD 63-82; rtd 82. *4591 West 16th Avenue, Vancouver, British Columbia, Canada, V6R 3E8* Vancouver (604) 224-4812

WOODHOUSE, James. b 29. Lon Univ BA52. Lich Th Coll. **d** 61 **p** 62. R Roos w Tunstall *York* 69-72; V Garton w Grimston and Hilston 69-72; V Nunthorpe 72-82; V Pocklington w Yapham-cum-Meltonby, Owsthorpe etc 82-83; P-in-c Millington w Gt Givendale 82-83; TR Pocklington Team 84-89; RD Pocklington 84-86; RD S Wold 86-90; V Coatham 89-94; rtd 94. *5 Cleveland Avenue, Stokesley, Middlesbrough, Cleveland TS9 5EZ* Stokesley (01642) 712310

WOODHOUSE, Canon Keith Ian. b 33. K Coll Lon 54. **d** 58 **p** 59. C Stockton St Chad CD *Dur* 58-61; C Man St Aid *Man* 61-64; V Peterlee *Dur* from 64; RD Easington from 72; Hon Can Dur Cathl from 79. *The Vicarage, Manor Way, Peterlee, Co Durham SR8 5QW* 0191-586 2630

WOODHOUSE, Patrick Henry Forbes. b 47. Ch Ch Ox BA69 MA81. St Jo Coll Nottm 69 Lon Coll of Div ALCD71 LTh71. **d** 72 **p** 73. C Birm St Martin *Birm* 72-74; C Whitchurch *Bris* 75-76; C Harpenden St Nic *St Alb* 76-80; Tanzania 80-81; Soc Resp Officer *Carl* 81-85; P-in-c Dean 81-85; Dir Soc Resp *Win* 85-90; V Chippenham St Andr w Tytherton Lucas *Bris* from 90. *The Vicarage, 54A St Mary Street, Chippenham, Wilts SN15 3JW* Chippenham (01249) 656834

WOODHOUSE, Ven Samuel Mostyn Forbes. b 12. Ch Ch Ox BA34 MA42. Wells Th Coll 35. **d** 36 **p** 37. Adn Lon and Can Res St Paul's Cathl *Lon* 67-78; rtd 78. *Under Copse Cottage, Redhill, Wrington, Bristol BS18 7SH* Wrington (01934) 862711

WOODHOUSE, Thomas Mark Bewes. b 66. Aston Tr Scheme 90 Westcott Ho Cam CTM95. **d** 95. C Cainscross w Selsley *Glouc* from 95. *Church House, 13 Frome Gardens, Stroud, Glos GL5 4LE* Stroud (01453) 756290

WOODHOUSE, William Henry. b 12. SS Coll Cam BA36 MA40. Chich Th Coll 36. **d** 38 **p** 39. R Yate *Bris* 61-74; P-in-c

Wapley w Codrington and Dodington 67-71; R N Cerney w Bagendon *Glouc* 74-82; RD Cirencester 77-82; rtd 82; Perm to Offic *Glouc* from 82. *2 Burford Road, Cirencester, Glos GL7 1AF* Cirencester (01285) 658938

WOODING JONES, Andrew David. b 61. Oak Hill Th Coll BA91. **d** 91 **p** 92. C Welling *Roch* 91-95; TV Crookes St Thos *Sheff* from 95. *79 Glebe Road, Sheffield S10 1FB* Sheffield (0114) 268 3463

WOODLAND, Robert Alan. b 29. Bps' Coll Cheshunt 59. **d** 61 **p** 62. V Oxhey All SS *St Alb* 66-76; V Hainault *Chelmsf* 76-81; R Bicknoller w Crowcombe and Sampford Brett *B & W* 81-89; rtd 90; Perm to Offic *B & W* from 90. *13 Paganel Close, Minehead, Somerset TA24 5HD* Minehead (01643) 704598

WOODLEY, David James. b 38. K Coll Lon BD61 AKC61. **d** 62 **p** 63. C Lancing St Jas *Chich* 62-64; C St Alb St Pet *St Alb* 64-67; Malaysia 67-70; Lic to Offic *Linc* 71-72; V Westoning w Tingrith *St Alb* 72-77; Asst Chapl HM Pris Wormwood Scrubs 77-78; Chapl HM Pris Cardiff 78-84; Chapl HM Rem Cen Risley 84-92; Chapl HM Pris Styal from 92. *HM Prison, Styal, Wilmslow, Cheshire SK9 4HR* Wilmslow (01625) 532141 Fax 548060

WOODLEY, Canon John Francis Chapman. b 33. Univ of Wales (Lamp) BA58. Edin Th Coll 58. **d** 60 **p** 61. C Edin All SS *Edin* 60-65; Chapl St Andr Cathl *Ab* 65-67; Prec 67-71; R Glas St Oswald *Glas* 71-77; P-in-c Cumbernauld 77-93; Can St Mary's Cathl from 82; CSG from 82; R Dalbeattie *Glas* from 93. *The Rectory, 319 High Street, Dalbeattie, Kirkcudbrightshire DG5 4DT* Dalbeattie (01556) 610671

WOODLEY, Ven Ronald John. b 25. Bps' Coll Cheshunt 50. **d** 53 **p** 54. V Middlesb Ascension *York* 66-71; R Stokesley 71-85; RD Stokesley 77-85; Can and Preb York Minster 82-91; Adn Cleveland 85-91; rtd 91. *52 South Parade, Northallerton, N Yorkshire DL7 8SL* Northallerton (01609) 778818

WOODMAN, Dr Brian Baldwin. b 35. Leeds Univ BA57 PhD73. N Ord Course 84. **d** 87 **p** 88. C Guiseley w Esholt *Bradf* 87-90; TV Bingley All SS 90-94; NSM St Merryn *Truro* from 94. *The Vicarage, St Merryn, Padstow, Cornwall PL28 8ND* Padstow (01841) 520379

WOODMAN, Christopher James. b 65. Chich Th Coll BTh93. **d** 93. C Leigh-on-Sea St Marg *Chelmsf* from 93. *45 Eaton Road, Leigh-on-Sea, Essex SS9 3PF* Southend-on-Sea (01702) 77863

WOODMAN, Oliver Nigel. b 47. FIPM MIPM73 HNC73. Sarum Th Coll 67. **d** 70 **p** 82. C Stepney St Dunstan and All SS *Lon* 70-71; NSM Ovingdean w Rottingdean and Woodingdean *Chich* 81-87; NSM Eastbourne St Sav and St Pet 88-93; Asst to RD Eastbourne from 93. *56 Upper Kings Drive, Eastbourne, E Sussex BN20 9AS* Eastbourne (01323) 507208

WOODMAN, Ven Peter Wilfred. b 36. Univ of Wales (Lamp) BA58. Wycliffe Hall Ox 58. **d** 60 **p** 61. C New Tredegar *Mon* 60-61; C Newport St Paul 61-64; C Llanfrechfa All SS 64-66; Abp of Wales's Messenger 66-67; V Llantillio Pertholey w Bettws Chpl etc *Mon* 67-74; V Bassaleg 74-90; Can St Woolos Cathl from 84; V Caerwent w Dinham and Llanfair Discoed etc from 90; Adn Mon from 93. *The Vicarage, Vicarage Gardens, Caerwent, Newport, Gwent NP6 4BF* Caldicot (01291) 424984

WOODMANSEY, Michael Balfour. b 55. Leic Univ BSc. Ridley Hall Cam. **d** 83 **p** 84. C St Paul's Cray St Barn *Roch* 83-89; C S Shoebury *Chelmsf* 89-93; R Stifford from 93. *The Rectory, High Road, North Stifford, Grays, Essex RM16 1UE* Grays Thurrock (01375) 372733

WOODROFFE, Ian Gordon. b 46. Edin Th Coll 69. **d** 72 **p** 73. C Soham *Ely* 72-75; P-in-c Swaffham Bulbeck 75-80; Youth Chapl 75-80; V Cam St Jas 80-87; Chapl Mayday Univ Hosp Thornton Heath from 87. *Mayday Hospital, Mayday Road, Thornton Heath, Surrey CR7 7YE* 0181-401 3105

WOODROW, Canon Norman Wilson. b 21. TCD BA44 MA50. CITC 46. **d** 46 **p** 47. I Saintfield *D & D* 64-93; RD Killinchy 79-93; Can Belf Cathl 85-93; rtd 93. *Kingswood, 12 The Grange, Saintfield, Co Down BT24 7NF* Saintfield (01238) 510447

WOODS, Canon Alan Geoffrey. b 42. TD93. ACCA65 FCCA80. Sarum Th Coll 67. **d** 70 **p** 71. C Bedminster St Fran *Bris* 70-73; Youth Chapl 73-76; Warden Legge Ho Res Youth Cen 73-76; P-in-c Neston 76-79; TV Gtr Corsham 79-81; CF (TA) 80-94; P-in-c Charminster *Sarum* 81-83; V Charminster and Stinsford 83-90; RD Dorchester 85-90; Chapl Dorchester Hosps 86-87; V Calne and Blackland *Sarum* from 90; RD Calne from 90; Chapl St Mary's Sch Calne from 90; Can and Preb Sarum Cathl *Sarum* from 92. *The Vicarage, Vicarage Close, Calne, Wilts SN11 8DD* Calne (01249) 812340 Fax as telephone

WOODS, Albert. b 12. St Paul's Coll Burgh St Chad's Coll Regina LTh47. **d** 41 **p** 42. V Upper w Nether Swell *Glouc*

71-78; rtd 78; Perm to Offic *Liv* 85-91. *4 Priors Court, Tolsey Quay, Tewkesbury, Glos GL20 5US* Tewkesbury (01684) 274228

WOODS, Allan Campbell. b 32. MIEH59. Ox NSM Course 85. **d** 89 **p** 90. NSM W Wycombe w Bledlow Ridge, Bradenham and Radnage *Ox* from 89. *4 Pitcher's Cottages, Bennett End, Radnage, High Wycombe, Bucks HP14 4EF* High Wycombe (01494) 482083

WOODS, Charles William. b 31. Lich Th Coll 55. **d** 58 **p** 59. C Hednesford *Lich* 58-62; V Wilnecote 62-67; V Basford 67-76; V Chasetown 76-81; P-in-c Donington 81-83; R from 83; V Boningale from 83; RD Shifnal 84-89. *Donington Rectory, Albrighton, Wolverhampton WV7 3EP* Albrighton (01902) 372279

WOODS, Christopher Guy Alistair. b 35. Dur Univ BA60. Clifton Th Coll 60. **d** 62 **p** 63. C Rainham *Chelmsf* 62-65; C Edin St Thos *Edin* 65-69; Sec Spanish and Portuguese Ch Aid Soc 69-79; C Willesborough w Hinxhill *Cant* 75-80; P-in-c Murston w Bapchild and Tonge 80-87; R 87-90; R Gt Horkesley *Chelmsf* from 90; RD Dedham and Tey from 91. *The Rectory, Ivy Lodge Road, Great Horkesley, Colchester CO6 4EN* Colchester (01206) 271242

WOODS, Christopher Samuel. b 43. Cant Univ (NZ) BA. Qu Coll Birm 75. **d** 76 **p** 77. C Childwall All SS *Liv* 76-79; V Parr Mt from 79. *The Vicarage, Traverse Street, St Helens, Merseyside WA9 1BW* St Helens (01744) 22778

WOODS, David Arthur. b 28. Bris Univ BA52. Tyndale Hall Bris 48. **d** 53 **p** 54. V Stapleford *S'well* 66-70; Miss to Seamen 70-93; Hon Chapl Miss to Seamen 70-93; V Fowey *Truro* 70-93; RD St Austell 80-88; rtd 93; Hon C Pelynt *Truro* from 93. *Linden, 7 Richmond Road, Pelynt, Looe, Cornwall PL13 2NH* Looe (01503) 220374

WOODS, David Benjamin. b 42. Linc Th Coll 88. **d** 90 **p** 91. C Louth *Linc* 90-93; P-in-c Ingoldmells w Addlethorpe from 93. *The Rectory, 73 Elmwood Drive, Ingoldmells, Skegness, Lincs PE25 1QG* Skegness (01754) 871494

WOODS, Edward Christopher John. b 44. NUI BA67. CITC 66. **d** 67 **p** 68. C Drumglass *Arm* 67-70; C Belf St Mark *Conn* 70-73; I Kilcolman *L & K* 73-78; RD Killarney 75-78; I Portarlington w Cloneyhurke and Lea *M & K* 78-84; Chan Kildare Cathl 81-84; I Killiney Ballybrack *D & G* 85-92; RD Killiney 90-93; I Dub Rathfarnham from 93. *Rathfarnham Rectory, Terenure, Dublin 6, Irish Republic* Dublin (1) 490-5543

WOODS, Eric John. b 51. Magd Coll Ox BA72 MA77 Trin Coll Cam BA77 MA83. Westcott Ho Cam 75. **d** 78 **p** 79. C Bris St Mary Redcliffe w Temple etc *Bris* 78-81; Hon C Clifton St Paul 81-83; Asst Chapl Bris Univ 81-83; R Wroughton 83-93; RD Wroughton 88-93; V Sherborne w Castleton and Lillington *Sarum* from 93. *The Vicarage, Abbey Close, Sherborne, Dorset DT9 3LQ* Sherborne (01935) 812452

WOODS, Frederick James (Fred). b 45. Southn Univ BA66 MPhil74 Fitzw Coll Cam BA76 MA79. Ridley Hall Cam 74. **d** 77 **p** 78. C Stratford-on-Avon w Bishopton *Cov* 77-81; V Warminster Ch Ch *Sarum* from 81; RD Heytesbury from 95. *The Vicarage, 13 Avon Road, Warminster, Wilts BA12 9PR* Warminster (01985) 212219

WOODS, Geoffrey Edward. b 49. Tyndale Hall Bris BD70. **d** 73 **p** 74. C Gipsy Hill Ch Ch *S'wark* 73-76; C Uphill *B & W* 76-79; R Swainswick w Langridge and Woolley 79-84. *22 Watergates, Colerne, Chippenham, Wilts SN14 8DR* Box (01225) 743675

WOODS, Howard Charles. b 04. Trin Coll Ox BA26 MA30. Westcott Ho Cam 32. **d** 33 **p** 34. R Stratton Audley w Godington *Ox* 64-71; rtd 71. *Manormead, Tilford Road, Hindhead, Surrey GU26 6RA* Hindhead (01428) 604780

WOODS, Canon John Mawhinney. b 19. Edin Th Coll 55. **d** 58 **p** 59. R Walpole St Peter *Ely* 60-75; R Inverness St Andr *Mor* 75-80; Provost St Andr Cathl Inverness 75-80; Hon Can St Andr Cathl Inverness from 80; V The Suttons w Tydd *Linc* 80-85; rtd 85; Perm to Offic *Nor* 85-93. *4 Trenowarth Place, King Street, King's Lynn, Norfolk PE30 1HL* King's Lynn (01553) 762569

WOODS, John William Ashburnham. b 22. Reading Univ BSc50. NW Ord Course 73 St Jo Coll Lusaka 69. **d** 71 **p** 74. Zambia 71-72; C Goole *Sheff* 73-75; P-in-c Firbeck w Letwell 75-76; R 76-82; P-in-c Woodsetts 75-76; V 76-82; Bp's Rural Adv 80-92; R Barnburgh w Melton on the Hill 82-92; RD Wath 86-92; rtd 92; NSM Birdsall w Langton *York* from 93. *The Vicarage, 2 Cromarty Cottages, Birdsall, Malton, N Yorkshire YO17 9NN* North Grimston (01944) 768374

WOODS, Joseph Richard Vernon. b 31. Solicitor 57. Cuddesdon Coll 58. **d** 60 **p** 61. C Newc St Gabr *Newc* 60-63; Trinidad and Tobago 63-67; Chapl Long Grove Hosp Epsom 67-76; P-in-c Ewell St Fran *Guildf* 76-79; V 79-87; V Englefield Green from 87. *The Vicarage, 21 Willow Walk, Englefield Green, Egham, Surrey TW20 0DQ* Egham (01784) 432553

WOODS, Michael Spencer. b 44. K Coll Lon BD66 AKC66 Hull Univ DipMin88. **d** 67 **p** 68. C Sprowston *Nor* 67-70; Malaysia

70-74; TV Hempnall *Nor* 74-79; TV Halesworth w Linstead and Chediston *St E* 79-80; TV Halesworth w Linstead, Chediston, Holton etc 80-85; TR Braunstone *Leic* 85-92; RD Sparkenhoe E 89-91; TR Gt Yarmouth *Nor* from 92. *The Rectory, 1 Osborne Avenue, Great Yarmouth, Norfolk NR30 4EE* Great Yarmouth (01493) 850666

WOODS, Canon Norman Harman. b 35. K Coll Lon BD62 AKC62. **d** 63 **p** 64. C Poplar All SS w St Frideswide *Lon* 63-68; C-in-c W Leigh CD *Portsm* 68-76; V Hythe *Cant* from 76; RD Elham 83-89; Hon Can Cant Cathl from 90. *St Leonard's Vicarage, Oak Walk, Hythe, Kent CT21 5DN* Hythe (01303) 266217

WOODS, Richard Thomas Evelyn Brownrigg. b 51. St Steph Ho Ox 83. **d** 85 **p** 86. C Southgate Ch Ch *Lon* 85-88; C Northn All SS w St Kath *Pet* 88-89; V Maybridge *Chich* from 89. *56 The Boulevard, Worthing, W Sussex BN13 1LA* Worthing (01903) 249463

✠**WOODS, Rt Rev Robert Wylmer.** b 14. KCMG89 KCVO71. Trin Coll Cam BA37 MA40. Westcott Ho Cam 37. **d** 38 **p** 39 **c** 71. C St Edm the King w St Nic Acons etc *Lon* 38-39; C Hoddesdon *St Alb* 39-42; CF (EC) 42-46; V Glen Parva and S Wigston *Leic* 46-51; Adn Singapore 51-58; R Tankersley *Sheff* 58-62; Adn Sheff 58-62; Dean of Windsor and Dom Chapl to The Queen 62-71; Bp Worc 71-81; rtd 81; Asst Bp Glouc from 81. *Torsend House, Tirley, Gloucester GL19 4EU* Gloucester (01452) 780327

WOODS, Ven Samuel Edward. b 10. Trin Coll Cam BA34 MA37. Westcott Ho Cam 35. **d** 36 **p** 37. New Zealand 36-46 and from 55; V Southport H Trin *Liv* 46-50; R Hatf *St Alb* 50-55; Adn Rangiora and Westland 55-59 and 63-68; Adn Sumner 59-63; Adn Timaru 68-71; Adn Akaroa and Asburton 73-74. *19B Sumnervale Drive, Sumner, Christchurch 8, New Zealand* Christchurch (3) 266521

WOODS, Theodore Frank Spreull. b 37. Wells Th Coll 60. **d** 62 **p** 63. C Stocking Farm CD *Leic* 62-67; Papua New Guinea 67-77; V Knighton St Jo *Leic* 77-80; Australia from 80. *257 Bennetts Road, Norman Park, Queensland, Australia 4170* Brisbane (7) 395-5723 or 354-3422

WOODS, Timothy James. b 52. AIB75 PACTA88 Cen Lon Poly BA78 MSc79. Qu Coll Birm 81. **d** 83 **p** 84. C Brierley Hill *Lich* 83-86; C Stoneydelph St Martin CD 86-88; World Development Officer 86-88; Chr Aid Area Sec (SE Lon) 88-91; Perm to Offic *S'wark* 88-91; Perm to Offic *Roch* 88-91; Perm to Offic *Chelmsf* 88-91; V Estover *Ex* from 91. *The Vicarage, 1 Hallerton Court, Hallerton Close, Plymouth PL6 8NP* Plymouth (01752) 703713

WOODS, Mrs Valerie Irene. b 44. Trin Coll Bris DipHE84. dss 84 **d** 87 **p** 94. Coleford w Staunton *Glouc* 84-87; C 87-88; TD Bedminster *Bris* 88-94; TV 94-95; Chapl HM Rem Cen Pucklechurch from 95. *HM Remand Centre, Pucklechurch, Bristol BS17 3QJ.* Bristol (0117) 937 2606   Fax 937 2729

WOODSFORD, Canon Andrew Norman. b 43. Nottm Univ BA65. Ridley Hall Cam 65. **d** 67 **p** 68. C Radcliffe-on-Trent *S'well* 67-70; P-in-c Ladybrook 70-73; P-in-c Barton in Fabis 73-81; P-in-c Thrumpton 73-81; R Gamston w Eaton and W Drayton 81-88; Chapl Bramcote Sch Gamston from 81; Warden of Readers *S'well* from 88; Hon Can S'well Minster from 93; RD Retford from 93. *The Rectory, Gamston, Retford, Notts DN22 0QB* Gamston (01777) 838706

WOODSIDE, David. b 60. St Jo Coll Dur BA81. Cranmer Hall Dur 87. **d** 90 **p** 91. C Stoke Newington St Mary *Lon* 90-92. *2A South Park Street, Chatteris, Cambs PE16 6AR* Chatteris (01354) 695948

WOODWARD, Anthony John. b 50. Salford Univ BSc78. St Jo Coll Nottm DipTh79. **d** 81 **p** 82. C Deane *Man* 81-84; CF 84-87; R Norris Bank *Man* 87-90; V Lostock St Thos and St Jo from 92. *9 Lowside Avenue, Lostock, Bolton BL1 5XQ* Bolton (01204) 848631

WOODWARD, Arthur Robert Harry (Bob). b 28. **d** 76 **p** 77. Rhodesia 76-80; Zimbabwe 80-87; Adn E Harare 82-87; R Wymington w Podington *St Alb* from 87; RD Sharnbrook from 89. *The Rectory, Manor Lane, Wymington, Rushden, Northants NN10 9LL* Rushden (01933) 57800

WOODWARD, Geoffrey Wallace. b 23. St Jo Coll Cam BA47 MA50. Westcott Ho Cam 47. **d** 49 **p** 50. V Nunthorpe *York* 65-72; V Scarborough St Martin 72-79; V Goathland 79-88; rtd 88; Chapl E Netherlands *Eur* 89-93. *Yemscroft, 2 Grange Drive, Cottingham, N Humberside HU16 5RE* Hull (01482) 841423

WOODWARD, James Welford. b 61. K Coll Lon BD82 AKC82 Birm Univ MPhil91. Westcott Ho Cam 83 Lambeth STh85. **d** 85 **p** 86. C Consett *Dur* 85-87; Bp's Dom Chapl *Ox* 87-90; Chapl Qu Eliz Hosp Birm from 90; Distr Chapl Co-ord S Birm HA from 90; Chapl Manager Univ Hosp Birm NHS Trust from 92. *Queen Elizabeth Hospital, Birmingham, B15 52TH, or 18 Westholme Croft, Bournville, Birmingham B30 1TR* 0121-472 1311 Ext 3104   Fax 627 2202

WOODWARD, Canon John Clive. b 35. Univ of Wales (Lamp) BA56. St Jo Coll Dur 56. **d** 58 **p** 59. C Risca *Mon* 58-63; C Chepstow 63-66; V Ynysddu 66-74; V Newport Ch Ch 74-84; Can St Woolos Cathl from 82; R Cyncoed from 84. *The Rectory, 256 Cyncoed Road, Cardiff CF2 6RU* Cardiff (01222) 752138

WOODWARD, Maurice George. b 29. Selw Coll Cam BA56 MA58. Wells Th Coll 56. **d** 58 **p** 59. CF (R of O) 63-94; V Barrow upon Soar *Leic* 64-77; Hon Chapl Leic Cathl 64-77; V Clare w Poslingford *St E* 77-85; P-in-c Stoke by Clare w Wixoe 84-85; R How Caple w Sollarshope, Sellack etc *Heref* 85-94; rtd 94; Perm to Offic *Glouc* from 95. *Wynfield, 16 Sherwood Road, Tetbury, Glos GL8 8BU* Tetbury (01666) 505717

WOODWARD, Canon Peter Cavell. b 36. St Cath Coll Cam BA58 MA62. Bps' Coll Cheshunt 58. **d** 60 **p** 61. C Chingford St Anne *Chelmsf* 60-63; Madagascar 63-75; V Weedon Bec *Pet* 75-76; P-in-c Everdon 75-76; V Weedon Bec w Everdon 76-81; RD Daventry 79-81; Can Pet Cathl from 81; V Brackley St Pet w St Jas from 81; Chapl Brackley Cottage Hosp from 81; RD Brackley 82-88. *The Vicarage, Old Town, Brackley, Northants NN13 5BZ* Brackley (01280) 702767

WOODWARD, Reginald Charles Huphnill. b 19. FRGS Lon Univ BA41 DipEd. Wells Th Coll 41. **d** 43 **p** 44. Lic to Offic *Linc* from 53; Teacher K Sch Grantham 53-74; Hd Master K Lower Sch Grantham 74-79; rtd 79. *104 Harrowby Road, Grantham, Lincs NG31 9DS* Grantham (01476) 71912

WOODWARD, Richard Tharby. b 39. Man Univ BA60. Chich Th Coll 60. **d** 62 **p** 63. C-in-c Beaconsfield St Mich CD *Ox* 69-76; TV Beaconsfield 76-94; rtd 94. *10 Baring Crescent, Beaconsfield, Bucks HP9 2NG* Beaconsfield (01494) 670690

WOODWARD, Roger David. b 38. W Midl Minl Tr Course 87. **d** 90 **p** 91. C Castle Bromwich SS Mary and Marg *Birm* 90-93; C Kingstanding St Luke from 93; C Kingstanding St Mark from 93. *77 Bannersgate Road, Sutton Coldfield, W Midlands B73 6TY* 0121-355 8497

WOODWARD-COURT, John Blunden. b 13. Ripon Hall Ox 52. **d** 53 **p** 54. P-in-c Snitterfield w Bearley *Cov* 55-74; P-in-c Barton-on-the-Heath 74-83; R Barcheston 76-83; R Cherington w Stourton 76-83; V Wolford w Burmington 76-83; rtd 83; Perm to Offic *Cov* from 83; Perm to Offic *Glouc* from 83; Perm to Offic *Ox* from 84. *2 Orchard Close, Lower Brailes, Banbury, Oxon OX15 5AH* Brailes (01608) 685411

WOODWARDS, Canon David George. b 36. K Coll Lon BD62 MTh73. Oak Hill Th Coll 62. **d** 64 **p** 65. C Heworth H Trin *York* 64-66; Nigeria 67-71; V Edwardstone w Groton *St E* 72-82; RD Sudbury 81-88; R Glemsford 82-88; P-in-c Stanstead w Shimplingthorne and Alpheton 85-86; P-in-c Hartest w Boxted 85-86; P-in-c Lawshall 85-86; P-in-c Hartest w Boxted, Somerton and Stanstead 86-88; Hon Can St E Cathl from 87; R Thorndon w Rishangles, Stoke Ash, Thwaite etc 88-94; RD Hartismere 88-93. *4 Cricketers Close, Sudbury, Suffolk CO10 6AL* Sudbury (01787) 374160

WOOKEY, Stephen Mark. b 54. Em Coll Cam BA76 MA80. Wycliffe Hall Ox 77. **d** 80 **p** 81. C Enfield Ch Ch Trent Park *Lon* 80-84; Asst Chapl Paris St Mich *Eur* 84-87; C Langham Place All So *Lon* from 87. *2 St Paul's Court, 56 Manchester Street, London W1M 5PA* 0171-487 5374

WOOLCOCK, Mrs Annette Elizabeth. b 56. Qu Coll Birm. **d** 94 **p** 95. C Hethersett w Canteloff w Lt and Gt Melton *Nor* from 94. *32 Harman Close, Steepletower, Hethersett, Norwich NR9 3PR* Norwich (01603) 812399

WOOLCOCK, Christine Ann. *See* FROUDE, Mrs Christine Ann

WOOLCOCK, Canon John. b 47. DipRK70 Open Univ BA82 BA86. Wm Temple Coll Rugby 69 Sarum & Wells Th Coll 70. **d** 72 **p** 73. C Kells *Carl* 72-76; C Barrow St Matt 76-78; R Distington 78-86; V Staveley w Kentmere 86-93; V Staveley, Ings and Kentmere 93; Soc Resp Officer 89-93; Hon Can Carl Cathl from 91; TR Egremont and Haile from 93. *The Rectory, Grove Road, Egremont, Cumbria CA22 2LU* Egremont (01946) 820268

WOOLDRIDGE, Derek Robert. b 33. Nottm Univ BA57. Oak Hill Th Coll. **d** 59 **p** 60. C Chesterfield H Trin *Derby* 59-63; C Heworth w Peasholme St Cuth *York* 63-70; R York St Paul from 70. *St Paul's Rectory, 100 Acomb Road, York YO2 4ER* York (01904) 792304

WOOLDRIDGE, John Bellamy. b 27. Tyndale Hall Bris 54. **d** 56 **p** 57. P-in-c Knutsford St Jo *Ches* 68-71; V Knutsford St Jo and Toft 71-79; V Gt Clacton *Chelmsf* 79-82; V Disley *Ches* 82-88; Min Buxton Trin Prop Chpl *Derby* 88-92; rtd 92; Lic to Offic *S'well* from 92. *227 Bramcote Lane, Nottingham NG8 2QL* Nottingham (0115) 928 8332

WOOLFENDEN, Dennis George. b 12. Leeds Univ BSc35. Cranmer Hall Dur 66. **d** 68 **p** 69. C Barking St Marg *Chelmsf* 68-72; R Wakes Colne w Chappel 72-76; V Elm Park St Nic Hornchurch 76-80; rtd 80; Perm to Offic *Chich* from 80; Perm to Offic *Portsm* from 90. *2 Tollhouse Close, Chichester, W Sussex PO19 1SE* Chichester (01243) 528593

WOOLHOUSE, Kenneth (Ken). b 38. BNC Ox BA61 MA65. Cuddesdon Coll 61. **d** 64 **p** 65. C Old Brumby *Linc* 64-67; Chapl Cov Cathl *Cov* 68-74; C-in-c Hammersmith SS Mich and Geo White City Estate CD *Lon* 75-81; Dir Past Studies Chich Th Coll 81-95; P-in-c Birdham w W Itchenor *Chich* 81-86; Chapl W Sussex Inst of HE 86-95; TV N Lambeth *S'wark* from 95. *22 Wincott Street, London SE11 4NT* 0171-582 4915

WOOLHOUSE, Miss Linda June. b 49. ACP76 CertEd70. W Midl Minl Tr Course 85. **d** 88 **p** 94. Hon Par Dn Old Swinford Stourbridge *Worc* 88-92; Par Dn 93-94; Community Chapl 92-93; C Old Swinford Stourbridge from 94. *10 Rectory Gardens, Old Swinford, Stourbridge, W Midlands DY8 2HB* Stourbridge (01384) 376587

WOOLLARD, Miss Bridget Marianne. b 56. K Coll Cam BA77 MA80 Sheff Univ PGCE78 St Jo Coll Dur BA81 Birm Univ MPhil87. Cranmer Hall Dur 79. **dss** 82 **d** 87 **p** 94. Battersea St Pet and St Paul *S'wark* 82-84; Chapl Southn Univ *Win* 84-89; Tutor Past Th and Dir Past Studies Qu Coll Birm 89-92; Telford Chr Coun Officer for Ind and Commerce *Lich* from 92; Perm to Offic *Heref* from 92. *Meeting Point House, Southwater Square, Town Centre, Telford, Shropshire TF3 4HS* Telford (01952) 291904 or 243205 Fax 290617

WOOLLARD, David John. b 39. Leic Univ BSc62. Trin Coll Bris DipHE88. **d** 88 **p** 89. C Clifton *York* 88-91; C York St Luke 91-94; V Selby St Jas from 94; V Wistow from 94. *St James's Vicarage, 14 Leeds Road, Selby, N Yorkshire YO8 0HX* Selby (01757) 702861

WOOLLASTON, Brian. b 53. CertEd76 DipTh83. St Paul's Grahamstown 81. **d** 83 **p** 84. C Kington w Huntington, Old Radnor, Kinnerton etc *Heref* 88-89; C Tupsley 89-91; V Newbridge-on-Wye and Llanfihangel Brynpabuan etc *S & B* from 91. *The Vicarage, Newbridge-on-Wye, Llandrindod Wells, Powys LD1 6LY* Llandrindod Wells (0159789) 272

WOOLLCOMBE, Mrs Juliet. b 38. St Mary's Coll Dur BA60 DipEd61. Gilmore Course 74. **dss** 77 **d** 87 **p** 94. St Marylebone Ch Ch *Lon* 77-80; Dean of Women's Min (Lon Area) 87-89; D-in-c Upton Snodsbury and Broughton Hackett etc *Worc* 89-94; NSM Pershore w Pinvin, Wick and Birlingham from 94. *19 Ashdale Avenue, Pershore, Worcs WR10 1PL* Pershore (02386) 556550

✠WOOLLCOMBE, Rt Rev Kenneth John. b 24. St Jo Coll Ox BA49 MA53 S Swanee Univ STD63 Trin Coll Hartford (USA) Hon DD75. Westcott Ho Cam 49. **d** 51 **p** 52 **c** 71. C Gt Grimsby St Jas *Linc* 51-53; Fell Chapl and Lect St Jo Coll Ox 53-60; Tutor St Jo Coll Ox 56-60; USA 60-63; Prof Dogmatic Th Gen Th Sem NY 60-63; Prin Edin Th Coll 63-71; Can St Mary's Cathl *Edin* 63-71; Bp Ox 71-78; Asst Bp Lon 78-81; Can Res and Prec St Paul's Cathl 81-89; rtd 89; Asst Bp Worc from 89. *9 Ashdale Avenue, Pershore, Worcs WR10 1PL* Pershore (01386) 556550

WOOLLEY, Canon Christopher Andrew Lempriere. b 15. Ch Ch Ox BA37 MA70. Ely Th Coll 37. **d** 39 **p** 40. Tanganyika 46-64; Tanzania 64-70; Adn Njombe 64-70; P-in-c Hanwell *Ox* 70-84; V Horley w Hornton 70-84; rtd 84; Perm to Offic *B & W* 86-91. *Springfield, Street Road, Glastonbury, Somerset BA6 9EG* Glastonbury (01458) 835175

WOOLLEY, Francis Bertram Hopkinson. b 43. Sarum & Wells Th Coll 75. **d** 78 **p** 79. C Halesowen *Worc* 78-81; TV Droitwich 81-86; TV Cam Ascension *Ely* 86-92; R Leverington from 92; P-in-c Wisbech St Mary from 92. *The Rectory, Gorefield Road, Leverington, Wisbech, Cambs PE13 5AS* Wisbech (01945) 581486

WOOLLEY, John Alexander. b 28. St Deiniol's Hawarden 61. **d** 63 **p** 64. C-in-c Gt Crosby St Luke *Liv* 65-71; R Croft w Southworth 71-75; Chapl Cherry Knowle & Ryhope Hosps Sunderland 75-83; Chapl Cell Barnes Hosp St Alb 83-93; Chapl Hill End Hosp St Alb 83-93; rtd 93; NSM Niton *Portsm* from 95; NSM Whitwell from 95; NSM St Lawrence from 95. *The Vicarage, Ashknowle Lane, Whitwell, Ventnor, Isle of Wight PO38 2PP* Isle of Wight (01983) 730745

WOOLMER, John Shirley Thursby. b 42. Wadh Coll Ox BA63 MA69. St Jo Coll Nottm 70. **d** 71 **p** 72. Asst Chapl Win Coll 72-75; C Ox St Aldate w H Trin *Ox* 75-82; C Ox St Aldate w St Matt 82; R Shepton Mallet w Doulting *B & W* from 82. *The Rectory, Peter Street, Shepton Mallet, Somerset BA4 5BL* Shepton Mallet (01749) 342163

WOOLSTENHOLMES, Cyril Esmond. b 16. Bede Coll Dur BA37 DipTh38 MA41. **d** 39 **p** 40. R Shadforth *Dur* 67-82; rtd 82. *12 Wearside Drive, The Sands, Durham DH1 1LE* 0191-384 3763

WOOLVEN, Ronald (Ron). b 36. Oak Hill Th Coll 60. **d** 63 **p** 64. C Romford Gd Shep Collier Row *Chelmsf* 63-68; C Widford 68-73; P-in-c Barling w Lt Wakering 73-84; V from 84. *154 Little Wakering Road, Great Wakering, Southend-on-Sea SS3 0JN* Southend-on-Sea (01702) 219200

WOOLVERIDGE, Gordon Hubert. b 27. Barrister-at-Law 52 CCC Cam BA51 MA55. S Dios Minl Tr Scheme 81. **d** 84 **p** 85. NSM St Edm the King w St Nic Acons etc *Lon* 84-85; NSM Chich St Paul and St Pet *Chich* 85-88; P-in-c Greatham w Empshott *Portsm* 88-90; P-in-c Hawkley w Prior's Dean 88-90; P-in-c Greatham w Empshott and Hawkley w Prior's Dean 90-92; rtd 92. *Brook House, Winfrith Newburgh, Dorchester, Dorset DT2 8JH* Dorchester (01305) 853633

WOOLWICH, Area Bishop of. *See* HALL, Rt Rev Albert Peter

WOOSTER, Patrick Charles Francis. b 38. Qu Coll Birm 63. **d** 65 **p** 66. C Chippenham St Andr w Tytherton Lucas *Bris* 65-70; C Cockington *Ex* 70-72; V Stone w Woodford *Glouc* 72-73; P-in-c Hill 72-73; V Stone w Woodford and Hill from 73. *The Vicarage, Stone, Berkeley, Glos GL13 9LB* Falfield (01454) 260277

WORCESTER, Archdeacon of. *See* BENTLEY, Ven Frank William Henry

WORCESTER, Bishop of. *See* GOODRICH, Rt Rev Philip Harold Ernest

WORCESTER, Dean of. *See* JEFFERY, Very Rev Robert Martin Colquhoun

WORDSWORTH, Jeremy Nathaniel. b 30. Clare Coll Cam BA54 MA58. Ridley Hall Cam 54. **d** 56 **p** 57. Chapl Sherborne Sch Dorset 63-71; PV and Succ S'wark Cathl *S'wark* 71-73; P-in-c Stone *Worc* 73-77; V Malvern St Andr 77-82; V Combe Down w Monkton Combe and S Stoke *B & W* 82-95; rtd 95. *4 The Glebe, Hinton Charterhouse, Bath BA3 6AB* Bath (01225) 722520

WORDSWORTH, Paul. b 42. Birm Univ BA64 Hull Univ DipMin89. Wells Th Coll 64. **d** 66 **p** 67. C Anlaby St Pet *York* 66-71; C Marfleet 71-72; TV 72-77; V Sowerby 77-90; P-in-c Sessay 77-90; V York St Thos w St Maurice from 90; Dioc Community Miss Project Ldr from 90. *St Thomas's Vicarage, 157 Haxby Road, York YO3 7JL* York (01904) 652228

WORGAN, Maurice William. b 40. Ely Th Coll 62 Sarum Th Coll 64. **d** 65 **p** 66. C Cranbrook *Cant* 65-69; C Maidstone St Martin 69-72; P-in-c Stanford w Postling and Radegund 72-73; R Lyminge w Paddlesworth 72-73; R Lyminge w Paddlesworth, Stanford w Postling etc 73-88; V Cant St Dunstan w H Cross from 88. *St Dunstan's Vicarage, 5 Harkness Drive, Canterbury, Kent CT2 7RW* Canterbury (01227) 463654

WORKMAN, David Andrew. b 22. MICS49 AMBIM78 FBIM80. Arm Aux Min Course 87. **d** 90 **p** 91. C Dundalk w Heynestown *Arm* from 90. *Dunbeag, Togher, Drogheda, Co Louth, Irish Republic* Drogheda (41) 52171

WORKMAN, John Lewis. b 26. St Deiniol's Hawarden 82. **d** 83 **p** 84. C Brecon St Mary and Battle w Llanddew *S & B* 83-86; Min Can Brecon Cathl 83-86; P-in-c Cwmbwrla 86-87; V 87-95; rtd 95. *69 Belgrave Court, Walter Road, Uplands, Swansea SA1 4PZ* Swansea (01792) 473649

WORLEY, William. b 37. TD89. Cranmer Hall Dur 69. **d** 72 **p** 73. C Consett *Dur* 72-76; V Seaton Carew from 76; CF (TA) from 77. *The Vicarage, 11 Ruswarp Grove, Seaton Carew, Hartlepool, Cleveland TS25 2BA* Hartlepool (01429) 262463

WORMALD, Roy Henry. b 42. Chich Th Coll 64. **d** 67 **p** 68. C Walthamstow St Mich *Chelmsf* 67-69; C Cov St Thos *Cov* 69-72; C Cov St Jo 69-72; C Wood Green St Mich *Lon* 72-77; P-in-c Hanwell St Mellitus 77-80; P-in-c Hanwell St Mellitus w St Mark 80-81; V 81-95; C Hillingdon St Jo from 95. *Glebe House, Royal Lane, Uxbridge, Middx UB8 3QR* Uxbridge (01895) 256427

WORN, Nigel John. b 56. Sarum & Wells Th Coll. **d** 84 **p** 85. C Walworth St Jo *S'wark* 84-88; Succ S'wark Cathl 88-92; V Mitcham Ascension from 92. *The Parsonage, Sherwood Park Road, Mitcham, Surrey CR4 1NE* 0181-764 1258

WORRALL, Frederick Rowland. b 27. **d** 86 **p** 87. NSM Chellaston *Derby* from 86; NSM Barrow-on-Trent w Twyford and Swarkestone from 94. *37 St Peter's Road, Chellaston, Derby DE7 1UU* Derby (01332) 701890

WORRALL, Peter Henry. b 62. CA Tr Coll DipEvang88 W Midl Minl Tr Course 93. **d** 95. C Bromsgrove St Jo *Worc* from 95. *6 Rock Hill, Bromsgrove, Worcs B61 7LJ* Bromsgrove (01527) 832087

WORRALL, Miss Suzanne. b 63. Trin Coll Bris BA86. **d** 87 **p** 94. Par Dn Kingston upon Hull St Nic *York* 87-91; Par Dn Kingston upon Hull Southcoates St Aid 91-94; C from 94. *76 Southcoates Avenue, Hull HU9 3HD* Hull (01482) 783233

WORSDALL, John Robin. b 33. Dur Univ BA57. Linc Th Coll 62. **d** 63 **p** 64. C Manthorpe w Londonthorpe *Linc* 63-66; C Folkingham w Laughton 66-68; V New Bolingbroke w Carrington 68-74; P-in-c S Somercotes 74-80; V N Somercotes 74-80; P-in-c Stickney 80-82; P-in-c E Ville and Mid Ville 80-82; P-in-c Stickford 80-82; V Stickney Gp from 82. *The Rectory, Horbling Lane, Stickney, Boston, Lincs PE22 8DQ* Boston (01205) 480049

WORSDELL, William Charles (Bill). b 35. AKC59. **d** 60 **p** 61. C Glouc St Aldate *Glouc* 60-66; V Devonport St Barn *Ex* 66-72; R Uplyme 72-77; R Withington and Compton Abdale w Haselton *Glouc* 77-87; V Badgeworth w Shurdington from 87. *The Vicarage, Shurdington, Cheltenham, Glos GL51 5TQ* Cheltenham (01242) 862241

WORSFOLD, Ms Caroline Jayne. b 61. St Steph Ho Ox. **d** 88 **p** 94. Chapl Asst Leic R Infirmary 88-90; C Sunderland Pennywell St Thos *Dur* 90-91; Chapl Cherry Knowle Hosp Sunderland from 91; Sunderland HA Chapl from 91. *Cherry Knowle Hospital, Ryhope, Sunderland SR2 0NB* 0191-565 6256

WORSFOLD, John. b 24. Keble Coll Ox BA50 MA50. Cuddesdon Coll 50. **d** 51 **p** 52. C Shirley St Geo *Cant* 63-80; C Croydon H Sav 80-84; C Croydon H Sav *S'wark* 85-89; rtd 90. *26 Links Road, West Wickham, Kent BR4 0QW* 0181-777 7463

WORSFOLD, Richard Vernon. b 64. Ex Univ LLB86. Cranmer Hall Dur BA94 DMS95. **d** 95. C Countesthorpe w Foston *Leic* from 95. *12 The Hawthorns, Countesthorpe, Leicester LE8 5RY* Leicester (0116) 277 6066

WORSLEY, Mrs Christine Anne. b 52. Hull Univ BA73 Bris Univ CertEd74. W Midl Minl Tr Course 82. **dss** 84 **d** 87 **p** 94. Smethwick St Mary *Birm* 84-87; Par Dn 87; Par Dn Smethwick H Trin w St Alb 87-89; Par Dn Cov Caludon *Cov* 89-91; Chapl Myton Hamlet Hospice from 92. *Wyken Vicarage, 56 Wyken Croft, Coventry CV2 3AD* Coventry (01203) 602332

WORSLEY, Howard John. b 61. Man Univ BA83 Leeds Univ PGCE85. St Jo Coll Nottm DTS92 MA93. **d** 93 **p** 94. C Huthwaite *S'well* from 93. *38 Chesterfield Road, Huthwaite, Sutton-in-Ashfield, Notts NG17 2PW* Mansfield (01623) 553808

WORSLEY, James Duncan. b 14. Dur Univ LTh40. Tyndale Hall Bris 37. **d** 40 **p** 41. V Ullenhall cum Aspley *Cov* 61-72; V Wappenbury w Weston under Wetherley 72-79; V Hunningham 72-79; Chapl Weston-under-Wetherley Hosp 72-79; rtd 79. *24 Banneson Road, Nether Stowey, Bridgwater, Somerset TA5 1NW* Nether Stowey (01278) 732169

WORSLEY, Richard John. b 52. Qu Coll Cam BA74 MA78. Qu Coll Birm DipTh79. **d** 80 **p** 81. C Styvechale *Cov* 80-84; V Smethwick H Trin w St Alb *Birm* 84-89; TV Cov Caludon *Cov* from 89. *Wyken Vicarage, 56 Wyken Croft, Coventry CV2 3AD* Coventry (01203) 602332

WORSNIP, Harry. b 29. Oldham Tech Coll HNC50. St Alb Minl Tr Scheme 89. **d** 92 **p** 93. NSM Arlesey w Astwick *St Alb* from 92. *28 Milburn Road, Bedford MK41 0NZ* Bedford (01234) 266422

WORSSAM, Richard Mark. b 61. St Jo Coll Dur BA83 Selw Coll Cam BA92. Ridley Hall Cam CTM93. **d** 93 **p** 94. C Green Street Green and Pratts Bottom *Roch* from 93. *9 Ringwood Avenue, Orpington, Kent BR6 7SY* Orpington (01689) 861742

WORSTEAD, Eric Henry. b 14. Lon Univ BD44 BA46 MTh54. **d** 64 **p** 64. Hon C Southborough St Thos *Roch* 67-72; Dep Prin Whitelands Coll Lon 67-72; P-in-c High Hurstwood *Chich* 72-78; rtd 78. *Flat 2, Waterside, Crowborough Hill, Crowborough, E Sussex TN6 2RS* Crowborough (01892) 664330

WORTH, Douglas Albert Victor. b 09. St Cath Coll Cam BA32 MA47. Wells Th Coll 32. **d** 33 **p** 34. Prin Lect Coll of SS Mark and Jo Chelsea 67-71; Perm to Offic *Glouc* from 71; rtd 74. *74 Barclay Court, Trafalgar Road, Cirencester, Glos GL7 2EN* Cirencester (01285) 658579

WORTH, Frederick Stuart. b 30. Oak Hill Th Coll 60. **d** 62 **p** 63. C Okehampton w Inwardleigh *Ex* 62-68; V Dunkeswell and Dunkeswell Abbey 68-78; P-in-c Luppitt 69-72; P-in-c Upottery 72-76; V Sheldon 73-78; RD Honiton 77-84 and 86-90; R Uplyme 78-86; R Uplyme w Axmouth from 86. *The Rectory, Rhode Lane, Uplyme, Lyme Regis, Dorset DT7 3TX* Lyme Regis (01297) 443256

WORTH, Thomas (Tom). b 23. Glouc Sch of Min 90. **d** 91 **p** 92. NSM Bourton-on-the-Water w Clapton *Glouc* 91-94; Perm to Offic from 94. *7 Station Meadow, Bourton-on-the-Water, Cheltenham, Glos GL54 2HG* Cotswold (01451) 822342

WORTHEN, Dr Jeremy Frederick. b 65. Rob Coll Cam BA86 MPhil88 Toronto Univ PhD92. Ripon Coll Cuddesdon DipTh93 DipMin94. **d** 94 **p** 95. C Bromley SS Pet and Paul *Roch* from 94. *13 Rochester Avenue, Bromley BR1 3DB* 0181-464 9532

WORTHEN, Peter Frederick. b 38. Oak Hill Th Coll 71. **d** 71 **p** 72. C Tonbridge SS Pet and Paul *Roch* 71-75; P-in-c High Halstow w Hoo St Mary 75-76; R High Halstow w All Hallows and Hoo St Mary 76-83; V Welling 83-93; TV Stantonbury and Willen *Ox* from 93. *Bradwell Church House, 1 Atterbrook, Bradwell, Milton Keynes MK13 9EY* Milton Keynes (01908) 320850

WORTHINGTON, George. b 35. AKC60. **d** 61 **p** 62. C Stockton St Pet *Dur* 61-65; C Poulton-le-Fylde *Blackb* 65-67; V Trawden 67-76; P-in-c Gressingham 76-78; P-in-c Arkholme 76-78; P-in-c Whittington 77-78; V Whittington w Arkholme and Gressingham 78-91; V Warton St Paul from 91. *The Vicarage, Church Road, Warton, Preston PR4 1BD* Freckleton (01772) 632227

WORTHINGTON, John Clare. b 17. St Jo Coll Cam BA39 MA46. Westcott Ho Cam 39 46. **d** 48 **p** 49. V Ellingham and Harbridge and Ibsley *Win* 65-85; RD Christchurch 79-82; rtd 85; Perm to Offic *Win* from 85. *Moorland Cottage, Godshill, Fordingbridge, Hants SP6 2LG* Fordingbridge (01425) 654448

WORTHINGTON, Mark. b 55. Solicitor 80 Leeds Poly BA77. Cranmer Hall Dur CTMin93. **d** 93 **p** 94. C Monkwearmouth St Andr *Dur* from 93. *10 Ashleigh Grove, Sunderland SR6 9EF* 0191-548 7112

WORTLEY, Prof John Trevor. b 34. FRHistS Dur Univ BA57 MA60 DD86 Lon Univ PhD69. Edin Th Coll 57. **d** 59 **p** 60. C Huddersfield St Jo *Wakef* 59-64; Canada from 64; Prof Hist Manitoba Univ from 69. *298 Yale Avenue, Winnipeg, Canada, R3M 0M1, or Manitoba University, Winnipeg, Canada, R3T 2N2* Winnipeg (204) 284-7554 or 474-9830

WORTON, David Reginald (Brother Paschal). b 56. St Steph Ho Ox 88. **d** 90 **p** 90. SSF from 77. *St Francis House, 68 Laurel Road, Liverpool L7 0LW* 0151-263 8581

WORTON, Norman. b 10. ALCD38. **d** 38 **p** 39. V Hove St Phil *Chich* 59-65; Australia from 65; rtd 75. *1112 Rawson Street, Mosman, NSW, Australia 2088*

WORWOOD, Canon Frank Edward. b 11. ALCD34. **d** 34 **p** 35. RD Bingham W *S'well* 61-81; R W Bridgford 61-81; Hon Can S'well Minster 72-81; rtd 81; Perm to Offic *S'well* from 81. *1 Eastwood Road, Radcliffe-on-Trent, Nottingham NG12 2FZ* Nottingham (0115) 933 5647

WOSTENHOLM, Dr David Kenneth. b 56. Edin Univ BSc77 MB, ChB80 Southn Univ BTh88. Chich Th Coll 82. **d** 85 **p** 86. C Leytonstone St Marg w St Columba *Chelmsf* 85-90; V Brighton Annunciation *Chich* from 90. *Annunciation Vicarage, 89 Washington Street, Brighton BN2 2SR* Brighton (01273) 681341

WOTHERSPOON, David Colin. b 36. Portsm Coll of Tech CEng65 MIMechE65. St Jo Coll Dur 76. **d** 78 **p** 79. C Blackb St Gabr *Blackb* 78-81; V Witton 81-90; Chapl Berne w Neuchatel *Eur* from 90. *St Ursula, Jubiläumsplatz 2, 3005 Berne, Switzerland* Berne (31) 351-0343 or 352-8567 Fax 352-8567

WOTTON, David Ashley. b 44. Chich Th Coll 71. **d** 74 **p** 75. C Allington and Maidstone St Pet *Cant* 74-77; C Ham St Andr *S'wark* 78-79; Chapl HM Rem Cen Latchmere Ho 78-79; C Tattenham Corner and Burgh Heath *Guildf* 85-88; P-in-c E Molesey St Mary 88-93; R Headley w Box Hill from 93; Offg Chapl RAF from 93. *The Rectory, Headley, Epsom, Surrey KT18 6LE* Leatherhead (01372) 377327

WOULDHAM, Ralph Douglas Astley. b 19. Leeds Univ BA48. Coll of Resurr Mirfield 48. **d** 50 **p** 51. V Cleadon *Dur* 69-79; V Lowick and Kyloe w Ancroft *Newc* 79-84; rtd 84. *55 Northumberland Road, Tweedmouth, Berwick-upon-Tweed TD15 2AS* Berwick-upon-Tweed (01289) 308240

WRAGG, John Gordon. b 17. Sheff Univ BA39. ALCD41. **d** 41 **p** 42. V Spittal *Newc* 62-75; R Wark 75-82; V Birtley 77-82; rtd 82. *21 The Croft, Filey, N Yorkshire YO14 9LT* Scarborough (01723) 514824

WRAGG, Peter Robert. b 46. Lon Univ BSc68. Sarum & Wells Th Coll 71. **d** 74 **p** 75. C Feltham *Lon* 74-79; TV Hackney 79-85; P-in-c Isleworth St Mary 85-94; V Feltham from 94. *The Vicarage, Cardinal Road, Feltham, Middx TW13 5AL* 0181-890 6681 or 890 2011

WRAIGHT, John Radford. b 38. St Chad's Coll Dur BA62 DipTh64. **d** 64 **p** 65. C Shildon *Dur* 64-67; C Newton Aycliffe 67-70; C Darlington St Jo 70-75; P-in-c Livingston LEP *Edin* 75-80; TV Carl H Trin and St Barn *Carl* 80-85; P-in-c Lindale w Field Broughton from 85. *The Vicarage, Windermere Road, Lindale, Grange-over-Sands, Cumbria LA11 6LB* Grange-over-Sands (015395) 34717

WRAKE, John. b 28. RMA. Clifton Th Coll 56. **d** 59 **p** 60. V Tilton w Lowesby *Leic* 66-73; R Maresfield *Chich* 73-79; rtd 93. *Parkfield, Batts Ridge Road, Maresfield, Uckfield, E Sussex TN22 2HJ* Uckfield (01825) 762727

WRAPSON, Donald. b 36. St Aid Birkenhead 61. **d** 65 **p** 66. C Bacup St Sav *Man* 65-69; C Wolv St Matt *Lich* 69-72; C Normanton *Derby* 72-78; V Dordon *Birm* 78-82; Chapl Birm Accident Hosp 82-93; Chapl Selly Oak Hosp Birm 82-93; Chapl S Birm Acute Unit Birm Gen Hosp from 93. *Birmingham General Hospital, Steelhouse Lane, Birmingham B4 6NH* 0121-236 8611

WRATTEN, Martyn Stephen. b 34. AKC58 St Boniface Warminster 58. **d** 59 **p** 60. C Wandsworth Common St Mary *S'wark* 59-62; C Putney St Mary 62-65; C Pembury *Roch* 65-70; R Stone 70-76; Chapl Joyce Green Hosp Dartford 70-73; Stone Ho Hosp Kent 73-76; Hillcrest Hosp and

Netherne Hosp Coulsdon 76-87; Hon C Netherne St Luke CD *S'wark* 76-87; V Gt Doddington *Pet* 87-88; V Gt Doddington and Wilby from 88. *The Vicarage, 72 High Street, Great Doddington, Wellingborough, Northants NN9 7TH* Wellingborough (01933) 226711

WRAW, John Michael. b 59. Linc Coll Ox BA81 Fitzw Ho Cam BA84. Ridley Hall Cam 82. **d** 85 **p** 86. C Bromyard *Heref* 85-88; TV Sheff Manor *Sheff* 88-92; V Clifton St Jas from 92. *Clifton Vicarage, 10 Clifton Crescent North, Rotherham, S Yorkshire S65 2AS* Rotherham (01709) 363082 or 836308

WRAY, Christopher. b 48. Hull Univ BA70 New Coll Ox DipTh73. Cuddesdon Coll 70. **d** 73 **p** 74. C Brighouse *Wakef* 73-76; C Almondbury 76-78; C Tong *Bradf* 78-80; V Ingleton w Chapel le Dale 80-86; R Brompton Regis w Upton and Skilgate *B & W* 86-91; V Yoxford and Peasenhall w Sibton *St E* 91-94. *The Boot and Shoe, Greystoke, Penrith, Cumbria CA11 7ST* Penrith (01768) 483343

WRAY, Christopher Brownlow. b 46. Open Univ BA91. Oak Hill Th Coll 86. **d** 88 **p** 89. C Quidenham *Nor* 88-91; TV Chippenham St Paul w Hardenhuish etc *Bris* from 91. *Hardenhuish Vicarage, 141 Malmesbury Road, Chippenham, Wilts SN15 1QA* Chippenham (01249) 650787

WRAY, Karl. b 51. St And Coll Greystoke 72 Ian Ramsey Coll 74 Coll of Resurr Mirfield 75. **d** 78 **p** 79. C Salford St Phil w St Steph *Man* 78-83; CF 83-86 and from 91; V Sculcoates St Paul w Ch Ch and St Silas *York* 86-89; V Carl St Luke Morton *Carl* from 92. *St Luke's Vicarage, Brownrigg Drive, Carlisle CA2 6PA* Carlisle (01228) 515693

WRAY, Kenneth Martin. b 43. Linc Th Coll 72. **d** 75 **p** 76. C Shipley St Paul *Bradf* 75-79; V Edlington *Sheff* 79-85; V Nether Hoyland St Pet from 85. *The Vicarage, 104 Hawshaw Lane, Hoyland, Barnsley, S Yorkshire S74 0HH* Barnsley (01226) 749231

WRAY, Martin John. b 51. St Steph Ho Ox 86. **d** 88 **p** 89. C E Boldon *Dur* 88-90; C Seaham w Seaham Harbour 90-92; P-in-c Chopwell from 92. *The Vicarage, Chopwell, Newcastle upon Tyne NE17 7AN* Ebchester (01207) 561248

WRAY, Michael. b 49. Univ of Wales (Cardiff) BSc(Econ)77 Keele Univ PGCE78 RGN87. Ripon Coll Cuddesdon 80. **d** 82 **p** 83. C Blackpool St Steph *Blackb* 82-83; C Torrisholme 83-84; NSM Headington St Mary *Ox* 93-95; C Kennington *Cant* from 95; CF (TA) from 95. *158 Canterbury Road, Kennington, Ashford, Kent TN24 9QE* Ashford (01233) 638058

WRAYFORD, Geoffrey John. b 38. Ex Coll Ox BA61 MA65. Linc Th Coll 61. **d** 63 **p** 64. C Cirencester *Glouc* 63-69; Chapl Chelmsf Cathl *Chelmsf* 69-74; V 70-74; V Canvey Is 74-76; TR 76-80; P-in-c Woodlands *B & W* 80-88; V 89-92; P-in-c Frome St Jo 80-88; P-in-c Frome Ch 80-85; P-in-c Frome St Mary 85-88; V Frome St Jo and St Mary 89-92; V Minehead from 92. *The Vicarage, 7 Paganel Road, Minehead, Somerset TA24 5ET* Minehead (01643) 703530

WREN, Christopher John. b 54. Dur Univ BEd76 MA85. St Steph Ho Ox 77. **d** 79 **p** 80. C Stockton St Pet *Dur* 79-82; C Newton Aycliffe 82-85; V Gateshead St Chad Bensham 85-91; TR Bensham from 91. *St Chad's Vicarage, Dunsmuir Grove, Gateshead, Tyne & Wear NE8 4QL* 0191-477 1964

WREN, Douglas Peter. b 59. Lanc Univ BA82. Trin Coll Bris BA88. **d** 88 **p** 89. C Nantwich *Ches* 88-91; C Chatham St Phil and St Jas *Roch* 91-94; R Kingsdown from 94. *The Rectory, School Lane, West Kingsdown, Sevenoaks, Kent TN15 6JB* West Kingsdown (01474) 852265

WREN, John Aubrey. b 46. St Chad's Coll Dur BA69. Cuddesdon Coll 72. **d** 74 **p** 75. C Fenny Stratford and Water Eaton *Ox* 74-77; TV Brighton Resurr *Chich* 77-84; V Eastbourne St Andr 84-92; V Hove St Barn and St Agnes from 92. *St Barnabas' Vicarage, 88 Sackville Road, Hove, E Sussex BN3 3HE* Brighton (01273) 732427

WREN, Canon Kathleen Ann. b 50. St Steph Ho Ox 83. **dss** 85 **d** 87. Gateshead St Cuth w St Paul *Dur* 85-86; Gateshead St Chad Bensham 86-91; Par Dn 87-91; Adv for Women's Min from 90; Par Dn Bensham 91-94; C from 94; Hon Can Dur Cathl from 93. *St Chad's Vicarage, Dunsmuir Grove, Gateshead, Tyne & Wear NE8 4QL* 0191-477 1964

WREN, Richard. b 35. S Dios Minl Tr Scheme. **d** 90 **p** 91. NSM Tisbury *Sarum* from 90. *Gaston House, Tisbury, Salisbury SP3 6LG* Tisbury (01747) 870674

WRENBURY, Rev and Rt Hon Lord (John Burton Buckley). b 27. Solicitor 52 K Coll Cam BA48 MA48. S'wark Ord Course 87. **d** 90 **p** 91. NSM Brightling, Dallington, Mountfield & Netherfield *Chich* from 90. *Oldcastle, Dallington, Heathfield, E Sussex TN21 9JP* Rushlake Green (01435) 830400

WRENN, Peter Henry. b 34. Lon Univ BA56. Qu Coll Birm 58. **d** 60 **p** 61. C Dronfield *Derby* 60-64; C Hessle *York* 64-65; V Loscoe *Derby* 65-70; Asst Chapl Solihull Sch W Midl 71-77; Chapl from 77. *63 Shakespeare Drive, Shirley, Solihull, W Midlands B90 2AN* 0121-744 3941 or 705 4409

WREXHAM, Archdeacon of. *See* WILLIAMS, Ven Edward Bryan

WRIGHT, Alan James. b 38. Chich Th Coll 63. **d** 66 **p** 67. C Edge Hill St Dunstan *Liv* 66-69; Swaziland 69-71; P-in-c Seaforth *Liv* 71-76; V Taunton All SS *B & W* from 76. *All Saints' Vicarage, Outer Circle, Taunton, Somerset TA1 2DE* Taunton (01823) 331545

WRIGHT, Alfred John. b 22. Wycliffe Hall Ox 66. **d** 66 **p** 67. C Newbury St Jo *Ox* 66-71; V E Challow 71-91; Chapl Community of St Mary V Wantage 75-89; rtd 91. *3 Latton Close, Southmoor, Abingdon, Oxon OX13 5AE* Longworth (01865) 820625

WRIGHT, Andrew David Gibson. b 58. St Andr Univ MTheol81. Ridley Hall Cam. **d** 83 **p** 84. C W Derby Gd Shep *Liv* 83-86; C Carl H Trin and St Barn *Carl* 86-88; V Wigan St Jas w St Thos *Liv* 88-91; Chapl St Edw Sch Ox from 91. *34 Oakthorpe Road, Oxford OX2 7BE, or St Edward's School, Oxford OX2 7NN* Oxford (01865) 319266 or 319204

WRIGHT, Anthony John. b 47. ACA70 FCA77. Ripon Coll Cuddesdon 86. **d** 88 **p** 89. C Kidderminster St Mary and All SS etc *Worc* 88-90; C Kidderminster St Mary and All SS w Trimpley etc 90-91; P-in-c Offenham and Bretforton from 91. *The Vicarage, Main Street, Offenham, Evesham, Worcs WR11 5RL* Evesham (01386) 442096

WRIGHT, Anthony Robert. b 49. Lanchester Poly BA70. St Steph Ho Ox 70. **d** 73 **p** 74. C Amersham on the Hill *Ox* 73-76; C Reading St Giles 76-78; P-in-c Prestwood 78-84; P-in-c Wantage 84-87; V 87-92; RD Wantage 84-92; P-in-c W w E Hanney 88-91; V Portsea St Mary *Portsm* from 92. *St Mary's Vicarage, Fratton Road, Portsmouth PO1 5PA* Portsmouth (01705) 822687

WRIGHT, Antony John. b 31. St Pet Coll Saltley CertEd53. Chan Sch Truro 76. **d** 79 **p** 80. NSM St Breoke *Truro* 79-84; TV Probus, Ladock and Grampound w Creed and St Erme 84-89; V Perranzabuloe from 89. *The Vicarage, Station Road, Perranporth, Cornwall TR6 0DD* Truro (01872) 573375

WRIGHT, Canon Barnabas Kenneth William. b 21. K Coll Lon BD43 AKC43 BA44. Linc Th Coll 43. **d** 44 **p** 45. R W Wickham St Jo *Cant* 63-72; RD Croydon Cen 66-72; RD E Charing 72-81; Hon Can Cant Cathl 72-86; V Ashford 72-81; R Barham w Bishopsbourne and Kingston 81-86; rtd 86. *Stable End, The Street, Newchurch, Romney Marsh, Kent TN29 0DZ* Dymchurch (01303) 874286

WRIGHT, Canon Barry Owen. b 38. S'wark Ord Course 66. **d** 69 **p** 70. C Plumstead Ascension *S'wark* 69-74; Hon C Welling 74-89; Hon Can S'wark Cathl 79-89; Sen Chapl W Midl Police *Birm* 89-93; Sen Chapl Metrop Police *Lon* from 93. *St Barnabas Vicarage, 7 Oakfields Road, London NW11 0JA* 0181-458 7828 or 200 2077 Fax 458 7828

WRIGHT, Miss Caroline Peggy. b 34. RMN75. Gilmore Ho 57. **dss** 59 **d** 88 **p** 94. Badsey *Worc* 62-66; Wickhamford 62-66; Wolverley 66-67; Warden St Mary's Abbey Leiston 67-74; Perm to Offic *St E* 74-88; Par Dn Bungay H Trin w St Mary from 88. *4 Kerrison Road, Bungay, Suffolk NR35 1RZ* Bungay (01986) 892023

WRIGHT, Charles Frederick Peter. b 16. Qu Coll Ox BA39 MA42. Westcott Ho Cam 40. **d** 41 **p** 42. Lic to Offic *Linc* from 69; rtd 81. *The Hermitage, Snelland, Lincoln LN3 5AA* Wickenby (01673) 885325

WRIGHT, Charles Kenneth (Ken). b 38. CEng73 MIMechE73 MBIM91. Sarum & Wells Th Coll DCM93. **d** 93 **p** 94. C Bridgwater St Mary, Chilton Trinity and Durleigh *B & W* from 93. *11 Alexandra Road, Bridgwater, Somerset TA6 3HE* Bridgwater (01278) 429565

WRIGHT, Dr Christopher Joseph Herbert (Chris). b 47. St Cath Coll Cam BA69 MA73 PhD77. Ridley Hall Cam 75. **d** 77 **p** 78. C Tonbridge SS Pet and Paul *Roch* 77-81; Perm to Offic *St Alb* from 82; India 83-88; Tutor and Dir Studies All Nations Chr Coll Ware 88-93; Prin from 93. *All Nations Christian College, Easneye, Ware, Herts SG12 8LX* Ware (01920) 461243 Fax 462997

WRIGHT, Christopher Nigel. b 39. Kelham Th Coll 60. **d** 65 **p** 66. C Latchford Ch Ch *Ches* 69-72; C Gt Budworth 72-75; C Wigan St Andr *Liv* 75-76; V New Springs 77-82; C Dovecot 82-85; C Rainford 85-89; rtd 89. *105 Ilfracombe Road, Sutton Leach, St Helens, Merseyside WA9 4NN* Marshalls Cross (01744) 821199

WRIGHT, Canon Clifford Nelson. b 35. K Coll Lon BD59 AKC59. **d** 60 **p** 61. C Stevenage *St Alb* 60-67; V Camberwell St Luke *S'wark* 67-81; RD Camberwell 75-80; Hon Can S'wark Cathl 79-80; TR Basingstoke *Win* 81-93; RD Basingstoke 84-93; Hon Can Win Cathl from 89; R Win St Matt from 93. *The Rectory, 44 Cheriton Road, Winchester, Hants SO22 5AY* Winchester (01962) 854849

WRIGHT, David Evan Cross. b 35. K Coll Lon BD64 AKC64. **d** 65 **p** 66. C Morpeth *Newc* 65-69; C Benwell St Jas 69-70; C Bushey *St Alb* 70-74; V High Wych 74-77; R High Wych and Gilston w Eastwick 77-80; V St Alb St Mary Marshalswick

80-89; P-in-c Sandridge 87-89; R Lenham w Boughton Malherbe *Cant* from 89. *The Vicarage, Old Ashford Road, Lenham, Maidstone, Kent ME17 2PX* Maidstone (01622) 858245

WRIGHT, David Hanson. b 14. Hertf Coll Ox BA36 MA46. **d** 61 **p** 62. C Westhoughton *Man* 62-67; C Bolton St Matt w St Barn 67-77; Hon C New Bury 77-79; Hon C Bolton St Phil 79-84; Perm to Offic from 84. *8 Moorside Avenue, Bolton BL1 6BE* Bolton (01204) 840121

WRIGHT, David Henry. b 23. Keble Coll Ox BA48. St Steph Ho Ox 52. **d** 54 **p** 55. V Wandsworth St Anne *S'wark* 66-73; P-in-c Stanley *St And* 73-75; R Dunkeld 73-92; R Strathtay 75-92; rtd 92. *Ground Flat, 83 Henderson Street, Bridge of Allan, Stirling FK9 4HG* Bridge of Allan (01786) 833954

WRIGHT, David William. b 63. Barrister 86 Liv Univ LLB85 Fitzw Coll Cam BA92. Westcott Ho Cam 90. **d** 93 **p** 94. C Chorlton-cum-Hardy St Clem *Man* from 93. *94 Hardy Lane, Chorlton-cum-Hardy, Manchester M21 8DN* 0161-881 9458

WRIGHT, Derek Anthony. b 35. ACP66 Lon Univ CertEd57. Cranmer Hall Dur 80. **d** 81 **p** 82. C Auckland St Andr and St Anne *Dur* 81-83; V Cornforth 83-87; P-in-c Thornley 87-88; R Gt and Lt Glemham, Blaxhall etc *St E* 88-90; V Evenwood *Dur* 90-93; P-in-c Satley and Tow Law from 93. *The Vicarage, 3 Church Lane, Tow Law, Bishop Auckland, Co Durham DL13 4HE* Bishop Auckland (01388) 730335

WRIGHT, Edward Albert. b 37. St Cath Soc Ox BA61 MA65. Cuddesdon Coll DipTh63. **d** 64 **p** 65. C Willesden St Andr *Lon* 64-68; Bahamas 68-71; V Lewisham St Steph and St Mark *S'wark* 72-80; V Ox St Barn and St Paul *Ox* from 80. *St Barnabas' Vicarage, St Barnabas Street, Oxford OX2 6BG* Oxford (01865) 57530

WRIGHT, Edward Maurice. b 54. **d** 88 **p** 91. C Maidstone St Luke *Cant* 88-93; R Cliffe at Hoo w Cooling *Roch* from 93. *St Helen's Rectory, Church Street, Cliffe, Rochester, Kent ME3 7PY* Medway (01634) 220220

WRIGHT, Frank Albert. b 51. Sarum & Wells Th Coll 80. **d** 83 **p** 84. C Buckm *Ox* 83-86; C Newport Pagnell w Lathbury and Moulsoe 86-89; TV W Slough from 89. *298 Stoke Poges Lane, Slough SL1 3LL* Slough (01753) 539062

WRIGHT, Canon Frank Sidney. b 22. St Pet Hall Ox BA45 MA47. Westcott Ho Cam 47. **d** 49 **p** 50. Can Res Man Cathl *Man* 66-74; Sub-Dean 72-74; Min Can 74-83; Tutor Man Univ 74-83; Angl Adv Granada TV 82; rtd 83; Perm to Offic *Carl* from 83; Perm to Offic *Ches* from 87. *Windyridge, Aaronstown Lonning, Brampton, Cumbria CA8 1QR* Brampton (016977) 2752

WRIGHT, Frederic Ian. b 64. City Univ BSc85. Wycliffe Hall Ox BTh94. **d** 94. C Carl St Jo *Carl* from 94. *68 Greystone Road, Carlisle CA1 2DG* Carlisle (01228) 20893 or 595792

WRIGHT, Frederick John (Fred). b 15. AKC42. **d** 42 **p** 43. R Romsley *Worc* 67-80; rtd 80. *Rosevear, 3 Dury Lane, Colne, Huntingdon, Cambs PE17 3NB* Ramsey (01487) 840518

WRIGHT, George Frederick. b 12. Kelham Th Coll 30. **d** 36 **p** 37. R E Markham and Askham *S'well* 62-77; P-in-c Headon w Upton 76-77; rtd 77; Perm to Offic *S'well* from 77. *Rutland House, Low Street, Collingham, Newark, Notts NG23 7NL* Newark (01636) 892876

WRIGHT, Gerald Grattan. b 32. Delaware State Coll BSc72. Ripon Hall Ox 73. **d** 76 **p** 77. Hon C Wolvercote w Summertown *Ox* 76-87; NSM from 88; C Ox St Mich w St Martin and All SS 87-88. *28 Davenant Road, Oxford OX2 8BX* Oxford (01865) 52617

WRIGHT, Graham. b 50. Oak Hill Th Coll 73. **d** 76 **p** 77. C Northn St Giles *Pet* 76-79; C Man Resurr *Man* 79-82; V Barkingside St Laur *Chelmsf* 82-88; Chapl K Geo V Hosp Ilford 82-88; P-in-c Yoxford *St E* 88-90; Chapl Suffolk Constabulary 88-90. *8-10 Dixons Fold, North Walsham Road, Norwich NR6 7QD* Norwich (01603) 459960

WRIGHT, Graham Ewen. b 44. Lon Univ DipRS. S'wark Ord Course 86. **d** 89 **p** 90. NSM Aveley and Purfleet *Chelmsf* from 89. *2 Palmers, Corringham, Stanford-le-Hope, Essex SS17 7JA* Stanford-le-Hope (01375) 671747

WRIGHT, Hugh Edward. b 57. BNC Ox BA79 MA87 Ex Univ CertEd81. Sarum & Wells Th Coll 85. **d** 87 **p** 88. C Hobs Moat *Birm* 87-90; C W Drayton *Lon* 90-92; V Oakfield St Jo *Portsm* from 92. *St John's Vicarage, Victoria Crescent, Ryde, Isle of Wight PO33 1DQ* Isle of Wight (01983) 562863

WRIGHT, Miss Jacqueline Anne. b 39. Dalton Ho Bris 67. **dss** 76 **d** 87 **p** 94. BCMS 71-88; Uganda 71-77; N Area Sec BCMS 78-88; Pudsey St Lawr and St Paul *Bradf* 82-87; Hon Par Dn 87-88; Par Dn Kingston upon Hull H Trin *York* 88-93; Hd of Min amongst Women CPAS from 93; Perm to Offic *Cov* from 93. *c/o CPAS, Athena Drive, Tachbrook Park, Warwick CV34 6NG* Warwick (01926) 334242 Fax 337613

WRIGHT, Mrs Jean. b 41. Man Univ BA63 CertEd64. Carl Dioc Tr Inst 88. **d** 91 **p** 94. NSM Kirkby Stephen w

Mallerstang etc *Carl* from 91. *Mains View, Crosby Garrett, Kirkby Stephen, Cumbria CA17 4PR* Kirkby Stephen (017683) 71457

WRIGHT, Canon John Richard Martin. b 12. St Jo Coll Dur BA34 MA37 DipTh35. **d** 35 **p** 36. R Barrow *St E* 53-76; V Denham St Mary 53-76; R Edmundbyers w Muggleswick *Dur* 76-80; rtd 80; Perm to Offic *St E* from 80. *11 Grosvenor Gardens, Bury St Edmunds, Suffolk IP33 2ES* Bury St Edmunds (01284) 703848

WRIGHT, John Alastair. b 30. FRSA72. Cranmer Hall Dur 62. **d** 64 **p** 65. Miss to Seamen 67-72; V Darlington St Luke *Dur* 72-78; Community Chapl Darlington 78-89; rtd 89. *4 Grasmere, Agar Nook, Coalville, Leics LE67 4SH* Coalville (01530) 837390

WRIGHT, John Douglas. b 42. Birm Univ BSc64 CertEd66. St Steph Ho Ox 69. **d** 69 **p** 70. C Swanley St Mary *Roch* 69-74; C Stockwell Green St Andr *S'wark* 74-79; V Leigh St Jo *Man* 79-82; P-in-c Whitehawk *Chich* from 82. *St Cuthman's Vicarage, 1 St Cuthman's Close, Whitehawk, Brighton BN2 5LJ* Brighton (01273) 699424

WRIGHT, John Gordon. b 27. Birm Univ MA51. St D Coll Lamp BA50. **d** 52 **p** 53. Chapl St Olave and St Sav Sch Orpington 68-86; Hon C Crayford *Roch* 68-76; Lic to Offic 76-86; R Whimple *Ex* 87-88; R Whimple, Talaton and Clyst St Lawr 89-90; rtd 90; Perm to Offic *Lich* from 90; Perm to Offic *Heref* 90-93. *Danesford, High Street, Albrighton, Wolverhampton WV7 3LA* Albrighton (01902) 373709

WRIGHT, John Harold. b 36. ATCL Dur Univ BA58 ACertCM. Ely Th Coll 58. **d** 61 **p** 62. C Boston *Linc* 61-64; C Willesborough w Hinxhill *Cant* 64-68; V Westwell 68-75; R Eastwell w Boughton Aluph 68-75; V Rolvenden 75-84; R Cheriton from 84. *St Martin's Rectory, Horn Street, Folkestone, Kent CT20 3JJ* Folkestone (01303) 238509

WRIGHT, Canon Joseph James. b 16. Lon Univ BD39 AKC39. Ely Th Coll 39. **d** 39 **p** 40. V Forest Gate Em w Upton Cross *Chelmsf* 62-84; Hon Can Chelmsf Cathl 82-84; rtd 84. *87 Burnham Road, Southminster, Essex CM0 7ES* Maldon (01621) 773640

WRIGHT, Canon Kenneth William. b 13. Coll of Resurr Mirfield 37. **d** 39 **p** 40. Hon Can Ch Ch *Ox* 70-79; TR Fenny Stratford and Water Eaton 74-79; rtd 80; Perm to Offic *S'well* 80-92. *St Martin's, Station Road, Collingham, Newark, Notts NG23 7RA* Newark (01636) 892800

WRIGHT, Canon Kenyon Edward. b 32. Glas Univ MA53 Fitzw Coll Cam BA55 Serampore Coll MTh61. Wesley Ho Cam 53. **d** 71 **p** 71. In Meth Ch 57-71; India 57-71; Dir Urban Min Cov Cathl *Cov* 71-81; Dir of Internat Min and Can Res 72-81; Public Preacher 72-74; Gen Sec Scottish Chs Coun 81-90; Dir Scottish Chs Ho Dunblane 81-90; Dir Kairos Trust 90-92; Hon C Knightswood H Cross Miss *Glas* from 91; rtd 92; P-in-c Glencarse *Bre* from 94. *122/124 Norse Road, Glasgow G14 9EH* 0141-954 0262 Fax 954 1411

WRIGHT, Leslie Vandernoll. b 24. Trin Hall Cam MA50. Ridley Hall Cam 49. **d** 51 **p** 52. Chapl Vevey *Eur* 68-73; Hd St Geo Sch Clarens 73-89; rtd 89; Chapl Lugano *Eur* 89-92. *Lime Tree House, 101 Lynwood Drive, Wimborne, Dorset BH21 1UU* Wimborne (01202) 888771

WRIGHT, Mrs Louisa Mary (Lisa). b 33. S'wark Ord Course. **d** 87 **p** 94. NSM Streatham Hill St Marg *S'wark* 87-95; Hon C Streatham St Leon from 95. *19 Hillside Road, London SW2 3HL* 0181-671 8037

WRIGHT, Canon Martin Neave. b 37. AKC61 Leic Univ DSRS67. St Boniface Warminster. **d** 62 **p** 63. C Corby St Columba *Pet* 62-65; Ind Chapl 65-71; Nigeria 71-75; P-in-c Honiley *Cov* 75-84; P-in-c Wroxall 75-84; Ind Chapl 75-84; Soc Resp Officer from 84; Hon Can Cov Cathl from 95. *The New Rectory, Baginton, Coventry CV8 3AR* Coventry (01203) 302508 or 227597

WRIGHT, Canon Michael. b 30. St Chad's Coll Dur BA55 DipTh56. **d** 56 **p** 57. V Louth St Mich *Linc* 62-73; R Stewton 62-73; R Warmsworth *Sheff* 73-86; Warden Dioc Readers' Assn 81-86; Hon Can Sheff Cathl 82-95; V Wath-upon-Dearne w Adwick-upon-Dearne 86-94; V Wath-upon-Dearne 94-95; RD Wath 92-95; rtd 95. *17 Ashfield Road, Sleaford, Lincs NG34 7DZ* Sleaford (01529) 415698

WRIGHT, Michael Christopher. b 44. Leeds Univ BA65 CertEd67 MSc75. Wells Th Coll 65. **d** 67 **p** 68. C Dormanstown *York* 67-69; Perm to Offic *Linc* 69-88; Perm to Offic *Sheff* from 71; Hd Master Eastmoor High Sch Wakef 84-87; Lic to Offic *Wakef* from 84; Hd Master Carleton High Sch Pontefract from 87. *Orchard End, Finkle Street, Hensall, Goole, N Humberside DN14 0QY* Whitley Bridge (01977) 661900

WRIGHT, Michael John. b 38. DipTM. Chich Th Coll 59. **d** 62 **p** 63. C Yate *Glouc* 62-65; C Kirby Moorside w Gillamoor *York* 65-68; V 68-72; V Bransdale cum Farndale 68-72; V Kirkbymoorside w Gillamoor, Farndale & Bransdale 72-73; Dioc Communications Officer 72-74; V Ormesby 74-80; P-in-c

Middlesb St Cuth 81-88; Perm to Offic 88-90; NSM W Acklam from 91. *25 Thornfield Road, Middlesbrough, Cleveland TS5 5DD* Middlesbrough (01642) 816247

WRIGHT, Nicholas John. b 65. Liv Univ BA87. Wycliffe Hall Ox 89. **d** 92 **p** 93. C Burley *Ripon* 92-95; C Brightside w Wincobank *Sheff* from 95. *44 Newman Drive, Sheffield S9 1LZ* Sheffield (0114) 249 2942

WRIGHT, Nicholas Mark (Nick). b 59. Loughb Univ BSc80. Qu Coll Birm 82. **d** 85 **p** 86. C Coney Hill *Glouc* 85-89; C Rotherham *Sheff* 89-91; TV Worc SE *Worc* from 91. *The Vicarage, 4 Silverdale Avenue, Worcester WR5 1PY* Worcester (01905) 353432

WRIGHT, Very Rev Dr Nicholas Thomas (Tom). b 48. Ex Coll Ox BA71 MA75 DPhil81. Wycliffe Hall Ox BA73. **d** 75 **p** 76. Fell Mert Coll Ox 75-78; Chapl 76-78; Chapl and Fell Down Coll Cam 78-81; Asst Prof NT Studies McGill Univ Montreal 81-86; Chapl and Fell Worc Coll Ox and Univ Lect Th 86-93; Tutor 86-93; Can Th Cov Cathl *Cov* from 92; Dean Lich from 93. *The Deanery, The Close, Lichfield, Staffs WS13 7LD* Lichfield (01543) 265120 Fax 250935

WRIGHT, Patricia. b 46. SRN68 DN68 DipHV69. S'wark Ord Course 80. **dss** 85 **d** 89. Chapl R Lon Hosp (Mile End) 83-89; Bethnal Green St Matt w St Jas the Gt *Lon* 85-87; St Botolph Aldgate w H Trin Minories 88-89; C from 89. *8 Royal Mint Street, London E1 8LG* 0171-265 1814

WRIGHT, Paul. b 54. K Coll Lon BD78 AKC78 Heythrop Coll Lon MTh90. Ripon Coll Cuddesdon 78. **d** 79 **p** 80. C Beckenham St Geo *Roch* 79-83; Chapl Ch Sch Richmond 83-85; C Richmond St Mary w St Matthias and St Jo *S'wark* 83-85; V Gillingham St Aug *Roch* 85-90; R Crayford from 90; RD Erith from 93. *The Rectory, 1 Claremont Crescent, Crayford, Dartford DA1 4RJ* Crayford (01322) 522078

WRIGHT, Paul Stephen. b 66. Westcott Ho Cam 90. **d** 93 **p** 94. C Upholland *Liv* from 93. *8 Beacon View Drive, Upholland, Skelmersdale, Lancs WN8 0HL* Skelmersdale (01695) 622181

WRIGHT, Canon Peter. b 35. Hull Univ MA. AKC61 St Boniface Warminster. **d** 62 **p** 63. C Goole *Sheff* 62-67; V Norton Woodseats St Chad 67-80; R Aston cum Aughton 80-84; P-in-c Ulley 80-84; R Aston cum Aughton and Ulley 84-93; TR Aston cum Aughton w Swallownest, Todwick & Ulley from 93; RD Laughton 85-93; Hon Can Sheff Cathl from 92. *The Rectory, 91 Worksop Road, Aston, Sheffield S31 0EB* Sheffield (0114) 287 2272

WRIGHT, Peter Gordon. b 27. St Aid Birkenhead 55. **d** 57 **p** 58. C Mansf Woodhouse *S'well* 57-61; V Coddington w Barnby in the Willows from 61. *All Saints' Vicarage, Coddington, Newark, Notts NG24 2QF* Newark (01636) 703084

WRIGHT, Peter Reginald. b 34. Dur Univ BA60. Linc Th Coll 60. **d** 62 **p** 63. C Lt Ilford St Mich *Chelmsf* 62-65; C Billingham St Aid *Dur* 65-68; TV 68-71; TR 71-76; Chapl Portsm Poly *Portsm* 76-87; Sec Chapls in HE Gen Syn Bd of Educn 88-95; rtd 95. *6 Garden Lane, Southsea, Hants PO5 3DP* Southsea (01705) 726651

WRIGHT, Peter Westrope. b 24. Kelham Th Coll 43. **d** 48 **p** 49. R E Blatchington *Chich* 59-73; P-in-c Lewes St Mich 73-75; TV Lewes All SS, St Anne, St Mich and St Thos 75-84; TR 84-87; rtd 89. *9 Powis Villas, Brighton BN1 3HD* Brighton (01273) 321768

WRIGHT, Philip. b 32. G&C Coll Cam BA53 MA57. Wells Th Coll 56. **d** 57 **p** 58. C Barnard Castle *Dur* 57-60; C Heworth St Mary 60-64; V Tow Law 64-70; V Tanfield 70-78; V Gateshead Ch Ch from 78. *Christ Church Vicarage, Bewick Road, Gateshead, Tyne & Wear NE8 4DR* 0191-477 1840

WRIGHT, Phillip. b 35. Kelham Th Coll 57 St Aid Birkenhead 59. **d** 61 **p** 62. C Goldthorpe *Sheff* 61-65; V Doncaster St Jude 65-71; V Kettering All SS *Pet* 71-82; V S Kirkby *Wakef* 82-94. *2 The Grove, Wickersley, Rotherham, S Yorkshire S66 0BP* Rotherham (01709) 543922

WRIGHT, Robert Charles. b 31. Roch Th Coll 65. **d** 67 **p** 68. C Manston *Ripon* 67-70; C Moor Allerton 70-74; P-in-c Terrington St John *Ely* 74-79; P-in-c Walpole St Andrew 74-75; P-in-c Tilney All Saints w Tilney St Lawrence 79; V Terrington St John 80-91; V Tilney St Lawrence 80-91; V Tilney All Saints 80-91; R Stiffkey and Cockthorpe w Morston, Langham etc *Nor* from 91. *The Rectory, Langham, Holt, Norfolk NR25 7BX* Binham (01328) 830246

WRIGHT, Canon Robert Doogan. b 24. TCD BA46. **d** 47 **p** 48. I Belf St Mark *Conn* 64-70; I Carrickfergus 70-82; Can Conn Cathl 79-86; I Killead w Gartree 82-86; Chan Conn Cathl 83-86; rtd 86. *123 Station Road, Greenisland, Carrickfergus, Co Antrim BT38 8UN* Belfast (01232) 862779

✠**WRIGHT, Rt Rev Royston Clifford.** b 22. Univ of Wales BA42. St Steph Ho Ox 43. **d** 45 **p** 46 **c** 86. C Bedwas *Mon* 45-47; C Newport St Jo Bapt 47-49; C Walton St Jo *Liv* 49-51; Chapl RNVR 50-51; Chapl RN 51-68; V Blaenavon w Capel Newydd *Mon* 68-74; RD Pontypool 73-74; Can St Woolos

Cathl 74-77; R Ebbw Vale 74-77; Adn Newport 77-86; Adn Mon 77-86; Bp Mon 86-91; rtd 91. *23 Rupert Brook Drive, Newport, Gwent NP9 3HP* Newport (01633) 250770

WRIGHT, Samuel John. b 18. St D Coll Lamp BA50. **d** 52 **p** 53. V Birkenhead St Pet w St Matt *Ches* 58-74; V Marbury 75-84; RD Malpas 84; rtd 85; Perm to Offic *Lich* from 85; Perm to Offic *St As* from 85. *Bodwen, Llansantffraid, Powys SY22 6AQ* Llansantffraid (01691) 828896

WRIGHT, Canon Simon Christopher. b 44. AKC67. **d** 68 **p** 69. C Bitterne Park *Win* 68-72; C Kirkby 72-74; V Wigan St Anne *Liv* 74-79; Abp's Dom Chapl *York* 79-84; Dir of Ords 79-84; V W Acklam from 84; RD Middlesbrough from 87; Can York Minster from 94. *The Vicarage, 50 Church Lane, Middlesbrough, Cleveland TS5 7EB* Middlesbrough (01642) 817150

WRIGHT, Stephen Irwin. b 58. Ex Coll Ox BA80 MA84 Selw Coll Cam BA85 MA90. Ridley Hall Cam 83. **d** 86 **p** 87. C Newbarns w Hawcoat *Carl* 86-90; C Burton and Holme 90-94; NSM Esh *Dur* from 94; NSM Hamsteels from 94. *The Vicarage, Church Street, Langley Park, Durham DH7 9TZ* 0191-373 6019

WRIGHT, Stephen Mark. b 60. Keele Univ BA83. Trin Coll Bris 86. **d** 89 **p** 90. C Thorne *Sheff* 89-92; CMS from 92; Nigeria from 93. *Bishopscourt, Cable Point, PO Box 216, Asaba, Delta State, Nigeria*

WRIGHT, Thomas Stephen (Tom). b 31. Fitzw Ho Cam BA54 MA58. Bps' Coll Cheshunt 56. **d** 57 **p** 58. C Bishop's Stortford St Mich *St Alb* 57-61; C St E Cathl *St E* 61-64; R Hartest w Boxted 64-82; Chapl RAF 64-71; RD Sudbury *St E* 70-81; P-in-c Somerton 71-82; P-in-c Stansfield 82-91; V Denston w Stradishall and Stansfield from 91; Min Can St E Cathl from 82. *The Rectory, Cornerstone Grove, Stradishall, Newmarket, Suffolk CB8 8YN* Haverhill (01440) 820580

WRIGHT, Tim Stanley. b 63. Derby Coll of Educn BEd86. St Jo Coll Dur 89. **d** 92 **p** 93. C Eccleshill *Bradf* from 92. *3 Hall Road, Eccleshall, Bradford, W Yorkshire BD2 2DP* Bradford (01274) 640286

WRIGHT, Timothy. b 63. NUU BSc85. Cranmer Hall Dur 86. **d** 89 **p** 90. C Bramcote *S'well* 89-93; I Glenavy w Tunny and Crumlin *Conn* from 93. *Glenavy Vicarage, 30 Crumlin Road, Glenavy, Crumlin, Co Antrim BT29 4LG* Crumlin (01849) 422361

WRIGHT, Timothy John. b 41. K Coll Lon BD63 AKC63. **d** 64 **p** 65. C Highfield *Ox* 64-68; Asst Chapl Worksop Coll Notts 68-71; Chapl Malvern Coll Worcs 71-77; Ho Master and Asst Chapl 77-87; Hd Master Jo Lyon Sch Harrow from 86. *Capers Mead, Whitmore Road, Harrow, Middx HA1 4AA* 0181-864 9964

WRIGHT, Timothy John. b 54. Nottm Univ BA76. Ripon Coll Cuddesdon 90. **d** 92 **p** 93. C Dawlish *Ex* from 92. *15 Cousens Close, Langstone Park, Dawlish, Devon EX7 9TE* Dawlish (01626) 862944

WRIGHT, Mrs Vyvienne Mary. b 35. S Dios Minl Tr Scheme 80. **dss** 83 **d** 87 **p** 94. Martock w Ash *B & W* 83-87; Hon C from 87. *29 North Street, Martock, Somerset TA12 6DH* Martock (01935) 823292

WRIGHT, William Charles Stuart. b 53. Ulster Poly BSc81. CITC BTh95. **d** 95. C Ballyholme *D & D* from 95. *The Parish Office, 68 Groomsport Road, Bangor, Co Down BT20 5NE* Bangor (01247) 274912

WRIGHT, William Easton. b 20. Linc Th Coll 52. **d** 53 **p** 54. R Offwell w Widworthy *Ex* 69-72; P-in-c Cotleigh 69-72; R Offwell, Widworthy, Cotleigh, Farway etc 72-85; rtd 85; Perm to Offic *Ex* from 85. *17 North Street, Ottery St Mary, Devon EX11 1DR* Ottery St Mary (01404) 813744

WRIGHT, Canon William Hutchinson. b 27. St Jo Coll Dur BA50 DipTh52. **d** 55 **p** 56. Ind Chapl *Dur* 59-92; Hon Can Dur Cathl 72-92; rtd 92. *109 Bishopton Road, Stockton-on-Tees, Cleveland TS18 4PL* Stockton-on-Tees (01642) 678817

WRIGHT, William Samuel. b 59. TCD DipTh87 BTh89. **d** 87 **p** 88. C Belf St Aid *Conn* 87-91; Sec Dioc Bd of Miss 90-91; I Cleenish w Mullaghdun *Clogh* from 91. *Cleenish Rectory, Bellanaleck, Enniskillen, Co Fermanagh BT92 2BP* Enniskillen (01365) 348259

WRIGHTSON, Bernard. b 25. Linc Th Coll. **d** 83 **p** 84. Hon C Alford w Rigsby *Linc* 83-86; Perm to Offic 86-89; NSM Mablethorpe w Trusthorpe 89-94. *Pipits Acre, 64 Church Lane, Mablethorpe, Lincs LN12 2NU* Mablethorpe (01507) 472394

WRIGLEY, Canon Philip Arthur. b 07. St Jo Coll Dur LTh33 BA34. St Aid Birkenhead 29. **d** 34 **p** 35. R Stoke Bliss w Kyre Wyard *Worc* 69-72; rtd 72; Hon C Worc City St Paul and Old St Martin etc *Worc* 72-76; Hon C Middleton *Man* 76-80; Perm to Offic *Heref* from 80. *Pencombe Hall, Pencombe, Bromyard, Herefordshire HR7 4RL* Pencombe (01885) 400625

WRIGLEY, William Vickers. b 10. K Coll Cam BA32 MA36. Wells Th Coll 32. **d** 33 **p** 35. V Hutton Buscel *York* 57-70; V Old Malton 70-75; rtd 76; Hon C Rillington w Scampston,

WRISDALE

Wintringham etc *York* 76-83; RD Buckrose 77-80. *Beech House, Low Moorgate, Rillington, Malton, N Yorkshire YO17 8JW* Rillington (01944) 758513

WRISDALE, Jean May. b 40. Local NSM Course. **d** 90 **p** 94. NSM Fotherby *Linc* from 90. *The Meadows, Livesey Road, Ludborough, S Humberside DN36 5SG* Grimsby (01472) 840474

WRIST-KNUDSEN, Svend Michael. b 61. Copenhagen Univ DipTh87. St Jo Coll Dur BA91. **d** 91 **p** 92. C Newton Aycliffe *Dur* 91-95; P-in-c Penzance St Jo *Truro* from 95. *11 Pendarves Road, Penzance, Cornwall TR18 2AJ* Penzance (01736) 65836

WYATT, Colin. b 27. Ex Coll Ox BA54 MA55 Lon Univ BD62. Tyndale Hall Bris 60. **d** 63 **p** 64. V Tetsworth *Ox* 67-72; Lect Bible Tr Inst Glas 72-74; R Hurworth *Dur* 74-79; P-in-c Dinsdale w Sockburn 74-76; R 76-79; R Sadberge 79-84; R Bacton w Wyverstone and Cotton *St E* 84-92; rtd 92. *20 Harrogate Road, Ripon, N Yorkshire HG4 1SR* Ripon (01765) 606810

WYATT, Canon David Stanley Chadwick. b 36. Fitzw Ho Cam BA59 MA71. Ely Th Coll 59. **d** 61 **p** 62. C Rochdale *Man* 61-63; Bp's Dom Chapl 63-68; R Salford St Paul w Ch Ch from 68; Hon Can Man Cathl from 82; P-in-c Salford Ordsall St Clem from 91. *St Paul's Church House, Broadwalk, Salford M6 5AN* 0161-736 8868

WYATT, Peter John. b 38. Kelham Th Coll 58. **d** 64 **p** 65. C N Stoneham *Win* 64-68; C Brixham *Ex* 68-69; Dominica 69-75; Zambia 76-78; P-in-c Ettington *Cov* 78-79; V Butlers Marston and the Pillertons w Ettington 79-86; V Codnor and Loscoe *Derby* 86-91; Chapl to the Deaf from 91. *10 Kirkstead Close, Oakwood, Derby DE21 2HN* Derby (01332) 280922

WYATT, Richard Norman. b 21. LVCM. **d** 84 **p** 85. C Puttenham and Wanborough *Guildf* 84-90; rtd 91; Perm to Offic *Chich* 91-93; P-in-c Stedham w Iping from 93. *The Rectory, Stedham, Midhurst, W Sussex GU29 0NQ* Midhurst (01730) 817570 Fax as telephone

WYATT, Royston Dennis. b 36. FRICS67. Sarum & Wells Th Coll 74. **d** 77 **p** 78. NSM Canford Magna *Sarum* 77-82; V Abbotsbury, Portesham and Langton Herring 82-88; Dioc Missr *Linc* 88-95; R Welford w Weston and Clifford Chambers *Glouc* from 95. *The Rectory, Church Lane, Welford on Avon, Stratford-upon-Avon, Warks CV37 8EL* Stratford-upon-Avon (01789) 750808

WYBREW, Canon Hugh Malcolm. b 34. Qu Coll Ox BA58 MA. Linc Th Coll 59. **d** 60 **p** 61. C E Dulwich St Jo *S'wark* 60-64; Tutor St Steph Ho Ox 65-71; Chapl Bucharest *Eur* 71-73; V Pinner *Lon* 73-83; Sec Fellowship of SS Alb and Sergius 84-86; Dean Jerusalem 86-89; V Ox St Mary Magd *Ox* from 89; Hon Can Gib Cathl *Eur* from 89. *15 Beaumont Street, Oxford OX1 2NA* Oxford (01865) 247836

WYER, Keith George. b 45. St Paul's Cheltenham CertEd66 K Coll Lon BD71 AKC71. St Aug Coll Cant 71. **d** 72 **p** 73. C Moseley St Mary *Birm* 72-76; Chapl RNR 73-92; V Walsall *Lich* 76-77; Min Walsall St Martin 77-79; Chapl Colston's Sch Bris 79-86; Chapl Kelly Coll Tavistock 86-92; Lic to Offic *Ex* 86-92; R Combe Martin and Berrynarbor from 92; RD Shirwell from 95. *The Rectory, Rectory Road, Combe Martin, Ilfracombe, Devon EX34 0NS* Combe Martin (01271) 883203

WYLAM, John. b 43. AKC66. **d** 67 **p** 68. C Derby St Bart *Derby* 67-70; SSF 70-73; C Seaton Hirst *Newc* 74-77; V Byker St Silas 77-83; V Alwinton w Holystone and Alnham from 83. *The Vicarage, Alwinton, Morpeth, Northd NE65 7BE* Rothbury (01669) 50203

WYLD, Kevin Andrew. b 58. St Cath Coll Ox BA79 MA85 Univ Coll Dur MSc83 Edin Univ BD85. Edin Th Coll 82. **d** 85 **p** 86. C Winlaton *Dur* 85-87; C Houghton le Spring 87-90; V Medomsley 90-95; P-in-c High Spen and Rowlands Gill from 95. *St Patrick's Vicarage, High Spen, Rowlands Gill, Tyne & Wear NE39 2AA* Rowlands Gill (01207) 542815

WYLD, Peter Houldsworth. b 20. Magd Coll Ox BA53 MA53. Cuddesdon Coll 53. **d** 55 **p** 56. USPG 66-74; Gen Ed 71-74; Dir C of E Enquiry Cen 74-78; C Hatf *St Alb* 78-79; R Appleton *Ox* 79-85; P-in-c Besselsleigh w Dry Sandford 85-89; rtd 89. *2 Jubilee Terrace, Oxford OX1 4LN* Oxford (01865) 792506

WYLIE, Alan. b 47. Is of Man Tr Inst 88. **d** 92 **p** 93. NSM Douglas St Geo and St Barn *S & M* from 92. *16 Albany Street, Douglas, Isle of Man IM2 3LE* Douglas (01624) 676745

WYLIE, Clive George. b 64. QUB BSc TCD BTh MITD MA. CITC. **d** 90 **p** 91. C Drumglass w Moygashel *Arm* 90-93; Bp's C Arm St Mark w Aghavilly from 93; I from 95; Hon VC Arm Cathl from 93. *The Rectory, 16 Derryhaw Road, Tynan, Armagh BT60 4SS* Caledon (01861) 568619

WYLIE, David Victor. b 61. ACA86 LSE BSc(Econ)82 Leeds Univ BA91. Coll of Resurr Mirfield 89. **d** 92 **p** 93. C Kilburn St Aug w St Jo *Lon* from 92. *122 Dibdin House, London W9 1QG* 0171-328 9301

WYLIE, Nigel Bruce. b 62. Trin Coll Bris 88. **d** 91 **p** 92. C Selly Park St Steph and St Wulstan *Birm* 91-94. *10 Regent Court,*

Winn Road, Southampton SO17 1GG Southampton (01703) 556456

WYLIE-SMITH, Ms Megan Judith. b 52. BD74. S'wark Ord Course 88. **d** 91 **p** 94. C Greenstead juxta Colchester *Chelmsf* 91-94; C W Ham from 94. *St Thomas' House, 29A Mortham Street, London E15 3LS* 0181-519 2118

WYNBURNE, John Paterson Barry. b 48. St Jo Coll Dur BA70. Wycliffe Coll Toronto MDiv72 Ridley Hall Cam 72. **d** 73 **p** 74. C Gt Stanmore *Lon* 73-76; Chapl Bucharest w Sofia *Eur* 76-77; C Dorking w Ranmore *Guildf* 77-80; V Send 80-88; V York Town St Mich 88-93; V Camberley St Mich Yorktown 93-95; TR Beaconsfield *Ox* from 95. *The Rectory, Wycombe End, Beaconsfield, Bucks HP9 1NB* Beaconsfield (01494) 673949

WYNES, Michael John. b 33. AKC57. **d** 58 **p** 59. R Berkley w Rodden *B & W* 68-77; V Priddy 77-86; V Westbury sub Mendip w Easton 77-86; C Milton 86-93; rtd 93; Perm to Offic *B & W* from 95. *23A Fairways, Wells, Somerset BA5 2DF* Wells (01749) 673778

WYNGARD, Canon Ernest Clive. b 30. Leeds Univ BA52. Coll of Resurr Mirfield 52. **d** 54 **p** 55. V Beamish *Dur* 67-80; RD Lanchester 74-80; V Dur St Giles 80-87; Hon Can Dur Cathl 83-94; V Greatham 87-94; Master Greatham Hosp 87-94; rtd 94. *16 Langholm Road, East Boldon, Tyne & Wear NE36 0ED* 0191-536 5275

WYNN-EVANS, James Naylor. b 34. Magd Coll Ox BA55 MA59. Linc Th Coll 57. **d** 59 **p** 60. C Goole *Sheff* 59-62; C Hatf 62-63; Chapl HM Borstal Hatf 62-67; C-in-c Dunscroft CD *Sheff* 63-67; Bp's Dom Chapl *Edin* 67-75; C Edin St Columba 67-69; R Edin St Marg 69-85; P-in-c Edin SS Phil and Jas 76-85; P-in-c Edin St Dav from 85; Can St Mary's Cathl 86-95. *1 Gayfield Place, Edinburgh EH7 4AB* 0131-556 1566

WYNNE, Alan John. b 46. St Luke's Coll Ex CertEd71. St Steph Ho Ox BA71 MA75. **d** 71 **p** 72. C Watford St Pet *St Alb* 71-74; Chapl Liddon Ho Lon 74-75; Chapl Abp Tenison Gr Sch Kennington 75-86; Hon C St Marylebone Annunciation Bryanston Street *Lon* 81-86; V Hoxton St Anne w St Columba 86-94; TR Poplar from 94. *Poplar Rectory, Newby Place, London E14 0EY* 0171-987 3133 or 538 9198   Fax 987 1605

WYNNE, Frederick John Gordon. b 44. Chu Coll Cam BA66 MA70. CITC DipTh84. **d** 84 **p** 85. C Dub St Patr Cathl Gp *D & G* 84-86; C Romsey *Win* 86-89; R Broughton, Bossington, Houghton and Mottisfont from 89. *The Rectory, Broughton, Stockbridge, Hants SO20 8AB* Romsey (01794) 301287

WYNNE, Preb Geoffrey. b 41. K Coll Lon BD64 AKC64 Lon Univ BSc(Soc)75 Heythrop Coll Lon MTh86. **d** 66 **p** 67. C Wolv St Pet *Lich* 66-70; Chapl Wolv Poly 70-79; Sen Chapl 79-92; Sen Chapl Wolv Univ from 92; Dir of Ords 76-83; Preb Lich Cathl from 83. *The Principal's House, 1 Compton Park, Wolverhampton WV3 9DU* W'hampton (0902) 712051 or 25747

WYNNE, James Arthur Hill. b 13. BSP45. **d** 47 **p** 48. V Coundon *Dur* 67-82; Perm to Offic *Dur* from 82; Perm to Offic *Newc* from 82. *44 Hermiston, Monkseaton, Whitley Bay, Tyne & Wear NE25 9AN* 0191-253 0302

WYNNE, Canon Richard William Maurice. b 19. TCD BA44 MA68. TCD Div Sch Div Test44. **d** 44 **p** 45. I Monkstown St Mary *D & G* 58-78; Preb Dunlavin St Patr Cathl Dub 76-87; I Dub St Ann w St Mark and St Steph *D & G* 78-87; Chmn, Nat Sec and Deputation Sec Miss to Seamen from 83; rtd 87. *17 Brookville Park, Stradbrook, Blackrock, Co Dublin, Irish Republic* Dublin (1) 289-2315

WYNNE, Canon Ronald Charles. b 16. Selw Coll Cam BA38 MA42 Cape Town Univ MA79. Bp's Coll Calcutta 41. **d** 42 **p** 43. Botswana 68-82; rtd 82; Perm to Offic *Glouc* from 83. *19 Ricardo Road, Minchinhampton, Stroud, Glos GL6 9BY* Brimscombe (01453) 883372

WYNNE, Trefor. b 35. St Mich Coll Llan 72. **d** 74 **p** 75. C Llangynwyd w Maesteg *Llan* 74-77; V Trealaw 77-83; R Llanbeulan w Llanfaelog and Tal-y-llyn *Ban* from 83; RD Llifon and Talybolion from 93. *The Rectory, Rhosneigr, Gwynedd LL64 5JX* Rhosneigr (01407) 810412

WYNNE-GREEN, Roy Rowland. b 36. Chich Th Coll 67. **d** 70 **p** 71. C Fleetwood *Blackb* 70-73; C Cen Torquay *Ex* 73-76; Chapl SW Hosp & Chapl Asst St Thos Hosp Lon 75-85; Chapl R Surrey Co Hosp Guildf from 85. *Surrey Hospital, Egerton Road, Guildford GU2 5XX, or 14 Broadacres, Guildford, Surrey GU3 3AZ* Guildford (01483) 571122

WYNNE-JONES, Dyfed. b 56. St Mich Coll Llan DipTh79. **d** 79 **p** 80. C Porthmadog *Ban* 79-82; R Llangelynnin w Rhoslefain 82-86; Dioc Youth Officer 82-88; V Llanllechid 86-88; Chapl RAF from 88. *Chaplaincy Services (RAF), HQ, Personnel and Training Command, RAF Innsworth, Gloucester GL3 1EZ* Gloucester (01452) 712612 Ext 5164   Fax 510828

WYNNE-JONES, Nicholas Winder. b 45. Jes Coll Ox BA67 MA72. Oak Hill Th Coll 69. **d** 72 **p** 73. C St Marylebone All So w SS Pet and Jo *Lon* 72-75; Chapl Stowe Sch Bucks 75-83; V

Gt Clacton *Chelmsf* from 83. *St John's Vicarage, Valley Road, Great Clacton, Clacton-on-Sea, Essex CO15 4AR*   Clacton-on-Sea (01255) 423435

WYNNE-OWEN, Canon David. b 99. St Chad's Coll Dur BA21 DipTh22. **d** 22 **p** 23. SSF from 47; Min 58-63; Min Gen 63-70; Can and Preb Sarum Cathl *Sarum* 66-70; rtd 70. *Glasshampton Monastery, Shrawley, Worcester WR6 6TG*   Great Witley (01299) 896345

WYNTER, Michael Pallant. b 48. Ripon Coll Cuddesdon DipMin95. **d** 95. C Hughenden *Ox* from 95. *Pipers Cottage, Pipers Lane, Great Kingshill, High Wycombe, Bucks HP15 6LW*   High Wycombe (01494) 714758

WYSS, Mrs Joan. b 30. St Chris Coll Blackheath. **d** 88. NSM Woodhorn w Newbiggin *Newc* 88-92; rtd 90. *11 Sandridge, Newbiggin-by-the-Sea, Northd NE64 6DX*   Ashington (01670) 813356

Y

YABBACOME, David Wallace. b 55. Bp Otter Coll BEd Linc Th Coll DipTh. **d** 83 **p** 84. C Egham Hythe *Guildf* 83-86; C Cen Telford *Lich* 86-87; TV 87-92; R Cheadle w Freehay from 92. *The Rectory, Cheadle, Stoke-on-Trent ST10 1HU*   Cheadle (01538) 753337

YABSLEY, Mrs Janet. b 42. St Alb Minl Tr Scheme 81. **dss** 84 **d** 87 **p** 94. Luton St Andr *St Alb* 84-87; Hon C Luton St Aug Limbury from 87. *11 Dale Road, Dunstable, Beds LU5 4PY*   Dunstable (01582) 661480

YACOMENI, Peter Frederick. b 34. Worc Coll Ox BA58 MA61. Wycliffe Hall Ox 58. **d** 60 **p** 61. C New Malden and Coombe *S'wark* 60-64; C Bethnal Green St Jas Less *Lon* 64-68; V Barton Hill St Luke w Ch Ch *Bris* 68-75; V Bishopsworth 75-86; RD Bedminster 84-86; P-in-c Wick w Doynton 86-87; V Wick w Doynton and Dyrham from 87; RD Bitton from 95. *The Vicarage, 78A High Street, Wick, Bristol BS15 5QH*   Bristol (0117) 973 3281

YAHAYA, Haruna. b 62. St Fran Coll Nigeria DipTh88 Trin Coll Bris 93. **d** 81 **p** 92. Nigeria 81-93; C Hirwaun *Llan* 93 and from 94. *142 Heol Keir Hardy, Aberdare, M Glam CF44 9AW*   Aberdare (01685) 814249

YALLOP, John. b 47. BA79. Oak Hill Th Coll 79. **d** 79 **p** 80. C Brinsworth w Catcliffe *Sheff* 79-81; C Heeley 81-83; C Pitsmoor Ch Ch 83-86; V Ellesmere St Pet 86-88; C Worksop St Jo *S'well* 90-94; P-in-c Cliftonville *Cant* from 94. *St Paul's Vicarage, Northdown Road, Margate, Kent CT9 2RD*   Thanet (01843) 220857

YANDELL, Canon Owen James. b 20. Trin Hall Cam BA42 MA46. Wycliffe Hall Ox 42. **d** 44 **p** 45. V Birkdale St Jo *Liv* 67-73; Dir of Educn 73-85; R Sefton 73-91; Hon Can Liv Cathl 76-91; rtd 91. *5 The Mews, Preseland Road, Crosby, Liverpool L23 5TJ*   0151-924 1019

YATES, Andrew Martin. b 55. St Chad's Coll Dur BA77. Linc Th Coll 78. **d** 80 **p** 81. C Brightside St Thos and St Marg *Sheff* 80-83; TV Haverhill w Withersfield, the Wrattings etc *St E* 84-90; Ind Chapl 84-90; R Aylesham w Adisham *Cant* from 90. *St Peter's Vicarage, Dorman Avenue North, Aylesham, Canterbury, Kent CT3 3BL*   Nonington (01304) 840266

YATES, Anthony Hugh. b 39. Univ of Wales BA62. Wycliffe Hall Ox 62. **d** 65 **p** 66. C Withington St Crispin *Man* 65-68; C Sheff Parson Cross St Cecilia *Sheff* 68-73; V Middlesb St Thos *York* 73-82; V Fenton *Lich* 82-95; V Kilburn St Aug w St Jo *Lon* from 95. *St Augustine's House, Kilburn Park Road, London NW6 5XB*   0171-624 1637

YATES, Dr Arthur Stanley. b 11. Lon Univ BD43 BA45 Leeds Univ PhD49. Ripon Hall Ox. **d** 61 **p** 62. Sen Lect Coll of SS Jo and Mark Plymouth 63-77; Lic to Offic *Ex* from 74; rtd 77; Ex Univ *Ex* from 77. *The Homestead, Thornhill Road, Plymouth PL3 5NA*   Plymouth (01752) 663774

YATES, David. b 56. Oak Hill Th Coll DipHE90. **d** 90 **p** 91. C Parkham, Alwington, Buckland Brewer etc *Ex* 90-93; C Watling Valley *Ox* from 93. *3 Daubeney Gate, Shenley Church End, Milton Keynes MK5 6EH*   Milton Keynes (01908) 505812

YATES, David Herbert. b 10. **d** 70 **p** 73. Rhodesia 70-80; rtd 80; C Verwood *Sarum* 80-85; Perm to Offic from 85. *Denewood House, 14 Denewood Road, West Moors, Wimborne, Dorset BH22 0LX*   Wimborne (01202) 871483

YATES, Francis Edmund (Frank). b 49. Ox Univ BEd72 Sheff Univ MEd88. Linc Th Coll CMinlStuds95. **d** 95. C

Chesterfield All SS *Derby* from 95. *5 Queen Street, Chesterfield, Derbyshire S40 4SF*   Chesterfield (01246) 279063

YATES, James Ainsworth. b 21. Bps' Coll Cheshunt 56. **d** 58 **p** 59. V Shillington *St Alb* 60-79; V Upper Gravenhurst 62-72; R Lower Gravenhurst 62-72; RD Shefford 69-79; V Upper w Lower Gravenhurst 72-79; V Sandon and Wallington w Rushden 79; R Sandon, Wallington and Rushden w Clothall 79-87; rtd 87. *97 Grove Road, Hitchin, Herts SG5 1SQ*   Hitchin (01462) 434959

YATES, Miss Joanna Mary. b 49. St Anne's Coll Ox BA71 MA74 K Coll Lon PGCE72. S'wark Ord Course 89. **d** 91 **p** 94. Promotions and Publications Officer Nat Soc 85-95; Chapl Church Ho Westmr 91-95; C Regent's Park St Mark *Lon* 91-95; C Finchley St Mary from 95. *28 Hendon Lane, London N3 1TR*   0181-343 1580

✠**YATES, Rt Rev John.** b 25. Jes Coll Cam BA49 MA52 Cheltenham & Glouc Coll of HE Hon DLitt92. Linc Th Coll 49. **d** 51 **p** 52 **c** 72. C Southgate Ch Ch *Lon* 51-54; Lic to Offic *Linc* 54-59; Tutor Linc Th Coll 54-59; Chapl 56-59; V Bottesford *Linc* 59-65; Prin Lich Th Coll 66-72; Preb Lich Cathl *Lich* 72; Lic to Offic 66-72; Suff Bp Whitby *York* 72-75; Bp Glouc 75-91; Bp at Lambeth (Hd of Staff) *Cant* 91-94; rtd 94. *14 Belle Vue Road, Andover, Hants SP10 2DF*   Andover (01264) 354996

YATES, Canon John Dennis. b 28. Wells Th Coll. **d** 57 **p** 58. R Moston St Jo *Man* 62-73; V Bury St Pet 73-76; R Ipswich St Mary at Stoke w St Pet & St Mary Quay *St E* 76-80; TR 80-85; TR Ipswich St Mary at Stoke w St Pet, Stoke Park 85-94; P-in-c Wherstead 77-94; Hon Can St E Cathl 87-94; rtd 94. *41 Princethorpe Road, Ipswich IP3 8NX*   Ipswich (01473) 721394

YATES, Keith Leonard. b 36. K Coll Lon BD AKC61 Nottm Univ MPhil79. Wells Th Coll. **d** 69 **p** 70. C Luton Ch Ch *St Alb* 69-73; Hon C Luton St Andr 73-76; R Grimoldby w Manby *Linc* 76-80; P-in-c Yarburgh 76-78; R 78-80; P-in-c Alvingham w N and S Cockerington 76-78; V 78-80; P-in-c Gt w Lt Carlton 77-78; R 78-80; Lect Sarum & Wells Th Coll 80-87; R Upper Chelsea H Trin w St Jude *Lon* from 87. *Upper Chelsea Rectory, 97A Cadogan Lane, London SW1X 9DU*   0171-235 3383

YATES, Kenneth. b 44. Leeds Univ CQSW80. Kelham Th Coll 65. **d** 70 **p** 71. C Leeds City *Ripon* 70-74; C Worksop Priory *S'well* 74-75; Hon C Bawtry w Austerfield 75-78; Hon C Cantley *Sheff* 80-83; Hon C Doncaster St Jude 83-86; Hon C Ashford St Matt *Lon* 86-88; TV Brighton Resurr *Chich* from 88. *St Alban's Vicarage, 10 Natal Road, Brighton BN2 4BN*   Brighton (01273) 602357

YATES, Michael Anthony. b 48. Oak Hill Th Coll. **d** 82 **p** 83. C Hebburn St Jo *Dur* 82-85; C Sheldon *Birm* 85-87; V Lea Hall 87-92; TV Old Brampton and Loundsley Green *Derby* from 92. *Church House, 6 Arden Close, Loundsley Green, Chesterfield, Derbyshire S40 4NE*   Chesterfield (01246) 276805

YATES, Michael John Whitworth. b 39. Selw Coll Cam BA62. Oak Hill Th Coll 62. **d** 64 **p** 65. C New Catton St Luke *Nor* 64-68; C Lowestoft St Jo 68-74; Perm to Offic *Bradf* from 75. *5 Belle Hill, Giggleswick, Settle, N Yorkshire BD24 0BA*   Settle (01729) 822690

YATES, Michael Peter. b 47. Leeds Univ BA69 MA70 MPhil85. Coll of Resurr Mirfield 69. **d** 71 **p** 72. C Crewe St Andr *Ches* 71-76; V Wheelock 76-79; Chapl Rainhill Hosp Liv 79-89; Chapl Barnsley Distr Gen Hosp from 89. *The Chaplain's Office, Barnsley Hospital, Gawber Road, Barnsley, S Yorkshire S75 2EP*   Barnsley (01226) 730000

YATES, Dr Paul David. b 47. Sussex Univ BA73 DPhil80. Sarum & Wells Th Coll 88. **d** 91 **p** 92. NSM Lewes All SS, St Anne, St Mich and St Thos *Chich* from 91. *17 St Swithun's Terrace, Lewes, E Sussex BN7 1UJ*   Brighton (01273) 473463

YATES, Peter Francis. b 47. Sheff Univ BA69 Nottm Univ DipTh71. Kelham Th Coll 69. **d** 74 **p** 75. C Mexborough *Sheff* 74-78; C Sevenoaks St Jo *Roch* 78-81; CSWG from 81; Lic to Offic *Chich* from 86. *The Monastery, Crawley Down, Crawley, W Sussex RH10 4LH*   Copthorne (01342) 712074

YATES, Raymond Paul (Ray). b 55. Oak Hill Th Coll BA88. **d** 88 **p** 89. C Bootle St Mary w St Paul *Liv* 88-91; C Drypool *York* 91-92; TV from 92. *383 Southcoates Lane, Hull HU9 3UN*   Hull (01482) 781090

YATES, Dr Roger Alan. b 47. MRCP77 Trin Coll Cam BA68 MB71 BChir71 MA72 Bris Univ PhD75. N Ord Course 84. **d** 87 **p** 88. NSM Wilmslow *Ches* from 87. *3 Racecourse Park, Wilmslow, Cheshire SK9 5LU*   Wilmslow (01625) 520246

YATES, Mrs Rosamund. b 63. Rob Coll Cam BA84 MA88. Oak Hill Th Coll BA93. **d** 93. C Holloway St Mary Magd *Lon* 93-95. *Wallsebaan 47, 3080 Tervuren, Belgium*   Brussels (2) 767-4845

YATES, Mrs Sian. b 57. Univ of Wales (Ban). Linc Th Coll 78. **d** 80 **p** 94. C Risca *Mon* 80-83; Chapl Ch Hosp Horsham 83-85; TD Haverhill w Withersfield, the Wrattings etc *St E* 85-90; Dioc Youth Chapl *Cant* 90-93; Par Dn Cant St Martin and St Paul 93-94; C from 94. *St Peter's Vicarage, Dorman Avenue*

North, Aylesham, Canterbury, Kent CT3 3BL   Nonington (01304) 840266

YATES, Canon Timothy Edward. b 35. Magd Coll Cam BA59 MA62 Uppsala Univ DTh78. Ridley Hall Cam 58. **d** 60 **p** 61. C Tonbridge SS Pet and Paul *Roch* 60-63; Tutor St Jo Coll Dur 63-71; Warden Cranmer Hall Dur 71-79; P-in-c Darley w S Darley *Derby* 79-82; R Darley 82-90; Dioc Dir of Ords from 85; Hon Can Derby Cathl from 89; Hon C Ashford w Sheldon and Longstone from 90. *Great Longstone Vicarage, Bakewell, Derbyshire DE45 1TB*   Great Longstone (01629) 640257

YATES, Warwick John (Ricky). b 52. Univ of Wales (Lamp) BA78. Wycliffe Hall Ox 87. **d** 89 **p** 90. C Hoddesdon *St Alb* 89-93; R Finmere w Mixbury, Cottisford, Hardwick etc *Ox* from 93. *The Rectory, Finmere, Buckingham MK18 4AT* Finmere (01280) 847184

YATES, William Herbert. b 35. Man Univ BA59. Chich Th Coll 60. **d** 61 **p** 62. C Blackpool St Steph *Blackb* 61-65; C Wednesbury St Jo *Lich* 65-69; V Porthill 69-78; R Norton in the Moors 78-84; R Church Aston from 84. *St Andrew's Rectory, Church Aston, Newport, Shropshire TF10 9JG* Newport (01952) 810942

YATES-ROUND, Joseph Laurence John. b 25. S'wark Ord Course 75. **d** 76 **p** 77. NSM Tonbridge SS Pet and Paul *Roch* 76-83; Chapl Palma and Balearic Is w Ibiza etc *Eur* 83-90; rtd 90. *5 Willowtree Grove, Road Heath, Alsager, Stoke-on-Trent ST7 3TE*   Alsager (01270) 883425

YEATS, Charles. b 56. Natal Univ BCom77 Witwatersrand Univ MBA79 Ball Coll Ox MA85 K Coll Lon MTh90. Wycliffe Hall Ox 85. **d** 87 **p** 88. C Islington St Mary *Lon* 87-90; Research Fell Whitefield Inst Ox 90-92; Chapl and Fell Univ Coll Dur from 92. *3 Bishop Cosin's Hall, Palace Green, Durham DH1 3RL*   0191-374 3878

YEATS, Peter Derek. b 62. Leeds Univ BA84. Cranmer Hall Dur 85. **d** 87 **p** 88. C Tynemouth Cullercoats St Paul *Newc* 87-90; USPG from 90. *c/o USPG, Partnership House, 157 Waterloo Road, London SE1 8XA*   0171-928 8681 Fax 928 2371

YEEND, Walter Archibald John. b 12. AKC40. **d** 40 **p** 41. C W Molesey *Guildf* 40-42; V from 45; C Westmr St Matt *Lon* 43-45. *The Vicarage, 518 Walton Road, West Molesey, Surrey KT8 0QF*   0181-979 2805

YELDHAM, Anthony Paul Richard. See KYRIAKIDES-YELDHAM, Anthony Paul Richard

YENDALL, John Edward Thomas. b 52. St Jo Coll Dur BA88. Cranmer Hall Dur. **d** 88 **p** 89. C Ban 88-90; C Mellteyrn w Botwnnog and Llandygwnnin etc 90-91; R Trefdraeth w Aberffraw and Llangwyfan etc from 91. *The Rectory, 1 Maes Glas, Bethel, Bodorgan, Anglesey, Gwynedd LL62 5ER* Bodorgan (01407) 840190

YEO (nee HARRISSON), Mrs Jennifer Marjorie. b 40. SRN62. Cant Sch of Min 87. **d** 90. NSM Kemsing w Woodlands *Roch* 90-91; Chapl Stone Ho Hosp Kent 90-91; NSM Totnes, Bridgetown & Berry Pomeroy & Dartington *Ex* from 95. *Clematis Cottage, 2 Brooking Barn, Ashprington, Totnes, Devon TQ9 7UL*   Harbertonford (01803) 732770

YEO, Lester John. b 55. Ex Coll Ox BA77 MA81. Coll of Resurr Mirfield 78. **d** 80 **p** 81. C Plymstock *Ex* 80-83; C Northam w Westward Ho! and Appledore 83-85; TV 85-89; P-in-c Devonport St Mark Ford 89-93; TV Thorverton, Cadbury, Upton Pyne etc 93-95; TR from 95. *The Vicarage, Thorverton, Exeter EX5 5NP*   Exeter (01392) 8605332

YEO, Richard Ellery. b 25. Ex Coll Ox MA49 DipEd49. Cant Sch of Min 86. **d** 89 **p** 90. NSM Broadstairs *Cant* 89-92; NSM Totnes, Bridgetown & Berry Pomeroy & Dartington *Ex* from 95. *Clematis Cottage, 2 Brooking Barn, Ashprington, Totnes, Devon TQ9 7UL*   Harbertonford (01803) 732770

YEOMAN, David. b 44. Univ of Wales DipTh69. St Mich Coll Llan 66. **d** 70 **p** 71. C Cardiff St Jo *Llan* 70-72; C Caerphilly 72-76; V Ystrad Rhondda w Ynyscynon 76-81; V Mountain Ash from 81. *The Vicarage, Duffryn Road, Mountain Ash, M Glam CF45 4DA*   Mountain Ash (01443) 473700

YEOMAN, Douglas. b 35. ACII63. **d** 77 **p** 78. NSM Edin St Martin *Edin* from 77; NSM Edin St Luke 79-90. *6 Craiglockhart Crescent, Edinburgh EH14 1EY*   0131-443 5449

YEOMAN, Miss Ruth Jane. b 60. Sheff Univ BSc82 MSc85 Dur Univ PGCE83. Ripon Coll Cuddesdon BA90. **d** 91 **p** 94. C Coleshill *Birm* 91-95; C Hodge Hill from 95; Dio Children's Adv from 95. *1 Ayala Croft, Bromford Bridge, Birmingham B36 8SN*   0121-747 9320

YEOMANS, Robert John. b 44. AKC66. **d** 67 **p** 68. C Pontesbury I and II *Heref* 67-70; Asst Youth Officer *St Alb* 70-72; Project Officer (Dio St Alb) Gen Syn Bd of Educn 73-77; V Is of Dogs Ch Ch and St Jo w St Luke *Lon* 77-87; V Waterloo St Jo w St Andr *S'wark* 87-93; Chapl Bris R Infirmary from 93. *The Chaplaincy Office, Bristol Royal Infirmary, Marlborough Street, Bristol BS2 8HW*   Bristol (0117) 923 0000 or 924 5275

YEOMANS, Thomas Henry. b 14. **d** 60 **p** 61. V Helme *Wakef* 62-71; V Wincle *Ches* 71-73; V Wincle and Wildboarclough 73-79; rtd 79; Perm to Offic *Ches* from 80. *14 Dean Close, Sandbach, Cheshire CW11 9XE*   Crewe (01270) 765638

YERBURGH, Canon David Savile. b 34. Magd Coll Cam BA57 MA61. Wells Th Coll 57. **d** 59 **p** 60. C Cirencester *Glouc* 59-63; C Bitterne Park *Win* 63-67; V Churchdown St Jo *Glouc* 67-74; RD Glouc N 73-74; V Charlton Kings St Mary 74-85; R Minchinhampton from 85; Hon Can Glouc Cathl 86-95. *The Rectory, Butt Street, Minchinhampton, Stroud, Glos GL6 9JP* Brimscombe (01453) 882289

YERBURGH, Peter Charles. b 31. Magd Coll Cam BA53 MA57. Wells Th Coll 53. **d** 55 **p** 56. Chapl Wells Cathl Sch 58-71; Chapl Durlston Court Sch Barton on Sea 71-91; rtd 91. *2 Mill Race Close, Mill Road, Salisbury SP2 7RX*   Salisbury (01722) 327796

YEULETT, George Eric. b 04. Qu Coll Cam BA27 MA30. Bps' Coll Cheshunt 27. **d** 28 **p** 29. C V W Acton St Martin *Lon* 53-71; rtd 71; Perm to Offic *Chich* from 76. *2 Poole Farm Court, South Road, Hailsham, E Sussex BN27 3NU*   Hailsham (01323) 842452

YEWDALL, Mrs Mary Doreen. b 23. Nottm Univ DipEd71 BTh85. E Midl Min Tr Course 76. **dss** 79 **d** 87 **p** 94. Kirkby in Ashfield St Thos *S'well* 79-81; Daybrook 81-87; Par Dn 87-89; rtd 89; Hon Par Dn Bilsthorpe *S'well* 89-91; Hon Par Dn Eakring 89-91; Hon Par Dn Winkburn 89-91; Hon Par Dn Maplebeck 89-91; NSM Norton *York* from 92. *2A The Avenue, Norton, Malton, N Yorkshire YO17 9EF*   Malton (01653) 697773

YIEND, Paul Martin. b 57. UEA BA80. St Jo Coll Nottm DTS92. **d** 92 **p** 94. C Bushbury *Lich* 92-95; France *Eur* from 95. *Boulevard de Metz 76/134, 59000 Lille, France*   France (33) 20 57 23 19   Fax 20 42 94 22

YIN, Canon Roy Henry Bowyer. b 10. K Coll Cam BA32 MA36. Cuddesdon Coll 32. **d** 33 **p** 34. Singapore from 64; rtd 75; Hon Can Singapore from 80. *114-A Newton Court, Newton Road, Singapore 1130*   Singapore (65) 252-5108

YONGE, James Mohun (Brother Amos). b 47. Keele Univ BA71. W Midl Minl Tr Course 91. **d** 94. SSF from 76. *The Society of St Francis, Glasshampton, Shrawley, Worcester WR6 6TQ* Worcester (01299) 896345

YORK, Canon Humphrey Bowmar. b 28. St Chad's Coll Dur BA54. **d** 55 **p** 56. P-in-c Lanlivery *Truro* 67-74; P-in-c Luxulyan 67-74; P-in-c Lanlivery w Luxulyan 74-83; RD Bodmin 76-82; R Antony w Sheviock 83-93; Hon Can Truro Cathl 90-93; rtd 93. *8 Huntingdon Street, Bradford-on-Avon, Wilts BA15 1RF*

YORK, Archbishop of. See HOPE, Most Rev and Rt Hon David Michael

YORK, Archdeacon of. See AUSTIN, Ven George Bernard

YORK, Dean of. See FURNELL, Very Rev Raymond

YORKE, Edward Frederick. b 06. G&C Coll Cam BA28 MA32. Tyndale Hall Bris 28. **d** 31 **p** 32. R Denver *Ely* 66-70; rtd 71; Hon C Portman Square St Paul *Lon* 84-88; Hon C Langham Place All So 88-90. *Flat 28, Grace Darling House, Vallis Close, Poole, Dorset BH15 1XZ*   Poole (01202) 681739

YORKE, John Andrew. b 47. Cranmer Hall Dur 70. **d** 73 **p** 74. C Spitalfields Ch Ch w All SS *Lon* 73-78; Canada 78-92; V Totland Bay *Portsm* from 92. *The Vicarage, Alum Bay New Road, Totland Bay, Isle of Wight PO39 0ES*   Isle of Wight (01983) 752031

YORKE, Canon Leslie Henry. b 09. Dur Univ LTh34. St Aug Coll Cant 33. **d** 33 **p** 34. V Christchurch *Win* 62-76; rtd 76; Perm to Offic *Chich* 76-88 and from 89; P-in-c Aldrington 88-89. *98 Wallace Avenue, Worthing, E Sussex BN11 5QA* Worthing (01903) 503756

YORKE, Very Rev Michael Leslie. b 39. Magd Coll Cam BA62 MA66. Cuddesdon Coll 62. **d** 64 **p** 65. C Croydon *Cant* 64-68; Succ Chelmsf Cathl *Chelmsf* 68-69; Prec and Chapl 69-73; Dep Dir Cathl Cen for Research and Tr 72-74; P-in-c Ashdon w Hadstock 74-76; R 76-78; Can Res Chelmsf Cathl 78-88; Vice-Provost 84-88; P-in-c N Lynn w St Marg and St Nic *Nor* 88-92; P-in-c King's Lynn St Marg w St Nic 92-94; Chmn Dioc Adv Bd for Min 90-94; Hon Can Nor Cathl 93-94; Provost Portsm from 94. *Provost's House, Pembroke Road, Portsmouth PO1 2NS*   Portsmouth (01705) 824400

YORKSTONE, Peter. b 48. Loughb Univ BTech72. Oak Hill Th Coll 79. **d** 81 **p** 82. C Blackpool St Thos *Blackb* 81-85; V Copp from 85. *St Anne's Vicarage, Copp Lane, Great Eccleston, Preston PR3 0ZN*   Great Eccleston (01995) 670231

YOUATT, Jennifer Alison. See MONTGOMERY, Mrs Jennifer Alison

YOULD, Dr Guy Martin. b 38. FSAScot75 Keble Coll Ox BA61 DipTh62 MA65 Magd Coll Ox BD68 Hull Univ PhD80. Lambeth STh75 St Steph Ho Ox 61. **d** 63 **p** 64. C Middlesb St Jo the Ev *York* 63-65; Chapl Magd Coll Ox 65-68; C Cowley St Jo *Ox* 65-68; Lic to Offic 68-71 and 87-93; Asst Chapl Radley Coll Abingdon 68-71; C W Kirby St Bridget *Ches* 71-74; Chapl

Loretto Sch Musselburgh 74; V Liscard St Mary w St Columba *Ches* 74-78; Australia 78-80; C Doncaster St Leon and St Jude *Sheff* 80-81; V Brodsworth w Hooton Pagnell, Frickley etc 81-87; Chapl St Mary's Sch Wantage 87-93; Lic to Offic *Ox* 87-93; R Chapel Chorlton, Maer and Whitmore *Lich* from 93. *Whitmore Rectory, Snape Hall Road, Whitmore Heath, Newcastle, Staffs ST5 5HS* Whitmore (01782) 680258

YOULE, Peter William. b 36. K Coll Lon BD92 AKC92. S'wark Ord Course. d 89 p 90. NSM Gt Totham *Chelmsf* 89-92; P-in-c Copford w Easthorpe 92-93; P-in-c Messing w Inworth 92-93; R Copford w Easthorpe and Messing w Inworth 93-95; rtd 95; Perm to Offic *Chelmsf* from 95. *3 Pear Tree Close, Haddenham, Ely, Cambs CB6 3UU* Ely (01353) 741786

YOUNG, Andrew John. b 50. St Jo Coll Dur BA73. Westcott Ho Cam 73. d 75 p 89. C Nailsworth *Glouc* 75-76; NSM Yeovil w Kingston Pitney *B & W* 89-93; NSM Tintinhull w Chilthorne Domer, Yeovil Marsh etc from 93. *17 Stone Lane, Yeovil, Somerset BA21 4NN* Yeovil (01935) 76394

YOUNG, Aubrey William. b 38. d 91 p 92. NSM Tallaght *D & G* from 91. *27 Flower Grove, Dun Laoghaire, Irish Republic* Dublin (1) 285-5069

YOUNG, Brian Thomas. b 42. Linc Th Coll 67. d 70 p 71. C Monkseaton St Mary *Newc* 70-73; C Berwick H Trin 73-77; P-in-c Gt Broughton *Carl* 77-80; P-in-c Gt Broughton and Broughton Moor 80; V 80-83; V Chorley *Ches* 83-90; V Alderley Edge from 90. *The Vicarage, Church Lane, Alderley Edge, Cheshire SK9 7UZ* Alderley Edge (01625) 583249

YOUNG, Canon Charles John. b 24. Qu Coll Birm 52. d 55 p 56. R Kirkby in Ashfield *S'well* 66-75; V Balderton 75-92; RD Newark 82-90; Hon Can S'well Minster 84-92; rtd 92; Bp's Chapl for Rtd Clergy *S'well* from 92. *9 The Paddocks, London Road, Newark, Notts NG24 1SS* Newark (01636) 613445

YOUNG, Ven Clive. b 48. St Jo Coll Dur BA70. Ridley Hall Cam 70. d 72 p 73. C Neasden cum Kingsbury St Cath *Lon* 72-75; C Hammersmith St Paul 75-79; P-in-c Old Ford St Paul w St Steph 79-82; V Old Ford St Paul w St Steph and St Mark 82-92; AD Tower Hamlets 88-92; Adn Hackney from 92; V St Andr Holborn from 92. *St Andrew's Vicarage, 5 St Andrew Street, London EC4A 3AB* 0171-353 3544 Fax 583 2750

YOUNG, Daniel George Harding. b 52. New Coll Ox BA73 MA83. Cranmer Hall Dur 77. d 80 p 81. C Bushbury *Lich* 80-83; Chapl Dean Close Sch Cheltenham from 83. *The White House, 2 Church Road, St Marks, Cheltenham, Glos GL51 7AH* Cheltenham (01242) 528922

YOUNG, Dr David. b 37. Open Univ PhD89. Lambeth STh79 Ely Th Coll 61 Linc Th Coll 64. d 67 p 68. C Crofton *Wakef* 67-68; C Heckmondwike 68-71; V Stainland 71-76; R Patrington w Winestead *York* 76-80; Chapl St Jo Hosp Linc 80-90; Chapl N Lincs Mental Health Unit from 90; Chapl Witham Court ESMI Unit from 90. *Westview, Ainsthorpe, Lincoln, LN1 2SG, or Witham Court, Fen Lane, North Hykeham, Lincoln LN6 8UZ* Lincoln (01522) 730912 or 500690

YOUNG, David John. b 43. Nottm Univ BA64 MPhil89. Lambeth STh87 Coll of Resurr Mirfield 64. d 66 p 67. C Warsop *S'well* 66-68; C Harworth 68-71; P-in-c Hackenthorpe Ch Ch *Derby* 71-73; TV Frecheville and Hackenthorpe 73-75; V Chaddesden St Phil 75-83; R Narborough and Huncote *Leic* 83-89; RD Guthlaxton I (Blaby) 87-90; Chapl Leic Univ 90-95; V Eyres Monsell from 95. *St Hugh's Vicarage, Pasley Road, Leicester LE2 9BU* Leicester (0116) 278 2954

YOUNG, David Charles. b 44. Or Coll Ox BA66 MA70. S'wark Ord Course 74. d 77 p 78. C Harborne St Pet *Birm* 77-81; P-in-c Edgbaston St Germain 81-83; P-in-c Birm St Paul 83-85; Perm to Offic *St Alb* from 85. *18 Tamar Walk, Leighton Buzzard, Beds LU7 8DD* Leighton Buzzard (01525) 382881

✠YOUNG, Rt Rev David Nigel de Lorentz. b 31. Ball Coll Ox BA54 MA58. Wycliffe Hall Ox 57. d 59 p 60 c 77. C Allerton *Liv* 59-62; C St Marylebone St Mark Hamilton Terrace *Lon* 62-63; CMS 63-67; Perm to Offic *Ches* 67-70; Perm to Offic *Man* 67-70; Lect Man Univ 67-70; V Burwell *Ely* 70-75; Hon Can Ely Cathl 75-77; Adn Huntingdon 75-77; V Gt w Lt Gidding and Steeple Gidding 75-77; R Hemingford Abbots 77; Bp Ripon from 77. *Bishop Mount, Ripon, N Yorkshire HG4 5DP* Ripon (01765) 602045 Fax 700758

YOUNG, Derek John. b 42. St D Coll Lamp DipTh73. d 73 p 74. C Griffithstown *Mon* 73-76; C Ebbw Vale 76-77; V Penmaen 77-81; V Penmaen and Crumlin 81-87; Chapl Oakdale Hosp Gwent from 83; V New Tredegar *Mon* from 87. *The Vicarage, Gorse Terrace, New Tredegar, Gwent NP2 6NR* Bargoed (01443) 821087

YOUNG, Desmond Terence. b 17. TCD BA40. d 41 p 42. P-in-c Thomastown *C & O* 62-74; I Inistioge w the Rower 62-74; RD Kells 65-74; C Roundhay St Edm *Ripon* 74-77; V Leeds Gipton Epiphany 77-83; rtd 83; Perm to Offic *Guildf* 83-94. *102 Wallace Avenue, Worthing, W Sussex BN11 5QA* Worthing (01903) 246973

YOUNG, Frederick Charles (Eric). b 32. TCD BA56 MA59 MLitt63 DTh68. d 58 p 59. C Dub Donnybrook *D & G* 58-63; C Taney Ch Ch 63-66; I Bray 66-70; I Dalkey St Patr 70-73; C Upper Norwood All SS w St Marg *Cant* 81-84; Warden Coll of Preachers 84-93; Dir from 94; P-in-c Morton w Hacconby *Linc* 84-90; V 90-93. *81 North Road, Bourne, Lincs PE10 9BT* Bourne (01778) 422929

YOUNG, Canon Geoffrey Maxwell. b 12. Ch Coll Cam BA34 MA38. Westcott Ho Cam 34. d 35 p 36. V W Malling w Offham *Roch* 67-81; Hon Can Roch Cathl 73-81; rtd 81; Perm to Offic *Roch* 82-84; Hon PV Roch Cathl from 84. *4 Albany Road, Rochester, Kent ME1 3ET* Medway (01634) 844608

YOUNG, George William. b 31. Lon Coll of Div ALCD55 LTh74. d 56 p 57. V Tylers Green *Ox* 69-80; Lic to Offic 80-84; Area Sec (W England) SAMS 80-84; Hon C Purley Ch Ch *S'wark* 84-87; V Beckenham St Jo *Roch* 87-92; rtd 92. *9 Shortacres, High Street, Nutfield, Redhill RH1 4HJ* Nutfield Ridge (01737) 822363

YOUNG, Henry Lawrence. b 19. TCD MA46. d 47 p 48. R Gt and Lt Casterton w Pickworth and Tickencote *Pet* 64-70; rtd 70; Hon C Perth St Jo *St And* from 70. *6 Pullar Terrace, Hillyland, Perth PH1 2QF* Perth (01738) 36797

YOUNG, Iain Clavering. b 56. Newc Poly BA79. Coll of Resurr Mirfield 80. d 83 p 84. C Wallsend St Luke *Newc* 83-86; C Horton 86-87; V 87-92; V Friern Barnet St Pet le Poer *Lon* from 92. *St Peter's Vicarage, 163 Colney Hatch Lane, London N10 1HA* 0181-883 1526

YOUNG, Jeremy Michael. b 54. Ch Coll Cam BA76 MA80 Lon Univ MTh94. Coll of Resurr Mirfield 78. d 80 p 81. C Whitworth w Spennymoor *Dur* 80-83; C Boxmoor St Jo *St Alb* 83-86; V Croxley Green St Oswald 86-94; Dir Theol CITC from 94. *27 Rostrevor Road, Rathgar, Dublin 6, Irish Republic* Dublin (1) 497 0331

YOUNG, Canon John David. b 37. DLC60 Lon Univ BD65 Sussex Univ MA77. Clifton Th Coll 62. d 65 p 66. C Plymouth St Jude *Ex* 65-68; Hd of RE Northgate Sch Ipswich 68-71; Lic to Offic *St E* 68-71; Chapl and Sen Lect Bp Otter Coll Chich 71-81; Chapl and Sen Lect W Sussex Inst of HE 77-81; Chapl and Sen Lect Coll of Ripon & York St Jo 81-87; C York St Paul *York* 87-88; Dioc Ev from 88; Can York Minster from 92. *73 Middlethorpe Grove, York YO2 2JX* York (01904) 704195

YOUNG, John Kenneth. Edin Th Coll 62. d 64 p 65. C Gosforth All SS *Newc* 64-67; C Newc St Gabr 67-69; R Bowers Gifford *Chelmsf* 69-72; R Bowers Gifford w N Benfleet 72-75; P-in-c Kirkwhelpington *Newc* 75-79; P-in-c Kirkheaton 75-79; P-in-c Cambo 77-79; P-in-c Kirkharle 77-79; V Kirkwhelpington, Kirkharle, Kirkheaton and Cambo 79-82; V Gosforth St Nic 82-92; V Healey and Slaley from 92. *Slaley Vicarage, Hexham, Northd NE47 0AA* Slaley (01434) 673609

YOUNG, Canon Jonathan Frederick. b 25. Univ of Wales (Lamp) BA51 Birm Univ MA81. St Mich Coll Llan 51. d 53 p 54. Lic to Offic *Ox* 59-74; SSJE 62-71; Bp's Chapl for Community Relns *Birm* 71-74; Chapl Coun for Soc Resp 74-85; Hon Can Birm Cathl 84-85; USA from 85; rtd 90. *193 Salem Street, Boston, Massachusetts 02113, USA*

YOUNG, Jonathan Priestland. b 44. AKC68. d 69 p 70. C Clapham H Trin *S'wark* 69-73; C Mitcham St Mark 73-74; V Godmanchester *Ely* 74-82; P-in-c Cam St Giles w St Pet 82; P-in-c Chesterton St Luke 82; TR Cam Ascension from 82; Chapl St Jo Coll Sch Cam 88-93. *Ascension Rectory, Cambridge CB4 3PS* Cambridge (01223) 361919 Fax 322710

YOUNG, Katharine Jane. See BOOTH, Mrs Katharine Jane

YOUNG, Kathleen Margaret. b 40. QUB BD BTh. d 88 p 90. C Carrickfergus *Conn* 88-92; I Belf St Paul w St Barn from 92. *The Parsonage, 50 Sunningdale Park, Belfast BT14 6RW* Belfast (01232) 715413

YOUNG, Mark Gilbert Campbell. b 60. Mert Coll Ox BA88. Wycliffe Hall Ox 86. d 91 p 92. C Holborn St Geo w H Trin and St Bart *Lon* 91-95; C St Pancras w St Jas and Ch from 95. *Flat 3, 58 Lambs Conduit Street, London WC1N 3LW* 0171-831 7234

YOUNG, Martin Edward. b 20. Or Coll Ox BA41 MA45. Cuddesdon Coll 41. d 43 p 44. R Wootton w Quinton *Pet* 64-72; R Wootton w Quinton and Preston Deanery 72-74; V Welford w Sibbertoft 78-82; V Welford w Sibbertoft and Marston Trussell 82-88; rtd 88. *2 Knutsford Lane, Long Buckby, Northampton NN6 7RL* Long Buckby (01327) 843929

YOUNG, Canon Noel. b 26. St Aid Birkenhead 53. d 56 p 57. V Leigh-on-Sea St Aid *Chelmsf* 60-72; I Kilnasoolagh *L & K* 73-78; I Tullow w Shillelagh, Aghold and Mullinacuff *C & O* 79-88; Preb Leighlin Cathl 83-88; Preb Ossory Cathl 83-88; Treas Ossory and Leighlin Cathls 85-88; I Templemore w Thurles and Kilfithmone 88-94; rtd 94. *31 Cherryfield, Coolgreany Road, Arklow, Co Wicklow, Irish Republic* Arklow (402) 33242

YOUNG, Norman Keith. b 35. E Anglian Minl Tr Course 85. d 87 p 88. C Burwell *Ely* 87-91; V Swaffham Bulbeck and Swaffham Prior w Reach 91-92; V Barnby Dun *Sheff* from 92; Ind Chapl from 92. *The Vicarage, Stainforth Road, Barnby Dun, Doncaster, S Yorkshire DN3 1AA* Doncaster (01302) 882835

YOUNG, Paul Goodwin. b 07. Em Coll Cam BA30 MA38. Coll of Resurr Mirfield 30. d 32 p 33. R Redmarley D'Abitot *Worc* 59-74; rtd 74; Perm to Offic *Ex* from 74. *8 Shepherds Meadow, Beaford, Winkleigh, Devon EX19 8NF* Beaford (018053) 351

YOUNG, Peter John. b 26. Pemb Coll Cam BA49 MA54. Ridley Hall Cam 49. d 51 p 52. Malaya 54-63; Malaysia from 63; rtd 92. *Peti Syrat 498, Jalan Sultan, 46760 Petaling Jaya, Selangor, Malaysia* Kuala Lumpur (3) 274-6172

YOUNG, Canon Raymond Grant. b 11. MBE81. d 43 p 44. Chapl to Deaf (Dios Win and Portsm) 70-81; Hon Can Win Cathl *Win* 77-81; rtd 81; Perm to Offic *Win* from 81. *66 Chalvington Road, Eastleigh, Hants SO5 3DT* Chandler's Ford (01703) 261519

YOUNG, Roger Edward. b 40. Dur Univ BSc62. Cuddesdon Coll 64. d 66 p 67. C Eglwysilan *Llan* 66-68; C Llanishen and Lisvane 68-74; C-in-c Rhydyfelin CD 74-78; TV Ystradyfodwg 78-81; V 81-88; Chapl Tyntyla, Llwynypia and Porth and Distr Hosps from 81; Dir of Tr for the NSM from 86; R Peterston-super-Ely w St Brides-super-Ely *Llan* from 88. *The Rectory, Peterston-super-Ely, Cardiff CF5 6LH* Peterston-super-Ely (01446) 760297

YOUNG, Canon Stanley. b 14. St Jo Coll Dur BA36. Ely Th Coll 36. d 37 p 38. V Long Crendon *Ox* 70-80; P-in-c Chearsley w Nether Winchendon 77-80; V Long Crendon w Chearsley and Nether Winchendon 80-94; Hon Can Ch Ch 81-94; rtd 94. *The Pightle, Church Lane, Chearsley, Aylesbury, Bucks HP18 0DH* Long Crendon (01844) 208402

YOUNG, Stephen. b 33. St Edm Hall Ox MA61. St Jo Coll Nottm 75 ALCD77. d 77 p 78. C Crofton *Portsm* 77-81; C Rainham *Chelmsf* 81-87; V Ramsgate Ch Ch *Cant* from 87. *The Vicarage, 23 Pegwell Road, Ramsgate, Kent CT11 0JB* Thanet (01843) 589848

YOUNG, Stephen Edward. b 52. K Coll Lon BD73 AKC73 Ch Ch Coll Cant CertEd74. d 75 p 76. C Walton St Mary *Liv* 75-79; C St Marylebone All SS *Lon* 83; C Pimlico St Gabr 83-85; Chapl Whitelands Coll of HE *S'wark* 85-88; Asst Chapl St Paul's Sch Barnes from 88; P in O from 91. *12 Florys Court, Augustus Road, London SW19 6RA* 0181-789 6162 or 748 9142

YOUNG, Stuart Kincaid. b 59. d 95. C Letchworth St Paul w Willian *St Alb* from 95. *89 Howard Drive, Letchworth, Herts SG6 2BX* Letchworth (01462) 673888

YOUNG, Walter Howlett. b 08. Clifton Th Coll 32. d 34 p 35. R Chelwood *B & W* 67-73; rtd 73; Perm to Offic *B & W* 73-94. *West Moorlands, 8 Watery Lane, Nailsea, Bristol BS19 2AX* Nailsea (01275) 852944

YOUNG, William Maurice. b 32. St Jo Coll Nottm 80. d 81 p 82. C Harlescott *Lich* 81-84; V Hadley 84-94; rtd 94. *Old Chapel School, Newport Street, Clun, Craven Arms, Shropshire SY7 8JZ* Craven Arms (01588) 640846

YOUNGER, Jeremy Andrew. b 46. Nottm Univ BA68 Bris Univ MA71. Wells Th Coll 68. d 70 p 71. C Basingstoke *Win* 70-74; C Harpenden St Nic *St Alb* 74-76; Dir Communications & Chapl Sarum & Wells Th Coll 77-81; V Clifton All SS w St Jo *Bris* 81-84; Relig Affairs Producer BBC Radio Nottm *S'well* 84-86; C Bow w Bromley St Leon *Lon* 86-88; Projects and Min Manager St Jas Piccadilly from 89; Hon C St Marylebone All SS from 89. *90 Harvist Road, London NW6 6HA* 0181-964 2930

YOUNGMAN, Donald Arthur. b 10. AKC37. d 37 p 38. P-in-c Rampton *Ely* 69-74; rtd 74. *4 Church Close, Hunstanton, Norfolk PE36 6BE* Hunstanton (01485) 533322

YOUNGMAN, Frank Arthur. b 05. Magd Coll Cam BA27 MA31. Westcott Ho Cam 35. d 35 p 36. R Studland *Sarum* 66-72; rtd 72. *4 Trinity Terrace, Corbridge, Northd NE45 5HW* Hexham (01434) 633166

YOUNGSON, David Thoms. b 38. Cuddesdon Coll 71. d 73 p 74. C Norton St Mary *Dur* 73-76; C Hartlepool St Paul 76-79;

P-in-c Stockton St Jo CD 79-84; V Stockton St Jo 84-86; V Owton Manor 86-90; rtd 90. *36 Stokesley Road, Seaton Carew, Hartlepool, Cleveland TS24 1EE*

YULE, John David. b 49. G&C Coll Cam BA70 MA74 PhD76. Westcott Ho Cam 79. d 81 p 82. C Cherry Hinton St Andr *Ely* 81-84; C Almondbury w Farnley Tyas *Wakef* 84-87; V Swavesey *Ely* from 87; V Fen Drayton w Conington from 87. *The Vicarage, Honey Hill, Fen Drayton, Cambridge CB4 5SF* Swavesey (01954) 31903

YULE, Robert White. b 49. FCMA81. St Jo Coll Nottm LTh88. d 88 p 89. C Wilford *S'well* 88-91; TV Bestwood from 91. *Emmanuel Vicarage, 10 Church View Close, Nottingham NG5 9QP* Nottingham (0115) 920 8879

Z

ZACHAU, Eric. b 31. AKC57. d 58 p 59. C Bishopwearmouth St Mich *Dur* 58-62; C Ryhope 62-63; V Beadnell *Newc* 63-69; V Earsdon 69-81; V Bamburgh and Lucker from 81; RD Bamburgh and Glendale from 92. *The Vicarage, 7 The Wynding, Bamburgh, Northd NE69 7DB* Bamburgh (016684) 295

ZAIR, Richard George. b 52. Newc Univ BSc74. Trin Coll Bris 75 St Jo Coll Dur 79. d 80 p 81. C Bishopsworth *Bris* 80-83; C New Malden and Coombe *S'wark* 83-91; Dir of Evang CPAS from 91; Perm to Offic *Cov* from 91. *64 Kingsway, Leamington Spa, Warks CV31 3LE* Leamington Spa (01926) 424634 Fax Warwick (01926) 337613

ZAMMIT, Mark Timothy Paul. b 60. Aston Tr Scheme 90 Sarum & Wells Th Coll DCTM94. d 94 p 95. C Bitterne Park *Win* from 94. *25 Lacon Close, Southampton SO2 4JA* Southampton (01703) 583540

ZASS-OGILVIE, Ian David. b 38. ARICS72 FRICS80. AKC65. d 66 p 67. C Washington *Dur* 66-70; Bp's Soc and Ind Adv for N *Dur* 70-73; Lic to Offic *Newc* 73-75; V Tynemouth St Jo 75-78; Hon C St Marylebone St Mary *Lon* 78-81; V Bromley St Jo *Roch* 81-84; R Keith *Mor* 84-88; R Huntly 84-88; R Aberchirder 84-88; R Edin St Pet *Edin* from 88. *3 Bright's Crescent, Edinburgh EH9 2DB* 0131-667 6224 Fax as telephone

ZEAL, Stanley Allan. b 33. Leeds Univ BA55. Coll of Resurr Mirfield. d 57 p 58. C Perry Hill St Geo *S'wark* 57-61; C Cobham *Guildf* 61-64; V Ash Vale 64-69; R Ash 64-69; Chapl Northfield Hosp Aldershot from 69; V Aldershot St Mich *Guildf* from 69. *St Michael's Vicarage, 120 Church Lane East, Aldershot, Hants GU11 3SS* Aldershot (01252) 20108

ZIETSMAN, Sheila. d 90. C Geashill w Killeigh and Ballycommon *M & K* 90-91; C Mullingar, Portnashangan, Moyliscar, Kilbixy etc from 91; Chapl Wilson's Hosp Sch Multyfarnham from 91. *Wilson's Hospital School, Multyfarnham, Mullingar, Westmeath, Irish Republic* Mullingar (44) 71171 Fax 71115

ZORAB, Mark Elston. b 53. FRICS77 MRAC75. Mon Dioc Tr Scheme 92. d 94. NSM Itton and St Arvans w Penterry and Kilgwrrwg etc *Mon* from 94. *Oak Cottage, Itton Road, Chepstow, Gwent NP6 6BQ* Chepstow (01291) 620919 Fax as telephone

ZOTOV, Mrs Carolyn Ann. b 47. Lady Mabel Coll CertEd68 Open Univ BA78 Nottm Univ DSpEd86. E Midl Min Tr Course CTPS91. d 92 p 94. NSM Hykeham *Linc* 92-94; NSM Aisthorpe w Scampton w Thorpe le Fallows etc 94; C Ingham w Cammeringham w Fillingham from 94. *2 The Green, Ingham, Lincoln LN1 2XT* Lincoln (01522) 730765

ZWALF, Willem Anthony Louis. b 46. AKC68. d 71 p 72. C Fulham St Etheldreda w St Clem *Lon* 71-74; Chapl City Univ 74-78; V Coalbrookdale *Heref* 78; P-in-c Ironbridge 78; P-in-c Lt Wenlock 78; R Coalbrookdale, Iron-Bridge and Lt Wenlock 78-90; V Wisbech SS Pet and Paul *Ely* from 90. *The Vicarage, Love Lane, Wisbech, Cambs PE13 1HP* Wisbech (01945) 583559

DEACONESSES

The biographies of women clergy are to be found in the preceding section.

ANDERSON, Mary. b 15. St Mary's Ho Dur 38. **dss** 43. Warden Dioc Ho *S'wark* 66-70; Clapham H Trin 70-75; rtd 75. *1 Barrett Crescent, Wokingham, Berks RG11 1UR* Wokingham (01734) 783676

BENNETT, Miss Doreen. b 29. St Mich Ho Ox 60. **dss** 79. Moreton *Ches* 78-80; Dewsbury Moor *Wakef* 80-86; W Germany 86-90; Germany 90-91; rtd 89. *6B Fairlawn Road, Lytham, Lytham St Annes, Lancs FY8 5PT* Lytham (01253) 795217

BLACKBURN, Mary Paterson. b 16. St Chris Coll Blackheath 45 Wm Temple Coll Rugby 59. **dss** 76. Sawston *Ely* 74-78; rtd 78. *30 Maple Avenue, Sawston, Cambridge CB2 4TB* Cambridge (01223) 833843

BRIERLY, Margaret Ann. b 32. Dalton Ho Bris 54. **dss** 85. Wreningham *Ches* 85-86; Tetsworth, Adwell w S Weston, Lewknor etc *Ox* from 86. *The Rectory, 46 High Street, Tetsworth, Thame, Oxon OX9 7AS* Tetsworth (01844) 281267

BUTLER, Miss Ann. b 41. St Mich Ho Ox 67 Dalton Ho Bris IDC69. **dss** 82. Bucknall and Bagnall *Lich* 82-87; Leyton St Mary w St Edw *Chelmsf* from 89. *14 Vicarage Road, London E10 5EA* 0181-558 4200

BYATT, Margaret Nelly. b 18. Bedf Coll Lon BA40. Lon Bible Coll DipTh50 Gilmore Ho 59. **dss** 62. Lee Gd Shep w St Pet *S'wark* 66-78; rtd 78. *41 Woodlands, Overton, Basingstoke, Hants RG25 3HW* Basingstoke (01256) 770347

COLEBROOK, Vera Gwendoline. b 06. Greyladies Coll Gilmore Ho 45. **dss** 49. Lewisham St Steph *S'wark* 61-67; rtd 67. *Flat 57, Charles Clore Court, 139 Appleford Road, Reading RG3 3NT* Reading (01734) 583960

COOK, Gwendoline. b 14. Greyladies Coll 50 St Andr Ho Ox 51. **dss** 56. Dss Ho Hindhead 69-74; rtd 74; Perm to Offic *S'wark* from 74. *2 Lancaster Avenue, London SW19 5DE* 0181-947 1096

COOPER, Janet Pamela. b 46. Glos Coll of Educn TCert67 Ox Poly CertEdD79. Trin Coll Bris DipHE83. **dss** 83. Patchway *Bris* 83-88; Perm to Offic *Glouc* from 90. *Bethel, Kington Mead Farm, Kington Road, Thornbury, Bristol BS12 1PQ* Thornbury (01454) 414230

CUZNER, Amabel Elizabeth Callow. b 17. Gilmore Ho 63. **dss** 72. Catshill *Worc* 72-82; rtd 82; Perm to Offic *Worc* from 82. *12 Blake Road, Catshill, Bromsgrove, Worcs B61 0LZ* Bromsgrove (01527) 835063

DAVIDSON, Helen Beatrice. b 98. Greyladies Coll 40. **dss** 45. Norbury St Steph *Cant* 48-50; rtd 50; Perm to Offic *Chich* 50-70. *Ridgemead House Nursing Home, Ridgemead Road, Egham, Surrey TW20 0YH* Egham (01784) 433463

DEE, Mary. b 21. **dss** 55. Cumnor *Ox* 76-81; rtd 81. *Flat 4, 45 Oxford Avenue, Bournemouth BH6 5HT* Bournemouth (01202) 424240

DENCE, Barbara Irene (Sister Verity). b 20. **dss** 52. CSA from 48. *St Andrew's House, 2 Tavistock Road, London W11 1BA* 0171-229 2662

DOROTHY, Sister. *See* WARR, Sister Dorothy Lilian Patricia

DUCKERING, Alice Muriel. b 18. Gilmore Ho 43. **dss** 46. USPG 45-70; Kegworth *Leic* 71-77; rtd 77. *23 Stuart Court, Kibworth, Leicester LE8 0LN*

ENTWISTLE, Phyllis. b 18. Gilmore Ho 49. **dss** 54. Northallerton w Kirby Sigston *York* 70-78; rtd 78. *15 Kent Road, Harrogate, N Yorkshire HG1 2LH* Harrogate (01423) 560564

ESSAM, Susan Catherine. b 46. Southn Univ BA67 CertEd68. Linc Th Coll DipTh74. **dss** 80. CMS from 83; Nigeria from 83. *c/o Bishopscourt, PO Box 6283, Jos, Plateau State, Nigeria* Jos (73) 52221

EVANS, Mrs Diana. b 59. Somerville Coll Ox BA81 MA85. St Steph Ho Ox 81. **dss** 84. Sherborne w Castleton and Lillington *Sarum* 84-88; Northn St Paul *Pet* from 93. *St Paul's Vicarage, 104 Semilong Road, Northampton NN2 6EX* Northampton (01604) 712688

EVENDEN, Joyce Nellie. b 15. Ranyard Tr Ho 46. **dss** 63. Wembley St Jo *Lon* 67-72; Warden Dss Ho Staines 72-76; rtd 76. *27 Dowe House, The Glebe, London SE3 9TU* 0181-318 2158

FINDER, Miss Patricia Constance. b 30. Dalton Ho Bris 63. **dss** 79. Clapham St Jas *S'wark* 79-90; rtd 90. *8 Brighton Road, Ilkley, W Yorkshire LS29 8PS* Ilkley (01943) 607023

FISH, Margaret. b 18. St Mich Ho Ox 49. **dss** 77. rtd 78; Perm to Offic *Nor* 78-89. *35 Ashwell Court, Norwich NR5 9BS* Norwich (01603) 746123

FROST, Constance Mary. b 09. Gilmore Ho 34. **dss** 37. Bilston *Lich* 49-73; rtd 73. *17 Church Way, Worthing, W Sussex BN13 1HD* Worthing (01903) 201596

GOUGH, Mrs Janet Ainley. b 46. SRN RSCN SCM Lon Univ CertRK73. Trin Coll Bris 70. **dss** 76. Leic H Apostles *Leic* 73-80; USA 80-81; Perm to Offic *Leic* from 81. *410 Hinckley Road, Leicester LE3 0WA* Leicester (0116) 285 4284

GREAVES, Dorothea Mary. b 16. St Denys Warminster 39. **dss** 62. Willesden St Andr *Lon* 63-76; rtd 76. *5 Norfolk House, Ellenslea Road, St Leonards-on-Sea, E Sussex TN37 6HZ* Hastings (01424) 432965

GRIERSON, Miss Janet. b 13. Westf Coll Lon BA34. Lambeth STh37 MA82 Greyladies Coll 34 K Coll Lon 34. **dss** 48. Prin Lect RE Summerfield Coll Kidderminster 63-75; rtd 75. *Flat 8, Parkview, Abbey Road, Malvern, Worcs WR14 3HG* Malvern (01684) 569341

HAMBLY, Miss Winifred Kathleen. b 18. Lambeth DipTh55 Gilmore Ho 54. **dss** 55. Cricklewood St Pet *Lon* 55-78; Eastbourne St Mich *Chich* from 78. *4 Tutts Barn Court, Tutts Barn Lane, Eastbourne, E Sussex BN22 8XP* Eastbourne (01323) 640735

HAMILTON, Miss Pamela Moorhead. b 43. SRN64 SCM66. Trin Coll Bris DipTh75. **dss** 77. Derby St Pet and Ch Ch w H Trin *Derby* 77-84; Bedworth *Cov* from 85. *10 William Street, Bedworth, Nuneaton, Warks CV12 9DS* Nuneaton (01203) 491608

HARRIS, Audrey Margaret. b 39. Dalton Ho Bris 68. **dss** 82. Collier Row St Jas *Chelmsf* 82-85; Woking St Mary *Guildf* from 85. *46 Hawthorn Road, Woking, Surrey GU22 0BA* Woking (01483) 764056

HARRISON, Mrs Ann. b 55. Ex Univ BSc77. Linc Th Coll DipHE81. **dss** 82. Acomb H Redeemer *York* 82-83; Lic to Offic *Wakef* 83-91. *The Rectory, 8 Viking Road, Stamford Bridge, York YO41 BR* Stamford Bridge (01759) 71353

HEDLEY, Elsie. b 16. Lon Univ DipTh51. St Chris Coll Blackheath 46. **dss** 58. St D Cathl *St D* 65-74; Bradford-on-Avon *Sarum* 74-75; rtd 75. *13A Connaught Road, Sidmouth, Devon EX10 8TT* Sidmouth (01395) 516963

HEWITT, Miss Joyce Evelyn. b 30. SRN51 SCM55. St Mich Ho Ox IDC61. **dss** 67. Spitalfields Ch Ch w All SS *Lon* 67-70; CMJ 71-73; Canonbury St Steph *Lon* 73-75; Chorleywood RNIB Coll for Blind Girls 75-80; rtd 90. *38 Ashridge Court, Station Road, Newbury, Berks RG14 7LL* Newbury (01635) 47829

HIDER, Margaret Joyce Barbara. b 25. St Mich Ho Ox 52. **dss** 77. Bris H Cross Inns Court *Bris* 77-84; Uphill *B & W* 84-89; rtd 89; Perm to Offic *B & W* from 89. *Bethany, 8 Uphill Way, Weston-super-Mare, Avon BS23 4TH* Weston-super-Mare (01934) 414191

HILDEGARD, Sister. *See* MOORE, Sister Hildegard

HINDE, Miss Mavis Mary. b 29. Lightfoot Ho Dur. **dss** 65. Ensbury *Sarum* 69-70; Portsea St Alb *Portsm* 70-76; Houghton Regis *St Alb* 77-85; Eaton Socon 85-94; rtd 94. *8 Burnt Close, Eynesbury, St Neots, Huntingdon, Cambs PE19 2LZ* St Neots (01480) 218219

HOWARD, Jean Elizabeth. b 37. Man Univ BA59 Univ of Wales (Cardiff) TDip61 Lon Univ DipTh BD86. St Mich Ho Ox 61. **dss** 82. Tottenham St Ann *Lon* 82-84; Dagenham *Chelmsf* 88-90; Perm to Offic from 90. *c/o Miss E Neeve, 4 Lavenham House, Brettenham Road, London E17 5AS* 0181-527 3013

JAMES, Grace. b 18. **dss** 72. Chatham St Wm *Roch* 70-78; rtd 79. *46 Oastview, Gillingham, Kent ME8 8JQ* Medway (01634) 360276

KELLY, Miss Philippa. b 14. St Chris Coll Blackheath 37. **dss** 61. Jamaica 69-71; Kidderminster St Mary *Worc* 72-75; rtd 75. *Dulverton Hall, St Martin's Square, Scarborough, N Yorkshire YO11 2DB* Scarborough (01723) 501806

LEACH, Edith. b 22. St Mich Ho Ox 51. **dss** 81. Halliwell St Luke *Man* 77-83; rtd 82. *13 London Road, Blackpool FY3 8DL* Blackpool (01253) 34616

McCLATCHEY, Mrs Diana. b 20. LMH Ox MA44 DPhil49 Lon Univ DBRS69. **dss** 71. Adv for Women's Min *Dur* 70-74; Adv Lay Min *Worc* 74-80; Wilden 80-85; rtd 85. *10 Bellars Lane, Malvern, Worcs WR14 2DN* Malvern (01684) 560336

MACCORMACK, Mrs June Elizabeth. b 45. Local NSM Course 82 St Jo Coll Nottm 85. **dss** 86. Bieldside *Ab* from 86. *5 Overton Park, Dyce, Aberdeen AB2 0FT* Aberdeen (01224) 722691

MOORE (nee STOWE), Mrs Ann Jessica Margaret. b 41. St Mich Ho Ox. **dss** 87. Watford *St Alb* 87-88; Spitalfields Ch Ch w All SS *Lon* 88-89; rtd 89. *168 Thorpe Road, Kirby Cross, Frinton-on-Sea, Essex CO13 0NQ* Frinton-on-Sea (01255) 851933

MOORE, Sister Hildegard. b 03. St Andr Ho Ox CWWCh38. **dss** 41. CSA from 41; Perm to Offic *Lon* from 41. *St Andrew's House, 2 Tavistock Road, London W11 1BA*   0171-229 2662

MOORHOUSE, Olga Marian. b 28. Dalton Ho Bris. **dss** 63. Fazakerley Em *Liv* 68-70; Huyton St Geo 70-76; Blurton *Lich* 76-88; rtd 88. *37 Rosalind Grove, Wednesfield, Wolverhampton WV11 3RZ*   Willenhall (01902) 630128

MORGAN, Beryl. b 19. Dalton Ho Bris 47. **dss** 77. Princess Marg Hosp Swindon 69-79; rtd 79. *Ty Clyd, Llanfihangel, Nant-Bran, Brecon, Powys LD3 9NA*   Sennybridge (0187482) 500

MULLER, Louise Irmgard. b 12. **dss** 64. Prestonville St Luke *Chich* 65-72; rtd 73. *24 Clifton Road, Worthing, W Sussex BN11 4DP*   Worthing (01903) 206541

NELSON, Olive Margaret. b 21. **dss** 52. Auckland St Andr and St Anne *Dur* 76; Heanor *Derby* 76-78; Littleover 78-82; rtd 82; Blagreaves St Andr CD *Derby* 82. *Address temp unknown*

OBEE, Sister Monica May. b 37. **dss** 82. Radford *Cov* from 82. *53 Cheveral Avenue, Coventry CV6 3ED*   Coventry (01203) 594350

OLD, Constance Nellie. b 11. St Cath Coll Lon 37 St Mich Ho Ox 38. **dss** 40. Pakistan 47-71; Gt Ilford St Andr *Chelmsf* 72-86; rtd 86. *230 Wanstead Park Road, Ilford, Essex IG1 3TT*   0181-554 2781

OLIVER, Miss Kathleen Joyce. b 44. Man Univ BA65. N Ord Course 80. **dss** 83. Littleborough *Man* from 83. *Littleborough Christian Care Centre, Lee House, Todmorden Road, Littleborough, Lancs OL15 9EA*   Littleborough (01706) 376477   Fax 374074

OLPHIN, Miss Maureen Rose. b 30. Lon Univ BSc Sheff Univ DipEd Man Univ DipTh. **dss** 84. Sheff St Barn and St Mary *Sheff* 84-90; rtd 90. *41A Queen Street, Mosborough, Sheffield S19 5BP*   Sheffield (0114) 247 3009

PALMER, Kathleen. b 09. Gilmore Ho 43. **dss** 65. Chapl Asst S Ockendon Hosp 65-70; S Ockendon *Chelmsf* 65-70; rtd 70; Lee St Marg *S'wark* 70-80; Lewisham St Mary 70-80. *25 Stuart Court, Kibworth, Leicester LE8 0LN*   Leicester (0116) 279 6326

PATRICK, Ruby Olivia. b 16. Gilmore Ho 69. **dss** 72. E Ham w Upton Park *Chelmsf* 72-74; Becontree St Eliz 74-75; Trinidad and Tobago 75-82; rtd 82. *41A New River Crescent, London N13 5RD*   0181-882 5146

PIERSON, Mrs Valerie Susan (Sue). b 44. CertEd65. Trin Coll Bris 76. **dss** 79. Fulham St Matt *Lon* from 79. *48 Peterborough Road, London SW6 3EB*   0171-736 4421

PLATT, Marjorie. b 18. Qu Coll Birm 76. **dss** 78. Hinckley St Mary *Leic* 78-85; Perm to Offic from 85. *216 Brookside, Burbage, Hinckley, Leics LE10 2TW*   Hinckley (01455) 233928

POLLARD, Shirley Ann. b 27. Wm Temple Coll Rugby 67 Cranmer Hall Dur 69. **dss** 84. Cramlington *Newc* 78-85; rtd 85. *3 Buttermere Drive, Worcester WR4 9HX*   Worcester (01905) 610724

RAIKES, Miss Gwynneth Marian Napier. b 51. Somerville Coll Ox MA72 Lon Univ BD81. Trin Coll Bris 79. **dss** 81. Asst Chapl Bris Poly *Bris* 81-86; Beckenham Ch Ch *Roch* from 86. *25 Rectory Road, Beckenham, Kent BR3 1HL*   0181-650 8025

RAINEY, Miss Irene May. b 14. SRN36 SCM38. Gilmore Ho 69. **dss** 72. Filton *Bris* 70-74; Crowthorne *Ox* 74-79; rtd 79. *12 Stevens Close, Cottenham, Cambridge CB4 4TT*   Cottenham (01954) 51634

RANSLEY, Frances Mary. b 12. St Andr Ho Portsm 52. **dss** 61. Linc St Jo *Linc* 69-72; rtd 72; Lic to Offic *Portsm* from 72. *The Home of Comfort, 17 Victoria Grove, Southsea, Hants PO5 1NF*   Portsmouth (01705) 820920

ROBINSON, Philippa. b 09. R Holloway Coll Lon BA31 Nottm Univ CTPS76. **dss** 75. Branksome St Aldhelm *Sarum* 76-83; Lic to Offic from 83; Tutor Bp's Cert 84-86. *132 Parkstone Avenue, Poole, Dorset BH14 9LS*   Poole (01202) 748415

SAMPSON, Miss Hazel. b 35. Lightfoot Ho Dur 58. **dss** 64. Chapl Asst Manor Hosp Walsall 69-76; Lich St Mary w St Mich *Lich* 76-95; rtd 95. *107 Walsall Road, Lichfield, Staffs WS13 8DD*   Lichfield (01543) 419664

SCHMIEGELOW, Miss Patricia Kate Lunn (Patti). b 37. St Mich Ho Ox IDC65. **dss** 86. The Hague *Eur* 86-89; Gen Sec Intercon Ch Soc from 92. *c/o Intercontinental Church Society, 175 Tower Bridge Road, London SE1 2AQ*   0171-407 4588   Fax 378 0541

SELWOOD, Miss Eveline Mary. b 34. **dss** 71. Huddersfield St Jo *Wakef* 76-79; King Cross 79-85; rtd 94. *27 Alverthorpe Road, Wakefield, W Yorkshire WF2 9NW*   Wakefield (01924) 378364

SILL, Grace Mary. b 11. St Chris Coll Blackheath 53. **dss** 62. Southmead Hosp Bris 63-77; rtd 77. *10 Tyndale Court, Chertsey Road, Bristol BS6 6NF*   Bristol (0117) 973 2903

SIMPSON, Mrs Elizabeth Ann. b 59. Lon Bible Coll BA80 Trin Coll Bris 84. **dss** 86. Thornbury *Glouc* 86-87; Beckenham Ch Ch *Roch* 87-90; Heydon, Gt and Lt Chishill, Chrishall etc *Chelmsf* 90-93; Shirwell, Loxhore, Kentisbury, Arlington, etc Ex from 93. *The Rectory, Shirwell, Barnstaple, Devon EX31 4JR*   Barnstaple (01271) 850436

SMEDBERG, Dr Daphne. b 17. MRCPsych MB, ChB DPM. S'wark Ord Course 73. **dss** 76. Chipstead *S'wark* from 76. *76 Woodplace Lane, Coulsdon, Surrey CR5 1NF*   Downland (01737) 554440

SNOW, Marjorie Eveline. b 07. St Chris Coll Blackheath 30. **dss** 45. Jamaica 57-72; rtd 72. *The Close, Vicarage Road, Staines, Middx TW18 4YG*   Staines (01784) 452094

SPROSON, Doreen. b 31. St Mich Ho Ox IDC58. **dss** 70. Wandsworth St Mich *S'wark* 68-71; Women's Sec CMS 71-74; Goole *Sheff* 74-76; Kirby Muxloe *Leic* 76-77; Perm to Offic *S'wark* from 85; rtd 91. *Flat 1, 27 St Leonards Road, London SW14 7LY*   0181-876 4281

STOWE, Ann Jessica Margaret. See MOORE, Mrs Ann Jessica Margaret

SYMES, Miss Annabel. b 41. AIMLS68. S Dios Minl Tr Scheme 79. **dss** 85. Barford St Martin, Dinton, Baverstock etc *Sarum* from 89; Chapl Asst Salisbury Hosps from 85. *7 Shaftesbury Road, Barford St Martin, Salisbury SP3 4BL*   Salisbury (01722) 744110

TAYLOR, Miss Jean. b 37. St Andr Coll Pampisford 62. **dss** 68. CSA 62-79; E Crompton *Man* from 79. *1A Crossley Street, Shaw, Oldham OL2 8EN*   Shaw (01706) 844061

TAYLOR, Muriel. b 28. CA Tr Coll 48. **dss** 76. Gateshead Fell *Dur* 76-86; Gateshead Harlow Green 86-88; rtd 88. *18 Beechwood Avenue, Gateshead, Tyne & Wear NE9 6PP*   0191-487 6902

THUMWOOD, Janet Elizabeth. b 30. STh60 DipREd61. Trin Coll Toronto 58. **dss** 62. CSF 66-77; rtd 90. *66 Headley Grove, Tadworth, Surrey KT20 5JF*   Tadworth (01737) 371076

TURNER, Miss Rosie (Poppy). b 22. St Mich Ho Ox 56. **dss** 61. Wealdstone H Trin *Lon* 62-70; CMJ 71-72; CMS 73-74; Dss Ho Hindhead 74-76; Sutton Ch Ch *S'wark* 77-80; rtd 80. *Bungalow 16, Huggens' College, College Road, Northfleet, Gravesend, Kent DA11 9DL*   Gravesend (01474) 357722

VAN DONGEN, Wilhelmina Gerardina. b 26. Qu Wilhelmina Coll Rotterdam Gen Teacher 45. St Chris Coll Blackheath 51. **dss** 76. Harold Hill St Geo *Chelmsf* 74-84; Hon Asst Rotterdam *Eur* 84-95. *14 Churchfield Road, Coggeshall, Colchester CO6 1QE*   Coggeshall (01376) 562919

VERITY, Sister. See DENCE, Barbara Irene

WARR, Sister Dorothy Lilian Patricia. b 14. Selly Oak Coll 38. **dss** 53. CSA from 53; St Mich Convalescent Home Westgate-on-Sea 65-74; rtd 75. *St Andrew's House, 2 Tavistock Road, London W11 1BA*   0171-229 2662

WEBB, Sybil Janet. b 20. SRN42 SCM43. Gilmore Course 69. **dss** 77. Worthing St Geo *Chich* 77-80; rtd 80. *42 Ham Road, Worthing, W Sussex BN11 2QX*   Worthing (01903) 202997

WRIGHT, Edith Mary. b 22. St Hugh's Coll Ox MA46 DipEd46. Gilmore Ho STh58. **dss** 61. St Marylebone St Mary *Lon* 58-71; Lect Linc Th Coll 71-73; Oatlands *Guildf* 73-76; Roehampton H Trin *S'wark* 76-82; rtd 82. *39A Radnor Road, Harrow, Middx HA1 1SA*   0181-863 7320

WRIGHT, Gloria Mary. b 40. **dss** 83. Smethwick St Matt w St Chad *Birm* 83-84; Tottenham H Trin *Lon* 84-86. *3 Barelees Cottages, Cornhill-on-Tweed, Northd TD12 4SF*   Crookham (01890) 820327

DIOCESAN, AREA, SUFFRAGAN AND ASSISTANT BISHOPS AND PROVINCIAL EPISCOPAL VISITORS IN ENGLAND, WALES, SCOTLAND AND IRELAND

CHURCH OF ENGLAND

BATH AND WELLS
Bishop of Bath and Wells — J L THOMPSON
Suffragan Bishop of Taunton — J H R LEWIS
Honorary Assistant Bishops — A K HAMILTON
J R G NEALE
R H M THIRD
J S WALLER
R P WILSON

BIRMINGHAM
Bishop of Birmingham — M SANTER
Suffragan Bishop of Aston — J M AUSTIN
Assistant Bishop — M H D WHINNEY
retiring Dec. 95
Honorary Assistant Bishop — A C DUMPER

BLACKBURN
Bishop of Blackburn — A D CHESTERS
Suffragan Bishop of Burnley — M W JARRETT
Suffragan Bishop of Lancaster — J NICHOLLS

BRADFORD
Bishop of Bradford — D J SMITH
Bishop of Beverley (Provincial — J S GAISFORD
Episcopal Visitor)

BRISTOL
Bishop of Bristol — B ROGERSON
Suffragan Bishop of Swindon — M D DOE
(formerly Malmesbury)

CANTERBURY
Archbishop of Canterbury, Primate — G L CAREY
of All England and Metropolitan
Suffragan Bishop of Dover — J R ALLEN
Suffragan Bishop of Maidstone — G H REID
Suffragan Bishop of Ebbsfleet — J RICHARDS
(Provincial Episcopal Visitor)
Suffragan Bishop of Richborough — R E BARNES
(Provincial Episcopal Visitor)
Honorary Assistant Bishop — R D SAY

CARLISLE
The Bishop of Carlisle — I HARLAND
Suffragan Bishop of Penrith — R GARRARD
Honorary Assistant Bishops — I M GRIGGS
G L HACKER
J R SATTERTHWAITE

CHELMSFORD
Bishop of Chelmsford — J WAINE retiring
April 1996
Area Bishop of Barking — R F SAINSBURY
Area Bishop of Bradwell — L A GREEN
Area Bishop of Colchester — E HOLLAND
Honorary Assistant Bishop — J N JOHNSON

CHESTER
Bishop of Chester — M A BAUGHEN
Suffragan Bishop of Birkenhead — M L LANGRISH
Suffragan Bishop of Stockport — G M TURNER
Honorary Assistant Bishop — A L WINSTANLEY

CHICHESTER
Bishop of Chichester — E W KEMP
Area Bishop of Horsham — L G UNWIN
Area Bishop of Lewes — I P M CUNDY
Honorary Assistant Bishops — D R J EVANS
M GREEN
J W HIND
E G KNAPP-FISHER
C C LUXMOORE
M H ST J MADDOCKS
M R J MANKTELOW
M E MARSHALL
S W PHIPPS

COVENTRY
Bishop of Coventry — S BARRINGTON-WARD
Suffragan Bishop of Warwick — G C HANDFORD
Honorary Assistant Bishop — V S NICHOLLS

DERBY
Bishop of Derby — J S BAILEY
Suffragan Bishop of Repton — F H A RICHMOND
Honorary Assistant Bishops — K J F SKELTON
R M C BEAK

DURHAM
Bishop of Durham — A M A TURNBULL
Suffragan Bishop of Jarrow — A SMITHSON
Honorary Assistant Bishop — P S M SELBY

ELY
Bishop of Ely — S W SYKES
Suffragan Bishop of Huntingdon — W G ROE

EXETER
Bishop of Exeter — G H THOMPSON
Suffragan Bishop of Crediton — P E COLEMAN
Suffragan Bishop of Plymouth — R S HAWKINS
Honorary Assistant Bishops — R F CARTWRIGHT
I C DOCKER
R C O GOODCHILD
P J PASTERFIELD

GLOUCESTER
Bishop of Gloucester — D E BENTLEY
Suffragan Bishop of Tewkesbury — J S WENT
designate
Honorary Assistant Bishops — C D BOND
C W J BOWLES
J GIBBS
F T HORAN
W S LLEWELLYN
M A MANN
R W WOODS

GUILDFORD
Bishop of Guildford — J W GLADWIN
Suffragan Bishop of Dorking — Vacant

HEREFORD
Bishop of Hereford — J K OLIVER
Suffragan Bishop of Ludlow — J C SAXBEE

LEICESTER
Bishop of Leicester — T F BUTLER
Assistant Bishop — W J D DOWN
Honorary Assistant Bishop — J E L MORT

LICHFIELD
Bishop of Lichfield — K N SUTTON
Area Bishop of Stafford and Bishop — M C SCOTT-JOYNT
of Winchester designate
Area Bishop of Shrewsbury — D M HALLATT
Area Bishop of Wolverhampton — M G BOURKE

LINCOLN
Bishop of Lincoln — R M HARDY
Suffragan Bishop of Grantham — W IND
Suffragan Bishop of Grimsby — D TUSTIN
Honorary Assistant Bishop — R S CUTTS

LIVERPOOL
Bishop of Liverpool — D S SHEPPARD
Suffragan Bishop of Warrington — M HENSHALL
Honorary Assistant Bishops — G C CHADWICK
J W ROXBURGH

LONDON
Bishop of London designate — R J C CHARTRES
Area Bishop of Edmonton — B J MASTERS
Suffragan Bishop of Fulham — J KLYBERG
Area Bishop of Kensington — Vacant
Area Bishop of Stepney — Vacant
Area Bishop of Willesden — G G DOW
Honorary Assistant Bishops — M E MARSHALL
M A P WOOD

MANCHESTER
Bishop of Manchester — C J MAYFIELD
Suffragan Bishop of Bolton — D BONSER
Suffragan Bishop of Hulme — C J F SCOTT
Suffragan Bishop of Middleton — S S VENNER

NEWCASTLE
Bishop of Newcastle — A A K GRAHAM
Assistant Bishop — K E GILL

NORWICH
Bishop of Norwich — P J NOTT
Suffragan Bishop of Lynn — D J CONNER
Suffragan Bishop of Thetford — H F De WAAL

OXFORD
Bishop of Oxford — R D HARRIES
Area Bishop of Buckingham — C J BENNETTS
Area Bishop of Dorchester — A J RUSSELL
Area Bishop of Reading — J F E BONE

Honorary Assistant Bishops	L J ASHTON
	A K CRAGG
	A R McD GORDON
	J RICHARDS
	S E VERNEY
	P K WALKER
	R C C WATSON
	M A P WOOD

PETERBOROUGH
| Bishop of Peterborough | W J WESTWOOD retiring Dec. 95 |
| Suffragan Bishop of Brixworth | P E BARBER |

PORTSMOUTH
Bishop of Portsmouth	K W STEVENSON
Honorary Assistant Bishops	E E CURTIS
	H D HALSEY
	E J K ROBERTS

RIPON
Bishop of Ripon	D N De L YOUNG
Suffragan Bishop of Knaresborough	M J MENIN
Honorary Assistant Bishops	R EMMERSON
	D A RAWCLIFFE

ROCHESTER
Bishop of Rochester	M J NAZIR-ALI
Suffragan Bishop of Tonbridge	B A SMITH
Honorary Assistant Bishops	C O BUCHANAN
	D R J EVANS

ST ALBANS
Bishop of St Albans	C W HERBERT
Suffragan Bishop of Bedford	J H RICHARDSON
Suffragan Bishop of Hertford	R J N SMITH
Honorary Assistant Bishops	D J FARMBROUGH
	R A K RUNCIE

ST EDMUNDSBURY AND IPSWICH
| Bishop of St Edmundsbury & Ipswich | J DENNIS |
| Suffragan Bishop of Dunwich | T J STEVENS |

SALISBURY
Bishop of Salisbury	D S STANCLIFFE
Area Bishop of Ramsbury	P St G VAUGHAN
Area Bishop of Sherborne	J D G KIRKHAM
Honorary Assistant Bishop	J K CAVELL

SHEFFIELD
Bishop of Sheffield	D R LUNN
Suffragan Bishop of Doncaster	M F GEAR
Honorary Assistant Bishops	K J F SKELTON
	K H PILLAR

SODOR AND MAN
| Bishop of Sodor and Man | N D JONES |

SOUTHWARK
Bishop of Southwark	R K WILLIAMSON
Area Bishop of Croydon	W D WOOD
Area Bishop of Kingston	J M WHARTON
Area Bishop of Woolwich	A P HALL
Honorary Assistant Bishops	E M H CAPPER
	J T HUGHES
	H W MONTEFIORE
	S W PHIPPS

SOUTHWELL
| Bishop of Southwell | P B HARRIS |
| Suffragan Bishop of Sherwood | A W MORGAN |

TRURO
| Bishop of Truro | M T BALL |
| Suffragan Bishop of St Germans | G R JAMES |

WAKEFIELD
| Bishop of Wakefield | N S McCULLOCH |
| Suffragan Bishop of Pontefract | J T FINNEY |

WINCHESTER
Bishop of Winchester designate	M C SCOTT-JOYNT
Suffragan Bishop of Basingstoke	D G ROWELL
Suffragan Bishop of Southampton	J F PERRY
Honorary Assistant Bishops	J A BAKER
	S H BURROWS
	L L REES
	H B D TAFTI

WORCESTER
| Bishop of Worcester | P H E GOODRICH |
| Suffragan Bishop of Dudley | R W N HOARE |

YORK
Archbishop of York, Primate of England and Metropolitan	D M HOPE
Suffragan Bishop of Hull	J S JONES
Suffragan Bishop of Selby	H V TAYLOR
Suffragan Bishop of Whitby	G BATES
Suffragan Bishop of Beverley (Provincial Episcopal Visitor)	J S GAISFORD

Honorary Assistant Bishops	C C BARKER
	G E I COCKIN
	R G G FOLEY
	D G GALLIFORD
	R J WOOD

EUROPE
Bishop of Gibraltar in Europe	J W HIND
Suffragan Bishop in Europe	H W SCRIVEN
Auxiliary Bishops	E M H CAPPER
	D P dos S de PINA CABRAL
	E N DEVENPORT
	M R J MANKTELOW
	J W ROWTHORN
	A W M WEEKES

CHURCH IN WALES

BANGOR
| Bishop of Bangor | B C MORGAN |

LLANDAFF
| Bishop of Llandaff | R T DAVIES |

MONMOUTH
| Bishop of Monmouth | R D WILLIAMS |

ST ASAPH
| Archbishop of Wales and Bishop of St Asaph | A R JONES |
| Assistant Bishop | D H JONES |

ST DAVIDS
| Bishop of St Davids | J I REES |

SWANSEA AND BRECON
| Bishop of Swansea and Brecon | D M BRIDGES |

SCOTTISH EPISCOPAL CHURCH

ABERDEEN AND ORKNEY
| Bishop of Aberdeen and Orkney | A B CAMERON |

ARGYLL AND THE ISLES
| Bishop of Argyll and the Isles | D M CAMERON |

BRECHIN
| Bishop of Brechin | R T HALLIDAY |

EDINBURGH
| Bishop of Edinburgh and Primus | R F HOLLOWAY |

GLASGOW AND GALLOWAY
| Bishop of Glasgow and Galloway | J M TAYLOR |

MORAY, ROSS AND CAITHNESS
| Bishop of Moray, Ross and Caithness | G MACGREGOR |

ST ANDREWS, DUNKELD AND DUNBLANE
| Bishop of St Andrews, Dunkeld and Dunblane | M G H HARE DUKE |

CHURCH OF IRELAND

ARMAGH
| Archbishop of Armagh and Primate of All Ireland and Metropolitan | R H A EAMES |

CLOGHER
| Bishop of Clogher | B D A HANNON |

CONNOR
| Bishop of Connor | S G POYNTZ |

DERRY AND RAPHOE
| Bishop of Derry and Raphoe | J MEHAFFEY |

DOWN AND DROMORE
| Bishop of Down and Dromore | G McMULLAN |

KILMORE, ELPHIN AND ARDAGH
| Bishop of Kilmore, Elphin and Ardagh | M H G MAYES |

TUAM, KILLALA AND ACHONRY
| Bishop of Tuam, Killala and Achonry | J R W NEILL |

CASHEL, WATERFORD, LISMORE, OSSORY, FERNS AND LEIGHLIN
| Bishop of Cashel and Ossory | N V WILLOUGHBY |

CORK, CLOYNE AND ROSS
| Bishop of Cork, Cloyne and Ross | R A WARKE |

DUBLIN AND GLENDALOUGH
| Archbishop of Dublin, Bishop of Glendalough, Primate of Ireland and Metropolitan | D A R CAIRD |

LIMERICK, ARDFERT, AGHADOE, KILLALOE, KILFENORA, CLONFERT, KILMACDUAGH AND EMLY
| Bishop of Limerick and Killaloe | E F DARLING |

MEATH AND KILDARE
| Bishop of Meath and Kildare | W N I EMPEY |

SUCCESSION OF ARCHBISHOPS AND BISHOPS

In a number of dioceses, especially for the medieval period, the dating of some episcopal appointments is not known for certain. For ease of reference, the date of consecration is given when known; or, in the case of more modern appointments, the date of confirmation of election. More information on the dates of individual bishops can be found in the Royal Historical Society's *Handbook of British Chronology*.

ENGLAND

PROVINCE OF CANTERBURY

Canterbury

597	Augustine
604	Laurentius
619	Mellitus
624	Justus
627	Honorius
655	Deusdedit
668	Theodorus
693	Berhtwald
731	Tatwine
735	Nothelm
740	Cuthbert
761	Bregowine
765	Jaenberht
793	Æthelheard
805	Wulfred
832	Feologild
833	Ceolnoth
870	Æthelred
890	Plegmund
914	Æthelhelm
923	Wulfhelm
942	Oda
959	Ælfsige
959	Byrhthelm
960	Dunstan
c988	Athelgar
990	Sigeric Serio
995	Ælfric
1005	Ælfheah
1013	Lyfing [Ælfstan]
1020	Æthelnoth
1038	Eadsige
1051	Robert of Jumièges
1052	Stigand
1070	Lanfranc
1093	Anselm
1114	Ralph d'Escures
1123	William de Corbeil
1139	Theobald of Bec
1162	Thomas Becket
1174	Richard [of Dover]
1184	Baldwin
1193	Hubert Walter
1207	Stephen Langton
1229	Richard le Grant
1234	Edmund Rich
1245	Boniface of Savoy
1273	Robert Kilwardby
1279	John Pecham
1294	Robert Winchelsey
1313	Walter Reynolds
1328	Simon Mepham
1333	John Stratford
1349	Thomas Bradwardine
1349	Simon Islip
1366	Simon Langham
1368	William Whittlesey
1375	Simon Sudbury
1381	William Courtenay
1396	Thomas Arundel[1]
1398	Roger Walden
1414	Henry Chichele
1443	John Stafford

1452	John Kempe
1454	Thomas Bourgchier
1486	John Morton
1501	Henry Deane
1503	William Warham
1533	Thomas Cranmer
1556	Reginald Pole
1559	Matthew Parker
1576	Edmund Grindal
1583	John Whitgift
1604	Richard Bancroft
1611	George Abbot
1633	William Laud
1660	William Juxon
1663	Gilbert Sheldon
1678	William Sancroft
1691	John Tillotson
1695	Thomas Tenison
1716	William Wake
1737	John Potter
1747	Thomas Herring
1757	Matthew Hutton
1758	Thomas Secker
1768	Frederick Cornwallis
1783	John Moore
1805	Charles Manners Sutton
1828	William Howley
1848	John Bird Sumner
1862	Charles Thomas Longley
1868	Archibald Campbell Tait
1883	Edward White Benson
1896	Frederick Temple
1903	Randall Thomas Davidson
1928	Cosmo Gordon Lang
1942	William Temple
1945	Geoffrey Francis Fisher
1961	Arthur Michael Ramsey
1974	Frederick Donald Coggan
1980	Robert Alexander Kennedy Runcie
1991	George Leonard Carey

London

	Theanus
	Eluanus
	Cadar
	Obinus
	Conanus
	Palladius
	Stephanus
	Iltutus
	Theodwinus
	Theodredus
	Hilarius
314	Restitutus
	Guitelinus
	Fastidius
	Vodinus
	Theonus
c604	Mellitus
664	Cedd[2]
666	Wini
675	Eorcenwald

693	Waldhere
716	Ingwald
745	Ecgwulf
772	Wigheah
782	Eadbeorht
789	Eadgar
793	Coenwalh
796	Eadbald
798	Heathoberht
803	Osmund
c811	Æthelnoth
824	Ceolberht
862	Deorwulf
898	Swithwulf
898	Heahstan
900	Wulfsige
c926	Æthelweard
926	Leofstan
926	Theodred
—	Wulfstan I
953	Brihthelm
959	Dunstan
964	Ælfstan
996	Wulfstan II
1004	Ælfhun
1014	Ælfwig
1035	Ælfweard
1044	Robert of Jumièges
1051	William
1075	Hugh of Orival
1086	Maurice
1108	Richard de Belmeis
1128	Gilbert [the Universal]
1141	Robert de Sigillo
1152	Richard de Belmeis II
1163	Gilbert Foliot
1189	Richard Fitz Neal
1199	William of Ste-Mere-Eglise
1221	Eustace de Fauconberg
1229	Roger Niger
1244	Fulk Basset
1260	Henry Wingham
1263	Henry of Sandwich
1274	John Chishull
1280	Richard Gravesend
1306	Ralph Baldock
1313	Gilbert Segrave
1317	Richard Newport
1319	Stephen Gravesend
1338	Richard Bintworth
1355	Michael Northburgh
1362	Simon Sudbury
1375	William Courtenay
1382	Robert Braybrooke
1404	Roger Walden
1406	Nicholas Bubwith
1407	Richard Clifford
1421	John Kempe
1426	William Gray
1431	Robert Fitz-Hugh
1436	Robert Gilbert
1450	Thomas Kempe
1489	Richard Hill
1496	Thomas Savage

[1] On 19 October 1399 Boniface IX annulled Arundel's translation to St Andrews and confirmed him in the See of Canterbury.
[2] See vacant for a term of years.

1502 William Warham	867 Ealhferth	**Bath and Wells**
1504 William Barons [Barnes]	877 Tunberht	BISHOPS OF WELLS
1506 Richard Fitz-James	879 Denewulf	909 Athelm
1522 Cuthbert Tunstall [Tonstall]	909 Frithestan	925 Wulfhelm I
1530 John Stokesley	931 Byrnstan	928 Ælfheah
1540 Edmund Bonner	934 Ælfheah I	938 Wulfhelm II
1550 Nicholas Ridley	951 Ælfsige I	956 Byrhthelm
1553 Edmund Bonner (rest.)	960 Brihthelm	974 Cyneweard
1559 Edmund Grindal	963 Æthelwold I	979 Sigegar
1570 Edwin Sandys	984 Ælfheah II	997 Ælfwine
1577 John Aylmer	1006 Cenwulf	999 Lyfing
1595 Richard Fletcher	1006 Æthelwold II	1018 Æthelwine (eject.)
1597 Richard Bancroft	c1014 Ælfsige II	1013 Brihtwine (dep.)
1604 Richard Vaughan	1032 Ælfwine	Æthelwine (rest.)
1607 Thomas Ravis	1043 Stigand	Beorhtwine (rest.)
1610 George Abbot	Ælfsige III?	1024 Brihtwig [also Merehwit]
1611 John King	1070 Walkelin	1033 Duduc
1621 George Montaigne [Mountain]	1107 William Giffard	1061 Gisa
1628 William Laud	1129 Henry of Blois	1088 John of Tours [de Villula]
1633 William Juxon	1174 Richard of Ilchester (Toclyve)	
1660 Gilbert Sheldon	1189 Godfrey de Lucy	BISHOPS OF BATH
1663 Humfrey Henchman	1205 Peter des Roches	1090 John of Tours [de Villula]
1676 Henry Compton	1244 Will. de Raleigh	1123 Godfrey
1714 John Robinson	1260 Aymer de Valance [of Lusignan]	1136 Robert
1723 Edmund Gibson	1262 John Gervaise	1174 Reg. Fitz Jocelin
1748 Thomas Sherlock	1268 Nicholas of Ely	1192 Savaric FitzGeldewin
1761 Thomas Hayter	1282 John of Pontoise	
1762 Richard Osbaldeston	1305 Henry Merewell [or Woodlock]	BATH AND GLASTONBURY
1764 Richard Terrick	1316 John Sandale	1206 Jocelin of Wells
1778 Robert Lowth	1320 Rigaud of Assier	
1787 Beilby Porteus	1323 John Stratford	BATH AND WELLS
1809 John Randolph	1333 Adam Orleton	1244 Roger of Salisbury
1813 William Howley	1346 William Edendon [Edington]	1248 William Bitton I
1828 Charles James Blomfield	1367 William of Wykeham	1265 Walter Giffard
1856 Archibald Campbell Tait	1404 Henry Beaufort	1267 William Bitton II
1869 John Jackson	1447 William of Waynflete	1275 Robert Burnell
1885 Frederick Temple	1487 Peter Courtenay	1293 William of March
1897 Mandell Creighton	1493 Thomas Langton	1302 Walter Hasleshaw
1901 Arthur Foley Winnington-Ingram	1501 Richard Fox	1309 John Droxford
	1529 Thomas Wolsey	1329 Ralph of Shrewsbury
1939 Geoffrey Francis Fisher	1531 Stephen Gardiner (dep.)	1364 John Barnet
1945 John William Charles Wand	1551 John Ponet [Poynet]	1367 John Harewell
1956 Henry Colville Montgomery Campbell	1553 Stephen Gardiner (rese.)	1386 Walter Skirlaw
	1556 John White (dep.)	1388 Ralph Erghum
1961 Robert Wright Stopford	1561 Robert Horne	1401 Henry Bowet
1973 Gerald Alexander Ellison	1580 John Watson	1407 Nicholas Bubwith
1981 Graham Douglas Leonard	1584 Thomas Cowper [Cooper]	1425 John Stafford
1991 David Michael Hope	1595 William Wickham [Wykeham]	1443 Thomas Beckington
	1596 William Day	1466 Robert Stillington
	1597 Thomas Bilson	1492 Richard Fox
†Westminster	1616 James Montague	1495 Oliver King
1540 Thomas Thirlby	1619 Lancelot Andrewes	1504 Adriano de Castello [di Corneto]
	1628 Richard Neile	1518 Thomas Wolsey
	1632 Walter Curll	1523 John Clerk
Winchester	1660 Brian Duppa	1541 William Knight
BISHOPS OF THE WEST SAXONS	1662 George Morley	1548 William Barlow
634 Birinus	1684 Peter Mews	1554 Gilbert Bourne
650 Ægilberht	1707 Jonathan Trelawney	1560 Gilbert Berkeley
	1721 Charles Trimnell	1584 Thomas Godwin
BISHOPS OF WINCHESTER	1723 Richard Willis	1593 John Still
660 Wine	1734 Benjamin Hoadly	1608 James Montague
670 Leutherius	1761 John Thomas	1616 Arthur Lake
676 Haedde	1781 Brownlow North	1626 William Laud
705 Daniel	1820 George Pretyman Tomline	1628 Leonard Mawe
744 Hunfrith	1827 Charles Richard Sumner	1629 Walter Curll
756 Cyneheard	1869 Samuel Wilberforce	1632 William Piers
778 Æthelheard	1873 Edward Harold Browne	1670 Robert Creighton
778 Ecbald	1891 Anthony Wilson Thorold	1673 Peter Mews
785 Dudd	1895 Randall Thomas Davidson	1685 Thomas Ken (dep.)
c785 Cyneberht	1903 Herbert Edward Ryle	1691 Richard Kidder
803 Eahlmund	1911 Edward Stuart Talbot	1704 George Hooper
814 Wigthegn	1923 Frank Theodore Woods	1727 John Wynne
825 Herefrith[1]	1932 Cyril Forster Garbett	1743 Edward Willes
838 Eadmund	1942 Mervyn George Haigh	1774 Charles Moss
c838 Eadhun	1952 Alwyn Terrell Petre Williams	1802 Richard Beadon
839 Helmstan	1961 Sherard Falkner Allison	1824 George Henry Law
852 Swithhun	1975 John Vernon Taylor	1845 Richard Bagot
	1985 Colin Clement Walter James	

[1] Never signed without Wigthegn

1854 Robert John Eden, Lord
      Auckland
1869 Anhur Charles Hervey
1894 George Wyndham Kennion
1921 St. John Basil Wynne Wilson
1937 Francis Underhill
1943 John William Charles Wand
1946 Harold William Bradfield
1960 Edward Barry Henderson
1975 John Monier Bickersteth
1987 George Leonard Carey
1991 James LawtonThompson

Birmingham

1905 Charles Gore
1911 Henry Russell Wakefield
1924 Ernest William Barnes
1953 John Leonard Wilson
1969 Laurence Ambrose Brown
1978 Hugh William Montefiore
1987 Mark Santer

Bristol

1542 Paul Bush
1554 John Holyman
1562 Richard Cheyney
1581 John Bullingham (held
      Gloucester and Bristol 1586-9)
1589 Richard Fletcher
[See vacant for ten years]
1603 John Thornborough
1617 Nicholas Felton
1619 Rowland Searchfield
1623 Robert Wright
1633 George Coke
1637 Robert Skinner
1642 Thomas Westfield
1644 Thomas Howell
1661 Gilbert Ironside
1672 Guy Carleton
1679 William Gulston
1684 John Lake
1685 Jonathan Trelawney
1689 Gilbert Ironside
1691 John Hall
1710 John Robinson
1714 George Smalridge
1719 Hugh Boulter
1724 William Bradshaw
1733 Charles Cecil
1735 Thomas Secker
1737 Thomas Gooch
1738 Joseph Butler
1750 John Conybeare
1756 John Hume
1758 Philip Yonge
1761 Thomas Newton
1782 Lewis Bagot
1783 Christopher Wilson
1792 Spencer Madan
1794 Henry Reginald Courtenay
1797 Ffolliott Herbert Walker
      Cornewall
1803 George Pelham
1807 John Luxmoore
1808 William Lort Mansel
1820 John Kaye
1827 Robert Gray
1834 Joseph Allen
[1836 to 1897 united with **Gloucester**]
1897 George Forrest Browne
1914 George Nickson
1933 Clifford Salisbury Woodward
1946 Frederick Arthur Cockin
1959 Oliver Stratford Tomkins
1975 Ernest John Tinsley
1985 Barry Rogerson

Chelmsford

1914 John Edwin Watts-Ditchfield
1923 Frederic Sumpter Guy Warman
1929 Henry Albert Wilson
1951 Sherard Falkner Allison
1962 John Gerhard Tiarks
1971 Albert John Trillo
1986 John Waine

Chichester

BISHOPS OF SELSEY

681 Wilfrid
716 Eadberht
731 Eolla
733 Sigga [Sigeferth]
765 Aaluberht
c765 Oswald [Osa]
780 Gislhere
786 Tota
c789 Wihthun
c811 Æthelwulf
824 Cynered
845 Guthheard
900 Wighelm
909 Beornheah
931 Wulfhun
943 Ælfred
955 Daniel
956 Brihthelm
963 Eadhelm
980 Æthelgar
990 Ordbriht
1009 Ælfmaer
1032 Æthelric I
1039 Grimketel
1047 Heca
1058 Æthelric II
1070 Stigand

BISHOPS OF CHICHESTER

1075 Stigand
1088 Godfrey
1091 Ralph Luffa
1125 Seffrid I [d'Escures Pelochin]
1147 Hilary
1174 John Greenford
1180 Seffrid II
1204 Simon FitzRobert
1215 Richard Poore
1218 Ranulf of Wareham
1224 Ralph Nevill
1245 Richard Wich
1254 John Climping
1262 Stephen Bersted [or Pagham]
1288 Gilbert de St. Leofard
1305 John Langton
1337 Robert Stratford
1362 William Lenn
1369 William Reade
1386 Thomas Rushock
1390 Richard Mitford
1396 Robert Waldby
1397 Robert Reade
1417 Stephen Patrington
1418 Henry de la Ware
1421 John Kempe
1421 Thomas Polton
1426 John Rickingale
1431 Simon Sydenham
1438 Richard Praty
1446 Adam de Moleyns
1450 Reginald Pecock
1459 John Arundel
1478 Edward Story
1504 Richard Fitz-James
1508 Robert Sherburne

1536 Richard Sampson
1543 George Day (dep.)
1552 John Scory
1553 George Day (rest.)
1557 John Christopherson
1559 William Barlow
1570 Richard Curtis
1586 Thomas Bickley
1596 Anthony Watson
1605 Lancelot Andrewes
1609 Samuel Harsnett
1619 George Carleton
1628 Richard Montague
1638 Brian Duppa
1642 Henry King
1670 Peter Gunning
1675 Ralph Brideoake
1679 Guy Carleton
1685 John Lake
1689 Simon Patrick
1691 Robert Grove
1696 John Williams
1709 Thomas Manningham
1722 Thomas Bowers
1724 Edward Waddington
1731 Francis Hare
1740 Matthias Mawson
1754 William Ashburnham
1798 John Buckner
1824 Robert James Carr
1831 Edward Maltby
1836 William Otter
1840 Philip Nicholas Shuttleworth
1842 Ashurst Turner Gilbert
1870 Richard Durnford
1896 Ernest Roland Wilberforce
1908 Charles John Ridgeway
1919 Winfrid Oldfield Burrows
1929 George Kennedy Allen Bell
1958 Roger Plumpton Wilson
1974 Eric Waldram Kemp

Coventry

1918 Huyshe Wolcott Yeatman-Biggs
1922 Charles Lisle Carr
1931 Mervyn George Haigh
1943 Neville Vincent Gorton
1956 Cuthbert Killick Norman
      Bardsley
1976 John Gibbs
1985 Simon Barrington-Ward

Derby

1927 Edmund Courtenay Pearce
1936 Alfred Edward John Rawlinson
1959 Geoffrey Francis Allen
1969 Cyril William Johnston Bowles
1988 Peter Spencer Dawes
1995 Jonathan Sansbury Bailey

Dorchester[1]

634 Birinus
650 Agilbert
c660 Ætla
c888 Ahlheard

Ely

1109 Hervey
1133 Nigel
1174 Geoffrey Ridel
1189 William Longchamp
1198 Eustace
1220 John of Fountains
1225 Geoffrey de Burgo
1229 Hugh of Northwold

---

[1] Originally a West Saxon, after Ahlheard's time a Mercian, bishopric. See transferred to Lincoln 1077.

1255 William of Kilkenny	1046 Leofric Bp. of Crediton and	1869 Frederick Temple
1258 Hugh of Balsham	Cornwall	1885 Edward Henry Bickersteth
1286 John of Kirkby	[See transferred to Exeter 1050]	1901 Herbert Edward Ryle
1290 William of Louth		1903 Archibald Robertson
1299 Ralph Walpole	BISHOPS OF CREDITON	1916 Rupert Ernest William Gascoyne
1303 Robert Orford	909 Eadwulf	Cecil
1310 John Ketton	934 Æthelgar	1936 Charles Edward Curzon
1316 John Hotham	953 Ælfwold I	1949 Robert Cecil Mortimer
1337 Simon Montacute	973 Sideman	1973 Eric Arthur John Mercer
1345 Thomas de Lisle	979 Ælfric	1985 Geoffrey Hewlett Thompson
1362 Simon Langham	987 Ælfwold II	
1367 John Barnet	1008 Ælfwold III	**Gloucester**
1374 Thomas Arundel	1015 Eadnoth	
1388 John Fordham	1027 Lyfing	1541 John Wakeman *alias* Wiche
1426 Philip Morgan	1046 Leofric[1]	1551 John Hooper
1438 Lewis of Luxembourg		1554 James Brooks
1444 Thomas Bourgchier	BISHOPS OF EXETER	1562 Richard Cheyney[2]
1454 William Grey	1050 Leofric	1581 John Bullingham[3]
1479 John Morton	1072 Osbern Fitz-Osbern	1598 Godfrey Goldsborough
1486 John Alcock	1107 Will. Warelwast	1605 Thomas Ravis
1501 Richard Redman	1138 Robert Warelwast	1607 Henry Parry
1506 James Stanley	1155 Robert II Of Chichester	1611 Giles Thompson
1515 Nicholas West	1161 Bartholomew	1612 Miles Smith
1534 Thomas Goodrich	1186 John the Chanter	1625 Godfrey Goodman
1555 Thomas Thirlby	1194 Henry Marshall	1661 William Nicolson
1559 Richard Cox	1214 Simon of Apulia	1672 John Pritchett
1600 Martin Heton	1224 William Brewer	1681 Robert Frampton
1609 Lancelot Andrewes	1245 Richard Blund	1691 Edward Fowler
1619 Nicolas Felton	1258 Walter Bronescombe	1715 Richard Willis
1628 John Buckeridge	1280 Peter Quinel [Wyvill]	1721 Joseph Wilcocks
1631 Francis White	1292 Thomas Bitton	1731 Elias Sydall
1638 Matthew Wren	1308 Walter Stapeldon	1735 Martin Benson
1667 Banjamin Laney	1327 James Berkeley	1752 James Johnson
1675 Peter Gunning	1328 John Grandisson	1760 William Warburton
1684 Francis Turner	1370 Thomas Brantingham	1779 James Yorke
1691 Simon Patrick	1395 Edmund Stafford	1781 Samuel Hallifax
1707 John Moore	1419 John Catterick	1789 Richard Beadon
1714 William Fleetwood	1420 Edmund Lacy	1802 George Isaac Huntingford
1723 Thomas Greene	1458 George Nevill	1815 Henry Ryder
1738 Robert Butts	1465 John Booth	1824 Christopher Bethell
1748 Thomas Gooch	1478 Peter Courtenay	1830 James Henry Monk
1754 Matthias Mawson	1487 Richard Fox	[1836 To 1897, united with Bristol]
1771 Edmund Keene	1493 Oliver King	
1781 James Yorke	1496 Richard Redman	BISHOPS OF GLOUCESTER AND
1808 Thomas Dampier	1502 John Arundel	BRISTOL
1812 Bowyer Edward Sparke	1505 Hugh Oldham	1836 James Henry Monk
1836 Joseph Allen	1519 John Veysey (resig.)	1856 Charles Baring
1845 Thomas Turton	1551 Miles Coverdale	1861 William Thomson
1864 Edward Harold Browne	1553 John Veysey (rest.)	1863 Charles John Ellicott[4]
1873 James Russell Woodford	1555 James Turberville	
1886 Alwyne Frederick Compton	1560 William Alley [or Allei]	BISHOPS OF GLOUCESTER
1905 Frederick Henry Chase	1571 William Bradbridge	1897 Charles John Ellicott
1924 Leonard Jauncey White-	1579 John Woolton	1905 Edgar Charles Sumner Gibson
Thomson	1595 Gervase Babington	1923 Arthur Cayley Headlam
1934 Bernard Oliver Francis	1598 William Cotton	1946 Clifford Salisbury Woodward
Heywood	1621 Valentine Carey	1954 Wilfred Marcus Askwith
1941 Harold Edward Wynn	1627 Joseph Hall	1962 Basil Tudor Guy
1957 Noel Baring Hudson	1642 Ralph Brownrigg	1975 John Yates
1964 Edward James Keymer	1660 John Gauden	1991 Peter John Ball
Roberts	1662 Seth Ward	1993 David Edward Bentley
1977 Peter Knight Walker	1667 Anthony Sparrow	
1990 Stephen Whitefield Sykes	1676 Thomas Lamplugh	**Guildford**
	1689 Jonathan Trelawney	
Exeter	1708 Offspring Blackall	1927 John Harold Greig
	1717 Lancelot Blackburn	1934 John Victor Macmillan
BISHOPS OF CORNWALL	1724 Stephen Weston	1949 Henry Colville Montgomery
870 Kenstec	1742 Nicholas Claget	Campbell
893 Asser	1747 George Lavington	1956 Ivor Stanley Watkins
931 Conan	1762 Frederick Keppel	1961 George Edmund Reindorp
950 Æthelge [ard]	1778 John Ross	1973 David Alan Brown
c955 Daniel	1792 William Buller	1983 Michael Edgar Adie
963 Wulfsige Comoere	1797 Henry Reginald Courtenay	1994 John Warren Gladwin
990 Ealdred	1803 John Fisher	
1009 Æthelsige	1807 George Pelham	**Hereford**
1018 Buruhwold	1820 William Carey	
1027 Lyfing, Bp. of Crediton	1830 Christopher Bethell	676 Putta
Cornwall and Worcester	1831 Henry Phillpotts	688 Tyrhtel
		710 Torhthere

[1] Removed See from Crediton.   [2] Also Bishop of Bristol.   [3] Held Gloucester and Bristol 1581-9.   [4] Gloucester only from 1897.

c731 Wahistod	1635 Theophilus Field	964 Wynsige
736 Cuthberht	1636 George Coke	975 Ælfheah
741 Podda	1661 Nicolas Monk	1004 Godwine
c758 Acca	1662 Herbert Croft	1020 Leofgar
c770 Headda	1691 Gilbert Ironside	1026 Brihtmaer
777 Aldberht	1701 Humphrey Humphries	1039 Wulfsige
786 Esne	1713 Philip Bisse	1053 Leofwine
c788 Ceolmund	1721 Benjamin Hoadly	1072 Peter
c798 Utel	1724 Henry Egerton	
801 Wulfheard	1746 James Beauclerk	**BISHOPS OF LICHFIELD,**
824 Beonna	1787 John Harley	**CHESTER, AND COVENTRY**[5]
c832 Eadwulf	1788 John Butler	1075 Peter
c839 Cuthwulf	1803 Ffolliott Herbert Walker	1086 Robert de Limesey[5]
866 Mucel	Cornewall	1121 Robert Peche
c866 Deorlaf	1808 John Luxmoore	1129 Roger de Clinton
888 Cynemund	1815 George Isaac Huntingford	1149 Walter Durdent
890 EadBar	1832 Edward Grey	1161 Richard Peche
c931 Tidhelm	1837 Thomas Musgrave	1183 Gerard La Pucelle
940 Wulfhelm	1848 Renn Dickson Hampden	1188 Hugh Nonant
c940 Ælfric	1868 James Atlay	1198 Geoffrey Muschamp
971 Æthelwulf	1895 John Percival	1215 William Cornhill
1016 Æthelstan	1918 Herbert Hensley Henson	1224 Alex. Stavensby
1056 Leofgar	1920 Martin Linton Smith	1240 Hugh Pattishall
1056 Ealdred, Bp of Hereford and	1931 Charles Lisle Carr	1246 Roger Weseham
Worcester	1941 Richard Godfrey Parsons	1258 Roger Longespee
1060 Walter	1949 Tom Longworth	1296 Walter Langton
1079 Robert Losinga	1961 Mark Allin Hodson	1322 Roger Northburgh
1096 Gerard	1974 John Richard Gordon Eastaugh	1360 Robert Stretton
1107 Reinhelm	1990 John Keith Oliver	1386 Walter Skirlaw
1115 Geoffrey de Clive		1386 Richard le Scrope
1121 Richard de Capella	**Leicester**	1398 John Burghill
1131 Robert de Bethune		1415 John Catterick
1148 Gilbert Foliot	Also *see* Lincoln	1420 William Heyworth
1163 Robert of Melun		1447 William Booth
1174 Robert Foliot	**NEW FOUNDATION**	1452 Nicholas Close
1186 William de Vere		1453 Reginald Boulers
1200 Giles de Braose	1927 Cyril Charles Bowman Bardsley	1459 John Hales
1216 Hugh of Mapenore	1940 Guy Vernon Smith	1493 William Smith
1219 Hugh Foliot	1953 Ronald Ralph Williams	1496 John Arundel
1234 Ralph Maidstone	1979 Cecil Richard Rutt	1503 Geoffrey Blyth
1240 Peter d'Aigueblanche	1991 Thomas Frederick Butler	1534 Rowland Lee
1269 John Breton		1541 [**Chester** formed as a bishopric]
1275 Thomas Cantilupe	**Lichfield**	1543 Richard Sampson
1283 Richard Swinfeld		1554 Ralph Baynes
1317 Adam Orleton	**BISHOPS OF MERCIA**	1560 Thomas Bentham
1327 Thomas Chariton		1580 William Overton
1344 John Trilleck	656 Diuma[1]	1609 George Abbot
1361 Lewis Charleton	658 Ceollach	1610 Richard Neile
1370 William Courtenay	659 Trumhere	1614 John Overall
1375 John Gilbert	662 Jaruman	1619 Thomas Morton
1389 John Trefnant		1632 Robert Wright
1404 Robert Mascall	**BISHOPS OF LICHFIELD**	1644 Accepted Frewen
1417 Edmund Lacy		1661 John Hackett
1420 Thomas Polton	669 Chad[2]	1671 Thomas Wood
1422 Thomas Spofford	672 Winfrith	1692 William Lloyd
1449 Richard Beauchamp	676 Seaxwulf	1699 John Hough
1451 Reginald Boulers	691 Headda[3]	1717 Edward Chandler
1453 John Stanbury	731 Aldwine	1731 Richard Smalbroke
1474 Thomas Milling	737 Hwita	1750 Fred. Cornwallis
1492 Edmund Audley	757 Hemele	1768 John Egerton
1502 Adriano de Castello [di Corneto]	765 Cuthfrith	1771 Brownlow North
1504 Richard Mayeu	769 Berhthun	1775 Richard Hurd
1516 Charles Booth	779 Hygeberht[4]	1781 James Cornwallis
1535 Edward Fox	801 Aldwulf	[4th Earl Cornwallis]
1539 John Skip	816 Herewine	1824 Henry Ryder
1553 John Harley	818 Æthelwald	1836 [Coventry transferred to
1554 Robert Parfew or Wharton	830 Hunberht	Worcester diocese]
1559 John Scory	836 Cyneferth	1836 Samuel Butler
1586 Herbert Westfaling	845 Tunberht	1840 James Bowstead
1603 Robert Bennett	869 Eadberht	1843 John Lonsdale
1617 Francis Godwin	883 Wulfred	1868 George Augustus Selwyn
1634 Augustine Lindsell	900 Wigmund or Wilferth	1878 William Dalrymple Maclagan
1635 Matthew Wren	915 Ælfwine	1891 Augustus Legge
	941 Wulfgar	
	949 Cynesige	

[1] Abp of the Mercians, the Lindisfari, and the Middle Angles.
[2] Bp of the Mercians and Lindisfari.
[3] Bp of Lichfield and Leicester.
[4] Abp of Lichfield after 787.
[5] 1102 Robert de Limesey, Bp of Lichfield, moved the See to Coventry. Succeeding Bishops are usually termed *of Coventry* until 1228. Then *Coventry and Lichfield* was the habitual title until the Reformation. *Chester* was used by some 12th-century Bishops, and popularly afterwards. After the Reformation *Lichfield and Coventry* was used until 1846.

1913 John Augustine Kempthorne
1937 Edward Sydney Woods
1953 Arthur Stretton Reeve
1975 Kenneth John Fraser
       Skelton
1984 Keith Norman Sutton

Lincoln

BISHOPS OF LINDSEY

634 Birinus
650 Agilbert
660 Aetlai
678 Eadhaed
680 Æthelwine
693 (?)Edgar
731 (?)Cyneberht
733 Alwig
750 Aldwulf
767 Ceolwulf
796 Eadwulf
839 Beorhtred
869 Burgheard
933 Ælfred
953 Leofwine
996 Sigefrith

BISHOPS OF LEICESTER

664 Wilfrid, tr. from York
679 Cuthwine
691 Headda[1] (founder of Lichfield
       Cathedral 705-37)
727 Aldwine
737 Torhthelm
764 Eadberht
785 Unwona
803 Wernberht
816 Raethhun
840 Ealdred
844 Ceolred
874 [See of Leicester removed to
       Dorchester]

BISHOPS OF DORCHESTER

(after it became a Mercian See)
c888 Ahlheard
900 Wigmund or Wilferth
909 Cenwulf
925 Wynsige
c951 Osketel
953 Leofwine
975 Ælfnoth
979 Æscwig
1002 Ælfheln
1006 Eadnoth I
1016 Æthelric
1034 Eadnoth II
1049 Ulf
1053 Wulfwig
1067 Remigius

BISHOPS OF LINCOLN

1072 Remigius
1094 Robert Bloett
1123 Alexander
1148 Robert de Chesney
1183 Walter de Coutances
1186 Hugh of Avalon
1203 William of Blois
1209 Hugh of Wells
1235 Robert Grosseteste
1254 Henry Lexington [Sutton]
1258 Richard Gravesend

1280 Oliver Sutton [Lexington]
1300 John Dalderby
1320 Henry Burghersh
1342 Thomas Bek
1347 John Gynewell
1363 John Bokyngham [Buckingham]
1398 Henry Beaufort
1405 Philip Repingdon
1420 Richard Fleming
1431 William Gray
1436 William Alnwick
1450 Marmaduke Lumley
1452 John Chedworth
1472 Thomas Rotherham [Scott]
1480 John Russell
1495 William Smith
1514 Thomas Wolsey
1514 William Atwater
1521 John Longland
1547 Henry Holbeach [Rands]
1552 John Taylor
1554 John White
1557 Thomas Watson
1560 Nicholas Bullingham
1571 Thomas Cooper
1584 William Wickham
1595 William Chaderton
1608 William Barlow
1614 Richard Neile
1617 George Monteigne [Mountain]
1621 John Williams
1642 Thomas Winniffe
1660 Robt. Sanderson
1663 Benjamin Laney
1667 William Fuller
1675 Thomas Barlow
1692 Thomas Tenison
1695 James Gardiner
1705 William Wake
1716 Edmund Gibson
1723 Richard Reynolds
1744 John Thomas
1761 John Green
1779 Thomas Thurlow
1787 George Pretyman [Pretyman
       Tomline after June 1803]
1820 George Pelham
1827 John Kaye
1853 John Jackson
1869 Christopher Wordsworth
1885 Edward King
1910 Edward Lee Hicks
1920 William Shuckburgh Swayne
1933 Frederick Cyril Nugent Hicks
1942 Henry Aylmer Skelton
1946 Leslie Owen
1947 Maurice Henry Harland
1956 Kenneth Riches
1975 Simon Wilton Phipps
1987 Robert Maynard Hardy

Norwich

BISHOPS OF DUNWICH

631 Felix
648 Thomas
c653 Berhtgils [Boniface]
c670 Bisi
c673 Æcce
693 Alric (?)
716 Eardred
731 Aldbeorht I

747 Æscwulf
747 Eardwulf
775 Cuthwine
775 Aldbeorht II
781 Ecglaf
781 Heardred
793 Ælfhun
798 Tidferth
824 Waermund[2]
825 Wilred
836 Husa
870 Æthelwold

BISHOPS OF ELMHAM

673 Beaduwine
706 Nothberht
c731 Heathulac
736 Æthelfrith
758 Eanfrith
c781 Æthelwulf
c785 Alhheard
814 Sibba
824 Hunferth
824 Hunbeorht
836 Cunda[3]
c933 Ælfred[4]
c945 Æthelweald
956 Eadwulf
970 Ælfric I
974 Theodred I
982 Theodred II
997 Æthelstan
1001 Ælfgar
1021 Ælfwine
1038 Ælfric II
1039 Ælfric III
1043 Stigand[5]
1043 Grimketel[6]
1044 Stigand (rest.)
1047 Æthelmaer

BISHOPS OF THETFORD

1070 Herfast
1086 William de Beaufai
1091 Herbert Losinga

BISHOPS OF NORWICH

1091 Herbert Losinga
1121 Everard of Montgomery
1146 William de Turbe
1175 John of Oxford
1200 John de Gray
1222 Pandulf Masca
1226 Thomas Blundeville
1239 William Raleigh
1245 Walter Suffield or Calthorp
1258 Simon Walton
1266 Roger Skerning
1278 William Middleton
1289 Ralph Walpole
1299 John Salmon
1325 [Robert de Baldock]
1325 William Ayermine
1337 Anthony Bek
1344 William of Norwich [Bateman]
1356 Thomas Percy
1370 Henry Spencer [Dispenser]
1407 Alexander Tottington
1413 Richard Courtenay
1416 John Wakeryng
1426 William Ainwick

---

[1] Bp of Leicester and Lichfield.
[2] Bp of Dunwich or Elmham.
[3] Bp of Elmham or Dunwich
[4] Bp of Elmham or Lindsey.
[5] Dep. before consecration.
[6] Bp of Selsey and Elmham.

1436 Thomas Brown	1812 William Jackson	669 Putta
1446 Walter Lyhert [le Hart]	1816 Edward Legge	676 Cwichelm
1472 James Goldwell	1827 Charles Lloyd	678 Gebmund
1499 Thomas Jane	1829 Richard Bagot	716 Tobias
1501 Richard Nykke	1845 Samuel Wilberforce	727 Aldwulf
1536 William Reppes [Rugge]	1870 John Fielder Mackarness	741 Dunn
1550 Thomas Thirlby	1889 William Stubbs	747 Eardwulf
1554 John Hopton	1901 Francis Paget	772 Diora
1560 John Parkhurst	1911 Charles Gore	785 Waermund I
1575 Edmund Freke	1919 Hubert Murray Burge	805 Beornmod
1585 Edmund Scambler	1925 Thomas Banks Strong	844 Tatnoth
1595 William Redman	1937 Kenneth Escott Kirk	868 Badenoth
1603 John Jegon	1955 Harry James Carpenter	868 Waermund II
1618 John Overall	1971 Kenneth John Woollcombe	868 Cuthwulf
1619 Samuel Harsnett	1978 Patrick Campbell Rodger	880 Swithwulf
1629 Francis White	1987 Richard Douglas Harries	900 Ceolmund
1632 Richard Corbet		c926 Cyneferth
1635 Matthew Wren		c934 Burhric
1638 Richard Montagu	## Peterborough	949 Beorhtsige
1641 Joseph Hall		955 [Daniel?] Rochester or Selsey
1661 Edward Reynolds	1541 John Chamber	964 Ælfstan
1676 Antony Sparrow	1557 David Pole	995 Godwine I
1685 William Lloyd	1561 Edmund Scambler	1046 Godwine II
1691 John Moore	1585 Richard Howland	1058 Siward
1708 Charles Trimnell	1601 Thomas Dove	1076 Arnost
1721 Thomas Green	1630 William Piers	1077 Gundulf
1723 John Leng	1633 Augustine Lindsell	1108 Ralph d'Escures
1727 William Baker	1634 Francis Dee	1115 Ernulf
1733 Robert Butts	1639 John Towers	1125 John
1738 Thomas Gooch	1660 Benjamin Laney	1137 John II
1748 Samuel Lisle	1663 Joseph Henshaw	1142 Ascelin
1749 Thomas Hayter	1679 William Lloyd	1148 Walter
1761 Philip Yonge	1685 Thomas White	1182 Waleran
1783 Lewis Bagot	1691 Richard Cumberland	1185 Gilbert Glanvill
1790 George Horne	1718 White Kennett	1215 Benedict of Sausetun [Sawston]
1792 Charles Manners Sutton	1729 Robert Clavering	1227 Henry Sandford
1805 Henry Bathurst	1747 John Thomas	1238 Richard Wendene
1837 Edward Stanley	1757 Richard Terrick	1251 Lawrence of St. Martin
1849 Samuel Hinds	1764 Robert Lambe	1274 Walter Merton
1857 John Thomas Pelham	1769 John Hinchliffe	1278 John Bradfield
1893 John Sheepshanks	1794 Spencer Madan	1283 Thomas Ingoldsthorpe
1910 Bertram Pollock	1813 John Parsons	1292 Thomas of Wouldham
1942 Percy Mark Herbert	1819 Herbert Marsh	1319 Hamo Hethe
1959 William Launcelot Scott	1839 George Davys	1353 John Sheppey
Fleming	1864 Francis Jeune	1362 William of Whittlesey
1971 Maurice Arthur Ponsonby	1868 William Connor Magee	1364 Thomas Trilleck
Wood	1891 Mandell Creighton	1373 Thomas Brinton
1985 Peter John Nott	1897 Edward Carr Glyn	1389 William Bottlesham [Bottisham]
	1916 Frank Theodore Woods	1400 John Bottlesham
## Oxford	1924 Cyril Charles Bowman Bardsley	1404 Richard Young
	1927 Claude Martin Blagden	1419 John Kempe
1542 Robert King[1]	1949 Spencer Stottisbury Gwatkin	1422 John Langdon
1558 [Thomas Goldwell]	Leeson	1435 Thomas Brouns
1567 Hugh Curen [Curwen]	1956 Robert Wright Stopford	1437 William Wells
1589 John Underhill	1961 Cyril Eastaugh	1444 John Low
1604 John Bridges	1972 Douglas Russell Feaver	1468 Thomas Rotherham [otherwise
1619 John Howson	1984 William John Westwood	Scott]
1628 Richard Corbet		1472 John Alcock
1632 John Bancroft	## Portsmouth	1476 John Russell
1641 Robert Skinner		1480 Edmund Audley
1663 William Paul	1927 Ernest Neville Lovett	1493 Thomas Savage
1665 Walter Blandford	1936 Frank Partridge	1497 Richard Fitz-James
1671 Nathaniel Crewe [Lord Crewe]	1942 William Louis Anderson	1504 John Fisher
1674 Henry Compton	1949 William Launcelot Scott	1535 John Hilsey [Hildesleigh]
1676 John Fell	Fleming	1540 Nicolas Heath
1686 Samuel Parker	1960 John Henry Lawrence Phillips	1544 Henry Holbeach
1688 Timothy Hall	1975 Archibald Ronald McDonald	1547 Nicholas Ridley
1690 John Hough	Gordon	1550 John Ponet [Poynet]
1699 William Talbot	1984 Timothy John Bavin	1551 John Scory
1715 John Potter	1995 Kenneth William Stevenson	1554 Maurice Griffith
1737 Thomas Secker		1560 Edmund Gheast [Guest]
1758 John Hume		1572 Edmund Freke
1766 Robert Lowth	## Rochester	1576 John Piers
1777 John Butler		1578 John Young
1788 Edward Smallwell	604 Justus	1605 William Barlow
1799 John Randolph	624 Romanus	1608 Richard Neile
1807 Charles Moss	633 Paulinus	1611 John Buckeridge
	644 Ithamar	
	664 Damianus	

[1] Bp Rheon. *in partibus*. Of Oseney 1542-5. See transferred to Oxford 1545

1628 Walter Curil
1630 John Bowle
1638 John Warner
1666 John Dolben
1683 Francis Turner
1684 Thomas Sprat
1713 Francis Atterbury
1723 Samuel Bradford
1731 Joseph Wilcocks
1756 Zachary Pearce
1774 John Thomas
1793 Samuel Horsley
1802 Thomas Dampier
1809 Walker King
1827 Hugh Percy
1827 George Murray
1860 Joseph Cotton Wigram
1867 Thomas Legh Claughton
1877 Anthony Wilson Thorold
1891 Randall Thomas Davidson
1895 Edward Stuart Talbot
1905 John Reginald Harmer
1930 Manin Linton Smith
1940 Christopher Maude Chavasse
1961 Richard David Say
1988 Anthony Michael Arnold
     Turnhull
1994 Michael James Nazir-Ali

St Albans

1877 Thomas Legh Claughton
1890 John Wogan Festing
1903 Edgar Jacob
1920 Michael Bolton Furse
1944 Philip Henry Loyd
1950 Edward Michael Gresford Jones
1970 Robert Alexander Kennedy
     Runcie
1980 John Bernard Taylor

St Edmundsbury and Ipswich

1914 Henry Bernard Hodgson
1921 Albert Augustus David
1923 Walter Godfrey Whittingham
1940 Richard Brook
1954 Arthur Harold Morris
1966 Leslie Wilfrid Brown
1978 John Waine
1986 John Dennis

Salisbury

BISHOPS OF SHERBORNE
 705 Ealdhelm
 709 Forthhere
 736 Hereweald
 774 Æthelmod
 793 Denefrith
 801 Wigberht
 825 Ealhstan
 868 Heahmund
 877 Æthelheah
 889 Wulfsige I
 900 Asser
c909 Æthelweard
c909 Waerstan
 925 Æthelbald
 925 Sigehelm
 934 Ælfred
 943 Wulfsige II
 958 Ælfwold I
 979 Æthelsige I
 992 Wulfsige III
1002 Æthelric
1012 Æthelsige II
1017 Brihtwine I

1017 Ælfmaer
1023 Brihtwine II
1045 Ælfwold II
1058 Hereman, Bp of Ramsbury

BISHOPS OF RAMSBURY
 909 Æthelstan
 927 Oda
 949 Ælfric I
 951 Osulf
 970 Ælfstan
 981 Wulfgar
 986 Sigeric
 993 Ælfric II
1005 Brihtwold
1045 Hereman[1]

BISHOPS OF SALISBURY
1078 Osmund
     Osmer
1107 Roger
1142 Jocelin de Bohun
1189 Hubert Walter
1194 Herbert Poore
1217 Richard Poore
1229 Robert Bingham
1247 William of York
1257 Giles of Bridport
1263 Walter de la Wyle
1274 Robert Wickhampton
1284 Walter Scammel
1287 Henry Brandeston
1289 William de la Corner
1292 Nicholas Longespee
1297 Simon of Ghent
1315 Roger de Mortival
1330 Robert Wyville
1375 Ralph Erghum
1388 John Waltham
1395 Richard Mitford
1407 Nicholas Bubwith
1407 Robert Hallum
1417 John Chaundler
1427 Robert Nevill
1438 William Aiscough
1450 Richard Beauchamp
1482 Lionel Woodville
1485 Thomas Langton
1494 John Blythe
1500 Henry Deane
1502 Edmund Audley
1525 Lorenzo Campeggio
1535 Nicholas Shaxton
1539 John Salcot [Capon]
1560 John Jewell
1571 Edmund Gheast [Guest]
1577 John Piers
1591 John Coldwell
1598 Henry Cotton
1615 Robert Abbot
1618 Martin Fotherby
1620 Robert Townson [Toulson]
1621 John Davenant
1641 Brian Duppa
1660 Humfrey Henchman
1663 John Earle
1665 Alexander Hyde
1667 Seth Ward
1689 Gilbert Burnet
1715 William Talbot
1721 Richard Wilis
1723 Benjamin Hoadly
1734 Thomas Sherlock
1748 John Gilbert
1757 John Thomas
1761 Robert Hay Drummond
1761 John Thomas
1766 John Hume

1782 Shute Barrington
1791 John Douglas
1807 John Fisher
1825 Thomas Burgess
1837 Edward Denison
1854 Walter Kerr Hamilton
1869 George Moberly
1885 John Wordsworth
1911 Frederic Edward Ridgeway
1921 St. Clair George Alfred
     Donaldson
1936 Ernest Neville Lovett
1946 Geoffrey Charles Lester Lunt
1949 William Louis Anderson
1963 Joseph Edward Fison
1973 George Edmund Reindorp
1982 John Austin Baker
1993 David Staffurth Stancliffe

Southwark

1905 Edward Stuart Talbot
1911 Hubert Murray Burge
1919 Cyril Forster Garbett
1932 Richard Godfrey Parsons
1942 Bertram Fitzgerald Simpson
1959 Arthur Mervyn Stockwood
1981 Ronald Oliver Bowlby
1991 Robert Kerr Williamson

Truro

1877 Edward White Benson
1883 Geo. Howard Wilkinson
1891 John Gott
1906 Charles William Stubbs
1912 Winfrid Oldfield Burrows
1919 Frederic Sumpter Guy Warman
1923 Walter Howard Frere
1935 Joseph Wellington Hunkin
1951 Edmund Robert Morgan
1960 John Maurice Key
1973 Graham Douglas Leonard
1981 Peter Mumford
1990 Michael Thomas Ball

Worcester

 680 Bosel
 691 Oftfor
 693 Ecgwine
 718 Wilfrid I
 745 Milred
 775 Waermund
 777 Tilhere
 781 Heathured
 798 Deneberht
 822 Heahberht
 845 Alhhun
 873 Waerferth
 915 Æthelhun
 922 Wilferth II
 929 Cenwald
 957 Dunstan
 961 Oswald
 992 Ealdwulf
1002 Wulfstan I
1016 Leofsige
1027 Lyfing
1033 Brihtheah
1040 Æltric Puttoc, Bp of York and
     Worcester
1041 Lyfing (restored)
1046 Ealdred Bp of Hereford and
     Worcester 1056-60
1062 Wulfstan II
1096 Samson

[1] Ramsbury was added to Sherborne in 1058 when Hereman became Bishop of Sherborne. The See was moved to Salisbury in 1078.

1115 Theulf	1375 Henry Wakefield	1641 John Prideaux
1125 Simon	1396 Robert Tideman of Winchcomb	1660 George Morley
1151 John of Pagham	1401 Richard Clifford	1662 John Gauden
1158 Aldred	1407 Thomas Peverel	1662 John Earle
1164 Roger of Gloucester	1419 Philip Morgan	1663 Robert Skinner
1180 Baldwin	1426 Thomas Polton	1671 Walter Blandford
1186 William of Northolt	1435 Thomas Bourgchier	1675 James Fleetwood
1191 Robert Fitz Ralph	1444 John Carpenter	1683 William Thomas
1193 Henry de Sully	1476 John Alcock	1689 Edward Stillingfleet
1196 John of Coutances	1487 Robert Morton	1699 William Lloyd
1200 Mauger	1497 Giovanni de' Gigli	1717 John Hough
1214 Walter de Gray	1499 Silvestro de' Gigli	1743 Isaac Maddox
1216 Silvester of Evesham	1521 Julius de Medici Guilio de	1759 James Johnson
1218 William of Blois	Medici [admin.]	1774 Brownlow North
1237 Walter Cantilupe	1523 Geronimo Ghinucci	1781 Richard Hurd
1266 Nicolas of Ely	1535 Hugh Latimer	1808 Ffoliott Herbert Walker
1268 Godfrey Giffard	1539 John Bell	Cornewall
1302 Walter Gainsborough	1544 Nicholas Heath (dep.)	1831 Robert James Carr
1308 Walter Reynolds	1552 John Hooper	1841 Henry Pepys
1313 Walter Maidstone	1554 Nicholas Heath (rest.)	1861 Henry Philpott
1317 Thomas Cobham	1555 Richard Pates	1891 John James Stewart Perowne
1327 Adam Orleton	1559 Edwin Sandys	1902 Charles Gore
1334 Simon Montacute	1571 Nicholas Bullingham	1905 Huyshe Wolcott Yeatman-Biggs
1337 Thomas Hempnall	1577 John Whitgift	1919 Ernest Harold Pearce
1339 Wulstan Bransford	1584 Edmund Freke	1931 Arthur William Thomson
1350 John Thoresby	1593 Richard Fletcher	Perowne
1353 Reginald Brian	1596 Thomas Bilson	1941 William Wilson Cash
1362 John Barnet	1597 Gervase Babington	1956 Lewis Mervyn Charles-Edwards
1364 William of Whittlesey	1610 Henry Parry	1970 Robert Wylmer Woods
1369 William Lenn	1617 John Thornborough	1982 Philip Harold Ernest Goodrich

PROVINCE OF YORK

York

BISHOPS

314 Eborius	1256 Sewal de Bovill	1743 Thomas Herring
625 Paulinus	1258 Godfrey Ludham [Kineton]	1747 Matthew Hutton
[Vacancy 633-64]	1266 Walter Giffard	1757 John Gilben
664 Cedda	1279 William Wickwane	1761 Roben Hay Drummond
664 Wilfrid I	1286 John Romanus [le Romeyn]	1777 William Markham
678 Bosa (ret.)	1298 Henry Newark	1808 Edward Venables Vernon
686 Bosa (rest.)	1300 Thomas Corbridge	Harcourt
691 Wilfrith (rest.)	1306 William Greenfield	1847 Thomas Musgrave
706 John of Beverley	1317 William Melton	1860 Charles Thos. Longley
718 Wilfrid II	1342 William de la Zouche	1863 William Thomson
	1352 John Thoresby	1891 William Connor Magee
ARCHBISHOPS	1374 Alexander Neville	1891 William Dalrymple Maclagan
	1388 Thomas Arundel	1909 Cosmo Gordon Lang
734 Egberht	1396 Robert Waldby	1929 William Temple
767 Æthelberht	1398 Richard le Scrope	1942 Cyril Forster Garbett
780 Eanbald I	1407 Henry Bowet	1956 Anhur Michael Ramsey
796 Eanbald II	1426 John Kempe	1961 Frederick Donald Coggan
808 Wulfsige	1452 William Booth	1975 Stuart Yarwonh Blanch
837 Wigmund	1464 George Nevill	1983 John Stapylton Habgood
854 Wulfhere	1476 Lawrence Booth	1995 David Michael Hope
900 Æthelbald	1480 Thomas Rotherham [Scott]	
c928 Hrothweard	1501 Thomas Savage	## Durham
931 Wulfstan I	1508 Christopher Bainbridge	
956 Osketel	1514 Thomas Wolsey	**BISHOPS OF LINDISFARNE[2]**
971 Oswald	1531 Edward Lee	635 Aidan
971 Edwald	1545 Robert Holgate	651 Finan
992 Ealdwulf[1]	1555 Nicholas Heath	661 Colman
1003 Wulfstan II	1561 Thomas Young	664 Tuda
1023 Ælfric Puttoc	1570 Edmund Grindal	[Complications involving Wilfrid and
1041 Æthelric	1577 Edwin Sandys	Chad]
1051 Cynesige	1589 John Piers	681 Eata
1061 Ealdred	1595 Matthew Hutton	685 Cuthberht
1070 Thomas I of Bayeux	1606 Tobias Matthew	[Vacancy during which Wilfrid
1100 Gerard	1628 George Montaigne [Mountain]	administered the see]
1109 Thomas II	1629 Samuel Harsnett	688 Eadberht
1119 Thurstan	1632 Richard Neile	698 Eadfenh
1143 William Fitzherbert	1641 John Williams	731 Æthelweald
1147 Henry Murdac	1660 Accepted Frewen	740 Cynewulf
1153 William Fitzherbert (rest.)	1664 Richard Sterne	781 Higbald
1154 Roger of Pont l'Eveque	1683 John Dolben	803 Ecgberht
1191 Geoffrey Plantagenet	1688 Thomas Lamplugh	821 Heathwred
1215 Walter de Gray	1691 John Sharp	830 Ecgred
	1714 William Dawes	845 Eanberht
	1724 Lancelot Blackburn	854 Eardwulf

[1] Ealdwulf and Wulfstan II held the Sees of York and Worcester together. Ælfric Puttoc held both 1040-1 and Ealdred 106-1.
[2] See transferred to Chester-le-Street 883.

BISHOPS OF HEXHAM

- 664 Wilfrith
- 678 Eata
- 681 Tunberht
- 684 Cuthbert
- 685 Eata (rest.)
- 687 John of Beverley
- 709 Acca
- 734 Frithoberht
- 767 Ahimund
- 781 Tilberht
- 789 Æthelberht
- 797 Heardred
- 800 Eanberht
- 813 Tidferth

BISHOPS OF CHESTER-LE-STREET[1]

- 899 Eardwulf
- 899 Cutheard
- 915 Tilred
- 925 Wigred
- 944 Uhtred
- 944 Seaxhelm
- 944 Ealdred
- 968 Ælfsige
- 990 Aldhun

BISHOPS OF DURHAM

- 990 Aldhun d. 1018
- [See vacant 1018-1020]
- 1020 Edmund
- c1040 Eadred
- 1041 Æthelric
- 1056 Æthelwine
- 1071 Walcher
- 1081 William of Saint Calais
- 1099 Ralph [Ranulf] Flambard
- 1133 Geoffrey Rufus
- 1143 William of Sainte-Barbe
- 1153 Hugh of le Puiset
- 1197 Philip of Poitiers
- 1217 Richard Marsh
- 1228 Richard Poore
- 1241 Nicholas Farnham
- 1249 Walter Kirkham
- 1261 Robert Stichill
- 1274 Robert of Holy Island
- 1284 Anthony Bek
- 1311 Richard Kellaw
- 1318 Lewis de Beaumont
- 1333 Richard of Bury
- 1345 Thomas Hatfield
- 1382 John Fordham
- 1388 Walter Skirlaw
- 1406 Thomas Langley
- 1438 Robert Nevill
- 1457 Lawrence Booth
- 1476 William Dudley
- 1485 John Shirwood
- 1494 Richard Fox
- 1502 William Senhouse [Sever]
- 1507 Christopher Bainbridge
- 1509 Thomas Ruthall
- 1523 Thomas Wolsey
- 1530 Cuthbert Tunstall
- 1561 James Pilkington
- 1577 Richard Barnes
- 1589 Matthew Hutton
- 1595 Tobias Matthew
- 1606 William James
- 1617 Richard Neile
- 1628 George Montaigne [Mountain]
- 1628 John Howson
- 1632 Thomas Morton
- 1660 John Cosin
- 1674 Nathaniel Crew [Lord Crew]

- 1721 William Talbot
- 1730 Edward Chandler
- 1750 Joseph Butler
- 1752 Richard Trevor
- 1771 John Egerton
- 1787 Thomas Thurlow
- 1791 Shute Barrington
- 1826 William Van Mildert
- 1836 Edward Maltby
- 1856 Chaarles Thomas Longley
- 1860 Henry Montague Villiers
- 1861 Charles Baring
- 1879 Joseph Barber Lightfoot
- 1890 Brooke Foss Westcott
- 1901 Handley Carr Glyn Moule
- 1920 Herbert Hensley Henson
- 1939 Alwyn Terrell Petre Williams
- 1952 Arthur Michael Ramsey
- 1956 Maurice Henry Harland
- 1966 Lan Thomas Ramsey
- 1973 John Stapylton Habgood
- 1984 David Edward Jenkins
- 1994 Anthony Michael Arnold Turnbull

Blackburn

- 1926 Percy Mark Herbert
- 1942 Wilfred Marcus Askwith
- 1954 Walter Hubert Baddeley
- 1960 Charles Robert Claxton
- 1972 Robert Arnold Schürhoff Martineau
- 1982 David Stewart Cross
- 1989 Alan David Chesters

Bradford

- 1920 Arthur William Thomson Perowne
- 1931 Alfred Walter Frank Blunt
- 1956 Frederick Donald Coggan
- 1961 Clement George St. Michael Parker
- 1972 Ross Sydney Hook
- 1981 Geoffrey John Paul
- 1984 Robert KerrWilliamson
- 1992 David James Smith

Carlisle

- 1133 Æthelwulf
- 1203 Bernard
- 1219 Hugh of Beaulieu
- 1224 Walter Mauclerc
- 1247 Silvester Everdon
- 1255 Thomas Vipont
- 1258 Robert de Chause
- 1280 Ralph Ireton
- 1292 John of Halton
- 1325 John Ross
- 1332 John Kirkby
- 1353 Gilbert Welton
- 1363 Thomas Appleby
- 1396 Robert Reade
- 1397 Thomas Merks
- 1400 William Strickland
- 1420 Roger Whelpdale
- 1424 William Barrow
- 1430 Marmaduke Lumley
- 1450 Nicholas Close
- 1452 William Percy
- 1462 John Kingscote
- 1464 Richard le Scrope
- 1468 Edward Story
- 1478 Richard Bell
- 1496 William Senhouse [Sever]

- 1504 Roger Layburne
- 1508 John Penny
- 1521 John Kite
- 1537 Robert Aldrich
- 1556 Owen Oglethorpe
- 1561 John Best
- 1570 Richard Barnes
- 1577 John May
- 1598 Henry Robinson
- 1616 Robert Snowden
- 1621 Richard Milbourne
- 1624 Richard Senhouse
- 1626 Francis White
- 1629 Barnabas Potter
- 1642 James Ussher
- 1660 Richard Sterne
- 1664 Edward Rainbowe
- 1684 Thomas Smith
- 1702 William Nicolson
- 1718 Samuel Bradford
- 1723 John Waugh
- 1735 George Fleming
- 1747 Richard Osbaldeston
- 1762 Charles Lyttleton
- 1769 Edmund Law
- 1787 John Douglas
- 1791 Edward Venables Vernon [Harcourt]
- 1808 Samuel Goodenough
- 1827 Hugh Percy
- 1856 Henry Montagu Villiers
- 1860 Samuel Waldegrave
- 1869 Harvey Goodwin
- 1892 John Wareing Bardsley
- 1905 John William Diggle
- 1920 Henry Herbert Williams
- 1946 Thomas Bloomer
- 1966 Sydney Cyril Bulley
- 1972 Henry David Halsey
- 1989 Lan Harland

Chester

- 1541 John Bird
- 1554 George Cotes
- 1556 Cuthbert Scott
- 1561 William Downham
- 1579 William Chaderton
- 1595 Hugh Bellott
- 1597 Richard Vaughan
- 1604 George Lloyd
- 1616 Thomas Morton
- 1619 John Bridgeman
- 1660 Brian Walton
- 1662 Henry Ferne
- 1662 George Hall
- 1668 John Wilkins
- 1673 John Pearson
- 1686 Thomas Cartwright
- 1689 Nicolas Stratford
- 1708 William Dawes
- 1714 Francis Gastrell
- 1726 Samuel Peploe
- 1752 Edmund Keene
- 1771 William Markham
- 1777 Beilby Porteus
- 1788 William Cleaver
- 1800 Henry William Majendie
- 1810 Bowyer Edward Sparke
- 1812 George Henry Law
- 1824 Charles James Blomfield
- 1828 John Bird Sumner
- 1848 John Graham
- 1865 William Jacobson
- 1884 William Stubbs
- 1889 Francis John Jayne
- 1919 Henry Luke Paget

---

[1] See transferred to Durham 995.

1932 Geoffrey Francis Fisher
1939 Douglas Henry Crick
1955 Gerald Alexander Ellison
1974 Hubert Victor Whitsey
1982 Michael Alfred Baughen

Liverpool

1880 John Charles Ryle
1900 Francis James Chavasse
1923 Albert Augustus David
1944 Clifford Arthur Martin
1966 Stuart Yarworth Blanch
1975 David Stuart Sheppard

Manchester

1848 James Prince Lee
1870 James Fraser
1886 James Moorhouse
1903 Edmund Arbuthnott Knox
1921 William Temple
1929 Frederic Sumpter Guy Warman
1947 William Derrick Lindsay Greer
1970 Patrick Campbell Rodger
1978 Stanley Eric Francis Booth-
       Clibborn
1993 Christopher John Mayfield

Newcastle

1882 Ernest Roland Wilberforce
1896 Edgar Jacob
1903 Arthur Thomas Lloyd
1907 Norman Dumenil John Straton
1915 Herbert Louis Wild
1927 Harold Ernest Bilbrough
1941 Noel Baring Hudson
1957 Hugh Edward Ashdown
1973 Ronald Oliver Bowlby
1981 Andrew Alexander Kenny
       Graham

Ripon

c678 Eadheath

NEW FOUNDATION
1836 Charles Thomas Longley
1857 Robert Bickersteth
1884 William Boyd Carpenter
1912 Thomas Wortley Drury
1920 Thomas Banks Strong
1926 Edward Arthur Burroughs
1935 Geoffrey Charles Lester Lunt
1946 George Armitage Chase
1959 John Richard Humpidge
       Moorman
1975 Stuart Hetley Price
1977 David Nigel de Lorentz Young

Sheffield

1914 Leonard Hedley Burrows
1939 Leslie Stannard Hunter
1962 Francis John Taylor
1971 William Gordon Fallows
1980 David Ramsay Lunn

Sodor and Man[1]

447 Germanus
      Conindrius
      Romulus
      Machutus
      Conanus
      Contentus
      Baldus
      Malchus
      Torkinus
      Brendanus
[Before 1080 Roolwer]
      William
      Hamond
1113 Wimund
1151 John
1160 Gamaliel
      Ragnald
      Christian of Argyle
      Michael
1203 Nicholas de Meaux
      Nicholas II
1217 Reginald
1226 John
1229 Simon of Argyle
1252 Richard
1275 Mark of Galloway
1305 Alan
1321 Gilbert Maclean
1329 Bernard de Linton
1334 Thomas
1348 William Russell
1387 John Donegan
1387 Michael
1392 John Sproten
1402 Conrad
1402 Theodore Bloc
1429 Richard Messing Andrew
1435 John Seyre
1455 Thomas Burton
1458 Thomas Kirklam
1472 Angus
1478 Richard Oldham
1487 Hugh Blackleach
1513 Hugh Hesketh
1523 John Howden
1546 Henry Man
1556 Thomas Stanley
1570 John Salisbury
1576 John Meyrick
1600 George Lloyd
1605 John Philips
1634 William Forster
1635 Richard Parr

1661 Samuel Rutter
1663 Isaac Barrow
1671 Henry Bridgman
1683 John Lake
1685 Baptist Levinz
1698 Thomas Wilson
1755 Mark Hildesley
1773 Richard Richmond
1780 George Mason
1784 Claudius Crigan
1814 George Murray
1828 William Ward
1838 James Bowstead
1840 Henry Pepys
1841 Thomas Vowler Short
1847 Walter Augustus Shirley
1847 Robert John Eden
1854 Horatio Powys
1877 Rowley Hill
1887 John Wareing Bardsley
1892 Norman Dumenil John Straton
1907 Thomas Wortley Drury
1912 James Denton Thompson
1925 Charles Leonard Thornton-
       Duesbery
1928 William Stanton Jones
1943 John Ralph Strickland Taylor
1954 Benjamin Pollard
1966 George Eric Gordon
1974 Vernon Sampson Nicholls
1983 Arthur Henry Attwell
1989 Noel Debroy Jones

Southwell

1884 George Ridding
1904 Edwyn Hoskyns
1926 Bernard Oliver Francis
       Heywood
1928 Henry Mosley
1941 Frank Russell Barry
1964 Gordon David Savage
1970 John Denis Wakeling
1985 Michael Humphrey Dickens
       Whinney
1988 Patrick Burnet Harris

Wakefield

1888 William Walsham How
1897 George Rodney Eden
1928 James Buchanan Seaton
1938 Campbell Richard Hone
1946 Henry McGowan
1949 Roger Plumpton Wilson
1958 John Alexander Ramsbotham
1968 Eric Treacy
1976 Colin Clement Walter James
1985 David Michael Hope
1991 Nigel Simeon McCullough

[1] Included in the province of York by Act of Parliament 1542. Prior to Richard Oldham there is some uncertainty as to several names and dates. From 1425 to 1553 there was an English and Scottish succession. It is not easy to say which claimant was Bishop either *de jure* or *de facto*.

BISHOPS SUFFRAGAN IN ENGLAND

Aston (Birmingham)
1954 Clement George St Michael
       Parker
1962 David Brownfield Porter
1972 Mark Green
1982 Michael Humphrey Dickens
       Whinney

1985 Colin Ogilvie Buchanan
1989-92 no appointment
1992 John Michael Austin

Barking (Chelmsford)
[in St Albans diocese to 1914]
1901 Thomas Stevens

1919 James Theodore Inskip
1948 Hugh Rowlands Gough
1959 William Frank Percival
       Chadwick
1975 Albert James Adams
1983 James William Roxburgh
1991 Roger Frederick Sainsbury

Barrow-in-Furness (Carlisle)

1889 Henry Ware
1909 Campbell West-Watson
1926 Henry Sidney Pelham
1944 in abeyance

Basingstoke (Winchester)

1973 Colin Clement Walter James
1977 Michael Richard John
      Manktelow
1993 Douglas Geoffrey Rowell

Bedford (St Albans)

1537 John Hodgkins[1]
1560-1879 in abeyance
1879 William Walsham How[2]
1888 Robert Claudius Billing[3]
1898-1935 in abeyance
1935 James Lumsden Barkway
1939 Aylmer Skelton
1948 Claude Thomas Thellusson
      Wood
1953 Angus Campbell MacInnes
1957 Basil Tudor Guy
1963 John Albert Trillo
1968 John Tyrrell Holmes Hare
1977 Andrew Alexander Kenny
      Graham
1981 David John Farmbrough
1993 John Henry Richardson

Berwick (Durham)

1536 Thomas Sparke
1572 in abeyance

Beverley (York)

1889 Robert Jarratt Crosthwaite
1923 in abeyance
1994 John Scott Gaisford

Birkenhead (Chester)

1965 Eric Arthur John Mercer
1974 Ronald Brown
1992 Michael Laurence Langrish

Bolton (Manchester)

1984 David George Galliford
1991 David Bonser

Bradwell (Chelmsford)

1968 William Neville Welch
1973 John Gibbs
1976 Charles Derek Bond
1992 Laurence Alexander Green

Bristol (Worcester)

1538 Henry Holbeach [Rands]
1542 became diocesan see

Brixworth (Peterborough)

1989 Paul Everard Barber

Buckingham (Oxford)

1914 Edward Domett Shaw
1921 Philip Herbert Eliot

1944 Roben Milton Hay
1960 Gordon David Savage
1964 George Christopher Cutts Pepys
1974 Simon Hedley Burrows
1994 Colin James Bennetts

Burnley (Blackburn)

[in Manchester diocese to 1926]
1901 Edwyn Hoskyns
1905 Alfred Pearson
1909 Henry Henn
1931 Edgar Priestley Swain
1950 Charles Keith Kipling Prosser
1955 George Edward Holderness
1970 Richard Charles Challinor
      Watson
1988 Ronald James Milner
1994 Martyn William Jarrett

Colchester (Chelmsford)

[in London diocese to 1845

in Rochester diocese to 1877
in St Albans diocese 1877-1914]
1536 William More
1541-91 in abeyance
1592 John Sterne
1608-1882 in abeyance
1882 Alfred Blomfield
1894 Henry Frank Johnson
1909 Robert Henry Whitcombe
1922 Thomas Alfred Chapman
1933 Charles Henry Ridsdale
1946 Frederick Dudley Vaughan
      Narborough
1966 Roderic Norman Coote
1988 Michael Edwin Vickers
1994 Edward Holland

Coventry (Worcester)

See also under Lichfield

1891 Henry Bond Bowlby
1894 Edmund Arbuthnott Knox
1903-18 no appointment
1918 became diocesan see

Crediton (Exeter)

1897 Robert Edward Trefusis
1930 William Frederick Surtees
1954 Wilfred Arthur Edmund Westall
1974 Philip John Pasterfield
1984 Peter Everard Coleman

Croydon (Southwark)

(in Canterbury diocese to 1985)

1904 Henry Horace Pereira
1924-1930 no appointment
1930 Edward Sydney Woods
1937 William Louis Anderson
1942 Maurice Henry Harland
1947 Cuthbert Killick Norman
      Bardsley
1957 John Taylor Hughes
1977 Geoffrey Stuart Snell
1985 Wilfred Denniston Wood

Derby (Southwell)

1889 Edward Ash Were
1909 Charles Thomas Abraham
1927 became diocesan see

Doncaster (Sheffield)

1972 Stuart Hetley Price
1976 David Stewart Cross
1982 William Michael Dermot
      Persson
1992 Michael Frederick Gear

Dorchester (Oxford)

*See also under Dorchester (diocesan
      see) and Lincoln*

1939 Gerald Burton Allen
1952 Kenneth Riches
1957 David Goodwin Loveday
1972 Peter Knight Walker
1979 Conrad John Eustace Meyer
1988 Anthony John Russell

Dorking (Guildford)

(in Winchester diocese to 1909)

1905 Cecil Henry Boutflower
1909-68 in abeyance
1968 Kenneth Dawson Evans
1986 David Peter Wilcox

Dover (Canterbury)

1537 Richard Yngworth
1545 Richard Thornden
1557-69 no appointment
1569 Richard Rogers
1597-1870 in abeyance
1870 Edward Parry
1890 George Rodney Eden
1898 William Walsh
1916 Harold Ernest Bilbrough
1927 John Victor Macmillan
1935 Alfred Careywollaston Rose
1957 Lewis Evan Meredith
1964 Anthony Paul Tremlett
1980 Richard Henry McPhail Third
1992 John Richard Allan Llewellin

Dudley (Worcester)

1974 Michael Ashley Mann
1977 Anthony Charles Dumper
1993 Rupert William Noel Hoare

Dunwich (St Edmundsbury and Ipswich)

See also under Norwich

1934 Maxwell Homfray Maxwell-
      Gumbleton
1945 Clement Mallory Ricketts
1955 Thomas Herbert Cashmore
1967 David Rokeby Maddock
1977 William Johnston
1980 Eric Nash Devenport
1992 Jonathan Sansbury Bailey

Ebbsfleet (Canterbury)

1994 John Richards

Edmonton (London)

1970 Alan Francis Bright Rogers
1975 William John Westwood
1985 Brian John Masters

---

[1] Appointed for the diocese of London
[2] Appointed for the diocese of London
[3] Appointed for the diocese of London, and retained title after resigning his suffragan duties in 1895
[4] From 1926 To 1980 Exercised the Bishop of London's extra-diocesan jurisdiction over chaplaincies in Northern and Central Europe

Fulham (London)[4]

1926 Basil Staunton Batty
1947 William Marshall Selwyn
1949 George Ernest Ingle
1955 Robert Wright Stopford
1957 Roderic Norman Coote
1966 Alan Francis Bright Rogers
1970 John Richard Satterthwaite[1]
1980-1982 no appointment
1982 Brian John Masters
1985 John Klyberg

Grantham (Lincoln)

1905 Welbore MacCarthy
1920 John Edward Hine
1930 Ernest Morell Blackie
1935 Arthur Ivan Greaves
1937 Algernon Augustus Markham
1949 Anthony Otter
1965 Ross Sydney Hook
1972 Dennis Gascoyne Hawker
1987 William Ind

Grimsby (Lincoln)

1935 Ernest Morell Blackie
1937 Anhur Ivan Greaves
1958 Kenneth Healey
1966 Gerald Fitzmaurice Colin
1979 David Tustin

Guildford (Winchester)

1874 John Sutton Utterton
1888 George Henry Sumner
1909 John Hugh Granville Randolph
1927 *became diocesan see*

Hertford (St Albans)

1968 Albert John Trillo
1971 Hubert Victor Whitsey
1974 Peter Mumford
1982 Kenneth Harold Pillar
1990 Robin Smith

Horsham (Chichester)

1968 Simon Wilton Phipps
1975 Ivor Colin Docker
1991 John William Hind
1993 Lindsay Goodall Urwin

Hull (York)

1538 Robert Sylvester (Pursglove)
1579-1891 in abeyance
1891 Richard Frederick Lefevre Blunt
1910 John Augustus Kempthome
1913 Francis Gurdon
1929-31 no appointment
1931 Bemard Oliver Francis
     Heywood
1934 Henry Townsend Vodden
1957 George Fredenck Townley
1965 Hubert Laurence Higgs
1977 Geoffrey John Paul
1981 Donald George Snelgrove
1994 James Stuart Jones

Hulme (Manchester)

1924 John Charles Hill
1930 Thomas Sherwood Jones

1945 Hugh Leycester Homby
1953 Kenneth Venner Ramsey
1975 David George Galliford
1984 Colin John Fraser Scott

Huntingdon (Ely)

1966 Robert Amold Schürhoff
     Martineau
1972 Eric St Quintin Wall
1980 William Gordon Roe

Ipswich (Norwich)

1536 Thomas Manning[2]
?-1899 in abeyance[3]
1899 George Carnac Fisher
1906 Henry Luke Paget
1909 *No appointment*
1914 *became diocesan see with*
     St Edmundsbury

Islington (London)

1898 Charles Henry Tumer
1923 in abeyance

Jarrow (Durham)

1906 George Nickson
1914 John Nathaniel Quirk
1924 Samuel Kirshbaum Knight
1932 James Geoffrey Gordon
1939 Leslie Owen
1944 David Colin Dunlop
1950 John Alexander Ramsbotham
1958 Mervyn Armstrong
1965 Alexander Kenneth Hamilton
1980 Michael Thomas Ball
1990 Alan Smithson

Kensington (London)

1901 Frederic Edward Ridgeway
1911 John Primatt Maud
1932 Bertram Fitzgerald Simpson
1942 Henry Colville Montgomery
     Campbell
1949 Cyril Eastaugh
1962 Edward James Keymer Roberts
1964 Ronald Cedric Osbourne
     Goodchild
1981 Mark Santer
1987 John Hughes
1994 no appointment

Kingston upon Thames (Southwark)

1905 Cecil Hook
1915 Samuel Mumford Taylor
1922 Percy Mark Herbert
1927 Frederick Ochterlony Taylor
     Hawkes
1952 Wiiliam Percy Gilpin
1970 Hugh William Montefiore
1978 Keith Norman Sutton
1984 Peter Stephen Maurice Selby
1992 John Martin Wharton

Knaresborough (Ripon)

1905 Lucius Fredenck Moses
     Bottomley Smith
1934 Paul Fulcrand Dalacour de
     Labilliere

1938 John Norman Bateman-
     Champain
1948 Henry Handley Vully de
     Candole
1965 John Howard Cruse
1972 Ralph Emmerson
1979 John Dennis
1987 Malcolm James Menin

Lancaster (Blackburn)

1936 Benjamim Pollard
1955 Anthony Leigh Egerton
     Hoskyns-Abrahall
1975 Dennis Fountain Page
1985 Ian Harland
1989 John Nicholls

Leicester (Peterborough)

See also under Lichfield and Lincoln

1888 Francis Henry Thicknesse
1903 Lewis Clayton
1913 Nomman MacLeod Lang
1927 *became diocesan see*

Lewes (Chichester)

1909 Leonard Hedley Burrows
1914 Herbert Edward Jones
1920 Henry Kemble Southwell
1926 Thomas William Cook
1929 William Champion Streatfield
1929 Hugh Maudsley Hordern
1946 Geoffrey Hodgson Warde
1959 James Herbert Lloyd Morrell
1977 Peter John Ball
1992 Lan Patrick Martin Cundy

Ludlow (Hereford)

1981 Stanley Mark Wood
1987 Lan Macdonald Griggs
1994 John Charles Saxbee

Lynn (Norwich)

1963 William Somers Llewellyn
1972 William Aubrey Aitken
1986 David Edward Bentley
1994 David John Conner

Maidstone (Canterbury)

1944 Leslie Owen
1946-56 no appointment
1956 Stanley Woodley Betts
1966-69 no appointment
1969 Geoffrey Lewis Tiarks
1976 Richard Henry McPhail Third
1980 Robert Maynard Hardy
1987 David James Smith
1992 Gavin Hunter Reid

Malmesbury (Bristol)

1927 Ronald Erskine Ramsay
1946 Ivor Stanley Watkins
1956 Edward James Keymer Roberts
1962 Clifford Leofric Purdy Bishop
1973 Frederick Stephen Temple
1983 Peter James Firth
1994 *renamed* **Swindon**

Marlborough

1537 Thomas Morley (Bickley)[1]
c1561-1888 *in abeyance*
1888 Alfred Earle[2]
1919 *in abeyance*

Middleton (Manchester)

1927 Richard Godfrey Parsons
1932 Cecil Wilfred Wilson
1938 Arthur Fawssett Alston
1943 Edward Worsfold Mowll
1952 Frank Woods
1958 Robert Nelson
1959 Edward Ralph Wickham
1982 Donald Alexander Tytler
1994 Stephen Squires Venner

Nottingham (Lincoln)

[in York diocese to 1837]
1567 Richard Barnes
1570-1870 in abeyance
1870 Henry Mackenzie
1877 Edward Trollope
1893 in abeyance
1979 John Dennis

Penrith (Carlisle)

See also Richmond

1537 John Bird[3]
1539-1888 in abeyance
1888 John James Pulleine[4]
1939 Grandage Edwards Powell
1944 Herbert Victor Turner
1959 Sydney Cyril Bulley
1967 Reginald Foskett
1970 William Edward Augustus Pugh
1979 George Lanyon Hacker
1994 Richard Garrard

Plymouth (Exeter)

1923 John Howard Bertram
        Masterman
1934 Francis Whitfield Daukes
1950 Norman Harry Clarke
1962 Wilfred Guy Sanderson
1972 Richard Fox Cartwright
1982 Kenneth Albert Newing
1988 Richard Stephen Hawkins

Pontefract (Wakefield)

1931 Campbell Richard Hone
1939 Tom Longworth
1949 Arthur Harold Morris
1954 George William Clarkson
.1961 Eric Treacy
1968 William Gordon Fallows
1971 Thomas Richard Hare
1993 John Finney

Ramsbury (Salisbury)

See also under Salisbury

1974 John Robert Geoffrey Neale
1989 Peter St George Vaughan

Reading (Oxford)

1889 James Leslie Randall
1909-1942 in abeyance
1942 Arthur Groom Parham
1954 Eric Henry Knell
1972 Eric Wild
1982 Ronald Graham Gregory Foley
1989 John Frank Ewan Bone

Repton (Derby)

1965 William Warren Hunt
1977 Stephen Edmund Verney
1986 Francis Henry Arthur
        Richmond

Richborough (Canterbury)

1995 Edwin Ronald Barnes

Richmond (Ripon)

1889 John James Pulleine[5]
1913 Francis Charles Kilner
1921 in abeyance

St Germans (Truro)

1905 John Rundle Comish
1918-1974 in abeyance
1974 Cecil Richard Rutt
1979 [Michael] Reginald Lindsay
        Fisher
1985 John Richard Allan Llewellin
1992 Graham Richard James

Selby (York)

1939 Henry St John Stirling
        Woollcombe
1941 Carey Fredenck Knyvett
1962 Douglas Noel Sargent
1971 Morris Henry St John
        Maddocks
1983 Clifford Conder Barker
1991 Humphrey Vincent Taylor

Shaftesbury (Salisbury)

[in Bistol diocese 1542-1836]
1539 John Bradley
  ?   *in abeyance*[6]

Sheffield (York)

1901 John Nathaniel Quirk
1914 *became diocesan see*

Sherborne (Salisbury)

1925 Robert Crowther Abbott
1928 Gerald Burton Allen
1936 Harold Nickinson Rodgers
1947 John Maurice Key
1960 VictorJoseph Pike
1976 John Dudley Galtrey Kirkham

Sherwood (Southwell)

1965 Kenneth George Thompson
1975 Harold Richard Darby
1989 Alan Wyndham Morgan

Shrewsbury (Lichfield)

1537 Lewis Thomas[7]
1561-1888 in abeyance
1888 Sir Lovelace Tomlinson Stamer
1905-40 in abeyance
1940 Eric Knightley Chetwode
        Hamilton
1944 Robert Leighton Hodson
1959 William Alonzo Parker
1969 Francis William Cocks
1980 Leslie Lloyd Rees
1987 John Dudley Davies
1994 David Marrison Hallatt

Southampton (Winchester)

1895 William Awdry
1896 George Carnac Fisher
1898 Hon. Arthur Temple Lyttelton
1903 James Macarthur
1921 Cecil Henry Boutflower
1933 Anhur Baillie Lumsdaine
        Karney
1943 Edmund Robert Morgan
1951 Kenneth Edward Norman
        Lamplugh
1972 John Kingsmill Cavell
1984 Edward David Cartwright
1988 John Freeman Perry

Southwark (Rochester)

1891 Huyshe Wolcott Yeatman-Biggs
1905 *became diocesan see*

Stafford (Lichfield)

1909 Edward Ash Were
1915 Lionel Payne Crawfurd
1934 Douglas Henry Crick
1938 Lempriere Durell Hammond
1958 Richard George Clitherow
1975 John Waine
1979 John Stevens Waller
1987 Michael Charles Scott-Joynt

Stepney (London)

1895 George Forres Browne
1897 Arthur Foley Winnington-
        Ingram
1901 Cosmo Gordon Lang
1909 Henry Luke Paget
1919 Henry Mosley
1928 Charles Edward Curzon
1936 Robert Hamilton Moberly
1952 Joost de Blank
1957 Francis Evered Lunt
1968 Ernest Urban Trevor
        Huddleston
1978 James Lawton Thompson
1992 Richard John Carew Chartres

Stockport (Chester)

1949 Frank Jackson Okell
1951 David Henry Saunders
        Saunders-Davies
1965 Rupert Gordon Strutt
1984 Frank Pilkington Sargeant
1994 Geoffrey Martin Turner

[1] Appointed for the diocese of London
[2] Appointed for the diocese of London, but retained the title while Dean of Exeter 1900-1918
[3] Appointed for the diocese of Lichfield
[4] Appointed for the diocese of Ripon
[5] His suffragan title was changed from Penrith to Richmond by Royal Warrant
[6] The date of Bradley's death is not known
[7] Not appointed for Lichfield, but probably for Llandaff

Swindon (Bristol)

1994 Michael David Doe

Taunton (Bath and Wells)

1538 William Finch
1559-1911 in abeyance
1911 Charles Fane De Salis
1931 George Arthur Hollis
1945 Harry Thomas
1955 Mark Allin Hodson
1962 Francis Horner West
1977 Peter John Nott
1986 Nigel Simeon McCulloch
1992 John Hubert Richard Lewis

Tewkesbury (Gloucester)

1938 Augustine John Hodson
1955 Edward Barry Henderson
1960 Forbes Trevor Horan
1973 Thomas Carlyle Joseph Robert
　　　Hamish Deakin
1986 Geoffrey David Jeremy Walsh

Thetford (Norwich)

See also under Norwich

1536 John Salisbury
1570-1894 in abeyance
1894 Arthur Thomas Lloyd
1903 John Philips Alcott Bowers
1926-45 no appointment
1945 John Walker Woodhouse
1953 Manin Patrick Grainge Leonard
1963 Eric William Bradley Cordingly
1977 Hugh Charles Blackburne

1981 Timothy Dudley-Smith
1992 Hugo Ferdinand De Waal

Tonbridge (Rochester)

1959 Russell Berridge White
1968 Henry David Halsey
1973 Philip Harold Ernest Goodrich
1982 David Henry Bartleet
1993 Brian Arthur Smith

Warrington (Liverpool)

1918 Martin Linton Smith
1920 Edwin Hone Kempson
1927 Herbert Gresford Jones
1946 Charles Robert Claxton
1960 Laurence Ambrose Brown
1970 John Monier Bickersteth
1976 Michael Henshall

Warwick (Coventry)

1980 Keith Appleby Arnold
1990 Clive Handford

Whalley (Blackburn)

[in Manchester diocese to 1926]

1909 Atherton Gwillym Rawstorne
1936 in abeyance

Whitby (York)

1923 Harry St John Stirling
　　　Woollcombe
1939 Harold Evelyn Hubbard

1947 Walter Hubert Baddeley
1954 Philip William Wheeldon
1961 George D'Oyly Snow
1972 John Yates
1976 Clifford Conder Barker
1983 Gordon Bates

Willesden (London)

1911 William Willcox Perrin
1929 Guy Vernon Smith
1940 Henry Colville Montgomery
　　　Campbell
1942 Edward Michael Gresford Jones
1950 Gerald Alexander Ellison
1955 George Ernest Ingle
1964 Graham Douglas Leonard
1974 Geoffrey Hewlett Thompson
1985 Thomas Frederick Butler
1992 Geoffrey Graham Dow

Wolverhampton (Lichfield)

1979 Barry Rogerson
1985 Christopher John Mayfield
1994 Michael Gay Bourke

Woolwich (Southwark)

1905 John Cox Leeke
1918 William Woodcock Hough
1932 Arthur Llewellyn Preston
1936 Leslie Hamilton Lang
1947 Robert William Stannard
1959 John Arthur Thomas Robinson
1969 David Stuart Sheppard
1975 Michael Eric Marshall
1984 Albert Peter Hall

WALES

Archbishops of Wales

1920 Alfred George Edwards
　　　(St Asaph, 1889–1934)
1934 Charles Alfred Howell Green
　　　(Bangor, 1928–44)
1944 David Lewis Prosser
　　　(St David's, 1927–50)
1949 John Morgan
　　　(Llandaff, 1939–57)
1957 Alfred Edwin Morris
　　　(Monmouth, 1945–67)
1968 William Glyn Hughes Simon
　　　(Llandaff, 1957–71)
1971 Gwilym Owen Williams
　　　(Bangor, 1957–82)
1983 Derrick Greenslade Childs
　　　(Monmouth, 1972–87)
1987 George Noakes
　　　(St David's, 1982–1991)
1991 Alwyn Rice Jones
　　　(St Asaph 1982–)

Bangor[1]

*c*550 Deiniol [*Daniel*]
*c*775 Elfod [*Elbodugen*]
1092 Herve
[*Vacancy* 1109–20]
1120 David the Scot
1140 Maurice (Meurig)
[*Vacancy* 1161–77]
1177 Guy Rufus [*Gwion Goch*]
[*Vacancy c*1190–5]
1195 Alan [*Alban*]
1197 Robert of Shrewsbury

[*Vacancies* 1212–15]
1215 Cadwgan
1237 Richard
1267 Anian or Einion
1307 Grufudd ab Iowerth
1309 Anian [Einion] Sais
1328 Matthew de Englefield
1357 Thomas de Ringstead
1366 Gervase de Castro
1371 Hywel ap Gronwy
1372 John Gilbert
1376 John Swaffham
1400 Richard Young
[*Vacancy c*1404–8]
1408 Benedict Nicolls
1418 William Barrow
1425 John Cliderow
1436 Thomas Cheriton
1448 John Stanbury
1453 James Blakedon
1465 Richard Edenham
1495 Henry Dean
1500 Thomas Pigot
1505 Thomas Penny
1509 Thomas Skevington
1534 John Salcot or Capon
1539 John Bird
1542 Arthur Bulkeley
1555 William Glynn
1559 Rowland Meyrick
1566 Nicholas Robinson
1586 Hugh Bellot
1596 Richard Vaughan
1598 Henry Rowlands
1616 Lewis Bayly

1632 David Dolben
1634 Edmund Griffith
1637 William Roberts
1666 Robert Morgan
1673 Humphrey Lloyd
1689 Humphrey Humphreys
1702 John Evans
1716 Benjamin Hoadley
1721 Richard Reynolds
1723 William Baker
1728 Thomas Sherlock
1734 Charles Cecil
1738 Thomas Herring
1743 Matthew Hutton
1748 Zachary Pearce
1756 John Egerton
1769 John Ewer
1775 John Moore
1783 John Warren
1800 William Cleaver
1807 John Randolph
1809 Henry William Majendie
1830 Christopher Bethell
1859 James Colquhoun Campbell
1890 Daniel Lewis Lloyd
1899 Watkin Herbert Williams
1925 Daniel Davies
1928 Charles Alfred Howell Green
　　　(Archbishop of Wales 1934)
1944 David Edwardes Davies
1949 John Charles Jones
1957 Gwilym Owen Williams
　　　(Archbishop of Wales 1971)
1982 John Cledan Mears
1992 Barry Cenydd Morgan

[1] Very few of the names of the Celtic bishops have been preserved.

Llandaff[1]

c550 Teiliau
c872 Cyfeiliag
c880 Libiau
c940 Marchlwys
 982 Gwyzan
c995 Bledri
1027 Joseph
1056 Herewald
1107 Urban
[Vacancy of six years]
1140 Uchtryd
1148 Nicolas ap Gwrgant
[Vacancy of two years]
1186 William Saltmarsh
1193 Henry of Abergavenny
1219 William of Goldcliff
1230 Elias of Radnor
1245 William de Burgh
1254 John de Ware
1257 William of Radnor
1266 Willam de Breuse or Brus
1297 John of Monmouth
1323 John of Eaglescliffe
1344 John Paschal
1361 Roger Cradock
1383 Thomas Rushook
1386 William Bottesham
1389 Edmund Bromfield
1393 Tideman de Winchcomb
1395 Andrew Barret
1396 John Burghill
1398 Thomas Peverel
1408 John de la Zouch [Fulford]
1425 John Wells
1441 Nicholas Ashby
1458 John Hunden
1476 John Smith
1478 John Marshall
1496 John Ingleby
1500 Miles Salley
1517 George de Athequa
1537 Robert Holdgate or Holgate
1545 Anthony Kitchin
1567 Hugh Jones
1575 William Blethin
1591 Gervase Babington
1595 William Morgan
1601 Francis Godwin
1618 George Carleton
1619 Theophilus Field
1627 William Murray
1640 Morgan Owen
1660 Hugh Lloyd
1667 Francis Davies
1675 William Lloyd
1679 William Beaw
1706 John Tyler
1725 Robert Clavering
1729 John Harris
1739 Matthias Mawson
1740 John Gilbert
1749 Edward Cressett
1755 Richard Newcome
1761 John Ewer
1769 Jonathan Shipley
1769 Shute Barrington
1782 Richard Watson
1816 Herbert Marsh
1819 William Van Mildert
1826 Charles Richard Sumner
1828 Edward Copleston
1849 Alfred Ollivant
1883 Richard Lewis
1905 Joshua Pritchard Hughes

1931 Timothy Rees
1939 John Morgan
      (Archbishop of Wales 1949)
1957 William Glyn Hughes Simon
      (Archbishop of Wales 1968)
1971 Eryl Stephen Thomas
1975 John Richard Worthington
      Poole-Hughes
1985 Roy Thomas Davies

Monmouth

1921 Charles Alfred Howell Green
1928 Gilbert Cunningham Joyce
1940 Alfred Edwin Monahan
1945 Alfred Edwin Morris
      (Archbishop of Wales 1957)
1968 Eryl Stephen Thomas
1972 Derrick Greenslade Childs
      (Archbishop of Wales 1983)
1986 Royston Clifford Wright
1991 Rowan Douglas Williams

St Asaph[2]

c560 Kentigern
c573 Asaph
1143 Gilbert
1152 Geoffrey of Monmouth
1154 Richard
1160 Godfrey
1175 Adam
1183 John I
1186 Reiner
1225 Abraham
1235 Hugh
1242 Hywel Ab Ednyfed
1249 Anian I or Einion
1267 John II
1268 Anian II
1293 Llywelyn de Bromfield
1315 Dafydd ap Bleddyn
1346 John Trevor I
1357 Llywelyn ap Madoc ab Ellis
1377 William de Spridlington
1382 Lawrence Child
1390 Alexander Bache
1395 John Trevor 11
1411 Robert de Lancaster
1433 John Lowe
1444 Reginald Pecock
1451 Thomas Bird alias Knight
1471 Richard Redman
1496 Michael Deacon
1500 Dafydd ab lorwerth
1504 Dafydd ab Owain
1513 Edmund Birkhead
1518 Henry Standish
1536 Robert Warton or Parfew
1555 Thomas Goldwell
1560 Richard Davies
1561 Thomas Davies
1573 William Hughes
1601 William Morgan
1604 Richard Parry
1624 John Hanmer
1629 John Owen
1660 George Griffith
1667 Henry Glemham
1670 Isaac Barrow
1680 William Lloyd
1692 Edward Jones
1703 George Hooper
1704 William Beveridge
1708 Will. Fleetwood

1715 John Wynne
1727 Francis Hare
1732 Thomas Tanner
1736 Isaac Maddox
1744 Samuel Lisle
1748 Robert Hay Drummond
1761 Richard Newcome
1769 Jonathan Shipley
1789 Samuel Hallifax
1790 Lewis Bagot
1802 Samuel Horsley
1806 William Cleaver
1815 John Luxmore
1830 William Carey
1846 Thomas Vowler Short
1870 Joshua Hughes
1889 Alfred George Edwards
      (Archbishop of Wales 1920)
1934 William Thomas Havard
1950 David Daniel Bartlett
1971 Harold John Charles
1982 Alwyn Rice Jones
      (Archbishop of Wales 1991)

St David's[3]

c601 David
c606 Cynog
 831 Sadyrnfyw
      Meurig
c840 Novis
      ?Idwal
c906 Asser
      Llunwerth
 944 Eneuris
c961 Rhydderch
c999 Morgeneu
1023 Morgeneu
1023 Erwyn
1039 Tramerin
1061 Joseph
1061 Bleddud
1072 Sulien
1078 Abraham
1080 Sulien (again)
1085 Wilfrid
1115 Bernard
1148 David Fitz-Gerald
1176 Peter de Leia
1203 Geoffrey de Henlaw
1215 Gervase [Iorwerth]
1231 Anselm le Gras
1248 Thomas le Waleys
1256 Richard de Carew
1280 Thomas Bek
1296 David Martin
1328 Henry Gower
1347 John Thoresby
1350 Reginald Brian
1352 Thomas Fastolf
1362 Adam Houghton
1389 John Gilbert
1397 Guy de Mohne
1408 Henry Chichele
1414 John Catterick
1415 Stephen Patrington
1418 Benedict Nichols
1434 Thomas Rodburn [Rudborne]
1442 William Lindwood
1447 John Langton
1447 John de la Bere
1460 Robert Tully
1482 Richard Martin
1483 Thomas Langton
1485 Hugh Pavy

[1] The traditional list of bishops of the Celtic Church has little historical foundation. But the names of the following, prior to Urban, may be regarded as fairly trustworthy though the dates are very uncertain.
[2] Prior to the Norman period there is considerable uncertainty as to names and dates.
[3] The following names occur in early records though the dates given cannot always be reconciled.

1496 John Morgan [Young]	1705 George Bull	1874 William Basil Tickell Jones
1505 Robert Sherborn	1710 Philip Bisse	1897 John Owen
1509 Edward Vaughan	1713 Adam Ottley	1927 David Lewis Prosser
1523 Richard Rawlins	1724 Richard Smallbrooke	(Archbishop of Wales 1944)
1536 William Barlow	1731 Elias Sydall	1950 William Thomas Havard
1548 Robert Ferrar	1732 Nicholas Claggett	1956 John Richards Richards
1554 Henry Morgan	1743 Edward Willes	1971 Eric Matthias Roberts
1560 Thomas Young	1744 Richard Trevor	1982 George Noakes
1561 Richard Davies	1753 Anthony Ellis	(Archbishop of Wales 1987)
1582 Marmaduke Middleton	1761 Samuel Squire	1991 John Ivor Rees
1594 Anthony Rudd	1766 Robert Lowth	
1615 Richard Milbourne	1766 Charles Moss	
1621 William Laud	1774 James Yorke	## Swansea and Brecon
1627 Theophilus Field	1779 John Warren	
1636 Roger Mainwaring	1783 Edward Smallwell	1923 Edward Latham Bevan
1660 William Lucy	1788 Samuel Horsley	1934 John Morgan
1678 William Thomas	1794 William Stewart	1939 Edward William Williamson
1683 Laurence Womock	1801 George Murray	1953 William Glyn Hughes Simon
1686 John Lloyd	1803 Thomas Burgess	1957 John James Absalom Thomas
1687 Thomas Watson	1825 John Banks Jenkinson	1976 Benjamin Noel Young Vaughan
[Vacancy 1699–1705]	1840 Connop Thirlwall	1988 Dewi Morris Bridges

SCOTLAND

Sources: Bp Dowden's *The Bishops of Scotland* (Glasgow 1912), for all the sees up to the Reformation, and for Aberdeen and Moray to the present time.

For bishops after the Reformation (and for a few of the earliest ones before Queen Margaret)—Grub, *Ecclesiastical History of Scotland* (Edinburgh 1861, 4 Vols.) and Bp Keith and Bp Russel, *Scottish Bishops* (2nd ed. Edinburgh 1824).

Scottish episcopal elections became subject immediately to Roman confirmation in 1192. The subordination of the Scottish Church to York became less direct in 1165, and its independence was recognized in a bill of Celestine III in 1192. St. Andrews was raised to metropolitan rank on 17 August 1472 and the Archbishop became primate of all Scotland with the same legative rights as the archbishop of Canterbury on 27 March 1487.

The dates in the margin are those of the consecration or translation to the particular see of the bishops named; or in the case of bishops elect, who are not known to have been consecrated, they are those of the election; or in the case of titular bishops, of the date of their appointment.

The date of the death has been given where there was a long interregnum, or where there is dislocation (as at the Reformation and at the Revolution), or for some special reason to make the history intelligible.

The extra information in the list of College Bishops is given for the reason just stated.

St Andrews

St Andrews, Dunkeld and Dunblane

906 Cellach I
915(?) Fothad I
955 Malisius I
963 Maelbridge
970 Cellach II
996(?) Malasius II
(?) Malmore
1025 Alwyn
1028 Maelduin
1055 Tuthald or Tuadal
1059 Fothad II
1077 ⎰ Gregory (elect)
to ⎱ Catharas (elect)
1107 ⎰ Edmarus (elect)
    ⎱ Godricus (elect)
1109 Turgot
1120 Eadmer (elect)
1127 Robert
1159 Waldeve (elect)
1160 Ernald
1165 Richard
1178 Hugh
1180 John the Scot
1198 Roger de Beaumon
1202 William Malveisin
1238 Geoffrey (elect)
1240 David de Bernham
1253 Robert de Stuteville (elect)
1254 Abel de Golin
1255 Gamelin
1273 William Wischard
1280 William Fraser
1298 William de Lamberton
1328 James Bennet
1342 William de Laundels
1385 Stephen de Pay (elect)

1386(?) Walter Trayl
1388 Alexander de Neville
1398 Thomas de Arundel
1401 Thomas Stewart (elect)
1402 Walter de Danielston (elect)
1403(?) Gilbert Greenlaw
1403 Henry Wardlaw
1408 John Trevor
1440 James Kennedy

ARCHBISHOPS

1465 Patrick Graham
1478 William Scheves
1497 James Stewart (elect)
1504 Alexander Stewart (elect)
1513 John Hepburn (elect)
1513 Innocenzo Cibo (elect)
1514 Andrew Forman
1522 James Betoun
1538 David Betoun [coadj.]
1547 John Hamilton
1551 Gavin Hamilton [coadj.]
    d. 1571
1572 John Douglas (titular)
1576 Patrick Adamson (titular)
    d. 1592
1611 George Gladstanes
1615 John Spottiswoode, d. 1639
1661 James Sharp
1679 Alexander Burnet
1684 Arthur Rose, d. 1704

BISHOPS OF FIFE

[1704 to 1726 See vacant]
1726 James Rose
1733 Robert Keith
1743 Robert White
1761 Henry Edgar

BISHOPS OF ST ANDREWS

1842 Patrick Torry
1853 Charles Wordsworth
1893 George Howard Wilkinson
1908 Charles Edward Plumb
1931 Edward Thomas Scott Reid
1938 James Lumsden Barkway
1949 Arnold Brian Burrowes
1955 John William Alexander Howe
1969 Michael Geoffrey Hare Duke
1994 Michael Harry George Henley

†Dunkeld

849(?) Tuathal
865(?) Flaithbertach
1114 Cormac
1147 Gregory
1170 Richard I
1178 Walter de Bidun (elect)
1183(?) John I, the Scot
1203 Richard II, de Prebenda
1212(?) John II, de Leycester
1214(?) Hugh de Sigillo
1229 Matthew Scot (elect)
1229 Gilbert
1236(?) Geoffrey de Liberatione
1252 Richard III, of Inverkeithing
1273(?) Robert de Stuteville
1283(?) Hugh de Strivelin [Stirling]
    (elect)
1283 William
1288 Matthew de Crambeth
1309 John de Leek (elect)
1312 William Sinclair
1337 Malcolm de Innerpeffray (elect)
1344 Richard de Pilmor
1347 Robert de Den (elect)

† Indicates a diocese no longer extant or united with another diocese

1347(?) Duncan de Strathearn
1355 John Luce
1370 John de Carrick (elect)
1371(?) Michael de Monymusk
1377(?) Andrew Umfray (elect)
1379 John de Peblys [? of Peebles]
1379 Robert de Derling
1390(?) Nicholas Duffield
1391 Robert Sinclair
1398(?) Robert de Cardeny
1430 William Gunwardby
1437 Donald MacNaughton (elect)
1438 James Kennedy
1440(?) Thomas Livingston
1440 Alexander de Lawedre [Lauder]
         (elect)
1442 James de Brois [Brewhous]
1447 William Turnbull (elect)
1448 John Ralston
1452(?) Thomas Lauder
1476 James Livingston
1483 Alexander Inglis (elect)
1484 George Brown
1515 Andrew Stewart (elect)
1516 Gavin Douglas
1524 Robert Cockburn
1526(?) George Crichton
1546 John Hamilton
1552 Robert Crichton
1572 James Paton (titular)
1585 Peter Rollock (titular)
1607 James Nicolson (titular)
1611(?) Alexander Lindsay dep. 1638
1662 George Haliburton
1665 Henry Guthrie
1677 William Lindsay
1679 Andrew Bruce
1686 John Hamilton
1717 Thomas Rattray
1743 John Alexander
1776(?) Charles Rose
1792 Jonathan Watson
1808 Patrick Torry
1842 Held with St Andrews

†Dunblane

1162 Laurence
c1180 Symon
1196 W[illelmus]
1198 Johathan
1215 Abraham
1225 Ralph (elect)
1227 Osbert
1233 Clement
1259 Robert de Prebenda
1284 William I
1296 Alpin
1301 Nicholas
1307 Nicholas de Balmyle
1318(?) Roger de Balnebrich (elect)
1322 Maurice
c1347 William II
c1361 Walter de Coventre
c1372 Andrew
c1380 Dougal
1403(?) Finlay or Dermoch
1419 William Stephen
1430 Michael Ochiltree
1447(?) Robert Lauder
1468 John Hepburn
1487 James Chisolm
1527 William Chisolm I
1561 William Chisom II [coadj.]
1575 Andrew Graham (titular)
1611 George Graham
1616 Adam Bellenden

1636 James Wedderburn
1661 Robert Leighton
1673 James Ramsay
1684 Robert Douglas
[1716 to 1731 See vacant]
1731 John Gillan
1735 Robert White
1744 Thomas Ogilvie (elect)
1774 Charles Rose, d. 1791
1776 Held with **Dunkeld**

Edinburgh

1634 William Forbes
1634 David Lindsay
1662 George Wishart
1672 Alexander Young
1679 John Paterson
1687 Alexander Rose
1720 John Fullarton
1727 Arthur Millar
1727 Andrew Lumsden
1733 David Freebairn
[1739 to 1776 See vacant]
1776 William Falconer
1787 William Abernethy Drummond
1806 Daniel Sandford
1830 James Walker
1841 Charles Hughes Terrot
1872 Henry Cotterill
1886 John Dowden
1910 George Henry Somerset
        Walpole
1929 Harry Seymour Reid
1939 Ernest Denny Logie Danson
1947 Kenneth Charles Harman
        Warner
1961 Kenneth Moir Carey
1975 Alastair Iain Macdonald
        Haggart
1986 Richard Frederick Holloway

Aberdeen

Aberdeen and Orkney

BISHOPS AT MURTHLAC
   (?) Beyn [Beanus]
   (?) Donort
   (?) Cormac

BISHOPS AT ABERDEEN
1132 Nechtan
c1150 Edward
c1172 Matthew
c1201 John
c1208 Adam de Kalder
1228 Matthew Scot (elect)
1230 Gilbert de Strivelyn
1240 Radulf de Lamley
1247 Peter de Ramsey
1258 Richard de Pottun
1272 Hugh de Bennum
1282 Henry le Chene
1329 Walter Herok (elect)
1329 Alexander I, de Kyninmund
1344 William de Deyn
1351 John de Rate
1356 Alexander II, de Kyninmund
1380 Adam de Tynyngham
1391 Gilbert de Grenlaw
1422 Henry de Lychton [Leighton]
c1441 Ingram de Lindsay
1458 Thomas Spens
1480 Robert Blackadder (elect)
1488 William Elphinstone
1515 Robert Forman (elect)
1516 Alexander Gordon

1519 Gavin Dunbar
1529 George Learmonth [coadj.]
1533 William Stewart
1547 William Gordon
1577 David Cunningham (elect)
1611 Peter Blackburn
1616 Alexander Forbes
1618 Patrick Forbes of Corse
1635 Adam Bellenden [Bannatyne]
1662 David Mitchell
1663 Alexander Burnet
1664 Patrick Scougal
1682 George Halyburton
[1715 to 1721 See vacant]
1721 Archibald Campbell
1724 James Gadderar
1733 William Dunbar
1746 Andrew Gerard
1768 Robert Kilgour
1786 John Skinner
1816 William Skinner
1857 Thomas George Spink Suther
1883 Arthur Gascoigne Douglas
1906 Rowland Ellis
1912 Anthony Mitchell
1917 Frederic Llewellyn Deane
1943 Herbert William Hall
1956 Edward Frederick Easson
1973 Ian Forbes Begg
1978 Frederick Charles Darwent
1992 Andrew Bruce Cameron

†Orkney

1035 Henry
1050 Turolf
1072 John I
1072 Adalbert
1073 Radulf
1108 Roger
1114 Radulf Novell
1102 William I, 'the Old'
1168(?) William II
1188(?) Bjarni
1224 Jofreyrr
1248 Henry I
1270 Peter
1286 Dolgfinn
1310 William III
c1369 William IV
c1384 Robert Sinclair
1384(?) John
1394 Henry II
1396(?) John Pak
1407 Alexander Vaus (elect)
1415 William Stephenson
1420 Thomas Tulloch
1461 William Tulloch
1477 Andrew Painter
1500 Edward Stewart
1524 John Benston [coadj.]
1526(?) Robert Maxwell
1541 Robert Reid
1559 Adam Bothwell
1611 James Law
1615 George Graham
1639 Robert Barron (elect)
1661 Thomas Sydserf
1664 Andrew Honeyman
1677 Murdo Mackenzie
1688 Andrew Bruce, See afterwards
        administered with **Caithness**
1857 Held with **Aberdeen**

Brechin

1153(?) Samson
1178 Turpin

1202 Radulf
1215 Hugh
1218 Gregory
1246 Albin
1269(?) William de Crachin (elect)
1275 William Comyn
1296 Nicholas
1298 John de Kyninmund
1328 Adam de Moravia
1350 Philip Wilde
1351 Patrick de Locrys [Leuchars]
1383 Stephen de Cellario
1411 Walter Forrester
1426 John de Crannach
1455 George Schoriswood
1464 Patrick Graham
1465 John Balfour
1489 William Meldrum
1523 John Hepburn
1557 Donald Campbell (elect)
1565(?) John Sinclair (elect)
1566 Alexander Campbell (titular)
1610 Andrew Lamb
1619 David Lindsay
1634 Thomas Sydserf
1635 Walter Whitford
1662 David Strachan
1672 Robert Laurie
1678 George Haliburton
1682 Robert Douglas
1684 Alexander Cairncross
1684 James Drummond
[1695 to 1709 Held with **Edinburgh**]
1709 John Falconar
1724 Robert Norrie
1726 John Ochterlonie
1742 James Rait
1778 George Innes
1787 William Abernethy Drummond
1788 John Strachan
1810 George Gleig
1840 David Moir
1847 Alexander Penrose Forbes
1876 Hugh Willoughby Jermyn
1904 Walter John Forbes Robberds
1935 Kenneth Donald Mackenzie
1944 Eric Graham
1959 John Chappell Sprott
1975 Lawrence Edward Luscombe
1990 Robert Halliday

Moray

Moray Ross and Caithness

1114 Gregory
1153(?) William
1164 Felix
1172 Simon de Tonei
1187 Richard de Lincoln
1203 Brice de Douglas
1224(?) Andrew de Moravia
1244(?) Simon
1251 Radulf de Leycester (elect)
1253 Archibald
1299 David de Moravia
1326 John de Pilmor
1363 Alexander Bur
1397 William de Spyny
1407 John de Innes
1415 Henry Leighton
1422 Columba de Dunbar
1437 John de Winchester
1460(?) James Stewart
1463 David Stewart
1477 William de Tulloch
1487 Andrew Stewart
1501(?) Andrew Forman
1516(?) James Hepburn
1525 Robert Shaw

1532(?) Alexander Stewart
1538(?) Patrick Hepburn
1574 George Douglas
1611 Alexander Douglas
1623 John Guthrie
1662 Murdo Mackenzie
1677 James Aitken
1680 Colin Falconer
1687 Alexander Rose
1688 William Hay
1707 Held with **Edinburgh**
1725 Held with **Aberdeen**
1727 William Dunbar
1737 George Hay (elect)
1742 William Falconar
1777 Arthur Petrie
1787 Andrew Macfarlane
1798 Alexander Jolly
1838 Held with **Ross**
1851 Robert Eden
1886 James Butler Knill Kelly
1904 Arthur John Maclean
1943 Piers Holt Wilson
1953 Duncan Macinnes
1970 George Minshull Sessford
1994 Gregor Macgregor

†Ross

1131(?) Macbeth
1150(?) Simon
1161 Gregory
1195 Reginald
1213 Andrew de Moravia (elect)
1215(?) Robert I
1250 Robert II
1272 Matthew
1275(?) Robert II de Fyvin
1295(?) Adam de Derlingtun (elect)
1297(?) Thomas de Dundee
1325 Roger
1351 Alexander Stewart
1372 Alexander de Kylwos
1398(?) Alexander de Waghorn
1418 Thomas Lyell (elect)
        Griffin Yonge (elect)
1420 John Bulloch
1441(?) Andrew de Munro (elect)
1441(?) Thomas Tulloch
1464(?) Henry Cockburn
1478 John Wodman
1481 William Elphinstone (elect)
1483 Thomas Hay
1492 John Guthrie
1498 John Frisel [Fraser]
c1507 Robert Cockburn
1525 James Hay
c1539 Robert Cairncross
1552 David Painter
1561(?) Henry Sinclair
1566 John Lesley
1575 Alexander Hepburn
1611 David Lindsay
1613 Patrick Lindsay
1633 John Maxwell
1662 John Paterson
1679 Alexander Young
1684 James Ramsay
[1696 See vacant or held with
        Caithness until 1727]
1727 Held with **Moray**
1742 Held with **Caithness**
1762 Robert Forbes
1777 Held with **Moray**
1819 David Low
1851 Held with **Moray**

†Caithness

c1146 Andrew

c1187 John
1214 Adam
1223(?) Gilbert de Moravia
1250(?) William
1263 Walter de Baltrodin
1273(?) Nicholas (elect)
1275 Archibald Herok
1278 Richard (elect)
1279(?) Hervey de Dundee (elect)
1282 Alan de St. Edmund
1295 John or James (elect)
1296 Adam de Derlingtun
1297 Andrew
1306 Fercard Belegaumbe
1328(?) David
1341 Alan de Moravia
1343 Thomas de Fingask
1370 Malcolm de Dumbrek
1381 Alexander Man
1414 Alexander Vaus
1425 John de Crannach
1428 Robert Strabrok
1446 John Innes
1448 William Mudy
1478(?) Prospero Camogli de
        Medici
1484(?) John Sinclair (elect)
1502 Andrew Stewart I
1517(?) Andrew Stewart II
1542 Robert Stewart (elect)
1600 George Gledstanes (elect)
1611 Alexander Forbes
1616 John Abernethy
1662 Patrick Forbes
1680 Andrew Wood
[1695 See vacant]
1731 Robert Keith
1741 Wm. Falconas
1762 Held with **Ross**
[1742 See Vacant]
1777 Held with **Moray**

Glasgow

Glasgow and Galloway

550(?) Kentigern or Mungo (No
        record of his successors)
1114(?) (Michael)
1118(?) John
1147 Herbert
1164 Ingram
1175 Jocelin
1199 Hugh de Roxburgh (elect)
1200 William Malveisin
1202 Florence (elect)
1208 Walter de St Albans
1233 William de Bondington
1259 Nicholas de Moffat (elect)
1259 John de Cheam
1268 Nicholas de Moffat (again
        elect)
1271 William Wischard (elect)
1273 Robert Wischard
1317 Stephen de Donydouer (elect)
1318 John de Eglescliffe
1323 John de Lindsay
1337 John Wischard
1339 William Rae
1367 Walter Wardlaw
1388 Matthew de Glendonwyn
1391 John Framisden (titular)
1408 William Lauder
1427 John Cameron
1447 James de Brois [Brewhouse]
1448 William Turnbull
1456 Andrew de Durrisdeer
1475 John Laing
1483 George Carmichael (elect)

ARCHBISHOPS

1483 Robert Blackadder (Archb. 9
     Jan. 1492)
1509 James Betoun I
1525 Gavin Dunbar
1551 Alexander Gordon
1552 James Betoun II, restored 1587
1571 John Porterfield (titular)
1573 James Boyd (titular)
1581 Robert Montgomery (titular)
1585 William Erskine (titular)
1610 John Spottiswoode
1615 James Law
1633 Patrick Lindsay
1661 Andrew Fairfoul
1664 Alexander Burnet, restored 1674
1671 Robert Leighton, resigned 1674,
     d. 1684
1679 Arthur Rose
1684 Alexander Cairncross d. 1701
1687 John Paterson,[1] d. 1708
[1708 Vacant]

BISHOPS

1731 Alexander Duncan, d. 1733
[1733 Vacant]
1787 Held with **Edinburgh**
1805 William Abernethy Drummond
1809–37 Held with **Edinburgh**
1837 Michael Russell
1848 Walter John Trower
1859 William Scott Wilson
1888 William Thomas Harrison
1904 Archibald Ean Campbell
1921 Edward Thomas Scott Reid
1931 John Russell Darbyshire
1938 John Charles Halland How
1952 Francis Hamilton Moncreiff
1974 Frederick Goldie
1981 Derek Alec Rawcliffe
1991 John Mitchell Taylor

†Galloway or Candida Casa or Whithorn[2]

     Ninian, d. 432(?)
 (?) Octa
 681 Trumwine
 731 Penthelm, d. 735(?)
 735 Frithowald, d. 764
 763 Pehtwine, d. 776
 777 Ethelbert
 791 Beadwulf
1140 Gilla-Aldan
1154 Christian
1189 John
1214 Walter
1235 Odo Ydonc (elect)
1235 Gilbert
1255 Henry
1294 Thomas de Kircudbright [de
     Daltoun]
1327 Simon de Wedale
1355 Michael Malconhalgh
1359(?) Thomas Macdowell (elect)
1359 Thomas
1364 Adam de Lanark
 (?) David Douglas, d. 1373
 (?) James Carron, resigned 1373
1378 Ingram de Kethnis (elect)
1379 Oswald
1380 Thomas de Rossy
 (?) Francis Ramsay, d. 1402
1406 Elisaeus Adougan
1414(?) Gilbert Cavan (elect)
1415 Thomas de Butil
1422 Alexander Vaus

1451 Thomas Spens
1457(?) Thomas Vaus (elect)
1459 Ninian Spot
1482(?) George Vaus
1508(?) James Betoun (elect)
1509(?) David Arnot
1526 Henry Wemyss
1541(?) Andrew Dury
1559(?) Alexander Gordon
1610 Gavin Hamilton
1612(?) William Couper
1619 Andrew Lamb
1635 Thomas Sydserf
1661 James Hamilton
1675 John Paterson
1679 Arthur Rose
1680 James Aitken
1688 John Gordon, d. 1726
1697 Held with **Edinburgh**
1837 Held with **Glasgow**

Argyll or Lismore

Argyll and The Isles
1193 Harald
1240 William
1253 Alan
1268 Laurence de Erganis
1300 Andrew
1342 Angusde Ergadia (elect)
1344 Martinde Ergaill
1387 John Dugaldi
1397(?) Bean Johannis
1420(?) Finlay de Albany
1428 George Lauder
1476 Robert Colquhoun
1504 David Hamilton
1532 Robert Montgomery
1539(?) William Cunningham (elect)
1553(?) James Hamilton (elect)
1580 Neil Campbell (titular)
1611 John Campbell (titular)
1613 Andrew Boyd
1637 James Fairlie
1662 David Fletcher
1665 John Young (elect)
1666 William Scroggie
1675 Arthur Rose
1679 Colin Falconer
1680 Hector Maclean
1688 Alexander Monro (elect)
     Held with **Ross**
1847 Alexander Ewing
1874 George Mackarness
1883 James Robert Alexander
     Chinnery-Haldane
1907 Kenneth Mackenzie
1942 Thomas Hannay
1963 Richard Knyvet Wimbush
1977 George Kennedy Buchanan
     Henderson
1992 Douglas MacLean Cameron

†The Isles

 900 Patrick
1080 Roolwer
1080 William
1095 Hamundr
1138 Wimund
1152 John I
1152(?) Ragnald
1154 Gamaliel
1170 Christian
1194 Michael
1210 Nicholas I
1219 Nicholas II of Meaux
1226(?) Reginald

1226 Simon
1249 Laurence (elect)
1253 Richard
1275 Gilbert (elect)
1275 Mark
1305 Alan
1324 Gilbert Maclelan
1328 Bernard de Linton
1331 Thomas de Rossy
1349 William Russell
1374 John Donkan
1387 Michael
1392 John Sproten (**Man**) (titular)
1402(?) Conrad (**Man**) (titular)
1402(?) Theodore Bloc (**Man**) (titular)
1410 Richard Messing (**Man**)
1422 Michael Anchire
1425(?) John Burgherlinus (**Man**)
1428 Angus I
1441(?) John Hectoris [McCachane]
     Macgilleon
1472 Angus II
1487 John Campbell
1511 George Hepburn
1514 John Campbell (elect)
1530(?) Ferchar MacEachan (elect)
1550(?) Roderick Maclean
1553(?) Alexander Gordon
1567 John Carswell (titular)
1573 John Campbell
1605 Andrew Knox
1619 Thomas Knox
1628 John Leslie
1634 Neil Campbell
1662 Robert Wallace
1677 Andrew Wood
1680 Archibald Graham [or
     McIlvernock]
     Held with **Orkney** and **Caithness**
1819 Held with **Argyll**

College Bishops, Consecrated without Sees

1705 John Sage, d. 1711
1705 John Fullarton
     (**Edinburgh** 1720), d. 1727
1709 Henry Christie, d. 1718
1709 John Falconar
     (**Fife** 1720), d. 1723
1711 Archibald Campbell
     (**Aberdeen** 1721), d. 1744
1712 James Gadderar
     (**Aberdeen** 1725, **Moray** 1725),
     d. 1733
1718 Arthur Millar
     (**Edinburgh** 1727), d. 1727
1718 William Irvine, d. 1725
1722 Andrew Cant, d. 1730
1722 David Freebairn
     (**Edinburgh** 1733)
1726 John Ochterlonie
     (**Brechin** 1731), d. 1742
1726 James Ross
     (**Fife** 1731), d. 1733
1727 John Gillan
     (**Dunblane** 1731), d. 1735
1727 David Ranken, d. 1728

Bishops who have held the Office of Primus

1704 Alexander Rose
     (**Edinburgh** 1704–20)
1720 John Fullarton
     (**Edinburgh** 1720–27)

[1] After the deposition of John Paterson at the Revolution the See ceased to be Archiepiscopal.
[2] The traditional founder of the See is St. Ninian. But nothing authentic is known of the bishops prior to the accession of Gilla-Aldan between 1133 and 1140.

1727 Arthur Millar
      (**Edinburgh** 1727)
1727 Andrew Lumsden
      (**Edinburgh** 1727–33)
1731 David Freebairn
      (**Edinburgh** 1733–39)
1738 Thomas Rattray
      (**Dunkeld** 1727–43)
1743 Robert Keith
      (**Caithness** 1731–41)
1757 Robert White
      (**Dunblane** 1735–43,
      St. Andrews 1743–61)
1762 William Falconar
      (**Orkney** and **Caithness**
      1741–62)
1782 Robert Kilgour
      (**Aberdeen** 1768–86)
1788 John Skinner
      (**Aberdeen** 1786–1816)
1816 George Gleig
      (**Brechin** 1810–40)

1837 James Walker
      (**Edinburgh** 1880–41)
1841 William Skinner
      (**Aberdeen** 1816–57)
1857 Charles H. Terrot
      (**Edinburgh** 1841–72)
1862 Robert Eden
      (**Moray, Ross,** and **Caithness**
      1851–86)
1886 Hugh W. Jermyn
      (**Brechin** 1875–1903)
1901 James B. K. Kelly
      (**Moray, Ross,** and **Caithness**
      1886–1904)
1904 George H. Wilkinson
      (**St. Andrews, Dunkeld,** and
      Dunblane 1893–1907)
1908 Walter J. F. Robberds
      (**Brechin** 1904–34)
1935 Arthur J. Maclean
      (**Moray, Ross,** and **Caithness**
      1904–43)

1943 E. D. Logie Danson
      (**Edinburgh** 1939–46)
1946 John C. H. How
      (**Glasgow and Galloway**
      1938–52)
1952 Thomas Hannay
      (**Argyll** and **The Isles** 1942–62)
1962 Francis Hamilton Moncreiff
      (**Glasgow and Galloway**
      1952–74)
1974 Richard Knyvet Wimbush
      (**Argyll and The Isles** 1963–77)
1977 Alastair Iain Macdonald Haggart
      (**Edinburgh** 1975–85)
1985 Lawrence Edward Luscombe
      (**Brechin** 1975–)
1990 George Kennedy Buchanan
      Henderson (**Argyll** and **The
      Isles** 1977–1992)
1992 Richard Frederick Holloway
      (**Edinburgh** 1986–)

IRELAND

PROVINCE OF ARMAGH

†Achonry

BISHOPS

*c*558 Cathfuidh
1152 Mael Ruanaid ua Ruadain
1159 Gille na Naehm O Ruadain
      [Gelasius]
1208 Clemens O Sniadaig
1220 Connmach O Torpaig [Carus]
1226 Gilla Isu O Cleirig [Gelasius]
1237 Tomas O Ruadhan
1238 Oengus O Clumain [Elias]
1251 Tomas O Maicin
1266 Tomas O Miadachain
      [Dionysus]
1286 Benedict O Bracain
1312 David of Kilheny
1348 David II
1348 Nicol Alias Muircheartach O
      hEadhra
1374 William Andrew
1385 Simon
*c*1390 Tomas mac Muirgheasa
      MacDonn-chadha
1401 Brian mac Seaain O hEadhra
1410 Maghnus O h Eadhra
1424 Donatus
1424 Richard Belmer
1436 Tadhg O Dalaigh
1442 James Blakedon
1449 Cornelius O Mochain
1463 Brian O hEasdhra [Benedictus]
1470 Nicholas Forden
1475 Robert Wellys
1484 Thomas fitzRichard
1484 Tomas O Conghalain
1489 John Bustamente
1492 Thomas Ford
1508 Eugenius O Flannagain
1522 Cormac O Snighe
1547 Thomas O Fihilly
1562 Eugene O'Harte
1613 Miler Magrath (with **Cashel**)
United to **Killala** 1622

†Annadown

BISHOPS

1189 Conn ua Mellaig [Concors]
1202 Murchad ua Flaithbertaig

1242 Tomas O Mellaig
1251 Conchobar [Concors]
1283 John de Ufford
1308 Gilbert O Tigernaig
1323 Jacobus O Cethernaig
1326 Robert Petit
1328 Albertus
1329 Tomas O Mellaig
1359 Dionysius
1393 Johannes
1394 Henry Trillow
1402 John Bryt
1408 John Wynn
1421 John Boner [Camere]
1425 Seean Mac Braddaigh
1428 Seamus O Lonnghargain
1431 Donatus O Madagain
1446 Thomas Salscot
1450 Redmund Bermingham
1458 Thomas Barrett
1496 Francis Brunand
1540 John Moore
[United to **Tuam** *c*1555]

†Ardagh

454 Mel
*c*670 Erard
874 Faelghus
      Cele 1048
1152 Mac Raith ua Morain
1172 Gilla Crist O hEothaig
      [Christianus]
      O'Tirlenain 1187
      ua hEislinnen
      Annud O Muiredaig 1216
1217 Robert
1224 M.
1228 Loseph mac Teichthechain
1229 Mac Raith Mac Serraig
1232 Gilla Isu mac in Scelaige O
      Tormaid [Gelasius]
1232 Iocelinus
1238 Brendan Mac Teichthechain
1256 Milo of Dunstable
1290 Matha O'h-Eothaig [Mattheus]
1323 Robert Wirsop (did not get
      possession)
1324 Mac Eoaighseoan
1347 Eoghan O Ferghail [Audovenus]

1368 William Mac Carmaic
1373 Cairbre O'Ferghail [Charles]
1373 John Aubrey
1392 Henry Nony (did not get
      possession)
1396 Comedinus Mac Bradaigh
      [Gilbert]
1400 Adam Leyns
1419 Conchobar O'Ferghail
      [Cornelius]
1425 Risdeard O'Ferghail
[1444 O'Murtry, not cons. res.]
1445 Cormac Mac Shamhradhain
1462 Seaan O'Ferghail
1467 Donatus O'Ferghail
1482 William O'Ferghail
1517 Ruaidri O'Maoileoin
1517 Rory O'Mallone [Roger O
      Melleine]
1541 Richard O'Ferrall
1553 Patrick MacMahon
[1572 John Garvey, not consecrated]
1583 Lysach O'Ferrall
1604 Robert Draper
1613 Thomas Moigne
1679 William Bedell
1633 John Richardson
1661 Robert Maxwell
1673 Francis Marsh
1682 William Sheridan
1692 Ulysses Burgh
1604–33 and 1661–92 and 1692–1751
      Held by the Bishops of
      Kilmore
1751–1839 Held by the Archbishops
      of **Tuam**
United to **Kilmore** 1839

Armagh

BISHOPS

444 Patrick
      Benignus 467
      Jarlath 481
      Cormac 497
      Dubthach 513
      Ailill I 526
      Ailill II 536
      David O'Faranan 551
      Carlaen 588

---

† Indicates a diocese no longer extant or united with another diocese.

MacLaisre 623
-640 Thomian MacRonan
Segeni 688
Suibhne 730
-732 Congusa
Affinth 794
-811 Nundha
-818 Artri
835 Forannan
Mael Patraic I 862
Fethgna 875
Cathasach MacRobartach 883
Mochta 893
900 Maelaithghin
Cellach
Mael Ciarain 915
Joseph 936
Mael Patraic II 936
Cathasach MacDolgen 966
Maelmiure 994
Airindach 1000
Maeltuile 1032
1032 Hugh O'Ferris
Mael Patraic III 1096
1099 Caincomrac O'Boyle

ARCHBISHOPS

1105 Cellach mac Aeda meic Mael Isu
[Celsus]
1132 Mael maedoc Ua Morgair
[Malachais]
1137 Gilla Meic Liac mac Diarmata
meic Ruaidri [Gelasius]
1174 Conchobar O Conchaille
[Concors]
1175 Gille in Coimhedh O Caran
[Gilbertus]
1180 Tomaltach O Conchobair
[Thomas]
1184 Mael Isu Ua Cerbaill
[Malachias]
1202 Echdonn mac Gilla Uidir
[Eugenius]
1217 Lucas Neterville
1227 Donatus O Fidabra
1240 Albert Suebeer of Cologne
1247 Reginald
1258 Abraham O'Conallain
1261 Mael Patraic O Scannail
1270 Nicol Mac Mael Isu
1303 Michael MacLochlainn (not
confirmed)
1304 Dionysius (not confirmed)
1306 John Taaffe
1307 Walter Jorz
1311 Roland Jorz
1324 Stephen Segrave
1334 David Mag Oireachtaigh
1347 Richard FitzRalph
1362 Milo Sweetman
1383 John Colton
1404 Nicholas Fleming
1418 John Swayne
1439 John Prene
1444 John Mey
1457 John Bole [Bull]
1471 John Foxhalls or Foxholes
1475 Edmund Connesburgh
1480 Ottaviano Spinelli [de Palatio]
1513 John Kite
1521 George Cromer
1543 George Dowdall
1552 Hugh Goodacre
1553 George Dowdall (again)
[1560 Donat MacTeague, not
recognized by the Crown,
1562]
1563 Adam Loftus

1568 Thomas Lancaster
1584 John Long
1589 John Garvey
1595 Henry Ussher
1613 Christopher Hampton
1625 James Ussher
[Interregnum 1656–61]
1661 John Bramhall
1663 James Margetson
1679 Michael Boyle
1703 Narcissus Marsh
1714 Thomas Lindsay
1724 Hugh Boulter
1742 John Hoadly
1747 George Stone
1765 Richard Robinson [afterwards
Baron Rokeby]
1795 William Newcome
1800 William Stuart
1822 John George Beresford
Clogher united to Armagh 1850–86
1862 Marcus Gervais Beresford
1886 Robert Bentknox
1893 Robert Samuel Gregg
1896 William Alexander
1911 John Baptist Crozier
1920 Charles Frederick D'Arcy
1938 John Godfrey FitzMaurice Day
1939 John Allen Fitzgerald Gregg
1959 James McCann
1969 George Otto Simms
1980 John Ward Armstrong
1986 Robert Henry Alexander Eames

Clogher

c493 MacCarthinn or Ferdachrioch
Ailill 869
1135 Cinaeth O Baigill
1135 Gilla Crist O Morgair
[Christianus] (moved his see to
Louth)

BISHOPS OF LOUTH

1135 Gilla Crist O Morgair
[Christianus]
1138 Aed O Ceallaide [Edanus]
1178 Mael Isu O Cerbaill [Malachias]
1187 Gilla Crist O Mucaran
[Christinus]
1194 Mael Isu Ua Mael Chiarain
1197 Gilla Tigernaig Mac Gilla
Ronain [Thomas]

BISHOPS OF CLOGHER

1218 Donatus O Fidabra
1228 Nehemias
1245 David O Bracain
1268 Michael Mac an tSair
1287 Matthew Mac Cathasaigh I
-1310 Henricus
1316 Gelasius O Banain
1320 Nicholas Mac Cathasaigh
1356 Brian Mac Cathmaoil [Bernard]
1362 Matthew Mac Cathasaigh II
—   Aodh O hEothaigh [alias O
Neill]
1373 John O Corcrain [Wurzburg]
1390 Art Mac Cathmhail
1433 Piaras Mag Uidhir [Petrus]
1450 Rossa mac Tomais Oig Mag
Uidhir [Rogerius]
1475 Florence Woolley
[1484 Niall mac Seamuis Mac
Mathghamna]
1484 John Edmund de Courci
1494 Seamus Mac Pilip Mac
Mathghamna

1500 Andreas
1502 Nehemias O Cluainin
1504 Giolla Padraig O Conalaigh
[Patrick]
1505 Eoghan Mac Cathmhail
[Eugenius]
1517 Padraig O Cuilin
1535 Aodh O Cearbhalain [Odo]
1517 Patrick O'Cullen
1535 Hugh O'Carolan
1570 Miler Magrath
1605 George Montgomery
1621 James Spottiswood
1645 Henry Jones
1661 John Leslie
1671 Robert Leslie
1672 Roger Boyle
1691 Richard Tennison
1697 St. George Ashe
1717 John Stearne
1745 Robert Clayton
1758 John Garnett
1782 John Hotham (bt. 1794)
1796 William Foster
1797 John Porter
1819 John George Beresford
1820 Percy Jocelyn
1822 Robert Ponsonby Tottenham
Loftus
United to **Armagh** 1850–86
1886 Charles Maurice Stack
1903 Charles Frederick D'Arcy
1908 Maurice Day
1923 James MacManaway
1944 Richard Tyner
1958 Alan Alexander Buchanan
1970 Richard Patrick Crosland
Hanson
1973 Robert William Heavener
1980 Gordon McMullan
1986 Brian Desmond Anthony
Hannon

Connor

506 Oengus MacNessa 514
Lughadh 543
640 Dimma Dubh. [the Black]
Duchonna the Pious 725
Cunnen or Cuinden 1038
Flann O'Sculu 1117
1124 Mael Maedoc Ua Morgair
[Malachias]
-1152 MaelPatraic O'Banain
1172 Nehemias
1178 Reginaldus
1226 Eustacius
1242 Adam
1245 Isaac de Newcastle-on-Tyne
1258 William de Portroyal
1261 William de Hay [or la Haye]
1263 Robert de Flanders
1275 Peter de Dunach
1293 Johannes
1320 Richard
1321 James de Couplith
1323 John de Eglecliff
1323 Robert Wirsop
1324 Jacabus O Cethernaig
1353 William Mercier
1374 Paulus
1389 Johannes
[1420 Seaan O Luachrain not
consecrated]
1423 Eoghan O'Domhnaill
1429 Domhnall O'Meraich
1431 John Fossade [Festade]
1459 Patricius

1459 Simon Elvington
United to **Down** 1441
1945 Charles King Irwin
1956 Robert Cyril Hamilton Glover
         Elliott
1969 Arthur Hamilton Butler
1981 William John McCappin
1987 Samuel Greenfield Poyntz
1995 James Edward Moore

Derry

Derry and Raphoe

         Caencomhrac 927
–937 Finachta MacKellach
–949 Mael Finnen

BISHOPS OF MAGHERA
(Where the See was in the twelfth and
the thirteenth centuries)

1107 Mael Coluim O Brolchain
—   Mael Brigte O Brolchain
1152 O Gormgaile Muiredach O
         Cobthaig [Mauricius]
1173 Amhlaim O Muirethaig
1185 Fogartach O Cerballain
         [Florentius]
c1230 Gilla in Coimhded O Cerballain
         [Germanus]
c1280 Fogartach O Cerballain II
         [Florentius]

BISHOPS OF DERRY
(Where the See was resettled)

1295 Enri Mac Airechtaig [O'Reghly]
         [of Ardagh]
1297 Gofraid MacLochlainn
         [Godfrey]
1316 Aed O Neill [Odo]
1319 Michael Mac Lochlainn
         [Maurice]
1349 Simon
1391 Johannes
1391 John Dongan
1394 Seoan O Mochain
1398 Aodh [Hugo]
1401 Seoan O Flannabhra
1415 Domhnall Mac Cathmhail
1419 Domhnall O Mearaich
1429 Eoghan O Domhnaill [Eugenius]
1433 John Oguguin
[1456 John Bole, appointment not
         completed, trld. to Armagh]
1458 Bartholomew O Flannagain
c1464 Johannes
1467 Nicholas Weston
1485 Domhnall O Fallamhain
1501 Seamus mac Pilip Mac
         Mathghamna [MacMahon]
1520 Ruaidhri O Domhnaill
1520 Rory O'Donnell
1554 Eugene O'Doherty
1568 F. [doubtful authority]
1569 Redmond O'Gallagher
[1603 Denis Campbell, not
         consecrated]
1605 George Montgomery
1610 Brutus Babington
[1611 Christopher Hampton,
         consecrated]
1613 John Tanner
1617 George Downham
1634 John Bramhall
1661 George Wild
1666 Robert Mossom
1680 Michael Ward
1681 Ezekiel Hopkins
1691 William King
1703 Charles Hickman
1714 John Hartstonge

1717 St. George Ashe
1718 William Nicolson
1727 Henry Downes
1735 Thomas Rundle
1743 Carew Reynell
1745 George Stone
1747 William Barnard
1768 Frederick Augustus Hervey
         [afterwards Earl of Bristol]
1803 William Knox
1831 Richard Ponsonby
Raphoe united to Derry from 1834
1853 William Higgin
1867 William Alexander
1896 George Alexander Chadwick,
         res.
1916 Joseph Irvine Peacocke
1945 Robert M'Neil Boyd
1958 Charles John Tyndall
1970 Cuthbert Irvine Peacocke
1975 Robert Henry Alexander
         Eames
1980 James Mehaffey

Down

Down and Dromore

         Fergus 584
         Suibhne 825
         Graithene 956
         Finghin 964
         Flaithbertach 1043
         MaelKevin 1086
—   Mael Muire 1117
         Oengus Ua Gormain 1123
—   [Anonymous]
c1124 Mael Maedoc O Morgair
         [Malachias]
1152 Mael Isu mac in Chleirig Chuirr
         [Malachias]
1175 Gilla Domangairt Mac
         Cormaic
c1176 Echmilid [Malachias]
c1202 Radulfus
1224 Thomas
1251 Randulphus
1258 Reginaldus
1265 Thomas Lydel
1277 Nicholas le Blund
1305 Thomas Ketel
1314 Thomas Bright
1328 John of Baliconingham
1329 Ralph of Kilmessan
1353 Richard Calf I
1365 Robert of Aketon
1367 William White
1369 Richard Calf [II]
1386 John Ross
1394 John Dongan
1413 John Cely *or* Sely
1445 Ralph Alderle

BISHOPS OF DOWN AND
CONNOR

1441 John Fossard
1447 Thomas Pollard
1451 Richard Wolsey
1456 Thomas Knight
1469 Tadhg O Muirgheasa
         [Thaddeus]
1489 Tiberio Ugolino
1520 Robert Blyth
1542 Eugene Magennis
1565 James MacCawell
1569 John Merriman
1572 Hugh Allen
1593 Edward Edgeworth
1596 John Charden
1602 Roben Humpston
1607 John Todd, res.

1612 James Dundas
1613 Robert Echlin
1635 Henry Leslie
1661 Jeremy Taylor
1667 Roger Boyle
1672 Thomas Hacket
1694 Samuel Foley
1695 Edward Walkington
1699 Edward Smyth
1721 Francis Hutchinson
1739 Carew Reynell
1743 John Ryder
1752 John Whitcombe
1752 Robert Downes
1753 Arthur Smyth
1765 James Traill
1784 William Dickson
1804 Nathaniel Alexander
1823 Richard Mant

BISHOPS OF DOWN, CONNOR
AND DROMORE

1849 Robert Bent Knox
1886 William Reeves
1892 Thomas James Welland
1907 John Baptist Crozier
1911 Charles Frederick D'Arcy
1919 Charles Thornton Primrose
         Grierson
1934 John Frederick McNeice
1942 Charles King Irwin

BISHOPS OF DOWN AND
DROMORE

1945 William Shaw Kerr
1955 Frederick Julian Mitchell
1970 George Alderson Quin
1980 Robert Henry Alexander Eames
1986 Gordon McMullan

†Dromore

         Mael Brighde 974
         Riagan 1101
1197 Ua Ruanada
1227 Geraldus
1245 Andreas
1284 Tigernach I
1290 Gervasius
—   Tigernach II
1309 Florentius Mac Donnocain
1351 Anonymous
1366 Milo
1369 Christophorus Cornelius 1382
1382 John O'Lannoy
1398 Thomas Orwell
1400 John Waltham
1402 Roger Appleby
1408 Richard Payl
1410 Marcus
1411 John Chourles
1414 Seaan O Ruanadha
1419 Nicholas Wartre
1429 Thomas Rackelf
1431 William
1431 David Chirbury
1450 Thomas Scrope [Bradley]
1450 Thomas Radcliff
1456 Donatus O h-Anluain
         [Ohendua]
1457 Richard Messing
1463 William Egremond
—   Aonghus [Aeneas] 1476
1476 Robert Kirke
1480 Yvo Guillen
1483 George Braua
1511 Tadhg O Raghallaigh
         [Thaddeus]
1536 Quintin O Quigley [Cogley]
1539 Roger McHugh

1540 Arthur Magennis
1607 John Todd
[1613 John Tanner, not consecrated]
1613 Theophilus Buckworth
1661 Robert Leslie
1661 Jeremy Taylor (administered the diocese)
1667 George Rust
1671 Essex Digby
1683 Capel Wiseman
1695 Tobias Pullein
1713 John Stearne
1717 Ralph Lambert
1727 Charles Cobbe
1732 Henry Maule
1744 Thomas Fletcher
1745 Jemmett Browne
1745 George Marlay
1763 John Oswald
1763 Edward Young
1765 Henry Maxwell
1766 William Newcome
1775 James Hawkins
1780 William de la Poer Beresford
1782 Thomas Percy
1811 George Hall
1812 John Leslie
1819 James Saurin
United to **Down** since 1842

†Elphin

Domnall mac Flannacain Ua Dubhthaig 1136
Muiredach O Dubhthaig 1150
1152 Mael Isu O Connachtain
Flannacan O Dubhthaig 1168
c1177 Tomaltach mac Aeda Ua Conchobhair [Thomas]
c1180 Florint Ua Riacain Ui Maelrvanaid
1206 Ardgar O Conchobhair
1226 Dionysius O Mordha
c1230 Alanus
1231 Donnchad mac Fingein O Conchobhair [Dionysius Donatus]
1245 Eoin O Mugroin
1247 Tomaltach macToirrdelbaig O Conchobhair [Thomas]
1260 Mael Sechlainn O Conchobhair [Milo]
1262 Tomas mac Fergail mac Diarmata
1266 Muiris O Conchobhair
[1285 Amiaim O Tommaltaig, not consecrated]
1285 Gilla Isu mac in Liathana O Conchobhair
1297 Maelsechlainn mac Briain [Malachias]
1303 Donnchad O Flannacain, [Donatus]
1307 Cathal O Conchobhair
1310 Mael Sechlainn Mac Aedha
1313 Lurint O Lachtnain [Laurence]
1326 Sean O Finnachta
1355 Carolus
1357 Gregory O Mochain
1372 Thomas Barrett
1383 Seoan O Mochain
1407 Seaan O Grada
1405 Gerald Caneton
1412 Thomas Colby
1418 Robert Fosten
1421 Edmund Barrett
1427 Johannes
1429 Laurence O Beolain
1429 William O hEidighean
1448 Conchobhar O Maolalaidh

1458 Nicholas O Flanagan
1487 Hugo Arward
1492 Rlocard mac Briain O gCuanach
1499 George Brana
1501 Cornelius O Flannagain
1508 Christopher Fisher
1525 John Maxey
1539 Wlillam Maginn 1541(?)
1539 Gabriel de Sancto Serio
1541 Conach or Con O'Negall or O'Shyagall
1552 Roland Burke [de Burgo]
1582 Thomas Chester
1583 John Lynch
1611 Edward King
1639 Henry Tilson
1661 John Parker
1667 John Hodson
1691 Simon Digby
1720 Henry Downes
1724 Theophilus Bolton
1730 Robert Howard
1740 Edward Synge
1762 William Gore
1772 Jemmett Browne
1775 Charles Dodgson
1795 John Law
1810 Power le Poer Trench
1819 John Leslie 1854
United to **Kilmore** and **Ardagh** on the death of Bp Beresford in 1841 when Bp Leslie became Bp of the united dioceses.

†Killala

Muiredach
Kellach
O Maolfogmair I 1137
O Maolfogmair II 1151
Imar O Ruaidhin 1176
1179 O Maolfogmair III
1199 Domnall Ua Becdha
1207 Cormac O'Tarpy
O'Kelly 1214
1226 Aengus O Maolfogmair [Elias]
Gille Cellaig O Ruaidhin
1253 Seoan O Laidlg
1281 Donnchad O Flaithbertaig [Donatus]
1307 John Tankard
Sean O Flaithim 1343
1344 James Bermingham
1347 William O Dubhda
1351 Robert Elyot
1381 Thomas Lodowys
1383 Conchobar O Coineoil [Cornelius]
1390 Thomas Horwell [Orwell]
1400 Thomas Barrett
1403 Muircheartach Cleirach mac Donnchadha O Dubhda
Connor O'Connell 1423
1427 Fergal Mac Martain
1431 Thaddaeus Mac Creagh
1432 Brian O Coneoil
1447 Robert Barrett
1452 Ruaidhri Bairead [Barrett]
1453 Thomas
1459 Richard Viel
Miler O'Connell
1461 Donatus O Conchobhair
1470 Tomas Bairead [Barrett]
1487 John de Tuderto [Seaan O Caissin]
1500 Thomas Clerke
1508 Malachias O Clumhain
1513 Risdeard Bairead
1545 Redmond O'Gallagher
1570 Donat O'Gallagher

1580 John O'Casey
1592 Owen O'Conor
1613 Miler Magrath
Achonry united to Killala 1622
1623 Archibald Hamilton
1630 Archibald Adair, dep., but subsequently restored
164? John Maxwell
1661 Henry Hall
1664 Thomas Bayly
1671 Thomas Otway
1680 John Smith
1681 William Smyth
1682 Richard Tennison
1691 William Lloyd
1717 Henry Downes
1720 Charles Cobbe
1727 Robert Howard
1730 Robert Clayton
173? Mordecai Cary
175? Richard Robinson [afterwards Baron Rokeby]
1759 Samuel Hutchinson
1781 William Cecil Pery
1784 William Preston
1787 John Law
1795 John Porter
1798 Joseph Stock
1810 James Verschoyle
United to **Tuam** since 1834

Kilmore

Kilmore, Elphin and Ardagh
—   Aed Ua Finn 1136
—   Muirchenach Ua Maelmoeherge 1149
1152 Tuathal Ua Connachtaig [Thadeus]
1202 Mi Ua Dobailen
—   Flann O Connachtaig [Florentius] 1231
1237 Congalach Mac Idneoil
1251 Simon O Ruairc
1286 Mauricius
—   Matha Mac Duibne 1314
1320 Padraig O Cridecain
—   Conchobhar Mac Conshnamha [Ford] 1355
1356 Richard O Raghilligh
1373 Johannes
1388 Thomas Rushook, O.P.
1392 Sean O Raghilligh I [John]
1398 Nicol Mac Bradaigh
1401 Sean O'Raghilligh II
1407 John Stokes
1409 David O'Fairchellaigh
1422 Domhnall O Gabhann
1445 Aindrias Mac Bradaigh
1455 Fear Sithe Mag Dhuibhne
1465 Sean O Raghilligh II
1476 Cormac Mag Shamhradhain
1480 Tomas MacBradaigh
1512 Diarmaid O Raghilligh
1530 Edmund Nugent
1540 Sean Mac Bradaigh
1585 John Garvey
1604 Robert Draper
1613 Thomas Moigne
1629 William Bedell
1643 Robert Maxwell
1673 Francis Marsh
1682 William Sheridan
1693 William Smyth
1699 Edward Wetenhall
1715 Timothy Godwin
1727 Josiah Hott
1742 Joseph Story
1757 John Cradock

1772 Denison Cumberland
1775 George Lewis Jones
1790 William Foster
1796 Charles Broderick
1802 George de la Poer Beresford
Ardagh united to Kilmore 1839
Elphin united to Kilmore 1841
1841 John Leslie
1854 Marcus Gervais Beresford
1862 Hamilton Verschoyle
1870 Charles Leslie
1870 Thomas Carson
1874 John Richard Darley
1884 Samuel Shone
1897 Alfred George Elliott
1915 William Richard Moore
1930 Arthur William Barton
1939 Albert Edward Hughes
1950 Frederick Julian Mitchell
1956 Charles John Tyndall
1959 Edward Francis Butler Moore
1981 William Gilbert Wilson
1993 Michael Hugh Gunton Mayes

†Mayo

Gerald 732
Muiredach [or Murray]
Mcinracht 732
Aidan 773
1172 Gilla Isu Ua Mailin
Cele O Dubhthaig 1210
1210 ?Patricius
1428 William Prendergast
1430 Nicholas 'Wogmay'
1439 Odo O h-Uiginn
1432 Martin Campania
1457 Simon de Duren
1493 John Bel
1541 Eugenius Macan Brehon
United to **Tuam** 1559

†Raphoe

Sean O Gairedain
Donell O Garvan
Felemy O Syda
Oengus O'Lappin 959
1150 Muiredhach O'Cofley
1156 Gille in Coimhded Ua Carain
[Gilbertus]
— Anonymous
1204 Mael Isu Ua Doirig
— Anonymous
1253 Mael Padraig O Scannail
[Patricius]
1263 John de Alneto
1265 Cairpre O Scuapa
1275 Fergal O Firghil [Florentius]
1306 Enri Mac-in-Chrossain
[Henricus]
1319 Tomas Mac Carmaic Ui
Domhnaill

1363 Padraig Mac Maonghail
1367 Conchobar Mac Carmaic Ui
Domhnaill [Cornelius]
1397 Seoan MacMenmain
1400 Eoin MacCarmaic [Johannes]
–1413 Anthony
–1414 Robert Rubire
1416 John McCormic
1420 Lochlainn O Gallchobhair I
[Laurentius]
1440 Cornelius Mac Giolla Brighde
1443 Lochlainn O Gallchobhair II
[Laurentius]
1479 John de Rogeriis
1482 Meanma Mac Carmail
[Menclaus Mac Carmacain]
1514 Conn O Cathain [Cornelius]
1534 Eamonn O Gallchobhair
1547 Arthur o'Gallagher
1563 Donnell Magonigle [or
McCongail]
[1603 Denis Campbell, not
consecrated]
1605 George Montgomery
1611 Andrew Knox
1633 John Leslie
1661 Robert Leslie
1671 Ezekiel Hopkins
1682 William Smyth
1693 Alexander Cairncross
1701 Robert Huntington
1702 John Pooley
1713 Thomas Lindsay
1714 Edward Synge
1716 Nicholas Forster
1744 William Barnard
1747 Philip Twysden
1753 Robert Downes
1763 John Oswald
1780 James Hawkins
1807 John George Beresford
1819 William Magee
1822 William Bissett
United to **Derry** since 1834

Tuam

Tuam, Killala and Achonry

BISHOPS
Murrough O'Nioc 1032
Hugh O'Hessian 1085
Cathusach Ua Conaill 1117
O Clerig 1137
Muiredach Ua Dubhthaig 1150

ARCHBISHOPS
1152 Aed Ua h-Oisin [Edanus]
1167 Cadhla Ua Dubhthaig
[Catholicus]
1202 Felix Ua Ruanada
1236 Mael Muire O Lachtain
[Marianus]
1250 Flann Mac Flainn [Florentius]

[1256 James O'Laghtnan, not
confirmed or consecrated]
1257 Walter de Salerno
1258 Tomaltach O Conchobair
[Thomas]
1286 Stephen de Fulbourn
1289 William de Bermingham
1312 Mael Sechlainn Mac Aeda
1348 Tomas MacCerbhaill
[MacCarwill]
1364 Eoin O Grada
1372 Gregory O Mochain I
1384 Gregory O Mochain II
1387 William O Cormacain
1393 Muirchertach mac Pilb O
Cellaigh
1410 John Babingle
1411 Cornelius
1430 John Bermingham [Winfield]
1438 Tomas mac Muirchearthaigh O
Cellaigh
1441 John de Burgo
1452 Donatus O Muiredaigh
1485 William Seoighe [Joyce]
1503 Philip Pinson
1506 Muiris O Fithcheallaigh
1514 Tomas O Maolalaidh
1537 Christopher Bodkin
1573 William O'Mullally or Lealy
Annadown united to Tuam c1555
Mayo united to Tuam 1559
1595 Nehemiah Donnellan
1609 William O'Donnell or Daniel
1629 Randolph or Ralph Barlow
1638 Richard Boyle
1645 John Maxwell
1661 Samuel Pullen
1667 John Parker
1679 John Vesey
1716 Edward Synge
1742 Josiah Hort
1752 John Ryder
1775 Jemmett Browne
1782 Joseph Dean Bourke [afterwards
Earl of Mayo]
1794 William Beresford [afterwards
Baron Decies]
1819 Power le Poer Trench
Killala united to Tuam from 1834

BISHOPS
1839 Thomas Plunket [afterwards
Baron Plunket]
1867 Charles Brodrick Bernard
1890 James O'Sullivan
1913 Benjamin John Plunket
1920 Arthur Edwin Ross
1923 John Ort
1928 John Mason Harden
1932 William Hardy Holmes
1939 John Winthrop Crozier
1958 Arthur Hamilton Butler
1970 John Coote Duggan
1986 John Robert Winder Neill

PROVINCE OF DUBLIN

†Ardfert

BISHOPS
Anmchad O h-Anmchada 1117
1152 Mael Brenain Ua Ronain
Gilla Mac Aiblen O'Anmehadha
1166
Domnall O Connairche 1193
1200 David Ua Duibdithrib
Anonymous 1217

1218 John
1218 Gilbertus
1237 Brendan
1253 Christianus
1257 Philippus
1265 Johannes
1286 Nicolaus
1288 Nicol O Samradain
1336 Ailin O hEichthighirn
1331 Edmund of Caermaerthen

1348 John de Valle
1372 Cornelius O Tigernach
1380 William Bull
1411 Nicholas FitzMaurice
1404 Nicholas Ball
1405 Tomas O Ceallaigh
1409 John Attilburgh [Artilburch]
1450 Maurice Stack
1452 Maurice O Conchobhair
1461 John Stack

1461 John Pigge
1473 Philip Stack
1495 John FitzGerald
[See vacant in 1534]
1536 James FitzMaurice
1588 Nicholas Kenan
1600 John Crosbie
1622 John Steere
1628 William Steere
1641 Thomas Fulwar
United to **Limerick** 1661

†Ardmore

1153 Eugenius
Incorporated with **Lismore** 1192

Cashel

Cashel, Waterford, Lismore, Ossor Ferns and Leighlin

BISHOPS
 Cormac MacCuillenan
 908
 Donnell O'Heney 1096 *or* 1098

ARCHBISHOPS
*c*1111 Mael los Ua h-Ainmire
 Mael Iosa Ua Fogludha
 [Mauricius] 1131
 Domnall Ua Conaing 1137
 Gilla Naomh O'Marty 1149
–1152 Donat O'Lonergan I
–*c*1160 M.
1172 Domnall O h-Ualla-chain
 [Donatus]
1186 Muirghes O h-Enna [Matheus]
*c*1208 Donnchad Ua Longargain I
 [Donatus]
1216 Donnchad Ua Longargain II
 [Donatus]
1224 Mairin O Briain [Marianus]
1238 David mac Ceallaig [O'Kelly]
1254 David Mac Cearbaill [Mac Carwill]
1290 Stiamna O Bracain
1303 Maurice Mac Cearbaill
1317 William FitzJohn
1327 Seoan Mac Cerbaill
1329 Walter le Rede
1332 Eoin O Grada
1346 Radulphus O Cellaigh [Kelly]
1362 George Roche [de Rupe]
1365 Tomas Mac Cearbhaill
1374 Philip of Torrington
1382 Michael
1384 Peter Hackett
1406 Richard O Hedian
1442 John Cantwell I
1452 John Cantwell II
1484 David Creagh
1504 Maurice FitzGerald
1525 Edmund Butler
1553 Roland Baron *or* FitzGerald
1567 James MacCawell
Emly united to Cashel 1569
1571 Miler Magrath
1623 Malcolm Hamilton
1630 Archibald Hamilton
1661 Thomas Fulwar
1667 Thomas Price
[See vacant 1685–91]
1691 Narcissus Marsh
1694 William Palliser
[1727 William Nicolson, not enthroned]
1727 Timothy Goodwin
1730 Theophilus Bolton
1744 Arthur Price

1752 John Whitcombe
1754 Michael Cox
1779 Charles Agar
1801 Charles Brodrick
1822 Richard Laurente
Waterford and **Lismore** united to Cashel from 1833; on the death of Abp Laurence in 1838 the province was united to Dublin and the see ceased to be an Archbishopric

BISHOPS
1839 Stephen Creagh Sandes
1843 Robert Daly
1872 Maurice FitzGerald Day
1900 Henry Stewart O'Hara
1919 Robert Miller
1931 John Frederick McNeice
1935 Thomas Arnold Harvey
1958 William Cecil De Pauley
1968 John Ward Armstrong
Ossory united to Cashel 1977
1980 Noel Vincent Willoughby

†Clonfert

 Moena, *or* Moynean, *or* Moeinend 572
 Cummin the Tall 662
 Ceannfaeladh 807
 Laithbheartach 822
 Ruthnel *or* Ruthme 826
 Cormac MacEdain 922
 Ciaran O'Gabbla 953
 Cathal 963
 Eochu 1031
 O'Corcoran 1095
 Muiredach Ua h-Enlainge 1117
 Gille Patraic Ua Ailcinned 1149
*c*1152 Petrus Ua Mordha
1172 Mail Isu mac in Baird
1179 Celechair Ua h-Armedaig
 Muirchertach Ua'Maeluidir 1187
 Domnall Ua Finn 1195
 Muirchertach Ua Carmacain 1204
1205 Mael Brigte Ua hErurain
1224 Cormac O Luimlin [Carus]
1248 Thomas
1259 Tomas mac Domnaill Moire O Cellaig
1266 Johannes de Alatre
1296 Robert
*c*1302 John
1308 Gregorius O Brocaig
1320 Robert Le Petit
1322 Seoan O Leaain
1347 Tomas mac Gilbert O Cellaigh l
1378 Muircheartach mac Pilib O Cellaigh [Maurice]
1393 William O Cormacain
1398 David Corre
1398 Enri O Conmaigh
1405 Tomasi O Cellaigh II
1410 Cobhthach O Madagain
1438 Seaan O hEidin
1441 John White
1447 Conchobhar O Maolalaidh
1448 Cornelius O Cuinnlis
1463 Matthaeus Mag Raith
1508 David de Burgo
1509 Dionysius O'Mordha
1534 Roland de Burgo
1536 Richard Nangle
1580 Hugh
1582 Stephen Kirwan
1602 Roland Lynch
1627 Robert Dawson

1644 William Baily
1665 Edward Wolley
1691 William FitzGerald
1722 Theophilus Bolton
1724 Arthur Price
1730 Edward Synye
1732 Mordecai Cary
1716 John Whitcombe
1752 Arthur Smyth
1753 William Carmichael
1758 William Gote
1762 John Oswald
1763 Denison Cumberland
1772 Walter Cope
1782 John Law
1787 Richard Marlay
1795 Charles Broderick
1796 Hugh Hamilton
1798 Matthew Young
1801 George de la l'oer Beresford
1802 Nathaniel Alexander
1804 Christopher Butson
United to **Killaloe** since 1834

†Clonmacnoise

–663 Baitan O'Cormac
–839 Joseph [of Rossmore]
 Maclodhar 890
 Cairbre Crom 904
 Loingsech 919
–940 Donough I
–953 Donough II
–966 Cormae O Cillin
 Maenach 971
 Conaing O'Cosgraigh 998
 Male Poil 1001
 Flaithbertach 1038
 Celechar 1067
 O'Mallaen 1093
 Christian Aherne 1104
?1111 Domnall mac Flannacain Ua Dubthaig
1152 Muirchertach Ua Maeluidir
 Cathal Ua Maeileoin 1207
*c*1207 Muirchertach Ua Muiricen
1214 Aed O Maeileoin I
1227 Aed O Maeileoin II [Elias]
1236 Thomas Fitzpatrick
1252 Tomas O Cuinn
1280 Anonymous
1282 Gilbert (not consecrated)
1290 William O Dubhthaig
1298 William O Finnen
1303 Domnall O Braein
1324 Lughaid O Dalaigh
1337 Henricus
1349 Simon
1369 Richard [Braybroke]
1371 Hugo
1388 Philippus O Maoil
1389 Milo Corr
1397 O'Gallagher
1397 Philip Nangle
1423 David Prendergast
1426 Cormac Mac Cochlain [Cornelius]
1444 Sean O Dalaigh
1449 Thomas
1458 Robertus
1458 William
1459 John
1487 Walter Blake
1509 Tomas O Maolalaidh
1516 Quintin O h-Uiginn
1539 Richard O'Hogan
1539 Florence Kirwan
1556 Peter Wall [Wale]
United to **Meath** 1569

†Cloyne

Reachtaidh 887
1148 Gilla na Naem O Muirchertaig
      [Nehemias]
Ua Dubcroin 1159
Ua Flannacain 1167
1177 Matthaeus Ua Mongaig
1201 Laurence Ua Suilleabain
1205 C.
1281 Luke
c1224 Florence
1226 Daniel
1237 David mac Cellaig [O'Kelly]
1240 Ailinn O Suilleabain
1247 Daniel
1265 Reginaldus
1275 Alan O Longain
1284 Nicholas of Effingham
1323 Maurice O Solchain
1333 John Brid
1351 John Whitekot
1363 John Swaffham
1376 Richard Wye
1394 Gerard Caneton
1413 Adam Payn
United to **Cork** 1418–1638
1638 George Synge
1661–1678 Held by the Bishops of
      Cork
1679 Patrick Sheridan
1683 Edward Jones
1693 William Palliser
1694 Tobias Pullein
1695 St. George Ashe
1697 John Pooley
1702 Charles Crow
1726 Henry Maule
1732 Edward Synge
1734 George Berkeley
1753 James Stopford
1759 Robert Johnson
1767 Frederick Augustus Hervery
1768 Charles Agar
1780 George Chinnery
1781 Richard Woodward
1794 William Bennett
1820 Charles Mongan Warhurton
1826 John Brinkley
United to **Cork** on the death of Bp
      Brinkley in 1835

Cork

Cork, Cloyne and Ross

Donnell 876
Soer Bhreatach 892
Dubhdhurn O'Stefam 959
Cathmogh 969
Mugron O'Mutan 1057
1138 Gregory
? Ua Menngorain 1147
1148 Gilla Aedha Ua Maigin
1174 [Gregorius] O h-Aedha [O Hea]
c1182 Reginaldus I
1187 Aicher
1192 Murchad Ua h-Aedha
      Anonymous 1214
1215 Mairin Ua Briain [Marianus]
1225 Gilbertus
1248 Laurentius
1265 William of Jerpoint
1267 Reginaldus
1277 Robert Mac Donnchada
1302 Seoan Mac Cearbaill [Mac
      Carwill]
1321 Philip of Slane
1327 Walter le Rede
1330 John of Ballyconingham
1347 John Roche

1359 Gerald de Barri
1396 Roger Ellesmere
1406 Richard Kynmoure
1409 Patrick Fox
1409 Milo fitzJohn
1425 John Paston
1418 Adam Payn
1429 Jordan Purcell
1472 William Roche (Coadjutor)
1463 Gerald FitzGerald
1490 Tadhg Mac Carthaigh
1499 John FitzEdmund FitzGerald
1499 Patrick Cant
1523 John Benet
1536 Dominic Tyrre [Tirrey]
1562 Roger Skiddy
1570 Richard Dyxon
1572 Matthew Sheyn
Ross united to Cork 1583
1583 William Lyon
1618 John Boyle
1620 Richard Boyle
1638 William Chappell
1661 Michael Boyle
1663 Edward Synge
1679 Edward Wetenhall
1699 Dive Downes
1710 Peter Browne
1735 Robert Clayton
1745 Jemmett Browne
1772 Isaac Mann
1789 Euseby Cleaver
1789 William Foster
1790 William Bennet
1794 Thomas Stopford
1805 John George Beresford
1807 Thomas St. Laurence
1831 Samuel Kyle
Cloyne united to Cork from 1835
1848 James Wilson
1857 William FitzGerald
1862 John Gregg
1878 Robert Samuel Gregg
1894 William Edward Meade
1912 Charles Benjamin Dowse
1933 William Edward Flewett
1938 Robert Thomas Hearn
1952 George Otto Simms
1957 Richard Gordon Perdue
1978 Samuel Greenfield Poyntz
1988 Robert Alexander Warke

Dublin

Dublin and Glendalough

BISHOPS
Sinhail 790
c1028 Dunan [Donatus]
1074 Gilla Patraic
1085 Donngus
1096 Samuel Ua'h-Aingliu

ARCHBISHOPS
1121 Grene [Gregorius]
1162 Lorcan Ua'Tuathail [Laurentius]
1182 John Cumin
1213 Henry de Loundres
Glendalough united to Dublin
1230 Luke
125? Fulk de Sandford
1279 John de Derlington
1286 John de Sandford
1295 Thomas de Chadworth
1296 William de Hotham
1299 Richard de Ferings
[1307 Richard de Havering, not
      consecrated]
1311 John de Leche
1317 Alexander de Bicknor

1349 John de St. Paul
1363 Thomas Minot
1376 Robert de Wikeford
1391 Robert Waldeby
1396 Richard Northalis
1397 Thomas Cranley
1418 Richard Talbot
1451 Michael Tregury
1472 John Walton
1484 Walter Fitzsimons
1512 William Rokeby
1521 Hugh Inge
1529 John Alan
1535 George Browne
1555 Hugh Curwin
1567 Adam Loftus
1605 Thomas Jones
1619 Lancelot Bulkeley
1661 James Margetson
1663 Michael Boyle
1679 John Parker
1682 Francis Marsh
1694 Narcissus Marsh
1703 William King
1730 John Hoadly
1743 Charles Cobbe
1765 William Carmichael
1766 Arthur Smyth
1772 John Cradock
1779 Robert Fowler
1801 Charles Agar [Earl of
      Normanton]
1809 Euseby Cleaver
1820 John George Beresford
1822 William Magee
1831 Richard Whately
Kildare united to Dublin 1846
1864 Richard Chenevix Trench, res.
1885 William Conyngham [Lord
      Plunket]
1897 Joseph Ferguson Peacocke
1915 John Henry Bernard
1919 Charles Frederick D'Arcy
1920 John Allen Fitzgerald Gregg
1939 Arthur William Barton
1956 George Otto Simms
1969 Alan Alexander Buchanan
1977 Henry Robert McAdoo
1985 Donald Arthur Richard Caird

†Emly

Raidghil 881
Ua Ruaich 953
Faelan 980
MaelFinan 1030
Diarmait Ua Flainnchua 1114
1152 Gilla in Choimhded Ua
      h-Ardmhail Mael Isu Ua
      Laigenain 1163
1172 Ua Meic Stia
1177 Charles O'Buacalla
1177 Isaac O'Hamery
1192 Ragnall Ua Flainnchua
1205 M.
1209 William
1212 Henry
1227 John Collingham
1238 Daniel
1238 Christianus
1251 Gilbert O'Doverty
1266 Florence or Laurence O'hAirt
1272 Matthew MacGormain
1275 David O Cossaig
1286 William de Clifford
1306 Thomas Cantock [Quantock]
1309 William Roughead
1335 Richard le Walleys
1353 John Esmond
1363 David Penlyn [Foynlyn]

1405 Nicholas Ball
1421 John Rishberry
1422 Robert Windell
1428 Thomas de Burgo
1428 Robert Portland
1445 Cornelius O Cuinnlis
1444 Robert
1448 Cornelius O Maolalaidh
1449 William O Hetigan
1476 Pilib O Cathail
1494 Donatus Mac Briain
1498 Cinneidigh Mac Briain
1507 Tomas O hUrthaille
1543 Angus O'Hernan
1551 Raymond de Burgo
United to **Cashel** 1569
Transferred to **Limerick** 1976

†Ferns

−598 Edar *or* Maedoc *or* Hugh
 Maeldogair 676
 Coman 678
 Diratus 693
 Cillenius 715
 Cairbre O'Kearney 1095
 Ceallach Ua Colmain 1117
 Mael Eoin Ua Dunacain 1125
 Ua Cattain 1135
1178 Loseph Ua h-Aeda
1186 Ailbe Ua Maelmuaid [Albinus]
1224 John of St. John
1254 Geoffrey of St. John
1258 Hugh of Lamport
1283 Richard of Northampton
1304 Simon of Evesham
1305 Robert Walrand
1312 Adam of Northampton
1347 Hugh de Saltu [of Leixlip]
1347 Geoffrey Grandfeld
1349 John Esmond
1350 William Charnells
1363 Thomas Dene
1400 Patrick Barret
1418 Robert Whittey
1453 Tadhg O Beirn
1457 John Purcell I
1479 Laurence Nevill
1505 Edmund Comerford
1510 Nicholas Comyn
1519 John Purcell II
1539 Alexander Devereux
1566 John Devereux
1582 Hugh Allen
Leighlin united to Ferns 1597
1600 Robert Grave
1601 Nicholas Statford
1605 Thomas Ram
1635 George Andrews
1661 Robert Price
1667 Richard Boyle
1683 Narcissus Marsh
1691 Bartholomew Vigors
1722 Josiah Hort
1727 John Hoadly
1730 Arthur Price
1734 Edward Synge
1740 George Stone
1743 William Cottrell
1744 Robert Downes
1752 John Garnet
1758 William Carmichael
1758 Thomas Salmon
1759 Richard Robinson
1761 Charles Jackson
1765 Edward Young
1772 Joseph Deane Bourke
1782 Walter Cope
1787 William Preston
1789 Euseby Cleaver

1809 Percy Jocelyn
1820 Robert Ponsonby Tottenham
 Loftus
1822 Thomas Elrington
United to **Ossory** 1835

†Glendalough

 Dairchell 678
 Eterscel 814
 Dungal 904
 Cormac 927
 Nuadha 920 [or Neva]
 Gilda Na Naomh *c*1080
 Cormac O'Mail 1101
 Aed Ua Modain 1126
1140 Anonymous
1152 Gilla na Naem
1157 Cinaed O Ronain [Celestinus]
1176 Maelcallann Ua Cleirchen
 [Malchus]
1186 Macrobius
1192 William Piro
1214 Robert de Bedford
United to **Dublin**
After the union with Dublin some rival
bishops appear
*c*1216 Bricheus
1468 John
1475 Michael
1481 Denis White
 John 1494
1494 Ivo Ruffi
1495 John
1500 Francis Fitzjohn of Corduba

†Iniscattery (Scattery Island)

 861 Aidan
 959 Cinaeda O'Chommind
 973 Scandlam O'Lenz
 O'Bruil 1069
 O'Bruil II 1081
 Dermot O Lennain 1119
 Aed Ua Bechain 1 188
 Cearbhal Ua'h-Enna [Carolus]
 1193
1360 Tomas Mac Mathghamhna
1392 John Donkan
1414 Richard Belmer
 Dionysius 1447
1447 John Grene
Incorporated with **Limerick**

†Kells

 Mael Finnen 968
*c*1152 Tuathal Ua Connachtarg
1185 Anonymous
1202 M. Ua Dobailen
Incorporated with **Meath**

†Kildare

 Conlaedh 520
 Hugh [or Hed] the Black 639
 Maeldoborcon 709
 Eutigern 762
 Lomthiull 787
 Snedbran 787
 Tuatchar 834
 Orthanach 840
 Aedgene Britt 864
 Macnghal 870
 Lachtnan 875
 Suibhne 881
 Scannal 885
 Lergus 888
 Mael Findan 950
 Annchadh 981
 Murrough McFlan 986

1030 MaelMartain
 MaelBrighde 1042
 Finn 1085
 MaelBrighde O Brolchan 1097
 Hugh [Heremon] 1100
 Ferdomnach 1101
 Cormac O Cathassaig 1146
 Ua Duibhin 1148
1152 Finn mac Mael Muire Mac
 Cianain
 Fin mac Gussain Ua Gormain
1161 Malachias Ua Brain
1177 Nehemias
1206 Cornelius Mac Fealain
1223 Ralph of Bristol
1233 John of Taunton
1258 Simon of Kilkenny
1280 Nicholas Cusack
1300 Walter Calf [de Veel]
1333 Richard Houlot
1352 Thomas Giffard
1366 Robert of Aketon [Acton]
1404 John Madock
1431 William fitzEdward
1449 Geoffrey Hereford
1456 John Bole [Bull]
1464 Richard Lang
1474 David Cone
1475 James Wall
 William Barret
1480 Edward Lane
1526 Thomas Dillon
1529 Walter Wellesley
1540 William Miagh
1550 Thomas Lancaster
1555 Thomas Leverous
1560 Alexander Craik
1564 Robert Daly
1583 Daniel Neylan
1604 William Pilsworth
1636 Robert Ussher
1644 William Golborne
1661 Thomas Price
1667 Ambrose Jones
1679 Anthony Dopping
1682 William Moreton
1705 Welbore Ellis
1731 Charles Cobbe
1743 George Stone
1745 Thomas Fletcher
1761 Richard Robinson
1765 Charles Jackson
1790 George Lewis Jones
1804 Charles Lindsay
United to **Dublin** after the death of Bp
Lindsay in 1846
1976 Separated from Dublin and
united to **Meath**

†Kilfenora

1172 Anonymous
1205 F.
1224 Johannes
1254 Christianus
 Anonymous 1264
1266 Mauricius
1273 Florentius O Tigernaig
1281 Congalach [O Lochlainn]
1291 G.
1299 Simon O Cuirrin
1303 Maurice O Briain
1323 Risdeard O Lochlainn
*c*1355 Dionysius
1372 Henricus
 Cornelius
1390 Patricius
1421 Feidhlimidh mac Mathghamhna
 O Lochlainn [Florentius]

1433 Fearghal
1434 Dionysius O Connmhaigh
1447 John Greni
1476 [? Denis] O Tombaigh
1491 Muircheartach mac Murchadha
     O Briain [Mauricius]
1514 Maurice O'Kelly
1541 John O'Neylan
–1585 Daniel, bishop-elect
1606 Bernard Adams [with Limerick
     q.v.]
1617 John Steere
1622 William Murray
[1628 Richard Betts, not consecrated]
1630 James Heygate
1638 Robert Sibthorp
1661–1741 Held by the Archbishops
    of Tuam
1742–52 Held by the Bishop of
    Clonfert
    United to **Killaloe** 1752

†Killaloe

BISHOPS

    O'Gerruidher 1054
    Domnall Ua hEnna 1098
    Mael Muire O Dunain 1117
    Domnall Ua Conaing 1131
    Domnall Ua Longargain 1137
    Tadg Ua Longargain 1161
    Donnchad mac Diarmata Ua
     Briain 1164
1179 Constantin mac Toirrdelbaig Ua
     Briain
1194 Diarmait Ua Conaing
1201 Conchobhar Ua h-Enna
    [Cornelius]
1217 Robert Travers
1221 Domnall Ua h-Enna [Donatus]
1231 Domnall O Cenneitig [Donatus]
1253 Isoc O Cormacain [Isaac]
1268 Mathgamain O h-Ocain [O
    Hogan]
1281 Maurice O h-Ocain
1299 David Mac Mathghamna [Mac
    Mahon]
1317 Tomas O Cormacain I
1323 Brian O Cosgraig
1326 David Mac Briain [David of
    Emly]
?1326 Natus O Heime
1343 Tomas O h-Ogain
1355 Tomas O Cormacain II
1389 Mathghamain Mag Raith
1400 Donatus Mag Raith
1409 Robert Mulfield
1418 Eugenius O Faolain
1423 Thadeus Mag Raith I
1429 Seamus O Lonnghargain
1443 Donnchadh mac
    Toirdhealbhaigh O Briain
1460 Thadeus Mag Raith II
1463 Matthaeus O Griobhtha
1483 Toirdhealbhach mac
    Mathghamhna O Briain
    [Theodoricus]
1523 Thadeus
1526 Seamus O Cuirrin
1546 Cornelius O Dea
1554 Turlough [or Terence] O'Brien II
1570 Maurice [or Murtagh] O'Brien-
    Arra
1613 John Rider
1633 Lewis Jones
1647 Edward Parry
1661 Edward Worth
1669 Daniel Wytter
1675 John Roan

1693 Henry Ryder
1696 Thomas Lindsay
1713 Thomas Vesey
1714 Nicholas Forster
1716 Charles Carr
1740 Joseph Story
1742 John Ryder
1743 Jemmet Browne
1745 Richard Chenevix
1746 Nicholas Synge
Kilfenora united to Killaloe 1752
1771 Robert Fowler
1779 George Chinnery
1780 Thomas Barnard
1794 William Knox
1803 Charles Dalrymple Lindsay
1804 Nathaniel Alexander
1804 Robert Ponsonby Tottenham
    Loftus
1820 Richard Mant
1823 Alexander Arbuthnot
1828 Richard Ponsonby
1831 Edmund Knox [with Clonfert]
Clonfert united to Killaloe 1834
Kilmacduagh united to Killaloe 1834
1834 Christopher Butson
1836 Stephen Crengh Sandes
1839 Ludlow Tonson [afterwards
    Baron Riversdale]
1862 William FitzGerald
1884 William Bennet Chester
1893 Frederick Richards Wynne
1897 Mervyn Archdall
1912 Charles Benjamin Dowse
1913 Thomas Sterling Berry, res.
1924 Henry Edmund Patton
1943 Robert M'Neil Boyd
1945 Hedley Webster
1953 Richard Gordon Perdue
1957 Henry Arthur Stanistreet
1972 Edwin Owen
1976 United to **Limerick**

†Kilmacduagh

? Ua Cleirig 1137
Imar Ua Ruaidin 1176
Rugnad O'Rowan 1178
1179 Mac Gilla Cellaig Ua Ruaidin
1206 Ua Cellaig
    Mael Muire O Connmaig 1224
1227 Aed [Odo]
    Conchobhar O Muiredaig 1247
1248 Gilla Cellaig O Ruaidin
    [Gilbertus]
1249 David yFredrakern
1254 Mauricius O Leaain
1284 David O Setachain
1290 Luirint O Lachtnain
    [Laurentius]
1307 Lucas
1326 Johannes
1360 Nicol O Leaain
1394 Gregory O Leaain
1405 Enri O Connmhaigh
1409 Dionysius
1409 Eugene O Faolain
1418 Diarmaid O Donnchadha
1419 Nicol O Duibhghiolla
1419 Seaan O Connmhaigh
1441 Dionysius O Donnchadha
1479 Cornelius O Mullony
1503 Matthaeus O Briain
1533 Christopher Bodkin
1573 Stephen O'Kirwan
[1584 Thomas Burke, not consecrated]
1587 Roland Lynch
1627–1836 Held in commendam by
    the Bishops of Clonfert
United to **Killaloe** since 1834

†Leighlin

–633 Laserian or Molaise
–865 Mainchin
–940 Conella McDonegan
    Daniel 969
    Cleitic O'Muinic 1050
c1096 Ferdomnac
    Mael Eoin Ua Dunacain 1125
    Sluaigedach Ua Cathain 1145
1152 Dungal O Caellaide
1192 Johannes
1197 Johannes
1202 Herlewin
1217 Richard [Fleming]
1228 William le Chauniver
1252 Thomas
1275 Nicholas Chever
1309 Maurice de Blanchville
1321 Meiler le Poer
1344 Radulphus O Ceallaigh
1349 Thomas of Brakenberg
1360 Johannes
1362 William (not consecrated)
1363 John Young
1371 Philip FitzPeter
1385 John Griffin
1398 Thomas Peverell
1400 Richard Bocomb
1419 John Mulgan
1432 Thomas Fleming
— Diarmaid 1464
1464 Milo Roche
1490 Nicholas Magwyr
1513 Thomas Halsey
1524 Mauricius O Deoradhain
1527 Matthew Sanders
1550 Robert Travers
1555 Thomas O'Fihelly
1567 Donnell or Daniel Cavanagh
1589 Richard Meredith
United to **Ferns** since 1597 on the
death of Bp Meredith

Limerick

*Limerick, Ardfert, Aghadoe, Killaloe,
Kilfenora, Clonfert, Kilmacduagh and
Emly*

–1106 Gilli alias Gilla Espaic
1140 Patricius
1150 Erolb [? = Harold]
1152 Torgesius
1179 Brictius
1203 Donnchad Ua'Briain [Donatus]
1207 Geoffrey
–1215 Edmund
1223 Hubert de Burgo
1252 Robert de Emly or Neil
1273 Gerald [or Miles] de Mareshall
1302 Robert de Dundonald
1312 Eustace de Aqua or de l'Eau
1336 Maurice de Rochfort
1354 Stephen Lawless
1360 Stephen Wall [de Valle]
1369 Peter Curragh
1399 Bernardus O Conchobhair
1400 Conchobhar O Deadhaidh
1426 John Mothel res.
Iniscattery incorporated with Limerick
1456 Thomas Leger
1458 William Russel, *alias* Creagh
1463 Thomas Arthur
[1486 Richard Stakpoll, not
    consecrated]
1486 John Dunowe
1489 John O'Phelan [Folan]
1524 Sean O Cuinn
1551 William Casey
1557 Hugh de Lacey or Lees, dep.

1571 William Casey (again)
1594 John Thornburgh
1604 Bernard Adams
1626 Francis Gough
1634 George Webb
1643 Robert Sibthorp
Ardfert united to Limerick 1661
1661 Edward Synge
1664 William Fuller
1667 Francis Marsh
1673 John Vesey
1679 Simon Digby
1692 Nathaniel Wilson
1695 Thomas Smyth
1725 William Burscough
1755 James Leslie
1771 James Averill
1772 William Gore
1784 William Cecil Pery
1794 Thomas Barnard
1806 Charles Morgan Warburton
1820 Thomas Elrington
1823 John Jebb
1834 Edmund Knox
1849 William Higgin
1854 Henry Griffin
1866 Charles Graves
1899 Thomas Bunbury
1907 Raymond D'Audemra Orpen
1921 Harry Vere White
1934 Charles King Irwin
1942 Evelyn Charles Hodges
1961 Robert Wyse Jackson
1970 Donald Arthur Richard Caird
Killaloe united to Limerick 1976
Emily transferred to Limerick 1976
1976 Edwin Owen
1984 Walton Hewcombe Francis
      Empey
1985 Edward Flewett Darling

†Lismore

      Ronan 764
      Cormac MacCuillenan 918
-999 Cinneda O'Chonmind
      Niall mac Meic Aedacain 1113
      Ua Daightig 1119
1121 Mael Isu Ua h-Ainmere
      Mael Muire Ua Loingsig 1150
1151 Gilla Crist Ua Connairche
      [Christianus]
1179 Felix
Ardmore incorporated with Lismore
      1192
1203 Malachias, O'Heda or O'Danus
1216 Thomas
1219 Robert of Bedford
1228 Griffin Christopher
1248 Ailinn O Suilleabain
1253 Thomas
1270 John Roche
1280 Richard Corre
1309 William Fleming
1310 R.
1322 John Leynagh
1356 Roger Cradock, provision
      annulled
1358 Thomas le Reve
United to **Waterford** 1363

Meath

Meath and Kildare

BISHOPS OF THE SEE OF
CLONARD
      Senach 588
-640 Colman 654
      Dubhduin O'Phelan 718
      Tole 738

-778 Fulartach 779
      Clothcu 796
      Clemens 826
      Cormac MacSuibhne
      Cumsuth 858
      Suarlech 870
      Ruman MacCathasaid 922
      Colman MacAilild 926
      Tuathal O'Dubhamaigh 1028

BISHOPS OF MEATH
1096 Mael Muire Ua Dunain
1128 Eochaid O Cellaig
1151 Etru Ua Miadacain [Eleuzerius]
1177 Echtigern mac Mael Chiarain
      [Eugenius]
1192 Simon Rochfort
(The See was transferred from Clonard
to Newtown near Trim, 1202)
Kells incorporated with Meath
1224 Donan De [Deodatus] (not
      consecrated)
1227 Ralph Petit
1231 Richard de la Corner
1253 Geoffrey Cusack
1255 Hugo de Taghmon
1283 Walter de Fulburn
1287 Thomas St. Leger
1322 Seoan Mac Cerbaill [John
      MacCarwill]
1327 William de Paul
1350 William St. Leger
1353 Nicholas [Allen]
1369 Stephen de Valle [Wall]
1380 William Andrew
1385 Alexander Petit *or* de Balscot
1401 Robert Montayne
1412 Edward Dant sey
[1430 Thomas Scurlog, apparently
      not consecrated]
1430 William Hadsor
1435 William Silk
1450 Edmund Ouldhall
1460 William Shirwood
1483 John Payne
1507 William Rokeby
1512 Hugh Inge
1523 Richard Wilson
1529 Edward Staples
1554 William Walsh
1563 Hugh Brady
Clonmacnoise united to Meath 1569
1584 Thomas Jones
1605 Roger Dod
1612 George Montgomery
1621 James Usher
1625 Anthony Martin
      [Interregnum 1650–61]
1661 Henry Leslie
1661 Henry Jones
1682 Anthony Dopping
1697 Richard Tennison
1705 William Moreton
1716 John Evans
1724 Henry Downes
1727 Ralph Lambert
1732 Welbore Ellis
1734 Arthur Price
1744 Henry Maule
1758 William Carmichael
1765 Richard Pococke
1765 Arthur Smyth
1766 Henry Maxwell
1798 Thomas Lewis O'Beirne
1823 Nathaniel Alexander
1840 Charles Dickinson
1842 Edward Stopford
1850 Thomas Stewart Townsend
1852 James Henderson Singer
1866 Samuel Butcher

1876 William Conyngham, Lord
      Plunket
1885 Charles Parsons Reichel
1894 Joseph Ferguson Peacocke
1897 James Bennett Keene
1919 Benjamin John Plunket
1926 Thomas Gibson George Collins
1927 John Orr
1938 William Hardy Holmes
1945 James McCann
1959 Robert Bonsall Pike
Kildare united to Meath 1976
1976 Donald Arthur Richard Caird
1985 Walton Newcombe Francis
      Empey

†Ossory

      Dermot 973
1152 Domnall Ua Fogartaig
1180 Felix Ua Duib Slaine
1202 Hugo de Rous [Hugo Rufus]
1220 Peter Mauveisin
1231 William of Kilkenny
1233 Walter de Brackley
1245 Geoffrey de Turville
1251 Hugh de Mapilton
1260 Geoffrey St. Leger
1287 Roger of Wexford
1289 Michael d'Exeter
1303 William FitzJohn
1317 Richard Ledred
1361 John de Tatenhale
1366 William
—   John of Oxford
1371 Alexander Petit [de Balscot]
1387 Richard Northalis
1396 Thomas Peverell
1399 John Waltham
1400 John Griffin
1400 John
1401 Roger Appleby
1402 John Waltham (again)
1407 Thomas Snell
1417 Patrick Foxe
1421 Dionysius O Deadhaidh
1427 Thomas Barry
1460 David Hacket
1479 Seaan O hEidigheain
1487 Oliver Cantwell
1528 Milo Baron [or FitzGerald]
1553 John Bale
1554 John Tonory
1567 Christopher Gaffney
1577 Nicholas Walsh
1586 John Horsfall
1610 Richard Deane
1613 Jonas Wheeler
1641 Griffith Williams
1672 John Parry
1678 Benjamin Parry
1678 Michael Ward
1680 Thomas Otway
1693 John Hartstonge
1714 Thomas Vesey
1731 Edward Tennison
1736 Charles Este
1741 Anthony Dopping
1743 Michael Cox
1754 Edward Maurice
1755 Richard Pococke
1765 Charles Dodgson
1775 William Newcome
1779 John Hotham
1782 William Heresford
1795 Thomas Lewis O'Beirne
1799 Hugh Hamilton
1806 John Kearney
1813 Robert Fowler
Ferns united to **Ossory** 1835

1842 James Thomas O'Brien
1874 Robert Samuel Gregg
1878 William Fakenham Walsh
1897 John Baptist Crozier
1907 Charles Frederick D'Arcy
1911 John Henry Bernard
1915 John Allen Fitzgerald Gregg
1920 John Godfrey FitzMaurice
      Day
1938 Ford Tichbourne
1940 John Percy Phair
1962 Henry Robert McAdoo
1977 United to **Cashel**

†Ross

Nechtan MacNechtain 1160
Isaac O'Cowen 1161
O'Carroll 1168
1177 Benedictus
1192 Mauricius
1198 Daniel
1224 Fineen O Clothna [Florentiusl
c1250 Malachy
1254 Mauricius
1269 Walter O Mithigein
1275 Peter O h-Uallachain [? Patrick]
1291 Laurentius
1310 Matthaeus O Finn
1331 Laurentius O h-Uallachain
1336 Dionysius
1379 Bernard O Conchobhair
1399 Peter Curragh
1400 Thadeus O Ceallaigh
1401 Mac Raith O hEidirsgeoil
      [Macrobius]
1402 Stephen Brown
1403 Matthew
1418 Walter Formay
1424 John Bloxworth
1426 Conchobhar Mac Fhaolchadha
      [Cornelius]
      Maurice Brown 1431

1431 Walter of Leicester
1434 Richard Clerk
1448 Domhnall O Donnobhain
      John 1460
1460 Robert Colynson
−1464 Thomas
1464 John Hornse *alias* Skipton
1473 Aodh O hEidirsgeoil [Odo]
1482 Tadhg Mac Carthaigh
1494 John Edmund Courci
1517 Seaan O Muirthile
1519 Tadgh O Raghallaigh
      [Thaddeus]
1523 Bonaventura
1526 Diarmaid Mac Carthaigh
1544 Dermot McDonnell
1551 John
1554 Maurice O'Fihelly
1559 Maurice O'Hea
1561 Thomas O'Herlihy
1582 William Lyon [with Cork and
      Cloyne after 1581]
United to **Cork** 1583

†Waterford

1096 Mael lus Ua h-Ainmere
1152 Toistius
1175 Augustinus Ua Selbaig
      Anonymous 1199
1200 Robert I
1204 David the Welshman
1210 Robert II [Breathnach]
1223 William Wace
1227 Walter
1232 Stephen
1250 Henry
1252 Philip
1255 Walter de Southwell
1274 Stephen de Fulbourn
1286 Walter de Fulbourn
1308 Matthew
1323 Nicholas Welifed

1338 Richard Francis
1349 Robert Elyot
1350 Roger Cradock
Lismore united to Waterford 1363
1363 Thomas le Reve
1394 Robert Read
1396 Thomas Sparklord
1397 John Deping
1400 Thomas Snell
1407 Roger of Appleby (*see under*
      Ossory)
1409 John Geese
1414 Thomas Colby
1421 John Geese (again)
1426 Richard Cantwell
1446 Robert Poer
1473 Richard Martin
1475 John Bulcomb
1480 Nicol O hAonghusa
1483 Thomas Purcell
1519 Nicholas Comyn
1551 Patrick Walsh
1579 Marmaduke Middleton
1582 Miler Magrath [in com. with
      Cashel, see below]
1589 Thomas Wetherhead *or* Walley
1592 Miler Magrath (again)
1608 John Lancaster
1619 Michael Boyle
1636 John Atherton
1641 Archibald Adair
1661 George Baker
1666 Hugh Gore
1691 Nathaniel Foy
1708 Thomas Mills
1740 Charles Este
1746 Richard Chenevix
1779 William Newcome
1795 Richard Marlay
1802 Power le Poer Trench
1810 Joseph Stock
1813 Richard Bourke
United to **Cashel** under Church
Temporalities Act 1833

CATHEDRALS

Church of England

(BATH AND) WELLS (St Andrew)   DEAN R LEWIS
CANS RES P G WALKER, G O FARRAN, P de N LUCAS
EDUCN OFFICER C M BONNEYWELL
BIRMINGHAM (St Philip)   PROVOST P A BERRY
CANS RES VEN C J G BARTON, A H F LUFF,
RT REV M H D WHINNEY   SUCC M F PALMER
BLACKBURN (St Mary)   PROVOST D FRAYNE
CANS RES K J PARFITT, J M TAYLOR
BRADFORD (St Peter)   PROVOST J S RICHARDSON
CAN RES K H COOK, C G LEWIS   CHAPL J P SMITH
BRISTOL (Holy Trinity)   DEAN A W CARR
CANS RES P F JOHNSON, A L J REDFERN, J L SIMPSON
SUCC R H CHUBB   CHAPL S A N DARLEY
CANTERBURY (Christ)   DEAN J A SIMPSON
CANS RES P G C BRETT, M J CHANDLER, R H C SYMON
VEN M S TILL   PREC S SEALY
CARLISLE (Holy Trinity)   DEAN H E C STAPLETON
CANS RES R A CHAPMAN, D T I JENKINS, D H DIXON,
VEN W F EWBANK, D W V WESTON
CHELMSFORD (St Mary, St Peter and St Cedd)
PROVOST J H MOSES   CANS RES D C KNIGHT, B P THOMPSON,
T THOMPSON, D SHERLOCK, F J HACKETT, J K HAYWARD,
J N JOHNSON   CHAPL J D JONES
CHESTER (Christ and Blessed Virgin Mary)
DEAN S S SMALLEY   CANS RES T J DENNIS, J W S NEWCOME,
O A CONWAY, R M REES
CHICHESTER (Holy Trinity)   DEAN J D TREADGOLD
CANS RES R T GREENACRE, F J HAWKINS, J F HESTER
PRIEST VICAR D NASON
COVENTRY (St Michael)   PROVOST J F PETTY
CANS RES P OESTREICHER, V F FAULL, J C BURCH
CHAPL A E DARBY
DERBY (All Saints)   PROVOST B H LEWERS
CANS RES G A CHESTERMAN, G O MARSHALL, R M PARSONS
DURHAM (Christ and Blessed Virgin Mary)
DEAN J R ARNOLD   CANS RES D W BROWN, R L COPPIN,
VEN J D HODGSON, G S PEDLEY, M C PERRY
PREC D J MEAKIN
ELY (Holy Trinity)   DEAN M J HIGGINS
CANS RES D J GREEN
EXETER (St Peter)   DEAN R M EYRE
CANS RES A C MAWSON, K C PARRY, D J ISON
PRIEST VICAR G DAXTER
GLOUCESTER (St Peter and Holy Trinity)
DEAN K N JENNINGS   CANS RES N CHATFIELD,
N C HEAVISIDES, R P GREENWOOD, R D M GREY
CHAPL J Y TILLIER
GUILDFORD (Holy Spirit)   DEAN A G WEDDERSPOON
CANS RES J M SCHOFIELD, R D FENWICK, F S TELFER
HEREFORD (Blessed Virgin Mary and St Ethelbert)
DEAN R A WILLIS   CANS RES P R ILES, A R OSBORNE,
J F BUTTERWORTH, J TILLER   SUCC A C HUTCHINSON
LEICESTER (St Martin)   PROVOST D N HOLE
CAN RES M T H BANKS, M WILSON   PREC J N CRAIG
LICHFIELD (Blessed Virgin Mary and St Chad)
DEAN N T WRIGHT   CANS RES A N BARNARD, J HOWE,
VEN R B NINIS, C W TAYLOR
LINCOLN (Blessed Virgin Mary)   DEAN B D JACKSON
CANS RES B R DAVIS, A J STOKES, V P WHITE
LIVERPOOL (Christ)   DEAN R D C WALTERS
CANS RES D J HUTTON, H G THOMAS, M M WOLFE,
M C BOYLING   CHAPL J C LYNN
LONDON (St Paul)   DEAN T E EVANS
CANS RES VEN G H CASSIDY, R J HALLIBURTON,
C J HILL, M J SAWARD   MIN CANS C J MANN,
J R LEES   CHAPL J M PAUL
MANCHESTER (St Mary, St Denys and St George)
DEAN K J RILEY   CANS RES J R ATHERTON, B DUNCAN,
VEN R B HARRIS, A E RADCLIFFE
NEWCASTLE (St Nicholas)   PROVOST N G COULTON
CANS RES R LANGLEY, P R STRANGE
NORWICH (Holy Trinity)   DEAN S G PLATTEN
CANS RES C J OFFER, R J HANMER, M F PERHAM

OXFORD (Christ Church)   DEAN J H DRURY
CANS RES RT REV A R McGORDON, O M T O'DONOVAN,
J M PEIRCE, J S K WARD
VEN F V WESTON   PREC A C BALLARD
PETERBOROUGH (St Peter, St Paul and St Andrew)
DEAN M BUNKER   CANS RES T R CHRISTIE, J HIGHAM,
T WILLMOTT
PORTSMOUTH (St Thomas of Canterbury)
PROVOST M L YORKE   CANS RES C J BRADLEY, J B HEDGES,
D T ISAAC
RIPON (St Peter and St Wilfrid)   DEAN J A R METHUEN
CANS RES D G FORD, M R GLANVILLE-SMITH,
P J MARSHALL   MIN CANS E D MURFET, M P SPURGEON,
D G PATON-WILLIAMS
ROCHESTER (Christ and Blessed Virgin Mary)
DEAN E F SHOTTER   CANS RES J M ARMSON, R J R LEA,
E R TURNER, VEN N L WARREN   SUCC S M GRIFFITHS
ST ALBANS (St Alban)   DEAN C A LEWIS
CANS RES C GARNER, G R S RITSON, M C SANSOM,
C R J FOSTER   PREC J BOARDMAN
ST EDMUNDSBURY (St James)   PROVOST J E ATWELL
CANS RES M E MINGINS, A M SHAW   SUCC W N PRICE
SALISBURY (Blessed Virgin Mary)   DEAN H G DICKINSON
CANS RES D J C DAVIES, D M K DURSTON, P D SLATER
SHEFFIELD (St Peter and St Paul)   PROVOST M SADGROVE
CANS RES T M PAGE VEN S R LOWE, J E M SINCLAIR,
C M SMITH
SODOR AND MAN (St German)   DEAN THE BISHOP
CAN PREC B H KELLY
SOUTHWARK (St Saviour and St Mary Overie)
PROVOST C B SLEE   CANS RES D J ATKINSON, M KITCHEN,
D S PAINTER, R S WHITE   SUCC G D SWINTON
SOUTHWELL (Blessed Virgin Mary)   PROVOST D LEANING
CANS RES M R AUSTIN, I G COLLINS, D P KEENE
VICAR CHORAL J A WARDLE
TRURO (St Mary)   DEAN D J SHEARLOCK
CANS RES VEN R L RAVENSCROFT, P R GAY, K P MELLOR
WAKEFIELD (All Saints)   PROVOST J E ALLEN
CANS RES R D BAXTER, I C KNOX, G P NAIRN-BRIGGS
D O'CONNOR   CHAPL A JENNINGS
WINCHESTER (Holy Trinity, St Peter St Paul and St
Swithun)   DEAN T R BEESON   CANS RES A F KNIGHT,
C STEWART, P B MORGAN, A K WALKER
WORCESTER (Christ and Blessed Virgin Mary)
DEAN R M C JEFFERY   CANS RES VEN F W H BENTLEY,
I M MacKENZIE, D G THOMAS   PREC T E HOLME
YORK (St Peter)   DEAN R FURNELL
CANS RES R METCALFE, E R NORMAN, J TOY
P J FERGUSON

Collegiate Churches

COLLEGIATE CHURCH OF ST PETER, Westminster
(Westminster Abbey)   DEAN M C O MAYNE
CANS P S BATES, D C GRAY, VEN A E HARVEY,
C D SEMPER   PREC B D FENTON   CHAPL J M GOODALL
QUEEN'S FREE CHAPEL OF ST GEORGE
Windsor Castle (St George's Chapel)   DEAN P R MITCHELL
CANS A A COLDWELLS, M A MOXON, D M STANESBY,
J A WHITE   MIN CANS T J HARVEY, A G GYLE

Diocese in Europe

GIBRALTAR (Holy Trinity)   DEAN B W HORLOCK
MALTA Valletta (St Paul)   PRO-CATHEDRAL
CAN Vacant
BRUSSELS (Holy Trinity)   PRO-CATHEDRAL
DEAN RT REV H W SCRIVEN *Bishop in Europe*
CAN N M WALKER

Church in Wales

The name of the Dean is given, together with other clergy holding full-time appointments.

BANGOR (St Deiniol) DEAN T E P EDWARDS
  MIN CAN E ROBERTS R W TOWNSEND
LLANDAFF (St Peter and St Paul) DEAN J ROGERS
  MIN CAN J F REDVERS HARRIS, N J K COURT
MONMOUTH Newport (St Woolos) DEAN D G LEWIS
  MIN CAN T J G S COOPER, D S TURNER
ST ASAPH (St Asaph) DEAN T R K GOULSTONE
  PRIEST VICAR R H GRIFFITHS MIN CAN C A MITCHELL
ST DAVIDS (St David and St Andrew) DEAN J W EVANS
  MIN CAN J O ESAU, R B WEBLEY
(SWANSEA AND) BRECON (St John the
  Evangelist) DEAN J HARRIS
  CAN RES E C JOHN MIN CAN M J BATCHELOR

Scottish Episcopal Church

For the members of the chapter the *Year Book and Directory of the Scottish Episcopal Church* should be consulted.

Aberdeen and Orkney

ABERDEEN (St Andrew) PROVOST W D WIGHTMAN

Argyll and The Isles

OBAN (St John) PROVOST A M MACLEAN
CUMBRAE (Holy Spirit) Cathedral of The Isles
  PROVOST D M CAMERON

Brechin

DUNDEE (St Paul) PROVOST M J BUNCE

Edinburgh

EDINBURGH (St Mary) PROVOST G J T FORBES
  CHAPL J CUTHBERT

Glasgow and Galloway

GLASGOW (St Mary) PROVOST P B FRANCIS
  CURATE M N OXLEY CHAPL D REID

Moray, Ross and Caithness

INVERNESS (St Andrew) PROVOST M E GRANT

St Andrews, Dunkeld and Dunblane

PERTH (St Ninian) PROVOST K G FRANZ
  CURATES R B ANKER-PETERSEN, M D ROBSON

Church of Ireland

Most Cathedrals are parish churches and the Dean is usually, but not always, the incumbent. For the members of the chapter the Church of Ireland Directory should be consulted. The name of the Dean is given, together with other clergy holding full-time appointments.

NATIONAL CATHEDRAL OF ST PATRICK, Dublin
  DEAN M E STEWART DEAN'S VICAR C R J BRADLEY
CATHEDRAL OF ST ANNE, Belfast J SHEARER
(St Anne's is a cathedral of the dioceses of Down and
  Dromore and of Connor)

PROVINCE OF ARMAGH

Armagh

ARMAGH (St Patrick) H CASSIDY

Clogher

CLOGHER (St Macartan) DEAN T R MOORE
  J S FRAZIER
ENNISKILLEN (St Macartin) T R MOORE *Dean of
  Clogher*

Derry and Raphoe

DERRY (St Columb) D C ORR
RAPHOE (St Eunan) S R WHITE

Down and Dromore

DOWN (Holy and Undivided Trinity) H LECKEY
  CAN RES J A B MAYNE
DROMORE (Christ the Redeemer) D R CHILLINGWORTH
  W B NEILL

Connor

LISBURN (Christ) J A FAIR *Dean of Connor*
  J T McCAMMON

Kilmore, Elphin and Ardagh

KILMORE (St Fethlimidh) J C COMBE
SLIGO (St Mary and St John the Baptist) S I McGEE
Dean of Elphin and Ardagh

Tuam, Killala and Achonry

TUAM (St Mary) A M A PREVITE
KILLALA (St Patrick) E G ARDIS
ACHONRY (St Crumnathy) Vacant

PROVINCE OF DUBLIN

Dublin and Glendalough

DUBLIN (Holy Trinity) Christ Church J T F PATERSON

Meath and Kildare

TRIM (St Patrick) J A G BARRETT *Dean of Clonmacnoise*
KILDARE (St Brigid) R K TOWNLEY

Cashel and Ossory

CASHEL (St John the Baptist) P J KNOWLES
WATERFORD (Blessed Trinity) Christ Church W B A NEILL
LISMORE (St Carthage) C W WEEKES
KILKENNY (St Canice) N N LYNAS *Dean of Ossory*
LEIGHLIN (St Laserian) C A FAULL
FERNS (St Edan) L D A FORREST

Cork, Cloyne and Ross

CORK (St Fin Barr) R L CLARKE
CLOYNE (St Colman) G P ST J HILLIARD
ROSS (St Fachtna) R C A HENDERSON

Limerick and Killaloe

LIMERICK (St Mary) J M G SIRR
KILLALOE (St Flannan) Vacant

ROYAL PECULIARS, THE CHAPEL ROYAL AND COLLEGE OF CHAPLAINS

Royal Peculiars

WESTMINSTER ABBEY
ST GEORGE'S CHAPEL, WINDSOR
See Collegiate Churches, p 824

The Chapel Royal

Dean of the Chapels Royal   THE BISHOP OF LONDON
Sub-Dean of the Chapels Royal   W J BOOTH

The Chapel Royal, St James's Palace, and The Queen's Chapel, St James's

Priests in Ordinary   G D WATKINS, S E YOUNG
Deputy Priests   T M THORNTON, J G M W MURPHY, M M H MOORE, A H MEAD, VEN M J COLCLOUGH
Chaplain, Hampton Court Palace   M M H MOORE
Chaplain, HM Tower of London   J G M W MURPHY

Domestic Chaplains to The Queen

Buckingham Palace   W J BOOTH
Windsor Castle   THE DEAN OF WINDSOR
Sandringham   G R HALL

Royal Chapel of All Saints, Windsor Great Park

Chaplain   M A MOXON

Royal Almonry

High Almoner   RT REV J B TAYLOR (Bishop of Albans)
Sub-Almoner   W J BOOTH

The College of Chaplains

Clerk of the Closet   RT REV J WAINE (Bishop of Chelmsford)
Deputy Clerk of the Closet   W J BOOTH

Chaplains to The Queen

J D A ADAMS	I A HARDAKER	K S POUND
P L ASHFORD	J G HASLAM	J C PRIESTLEY
VEN F W H BENTLEY	J F HESTER	J P ROBSON
R A BOWDEN	C A C HILL	I G SMITH-
E BUCHANAN	C J HILL	CAMERON
D J BURGESS	K HUXLEY	J A STANLEY
R S CLARKE	G JONES	J SYKES
J O COLLING	M A MOXON	L F WEBBER
D C GRAY	J G M W MURPHY	D H WHEATON
D N GRIFFITHS	D G PALMER	
G R HALL	G S PEDLEY	

Extra Chaplains to The Queen

A D CAESAR	J R W STOTT	S A WILLIAMS
J S D MANSEL	E J G WARD	E A JAMES

The Queen's Chapel of the Savoy

Chaplain   W P ROBSON

Royal Memorial Chapel, Sandhurst

Chaplain   A J HEAGERTY

Royal Foundation of St Katharine in Ratcliffe

Master   M A JOHNSON

DIOCESAN OFFICES

CHURCH OF ENGLAND

BATH AND WELLS Diocesan Office, The Old Deanery, Wells, Somerset BA5 2UG
Tel: Wells (01749) 670777 Fax (01749) 674240

BIRMINGHAM Diocesan Office, 175 Harborne Park Road, Harborne, Birmingham B17 0BH
Tel: Birmingham (0121) 427 5141 Fax (0121) 428 1114

BLACKBURN Church House, Cathedral Close, Blackburn, Lancs BB1 5AA
Tel: Blackburn (01254) 54421 Fax (01254) 667309

BRADFORD Diocesan Office, Cathedral Hall, Stott Hill, Bradford, W Yorkshire BD1 4ET
Tel: Bradford (01274) 725958 Fax (01274) 726343

BRISTOL Diocesan Church House, 23 Great George Street, Bristol BS15QZ
Tel: Bristol (0117) 921 4411 Fax (0117) 925 0460

CANTERBURY Diocesan House, Lady Wootton's Green, Canterbury, Kent CT1 1NQ
Tel: Canterbury (01227) 459401 Fax (01227) 450964

CARLISLE Church House, West Walls, Carlisle, Cumbria CA3 8UE
Tel: Carlisle (01228) 22573 Fax (01228) 48769

CHELMSFORD Guy Harlings, 53 New Street, Chelmsford, Essex CM1 1AT
Tel: Chelmsford (01245) 266731 Fax (01245) 492786

CHESTER Diocesan House, Raymond Street, Chester CH1 4PN
Tel: Chester (01244) 379222 Fax (01244) 383835

CHICHESTER Diocesan Church House, 211 New Church Road, Hove, E Sussex BN3 4ED
Tel: Brighton (01273) 421021 Fax (01273) 421041

COVENTRY Church House, Palmerston Road, Coventry CV5 6FJ
Tel/Fax: Coventry (01203) 674328

DERBY Derby Church House, Full Street, Derby DE1 3DR
Tel: Derby (01332) 382233 Fax (01332) 292969

DURHAM Diocesan Office, Auckland Castle, Market Place, Bishop Auckland,
 Co. Durham DL14 7QJ
Tel: Bishop Auckland (01388) 604515 Fax (01388) 603695

ELY Diocesan Office, Bishop Woodford House, Barton Road, Ely, Cambs CB7 4DX
Tel: Ely (01353) 663579 Fax (01353) 666148

EUROPE Diocesan Office, 14 Tufton Street, Westminster, London, SW1P 3QZ
Tel: (0171) 976 8001 Fax (0171) 976 8002

EXETER Diocesan House, Palace Gate, Exeter, Devon EX1 1HX
Tel: Exeter (01392) 72686 Fax (01392) 499594

GLOUCESTER Church House, College Green, Gloucester GL1 2LY
Tel: Gloucester (01452) 410022 Fax (01452) 308324

GUILDFORD Diocesan House, Quarry Street, Guildford, Surrey GU1 3XG
Tel: Guildford (01483) 571826 Fax (01483) 67896

HEREFORD Diocesan Office, The Palace, Hereford HR4 9BL
Tel: Hereford (01432) 353863/4 Fax (01432) 352952

LEICESTER Church House, 3/5 St Martin's East, Leicester LE1 5FX
Tel: Leicester (0116) 262 7445 Fax (0116) 253 2889

LICHFIELD St Mary's House, The Close, Lichfield, Staffs WS13 7LD
Tel: Lichfield (01543) 414551 Fax (01543) 250935

LINCOLN Diocesan Office, The Old Palace, Lincoln LN2 1PU
Tel: Lincoln (01522) 529241 Fax (01522) 512717

LIVERPOOL Church House, 1 Hanover Street, Liverpool L1 3DW
Tel: (0151) 709 9722 Fax (0151) 709 2885

LONDON London Diocesan House, 36 Causton Street, London SW1P 4AU
Tel: (0171) 932 1100 Fax (0171) 932 1112

MANCHESTER Diocesan Church House, 90 Deansgate, Manchester M3 2GH
Tel: (0161) 833 9521 Fax (0161) 833 2751

NEWCASTLE Church House, Grainger Park Road, Newcastle upon Tyne NE4 8SX
Tel: (0191) 226 0622 Fax (0191) 226 0730

NORWICH Diocesan Office, 109 Dereham Road, Easton, Norwich, Norfolk NR9 5ES
Tel: Norwich (01603) 880853 Fax (01603) 881083

OXFORD Diocesan Church House, North Hinksey, Oxford OX2 0NB
Tel: Oxford (01865) 244566 Fax (01865) 790470

PETERBOROUGH	The Palace, Peterborough, Cambs PE1 1YB *Tel:* Peterborough (01733) 64448/9 Fax (01733) 555271
PORTSMOUTH	Cathedral House, St Thomas's Street, Portsmouth, Hants PO1 2HA *Tel:* Portsmouth (01705) 825731 Fax (01705) 752967
RIPON	Ripon Diocesan Office, St Mary's Street, Leeds LS9 7DP *Tel:* Leeds (0113) 248 7487 Fax (0113) 249 1129
ROCHESTER	St Nicholas Church, Boley Hill, Rochester, Kent ME1 1SL *Tel:* Medway (01634) 830333 Fax (01634) 829463
ST ALBANS	Holywell Lodge, 41 Holywell Hill, St Albans, Herts AL1 1HE *Tel:* St Albans (01727) 854532 Fax (01727) 844469
ST EDMUNDSBURY AND IPSWICH	Diocesan House, 13/15 Tower Street, Ipswich, Suffolk IP1 3BG *Tel:* Ipswich (01473) 211028 Fax (01473) 232407
SALISBURY	Church House, Crane Street, Salisbury, Wilts SP12QB *Tel:* Salisbury (01722) 411922 Fax (01722) 411990
SHEFFIELD	Diocesan Church House, 95–99 Effingham St, Rotherham S65 1BL *Tel:* Sheffield (01709) 837547 Fax (01709) 837556
SODOR AND MAN	c/o Cooil Voorath, The Cronk, Ballaugh, Isle of Man IM7 5AX *Tel:* Douglas (01624) 897880 Fax (01624) 843374
SOUTHWARK	Trinity House, 4 Chapel Court, Borough High Street, London SE1 1HW *Tel:* (0171) 403 8686 Fax (0171) 403 4770
SOUTHWELL	Dunham House, Westgate, Southwell, Notts NG25 OJL *Tel:* Southwell (01636) 814331 Fax (01636) 815084
TRURO	Diocesan House, Kenwyn, Truro, Cornwall TR1 3DU *Tel:* Truro (01872) 74351 Fax (01872) 222510
WAKEFIELD	Church House, 1 South Parade, Wakefield, W Yorkshire WF1 1LP *Tel:* Wakefield (01924) 371802 Fax (01924) 364834
WINCHESTER	Church House, 9 The Close, Winchester, Hants S023 9LS *Tel:* Winchester (01962) 844644 Fax (01962) 841815
WORCESTER	The Old Palace, Deansway, Worcester WR1 2JE *Tel:* Worcester (01905) 20537/8 and 28764 Fax (01905) 612302
YORK	Church House, Ogleforth, York, N Yorkshire YO1 2JE *Tel:* York (01904) 611696 Fax (01904) 620375

SCOTTISH EPISCOPAL CHURCH

ABERDEEN AND ORKNEY	Diocesan Centre, 39 King's Cres, Aberdeen AB2 3HP *Tel:* (01224) 636653 Fax (01224) 636186
ARGYLL AND THE ISLES	The Pines, Ardconnel Road, Oban PA34 5DR *Tel/Fax:* (01631) 66912
BRECHIN	The Bishop's Room, St Paul's Cathedral, 1 High St, Dundee DD1 1TD *Tel:* (01382) 229230 9am–12 noon Fax (01382) 203446
EDINBURGH	Diocesan Centre, Walpole Hall, Chester St, Edinburgh EH3 7EN *Tel:* (0131) 226 3358 Fax (0131) 225 3181
GLASGOW AND GALLOWAY	The Diocesan Office, 5 St Vincent Pl, Glasgow, G1 2DH *Tel:* (0141) 221 5720/2694 Fax (0141) 221 7014
MORAY AND CAITHNESS	Diocesan Office, 11 Kenneth St, Inverness, IV3 5NR *Tel/Fax:* (01463) 226255 (mornings only)
ST ANDREWS, DUNKELD AND DUNBLANE	Perth Diocesan Centre, N Methven St, Perth, PH1 5PP *Tel:* (01738) 443173 Fax (01738) 443174

CHURCH IN WALES

BANGOR
Diocesan Secretary, Bangor Diocesan Board of Finance, The Cathedral Close, Bangor, Gwynedd LL57 1RL
Tel: (01248) 354999 Fax (01248) 353882

LLANDAFF
Diocesan Secretary, Llandaf Diocesan Board of Finance, Heol Fair, Llandaff, Cardiff CF5 2EE
Tel: (01222) 578899 Fax (01222) 576198

MONMOUTH
Diocesan Secretary, Monmouth Diocesan Board of Finance, 64 Caerau Road, Newport NP9 4HJ
Tel: (01633) 267490 Fax (01633) 265586

ST ASAPH
Diocesan Secretary, St Asaph Diocesan Board of Finance, High Street, St Asaph, Clwyd LL17 0RD
Tel: (01745) 582245 Fax (01745) 583556

ST DAVIDS
Diocesan Secretary, St Davids Diocesan Board of Finance, Abergwili, Carmarthen, Dyfed SA31 2JG
Tel: (01267) 236145 Fax (01267) 223046

SWANSEA AND BRECON
Diocesan Secretary, Swansea & Brecon Diocesan Board of Finance, House of the Good Shepherd, Eastmoor, Clyne Common, Swansea SA3 3JA
Tel/Fax: (01792) 402616

CHURCH OF IRELAND

PROVINCE OF ARMAGH

ARMAGH
Church House, 46 Abbey St, Armagh, BT61 7DZ
Tel: (08 01861) 522858 Fax (08 01861) 527823

CLOGHER
The Deanery, 10 Augher Rd, Clogher, Co Tyrone BT76 0AD
Tel/Fax: (08 016625) 48235

CONNOR
Diocesan Office, Church of Ireland House, 12 Talbot St, Belfast BT12QH
Tel: (08 01232) 322268/323188 Fax (08 01232) 323554

DERRY AND RAPHOE
Diocesan Office, London St, Londonderry BT48 6RQ
Tel: (08 01504) 262440

DOWN AND DROMORE
Diocesan Office, Church of Ireland House, 12 Talbot St, Belfast BT12QH
Tel: (08 01232) 322268/323188 Fax (08 01232) 323554

KILMORE
Killinagh Rectory, Blacklion, Sligo
Tel: (072) 53010 Fax (072) 53010

ELPHIN AND ARDAGH
Carrowkeel Lodge, Castlebaldwin, Co Sligo
Tel: (079) 66015 Fax (079) 66015

TUAM, KILLALA AND ACHONRY
Luimnagh West, Corrandulla, Co Galway
Tel: (091) 91482 Fax (091) 91386

PROVINCE OF DUBLIN

CASHEL, WATERFORD, LISMORE, OSSORY AND LEIGHLIN
Diocesan Office, St Canice's Library, Kilkenny
Tel: (056) 61910/27248 Fax (056) 64399

CORK, CLOYNE AND ROSS
St Nicholas House, 14 Cove St, Cork
Tel: (021) 272262 Fax (021) 968467

DUBLIN AND GLENDALOUGH
Diocesan Office, Church of Ireland House, Church Avenue, Rathmines, Dublin
Tel: 4966981 Fax 4972865

FERNS
Garranvabby, The Rower, Thomastown, Co Kilkenny
Tel: (051) 23637

KILLALOE, CLONFERT, LIMERICK AND ARDFERT
St Cronan's Rectory, Roscrea, Co Tipperary
Tel: (0505) 21725 Fax (0505) 21993

MEATH AND KILDARE
Rivendell, 26 Oaklawn West, Leixlip, Co Kildare
Tel/Fax: 01 6243534

ARCHDEACONRIES, DEANERIES AND RURAL DEANS OF THE CHURCH OF ENGLAND AND THE CHURCH IN WALES

The numbers given to the deaneries below correspond to those given in the benefice entries in the combined benefice and church index for England (page 839) and for Wales (page 1017). Where an archdeaconry comes within the jurisdiction of suffragan or area bishop under an established scheme, the respective bishop is indicated.

The dioceses of Liverpool, London and Manchester and the three Nottingham deaneries in the diocese of Southwell, use the title Area Dean.

CHURCH OF ENGLAND

BATH AND WELLS

ARCHDEACONRY OF WELLS

1. AXBRIDGE   V L DALEY
2. BRUTON   P W M REVELL
3. CARY   P W M REVELL
4. FROME   D OLIVE
5. GLASTONBURY   B H ADAMS
6. IVELCHESTER   H A HALLETT
7. MERSTON   M D ELLIS
8. SHEPTON MALLET   *Vacant*

ARCHDEACONRY OF BATH

9. BATH   A R WALLACE
10. CHEW MAGNA   T K VIVIAN
11. LOCKING   G W HOBDEN
12. MIDSOMER NORTON   P M HAND
13. PORTISHEAD   A Q H WHEELER

ARCHDEACONRY OF TAUNTON

14. BRIDGWATER   R E J PACKER
15. CREWKERNE AND ILMINSTER   M S KIVETT
16. EXMOOR   H E ALLEN
17. QUANTOCK   J D A STEVENS
18. TAUNTON   R E FLOWER
19. TONE   T W STOKES

BIRMINGHAM

ARCHDEACONRY OF BIRMINGHAM

1. BIRMINGHAM CITY   J H LANGSTAFF
2. EDGBASTON   I M MICHAEL
3. HANDSWORTH   R J MORRIS
4. KINGS NORTON   C J W JACKSON
5. WARLEY   D RAYNER

ARCHDEACONRY OF ASTON

6. ASTON   D E NEWSOME
7. BORDESLEY   S A HOLLOWAY
8. MOSELEY   H J OSBORNE
9. SUTTON COLDFIELD   E G LONGMAN
10. YARDLEY   R H POSTILL

ARCHDEACONRY OF COLESHILL

11. COLESHILL   C J BOYLE
12. POLESWORTH   J D POTTER
13. SOLIHULL   A J M DOW

BLACKBURN

ARCHDEACONRY OF BLACKBURN

1. ACCRINGTON   P H DEARDEN
2. BLACKBURN   P S GRIERSON
3. BURNLEY   R McCULLOUGH
4. CHORLEY   P K WARREN
5. DARWEN   R P CARTMELL
6. LEYLAND   T TAYLOR
7. PENDLE   J C PRIESTLEY
8. WHALLEY   P A SMITH

ARCHDEACONRY OF LANCASTER

9. BLACKPOOL   S EDWARDS
10. GARSTANG   R G GREENALL
11. KIRKHAM   J H CATLEY
12. LANCASTER   P J BALLARD
13. POULTON   D E REEVES
14. PRESTON   J R POWELL
15. TUNSTALL   W G BOWNESS

BRADFORD

ARCHDEACONRY OF BRADFORD

1. AIREDALE   S R CROWE
2. BOWLING AND HORTON   W HOLLIDAY
3. CALVERLEY   J N WHITE
4. OTLEY   P J C MARSHALL

ARCHDEACONRY OF CRAVEN

5. BOWLAND   G WALKER
6. EWECROSS   J M BEARPARK
7. SKIPTON   C J HAYWARD
8. SOUTH CRAVEN   G D N SMITH

BRISTOL

ARCHDEACONRY OF BRISTOL

1. BEDMINSTER   B E PEARCE
2. BITTON   P F YACOMENI
3. BRISLINGTON   J N HARRISON
4. BRISTOL CITY   C A SUNDERLAND
5. CLIFTON   F SMITH
6. HORFIELD   J M PERRIS
7. STAPLETON   R J BURBRIDGE
8. WESTBURY AND SEVERNSIDE   P R BAILEY

ARCHDEACONRY OF SWINDON

9. CHIPPENHAM   A D FENSOME
10. CRICKLADE   G K WITHINGTON
11. HIGHWORTH   A N GRAHAM
12. MALMESBURY   R K EAST
13. WROUGHTON   L R HURRELL

CANTERBURY

ARCHDEACONRY OF CANTERBURY

1. BRIDGE, EAST   R GILBERT
2. BRIDGE, WEST   C R DUNCAN
3. CANTERBURY   P T MACKENZIE
4. DOVER   P W A BOWERS
5. ELHAM   R G HUMPHRISS
6. OSPRINGE   *Vacant*
7. RECULVER   R W COTTON
8. SANDWICH   B A HAWKINS
9. THANET   N A S BURY

ARCHDEACONRY OF MAIDSTONE

10. CHARING, EAST   C G PREECE
11. CHARING, WEST   J RECORD
12. LYMPNE NORTH   L WILLIAMS
13. LYMPNE SOUTH   L J HAMMOND
14. SITTINGBOURNE   G H SPENCER
15. SUTTON   G H SIDAWAY

CARLISLE

ARCHDEACONRY OF CARLISLE

1. APPLEBY   C R LEVEY
2. BRAMPTON   J S CASSON
3. CARLISLE   G P RAVALDE
4. PENRITH   B DAWSON

ARCHDEACONRY OF WEST CUMBERLAND

5. CALDER   P R BRYAN
6. DERWENT   M R BRAITHWAITE
7. SOLWAY   P J SWAIN

DEANERIES AND RURAL DEANS

ARCHDEACONRY OF WESTMORLAND AND FURNESS

8. FURNESS   D SANDERSON
9. KENDAL   G A HOWE
10. WINDERMERE   C L V ATKINSON

CHELMSFORD

ARCHDEACONRY OF WEST HAM (BISHOP OF BARKING)

1. BARKING AND DAGENHAM   J A A FLETCHER
2. HAVERING   B J LEWIS
3. NEWHAM   J P WHITWELL
4. REDBRIDGE   T H SHANNON
5. WALTHAM FOREST   D S AINGE

ARCHDEACONRY OF SOUTHEND (BISHOP OF BRADWELL)

6. BASILDON   P D ASHTON
7. BRENTWOOD   R B WHITE
8. CHELMSFORD NORTH   C E HOPKINSON
9. CHELMSFORD SOUTH   D J ATKINS
10. HADLEIGH   P J SANDBERG
11. MALDON AND DENGIE   P J MASON
12. ROCHFORD   P F TAYLOR
13. SOUTHEND-ON-SEA   M A BALLARD
14. THURROCK   S BAILEY

ARCHDEACONRY (AND BISHOP) OF COLCHESTER

15. BELCHAMP   P J STREET
16. BRAINTREE   J F H SHEAD
17. COLCHESTER   R M WILSON
18. DEDHAM AND TEY   C G A WOODS
19. DUNMOW   A R JACK
20. HALSTEAD AND COGGESHALL   B E ROSE
21. HARWICH   P E BALL
22. NEWPORT AND STANSTED   C BISHOP
23. SAFFRON WALDEN   B J MACDONALD-MILNE
24. ST OSYTH   N G E ISSBERNER
25. WITHAM   C J SLY

ARCHDEACONRY OF HARLOW (BISHOP OF BARKING)

26. EPPING FOREST   D DRISCOLL
27. HARLOW   M D WEBSTER
28. ONGAR   E J SIBSON

CHESTER

ARCHDEACONRY OF CHESTER

1. BIRKENHEAD   A J POULTER
2. CHESTER   C W J SAMUELS
3. FRODSHAM   A R RIDLEY
4. GREAT BUDWORTH   G L DAVIES
5. MALPAS   J M G DAVIES
6. MIDDLEWICH   P D GARDNER
7. WALLASEY   B E LEE
8. WIRRAL NORTH   R E MORRIS
9. WIRRAL SOUTH   J C CLARKE

ARCHDEACONRY OF MACCLESFIELD

10. BOWDON   D ASHWORTH
11. CONGLETON   E J GORDON
12. KNUTSFORD   N D ROGERS
13. MACCLESFIELD   D W MOIR
14. MOTTRAM   J H DARCH
15. NANTWICH   D ROSTRON
16. CHADKIRK   D C SPEEDY
17. CHEADLE   S P ISHERWOOD
18. STOCKPORT   A M FAIRHURST

CHICHESTER

ARCHDEACONRY OF CHICHESTER

1. ARUNDEL AND BOGNOR   A M G WELLS
2. BRIGHTON   E W M WALKER
3. CHICHESTER   K W CATCHPOLE
4. HOVE   J M P CALDICOTT
5. WORTHING   P R ROBERTS

ARCHDEACONRY OF HORSHAM

6. CUCKFIELD   I J BRACKLEY
7. EAST GRINSTEAD   A F HAWKER
8. HORSHAM   J D MORRIS
9. HURST   R L CLARKE
10. MIDHURST   M C JUDGE
11. PETWORTH   D S POLLARD
12. STORRINGTON   G A EVANS
13. WESTBOURNE   T J INMAN

ARCHDEACONRY OF LEWES AND HASTINGS

14. BATTLE AND BEXHILL   J W COTTON
15. DALLINGTON   D D FRICKER
16. EASTBOURNE   N S READE
17. HASTINGS   C L RICHARDSON
18. LEWES AND SEAFORD   H M MOSELEY
19. ROTHERFIELD   R J GOODCHILD
20. RYE   M SHEPPARD
21. UCKFIELD   C J PETERS

COVENTRY

ARCHDEACONRY OF COVENTRY

1. COVENTRY EAST   D J HOWARD
2. COVENTRY NORTH   N J TAYLOR
3. COVENTRY SOUTH   R D ALLON-SMITH
4. KENILWORTH   R D TURNER
5. NUNEATON   J F LAW
6. RUGBY   P WATKINS

ARCHDEACONRY OF WARWICK

7. ALCESTER   J F GANJAVI
8. FOSSE   S A BEAKE
9. SHIPSTON   N J MORGAN
10. SOUTHAM   P R BROWN
11. WARWICK AND LEAMINGTON   K LINDOP

DERBY

ARCHDEACONRY OF CHESTERFIELD

1. ALFRETON   *Vacant*
2. BAKEWELL AND EYAM   M F COLLIER
3. BOLSOVER AND STAVELEY   J EASTON
4. BUXTON   J C TOMLINSON
5. CHESTERFIELD   S MILLINGTON
6. GLOSSOP   J H K NORTON
7. WIRKSWORTH   J O GOLDSMITH

ARCHDEACONRY OF DERBY

8. ASHBOURNE   D H SANSUM
9. DERBY NORTH   G O MARSHALL
10. DERBY SOUTH   D C MACDONALD
11. DUFFIELD   A T REDMAN
12. HEANOR   C L BLAKEY
13. ILKESTON   G R PERCY
14. LONGFORD   D MILNER
15. MELBOURNE   F ROSS
16. REPTON   J R P BARKER

DURHAM

ARCHDEACONRY OF DURHAM

1. CHESTER LE STREET   F WHITE
2. DURHAM   D J BELL
3. EASINGTON   K I WOODHOUSE
4. GATESHEAD   H DITCHBURN
5. GATESHEAD WEST   T L JAMIESON
6. HOUGHTON LE SPRING   D GUEST
7. JARROW   E G STEPHENSON
8. LANCHESTER   P WATERHOUSE
9. WEARMOUTH   R I DAVISON

ARCHDEACONRY OF AUCKLAND

10. AUCKLAND   R CUTHBERTSON
11. BARNARD CASTLE   T J D OLLIER
12. DARLINGTON   P H E THOMAS
13. HARTLEPOOL   M H WHITEHEAD
14. SEDGEFIELD   M Q KING
15. STANHOPE   C N LOVELL
16. STOCKTON   R I SMITH

ELY

ARCHDEACONRY OF ELY

1. BOURN R STEPHENSON
2. CAMBRIDGE B N JONES
3. FORDHAM M G F SHEARS
4. LINTON A F HOMER
5. NORTH STOWE H K McCURDY
6. QUY F J KILNER
7. SHELFORD K F M FISHER
8. SHINGAY J K GREASLEY

ARCHDEACONRY OF HUNTINGDON

9. HUNTINGDON W R KING
10. LEIGHTONSTONE J HINDLEY
11. ST IVES S O LEEKE
12. ST NEOTS B CURRY
13. YAXLEY M SOULSBY

ARCHDEACONRY OF WISBECH

14. ELY R J MACKLIN
15. FELTWELL J B ROWSELL
16. FINCHAM R D TOMKINSON
17. LYNN MARSHLAND A R TREEN
18. MARCH P BAXANDALL
19. WISBECH R D BULL

EXETER

ARCHDEACONRY OF EXETER

1. AYLESBEARE R J GIBBS
2. CADBURY A E GEERING
3. CHRISTIANITY B R TUBBS
4. CULLOMPTON B PETTY
5. HONITON D A GUNN-JOHNSON
6. KENN C R EVANS
7. OTTERY J V MAPSON
8. TIVERTON R C THORP

ARCHDEACONRY OF TOTNES

9. HOLSWORTHY L BROOKHOUSE
10. IPPLEPEN P W DARBY
11. MORETON P J GREGSON
12. OKEHAMPTON R C CHAMBERLAIN
13. TOTNES J CRUSE
14. WOODLEIGH P HANCOCK

ARCHDEACONRY OF BARNSTAPLE

15. BARNSTAPLE N JACKSON-STEVENS
16. CHULMLEIGH *Vacant*
17. HARTLAND W G BLAKEY
18. SHIRWELL K G WYER
19. SOUTH MOLTON M J HOMEWOOD
20. TORRINGTON R J P ACWORTH

ARCHDEACONRY OF PLYMOUTH

21. IVYBRIDGE R J CARLTON
22. PLYMOUTH DEVONPORT M D D JONES
23. PLYMOUTH MOORSIDE J M KIRKPATRICK
24. PLYMOUTH SUTTON P H W HAWKINS
25. TAVISTOCK G M COTTER

GLOUCESTER

ARCHDEACONRY OF GLOUCESTER

1. BISLEY B C E COKER
2. DURSLEY C RAWLINSON
3. FOREST NORTH T WILLIAMS
4. FOREST SOUTH D F F EVANS
5. GLOUCESTER CITY M W BUTLER
6. GLOUCESTER NORTH J O'BRIEN
7. HAWKESBURY D B SMALL
8. STONEHOUSE S J RIGGS
9. TEWKESBURY J H MEAD

ARCHDEACONRY OF CHELTENHAM

10. CHELTENHAM D C NYE
11. CAMPDEN T R C OVERTHROW
12. CIRENCESTER H S RINGROSE

13. FAIRFORD P J GREEN
14. NORTHLEACH G B THOMAS
15. STOW R F ROTHERY
16. TETBURY J D STRONG
17. WINCHCOMBE M J PAGE

GUILDFORD

ARCHDEACONRY OF SURREY

1. ALDERSHOT M S KING
2. CRANLEIGH M C HUGHES
3. FARNHAM J N E BUNDOCK
4. GODALMING R C D MACKENNA
5. GUILDFORD M D B LEWIS
6. SURREY HEATH D HOLT

ARCHDEACONRY OF DORKING

7. DORKING A S W CULLIS
8. EMLY C M SCOTT
9. EPSOM D W RENSHAW
10. LEATHERHEAD D J EATON
11. RUNNYMEDE A J MAGOWAN
12. WOKING M F HERBERT

HEREFORD

ARCHDEACONRY OF HEREFORD

1. ABBEYDORE F E RODGERS
2. BROMYARD D W GOULD
3. HEREFORD CITY P T WOOD
4. HEREFORD RURAL U J SUMMERS
5. KINGTON AND WEOBLEY S HOLLINGHURST
6. LEDBURY C N H ATTWOOD
7. LEOMINSTER M W HOOPER
8. ROSS AND ARCHENFIELD P TARLING

ARCHDEACONRY OF LUDLOW

9. BRIDGNORTH R SHARP
10. CLUN FOREST R T SHAW
11. CONDOVER M S STEDMAN
12. LUDLOW R A HORSFIELD
13. PONTESBURY P TOWNER
14. TELFORD SEVERN GORGE C HILL

LEICESTER

ARCHDEACONRY OF LEICESTER

1. CHRISTIANITY (LEICESTER) NORTH A W ROBINSON
2. CHRISTIANITY (LEICESTER) SOUTH M T H BANKS
3. FRAMLAND (Melton) G J JOHNSON
4. GARTREE FIRST DEANERY (Harborough) S R LONG
5. GARTREE SECOND DEANERY (Wigston) B R GLOVER
6. GOSCOTE K R COURT

ARCHDEACONRY OF LOUGHBOROUGH

7. AKELEY EAST (Loughborough) S SAMUEL
8. AKELEY SOUTH (Coalville) J RICHARDSON
9. AKELEY WEST (Ashby) C P DOBBIN
10. GUTHLAXTON FIRST DEANERY (Blaby) P BURROWS
11. GUTHLAXTON SECOND DEANERY (Lutterworth) P J C CLEMENTS
12. SPARKENHOE EAST G T WILLETT
13. SPARKENHOE WEST (Hinckley and Bosworth) B DAVIS

LICHFIELD

ARCHDEACONRY OF LICHFIELD (BISHOP OF WOLVERHAMPTON)

1. LICHFIELD E G H TOWNSHEND
2. PENKRIDGE T H GREEN
3. RUGELEY A F CREBER
4. TAMWORTH J A WIDDAS
5. TRYSULL J D MAKEPEACE
6. WALSALL P A R HAMMERSLEY
7. WEDNESBURY I B COOK
8. WEST BROMWICH M C RUTTER
9. WOLVERHAMPTON P J CHAPMAN

DEANERIES AND RURAL DEANS

ARCHDEACONRY OF STOKE-ON-TRENT
(BISHOP OF STAFFORD)

10. ALSTONFIELD   *Vacant*
11. CHEADLE   N JEFFERYES
12. ECCLESHALL   M J POPE
13. LEEK   J P EADES
14. NEWCASTLE   M D HARDING
15. STAFFORD   J POTTS
16. STOKE NORTH   B L WILLIAMS
17. STOKE   J W PAWSON
18. TRENTHAM   G L SIMPSON
19. TUTBURY   D B SIMMONDS
20. UTTOXETER   J B HALL

ARCHDEACONRY OF SALOP
(BISHOP OF SHREWSBURY)

21. EDGMOND   R T HIBBERT
22. ELLESMERE   M W H GRAY
23. HODNET   P M JAMES
24. OSWESTRY   D N AUSTERBERRY
25. SHIFNAL   R B BALKWILL
26. SHREWSBURY   R W D BIDDLE
27. TELFORD   C HILL
28. WEM AND WHITCHURCH   R D JENKINS
29. WROCKWARDINE   C S COOKE

LINCOLN

ARCHDEACONRY OF STOW

1. AXHOLME, ISLE OF   J GIBBONS
2. CORRINGHAM   G S RICHARDSON
3. LAWRES   M J SILLEY
4. MANLAKE   A G D HAYDAY
5. WEST WOLD   M J CARTWRIGHT
6. YARBOROUGH   S PHILLIPS

ARCHDEACONRY OF LINDSEY

7. BOLINGBROKE   R W B MASSINGBERD-MUNDY
8. CALCEWAITHE AND CANDLESHOE   P F COATES
9. GRIMSBY AND CLEETHORPES   J W ELLIS
10. HAVERSTOE   H W P HALL
11. HORNCASTLE   S W PEARCE
12. LOUTHESK   S D HOLDAWAY

ARCHDEACONRY OF LINCOLN

13. AVELAND AND NESS w STAMFORD   J M WARWICK
14. BELTISLOE   R BURGESS
15. CHRISTIANITY   I W MACKIE
16. ELLOE EAST   P HILL
17. ELLOE WEST   K A ALMOND
18. GRAFFOE   R G BILLINGHURST
19. GRANTHAM   R P REISS
20. HOLLAND EAST   W G PAGE
21. HOLLAND WEST   J W THACKER
22. LAFFORD   J S THOROLD
23. LOVEDEN   G R SHRIMPTON

LIVERPOOL

ARCHDEACONRY OF LIVERPOOL

1. BOOTLE   R CAPPER
2. HUYTON   J A STANLEY
3. LIVERPOOL NORTH   G J BUTLAND
4. LIVERPOOL SOUTH   J V ROBERTS
5. SEFTON   F A BRISCOE
6. TOXTETH AND WAVERTREE   M M WOLFE
7. WALTON   A B HAWLEY
8. WEST DERBY   J R I WIKELEY

ARCHDEACONRY OF WARRINGTON

9. NORTH MEOLS   J M BURGESS
10. ST HELENS   C H B BYWORTH
11. ORMSKIRK   M J SMOUT
12. WARRINGTON   J O COLLING
13. WIDNES   *Vacant*
14. WIGAN EAST   K M FORREST
15. WIGAN WEST   D LYON
16. WINWICK   R BRITTON

LONDON

ARCHDEACONRY OF LONDON

1. THE CITY   A J TANNER

ARCHDEACONRY OF CHARING CROSS
(BISHOP OF FULHAM)

2. WESTMINSTER PADDINGTON   R F BUSHAU
3. WESTMINSTER ST MARGARET   A C C COURTAULD
4. WESTMINSTER ST MARYLEBONE   J SLATER

ARCHDEACONRY OF HACKNEY
(BISHOP OF STEPNEY)

5. HACKNEY   W M MACNAUGHTON
6. ISLINGTON   S J W COX
7. TOWER HAMLETS   J D M PATON

ARCHDEACONRY OF MIDDLESEX
(BISHOP OF KENSINGTON)

8. CHELSEA   D R WATSON
9. HAMMERSMITH   S J TAYLOR
10. HAMPTON   D H PALMER
11. HOUNSLOW   P G HUTTON
12. KENSINGTON   I L ROBSON
13. SPELTHORNE   D C PEMBERTON

ARCHDEACONRY OF HAMPSTEAD
(BISHOP OF EDMONTON)

14. BARNET, CENTRAL   M H McGOWAN
15. BARNET, WEST   P G BAKER
16. CAMDEN, NORTH (Hampstead)   P J W BUCKLER
17. CAMDEN, SOUTH (Holborn and St Pancras)   C G POPE
18. ENFIELD   J D TRIGG
19. HARINGEY, EAST   R B PEARSON
20. HARINGEY, WEST   G B SEABROOK

ARCHDEACONRY OF NORTHOLT
(BISHOP OF WILLESDEN)

21. BRENT   J B ROOT
22. EALING   W H TAYLOR
23. HARROW   P VANNOZZI
24. HILLINGDON   P J BALL

MANCHESTER

ARCHDEACONRY OF MANCHESTER

1. ARDWICK   A DURRANS
2. ECCLES   *Vacant*
3. HEATON   A PUGMIRE
4. HULME   G A WHEALE
5. MANCHESTER, NORTH   C S FORD
6. SALFORD   P D FOSTER
7. STRETFORD   W J TWIDELL
8. WITHINGTON   N W DAWSON

ARCHDEACONRY OF BOLTON

9. BOLTON   R F OLDFIELD
10. BURY   G G ROXBY
11. DEANE   D W GATENBY
12. FARNWORTH   A E BALLARD
13. LEIGH   P W LEAKEY
14. RADCLIFFE AND PRESTWICH   R W WARNER
15. ROSSENDALE   J A ARMES
16. WALMSLEY   D J BRIERLEY

ARCHDEACONRY OF ROCHDALE

17. ASHTON-UNDER-LYNE   C A E LAWRENCE
18. HEYWOOD AND MIDDLETON   *Vacant*
19. OLDHAM   C H RAZZALL
20. ROCHDALE   B H LOCKE
21. SADDLEWORTH   L R TOONE
22. TANDLE   D SHARPLES

NEWCASTLE

ARCHDEACONRY OF NORTHUMBERLAND

1. BEDLINGTON   J R PRINGLE
2. BELLINGHAM   T R HARPER
3. CORBRIDGE   M F FENWICK
4. HEXHAM   K FLETCHER
5. NEWCASTLE CENTRAL   F R DEXTER (ACTING)
6. NEWCASTLE EAST   P C DODD
7. NEWCASTLE WEST   V G ASHWIN
8. TYNEMOUTH   W N STOCK

ARCHDEACONRY OF LINDISFARNE

9. ALNWICK   B COWEN
10. BAMBURGH AND GLENDALE   E ZACHAU
11. MORPETH   A S CRAIG
12. NORHAM   W P HEWITT

NORWICH

ARCHDEACONRY OF NORWICH

1. NORWICH EAST   H R G COOKE
2. NORWICH NORTH   M H STAGG
3. NORWICH SOUTH   P R OLIVER

ARCHDEACONRY OF NORFOLK

4. BLOFIELD   C G WAY
5. DEPWADE   P E HALLS
6. GREAT YARMOUTH   C W COUSINS
7. HUMBLEYARD   P J STEPHENS
8. LODDON   C R CHAPMAN
9. LOTHINGLAND   W A STEWART
10. REDENHALL   M E ELLSON
11. THETFORD AND ROCKLAND   A D McGREGOR
12. TUNSTEAD   M W SMITH
13. WAXHAM   W J CAMERON

ARCHDEACONRY OF LYNN

14. BRECKLAND   J H RICHARDSON
15. BRISLEY AND ELMHAM   B R A COLE
16. BURNHAM AND WALSINGHAM   A J BELL
17. HEACHAM AND RISING   G R HALL
18. HINGHAM AND MITFORD   D J BOURNE
19. HOLT   P J G BARNES-CLAY
20. INGWORTH   P B FOREMAN
21. LYNN   S R NAIRN
22. REPPS   D F HAYDEN
23. SPARHAM   M F C TAYLOR

OXFORD

ARCHDEACONRY OF OXFORD
(BISHOP OF DORCHESTER)

1. ASTON AND CUDDESDON   J Y CROWE
2. BICESTER AND ISLIP   G G CHAPMAN
3. CHIPPING NORTON   M J CHADWICK
4. COWLEY   P S M JUDD
5. DEDDINGTON   T WIMBUSH
6. HENLEY   P E NIXON
7. OXFORD   A M GANN
8. WITNEY   R E MEREDITH
9. WOODSTOCK   A W DAVIES

ARCHDEACONRY OF BERKSHIRE
(BISHOP OF READING)

10. ABINGDON   D P PRITCHARD
11. BRACKNELL   C G CLARKE
12. BRADFIELD   R B HOWELL
13. MAIDENHEAD   D D J ROSSDALE
14. NEWBURY   C T SCOTT-DEMPSTER
15. READING   B SHENTON
16. SONNING   J W RATINGS
17. VALE OF WHITE HORSE   D J HOWSON
18. WALLINGFORD   C J STOTT
19. WANTAGE   A WADGE

ARCHDEACONRY
(AND BISHOP) OF BUCKINGHAM

20. AMERSHAM   A M PRIDDIS
21. AYLESBURY   T J HIGGINS
22. BUCKINGHAM   D G MEARA
23. BURNHAM   S N D BROWN

24. CLAYDON   D W OWEN
25. MILTON KEYNES   D K MIELL
26. MURSLEY   N J COTTON
27. NEWPORT   S J A WESTON
28. WENDOVER   A W BENNETT
29. WYCOMBE   D J ROBERTSON

PETERBOROUGH

ARCHDEACONRY OF NORTHAMPTON

1. BRACKLEY   S E CRAWLEY
2. BRIXWORTH   B LEE
3. DAVENTRY   J A ROBERTS
4. NORTHAMPTON   K E ANDERSON
5. TOWCESTER   M H CHAMPNEYS
6. WELLINGBOROUGH   J R WESTWOOD
7. WOOTTON   J T SHORT

ARCHDEACONRY OF OAKHAM

8. BARNACK   B HARRIS
9. CORBY   M A CRAGGS
10. HIGHAM   D R BIRD
11. KETTERING   J SIMMONS
12. OUNDLE   M W R COVINGTON
13. PETERBOROUGH   T R CHRISTIE
14. RUTLAND   A M S WILSON

PORTSMOUTH

ARCHDEACONRY OF PORTSMOUTH

1. BISHOPS WALTHAM   D E HENLEY
2. FAREHAM   R J S EVENS
3. GOSPORT   D G JAMES
4. HAVANT   P HANCOCK
5. PETERSFIELD   B E COOK
6. PORTSMOUTH   K M L H BANTING

ARCHDEACONRY OF ISLE OF WIGHT

7. WIGHT, EAST   A P MENNISS
8. WIGHT, WEST   A BROWN

RIPON

ARCHDEACONRY OF RICHMOND

1. HARROGATE   A C BETTS
2. RICHMOND   C N H WHITE
3. RIPON   R T COOPER
4. WENSLEY   C W MALPASS

ARCHDEACONRY OF LEEDS

5. ALLERTON   C R CORNWELL
6. ARMLEY   F SUDWORTH
7. HEADINGLEY   G C DARVILL
8. WHITKIRK   K A PAYNE

ROCHESTER

ARCHDEACONRY OF ROCHESTER

1. COBHAM   D L WILLIAMS
2. DARTFORD   A T WATERMAN
3. GILLINGHAM   S H DUNN
4. GRAVESEND   C D GOBLE
5. ROCHESTER   K A GARDINER
6. STROOD   B R INGRAM

ARCHDEACONRY OF TONBRIDGE

7. MALLING   R B STEVENSON
8. SEVENOAKS   B E S GODFREY
9. SHOREHAM   C C HORN
10. TONBRIDGE   D G St L WINTER
11. TUNBRIDGE WELLS   R E WHYTE

ARCHDEACONRY OF BROMLEY

12. BECKENHAM   D S R REDMAN
13. BROMLEY   P R HENWOOD
14. ERITH   P WRIGHT
15. ORPINGTON   R R LUNNON
16. SIDCUP   D L KNIGHT

DEANERIES AND RURAL DEANS

ST ALBANS

ARCHDEACONRY OF ST ALBANS

1. ALDENHAM S PURVIS
2. BARNET G R HUDDLESTON
3. BERKHAMSTED J A S PAYNE COOK
4. BISHOP'S STORTFORD J L PELLEY
5. BUNTINGFORD P J M BRIGHT
6. CHESHUNT J H SPRINGBETT
7. HATFIELD P J SMITH
8. HERTFORD J RISBY
9. HITCHIN F J C MERCURIO
10. RICKMANSWORTH B L DRIVER
11. ST ALBANS A R HURLE
12. STEVENAGE M BARNSLEY
13. WATFORD J B BROWN
14. WHEATHAMPSTEAD T PURCHAS

ARCHDEACONRY OF BEDFORD

15. AMPTHILL D LEWTHWAITE
16. BEDFORD J R BROWN
17. BIGGLESWADE J D WATSON
18. DUNSTABLE K A STEELE
19. ELSTOW J K DIXON
20. LUTON R I CHEETHAM
21. SHARNBROOK A R H WOODWARD
22. SHEFFORD *Vacant*

ST EDMUNDSBURY AND IPSWICH

ARCHDEACONRY OF IPSWICH

1. BOSMERE R S STRINGER
2. COLNEYS G L GRANT
3. HADLEIGH S C MORRIS
4. IPSWICH K B JONES
5. SAMFORD R F PALLANT
6. STOWMARKET J R HARROLD
7. WOODBRIDGE N DAVIS

ARCHDEACONRY OF SUDBURY

8. CLARE E J BETTS
9. IXWORTH D M B MATHERS
10. LAVENHAM B H MANNING
11. MILDENHALL G C SMITH
12. SUDBURY L F SIMPKINS
13. THINGOE R W CLIFTON

ARCHDEACONRY OF SUFFOLK

14. BECCLES AND SOUTH ELMHAM J M S FALKNER
15. HALESWORTH P E BUSTIN
16. HARTISMERE M P BEEK
17. HOXNE D J STREETER
18. LOES D A S BOYES
19. SAXMUNDHAM D C LOWE

SALISBURY

ARCHDEACONRY OF SHERBORNE

1. BEAMINSTER E G A W PAGE-TURNER
2. DORCHESTER K J SCOTT
3. LYME BAY E G A W PAGE-TURNER
4. SHERBORNE R S GLEN
5. WEYMOUTH K A HUGO

ARCHDEACONRY OF DORSET

6. BLACKMORE VALE D DICKER
7. MILTON AND BLANDFORD G S M SQUAREY
8. POOLE S D LAKE
9. PURBECK P G HARDMAN
10. WIMBORNE D R PRICE

ARCHDEACONRY OF SARUM

11. ALDERBURY M C GALLAGHER
12. AVON M J BRIDGER
13. CHALKE M E RIDLEY
14. HEYTESBURY F J WOODS
15. SALISBURY D P SCRACE
16. WYLYE AND WILTON B THOMAS

ARCHDEACONRY OF WILTS

17. BRADFORD C F BROWN
18. CALNE A G WOODS
19. DEVIZES B A TIGWELL
20. MARLBOROUGH H G PEARSON
21. PEWSEY D M RYDER

SHEFFIELD

ARCHDEACONRY OF SHEFFIELD

1. ATTERCLIFFE M L FUDGER
2. ECCLESALL K E JONES
3. ECCLESFIELD T W ELLIS
4. HALLAM A NEWMAN
5. LAUGHTON H J PATRICK
6. ROTHERHAM B H COOPER
7. TANKERSLEY P J CRAIG-WILD

ARCHDEACONRY OF DONCASTER

8. ADWICK-LE-STREET R A FITZHARRIS
9. DONCASTER P J BOULTON-LEA
10. DONCASTER, WEST R M HARVEY
11. SNAITH AND HATFIELD J W SWEED
12. WATH C W M BALDOCK

SODOR AND MAN

1. CASTLETOWN G B CLAYTON
2. DOUGLAS D WHITWORTH
3. PEEL B H PARTINGTON
4. RAMSEY J H SHEEN

SOUTHWARK

ARCHDEACONRY OF LEWISHAM
(BISHOP OF WOOLWICH)

1. GREENWICH *Vacant*
2. DEPTFORD W G CORNECK
3. LEWISHAM, EAST D GARLICK
4. LEWISHAM, WEST J O ARDLEY

ARCHDEACONRY OF SOUTHWARK
(BISHOP OF WOOLWICH)

5. BERMONDSEY P D MAURICE
6. CAMBERWELL R W G BOMFORD
7. DULWICH J B NAYLOR
8. SOUTHWARK AND NEWINGTON M A HART

ARCHDEACONRY OF LAMBETH
(BISHOP OF KINGSTON)

9. BRIXTON L DENNEN
10. CLAPHAM D J HOUGHTON
11. LAMBETH C R TRUSS
12. MERTON I C DAVIES
13. STREATHAM J R WILCOX

ARCHDEACONRY OF WANDSWORTH
(BISHOP OF KINGSTON)

14. BATTERSEA P CLARK
15. KINGSTON C J DAVIES
16. RICHMOND AND BARNES R AMES-LEWIS
17. TOOTING M D MARSHALL
18. WANDSWORTH A N TREDENNICK

ARCHDEACONRY
(AND BISHOP) OF CROYDON

19. CATERHAM V M HAMER
20. CROYDON ADDINGTON L A D WATSON
21. CROYDON CENTRAL G S DERRIMAN
22. CROYDON SOUTH A C WAIT
23. CROYDON NORTH P L WASHINGTON

ARCHDEACONRY OF REIGATE
(BISHOP OF CROYDON)

24. GODSTONE D A RICHARDSON
25. REIGATE R H McLEAN
26. SUTTON M R GOODLAD

SOUTHWELL

ARCHDEACONRY OF NEWARK

1. BAWTRY G A MUMFORD
2. MANSFIELD J M BURGESS
3. NEWARK R A J HILL
4. NEWSTEAD F G GREEN
5. RETFORD A N WOODSFORD
6. WORKSOP G E JONES

ARCHDEACONRY OF NOTTINGHAM

7. BEESTON C J HALL
8. BINGHAM G B BARRODALE
9. BINGHAM SOUTH T SISSON
10. BINGHAM WEST S J SMITH
11. GEDLING R D A MORE
12. NOTTINGHAM CENTRAL S E DYAS
13. NOTTINGHAM NORTH C GALE
14. NOTTINGHAM WEST A S G HART
15. SOUTHWELL M J BROCK

TRURO

ARCHDEACONRY OF CORNWALL

1. ST AUSTELL J B SAUNDERS
2. CARNMARTH NORTH N J POCOCK
3. CARNMARTH SOUTH R G GILBERT
4. KERRIER J T McCABE
5. PENWITH M H FISHER
6. POWDER M J ADAMS
7. PYDAR J G SLEE

ARCHDEACONRY OF BODMIN

8. STRATTON B G DORRINGTON
9. TRIGG MAJOR J D FERGUSON
10. TRIGG MINOR AND BODMIN I H MORRIS
11. WIVELSHIRE, EAST R OAKES
12. WIVELSHIRE, WEST K P MELLOR

WAKEFIELD

ARCHDEACONRY OF HALIFAX

1. ALMONDBURY M W THOMAS
2. BRIGHOUSE AND ELLAND B FIRTH
3. CALDER VALLEY P N CALVERT
4. HALIFAX J C WIDDOWS
5. HUDDERSFIELD E O ROBERTS
6. KIRKBURTON D BARRACLOUGH

ARCHDEACONRY OF PONTEFRACT

7. BARNSLEY J L HUDSON
8. BIRSTALL R M WELLER
9. CHEVET *Vacant*
10. DEWSBURY F J MARSH
11. PONTEFRACT W T HICKS
12. WAKEFIELD B S ELLIS

WINCHESTER

ARCHDEACONRY OF BASINGSTOKE

1. ALRESFORD C R SMITH
2. ALTON J RICHARDS
3. ANDOVER M HARLEY
4. BASINGSTOKE A D PICTON
5. ODIHAM R C HUBBLE
6. WHITCHURCH N P CUMMING

ARCHDEACONRY OF WINCHESTER

7. BOURNEMOUTH D H R JONES
8. CHRISTCHURCH A SESSFORD
9. EASTLEIGH A G HARBIDGE
10. LYNDHURST M G ANDERSON

11. ROMSEY D B KINGTON
12. SOUTHAMPTON B J HARTNELL
13. WINCHESTER R J H TEARE

CHANNEL ISLANDS

14. GUERNSEY J R FENWICK
15. JERSEY J N SEAFORD

WORCESTER

ARCHDEACONRY OF WORCESTER

1. EVESHAM G S CROSS
2. MALVERN P C G BILLINGHAM
3. MARTLEY AND WORCESTER WEST J W HERBERT
4. PERSHORE C J RIDOUT
5. UPTON J R PARKINSON
6. WORCESTER EAST M A O LEWIS

ARCHDEACONRY OF DUDLEY

7. BROMSGROVE D C SALT
8. DROITWICH W D S WELLS
9. DUDLEY J C EVEREST
10. HIMLEY W M SMITH
11. KIDDERMINSTER A J POSTLETHWAITE
12. STOURBRIDGE D O BELL
13. STOURPORT B GILBERT

YORK

ARCHDEACONRY OF YORK
(BISHOP OF SELBY)

1. AINSTY, NEW J A RENDALL
2. BUCKROSE F B WILLIAMS
3. BULMER AND MALTON E T CHAPMAN
4. DERWENT F G HUNTER
5. EASINGWOLD G C GALLEY
6. SELBY D G RICHARDSON
7. SOUTH WOLD J V ANDREWS
8. YORK, CITY OF R G FLETCHER

ARCHDEACONRY OF EAST RIDING
(BISHOP OF HULL)

9. BEVERLEY M L KAVANAGH
10. BRIDLINGTON J C MEEK
11. HARTHILL R I JONES
12. HOLDERNESS, NORTH *Vacant*
13. HOLDERNESS, SOUTH I R S WALKER
14. HOWDEN D C BAILEY
15. HULL F A GORDON-KERR
16. SCARBOROUGH M D B LONG

ARCHDEACONRY OF CLEVELAND
(BISHOP OF WHITBY)

17. GUISBOROUGH T N EVANS
18. HELMSLEY D E NEWTON
19. MIDDLESBROUGH S C WRIGHT
20. MOWBRAY D G BILES
21. PICKERING F J A HEWITT
22. STOKESLEY D F LICKESS
23. WHITBY N N JONES

CHURCH IN WALES

ST ASAPH

ARCHDEACONRY OF ST ASAPH

1. ST ASAPH   R W ROWLAND
2. DENBIGH   C W EVANS
3. DYFFRYN CLWYD   D J WILLIAMS
4. HOLYWELL   J T EVANS
5. LLANRWST   W D JENKINS
6. RHOS   D J ROBERTS

ARCHDEACONRY OF MONTGOMERY

7. CEDEWAIN   P B JONES
8. CAEREINION   G MORGAN
9. LLANFYLLIN   C F CARTER
10. POOL   B LETSON

ARCHDEACONRY OF WREXHAM

11. BAN ISYCOED   P R OWENS
12. EDEYRNION   R S THOMAS
13. LLANGOLLEN   G C JONES
14. MOLD   J B JONES
15. PENLLYN   G W JONES
16. WREXHAM   R A SUTER

BANGOR

ARCHDEACONRY OF BANGOR

1. ARFON   I THOMAS
2. ARLLECHWEDD   G B HUGHES
3. LIFTON AND TALYBOLION   T WYNNE
4. MENAI AND MALLTRAETH   J F W JONES
5. TINDAETHWY   G M HUGHES
6. TWRCELYN   G W EDWARDS

ARCHDEACONRY OF MEIRIONNYDD

7. ARDUDWY   R A BEACON
8. ARWYSTLI   D J PARRY
9. CYFEILIOG AND MAWDDWY   G J VAUGHAN-JONES
10. EIFIONYDD   W JONES
11. LLYN   W L JONES
12. YSTUMANER   J M RILEY

ST DAVIDS

ARCHDEACONRY OF ST DAVIDS

1. CASTLEMARTIN   A THOMAS
2. DAUGLEDDAU   W H WATKINS
3. DEWISLAND AND FISHGUARD   R J E W REES
4. NARBERTH   M BUTLER
5. ROOSE   A CRAVEN

ARCHDEACONRY OF CARDIGAN

6. CEMAIS AND SUB-AERON   E L THOMAS
7. EMLYN   J H ROWLANDS
8. GLYN AERON   *Vacant*
9. LAMPETER AND ULTRA-AERON   E D GRIFFITHS
10. LLANBADARN FAWR   R H WILLIAMS

ARCHDEACONRY OF CARMARTHEN

11. CARMARTHEN   J K DAVIES
12. CYDWELI   S R THOMAS

13. DYFFRYN AMAN   R I PROTHEROE
14. LLANGADOG AND LLANDEILO   B T RICE
15. ST CLEARS   M G R MORRIS

LLANDAFF

ARCHDEACONRY OF LLANDAFF

1. BRIDGEND   E J EVANS
2. CAERPHILLY   M J SHORT
3. CARDIFF   H G CLARKE
4. LLANTWIT MAJOR AND COWBRIDGE   D V GINN
5. LLANDAFF   M M DAVIES
6. PENARTH AND BARRY   N H COLLINS

ARCHDEACONRY OF MARGAM

7. ABERDARE   N C H BROWN
8. MARGAM   P G WHITE
9. MERTHYR TYDFIL   S S MORGAN
10. NEATH   P RAIKES
11. PONTYPRIDD   J H S THOMAS
12. RHONDDA   N CAHILL

MONMOUTH

ARCHDEACONRY OF MONMOUTH

1. ABERGAVENNY   D K POPE
2. CHEPSTOW   J P HARRIS
3. MONMOUTH   J K C DENERLEY
4. NETHERWENT   T H J PALMER
5. RAGLAN-USK   C R F CALE

ARCHDEACONRY OF NEWPORT

6. BASSALEG   P VANN
7. BEDWELLTY   R J SUMMERS
8. BLAENAU GWENT   D J JONES
9. NEWPORT   K W SHARPE
10. PONTYPOOL   D G BRUNNING

SWANSEA AND BRECON

ARCHDEACONRY OF BRECON

1. BRECON   B M JONES
2. BUILTH   P A C PEARCEY
3. CRICKHOWELL   J R ELLIS
4. HAY   P DIXON
5. MAELIENYDD   N D HALL

ARCHDEACONRY OF GOWER

6. CLYNE   E M WASTELL
7. CWMTAWE   D H E MOSFORD
8. GOWER   J W GRIFFIN
9. LLWCHWR   C J COLEBROOK
10. PENDERI   A G LEE
11. SWANSEA   D E LEWIS

ENGLISH BENEFICES AND CHURCHES

An index of benefices, conventional districts, local ecumenical projects, and proprietary chapels (shown in bold type), together with entries for churches and other licensed places of worship listed on the Parish Index of the Central Board of Finance. Where the church name is the same as that of the benefice (or as that of the place whose name forms the beginning of the benefice name), the church entry is omitted. Church dedications are indicated in brackets.

The benefice entry gives the full legal name, followed by the diocese, its deanery number (page 830), the patron(s), and the name(s) and appointment(s) of clergy serving there (if there are none, the telephone number of the parsonage house is given). The following are the main abbreviations used; for others see the full list of abbreviations.

C	Curate	P	Patron(s)
C-in-c	Curate-in-charge	P-in-c	Priest-in-charge
Dn-in-c	Deacon-in-charge	Par Dn	Parish Deacon
Dss	Deaconess	R	Rector
Hon C	Honorary Curate	TM	Team Minister
Hon Par Dn	Honorary Parish Deacon	TR	Team Rector
Min	Minister	TV	Team Vicar
NSM	Non-stipendiary Minister	V	Vicar

Listed below are the elements in place names which are not normally treated as substantive in the index:

CENTRAL	HIGHER	MUCH	OVER
EAST	LITTLE	NETHER	SOUTH
GREAT	LOW	NEW	THE
GREATER	LOWER	NORTH	UPPER
HIGH	MIDDLE	OLD	WEST

Thus, WEST WIMBLEDON (Christ Church) appears as **WIMBLEDON, WEST (Christ Church)** and CENTRAL TELFORD as **TELFORD, CENTRAL**. The only exception occurs where the second element of the place name is a common noun – thus, NEW LANE remains as **NEW LANE**, and WEST TOWN as **WEST TOWN**.

AB KETTLEBY Group, The (St James) *Leic 3* **P** *V Rothley, K J M Madocks Wright Esq, and MMCET (jt)*
P-in-c R W WIDDOWSON
ABBAS and Templecombe w Horsington *B & W 2* **P** *Bp and Ch Trust Fund (jt)* **R** A J ROSE
ABBERLEY (St Mary) Shrawley, Witley, Astley and Abberley *Worc*
ABBERLEY (St Michael) as above
ABBERTON (St Andrew) Fingringhoe w E Donyland and Abberton etc *Chelmsf*
ABBERTON (St Edburga), The Flyfords, Naunton Beauchamp and Bishampton w Throckmorton *Worc 4* **P** *Bp and Croome Estate Trustees (1 turn), and Ld Chan (1 turn)*
R D E HASSELL
ABBESS RODING (St Edmund), Beauchamp Roding and White Roding *Chelmsf 19* **P** *Viscount Gough (1 turn) and Bp (2 turns)* **R** *Vacant* White Roding (01279) 876313
ABBEY CHAPEL (St Mary) Annesley Our Lady and All SS *S'well*
ABBEY HEY (St George) *Man 1* **P** *Bp*
P-in-c I C J GORTON
ABBEY HULTON (St John) Bucknall and Bagnall *Lich*
ABBEY WOOD (St Michael and All Angels) *S'wark 1*
P *Bp* **V** M W NEALE, **NSM** D C ROBINSON
ABBEY WOOD (William Temple) Thamesmead *S'wark*
ABBEYDALE (St John the Evangelist) *Sheff 2* **P** *Lady Judith Roberts, Mrs C Longworth, P Hayward Esq and J Roebuck Esq (jt)* **V** G G MacINTOSH
ABBEYDALE (St Peter) Sheff Abbeydale St Pet *Sheff*
ABBEYDORE (St Mary) Ewyas Harold w Dulas, Kenderchurch etc *Heref*
ABBOTS BICKINGTON (St James) and Bulkworthy *Ex 9*
P *Bp* **V** *Vacant*
ABBOTS BROMLEY (St Nicholas) w Blithfield *Lich 3* **P** *Bp and D&C (jt)* **V** *Vacant* Burton-on-Trent (01283) 840242
ABBOTS LANGLEY (St Lawrence) *St Alb 13* **P** *Bp*
V B K ANDREWS, **C** R W NEILL
ABBOTS LEIGH (Holy Trinity) w Leigh Woods *Bris 5*
P *Bp* **V** P W ROWE
ABBOTS MORTON (St Peter) Church Lench w Rous Lench and Abbots Morton *Worc*
ABBOTS RIPTON (St Andrew) w Wood Walton *Ely 9*
P *Lord de Ramsey (2 turns), D&C (1 turn)*
P-in-c B J HYDER-SMITH
ABBOTSBURY (St Mary) Highweek and Teigngrace *Ex*
ABBOTSBURY (St Nicholas), Portesham and Langton Herring *Sarum 5* **P** *Hon Charlotte Morrison and P R FitzGerald Esq (jt), and Bp (alt)* **V** P T SEAL
ABBOTSHAM (St Helen) Parkham, Alwington, Buckland Brewer etc *Ex*
ABBOTSKERSWELL (Blessed Virgin Mary) *Ex 11*
P *Ld Chan* **P-in-c** J G A IVE, **Par Dn** P FIVE (nee KNOTT)

ABBOTSLEY (St Margaret) *Ely 12* **P** *Ball Coll Ox*
P-in-c B CURRY
ABBOTSWOOD (St Nicholas Family Centre) Yate New Town *Bris*
ABBOTTS ANN (St Mary) and Upper Clatford and Goodworth Clatford *Win 3* **P** *T P de Paravicini Esq and Bp (jt)* **R** P M GILKS, **NSM** N J JUDD, J A TAYLOR
ABDON (St Margaret) *Heref 12* **P** *Bp* **R** I E GIBBS
ABENHALL (St Michael) w Mitcheldean *Glouc 3* **P** *DBP*
P-in-c R G STURMAN
ABERFORD (St Ricarius) Micklefield w Aberford *York*
ABINGDON (Christ Church) (St Helen) (St Michael and All Angels) (St Nicholas) *Ox 10* **P** *Patr Bd*
TR M A J GOODE, **TV** G N MAUGHAN, M LOVERING, **C** J M LOVERING, T R PERRY, **NSM** M C SAMS, G W COX, A MITRA, S D COE, N J MITRA
ABINGER (St James) cum Coldharbour *Guildf 7* **P** *Ch Patr Trust and J P M H Evelyn Esq (alt)* **R** A N BERRY
ABINGTON (St Peter and St Paul) *Pet 4* **P** *Bp*
R F E PICKARD, **C** A Q MICKLETHWAITE
ABINGTON, GREAT (St Mary the Virgin) w LITTLE (St Mary) *Ely 4* **P** *MMCET* **P-in-c** G C MILLS
ABINGTON PIGOTTS (St Michael and All Angels) Shingay Gp of Par *Ely*
ABNEY (Mission Room) Bradwell *Derby*
ABRAM (St John) *Liv 14* **P** *R Wigan* **V** J JORDAN
ABRIDGE (Holy Trinity) Lambourne w Abridge and Stapleford Abbotts *Chelmsf*
ABSON (St James the Great) Pucklechurch and Abson *Bris*
ABTHORPE (St John the Baptist) Silverstone and Abthorpe w Slapton *Pet*
ACASTER MALBIS (Holy Trinity) *York 1*
P *R A G Raimes Esq* **V** P RATHBONE
ACASTER SELBY (St John) Appleton Roebuck w Acaster Selby *York*
ACCRINGTON (Christ Church) *Blackb 1* **P** *Bp and V S Shore H Trin (jt)* **V** K LOGAN
ACCRINGTON (St James) (St Paul) (St Andrew) (St Peter) *Blackb 1* **P** *DBP* **TR** F R COOKE, **TV** A D LYON, A FISHWICK
ACCRINGTON (St John) w Huncoat (St Augustine) *Blackb 1* **P** *Bp and V Accrington St Jas w St Paul (jt)*
V D E CROOK, **C** G BILLINGTON
ACCRINGTON (St Mary Magdalen) Milnshaw *Blackb 1*
P *V Accrington St Jas* **V** M C R SOWERBY
ACKLAM (St John the Baptist) Burythorpe, Acklam and Leavening w Westow *York*
ACKLAM, WEST (St Mary) *York 19* **P** *Trustees*
V S C WRIGHT, **C** D S WATSON, **NSM** M J WRIGHT
ACKLETON (Mission Room) Worfield *Heref*
ACKLINGTON (St John the Divine) Warkworth and Acklington *Newc*
ACKWORTH (All Saints) (St Cuthbert) *Wakef 11* **P** *Duchy of Lanc* **R** P MOORHOUSE

ACLE (St Edmund) w Fishley and North Burlingham *Nor 4*
  P *Bp and Ch Soc Trust (jt)*   **R** C G WAY
ACOCKS GREEN (St Mary) *Birm 10* **P** *Trustees*
  V R H POSTILL
ACOL (St Mildred) Birchington w Acol and Minnis Bay *Cant*
ACOMB (Holy Redeemer) *York 8* **P** *The Crown*
  V J BEECH
ACOMB (St Stephen) *York 8* **P** *J H Murray Esq and*
  J B Deby Esq (jt) **V** M E G WARCHUS, **C** R J FISHER,
  P A BROOKFIELD
ACOMB MOOR (James the Deacon) *York 8* **P** *Abp*
  V R W A GUIVER
ACRISE (St Martin) Hawkinge w Acrise and Swingfield *Cant*
ACTON (All Saints) w Great Waldingfield *St E 12* **P** *Bp*
  NSM D L C RUTHERFORD
ACTON (St Mary) *Lon 22* **P** *Bp* **C** S M MAINA,
  Hon C J F FOX, **NSM** P M SMEDLEY
ACTON (St Mary) and Worleston, Church Minshull and
  Wettenhall *Ches 15* **P** *Bp, V Over St Chad, and*
  R C Roundell Esq (jt) **V** M J RYLANDS,
  C J A KENDALL, A C RYLANDS
ACTON, EAST (St Dunstan w St Thomas) *Lon 22* **P** *Bp*
  V W J MORGAN, **C** P B D CRICK
ACTON, NORTH (St Gabriel) *Lon 22* **P** *Bp*
  V E J ALCOCK, **NSM** C C SLIPPER
ACTON, WEST (St Martin) *Lon 22* **P** *Bp*
  P-in-c N P HENDERSON, **Hon C** J M UCHIDA
ACTON BEAUCHAMP (St Giles) and Evesbatch w Stanford
  Bishop *Heref 2* **P** *Bp and MMCET (alt)*
  P-in-c B R CONAWAY
ACTON BURNELL (St Mary) Condover w Frodesley,
  Acton Burnell etc *Heref*
ACTON GREEN (St Alban) (St Peter) (All Saints) *Lon 22*
  P *Bp* **V** J M V WILLMINGTON, **C** R M REEVE
ACTON ROUND (St Mary) *Heref 9* **P** *DBP*
  Hon C H J PATTERSON
ACTON SCOTT (St Margaret) *Heref 11* **P** *DBP* **R** *Vacant*
ACTON TRUSSELL (St James) Penkridge Team *Lich*
ACTON TURVILLE (St Mary) Badminton w Lt Badminton,
  Acton Turville etc *Glouc*
ADBASTON (St Michael and All Angels) Croxton w
  Broughton and Adbaston *Lich*
ADDERBURY (St Mary) w Milton *Ox 5* **P** *New Coll Ox*
  V J E HOLBROOK
ADDERLEY (St Peter) *Lich 23* **P** *Lt-Col Sir John*
  Corbet, Bt **P-in-c** G D PRICE
ADDINGHAM (St Michael), Edenhall, Langwathby and
  Culgaith *Carl 4* **P** *D&C* **V** R A MOATT,
  NSM A R BEAUMONT
ADDINGHAM (St Peter) *Bradf 4* **P** *J R Thompson-*
  Ashby Esq **R** M J CASTERTON, **Hon C** J E LLOYD
ADDINGTON (St Margaret) Birling, Addington, Ryarsh
  and Trottiscliffe *Roch*
ADDINGTON (St Mary) Winslow w Gt Horwood and
  Addington *Ox*
ADDINGTON (St Mary) *S'wark 20* **P** *Abp* **V** P ADAMS,
  C N G MARNS, **NSM** B J HESELTINE
ADDINGTON, GREAT (All Saints) w Little Addington
  Pet 10 **P** *Bp* **NSM** P R NEEDLE
ADDINGTON, LITTLE (St Mary the Virgin) Gt w Lt
  Addington *Pet*
ADDINGTON, NEW (St Edward) *S'wark 20* **P** *Bp*
  V J A F GALBRAITH, **C** A O NICOLL, P M BALLAMAN
ADDISCOMBE (St Mary Magdalene) *S'wark 21*
  P *Trustees* **V** M R M°KINNEY, **C** R W J MYERS,
  H H NESBITT
ADDISCOMBE (St Mildred) *S'wark 21* **P** *Bp*
  V G D S GALILEE
ADDLESTONE (St Augustine) (St Paul) *Guildf 11* **P** *Bp*
  V W M POWELL, **C** L C SMITH, **NSM** A G BARDELL
ADDLETHORPE (St Nicholas) Ingoldmells w Addlethorpe
  Linc
ADEL (St John the Baptist) *Ripon 7* **P** *Brig R G Lewthwaite,*
  D R Lewthwaite Esq, and J V Lewthwaite Esq (jt)
  R G C DARVILL, **C** A W SEWELL
ADEYFIELD (St Barnabas) Hemel Hempstead *St Alb*
ADISHAM (Holy Innocents) Aylesham w Adisham *Cant*
ADLESTROP (St Mary Magdalene) Broadwell, Evenlode,
  Oddington and Adlestrop *Glouc*
ADLINGFLEET (All Saints) The Marshland *Sheff*
ADLINGTON (St John's Mission Church) Prestbury *Ches*
ADLINGTON (St Paul) *Blackb 4* **P** *Bp* **V** D F C MORGAN
ADSTOCK (St Cecilia) Lenborough *Ox*
ADSTONE (All Saints) Blakesley w Adstone and Maidford
  etc *Pet*
ADSWOOD (St Gabriel's Mission Church) Stockport South
  West *Ches*

ADVENT (St Adwena) Lanteglos by Camelford w Advent
  Truro
ADWELL (St Mary) Tetsworth, Adwell w S Weston,
  Lewknor etc *Ox*
ADWICK-LE-STREET (St Laurence) *Sheff 8* **P** *J C M*
  Fullerton Esq **R** P A INGRAM
ADWICK-UPON-DEARNE (St John the
  Baptist) Barnburgh w Melton on the Hill etc *Sheff*
AFFPUDDLE (St Lawrence) Bere Regis and Affpuddle w
  Turnerspuddle *Sarum*
AIGBURTH (St Anne) *Liv 4* **P** *Trustees* **V** J C ANDERS
AIKTON (St Andrew) *Carl 3* **P** *Earl of Lonsdale* **R** *Vacant*
  Wigton (016973) 42229
AINDERBY STEEPLE (St Helen) w Yafforth and Kirby
  Wiske w Maunby *Ripon 4* **P** *Bp and Duke of Northd (jt)*
  R *Vacant* Northallerton (01609) 773346
AINSDALE (St John) *Liv 9* **P** *R Walton, Bp, and Adn (jt)*
  V A RENSHAW, **C** U R SHONE
AINSTABLE (St Michael and All Angels) Kirkoswald,
  Renwick and Ainstable *Carl*
AINSWORTH (Christ Church) *Man 14* **P** *Bp*
  V A T FLAHERTY
AINTREE (St Giles) *Liv 7* **P** *Bp* **V** D K KING
AINTREE (St Peter) *Liv 7* **P** *R Sefton*
  P-in-c R A BYWORTH
AIREDALE (Holy Cross) w Fryston *Wakef 11* **P** *Bp*
  V J D WILKINSON, **C** P WHITTINGHAM
AIRMYN (St David) Hook w Airmyn *Sheff*
AISHOLT (All Saints) *B & W 14* **P** *MMCET*
  P-in-c R R EARNSHAW
AISLABY (St Margaret) and Ruswarp *York 23* **P** *Abp*
  P-in-c D W PROUT
AISTHORPE (St Peter) w Scampton w Thorpe le Fallows w
  Brattleby *Linc 3* **P** *DBP and J M Wright Esq (jt)*
  R M J SILLEY
AKELEY (St James) N Buckm *Ox*
ALBERBURY (St Michael and All Angels) w Cardeston
  Heref 13 **P** *Bp and Sir Michael Leighton, Bt (alt)*
  V H J EDWARDS
ALBOURNE (St Bartholomew) w Sayers Common and
  Twineham *Chich 9* **P** *Bp (2 turns), Ex Coll Ox (1 turn)*
  R D M SWYER
ALBRIGHTON (St John the Baptist) Leaton and Albrighton
  w Battlefield *Lich*
ALBRIGHTON (St Mary Magdalene) *Lich 25*
  P *Haberdashers' Co and Ch Hosp Horsham (alt)*
  V R B BALKWILL
ALBURGH (All Saints) Earsham w Alburgh and Denton
  Nor
ALBURY (St Mary) Lt Hadham w Albury *St Alb*
ALBURY (St Peter and St Paul) (St Martha) *Guildf 2*
  P *Marquess of Linlithgow and R G H Smith Esq (jt)*
  R D H GUMMER
ALBURY Tiddington (St Helen) Holton and Waterperry w
  Albury and Waterstock *Ox*
ALBY (St Ethelbert) Erpingham w Calthorpe, Ingworth,
  Aldborough etc *Nor*
ALCESTER (St Nicholas) and Arrow w Oversley and Weethley
  Cov 7 **P** *Marquess of Hertf* **R** D C CAPRON
ALCISTON (not known) Berwick w Selmeston and Alciston
  Chich
ALCOMBE (St Michael the Archangel) *B & W 16* **P** *Bp*
  V A F MILLS
ALCONBURY (St Peter and St Paul) w Alconbury Weston
  Ely 9 **P** *D&C Westmr* **V** J A COOMBE
ALDBOROUGH (St Andrew) w Boroughbridge and Roecliffe
  Ripon 3 **P** *D&C York and Bp (alt)* **V** R T COOPER,
  C P J SMITH
ALDBOROUGH (St Mary) Erpingham w Calthorpe,
  Ingworth, Aldborough etc *Nor*
ALDBOROUGH HATCH (St Peter) *Chelmsf 4*
  P *The Crown* **V** M J TRODDEN
ALDBOURNE (St Michael) Whitton *Sarum*
ALDBROUGH (St Bartholomew) and Mappleton w Goxhill
  and Withernwick *York 12* **P** *Ld Chan, Abp, and Adn*
  E Riding (by turn) **V** N W STOCKBRIDGE,
  NSM S FOSTER
ALDBROUGH (St Paul) Forcett and Aldbrough and
  Melsonby *Ripon*
ALDBURY (St John the Baptist) Tring *St Alb*
ALDEBURGH (St Peter and St Paul) w Hazlewood *St E 19*
  P *Mrs A C V Wentworth* **V** A H MOORE,
  NSM J A BIRCH
ALDEBY (St Mary) The Raveningham Gp *Nor*
ALDENHAM (St John the Baptist) *St Alb 1* **P** *Lord*
  Aldenham **P-in-c** G H BOLT, **NSM** M V BOLT
ALDERBROOK (St Richard) Crowborough *Chich*
ALDERBURY (St Mary the Virgin) Alderbury Team *Sarum*

ALDERBURY Team, The (St Mary the Virgin) *Sarum 11*
  P *Patr Bd* **TR** G ROWSTON, **TV** P R BOSHER,
  C H B SKELDING, **NSM** G F H MITCHELL
ALDERCAR (St John) Langley Mill *Derby*
ALDERFORD (St John the Baptist) w Attlebridge and
  Swannington *Nor 23* **P** *Bp and D&C (alt)*
  P-in-c J P PILLINGWORTH
ALDERHOLT (St James) *Sarum 10* **P** *DBP*
  V P J MARTIN
ALDERLEY (St Kenelm) Kingswood w Alderley and
  Hillesley *Glouc*
ALDERLEY (St Mary) *Ches 12* **P** *Trustees*
  P-in-c B C REEVE
ALDERLEY EDGE (St Philip) *Ches 12* **P** *Trustees*
  V B T YOUNG
ALDERMASTON (St Mary the Virgin) w Wasing and
  Brimpton *Ox 12* **P** *Bp, DBP, Sir William Mount, Bt, and*
  Worc Coll Ox (jt) **V** R B MILLER
ALDERMINSTER (St Mary and Holy Cross) and Halford
  Cov 9 **P** *Bp and SMF (jt)* **P-in-c** D R TILLEY
ALDERNEY (St Anne) *Win 14* **P** *The Crown*
  V S C INGHAM
ALDERSBROOK (St Gabriel) *Chelmsf 4* **P** *R Wanstead*
  V D J DALAIS
ALDERSHOT (Holy Trinity) *Guildf 1* **P** *CPAS*
  V R F PARKER
ALDERSHOT (St Augustine) *Guildf 1* **P** *Bp*
  V K M HODGES
ALDERSHOT (St Michael) (Ascension) *Guildf 1* **P** *Bp*
  V S A ZEAL, **C** C WAREHAM
ALDERSLEY (Christ the King) Tettenhall Regis *Lich*
ALDERTON (St Andrew) w Ramsholt and Bawdsey *St E 7*
  P *Sir Anthony Quilter (1 turn), F G A Beckett Esq (2 turns),*
  and Bp (1 turn) **P-in-c** M H INMAN
ALDERTON (St Giles) Sherston Magna, Easton Grey,
  Luckington etc *Bris*
ALDERTON (St Margaret) Stoke Bruerne w Grafton Regis
  and Alderton *Pet*
ALDERTON (St Margaret of Antioch), Great Washbourne,
  Dumbleton and Wormington *Glouc 17* **P** *M A E Casey Esq*
  (1 Turn), Bp (2 turns), and Hon S K L Evetts (1 turn)
  R P W SMITH
ALDERWASLEY (All Saints) Wirksworth *Derby*
ALDFIELD (St Lawrence) Fountains Gp *Ripon*
ALDFORD (St John the Baptist) and Bruera *Ches 5* **P** *Duke*
  of Westmr and D&C (alt) **R** C A BARTON
ALDHAM (St Margaret and St Catherine) Marks Tey w
  Aldham and Lt Tey *Chelmsf*
ALDHAM (St Mary) Elmsett w Aldham *St E*
ALDINGBOURNE (St Mary the Virgin), Barnham and
  Eastergate *Chich 1* **P** *Bp and D&C (jt)* **R** D J FARNHAM
ALDINGHAM (St Cuthbert) and Dendron and Rampside
  Carl 8 **P** *The Crown and V Dalton-in-Furness (alt)*
  P-in-c C E POTTER
ALDINGTON (St Martin) w Bonnington and Bilsington
  Cant 12 **P** *Abp* **R** L WILLIAMS
ALDRIDGE (St Mary the Virgin) (St Thomas) *Lich 6*
  P *MMCET* **R** N J H REEVES, **C** G R DAVIES,
  J A WHITING
ALDRINGHAM (St Andrew) w Thorpe, Knodishall w Buxlow
  and Friston *St E 19* **P** *Mrs A C V Wentworth, Ch Patr*
  Trust, and Ch Soc Trust (by turn) **P-in-c** C E BROOKS
ALDRINGTON (St Leonard) *Chich 4* **P** *Bp*
  TR S J TERRY, **TV** T P J BODKIN
ALDSWORTH (St Bartholomew) Sherborne, Windrush, the
  Barringtons etc *Glouc*
ALDWARK (St Stephen) Alne *York*
ALDWICK (St Richard) *Chich 1* **P** *Bp* **V** L C J NAGEL,
  C D A WALLER
ALDWINCLE (St Peter) w Thorpe Achurch and Pilton w
  Wadenhoe and Stoke Doyle *Pet 12* **P** *Soc Merchant*
  Venturers Bris (2 turns), G C Capron Esq (1 turn), and
  Wadenhoe Trust (1 turn) **P-in-c** J A ROSE
ALDWORTH (St Mary the Virgin) Basildon w Aldworth and
  Ashampstead *Ox*
ALEXANDRA PARK (St Andrew) *Lon 20* **P** *Bp*
  V A F PYBUS,
ALFINGTON (St James and St Anne) Ottery St Mary,
  Alfington, W Hill, Tipton etc *Ex*
ALFOLD (St Nicholas) and Loxwood *Guildf 2* **P** *Bp and*
  CPAS (jt) **R** K A SHORT
ALFORD (All Saints) Six Pilgrims *B & W*
ALFORD (St Wilfrid) w Rigsby *Linc 8* **P** *Bp*
  P-in-c A READER-MOORE, **C** R J BENSON
ALFRETON (St Martin) *Derby 1* **P** *Bp* **V** *Vacant* Alfreton
  (01773) 833280

ALFRICK (St Mary Magdalene) and Lulsley and Suckley and
  Leigh and Bransford *Worc 3* **P** *Prime Min and Bp (alt)*
  R M R WESTALL
ALFRISTON (St Andrew) w Lullington, Litlington and West
  Dean *Chich 18* **P** *Ld Chan (3 turns), R A Brown Esq*
  (1 turn), and Duke of Devonshire (1 turn) **R** F J FOX-
  WILSON
ALGARKIRK (St Peter and St Paul) Sutterton w Fosdyke
  and Algarkirk *Linc*
ALHAMPTON (Mission Church) Ditcheat w E Pennard and
  Pylle *B & W*
ALKBOROUGH (St John the Baptist) *Linc 4* **P** *Em Coll*
  Cam and Bp (alt) **V** G P GUNNING
ALKERTON (St Michael and All Angels) Horley w Hornton
  and Hanwell, Shenington etc *Ox*
ALKHAM (St Anthony) w Capel le Ferne and Hougham
  Cant 4 **P** *Abp* **V** *Vacant* Folkestone (01303) 50252
ALKMONTON (St John), Cubley, Marston, Montgomery and
  Yeaveley *Derby 14* **P** *Bp (3 turns), V Shirley (1 turn)*
  P-in-c M G HUGGETT
ALL CANNINGS (All Saints) Bishop's Cannings, All
  Cannings etc *Sarum*
ALL STRETTON (St Michael and All Angels) Church
  Stretton *Heref*
ALLENDALE (St Cuthbert) w Whitfield *Newc 4* **P** *Viscount*
  Allendale and J C Blackett-Ord Esq (alt) **R** R A BAILY
ALLENS CROSS (St Bartholomew) *Birm 4* **P** *Bp*
  P-in-c D W JAMES
ALLENS GREEN (Mission Church) High Wych and Gilston
  w Eastwick *St Alb*
ALLEN'S ROUGH (Worship Centre) Willenhall H Trin *Lich*
ALLENSMORE (St Andrew) Kingstone w Clehonger, Eaton
  Bishop etc *Heref*
ALLENTON (St Edmund) and Shelton Lock *Derby 15*
  P *Bp* **V** A LUKE
ALLER (St Andrew) Langport Area Chs *B & W*
ALLERSTON (St John) Brompton-by-Sawdon w Snainton,
  Ebberston etc *York*
ALLERTHORPE (St Botolph) Barmby Moor w Allerthorpe,
  Fangfoss and Yapham *York*
ALLERTON (All Hallows) *Liv 4* **P** *J Bibby Esq*
  V G J BUTLAND, **NSM** A M SMITH
ALLERTON (not known) Mark w Allerton *B & W*
ALLERTON (St Peter) (St Francis of Assisi) *Bradf 1* **P** *Bp*
  V C WARD, **C** M WARD
ALLERTON BYWATER (St Mary) Kippax w Allerton
  Bywater *Ripon*
ALLESLEY (All Saints) *Cov 2* **P** *J R W Thomson-Bree Esq*
  R J T H BRITTON, **C** J BURROWS
ALLESLEY PARK (St Christopher) and Whoberley *Cov 3*
  P *Bp* **V** F J CURTIS
ALLESTREE (St Edmund) *Derby 11* **P** *Bp*
  V A T REDMAN, **C** P THOMPSON, **NSM** C C WARNER,
  A J CLARK
ALLESTREE (St Nicholas) *Derby 11* **P** *Bp* **V** W F BATES
ALLEXTON (St Peter) Hallaton w Horninghold, Allexton,
  Tugby etc *Leic*
ALLHALLOWS (All Saints) *Carl 7* **P** *Bp* **V** *Vacant* Low
  Ireby (016973) 71295
ALLINGTON (St John the Baptist) Bourne Valley *Sarum*
ALLINGTON (St Nicholas) and Maidstone St Peter *Cant 15*
  P *Abp* **R** A WATSON
ALLINGTON (St Swithin) Bridport *Sarum*
ALLINGTON, EAST (St Andrew), Slapton and Strete *Ex 14*
  P *Bp* **R** *Vacant* Stoke Fleming (01803) 770378
ALLINGTON, WEST (Holy Trinity) w East Allington and
  Sedgebrook *Linc 19* **P** *Ld Chan* **NSM** S J HADLEY
ALLITHWAITE (St Mary) *Carl 10* **P** *Bp*
  P-in-c H G WHITTY
ALLONBY (Christ Church) *Carl 7* **P** *D&C and V Bromfield*
  w Waverton (jt) **V** J LEONARDI
ALMELEY (St Mary) Lyonshall w Titley, Almeley and
  Kinnersley *Heref*
ALMER (St Mary) Red Post *Sarum*
ALMONDBURY (St Michael and St Helen) (St Mary) (All
  Hallows) w Farnley Tyas *Wakef 1* **P** *DBP*
  TR M W THOMAS, **TV** S V BROOKS, **C** A W FROUD
ALMONDSBURY (St Mary the Virgin) *Bris 8* **P** *Bp*
  V I T HOLDCROFT
ALNE (St Mary) *York 5* **P** *CPAS and MMCET (alt)*
  NSM R WADSWORTH
ALNE, GREAT (St Mary Magdalene) Kinwarton w Gt Alne
  and Haselor *Cov*
ALNHAM (St Michael and All Angels) Alwinton w
  Holystone and Alnham *Newc*
ALNMOUTH (St John the Baptist) Lesbury w Alnmouth
  Newc

ALNWICK (St Michael and St Paul) *Newc 9* **P** *Trustees of the late Duke of Northd* **V** C P ANDREWS, **C** J E HAMPSON

ALPERTON (St James) *Lon 21* **P** *CPAS* **V** J B ROOT, **C** D J SIMPSON, **NSM** A S JACOB

ALPHAMSTONE (not known) w Lamarsh and Pebmarsh *Chelmsf 15* **P** *Earl of Verulam and Ld Chan (alt)* **R** *Vacant* Twinstead (01787) 269646

ALPHETON (St Peter and St Paul) Lawshall w Shimplingthorne and Alpheton *St E*

ALPHINGTON (St Michael and All Angels) *Ex 3* **P** *DBP* **R** L M BATE

ALRESFORD (St Andrew) *Chelmsf 24* **P** *Bp* **R** G R COBB, **NSM** J R PANTRY

ALRESFORD, NEW (St John the Baptist) w Ovington and Itchen Stoke *Win 1* **P** *Bp* **R** G C G TRASLER **P-in-c** T M W PINNER, **NSM** D B ROGERS

ALRESFORD, OLD (St Mary) and Bighton *Win 1* **P** *Bp*

ALREWAS (All Saints) *Lich 1* **P** *Bp* **V** S J MORRIS

ALSAGER (Christ Church) *Ches 11* **P** *Bp* **V** J E VARTY

ALSAGER (St Mary Magdalene) (St Patrick's Mission Church) *Ches 11* **P** *Bp* **V** J RICHARDSON, **Hon C** J WATSON

ALSAGERS BANK (St John) Silverdale and Alsagers Bank *Lich*

ALSOP EN LE DALE (St Michael and All Angels) Parwich w Alsop en le Dale *Derby*

ALSTON Team, The (St Augustine) *Newc 4* **P** *Bp* **TR** L T ATHERTON, **TV** J R KELLY

ALSTONE (St Margaret) Overbury w Teddington, Alstone etc *Worc*

ALSTONFIELD (St Peter), Butterton, Warslow w Elkstone and Wetton *Lich 10* **P** *Miss A I M Harpur-Crewe, Bp, and V Mayfield (jt)* **V** *Vacant* Alstonefield (01335) 310216

ALSWEAR (not known) Bishopsnympton, Rose Ash, Mariansleigh etc *Ex*

ALTARNON (St Nonna) w Bolventor, Laneast and St Clether *Truro 9* **P** *Bp, D&C, and SMF (jt)* **P-in-c** W M CARTWRIGHT

ALTCAR (St Michael and All Angels) *Liv 5* **P** *Bp* **P-in-c** R J LEE

ALTHAM (St James) w Clayton le Moors *Blackb 1* **P** *DBP and Trustees (alt)* **V** P H DEARDEN, **C** S P C COOPER

ALTHORNE (St Andrew) Creeksea w Althorne, Latchingdon and N Fambridge *Chelmsf*

ALTHORPE (St Oswald) N Axholme Gp *Linc*

ALTOFTS (St Mary Magdalene) *Wakef 9* **P** *Meynall Ingram Trustees* **V** S K L VICK

ALTON (All Saints) *Win 2* **P** *Bp* **V** M C SURMAN

ALTON (St Lawrence) *Win 2* **P** *D&C* **V** R W S L GUSSMAN, **C** C J ELLIOTT

ALTON (St Peter) w Bradley-le-Moors and Oakamoor w Cotton *Lich 11* **P** *Earl of Shrewsbury and Talbot, DBP, and R Cheadle (jt)* **V** *Vacant* Oakamoor (01538) 702469

ALTON BARNES (St Mary the Virgin) Swanborough *Sarum*

ALTON COMMON (Mission Room) Alton w Bradley-le-Moors and Oakamoor w Cotton *Lich*

ALTON PANCRAS (St Pancras) Piddletrenthide w Plush, Alton Pancras etc *Sarum*

ALTRINCHAM (St George) *Ches 10* **P** *V Bowdon* **V** B R McCONNELL, **C** S J ARTUS, **Hon C** R E CORK

ALTRINCHAM (St John the Evangelist) *Ches 10* **P** *Bp* **V** D P BROCKBANK

ALVANLEY (St John the Evangelist) *Ches 3* **P** *Bp* **P-in-c** A R RIDLEY

ALVASTON (St Michael and All Angels) *Derby 15* **P** *PCC* **P-in-c** C F MEEHAN

ALVECHURCH (St Lawrence) *Worc 7* **P** *Bp* **R** D H MARTIN

ALVEDISTON (St Mary) Chalke Valley W *Sarum*

ALVELEY (St Mary the Virgin) and Quatt *Heref 9* **P** *J W H Thompson Esq and Lady Labouchere (jt)* **P-in-c** W WATSON, **NSM** W R PRYCE

ALVERDISCOTT (All Saints) Newton Tracey, Alverdiscott, Huntshaw etc *Ex*

ALVERSTOKE (St Faith) (St Francis) (St Mary) *Portsm 3* **P** *Bp* **R** E A GOODYER, **C** J A GORDON

ALVERSTONE (Church Hall) Brading w Yaverland *Portsm*

ALVERTHORPE (St Paul) *Wakef 12* **P** *Bp* **V** A MAUCHAN

ALVESCOT (St Peter) Shill Valley and Broadshire *Ox*

ALVESTON (St Helen) *Bris 8* **P** *D&C* **V** D J POLE

ALVESTON (St James) *Cov 8* **P** *R Hampton Lucy w Charlecote and Loxley* **V** R E WILLIAMS

ALVINGHAM (St Adelwold) Mid Marsh Gp *Linc*

ALVINGTON (St Andrew) Woolaston w Alvington and Aylburton *Glouc*

ALVINGTON, WEST (All Saints) Malborough w S Huish, W Alvington and Churchstow *Ex*

ALWALTON (St Andrew) and Chesterton *Ely 13* **P** *Sir Stephen Hastings* **P-in-c** R A D STURT

ALWINGTON (St Andrew) Parkham, Alwington, Buckland Brewer etc *Ex*

ALWINTON (St Michael and All Angels) w Holystone and Alnham *Newc 9* **P** *Ld Chan and Trustees of the late Duke of Northd (alt)* **V** J WYLAM

ALWOODLEY (St Barnabas) Moor Allerton *Ripon*

AMBERGATE (St Anne) and Heage *Derby 11* **P** *V Duffield and Exors M A T Johnson Esq* **R** D J T RYMER

AMBERLEY (Holy Trinity) *Glouc 8* **P** *DBP* **P-in-c** M O TUCKER

AMBERLEY (no dedication) Marden w Amberley and Wisteston *Heref*

AMBERLEY (St Michael) w North Stoke and Parham, Wiggonholt and Greatham *Chich 12* **P** *Bp and Parham Estate Trustees (jt)* **P-in-c** C R JENKINS

AMBLE (St Cuthbert) *Newc 9* **P** *Bp* **V** J A MACNAUGHTON

AMBLECOTE (Holy Trinity) *Worc 12* **P** *Bp* **V** P TONGUE

AMBLESIDE (St Mary) w Brathay *Carl 10* **P** *DBP* **V** L G HIGDON, **NSM** D HARRISON

AMBROSDEN (St Mary the Virgin) w Merton and Piddington *Ox 2* **P** *Trustees F A W Page-Turner Esq, Ex Coll Ox, and DBF (jt)* **V** G G CHAPMAN, **NSM** L K ROSE

AMCOTTS (St Mark) N Axholme Gp *Linc*

AMERSHAM (St Mary the Virgin) *Ox 20* **P** *Capt F Tyrwhitt Drake* **R** A M PRIDDIS, **C** W D BRIERLEY

AMERSHAM ON THE HILL (St Michael and All Angels) *Ox 20* **P** *Bp* **V** G B GRIFFITHS

AMESBURY (St Mary and St Melor) *Sarum 12* **P** *D&C* **V** P R LEWIS

AMINGTON (St Editha) *Birm 12* **P** *Bp* **V** M A HARRIS

AMOTHERBY (St Helen) Street TM *York*

AMPFIELD (St Mark) Hursley and Ampfield *Win*

AMPLEFORTH (St Hilda) and Oswaldkirk and Gilling East *York 18* **P** *Abp and Trin Coll Cam (jt)* **R** D E NEWTON

AMPNEYS (St Mary) (St Peter) (Holy Rood) w Driffield and Poulton, The *Glouc 13* **P** *Bp and Col Sir Piers Bengough (jt)* **P-in-c** P H NAYLOR

AMPORT (St Mary), Grateley, Monxton and Quarley *Win 3* **P** *D&C Chich, T P de Paravicini Esq, Mrs E D Collie, Bp, and R Foundn of St Kath (jt)* **V** R S BENNETT

AMPTHILL (St Andrew) w Millbrook and Steppingley *St Alb 15* **P** *Ld Chan* **C** D J MUSKETT

AMPTON (St Peter) Blackbourne *St E*

AMWELL, GREAT (St John the Baptist) w St Margaret's *St Alb 8* **P** *Bp and Haileybury and Imp Service Coll (jt)* **P-in-c** B F J GOODWIN

AMWELL, LITTLE (Holy Trinity) *St Alb 8* **P** *Ch Patr Trust* **V** J V BUDD, **NSM** M HARDING

ANCASTER (St Martin) Ancaster Wilsford Gp *Linc*

ANCASTER WILSFORD Group, The *Linc 23* **P** *Bp (2 turns), DBP (1 turn), and Mrs G V Hoare (1 turn)* **NSM** J E COULTHURST

ANCHORSHOLME (All Saints) *Blackb 9* **P** *Bp, V Bispham, and Ch Soc Trust (jt)* **V** P R NUNN

ANCOATS (All Souls) Man Gd Shep *Man*

ANCROFT (St Anne) Lowick and Kyloe w Ancroft *Newc*

ANDERBY (St Andrew) Sutton, Huttoft and Anderby *Linc*

ANDOVER (St Mary the Virgin) (St Thomas) w Foxcott *Win 3* **P** *St Mary's Coll Win* **V** A R WILDS, **C** M A AIKMAN

ANDOVER, WEST (St Michael and All Angels) *Win 3* **P** *Bp* **V** J R TARR

ANDREAS (St Andrew) *S & M 4* **P** *The Crown* **R** R C GEDDES

ANDREAS (St Jude Chapelry) *S & M 4* **P** *R Andreas* **V** R C GEDDES

ANERLEY Christ Church *Roch 12* **P** *CPAS* **V** *Vacant* 0181-778 4800

ANFIELD (St Columba) *Liv 7* **P** *Bp* **V** P B CAVANAGH, **NSM** K L MILLER

ANFIELD (St Margaret) *Liv 3* **P** *Bp* **P-in-c** C J GRAY

ANGELL TOWN (St John the Evangelist) *S'wark 9* **P** *Bp* **V** M S ARMITAGE, **NSM** D J DERRICK

ANGERSLEIGH (St Michael) Trull w Angersleigh *B & W*

ANGMERING (St Margaret) *Chich 1* **P** *J F P Somerset Esq* **R** A M G WELLS, **C** M J T PAYNE

ANLABY (St Peter) *York 15* **P** *Trustees* **V** F A GORDON-KERR

ANLABY COMMON (St Mark) Hull *York 15* **P** *Abp* **V** C A G KERR

ANMER (St Mary) Dersingham w Anmer and Shernborne *Nor*

ANNESLEY (Our Lady and All Saints) *S'well 4* **P** *Exors Major R P Chaworth-Musters* **V** J C WILSON

ANNFIELD PLAIN (St Aidan) Collierley w Annfield Plain *Dur*

ANNSCROFT (Christ Church) Longden and Annscroft w Pulverbatch *Heref*

ANSFORD (St Andrew) Castle Cary w Ansford *B & W*

ANSLEY (St Lawrence) *Cov 5* **P** *Ch Patr Trust* **V** J R JASPER

ANSLOW (Holy Trinity) *Lich 19* **P** *MMCET* **V** M D BIRT

ANSTEY (St George) Hormead, Wyddial, Anstey, Brent Pelham etc *St Alb*

ANSTEY (St Mary) *Leic 12* **P** *R Thurcaston* **R** J E HALL

ANSTEY, EAST (St Michael) Bishopsnympton, Rose Ash, Mariansleigh etc *Ex*

ANSTEY, WEST (St Petrock) as above

ANSTON (St James) *Sheff 5* **P** *Bp* **V** P J COGHLAN, **C** S G MILLWOOD

ANSTY (St James) Bulkington w Shilton and Ansty *Cov*

ANSTY (St James) Tisbury *Sarum*

ANSTY (St John) Cuckfield *Chich*

ANTINGHAM (St Mary) Trunch *Nor*

ANTONY (St James the Great) w Sheviock *Truro 11* **P** *Bp and Col Sir John Carew-Pole, Bt (alt)* **NSM** K J PIPER

ANTROBUS (St Mark) *Ches 4* **P** *V Gt Budworth* **P-in-c** J E DRAYTON

ANWICK (St Edith) Kirkby Laythorpe *Linc*

APETHORPE (St Leonard) *Pet 12* **P** *Lord Brassey* **V** *Vacant*

APLEY (St Andrew) Bardney *Linc*

APPERLEY (Holy Trinity) Deerhurst, Apperley w Forthampton and Chaceley *Glouc*

APPLEBY (St Bartholomew) Winterton Gp *Linc*

APPLEBY (St Lawrence) *Carl 1* **P** *D&C and Bp (jt)* **V** P E P NORTON, **C** E M SMITH

APPLEBY GROUP, The *Leic 9* **P** *DBP, MMCET, Bp, Ld Chan (by turn)* **R** D J K WALLER

APPLEBY MAGNA (St Michael and All Angels) The Appleby Gp *Leic*

APPLEDORE (St Mary) Northam w Westward Ho! and Appledore *Ex*

APPLEDORE (St Peter and St Paul) w Brookland and Fairfield and Brenzett w Snargate and Kenardington *Cant 13* **P** *Abp* **V** L J HAMMOND, **C** M S WING

APPLEDRAM (St Mary the Virgin) *Chich 3* **P** *D&C* **P-in-c** M A COLLIS

APPLEFORD (St Peter and St Paul) Sutton Courtenay w Appleford *Ox*

APPLESHAW (St Peter) and Kimpton and Thruxton and Fyfield *Win 3* **P** *Bp, D&C, and M H Routh Esq (jt)* **R** I J TOMLINSON

APPLETHWAITE (St Mary) *Carl 10* **P** *Bp* **V** D R JACKSON

APPLETON (All Saints) Street TM *York*

APPLETON (St Lawrence) *Ox 10* **P** *Magd Coll Ox* **P-in-c** R G PENMAN

APPLETON (St Mary Magdalene) Stockton Heath *Ches*

APPLETON-LE-MOORS (Christ Church) Lastingham w Appleton-le-Moors, Rosedale etc *York*

APPLETON ROEBUCK (All Saints) w Acaster Selby *York 1* **P** *Abp* **P-in-c** J M RODEN

APPLETON THORN (St Cross) Stretton and Appleton Thorn *Ches*

APPLETON WISKE (St Mary) Gt Smeaton w Appleton Wiske and Birkby etc *Ripon*

APPLETREEWICK (St John the Baptist) Burnsall w Rylstone *Bradf*

APPLEY BRIDGE (All Saints) *Blackb 4* **P** *Bp* **V** J P ATACK

APULDRAM (St Mary the Virgin) Appledram *Chich*

ARBORFIELD (St Bartholomew) w Barkham *Ox 16* **P** *DBP* **P-in-c** D B ROWE, **Hon C** H M WAKELING, **NSM** J WAKELING

ARBORY (St Columba) *S & M 1* **P** *The Crown* **V** G B CLAYTON

ARBOURTHORNE (St Paul) Sheff Manor *Sheff*

ARDELEY (St Lawrence) *St Alb 5* **P** *D&C St Paul's* **P-in-c** E J POOLE

ARDINGLY (St Peter) *Chich 6* **P** *MMCET* **R** R P SYMMONS, **NSM** K I GOSS

ARDINGTON (Holy Trinity) Wantage Downs *Ox*

ARDLEIGH (St Mary the Virgin) *Chelmsf 18* **P** *Ld Chan* **P-in-c** T C DIAPER

ARDLEIGH GREEN (All Saints) Squirrels Heath *Chelmsf*

ARDLEY (St Mary) Fritwell w Souldern and Ardley w Fewcott *Ox*

ARDSLEY (Christ Church) *Sheff 12* **P** *R Darfield* **V** R G R EVANS

ARDSLEY, EAST (St Gabriel) (St Michael) *Wakef 12* **P** *E C S J G Brudenell Esq* **V** K G WILLIAMS

ARDSLEY, WEST *Wakef 10* **P** *E C S J G Brudenell Esq* **V** T R KING

ARDWICK (St Benedict) *Man 1* **P** *Keble Coll Ox* **R** *Vacant* 0161–223 0154

ARDWICK (St Jerome and St Silas) Man Gd Shep *Man*

ARELEY KINGS (St Bartholomew) *Worc 13* **P** *R Martley* **P-in-c** A J VESSEY

ARKENDALE (St Bartholomew) Farnham w Scotton, Staveley, Copgrove etc *Ripon*

ARKENGARTHDALE (St Mary) Swaledale *Ripon*

ARKESDEN (St Mary the Virgin) Clavering w Langley and Arkesden *Chelmsf*

ARKHOLME (St John the Baptist) Whittington w Arkholme and Gressingham *Blackb*

ARKLEY (St Peter) Chipping Barnet w Arkley *St Alb*

ARKSEY (All Saints) *Sheff 8* **P** *DBP* **V** C J A HICKLING

ARLECDON (St Michael) Frizington and Arlecdon *Carl*

ARLESEY (St Andrew) (St Peter) w Astwick *St Alb 22* **P** *DBP* **NSM** H WORSNIP, C M EAGGER

ARLEY (St Michael) (St Wilfred) *Cov 5* **P** *A C D Ransom Esq and N W H Sylvester Esq (jt)* **R** G F KIMBER, **C** G M KIMBER

ARLEY, UPPER (St Peter) Kidderminster St Mary and All SS w Trimpley etc *Worc*

ARLINGHAM (St Mary the Virgin) Frampton on Severn, Arlingham, Saul etc *Glouc*

ARLINGTON (St James) Shirwell, Loxhore, Kentisbury, Arlington, etc *Ex*

ARLINGTON (St Pancras), Folkington and Wilmington *Chich 18* **P** *Bp Lon, Mrs M P Gwynne-Longland, and Duke of Devonshire (by turn)* **P-in-c** J D E SMITH

ARMATHWAITE (Christ and St Mary) Hesket-in-the-Forest and Armathwaite *Carl*

ARMINGHALL (St Mary) Stoke H Cross w Dunston, Arminghall etc *Nor*

ARMITAGE (Holy Trinity) (St John the Baptist) *Lich 3* **P** *Bp* **R** D R H THOMAS

ARMITAGE BRIDGE (St Paul) Newsome and Armitage Bridge *Wakef*

ARMLEY (St Bartholomew) w New Wortley (St Mary) *Ripon 6* **P** *Bp, DBP, and Hyndman Trustees (jt)* **V** T W LIPSCOMB, **C** A J GILBERT

ARMLEY, UPPER (Christ Church) *Ripon 6* **P** *Ch Patr Trust* **V** F SUDWORTH, **C** T P PARKER, R J TWITTY

ARMLEY HEIGHTS (Church of the Ascension) Upper Armley *Ripon*

ARMTHORPE (St Leonard and St Mary) *Sheff 9* **P** *Bp* **R** J C BARNES, **C** M G COCKAYNE

ARNCLIFFE (St Oswald) Kettlewell w Conistone, Hubberholme etc *Bradf*

ARNE (St Nicholas) Wareham *Sarum*

ARNESBY (St Peter) w Shearsby and Bruntingthorpe *Leic 10* **P** *Bp* **P-in-c** A W JOHNSON, **Hon C** J C DUDLEY

ARNOLD (St Mary) *S'well 11* **P** *Bp* **V** A CLARKE, **C** J A BANKS

ARNSIDE (St James) *Carl 9* **P** *Bp* **P-in-c** D HAMPSON

ARRETON (St George) *Portsm 7* **P** *Bp* **V** D H HEATLEY

ARRINGTON (St Nicholas) *Ely 8* **P** *Bp and DBP (alt)* **V** N A BRICE

ARROW (Holy Trinity) Alcester and Arrow w Oversley and Weethley *Cov*

ARTHINGTON (St Peter) Pool w Arthington *Ripon*

ARTHINGWORTH (St Andrew) and Harrington w Oxendon and East Farndon *Pet 2* **P** *St Jo Coll Ox (2 turns), E G Nugee Esq (2 turns), and Bp (1 turn)* **R** T H ROPER

ARTHURET (St Michael and All Angels) *Carl 2* **P** *Sir Charles Graham, Bt* **R** J L HIGGINS

ARUNDEL (St Nicholas) w Tortington and South Stoke *Chich 1* **P** *Bp (2 turns), Duke of Norfolk (1 turn)* **V** M H WEAVER

ASBY (St Peter) *Carl 1* **P** *Bp* **P-in-c** D C WOOD

ASCOT, NORTH (St Mary and St John) Ascot Heath *Ox*

ASCOT, SOUTH (All Souls) *Ox 11* **P** *Bp* **V** D S JONES

ASCOT HEATH (All Saints) *Ox 11* **P** *Bp* **R** P le S V NASH-WILLIAMS, **C** J M R BAKER

ASCOTT UNDER WYCHWOOD (Holy Trinity) Chadlington and Spelsbury, Ascott under Wychwood *Ox*

ASFORDBY (All Saints) *Leic 3* **P** *DBP* **R** R W WIDDOWSON

ASGARBY (St Andrew) Kirkby Laythorpe *Linc*

ASH (Christ Church) *Lich 28* **P** *R Whitchurch* **P-in-c** J H TYERS

ASH (Holy Trinity) Martock w Ash *B & W*
ASH (St Nicholas) w Westmarsh *Cant 1* P *Abp*
V DJBARNES
ASH (St Peter) *Guildf 1* P *Win Coll* R H F JACKSON
ASH (St Peter and St Paul) *Roch 1* P *J R A B Scott Esq*
R L W G KEVIS, NSM E M R WALKER
ASH (Thomas Chapel) Sampford Peverell, Uplowman,
Holcombe Rogus etc *Ex*
ASH PRIORS (Holy Trinity) Lydeard St Lawrence w
Brompton Ralph etc *B & W*
ASH VALE (St Mary) *Guildf 1* P *Bp* V P C BAKER
ASHAMPSTEAD (St Clement) Basildon w Aldworth and
Ashampstead *Ox*
ASHBOCKING (All Saints) Clopton w Otley, Swilland and
Ashbocking *St E*
ASHBOURNE (St John the Baptist) *Derby 8* P *Wright
Trustees* V D H SANSUM
ASHBOURNE (St Oswald) w Mapleton *Derby 8* P *Bp*
V D H SANSUM
ASHBRITTLE (St John the Baptist) Wellington and Distr
B & W
ASHBURNHAM (St Peter) w Penhurst *Chich 14*
P *Ashburnham Chr Trust* P-in-c K L BARHAM
ASHBURTON (St Andrew) w Buckland in the Moor and
Bickington *Ex 11* P *D&C* V P J GREGSON
ASHBURY (St Mary the Virgin), Compton Beauchamp and
Longcot w Fernham *Ox 17* P *Ld Chan*
NSM A K WEAVER
ASHBY (St Catherine) Bottesford w Ashby *Linc*
ASHBY (St Mary) Somerleyton, Ashby, Fritton, Herringfleet
etc *Nor*
ASHBY (St Mary) Thurton *Nor*
ASHBY (St Paul) Bottesford w Ashby *Linc*
ASHBY, WEST (All Saints) Hemingby *Linc*
ASHBY-BY-PARTNEY (St Helen) Partney *Linc*
ASHBY-CUM-FENBY (St Peter) Ravendale Gp *Linc*
ASHBY DE LA LAUNDE (St Hibald) Digby *Linc*
ASHBY-DE-LA-ZOUCH (Holy Trinity) *Leic 9* P *Bp*
V L A DUTTON
ASHBY-DE-LA-ZOUCH (St Helen) w Coleorton *Leic 9*
P *D A G Shields Esq* V C P DOBBIN, C J S KNEE,
NSM S A B WALTERS
ASHBY FOLVILLE (St Mary) S Croxton Gp *Leic*
ASHBY MAGNA (St Mary) Willoughby Waterleys, Peatling
Magna etc *Leic*
ASHBY PARVA (St Peter) Leire w Ashby Parva and Dunton
Bassett *Leic*
ASHBY PUERORUM (St Andrew) Fulletby w Greetham
and Ashby Puerorum *Linc*
ASHBY ST LEDGERS (St Mary) Daventry, Ashby St
Ledgers, Braunston etc *Pet*
ASHCHURCH (St Nicholas) *Glouc 9* P *K Storey Esq*
R K R CORLESS, C D G S BATTERSBY
ASHCOMBE (St Nectan) Teignmouth, Ideford w Luton,
Ashcombe etc *Ex*
ASHCOTT (All Saints) Shapwick w Ashcott and Burtle
B & W
ASHDON (All Saints) w Hadstock *Chelmsf 23* P *E H Vestey
Esq and Ld Chan (alt)* R J D SAVILLE
ASHE (Holy Trinity and St Andrew) N Waltham and
Steventon, Ashe and Deane *Win*
ASHEN (St Augustine) Ridgewell w Ashen, Birdbrook and
Sturmer *Chelmsf*
ASHENDON (St Mary) Ludgershall w Wotton Underwood
and Ashendon *Ox*
ASHFIELD, GREAT (All Saints) Badwell Ash w Gt
Ashfield, Stowlangtoft etc *St E*
ASHFIELD CUM THORPE (St Mary) Earl Soham w
Cretingham and Ashfield cum Thorpe *St E*
ASHFORD (St Hilda) *Lon 13* P *Bp* V S J BLOOD
ASHFORD (St Mary the Virgin) *Cant 10* P *Abp*
V J W EVERETT, C D D CHAMP
ASHFORD (St Matthew) *Lon 13* P *Ld Chan*
V R E HORTON
ASHFORD (St Peter) Pilton w Ashford *Ex*
ASHFORD, South (St Francis of Assisi) *Cant 10* P *Abp*
P-in-c I L GARRETT
ASHFORD, SOUTH (Christ Church) *Cant 10* P *Abp*
P-in-c B L H CARPENTER, C M J ASQUITH
ASHFORD BOWDLER (St Andrew) Ludlow, Ludford,
Ashford Carbonell etc *Heref*
ASHFORD CARBONELL (St Mary) as above
ASHFORD COMMON (St Benedict) Upper Sunbury St Sav
Lon
ASHFORD HILL (St Paul) w Headley *Win 6*
P *V Kingsclere* V B G G MARSHALL

ASHFORD IN THE WATER (Holy Trinity) w Sheldon and
Great Longstone *Derby 2* P *V Bakewell*
V C A THROWER, Hon C T E YATES
ASHILL (Blessed Virgin Mary) Ilminster and District *B & W*
ASHILL (St Nicholas) w Saham Toney *Nor 14* P *Bp and
New Coll Ox (alt)* R M J DOWN, NSM A D WALKER
ASHILL (St Stephen) Uffculme *Ex*
ASHINGDON (St Andrew) w South Fambridge *Chelmsf 12*
P *CCC Cam* R *Vacant* Southend-on-Sea (01702) 544327
ASHINGTON (Holy Sepulchre) *Newc 11* P *Bp*
V C H KNIGHTS
ASHINGTON (St Matthew) Canford Magna *Sarum*
ASHINGTON (St Peter and St Paul), Washington and Wiston
w Buncton *Chich 12* P *Bp and R H Goring Esq (alt)*
R J M WALKER
ASHINGTON (St Vincent) Chilton Cantelo, Ashington,
Mudford, Rimpton etc *B & W*
ASHLEWORTH (St Bartholomew) Hasfield w Tirley and
Ashleworth *Glouc*
ASHLEY (St Elizabeth) Hale and Ashley *Ches*
ASHLEY (St James), Crudwell, Hankerton, Long Newnton and
Oaksey *Bris 12* P *Trustees* R B RAVEN
ASHLEY (St John the Baptist) *Lich 12* P *Meynell
Ch Trustees* P-in-c M R H TURNER
ASHLEY (St Mary the Virgin) w Weston by Welland and
Sutton Bassett *Pet 9* P *Bp and DBP (alt)* R *Vacant*
Medbourne Green (0185883) 827
ASHLEY (St Mary) w Silverley *Ely 4* P *Bp and DBP (alt)*
R A F HOMER
ASHLEY (St Peter and St Paul) Somborne w Ashley *Win*
ASHLEY GREEN (St John the Evangelist) Gt Chesham *Ox*
ASHMANHAUGH (St Swithin) Horning w Beeston St
Laurence and Ashmanhaugh *Nor*
ASHMANSWORTH (St James) Highclere and
Ashmansworth w Crux Easton *Win*
ASHMORE (St Nicholas) Tollard Royal w Farnham,
Gussage St Michael etc *Sarum*
ASHMORE PARK (St Alban) Wednesfield *Lich*
ASHOVER (All Saints) and Brackenfield *Derby 5* P *Rev
J J C Nodder and DBF (jt)* R T B JOHNSON,
NSM A L SMITH, R SMITH
ASHOW (The Assumption of Our Lady) Stoneleigh w Ashow
and Baginton *Cov*
ASHPERTON (St Bartholomew) Bosbury w Wellington
Heath etc *Heref*
ASHPRINGTON (St David), Cornworthy and Dittisham
Ex 13 P *Bp* P-in-c R A KING
ASHREIGNEY (St James) *Ex 16* P *DBP* R P J NORMAN
ASHTEAD (St George) (St Giles) *Guildf 10* P *Bp*
R C C HUGHES, C J D STRIDE, T H PATTERSON
ASHTON (Annunciation) Breage w Germoe *Truro*
ASHTON (Chapel) Oundle *Pet*
ASHTON (St John the Baptist) Christow, Ashton, Trusham
and Bridford *Ex*
ASHTON (St Michael and All Angels) Roade and Ashton w
Hartwell *Pet*
ASHTON, WEST (St John) Trowbridge St Thos and W
Ashton *Sarum*
ASHTON GATE (St Francis) Bedminster *Bris*
ASHTON GIFFORD *Sarum 16* P *DBP, Ld Chan, and Pemb
Coll Ox (by turn)* R J H TIPPING, NSM G I DUFF
ASHTON HAYES (St John the Evangelist) *Ches 2* P *Keble
Coll Ox* V W B FAULL
ASHTON-IN-MAKERFIELD (Holy Trinity) *Liv 15* P *Bp*
R D R ABBOTT
ASHTON-IN-MAKERFIELD (St Thomas) *Liv 15*
P *R Ashton-in-Makerfield H Trin* V D G MELLORS,
C W FORSTER, NSM D HART
ASHTON KEYNES (Holy Cross), Leigh and Minety *Bris 12*
P *Bp* V P S HUGHES
ASHTON ON MERSEY (St Mary Magdalene) *Ches 10*
P *Trustees* V G J SKINNER, C G R PATCHELL,
A R GARNER
ASHTON-ON-RIBBLE (St Andrew) *Blackb 14* P *Trustees*
V J R POWELL
ASHTON-ON-RIBBLE (St Michael and All Angels) w Preston
(St Mark) *Blackb 14* P *Bp* V W G GRIMES
ASHTON UNDER HILL (St Barbara) Overbury w
Teddington, Alstone etc *Worc*
ASHTON-UNDER-LYNE (Christ Church) *Man 17* P *Bp*
V C LAYCOCK, C M E DICKER
ASHTON-UNDER-LYNE (Holy Trinity) *Man 17*
P *Trustees* P-in-c D J WISEMAN
ASHTON-UNDER-LYNE (St James) (Queen Victoria
Memorial Church) *Man 17* P *Bp and Lord Deramore (jt)*
V *Vacant* 0161-330 2771
ASHTON-UNDER-LYNE (St Michael and All Angels)
(St Gabriel) *Man 17* P *Lord Deramore* NSM R FOX

ASHTON-UNDER-LYNE (St Peter) *Man 17* **P** *R Ashton-under-Lyne St Mich* **V** A BROWN

ASHTON UPON MERSEY (St Martin) *Ches 10* **P** *SMF* **R** P M FREEMAN

ASHURST (St James) *Chich 12* **P** *MMCET* **R** *Vacant*

ASHURST (St Martin of Tours) Speldhurst w Groombridge and Ashurst *Roch*

ASHURST WOOD (St Dunstan) Forest Row *Chich*

ASHWATER (St Peter ad Vincula), Halwill, Beaworthy, Clawton and Tetcott w Luffincott *Ex 9* **P** *Ld Chan (1 turn), Major L J Melhuish, Lt-Col Sir John Molesworth-St Aubyn Bt, and Bp (jt) (2 turns)* **R** L BROOKHOUSE

ASHWELL (St Mary) Cottesmore and Barrow w Ashwell and Burley *Pet*

ASHWELL (St Mary the Virgin) w Hinxworth and Newnham *St Alb 5* **P** *Bp, R Smyth Esq, and N J A Farr Esq (jt) (1 turn), Bp (3 turns)* **R** P J M BRIGHT, **Hon C** J LAING, **NSM** C H BROWNLIE

ASHWELLTHORPE (All Saints) Wreningham *Nor*

ASHWICK (St James) w Oakhill and Binegar *B & W 8* **P** *Bp* **P-in-c** J C ANDREWS

ASHWICKEN (All Saints) Gayton Gp of Par *Nor*

ASHWORTH (St James) Norden w Ashworth *Man*

ASKAM (St Peter) Ireleth w Askam *Carl*

ASKERN (St Peter) *Sheff 8* **P** *Bp* **V** A T COATES

ASKERSWELL (St Michael), Loders and Powerstock *Sarum 3* **P** *Ld Chan, Lady Laskey, Bp, and D&C (by turn)* **R** E G A W PAGE-TURNER

ASKHAM (Church Centre) Ireleth w Askam *Carl*

ASKHAM (St Nicholas) E Markham w Askham, Headon w Upton and Grove *S'well*

ASKHAM (St Peter) Lowther and Askham *Carl*

ASKHAM BRYAN (St Nicholas) *York 1* **P** *Trustees of Rev G Nussey* **NSM** G G HOLMAN

ASKHAM RICHARD (St Mary) Healaugh w Wighill, Bilbrough and Askham Richard *York*

ASKRIGG (St Oswald) w Stallingbusk *Ripon 4* **P** *V Aysgarth* **V** C W MALPASS

ASLACKBY (St James) Rippingale Gp *Linc*

ASLACTON (St Michael) Bunwell, Carleton Rode, Tibenham, Gt Moulton etc *Nor*

ASLOCKTON (St Thomas) Whatton w Aslockton, Hawksworth, Scarrington etc *S'well*

ASPALL (St Mary of Grace) Debenham w Aspall and Kenton *St E*

ASPATRIA (St Kentigern) w Hayton *Carl 7* **P** *Bp* **P-in-c** B ROWE, **NSM** J M BEAZLEY

ASPENDEN (St Mary), Buntingford and Westmill *St Alb 5* **P** *CPAS, MCET, and K Coll Lon (jt)* **R** N J RICHARDS, **NSM** M CAPEL-EDWARDS, P J ALEXANDER

ASPLEY (St Margaret) *S'well 14* **P** *Trustees* **V** D WARD, **C** I A HILTON

ASPLEY GUISE (St Botolph) w Husborne Crawley and Ridgmont *St Alb 15* **P** *Ld Chan (1 turn), Trustees Bedf Estates (1 turn), cnd Bp (2 turns)* **R** J E INGHAM

ASPULL (St Elizabeth) *Liv 14* **P** *R Wigan* **V** B WHITEHEAD

ASSINGTON (St Edmund) w Newton Green and Little Cornard *St E 12* **P** *DBP (1 turn), Peterho Cam (1 turn), and Bp (2 turns)* **R** A R GEORGE

ASTBURY (St Mary) and Smallwood *Ches 11* **P** *Sir Richard Baker Wilbraham, Bt* **R** E J A BRAZIER

ASTERBY Group, The *Linc 11* **P** *Bp, DBP, J N Heneage Esq, F Smith Esq, and Mrs J Fox (jt)* **R** *Vacant* Louth (01507) 343345

ASTHALL (St Nicholas) Burford w Fulbrook, Taynton, Asthall etc *Ox*

ASTLEY (St Mary the Virgin) Chilvers Coton w Astley *Cov*

ASTLEY (St Mary), Clive, Grinshill and Hadnall *Lich 28* **P** *D R B Thompson Esq* **V** S W DEANE

ASTLEY (St Peter) Shrawley, Witley, Astley and Abberley *Worc*

ASTLEY (St Stephen) *Man 13* **P** *V Leigh St Mary* **V** C A BRACEGIRDLE, **C** R TAGUE

ASTLEY ABBOTTS (St Calixtus) Bridgnorth, Tasley, Astley Abbotts, Oldbury etc *Heref*

ASTLEY BRIDGE (St Paul) *Man 16* **P** *The Crown* **V** T P CHALLIS, **NSM** B E HAWORTH

ASTON (St Giles) Wigmore Abbey *Heref*

ASTON (St Mary) Woore and Norton in Hales *Lich*

ASTON (St Mary) Stevenage St Mary Sheppall w Aston *St Alb*

ASTON (St Saviour) Stone St Mich w Aston St Sav *Lich*

ASTON, LITTLE (St Peter) *Lich 1* **P** *Trustees* **V** S HUYTON

ASTON, NORTH (St Mary the Virgin) Steeple Aston w N Aston and Tackley *Ox*

ASTON ABBOTS (St James the Great) Wingrave w Rowsham, Aston Abbotts and Cublington *Ox*

ASTON BOTTERELL (St Michael and All Angels) Ditton Priors w Neenton, Burwarton etc *Heref*

ASTON BY SUTTON (St Peter) *Ches 3* **P** *B H Talbot Esq* **P-in-c** J E DRAYTON, **NSM** T A WHYTE

ASTON CANTLOW (St John the Baptist) and Wilmcote w Billesley *Cov 7* **P** *SMF* **V** T J HENDERSON, **C** H C J M KEEP

ASTON CLINTON (St Michael and All Angels) w Buckland and Drayton Beauchamp *Ox 22* **P** *Exors Major S W Jenney, Jes Coll Ox, and Bp (by turn)* **R** A W BENNETT, **NSM** I CORNISH

ASTON cum AUGHTON (All Saints) w Swallownest, Todwick and Ulley *Sheff 5* **P** *Bp* **TR** P WRIGHT, **TV** D C BLISS, S K PROCTOR, H LIDDLE

ASTON EYRE (not known) Morville w Aston Eyre *Heref*

ASTON FLAMVILLE (St Peter) Burbage w Aston Flamville *Leic*

ASTON INGHAM (St John the Baptist) Linton w Upton Bishop and Aston Ingham *Heref*

ASTON JUXTA BIRMINGHAM (St James) *Birm 6* **P** *V Aston* **V** *Vacant* 0121–327 3230

ASTON JUXTA BIRMINGHAM (St Peter and St Paul) *Birm 6* **P** *Aston Trustees* **V** G K SINCLAIR, **C** E M HATCHMAN

ASTON LE WALLS (St Leonard) Byfield w Boddington and Aston le Walls *Pet*

ASTON-ON-TRENT (All Saints) and Weston-on-Trent *Derby 15* **P** *Winterbottom Trustees and Bp (alt)* **R** B H MUNRO

ASTON ROWANT (St Peter and St Paul) Chinnor w Emmington and Sydenham etc *Ox*

ASTON SANDFORD (St Michael and All Angels) Haddenham w Cuddington, Kingsey etc *Ox*

ASTON SOMERVILLE (St Mary) Childswyckham w Aston Somerville, Buckland etc *Glouc*

ASTON-SUB-EDGE (St Andrew) Willersey, Saintbury, Weston-sub-Edge etc *Glouc*

ASTON TIRROLD (St Michael) S w N Moreton, Aston Tirrold and Aston Upthorpe *Ox*

ASTON UPTHORPE (All Saints) as above

ASTWICK (St Guthlac) Arlesey w Astwick *St Alb*

ASTWOOD (St Peter) Sherington w Chicheley, N Crawley, Astwood etc *Ox*

ASTWOOD BANK (St Matthias and St George) *Worc 7* **P** *DBP* **P-in-c** P G HARRISON, **NSM** I J MERRY

ASWARBY (St Denys) S Lafford *Linc*

ASWARDBY (St Helen) w Sausthorpe *Linc 7* **P** *DBP* **R** G ROBSON

ATCHAM (St Eata) Shrewsbury St Giles w Sutton and Atcham *Lich*

ATHELINGTON (St Peter) Stradbroke, Horham, Athelington and Redlingfield *St E*

ATHERINGTON (St Mary) and High Bickington *Ex 16* **P** *DBP and D&C (alt)* **P-in-c** H G POLLOCK

ATHERSLEY (St Helen) *Wakef 7* **P** *Bp* **V** N T B STRAFFORD, **C** D ROBINSON

ATHERSTONE (St Mary) *Cov 5* **P** *V Mancetter* **V** P I HARRIS

ATHERTON (St John the Baptist) (St George) (St Philip) *Man 13* **P** *Bp* **TR** W BALDWIN, **TV** J A READ

ATLOW (St Philip and St James) Hulland, Atlow, Bradley and Hognaston *Derby*

ATTENBOROUGH (St Mary the Virgin) *S'well 7* **P** *CPAS* **V** B DAWSON, **C** A M M PARKER

ATTERCLIFFE (Hill Top Chapel) Darnall-cum-Attercliffe *Sheff*

ATTERCLIFFE (St Alban) as above

ATTLEBOROUGH (Assumption of the Blessed Virgin Mary) w Besthorpe *Nor 11* **P** *CR and Mrs S P J Scully (jt)* **R** J A AVES

ATTLEBOROUGH (Holy Trinity) *Cov 5* **P** *V Nuneaton* **V** *Vacant* Nuneaton (01203) 382926

ATTLEBRIDGE (St Andrew) Alderford w Attlebridge and Swannington *Nor*

ATWICK (St Lawrence) Hornsea w Atwick *York*

ATWORTH (St Michael and All Angels) w Shaw and Whitley *Sarum 17* **P** *D&C Bris and R Melksham (alt)* **P-in-c** G R J FORCE-JONES

AUBOURN (St Peter) w Haddington *Linc 18* **P** *Capt H N Nevile* **P-in-c** E I SLATER

AUCKLAND (St Andrew) (St Anne) *Dur 10* **P** *Bp* **V** J MARSHALL

AUCKLAND (St Helen) *Dur 10* **P** *Bp* **P-in-c** R I McTEER

AUCKLAND (St Peter) *Dur 10* **P** *The Crown* **V** P K LEE

AUCKLEY (St Saviour) Finningley w Auckley *S'well*

AUDENSHAW (St Hilda) *Man 17* **P** *Bp* **V** J H KERSHAW

AUDENSHAW (St Stephen) *Man 17* **P** *Bp* **V** P R DIXON
AUDLEM (St James the Great) *Ches 15* **P** *Bp*
V D ROSTRON
AUDLEY (St James the Great) *Lich 14* **P** *Ch Soc Trust*
V P T W DAVIES
AUGHTON (All Saints) Bubwith w Skipwith *York*
AUGHTON (Christ Church) *Liv 11* **P** *R Aughton St Mich*
V R MOUGHTIN, **C** J L ROBERTS
AUGHTON (St Michael) *Liv 11* **P** *Bp* **R** M J SMOUT,
C J M MATTHEWS
AUGHTON (St Saviour) Halton w Aughton *Blackb*
AUKBOROUGH (St John the Baptist) Alkborough *Linc*
AULT HUCKNALL (St John the Baptist) *Derby 3* **P** *Duke
of Devonshire* **V** K H WAYNE
AUNSBY (St Thomas of Canterbury) S Lafford *Linc*
AUST (not known) Olveston *Bris*
AUSTERFIELD (St Helen) Bawtry w Austerfield and
Misson *S'well*
AUSTREY (St Nicholas) and Warton (Holy Trinity) *Birm 12*
P *Ld Chan and V Polesworth St Editha (alt)*
V W R STUART-WHITE
AUSTWICK (Epiphany) Clapham-with-Keasden and
Austwick *Bradf*
AVEBURY (St James) Upper Kennett *Sarum*
AVELEY (St Michael) and Purfleet *Chelmsf 14* **P** *Bp*
V C J NORRIS, **NSM** G E WRIGHT
AVENING (Holy Cross) w Cherington *Glouc 16*
P *Mrs D C Fetherston-Godley (1 turn), D&C (2 turns)*
NSM C CARTER
AVERHAM (St Michael and All Angels) w Kelham *S'well 3*
P *DBP* **NSM** A CARMSTRONG, M B ARMSTRONG
AVETON GIFFORD (St Andrew) *Ex 14* **P** *Bp* **R** J S COLE
AVINGTON (St Mary) Itchen Valley *Win*
AVON DASSETT (St Peter and St Clare) w Farnborough and
Fenny Compton *Cov 8* **P** *G V L Holbech Esq and Mrs
A D Seyfried (jt), CCC Ox, and Bp(alt)* **R** D P PYM
AVON VALLEY *Sarum 12* **P** *Bp (3 turns), MOD (2 turns),
and Ch Hosp (1 turn)* **V** *Vacant* Stonehenge (01980) 670353
AVONMOUTH (St Andrew) *Bris 8* **P** *Bp* **V** C F PENN
AWBRIDGE (All Saints) w Sherfield English *Win 11* **P** *Bp
and CPAS (jt)* **R** D E APPLIN
AWLISCOMBE (St Michael and All Angels) Honiton,
Gittisham, Combe Raleigh, Monkton etc *Ex*
AWRE (St Andrew) Newnham w Awre and Blakeney *Glouc*
AWSWORTH (St Peter) w Cossall *S'well 7* **P** *Bp*
P-in-c D McMANN
AXBRIDGE (St John the Baptist) w Shipham and Rowberrow
B & W 1 **P** *Bp and D&C (alt)* **R** J SMITH
AXFORD (St Michael) Whitton *Sarum*
AXHOLME Group, The NORTH *Linc 1* **P** *The Crown*
V J GIBBONS
AXMINSTER (St Mary), Chardstock, Combe Pyne and
Rousdon *Ex 5* **P** *Bp* **TR** J H GOOD, **TV** A J ASHWELL
AXMOUTH (St Michael) Uplyme w Axmouth *Ex*
AYCLIFFE (Church Centre) Dover St Mary *Cant*
AYCLIFFE (St Andrew) *Dur 14* **P** *D&C* **V** P D DAVEY
AYLBURTON (St Mary) Woolaston w Alvington and
Aylburton *Glouc*
AYLBURTON COMMON (Mission Church) Lydney *Glouc*
AYLESBEARE (Blessed Virgin Mary), Rockbeare, Farringdon,
Clyst Honiton and Sowton *Ex 1* **P** *Bp and D&C (jt)*
NSM P PULLIN
AYLESBURY (St Mary the Virgin) w Bierton and Hulcott
Ox 21 **P** *Bp and Patr Bd (jt)* **TR** T J HIGGINS,
TV V J HICKS, P D ATKINSON
AYLESBY (St Lawrence) Keelby w Riby and Aylesby *Linc*
AYLESFORD (St Peter and St Paul) *Roch 7* **P** *D&C*
V P E FRANCIS, **C** K D CRINKS
AYLESHAM (St Peter) w Adisham *Cant 1* **P** *Abp*
R A M YATES
AYLESTONE (St Andrew) w St James *Leic 2* **P** *Bp*
R A RACE, **C** H BRADLEY, D H LEIGH
AYLESTONE PARK (Church of the Nativity) Aylestone St
Andr w St Jas *Leic*
AYLMERTON (St John the Baptist) w Runton *Nor 22*
P *Bp* **R** P H ATKINS
AYLSHAM (St Michael) *Nor 20* **P** *D&C Cant*
V R D BRANSON
AYLTON (not known) Tarrington w Stoke Edith, Aylton,
Pixley etc *Heref*
AYMESTREY (St John the Baptist and St Alkmund) and
Leinthall Earles w Wigmore and Leinthall Starkes *Heref 7*
P *Ld Chan and Bp (alt)* **P-in-c** S B THOMAS,
NSM J W M ROBINSON
AYNHO (St Michael) and Croughton w Evenley *Pet 1* **P** *Bp,
Ms E A J Cartwright-Hignett, and Magd Coll Ox (by turn)*
R G J GREEN

AYOT ST LAWRENCE (St Lawrence) Kimpton w Ayot St
Lawrence *St Alb*
AYOT ST PETER (St Peter) Welwyn w Ayot St Peter *St Alb*
AYSGARTH (St Andrew) and Bolton cum Redmire *Ripon 4*
P *Trin Coll Cam and R Wensley (alt)* **V** A E ATKINSON,
Hon C J H RICHARDSON
AYSTON (St Mary the Virgin) Uppingham w Ayston and
Wardley w Belton *Pet*
AYTHORPE (St Mary) w High and Leaden Roding
Chelmsf 19 **P** *Ld Chan and Ch Soc Trust and Bp (by turn)*
R *Vacant* White Roding (01279) 876387
AYTON, EAST (St John the Baptist) Seamer w E Ayton
York
AYTON, GREAT (All Saints) (Christ Church) w Easby and
Newton in Cleveland *York 22* **P** *Abp* **V** P H PEVERELL
BABBACOMBE (All Saints) *Ex 10* **P** *V St Marychurch*
V *Vacant* Torquay (01803) 323002
BABCARY (Holy Cross) Six Pilgrims *B & W*
BABRAHAM (St Peter) *Ely 7* **P** *H R T Adeane Esq*
P-in-c R L POWELL
BABWORTH (All Saints) w Sutton-cum-Lound *S'well 5*
P *Bp and Major Sir James Whitaker, Bt (jt)*
R G E HOLLOWAY
BACKFORD (St Oswald) and Capenhurst *Ches 9* **P** *Bp*
P-in-c G F PARSONS
BACKWELL (St Andrew) w Chelvey and Brockley *B & W 13*
P *DBP* **R** *Vacant* Flax Bourton (01275) 462391
BACKWORTH (St John) Earsdon and Backworth *Newc*
BACONSTHORPE (St Mary) Barningham w Matlaske w
Baconsthorpe etc *Nor*
BACTON (St Andrew) w Edingthorpe w Witton and Ridlington
Nor 12 **P** *Duchy of Lanc (1 turn), Bp and Earl of
Kimberley (1 turn)* **P-in-c** J M S PICKERING
BACTON (St Faith) Ewyas Harold w Dulas, Kenderchurch
etc *Heref*
BACTON (St Mary the Virgin) w Wyverstone and Cotton
St E 6 **P** *MMCET, Ld Chan, and J C S Priston Esq
(by turn)* **P-in-c** R W JACK
BACUP (Christ Church) *Man 15* **P** *Trustees*
P-in-c M L GOODER
BACUP (St John the Evangelist) *Man 15* **P** *Wm Hulme
Trustees* **V** M HOLT
BACUP (St Saviour) *Man 15* **P** *Ch Soc Trust*
V D H KINGHAM
BADBY (St Mary) w Newham and Charwelton w Fawsley and
Preston Capes *Pet 3* **P** *Bp* **R** S P ADAMS
BADDESLEY, NORTH (All Saints' Mission
Church) Chilworth w N Baddesley *Win*
BADDESLEY, NORTH (St John the Baptist) Valley Park
Win
BADDESLEY, SOUTH (St Mary the Virgin) Boldre w S
Baddesley *Win*
BADDESLEY CLINTON (St Michael) *Birm 13*
P *T W Ferrers-Walker Esq* **R** A V WILLMONT
BADDESLEY ENSOR (St Nicholas) w Grendon *Birm 12*
P *Bp, V Polesworth, and PCC (jt)* **V** K HODSON
BADDILEY (St Michael) and Wrenbury w Burleydam
Ches 15 **P** *V Acton and Bp (alt)* **M** M ROWLANDS
BADDOW, GREAT (Meadgate Church Centre) (St Mary the
Virgin) (St Paul) *Chelmsf 9* **P** *Patr Bd*
TV P C NICHOLSON
BADDOW, LITTLE (St Mary the Virgin) *Chelmsf 9* **P** *Bp*
R R E TURNER
BADGER (St Giles) Beckbury, Badger, Kemberton, Ryton,
Stockton etc *Lich*
BADGEWORTH (Holy Trinity) w Shurdington *Glouc 11*
P *Bp* **V** W C WORSDELL, **NSM** P F SMITH
BADGWORTH (St Congar) Crook Peak *B & W*
BADINGHAM (St John the Baptist) w Bruisyard, Cransford
and Dennington *St E 18* **P** *R C Rous Esq (1 turn), DBP
(2 turns)* **R** B G MIDDLETON
BADLESMERE (St Leonard) Selling w Throwley, Sheldwich
w Badlesmere etc *Cant*
BADMINTON (St Michael and All Angels) w Little
Badminton, Acton Turville and Hawkesbury *Glouc 7*
P *Duke of Beaufort* **P-in-c** P R BERROW
BADMINTON, LITTLE (St Michael and All Angels) see
above
BADSEY (St James) w Aldington and Wickhamford *Worc 1*
P *Ch Ch Ox* **V** P D MITCHELL
BADSHOT LEA (St George) Conventional District *Guildf 3*
C-in-c E HUGHES
BADSWORTH (St Mary the Virgin) *Wakef 11* **P** *DBP*
R R H TAYLOR
BADWELL ASH (St Mary) w Great Ashfield, Stowlangtoft,
Langham and Hunston *St E 9* **P** *Bp (2 turns), DBP
(1 turn)* **P-in-c** F H POTTER
BAG ENDERBY (St Margaret) S Ormsby Gp *Linc*

BAGBOROUGH (St Pancras) Bishops Lydeard w
Bagborough and Cothelstone *B & W*
BAGBY (St Mary) Thirkleby w Kilburn and Bagby *York*
BAGENDON (St Margaret) Stratton, N Cerney, Baunton
and Bagendon *Glouc*
BAGINTON (St John the Baptist) Stoneleigh w Ashow and
Baginton *Cov*
BAGNALL (St Chad) Bucknall and Bagnall *Lich*
BAGSHOT (Good Shepherd) Wexcombe *Sarum*
BAGSHOT (St Anne) *Guildf 6* **P** *Ld Chan* **V** D HOLT
BAGULEY Brooklands (St John the Divine) *Man 8* **P** *Bp and*
A W Hargreaves Esq (jt) **V** J C FINDON,
C O E SIBBALD, **NSM** A W HARGREAVES
BAGWORTH (The Holy Rood) Thornton, Bagworth and
Stanton *Leic*
BAILDON (St John the Evangelist) (St Hugh Mission Church)
(St James) *Bradf 1* **P** *Major M W V Hammond-Maude*
V J D NOWELL, **C** S NAYLOR, E A THOMAS (nee
REEVES)
BAINTON (St Andrew) w North Dalton, Middleton-on-the-
Wolds and Kilnwick *York 11* **P** *Abp, St Jo Coll Ox, and*
Exors M P Winter (jt) **R** H L ARTLEY,
NSM C CONNER
BAINTON (St Mary) Barnack w Ufford and Bainton *Pet*
BAKEWELL (All Saints) *Derby 2* **P** *D&C Lich*
V E R URQUHART, **NSM** L E ELLSWORTH
BALBY (St John the Evangelist) *Sheff 10* **P** *Bp*
V G J MARCER
BALCOMBE (St Mary) *Chich 6* **P** *P A D Secretan Esq*
R N G PRINT
BALDERSBY (St James) w Dalton, Dishforth and Skipton on
Swale *York 20* **P** *Abp and Viscount Downe (jt)*
V D F BAKER
BALDERSTONE (St Leonard) *Blackb 2* **P** *V Blackb*
V D E ASHFORTH
BALDERSTONE (St Mary) *Man 20* **P** *Trustees*
V I C THOMPSON, **C** G J CROSSLEY
BALDERTON (St Giles) *S'well 3* **P** *Ld Chan*
P-in-c W H THACKRAY
BALDHU (St Michael) Highertown and Baldhu *Truro*
BALDOCK (St Mary the Virgin) w Bygrave *St Alb 12*
P *Marquess of Salisbury and Bp (alt)* **C** T E JESSIMAN
BALDWIN (St Luke) Marown *S & M*
BALE (All Saints) Gunthorpe w Bale w Field Dalling,
Saxlingham etc *Nor*
BALHAM (St Mary and St John the Divine) *S'wark 17* **P** *Bp*
and Keble Coll Ox (jt) **V** D A NICHOLSON, **C** P J ROSE-
CASEMORE, **NSM** J B SMITH
BALHAM HILL (Ascension) *S'wark 17* **P** *Bp*
P-in-c A P B WHITE
BALKWELL (St Peter) *Newc 8* **P** *Bp* **V** P S McCONNELL
BALLAM (St Matthew) Ribby w Wrea *Blackb*
BALLAUGH (St Mary) (St Mary Old Church) *S & M 3*
P *The Crown* **R** J L EVANS
BALLIDON (All Saints) Wirksworth *Derby*
BALLINGER (St Mary Mission Hall) Gt Missenden w
Ballinger and Lt Hampden *Ox*
BALLINGHAM (St Dubricius) Lt Dewchurch, Aconbury w
Ballingham and Bolstone *Heref*
BALSALL COMMON (St Peter) *Birm 13* **P** *Bp* **V** *Vacant*
Berkswell (01676) 532721
BALSALL HEATH (St Barnabas) Sparkbrook St Agatha w
Balsall Heath St Barn *Birm*
BALSALL HEATH (St Paul) *Birm 8* **P** *Bp*
V J D HANNAH, **C** P M HOLLINGSWORTH
BALSCOTE (St Mary Magdalene) Broughton w N
Newington and Shutford etc *Ox*
BALSHAM (Holy Trinity) *Ely 4* **P** *Charterhouse*
R W N C GIRARD
BALTERLEY (All Saints' Memorial Church) Barthomley
Ches
BALTONSBOROUGH (St Dunstan) w Butleigh and West
Bradley *B & W 5* **P** *Bp* **V** B H ADAMS
BAMBER BRIDGE (St Aidan) *Blackb 6* **P** *Bp*
V M L HARTLEY, **C** J M TURNER
BAMBER BRIDGE (St Saviour) *Blackb 6* **P** *V Blackb*
V W T BARNES
BAMBURGH (St Aidan) and Lucker *Newc 10* **P** *Lord*
Armstrong (2 turns), Newc Dioc Soc (1 turn)
V E ZACHAU
BAMFORD (St John the Baptist) *Derby 2*
P *A C H Barnes Esq* **R** N P GOWER
BAMFORD (St Michael) *Man 20* **P** *Bp* **V** S B GREY
BAMFURLONG (Good Shepherd) Abram *Liv*
BAMPTON (Holy Trinity) (St James) (St Mary) w Clanfield
Ox 5 **P** *Bp, DBP, St Jo Coll Ox, D&C Ex, and*
B Babington-Smith Esq (jt) **V** A C G SCOTT,
NSM S A BAREHAM

BAMPTON (St Michael and All Angels), Morebath,
Clayhanger and Petton *Ex 8* **P** *DBP and D&C (jt)*
V P P OCKFORD
BAMPTON (St Patrick) Shap w Swindale and Bampton w
Mardale *Carl*
BAMPTON ASTON (St James) Bampton w Clanfield *Ox*
BAMPTON LEW (Holy Trinity) as above
BAMPTON PROPER (St Mary) as above
BANBURY (St Mary) *Ox 5* **P** *Bp* **TR** D A INESON,
TV P N TOVEY, **C** D W TOWNSEND, D JACKSON,
NSM S R FAIRBAIRN, V W BALL
BANHAM (St Mary) Quidenham *Nor*
BANKFOOT (St Matthew) *Bradf 2* **P** *Bp* **V** J W TURNER
BANKS (St Stephen in the Banks) *Liv 9* **P** *R N Meols*
V B J GERRARD
BANNINGHAM (St Botolph) Felmingham, Skeyton, Colby,
Banningham etc *Nor*
BANSTEAD (All Saints) *Guildf 9* **P** *Bp* **V** D N CHANCE,
C W D GULLIFORD
BANWELL (St Andrew) *B & W 11* **P** *D&C Bris*
V C A R MOORSOM
BAPCHILD (St Lawrence) Murston w Bapchild and Tonge
Cant
BAR HILL (not known) *Ely 5* **P** *Bp* **V** *Vacant* Crafts Hill
(01954) 781629
BARBON (St Bartholomew) Kirkby Lonsdale *Carl*
BARBOURNE (St Stephen) *Worc 6* **P** *Bp* **V** S W CURRIE
BARBROOK (St Bartholomew) Lynton, Brendon,
Countisbury, Lynmouth etc *Ex*
BARBY (St Mary) w Kilsby *Pet 3* **P** *Bp* **R** J A ROBERTS
BARCHESTON (St Martin) *Cov 9* **P** *Bp* **R** D C BROWN
BARCOMBE (St Francis) (St Mary the Virgin) *Chich 18*
P *Ld Chan* **R** D PEARSON-MILES, **NSM** R A MOORE
BARDFIELD (St Peter and St Paul) Gt and Lt Bardfield w
Gt and Saling *Chelmsf*
BARDFIELD, GREAT (St Mary the Virgin) and Little (St
Katherine) w Great and Little (Bardfield) Saling
Chelmsf 19 **P** *Ch Union Trust, and Bp (jt)*
V M J ATKINSON
BARDNEY (St Laurence) *Linc 11* **P** *DBP (1 turn), Bp*
(2 turns), and St Jo Coll Cam (1 turn) **R** S GREEN,
Hon C J A GREEN
BARDON HILL (St Peter) Coalville and Bardon Hill *Leic*
BARDSEA (Holy Trinity) *Carl 8* **P** *DBP* **V** *Vacant*
BARDSEY (All Hallows) *Ripon 1* **P** *G L Fox Esq*
V R J PEARSON
BARDSLEY (Holy Trinity) *Man 17* **P** *Wm Hulme Trustees*
V L S IRELAND, **Hon C** L A IRELAND
BARDWELL (St Peter and St Paul) Blackbourne *St E*
BARE (St Christopher) *Blackb 12* **P** *Bp* **V** D L HEAP
BARFORD (St Botolph) Barnham Broom *Nor*
BARFORD (St John) Deddington w Barford, Clifton and
Hempton *Ox*
BARFORD (St Michael) as above
BARFORD (St Peter) w Wasperton and Sherbourne *Cov 8*
P *Major J M Mills, R Hampton Lucy, and Lady Jeryl*
Smith-Ryland (jt) **R** G BENFIELD
BARFORD, GREAT (All Saints) Roxton w Gt Barford
St Alb
BARFORD ST MARTIN (St Martin), Dinton, Baverstock and
Burcombe *Sarum 13* **P** *All So Coll Ox, A K I Mackenzie-*
Charrington Esq, Bp, and St Jo Hosp Wilton (jt)
R J LEEMING, **Dss** A SYMES
BARFREYSTONE (St Nicholas) Eythorne and Elvington w
Waldershare etc *Cant*
BARHAM (St Giles) Spaldwick w Barham and Woolley *Ely*
BARHAM (St John the Baptist) w Bishopsbourne and Kingston
Cant 1 **P** *Abp* **R** A A DUKE
BARHAM (St Mary) Claydon and Barham *St E*
BARHOLME (St Martin) Uffington Gp *Linc*
BARKBY (St Mary) Syston TM *Leic*
BARKESTONE (St Peter and St Paul) w Plungar, Redmile and
Stathern *Leic 3* **P** *The Crown and Peterho Cam (alt)*
P-in-c G SPENCER, **C** M TURNER
BARKHAM (St James) Arborfield w Barkham *Ox*
BARKING (St Erkenwald) *Chelmsf 1* **P** *Bp* **V** G R WISKER
BARKING (St Margaret) (St Patrick) *Chelmsf 1* **P** *Patr Bd*
P-in-c J B PARSONS, **TV** D SILVESTER, **C** M OKELLO,
A R B JOWITT, M BARKER, **NSM** J G FROUD
BARKING (St Mary) Ringshall w Battisford, Barking w
Darmsden etc *St E*
BARKINGSIDE (Holy Trinity) *Chelmsf 4* **P** *V Ilford*
V C REEVES
BARKINGSIDE (St Cedd) *Chelmsf 4* **P** *Bp*
P-in-c M J KETLEY
BARKINGSIDE (St Francis of Assisi) *Chelmsf 4* **P** *Bp*
V M JENNINGS

BARKINGSIDE (St George) *Chelmsf 4* **P** *Bp*
V J V FISHER
BARKINGSIDE (St Laurence) *Chelmsf 4* **P** *Bp*
V G R LOCK
BARKISLAND (Christ Church) w West Scammonden
Wakef 4 **P** *V Halifax* **V** *Vacant*
BARKSTON (St Nicholas) and Hough Group, The *Linc 23*
P *Capt Sir Anthony Thorold, Bt, Rev J R H and Rev*
H C Thorold, Lord Brownlow, and Sir Lyonel Tollemache, Bt
(by turn) **NSM** S N SHRIMPTON
R G R SHRIMPTON,
BARKSTON ASH (Holy Trinity) Sherburn in Elmet w
Saxton *York*
BARKWAY (St Mary Magdalene), Reed and Buckland w
Barley *St Alb 5* **P** *The Crown and DBP (alt)*
R C C KEVILL-DAVIES
BARKWITH Group, The *Linc 5* **P** *D&C, J N Heneage Esq,*
K Coll Lon, and DBP (by turn) **P-in-c** I S PARTRIDGE
BARKWITH, EAST (St Mary) Barkwith Gp *Linc*
BARLASTON (St John the Baptist) *Lich 18* **P** *Countess of*
Sutherland **V** G L SIMPSON
BARLAVINGTON (St Mary), Burton w Coates and Sutton w
Bignor *Chich 11* **P** *Lord Egremont and Miss*
J B Courtauld (jt) **R** *Vacant* Sutton (017987) 220
BARLBOROUGH (St James) *Derby 3* **P** *S R Sitwell Esq*
R H J DOBBIN
BARLBY (All Saints) w Riccall *York 4* **P** *Abp and V*
Hemingbrough (jt) **V** C J SIMMONS
BARLESTONE (St Giles) *Leic 13* **P** *Bp*
P-in-c L R CARPENTER, **NSM** J A DOWNS
BARLEY (St Margaret of Antioch) Barkway, Reed and
Buckland w Barley *St Alb*
BARLING (All Saints) w Little Wakering *Chelmsf 12* **P** *D&C*
St Paul's and Bp (alt) **V** R WOOLVEN
BARLING MAGNA (All Saints) Barling w Lt Wakering
Chelmsf
BARLINGS (St Edward) *Linc 3* **P** *DBP*
(2 turns), Earl of Scarborough (1 turn) **V** R G SPAIGHT
BARLOW (not known) Brayton *York*
BARLOW (St Lawrence) *Derby 5* **P** *R Stavely* **V** *Vacant*
Sheffield (0114) 289 0269
BARLOW, GREAT (St Lawrence) Barlow *Derby*
BARLOW MOOR (Emmanuel) Didsbury St Jas and Em
Man
BARMBY MARSH (St Helen) Howden TM *York*
BARMBY MOOR (St Catherine) w Allerthorpe, Fangfoss and
Yapham *York 7* **P** *Abp* **R** V P HEWETSON
BARMING (St Margaret of Antioch) w West Barming
Roch 7 **P** *Ld Chan* **R** A DAUNTON-FEAR
BARMING HEATH (St Andrew) *Cant 15* **P** *Abp*
V B REED
BARMSTON (All Saints) Skipsea w Ulrome and Barmston w
Fraisthorpe *York*
BARNACK (St John the Baptist) w Ufford and Bainton *Pet 8*
P *Bp and St Jo Coll Cam (alt)* **R** G AUSTEN
BARNACRE (All Saints) w Calder Vale *Blackb 10* **P** *Bp and*
Mrs V O Shepherd-Cross (alt) **P-in-c** P J PIKE
BARNARD CASTLE (St Mary) w Whorlton *Dur 11* **P** *Trin*
Coll Cam **V** P W LIND-JACKSON, **C** V J BROWN,
NSM G KIRTLEY
BARNARDISTON (All Saints) Hundon w Barnardiston *St E*
BARNBURGH (St Peter) w Melton on the Hill and Aldwick-
upon-Dearne *Sheff 12* **P** *Ld Chan (2 turns), Bp (1 turn)*
R J R SMITH
BARNBY (St John the Baptist) Worlingham w Barnby and N
Cove *St E*
BARNBY, EAST (Mission Chapel) Lythe w Ugthorpe *York*
BARNBY DUN (St Peter and St Paul) *Sheff 9* **P** *Bp*
V N K YOUNG, **NSM** D OTTEWELL
BARNBY IN THE WILLOWS (All Saints) Coddington w
Barnby in the Willows *S'well*
BARNEHURST (St Martin) *Roch 14* **P** *Bp*
V D F SPRINGTHORPE
BARNES (Holy Trinity) *S'wark 16* **P** *R Barnes St Mary*
P-in-c G HOLDSTOCK
BARNES (St Mary) *S'wark 16* **P** *D&C St Paul's*
P-in-c R AMES-LEWIS
BARNES (St Michael and All Angels) *S'wark 16* **P** *D&C*
St Paul's **R** B RUDDOCK, **NSM** A J ROBERTS
BARNET (Christ Church) S Mimms Ch Ch *Lon*
BARNET (St Stephen) Chipping Barnet w Arkley *St Alb*
BARNET, EAST (St Mary the Virgin) *St Alb 2*
P *The Crown* **R** A J PROUD, **NSM** A E DAVIE (nee
JONES)
BARNET, NEW (St James) *St Alb 2* **P** *Ch Patr Trust*
V B R PENFOLD
BARNET VALE (St Mark) *St Alb 2* **P** *Bp* **V** C J GAY

BARNETBY LE WOLD (St Barnabas) N Wolds Gp *Linc*
BARNEY (St Mary), Fulmodeston w Croxton, Hindringham
and Thursford *Nor 19* **P** *CCC Cam, Lord Hastings, and*
D&C (by turn) **P-in-c** J P S DENNY
BARNHAM (St Gregory) Blackbourne *St E*
BARNHAM (St Mary) Aldingbourne, Barnham and
Eastergate *Chich*
BARNHAM BROOM (St Peter and St Paul) *Nor 18*
P *Patr Bd* **TV** P M HOPKINS
BARNINGHAM (St Andrew) Hopton, Market Weston,
Barningham etc *St E*
BARNINGHAM (St Mary the Virgin) w Matlaske w
Baconsthorpe w Plumstead w Hempstead *Nor 19* **P** *Duchy*
of Lanc (1 turn), Sir Charles Mott-Radclyffe, CPAS and
D&C (jt) (1 turn) **R** *Vacant* Matlaske (026377) 420
BARNINGHAM (St Michael and All Angels) w Hutton Magna
and Wycliffe *Ripon 2* **P** *Bp and V Gilling and Kirkby*
Ravensworth (jt) **R** W A CLAYTON
BARNINGHAM, LITTLE (St Andrew) Wickmere w Lt
Barningham, Itteringham etc *Nor*
BARNINGHAM WINTER (St Mary the
Virgin) Barningham w Matlaske w Baconsthorpe etc *Nor*
BARNOLDBY LE BECK (St Helen) *Linc 10* **P** *Ld Chan*
P-in-c I R SHELTON
BARNOLDSWICK (Holy Trinity) (St Mary le Gill) w
Bracewell *Bradf 7* **P** *Bp* **V** J R LANCASTER,
C A W MARKS
BARNSBURY (St Andrew) *Lon 6* **P** *Patr Bd*
TR A E HARVEY, **TV** C M S R THOMAS, R W WALL
BARNSLEY Old Town (St Paul) Barnsley St Mary *Wakef*
BARNSLEY (St Edward the Confessor) *Wakef 7* **P** *Bp*
V G H HALL
BARNSLEY (St George's Parish Church Centre) *Wakef 7*
P *Bp* **V** P J MUNBY, **C** C J WADE
BARNSLEY (St Mary) Bibury w Winson and Barnsley *Glouc*
BARNSLEY (St Mary) *Wakef 7* **P** *Bp* **R** I E WILDEY
BARNSLEY (St Peter and St John the Baptist) *Wakef 7*
P *Bp* **V** *Vacant* Barnsley (01226) 282220
BARNSTAPLE (St Peter and St Mary Magdalene) (Holy
Trinity) w Goodleigh, Landkey and Sticklepath *Ex 15*
P *DBP* **TV** M J PEARSON, D J PHIPPS, G CHAVE-COX,
P-in-c C PUCKRIN, **Hon C** P D PILDITCH,
NSM G F SQUIRE
BARNSTON (Christ Church) *Ches 8* **P** *Bp*
V G P BENSON, **C** N A J BELCHER
BARNSTON (St Mary the Virgin) and Little Dunmow
Chelmsf 19 **P** *CPAS* **R** A R JACK
BARNSTONE (St Mary Mission Room) Cropwell Bishop w
Colston Bassett, Granby etc *S'well*
BARNT GREEN (St Andrew) Cofton Hackett w Barnt
Green *Birm*
BARNTON (Christ Church) *Ches 4* **P** *Bp*
P-in-c D H McINTOSH, **NSM** G H BUCHAN
BARNWELL (All Saints) (St Andrew) w Tichmarsh, Thurning
and Clapton *Pet 12* **P** *Soc of Merchant Venturers,*
MMCET, Em Coll Cam, and DBP (by turn)
R P C H A TRENCHARD
BARNWOOD (St Lawrence) *Glouc 5* **P** *D&C*
V M S RILEY
BARR, GREAT (St Margaret) *Lich 6*
P *E G A Farnham Esq* **V** J S REANEY
BARRINGTON (All Saints) *Ely 8* **P** *Trin Coll Cam*
V M W BAKER
BARRINGTON (Blessed Virgin Mary) Ilminster and District
B & W
BARRINGTON, GREAT (St Mary) Sherborne, Windrush,
the Barringtons etc *Glouc*
BARRINGTON, LITTLE (St Peter) as above
BARROW (All Saints) w Denham St Mary and Higham Green
St E 13 **P** *Bp, St Jo Coll Cam, and D W Barclay Esq*
(by turn) **R** J B DAVIS
BARROW and Goxhill *Linc 6* **P** *Ld Chan*
P-in-c C MACDONALD
BARROW (St Bartholomew) *Ches 2* **P** *D Okell Esq*
P-in-c P T CHANTRY, **NSM** H F CHANTRY
BARROW (St Giles) Broseley w Benthall, Jackfield, Linley
etc *Heref*
BARROW, NORTH (St Nicholas) Six Pilgrims *B & W*
BARROW, SOUTH (St Peter) as above
BARROW GURNEY (Blessed Virgin Mary and St Edward
King and Martyr) *B & W 13* **P** *Major M A Gibbs*
P-in-c J B BISHOP
BARROW HILL (St Andrew) Staveley and Barrow Hill
Derby
BARROW-IN-FURNESS (St Aidan) *Carl 8* **P** *Bp*
V D L E BERRY
BARROW-IN-FURNESS (St George) (St Luke) *Carl 8*
P *Bp* **TV** M S WILKINSON, **P-in-c** P E MANN

BARROW-IN-FURNESS (St James) *Carl 8*   P *DBP*
  P-in-c C J LAXON
BARROW-IN-FURNESS (St John the Evangelist) *Carl 8*
  P *DBP* V   *Vacant* Barrow-in-Furness (0229) 821101
BARROW-IN-FURNESS (St Mark) *Carl 10*   P *Bp*
  V P G DAY
BARROW-IN-FURNESS (St Mary the Virgin) Walney Is
  Carl
BARROW-IN-FURNESS (St Matthew) *Carl 8*   P *Bp*
  V C G JOHNSON,   C M G CROOK
BARROW-ON-HUMBER (Holy Trinity) Barrow and
  Goxhill *Linc*
BARROW-ON-TRENT (St Wilfrid) w Twyford and
  Swarkestone *Derby 15*   P *Repton Sch and*
  Exors H F Harpur-Crewe Esq (jt)   P-in-c R HILL,
  NSM F R WORRALL
BARROW UPON SOAR (Holy Trinity) w Walton le Wolds
  Leic 7   P *St Jo Coll Cam and DBP (jt)*   R S J MITCHELL
BARROWBY (All Saints) and Gonerby, Great *Linc 19*
  P *R Grantham, and Duke of Devonshire (by turn)*
  R P HOPKINS
BARROWDEN (St Peter) and Wakerley w South Luffenham
  Pet 8   P *Burghley Ho Preservation Trust and Ball Coll Ox*
  (alt)   R B SCOTT
BARROWFORD (St Thomas) *Blackb 7*   P *DBF*
  V B MORGAN
BARSHAM (Holy Trinity) Wainford *St E*
BARSHAM, EAST (All Saints) w North Barsham (All Saints)
  and West Barsham (Assumption of the Blessed Virgin Mary)
  Nor 16   P *Capt J D A Keith*   R A M THOMSON
BARSTON (St Swithin) *Birm 13*   P *MMCET*
  P-in-c E W RUSSELL
BARTHOMLEY (St Bertoline) *Ches 11*   P *Lord O'Neill*
  R O J HORROCKS
BARTLEY (Mission Church) Copythorne and Minstead *Win*
BARTLEY GREEN (St Michael and All Angels) *Birm 2*
  P *Bp*   C A H PERRY
BARTLOW (St Mary) *Ely 4*   P *Brig A N Breitmeyer*
  R J H THOMSON
BARTON (St Cuthbert w St Mary) and Manfield and Cleasby
  w Stapleton *Ripon 2*   P *Bp, D&C, and V Forcett and*
  Stanwick w Aldbrough (jt)   V R W GROSSE
BARTON (St Lawrence) *Blackb 10*   P *DBP*
  V J H RANDELL
BARTON (St Mark's Chapel) w Peel Green (St Michael and
  All Angels) (St Catherine) *Man 2*   P *Bp and TR Eccles*
  V *Vacant* 0161–789 3751
BARTON (St Martin) Torquay St Martin Barton *Ex*
BARTON (St Michael), Pooley Bridge and Martindale
  Carl 4   P *Bp and Earl of Lonsdale (jt)* V *Vacant* Pooley
  Bridge (017684) 86220
BARTON (St Paul) *Portsm 8*   P *R Whippingham*
  P-in-c C G LANE
BARTON (St Peter) *Ely 1*   P *Ld Chan*   V H D SEARLE
BARTON, GREAT (Holy Innocents) *St E 13*   P *Sir Michael*
  Bunbury, Bt V   *Vacant* Great Barton (0128487) 274
BARTON BENDISH (St Andrew) w Beachamwell and
  Shingham *Ely 16*   P *Bp and DBP (alt)*   P-in-c M TUCKER
BARTON HARTSHORN (St James) Swan *Ox*
BARTON HILL (St Luke w Christ Church) *Bris 4*   P *V Bris*
  St Phil (2 turns) and CPAS (1 turn)   V C A SUNDERLAND
BARTON IN FABIS (St George) *S'well 10*   P *Ld Chan*
  R A C SUTHERLAND,   NSM J M GORICK
BARTON-LE-CLEY (St Nicholas) w Higham Gobion and
  Hexton *St Alb 15*   P *The Crown (3 turns), Mrs*
  F A A Cooper (1 turn)   P P H WHITTAKER
BARTON-LE-STREET (St Michael) Street TM *York*
BARTON MILLS (St Mary) Mildenhall *St E*
BARTON-ON-THE-HEATH (St Lawrence) Long Compton,
  Whichford and Barton-on-the-Heath *Cov*
BARTON SEAGRAVE (St Botolph) w Warkton *Pet 11*
  P *Ch Soc Trust (2 turns), Duke of Buccleugh (1 turn)*
  R J A WARDLE,   C D M TALBOT,   C R EVANS,
  P G McGLINCHEY,   Hon C G MORGAN,
  NSM H EASTWOOD
BARTON ST DAVID (St David) Keinton Mandeville w
  Lydford-on-Fosse etc *B & W*
BARTON STACEY (All Saints) and Bullington and
  Hurstbourne Priors and Longparish *Win 6*   P *Bp, D&C, and*
  J Woodcock Esq (jt)   V W ROBSON
BARTON TURF (St Michael) Neatishead, Barton Turf and
  Irstead *Nor*
BARTON UNDER NEEDWOOD (St James) *Lich 19*
  P *Bp*   V A J WOOD
BARTON UPON HUMBER (St Mary) *Linc 6*   P *Bp*
  V E J P HEPWORTH,   C P C PATRICK
BARTON UPON IRWELL (St Catherine) Barton w Peel
  Green *Man*

BARWELL (St Mary) w Potters Marston and Stapleton
  Leic 13   P *R J W Titley Esq*   R *Vacant* Earl Shilton
  (01455) 843866
BARWICK (St Mary Magdalene) *B & W 7*   P *Ms Y L Bennett*
  and Ms R S Mullen (jt)   R *Vacant* Yeovil (01935) 20661
BARWICK IN ELMET (All Saints) *Ripon 8*   P *Duchy of*
  Lanc   R R B B WILD
BASCHURCH (All Saints) and Weston Lullingfield w Hordley
  Lich 22   P *Ch Patr Trust and Bp (jt)*   R D R D JONES
BASCOTE HEATH (Chapel) Radford Semele and Ufton *Cov*
BASEGREEN (St Peter) Gleadless *Sheff*
BASFORD (St Aidan) *S'well 13*   P *Bp*   C J HEMSTOCK,
  P HEMSTOCK
BASFORD (St Leodegarius) w Hyson Green *S'well 13*   P *Bp*
  and CPAS (jt)   P-in-c G J BURTON,
  C E A CARRINGTON,   R M M CREIGHTON
BASFORD (St Mark) *Lich 14*   P *Bp*   V I NICKLIN
BASFORD, NEW (St Augustine) Basford w Hyson Green
  S'well
BASHLEY (St John) Milton *Win*
BASILDON (St Andrew) (Holy Cross) *Chelmsf 6*   P *Bp*
  V J R CARR
BASILDON (St Stephen) w Aldworth and Ashampstead
  Ox 12   P *St Jo Coll Cam, Simeon's Trustees, and DBF*
  (by turn)   P-in-c M O M MILLS-POWELL
BASILDON, (St Martin of Tours) *Chelmsf 6*   P *Bp*
  R L F WEBBER
BASING (St Mary) *Win 4*   P *Magd Coll Ox*
  V A D PICTON,   C J M STAGG,   NSM C E EDMONDS (nee
  HARRIS)
BASINGSTOKE (All Saints) (St Michael) *Win 4*   P *Patr Bd*
  TR P P WELSH,   TV P FURBER,   T H ROBERTS,
  M D BAILEY,   A M BURDEN,   C S T HORNE,
  NSM E A GEORGE,   J A WIBREW
BASINGSTOKE Brighton Hill (Christ the King) Basingstoke
  Win
BASINGSTOKE Popley (Bethlehem Chapel) as above
BASINGSTOKE South Ham (St Peter) as above
BASLOW (St Anne) w Curbar and Stoney Middleton
  Derby 2   P *Duke of Devonshire and V Hathersage (jt)*
  V G R ORCHARD
BASSENTHWAITE (St Bega) (St John), Isel and Setmurthy
  Carl 6   P *Bp, D&C, and Miss M E Burkett (by turn)*
  P-in-c R G HIRST
BASSINGBOURN (St Peter and St Paul) *Ely 8*   P *D&C*
  Westmr V E DUCKETT
BASSINGHAM (St Michael and All Angels) *Linc 18*
  P *CCC Ox*   P-in-c E I SLATER,
  NSM J R D SCARBOROUGH
BASSINGTHORPE (St Thomas a Becket) Ingoldsby *Linc*
BASTON (St John the Baptist) Ness Gp *Linc*
BASWICH (Holy Trinity) *Lich 15*   P *Bp*   V M V ROBERTS
BATCOMBE (Blessed Virgin Mary) Bruton and Distr *B & W*
BATCOMBE (St Mary) Yetminster w Ryme Intrinseca and
  High Stoy *Sarum*
BATH Abbey (St Peter and St Paul) w St James *B & W 9*
  P *Simeon's Trustees*   R R G ASKEW,   C C R M ROBERTS,
  N M COULTHARD
BATH Bathwick (St John the Baptist) (Blessed Virgin Mary)
  B & W 9   P *Bp*   R D J PROTHERO,   C L A PINFIELD
BATH (Christ Church) Proprietary Chapel *B & W 11*
  P *R Walcot*   NSM C R BURROWS,   V S ROBERTS
BATH (Holy Trinity) *B & W 9*   P *SMF*   R G OAKES
BATH Odd Down (St Philip and St James) w Combe Hay
  B & W 9   P *Simeon's Trustees*   V A BAIN,
  NSM T D H CATCHPOOL,   M JOYCE
BATH (St Barnabas) w Englishcombe *B & W 9*   P *Bp*
  V T R BONIWELL
BATH (St Bartholomew) *B & W 9*   P *Simeon's Trustees*
  V I R LEWIS
BATH (St Luke) *B & W 9*   P *Simeon's Trustees*
  V D F PERRYMAN,   C S C COUPLAND,   A J SYMONDS
BATH St Mary Magdalene Holloway (Extra-parochial
  Chapelry) *B & W 11*   P *Bath Municipal Charities for*
  Ld Chan,   Chapl W G BURMAN
BATH (St Michael) w St Paul *B & W 9*   P *Exors Rev*
  W G M C Colburn, and Rev D B Bubbers, Canon
  A R Henderson and CPAS (jt)   R A R WALLACE
BATH (St Saviour) w Swainswick and Woolley *B & W 9*
  P *Ch Patr Trust and Oriel Coll Ox (jt)*   R P J SOURBUT,
  C T M STAPLES,   NSM N J L PEARCE
BATH (St Stephen) Charlcombe w Bath St Steph *B & W*
BATH Twerton-on-Avon (Ascension) (St Michael) *B & W 9*
  P *Patr Bd*   TR K L SHILL,   TV G I WILTON,
  A E H TURNER,   NSM G L WILTON
BATH Walcot (St Andrew) (St Swithin) *B & W 9*   P *Simeon's*
  Trustees   R G M DODDS,   C M C LLOYD WILLIAMS

BATH Weston (All Saints) w North Stoke and Langridge
B & W 9 **P** *Ld Chan* **R** T P WATSON, P J WHITWORTH,
C A N PERRY

BATH Weston (St John the Evangelist) (Emmanuel) w Kelston
B & W 9 **P** *Ld Chan* **R** C D G PATTERSON,
C T STEWART

BATH Widcombe (St Matthew) (St Thomas a Becket)
B & W 9 **P** *Simeon's Trustees* **V** R A RUSSELL,
NSM P J BETTS

BATHAMPTON (St Nicholas) w Claverton *B & W 9* **P** *D&C*
Bris and Personal Reps R L D Skrine Esq (jt)
R O J D BAYLEY

BATHEALTON (St Bartholomew) Wellington and Distr
B & W

BATHEASTON (St John the Baptist) (St Catherine)
B & W 9 **P** *Ch Ch Ox* **V** J W B PERRY

BATHFORD (St Swithun) *B & W 9* **P** *D&C Bris*
V M J TURNER

BATLEY (All Saints) *Wakef 10* **P** E C S J G *Brudenell Esq*
and Trustees D Stubley Esq (jt) **V** K WILLIAMS

BATLEY (St Thomas) *Wakef 10* **P** *V Batley* **V** L C DEW

BATLEY CARR (Holy Trinity) *Dewsbury Wakef*

BATSFORD (St Mary) Moreton-in-Marsh w Batsford,
Todenham etc *Glouc*

BATTERSEA (Christ Church and St Stephen) *S'wark 14*
P *Bp and V Battersea St Mary (alt)* **V** P CLARK,
C B J WALLIS

BATTERSEA (St Luke) *S'wark 14* **P** *Bp* **V** J A RUSSELL,
C A BIENFAIT, **Hon C** J A BAKER

BATTERSEA (St Mary) *S'wark 14* **P** *Earl Spencer*
V J M CLARKE, **C** J N MORRIS

BATTERSEA (St Peter) (St Paul) *S'wark 14* **P** *V Battersea
St Mary* **V** M A WIMSHURST

BATTERSEA (St Philip w St Bartholomew) *S'wark 14*
P *Bp* **V** I R FORSTER

BATTERSEA (St Saviour) *S'wark 14* **P** *CPAS and Ch Patr
Soc (jt)* **C** A BAKER

BATTERSEA Wandsworth Common (St Michael) *S'wark 14*
P *V Battersea St Mary* **V** A C HORTON

BATTERSEA PARK (All Saints) *S'wark 14* **P** *Bp*
P-in-c A J GADD, **Hon C** I G SMITH-CAMERON

BATTERSEA RISE (St Mark) *S'wark 14* **P** *V Battersea
St Mary* **V** P J S PERKIN, **C** A J BAUGHEN

BATTISFORD (St Mary) Ringshall w Battisford, Barking w
Darmsden etc *St E*

BATTLE (Church of the Ascension) (St Mary the Virgin)
Chich 14 **P** *The Crown* **V** W A V CUMMINGS

BATTLE HILL (Good Shepherd) Willington Team *Newc*

BATTLESDEN (St Peter and All Saints) Woburn w
Eversholt, Milton Bryan, Battlesden etc *St Alb*

BATTYEFORD (Christ the King) *Wakef 10* **P** *V Mirfield*
V D B FOSS, **Hon C** R E WHITNALL

**BAUGHURST (St Stephen) and Ramsdell and Wolverton w
Ewhurst and Hannington** *Win 4* **P** *Ld Chan, Duke of
Wellington, and Bp (by turn)* **R** A E BARTON

BAULKING (St Nicholas) Uffington, Shellingford,
Woolstone and Baulking *Ox*

BAUMBER (St Swithin) Hemingby *Linc*

BAUNTON (St Mary Magdalene) Stratton, N Cerney,
Baunton and Bagendon *Glouc*

BAVERSTOCK (St Editha) Barford St Martin, Dinton,
Baverstock etc *Sarum*

BAWBURGH (St Mary and St Walstan) Cringleford w
Colney and Bawburgh *Nor*

BAWDESWELL (All Saints) w Foxley *Nor 23* **P** *Bp*
P-in-c G L HUMPHRIES

BAWDRIP (St Michael and All Angels) Woolavington w
Cossington and Bawdrip *B & W*

BAWDSEY (St Mary) Alderton w Ramsholt and Bawdsey
St E

BAWTRY (St Nicholas) w Austerfield and Misson *S'well 1*
P *Bp* **V** J N GREEN, **Hon C** P E SARGAN

BAXENDEN (St John) *Blackb 1* **P** *Bp* **V** M C IRELAND

BAXTERGATE (St Ninian) Whitby *York*

**BAXTERLEY (not known) w Hurley and Wood End and
Merevale w Bentley** *Birm 12* **P** *Ld Chan (1 turn), Bp and
Sir William Dugdale, Bt (1 turn)* **R** D R CARRIVICK

BAYDON (St Nicholas) Whitton *Sarum*

BAYFORD (Mission Room) Charlton Musgrove,
Cucklington and Stoke Trister *B & W*

BAYFORD (St Mary) Lt Berkhamsted and Bayford,
Essendon etc *St Alb*

BAYLHAM (St Peter) Gt and Lt Blakenham w Baylham and
Nettlestead *St E*

BAYSTON HILL (Christ Church) *Lich 26* **P** *V Shrewsbury
H Trin w St Julian* **V** G C GRIFFITHS,
Hon C M H TUPPER

BAYSWATER (St Matthew) *Lon 2* **P** *Exors Dame Jewell
Magnus-Allcroft* **V** G M EVANS

BAYTON (St Bartholomew) Mamble w Bayton, Rock w
Heightington etc *Worc*

BEACHAMPTON (Assumption of the Blessed Virgin Mary)
Nash w Thornton, Beachampton and Thornborough *Ox*

BEACHAMWELL (St Mary) Barton Bendish w
Beachamwell and Shingham *Ely*

BEACHLEY (St John the Evangelist) Tidenham w Beachley
and Lancaut *Glouc*

**BEACONSFIELD (St Mary and All Saints) (St Michael and
All Angels)** *Ox 20* **P** *Patr Bd* **TR** J P B WYNBURNE,
TV H EDEN, **C** W J ADAM, **NSM** W T EVANS,
R A JOHNSON, G R ANDERSON, A M CAW

BEADLAM (St Hilda) Kirkdale *York*

BEADNELL (St Ebba) w Ellingham *Newc 10* **P** *D&C Dur
and V Bamburgh (jt)* **V** *Vacant* Seahouses (01665) 720223

BEAFORD (All Saints), Roborough and St Giles in the Wood
Ex 20 **P** *Bp, Ld Chan, and M M CET (by turn)*
P-in-c T C OAKLEY

**BEALINGS, GREAT (St Mary) and LITTLE (All Saints) w
Playford and Culpho** *St E 7* **P** *Lord Cranworth (1 turn), Bp
(3 turns)* **R** M P SKLIROS

BEAMINSTER AREA (St Mary of the Annunciation)
Sarum 1 **P** *Patr Bd* **TR** T M F BILES, **TV** R LEGG,
R H P THORNBURGH, **C** P G STEELE

BEAMISH (St Andrew) Stanley *Dur*

BEARD (St James the Less) New Mills *Derby*

BEARLEY (St Mary the Virgin) Snitterfield w Bearley *Cov*

BEARPARK (St Edmund) and Ushaw Moor *Dur 2* **P** *D&C
and Bp (alt)* **TR** L G BARRON

BEARSTED (Holy Cross) w Thurnham *Cant 15* **P** *Abp*
V G H SIDAWAY, **C** P J HESKETH

BEARWOOD (St Catherine) *Ox 16* **P** *Bp* **R** H D ETCHES

BEARWOOD (St Mary the Virgin) *Birm 5* **P** *V Smethwick*
V H G JAMES

BEAUCHAMP RODING (St Botolph) Abbess Roding,
Beauchamp Roding and White Roding *Chelmsf*

BEAUDESERT (St Nicholas) and Henley-in-Arden w Ullenhall
Cov 7 **P** *M M CET, Bp, and High Bailiff of Henley-in-
Arden (jt)* **R** J F GANJAVI

**BEAULIEU (Blessed Virgin and Holy Child) and Exbury and
East Boldre** *Win 10* **P** *Bp and Lord Montagu of
Beaulieu (jt)* **V** D T P ABERNETHY,
Hon C E M SINGLETON

BEAUMONT CUM MOZE (St Leonard and St Mary)
Tendring and Lt Bentley w Beaumont cum Moze *Chelmsf*

BEAUMONT LEYS (Christ the King) *Leic 2* **P** *Bp*
V C R OXLEY, **NSM** P J OXLEY

BEAUWORTH (St James) Cheriton w Tichborne and
Beauworth *Win*

BEAUXFIELD (St Peter) Whitfield w Guston *Cant*

BEAWORTHY (St Alban) Ashwater, Halwill, Beaworthy,
Clawton etc *Ex*

BEBINGTON (St Andrew) *Ches 8* **P** *Ch Soc Trust*
R S L JAMES, **C** G J COUSINS, P M FROGGATT

BEBINGTON, HIGHER (Christ Church) *Ches 8*
P *C J C Saunders-Griffiths Esq* **V** R K FAULKNER,
C G D MASSEY, **Hon C** R RAWLINSON

**BECCLES (St Michael the Archangel) (St Luke's Church
Centre)** *St E 14* **P** *Patr Bd* **TR** A H R THOMAS,
TV Y P IRVINE

BECK ROW (St John) Mildenhall *St E*

**BECKBURY (St Milburga), Badger, Kemberton, Ryton,
Stockton and Sutton Maddock** *Lich 25* **P** *Lord Hamilton of
Dalzell, Oriel Coll Ox, and M M CET (2 turns), Ld
Chan (1 turn)* **R** D F CHANTREY,
NSM P H J THORNEYCROFT

BECKENHAM (Christ Church) *Roch 12* **P** *Ch Trust Fund
Trust* **C** R E SEED, **Hon C** J T ANSCOMBE,
NSM M D COOKE, **Dss** G M N RAIKES

BECKENHAM (Holy Trinity) Penge Lane H Trin *Roch*

BECKENHAM (St Barnabas) *Roch 12* **P** *Keble Coll Ox*
P-in-c P MARR

BECKENHAM (St George) *Roch 12* **P** *Bp*
R D G E CARPENTER, **C** R CHAVNER

BECKENHAM (St James) Elmers End *Roch 12* **P** *Bp*
V L C STAPLETON

BECKENHAM (St John the Baptist) Eden Park *Roch 12*
P *Ch Trust Fund Trust, Bp and Adn Bromley (jt)*
V M L JEFFERIES, **C** P J AVANN

BECKENHAM (St Michael and All Angels) w St Augustine
Roch 12 **P** *SMF and Bp (jt)* **V** R S FAYERS

BECKENHAM, NEW (St Paul) *Roch 12* **P** *Bp* **V** J FROST

BECKERMET (St Bridget) (St Bridget Old Church) (St John)
w Ponsonby *Carl 5* **P** *Bp, Adn W Cumberland,
P Stanley Esq, and PCCs of Beckermet St Jo and
St Bridget (jt)* **V** P EVANS

BECKFORD (St John the Baptist) Overbury w Teddington, Alstone etc *Worc*

BECKHAM, WEST (St Helen and All Saints) Weybourne Gp *Nor*

BECKINGHAM (All Saints) Brant Broughton and Beckingham *Linc*

BECKINGHAM (All Saints) w Walkeringham *S'well 1* **P** *Bp and Ld Chan (alt)* **V** D HOLLIS

BECKINGTON (St George) w Standerwick, Berkley, Rodden, Lullington and Orchardleigh *B & W 4* **P** *Bp (3 turns), Ch Soc Trust (1 turn), and Exors A Duckworth Esq* **R** A F HOGARTH

BECKLEY (All Saints) and Peasmarsh *Chich 20* **P** *Univ Coll Ox and SS Coll Cam (alt)* **R** C F HOPKINS

BECKLEY (Assumption of the Blessed Virgin Mary) *Ox 1* **P** *W A Cooke Esq* **V** *Vacant*

BECKTON (St Mark) *Chelmsf 3* **P** *Bp* **V** *Vacant*

BECKWITHSHAW (St Michael and All Angels) Pannal w Beckwithshaw *Ripon*

BECONTREE (St Elizabeth) *Chelmsf 1* **P** *Bp* **P-in-c** R LOVE

BECONTREE (St George) Dagenham *Chelmsf*

BECONTREE (St Mary) *Chelmsf 1* **P** CPAS **V** R HERBERT, **C** A NEWTON

BECONTREE SOUTH (St Alban) (St John the Divine) (St Martin) *Chelmsf 1* **P** *Patr Bd* **TR** P HAWORTH, **C** G W J NUNN, **NSM** V D DRURY

BECONTREE WEST (St Cedd) (St Peter) (St Thomas) *Chelmsf 1* **P** *DBP* **TV** D P RITCHIE, R J COWEN

BEDALE (St Gregory) *Ripon 4* **P** *Sir Henry Beresford-Peirce Bt* **R** M D EMMEL, **C** S C WHITEHOUSE, **NSM** A L WOODHOUSE

BEDDINGHAM (St Andrew) Glynde, W Firle and Beddingham *Chich*

BEDDINGTON (St Francis' Church Hall) S Beddington St Mich *S'wark*

BEDDINGTON (St Mary) *S'wark 26* **P** *K Bond Esq* **R** L S TILLETT

BEDDINGTON, SOUTH (St Michael and All Angels) *S'wark 26* **P** *Bp* **V** J M DEAN

BEDFIELD (St Nicholas) Worlingworth, Southolt, Tannington, Bedfield etc *St E*

BEDFONT, EAST (St Mary the Virgin) *Lon 11* **P** *Ld Chan* **V** P G HUTTON

BEDFORD (All Saints) *St Alb 16* **P** *Bp* **V** N J ELDER, **C** P M WISE

BEDFORD (Christ Church) *St Alb 16* **P** *Bp* **V** D R HARRIS, **C** N C STYLES

BEDFORD (St Andrew) *St Alb 16* **P** *Ld Chan* **V** C M DENT, **C** M J LAWSON

BEDFORD (St John the Baptist) (St Leonard) *St Alb 16* **P** *MMCET* **R** M J PARKER, **C** M C NEWBON, **NSM** E M HOUGHTON

BEDFORD (St Mark) *St Alb 16* **P** *Bp* **V** C ROYDEN

BEDFORD (St Martin) *St Alb 16* **P** *Bp* **V** M P R LINSKILL

BEDFORD (St Michael and All Angels) *St Alb 16* **P** *Bp* **V** J R FOWLER

BEDFORD (St Paul) *St Alb 16* **P** *Bp* **V** C P COLLINGWOOD, **C** P SHAYLER-WEBB, **NSM** M H BULL

BEDFORD (St Peter de Merton) w St Cuthbert *St Alb 16* **P** *Ld Chan* **R** G E W BUCKLER

BEDFORD LEIGH (St Thomas) (All Saints Mission) *Man 13* **P** *V Leigh St Mary* **V** J WISEMAN, **C** A C BEDELL

BEDFORD PARK (St Michael and All Angels) *Lon 11* **P** *Bp* **V** P A BUTLER, **C** G I SWENSSON, **Hon C** G I BALL

BEDGROVE (Holy Spirit) *Ox 21* **P** *DBP* **V** W F MASON, **C** D C CHEDZEY

BEDHAMPTON (St Nicholas's Mission Church) (St Thomas) *Portsm 4* **P** *Bp* **R** I G COOMBER

BEDINGFIELD (St Mary) *St E 16* **P** *MMCET* **P-in-c** R H SMITH

BEDINGHAM (St Andrew) Hempnall *Nor*

BEDLINGTON (St Cuthbert) *Newc 1* **P** *D&C Dur* **V** M D J SAVAGE

BEDMINSTER (St Aldhelm) (St Paul) *Bris 1* **P** *Bp* **TR** R V HEADING, **TM** V I WOODS, **TV** D P LLOYD, **C** D J GOODHEW, **NSM** A L CRETNEY, R A LANE

BEDMINSTER (St Michael and All Angels) *Bris 1* **P** *Bp* **V** T J BAILLIE, **C** R W DENT

BEDMINSTER DOWN (St Oswald) *Bris 1* **P** *Bp* **V** C M PILGRIM

BEDMONT (Ascension) Abbots Langley *St Alb*

BEDNALL (All Saints) Penkridge Team *Lich*

BEDSTONE (St Mary) Clungunford w Clunbury and Clunton, Bedstone etc *Heref*

BEDWORTH (All Saints) *Cov 5* **P** *Patr Bd* **TR** K I HOBBS, **C** T P EDGE, P J NORTON, **Dss** P M HAMILTON

BEDWYN, GREAT (St Mary), Little Bedwyn and Savernake Forest *Sarum 21* **P** *Bp* **V** T SALISBURY

BEDWYN, LITTLE (St Michael) Gt and Lt Bedwyn and Savernake Forest *Sarum*

BEECH (St Peter) Alton St Lawr *Win*

BEECH, HIGH (Holy Innocents) Waltham H Cross *Chelmsf*

BEECH HILL (St Mary the Virgin), Grazeley and Spencers Wood *Ox 15* **P** *Bp* **P-in-c** G O SHAW, **NSM** K P WIGGINS, A S HOLMES

BEECHDALE ESTATE (St Chad) Blakenall Heath *Lich*

BEECHINGSTOKE (St Stephen) Swanborough *Sarum*

BEEDING (St Peter) and Bramber w Botolphs *Chich 12* **P** *Bp* **R** D J WHITE

BEEDING, LOWER (Holy Trinity) (St John the Evangelist) *Chich 8* **P** *Bp* **V** T A MARTIN

BEEDON (St Nicholas) and Peasemore w West Ilsley and Farnborough *Ox 14* **P** *Bp* **P-in-c** P M RENOUF, **NSM** B D SIMS

BEEFORD (St Leonard) w Frodingham and Foston *York 12* **P** *Abp and Ch Soc Trust (jt)* **R** J D WAUD

BEELEY (St Anne) and Edensor *Derby 2* **P** *Duke of Devonshire* **P-in-c** R A BEDDOES

BEELSBY (St Andrew) Ravendale Gp *Linc*

BEENHAM VALENCE (St Mary) Woolhampton w Midgham and Beenham Valance *Ox*

BEER (St Michael) and Branscombe *Ex 5* **P** *Lord Clinton and D&C (jt)* **V** N H FREATHY

BEER HACKETT (St Michael) Bradf Abbas and Thornford w Beer Hackett *Sarum*

BEERCROCOMBE (St James) Hatch Beauchamp w Beercrocombe, Curry Mallet etc *B & W*

BEESANDS (St Andrew) Stokenham w Sherford *Ex*

BEESBY (St Andrew) Saleby w Beesby and Maltby *Linc*

BEESTON (St Andrew) Sprowston w Beeston *Nor*

BEESTON (St John the Baptist) *S'well 7* **P** *Duke of Devonshire* **V** S A LOWE, **C** R HARDWICK

BEESTON (St Laurence) Horning w Beeston St Laurence and Ashmanhaugh *Nor*

BEESTON (St Mary the Virgin) *Ripon 6* **P** *V Leeds St Pet* **V** J F DICKINSON, **C** D J PEAT

BEESTON HILL (Holy Spirit) *Ripon 6* **P** *V Leeds St Pet* **P-in-c** J P GUTTERIDGE

BEESTON NEXT MILEHAM (St Mary the Virgin) Litcham w Kempston, E and W Lexham, Mileham etc *Nor*

BEESTON REGIS (All Saints) *Nor 22* **P** *Duchy of Lanc* **R** S H GILBERT

BEESTON RYLANDS (St Mary) Beeston *S'well*

BEETHAM (St Michael and All Angels) *Carl 9* **P** *Bp* **P-in-c** P K BARBER

BEETLEY (St Mary) Swanton Morley w Beetley w E Bilney and Hoe *Nor*

BEGBROKE (St Michael) Yarnton w Begbroke and Shipton on Cherwell *Ox*

BEIGHTON (All Saints) Freethorpe w Wickhampton, Halvergate etc *Nor*

BEIGHTON (St Mary the Virgin) *Sheff 1* **P** *Bp* **V** G TAYLOR

BEKESBOURNE (St Peter) Patrixbourne w Bridge and Bekesbourne *Cant*

BELAUGH (St Peter) Wroxham w Hoveton and Belaugh *Nor*

BELBROUGHTON (Holy Trinity) w Fairfield and Clent *Worc 12* **P** *Ld Chan and St Jo Coll Ox (alt)* **R** D SHARPLES

BELCHALWELL (St Aldheim) Hazelbury Bryan and the Hillside Par *Sarum*

BELCHAMP OTTEN (St Ethelbert and All Saints) w Belchamp Walter and Bulmer *Chelmsf 15* **P** *M Raymond Esq (1 turn), DBP (2 turns)* **R** *Vacant* Clare (01787) 277318

BELCHAMP ST PAUL (St Paul and St Andrew) *Chelmsf 15* **P** *D&C Windsor* **P-in-c** H A HARKER

BELCHAMP WALTER (St Mary the Virgin) Belchamp Otten w Belchamp Walter and Bulmer *Chelmsf*

BELCHFORD (St Peter and St Paul) *Linc 11* **P** *Ld Chan* **R** *Vacant*

BELFIELD (St Ann) *Man 20* **P** *Bp* **V** D K BARNES

BELFORD (St Mary) *Newc 10* **P** *Bp* **P-in-c** A J HUGHES

BELGRAVE (St Gabriel) Leic Resurr *Leic*

BELGRAVE (St Michael and All Angels) as above

BELGRAVE (St Paul) Wilnecote *Lich*

BELGRAVE (St Peter) Leic Resurr *Leic*

BELHUS PARK (All Saints) *Chelmsf 14* **P** *Bp* **P-in-c** R W SPRINGETT

BELLE GREEN (Mission) Ince Ch Ch *Liv*

BELLEAU (St John the Baptist) Wold-Marsh Gp *Linc*
BELLERBY (St John) Leyburn w Bellerby *Ripon*
BELLFIELD (St Mark) Sutton St Jas and Wawne *York*
BELLINGDON (St John the Evangelist) Gt Chesham *Ox*
BELLINGHAM (St Cuthbert) N Tyne and Redesdale Team *Newc*
BELLINGHAM (St Dunstan) *S'wark 3* **P** *Bp*
Hon **C** R B CRANE, **NSM** J M WALLACE
BELMONT (St Anselm) *Lon 23* **P** *Bp* **V** W M DAVIES,
C A FRANCIS
BELMONT (St John) *S'wark 26* **P** *R Cheam*
V E C PROBERT, **C** S H L CAWDELL
BELMONT (St Mary Magdalene) *Dur 2* **P** *The Crown*
P-in-c J W ELLIOTT
BELMONT (St Peter) *Man 16* **P** *V Bolton-le-Moors St Pet*
P-in-c B P HUMPHRIES
BELPER (Christ Church) (St Faith's Mission Church) and
Milford *Derby 11* **P** *Bp* **NSM** B WESSON
BELPER (St Peter) *Derby 11* **P** *V Duffield*
V D M WHITE, **C** L M PLAYER, P T WALLER
BELSIZE PARK (St Peter) *Lon 16* **P** *D&C Westmr*
V D E BARNES, **C** C F WILSON
BELSTEAD (St Mary the Virgin) Copdock w Washbrook
and Belstead *St E*
BELSTONE (St Mary) S Tawton and Belstone *Ex*
BELTINGHAM (St Cuthbert) w Henshaw *Newc 4*
P *V Haltwhistle* **P-in-c** K FLETCHER, **C** G A PRICE
BELTON (All Saints) and Burgh Castle *Nor 6* **P** *Bp and*
Ld Chan (alt) **R** J J QUINN
BELTON in the Isle of Axholme (All Saints) *Linc 1* **P** *Bp*
V A D O'BRIEN
BELTON (St John the Baptist) Hathern, Long Whatton and
Diseworth w Belton etc *Leic*
BELTON (St Peter) Uppingham w Ayston and Wardley w
Belton *Pet*
BELTON (St Peter and St Paul) Barkston and Hough Gp
Linc
BELVEDERE (All Saints) *Roch 14* **P** *DBP* **V** G LAMBERT
BELVEDERE (St Augustine) *Roch 14* **P** *Bp*
V P ROYSTON-BALL
BEMBRIDGE (Holy Trinity) (St Luke's Mission Church)
Portsm 7 **P** *V Brading* **V** A P MENNISS
BEMERTON (St Andrew) (St John the Evangelist) (St Michael
and All Angels) *Sarum 15* **P** *Prime Min (2 turns) and Bp*
(1 turn) **P-in-c** A R ARCHER, **C** P D NEWTON,
NSM P CURZEN
BEMPTON (St Michael) *York 10* **P** *DBP* **V** *Vacant*
BEN RHYDDING (St John the Evangelist) *Bradf 4*
P *V Ilkey* **V** B GREGORY
BENCHILL (St Luke) *Man 8* **P** *Bp* **V** D T THOMAS,
C C MacLAREN
BENEFIELD (St Mary the Virgin) and Southwick w Glapthorn
Pet 12 **P** *Mrs G S Watts-Russell and G C Capron Esq (alt)*
R *Vacant* Oundle (01832) 274026
BENENDEN (St George and St Margaret) *Cant 11* **P** *Abp*
V C F SMITH, **NSM** J T M DESROSIERS
BENFIELDSIDE (St Cuthbert) *Dur 8* **P** *Bp*
P-in-c M JACKSON, **C** N P d'E CHITTENDEN
BENFLEET, NORTH (All Saints) Bowers Gifford w N
Benfleet *Chelmsf*
BENFLEET, SOUTH (St Mary the Virgin) *Chelmsf 10*
P *D&C Westmr* **V** M E GALLOWAY
BENGEO (Holy Trinity) (St Leonard) and Christ Church
St Alb 8 **P** *R M A Smith Esq* **R** I PEARSON
BENGEWORTH (St Peter) *Worc 1* **P** *Bp* **V** L L BURN,
C B J PYKE
BENHALL (St Mary) Sternfield w Benhall and Snape *St E*
BENHILTON (All Saints) *S'wark 26* **P** *Bp*
V M A JOADES, **Hon C** J P WICKENS
BENINGTON (All Saints) w Leverton *Linc 20* **P** *Ld Chan*
R K M TOMLIN
BENINGTON (St Peter) w Walkern *St Alb 12* **P** *Trustees*
Ripon Coll Ox and K Coll Cam (alt), and Bp
P-in-c J N PRICE
BENNIWORTH (St Julian) Asterby Gp *Linc*
BENSHAM (St Chad) *Dur 4* **P** *Bp* **TR** C J WREN,
C K A WREN, M WARNER
BENSINGTON (St Helen) Benson *Ox*
BENSON (St Helen) *Ox 1* **P** *Ch Ch Ox* **V** A R HAWKEN
BENTHALL (St Bartholomew) Broseley w Benthall,
Jackfield, Linley etc *Heref*
BENTHAM (St John the Baptist) *Bradf 6* **P** *Bp*
P-in-c M J BAMFORTH
BENTHAM (St Margaret) *Bradf 6* **P** *Bp*
V J M BEARPARK
BENTILEE (St Stephen) Bucknall and Bagnall *Lich*
BENTLEY (Emmanuel) *Lich 9* **P** *Bp and Personal Reps*
Sir Alfred Owen (jt) **V** J S BARNES

BENTLEY (St Mary) and Binsted *Win 2* **P** *Adn Surrey and*
D&C (jt) **R** J M CAMPBELL
BENTLEY (St Mary) w Tattingstone *St E 5* **P** *Bp and*
DBP (alt) **V** *Vacant* Great Wenham (01473) 311495
BENTLEY (St Peter) *Sheff 8* **P** *Bp* **V** R A FITZHARRIS
BENTLEY (St Peter) Rowley w Skidby *York*
BENTLEY, GREAT (St Mary the Virgin) and Frating w
Thorrington *Chelmsf 24* **P** *St Jo Coll Cam and Bp (alt)*
R W B METCALFE
BENTLEY, LITTLE (St Mary) Tendring and Lt Bentley w
Beaumont cum Moze *Chelmsf*
BENTLEY, LOWER (St Mary) Tardebigge *Worc*
BENTLEY, NEW (St Philip and St James) *Sheff 8* **P** *Bp*
V S P DICKINSON
BENTLEY COMMON (St Paul) *Chelmsf 7* **P** *Bp*
P-in-c R A L ROSE
BENTLEY HEATH (St James) Dorridge *Birm*
BENTWORTH (St Mary) and Shalden and Lasham *Win 2*
P *J L Jervoise Esq* **R** J C R WEBB
BENWELL Team, The (St James) (St John) (Venerable Bede)
Newc 7 **P** *Bp* **TR** R D TAYLOR, **TV** A P RUGG,
P WATSON
BEOLEY (St Leonard) (St Andrew's Church Centre) *Worc 7*
P *Patr Bd* **V** D ROGERS
BEPTON (St Mary) Cocking, Bepton and W Lavington
Chich
BERDEN (St Nicholas) Manuden w Berden *Chelmsf*
BERE ALSTON (Holy Trinity) Bere Ferrers *Ex*
BERE FERRERS (St Andrew) *Ex 25* **P** *DBP*
R D J PASKINS
BERE REGIS (St John the Baptist) and Affpuddle w
Turnerspuddle *Sarum 7* **P** *Ball Coll Ox (2 turns), Bp*
(1 turn) **R** G H ROBLIN
BERECHURCH (St Margaret w St Michael) *Chelmsf 17*
P *Bp* **V** R I WILKINSON
BERGH APTON (St Peter and St Paul) Thurton *Nor*
BERGHOLT, EAST (St Mary the Virgin) *St E 5* **P** *Em Coll*
Cam **R** J P DRUCE
BERGHOLT, WEST (St Mary the Virgin) *Chelmsf 18*
P *Bp* **R** W C FREWIN
BERINSFIELD (St Mary and St Berin) Dorchester *Ox*
BERKELEY (St Mary the Virgin) w Wick, Breadstone and
Newport *Glouc 2* **P** *R J G Berkeley Esq and Sir Hugo*
Huntington-Whiteley (jt) **V** S G RICHARDS,
NSM R P CHIDLAW
BERKHAMSTED (St Mary) *St Alb 3* **P** *Duchy of Cornwall*
R J T TABOR
BERKHAMSTED, GREAT (All Saints) (St Peter) *St Alb 3*
P *Bp* **R** H R DAVIS, **NSM** J MACPHERSON
BERKHAMSTED, LITTLE (St Andrew) and Bayford,
Essendon and Ponsbourne *St Alb 8* **P** *Marquess of Salisbury*
(2 turns), CPAS (1 turn), and Bp (1 turn)
P-in-c J H B COTTON, **C** P M HIGHAM (nee ANNS),
Hon C M E COTTON
BERKHAMSYTCH (St Mary and St John) Ipstones w
Berkhamsytch and Onecote w Bradnop *Lich*
BERKLEY (Blessed Virgin Mary) Beckington w
Standerwick, Berkley, Rodden etc *B & W*
BERKSWELL (St John the Baptist) *Cov 4* **P** *Trustees*
Col C J H Wheatley **R** G BAISLEY
BERKSWICH (Holy Trinity) Baswich (or Berkswich) *Lich*
BERMONDSEY (St Anne) (St Augustine) *S'wark 5* **P** *Bp*
and F W Smith Esq (alt) **P-in-c** S L WILMOT
BERMONDSEY (St Crispin w Christ Church) *S'wark 5*
P *Hyndman Trustees* **P** G GRAY
BERMONDSEY St Hugh Charterhouse Mission Conventional
District *S'wark 5* **Min** D J FUDGER
BERMONDSEY (St James w Christ Church) *S'wark 5*
P *The Crown, Bp, and R Bermondsey St Mary (by turn)*
P-in-c S L WILMOT, **C** I J DAVOLL, R D BAINBRIDGE
BERMONDSEY (St Katharine) w St Bartholomew *S'wark 5*
P *Bp and R Rotherhithe St Mary w All SS (jt)*
V T HOPPERTON
BERMONDSEY (St Mary Magdalen w St Olave, St John and
St Luke) *S'wark 5* **P** *Ch Patr Soc (2 turns), Ld Chan*
(1 turn), and Bp (1 turn) **P-in-c** J A BRADSHAW
BERNEY, GREAT (St John) Langdon Hills *Chelmsf*
BERRICK SALOME (St Helen) Chalgrove w Berrick Salome
Ox
BERRINGTON (All Saints) and Betton Strange *Heref 11*
P *DBP* **P-in-c** J C WALNE
BERROW (Blessed Virgin Mary) and Breane *B & W 1* **P** *Adn*
Wells **R** S LOW
BERROW (St Faith) w Pendock, Eldersfield, Hollybush and
Birtsmorton *Worc 5* **P** *Bp, D&C, and Sir Berwick*
Lechmere, Bt (jt) **R** J R PARKINSON
BERRY POMEROY (St Mary) Totnes, Bridgetown and
Berry Pomeroy and Dartington *Ex*

BERRYNARBOR (St Peter) Combe Martin and Berrynarbor *Ex*

BERSTED, NORTH (Holy Cross) Conventional District *Chich 1* **C-in-c** G A TOOLEY

BERSTED, SOUTH (St Mary Magdalene) w NORTH (St Peter) *Chich 1* **P** *Abp* **P-in-c** D H THORNLEY

BERWICK (Holy Trinity) (St Mary) *Newc 12* **P** *Bp (2 turns), D&C Dur (1 turn)* **V** A HUGHES

BERWICK (St John) Chalke Valley W *Sarum*

BERWICK (St Michael and All Angels) w Selmeston and Alciston *Chich 18* **P** *Miss I M Newson and Miss R Fitzherbert (1 turn), D&C (1 turn)* **R** P SMITH

BERWICK PARK (Good Shepherd) Wood Green St Mich w Bounds Green St Gabr etc *Lon*

BERWICK ST JAMES (St James) Lower Wylye and Till Valley *Sarum*

BESFORD (St Peter's Chapelry) Defford w Besford *Worc*

BESSACARR, WEST (St Francis of Assisi) *Sheff 9* **P** *Bp* **V** A C GRIFFITHS

BESSELSLEIGH (St Lawrence) w Dry Sandford *Ox 10* **P** *Ox Ch Trust* **P-in-c** R G PENMAN

BESSINGBY (St Magnus) (St Mark) *York 10* **P** *Reps George Wright Esq* **V** T J DAVIDSON

BESSINGHAM (St Mary) Roughton and Felbrigg, Metton, Sustead etc *Nor*

BESTHORPE (All Saints) Attleborough w Besthorpe *Nor*

BESTHORPE (Holy Trinity) Collingham w S Scarle and Besthorpe and Girton *S'well*

BESTWOOD (no dedication) (St Mark) (St Matthew on the Hill) (St Philip) (Emmanuel) *S'well 13* **P** *Patr Bd* **TM** S J GRIFFITHS, **TV** S LEES, R W YULE, N G SHAW, **C** K J HITCHMAN, **NSM** V I VIVIAN

BESTWOOD/RISE PARK Local Ecumenical Project *S'well 10* **Min** S J GRIFFITHS

BESTWOOD RISE PARK Bestwood *S'well*

BESWICK (St Margaret) Hutton Cranswick w Skerne, Watton and Beswick *York*

BETCHWORTH (St Michael and All Angels) *S'wark 25* **P** *D&C Windsor* **V** *Vacant* Betchworth (01737) 842102

BETHERSDEN (St Margaret) w High Halden *Cant 11* **P** *Abp* **V** *Vacant* Bethersden (01233) 820266

BETHESDA (Shared Church) Hallwood *Ches*

BETHNAL GREEN (St Barnabas) *Lon 7* **P** *D&C Cant* **P-in-c** J D M PATON, **NSM** F M ROLLINSON, P STORR VENTER

BETHNAL GREEN (St James the Less) *Lon 7* **P** *CPAS* **P-in-c** B S CASTLE, **Hon C** W C HARRAP

BETHNAL GREEN (St Matthew w St James the Great) *Lon 7* **P** *Bp* **R** C J C BEDFORD, **C** S A WILLIS

BETHNAL GREEN (St Peter) (St Thomas) *Lon 7* **P** *City Corp* **V** J M V WEIR

BETLEY (St Margaret) and Keele *Lich 14* **P** T G H Howard-Sneyd Esq and DBP (jt) **V** J S WHITEHEAD, **C** G F COOKE **NSM** T E BIDDINGTON

BETTESHANGER (St Mary the Virgin) Eastry and Northbourne w Tilmanstone etc *Cant*

BETTISCOMBE (St Stephen) Marshwood Vale TM *Sarum*

BETTON STRANGE (St Margaret) Berrington and Betton Strange *Heref*

BETTWS-Y-CRWYN (St Mary) Clun w Bettws-y-Crwyn and Newc *Heref*

BEVENDEAN (Holy Nativity) Moulsecoomb *Chich*

BEVERLEY (St Mary) *York 9* **P** *Abp* **V** D W HOSKIN, **Hon C** H A HALL, **NSM** D S SIMON

BEVERLEY (St Nicholas) *York 9* **P** *Abp* **V** M L KAVANAGH, **C** J F TWOMEY, **NSM** L C MUNT

BEVERLEY MINSTER (St John and St Martin) *York 9* **P** *Simeon's Trustees* **V** P R FORSTER, **C** M P DUNNING, B S DIXON

BEVERSTON (St Mary the Virgin) Tetbury w Beverston *Glouc*

BEWBUSH (Community Centre) Ifield *Chich*

BEWCASTLE (St Cuthbert), Stapleton and Kirklinton w Hethersgill *Carl 2* **P** *Bp, D&C, and DBP (jt)* **R** J R REPATH

BEWDLEY (St Anne) Ribbesford w Bewdley and Dowles *Worc*

BEWERLEY GRANGE (Chapel) Upper Nidderdale *Ripon*

BEWHOLME (St John the Baptist) Sigglesthorne and Rise w Nunkeeling and Bewholme *York*

BEWICK, OLD (Holy Trinity) Glendale Gp *Newc*

BEXHILL (All Saints) Sidley *Chich*

BEXHILL (St Andrew) Conventional District *Chich 14* **NSM** G G DANIELS

BEXHILL (St Augustine) *Chich 14* **P** *Bp* **V** E F P BRYANT

BEXHILL (St Barnabas) *Chich 14* **P** *Bp* **V** T M J VAN CARRAPIETT

BEXHILL (St Mark) *Chich 14* **P** *Bp* **R** J J W EDMONDSON, **Hon C** E V WHEELER

BEXHILL (St Peter) (St Michael) (Good Shepherd) *Chich 14* **P** *Bp* **TR** J W COTTON, **TV** R L HAWKES, **C** N P ELY, **Hon Par Dn** E A HAWKES

BEXHILL (St Stephen) *Chich 14* **P** *Bp* **V** D R FROST

BEXLEY (St John the Evangelist) *Roch 16* **P** *The Crown* **V** J A PEAL, **Hon C** A F DALLING, **NSM** J PEAL

BEXLEY (St Mary) *Roch 16* **P** *Bp* **V** D L KNIGHT, **Hon C** G ATFIELD

BEXLEYHEATH (Christ Church) *Roch 14* **P** *Bp* **V** M G GRIBBLE, **C** A M HORTON, A E COOKE

BEXLEYHEATH (St Peter) *Roch 14* **P** *Bp* **V** M H CLUMGAIR

BEXWELL (St Mary) Downham Market w Bexwell *Ely*

BEYTON (All Saints) Rougham, Beyton w Hessett and Rushbrooke *St E*

BIBURY (St Mary) w Winson and Barnsley *Glouc 13* **P** *Bp and W H Wykeham-Musgrave Esq (alt)* **V** *Vacant* Cirencester (01285) 740387

BICESTER (St Edburg) w Bucknell, Caversfield and Launton *Ox 2* **P** *Patr Bd* **TR** J S BAGGLEY, **TV** J D NIXON, S P HALL

BICKENHILL (St Peter) *Birm 13* **P** *Birm Dioc Trustees* **P-in-c** A J EYLES

BICKER (St Swithin) and Wigtoft *Linc 21* **P** *Bp and D&C (alt)* **V** N A G BURNET

BICKERSHAW (St James and St Elizabeth) *Liv 14* **P** *Bp* **V** J JORDAN, **NSM** M E WEYMONT

BICKERSTAFFE Four Lane Ends (not known) Bickerstaffe and Melling *Liv*

BICKERSTAFFE (Holy Trinity) and Melling *Liv 11* **P** *Lord Derby and R Halsall (jt)* **V** N K LEIPER

BICKERTON (Holy Trinity) w Bickley *Ches 5* **P** *DBP, Marchioness of Cholmondeley, Adn, and Bp (jt)* **P-in-c** D R BUCKLEY

BICKINGTON (St Andrew) Fremington *Ex*

BICKINGTON (St Mary the Virgin) Ashburton w Buckland in the Moor and Bickington *Ex*

BICKINGTON, HIGH (St Mary) Atherington and High Bickington *Ex*

BICKLEIGH Roborough (St Mary the Virgin) and Shaugh Prior *Ex 21* **P** *Patr Bd* **TR** R J CARLTON, **C** R OLLIFF

BICKLEIGH (St Mary) Silverton, Butterleigh, Bickleigh and Cadeleigh *Ex*

BICKLEIGH DOWN (School) Bickleigh (Roborough) and Shaugh Prior *Ex*

BICKLEY (St George) *Roch 13* **P** *SMF* **V** D A S HERBERT

BICKLEY (St Wenefrede) Bickerton w Bickley *Ches*

BICKNACRE (St Andrew) Woodham Ferrers and Bicknacre *Chelmsf*

BICKNOLLER (St George) w Crowcombe and Sampford Brett *B & W 17* **P** *Bp and V Stogumber (jt)* **R** M D BOLE

BICKNOR (St James) Bredgar w Bicknor and Frinsted w Wormshill etc *Cant*

BICTON (Holy Trinity), Montford w Shrawardine and Fitz *Lich 26* **P** *Earl of Powis, N E E Stephens Esq, and C J Wingfield Esq (jt)* **R** K J F MACLEAN

BICTON (St Mary) E Budleigh w Bicton and Otterton *Ex*

BIDBOROUGH (St Lawrence) *Roch 10* **P** *Mabledon Trust* **R** M R HODGE

BIDDENDEN (All Saints) and Smarden *Cant 11* **P** *Abp* **P-in-c** B K MELBOURNE

BIDDENHAM (St James) *St Alb 16* **P** *Bp* **NSM** D G MASON

BIDDESTONE (St Nicholas) w Slaughterford *Bris 9* **P** *Win Coll* **P-in-c** J N A BRADBURY, **C** R V C LEWIS

BIDDISHAM (St John the Baptist) Crook Peak *B & W*

BIDDLESDEN (St Margaret) Westbury w Turweston, Shalstone and Biddlesden *Ox*

BIDDULPH (St Lawrence) *Lich 13* **P** *MMCET* **V** A J PIGGOTT, **C** N D GREW

BIDDULPH MOOR (Christ Church) *Lich 13* **P** *MMCET* **R** J McGUIRE

BIDEFORD (St Mary) (St Peter East the Water) *Ex 17* **P** *DBP* **R** P G SMITH, **C** I W MACKENZIE

BIDFORD-ON-AVON (St Laurence) *Cov 7* **P** *Bp* **V** D A HALL, **NSM** M M DEIMEL

BIDSTON (St Oswald) *Ches 1* **P** *Bp* **V** S M MANSFIELD, **C** S CHESTERS

BIELBY (St Giles) Seaton Ross Gp of Par *York*

BIERLEY (St John the Evangelist) *Bradf 2* **P** *DBP* **V** I R LANE, **C** T H C MEYRICK

BIERLEY, EAST (St Luke) Birkenshaw w Hunsworth *Wakef*

BIERTON (St James the Great) Aylesbury w Bierton and Hulcott *Ox*

BIGBURY (St Lawrence), Ringmore and Kingston *Ex 14*
  P *MMCET and Canon N M Ramm (alt)*
  NSM A DROWLEY
BIGBY (All Saints) N Wolds Gp *Linc*
BIGGIN (St Thomas) Hartington, Biggin and Earl Sterndale
  Derby
BIGGIN HILL (St Mark) *Roch 13* **P** *Bp*
  V E H HESELWOOD, **C** R J POWELL,
  NSM E J G STRICKLAND (nee CUTTS)
BIGGLESWADE (St Andrew) *St Alb 17* **P** *Bp*
  V R F SIBSON, **C** N D BARNES
BIGHTON (All Saints) Old Alresford and Bighton *Win*
BIGNOR (Holy Cross) Barlavington, Burton w Coates,
  Sutton and Bignor *Chich*
BIGRIGG (St John) Egremont and Haile *Carl*
BILBOROUGH (St John the Baptist) *S'well 14* **P** *Bp*
  V A S G HART, **C** E P BAILEY
BILBOROUGH (St Martin) w Strelley *S'well 14* **P** *SMF*
  P-in-c D J HOWARD
BILBROOK (Holy Cross) Codsall *Lich*
BILBROUGH (St James) Healaugh w Wighill, Bilbrough and
  Askham Richard *York*
BILDESTON (St Mary Magdalene) w Wattisham *St E 3*
  P *Abp, Bp, and CPAS (by turn)* **P-in-c** J A COHEN
BILHAM *Sheff 12* **P** *Bp, Major W Warde-Aldam,*
  W G A Warde-Norbury Esq, and Mrs P Williams (jt)
  V G K BOSTOCK
BILLERICAY (St Mary Magdalen) (Christ Church) and Little
  Burstead *Chelmsf 6* **P** *Bp* **TR** P D ASHTON,
  TV N HAWKINS, G T WAKEFIELD, **C** J E EATON,
  NSM M L ASHTON,
BILLESDON (St John the Baptist) and Skeffington *Leic 4*
  P *Bp* **V** D VOSBORNE
BILLESLEY COMMON (Holy Cross) *Birm 8* **P** *Bp*
  V *Vacant* 0121–444 1737
BILLING, GREAT (St Andrew) w LITTLE (All Saints)
  Pet 4 **P** *BNC Ox and Bp (alt)* **R** K P ASHBY,
  NSM M J WALTON
BILLINGBOROUGH (St Andrew) *Linc 13* **P** *The Crown*
  P-in-c C H WILSON
BILLINGE (St Aidan) *Liv 15* **P** *R Wigan* **V** D LYON
BILLINGFORD (St Leonard) Scole, Brockdish, Billingford,
  Thorpe Abbots etc *Nor*
BILLINGFORD (St Peter) N Elmham w Billingford and
  Worthing *Nor*
BILLINGHAM (St Aidan) (St Luke) *Dur 16* **P** *Patr Bd*
  TR C O HURFORD, **TV** D R HANSON
BILLINGHAM (St Cuthbert) *Dur 16* **P** *D&C*
  V R I SMITH, **C** M N VERNON
BILLINGHAM (St Mary Magdalene) Wolviston *Dur*
BILLINGHAY (St Michael) *Linc 22* **P** *Sir Stephen Hastings*
  V *Vacant* Billinghay (01526) 861321
BILLINGSHURST (St Mary the Virgin) *Chich 8* **P** *Bp*
  V D C PAIN
BILLINGSLEY (St Mary) w Sidbury, Middleton Scriven,
  Chetton, Glazeley, Deuxhill and Chelmarsh *Heref 9* **P** *Bp*
  and Woodward Schools (jt) **R** P R J LAMB
BILLINGTON (St Michael and All Angels) Leighton
  Buzzard w Eggington, Hockliffe etc *St Alb*
BILLOCKBY (All Saints) Rollesby w Burgh w Billockby w
  Ashby w Oby etc *Nor*
BILLY MILL (St Aidan) Cullercoats St Geo *Newc*
BILNEY, EAST (St Mary) Swanton Morley w Beetley w E
  Bilney and Hoe *Nor*
BILSBORROW (St Hilda) *Blackb 10* **P** *V St Michael's-on-*
  Wyre **V** A WHITTAKER
BILSBY (Holy Trinity) w Farlesthorpe *Linc 8* **P** *Bp*
  P-in-c A READER-MOORE
BILSDALE MIDCABLE (St John) Upper Ryedale *York*
BILSDALE PRIORY (St Hilda) Ingleby Greenhow w
  Bilsdale Priory, Kildale etc *York*
BILSINGTON (St Peter and St Paul) Aldington w
  Bonnington and Bilsington *Cant*
BILSON (Mission Church) Cinderford St Steph w Littledean
  Glouc
BILSTHORPE (St Margaret) *S'well 15* **P** *DBP*
  R H H WILCOX
BILSTON (St Leonard) (St Chad) (St Mary the Virgin)
  Lich 9 **P** *Patr Bd* **TR** P J CHAPMAN,
  TV G E MORRIS, G WARREN, **C** C P MAYO
BILTON (St John the Evangelist) *Ripon 1* **P** *Bp*
  V A L GLASBY, **C** J CHEVERTON,
  NSM K A FITZSIMONS
BILTON (St Mark) *Cov 6* **P** *N M Assheton Esq*
  R C S HARPER, **C** J K FRENCH
BILTON, NEW (St Oswald) *Cov 6* **P** *Dioc Trustees*
  V *Vacant* Rugby (01788) 544011

BILTON-IN-AINSTY (St Helen) Tockwith and Bilton w
  Bickerton *York*
BILTON IN HOLDERNESS (St Peter) *York 13* **P** *Abp*
  V R J E MAJOR
BINBROOK Group, The (St Mary) *Linc 10* **P** *Ld Chan, DBP*
  and M M Sleight Esq (alt) **R** T J WALKER
BINCOMBE (Holy Trinity) w Broadwey, Upwey and Buckland
  Ripers *Sarum 5* **P** *G&C Coll Cam (2 turns),*
  Miss M B F Frampton (1 turn), and Bp (1 turn)
  R R A C SIMMONS, **NSM** N E MOSS
BINEGAR (Holy Trinity) Ashwick w Oakhill and Binegar
  B & W
BINFIELD (All Saints) (St Mark) *Ox 11* **P** *Ld Chan*
  R O R M BLATCHLY, **Hon C** G A WILLIS
BINGFIELD (St Mary) St Oswald in Lee w Bingfield *Newc*
BINGHAM (St Mary and All Saints) *S'well 8* **P** *The Crown*
  R D L HARPER, **Hon C** J B DAVIS
BINGLEY (All Saints) *Bradf 1* **P** *Bp* **TR** S P KELLY,
  TV P WILLOX
BINGLEY (Holy Trinity) *Bradf 1* **P** *Bp* **P-in-c** A J CLARKE
BINHAM (St Mary) Stiffkey and Cockthorpe w Morston,
  Langham etc *Nor*
BINLEY (St Bartholomew) *Cov 1* **P** *Bp* **V** D J HOWARD,
  C T D BUCKLEY, G L PRINGLE
BINLEY WOODS Local Ecumenical Project *Cov 1*
  Min T D BUCKLEY
BINSEY (St Margaret) Ox St Thos w St Frideswide and
  Binsey *Ox*
BINSTEAD (Holy Cross) *Portsm 7* **P** *Bp*
  R S M CHALONER, **NSM** T I CARD
BINSTED (Holy Cross) Bentley and Binsted *Win*
BINSTED (St Mary) Walberton w Binsted *Chich*
BINTON (St Peter) Temple Grafton w Binton *Cov*
BINTREE (St Swithin) Twyford, Guist, Bintree,
  Themelthorpe etc *Nor*
BIRCH (St Agnes) *Man 3* **P** *Bp* **R** C D NEWELL,
  C M K J SMITH
BIRCH (St James) w Fallowfield *Man 4* **P** *Bp*
  P-in-c W G RAINES
BIRCH (St Mary) Rhodes *Man*
BIRCH w Layer Breton and Layer Marney *Chelmsf 20*
  P *Col J G Round, N S Charrington Esq, and Bp (jt)*
  R P C SPENCER
BIRCH-IN-RUSHOLME (St James) Birch w Fallowfield
  Man
BIRCHAM, GREAT (St Mary the Virgin) Docking, The
  Birchams, Stanhoe and Sedgeford *Nor*
BIRCHAM NEWTON (All Saints) as above
BIRCHANGER (St Mary the Virgin) *Chelmsf 22* **P** *New Coll*
  Ox **R** *Vacant* Bishop Stortford 812310
BIRCHENCLIFFE (St Philip the Apostle) *Wakef 5*
  P *V Lindley* **P-in-c** R E WHITEHOUSE
BIRCHES HEAD (St Matthew) Hanley H Ev *Lich*
BIRCHFIELD (Holy Trinity) *Birm 3* **P** *Bp* **V** R W HUNT,
  C A St L J WICKENS, **NSM** V JORDINSON
BIRCHILLS, THE (St Andrew) Walsall St Andr *Lich*
BIRCHIN COPPICE (St Peter) Kidderminster St Jo and H
  Innocents *Worc*
BIRCHINGTON (All Saints) w Acol and Minnis Bay *Cant 9*
  P *Abp* **V** F R SMALE, **C** S D MANSFIELD
BIRCHMOOR (St John) Polesworth *Birm*
BIRCHOVER (St Michael) Youlgreave, Middleton, Stanton-
  in-Peak etc *Derby*
BIRCHWOOD (Mission Church) Churchstanton, Buckland
  St Mary and Otterford *B & W*
BIRCHWOOD (St Luke) *Linc 15* **P** *Bp* **V** *Vacant* Lincoln
  (01522) 683507
BIRCHWOOD (Transfiguration) Padgate *Liv*
BIRCLE (St John the Baptist) *Man 10* **P** *R Middleton*
  St Leon **V** A R BROCKBANK
BIRDBROOK (St Augustine) Ridgewell w Ashen, Birdbrook
  and Sturmer *Chelmsf*
BIRDHAM (St James) W Wittering and Birdham w Itchenor
  Chich
BIRDINGBURY (St Leonards) Leamington Hastings and
  Birdingbury *Cov*
BIRDLIP (St Mary in Hamlet) Brimpsfield, Cranham,
  Elkstone and Syde *Glouc*
BIRDSALL (St Mary) w Langton *York 2* **P** *Lord Middleton*
  and Ld Chan (alt) **NSM** J W A WOODS
BIRKBY (St Peter) Gt Smeaton w Appleton Wiske and
  Birkby etc *Ripon*
BIRKDALE Carr Lane (St Mary) Birkdale St Jo *Liv*
BIRKDALE (St James) *Liv 9* **P** *Trustees* **V** J S BELLAMY,
  NSM I D DAWSON
BIRKDALE (St John) *Liv 9* **P** *Trustees* **V** J W C HARDING

BIRKDALE (St Peter) *Liv 9* **P** *Trustees* **V** MISTOCKLEY
BIRKENHEAD (Christ Church) *Ches 1* **P** *Bp* **V** *Vacant*
0151–652 5647 or 652 3990
BIRKENHEAD (St James) w St Bede *Ches 1* **P** *Trustees*
V STPENDLEBURY, **C** DRNUGENT
BIRKENHEAD (St Winifred) Welsh Church *Ches 1*
C-in-c DTPEVANS
BIRKENHEAD PRIORY (Christ the King) *Ches 1* **P** *Bp,*
Simeon's Trustees, and Ch Patr Trust (jt)
TR DWALKER, **C** DJBURLEIGH, **NSM** SHUGHES
BIRKENSHAW (St Paul) w Hunsworth *Wakef 8*
P *V Birstall* **V** IMGASKELL
BIRKIN (St Mary) Haddlesey w Hambleton and Birkin *York*
BIRLEY (St Peter) Canon Pyon w Kings Pyon and Birley
Heref
BIRLING (All Saints), Addington, Ryarsh and Trottiscliffe
Roch 7 **P** *Bp* **R** GCMMILES, **NSM** BEHURD
BIRLING, LOWER (Christ Church) Snodland All SS w Ch
Ch Roch
BIRLINGHAM (St James the Great) Pershore w Pinvin,
Wick and Birlingham *Worc*
BIRMINGHAM (Bishop Latimer w All Saints) *Birm 1*
P *St Martin's Trustees* **R** RFBASHFORD
BIRMINGHAM (St George) *Birm 1* **P** *St Martin's Trustees*
R RAKENWAY
BIRMINGHAM (St John the Evangelist) Ladywood *Birm 1*
P *R Birm St Martin w Bordesley* **V** RJTETLOW,
C JMMASON
BIRMINGHAM (St Luke) *Birm 1* **P** *Trustees*
V RCHINGLEY, **C** SCCARTER, **NSM** BHINGLEY
BIRMINGHAM (St Martin) w Bordesley St Andrew *Birm 1*
P *St Martin's Trustees* **R** JGWESSON, **C** ADJCOE,
QDWARBRICK, SJMVETTERS
BIRMINGHAM (St Paul) *Birm 1* **P** *St Martin's Trustees*
V DLCLARINGBULL
BIRMINGHAM (St Peter) *Birm 1* **P** *Bp* **V** CFMORTON
BIRSTALL (St James the Greater) and Wanlip *Leic 6* **P** *Bp*
and C A Palmer-Tomkinson Esq (jt) **V** CABRADSHAW,
C HCBAKER
BIRSTALL (St Peter) *Wakef 8* **P** *Bp* **V** RMWELLER
BIRSTWITH (St James) *Ripon 1* **P** *Exors Col*
B C Greenwood **P-in-c** WAWILBY
BIRTLES (St Catherine) *Ches 13* **P** *Bp* **V** WFIWHINTON
BIRTLEY (St Giles) Chollerton w Birtley and Thockrington
Newc
BIRTLEY (St John the Evangelist) *Dur 1* **P** *R Chester-le-*
Street **V** FWHITE, **C** DMJOHNSON
BIRTSMORTON (St Peter and St Paul) Berrow w Pendock,
Eldersfield, Hollybush etc *Worc*
BIRWOOD (Mission church) Churcham w Bulley and
Minsterworth *Glouc*
BISBROOKE (St John the Baptist) Morcott w Glaston and
Bisbrooke *Pet*
BISCATHORPE (St Helen) Asterby Gp *Linc*
BISCOT (Holy Trinity) *St Alb 20* **P** *Bp* **V** EEWEST
BISHAM (All Saints) Gt Marlow w Marlow Bottom, Lt
Marlow and Bisham *Ox*
BISHAMPTON (St James) Abberton, The Flyfords,
Naunton Beauchamp etc *Worc*
BISHOP AUCKLAND (St Andrew) (St Anne) Auckland St
Andr and St Anne *Dur*
BISHOP AUCKLAND (St Peter) Auckland St Pet *Dur*
BISHOP AUCKLAND Woodhouse Close Area of Ecumenical
Experiment (Conventional District) *Dur 10*
C-in-c PSINCLAIR
BISHOP BURTON (All Saints) w Walkington *York 9* **P** *Abp*
and DBP (alt) **R** DGKIRBY
BISHOP CAUNDLE (not known) The Caundles w Folke
and Holwell *Sarum*
BISHOP MIDDLEHAM (St Michael) *Dur 14* **P** *Ld Chan*
P-in-c VSHEDDEN
BISHOP MONKTON (St John the Baptist) and Burton
Leonard *Ripon 3* **P** *D&C* **P-in-c** PHULETT
BISHOP NORTON (St Peter), Waddingham and Snitterby
Linc 6 **P** *Bp and The Crown (alt)* **R** DJATKINSON
BISHOP SUTTON (Holy Trinity) and Stanton Drew and
Stowey *B & W 10* **P** *Bp and Adn Bath (alt)* **V** JHIGGINS
BISHOP THORNTON (St John the Evangelist) Markington
w S Stainley and Bishop Thornton *Ripon*
BISHOP WILTON (St Edith) w Full Sutton, Kirby Underdale
and Bugthorpe *York 7* **P** *Abp, D&C, and Earl of Halifax*
(jt) (3 turns), Ld Chan (1 turn) **R** JCFINNEMORE
BISHOPDALE (Mission Room) Aysgarth and Bolton cum
Redmire *Ripon*
BISHOP'S CANNINGS (St Mary the Virgin), All Cannings
and Etchilhampton *Sarum 19* **P** *DBP* **P-in-c** APJEANS

BISHOP'S CASTLE (St John the Baptist) w Mainstone
Heref 10 **P** *Earl of Powis and Ld Chan (alt)*
V KMCROUCH, **C** KBCOLLINS
BISHOP'S CLEEVE (St Michael and All Angels) *Glouc 9*
P *DBP* **R** JHMEAD, **C** MJOHNSON, JCCORNELL
BISHOP'S FROME (St Mary the Virgin) w Castle Frome and
Fromes Hill *Heref 2* **P** *Bp* **R** BRCONAWAY
BISHOPS GREEN (Community Church) Burghclere w
Newtown and Ecchinswell w Sydmonton *Win*
BISHOP'S HATFIELD (St Etheldreda) Hatf *St Alb*
BISHOP'S HULL (St John the Evangelist) Taunton St Jo
B & W
BISHOPS HULL (St Peter and St Paul) *B & W 18* **P** *Adn*
Taunton **V** CMSRANDALL
BISHOP'S ITCHINGTON (St Michael) *Cov 10* **P** *Bp*
P-in-c MCGREEN
BISHOP'S LAVINGTON (All Saints) W Lavington and the
Cheverells *Sarum*
BISHOPS LYDEARD (Blessed Virgin Mary) w Bagborough
and Cothelstone *B & W 18* **P** *D&C (3 turns), Ms*
P M G Mitford (1 turn) **R** *Vacant* Bishops Lydeard (01823)
432414
BISHOPS NORTON (St John the Evangelist) Twigworth,
Down Hatherley, Norton, The Leigh etc *Glouc*
BISHOP'S STORTFORD (Holy Trinity) *St Alb 4* **P** *Bp*
R JRHAYNES
BISHOP'S STORTFORD (St Michael) *St Alb 4* **P** *Bp*
V RAVMARCHAND, **C** LKLIMAS,
Hon C BHTALBOTT, **NSM** DCHINGE
BISHOP'S SUTTON (St Nicholas) and Ropley and West
Tisted *Win* **P** *Peache Trustees* **R** RJSUCH,
NSM TJRIVIERE
BISHOP'S TACHBROOK (St Chad) *Cov 10* **P** *Bp*
V WRLARGE
BISHOPS TAWTON (St John the Baptist) Newport, Bishops
Tawton and Tawstock *Ex*
BISHOPS WALTHAM (St Peter) *Portsm 1* **P** *Bp*
R SEWILKINSON, **C** GEDHITCHINS
BISHOP'S WOOD (St Mary) Hartlebury *Worc*
BISHOPSBOURNE (St Mary) Barham w Bishopsbourne and
Kingston *Cant*
BISHOPSNYMPTON (St Mary the Virgin), Rose Ash,
Mariansleigh, Molland, Knowstone, East Anstey and West
Anstey *Ex 19* **P** *DBP* **TR** CSTULL, **C** RESHORTER
BISHOPSTEIGNTON (St John the Evangelist) Teignmouth,
Ideford w Luton, Ashcombe etc *Ex*
BISHOPSTOKE (St Mary) (St Paul) *Win 9* **P** *Bp*
R DJCOTTRILL, **C** MMULLINS, **Hon C** NJACKSON
BISHOPSTON (Church of the Good Shepherd) (St Michael
and All Angels) *Bris 6* **P** *Patr Bd* **TV** HWWARDALE,
P-in-c RVBRAZIER
BISHOPSTONE (St Andrew) *Chich 18* **P** *Bp Lon*
V RCWALLIS
BISHOPSTONE (St John the Baptist) Chalke Valley E *Sarum*
BISHOPSTONE (St Lawrence) *Heref 4* **P** *Major*
D J C Davenport **P-in-c** GUSHER
BISHOPSTROW (St Aldhelm) and Boreham *Sarum 14*
P *DBP* **P-in-c** DRABRETT
BISHOPSWOOD (All Saints) Walford and Saint John, w
Bishopswood etc *Heref*
BISHOPSWOOD (St John the Evangelist) *Lich 2*
P *V Brewood* **V** THGREEN
BISHOPSWORTH (St Peter) *Bris 1* **P** *Bp*
V PGHUZZEY, **C** LJEGOODHEW,
Hon C WJBISHOP, **NSM** PJBEVAN
BISHOPTHORPE (St Andrew) *York 1* **P** *Abp*
V PRATHBONE
BISHOPTON (St Peter) w Great Stainton *Dur 16*
P *Ld Chan* **V** PSATKINSON
BISHOPWEARMOUTH (Christ Church) *Dur 9* **P** *Bp*
V RIDAVISON, **NSM** BJABBOTT
BISHOPWEARMOUTH (Good Shepherd) *Dur 9* **P** *Bp*
V *Vacant* 0191–565 6870
BISHOPWEARMOUTH (St Gabriel) *Dur 9*
P *V Sunderland* **V** ATHORP, **C** RJDOWNES,
NSM HMTHORP
BISHOPWEARMOUTH (St Luke Pallion) Pallion *Dur*
BISHOPWEARMOUTH (St Mary) Millfield St Mary *Dur*
BISHOPWEARMOUTH (St Nicholas) *Dur 9* **P** *Bp*
V *Vacant* 0191–522 6444
BISLEY (All Saints), Oakridge, Miserden and Edgeworth
Glouc 1 **P** *Major M T N H Wills, Ld Chan, and Bp*
(by turn) **V** IEDFARROW
BISLEY (St John the Baptist) and West End (Holy Trinity)
Guildf 6 **P** *Bp* **R** IATERRY, **NSM** DHROBINSON
BISPHAM (All Hallows) *Blackb 9* **P** *Ch Soc Trust*
R SJCOX, **C** JMFEARNLEY, **Hon C** LFRASER
BISTERNE (St Paul) Ringwood *Win*

BITCHFIELD (St Mary Magdalene) Ingoldsby *Linc*

BITTADON (St Peter) Ilfracombe, Lee, Woolacombe, Bittadon etc *Ex*

BITTERING PARVA (St Peter and St Paul) Gressenhall w Longham w Wendling etc *Nor*

BITTERLEY (St Mary) w Middleton, Stoke St Milborough w The Heath and Hopton Cangeford, Clee St Margaret and Cold Weston *Heref 12* **P** *Bp, DBP, Walcott Trustees, and Miss M F Rouse-Boughton (jt)* **R** A G SEABROOK

BITTERNE (Holy Saviour) *Win 12* **P** *Bp* **V** P HARRIS, **C** D S SNUGGS

BITTERNE PARK (All Hallows) (Ascension) *Win 12* **P** *Bp* **V** J R EVANS, **C** M T P ZAMMIT, D E CHANDLER, **NSM** B L STREVENS

BITTESWELL (St Mary) *Leic 11* **P** *Haberdashers' Co* **P-in-c** M H W COUSSENS

BITTON (St Mary) Warmley, Syston and Bitton *Bris*

BIX (St James) Nettlebed w Bix and Highmore *Ox*

BLABY (All Saints) *Leic 10* **P** *Bp* **NSM** C W DOIDGE

BLACK BOURTON (St Mary the Virgin) Shill Valley and Broadshire *Ox*

BLACK NOTLEY (St Peter and St Paul) *Chelmsf 16* **P** *St Jo Coll Cam* **R** A G MORRISON

BLACK TORRINGTON (St Mary), Bradford w Cookbury, Thornbury and Highampton *Ex 9* **P** *DBP* **P-in-c** H J MAYELL

BLACKAWTON (St Michael) and Stoke Fleming *Ex 14* **P** *Bp and DBP (jt)* **V** R H WHITE

BLACKBIRD LEYS (Holy Family) *Ox 4* **P** *Bp* **V** J A RAMSAY

BLACKBOURNE *St E 9* **P** *Patr Bd* **TR** P M OLIVER, **TV** R H NORBURN, E S FOGDEN, **NSM** A DAY

BLACKBURN (Christ Church w St Matthew) *Blackb 2* **P** *Bp* **V** J G RILEY, **Hon Par Dn** L A RILEY

BLACKBURN (Church of the Redeemer) *Blackb 2* **P** *Bp* **V** S D BESSANT

BLACKBURN (Saviour) *Blackb 2* **P** *CPAS* **V** A K ROYLE

BLACKBURN (St Aidan) *Blackb 5* **P** *Bp* **V** J S McDONALD

BLACKBURN (St Andrew) Livesey *Blackb*

BLACKBURN (St Barnabas) *Blackb 2* **P** *Bp* **V** H H DANIEL

BLACKBURN (St Bartholomew) Ewood *Blackb*

BLACKBURN (St Gabriel) *Blackb 2* **P** *Bp* **V** J CORBYN, **C** B R McCONKEY

BLACKBURN (St James) *Blackb 2* **P** *Bp* **C** G D CLANE, E J H LANE

BLACKBURN (St Luke) w St Philip *Blackb 2* **P** *Bp* **V** P S GRIERSON

BLACKBURN (St Michael and All Angels) (Holy Trinity Worship Centre) w St John the Evangelist *Blackb 2* **P** *V Blackb* **V** S J LOCKE, **NSM** E G HUNT

BLACKBURN (St Silas) *Blackb 2* **P** *Trustees* **V** B STEVENSON

BLACKBURN (St Stephen) *Blackb 2* **P** *Trustees* **V** A A WELSH

BLACKBURN St Thomas (St Jude) *Blackb 2* **P** *Bp and Trustees (alt)* **V** P R HAPGOOD-STRICKLAND

BLACKDOWN (Holy Trinity) Beaminster Area *Sarum*

BLACKFEN (Good Shepherd) Lamorbey H Redeemer *Roch*

BLACKFORD (Holy Trinity) Wedmore w Theale and Blackford *B & W*

BLACKFORD (St John the Baptist) Rockcliffe and Blackford *Carl*

BLACKFORD (St Michael) Camelot Par *B & W*

BLACKFORDBY (St Margaret) *Leic 9* **P** *Bp* **V** M J PENNY

BLACKHALL (St Andrew) *Dur 3* **P** *Bp* **V** W E L BROAD

BLACKHAM (All Saints) Withyham St Mich *Chich*

BLACKHEATH (All Saints) *S'wark 3* **P** *V Lewisham St Mary* **V** H K BURGIN

BLACKHEATH (Ascension) *S'wark 3* **P** *V Lewisham St Mary* **P-in-c** P C KNAPPER, **Hon C** E R NEWNHAM, **NSM** J M PRESTON

BLACKHEATH (St John the Evangelist) *S'wark 1* **P** *CPAS* **V** J A de B WILMOT, **Hon C** J McALLEN, **NSM** A M BESWETHERICK

BLACKHEATH (St Martin) and Chilworth *Guildf 2* **P** *Bp* **V** E GIBBONS

BLACKHEATH (St Paul) *Birm 5* **P** *Bp* **V** D H GARNER, **C** C WAUDBY

BLACKHEATH PARK (St Michael and All Angels) *S'wark 1* **P** *Bp* **V** H L WHYTE, **C** D N LEAVER, **NSM** A SCOTT

BLACKHILL (St Aidan) *Dur 8* **P** *Bp* **V** *Vacant* Consett (01207) 502155

BLACKLAND (St Peter) Calne and Blackland *Sarum*

BLACKLANDS Hastings (Christchurch and St Andrew) *Chich 17* **P** *Ch Patr Trust* **V** P J LE SUEUR

BLACKLEY (Holy Trinity) *Man 5* **P** *Bp* **R** P A STAMP

BLACKLEY (St Andrew) *Man 5* **P** *Bp* **R** D J ERRIDGE, **C** T M MALONEY

BLACKLEY (St Paul) *Man 5* **P** *Bp* **R** M J ROBINSON

BLACKLEY (St Peter) *Man 5* **P** *D&C* **R** L St J R AITKEN

BLACKLEY White Moss (St Mark) *Man 5* **P** *D&C* **R** R LEATHERBARROW

BLACKMOOR (St Matthew) *Portsm 5* **P** *Earl of Selborne* **V** *Vacant* Bordon (01420) 473548

BLACKMORE (St Laurence) and Stondon Massey *Chelmsf 28* **P** *Bp* **V** I E CRAWFORD

BLACKPOOL (Christ Church w All Saints) (St Andrew) *Blackb 9* **P** *Bp and Trustees (jt)* **V** P GASCOIGNE

BLACKPOOL (Holy Cross) South Shore *Blackb 9* **P** *Bp* **V** S EDWARDS

BLACKPOOL (Holy Trinity) S Shore H Trin *Blackb*

BLACKPOOL (St John) *Blackb 9* **P** *Trustees* **V** R IMPEY, **C** A V WEST

BLACKPOOL (St Mark) *Blackb 9* **P** *CPAS* **V** E W GRAY, **C** D M HANKEY

BLACKPOOL (St Mary) South Shore *Blackb 9* **P** *Bp* **V** M F WOOD, **Hon C** N SMITH

BLACKPOOL (St Michael and All Angels) *Blackb 9* **P** *Bp* **V** D H JENKINS

BLACKPOOL St Paul *Blackb 9* **P** *Trustees* **V** C J ENTWISTLE, **C** P I IMPEY

BLACKPOOL (St Peter) S Shore St Pet *Blackb*

BLACKPOOL (St Stephen on the Cliffs) *Blackb 9* **P** *Bp, R Bispham All Hallows, and Ch Wardens (jt)* **V** P WALSH

BLACKPOOL (St Thomas) *Blackb 9* **P** *CPAS* **V** G A FISHER, **C** G P H NEWTON

BLACKPOOL (St Wilfrid) Mereside *Blackb 9* **P** *Bp* **V** P H HUDSON

BLACKROD (St Catherine) (Scot Lane School) *Man 11* **P** *V Bolton-le-Moors St Pet* **V** R C COOPER

BLACKTOFT (Holy Trinity) Howden TM *York*

BLACKWATER (St Barnabas) Arreton *Portsm*

BLACKWELL (All Saints) Darlington St Cuth *Dur*

BLACKWELL (St Catherine) The Lickey *Birm*

BLACKWELL (St Werburgh) *Derby 1* **P** *Bp* **P-in-c** M N W EDWARDS

BLADON (St Martin) w Woodstock *Ox 9* **P** *Duke of Marlborough* **R** R J HUMPHREYS

BLAGDON (St Andrew) w Compton Martin and Ubley *B & W 10* **P** *Bp and Sir John Wills Bt (jt)* **R** H A MATTHEWS, **NSM** G D TEAGUE

BLAGREAVES (St Andrew) *Derby 10* **P** *Bp, Churchwardens, and CPAS (jt)* **V** K W HORLESTON

BLAISDON (St Michael and All Angels) Westbury-on-Severn w Flaxley and Blaisdon *Glouc*

BLAKEDOWN (St James the Great) Churchill-in-Halfshire w Blakedown and Broome *Worc*

BLAKEMERE (St Leonard) Madley w Tyberton, Preston-on-Wye and Blakemere *Heref*

BLAKENALL HEATH (Christ Church) *Lich 6* **P** *Patr Bd* **TR** D P LINGWOOD, **TV** C D C THORPE, J P HERBERT, **C** C M MASON

BLAKENEY (All Saints) Newnham w Awre and Blakeney *Glouc*

BLAKENEY (St Nicholas w St Mary and St Thomas) w Cley, Wiveton, Glandford and Letheringsett *Nor 19* **P** *Bp and Keble Coll Ox (jt)* **R** N R MARTIN, **NSM** R H ROE

BLAKENHALL (St Luke) Wolv St Luke *Lich*

BLAKENHAM, GREAT (St Mary) and LITTLE (St Mary) w Baylham and Nettlestead *St E 1* **P** *Bp and MMCET (jt)* **R** *Vacant* Ipswich (01473) 623840

BLAKESLEY (St Mary) w Adstone and Maidford and Farthingstone *Pet 5* **P** *Sons of Clergy Corp, Bp, Hertf Coll Ox, and Capt R Grant-Renwick (by turn)* **R** A F RIDLEY

BLANCHLAND (St Mary's Abbey) w Hunstanworth and Edmundbyers and Muggleswick *Newc 3* **P** *D E Scott-Harden Esq, Lord Crewe's Trustees and D&C (alt)* **R** M A CUMING

BLANDFORD FORUM (St Peter and St Paul) and Langton Long *Sarum 7* **P** *Bp* **R** B W J LOMAX, **C** M W FEARN, **Hon C** M C MILES, **NSM** H J TRENCHARD

BLANDFORD ST MARY (St Mary) Spetisbury w Charlton Marshall and Blandford St Mary *Sarum*

BLANKNEY (St Oswald) Metheringham w Blankney and Dunston *Linc*

BLASTON (St Giles) Six Saints circa Holt *Leic*

BLATCHINGTON, EAST (St John the Evangelist) (St Peter) *Chich 19* **P** *Bp* **R** R S CRITTALL

BLATCHINGTON, WEST (St Peter) *Chich 4* **P** *Bp* **R** M S PORTEOUS, **NSM** J FOX

BLAXHALL (St Peter) Gt and Lt Glemham, Blaxhall etc *St E*

BLEADON (St Peter and St Paul) *B & W 11*   **P** *Guild of All So*   **R** D T PARKINSON

BLEAN (St Cosmus and St Damian) *Cant 3*   **P** *Master of Eastbridge Hosp*   **P-in-c** D R WITTS

BLEASBY (St Mary) Thurgarton w Hoveringham and Bleasby etc *S'well*

BLEASDALE (St Eadmor) Whitechapel w Admarsh-in-Bleasdale *Blackb*

BLEATARN (Chapel of Ease) Brough w Stainmore, Musgrave and Warcop *Carl*

BLEDINGTON (St Leonard) Westcote w Icomb and Bledington *Glouc*

BLEDLOW (Holy Trinity) w Saunderton and Horsenden *Ox 21*   **P** *Lord Carrington*   **R** C C G SHAW

BLEDLOW RIDGE (St Paul) W Wycombe w Bledlow Ridge, Bradenham and Radnage *Ox*

BLENDON (St James) Bexley St Jo *Roch*

BLENDON (St James the Great) *Roch 16*   **P** *The Crown*   **V** A KEELER

BLENDWORTH (Holy Trinity) w Chalton w Idsworth *Portsm 4*   **P** *Bp*   **P-in-c** R W REED

BLETCHINGDON (St Giles) Kirtlington w Bletchingdon, Weston etc *Ox*

BLETCHINGLEY (St Andrew) (St Mary) *S'wark 24*   **P** *Em Coll Cam*   **NSM** P H BRADSHAW

BLETCHLEY (St Mary) *Ox 25*   **P** *DBP*   **R** I J PUSEY,   **C** A MACKENZIE,   LI WICKINGS,   S J L CANSDALE

BLETCHLEY, NORTH (Whaddon Way Church) Conventional District *Ox 25*   **NSM** J M LAWRENCE

BLETSOE (St Mary) Riseley w Bletsoe *St Alb*

BLEWBURY (St Michael and All Angels), Hagbourne and Upton *Ox 18*   **P** *Bp*   **R** E G CLEMENTS,   **C** J H TOMLINSON

BLICKLING (St Andrew) Saxthorpe w Corpusty, Blickling, Oulton etc *Nor*

BLIDWORTH (St Mary) *S'well 2*   **P** *Ld Chan*   **V** R BEARDALL

BLIDWORTH, NEW (St Andrew) Blidworth *S'well*

BLINDLEY HEATH (St John the Evangelist) *S'wark 24*   **P** R GODSTONE   **P-in-c** H G C CLARKE

BLISLAND (St Protus and St Hyacinth) w St Breward *Truro 10*   **P** *SMF and D&C (alt)*   **R** F E HARRIS

BLISWORTH (St John the Baptist) *Pet 5*   **P** *MMCET*   **R** H BUNKER

BLITHFIELD (St Leonard) Abbots Bromley w Blithfield *Lich*

BLO' NORTON (St Andrew) Garboldisham w Blo' Norton, Riddlesworth etc *Nor*

BLOCKLEY (St Peter and St Paul) w Aston Magna and Bourton on the Hill *Glouc 10*   **P** *Lord Dulverton and DBP (jt)*   **V** G A NEALE

BLOFIELD (St Andrew) w Hemblington *Nor 4*   **P** *G&C Coll Cam*   **R** *Vacant* Norwich (01603) 713160

BLOOMSBURY (St George) w Woburn Square (Christ Church) *Lon 17*   **P** *Ld Chan*   **P-in-c** M DAY

BLORE RAY (St Bartholomew) Ilam w Blore Ray and Okeover *Lich*

BLOXHAM (Our Lady of Bloxham) w Milcombe and South Newington *Ox 5*   **P** *Ex Coll Ox and Eton Coll (jt)*   **V** J R A STROYAN

BLOXHOLME (St Mary) Digby *Linc*

BLOXWICH (All Saints) (Holy Ascension) *Lich 6*   **P** *Patr Bd*   **TR** S C RAWLING,   **TV** M H HAWKSWORTH,   **C** D A MAYO

BLOXWORTH (St Andrew) Red Post *Sarum*

BLUBBERHOUSES (St Andrew) Leathley w Farnley, Fewston and Blubberhouses *Bradf*

BLUCHER (St Cuthbert) Newburn *Newc*

BLUE BELL HILL (St Alban) Chatham St Steph *Roch*

BLUNDELLSANDS (St Michael) *Liv 5*   **P** *Trustees*   **V** P C N CONDER

BLUNDELLSANDS (St Nicholas) *Liv 5*   **P** *Trustees*   **V** R D BAKER

BLUNDESTON (St Mary) Somerleyton, Ashby, Fritton, Herringfleet etc *Nor*

BLUNHAM (St Edmund and St James) w Tempsford and Little Barford *St Alb 17*   **P** *Ball Coll Ox and The Crown (alt)*   **P-in-c** R D SEYMOUR-WHITELEY

BLUNSDONS, The (St Leonard) (St Andrew) *Bris 10*   **P** *Bp*   **R** J L WARE

BLUNTISHAM (St Mary) cum Earith w Colne and Woodhurst *Ely 11*   **P** *Ch Ch Ox*   **R** C BACKHOUSE

BLURTON (St Bartholomew) (St Alban) *Lich 18*   **P** *Bp*   **V** P J MOCKFORD,   **C** B M S CHAMBERS

BLYBOROUGH (St Alkmund) Glentworth Gp *Linc*

BLYFORD (All Saints) Halesworth w Linstead, Chediston, Holton etc *St E*

BLYMHILL (St Mary) w Weston-under-Lizard *Lich 2*   **P** *Earl of Bradf*   **P-in-c** J R McMANUS,   **Hon C** R C W DAMPIER

BLYTH (St Cuthbert) *Newc 1*   **P** *Bp*   **V** J G O'CONNOR

BLYTH (St Mary) *Newc 1*   **P** *Bp*   **V** B BENISON

BLYTH (St Mary and St Martin) *S'well 6*   **P** *Trin Coll Cam*   **V** R E WHEATON

BLYTHBURGH (Holy Trinity) w Reydon *St E 15*   **P** *Exors Earl of Stradbroke (2 turns), Sir Charles Blois Bt (1 turn)*   **V** H V EDWARDS,   **Hon C** A K E SORENSEN

BLYTON (St Martin) Corringham and Blyton Gp *Linc*

BOARHUNT (St Nicholas) Southwick w Boarhunt *Portsm*

BOARSTALL (St James) Brill, Boarstall, Chilton and Dorton *Ox*

BOBBING (St Bartholomew) Sittingbourne H Trin w Bobbing *Cant*

BOBBINGTON (Holy Cross) Wombourne w Trysull and Bobbington *Lich*

BOBBINGWORTH (St Germain) Fyfield, Moreton w Bobbingworth and Willingale etc *Chelmsf*

BOCKING (St Mary) *Chelmsf 16*   **P** *Abp*   **R** A M HAIG

BOCKING (St Peter) *Chelmsf 16*   **P** *Abp*   **V** M C S BEVER

BOCKLETON (St Michael) w Leysters *Heref 7*   **P** *Bp*   **P-in-c** C L BEEVERS

BOCONNOC (not known) Lostwithiel, St Winnow w St Nectan's Chpl etc *Truro*

BODDINGTON (St John the Baptist) Byfield w Boddington and Aston le Walls *Pet*

BODDINGTON (St Mary Magdalene) Staverton w Boddington and Tredington etc *Glouc*

BODENHAM (St Michael and All Angels) w Hope-under-Dinmore, Felton and Preston Wynne *Heref 4*   **P** *Bp*   **P-in-c** C M HILL

BODHAM (All Saints) Weybourne Gp *Nor*

BODIAM (St Giles) *Chich 20*   **P** *All So Coll Ox*   **P-in-c** R K BAKER

BODICOTE (St John the Baptist) *Ox 5*   **P** *New Coll Ox*   **V** C J BUTLAND

BODINNICK (St John) Lanteglos by Fowey *Truro*

BODLE STREET GREEN (St John the Evangelist) Warbleton and Bodle Street Green *Chich*

BODMIN (St Leonard) (St Petroc) w Lanhydrock and Lanivet *Truro 10*   **P** *DBP*   **TR** K ROGERS,   **TV** S R F DRAKELEY,   **NSM** F B J COOMBES

BODNEY (St Mary) Hilborough w Bodney *Nor*

BOGNOR (St Wilfrid) *Chich 1*   **P** *Abp*   **P-in-c** R P CALDER

BOLAM (St Andrew) Heighington *Dur*

BOLAM (St Andrew) w Whalton and Hartburn w Meldon *Newc 11*   **P** *Ld Chan (2 turns), J I K Walker Esq (1 turn), and D&C Dur (1 turn)*   **R** W A GOFTON

BOLAS MAGNA (St John the Baptist) Tibberton w Bolas Magna and Waters Upton *Lich*

BOLDMERE (St Michael) *Birm 9*   **P** *Birm Dioc Trustees*   **V** J D PIGOTT,   **C** J R WARREN

BOLDON (St Nicholas) *Dur 7*   **P** *Bp*   **R** T A MIDDLETON

BOLDON, EAST (St George) *Dur 7*   **P** *Bp*   **V** E G STEPHENSON

BOLDRE (St John the Baptist) w South Baddesley *Win 10*   **P** *Bp and Lord Teynham (jt)*   **V** G S S WATTS

BOLDRE, EAST (St Paul) Beaulieu and Exbury and E Boldre *Win*

BOLDRON (Mission Room) Startforth and Bowes and Rokeby w Brignall *Ripon*

BOLE (St Martin) N Wheatley, W Burton, Bole, Saundby, Sturton etc *S'well*

BOLINGBROKE (St Peter and St Paul) Marden Hill Gp *Linc*

BOLINGBROKE, NEW (St Peter) Sibsey w Frithville *Linc*

BOLLINGHAM (St Silas) Eardisley w Bollingham, Willersley, Brilley etc *Heref*

BOLLINGTON (Holy Trinity) Rostherne w Bollington *Ches*

BOLLINGTON (St John the Baptist) *Ches 13*   **P** *V Prestbury*   **V** M A WHETTER,   **C** S C DAVIS

BOLLINGTON CROSS (St Oswald) Bollington St Jo *Ches*

BOLNEY (St Mary Magdalene) *Chich 6*   **P** *K Coll Lon*   **V** A R HARCUS

BOLNHURST (St Dunstan) Keysoe w Bolnhurst and Lt Staughton *St Alb*

BOLSOVER (St Mary and St Laurence) *Derby 3*   **P** *Bp*   **V** J EASTON

BOLSTERSTONE (St Mary) *Sheff 7*   **P** *R B Rimington Wilson Esq*   **V** K J BARNARD,   **C** C E BARNARD,   **Hon C** P B MIALL

BOLTBY (Holy Trinity) Felixkirk w Boltby *York*
BOLTON (All Saints) *Carl 1*   **P** *V Morland w Thrimby etc*
P-in-c D C WOOD
BOLTON (All Saints) w Ireby and Uldale *Carl 6*   **P** *Earl of
Lonsdale, D&C, and Qu Coll Ox (by turn)*   **R** *Vacant Low
Ireby* (016973) 71307
BOLTON Breightmet (St James) *Man 16*   **P** *The Crown*
V J H SMITH
BOLTON Chapel (unknown) Whittingham and Edlingham w
Bolton Chapel *Newc*
BOLTON (St James w St Chrysostom) *Bradf 3*   **P** *Bp*
V B LOFTHOUSE,   **C** M A COOPER
BOLTON (St John the Evangelist) Top o' th' Moss *Man 16*
P *The Crown*   **V** H CALLAGHAN
BOLTON (St Thomas) *Man 9*   **P** *Trustees*   **V** D R OTTLEY,
NSM A PIERCE
BOLTON ABBEY (St Mary and St Cuthbert) *Bradf 7*
P *Duke of Devonshire*   **NSM** J A TURNBULL
BOLTON BY BOWLAND (St Peter and St Paul) w
Grindleton *Bradf 5*   **P** *Bp and V Hurst Green and
Mitton (jt)*   **R** D W MEWIS
BOLTON LE MOORS (St Bede) *Man 11*   **P** *Bp* **V** *Vacant*
Bolton (01204) 61496
BOLTON LE MOORS (St Matthew w St Barnabas) *Man 9*
P *Bp*   **V** E G F SWINNERTON
BOLTON LE MOORS (St Paul) (Emmanuel) *Man 9*
P *Patr Bd*   **TR** W J GASH,   **TV** M I McNAMARA
BOLTON LE MOORS (St Peter) *Man 9*   **P** *Bp*
V A WOLSTENCROFT,   **C** C E VANN
BOLTON LE MOORS (St Philip) *Man 9*   **P** *Bp and Hulme
Trustees (alt)*   **V** M W J HILLS,   **NSM** G BUSH
BOLTON LE MOORS (St Simon and St Jude) *Man 9*
P *Trustees*   **V** F G DOWNING
BOLTON LE SANDS (Holy Trinity) *Blackb 15*   **P** *Bp*
V R D HACKING,   **NSM** R FOSTER
BOLTON ON SWALE (St Mary) Easby w Brompton on
Swale and Bolton on Swale *Ripon*
BOLTON PERCY (All Saints) *York 1*   **P** *Abp*
P-in-c F A R MINAY
BOLTON-UPON-DEARNE (St Andrew the Apostle)
Sheff 12   **P** *Meynall Ch Trust*   **V** D G STAFFORD
BOLVENTOR (Holy Trinity) Altarnon w Bolventor, Laneast
and St Clether *Truro*
BOMERE HEATH (Mission Room) Leaton and Albrighton
w Battlefield *Lich*
BONBY (St Andrew) *Linc 6*   **P** *DBP* **V** *Vacant*
BONCHURCH (St Boniface) (St Boniface Old Church)
Portsm 7   **P** *Ch Patr Trust*   **R** A TEDMAN
BONDLEIGH (St James the Apostle) N Tawton, Bondleigh,
Sampford Courtenay etc *Ex*
BONINGALE (St Chad) *Lich 25*   **P** *MMCET*
V C W WOODS
BONNINGTON (St Rumwold) Aldington w Bonnington and
Bilsington *Cant*
BONSALL (St James the Apostle) Wirksworth *Derby*
BOOKER (St Birinus' Mission Church) High Wycombe *Ox*
BOOKHAM, GREAT (St Nicholas) *Guildf 10*   **P** *Bp*
R A C WARNER,   **NSM** M E BIDE
BOOKHAM, LITTLE (not known) Effingham w Lt
Bookham *Guildf*
BOOSBECK (St Aidan) w Moorsholm *York 17*   **P** *Abp*
V *Vacant* Guisborough (01287) 651728
BOOTHBY GRAFFOE (St Andrew) Graffoe Gp *Linc*
BOOTHBY PAGNELL (St Andrew) Ingoldsby *Linc*
BOOTHSTOWN (St Andrew's Church Institute) Worsley
Man
BOOTLE (Christ Church) *Liv 1*   **P** *Bp*   **V** T RICH
BOOTLE (St Leonard) *Liv 1*   **P** *Simeon's Trustees*
V C D BENGE
BOOTLE (St Mary w St Paul) *Liv 1*   **P** *Bp and Trustees (jt)*
V P H JORDAN,   **C** C I KIDD
BOOTLE (St Matthew) *Liv 1*   **P** *Bp*   **V** C H JONES
**BOOTLE (St Michael and All Angels), Corney, Whicham and
Whitbeck** *Carl 5*   **P** *Earl of Lonsdale*   **R** M C RIDYARD
BORASTON (not known) Burford I *Heref*
BORDEN (St Peter and St Paul) *Cant 14*   **P** *SMF*
V H I J SUCH
BORDESLEY (St Alban and St Patrick) *Birm 7*   **P** *Keble
Coll Ox* **V** *Vacant* 0121–440 4605
BORDESLEY (St Benedict) *Birm 10*   **P** *Keble Coll Ox*
V *Vacant* 0121–772 2726
BORDESLEY (St Oswald) Small Heath St Aid w St Greg
and St Oswald *Birm*
BORDESLEY GREEN (St Paul) *Birm 10*   **P** *The Crown*
V G C TURNER
BORDON (St Mark) Headley All SS *Guildf*
BOREHAM (St Andrew) *Chelmsf 9*   **P** *Bp*
P-in-c D W A KING

BOREHAM (St John the Evangelist) Bishopstrow and
Boreham *Sarum*
**BOREHAMWOOD (All Saints) (Holy Cross) (St Michael and
All Angels)** *St Alb 1*   **P** *Patr Bd*   **TR** S PURVIS,
TV P W WATSON,   M E PARTRIDGE,   **C** S D EDWARDS
BORLEY (not known) Pentlow, Foxearth, Liston and Borley
Chelmsf
BOROUGH GREEN (Good Shepherd) *Roch 9*   **P** *Bp*
V A J POWELL
BOROUGHBRIDGE (St James) Aldborough w
Boroughbridge and Roecliffe *Ripon*
BORROWASH (St Stephen's Chapel) Ockbrook *Derby*
BORROWDALE (St Andrew) *Carl 6*   **P** *V Crosthwaite*
P-in-c J T ROOKE
BORSTAL (St Matthew) *Roch 5*   **P** *V Rochester St Marg*
V J KING
BORWICK (St Mary) Warton St Oswald w Yealand Conyers
Blackb
**BOSBURY (Holy Trinity) w Wellington Heath, Stretton
Grandison, Ashperton and Canon Frome** *Heref 6*   **P** *Bp and
D&C (jt)*   **V** J R HAWKINS
BOSCASTLE w Davidstow *Truro 10*   **P** *Duchy of Cornwall
(1 turn), DBP (2 turns)*   **TR** J M AYLING,
Hon C S W DORAN
BOSCOMBE (St Andrew) Bourne Valley *Sarum*
BOSCOMBE (St Andrew) *Win 7*   **P** *Bp*   **V** N A CARTER
BOSCOMBE (St John) *Win 7*   **P** *Peache Trustees*
V G A TAYLOR,   **C** T D HANSON,   **NSM** P H DRAPER
BOSCOPPA *Truro 1*   **P** *Prime Min*   **V** P G J HUGHES
BOSHAM (Holy Trinity) *Chich 13*   **P** *Bp*   **V** T J INMAN,
NSM J V EMERSON
**BOSLEY (St Mary the Virgin) and North Rode (St Michael) w
Wincle (St Michael) and Wildboarclough (St Saviour)**
Ches 13   **P** *Bp, V Prestbury, and Earl of Derby (jt)*
P-in-c D W MOIR
BOSSALL (St Botolph) Sand Hutton *York*
BOSSINGTON (St James) Broughton, Bossington,
Houghton and Mottisfont *Win*
BOSTALL HEATH (St Andrew) *Roch 14*   **P** *DBP*
V S C VARNEY
BOSTON (St Botolph) (St Christopher) *Linc 20*   **P** *Bp*
C J A PATRICK
BOSTON SPA (St Mary) *York 1*   **P** *Ch Ch Ox*
V R M C SEED
BOTCHERBY (St Andrew) Carl St Aid and Ch Ch *Carl*
BOTESDALE (St Botolph) Redgrave cum Botesdale w
Rickinghall *St E*
BOTHAL (St Andrew) and Pegswood w Longhirst *Newc 11*
P *Bp*   **R** K M TRIVASSE
BOTHAMSALL (Our Lady and St Peter) Elkesley w
Bothamsall *S'well*
BOTHENHAMPTON (Holy Trinity) Bridport *Sarum*
BOTLEY (All Saints) *Portsm 1*   **P** *Bp*   **R** A N STAMP,
C K F ARVIDSSON
BOTLEY (St Peter and St Paul) N Hinksey and Wytham *Ox*
BOTLEYS and Lyne (Holy Trinity) *Guildf 11*   **P** *Bp*
V A B OLSEN
BOTOLPHS (St Botolph) Beeding and Bramber w Botolphs
Chich
BOTTESFORD (St Mary the Virgin) and Muston *Leic 3*
P *Duke of Rutland*   **P-in-c** G SPENCER,   **C** M TURNER
BOTTESFORD (St Peter) w Ashby *Linc 4*   **P** *Patr Bd*
TR M J BOUGHTON,   **TV** D C PEACOCK,   I ROBINSON,
C N H BALLARD,   **NSM** M L MILLSON
BOTTISHAM (Holy Trinity) and Lode with Longmeadow
Ely 6   **P** *Trin Coll Cam and Bp (jt)*   **V** *Vacant* Cambridge
(01223) 812367
BOTUS FLEMING (St Mary) Landrake w St Erney and
Botus Fleming *Truro*
BOUGHTON (All Saints) *Ely 16*   **P** *Bp* **R** *Vacant*
BOUGHTON (St John the Baptist) Pitsford w Boughton *Pet*
BOUGHTON (St Matthew) Ollerton w Boughton *S'well*
BOUGHTON ALUPH (All Saints) Westwell, Hothfield,
Eastwell and Boughton Aluph *Cant*
BOUGHTON ALUPH (St Christopher) as above
BOUGHTON MALHERBE (St Nicholas) Lenham w
Boughton Malherbe *Cant*
BOUGHTON MONCHELSEA (St Augustine) (St Peter)
Cant 15   **P** *Abp*   **V** R G DAVIS,   **C** R S WILKINSON
**BOUGHTON UNDER BLEAN (St Barnabas) (St Peter and
St Paul) w Dunkirk and Hernhill** *Cant 6*   **P** *Abp*
V J W R MOWLL
BOULGE (St Michael) w Burgh and Grundisburgh *St E 7*
P *Bp and DBP (jt)*   **R** N DAVIS
BOULMER (St Andrew) Longhoughton w Howick *Newc*
**BOULTHAM (Holy Cross) (St Helen) (St Mary Magdalene)
(St Matthew)** *Linc 15*   **P** *DBP*   **P-in-c** D J OSBOURNE,
C P TAYLOR

BOULTON (St Mary the Virgin) *Derby 15* **P** *Bp*
P-in-c R J HARRIS, **C** A G MURPHIE
BOUNDSTONE (Mission Church) Wrecclesham *Guildf*
BOURN (St Helena and St Mary) and Kingston w Caxton and
Longstowe *Ely 1* **P** *Bp, Ch Coll Cam, D&C Windsor, and*
Selw Coll Cam (jt) **R** J C B PEMBERTON,
NSM C M PEMBERTON
BOURNE (St Peter and St Paul) *Linc 13* **P** *DBP*
V J M WARWICK
BOURNE (St Thomas on the Bourne) *Guildf 3* **P** *Adn*
Surrey **V** J R H HUBBARD, **C** J R SINGLETON,
H S HOUSTON (nee LOVELL)
BOURNE, LOWER (St Martin) Bourne *Guildf*
BOURNE END (St John) Sunnyside w Bourne End *St Alb*
BOURNE END (St Mark) Hedsor and Bourne End *Ox*
BOURNE STREET (St Mary) Pimlico St Mary Graham
Terrace *Lon*
BOURNE VALLEY *Sarum 11* **P** *Patr Bd*
TR S P BURTWELL, **TV** P F B FISKE, I SYKES
BOURNEMOUTH (Christ Church) Westbourne Ch Ch CD
Win
BOURNEMOUTH (Holy Epiphany) *Win 7* **P** *Bp*
V R S COSSINS, **Hon C** D G KINGSLAND
BOURNEMOUTH Queen's Park (St Barnabas) Holdenhurst
Win
BOURNEMOUTH (St Alban) *Win 7* **P** *Bp*
P-in-c J C WHITE
BOURNEMOUTH (St Ambrose) *Win 7* **P** *Bp*
P-in-c G J WHEELER
BOURNEMOUTH (St Andrew) Bennett Road *Win 7*
P *Trustees* **V** A R ROAKE
BOURNEMOUTH (St Augustine) *Win 7* **P** *Bp*
P-in-c P MANHOOD
BOURNEMOUTH (St Clement) *Win 7* **P** *DBP*
P-in-c G J WHITING
BOURNEMOUTH (St Francis) *Win 7* **P** *CR*
V P G BERRETT, **NSM** A J JORDAN
BOURNEMOUTH (St John) (St Michael and All Angels)
Win 7 **P** *Bp and Exors R Ives Esq (jt)* **V** K J RANDALL,
C K E W MATHERS, **Hon C** K D MATHERS (nee
STEWART)
BOURNEMOUTH (St Luke) *Win 7* **P** *Bp* **V** S HOLMES
BOURNEMOUTH (St Mary) *Win 7* **P** *DBP* **V** *Vacant*
Bournemouth (01202) 398376
BOURNEMOUTH (St Peter) (St Swithun) (St Stephen) and
Holy Trinity *Win 7* **P** *Patr Bd* **TR** D H R JONES,
TV J H S STEVEN, R C N HARGER, **Hon C** H G JAMES
BOURNVILLE (St Andrew) Weston-super-Mare St Andr
Bournville *B & W*
BOURNVILLE (St Francis) *Birm 8* **P** *Bp*
V K WITHINGTON, **NSM** H A AYKROYD
BOURTON (Holy Trinity) Wenlock *Heref*
BOURTON (St George) Upper Stour *Sarum*
BOURTON (St James) Shrivenham w Watchfield and
Bourton *Ox*
BOURTON (St Peter) w Frankton and Stretton on Dunsmore
w Princethorpe *Cov 6* **P** *Bp (2 turns), Simeon's Trustees*
(1 turn), and Mrs J H Shaw-Fox (1 turn) **R** R C ROGERS
BOURTON, GREAT (All Saints) Cropredy w Gt Bourton
and Wardington *Ox*
BOURTON ON THE HILL (St Lawrence) Blockley w Aston
Magna and Bourton on the Hill *Glouc*
BOURTON-ON-THE-WATER (St Lawrence) w Clapton
Glouc 15 **P** *Wadh Coll Ox* **P-in-c** E A FARLEY
BOVEY, NORTH (St John the Baptist) Moretonhampstead,
N Bovey and Manaton *Ex*
BOVEY TRACEY (St John the Evangelist) w Chudleigh
Knighton and Heathfield *Ex 11* **P** *DBP and Guild of*
All So (jt) **P-in-c** D J STANTON
BOVEY TRACEY (St Peter and St Paul and St Thomas of
Canterbury) w Hennock *Ex 11* **P** *Prime Min (2 turns),*
MMCET (1 turn) **V** C H SARALIS, **NSM** C V L CURD
BOVINGDON (St Lawrence) *St Alb 3* **P** *Ch Soc Trust*
V T J MARSHALL, **Hon C** R H METCALFE
BOW (Holy Trinity) (All Hallows) *Lon 7* **P** *Patr Bd*
TR J M PEET
BOW (St Bartholomew) w Broad Nymet *Ex 2* **P** *DBP*
R J C HALL
BOW (St Mary) w Bromley (St Leonard) *Lon 7* **P** *Bp*
R G W GARNER, **NSM** D F WAXHAM
BOW BRICKHILL (All Saints) Gt Brickhill w Bow Brickhill
and Lt Brickhill *Ox*
BOW COMMON (St Paul) *Lon 7* **P** *Bp* **P-in-c** D G ROSS
BOWBROOK NORTH: Feckenham and Hanbury and Stock
and Bradley *Worc 8* **P** *Bp and D&C (jt)*
R E J ROTHWELL

BOWBROOK SOUTH: Crowle w Bredicot and Hadzor w
Oddingley and Tibberton and Himbleton and Huddington
Worc 8 **P** *Bp, D&C, R J G Berkeley Esq, and*
J F Bennett Esq (jt) **R** W D S WELLS
BOWBURN (Christ the King) Cassop cum Quarrington *Dur*
BOWDEN, GREAT (St Peter and St Paul) w Welham,
Glooston and Cranoe *Leic 4* **P** *Bp and E Brudenell Esq*
P-in-c I W Y GEMMELL
BOWDEN, LITTLE (St Hugh) Market Harborough
Transfiguration and Lt Bowden *Leic*
BOWDEN, LITTLE (St Nicholas) as above
BOWDEN HILL (St Anne) Lacock w Bowden Hill *Bris*
BOWDON (St Luke) (St Mary the Virgin) *Ches 10* **P** *Bp*
V K E HINE
BOWERCHALKE (Holy Trinity) Chalke Valley W *Sarum*
BOWERS GIFFORD (St John) (St Margaret) w North
Benfleet *Chelmsf 6* **P** *Em Coll Cam and Brig R H C Bryhers*
(alt) **R** *Vacant* Basildon (01268) 552219
BOWES (St Giles) Startforth and Bowes and Rokeby w
Brignall *Ripon*
BOWES PARK (St Michael-at-Bowes) Wood Green St Mich
w Bounds Green St Gabr etc *Lon*
BOWLEE (St Thomas) Rhodes *Man*
BOWLING (St John) *Bradf 2* **P** *V Bradford* **V** H K ASTIN
BOWLING (St Stephen) *Bradf 2* **P** *CPAS* **V** *Vacant*
Bradford (01274) 720784
BOWNESS (St Michael) *Carl 3* **P** *Earl of Lonsdale*
P-in-c J T SPENCE
BOWTHORPE (St Michael) *Nor 3* **P** *Bp and CPAS (jt)*
V R J SIMPSON
BOX (St Barnabas) Minchinhampton *Glouc*
BOX (St Thomas a Becket) w Hazlebury and Ditteridge
Bris 9 **P** *Bp* **R** J R FLORY, **NSM** J AYERS,
J D POTTER
BOX HILL (St Andrew) Headley w Box Hill *Guildf*
BOXFORD (St Andrew) Welford w Wickham and Gt
Shefford, Boxford etc *Ox*
BOXFORD (St Mary) *St E 12* **P** *The Crown*
R E C HAMLYN
BOXGROVE (St Mary and St Blaise) Chich *3* **P** *Duke of*
Richmond and Gordon **V** J M HASELOCK
BOXLEY (St Mary the Virgin and All Saints) w Detling
Cant 13 **P** *Abp* **V** M M BRADSHAW
BOXMOOR (St John the Evangelist) *St Alb 3* **P** *Bp*
P-in-c P V HUGHES, **C** J M HALLOWS,
NSM E J HUGHES
BOXTED (Holy Trinity) Glem Valley United Benefice *St E*
BOXTED (St Peter) w Langham *Chelmsf 18* **P** *Bp and Duchy*
of Lanc (alt) **R** J A CARDELL-OLIVER
BOXWELL (St Mary the Virgin), Leighterton, Didmarton,
Oldbury-on-the-Hill and Sopworth *Glouc 16* **P** *Duke of*
Beaufort and J F B Hutley Esq (alt)
R N C J MULHOLLAND
BOXWORTH (St Peter) *Ely 1* **P** *G E P Thornhill Esq*
R H A MOSEDALE
BOYATT WOOD (St Peter) *Win 9* **P** *Bp*
V D WALFORD, **NSM** A WALFORD
BOYLESTONE (St John the Baptist) Ch Broughton w
Barton Blount, Boylestone etc *Derby*
BOYNE HILL (All Saints) *Ox 13* **P** *Bp* **V** N J BROWN
BOYNTON (St Andrew) Rudston w Boynton and Kilham
York
BOYTHORPE (St Francis) Chesterfield St Aug *Derby*
BOYTON (Holy Name), North Tamerton, Werrington w St
Giles-in-the-Heath and Virginstow *Truro 9* **P** *Duke of*
Cornwall, MMCET, Ld Chan, and R Williams Esq
(by turn) **R** A J M BROWNRIDGE
BOYTON (St Andrew) w Capel St Andrew and Hollesley
St E 7 **P** *Mary Warner Charity and DBP (alt)*
R J M GATES
BOYTON (St Mary the Virgin) Ashton Gifford *Sarum*
BOZEAT (St Mary) w Easton Maudit *Pet 6* **P** *Bp and*
Marquess of Northn (alt) **V** P H BLIGH
BRABOURNE (St Mary the Blessed Virgin) w Smeeth
Cant 12 **P** *Abp* **P-in-c** J W TIPPING, **Hon C** R L LE
ROSSIGNOL
BRACEBOROUGH (St Margaret) Uffington Gp *Linc*
BRACEBRIDGE (All Saints) *Linc 15* **P** *Mrs B M Ellison-*
Lendrum **V** A J KERSWILL
BRACEBRIDGE HEATH (St John the Evangelist) *Linc 15*
P *Bp* **V** I W MACKIE, **NSM** J M CLARK
BRACEBY (St Margaret) Sapperton w Braceby *Linc*
BRACEWELL (St Michael) Barnoldswick w Bracewell *Bradf*
BRACKENFIELD (Holy Trinity) Ashover and Brackenfield
Derby
BRACKLEY (St Peter w St James) *Pet 1* **P** *Bp*
V P C WOODWARD

BRACKNELL (Holy Trinity) *Ox 11* **P** *Bp*
TR C G CLARKE, **TV** C H REDGRAVE, C ALLSOPP,
C A J DUFF, T D COCKELL, H F COCKELL
BRACON ASH (St Nicholas) Wreningham *Nor*
BRADBOURNE (All Saints) Wirksworth *Derby*
BRADDAN (St Brendan) *S & M 2* **P** *Bp* **V** D WHITWORTH
BRADDEN (St Michael) Greens Norton w Bradden and
Lichborough *Pet*
**BRADELEY (St Mary and All Saints), Church Eaton and
Moreton** *Lich 15* **P** *Bp and V Gnosall (jt)* **R** T W B FOX
BRADENHAM (St Botolph) W Wycombe w Bledlow Ridge,
Bradenham and Radnage *Ox*
BRADENHAM, WEST (St Andrew) Shipdham w E and W
Bradenham *Nor*
BRADENSTOKE (St Mary) Lyneham w Bradenstoke *Sarum*
BRADFIELD (St Andrew) and Stanford Dingley *Ox 12*
P *Ch Soc Trust* **P-in-c** H W ELLIS
BRADFIELD (St Clare) Cockfield w Bradfield St Clare,
Felsham etc *St E*
BRADFIELD (St George) Gt and Lt Whelnetham w
Bradfield St George *St E*
BRADFIELD (St Giles) Trunch *Nor*
BRADFIELD (St Laurence) Mistley w Manningtree and
Bradfield *Chelmsf*
BRADFIELD (St Nicholas) *Sheff 7* **P** *V Ecclesfield*
R G V LETTS
BRADFIELD COMBUST (All Saints) Hawstead and
Nowton w Stanningfield etc *St E*
BRADFORD (All Saints) Black Torrington, Bradf w
Cookbury etc *Ex*
BRADFORD (St Augustine) Undercliffe *Bradf 3* **P** *V Bradf*
C N R SHORT
BRADFORD (St Clement) *Bradf 3* **P** *Bp (2 turns) and
Trustees (1 turn)* **P-in-c** D P BANBURY,
NSM M HARGREAVES
BRADFORD (St Columba w St Andrew) *Bradf 2* **P** *Bp*
V C I JUDD
BRADFORD (St Giles) w Oake, Hillfarrance and Heathfield
B & W 19 **P** *Bp and M V Spurway Esq (jt)*
R K G X TINGAY
BRADFORD (St Oswald) Chapel Green *Bradf 2* **P** *Bp*
P-in-c W HOLLIDAY, D J PISIORHO, C D J POOLE
BRADFORD (St Wilfrid) Lidget Green *Bradf 2* **P** *Bp*
V P M BILTON, **NSM** G A BRIGHOUSE
BRADFORD, WEST (St Catherine) Waddington *Bradf*
**BRADFORD ABBAS (St Mary the Virgin) and Thornford w
Beer Hackett** *Sarum 4* **P** *Major K S D Wingfield Digby and
Win Coll (alt)* **R** D A K GREENE
BRADFORD-ON-AVON (Christ Church) *Sarum 17*
P *V Bradf H Trin* **V** D R R SEYMOUR,
NSM B F CHAPMAN
BRADFORD-ON-AVON (Holy Trinity) *Sarum 17* **P** *D&C*
V W A MATTHEWS, **C** R J PRESS
BRADFORD ON TONE (St Giles) Bradf w Oake,
Hillfarrance and Heathfield *B & W*
**BRADFORD PEVERELL (Church of the Assumption),
Stratton, Frampton and Sydling St Nicholas** *Sarum 2*
P *Win Coll and Bp (alt)* **R** K J SCOTT, **NSM** S C CHALK
BRADING (St Mary the Virgin) w Yaverland *Portsm 7*
P *Hon Mrs I S T Monck and Trin Coll Cam (jt)* **R** *Vacant*
Isle of Wight (01983) 407262
BRADLEY (All Saints) Hulland, Atlow, Bradley and
Hognaston *Derby*
BRADLEY (All Saints) The Candover Valley *Win*
BRADLEY (St George) Gt and Lt Coates w Bradley *Linc*
BRADLEY (St John the Baptist) Bowbrook N *Worc*
BRADLEY (St Martin) *Lich 9* **P** *Baldwin Pugh Trustees*
V R M WALKER
BRADLEY (St Mary) Cononley w Bradley *Bradf*
BRADLEY (St Thomas) *Wakef 5* **P** *Bp* **V** D R WARD
BRADLEY, GREAT (St Mary the Virgin) Haverhill w
Withersfield, the Wrattings etc *St E*
BRADLEY, LITTLE (All Saints) as above
BRADLEY, NORTH (St Nicholas) Southwick and Heywood
Sarum 17 **P** *Win Coll* **P-in-c** P M POTTER
BRADLEY, WEST (not known) Baltonsborough w Butleigh
and W Bradley *B & W*
BRADLEY-LE-MOORS (St Leonard) Alton w Bradley-le-
Moors and Oakamoor w Cotton *Lich*
BRADLEY STOKE (Christ the King) Stoke Gifford *Bris*
BRADMORE (Mission Room) Bunny w Bradmore *S'well*
BRADNINCH (St Disen) and Clyst Hydon *Ex 4* **P** *D&C and
D&C Windsor (jt)* **R** D L D ROBOTTOM
BRADNOP (Mission Church) Ipstones w Berkhamsytch and
Onecote w Bradnop *Lich*
BRADOC (Blessed Virgin Mary) Liskeard, St Keyne, St
Pinnock, Morval etc *Truro*
BRADPOLE (Holy Trinity) Bridport *Sarum*

BRADSHAW (St John the Evangelist) *Wakef 4* **P** *Bp*
V C H AYNES
BRADSHAW (St Maxentius) *Man 16* **P** *V Bolton-le-Moors
St Pet* **V** D M DUNN, **C** S C EDWARDS, S H AWORTH
BRADSTONE (St Nonna) Kelly w Bradstone *Ex*
BRADWELL (St Barnabas) *Derby 2* **P** *D&C Lich*
V J VAUGHAN
BRADWELL (St Barnabas) Wolstanton *Lich*
BRADWELL (St Laurence and Methodist
United) Stantonbury and Willen *Ox*
BRADWELL (St Nicholas) *Nor 6* **P** *Bp* **R** R J TUCK
BRADWELL, NEW (St James) Stantonbury and Willen *Ox*
BRADWELL AND PATTISWICK (Holy Trinity) Stisted w
Bradwell and Pattiswick *Chelmsf*
BRADWELL ON SEA (St Thomas) *Chelmsf 11* **P** *Bp*
P-in-c M W WALLACE
BRADWORTHY (St John the Baptist) *Ex 9* **P** *The Crown*
P-in-c N P G LAST
**BRAFFERTON (St Peter) w Pilmoor, Myton on Swale and
Thormanby** *York 5* **P** *Abp and Sir Anthony Milnes
Coates (jt)* **V** J D HARRIS-DOUGLAS
BRAFIELD ON THE GREEN (St Laurence) Gt and Lt
Houghton w Brafield on the Green *Pet*
BRAILES (St George) *Cov 9* **P** *Provost and Chapter*
V N J MORGAN, **NSM** J W ROLFE
**BRAILSFORD (All Saints) w Shirley and Osmaston w
Edlaston** *Derby 8* **P** *Bp, Earl Ferrers, and Sir Peter
Walker-Okeover, Bt (by turn)* **R** I ALDERSLEY,
NSM C L JOHNSON
BRAINTREE (St Michael) *Chelmsf 16* **P** *Ch Trust Fund
Trust* **V** B DAVIES, **C** A McHAFFIE
BRAINTREE (St Paul) *Chelmsf 16* **P** *Ch Trust Fund Trust*
V S R LLOYD
BRAISHFIELD (All Saints) Michelmersh, Timsbury, Farley
Chamberlayne etc *Win*
BRAITHWAITE (St Herbert) Thornthwaite cum Braithwaite
and Newlands *Carl*
BRAITHWELL (St James) Bramley and Ravenfield w
Hooton Roberts etc *Sheff*
BRAMBER (St Nicholas) Beeding and Bramber w Botolphs
Chich
BRAMBLETON (not known) Bourne *Guildf*
BRAMCOTE (St Michael and All Angels) *S'well 7* **P** *CPAS*
NSM D EDINBOROUGH, J HENDERSON, J P SMITHURST
BRAMDEAN (St Simon and St Jude) Hinton Ampner w
Bramdean and Kilmeston *Win*
BRAMDEAN COMMON (Church in the Wood) as above
BRAMERTON (St Peter) Rockland St Mary w Hellington,
Bramerton etc *Nor*
BRAMFIELD (St Andrew) Thorington w Wenhaston,
Bramfield & Walberswick *St E*
BRAMFIELD (St Andrew) w Stapleford and Waterford
St Alb 8 **P** *R M A Smith Esq and Grocers' Co (alt)*
R G D BOOKER
BRAMFORD (St Mary the Virgin) *St E 1* **P** *D&C Cant*
P-in-c R J DEDMAN
BRAMHALL (St Michael and All Angels) (Hall Chapel)
Ches 17 **P** *Trustees* **C** R J ISHERWOOD, T S McCABE,
NSM L M DADSON
BRAMHAM (All Saints) *York 1* **P** *G Lane Fox Esq*
V J R D SHAW
BRAMHOPE (St Giles) *Ripon 7* **P** *Trustees* **V** J R WARD
BRAMLEY (Holy Trinity) and Grafham *Guildf 2*
P *Ld Chan* **V** M F H GODWIN
**BRAMLEY (St Francis) and Ravenfield w Hooton Roberts and
Braithwell** *Sheff 6* **P** *Patr Bd* **R** D S WALKER,
TV P J HOPPER, **C** C P SMITH
BRAMLEY (St James) *Win 4* **P** *Qu Coll Ox*
V R C TOOGOOD
BRAMLEY (St Peter) *Ripon 6* **P** *DBP* **TV** S P RANDALL
BRAMPFORD SPEKE (St Peter) Thorverton, Cadbury,
Upton Pyne etc *Ex*
BRAMPTON (St Mark) *Derby 5* **P** *Bp* **V** *Vacant*
Chesterfield (01246) 234015
**BRAMPTON (St Martin) and Farlam and Castle Carrock w
Cumrew** *Carl 2* **P** *Bp, D&C, Mrs J M Matthews, and Mrs
S C Dean (jt)* **R** N N STEADMAN, **C** G SMITH
BRAMPTON (St Mary Magdalene) *Ely 9* **P** *Bp*
R M R GREENFIELD
BRAMPTON (St Peter) Buxton w Oxnead, Lammas and
Brampton *Nor*
BRAMPTON (St Peter) Hundred River *St E*
BRAMPTON (St Thomas the Martyr) *Derby 5* **P** *Bp*
R C J C FRITH, **C** B J H PORTER, S R PITE,
P D L WILKINSON, **NSM** J A HENDERSON
BRAMPTON, OLD (Cutthorpe Institute) Old Brampton and
Loundsley Green *Derby*

**BRAMPTON, OLD (St Peter and St Paul) and Loundsley
Green** *Derby 5* **P** *Bp* **TR** PJBOWLES, **TV** MAYATES
BRAMPTON ABBOTTS (St Michael) Ross w Brampton
Abbotts, Bridstow, Peterstow etc *Heref*
BRAMPTON ASH (St Mary) w Dingley and Braybrooke
Pet 11 **P** *Earl Spencer (2 turns), DBP (1 turn)*
R RJCHAPMAN, **NSM** NMCLARKE
BRAMPTON BIERLOW (Christ Church) *Sheff 12*
P *V Wath-upon-Dearne* **V** CWMBALDOCK
BRAMPTON BRYAN (St Barnabas) Wigmore Abbey *Heref*
BRAMSHALL (St Laurence) Uttoxeter w Bramshall *Lich*
BRAMSHAW (St Peter) and Landford w Plaitford *Sarum 11*
P *Bp and D&C (alt)* **R** DPCLACEY
BRAMSHILL (Mission Church) Eversley *Win*
BRAMSHOTT (St Mary the Virgin) and Liphook *Portsm 5*
P *Qu Coll Ox* **R** RAEWBANK, **NSM** FJHEAL
BRANCASTER (St Mary the Virgin) Hunstanton St Mary w
Ringstead Parva etc *Nor*
BRANCEPETH (St Brandon) *Dur 2* **P** *Bp*
NSM RMAYLAND
BRANCEPETH, NEW (St Catherine) Brandon *Dur*
BRANDESBURTON (St Mary) *York 12* **P** *St Jo Coll Cam*
R *Vacant* Hornsea (01964) 542015
BRANDESTON (All Saints) w Kettleburgh *St E 18* **P** *Capt
J L Round-Turner (2 turns), C Austin Esq (1 turn)*
P-in-c RJDIXON, **NSM** PGVELLACOTT
BRANDLESHOLME (St Francis House Chapel) Elton All
SS *Man*
BRANDON (Chapel) Barkston and Hough Gp *Linc*
BRANDON (St John the Evangelist) *Dur 2* **P** *R Brancepeth*
V DBGODSELL, **C** PBROWN
BRANDON (St Peter) and Santon Downham w Elveden
St E 11 **P** *Exors Earl of Iveagh* **R** *Vacant* Thetford
(01842) 811907
BRANDON PARVA (All Saints) Barnham Broom *Nor*
BRANDSBY (All Saints) Crayke w Brandsby and Yearsley
York
BRANDWOOD (St Bede) *Birm 4* **P** *Bp* **V** NHBENSON,
NSM HCBENSON
BRANKSEA ISLAND (St Mary) Parkstone St Pet w
Branksea and St Osmund *Sarum*
BRANKSOME (St Aldhelm) (St Francis) *Sarum 8* **P** *Bp*
P-in-c SDLAKE
BRANKSOME (St Clement) (St Barnabas) *Sarum 8*
P *MMCET* **V** MGBOULTER
BRANKSOME PARK (All Saints) *Sarum 8* **P** *MMCET*
V *Vacant* Poole (01202) 708202
BRANSCOMBE (St Winifred) Beer and Branscombe *Ex*
BRANSDALE (St Nicholas) Kirkbymoorside w Gillamoor,
Farndale & Bransdale *York*
BRANSFORD (St John the Baptist) Alfrick, Lulsley,
Suckley, Leigh and Bransford *Worc*
BRANSGORE (St Mary the Virgin) *Win 8*
P *P W J Jesson Esq* **V** PCELKINS
BRANSHOLME (St John) Sutton St Jas and Wawne *York*
BRANSTON (All Saints) w Nocton and Potterhanworth
Linc 18 **P** *Stowe Sch (2 turns), Ld Chan (1 turn) and Br
Field ProductsLtd (1 turn)* **R** DFREAGON
BRANSTON (St Saviour) *Lich 19* **P** *Simeon's Trustees*
V DBSIMMONDS
BRANSTON BY BELVOIR (St Guthlac) High Framland
Par *Leic*
BRANT BROUGHTON (St Helen) and Beckingham *Linc 23*
P *Bp, Exors Sir Richard Sutton, Bt, and Rev J R H and Rev
H C Thorold (by turn)* **R** *Vacant* Loveden (01400) 72449
BRANT ROAD (Church Centre) Bracebridge *Linc*
BRANTHAM (St Michael and All Angels) w Stutton *St E 5*
P *Bp and Em Coll Cam (alt)* **R** ASJONES
BRANTINGHAM (All Saints) Elloughton and Brough w
Brantingham *York*
BRANXTON (St Paul) *Newc 12* **P** *Abp* **V** RWHOWE
BRASSINGTON (St James) Wirksworth *Derby*
BRASTED (St Martin) *Roch 8* **P** *Abp*
P-in-c SMBANNISTER
BRATHAY (Holy Trinity) Ambleside w Brathay *Carl*
BRATOFT (St Peter and St Paul) w Irby-in-the-Marsh
Linc 8 **P** *Bp* **P-in-c** TSTEELE
BRATTLEBY (St Cuthbert) Aisthorpe w Scampton w
Thorpe le Fallows etc *Linc*
BRATTON (St James the Great) (Oratory) *Sarum 14*
P *V Westbury* **V** *Vacant* Bratton (01380) 830374
BRATTON CLOVELLY (St Mary the Virgin) Okehampton
w Inwardleigh, Bratton Clovelly etc *Ex*
BRATTON FLEMING (St Peter) Shirwell, Loxhore,
Kentisbury, Arlington, etc *Ex*
BRATTON ST MAUR (St Nicholas) Bruton and Distr
B & W

**BRAUGHING (St Mary the Virgin) w Furneux Pelham and
Stocking Pelham** *St Alb 4* **P** *Bp and Lord Hamilton (alt)*
R RHNOKES
BRAUNSTON (All Saints) Daventry, Ashby St Ledgers,
Braunston etc *Pet*
BRAUNSTON (All Saints) Oakham, Hambleton, Egleton,
Braunston and Brooke *Pet*
BRAUNSTONE (St Peter) (St Crispin) *Leic 12* **P** *Bp*
TR RKDANIEL
BRAUNTON (St Brannock) *Ex 15* **P** *Bp* **V** RPREEVE,
C IJWHEATLEY, **Hon C** LABUTTLE
BRAXTED, GREAT (All Saints) Tolleshunt Knights w
Tiptree and Gt Braxted *Chelmsf*
BRAXTED, LITTLE (St Nicholas) Wickham Bishops w Lt
Braxted *Chelmsf*
BRAY (St Michael) and Braywood *Ox 13* **P** *Bp*
V GDREPATH, **C** JFRAMSBOTTOM
BRAY, HIGH (All Saints) S Molton w Nymet St George,
High Bray etc *Ex*
BRAYBROOKE (All Saints) Brampton Ash w Dingley and
Braybrooke *Pet*
BRAYDESTON (St Michael) Brundall w Braydeston and
Postwick *Nor*
BRAYTON (St Wilfrid) *York 6* **P** *Abp*
TR DHREYNOLDS, **TV** RMITCHINSON,
PEGRIGSBY, **NSM** KMANNERS
BREADSALL (All Saints) *Derby 13* **P** *Miss A I M Harpur-
Crewe* **P-in-c** RTSHORTHOUSE
BREADSTONE (St Michael and All Angels) Berkeley w
Wick, Breadstone and Newport *Glouc*
BREAGE (St Breaca) w Germoe *Truro 4* **P** *The Crown*
NSM GEGRIFFITHS
BREAM (St James) *Glouc 4* **P** *Bp* **V** AGKENDALL,
NSM GMPEMBERY
BREAMORE (St Mary) *Win 8* **P** *Sir Westrow Hulse, Bt*
P-in-c GFWNEWELL
BREAN (St Bridget) Berrow and Breane *B & W*
BREARTON (St John the Baptist) Knaresborough *Ripon*
BREASTON (St Michael) Wilne and Draycott w Breaston
Derby
BRECKLES (St Margaret) Caston w Griston, Merton,
Thompson etc *Nor*
BREDBURY (St Barnabas) *Ches 16* **P** *V Bredbury St Mark*
V CRWINDLE
BREDBURY (St Mark) *Ches 16* **P** *Bp* **V** NTOPPING
BREDE (St George) w Udimore *Chich 20* **P** *Bp and Mrs
M E Crook (alt)* **R** RWCOTTON
**BREDENBURY (St Andrew) w Grendon Bishop and Wacton,
Edwyn Ralph, Collington, Thornbury, Pencombe and
Marston Stannett and Little Cowarne** *Heref 2* **P** *DBP,
V Bromyard, and Lt-Col H H Barneby (jt)*
R CIFLETCHER
BREDFIELD (St Andrew) Ufford w Bredfield and Haseketon
St E
**BREDGAR (St John the Baptist) w Bicknor and Frinsted w
Wormshill and Milsted** *Cant 17* **P** *Abp, Lord Kingsdown,
M Nightingale Esq, and S McCandlish Esq (jt)*
R PNSHAYNES
BREDHURST (St Peter) S Gillingham *Roch*
BREDICOT (St James the Less) Bowbrook S *Worc*
BREDON (St Giles) w Bredon's Norton *Worc 4* **P** *Bp*
R CJRIDOUT
BREDON'S NORTON (not known) Bredon w Bredon's
Norton *Worc*
BREDWARDINE (St Andrew) Cusop w Clifford,
Hardwicke, Bredwardine etc *Heref*
BREDY, LITTLE (St Michael and All Angels) Bride Valley
Sarum
**BREEDON-ON-THE-HILL (St Mary and St Hardulph) cum
Isley Walton and Worthington** *Leic 9* **P** *D A G Shields Esq
and Ch Coll Cam (alt)* **R** SJDFOSTER,
NSM JWADAWSON
**BREIGHTMET Top o' th' Moss (St John the
Evangelist)** Bolton St John *Man*
BREINTON (St Michael) (Mission Hall) *Heref 4* **P** *Bp*
V *Vacant* Hereford (01432) 273447
BREMHILL (St Martin) Derry Hill w Bremhill and Foxham
Sarum
BRENCHLEY (All Saints) *Roch 11* **P** *D&C Cant*
V JFBOYCE
BRENDON (St Brendon) Lynton, Brendon, Countisbury,
Lynmouth etc *Ex*
BRENT, EAST (The Blessed Virgin Mary) Brent Knoll, E
Brent and Lympsham *B & W*
BRENT, SOUTH (St Petroc) and Rattery *Ex 13* **P** *Bp and
Sir R V Carew, Bt (jt)* **V** JHHARPER
BRENT ELEIGH (St Mary) Monks Eleigh w Chelsworth
and Brent Eleigh etc *St E*

BRENT KNOLL (St Michael) and East Brent and Lympsham
B & W 1 **P** *Adn Wells (1 turn), Bp (2 turns)*
R J S WELLS
BRENT PELHAM (St Mary the Virgin) Hormead, Wyddial, Anstey, Brent Pelham etc *St Alb*
BRENTFORD (St Paul w St Lawrence and St George) (St Faith) *Lon 11* **P** *Bp* **TV** P G WHITESIDE,
C M J BULMAN, **Hon C** J S BOWDEN
BRENTOR (Christ Church) Lydford and Brent Tor *Ex*
BRENTOR (St Michael) as above
BRENTRY (St Mark) Henbury *Bris*
BRENTS (St John the Evangelist) and Davington w Oare and Luddenham, The *Cant 6* **P** *Abp and Ld Chan (alt)*
V *Vacant* Faversham (01795) 533272
BRENTWOOD (St George the Martyr) *Chelmsf 7* **P** *DBP*
V G F JENKINS
BRENTWOOD (St Thomas) *Chelmsf 7* **P** *DBP*
P-in-c R B WHITE, **C** P C BANKS
BRENZETT (St Eanswith) Appledore w Brookland, Fairfield, Brenzett etc *Cant*
BRERETON (St Michael) *Lich 3* **P** *R Rugeley* **V** *Vacant* Rugeley (01889) 582466
BRERETON (St Oswald) w Swettenham *Ches 11* **P** *DBP and MMCET (jt)* **R** J M INNES
BRESSINGHAM (St John the Baptist) w North and South Lopham and Fersfield *Nor 10* **P** *R D A Woode Esq, MMCET, and St Jo Coll Cam (by turn)* **R** D M HUNTER
BRETBY (St Wystan) w Newton Solney *Derby 16* **P** *Bp and DBP (alt)* **P-in-c** C N DODD
BRETFORTON (St Leonard) Offenham and Bretforton *Worc*
BRETHERTON (St John the Baptist) *Blackb 4*
P *R Croston* **P-in-c** D P NESTOR
BRETTENHAM (St Andrew) Garboldisham w Blo' Norton, Riddlesworth etc *Nor*
BRETTENHAM (St Mary) Rattlesden w Thorpe Morieux and Brettenham *St E*
BRETTON PARK (St Bartholomew) Woolley *Wakef*
BREWHAM, SOUTH (St John the Baptist) Bruton and Distr *B & W*
BREWOOD (St Mary and St Chad) *Lich 2* **P** *Bp*
V T H GREEN
BRICETT, GREAT (St Mary and St Lawrence) Ringshall w Battisford, Barking w Darmsden etc *St E*
BRICKENDON (Holy Cross and St Alban) Lt Berkhamsted and Bayford, Essendon etc *St Alb*
BRICKET WOOD (St Luke) *St Alb 1* **P** *CPAS*
V N M LADD, **NSM** A J WILLIAMSON, A de C LADD
BRICKHILL, GREAT (St Mary) w Bow Brickhill and Little Brickhill *Ox 26* **P** *Sir Philip Duncombe, Bt, Bp, and St Edw Sch Ox (by turn)* **R** S J TOZE
BRICKHILL, LITTLE (St Mary Magdalene) Gt Brickhill w Bow Brickhill and Lt Brickhill *Ox*
BRICKHILL, NORTH (St Mark) Bedf St Mark *St Alb*
BRICKLEHAMPTON (St Michael) Elmley Castle w Bricklehampton and Combertons *Worc*
BRIDE VALLEY *Sarum 3* **P** *Patr Bd* **TR** J D ATKINSON, **TV** A M B SALMON
BRIDEKIRK (St Bridget) *Carl 6* **P** *Trustees* **V** *Vacant* Cockermouth (01900) 822257
BRIDESTOWE (St Bridget) Okehampton w Inwardleigh, Bratton Clovelly etc *Ex*
BRIDFORD (St Thomas a Becket) Christow, Ashton, Trusham and Bridford *Ex*
BRIDGE (St Peter) Patrixbourne w Bridge and Bekesbourne *Cant*
BRIDGE SOLLARS (St Andrew) Kenchester and Bridge Sollers *Heref*
BRIDGEMARY (St Matthew) *Portsm 3* **P** *Bp*
V J R H RAILTON, **NSM** G A BARKER
BRIDGERULE (St Bridget) Pyworthy, Pancrasweek and Bridgerule *Ex*
BRIDGETOWN (St John the Evangelist) Totnes, Bridgetown and Berry Pomeroy and Dartington *Ex*
BRIDGFORD, EAST (St Peter) and Kneeton *S'well 8*
P *Magd Coll Ox (2 turns), C G Neale Esq (1 turn)*
R A HAYDOCK
BRIDGFORD, WEST (St Giles) (St Luke) *S'well 10*
P *Waddington Trustees* **R** P N HUMPHREYS,
C J H FROST, **NSM** G CLEAVER
BRIDGHAM (St Mary) E w W Harling and Bridgham w Roudham *Nor*
BRIDGNORTH (St Mary Magdalene) (St Leonard) (St James), Tasley, Astley Abbotts, Oldbury and Quatford *Heref 9* **P** *DBP (3 turns) and Ld Chan (1 turn)*
TR A A ROBERTS, **TV** M J KNEEN, L A WALKER,
C N J WILL, **Hon C** W A D BAKER, K SMALLEY

BRIDGWATER (Holy Trinity) *B & W 14* **P** *Bp*
V J P HART, **NSM** J K L POWELL
BRIDGWATER (St Francis of Assisi) *B & W 14* **P** *Bp*
V D ARNOTT
BRIDGWATER (St John the Baptist) *B & W 14* **P** *Bp*
V I G PIDOUX
BRIDGWATER (St Mary) and Chilton Trinity and Durleigh *B & W 14* **P** *Ld Chan* **V** R E J PACKER, **C** C K WRIGHT
BRIDLINGTON (Emmanuel) *York 10* **P** *Trustees*
V M EXLEY
BRIDLINGTON (Holy Trinity) and Sewerby w Marton *York 10* **P** *Abp* **V** T C WILLIS
BRIDLINGTON (St Mary's Priory Church) *York 10*
P *Simeon's Trustees* **R** J C MEEK, **C** P E JARAM
BRIDLINGTON QUAY (Christ Church) *York 10*
P *R Bridlington Priory* **V** J G COUPER
BRIDPORT (St Mary) *Sarum 3* **P** *Patr Bd (2 turns) and Ld Chan (1 turn)* **TR** T N STUBBS, **TV** M A ALLCHIN, R W SHAMBROOK, **Hon C** J A FRY
BRIDSTOW (St Bridget) Ross w Brampton Abbotts, Bridstow, Peterstow etc *Heref*
BRIERCLIFFE (St James) *Blackb 3* **P** *Hulme Trustees*
V P H HALLAM, **C** J F EDGE
BRIERFIELD (St Luke) *Blackb 7* **P** *Bp* **V** *Vacant* Nelson (01282) 613235
BRIERLEY (St Paul) Felkirk w Brierley *Wakef*
BRIERLEY HILL (St Michael) (St Paul) *Worc 10*
P *TR Wordsley* **R** C S MINCHIN
BRIGG (St John the Evangelist) *Linc 6* **P** *Bp*
C M E THORNE, P J GREEN
BRIGHAM (St Bridget) *Carl 6* **P** *Earl of Lonsdale*
V C GODDARD
BRIGHOUSE (St Martin) (St Chad) and Clifton *Wakef 2*
P *Bp* **TR** W G HARRIS-EVANS, **TV** D C BROOKES, G MANN, **C** J R JENKINS
BRIGHSTONE (St Mary the Virgin) and Brooke w Mottistone *Portsm 8* **P** *Bp (2 turns), D&C St Paul's (1 turn)*
R T W EADY
BRIGHTLING (St Thomas of Canterbury) Dallington, Mountfield and Netherfield *Chich 15* **P** *Bp, Adn Lewes and Hastings, Mrs R Hope Grissell, P S Wilmot-Sitwell Esq, and N S Cobbold Esq (jt)* **R** D D FRICKER,
NSM J B B WRENBURY
BRIGHTLINGSEA (All Saints) (St James) *Chelmsf 24*
P *Ld Chan* **V** *Vacant* Brightlingsea (01206) 302407
BRIGHTON (Annunciation) *Chich 2* **P** *Wagner Trustees*
V D K WOSTENHOLM
BRIGHTON (Good Shepherd) Preston *Chich 2* **P** *Bp*
V P M COLLINS, **C** A G LOW
BRIGHTON (Resurrection) (St Alban) (St Luke) St Martin w St Wilfrid) *Chich 2* **P** *Patr Bd* **TR** B L BRANDIE,
TV H A CAMM, K YATES, **C** W P STAFFORD-WHITTAKER, J K T ELDRIDGE, **NSM** A D OTTERWELL
BRIGHTON (St Augustine and St Saviour) *Chich 2* **P** *Bp*
V T G BUXTON
BRIGHTON (St Bartholomew) *Chich 2* **P** *Wagner Trustees*
V V W HOUSE, **NSM** H N ANNIS
BRIGHTON (St George w St Anne and St Mark) *Chich 2*
P *Bp and V Brighton (jt)* **V** B J LOVATT,
C G V RICKETTS
BRIGHTON (St John) Preston *Chich*
BRIGHTON (St Mary the Virgin) Kemp Town St Mary *Chich*
BRIGHTON (St Matthias) *Chich 2* **P** *V Preston*
V K L W SYLVIA, **C** B S TYLER
BRIGHTON (St Michael and All Angels) *Chich 2*
P *V Brighton* **V** F G JACKSON, **NSM** D G HEWETSON, J F KEYS
BRIGHTON (St Paul) *Chich 2* **P** *Wagner Trustees*
V G R O'LOUGHLIN, **Hon C** J N BALDRY
BRIGHTON (St Peter) (St Nicholas) (Chapel Royal) *Chich 2*
P *Bp* **TR** E W M WALKER, **TV** W R D CAPSTICK, D F MOODY, **C** J C WALL, **NSM** M J WELLS
BRIGHTON, NEW (All Saints) *Ches 7* **P** *DBP*
NSM E R ROYDEN
BRIGHTON, NEW (Emmanuel) *Ches 7* **P** *Bp*
P-in-c A J JEYNES, **C** B D HARRY
BRIGHTON, NEW (St James) *Ches 7* **P** *Bp*
V A J JEYNES, **C** B D HARRY
BRIGHTSIDE (St Thomas and St Margaret) w Wincobank *Sheff 3* **P** *The Crown and Sheff Ch Burgesses (alt)*
V S HOPE, **C** N J WRIGHT
BRIGHTWALTON (All Saints) w Catmore, Leckhampstead, Chaddleworth and Fawley *Ox 14* **P** *Bp, P L Wroughton Esq, and D&C Westmr (jt)* **R** A A D SMITH
BRIGHTWELL (St Agatha) w Sotwell *Ox 18* **P** *Bp*
P-in-c J M SPURRELL

BRIGHTWELL (St John the Baptist) Martlesham w
Brightwell *St E*
BRIGHTWELL BALDWIN (St Bartholomew) Ewelme,
Brightwell Baldwin, Cuxham w Easington *Ox*
BRIGNALL (St Mary) Startforth and Bowes and Rokeby w
Brignall *Ripon*
BRIGSLEY (St Helen) Ravendale Gp *Linc*
BRIGSTOCK (St Andrew) w Stanion *Pet 9* **P** *Bp*
V R D HOWE
BRILL (All Saints), Boarstall, Chilton and Dorton *Ox 21*
P *Sir John Aubrey-Fletcher, Bt and Earl Temple of
Stowe (jt)* **V** P R BUGG
BRILLEY (St Mary) Eardisley w Bollingham, Willersley,
Brilley etc *Heref*
BRIMFIELD (St Michael) Orleton w Brimfield *Heref*
BRIMINGTON (St Michael) *Derby 3* **P** *V Chesterfield*
R D C TRUBY, **NSM** J V LEWIS
BRIMPSFIELD (St Michael), Cranham, Elkstone and Syde
Glouc 1 **P** *Bp, Wg Comdr H T Price, Mrs N Owen, and
DBP (jt)* **R** P NEWING
BRIMPTON (St Peter) Aldermaston w Wasing and Brimpton
Ox
BRIMSCOMBE (Holy Trinity) Woodchester and
Brimscombe *Glouc*
BRINDLE (St James) *Blackb 4* **P** *Trustees*
P-in-c A SOWERBUTTS
BRINGHURST (St Nicholas) Six Saints circa Holt *Leic*
BRINGTON (All Saints) w Molesworth and Old Weston
Ely 10 **P** *Bp* **R** G L NORTH
BRINGTON (St Mary w St John) w Whilton and Norton
Pet 3 **P** *DBP and Earl Spencer (alt)*
P-in-c J J RICHARDSON
BRININGHAM (St Maurice) Brinton, Briningham,
Hunworth, Stody etc *Nor*
BRINKBURN (not known) Longframlington w Brinkburn
Newc
BRINKHILL (St Philip) S Ormsby Gp *Linc*
BRINKLEY (St Mary), Burrough Green and Carlton *Ely 4*
P *St Jo Coll Cam, Mrs B O Killander, and E H Vestey Esq
(by turn)* **P-in-c** J S ASKEY
BRINKLOW (St John the Baptist) *Cov 6* **P** *Ld Chan*
R P S RUSSELL
BRINKWORTH (St Michael and All Angels) w Dauntsey
Bris 12 **P** *Bp* **R** D ORMSTON
BRINNINGTON (St Luke) w Portwood St Paul *Ches 18*
P *Bp* **V** S B WOODHEAD
BRINSCALL (St Luke) Heapey St Barnabas and Withnell St
Paul *Blackb*
BRINSLEY (St James the Great) w Underwood *S'well 4*
P *Bp* **V** *Vacant* Langley Mill (01773) 713978
BRINSOP (St George) Credenhill w Brinsop, Mansel Lacey,
Yazor etc *Heref*
BRINSWORTH (St Andrew) w Catcliffe and Treeton *Sheff 6*
P *Patr Bd* **TR** B SWINDELL, **TV** L E G BONIFACE,
C M J SNOW
**BRINTON (St Andrew), Briningham, Hunworth, Stody,
Swanton Novers and Thornage** *Nor 19* **P** *J S Howlett Esq,
Lord Hastings, and DBP (by turn)* **NSM** F N WARD
BRISLEY (St Bartholomew) Colkirk w Oxwick w Pattesley,
Whissonsett etc *Nor*
BRISLINGTON (St Anne) *Bris 3* **P** *Bp* **P-in-c** S J ORAM
BRISLINGTON (St Christopher) *Bris 3* **P** *Simeon's
Trustees* **P-in-c** C R EDWARDS
BRISLINGTON (St Cuthbert) *Bris 3* **P** *Bp*
P-in-c G R M FISON
BRISLINGTON (St Luke) *Bris 3* **P** *Bp* **P-in-c** S W JONES,
NSM C A G LEGGATE
BRISTOL (Christ the Servant) Stockwood *Bris 3* **P** *Bp*
V J N HARRISON, **C** P M KNIGHT, **Hon C** P A WALL
BRISTOL (Holy Cross) Inns Court *Bris 3* **P** *Bris Ch Trustees*
V *Vacant* Bristol (0117) 966 4123
BRISTOL Lockleaze (St Mary Magdalene w St Francis)
Bris 6 **P** *Bp* **V** P H DENYER, **C** K A MacKINNON
BRISTOL Redfield (St Leonard) E Bris *Bris*
BRISTOL St Aidan w St George *Bris 2* **P** *Bp and SMF*
V *Vacant*
BRISTOL (St Andrew) Hartcliffe *Bris 1* **P** *Bp*
V J J HASLER, **C** R C NIXSON
BRISTOL (St Andrew w St Bartholomew) *Bris 6* **P** *Bp*
P-in-c M A TAYLOR, **NSM** V J HOWLETT
**BRISTOL (St Mary the Virgin) Redcliffe w Temple and
Bedminster St John the Baptist** *Bris 1* **P** *Bp*
V M A WHATMOUGH, **C** P J HAYWARD,
NSM G G STIMPSON, **C** R PIPE-WOLFERSTAN
BRISTOL (St Matthew and St Nathanael) (St Katharine)
Bris 6 **P** *Bp and CPAS (jt)* **V** R V BRAZIER,
C R J SHIRRAS

BRISTOL (St Michael) (St Paul) *Bris 5* **P** *Bp and Bris Ch
Trustees (jt)* **R** A C BRYER, **C** A V I BERNERS-WILSON
(or SILLETT), **C** W JAGE-BOWLER
BRISTOL St Paul's (St Agnes) *Bris 4* **P** *Ld Chan and
Patr Bd (alt)* **TR** D C SELF, **TV** J M FRANCIS,
NSM P BARTLE-JENKINS
BRISTOL (St Philip and St Jacob w Emmanuel) *Bris 4*
P *Trustees* **V** M M WIDDECOMBE
**BRISTOL, The City of (Christ Church w St George) (St James
w St Peter) (St Stephen w St James and St John the Baptist)**
Bris 4 **P** *Ld Chan (1 turn), Trustees (2 turns)*
R E A MORRIS
BRISTOL, EAST (St Aidan) Bristol St Aid w St Geo *Bris*
BRISTOL, EAST (St Ambrose) (St Matthew) (St Leonard)
Bris 2 **P** *Patr Bd* **TR** R D JAMES, **TV** B W JONES,
C D A IZZARD, **Hon C** C L SUTCH, **N G BAILEY**
BRISTOL, EAST (St George) Bristol St Aid w St Geo *Bris*
BRISTON (All Saints) w Burgh Parva and Melton Constable
Nor 19 **P** *Bp and Lord Hastings (jt)* **R** H J BLACKER
BRITFORD (St Peter) *Sarum 11* **P** *D&C*
P-in-c R P HOLLINGSHURST
BRITWELL (St George) W Slough *Ox*
BRITWELL SALOME (St Nicholas) Swyncombe w Britwell
Salome *Ox*
**BRIXHAM (St Mary) (All Saints) w Churston Ferrers and
Kingswear** *Ex 10* **P** *The Crown* **TR** I D CAMPBELL,
TV A S ALLEN, **D R MILTON, **C** J E HOWES
BRIXTON (St Mary) Yealmpton and Brixton *Ex*
BRIXTON St Matthew *S'wark 9* **P** *Abp*
V C B OXENFORTH
BRIXTON (St Paul) *S'wark 9* **P** *Ch Soc Trust*
V N J STONE
BRIXTON, EAST (St Jude) *S'wark 9* **P** *Ch Soc Trust*
P-in-c W P NASH
BRIXTON, NORTH (Christ Church) Brixton Rd Ch Ch
S'wark
BRIXTON DEVERILL (St Michael) The Deverills *Sarum*
BRIXTON HILL (St Saviour) *S'wark 9* **P** *Ch Soc Trust*
P-in-c S F COUGHTREY, **Hon C** J MARSHALL
BRIXTON ROAD (Christ Church) *S'wark 9* **P** *CPAS*
V N P GODFREY, **Hon C** V A ROBERTS
BRIXWORTH (All Saints) w Holcot *Pet 2* **P** *Bp*
V A J WATKINS
BRIZE NORTON (St Britius) Minster Lovell and Brize
Norton *Ox*
**BROAD Town (Christ Church), Clyffe Pypard, Hilmarton and
Tockenham** *Sarum 18* **P** *Ld Chan, DBP, and Prime Min
(by turns)* **R** A G CAPES
BROAD BLUNSDON (St Leonard) Blunsdons, The *Bris*
BROAD CAMPDEN (St Michael and All Angels) Chipping
Campden w Ebrington *Glouc*
BROAD HINTON (St Peter ad Vincula) Upper Kennett
Sarum
BROAD LANE (Licensed Room) Wybunbury w Doddington
Ches
BROAD OAK (St George) Heathfield *Chich*
BROADBOTTOM (St Mary Magdalene) Mottram in
Longdendale *Ches*
BROADBRIDGE HEATH (St John) Horsham *Chich*
BROADCHALKE (All Saints) Chalke Valley W *Sarum*
BROADCLYST (St John the Baptist) Pinhoe and Broadclyst
Ex
BROADFIELD (Christ the Lord) Southgate *Chich*
BROADHEATH (Christ Church), Crown East and Rushwick
Worc 3 **P** *Bp and D&C (jt)* **V** G T M NOTT
BROADHEATH (St Alban) *Ches 10* **P** *Bp* **V** J BEANEY,
C A R ROWE
**BROADHEMBURY (St Andrew the Apostle and Martyr),
Payhembury and Plymtree** *Ex 7* **P** *W Drewe Esq, Ex Coll
Ox, and Or Coll Ox (by turn)* **R** A M ROBERTS
**BROADHEMPSTON (St Peter and St Paul), Woodland,
Staverton w Landscove and Littlehempston** *Ex 13* **P** *Prime
Min (1 turn), D&C and Bp (1 turn)* **R** J CRUSE
**BROADMAYNE (St Martin), West Knighton, Owermoigne
and Warmwell** *Sarum 2* **P** *Major G A M Cree (1 turn),
MMCET (2 turns), and Sir Robert Williams, Bt (1 turn)*
R R B GREGORY
BROADOAK (St Paul) Symondsbury and Chideock *Sarum*
BROADSTAIRS (Holy Trinity) *Cant 9* **P** *V St Peter-in-
Thanet* **R** M W HAYTON
BROADSTONE (not known) Diddlebury w Munslow,
Holdgate and Tugford *Heref*
BROADSTONE (St John the Baptist) *Sarum 8* **P** *Bp*
V M FREDRIKSEN, **NSM** D J MADDOX
BROADWAS (St Mary Magdalene) Martley and
Wichenford, Knightwick etc *Worc*

BROADWATER (St Mary) (St Stephen) Chich 5 **P** Patr Bd
TR P J DOMINY, **TV** G C A STOREY, J M NEVILL,
C T J GREENSLADE, **Hon Par Dn** E T HARDING
BROADWATER DOWN Tunbridge Wells St Mark Roch
BROADWATERS (St Oswald) Kidderminster St Mary and
All SS w Trimpley etc Worc
BROADWAY (St Aldhem and St Eadburga) Ilminster and
District B & W
BROADWAY (St Eadburgha) (St Michael and All Angels)
Worc 1 **P** Peache Trustees **V** P J BURCH
BROADWELL (Good Shepherd) Coleford w Staunton Glouc
BROADWELL (St Paul), Evenlode, Oddington and Adlestrop
Glouc 15 **P** Bp, Ch Soc Trust, Lord Leigh, and DBP (jt)
P-in-c R N MANN
BROADWELL (St Peter and St Paul) Shill Valley and
Broadshire Ox
BROADWEY (St Nicholas) Bincombe w Broadwey, Upwey
and Buckland Ripers Sarum
BROADWINDSOR (St John the Baptist) Beaminster Area
Sarum
BROADWOODKELLY (All Saints) Ex 16 **P** DBP
R P J NORMAN
BROADWOODWIDGER (St Nicholas) Ex 25 **P** Bp
P-in-c J H HEATH
BROCKDISH (St Peter and St Paul) Scole, Brockdish,
Billingford, Thorpe Abbots etc Nor
BROCKENHURST (St Nicholas) (St Saviour) Win 10
P Trustees of E Mourant Esq **Hon C** R DROWN
BROCKHALL (St Peter and St Paul) Flore w Dodford and
Brockhall Pet
BROCKHAM GREEN (Christ Church) S'wark 25
P Hon J L Hamilton **P-in-c** J M A WILLANS
BROCKHAMPTON (Chapel) Bromyard Heref
BROCKHAMPTON (All Saints) Fownhope w Mordiford,
Brockhampton etc Heref
BROCKHOLES (St George) Honley Wakef
BROCKLESBY (All Saints) Gt Limber w Brocklesby Linc
BROCKLEY (St Andrew) Chevington w Hargrave and
Whepstead w Brockley St E
BROCKLEY HILL (St Saviour) S'wark 4 **P** V Forest Hill
Ch Ch **V** C G SMITH, **C** A E SMITH **NSM** R O SMITH
BROCKMOOR (St John) Worc 10 **P** Prime Min
V F M TRETHEWEY
BROCKWORTH (St George) Glouc 6 **P** DBP
P-in-c M M ENNIS, **C** W J BOON
BROCTON (All Saints) Baswich (or Berkswich) Lich
BRODSWORTH (St Michael and All Angels) Bilham Sheff
BROKENBOROUGH (St John the Baptist) Malmesbury w
Westport and Brokenborough Bris
BROKERS WOOD (All Saints) Dilton Marsh Sarum
BROMBOROUGH (St Barnabas) Ches 9 **P** D&C
R W J HOGG, **C** N TIVEY
BROME (St Mary) N Hartismere St E
BROMESWELL (St Edmund) Eyke w Bromeswell,
Rendlesham, Tunstall etc St E
BROMFIELD (St Mary the Virgin) Culmington w Onibury,
Bromfield etc Heref
BROMFIELD (St Mungo) w Waverton Carl 7 **P** Bp
P-in-c P J SWAIN
BROMFORD FIRS (not Known) Hodge Hill Birm
BROMHAM (St Nicholas), Chittoe and Sandy Lane
Sarum 18 **P** DBP and S Spicer Esq (jt) **R** R G BROWN
BROMHAM (St Owen) w Oakley and Stagsden St Alb 19
P Bp **V** D V DRAPER, **C** J G S MORGAN
BROMLEY (All Hallows) Bow H Trin and All Hallows Lon
BROMLEY (Christ Church) Roch 13 **P** CPAS
V M C LAWSON, **C** R B C STANDRING, Pde GREY-
WARTER, **Hon C** N E BAINES, **NSM** C D HARLEY
BROMLEY (Holy Trinity Mission Church) Pensnett Worc
BROMLEY (St Andrew) Roch 13 **P** Bp **V** H A ATHERTON
BROMLEY (St John the Evangelist) Roch 13 **P** Bp
V C D ELLIOTT
BROMLEY (St Mark) Roch 13 **P** V Bromley SS Pet & Paul
V A T VOUSDEN, **C** M B MUDIE
BROMLEY (St Peter and St Paul) Roch 13 **P** Bp
V P H D'A LOCK, **C** J F WORTHEN
BROMLEY, GREAT (St George) The Bromleys Chelmsf
BROMLEY COMMON (Holy Trinity) Roch 13 **P** The
Crown **V** H P C BROADBENT, **NSM** K C BARNES
BROMLEY COMMON (St Augustine) Roch 13 **P** Bp
V B J ASH, **C** R ARDING
BROMLEY COMMON (St Luke) Roch 13 **P** Bp
P-in-c G D GRAHAM, **C** H HESELWOOD
BROMLEY CROSS (St Andrew's Mission
Church) Walmsley Man
BROMLEYS, The Chelmsf 21 **P** CR and Wadh Coll Ox
(alt) **P-in-c** T C DIAPER

BROMPTON (Holy Trinity) w Onslow Square St Paul Lon 8
P Bp and MMCET (jt) **V** J A K MILLAR,
C N G P GUMBEL, S C R LEES, S G DOWNHAM, N K LEE
BROMPTON (St Thomas) w Deighton York 20 **P** D&C
Dur **V** M S SNOWBALL
BROMPTON, NEW (St Luke) Roch 3 **P** Bp
V J L C ABLEWHITE
BROMPTON, WEST (St Mary) (St Peter) Lon 8 **P** Bp
V S G H BARTLETT
**BROMPTON-BY-SAWDON (All Saints) w Snainton,
Ebberston and Allerston** York 21 **P** Abp
V T E D THOMAS
BROMPTON ON SWALE (St Paul) Easby w Brompton on
Swale and Bolton on Swale Ripon
BROMPTON RALPH (The Blessed Virgin Mary) Lydeard St
Lawrence w Brompton Ralph etc B & W
**BROMPTON REGIS (Blessed Virgin Mary) w Upton and
Skilgate** B & W 16 **P** Bp, Em Coll Cam, and Keble Coll
Ox (jt) **P-in-c** J CLOWES
BROMSBERROW (St Mary the Virgin) Redmarley
D'Abitot, Bromesberrow w Pauntley etc Glouc
BROMSGROVE (All Saints) Worc 7 **P** V Bromsgrove
St Jo **V** J E COOK, **NSM** J E SHAW-HAMILTON
BROMSGROVE (St John the Baptist) Worc 7 **P** D&C
V J H DAVIES, **C** P H WORRALL, **NSM** G GILES (nee
WILLIAMS)
BROMWICH, WEST (All Saints) Lich 8 **P** Bp
V M MORETON, **C** K A MUNDY, R K BELL
BROMWICH, WEST (Good Shepherd w St John) Lich 8
P Bp **C** R J HUDSON-WILKIN
BROMWICH, WEST (Holy Trinity) Lich 8 **P** Peache
Trustees **V** G St C CAMPBELL, **C** M T SHARPE
BROMWICH, WEST (St Andrew) (Christ Church) Lich 8
P Bp and V W Bromwich All SS (jt) **V** K WILKIN,
C S PETTY
BROMWICH, WEST (St Francis of Assisi) Lich 8 **P** Bp
C S J GOODMAN
BROMWICH, WEST St James Hill Top Lich 8 **P** Bp
V M C RUTTER, **C** J MITSON
BROMWICH, WEST (St Paul) Golds Hill Lich 8
P V Tipton St Martin **P-in-c** M C RUTTER
BROMWICH, WEST (St Peter) Lich 8 **P** Bp
P-in-c G D STARKEY
BROMWICH, WEST (St Philip) Lich 8 **P** Bp
V R C DESON
BROMYARD (St Peter) Heref 2 **P** Bp **V** D W GOULD,
C P D HALL
BROMYARD DOWNS (Mission Church) Bromyard Heref
BRONDESBURY (Christ Church) (St Laurence) Lon 21
P Ld Chan **P-in-c** E V LAKE
BRONDESBURY (St Anne) w Kilburn (Holy Trinity) Lon 21
P Bp and Ch Patr Soc (alt) **P-in-c** F B CAPIE,
NSM D NEW
BROOK (St Mary) Wye w Brook Cant
BROOKE (St Mary the Virgin) Brighstone and Brooke w
Mottistone Portsm
BROOKE (St Peter) Oakham, Hambleton, Egleton,
Braunston and Brooke Pet
**BROOKE (St Peter), Kirstead, Mundham w Seething and
Thwaite** Nor 5 **P** G&C Coll Cam, Gt Hosp and Countess
Ferrers and Ld Chan (by turn) **R** P E HALLS
BROOKE STREET (St Alban the Martyr) Holborn St Alb w
Saffron Hill St Pet Lon
BROOKEND (Mission Room) Sharpness w Purton and
Brookend Glouc
BROOKFIELD (St Anne), Highgate Rise Lon 17 **P** Bp
P-in-c C G POPE
BROOKFIELD (St Margaret) York 22 **P** Abp
V R W SMITH
BROOKFIELD (St Mary) Lon 17 **P** Bp **V** C G POPE,
C C D MITCHELL
BROOKHURST (St Peter's Chapel) Eastham Ches
BROOKING (St Barnabas) Totnes, Bridgetown & Berry
Pomeroy & Dartington Ex
BROOKLAND (St Augustine) Appledore w Brookland,
Fairfield, Brenzett etc Cant
BROOKLANDS Baguley Man
BROOKMANS PARK (St Michael) N Mymms St Alb
BROOKSBY (St Michael and All Angels) Upper Wreake
Leic
BROOKSIDE (Pastoral Centre) Cen Telford Lich
BROOKTHORPE (St Swithun) The Edge, Pitchcombe,
Harescombe and Brookthorpe Glouc
BROOKWOOD (St Saviour) Woking St Jo Guildf
BROOM (St Matthew) Bidford-on-Avon Cov
BROOM LEYS (St David) Leic 8 **P** Bp **V** J W STEVENSON

BROOM VALLEY (St Barnabas) Rotherham *Sheff*

BROOME (St Michael) Ditchingham, Hedenham and Broome *Nor*

BROOME (St Peter) Churchill-in-Halfshire w Blakedown and Broome *Worc*

BROOMFIELD (St Margaret) Hollingbourne and Hucking w Leeds and Broomfield *Cant*

BROOMFIELD (St Mary and All Saints) Kingston St Mary w Broomfield etc *B & W*

BROOMFIELD (St Mary w St Leonard) *Chelmsf 8* **P** *Bp* **P-in-c** A W D RITSON

BROOMFLEET (St Mary) S Cave and Ellerker w Broomfleet *York*

BROOMHILL (St Mark) Sheff St Mark Broomhill *Sheff*

BROSELEY (All Saints) w Benthall, Jackfield, Linley, Willey and Barrow *Heref 14* **P** *Patr Bd* **R** M A KINNA, **C** T J STEAD, **NSM** A A BRACE

BROTHERTOFT Group, The (Christ Church) (St Gilbert of Sempringham) *Linc 21* **P** *Bp (2 turns), V Algarkirk (1 turn)* **V** J W THACKER, **NSM** D J CLARKE

BROTHERTON (St Edward the Confessor) *Wakef 11* **P** *D&C York* **P-in-c** M BAMFORD

BROTTON PARVA (St Margaret) *York 17* **P** *Abp* **R** E SMITS

BROUGH (All Saints) Elloughton and Brough w Brantingham *York*

BROUGH (St Michael) w Stainmore, Musgrave and Warcop *Carl 1* **P** *Bp (2 turns) and Lord Hothfield (1 turn)* **R** R M F HAIGH, **C** D B de M LEATHES

BROUGHAM (St Wilfrid Chapel) Clifton, Brougham and Cliburn *Carl*

BROUGHTON (All Saints) Warboys w Broughton and Bury w Wistow *Ely*

BROUGHTON (All Saints), Marton and Thornton *Bradf 7* **P** *Ch Ch Ox and Exors Dame Harriet Nelson (jt)* **R** T VAUGHAN

BROUGHTON (St Andrew) w Loddington and Cransley and Thorpe Malsor *Pet 11* **P** *Ld Chan (1 turn), Bp (2 turns), and Keble Coll Ox (1 turn)* **R** R M GILES

BROUGHTON (St James) (St Clement and St Matthias) *Man 6* **P** *Patr Bd* **P-in-c** C W READ

BROUGHTON (St John the Baptist) *Blackb 14* **P** *Trustees* **V** S J FINCH, **C** J E C PERCIVAL

BROUGHTON (St John the Evangelist) *Man 6* **P** *Bp* **R** J APPLEGATE

BROUGHTON (St Mary) *Lich 28* **P** *D R B Thompson Esq* **P-in-c** E A HADLEY

BROUGHTON (St Mary) *Linc 6* **P** *MMCET* **P-in-c** J W COTTON

BROUGHTON (St Mary Magdalene) (Holy Innocents) and Duddon *Carl 8* **P** *V Millom, Lt-Col D A S Pennefather, and Ch Patr Trust (by turn)* **V** P F BARNES

BROUGHTON (St Mary the Virgin) w North Newington and Shutford, Wroxton w Balscote and Drayton *Ox 5* **P** *Lord Saye and Sele, New Coll Ox, and Bp (by turn)* **R** *Vacant Banbury (01295) 730344*

BROUGHTON (St Mary) w Bossington and Houghton and Mottisfont *Win 11* **P** *Ld Chan (1 turn), E J M Dent Esq and Ms M Dent, A Humbert Esq and Miss R A Humbert (jt) (2 turns)* **R** F J G WYNNE

BROUGHTON (St Peter) Croxton w Broughton and Adbaston *Lich*

BROUGHTON, GREAT (Christ Church) and Broughton Moor *Carl 7* **P** *Bp* **P-in-c** J V HINE

BROUGHTON, LOWER (Ascension) *Man 6* **P** *Trustees* **R** *Vacant 0161–834 4370*

BROUGHTON, NETHER (St Mary the Virgin) Old Dalby and Nether Broughton *Leic*

BROUGHTON, UPPER (St Luke) Hickling w Kinoulton and Broughton Sulney *S'well*

BROUGHTON ASTLEY (St Mary) *Leic 10* **P** *Woodard Schs* **R** P BURROWS, **C** N M HUNT

BROUGHTON GIFFORD (St Mary the Virgin), Great Chalfield and Holt St Katharine *Sarum 17* **P** *D&C Bris (3 turns), Ld Chan (2 turns), and R C Floyd Esq (1 turn)* **R** *Vacant Trowbridge (01225) 782289*

BROUGHTON HACKETT (St Leonard) Peopleton and White Ladies Aston w Churchill etc *Worc*

BROUGHTON IN FURNESS (St Mary Magdalene) Broughton and Duddon *Carl*

BROUGHTON MILLS (Holy Innocents) as above

BROUGHTON MOOR (St Columba) Gt Broughton and Broughton Moor *Carl*

BROUGHTON POGGS (St Peter) Shill Valley and Broadshire *Ox*

BROWN CANDOVER (St Peter) The Candover Valley *Win*

BROWN EDGE (St Anne) *Lich 13* **P** *Bp* **V** D J FAIRWEATHER

BROWNHILL (St Saviour) *Wakef 10* **P** *V Batley* **V** R ADAIR

BROWNSWOOD PARK (St John the Evangelist) *Lon 5* **P** *City Corp* **P-in-c** A G SCOTT

BROXBOURNE (St Augustine) w Wormley *St Alb 6* **P** *Bp and Peache Trustees (jt)* **R** R A POTTER, **C** B E C PATE, R H TOTTERDELL

BROXHOLME (All Saints) Saxilby Gp *Linc*

BROXTED (St Mary the Virgin) w Chickney and Tilty and Great and Little Easton *Chelmsf 19* **P** *Mrs F Spurrier (2 turns), DBP (1 turn), and MMCET (1 turn)* **R** J M FILBY

BROXTOWE (St Martha) *S'well 14* **P** *Bp* **V** J S M HARDING

BRUERA (St Mary) Aldford and Bruera *Ches*

BRUISYARD (St Peter) Badingham w Bruisyard, Cransford and Dennington *St E*

BRUMBY, OLD (St Hugh) *Linc 4* **P** *Bp* **TR** A G D HAYDAY

BRUNDALL (St Lawrence) w Braydeston and Postwick *Nor 4* **P** *Bp and MMCET (jt)* **R** R M BAKER, **C** R J ESPIN-BRADLEY

BRUNDISH (St Lawrence) Wilby w Brundish *St E*

BRUNSTEAD (St Peter) Stalham and E Ruston w Brunstead *Nor*

BRUNSWICK (Christ Church) *Man 4* **P** *Ch Soc Trust* **P-in-c** S J T GATENBY

BRUNSWICK (St Cuthbert) Ch the King in the Dio of Newc *Newc*

BRUNTCLIFFE (St Andrew) *Wakef 8* **P** *V Batley and V St Peter Morley (alt)* **V** J VICKERMAN

BRUNTINGTHORPE (St Mary) Arnesby w Shearsby and Bruntingthorpe *Leic*

BRUNTON PARK (St Aidan) Ch the King in the Dio of Newc *Newc*

BRUSHFORD (St Mary the Virgin) *Ex 16* **P** *D&C* **V** P J NORMAN

BRUSHFORD (St Nicholas) Dulverton and Brushford *B & W*

BRUTON (Blessed Virgin Mary) and District *B & W 2* **P** *Patr Bd* **TR** D J RICHARDS, **TV** O D WILLIAMS, **C** J F M MILES (nee HOARE), **Hon C** D C BARKER

BRYANSTON SQUARE (St Mary) w St Marylebone (St Mark) *Lon 4* **P** *The Crown* **R** D EVANS

BRYHER (All Saints) Scilly Is *Truro*

BRYMPTON (St Andrew) Odcombe, Brympton, Lufton and Montacute *B & W*

BRYN (St Chad) Clun w Bettws-y-Crwyn and Newc *Heref*

BRYN (St Peter) *Liv 15* **P** *Bp* **V** D J HOOTON

BUBBENHALL (St Giles) Ryton on Dunsmore w Bubbenhall *Cov*

BUBWITH (All Saints) w Skipwith *York 4* **P** *Abp and D&C, and Ld Chan (alt)* **V** B EVES

BUCKDEN (St Mary) *Ely 12* **P** *Bp* **V** R C BENDING

BUCKENHAM, NEW (St Martin) Quidenham *Nor*

BUCKENHAM, OLD (All Saints) as above

BUCKERELL (St Mary and St Giles) Feniton, Buckerell and Escot *Ex*

BUCKFAST SANCTUARY (not known) Buckfastleigh w Dean Prior *Ex*

BUCKFASTLEIGH (Holy Trinity) (St Luke's Mission) w Dean Prior *Ex 13* **P** *D&C (2 turns), DBP (1 turn)* **V** P E WILSON, **NSM** J N CIRWIN

BUCKHORN WESTON (St John the Baptist) Gillingham *Sarum*

BUCKHURST HILL (St Elisabeth) (St John the Baptist) (St Stephen) *Chelmsf 26* **P** *Patr Bd* **TV** B M EAVES, **P-in-c** K P HALLETT, **C** J A W BRICE

BUCKINGHAM (St Peter and St Paul) w Radclive cum Chackmore *Ox 22* **P** *Bp (2 turns), New Coll Ox (1 turn)* **V** D G MEARA, **C** P HARDY, **Par Dn** P HARDY, **NSM** R M BUNDOCK

BUCKINGHAM, NORTH *Ox 22* **P** *Ch Soc Trust, Mrs J M Williams, and D J Robarts Esq (by turn)* **R** N A THORP

BUCKLAND (All Saints) Aston Clinton w Buckland and Drayton Beauchamp *Ox*

BUCKLAND (St Mary the Virgin) *Ox 17* **P** *DBP, Bp and Or Coll Ox (by turn)* **V** C R RUDD

BUCKLAND (St Mary the Virgin) *S'wark 25* **P** *All So Coll Ox* **R** *Vacant Betchworth (0173784) 3360*

BUCKLAND (St Michael) Childswyckham w Aston Somerville, Buckland etc *Glouc*

BUCKLAND, EAST (St Michael) S Molton w Nymet St George, High Bray etc *Ex*

BUCKLAND, WEST (Blessed Virgin Mary) Wellington and Distr *B & W*

BUCKLAND, WEST (St Peter) Swimbridge and W
Buckland *Ex*

BUCKLAND BREWER (St Mary and St
Benedict) Parkham, Alwington, Buckland Brewer etc *Ex*

BUCKLAND DINHAM (St Michael and All Angels) Mells
w Buckland Dinham, Elm, Whatley etc *B & W*

BUCKLAND FILLEIGH (St Mary and Holy
Trinity) Shebbear, Buckland Filleigh, Sheepwash etc *Ex*

**BUCKLAND IN DOVER (St Andrew) w Buckland Valley
(St Nicholas)** *Cant 4* **P** *Abp* **R** L G TYZACK,
C G G GILL

BUCKLAND IN THE MOOR (St Peter) Ashburton w
Buckland in the Moor and Bickington *Ex*

BUCKLAND MONACHORUM (St Andrew) *Ex 25* **P** *Bp*
V G M COTTER

BUCKLAND NEWTON (Holy Rood) Dungeon Hill *Sarum*

BUCKLAND RIPERS (St Nicholas) Bincombe w Broadwey,
Upwey and Buckland Ripers *Sarum*

BUCKLAND ST MARY (Blessed Virgin
Mary) Churchstanton, Buckland St Mary and Otterford
B & W

BUCKLAND TOUT SAINTS (St Peter) Charleton w
Buckland Tout Saints etc *Ex*

BUCKLAND VALLEY (St Nicholas) Buckland in Dover w
Buckland Valley *Cant*

BUCKLEBURY (St Mary) w Marlston *Ox 14*
P *C J Pratt Esq* **V** A D R HOLMES

BUCKLEBURY, UPPER (All Saints) Bucklebury w
Marlston *Ox*

BUCKLERS HARD (St Mary) Beaulieu and Exbury and E
Boldre *Win*

BUCKLESHAM (St Mary) Nacton and Levington w
Bucklesham and Foxhall *St E*

BUCKMINSTER (St John the Baptist) Wymondham w
Edmondthorpe, Buckminster etc *Leic*

BUCKNALL (St Margaret) Woodhall Spa Gp *Linc*

BUCKNALL (St Mary the Virgin) and Bagnall *Lich 17*
P *Patr Bd* **TR** G O STONE, **TV** M R EAST,
G F SMALL, J V CHAPMAN

**BUCKNELL (St Mary) w Chapel Lawn, Llanfair Waterdine
and Stowe** *Heref 10* **P** *Earl of Powis, Grocers' Co, and
J Coltman Rogers Esq (jt)* **P-in-c** E LLOYD

BUCKNELL (St Peter) Bicester w Bucknell, Caversfield and
Launton *Ox*

BUCKS MILLS (St Anne) Parkham, Alwington, Buckland
Brewer etc *Ex*

BUCKWORTH (All Saints) *Ely 9* **P** *Bp* **R** J A COOMBE

BUDBROOKE (St Michael) *Cov 4* **P** *MMCET*
V T J JOHNSON

**BUDE HAVEN (St Michael and All Angels) and
Marhamchurch** *Truro 8* **P** *Bp and PCC (jt)*
R P TWISLETON

BUDLEIGH, EAST (All Saints) w Bicton and Otterton *Ex 1*
P *Lord Clinton* **V** M A J HARDING

BUDLEIGH SALTERTON (St Peter) *Ex 1* **P** *Lord Clinton*
V R J GIBBS

BUDOCK (St Budock) *Truro 3* **P** *Bp*
P-in-c M J W WARNER

BUDWORTH, GREAT (St Mary and All Saints) *Ches 4*
P *Ch Ch Ox* **V** G D MILLS

BUDWORTH, LITTLE (St Peter) Whitegate w Lt Budworth
Ches

BUGBROOKE (St Michael and All Angels) w Rothersthorpe
Pet 3 **P** *Exors E W Harrison (2 turns), DBP (1 turn)*
R T R PARTRIDGE

BUGLAWTON (St John the Evangelist) *Ches 11*
P *R Astbury* **V** M L EAMAN

BUGTHORPE (St Andrew) Bishop Wilton w Full Sutton,
Kirby Underdale etc *York*

**BUILDWAS (Holy Trinity) and Leighton w Eaton Constantine
and Wroxeter** *Lich 29* **P** *Bp, Lord Barnard, and
MMCET (jt)* **R** D K B HAWKINS

BULCOTE (Holy Trinity) Burton Joyce w Bulcote *S'well*

BULFORD (St Leonard) Avon Valley *Sarum*

BULKELEY (All Saints) Bickerton w Bickley *Ches*

BULKINGTON (Christ Church) Seend and Bulkington
Sarum

BULKINGTON (St James) w Shilton and Ansty *Cov 5*
P *Ld Chan* **V** *Vacant* Bedworth (01203) 312396

BULKWORTHY (St Michael) Abbots Bickington and
Bulkworthy *Ex*

BULLEY (St Michael and All Angels) Churcham w Bulley
and Minsterworth *Glouc*

BULLINGHOPE, UPPER (St Peter) and Lower w Grafton
Heref 3 **P** *Bp* **V** T P JONES

BULLINGTON (St Michael and All Angels) Barton Stacey
and Bullington etc *Win*

BULMER (St Andrew) Belchamp Otten w Belchamp Walter
and Bulmer *Chelmsf*

BULMER (St Martin) w Dalby, Terrington and Welburn
York 3 **P** *Abp and Hon S B G Howard (jt)*
R E T CHAPMAN

BULPHAN (St Mary the Virgin) Orsett and Bulphan and
Horndon on the Hill *Chelmsf*

BULWELL (St John the Divine) *S'well 13* **P** *Bp*
V J P FEWKES, **C** B A STARK

BULWELL (St Mary the Virgin and All Souls) *S'well 13*
P *Bp* **R** W S BEASLEY, **C** K K BARRON

**BULWICK (St Nicholas) and Blatherwycke w Harringworth
and Laxton** *Pet 8* **P** *G T G Conant Esq (3 turns), F & A
George Ltd (1 turn)* **R** M R A WILSON

BUNBURY (St Boniface) and Tilstone Fearnall *Ches 5*
P *Haberdashers' Co* **V** J E W BOWERS

BUNCTON (All Saints) Ashington, Washington and Wiston
with Buncton *Chich*

BUNGAY (Holy Trinity) w St Mary *St E 14* **P** *DBP*
V I S MORGAN, **C** C P WRIGHT

BUNNY (St Mary the Virgin) w Bradmore *S'well 9*
P *Ld Chan* **V** *Vacant* Nottingham (0115) 921 7805

**BUNWELL (St Michael and All Angels), Carleton Rode,
Tibenham, Great Moulton and Aslacton** *Nor 5* **P** *Bp and
DBP (alt)* **R** S SWIFT

BURBAGE (All Saints) Wexcombe *Sarum*

BURBAGE (Christ Church) Buxton w Burbage and King
Sterndale *Derby*

BURBAGE (St Catherine) w Aston Flamville *Leic 13*
P *Ball Coll Ox* **R** F D JENNINGS, **C** A S REED

BURCOMBE (St John the Baptist) Barford St Martin,
Dinton, Baverstock etc *Sarum*

BURES (St Mary the Virgin) *St E 12* **P** *DBP*
V R L C KING

BURFORD First Portion *Heref 12* **P** *DBP, Bp Birm, Bp, and
J J C Caldwell Esq (jt)* **R** D S DORMOR

**BURFORD Second Portion (St Mary) w Greete and Hope
Bagot** *Heref 12* **P** *DBP* **R** D S DORMOR

**BURFORD (St John the Baptist) w Fulbrook, Taynton,
Asthall, Swinbrook and Widford** *Ox 8* **P** *Bp and Capt
D Mackinnon (jt)* **NSM** C R TADMAN-ROBINS

BURFORD Third Portion (St Mary) w Little Hereford
Heref 12 **P** *DBP and Bp Birm (jt)* **R** D S DORMOR

BURGATE (St Mary) N Hartismere *St E*

BURGESS HILL (St Andrew) *Chich 9* **P** *Bp*
V I G PRIOR, **NSM** S C M McLARNON

BURGESS HILL (St John the Evangelist) (St Edward)
Chich 9 **P** *Patr Bd* **TR** M C KNOWLES,
C P L OXBORROW

BURGH (St Botolph) Boulge w Burgh and Grundisburgh
St E

BURGH (St Margaret and St Mary) Rollesby w Burgh w
Billockby w Ashby w Oby etc *Nor*

BURGH (St Peter) The Raveningham Gp *Nor*

**BURGH-BY-SANDS (St Michael) and Kirkbampton w
Kirkandrews on Eden, Beaumont and Grinsdale** *Carl 3*
P *DBP and Earl of Lonsdale (jt)* **R** D R KING

BURGH CASTLE (St Peter and St Paul) Belton and Burgh
Castle *Nor*

BURGH HEATH (St Mary the Virgin) Tattenham Corner
and Burgh Heath *Guildf*

BURGH LE MARSH (St Peter and St Paul) *Linc 8* **P** *Bp*
P-in-c T STEELE

BURGH-NEXT-AYLSHAM (St Mary) Marsham w Burgh-
next-Aylsham *Nor*

BURGH-ON-BAIN (St Helen) Asterby Gp *Linc*

BURGH PARVA (St Mary) Briston w Burgh Parva and
Melton Constable *Nor*

**BURGHCLERE (Ascension) (All Saints) w Newtown and
Ecchinswell w Sydmonton** *Win 6* **P** *Earl of Carnarvon*
R C A LE PREVOST

BURGHFIELD (St Mary the Virgin) *Ox 12* **P** *Earl of
Shrewsbury* **R** A B GRUNDY, **NSM** J N COOPER

BURGHILL (St Mary the Virgin) *Heref 4* **P** *DBP*
P-in-c M A KELK

BURGHWALLIS (St Helen) w Skelbrooke *Sheff 8* **P** *Mrs
E H I Donovan-Anne (2 turns), Bp (1 turn)*
P-in-c A D LENNON

BURHAM (Methodist Church) and Wouldham *Roch 5* **P** *Bp
and Ld Chan (alt)* **R** W S AITKEN

BURITON (St Mary the Virgin) *Portsm 5* **P** *Bp*
R C LOWSON, **C** O E ANDERSON

BURLESCOMBE (St Mary) Sampford Peverell, Uplowman,
Holcombe Rogus etc *Ex*

BURLEY (St Matthias) *Ripon 7* **P** *G M Bedford Esq,
J C Yeadon Esq, E Beety Esq, Mrs M E Dunham, and Mrs
L M Rawse (jt)* **V** M J WINBOLT LEWIS,
C A B CHAPMAN

BURLEY IN WHARFEDALE (St Mary the Virgin) *Bradf 4*
P *Bp* **V** PJSUTCLIFFE, **NSM** DPHALLIDAY
BURLEY VILLE (St John the Baptist) *Win 8*
P *V Ringwood* **V** AGCLARKSON
BURLEYDAM (St Mary and St Michael) Baddiley and
Wrenbury w Burleydam *Ches*
BURLINGHAM (St Andrew) Acle w Fishley and N
Burlingham *Nor*
BURLINGHAM (St Edmund) w Lingwood, Strumpshaw w
Hassingham and Buckenham *Nor 4* **P** *Ch Soc Trust,*
MMCET, and Bp (jt) **P-in-c** VMELPHICK
BURLTON (St Anne) Loppington w Newtown *Lich*
BURMANTOFTS (St Stephen and St Agnes) *Ripon 5*
P *Ch Trust Fund Trust* **C** RHJAMIESON
BURMARSH (All Saints) Dymchurch w Burmarsh and
Newchurch *Cant*
BURMINGTON (St Nicholas and St Barnabas) Wolford w
Burmington *Cov*
BURNAGE (St Margaret) *Man 3* **P** *Bp* **R** APUGMIRE,
C ARBRADLEY
BURNAGE (St Nicholas) *Man 8* **P** *Trustees* **R** *Vacant*
0161-432 3384
BURNBY (St Giles) *York 7* **P** *Trustees* **R** KGSKIPPER
BURNESIDE (St Oswald) *Carl 9* **P** *J A Cropper Esq,*
Mrs B Snowdon and Mrs E Bingham (jt) **V** NLDAVIES,
Hon Par Dn JLTYRER
BURNESTON (St Lambert) Kirklington w Burneston and
Wath and Pickhill *Ripon*
BURNETT (St Michael) Keynsham *B & W*
BURNEY LANE (Christ Church) *Birm 10* **P** *Bp*
V MCHESTER
BURNHAM (St Andrew) *B & W 1* **P** *D&C* **V** REPITT
BURNHAM (St Mary the Virgin) *Chelmsf 11*
P *N D Beckett Esq and Walsingham Coll Trust (jt)*
V RJWEBB
BURNHAM (St Peter) w Dropmore, Hitcham and Taplow
Ox 23 **P** *Patr Bd* **TR** SNDBROWN, **TV** ACDIBDEN,
TRHEWSON, MRWHITE
BURNHAM DEEPDALE (St Mary) Hunstanton St Mary w
Ringstead Parva etc *Nor*
BURNHAM NORTON (St Margaret) Burnham Gp of Par
Nor
BURNHAM-ON-CROUCH (St Mary the Virgin) Burnham
Chelmsf
BURNHAM-ON-SEA (St Andrew) as above
BURNHAM OVERY (St Clement) Burnham Gp of Par *Nor*
BURNHAM THORPE (All Saints) as above
BURNHAM ULPH (All Saints) as above
BURNHAM WESTGATE (St Mary), Burnham Norton,
Burnham Overy, Burnham Thorpe, and Burnham Sutton w
Ulph (The Burnham Group of Parishes) *Nor 16* **P** *Ch Coll*
Cam (1 turn), Ld Chan (2 turns), and DBP (1 turn)
R *Vacant* Fakenham (01328) 738317
BURNLEY Habergham Eaves (St Matthew the Apostle) (Holy
Trinity) *Blackb 3* **P** *R Burnley* **V** RMcCULLOUGH
BURNLEY (St Andrew) w St Margaret *Blackb 3*
P *R Burnley* **V** BROBINSON, **Hon C** BTONGE
BURNLEY (St Catherine) (St Alban) and St Paul *Blackb 3*
P *R Burnley* **V** RWILLIAMS
BURNLEY (St Cuthbert) *Blackb 3* **P** *R Burnley* **V** HLEE
BURNLEY (St James) *Blackb 3* **P** *The Crown*
P-in-c BROBINSON
BURNLEY (St Mark) *Blackb 3* **P** *Bp* **V** ACTAYLOR
BURNLEY (St Peter) *Blackb 3* **P** *Bp* **R** DFTOWERS
BURNLEY (St Stephen) *Blackb 3* **P** *R Burnley*
P-in-c JBSWALLOW
BURNLEY, WEST (All Saints) *Blackb 3* **P** *Bp and V Burnley*
St Pet (jt) **V** JHODGSON, **C** LADAM, ARWOOD
BURNMOOR (St Barnabas) *Dur 6* **P** *Lord Lambton*
R MGBISHOP
BURNOPFIELD (St James) *Dur 8* **P** *Bp* **V** *Vacant*
Burnopfield (01207) 70261
BURNSALL (St Wilfrid) w Rylstone *Bradf 7* **P** *Exors Earl of*
Craven and CPAS (jt) **R** CDECLARKE
BURNT YATES (St Andrew) Ripley *Ripon*
BURNTWOOD (Christ Church) *Lich 1* **P** *D&C*
P-in-c DAWEAVER, **C** NJCARTER
BURPHAM (St Luke) Guildford *Guildf 5* **P** *Bp*
V CJMATTHEWS
BURPHAM (St Mary the Virgin) *Chich 1* **P** *D&C*
NSM GABLACKWELL
BURRADON (Good Shepherd) Weetslade *Newc*
BURRILL (Mission Church) Bedale *Ripon*
BURRINGTON (Holy Trinity) *Ex 16* **P** *DBP*
P-in-c HGPOLLOCK
BURRINGTON (Holy Trinity) and Churchill *B & W 11*
P *D&C Bris and Burrington PCC (jt)* **V** JCABDY
BURRINGTON (St George) Wigmore Abbey *Heref*

BURROUGH GREEN (St Augustine of
Canterbury) Brinkley, Burrough Green and Carlton *Ely*
BURROUGH HILL Parishes, The: Burrough on the Hill,
Great Dalby, Little Dalby, Pickwell and Somerby *Leic 3*
P *Bp, DBP, and Mrs M Burdett Fisher (jt)*
P-in-c RJSTRETTON
BURROUGH ON THE HILL (St Mary the
Virgin) Burrough Hill Pars *Leic*
BURROWBRIDGE (St Michael) Stoke St Gregory w
Burrowbridge and Lyng *B & W*
BURRSVILLE (St Mark) Gt Clacton *Chelmsf*
BURSCOUGH BRIDGE (St John) (St Andrew) (St Cyprian)
Liv 11 **P** *V Ormskirk* **V** BROBINSON,
C ARWOODHOUSE
BURSDON MOOR (St Martin) Parkham, Alwington,
Buckland Brewer etc *Ex*
BURSEA (Chapel) Holme-on-Spalding Moor *York*
BURSLEDON Pilands Wood (St Paul) Bursledon *Win*
BURSLEDON (St Leonard) *Win 9* **P** *Bp*
V PAVARGESON
BURSLEM (St John the Baptist) (St Paul) *Lich 16* **P** *Bp and*
MMCET (jt) **R** CRJOHNSON, **C** DPCOOPER
BURSLEM (St Werburgh) *Lich 16* **P** *Bp* **V** KLROUND
BURSTALL (St Mary the Virgin) Sproughton w Burstall
St E
BURSTEAD, GREAT (St Mary Magdalene) *Chelmsf 6*
P *Bp* **V** BJRODWELL
BURSTEAD, LITTLE (St Mary) Billericay and Lt Burstead
Chelmsf
BURSTOCK (St Andrew) Beaminster Area *Sarum*
BURSTON (St Mary) Winfarthing w Shelfanger w Burston w
Gissing etc *Nor*
BURSTON (St Rufin) Salt and Sandon w Burston *Lich*
BURSTOW (St Bartholomew) *S'wark 25* **P** *Ld Chan*
R GBTALBOT, **Hon C** KWRAMSAY
BURSTWICK (All Saints) w Thorngumbald *York 13* **P** *Abp*
V FWRLATOUCHE
BURTLE (St Philip and St James) Shapwick w Ashcott and
Burtle *B & W*
BURTON (All Saints) w Christ Church *Lich 19* **P** *CPAS and*
Ch Soc Trust (jt) **V** RPOAKLEY
BURTON (St James) and Holme *Carl 9* **P** *Simeon's*
Trustees **V** JJCNODDER
BURTON (St Luke) and Sopley *Win 8* **P** *Bp and D&C Cant*
(alt) **V** ASESSFORD
BURTON (St Nicholas) and Shotwick *Ches 9* **P** *D&C*
(1 turn) and St Jo Hosp Lich (2 turns) **V** HJALDRIDGE
BURTON w COATES (St Agatha) Barlavington, Burton w
Coates, Sutton and Bignor *Chich*
BURTON AGNES (St Martin) w Harpham and Lowthorpe w
Ruston Parva *York 11* **P** *Ld Chan (2 turns), C T Legard*
Esq (1 turn) **R** DSHAWKINS
BURTON BRADSTOCK (St Mary) Bride Valley *Sarum*
BURTON BY LINCOLN (St Vincent) *Linc 2* **P** *Lord*
Monson **R** *Vacant*
BURTON COGGLES (St Thomas a Becket) Ingoldsby *Linc*
BURTON DASSETT (All Saints) *Cov 8* **P** *Bp*
V PTFRANCIS
BURTON FLEMING (St Cuthbert) w Fordon, Grindale and
Wold Newton *York 10* **P** *Abp and MMCET (jt)*
V JRBROADHURST
BURTON GREEN (Chapel of Ease) Kenilworth St Nic *Cov*
BURTON HASTINGS (St Botolph) Wolvey w Burton
Hastings, Copston Magna etc *Cov*
BURTON IN LONSDALE (All Saints) Thornton in
Lonsdale w Burton in Lonsdale *Bradf*
BURTON JOYCE (St Helen) w Bulcote *S'well 11*
P *MMCET* **V** AGRAHAM
BURTON LATIMER (St Mary the Virgin) *Pet 11* **P** *Bp*
R JSIMMONS
BURTON LAZARS (St James) Melton Mowbray *Leic*
BURTON LEONARD (St Leonard) Bishop Monkton and
Burton Leonard *Ripon*
BURTON-ON-TRENT (All Saints) Burton All SS w Ch Ch
Lich
BURTON-ON-TRENT (St Aidan) Shobnall *Lich*
BURTON-ON-TRENT (St Chad) *Lich 19* **P** *Bp*
V MPSKILLINGS
BURTON-ON-TRENT (St Modwen) (St Paul) *Lich 19* **P** *Bp*
and Lord Burton (jt) **V** DMMORRIS,
Hon Par Dn VRMORRIS
BURTON OVERY (St Andrew) Gaulby *Leic*
BURTON PEDWARDINE (St Andrew and the Blessed
Virgin Mary and St Nicholas) Heckington *Linc*
BURTON PIDSEA (St Peter) and Humbleton w Elsternwick
York 13 **P** *Ld Chan and D&C (alt)* **V** *Vacant* Withernsea
(01964) 671074

BURTON UPON STATHER (St Andrew) Flixborogh w Burton upon Stather *Linc*
BURTONWOOD (St Michael) *Liv 16* **P** *R Warrington* **V** R S NAYLOR, **Hon C** F H BOARDMAN
BURWARDSLEY (St John) Harthill and Burwardsley *Ches*
BURWASH (St Bartholomew) *Chich 14* **P** *BNC Ox* **P-in-c** R D VINCENT
BURWASH WEALD (St Philip) *Chich 15* **P** *Bp* **P-in-c** J N STOCKWELL
BURWELL (St Andrew) (St Mary) *Ely 3* **P** *DBP* **V** *Vacant* Newmarket (01638) 741262
BURY (Christ the King) *Man 10* **P** *Patr Bd* **V** P R FRENCH
BURY (Holy Cross) Warboys w Broughton and Bury w Wistow *Ely*
BURY (Holy Trinity) *Man 10* **P** *Patr Bd* **V** *Vacant* 0161–764 2006
BURY (St John the Evangelist) and Houghton *Chich 11* **P** *Pemb Coll Ox* **V** *Vacant* Bury (01798) 831677
BURY (St John w St Mark) *Man 10* **P** *R Bury St Mary* **V** R W LAWRANCE
BURY (St Mary the Virgin) *Man 10* **P** *Earl of Derby* **R** J R SMITH
BURY (St Paul) *Man 10* **P** *Trustees* **V** A BORSBEY
BURY (St Peter) *Man 10* **P** *R Bury St Mary* **V** G G ROXBY, **C** R J E CLACK, **Hon C** F E F WARD, **NSM** J M SMITH
BURY, NEW (St James) *Man 12* **P** *Bp* **TR** A OWENS, **C** A COMBER, **NSM** D N BIRD, E FODEN, A L OWENS
BURY ST EDMUNDS (All Saints) *St E 13* **P** *Bp* **P-in-c** G J WEBB
BURY ST EDMUNDS (Cathedral of St James) District *St E* **V** *Vacant*
BURY ST EDMUNDS (Christ Church) Moreton Hall *St E 13* **P** *Bp, V Bury St Edm St Jas, and V Bury St Edm St Mary (jt)* **V** J L ALDERTON-FORD
BURY ST EDMUNDS (St George) *St E 13* **P** *Bp* **V** D W HERRICK, **C** A W SPENCER
BURY ST EDMUNDS (St John the Evangelist) *St E 13* **P** *Bp* **P-in-c** D R UNDERWOOD, **C** A HASLEHURST (nee STERLING), **NSM** D MAUDLIN
BURY ST EDMUNDS (St Mary) (St Peter's District Church) *St E 13* **P** *Hyndman Trustees* **P-in-c** J D HAYDEN, **C** I D TWEEDIE-SMITH, **NSM** E M ELLIOTT
BURYTHORPE (All Saints), Acklam and Leavening w Westow *York 2* **P** *Abp* **R** *Vacant* Burythorpe (0165385) 220
BUSBRIDGE (St John the Baptist) *Guildf 4* **P** *DBP* **R** J TRICKEY
BUSCOT (St Mary) Gt Coxwell w Buscot, Coleshill & Eaton Hastings *Ox*
BUSH END (St John the Evangelist) Hatf Broad Oak and Bush End *Chelmsf*
BUSH HILL PARK (St Mark) *Lon 18* **P** *Bp* **V** D G BROOKER
BUSH HILL PARK (St Stephen) *Lon 18* **P** *V Edmonton All SS* **V** R J ANNIS
BUSHBURY (St Mary) *Lich 9* **P** *Patr Bd* **TR** R A HINTON, **TV** N R HOGG, P I DENNISON, **C** S J OSBOURNE
BUSHEY (Holy Trinity) (St James) (St Paul) *St Alb 1* **P** *Bp* **R** I C COOPER, **C** I S TATTUM, C M PUNSHON, **Hon C** W A PENNEY
BUSHEY HEATH (St Peter) *St Alb 1* **P** *Bp* **V** W R LOW
BUSHLEY (St Peter) Longdon, Castlemorton, Bushley, Queenhill etc *Worc*
BUSHMEAD Conventional District *St Alb 20* **C-in-c** M A SLATER
BUSSAGE (St Michael and All Angels) *Glouc 1* **P** *Bp* **V** H J van der LINDE
BUTCOMBE (St Michael and All Angels) Wrington w Butcombe *B & W*
BUTLEIGH (St Leonard) Baltonsborough w Butleigh and W Bradley *B & W*
BUTLERS MARSTON (St Peter and St Paul) and the Pillertons w Ettington *Cov 9* **P** *Ch Ch Ox (1 turn), Bp, Major & Mrs J E Shirley, and Miss M L P Shirley (1 turn), and Mr & Mrs G Howell (1 turn)* **V** D CHING
BUTLEY (St John the Baptist) Orford w Sudbourne, Chillesford, Butley and Iken *St E*
BUTTERCRAMBE (St John the Evangelist) Sand Hutton *York*
BUTTERLEIGH (St Matthew) Silverton, Butterleigh, Bickleigh and Cadeleigh *Ex*
BUTTERMERE (St James) Lorton and Loweswater w Buttermere *Carl*
BUTTERMERE (St James the Great) Wexcombe *Sarum*
BUTTERSHAW (St Aidan) Shelf St Mich w Buttershaw St Aid *Bradf*

BUTTERSHAW (St Paul) *Bradf 2* **P** *Bp* **V** P STREET
BUTTERTON (St Bartholomew) Alstonfield, Butterton, Warslow w Elkstone etc *Lich*
BUTTERTON (St Thomas) Newc w Butterton *Lich*
BUTTERWICK (Mission Chapel) Street TM *York*
BUTTERWICK (St Andrew) Freiston w Butterwick *Linc*
BUTTERWICK (St Nicholas) Langtoft w Foxholes, Butterwick, Cottam etc *York*
BUTTERWICK, EAST (St Andrew) Messingham *Linc*
BUTTERWICK, WEST (St Mary) *Linc 1* **P** *V Owston* **V** *Vacant*
BUTTSBURY (St Mary) Ingatestone w Buttsbury *Chelmsf*
BUXHALL (St Mary) w Shelland *St E 6* **P** *Bp* **R** *Vacant* Rattlesden (014493) 236
BUXTED (St Margaret the Queen) (St Mary) and Hadlow Down *Chich 21* **P** *Abp, Bp, and Wagner Trustees (jt)* **R** R WOLLEY
BUXTON (St Andrew) w Oxnead, Lammas and Brampton *Nor 20* **P** *Bp* **R** G R DRAKE
BUXTON (St Anne) (St John the Baptist) (St Mary the Virgin) w Burbage and King Sterndale *Derby 4* **P** *Patr Bd* **TR** J C TOMLINSON, **TV** M J LEWIS, C M SCARGILL
BUXTON (Trinity Chapel) Proprietary Chapel *Derby 4* **C-in-c** S D N VIBERT
BUXWORTH (St James) Chinley w Buxworth *Derby*
BYERS GREEN (St Peter) *Dur 10* **P** *Bp* **P-in-c** A L BELL
BYFIELD (Holy Cross) w Boddington and Aston le Walls *Pet 1* **P** *Bp, CCC Ox, and Em Coll Cam (by turn)* **R** S E WEST-LINDELL
BYFLEET (St Mary) *Guildf 12* **P** *Ld Chan* **R** R D TRUMPER, **C** M A McCAGHREY, **NSM** A G BARDELL
BYFLEET, WEST (St John) *Guildf 12* **P** *Bp* **V** L S SMITH
BYFORD (St John the Baptist) Letton w Staunton, Byford, Mansel Gamage etc *Heref*
BYGRAVE (St Margaret of Antioch) Baldock w Bygrave *St Alb*
BYKER (St Anthony) *Newc 6* **P** *Bp* **V** D C MUMFORD, **C** J DRAY
BYKER St Mark and Walkergate (St Oswald) *Newc 6* **P** *Bp and Ch Trust Fund Trust (jt)* **V** K MOULDER, **C** H A CHARTERIS
BYKER (St Martin) Newcastle upon Tyne *Newc 6* **P** *Bp* **V** *Vacant* 0191–265 5931
BYKER (St Michael w St Lawrence) *Newc 6* **P** *Bp* **P-in-c** S J LIDDLE
BYKER (St Silas) *Newc 6* **P** *Bp* **V** *Vacant* 0191–265 5353
BYLAND, OLD (All Saints) Upper Ryedale *York*
BYLAUGH (St Mary) Lyng, Sparham, Elsing and Bylaugh *Nor*
BYLEY CUM LEES (St John the Evangelist) Middlewich w Byley *Ches*
BYRNESS (St Francis) N Tyne and Redesdale Team *Newc*
BYTHAM, LITTLE (St Medardus) Castle Bytham w Creeton *Linc*
BYTHORN (St Lawrence) Keyston and Bythorn *Ely*
BYTON (St Mary) Pembridge w Moorcourt, Shobdon, Staunton etc *Heref*
BYWELL (St Peter) *Newc 3* **P** *Adn Northd* **V** T EMMETT
BYWORTH (St Francis) Farnham *Guildf*
CABLE STREET (St Mary) St Geo-in-the-East St Mary *Lon*
CABOURN (St Nicholas) Swallow *Linc*
CADBURY (St Michael and All Angels) Thorverton, Cadbury, Upton Pyne etc *Ex*
CADBURY, NORTH (St Michael the Archangel) Camelot Par *B & W*
CADBURY, SOUTH (St Thomas a Becket) as above
CADDINGTON (All Saints) *St Alb 20* **P** *D&C St Paul's* **V** A J D SMITH
CADEBY (All Saints) Market Bosworth, Cadeby w Sutton Cheney etc *Leic*
CADELEIGH (St Bartholomew) Silverton, Butterleigh, Bickleigh and Cadeleigh *Ex*
CADGWITH (St Mary) St Ruan w St Grade and Landewednack *Truro*
CADISHEAD (St Mary the Virgin) *Man 2* **P** *Bp* **V** D RIDLEY, **C** L RIDLEY
CADMORE END (St Mary le Moor) Lane End w Cadmore End *Ox*
CADNEY (All Saints) *Linc 6* **P** *Bp* **V** *Vacant*
CADOGAN SQUARE (St Simon Zelotes) Upper Chelsea St Simon *Lon*
CAERHAYS (St Michael) St Goran w St Mich Caerhays *Truro*
CAGE GREEN (Church Hall) Tonbridge SS Pet and Paul *Roch*

CAINSCROSS (St Matthew) w Selsley *Glouc 8*   **P** *Bp and Sir Charles Marling, Bt (alt)*   **V**   G G C MINORS,   **C**   T M B WOODHOUSE

CAISTER NEXT YARMOUTH (Holy Trinity) (St Edmund) *Nor 6*   **P** *SMF*   **P-in-c** T C THOMPSON

CAISTOR (St Edmund) Stoke H Cross w Dunston, Arminghall etc *Nor*

CAISTOR (St Peter and St Paul) w Clixby *Linc 5*   **P** *Bp*   **V** *Vacant* Caistor (01472) 851339

CALBOURNE (All Saints) w Newtown *Portsm 8*   **P** *Bp*   **V** *Vacant*

CALCOT (St Birinus) *Ox 15*   **P** *Magd Coll Ox*   **V**   A D BARNES

CALDBECK (St Mungo) (Fellside), Castle Sowerby and Sebergham *Carl 3*   **P** *Bp and D&C (alt)*   **R**   R C JOHNS

CALDECOTE (All Saints) *St Alb 17*   **P** *Grocers' Co*   **V**   P R CRESSALL

CALDECOTE (St John the Evangelist) Gretton w Rockingham and Caldecote *Pet*

CALDECOTE (St Michael and All Angels) Toft w Caldecote and Childerley *Ely*

CALDECOTE (St Theobald and St Chad) Weddington and Caldecote *Cov*

CALDER GROVE (St John the Divine) Chapelthorpe *Wakef*

CALDER VALE (Mission) Barnacre w Calder Vale *Blackb*

CALDER VALE (St John the Evangelist) as above

CALDERBROOK (St James the Great) *Man 20*   **P** *Bp*   **V** *Vacant* Littleborough (01706) 378414

CALDMORE (St Michael and All Angels) *Lich 6*   **P** *Bp*   **P-in-c** F R MILLER,   **C**   N A MPUNZI

CALDWELL (Chapel) Forcett and Aldbrough and Melsonby *Ripon*

CALDWELL (St Giles) Stapenhill w Cauldwell *Derby*

CALDY (Church of the Resurrection and All Saints) W Kirby St Bridget *Ches*

CALEDONIAN ROAD (All Saints Hall) Barnsbury *Lon*

CALIFORNIA (St Mary and St John) *Ox 16*   **P** *DBP*   **V** *Vacant* Eversley (01734) 730030

CALLINGTON (St Mary) S Hill w Callington *Truro*

CALLOW END (St James) Powyke *Worc*

CALMORE (St Anne) Totton *Win*

CALNE (Holy Trinity) (St Mary the Virgin) and Blackland *Sarum 18*   **P** *Bp*   **V**   A G WOODS,   **C**   M T B EVANS,   S P V CADE

CALOW (St Peter) and Sutton cum Duckmanton *Derby 3*   **P** *Bp and V Chesterfield (jt)*   **R**   N V JOHNSON

CALSHOT (St George) Fawley *Win*

CALSTOCK (St Andrew) *Truro 11*   **P** *Duchy of Cornwall*   **R**   J A C WILSON

CALSTONE WELLINGTON (St Mary the Virgin) Oldbury *Sarum*

CALTHORPE (Our Lady w St Margaret) Erpingham w Calthorpe, Ingworth, Aldborough etc *Nor*

CALTHWAITE (All Saints) Hesket-in-the-Forest and Armathwaite *Carl*

CALTON (St Mary the Virgin), Cauldon, Grindon and Waterfall *Lich 10*   **P** *Bp*   **R**   J R TYE

CALVELEY CHURCH (not known) Bunbury and Tilstone Fearnall *Ches*

CALVERHALL or CORRA (Holy Trinity) Ightfield w Calverhall *Lich*

CALVERLEIGH (St Mary the Virgin) Washfield, Stoodleigh, Withleigh etc *Ex*

CALVERLEY (St Wilfrid) *Bradf 3*   **P** *Bp*   **V**   J H WALKER

CALVERTON (All Saints) *Ox 25*   **P** *DBP*   **R**   C H J CAVELL-NORTHAM

CALVERTON (St Wilfrid) *S'well 15*   **P** *Bp*   **V** *Vacant* Nottingham (0115) 965 2552

CAM (St George) w Stinchcombe *Glouc 2*   **P** *Bp*   **V**   C M MALKINSON

CAM, LOWER (St Bartholomew) w Coaley *Glouc 2*   **P** *Bp*   **V**   I A ROBB

CAMBER (St Thomas) Rye *Chich*

CAMBERLEY (St Martin) Old Dean *Guildf 6*   **P** *Bp*   **V**   M N CORNELL

CAMBERLEY (St Michael) Yorktown *Guildf 6*   **P** *Bp*   **V**   J P B WYNBURNE

CAMBERLEY (St Paul) (St Mary) *Guildf 6*   **P** *Bp*   **TR**   R S CROSSLEY,   **TV**   P D BRYER,   J H G CARTER,   **C**   B APPLETON, **Hon C** A C LONG, **NSM** C SIMONS

CAMBERLEY HEATHERSIDE (Community Centre) Camberley St Paul *Guildf*

CAMBERWELL (All Saints) Blenheim Grove *S'wark 6*   **P** *Ch Trust Fund Trust*   **V** *Vacant* 0171–639 3052

CAMBERWELL (Christ Church) *S'wark 6*   **P** *Trustees*   **V**   H R BALFOUR

CAMBERWELL (St George) *S'wark 6*   **P** *Bp and Trin Coll Cam (jt)*   **V**   S J ROBERTS, **Hon C** J E PAWSEY

CAMBERWELL (St Giles) (St Matthew) *S'wark 6*   **P** *Bp*   **V**   R W G BOMFORD,   **C**   S M SICHEL, **Hon C** S D HAINES, **NSM** H D POTTER

CAMBERWELL (St Luke) *S'wark 6*   **P** *Bp*   **V**   A P DAVEY

CAMBERWELL (St Matthew) Herne Hill *S'wark*

CAMBERWELL (St Michael and All Angels w All Souls w Emmanuel) *S'wark 8*   **P** *DBP*   **V** P VOWLES,   **P-in-c** M A HART

CAMBERWELL (St Philip) and St Mark *S'wark 5*   **P** *The Crown*   **V**   N A W DAVIS

CAMBO (Holy Trinity) Kirkwhelpington, Kirkharle, Kirkheaton and Cambo *Newc*

CAMBOIS (St Peter) (St Andrew's Mission Church) *Newc 1*   **P** *D&C*   **P-in-c** J M PENNINGTON

CAMBORNE (St Martin and St Meriadoc) *Truro 2*   **P** *Ch Soc Trust*   **R**   N J POCOCK,   **C**   D A TREBY, **Hon C** G E BOTTOMLEY, **NSM** D E HARVEY

CAMBRIDGE Ascension (St Giles) (St Luke the Evangelist) (St Augustine of Canterbury) (All Souls Chapel) *Ely 2*   **P** *Bp*   **TR** J P YOUNG,   **TV** C A SINDALL,   **C** P A KING, **NSM** O R SPENCER-THOMAS

CAMBRIDGE (Holy Cross) *Ely 2*   **P** *Bp*   **V**   A L HARGRAVE

CAMBRIDGE (Holy Sepulchre) (St Andrew the Great) *Ely 2*   **P** *PCC*   **V**   M H ASHTON,   **C**   G R WALTER,   C J DAVIS,   C B G ASH

CAMBRIDGE (Holy Trinity) *Ely 2*   **P** *D&C and Peache Trustees (jt)*   **V**   D HUMPHRIES,   C D HANCOCK,   **C**   N G JONES, **Hon C** G G AKURU

CAMBRIDGE (St Andrew the Less) (Christ Church) *Ely 2*   **P** *Ch Trust Fund Trust*   **V**   M L DIAMOND

CAMBRIDGE (St Barnabas) *Ely 2*   **P** *V Cam St Paul*   **V**   L J BROWNE,   **C**   L E J SMYTH,   **NSM** J E KEILLER

CAMBRIDGE (St Benedict) *Ely 2*   **P** *CCC Cam*   **V**   R A L SMYTH

CAMBRIDGE (St Botolph) *Ely 2*   **P** *Qu Coll Cam*   **NSM**   W HORBURY

CAMBRIDGE (St Clement) *Ely 2*   **P** *Jes Coll Cam*   **V** *Vacant*

CAMBRIDGE (St Edward King and Martyr) Proprietary Chapel *Ely 2*,   F N WATTS

CAMBRIDGE (St James) *Ely 2*   **P** *Bp*   **V**   H W DAWES,   **C**   B SNELL

CAMBRIDGE (St John the Evangelist) Cherry Hinton St Jo *Ely*

CAMBRIDGE (St Mark) *Ely 2*   **P** *DBP*   **V**   P A SPENCE

CAMBRIDGE (St Martin) (St Thomas) *Ely 2*   **P** *V Cam St Paul*   **V**   S D ARMSTRONG,   **C**   S C HOWARD

CAMBRIDGE (St Mary the Great) w St Michael *Ely 2*   **P** *Trin Coll Cam*   **V**   J R BINNS,   **C**   C M FARRINGTON,   D L GOSLING, **Hon C** A S HOPKINSON

CAMBRIDGE (St Mary the Less) *Ely 2*   **P** *Peterho Cam*   **V**   R A H GREANY, **Hon C** A K BERGQUIST,   **NSM** N J HANCOCK,   J B QUASH

CAMBRIDGE (St Matthew) *Ely 2*   **P** *V Cam St Andr the Less*   **P-in-c** E P J FOSTER

CAMBRIDGE (St Paul) *Ely 2*   **P** *Ch Trust Fund Trust*   **V**   M S BECKETT

CAMBRIDGE (St Philip) (St Stephen) *Ely 2*   **P** *Ch Trust Fund Trust*   **V**   S TAYLOR,   **C**   N CUTLER,   **NSM**   T R MONTGOMERY

CAMDEN SQUARE (St Paul) *Lon 17*   **P** *D&C St Paul's*   **V**   P DYSON

CAMDEN TOWN (St Michael) (All Saints and St Thomas) *Lon 17*   **P** *D&C St Paul's*   **V**   A R B PAGE

CAMEL, WEST (All Saints) Queen Camel w W Camel, Corton Denham etc *B & W*

CAMELFORD (St Julitta) Lanteglos by Camelford w Advent *Truro*

CAMELFORD (St Thomas of Canterbury) as above

CAMELOT Parishes, The *B & W 3*   **P** *Patr Bd*   **TV**   J M THOROGOOD,   **NSM**   K L BRUTON

CAMELSDALE (St Paul) *Chich 10*   **P** *The Crown*   **V**   G BOTTOMLEY

CAMERTON (St Peter) w Dunkerton, Foxcote and Shoscombe *B & W 12*   **P** *Bp*   **R**   D E COOPER

CAMERTON (St Peter), Seaton and West Seaton *Carl 7*   **P** *D&C and Ch Trust Fund Trust (jt)*   **V**   J D KELLY

CAMMERINGHAM (St Michael) Ingham w Cammeringham w Fillingham *Linc*

CAMP HILL (St Mary and St John) w Galley Common *Cov 5*   **P** *Bp*   **V**   S D SNEATH

CAMPBELL ROOMS (not known) Parr Mt *Liv*

CAMPSALL (St Mary Magdalene) *Sheff 8*   **P** *Bp*   **V**   T B CLARK

CAMPSEA ASHE (St John the Baptist) w Marlesford, Parham and Hacheston *St E 18*   **P** *Prime Min, Ch Soc Trust, and J S Schreiber Esq (by turn)*   **R** *Vacant* Wickham Market (01728) 746747

CAMPTON (All Saints) Meppershall w Campton and Stondon *St Alb*
CANDLESBY (St Benedict) Partney *Linc*
CANDOVER VALLEY, THE *Win 1* **P** *D&C and Lord Ashburton (jt)* **R** C R SMITH
CANEWDON (St Nicholas) w Paglesham *Chelmsf 12* **P** *D&C Westmr and Hyndman Trustees (jt)* **V** N J KELLY
CANFIELD, GREAT (St Mary) *Chelmsf 19* **P** *A C Sainthill Esq* **R** *Vacant* Bishop's Stortford (0279) 871300
CANFIELD, LITTLE (All Saints) Takeley w Lt Canfield *Chelmsf*
CANFORD CLIFFS (Transfiguration) and Sandbanks *Sarum 8* **P** *Bp* **P-in-c** J C OAKES
CANFORD HEATH (St Paul) Oakdale St Geo *Sarum*
CANFORD MAGNA (Bearwood) (Lantern) *Sarum 10* **P** *Patr Bd* **TR** P H LAWRENCE, **TV** A D EDWARDS, R J GROVES, **NSM** A SIMPSON, D A PHILLIPS, I CHALLIS
CANLEY (St Stephen) *Cov 3* **P** *Bp* **V** P H SMITH
CANNING TOWN (St Cedd) *Chelmsf 3* **P** *Bp* **V** *Vacant* 0171–474 3711
CANNING TOWN (St Matthias) *Chelmsf 3* **P** *Bp* **C** R H WILLIAMS
CANNINGTON (Blessed Virgin Mary), Otterhampton, Combwich and Stockland *B & W 14* **P** *Bp* **R** P MARTIN, **NSM** R H BARBER
CANNOCK (St Luke) *Lich 3* **P** *Patr Bd* **TR** K M JUKES, **TV** P J DREWETT, P A GRAYSMITH (formerly SMITH), N PURVEY-TYRER, **C** M A HOLDSWORTH, P J GRAYSMITH (nee GRAY), A J BETTS
CANON FROME (St James) Bosbury w Wellington Heath etc *Heref*
CANON PYON (St Lawrence) w Kings Pyon and Birley *Heref 7* **P** *Bp and D&C (alt)* **V** C M BURKE
CANONBURY (St Stephen) *Lon 6* **P** *V Islington St Mary* **V** D P LITTLE, **NSM** M E EVANS
CANTERBURY (All Saints) *Cant 3* **P** *Abp* **V** B J COOPER
CANTERBURY (St Dunstan w Holy Cross) *Cant 3* **P** *Abp* **V** M W WORGAN
CANTERBURY (St Martin) (St Paul) *Cant 3* **P** *Abp* **R** P T MACKENZIE, **C** S YATES, **Hon C** P V LLOYD
CANTERBURY (St Mary Bredin) *Cant 3* **P** *Simeon's Trustees* **V** J M GLEDHILL, **C** M J BURRELL
CANTERBURY (St Peter w St Alphege) (St Mildred) and St Margaret w St Mary de Castro *Cant 3* **P** *The Crown* **R** D M H HAYES
CANTERBURY (St Stephen) Hackington *Cant*
CANTLEY (St Margaret) Reedham w Cantley w Limpenhoe and Southwood *Nor*
CANTLEY (St Wilfrid) *Sheff 9* **P** *Guild of All So* **V** R J OAKLEY, **C** T A PARKINSON, J W MATHER
CANTLEY, NEW (St Hugh of Lincoln) *Sheff 9* **P** *Guild of All So* **V** C J FLETCHER
CANTRIL FARM (St Jude) *Liv 2* **P** *Bp and R W Derby (jt)* **V** C WARRILOW, **C** V J ENEVER
CANVEY ISLAND (St Anne) (St Katherine's Worship Centre) (St Nicholas) *Chelmsf 10* **P** *Bp and Patr Bd (jt)* **TR** D J ELLA, **TV** A J FORAN, **C** M D MOORE, **NSM** J E MOORE
CANWELL (St Mary, St Giles and All Saints) *Lich 4* **P** *Bp* **V** H J BAKER
CANWICK (All Saints) Washingborough w Heighington and Canwick *Linc*
CAPEL (St John the Baptist) *Guildf 7* **P** *Ld Chan* **V** R J WHITTLE
CAPEL St Mary w Little Wenham and Great Wenham *St E 5* **P** *Bp and SMF (jt)* **R** B A TOLL
CAPEL LE FERNE (St Radigund) Alkham w Capel le Ferne and Hougham *Cant*
CAPENHURST (Holy Trinity) Backford and Capenhurst *Ches*
CAPESTHORNE (Holy Trinity) w Siddington and Marton *Ches 13* **P** *Exors Lt-Col Sir Walter Bromley-Davenport* **V** J B WARBURTON
CAR COLSTON (St Mary) w Screveton *S'well 8* **P** *H S Blagg Esq* **R** J PULMAN
CARBIS BAY (St Anta and All Saints) w Lelant (St Uny) *Truro 5* **P** *Bp* **NSM** E A TUGWELL
CARBROOKE (St Peter and St Paul) Watton w Carbrooke and Ovington *Nor*
CARBURTON (St Giles) Worksop Priory *S'well*
CARDESTON (St Michael) Alberbury w Cardeston *Heref*
CARDINGTON (St James) *Heref 11* **P** *Rt Hon Sir Frederick Corfield* **V** M BROMFIELD
CARDINGTON (St Mary) *St Alb 19* **P** *S C Whitbread Esq* **V** N P MORRELL, **Hon C** L R MOORE

CARDYNHAM (St Mewbud) *Truro 10* **P** *DBP and Personal Reps R M Coode Esq (jt)* **P-in-c** R D C WHITEMAN, **NSM** J F KIRBY
CAREBY (St Stephen) Castle Bytham w Creeton *Linc*
CARHAM (St Cuthbert) Cornhill w Carham *Newc*
CARHAMPTON (St John the Baptist) Dunster, Carhampton and Withycombe w Rodhuish *B & W*
CARHARRACK (St Piran's Mission Church) St Day *Truro*
CARISBROOKE (St John the Baptist) Newport St Jo *Portsm*
CARISBROOKE (St Mary the Virgin) *Portsm 8* **P** *Qu Coll Ox* **P-in-c** M A J EXELL
CARISBROOKE St Nicholas in the Castle *Portsm 8* **P** *Qu Coll Ox* **V** *Vacant*
CARLBY (St Stephen) Ness Gp *Linc*
CARLECOATES (St Anne) Penistone and Thurlstone *Wakef*
CARLETON (St Mary the Virgin) and Lothersdale *Bradf 7* **P** *Ch Ch Ox* **R** S G HOARE, **NSM** B M WILKINSON (nee PHILPOTT)
CARLETON (St Michael) *Wakef 11* **P** *V Pontefract* **V** F L BROOKS
CARLETON (St Peter) Rockland St Mary w Hellington, Bramerton etc *Nor*
CARLETON, EAST (St Mary) Swardeston w E Carleton, Intwood, Keswick etc *Nor*
CARLETON IN CRAVEN Carleton and Lothersdale *Bradf*
CARLETON RODE (All Saints) Bunwell, Carleton Rode, Tibenham, Gt Moulton etc *Nor*
CARLIN HOW (St Helen) Loftus and Carlin How w Skinningrove *York*
CARLINGHOW (St John the Evangelist) *Wakef 10* **P** *V Brownhill and V Batley (alt)* **V** *Vacant* Batley (01924) 472576
CARLISLE Belah (St Mark) Stanwix *Carl*
CARLISLE Harraby (St Elizabeth) Harraby *Carl*
CARLISLE (Holy Trinity) (St Barnabas) *Carl 3* **P** *Patr Bd* **TR** D C ELLIS, **TV** G M DYER, D T LEWIS, **NSM** T N DYER
CARLISLE (St Aidan) and Christ Church *Carl 3* **P** *Bp* **V** N M E CLAPP
CARLISLE (St Cuthbert) *Carl 3* **P** *D&C* **P-in-c** A N DAVIS
CARLISLE (St Herbert) w St Stephen *Carl 3* **P** *Bp* **P-in-c** G F GILCHRIST
CARLISLE (St James) Denton Holme *Carl*
CARLISLE (St John the Evangelist) *Carl 3* **P** *CPAS* **V** P J BYE, **C** F I WRIGHT, **NSM** C G Y HYSLOP
CARLISLE (St Luke) Morton *Carl 3* **P** *Bp* **V** K W RAY
CARLISLE Stanwix (St Michael) Stanwix *Carl*
CARLISLE Upperby (St John the Baptist) Upperby St Jo *Carl*
CARLTON (St Aidan) Helmsley *York*
CARLTON (St Andrew) Nailstone and Carlton w Shackerstone *Leic*
CARLTON (St Bartholomew) Guiseley w Esholt *Bradf*
CARLTON (St Botolph) Whorlton w Carlton and Faceby *York*
CARLTON (St John the Baptist) *S'well 11* **P** *Bp* **V** A M LUCKCUCK
CARLTON (St John the Evangelist) *Wakef 7* **P** *DBP* **P-in-c** J L HUDSON
CARLTON (St Mary) Harrold and Carlton w Chellington *St Alb*
CARLTON (St Peter) Brinkley, Burrough Green and Carlton *Ely*
CARLTON (St Peter) Kelsale-cum-Carlton, Middleton-cum-Fordley etc *St E*
CARLTON, EAST (St Peter) Cottingham w E Carlton *Pet*
CARLTON, GREAT (St John the Baptist) Mid Marsh Gp *Linc*
CARLTON, NORTH (St Luke) w SOUTH (St John the Baptist) *Linc 3* **P** *Lord Monson* **P-in-c** M J SILLEY
CARLTON BY SNAITH (St Mary) and Drax *York 6* **P** *Abp and Ch Trust Fund Trust (jt)* **V** *Vacant* Selby (01757) 618313
CARLTON COLVILLE (St Peter) w Mutford and Rushmere *Nor 9* **P** *Bp, G&C Coll Cam, and Simeon's Trustees (jt)* **R** A T SMITH
CARLTON CURLIEU (St Mary the Virgin) Gaulby *Leic*
CARLTON FOREHOE (St Mary) Barnham Broom *Nor*
CARLTON HUSTHWAITE (St Mary) Coxwold and Husthwaite *York*
CARLTON-IN-LINDRICK (St John the Evangelist) *S'well 6* **P** *Ld Chan* **R** J OGLEY, **Hon C** J H SIMPSON
CARLTON-IN-THE-WILLOWS (St Paul) *S'well 11* **P** *MMCET* **R** J F McGINLEY
CARLTON-LE-MOORLAND (St Mary) w Stapleford *Linc 18* **P** *Lord Middleton* **P-in-c** E I SLATER

CARLTON MINIOTT (St Lawrence) Thirsk *York*

CARLTON-ON-TRENT (St Mary) Sutton w Carlton and Normanton upon Trent etc *S'well*

CARLTON SCROOP (St Nicholas) Caythorpe *Linc*

CARNABY (St John the Baptist) *York 10* P *Abp*
V T J DAVIDSON

CARNFORTH (Christ Church) *Blackb 15* P *Bp* V *Vacant* Carnforth (01524) 732948

CARR CLOUGH (St Andrew) Kersal Moor *Man*

CARR MILL (St David) *Liv 10* P *V St Helens St Mark and Bp (jt)* P-in-c J R BROUGHTON

CARRINGTON (St John the Evangelist) *S'well 13* P *Bp* V *Vacant* Nottingham (0115) 962 1291

CARRINGTON (St Paul) Sibsey w Frithville *Linc*

CARSHALTON (All Saints) *S'wark 26* P *Bp*
R L C EDWARDS

CARSHALTON BEECHES (Good Shepherd) *S'wark 26* P *Bp* V C WHEATON, C P H CUNLIFFE

CARSINGTON (St Margaret) Wirksworth *Derby*

CARTERTON (St John the Evangelist) *Ox 8* P *Ch Ch Ox* V R K BILLINGS

CARTMEL (St Mary and St Michael) *Carl 10* P *R H Cavendish Esq* V C L V ATKINSON

CARTMEL FELL (St Anthony) *Carl 9* P *Bp* V K PARTINGTON

CASSINGTON (St Peter) Eynsham and Cassington *Ox*

CASSOP cum Quarrington *Dur 14* P *Bp* V J THOMPSON

CASTERTON (Holy Trinity) Kirkby Lonsdale *Carl*

CASTERTON, GREAT (St Peter and St Paul) and LITTLE (All Saints) w Pickworth and Tickencote *Pet 8* P *Burghley Ho Preservation Trust (2 turns), Lord Chesham (1 turn), and Bp (1 turn)* R B HARRIS

CASTLE ACRE (St James) w Newton, Rougham and Southacre *Nor 15* P *Viscount Coke, T F North Esq, Bp and H Birkbeck Esq (jt) (by turn)* P-in-c R W GYTON

CASTLE ASHBY (St Mary Magdalene) Yardley Hastings, Denton and Grendon etc *Pet*

CASTLE BOLTON (St Oswald) Aysgarth and Bolton cum Redmire *Ripon*

CASTLE BROMWICH (St Clement) *Birm 11* P *Bp* V W J SILLITOE, Hon C M W MORECROFT, NSM P A SILLITOE

CASTLE BROMWICH (St Mary and St Margaret) *Birm 11* P *Earl of Bradf* R C J BOYLE, C S CONLON

CASTLE BYTHAM (St James) w Creeton *Linc 14* P *D&C, Bp, Ld Chan, and DBP (by turn)* R B J BENNETT

CASTLE CAMPS (All Saints) *Ely 4* P *Charterhouse* P-in-c J H THOMSON, NSM M W B O'LOUGHLIN

CASTLE CARROCK (St Peter) Brampton and Farlam and Castle Carrock w Cumrew *Carl*

CASTLE CARY (All Saints) w Ansford *B & W 3* P *Bp* V P W M REVELL, C R H AXFORD

CASTLE CHURCH (St Mary) *Lich 15* P *Bp* V J T H PYE

CASTLE COMBE (St Andrew) *Bris 9* P *Bp* P-in-c J N A BRADBURY, C R V C LEWIS

CASTLE DONINGTON (St Edward the King and Martyr) and Lockington cum Hemington *Leic 7* P *Lady Gretton and C H C Coaker Esq (jt)* V B WHITEHEAD, NSM L R F TESTA

CASTLE EATON (St Mary the Virgin) Meysey Hampton w Marston Meysey and Castle Eaton *Glouc*

CASTLE EDEN (St James) w Monkhesleden *Dur 3* P *Bp* R G G DEWHURST

CASTLE FROME (St Michael) Bishop's Frome w Castle Frome and Fromes Hill *Heref*

CASTLE HEDINGHAM (St Nicholas) Sible Hedingham w Castle Hedingham *Chelmsf*

CASTLE HILL (St Philip) Hindley All SS *Liv*

CASTLE RISING (St Lawrence) *Nor 17* P *G Howard Esq* P-in-c G R HALL

CASTLE SOWERBY (St Kentigern) Caldbeck, Castle Sowerby and Sebergham *Carl*

CASTLE TOWN (St Thomas and St Andrew) *Lich 15* P *Hyndman Trustees* V A L HUGHES

CASTLE VALE (St Cuthbert of Lindisfarne) *Birm 9* P *Bp* R S W POWELL

CASTLE VIEW ESTATE (St Francis) Langley Marish *Ox*

CASTLECROFT (The Good Shepherd) Tettenhall Wood *Lich*

CASTLEFORD (All Saints) *Wakef 11* P *Duchy of Lanc* R W T HICKS

CASTLEFORD (St Michael and All Angels) Smawthorpe St Mich *Wakef*

CASTLEMORTON (St Gregory) Longdon, Castlemorton, Bushley, Queenhill etc *Worc*

CASTLESIDE (St John the Evangelist) *Dur 8* P *Bp* V R L FERGUSON

CASTLETHORPE (St Simon and St Jude) Hanslope w Castlethorpe *Ox*

CASTLETON (St Edmund) Hope and Castleton *Derby*

CASTLETON (St Mary Magdalene) Sherborne w Castleton and Lillington *Sarum*

CASTLETON (St Michael and St George) Danby *York*

CASTLETON MOOR (St Martin) *Man 18* P *Bp* V I McVEETY

CASTLETOWN (St Margaret) N Hylton St Marg Castletown *Dur*

CASTLETOWN (St Mary) *S & M 1* P *Bp* V S T M R DEAN, C S M WATTERSON, NSM J R GULLAND

CASTON (St Cross) w Griston, Merton, Thompson, Stow Bedon and Breckles *Nor 14* P *Bp and Lord Walsingham (alt)* R J H RICHARDSON

CASTOR (St Kyneburgha) w Sutton and Upton *Pet 13* P *Bp (2 turns) and Mrs V S V Gunnery (1 turn)* R *Vacant* Peterborough (01733) 380244

CATCLIFFE (St Mary) Brinsworth w Catcliffe and Treeton *Sheff*

CATCOTT (St Peter) W Poldens *B & W*

CATERHAM (St Mary the Virgin) (St Laurence) (St Paul) *S'wark 19* P *Bp* C T MOAT, V M HAMER, Hon C E M HILL, M J WEST, P D JONES

CATERHAM VALLEY (St John the Evangelist) *S'wark 19* P *Bp* P-in-c C M S SNOW

CATESBY (St Mary) Daventry, Ashby St Ledgers, Braunston etc *Pet*

CATFIELD (All Saints) Sutton w Ingham and Catfield *Nor*

CATFORD (St Andrew) *S'wark 3* P *Bp* V R B JORDAN

CATFORD (St John) and Downham *S'wark 3* P *Bp* TR J D FRYAR, TV D E RHYS, P H ALLEN

CATFORD (St Laurence) *S'wark 3* P *Bp* V C F PICKSTONE, C C A M BRADDICK-SOUTHGATE

CATHERINGTON (All Saints) and Clanfield *Portsm 4* P *Bp* V C BEARDSLEY

CATHERSTON LEWESTON (St Mary) Charmouth and Catherston Leweston *Sarum*

CATON (St Paul) w Littledale *Blackb 12* P *V Lanc* V J R TATE

CATSFIELD (St Laurence) and Crowhurst *Chich 14* P *Bp and J P Papillon (alt)* R D J TAYLOR

CATSHILL (Christ Church) and Dodford *Worc 7* P *Bp and V Bromsgrove St Jo (alt)* P-in-c R M HARDING, C W J RIOCH

CATTERICK (St Anne) *Ripon 2* P *Bp* V W R HOGG

CATTHORPE (St Thomas) Swinford w Catthorpe, Shawell and Stanford *Leic*

CATTISTOCK (St Peter and St Paul) Melbury *Sarum*

CATTON (All Saints) Stamford Bridge Gp of Par *York*

CATTON (St Nicholas and the Blessed Virgin Mary) Walton on Trent w Croxall etc *Derby*

CATTON, NEW (Christ Church) *Nor 2* P *R Colegate St Geo* P-in-c K G CROCKER, C S C STOKES

CATTON, NEW (St Luke) *Nor 2* P *CPAS* V D A G G DOLMAN

CATTON, OLD (St Margaret) *Nor 2* P *D&C* V A D RAYMENT, Hon C H E QUINN

CATWICK (St Michael) Leven w Catwick *York*

CATWORTH, GREAT Catworth Magna *Ely*

CATWORTH MAGNA (St Leonard) *Ely 10* P *BNC Ox* P-in-c J HINDLEY, NSM B A BEARCROFT, J RAWLINSON

CAULDON (St Mary and St Laurence) Calton, Cauldon, Grindon and Waterfall *Lich*

CAUNDLE MARSH (St Peter and St Paul) The Caundles w Folke and Holwell *Sarum*

CAUNDLES w Folke and Holwell, The *Sarum 4* P *Major K S D Wingfield Digby, Bp, and D&C (jt)* R D J HILLIER

CAUNTON (St Andrew) Norwell w Ossington, Cromwell and Caunton *S'well*

CAUSEWAY HEAD (St Paul) Silloth *Carl*

CAUTLEY (St Mark) Sedbergh, Cautley and Garsdale *Bradf*

CAVENDISH (St Mary) Clare w Poslingford, Cavendish etc *St E*

CAVENHAM (St Andrew) Mildenhall *St E*

CAVERSFIELD (St Laurence) Bicester w Bucknell, Caversfield and Launton *Ox*

CAVERSHAM (St Andrew) *Ox 15* P *Bp* R W B CARPENTER, NSM A TYLER

CAVERSHAM (St John the Baptist) *Ox 15* P *Bp* V S M BROWE, NSM C E ROWE

CAVERSHAM (St Peter) (Park Church) and Mapledurham *Ox 15* P *Eton Coll (1 turn) and Ch Ch Ox (3 turns)* R R J KINGSBURY, C P J ABREY, S J NUNN, NSM J DUNN

CAVERSHAM HEIGHTS (St Andrew) Caversham St Andr *Ox*

CAVERSHAM PARK Local Ecumenical Project *Ox 15* **Min** P J ABREY

CAVERSWALL (St Peter) and Weston Coyney w Dilhorne *Lich 11* **P** *D&C* **V** N JEFFERYES, **C** D J R FLEET, **NSM** J A JEFFERYES

CAWOOD (All Saints) *York 6* **P** *Abp* **P-in-c** R E MESSER

CAWSAND (St Andrew's Mission Church) Maker w Rame *Truro*

CAWSTON (St Agnes) w Haveringland, Booton and Brandiston *Nor 20* **P** *Pemb Coll Cam (3 turns), DBP (1 turn)* **R** M C KING

CAWTHORNE (All Saints) *Wakef 7* **P** S W Fraser Esq **V** R T G SHARP

CAWTHORPE, LITTLE (St Helen) Legbourne *Linc*

CAXTON (St Andrew) Bourn and Kingston w Caxton and Longstowe *Ely*

CAYNHAM (St Mary) Ludlow, Ludford, Ashford Carbonell etc *Heref*

CAYTHORPE (St Aidan) Lowdham w Caythorpe, and Gunthorpe *S'well*

CAYTHORPE (St Vincent) *Linc 23* **P** *Bp, J F Fane Esq, and S J Packe-Drury-Lowe Esq (by turn)* **R** *Vacant* Loveden (01400) 73114

CAYTON (St John the Baptist) w Eastfield *York 16* **P** *Abp* **V** M D B LONG, **C** P OVEREND

CENTRAL: *see under substantive place name.*

CERNE ABBAS (St Mary) w Godmanstone and Minterne Magna *Sarum 2* **P** *Adn Sherborne (1 turn), D H C Batten Esq (1 turn), Lord Digby (2 turns), and G E H Gallia Esq (1 turn)* **V** *Vacant* Cerne Abbas (01300) 341251

CERNEY, NORTH (All Saints) Stratton, N Cerney, Baunton and Bagendon *Glouc*

CERNEY, SOUTH (All Hallows) w Cerney Wick and Down Ampney *Glouc 13* **P** *Bp and Ch Ch Ox (alt)* **V** J R CALVERT, **NSM** J T THOMAS

CERNEY WICK (Holy Trinity) S Cerney w Cerney Wick and Down Ampney *Glouc*

CHACELEY (St John the Baptist) Deerhurst, Apperley w Forthampton and Chaceley *Glouc*

CHACEWATER (St Paul) *Truro 6* **P** *V Kenwyn* **V** *Vacant* Truro (01872) 560225

CHACOMBE (St Peter and St Paul) Middleton Cheney w Chacombe *Pet*

CHADDERTON (Christ Church) (St Saviour) *Man 22* **P** *Trustees* **V** D P BANTING, **C** D K PHILLIPS

CHADDERTON (Emmanuel) (St George) *Man 22* **P** *Trustees* **V** E STOTT

CHADDERTON (St Luke) *Man 22* **P** *Bp* **V** G G MARSHALL

CHADDERTON (St Mark) *Man 22* **P** *The Crown* **V** A COOKE

CHADDERTON (St Matthew) *Man 22* **P** *The Crown* **V** R W BAILEY

CHADDESDEN (St Mary) *Derby 9* **P** *MMCET* **C** T M BINLEY

CHADDESDEN (St Philip) *Derby 9* **P** *Bp* **V** T G REILLY

CHADDESLEY CORBETT (St Cassian) and Stone *Worc 11* **P** *Ld Chan* **V** J A COX

CHADDLEWORTH (St Andrew) Brightwalton w Catmore, Leckhampstead etc *Ox*

CHADKIRK (St Chad) *Ches 16* **P** *R Stockport St Mary* **V** T D BARLOW, **C** T R PARKER

CHADLINGTON (St Nicholas) and Spelsbury, Ascott under Wychwood *Ox 3* **P** *Bp and Ch Ch Ox (alt)* **V** T C G THORNTON

CHADSMOOR (St Aidan) Cannock *Lich*

CHADSMOOR (St Chad) as above

CHADWELL (Emmanuel) (St Mary) *Chelmsf 14* **P** *Ch Soc Trust* **R** S BAILEY, **C** D WILLS

CHADWELL HEATH (St Chad) *Chelmsf 1* **P** *Vs Dagenham and Ilford (alt)* **V** J A A FLETCHER, **C** A COMFORT

CHAFFCOMBE (St Michael and All Angels) Chard Furnham w Chaffcombe, Knowle St Giles etc *B & W*

CHAGFORD (St Michael) w Gidleigh and Throwleigh *Ex 12* **P** *Lady Anne Hayter-Hames, Guild of All So, and Bp (jt)* **R** P L BAYCOCK

CHAILEY (St Peter) *Chich 21* **P** *J P B Tillard Esq* **R** C R ABBOTT

CHALBURY (All Saints) Horton and Chalbury *Sarum*

CHALDON (St Peter and St Paul) *S'wark 19* **P** *Bp* **R** *Vacant* Caterham (01883) 43668

CHALDON HERRING (St Nicholas) The Lulworths, Winfrith Newburgh and Chaldon *Sarum*

CHALE (St Andrew) *Portsm 8* **P** *Keble Coll Ox* **R** J W RUSSELL

CHALFIELD, GREAT (All Saints) Broughton Gifford, Gt Chalfield and Holt *Sarum*

CHALFONT, LITTLE (St George) Chenies and Lt Chalfont, Latimer and Flaunden *Ox*

CHALFONT ST GILES *Ox 20* **P** *Bp* **R** P W POOLE

CHALFONT ST PETER (St Peter) *Ox 20* **P** *St Jo Coll Ox* **R** D M MURRAY, **C** J P E SIBLEY, **NSM** L WARRINER, P J RINGER

CHALFORD (Christ Church) and France Lynch *Glouc 1* **P** *Adn Glouc and DBP (jt)* **V** P R KESLAKE

CHALGRAVE (All Saints) *St Alb 18* **P** *DBP* **P-in-c** K A STEELE

CHALGROVE (St Mary) w Berrick Salome *Ox 1* **P** *Ch Ch Ox* **V** I G H COHEN

CHALK (St Mary) *Roch 4* **P** *R Milton* **V** J R FRY

CHALKE VALLEY East *Sarum 13* **P** *D&C, CCC Ox, and Bp (by turn)* **R** P BYRON-DAVIES

CHALKE VALLEY West *Sarum 13* **P** *Bp, DBP, and K Coll Cam (by turn)* **V** S H WILLCOX

CHALLACOMBE (Holy Trinity) Shirwell, Loxhore, Kentisbury, Arlington, etc *Ex*

CHALLOCK (St Cosmas and St Damian) Chilham w Challock and Molash *Cant*

CHALLOW, EAST (St Nicolas) Hanney, Denchworth and E Challow *Ox*

CHALLOW, WEST (St Laurence) Ridgeway *Ox*

CHALTON (St Michael and All Angels) Blendworth w Chalton w Idsworth *Portsm*

CHALVEY (St Peter) Upton cum Chalvey *Ox*

CHALVINGTON (St Bartholomew) Laughton w Ripe and Chalvington *Chich*

CHAMBERSBURY Hemel Hempstead (Holy Trinity) (St Mary) (St Benedict) *St Alb 3* **P** *DBP* **TR** M R ABBOTT, **TV** C L TERRY, J B THOMAS, **Hon C** D A BUTLER

CHANDLER'S FORD (St Boniface) (St Martin in the Wood) *Win 9* **P** *Bp* **V** A G HARBIDGE, **C** J H T de GARIS, **NSM** V L MOFFITT

CHANTRY (Holy Trinity) Mells w Buckland Dinham, Elm, Whatley etc *B & W*

CHAPEL ALLERTON (St Matthew) *Ripon 5* **P** *V Leeds St Pet* **V** S JARRATT

CHAPEL CHORLTON (St Laurence), Maer and Whitmore *Lich 12* **P** *Bp and R G D Cavenagh-Mainwaring Esq (jt)* **R** G M YOULD

CHAPEL-EN-LE-FRITH (St Thomas a Becket) *Derby 4* **P** *PCC* **V** N R BRALESFORD

CHAPEL HOUSE (Holy Nativity) Whorlton *Newc*

CHAPEL LAWN (St Mary) Bucknell w Chapel Lawn, Llanfair Waterdine etc *Heref*

CHAPEL LE DALE (St Leonard) Ingleton w Chapel le Dale *Bradf*

CHAPEL PLAISTER (not known) Box w Hazlebury and Ditteridge *Bris*

CHAPEL ST LEONARDS (St Leonard) w Hogsthorpe *Linc 8* **P** *V Willoughby St Helen* **P-in-c** J D DUCKETT

CHAPELTHORPE (St James) *Wakef 9* **P** *V Sandal* **V** J F WHITE, **C** J TRAFFORD

CHAPELTOWN (St John the Baptist) *Sheff 7* **P** *Bp* **V** P J CRAIG-WILD, **C** D E CRAIG-WILD, M V GILBERT

CHAPL Whiteley Village *Guildf* , J T BEECH

CHAPMANSLADE (St Philip and St James) Corsley *Sarum*

CHAPPEL (St Barnabas) Gt Tey and Wakes Colne w Chappel *Chelmsf*

CHARBOROUGH (St Mary) Red Post *Sarum*

CHARD (Blessed Virgin Mary) *B & W 15* **P** *Bp* **V** M S KIVETT

CHARD Furnham (Good Shepherd) w Chaffcombe, Knowle St Giles and Cricket Malherbie *B & W 15* **P** *R Shepton Beauchamp etc and R Bishops Lydeard etc (jt)* **P-in-c** F R HAZELL

CHARDSTOCK (All Saints) Axminster, Chardstock, Combe Pyne and Rousdon *Ex*

CHARDSTOCK (St Andrew) as above

CHARFIELD (St John) *Glouc 7* **P** *R W Neeld Esq* **R** K G GRANT

CHARFORD (St Andrew) Bromsgrove St Jo *Worc*

CHARING (St Peter and St Paul) w Charing Heath (Holy Trinity) and Little Chart *Cant 10* **P** *Abp and D&C (jt)* **V** B CHALMERS

CHARLBURY (St Mary the Virgin) w Shorthampton *Ox 3* **P** *St Jo Coll Ox* **V** M J CHADWICK

CHARLCOMBE (Blessed Virgin Mary) w Bath (St Stephen) *B & W 9* **P** *DBP and Simeon's Trustees (jt)* **R** R OSBORNE

CHARLECOTE (St Leonard) Hampton Lucy w Charlecote and Loxley *Cov*

CHARLES (St John the Baptist) S Molton w Nymet St George, High Bray etc *Ex*

CHARLES w St Matthias, Plymouth *Ex 24* **P** *Ch Patr Trust* **P-in-c** R S WILLIAMS, **C** G M ROBERTS
CHARLESTOWN (St George) Pendleton St Thos w Charlestown *Man*
CHARLESTOWN (St Paul) *Truro 1* **P** *The Crown* **V** D R APPS, **Hon C** A D J JAGO, **NSM** D C B PECKETT
CHARLESTOWN (St Thomas the Apostle) *Wakef 4* **P** *V Halifax* **P-in-c** K WARD
CHARLESWORTH (St John the Evangelist) and Dinting Vale *Derby 6* **P** *The Crown (2 turns), Bp (1 turn)* **C** A W WARD, **NSM** S M McLEOD
CHARLETON (St Mary) w Buckland Tout Saints, East Portlemouth, South Pool and Chivelstone *Ex 14* **P** *Ld Chan (2 turns), E Roberts Esq, S Tyler Esq and N Tyler Esq (1 turn), Bp (1 turn), and DBP (1 turn)* **R** *Vacant* Frogmore (01548) 531211
CHARLTON (Holy Trinity) Wantage *Ox*
CHARLTON (St John) Cropthorne w Charlton *Worc*
CHARLTON (St John the Baptist) Garsdon, Lea and Cleverton and Charlton *Bris*
CHARLTON (St John the Baptist) The Donheads *Sarum*
CHARLTON (St Luke w Holy Trinity) (St Richard) *S'wark 1* **P** *Viscount Gough* **R** J G HESKINS, **Hon C** G M HESKINS, **NSM** J R GRIFFITHS
CHARLTON (St Peter) Uphavon w Rushall and Charlton *Sarum*
CHARLTON (St Thomas the Apostle) Andover w Foxcott *Win*
CHARLTON, SOUTH (St James) Glendale Gp *Newc*
CHARLTON ABBOTS (St Martin) Sevenhampton w Charlton Abbotts and Hawling etc *Glouc*
CHARLTON ADAM (St Peter and St Paul) Somerton w Compton Dundon, the Charltons etc *B & W*
CHARLTON ALL SAINTS (All Saints) *Sarum 11* **P** *V Downton* **P-in-c** R P HOLLINGSHURST
CHARLTON HORETHORNE (St Peter and St Paul) Henstridge and Charlton Horethorne w Stowell *B & W*
CHARLTON-IN-DOVER (St Peter and St Paul) *Cant 4* **P** *Keble Coll Ox* **R** N D L DE KEYSER
CHARLTON KINGS (Holy Apostles) *Glouc 14* **P** *R Cheltenham* **P-in-c** R COPPING
CHARLTON KINGS (St Mary) *Glouc 11* **P** *Bp* **V** G T BRYANT, **C** P G JAMIESON
CHARLTON MACKRELL (Blessed Virgin Mary) Somerton w Compton Dundon, the Charltons etc *B & W*
CHARLTON MARSHALL (St Mary the Virgin) Spetisbury w Charlton Marshall and Blandford St Mary *Sarum*
CHARLTON MUSGROVE (St John) (St Stephen), Cucklington and Stoke Trister *B & W 2* **P** *Bp* **P-in-c** R D THATCHER
CHARLTON ON OTMOOR (St Mary) Islip w Charlton on Otmoor, Oddington, Noke etc *Ox*
CHARLWOOD (St Nicholas) *S'wark 25* **P** *DBP* **R** W G CAMPEN, **Hon C** R C GAUNT
CHARMINSTER (St Mary the Virgin) and Stinsford *Sarum 2* **P** *Hon Charlotte Morrison and P R FitzGerald (jt), and Bp (alt)* **P-in-c** G M BOULT
CHARMOUTH (St Andrew) and Catherston Leweston *Sarum 3* **P** *MMCET* **P-in-c** R H BLANKLEY
CHARNEY BASSETT (St Peter) Cherbury *Ox*
CHARNOCK RICHARD (Christ Church) *Blackb 4* **P** *DBF* **P-in-c** R A PETTITT
CHARSFIELD w Debach (St Peter), Monewden, Hoo, Dallinghoo and Letheringham *St E 18* **P** *MMCET and CPAS, Ld Chan, and Ch Patr Trust (by turn)* **V** G R ADDINGTON HALL
CHART, GREAT (St Mary) *Cant 10* **P** *Abp* **R** A J DAVIS
CHART, LITTLE (St Mary) Charing w Charing Heath and Lt Chart *Cant*
CHART SUTTON (St Michael) Sutton Valence w E Sutton and Chart Sutton *Cant*
CHARTERHOUSE-ON-MENDIP (St Hugh) Blagdon w Compton Martin and Ubley *B & W*
CHARTHAM (St Mary) *Cant 2* **P** *Abp* **R** C C BARLOW
CHARWELTON (Holy Trinity) Badby w Newham and Charwelton w Fawsley etc *Pet*
CHASETOWN (St Anne) (St John) *Lich 1* **P** *V Burntwood* **P-in-c** M J WITHEY
CHASETOWN (St John) Chase Terrace St Jo Distr Ch *Lich*
CHASTLETON (St Mary the Virgin) Lt Compton w Chastleton, Cornwell etc *Ox*
CHATBURN (Christ Church) *Blackb 8* **P** *DBF* **V** W DRAIN
CHATHAM (St Mary and St John) *Roch 5* **P** *D&C* **R** R C PAGET
CHATHAM (St Paul w All Saints) *Roch 5* **P** *Bp* **V** *Vacant* Medway (01634) 845419

CHATHAM (St Philip and St James) *Roch 5* **P** *Ch Soc Trust* **V** G J ACKERLEY, **C** D J CHAMBERLIN
CHATHAM (St Stephen) *Roch 5* **P** *Bp* **V** C J D WALKER, **C** J L STEVENTON, **Hon C** O MATON
CHATHAM (St William) (St David) *Roch 5* **P** *Bp* **V** S F MORRIS, **C** S STAFF, **NSM** A J FIDDYMENT
CHATTERIS (St Peter and St Paul) *Ely 18* **P** *G&C Coll Cam* **V** C J MYHILL
CHATTISHAM (All Saints and St Margaret) Hintlesham w Chattisham *St E*
CHATTON (Holy Cross) Glendale Gp *Newc*
CHAULDEN (St Stephen) Hemel Hempstead *St Alb*
CHAVEY DOWN (St Martin) Winkfield and Cranbourne *Ox*
CHAWLEIGH (St James) w Cheldon *Ex 16* **P** *Bp* **R** R A GRINSTED, **C** K A ELLIOTT
CHAWTON (St Nicholas) and Farringdon *Win 2* **P** *Bp* **R** G A HODGE
CHEADLE (All Hallows) (St Philip's Mission Church) *Ches 17* **P** *R Cheadle* **V** R I McLAREN
CHEADLE (St Cuthbert) (St Mary) *Ches 17* **P** *Ch Soc Trust* **R** D S ALLISTER, **C** J E M NEWMAN, M I A SMITH, **NSM** S POOLE, N CHALL
CHEADLE (St Giles) w Freehay *Lich 11* **P** *DBP* **R** D W YABBACOME, **C** P W DAVEY
CHEADLE HEATH (St Augustine) *Ches 18* **P** *Bp* **V** *Vacant* 0161–477 3541
CHEADLE HULME (All Saints) *Ches 17* **P** *Bp* **C** D TAYLOR
CHEADLE HULME (Emmanuel) Conventional District *Ches 17* **Min** G J RENISON
CHEADLE HULME (St Andrew) *Ches 17* **P** *R Cheadle* **V** C P COOK, **C** D W GUEST
CHEAM (St Dunstan) (St Alban the Martyr) (St Oswald) *S'wark 26* **P** *St Jo Coll Ox* **R** T J de L SURTEES, **C** H R NAUNTON, F T LYNN
CHEAM COMMON (St Philip) *S'wark 26* **P** *R Cheam* **V** M R GOODLAD, **C** S H CAWDELL
CHEARSLEY (St Nicholas) Long Crendon w Chearsley and Nether Winchendon *Ox*
CHEBSEY (All Saints), Ellenhall and Seighford-with-Creswell *Lich 12* **P** *D&C, Trustees Earl of Lich, Personal Reps Major C Eld, and Qu Eliz Grant Trustees (jt)* **V** G G HODSON
CHECKENDON (St Peter and St Paul) Langtree *Ox*
CHECKLEY (Mission Room) Fownhope w Mordiford, Brockhampton etc *Heref*
CHECKLEY (St Mary and All Saints) *Lich 20* **P** *Mrs M Philips* **P-in-c** A G SADLER, **C** A O L HODGSON
CHEDBURGH (All Saints) w Depden, Rede and Hawkedon *St E 8* **P** *Bp (1 turn), Ld Chan (4 turns)* **R** D O WALL
CHEDDAR (St Andrew) *B & W 1* **P** *D&C* **V** V L DALEY, **C** R M HOVEY, **NSM** R D H BURSELL
CHEDDINGTON (St Giles) w Mentmore and Marsworth *Ox 26* **P** *Bp and Earl of Rosebery (jt)* **R** R A HALE
CHEDDLETON (St Edward the Confessor) *Lich 13* **P** *Bp* **V** D M TINSLEY
CHEDDON FITZPAINE (The Blessed Virgin Mary) Kingston St Mary w Broomfield etc *B & W*
CHEDGRAVE (All Saints) w Hardley and Langley *Nor 8* **P** *Gt Hosp (1 turn), Sir Christopher Beauchamp, Bt (2 turns)* **R** D A J MacPHERSON
CHEDISTON (St Mary) Halesworth w Linstead, Chediston, Holton etc *St E*
CHEDWORTH (St Andrew), Yanworth and Stowell, Coln Rogers and Coln St Denys *Glouc 14* **P** *Ld Chan (2 turns), Qu Coll Ox (1 turn)* **NSM** D W HUTCHIN
CHEDZOY (The Blessed Virgin Mary) Weston Zoyland w Chedzoy *B & W*
CHEETHAM (St John the Evangelist) *Man 5* **P** *Bp* **R** J PRESTON
CHEETHAM St Luke and Lower Crumpsall (St Thomas) *Man 5* **P** *Bp and CPAS (jt)* **R** H W MAYOR
CHEETHAM (St Mark) Barton w Peel Green *Man*
CHEETHAM (St Mark) (Hamilton Memorial Hall) *Man 5* **P** *D&C* **R** *Vacant* 0161–792 7161
CHEETWOOD *Man 5* **P** *D&C* **R** *Vacant*
CHELBOROUGH, EAST (St James) Melbury *Sarum*
CHELBOROUGH, WEST (St Andrew) as above
CHELDON (St Mary) Chawleigh w Cheldon *Ex*
CHELFORD (St John the Evangelist) w Lower Withington *Ches 12* **P** *J M Dixon Esq* **V** J F ELLIS
CHELL (St Michael) *Lich 16* **P** *Patr Bd* **TR** C S BUTLER
CHELL HEATH (Saviour) Chell *Lich*
CHELLASTON (St Peter) *Derby 15* **P** *Bp* **V** N GUTHRIE, **NSM** F R WORRALL
CHELMARSH (St Peter) Billingsley w Sidbury, Middleton Scriven etc *Heref*

CHELMONDISTON (St Andrew) and Erwarton w Harkstead
St E 5 **P** *Ld Chan (1 turn), Bp (2 turns)* **R** R D NEWTON
CHELMORTON AND FLAGG (St John the
Baptist) Taddington, Chelmorton and Flagg, and Monyash
Derby
CHELMSFORD (All Saints) (St Michael's Church Centre)
Chelmsf 8 **P** *Bp* **P-in-c** I L MORRIS, C D W LOWMAN
CHELMSFORD (Ascension) *Chelmsf 8* **P** *Bp*
P-in-c I L MORRIS, C D W LOWMAN
CHELMSFORD (St Andrew) *Chelmsf 8* **P** *Bp*
P-in-c A L COZENS
CHELMSLEY WOOD (St Andrew) *Birm 11* **P** *Bp*
TR D T SHAW, **TV** G BLOOMFIELD
CHELSEA (All Saints) (Old Church) *Lon 8*
P *R Chelsea St Luke and Earl Cadogan (jt)* **V** P D ELVY
CHELSEA (St John w St Andrew) (St John) *Lon 8* **P** *CPAS*
and Lon Coll of Div (jt) **V** J O SMITH
CHELSEA (St Luke) (Christ Church) *Lon 8* **P** *Earl*
Cadogan **R** D R WATSON, C G C BEAUCHAMP,
Hon C S A WATSON
CHELSEA (St Saviour) Upper Chelsea St Sav *Lon*
CHELSEA, UPPER (Holy Trinity) (St Jude) *Lon 8* **P** *Earl*
Cadogan **R** K L YATES, **Hon C** P E P BRICE
CHELSEA, UPPER (St Saviour) *Lon 8* **P** *R Upper Chelsea*
Holy Trin w St Jude **V** *Vacant* 0171–235 3468
CHELSEA, UPPER (St Simon Zelotes) *Lon 8* **P** *Hyndman*
Trustees **P-in-c** J J G JAMES
CHELSFIELD (St Martin of Tours) *Roch 15* **P** *All So*
Coll Ox **R** L G VIRGO, **Hon C** R S BODY
CHELSHAM (St Christopher) Warlingham w Chelsham and
Farleigh *S'wark*
CHELSHAM (St Leonard) as above
CHELSTON (St Peter) Cockington *Ex*
CHELSWORTH (All Saints) Monks Eleigh w Chelsworth
and Brent Eleigh etc *St E*
CHELTENHAM (All Saints) *Glouc 11* **P** *Bp*
V W J JENNINGS
CHELTENHAM (Christ Church) *Glouc 11* **P** *Simeon's*
Trustees **V** E A CROFTON, C S N CRONK,
NSM F M BAYNE
CHELTENHAM (Emmanuel) *Glouc 11* **P** *Bp*
P-in-c I E BURBERY, **NSM** B E TORODE
CHELTENHAM (St Luke and St John) *Glouc 11*
P *R Cheltenham and Simeon's Trustees (alt)*
P-in-c M J LODGE
CHELTENHAM (St Mark) (St Silas) (St Barnabas) (St
Aidan) (Emmanuel) *Glouc 11* **P** *Patr Bd*
TR D G WILLIAMS, **TV** D SCOTT, R T SWAIN,
R W S SUFFERN, C R J FACER, K G W WEBB,
NSM H J DAVIES
CHELTENHAM (St Mary) (St Matthew) (St Paul) (Holy
Trinity) *Glouc 11* **P** *Patr Bd* **TR** T P WATSON,
TV M R BAILEY, S J TYRRELL, C M J SCHORAH,
D I GIBSON, **NSM** A B MARTIN-DOYLE
CHELTENHAM (St Michael) *Glouc 11* **P** *Bp*
V D I LAWRENCE, **NSM** G L EDWARDS, M E THAME
CHELTENHAM (St Peter) *Glouc 11* **P** *DBP*
V W F J EVERITT
CHELTENHAM (St Stephen) *Glouc 11* **P** *Bp*
P-in-c J H HEIDT, C R NORTHING, **NSM** B E TORODE
CHELVESTON (St John the Baptist) Higham Ferrers w
Chelveston *Pet*
CHELVEY (St Bridget) Backwell w Chelvey and Brockley
B & W
CHELWOOD (St Leonard) Publow w Pensford, Compton
Dando and Chelwood *B & W*
CHELWOOD GATE (not known) Danehill *Chich*
CHENIES (St Michael) and Little Chalfont, Latimer and
Flaunden *Ox 23* **P** *Bedf Estates Trustees and Lord*
Chesham (jt) **R** D F LAMBERT, C A W BAINES
CHEQUERBENT (St Thomas) Westhoughton *Man*
CHEQUERFIELD (St Mary) Pontefract St Giles *Wakef*
CHERBURY *Ox 17* **P** *Bp, Jes Coll Ox, and Worc Coll*
Ox (jt) **R** D J HOWSON
CHERHILL (St James the Great) Oldbury *Sarum*
CHERINGTON (St John the Baptist) w Stourton *Cov 9*
P *Bp* **R** D C BROWN
CHERINGTON (St Nicholas) Avening w Cherington *Glouc*
CHERITON (All Souls) w Newington *Cant 5* **P** *Abp*
V G H GREEN
CHERITON (St Martin) *Cant 5* **P** *Abp* **R** J H WRIGHT
CHERITON (St Michael and All Angels) w Tichborne and
Beauworth *Win 1* **P** *The Crown* **R** E WILLIAMS
CHERITON, NORTH (St John the Baptist) Camelot Par
B & W
CHERITON BISHOP (St Mary) *Ex 6* **P** *Bp* **R** *Vacant*
Cheriton Bishop (0164724) 517
CHERITON FITZPAINE (St Matthew) N Creedy *Ex*

CHERRY BURTON (St Michael) *York 9*
P *R H Burton Esq* **P-in-c** E A CULLING
CHERRY HINTON (St Andrew) *Ely 2* **P** *Peterho Cam*
V C D BOULTON, **Hon C** W G PRENTICE
CHERRY HINTON (St John the Evangelist) *Ely 2* **P** *Bp*
V B N JONES, C R A DARMODY
CHERRY WILLINGHAM (St Peter and St Paul) w Greetwell
Linc 3 **P** *D&C* **V** K J SAUNDERS
CHERTSEY (St Peter w All Saints) *Guildf 11*
P *Haberdashers' Co* **V** D L H HEAD
CHESELBOURNE (St Martin) Milton Abbas, Hilton w
Cheselbourne etc *Sarum*
CHESHAM, GREAT (Christ Church) (Emmanuel) (St Mary
the Virgin) *Ox 20* **P** *Patr Bd* **TR** R J SALISBURY,
TV J A HAWKINS, C S N AUSTEN, W M C STILEMAN,
M M HALL, **NSM** A DAVIS, A W MEEK, D J UPCOTT,
J O EDIS
CHESHAM BOIS (St Leonard) *Ox 20* **P** *Peache Trustees*
R G C ROWLANDSON, C S P DUST, **NSM** D J BUTLER,
C CLARE, M S McCRUM
CHESHUNT (St Mary the Virgin) *St Alb 6* **P** *Marquess of*
Salisbury **V** T D LEWIS LLOYD, C S R MEPHAM,
J G F KESTER, **NSM** D R PEPPER
CHESSINGTON (St Mary the Virgin) *Guildf 9* **P** *Mert Coll*
Ox **V** P M FLYNN, C B STEADMAN-ALLEN
CHESTER (Holy Trinity without the Walls) *Ches 2* **P** *Bp*
R P L WILLIAMS, C D A GUEST
CHESTER (St Mary on the Hill) *Ches 2* **P** *Duke of Westmr*
R C W J SAMUELS, **Hon C** J R CARHART
CHESTER (St Paul) *Ches 2* **P** *R Ches* **V** N W PYATT
CHESTER Team, The (Christ Church) (St Barnabas) (St John
the Baptist) (St Peter) (St Thomas of Canterbury) *Ches 2*
P *DBP* **TR** R S LUNT, **TV** C M POTTER, J L GOODE
CHESTER LE STREET (St Mary and St Cuthbert) *Dur 1*
P *St Jo Coll Dur* **P-in-c** S K PRIOR, C P W JUDSON,
S A K ALLABY, M R JUDSON
CHESTER SQUARE (St Michael) (St Philip) *Lon 3* **P** *Duke*
of Westmr C C P GUINNESS, **NSM** M L STEVENS
CHESTERBLADE (The Blessed Virgin Mary) Evercreech w
Chesterblade and Milton Clevedon *B & W*
CHESTERFIELD (Holy Trinity) (Christ Church) *Derby 5*
P *CPAS* **R** N D GREENWOOD, C S M POTTER
CHESTERFIELD (St Augustine) *Derby 5* **P** *Bp*
V F E WILLETT, C J M MacLEOD
CHESTERFIELD (St Mary and All Saints) *Derby 5* **P** *Bp*
V M R KNIGHT, C F E YATES, **NSM** D KING,
J E HUNT
CHESTERFORD, GREAT (All Saints) w LITTLE (St Mary
the Virgin) *Chelmsf 23* **P** *Bp* **V** A KEMP
CHESTERTON (Good Shepherd) *Ely 2* **P** *Bp*
V A R McKEARNEY, C G J GILES
CHESTERTON (Holy Trinity) (St Chad) *Lich 14* **P** *Prime*
Min **V** V T OXFORD
CHESTERTON (St Andrew) *Ely 2* **P** *Trin Coll Cam*
V J M R SHELDON, C L DAZELEY
CHESTERTON (St George) *Ely 2* **P** *Bp* **V** P K REED
CHESTERTON (St Giles) *Cov 8* **P** *Lady Willoughby*
de Broke **V** J R WILLIAMS
CHESTERTON (St Lawrence) Cirencester *Glouc*
CHESTERTON (St Michael) Alwalton and Chesterton *Ely*
CHESTERTON w Middleton Stoney and Wendlebury *Ox 2*
P *New Coll Ox, Ch Ch Ox, and Bp (by turn)* **V** *Vacant*
Bicester (01869) 252387
CHESTERTON, GREAT (St Mary) Chesterton w Middleton
Stoney and Wendlebury *Ox*
CHESWARDINE (St Swithun), Childs Ercall, Hales,
Hinstock, Sambrook and Stoke on Tern *Lich 23* **P** *Bp, Adn*
Salop, R Edgmond w Kynnersley and Preston Wealdmoors,
Lt-Col Sir John Corbet, Bt, and R N C Hall Esq (jt)
C G E B LLOYD
CHETNOLE (St Peter) Yetminster w Ryme Intrinseca and
High Stoy *Sarum*
CHETTISHAM (St Michael and All Angels) *Ely 14* **P** *D&C*
P-in-c F J KILNER, C A F PLEDGER
CHETTLE (St Mary) Tollard Royal w Farnham, Gussage St
Michael etc *Sarum*
CHETTON (St Giles) Billingsley w Sidbury, Middleton
Scriven etc *Heref*
CHETWODE (St Mary and St Nicholas) Swan *Ox*
CHETWYND (St Michael and All Angels) Newport w
Longford and Chetwynd *Lich*
CHEVELEY (St Mary) *Ely 4* **P** *DBP and Mrs D A Bowlby*
(alt) **R** A F HOMER
CHEVENING (St Botolph) *Roch 8* **P** *Abp* **R** *Vacant*
Sevenoaks (01732) 453555
CHEVERELL, GREAT (St Peter) W Lavington and the
Cheverells *Sarum*
CHEVERELL, LITTLE (St Peter) as above

CHEVINGTON (All Saints) w Hargrave and Whepstead w Brockley *St E 13*   **P** *DBP (1 turn), Guild of All So (2 turns), and Bp (2 turns)*   **R** J W MOTT

CHEVINGTON (St John the Divine) *Newc 9*   **P** *Bp*   **V** J P H CLARK

CHEVITHORNE (St Thomas) Tiverton St Pet w Chevithorne *Ex*

CHEW MAGNA (St Andrew) w Dundry *B & W 10*   **P** *Mrs D H F Luxmoore-Ball*   **V** M W MATTHEWS

CHEW STOKE (St Andrew) w Nempnett Thrubwell *B & W 10*   **P** *Bp and SMF (jt)*   **R** T K VIVIAN

CHEWTON (Mission Church) Keynsham *B & W*

CHEWTON MENDIP (St Mary Magdalene) w Ston Easton, Litton and Emborough *B & W 8*   **P** *Earl Waldegrave (2 turns), Bp (1 turn)*   **R** A G BROWE

CHEYLESMORE (Christ Church) *Cov 3*   **P** *Ch Trust Fund Trust*   **V** A F MUNDEN

CHICHELEY (St Laurence) Sherington w Chicheley, N Crawley, Astwood etc *Ox*

CHICHESTER (St Pancras and St John) *Chich 3*   **P** *Simeon's Trustees (2 turns), St Jo Chpl Trustees (1 turn)*   **R** R B M GRIFFITHS

CHICHESTER (St Paul) and St Peter the Great *Chich 3*   **P** *D&C*   **V** K W CATCHPOLE,   **C** C M B HUXTABLE,   **NSM** M G STONE

CHICHESTER (St Wilfred) Parklands St Wilfrid CD *Chich*

CHICKERELL (St Mary) w Fleet *Sarum 5*   **P** *Bp* **R** *Vacant* Weymouth (01305) 784915

CHICKLADE (All Saints) Tisbury *Sarum*

CHIDDINGFOLD (St Mary) *Guildf 4*   **P** *Ld Chan*   **R** D E WEBSTER

CHIDDINGLY (not known) w East Hoathly *Chich 21*   **P** *Bp*   **R** M B LEA

CHIDDINGSTONE (St Mary) w Chiddingstone Causeway *Roch 10*   **P** *Abp and Bp (jt)*   **R** J R LEE,   **NSM** E J LORIMER

CHIDDINGSTONE CAUSEWAY (St Luke) Chiddingstone w Chiddingstone Causeway *Roch*

CHIDEOCK (St Giles) Symondsbury and Chideock *Sarum*

CHIDHAM (St Mary) *Chich 13*   **P** *Bp*   **P-in-c** B R COOK

CHIEVELEY (St Mary the Virgin) w Winterbourne and Oare *Ox 14*   **P** *Adn Berks*   **V** C T SCOTT-DEMPSTER

CHIGNAL SMEALEY (St Nicholas) see below

CHIGNALS w Mashbury, The *Chelmsf 8*   **P** *CPAS (2 turns), Bp (1 turn)*   **P-in-c** A L COZENS

CHIGWELL (St Mary) (St Winifred) see 8/76bx *Chelmsf 26*   **P** *Bp* **TM** *Vacant* 0181–500 3510

CHIGWELL (St Mary) (St Winifred) and Chigwell Row *Chelmsf 26*   **P** *The Crown, and Patr Bd (by turn)*   **TR** P J TRENDALL,   **TV** R C MATTHEWS,   **C** E R STEINBERG,   **NSM** V N ARNOLD

CHIGWELL ROW (All Saints) Chigwell and Chigwell Row *Chelmsf*

CHILBOLTON (St Mary) cum Wherwell *Win 3*   **P** *Bp and Marquess of Camden (alt)*   **R** F E WILLIAMS

CHILCOMB (St Andrew) Win All SS w Chilcomb and Chesil *Win*

CHILCOMBE (not known) Bride Valley *Sarum*

CHILCOMPTON (St John the Baptist) w Downside and Stratton on the Fosse *B & W 12*   **P** *Bp, MMCET, and V Midsomer Norton (jt)*   **R** S J TUDGEY

CHILCOTE (St Matthew's Chapel) Clifton Campville w Edingale *Lich*

CHILDE OKEFORD (St Nicholas), Okeford Fitzpaine, Manston, Hammoon and Handford *Sarum 6*   **P** *G A L Pitt-Rivers Esq and DBP (alt)*   **R** *Vacant* Child Okeford (01258) 860547

CHILDERDITCH (All Saints and St Faith) Gt Warley w Childerditch and Ingrave *Chelmsf*

CHILDREY (St Mary the Virgin) Ridgeway *Ox*

CHILDS ERCALL (St Michael and All Angels) Cheswardine, Childs Ercall, Hales, Hinstock etc *Lich*

CHILDSWYCKHAM (St Mary the Virgin) w Aston Somerville, Buckland and Snowshill *Glouc 17*   **P** *Bp*   **R** *Vacant* Broadway (01386) 852240

CHILDWALL (All Saints) *Liv 4*   **P** *Bp*   **V** E BRAMHALL,   **C** J A DAWSWELL

CHILDWALL (St David) *Liv 4*   **P** *Bp*   **V** S W C GOUGH

CHILDWALL VALLEY (St Mark) Gateacre *Liv*

CHILDWICK (St Mary) St Alb St Mich *St Alb*

CHILFROME (Holy Trinity) Melbury *Sarum*

CHILHAM (St Mary) w Challock and Molash *Cant 2*   **P** *Abp and Viscount Massereene and Ferrard (jt)*   **V** C R DUNCAN

CHILLENDEN (All Saints) Nonington w Wymynswold and Goodnestone etc *Cant*

CHILLESFORD (St Peter) Orford w Sudbourne, Chillesford, Butley and Iken *St E*

CHILLINGHAM (St Peter) Glendale Gp *Newc*

CHILLINGTON (St James) Ilminster and District *B & W*

CHILMARK (St Margaret of Antioch) Tisbury *Sarum*

CHILTHORNE DOMER (Blessed Virgin Mary) Tintinhull w Chilthorne Domer, Yeovil Marsh etc *B & W*

CHILTINGTON, EAST (not known) Plumpton w E Chiltington cum Novington *Chich*

CHILTINGTON, WEST (St Mary) *Chich 12*   **P** *Bp*   **R** G A EVANS

CHILTON (All Saints) Harwell w Chilton *Ox*

CHILTON (St Aidan) *Dur 14*   **P** *Bp*   **P-in-c** S G RADLEY

CHILTON (St Mary) Brill, Boarstall, Chilton and Dorton *Ox*

CHILTON CANTELO (St James) w Ashington, Mudford, Rimpton and Marston Magna *B & W 7*   **P** *DBP and D&C, D&C Bris, and Bp Lon (by turn)*   **R** E D WHITE

CHILTON FOLIAT (St Mary) Whitton *Sarum*

CHILTON MOOR (St Andrew) *Dur 6*   **P** *Bp* **V** *Vacant* 0191–385 2468

CHILTON POLDEN (St Edward) W Poldens *B & W*

CHILTON TRINITY (Holy Trinity) Bridgwater St Mary, Chilton Trinity and Durleigh *B & W*

CHILVERS COTON (All Saints) w Astley *Cov 5*   **P** *Viscount Daventry*   **V** J D PHILPOTT,   **C** J P WELBY

CHILWELL (Christ Church) *S'well 7*   **P** *CPAS*   **V** I S CHISHOLM,   **C** A J HULME,   **G B** McGUINNESS

CHILWORTH (St Denys) w North Baddesley *Win 11*   **P** *Mrs P M A T Chamberlayne-Macdonald* **V** *Vacant* Southampton (01703) 732393

CHILWORTH (St Thomas) Blackheath and Chilworth *Guildf*

CHINEHAM (Christ Church) *Win 4*   **P** *Bp*   **V** P J LAW

CHINESE CONGREGATION St Martin-in-the-Fields *Lon*

CHINGFORD (All Saints) (St Peter and St Paul) *Chelmsf 5*   **P** *Bp*   **R** N J EDWARDS,   **C** W G CAMPBELL-TAYLOR,   J W STREETING

CHINGFORD (St Anne) *Chelmsf 5*   **P** *Bp*   **V** J A L HARRISSON,   **Hon C** P G ROLPH

CHINGFORD (St Edmund) *Chelmsf 5*   **P** *Bp*   **V** E C FORD

CHINLEY (St Mary) w Buxworth *Derby 6*   **P** *Bp*   **P-in-c** E D PACKHAM

CHINNOCK, EAST (Blessed Virgin Mary) W Coker w Hardington Mandeville, E Chinnock etc *B & W*

CHINNOCK, MIDDLE (St Margaret) Norton sub Hamdon, W Chinnock, Chiselborough etc *B & W*

CHINNOCK, WEST (Blessed Virgin Mary) as above

CHINNOR (St Andrew) w Emmington and Sydenham and Aston Rowant w Crowell *Ox 1*   **P** *Bp, DBP, and Peache Trustees (jt)*   **R** R A CARTMILL,   **C** R G HARNISH

CHIPPENHAM (St Andrew) w Tytherton Lucas *Bris 9*   **P** *Ch Ch Ox*   **V** P H F WOODHOUSE,   **C** S M J CROSSMAN

CHIPPENHAM (St Margaret) *Ely 3*   **P** *Mrs A Crawley*   **P-in-c** D J KIGHTLEY

CHIPPENHAM (St Paul) w Hardenhuish and Langley Burrell *Bris 9*   **P** *Patr Bd*   **TR** J A SMITH,   **TV** C B WRAY

CHIPPENHAM (St Peter) *Bris 9*   **P** *Bp*   **V** A D FENSOME,   **Hon C** S J STEVENS,   **NSM** D C THURNELL

CHIPPERFIELD (St Paul) *St Alb 10*   **P** *Trustees*   **P-in-c** A M BUTLER

CHIPPING (St Bartholomew) and Whitewell (St Michael) *Blackb 8*   **P** *Bp and Hulme Trustees (jt)*   **V** H F K CHEALL

CHIPPING BARNET (St John the Baptist) w Arkley *St Alb 2*   **P** *The Crown*   **TR** A G K ESDAILE,   **TV** J A STONE,   C J SWIFT,   **C** B L M PHILLIPS

CHIPPING CAMPDEN (St James) w Ebrington *Glouc 10*   **P** *Peache Trustees (1 turn), Earl of Harrowby (2 turns)*   **V** S J OBERST

CHIPPING NORTON (St Mary the Virgin) *Ox 3*   **P** *D&C Glouc*   **C** J D PORTER

CHIPPING ONGAR (St Martin) w Shelley *Chelmsf 28*   **P** *Guild of All So and Keble Coll Ox*   **R** E J SIBSON

CHIPPING SODBURY (St John the Baptist) and Old Sodbury *Glouc 7*   **P** *D&C Worc*   **V** N R E JACOBS,   **C** E P A GREEN

CHIPPING WARDEN (St Peter and St Paul) Culworth w Sulgrave and Thorpe Mandeville etc *Pet*

CHIPSTABLE (All Saints) Wiveliscombe w Chipstable, Huish Champflower etc *B & W*

CHIPSTEAD (Good Shepherd) Chevening *Roch*

CHIPSTEAD (St Margaret of Antioch) *S'wark 25*   **P** *Abp*   **R** J M P GOODDEN,   **Dss** D SMEDBERG

CHIRBURY (St Michael) *Heref 13*   **P** *Sir David Wakeman, Bt and Bp (alt)*   **V** P D HARRATT

CHIRTON (St John the Baptist) Redhorn *Sarum*

CHISELBOROUGH (St Peter and St Paul) Norton sub Hamdon, W Chinnock, Chiselborough etc *B & W*

CHISHILL, GREAT (St Swithun) Heydon, Gt and Lt Chishill, Crishall etc *Chelmsf*

CHISHILL, LITTLE (St Nicholas) as above

CHISELDON (Holy Cross) Ridgeway *Sarum*

CHISLEHURST (Annunciation) *Roch 13* **P** *Keble Coll*
V W B BEER
CHISLEHURST (Christ Church) *Roch 13* **P** *CPAS*
V J M ADAMS, **C** D J LITTLE
CHISLEHURST (St Nicholas) *Roch 13* **P** *Bp*
R J C ALLEN, **NSM** J B HURN
CHISLET (St Mary the Virgin) St Nicholas at Wade w Sarre
and Chislet w Hoath *Cant*
CHISWICK (St Michael) *Lon 11* **P** *V St Martin-in-the-*
Fields **P-in-c** N C FINCHAM
CHISWICK (St Nicholas w St Mary Magdalene) *Lon 11*
P *D&C St Paul's* **V** P A TUFT, **C** N G KELLEY,
NSM D W RANDALL
CHISWICK (St Paul) Grove Park *Lon 11* **P** *V Chiswick*
V M C RILEY
CHITHURST (St Mary) Rogate w Terwick and Trotton w
Chithurst *Chich*
CHITTERNE (All Saints and St Mary) Tilshead, Orcheston
and Chitterne *Sarum*
CHITTERNE (St Mary) as above
CHITTLEHAMHOLT (St John) S Molton w Nymet St
George, High Bray etc *Ex*
CHITTLEHAMPTON (St Hieritha) as above
CHITTS HILL (St Cuthbert) *Lon 19* **P** *CPAS*
V D M DALEY
CHIVELSTONE (St Sylvester) Charleton w Buckland Tout
Saints etc *Ex*
CHOBHAM (St Lawrence) w Valley End *Guildf 6* **P** *Bp and*
Brig R W Acworth (alt) **V** A J H SALMON
CHOLDERTON (St Nicholas) Bourne Valley *Sarum*
CHOLESBURY (St Lawrence) Hawridge w Cholesbury and
St Leonard *Ox*
CHOLLERTON w Birtley and Thockrington *Newc 2*
P *Mrs P I Enderby (2 turns), Newc Dioc Soc (1 turn)*
R J A PYLE
CHOLSEY (St Mary) *Ox 18* **P** *Ld Chan* **V** A M PETIT
CHOPPARDS (Mission Room) Upper Holme Valley *Wakef*
CHOPPINGTON (St Paul the Apostle) *Newc 1* **P** *D&C*
V G EVANS, **NSM** J M GRIEVE (nee
BELL)
CHOPWELL (St John the Evangelist) *Dur 5* **P** *Bp*
P-in-c M J WRAY
CHORLEY (All Saints) *Blackb 4* **P** *Bp* **V** E N STRASZAK
CHORLEY (St George) *Blackb 4* **P** *R Chorley*
V K BARRETT, **C** A R HODGSON
CHORLEY (St James) *Blackb 4* **P** *R Chorley*
V G THOMAS
CHORLEY (St Laurence) *Blackb 4* **P** *Bp*
R J R K FENWICK, **C** P WALLINGTON
CHORLEY (St Peter) *Blackb 4* **P** *R Chorley* **V** J D BURNS
CHORLEY (St Philip) Alderley Edge *Ches*
CHORLEYWOOD (Christ Church) *St Alb 10* **P** *CPAS*
V J S KINGSLEY-SMITH, **C** T A STACEY
CHORLEYWOOD (St Andrew) *St Alb 10* **P** *Bp*
V G EDPYTCHES, **C** B J KISSELL, B A SKINNER,
M O KNIGHT, **NSM** J G ROBERTS, J W SUTTON,
R W MAYNARD
CHORLTON-CUM-HARDY (St Clement) (St Barnabas)
Man 4 **P** *D&C* **R** R J GILPIN, **C** D W WRIGHT
CHORLTON-CUM-HARDY (St Werburgh) *Man 4* **P** *Bp*
R A R M SEAMAN
CHRISHALL (Holy Trinity) Heydon, Gt and Lt Chishill,
Chrishall etc *Chelmsf*
CHRIST THE KING in the Diocese of Newcastle *Newc 5*
P *Patr Bd* **TR** R K KENNEDY, **TV** C J CLINCH,
G G KEYES
CHRISTCHURCH (Holy Trinity) *Win 8* **P** *Bp*
V H M WILLIAMS, **C** J C COWBURN, M S LOWE,
P A MacCARTY, A HAWTHORNE
CHRISTCHURCH Stourvale (St George) Christchurch *Win*
CHRISTIAN MALFORD (All Saints) Draycot *Bris*
CHRISTLETON (St James) *Ches 2* **P** *Exors*
Major H C L Garnett **R** K P LEE
CHRISTON (Blessed Virgin Mary) Crook Peak *B & W*
CHRISTOW (St James), Ashton, Trusham and Bridford
Ex 6 **P** *SMF, MMCET, Viscount Exmouth, Bp, and*
E A Beard Esq (jt) **R** J R C TAYLOR,
NSM M D A WILLIAMS
CHUDLEIGH (St Mary and St Martin) *Ex 11* **P** *MMCET*
V C T PIDSLEY
CHUDLEIGH KNIGHTON (St Paul) Bovey Tracey St
John, Chudleigh Knighton etc *Ex*
CHULMLEIGH (St Mary Magdalene) *Ex 16* **P** *MMCET*
R R A GRINSTED, **C** K A ELLIOTT
CHURCH ASTON (St Andrew) *Lich 21* **P** *R Edgmond*
R W H YATES
CHURCH BRAMPTON (St Botolph) w Chapel Brampton and
Harleston, East Haddon and Holdenby *Pet 2* **P** *Earl*

Spencer, Bp, The Crown, and CCC Ox (by turn)
P-in-c J J RICHARDSON
CHURCH BROUGHTON (St Michael and All Angels) w
Barton Blount, Boylestone, Sutton on the Hill and Trusley
Derby 14 **P** *Exors R H R Buckston, Worc Coll Ox,*
Mrs F H Coke-Steel (2 turns each), Miss C M Auden and
J W Prast Esq (1 turn ea **R** *Vacant* Sudbury (01283) 585296
CHURCH CONISTON (St Andrew) *Carl 8* **P** *Peache*
Trustees **P-in-c** M H CANNON
CHURCH EATON (St Editha) Bradeley, Church Eaton and
Moreton *Lich*
CHURCH HONEYBOURNE (St Ecgwyn) Pebworth w
Dorsington and Honeybourne *Glouc*
CHURCH HULME (St Luke) *Ches 11* **P** *V Sandbach*
V J EARDLEY
CHURCH KIRK (St James) *Blackb 1* **P** *Hulme Trustees*
R N A ASHTON
CHURCH KNOWLE (St Peter) Corfe Castle, Church
Knowle, Kimmeridge etc *Sarum*
CHURCH LANGTON (St Peter) w Tur Langton, Thorpe
Langton and Stonton Wyville *Leic 4* **P** *Bp and*
E Brudenell Esq (jt) **P-in-c** I W Y GEMMELL,
K F SHEPHERD
CHURCH LAWFORD (St Peter) Wolston and Church
Lawford *Cov*
CHURCH LAWTON (All Saints) *Ches 11*
P *J A Lawton Esq* **R** G L JOYCE
CHURCH LENCH (All Saints) w Rous Lench and Abbots
Morton *Worc 1* **P** *Bp* **P-in-c** F R HIGGINS
CHURCH MINSHULL (St Bartholomew) Acton and
Worleston, Church Minshull and Wettenhall *Ches*
CHURCH OAKLEY (St Leonard) and Wootton (St Lawrence)
Win 4 **P** *Qu Coll Ox and D&C (alt)* **R** C L ATKINS
CHURCH PREEN (St John the Baptist) Wenlock *Heref*
CHURCH STRETTON (St Laurence) *Heref 11* **P** *Ch Patr*
Trust **R** M S STEDMAN, **NSM** D E JANES
CHURCHAM (St Andrew) w Bulley and Minsterworth
Glouc 3 **P** *Bp and D&C (alt)* **V** G P JENKINS
CHURCHDOWN (St Andrew) (St Bartholomew) *Glouc 6*
P *D&C* **V** T E MASON
CHURCHDOWN (St John the Evangelist) *Glouc 6* **P** *Bp*
V E F GILES
CHURCHILL (All Saints) Kingham w Churchill, Daylesford
and Sarsden *Ox*
CHURCHILL (St John the Baptist) Burrington and
Churchill *B & W*
CHURCHILL (St Michael) Peopleton and White Ladies
Aston w Churchill etc *Worc*
CHURCHILL-IN-HALFSHIRE (St James) w Blakedown and
Broome *Worc 12* **P** *Viscount Cobham and*
N A Bourne Esq (alt) **R** N J DAVIS
CHURCHOVER (Holy Trinity) w Willey *Cov 6* **P** *Bp*
P-in-c P S BALLANTINE
CHURCHSTANTON (St Peter and St Paul), Buckland
St Mary and Otterford *B & W 18* **P** *DBP and*
Mrs M E Mcdonald (jt) **P-in-c** R G CLARKE
CHURCHSTOKE (St Nicholas) w Hyssington and Sarn
Heref 10 **P** *The Crown (1 turn), Earl of Powis (2 turns)*
V W T BRYAN, **NSM** I R BALL, G LLOYD
CHURCHSTOW (St Mary) Malborough w S Huish, W
Alvington and Churchstow *Ex*
CHURSTON FERRERS (St Mary the Vigin) Brixham w
Churston Ferrers and Kingswear *Ex*
CHURT (St John the Evangelist) *Guildf 3* **P** *Adn Surrey*
V C H PONTIN
CHURWELL (All Saints) Morley St Pet w Churwell *Wakef*
CHUTE (St Nicholas) Wexcombe *Sarum*
CHYNGTON (St Luke) Seaford w Sutton *Chich*
CINDERFORD (St John the Evangelist) *Glouc 4*
P *The Crown* **V** J W HOLDER
CINDERFORD (St Stephen) w Littledean *Glouc 4* **P** *Ch Patr*
Trust **V** G C BOWYER, **NSM** B J DAVIES
CINDERHILL (Christ Church) *S'well 14* **P** *Bp*
P-in-c M J O'CONNELL
CINNAMON BROW (Resurrection) Padgate *Liv*
CIPPENHAM (St Andrew) W Slough *Ox*
CIRENCESTER (St John the Baptist) *Glouc 12* **P** *Bp*
V H S RINGROSE, **C** J G LEWIS-ANTHONY,
NSM P G W PRIDGEON
CLACTON, GREAT (St John the Baptist) *Chelmsf 24*
P *Ch Patr Trust* **V** N W WYNNE-JONES, **C** S MARSHALL
CLACTON, LITTLE (St James) Weeley and Lt Clacton
Chelmsf
CLACTON-ON-SEA (St Christopher) (St James)
Chelmsf 24 **P** *Bp* **V** A P D SPOONER, **C** T D WATSON,
NSM I A O LEE
CLACTON-ON-SEA (St Paul) *Chelmsf 24* **P** *Ch Patr*
Trust **V** N G E ISSBERNER, **Hon C** D W HART

CLAINES (St John the Baptist) *Worc 6*   **P** *Bp*
  V A W BROOKSBANK
CLANDON, EAST (St Thomas of Canterbury) and WEST (St Peter and St Paul) *Guildf 5*   **P** *Earl of Onslow and Bp*
  (alt)   **R** J B SMITH
CLANFIELD (St James) Catherington and Clanfield *Portsm*
CLANFIELD (St Stephen) Bampton w Clanfield *Ox*
CLANNABOROUGH (St Petrock) N Creedy *Ex*
CLAPHAM (St James) *S'wark 10*   **P** *CPAS*   **V** C E GALE
CLAPHAM (St Mary the Virgin) Findon w Clapham and Patching *Chich*
CLAPHAM (St Thomas of Canterbury) *St Alb 19*
  P *MMCET*   **V** M K M SCOTT
CLAPHAM Team Ministry, The (Christ Church and St John) (Holy Spirit) (Holy Trinity) (St John the Evangelist) (St Paul) (St Peter) *S'wark 10*   **P** *Patr Bd*
  TR D O ISHERWOOD, **TV** D N HEAD, D J HOUGHTON, H M CUNLIFFE, **C** J P HAWES, **Hon C** R F VICKERY, C HERBERT, **NSM** S MOSS
CLAPHAM COMMON (St Barnabas) *S'wark 14*
  P *Ch Trust Fund Trust*   **V** D PAGE
CLAPHAM PARK (All Saints) *S'wark 10*   **P** *CPAS and TR Clapham (jt)*   **V** N COOPER
CLAPHAM PARK (St Stephen) *S'wark 11*   **P** *Trustees*
  V *Vacant* 0181–671 8276
CLAPHAM-WITH-KEASDEN (St James) and Austwick *Bradf 6*   **P** *Bp*   **V** J DALBY
CLAPTON (St James) Bourton-on-the-Water w Clapton *Glouc*
CLAPTON (St Peter) Barnwell w Tichmarsh, Thurning and Clapton *Pet*
CLAPTON, UPPER (St Matthew) *Lon 5*   **P** *D&C Cant*
  V L W S PHILLIPS
CLARBOROUGH (St John the Baptist) w Hayton *S'well 5*
  P *Bp*   **P-in-c** R GOODHAND
CLARE (St Peter and St Paul) w Poslingford, Cavendish, Stoke by Clare w Wixoe *St E 8*   **P** *Lady Loch*   **R** W J A RANKIN
CLAREMONT (Holy Angels) *Man 6*   **P** *Bp*   **V** A BUTLER, **C** P BUTLER
CLARENDON PARK (St John the Baptist) w Knighton (St Michael and All Angels) *Leic 2*   **P** *Bp*
  TR M W STEPHENSON, **TV** S I SKIDMORE, **Hon C** A J BALLARD, **NSM** S L LANCASTER
CLATFORD, UPPER (All Saints) Abbotts Ann and Upper and Goodworth Clatford *Win*
CLATWORTHY (St Mary Magdalene) Wiveliscombe w Chipstable, Huish Champflower etc *B & W*
CLAUGHTON (St Chad) Hornby w Claughton *Blackb*
CLAUGHTON VILLAGE (St Bede) Birkenhead St Jas w St Bede *Ches*
CLAVERDON (St Michael and All Angels) w Preston Bagot *Cov 7*   **P** *Bp*   **P-in-c** C P C HUNT
CLAVERHAM (St Barnabas) Yatton Moor *B & W*
CLAVERING (St Mary and St Clement) w Langley and Arkesden *Chelmsf 22*   **P** *Ch Hosp and Keble Coll Ox (alt)*
  V D S McGUFFIE
CLAVERLEY (All Saints) (Heathton Mission) w Tuckhill *Heref 9*   **P** *Bp and Miss L Amphlett (jt)*   **V** R SHARP
CLAVERTON (Blessed Virgin Mary) Bathampton w Claverton *B & W*
CLAVERTON DOWN (St Hugh) as above
CLAWTON (St Leonard) Ashwater, Halwill, Beaworthy, Clawton etc *Ex*
CLAXBY (St Mary) Walesby *Linc*
CLAXTON (St Andrew) Rockland St Mary w Hellington, Bramerton etc *Nor*
CLAY CROSS (St Bartholomew N Wingfield, Clay Cross and Pilsley *Derby*
CLAY HILL (St John the Baptist) (St Luke) *Lon 18*
  P *V Enfield St Andr and Bp (jt)*   **V** J H NODDINGS
CLAYBROOKE (St Peter) cum Wibtoft and Frolesworth *Leic 11*   **P** *The Crown and Adn Loughb (by turn)*
  P-in-c J M BRADSHAW
CLAYDON and Barham *St E 1*   **P** *G R Drury Esq*
  R T W BROADBENT, **C** S M EVANS
CLAYDON (St James the Great) w Mollington *Ox 5*   **P** *Bp*
  P-in-c R J CHARD, **NSM** D B ADDLEY
CLAYDONS, The (St Mary) (All Saints) *Ox 24*   **P** *Sir Ralph Verney, Bt*   **R** C DRAPER
CLAYGATE (Holy Trinity) *Guildf 8*   **P** *Ch Patr Trust*
  V J T HENDERSON, **C** J WHITE
CLAYHANGER (St Peter) Bampton, Morebath, Clayhanger and Petton *Ex*
CLAYHIDON (St Andrew) Hemyock w Culm Davy, Clayhidon and Culmstock *Ex*
CLAYPOLE (St Peter) *Linc 23*   **P** *DBP*   **R** G MUNN
CLAYTON (St James the Great) *Lich 14*   **P** *Bp*
  V R K LEGG, **C** P H SMITH

CLAYTON (St John the Baptist) *Bradf 2*   **P** *V Bradf*
  V J A N B HOWELL
CLAYTON (St John the Baptist) w Keymer *Chich 9*   **P** *BNC Ox*   **R** R L CLARKE, **C** J P COOPER
CLAYTON BROOK (Community Church) Whittle-le-Woods *Blackb*
CLAYTON LE MOORS (All Saints) Altham w Clayton le Moors *Blackb*
CLAYTON LE MOORS (St James) as above
CLAYTON WEST w HIGH HOYLAND (All Saints) High Hoyland, Scissett and Clayton W *Wakef*
CLAYWORTH (St Peter) Everton and Mattersey w Clayworth *S'well*
CLEADON (All Saints) *Dur 7*   **P** *R Whitburn*   **V** N SHAW, **NSM** J P TALBOT
CLEADON PARK (St Mark and St Cuthbert) *Dur 7*   **P** *Bp*
  P-in-c P R C HAMILTON-MANON
CLEARWELL (St Peter) Newland and Redbrook w Clearwell *Glouc*
CLEASBY (St Peter) Barton and Manfield and Cleasby w Stapleton *Ripon*
CLEATOR MOOR (St John the Evangelist) w Cleator (St Leonard) *Carl 5*   **P** *Earl of Lonsdale and Bp (alt)*
  V J A McKINNEY, **C** B PEDDER
CLECKHEATON (St John the Evangelist) *Wakef 8*
  P *V Birstall*   **V** M G INMAN
CLECKHEATON (St Luke) (Whitechapel) *Wakef 8*   **P** *Bp and Sir Martin Wilson (jt)*   **V** D ACKROYD
CLEDFORD (Mission Room) Middlewich w Byley *Ches*
CLEE, NEW (St John the Evangelist) (St Stephen) *Linc 9*
  P *Bp*   **V** J WELLIS, **C** P FOSTER
CLEE, OLD (Holy Trinity and St Mary the Virgin) *Linc 9*
  P *Bp*   **V** R S R PATSTON
CLEE ST MARGARET (St Margaret) Bitterley w Middleton, Stoke St Milborough etc *Heref*
CLEETHORPE (Christ Church) Clee *Linc*
CLEETHORPES St Aidan *Linc 9*   **P** *Bp*   **V** *Vacant*
CLEETHORPES (St Francis) (St Peter) *Linc 9*   **P** *Bp*
  TR T H ROBINSON, **TV** M F JONES, T H ATKINSON, **Hon C** D H WEBSTER
CLEETON (St Mary) Stottesdon w Farlow, Cleeton and Silvington *Heref*
CLEEVE (Holy Trinity) Yatton Moor *B & W*
CLEEVE, OLD (St Andrew), Leighland and Treborough *B & W 16*   **P** *Selw Coll Cam (2 turns), Personal Reps G R Wolseley Esq (1 turn)*   **R** H E ALLEN, **C** R A R FIGG
CLEEVE HILL (St Peter) Bishop's Cleeve *Glouc*
CLEEVE PRIOR (St Andrew) and The Littletons *Worc 1*
  P *D&C and Ch Ch Ox (alt)*   **V** D R EVANS
CLEHONGER (All Saints) Kingstone w Clehonger, Eaton Bishop etc *Heref*
CLENCHWARTON (St Margaret) *Ely 17*   **P** *Bp*
  P-in-c A J DAVEY
CLENT (St Leonard) Belbroughton w Fairfield and Clent *Worc*
CLEOBURY MORTIMER (St Mary the Virgin) w Hopton Wafers, Neen Sollars and Milson, Neen Savage w Kinlet *Heref 12*   **P** *Patr Bd (2 turns), Ld Chan (1 turn)*
  R R A HORSFIELD, **C** P E HUNT, **NSM** B H GADD
CLEOBURY NORTH (St Peter and St Paul) Ditton Priors w Neenton, Burwarton etc *Heref*
CLERKENWELL (Holy Redeemer) (St Mark) *Lon 6*
  P *Trustees and City Corp (jt)*   **P-in-c** P A BAGOTT, **NSM** L S A MARSH
CLERKENWELL (St James and St John) (St Peter) *Lon 6*
  P *Ch Patr Trust and PCC (jt)*   **P-in-c** T C COLLETT-WHITE
CLEVEDON (St Andrew) (Christ Church) (St Peter)
  B & W 13   **P** *Simeon's Trustees (1 turn), Ld Chan (2 turns)*   **V** M G W HAYES, **C** P BURDEN, **NSM** J RITCHIE, J E G ANGLE
CLEVEDON (St John the Evangelist) *B & W 13*   **P** *SMF*
  V D S M SMITH, **C** C D EPPS
CLEVEDON, EAST (All Saints) and Walton w Weston w Clapton in Gordano *B & W 13*   **P** *Bp and SMF (jt)*
  R J F SMART, **C** M E RICHARDS
CLEVELEYS (St Andrew) *Blackb 13*   **P** *Trustees*
  V D E REEVES, **C** C R HUGGETT
CLEWER (St Andrew) *Ox 13*   **P** *Eton Coll*
  P-in-c I N RANDALL
CLEWER (St Stephen) New Windsor *Ox*
CLEY (St Margaret) Blakeney w Cley, Wiveton, Glandford etc *Nor*
CLIBURN (St Cuthbert) Clifton, Brougham and Cliburn *Carl*
CLIDDESDEN (St Lawrence) and Ellisfield w Farleigh Wallop and Dummer *Win 4*   **P** *Earl of Portsm and DBP (jt)*
  R *Vacant* Basingstoke (01256) 381217
CLIFFE (St Andrew) Hemingbrough *York*

CLIFFE, NORTH (St John) N Cave w Cliffe *York*
CLIFFE AT HOO (St Helen) w Cooling *Roch 6* **P** *D&C*
R E M WRIGHT
CLIFFE VALE (St Stephen) Hartshill *Lich*
CLIFFORD (St Luke) *York 1* **P** *G Lane-Fox Esq*
P-in-c R M C SEED, **C** A STOKER
CLIFFORD (St Mary the Virgin) Cusop w Clifford,
Hardwicke, Bredwardine etc *Heref*
CLIFFORD CHAMBERS (St Helen) Welford w Weston and
Clifford Chambers *Glouc*
CLIFFORDS MESNE (St Peter) Newent and Gorsley w
Cliffords Mesne *Glouc*
CLIFFSEND (St Mary the Virgin) St Laurence in the Isle of
Thanet *Cant*
CLIFTON (All Saints) *St Alb 22* **P** *Bp* **R** J K DIXON
CLIFTON (All Saints w St John) *Bris 5* **P** *Bp*
V P G COBB, **NSM** R DURBIN
CLIFTON (Christ Church w Emmanuel) *Bris 5* **P** *Simeon's*
Trustees **V** P M BERG, **C** R A HIGGINS, R D JAMES
CLIFTON (Holy Trinity) *Derby 8* **P** *Mrs M F Stanton,*
T W Clowes Esq, and V Ashbourne (by turn) **V** *Vacant*
Ashbourne (01335) 342199
CLIFTON (Holy Trinity, St Andrew the Less and St Peter)
Bris 5 **P** *Simeon's Trustees* **V** G G HOWARD
CLIFTON (Mission Church) Conisbrough *Sheff*
CLIFTON (St Anne) *Man 2* **P** *Bp* **P-in-c** P J BARNETT
CLIFTON (St Cuthbert), Brougham and Cliburn *Carl 4*
P *Earl of Lonsdale and Lord Hothfield (alt)* **R** *Vacant*
Penrith (01768) 64766
CLIFTON (St Francis) (St Mary the Virgin) *S'well 10*
P *DBP* **TR** E P FORSHAW, **TV** S BROCKLEHURST,
NSM L FOX
CLIFTON (St James) *Sheff 6* **P** *Bp* **V** J M WRAW,
C G R HOLMES
CLIFTON (St John the Evangelist) Brighouse and Clifton
Wakef
CLIFTON (St Luke) *Carl 4* **P** *R Workington*
V P M BADEN
CLIFTON (St Philip and St James) *York 8* **P** *Trustees*
V R G FLETCHER, **C** A W ALLINGTON,
NSM N E ECKERSLEY
CLIFTON (St Paul) Bris St Mich and St Paul *Bris*
CLIFTON, NEW (Holy Trinity) Clifton *S'well*
CLIFTON, NORTH (St George) Harby w Thorney and N
and S Clifton *S'well*
CLIFTON CAMPVILLE (St Andrew) w Edingale *Lich 4*
P *Bp and Major F C Piper-Wolferstan (jt)*
R A C SOLOMON
CLIFTON GREEN (St Thomas) *Man 2* **P** *Bp*
V K J MASSEY
CLIFTON HAMPDEN (St Michael and All
Angels) Dorchester *Ox*
CLIFTON-ON-TEME (St Kenelm), Lower Sapey and the
Shelsleys *Worc 3* **P** *Bp and A F Evans Esq (jt)*
R P C OWEN
CLIFTON REYNES (St Mary the Virgin) Lavendon w Cold
Brayfield, Clifton Reynes etc *Ox*
CLIFTON UPON DUNSMORE (St Mary) and Newton
Cov 6 **P** *H A F W Boughton Leigh Esq*
P-in-c P S BALLANTINE
CLIFTONVILLE (St Paul) *Cant 9* **P** *Ch Patr Trust*
P-in-c J YALLOP
CLIPPESBY (St Peter) Rollesby w Burgh w Billockby w
Ashby w Oby etc *Nor*
CLIPSHAM (St Mary) Greetham and Thistleton w Stretton
and Clipsham *Pet*
CLIPSTON (All Saints) w Naseby and Haselbech w Kelmarsh
Pet 2 **P** *Ch Coll Cam, DBP, M F Harris Esq, and Miss*
C V Lancaster (by turn) **R** D W FAULKS
CLIPSTONE (All Saints) *S'well 2* **P** *Bp* **V** *Vacant*
Mansfield (01623) 23916
CLITHEROE (St James) *Blackb 8* **P** *Trustees*
R R PHILPOTT
CLITHEROE (St Mary Magdalene) *Blackb 8*
P J R Peel Esq **V** J A D ROBERTS, **NSM** P W SHEPHERD
CLITHEROE (St Paul) Low Moor *Blackb 8* **P** *Bp*
V R NICHOLSON
CLIVE (All Saints) Astley, Clive, Grinshill and Hadnall *Lich*
CLIVE VALE (All Souls) Hastings All So *Chich*
CLODOCK (St Clydog) and Longtown w Craswall,
Llanveynoe, St Margaret's, Michaelchurch Escley and
Newton *Heref 1* **P** *DBP (2 turns), MMCET (1 turn)*
V F E RODGERS, **NSM** G G DAVIES
CLOFORD (St Mary) Nunney and Witham Friary, Marston
Bigot etc *B & W*
CLOPHILL (St Mary the Virgin) *St Alb 22* **P** *Ball Coll Ox*
R P J SWINDELLS

CLOPTON (St Mary) w Otley, Swilland and Ashbocking
St E 7 **P** *Ld Chan and Bp (alt)* **R** B WAKELING
CLOSWORTH (All Saints) E Coker w Sutton Bingham and
Closworth *B & W*
CLOTHALL (St Mary Virgin) Sandon, Wallington and
Rushden w Clothall *St Alb*
CLOUGHTON (St Mary) *York 16* **P** *V Scalby*
P-in-c S RICHARDSON
CLOVELLY (All Saints) Parkham, Alwington, Buckland
Brewer etc *Ex*
CLOVELLY (St Peter) as above
CLOWNE (St John the Baptist) *Derby 3* **P** *Ld Chan*
R L R R HARRIS
CLOWS TOP (Mission Room) Mamble w Bayton, Rock w
Heightington etc *Worc*
CLUBMOOR (St Andrew) *Liv 8* **P** *Bp* **V** R J G PANTER
CLUMBER PARK (St Mary the Virgin) Worksop Priory
S'well
CLUN (St George) w Bettws-y-Crwyn and Newcastle
Heref 10 **P** *Earl of Powis* **V** R T SHAW,
Hon C J E M ROBERTS
CLUNBURY (St Swithin) Clungunford w Clunbury and
Clunton, Bedstone etc *Heref*
CLUNGUNFORD (St Cuthbert) w Clunbury and Clunton,
Bedstone and Hopton Castle *Heref 10* **P** *Earl of Powis, Mrs*
S B Rocke, M S C Brown Esq, and Sir Hugh Ripley, Bt (jt)
P-in-c S B BELL
CLUNTON (St Mary) Clungunford w Clunbury and
Clunton, Bedstone etc *Heref*
CLUTTON (St Augustine of Hippo) w Cameley *B & W 10*
P *Earl of Warw (2 turns), Exors J P Hippisley Esq (1 turn)*
R A V SAUNDERS, **NSM** J P KNOTT
CLYFFE PYPARD (St Peter) Broad Town, Clyffe Pypard,
Hilmarton etc *Sarum*
CLYMPING (St Mary the Virgin) and Yapton w Ford
Chich 1 **P** *Bp (2 turns), Ld Chan (1 turn)* **V** G HOWELLS
CLYST HONITON (St Michael and All Angels) Aylesbeare,
Rockbeare, Farringdon etc *Ex*
CLYST HYDON (St Andrew) Bradninch and Clyst Hydon
Ex
CLYST ST GEORGE (St George) Clyst St Mary, Clyst St
George etc *Ex*
CLYST ST LAWRENCE (St Lawrence) Whimple, Talaton
and Clyst St Lawr *Ex*
CLYST ST MARY (St Mary), Clyst (St George) and
Woodbury Salterton *Ex 1* **P** *Lord Wraxall, D&C, and*
S Radcliffe Esq (jt) **R** G L ROWE
COALBROOKDALE (Holy Trinity), Iron-Bridge and Little
Wenlock *Heref 14* **P** *Bp, Lord Forester, and Vs Madeley*
and Much Wenlock (jt) **R** B A NORTH
COALEY (St Bartholomew) Lower Cam w Coaley *Glouc*
COALPIT HEATH (St Saviour) *Bris 7* **P** *Bp* **V** *Vacant*
Winterbourne (01454) 775129
COALVILLE (Christ Church) and Bardon Hill *Leic 8*
P *Simeon's Trust and R Hugglescote (jt)* **V** *Vacant* Coalville
(01530) 838287
COATES (Holy Trinity) *Ely 18* **P** *Ld Chan* **P-in-c** B E WAY
COATES (St Edith) Stow Gp *Linc*
COATES (St Matthew), Rodmarton and Sapperton w
Frampton Mansell *Glouc 12* **P** *Bp, Lord Bathurst, and*
Guild of All So (jt) **R** R A BOWDEN,
NSM J M FRANCIS, S EMSON
COATES, GREAT (St Nicholas) and LITTLE (Bishop Edward
King Church) (St Michael) w Bradley *Linc 9* **P** *Patr Bd*
TR A V DOUGLAS, **TV** C M WOADDEN,
P A GOLDSMITH, **C** J C NEALE, **NSM** S GOLDSMITH
COATES, NORTH (St Nicholas) North-Chapel Parishes,
The *Linc*
COATHAM (Christ Church) *York 17* **P** *Trustees*
V J A WILSON
COATHAM, EAST (Christ Church) Coatham *York*
COBBOLD ROAD (St Saviour) (St Mary) *Lon 9* **P** *Bp*
V J D WHEELER
COBHAM Sole Street (St Mary's Church Room) Cobham w
Luddesdowne and Dode *Roch*
COBHAM (St Andrew) (St John the Divine) *Guildf 10*
P *D C H Combe Esq* **V** B L PREECE, **C** P F SMITH,
Hon C P G VICKERS
COBHAM (St Mary Magdalene) w Luddesdowne and Dode
Roch 1 **P** *Earl of Darnley and CPAS (alt)*
P-in-c M P P HOWARD
COBRIDGE (Christ Church) Hanley H Ev *Lich*
COCKAYNE HATLEY (St John the Baptist) Potton w
Sutton and Cockayne Hatley *St Alb*

COCKERHAM (St Michael) w Winmarleigh St Luke and Glasson Christ Church *Blackb 12* **P** *Bp (2 turns), Trustees (1 turn)* **V** R N HAMBLIN

COCKERINGTON, SOUTH (St Leonard) Mid Marsh Gp *Linc*

COCKERMOUTH (All Saints) (Christ Church) w Embleton and Wythop *Carl 6* **P** *Patr Bd* **TR** D THOMSON, **TV** I M RUMSEY, **NSM** J M CHAMBERLIN

COCKERNHOE (St Hugh) Luton St Fran *St Alb*

COCKERTON (St Mary) *Dur 12* **P** *Bp* **P-in-c** S D CONWAY, **C** M L DENT

COCKFIELD (St Mary) *Dur 11* **P** *Bp* **R** *Vacant* Bishop Auckland (01388) 718447

COCKFIELD (St Peter) w Bradfield St Clare, Felsham and Gedding *St E 10* **P** *St Jo Coll Cam (3 turns), Bp (2 turns), and Lt-Col J G Aldous (1 turn)* **R** B H MANNING, **NSM** H M FORD

COCKING (not known), Bepton and West Lavington *Chich 10* **P** *Ld Chan, Bp and Cowdray Trust (alt)* **P-in-c** F J R OTTO

COCKINGTON (St George and St Mary) (St Matthew) *Ex 10* **P** *Bp* **V** A K F MACEY

COCKLEY CLEY (All Saints) w Gooderstone *Nor 14* **P** *Bp* **P-in-c** A C FOOTTIT

COCKSHUTT (St Simon and St Jude) Petton w Cockshutt, Welshampton and Lyneal etc *Lich*

COCKYARD (Church Hall) Chapel-en-le-Frith *Derby*

CODDENHAM (St Mary) w Gosbeck and Hemingstone w Henley *St E 1* **P** *Pemb Coll Cam (2 turns), Lord de Saumarez (1 turn)* **R** *Vacant* Coddenham (0144979) 419

CODDINGTON (All Saints) Colwall w Upper Colwall and Coddington *Heref*

CODDINGTON (All Saints) w Barnby in the Willows *S'well 3* **P** *Bp* **V** P G WRIGHT

CODDINGTON (St Mary) Farndon and Coddington *Ches*

CODFORD (St Mary) Ashton Gifford *Sarum*

CODFORD (St Peter) as above

CODICOTE (St Giles) *St Alb 7* **P** *Abp* **V** P J SMITH, **NSM** J N HOLDEN

CODNOR (St James) *Derby 12* **P** *The Crown* **V** M M MOOKERJI

CODSALL (St Nicholas) *Lich 2* **P** *Bp and Lady Wrottesley (jt)* **V** A E WILLIAMS, **C** G E T BENNETT

CODSALL WOOD (St Peter) Codsall *Lich*

COFFEEHALL (Community Church) Woughton *Ox*

COFFINSWELL (St Bartholomew) Kingskerswell w Coffinswell *Ex*

COFTON (St Mary) Kenton, Mamhead, Powderham, Cofton and Starcross *Ex*

COFTON HACKETT (St Michael) w Barnt Green *Birm 4* **P** *Bp* **P-in-c** R S FIELDSON

COGENHOE (St Peter) *Pet 7* **P** *DBP* **R** D W JOHNSON

COGGES (St Mary) and Leigh, South *Ox 8* **P** *Bp and Payne Trustees (jt)* **V** S L BESSENT, **C** G R HOCKEN

COGGESHALL (St Peter ad Vincula) w Markshall *Chelmsf 20* **P** *Bp (2 turns), SMF (1 turn)* **V** D A M BEETON, **NSM** F J JACKSON

COGGESHALL, LITTLE (St Nicholas) Coggeshall w Markshall *Chelmsf*

COKER, EAST (St Michael and All Angels) w Sutton Bingham and Closworth *B & W 7* **P** *D&C Ex* **V** D J HUNT

COKER, WEST (St Martin of Tours) w Hardington Mandeville, East Chinnock and Pendomer *B & W 7* **P** *MMCET and Ox Chs Trust, and DBP (alt)* **R** D M OSMOND

COLATON RALEIGH (St John the Baptist) Newton Poppleford, Harpford and Colaton Raleigh *Ex*

COLBURN (St Cuthbert) Hipswell *Ripon*

COLBURY (Christ Church) *Win 10* **P** *Mrs A V Barker-Mill* **P-in-c** B L PICKETT

COLBY (Belle Abbey Church) Arbory *S & M*

COLBY (St Giles) Felmingham, Skeyton, Colby, Banningham etc *Nor*

COLCHESTER (Christ Church w St Mary at the Walls) *Chelmsf 17* **P** *Bp* **R** A J ROSE, **NSM** L K SPENDLOVE

COLCHESTER (St Anne) *Chelmsf 17* **P** *Bp* **V** T V HODDER

COLCHESTER (St Barnabas) Old Heath *Chelmsf 17* **P** *Bp* **V** R W F BEAKEN

COLCHESTER (St Botolph w Holy Trinity and St Giles) *Chelmsf 17* **P** *Bp* **P-in-c** M K TAILBY, **Hon C** P B J GREGORY

COLCHESTER (St James) w All Saints and St Nicholas and St Runwald *Chelmsf 17* **P** *Bp* **P-in-c** P S WALKER, **C** M J CATTERICK, **Hon C** P S LANSLEY

COLCHESTER (St John the Evangelist) *Chelmsf 17* **P** *Adn Colchester* **V** B W NICHOLSON, **C** P D PEARSON, **NSM** P H ADAMS

COLCHESTER (St Michael) Myland *Chelmsf 17* **P** *Ball Coll Ox* **R** J F BLORE

COLCHESTER (St Paul) *Chelmsf 17* **P** *Bp* **V** H D WINTER

COLCHESTER (St Peter) *Chelmsf 17* **P** *Simeon's Trustees* **V** R M WILSON

COLCHESTER (St Stephen) Colchester, New Town and The Hythe *Chelmsf*

COLCHESTER, New Town and The Hythe (St Stephen, St Mary Magdalen and St Leonard) *Chelmsf 17* **P** *Ball Coll Ox (2 turns), Ld Chan (1 turn)* **R** J SHILLAKER, **C** C F SHILLAKER, **Par Dn** C F SHILLAKER

COLD ASH (St Mark) Hermitage and Hampstead Norreys, Cold Ash etc *Ox*

COLD ASHBY (St Denys) Guilsborough w Hollowell and Cold Ashby *Pet*

COLD ASHTON (Holy Trinity) Marshfield w Cold Ashton and Tormarton etc *Bris*

COLD ASTON (St Andrew) w Notgrove and Turkdean *Glouc 14* **P** *Ld Chan (2 turns), Bp (1 turn)* **C** R A B MORRIS

COLD BRAYFIELD (St Mary) Lavendon w Cold Brayfield, Clifton Reynes etc *Ox*

COLD HIGHAM (St Luke) Pattishall w Cold Higham and Gayton w Tiffield *Pet*

COLD KIRBY (St Michael) Upper Ryedale *York*

COLD NORTON (St Stephen) Purleigh, Cold Norton and Stow Maries *Chelmsf*

COLD OVERTON (St John the Baptist) Whatborough Gp of Par *Leic*

COLD SALPERTON (All Saints) Dowdeswell and Andoversford w the Shiptons etc *Glouc*

COLDEAN (St Mary Magdalene) Moulsecoomb *Chich*

COLDEN (Holy Trinity) *Win 9* **P** *V Twyford* **V** A C MILLAR

COLDHAM (St Etheldreda) *Ely 19* **P** *Bp* **V** J E BARRETT

COLDHARBOUR (Christ Church) Abinger cum Coldharbour *Guildf*

COLDHURST (Holy Trinity) Oldham *Man*

COLDRED (St Pancras) Eythorne and Elvington w Waldershare etc *Cant*

COLDRIDGE (St Matthew) Lapford, Nymet Rowland and Coldridge *Ex*

COLDWALTHAM (St Giles) and Hardham *Chich 12* **P** *D&C and Col Sir B W de S Barttelot, Bt (jt)* **P-in-c** K B ELLWOOD, **NSM** C S STRIDE

COLEBROOKE (St Andrew) *Ex 2* **P** *D&C* **V** J C HALL

COLEBY (All Saints) Graffoe Gp *Linc*

COLEFORD (Holy Trinity) w Holcombe *B & W 12* **P** *Bp and V Kilmersdon (jt)* **V** P M DOWN

COLEFORD (St John the Evangelist) w Staunton *Glouc 4* **P** *Bp* **V** P W SEMPLE, **Hon C** A W WEARMOUTH

COLEHILL (St Michael and All Angels) *Sarum 10* **P** *Wimborne Minster Sch* **P-in-c** J W GOODALL, **C** D J J R LINAKER

COLEMAN'S HATCH (Holy Trinity) Hartfield w Coleman's Hatch *Chich*

COLEORTON (St Mary the Virgin) Ashby-de-la-Zouch St Helen w Coleorton *Leic*

COLERNE (St John the Baptist) w North Wraxall *Bris 9* **P** *New Coll Ox and Or Coll Ox (alt)* **R** *Vacant* Box (01225) 742742

COLESBOURNE (St James) *Glouc 12* **P** *H W G Elwes Esq* **V** *Vacant*

COLESHILL (All Saints) Amersham *Ox*

COLESHILL (All Saints) Gt Coxwell w Buscot, Coleshill & Eaton Hastings *Ox*

COLESHILL (St Peter and St Paul) *Birm 11* **P** *K S D Wingfield Digby Esq* **V** R G BOLLARD, **C** J E SALTER

COLEY Norwood Green (St George) Coley *Wakef*

COLEY (St John the Baptist) *Wakef 2* **P** *V Halifax* **V** A M EARNSHAW, **Hon C** R C DOWSON

COLGATE (St Saviour) *Chich 8* **P** *Mrs E C Calvert* **P-in-c** P H ADDENBROOKE

COLINDALE (St Matthias) *Lon 15* **P** *Bp* **V** M R POOLE

COLKIRK (St Mary) w Oxwick w Pattesley, Whissonsett, Horningtoft and Brisley *Nor 15* **P** *DBP, Ch Coll Cam, and C S P D Lane Esq (jt)* **NSM** K D BLOGG

COLLATON (St Mary the Virgin) Stoke Gabriel and Collaton St Mary *Ex*

COLLIER ROW (St James) and Havering-atte-Bower *Chelmsf 2* **P** *C P A S and Bp (jt)* **V** C G T HERBERT, **C** R J GARNETT

COLLIER STREET (St Margaret) Yalding w Collier Street *Roch*

COLLIERLEY (St Thomas) w Annfield Plain *Dur 8* **P** *Bp and The Crown (alt)* **V** G H LAWES

COLLIERS END (St Mary) High Cross *St Alb*

COLLINGBOURNE DUCIS (St Andrew) Wexcombe *Sarum*

COLLINGBOURNE KINGSTON (St Mary) as above

COLLINGHAM (All Saints) (St John the Baptist) w South Scarle and Besthorpe and Girton *S'well 3* **P** *Ld Chan and D&C Pet (alt)* **R** A A CONN, **NSM** S A DAVENPORT

COLLINGHAM (St Oswald) w Harewood *Ripon 1* **P** *Earl of Harewood and G H H Wheler Esq (jt)* **V** P F ROBERTS

COLLINGTON (St Mary) Bredenbury w Grendon Bishop and Wacton etc *Heref*

COLLINGTREE (St Columba) w Courteenhall and Milton Malsor *Pet 7* **P** *Major Sir Hereward Wake, G Phipps-Walker, and Hyndman Trustees (by turn)* **R** R J ORMSTON

COLLYHURST (The Saviour) *Man 5* **P** *Bp and Trustees (jt)* **R** D W BAILEY, **NSM** M B ROGERS

COLLYWESTON (St Andrew) Easton on the Hill, Collyweston w Duddington etc *Pet*

COLMWORTH (St Denys) Wilden w Colmworth and Ravensden *St Alb*

COLN ROGERS (St Andrew) Chedworth, Yanworth and Stowell, Coln Rogers etc *Glouc*

COLN ST ALDWYNS (St John the Baptist), Hatherop, Quenington, Eastleach and Southrop *Glouc 13* **P** *Earl St Aldwyn, D&C, Wadh Coll Ox, and DBP (jt)* **P-in-c** A M ROSS

COLN ST DENYS (St James the Great) Chedworth, Yanworth and Stowell, Coln Rogers etc *Glouc*

COLNBROOK (St Thomas) Riverside *Ox*

COLNE (Christ Church) *Blackb 7* **P** *DBF* **V** J C PRIESTLEY

COLNE (Holy Trinity) *Blackb 7* **P** *Bp* **V** G S INGRAM, **NSM** K ALLEN

COLNE (St Bartholomew) *Blackb 7* **P** *DBF* **R** P J MOTT

COLNE (St Helen) Bluntisham cum Earith w Colne and Woodhurst *Ely*

COLNE ENGAINE (St Andrew) Earls Colne w White Colne and Colne Engaine *Chelmsf*

COLNEY (St Andrew) Cringleford w Colney and Bawburgh *Nor*

COLNEY (St Peter) *St Alb 1* **P** *Bp* **V** M T BEER, **Hon C** J M BEER, **NSM** R W HEINZE

COLNEY HEATH (St Mark) *St Alb 7* **P** *Trustees* **V** D R VENESS, **Hon C** A D T GORTON, **NSM** B R McMAHON

COLSTERWORTH Group, The (St John the Baptist) *Linc 14* **P** *Bp (2 turns), Mrs R S McCorquodale and Rev J R H and Rev H C Thorold (1 turn)* **R** J COOK, **NSM** P C HOLLINGSHEAD

COLSTON BASSETT (St John the Divine) Cropwell Bishop w Colston Bassett, Granby etc *S'well*

COLTISHALL (St John the Baptist) w Great Hautbois and Horstead *Nor 20* **P** *D&C and K Coll Cam (jt)* **R** H D TOLLER, **NSM** N H KHAMBATTA

COLTON (Holy Trinity) w Satterthwaite and Rusland *Carl 10* **P** *V Hawksheod etc and Landowners (jt)* **P-in-c** D A SOUTHWARD, **NSM** S WAREHAM

COLTON (St Andrew) Easton w Colton and Marlingford *Nor*

COLTON (St Mary the Virgin) *Lich 3* **P** *Bp* **P-in-c** T THAKE

COLTON (St Paul) Bolton Percy *York*

COLWALL (St Crispin's Chapel) (St James the Great) w Upper Colwall (Good Shepherd) and Coddington *Heref 6* **P** *Bp* **R** C N H ATTWOOD, **C** E J CLARK-KING

COLWICH (St Michael and All Angels) w Great Haywood *Lich 3* **P** *Bp and Trustees (jt)* **V** T THAKE, **C** H M FULLARTON

COLWICK (St John the Baptist) Netherfield w Colwick *S'well*

COLYFORD (St Michael) Colyton, Southleigh, Offwell, Widworthy etc *Ex*

COLYTON (St Andrew), Southleigh, Offwell, Widworthy, Farway, Northleigh and Musbury *Ex 5* **P** *Patr Bd* **TR** D A GUNN-JOHNSON, **TV** D R WINNINGTON-INGRAM, **NSM** A RICHMOND, G A SMITH

COMBE (St Lawrence) Stonesfield w Combe *Ox*

COMBE (St Swithin) W Woodhay w Enborne, Hampstead Marshall etc *Ox*

COMBE DOWN (Holy Trinity) (St Andrew) w Monkton Combe and South Stoke *B & W 9* **P** *R Bath, Ox Chs Trust, and Comdr H R Salmer (jt)* **C** P A EAST, **NSM** S TRICKETT

COMBE FLOREY (St Peter and St Paul) Lydeard St Lawrence w Brompton Ralph etc *B & W*

COMBE HAY (not known) Bath Odd Down w Combe Hay *B & W*

COMBE-IN-TEIGNHEAD (All Saints) Stoke-in-Teignhead w Combe-in-Teignhead etc *Ex*

COMBE MARTIN (St Peter) and Berrynarbor *Ex 18* **P** *Bp* **R** K G WYER, **Hon C** R O H EPPINGSTONE

COMBE PYNE (St Mary the Virgin) Axminster, Chardstock, Combe Pyne and Rousdon *Ex*

COMBE RALEIGH (St Nicholas) Honiton, Gittisham, Combe Raleigh, Monkton etc *Ex*

COMBE ST NICHOLAS (St Nicholas) w Wambrook *B & W 15* **P** *Bp and T V D Eames Esq (jt)* **P-in-c** P REGAN

COMBERFORD (St Mary and St George) Wigginton *Lich*

COMBERTON (St Mary) *Ely 1* **P** *Jes Coll Cam* **V** R STEPHENSON, **NSM** M J REISS

COMBERTON, GREAT (St Michael) Elmley Castle w Bricklehampton and Combertons *Worc*

COMBERTON, LITTLE (St Peter) as above

COMBROKE (St Mary and St Margaret) w Compton Verney *Cov 8* **P** *Bp* **V** R MIGHALL

COMBS (St Mary) *St E 6* **P** *Bp* **P-in-c** P H MILLER

COMBWICH (St Peter) Cannington, Otterhampton, Combwich and Stockland *B & W*

COMER GARDENS (St David) Worc St Clem *Worc*

COMMONDALE (St Peter) Danby *York*

COMPSTALL (St Paul) Werneth *Ches*

COMPTON (All Saints) and Otterbourne *Win 13* **P** *Bp and Mrs P M A T Chamberlayne-Macdonald (jt)* **R** P L S BARRETT

COMPTON (St Mary) Farnham *Guildf*

COMPTON (St Mary and St Nicholas) w East Ilsley *Ox 14* **P** *Bp* **V** J B LEWIS

COMPTON (St Mary), the Mardens, Stoughton and Racton *Chich 13* **P** *Bp Lon (1 turn), Bp (2 turns)* **V** *Vacant* Compton (0170131) 578252

COMPTON (St Nicholas) w Shackleford and Peper Harow *Guildf 4* **P** *Bp and Major J R More-Molyneux (jt)* **R** J M FELLOWS

COMPTON, LITTLE (St Denys) w Chastleton, Cornwell, Little Rollright and Salford *Ox 3* **P** *Ch Ch Ox, DBP, and Bp (by turn)* **P-in-c** G P EVANS, **NSM** S U LAMBERT

COMPTON, NETHER (St Nicholas) Queen Thorne *Sarum*

COMPTON, OVER (St Michael) as above

COMPTON ABBAS (St Mary the Virgin) Shaston *Sarum*

COMPTON ABDALE (St Oswald) Withington and Compton Abdale w Haselton *Glouc*

COMPTON BASSETT (St Swithin) Oldbury *Sarum*

COMPTON BEAUCHAMP (St Swithun) Ashbury, Compton Beauchamp and Longcot w Fernham *Ox*

COMPTON BISHOP (St Andrew) Crook Peak *B & W*

COMPTON CHAMBERLAYNE (St Michael) Fovant, Sutton Mandeville and Teffont Evias etc *Sarum*

COMPTON DANDO (Blessed Virgin Mary) Publow w Pensford, Compton Dando and Chelwood *B & W*

COMPTON DUNDON (St Andrew) Somerton w Compton Dundon, the Charltons etc *B & W*

COMPTON GREENFIELD (All Saints) Pilning w Compton Greenfield *Bris*

COMPTON MARTIN (St Michael) Blagdon w Compton Martin and Ubley *B & W*

COMPTON PAUNCEFOOT (Blessed Virgin Mary) Camelot Par *B & W*

COMPTON VALENCE (St Thomas a Beckett) The Winterbournes and Compton Valence *Sarum*

CONCHAN (St Peter) Onchan *S & M*

CONDICOTE (St Nicholas) Longborough, Sezincote, Condicote and the Swells *Glouc*

CONDOVER (St Andrew and St Mary) w Frodesley, Acton Burnell and Pitchford *Heref 11* **P** *Bp, Rev E W Serjeantson, and Mrs C R Colthurst (jt)* **R** F T RUMBALL

CONEY HILL (St Oswald) *Glouc 5* **P** *The Crown* **V** I F CALDER, **C** M SHARLAND

CONEY WESTON (St Mary) Hopton, Market Weston, Barningham etc *St E*

CONEYSTHORPE (Chapel) Street TM *York*

CONGERSTONE (St Mary the Virgin) Market Bosworth, Cadeby w Sutton Cheney etc *Leic*

CONGHAM (St Andrew) Grimston, Congham and Roydon *Nor*

CONGLETON (St James) *Ches 11* **P** *Bp* **P-in-c** A J BURTON

CONGLETON (St Peter) *Ches 1* **P** *Simeon's Trustees* **V** R P SCOONES

CONGLETON (St Stephen) *Ches 11* **P** *Bp* **P-in-c** R P SCOONES

CONGRESBURY (St Andrew) w Puxton and Hewish St Ann *B & W 11* **P** M M CET **V** R H SALMON

CONINGSBY (St Michael and All Angels) w Tattershall
Linc 11　P DBP and Baroness Willoughby de Eresby (alt)
P-in-c J R MOORE, **NSM** M DONE
CONINGTON (St Mary) Fen Drayton w Conington Ely
CONISBROUGH (St Peter) Sheff 10　P Bp　V P A JEPPS,
C D R SHERWIN
CONISCLIFFE (St Edwin) Dur 12　P Bp　**P-in-c** P CRICK
CONISHOLME (St Peter) Somercotes and Grainthorpe w
Conisholme Linc
CONISTON (St Andrew) Church Coniston Carl
CONISTON COLD (St Peter) Kirkby-in-Malhamdale w
Coniston Cold Bradf
CONISTONE (St Mary) Kettlewell w Conistone,
Hubberholme etc Bradf
CONONLEY (St John the Evangelist) w Bradley Bradf 8
P Bp　**V** C R PENFOLD, **Hon C** S I PENFOLD
CONSETT (Christ Church) Dur 8　P Bp　V J HOGARTH,
C S C FOSTER
CONSTABLE LEE (St Paul) Man 15　P CPAS
V P HEYWOOD
CONSTANTINE (St Constantine) Truro 4　P D&C
V A J WADE
COOKBURY (St John the Baptist and the Seven
Maccabes) Black Torrington, Bradf w Cookbury etc Ex
COOKHAM (Holy Trinity) Ox 13　P Bp　P Mrs K E Rogers
V D D J ROSSDALE, **Hon C** A W WELLING
COOKHAM DEAN (St John the Baptist) Ox 13
P V Cookham　**V** J F W V COPPING
COOKHILL (St Paul) Inkberrow w Cookhill and Kington w
Dormston Worc
COOKLEY (St Michael and All Angels) Cratfield w
Heveningham and Ubbeston etc St E
COOKLEY (St Peter) Wolverley and Cookley Worc
COOKRIDGE (Holy Trinity) Ripon 7　P R Adel
V J F HAMILTON
COOMBE (Christ Church) New Malden and Coombe S'wark
COOMBE BISSET (St Michael and All Angels) Chalke
Valley E Sarum
COOMBES (not known) Lancing w Coombes Chich
COOMBS WOOD (St Ambrose) Blackheath Birm
COOPERSALE (St Alban) Epping Distr Chelmsf
COPDOCK (St Peter) w Washbrook and Belstead St E 5
P DBP **R** Vacant
**COPFORD (St Michael and All Angels) w Easthorpe and
Messing w Inworth** Chelmsf 25　P Ld Chan, Duchy of Lanc,
and DBP (by turn)　**R** Vacant Tiptree (01621) 815434
COPGROVE (St Michael) Farnham w Scotton, Staveley,
Copgrove etc Ripon
COPLE (All Saints) w Willington St Alb 17　P Bp and
D&C Ox (alt)　**V** J A TERRY
COPLEY Wakef 4　P V Halifax　V Vacant Halifax (01422)
652964
COPMANTHORPE (St Giles) York 1　P R Micklegate
H Trin　**V** J C STONEHOUSE
COPP (St Anne) Blackb 10　P V St Michael's-on-Wyre
V P YORKSHIRE
COPPENHALL (All Saints and St Paul) Crewe All SS and St
Paul Ches
COPPENHALL (St Laurence) Penkridge Team Lich
COPPENHALL (St Michael) Ches 15　P Bp　**R** J MACKEY
COPPULL (not known) Blackb 4　P R Standish
V J HUDSON
COPPULL (St John) Blackb 4　P R Standish　**R** J STEWART
COPSTON MAGNA (St John) Wolvey w Burton Hastings,
Copston Magna etc Cov
COPT OAK (St Peter) Oaks in Charnwood and Copt Oak
Leic
COPTHORNE (St John the Evangelist) Chich 7　P Bp
V Vacant Copthorne (01342) 712063
COPYTHORNE (St Mary) and Minstead Win 10　P Bp Liv
and J P Green Esq (jt)　**P-in-c** J W PRAGNELL
CORBRIDGE w Halton (St Andrew) and Newton Hall
Newc 3　P D&C Carl　**V** L CONSTANTINE,
NSM H H HUNTER
CORBY (Epiphany) (St John the Baptist) Pet 9
P E Brudenell Esq　**P-in-c** P G LAMBERT
CORBY (St Columba and the Northern Saints) Pet 9　P Bp
V M W EDEN
**CORBY (St Peter and St Andrew) (Kingswood Church) w
Great and Little Oakley** Pet 9　P Bp, Boughton Estates, and
H W G de Capell Brooke Esq (jt)　**TR** M A CRAGGS,
TV M D GLENN
CORBY GLEN (St John the Evangelist) Linc 14　P Ld Chan
(2 turns), Sir Simon Benton Jones, Bt (1 turn)
NSM I K WILLIAMS
CORELEY (St Peter) w Doddington Heref 12　P DBP and
Mrs R C Woodward (jt)　**P-in-c** D M BURGESS
CORFE (St Nicholas) Pitminster w Corfe B & W

**CORFE CASTLE (St Edward the Martyr), Church Knowle,
Kimmeridge Steeple w Tyneham** Sarum 9　P Major
M J A Bond and Major J C Mansel (jt)　**R** M A STRIKE
CORFE MULLEN (St Hubert) Sarum 10　P Bp
R A B ELKINS, **C** A F DAWTRY
CORHAMPTON (not known) Meonstoke w Corhampton
cum Exton Portsm
CORLEY (not known) Fillongley and Corley Cov
CORNARD, GREAT (St Andrew) St E 12　P Bp
P-in-c P F HOCKING
CORNARD, LITTLE (All Saints) Assington w Newton
Green and Lt Cornard St E
CORNELLY (St Cornelius) Tregony w St Cuby and Cornelly
Truro
CORNEY (St John the Baptist) Bootle, Corney, Whicham
and Whitbeck Carl
CORNFORTH (Holy Trinity) Dur 14　P Bp V Vacant
Ferryhill (01740) 654591
CORNHILL (St Helen) w Carham Newc 12　P Abp (2 turns),
E M Straker-Smith Esq (1 turn)　**V** R W HOWE
CORNHOLME (St Michael and All Angels) Wakef 3
P DBP　**V** N J WHETTON
CORNISH HALL END (St John the
Evangelist) Finchingfield and Cornish Hall End Chelmsf
CORNWELL (St Peter) Lt Compton w Chastleton, Cornwell
etc Ox
CORNWOOD (St Michael and All Angels) Ex 21　P Bp
NSM D HALL
CORNWORTHY (St Peter) Ashprington, Cornworthy and
Dittisham Ex
CORONATION SQUARE (St Aidan) Cheltenham St Mark
Glouc
CORRINGHAM (St John the Evangelist) (St Mary the Virgin)
Chelmsf 14　P SMF　**P-in-c** M HUME
CORRINGHAM (St Lawrence) and Blyton Group, The
Linc 2　P Ld Chan (2 turns), Bp (1 turn), and
Meynell Ch Trustees (1 turn)　**V** M W PAGE-CHESTNEY,
NSM S V PAGE-CHESTNEY
CORSCOMBE (St Mary the Virgin) Melbury Sarum
CORSE (St Margaret) Hartpury w Corse and Staunton Glouc
CORSENSIDE (All Saints) N Tyne and Redesdale Team
Newc
CORSENSIDE (St Cuthbert) as above
CORSHAM, GREATER (St Bartholomew) Bris 9
P Patr Bd　**TR** R G CLIFTON, **TV** V W BEYNON,
C I BUTCHER, **NSM** L F FLOWERDAY
CORSLEY (St Mary the Virgin) Sarum 14　P DBP
P-in-c R SHARPE
CORSTON (All Saints) Saltford w Corston and Newton St
Loe B & W
CORSTON (All Saints) Gt Somerford, Lt Somerford, Seagry,
Corston etc Bris
CORTON (St Bartholomew) Hopton w Corton Nor
CORTON (St Bartholomew) Abbotsbury, Portesham and
Langton Herring Sarum
CORTON DENHAM (St Andrew) Queen Camel w W
Camel, Corton Denham etc B & W
CORYTON (St Andrew) Marystowe, Coryton, Stowford,
Lewtrenchard etc Ex
COSBY (St Michael and All Angels) Leic 10　P Bp
V S B HEYGATE
COSELEY (Christ Church) (St Cuthbert) Worc 10　P Bp
V M T C BAYNES
COSELEY (St Chad) Worc 10　P Bp　**P-in-c** A HOWES
COSGROVE (St Peter and St Paul) Potterspury, Furtho,
Yardley Gobion and Cosgrove Pet
COSHAM (St Philip) Portsm 6　P Bp　**V** T E LOUDEN,
C M J THOMSON
COSSALL (St Catherine) Awsworth w Cossall S'well
COSSINGTON (All Saints) Sileby, Cossington and Seagrave
Leic
COSSINGTON (Blessed Virgin Mary) Woolavington w
Cossington and Bawdrip B & W
COSTESSEY (St Edmund) Nor 2　P Gt Hosp Nor
C A KNIGHT
COSTESSEY, NEW (St Helen) Costessey Nor
COSTOCK (St Giles) E and W Leake, Stanford-on-Soar,
Rempstone etc S'well
COSTON (St Andrew) Wymondham w Edmondthorpe,
Buckminster etc Leic
COTEBROOKE (St John and Holy Cross) Tarporley Ches
COTEHELE HOUSE (Chapel) Calstock Truro
COTEHILL (St John the Evangelist) and Cumwhinton Carl 2
P The Crown　**P-in-c** F W BOVILL, **NSM** P N DOWNHAM
COTES HEATH (St James) Standon and Cotes Heath Lich
COTESBACH (St Mary) Lutterworth w Cotesbach Leic
COTGRAVE (All Saints) S'well 8　P DBP
R G B BARRODALE, **C** S SPENCER, **NSM** R A SPRAY

COTHAM (St Saviour w St Mary) *Bris 5* **P** *Bp*
V GNBOUNDY

COTHELSTONE (St Thomas of Canterbury) Bishops Lydeard w Bagborough and Cothelstone *B & W*

COTHERIDGE (St Leonard) Martley and Wichenford, Knightwick etc *Worc*

COTHERSTONE (St Cuthbert) Romaldkirk w Laithkirk *Ripon*

COTLEIGH (St Michael and All Angels) Yarcombe, Membury, Upottery and Cotleigh *Ex*

COTMANHAY (Christ Church) *Derby 13* **P** *Bp*
V JDHOLT, C RGHOLLINGS

COTON (St Peter) *Ely 1* **P** *St Cath Coll Cam*
R HDSEARLE

COTON IN THE ELMS (St Mary) Walton on Trent w Croxall etc *Derby*

COTTAM (Holy Trinity) Rampton w Laneham, Treswell, Cottam and Stokeham *S'well*

COTTENHAM (All Saints) *Ely 5* **P** *Bp* **R** I MGFRIARS

COTTERED (St John the Baptist) w Broadfield and Throcking *St Alb 5* **P** *Bp* **P-in-c** E JPOOLE, **NSM** CPOLHILL

COTTERIDGE (St Agnes) *Birm 4* **P** *R Kings Norton*
V MWBLOOD, **NSM** RRCOLLINS

COTTERSTOCK (St Andrew) Warmington, Tansor, Cotterstock and Fotheringhay *Pet*

COTTESBROOKE (All Saints) w Great Creaton and Thornby *Pet 2* **P** *Bp (2 turns), MacDonald-Buchanan Trustees (1 turn)* **P-in-c** WGGIBBS

COTTESMORE (St Nicholas) and Barrow w Ashwell and Burley *Pet 14* **P** *E R Hanbury Esq, Viscount Downe, and DBP (by turn)* **R** MHWROGERS

COTTIMORE (St John) Walton-on-Thames *Guildf*

COTTINGHAM (St Mary) *York 15* **P** *Abp* **R** TGGRIGG

COTTINGHAM (St Mary Magdalene) w East Carlton *Pet 9* **P** *BNC Ox and Sir Geoffrey Palmer Bt (alt)* **R** *Vacant* Rockingham (01536) 771277

COTTINGLEY (St Michael and All Angels) *Bradf 1* **P** *Bp*
V *Vacant* Bradford (01274) 562278

COTTINGWITH, EAST (St Mary) Elvington w Sutton on Derwent and E Cottingwith *York*

COTTISFORD (St Mary the Virgin) Finmere w Mixbury, Cottisford, Hardwick etc *Ox*

COTTON (St Andrew) Bacton w Wyverstone and Cotton *St E*

COTTON (St John the Baptist) Alton w Bradley-le-Moors and Oakamoor w Cotton *Lich*

COTTON MILL (St Julian) St Alb St Steph *St Alb*

COUGHTON (St Peter) *Cov 7* **P** *Bp*
P-in-c FJBALLINGER

COULSDON (St Andrew) *S'wark 22* **P** *Bp* **V** CJELUNN,
Hon C KVMcKIE

COULSDON (St John) *S'wark 22* **P** *Abp* **R** SHMASLEN,
C NDBIDEN, RWHARE

COULSTON, EAST (St Thomas of Canterbury) Edington and Imber, Erlestoke and E Coulston *Sarum*

COUND (St Peter) *Heref 11* **P** *Bp* **R** *Vacant*

COUNDON (St James) *Dur 10* **P** *Bp* **V** HHUTCHINSON

COUNTESS WEAR (St Luke) Wear St Luke *Ex*

COUNTESS WEAR (St Luke's Hall) as above

COUNTESTHORPE (St Andrew) w Foston *Leic 10* **P** *DBP and Bp (alt)* **V** AWJOHNSON, C RVWORSFOLD,
NSM MDGILLESPIE

COUNTISBURY (St John the Evangelist) Lynton, Brendon, Countisbury, Lynmouth etc *Ex*

COURTEENHALL (St Peter and St Paul) Collingtree w Courteenhall and Milton Malsor *Pet*

COVE (St John the Baptist) (St Christopher) *Guildf 1* **P** *Bp*
TR MSKING, **TV** JPSTEWART, PADOBSON,
C HO'SULLIVAN

COVEHITHE (St Andrew) Wrentham w Benacre, Covehithe, Frostenden etc *St E*

COVEN (St Paul) *Lich 2* **P** *V Brewood*
P-in-c KLWASSALL

COVEN HEATH (Mission Church) Bushbury *Lich*

COVENEY (St Peter ad Vincula) *Ely 14* **P** *Bp*
R RJMACKLIN

COVENHAM (Annunciation of the Blessed Virgin Mary) Fotherby *Linc*

COVENT GARDEN (St Paul) *Lon 3* **P** *Bp* **R** DELLIOTT

COVENTRY Caludon (St Paul) *Cov 1* **P** *Bp and Ld Chan (alt)*
TV RJWORSLEY, MMCLARKE, **TV** NDADAMS,
C WMSMITH, CADAMS

COVENTRY Holbrooks (St Luke) Holbrooks *Cov*

COVENTRY (Holy Trinity) *Cov 2* **P** *Ld Chan*
V DAURQUHART, C ADBRADLEY, PJHARWOOD

COVENTRY (St Francis of Assisi) North Radford *Cov 2*
P *Bp* **V** NJTAYLOR, **NSM** MJROWBERRY

COVENTRY (St George) *Cov 2* **P** *Bp* **V** LNJANICKER

COVENTRY (St John the Baptist) *Cov 2* **P** *Trustees*
R GTSSOUTHGATE

COVENTRY (St Mary Magdalen) *Cov 3* **P** *Bp*
V CHKNOWLES, C DRWINTLE

COVENTRY EAST (St Anne and All Saints) (St Barnabas) (St Margaret) (St Peter) *Cov 1* **P** *Patr Bd*
TR WADBERRYMAN, **TV** NAJBLACKWELL,
PGEDWARDS, SMUKHERJEE, C AWWILLSON,
SEDWARDS, **NSM** PNASPINALL

COVERACK (St Peter) St Keverne *Truro*

COVERDALE (St Botolph) Middleham w Coverdale and E Witton *Ripon*

COVINGHAM (St Paul) Swindon Dorcan *Bris*

COVINGTON (All Saints) *Ely 10* **P** *Sir Stephen Hastings*
P-in-c JHINDLEY, **NSM** BABEARCROFT,
JRAWLINSON

COWARNE, LITTLE (not known) Bredenbury w Grendon Bishop and Wacton etc *Heref*

COWARNE, MUCH (St Mary the Virgin) Stoke Lacy, Moreton Jeffries w Much Cowarne etc *Heref*

COWBIT (St Mary) *Linc 17* **P** *Ld Chan, DBP, and V Moulton (by turn)* **V** *Vacant* Holbeach (01406) 370152

COWCLIFFE (St Hilda) N Huddersfield *Wakef*

COWDEN (St Mary Magdalene) w Hammerwood *Chich 7*
P *Ch Soc Trust* **R** *Vacant* Cowden (01342) 850221

COWES (Holy Trinity) and Cowes (St Mary the Virgin) *Portsm 8* **P** *Trustees and V Carisbrooke St Mary the Virgin (jt)* **V** RJEMBLIN, **Hon C** IRDOWSE

COWES (St Faith) *Portsm 8* **P** *Bp* **V** *Vacant* Isle of Wight (01983) 292656

COWES, EAST (St James) Whippingham w E Cowes *Portsm*

COWESBY (St Michael) *York 20* **P** *Abp*
P-in-c PRARHOARE

COWFOLD (St Peter) *Chich 9* **P** *Bp Lon* **V** GLDRIVER

COWGATE (St Peter) *Newc 7* **P** *Bp* **V** TDDAWSON

COWGILL (St John the Evangelist) Dent w Cowgill *Bradf*

COWICK (Holy Trinity) Gt Snaith *Sheff*

COWLAM (St Mary) Sledmere and Cowlam w Fridaythorpe, Fimer etc *York*

COWLEIGH (St Peter) Malvern Link w Cowleigh *Worc*

COWLEY (St James) (St Francis) *Ox 4* **P** *Patr Bd*
TV PAKNIGHTS, C PDSTANWAY, **NSM** WCHAND

COWLEY (St John) (St Alban) (St Bartholomew) (St Mary and St John) *Ox 4* **P** *St Steph Ho Ox* **V** CPIRVINE,
C PMDOLL, **NSM** ALFORBES

COWLEY (St Laurence) *Lon 24* **P** *Bp*
P-in-c RCHRISTIAN

COWLEY (St Mary) Coberley w Cowley *Glouc*

COWLEY CHAPEL (St Antony) Thorverton, Cadbury, Upton Pyne etc *Ex*

COWLING (Holy Trinity) *Bradf 8* **P** *Bp* **V** RDCARTER

COWLINGE (St Margaret) Wickhambrook w Lydgate, Ousden and Cowlinge *St E*

COWPEN (St Benedict) Horton *Newc*

COWPLAIN (St Wilfrid) *Portsm 4* **P** *Bp* **V** PHANCOCK,
C APMARSDEN

COWTONS, The (All Saints) (St Luke's Pastoral Centre) *Ripon 2* **P** *V Gilling (1 turn), DBP (2 turns)* **V** *Vacant* Darlington (01325) 378230

COX GREEN (Good Shepherd) *Ox 13* **P** *Bp*
P-in-c VJBROOKS

COXHEATH (Chapel) w East Farleigh, Hunton and Linton *Roch 7* **P** *Abp, Ld Chan and Lord Cornwallis (by turn)*
R RJCASTLE, **NSM** HCHBIRD, GRELLMORE

COXHOE (St Mary) *Dur 14* **P** *Bp* **V** *Vacant* 0191–3770222

COXLEY (Christ Church), Henton and Wookey *B & W 8*
P *Bp* **V** RRBPLOWMAN

COXWELL, GREAT (St Giles) w Buscot, Coleshill and Eaton Hastings *Ox 17* **P** *Bp and Lord Faringdon (jt)*
V RCSWANBOROUGH

COXWELL, LITTLE (St Mary) Gt Faringdon w Lt Coxwell *Ox*

COXWOLD (St Michael) and Husthwaite *York 5* **P** *Abp*
V DFJOHNSON

CRABBS CROSS (St Peter) Redditch, The Ridge *Worc*

CRADLEY (St James) w Mathon and Storridge *Heref 6*
P *Bp and D&C Westmr (jt)* **P-in-c** GPHOWELL,
NSM MDVOCKINS

CRADLEY (St Peter) (St Katherine's Mission Church) *Worc 9* **P** *R Halesowen* **V** DJBLACKBURN,
C RJROSOMAN

CRADLEY HEATH (St Luke) Reddal Hill St Luke *Worc*

CRAGHEAD (St Thomas) Stanley *Dur*

CRAKEHALL (St Gregory) *Ripon 4* **P** *Sir Henry Beresford-Peirse, Bt* **V** *Vacant*

CRAMBE (St Michael) Whitwell w Crambe, Flaxton, Foston etc *York*

CRAMLINGTON (St Nicholas) *Newc 1* **P** *Bp*
TR M N F HAIG, **TV** A PATTISON, V C NICHOLSON,
TV M F LAYBOURNE
CRAMPMOOR (St Swithun) Romsey *Win*
CRANBORNE (St Mary and St Bartholomew) w Boveridge,
Edmondsham, Wimborne St Giles and Woodlands
Sarum 10 **P** *Marquess of Salisbury, Earl of Shaftesbury,*
and Mrs C M Medlycott (jt) **R** B R DIXON
CRANBOURNE (St Peter) Winkfield and Cranbourne *Ox*
CRANBROOK (St Dunstan) *Cant 11* **P** *Abp*
V G S BRIDGEWATER, **NSM** J P MOY
CRANFIELD (St Peter and St Paul) and Hulcote w Salford
St Alb 19 **P** *MMCET* **R** *Vacant* Bedford (01234) 750214
CRANFORD (Holy Angels) (St Dunstan) *Lon 11*
P *R J G Berkeley Esq and Sir Hugo Huntingdon-*
Whiteley (jt) **R** N G T WHEELER
CRANFORD (St Andrew) (St John the Baptist) w Grafton
Underwood and Twywell *Pet 11* **P** *Boughton Estates, DBP,*
and Sir John Robinson (by turn) **R** D H P FOOT
CRANHAM (All Saints) *Chelmsf 2* **P** *St Jo Coll Ox*
P-in-c T W PAGE, **C** A J D E ABSALOM
CRANHAM (St James the Great) Brimpsfield, Cranham,
Elkstone and Syde *Glouc*
CRANHAM PARK Moor Lane (not known) Cranham Park
Chelmsf
CRANHAM PARK (St Luke) *Chelmsf 2* **P** *Bp*
V J F DUNNETT, **C** R G SAUNDERS
CRANLEIGH (St Nicolas) *Guildf 2* **P** *Bp*
R N P NICHOLSON, **C** S N PAUL
CRANMORE, WEST (St Bartholomew) Shepton Mallet w
Doulting *B & W*
CRANOE (St Michael) Gt Bowden w Welham, Glooston and
Cranoe *Leic*
CRANSFORD (St Peter) Badingham w Bruisyard, Cransford
and Dennington *St E*
CRANSLEY (St Andrew) Broughton w Loddington and
Cransley etc *Pet*
CRANTOCK (St Carantoc) *Truro 7* **P** *SMF*
NSM M WILLS
CRANWELL (St Andrew) *Linc 22* **P** *DBP* **V** *Vacant*
CRANWICH (St Mary) *Nor 14* **P** *CPAS*
P-in-c G H WHEATLEY
CRANWORTH (St Mary the Virgin) Reymerston w
Cranworth, Letton, Southburgh etc *Nor*
CRASSWALL (St Mary) Clodock and Longtown w
Craswall, Llanveynoe etc *Heref*
CRASTER (Mission Church) Embleton w Rennington and
Rock *Newc*
CRATFIELD (St Mary) w Heveningham and Ubbeston w
Huntingfield and Cookley *St E 15* **P** *Hon Mrs S Peel and*
Simeon's Trustees (alt) **P-in-c** L M HIPKINS
CRATHORNE (All Saints) *York 22* **P** *Lord Crathorne,*
Hon David Dugdale, and J Southern Esq (jt)
P-in-c P KITCHING
CRAWCROOK (Church of the Holy Spirit) Greenside *Dur*
CRAWFORD (District Church) Upholland *Liv*
CRAWLEY (St John the Baptist) *Chich 7* **P** *Bp*
TR K D RICHARDS, **TV** S HARDAKER, R C MARSH,
B L HACKSHALL, **C** D G STANIFORD, J M BALDWIN,
Hon C I W NATHANIEL
CRAWLEY (St Mary) and Littleton and Sparsholt w Lainston
Win 13 **P** *Ld Chan and DBP (alt)* **R** D G WILLIAMS
CRAWLEY, NORTH (St Firmin) Sherington w Chicheley, N
Crawley, Astwood etc *Ox*
CRAWLEY DOWN (All Saints) *Chich 7* **P** *R Worth*
V W J L STRONG
CRAWSHAWBOOTH (St John) Goodshaw and
Crawshawbooth *Man*
CRAY (St Mary and St Paulinus) St Mary Cray and St Paul's
Cray *Roch*
CRAY, NORTH (St James) w Ruxley *Roch 16* **P** *Bp*
R P H ROLTON
CRAYFORD (St Paulinus) *Roch 14* **P** *Bp* **R** P WRIGHT,
C J M HULME, J PEAL
CRAYKE (St Cuthbert) w Brandsby and Yearsley *York 5*
P *The Crown and Abp (alt)* **NSM** R W DAVILL
CRAZIES HILL (Mission Room) Wargrave *Ox*
CREACOMBE (St Michael and All Angels) Witheridge,
Thelbridge, Creacombe, Meshaw etc *Ex*
CREAKE, NORTH (St Mary) and SOUTH (St Mary) w
Waterden, Syderstone w Barmer and Sculthorpe *Nor 16*
P *Bp, Earl Spencer, Earl of Leic, Guild of All So,*
J Labouchere Esq, Mrs M E Russell, and DBP (jt)
R A M THOMSON
CREATON, GREAT (St Michael and All
Angels) Cottesbrooke w Gt Creaton and Thornby *Pet*

CREDENHILL (St Mary) w Brinsop, Mansel Lacey, Yazor
and Wormesley *Heref 4* **P** *Major D J Davenport (2 turns),*
Bp (1 turn), and R Ecroyd Esq (1 turn) **R** G USHER
CREDITON (Holy Cross) (St Lawrence) and Shobrooke
Ex 2 **P** *12 Govs of Crediton Ch* **R** A E GEERING
CREECH ST MICHAEL (St Michael) *B & W 18*
P *MMCET* **V** D G MANNING
CREED (St Crida) Probus, Ladock and Grampound w Creed
and St Erme *Truro*
CREEDY, NORTH: Cheriton Fitzpaine, Woolfardisworthy
East, Kennerleigh, Washford Pyne, Puddington, Poughill,
Stockleigh English, Morchard Bishop, Stockleigh Pomeroy,
Down St Mary and Clannaborough *Ex 2* **P** *Ld Chan*
(1 turn), DBP (3 turns), **TR** B SHILLINGFORD,
TV S G C SMITH, **AR** GARDINER
CREEKMOOR (Christ Church) Oakdale St Geo *Sarum*
CREEKSEA (All Saints) w Althorne and Latchingdon w North
Fambridge *Chelmsf 11* **P** *Bp, Abp and Ld Chan (by turn)*
NSM D I GORDON, E S LANGAN
CREETING (St Peter) Creeting St Mary, Creeting St Peter
etc *St E*
CREETING ST MARY (St Mary), Creeting (St Peter) and
Earl Stonham w Stonham Parva *St E 1* **P** *DBP (2 turns),*
Pemb Coll Cam (1 turn) **R** A PYKE
CREETON (St Peter) Castle Bytham w Creeton *Linc*
CREGNEISH (St Peter) Rushen *S & M*
CRESSAGE (Christ Church) Wenlock *Heref*
CRESSBROOK (St John the Evangelist) Tideswell *Derby*
CRESSING (All Saints) *Chelmsf 16* **P** *Bp* **R** *Vacant*
Braintree (01376) 343740
CRESSINGHAM, GREAT (St Michael) and LITTLE (St
Andrew), w Threxton *Nor 14* **P** *Bp and Sec of State for*
Defence **P-in-c** A C FOOTTIT
CRESSWELL (St Bartholomew) and Lynemouth *Newc 11*
P *Bp* **V** P WHITEHEAD
CRESWELL (St Mary Magdalene) Elmton *Derby*
CRETINGHAM (St Peter) Earl Soham w Cretingham and
Ashfield cum Thorpe *St E*
CREWE (All Saints and St Paul) *Ches 15* **P** *Bp*
V P D BRADBROOK
CREWE (Christ Church) (St Peter) *Ches 15* **P** *Bp*
V W C W FOSS
CREWE (St Andrew w St John the Baptist) *Ches 15* **P** *Bp*
V W J BAKER
CREWE (St Barnabas) *Ches 15* **P** *Bp* **V** R D POWELL
CREWE GREEN (St Michael and All Angels) Haslington w
Crewe Green *Ches*
CREWKERNE (St Bartholomew) w Wayford *B & W 15*
P *Ld Chan* **R** P B CURTIS
CREWTON (St Peter) Boulton *Derby*
CRICH (St Mary) *Derby 1* **P** *Ch Trust Fund Trust* **V** *Vacant*
Ambergate (01773) 852449
CRICK (St Margaret) and Yelvertoft w Clay Coton and
Lilbourne *Pet 2* **P** *MMCET and St Jo Coll Ox (jt)*
R R M BARLOW
CRICKET MALHERBIE (St Mary Magdalene) Chard
Furnham w Chaffcombe, Knowle St Giles etc *B & W*
CRICKET ST THOMAS (St Thomas) Thorncombe w
Winsham and Cricket St Thomas *B & W*
CRICKLADE (St Sampson) w Latton *Bris 10* **P** *D&C, Bp,*
and Hon P N Eliot (by turn) **V** G K WITHINGTON,
NSM A EVANS
CRICKLEWOOD (St Gabriel and St Michael) *Lon 21*
P *Bp* **P-in-c** M R ALDRIDGE, **C** R W HARRISON
CRICKLEWOOD (St Peter) *Lon 21* **P** *Bp*
P-in-c K MITCHELL
CRIFTINS (St Matthew) *Lich 22* **P** *Bp*
P-in-c D R D JONES, **C** A C NETHERWOOD
CRIMPLESHAM (St Mary) w Stradsett *Ely 16* **P** *Bp*
V P F KEELING
CRINGLEFORD (St Peter) w Colney and Bawburgh *Nor 7*
P *Gt Hosp Nor, Exors E H Barclay Esq and D&C (alt)*
R C J BLACKMAN
CROCKENHILL (All Souls) *Roch 2* **P** *Bp*
V S CHEMMING CLARK
CROCKERNWELL (Holy Trinity) Cheriton Bishop *Ex*
CROCKHAM HILL (Holy Trinity) *Roch 10*
P *J St A Warde Esq* **C** R JONES
CROFT (All Saints) Wainfleet Gp, The *Linc*
CROFT (Christ Church) w Southworth *Liv 16* **P** *Bp*
R W R D ALEXANDER
CROFT (St Michael and All Angels) Eye, Croft w Yarpole
and Lucton *Heref*
CROFT (St Michael and All Angels) and Stoney Stanton
Leic 13 **P** *Bp and A I Steel Esq (jt)* **C** C HURST
CROFT (St Peter) Middleton Tyas w Croft and Eryholme
Ripon

CROFTON (All Saints) *Wakef 9* **P** *Duchy of Lanc* **R** *Vacant*
Wakefield (01924) 862966
CROFTON (Holy Rood) (St Edmund) *Portsm 2* **P** *Bp*
V M T CHRISTIAN-EDWARDS, C S JONES,
Hon C O B STARES
CROFTON (St Paul) *Roch 15* **P** *V Orpington* V C J REED
CROFTON PARK (St Hilda w St Cyprian) *S'wark 4*
P *V Lewisham St Mary* V S G BATES, NSM R O SMITH
CROGLIN (St John the Baptist) *Carl 2* **P** *D&C*
P-in-c J S CASSON
CROMER (St Peter and St Paul) *Nor 22* **P** *CPAS*
V D F HAYDEN, C T D B PIERCE
CROMFORD (St Mary) Matlock Bath and Cromford *Derby*
CROMHALL (St Andrew) w Tortworth and Tytherington
Glouc 7 **P** *Earl of Ducie, Or Coll Ox, and MMCET (jt)*
P-in-c P M LYES-WILSDON
CROMPTON, EAST (St James) *Man 22* **P** *Bp*
C G TURNER, Hon C S TURNER, Dss J TAYLOR
CROMPTON, HIGH (St Mary) *Man 22* **P** *Bp*
V H S EDWARDS
CROMPTON FOLD (St Saviour) E Crompton *Man*
CROMWELL (St Giles) Norwell w Ossington, Cromwell and
Caunton *S'well*
CRONDALL (All Saints) and Ewshot *Guildf 3* **P** *Bp*
V P M RICH
CROOK (St Catherine) *Carl 9* **P** *CPAS* V R A MACHIN
CROOK (St Catherine) *Dur 15* **P** *R Brancepeth*
R A FEATHERSTONE, C J V HALLETT
CROOK PEAK *B & W 1* **P** *Ld Chan, Bp, Bp Lon, and*
R M Dod Esq (by turn) R G GOULD
CROOKES (St Thomas) *Sheff 4* **P** *Patr Bd*
TR M J BREEN, TV A D WOODING JONES
CROOKES (St Timothy) *Sheff 4* **P** *Sheff Ch Burgesses*
V P R TOWNSEND
CROOKHAM (Christ Church) *Guildf 1* **P** *V Crondall and*
Ewshot V F J M EVANS, NSM N A P EVANS
CROOKHORN (Good Shepherd) *Portsm 4* **P** *Simeon's*
Trustees V D CONNOLLY
CROPREDY (St Mary the Virgin) w Great Bourton and
Wardington *Ox 5* **P** *Bp* V P G ATKINSON
CROPTHORNE (St Michael) w Charlton *Worc 4* **P** *D&C*
(2 turns), Bp (1 turn) P-in-c K A BOYCE, C I SCOTT
CROPTON (St Gregory) Lastingham w Appleton-le-Moors,
Rosedale etc *York*
CROPWELL BISHOP (St Giles) w Colston Bassett, Granby w
Elton, Langar cum Barnstone and Tythby w Cropwell Butler
S'well 8 **P** *CPAS and Bp, Ld Chan (alt)*
V A O WIGRAM, NSM J A CONLEY
CROSBY (St George) (St Michael) *Linc 4* **P** *Sir Reginald*
Sheffield, Bt C K N JAMES
CROSBY, GREAT (All Saints) *Liv 5* **P** *R Sefton, Bp,*
V St Luke, and CPAS (jt) V N J PATTERSON
CROSBY, GREAT (St Faith) *Liv 1* **P** *St Chad's Coll Dur*
V R CAPPER, C C KETLEY, Hon C D A SMITH,
NSM G GILFORD
CROSBY, GREAT (St Luke) *Liv 5* **P** *R Sefton*
V D H TROLLOPE, C D J WILLIAMS, NSM W J PIERCE
CROSBY GARRETT (St Andrew) Kirkby Stephen w
Mallerstang etc *Carl*
CROSBY-ON-EDEN (St John the Evangelist) Irthington,
Crosby-on-Eden and Scaleby *Carl*
CROSBY RAVENSWORTH (St Lawrence) *Carl 1* **P** *DBP*
P-in-c D C WOOD
CROSCOMBE (Blessed Virgin Mary) Pilton w Croscombe, N
Wootton and Dinder *B & W*
CROSLAND, SOUTH (Holy Trinity) *Wakef 1*
P *R Almondbury* V M C RUSSELL, NSM R T TUCK
CROSLAND MOOR (St Barnabas) *Wakef 5* **P** *Bp*
V M STOREY, NSM D A KIRBY
CROSS GREEN (St Hilda) Leeds Richmond Hill *Ripon*
CROSS GREEN (St Saviour) as above
CROSS HEATH (St Michael and All Angels) *Lich 14* **P** *Bp*
V *Vacant* Newcastle-under-Lyme (01782) 617241
CROSS IN HAND (St Bartholomew) Waldron *Chich*
CROSS ROADS cum Lees (St James) *Bradf 8* **P** *Bp*
V D N WILLIAMS
CROSS STONE (St Paul) Todmorden *Wakef*
CROSSCANONBY (St John the Evangelist) *Carl 7* **P** *D&C*
V J LEONARDI
CROSSCRAKE (St Thomas) and Preston Patrick *Carl 9*
P *Bp and J Heversham and Milnthorpe (jt)* V *Vacant*
Sedgwick (015395) 60333
CROSSENS (St John) *Liv 9* **P** *Trustees* V R S J CHARLES
CROSSFLATTS (St Aidan) Bingley All SS *Bradf*
CROSSPOOL (St Columba) *Sheff 4* **P** *Bp* V M R BURKE
CROSTHWAITE (St Kentigern) Keswick *Carl 6* **P** *Bp*
V R T HUGHES

CROSTHWAITE (St Mary) Kendal *Carl 9* **P** *DBP*
V K PARTINGTON
CROSTON (St Michael and All Angels) *Blackb 4*
P *M G Rawstorne Esq* R R J BRUNSWICK
CROSTWICK (St Peter) Spixworth w Crostwick and
Frettenham *Nor*
CROSTWIGHT (All Saints) Smallburgh w Dilham w Honing
and Crostwight *Nor*
CROUCH END HILL (Christ Church) Hornsey Ch Ch *Lon*
CROUGHTON (All Saints) Aynho and Croughton w
Evenley *Pet*
CROWAN (St Crewenna) w Godolphin *Truro 4* **P** *Bp and*
D L C Roberts Esq (alt) V P DOUGLASS
CROWBOROUGH (All Saints) *Chich 19* **P** *Ld Chan*
V A C J CORNES, C A RAYNES, NSM J A HOBBS
CROWCOMBE (Holy Ghost) Bicknoller w Crowcombe and
Sampford Brett *B & W*
CROWELL (Nativity of the Blessed Virgin Mary) Chinnor w
Emmington and Sydenham etc *Ox*
CROWFIELD (All Saints) w Stonham Aspal and Mickfield
St E 1 **P** *DBP, Bp, and Lord de Saumarez (alt)*
P-in-c H M WILSON
CROWHURST (St George) Catsfield and Crowhurst *Chich*
CROWHURST (St George) Lingfield and Crowhurst *S'wark*
CROWLAND (St Mary and St Bartholomew and St Guthlac)
Linc 17 **P** *Earl of Normanton* R J A CRUST
CROWLE (St John the Baptist) Bowbrook S *Worc*
CROWLE (St Oswald) *Linc 1* **P** *Bp* V D SCHOFIELD,
Hon C D E CORNELIUS
CROWMARSH GIFFORD (St Mary
Magdalene) Wallingford w Crowmarsh Gifford etc *Ox*
CROWN EAST AND RUSHWICK (St
Thomas) Broadheath, Crown E and Rushwick *Worc*
CROWNHILL (Ascension) Plymouth Crownhill Ascension
Ex
CROWTHORNE (St John the Baptist) *Ox 16* **P** *Bp*
V B R SPENCE, NSM T WALT
CROWTON (Christ Church) Norley and Crowton *Ches*
CROXALL-CUM-OAKLEY (St John the Baptist) Walton
on Trent w Croxall etc *Derby*
CROXBY (All Saints) Swallow *Linc*
CROXDALE (St Bartholomew) and Tudhoe *Dur 10* **P** *D&C*
R P E B WELBY
CROXDEN (St Giles) Rocester and Croxden w Hollington
Lich
CROXLEY GREEN (All Saints) *St Alb 10*
P *V Rickmansworth* V L G-H LEE
CROXLEY GREEN (St Oswald) *St Alb 10* **P** *Bp*
V A M LOVEGROVE
CROXTETH (St Paul) *Liv 8* **P** *R W Derby and Bp (jt)*
V I G BROOKS
CROXTON (All Saints) Thetford *Nor*
CROXTON Group, The SOUTH (St John the Baptist)
Leic 3 **P** *DBP, Ch Soc Trust, and MMCET (jt)*
R M E LAMBERT
CROXTON (St James) and Eltisley *Ely 1* **P** *Bp*
R T J MARKS
CROXTON (St John the Evangelist) *Linc 6* **P** *Ld Chan*
R S PHILLIPS
CROXTON (St Paul) w Broughton and Adbaston *Lich 12*
P *Bp and J Hall Esq* V M W WELSH
CROXTON KERRIAL (St Botolph and St John the
Baptist) High Framland Par *Leic*
CROYDE (St Mary Magdalene) Georgeham *Ex*
CROYDON (All Saints) w Clopton *Ely 8* **P** *Bp and DBP*
(alt) R N A BRICE
CROYDON (Christ Church) Broad Green *S'wark 21*
P *Simeon's Trustees* V C J ROSEWEIR
CROYDON (Holy Saviour) *S'wark 23* **P** *Bp*
NSM P L GIBBS
CROYDON (St Andrew) *S'wark 21* **P** *Trustees*
V P D HENDRY
CROYDON (St Augustine) *S'wark 21* **P** *Bp*
V G S DERRIMAN, NSM A SMITH
CROYDON (St John the Baptist) *S'wark 21* **P** *Abp*
V C J L BOSWELL, C R H G BRAND,
Hon C S J F GEDGE, K V G SMITH, NSM P D F SMITH
CROYDON (St Matthew) *S'wark 21* **P** *V Croydon*
V R TAYLOR, C A P WHITE
CROYDON (St Michael and All Angels w St James)
S'wark 21 **P** *Trustees* V *Vacant* 0181–680 8413
CROYDON (St Peter) *S'wark 21* **P** *V Croydon*
V S J KNOWERS
CROYDON Woodside (St Luke) *S'wark 23* **P** *Bp*
V P EVANS
CROYDON, SOUTH (Emmanuel) *S'wark 22* **P** *Ch Trust*
Fund Trust NSM D J RICHARDSON, S J H GOATCHER
CROYDON, SOUTH (St Augustine) Croydon St Aug *S'wark*

CROYLAND (St Mary and St Bartholomew and St Guthlac) Crowland *Linc*

CRUDWELL (All Saints) Ashley, Crudwell, Hankerton, Long Newnton etc *Bris*

CRUMPSALL (St Matthew w St Mary) *Man 5* **P** *Bp* **P-in-c** A-M C BIRD (nee BAKER)

CRUNDALE (St Mary the Blessed Virgin) w Godmersham *Cant 2* **P** *Abp* **P-in-c** R I MARTIN

CRUWYS MORCHARD (Holy Cross) Washfield, Stoodleigh, Withleigh etc *Ex*

CRUX EASTON (St Michael and All Angels) Highclere and Ashmansworth w Crux Easton *Win*

CUBBINGTON (St Mary) *Cov 11* **P** *Bp* **V** K LINDOP

CUBERT (St Cubert) *Truro 7* **P** *DBP* **V** P E TIDMARSH

CUBLEY (St Andrew) Alkmonton, Cubley, Marston, Montgomery etc *Derby*

CUBLINGTON (St Nicholas) Wingrave w Rowsham, Aston Abbotts and Cublington *Ox*

CUCKFIELD (Holy Trinity) *Chich 6* **P** *Bp* **V** N G WETHERALL

CUCKLINGTON (St Lawrence) Charlton Musgrove, Cucklington and Stoke Trister *B & W*

CUDDESDON (All Saints) *Ox 1* **P** *Bp* **V** J H GARTON

CUDDINGTON (St Mary) *Guildf 9* **P** *Bp* **V** C H CHEESEMAN

CUDDINGTON (St Nicholas) Haddenham w Cuddington, Kingsey etc *Ox*

CUDHAM (St Peter and St Paul) and Downe *Roch 15* **P** *Ch Soc Trust and Bp (jt)* **V** T R HATWELL, **NSM** N K HINTON

CUDWORTH (St John) *Wakef 7* **P** *Bp* **V** D GLOVER

CUDWORTH (St Michael) Ilminster and District *B & W*

CUFFLEY (St Andrew) Northaw *St Alb*

CULBONE (St Beuno) Oare w Culbone *B & W*

CULFORD (St Mary), West Stow and Wordwell w Flempton, Hengrave and Lackford *St E 13* **P** *Bp (2 turns), R W Gough Esq (1 turn)* **R** R W CLIFTON

CULGAITH (All Saints) Addingham, Edenhall, Langwathby and Culgaith *Carl*

CULHAM (St Paul) Dorchester *Ox*

CULLERCOATS (St George) *Newc 8* **P** *Patr Bd* **TR** G F REVETT, **TV** J T SHONE, M SLACK, **C** C P M PATTERSON, **Hon C** R A MACEY, **NSM** D HOOD

CULLINGWORTH (St John the Evangelist) *Bradf 8* **P** *Bp* **P-in-c** M COWGILL

CULLOMPTON (St Andrew) (Langford Chapel) *Ex 4* **P** *CPAS* **V** D A SAUNDERS, **C** J G PERKIN, A DELANEY

CULM DAVY (St Mary's Chapel) Hemyock w Culm Davy, Clayhidon and Culmstock *Ex*

CULMINGTON (All Saints) w Onibury, Bromfield and Stanton Lacy *Heref 12* **P** *Lady Magnus-Allcroft (1 turn), Earl of Plymouth (2 turns)* **R** K J M EWEN, **NSM** E H M PERKS

CULMSTOCK (All Saints) Hemyock w Culm Davy, Clayhidon and Culmstock *Ex*

CULPHO (St Botolph) Gt and Lt Bealings w Playford and Culpho *St E*

CULWORTH (St Mary the Virgin) w Sulgrave and Thorpe Mandeville and Chipping Warden w Edgcote *Pet 1* **P** *Ch Patr Trust (1 turn), T M Sergison-Brooke Esq (1 turn), DBP (2 turns), and D L P Humfrey Esq (1 turn)* **R** S E CRAWLEY

CUMBERWORTH (St Helen) Sutton, Huttoft and Anderby *Linc*

CUMBERWORTH (St Nicholas), Denby and Denby Dale *Wakef 6* **P** *Bp and V Penistone (jt)* **R** D J CLARKSON

CUMDIVOCK (St John) Dalston *Carl*

CUMMERSDALE (St James) Denton Holme *Carl*

CUMNOR (St Michael) *Ox 10* **P** *St Pet Coll Ox* **V** N D DURAND, **C** L E FLETCHER, **NSM** C H HOLMES

CUMREW (St Mary the Virgin) Brampton and Farlam and Castle Carrock w Cumrew *Carl*

CUMWHINTON (St John's Hall) Cotehill and Cumwhinton *Carl*

CUMWHITTON (St Mary the Virgin) Hayton w Cumwhitton *Carl*

CUNDALL (St Mary and All Saints) Kirby-on-the-Moor, Cundall w Norton-le-Clay etc *Ripon*

CURBAR (All Saints) Baslow w Curbar and Stoney Middleton *Derby*

CURBRIDGE (St Barnabas) Sarisbury *Portsm*

CURBRIDGE (St John the Baptist) Witney *Ox*

CURDRIDGE (St Peter) *Portsm 1* **P** *D&C Win* **V** A N STAMP, **C** K F ARVIDSSON

CURDWORTH (St Nicholas and St Peter ad Vincula) (St George) *Birm 9* **P** *Bp and Lord Norton (jt)* **R** M GARLAND, **NSM** C HOARE

CURRY, NORTH (St Peter and St Paul) *B & W 18* **P** *D&C* **V** C H TOWNSHEND

CURRY MALLET (All Saints) Hatch Beauchamp w Beercrocombe, Curry Mallet etc *B & W*

CURRY RIVEL (St Andrew) w Fivehead and Swell *B & W 15* **P** *D&C Bris (1 turn), P G H Speke Esq (2 turns)* **R** P C LAMBERT

CURY (St Corentine) and Gunwalloe w St Mawgan-in-Meneage *Truro 4* **P** *Bp* **R** P R LONG

CUSOP (St Mary) w Clifford, Hardwicke, Bredwardine, Brobury and Moccas *Heref 1* **P** *CPAS, MMCET, R T G Chester Master Esq, and S Penoyre Esq (jt)* **R** P W M BYLLAM-BARNES, **NSM** C P STUTZ

CUTCOMBE (St John the Evangelist) Exton and Winsford and Cutcombe w Luxborough *B & W*

CUTSDEAN (St James) The Guitings, Cutsdean and Farmcote *Glouc*

CUXHAM (Holy Rood) Ewelme, Brightwell Baldwin, Cuxham w Easington *Ox*

CUXTON (St Michael and All Angels) and Halling *Roch 6* **P** *Bp and D&C (jt)* **R** R I KNIGHT

CUXWOLD (St Nicholas) Swallow *Linc*

CWM HEAD (St Michael) Wistanstow *Heref*

DACRE (Holy Trinity) w Hartwith and Darley w Thornthwaite *Ripon 3* **P** *Bp, D&C, V Masham and Healey, and Mrs K A Dunbar (jt)* **V** F A CHAPPELL, **C** M J DUXBURY

DACRE (St Andrew) *Carl 4* **P** *Trustees* **P-in-c** P J WILSON

DADLINGTON (St James) Stoke Golding w Dadlington *Leic*

DAGENHAM (St Luke) (St Peter and St Paul) *Chelmsf 1* **P** *Patr Bd* **TR** R M REITH, **TV** H K SYMES-THOMPSON, **C** B J ROBSON, **NSM** A HILL

DAGENHAM (St Martin) Becontree S *Chelmsf*

DAGLINGWORTH (Holy Rood) w the Duntisbournes and Winstone *Glouc 12* **P** *Ld Chan, DBP, and CCC Ox (by turn)* **P-in-c** P NEWING, **NSM** E HISCOX, J M FRANCIS

DAGNALL (All Saints) Kensworth, Studham and Whipsnade *St Alb*

DAISY HILL (St James) *Man 11* **P** *Bp* **V** R COWARD

DALBURY (All Saints) Longford, Long Lane, Dalbury and Radbourne *Derby*

DALBY (St James) Patrick *S & M*

DALBY (St Lawrence and Blessed Edward King) Partney *Linc*

DALBY (St Peter) Bulmer w Dalby, Terrington and Welburn *York*

DALBY, GREAT (St Swithun) Burrough Hill Pars *Leic*

DALBY, LITTLE (St James) as above

DALBY, OLD (St John the Baptist) and Nether Broughton *Leic 3* **P** *Bp* **P-in-c** R W WIDDOWSON, **C** R A WHITE

DALE ABBEY (All Saints) Stanton-by-Dale w Dale Abbey *Derby*

DALE HEAD (St James) Long Preston w Tosside *Bradf*

DALHAM (St Mary) Gazeley w Dalham, Moulton and Kentford *St E*

DALLAM (St Mark) *Liv 12* **P** *R Warrington and Bp (jt)* **V** P J MARSHALL

DALLINGHOO (St Mary) Charsfield w Debach, Monewden, Hoo etc *St E*

DALLINGTON (St Giles) Brightling, Dallington, Mountfield & Netherfield *Chich*

DALLINGTON (St Mary) *Pet 7* **P** *Earl Spencer* **V** A E PANTON

DALLOWGILL (St Peter) Fountains Gp *Ripon*

DALSTON (Holy Trinity) (St Philip) *Lon 5* **P** *Bp* **V** J F WILLARD

DALSTON (St Mark w St Bartholomew) *Lon 5* **P** *Ch Patr Trust* **V** D H PATEMAN

DALSTON (St Michael) *Carl 3* **P** *Bp* **P-in-c** P KYBIRD, **C** J R BAXENDALE, **NSM** H J CARTER

DALTON (Holy Trinity) Newburn *Newc*

DALTON (Holy Trinity) *Sheff 6* **P** *Bp* **V** J R CORBYN

DALTON (St James) Gilling and Kirkby Ravensworth *Ripon*

DALTON (St John the Evangelist) Baldersby w Dalton, Dishforth etc *York*

DALTON (St Michael and All Angels) *Liv 11* **P** *Bp* **V** T C BARTON

DALTON, NORTH (All Saints) Bainton w N Dalton, Middleton-on-the-Wolds etc *York*

DALTON, SOUTH Dalton le Dale *Dur*

DALTON HOLME (St Mary) Etton w Dalton Holme *York*

DALTON-IN-FURNESS (St Mary) *Carl 8* **P** *Bp* **V** S J SKINNER, **C** I K HOOK, K KITCHIN, **NSM** J M SKINNER

DALTON LE DALE (Holy Trinity) (St Andrew) *Dur 3*
P *D&C* P-in-c A MILNE
DALWOOD (St Peter) Stockland w Dalwood *Ex*
DAMERHAM (St George) W Downland *Sarum*
DANBURY (St John the Baptist) *Chelmsf 9* P *Lord Fitzwalter* R *Vacant* Danbury (01245) 223140
DANBY (St Hilda) *York 23* P *Viscount Downe*
V T M RHODES
DANBY WISKE (not known) Gt Smeaton w Appleton Wiske and Birkby etc *Ripon*
DANEHILL (All Saints) *Chich 21* P *Ch Soc Trust*
P-in-c J M REX
DANESMOOR (St Barnabas) N Wingfield, Clay Cross and Pilsley *Derby*
DARBY END (St Peter) *Worc 9* P *Bp* V N LAMBERT
DARBY GREEN (St Barnabas) *Win 5* P *Bp*
V J P H TYRRELL
DARENTH (St Margaret) *Roch 2* P *D&C* V R J FORD
DARESBURY (All Saints) *Ches 4* P *D G Greenhall Esq*
V D W SMITH
DARFIELD (All Saints) *Sheff 12* P *MMCET* R *Vacant* Barnsley (01226) 752236
DARLASTON (All Saints) *Lich 7* P *Simeon's Trustees*
V *Vacant* 0121–568 6618
DARLASTON (St Lawrence) *Lich 7* P *Bp and Simeon's Trustees (jt)* R G W LLOYD
DARLEY (Christ Church) Dacre w Hartwith and Darley w Thornthwaite *Ripon*
DARLEY (St Helen) *Derby 7* P *Bp* R R E QUARTON
DARLEY, SOUTH (St Mary the Virgin), Elton and Winster *Derby 7* P *Bp and DBF (jt)* R *Vacant* Winster (01629) 650256
DARLEY ABBEY (St Matthew) *Derby 9* P *DBP*
V D MOWBRAY
DARLINGSCOTT (St George) Tredington and Darlingscott w Newbold on Stour *Cov*
DARLINGTON (Holy Trinity) (Salutation Church) *Dur 12*
P *Adn Dur* V R C WARDALE, C A V MACKEITH (nee GODFREY), C M BLAKESLEY
DARLINGTON (St Cuthbert) *Dur 12* P *Lord Barnard*
P-in-c G V MILLER, C J R DOBSON
DARLINGTON St Hilda and (St Columba) *Dur 12* P *Bp*
V *Vacant*
DARLINGTON (St James) *Dur 12* P *The Crown*
V I L GRIEVES, NSM C M WILSON
DARLINGTON (St Mark) w St Paul *Dur 12* P *Bp and St Jo Coll Dur* V J R PILKINGTON
DARLINGTON (St Matthew) and St Luke *Dur 12* P *Bp*
V J R RICE-OXLEY, NSM B HOLMES
DARLINGTON, EAST (St John) (St Herbert) *Dur 12*
P *The Crown* TR J CLASPER
DARLTON (St Giles) Dunham-on-Trent w Darlton, Ragnall etc *S'well*
DARNALL (Church of Christ) Darnall-cum-Attercliffe *Sheff*
DARNALL-CUM-ATTERCLIFFE *Sheff 1* P *Patr Bd*
TR J H MARTIN, TV M L FUDGER
DARRINGTON (St Luke and All Saints) w Wentbridge *Wakef 11* P *Bp* V C DAWSON
DARSHAM (All Saints) *St E 19* P *Exors Earl of Stradbroke* V R J GINN
DARTFORD (Christ Church) *Roch 2* P *V Dartford H Trin*
V D B KITLEY, NSM C CROOK
DARTFORD (Holy Trinity) *Roch 2* P *Bp*
V M J HENWOOD
DARTFORD (St Alban) *Roch 2* P *V Dartford H Trin*
V A T WATERMAN
DARTFORD (St Edmund the King and Martyr) *Roch 2*
P *Bp* V R P CALLAGHAN
DARTINGTON (Old St Mary's Church Tower) Totnes, Bridgetown and Berry Pomeroy and Dartington *Ex*
DARTINGTON (St Mary) as above
DARTMOUTH (St Petrox) (St Saviour) *Ex 13* P *DBP and Sir John Seale, Bt (jt)* Hon C P A RILEY
DARTON (All Saints) *Wakef 7* P *Bp* V W R PLIMMER
DARWEN (St Barnabas) *Blackb 5* P *Bp* V P H SMITH
DARWEN (St Cuthbert) w Tockholes St Stephen *Blackb 5*
P *Bp* V J COOPER, C I J J DEWAR
DARWEN (St Peter) w Hoddlesden St Paul *Blackb 5*
P *V Blackburn and DBP (jt)* TV D M BEAL,
C S D BURTON-JONES
DARWEN, LOWER (St James) *Blackb 5* P *V Blackb*
V R P CARTMELL
DARWEN, OVER (St James) *Blackb 5* P *V Blackb*
V J FARADAY
DASSETT MAGNA (All Saints) Burton Dassett *Cov*
DATCHET (St Mary the Virgin) Riverside *Ox*
DATCHWORTH (All Saints) w Tewin *St Alb 10* P *Bp and Jes Coll Cam (alt)* R P R BETTS

DAUBHILL (St George the Martyr) *Man 9* P *Trustees*
V S J ABRAM
DAUNTSEY (St James Great) Brinkworth w Dauntsey *Bris*
DAVENHAM (St Wilfrid) *Ches 6* P *Bp* R C J REES,
C P M CLARK
DAVENTRY (Holy Cross), Ashby St Ledgers, Braunston, Catesby, Hellidon, Staverton and Welton *Pet 3* P *Patr Bd*
TR K SMALLDON, TV J W HARGREAVES,
G HOWARD, C P MOSELING, NSM E THORPE
DAVIDSTOW (St David) Boscastle w Davidstow *Truro*
DAVINGTON (St Mary Magdalene) The Brents and Davington w Oare and Luddenham *Cant*
DAVYHULME (Christ Church) *Man 7* P *Bp* V A J WATTS
DAVYHULME (St Mary) *Man 7* P *Bp* V S J WINWARD
DAWDON (St Hild and St Helen) *Dur 3* P *Bp*
V J C G POLLOCK
DAWLEY (Holy Trinity) Cen Telford *Lich*
DAWLEY (St Jerome) *Lon 24* P *Hyndman Trustees*
P-in-c D HONOUR
DAWLISH (St Gregory) *Ex 6* P *D&C* V W D S LARK,
C T J WRIGHT, Hon C C R EVANS
DAWLISH WARREN (Church Hall) Kenton, Mamhead, Powderham, Cofton and Starcross *Ex*
DAYBROOK (St Paul) *S'well 13* P *Bp* V A L WHEALE,
Hon C D J DAVIES
DAYLESFORD (St Peter) Kingham w Churchill, Daylesford and Sarsden *Ox*
DE BEAUVOIR TOWN (St Peter) *Lon 5* P *Bp*
V A WINDROSS, NSM I C CZERNIAWSKA EDGECUMBE
DEAL (St Andrew) *Cant 8* P *Abp* R J D KING
DEAL (St George the Martyr) *Cant 8* P *Abp* V G W LINGS
DEAL (St Leonard) (St Richard) and Sholden (St Nicholas) *Cant 8* P *Abp* C R O WOODHAMS, G F MACK,
NSM R C NELSON
DEAN (All Hallows) The Stodden Churches *St Alb*
DEAN (St Oswald) *Carl 6* P *A R Sherwen Esq and R Workington (jt)* R P M BADEN
DEAN, EAST (All Saints) *Chich 13* P *Bp* V P M JENKINS
DEAN, EAST (St Simon and St Jude) w Friston and Jevington *Chich 16* P *Duke of Devonshire (1 turn), D&C (2 turns)*
R A H H HARBOTTLE
DEAN, EAST (St Winifred) Lockerley and E Dean w E and W Tytherley *Win*
DEAN, WEST (All Saints) Alfriston w Lullington, Litlington and W Dean *Chich*
DEAN, WEST (St Andrew) *Chich 13* P *D&C*
V P M JENKINS
DEAN, WEST (St Mary) Alderbury Team *Sarum*
DEAN COURT (St Andrew) Cumnor *Ox*
DEAN FOREST (Holy Trinity) *Glouc 4* P *The Crown*
V A N JAMES
DEAN FOREST (St Paul) *Glouc 4* P *Bp* V I L DAVIES,
NSM G W J BATTEN
DEAN PRIOR (St George the Martyr) Buckfastleigh w Dean Prior *Ex*
DEANE (All Saints) N Waltham and Steventon, Ashe and Deane *Win*
DEANE (St Mary the Virgin) *Man 11* P *Patr Bd*
TR R B JACKSON, TV A R HAZLEHURST,
C C D MOORE
DEANSHANGER (Holy Trinity) Passenham *Pet*
DEARHAM (St Mungo) *Carl 7* P *Bp* V *Vacant* Maryport (01900) 812320
DEARNLEY (St Andrew) *Man 20* P *Bp* V *Vacant* Littleborough (01706) 78466
DEBDEN (St Mary the Virgin) and Wimbish w Thunderley *Chelmsf 23* P *Bp* R A K GAIR
DEBENHAM (St Mary Magdalene) w Aspall and Kenton *St E 18* P *Lord Henniker (2 turns), Bp (1 turn)*
P-in-c G E NOBLE
DEDDINGTON (St Peter and St Paul) Barford, Clifton and Hempton *Ox 5* P *D&C Windsor and Bp (jt)*
V K G REEVES, C E J NEWELL
DEDHAM (St Mary the Virgin) *Chelmsf 18* P *Duchy of Lanc and Lectureship Trustees (alt)* V G G MOATE
DEDWORTH (All Saints) *Ox 13* P *Bp* P-in-c L M BROWN
DEEPCAR (St John the Evangelist) *Sheff 7* P *Bp*
V M WOODHEAD
DEEPING (St Nicholas) Spalding St Jo w Deeping St Nicholas *Linc*
DEEPING, WEST (St Andrew) Uffington Gp *Linc*
DEEPING ST JAMES (St James) *Linc 13* P *Burghley Ho Preservation Trust* V S R HAWORTH
DEERHURST (St Mary) and Apperley w Forthampton and Chaceley *Glouc 9* P *Bp, Exors G J Yorke Esq, and V Longdon (jt)* P-in-c J E FORRYAN
DEFFORD (St James) w Besford *Worc 4* P *D&C Westmr*
V P J THOMAS

DEIGHTON (All Saints) Brompton w Deighton *York*
DELABOLE (St John the Evangelist) St Teath *Truro*
DELAMERE (St Peter) *Ches 6* **P** *The Crown* **R** *Vacant*
Sandiway (01606) 882184
DELAVAL (Our Lady) *Newc 1* **P** *Lord Hastings*
V MSJONES, **Hon C** FRHOWE
DEMBLEBY (St Lucia) S Lafford *Linc*
DENABY, OLD (Mission Church) Mexborough *Sheff*
DENABY MAIN (All Saints) *Sheff 8* **P** *Bp* **V** RCDAVIES
DENBURY (St Mary the Virgin) Ogwell and Denbury *Ex*
DENBY (St John the Evangelist) Cumberworth, Denby and
Denby Dale *Wakef*
DENBY (St Mary the Virgin) *Derby 12* **P** *Exors Capt*
P J B Drury-Lowe **P-in-c** DJPHYPERS
DENBY DALE (Holy Trinity) Cumberworth, Denby and
Denby Dale *Wakef*
DENCHWORTH (St James) Hanney, Denchworth and E
Challow *Ox*
DENDRON (St Matthew) Aldingham and Dendron and
Rampside *Carl*
DENESIDE (All Saints) Seaham w Seaham Harbour *Dur*
DENFORD (Holy Trinity) w Ringstead *Pet 10* **P** *L Stopford-*
Sackville Esq **V** FCOLEMAN
DENGIE (St James) w Asheldham *Chelmsf 11*
P *D&C St Paul's and Bp* **P-in-c** IMFINN
DENHAM (St John the Baptist) Hoxne w Denham, Syleham
and Wingfield *St E*
DENHAM (St Mark) (St Mary the Virgin) *Ox 20*
P L J Way Esq **R** JAHIRST
DENHAM (St Mary) Barrow w Denham St Mary and
Higham Green *St E*
DENHAM, NEW (St Francis) Denham *Ox*
DENHOLME GATE (St Paul) *Bradf 8* **P** *Bp*
P-in-c CBHOLLIS
DENMEAD (All Saints) *Portsm 4* **P** *Ld Chan*
V JRHERKLOTS, **NSM** FRSTRANACK
DENNINGTON (St Mary) Badingham w Bruisyard,
Cransford and Dennington *St E*
DENSHAW (Christ Church) *Man 21* **P** *Bp*
V SCLCLAYTON
DENSTON (St Nicholas) w Stradishall and Stansfield *St E 8*
P *Mrs G S M MacRae and Ld Chan (alt)*
V TSWRIGHT, **NSM** PWde VOIL
DENSTONE (All Saints) w Ellastone and Stanton *Lich 20*
P *Bp and Col Sir Walter Bromley-Davenport (jt)*
V JRCLATWORTHY
DENT (St Andrew) w Cowgill *Bradf 6* **P** *Bp and Sidesmen of*
Dent (alt) **V** CAMITCHELL
DENTON (Christ Church) *Man 17* **P** *Bp* **R** JKTUTTON,
C GWHITTAKER
DENTON Dane Bank (St George) Denton Ch Ch *Man*
DENTON (Holy Spirit) *Newc 7* **P** *Bp* **V** BCHURST
DENTON (St Andrew) Harlaxton *Linc*
DENTON (St Helen) Weston w Denton *Bradf*
DENTON (St Lawrence) *Man 17* **P** *Earl of Wilton*
R RCASSIDY
DENTON (St Leonard) w South Heighton and Tarring Neville
Chich 18 **P** *MMCET and Bp (alt)* **R** NAMANNING
DENTON (St Margaret) Yardley Hastings, Denton and
Grendon etc *Pet*
DENTON (St Mary) Earsham w Alburgh and Denton *Nor*
DENTON (St Mary) and Ingleton *Dur 12* **P** *V Staindrop*
(2 turns), V Gainford (1 turn) **P-in-c** JWBOOCOCK
DENTON (St Mary Magdalene) Elham w Denton and
Wootton *Cant*
DENTON HOLME (St James) *Carl 3* **P** *Trustees*
V JDRUSHTON, **C** PMACKROYD
DENVER (St Mary) *Ely 16* **P** *G&C Coll Cam*
P-in-c JKISAACS
DENVILLE (Christchurch Centre) Havant *Portsm*
DEOPHAM (St Andrew) High Oak *Nor*
DEPDEN (St Mary the Virgin) Chedburgh w Depden, Rede
and Hawkedon *St E*
DEPTFORD Brockley (St Peter) *S'wark 2* **P** *Bp*
V TJLHARPER, **C** BAABAYOMI-COLE
DEPTFORD Edward Street (St Mark) Deptford St Paul
S'wark
DEPTFORD (St John) (Holy Trinity) *S'wark 2* **P** *Peache*
Trustees and Ch Trust Fund Trust (jt) **V** AIKEECH
DEPTFORD (St Nicholas) (St Luke) *S'wark 2* **P** *MMCET,*
Peache Trustees, and CPAS (jt) **V** WGCORNECK
DEPTFORD (St Paul) (St Mark) *S'wark 2* **P** *Bp*
R PWFELLOWS
DERBY Mill Hill *Derby 10* **P** *CPAS* **P-in-c** DNGOUGH
DERBY (St Alkmund and St Werburgh) *Derby 9* **P** *Simeon's*
Trustees **V** PACORRIE, **C** MPWATSON,
NSM RJELGAR

DERBY (St Andrew w St Osmund) *Derby 10* **P** *Bp*
V DCMACDONALD, **C** NKPRITCHARD
DERBY (St Anne) (St John the Evangelist) *Derby 9* **P** *Bp*
V CMGBRINKWORTH
DERBY (St Augustine) *Derby 10* **P** *V Derby St Chad*
P-in-c MWSPARSONS, **C** TMHOWARTH
DERBY (St Barnabas) *Derby 9* **P** *Bp* **V** GDKENDREW
DERBY (St Bartholomew) *Derby 10* **P** *Bp* **V** AGMESSOM
DERBY St James the Great *Derby 10* **P** *Bp*
P-in-c MRFUTERS
DERBY (St Luke) *Derby 9* **P** *Bp* **V** DJMELLOR,
C JHFLINT
DERBY (St Mark) *Derby 9* **P** *Bp* **V** LNCHILDS,
NSM BAKEELING
DERBY (St Paul) *Derby 9* **P** *Bp* **V** JFLEE
DERBY (St Peter and Christ Church w Holy Trinity)
Derby 10 **P** *CPAS* **V** CJCHILTON
DERBY (St Thomas the Apostle) *Derby 10* **P** *Bp* **V** *Vacant*
Derby (01332) 343470
DERBY, WEST (Good Shepherd) *Liv 8* **P** *Bp and*
R W Derby (jt) **V** TRSTRATFORD, **C** ARBECK
DERBY, WEST (St James) *Liv 8* **P** *Trustees*
V PWPLUNKETT
DERBY, WEST St John *Liv 8* **P** *Trustees* **V** TPENENER
DERBY, WEST (St Luke) *Liv 2* **P** *Bp* **V** JHWELCH,
C SELLIS
DERBY, WEST (St Mary) *Liv 8* **P** *Bp*
TR JRIWIKELEY, **TV** TMLATHAM, **C** MEJABREY,
JEBOWEN
DERBYHAVEN (Chapel) Malew *S & M*
DEREHAM, EAST (St Nicholas) and Scarning *Nor 18*
P *Ld Chan* **R** DWARIDER, **C** SJABBOTT, **Sen Asst**
Priest AJTODD
DEREHAM, WEST (St Andrew) *Ely 16* **P** *Bp*
P-in-c JKISAACS
DERRINGHAM BANK (Ascension) *York 15* **P** *Abp*
V SJWHALEY, **C** PNASENIOR, **NSM** JBRAY
DERRINGTON (St Matthew), Haughton and Ranton
Lich 15 **P** *Bp, Mrs M N Nutt, and Trustees Earl of Lich*
(jt) **R** GKSMITH
DERRY Hill (Christ Church) w Bremhill and Foxham
Sarum 18 **P** *Prime Min and V Calne and Blackland*
V JRCARDWELL, **NSM** JWSCOTT
DERSINGHAM (St Nicholas) w Anmer and Shernborne
Nor 17 **P** *Ld Chan* **R** TPJARDINE
DESBOROUGH (St Giles) *Pet 11* **P** *Bp*
V RJCHAPMAN, **NSM** NMCLARKE
DESFORD (St Martin) and Peckleton w Tooley *Leic 12*
P *Ld Chan* **R** DJSENIOR
DETHICK (St John the Baptist) Tansley, Dethick, Lea and
Holloway *Derby*
DETLING (St Martin) Boxley w Detling *Cant*
DEVERILLS, The *Sarum 14* **P** *DBP (3 turns), Bp (1 turn)*
C CNVON BENZON
DEVIZES (St John) (St Mary) *Sarum 19* **P** *Ld Chan*
R CBRYANT, **Hon C** LMCATER
DEVIZES (St Peter) *Sarum 19* **P** *Bp* **V** BATIGWELL
DEVONPORT (St Aubyn) *Ex 22* **P** *The Crown and R Stoke*
Damerel (alt) **P-in-c** GDCRYER, **C** PAWJONES,
Hon C JGODFREY
DEVONPORT (St Barnabas) *Ex 22* **P** *R Stoke Damerel*
V JESUMMERS
DEVONPORT (St Bartholomew) *Ex 22* **P** *Bp*
P-in-c JMROBINSON
DEVONPORT (St Boniface) (St Philip) *Ex 22* **P** *Bp*
TR PJLOW, **TV** NRCPEARKES
DEVONPORT (St Mark) Ford *Ex 22* **P** *Trustees*
P-in-c JMROBINSON
DEVONPORT (St Michael) Stoke *Ex 22* **P** *R Stoke*
Damerel **P-in-c** RJHILL
DEVONPORT ST BUDEAUX *Ex 22* **P** *V Plymouth St Andr*
w St Paul and St Geo **V** MDDJONES, **C** SMHAYNES
DEVORAN (St John the Evangelist and St Petroc) *Truro 6*
P *Bp* **V** MCPALMER
DEWCHURCH, LITTLE (St David) and Aconbury w
Ballingham and Bolstone *Heref 3* **P** *D&C and Bp (alt)*
V TPJONES
DEWCHURCH, MUCH (St David) Much Birch w Lt Birch,
Much Dewchurch etc *Heref*
DEWLISH (All Saints) Milborne St Andrew w Dewlish
Sarum
DEWSALL (St Michael) w Callow *Heref 3* **P** *D&C*
R TPJONES
DEWSBURY (All Saints) (St Mark) (St Matthew and St John)
Wakef 10 **P** *Bp, Adn Pontefract, RD Dewsbury, and Lay*
Chmn Dewsbury Deanery Syn (jt) **TR** JAHAWLEY,
TV JALAWSON

DEWSBURY MOOR (St John the Evangelist) Dewsbury *Wakef*
DHOON (Christ Church) Maughold *S & M*
DIBDEN (All Saints) *Win 10* **P** *MMCET*
R JDALDERMAN, **C** MRPOWIS
DIBDEN PURLIEU (St Andrew) Dibden *Win*
DICKER, UPPER (Holy Trinity) Hellingly and Upper Dicker *Chich*
DICKLEBURGH (All Saints) w Langmere and Shimpling, Thelveton w Frenze, Rushall *Nor 10* **P** *Ld Chan, Bp, Trin Coll Cam, MMCET, and Lady Mann (by turn)*
R SJOSPIKIN
DIDBROOK (St George) Toddington, Stanton, Didbrook w Hailes etc *Glouc*
DIDCOT (All Saints) *Ox 18* **P** *BNC Ox*
P-in-c PADALLAWAY, **C** JMIMPEY
DIDCOT (St Peter) *Ox 18* **P** *Bp* **P-in-c** NJGANDY
DIDDINGTON (St Laurence) *Ely 12* **P** *G E P Thornhill Esq*
V PGLEWIS
DIDDLEBURY (St Peter) w Munslow, Holdgate and Tugford *Heref 12* **P** *Bp (3 turns), D&C(1 turn)* **R** IEGIBBS
DIDLINGTON (St Michael) *Nor 14* **P** *CPAS*
P-in-c ACFOOTTIT
DIDMARTON (St Lawrence) Boxwell, Leighterton, Didmarton, Oldbury etc *Glouc*
DIDSBURY (Christ Church) Barlow Moor Road *Man 8*
P *Trustees* **R** CJSJONES
DIDSBURY (St James) (Emmanuel) *Man 8* **P** *Patr Bd*
TR DMHUGHES, **TV** JKMILLS
DIGBY (St Thomas of Canterbury) *Linc 22* **P** *DBP and Mrs H E Gillatt (alt)* **P-in-c** RJMORRISON
DIGMOOR (Christ the Servant) Upholland *Liv*
DIGSWELL (St John the Evangelist) (Christ the King) and Panshanger *St Alb 7* **P** *Patr Bd* **TR** JDTHOMPSON,
TV RAFLETCHER, **C** TWGLADWIN,
NSM RBEARDLEY, GGBROWN, KESUCKLING, JMANNIS
DILHAM (St Nicholas) Smallburgh w Dilham w Honing and Crostwight *Nor*
DILHORNE (All Saints) Caverswall and Weston Coyney w Dilhorne *Lich*
DILSTON (St Mary Magdalene) Corbridge w Halton and Newton Hall *Newc*
DILTON or LEIGH (Holy Saviour) Westbury *Sarum*
DILTON MARSH (Holy Trinity) *Sarum 14* **P** *Bp*
V SFTREEBY
DILWYN AND STRETFORD (St Mary the Virgin) Leominster *Heref*
DINDER (St Michael and All Angels) Pilton w Croscombe, N Wootton and Dinder *B & W*
DINEDOR (St Andrew) Holme Lacy w Dinedor *Heref*
DINGLEY (All Saints) Brampton Ash w Dingley and Braybrooke *Pet*
DINNINGTON (St Leonard) *Sheff 5* **P** *J C Athorpe Esq*
R SPBAILEY, **C** MJCAMERON
DINNINGTON (St Matthew) Ch the King in the Dio of Newc *Newc*
DINNINGTON (St Nicholas) Merriott w Hinton, Dinnington and Lopen *B & W*
DINSDALE (St John the Baptist) w Sockburn *Dur 12*
P *D&C and Sherburn Hosp (alt)* **R** RRAGRAHAM
DINTING VALE (Holy Trinity) Charlesworth and Dinting Vale *Derby*
DINTON (St Mary) Barford St Martin, Dinton, Baverstock etc *Sarum*
DINTON (St Peter and St Paul) Stone w Dinton and Hartwell *Ox*
DIPTFORD (St Mary the Virgin), North Huish, Harberton and Harbertonford *Ex 13* **P** *Mrs E P Buchanan-Allen, D&C, and Bp (jt)* **R** PADWILLIS, **Hon C** JTGEORGE,
DALAWES
DIPTON (St John the Evangelist) and Leadgate *Dur 8* **P** *Bp*
V DGHERON
DISCOED (St Michael) Presteigne w Discoed, Kinsham and Lingen *Heref*
DISEWORTH (St Michael and All Angels) Hathern, Long Whatton and Diseworth w Belton etc *Leic*
DISHFORTH (Christ Church) Baldersby w Dalton, Dishforth etc *York*
DISHLEY (All Saints) and Thorpe Acre *Leic 7* **P** *Bp*
V EKWHITLEY, **C** GAOJESSON, **NSM** CMPARKER
DISLEY (St Mary the Virgin) *Ches 16* **P** *Lord Newton*
V PSDANIEL
DISS Heywood (St James the Great) Diss *Nor*
DISS (St Mary) *Nor 10* **P** *Bp* **R** GCJAMES,
NSM BJSASADA
DISTINGTON (Holy Spirit) *Carl 7* **P** *Earl of Lonsdale*
P-in-c DJTIZZARD

DITCHEAT (St Mary Magdalene) w East Pennard and Pylle
B & W 8 **P** *Bp and Canon D S Salter (jt)*
P-in-c SMMUNNS
DITCHINGHAM (St Mary), Hedenham and Broome *Nor 5*
P *Countess Ferrers and Bp (jt)* **P-in-c** JSREAD
DITCHLING (St Margaret) *Chich 9* **P** *Bp* **V** KCJEFFERY
DITTERIDGE (St Christopher) Box w Hazlebury and Ditteridge *Bris*
DITTISHAM (St George) Ashprington, Cornworthy and Dittisham *Ex*
DITTON (St Michael) *Liv 13* **P** *Patr Bd* **TR** DRLESLIE,
TV JNMANSFIELD, RSBRIDSON, **C** DJROSCOE
DITTON (St Peter ad Vincula) *Roch 7* **P** *Ch Trust Fund Trust* **R** JRTERRANOVA, **C** RAKNAPP (nee STOCKER)
DITTON PRIORS (St John the Baptist) w Neenton, Burwarton, Cleobury North, Aston Botterell, Wheathill and Loughton *Heref 9* **P** *Bp, Viscount Boyne, and Princess Josephine zu Loewenstein (jt)* **P-in-c** DHGOOD
DIXTON (St Peter) *Heref 8* **P** *DBP* **V** BEDWPHILLIPS,
NSM JSTUNNICLIFFE
DOBCROSS (Holy Trinity) w Scouthead (St Paul) *Man 21*
P *Bp* **V** CWMBARLOW
DOBWALLS (St Peter) Liskeard, St Keyne, St Pinnock, Morval etc *Truro*
DOCCOMBE (Chapel) Moretonhampstead, N Bovey and Manaton *Ex*
DOCK (Mission Church) Immingham *Linc*
DOCKENFIELD (Church of the Good Shepherd) Frensham *Guildf*
DOCKING (StMary), The Birchams, Stanhoe and Sedgeford
Nor 17 **P** *Bp, D&C, and Mrs A J Ralli (3 turns), The Crown (1 turn)* **P-in-c** MPADAMS
DOCKLOW (St Bartholomew) Leominster *Heref*
DODBROOKE (St Thomas a Beckett) Kingsbridge and Dodbrooke *Ex*
DODDERHILL (St Augustine) Droitwich Spa *Worc*
DODDINGHURST (All Saints) and Mountnessing
Chelmsf 7 **P** *Bp* **P-in-c** AJABBEY
DODDINGTON (All Saints) Quantoxhead *B & W*
DODDINGTON (St John) Wybunbury w Doddington *Ches*
DODDINGTON (St John the Baptist) Coreley w Doddington *Heref*
DODDINGTON (St John the Baptist), Newnham and Wychling *Cant 6* **P** *Abp, Adn, and Exors Sir John Croft, Bt (jt)* **V** DKINNES
DODDINGTON (St Mary and St Michael) Glendale Gp *Newc*
DODDINGTON (St Mary) w Benwick *Ely 18* **P** *Lady Glover-Hurlimann and Bp (alt)* **P-in-c** ALWAY
DODDINGTON (St Peter) Skellingthorpe w Doddington *Linc*
DODDINGTON, GREAT (St Nicholas) and Wilby *Pet 6*
P *Exors Lt-Col H C M Stockdale and Ld Chan (alt)*
V MSWRATTEN
DODDISCOMBSLEIGH (St Michael) Dunsford and Doddiscombsleigh *Ex*
DODFORD (Holy Trinity and St Mary) Catshill and Dodford *Worc*
DODFORD (St Mary the Virgin) Flore w Dodford and Brockhall *Pet*
DODLESTON (St Mary) *Ches 2* **P** *D&C*
R KGHORSWELL
DODWORTH (St John the Baptist) *Wakef 7* **P** *V Silkstone*
V PHUMPLEBY
DOGMERSFIELD (All Saints) Hartley Wintney, Elvetham, Winchfield etc *Win*
DOLPHINHOLME (St Mark) w Quernmore St Peter
Blackb 12 **P** *Bp and V Lanc (alt)* **V** LJHAKES
DOLTON (St Edmund) *Ex 20* **P** *Ch Soc Trust*
NSM DJURSELL
DONCASTER Holy Trinity *Sheff 9* **P** *SMF* **V** JHARRIS,
C JBFGRANT
DONCASTER Intake (All Saints) *Sheff 9* **P** *Bp*
V BGFRETWELL
DONCASTER (St George) (St Edmund's Church Centre)
Sheff 9 **P** *Bp* **V** HJJBIRD
DONCASTER (St James) *Sheff 10* **P** *Hyndman Trustees*
V DPOLLARD
DONCASTER (St Jude) *Sheff 10* **P** *Bp* **V** MHJAMES
DONCASTER (St Leonard and St Jude) *Sheff 8* **P** *The Crown* **V** NJPAY
DONCASTER (St Mary) *Sheff 9* **P** *Hyndman Trustees*
V JBTHOMSON
DONHEAD ST ANDREW (St Andrew) The Donheads *Sarum*

DONHEAD ST MARY (St Mary the Virgin) as above
DONHEADS, The *Sarum 13* **P** *DBP and New Coll Ox*
(alt) **P-in-c** TCCURRY
DONINGTON (St Cuthbert) *Lich 25* **P** *MMCET*
  R CWWOODS
DONINGTON (St Mary and the Holy Rood) *Linc 21*
  P *Simeon's Trustees* **V** *Vacant* Spalding (01775) 820418
DONINGTON-ON-BAIN (St Andrew) Asterby Gp *Linc*
DONISTHORPE (St John) and Moira w Stretton-en-le-Field
  Leic 9 **P** *Ch Soc Trust (1 turn), and Bp (3 turns)*
  V AJBURGESS, **Hon C** WPOPEJOY
DONNINGTON (St George) *Chich 3* **P** *Bp*
  P-in-c PTRAFFORD
DONNINGTON WOOD (St Matthew) *Lich 27* **P** *Bp*
  P-in-c AJCOOPER
DONNISON (School) Sunderland *Dur*
DONYATT (The Blessed Virgin Mary) Ilminster and District
  B & W
DONYLAND, EAST (St Lawrence) Fingringhoe w E
  Donyland and Abberton etc *Chelmsf*
DORCHESTER (St George) (St Mary the Virgin) (St Peter,
  Holy Trinity and All Saints) *Sarum 2* **P** *Patr Bd (3 turns),*
  Ld Chan (1 turn) **TR** REHJOHNSON,
  TV DJLETCHER, DCWFAYLE, **C** TJCOOK,
  NSM IMGSCOTT, GJMUGRIDGE, PFTURNBULL
DORCHESTER (St Peter and St Paul) *Ox 1* **P** *Patr Bd*
  TR JYCROWE, **TV** ATAWN, WJMCOOMBS,
  MPPULESTON, **NSM** RMGODFREY,
  MCRBRAYBROOKE, MDCHAPMAN
DORDON (St Leonard) *Birm 12* **P** *V Polesworth*
  V JDPOTTER
DORE (Christ Church) *Sheff 2* **P** *Sir Stephen Hastings*
  V DGWILLIAMS
DORKING (St Martin) w Ranmore *Guildf 7* **P** *Bp*
  V MJFARRANT, **C** RJCNEWTON
DORKING (St Paul) *Guildf 7* **P** *Ch Patr Trust*
  V ASWCULLIS, **C** TJCWARD
DORMANSLAND (St John) *S'wark 24* **P** *Bp*
  V DARICHARDSON
DORMANSTOWN (All Saints) *York 17* **P** *Abp*
  V JEDCAVE
DORMINGTON (St Peter) Fownhope w Mordiford,
  Brockhampton etc *Heref*
DORMSTON (St Nicholas) Inkberrow w Cookhill and
  Kington w Dormston *Worc*
DORNEY (St James the Less) Riverside *Ox*
DORRIDGE (St Philip) *Birm 13* **P** *Bp* **V** JASTEVENS,
  C PAREYNOLDS
DORRINGTON (St Edward) w Leebotwood, Longnor,
  Stapleton, Smethcote and Woolstaston *Heref 11* **P** *DBP*
  and J J C Coldwell Esq (jt) **R** RSPAYNE
DORRINGTON (St James) Digby *Linc*
DORSINGTON (St Peter) Pebworth w Dorsington and
  Honeybourne *Glouc*
DORSTONE (St Faith) Peterchurch w Vowchurch,
  Turnastone and Dorstone *Heref*
DORTON (St John the Baptist) Brill, Boarstall, Chilton and
  Dorton *Ox*
DOSTHILL (St Paul) *Birm 12* **P** *Bp* **V** RGSHARPE
DOTTERY (St Saviour) Askerswell, Loders and Powerstock
  Sarum
DOUGLAS (Christ Church) *Blackb 4* **P** *Bp*
  V BEHARDING
DOUGLAS (St George) and St Barnabas w (All Saints)
  S & M 2 **P** *Bp* **V** DAWILLOUGHBY, **C** NAWELLS,
  Hon C JPHEBDEN, **NSM** AWYLIE
DOUGLAS (St Matthew the Apostle) *S & M 2* **P** *Bp*
  V DWHITWORTH, **Hon C** JWRCSARKIES,
  NSM NPILLING
DOUGLAS (St Ninian) *S & M 2* **P** *CPAS*
  V GCGRINHAM, **NSM** GBQUINN
DOUGLAS (St Thomas the Apostle) *S & M 2* **P** *Bp*
  V SEMOURANT
DOUGLAS-IN-PARBOLD (Christ Church) Douglas *Blackb*
DOULTING (St Aldhelm) Shepton Mallet w Doulting *B & W*
DOVE HOLES (St Paul) Wormhill, Peak Forest w Peak Dale
  and Dove Holes *Derby*
DOVECOT (Holy Spirit) *Liv 2* **P** *Bp*
  P-in-c DGRBEARDSLEY, **C** DMARSHALL,
  LHCOOPER
DOVER Buckland Valley (St Nicholas) Buckland in Dover w
  Buckland Valley *Cant*
DOVER (St Martin) *Cant 4* **P** *CPAS* **V** HKOPSCH
DOVER (St Mary the Virgin) *Cant 4* **P** *Abp, Ld Warden of*
  Cinque Ports, and Ld Lt of Kent (jt) **V** GJBATTEN
DOVER (St Peter and St Paul) Charlton-in-Dover *Cant*
DOVERCOURT (All Saints) and Parkeston *Chelmsf 21*
  P *Patr Bd* **TR** SHARDIE, **TV** RMCPAXON

DOVERDALE (St Mary) Ombersley w Doverdale *Worc*
DOVERIDGE (St Cuthbert) *Derby 14* **P** *Duke of*
  Devonshire **P-in-c** DMILNER, **NSM** PRJONES
DOVERSGREEN (St Peter) Reigate St Luke S Park *S'wark*
DOWDESWELL (St Michael) and Andoversford w the
  Shiptons and Cold Salperton *Glouc 14* **P** *Mrs L E Evans,*
  MMCET, and Bp (jt) **P-in-c** GBTHOMAS
DOWLAND (not known) Iddesleigh w Dowland *Ex*
DOWLES Button Oak (St Andrew) Ribbesford w Bewdley
  and Dowles *Worc*
DOWLISHWAKE (St Andrew) Ilminster and District *B & W*
DOWN, East (St John the Baptist) Shirwell, Loxhore,
  Kentisbury, Arlington, etc *Ex*
DOWN AMPNEY (All Saints) S Cerney w Cerney Wick and
  Down Ampney *Glouc*
DOWN HATHERLEY (St Mary and Corpus
  Christi) Twigworth, Down Hatherley, Norton, The Leigh
  etc *Glouc*
DOWN ST MARY (St Mary the Virgin) N Creedy *Ex*
DOWNDERRY (St Nicholas) St Germans *Truro*
DOWNE (St Mary Magdalene) Cudham and Downe *Roch*
DOWNEND (Christ Church) (Church Centre) *Bris 7*
  P *Peache Trustees* **V** AOJOYCE, **C** WBMDOWIE,
  RHHAYES, **Hon C** GCHART
DOWNHAM (St Barnabas) Catford (Southend) and
  Downham *S'wark*
DOWNHAM (St Leonard) *Blackb 8* **P** *Lord Clitheroe*
  V *Vacant* Clitheroe (01200) 41379
DOWNHAM (St Leonard) *Ely 14* **P** *Bp* **R** RJMACKLIN
DOWNHAM (St Luke) Catford (Southend) and Downham
  S'wark
DOWNHAM (St Margaret) w South Hanningfield *Chelmsf 9*
  P *Bp* **R** DJATKINS, **NSM** JMALLWRIGHT
DOWNHAM, NORTH (St Mark) Catford (Southend) and
  Downham *S'wark*
DOWNHAM MARKET (St Edmund) w Bexwell *Ely 16*
  P *Bp* **R** PFKEELING
DOWNHEAD (All Saints) Leigh upon Mendip w Stoke St
  Michael *B & W*
DOWNHOLME (St Michael and All Angels) and Marske
  Ripon 2 **P** *Bp* **C** JGHAIGH
DOWNLEY (St James the Great) High Wycombe *Ox*
DOWNS BARN and NEAT HILL (Community
  Church) Stantonbury and Willen *Ox*
DOWNSBY (St Andrew) Rippingale Gp *Linc*
DOWNSIDE (St Michael's Chapel) Ockham w Hatchford
  Guildf
DOWNSWAY (All Souls Worship Centre) Southwick *Chich*
DOWNTON (St Giles) Wigmore Abbey *Heref*
DOWNTON (St Lawrence) *Sarum 11* **P** *Win Coll*
  V MCGALLAGHER
DOYNTON (Holy Trinity) Wick w Doynton and Dyrham
  Bris
DRAKES BROUGHTON (St Barnabas) Stoulton w Drake's
  Broughton and Pirton etc *Worc*
DRAUGHTON (St Augustine) Skipton H Trin *Bradf*
DRAUGHTON (St Catherine) Maidwell w Draughton,
  Lamport w Faxton *Pet*
DRAX (St Peter and St Paul) Carlton and Drax *York*
DRAYCOT *Bris 9* **P** *Bp, D&C Sarum, and R W Neeld Esq*
  (jt) **R** TWHARRIS
DRAYCOTT (St Mary) Wilne and Draycott w Breaston
  Derby
DRAYCOTT (St Peter) Rodney Stoke w Draycott *B & W*
DRAYCOTT IN THE CLAY (St Augustine) Hanbury w
  Newborough *Lich*
DRAYCOTT-LE-MOORS (St Margaret) w Forsbrook
  Lich 11 **P** *Bp* **R** BLWHITTAKER, **C** JCWATERS
DRAYTON (Iron Mission Room) Chaddesley Corbett and
  Stone *Worc*
DRAYTON (St Catherine) Langport Area Chs *B & W*
DRAYTON (St Leonard and St Catherine) Dorchester *Ox*
DRAYTON (St Margaret) w Felthorpe *Nor 2* **P** *Bp*
  R PHHARRISON
DRAYTON (St Peter) Broughton w N Newington and
  Shutford etc *Ox*
DRAYTON (St Peter) Berks *Ox 10* **P** *Bp*
  P-in-c SMCOLE-KING, **NSM** TASCOTT
DRAYTON, EAST (St Peter) Dunham-on-Trent w Darlton,
  Ragnall etc *S'well*
DRAYTON, LITTLE (Christ Church) *Lich 23* **P** *V Drayton*
  in Hales **V** JODAVIES
DRAYTON, WEST (St Martin) *Lon 24* **P** *Bp*
  V TSAMUEL, **C** RPHARLEY
DRAYTON, WEST (St Paul) Gamston w Eaton and W
  Drayton *S'well*
DRAYTON BASSETT (St Peter) *Lich 4* **P** *Bp*
  R HJBAKER

DRAYTON-BEAUCHAMP (St Mary the Virgin) Aston
Clinton w Buckland and Drayton Beauchamp *Ox*
DRAYTON IN HALES (St Mary) *Lich 23* **P** *Lt-Col Sir John
Corbet, Bt* **P-in-c** G D PRICE, **NSM** J T SMITH
DRAYTON PARSLOW (Holy Trinity) Stewkley w Soulbury
and Drayton Parslow *Ox*
DRESDEN (Resurrection) *Lich 17* **P** *V Blurton*
V H F HARPER
DREWSTEIGNTON (Holy Trinity) *Ex 12* **P** *Exors
B Drewe* **R** C J L NAPIER, **NSM** J G WITHERS
DRIFFIELD (St Mary) The Ampneys w Driffield and
Poulton *Glouc*
DRIFFIELD, GREAT (All Saints) and LITTLE (St Peter)
York 11 **P** *Abp* **V** R E CARLILL
DRIGG (St Peter) Seascale and Drigg *Carl*
DRIGHLINGTON (St Paul) *Wakef 8* **P** *Bp* **V** P A CRABB
DRIMPTON (St Mary) Beaminster Area *Sarum*
DRINGHOUSES (St Edward the Confessor) *York 8* **P** *Abp*
V A M GIRLING, **C** S E FLETCHER
DRINKSTONE (All Saints) Woolpit w Drinkstone *St E*
**DROITWICH SPA (St Andrew w St Mary de Witton)
(St Nicholas) (St Peter) (St Richard)** *Worc 8* **P** *Bp*
TR P BRISTOW, **TV** P A HARVEY, S K BANYARD
Hon C S W GODFREY, **NSM** R M WILTSHIRE
DRONFIELD (St John the Baptist) w Holmesfield *Derby 5*
P *Ld Chan* **TR** D G PALMER, **TV** R P TUCKER,
P R SANDFORD, M D LILES
DROPMORE (St Anne) Burnham w Dropmore, Hitcham
and Taplow *Ox*
DROXFORD (St Mary and All Saints) *Portsm 1* **P** *Bp*
R D E HENLEY
DROYLSDEN (St Andrew) *Man 17* **P** *Bp* **R** *Vacant* 0161–
370 3242
DROYLSDEN (St Martin) *Man 17* **P** *Bp*
V R LIVINGSTON
DROYLSDEN (St Mary) (St John) *Man 17* **P** *Bp*
R M J WILLIAMSON
DRY DODDINGTON (St James) Claypole *Linc*
DRY DRAYTON (St Peter and St Paul) *Ely 5* **P** *MMCET*
P-in-c G A LAY
DRY SANDFORD (St Helen) Besselsleigh w Dry Sandford
Ox
DRYBROOK (Holy Trinity) Dean Forest H Trin *Glouc*
DRYPOOL (St Columba) (St John) *York 15* **P** *Patr Bd*
TR P R W HARRISON, **TV** R P YATES, M BURLEY,
P A WICK, **C** J A EVANS
DUCKLINGTON (St Bartholomew) *Ox 8* **P** *DBP*
P-in-c C HORSEMAN, **NSM** R J EDY
DUCKMANTON (St Peter and St Paul) Calow and Sutton
cum Duckmanton *Derby*
DUDDENHOE END (The Hamlet Church) Heydon, Gt and
Lt Chishill, Chrishall etc *Chelmsf*
DUDDESTON w Nechells St Clement *Birm 1* **P** *Bp and
V Aston-juxta-Birm (jt)* **V** J H LANGSTAFF,
C M O HEFFERNAN
DUDDINGTON (St Mary) Easton on the Hill, Collyweston
w Duddington etc *Pet*
DUDDO (All Saints) Norham and Duddo *Newc*
DUDDON (St Peter) Tarvin *Ches*
DUDLESTON (St Mary the Virgin) *Lich 22* **P** *V Ellesmere*
P-in-c D R D JONES, **C** A C NETHERWOOD
DUDLEY Eve Hill (St James the Great) *Worc 9* **P** *V Dudley*
V *Vacant* Dudley (01384) 253570
DUDLEY Holly Hall (St Augustine) *Worc 9* **P** *V Dudley*
P-in-c M C WARREN, **C** A T JUDD
DUDLEY Kate's Hill (St John) *Worc 9* **P** *V Dudley*
V J W KNIGHTS
DUDLEY (St Andrew) Netherton St Andr *Worc*
DUDLEY (St Barnabas) *Worc 9* **P** *Bp* **V** P G GREEN
DUDLEY (St Edmund King and Martyr) *Worc 9*
P *V Dudley* **V** M C BRAIN
DUDLEY (St Francis) *Worc 9* **P** *Bp* **V** J G PRYSOR-
JONES, **C** J W BESWICK, **NSM** G S JOHNSTON
DUDLEY (St Paul) Weetslade *Newc*
DUDLEY (St Thomas and St Luke) *Worc 9* **P** *Bp*
V M J GOSS
DUDLEY WOOD (St John) *Worc 9* **P** *V Netherton*
V S G F OWENS
DUFFIELD (St Alkmund) *Derby 11* **P** *Ch Soc Trust*
V D A WILKINSON, **Hon C** J B WELLER
DUFTON (St Cuthbert) Long Marton w Dufton and w
Milburn *Carl*
DUKINFIELD (St John) (St Alban Mission Church) *Ches 14*
P *R Stockport St Mary* **P-in-c** T J HAYES
DUKINFIELD (St Mark) (St Luke) *Ches 14* **P** *Bp*
V E W D THOMAS

DULAS (St Michael) Ewyas Harold w Dulas, Kenderchurch
etc *Heref*
DULCOTE (All Saints) Wells St Cuth w Wookey Hole
B & W
DULLINGHAM (St Mary) *Ely 4* **P** *P B Taylor Esq*
P-in-c J S ASKEY
DULOE (St Cuby) w Herodsfoot *Truro 12* **P** *Ball Coll Ox*
R *Vacant* Looe (01503) 263974
DULVERTON (All Saints) and Brushford *B & W 16* **P** *D&C
and E A M H M Herbert Esq (jt)* **R** A R N APPLEBY
DULWICH (St Barnabas) *S'wark 7* **P** *Bp*
V R M CATTLEY, **C** R P GRAFTON, **Hon C** J G WINTER,
M E JACKSON, **NSM** J B ROTHWOOD
DULWICH (St Clement) St Peter *S'wark 7* **P** *Bp*
V P J E MACAN, **C** J M McLAREN
DULWICH, EAST (St John) *S'wark 7* **P** *Ripon Coll
Cuddesdon* **V** J B NAYLOR, **C** P E COLLIER,
NSM R A SHAW
DULWICH, NORTH (St Faith) *S'wark 7* **P** *Bp*
V S M BURDETT
DULWICH, SOUTH (St Stephen) *S'wark 7* **P** *Dulwich
Coll* **V** N H THOMPSON, **C** A P ROBBINS-COLE
DULWICH, WEST (All Saints) *S'wark 13* **P** *Bp*
V R J TITLEY, **C** S J ROBBINS-COLE
DULWICH, WEST (Emmanuel) *S'wark 13* **P** *Bp*
V C H KEY
DUMBLETON (St Peter) Alderton, Gt Washbourne,
Dumbleton etc *Glouc*
DUMMER (All Saints) Cliddesden and Ellisfield w Farleigh
Wallop etc *Win*
**DUNCHIDEOCK (St Michael and All Angels) and Shillingford
St George w Ide** *Ex 6* **P** *D&C and Mrs J M Michelmore
(alt)* **R** J W G GODECK
DUNCHURCH (St Peter) *Cov 6* **P** *Bp*
V R P C ELVERSON, **NSM** J W T ROGERS
DUNCTON (Holy Trinity) *Chich 11* **P** *Lord Egremont*
R *Vacant*
DUNDRY (St Michael) Chew Magna w Dundry *B & W*
DUNGEON HILL *Sarum 4* **P** *DBP, Col J L Yeatman,
Mrs C B Ireland-Smith, and N G Halsey Esq (jt)*
R D HOPLEY
**DUNHAM, GREAT (St Andrew) and LITTLE (St Margaret),
w Great and Little Fransham and Sporle** *Nor 15* **P** *Hertf
Coll Ox, Ch Soc Trust, Magd Coll Cam, and DBP
(by turn)* **R** B R A COLE
DUNHAM MASSEY (St Margaret) (St Mark) (All Saints)
Ches 10 **P** *J G Turnbull Esq* **P-in-c** B HIGGINS
DUNHAM-ON-THE-HILL (St Luke) Helsby and Dunham-
on-the-Hill *Ches*
**DUNHAM-ON-TRENT (St Oswald) w Darlton, Ragnall,
Fledborough and East Drayton** *S'well 5* **P** *Bp (2 turns),
D&C York (1 turn)* **R** J CALVERT
DUNHOLME (St Chad) Welton and Dunholme w Scothern
Linc
DUNKERTON (All Saints) Camerton w Dunkerton,
Foxcote and Shoscombe *B & W*
**DUNKESWELL (Holy Trinity) (St Nicholas), Sheldon and
Luppitt** *Ex 5* **P** *MMCET and Bp (jt)* **V** N J WALL
DUNMOW, GREAT (St Mary the Virgin) *Chelmsf 19*
P *Ld Chan* **P-in-c** K G HOLLOWAY, **NSM** R DREW
DUNMOW, LITTLE (not known) Barnston and Lt
Dunmow *Chelmsf*
DUNNINGTON (not known) Salford Priors *Cov*
DUNNINGTON (St Nicholas) Beeford w Frodingham and
Foston *York*
DUNNINGTON (St Nicholas) *York 4* **P** *Abp*
R J D WALKER, **C** C J COPLAND
DUNS TEW (St Mary Magdalen) Westcote Barton w Steeple
Barton, Duns Tew etc *Ox*
DUNSBY (All Saints) Rippingale Gp *Linc*
DUNSCROFT (St Edwin) *Sheff 11* **P** *Bp* **V** S J RAINE
DUNSDEN (All Saints) Shiplake w Dunsden *Ox*
DUNSFOLD (St Mary and All Saints) *Guildf 2* **P** *Ld Chan*
R G S M WILLIS
DUNSFORD (St Mary) and Doddiscombsleigh *Ex 6* **P** *Exors
Lt-Col F E A Fulford (2 turns), J F N Buckingham Esq
(1 turn)* **V** *Vacant* Christow (01647) 52490
DUNSFORTH (St Mary) Aldborough w Boroughbridge and
Roecliffe *Ripon*
DUNSLAND (Mission Church) Ashwater, Halwill,
Beaworthy, Clawton etc *Ex*
DUNSLEY (Mission Room) Aislaby and Ruswarp *York*
DUNSMORE (Chapel of the Ressurection) Ellesborough,
The Kimbles and Stoke Mandeville *Ox*
DUNSOP BRIDGE (St George) Slaidburn *Bradf*
**DUNSTABLE (St Augustine of Canterbury) (St Fremund the
Martyr) (St Peter)** *St Alb 18* **P** *Bp* **TV** D W KESTERTON,
A J M SINCLAIR, J H HARRIS, K D BURN

DUNSTALL (St Mary) w Rangemore and Tatenhill *Lich 19*
  P *Lord Burton, Sir Rupert Hardy, Bt, and Bp (jt)* **R** *Vacant*
  Barton under Needwood (01283) 712509
DUNSTAN (St Leonard) Penkridge Team *Lich*
DUNSTAN (St Peter) Metheringham w Blankney and
  Dunston *Linc*
DUNSTER (St George), Carhampton and Withycombe w
  Rodhuish *B & W 16* **P** *Bp* **R** M P GRANTHAM
DUNSTON (Church House) Newbold and Dunston *Derby*
DUNSTON (St Nicholas) w (Christ Church) *Dur 5* **P** *Bp*
  V K TEASDALE
DUNSTON (St Remigius) Stoke H Cross w Dunston,
  Arminghall etc *Nor*
DUNSWELL (St Faith's Mission Church) Hull Newland St
  Jo *York*
DUNTERTON (All Saints) Milton Abbot, Dunterton,
  Lamerton etc *Ex*
DUNTISBOURNE ABBOTS (St Peter) Daglingworth w the
  Duntisbournes and Winstone *Glouc*
DUNTISBOURNE ROUS (St Michael and All Angels) as
  above
DUNTON (St Martin) Schorne *Ox*
DUNTON (St Mary Magdalene) w Wrestlingworth and
  Eyeworth *St Alb 17* **P** *Ld Chan and DBP (alt)* **R** *Vacant*
  Wrestlingworth (01767) 631596
DUNTON BASSETT (All Saints) Leire w Ashby Parva and
  Dunton Bassett *Leic*
DUNWICH (St James) Westleton w Dunwich *St E*
DURHAM (St Cuthbert) *Dur 2* **P** *D&C* **C** R N INNES,
  NSM B MIDDLEBROOK
DURHAM (St Giles) *Dur 2* **P** *D&C* **V** T W THUBRON,
  NSM D J WILSON
DURHAM (St Margaret of Antioch) *Dur 2* **P** *D&C*
  R *Vacant* 0191–384 3623
DURHAM (St Nicholas) *Dur 2* **P** *CPAS* **V** M J WILCOCK
DURHAM (St Oswald King and Martyr) *Dur 2* **P** *D&C*
  V B J H de la MARE, **C** J HIRST
DURLEIGH (not known) Bridgwater St Mary, Chilton
  Trinity and Durleigh *B & W*
DURLEY (Holy Cross) *Portsm 1* **P** *Ld Chan*
  R A N STAMP, **C** K F ARVIDSSON
DURNFORD (St Andrew) Woodford Valley *Sarum*
DURRINGTON (All Saints) *Sarum 12* **P** *D&C Win*
  R P H TAMPLIN
DURRINGTON (St Symphorian) *Chich 5* **P** *Bp*
  V R N AITON, **C** R A BROMFIELD
DURSLEY (St James the Great) *Glouc 2* **P** *Bp*
  R J B HUNNISETT
DURSTON (St John the Baptist) N Newton w St
  Michaelchurch, Thurloxton etc *B & W*
DURWESTON (St Nicholas) Pimperne, Stourpaine,
  Durweston and Bryanston *Sarum*
DUSTON Team, The (St Francis) (St Luke) *Pet 7* **P** *Bp*
  TV N G TUCK
DUSTON, NEW (Mission Church) Duston Team *Pet*
DUTTON (Licensed Room) Lt Leigh and Lower Whitley
  Ches
DUXFORD (St Peter) w St John *Ely 7* **P** *Bp* **R** *Vacant*
  Cambridge (01223) 832137
DYMCHURCH (St Peter and St Paul) w Burmarsh and
  Newchurch *Cant 13* **P** *Abp* **R** P N ASHMAN
DYMOCK (St Mary the Virgin) w Donnington and Kempley
  Glouc 3 **P** *Pemb Coll Ox, Bp, and R D Marcon Esq (by*
  turn) **P-in-c** R HART
DYRHAM (St Peter) Wick w Doynton and Dyrham *Bris*
EAGLE (All Saints) Swinderby *Linc*
EAKRING (St Andrew) *S'well 15* **P** *DBP* **R** H H WILCOX
EALING (All Saints) *Lon 22* **P** *Bp*
  P-in-c N P HENDERSON, **NSM** R W BUCKLEY
EALING (Ascension) Hanger Hill Ascension and W Twyford
  St Mary *Lon*
EALING (Christ the Saviour) *Lon 22* **P** *Bp* **V** A F DAVIS,
  NSM D E BIRT
EALING (St Barnabas) *Lon 22* **P** *Bp*
  V G A REDDINGTON, **NSM** M J JOACHIM
EALING (St Mary) *Lon 22* **P** *Bp* **V** D R HOLT,
  C M S STARKEY, V A CORY
EALING (St Paul) *Lon 22* **P** *Bp* **V** M P MELLUISH,
  C R J THOMPSON
EALING (St Peter) Mount Park *Lon 22* **P** *Bp*
  V W H TAYLOR, **C** C D EYDEN, **NSM** J H ROBINSON
EALING (St Stephen) Castle Hill *Lon 22* **P** *D&C St Paul's*
  V D C RUNCORN, **C** M K HARGREAVES, J A SEARLE,
  NSM J M WINFIELD
EALING, WEST (St John) w St James *Lon 22* **P** *Bp*
  V I N FISHWICK, **C** M Q BRATTON
EALING COMMON (St Matthew) *Lon 22* **P** *Bp*
  V P G WATKINS

EARBY (All Saints) *Bradf 7* **P** *Bp* **V** R C WALLACE,
  NSM G L HALL
EARDISLAND (St Mary the Virgin) *Heref 7* **P** *Bp Birm*
  P-in-c S B THOMAS
EARDISLEY (St Mary Magdalene) w Bollingham, Willersley,
  Brilley, Michaelchurch, Whitney and Winforton *Heref 5*
  P *Bp, Mrs C E Hope, and Exors Mrs A M Dew (jt)*
  R K NEWBON
EARL SHILTON (St Simon and St Jude) w Elmesthorpe
  Leic 13 **P** *Bp* **V** G GITTINGS
EARL SOHAM (St Mary) w Cretingham and Ashfield cum
  Thorpe *St E 18* **P** *Lord Henniker, Ld Chan, and Wadh Coll*
  Ox (by turn) **P-in-c** D A S BOYES
EARL STERNDALE (St Michael and All
  Angels) Hartington, Biggin and Earl Sterndale *Derby*
EARL STONHAM (St Mary) Creeting St Mary, Creeting St
  Peter etc *St E*
EARLESTOWN (St John the Baptist) *Liv 16*
  P *R Wargrave* **V** M BUCKLEY
EARLEY (St Nicolas) *Ox 15* **P** *DBP* **P-in-c** T C PLATTS,
  Hon C W P COOPER
EARLEY (St Peter) *Ox 15* **P** *DBP* **V** R R D SPEARS,
  C J R HICKS
EARLEY Trinity *Ox 15* **P** *DBP* **V** *Vacant* Reading (01734)
  868615
EARLEY, LOWER Trinity Church Local Ecumenical Project
  Ox 15 Vacant
EARLHAM (St Anne) *Nor 3* **P** *Bp* **V** P R OLIVER,
  C T MELBOURNE, N A SULLIVAN
EARLHAM (St Elizabeth) *Nor 3* **P** *Bp* **R** J PANTING
EARLHAM (St Mary) *Nor 3* **P** *Trustees*
  NSM P G RUTHERFORD
EARLS BARTON (All Saints) *Pet 6* **P** *DBP*
  V M C W WEBBER
EARLS COLNE (St Andrew) w White Colne and Colne
  Engaine *Chelmsf 20* **P** *DBP, Ch Hosp, and Keble Coll Ox*
  (by turn) **R** J E F JASPER
EARL'S COURT (St Cuthbert) (St Matthias) *Lon 12*
  P *Trustees* **V** J VINE, **NSM** W J A KIRKPATRICK
EARLS CROOME (St Nicholas) Ripple, Earls Croome w
  Hill Croome and Strensham *Worc*
EARLSDON (St Barbara) *Cov 3* **P** *Bp* **V** T C BROOKE
EARLSFIELD (St Andrew) *S'wark 18* **P** *Bp*
  V C W PRITCHARD
EARLSFIELD (St John the Divine) *S'wark 18* **P** *Bp*
  V C E ROBERTS
EARLSHEATON (St Peter) *Wakef 10* **P** *R Dewsbury*
  V G R WALKER
EARLY (St Bartholomew) Reading St Luke w St Bart *Ox*
EARNLEY (not known) and East Wittering *Chich 3* **P** *Bp*
  (2 turns), Bp Lon (1 turn) **R** J H LYON
EARNSHAW BRIDGE (St John) Leyland St Jo *Blackb*
EARSDON (St Alban) and Backworth *Newc 8* **P** *Bp*
  V N WILSON
EARSHAM (All Saints) w Alburgh and Denton *Nor 10*
  P *Abp, J M Meade Esq, and St Jo Coll Cam (by turn)*
  R J S READ
EARSWICK, NEW (St Andrew) Huntington *York*
EARTHAM (St Margaret) Slindon, Eartham and Madehurst
  Chich
EASBY (Chapel) Gt Ayton w Easby and Newton in
  Cleveland *York*
EASBY (St Agatha) w Brompton on Swale and Bolton on Swale
  Ripon 2 **P** *Bp* **V** A GLEDHILL
EASEBOURNE (St Mary) *Chich 10* **P** *Cowdray Trust*
  V M C JUDGE, **NSM** S J CHAPMAN
EASINGTON (All Saints) w Liverton *York 17* **P** *Ld Chan*
  R E J HOSKIN
EASINGTON (All Saints) w Skeffling, Kilnsea and Holmpton
  York 13 **P** *Ld Chan* **R** W J G HEALE
EASINGTON (St Hugh) Banbury *Ox*
EASINGTON (St Mary) *Dur 3* **P** *Bp* **R** N P VINE
EASINGTON (St Peter) Ewelme, Brightwell Baldwin,
  Cuxham w Easington *Ox*
EASINGTON COLLIERY (Ascension) *Dur 3* **P** *Bp*
  V *Vacant* 0191–527 0272
EASINGWOLD (St John the Baptist and All Saints) w
  Raskelfe *York 5* **P** *Abp* **V** T HART
EAST: *see also under substantive place names*
EAST FERRY (St Mary the Virgin) Scotter w E Ferry *Linc*
EAST LANE (St Mary) W Horsley *Guildf*
EAST ORCHARD (St Thomas) Shaston *Sarum*
EASTBOURNE (All Saints) *Chich 16* **P** *Trustees*
  V G T RIDEOUT, **C** C K MACDONALD,
  Hon C P S PLUNKETT
EASTBOURNE (All Souls) *Chich 16* **P** *Ch Soc Trust and*
  J H Cordle Esq (jt) **V** R H G MASON
EASTBOURNE (Christ Church) *Chich 16* **P** *V Eastbourne*
  V P A S FORDHAM

EASTBOURNE (Holy Trinity) *Chich 16* **P** *V Eastbourne*
V K H BLYTH, **C** P DUNTHORNE, **NSM** K C LEFROY
(nee CLARK)
EASTBOURNE (St Andrew) *Chich 16* **P** *Bp*
V A F STONE, **C** R J S CATCHPOLE
EASTBOURNE (St Elisabeth) *Chich 16* **P** *Bp* **V** B H KING
EASTBOURNE (St John) Meads *Chich 16* **P** *Trustees*
V A McCABE, **NSM** B H JEFFORD
EASTBOURNE (St Mary) *Chich 16* **P** *Bp* **V** N S READE,
C K R C AGNEW, **NSM** A M WINDROSS
EASTBOURNE (St Michael and All Angels) Ocklynge
Chich 16 **P** *V Eastbourne* **V** J C T HARRINGTON,
Dss W K HAMBLY
EASTBOURNE (St Philip) *Chich 16* **P** *Bp* **V** R C COLES
EASTBOURNE (St Richard of Chichester) Langney *Chich*
EASTBOURNE (St Saviour and St Peter) *Chich 16* **P** *Keble*
Coll Ox **V** D MOTTERSHEAD, **Hon Par Dn** B R RUNDLE
EASTBURY (St James the Great) and East Garston *Ox 14*
P *Bp and Ch Ch Ox (alt)* **P-in-c** W J STEWART
EASTCHURCH (All Saints) w Leysdown and Harty *Cant 14*
P *Abp and Keble Coll Ox (jt)* **R** L C MEPSTED
EASTCOMBE (St Augustine) Bussage *Glouc*
EASTCOTE (St Lawrence) *Lon 24* **P** *Bp* **V** D COLEMAN,
C A V COLEMAN
EASTER, HIGH (St Mary the Virgin) and Good Easter w
Margaret Roding *Chelmsf 19* **P** *Bp Lon, Trustees*
R K Shepherd Esq, and D&C St Paul's (by turn)
R G F BARTLAM
EASTERGATE (St George) Aldingbourne, Barnham and
Eastergate *Chich*
EASTERN GREEN (St Andrew) *Cov 3* **P** *R Allesley*
V J A DAVIES
EASTERTON (St Barnabas) Market Lavington and
Easterton *Sarum*
EASTFIELD (Holy Nativity) Cayton w Eastfield *York*
EASTGATE (All Saints) w Rookhope *Dur 15* **P** *Bp and
Ld Chan (alt)* **V** C N LOVELL
**EASTHAM (St Mary the Blessed Virgin) (St Peter's Chapel)
(Chapel of the Holy Spirit)** *Ches 9* **P** *D&C*
V A L WINSTANLEY, **C** D W JACKSON
EASTHAM (St Peter and St Paul) Teme Valley S *Worc*
EASTHAMPSTEAD (St Michael and St Mary Magdalene)
Ox 11 **P** *Ch Ch Ox* **R** O SIMON, **C** G F THEOBALD,
R G BURGESS, D B TONKINSON
EASTHOPE (St Peter) Wenlock *Heref*
EASTHORPE (St Mary the Virgin) Copford w Easthorpe
and Messing w Inworth *Chelmsf*
EASTINGTON (St Michael and All Angels) and Frocester
Glouc 8 **P** *Lady Cooper and DBP (alt)* **R** N E L BAKER
EASTLEACH (St Andrew) Coln St Aldwyns, Hatherop,
Quenington etc *Glouc*
EASTLEIGH (All Saints) *Win 9* **P** *Bp* **V** R P DAVIES,
C M P BENWELL
EASTLEIGH Nightingale Avenue (St Francis) Eastleigh *Win*
EASTLING (St Mary) w Ospringe and Stalisfield w Otterden
Cant 6 **P** *The Crown* **R** D W TURTON
EASTMOORS (St Mary Magdalene) Helmsley *York*
EASTNEY (St Margaret) *Portsm 6* **P** *Bp* **V** P H KELLY,
NSM A DEAN
EASTNOR (St John the Baptist) Ledbury w Eastnor *Heref*
EASTOFT (St Bartholomew) The Marshland *Sheff*
EASTON (All Hallows) *Bris 2* **P** *R Bris St Steph* **V** *Vacant*
Bristol (0117) 955 2477
EASTON (All Saints) Wickham Market w Pettistree and
Easton *St E*
**EASTON (Holy Trinity w St Gabriel and St Lawrence and St
Jude)** *Bris 4* **P** *Trustees* **V** W R DONALDSON,
C N R HOPKIN
EASTON (St Mary) Itchen Valley *Win*
EASTON (St Paul) Westbury sub Mendip w Easton *B & W*
EASTON (St Peter) *Ely 10* **P** *Bp* **P-in-c** J ALFORD
EASTON (St Peter) w Colton and Marlingford *Nor 18*
P *Ld Chan, E C Evans-Lombe Esq, and Adn Norfolk
(by turn)* **P-in-c** J B LUMBY
EASTON, GREAT (St Andrew) Six Saints circa Holt *Leic*
EASTON, GREAT (St John and St Giles) Broxted w
Chickney and Tilty etc *Chelmsf*
EASTON, LITTLE (not known) as above
EASTON GREY (not known) Sherston Magna, Easton
Grey, Luckington etc *Bris*
EASTON IN GORDANO (St George) Pill w Easton in
Gordano and Portbury *B & W*
EASTON MAUDIT (St Peter and St Paul) Bozeat w Easton
Maudit *Pet*
EASTON NESTON (St Mary) Towcester w Easton Neston
Pet

EASTON ON THE HILL (All Saints) and Collyweston w
Duddingtonand Tixover *Pet 8* **P** *Ld Chan, Bp, and Burghley
Ho Preservation Trust (by turn)* **NSM** R C TROUNSON,
P J ALLEN
EASTON ROYAL (Holy Trinity) Pewsey TM *Sarum*
EASTRINGTON (St Michael) Howden TM *York*
EASTROP (St Mary) *Win 4* **P** *CPAS* **R** C L HAWKINS
EASTRY (St Mary Blessed Virgin) and Northbourne w
Tilmanstone and Betteshanger w Ham *Cant 8* **P** *Abp and
Lord Northbourne (jt)* **R** C A TOMKINS, **C** S C TURNER
(formerly BENBOW)
EASTTHORPE (St Paul) and Upper Hopton *Wakef 10*
P *V Mirfield* **V** S G D PARKINSON
EASTVILLE (St Anne w St Mark and St Thomas) *Bris 4*
P *Bp* **V** *Vacant* Bristol (0117) 952 0202
EASTVILLE (St Paul) Stickney Gp *Linc*
EASTWELL (St Michael) Scalford w Goadby Marwood and
Wycombe etc *Leic*
EASTWICK (St Botolph) High Wych and Gilston w
Eastwick *St Alb*
EASTWOOD (St David) *Chelmsf 10* **P** *Bp* **V** M J TAYLOR
EASTWOOD (St Laurence and All Saints) *Chelmsf 10*
P *Ld Chan* **V** N L RANSOM
EASTWOOD (St Mary) *S'well 4* **P** *J N Plumptre Esq*
R E A C CARDWELL, **C** J CURRIN
EATON (All Saints) Gamston w Eaton and W Drayton
S'well
EATON (Christ Church) and Hulme Walfield *Ches 11* **P** *Bp
and R Astbury (alt)* **V** R B ROBERTS
EATON (Christ Church) (St Andrew) *Nor 3* **P** *D&C*
V A BEARDSMORE, **C** J B SCOTT
EATON (St Denys) Scalford w Goadby Marwood and
Wycombe etc *Leic*
EATON (St Thomas) Tarporley *Ches*
EATON, LITTLE (St Paul) Holbrook and Lt Eaton *Derby*
EATON BISHOP (St Michael and All Angels) Kingstone w
Clehonger, Eaton Bishop etc *Heref*
EATON BRAY (St Mary the Virgin) w Edlesborough
St Alb 18 **P** *DBP* **V** M P J BONNEY
EATON HASTINGS (St Michael and All Angels) Gt
Coxwell w Buscot, Coleshill & Eaton Hastings *Ox*
EATON SOCON (St Mary) *St Alb 17* **P** *E W Harper Esq*
V J D WATSON, **C** V E RAYMER
EATON SQUARE (St Peter) Pimlico St Pet w Westmr Ch Ch
Lon
EATON-UNDER-HEYWOOD (St Edith) Hope Bowdler w
Eaton-under-Heywood *Heref*
EBBERSTON (St Mary) Brompton-by-Sawdon w Snainton,
Ebberston etc *York*
EBBESBOURNE WAKE (St John the Baptist) Chalke
Valley W *Sarum*
EBCHESTER (St Ebba) *Dur 8* **P** *Bp*
P-in-c A E HARRISON
EBERNOE (Holy Trinity) N Chapel w Ebernoe *Chich*
EBONY (St Mary the Virgin) Wittersham w Stone-in-Oxney
and Ebony *Cant*
EBREY WOOD (Mission Chapel) Uffington, Upton Magna
and Withington *Lich*
EBRINGTON (St Eadburgha) Chipping Campden w
Ebrington *Glouc*
ECCHINSWELL (St Lawrence) Burghclere w Newtown and
Ecchinswell w Sydmonton *Win*
ECCLES (St Mary the Virgin) Quidenham *Nor*
ECCLES (St Mary the Virgin) (St Andrew) *Man 2*
P *Ld Chan and Patr Bd (alt)* **TR** N JONES,
TV M W SAUNDERS
ECCLESALL (St Gabriel) Greystones *Sheff*
ECCLESALL BIERLOW (All Saints) *Sheff 2* **P** *Provost
Sheff* **V** C P WILLIAMS, **C** E HOPE, P J HUGHES
ECCLESFIELD (St Mary the Virgin) *Sheff 3* **P** *DBF*
V J O FORRESTER
ECCLESFIELD (St Paul) Sheff St Paul Wordsworth Avenue
Sheff
ECCLESHALL (Holy Trinity) *Lich 12* **P** *Bp* **V** J S COOKE
ECCLESHILL (St Luke) *Bradf 3* **P** *V Bradf*
V A S TREASURE, **C** T S WRIGHT
ECCLESTON (Christ Church) *Liv 10* **P** *F Webster Esq, Lord
Blanch, Canon J A Lawton, Rev D G Mellors, and Bp (jt)*
V C D HENDRICKSE
ECCLESTON (St Luke) *Liv 10* **P** *Trustees* **V** A W HARDY
ECCLESTON (St Mary the Virgin) *Blackb 4* **P** *DBP*
R A H McMICHAEL
ECCLESTON (St Mary the Virgin) and Pulford *Ches 2*
P *Duke of Westmr* **R** F H LINN
ECCLESTON (St Thomas) *Liv 10* **P** *Bp* **V** S P ATTWATER
ECCLESTON, GREAT Copp *Blackb*
ECCLESTON PARK (St James) *Liv 10* **P** *Bp*
V A OVEREND

ECKINGTON (Holy Trinity) *Worc 4*   **P** *D&C Westmr*
  V P J THOMAS
ECKINGTON (St Peter and St Paul) w Handley and Ridgeway
  Derby 3   **P** *The Crown and Patr Bd (alt)*
  TR N R HARVEY,   **C** H E PATTEN (nee STARNS)
ECKINGTON, UPPER (St Luke) Eckington w Handley and
  Ridgeway *Derby*
ECTON (St Mary Magdalene) *Pet 6*   **P** *The Crown*
  R P E NAYLOR
EDALE (Holy and Undivided Trinity) *Derby 2*   **P** *Rep*
  Landowners   **P-in-c** A J G MURRAY-LESLIE
EDBURTON (St Andrew) Poynings w Edburton, Newtimber
  and Pyecombe *Chich*
EDENBRIDGE (St Peter and St Paul) *Roch 10*   **P** *Bp*
  V S A J MITCHELL,   **C** R JONES
EDENFIELD (not known) and Stubbins *Man 10*   **P** *Bp*
  V G N HIGHAM
EDENHALL (St Cuthbert) Addingham, Edenhall,
  Langwathby and Culgaith *Carl*
EDENHAM (St Michael) w Witham-on-the-Hill *Linc 13*
  P *Bp and Baroness Willoughby de Eresby (alt)*
  V A T HAWES
EDENSOR (St Paul) *Lich 17*   **P** *Prime Min*
  V C CRUMPTON
EDENSOR (St Peter) Beeley and Edensor *Derby*
EDGBASTON (St Augustine) *Birm 2*   **P** *Bp*   **V** R F PRICE
EDGBASTON (St Bartholomew) *Birm 2*   **P** *Sir Euan*
  Anstruther-Gough-Calthorpe, Bt   **V** E D COOMBES
EDGBASTON (St George w St Michael) (St Michael's Hall)
  Birm 2   **P** *Sir Euan Anstruther-Gough-Calthorpe, Bt*
  V R W GRIMLEY,   **NSM** J L HUGHES
EDGBASTON (St Germain) *Birm 2*   **P** *Trustees*
  V A P NORRIS,   **C** D J SMITH
EDGBASTON (St Mary and St Ambrose) *Birm 2*   **P** *Bp and*
  Sir Euan Anstruther-Gough-Calthorpe, Bt (jt)
  V A J WARD,   **NSM** P M EATON
EDGCOTE (St James) Culworth w Sulgrave and Thorpe
  Mandeville etc *Pet*
EDGCOTT (St Michael) Swan *Ox*
EDGE, THE (St John the Baptist), Pitchcombe, Harescombe
  and Brookthorpe *Glouc 1*   **P** *Bp and D&C (jt)*
  P-in-c E A POWELL
EDGE HILL (St Dunstan) Earle Road *Liv 6*   **P** *Trustees*
  V R F JONES
EDGE HILL (St Mary) *Liv 3*   **P** *Bp*   **V** A GODSON
EDGEFIELD (School Room) Worsley *Man*
EDGEFIELD (St Peter and St Paul) Wickmere w Lt
  Barningham, Itteringham etc *Nor*
EDGESIDE (St Anne) *Man 15*   **P** *Trustees*
  P-in-c R J CARMYLLIE
EDGEWORTH (St Mary) Bisley, Oakridge, Miserden and
  Edgeworth *Glouc*
EDGMOND (St Peter) w Kynnersley and Preston Wealdmoors
  Lich 21   **P** *Bp, Adn Salop, Chan Lich, MMCET, and*
  Preston Trust Homes Trustees (jt)   **R** W E WARD,
  NSM R G R SMITH
EDGTON (St Michael the Archangel) Lydbury N w Hopesay
  and Edgton *Heref*
EDGWARE Burnt Oak (St Alphege) Hendon St Alphage
  Lon
EDGWARE (St Andrew) (St Margaret) (St Peter) *Lon 15*
  P *MMCET*   **R** C M BEDFORD,   **C** R M GOLDENBERG,
  R A LEE,   J A FAIRBAIRN
EDINGALE (Holy Trinity) Clifton Campville w Edingale
  Lich
EDINGLEY (St Giles) w Halam *S'well 15*   **P** *Bp*
  P-in-c I G COLLINS
EDINGTHORPE (All Saints) Bacton w Edingthorpe w
  Witton and Ridlington *Nor*
EDINGTON (St George) W Poldens *B & W*
EDINGTON (St Mary, St Katharine and All Saints) and
  Imber, Erlestoke and East Coulston *Sarum 19*   **P** *Bp*
  P-in-c D J BELCHER
EDITH WESTON (St Mary) w North Luffenham and Lyndon
  w Manton *Pet 14*   **P** *Baroness Willoughby de Eresby,*
  Sir John Conant, and Em CollCam (by turn)
  R R J M BLACKALL
EDITHMEAD (Mission) Burnham *B & W*
EDLASTON (St James) Brailsford w Shirley and Osmaston
  w Edlaston *Derby*
EDLINGHAM (St John the Baptist w Bolton
  Chapel) Whittingham and Edlingham w Bolton Chapel
  Newc
EDLINGTON (St Helen) Hemingby *Linc*
EDLINGTON (St John the Baptist) *Sheff 10*   **P** *Bp*
  V J T ARCHER

EDMONDSHAM (St Nicholas) Cranborne w Boveridge,
  Edmondsham etc *Sarum*
EDMONDTHORPE (St Michael and All
  Angels) Wymondham w Edmondthorpe, Buckminster etc
  Leic
EDMONTON (All Saints) (St Michael) *Lon 18*
  P *D&C St Paul's*   **V** B W OAKLEY,   **C** J E CLARK
EDMONTON (St Aldhelm) *Lon 18*   **P** *V Edmonton All SS*
  V J E HALL
EDMONTON (St Alphege) *Lon 18*   **P** *Bp*   **V** C W COPPEN
EDMONTON (St Mary w St John) (St Mary's Centre)
  Lon 18   **P** *D&C St Paul's*   **V** D W GOUGH,
  Hon C J S ALDIS
EDMONTON (St Peter w St Martin) *Lon 18*   **P** *Bp*
  V B M SMITH
EDMUNDBYERS (St Edmund) Blanchland w
  Hunstanworth and Edmundbyers etc *Newc*
EDSTASTON (St Mary the Virgin) Tilstock, Edstaston and
  Whixall *Lich*
EDSTON (St Michael) Kirby Misperton w Normanby,
  Edston and Salton *York*
EDVIN LOACH (St Mary) w Tedstone Delamere, Tedstone
  Wafer, Upper Sapey, Wolferlow and Whitbourne *Heref 2*
  P *Bp, BNC Ox, Sir Francis Winnington Bt, and D P Barneby*
  Esq (jt)   **R** R J COLBY,   **NSM** D G WILLIAMS
EDWALTON (Holy Rood) *S'well 9*   **P** *Exors Major R P*
  Chaworth-Musters   **V** D C BIGNELL,
  NSM P A EDWARDS
EDWARDSTONE (St Mary the Virgin) w Groton and Little
  Waldingfield *St E 12*   **P** *DBP (2 turns) and Hon Thomas*
  Lindsay (1 turn)   **R** R K TITFORD
EDWINSTOWE (St Mary) w Carburton *S'well 6*   **P** *Earl*
  Manvers' Trustees   **V** *Vacant* Mansfield (01623) 822430
EDWYN RALPH (St Michael) Bredenbury w Grendon
  Bishop and Wacton etc *Heref*
EFFINGHAM (St Lawrence) w Little Bookham *Guildf 10*
  P *Keble Coll Ox*   **V** A P HODGETTS
EFFORD (St Paul) Plymouth Em, Efford and Laira *Ex*
EGDEAN (St Bartholomew) Chich 11   **P** *Bp* **R** *Vacant*
EGERTON (St James) w Pluckley *Cant 10*   **P** *Abp*
  R M J HIGGS
EGG BUCKLAND (St Edward) *Ex 23*   **P** *Ld Chan*
  V T R J DICKENS,   **C** R HURLEY
EGGESFORD (All Saints) Wembworthy w Eggesford *Ex*
EGGINTON (St Michael) Leighton Buzzard w Eggington,
  Hockliffe etc *St Alb*
EGGINTON (St Wilfrid) Etwall w Egginton *Derby*
EGGLESCLIFFE (St John the Baptist) *Dur 16*   **P** *Bp*
  R R V CHADWICK
EGGLESTON (Holy Trinity) *Dur 11*   **P** *The Crown*
  V G LINDEN
EGHAM (St John the Baptist) *Guildf 11*   **P** *Ch Soc Trust*
  V A J MAGOWAN,   **C** A J FACEY,   **Hon C** J H GOODING
EGHAM HYTHE (St Paul) *Guildf 11*   **P** *Bp*
  V A J BUTCHER
EGLETON (St Edmund) Oakham, Hambleton, Egleton,
  Braunston and Brooke *Pet*
EGLINGHAM (St Maurice) Glendale Gp *Newc*
EGLOSHAYLE (St Petroc) St Breoke and Egloshayle *Truro*
EGLOSKERRY (St Petrock and St Keri), North Petherwin,
  Tremaine and Tresmere *Truro 9*   **P** *Duchy of Cornwall and*
  Bp (alt)   **V** G PENGELLY
EGMANTON (Our Lady of Egmanton) *S'well 3*   **P** *SMF*
  V C C LEVY
EGREMONT (St John) *Ches 7*   **P** *Bp*   **V** B E LEE,
  C T JORDAN
EGREMONT (St Mary and St Michael) and Haile *Carl 5*
  P *Patr Bd*   **TR** J WOOLCOCK,   **TV** N J P HAYTON,
  C M E IVEY (nee HODGE), **NSM** B J JEAPES (nee PORTER)
EGTON (St Hilda) w Grosmont *York 23*   **P** *Abp*
  V D C KING
EGTON-CUM-NEWLAND (St Mary the Virgin) and Lowick
  Carl 8   **P** *Trustees*   **P-in-c** G WEMYSS
EIGHT ASH GREEN (All Saints) Fordham *Chelmsf*
EIGHTON BANKS (St Thomas) *Dur 4*   **P** *Bp*
  V A W HODGSON,   **NSM** E CARR
ELBERTON (St John) Littleton on Severn w Elberton *Bris*
ELBURTON (St Matthew) *Ex 24*   **P** *CPAS*
  V K H S COOMBE
ELDENE (not known) Swindon Dorcan *Bris*
ELDERSFIELD (St John the Baptist) Berrow w Pendock,
  Eldersfield, Hollybush etc *Worc*
ELDON (St Mark) Shildon w Eldon *Dur*
ELDWICK (St Lawrence) Bingley All SS *Bradf*

ELFORD (St Peter) Lich 4 **P** Bp **P-in-c** B L COX
ELHAM (St Mary the Virgin) w Denton and Wootton Cant 5
  P Abp and Mert Coll Ox (jt) **Hon C** R J C LLOYD
ELING (St Mary) Totton Win
ELKESLEY (St Giles) w Bothamsall S'well 5 **P** SMF
  V Vacant Gamston (01777) 838293
ELKINGTON, SOUTH (All Saints) Louth Linc
ELKSTONE (St John the Baptist) Alstonfield, Butterton,
  Warslow w Elkstone etc Lich
ELKSTONE (St John the Evangelist) Brimpsfield, Cranham,
  Elkstone and Syde Glouc
ELLACOMBE (Christ Church) Torquay St Jo and
  Ellacombe Ex
ELLAND (All Saints) (St Mary the Virgin) Wakef 2 **P** Bp,
  Adn Halifax, and V Halifax (jt) **TR** N M WOOD,
  TV M R FREEMAN, **C** J R GARRARD,
  NSM B S COCKCROFT
ELLASTONE (St Peter) Denstone w Ellastone and Stanton
  Lich
ELLEL (St John the Evangelist) Blackb 12 **P** V Cockerham
  P-in-c A J GWILLIM
ELLENBROOK (St Mary's Chapel) Worsley Man
ELLENHALL (St Mary) Chebsey, Ellenhall and Seighford-
  with-Creswell Lich
ELLERBURNE (St Hilda) Thornton Dale and Ellerburne w
  Wilton York
ELLERBY (St James) Swine York
ELLERKER (not known) S Cave and Ellerker w Broomfleet
  York
**ELLESBOROUGH (St Peter and St Paul), The Kimbles and
  Stoke Mandeville** Ox 28 **P** Chequers Trustees, Hon I Hope-
  Morley, and D&C Linc (by turn) **R** A D WILLIS,
  NSM D J FREEMAN, H W HESLOP, N M DICK
ELLESMERE (St Mary) and Welsh Frankton Lich 22 **P** Bp
  V P J EDGE, **NSM** M W H GRAY
ELLESMERE (St Peter) Sheff 3 **P** Bp
  V F S K WAINAINA, **NSM** J L BROWN
ELLESMERE PORT Ches 9 **P** Bp **TR** D C GARNETT,
  TV R A WIFFEN, **C** M LEWIS
ELLINGHAM (St Mary) Gillingham w Geldeston, Stockton,
  Ellingham etc Nor
**ELLINGHAM (St Mary and All Saints) and Harbridge and
  Ibsley** Win 8 **P** Earl of Normanton **V** Vacant Ringwood
  (01425) 473723
ELLINGHAM (St Maurice) Beadnell w Ellingham Newc
**ELLINGHAM, LITTLE (St Peter) w GREAT (St James) w
  Rockland (All Saints) and (St Andrew and St Peter)** Nor 11
  P Bp and CCC Cam (alt) **R** M N WILLIAMS
ELLINGTON (All Saints) Ely 10 **P** Peterho Cam
  P-in-c J ALFORD
ELLISFIELD (St Martin) Cliddesden and Ellisfield w
  Farleigh Wallop etc Win
ELLISTOWN (St Christopher) Hugglescote w Donington,
  Ellistown and Snibston Leic
ELLOUGHTON (St Mary) and Brough w Brantingham
  York 14 **P** Abp and D&C Dur (jt) **V** W E J MASH,
  C J E PETERSEN
ELM (All Saints) Ely 19 **P** Bp **V** J E BARRETT
ELM (St Mary Magdalene) Mells w Buckland Dinham, Elm,
  Whatley etc B & W
ELM PARK (St Nicholas) Hornchurch Chelmsf 2 **P** Bp
  V R B LLOYD, **NSM** M S McCREADY
ELMBRIDGE (St Mary) Elmley Lovett w Hampton Lovett
  and Elmbridge etc Worc
ELMDON (St Nicholas) Heydon, Gt and Lt Chishill,
  Chrishall etc Chelmsf
**ELMDON (St Nicholas) (St Stephen's Church Centre) (St
  Nicholas's Hall)** Birm 13 **P** Ch Trust Fund Trust
  R A S GRAESSER
ELMDON HEATH (St Francis of Assisi) Solihull Birm
ELMESTHORPE (St Mary) Earl Shilton w Elmesthorpe Leic
ELMHAM, NORTH (St Mary) w Billingford and Worthing
  Nor 15 **P** Bp (1 turn), Viscount Coke (2 turns), and G & C
  Coll Cam (1 turn) **R** N TEWKESBURY
**ELMHAM, SOUTH (St Cross) (St James) (St Margaret) (St
  Peter) (St Michael and All Angels) and Ilketshall** St E 14
  P Bp (3 turns), Ld Chan (1 turn), and Duke of Norfolk
  (1 turn) **R** J M S FALKNER, **NSM** R A FINCH
ELMHURST (Mission Room) Lich St Chad Lich
**ELMLEY CASTLE (St Mary) w Bricklehampton and the
  Combertons** Worc 4 **P** Bp **R** S K CLARK
**ELMLEY LOVETT (St Michael) w Hampton Lovett and
  Elmbridge w Rushdock** Worc 8 **P** Bp and Ch Coll Cam
  (alt) **P-in-c** J READER
ELMORE (St John the Baptist) Hardwicke, Quedgeley and
  Elmore w Longney Glouc

ELMSALL, NORTH (St Margaret) Badsworth Wakef
ELMSALL, SOUTH (St Mary the Virgin) Wakef 11 **P** Bp
  V M E ROGERS, **C** S A STACEY (nee O'BRIEN)
ELMSETT (St Peter) w Aldham St E 3 **P** Bp and MMCET
  (alt) **P-in-c** I A WILSON
ELMSTEAD (St Anne and St Laurence) Chelmsf 21 **P** Jes
  Coll Cam **V** R G SMITH
ELMSTED (St James the Great) w Hastingleigh Cant 2
  P Abp **C** P G COX
ELMSTONE (not known) Wingham w Elmstone and Preston
  w Stourmouth Cant
ELMSTONE HARDWICKE (St Mary Magdalene) Swindon
  w Uckington and Elmstone Hardwicke Glouc
ELMSWELL (St John) St E 10 **P** MMCET
  R J A C PERROTT
ELMTON (St Peter) Derby 3 **P** Bp **V** B M CROWTHER-
  ALWYN
ELSDON (St Cuthbert) N Tyne and Redesdale Team Newc
ELSECAR (Holy Trinity) Sheff 7 **P** Sir Stephen Hastings
  V J G FAIRHURST
ELSENHAM (St Mary the Virgin) Henham and Elsenham w
  Ugley Chelmsf
ELSFIELD (St Thomas of Canterbury) Marston w Elsfield
  Ox
ELSHAM (All Saints) N Wolds Gp Linc
ELSING (St Mary) Lyng, Sparham, Elsing and Bylaugh Nor
ELSON (St Thomas) Portsm 3 **V** K W JACKSON
ELSTEAD (St James) Guildf 4 **P** Adn Surrey **R** W D LANG
ELSTED (St Paul) Harting w Elsted and Treyford cum
  Didling Chich
ELSTERNWICK (St Laurence) Burton Pidsea and
  Humbleton w Elsternwick York
ELSTON (All Saints) w Elston Chapelry S'well 3
  P J C S Darwin Esq **R** G A FIRTH
ELSTOW (St Mary and St Helena) St Alb 19
  P S C Whitbread Esq **V** R W HUBAND
ELSTREE (St Nicholas) St Alb 1 **P** Ld Chan
  R W J ELLIOTT
ELSWICK, HIGH (St Paul) Newc 7 **P** Trustees
  V B E SEAMAN
ELSWICK, HIGH (St Philip) Newc St Phil and St Aug Newc
ELSWICK, LOW (St Stephen) Newc 7 **P** Ch Soc Trust
  V G R CURRY
ELSWORTH (Holy Trinity) w Knapwell Ely 1 **P** Bp
  (4 turns), The Crown (1 turn) **R** H A MOSEDALE
ELTHAM (Holy Trinity) S'wark 1 **P** Bp **V** J P H JOHN,
  C G W OWEN, **Hon C** A GURNEY
ELTHAM (St Barnabas) S'wark 1 **P** Bp **V** J E NEAL
ELTHAM (St John the Baptist) S'wark 1 **P** DBP
  V P V L JOHNSTONE
ELTHAM (St Saviour) S'wark 1 **P** Bp **V** S M CAPLE
ELTHAM, NEW (All Saints) S'wark 1 **P** Bp
  V B M BRANCHE
ELTHAM PARK (St Luke) S'wark 1 **P** Bp
  V J C THEWLIS, **NSM** M J MABBS, I NASH
ELTISLEY (St Pandionia and St John the Baptist) Croxton
  and Eltisley Ely
ELTON (All Saints) S Darley, Elton and Winster Derby
ELTON (All Saints) Ely 13 **P** Sir Peter Proby
  R P O POOLEY
ELTON (All Saints) Man 10 **P** R Bury St Mary
  V I E WALTER, **C** I BLAY, **Hon C** P J BEDDINGTON
ELTON (no dedication) Longnewton w Elton Dur
ELTON (St Mary the Virgin) Wigmore Abbey Heref
ELTON (St Stephen) Man 10 **P** V Elton All SS
  V B J TURNER
ELTON-ON-THE-HILL (St Michael) Cropwell Bishop w
  Colston Bassett, Granby etc S'well
ELVASTON (St Bartholomew) and Shardlow Derby 15
  P Earl of Harrington and DBP (alt) **P-in-c** P E HARDING
ELVEDEN (St Andrew and St Patrick) Brandon and Santon
  Downham w Elveden St E
**ELVINGTON (Holy Trinity) w Sutton on Derwent and East
  Cottingwith** York 4 **P** Lt Col J Darlington **R** S E MUTCH
ELWICK HALL (St Peter) Hart w Elwick Hall Dur
ELWORTH (St Peter) and Warmingham Ches 11
  P V Sandbach, Q H Crewe Esq and J C Crewe Esq (alt)
  R C D JEFFERSON
ELY (Holy Trinity w St Mary) (St Peter) Ely 14 **P** D&C
  P-in-c F J KILNER, **C** A F PLEDGER, M E RABY
EMBERTON (All Saints) Olney w Emberton Ox
EMBLETON (Holy Trinity) w Rennington and Rock Newc 9
  P Mert Coll Ox **V** J M MOUNTNEY
EMBLETON (St Cuthbert) Cockermouth w Embleton and
  Wythop Carl
EMBROOK (Community of St Nicholas) Wokingham St
  Paul Ox

EMBSAY (St Mary the Virgin) w Eastby *Bradf 7*
P *R Skipton H Trin* **P-in-c** A KITCHEN
EMERY DOWN (Christ Church) Lyndhurst and Emery
Down *Win*
EMLEY (St Michael the Archangel) *Wakef 6* P *Lord Savile*
P-in-c J A WILLIAMS
EMMER GREEN (St Barnabas) *Ox 15* P *Bp*
R N J HARDCASTLE
EMMINGTON (St Nicholas) Chinnor w Emmington and
Sydenham etc *Ox*
EMNETH (St Edmund) *Ely 19* P *Bp* **P-in-c** J A COOMBS
EMPINGHAM (St Peter) and Exton w Horn w Whitwell
Pet 14 P *Bp and Earl of Gainsborough (alt)*
P-in-c B FERNYHOUGH
EMPSHOTT (Holy Rood) Greatham w Empshott and
Hawkley w Prior's Dean *Portsm*
EMSCOTE (All Saints) *Cov 11* P *Earl of Warw*
V A PLURY, C A G R BRISTOW, M G COZENS
EMSWORTH (St James) Warblington and Emsworth *Portsm*
ENBORNE (St Michael and All Angels) W Woodhay w
Enborne, Hampstead Marshall etc *Ox*
ENDCLIFFE (St Augustine) *Sheff 2* P *Ch Burgesses*
V M R GOATER
ENDERBY (St John the Baptist) w Lubbesthorpe and
Thurlaston *Leic 10* P *Bp and F B Drummond Esq*
V R A SHELLEY, Hon C T J R KING
ENDON (St Luke) w Stanley *Lich 13*
P *R Leek and Meerbrook* V E OSMAN,
NSM J FORRESTER
ENFIELD (Christ Church) Trent Park *Lon 18* P *Ch Trust*
Fund Trust V P A E REES, C J E ROBSON,
S J NORTHAM, A G PURSER
ENFIELD (St Andrew) *Lon 18* P *Trin Coll Cam*
V M M EDGE, C M G OATES, Hon C O R COPE
ENFIELD (St George) *Lon 18* P *Bp* V *Vacant Lea Valley*
(01992) 762581
ENFIELD (St James) (St Barnabas) *Lon 18* P *V Enfield*
V J M BOWERS, C R H WHITTINGTON, J D MITCHELL
ENFIELD (St Michael and All Angels) *Lon 18* P *V Enfield*
V G H G PLASTOW
ENFIELD (St Peter and St Paul) *Lon 18* P *Bp*
V J C VAUGHAN
ENFIELD CHASE (St Mary Magdalene) *Lon 18* P *Bp*
V J A SAMPFORD, NSM R H DUNN
ENFORD (All Saints) Avon Valley *Sarum*
ENGLEFIELD (St Mark) Theale and Englefield *Ox*
ENGLEFIELD GREEN (St Jude) *Guildf 11* P *Bp*
V J R V WOODS
ENGLISH BICKNOR (St Mary) Forest of Dean Ch Ch w
English Bicknor *Glouc*
ENGLISHCOMBE (St Peter) Bath St Barn w Englishcombe
B & W
ENHAM ALAMEIN (St George) Smannell w Enham
Alamein *Win*
ENMORE (St Michael) Spaxton w Goathurst, Enmore and
Charlynch *B & W*
ENMORE GREEN (St John the Evangelist) Shaston *Sarum*
ENNERDALE (St Mary) Lamplugh w Ennerdale *Carl*
ENSBURY PARK (St Thomas) *Sarum 8* P *Bp*
V E FARROW
ENSTONE (St Kenelm) and Heythrop *Ox 3* P *Bp*
V A R MOORE
ENVILLE (St Mary the Virgin) Kinver and Enville *Lich*
EPPERSTONE (Holy Cross) *S'well 11* P *Bp, Ld Chan, and*
Comdr M B P Francklin (by turn) R M J BROCK
EPPING District (All Saints) (St John the Baptist)
Chelmsf 26 P *Patr Bd* TR P W NOKES, TV C F J BARD,
J M GLASSPOOL, NSM J H B DODD, P A EVANS
EPPLETON (All Saints) *Dur 6* P *The Crown*
V J J STEPHENSON
EPSOM (St Barnabas) *Guildf 9* P *Bp* V M C PRESTON
EPSOM (St Martin) (St Stephen on the Downs) *Guildf 9*
P *Bp* V D A SMETHURST, C A J SHUTT, R C HOAD,
Hon C M D RANKEN
EPSOM COMMON (Christ Church) *Guildf 9* P *Bp*
V M J C WILSON, C C G POTTER, M K WILSON
EPWELL (St Anne) w Sibford, Swalcliffe and Tadmarton
Ox 5 P *Worc Coll Ox (1 turn), New Coll Ox (2 turns)*
R T WIMBUSH, NSM S T B FORBES ADAM
EPWORTH (St Andrew) and Wroot *Linc 1* P *Prime Min*
(2 turns), Ld Chan (1 turn) **P-in-c** J D BROWN
ERCALL MAGNA (St Michael and All Angels) (St Mary
Mission Church) *Lich 29* P *Lord Barnard* V K D MINTY
ERDINGTON (St Barnabas) *Birm 6* P *Aston Trustees*
V P R SPENCER
ERDINGTON (St Chad) *Birm 6* P *Bp* V A R BROOKS
ERIDGE GREEN (Holy Trinity) Frant w Eridge *Chich*
ERISWELL (St Laurence and St Peter) Mildenhall *St E*

ERITH (Christ Church) *Roch 14* P *Bp* V J DRAYCOTT
ERITH Northumberland Heath (St Paul) *Roch 14* P *C P A S*
V J R G WATSON, C I F DURNDELL
ERITH (St John the Baptist) *Roch 14* P *Bp* **P-in-c** J DAY,
C J DAY
ERLESTOKE (Holy Saviour) Edington and Imber, Erlestoke
and E Coulston *Sarum*
ERMINGTON (St Peter and St Paul) and Ugborough *Ex*
P *Prime Min (1 turn), Bp and Grocers' Co (jt) (3 turns)*
I E J PERRY
ERNESETTLE (St Aidan) *Ex 22* P *Bp* V G J SMITH
ERPINGHAM (St Mary) w Calthorpe, Ingworth, Aldborough,
Thurgarton and Alby w Thwaite *Nor 20* P *Bp, Lord*
Walpole, Gt Hosp Nor, Mrs S M Lilly, and DBP (by turn)
R B T FAULKNER
ERWARTON (St Mary the Virgin) Chelmondiston and
Erwarton w Harkstead *St E*
ERYHOLME (St Mary) Middleton Tyas w Croft and
Eryholme *Ripon*
ESCOMB (no dedication) *Dur 10* P *Bp* V N M J-
W BEDDOW
ESCOT (St Philip and St James) Feniton, Buckerell and Escot
Ex
ESCRICK (St Helen) and Stillingfleet w Naburn *York 4*
P *Abp, D&C, and N C Forbes Adam Esq (jt)*
R G D HARRIS
ESH (St Michael and All Angels) *Dur 8* P *The Crown*
P-in-c G M POCOCK, NSM S I WRIGHT
ESHER (Christ Church) (St George) *Guildf 8* P *Wadh Coll*
Ox R C M SCOTT, C J BROWN
ESHOLT (St Paul) Guiseley w Esholt *Bradf*
ESKDALE (St Catherine) (St Bega's Mission), Irton,
Muncaster and Waberthwaite *Carl 5* P *Bp, Adn*
W Cumberland, Mrs P Gordon-Duff-Pennington, and
P Stanley Esq (jt) V G M STONESTREET,
NSM I M HALL
ESKDALESIDE (St John) w Ugglebarnby and Sneaton
York 23 P *Abp* V N N JONES
ESSENDINE (St Mary the Virgin) Ryhall w Essendine *Pet*
ESSENDON (St Mary the Virgin) Lt Berkhamsted and
Bayford, Essendon etc *St Alb*
ESSINGTON (St John the Evangelist) *Lich 9* P *Bp,*
R Bushbury, R Wednesfield, and Simeon's Trustees (jt)
V B PRENTICE
ESTON (Christ Church) w Normanby *York 19* P *Abp*
TR A G C LEIGHTON, TV L N CAVAN
ESTOVER (Christ Church) *Ex 23* P *Bp* V T J WOODS,
C S F AUSTIN
ETAL (St Mary the Virgin) Ford and Etal *Newc*
ETCHILHAMPTON (St Andrew) Bishop's Cannings, All
Cannings etc *Sarum*
ETCHING HILL (The Holy Spirit) Rugeley *Lich*
ETCHINGHAM (Assumption and St Nicholas) *Chich 15*
P *Bp* R B C GURD
ETHERLEY (St Cuthbert) *Dur 10* P *Bp* R D G F HINGE
ETON (St John the Evangelist) Riverside *Ox*
ETON WICK (St John the Baptist) as above
ETTINGSHALL (Holy Trinity) *Lich 9* P *Bp* V A J JONES
ETTINGTON (Holy Trinity and St Thomas of
Canterbury) Butlers Marston and the Pillertons w
Ettington *Cov*
ETTON (St Mary) w Dalton Holme *York 9* P *Lord Hotham*
NSM J M WATERS
ETTON (St Stephen) w Helpston and Maxey *Pet 13* P *Sir*
Stephen Hastings (2 turns), D&C (1 turn) R *Vacant*
Peterborough (01733) 253456
ETWALL (St Helen) w Egginton *Derby 14* P *Bp,*
Sir H J M Every, Major J W Chandos-Pole, and DBP
(by turn) **P-in-c** S L RAYNER
EUSTON (St Genevieve) Blackbourne *St E*
EUXTON (not known) *Blackb 4* P *Bp* V P D TAYLOR
EVEDON (St Mary) Kirkby Laythorpe *Linc*
EVENLEY (St George) Aynho and Croughton w Evenley *Pet*
EVENLODE (St Edward King and Martyr) Broadwell,
Evenlode, Oddington and Adlestrop *Glouc*
EVENWOOD (St Paul) *Dur 11* P *Bp* **P-in-c** G LIDDLE
EVERCREECH (St Peter) w Chesterblade and Milton
Clevedon *B & W 2* P *DBP* V R J M WILLCOX
EVERDON (St Mary) Weedon Bec w Everdon *Pet*
EVERINGHAM (St Everilda) Seaton Ross Gp of Par *York*
EVERSDEN, GREAT (St Mary) Haslingfield w Harlton and
Gt and Lt Eversden *Ely*
EVERSDEN, LITTLE (St Helen) as above
EVERSHOLT (St John the Baptist) Woburn w Eversholt,
Milton Bryan, Battlesden etc *St Alb*
EVERSHOT (St Osmund) Melbury *Sarum*

EVERSLEY (St Mary) *Win 5* **P** *DBP* **R** G D FULLER
EVERTON (Holy Trinity) and Mattersey w Clayworth
S'well 1 **P** *Ld Chan (2 turns), Bp (2 turns)*
R G A MUMFORD
EVERTON (St George) *Liv 3* **P** *Bp* **V** P H SPIERS,
C D P WILLIAMS
EVERTON (St John Chrysostom) (Emmanuel) *Liv 3* **P** *Adn,
CPAS, and PCC (jt)* **V** *Vacant* 0151–263 3755
EVERTON (St Mary) Milford *Win*
EVERTON (St Mary) w Tetworth *Ely 12* **P** *Clare Coll Cam*
P-in-c B CURRY
EVERTON (St Peter) *Liv 3* **P** *Patr Bd* **TR** H CORBETT
EVESBATCH (St Andrew) Acton Beauchamp and Evesbatch
w Stanford Bishop *Heref*
EVESHAM (All Saints w St Lawrence) *Worc 1* **P** *Bp*
V R N ARMITAGE, **NSM** A E WHITEHOUSE
EVINGTON (St Denys) *Leic 1* **P** *Bp* **V** C FINCH,
C I L JOHNSON, S F REDGRAVE, **Hon C** S A PATERSON
EVINGTON (St Stephen) Twigworth, Down Hatherley,
Norton, The Leigh etc *Glouc*
EVINGTON, NORTH (St Stephen) *Leic 1* **P** *Bp*
P-in-c I St C RICHARDS, **NSM** W C BURLEIGH
EWELL (St Francis of Assisi) Ruxley Lane *Guildf 9* **P** *Bp*
V S G THOMAS
EWELL (St Mary the Virgin) *Guildf 9* **P** *Bp*
V W R HANFORD, **Hon Par Dn** A J LYNN
EWELL, WEST (All Saints) *Guildf 9* **P** *Bp* **V** A J HURD
EWELME (St Mary the Virgin), Brightwell Baldwin, Cuxham
w Easington *Ox 1* **P** *F D Wright Esq and Mert Coll Ox,
Prime Min (alt)* **R** M W GARNER
EWERBY (St Andrew) Kirkby Laythorpe *Linc*
EWHURST (St James the Great) *Chich 20* **P** *K Coll Cam*
P-in-c R K BAKER, **C** A WILLIAMS
EWHURST (St Peter and St Paul) *Guildf 2* **P** *Ld Chan*
R D H LEWIS
EWOOD (St Bartholomew) *Blackb 5* **P** *Bp* **V** *Vacant*
Blackburn (01254) 251206
EWSHOT (St Mary the Virgin) Crondall and Ewshot *Guildf*
EWYAS HAROLD (St Michael and All Angels) w Dulas,
Kenderchurch, Abbeydore, Bacton, Kentchurch, Llangua,
Rowlestone, Llancillo, Walterstone, Kilpeck, St Devereux and
Wormbridge *Heref 1* **P** *Patr Bd* **P-in-c** A L MOORE,
C E C GARRETT
EXBOURNE (St Mary the Virgin) Hatherleigh, Meeth,
Exbourne and Jacobstowe *Ex*
EXBURY (St Katherine) Beaulieu and Exbury and E Boldre
Win
EXE, WEST (St Paul) *Ex 8* **P** *Peache Trustees*
P-in-c M J PARTRIDGE
EXE VALLEY Washfield, Stoodleigh, Withleigh etc *Ex*
EXETER (St David) (St Michael and All Angels) *Ex 3*
P *D&C* **V** J M HENTON, **C** P BENTLEY, **NSM** P A LEE
EXETER (St James) *Ex 3* **P** *D&C* **R** B R TUBBS,
C C E DEACON
EXETER (St Leonard w Holy Trinity) *Ex 3* **P** *CPAS*
R J C SKINNER, **C** H J CUNNINGTON,
NSM J F SEARLE
EXETER (St Mark) *Ex 3* **P** *Bp* **P-in-c** S CROFT,
NSM R J A BARRETT
EXETER (St Mary Steps) *Ex 3* **P** *SMF* **R** *Vacant* Exeter
(01392) 77685
EXETER (St Paul) Heavitree w Ex St Paul *Ex*
EXETER (St Sidwell) (St Matthew) *Ex 3* **P** *D&C*
C P K CRANCH
EXETER (St Thomas the Apostle) (Emmanuel) (St Andrew)
(St Philip) *Ex 3* **P** *Bp* **TR** A WHITE, **TV** D B M GILL,
R A BOWYER, **C** N T MACNEILL
EXETER, CENTRAL (St Martin) (St Mary Arches)
(St Olave) (St Pancras) (St Petrock) (St Stephen) *Ex 3*
P *Patr Bd* **TR** M R SELMAN, **Hon C** M J HATT,
NSM A A HALL
EXFORD (St Mary Magdalene), Exmoor, Hawkridge and
Withypool *B & W 16* **P** *Bp (1 turn), Peterho Cam
(2 turns)* **R** R J RAY
EXHALL (St Giles) *Cov 5* **P** *Bp* **V** M POWELL,
C S L BUSHELL
EXHALL (St Giles) w Wixford *Cov 7* **V** E F WILLIAMS
EXMINSTER (St Martin) and Kenn *Ex 6* **P** *Mrs M P L Bate
and 12 Govs of Crediton Ch (jt)* **R** *Vacant* Exeter (01392)
824283
EXMOOR (St Luke) Exford, Exmoor, Hawkridge and
Withypool *B & W*
EXMOUTH (All Saints) Withycombe Raleigh *Ex*
EXMOUTH (Holy Trinity) Littleham w Exmouth *Ex*
EXMOUTH (St Andrew) as above
EXMOUTH (St Saviour) as above
EXNING (St Agnes) Newmarket St Mary w Exning St Agnes
St E

EXNING (St Martin) (St Philip) w Landwade *St E 11*
P *D&C Cant* **V** C T CATTON, **C** P J LILEY,
NSM C T McCARTY
EXTON (St Andrew) Woodbury *Ex*
EXTON (St Peter and St Paul) Empingham and Exton w
Horn w Whitwell *Pet*
EXTON (St Peter and St Paul) Meonstoke w Corhampton
cum Exton *Portsm*
EXTON (St Peter) and Winsford and Cutcombe w Luxborough
B & W 16 **P** *Ld Chan (2 turns), Em Coll Cam (1 turn), and
G A Warren Esq and D M Warren Esq (1 turn)*
R C J BUDDEN
EXWICK (St Andrew) *Ex 3* **P** *Lord Wraxall*
V J FAIRWEATHER
EYAM (St Lawrence) *Derby 2* **P** *Earl Temple* **R** D G SHAW
EYDON (St Nicholas) Woodford Halse w Eydon *Pet*
EYE (St Matthew) *Pet 13* **P** *Bp* **V** S CHOLROYD
EYE (St Peter and St Paul) w Braiseworth and Yaxley
St E 16 **P** *SMF* **V** R H SMITH
EYE (St Peter and St Paul), Croft w Yarpole and Lucton
Heref 7 **P** *Exors Mrs E Parr (2 turns), Ld Chan (2 turns),
Lucton Sch (1 turn)* **P-in-c** M W HOOPER
EYEWORTH (All Saints) Dunton w Wrestlingworth and
Eyeworth *St Alb*
EYKE (All Saints) w Bromeswell, Rendlesham, Tunstall and
Wantisden *St E 7* **P** *Bp, Mrs R M L Darling,
J H Kemball Esq, and MMCET (jt)* **P-in-c** N D G DEAR
EYNESBURY (St Mary) *Ely 12* **P** *Bp* **R** T J McCABE
EYNSFORD (St Martin) w Farningham and Lullingstone
Roch 9 **P** *D&C* **R** R A FREEMAN
EYNSHAM (St Leonard) and Cassington *Ox 9* **P** *Wycliffe
Hall Ox and Ch Ch Ox (alt)* **V** I R BENTLEY,
C T R DAVIES, **NSM** C A W SANDERS
EYPE (St Peter) Symondsbury and Chideock *Sarum*
EYRES MONSELL (St Hugh) *Leic 2* **P** *Bp* **V** D J YOUNG
EYTHORNE (St Peter and St Paul) and Elvington w
Waldershare and Barfreystone w Sherdswell and Coldred
Cant 4 **P** *Abp, St Jo Coll Ox, and Earl of Guilford (jt)*
R L P SMITH, **NSM** M G HINTON, P M O OLIVER,
M M MOWER
EYTON (All Saints) Leominster *Heref*
EYTON (St Catherine) Wellington, All SS w Eyton *Lich*
FACCOMBE (St Barnabas) Hurstbourne Tarrant,
Faccombe, Vernham Dean etc *Win*
FACEBY (St Mary Magdalene) Whorlton w Carlton and
Faceby *York*
FACIT (St John the Evangelist) (St Michael the Archangel)
Man 20 **P** *Bp* **V** *Vacant* Whitworth (01706) 853931
FAILAND (St Bartholomew) Wraxall *B & W*
FAILSWORTH (Holy Family) *Man 19* **P** *Bp*
R P R LOMAS
FAILSWORTH (Holy Trinity) *Man 19* **P** *The Crown*
R R W STEPHENS
FAILSWORTH (St John) (St John the Evangelist) *Man 19*
P *Bp* **R** *Vacant* 0161–681 2734
FAIR OAK (St Thomas) *Win 9* **P** *Bp* **V** K M BELL
FAIRBURN (St James) Ledsham w Fairburn *York*
FAIRFIELD (St John the Divine) *Liv 3* **P** *MMCET*
V D J ROWLAND
FAIRFIELD (St Mark) Belbroughton w Fairfield and Clent
Worc
FAIRFIELD (St Matthew) *Linc 9* **P** *Bp* **V** D P ROWETT
FAIRFIELD (St Peter) *Derby 4* **P** *Ch Govs*
V A J SIDEBOTTOM, **NSM** P D BRIDGWATER
FAIRFIELD (St Thomas a Becket) Appledore w Brookland,
Fairfield, Brenzett etc *Cant*
FAIRFORD (St Mary the Virgin) *Glouc 13* **P** *D&C*
V P J GREEN
FAIRHAVEN (St Paul) *Blackb 11* **P** *J C Hilton Esq*
V J R HASLAM
FAIRLIGHT, Guestling and Pett *Chich 20* **P** *Patr Bd*
R J R BALCH, **Hon C** D M OWEN
FAIRSEAT (Holy Innocents) Stansted w Fairseat and Vigo
Roch
FAIRSTEAD (St Mary) w Terling and White Notley w
Faulkbourne *Chelmsf 25* **P** *Bp, Exors Lord Rayleigh, and
C W O Parker Esq (by turn)* **R** J M HALL
FAIRWARP (Christ Church) *Chich 21* **P** *Bp*
P-in-c I GIBSON
FAIRWEATHER GREEN (St Saviour) *Bradf 1* **P** *Bp*
V S BETSON
FAKENHAM (St Peter and St Paul) w Alethorpe *Nor 16*
P *Trin Coll Cam* **R** A J BELL, **C** C S R WALTER
FAKENHAM MAGNA (St Peter) Blackbourne *St E*
FALCONWOOD (Bishop Ridley Church) *Roch 14* **P** *Bp*
V R J IRETON

FALDINGWORTH (All Saints) Wickenby Gp *Linc*

FALFIELD (St George) w Rockhampton *Glouc 7* **P** *Adn Glouc, V Thornbury, J Leigh Esq, and Bp (by turn)* **P-in-c** R W MARTIN

FALINGE (St Edmund) Rochdale *Man*

FALKENHAM (St Ethelbert) Kirton w Falkenham *St E*

FALMER (St Laurence) Stanmer w Falmer *Chich*

FALMOUTH (All Saints) *Truro 3* **P** *Bp* **V** J S SCANTLEBURY

FALMOUTH (King Charles the Martyr) *Truro 3* **P** *Bp* **R** R G GILBERT, **C** E B L BROWNING, **NSM** J B BENNETTS

FALSTONE (St Peter) N Tyne and Redesdale Team *Newc*

FAMBRIDGE, NORTH (Holy Trinity) Creeksea w Althorne, Latchingdon and N Fambridge *Chelmsf*

FAMBRIDGE, SOUTH (All Saints) Ashingdon w S Fambridge *Chelmsf*

FANGFOSS (St Martin) Barmby Moor w Allerthorpe, Fangfoss and Yapham *York*

FAR FOREST (Holy Trinity) Mamble w Bayton, Rock w Heightington etc *Worc*

FAR HEADINGLEY St Chad (St Oswald) *Ripon 7* **P** *Lord Grimthorpe* **V** B M OVEREND, **C** J P CLARKE, S C COWLING

FARCET (St Mary) Stanground and Farcet *Ely*

FAREHAM (Holy Trinity) (St Columba) *Portsm 2* **P** *Bp* **TR** I J AGGER, **TV** A TREMLETT, **C** N R RALPH, **Hon C** A P BURR, **NSM** D M JACKSON, R V JAGGER

FAREHAM (St John the Evangelist) *Portsm 2* **P** *CPAS* **V** H CHANT

FAREHAM (St Peter and St Paul) *Portsm 2* **P** *Bp* **V** R C H FRANKLIN, **C** R A WHITE

FAREWELL (St Bartholomew) *Lich 1* **P** *MMCET* **P-in-c** M J BUTT

FARFORTH (St Peter) S Ormsby Gp *Linc*

FARINGDON, GREAT (All Saints) w Little Coxwell *Ox 17* **P** *Simeon's Trustees* **V** A J BAILEY, **NSM** M R STARR

FARINGDON, LITTLE (not known) Shill Valley and Broadshire *Ox*

FARINGTON (St Paul) *Blackb 6* **P** *V Penwortham* **V** P E M HOLLANDS

FARLAM (St Thomas a Becket) Brampton and Farlam and Castle Carrock w Cumrew *Carl*

FARLEIGH (St Mary) Warlingham w Chelsham and Farleigh *S'wark*

FARLEIGH, EAST (not known) Coxheath w E Farleigh, Hunton and Linton *Roch*

FARLEIGH, WEST (All Saints) Wateringbury w Teston and W Farleigh *Roch*

FARLEIGH HUNGERFORD (St Leonard) Rode Major *B & W*

FARLEIGH WALLOP (St Andrew) Cliddesden and Ellisfield w Farleigh Wallop etc *Win*

FARLESTHORPE (St Andrew) Bilsby w Farlesthorpe *Linc*

FARLEY (All Saints) Alderbury Team *Sarum*

FARLEY CHAMBERLAYNE (St John) Michelmersh, Timsbury, Farley Chamberlayne etc *Win*

FARLEY GREEN (St Michael) Albury w St Martha *Guildf*

FARLEY HILL (St John the Baptist) *St Alb 20* **P** *Bp* **V** R E MERRY

FARLEY HILL (St John the Evangelist) Swallowfield *Ox*

FARLINGTON (St Andrew) (Church of the Resurrection) *Portsm 6* **P** *Dr R A L Leatherdale and E G Nugee Esq (jt)* **R** J R PINDER, **C** C B RANKINE, **NSM** J L FELLOWS

FARLINGTON (St Leonard) Sheriff Hutton and Farlington *York*

FARLOW (St Giles) Stottesdon w Farlow, Cleeton and Silvington *Heref*

FARMBOROUGH (All Saints) and Marksbury and Stanton Prior *B & W 9* **P** *MMCET (3 turns), Duchy of Cornwall (1 turn), and DBF (1 turn)* **R** A KENNEDY

FARMCOTE (St Faith) The Guitings, Cutsdean and Farmcote *Glouc*

FARMINGTON (St Peter) Northleach w Hampnett and Farmington *Glouc*

FARMOOR (St Mary) Cumnor *Ox*

FARNBOROUGH (All Saints) Beedon and Peasemore w W Ilsley and Farnborough *Ox*

FARNBOROUGH (St Botolph) Avon Dassett w Farnborough and Fenny Compton *Cov*

FARNBOROUGH (St Giles) (St Nicholas) *Roch 15* **P** *Em Coll Cam* **C** W A CRANIDGE

FARNBOROUGH (St Peter) *Guildf 1* **P** *CPAS* **R** A C P RODDINGTON, **C** A L FLOWERDAY, S D PAYNTER, E B PHILLIPS, **NSM** M JAMES

FARNBOROUGH, SOUTH (St Mark) *Guildf 1* **P** *Bp* **V** I C HEDGES

FARNCOMBE (St John the Evangelist) *Guildf 4* **P** *Bp* **R** T W KING, **C** D HENLEY

FARNDALE (St Mary) Kirkbymoorside w Gillamoor, Farndale & Bransdale *York*

FARNDON (St Chad) and Coddington *Ches 5* **P** *Duke of Westmr and D&C (jt)* **V** D A BOYD

FARNDON (St Peter) w Thorpe, Hawton and Cotham *S'well 3* **P** *Ld Chan* **R** J B QUARRELL

FARNDON, EAST (St John the Baptist) Arthingworth, Harrington w Oxendon and E Farndon *Pet*

FARNHAM (St Andrew) *Guildf 3* **P** *Bp* **R** A K TUCK, **C** M S NICHOLLS, S E FORD, **NSM** M BLAKE

FARNHAM (St Laurence) Tollard Royal w Farnham, Gussage St Michael etc *Sarum*

FARNHAM (St Mary) Gt and Lt Glemham, Blaxhall etc *St E*

FARNHAM (St Mary the Virgin) *Chelmsf 22* **P** *Lt-Col W D Gosling* **P-in-c** R WALLACE

FARNHAM (St Oswald) w Scotton and Staveley and Copgrove and Arkendale *Ripon 1* **P** *Bp, DBP, R Knaresborough, MMCET, and Major Sir Arthur Collins (jt)* **R** P GARNER

FARNHAM COMMON (St John the Evangelist) Farnham Royal w Hedgerley *Ox*

FARNHAM ROYAL (St Mary the Virgin) w Hedgerley *Ox 23* **P** *Bp and Eton Coll (jt)* **R** M D SMITH, **C** P A ROBERTS, **NSM** S F BEDWELL

FARNHAM ROYAL SOUTH (St Michael) W Slough *Ox*

FARNINGHAM (St Peter and St Paul) Eynsford w Farningham and Lullingstone *Roch*

FARNLEY (All Saints) Leathley w Farnley, Fewston and Blubberhouses *Bradf*

FARNLEY (St Michael) *Ripon 6* **P** *Bp* **R** *Vacant* Leeds (0113) 263 8064

FARNLEY, NEW (St James) Farnley *Ripon*

FARNLEY TYAS (St Lucias) Almondbury w Farnley Tyas *Wakef*

FARNSFIELD (St Michael) *S'well 15* **P** *Bp* **V** D J BARTLETT, **NSM** F CLARKE

FARNWORTH (All Saints) E Farnworth and Kearsley *Man*

FARNWORTH (St George) New Bury *Man*

FARNWORTH (St John) E Farnworth and Kearsley *Man*

FARNWORTH (St Luke) (Bold Mission) (Cronton Mission) *Liv 13* **P** *V Prescot St Mary* **V** M C FREEMAN

FARNWORTH (St Peter) E Farnworth and Kearsley *Man*

FARNWORTH, EAST (All Saints) (St John) (St Peter) (St Thomas) and Kearsley *Man 12* **P** *Bp (2 turns), Ld Chan (1 turn)* **TR** D T N PARRY, **TV** B HARTLEY, F M SHAW, **Hon C** M M PARRY

FARRINGDON (All Saints) Chawton and Farringdon *Win*

FARRINGDON (St Petrock and St Barnabas) Aylesbeare, Rockbeare, Farringdon etc *Ex*

FARRINGTON GURNEY (St John the Baptist) *B & W 12* **P** *Bp* **V** R E INGLESBY

FARSLEY (St John the Evangelist) *Bradf 3* **P** *V Calverley* **V** J N WHITE

FARTHINGHOE (St Michael and All Angels) w Hinton-in-the-Hedges w Steane *Pet 1* **P** *Ld Chan and Bp (alt)* **R** M BERRY

FARTHINGSTONE (St Mary the Virgin) Blakesley w Adstone and Maidford etc *Pet*

FARWAY (St Michael and All Angels) Colyton, Southleigh, Offwell, Widworthy etc *Ex*

FATFIELD (St George) *Dur 1* **P** *Lord Lambton* **P-in-c** R S WILSON, **C** A J FARISH

FAULKBOURNE (St Germanus) Fairstead w Terling and White Notley etc *Chelmsf*

FAULS (Holy Emmanuel) *Lich 28* **P** *V Prees* **V** D J TITLEY

FAVERSHAM (St Mary of Charity) *Cant 6* **P** *D&C* **V** G R D MANLEY, **C** D G RIDLEY

FAWDON (St Mary the Virgin) Newc Epiphany *Newc*

FAWKENHURST *Cant 12* **P** *DBP* **R** *Vacant*

FAWKHAM (St Mary) and Hartley *Roch 1* **P** *Bp and D&C (jt)* **R** G B McCORMACK

FAWLEY (All Saints) *Win 10* **P** *Bp* **R** G J PHILBRICK, **C** C F PETTET

FAWLEY (St Mary) Brightwalton w Catmore, Leckhampstead etc *Ox*

FAWLEY (St Mary the Virgin) Hambleden Valley *Ox*

FAWSLEY (St Mary the Virgin) Badby w Newham and Charwelton w Fawsley etc *Pet*

FAZAKERLEY (Emmanuel) (St Paul) *Liv 7* **P** *Patr Bd* **TR** D H HARRISON, **TV** R J DRIVER, J E DUFFIELD

FAZAKERLEY Sparrow Hall (St George) Fazakerley Em *Liv*

FAZAKERLEY (St Nathanael) Walton-on-the-Hill *Liv*
FAZELEY (St Paul) (St Barnabas) *Lich 4* **P** *Bp*
  V H J BAKER
FEATHERSTONE (All Saints) *Wakef 11* **P** *Ch Ch Ox*
  V N CLEWS
FEATHERSTONE (School Chapel) Haltwhistle and
  Greenhead *Newc*
FECKENHAM (St John the Baptist) Bowbrook N *Worc*
FEERING (All Saints) *Chelmsf 20* **P** *Bp* **V** A R MOODY
FELBRIDGE (St John) *S'wark 24* **P** *DBP* **V** S G BOWEN
FELBRIGG (St Margaret) Roughton and Felbrigg, Metton,
  Sustead etc *Nor*
FELIXKIRK (St Felix) w Boltby *York 20* **P** *Abp*
  P-in-c P R A R HOARE
FELIXSTOWE (St John the Baptist) (St Edmund) *St E 2*
  P *Bp* **V** K FRANCIS, **C** J R GLAISTER
FELIXSTOWE (St Peter and St Paul) (St Andrew)
  (St Nicholas) *St E 2* **P** *Ch Trust Fund Trust*
  V H L BOREHAM
FELKIRK (St Peter) w Brierley *Wakef 7* **P** *Bp*
  V A N DAWKINS
FELLING (Christ Church) *Dur 4* **P** *CPAS* **V** M HOUGH
FELLISCLIFFE (Mission Church) Hampsthwaite and
  Killinghall *Ripon*
FELMERSHAM (St Mary) *St Alb 21* **P** *Bp*
  P-in-c D E CLAYPOLE WHITE
FELMINGHAM (St Andrew), Skeyton, Colby, Banningham,
  Tuttington and Suffield *Nor 12* **P** *Bp, D&C, P H C Barber*
  Esq, and J T D Shaw Esq (jt) **R** T S LAWES
FELPHAM (St Mary the Virgin) w Middleton *Chich 1*
  P *D&C* **R** R D HARRIS
FELSHAM (St Peter) Cockfield w Bradfield St Clare,
  Felsham etc *St E*
FELSTED (Holy Cross) *Chelmsf 16* **P** *CPAS*
  P-in-c D A HOLGATE
FELTHAM (Christ Church) (St Dunstan) *Lon 11* **P** *Bp*
  V P R WRAGG, **C** M WALTER, **NSM** M J COLLETT
FELTHORPE (St Margaret) Drayton w Felthorpe *Nor*
FELTON (St Katharine and the Noble Army of
  Martyrs) Winford w Felton Common Hill *B & W*
FELTON (St Michael and All Angels) *Newc 9* **P** *Bp*
  V *Vacant* Felton (01670) 787263
FELTON (St Michael the Archangel) Bodenham w Hope-
  under-Dinmore, Felton etc *Heref*
FELTON, WEST (St Michael) *Lich 24* **P** *Bp*
  R A M BRANNAGAN
FELTWELL (St Mary) w St Nicholas *Ely 15* **P** *Bp*
  P-in-c P J SHEPHERD
FEN DITTON (Holy Cross) (St Mary Magdalene) (St Mary
  the Virgin) *Ely 6* **P** *Bp* **V** L A MARSH
FEN DRAYTON (St Mary the Virgin) w Conington *Ely 5*
  P *The Crown and Ch Coll Cam (alt)* **V** J D YULE
FENCE-IN-PENDLE (St Anne) and Newchurch-in-Pendle
  Blackb 7 **P** *Ld Chan* **V** T N HOWARD,
  NSM E J BOOTH
FENCOTE (St Andrew) Kirkby Fleetham w Langton on
  Swale and Scruton *Ripon*
FENHAM (St James and St Basil) *Newc 7* **P** *Bp*
  V V G ASHWIN, **C** J M BREARLEY
FENISCLIFFE (St Francis) *Blackb 5* **P** *Bp* **V** P D LAW-
  JONES
FENISCOWLES (Immanuel) *Blackb 5* **P** *V Blackb*
  V J R CREE, **NSM** M J WEDGEWORTH
FENITON (St Andrew), Buckerell and Escot *Ex 7* **P** *DBP,*
  D&C and J M Kennaway Esq (jt) **P-in-c** R J GORDON
FENNY BENTLEY (St Edmund King and Martyr), Kniveton,
  Thorpe and Tissington *Derby 8* **P** *Bp and Sir John*
  FitzHerbert, Bt (jt) **R** V C BROWN
FENNY DRAYTON (St Michael and All Angels) Higham-
  on-the-Hill w Fenny Drayton and Witherley *Leic*
FENNY STRATFORD (St Martin) *Ox 25* **P** *Bp*
  V S L HUCKLE, **NSM** I W THOMAS
FENSTANTON (St Peter and St Paul) *Ely 9* **P** *Bp*
  V P S G CAMERON
FENTON (All Saints) Brant Broughton and Beckingham
  Linc
FENTON (Christ Church) *Lich 17* **P** *R Stoke-on-Trent*
  NSM A H TOWNSEND
FENWICK and MOSS (St John) Fishlake w Sykehouse, Kirk
  Bramwith, Fenwick etc *Sheff*
FEOCK (St Feock) *Truro 6* **P** *Bp* **P-in-c** D J P HEWLETT,
  NSM I F FRITH
FERHAM PARK (St Paul) Masbrough *Sheff*
FERNDOWN (St Mary) Hampreston *Sarum*
FERNHAM (St John the Evangelist) Ashbury, Compton
  Beauchamp and Longcot w Fernham *Ox*
FERNHURST (St Margaret) *Chich 10* **P** *Cowdray Trust*
  V W S CROFT

FERNILEE (Holy Trinity) Whaley Bridge *Ches*
FERRIBY, NORTH (All Saints) *York 15* **P** *Patr Bd*
  TR C J ASTILL, **TV** R H O HILL
FERRIBY, SOUTH (St Nicholas) *Linc 6* **P** *Bp* **R** *Vacant*
  Barton on Humber (01469) 635258
FERRING (St Andrew) *Chich 5* **P** *D&C* **V** A K McNICOL
FERRYBRIDGE (St Andrew) *Wakef 11* **P** *D&C York*
  V G HOLLAND
FERRYHILL (St Luke) (St Martha and St Mary) *Dur 14*
  P *D&C* **V** K LUMSDON, **C** I H JORYSZ
FERSFIELD (St Andrew) Bressingham w N and S Lopham
  and Fersfield *Nor*
FETCHAM (St Mary) *Guildf 10* **P** *Bp* **R** D J BAKER
FEWSTON (St Michael and St Lawrence) Leathley w
  Farnley, Fewston and Blubberhouses *Bradf*
FIDDINGTON (St Martin) Stogursey w Fiddington *B & W*
FIELD BROUGHTON (St Peter) Lindale w Field Broughton
  Carl
FIELD DALLING (St Andrew) Gunthorpe w Bale w Field
  Dalling, Saxlingham etc *Nor*
FIFEHEAD MAGDALEN (St Mary Magdalene) Gillingham
  Sarum
FIFEHEAD NEVILLE (All Saints) Hazelbury Bryan and the
  Hillside Par *Sarum*
FIFIELD (St John the Baptist) Shipton-under-Wychwood w
  Milton-under-Wychwood *Ox*
FIFIELD BAVANT (St Martin) Chalke Valley W *Sarum*
FIGHELDEAN (St Michael and All Angels) Avon Valley
  Sarum
FILBY (All Saints), Thrigby, Mautby, Stokesby, Runham and
  Burgh w Billockby *Nor 6* **P** *Bp, Adn Nor, DBP,*
  Mrs Z K Cognetti, R T Daniel Esq, and I F M Lucas Esq (jt)
  R *Vacant* Great Yarmouth (01493) 369237
FILEY (St John) (St Oswald) *York 16* **P** *PCC*
  V C W HUMPHRIES, **C** N P ARMSTRONG,
  E BUTTERWORTH
FILKINS (St Peter) Shill Valley and Broadshire *Ox*
FILLEIGH (St Paul) S Molton w Nymet St George, High
  Bray etc *Ex*
FILLINGHAM (St Andrew) Ingham w Cammeringham w
  Fillingham *Linc*
FILLONGLEY (St Mary and All Saints) and Corley *Cov 5*
  P *Bp and Ch Soc Trust (jt)* **V** J F LAW
FILTON (St Peter) *Bris 6* **P** *Bp* **R** B R ARMAN,
  NSM E M DESMOND
FIMBER (St Mary) Sledmere and Cowlam w Fridaythorpe,
  Fimer etc *York*
FINBOROUGH, GREAT (St Andrew) w Onehouse and
  Harleston *St E 6* **P** *Bp* **P-in-c** N J HARTLEY
FINBOROUGH, LITTLE (St Mary) Hitcham w Lt
  Finborough *St E*
FINCHAM (St Martin) *Ely 16* **P** *Bp* **P-in-c** G PARROTT
FINCHAMPSTEAD (St James) *Ox 16* **P** *DBP*
  R D T CROSSLEY
FINCHFIELD (St Thomas) Tettenhall Wood *Lich*
FINCHINGFIELD (St John the Baptist) and Cornish Hall End
  Chelmsf 16 **P** *Mrs E M Bishop* **P-in-c** J F H SHEAD
FINCHLEY (Christ Church) *Lon 14* **P** *Ch Patr Trust*
  V T D ATKINS, **C** W J MUSSON
FINCHLEY (Holy Trinity) *Lon 16* **P** *Bp* **V** L B HILL
FINCHLEY (St Mary) *Lon 14* **P** *Bp* **R** D J BARNETT,
  C D H P BROWN, J M YATES
FINCHLEY (St Paul) (St Luke) *Lon 14* **P** *Simeon Trustees*
  and Ch Patr Trust (jt) **V** P M TEMPLEMAN,
  C A G THOM
FINCHLEY, EAST (All Saints) *Lon 14* **P** *Bp*
  V C R HARDY
FINDERN (All Saints) *Derby 16* **P** *Bp* **V** C R WILSON
FINDON (St John the Baptist) w Clapham and Patching
  Chich 5 **P** *Abp, Bp, and J E P Somerset Esq (jt)*
  V Z E ALLEN
FINDON VALLEY (All Saints) *Chich 5* **P** *Bp*
  V Q M RONCHETTI
FINEDON (St Mary the Virgin) *Pet 10* **P** *Bp*
  V J P BEAUMONT
FINGEST (St Bartholomew) Hambleden Valley *Ox*
FINGHALL (St Andrew) Spennithorne w Finghall and
  Hauxwell *Ripon*
FINGRINGHOE (St Andrew) w East Donyland and Abberton
  w Langenhoe *Chelmsf 17* **P** *Bp (3 turns), Ld Chan (1*
  turn) **R** R J HANDSCOMBE, **C** R WILKINSON
FINHAM (St Martin in the Fields) *Cov 3* **P** *Bp*
  V D T PETTIFOR, **C** D E KERR
FINMERE (St Michael) w Mixbury, Cottisford, Hardwick w
  Tusmore and Newton Purcell w Shelswell *Ox 2* **P** *Bp,*
  J F Vallings Esq, and Baroness von Maltzahn (jt)
  R W J YATES

FINNINGHAM (St Bartholomew) Walsham le Willows and
Finningham w Westhorpe *St E*
FINNINGLEY (Holy Trinity and St Oswald) w Auckley
S'well 1 **P** *DBP* **R** JDJGOODMAN,
NSM JFCHAFFEY
FINSBURY (St Clement) (St Barnabas) (St Matthew) *Lon 5*
P *D&C St Paul's* **V** *Vacant* 0171–2539140
FINSBURY PARK (St Thomas) *Lon 5* **P** *Abp*
V SRCOLES
FINSTALL (St Godwald) *Worc 7* **P** *V Stoke Prior*
V FTHOLT
FINSTHWAITE (St Peter) Leven Valley *Carl*
FIR TREE (St Mary the Virgin) Howden-le-Wear and
Hunwick *Dur*
FIR VALE (St Cuthbert) Sheff St Cuth *Sheff*
FIRBANK (St John the Evangelist), Howgill and Killington
Bradf 6 **P** *Ld Chan and V Sedbergh (alt)* **V** LFOSTER,
Hon C AWFELL
FIRBECK (St Martin) w Letwell *Sheff 5* **P** *Bp* **R** PIRESON
FIRLE, WEST (St Peter) Glynde, W Firle and Beddingham
Chich
FIRSBY (St Andrew) w Great Steeping *Linc 7*
P *Mrs J M Fox-Robinson* **R** GROBSON
FISH HALL (Mission Church) Tonbridge SS Pet and Paul
Roch
FISHBOURNE, NEW (St Peter and St Mary) *Chich 3*
P *Ld Chan* **R** MACOLLIS
FISHBURN (St Catherine) Sedgefield *Dur*
FISHERMEAD (Trinity Church) Woughton *Ox*
FISHERTON ANGER (St Paul) *Sarum 15* **P** *Ch Patr*
Trust **P-in-c** RACHARKHAM, **NSM** MGHUXTABLE
FISHLAKE (St Cuthbert) w Sykehouse, Kirk Bramwith,
Fenwick and Moss *Sheff 11* **P** *Duchy of Lanc (1 turn),*
D&C Dur (2 turns), and Bp (1 turn) **R** JMOSGERBY,
NSM ESATHERFOLD
FISHLEY (St Mary) Acle w Fishley and N Burlingham *Nor*
FISHPOND (St John the Baptist) Marshwood Vale TM
Sarum
FISHPONDS (All Saints) *Bris 7* **P** *Bp*
V RJBURBRIDGE, **C** JAKINGS
FISHPONDS (St John) *Bris 7* **P** *Bp* **V** JGBRAY,
C EFCULLY, NRWALLACE
FISHPONDS (St Mary) *Bris 7* **P** *Bp* **V** RGMINSON,
NSM KRGMILES
FISHTOFT (St Guthlac) *Linc 20* **P** *DBP* **R** JBPAVEY
FISKERTON (St Clement) w Reepham *Linc 3* **P** *D&C and*
Mercers' Co (jt) **R** MKROBERTS
FITTLETON (All Saints) Avon Valley *Sarum*
FITTLEWORTH (St Mary the Virgin) Stopham and
Fittleworth *Chich*
FITTON HILL (St Cuthbert) Bardsley *Man*
FITZ (St Peter and St Paul) Bicton, Montford w Shrawardine
and Fitz *Lich*
FITZHEAD (St James) Milverton w Halse and Fitzhead
B & W
FITZWILLIAM (St Maurice) Kinsley w Wragby *Wakef*
FIVE ASHES (Church of the Good Shepherd) Mayfield
Chich
FIVE OAK GREEN (St Luke) Tudeley w Capel *Roch*
FIVEHEAD (St Martin) Curry Rivel w Fivehead and Swell
B & W
FIXBY (St Francis) N Huddersfield *Wakef*
FLACKWELL HEATH (Christ Church) *Ox 29* **P** *DBP*
P-in-c CDBULL
FLADBURY (St John the Baptist), Wyre Piddle and Moor
Worc 4 **P** *Bp* **R** KABOYCE, **NSM** SJGIBBONS
FLAGG (School Mission Room) Taddington, Chelmorton
and Flagg, and Monyash *Derby*
FLAMBOROUGH (St Oswald) *York 10* **P** *Abp* **V** *Vacant*
Bridlington (01262) 850336
FLAMSTEAD (St Leonard) *St Alb 14* **P** *Univ Coll Ox*
C DJKERR, **Hon C** GHKING, **NSM** JJSTRATTON
FLAUNDEN (St Mary Magdalene) Chenies and Lt
Chalfont, Latimer and Flaunden *Ox*
FLAWBOROUGH (St Peter) Staunton w Flawborough
S'well
FLAX BOURTON (St Michael and All Angels) *B & W 13*
P *Lord Wraxall* **P-in-c** JBBISHOP
FLAXLEY (St Mary the Virgin) Westbury-on-Severn w
Flaxley and Blaisdon *Glouc*
FLAXTON (St Lawrence) Whitwell w Crambe, Flaxton,
Foston etc *York*
FLECKNEY (St Nicholas) and Kilby *Leic 5* **P** *Bp and*
Hon Ann Brooks (jt) **V** BRGLOVER
FLECKNOE (St Mark) Grandborough w Willoughby and
Flecknoe *Cov*
FLEET (All Saints) (St Philip and St James) *Guildf 1* **P** *Bp*
V CHJOBSON, **C** PPMOYSE

FLEET (Holy Trinity) Chickerell w Fleet *Sarum*
FLEET (St Mary Magdalene) w Gedney *Linc 16*
P *The Crown and DBP (alt)* **R** DFBRATLEY
FLEETWOOD (St David) *Blackb 13* **P** *Bp and Meynell*
Trustees (jt) **V** EKSILLIS
FLEETWOOD (St Nicholas) *Blackb 13* **P** *Bp and Meynell*
Trustees (jt) **V** JTALLANT
FLEETWOOD (St Peter) *Blackb 13* **P** *Meynell Trustees*
V JCAYTON
FLEMPTON (St Catherine of Alexandria) Culford, W Stow
and Wordwell w Flempton etc *St E*
FLETCHAMSTEAD (St James) *Cov 3* **P** *Bp*
V RJCOOKE, **C** EASMITH (nee HOWSE)
FLETCHING (St Mary and St Andrew) *Chich 21* **P** *Abp*
NSM JDGRAY
FLETTON (St Margaret) *Ely 13* **P** *Sir Stephen Hastings*
P-in-c DGSTEVENS
FLIMBY (St Nicholas) *Carl 7* **P** *Bp* **P-in-c** WKELLY,
C ABUTLER
FLIMWELL (St Augustine of Canterbury) Ticehurst and
Flimwell *Chich*
FLINTHAM (St Augustine of Canterbury) *S'well 8*
P *M T Hildyard Esq* **V** JPULMAN
FLITCHAM (St Mary the Virgin) Sandringham w W
Newton and Appleton etc *Nor*
FLITTON (St John the Baptist) Silsoe, Pulloxhill and Flitton
St Alb
FLITWICK (St Andrew) (St Peter and St Paul) *St Alb 15*
P *DBP* **V** MFJBRADLEY, **C** SMORTON
FLIXBOROUGH (All Saints) w Burton upon Stather *Linc 4*
P *Sir Reginald Sheffield, Bt* **V** PBHEARN,
Hon C DECORNELIUS
FLIXTON (St John) *Man 7* **P** *Bp* **V** JADEY,
NSM RWGREEN, BRCORKE
FLIXTON (St Mary) S Elmham and Ilketshall *St E*
FLIXTON (St Michael) *Man 7* **P** *Bp* **R** WJTWIDELL,
C AJHARDY
FLOCKTON (St James the Great) cum Denby Grange
Wakef 6 **P** *R Carter's Trustees* **P-in-c** MESMITH
FLOOKBURGH (St John the Baptist) *Carl 10*
P *R H Cavendish Esq* **P-in-c** NJASH
FLORDON (St Michael) Tasburgh w Tharston, Forncett and
Flordon *Nor*
FLORE (All Saints) w Dodford and Brockhall *Pet 3* **P** *Bp and*
Ch Ch Ox (alt) **V** JWLATHAM
FLOWTON (St Mary) Somersham w Flowton and Offton w
Willisham *St E*
FLUSHING (St Peter) Mylor w Flushing *Truro*
FLYFORD FLAVELL (St Peter) Abberton, The Flyfords,
Naunton Beauchamp etc *Worc*
FOBBING (St Michael) *Chelmsf 14* **P** *The Crown*
P-in-c GWDAVIES
FOLESHILL (St Laurence) *Cov 2* **P** *Ld Chan*
V MRCLEVELAND
FOLESHILL (St Paul) *Cov 2* **P** *Ld Chan* **V** AJCANNING
FOLEY PARK (Holy Innocents) Kidderminster St Jo and H
Innocents *Worc*
FOLKE (St Lawrence) The Caundles w Folke and Holwell
Sarum
FOLKESTONE Foord (St John the Baptist) Foord St Jo
Cant
FOLKESTONE (Holy Trinity w Christ Church) *Cant 5*
P *Abp* **P-in-c** JCTAPPER, **NSM** GMCALVER
FOLKESTONE (St Augustine) (St Mary and St Eanswythe)
Cant 5 **P** *Abp* **V** JWDILNOT, **C** BDRWOOD
FOLKESTONE (St George) Sandgate St Paul w Folkestone
St Geo *Cant*
FOLKESTONE (St Peter) *Cant 5* **P** *Trustees*
V MAHOUGHTON
FOLKESTONE (St Saviour) *Cant 5* **P** *Abp*
V GJBUTLER, **C** NAMAXTED
FOLKESWORTH (St Helen) Stilton w Denton and
Caldecote etc *Ely*
FOLKINGHAM (St Andrew) S Lafford *Linc*
FOLKINGTON (St Peter ad Vincula) Arlington, Folkington
and Wilmington *Chich*
FOLKTON (St John) Willerby w Ganton and Folkton *York*
FOLLIFOOT (St Joseph and St James) Spofforth w Kirk
Deighton *Ripon*
FONTHILL BISHOP (All Saints) Tisbury *Sarum*
FONTHILL GIFFORD (Holy Trinity) as above
FONTMELL MAGNA (St Andrew) The Iwernes, Sutton
Waldron and Fontmell Magna *Sarum*
FOOLOW (St Hugh) Eyam *Derby*
FOORD (St John the Baptist) *Cant 5* **P** *CPAS*
V HWJHARLAND, **C** DPMOUNCER

FOOTS CRAY (All Saints) *Roch 16* **P** *Ld Chan*
P-in-c G S COLVILLE
FORCETT (St Cuthbert) and Aldbrough and Melsonby
Ripon 2 **P** *DBP and Univ Coll Ox (alt)* **R** M D GRAY
FORD (St Andrew) Clymping and Yapton w Ford *Chich*
FORD (St John of Jerusalem) Leominster *Heref*
FORD (St John the Evangelist) Colerne w N Wraxall *Bris*
FORD (St Michael) *Heref 13* **P** *Bp* **V** H J EDWARDS
FORD (St Michael and All Angels) and Etal *Newc 12* **P** *Lord Joicey* **R** W P HEWITT
FORD END (St John the Evangelist) Gt Waltham w Ford End *Chelmsf*
FORDCOMBE (St Peter) Penshurst and Fordcombe *Roch*
FORDHAM (All Saints) *Chelmsf 18* **P** *Reform Ch Trust, Ball Coll Ox (alt)* **R** M R J NEVILLE
FORDHAM (St Peter and St Mary Magdalene) *Ely 3* **P** *Jes Coll Cam* **V** *Vacant* Newmarket (01638) 720266
FORDHOUSES (St James) Bushbury *Lich*
FORDINGBRIDGE (St Mary) *Win 8* **P** *K Coll Cam*
P-in-c T E DAYKIN, **C** M E PINNOCK, **NSM** C E ROLFE
FORDON (St James) Burton Fleming w Fordon, Grindale etc *York*
FORDWICH (St Mary the Virgin) Sturry w Fordwich and Westbere w Hersden *Cant*
FOREMARK (St Saviour) *Derby 16* **P** *Major F R D Burdett Fisher (1 turn), Exors H F Harpur-Crewe Esq (2 turns)*
V J R P BARKER
FOREST (St Stephen) Rainow w Saltersford and Forest *Ches*
FOREST GATE (All Saints) *Chelmsf 3* **P** *Bp*
P-in-c J H SETTIMBA
FOREST GATE (Emmanuel w St Peter) Upton Cross
Chelmsf 3 **P** *Bp* **P-in-c** W D N WEIR,
C A M W WILSON, **NSM** A R EASTER
FOREST GATE (St Edmund) *Chelmsf 3* **P** *Bp*
V C C DALLISTON, **C** M R JUDGE
FOREST GATE (St James) Stratford St Jo and Ch Ch w Forest Gate St Jas *Chelmsf*
FOREST GATE (St Mark) *Chelmsf 3* **P** *Ch Patr Trust*
V P J STOW
FOREST GATE (St Saviour) w West Ham (St Matthew)
Chelmsf 3 **P** *Patr Bd* **TR** J H WILLIAMS
FOREST GREEN (Holy Trinity) Ockley, Okewood and Forest Green *Guildf*
FOREST HILL (Christ Church) (St Paul) *S'wark 4* **P** *Bp and Earl of Dartmouth (jt)* **V** C D HARRISON,
C J P H ALLAIN CHAPMAN, **NSM** T G BURMAN
FOREST HILL (St Augustine) Honor Oak Park *S'wark 4*
P *Bp* **V** M J R COUNSELL, **Hon C** R O SMITH, S COOK
FOREST HILL (St Nicholas) Wheatley w Forest Hill and Stanton St John *Ox*
FOREST-IN-TEESDALE (St Mary the Virgin) Middleton-in-Teesdale w Forest and Frith *Dur*
FOREST OF DEAN (Christ Church) w English Bicknor
Glouc 4 **P** *The Crown (3 turns), SMF (1 turn)*
P-in-c A E WELLS
FOREST ROW (Holy Trinity) *Chich 7* **P** *V E Grinstead*
V R N HARLEY, **NSM** A W B LEACH
FOREST TOWN (St Alban) *S'well 2* **P** *Bp*
P-in-c H R SMITH
FORESTSIDE (Christ Church) Stansted *Chich*
FORMBY (Holy Trinity) *Liv 5* **P** *Trustees* **V** C A QUINE,
C D A LAMB, **NSM** P J UPTON-JONES
FORMBY (St Luke) *Liv 5* **P** *Bp* **V** *Vacant* Formby (01704) 877655
FORMBY (St Peter) *Liv 5* **P** *R Walton* **V** P WORMROD
FORNCETT (St Peter) Tasburgh w Tharston, Forncett and Flordon *Nor*
FORNCETT END (St Edmund) as above
FORNHAM (All Saints) (St Martin) w Timworth *St E 13*
P *Bp* **P-in-c** R W CLIFTON, **C** P BARHAM
FORRABURY (St Symphorian) Boscastle w Davidstow *Truro*
FORSBROOK (St Peter) Draycott-le-Moors w Forsbrook *Lich*
FORTHAMPTON (St Mary) Deerhurst, Apperley w Forthampton and Chaceley *Glouc*
FORTON (All Saints) *Lich 12* **P** *D&C* **P-in-c** R T HIBBERT
FORTON (St John the Evangelist) *Portsm 3* **P** *DBP*
P-in-c H O ALBY, **NSM** D KING
FORTY HILL (Jesus Church) *Lon 18* **P** *V Enfield*
V P N L PYTCHES
FOSDYKE (All Saints) Sutterton w Fosdyke and Algarkirk *Linc*
FOSTON (All Saints) Whitwell w Crambe, Flaxton, Foston etc *York*
FOSTON (St Bartholomew) Countesthorpe w Foston *Leic*

FOSTON (St Peter) Long Bennington w Foston *Linc*
FOSTON-ON-THE-WOLDS (St Andrew) Beeford w Frodingham and Foston *York*
FOTHERBY (St Mary) *Linc 12* **P** *Ld Chan (1 turn), DBP, MMCET and M M Sleight Esq (1 turn), and Bp (1 turn)*
NSM A HUNDLEBY, J M WRISDALE
FOTHERINGHAY (St Mary and All Saints) Warmington, Tansor, Cotterstock and Fotheringhay *Pet*
FOULDEN (All Saints) Oxborough w Foulden and Caldecote *Nor*
FOULNESS (St Mary the Virgin) Gt Wakering w Foulness *Chelmsf*
FOULRIDGE (St Michael and All Angels) *Blackb 7* **P** *Bp*
V G SENIOR
FOULSHAM (Holy Innocents) Hindolveston and Guestwick
Nor 23 **P** *Lord Hastings, Mrs M E E Bulwer-Long and D&C (alt)* **P-in-c** C J ENGELSEN
FOUNTAINS Group, The *Ripon 3* **P** *D&C* **R** T KEDDIE,
C M J STEWART
FOUR ELMS (St Paul) Hever, Four Elms and Mark Beech *Roch*
FOUR MARKS (Good Shepherd) *Win 2* **P** *Bp*
V C M NOYCE
FOUR OAKS (All Saints) *Birm 9* **P** *Bp*
V D E McCORMACK, **C** J S CURRY
FOURSTONES (St Aidan) Warden w Newbrough *Newc*
FOVANT (St George), Sutton Mandeville and Teffont Evias w Teffont Magna and Compton Chamberlayne *Sarum 13*
P *Reformation Ch Trust, Bp, and Ch Soc Trust (jt)*
R J C EADE
FOWEY (St Fimbarrus) *Truro 1* **P** *Ch Soc Trust*
V D J N MADDOCK
FOWLMERE (St Mary) *Ely 8* **P** *Bp* **P-in-c** J B MYNORS
FOWNHOPE (St Mary) w Mordiford, Brockhampton and Fawley and Woolhope *Heref 4* **P** *D&C (4 turns), and Major R J Hereford (1 turn)* **R** A E DICKSON
FOXCOTE (St James the Less) Camerton w Dunkerton, Foxcote and Shoscombe *B & W*
FOXDALE (St Paul) *S & M 3* **P** *The Crown and Bp (alt)*
V B H PARTINGTON, **NSM** H G R SLADE
FOXEARTH (St Peter and St Paul) Pentlow, Foxearth, Liston and Borley *Chelmsf*
FOXHAM (St John the Baptist) Derry Hill w Bremhill and Foxham *Sarum*
FOXHILL (Chapel) Frodsham *Ches*
FOXHOLE (St Boniface) Paignton St Jo *Ex*
FOXHOLES (St Mary) Langtoft w Foxholes, Butterwick, Cottam etc *York*
FOXLEY (not known) Sherston Magna, Easton Grey, Luckington etc *Bris*
FOXLEY (St Thomas) Bawdeswell w Foxley *Nor*
FOXT (St Mark the Evangelist) w Whiston *Lich 11*
P *Mrs G I A Dalrymple-Hamilton and Mrs C I Townley (alt)* **NSM** J B HARROP
FOXTON (St Andrew) w Gumley and Laughton and Lubenham
Leic 4 **P** *Bp, A M Finn Esq, and D&C Linc (by turn)*
V *Vacant* East Langton (01858) 545245
FOXTON (St Laurence) *Ely 8* **P** *Bp* **P-in-c** W G THOMAS,
NSM R M NANCARROW
FOY (St Mary) How Caple w Sollarshope, Sellack etc *Heref*
FRADLEY (St Stephen) Alrewas *Lich*
FRADSWELL (St James the Less), Gayton, Milwich and Weston on Trent *Lich 15* **P** *Bp, Personal Reps of Earl of Harrowby, Hertf Coll Ox and T J A Dive Esq (jt)*
P-in-c J LILLEY, **C** J M OAKES
FRAISTHORPE (St Edmund) Skipsea w Ulrome and Barmston w Fraisthorpe *York*
FRAMFIELD (St Thomas a Becket) *Chich 21*
P *Mrs E R Wix* **V** G T DAINTREE
FRAMILODE (St Peter) Frampton on Severn, Arlingham, Saul etc *Glouc*
FRAMINGHAM EARL (St Andrew) Poringland *Nor*
FRAMINGHAM PIGOT (St Andrew) Thurton *Nor*
FRAMLAND Parishes, The HIGH *Leic 3* **P** *Duke of Rutland and Sir Lyonel Tollemache, Bt (jt)* **R** A E H CLAYTON
FRAMLINGHAM (St Michael) w Saxtead *St E 18* **P** *Pemb Coll Cam* **R** R W WILLCOCK, **C** E S HEBBLETHWAITE
FRAMPTON (St Mary) Bradf Peverell, Stratton, Frampton etc *Sarum*
FRAMPTON (St Mary) (St Michael) w Kirton in Holland
Linc 21 **P** *Mercers Co (2 turns), Trustees (1 turn)*
P-in-c E HORNER
FRAMPTON COTTERELL (St Peter) *Bris 7* **P** *SMF*
P-in-c S E RUSHTON
FRAMPTON MANSELL (St Luke) Coates, Rodmarton and Sapperton etc *Glouc*
FRAMPTON ON SEVERN (St Mary), Arlingham, Saul, Fretherne and Framilode *Glouc 8* **P** *DBP, V Standish w*

Haresfield etc, Brig Sir Jeffrey Darell, Bt, and Bp (jt)
V PCHEESMAN

FRAMSDEN (St Mary) Helmingham w Framsden and
Pettaugh w Winston *St E*

FRAMWELLGATE MOOR (St Aidan) Dur St Cuth *Dur*

FRANCE LYNCH (St John the Baptist) Chalford and
France Lynch *Glouc*

FRANCHE (St Barnabas) Kidderminster St Mary and All SS
w Trimpley etc *Worc*

FRANKBY (St John the Divine) w Greasby St Nicholas
Ches 8 **P** *D&C* **V** GM BREFFITT, **C** M R SHORT

FRANKLEY (St Leonard) *Birm 4* **P** *Bp* **R** M T DENNY

FRANKTON (St Nicholas) Bourton w Frankton and
Stretton on Dunsmore etc *Cov*

FRANSHAM, GREAT (All Saints) Gt and Lt Dunham w Gt
and Lt Fransham and Sporle *Nor*

FRANSHAM, LITTLE (St Mary) as above

FRANT (St Alban) w Eridge *Chich 19* **P** *Bp and Marquess of
Abergavenny (jt)* **R** E G DORE

FREASLEY (St Mary) Dordon *Birm*

FRECHEVILLE (St Cyprian) *Sheff 2* **P** *Bp*
R M J GILLINGHAM

FRECKENHAM (St Andrew) Mildenhall *St E*

FRECKLETON (Holy Trinity) *Blackb 11* **P** *Bp*
V S F BRIAN

FREEBY (St Mary) Melton Mowbray *Leic*

FREEHAY (St Chad) Cheadle w Freehay *Lich*

FREELAND (St Mary the Virgin) Hanborough and Freeland
Ox

FREEMANTLE (Christ Church) *Win 12* **P** *Bp* **R** R G DISS

**FREETHORPE (All Saints) w Wickhampton, Halvergate,
Tunstall, Beighton and Moulton** *Nor 4* **P** *Bp, Ch Soc Trust,
and K M Mills Esq (jt)* **R** R F GIBSON

FREISTON (St James) w Butterwick *Linc 20* **P** *Bp*
V B R GRELLIER, **NSM** L HALL, R T WESTLAND

FREMINGTON (St Peter) *Ex 15* **P** MMCET
V P H HOCKEY

FRENCHAY (St John the Baptist) and Winterbourne Down
Bris 7 **P** *St Jo Coll Ox and SMF (jt)* **R** R J THOMAS,
Hon C C F MOSELEY

FRENSHAM (St Mary the Virgin) *Guildf 3* **P** *Ld Chan*
V A L PETTERSEN, **NSM** J C NEWELL PRICE

**FRESHFORD (St Peter) w Limpley Stoke and Hinton
Charterhouse** *B & W 9* **P** *Simeon's Trustees and V Norton
St Phil (jt)* **R** D J CLARK

FRESHWATER (All Saints) (St Agnes) *Portsm 8* **P** *St Jo
Coll Cam* **R** B W E BANKS

**FRESSINGFIELD (St Peter and St Paul), Menham, Metfield,
Weybread and Withersdale** *St E 17* **P** *Bp, Em Coll Cam,
Ch Soc Trust, and SMF (jt)* **R** G WOOD,
NSM P A SCHWIER, C D BURKE, R A WILLIS

FRESTON (St Peter) Holbrook w Freston and Woolverstone
St E

FRETHERNE (St Mary the Virgin) Frampton on Severn,
Arlingham, Saul etc *Glouc*

FRETTENHAM (St Swithin) Spixworth w Crostwick and
Frettenham *Nor*

FRIAR PARK (St Francis of Assisi) W Bromwich St Fran
Lich

FRIARMERE (St Thomas) *Man 21* **P** *Bp* **V** D J COX

FRICKLEY (All Saints) Bilham *Sheff*

FRIDAY BRIDGE (St Mark) *Ely 19* **P** *Bp* **V** J E BARRETT

FRIDAYTHORPE (St Mary) Sledmere and Cowlam w
Fridaythorpe, Fimer etc *York*

FRIERN BARNET (All Saints) *Lon 14* **P** *Bp*
V A V BENJAMIN

**FRIERN BARNET (St James the Great) (St John the
Evangelist)** *Lon 14* **P** *D&C St Paul's* **C** T G CLEMENT

FRIERN BARNET (St Peter le Poer) *Lon 14*
P *D&C St Paul's* **V** I C YOUNG

FRIESTHORPE (St Peter) Wickenby Gp *Linc*

FRIETH (St John the Baptist) Hambleden Valley *Ox*

FRIEZLAND (Christ Church) St Anne Lydgate w Ch Ch
Friezland *Man*

FRILSHAM (St Frideswide) Hermitage and Hampstead
Norreys, Cold Ash etc *Ox*

FRIMLEY (St Francis) (St Peter) *Guildf 6* **P** *R Ash*
R N C TURTON, **C** B M JONES, J F WHITMORE,
Hon C H E B SKEET

FRIMLEY GREEN (St Andrew) *Guildf 6* **P** *Bp*
V B K BESSANT

FRINDSBURY (All Saints) w Upnor (St Phillip and St James)
Roch 6 **P** *Bp* **V** W J N DURANT

FRING (All Saints) Snettisham w Ingoldisthorpe and Fring
Nor

FRINGFORD (St Michael) Stratton Audley and Godington,
Fringford etc *Ox*

FRINSTED (St Dunstan) Bredgar w Bicknor and Frinsted w
Wormshill etc *Cant*

**FRINTON (St Mary Magdalene) (St Mary the Virgin Old
Church)** *Chelmsf 24* **P** CPAS **C** D W BARTLETT,
NSM H LAWRENCE

**FRISBY-ON-THE-WREAKE (St Thomas of
Canterbury)** Upper Wreake *Leic*

FRISKNEY (All Saints) *Linc 8* **P** *Bp* **P-in-c** J DUMAT

FRISTON (St Mary Magdalene) Aldringham w Thorpe,
Knodishall w Buxlow etc *St E*

FRISTON (St Mary the Virgin) E Dean w Friston and
Jevington *Chich*

FRITCHLEY (Mission Room) Crich *Derby*

FRITHELSTOCK (St Mary and St Gregory) Gt and Lt
Torrington and Frithelstock *Ex*

FRITHVILLE (St Peter) Sibsey w Frithville *Linc*

FRITTENDEN (St Mary) Sissinghurst w Frittenden *Cant*

FRITTON (St Catherine) Hempnall *Nor*

FRITTON (St Edmund) Somerleyton, Ashby, Fritton,
Herringfleet etc *Nor*

FRITWELL (St Olave) w Souldern and Ardley w Fewcott
Ox 2 **P** *DBP, St Jo Coll Cam, and Wadh Coll Ox
(by turn)* **R** J W THOMPSON

FRIZINGHALL (St Margaret) Shipley St Paul and
Frizinghall *Bradf*

FRIZINGTON (St Paul) and Arlecdon *Carl 5* **P** *Bp*
P-in-c J A McKINNEY

FROCESTER (St Andrew) Eastington and Frocester *Glouc*

FRODESLEY (St Mark) Condover w Frodesley, Acton
Burnell etc *Heref*

FRODINGHAM (St Lawrence) *Linc 4* **P** *Lord St Oswald*
V M P COONEY, **NSM** M DUNFORD

FRODINGHAM, NORTH (St Elgin) Beeford w
Frodingham and Foston *York*

FRODSHAM (St Lawrence) *Ches 3* **P** *Ch Ch Ox* **V** *Vacant*
Frodsham (01928) 733378

FROGMORE (Holy Trinity) *St Alb 1* **P** CPAS
V G R BARTER, **NSM** N A WARD

FROLESWORTH (St Nicholas) Claybrooke cum Wibtoft
and Frolesworth *Leic*

FROME (Christ Church) *B & W 4* **P** *Bp* **V** T A THOMAS,
NSM P E LAWLESS

FROME (Holy Trinity) *B & W 4* **P** *Bp* **V** *Vacant* Frome
(01373) 462586

FROME (St John the Baptist) (Blessed Virgin Mary)
B & W 4 **P** *Bp and DBP (jt)* **V** J G PESCOD,
C I M TUCKER

FROME ST QUINTON (St Mary) Melbury *Sarum*

FROME VAUCHURCH (St Mary) as above

FROMES HILL (St Matthew) Bishop's Frome w Castle
Frome and Fromes Hill *Heref*

FROSTENDEN (All Saints) Wrentham w Benacre,
Covehithe, Frostenden etc *St E*

FROSTERLEY (St Michael and All Angels) Stanhope w
Frosterley *Dur*

FROXFIELD (All Saints) Whitton *Sarum*

FROXFIELD (St Peter) Steep and Froxfield w Privett *Portsm*

FROXFIELD (St Peter on the Green) as above

**FROYLE (Assumption of the Blessed Virgin Mary) and
Holybourne** *Win 2* **P** *Guild of All So and D&C (jt)*
V C R ARDAGH-WALTER

FRYERNING (St Mary the Virgin) w Margaretting
Chelmsf 7 **P** *Wadh Coll Ox* **P-in-c** J D BROWN,
NSM F DRAKE

FRYSTON (St Peter) Airedale w Fryston *Wakef*

FUGGLESTONE (St Peter) Wilton w Netherhampton and
Fugglestone *Sarum*

FULBECK (St Nicholas) Caythorpe *Linc*

FULBOURN (St Vigor w All Saints) *Ely 6* **P** *St Jo Coll
Cam* **R** B E KERLEY

FULBROOK (St Gabriel) Walsall St Gabr Fulbrook *Lich*

FULBROOK (St James the Great) Burford w Fulbrook,
Taynton, Asthall etc *Ox*

FULFORD (St Oswald) *York 8* **P** *Abp* **V** R A HALL,
NSM M COOPER

FULFORD-IN-STONE (St Nicholas) w Hilderstone *Lich 18*
P *D&C* **V** P D BROOKS

FULHAM (All Saints) *Lon 9* **P** *Bp* **V** K N BOWLER,
C M J HUGHES

FULHAM (Christ Church) *Lon 9* **P** CPAS **V** *Vacant*
0171–736 4261

FULHAM (St Alban) (St Augustine) *Lon 9* **P** *Bp and City
Corp (jt)* **V** G PALMER, **Hon C** G R J SHEA

FULHAM (St Andrew) Fulham Fields *Lon 9* **P** *Bp*
V D R PAGET

FULHAM (St Dionis) Parson's Green *Lon 9* **P** *Bp*
P-in-c A S ATKINS, **Past Asst** K D MENTZEL

FULHAM (St Etheldreda) (St Clement) *Lon 9* **P** *Bp*
P-in-c J F H HENLEY
FULHAM (St Mary) North End *Lon 9* **P** *Ch Soc Trust*
V R W CURL, **C** M D REDHOUSE
FULHAM (St Matthew) *Lon 9* **P** *Ch Patr Trust*
V G Q D PIPER, **C** N D BEYNON, **Dss** V S PIERSON
FULHAM (St Peter) *Lon 9* **P** *Bp* **V** *Vacant* 0171–385 2045
FULKING (Good Shepherd) Poynings w Edburton,
Newtimber and Pyecombe *Chich*
FULL SUTTON (St Mary) Bishop Wilton w Full Sutton,
Kirby Underdale etc *York*
FULLETBY (St Andrew) w Greetham and Ashby Puerorum
Linc 11 **P** *D&C (2 turns), Keble Coll Ox (1 turn)*
R *Vacant* Winceby (01507) 588671
FULMER (St James) Gerrards Cross and Fulmer *Ox*
FULMODESTON (Christ Church) Barney, Fulmodeston w
Croxton, Hindringham etc *Nor*
FULSHAW (St Anne) Wilmslow *Ches*
FULSTOW (St Laurence) Fotherby *Linc*
FULWELL (St Michael and St George) Teddington SS Pet
and Paul and Fulwell *Lon*
FULWOOD (Christ Church) *Blackb 14* **P** *V Lanc*
V E J BURNS
FULWOOD (Christ Church) *Sheff 4* **P** *CPAS*
V P H HACKING, **C** G J McGRATH
FULWOOD Lodge Moor (St Luke) Lodge Moor St Luke
Sheff
FUNDENHALL (St Nicholas) Wreningham *Nor*
FUNTINGTON (St Mary) and Sennicotts *Chich 13* **P** *Bp*
V D A JOHNSON
FUNTLEY (St Francis) Fareham SS Pet and Paul *Portsm*
FURNACE GREEN (St Andrew) Southgate *Chich*
FURNESS VALE (St John) Disley *Ches*
FURNEUX PELHAM (St Mary the Virgin) Braughing w
Furneux Pelham and Stocking Pelham *St Alb*
FURNHAM (Good Shepherd) Chard Furnham w
Chaffcombe, Knowle St Giles etc *B & W*
FURTHO (St Bartholomew) Potterspury, Furtho, Yardley
Gobion and Cosgrove *Pet*
FURZE PLATT (St Peter) *Ox 13* **P** *Bp*
V J E R POLLARD, **NSM** M W SKINNER
FURZEBANK (Worship Centre) Willenhall H Trin *Lich*
FURZTON (not known) Watling Valley *Ox*
FYFIELD (St Nicholas) Upper Kennett *Sarum*
FYFIELD (St Nicholas) Appleshaw, Kimpton, Thruxton and
Fyfield *Win*
FYFIELD (St Nicholas) w Tubney and Kingston Bagpuize
Ox 10 **P** *St Jo Coll Ox* **V** K J TRIPLOW
**FYFIELD (St Nicholas), Moreton w Bobbingworth and
Willingale w Shellow and Berners Roding** *Chelmsf 28*
P *Ld Chan, St Jo Coll Cam, MMCET, and Major G N Capel-
Cure (by turn)* **R** R MORGAN, **NSM** R H R DARK
FYLINGDALES (St Stephen) and Hawsker cum Stainsacre
York 23 **P** *Abp* **V** *Vacant* Whitby (01947) 880232
GADDESBY (St Luke) S Croxton Gp *Leic*
GADDESDEN, GREAT (St John the Baptist) *St Alb 3*
P *N G Halsey Esq* **P-in-c** N ROSKROW,
Hon C P M ROSKROW
GADDESDEN, LITTLE (St Peter and St Paul) *St Alb 3*
P *Bp* **P-in-c** N ROSKROW, **Hon C** P M ROSKROW
GADEBRIDGE (St Peter) Hemel Hempstead *St Alb*
GAINFORD (St Mary) *Dur 11* **P** *Trin Coll Cam*
V T J D OLLIER
GAINSBOROUGH (All Saints) *Linc 2* **P** *Bp* **V** P W DADD
GAINSBOROUGH (St George) *Linc 2* **P** *Bp*
P-in-c J STAFF
GAINSBOROUGH (St John the Divine) *Linc 2* **P** *Bp*
V B M DODDS
GALLEY COMMON (St Peter) Camp Hill w Galley
Common *Cov*
GALLEYWOOD (Junior School Worship
Centre) Galleywood Common *Chelmsf*
GALLEYWOOD COMMON (St Michael and All Angels)
Chelmsf 9 **P** *CPAS* **V** R WAKELY, **C** R T BASHFORD
GALMINGTON (St Michael) Wilton *B & W*
GALMPTON (Chapel of The Good Shepherd) Brixham w
Churston Ferrers and Kingswear *Ex*
GAMBLESBY (St John) Addingham, Edenhall, Langwathby
and Culgaith *Carl*
GAMESLEY (Bishop Geoffrey Allen Church and County
Centre) Charlesworth and Dinting Vale *Derby*
**GAMLINGAY (St Mary the Virgin) w Hatley (St George) and
East Hatley** *Ely 12* **P** *Bp and Down Coll Cam (jt)*
P-in-c A J COLE
GAMLINGAY HEATH (St Sylvester) Gamlingay w Hatley
St Geo and E Hatley *Ely*
GAMSTON and Bridgford *S'well 5* **P** *DBP*
R J A S WOOD, **NSM** B E F CLANCEY

GAMSTON (St Peter) w Eaton and West Drayton *S'well 5*
P *D&C York and Bp (alt)* **R** C F ANDREWS
GANAREW (St Swithin) Llangarron w Llangrove,
Whitchurch and Ganarew *Heref*
GANTON (St Nicholas) Willerby w Ganton and Folkton
York
**GARBOLDISHAM (St John the Baptist) w Blo' Norton,
Riddlesworth, Brettenham and Rushford** *Nor 11* **P** *DBP,
Sir John Musker, Mrs C Noel, and C P B Goldson Esq
(by turn)* **P-in-c** J HANDLEY, **A V** HEDGES
GARFORD (St Luke) Marcham w Garford *Ox*
GARFORTH (St Mary the Virgin) *Ripon 8* **P** *DBP*
R R G N PLANT
GARGRAVE (St Andrew) *Bradf 5* **P** *Bp* **P-in-c** M W BULL
GARRETTS GREEN (St Thomas) *Birm 11* **P** *Bp*
V A E ASH
GARRIGILL (St John) Alston Team *Newc*
GARSDALE (St John the Baptist) Sedbergh, Cautley and
Garsdale *Bradf*
GARSDON (All Saints), Lea and Cleverton and Charlton
Bris 12 **P** *Ch Soc Trust and Bp (jt)* **R** R K EAST
GARSINGTON (St Mary) and Horspath *Ox 1* **P** *DBP and
Trin Coll Ox (jt)* **R** *Vacant* Garsington (0186736) 381
GARSTANG (St Helen) Churchtown *Blackb 10*
P *A R Pedder Esq* **V** R BRAITHWAITE
GARSTANG (St Thomas) *Blackb 10* **P** *V Churchtown
St Helen* **V** R G GREENALL
GARSTON (St Michael) *Liv 4* **P** *Trustees*
V W N LETHEREN, **C** E M STOREY
GARSTON, EAST (All Saints) Eastbury and E Garston *Ox*
GARSWOOD (St Andrew) Ashton-in-Makerfield H Trin *Liv*
GARTHORPE (St Mary) Wymondham w Edmondthorpe,
Buckminster etc *Leic*
GARTHORPE (St Mary) N Axholme Gp *Linc*
GARTON IN HOLDERNESS (St Michael) Roos and
Garton in Holderness w Tunstall etc *York*
GARTON-ON-THE-WOLDS (St Michael and All
Angels) Wetwang and Garton-on-the-Wolds w Kirkburn
York
GARVESTON (St Margaret) Barnham Broom *Nor*
GARWAY (St Michael) St Weonards w Orcop, Garway,
Tretire etc *Heref*
GASTARD (St John the Baptist) Gtr Corsham *Bris*
GATCOMBE (St Olave) *Portsm 8* **P** *Qu Coll Ox*
R J W RUSSELL
GATE BURTON (St Helen) Lea Gp *Linc*
GATE HELMSLEY (St Mary) Sand Hutton *York*
GATEACRE (St Stephen) *Liv 4* **P** *Bp*
TR A T E TREHERNE, **TV** V E HUGHES,
A W ROBINSON, **C** S McGANITY, P G WHITTINGTON
GATEFORTH (St Mary's Mission Room) Haddlesey w
Hambleton and Birkin *York*
GATELEY (St Helen) Gt and Lt Ryburgh w Gateley and
Testerton *Nor*
GATESHEAD (Christ Church) *Dur 4* **P** *Bp* **V** P WRIGHT
GATESHEAD Harlow Green (St Ninian) *Dur 4* **P** *Bp*
V *Vacant* 0191–487 6685
GATESHEAD Lobley Hill (All Saints) Lobley Hill *Dur*
GATESHEAD (St Chad) Bensham *Dur*
**GATESHEAD (St Edmund's Chapel w Holy Trinity)
(Venerable Bede)** *Dur 4* **P** *Bp and The Crown (alt)*
TR K HUXLEY, **TV** P J WILCOX, J D FINKPIN
GATESHEAD (St George) *Dur 4* **P** *Trustees*
V E M T UNDERHILL
GATESHEAD (St Helen) *Dur 4* **P** *Bp* **V** B M HARRISON
GATESHEAD FELL (St John) *Dur 4* **P** *Bp* **R** *Vacant*
0191–487 3537
GATLEY (St James) *Ches 17* **P** *R Stockport St Thos*
V P O MOULTON
GATTEN (St Paul) *Portsm 7* **P** *Ch Patr Trust*
V P G ALLEN
GATTON (St Andrew) Merstham and Gatton *S'wark*
GAULBY (St Peter) *Leic 5* **P** *MMCET, Ch Soc Trust, and
Sir Geoffrey Palmer, Bt (jt)* **R** A F B CHEESMAN
GAUTBY (All Saints) Bardney *Linc*
GAWBER (St Thomas) *Wakef 7* **P** *V Darton*
V D TURNER, **NSM** B BENFORD
GAWCOTT (Holy Trinity) Lenborough *Ox*
GAWSWORTH (St James) *Ches 13* **P** *T R R Richards Esq*
R K V POVEY
GAWTHORPE (St Mary) and Chickenley Heath *Wakef 10*
P *Bp* **V** S MITCHELL
GAYDON (St Giles) w Chadshunt *Cov 8* **P** *Bp*
V P T FRANCIS
**GAYHURST (St Peter) w Ravenstone, Stoke Goldington and
Weston Underwood** *Ox 27* **P** *Bp and Lord Hesketh (jt)*
R S J A WESTON

**GAYTON Group of Parishes, The: Gayton (St Nicholas),
Gayton Thorpe w East Walton, Westacre, Ashwicken w
Leziate and Bawsey (Eastern)** *Nor 21* **P** *Bp and Capt
H Birkbeck (alt)* **R** LJMIDDLETON

GAYTON (St Mary) Pattishall w Cold Higham and Gayton
w Tiffield *Pet*

GAYTON (St Peter) Fradswell, Gayton, Milwich and Weston
Lich

GAYTON LE WOLD (St Peter) Asterby Gp *Linc*

GAYTON THORPE (St Mary) Gayton Gp of Par *Nor*

GAYWOOD (St Faith), Kings Lynn *Nor 21* **P** *Patr Bd*
TR AJHAWES, **TV** PMFARROW,
C LAHUMPHREYS, **NSM** KMLEES

GAZELEY (All Saints) w Dalham, Moulton and Kentford
St E 11 **P** *Bp (2 turns), Personal Reps Major the Hon J P
Philipps (1 turn), and Ch Coll Cam (1 turn)*
V BRWHAYES

GEDDING (St Mary the Virgin) Cockfield w Bradfield St
Clare, Felsham etc *St E*

GEDDINGTON (St Mary Magdalene) w Weekley *Pet 11*
P *Boughton Estates* **V** RBDORRINGTON

GEDLING (All Hallows) *S'well 11* **P** *DBP*
R MHFBEACH, **C** KGRIFFIN

GEDNEY (St Mary Magdalene) Fleet w Gedney *Linc*

GEDNEY DROVE END (Christ Church) Lutton w Gedney
Drove End, Dawsmere *Linc*

GEDNEY HILL (Holy Trinity) (St Polycarp) *Linc 16* **P** *Bp*
P-in-c JMONTAGUE

GEE CROSS (Holy Trinity) (St Philip's Mission Room)
Ches 14 **P** *V Werneth* **V** GDOSGOOD

GELDESTON (St Michael) Gillingham w Geldeston,
Stockton, Ellingham etc *Nor*

GENTLESHAW (Christ Church) *Lich 1* **P** *MMCET*
P-in-c MJBUTT

GEORGEHAM (St George) *Ex 15* **P** *MMCET*
R DWTRUDMAN

GERMAN (St German) *S & M 3* **P** *Bp* **V** BHKELLY,
C WHMARTIN

GERMAN (St John the Baptist) *S & M 3* **P** *Bp*
V BHPARTINGTON, **NSM** HGRSLADE

GERMANSWEEK (St German) Okehampton w
Inwardleigh, Bratton Clovelly etc *Ex*

GERMOE (St Germoe) Breage w Germoe *Truro*

GERRANS (St Gerran) w St Anthony in Roseland *Truro 6*
P *Bp* **P-in-c** DPOWELL

GERRARDS CROSS (St James) and Fulmer *Ox 20* **P** *Bp
and Simeon's Trustees (jt)* **R** NARUSSELL, **C** TCLING

GESTINGTHORPE (St Mary) Gt and Lt Maplestead w
Gestingthorpe *Chelmsf*

**GIDDING, GREAT (St Michael) w LITTLE (St John) and
Steeple Gidding** *Ely 10* **P** *Sir Stephen Hastings and Bp
(alt)* **P-in-c** JHINDLEY, **NSM** IDMGIBSON,
CMFURLONG (nee DAVIES)

GIDEA PARK (St Michael) *Chelmsf 2* **P** *Bp*
V ERPILKINGTON, **C** GPTUFFIN

GIDLEIGH (Holy Trinity) Chagford w Gidleigh and
Throwleigh *Ex*

GIGGETTY LANE (The Venerable Bede) Wombourne w
Trysull and Bobbington *Lich*

GIGGLESWICK (St Alkelda) and Rathmell w Wigglesworth
Bradf 5 **P** *Bp and Ch Trust Fund Trust (jt)*
V GDRHODES

GILCRUX (St Mary) Plumbland and Gilcrux *Carl*

GILDERSOME (St Peter) *Wakef 8* **P** *V Batley*
V DRDMARTINEAU

GILLAMOOR (St Aidan) Kirkbymoorside w Gillamoor,
Farndale & Bransdale *York*

GILLCAR (St Silas) Sheff St Silas Broomhall *Sheff*

GILLING (St Agatha) and Kirkby Ravensworth *Ripon 2*
P *Bp and Mrs M W Ringrose-Wharton (jt)*
P-in-c JIWILLIAMSON

GILLING EAST (Holy Cross) Ampleforth and Oswaldkirk
and Gilling E *York*

GILLINGHAM (Holy Trinity) *Roch 3* **P** *Bp*
V DWGREEN

GILLINGHAM (St Augustine) *Roch 3* **P** *Bp*
V PRWILLIAMS, **NSM** PMATTHIAS

GILLINGHAM (St Barnabas) *Roch 3* **P** *Bp*
V DFPRESTON, **NSM** HJCONNELL

GILLINGHAM (St Mark) *Roch 3* **P** *Hyndman Trustees*
V COBUCHANAN, **C** PTKERR, JKERR

GILLINGHAM (St Mary Magdalene) *Roch 3* **P** *DBP*
V OPHARVEY, **C** MDPALMER

GILLINGHAM (St Mary the Virgin) *Sarum 6* **P** *Bp*
TR JMcNEISH, **TV** PBIRT, WTRIDDING,
C JRPARKER, **NSM** JRHEDGES

**GILLINGHAM (St Mary) w Geldeston w Stockton w
Ellingham St Mary and Kirby Cane** *Nor 8* **P** *Ld Chan
(1 turn), Bp, MMCET and Ch Trust Fund Trust (1 turn)*
R CHRWHITEMAN, **NSM** RDHARVEY

GILLINGHAM, SOUTH (St Matthew) *Roch 3* **P** *Patr Bd*
TR SHDUNN, **TV** GEHOVENDEN, ACOEHRING,
C BTKNAPP

GILLOW HEATH (Mission Room) Biddulph *Lich*

**GILMORTON (All Saints) w Peatling Parva and Kimcote cum
Walton** *Leic 11* **P** *Bp and Guild All So (jt)* **R** *Vacant*
Lutterworth (01455) 552119

GILSLAND (St Mary Magdalene) w Nether Denton *Carl 2*
P *Bp* **P-in-c** PAGREENHALGH

GILSTEAD (St Wilfrid) Bingley H Trin *Bradf*

GILSTON (St Mary) High Wych and Gilston w Eastwick
St Alb

GIMINGHAM (All Saints) Trunch *Nor*

GIPPING (Chapel of St Nicholas) Old Newton w
Stowupland *St E*

GIPSY HILL (Christ Church) *S'wark 13* **P** *CPAS*
C SMELLUISH

GIRLINGTON (St Philip) *Bradf 1* **P** *Simeon's Trustees*
V ADGREENHILL

GIRTON (St Andrew) *Ely 5* **P** *Ld Chan*
R RGJMACKINTOSH

GIRTON (St Cecilia) Collingham w S Scarle and Besthorpe
and Girton *S'well*

GISBURN (St Mary the Virgin) *Bradf 5* **P** *Bp*
P-in-c GWALKER

GISLEHAM (Holy Trinity) Kessingland w Gisleham *Nor*

GISLINGHAM (St Mary) Thornhams Magna and Parva,
Gislingham and Mellis *St E*

GISSING (St Mary the Virgin) Winfarthing w Shelfanger w
Burston w Gissing etc *Nor*

GITTISHAM (St Michael) Honiton, Gittisham, Combe
Raleigh, Monkton etc *Ex*

GIVENDALE, GREAT (St Ethelberga) Pocklington and
Owsthorpe and Kilnwick Percy etc *York*

GLAISDALE (St Thomas) *York 23* **P** *Abp* **V** BHARRISON

GLANDFORD (St Martin) Blakeney w Cley, Wiveton,
Glandford etc *Nor*

GLANTON (St Peter) Whittingham and Edlingham w Bolton
Chapel *Newc*

GLAPTHORN (St Leonard) Benefield and Southwick w
Glapthorn *Pet*

GLAPWELL (St Andrew) Ault Hucknall *Derby*

GLASCOTE (St George) and Stonydelph *Lich 4* **P** *Patr Bd*
TR BRFROCHE, **TV** CEBERESFORD,
DSMcDONOUGH, **C** SMGRIFFITHS

GLASSHOUGHTON (St Paul) *Wakef 11* **P** *Bp*
V GDRIVER

GLASSON (Christ Church) Cockerham w Winmarleigh and
Glasson *Blackb*

GLASTON (St Andrew) Morcott w Glaston and Bisbrooke
Pet

**GLASTONBURY (St John the Baptist) (St Benedict) w Meare,
West Pennard and Godney** *B & W 5* **P** *Bp* **V** PJRILEY,
C GRWITTS, EMCROSS, JGSUMNER,
Hon C WMMARSHALL

GLATTON (St Nicholas) *Ely 13* **P** *Bp* **R** *Vacant*

GLAZEBURY (All Saints) w Hollinfare *Liv 16* **P** *Bp and R
Warrington (jt)* **R** BCCLARK, **NSM** JBENT

GLAZELEY (St Bartholomew) Billingsley w Sidbury,
Middleton Scriven etc *Heref*

GLEADLESS (Christ Church) *Sheff 1* **P** *DBP*
TR CJWHEDLEY, **TV** AMCOLEBY, **C** APFEREDAY,
NSM SDHOLDAWAY

GLEADLESS VALLEY (Holy Cross) *Sheff 1* **P** *DBP*
TR *Vacant* Sheffield (0114) 239 8852

**GLEMHAM, GREAT (All Saints) and LITTLE (St Andrew),
Blaxhall, Stratford St Andrew and Farnham** *St E 19* **P** *Earl
of Guilford, C J V Hope Johnstone Esq, and P M Cobbold Esq
(1 turn), and DBP (1 turn)* **P-in-c** MIBLACKALL

**GLEMSFORD (St Mary the Virgin), Hartest w Boxted,
Somerton and Stanstead (Glem Valley United Benefice)**
St E 12 **P** *Bp, Prime Min, and Ch Soc Trust (by turn)*
C BASAMPSON

GLEN AULDYN (Mission Church) Lezayre *S & M*

GLEN PARVA and South Wigston *Leic 5* **P** *Bp* **V** PDAY,
C SAHOY, **NSM** PGHOLMES

GLENDALE Group, The *Newc 10* **P** *Patr Bd (4 turns),
Ld Chan (1 turn)* **TR** RBSBURSTON,
TV MDCATLING, **NSM** TRROCHESTER, GJONES

GLENFIELD (St Peter) *Leic 12* **P** *Bp*
R ALLATTIMORE, **C** JJPRICE

GLENHOLT (St Anne) Bickleigh (Roborough) and Shaugh
Prior *Ex*

GLENTHAM (St Peter) Owmby Gp *Linc*

GLENTWORTH Group, The (St Michael) *Linc 2* **P** *Bp,
Earl of Scarbrough, MMCET, and Ch Soc Trust (jt)*
P-in-c M DAWSON

GLINTON (St Benedict) Peakirk w Glinton and
Northborough *Pet*

GLODWICK (St Mark w Christ Church) *Man 19* **P** *Bp*
V M A NARUSAWA

GLOOSTON (St John the Baptist) Gt Bowden w Welham,
Glooston and Cranoe *Leic*

GLOSSOP (All Saints) *Derby 6* **P** *Patr Bd*
V F K WHITEHEAD

GLOUCESTER (St Aldate) Finlay Road *Glouc 5* **P** *Bp*
V D C SAWYER

GLOUCESTER (St Barnabas) Tuffley *Glouc*

GLOUCESTER (St Catharine) *Glouc 5* **P** *Bp*
V R J LLEWELYN, **NSM** J R MURPHY

GLOUCESTER (St George) w Whaddon *Glouc 5* **P** *Bp*
V B A McQUILLEN, **C** J E TAYLOR, D J RUSSELL

GLOUCESTER (St James and All Saints) *Glouc 5* **P** *Bp*
V M W BUTLER, **C** A J FITCH, S A BOWEN,
NSM V J FRAY

GLOUCESTER (St Stephen) *Glouc 5* **P** *Bp*
V D G HUMPHRIES

GLOUCESTER (St Mark) *Glouc 5* **P** *Bp*
P-in-c A M LYNETT

**GLOUCESTER (St Mary de Crypt) (St John the Baptist)
(Christ Church) (St Mary de Lode and St Nicholas)**
Glouc 5 **P** *D&C, Bp, and Ld Chan (by turn)*
R D A BRAZINGTON, **C** S B MORRIS,
Hon C M J P BINGHAM

GLOUCESTER (St Michael) Tuffley *Glouc*

GLOUCESTER (St Oswald) Coney Hill *Glouc*

GLOUCESTER (St Paul) *Glouc 5* **P** *Bp* **V** R C KEY,
C D E S PRIMROSE

**GLOUCESTER DOCKS Mariners' Church Proprietary
Chapel** *Glouc 5* **P** *Ch Soc Trust* **Chapl** S G GWILT

GLOUCESTER ROAD (St Stephen) S Kensington St Steph
Lon

GLUSBURN (All Saints) Sutton *Bradf*

GLYMPTON (St Mary) Wootton w Glympton and
Kiddington *Ox*

GLYNDE (St Mary), West Firle and Beddingham *Chich 18*
P *Bp and D&C Windsor (alt)* **V** P A LYNN

GNOSALL (St Lawrence) *Lich 12* **P** *Bp* **V** M J POPE

GOADBY (St John the Baptist) Billesdon and Skeffington
Leic

GOADBY MARWOOD (St Denys) Scalford w Goadby
Marwood and Wycombe etc *Leic*

GOATHILL (St Peter) Milborne Port w Goathill *B & W*

GOATHLAND (St Mary) *York 23* **P** *Abp*
P-in-c E NEWLYN

GOATHURST (St Edward the King and Martyr) Spaxton w
Goathurst, Enmore and Charlynch *B & W*

GOBOWEN (All Saints) Hengoed w Gobowen *Lich*

GOBOWEN ROAD (Mission Room) Oswestry *Lich*

GODALMING (St Peter and St Paul) *Guildf 4* **P** *Bp*
V F J ASHE, **C** D R TOMLINSON, J C TOMLINSON (nee
MILLS)

GODINGTON (Holy Trinity) Stratton Audley and
Godington, Fringford etc *Ox*

GODLEY cum Newton Green (St John the Baptist) *Ches 14*
P *R Cheadle* **P-in-c** R H WHITE

GODMANCHESTER (St Mary) *Ely 9* **P** *D&C Westmr*
V N R T FOLLETT, **NSM** J G CRADDOCK

GODMANSTONE (Holy Trinity) Cerne Abbas w
Godmanstone and Minterne Magna *Sarum*

GODMERSHAM (St Lawrence the Martyr) Crundale w
Godmersham *Cant*

GODNEY (Holy Trinity) Glastonbury w Meare, W Pennard
and Godney *B & W*

GODOLPHIN (St John the Baptist) Crowan w Godolphin
Truro

GODSHILL (All Saints) *Portsm 7* **P** *Guild of All So*
P-in-c J M RYDER

GODSHILL (St Giles) Fordingbridge *Win*

GODSTONE (St Nicholas) *S'wark 24* **P** *C K G Hoare Esq*
R R E WATTS

GOFF'S OAK (St James) *St Alb 6* **P** *V Cheshunt*
V J W BRIDSTRUP

GOLBORNE (St Thomas) *Liv 16* **P** *Bp* **R** R PLANT

GOLCAR (St John the Evangelist) *Wakef 5*
P *V Huddersfield* **V** R M F CROMPTON,
C P H AINSWORTH

GOLDEN GREEN (Mission) Hadlow *Roch*

GOLDEN VALLEY (St Matthias) Riddings and Ironville
Derby

GOLDENHILL (St John the Evangelist) *Lich 16* **P** *Bp*
V J C G SELVINI

GOLDERS Green (St Alban the Martyr and St Michael)
Lon 15 **P** *Bp* **V** P G BAKER, **C** D L MUNCHIN

GOLDHANGER (St Peter) w Little Totham *Chelmsf 11*
P *Ld Chan* **R** D J ALLAN

GOLDINGTON (St Mary the Virgin) *St Alb 16* **P** *Bp*
V T MAINES, **C** Q D CHANDLER, **NSM** D G PRESTON

GOLDSBOROUGH (St Mary) Knaresborough *Ripon*

GOLDSWORTH PARK (St Andrew) *Guildf 12* **P** *Bp*
V R J N COOK

**GOLDTHORPE (St John the Evangelist and St Mary
Magdalene) w Hickleton** *Sheff 12* **P** *CR (2 turns), Earl of
Halifax (1 turn)* **V** A J DELVES, **C** M W OSBORNE

GOMERSAL (St Mary) *Wakef 8* **P** *Bp* **V** M G RAWSON

GONALSTON (St Laurence) *S'well 11* **P** *Comdr M B P
Francklin, Bp, and Ld Chan (by turn)* **R** M J BROCK

GONERBY, GREAT (St Sebastian) Barrowby and Gt
Gonerby *Linc*

GOOD EASTER (St Andrew) High and Gd Easter w
Margaret Roding *Chelmsf*

GOODERSTONE (St George) Cockley Cley w Gooderstone
Nor

GOODLEIGH (St Gregory) Barnstaple *Ex*

GOODMANHAM (All Saints) *York 7* **P** *Abp*
R A CLEMENTS

GOODMAYES (All Saints) *Chelmsf 4* **P** *Hyndman
Trustees* **V** C R KEATING

GOODMAYES (St Paul) *Chelmsf 4* **P** *Bp* **V** B J RUTT-
FIELD

GOODNESTONE (Holy Cross) Nonington w Wymynswold
and Goodnestone etc *Cant*

GOODRICH (St Giles) Walford and Saint John, w
Bishopswood etc *Heref*

GOODRINGTON (St George) *Ex 10* **P** *Bp*
V B D PROTHERO

GOODSHAW (St Mary and All Saints) and Crawshawbooth
Man 15 **P** *Bp and Wm Hulme Trustees (jt)*
P-in-c J A ARMES

GOODWORTH CLATFORD (St Peter) Abbotts Ann and
Upper and Goodworth Clatford *Win*

**GOOLE (St John the Evangelist) (St Mary) (Mariners' Club
and Chapel)** *Sheff 11* **P** *Bp* **V** T E LEACH,
C M WIGGLESWORTH, **NSM** K W SARGEANTSON

GOOSE GREEN (St Paul) *Liv 15* **P** *Bp* **V** J J HARTLEY,
C P HRYZIUK

GOOSEY (All Saints) Stanford in the Vale w Goosey and
Hatford *Ox*

GOOSNARGH (St Mary the Virgin) w Whittingham
Blackb 10 **P** *Bp* **V** B M BEAUMONT

GOOSTREY (St Luke) *Ches 11* **P** *V Sandbach*
V A G SPARHAM

GORAN HAVEN (St Just) St Goran w St Mich Caerhays
Truro

GOREFIELD (St Paul) *Ely 19* **P** *Bp*
P-in-c N A WHITEHOUSE

GORING (St Thomas of Canterbury) w South Stoke *Ox 6*
P *Ch Ch Ox* **V** P E NIXON, **C** R N F COLLINS

GORING-BY-SEA (St Mary) (St Laurence) *Chich 4* **P** *Bp*
V M J HORE, **C** C H LOVELESS, **Hon C** P MATTHEWS,
NSM K J TUFFEL

GORLESTON (St Andrew) *Nor 6* **P** *Ch Trust Fund Trust*
C L R COLLINSON, D R HARRISON,
NSM A T CADMORE

GORLESTON (St Mary Magdalene) *Nor 6* **P** *Bp and
Ch Trust Fund Trust (jt)* **V** T W RIESS

GORNAL, LOWER (St James the Great) *Worc 10* **P** *Bp*
V P E HUTCHINSON

GORNAL, UPPER (St Peter) *Worc 10* **P** *V Sedgley All SS*
V M K BATE

GORSLEY (Christ Church) Newent and Gorsley w Cliffords
Mesne *Glouc*

GORTON (Emmanuel) *Man 1* **P** *Bp* **R** M R J WILLIAMS,
C S S AGGREY

GORTON (Our Lady and St Thomas) *Man 1* **P** *Trustees*
R R G J HERRON

GORTON (St James) *Man 1* **P** *D&C* **C** S S AGGREY

GORTON (St Philip) *Man 1* **P** *The Crown* **R** *Vacant*
0161–231 2201

GOSBECK (St Mary) Coddenham w Gosbeck and
Hemingstone w Henley *St E*

GOSBERTON (St Peter and St Paul) *Linc 17* **P** *D&C*
V T G WILLIAMSON

**GOSBERTON CLOUGH (St Gilbert and St Hugh) and
Quadring** *Linc 17* **P** *Bp* **V** *Vacant* Spalding (01775)
680906

GOSCOTE, EAST (St Hilda) Syston TM *Leic*
GOSFIELD (St Katherine) *Chelmsf* 20 **P** *Mrs G M Lowe and Mrs M A Wilson* **V** *Vacant* Halstead (01787) 473857
GOSFORTH (All Saints) *Newc* 5 **P** *Bp* **V** R B HILL, **C** E J NOBLE
GOSFORTH (St Hugh) Newc Epiphany *Newc*
GOSFORTH (St Mary) w Nether Wasdale and Wasdale Head *Carl* 5 **P** *Bp, Earl of Lonsdale, V St Bees, and PCCs (jt)* **P-in-c** C B GALLOWAY
GOSFORTH (St Nicholas) *Newc* 5 **P** *Bp* **V** A M ROFF, **C** T P GIBBONS
GOSFORTH, NORTH (St Columba) Ch the King in the Dio of Newc *Newc*
GOSFORTH VALLEY (St Andrew) Dronfield w Holmesfield *Derby*
GOSPEL END (St Barnabas) Sedgley All SS *Worc*
GOSPEL LANE (St Michael) *Birm* 13 **P** *Bp* **V** R K JOHNSON, **C** C A HIBBERD
GOSPORT (Christ Church) *Portsm* 3 **P** *Bp* **V** D G JAMES, **C** B M HAMMOND, **NSM** R A FORSE
GOSPORT (Holy Trinity) *Portsm* 3 **P** *DBP* **V** J R CAPPER
GOSSOPS GREEN (St Alban) Ifield *Chich*
GOTHAM (St Lawrence) *S'well* 10 **P** *Bp* **P-in-c** D C GORICK, **NSM** J H MOORE, A C SUTHERLAND, J M GORICK
GOUDHURST (St Mary the Virgin) w Kilndown *Cant* 11 **P** *Abp and Prime Min (alt)* **V** R C CAMPBELL-SMITH
GOULCEBY (All Saints) Asterby Gp *Linc*
GOXHILL (All Saints) Barrow and Goxhill *Linc*
GOXHILL (St Giles) Aldbrough, Mappleton w Goxhill and Withernwick *York*
GRADE (St Grada and the Holy Cross) St Ruan w St Grade and Landewednack *Truro*
GRAFFHAM (St Giles) w Woolavington *Chich* 11 **P** *Bp* **P-in-c** K F HYDE-DUNN
GRAFFOE GROUP *Linc* 18 **P** *Ch Coll Cam, D&C and DBP, Vicountess Chaplin, Or Coll Ox, J C M Fullerton Esq (by turn)* **V** *Vacant* Lincoln (01522) 810246
GRAFHAM (All Saints) *Ely* 10 **P** *Bp* **P-in-c** J ALFORD
GRAFHAM (St Andrew) Bramley and Grafham *Guildf*
GRAFTON, EAST (St Nicholas) Wexcombe *Sarum*
GRAFTON FLYFORD (St John the Baptist) Abberton, The Flyfords, Naunton Beauchamp etc *Worc*
GRAFTON REGIS (St Mary) Stoke Bruerne w Grafton Regis and Alderton *Pet*
GRAFTON UNDERWOOD (St James the Apostle) Cranford w Grafton Underwood and Twywell *Pet*
GRAHAME PARK (St Augustine) Conventional District *Lon* 15 **C-in-c** A K DANGERFIELD, **C** J P CARLISLE
GRAIN (St James) w Stoke *Roch* 6 **P** *DBP* **V** *Vacant* Medway (01634) 270263
GRAINSBY (St Nicholas) North-Chapel Parishes, The *Linc*
GRAINTHORPE (St Clement) Somercotes and Grainthorpe w Conisholme *Linc*
GRAMPOUND (St Nun) Probus, Ladock and Grampound w Creed and St Erme *Truro*
GRAMPOUND ROAD Mission Church as above
GRANBOROUGH (St John the Baptist) Schorne *Ox*
GRANBY (All Saints) Cropwell Bishop w Colston Bassett, Granby etc *S'well*
GRANDBOROUGH (St Peter) w Willoughby and Flecknoe *Cov* 6 **P** *Bp* **P-in-c** A J HOBSON
GRANE (St Stephen) Haslingdon w Grane and Stonefield *Blackb*
GRANGE (Holy Trinity) Borrowdale *Carl*
GRANGE (St Andrew) *Ches* 3 **P** *Bp* **V** D R FELIX, **C** D E WATSON
GRANGE FELL (not known) Grange-over-Sands *Carl*
GRANGE MOOR (St Bartholomew) Kirkheaton *Wakef*
GRANGE-OVER-SANDS (St Paul) *Carl* 10 **P** *Bp* **V** A GIBSON
GRANGE PARK (St Peter) *Lon* 18 **P** *Bp* **V** S P STARTUP
GRANGE VILLA (St Columba) W Pelton *Dur*
GRANGETOWN (St Aidan) *Dur* 9 **P** *V Ryhope* **V** C COLLINS
GRANGETOWN (St Hilda of Whitby) *York* 19 **P** *Abp* **V** R G S DEADMAN
GRANSDEN, GREAT (St Bartholomew) w LITTLE (St Peter and St Paul) *Ely* 12 **P** *Clare Coll Cam* **R** R K D WATKINS-WRIGHT
GRANTCHESTER (St Andrew and St Mary) *Ely* 7 **P** *CCC Cam* **V** J S BEER
GRANTHAM (St Anne) (St Wulfram) (Ascension) (Epiphany) *Linc* 19 **P** *Bp* **TR** R PREISS, **TV** P J MANDER, P N WEBB, **TV** M THURLEY, G A PLUMB, C P CRAVEN, **C** D E ALLEN, **NSM** J T FARLEY, F H LONG, R J MILLER
GRANVILLES WOOTTON (St Mary the Virgin) Dungeon Hill *Sarum*

GRAPPENHALL (St Wilfrid) *Ches* 4 **P** *P G Greenall Esq* **R** M B KELLY, **Hon C** S BECKETT, **NSM** M JONES
GRASBY (All Saints) *Linc* 5 **P** *Lord Tennyson* **V** *Vacant*
GRASMERE (St Oswald) *Carl* 10 **P** *Qu Coll Ox* **P-in-c** W E R WILKINSON, **NSM** A MANNING
GRASSENDALE (St Mary) *Liv* 4 **P** *Trustees* **V** M E GREENWOOD
GRATELEY (St Leonard) Amport, Grateley, Monxton and Quarley *Win*
GRATWICH (St Mary the Virgin) Kingstone w Gratwich *Lich*
GRAVELEY (St Botolph) w Papworth St Agnes w Yelling and Toseland *Ely* 1 **P** *Jes Coll Cam, T J H Sperling Esq, and Ld Chan (by turn)* **R** T J MARKS
GRAVELEY (St Mary) Gt and Lt Wymondley w Graveley and Chivesfield *St Alb*
GRAVELLY HILL (All Saints) *Birm* 6 **P** *Bp* **V** D E NEWSOME, **C** M A L BARZEY
GRAVENEY (All Saints) Preston next Faversham, Goodnestone and Graveney *Cant*
GRAVENHURST, UPPER (St Giles) w Lower Gravenhurst *St Alb* 22 **P** *Bp* **P-in-c** P J SWINDELLS, **NSM** C M EAGGER
GRAVESEND (Holy Family) w Ifield *Roch* 4 **P** *Bp and Lt-Col F B Edmeades (jt)* **R** R J R AMYS
GRAVESEND (St Aidan) *Roch* 4 **P** *Bp* **V** B PEARSON, **NSM** J P LITTLEWOOD
GRAVESEND (St George) *Roch* 4 **P** *Bp* **R** D G WILLEY, **C** J P A ELVIN
GRAVESEND (St Mary) *Roch* 4 **P** *R Gravesend* **V** C W KITCHENER, **NSM** E C KITCHENER
GRAYINGHAM (St Radegunda) *Linc* 6 **P** *Bp* **R** D I WALKER
GRAYRIGG (St John the Evangelist), Old Hutton and New Hutton *Carl* 9 **P** *V Kendal* **P-in-c** A M R STOCKLEY
GRAYS THURROCK (St Peter and St Paul) *Chelmsf* 14 **P** *DBP* **TR** R J WIGGS, **TV** P E PIMENTEL, **C** M IVIN, S D MASON, **NSM** J K EDWARDS
GRAYSHOTT (St Luke) *Guildf* 3 **P** *Bp* **V** W J MEYER, **NSM** D J LUSBY
GRAYSWOOD (All Saints) *Guildf* 4 **P** *Bp* **P-in-c** A J SHAW
GRAYTHWAITE (Mission Room) Hawkshead and Low Wray w Sawrey *Carl*
GRAZELEY (Holy Trinity) Beech Hill, Grazeley and Spencers Wood *Ox*
GREASBROUGH (St Mary) *Sheff* 6 **P** *Sir Stephen Hastings* **C** J HELLEWELL
GREASBY (St Nicholas) Frankby w Greasby *Ches*
GREASLEY (St Mary) *S'well* 4 **P** *Bp* **V** T A JOYCE, **C** G CHATFIELD
GREAT: *see also under substantive place names*
GREAT CAMBRIDGE ROAD (St John the Baptist and St James) *Lon* 19 **P** *D&C St Paul's* **V** P B LYONS, **Hon C** P E STURAY
GREAT GLEN (St Cuthbert), Stretton Magna and Wistow cum Newton Harcourt *Leic* 5 **P** *Bp and Hon Ann Brooks (jt)* **V** J F WELLINGTON
GREAT MOOR (St Saviour) Stockport St Sav *Ches*
GREATER: *see under substantive place name*
GREATFORD (St Thomas a Becket) Uffington Gp *Linc*
GREATHAM (not known) Amberley w N Stoke and Parham, Wiggonholt etc *Chich*
GREATHAM (St John the Baptist) *Dur* 13 **P** *Trustees* **P-in-c** D C COULING
GREATHAM w Empshott and Hawkley w Prior's Dean *Portsm* 5 **P** *DBP* **R** W C DAY
GREATSTONE (St Peter) Lydd *Cant*
GREATWORTH (St Peter) and Marston St Lawrence w Warkorth and Thenford *Pet* 1 **P** *Bp (2 turns), DBP (1 turn)* **R** A E TURNER
GREAVE FOLD (Holy Innocents) Chadkirk *Ches*
GREEN HAMMERTON (St Thomas) Whixley w Green Hammerton *Ripon*
GREEN HAWORTH (St Clement) Accrington *Blackb*
GREEN HEATH (St Saviour) Hednesford *Lich*
GREEN STREET GREEN (St Mary) and Pratts Bottom *Roch* 15 **P** *Bp* **V** P MILLER, **C** R M WORSSAM
GREEN VALE (Holy Trinity) Stockton Green Vale H Trin CD *Dur*
GREENFIELD (St Mary) *Man* 21 **P** *Bp* **V** L R TOONE
GREENFIELDS (United Church) Shrewsbury All SS w St Mich *Lich*
GREENFORD (Holy Cross) (St Edward the Confessor) *Lon* 22 **P** *K Coll Cam* **R** N RICHARDSON, **C** J R BAKER, S J ROGERS
GREENFORD, NORTH (All Hallows) *Lon* 22 **P** *Bp* **P-in-c** M WHEELER
GREENGATES (St John the Evangelist) *Bradf* 3 **P** *D&C* **V** T COLLIN

GREENHAM (St Mary the Virgin) *Ox 14* **P** *Bp*
  V J P H CLARKE
GREENHAM (St Peter) Wellington and Distr *B & W*
GREENHEAD (St Cuthbert) Haltwhistle and Greenhead
  Newc
GREENHILL (St John the Baptist) *Lon 23* **P** *Bp, Adn, and*
  V Harrow St Mary (jt) **P-in-c** J F SPINKS
GREENHILL (St Peter) *Sheff 2* **P** *Bp* **V** L C JENKINS
GREENHITHE (St Mary) *Roch 2* **P** *Ch Soc Trust and*
  Canon T L Livermore (jt) **R** R D BARRON
GREENHOW HILL (St Mary) Upper Nidderdale *Ripon*
GREENLANDS (St Anne) *Blackb 9* **P** *Bp and V Blackpool*
  St Steph (jt) **V** S L JONES
GREENLANDS (St John the Evangelist) Ipsley *Worc*
GREENS NORTON (St Bartholomew) w Bradden and
  Lichborough *Pet 5* **P** *J E Grant-Ives Esq (1 turn), The*
  Crown (3 turns), and Melanesian Miss Trust (1 turn)
  R J D V EVANS
GREENSIDE (St John) *Dur 5* **P** *R Ryton w Hedgefield*
  P-in-c P D SADDINGTON
GREENSTEAD (St Andrew) (St Edmund's Church Hall)
  (St Matthew) *Chelmsf 17* **P** *Ld Chan*
  P-in-c B L BIRCHMORE, **C** B S RAWLINGS,
  J H DELFGOU, **NSM** J D MITSON
GREENSTEAD GREEN (St James Apostle) Halstead St
  Andr w H Trin and Greenstead Green *Chelmsf*
GREENSTED-JUXTA-ONGAR (St Andrew) w Stanford
  Rivers *Chelmsf 28* **P** *Bp Lon and Duchy of Lanc (alt)*
  R T A GARDINER
GREENWICH (St Alfege w St Peter and St Paul) *S'wark 1*
  P *The Crown* **V** G S HARCOURT, **C** R P H BUCK
GREENWICH, EAST (Christ Church) (St Andrew and
  St Michael) *S'wark 1* **P** *V Greenwich St Alfege etc*
  C T W HURCOMBE
GREETE (St James) Burford II w Greete and Hope Bagot
  Heref
GREETHAM (All Saints) Fulletby w Greetham and Ashby
  Puerorum *Linc*
GREETHAM (St Mary the Virgin) and Thistleton w Stretton
  and Clipsham *Pet 14* **P** *Bp and Sir David Davenport-*
  Handley (alt) **V** P TOWNSEND
GREETLAND (St Thomas) and West Vale *Wakef 2*
  P *V Halifax* **V** D J HUMPHRIES
GREETWELL (All Saints) Cherry Willingham w Greetwell
  Linc
GREINTON (St Michael and All Angels) *B & W 5* **P** *Bp*
  R *Vacant*
GRENDON (All Saints) Baddesley Ensor w Grendon *Birm*
GRENDON (St Mary) Yardley Hastings, Denton and
  Grendon etc *Pet*
GRENDON BISHOP (St John the Baptist) Bredenbury w
  Grendon Bishop and Wacton etc *Heref*
GRENDON UNDERWOOD (St Leonard) Swan *Ox*
GRENOSIDE (St Mark) *Sheff 3* **P** *Bp and*
  V Ecclesfield (jt) **V** M W G STIBBE, **C** P E BOLD
GRESHAM (All Saints) *Nor 22* **P** *Guild of All So*
  P-in-c D F HAYDEN
GRESLEY (St George and St Mary) *Derby 16* **P** *Simeon's*
  Trustees **V** W B HERD
GRESSENHALL (Assumption of the Blessed Virgin Mary) w
  Longham w Wendling and Bittering Parva *Nor 15*
  P *Ld Chan (1 turn), J E T H Dodson Esq (2 turns)*
  R J E BELHAM
GRESSINGHAM (St John the Evangelist) Whittington w
  Arkholme and Gressingham *Blackb*
GRETTON (Christ Church) Winchcombe, Gretton, Sudeley
  Manor etc *Glouc*
GRETTON (St James the Great) w Rockingham and Caldecote
  Pet 9 **P** *Bp (2 turns), Comdr L M M Saunders-Watson*
  (1 turn) **V** G H RICHMOND
GREWELTHORPE (St James) Fountains Gp *Ripon*
GREYSTEAD (St Luke) N Tyne and Redesdale Team *Newc*
GREYSTOKE (St Andrew), Matterdale, Mungrisdale and
  Watermillock *Carl 4* **P** *DBP* **TR** R P H FRANK,
  TV R WALKER
GREYSTONES (St Gabriel) Ecclesall *Sheff*
GREYSTONES (St Gabriel) *Sheff 2* **P** *Provost Sheff*
  V P W BECKLEY
GREYWELL (St Mary) Newnham w Nately Scures w
  Mapledurwell etc *Win*
GRIMEHILLS (St Mary) Darwen St Barn *Blackb*
GRIMETHORPE (St Luke) *Wakef 7* **P** *Bp* **V** *Vacant*
  Barnsley (01226) 711331
GRIMLEY (St Bartholomew) w Holt *Worc 3* **P** *Bp*
  P-in-c C P COPELAND
GRIMOLDBY (St Edith) Mid Marsh Gp *Linc*
GRIMSARGH (St Michael) *Blackb 14* **P** *R Preston*
  V A J HASLAM

GRIMSBURY (St Leonard) Banbury *Ox*
GRIMSBY (St Augustine of Hippo) *Linc 9* **P** *TR Gt Grimsby*
  SS Mary and Jas **V** M C KING
GRIMSBY, GREAT (St Andrew w St Luke and All Saints)
  Linc 9 **P** *Bp* **P-in-c** M M E ISAM, **C** J A MUSTON
GRIMSBY, GREAT (St Mary and St James) (St Hugh)
  (St Mark) (St Martin) *Linc 9* **P** *Bp* **TR** M O HUNTER,
  TV M STEPHENS, G A CURTIS, S J POTHEN,
  P R DOWN, **C** S D MASON, **Hon C** E MARSHALL
GRIMSBY, LITTLE (St Edith) Fotherby *Linc*
GRIMSTEAD, EAST (Holy Trinity) Alderbury Team *Sarum*
GRIMSTEAD, WEST (St John) as above
GRIMSTON (St Botolph), Congham and Roydon *Nor 21*
  P *Qu Coll Cam, Bp, and G Howard Esq (jt)*
  R W A HOWARD
GRIMSTON (St John the Baptist) Ab Kettleby Gp *Leic*
GRIMSTON, NORTH (St Nicholas) Settrington w N
  Grimston and Wharram *York*
GRINDALE (St Nicholas) Burton Fleming w Fordon,
  Grindale etc *York*
GRINDLEFORD (St Helen) Eyam *Derby*
GRINDLETON (St Ambrose) Bolton by Bowland w
  Grindleton *Bradf*
GRINDON (All Saints) Calton, Cauldon, Grindon and
  Waterfall *Lich*
GRINDON (St James) and Stillington *Dur 16* **P** *Bp*
  V M GOODALL
GRINDON (St Oswald) Sunderland Pennywell St Thos *Dur*
GRINGLEY-ON-THE-HILL (St Peter and St Paul) *S'well 1*
  P *Bp* **P-in-c** D HOLLIS
GRINSDALE (St Kentigern) Burgh-by-Sands and
  Kirkbampton w Kirkandrews etc *Carl*
GRINSHILL (All Saints) Astley, Clive, Grinshill and
  Hadnall *Lich*
GRINSTEAD, EAST (St Mary the Virgin) *Chich 7* **P** *Bp*
  V G BOND
GRINSTEAD, EAST (St Swithun) *Chich 7* **P** *Bp*
  V J R BROWN, **C** E J POLLARD, S ATTWATER,
  NSM I M EDYE
GRINSTEAD, WEST (St George) *Chich 8* **P** *Bp*
  R W E M HARRIS
GRINTON (St Andrew) Swaledale *Ripon*
GRISTHORPE (St Thomas) Filey *York*
GRISTON (St Peter and St Paul) Caston w Griston, Merton,
  Thompson etc *Nor*
GRITTLETON (St Mary the Virgin) Stanton St Quintin,
  Hullavington, Grittleton etc *Bris*
GRIZEBECK (The Good Shepherd) Kirkby Ireleth *Carl*
GROBY (St Philip and St James) Ratby w Groby *Leic*
GROOMBRIDGE (St John the Evangelist) Speldhurst w
  Groombridge and Ashurst *Roch*
GROOMBRIDGE, NEW (St Thomas) *Chich 19*
  P *R Withyham* **V** C M HENLEY
GROSMONT (St Matthew) Egton w Grosmont *York*
GROSVENOR CHAPEL (no dedication) Chapel of Ease in the
  parish of Hanover Square St George w St Mark *Lon 3*
  C-in-c S J HOBBS
GROTON (St Bartholomew) Edwardstone w Groton and Lt
  Waldingfield *St E*
GROVE (St Helen) E Markham w Askham, Headon w
  Upton and Grove *S'well*
GROVE (St John the Baptist) *Ox 19* **P** *D&C Windsor*
  V R J FRENCH, **C** K M SINGLETON, R W FRAY
GROVE GREEN (St John) Local Ecumenical Project
  Cant 15 **Min** S P WALKER
GROVEHILL (Resurrection) Hemel Hempstead *St Alb*
GRUNDISBURGH (St Mary the Virgin) Boulge w Burgh
  and Grundisburgh *St E*
GUARLFORD (St Mary) Newland, Guarlford and
  Madresfield *Worc*
GUERNSEY (Holy Trinity) *Win 14* **P** *Trustees* **V** J BERRY
GUERNSEY L'Islet (St Mary) Guernsey St Sampson *Win*
GUERNSEY (St Andrew de la Pommeraye) *Win 14* **P** *The*
  Crown **R** J A GUILLE
GUERNSEY (St John the Evangelist) *Win 14* **P** *Trustees*
  V P HENRY
GUERNSEY (St Marguerite de la Foret) *Win 14* **P** *The*
  Crown **R** W A CANHAM
GUERNSEY (St Martin) *Win 14* **P** *The Crown*
  R F M TRICKEY
GUERNSEY (St Matthew) *Win 14* **P** *R Ste Marie du Castel*
  V M R STARR, **NSM** L S LE VASSEUR
GUERNSEY (St Michel du Valle) *Win 14* **P** *The Crown*
  R E J WIDDOWS
GUERNSEY (St Peter Port) *Win 14* **P** *The Crown*
  R J R FENWICK, **NSM** G J BARRETT
GUERNSEY (St Philippe de Torteval) *Win 14* **P** *The Crown*
  R *Vacant* Guernsey (01481) 63544

GUERNSEY (St Pierre du Bois) *Win 14* **P** *The Crown*
R N GRIFFITHS
GUERNSEY (St Sampson) *Win 14* **P** *The Crown*
R J E IRONSIDE
GUERNSEY (St Saviour) (Chapel of St Apolline) *Win 14*
P *The Crown* **R** L G H CRASKE
GUERNSEY (St Stephen) *Win 14* **P** *R St Peter Port*
V M C MILLARD, **Hon C** H S RIDGE,
NSM R G BELLINGER
GUERNSEY (Ste Marie du Castel) *Win 14* **P** *The Crown*
R M R STARR, **NSM** L S LE VASSEUR
GUESTLING (St Lawrence) Fairlight, Guestling and Pett
Chich
GUESTWICK (St Peter) Foulsham w Hindolveston and
Guestwick *Nor*
GUILDEN MORDEN (St Mary) Shingay Gp of Par *Ely*
GUILDEN SUTTON (St John the Baptist) Plemstall w
Guilden Sutton *Ches*
GUILDFORD (All Saints) *Guildf 5* **P** *Bp* **V** B J COLEMAN
GUILDFORD (Christ Church) *Guildf 5* **P** *Simeon's*
Trustees **V** J J R COLLINGWOOD, **C** P H BOUGHTON,
E M V BOUGHTON, **NSM** D H BEVIS
GUILDFORD (Holy Spirit) Burpham *Guildf*
GUILDFORD (Holy Trinity) (St Mary) (St Michael)
Guildf 5 **P** *Bp* **C** S A BAKER, D A CAMERON,
NSM J G TODD
GUILDFORD (St Clare) Westborough *Guildf*
GUILDFORD (St Francis) as above
GUILDFORD (St Luke) Burpham *Guildf*
GUILDFORD (St Nicolas) *Guildf 5* **P** *Bp*
R A H NORMAN, **C** P M BLEE
GUILDFORD (St Saviour) *Guildf 5* **P** *Simeon's Trustees*
R D J BRACEWELL
GUILSBOROUGH (St Ethelreda) w Hollowell and Cold
Ashby *Pet 2* **P** *J L Lowther Esq (2 turns) and Bp (1 turn)*
V W G GIBBS
GUISBOROUGH (St Nicholas) *York 17* **P** *Abp*
R P L BISHOP, **C** N O TUFFNELL
GUISELEY (St Oswald King and Martyr) w Esholt *Bradf 4*
P *Patr Bd* **TR** G B ATHERTON, **TV** P HARTLEY,
NSM T H BAXTER
GUIST (St Andrew) Twyford, Guist, Bintree, Themelthorpe
etc *Nor*
GUITING POWER (St Michael) The Guitings, Cutsdean
and Farmcote *Glouc*
GUITINGS, Cutsdean and Farmcote, The *Glouc 15*
P *E R Cochrane Esq and Ch Ch Ox (alt)* **V** *Vacant* Guiting
Power (01451) 850268
GULDEFORD, EAST (St Mary) Rye *Chich*
GULVAL (St Gulval) *Truro 5* **P** *Ld Chan* **V** A K TORRY
GULWORTHY (St Paul) Tavistock and Gulworthy *Ex*
GUMLEY (St Helen) Foxton w Gumley and Laughton and
Lubenham *Leic*
GUNBY (St Nicholas) Witham Gp *Linc*
GUNBY (St Peter) Welton-le-Marsh w Gunby *Linc*
GUNHOUSE (otherwise Gunness) (St Barnabas) w Burringham
Linc 4 **P** *Bp Lon* **R** *Vacant* Scunthorpe (01724) 783550
GUNN CHAPEL (Holy Name) Swimbridge and W Buckland
Ex
GUNNESS (St Barnabas) Gunhouse w Burringham *Linc*
GUNNISLAKE (St Anne) Calstock *Truro*
GUNTHORPE (St John the Baptist) Lowdham w Caythorpe,
and Gunthorpe *S'well*
GUNTHORPE (St Mary) w Bale w Field Dalling, Saxlingham
and Sharrington *Nor 19* **P** *Keble Coll Ox, MMCET, Bp,*
and DBP (by turn) **R** M R WARD
GUNTON St Peter (St Benedict) *Nor 9* **P** *CPAS* **R** *Vacant*
Lowestoft (01502) 572600
GUNWALLOE (St Winwalloe) Cury and Gunwalloe w
Mawgan *Truro*
GURNARD (All Saints) *Portsm 8* **P** *Bp* **R** C B BURLAND
GUSSAGE (St Andrew) Handley w Gussage St Andrew and
Pentridge *Sarum*
GUSSAGE ALL SAINTS (All Saints) Tollard Royal w
Farnham, Gussage St Michael etc *Sarum*
GUSSAGE ST MICHAEL (St Michael) as above
GUSTARD WOOD (St Peter) Wheathampstead *St Alb*
GUSTON (St Martin of Tours) Whitfield w Guston *Cant*
GUYHIRN (St Mary Magdalene) w Ring's End *Ely 19*
P *Bp* **V** R J SEAMAN
GWEEK (Mission Church) Constantine *Truro*
GWENNAP (St Weneppa) St Stythians w Perranarworthal
and Gwennap *Truro*
GWINEAR (St Winnear) Phillack w Gwithian and Gwinear
Truro
GWITHIAN (St Gwithian) as above
HABBERLEY (St Mary) *Heref 13* **P** *Bp*
P-in-c W K ROWELL

HABERGHAM (All Saints) W Burnley *Blackb*
HABERGHAM EAVES (St Matthew the Apostle) Burnley
(Habergham Eaves) St Matt w H Trin *Blackb*
HABROUGH Group, The (St Margaret) *Linc 10* **P** *DBP*
P-in-c B A HARRISON
HABTON, GREAT (St Chad) Kirby Misperton w
Normanby, Edston and Salton *York*
HACCOMBE (St Blaise) Stoke-in-Teignhead w Combe-in-
Teignhead etc *Ex*
HACCONBY (St Andrew) Morton w Hacconby *Linc*
HACHESTON (St Andrew) Campsea Ashe w Marlesford,
Parham and Hacheston *St E*
HACKBRIDGE and North Beddington (All Saints)
S'wark 26 **P** *Bp* **P-in-c** A O ROLAND
HACKENTHORPE (Christ Church) *Sheff 2* **P** *Bp*
V S J WILLETT
HACKFORD (St Mary the Virgin) High Oak *Nor*
HACKINGTON (St Stephen) *Cant 3* **P** *Adn Cant*
C D CRABTREE, **Hon C** M A MASCALL
HACKNESS (St Peter) w Harwood Dale *York 16* **P** *Lord*
Derwent **P-in-c** W F CURTIS
HACKNEY Mount Pleasant Lane (St Matthew) Upper
Clapton St Matt *Lon*
HACKNEY (St James) (St John) *Lon 5* **P** *Patr Bd*
TV A E MEERE, **C** I McDOWELL
HACKNEY (St Thomas) Stamford Hill St Thos *Lon*
HACKNEY, OVER (Mission Room) Darley *Derby*
HACKNEY, SOUTH (St John) (Christ Church) *Lon 5*
P *Lord Amherst* **R** N R J FUNNELL, **C** P A FARQUHAR
HACKNEY, SOUTH (St Michael and All Angels) London
Fields w Haggerston (St Paul) *Lon 5* **P** *R S Hackney St Jo*
w Ch Ch **V** A N EVERETT, **NSM** J M KING, H LODER
HACKNEY, WEST St Barnabas (St Paul) *Lon 5* **P** *Bp*
R F A PRESTON, **C** E J BRACK
HACKNEY MARSH (All Souls) *Lon 5* **P** *Patr Bd*
TR A P HOBSON, **TV** D N WINTERBURN,
C P W STONE, R A FAIRHURST
HACKNEY WICK (St Mary of Eton) (St Augustine) *Lon 5*
P *Eton Coll* **C** P J BOARDMAN
HACKTHORN (St Michael and All Angels) w Cold Hanworth
Linc 3 **P** *Mrs B K Eley* **P-in-c** I R HOWITT
HADDENHAM (Holy Trinity) *Ely 14* **P** *Adn Ely*
V M P WADSWORTH
HADDENHAM (St Mary the Virgin) w Cuddington, Kingsey
and Aston Sandford *Ox 20* **P** *D&C Roch*
V D W A GREGG, **Hon C** P McEACHRAN
HADDLESEY (St John the Baptist) Haddlesey w Hambleton
and Birkin *York*
HADDISCOE (St Mary) The Raveningham Gp *Nor*
HADDLESEY w Hambleton and Birkin *York 6* **P** *Abp and*
Simeon's Trustees (jt) **R** A G GREENHOUGH
HADDON (St Mary) Stilton w Denton and Caldecote etc *Ely*
HADDON, EAST (St Mary the Virgin) Church Brampton,
Chapel Brampton, Harleston etc *Pet*
HADDON, OVER (St Anne) Bakewell *Derby*
HADDON, WEST (All Saints) w Winwick and Ravensthorpe
Pet 2 **P** *DBP* **V** D STAPLES
HADFIELD (St Andrew) *Derby 6* **P** *Bp* **V** A BUCKLEY
HADHAM, LITTLE (St Cecilia) w Albury *St Alb 4* **P** *Bp*
Lon **R** J TAPLIN
HADHAM, MUCH (St Andrew) *St Alb 4* **P** *Bp Lon*
R M A McADAM
HADLEIGH (St Barnabas) *Chelmsf 10* **P** *Bp*
NSM M A BOYS
HADLEIGH (St James the Less) *Chelmsf 10*
P *Dr P W M Copeman* **R** *Vacant* Southend-on-Sea (01702)
558992
HADLEIGH (St Mary) w Layham and Shelley *St E 2* **P** *Abp*
and St Jo Coll Cam (alt) **P-in-c** S C MORRIS,
C C L WINGFIELD, **NSM** J M WILLIS, J H DOSSOR
HADLEY (Holy Trinity) *Lich 27* **P** *Bp, Adn Salop,*
V Wrockwardine, R Kynnersley, and V Wellington w
Eyton (jt) **P-in-c** V C SWEET
HADLEY WOOD (St Paul) Enfield Ch Ch Trent Park *Lon*
HADLOW (St Mary) *Roch 10* **P** *Exors Miss I N King*
V M M CAMP
HADLOW DOWN (St Mark) Buxted and Hadlow Down
Chich
HADNALL (St Mary Magdalene) Astley, Clive, Grinshill
and Hadnall *Lich*
HADSTOCK (St Botolph) Ashdon w Hadstock *Chelmsf*
HADZOR w Oddingley (St James) Bowbrook S *Worc*
HAGBOURNE (St Andrew) Blewbury, Hagbourne and
Upton *Ox*
HAGGERSTON (All Saints) *Lon 5* **P** *Ld Chan*
P-in-c J F WILLARD, **C** R J S PEARSON
HAGGERSTON (St Chad) *Lon 5* **P** *The Crown*
V D H T LEE

HAGLEY (St John the Baptist) *Worc 12* **P** *Viscount Cobham*
R *Vacant* Kidderminster (01562) 882442
HAGLEY, WEST (St Saviour) Hagley *Worc*
HAGNABY (St Andrew) Marden Hill Gp *Linc*
HAGWORTHINGHAM (Holy Trinity) as above
HAIGH (St David) *Liv 14* **P** *R Wigan* **V** G J T TAYLOR
HAIL WESTON (St Nicholas) *Ely 12* **P** *Mert Coll Ox*
V W N BROOK
HAILE (not known) Egremont and Haile *Carl*
HAILES (Chapel) Toddington, Stanton, Didbrook w Hailes
etc *Glouc*
HAILEY (St John the Evangelist) Witney *Ox*
HAILSHAM (St Mary) *Chich 16* **P** *Ch Soc Trust*
V R G H PORTHOUSE, **C** W K PUGH, J R JAMES
HAINAULT (St Paul) *Chelmsf 4* **P** *Bp*
V M W LEARMOUTH
HAINFORD (All Saints) Hevingham w Hainford and
Stratton Strawless *Nor*
HAINTON (St Mary) Barkwith Gp *Linc*
HALA (St Paul's Centre) Scotforth *Blackb*
HALAM (St Michael) Edingley w Halam *S'well*
HALBERTON (St Andrew) Sampford Peverell, Uplowman,
Holcombe Rogus etc *Ex*
HALDEN, HIGH (St Mary the Virgin) Bethersden w High
Halden *Cant*
HALDENS (Christ the King) Digswell and Panshanger
St Alb
HALDON (St Mary) Teignmouth, Ideford w Luton, Ashcombe etc *Ex*
HALE (St David) Timperley *Ches*
HALE (St John the Evangelist) *Guildf 3* **P** *Bp*
V H I J SOUTHERN, **C** P A BARLOW
HALE (St Mary) *Liv 13* **P** *Trustees* **P-in-c** J D ENGEL,
NSM W O BALMER
HALE (St Mary) w South Charford *Win 8*
P *P N Hickman Esq* **P-in-c** T E DAYKIN,
NSM C E ROLFE
HALE (St Peter) and Ashley *Ches 10* **P** *V Bowdon*
V D ASHWORTH, **C** P J MACKRIELL
HALE, GREAT (St John the Baptist) Helpringham w Hale
Linc
HALE, UPPER (St Mark) Hale *Guildf*
HALEBANK (St Mary Mission) as above
HALES (St Mary) Cheswardine, Childs Ercall, Hales,
Hinstock etc *Lich*
HALESOWEN (St John the Baptist) *Worc 9* **P** *Patr Bd*
TR J C EVEREST, **TV** S R BUCKLEY, B A L CAMP,
C J A PARSONS, **Hon C** C A KENT
**HALESWORTH (St Mary) w Linstead, Chediston, Holton
St Peter, Blyford, Spexhall, Wissett and Walpole** *St E 15*
P *Ld Chan and DBP (alt)* **TR** L W DOOLAN,
TV A B NORTON, W M BULMAN, **C** T J N L'ESTRANGE
HALEWOOD (St Nicholas) (St Mary) *Liv 4* **P** *Bp*
TM C DOWDLE, **TV** J H TYNDALL,
NSM C CRITCHLEY
HALFORD (Our Blessed Lady) Alderminster and Halford
Cov
HALFORD (St Thomas) Sibdon Carwood w Halford *Heref*
HALFWAY (St Peter) Minster in Sheppey *Cant*
HALIFAX Haley Hill (All Souls) *Wakef 4* **P** *Simeon's
Trustees* **P-in-c** A P BOWSHER
HALIFAX (Holy and Undivided Trinity) *Wakef 4* **P** *Bp and
V Halifax (jt)* **V** G R CALVERT
HALIFAX (St Anne in the Grove) *Wakef 2* **P** *V Halifax*
V D BURROWS
HALIFAX (St Augustine) *Wakef 4* **P** *Trustees*
V P W GOODMAN
HALIFAX (St Hilda) *Wakef 4* **P** *Bp* **V** J C WIDDOWS
HALIFAX (St John the Baptist) *Wakef 4* **P** *The Crown*
V A A ROSS
HALIFAX (St John the Baptist in the Wilderness) *Wakef 3*
P *V Halifax* **V** *Vacant* Halifax (01422) 882572
HALIFAX (St Jude) *Wakef 4* **P** *Trustees*
V D R G LOCKYER
HALIFAX (St James and St Mary) Halifax H Trin *Wakef*
HALL GREEN (Ascension) *Birm 13* **P** *Bp, V Yardley, and
Vice-Chmn of PCC (jt)* **V** J G RUSSELL
HALL GREEN (St Peter) *Birm 8* **P** *Bp* **P-in-c** N E BALL
HALL STREET (St Andrew) Stockport St Mary *Ches*
HALLAM, WEST (St Wilfred) and Mapperley *Derby 13*
P *Bp* **R** E C LYONS, **Hon C** S KRZEMINSKI,
NSM S G WATHEN
**HALLATON (St Michael and All Angels) w Horninghold and
Allexton, Tugby and East Norton and Slawston** *Leic 4*
P *Bp, DBP, and E Brudenell Esq (jt)* **R** J ADAMS
HALLING (St John the Baptist) Cuxton and Halling *Roch*

**HALLINGBURY, GREAT (St Giles) (St Andrew) and
LITTLE (St Mary the Virgin)** *Chelmsf 27* **P** *Bp and Govs
Charterhouse (jt)* **R** T J G LOW
HALLIWELL (St Luke) *Man 9* **P** *MMCET* **C** P E BERRY
HALLIWELL (St Margaret) *Man 9* **P** *Trustees*
V D McCOULOUGH
HALLIWELL (St Paul) *Man 9* **P** *Ch Soc Trust*
P-in-c I BROWN
**HALLIWELL (St Peter) (Barrow Bridge Mission) (St Andrew's
Mission Church)** *Man 9* **P** *Trustees* **V** R F OLDFIELD,
C G HARPER, M R S SMITH
HALLIWELL (St Thomas) Bolton St Thos *Man*
HALLOUGHTON (St James) Thurgarton w Hoveringham
and Bleasby etc *S'well*
HALLOW (St Philip and St James) *Worc 3* **P** *Bp*
V J W HERBERT
HALLWOOD (St Mark) *Ches 3* **P** *DBP*
V J C WILKINSON, **C** P B WAINWRIGHT
HALSALL (St Cuthbert) *Liv 11* **P** *Brig D H Blundell-
Hollinshead-Blundell* **R** P GOODRICH
HALSE (Mission Church) Brackley St Pet w St Jas *Pet*
HALSE (St James) Milverton w Halse and Fitzhead *B & W*
HALSETOWN (St John's in the Fields) *Truro 5* **P** *D&C*
NSM J DIBB SMITH
HALSHAM (All Saints) Keyingham w Ottringham, Halsham
and Sunk Is *York*
**HALSTEAD (St Andrew) w Holy Trinity and Greenstead
Green** *Chelmsf 20* **P** *Bp* **V** B E ROSE, **C** P J MOSSOP
HALSTEAD (St Margaret) Knockholt w Halstead *Roch*
HALSTOCK (St Mary) Melbury *Sarum*
**HALSTOW, HIGH (St Margaret) (All Hallows) and Hoo
(St Mary)** *Roch 6* **P** *MMCET and Ch Soc Trust (jt)*
R P S McVEAGH
HALSTOW, LOWER (St Margaret) Upchurch w Lower
Halstow *Cant*
HALTER DEVIL (Mission Room) Mugginton and
Kedleston *Derby*
HALTON (St Andrew) Corbridge w Halton and Newton
Hall *Newc*
HALTON (St Mary) *Ches 3* **P** *Bp* **V** R J SAMUELS,
C A E SAMUELS
HALTON (St Michael and All Angels) *Ox 28* **P** *DBF*
R *Vacant*
**HALTON (St Oswald and St Cuthbert and King
Alfwald)** Corbridge w Halton and Newton Hall *Newc*
HALTON (St Wilfred) w Aughton *Blackb 15* **P** *Exors of
R T Sanderson Esq* **R** M P KEIGHLEY
HALTON, EAST (St Peter) Habrough Gp *Linc*
HALTON, WEST (St Etheldreda) Alkborough *Linc*
HALTON HOLGATE (St Andrew) *Linc 7* **P** *Bp*
R G ROBSON
HALTON QUAY (St Indract's Chapel) St Dominic,
Landulph and St Mellion w Pillaton *Truro*
HALTON WEST (Mission Church) Hellifield *Bradf*
HALTWHISTLE (Holy Cross) and Greenhead *Newc 4*
P *Bp* **V** G A NEWMAN
HALVERGATE (St Peter and St Paul) Freethorpe w
Wickhampton, Halvergate etc *Nor*
HALWELL (St Leonard) w Moreleigh *Ex 13* **P** *Bp (1 turn)
and D&C (2 turns)* **V** *Vacant*
HALWILL (St Peter and St James) Ashwater, Halwill,
Beaworthy, Clawton etc *Ex*
HAM (All Saints) Wexcombe *Sarum*
HAM (St Andrew) *S'wark 15* **P** *K Coll Cam*
V D R MOORE, **Hon C** D S MARKWELL
HAM (St Barnabas Mission Church) Combe St Nicholas w
Wambrook *B & W*
HAM (St James the Less) Plymouth St Jas Ham *Ex*
HAM (St Richard) *S'wark 16* **P** *Bp* **V** W G M LEWIS,
Hon C P H BUSS
**HAM, EAST (St Bartholomew) (St Mary Magdalene) w Upton
Park** *Chelmsf 3* **P** *Patr Bd* **TR** F R BENTLEY,
TV J BROWN, D JONES, **C** K M RUMENS, S I LAMB
HAM, EAST (St George w St Ethelbert) *Chelmsf 3* **P** *Bp*
P-in-c P C TURNER
HAM, EAST (St Paul) *Chelmsf 3* **P** *Ch Patr Trust* **V** *Vacant*
0181-472 5531
HAM, HIGH (St Andrew) Langport Area Chs *B & W*
HAM, LOW (Chapel) as above
HAM, WEST (All Saints) *Chelmsf 3* **P** *The Crown*
TV R A LEWIS, **P-in-c** U E E J SCHARF, **C** M J WYLIE-
SMITH
HAM, WEST (St Matthew) Forest Gate St Sav w W Ham St
Matt *Chelmsf*
HAMBLE LE RICE (St Andrew) *Win 9* **P** *St Mary's Coll
Win* **V** J W TRAVERS

HAMBLEDEN VALLEY (St Mary the Virgin) *Ox 29* **P** *Bp, Viscount Hambleden, and Miss M Mackenzie (jt)* **P-in-c** M M FITZWILLIAMS, **C** P R NICOLSON, **NSM** C L WODEHOUSE

HAMBLEDON (St Peter) *Guildf 4* **P** *MMCET* **P-in-c** G B CHARRETT

HAMBLEDON (St Peter and St Paul) *Portsm 1* **P** *Ld Chan* **P-in-c** R W H KINGSTON

HAMBLETON (Blessed Virgin Mary) w Out Rawcliffe *Blackb 10* **P** *V Kirkham and V St Michaels-on-Wyre (jt)* **V** P P F WARD

HAMBLETON (St Andrew) Oakham, Hambleton, Egleton, Braunston and Brooke *Pet*

HAMBLETON (St Mary) Haddlesey w Hambleton and Birkin *York*

HAMBRIDGE (St James the Less) Kingsbury Episcopi w E Lambrook, Hambridge etc *B & W*

HAMER (All Saints) *Man 20* **P** *Bp* **V** M JONES

HAMERINGHAM (All Saints) w Scrafield and Winceby *Linc 11* **P** *DBP* **R** *Vacant*

HAMERTON (All Saints) *Ely 10* **P** *G R Petherick Esq* **NSM** I D M GIBSON

HAMMER (St Michael) Linchmere *Chich*

HAMMERFIELD (St Francis of Assisi) Boxmoor St Jo *St Alb*

HAMMERFIELD (St Francis of Assisi) as above

HAMMERSMITH (Holy Innocents) *Lon 9* **P** *Bp* **V** M W GRANT, **NSM** G MORGAN

HAMMERSMITH (St John the Evangelist) *Lon 9* **P** *V Hammersmith St Paul* **P-in-c** M P ANDREW, **NSM** A H MEAD

HAMMERSMITH (St Luke) *Lon 9* **P** *Bp* **P-in-c** S J TAYLOR

HAMMERSMITH (St Matthew) *Lon 9* **P** *Trustees* **V** G H CHIPLIN

HAMMERSMITH (St Michael and St George) White City Estate Conventional District *Lon 9* **C-in-c** S J TAYLOR, **C** D W CHERRY

HAMMERSMITH (St Paul) *Lon 9* **P** *Bp* **V** R A M THACKER, **NSM** P E BATES

HAMMERSMITH (St Peter) *Lon 9* **P** *Bp* **V** G W F LANG

HAMMERSMITH (St Simon) *Lon 9* **P** *Simeon's Trustees* **V** J J CLARK, **C** J TATE

HAMMERSMITH, NORTH (St Katherine) *Lon 9* **P** *Bp* **V** *Vacant* 0181-743 3951

HAMMERWICH (St John the Baptist) *Lich 1* **P** *Hammerwich Ch Lands Trustees* **P-in-c** E G H TOWNSHEND, **C** V M STEADY

HAMMERWOOD (St Stephen) Cowden w Hammerwood *Chich*

HAMMOON (St Paul) Childe Okeford, Okeford Fitzpaine, Manston etc *Sarum*

HAMNISH (St Dubricius and All Saints) Kimbolton w Hamnish and Middleton-on-the-Hill *Heref*

HAMPDEN, GREAT (St Mary Magdalene) Prestwood and Gt Hampden *Ox*

HAMPDEN, LITTLE (not known) Gt Missenden w Ballinger and Lt Hampden *Ox*

HAMPDEN PARK (St Mary-in-the-Park) *Chich 16* **P** *Bp* **V** F R SEARLE

HAMPNETT (St George) Northleach w Hampnett and Farmington *Glouc*

HAMPNETT, WEST (St Peter) *Chich 3* **P** *Bp* **P-in-c** K W CATCHPOLE

HAMPRESTON (All Saints) *Sarum 10* **P** *Patr Bd* **TR** R G L LUTHER, **TV** C M STRAIN, **C** M J RAINSBURY, **Hon C** M A BARBER

HAMPSTEAD Belsize Park (St Peter) Belsize Park *Lon*

HAMPSTEAD (Christ Church) *Lon 16* **P** *Trustees* **P-in-c** P D CONRAD

HAMPSTEAD Downshire Hill (St John) Proprietary Chapel *Lon 16 Vacant*

HAMPSTEAD (Emmanuel) West End *Lon 16* **P** *Trustees* **P-in-c** P J GALLOWAY

HAMPSTEAD (St John) *Lon 16* **P** *DBP* **V** P J W BUCKLER, **C** I L PHILLIPS, P Z KASHOURIS

HAMPSTEAD St Stephen w (All Hallows) *Lon 16* **P** *DBP and D&C Cant (jt)* **V** D N C HOULDING, **NSM** M O BRACKLEY, S D DEWEY

HAMPSTEAD, SOUTH (St Saviour) *Lon 16* **P** *V Hampstead St Jo* **P-in-c** A C PAVLIBEYI

HAMPSTEAD, WEST (Holy Trinity) *Lon 16* **P** *MMCET* **V** M NOLAN

HAMPSTEAD, WEST (St Cuthbert) *Lon 16* **P** *Ch Trust Fund Trust* **V** C O MASON

HAMPSTEAD, WEST (St James) *Lon 16* **P** *Trustees* **C** S J GRIGG

HAMPSTEAD, WEST (St Luke) *Lon 16* **P** *CPAS* **V** B J MORRISON

HAMPSTEAD GARDEN SUBURB (St Jude on the Hill) *Lon 15* **P** *Bp* **V** A R G WALKER

HAMPSTEAD NORREYS (St Mary) Hermitage and Hampstead Norreys, Cold Ash etc *Ox*

HAMPSTHWAITE (St Thomas a Becket) and Killinghall *Ripon 1* **P** *Exors Sir Cecil Aykroys, Bt, Sir Thomas Ingilby, Bt, and Bp* **V** *Vacant* Harrogate (01423) 770337

HAMPTON (All Saints) *Lon 10* **P** *Ld Chan* **V** W D F VANSTONE

HAMPTON (St Andrew) Herne Bay Ch Ch *Cant*

HAMPTON (St Andrew) *Worc 1* **P** *Ch Ch Ox* **V** J R N J BOMYER, **NSM** G KNEE

HAMPTON (St Mary the Virgin) *Lon 10* **P** *The Crown Vacant*

HAMPTON BISHOP (St Andrew) Tupsley w Hampton Bishop *Heref*

HAMPTON GAY (St Giles) Kirtlington w Bletchingdon, Weston etc *Ox*

HAMPTON HILL (St James) *Lon 10* **P** *V Hampton St Mary* **V** B LEATHARD

HAMPTON IN ARDEN (St Mary and St Bartholomew) *Birm 13* **P** *Guild of All So* **V** J DE WIT

HAMPTON LOVETT (St Mary and All Saints) Elmley Lovett w Hampton Lovett and Elmbridge etc *Worc*

HAMPTON LUCY (St Peter ad Vincula) w Charlecote and Loxley *Cov 8* **P** *Sir Edmund Fairfax-Lucy, Bt (3 turns), Col A M H Gregory-Hood (1 turn)* **R** *Vacant* Stratford-upon-Avon (01789) 840244

HAMPTON POYLE (St Mary the Virgin) Kidlington w Hampton Poyle *Ox*

HAMPTON WICK (St John the Baptist) Teddington St Mark and Hampton Wick St Jo *Lon*

HAMSEY (St Peter) *Chich 18* **P** *Bp* **P-in-c** D BASTIDE

HAMSTALL RIDWARE (St Michael and All Angels) The Ridwares and Kings Bromley *Lich*

HAMSTEAD (St Bernard) *Birm 3* **P** *Bp* **C** H A C MORSE

HAMSTEAD (St Paul) *Birm 3* **P** *Bp* **V** J W MASDING, **C** J E DOUGLAS

HAMSTEAD MARSHALL (St Mary) W Woodhay w Enborne, Hampstead Marshall etc *Ox*

HAMSTEELS (St John the Baptist) *Dur 8* **P** *The Crown* **NSM** S I WRIGHT

HAMSTERLEY (St James) and Witton-le-Wear *Dur 10* **P** *Bp and The Crown (alt)* **P-in-c** G W WEBSTER

HAMWORTHY (St Gabriel) (St Michael) *Sarum 8* **P** *MMCET* **P-in-c** J E WARING, **C** G F PERRYMAN, J W POOLE

HANBOROUGH (St Peter and St Paul) and Freeland *Ox 9* **P** *St Jo Coll Ox* **R** C A RANDALL

HANBURY (St Mary the Virgin) Bowbrook N *Worc*

HANBURY (St Werburgh) w Newborough *Lich 19* **P** *DBP* **NSM** D C FELIX

HANCHURCH (Chapel of Ease) Trentham *Lich*

HANDCROSS (All Saints) Slaugham *Chich*

HANDFORTH (St Chad) *Ches 17* **P** *R Cheadle* **V** S P ISHERWOOD, **C** P MASON

HANDLEY (All Saints) Tattenhall and Handley *Ches*

HANDLEY (St John the Baptist) Eckington w Handley and Ridgeway *Derby*

HANDLEY (St Mark) N Wingfield, Clay Cross and Pilsley *Derby*

HANDLEY (St Mary) w Gussage St Andrew and Pentridge *Sarum 7* **P** *D&C Windsor and Earl of Shaftesbury (alt)* **R** R E WOOD

HANDSACRE (St Luke) Armitage *Lich*

HANDSWORTH (St Andrew) *Birm 3* **P** *Bp* **V** D J COLLYER, **C** J AUSTEN

HANDSWORTH (St James) *Birm 3* **P** *Bp* **V** R J MORRIS, **C** J V MARCH, A G BUCKNALL

HANDSWORTH (St Mary) *Sheff 1* **P** *DBP* **C** H M HOTCHIN

HANDSWORTH (St Mary) (Epiphany) *Birm 3* **P** *Bp* **R** B A HALL, **C** C M FEAK, **Hon C** T W WARD

HANDSWORTH (St Michael) (St Peter) *Birm 3* **P** *Bp* **V** D HARE

HANDSWORTH Woodhouse (St James) *Sheff 1* **P** *Bp* **V** B R CRANWELL, **C** P D BURRIDGE-BUTLER, **Hon C** P E LAWRIE

HANFORD (St Matthias) *Lich 18* **P** *Bp* **P-in-c** J P HARTLEY

HANGER HILL (Ascension) and West Twyford *Lon 22* **P** *Bp and DBP (jt)* **V** *Vacant* 0181-569 9920

HANGING HEATON (St Paul) *Wakef 10* **P** *R Dewsbury* **V** J M WELLS

HANGLETON (St Helen) (St Richard) *Chich 4* **P** *Bp* **C** B W DOYLE

HANHAM (Christ Church) (St George) *Bris 2* **P** *Bp*
V SWCOOK, **NSM** JAPLUMMER
HANKERTON (Holy Cross) Ashley, Crudwell, Hankerton,
Long Newnton etc *Bris*
HANLEY (All Saints) Stoke-upon-Trent *Lich*
HANLEY Holy Evangelists (St Luke) *Lich 16* **P** *Bp*
TR RPOWEN, **TV** JHSTERLING, **NSM** CLOWNDES
HANLEY (St Chad) Hanley H Ev *Lich*
HANLEY CASTLE (St Mary), Hanley Swan and Welland
Worc 5 **P** *Ld Chan and Sir Berwick Lechmere, Bt (alt)*
V SJSWAIN
HANLEY CHILD (St Michael and All Angels) Teme
Valley S *Worc*
HANLEY SWAN (St Gabriel) Hanley Castle, Hanley Swan
and Welland *Worc*
HANLEY WILLIAM (All Saints) Teme Valley S *Worc*
HANNAH (St Andrew) cum Hagnaby w Markby *Linc 8* **P** *Bp*
and Mrs E Smyth (alt) **P-in-c** AREADER-MOORE
HANNEY (St James the Great), Denchworth and East Challow
Ox 19 **P** *Bp (2 turns), Worc Coll Ox (1 turn)*
V AHOGG
HANNINGFIELD, EAST (All Saints) *Chelmsf 9* **P** *CPAS*
P-in-c HAMATTY
HANNINGFIELD, WEST (St Mary and St Edward)
Chelmsf 9 **P** *DBP* **P-in-c** BGHALL
HANNINGTON (All Saints) Baughurst, Ramsdell,
Wolverton w Ewhurst etc *Win*
HANNINGTON (St John the Baptist) Highworth w
Sevenhampton and Inglesham etc *Bris*
HANNINGTON (St Peter and St Paul) Walgrave w
Hannington and Wold and Scaldwell *Pet*
HANOVER SQUARE (St George) (St Mark) *Lon 3* **P** *Bp*
R WMATKINS, **C** SJHOBBS
HANSLOPE (St James the Great) w Castlethorpe *Ox 27*
P *Bp* **C** MGBEAKE
HANWELL (St Mary) (St Christopher) *Lon 22* **P** *Bp*
R MRGRAYSHON, **C** DJBURGESS, JRLUCAS,
NSM RWEBB
HANWELL (St Mellitus w St Mark) *Lon 22* **P** *Bp*
P-in-c JOHEREWARD
HANWELL (St Peter) Horley w Hornton and Hanwell,
Shenington etc *Ox*
HANWELL (St Thomas) *Lon 22* **P** *The Crown*
V PAANDREWS
HANWOOD, GREAT (St Thomas) *Heref 13* **P** *Lt-Col*
H de Grey-Warter **R** PTOWNER
HANWORTH (All Saints) *Lon 11* **P** *Bp* V JAFLETCHER
HANWORTH (St Bartholomew) Roughton and Felbrigg,
Metton, Sustead etc *Nor*
HANWORTH (St George) *Lon 11* **P** *Lee Abbey Trust*
P-in-c PSWILLIAMSON
HANWORTH (St Richard of Chichester) *Lon 11* **P** *Bp*
V AJACKSON
HAPPISBURGH (St Mary the Virgin), Walcot, Hempstead w
Eccles and Lessingham and Sea Palling *Nor 13* **P** *Bp*
(3 turns), K Coll Cam (2 turns), E C Evans-Lombe Esq
andBp (1 turn) **R** JALINES
HAPTON (St Margaret) Padiham *Blackb*
HAPTON (St Margaret) Wreningham *Nor*
HARBERTON (St Andrew) Diptford, N Huish, Harberton
and Harbertonford *Ex*
HARBERTONFORD (St Peter) as above
HARBLEDOWN (St Michael and All Angels) *Cant 3*
P *Abp* **P-in-c** MAMORRIS
HARBORNE (St Faith and St Laurence) *Birm 2* **P** *Bp*
V IMMICHAEL, **NSM** TRBOTT
HARBORNE (St Peter) *Birm 2* **P** *Bp* V CJEVANS,
C JDRCOX
HARBORNE HEATH (St John the Baptist) *Birm 2*
P *Ch Soc Trust* V JPHUGHES, **C** JKSDENNISTON,
GPLANHAM
HARBOROUGH MAGNA (All Saints) *Cov 6* **P** *AHFW*
Boughton-Leigh Esq **R** PSRUSSELL
HARBRIDGE (All Saints) Ellingham and Harbridge and
Ibsley *Win*
HARBURY (All Saints) and Ladbroke *Cov 10* **P** *Bp*
R PRBROWN
HARBY (All Saints) w Thorney and North and South Clifton
S'well 3 **P** *Ld Chan and Bp (alt)* **R** *Vacant* Spalford
(01522) 778258
HARBY (St Mary the Virgin), Long Clawson and Hose
Leic 3 **P** *Duke of Rutland, Bp and DBP (alt)*
P-in-c GSPENCER, **C** MTURNER
HARDEN (St Saviour) and Wilsden *Bradf 8* **P** *Bp, Adn,*
V Bradf, and R Bingley Esq (jt) V JCPEET
HARDENHUISH (St Nicholas) Chippenham St Paul w
Hardenhuish etc *Bris*
HARDHAM (St Botolph) Coldwaltham and Hardham *Chich*

HARDINGHAM (St George) Barnham Broom *Nor*
HARDINGSTONE (St Edmund) and Horton and Piddington
Pet 7 **P** *Bp* V BHSTEVENS
HARDINGTON MANDEVILLE (Blessed Virgin Mary) W
Coker w Hardington Mandeville, E Chinnock etc *B & W*
HARDLEY (St Margaret) Chedgrave w Hardley and Langley
Nor
HARDMEAD (St Mary) Sherington w Chicheley, N
Crawley, Astwood etc *Ox*
HARDRAW (St Mary and St John) Hawes and Hardraw
Ripon
HARDRES, LOWER (St Mary) Petham and Waltham w
Lower Hardres etc *Cant*
HARDRES, UPPER (St Peter and St Paul) as above
HARDSTOFT (St Peter) Ault Hucknall *Derby*
HARDWICK (St James) Stockton St Jas *Dur*
HARDWICK (St Leonard) Mears Ashby and Hardwick and
Sywell etc *Pet*
HARDWICK (St Margaret) Hempnall *Nor*
HARDWICK (St Mary) *Ely 1* **P** *Bp* **R** DGDEBOYS,
NSM AGWILMAN
HARDWICK, EAST (St Stephen) *Wakef 11* **P** *Cawood*
Trustees V FLBROOKS **C** SVBROOKS
HARDWICK-CUM-TUSMORE (St Mary) Finmere w
Mixbury, Cottisford, Hardwick etc *Ox*
HARDWICKE (Holy Trinity) Cusop w Clifford, Hardwicke,
Bredwardine etc *Heref*
HARDWICKE (St Mary the Virgin) Schorne *Ox*
HARDWICKE (St Nicholas), Quedgeley and Elmore w
Longney *Glouc 8* **P** *Adn Glouc and Sir John Guise (1 turn),*
Bp (2 turns), and Ld Chan (1 turn) **R** GJBSTICKLAND,
C GEHISCOCK, **NSM** MECWHATSON
HAREBY (St Peter and St Paul) Marden Hill Gp *Linc*
HAREFIELD (St Mary the Virgin) *Lon 24* **P** *Viscount*
Daventry V AJRGANDON, **C** JDCORNISH
HARESCOMBE (St John the Baptist) The Edge,
Pitchcombe, Harescombe and Brookthorpe *Glouc*
HARESFIELD (St Peter) Standish w Haresfield and Moreton
Valence etc *Glouc*
HAREWOOD (Methodist Chapel) Collingham w Harewood
Ripon
HARFORD (St Petroc) Ivybridge w Harford *Ex*
HARGRAVE (All Saints) Stanwick w Hargrave *Pet*
HARGRAVE (St Edmund) Chevington w Hargrave and
Whepstead w Brockley *St E*
HARGRAVE (St Peter) *Ches 5* **P** *Bp* **P-in-c** RMPOWLEY
HARKSTEAD (St Mary) Chelmondiston and Erwarton w
Harkstead *St E*
HARLASTON (St Matthew) *Lich 4* **P** *Bp* **R** *Vacant*
HARLAXTON (St Mary and St Peter) *Linc 19* **P** *Bp,*
Sir Richard Welby, Bt, D&C, and DBP (jt)
P-in-c FCTHORNETT
HARLESCOTT (Holy Spirit) *Lich 26* **P** *Bp*
V MFWALKER, **C** IMBROTHERSTON, DGRASBY,
NSM DWGUFFINDELL
HARLESDEN (All Souls) *Lon 21* **P** *The Crown*
V MDMOORHEAD, **C** APSHACKERLEY,
NSM MDENGLER
HARLESDEN (St Mark) Kensal Rise St Mark and St Martin
Lon
HARLESTON (St Augustine) Gt Finborough w Onehouse
and Harleston *St E*
HARLESTON (St John the Baptist) Redenhall, Harleston,
Wortwell and Needham *Nor*
HARLESTON (St Andrew) Church Brampton, Chapel
Brampton, Harleston etc *Pet*
HARLEY (St Mary) Wenlock *Heref*
HARLING, EAST (St Peter and St Paul) w West Haling and
Bridgham w Roudham *Nor 11* **P** *Ld Chan (1 turn), DBP,*
Sir Robin Nugent Bt, and Mrs Juliet Barry and
C D F Musker Esq (3 turns) **P-in-c** JHANDLEY
HARLINGTON (Christ Church) Waltham Avenue
Conventional District *Lon 24* **C-in-c** RNMcCANN
HARLINGTON (St Mary the Virgin) *St Alb 18* **P** *Bp*
V SJWILLIAMS
HARLINGTON (St Peter and St Paul) *Lon 24* **P** *Bp*
R DRJENKINS
HARLOW (St Mary and St Hugh w St John the Baptist)
Chelmsf 27 **P** *Simeon's Trustees and Bp (alt)*
V SPEMOURANT, **C** JGBLAKELEY,
NSM JCMOURANT
HARLOW (St Mary Magdalene) *Chelmsf 27* **P** *V Harlow*
St Mary and St Hugh etc V GRSMITH,
C MJHAMPSON, **Hon C** GRNEAVE
HARLOW GREEN (St Ninian) Gateshead Harlow Green
Dur

HARLOW HILL (All Saints) Low Harrogate St Mary *Ripon*
HARLOW Town Centre St Paul's w St Mary's Little Parndon
  Chelmsf 27 **P** *Patr Bd* **TR** G OGILVIE,
  TV A R B HIGGS
HARLSEY, EAST (St Oswald) Osmotherley w Harlsey and
  Ingleby Arncliffe *York*
HARLTON (The Assumption of the Blessed Virgin
  Mary) Haslingfield w Harlton and Gt and Lt Eversden *Ely*
HARMANSWATER (St Paul) Bracknell *Ox*
HARMER HILL (St Andrew) Myddle *Lich*
HARMONDSWORTH (St Mary) *Lon 24* **P** *DBP*
  P-in-c J P ADAMS
HARMSTON (All Saints) Graffoe Gp *Linc*
HARNHAM (St George) (All Saints) *Sarum 15* **P** *Bp*
  (1 turn), *V Britford (2 turns)* **P-in-c** D P SCRACE
HARNHILL (St Michael and All Angels) The Ampneys w
  Driffield and Poulton *Glouc*
HAROLD HILL (St George) *Chelmsf 2* **P** *Bp*
  V S R JONES, **C** T D HULL
HAROLD HILL (St Paul) *Chelmsf 2* **P** *Bp*
  P-in-c E W COCKETT
HAROLD WOOD (St Peter) *Chelmsf 2* **P** *New Coll Ox*
  V W P BENN, **C** P A WILLIAMS, M W LUCAS
HAROME (St Saviour) w Stonegrave, Nunnington and Pockley
  York 18 **P** *Lady Clarissa Collin, Abp, Adn Cleveland and*
  V Helmsley (jt), The Crown, and Abp (by turn)
  R J M MATHER
HARPENDEN (St John the Baptist) *St Alb 14* **P** *DBP*
  V G A J MARTIN, **C** D C MYLNE
HARPENDEN (St Nicholas) (All Saints) *St Alb 14*
  P *Ld Chan* **R** N COLLINGS, **C** D G WILLIAMS,
  Hon C E M SHEGOG, **NSM** D PRICE
HARPFORD (St Gregory the Great) Newton Poppleford,
  Harpford and Colaton Raleigh *Ex*
HARPHAM (St John of Beverley) Burton Agnes w Harpham
  and Lowthorpe etc *York*
HARPLEY (St Lawrence) Gt and Lt Massingham and
  Harpley *Nor*
HARPOLE (All Saints) Kislingbury and Harpole *Pet*
HARPSDEN (St Margaret) w Bolney *Ox 6* **P** *All So Coll*
  Ox **P-in-c** P J FOX
HARPSWELL (St Chad) Glentworth Gp *Linc*
HARPTREE, EAST (St Laurence) w WEST (Blessed Virgin
  Mary) and Hinton Blewett *B & W 10* **P** *Duchy of*
  Cornwall **R** R G HARVEY
HARPUR HILL (St James) Buxton w Burbage and King
  Sterndale *Derby*
HARPURHEY cum Moston (Christ Church) *Man 5* **P** *Bp,*
  Dean, K Greenwood Esq, Mrs M V Johnson, and
  V Morley Esq (jt) **R** T R HINDLEY
HARPURHEY (St Stephen) *Man 5* **P** *Bp* **R** T R HINDLEY
HARRABY (St Elisabeth) *Carl 3* **P** *Bp*
  P-in-c D C BICKERSTETH, **C** M J MURRAY,
  NSM I DAVIES
HARRIETSHAM (St John the Baptist) w Ulcombe *Cant 15*
  P *The Crown* **R** A C STOCKBRIDGE
HARRINGAY (St Paul) *Lon 19* **P** *Bp* **V** J F SEELEY
HARRINGTON (St Mary) *Carl 7* **P** *Exors*
  E S C Curwen Esq **R** J D HODGKINSON
HARRINGTON (St Mary) S Ormsby Gp *Linc*
HARRINGTON (St Peter and St Paul) Arthingworth,
  Harrington w Oxendon and E Farndon *Pet*
HARRINGWORTH (St John the Baptist) Bulwick,
  Blatherwycke w Harringworth and Laxton *Pet*
HARROGATE (St Mark) *Ripon 1* **P** *Peache Trustees*
  V P D G HOOPER
HARROGATE (St Wilfrid and St Luke) *Ripon 1* **P** *Bp*
  V B R PEARSON, **C** D P A FEENEY, **NSM** G P CORNISH
HARROGATE, HIGH (Christ Church) *Ripon 1* **P** *Bp*
  V J E COLSTON, **C** P J CONWAY
HARROGATE, HIGH (St Peter) *Ripon 1* **P** *Ch Patr Trust*
  V A M SHEPHERD, **NSM** L J WASSELL
HARROGATE, LOW (St Mary) *Ripon 4* **P** *Peache*
  Trustees **V** M W SOAR
HARROLD (St Peter and All Saints) and Carlton w
  Chellington *St Alb 21* **P** *Bp* **R** J P SMITH
HARROW (Church of the Holy Spirit) Kenton *Lon*
HARROW (St Paul) Roxeth *Lon*
HARROW (Trinity) (St Michael) *Lon 23* **P** *Bp*
  C A R SALISBURY
HARROW, NORTH (St Alban) *Lon 23* **P** *Bp*
  V P HEMINGWAY, **Hon C** D S ARDEN
HARROW GREEN (Holy Trinity and St Augustine of
  Hippo) Leytonstone H Trin Harrow Green *Chelmsf*
HARROW ON THE HILL (St Mary) *Lon 23* **P** *Bp, Adn,*
  and Hd Master Harrow Sch (jt) **V** R F SWAN,
  C J M RUSHTON

HARROW WEALD (All Saints) *Lon 23* **P** *Bp, Adn,*
  V Harrow St Mary, and R Bushey (jt) **V** F D JAKEMAN,
  C M RAJKOVIC, F C PAPANTONIOU
HARROWBARROW (All Saints) Calstock *Truro*
HARROWDEN, GREAT (All Saints) w LITTLE (St Mary the
  Virgin) and Orlingbury *Pet 6* **P** *Sir Stephen Hastings and*
  Bp (alt) **V** J E COOPER
HARSTON (All Saints) w Hauxton *Ely 7* **P** *Bp (2 turns),*
  D&C (1 turn) **P-in-c** J PARR, **NSM** S CHRISTOU,
  R G HOWELLS
HARSTON (St Michael and All Angels) High Framland Par
  Leic
HARSWELL (St Peter) Seaton Ross Gp of Par *York*
HART (St Mary Magdalene) w Elwick Hall *Dur 13* **P** *Bp and*
  DBP (alt) **V** J E LUND
HART COMMON (not known) Westhoughton *Man*
HARTBURN (All Saints) Stockton St Pet *Dur*
HARTBURN (St Andrew) Bolam w Whalton and Hartburn
  w Meldon *Newc*
HARTCLIFFE (St Andrew) Bris St Andr Hartcliffe *Bris*
HARTEST (All Saints) Glem Valley United Benefice *St E*
HARTFIELD (St Mary) w Coleman's Hatch *Chich 19*
  P *Earl de la Warr* **R** P T CRAIG
HARTFORD (All Saints) Huntingdon *Ely*
HARTFORD (All Souls) Hartley Wintney, Elvetham,
  Winchfield etc *Win*
HARTFORD (St John the Baptist) *Ches 6* **P** *Mrs I H Wilson,*
  Mrs R H Emmet, and Mrs J M Wearne (jt)
  V P D GARDNER, **C** R S MUNRO
HARTHILL (All Hallows) and Thorpe Salvin *Sheff 5* **P** *Bp*
  R P MORLEY
HARTHILL (All Saints) and Burwardsley *Ches 5* **P** *Bp and*
  G R Barbour Esq (jt) **P-in-c** D R BUCKLEY
HARTING (St Mary and St Gabriel) w Elsted and Treyford
  cum Didling *Chich 10* **P** *Bp* **R** D R C GIBBONS
HARTINGTON (St Giles), Biggin and Earl Sterndale
  Derby 4 **P** *Duke of Devonshire* **V** D V GIBLING
HARTISMERE, NORTH *St E 16* **P** *MMCET, K Coll Cam,*
  Bp, and DBP (jt) **R** C M IDLE
HARTLAND (St Nectan) Parkham, Alwington, Buckland
  Brewer etc *Ex*
HARTLAND COAST as above
HARTLEBURY (St James) *Worc 13* **P** *Bp*
  P-in-c M E STANTON-HYDE
HARTLEPOOL (Holy Trinity) (St Mark's Centre) *Dur 13*
  P *Bp* **C** K A WALTON
HARTLEPOOL (St Aidan) (St Columba) *Dur 13* **P** *Bp*
  V M H WHITEHEAD, **C** A C JONES
HARTLEPOOL (St Hilda) (St Barnabas) *Dur 13* **P** *Bp*
  P-in-c J L COOK
HARTLEPOOL (St Luke) *Dur 13* **P** *Bp* **V** P TOWNSEND
HARTLEPOOL (St Oswald) *Dur 13* **P** *Bp*
  P-in-c B R TURNBULL
HARTLEPOOL (St Paul) *Dur 13* **P** *Bp*
  P-in-c R E MASSHEDAR
HARTLEY (All Saints) Fawkham and Hartley *Roch*
HARTLEY, NEW (St Michael and All Angels) Delaval *Newc*
HARTLEY BROOK (Mission Hall) Becontree St Mary
  Chelmsf
HARTLEY MAUDITT (St Leonard) E and W Worldham,
  Hartley Mauditt w Kingsley etc *Win*
HARTLEY WESPALL (St Mary) Sherfield-on-Loddon and
  Stratfield Saye etc *Win*
HARTLEY WINTNEY (St John the Evangelist), Elvetham,
  Winchfield and Dogmersfield *Win 5* **P** *Bp and Sir Euan*
  Anstruther-Gough-Calthorpe, Bt (jt)
  V P E de D WARBURTON, **C** M K NICHOLAS
HARTLIP (St Michael and All Angels) Newington w Hartlip
  and Stockbury *Cant*
HARTOFT (Mission Room) Lastingham w Appleton-le-
  Moors, Rosedale etc *York*
HARTON (St Peter) (St Lawrence) *Dur 7* **P** *D&C* **V** *Vacant*
  0191–456 1855
HARTPLAIN *Portsm 4* **P** *DBP* **V** M S COOPER
HARTPURY (St Mary the Virgin) w Corse and Staunton
  Glouc 6 **P** *Bp (2 turns), DBP (1 turn)* **P-in-c** J G EVANS
HARTSHEAD (St Peter) and Hightown *Wakef 8*
  P *R Dewsbury* **V** J van der VALK
HARTSHILL (Holy Trinity) *Cov 5* **P** *V Mancetter*
  V P C CANNING, **NSM** P DODDS
HARTSHILL (Holy Trinity) *Lich 17* **P** *Bp* **V** J A WALSH
HARTSHORNE (St Peter) *Derby 16* **P** *MMCET*
  R I R WILLIAMS-HUNTER
HARTWELL (St John the Baptist) Roade and Ashton w
  Hartwell *Pet*
HARTWITH (St Jude) Dacre w Hartwith and Darley w
  Thornthwaite *Ripon*

HARTY (St Thomas Apostle) Eastchurch w Leysdown and Harty *Cant*

HARVINGTON (St James), Norton and Lenchwick *Worc 1*　**P** *D&C*　**R** S C LITTLE

HARWELL (St Matthew) w Chilton *Ox 18*　**P** *DBP and CPAS (jt)*　**R** C J STOTT,　**C** M P CARNEY

HARWICH (St Nicholas) *Chelmsf 21*　**P** *Bp*　P-in-c S HARDIE

HARWOOD (Christ Church) *Man 16*　**P** *DBP*　**V** D J BRIERLEY,　**C** S J BEACH,　**Hon C** D A HILES,　**NSM** H MOLLOY,　M J FROST

HARWOOD, GREAT (St Bartholomew) *Blackb 8*　**P** *V Blackb*　**V** K PARKELL

HARWOOD, GREAT (St John) *Blackb 8*　**P** *Bp and V Gt Harwood St Bart (jt)*　**V** B DARBYSHIRE

HARWOOD DALE (St Margaret) Hackness w Harwood Dale *York*

HARWORTH (All Saints) *S'well 1*　**P** *Sir James Whitaker, Bt*　**V** J A BRITTON

HASBURY (St Margaret) Halesowen *Worc*

HASCOMBE (St Peter) *Guildf 4*　**P** *SMF*　**R** R C D MACKENNA

HASELBECH (St Michael) Clipston w Naseby and Haselbech w Kelmarsh *Pet*

HASELBURY PLUCKNETT (St Michael and All Angels), Misterton and North Perrott *B & W 15*　**P** *Ld Chan (2 turns), Bp (2 turns), and H W F Hoskyns Esq (1 turn)*　**V** R D MARTIN

HASELEY (St Mary) Hatton w Haseley, Rowington w Lowsonford etc *Cov*

HASELEY, GREAT (St Peter) Gt w Lt Milton and Gt Haseley *Ox*

HASELOR (St Mary and All Saints) Kinwarton w Gt Alne and Haselor *Cov*

HASELTON (St Andrew) Withington and Compton Abdale w Haselton *Glouc*

HASFIELD (St Mary) w Tirley and Ashleworth *Glouc 6*　**P** *W G F Meath-Baker Esq, Ld Chan, and Bp (by turn)*　P-in-c G E PARSONS

HASKETON (St Andrew) Ufford w Bredfield and Hasketon *St E*

HASLAND (St Paul) *Derby 5*　**P** *V Chesterfield*　P-in-c C W D VOGT

HASLEMERE (St Bartholomew) (St Christopher) *Guildf 4*　**P** *Ld Chan*　**R** A C EDMONDS,　**C** T A REDFEARN,　**Hon C** D C G BROWN

HASLINGDEN (St James) w Grane and Stonefold *Blackb 1*　**P** *Bp and Hulme Trustees (jt)*　**V** D B WEBB

HASLINGFIELD (All Saints) w Harlton and Eversden, Great w Little *Ely 1*　**P** *Qu Coll Cam, Ld Chan, Jes Coll Cam (by turn)*　**R** J P GILDING

HASLINGTON (St Matthew) w Crewe Green St Michael *Ches 15*　**P** *Bp*　**V** P H GEDDES

HASSALL GREEN (St Philip) Wheelock *Ches*

HASSINGHAM (St Mary) Burlingham St Edmund w Lingwood, Strumpshaw etc *Nor*

HASTINGLEIGH (St Mary the Virgin) Elmsted w Hastingleigh *Cant*

HASTINGS (All Souls) Clive Vale *Chich 17*　**P** *R Upper St Leon*　**V** B TRILL

HASTINGS (Christ Church and St Andrew) Blacklands Hastings Ch Ch and St Andr *Chich*

HASTINGS (Emmanuel and St Mary in the Castle) *Chich 17*　**P** *MMCET and Hyndman Trustees (alt)*　**V** P A O'GORMAN

HASTINGS (Holy Trinity) *Chich 17*　**P** *Bp*　**V** C TOLWORTHY

HASTINGS (St Clement) (All Saints) *Chich 17*　**P** *Bp*　**R** C L RICHARDSON,　**C** G J BUTTERWORTH,　**NSM** D F FENTIMAN

HASWELL (St Paul) S Hetton w Haswell *Dur*

HATCH, WEST (St Andrew) Hatch Beauchamp w Beercrocombe, Curry Mallet etc *B & W*

HATCH BEAUCHAMP (St John the Baptist) w Beercrocombe, Curry Mallet and West Hatch *B & W 18*　**P** *Duchy of Cornwall (1 turn), Ch Trust Fund Trust (2 turns), and D&C (1 turn)*　**R** R H M JAY

HATCH END (St Anselm) *Lon 23*　**P** *Bp*　**V** C PEARCE

HATCHAM St Catherine *S'wark 2*　**P** *Haberdashers' Co*　**V** M N A TORRY,　**C** M J JACKSON,　**Hon C** D H HAINES,　R M G MORRELL,　**NSM** J M L L BOGLE,　A R TYLER

HATCHAM (St James) (St George) (St Michael) *S'wark 2*　**P** *Ch Patr Soc*　**V** F Y-C HUNG,　**C** C LITTLE,　**NSM** E O ADOYO

HATCHAM PARK (All Saints) *S'wark 2*　**P** *Hyndman Trustees (2 turns), Haberdashers' Co (1 turn)*　**V** O J BEAMENT,　**NSM** B E WEST

HATCLIFFE (St Mary) Ravendale Gp *Linc*

HATFIELD (St Etheldreda) (St John) (St Michael and All Angels) (St Luke) *St Alb 7*　**P** *Marquess of Salisbury*　**R** W C D TODD,　**C** R J SUTTON,　J H HORNER

HATFIELD (St Lawrence) *Sheff 11*　**P** *Bp*　**V** J W SWEED,　**NSM** G BECKETT

HATFIELD (St Leonard) Leominster *Heref*

HATFIELD BROAD OAK (St Mary the Virgin) and Bush End *Chelmsf 27*　**P** *Bp*　P-in-c D P HODGSON

HATFIELD HEATH (Holy Trinity) and Sheering *Chelmsf 27*　**P** *V Hatfield Broad Oak*　**R** T J POTTER

HATFIELD HYDE (St Mary Magdalene) *St Alb 7*　**P** *Marquess of Salisbury*　**V** M L BANKS

HATFIELD PEVEREL (St Andrew) w Ulting *Chelmsf 25*　**P** *Bp*　**V** *Vacant* Chelmsford (01245) 380958

HATFIELD REGIS Hatf Broad Oak and Bush End *Chelmsf*

HATHERDEN (Christ Church) w Tangley and Weyhill and Penton Mewsey *Win 3*　**P** *Bp and Qu Coll Ox (jt)*　**V** R E WHETTINGSTEEL

HATHERLEIGH (St John the Baptist) Meeth, Exbourne and Jacobstowe *Ex 12*　**P** *CPAS, Lord Clinton, DBP, and Keble Coll Ox (jt)*　P-in-c R A L WELBY

HATHERN (St Peter and St Paul), Long Whatton and Diseworth w Belton and Osgathorpe *Leic 7*　**P** *Ld Chan, Haberdashers' Co, and Bp (by turn)*　**R** S SAMUEL,　**C** S M CHANTRY

HATHEROP (St Nicholas) Coln St Aldwyns, Hatherop, Quenington etc *Glouc*

HATHERSAGE (St Michael and All Angels) *Derby 2*　**P** *Duke of Devonshire*　**V** J W ALLUM

HATHERTON (St Saviour) *Lich 2*　**P** *A R W Littleton Esq*　**V** K M JUKES

HATLEY ST GEORGE (St George) Gamlingay w Hatley St Geo and E Hatley *Ely*

HATTERS LANE (St Andrew) High Wycombe *Ox*

HATTERSLEY (St Barnabas) *Ches 14*　**P** *Bp*　**V** P A BROWN

HATTON (All Saints) Marston on Dove w Scropton *Derby*

HATTON (Chapel of Ease) E Bedfont *Lon*

HATTON (Holy Trinity) w Haseley, Rowington w Lowsonford and Honiley and Wroxall *Cov 4*　**P** *Bp*　**R** B A RITCHIE

HATTON (St Stephen) Hemingby *Linc*

HAUGH (St Leonard) S Ormsby Gp *Linc*

HAUGHLEY (St Mary the Virgin) w Wetherden *St E 6*　**P** *Ld Chan and Bp (alt)*　P-in-c D P BURRELL

HAUGHTON (Mission Room) Bunbury and Tilstone Fearnall *Ches*

HAUGHTON (St Anne) *Man 17*　**P** *DBP*　P-in-c I L JOHNSON

HAUGHTON (St Chad) W Felton *Lich*

HAUGHTON (St Giles) Derrington, Haughton and Ranton *Lich*

HAUGHTON (St Mary the Virgin) *Man 17*　**P** *Bp*　**R** M J DOWLAND

HAUGHTON LE SKERNE (St Andrew) *Dur 12*　**P** *Bp*　**R** C C MARNHAM,　**C** M J NORMAN

HAUTBOIS, GREAT (Holy Trinity) Coltishall w Gt Hautbois and Horstead *Nor*

HAUXTON (St Edmund) Harston w Hauxton *Ely*

HAUXWELL (St Oswald) Spennithorne w Finghall and Hauxwell *Ripon*

HAVANT (St Faith) *Portsm 4*　**P** *Bp*　**R** D F BROWN

HAVENSTREET (St Peter) *Portsm 7*　**P** *SMF*　**V** S M CHALONER,　**NSM** T I CARD

HAVERHILL (St Mary the Virgin) w Withersfield, the Wrattings, the Thurlows and the Bradleys *St E 8*　**P** *Patr Bd*　**TR** E J BETTS,　**C** B RAISTRICK

HAVERIGG (St Luke) Millom *Carl*

HAVERING-ATTE-BOWER (St John) Collier Row St Jas and Havering-atte-Bower *Chelmsf*

HAVERINGLAND (St Peter) Cawston w Haveringland, Booton and Brandiston *Nor*

HAVERSHAM (St Mary) w Little Linford, Tyringham w Filgrave *Ox 27*　**P** *CPAS*　P-in-c S A WEEDEN

HAVERSTOCK HILL (Holy Trinity) w Kentish Town St Barnabas *Lon 17*　**P** *D&C St Paul's*　P-in-c G C ROWLANDS,　**C** N P PAINE DAVEY

HAVERTHWAITE (St Anne) Leven Valley *Carl*

HAWES (St Margaret) and Hardraw *Ripon 4*　**P** *Bp, V Aysgarth and Bolton cum Redmire, Mrs R Metcalfe, and W H Willan Esq (jt)*　**V** W M SIMMS

HAWES SIDE (St Christopher) *Blackb 9*　**P** *Bp*　**V** R G RAINFORD

HAWKCHURCH (St John the Baptist) Marshwood Vale **TM** *Sarum*

HAWKEDON (St Mary) Chedburgh w Depden, Rede and Hawkedon *St E*

HAWKESBURY (St Mary) Badminton w Lt Badminton, Acton Turville etc *Glouc*

HAWKHURST (St Laurance) *Cant 11* **P** *Ch Ch Ox* **V** J RECORD

HAWKINGE (St Luke) w Acrise and Swingfield *Cant 5* **P** *Abp* **R** C A SPARKES

HAWKLEY (St Peter and St Paul) Greatham w Empshott and Hawkley w Prior's Dean *Portsm*

HAWKRIDGE (St Giles) Oxford, Exmoor, Hawkridge and Withypool *B & W*

HAWKSHAW LANE (St Mary) *Man 10* **P** *F Whowell Esq* **V** E A RUEHORN

HAWKSHEAD (St Michael and All Angels) and Low Wray w Sawrey *Carl 10* **P** *Bp* **V** D A SOUTHWARD

HAWKSWOOD Hailsham *Chich*

HAWKSWORTH (St Mary and All Saints) Whatton w Aslockton, Hawksworth, Scarrington etc *S'well*

HAWKSWORTH WOOD (St Mary) *Ripon 7* **P** *Patrons Leeds St Pet* **V** R BROWN, **C** K D JACKSON

HAWKWELL (Emmanuel) (St Mary the Virgin) *Chelmsf 12* **P** *CPAS* **R** A R HIGTON, **C** S F KIMBER

HAWKWOOD (St Francis) Chingford SS Pet and Paul *Chelmsf*

HAWLEY (Holy Trinity) *Guildf 1* **P** *Keble Coll Ox* **V** I M HANCOCK, **C** R A SEABROOK

HAWLEY, SOUTH (All Saints) Hawley H Trin *Guildf*

HAWLING (St Edward) Sevenhampton w Charlton Abbotts and Hawling etc *Glouc*

HAWNBY (All Saints) Upper Ryedale *York*

HAWORTH (St Michael and All Angels) *Bradf 8* **P** *V Bradf and Haworth Ch Lands Trust (jt)* **R** *Vacant* Haworth (01535) 642169

HAWRIDGE (St Mary) w Cholesbury and St Leonard *Ox 28* **P** *Bp, Chpl Trust, and Neale's Charity (jt)* **R** G A de BURGH-THOMAS, **NSM** P R BINNS

HAWSKER (All Saints) Fylingdales and Hawsker cum Stainsacre *York*

HAWSTEAD (All Saints) and Nowton w Stanningfield and Bradfield Combust *St E 13* **P** *Mrs J Oakes (2 turns), Bp (3 turns)* **R** K A FINNIMORE

HAWTHORN (St Michael and All Angels) *Dur 3* **P** *I Pemberton Esq* **P-in-c** A MILNE

HAWTON (All Saints) Farndon w Thorpe, Hawton and Cotham *S'well*

HAXBY (St Mary) w Wigginton *York 8* **P** *Abp and Ld Chan (alt)* **TR** M W ESCRITT, **TV** A A HORSMAN, **NSM** L PERRINS

HAXEY (St Nicholas) *Linc 1* **P** *Ld Chan* **V** T W THOMPSON

HAY MILL (St Cyprian) Yardley St Cypr Hay Mill *Birm*

HAYDOCK (St James) *Liv 16* **P** *R Ashton-in-Makerfield* **V** R MIDDLETON, **NSM** G J HARDMAN

HAYDOCK (St Mark) *Liv 10* **P** *MMCET* **V** P POTTER, **NSM** G SMITH, G A SMITH

HAYDON BRIDGE (St Cuthbert) *Newc 4* **P** *Bp* **V** K FLETCHER, **C** G A PRICE

HAYDON WICK (St John) Rodbourne Cheney *Bris*

HAYES (St Anselm) *Lon 24* **P** *Bp* **V** *Vacant* 0181–573 0958

HAYES (St Edmund of Canterbury) *Lon 24* **P** *Bp* **V** P J BALL, **C** W A BROOKER, **NSM** J R MOTHERSOLE

HAYES (St Mary) *Lon 24* **P** *Keble Coll Ox* **R** *Vacant* 0181–573 2470

HAYES (St Mary the Virgin) *Roch 13* **P** *D&C* **R** P G H THOMAS, **C** F L MATTHEWS

HAYES (St Nicholas) Raynton Drive Conventional District *Lon 24* **C-in-c** D M BRADSHAW, **C** J W KNILL-JONES

HAYFIELD (St Matthew) *Derby 6* **P** *Resident Freeholders* **V** D M ROWLEY

HAYLE (St Elwyn) *Truro 5* **P** *D&C* **P-in-c** A T NEAL, **C** M A TREMBATH, **CC** McQUILLEN-WRIGHT

HAYLING, SOUTH (St Mary) (St Andrew) w North Hayling *Portsm 4* **P** *DBP* **V** P S GROYLE, **C** B M C MORRIS, **NSM** M G BULL

HAYNES (St Mary) (Mission Room) *St Alb 22* **P** *Bp* **P-in-c** K LORAINE

HAYTON (St James) Aspatria w Hayton *Carl*

HAYTON (St Martin) Shiptonthorpe w Hayton *York*

HAYTON (St Mary Magdalene) w Cumwhitton *Carl 2* **P** *D&C* **V** A SPYE

HAYTON (St Peter) Clarborough w Hayton *S'well*

HAYWARDS HEATH (St Richard) *Chich 6* **P** *Bp* **V** C R BEARD

HAYWARDS HEATH (St Wilfrid) (Church of the Ascension) (Church of the Good Shepherd) (Church of the Presentation) *Chich 6* **P** *Bp* **TR** I J BRACKLEY, **TV** G PIPER, K G SWABY, C J MIDLANE, **NSM** D J HOLLIS, J SEDGLEY

HAYWOOD, GREAT (St Stephen) Colwich w Gt Haywood *Lich*

HAZELBURY BRYAN (St Mary and St James) and the Hillside Parishes *Sarum 6* **P** *Duke of Northd (2 turns), M J Scott-Williams Esq, G A L Pitt-Rivers Esq, Exors F N Kent Esq, and Bp (1 turn each)* **R** S GILL

HAZELWELL (St Mary Magdalen) *Birm 8* **P** *Bp* **V** A C PRIESTLEY

HAZELWOOD (St John the Evangelist) *Derby 11* **P** *Bp* **V** *Vacant* Derby (01332) 840161

HAZLEMERE (Holy Trinity) *Ox 29* **P** *Peache Trustees* **V** P C COLLIER, **C** A M RIMMER

HEACHAM (St Mary) *Nor 17* **P** *Bp* **V** P W L RATCLIFFE

HEADBOURNE WORTHY (St Swithun) *Win 13* **P** *Univ Coll Ox and Exors Lord Northbrook (alt)* **R** *Vacant*

HEADCORN (St Peter and St Paul) *Cant 15* **P** *Abp* **V** *Vacant* Headcorn (01622) 890342

HEADINGLEY (St Chad) Far Headingley St Chad *Ripon*

HEADINGLEY (St Michael and All Angels) *Ripon 7* **P** *V Leeds St Pet* **V** M A CROSS, **C** J M LEAK, P THIRST, A D NORWOOD, **NSM** D W PEAT

HEADINGLEY (St Oswald) Far Headingley St Chad *Ripon*

HEADINGTON (St Andrew) *Ox 4* **P** *Keble Coll Ox* **V** W M BREWIN

HEADINGTON (St Mary) *Ox 4* **P** *Bp* **V** C J WALKER

HEADINGTON QUARRY (Holy Trinity) *Ox 4* **P** *Bp* **P-in-c** T D HONEY

HEADLESS CROSS (St Luke) Redditch, The Ridge *Worc*

HEADLEY (All Saints) *Guildf 3* **P** *Patr Bd* **TR** R W WOODGER, **TV** S GOODWIN, **C** B NICOLE, **NSM** S E GOODWIN, P A GODFREY

HEADLEY (St Mary the Virgin) w Box Hill (St Andrew) *Guildf 9* **P** *Bp* **R** D A WOTTON, **Hon C** A F TATHAM

HEADLEY (St Peter) Ashford Hill w Headley *Win*

HEADON (St Peter) E Markham w Askham, Headon w Upton and Grove *S'well*

HEADSTONE (St George) *Lon 23* **P** *Bp* **P-in-c** S R KEEBLE

HEAGE (St Luke) Ambergate and Heage *Derby*

HEALAUGH (St John the Baptist) w Wighill, Bilbrough and Askham Richard *York 1* **P** *Abp (3 turns), A G Wailes Fairburn Esq (1 turn)* **V** K BAILES

HEALD GREEN (St Catherine) *Ches 17* **P** *Bp* **V** R D CLARKE, **C** T B SMITH

HEALEY (Christ Church) *Man 20* **P** *Bp* **P-in-c** J D QUANCE

HEALEY (St John) and Slaley *Newc 3* **P** *Bp and V Bywell St Pet (jt)* **V** J K YOUNG

HEALEY (St Paul) Masham and Healey *Ripon*

HEALEY (War Memorial Mission) S Ossett *Wakef*

HEALING (St Peter and St Paul) and Stallingborough *Linc 10* **P** *Bp* **P-in-c** D E KING

HEAMOOR (St Thomas) Madron *Truro*

HEANOR (St Laurence) *Derby 12* **P** *Wright Trustees* **V** C L BLAKEY

HEANTON PUNCHARDON (St Augustine) w Marwood *Ex 15* **P** *CPAS (3 turns), St Jo Coll Cam (1 turn)* **R** J E DYKES

HEAP BRIDGE (St Thomas and St George) Bury Ch King *Man*

HEAPEY (St Barnabas) and Withnell *Blackb 4* **P** *V Leyland* **V** G R LOXHAM

HEAPHAM (All Saints) Lea Gp *Linc*

HEARTSEASE (St Francis) Nor Heartsease St Fran *Nor*

HEATH (All Saints) *Derby 5* **P** *Duke of Devonshire and Simeon's Trustees (jt)* **V** B M SPROSTON

HEATH (Mission Church) Uttoxeter w Bramshall *Lich*

HEATH, LITTLE (Christ Church) *St Alb 2* **P** *Ch Patr Trust* **V** I D BROWN, **NSM** A HARDING, R H WIKNER

HEATH, THE (not known) Bitterley w Middleton, Stoke St Milborough etc *Heref*

HEATH AND REACH (St Leonard) *St Alb 18* **P** *V Leighton Buzzard* **P-in-c** D RIDGEWAY

HEATH HAYES (St John) Cannock *Lich*

HEATH TOWN (Holy Trinity) Wednesfield Heath *Lich*

HEATHER (St John the Baptist) Ibstock w Heather *Leic*

HEATHERLANDS (St John) *Sarum 8* **P** *MMCET* **V** G A G LOUGHLIN, **C** D N ANDREW, J P M MARTIN

HEATHERYCLEUGH (St Thomas) *Dur 15* **P** *Bp* **V** D M SKELTON

HEATHFIELD (All Saints) *Chich 15* **P** *Bp* **V** B JACKSON

HEATHFIELD (St Catherine) Bovey Tracey St John, Chudleigh Knighton etc *Ex*

HEATHFIELD (St John the Baptist) Bradf w Oake, Hillfarrance and Heathfield *B & W*

HEATHFIELD (St Richard) *Chich 15* **P** *Bp* **V** *Vacant* Heathfield (01435) 862744

HEATON (Christ Church) *Man 9* **P** *R Deane St Mary*
V D B GRIFFITHS, **C** A BRADBROOK
HEATON (St Barnabas) *Bradf 1* **P** *Trustees*
V R S ANDERSON
HEATON (St Martin) *Bradf 1* **P** *Bp* **V** A J BURNISTON
HEATON CHAPEL (St Thomas) Heaton Norris St Thos
Man
HEATON MERSEY (St John the Baptist) *Man 3* **P** *Bp*
P-in-c M H MAXWELL
HEATON MOOR (St Paul) *Man 3* **P** *Trustees*
R S E W GUY
HEATON NORRIS (Christ w All Saints) *Man 3* **P** *Bp*
R M K BOOTH
HEATON NORRIS (St Thomas) *Man 3* **P** *D&C*
R R CROFT
HEATON REDDISH (St Mary) *Man 3* **P** *Trustees*
R W J McKAE
**HEAVITREE (St Michael and All Angels) (St Lawrence)
(St Loye) w Exeter St Paul** *Ex 3* **P** *Patr Bd*
TR M S HART, **TV** J D A WILLIAMS,
C G L COLLINGWOOD, **NSM** P R MORRELL
HEBBURN (St Cuthbert) *Dur 7* **P** *TR Jarrow*
P-in-c J B HUNT
HEBBURN (St John) *Dur 7* **P** *Bp* **P-in-c** C S ROGERSON
HEBBURN (St Oswald) *Dur 7* **P** *The Crown*
P-in-c L H SKINNER
HEBDEN (St Peter) Linton in Craven *Bradf*
HEBDEN BRIDGE (St James) *Wakef 3* **P** *V Halifax*
V M W PARROTT, **NSM** C J WARDMAN
HEBRON (St Cuthbert) Longhorsley and Hebron *Newc*
HECK (St John the Baptist) Gt Snaith *Sheff*
HECKFIELD (St Michael) w Mattingley and Rotherwick
Win 5 **P** *New Coll Ox (2 turns), Bp (1 turn)*
V A E BENNETT
HECKINGTON (St Andrew) *Linc 22* **P** *Bp (2 turns),
Ven A C Foottit (1 turn)* **P-in-c** D F BOUTLE
HECKMONDWIKE (All Souls) (St James) *Wakef 8*
P *V Birstall* **V** J F LOWE
HEDDINGTON (St Andrew) Oldbury *Sarum*
HEDDON-ON-THE-WALL (St Andrew) *Newc 3*
P *Ld Chan* **P-in-c** P J BRYARS
HEDENHAM (St Peter) Ditchingham, Hedenham and
Broome *Nor*
HEDGE END (St John the Evangelist) *Win 9* **P** *Bp*
V C J BANNISTER
HEDGE END (St Luke) *Win 9* **P** *Bp* **V** D S FARLEY
HEDGEFIELD (St Hilda) Ryton w Hedgefield *Dur*
HEDGERLEY (St Mary the Virgin) Farnham Royal w
Hedgerley *Ox*
HEDNESFORD (St Peter) *Lich 3* **P** *Bp* **V** D J DITCH,
C V C AGGETT, B N WHITMORE
HEDON (St Augustine) w Paull *York 13* **P** *Abp*
V J D HARGREAVE
HEDSOR (St Nicholas) and Bourne End *Ox 29* **P** *Bp*
P-in-c J E SCLATER, **Hon C** B BRITTON,
NSM R G FORDHAM
HEDWORTH (St Nicholas) *Dur 7* **P** *The Crown*
V W P B CARLIN
HEELEY (Christ Church) *Sheff 1* **P** *The Crown* **V** *Vacant*
Sheffield (0114) 255 7718
HEENE (St Botolph) *Chich 5* **P** *D&C* **R** P R ROBERTS,
C C G H KASSELL
HEIGHAM (Holy Trinity) *Nor 3* **P** *Ch Trust Fund Trust*
P-in-c A M STRANGE, **C** J H VALENTINE,
NSM C J SCOTT
HEIGHAM (St Barnabas) (St Bartholomew) *Nor 3* **P** *Bp*
V D M JONES
HEIGHAM (St Thomas) *Nor 3* **P** *Bp* **V** N J H GARRARD,
NSM E HUTCHEON
HEIGHINGTON (not known) Washingborough w
Heighington and Canwick *Linc*
HEIGHINGTON (St Michael) *Dur 12* **P** *D&C*
V P H E THOMAS
HEIGHTINGTON (St Giles) Mamble w Bayton, Rock w
Heightington etc *Worc*
HELFORD (St Paul's Mission Church) Manaccan w St
Anthony-in-Meneage and St Martin *Truro*
HELHOUGHTON (All Saints) South Raynham, E w W
Raynham, Helhoughton, etc *Nor*
HELIDON (St John the Baptist) Daventry, Ashby St
Ledgers, Braunston etc *Pet*
HELIONS BUMPSTEAD (St Andrew) Steeple Bumpstead
and Helions Bumpstead *Chelmsf*
HELLAND (St Helena) *Truro 10* **P** *MMCET*
P-in-c R D C WHITEMAN, J L BRENDON-COOK
HELLESDON (St Mary) (St Paul and St Michael) *Nor 2*
P *Bp* **V** D M HOARE, **C** J M FOLLETT,
M W L PICKETT, **Hon C** G M BRIDGES

HELLIFIELD (St Aidan) *Bradf 5* **P** *Ch Ch Ox*
V G WALKER
HELLINGLY (St Peter and St Paul) and Upper Dicker
Chich 15 **P** *Abp and Bp (jt)* **V** R E CHATWIN,
NSM D J SWANEPOEL
**HELMDON (St Mary Magdalene) w Stuchbury and Radstone
and Syresham w Whitfield** *Pet 1* **P** *Ox Univ, Mert Coll Ox,
and Worc Coll Ox (3 turns), Bp (1 turn), and DBP
(1 turn)* **P-in-c** J H ROBERTS
HELME (Christ Church) *Wakef 1* **P** *Bp*
P-in-c M C RUSSELL, **NSM** R T TUCK
**HELMINGHAM (St Mary) w Framsden and Pettaugh w
Winston** *St E 18* **P** *Ld Chan, MMCET, and Lord
Tollemache (by turn)* **R** *Vacant* Helmingham (01473)
890858
HELMSLEY (All Saints) *York 18* **P** *Lord Feversham*
V R C HOLMES
HELMSLEY, UPPER (St Peter) Sand Hutton *York*
HELPERTHORPE (St Peter) Weaverthorpe w Helperthorpe,
Luttons Ambo etc *York*
HELPRINGHAM (St Andrew) w Hale *Linc 22* **P** *Ld Chan
(2 turns), D&C (1 turn), and DBP (1 turn)*
R P R MASTERTON
HELPSTON (St Botolph) Etton w Helpston and Maxey *Pet*
HELSBY (St Paul) and Dunham-on-the-Hill *Ches 3* **P** *Bp*
V A R RIDLEY, **C** C E LARSEN, J E PEARCE
HELSINGTON (St John the Baptist) *Carl 9* **P** *V Kendal
H Trin* **V** *Vacant*
HELSTON (St Michael) and Wendron *Truro 4* **P** *Patr Bd*
TR D G MILLER, **C** P D SAYLE
HEMBLINGTON (All Saints) Blofield w Hemblington *Nor*
HEMEL HEMPSTEAD Apsley End (St
Mary) Chambersbury (Hemel Hempstead) *St Alb*
HEMEL HEMPSTEAD Bennetts End (St Benedict) as above
HEMEL HEMPSTEAD Leverstock Green (Holy Trinity) as
above
HEMEL HEMPSTEAD (St Mary) *St Alb 3* **P** *Ld Chan*
TR N D B ABBOTT, **TV** F A JACKSON, M J AINSWORTH,
G R KEGG, D J BEVINGTON, **NSM** T J BARTON
HEMINGBROUGH (St Mary the Virgin) *York 4* **P** *Abp*
V *Vacant* Selby (01757) 638528
HEMINGBY (St Margaret) *Linc 11* **P** *Bp (2 turns), Ld Chan
(2 turns), and DBP (1 turn)* **R** D J LAWRENCE
HEMINGFORD ABBOTS (St Margaret of Antioch) *Ely 9*
P *Lord Hemingford* **P-in-c** S R TALBOT
HEMINGFORD GREY (St James) *Ely 9* **P** *Mrs G A Scott*
P-in-c S R TALBOT
HEMINGSTONE (St Gregory) Coddenham w Gosbeck and
Hemingstone w Henley *St E*
HEMINGTON (St Peter and St Paul) Polebrook and Lutton
w Hemington and Luddington *Pet*
HEMINGTON (The Blessed Virgin Mary) Norton St Philip
w Hemington, Hardington etc *B & W*
HEMLEY (All Saints) Waldringfield w Hemley and
Newbourn *St E*
HEMLINGTON (St Timothy) *York 22* **P** *Abp*
V I M GRAHAM
HEMPNALL (St Margaret) *Nor 5* **P** *Ld Chan (1 turn),
Patr Bd (5 turns)* **TR** E J GREEN, **TV** C M MAHONY,
C M H WINDRIDGE, **Hon C** D M GREEN
HEMPSTEAD (All Saints) Barningham w Matlaske w
Baconsthorpe etc *Nor*
HEMPSTEAD (All Saints) S Gillingham *Roch*
HEMPSTEAD (St Andrew) Radwinter w Hempstead
Chelmsf
HEMPSTEAD (St Andrew) Happisburgh, Walcot,
Hempstead w Eccles etc *Nor*
HEMPSTED (St Swithun) *Glouc 5* **P** *Bp*
P-in-c M J D IRVING, **NSM** J E NEWELL
HEMPTON (Holy Trinity) and Pudding Norton *Nor 16*
P *The Crown* **V** *Vacant*
HEMPTON (St John the Evangelist) Deddington w Barford,
Clifton and Hempton *Ox*
HEMSBY (St Mary) *Nor 6* **P** *Major R A Ferrier*
V W D B WILLIAMS, **Hon C** C A POWLES
HEMSWELL (All Saints) Glentworth Gp *Linc*
HEMSWORTH (St Helen) *Wakef 11* **P** *Bp* **R** M DAVIES
**HEMYOCK (St Mary) w Culm Davy, Clayhidon and
Culmstock** *Ex 4* **P** *DBP, SMF, and D&C (jt)*
R A C B GROSSE
HENBURY (St Mary the Virgin) *Bris 8* **P** *Lord Middleton
(1 turn), Bp (3 turns)* **V** H B TROTTER, **C** B D JOY
HENBURY (St Thomas) *Ches 13* **P** *Bp* **V** J B PEEL
HENDFORD (St Mary the Virgin and All Saints) Yeovil H
Trin *B & W*
HENDON (All Saints) Childs Hill *Lon 15* **P** *Bp*
V J P WAINWRIGHT
HENDON (Christ Church) *Lon 15* **P** *Bp* **V** R E PARSONS

HENDON (St Alphage) *Lon 15* **P** *Bp* **V** H D MOORE
HENDON (St Ignatius) *Dur 9* **P** *Bp* **P-in-c** A M BARTLETT
HENDON (St Mary) (St Mary Magdalene) *Lon 15* **P** *Bp*
  V R E PARSONS, **C** A J WARD, J S CLARKE
HENDON (St Paul) Mill Hill *Lon 15* **P** *Bp*
  V M D KETTLE, **C** C A COTTON, S R J ELLIOTT
HENDON, WEST (St John) *Lon 15* **P** *Bp* **V** J M WARNER
HENDRED, EAST (St Augustine of Canterbury) Wantage
  Downs *Ox*
HENDRED, WEST (Holy Trinity) as above
HENFIELD (St Peter) w Shermanbury and Woodmancote
  Chich 9 **P** *Bp* **V** P C KEFFORD, **C** R M WATTS,
  NSM A McNEIL
HENGOED w Gobowen *Lich 24* **P** R Selattyn **V** *Vacant*
  Oswestry (01691) 661226
HENGROVE (Christ Church) *Bris 3* **P** *Bp and Simeon's*
  Trustees (alt) **V** P S FREAR
HENHAM (St Mary the Virgin) and Elsenham w Ugley
  Chelmsf 22 **P** *Ch Hosp, Ch Soc Trust, and Bp (jt)*
  P-in-c R W FARR
HENLEAZE (St Peter) *Bris 5* **P** *Bp* **V** F SMITH,
  Hon C S M TYLER (nee WAITE), **NSM** B J PULLAN
HENLEY on Thames w Remenham *Ox 6* **P** *Bp and Jes Coll*
  Ox (jt) **R** A PYBURN
HENLEY (St Peter) Coddenham w Gosbeck and
  Hemingstone w Henley *St E*
HENLEY IN ARDEN (St John the Baptist) Beaudesert and
  Henley-in-Arden w Ullenhall *Cov*
HENLEY-ON-THAMES (Holy Trinity) Rotherfield Greys H
  Trin *Ox*
HENLOW (St Mary the Virgin) *St Alb 22* **P** *Ld Chan*
  V C G MATTOCK
HENNOCK (St Mary) Bovey Tracey SS Pet, Paul and Thos
  w Hennock *Ex*
HENNY, GREAT (St Mary) and LITTLE w Middleton and
  Wickam St Paul w Twinstead *Chelmsf 15*
  P *Earl of Verulam, Bp, D&C St Paul's, and Ld Chan*
  (by turn) **R** B A CAREW
HENSALL (St Paul) Gt Snaith *Sheff*
HENSHAW (All Hallows) Beltingham w Henshaw *Newc*
HENSINGHAM (St John) (Keekle Mission) *Carl 5*
  P *Trustees* **V** I G MAINEY, **C** J H A LEGGETT
HENSTEAD (St Mary) Wrentham w Benacre, Covehithe,
  Frostenden etc *St E*
HENSTRIDGE (St Nicholas) and Charlton Horethorne w
  Stowell *B & W 7* **P** *Bp (2 turns), K S D*
  Wingfield Digby Esq (1 turn) **R** P HALLETT
HENTLAND (St Dubricius) How Caple w Sollarshope,
  Sellack etc *Heref*
HENTON (Christ Church) Coxley, Henton and Wookey
  B & W
HEPPLE (Christ Church) Rothbury *Newc*
HEPTONSTALL (St Thomas a Becket and St Thomas the
  Apostle) *Wakef 3* **P** *V Halifax* **V** *Vacant* Hebden Bridge
  (01422) 842004
HEPWORTH (Holy Trinity) Upper Holme Valley *Wakef*
HEPWORTH (St Peter) w Hinderclay, Wattisfield and
  Thelnetham *St E 9* **P** *Bp, K Coll Cam, MMCET, and*
  P J Holt-Wilson Esq (jt) **R** J W FULTON
HEREFORD (All Saints) (St Barnabas Church Centre)
  Heref 3 **P** *D&C Windsor* **P-in-c** A P MOTTRAM,
  NSM G N PRIDAY
HEREFORD (Holy Trinity) *Heref 3* **P** *Bp*
  P-in-c J A BARRIE, **C** R D KING
HEREFORD (St John the Baptist) *Heref 3* **P** *D&C*
  P-in-c R A WILLIS
HEREFORD (St Martin) (St Francis)—South Wye Team
  Ministry *Heref 3* **P** *Bp, D&C and Provost*
  Worc Coll Ox (jt) **TR** T P JONES, **TV** R C GREEN,
  A J HARDING, P G HADDLETON, **NSM** M E FRAMPTON
HEREFORD (St Nicholas) *Heref 3* **P** *Ld Chan*
  P-in-c R NORTH
HEREFORD (St Paul) Tupsley w Hampton Bishop *Heref*
HEREFORD (St Peter w St Owen) (St James) *Heref 3*
  P *Simeon's Trustees* **V** P T WOOD, **C** C D PINES
HEREFORD, LITTLE (St Mary Magdalene) Burford III w
  Lt Heref *Heref*
HERMITAGE (Holy Trinity) and Hampstead Norreys, Cold
  Ash and Yattendon w Frilsham *Ox 14* **P** *Patr Bd*
  TR P R ALLIN, **TV** M J WARREN, **NSM** D B WINTER
HERMITAGE (St Mary) Yetminster w Ryme Intrinseca and
  High Stoy *Sarum*
HERNE (St Martin) *Cant 7* **P** *Abp* **V** P D SALES
HERNE BAY (Christ Church) (St Andrew's Church and
  Centre) *Cant 7* **P** *Simeon's Trustees* **V** R W COTTON,
  C M C BREADMORE, **Hon C** S A MUST

HERNE BAY (St Bartholomew) Reculver and Herne Bay St
  Bart *Cant*
HERNE HILL (St John) (St Paul) *S'wark 7* **P** *Bp and*
  Trustees (jt) **V** A O LADIPO, **C** A M RUMBLE
HERNER (Chapel) Newport, Bishops Tawton and Tawstock
  Ex
HERNHILL (St Michael) Boughton under Blean w Dunkirk
  and Hernhill *Cant*
HERODSFOOT (All Saints) Duloe w Herodsfoot *Truro*
HERONSGATE (St John the Evangelist) Mill End and
  Heronsgate w W Hyde *St Alb*
HERRIARD (St Mary) w Winslade and Long Sutton and South
  Warnborough and Tunworth and Upton Grey and Weston
  Patrick *Win 5* **P** *Bp, Qu Coll Ox, St Jo Coll Ox, Viscount*
  Camrose, and J L Jervoise Esq (jt) **V** T J B JENKYNS,
  NSM B J SMITH
HERRINGFLEET (St Margaret) Somerleyton, Ashby,
  Fritton, Herringfleet etc *Nor*
HERRINGSWELL (St Ethelbert) Mildenhall *St E*
HERRINGTHORPE (St Cuthbert) *Sheff 6* **P** *Bp*
  V B H COOPER
HERRINGTON *Dur 6* **P** *Bp* **P-in-c** K WALKER,
  C D BODDY
HERSHAM (St Peter) *Guildf 8* **P** *Bp* **V** N J WHITEHEAD,
  C A C JONAS
HERSTMONCEUX (All Saints) and Wartling *Chich 15*
  P *Bp* **R** M R FRANCIS
HERSTON (St Mark) Swanage and Studland *Sarum*
HERTFORD (All Saints) *St Alb 8* **P** *Ld Chan and Marquess*
  Townshend (alt) **V** W St J KEMM
HERTFORD (St Andrew) *St Alb 8* **P** *Duchy of Lanc*
  R G C EDWARDS, **C** P M QUINT
HERTFORD HEATH (Holy Trinity) Lt Amwell *St Alb*
HERTINGFORDBURY (St Mary) *St Alb 8* **P** *The Crown*
  P-in-c J BIRTWISTLE, **C** R A CARUANA
HESKET-IN-THE-FOREST (St Mary the Virgin) and
  Armathwaite *Carl 4* **P** *D&C and E P Ecroyd Esq (jt)*
  V D C CROOK
HESKETH (All Saints) w Becconsall *Blackb 6* **P** *Trustees*
  R K POWELL
HESLERTON, EAST (St Andrew) Sherburn and W and E
  Heslerton w Yedingham *York*
HESLERTON, WEST (All Saints) as above
HESLINGTON (St Paul) *York 4* **P** *Abp* **V** F G HUNTER
HESSAY (St John the Baptist) Rufforth w Moor Monkton
  and Hessay *York*
HESSENFORD (St Anne) St Germans *Truro*
HESSETT (St Ethelbert) Rougham, Beyton w Hessett and
  Rushbrooke *St E*
HESSLE (All Saints) *York 15* **P** *Ld Chan* **V** K A DAVID,
  C H C STOKER, J L CAMPBELL
HESTER WAY LANE (St Silas) Cheltenham St Mark *Glouc*
HESTON (All Saints) (St Leonard) *Lon 11* **P** *Bp*
  V T J L MAIDMENT, **NSM** V F FRAY
HESWALL (Church of the Good Shepherd) (St Peter) *Ches 8*
  P *Exors Lt-Col Sir Walter Bromley-Davenport*
  R R E MORRIS, **C** R J RENDALL, K P OWEN
HETHE (St Edmund and St George) Stratton Audley and
  Godington, Fringford etc *Ox*
HETHEL (All Saints) Wreningham *Nor*
HETHERSETT (St Remigius) w Canteloff w Little Melton and
  Great Melton *Nor 7* **P** *G&C Coll Cam, E C Evans-*
  Lombe Esq, and Em Coll Cam (by turn)
  C A E WOOLCOCK, **NSM** J M TALBOT
HETHERSGILL (St Mary) Bewcastle, Stapleton and
  Kirklinton etc *Carl*
HETTON, SOUTH (Holy Trinity) w Haswell *Dur 3* **P** *Bp*
  P-in-c C TODD
HETTON-LE-HOLE (St Nicholas) *Dur 6* **P** *Bp*
  R R O DICK, **C** C A DICK
HEVENINGHAM (St Margaret) Cratfield w Heveningham
  and Ubbeston etc *St E*
HEVER (St Peter), Four Elms and Mark Beech *Roch 10*
  P *Bp and C Talbot Esq (jt)* **R** P J PLUMLEY
HEVERSHAM (St Peter) and Milnthorpe *Carl 9*
  P *Trin Coll Cam* **V** J C HANCOCK
HEVINGHAM (St Mary and St Botolph) w Hainford and
  Stratton Strawless *Nor 20* **P** *Bp and Sir Thomas*
  Beevor Bt (jt) **R** P B FOREMAN, **NSM** A E KERRISON
HEWELSFIELD (St Mary Magdalene) St Briavels w
  Hewelsfield *Glouc*
HEWISH (Good Shepherd) Crewkerne w Wayford *B & W*
HEWORTH (Holy Trinity) (Christ Church) (St Wulstan)
  York 8 **P** *Patr Bd* **TR** D ANDREW,
  TV T McDONOUGH, P W WHITE
HEWORTH (St Alban) *Dur 4* **P** *V Heworth St Mary*
  P-in-c C M HOOPER

HEWORTH (St Mary) *Dur 4* **P** *Bp* **P-in-c** W D TAYLOR
HEXHAM (St Andrew) *Newc 4* **P** *Mercers' Co and Viscount Allendale (alt)* **R** M NELSON, **C** D J IRVINE, **NSM** E M NICHOLAS
HEXTABLE (St Peter) Swanley St Paul *Roch*
HEXTHORPE (St Jude) Doncaster St Jude *Sheff*
HEXTON (St Faith) Barton-le-Cley w Higham Gobion and Hexton *St Alb*
HEY (St John the Baptist) *Man 21* **P** *R Aston-under-Lyne St Mich* **V** *Vacant* 0161–624 1182
HEYBRIDGE (St Andrew) (St George) w Langford *Chelmsf 11* **P** *D&C St Paul's and Lord Byron (alt)* **V** *Vacant* Maldon (01621) 856938
HEYBROOK BAY (Holy Nativity) Wembury *Ex*
HEYDON (Holy Trinity), Great Chishill and Little Chishill, Chrishall, Elmdon w Wenden Lofts and Strethall *Chelmsf 23* **P** *Patr Bd* **R** D W PARROTT, **C** P D DAKIN, **NSM** C E DAKIN (nee HOLLETT)
HEYDON (St Peter and St Paul) Saxthorpe w Corpusty, Blickling, Oulton etc *Nor*
HEYDOUR (St Michael and All Angels) Ancaster Wilsford Gp *Linc*
HEYFORD (St Peter and St Paul) w Stowe Nine Churches *Pet 3* **P** *J L R Crawley Esq and DBP (alt)* **R** D EVANS
HEYFORD, LOWER (St Mary) The Heyfords w Rousham and Somerton *Ox*
HEYFORD, UPPER (St Mary) as above
HEYFORDS w Rousham and Somerton, The *Ox 2* **P** *New Coll Ox, CCC Ox, L Cottrell-Dormer Esq, and P W G Barnes Esq (by turn)* **P-in-c** N B W JAMES
HEYHOUSES (St Nicholas) Sabden and Pendleton *Blackb*
HEYHOUSES ON SEA (St Anne) *Blackb 11* **P** *J C Hilton Esq* **V** M S MALKINSON, **C** N L STIMPSON
HEYSHAM (St Peter) (St Andrew) (St James) *Blackb 12* **P** *C E C Royds Esq* **R** E LACEY, **C** S J HUNT
HEYSHOTT (St James) *Chich 10* **P** *Bp* **P-in-c** C BOXLEY
HEYSIDE (St Mark) *Man 22* **P** *Trustees* **V** R MORRIS, **NSM** G F WEIR, S WALKER
HEYTESBURY (St Peter and St Paul) and Sutton Veny *Sarum 14* **P** *Bp* **R** A R WEBB
HEYTHROP (St Nicholas) Enstone and Heythrop *Ox*
HEYWOOD (St James) *Man 18* **P** *Bp* **V** S A EVASON
HEYWOOD (St Luke) (All Souls) *Man 18* **P** *Bp and R Bury St Mary (jt)* **V** C KNOWLES, **C** P N BARRATT, **NSM** I TAYLOR
HEYWOOD (St Margaret) *Man 18* **P** *Bp* **V** I J STAMP, **NSM** A BROWN, M S THORP
HIBALDSTOW (St Hibald) Scawby, Redbourne and Hibaldstow *Linc*
HICKLETON (St Wilfrid) Goldthorpe w Hickleton *Sheff*
HICKLING (St Luke) w Kinoulton and Broughton Sulney (Upper Broughton) *S'well 9* **P** *Prime Min, Qu Coll Cam, and Bp (by turn)* **R** *Vacant* Kinoulton (01949) 81657
HICKLING (St Mary) Ludham, Potter Heigham and Hickling *Nor*
HIGH: *see also under substantive place names*
HIGH CROSS (St John the Evangelist) *St Alb 8* **P** *DBP* **V** H J SHARMAN
HIGH HOYLAND (All Saints), Scissett and Clayton West *Wakef 6* **P** *Bp* **R** M F CLEVERLEY
HIGH LANE (St Thomas) *Ches 16* **P** *R Stockport* **V** I C WATTS, **NSM** C BULL
HIGH OAK *Nor 7* **P** *Bp, D&C Cant, Earl of Kimberley, A E H Heber-Percy Esq, and D&C (jt)* **P-in-c** P J STEPHENS
HIGH SPEN (St Patrick) and Rowlands Gill *Dur 5* **P** *Bp* **P-in-c** K A WYLD
HIGHAM (St John the Evangelist) Padiham *Blackb*
HIGHAM (St John the Evangelist) and Merston *Roch 6* **P** *St Jo Coll Cam* **V** J F SOUTHWARD
HIGHAM (St Mary), Holton St Mary, Raydon and Stratford St Mary *St E 3* **P** *Duchy of Lanc, Reformation Ch Trust, and Sir Joshua Rowley, Bt (by turn)* **R** T R J WELLS
HIGHAM FERRERS (St Mary the Virgin) w Chelveston *Pet 10* **P** *Sir Stephen Hastings and Bp (alt)* **V** E BUCHANAN
HIGHAM GOBION (St Margaret) Barton-le-Cley w Higham Gobion and Hexton *St Alb*
HIGHAM GREEN (St Stephen) Barrow w Denham St Mary and Higham Green *St E*
HIGHAM HILL (St Andrew) Walthamstow St Andr *Chelmsf*
HIGHAM-ON-THE-HILL (St Peter) w Fenny Drayton and Witherley *Leic 13* **P** *D&C, and Lord O'Neill (jt)* **P-in-c** M CHARLES
HIGHAMPTON (Holy Cross) Black Torrington, Bradf w Cookbury etc *Ex*
HIGHAMS PARK (All Saints) Hale End *Chelmsf 5* **P** *Bp* **V** M OAKES

HIGHBRIDGE (St John the Evangelist) *B & W 1* **P** *Bp* **V** M F W BOND
HIGHBROOK (All Saints) and West Hoathly *Chich 6* **P** *Ld Chan* **V** A C CARR
HIGHBURY (Christ Church) (St John) (St Saviour) *Lon 6* **P** *Ch Trust Fund Trust and Islington Ch Trust (jt)* **V** J R LITTLEWOOD, **C** N F MASON, **NSM** T J I WITTER
HIGHBURY NEW PARK (St Augustine) *Lon 6* **P** *Trustees* **V** P M ALLCOCK
HIGHCLERE (St Michael and All Angels) and Ashmansworth w Crux Easton *Win 6* **P** *Earl of Carnarvon* **R** T F HORSINGTON
HIGHCLIFFE (St Mark) w Hinton Admiral *Win 8* **P** *Sir George Tapps-Gervis-Meyrick, Bt, and Bp (alt)* **V** J R WILLIAMS, **C** E C BOOTH, **Hon C** K G DAVIS
HIGHER: *see also under substantive place names*
HIGHER FOLD Leigh (St Matthew) *Bedf Leigh Man*
HIGHERTOWN (All Saints) and Baldhu *Truro 6* **P** *Bp and Viscount Falmouth (alt)* **V** *Vacant*
HIGHFIELD (All Saints) *Ox 4* **P** *Bp* **V** J E COCKE
HIGHFIELD (St Catherine) New Bury *Man*
HIGHFIELD (St Mary) Sheff St Mary Bramhall Lane *Sheff*
HIGHFIELD (St Matthew) *Liv 15* **P** *Trustees* **V** W H HARRINGTON
HIGHFIELD (St Paul) Hemel Hempstead *St Alb*
HIGHGATE (All Saints) *Lon 20* **P** *Bp* **V** D H HUBBARD, **Hon C** J S BOWDEN
HIGHGATE (St Augustine) *Lon 20* **P** *Bp* **V** T BUGBY
HIGHGATE (St Michael) *Lon 20* **P** *Bp* **V** J J FIELDING, **C** A D TAYLOR
HIGHGATE CENTRE Bredbury St Barn *Ches*
HIGHGATE RISE (St Anne) Brookfield St Anne, Highgate Rise *Lon*
HIGHLEY (St Mary) *Heref 9* **P** *MMCET* **V** C G WILLIAMS, **C** O S DALE
HIGHMORE (St Paul) Nettlebed w Bix and Highmore *Ox*
HIGHNAM (Holy Innocents), Lassington, Rudford, Tibberton and Taynton *Glouc 3* **P** *D&C, T J Fenton Esq, and A E Woolley (jt)* **R** M CLARKE, **Hon C** G N CRAGO
HIGHTERS HEATH (Immanuel) *Birm 8* **P** *Bp* **V** N C M SALTER
HIGHTOWN (St Barnabas) Hartshead and Hightown *Wakef*
HIGHTOWN (St Stephen) *Liv 5* **P** *Bp* **P-in-c** F A BRISCOE
HIGHWEEK (All Saints) (St Mary) and Teigngrace *Ex 11* **P** *Bp* **R** C R KNOTT
HIGHWORTH (St Michael) w Sevenhampton and Inglesham and Hannington *Bris 12* **P** *Bp (4 turns), Mrs M G Hussey-Freke (1 turn)* **V** A N GRAHAM, **C** D S MOSS
HILBOROUGH (All Saints) w Bodney *Nor 14* **P** *DBP* **P-in-c** A C FOOTTIT
HILDENBOROUGH (St John the Evangelist) *Roch 10* **P** *V Tonbridge* **V** R J BAWTREE, **C** B S SENIOR, **NSM** E M TOY
HILDERSHAM (Holy Trinity) *Ely 4* **P** *Trustees* **R** *Vacant*
HILDERSTONE (Christ Church) Fulford w Hilderstone *Lich*
HILFIELD (St Nicholas) Yetminster w Ryme Intrinseca and High Stoy *Sarum*
HILGAY (All Saints) *Ely 16* **P** *Hertf Coll Ox* **R** A G COCHRANE
HILL (St James) *Birm 9* **P** *Bp* **V** R D HINDLEY, **C** A M WEAVER (nee ROBBINS)
HILL (St Michael) Stone w Woodford and Hill *Glouc*
HILL CROOME (St Mary) Ripple, Earls Croome w Hill Croome and Strensham *Worc*
HILL TOP (Mission Room) Greasley *S'well*
HILLESDEN (All Saints) Lenborough *Ox*
HILLESLEY (St Giles) Kingswood w Alderley and Hillesley *Glouc*
HILLFARRANCE (Holy Cross) Bradf w Oake, Hillfarrance and Heathfield *B & W*
HILLINGDON (All Saints) *Lon 24* **P** *Bp* **V** A P GODSALL
HILLINGDON (St John the Baptist) *Lon 24* **P** *Bp* **V** L D MACKENZIE, **C** R H WORMALD
HILLINGTON (St Mary the Virgin) *Nor 17* **P** *Major the Hon G Dawnay* **P-in-c** G R HALL
HILLMORTON (St John the Baptist) *Cov 6* **P** *Bp and TR Rugby* **V** A P HAINES, **C** I R WHITEHEAD
HILLOCK (St Andrew) *Man 14* **P** *Bp and R Stand All SS* **V** K B ASHWORTH
HILLSBOROUGH and Wadsley Bridge (Christ Church) *Sheff 4* **P** *Ch Patr Trust* **V** A NEWMAN, **C** J E ASHTON
HILLTOP (Mission Room) Endon w Stanley *Lich*
HILMARTON (St Lawrence) Broad Town, Clyffe Pypard, Hilmarton etc *Sarum*

HILPERTON (St Michael and All Angels) w Whaddon and Staverton w Hilperton Marsh *Sarum 17* **P** *R Trowbridge St Jas and Viscount Long (alt)* **R** R B HICKS

HILPERTON MARSH (St Mary) Hilperton w Whaddon and Staverton etc *Sarum*

HILSTON (St Margaret) Roos and Garton in Holderness w Tunstall etc *York*

HILTON (All Saints) Milton Abbas, Hilton w Cheselbourne etc *Sarum*

HILTON (St Mary Magdalene) *Ely 9* **P** *Bp*
V P S G CAMERON

HILTON IN CLEVELAND (St Peter) *York 22* **P** *DBP*
P-in-c M D A DYKES

HIMBLETON (St Mary Magdalen) Bowbrook S *Worc*

HIMLEY (St Michael and All Angels) *Lich 5* **P** *Bp*
P-in-c S E ABLEWHITE

HINCASTER (Mission Room) Heversham and Milnthorpe *Carl*

HINCHLEY WOOD (St Christopher) *Guildf 8* **P** *Bp*
V R D ROBINSON

HINCKLEY (Assumption of St Mary the Virgin) (St Francis) (St Paul) *Leic 13* **P** *Bp* **V** B DAVIS, **C** A S REED, **NSM** B STANTON

HINCKLEY (Holy Trinity) (St John the Evangelist) *Leic 13* **P** *DBP* **TR** G D HAYLES, **TV** J N JEE

HINDERCLAY (St Mary) Hepworth, Hinderclay, Wattisfield and Thelnetham *St E*

HINDERWELL (St Hilda) w Roxby *York 23* **P** *Abp*
R D J DERMOTT

HINDHEAD (St Alban) *Guildf 3* **P** *Adn Surrey*
V J N E BUNDOCK, **NSM** P J SMITH

HINDLEY (All Saints) *Liv 14* **P** *R Wigan* **V** D P LUND,
C W L WHITFORD

HINDLEY (St Peter) *Liv 14* **P** *St Pet Coll Ox*
V I S CARTER

HINDLEY GREEN (St John) *Liv 14* **P** *Bp* **V** S B SMITH

HINDLIP (St James) Salwarpe and Hindlip w Martin Hussingtree *Worc*

HINDOLVESTON (St George) Foulsham w Hindolveston and Guestwick *Nor*

HINDON (St John the Baptist) Tisbury *Sarum*

HINDRINGHAM (St Martin) Barney, Fulmodeston w Croxton, Hindringham etc *Nor*

HINDSFORD (St Anne) *Man 13* **P** *Bp* **V** A S WELLS

HINGHAM (St Andrew) w Wood Rising w Scoulton *Nor 18* **P** *Earl of Verulam and Trustees (alt)* **R** D J BOURNE

HINKSEY, NEW (St John the Evangelist) S Hinksey *Ox*

HINKSEY, NORTH (St Lawrence) and Wytham *Ox 7*
P *Bp* **P-in-c** R E H BATES, **Hon C** R T BECKWITH

HINKSEY, SOUTH (St Lawrence) *Ox 7* **P** *Bp*
V E J C DAVIS, **Hon C** B SINGH

HINSTOCK (St Oswald) Cheswardine, Childs Ercall, Hales, Hinstock etc *Lich*

HINTLESHAM (St Nicholas) w Chattisham *St E 3*
P *St Chad's Coll Dur (3 turns), Bp (1 turn)* **R** *Vacant* Hintlesham (01473) 652258

HINTON ADMIRAL (St Michael and All Angels) Highcliffe w Hinton Admiral *Win*

HINTON AMPNER (All Saints) w Bramdean and Kilmeston *Win 1* **P** *D&C and The Crown (alt)* **P-in-c** A R CROAD

HINTON BLEWETT (St Margaret) E w W Harptree and Hinton Blewett *B & W*

HINTON CHARTERHOUSE (St John the Baptist) Freshford, Limpley Stoke and Hinton Charterhouse *B & W*

HINTON-IN-THE-HEDGES (Holy Trinity) Farthinghoe w Hinton-in-the-Hedges w Steane *Pet*

HINTON MARTEL (St John the Evangelist) *Sarum 10* **P** *Earl of Shaftesbury* **R** *Vacant* Witchampton (01258) 840256

HINTON-ON-THE-GREEN (St Peter) Sedgeberrow w Hinton-on-the-Green *Worc*

HINTON PARVA (St Swithun) Lyddington and Wanborough and Bishopstone etc *Bris*

HINTON ST GEORGE (St George) Merriott w Hinton, Dinnington and Lopen *B & W*

HINTON ST MARY (St Mary) Sturminster Newton and Hinton St Mary *Sarum*

HINTON WALDRIST (St Margaret) Cherbury *Ox*

HINTS (St Bartholomew) *Lich 4* **P** *Personal Reps A E Jones Esq* **P-in-c** H J BAKER

HINXHILL (St Mary) Mersham w Hinxhill *Cant*

HINXTON (St Mary and St John) *Ely 7* **P** *Jes Coll Cam*
V *Vacant*

HINXWORTH (St Nicholas) Ashwell w Hinxworth and Newnham *St Alb*

HIPSWELL (St John the Evangelist) *Ripon 2* **P** *Bp*
V G K TIBBO

HISTON (St Andrew) *Ely 5* **P** *MMCET*
V H K McCURDY, **C** J M PRATT

HITCHAM (All Saints) w Little Finborough *St E 10* **P** *Bp and Pemb Coll Ox (alt)* **P-in-c** R S EXCELL

HITCHAM (St Mary) Burnham w Dropmore, Hitcham and Taplow *Ox*

HITCHIN (Holy Saviour) (St Faith) (St Mark) (St Mary) *St Alb 9* **P** *Patr Bd* **TR** L E OGLESBY, **TV** W T A MATTHEWS, F J C MERCURIO, **C** R B REYNOLDS, **NSM** F S E GIBBS

HITTISLEIGH (St Andrew) *Ex 12* **P** *Bp* **V** C J L NAPIER

HIXON (St Peter) w Stowe-by-Chartley *Lich 20* **P** *DBP*
P-in-c J LILLEY, **C** J M OAKES

HOAR CROSS (Holy Angels) w Newchurch *Lich 19* **P** *Bp and Meynell Ch Trustees* **P-in-c** H HUGHES

HOARWITHY (St Catherine) How Caple w Sollarshope, Sellack etc *Heref*

HOATH (Holy Cross) St Nicholas at Wade w Sarre and Chislet w Hoath *Cant*

HOATHLY, EAST (not known) Chiddingly w E Hoathly *Chich*

HOATHLY, WEST (St Margaret) Highbrook and W Hoathly *Chich*

HOBS MOAT (St Mary) *Birm 13* **P** *Bp* **V** D A LEAHY,
C A W MOORE

HOBY (All Saints) Upper Wreake *Leic*

HOCKERILL (All Saints) *St Alb 4* **P** *Bp Lon*
V A J ALLSOP, **C** R W C PAGE, **NSM** A I JOHNSTON

HOCKERING (St Michael), Honingham, East Tuddenham and North Tuddenham *Nor 18* **P** *J V Berney Esq (1 turn), DBP (2 turns)* **R** A R DAWSON

HOCKERTON (St Nicholas) Kirklington w Hockerton *S'well*

HOCKHAM w Shropham Group of Parishes (Great w Little Hockham w Larling w Illington w Shropham, Snetterton and Wretham) *Nor 11* **P** *Bp, Major E H C Garnier, DBP, and Charterhouse (jt)* **P-in-c** J H RICHARDSON

HOCKHAM, GREAT (Holy Trinity) Hockham w Shropham Gp of Par *Nor*

HOCKLEY (St Matthew) Wilnecote *Lich*

HOCKLEY (St Peter and St Paul) *Chelmsf 12*
P *Wadh Coll Ox* **V** J N JOHNSON

HOCKLIFFE (St Nicholas) Leighton Buzzard w Eggington, Hockliffe etc *St Alb*

HOCKWOLD (St James) w Wilton *Ely 15* **P** *G&C Coll Cam* **R** A J ROWE

HOCKWORTHY (St Simon and St Jude) Sampford Peverell, Uplowman, Holcombe Rogus etc *Ex*

HODDESDON (St Catherine and St Paul) *St Alb 6*
P *Peache Trustees* **V** J H SPRINGBETT, **C** R J DOULTON

HODDLESDEN (St Paul) Darwen St Pet w Hoddlesden *Blackb*

HODGE HILL (St Philip and St James) *Birm 11* **P** *Bp*
TR R J TAYLOR, **TV** W E DUDLEY, **C** R J YEOMAN

HODNET (St Luke) w Weston under Redcastle *Lich 23*
P *A E H Heber-Percy Esq* **R** J H GRAHAM

HODTHORPE (St Martin) Whitwell *Derby*

HOE (St Andrew) Swanton Morley w Beetley w E Bilney and Hoe *Nor*

HOE, WEST (St Michael) Plymouth St Andr and St Paul Stonehouse *Ex*

HOE BENHAM (not known) Welford w Wickham and Gt Shefford, Boxford etc *Ox*

HOGGESTON (Holy Cross) Schorne *Ox*

HOGHTON (Holy Trinity) *Blackb 6* **P** *V Leyland*
P-in-c M SAWLE

HOGNASTON (St Bartholomew) Hulland, Atlow, Bradley and Hognaston *Derby*

HOGSTHORPE (St Mary) Chapel St Leonards w Hogsthorpe *Linc*

HOLBEACH (All Saints) *Linc 16* **P** *Bp* **V** P HILL,
C D M McCORMICK

HOLBEACH FEN (St John) *Linc 16* **P** *Bp*
P-in-c D A CARNEY

HOLBEACH MARSH (St Luke) (St Mark) (St Martin) (St Matthew) *Linc 16* **P** *V Holbeach* **V** *Vacant* Holbeach (01406) 22337

HOLBECK (St Luke the Evangelist) *Ripon 6* **P** *Bp, V Leeds St Pet, and Meynell Ch Trust (jt)* **P-in-c** C P JOHNSON,
C M JARVIS, J T HODGES

HOLBETON (All Saints) *Ex 21* **P** *The Crown*
P-in-c T R DEACON

HOLBORN (St Alban the Martyr) w Saffron Hill St Peter *Lon 1* **P** *D&C St Paul's* **V** H LEVETT, **C** K J MORRIS

HOLBORN (St George the Martyr) Queen Square (Holy Trinity) (St Bartholomew) Grays Inn Road *Lon 1*
P *Ch Soc Trust* **R** D K WERNER

HOLBORN (St-Giles-in-the-Fields) St Giles-in-the-Fields *Lon*
HOLBROOK (All Saints) w Freston and Woolverstone *St E* 5　**P** *Bp*　**P-in-c** A B LEIGHTON
HOLBROOK (St Michael) and Little Eaton *Derby* 11 **P** *DBP*　**V** M J FENTON,　**NSM** P J OWEN-JONES
HOLBROOK ROAD (St Swithin) Belper *Derby*
HOLBROOK (St Luke) *Cov* 2　**P** *Bp*　**V** J F TWISLETON, **C** S J BROWN
HOLBURY (Good Shepherd) Fawley *Win*
HOLCOMBE (Emmanuel) (Canon Lewis Hall) *Man* 10 **P** *R Bury St Mary*　**R** C R HONOUR
HOLCOMBE (St Andrew) Coleford w Holcombe *B & W*
HOLCOMBE (St George) Dawlish *Ex*
HOLCOMBE BURNELL (St John the Baptist) Tedburn St Mary, Whitestone, Oldridge etc *Ex*
HOLCOMBE ROGUS (All Saints) Sampford Peverell, Uplowman, Holcombe Rogus etc *Ex*
HOLCOT (St Mary and All Saints) Brixworth w Holcot *Pet*
HOLDENHURST (St John the Evangelist) *Win* 7　**P** *Bp* **V** *Vacant* Bournemouth (01202) 393438
HOLDGATE (Holy Trinity) Diddlebury w Munslow, Holdgate and Tugford *Heref*
HOLFORD (St Mary the Virgin) Quantoxhead *B & W*
HOLKHAM (St Withiburga) w Egmere w Warham, Wells-next-the-Sea and Wighton *Nor* 16　**P** *Viscount Coke (2 turns), M J Beddard Esq (2 turns), and D&C (1 turn)* **R** W A J SAYER
HOLLACOMBE (St Petroc) Holsworthy w Hollacombe and Milton Damerel *Ex*
HOLLAND, GREAT (All Saints) Kirby-le-Soken w Gt Holland *Chelmsf*
HOLLAND, NEW (Christ Church) Barrow and Goxhill *Linc*
HOLLAND FEN (All Saints) Brothertoft Gp *Linc*
HOLLAND-ON-SEA (St Bartholomew) *Chelmsf* 24 **P** *Ch Patr Trust*　**V** G A CATCHPOLE,　**NSM** P C COTTON
HOLLESLEY (All Saints) Boyton w Capel St Andrew and Hollesley *St E*
HOLLINFARE (St Helen) Glazebury w Hollinfare *Liv*
HOLLINGBOURNE (All Saints) and Hucking w Leeds and Broomfield *Cant* 15　**P** *Abp*　**V** D C BROOKES
HOLLINGDEAN (St Richard) Brighton St Matthias *Chich*
HOLLINGTON (St John the Evangelist) Rocester and Croxden w Hollington *Lich*
HOLLINGTON (St John the Evangelist) (St Peter and St Paul) *Chich* 17　**P** *Ch Patr Trust*　**V** M G H LACKEY, **C** T COLEMAN
HOLLINGTON (St Leonard) (St Anne) *Chich* 17 **P** *E G Brabazon Esq*　**R** A J TURNER,　**C** S R NUNN
HOLLINGWOOD (St Francis) Staveley and Barrow Hill *Derby*
HOLLINGWORTH (St Hilda) Milnrow *Man*
HOLLINGWORTH (St Mary) *Ches* 14　**P** *Trustees* **V** E PRATT
HOLLINSWOOD (not known) Cen Telford *Lich*
HOLLINWOOD (St Margaret) *Man* 19　**P** *R Prestwich St Mary*　**V** A GEORGE
HOLLOWAY (Emmanuel) Tollington *Lon*
HOLLOWAY Hanley Road (St Saviour) as above
HOLLOWAY (St Francis of Assisi) W Holl St Luke *Lon*
HOLLOWAY (St Mary Magdalene) *Lon* 6　**P** *Bp and V Islington St Mary (jt)*　**V** S J W COX
HOLLOWAY, UPPER (All Saints) Tufnell Park St Geo and All SS *Lon*
HOLLOWAY, UPPER (St Peter) (St John) *Lon* 6　**P** *CPAS and Islington Ch Trust (jt)*　**C** E E BACK
HOLLOWAY, WEST (St Luke) *Lon* 6　**P** *Lon Coll Div Trustees*　**V** T J PIGREM
HOLLOWELL (St James) Guilsborough w Hollowell and Cold Ashby *Pet*
HOLLY HILL (Church Centre) Frankley *Birm*
HOLLYBUSH (All Saints) Berrow w Pendock, Eldersfield, Hollybush etc *Worc*
HOLLYM (St Nicholas) Patrington w Hollym, Welwick and Winestead *York*
HOLMBRIDGE (St David) Upper Holme Valley *Wakef*
HOLMBURY ST MARY (St Mary the Virgin) Wotton and Holmbury St Mary *Guildf*
HOLMCROFT (St Bertelin) Stafford *Lich*
HOLME (Holy Trinity) Burton and Holme *Carl*
HOLME (St Giles) Langford w Holme *Carl*
HOLME (St Giles) w Conington *Ely* 13　**P** *Ld Chan and J H B Heathcote Esq (alt)*　**V** *Vacant* Ramsey (01487) 830622
HOLME, EAST (St John the Evangelist) Wareham *Sarum*
HOLME CULTRAM (St Cuthbert) *Carl* 3　**P** *V Holme Cultram St Mary*　**V** A D WHIPP

HOLME CULTRAM (St Mary) *Carl* 3　**P** *Ox Univ* **V** A D WHIPP
HOLME EDEN (St Paul) *Carl* 2　**P** *DBP*　**V** J S CASSON
HOLME HALE (St Andrew) Necton, Holme Hale w N and S Pickenham *Nor*
HOLME-IN-CLIVIGER (St John) *Blackb* 3 **P** *Mrs C P Creed*　**P-in-c** A R FREARSON
HOLME LACY w Dinedor *Heref* 3　**P** *Patr Bd* **V** T P JONES
HOLME-NEXT-THE-SEA (St Mary) Hunstanton St Mary w Ringstead Parva etc *Nor*
HOLME-ON-SPALDING MOOR (All Saints) (Old School Mission Room) *York* 7　**P** *St Jo Coll Cam*　**V** D S COOK
HOLME PIERREPONT (St Edmund) Radcliffe-on-Trent and Shelford etc *S'well*
HOLME RUNCTON (St James) w South Runcton and Wallington *Ely* 16　**P** *Bp*　**R** J C W NOLAN
HOLME VALLEY, The UPPER *Wakef* 6　**P** *Patr Bd* **TR** J M SAUSBY,　**TV** J N CAPSTICK,　L GREENWOOD, F G LEE,　**NSM** M D ELLERTON
HOLME WOOD (St Christopher) Tong *Bradf*
HOLMER (St Bartholomew) (St Mary) w Huntington *Heref* 3　**P** *D&C*　**V** G FLEMING
HOLMER GREEN (Christ Church) Penn Street *Ox*
HOLMES CHAPEL (St Luke) Church Hulme *Ches*
HOLMESDALE (St Philip) Dronfield w Holmesfield *Derby*
HOLMESFIELD (St Swithin) as above
HOLMEWOOD (St Alban Mission) Heath *Derby*
HOLMFIELD (St Andrew) *Wakef* 4　**P** *Bp*　**V** G A BANKS
HOLMFIRTH (Holy Trinity) Upper Holme Valley *Wakef*
HOLMPTON (St Nicholas) Easington w Skeffling, Kilnsea and Holmpton *York*
HOLMSIDE (St John the Evangelist) *Dur* 8　**P** *The Crown* **P-in-c** B DAVISON
HOLMWOOD (St Mary Magdalene) *Guildf* 7　**P** *Bp* **V** D J SAYER
HOLMWOOD, NORTH (St John the Evangelist) *Guildf* 12 **P** *Bp*　**V** W C FREDERICK
HOLNE (St Mary the Virgin) Widecombe-in-the-Moor, Leusdon, Princetown etc *Ex*
HOLNEST (Church of the Assumption) Dungeon Hill *Sarum*
HOLSWORTHY (St Peter and St Paul) w Hollacombe and Milton Damerel *Ex* 9　**P** *DBP and Mrs F M Palmer (jt)* **R** R M REYNOLDS
HOLT (St Andrew) w High Kelling *Nor* 19　**P** *St Jo Coll Cam*　**R** S S GREGORY,　**NSM** D M HOWELL
HOLT (St James) Wimborne Minster and Holt *Sarum*
HOLT (St Katharine) Broughton Gifford, Gt Chalfield and Holt *Sarum*
HOLT (St Martin) Grimley w Holt *Worc*
HOLTBY (Holy Trinity) Stockton-on-the-Forest w Holtby and Warthill *York*
HOLTON (St Bartholomew) and Waterperry w Albury and Waterstock *Ox* 1　**P** *DBP*　**R** *Vacant* Wheatley (01865) 872460
HOLTON (St Nicholas) Camelot Par *B & W*
HOLTON (St Peter) Halesworth w Linstead, Chediston, Holton etc *St E*
HOLTON-CUM-BECKERING (All Saints) Wickenby Gp *Linc*
HOLTON-LE-CLAY (St Peter) and Tetney *Linc* 10　**P** *Ld Chan (2 turns), Bp (1 turn)*　**V** J M THOMPSON
HOLTON-LE-MOOR (St Luke) S Kelsey Gp *Linc*
HOLTON ST MARY (St Mary) Higham, Holton St Mary, Raydon and Stratford *St E*
HOLTS (St Hugh) Conventional District *Man* 18 **C-in-c** B A HARRISON
HOLTSPUR (St Thomas) Beaconsfield *Ox*
HOLTYE (St Peter) Cowden w Hammerwood *Chich*
HOLWELL (St Laurence) The Caundles w Folke and Holwell *Sarum*
HOLWELL (St Leonard) Ab Kettleby Gp *Leic*
HOLWELL (St Mary the Virgin) Shill Valley and Broadshire *Ox*
HOLWELL (St Peter) Ickleford w Holwell *St Alb*
HOLWORTH (St Catherine by the Sea) Broadmayne, W Knighton, Owermoigne etc *Sarum*
HOLY ISLAND (St Mary the Virgin) *Newc* 12　**P** *Bp* **V** D ADAM,　**Hon C** C E TRISTRAM
HOLYBOURNE (Holy Rood) Froyle and Holybourne *Win*
HOLYMOORSIDE (St Peter) Brampton St Thos *Derby*
HOLYSTONE (St Mary the Virgin) Alwinton w Holystone and Alnham *Newc*
HOLYWELL (St John the Baptist) w Needingworth *Ely* 11 **P** *Bp*　**R** O SWAN
HOLYWELL (St Mary) Seghill *Newc*

HOMERSFIELD (St Mary) S Elmham and Ilketshall *St E*
HOMERTON (Christ Church on the Mead) Hackney Marsh
Lon
HOMERTON (St Barnabas w St Paul) as above
HOMERTON (St Luke) *Lon 5* **P** *St Olave Hart Street
Trustees* **V** C D HEWITT
HOMINGTON (St Mary the Virgin) Chalke Valley E *Sarum*
HONEYCHURCH (St Mary) N Tawton, Bondleigh,
Sampford Courtenay etc *Ex*
HONICKNOWLE (St Francis) *Ex 23* **P** *Ld Chan*
V P J MORGAN
HONILEY (St John the Baptist) Hatton w Haseley,
Rowington w Lowsonford etc *Cov*
HONING (St Peter and St Paul) Smallburgh w Dilham w
Honing and Crostwight *Nor*
HONINGHAM (St Andrew) Hockering, Honingham, E and
N Tuddenham *Nor*
HONINGTON (All Saints) Shipston-on-Stour w Honington
and Idlicote *Cov*
HONINGTON (All Saints) Blackbourne *St E*
HONINGTON (St Wilfred) Barkston and Hough Gp *Linc*
**HONITON (St Michael) (St Paul), Gittisham, Combe Raleigh,
Monkton and Awliscombe** *Ex 5* **P** *DBP*
TR J W I TREVELYAN, **TV** A J WADSWORTH,
C A J H EDWARDS, **Hon C** R C H SAUNDERS
HONLEY (St Mary) *Wakef 1* **P** *R Almondbury*
V R N WHITTINGHAM
HOO (All Hallows) High Halstow w All Hallows and Hoo St
Mary *Roch*
HOO (St Andrew and St Eustachius) Charsfield w Debach,
Monewden, Hoo etc *St E*
HOO (St Werburgh) *Roch 6* **P** *D&C* **V** D A LOW
HOOBROOK (St Cecilia) Kidderminster St Geo *Worc*
HOOE (St John the Evangelist) *Ex 24* **P** *Keble Coll Ox*
V *Vacant* Plymouth (01752) 403076
HOOE (St Oswald) *Chich 14* **P** *Bp* **V** P C CLEMENTS
HOOK (St John the Evangelist) *Win 5* **P** *Bp*
R S J FOSTER, **NSM** M R M JAGGS
HOOK (St Mary the Virgin) w Airmyn *Sheff 11* **P** *Bp and
Ch Soc Trust (jt)* **V** H BAGNALL
HOOK (St Mary) w Warsash *Portsm 2* **P** *Bp*
V T A J READER, **NSM** J B LOWATER
HOOK (St Paul) *S'wark 15* **P** *The Crown*
V M C DEARNLEY
HOOK COMMON (Good Shepherd) Upton-upon-Severn
Worc
**HOOK NORTON (St Peter) w Great Rollright, Swerford and
Wigginton** *Ox 3* **P** *Bp, DBP, BNC Ox, and Jes Coll
Ox (jt)* **P** J ACREMAN, **Hon C** C G TURNER
HOOKE (St Giles) Beaminster Area *Sarum*
HOOLE (All Saints) *Ches 2* **P** *Simeon's Trustees*
NSM M S SEARLE
HOOLE (St Michael) *Blackb 6* **P** *Reps of Mrs E A Dunne
and Mrs D Downes (jt)* **R** H PUGH
HOOLEY (Mission Hall) Redhill St Jo *S'wark*
HOOTON (St Paul) *Ches 9* **P** *Trustees* **V** R W CAMPBELL
HOOTON PAGNELL (All Saints) Bilham *Sheff*
HOOTON ROBERTS (St John) Bramley and Ravenfield w
Hooton Roberts etc *Sheff*
HOPE (Holy Trinity) w Shelve *Heref 13* **P** *New Coll Ox
(3 turns), J J C Coldwell Esq (1 turn)* **R** N D MINSHALL
HOPE (St James) *Man 6* **P** *Trustees* **V** D SHARPLES
HOPE (St Peter) and Castleton *Derby 2* **P** *Bp and D&C
Lich (jt)* **V** M F COLLIER
HOPE BAGOT (St John the Baptist) Burford II w Greete
and Hope Bagot *Heref*
HOPE BOWDLER (St Andrew) w Eaton-under-Heywood
Heref 11 **P** *DBP, Bp Birm, and Mrs R Bell (jt)*
R M BROMFIELD
HOPE COVE (St Clements) Malborough w S Huish, W
Alvington and Churchstow *Ex*
HOPE MANSEL (St Michael) Ross w Brampton Abbotts,
Bridstow, Peterstow etc *Heref*
HOPE-UNDER-DINMORE (St Mary the Virgin) Bodenham
w Hope-under-Dinmore, Felton etc *Heref*
HOPESAY (St Mary the Virgin) Lydbury N w Hopesay and
Edgton *Heref*
**HOPTON (All Saints), Market Weston, Barningham and
Coney Weston** *St E 9* **P** *Ld Chan and Bp (alt)*
R C P GANE
HOPTON (St Peter) Salt and Sandon w Burston *Lich*
HOPTON w Corton *Nor 9* **P** *Ld Chan and D&C (alt)*
P-in-c J B SIMPSON
HOPTON, UPPER (St John the Evangelist) Eastthorpe and
Upper Hopton *Wakef*
HOPTON CASTLE (St Edward) Clungunford w Clunbury
and Clunton, Bedstone etc *Heref*

HOPTON WAFERS (St Michael and All Angels) Cleobury
Mortimer w Hopton Wafers etc *Heref*
HOPWAS (St Chad) Tamworth *Lich*
HOPWOOD (St John) *Man 18* **P** *R Bury St Mary*
V J R BROCKLEHURST
HORAM (Christ Church) (St James) *Chich 15* **P** *Bp*
V K A MEPHAM
HORBLING (St Andrew) *Linc 13* **P** *Bp*
P-in-c C H WILSON
**HORBURY (St Peter and St Leonard) w Horbury Bridge
(St John)** *Wakef 12* **P** *Provost* **V** O J AISBITT
HORBURY JUNCTION (St Mary) *Wakef 12* **P** *DBP*
P-in-c S GOLDTHORPE, **NSM** M C ALDCROFT
HORDEN (St Mary) *Dur 3* **P** *Bp* **V** A BOWSER
HORDLE (All Saints) *Win 10* **P** *Bp* **V** M G ANDERSON,
Hon C R S HALSE, D PRICE, **NSM** J G SMITH,
P E HEAD
HORDLEY (St Mary the Virgin) Baschurch and Weston
Lullingfield w Hordley *Lich*
HORFIELD (Holy Trinity) *Bris 6* **P** *Bp* **R** J H WILSON,
C D R JOHNSON, **NSM** G CALWAY
HORFIELD (St Gregory) *Bris 6* **P** *Bp*
V D D HOLLOWAY, **Hon C** R D WALKER,
NSM A R GOOD
HORHAM (St Mary) Stradbroke, Horham, Athelington and
Redlingfield *St E*
HORKESLEY, GREAT (All Saints) (St John) *Chelmsf 18*
P *Ball Coll Ox* **R** C G A WOODS
HORKESLEY, LITTLE (St Peter and St
Paul) Wormingford, Mt Bures and Lt Horkesley *Chelmsf*
HORKSTOW (St Maurice) *Linc 6* **P** *DBP* **V** *Vacant*
HORLEY (St Bartholomew) (St Francis) (St Wilfrid)
S'wark 25 **P** *Patr Bd* **TR** P R MAY, **TV** J J LEPINE,
K B ROBINSON
**HORLEY (St Etheldreda) w Hornton and Hanwell, Shenington
and Alkerton** *Ox 5* **P** *Ld Chan, Lord De La Warr, and
DBP (by turn)* **R** A LANCASHIRE
HORLEY ROW (St Wilfrid) Horley *S'wark*
**HORMEAD (St Mary), Wyddial, Anstey, Brent Pelham and
Meesden** *St Alb 5* **P** *St Jo Coll Cam, Ch Coll Cam, and Bp
(by turn)* **P-in-c** G A DREW
HORMEAD (St Nicholas) Hormead, Wyddial, Anstey, Brent
Pelham etc *St Alb*
HORN HILL (St Paul) Chalfont St Peter *Ox*
HORN PARK (St Francis) Eltham St Jo *S'wark*
HORNBLOTTON (St Peter) Six Pilgrims *B & W*
HORNBY (St Margaret) w Claughton *Blackb 15*
P *D R Battersby Esq and DBF (alt)* **V** I H RENNIE
HORNBY (St Mary) *Ripon 4* **P** *D&C York* **V** *Vacant*
HORNCASTLE (St Mary the Virgin) w Low Toynton
Linc 11 **P** *Bp (2 turns), Baroness Willoughby de Eresby
(1 turn)* **V** N A THORNLEY, **C** J F PARKIN,
D C PAYNE, **NSM** A C FORD
HORNCHURCH Elm Park (St Nicholas) Elm Park St Nic
Hornchurch *Chelmsf*
HORNCHURCH (Holy Cross) *Chelmsf 2* **P** *Bp and
New Coll Ox (alt)* **V** R B N HAYCRAFT,
NSM S M PAPWORTH
**HORNCHURCH (St Andrew) (St George) (St Matthew and St
John)** *Chelmsf 2* **P** *New Coll Ox* **V** H R DIBBENS,
C B A BAKER, D C BARNES, P J F GOODEY
HORNCHURCH, SOUTH (St John and St Matthew)
Chelmsf 2 **P** *MMCET* **P-in-c** M E PORTER
HORNDALE (St Francis) Newton Aycliffe *Dur*
**HORNDON, EAST (St Francis) and West Horndon w Little
Warley** *Chelmsf 7* **P** *Bp and Brentwood Sch*
P-in-c C F WELLS
HORNDON ON THE HILL (St Peter and St Paul) Orsett
and Bulphan and Horndon on the Hill *Chelmsf*
HORNE (St Mary) *S'wark 24* **P** *Bp* **R** W G WOOD
**HORNING (St Benedict) w Beeston St Laurence and
Ashmanhaugh** *Nor 12* **P** *Bp and Sir Ronald
Preston, Bt (jt)* **R** H A R EDGELL
HORNINGHOLD (St Peter) Hallaton w Horninghold,
Allexton, Tugby etc *Leic*
HORNINGLOW (St John the Divine) *Lich 19* **P** *Trustees*
V P J JEFFERIES, **C** M W HILL
HORNINGSEA (St Peter) *Ely 6* **P** *St Jo Coll Cam*
P-in-c L A MARSH
HORNINGSHAM (St John the Baptist) Warminster St
Denys, Upton Scudamore etc *Sarum*
HORNINGTOFT (St Edmund) Colkirk w Oxwick w
Pattesley, Whissonsett etc *Nor*
HORNSEA (St Nicholas) w Atwick *York 12* **P** *Ld Chan*
V B H WILCOX
HORNSEY (Christ Church) *Lon 20* **P** *Bp*
V J E TOWNSEND

HORNSEY (Holy Innocents) *Lon 20* **P** *Bp*
P-in-c N H ASBRIDGE
HORNSEY (St Mary) (St George) *Lon 20* **P** *Bp*
R G B SEABROOK, **C** P D RABIN
**HORNSEY RISE Whitehall Park Team, The (St Mary)
(St Andrew)** *Lon 6* **P** *Patr Bd* **TR** M J COLMER,
TV S P SAYERS, **C** F M HINTON
HORNTON (St John the Baptist) Horley w Hornton and
Hanwell, Shenington etc *Ox*
HORRABRIDGE (St John the Baptist) Sampford Spiney w
Horrabridge *Ex*
HORRINGER (St Leonard) cum Ickworth *St E 13* **P** *DBP*
R *Vacant* Horringer (01284) 735206
HORSEHEATH (All Saints) *Ely 4* **P** *Charterhouse*
P-in-c W N C GIRARD
HORSELL (St Mary the Virgin) *Guildf 12* **P** *Bp*
C W A PRESCOTT, **NSM** B ASHLEY
HORSENDON (St Michael and All Angels) Bledlow w
Saunderton and Horsenden *Ox*
HORSEY (All Saints) Winterton w E and W Somerton and
Horsey *Nor*
HORSFORD (All Saints) and Horsham w Newton St Faith
Nor 2 **P** *Bp* **V** J B BOSTON
HORSFORTH (St Margaret) *Ripon 7* **P** *Bp*
V M E SIDDLE, **C** D P RYAN
**HORSHAM (Holy Trinity) (St Leonard) (St Mary the Virgin)
(St Peter in the Causeway)** *Chich 8* **P** *Patr Bd*
TR D E E TANSILL, **TV** D J PROUD, T R J GODDEN,
B E STATHAM, **C** G C PICKERING, P H JONES,
NSM C SHORT, B SINTON
HORSHAM ST FAITH (St Mary and Andrew) Horsford
and Horsham w Newton St Faith *Nor*
HORSINGTON (All Saints) Woodhall Spa Gp *Linc*
HORSINGTON (St John the Baptist) Abbas and
Templecombe w Horsington *B & W*
HORSLEY (Holy Trinity) N Tyne and Redesdale Team
Newc
HORSLEY (St Clement) *Derby 12* **P** *Bp* **P-in-c** P SWALES
HORSLEY (St Martin) and Newington Bagpath w Kingscote
Glouc 16 **P** *Bp (2 turns), DBP (1 turn)* **V** G DEWHURST
HORSLEY, EAST (St Martin) *Guildf 10* **P** *D&C Cant*
R B J PARADISE
HORSLEY, WEST (St Mary) *Guildf 10*
P *Col A R N Weston* **R** P E B ROBINSON
HORSLEY HILL South Shields (St Lawrence the Martyr)
Dur 7 **P** *D&C* **V** G BUTTERY
HORSLEY WOODHOUSE (St Susanna) *Derby 12* **P** *Bp*
P-in-c D J PHYPERS
HORSMONDEN (St Margaret) *Roch 11* **P** *Bp*
P-in-c J M SAUNDERS
HORSPATH (St Giles) Garsington and Horspath *Ox*
HORSTEAD (All Saints) Coltishall w Gt Hautbois and
Horstead *Nor*
HORSTED, LITTLE (St Michael and All Angels) *Chich 21*
P *Rt Rev P J Ball* **R** C J PETERS, **NSM** C HOWARTH,
R C DALLING
HORSTED KEYNES (St Giles) *Chich 6* **P** *Bp*
R D A STONEBANKS
HORTON (All Saints) *Bradf 2* **P** *J F Bardsley Esq*
P-in-c W HOLLIDAY, **C** D J POOLE
HORTON (St James the Elder) and Little Sodbury *Glouc 7*
P *Duke of Beaufort (1 turn), CPAS (2 turns)*
R K V ENSOR
HORTON (St Mary Magdalene) Hardingstone and Horton
and Piddington *Pet*
HORTON (St Mary the Virgin) *Newc 1* **P** *V Woodhorn w
Newbiggin* **V** J D HOPKINS
HORTON (St Michael and All Angels) Riverside *Ox*
HORTON (St Michael), Lonsdon and Rushton Spencer
Lich 13 **P** *Bp and R Leek and Meerbrook (jt)*
V E J TOMLINSON
HORTON (St Peter) Ilminster and District *B & W*
HORTON (St Wolfrida) and Chalbury *Sarum 10* **P** *Earl of
Shaftesbury* **V** *Vacant*
HORTON, GREAT (St John the Evangelist) *Bradf 2*
P *V Bradf* **V** S ALLEN, **C** J D BREWSTER,
NSM L J SLOW
HORTON-CUM-STUDLEY (St Barnabas) *Ox 1*
P *V Beckley* **V** *Vacant*
HORTON-IN-RIBBLESDALE (St Oswald) Langcliffe w
Stainforth and Horton *Bradf*
HORTON KIRBY (St Mary) *Roch 2* **P** *Bp* **V** L E LAKER
**HORWICH (Holy Trinity) (St Catherine) (St Elizabeth) and
Rivington** *Man 11* **P** *Patr Bd* **TR** D W GATENBY,
TV G C BURROWS, W P BREW, **C** C R DUXBURY,
Hon C B H CRASTON (nee FULLALOVE), **NSM** J JERMY,
T LITHERLAND

HORWOOD (St Michael) Newton Tracey, Alverdiscott,
Huntshaw etc *Ex*
HORWOOD, GREAT (St James) Winslow w Gt Horwood
and Addington *Ox*
HORWOOD, LITTLE (St Nicholas) Mursley w Swanbourne
and Lt Horwood *Ox*
HOSE (St Michael) Harby, Long Clawson and Hose *Leic*
HOTHAM (St Oswald) *York 14* **P** *Ld Chan*
R P N HAYWARD
HOTHFIELD (St Margaret) Westwell, Hothfield, Eastwell
and Boughton Aluph *Cant*
HOUGH GREEN (All Saints) Ditton St Mich *Liv*
HOUGH-ON-THE-HILL (All Saints) Barkston and Hough
Gp *Linc*
HOUGHAM (All Saints) as above
HOUGHAM (St Laurence) Alkham w Capel le Ferne and
Hougham *Cant*
HOUGHTON (All Saints) Broughton, Bossington, Houghton
and Mottisfont *Win*
HOUGHTON (St Giles) Walsingham and Houghton *Nor*
HOUGHTON (St John the Evangelist) (St Peter) *Carl 3*
P *Trustees* **V** A M MacLEAY, **C** S R GALES
HOUGHTON (St Martin) E and W Rudham, Houghton-
next-Harpley etc *Nor*
HOUGHTON (St Mary) w Wyton *Ely 9* **P** *Bp*
R D D BILLINGS
HOUGHTON (St Nicholas) Bury and Houghton *Chich*
**HOUGHTON, GREAT (St Mary) and LITTLE (St Mary the
Blessed Virgin) w Brafield on the Green** *Pet 7* **P** *Magd Coll
Ox, Mrs A C Usher, and C G V Davidge Esq (jt)*
NSM S A TEBBUTT
**HOUGHTON, GREAT (St Michael and All Angels)
Conventional District** *Sheff 12*
C-in-c J P MILTON-THOMPSON
HOUGHTON, NEW (Christ Church) E Scarsdale *Derby*
HOUGHTON CONQUEST (All Saints) Wilshamstead and
Houghton Conquest *St Alb*
HOUGHTON LE SPRING (St Michael and All Angels)
Dur 6 **P** *Bp* **R** I G WALLIS, **C** P D ASHDOWN,
NSM D NEWTON
**HOUGHTON-ON-THE-HILL (St Catharine) Keyham and
Hungarton** *Leic 5* **P** *Bp* **R** O S BENNETT
HOUGHTON REGIS (All Saints) (St Thomas) *St Alb 18*
P *DBP* **V** G M NEAL, **C** C W WOOD
HOUND (St Edward the Confessor) (St Mary the Virgin)
Win 9 **P** *St Mary's Coll Win* **V** R W GOODHEW
HOUNSLOW (Holy Trinity) (St Paul) *Lon 11* **P** *Bp*
V O C M ROSS, **NSM** L LAWRENCE, N LAWRENCE
HOUNSLOW (St Mary the Virgin) Isleworth St Mary *Lon*
HOUNSLOW (St Stephen) *Lon 11* **P** *Bp* **V** R L RAMSDEN
HOUNSLOW WEST (Good Shepherd) *Lon 11* **P** *Bp*
V C J FULLER
**HOVE (All Saints) (St Andrew Old Church) (St John the
Baptist) (Holy Trinity)** *Chich 4* **P** *Bp*
TR J M P CALDICOTT, **TV** J S G COTMAN, C R BREEDS,
D A COTT, **C** I N CHANDLER, **NSM** H CHELLICAR
HOVE (Bishop Hannington Memorial Church) (Holy Cross)
Chich 4 **P** *Trustees* **V** A P BAKER,
C G L WINCHESTER, D F P RUTHERFORD
HOVE (St Barnabas) and St Agnes *Chich 4* **P** *Bp and V Hove
(alt)* **V** J A WREN, **NSM** T J MacDONALD
HOVE (St Patrick) *Chich 4* **P** *Bp, V Hove, and
V Brighton (jt)* **V** A B SHARPE, **NSM** D P WEBBER
HOVE (St Philip) Aldrington *Chich*
HOVERINGHAM (St Michael) Thurgarton w Hoveringham
and Bleasby etc *S'well*
HOVETON (St John) Wroxham w Hoveton and Belaugh *Nor*
HOVETON (St Peter) as above
HOVINGHAM (All Saints) Street TM *York*
**HOW CAPLE (St Andrew and St Mary) w Sollarshope,
Sellack, Kings Caple, Foy, Hentland and Hoarwithy**
Heref 8 **P** *Bp, D&C, and Brig A F L Clive (jt)*
P-in-c D J ENOCH
HOWDEN Team Ministry, The (St Peter) *York 14* **P** *Abp
(4 turns), Ld Chan (1 turn)* **TR** J H HARKER,
TV M R G SMITH, R HUNTER, **C** S F JONES
HOWDEN-LE-WEAR and Hunwick *Dur 15* **P** *Bp and
V Auckland St Andr (alt)* **V** *Vacant* Bishop Auckland
(01388) 604456
HOWE (St Mary the Virgin) Poringland *Nor*
HOWE BRIDGE (St Michael and All Angels) *Man 13*
P *DBP* **V** D H BRACEY
HOWELL (St Oswald) Heckington *Linc*
HOWELL HILL (St Paul) *Guildf 9* **P** *Bp*
C S M HENWOOD (nee OAKLEY), **NSM** F L McGILL
HOWGILL (Holy Trinity) Firbank, Howgill and Killington
Bradf

HOWICK (St Michael and All Angels) Longhoughton w Howick *Newc*

HOWLE HILL (St John the Evangelist) Walford and Saint John, w Bishopswood etc *Heref*

HOWSHAM (St John) Sand Hutton *York*

HOXNE (St Peter and St Paul) w Denham, Syleham and Wingfield *St E 17* **P** *Bp and DBP (jt)* **R** A R LOWE, NSM R J CLARK

HOXTON (Holy Trinity) (St Mary) *Lon 5* **P** *Bp* **V** S M WILSON

HOXTON (St Anne) (St Columba) *Lon 5* **P** *The Crown* **V** G R BUSH

HOXTON (St John the Baptist) Shoreditch St Leon and Hoxton St Jo *Lon*

HOYLAKE (Holy Trinity and St Hildeburgh) *Ches 8* **P** *Bp* **V** J K BALL

HOYLAND, NETHER (St Andrew) *Sheff 7* **P** *Bp* **V** C GREENWELL

HOYLAND, NETHER (St Peter) *Sheff 7* **P** *Sir Stephen Hastings* **V** K M WRAY

HOYLANDSWAINE (St John the Evangelist) and Silkstone w Stainborough *Wakef 7* **P** *Bp* **V** D BIRCH

HUBBERHOLME (St Michael and All Angels) Kettlewell w Conistone, Hubberholme etc *Bradf*

HUCCABY (St Raphael) Widecombe-in-the-Moor, Leusdon, Princetown etc *Ex*

HUCCLECOTE (St Philip and St James) *Glouc 5* **P** *Bp* **V** P H KENCHINGTON

HUCKING (St Margaret) Hollingbourne and Hucking w Leeds and Broomfield *Cant*

HUCKLOW, GREAT (Mission Room) Bradwell *Derby*

HUCKNALL TORKARD (St Mary Magdalene) (St Peter and St Paul) (St John's Mission Church) *S'well 8* **P** *Bp* **TR** F G GREEN, **TV** P HUNTER, C M BROWNE, C J E DAVIES, NSM R HALLETT

HUDDERSFIELD (Holy Trinity) *Wakef 5* **P** *Simeon's Trustees* **V** E O ROBERTS, C B PEACE, E J A McCULLAGH, NSM R C SWINDELL, P T WILCOCK

HUDDERSFIELD (St John the Evangelist) N Huddersfield *Wakef*

HUDDERSFIELD (St Peter) *Wakef 5* **P** *DBP* **V** B W MAGUIRE, C R A LANE, D A EARL, NSM D KENT

HUDDERSFIELD (St Thomas) *Wakef 5* **P** *DBP* **V** R S GILES, C T C K SLEDGE

HUDDERSFIELD, NORTH (St Cuthbert) *Wakef 5* **P** *DBP* **TR** M J LOWLES

HUDDINGTON (St James) Bowbrook S *Worc*

HUDSWELL (St Michael and All Angels) Richmond w Hudswell *Ripon*

HUGGATE (St Mary) Pocklington and Owsthorpe and Kilnwick Percy etc *York*

HUGGLESCOTE (St John the Baptist) w Donington, Ellistown and Snibston *Leic 8* **P** *Bp* **TR** J RICHARDSON, C M D WEBB

HUGHENDEN (St Michael) *Ox 29* **P** *DBP* **P-in-c** C H OVERTON, C M P WYNTER, NSM F J FRIEND

HUGHLEY (St John the Baptist) Wenlock *Heref*

HUISH (St James the Less) Shebbear, Buckland Filleigh, Sheepwash etc *Ex*

HUISH (St Nicholas) Swanborough *Sarum*

HUISH, SOUTH (Holy Trinity) Malborough w S Huish, W Alvington and Churchstow *Ex*

HUISH CHAMPFLOWER (St Peter) Wiveliscombe w Chipstable, Huish Champflower etc *B & W*

HUISH EPISCOPI (Blessed Virgin Mary) Langport Area Chs *B & W*

HULCOTE (St Nicholas) Cranfield and Hulcote w Salford *St Alb*

HULCOTT (All Saints) Aylesbury w Bierton and Hulcott *Ox*

HULL (Holy Apostles) Kingston upon Hull H Trin *York*

HULL Lowgate (St Mary the Virgin) Kingston upon Hull St Mary *York*

HULL Newington (St John the Baptist) Newington w Dairycoates *York*

HULL Newland (St John) *York 15* **P** *Abp* **V** M TINKER, C C B HOBBS, J C WEETMAN, M C BRAILSFORD

HULL Sculcoates (St Mary) *York 15* **P** *V Sculcoates* NSM J G LEEMAN, K FORSTER

HULL Sculcoates (St Stephen) *York 15* **P** *Ld Chan (2 turns), V Hull H Trin (1 turn), and Abp (1 turn)* **V** F A C S BOWN

HULL (St Cuthbert) *York 15* **P** *Abp* **V** J D DAGLISH

HULL (St George) Marfleet *York*

HULL (St Giles) as above

HULL (St Hilda) as above

HULL (St Martin) (Transfiguration) *York 15* **P** *Abp* **V** E WILSON, C M A HILL

HULL (St Philip) Marfleet *York*

HULL (St Thomas) Derringham Bank *York*

HULL, NORTH (St Michael and All Angels) *York 15* **P** *Abp* **V** D A WALKER, C T C GILL

HULLAND (Christ Church), Atlow, Bradley and Hognaston *Derby 8* **P** *Bp, D&C Lich, Trustees, and Exors Col* I P A M Walker-Okeover (by turn) **R** R K SMITH

HULLAVINGTON (St Mary Magdalene) Stanton St Quintin, Hullavington, Grittleton etc *Bris*

HULLBRIDGE (St Thomas of Canterbury) *Chelmsf 12* **P** *Bp* **V** *Vacant* Southend-on-Sea (01702) 232017

HULME (Ascension) *Man 4* **P** *Trustees* **R** J A R METHUEN, C M THOMPSON, Hon C H C WEST

HULME WALFIELD (St Michael) Eaton and Hulme Walfield *Ches*

HULTON, LITTLE (St John the Baptist) Walkden Moor w Lt Hulton *Man*

HULTON, OVER (St Andrew) Deane *Man*

HUMBER (St Mary the Virgin) Leominster *Heref*

HUMBERSTON (St Peter) *Linc 10* **P** *Bp* **V** I H TINKLER

HUMBERSTONE (St Mary) *Leic 1* **P** *DBP* **P-in-c** W J D DOWN

HUMBERSTONE, NEW (St Barnabas) *Leic 1* **P** *Bp* **P-in-c** S F BOULD, C R G BIRCHALL

HUMBLE, WEST (St Michael) Mickleham *Guildf*

HUMBLETON (St Peter) Burton Pidsea and Humbleton w Elsternwick *York*

HUMPHREY PARK (St Clement) Urmston *Man*

HUMSHAUGH (St Peter) w Simonburn and Wark *Newc 2* **P** *Bp* **R** S V PRINS

HUNCOAT (St Augustine) Accrington St Jo w Huncoat *Blackb*

HUNCOTE (St James the Greater) Narborough and Huncote *Leic*

HUNDLEBY (St Mary) Spilsby w Hundleby *Linc*

HUNDON (All Saints) w Barnardiston *St E 8* **P** *Jes Coll Cam (2 turns), Ridley Hall Cam (1 turn)* **R** J J COOPER

HUNDRED RIVER Benefice, The *St E 14* **P** *DBP, Shadingfield Properties Ltd, Bp, Miss to Seamen, and F D L Barnes Esq (by turn)* **R** C J ATKINSON

HUNGARTON (St John the Baptist) Houghton-on-the-Hill, Keyham and Hungarton *Leic*

HUNGERFORD (St Lawrence) and Denford *Ox 14* **P** *D&C Windsor* **V** A W SAWYER

HUNMANBY (All Saints) w Muston *York 16* **P** *M M CET* **V** J W R HATTAN

HUNNINGHAM (St Margaret) *Cov 10* **P** *Ld Chan* **P-in-c** P J CROOKS

HUNSDON (St Dunstan) (St Francis) w Widford and Wareside *St Alb 8* **P** *DBP* **R** J RISBY

HUNSINGORE (St John the Baptist) Lower Nidderdale *Ripon*

HUNSLET (St Mary) *Ripon 6* **P** *Bp (2 turns) and V Leeds St Pet (1 turn)* **V** P GREENWELL

HUNSLET MOOR (St Peter) and St Cuthbert *Ripon 6* **P** *Bp* **P-in-c** A J PEARSON

HUNSLEY (St Peter) Rowley w Skidby *York*

HUNSTANTON (St Edmund) w Ringstead *Nor 17* **P** *H Le Strange Esq* **V** M H SELLORS

HUNSTANTON (St Mary) w Ringstead Parva, Holme-next-the-Sea, Thornham, Brancaster, Burnham Deepdaleand Titchwell *Nor 17* **P** *Bp, Exors of the late H le Strange Esq, and Exors of the late H S N Simms-Adams Esq (jt)* **R** L H CAMPBELL, C D J ROPER

HUNSTANWORTH (St James) Blanchland w Hunstanworth and Edmundbyers etc *Newc*

HUNSTON (St Leodegar) N Mundham w Hunston and Merston *Chich*

HUNSTON (St Michael) Badwell Ash w Gt Ashfield, Stowlangtoft etc *St E*

HUNTINGDON (All Saints w St John the Baptist) (St Barnabas) (St Mary) *Ely 9* **P** *Bp* **TR** W R KING, **TV** A M GUITE, NSM M A GUITE

HUNTINGFIELD (St Mary) Cratfield w Heveningham and Ubbeston etc *St E*

HUNTINGTON (All Saints) *York 8* **P** *Patr Bd* **TR** K J DAVIES, **TV** C J CULLWICK, O J LAMBERT

HUNTINGTON (St Luke) *Ches 2* **P** *Bp* **V** D M WILSON

HUNTINGTON (St Mary Magdalene) Holmer w Huntington *Heref*

HUNTINGTON (St Thomas) Cannock *Lich*

HUNTINGTON (St Thomas a Becket) Kington w Huntington, Old Radnor, Kinnerton etc *Heref*

HUNTLEY (St John the Baptist) and Longhope *Glouc 3* **P** *Bp* **R** A J MINCHIN

HUNTON (St James) Wonston and Stoke Charity w Hunton *Win*

HUNTON (St Mary) Coxheath w E Farleigh, Hunton and Linton *Roch*
HUNTS CROSS (St Hilda) *Liv 4* **P** *Bp* **V** G A PERERA
HUNTSHAM (All Saints) Sampford Peverell, Uplowman, Holcombe Rogus etc *Ex*
HUNTSHAW (St Mary Magdalene) Newton Tracey, Alverdiscott, Huntshaw etc *Ex*
HUNTSPILL (St Peter and All Hallows) *B & W 1* **P** *Ball Coll Ox* **R** G M WALSH
HUNWICK (St Paul) Howden-le-Wear and Hunwick *Dur*
HUNWORTH (St Lawrence) Brinton, Briningham, Hunworth, Stody etc *Nor*
HURDSFIELD (Holy Trinity) *Ches 13* **P** *Hyndman Trustees* **V** J G TSIPOURAS
HURLEY (Resurrection) Baxterley w Hurley and Wood End and Merevale etc *Birm*
HURLEY (St Mary the Virgin) and Stubbings *Ox 13* **P** *DBP* **V** S J WELCH, **NSM** M W SKINNER
HURSLEY (All Saints) and Ampfield *Win 11* **P** *T H Faber Esq and Lord Lifford (jt)* **V** R B EDWARDS
HURST Fawkenhurst *Cant*
HURST (St John the Evangelist) *Man 17* **P** *The Crown* **V** J M MacGILLIVRAY, **C** L CONNOLLY
HURST (St Nicholas) *Ox 16* **P** *Bp* **V** D H LOVERIDGE
HURST GREEN (Holy Trinity) *Chich 15* **P** *Bp* **V** B C GURD
HURST GREEN (St John the Evangelist) *S'wark 24* **P** *Bp* **V** D F G BUTLIN, **NSM** M J SELLER
HURST GREEN (St John the Evangelist) and Mitton *Bradf 5* **P** *Bp and J E R Aspinall Esq (jt)* **V** J T BIRBECK
HURSTBOURNE PRIORS (St Andrew) Barton Stacey and Bullington etc *Win*
HURSTBOURNE TARRANT (St Peter) and Faccombe and Vernham Dean and Linkenholt *Win 3* **P** *Bp* **V** M HARLEY
HURSTPIERPOINT (Holy Trinity) (St George) *Chich 9* **P** *Woodard Schs* **R** D M REEVE
HURSTWOOD, HIGH (Holy Trinity) *Chich 21* **P** *Abp* **P-in-c** I GIBSON, **NSM** M COXHEAD
HURWORTH (All Saints) *Dur 12* **P** *Ch Soc Trust* **R** R R A GRAHAM
HUSBANDS BOSWORTH (All Saints) w Mowsley and Knaptoft and Theddingworth *Leic 4* **P** *DBP (2 turns), Bp (1 turn)* **R** J HICKLING, **NSM** R H HUTCHINGS
HUSBORNE CRAWLEY (St Mary Magdalene or St James) Aspley Guise w Husborne Crawley and Ridgmont *St Alb*
HUSTHWAITE (St Nicholas) Coxwold and Husthwaite *York*
HUTHWAITE (All Saints) *S'well 4* **P** *V Sutton-in-Ashfield* **V** P HILL, **C** H J WORSLEY
HUTTOFT (St Margaret) Sutton, Huttoft and Anderby *Linc*
HUTTON (All Saints) (St Peter) *Chelmsf 7* **P** *D&C St Paul's* **R** W H REED, **C** S M WOOD
HUTTON (Blessed Virgin Mary) *B & W 11* **P** *DBP* **R** B N STEVENSON
HUTTON, NEW (St Stephen) Grayrigg, Old Hutton and New Hutton *Carl*
HUTTON, OLD (St John the Evangelist) as above
HUTTON BONVILLE (St Laurence) Gt Smeaton w Appleton Wiske and Birkby etc *Ripon*
HUTTON BUSCEL (St Matthew) Wykeham and Hutton Buscel *York*
HUTTON CRANSWICK (St Peter) w Skerne, Watton and Beswick *York 11* **P** *Abp* **V** J McNAUGHTON
HUTTON HENRY (St Francis) Wingate Grange *Dur*
HUTTON-IN-THE-FOREST (St James) Skelton and Hutton-in-the-Forest w Ivegill *Carl*
HUTTON-LE-HOLE (St Chad) Lastingham w Appleton-le-Moors, Rosedale etc *York*
HUTTON MAGNA (St Mary) Barningham w Hutton Magna and Wycliffe *Ripon*
HUTTON ROOF (St John the Divine) Kirkby Lonsdale *Carl*
HUTTON RUDBY (All Saints) Rudby in Cleveland w Middleton *York*
HUTTONS AMBO (St Margaret) Whitwell w Crambe, Flaxton, Foston etc *York*
HUXHAM (St Mary the Virgin) Stoke Canon, Poltimore w Huxham and Rewe etc *Ex*
HUXLEY (St Andrew) Hargrave *Ches*
HUYTON (St George) *Liv 2* **P** *Bp* **V** D G TOWLER, **C** T R PLACE
HUYTON (St Michael) *Liv 2* **P** *Lord Derby* **V** J A STANLEY, **C** J R SKINNER, G C ELSMORE
HUYTON QUARRY (St Gabriel) *Liv 2* **P** *V Huyton St Mich* **V** N F BOON
HYDE (St George) *Ches 14* **P** *R Stockport St Mary* **V** J H DARCH, **C** P F REYNOLDS

HYDE (St Thomas) *Ches 14* **P** *Bp* **P-in-c** J MARTIN
HYDE, EAST (Holy Trinity) Woodside w E Hyde *St Alb*
HYDE, WEST (St Thomas) Mill End and Heronsgate w W Hyde *St Alb*
HYDE COMMON (Holy Ascension) *Win 8* **P** *Keble Coll Ox* **P-in-c** B R CASSIDY
HYDE HEATH (Mission Church) Lt Missenden *Ox*
HYDE PARK CRESCENT (St John) Paddington St Jo w St Mich *Lon*
HYDNEYE (St Peter) Conventional District *Chich 16* **C-in-c** M G ONIONS
HYKEHAM (All Saints) (St Hugh) (St Michael and All Angels) *Linc 18* **P** *Ld Chan and Bp (alt)* **TR** E L RENNARD, **TV** J FREEBAIRN-SMITH, **C** M R RENNARD
HYLTON, NORTH (St Margaret) Castletown *Dur 9* **P** *Bp* **NSM** C P A LOCKHART
HYLTON, SOUTH (St Mary) *Dur 9* **P** *Bp* **V** J E RUSCOE
HYSSINGTON (St Etheldreda) Churchstoke w Hyssington and Sarn *Heref*
HYTHE Butts Ash (St Anne) Hythe *Win*
HYTHE (St John the Baptist) *Win 10* **P** *Bp* **V** P D BAIRD, **Hon C** J M WEBSTER, **NSM** J M MEW
HYTHE (St Leonard) (St Michael and All Angels) *Cant 5* **P** *R Saltwood* **V** N H WOODS, **C** A C DENHAM
HYTHE, WEST (St Mary) Sellindge w Monks Horton and Stowting etc *Cant*
IBBERTON (St Eustace) Hazelbury Bryan and the Hillside Par *Sarum*
IBSTOCK (St Denys) w Heather *Leic 8* **P** *Bp and MMCET (jt)* **R** R N EVERETT
IBSTONE (St Nicholas) Stokenchurch and Ibstone *Ox*
ICKBURGH (St Peter) w Langford *Nor 14* **P** *Bp* **P-in-c** G H WHEATLEY
ICKENHAM (St Giles) *Lon 24* **P** *Eton Coll* **NSM** P ROBINSON, K R TOMBS
ICKFORD (St Nicholas) Worminghall w Ickford, Oakley and Shabbington *Ox*
ICKHAM (St John the Evangelist) Littlebourne and Ickham w Wickhambreaux etc *Cant*
ICKLEFORD (St Katherine) w Holwell *St Alb 9* **P** *DBP* **R** R I OAKLEY
ICKLESHAM (St Nicolas) Winchelsea and Icklesham *Chich*
ICKLETON (St Mary Magdalene) *Ely 7* **P** *Ld Chan* **V** *Vacant*
ICKLINGHAM (All Saints w St James) Mildenhall *St E*
ICOMB (St Mary) Westcote w Icomb and Bledington *Glouc*
IDBURY (St Nicholas) Shipton-under-Wychwood w Milton-under-Wychwood *Ox*
IDDESLEIGH (St James) w Dowland *Ex 20* **P** *Bp* **R** *Vacant*
IDE (St Ida) Dunchideock and Shillingford St George w Ide *Ex*
IDE HILL (St Mary the Virgin) Sundridge w Ide Hill *Roch*
IDEFORD (St Mary the Virgin) Teignmouth, Ideford w Luton, Ashcombe etc *Ex*
IDEN (All Saints) Rye *Chich*
IDLE (Holy Trinity) *Bradf 3* **P** *V Calverley* **V** D A JOHNSON
IDLICOTE (St James the Great) Shipston-on-Stour w Honington and Idlicote *Cov*
IDRIDGEHAY (St James) Wirksworth *Derby*
IDSWORTH (St Hubert) Blendworth w Chalton w Idsworth *Portsm*
IFFLEY (St Mary the Virgin) *Ox 4* **P** *Ch Ch Ox* **R** P S M JUDD, **C** R M COWLES, **NSM** D G EVERETT, D G S BARTON
IFIELD (St Margaret) *Chich 7* **P** *Bp* **TR** D L PARKER, **TV** W T MARSTON, P D WOOD, N A FLINT, **NSM** M WICKENS
IFIELD (St Margaret) Gravesend H Family w Ifield *Roch*
IFORD (St Nicholas) w Kingston and Rodmell *Chich 18* **P** *Bp* **V** G M DAW
IFORD (St Saviour) *Win 7* **P** *Bp* **V** I M SCOTT-THOMPSON, **NSM** N M BENCE, W MACDONALD
IGHTFIELD (St John the Baptist) w Calverhall *Lich 28* **P** *T C Heywood-Lonsdale Esq* **P-in-c** J H TYERS
IGHTHAM (St Peter) *Roch 9* **P** *Sir John Winnifrith* **R** J H B TALBOT
IKEN (St Botolph) Orford w Sudbourne, Chillesford, Butley and Iken *St E*
ILAM (Holy Cross) w Blore Ray and Okeover *Lich 10* **P** *Sir Peter Walker-Okeover* **P-in-c** P E R HALL
ILCHESTER (St Mary Major) w Northover, Limington, Yeovilton and Podimore *B & W 6* **P** *Bp Lon (7 turns), Bp (1 turn), and Wadh Coll Ox (1 turn)* **R** C F H SUTCLIFFE
ILDERTON (St Michael) Glendale Gp *Newc*
ILFORD, GREAT (St Alban) *Chelmsf 4* **P** *Bp* **V** D I MILNES, **Hon C** M R GRIFFIN

ILFORD, GREAT (St Andrew) *Chelmsf 4* **P** *Bp*
V P L DEEMING
ILFORD, GREAT (St Clement) (St Margaret of Antioch)
Chelmsf 4 **P** *Patr Bd* **TR** T H SHANNON,
C Q B D PEPPIATT
ILFORD, GREAT (St John the Evangelist) *Chelmsf 4* **P** *Bp*
V G M TARRY
ILFORD, GREAT (St Luke) *Chelmsf 4* **P** *Bp*
V K A L HINDS
ILFORD, GREAT (St Mary) *Chelmsf 4* **P** *V Ilford*
V J B BARNES
ILFORD, LITTLE (St Barnabas) *Chelmsf 3* **P** *Bp*
R B J ARSCOTT
ILFORD, LITTLE (St Michael and All Angels) *Chelmsf 3*
P *Hertf Coll Ox* **R** J P WHITWELL, **C** L C WINKETT,
NSM A C CLARKE
**ILFRACOMBE (Holy Trinity) (St Peter), Lee, Woolacombe,
Bittadon and Mortehoe** *Ex 15* **P** *Patr Bd*
TR N JACKSON-STEVENS, **TV** R G PECKHAM,
C S C E LAIRD
ILFRACOMBE (St Philip and St James) w West Down
Ex 15 **P** *Bp and Ch Trust Fund Trust (jt)*
V C E G TENNANT
ILKESTON (Holy Trinity) *Derby 13* **P** *Bp*
P-in-c W F P ENOCH, **NSM** K W G JOHNSON
ILKESTON (St John the Evangelist) *Derby 13* **P** *V Ilkeston
St Mary* **V** *Vacant* Nottingham (0115) 932 5446
ILKESTON (St Mary the Virgin) *Derby 13* **P** *Bp*
V J R HENSON, **C** C L HUGHES
ILKETSHALL ST ANDREW (St Andrew) Wainford *St E*
ILKETSHALL ST JOHN (St John the Baptist) S Elmham
and Ilketshall *St E*
ILKETSHALL ST LAWRENCE (St Lawrence) as above
ILKETSHALL ST MARGARET (St Margaret) as above
ILKLEY (All Saints) *Bradf 4* **P** *Hyndman Trustees*
V P J C MARSHALL, **NSM** N H TUCKER
ILKLEY (St Margaret) *Bradf 4* **P** *CR* **V** R D HOYAL,
NSM A G BROWN
ILLINGWORTH (St Mary) *Wakef 4* **P** *V Halifax*
V L T McKENNA
ILLOGAN (not known) *Truro 2* **P** *Ch Soc Trust*
R D J STEVENS, **C** J S WOOD
ILMER (St Peter) Princes Risborough w Ilmer *Ox*
**ILMINGTON (St Mary) and Stretton-on-Fosse and Ditchford
w Preston-on-Stour w Whitchurch and Atherstone-on-Stour**
Cov 9 **P** *Bp, MMCET, and Ms C A Alston-Roberts-
West (jt)* **P-in-c** V L STORY
ILMINSTER (Blessed Virgin Mary) and District *B & W 15*
P *Patr Bd* **TR** J P CREED, **TV** J R J HISCOX,
J T TYLER, **C** M M MASLEN (formerly CHILD),
NSM R E MASLEN
ILSINGTON (St Michael) *Ex 11* **P** *D&C Windsor*
P-in-c C J L CURD
ILSLEY, EAST (St Mary) Compton w E Ilsley *Ox*
ILSLEY, WEST (All Saints) Beedon and Peasemore w W
Ilsley and Farnborough *Ox*
ILSTON (St Michael and All Angels) Gaulby *Leic*
ILTON (St Peter) Ilminster and District *B & W*
IMMINGHAM (St Andrew) *Linc 10* **P** *DBP*
V H W P HALL, **C** C M J THODY, **Hon C** W E H COSENS
IMPINGTON (St Andrew) *Ely 5* **P** *Adn Ely* **C** J M PRATT
INCE (St James) Thornton le Moors w Ince and Elton *Ches*
INCE IN MAKERFIELD (Christ Church) (St Christopher)
Liv 14 **P** *Simeon's Trustees* **V** C J CROOKS
INCE IN MAKERFIELD (St Mary) *Liv 14* **P** *Simeon's
Trustees* **V** *Vacant* Wigan (01942) 864383
INDIAN QUEEN (St Francis) St Enoder *Truro*
INGATESTONE (St Edmund and St Mary) w Buttsbury
Chelmsf 7 **P** *Bp* **P-in-c** P E COULTON
INGESTRE (St Mary the Virgin) Stafford St Jo and Tixall w
Ingestre *Lich*
INGHAM (All Saints) w Cammeringham w Fillingham *Linc 3*
P *Bp and Ball Coll Ox (jt)* **V** M J SILLEY,
C C A ZOTOV, **Hon C** D J PRYOR
INGHAM (Holy Trinity) Sutton w Ingham and Catfield *Nor*
INGHAM (St Bartholomew) Blackbourne *St E*
INGLEBY ARNCLIFFE (All Saints) Osmotherley w Harlsey
and Ingleby Arncliffe *York*
INGLEBY BARWICK Conventional District *York 22*
C-in-c J M E COOPER
INGLEBY BARWICK (St Francis) Stainton-in-Cleveland
York
**INGLEBY GREENHOW (St Andrew) w Bilsdale Priory,
Kildale and Westerdale** *York 22* **P** *Abp, Adn Cleveland, Bp
Whitby, Viscount de l'Isle, R G Beckett Esq, and Mrs
C M Sutcliffe (jt)* **V** M K TIMBRELL
INGLETON (St John the Evangelist) Denton and Ingleton
Dur

INGLETON (St Mary the Virgin) w Chapel le Dale *Bradf 6*
P *Bp* **V** *Vacant* Ingleton (015242) 41440
INGOL (St Margaret) *Blackb 14* **P** *Bp* **V** A N WIBBERLEY
INGOLDISTHORPE (St Michael) Snettisham w
Ingoldisthorpe and Fring *Nor*
INGOLDMELLS (St Peter and St Paul) w Addlethorpe
Linc 8 **P** *Ld Chan and Wadh Coll Ox (alt)*
P-in-c D B WOODS
INGOLDSBY (St Bartholomew) *Linc 14* **P** *Ch Coll Cam,
Sir Lyonel Tollemache, Bt, D&C, Bp, and DBP (by turn)*
R R BURGESS, **NSM** K A C BROWN, I R WALTERS
INGRAM (St Michael) Glendale Gp *Newc*
INGRAVE (St Nicholas) Gt Warley w Childerditch and
Ingrave *Chelmsf*
INGRAVE (St Stephen) Conventional District *Chelmsf 7*
C-in-c J R YELAND
INGROW (St John the Evangelist) cum Hainworth *Bradf 8*
P *Bp* **P-in-c** D M ROBINSON, **C** S A BANKS
INGS (St Anne) Staveley, Ings and Kentmere *Carl*
INGWORTH (St Lawrence) Erpingham w Calthorpe,
Ingworth, Aldborough etc *Nor*
INHAM NOOK (St Barnabas) Chilwell *S'well*
INKBERROW (St Peter) w Cookhill and Kington w Dormston
Worc 1 **P** *Bp* **R** G S CROSS, **NSM** F M BATTIN (nee
WEBB)
INKERSALL (St Columba) Staveley and Barrow Hill *Derby*
INKPEN (St Michael) W Woodhay w Enborne, Hampstead
Marshall etc *Ox*
INNS COURT (Holy Cross) Bris H Cross Inns Court *Bris*
INSKIP (St Peter) *Blackb 10* **P** *V St Michael's-on-Wyre*
V G M HILTON-TURVEY
INSTOW (All Saints Chapel) (St John the Baptist) *Ex 17*
P *Christie Trustees* **R** G A SATTERLY
INTWOOD (All Saints) Swardeston w E Carleton, Intwood,
Keswick etc *Nor*
INWARDLEIGH (St Petroc) Okehampton w Inwardleigh,
Bratton Clovelly etc *Ex*
INWORTH (All Saints) Copford w Easthorpe and Messing w
Inworth *Chelmsf*
IPING (St Mary) Stedham w Iping *Chich*
IPPLEPEN (St Andrew) w Torbryan *Ex 10* **P** *D&C
Windsor* **V** P W DARBY
IPSDEN (St Mary the Virgin) Langtree *Ox*
IPSLEY (St Peter) *Worc 7* **P** *Patr Bd* **TR** R M ADAMS,
TV A J KELSO, A E J TOSTEVIN, **C** M D ALLABY,
NSM J W DAVEY
**IPSTONES (St Leonard) w Berkhamsytch and Onecote w
Bradnop** *Lich 11* **P** *Bp and R Leek and Meerbrook (jt)*
V S G PRICE
IPSWICH (All Hallows) *St E 4* **P** *Bp* **C** V B A BRECHIN,
NSM R F ALLARD
IPSWICH (All Saints) *St E 4* **P** *Bp* **V** A G WILCOX
IPSWICH (St Andrew) *St E 4* **P** *Bp* **V** G I HOUSE
IPSWICH (St Augustine of Hippo) *St E 4* **P** *Bp*
V J E N ELLISTON, **C** D J PARMENTER
IPSWICH (St Bartholomew) *St E 4* **P** *Bp* **V** J E BURROWS
IPSWICH (St Clement w St Luke) (Holy Trinity) *St E 4*
P *Ch Patr Trust* **P-in-c** R G WARREN
IPSWICH (St Francis) (St Clare's Church Centre) *St E 4*
P *Bp* **TV** N J ANSTEY, C G G EVERETT,
C C M EVERETT
IPSWICH (St Helen) (St James) *St E 4* **P** *Ch Patr Trust*
R D P HAZLEWOOD
IPSWICH (St John the Baptist) *St E 4* **P** *Simeon's Trustees*
V I J MANN, **C** J N BEAUCHAMP
IPSWICH (St Margaret) *St E 4* **P** *Simeon's Trustees*
V D CUTTS, **C** J M GOSNEY
IPSWICH (St Mary at Stoke) w (St Peter), Stoke Park
St E 4 **P** *Bp* **TR** I D J MORGAN, **TV** C M LACK,
TV J D HAYDEN
IPSWICH (St Mary at the Elms) *St E 4* **P** *PCC* **V** *Vacant*
Ipswich (01473) 252822
IPSWICH (St Mary-le-Tower) (St Nicholas) *St E 4* **P** *Bp*
(3 turns), Ch Patr Trust (1 turn) **V** K B JONES
IPSWICH (St Matthew) *St E 4* **P** *Ld Chan*
R P D HARDINGHAM, **P-in-c** P W GIBBS,
C P R DALTRY
IPSWICH (St Michael) *St E 4* **P** *Simeon's Trustees*
P-in-c S H COWLEY
IPSWICH (St Thomas) *St E 4* **P** *Bp* **V** M F WEST,
NSM B F ROSE, E A T ARNOLD
IRBY (St Chad's Mission Church) Thurstaston *Ches*
IRBY-IN-THE-MARSH (All Saints) Bratoft w Irby-in-the-
Marsh *Linc*
IRBY ON HUMBER (St Andrew) Laceby *Linc*
IRCHESTER (St Katharine) *Pet 10* **P** *Bp* **V** P A PAYNTON
IRCHESTER, LITTLE (St John) Irchester *Pet*
IREBY (St James) Bolton w Ireby and Uldale *Carl*

IRELAND WOOD (St Paul) *Ripon 7* **P** *R Adel*
C M SFOY, CC GARRUD
IRELETH w Askam (St Peter) *Carl 8* **P** *V Dalton-in-Furness* **V** D SANDERSON
IRLAM (St John the Baptist) *Man 2* **P** *Trustees*
V P J P WETZ
IRNHAM (St Andrew) Corby Glen *Linc*
IRON ACTON (St James the Less) *Bris 7* **P** *Ch Ch Ox*
R A F WAKER
IRON-BRIDGE (St Luke) Coalbrookdale, Iron-Bridge and Lt Wenlock *Heref*
IRONVILLE (Christ Church) Riddings and Ironville *Derby*
IRSTEAD (St Michael) Neatishead, Barton Turf and Irstead *Nor*
IRTHINGTON (St Kentigern), Crosby-on-Eden and Scaleby
Carl 2 **P** *Bp* **V** J G PEART
IRTHLINGBOROUGH (St Peter) *Pet 10* **P** *Sir Stephen Hastings* **R** R G KNIGHT
IRTON (St Paul) Eskdale, Irton, Muncaster and Waberthwaite *Carl*
ISEL (St Michael) Bassenthwaite, Isel and Setmurthy *Carl*
ISFIELD (St Margaret) *Chich 21* **P** *Abp* **R** C J PETERS, NSM C HOWARTH, R C DALLING
ISHAM (St Peter) w Pytchley *Pet 11* **P** *Bp*
R P R GATENBY
ISLE ABBOTTS (Blessed Virgin Mary) Ilminster and District *B & W*
ISLE BREWERS (All Saints) as above
ISLE OF DOGS (Christ Church) (St John) (St Luke) *Lon 7*
P *Bp* **V** N R HOLTAM, **C** C L OWENS, E A CARNELLEY
ISLEHAM (St Andrew) *Ely 3* **P** *Ld Chan*
P-in-c D J KIGHTLEY
ISLEWORTH (All Saints) *Lon 11* **P** *D&C Windsor*
V *Vacant* 0181–560 6662
ISLEWORTH (St Francis of Assisi) *Lon 11* **P** *Bp* **V** *Vacant* 0181–560 4839
ISLEWORTH (St John the Baptist) *Lon 11*
P *V Isleworth All SS* **P-in-c** P R MYLES, **C** V K LUCAS
ISLEWORTH (St Luke) Spring Grove St Mary *Lon*
ISLEWORTH (St Mary the Virgin) *Lon 11* **P** *Bp* **V** *Vacant* 0181–560 6166
ISLEY WALTON (All Saints) Breedon cum Isley Walton and Worthington *Leic*
ISLINGTON (St James the Apostle) (St Peter) *Lon 6* **P** *Bp*
V E H JONES
ISLINGTON (St Jude and St Paul) Mildmay Grove St Jude and St Paul *Lon*
ISLINGTON (St Mary) *Lon 6* **P** *CPAS*
V G L CLAYDON, **C** N D R NICHOLLS
ISLIP (St Nicholas) *Pet 10* **P** *L G Stopford-Sackville Esq*
P-in-c F COLEMAN
ISLIP (St Nicholas) w Charlton on Otmoor, Oddington, Noke and Woodeaton *Ox 2* **P** *D&C Westmr, Rev E H W Crusha, and Qu Coll Ox (jt)* **R** R L STURCH
ISTEAD RISE (St Barnabas) *Roch 4* **P** *Bp* **V** S R DYER, NSM A C DYER
ITCHEN ABBAS (St John the Baptist) Itchen Valley *Win*
ITCHEN VALLEY, THE *Win 1* **P** *Ld Chan*
R J M STEVENETTE, NSM J B NAPIER
ITCHENOR, WEST (St Nicholas) W Wittering and Birdham w Itchenor *Chich*
ITCHINGFIELD (St Nicholas) w Slinfold *Chich 7* **P** *Bp*
R J D GILPIN, NSM P GRAVES
IVEGILL (Christ Church) Skelton and Hutton-in-the-Forest w Ivegill *Carl*
IVER (St Peter) *Ox 23* **P** *Trustees* **V** A D ROSE
IVER HEATH (St Margaret) *Ox 23* **P** *Trustees*
R D S REYNISH
IVINGHOE (St Mary the Virgin) w Pitstone and Slapton
Ox 26 **P** *Bp and Ch Ch Ox (jt)* **V** P A LAWRENCE
IVINGTON (St John) Leominster *Heref*
IVY HATCH (not known) Ightham *Roch*
IVY ROW (Mission Room) Roos and Garton in Holderness w Tunstall etc *York*
IVYBRIDGE (St John the Evangelist) w Harford *Ex 21*
P *Bp* **V** F H COLES, **C** W G HAMILTON, B J DANSIE
IVYCHURCH (St George) St Mary's Bay w St Mary-in-the-Marsh etc *Cant*
IWADE (All Saints) *Cant 14* **P-in-c** J P LEFROY
IWERNE COURTNEY (St Mary) The Iwernes, Sutton Waldron and Fontmell Magna *Sarum*
IWERNE MINSTER (St Mary) as above
IWERNE STEPLETON (St Mary) as above
IWERNES, Sutton Waldron and Fontmell Magna, The
Sarum 7 **P** *Bp, D&C Windsor, DBP, and G A L F Pitt-Rivers Esq (jt)* **V** E A SELLGREN, NSM J H SIMMONS
IXWORTH (St Mary) Blackbourne *St E*
IXWORTH THORPE (All Saints) as above

JACKFIELD (St Mary) Broseley w Benthall, Jackfield, Linley etc *Heref*
JACOBSTOW (St James) St Gennys, Jacobstow w Warbstow and Treneglos *Truro*
JACOBSTOWE (St James) Hatherleigh, Meeth, Exbourne and Jacobstowe *Ex*
JARROW (St John the Baptist) (St Mark) (St Paul) (St Peter)
Dur 7 **P** *Bp* **TV** J D PICKERING, P A BAKER, NSM A RAINE
JARROW GRANGE (Christ Church) *Dur 7* **P** *Lord Northbourne* **R** N SWAINSON
JARVIS BROOK (St Michael and All Angels) *Chich 19*
P *Bp* **V** I E MORRISON
JERSEY (All Saints) *Win 15* **P** *R St Helier, Bp, and The Crown (by turn)* **P-in-c** G J HOUGHTON
JERSEY Gouray (St Martin) *Win 15* **P** *Bp and The Crown (alt)* **V** *Vacant* Jersey (01534) 54294
JERSEY Greve d'Azette (St Nicholas) Jersey St Clem *Win*
JERSEY (Holy Trinity) *Win 15* **P** *The Crown* **R** A KEOGH
JERSEY Millbrook (St Matthew) *Win 15* **P** *The Crown*
V *Vacant* Jersey (01534) 20934
JERSEY (St Andrew) *Win 15* **P** *Dean of Jersey*
V D J SPRINGHAM
JERSEY (St Brelade) (Communicare Chapel) (St Aubin)
Win 15 **P** *The Crown* **R** M A HALLIWELL, **C** P J WILKIN, Hon **C** J M GURDON
JERSEY (St Clement) *Win 15* **P** *The Crown* **R** M BEAL
JERSEY (St Helier) *Win 15* **P** *The Crown*
R J N SEAFORD, NSM A D WILLIAMS
JERSEY (St James) *Win 15* **P** *Bp* **V** D V WASTIE, NSM A F PEARCE
JERSEY (St John) *Win 15* **P** *The Crown*
P-in-c A J THEWLIS
JERSEY (St Lawrence) *Win 15* **P** *The Crown* **R** *Vacant* Jersey (01534) 20934
JERSEY (St Luke) *Win 15* **P** *Bp and The Crown (alt)*
V D V WASTIE, NSM J D DODD, A F PEARCE
JERSEY (St Mark) *Win 15* **P** *Bp* **V** C I BUCKLEY
JERSEY (St Martin) *Win 15* **P** *The Crown* **R** L J TURNER
JERSEY (St Mary) *Win 15* **P** *The Crown* **R** A HART
JERSEY (St Ouen) (St George) *Win 15* **P** *The Crown*
R R G SPECK
JERSEY (St Paul) Proprietary Chapel *Win 15*
Min P J BROOKS
JERSEY (St Peter) *Win 15* **P** *The Crown* **R** B J GILES
JERSEY (St Saviour) *Win 15* **P** *The Crown*
R A C SWINDELL, NSM J J ILTON
JERSEY (St Simon) *Win 15* **P** *R St Helier, Bp, and The Crown (by turn)* **V** *Vacant* Jersey (01534) 24885
JERSEY DE GROUVILLE (St Martin) (St Peter la Roque)
Win 15 **P** *The Crown* **P-in-c** F R A MASON
JESMOND (Clayton Memorial Church) *Newc 5* **P** *Trustees*
V D R J HOLLOWAY, **C** J J S PRYKE, C J P HOBBS
JESMOND (Holy Trinity) *Newc 5* **P** *Trustees*
V M C LIPPIATT
JEVINGTON (St Andrew) E Dean w Friston and Jevington *Chich*
JOYDENS WOOD (St Barnabas) *Roch 16* **P** *Bp*
V D H HORTON
JURBY (St Patrick) *S & M 4* **P** *Bp* **V** R C GEDDES
KEA (All Hallows) (Old Church) *Truro 6* **P** *V St Clement*
V R J REDRUP
KEAL, EAST (St Helen) Marden Hill Gp *Linc*
KEAL, WEST (St Helen) as above
KEARSLEY MOOR (St Stephen) *Man 6* **P** *R E Farnworth and Kearsley* **V** K F WAINWRIGHT
KEASDEN (St Matthew) Clapham-with-Keasden and Austwick *Bradf*
KEDDINGTON (St Margaret) Louth *Linc*
KEDINGTON (St Peter and St Paul) *St E 8* **P** *Walsingham Coll Trust* **P-in-c** J F M WILLIAMS
KEEDWELL HILL (Ascension) Long Ashton *B & W*
KEELBY (St Bartholomew) w Riby and Aylesby *Linc 10*
P *DBP (2 turns), J E Spillman Esq (1 turn)* **V** A S CAVE
KEELE (St John the Baptist) Betley and Keele *Lich*
KEEVIL (St Leonard) Steeple Ashton w Semington and Keevil *Sarum*
KEGWORTH (St Andrew) *Leic 7* **P** *Ch Coll Cam*
R R L NASH
KEIGHLEY (All Saints) *Bradf 8* **P** *Bp and R Keighley St Andr* **P-in-c** N DANIELS, Hon **C** C P HUTCHINSON
KEIGHLEY (St Andrew) *Bradf 8* **P** *Bp* **C** S I TAYLOR
KEINTON MANDEVILLE (St Mary Magdalene) w Lydford-on-Fosse, Barton St David and Kingweston *B & W 3* **P** *Ch Soc Trust, J H Cordle and Dr O W Holmes (1 turn), A J Whitehead (2 turns), Bp (1 turn), and Mrs E J Burden (1 turn)* **P-in-c** P N LITTLEWOOD

KELBROOK (St Mary) *Bradf 7* **P** *Bp* **V** *Vacant* Earby
(01282) 842984
KELBY (St Andrew) Ancaster Wilsford Gp *Linc*
KELHAM (St Wilfrid) Averham w Kelham *S'well*
KELLET, NETHER (St Mark) Bolton le Sands *Blackb*
KELLET, OVER (St Cuthbert) *Blackb 15* **P** *Reformation Ch
Trust* **V** K CLAPHAM
KELLING (St Mary) Weybourne Gp *Nor*
KELLINGTON (St Edmund) w Whitley *Wakef 11* **P** *DBP*
V *Vacant* Whitley Bridge (01977) 662876
KELLOE (St Helen) *Dur 14* **P** *Bp* **V** *Vacant* 0191–377 1053
KELLS (St Peter) *Carl 5* **P** *Bp* **V** T J HYSLOP,
NSM W D MAHONEY
KELLY (St Mary the Virgin) w Bradstone *Ex 25*
P *W F Kelly Esq* **P-in-c** J H HEATH
KELMARSH (St Denys) Clipston w Naseby and Haselbech
w Kelmarsh *Pet*
KELMSCOTT (St George) Shill Valley and Broadshire *Ox*
KELSALE (St Peter) Kelsale-cum-Carlton, Middleton-cum-
Fordley etc *St E*
**KELSALE-CUM-CARLTON, Middleton-cum-Fordley and
Theberton w Eastbridge** *St E 19* **P** *DBP, Prime Min, and
Ch Patr Trust (by turn)* **R** R S SMITH
KELSALL (St Philip) *Ches 2* **P** *V Tarvin* **V** F C CONANT
KELSEY Group, The SOUTH (St Mary) *Linc 5* **P** *Bp
(3 turns), M F Young Esq (1 turn)* **R** *Vacant* North Kelsey
(01652) 678251
KELSEY, NORTH (All Hallows) *Linc 6* **P** *Bp* **V** *Vacant*
North Kelsey (01652) 678205
KELSHALL (St Faith) Therfield w Kelshall *St Alb*
KELSTON (St Nicholas) Bath Weston St Jo w Kelston
B & W
KELVEDON (St Mary the Virgin) *Chelmsf 25* **P** *Bp*
V D J D THORNTON
KELVEDON HATCH (St Nicholas) *Chelmsf 7* **P** *Bp*
P-in-c R A L ROSE
KEMBERTON (St Andrew) Beckbury, Badger, Kemberton,
Ryton, Stockton etc *Lich*
**KEMBLE (All Saints), Poole Keynes, Somerford Keynes and
Sharncote** *Glouc 12* **P** *DBP, Duchy of Lanc, and
Mrs L R Rank (by turn)* **V** G R MARTIN
KEMERTON (St Nicholas) Woolstone w Gotherington and
Oxenton etc *Glouc*
KEMP TOWN (St Mary) *Chich 2* **P** *Bp, Mrs R A Hinton,
A C R Elliott Esq, and Canon D Walker (jt)* **V** J E LLOYD-
JAMES, NSM P C BROWNE
**KEMPSEY (St Mary the Virgin) and Severn Stoke w Croome
d'Abitot** *Worc 5* **P** *D&C and Earl of Cov (alt)*
R F J MUSHEN, **C** H C HANKE
KEMPSFORD (St Mary) w Welford *Glouc 13* **P** *Bp*
P-in-c J F GREGORY
KEMPSHOTT (St Mark) *Win 4* **P** *Bp* **V** K V BATT,
C P F D TAYLOR
KEMPSTON (All Saints) *St Alb 16* **P** *Bp* **V** *Vacant* Bedford
(01234) 852241
KEMPSTON (Transfiguration) *St Alb 16* **P** *Bp*
V J R BROWN, **C** R F WATSON, NSM G A WEBB,
V E HOLLIS
KEMSING (St Mary the Virgin) w Woodlands *Roch 9*
P *DBP* **V** C C HORN, NSM J G GOULDING
KENARDINGTON (St Mary) Appledore w Brookland,
Fairfield, Brenzett etc *Cant*
KENCHESTER (St Michael) and Bridge Sollers *Heref 4*
P *Ld Chan* **P-in-c** G USHER
KENCOT (St George) Shill Valley and Broadshire *Ox*
KENDAL (Holy Trinity) (All Hallows Chapel) *Carl 9* **P** *Trin
Coll Cam* **V** G A HOWE, **C** J J RICHARDS,
J E MAYCOCK, NSM P SMITH
KENDAL (St George) *Carl 9* **P** *V Kendal H Trin*
V A R BILLINGS
KENDAL (St Thomas) *Carl 9* **P** *CPAS* **V** R A MACHIN
KENDERCHURCH (St Mary) Ewyas Harold w Dulas,
Kenderchurch etc *Heref*
KENDRAY (St Andrew) *Sheff 12* **P** *V Ardsley*
V S DONALD
KENILWORTH (St John) *Cov 4* **P** *Simeon's Trustees*
V R D TURNER, **C** I D GOW
KENILWORTH (St Nicholas) (St Barnabas) *Cov 4*
P *Ld Chan* **V** D J RAKE, **C** B P BAISLEY
KENLEY (All Saints) *S'wark 22* **P** *Abp* **V** R C HAGON,
Hon C S C CONWAY
KENLEY (St John the Baptist) Wenlock *Heref*
KENN (St Andrew) Exminster and Kenn *Ex*
KENN (St John the Evangelist) Yatton Moor *B & W*
KENNERLEIGH (St John the Baptist) N Creedy *Ex*
KENNET, EAST (Christ Church) Upper Kennett *Sarum*
KENNETT (St Nicholas) *Ely 3* **P** *Mrs M F de Packh*
R *Vacant*

KENNETT, UPPER *Sarum 20* **P** *Bp* **TV** W J SELLERS,
NSM G M MacKICHAN
KENNINGHALL (St Mary) Quidenham *Nor*
KENNINGTON (St John the Divine w St James the Apostle)
S'wark 9 **P** *Ripon Coll Cuddesdon and Bp (jt)*
V L DENNEN, NSM W C BEAVER, P ANSDELL-EVANS
KENNINGTON (St Mark) *S'wark 11* **P** *Abp*
V J M STARR, **Hon C** M K BARLING
KENNINGTON (St Mary) *Cant 10* **P** *Abp*
V C G PREECE, **C** M WRAY
KENNINGTON (St Swithun) *Ox 10* **P** *Bp*
V H BLOOMFIELD, **Hon C** E A JOHNSON
KENNINGTON CROSS (St Anselm) N Lambeth *S'wark*
KENNINGTON PARK (St Agnes) *S'wark 8* **P** *Trustees*
V S C EVERSON
KENNY HILL (St James) Mildenhall *St E*
KENSAL GREEN (St John) *Lon 2* **P** *Bp* **V** R D BEAL
KENSAL RISE (St Mark) (St Martin) *Lon 21* **P** *St Olave
Hart Street Trustees and Bp (jt)* **V** N L JACKSON
KENSAL TOWN (St Thomas) (St Andrew) (St Philip)
Lon 12 **P** *Hyndman Trustees* **V** D FLETCHER,
Hon C P J MATHIE
KENSINGTON (St Barnabas) *Lon 12* **P** *V Kensington
St Mary Abbots w St Geo and Ch Ch* **V** J D IRVINE,
NSM P G BLUNDELL
KENSINGTON (St Helen) (Holy Trinity) *Lon 12* **P** *Bp*
V A SIMPSON
KENSINGTON (St James) Notting Dale St Clem w St Mark
and St Jas *Lon*
KENSINGTON (St John the Baptist) *Lon 12* **P** *Trustees*
V G F BRIGHT
KENSINGTON (St Mary Abbots) (St George) (Christ Church)
Lon 12 **P** *Bp* **V** I L ROBSON, **C** F J GELLI,
M G FULLER
KENSINGTON (St Philip) Earl's Court *Lon 12* **P** *Bp*
V M B E FORREST
KENSINGTON, SOUTH (Holy Trinity w All Saints) *Lon 3*
P *D&C Westmr* **P-in-c** M S ISRAEL
KENSINGTON, SOUTH (St Augustine) *Lon 3* **P** *Keble Coll
Ox* **V** K V HEWITT, **Hon C** G JOHNSON
KENSINGTON, SOUTH (St Jude) *Lon 3* **P** *Exors Dame
Jewell Magnus-Allcroft* **V** D A STONE
KENSINGTON, SOUTH (St Luke) *Lon 8* **P** *Ch Patr Trust*
V W R HEALD
KENSINGTON, SOUTH (St Stephen) *Lon 12* **P** *Guild of
All So* **V** C G COLVEN, **Hon C** K N COCKING
KENSINGTON, WEST (St Mary) Fulham St Mary N End
Lon
KENSINGTON, WEST The Boltons (St Mary) W Brompton
St Mary w St Pet *Lon*
KENSWORTH (St Mary the Virgin), Studham and Whipsnade
St Alb 18 **P** *Ld Chan and D&C St Paul's (alt)*
V P M PALMER
KENT TOWN E Molesey St Paul *Guildf*
KENTCHURCH (St Mary) Ewyas Harold w Dulas,
Kenderchurch etc *Heref*
KENTFORD (St Mary) Gazeley w Dalham, Moulton and
Kentford *St E*
KENTISBEARE (St Mary) w Blackborough *Ex 4* **P** *Exors
G C Wyndham Esq* **R** D A SAUNDERS
KENTISBURY (St Thomas) Shirwell, Loxhore, Kentisbury,
Arlington, etc *Ex*
KENTISH TOWN (St Benet and All Saints) (St Luke)
Lon 17 **P** *Prime Min and D&C St Paul's (alt)*
V R N ARNOLD, **C** R P P MARTIN
KENTISH TOWN (St Martin) (St Andrew) *Lon 17* **P** *Exors
Dame Jewell Magnus-Allcroft* **V** *Vacant* 0171–485 3807
KENTISH TOWN (St Silas the Martyr) *Lon 17* **P** *Bp*
V G C ROWLANDS, **C** N P PAINE DAVEY
KENTMERE (St Cuthbert) Staveley, Ings and Kentmere
Carl
KENTON (All Saints) Debenham w Aspall and Kenton *St E*
**KENTON (All Saints), Mamhead, Powderham, Cofton and
Starcross** *Ex 6* **P** *Earl of Devon, D&C, D&C Sarum, and
SMF (jt)* **R** R J WEBBER, **Hon C** P DAWKES
KENTON (Ascension) *Newc 5* **P** *Bp* **V** V T DICKINSON
KENTON (St Mary the Virgin) *Lon 23* **P** *Bp*
V D J SHERWOOD
KENTON, SOUTH (Annunciation) Wembley Park St Aug
Lon
KENWYN (St Keyne) w St Allen *Truro 6* **P** *Bp*
R M S BYROM
KERESLEY (St Thomas) and Coundon *Cov 2* **P** *Bp*
V K J MOBBERLEY, **C** E A DONALDSON,
NSM S MOBBERLEY
KERESLEY END (Church of the Ascension) Keresley and
Coundon *Cov*
KERRIDGE (Holy Trinity) Bollington St Jo *Ches*

KERSAL, LOWER (St Aidan) *Man 6* **P** *Bp*
V G D MORRIS

KERSAL MOOR (St Paul) *Man 6* **P** *Trustees*
R S FLETCHER, **C** S R BULLOCK (nee WHEALE)

KERSEY (St Mary) w Lindsey *St E 3* **P** *Bp*
P-in-c J A COHEN

KERSWELL GREEN (St John the Baptist) Kempsey and
Severn Stoke w Croome d'Abitot *Worc*

KESGRAVE (All Saints) *St E 4* **P** *Bp* **V** D R W HARES,
C C A GARRARD

KESSINGLAND (St Edmund) w Gisleham *Nor 9* **P** *Ld Chan*
(1 turn), Bp (2 turns) **P-in-c** J S HUNT

KESTON (not known) (St Audrey) *Roch 13* **P** *D&C*
R M R KEIRLE

KESWICK (All Saints) Swardeston w E Carleton, Intwood,
Keswick etc *Nor*

KESWICK (St John) *Carl 6* **P** *Trustees* **P-in-c** B SMITH

KESWICK, EAST (St Mary Magdalene) Bardsey *Ripon*

KETLEY (St Mary the Virgin) and Oakengates *Lich 27*
P *Bp* **V** D P SMITH

KETTERING (All Saints) *Pet 11* **P** *SMF* **V** *Vacant*
Kettering (01536) 513376

KETTERING (St Andrew) *Pet 11* **P** *Bp* **V** *Vacant* Kettering
(01536) 512754

KETTERING (St Mary the Virgin) (St John the Evangelist)
Pet 11 **P** *SMF* **V** *Vacant* Kettering (01536) 512736

KETTERING (St Peter and St Paul) (St Michael and All
Angels) *Pet 11* **P** *Comdr L M M Saunders Watson*
R *Vacant* Kettering (01536) 513385

KETTERINGHAM (St Peter) Swardeston w E Carleton,
Intwood, Keswick etc *Nor*

KETTLEBASTON (St Mary) *St E 10* **P** *Guild of All So*
P-in-c R A BIRD

KETTLEBROOK (St Andrew) Tamworth *Lich*

KETTLEBURGH (St Andrew) Brandeston w Kettleburgh
St E

KETTLENESS (St John the Baptist) Lythe w Ugthorpe *York*

KETTLESTONE AND PENSTHORPE (All Saints) Gt w Lt
Snoring w Kettlestone and Pensthorpe *Nor*

KETTLETHORPE (St Peter and St Paul) Saxilby Gp *Linc*

KETTLEWELL (St Mary) w Conistone, Hubberholme and
Arncliff w Halton Gill *Bradf 8* **P** *Bp, Mrs A M Harries and*
W R G Bell Esq (jt) **V** A B KNAPP

KETTON (St Mary the Virgin) w Tinwell *Pet 8*
P *Bp (3 turns), Burghley Ho Preservation Trust (1 turn)*
R M W M SAUNDERS

KEW (St Anne) *S'wark 16* **P** *The Crown* **V** P McCRORY

KEW (St Francis) *Liv 9* **P** *Bp, Adn Warrington, and V*
Southport All SS & All So (jt) **V** *Vacant* Southport (01704)
28549

KEW (St Philip and All Saints) (St Luke) *S'wark 16* **P** *Bp*
V N P DARBY

KEWSTOKE (St Paul) w Wick St Lawrence *B & W 11*
P *Ld Chan* **V** P A M WEST

KEXBY (St Paul) w Wilberfoss *York 7* **P** *Viscount de Vesci*
and Lord Egremont (alt) **P-in-c** I D GOMERSALL

KEYHAM (All Saints) Houghton-on-the-Hill, Keyham and
Hungarton *Leic*

KEYHAM, NORTH (St Thomas) *Ex 22* **P** *Bp*
V J M B SMETHURST

KEYINGHAM (St Nicholas) w Ottringham, Halsham and
Sunk Island *York 13* **P** *Abp (3 turns), DBP (1 turn)*
R I R S WALKER, **Hon C** S J WALKER

KEYMER (St Cosmas and St Damian) Clayton w Keymer
Chich

KEYMER (St Francis of Assisi) as above

KEYNSHAM (St Francis) (St John the Baptist) *B & W 10*
P *Patr Bd* **TR** P I ALLTON, **TV** S M STEVENETTE,
C N GANE, **NSM** A A J CLARIDGE, M A SNOOK

KEYSOE (St Mary the Virgin) w Bolnhurst and Little
Staughton *St Alb 21* **P** *CCC Ox (1 turn), Bp (2 turns)*
V J C LAIRD

KEYSTON (St John the Baptist) and Bythorn *Ely 10*
P *Sir Stephen Hastings (2 turns), Bp (1 turn)*
P-in-c J HINDLEY, **NSM** B A BEARCROFT,
J RAWLINSON

KEYWORTH (St Mary Magdalene) *S'well 9* **P** *Bp*
P-in-c T SISSON

KIBWORTH (St Wilfrid) and Smeeton Westerby and
Saddington *Leic 5* **P** *Mert Coll Ox and Bp (jt)*
P-in-c S M LEE

KIDBROOKE (St James) (St Nicholas) (Holy Spirit)
S'wark 1 **P** *Patr Bd* **TR** K W HITCH, **TV** I SALONIA,
NSM K F SITCH

KIDDERMINSTER (St George) (St Chad) (St John the
Baptist Church Hall) *Worc 11* **P** *Patr Bd*
TR N J W BARKER, **TV** A M JONES

KIDDERMINSTER (St John the Baptist) (Holy Innocents)
Worc 11 **P** *Patr Bd* **TR** H SMITH, **TV** C F RAVEN,
L M GIBSON, **C** K D SHILVOCK

KIDDERMINSTER (St Mary and All Saints) w Trimpley,
Franche, Broadwaters and Upper Arley *Worc 11* **P** *Bp*
TR A J POSTLETHWAITE, **TV** P J RAHILLY,
S D HARROP, **C** A M HUGHES

KIDDINGTON (St Nicholas) Wootton w Glympton and
Kiddington *Ox*

KIDLINGTON (St Mary the Virgin) w Hampton Poyle *Ox 7*
P *Patr Bd* **TR** G C M SMITH, **TV** R G COPPEN,
C J LONGUET-HIGGINS, **NSM** B DOUBTFIRE,
J A TURNER

KIDLINGTON, SOUTH (St John the Baptist) Kidlington w
Hampton Poyle *Ox*

KIDMORE END (St John the Baptist) *Ox 6* **P** *Bp*
V G D FOULIS BROWN

KIDSGROVE (St Thomas) *Lich 14* **P** *MMCET*
V R FARNWORTH, **C** J J REDFEARN

KILBURN (Mission Room) Horsley *Derby*

KILBURN Priory Road (St Mary w All Souls) *Lon 16* **P** *Bp*
and Ch Patr Trust (jt) **V** *Vacant*

KILBURN (St Augustine) (St John) *Lon 2* **P** *SMF*
V A H YATES, **C** D V WYLIE

KILBURN (St Mary) Thirkleby w Kilburn and Bagby *York*

KILBURN, WEST (St Luke) (St Simon) (St Jude) *Lon 2*
P *CPAS* **V** R D de BERRY, **C** E J BARRATT

KILBY (St Mary Magdalene) Fleckney and Kilby *Leic*

KILDALE (St Cuthbert) Ingleby Greenhow w Bilsdale
Priory, Kildale etc *York*

KILDWICK (St Andrew) *Bradf 8* **P** *Ch Ch Ox* **V** P MOORE

KILHAM (All Saints) Rudston w Boynton and Kilham *York*

KILKHAMPTON (St James the Great) w Morwenstow
Truro 8 **P** *DBP and Bp (jt)* **R** B G DORRINGTON

KILLAMARSH (St Giles) *Derby 3* **P** *The Crown*
R R J BRADSHAW

KILLERTON (Holy Evangelist) Pinhoe and Broadclyst *Ex*

KILLINGHALL (St Thomas the Apostle) Hampsthwaite and
Killinghall *Ripon*

KILLINGHOLME, NORTH AND SOUTH (St
Denys) Habrough Gp *Linc*

KILLINGTON (All Saints) Firbank, Howgill and Killington
Bradf

KILLINGWORTH (St John) *Newc 1* **P** *V Longbenton*
St Bart **V** M L MALLESON

KILMERSDON (St Peter and St Paul) w Babington
B & W 12 **P** *Lord Hylton* **R** C P J TURNER

KILMESTON (St Andrew) Hinton Ampner w Bramdean and
Kilmeston *Win*

KILMINGTON (St Giles) w Shute *Ex 5* **P** *Bp and D&C*
(alt) **V** D J R MOSELEY

KILMINGTON (St Mary the Virgin) Upper Stour *Sarum*

KILNDOWN (Christ Church) Goudhurst w Kilndown *Cant*

KILNGREEN (Diggle Mission Church) Saddleworth *Man*

KILNHURST (St Thomas) *Sheff 12* **P** *Ld Chan*
V N H ELLIOTT

KILNSEA (St Helen) Easington w Skeffling, Kilnsea and
Holmpton *York*

KILNWICK (All Saints) Bainton w N Dalton, Middleton-on-
the-Wolds etc *York*

KILNWICK PERCY (St Helen) Pocklington and Owsthorpe
and Kilnwick Percy etc *York*

KILPECK (St Mary and St David) Ewyas Harold w Dulas,
Kenderchurch etc *Heref*

KILSBY (St Faith) Barby w Kilsby *Pet*

KILTON (St Nicholas) Quantoxhead *B & W*

KILVERSTONE (St Andrew) Thetford *Nor*

KILVINGTON (St Mary) *S'well 3* **P** *E G Staunton Esq*
R *Vacant*

KILVINGTON, SOUTH (St Wilfrid) Thirsk *York*

KILWORTH, NORTH (St Andrew) w SOUTH (St Nicholas)
and Misterton *Leic 11* **P** *Ld Chan, R R D Belgrave Esq, and*
Rev C E N Richards (by turn) **R** H J EDWARDS

KIMBERLEY (Holy Trinity) *S'well 7* **P** *Bp* **R** D W WILDE

KIMBERLEY (St Peter) Barnham Broom *Nor*

KIMBERWORTH (St Thomas) (St Mark) *Sheff 6* **P** *Bp*
V N J BUCK, **C** E M DRAX

KIMBERWORTH PARK (St John) *Sheff 6* **P** *Bp*
V K THOMPSON

KIMBLE, GREAT (St Nicholas) Ellesborough, The Kimbles
and Stoke Mandeville *Ox*

KIMBLE, LITTLE (All Saints) as above

KIMBLESWORTH (St Philip and St James) Sacriston and
Kimblesworth *Dur*

KIMBOLTON (St Andrew) *Ely 10* **P** *Trustees Duke of Man* **V** R A FROST

KIMBOLTON (St James the Great) w Hamnish and Middleton-on-the-Hill *Heref 7* **P** *Bp* **P-in-c** C L BEEVERS

KIMCOTE (All Saints) Gilmorton w Peatling Parva and Kimcote etc *Leic*

KIMMERIDGE (St Nicholas of Myra) Corfe Castle, Church Knowle, Kimmeridge etc *Sarum*

KIMPTON (St Peter and St Paul) Appleshaw, Kimpton, Thruxton and Fyfield *Win*

KIMPTON (St Peter and St Paul) w Ayot St Lawrence *St Alb 14* **P** *Bp* **R** C J WHARTON

KINETON (St Peter) *Cov 8* **P** *Lady Willoughby de Broke* **V** R MIGHALL

KING CROSS (St Paul) *Wakef 4* **P** *Bp* **V** *Vacant* Halifax (01422) 352933

KING STERNDALE (Christ Church) Buxton w Burbage and King Sterndale *Derby*

KINGHAM (St Andrew) w Churchill, Daylesford and Sarsden *Ox 3* **P** *Ch Soc Trust* **R** J E ANDREWS, **NSM** T J MANN

KINGS BROMLEY (All Saints) The Ridwares and Kings Bromley *Lich*

KING'S CAPLE (St John the Baptist) How Caple w Sollarshope, Sellack etc *Heref*

KING'S CLIFFE (All Saints) *Pet 8* **P** *Bp* **R** J HUMPHRIES

KINGS HEATH (All Saints) *Birm 8* **P** *V Moseley St Mary* **P-in-c** J L WILKINSON, **C** D R M MONTEITH

KINGS HEATH (St Augustine) *Pet 7* **P** *Bp* **V** O R PAGE, **NSM** J C MICKLETHWAITE

KING'S HILL (St Andrew) Wednesbury St Bart *Lich*

KINGS LANGLEY (All Saints) *St Alb 3* **P** *Abp* **V** P R STEARN

KING'S LYNN (All Saints) S Lynn *Nor*

KING'S LYNN (St John the Evangelist) *Nor 21* **P** *Bp* **V** *Vacant* King's Lynn (01553) 773034

KING'S LYNN (St Margaret) (St Edmund) w St Nicholas *Nor 21* **P** *D&C* **P-in-c** W R HURDMAN

KING'S LYNN (St Peter) W Lynn *Ely*

KINGS NORTON (St John the Baptist) Gaulby *Leic*

KINGS NORTON (St Nicholas) *Birm 4* **P** *Patr Bd* **TR** M F LEIGH, **TV** E I PITTS, R BRISTOW, S C WINTER, **NSM** M G HUDSON

KING'S PYON (St Mary the Virgin) Canon Pyon w Kings Pyon and Birley *Heref*

KINGS RIPTON (St Peter) *Ely 9* **P** *Lord de Ramsey* **P-in-c** B J HYDER-SMITH

KING'S STANLEY (St George) The Stanleys *Glouc*

KING'S SUTTON (St Peter and St Paul) and Newbottle and Charlton *Pet 1* **P** *SMF and Lady Townsend (jt)* **V** J D CORBETT

KING'S WALDEN (St Mary) and Offley w Lilley *St Alb 9* **P** *Sir Thomas Pilkington, Bt (2 turns), St Jo Coll Cam (1 turn), D K C Salusbury-Hughes Esq and Mrs P A L McGrath (2 turns)* **P-in-c** J SCHILD

KING'S WORTHY (St Mary) (St Mary's Chapel) *Win 13* **P** *Univ Coll Ox and Exors Lord Northbrook (alt)* **R** R A CORNE

KINGSBRIDGE (St Edmund the King and Martyr) and Dodbrooke *Ex 14* **P** *Bp* **R** C C ROBINS

KINGSBURY (Holy Innocents) *Lon 21* **P** *D&C St Paul's* **V** D E NENO, **NSM** A J HOPKINS

KINGSBURY (St Andrew) *Lon 21* **P** *The Crown* **V** J T SMITH

KINGSBURY (St Peter and St Paul) *Birm 12* **P** *Bp* **P-in-c** M D MARSH

KINGSBURY EPISCOPI (St Martin) w East Lambrook, Hambridge and Earnshill *B & W 15* **P** *Bp (2 turns), D&C (1 turn)* **V** D A BURTON

KINGSCLERE (St Mary) *Win 6* **P** *Bp* **V** H B LEATHLEY, **NSM** A J ASKEW

KINGSCLERE WOODLANDS (St Paul) Ashford Hill w Headley *Win*

KINGSCOTE (St John the Baptist) Horsley and Newington Bagpath w Kingscote *Glouc*

KINGSDON (All Saints) Somerton w Compton Dundon, the Charltons etc *B & W*

KINGSDOWN (St Edmund the King and Martyr) *Roch 9* **P** *D&C* **R** D P WREN

KINGSDOWN (St John the Evangelist) Ringwould w Kingsdown *Cant*

KINGSEY (St Nicholas) Haddenham w Cuddington, Kingsey etc *Ox*

KINGSHURST (St Barnabas) *Birm 11* **P** *Bp* **V** *Vacant* 0121–770 3972

KINGSKERSWELL (St Mary) w Coffinswell *Ex 10* **P** *V St Marychurch* **V** J F LEONARD

KINGSLAND (St Michael and All Angels) *Heref 7* **P** *DBP* **R** S B THOMAS

KINGSLEY (All Saints) E and W Worldham, Hartley Mauditt w Kingsley etc *Win*

KINGSLEY (St John the Evangelist) *Ches 3* **P** *V Frodsham* **P-in-c** R H N ROBB, **C** C SQUIRE

KINGSLEY (St Werburgh) *Lich 11* **P** *Mrs G I A Dalrymple-Hamilton* **P-in-c** L R PRICE

KINGSLEY MOOR (St John the Baptist) Kingsley *Lich*

KINGSNORTH (St Michael and All Angels) w Shadoxhurst *Cant 10* **P** *Abp* **P-in-c** S E McLACHLAN

KINGSNYMPTON (St James) S Molton w Nymet St George, High Bray etc *Ex*

KINGSTAG (not known) Stock and Lydlinch *Sarum*

KINGSTANDING (St Luke) *Birm 3* **P** *Bp* **V** D J A SMITH, **C** R D WOODWARD

KINGSTANDING (St Mark) *Birm 3* **P** *Bp* **V** R A FARRELL, **C** R D WOODWARD, **Hon C** A BARTLETT

KINGSTEIGNTON (St Michael) *Ex 11* **P** *Bp* **V** C H BENSON

KINGSTHORPE (St John the Baptist) w St David, Northampton *Pet 4* **P** *Patr Bd* **TR** M R H BAKER, **TV** R J LEE, D M FAREY, **C** B B C PROWSE, **NSM** V A BARFORD

KINGSTON (All Saints and St Andrew) Bourn and Kingston w Caxton and Longstowe *Ely*

KINGSTON (St Giles) Barham w Bishopsbourne and Kingston *Cant*

KINGSTON (St James) Bigbury, Ringmore and Kingston *Ex*

KINGSTON (St James) Shorwell w Kingston *Portsm*

KINGSTON (St James), Langton Matravers and Worth Matravers *Sarum 9* **P** *Bp, Lt-Col H E Scott, and R Swanage and Studland (jt)* **R** R N K WATTON

KINGSTON (St Pancras) Iford w Kingston and Rodmell *Chich*

KINGSTON (St Winifred) and Ratcliffe-on-Soar *S'well 10* **P** *Lord Belper* **P-in-c** D C GORICK, **NSM** J H MOORE, A C SUTHERLAND, J M GORICK

KINGSTON BAGPUIZE (St John the Baptist) Fyfield w Tubney and Kingston Bagpuize *Ox*

KINGSTON BUCI (St Julian) *Chich 4* **P** *Lord Egremont* **R** S C KERSLEY, **C** E K HOWARD

KINGSTON DEVERILL (St Mary) The Deverills *Sarum*

KINGSTON HILL (St Paul) *S'wark 15* **P** *DBP* **V** R M de VIAL

KINGSTON LACY (St Stephen) Sturminster Marshall, Kingston Lacy and Shapwick *Sarum*

KINGSTON LISLE (St John the Baptist) Ridgeway *Ox*

KINGSTON PARK (not known) Newc Epiphany *Newc*

KINGSTON SEYMOUR (All Saints) Yatton Moor *B & W*

KINGSTON ST MARY (Blessed Virgin Mary) Broomfield and Cheddon Fitzpaine *B & W 18* **P** *D&C Bris and Bp (alt)* **R** G C H WATSON, **NSM** M M T DOBLE

KINGSTON UPON HULL (Holy Trinity) *York 15* **P** *Patr Soc* **V** J W WALLER, **C** J M BEADLE, **Hon C** M BATES

KINGSTON UPON HULL Southcoates (St Aidan) *York 15* **P** *Simeon's Trustees* **V** M A FRYER, **C** S WORRALL

KINGSTON UPON HULL (St Alban) *York 15* **P** *Abp* **V** E T FORWARD

KINGSTON UPON HULL (St Mary) *York 15* **P** *Abp* **P-in-c** D A ROGERS

KINGSTON UPON HULL (St Matthew w St Barnabas) *York 15* **P** *V Hull H Trin* **V** J A BAGSHAWE

KINGSTON UPON HULL (St Nicholas) *York 15* **P** *Abp* **V** R A SCRIVENER, **C** M R B HILLS

KINGSTON UPON THAMES (All Saints) (St John the Evangelist) *S'wark 15* **P** *K Coll Cam* **V** J BATES, **C** A MILLS, **Hon C** E J RICHARDSON, **NSM** A I SMITH

KINGSTON UPON THAMES (St Luke) *S'wark 15* **P** *Bp* **V** *Vacant* 0181–546 4064

KINGSTON VALE (St John the Baptist) *S'wark 15* **P** *Bp* **P-in-c** P S HAUGHTON

KINGSTONE (St John and All Saints) Ilminster and District *B & W*

KINGSTONE (St John the Baptist) w Gratwich *Lich 20* **P** *Bp* **P-in-c** A G SADLER, **C** R M VIDAL-HALL

KINGSTONE (St Michael and All Angels) w Clehonger, Eaton Bishop, Allensmore and Thruxton *Heref 1* **P** *Bp (2 turns), Prime Min (1 turn)* **R** B A M GILLETT, **C** W R PRIDIE

KINGSWEAR (St Thomas of Canterbury) Brixham w Churston Ferrers and Kingswear *Ex*

KINGSWINFORD (St Mary) *Worc 10* **P** *DBP* **V** J S LUNGLEY, **C** N C PEDLEY, P MARTIN

KINGSWOOD (Church of the Ascension) (Holy Trinity) *Bris 2* **P** *Patr Bd* **TR** R NEWTON, **TV** S C AIREY, **C** R D M MARTIN

KINGSWOOD (St Andrew) S'wark 25 P Bp and
  R&S Ch Trust (jt) V P V FISHER, Hon C R F SHAW
KINGSWOOD (St Mary the Virgin) w Alderley and Hillesley
  Glouc 7 P Bp, DBP and R M G S Hale Esq (jt)
  P-in-c S W ELDRIDGE
KINGSWOOD, LOWER (Wisdom of God) Kingswood
  S'wark
KINGTON (St James) Inkberrow w Cookhill and Kington w
  Dormston Worc
KINGTON (St Mary) w Huntington, Old Radnor, Kinnerton
  and Knill Heref 5 P Bp, D&C, and D&C Worc (jt)
  R H D G JENKYNS, C G T G SYKES
KINGTON (St Michael) Bris 9 P Patr Bd V Vacant
KINGTON, WEST (St Mary the Virgin) Bris 9 P Bp
  P-in-c J N A BRADBURY, C R V C LEWIS
KINGTON LANGLEY (St Peter) Draycot Bris
KINGTON MAGNA (All Saints) Gillingham Sarum
KINGWESTON (All Saints) Keinton Mandeville w Lydford-
  on-Fosse etc B & W
KINLET (St John the Baptist) Cleobury Mortimer w Hopton
  Wafers etc Heref
KINNERLEY (St Mary) w Melverley and Knockin w
  Maesbrook Lich 24 R D N AUSTERBERRY
KINNERSLEY (St James) Lyonshall w Titley, Almeley and
  Kinnersley Heref
KINNERTON (St Mary the Virgin) Kington w Huntington,
  Old Radnor, Kinnerton etc Heref
KINNERTON, HIGHER (All Saints) Dodleston Ches
KINNINVIE (Mission Room) Barnard Castle w Whorlton
  Dur
KINOULTON (St Luke) Hickling w Kinoulton and
  Broughton Sulney S'well
KINSBOURNE GREEN (St Mary) Harpenden St Nic St Alb
KINSHAM (All Saints) Presteigne w Discoed, Kinsham and
  Lingen Heref
KINSLEY (Ascension) w Wragby Wakef 11 P Bp and Lord
  St Oswald (jt) V J F HARPER
KINSON (St Andrew) (St Philip) Sarum 8 P Patr Bd
  TR V R BARRON, TV R C HARRISON, C D E COURT,
  NSM R J HARRISON
KINTBURY (St Mary the Virgin) w Avington Ox 14 P DBP
  (2 turns), Bp (1 turn) P-in-c D A PLUMMER
KINVER (St Peter) and Enville Lich 5 P Bp, Mrs E Bissill,
  and DBP (jt) R W F R BATSON, Hon C M MORRIS
KINWARTON (St Mary the Virgin) w Great Alne and Haselor
  Cov 7 P Bp P-in-c S R BURCH
KIPPAX (St Mary the Virgin) w Allerton Bywater Ripon 8
  P Bp TR K A PAYNE, TV J SYKES, C E M JONES,
  P J COWPER
KIPPINGTON (St Mary) Roch 8 P DBP V J B LOWE
KIRBY, WEST (St Andrew) Ches 8 P D&C R D C KELLY
KIRBY, WEST (St Bridget) Ches 8 P D&C
  R D M FERRIDAY, C K G LOWE
KIRBY BEDON (St Andrew) Rockland St Mary w
  Hellington, Bramerton etc Nor
KIRBY BELLARS (St Peter) Upper Wreake Leic
KIRBY CANE (All Saints) Gillingham w Geldeston,
  Stockton, Ellingham etc Nor
KIRBY GRINDALYTHE (St Andrew) Weaverthorpe w
  Helperthorpe, Luttons Ambo etc York
KIRBY KNOWLE (St Wilfrid) York 20 P Abp
  P-in-c P R A R HOARE
KIRBY-LE-SOKEN (St Michael) w Great Holland
  Chelmsf 24 P Bp and CPAS (jt) R A H P BEAUCHAMP
KIRBY MISPERTON (St Laurence) w Normanby, Edston and
  Salton York 21 P Countess Feversham, Abp, and St Jo Coll
  Cam (by turn) R D R SAMWAYS
KIRBY MUXLOE (St Bartholomew) Leic 12 P Bp
  TR G H SUART, TV J A COUTTS
KIRBY-ON-THE-MOOR (All Saints), Cundall w Norton-le-
  Clay and Skelton-cum-Newby Ripon 3 P Bp, Sir Arthur
  Collins, and R E J Compton Esq (jt) P-in-c J FOSTER
KIRBY SIGSTON (St Lawrence) Northallerton w Kirby
  Sigston York
KIRBY UNDERDALE (All Saints) Bishop Wilton w Full
  Sutton, Kirby Underdale etc York
KIRBY WISKE (St John the Baptist) Ainderby Steeple w
  Yafforth and Kirby Wiske etc Ripon
KIRDFORD (St John the Baptist) Chich 11 P Lord
  Egremont S GUISE
KIRK BRAMWITH (St Mary) Fishlake w Sykehouse, Kirk
  Bramwith, Fenwick etc Sheff
KIRK DEIGHTON (All Saints) Spofforth w Kirk Deighton
  Ripon
KIRK ELLA (St Andrew) York 15 P Patr Bd
  TR J A G SCOTT, TV W D NICHOL, NSM B S BOWES

KIRK FENTON (St Mary) w Kirkby Wharfe and Ulleskelfe
  York 1 P Abp and Trustees of Capt J Fielden
  V R A CLEGG
KIRK HALLAM (All Saints) Derby 13 P Bp V D E PEET
KIRK HAMMERTON (St John the Baptist) Lower
  Nidderdale Ripon
KIRK IRETON (Holy Trinity) Wirksworth Derby
KIRK LANGLEY (St Michael) Derby 11 P G Meynell Esq
  and J M Clark-Maxwell Esq (alt) P-in-c K JARDIN,
  NSM E DIXON, H M MEYNELL
KIRK MAUGHOLD (St Maughold) Maughold S & M
KIRK SANDALL and Edenthorpe (Good Shepherd) Sheff 9
  P Ld Chan R P J BOULTON-LEA
KIRK SMEATON (St Peter) Womersley and Kirk Smeaton
  Wakef
KIRKANDREWS ON EDEN (St Mary) Burgh-by-Sands
  and Kirkbampton w Kirkandrews etc Carl
KIRKANDREWS ON ESK (St Andrew) Nicholforest and
  Kirkandrews on Esk Carl
KIRKBAMPTON (St Peter) Burgh-by-Sands and
  Kirkbampton w Kirkandrews etc Carl
KIRKBRIDE (St Bridget) S & M 4 P The Crown
  R J H SHEEN
KIRKBRIDE (St Bridget or St Bride) w Newton Arlosh
  Carl 3 P Earl of Lonsdale and V Holme Cultram (alt)
  P-in-c J T SPENCE
KIRKBURN (St Mary) Wetwang and Garton-on-the-Wolds
  w Kirkburn York
KIRKBURTON (All Hallows) Wakef 6 P Bp
  V D BARRACLOUGH
KIRKBY (St Andrew) S Kelsey Gp Linc
KIRKBY (St Chad) (St Mark) (St Martin) (St Andrew) Liv 7
  P Patr Bd TR A B HAWLEY, TV A M DOYLE,
  N M NELSON, J M MORRELL, C P S HUDD, S HOWARD
KIRKBY, SOUTH (All Saints) Wakef 11 P Guild of All So
  V T H KAYE
KIRKBY FLEETHAM (St Mary) w Langton on Swale and
  Scruton Ripon 4 P Bp Ripon and D&C York (jt)
  R K McLEOD
KIRKBY GREEN (Holy Cross) Scopwick Gp Linc
KIRKBY IN ASHFIELD (St Thomas) S'well 4 P Bp
  P-in-c M EVANS
KIRKBY IN ASHFIELD (St Wilfrid) S'well 4 P Bp
  R A BUTT
KIRKBY-IN-CLEVELAND (St Augustine) York 22 P Abp
  V D J BOASE
KIRKBY-IN-MALHAMDALE (St Michael the Archangel) w
  Coniston Cold Bradf 5 P Bp and D&C (jt)
  V B W NEWTH
KIRKBY IRELETH (St Cuthbert) Carl 8 P D&C York
  V G MURFET
KIRKBY LAYTHORPE (St Denys) Linc 22 P Bp and DBP
  (alt) R R J ABRAHAM
KIRKBY LONSDALE (St Mary the Virgin) Carl 9
  P Patr Bd TR G W BETTRIDGE, TV R J A MITCHELL,
  C K W BATEMAN, NSM P FINLINSON
KIRKBY MALHAM (St Michael the Archangel) Kirkby-in-
  Malhamdale w Coniston Cold Bradf
KIRKBY MALLORY (All Saints) Newbold de Verdun and
  Kirkby Mallory Leic
KIRKBY MALZEARD (St Andrew) Fountains Gp Ripon
KIRKBY-ON-BAIN (St Mary) Thornton Gp Linc
KIRKBY OVERBLOW (All Saints) Ripon 1 P Bp
  R P A SUMMERS
KIRKBY RAVENSWORTH (St Peter and St Felix) Gilling
  and Kirkby Ravensworth Ripon
KIRKBY STEPHEN (not known) w Mallerstang and Crosby
  Garrett w Soulby Carl 1 P Bp, Earl of Lonsdale, and
  Lord Hothfield (jt) R W F GREETHAM,
  C D B de M LEATHES, NSM I F MacDOUGALL,
  J WRIGHT
KIRKBY THORE (St Michael) w Temple Sowerby and
  Newbiggin Carl 1 P Lord Hothfield (3 turns),
  Major and Mrs Sawrey-Cookson (1 turn)
  R I L McLOUGHLIN
KIRKBY UNDERWOOD (St Mary and All
  Saints) Rippingale Gp Linc
KIRKBY WHARFE (St John the Baptist) Kirk Fenton w
  Kirkby Wharfe and Ulleskelfe York
KIRKBY WOODHOUSE (St John the Evangelist) S'well 4
  P Bp V M J MACDONALD
KIRKBYMOORSIDE (All Saints) w Gillamoor, Farndale and
  Bransdale York 18 P Countess Feversham V J D PURDY
KIRKCAMBECK (St Kentigern) Lanercost w Kirkcambeck
  and Walton Carl
KIRKDALE (St Gregory) York 18 P Ox Univ
  V J M WARDEN

KIRKDALE (St Lawrence) *Liv 3* **P** *CPAS*
P-in-c E D DELVE
KIRKDALE (St Mary and St Athanasius) *Liv 3* **P** *Simeon's*
Trustees **P-in-c** J C M BISSEX
KIRKDALE (St Paul) Bootle St Mary w St Paul *Liv*
KIRKHAM (St Michael) *Blackb 11* **P** *Ch Ch Ox*
V J K BROCKBANK
KIRKHAUGH (Holy Paraclete) Alston Team *Newc*
KIRKHEATON (St Bartholomew) Kirkwhelpington,
Kirkharle, Kirkheaton and Cambo *Newc*
KIRKHEATON (St John the Baptist) *Wakef 1* **P** *Ch Trust*
Fund Trust **R** W L HALLING, **C** D E MALE
KIRKHOLT (St Thomas) *Man 20* **P** *Bp* **V** B H LOCKE,
C J HILDITCH
KIRKLAND (Mission Church) Lamplugh w Ennerdale *Carl*
KIRKLAND (St Lawrence) Skirwith, Ousby and Melmerby
w Kirkland *Carl*
KIRKLEATHAM (St Cuthbert) (St Hilda) *York 17* **P** *Abp*
C G J PACEY
KIRKLEVINGTON (St Martin) *York 22* **P** *Abp*
V D MOORE
KIRKLEY (St Peter and St John) *Nor 9* **P** *Bp and DBP (jt)*
R J T EYRE
**KIRKLINGTON (St Michael) w Burneston and Wath and
Pickhill** *Ripon 4* **P** *Ch Soc Trust, Mrs M St B Anderson,
G W Prior-Wandesforde Esq, and DBP (jt)* **R** C N R MANSELL
KIRKLINGTON (St Swithin) w Hockerton *S'well 15* **P** *Bp*
P-in-c D J BARTLETT
KIRKLINTON (St Cuthbert) Bewcastle, Stapleton and
Kirklinton etc *Carl*
KIRKNEWTON (St Gregory) Glendale Gp *Newc*
KIRKOSWALD (St Oswald), Renwick and Ainstable *Carl 4*
P *Bp and E P Ecroyd Esq (jt)* **V** D M FOWLER
KIRKSTALL (St Stephen) *Ripon 3* **P** *Patrons Leeds St Pet*
V P J BRINDLE, **C** A H BATCHELOR
KIRKSTEAD (St Leonard) Woodhall Spa Gp *Linc*
KIRKTHORPE (St Peter) Warmfield *Wakef*
**KIRKWHELPINGTON (St Bartholomew) w Kirkharle,
Kirkheaton and Cambo** *Newc 11* **P** *Ld Chan (2 turns),
J P P Anderson Esq (1 turn), and Bp (1 turn)*
V F B RODRIGUEZ-VEGLIO
KIRMINGTON (St Helen) *Linc 6* **P** *Earl of Yarborough*
V S PHILLIPS
KIRMOND-LE-MIRE (St Martin) Walesby *Linc*
KIRSTEAD (St Margaret) Brooke, Kirstead, Mundham w
Seething and Thwaite *Nor*
KIRTLING (All Saints) *Ely 4* **P** *Mrs D A Bowlby and
Countess Ellesmere (alt)* **V** A F HOMER
**KIRTLINGTON (St Mary the Virgin) w Bletchingdon,
Weston-on-The Green and Hampton Gay** *Ox 2* **P** *Qu Coll
Ox, St Jo Coll Ox, and C G R Buxton Esq (jt)* **R** *Vacant*
Bletchington (01869) 350224
KIRTON (Holy Trinity) *S'well 3* **P** *SMF* **R** C C LEVY
KIRTON (St Mary and St Martin) w Falkenham *St E 2*
P *Ld Chan* **P-in-c** J E SWAIN
KIRTON IN LINDSEY (St Andrew) *Linc 6* **P** *Bp*
V D I WALKER
KISLINGBURY (St Luke) and Harpole *Pet 3* **P** *Bp and Sir
Stephen Hastings (alt)* **R** *Vacant* Northampton (01604)
830322
KITTISFORD (St Nicholas) Wellington and Distr *B & W*
KLIVE (Blessed Virgin Mary) Quantoxhead *B & W*
KNAITH (St Mary) Lea Gp *Linc*
KNAPHILL (Holy Trinity) *Guildf 12* **P** *V Woking St Jo*
V R B WATSON
KNAPTON (St Peter) Trunch *Nor*
KNAPWELL (All Saints) Elsworth w Knapwell *Ely*
KNARESBOROUGH (Holy Trinity) (St John the Baptist)
Ripon 1 **P** *Bp and Earl of Harewood (jt)* **R** A C BETTS,
C D J WHEELER, T M TUNLEY
KNARESDALE (St Jude) Alston Team *Newc*
**KNEBWORTH (St Martin) (St Mary the Virgin and
St Thomas of Canterbury)** *St Alb 12* **P** *Hon
D A Fromanteel* **R** T W HARFORD
KNEESALL (St Bartholomew) w Laxton and Wellow
S'well 3 **P** *DBP and Bp (jt)* **V** V E RAMPTON
KNEETON (St Helen) E Bridgford and Kneeton *S'well*
KNIGHTLEY (Christ Church) High Offley and Norbury
Lich
KNIGHTON (St John the Baptist) Clarendon Park St Jo w
Knighton St Mich *Leic*
KNIGHTON (St Mary Magdalene) (St Guthlac) *Leic 2*
P *Bp* **V** C D ALLEN, **C** L R CURTIS, **NSM** M R SEDEN
KNIGHTON (St Michael and All Angels) Clarendon Park St
Jo w Knighton St Mich *Leic*

KNIGHTON (Village Hall) Mucklestone *Lich*
KNIGHTON, WEST (St Peter) Broadmayne, W Knighton,
Owermoigne etc *Sarum*
KNIGHTON-ON-TEME (St Michael and All Angels) Teme
Valley N *Worc*
**KNIGHTS ENHAM (St Michael and All Angels) (St Paul's
Church Centre)** *Win 3* **P** *Bp* **R** A EDMEADS,
NSM J M BENTALL
KNIGHTWICK (St Mary) Martley and Wichenford,
Knightwick etc *Worc*
KNILL (St Michael and All Angels) Kington w Huntington,
Old Radnor, Kinnerton etc *Heref*
KNIPTON (All Saints) High Framland Par *Leic*
KNIVETON (St Michael and All Angels) Fenny Bentley,
Kniveton, Thorpe and Tissington *Derby*
KNOCKHOLT (St Katharine) w Halstead *Roch 8* **P** *D&C*
R D M FLAGG
KNOCKIN (St Mary) Kinnerley w Melverley and Knockin w
Maesbrook *Lich*
KNODISHALL (St Lawrence) Aldringham w Thorpe,
Knodishall w Buxlow etc *St E*
KNOOK (St Margaret) Heytesbury and Sutton Veny *Sarum*
KNOSSINGTON (St Peter) Whatborough Gp of Par *Leic*
KNOTTING (St Margaret) Sharnbrook and Knotting w
Souldrop *St Alb*
KNOTTINGLEY (St Botolph) *Wakef 11* **P** *Bp and
V Pontefract (alt)* **V** H N LAWRANCE,
C C D LETHBRIDGE
KNOTTY ASH (St John) *Liv 2* **P** *R W Derby*
V J G M ROOKE
KNOWBURY Clee Hill (St Peter Mission Room) Wigmore
Abbey *Heref*
KNOWBURY (St Paul) *Heref 12* **P** *Bp*
P-in-c D M BURGESS
KNOWL HILL (St Peter) w Littlewick *Ox 13* **P** *Bp and
Trustees (alt)* **V** P NEWTON
KNOWLE (Holy Nativity) *Bris 3* **P** *Bp* **V** K NEWTON,
C K G PERKINTON, **NSM** J F HOUSE
KNOWLE (Mission Room) Coreley w Doddington *Heref*
KNOWLE (St Barnabas) *Bris 3* **P** *Bp*
P-in-c R K A THOMPSON, **C** J V THOMPSON (nee LILLIE)
KNOWLE (St Boniface) Crediton and Shobrooke *Ex*
KNOWLE (St John) E Budleigh w Bicton and Otterton *Ex*
KNOWLE (St John the Baptist) (St Lawrence and St Anne)
Birm 13 **P** *Bp* **V** A J M DOW, **C** D G RICHARDS
KNOWLE (St Martin) *Bris 3* **P** *Bp* **V** *Vacant* Bristol (0117)
977 6275
KNOWSLEY (St Mary) *Liv 2* **P** *Lord Derby*
V E F H GRIMSHAW, **Hon C** J T LEIGHTON
KNOWSTONE (St Peter) Bishopsnympton, Rose Ash,
Mariansleigh etc *Ex*
KNOYLE, EAST (St Mary the Virgin), Semley and Sedgehill
Sarum 13 **P** *Bp and Ch Ch Ox* **NSM** R B C DUFFIELD
KNOYLE, WEST (St Mary the Virgin) Mere w W Knoyle
and Maiden Bradley *Sarum*
KNUTSFORD (St Cross) Cross Town *Ches 12*
P *Mrs J Singer* **V** J R HEATON
KNUTSFORD (St John the Baptist) and Toft *Ches 12* **P** *Bp
(3 turns), Mrs L M Anderson (1 turn)* **V** M W WALTERS,
C S L THORP, **NSM** P S BENSON
KNUTTON (St Mary) *Lich 14* **P** *Brig Sir Alex Gibbons and
T H G Howard-Sneyd Esq (alt)* **V** P G HOUGH,
C P M JELF, **NSM** K R STABLES
KNUZDEN (St Oswald) *Blackb 2* **P** *Bp* **V** C J NELSON,
NSM K THOMAS
KNYPERSLEY (St John the Evangelist) *Lich 13* **P** *CPAS*
V A E BACKHOUSE
KYME, NORTH (St Luke) Kirkby Laythorpe *Linc*
KYME, SOUTH (St Mary and All Saints) as above
KYNNERSLEY (St Chad) Edgmond w Kynnersley and
Preston Wealdmoors *Lich*
KYRE WYARD (St Mary) Teme Valley S *Worc*
LACEBY (St Margaret) *Linc 10* **P** *Earl of Yarborough and
Ridley Hall Cam (jt)* **R** A J ADAMSON
LACEY GREEN (Church Hall) Wilmslow *Ches*
LACEY GREEN (St John the Evangelist) *Ox 21* **P** *R Princes
Risborough* **V** P R L HALE
LACH DENNIS (All Saints) Lostock Gralam *Ches*
LACHE (St Mark) cum Saltney *Ches 2* **P** *Bp*
V S A WILCOCKSON, **C** B V GAUGE, S R BEAK
LACKFORD (St Lawrence) Culford, W Stow and Wordwell
w Flempton etc *St E*
LACOCK (St Cyriac) w Bowden Hill *Bris 9* **P** *A M Burnett-
Brown Esq (2 turns), Ms Z M Dunlop (1 turn)*
P-in-c C A M MANN
LADBROKE (All Saints) Harbury and Ladbroke *Cov*
LADDINGFORD (St Mary) Yalding w Collier Street *Roch*

LADOCK (St Ladoca) Probus, Ladock and Grampound w Creed and St Erme *Truro*

LADY BAY (All Hallows) *S'well 10* **P** *Bp*
V R W BRECKLES

LADYBARN (St Chad) *Man 8* **P** *Bp* **R** D K PRYCE

LADYBROOK (St Mary the Virgin) *S'well 2* **P** *Bp*
V W STOCKTON

LADYWOOD (St John the Evangelist) Birm St Jo Ladywood *Birm*

LAFFORD, SOUTH *Linc 22* **P** *G Heathcote Esq, Bp, J Wilson Esq, D&C, DBP, N Playne Esq, Sir B Welby, Bt, and Baroness Willoughby de Eresby (by turn)*
R S H SPEERS, **C** A C R BALFOUR, **NSM** R S CUTTS

LAINDON (St Nicholas) w Dunton *Chelmsf 6* **P** *Bp*
R N C PAUL

LAIRA (St Augustine) Plymouth Em, Efford and Laira *Ex*

LAIRA (St Mary the Virgin) as above

LAISTERDYKE (St Mary) *Bradf 3* **P** *Simeon's Trustees*
V A F POPPLEWELL

LAITHKIRK (not known) Romaldkirk w Laithkirk *Ripon*

LAKE (Good Shepherd) *Portsm 7* **P** *Bp* **V** *Vacant*

LAKENHAM (St Alban) *Nor 3* **P** *D&C*
P-in-c D K ALEXANDER

LAKENHAM (St John the Baptist and All Saints) *Nor 3*
P *D&C* **V** A L BEWLEY

LAKENHAM (St Mark) w Trowse *Nor 1* **P** *D&C*
V J L WILSON

LAKENHEATH (St Mary) *St E 11* **P** *D&C Ely* **V** *Vacant* Thetford (01842) 860683

LALEHAM (All Saints) *Lon 13* **V** P R BROWN

LAMARSH (Holy Innocents) Alphamstone w Lamarsh and Pebmarsh *Chelmsf*

LAMBERHURST (St Mary) and Matfield *Roch 11* **P** *D&C and V Brenchley (jt)* **V** R J MIDDLEWICK

LAMBETH, NORTH (St Anselm) (St Mary's Mission) (St Peter) *S'wark 11* **P** *The Crown (1 turn), Patr Bd (2 turns)* **TR** I HARPER, **TV** K WOOLHOUSE, R H CRAIG

LAMBETH, SOUTH (St Anne and All Saints) *S'wark 11* **P** *Abp and Bp* **Hon C** T J JEFFREYS

LAMBETH, SOUTH (St Stephen) *S'wark 11* **P** *CPAS*
V I D FARLEY

LAMBLEY (Holy Trinity) *S'well 11* **P** *Rev W J Gull*
P-in-c N PEYTON

LAMBLEY (St Mary and St Patrick) Alston Team *Newc*

LAMBOURN (St Michael and All Angels) *Ox 14* **P** *Bp*
V W J STEWART

LAMBOURNE (St Mary and All Saints) w Abridge and Stapleford Abbotts *Chelmsf 26* **P** *CCC Cam and Ld Chan (alt)* **P-in-c** R J HOARE

LAMBROOK, EAST (St James) Kingsbury Episcopi w E Lambrook, Hambridge etc *B & W*

LAMERTON (St Peter) Milton Abbot, Dunterton, Lamerton etc *Ex*

LAMESLEY (St Andrew) *Dur 4* **P** *Bp* **V** N B WARNER

LAMMAS (St Andrew) Buxton w Oxnead, Lammas and Brampton *Nor*

LAMORBEY (Holy Redeemer) *Roch 16* **P** *Bp*
V N I KERR, **C** I SHAW

LAMORBEY (Holy Trinity) *Roch 16* **P** *D Malcolm Esq*
V D V COSSAR

LAMORRAN (Holy Trinity) and Merther *Truro 6*
P *Viscount Falmouth* **R** *Vacant* Truro (01872) 52431

LAMORRAN Tresillian (Holy Trinity) Lamorran and Merther *Truro*

LAMPLUGH (St Michael) w Ennerdale *Carl 5* **P** *Trustees*
R J P SIMPSON

LAMPORT (All Saints) Maidwell w Draughton, Lamport w Faxton *Pet*

LAMYATT (St Mary and St John) Bruton and Distr *B & W*

LANCASTER (Christ Church) (Christ Church Worship Centre) w St John and St Anne *Blackb 12* **P** *V Lanc and Trustees (alt)* **V** P J BALLARD, **C** A ROUNDHILL, **NSM** B K HARDING

LANCASTER (St Chad) Skerton St Chad *Blackb*

LANCASTER (St Mary) *Blackb 12* **P** *Trustees*
V M E BARTLETT, **C** G W NELSON, **TEA** PARK

LANCASTER (St Paul) Scotforth *Blackb*

LANCASTER (St Thomas) *Blackb 12* **P** *CPAS*
V P G GUINNESS, **C** D R WHEELER, T A MAPSTONE

LANCHESTER (All Saints) *Dur 8* **P** *Ld Chan*
V P WATERHOUSE

LANCING (St James the Less) w Coombes *Chich 5*
P *Bp Lon* **R** R G RUSSELL, **C** M L CATHERALL

LANCING (St Michael and All Angels) *Chich 5* **P** *Bp*
V B G CARTER

LANDBEACH (All Saints) *Ely 6* **P** *CCC Cam*
R D P E REINDORP

LANDCROSS (Holy Trinity), Littleham, Monkleigh and Weare Giffard *Ex 17* **P** *Bp* **R** G J HANSFORD

LANDEWEDNACK (St Wynwallow) St Ruan w St Grade and Landewednack *Truro*

LANDFORD (St Andrew) Bramshaw and Landford w Plaitford *Sarum*

LANDKEY (St Paul) Barnstaple *Ex*

LANDRAKE (St Michael) w St Erney and Botus Fleming *Truro 11* **P** *Bp and MMCET (jt)* **V** G W SMYTH

LANDSCOVE (St Matthew) Broadhempston, Woodland, Staverton etc *Ex*

LANDULPH (St Leonard and St Dilpe) St Dominic, Landulph and St Mellion w Pillaton *Truro*

LANDYWOOD (St Andrew) Gt Wyrley *Lich*

LANE END (Holy Trinity) w Cadmore End *Ox 29* **P** *Bp*
V R H JENNINGS

LANEAST (St Sidwell and St Gulvat) Altarnon w Bolventor, Laneast and St Clether *Truro*

LANEHAM (St Peter) Rampton w Laneham, Treswell, Cottam and Stokeham *S'well*

LANERCOST (St Mary Magdalene) w Kirkcambeck and Walton *Carl 2* **P** *Bp, Adn, Earl of Carlisle, and PCC Lanercost (jt)* **P-in-c** C J MORRIS

LANESIDE (St Peter) *Blackb 1* **P** *V Haslingden St Jas*
V J W FINCH

LANGAR (St Andrew) Cropwell Bishop w Colston Bassett, Granby etc *S'well*

LANGCLIFFE (St John the Evangelist) w Stainforth and Horton-in-Ribblesdale *Bradf 5* **P** *Bp, Adn Craven, W R G Bell Esq, N Caton Esq, and Churchwardens of Horton-in-Ribblesdale (jt)* **V** *Vacant* Settle (01729) 823010

LANGDALE (Holy Trinity) (Mission Chapel) *Carl 10*
P *R Grasmere* **NSM** A P MANNING

LANGDALE END (St Peter) Wykeham and Hutton Buscel *York*

LANGDON, EAST (St Augustine) St Margarets-at-Cliffe w Westcliffe etc *Cant*

LANGDON, WEST (St Mary the Virgin) as above

LANGDON HILLS (St Mary and All Saints) *Chelmsf 6*
P *D&C St Paul's* **R** A BARRETT, **C** A P PARSONS

LANGFORD (Blessed Virgin Mary) Burrington and Churchill *B & W*

LANGFORD (St Andrew) *St Alb 22* **P** *Ld Chan*
V G BRADSHAW

LANGFORD (St Bartholomew) w Holme *S'well 3* **P** *Bp*
P-in-c J L SMITH

LANGFORD (St Giles) Heybridge w Langford *Chelmsf*

LANGFORD (St Matthew) Shill Valley and Broadshire *Ox*

LANGFORD, LITTLE (St Nicholas of Mira) Yarnbury *Sarum*

LANGFORD BUDVILLE (St Peter) Wellington and Distr *B & W*

LANGHAM (not known) Gillingham *Sarum*

LANGHAM (St Mary the Virgin) Boxted w Langham *Chelmsf*

LANGHAM (St Mary the Virgin) Badwell Ash w Gt Ashfield, Stowlangtoft etc *St E*

LANGHAM (St Peter and St Paul) *Pet 14* **P** *Bp*
V A J F DULLEY

LANGHAM EPISCOPI (St Andrew and St Mary) Stiffkey and Cockthorpe w Morston, Langham etc *Nor*

LANGHAM PLACE (All Souls) *Lon 4* **P** *The Crown*
R R T BEWES, **C** J R M COOK, A RIDER, S M WOOKEY, R I TICE, **Hon C** J R W STOTT

LANGHO BILLINGTON (St Leonard) *Blackb 8*
P *V Blackb* **V** Q H WILSON

LANGLEY (All Saints and Martyrs) and Parkfield *Man 18*
P *Patr Bd* **TV** R J SMITH

LANGLEY (St Francis) Fawley *Win*

LANGLEY (St John) Birm 5 **P** *Bp* **V** R T ETHERIDGE

LANGLEY (St John the Evangelist) Clavering w Langley and Arkesden *Chelmsf*

LANGLEY (St Mary) Otham w Langley *Cant*

LANGLEY (St Mary the Virgin) Wolverton w Norton Lindsey and Langley *Cov*

LANGLEY (St Michael) Chedgrave w Hardley and Langley *Nor*

LANGLEY (St Michael and All Angels) *Birm 5* **P** *The Crown* **P-in-c** R T ETHERIDGE

LANGLEY BURRELL (St Peter) Chippenham St Paul w Hardenhuish etc *Bris*

LANGLEY GREEN (St Leonard) Ifield *Chich*

LANGLEY MARISH (St Mary the Virgin) *Ox 23*
P *Patr Bd* **TR** J R HURST, **TV** A W CLEEVE, J N DAY, J G HAMMERSLEY, **NSM** M E COLEMAN

**LANGLEY MARSH (St Luke Mission
Church)** Wiveliscombe w Chipstable, Huish Champflower
etc *B & W*

LANGLEY MILL (St Andrew) *Derby 12* **P** *V Heanor*
V I R JONAS

LANGLEY PARK (All Saints) Esh *Dur*

LANGLEY PARK (St Peter's Church Hall) Beckenham St
Barn *Roch*

LANGLEY STREET (Mission Room) Derby St Barn *Derby*

LANGLEYBURY (St Paul) *St Alb 13* **P** *D W A Loyd Esq*
V F H GIMSON

LANGNEY (St Richard of Chichester) *Chich 16* **P** *Bp*
V R E BUTLER

LANGOLD (St Luke) *S'well 6* **P** *Bp* **P-in-c** I R LILLEY

LANGPORT Area Churches, The *B & W 6* **P** *Patr Bd*
TR TV COOK, **TV** S J CONNOR, **Hon C** A H G JONES

LANGRICK (St Margaret of Scotland) Brothertoft Gp *Linc*

LANGRIDGE (St Mary Magdalene) Bath Weston All SS w
N Stoke and Langridge *B & W*

LANGRISH (St John the Evangelist) *Portsm 5* **P** *Bp*
V P R WADSWORTH, **C** A D RICHARDS

LANGSTONE (St Nicholas) Havant *Portsm*

LANGTOFT (St Michael) Ness Gp *Linc*

**LANGTOFT (St Peter) w Foxholes, Butterwick, Cottam and
Thwing** *York 11* **P** *Abp and Keble Coll Ox (2 turns),
Ld Chan (1 turn)* **R** R EVELEIGH

LANGTON (St Andrew) Birdsall w Langton *York*

LANGTON (St Margaret) Woodhall Spa Gp *Linc*

LANGTON (St Peter) as above

LANGTON, GREAT (St Wilfrid) Kirkby Fleetham w
Langton on Swale and Scruton *Ripon*

LANGTON, GREAT (The Good Shepherd) as above

LANGTON BY PARTNEY (St Peter and St Paul) w Sutterby
Linc 7 **P** *Mrs D E P Douglas* **R** G ROBSON

LANGTON-BY-WRAGBY (St Giles) Wragby *Linc*

LANGTON GREEN (All Saints) *Roch 11* **P** *R Speldhurst*
V B D SIMMONS

LANGTON HERRING (St Peter) Abbotsbury, Portesham
and Langton Herring *Sarum*

LANGTON LONG (All Saints) Blandford Forum and
Langton Long *Sarum*

LANGTON MATRAVERS (St George) Kingston, Langton
Matravers and Worth Matravers *Sarum*

LANGTON ON SWALE (St Wilfrid) Kirkby Fleetham w
Langton on Swale and Scruton *Ripon*

LANGTREE *Ox 6* **P** *Patr Bd* **TV** C D ROGERS,
D R OSBORN

LANGTREE (not known) Shebbear, Buckland Filleigh,
Sheepwash etc *Ex*

LANGWATHBY (St Peter) Addingham, Edenhall,
Langwathby and Culgaith *Carl*

LANGWITH, UPPER (Holy Cross) E Scarsdale *Derby*

LANGWORTH (St Hugh) Barlings *Linc*

LANHYDROCK (St Hydrock) Bodmin w Lanhydrock and
Lanivet *Truro*

LANIVET (St Ia) as above

LANLIVERY (St Brevita) w Luxulyan *Truro 10* **P** *Bp
(1 turn), Adn Bodmin (1 turn), and DBP (2 turns)*
V D J KEIGHLEY

LANNER (Christ Church) Redruth w Lanner and Treleigh
Truro

LANREATH (St Marnarck) *Truro 12* **P** *J B Kitson Esq and
Mrs S R Parker (alt)* **R** A R INGLEBY

LANSALLOS (St Ildierna) *Truro 12* **P** *DBP and W Gundry-
Mills Esq (alt)* **R** J K P S ROBERTSHAW

LANSDOWN (St Stephen) Charlcombe w Bath St Steph
B & W

LANTEGLOS BY CAMELFORD (St Julitta) w Advent
Truro 10 **P** *Duchy of Cornwall* **R** I H MORRIS

LANTEGLOS BY FOWEY (St Wyllow) *Truro 12* **P** *D&C*
P-in-c J S HALKES

LAPAL (St Peter) Halesowen *Worc*

**LAPFORD (St Thomas of Canterbury), Nymet Rowland and
Coldridge** *Ex 16* **P** *Bp* **P-in-c** D G BACON

LAPLEY (All Saints) w Wheaton Aston *Lich 2* **P** *Keble Coll
Ox* **V** J R McMANUS, **Hon C** R C W DAMPIER

LAPWORTH (St Mary the Virgin) *Birm 13* **P** *Mert Coll
Ox* **R** A V WILLMONT

LARCHFIELD (St George) Boyne Hill *Ox*

LARKFIELD (Holy Trinity) *Roch 7* **P** *DBP*
V D J WALKER

LARLING (St Ethelbert) Hockham w Shropham Gp of Par
Nor

LASBOROUGH (St Mary) Shipton Moyne w Westonbirt
and Lasborough *Glouc*

LASHAM (St Mary) Bentworth and Shalden and Lasham
Win

LASHBROOK (Mission Room) Shiplake w Dunsden *Ox*

**LASTINGHAM (St Mary) w Appleton-le-Moors, Rosedale and
Cropton** *York 18* **P** *Abp (2 turns), Ld Chan (1 turn)*
V D H BRYANT, **C** C M HADDON-REECE (nee STREETER)

LATCHFORD (Christ Church) *Ches 4* **P** *R Grappenhall*
V C J P CRISALL, **NSM** W P POVEY

LATCHFORD (St James) (St Hilda) *Ches 4*
P *R Grappenhall* **V** J T OWEN

LATCHINGDON (Christ Church) Creeksea w Althorne,
Latchingdon and N Fambridge *Chelmsf*

LATHBURY (All Saints) Newport Pagnell w Lathbury and
Moulsoe *Ox*

LATHOM PARK (St John) Ormskirk *Liv*

LATIMER (St Mary Magdalene) Chenies and Lt Chalfont,
Latimer and Flaunden *Ox*

LATTON (St John the Baptist) Cricklade w Latton *Bris*

LAUGHTON (All Saints) Corringham and Blyton Gp *Linc*

LAUGHTON (All Saints) w Ripe and Chalvington *Chich 18*
P *Earl of Chich, Hertf Coll Ox, and BNC Ox (by turn)*
R R N KENWARD

LAUGHTON (St Luke) Foxton w Gumley and Laughton
and Lubenham *Leic*

LAUGHTON-EN-LE-MORTHEN (All Saints) w Throapham
Sheff 5 **P** *Bp* **V** R W IVELL

LAUNCELLS (St Andrew and St Swithin) Stratton and
Launcells *Truro*

**LAUNCESTON (St Mary Magdalene) (St Thomas the
Apostle)** *Truro 9* **P** *Bp and PCC (jt)*
V T J G NEWCOMBE, **C** B N GORDON-TAYLOR

LAUNCESTON (St Stephen) St Steph by Launceston *Truro*

**LAUNTON (Assumption of the Blessed Virgin
Mary)** Bicester w Bucknell, Caversfield and Launton *Ox*

LAVANT (St Mary) (St Nicholas) *Chich 3* **P** *Earl of March
and Kinrara* **R** P G ATKINSON

LAVENDER HILL (Ascension) *S'wark 14* **P** *Keble Coll Ox*
V J H CUTHBERT

**LAVENDON (St Michael) w Cold Brayfield, Clifton Reynes
and Newton Blossomville** *Ox 27* **P** *T V Sutthery Esq,
Rev S F Hamill-Stewart, Exors M E Farrer Esq, and Bp (jt)*
R P J BOYLES

LAVENHAM (St Peter and St Paul) *St E 10* **P** *G & C Coll
Cam* **P-in-c** D M STIFF

**LAVER, HIGH (All Saints) w Magdalen Laver and Little
Laver and Matching** *Chelmsf 28* **P** *Bp*
P-in-c P T C MASHEDER

LAVER, LITTLE (St Mary the Virgin) High Laver w
Magdalen Laver and Lt Laver etc *Chelmsf*

LAVERSTOCK (St Andrew) *Sarum 15* **P** *D&C*
P-in-c K ROBINSON

LAVERSTOKE (St Mary) Overton w Laverstoke and
Freefolk *Win*

LAVERTON (The Blessed Virgin Mary) Norton St Philip w
Hemington, Hardington etc *B & W*

LAVINGTON, WEST and the Cheverells *Sarum 19* **P** *Bp*
R H G HOSKINS

LAVINGTON, WEST (St Mary Magdalene) Cocking,
Bepton and W Lavington *Chich*

LAWFORD (St Mary) *Chelmsf 21* **P** *St Jo Coll Cam*
R P E BALL, **NSM** C M MITSON

LAWHITTON (St Michael) Lezant w Lawhitton and S
Petherwin w Trewen *Truro*

LAWLEY (St John the Evangelist) Cen Telford *Lich*

LAWRENCE WESTON (St Peter) *Bris 8* **P** *Bp*
V S R P SPILSBURY

LAWSHALL (All Saints) w Shimplingthorne and Alpheton
St E 12 **P** *DBP and Lord de Saumarez (alt)*
R D F FOSBUARY

LAWTON (All Saints) Church Lawton *Ches*

LAWTON MOOR (St Michael) *Man 8* **P** *Bp*
V K BUTTERWORTH

LAXEY (Christ Church) *S & M 2* **P** *Bp* **V** C M UPTON

LAXFIELD (All Saints) *St E 17* **P** *Simeon's Trustees*
P-in-c M G T WALKEY

LAXTON (All Saints) Bulwick, Blatherwycke w
Harringworth and Laxton *Pet*

LAXTON (St Michael) Kneesall w Laxton and Wellow *S'well*

LAXTON (St Peter) Howden TM *York*

LAYER BRETON (St Mary the Virgin) Birch w Layer
Breton and Layer Marney *Chelmsf*

LAYER-DE-LA-HAYE (St John the Baptist) *Chelmsf 17*
P *Bp* **V** M H CLARKE

LAYER MARNEY (St Mary the Virgin) Birch w Layer
Breton and Layer Marney *Chelmsf*

LAYHAM (St Andrew) Hadleigh w Layham and Shelley *St E*

LAYSTON W BUNTINGFORD (St Peter) Aspenden,
Buntingford and Westmill *St Alb*

LAYTON, EAST (Christ Church) Forcett and Aldbrough
and Melsonby *Ripon*

LAZONBY (St Nicholas) Gt Salkeld w Lazonby *Carl*

LEA Group, The (St Helen) *Linc 2* **P** *Bp, DBP, Exors Lt Col
J E W G Sandars (jt)* **R** J S CROFT

LEA (St Christopher) (St Barnabas) *Blackb 14* **P** *Bp*
V G LEWIS

LEA (St Giles) Garsdon, Lea and Cleverton and Charlton
Bris

LEA, THE (St John the Baptist) Ross w Brampton Abbotts,
Bridstow, Peterstow etc *Heref*

LEA AND HOLLOWAY (Christ Church) Tansley, Dethick,
Lea and Holloway *Derby*

LEA CROSS (St Anne) Pontesbury I and II *Heref*

LEA HALL (St Richard) *Birm 10* **P** *Bp*
P-in-c P M BRACHER

LEA MARSTON (St John the Baptist) The Whitacres and
Shustoke *Birm*

LEADEN RODING (St Michael) Aythorpe w High and
Leaden Roding *Chelmsf*

LEADENHAM (St Swithin) *Linc 23* **P** *P R Reeve Esq*
R *Vacant* Loveden (01400) 73253

LEADGATE (St Ives) Dipton and Leadgate *Dur*

LEAFIELD (St Michael and All Angels) Ramsden, Finstock
and Fawler, Leafield etc *Ox*

LEAGRAVE (St Luke) *St Alb 20* **P** *Bp* **V** M D PETITT,
C S M HARDWICKE

LEAHOLM (St James' Chapel) Glaisdale *York*

LEAKE (St Mary) w Over and Nether Silton and Kepwick
York 20 **P** *Abp* **P-in-c** P R A R HOARE

**LEAKE, EAST (St Mary), WEST (St Helena), Stanford-on-
Soar, Rempstone and Costock** *S'well 10* **P** *Bp, DBP, Lord
Belper, and SS Coll Cam (jt)* **R** S J SMITH,
C K WAKEFIELD, **NSM** G C HETHERINGTON,
D M FISHER

LEAKE, NEW (St Jude) Stickney Gp *Linc*

LEAKE, OLD (St Mary) w Wrangle *Linc 20* **P** *Bp and DBP
(alt)* **V** *Vacant* Boston (01205) 870130

LEAM LANE (St Andrew) *Dur 4* **P** *Bp* **P-in-c** I JELLEY

LEAMINGTON, SOUTH (St John the Baptist) *Cov 11*
P *Bp* **V** D W LAWSON

LEAMINGTON HASTINGS (All Saints) and Birdingbury
Cov 6 **P** *Bp and Mrs H M O Lodder (alt)*
P-in-c H J H STEVINSON, **NSM** J M STEVINSON

LEAMINGTON PRIORS (All Saints) *Cov 11* **P** *Bp*
P-in-c G F WARNER, **C** M E JACKSON

LEAMINGTON PRIORS (St Mary) *Cov 11* **P** *Ch Patr
Trust* **V** M P M BOOKER, **C** M WARNES

LEAMINGTON PRIORS (St Paul) *Cov 11* **P** *Ch Patr
Trust* **V** B MERRINGTON

LEAMINGTON SPA (Holy Trinity) and Old Milverton
Cov 11 **P** *Bp and M Heber-Percy Esq (jt)*
P-in-c G F WARNER

LEAMINGTON SPA (St Mark New Milverton) New
Milverton *Cov*

LEAMORE (St Aidan) Blakenall Heath *Lich*

LEASINGHAM (St Andrew) *Linc 22* **P** *DBP*
P-in-c G SMITH

LEASOWE (St Chad) *Ches 7* **P** *Bp* **V** D M SHEPHERD

LEATHERHEAD (All Saints) (St Mary and St Nicholas)
Guildf 10 **P** *D&C Roch* **V** D J EATON, **C** M J PROCTOR

**LEATHLEY (St Oswald) w Farnley, Fewston and
Blubberhouses** *Bradf 4* **P** *Bp and G N le G Horton-
Fawkes Esq* **R** *Vacant* Leeds (0113) 284 3692

LEATON (Holy Trinity) and Albrighton w Battlefield *Lich 26*
P *Col H Lloyd and J F Sparrow Esq (jt)*
V P M GOLDTHORPE

LEAVELAND (St Laurence) Selling w Throwley, Sheldwich
w Badlesmere etc *Cant*

LEAVENHEATH (St Matthew) Stoke by Nayland w
Leavenheath *St E*

LEAVENING (not known) Burythorpe, Acklam and
Leavening w Westow *York*

LEAVESDEN (All Saints) *St Alb 13* **P** *Bp*
V C P HUITSON, **C** A G CARTER, J A BIRDSEYE

LECHLADE (St Lawrence) *Glouc 13* **P** *Em Coll Cam*
V S C PARSONS

LECK (St Peter) Tunstall w Melling and Leck *Blackb*

LECKFORD (St Nicholas) Stockbridge and Longstock and
Leckford *Win*

LECKHAMPSTEAD (Assumption of the Blessed Virgin
Mary) N Buckm *Ox*

LECKHAMPSTEAD (St James) Brightwalton w Catmore,
Leckhampstead etc *Ox*

LECKHAMPTON (St Christopher) Leckhampton SS Phil
and Jas w Cheltenham St Jas *Glouc*

LECKHAMPTON (St Peter) *Glouc 11* **P** *Bp* **R** A C BERRY

**LECKHAMPTON (St Philip and St James) w Cheltenham
(St James)** *Glouc 10* **P** *Bp* **V** D C NYE,
C R C PARRISH, R E ROBERTS, **NSM** J KNIGHT

LECONFIELD (St Catherine) Lockington and Lund and
Scorborough w Leconfield *York*

**LEDBURY (St Michael and All Angels) (St Katherine's
Chapel) w Eastnor** *Heref 6* **P** *Bp and J F S Hervey-
Bathurst Esq (jt)* **R** C M OLDROYD, **C** J N CLARK-KING
(formerly KING), R J TRAFFORD-ROBERTS

LEDGEMOOR (Mission Room) Canon Pyon w Kings Pyon
and Birley *Heref*

LEDSHAM (All Saints) w Fairburn *York 6* **P** *G H H
Wheler Esq* **V** P WARREN

LEDSTON LUCK (not known) Ledsham w Fairburn *York*

LEE (Good Shepherd) (St Peter) *S'wark 3* **P** *R Lee St Marg*
V J R GILES, **C** S G SPEAR, **Hon C** A E HOAD,
NSM M MONK

LEE (St Augustine) Grove Park *S'wark 3* **P** *Bp*
V G A BERRIMAN

LEE (St John the Baptist) *Ox 28* **P** *Bp* **V** G A de BURGH-
THOMAS

LEE (St Margaret) *S'wark 3* **P** *Ld Chan* **R** R C B BUTLER

LEE (St Matthew) Ilfracombe, Lee, Woolacombe, Bittadon
etc *Ex*

LEE (St Mildred) Burnt Ash Hill *S'wark 3* **P** *Bp*
V M C HILL, **Hon C** R C HENSON, A HILL

LEE BROCKHURST (St Peter) *Lich 28* **P** *Lord Barnard*
V N MacGREGOR

LEE MOOR (Mission Church) Bickleigh (Roborough) and
Shaugh Prior *Ex*

LEE-ON-THE-SOLENT (St Faith) *Portsm 3* **P** *Bp*
V P A SUTTON, **C** T STOTT

LEEBOTWOOD (St Mary) Dorrington w Leebotwood,
Longnor, Stapleton etc *Heref*

LEEDS (All Hallows) *Ripon 7* **P** *Bp and DBP (jt)*
V A C JENKINS

LEEDS (All Souls) *Ripon 7* **P** *V Leeds St Pet, Simeon's
Trustees, and DBP (jt)* **V** R L A PATERSON

LEEDS Belle Isle (St John and St Barnabas) *Ripon 6* **P** *Bp*
V D J HOPKINSON, **C** C M DAVEY

LEEDS (Emmanuel) *Ripon 7* **P** *Trustees*
P-in-c S J ROBINSON

LEEDS Gipton (Church of the Epiphany) *Ripon 5* **P** *Bp*
V *Vacant* Leeds (0113) 249 1845

LEEDS Halton (St Wilfrid) *Ripon 5* **P** *Bp* **V** *Vacant* Leeds
(0113) 264 7000

LEEDS (Parish Church) Leeds City *Ripon*

LEEDS Richmond Hill (All Saints) (St Hilda) (St Saviour)
Ripon 8 **P** *Bp and Keble Coll Ox (jt)* **C** N P GEORGE

LEEDS (St Aidan) *Ripon 5* **P** *V Leeds St Pet*
V A L TAYLOR, **C** S SMITH, P A BICKNELL (nee
RIDING), J S WEBB

LEEDS (St Cyprian and St James) Harehills *Ripon 5* **P** *Bp*
V H A THOMPSON

LEEDS (St George) *Ripon 7* **P** *Simeon's Trustees*
V D J L HAWKINS, **C** J E MORRIS, P K ELLEM,
NSM M B HANSON

LEEDS (St Nicholas) Hollingbourne and Hucking w Leeds
and Broomfield *Cant*

LEEDS (St Wilfrid) *Ripon 5* **P** *Bp* **V** D BOOTH

LEEDS CITY (St Peter) (Holy Trinity) *Ripon 5* **P** *DBP*
TR S J OLIVER, **TV** C R CORNWELL, N S HOWE,
C H BEGLEY, P F HUNT

LEEDSTOWN (St James's Mission Church) Crowan w
Godolphin *Truro*

**LEEK (All Saints) (St Edward the Confessor) (St John the
Evangelist) (St Luke) (St Paul) and Meerbrook** *Lich 13*
P *Patr Bd* **TR** K E JONES, **TV** J P EADES,
K R HAYWOOD, **C** U D PATEL, **NSM** T WARNER

LEEK WOOTTON (All Saints) *Cov 4* **P** *Lord Leigh*
P-in-c G R CORNWALL-JONES

LEEMING (St John the Baptist) *Ripon 4* **P** *R Kirklington w
Burneston etc* **P-in-c** M D EMMEL

LEEMING BAR (St Augustine) Bedale *Ripon*

LEES HILL (Mission Hall) Lanercost w Kirkcambeck and
Walton *Carl*

LEESFIELD Knoll's Lane (St Agnes) Leesfield *Man*

LEESFIELD (St Thomas) *Man 19* **P** *Bp* **V** H G SMITH,
NSM A KERR

LEFTWICH (Farm of the Good Shepherd) Davenham *Ches*

LEGBOURNE (All Saints) *Linc 12* **P** *Ch Trust Fund Trust
and Bp (jt)* **V** *Vacant* Louth (01507) 602535

LEGBURTHWAITE (Mission Church) St Johns-in-the-Vale
w Wythburn *Carl*

LEGH, HIGH (St John) Over Tabley and High Legh *Ches*

LEGSBY (St Thomas) *Linc 5* **P** *Bp* **V** M J CARTWRIGHT,
NSM D LINKPIN

**LEICESTER Christ the Saviour (St Hilda) (St Peter)
(St Saviour)** *Leic 1* **P** *Bp* **V** S F BOULD,
NSM A D BREAR

LEICESTER (Holy Apostles) (St Oswald) *Leic 2* **P** *DBP and Ridley Hall Cam (jt)* **V** J C RAINER, **NSM** R MILLER

LEICESTER (Holy Spirit) (St Andrew) (St Nicholas) *Leic 2* **P** *Bp* **TV** M G IPGRAVE, **C** J Z RAY, **Hon C** R SEMEONOFF

LEICESTER (Holy Trinity w St John the Divine) *Leic 2* **P** *Peache Trustees* **V** R W MORGAN, **C** A C WARD, J M A LEE, **Hon C** F R ENTWISTLE

LEICESTER (Martyrs) *Leic 2* **P** *Bp* **V** R J FREEMAN, **C** B A ROBERTSON

LEICESTER Resurrection (St Alban) *Leic 1* **P** *Bp* **TR** A W ROBINSON, **TV** M J COURT, M WAGSTAFF

LEICESTER (St Aidan) *Leic 2* **P** *Bp* **V** C DUNKLEY, **C** D P HOWELL (formerly WILLIAMS)

LEICESTER (St Alban) *Leic Resurr Leic*

LEICESTER (St Anne) *Leic 2* **P** *Bp* **V** I W HARRISON, **NSM** J M A SEMEONOFF

LEICESTER (St Augustine) *Leic 2* **P** *Bp* **P-in-c** P A NAYLOR

LEICESTER (St Barnabas) New Humberstone *Leic*

LEICESTER (St Chad) *Leic 1* **P** *Bp* **P-in-c** T S G VALE

LEICESTER (St Christopher) *Leic 2* **P** *MMCET* **V** A TELFORD

LEICESTER (St Elizabeth) Nether Hall *Leic 1* **P** *DBP* **P-in-c** M E C DREW

LEICESTER (St Hilda) Leic Ch Sav *Leic*

LEICESTER (St James the Greater) *Leic 2* **P** *Bp* **V** G RICHERBY, **C** R R POWELL, **Hon C** A S IRESON, **NSM** A T HELM

LEICESTER (St Margaret and All Saints) *Leic 2* **P** *Bp* **P-in-c** P A NAYLOR, **C** M J PEERS

LEICESTER (St Mary de Castro) *Leic 2* **P** *Bp* **V** D L CAWLEY, **Hon C** M N G STEWART

LEICESTER (St Paul) *Leic 2* **P** *Bp* **V** G W H SEALY

LEICESTER (St Peter) Leic Ch Sav *Leic*

LEICESTER (St Philip) *Leic 1* **P** *Adn Leic, V Evington, V Leic H Trin, G A Cooling Esq, and A S Price Esq (jt)* **P-in-c** C FINCH, **C** S F REDGRAVE

LEICESTER (St Saviour) Leic Ch Sav *Leic*

LEICESTER (St Theodore of Canterbury) *Leic 1* **P** *Bp* **V** J J LEONARD

LEICESTER FOREST EAST (St Andrew) Kirby Muxloe *Leic*

LEIGH (All Saints) Ashton Keynes, Leigh and Minety *Bris*

LEIGH (All Saints) *Lich 20* **P** *Bp* **V** A G SADLER

LEIGH (St Andrew) Yetminster w Ryme Intrinseca and High Stoy *Sarum*

LEIGH (St Bartholomew) *S'wark 25* **P** *N J Charrington Esq* **P-in-c** J M A WILLANS

LEIGH (St Catherine) Twigworth, Down Hatherley, Norton, The Leigh etc *Glouc*

LEIGH (St Clement) *Chelmsf 10* **P** *Bp* **R** S F JONES, **C** R J FARMER

LEIGH (St Edburga) Alfrick, Lulsley, Suckley, Leigh and Bransford *Worc*

LEIGH (St John the Evangelist) *Man 13* **P** *Bp* **V** R R USHER

LEIGH (St Mary) *Roch 10* **P** *Ch Trust Fund Trust* **V** T V E OVERTON

LEIGH (St Mary the Virgin) *Man 13* **P** *Bp* **V** J T FINNEY

LEIGH, LITTLE (St Michael and All Angels) and Lower Whitley *Ches 4* **P** *P G Greenall Esq and V Gt Budworth (alt)* **P-in-c** J E DRAYTON, **NSM** R BIGGIN

LEIGH, NORTH (St Mary) *Ox 9* **P** *Ld Chan* **V** *Vacant* Freeland (01993) 881136

LEIGH, SOUTH (St James the Great) Cogges and S Leigh *Ox*

LEIGH, WEST (St Alban) *Portsm 4* **P** *Bp* **V** S EVANS, **C** D C OSBORNE

LEIGH-ON-SEA (St Aidan) the Fairway *Chelmsf 10* **P** *Bp* **V** C J ELLIOTT, **NSM** J M BARHAM

LEIGH-ON-SEA (St James) *Chelmsf 10* **P** *Bp* **V** B J SCHOOLING, **NSM** C R BEECHAM, T E C SHARPE, **Hon Par Dn** E J A INGRAM

LEIGH-ON-SEA (St Margaret) *Chelmsf 10* **P** *Bp* **V** R H S EASTOE, **C** C J WOODMAN

LEIGH PARK (St Francis) *Portsm 4* **P** *Bp* **P-in-c** R C WHITE, **C** J W DRAPER, R A ORCHIN

LEIGH UPON MENDIP (St Giles) w Stoke St Michael *B & W 4* **P** *DBP and V Doulting (jt)* **V** P D WINKS

LEIGH WOODS (St Mary the Virgin) Abbots Leigh w Leigh Woods *Bris*

LEIGHLAND (St Giles) Old Cleeve, Leighland and Treborough *B & W*

LEIGHS, GREAT (St Mary the Virgin) *Chelmsf 8* **P** *Linc Coll Ox* **P-in-c** H ANSELL

LEIGHS, LITTLE (St John) *Chelmsf 8* **P** *Reformation Ch Trust* **R** *Vacant*

LEIGHTERTON (St Andrew) Boxwell, Leighterton, Didmarton, Oldbury etc *Glouc*

LEIGHTON (Holy Trinity) Trelystan *Heref*

LEIGHTON (St Mary) Buildwas and Leighton w Eaton Constantine etc *Lich*

LEIGHTON BROMSWOLD (St Mary) *Ely 10* **P** *Bp* **V** G L NORTH

LEIGHTON BUZZARD (All Saints) w Eggington, Hockliffe and Billington *St Alb 18* **P** *Bp* **V** J A L HULBERT, **C** A T BELL, E M CONSTANTINE, **NSM** V H SMITH

LEIGHTON-CUM-MINSHULL VERNON (St Peter) *Ches 15* **P** *Bp* **V** G D GEDDES

LEINTHALL EARLES (St Andrew) Aymestrey and Leinthall Earles w Wigmore etc *Heref*

LEINTHALL STARKES (St Mary Magdalene) as above

LEINTWARDINE Adforton (St Andrew) Wigmore Abbey *Heref*

LEINTWARDINE (St Mary Magdalene) as above

LEIRE (St Peter) w Ashby Parva and Dunton Bassett *Leic 11* **P** *Ball Coll Ox, Exors Major T G F Paget, and Adn Loughb (by turn)* **R** C D BRADLEY

LEISTON (St Margaret) *St E 19* **P** *Haberdashers' Co* **V** D C LOWE

LELANT (St Uny) Carbis Bay w Lelant *Truro*

LEMINGTON, LOWER (St Leonard) Moreton-in-Marsh w Batsford, Todenham etc *Glouc*

LEMSFORD (St John the Evangelist) *St Alb 7* **P** *Lord Brocket* **P-in-c** R S INGAMELLS, **NSM** J E FORDHAM

LENBOROUGH *Ox 23* **P** *Ch Ch Ox, Cam Univ, and New Coll Ox (2 turns), Ld Chan (1 turn)* **V** J HUDSON

LENHAM (St Mary) w Boughton Malherbe *Cant 15* **P** *Viscount Chilston and Lord Cornwallis (jt)* **R** D E C WRIGHT

LENTON (Holy Trinity) (Priory Church of St Anthony) *S'well 14* **P** *CPAS* **P-in-c** W R LOVATT, **C** I D BUNTING, D CHAPMAN

LENTON (St Peter) Ingoldsby *Linc*

LENTON ABBEY (St Barnabas) *S'well 14* **P** *CPAS* **V** G GREGORY, **C** P A WILLIAMS

LENWADE (All Saints) Weston Longville w Morton and the Witchinghams *Nor*

LEOMINSTER (St Peter and St Paul) *Heref 7* **P** *Patr Bd* **TR** M W HOOPER, **TV** G L JONES, J E LEWIS, P J PRIVETT, **C** S STRUTT, **NSM** J S POLLOCK

LEONARD STANLEY (St Swithun) The Stanleys *Glouc*

LEPTON (St John) *Wakef 6* **P** *R Kirkheaton* **V** G F WHITCROFT

LESBURY (St Mary) w Alnmouth *Newc 9* **P** *Dioc Soc* **V** B COWEN

LESNEWTH (St Michael and All Angels) Boscastle w Davidstow *Truro*

LESSINGHAM (All Saints) Happisburgh, Walcot, Hempstead w Eccles etc *Nor*

LETCHWORTH (St Mary the Virgin) (St Michael) *St Alb 9* **P** *Guild of All So* **R** *Vacant* Letchworth (01462) 684822

LETCHWORTH (St Paul) w Willian *St Alb 9* **P** *Bp* **V** G E TURNER, **C** S K YOUNG, **NSM** M P DACK

LETCOMBE BASSETT (St Michael and All Angels) Ridgeway *Ox*

LETCOMBE REGIS (St Andrew) as above

LETHERINGHAM (St Mary) Charsfield w Debach, Monewden, Hoo etc *St E*

LETHERINGSETT (St Andrew) Blakeney w Cley, Wiveton, Glandford etc *Nor*

LETTON (St John the Baptist) w Staunton, Byford, Mansel Gamage and Monnington *Heref 5* **P** *Sir John Cotterell, Bt (2 turns), Exors Mrs Dew (1 turn), Ch Ch Ox (3 turns), and DBP (1 turn)* **P-in-c** R A BINT

LETTY GREEN (St John) Hertingfordbury *St Alb*

LETWELL (St Peter) Firbeck w Letwell *Sheff*

LEUSDON (St John the Baptist) Widecombe-in-the-Moor, Leusdon, Princetown etc *Ex*

LEVEDALE (Mission Church) Penkridge Team *Lich*

LEVEN (Holy Trinity) w Catwick *York 12* **P** *Exors Sir Henry Strickland-Constable, Bt and Simeon's Trustees (alt)* **R** *Vacant* Hornsea (01964) 543793

LEVEN VALLEY *Carl 10* **P** *Mrs C M Chaplin, V Colton, and Bp (jt)* **P-in-c** G G DOUGLAS

LEVENS (St John the Evangelist) *Carl 9* **P** *Trustees* **V** *Vacant* Sedgwick (015395) 60233

LEVENSHULME (St Mark) *Man 3* **P** *Bp* **R** N P TAYLOR

LEVENSHULME (St Peter) *Man 3* **P** *Trustees* **R** R A J AXTELL

LEVENSHULME, SOUTH (St Andrew) *Man 3* **P** *Bp* **R** J L CLEGG

LEVER, GREAT (St Michael w St Bartholomew) E Farnworth and Kearsley *Man*

LEVER, GREAT (St Michael w St Bartholomew) *Man 12*
  P *Bp* **R** E J HALLIDAY
LEVER, LITTLE (St Matthew) *Man 12* **P** *V Bolton-le-*
  Moors St Pet **V** S F BRANDES, **NSM** I C ANTHONY
LEVER BRIDGE (St Stephen and All Martyrs) *Man 9*
  P *The Crown* **V** D A AKKER
LEVERINGTON (St Leonard) *Ely 19* **P** *Bp*
  R F B H WOOLLEY, **C** J A COOMBS, P C OWEN-JONES
LEVERTON (St Helen) Benington w Leverton *Linc*
LEVERTON, NORTH and SOUTH (St Martin) (All Saints)
  S'well 5 **P** *Bp* **V** R AKERMAN, **Hon C** I CARTER (nee
  O'NEILL)
LEVINGTON (St Peter) Nacton and Levington w
  Bucklesham and Foxhall *St E*
LEVISHAM (St John the Baptist) Middleton w Newton,
  Levisham and Lockton *York*
LEWANNICK (St Martin) North Hill and Lewannick *Truro*
LEWES All Saints (St Mary) (St Anne) (St Michael)
  (St Thomas at Cliffe) *Chich 18* **P** *Ld Chan (3 turns),*
  Patr Bd (1 turn) **TR** B KEETON, **TV** P J BENFIELD,
  C G L LINNEGAR, **NSM** R V CHEBBORN, P D YATES
LEWES (St John sub Castro) *Chich 18* **P** *Bp* **R** R M BELL
LEWES (St John the Baptist) Southover *Chich*
LEWISHAM (St Mary) *S'wark 3* **P** *Earl of Dartmouth*
  V D GARLICK
LEWISHAM (St Stephen) and St Mark *S'wark 3* **P** *Keble*
  Coll Ox **V** G KIRK, **Hon C** F D GARDOM
LEWISHAM (St Swithun) Hither Green *S'wark 3*
  P *V Lewisham St Mary* **V** R DANIELL, **NSM** E BAKER
LEWKNOR (St Margaret) Tetsworth, Adwell w S Weston,
  Lewknor etc *Ox*
LEWSEY (St Hugh) Luton Lewsey St Hugh *St Alb*
LEWTRENCHARD (St Peter) Marystowe, Coryton,
  Stowford, Lewtrenchard etc *Ex*
LEXDEN (St Leonard) *Chelmsf 17* **P** *Bp* **R** *Vacant*
  Colchester (01206) 578160
LEXHAM, EAST (St Andrew) Litcham w Kempston, E and
  W Lexham, Mileham etc *Nor*
LEXHAM, WEST (St Nicholas) as above
LEYBOURNE (St Peter and St Paul) *Roch 7*
  P *Major Sir David Hawley, Bt* **P-in-c** C D DENCH
LEYBURN (St Matthew) w Bellerby *Ripon 4* **P** *Lord Bolton*
  and Mrs M E Scragg (alt) **V** J B BLACKMAN
LEYFIELDS (St Francis) Tamworth *Lich*
LEYLAND (St Ambrose) *Blackb 6* **P** *V Leyland*
  V A F RANSON
LEYLAND (St Andrew) *Blackb 6* **P** *CPAS*
  V K HORSFALL, **C** K HOWLES
LEYLAND (St James) *Blackb 6* **P** *Sir Henry Farington, Bt*
  V R A MOORE, **NSM** M H PENMAN
LEYLAND (St John) *Blackb 6* **P** *V Leyland St Andr and*
  CPAS (jt) **V** I SMITH
LEYSTERS (St Andrew) Bockleton w Leysters *Heref*
LEYTON (All Saints) *Chelmsf 5* **P** *V St Mary's Leyton*
  V D S LOCK, **NSM** M R NIE
LEYTON (Christ Church) *Chelmsf 5* **P** *Ch Trust Fund*
  Trust **V** M E BURKILL
LEYTON (Emmanuel) *Chelmsf 5* **P** *Bp* **V** T B JONES
LEYTON (St Catherine) (St Paul) *Chelmsf 5*
  P *V Leyton St Mary w St Edw* **V** A J HOWARD
LEYTON St Luke *Chelmsf 5* **P** *Bp* **P-in-c** D S AINGE
LEYTON (St Mary w St Edward) *Chelmsf 5* **P** *Simeon's*
  Trustees **V** D S AINGE, **C** N JOHN, **Dss** A BUTLER
LEYTONSTONE (Holy Trinity) Harrow Green *Chelmsf 5*
  P *Bp* **P-in-c** T C N SCOTT
LEYTONSTONE (St Andrew) *Chelmsf 5* **P** *Bp*
  P-in-c J P SHEEHY
LEYTONSTONE (St John the Baptist) *Chelmsf 5* **P** *Bp*
  V R C FIELD, **C** A E MELANIPHY
LEYTONSTONE (St Margaret w St Columba) *Chelmsf 5*
  P *Bp* **V** J P SHEEHY, **C** P A BOSTOCK,
  J C RAVENSDALE
LEZANT (St Briochus) w Lawhitton and South Petherwin w
  Trewen *Truro 9* **P** *Bp and Ox Univ (jt)*
  P-in-c T J FULLER, **NSM** J MARSHALL
LEZAYRE (Holy Trinity) *S & M 4* **P** *The Crown*
  V B E SHEPHARD
LEZAYRE (St Olave) Ramsey *S & M 4* **P** *The Crown and Bp*
  (alt) **V** J H SHEEN, **NSM** A HADWIN
LICHBOROUGH (St Martin) Greens Norton w Bradden
  and Lichborough *Pet*
LICHFIELD (Christ Church) *Lich 1* **P** *Bp*
  I I W WILLIAMS, **NSM** P F HARRIS
LICHFIELD (St Chad) *Lich 1* **P** *D&C*
  R E G H TOWNSHEND, **C** A M DAFFERN, D D SCEATS,
  NSM B WILLIAMS, D J SHERIDAN
LICHFIELD (St John's Hospital) *Lich 1* **P** *Bp* **I** *Vacant*
  Lichfield (01543) 264169

LICHFIELD (St Mary) (St Michael) *Lich 1* **P** *D&C*
  R D A SMITH, **NSM** J PATTEN, J ANKETELL,
  J G LISTER
LICKEY, THE (Holy Trinity) *Birm 4* **P** *V Bromsgrove*
  V P D CHIPPENDALE
LIDEN (St Timothy) Swindon Dorcan *Bris*
LIDLINGTON (St Margaret) Marston Morteyne w
  Lidlington *St Alb*
LIFTON (St Mary) *Ex 25* **P** *Countess de Wolovey*
  P-in-c J H HEATH
LIGHTBOWNE (St Luke) *Man 5* **P** *D&C* **R** A J L LEWIS
LIGHTCLIFFE (St Matthew) *Wakef 2* **P** *V Halifax*
  V D WILDING
LIGHTHORNE (St Laurence) *Cov 8* **P** *Lady Willoughby*
  de Broke **R** J R WILLIAMS
LIGHTWATER (All Saints) *Guildf 6* **P** *Ld Chan and Bp*
  (alt) **V** M J HORTON
LILBOURNE (All Saints) Crick and Yelvertoft w Clay
  Coton and Lilbourne *Pet*
LILLESHALL (St John the Evangelist) (St Michael and All
  Angels) and Sheriffhales *Lich 21* **P** *Bp*
  V D J BUTTERFIELD
LILLEY (St Peter) King's Walden and Offley w Lilley *St Alb*
LILLINGSTONE DAYRELL (St Nicholas) N Buckm *Ox*
LILLINGSTONE LOVELL (Assumption of the Blessed
  Virgin Mary) as above
LILLINGTON (St Martin) Sherborne w Castleton and
  Lillington *Sarum*
LILLINGTON (St Mary Magdalene) *Cov 11* **P** *Bp*
  V T M H BOYNS, **C** N MORGAN
LILLIPUT (Holy Angels) *Sarum 8* **P** *Bp* **V** C HODGE,
  NSM A E RUTHERFORD
LIMBER MAGNA (St Peter) w Brocklesby *Linc 6* **P** *Earl of*
  Yarborough **V** S PHILLIPS, **C** C H LILLEY,
  Hon C S W ANDREW
LIMEHOUSE (St Anne) (St Peter) *Lon 7* **P** *BNC Ox*
  R J F D PEARCE, **C** A C TRESIDDER,
  Hon Par Dn A E PEARCE
LIMESIDE (St Chad) Oldham St Chad Limeside *Man*
LIMINGTON (The Blessed Virgin Mary) Ilchester w
  Northover, Limington, Yeovilton etc *B & W*
LIMPENHOE (St Botolph) Reedham w Cantley w
  Limpenhoe and Southwood *Nor*
LIMPLEY STOKE (St Mary) Freshford, Limpley Stoke and
  Hinton Charterhouse *B & W*
LIMPSFIELD (St Andrew) (St Peter) and Titsey *S'wark 24*
  P *Bp* **R** D J PARSONS, **C** S J FLATT, M H KELLY
LINBY (St Michael) w Papplewick *S'well 4*
  P *T W A Cundy Esq* **R** K H TURNER
LINCHMERE (St Peter) *Chich 10* **P** *DBP*
  P-in-c F H ANDERSON
LINCOLN Minster Group, The (St Mary Magdalene)
  (St Michael on the Mount) (St Peter in Eastgate) *Linc 15*
  P *Adn Linc, D&C, and Bp (by turn)* **R** J B BAYLEY,
  Hon C W M JACOB
LINCOLN (St Botolph by Bargate) *Linc 15* **P** *Bp* **V** *Vacant*
  Lincoln (01522) 520469
LINCOLN (St Faith) (St Martin) (St Peter-at-Arches)
  Linc 15 **P** *Bp* **P-in-c** L C ACKLAM, **C** CHILLIAM
LINCOLN (St George) Swallowbeck *Linc 15* **P** *Bp and*
  V Skellingthorpe (jt) **P-in-c** I G SILK, **NSM** J A DUFF
LINCOLN (St Giles) *Linc 15* **P** *Bp* **V** E B BARLOW
LINCOLN (St John the Baptist) (St John the Evangelist)
  Linc 15 **P** *Bp* **V** G WARD
LINCOLN (St Mary-le-Wigford) (St Benedict) (St Mark)
  Linc 15 **P** *Bp* **V** K R COOK
LINCOLN (St Nicholas) (St John) Newport *Linc 15* **P** *Bp*
  and D&C (alt) **V** B L WISKEN
LINCOLN (St Peter-at-Gowts) (St Andrew) *Linc 15* **P** *Bp*
  P-in-c P D GODDEN
LINCOLN (St Swithin) (All Saints) *Linc 15* **P** *Bp*
  P-in-c D G KERRIDGE
LINDAL IN MARTON (St Peter) Pennington w Lindal and
  Marton *Carl*
LINDALE (St Paul) w Field Broughton *Carl 10* **P** *Bp*
  P-in-c J R WRAIGHT
LINDFIELD (All Saints) *Chich 6* **P** *Ch Soc Trust*
  C M I CLUTTERBUCK, R C JACKSON
LINDLEY (St Stephen) *Wakef 5* **P** *V Huddersfield*
  V M T A HAYNES
LINDOW (St John) *Ches 12* **P** *Bp* **V** R D PETERS
LINDRIDGE (St Lawrence) Teme Valley N *Worc*
LINDSELL (St Mary the Virgin) Stebbing w Lindsell
  Chelmsf
LINDSEY (St Peter) Kersey w Lindsey *St E*
LINFORD (St Francis) E and W Tilbury and Linford
  Chelmsf

LINFORD, GREAT (St Andrew) Stantonbury and Willen *Ox*

LINFORD, LITTLE (St Leonard) Haversham w Lt Linford, Tyringham w Filgrave *Ox*

LINGDALE (Mission Room) Boosbeck w Moorsholm *York*

LINGEN (St Michael and All Angels) Presteigne w Discoed, Kinsham and Lingen *Heref*

LINGFIELD (St Peter and St Paul) and Crowhurst *S'wark 24* **P** *Bp* **V** EJSPLAXTON, **C** DCEDWARDS

LINGWOOD (St Peter) Burlingham St Edmund w Lingwood, Strumpshaw etc *Nor*

LINKENHOLT (St Peter) Hurstbourne Tarrant, Faccombe, Vernham Dean etc *Win*

LINKINHORNE (St Mellor) *Truro 12* **P** *DBP* **V** PRMEDLEY

LINLEY (St Leonard) Broseley w Benthall, Jackfield, Linley etc *Heref*

LINLEY GREEN (not known) Acton Beauchamp and Evesbatch w Stanford Bishop *Heref*

LINSLADE (St Barnabas) (St Mary) *Ox 26* **P** *Bp* **V** MJPEEL, **C** HLKIRK

LINSTEAD PARVA (St Margaret) Halesworth w Linstead, Chediston, Holton etc *St E*

LINTHORPE (St Barnabas) *York 19* **P** *Abp* **V** IDREID, **C** AMLAIRD, **NSM** RAMORRIS

LINTHWAITE (Christ Church) *Wakef 5* **P** *R Almondbury* **V** CHCOON

LINTON (Christ Church) and Castle Gresley *Derby 16* **P** *Bp* **V** WCEROSE

LINTON (St Aidan) Ashington *Newc*

LINTON (St Mary) *Ely 4* **P** *Bp* **V** JHTHOMSON, **C** LLRANDALL, **NSM** MWBO'LOUGHLIN

LINTON (St Mary the Virgin) w Upton Bishop and Aston Ingham *Heref 8* **P** *St Jo Coll Ox, D&C, and Preb H L Whatley (jt)* **R** AFRICKETTS

LINTON (St Nicholas) Coxheath w E Farleigh, Hunton and Linton *Roch*

LINTON IN CRAVEN (St Michael) *Bradf 7* **P** *D&C* **R** CJHAYWARD

LINWOOD (St Cornelius) *Linc 5* **P** *MMCET* **R** MJCARTWRIGHT, **NSM** DLINKPIN

LIPHOOK (Church Centre) Bramshott and Liphook *Portsm*

LISCARD (St John) Egremont St Jo *Ches*

LISCARD (St Mary w St Columba) *Ches 7* **P** *Bp* **V** TGRIFFITHS

LISCARD (St Thomas) *Ches 7* **P** *Bp* **P-in-c** RTNELSON

LISKEARD (St Martin), St Keyne, St Pinnock, Morval and Bradoc *Truro 12* **P** *Patr Bd (2 turns), Ld Chan (1 turn)* **TR** MGSELLIX, **TV** MGRIFFITHS

LISS (St Mary) (St Peter) (St Saviour) *Portsm 5* **P** *Bp* **R** BECOOK, **C** MJLANE, **Hon C** DJVARNEY

LISSET (St James of Compostella) Beeford w Frodingham and Foston *York*

LISSINGTON (St John the Baptist) Wickenby Gp *Linc*

LISTON (not known) Pentlow, Foxearth, Liston and Borley *Chelmsf*

LITCHAM (All Saints) w Kempston, East and West Lexham, Mileham, Beeston-next-Mileham, Stanfield, Tittleshall and Godwick *Nor 15* **P** *Bp, Earl of Leic, Ch Soc Tr, DBP, Mrs E M Olesen, and N W D Foster Esq (jt)* **R** PWRUSHTON

LITCHFIELD (St James the Less) Whitchurch w Tufton and Litchfield *Win*

LITHERLAND (St Andrew) *Liv 1* **P** *Bp* **P-in-c** CHKIRKE

LITHERLAND (St John and St James) *Liv 1* **P** *CPAS* **V** *Vacant* 0151–9223612

LITHERLAND (St Paul) Hatton Hill *Liv 1* **P** *Bp* **P-in-c** JWWHITLEY

LITHERLAND (St Philip) *Liv 1* **P** *Trustees* **V** ASCAIFE, **C** ICCOWELL, **Hon C** JTLEIGHTON

LITLINGTON (St Catherine) Shingay Gp of Par *Ely*

LITLINGTON (St Michael the Archangel) Alfriston w Lullington, Litlington and W Dean *Chich*

LITTLE: *see also under substantive place names*

LITTLE BIRCH (St Mary) Much Birch w Lt Birch, Much Dewchurch etc *Heref*

LITTLEBOROUGH (Holy Trinity) *Man 20* **P** *TR Rochdale* **V** JBPETTIFER, **Dss** KJOLIVER

LITTLEBOURNE (St Vincent) and Ickham w Wickhambreaux and Stodmarsh *Cant 1* **P** *Abp, D&C, Ch Trust Fund Trust, and Adn Cant (jt)* **R** AJALLAN

LITTLEBURY (Holy Trinity) Saffron Walden w Wendens Ambo and Littlebury *Chelmsf*

LITTLEBURY GREEN (St Peter) as above

LITTLEDEAN (St Ethelbert) Cinderford St Steph w Littledean *Glouc*

LITTLEHAM (St Margaret) w Exmouth *Ex 1* **P** *Patr Bd* **TR** KFMIDDLETON, **C** JEDICKER, **Hon C** EMMORRIS, **NSM** MKWEATHERLEY

LITTLEHAM (St Swithin) Landcross, Littleham, Monkleigh etc *Ex*

LITTLEHAMPTON (St James) (St Mary) and Wick *Chich 1* **P** *Bp* **TR** RJCASWELL, **TV** JSAHUDSON, JSBLOOMFIELD

LITTLEHEMPSTON (St John the Baptist) Broadhempston, Woodland, Staverton etc *Ex*

LITTLEMOOR (St Francis of Assisi) Preston w Sutton Poyntz and Osmington w Poxwell *Sarum*

LITTLEMORE (St Mary the Virgin and St Nicholas) *Ox 4* **P** *Or Coll Ox* **V** DGNICHOLLS

LITTLEOVER (St Peter) *Derby 10* **P** *PCC* **V** WBGMATHER, **C** MJARCHER, APLSMITH, **NSM** EAMATHER

LITTLEPORT (St George) (St Matthew) *Ely 14* **P** *Bp* **V** AGFVILLER

LITTLETON (St Catherine of Alexandria) Crawley and Littleton and Sparsholt w Lainston *Win*

LITTLETON (St Mary Magdalene) *Lon 13* **P** *C W L Barratt Esq* **R** *Vacant* Chertsey (01932) 562249

LITTLETON, HIGH (Holy Trinity) *B & W 12* **P** *Hyndman Trustees* **V** PMHAND

LITTLETON, NORTH (St Nicholas) Cleeve Prior and The Littletons *Worc*

LITTLETON, SOUTH (St Michael the Archangel) as above

LITTLETON DREW (All Saints) Nettleton w Littleton Drew *Bris*

LITTLETON ON SEVERN (St Mary of Malmesbury) w Elberton *Bris 8* **P** *Bp* **P-in-c** ITHOLDCROFT

LITTLEWICK (St John the Evangelist) Knowl Hill w Littlewick *Ox*

LITTLEWICK (St Thomas) Horsell *Guildf*

LITTLEWORTH (Holy Ascension) *Ox 17* **P** *Or Coll Ox* **V** CRRUDD

LITTON (Christ Church) Tideswell *Derby*

LITTON (St Mary the Virgin) Chewton Mendip w Ston Easton, Litton etc *B & W*

LITTON CHENEY (St Mary) Bride Valley *Sarum*

LIVERMERE, GREAT (St Peter) Blackbourne *St E*

LIVERPOOL (All Souls) Springwood *Liv 4* **P** *The Crown* **V** SPWEST

LIVERPOOL (Christ Church) Norris Green *Liv 8* **P** *Bp* **V** PWDAWKIN

LIVERPOOL (Our Lady and St Nicholas w St Anne) *Liv 3* **P** *Patr Bd* **TR** NAFRAYLING, **TV** DRCAPES, SSWILLIAMS, **Hon C** JSWILLIAMS

LIVERPOOL (St Christopher) Norris Green *Liv 8* **P** *Bp* **V** WMTODD

LIVERPOOL (St Luke in the City) (St Bride w St Saviour) (St Michael in the City) (St Stephen w St Catherine) *Liv 6* **P** *Patr Bd* **TR** NBLACK, **TV** MJFRY

LIVERPOOL (St Paul) Stoneycroft *Liv 8* **P** *St Chad's Coll Dur* **V** JCBAKER, **NSM** DBENSON

LIVERPOOL (St Philip w St David) *Liv 3* **P** *Bp* **P-in-c** JAGARNETT

LIVERSEDGE (Christ Church) *Wakef 8* **P** *V Birstall* **V** DFHANDLEY

LIVERTON (St Martin) Easington w Liverton *York*

LIVERTON MINES (St Hilda) as above

LIVESEY (St Andrew) *Blackb 5* **P** *Trustees* **V** *Vacant* Blackburn (01254) 259422

LLANCILLO (St Peter) Ewyas Harold w Dulas, Kenderchurch etc *Heref*

LLANDINABO (St Junabius) Much Birch w Lt Birch, Much Dewchurch etc *Heref*

LLANFAIR WATERDINE (St Mary) Bucknell w Chapel Lawn, Llanfair Waterdine etc *Heref*

LLANGARRON (St Deinst) w Llangrove, Whitchurch and Ganarew *Heref 8* **P** *Bp, DBP, and D&C (jt)* **R** WCMASSEY

LLANGROVE (Christ Church) Llangarron w Llangrove, Whitchurch and Ganarew *Heref*

LLANGUA (St James) Ewyas Harold w Dulas, Kenderchurch etc *Heref*

LLANVEYNOE (St Beuno and St Peter) Clodock and Longtown w Craswall, Llanveynoe etc *Heref*

LLANWARNE (Christ Church) Much Birch w Lt Birch, Much Dewchurch etc *Heref*

LLANYBLODWEL (St Michael) and Trefonen *Lich 24* **P** *Bp and Earl of Powis (jt)* **R** CRBALL

LLANYMYNECH (St Agatha) *Lich 24* **P** *Bp* **R** TVILLIERS

LOBLEY HILL (All Saints) *Dur 5* **P** *Bp* **V** RKHOPPER

LOCKERLEY (St John) and East Dean w East and West Tytherley *Win 11* **P** *DBP (1 turn), H B G Dalgety Esq (2 turns)* **V** MEBURSON-THOMAS

LOCKING (St Augustine) *B & W 11* **P** *MMCET* **V** MCCOTTERELL

LOCKINGE (All Saints) Wantage Downs *Ox*
LOCKINGE, WEST (All Souls) as above
LOCKINGTON (St Mary) and Lund and Scorborough w Leconfield *York 9* **P** *Abp* **R** C M F WHITEHEAD
LOCKINGTON (St Nicholas) Castle Donington and Lockington cum Hemington *Leic*
LOCKS HEATH (St John the Baptist) *Portsm 2* **P** *Bp* **V** R J S EVENS, **C** J M MAYBURY, **NSM** P A BOGGUST, D A WEIR
LOCKTON (St Giles) Middleton w Newton, Levisham and Lockton *York*
LODDINGTON (St Leonard) Broughton w Loddington and Cransley etc *Pet*
LODDINGTON (St Michael and All Angels) *Leic 3* **P** *Bp* **P-in-c** G J JOHNSON
LODDISWELL (St Michael and All Angels) Woodleigh and Loddiswell *Ex*
LODDON (Holy Trinity), Sisland w Hales and Heckingham *Nor 8* **P** *Bp (3 turns), E G Gilbert Esq (1 turn)* **P-in-c** C R CHAPMAN
LODE (St James) Bottisham and Lode w Long Meadow *Ely*
LODERS (St Mary Magdalene) Askerswell, Loders and Powerstock *Sarum*
LODGE, THE (St John) Weston Rhyn and Selattyn *Lich*
LODGE MOOR (St Luke) *Sheff 4* **P** C P A S **V** *Vacant* Sheffield (0114) 230 5271
LODSWORTH (St Peter) Lurgashall, Lodsworth and Selham *Chich*
LOFTHOUSE (Christ Church) *Ripon 8* **P** *DBP* **V** N G BURTON
LOFTUS-IN-CLEVELAND (St Leonard) and Carlin How w Skinningrove *York 17* **P** *Ld Chan (2 turns), Abp (1 turn)* **R** S GALLAGHER
LOLWORTH (All Saints) *Ely 5* **P** *SMF* **R** *Vacant* Crafts Hill (01954) 781001
LONAN (All Saints) *S & M 2* **P** *The Crown* **V** C M UPTON
LONDESBOROUGH (All Saints) *York 7* **P** *R F Ashwin Esq* **R** K G SKIPPER
LONDON Roscoe Street (St Luke's Church Centre) St Giles Cripplegate w St Bart Moor Lane etc *Lon*
LONDON, LITTLE (St Stephen) Bramley *Win*
LONDON CITY CHURCHES:
All Hallows Berkynchirche-by-the-Tower w St Dunstan-in-the-East *Lon 1* **P** *Abp* **V** P A DELANEY, **C** I C THURSTON, **Hon C** G R de MELLO, M D C FORRER, S VAN CULIN
St Andrew-the-Wardrobe w St Ann, Blackfriars *Lon 1* **P** *PCC and Mercers' Co (jt)* **R** J W PAUL
St Bartholomew the Great, Smithfield *Lon 1* **P** *D&C Westmr* **R** M R DUDLEY, **Hon C** A C WINTER
St Bartholomew the Less, Smithfield Gate *Lon 1* **P** *St Bart's Hosp* **V** A M WHAWELL
St Botolph Aldgate w Holy Trinity Minories *Lon 1* **P** *Bp* **V** B J LEE, **C** P WRIGHT, E J JONES, **Hon C** J W HOLDEN, F P COLEMAN, K LEECH
St Botolph without Bishopgate *Lon 1* **P** *D&C St Paul's* **R** A J TANNER, **Hon C** H J M TURNER
St Bride Fleet Street w Bridewell and Trinity Gough Square *Lon 1* **P** *D&C Westmr* **R** J OATES
St Clement Eastcheap w St Martin Orgar *Lon 1* **P** *D&C St Paul's* **P-in-c** M J WOODGATE, **Hon C** M B KIDDLE
St Edmund the King and St Mary Woolnoth w St Nicholas Acons, All Hallows Lombard Street, St Benet Gracechurch, St Leonard Eastcheap, St Dionis Backchurch and St Mary Woolchurch, Haw *Lon 1* **P** *The Crown (3 turns), D&C Cant (1 turn), Bp (1 turn), and Abp (1 turn)* **R** R HAYES
St Giles Cripplegate w St Bartholomew Moor Lane and St Alphage London Wall and St Luke Old Street w St Mary Charterhouse and St Paul Clerkenwell *Lon 1* **P** *D&C St Paul's* **R** D RHODES, **C** M ROBINSON, **Hon C** E F TINKER, **NSM** S NIGHTINGALE
St Helen, Bishopsgate w St Andrew Undershaft and St Ethelburga, Bishopsgate and St Martin Outwich and St Mary Axe *Lon 1* **R** R C LUCAS, **C** H PALMER, R M COOMBS, G J MOTE, C E SANDOM, W T TAYLOR
St James Garlickhythe w St Michael Queenhithe and Holy Trinity-the-Less *Lon 1* **P** *D&C St Paul's* **R** J W PAUL, **Hon C** W D BAKER
St Magnus the Martyr w St Margaret New Fish Street and St Michael Crooked Lane *Lon 1* **P** *DBP* **R** M J WOODGATE
St Margaret Lothbury and St Stephen Coleman Street w St Christopher-le-Stocks, St Bartholomew-by-the-Exchange, St Olave Old Jewry, St Martin Pomeroy, St Mildred Poultry and St Mary Colechurch *Lon 1* **P** *Simeon's Trustees* **R** T S FARRELL

St Mary at Hill w St Andrew Hubbard, St George Botolph Lane and St Botolph by Billingsgate *Lon 1* **P** *Ball Coll Ox (2 turns), PCC (1 turn), and Abp (1 turn)* **R** B A C KIRK-DUNCAN
St Mary le Bow w St Pancras Soper Lane, All Hallows Honey Lane, All Hallows Bread Street, St John the Evangelist Watling Street, St Augustine w St Faith under St Paul's and St Mildred Bread Street w St Margaret Moyses *Lon 1* **P** *Grocers' Co (1 turn), Abp (2 turns)* **R** V A STOCK, **NSM** J-H D BOWDEN
St Michael Cornhill w St Peter le Poer and St Benet Fink *Lon 1* **P** *Drapers' Co* **R** D B EVANS (or BURTON EVANS)
St Olave Hart Street w All Hallows Staining and St Catherine Coleman *Lon 1* **P** *Trustees* **R** J F COWLING, **Hon Par Dn** P D PERKINS
St Peter Cornhill *Lon 1* **P** *City Corp* **P-in-c** J H L CROSS
St Sepulchre w Christ Church Greyfriars and St Leonard Foster Lane *Lon 1* **P** *St Jo Coll Ox* **R** *Vacant*
St Stephen Walbrook w St Swithun London Stone w St Benet Sherehog and St Mary Bothaw w St Laurence Pountney *Lon 1* **P** *Grocers' Co and Magd Coll Cam (alt)* **R** E C VARAH
St Vedast w St Michael-le-Querne, St Matthew Friday Street, St Peter Cheap, St Alban Wood Street, St Olave Silver Street, St Michael Wood Street, St Mary Staining, St Anne and St Agnes and St John Zachary Gresham Street *Lon 1* **P** *D&C St Paul's* **P-in-c** M J COLCLOUGH
LONDON DOCKS (St Peter) w Wapping St John *Lon 7* **P** *Bp* **R** D PEEL, **C** S J HOYLE
LONDON GUILD CHURCHES:
All Hallows London Wall *Lon 1* **P** *Ld Chan* **P-in-c** A J TANNER
St Andrew Holborn *Lon 1* **P** *Bp* **V** C YOUNG
St Benet Paul's Wharf *Lon 1* **P** *Bp* **V** A P HAWKINS
St Botolph without Aldersgate *Lon 1* **P** *Bp* **V** T S FARRELL
St Dunstan in the West *Lon 1* **P** *Abp* **P-in-c** A T J SALTER
St Katharine Cree *Lon 1* **P** *Bp* **V** *Vacant* 0171–283 5733
St Lawrence Jewry *Lon 1* **P** *City Corp* **V** D J BURGESS
St Margaret Pattens *Lon 1* **P** *Ld Chan* **P-in-c** A G C PEARSON
St Martin Ludgate *Lon 1* **P** *D&C St Paul's* **P-in-c** T E EVANS
St Mary Abchurch *Lon 1* **P** *CCC Cam* **P-in-c** O R CLARKE
St Mary Aldermary *Lon 1* **P** *The Crown and Ld Chan (alt)* **P-in-c** V A STOCK
St Michael Paternoster Royal *Lon 1* **P** *Bp* **V** G JONES
LONDONDERRY (St Mark) (Holy Trinity) *Birm 5* **P** *Bp* **V** *Vacant* 0121–429 1149
LONDONTHORPE (St John the Baptist) Grantham *Linc*
LONG ASHTON (All Saints) *B & W 13* **P** *Bp* **V** H B TASKER
LONG BENNINGTON (St Swithin) w Foston *Linc 19* **P** *Duchy of Lanc* **P-in-c** R S EYRE, **NSM** C C MUNN
LONG BENTON (St Bartholomew) *Newc 6* **P** *Ball Coll Ox* **V** R W GOUNDRY, **C** R J PIMM
LONG BENTON (St Mary Magdalene) *Newc 6* **P** *Ball Coll Ox* **V** A J SHIPTON
LONG BREDY (St Peter) Bride Valley *Sarum*
LONG BUCKBY (St Lawrence) w Watford *Pet 2* **P** *Bp and Ld Chan (alt)* **V** M P TANNER
LONG BURTON (St James) Dungeon Hill *Sarum*
LONG CLAWSON (St Remigius) Harby, Long Clawson and Hose *Leic*
LONG COMPTON (St Peter and St Paul), Whichford and Barton-on-the-Heath *Cov 9* **P** *Bp, Trin Coll Ox, and Ch Ch Ox (by turn)* **V** E J RAINSBERRY
LONG CRENDON (St Mary the Virgin) w Chearsley and Nether Winchendon *Ox 21* **P** *Bp and R V Spencer-Bernard Esq (jt)* **P-in-c** R J ACKSON
LONG CRICHEL (St Mary) Witchampton and Hinton Parva, Long Crichel etc *Sarum*
LONG CROSS (Christ Church) *Guildf 11* **P** *J D Tringham Esq* **V** A BOLSEN
LONG DITTON (St Mary) *S'wark 15* **P** *Bp* **R** D LANKEY
LONG EATON (St John) *Derby 13* **P** *Bp* **V** G R PERCY, **C** L A DESHPANDE
LONG EATON (St Laurence) *Derby 13* **P** *Bp* **V** G M KNOX
LONG HANBOROUGH (Christ Church) Hanborough and Freeland *Ox*
LONG ITCHINGTON (Holy Trinity) and Marton *Cov 10* **P** *Bp* **V** *Vacant* Southam (01926) 812518
LONG LANE (Christ Church) Longford, Long Lane, Dalbury and Radbourne *Derby*
LONG LAWFORD (St John) Newbold on Avon *Cov*
LONG LOAD (Christ Church) Langport Area Chs *B & W*

LONG MARSTON (All Saints) Tring *St Alb*
LONG MARSTON (All Saints) *York 1* **P** *Col E C York*
  R J A RENDALL
LONG MARTON (St Margaret and St James) w Dufton and
  w Milburn *Carl 1* **P** *Lord Hothfield* **R** A HERBERT
LONG MELFORD (Holy Trinity) (St Catherine) *St E 12*
  P *Bp* **R** C J SANSBURY
LONG NEWNTON (Holy Trinity) Ashley, Crudwell,
  Hankerton, Long Newnton etc *Bris*
LONG PRESTON (St Mary the Virgin) w Tosside *Bradf 5*
  P *D&C Ch Ch Ox and V Gisburn (alt)* **V** L E AUSTIN
LONG RISTON (St Margaret) Skirlaugh w Long Riston
  York
LONG STANTON (All Saints) w St Michael *Ely 5* **P** *Magd*
  Coll Cam and Bp (alt) **P-in-c** G A LAY
LONG STANTON (St Michael and All Angels) Wenlock
  Heref
LONG SUTTON (All Saints) Herriard w Winslade and Long
  Sutton etc *Win*
LONG SUTTON (Holy Trinity) Langport Area Chs *B & W*
LONG SUTTON (St Mary) Sutton St Mary *Linc*
LONG WHATTON (All Saints) Hathern, Long Whatton and
  Diseworth w Belton etc *Leic*
LONG WITTENHAM (St Mary the Virgin) Dorchester *Ox*
LONGBOROUGH (St James), Sezincote, Condicote and the
  Swells *Glouc 15* **P** *Lord Leigh, Mrs S Peake, DBP, and*
  Ch Ch Ox (by turn) **R** E B HYDE
LONGBRIDGE (St John the Baptist) *Birm 4* **P** *Bp*
  V M S BRIDGEN
LONGBRIDGE DEVERILL (St Peter and St Paul) The
  Deverills *Sarum*
LONGCOT (St Mary the Virgin) Ashbury, Compton
  Beauchamp and Longcot w Fernham *Ox*
LONGDEN (St Ruthen) and Annscroft w Pulverbatch
  Heref 13 **P** *Bp and MMCET (jt)*
  P-in-c N J CHARRINGTON, **Hon C** J J WADDINGTON-
  FEATHER, J F JONES (nee HUBBARD)
LONGDON (St James) *Lich 1* **P** *Bp* **P-in-c** J W ALLAN
LONGDON (St Mary), Castlemorton, Bushley, Queenhill w
  Holdfast *Worc 5* **P** *Bp, D&C Westmr, and Ch Union*
  Trustees (jt) **V** *Vacant* Birtsmorton (0168481) 256
LONGDON-UPON-TERN (St Bartholomew), Rodington,
  Uppington and Wrockwardine *Lich 29* **P** *Lord Barnard,*
  V M E Holt Esq, MMCET, and Bp (jt) **C** G HORNER,
  NSM P M MILLICHAMP
LONGFIELD (Mission Room) (St Mary Magdalene) *Roch 1*
  P *Ld Chan* **R** J R CHALLICE
LONGFLEET (St Mary) *Sarum 8* **P** *MMCET*
  P-in-c A N PERRY
LONGFORD (St Chad), Long Lane, Dalbury and Radbourne
  Derby 14 **P** *Bp, R Church Broughton, and*
  Major J W Chandos-Pole (jt) **R** *Vacant* Kirk Langley
  (01332) 824560
LONGFORD (St Thomas) *Cov 2* **P** *Bp* **V** D I BRUCE
LONGFRAMLINGTON (St Mary the Virgin) w Brinkburn
  Newc 9 **P** *Bp* **V** *Vacant* Longframlington (01665) 570272
LONGHAM (St Andrew and St Peter) Gressenhall w
  Longham w Wendling etc *Nor*
LONGHILL (St Margaret) Sutton St Mich *York*
LONGHIRST (St John the Evangelist) Bothal and Pegswood
  w Longhirst *Newc*
LONGHOPE (All Saints) Huntley and Longhope *Glouc*
LONGHORSLEY (St Helen) and Hebron *Newc 11*
  P *Ld Chan* **V** J DEWAR
LONGHOUGHTON (St Peter and St Paul) w Howick
  Newc 9 **P** *Trustees of the late Duke of Northd and Bp*
  (alt) **V** C SCOTT
LONGLEVENS (Holy Trinity) Wotton St Mary *Glouc*
LONGNEWTON (St Mary) w Elton *Dur 16* **P** *Bp and*
  St Chad's Coll Dur (alt) **NSM** A I TRIMBLE
LONGNEY (St Lawrence) Hardwicke, Quedgeley and
  Elmore w Longney *Glouc*
LONGNOR (St Bartholomew), Quarnford and Sheen *Lich 10*
  P *Bp, V Alstonfield, and Miss A I M Harpur-Crewe (jt)*
  V A C F NICOLL
LONGNOR (St Mary) Dorrington w Leebotwood, Longnor,
  Stapleton etc *Heref*
LONGPARISH (St Nicholas) Barton Stacey and Bullington
  etc *Win*
LONGRIDGE (St Lawrence) (St Paul) *Blackb 14*
  P *Trustees* **V** R W E AWRE, **C** G ROUSE
LONGSDON (St Chad) Horton, Lonsdon and Rushton
  Spencer *Lich*
LONGSIGHT (St John w St Cyprian) *Man 3* **P** *Prime Min*
  and Bp (alt) **P-in-c** C D NEWELL, **C** M K J SMITH
LONGSIGHT (St Luke) *Man 1* **P** *D&C and Trustees (jt)*
  R P N CLARK, **C** V I MORGAN

LONGSLEDDALE (St Mary) Skelsmergh w Selside and
  Longsleddale *Carl*
LONGSOLE (Mission Room) Barming *Roch*
LONGSTOCK (St Mary) Stockbridge and Longstock and
  Leckford *Win*
LONGSTONE, GREAT (St Giles) Ashford w Sheldon and
  Longstone *Derby*
LONGSTOWE (St Mary) Bourn and Kingston w Caxton and
  Longstowe *Ely*
LONGTHORPE (St Botolph) *Pet 13* **P** *Sir Stephen*
  Hastings **V** H C SMART, **NSM** L M ELLIOTT (nee
  JUTSUM)
LONGTON (St Andrew) *Blackb 6* **P** *A F Rawstorne Esq*
  V A PARKINSON, **C** W J ROUTH
LONGTON (St James and St John) *Lich 17* **P** *Bp*
  R P N SUCH
LONGTON (St Mark) Edensor *Lich*
LONGTON (St Mary and St Chad) *Lich 17* **P** *Bp*
  V P LOCKETT
LONGTON, NEW (All Saints) *Blackb 6* **P** *Bp*
  V D M ROGERS
LONGWELL GREEN (All Saints) *Bris 2* **P** *Bp*
  P-in-c P S SHIPP
LONGWOOD (St Mark) *Wakef 5* **P** *V Huddersfield*
  V J A HUNT
LONGWORTH (St Mary) Cherbury *Ox*
LOOE, WEST (St Nicholas) St Martin w E and W Looe
  Truro
LOOSE (All Saints) *Cant 15* **P** *Abp* **V** R C COATES
LOPEN (All Saints) Merriott w Hinton, Dinnington and
  Lopen *B & W*
LOPHAM NORTH (St Nicholas) Bressingham w N and S
  Lopham and Fersfield *Nor*
LOPHAM SOUTH (St Andrew) as above
LOPPINGTON (St Michael and All Angels) w Newtown
  Lich 28 **P** *Bp and R Wem (jt)* **P-in-c** N MacGREGOR,
  NSM K M SOMERVELL
LORD'S HILL Local Ecumenical Project *Win 12* **P** *Bp*
  V J L H PAGE
LORTON (St Cuthbert) and Loweswater w Buttermere
  Carl 6 **P** *Bp and Earl of Lonsdale (alt)*
  V M R BRAITHWAITE
LOSCOE (St Luke) *Derby 12* **P** *Bp* **C** A LOVE
LOSTOCK (St Thomas and St John) *Man 11* **P** *Bp and*
  TR Deane St Mary the Virgin (jt) **V** A J WOODWARD
LOSTOCK GRALAM (St John the Evangelist) *Ches 6*
  P *V Witton* **V** K W DAVEY
LOSTOCK HALL (St James) *Blackb 6* **P** *Bp* **V** S BAXTER
LOSTWITHIEL (St Bartholomew), St Winnow w St Nectan's
  Chapel, St Veep and Boconnoc *Truro 10* **P** *D&C and*
  A D G Fortescue Esq (jt) **R** A E ALLARDICE,
  Hon C F E STUBBINGS
LOTHERSDALE (Christ Church) Carleton and Lothersdale
  Bradf
LOTHERTON (St James) Micklefield w Aberford *York*
LOTTISHAM (The Blessed Virgin Mary) Baltonsborough w
  Butleigh and W Bradley *B & W*
LOUDWATER (St Peter) *Ox 21* **P** *MMCET*
  V T G BUTLIN
LOUGHBOROUGH (All Saints) (Holy Trinity) *Leic 7* **P** *Bp*
  and Em Coll Cam (jt) **R** S A CHERRY,
  NSM G MITCHELL
LOUGHBOROUGH (Emmanuel) *Leic 7* **P** *Em Coll Cam*
  R M N PHILLIPS, **C** P G DAY, N LAYTON,
  NSM R BOOKLESS, R W B ARDILL
LOUGHBOROUGH (Good Shepherd) *Leic 7* **P** *Bp*
  V P H CLAY
LOUGHBOROUGH (St Peter) *Leic 7* **P** *Bp*
  V D PATERSON
LOUGHTON (All Saints) Watling Valley *Ox*
LOUGHTON (not known) Ditton Priors w Neenton,
  Burwarton etc *Heref*
LOUGHTON (St John the Baptist) (St Gabriel) (St Nicholas)
  Chelmsf 26 **P** *Patr Bd* **TR** G K WELCH,
  TV J DELFGOU, **C** M E WINDIATE, **Hon C** O B WELLS,
  NSM F C W MELLOR
LOUGHTON (St Mary the Virgin) *Chelmsf 26* **P** *Bp*
  P-in-c D J BROOMFIELD
LOUGHTON (St Michael and All Angels) *Chelmsf* **P** *Bp*
  P-in-c K G GARRETT
LOUND (St Anne) Babworth w Sutton-cum-Lound *S'well*
LOUND (St John the Baptist) Somerleyton, Ashby, Fritton,
  Herringfleet etc *Nor*
LOUNDSLEY GREEN (Church of the Ascension) Old
  Brampton and Loundsley Green *Derby*
LOUTH (Holy Trinity) (St James) (St Michael) *Linc 12*
  P *Patr Bd* **TR** S D HOLDAWAY, **TV** B A HILL,
  C R L HOWLETT, **NSM** R W MANSFIELD

LOVERSALL (St Katherine) Wadworth w Loversall *Sheff*
LOVINGTON (St Thomas a Becket) Six Pilgrims *B & W*
LOW: *see also under substantive place names*
LOW FELL (St Helen) Gateshead St Helen *Dur*
LOW HILL (Good Shepherd) Bushbury *Lich*
LOW MOOR (Holy Trinity) *Bradf 2* **P** *V Bradf*
 V D F BROWN
LOW MOOR (St Mark) *Bradf 2* **P** *Bp* **P-in-c** S J LORD,
 NSM L B ISIORHO (neeNORTHALL)
LOW VALLEY (St Matthew) Darfield *Sheff*
LOWDHAM (St Mary the Virgin) w Caythorpe, and
 Gunthorpe *S'well 11* **P** *Bp* **V** E ASHBY,
 NSM M A KEENE
LOWER: *see also under substantive place names*
LOWER MANOR (St Andrew) Sheff Manor *Sheff*
LOWER WINDRUSH *Ox 8* **P** *Bp, DBP, St Jo Coll Ox,
 D&C Ex, and B Babington-Smith Esq (jt)*
 Hon C P P SYMES
LOWER WYLYE and Till Valley *Sarum 16* **P** *Earl of
 Pembroke, D&C Windsor, and DBP (by turn)*
 R D K HASTINGS
LOWESBY (All Saints) Whatborough Gp of Par *Leic*
LOWESTOFT (Christ Church) *Nor 9* **P** CPAS
 V P R MOON
LOWESTOFT (Good Shepherd) Lowestoft St Marg *Nor*
LOWESTOFT (St Andrew) *Nor 9* **P** *Ch Patr Tr*
 V P J MEADER
LOWESTOFT (St Margaret) *Nor 9* **P** *Patr Bd*
 TR M C GRAY, **C** L F GANDIYA
LOWESWATER (St Bartholomew) Lorton and Loweswater
 w Buttermere *Carl*
LOWFIELD HEATH (St Michael) Crawley *Chich*
LOWGATE (St Mary) Hexham *Newc*
LOWICK (St John the Baptist) and Kyloe w Ancroft
 Newc 12 **P** *D&C Dur (2 turns), Bp (1 turn)*
 V W P HEWITT
LOWICK (St Luke) Egton-cum-Newland and Lowick *Carl*
LOWICK (St Peter) w Sudborough and Slipton *Pet 10* **P** L G
 Stopford-Sackville Esq and Bp (alt) **P-in-c** R D HOWE
LOWSONFORD (St Luke) Hatton w Haseley, Rowington w
 Lowsonford etc *Cov*
LOWTHER (St Michael) and Askham *Carl 1* **P** *Earl of
 Lonsdale* **R** D J RADCLIFFE
LOWTHORPE (St Martin) Burton Agnes w Harpham and
 Lowthorpe etc *York*
LOWTON (St Luke) *Liv 16* **P** *Bp* **R** *Vacant* Ashton-in-
 Makerfield (01942) 728434
LOWTON (St Mary) *Liv 16* **P** *Bp* **V** R BRITTON,
 C R H D SMITH
LOXBEARE (St Michael and All Angels) Washfield,
 Stoodleigh, Withleigh etc *Ex*
LOXHORE (St Michael and All Angels) Shirwell, Loxhore,
 Kentisbury, Arlington, etc *Ex*
LOXLEY (St Nicholas) Hampton Lucy w Charlecote and
 Loxley *Cov*
LOXTON (St Andrew) Crook Peak *B & W*
LOXWOOD (St John the Baptist) Alfold and Loxwood
 Guildf
LOZELLS (St Paul and St Silas) *Birm 6* **P** *Aston Patr
 Trust* **C** E B WATSON
LUBENHAM (All Saints) Foxton w Gumley and Laughton
 and Lubenham *Leic*
LUCCOMBE (The Blessed Virgin Mary) Selworthy,
 Timberscombe, Wootton Courtenay etc *B & W*
LUCKER (St Hilda) Bamburgh and Lucker *Newc*
LUCKINGTON (St Mary) Sherston Magna, Easton Grey,
 Luckington etc *Bris*
LUDBOROUGH (St Mary) Fotherby *Linc*
LUDDENDEN (St Mary) w Luddenden Foot *Wakef 3* **P** *Bp
 and V Halifax (alt)* **V** M J MORPHY
LUDDESDOWN (St Peter and St Paul) Cobham w
 Luddesdowne and Dode *Roch*
LUDDINGTON (All Saints) Stratford-on-Avon w Bishopton
 Cov
LUDDINGTON (St Margaret) Polebrook and Lutton w
 Hemington and Luddington *Pet*
LUDDINGTON (St Oswald) N Axholme Gp *Linc*
LUDFORD (St Giles) Ludlow, Ludford, Ashford Carbonell
 etc *Heref*
LUDFORD MAGNA (St Mary) Binbrook Gp *Linc*
LUDGERSHALL (St James) Tidworth, Ludgershall and
 Faberstown *Sarum*
LUDGERSHALL (St Mary the Virgin) w Wotton Underwood
 and Ashendon *Ox 24* **P** CPAS *and Bp (jt)* **R** C S JEE
LUDGVAN (St Ludgvan and St Paul) *Truro 5*
 P *Lord St Levan* **R** A PARSONS, NSM H M POOLE
LUDHAM (St Catherine), Potter Heigham and Hickling
 Nor 13 **P** *Bp and Major J M Mills (jt)* **V** W J CAMERON

LUDLOW (St Laurence) (St John), Ludford, Ashford
 Carbonell, Ashford Bowdler, Caynham and Richards Castle
 Heref 12 **P** *Patr Bd* **TR** B L CURNEW,
 TV J V ROBERTS, **C** G EVANS, NSM G H EARNEY
LUFFENHAM, NORTH (St John the Baptist) Edith Weston
 w N Luffenham and Lyndon w Manton *Pet*
LUFFENHAM, SOUTH (St Mary the Virgin) Barrowden
 and Wakerley w S Luffenham *Pet*
LUFTON (St Peter and St Paul) Odcombe, Brympton,
 Lufton and Montacute *B & W*
LUGWARDINE (St Peter) w Bartestree, Weston Beggard and
 Dormington *Heref 4* **P** *D&C (3 turns), and A T Foley Esq
 (1 turn)* **V** D J BOWEN
LULLINGSTONE (St Botolph) Eynsford w Farningham and
 Lullingstone *Roch*
LULLINGTON (All Saints) Beckington w Standerwick,
 Berkley, Rodden etc *B & W*
LULLINGTON (All Saints) *Derby 16* **P** *Bp* **V** W F BATES,
 J H LISTER
LULLINGTON (not known) Alfriston w Lullington,
 Litlington and W Dean *Chich*
LULWORTHS, (St Andrew) (Holy Trinity) Winfrith
 Newburgh and Chaldon, The *Sarum 9* **P** *Bp (3 turns),
 Col Sir Joseph Weld (1 turn)* **P-in-c** W A ROGERS
LUMB (St Michael) Newchurch *Man*
LUMLEY (Christ Church) *Dur 1* **P** *Bp* **V** J R STRINGER
LUND (All Saints) Lockington and Lund and Scorborough
 w Leconfield *York*
LUND (St John the Evangelist) *Blackb 11* **P** *Ch Ch Ox*
 V J K BRIGHAM
LUNDWOOD (St Mary Magdalene) *Wakef 7* **P** *Bp*
 V M GARSIDE
LUNDY ISLAND St Helen Extra Parochial Place *Ex 15*
 P-in-c W G BLAKEY
LUPPITT (St Mary) Dunkeswell, Sheldon and Luppitt *Ex*
LUPSET (St George) *Wakef 12* **P** *Bp* **V** G CLAY,
 C E J CLAY
LUPTON (All Saints) Kirkby Lonsdale *Carl*
LURGASHALL (St Laurence), Lodsworth and Selham
 Chich 11 **P** *Cowdray Trust and Lord Egremont (alt)*
 R D H R CORNISH
LUSBY (St Peter) Marden Hill Gp *Linc*
LUSTLEIGH (St John the Baptist) *Ex 11* **P** *Bp*
 NSM K E JACKSON
LUTON (All Saints) (St Peter) *St Alb 20* **P** *Bp*
 V G S N PRASADAM, **C** J PRASADAM
LUTON (Christ Church) *Roch 5* **P** *R Chatham*
 R C D COLLINS, **C** M R EAREY, S P DAVIE
LUTON Lewsey (St Hugh) *St Alb 20* **P** *Bp*
 V A G FORMAN, **C** D R ELLIOTT
LUTON Limbury (St Augustine of Canterbury) *St Alb 20*
 P *Bp* **V** R I CHEETHAM, Hon C J YABSLEY
LUTON (St Andrew) *St Alb 20* **P** *Bp* **V** R J BASS,
 NSM T SHACKLADY
LUTON (St Anne) *St Alb 20* **P** *Peache Trustees, Bp, and
 V Luton (jt)* **V** P C BUDGELL, Hon C R A BUDGELL
LUTON (St Christopher) Round Green *St Alb 20* **P** *Bp*
 V R B ETHERINGTON, NSM F M G ETHERINGTON
LUTON (St Francis) *St Alb 20* **P** *Peache Trustees, Bp, and
 V Luton (jt)* **V** A T SHARP, **C** J DANIEL
LUTON (St John) Teignmouth, Ideford w Luton, Ashcombe
 etc *Ex*
LUTON (St Mary) *St Alb 20* **P** *Peache Trustees*
 V N P J BELL, **C** D H HAGUE, S M HUDSPITH,
 R M LILLINGTON
LUTON (St Matthew) High Town *St Alb 20* **P** *Ch Patr
 Trust* **V** M J PRITCHARD
LUTON (St Paul) *St Alb 20* **P** *Peache Trustees*
 V A SELLERS, NSM C A PULLINGER
LUTON (St Saviour) *St Alb 20* **P** *Bp*
 NSM D C ANDERSON, P J MOSS
LUTTERWORTH (St Mary) w Cotesbach *Leic 11*
 P *The Crown (3 turns), Ld Chan (1 turn)*
 R M H W COUSSENS, **C** M A HAND
LUTTON (St Nicholas) w Gedney Drove End, Dawsmere
 Linc 16 **P** *The Crown, Ld Chan, and V Long Sutton
 (by turn)* **V** *Vacant* Holbeach (01406) 364199
LUTTON (St Peter) Polebrook and Lutton w Hemington and
 Luddington *Pet*
LUTTONS AMBO (St Mary) Weaverthorpe w Helperthorpe,
 Luttons Ambo etc *York*
LUXBOROUGH (Blessed Virgin Mary) Exton and Winsford
 and Cutcombe w Luxborough *B & W*
LUXULYAN (St Cyrus and St Julietta) Lanlivery w
 Luxulyan *Truro*

LYDBROOK (Holy Jesus) *Glouc 4* **P** *Bp* **V** M J FOSTER

LYDBURY NORTH (St Michael and All Angels) w Hopesay and Edgton *Heref 10* **P** *Earl of Powis (3 turns), Mrs R E Bell (1 turn)* **R** A F DENYER

LYDD (All Saints) *Cant 13* **P** *Abp* **R** *Vacant* Lydd (01679) 20345

LYDDEN (St Mary the Virgin) Temple Ewell w Lydden *Cant*

LYDDINGTON (All Saints) and Wanborough and Bishopstone w Hinton Parva *Bris 11* **P** *Bp and Ld Chan (alt)* **R** R W SANDAY

LYDDINGTON (St Andrew) w Stoke Dry and Seaton *Pet 14* **P** *Bp, Burghley Ho Preservation Trust, and R E M Elborne Esq (by turn)* **NSM** B R H TAYLOR

LYDEARD ST LAWRENCE (St Lawrence) w Brompton Ralph, Combe Florey, Ash Priors and Tolland *B & W 19* **P** *Ld Chan (2 turns), W H J Hancock Esq (2 turns), and MMCET (1 turn)* **R** J C F HAWNT

LYDFORD (St Petrock) and Brent Tor *Ex 25* **P** *Bp (3 turns), Duchy of Cornwall (1 turn)* **P-in-c** J D A HUTCHINGS, **Hon C** R D ORMSBY, D C ORMSBY

LYDFORD ON FOSSE (St Peter) Keinton Mandeville w Lydford-on-Fosse etc *B & W*

LYDGATE (St Anne), w (Christ Church), Friezland *Man 21* **P** *Bp* **V** R I S WHITE, **NSM** E OGDEN

LYDGATE (St Mary) Wickhambrook w Lydgate, Ousden and Cowlinge *St E*

LYDHAM (Holy Trinity) Wentnor w Ratlinghope, Myndtown, Norbury etc *Heref*

LYDIARD MILLICENT (All Saints) The Lydiards *Bris*

LYDIARD TREGOZE (St Mary) as above

LYDIARDS, The *Bris 13* **P** *Patr Bd* **TR** A HETHERINGTON, **TV** P A WALKER, R J BURLES, **C** W H ANDREW, **Hon C** R E WALKER

LYDIATE (St Thomas) *Liv 11* **P** *R Halsall* **V** A A DAVIES

LYDLINCH (St Thomas a Beckett) Stock and Lydlinch *Sarum*

LYDNEY (St Mary the Virgin) *Glouc 4* **P** *Ld Chan* **V** D F F EVANS, **NSM** M D MILLER

LYE, THE (Christchurch) and Stambermill *Worc 12* **P** *Bp and CPAS (alt)* **V** D M WOODHOUSE

LYFORD (St Mary) Cherbury *Ox*

LYME REGIS (St Michael the Archangel) *Sarum 3* **P** *Bp* **V** M J DELL, **Hon C** N TAYLOR

LYMINGE (St Mary and St Ethelburga) w Paddlesworth and Stanford w Postling and Radegund *Cant 5* **P** *Abp* **R** F KENT

LYMINGTON (St Thomas the Apostle) *Win 10* **P** *Bp* **V** M J JOINT, **C** J T McDOWALL

LYMINGTON Woodside (All Saints) Lymington *Win*

LYMINSTER (St Mary Magdalene) *Chich 1* **P** *Eton Coll on nomination of BNC Ox* **V** J E SLEGG

LYMM (St Mary the Virgin) *Ches 4* **P** *Bp* **R** G L DAVIES

LYMPNE (St Stephen) Sellindge w Monks Horton and Stowting etc *Cant*

LYMPSHAM (St Christopher) Brent Knoll, E Brent and Lympsham *B & W*

LYMPSTONE (Nativity of the Blessed Virgin Mary) *Ex 1* **P** *SMF* **P-in-c** J CLAPHAM

LYNCH (St Luke) w Iping Marsh and Milland *Chich 10* **P** *Cowdray Trust and Bp (jt)* **V** M J SMITH

LYNCHMERE Linchmere *Chich*

LYNCOMBE (St Bartholomew) Bath St Bart *B & W*

LYNDHURST (St Michael) and Emery Down *Win 10* **P** *Bp and P J P Green Esq (alt)* **V** P F MURPHY

LYNDON (St Martin) Edith Weston w N Luffenham and Lyndon w Manton *Pet*

LYNEAL (St John the Evangelist) Petton w Cockshutt, Welshampton and Lyneal etc *Lich*

LYNEHAM (St Michael) w Bradenstoke *Sarum 18* **P** *Ld Chan* **V** *Vacant*

LYNEMOUTH (St Aidan) Cresswell and Lynemouth *Newc*

LYNESACK (St John the Evangelist) *Dur 11* **P** *Bp* **V** *Vacant* Bishop Auckland (01388) 718291

LYNG (St Bartholomew) Stoke St Gregory w Burrowbridge and Lyng *B & W*

LYNG (St Margaret), Sparham, Elsing and Bylaugh *Nor 23* **P** *DPB and E C Evans-Lombe Esq* **R** M F C TAYLOR

LYNGFORD (St Peter) Taunton Lyngford *B & W*

LYNMOUTH (St John the Baptist) Lynton, Brendon, Countisbury, Lynmouth etc *Ex*

LYNN, NORTH (St Edmund) King's Lynn St Marg w St Nic *Nor*

LYNN, SOUTH (All Saints) *Nor 21* **P** *Bp* **R** *Vacant* King's Lynn (01553) 771779

LYNN, WEST (St Peter) *Ely 17* **P** *DBP* **P-in-c** A J DAVEY

LYNSTED (St Peter and St Paul) Teynham w Lynsted and Kingsdown *Cant*

LYNTON (St Mary the Virgin), Brendon, Countisbury, Lynmouth, Barbrook, Parracombe and Martinhoe *Ex 18* **P** *DBP* **TR** *Vacant* Lynton (01598) 53251

LYONS (St Michael and All Angels) *Dur 6* **P** *The Crown* **R** R L BURR

LYONSDOWN (Holy Trinity) *St Alb 2* **P** *Ch Patr Trust* **V** G R HUDDLESTON

LYONSHALL (St Michael and All Angels) w Titley, Almeley and Kinnersley *Heref 5* **P** *Bp, D&C, and Ch Patr Trust (jt)* **V** D R LOWE

LYSTON (not known) Pentlow, Foxearth, Liston and Borley *Chelmsf*

LYTCHETT MATRAVERS (St Mary the Virgin) *Sarum 8* **P** *DBP* **P-in-c** P J A HASTINGS

LYTCHETT MINSTER (not known) *Sarum 8* **P** *Bp* **V** E C CARDALE, **C** J LYNAS

LYTHAM (St Cuthbert) *Blackb 11* **P** *DBP* **V** G I HIRST

LYTHAM (St John the Divine) *Blackb 11* **P** *J C Hilton Esq* **V** C J CARLISLE

LYTHE (St Oswald) w Ugthorpe *York 23* **P** *Abp* **V** W SMITH

MABE (St Laudus) *Truro 3* **P** *Bp* **V** *Vacant* Falmouth (01326) 373201

MABLETHORPE (St Mary) w Trusthorpe *Linc 8* **P** *Bp Lon (2 turns), Bp Linc (1 turn)* **P-in-c** S J HOLMES

MACCLESFIELD (St John the Evangelist) *Ches 13* **P** *Bp* **V** R M SALENIUS

MACCLESFIELD (St Paul) *Ches 13* **P** *Bp* **V** S R MARSH

MACCLESFIELD Team Parish, The (All Saints) (Christ Church) (St Michael and All Angels) (St Peter) *Ches 13* **P** *Patr Bd* **TR** J BRIGGS, **TV** J C G STALEY, **C** J S BISHOP, **NSM** J A MYNETT

MACKWORTH (All Saints) *Derby 11* **P** *J M Clark-Maxwell Esq* **P-in-c** K JARDIN, **NSM** E DIXON

MACKWORTH (St Francis) *Derby 9* **P** *Bp* **V** B W G HACKNEY, **C** M J CAIN

MADEHURST (St Mary Magdalene) Slindon, Eartham and Madehurst *Chich*

MADELEY (All Saints) *Lich 14* **P** *J C Crewe Esq* **V** M N GRIFFIN

MADELEY (St Michael) *Heref 14* **P** *Patr Bd* **TR** R L PAMPLIN, **TV** H A SCRIVEN, K F McGARAHAN, **C** K S EVANS

MADINGLEY (St Mary Magdalene) *Ely 5* **P** *Bp* **V** *Vacant*

MADLEY (Nativity of the Blessed Virgin Mary) w Tyberton, Preston-on-Wye and Blakemere *Heref 1* **P** *D&C* **V** T R N JONES, **NSM** R S JONES

MADRESFIELD (St Mary) Newland, Guarlford and Madresfield *Worc*

MADRON (St Maddern) *Truro 5* **P** *Bp* **V** N H TOOGOOD

MAER (St Peter) Chapel Chorlton, Maer and Whitmore *Lich*

MAESBROOK (St John) Kinnerley w Melverley and Knockin w Maesbrook *Lich*

MAESBURY (St John the Baptist) Oswestry *Lich*

MAGDALEN LAVER (St Mary Magdalen) High Laver w Magdalen Laver and Lt Laver etc *Chelmsf*

MAGHAM DOWN (St Mark) Hailsham *Chich*

MAGHULL (St Andrew) (St James) (St Peter) *Liv 11* **P** *Patr Bd* **TR** J M GOODCHILD, **TV** B A MUSK, K DAGGER, **Hon C** W H TULLOCH, **NSM** C R SANDS

MAIDA VALE (St Peter) Paddington St Pet *Lon*

MAIDA VALE (St Saviour) Paddington St Sav *Lon*

MAIDEN BRADLEY (All Saints) Mere w W Knoyle and Maiden Bradley *Sarum*

MAIDEN NEWTON (St Mary) Melbury *Sarum*

MAIDENHEAD (All Saints) Boyne Hill *Ox*

MAIDENHEAD (St Andrew and St Mary Magdalene) *Ox 13* **P** *Peache Trustees* **V** T K PARKIN, **NSM** N W SANDERS, R D MANDERSON

MAIDENHEAD (St Luke) *Ox 13* **P** *Bp* **V** *Vacant* Maidenhead (01628) 22733

MAIDFORD (St Peter and St Paul) Blakesley w Adstone and Maidford etc *Pet*

MAIDS MORETON (St Edmund) N Buckm *Ox*

MAIDSTONE (All Saints) (St Philip) w St Stephen Tovil *Cant 15* **P** *Abp* **V** C J MORGAN-JONES, **C** D W FRITH, I C BLACK

MAIDSTONE Barming Heath (St Andrew) Barming Heath *Cant*

MAIDSTONE (St Faith) *Cant 15* **P** *Abp* **V** I H CROFTS

MAIDSTONE (St Luke the Evangelist) *Cant 15* **P** *Trustees* **C** J F ELDRIDGE

MAIDSTONE (St Martin) *Cant 15* **P** *Abp* **V** P M RAMPTON, **C** R G DAVIS, B A WALLES

MAIDSTONE (St Michael and All Angels) *Cant 15* **P** *Abp* **V** P J GIBBONS

MAIDSTONE (St Paul) *Cant 15* P *Abp* V N H TAYLOR
MAIDWELL (St Mary) w Draughton and Lamport w Faxton
Pet 2 P *Bp (3 turns), Sir Ian Isham (1 turn)*
P-in-c B LEE
MAINSTONE (St John the Baptist) Bishop's Castle w
Mainstone *Heref*
MAISEMORE (St Giles) *Glouc 6* P *Bp*
P-in-c G E PARSONS
MAKER (St Mary and St Julian) w Rame *Truro 11* P *The
Crown and Earl of Mount Edgcumbe (jt)* V R A DOYLE
MALBOROUGH (All Saints) w South Huish, West Alvington
and Churchstow *Ex 14* P *Bp and D&C (jt)*
V D J NEWPORT, Hon C M A FREEMAN (nee ADAMS)
MALDEN (St James) *S'wark 15* P *Bp* V C J DAVIES,
C E H LEE, Hon C A HARDY, NSM M M SLATTERY
MALDEN (St John) *S'wark 15* P *Mert Coll Ox*
V P J KNIGHT
MALDEN, NEW (St John the Divine) and Coombe (Christ
Church) *S'wark 15* P *CPAS* V J S DOWNEY,
C A W EVERETT, N M GENDERS, NSM I R L PRIOR
MALDON (All Saints w St Peter) *Chelmsf 11* P *Bp*
P-in-c P J MASON
MALDON (St Mary) w Mundon *Chelmsf 11*
P *D&C Westmr* R A M A McINTOSH
MALEW Ballasalla (St Mary the Virgin) Malew *S & M*
MALEW (St Mark) (St Moluag or St Lupus) *S & M 1*
P *The Crown* V M ROBERTS, NSM G BARKER
MALIN BRIDGE (St Polycarp) *Sheff 4* P *Bp*
V A WHITELEY
MALINS LEE (St Leonard) Cen Telford *Lich*
MALLERSTANG (St Mary) Kirkby Stephen w Mallerstang
etc *Carl*
MALLING, EAST (St James) *Roch 7* P *D&C* V *Vacant*
West Malling (01732) 843282
MALLING, SOUTH (St Michael) *Chich 18* P *MMCET*
V A T HINDLEY
MALLING, WEST (St Mary) w Offham *Roch 7* P *Ld Chan
and DBP (alt)* V R B STEVENSON
MALMESBURY (St Peter and St Paul) w Westport and
Brokenborough *Bris 12* P *Ch Trust Fund Trust*
V D LITTLEFAIR
MALPAS (St Andrew) Truro St Paul and St Clem *Truro*
MALPAS (St Oswald) and Threapwood *Ches 5* P *DBF*
R T ETHERIDGE
MALTBY (St Bartholomew) (Ascension) (Venerable Bede)
Sheff 5 P *Bp* TR V J FILER, TV I HOLLIN,
C G N RAINEY
MALTON, NEW (St Michael) *York 3* P *Sir Stephen
Hastings* V R ROGERS
MALTON, OLD (St Mary the Virgin) *York 3* P *Sir Stephen
Hastings* V J C MANCHESTER
MALVERN (Holy Trinity) (St James) *Worc 2* P *Bp and
D&C Westmr (jt)* V P C G BILLINGHAM, C C A MOSS
MALVERN (St Andrew) *Worc 2* P *Bp* V *Vacant* Malvern
(016845) 3912
MALVERN, GREAT (Christchurch) *Worc 2* P *Bp*
P-in-c P M J GINEVER, C J D HAYWARD
MALVERN, GREAT (St Mary and St Michael) *Worc 2*
P *Bp* P-in-c J W CHARLEY
MALVERN, LITTLE (St Giles), Malvern Wells and Wyche
Worc 2 P *Bp, V Malvern, and Exors
T M Berington Esq (jt)* P-in-c M H J DUNN,
NSM E G KNOWLES
MALVERN, WEST (St James) Malvern H Trin and St Jas
Worc
MALVERN LINK (Church of the Ascension) (St Matthias) w
Cowleigh *Worc 2* P *Patr Bd* TR G LYALL,
TV R J PRESTON, C A R N WILLIAMS,
NSM J H SADLER, Hon Par Dn R HERBERT
MAMBLE (St John the Baptist) w Bayton, Rock w
Heightington w Far Forest *Worc 4* P *Ld Chan and
R Ribbesford w Bewdley etc (alt)* V R MANN
MAMHEAD (St Thomas the Apostle) Kenton, Mamhead,
Powderham, Cofton and Starcross *Ex*
MANACCAN (St Manaccus and St Dunstan) w St Anthony-in-
Meneage and St Martin-in-Meneage *Truro 4* P *Ld Chan*
V J T McCABE
MANATON (St Winifred) Moretonhampstead, N Bovey and
Manaton *Ex*
MANBY (St Mary) Mid Marsh Gp *Linc*
MANCETTER (St Peter) *Cov 5* P *Ch Patr Trust*
V A S MAIRS
MANCHESTER (Apostles) w Miles Platting *Man 1* P *DBP*
R A DURRANS, C P J CLEMENT
MANCHESTER Clayton (St Cross w St Paul) *Man 1* P *Bp*
R N J PRIOR

MANCHESTER (Good Shepherd) (Church of the
Resurrection) *Man 1* P *Prime Min* P-in-c T S R CHOW,
NSM A-M HUMPHREYS
MANCHESTER (St Ann) *Man 4* P *Bp* R M ARUNDEL
MANCHESTER (St John Chrysostom) Victoria Park *Man 4*
P *Bp* R *Vacant* 0161–224 4152
MANCHESTER Whitworth (not known) *Man 4* P *Bp*
TV A P JOHNSON, TV A J SERVANT, C K S EOKEKE
MANEA (St Nicholas) *Ely 18* P *Bp* P-in-c S TOOKE
MANEY (St Peter) *Birm 9* P *Bp* V J C W ROSE
MANFIELD (All Saints) Barton and Manfield and Cleasby
w Stapleton *Ripon*
MANGOTSFIELD (St James) *Bris 7* P *Peache Trustees*
V K M BOXALL
MANLEY (St John the Evangelist) Alvanley *Ches*
MANNINGFORD BRUCE (St Peter) Swanborough *Sarum*
MANNINGHAM (St Chad) *Bradf 1* P *Keble Coll Ox*
V S R CROWE
MANNINGHAM (St Mary Magdalene and St Michael and All
Angels) (St Paul and St Jude) *Bradf 1* P *Patr Bd*
TR G MOFFAT, TV G J PETERS, B W PIERCE,
NSM L F CRAWLEY
MANNINGS HEATH (Church of the Good
Shepherd) Nuthurst *Chich*
MANOR PARK (St Barnabas) Lt Ilford St Barn *Chelmsf*
MANOR PARK (St John the Baptist) W Slough *Ox*
MANOR PARK (St John the Evangelist) Lt Ilford St Mich
Chelmsf
MANOR PARK (St Mary the Virgin) as above
MANOR PARK (St Michael and All Angels) as above
MANOR PARK (William Temple) Sheff Manor *Sheff*
MANSEL LACY (St Michael) Credenhill w Brinsop, Mansel
Lacey, Yazor etc *Heref*
MANSERGH (St Peter) Kirkby Lonsdale *Carl*
MANSFIELD Oak Tree Lane *S'well 2* P *DBP* V *Vacant*
MANSFIELD (St Augustine) *S'well 2* P *Bp*
V J M BURGESS
MANSFIELD (St John the Evangelist) *S'well 2* P *Bp*
P-in-c A R HOWE, C B HALL
MANSFIELD (St Lawrence) *S'well 2* P *Bp*
P-in-c D J HULL
MANSFIELD (St Mark) *S'well 2* P *Bp* P-in-c M J DOBBS
MANSFIELD (St Peter and St Paul) *S'well 2* P *Bp*
V R T WARBURTON, C R J St C HARLOW-TRIGG
MANSFIELD WOODHOUSE (St Edmund King and Martyr)
S'well 2 P *Bp* V D B STEVEN, C P C WHITEHEAD,
B V WILL
MANSTON (St Catherine) St Laurence in the Isle of Thanet
Cant
MANSTON (St James) *Ripon 8* P *R Barwick in Elmet*
V R W SHAW, C S J HILL, R E HAYES, A J MARRIOTT
(nee REID)
MANSTON (St Nicholas) Childe Okeford, Okeford
Fitzpaine, Manston etc *Sarum*
MANTHORPE (St John the Evangelist) Grantham *Linc*
MANTON (St Hibald) *Linc 6* P *Bp* R D I WALKER
MANTON (St Mary the Virgin) Edith Weston w N
Luffenham and Lyndon w Manton *Pet*
MANUDEN (St Mary the Virgin) w Berden *Chelmsf 22*
P *Patr Bd and Ch Hosp (alt)* P-in-c C BISHOP
MAPERTON (St Peter and St Paul) Camelot Par *B & W*
MAPLEBECK (St Radegund) *S'well 15* P *Sir Stephen
Hastings* V H H WILCOX
MAPLEDURHAM (St Margaret) Caversham and
Mapledurham *Ox*
MAPLEDURWELL (St Mary) Newnham w Nately Scures w
Mapledurwell etc *Win*
MAPLESTEAD, GREAT (St Giles) and LITTLE (St John) w
Gestingthorpe *Chelmsf 15* P *Bp* V *Vacant* Hedingham
(01787) 60294
MAPPERLEY (Holy Trinity) W Hallam and Mapperley
Derby
MAPPLEBOROUGH GREEN (Holy Ascension) Studley
Cov
MAPPLETON (All Saints) Aldbrough, Mappleton w Goxhill
and Withernwick *York*
MAPPLETON (St Mary) Ashbourne w Mapleton *Derby*
MAPPOWDER (St Peter and St Paul) Hazelbury Bryan and
the Hillside Par *Sarum*
MARAZION (All Saints) *Truro 5* P V *St Hilary*
V A K TORRY
MARBURY (St Michael) *Ches 5* P *Bp* V G H SANSOME
MARCH (St John) *Ely 18* P *Bp* R A T SCHOFIELD
MARCH (St Mary) *Ely 18* P *Bp* R D W SPENCER
MARCH (St Peter) *Ely 18* P *Bp* R D W SPENCER
MARCH (St Wendreda) *Ely 18* P *MMCET*
R P BAXANDALL, Hon Par Dn S M BARCLAY

MARCHAM (All Saints) w Garford *Ox 10*   **P** *Ch Ch Ox*
V   D P PRITCHARD,   **NSM** J C COTTERILL
MARCHINGTON (St Peter) w Marchington Woodlands
Lich 20   **P** *V Hanbury w Newborough*
P-in-c A G SADLER,   **C**   R M VIDAL-HALL
MARCHINGTON WOODLANDS (St John) Marchington
w Marchington Woodlands *Lich*
MARCHWOOD (St John) *Win 10*   **P** *Bp*   **R** J D CURTIS
MARCLE, LITTLE (St Michael and All Angels) *Heref 6*
P *Bp*   **P-in-c** C M OLDROYD
MARCLE, MUCH (St Bartholomew) *Heref 6*   **P** *E Money-
Kyrle Esq* **V** *Vacant* Much Marcle (0153184) 643
MARDEN (All Saints) Redhorn *Sarum*
MARDEN (St Hilda) Cullercoats St Geo *Newc*
MARDEN (St Mary the Virgin) w Amberley and Wisteston
Heref 4   **P** *D&C*   **P-in-c** U J SUMMERS
MARDEN (St Michael and All Angels) *Cant 11*   **P** *Abp*
V   J M BOURNE
MARDEN, EAST (St Peter) Compton, the Mardens,
Stoughton and Racton *Chich*
MARDEN, NORTH (St Mary) as above
MARDEN ASH (St James) High Ongar w Norton
Mandeville *Chelmsf*
MARDEN HILL Group, The *Linc 7*   **P** *Bp (2 turns), B Eley
Esq and DBP, Baroness Willoughby, Duchy of Lanc, J Pain
Esq and M Dudley Hewitt Esq, A Lee Esq (1 each)*
R   A M SULLIVAN
MAREHAM-LE-FEN (St Helen) and Revesby *Linc 11*   **P** *Bp
and Mrs A D Lee (alt)*   **R** S JONES-CRABTREE
MAREHAM ON THE HILL (All Saints) *Linc 11*   **P** *Bp*
V *Vacant*
MARESFIELD (St Bartholomew) *Chich 21*   **P** *Ch Trust Fund
Trust*   **R** M T A BULMAN
MARFLEET (St Giles) (St George) (St Hilda) (St Philip)
York 15   **P** *Patr Bd*   **TR** A PATTERSON,
TV S W OSMAN,   J G F GRAHAM-BROWN,
M A DONALDSON
MARGARET MARSH (St Margaret) Shaston *Sarum*
MARGARET RODING (St Margaret) High and Gd Easter
w Margaret Roding *Chelmsf*
MARGARET STREET (All Saints) St Marylebone All SS
Lon
MARGARETTING (St Margaret) Fryerning w Margaretting
Chelmsf
MARGATE (All Saints) *Cant 9*   **P** *Abp*
V   M J A ANDERSON
MARGATE Cliftonville (St Paul) Cliftonville *Cant*
MARGATE (Holy Trinity) *Cant 9*   **P** *Ch Patr Trust*
V   K M THORPE,   **C** T C WILSON,   R J MARSDEN,
NSM   E M SHEARCROFT
MARGATE (St John the Baptist in Thanet) *Cant 9*   **P** *Abp*
C   G T ARNOLD
MARHAM (Holy Trinity) *Ely 16*   **P** *St Jo Coll Cam*
P-in-c   G PARROTT
MARHAMCHURCH (St Marwenne) Bude Haven and
Marhamchurch *Truro*
MARHOLM (St Mary the Virgin) *Pet 13*   **P** *Sir Stephen
Hastings*   **P-in-c** P M HAWKINS
MARIANSLEIGH (St Mary) Bishopsnympton, Rose Ash,
Mariansleigh etc *Ex*
MARISHES, THE (Chapel) Pickering *York*
MARK (Holy Cross) w Allerton *B & W 1*   **P** *Bp and
D&C (jt)*   **R** M T PAVEY
MARK BEECH (Holy Trinity) Hever, Four Elms and Mark
Beech *Roch*
MARK CROSS (St Mark) Rotherfield w Mark Cross *Chich*
MARKBY (St Peter) Hannah cum Hagnaby w Markby *Linc*
**MARKET BOSWORTH (St Peter), Cadeby w Sutton Cheney
and Congerstone** *Leic 13*   **P** *DBP*   **TR** J F PLANT,
TV M M FOWLER
MARKET DEEPING (St Guthlac) *Linc 13*   **P** *Ld Chan*
R S D EARIS
MARKET DRAYTON (St Mary) Drayton in Hales *Lich*
MARKET HARBOROUGH (St Dionysius) *Leic 4*   **P** *Bp*
P-in-c C J E MOODY,   **C** S J BISHOP,   J G GIBBINS
**MARKET HARBOROUGH (Transfiguration) and Little
Bowden** *Leic 4*   **P** *Bp*   **P-in-c** C J E MOODY
**MARKET LAVINGTON (St Mary of the Assumption) and
Easterton** *Sarum 19*   **P** *Bp and Ch Ch Ox (alt)*
V D J GREENMAN
MARKET OVERTON (St Peter and St Paul) Teigh w
Whissendine and Market Overton *Pet*
MARKET RASEN (St Thomas the Apostle) *Linc 5*
P *Ld Chan*   **V** M J CARTWRIGHT,   **NSM** D LINKPIN
MARKET STAINTON (St Michael and All Angels) Asterby
Gp *Linc*

MARKET WEIGHTON (All Saints) *York 7*   **P** *Abp*
V   A CLEMENTS
MARKET WESTON (St Mary) Hopton, Market Weston,
Barningham etc *St E*
MARKFIELD (St Michael) *Leic 12*   **P** *MMCET*
R   G T WILLETT
**MARKHAM, EAST (St John the Baptist) w Askham, Headon
w Upton and Grove** *S'well 5*   **P** *Grove Settled Estate
Trustees and SMF (jt)*   **R** J H LITTLE
MARKHAM CLINTON (All Saints) Tuxford w Weston and
Markham Clinton *S'well*
**MARKINGTON (St Michael) w South Stainley and Bishop
Thornton** *Ripon 3*   **P** *Bp, D&C, Prust Trust and Bn and
N A Hudleston Esq (jt) (by turn)* **V** *Vacant* Ripon (01765)
677282
MARKS GATE (St Mark) Chadwell Heath *Chelmsf 1*   **P** *Bp*
V   R K GAYLER
MARKS TEY (St Andrew) w Aldham and Little Tey
Chelmsf 18   **P** *CPAS, Ch Patr Trust and MMCET (jt)*
R B SNELLING,   **Hon C** S G HUCKLE
MARKSBURY (St Peter) Farmborough, Marksbury and
Stanton Prior *B & W*
MARKYATE STREET (St John the Baptist) *St Alb 14*
P *Bp*   **V** M J CROW,   **C** C E HARDMAN,
NSM P J C McGRANAGHAN
MARLBOROUGH (St Mary the Virgin) *Sarum 20*
P *Patr Bd*   **TR** H G PEARSON,   **TV** J R SARGANT,
C A MANN,   **NSM** P H JOHNS
MARLBROOK (St Luke) Catshill and Dodford *Worc*
MARLDON (St John the Baptist) *Ex 10*   **P** *Bp*
V G L BROCKHOUSE
MARLESFORD (St Andrew) Campsea Ashe w Marlesford,
Parham and Hacheston *St E*
MARLEY HILL (St Cuthbert) *Dur 5*   **P** *The Crown*
V *Vacant* 0191–488 7897
MARLINGFORD (Assumption of the Blessed Virgin
Mary) Easton w Colton and Marlingford *Nor*
**MARLOW, GREAT (All Saints) w Marlow Bottom, Little
Marlow and Bisham** *Ox 29*   **P** *Patr Bd*   **TR** N J MOLONY,
TV A A EAGLES,   S E IRWIN
MARLOW, LITTLE (St John the Baptist) Gt Marlow w
Marlow Bottom, Lt Marlow and Bisham *Ox*
MARLOW BOTTOM (St Mary the Virgin) as above
MARLPIT HILL (St Paulinus) Edenbridge *Roch*
MARLPOOL (All Saints) *Derby 12*   **P** *V Heanor*
V D PERKINS
MARLSTON (St Mary) Bucklebury w Marlston *Ox*
MARNHULL (St Gregory) *Sarum 6*   **P** *DBF*
P-in-c R D G WEYMAN
MAROWN (Old Parish Church) (St Runius) *S & M 3*
P *The Crown*   **V** A M CONVERY
MARPLE (All Saints) *Ches 16*   **P** *R Stockport St Mary*
V M A LOWE,   **C** S J WILSON,   **NSM** B J LOWE
MARPLE, LOW (St Martin) *Ches 16*   **P** *Keble Coll Ox*
V J H CAM
MARR (St Helen) Bilham *Sheff*
MARSDEN (St Bartholomew) *Wakef 5*   **P** *R Almondbury*
V D MATHERS
MARSDEN, GREAT *Blackb 7*   **P** *The Crown*   **V** M J HOY,
C B PARKINSON
MARSDEN, LITTLE (St Paul) *Blackb 7*   **P** *Bp*
V J M HALL,   **C** G J HUMPHRYES
MARSH (St George) Lanc St Mary *Blackb*
MARSH (St James chapel) Huddersfield H Trin *Wakef*
MARSH BALDON (St Peter) Dorchester *Ox*
MARSH FARM (Holy Cross) *St Alb 20*   **P** *Bp*
V J R BELITHER
MARSH GIBBON (St Mary the Virgin) Swan *Ox*
MARSHAM (All Saints) w Burgh-next-Aylsham *Nor 20*
P *Bp, Mercers of the City of Lon, and J M Roberts Esq (jt)*
R R J HEWETSON
MARSHCHAPEL (St Mary the Virgin) North-Chapel
Parishes, The *Linc*
**MARSHFIELD (St Mary the Virgin) w Cold Ashton and
Tormarton w West Littleton** *Bris 7*   **P** *New Coll Ox and Bp
(alt)*   **V** M P WESTLAKE,   **Hon C** J CREIGHTON
MARSHLAND, The *Sheff 11*   **P** *Ld Chan and Bp (alt)*
V *Vacant* Goole (01405) 704643
MARSHLAND ST JAMES (St James) *Ely 17*   **P** *Bp*
P-in-c A R TREEN
MARSHWOOD VALE Team Ministry, The (St Mary)
Sarum 3   **P** *Patr Bd*   **TR** R H FAIRBROTHER,
C D D PAIRMAN
MARSKE (St Edmund) Downholme and Marske *Ripon*
MARSKE, NEW (St Thomas) *York 17*   **P** *Abp*
V R F ROWLING
MARSKE IN CLEVELAND (St Mark) *York 17*
P *Trustees*   **V** D H LAMBERT,   **C** M A PASKETT

MARSTON (St Alban) Stafford *Lich*
MARSTON (St Lawrence) Greatworth and Marston St
    Lawrence etc *Pet*
MARSTON (St Leonard) Stafford *Lich*
MARSTON (St Mary) Barkston and Hough Gp *Linc*
MARSTON (St Nicholas) w Elsfield *Ox 4* **P** *Bp and D&C*
    (jt) **V** A R PRICE
MARSTON, NEW (St Michael and All Angels) *Ox 4* **P** *Bp*
    P-in-c E C MILLER
MARSTON, NORTH (Assumption of the Blessed Virgin
    Mary) Schorne *Ox*
MARSTON, SOUTH (St Mary Magdalene) Stratton St
    Margaret w S Marston etc *Bris*
MARSTON BIGOT (St Leonard) Nunney and Witham
    Friary, Marston Bigot etc *B & W*
MARSTON GREEN (St Leonard) *Birm 11* **P** *Birm Dioc*
    Trustees **V** R V ALLEN, **NSM** D M WHITMORE
MARSTON MAGNA (Blessed Virgin Mary) Chilton
    Cantelo, Ashington, Mudford, Rimpton etc *B & W*
MARSTON MEYSEY (St James) Meysey Hampton w
    Marston Meysey and Castle Eaton *Glouc*
MARSTON MONTGOMERY (St Giles) Alkmonton,
    Cubley, Marston, Montgomery etc *Derby*
MARSTON MORTEYNE (St Mary the Virgin) w Lidlington
    St Alb 19 **P** *Bp and St Jo Coll Cam (alt)*
    R J GREENWAY
MARSTON SICCA (St James the Great) Quinton w Marston
    Sicca *Glouc*
MARSTON TRUSSELL (St Nicholas) Welford w Sibbertoft
    and Marston Trussell *Pet*
MARSTON UPON DOVE (St Mary) w Scropton *Derby 14*
    P *N J M Spurrier Esq* **V** *Vacant* Etwall (01283) 733433
MARSTOW (St Matthew) Walford and Saint John, w
    Bishopswood etc *Heref*
MARSWORTH (All Saints) Cheddington w Mentmore and
    Marsworth *Ox*
MARTHALL (All Saints) *Ches 12* **P** *DBP*
    P-in-c L R THOMAS
MARTHAM (St Mary) and Repps with Bastwick, Thurne and
    Clippesby *Nor 6* **P** *Bp, D&C, DBP and K Edw VI Gr Sch*
    (jt) **V** P S PAINE
MARTIN (All Saints) W Downland *Sarum*
MARTIN (Holy Trinity) Scopwick Gp *Linc*
MARTIN (St Michael) Thornton Gp *Linc*
MARTIN HUSSINGTREE (St Michael) Salwarpe and
    Hindlip w Martin Hussingtree *Worc*
MARTINDALE (Old Church) Barton, Pooley Bridge and
    Martindale *Carl*
MARTINDALE (St Peter) as above
MARTINHOE (St Martin) Lynton, Brendon, Countisbury,
    Lynmouth etc *Ex*
MARTLESHAM (St Mary the Virgin) w Brightwell *St E 2*
    P *Bp* **R** B D LILLISTONE, **C** T P B BREENE
MARTLEY (St Peter) and Wichenford, Knightwick and
    Doddenham, Broadwas and Cotheridge *Worc 3* **P** *D&C*
    (2 turns), Bp (1 turn) **R** W N RICHARDS,
    C A M HOUGH, **NSM** J C GUISE
MARTOCK (All Saints) w Ash *B & W 6* **P** *Bp*
    V T J FARMILOE, **Hon C** V M WRIGHT
MARTON (Room) Sinnington *York*
MARTON (St Esprit) Long Itchington and Marton *Cov*
MARTON (St James) Capesthorne w Siddington and Marton
    Ches
MARTON (St Margaret of Antioch) Lea Gp *Linc*
MARTON (St Mark) *Heref 13* **P** *V Chirbury*
    V P D HARRATT
MARTON (St Mary) Stillington and Marton w Moxby *York*
MARTON (St Paul) *Blackb 9* **P** *V Poulton-le-Fylde*
    V M PICKERING, **C** M A GISBOURNE
MARTON-CUM-GRAFTON (Christ Church) Gt and Lt
    Ouseburn w Marton-cum-Grafton *Ripon*
MARTON-IN-CHIRBURY (St Mark) Marton *Heref*
MARTON-IN-CLEVELAND (St Cuthbert) *York 19* **P** *Abp*
    V G FISHER, **C** N C SINCLAIR
MARTON IN CRAVEN (St Peter) Broughton, Marton and
    Thornton *Bradf*
MARTON MOSS (St Nicholas) *Blackb 9* **P** *Bp* **V** *Vacant*
    Blackpool (01253) 762658
MARTYR WORTHY (St Swithun) Itchen Valley *Win*
MARWOOD (St Michael and All Angels) Heanton
    Punchardon w Marwood *Ex*
MARYFIELD (St Philip and St James) Antony w Sheviock
    Truro
MARYPORT (St Mary) (Christ Church) *Carl 7* **P** *Trustees*
    P-in-c W KELLY, **C** A BUTLER
MARYSTOWE (St Mary the Virgin), Coryton, Stowford,
    Lewtrenchard and Thrushelton *Ex 25* **P** *P T L Newman Esq,*

*   Mrs A M Baring-Gould Almond, Air Cdre P L Donkin, and*
*   R H Wollocombe Esq (by turn)* **V** G W BALL
MARYTAVY (St Mary) *Ex 25* **P** *Guild of All So* **R** *Vacant*
    Mary Tavy (01822) 810516
MASBROUGH (St Paul) *Sheff 6* **P** *Bp and Ld Chan (alt)*
    V M O C JOY
MASHAM (St Mary the Virgin) and Healey *Ripon 3* **P** *Trin*
    Coll Cam **V** B ABELL
MASSINGHAM, GREAT (St Mary) and LITTLE (St
    Andrew) and Harpley *Nor 15* **P** *Bp, J H Brereton Esq, and*
    DBP (jt) **R** H C BRADBURY
MASTIN MOOR (St Paul) Staveley and Barrow Hill *Derby*
MATCHBOROUGH (Christ Church) Ipsley *Worc*
MATCHING (St Mary) High Laver w Magdalen Laver and
    Lt Laver etc *Chelmsf*
MATCHING GREEN (St Edmund) as above
MATFEN (Holy Trinity) Stamfordham w Matfen *Newc*
MATFIELD (St Luke) Lamberhurst and Matfield *Roch*
MATHON (St John the Baptist) Cradley w Mathon and
    Storridge *Heref*
MATLASKE (St Peter) Barningham w Matlaske w
    Baconsthorpe etc *Nor*
MATLOCK (St Giles) (St John the Baptist) *Derby 7* **P** *Bp*
    R P D PETERKEN
MATLOCK BANK (All Saints) *Derby 7* **P** *Bp*
    V J O GOLDSMITH, **NSM** K J ORFORD,
    M L GOLDSMITH
MATLOCK BATH (Holy Trinity) and Cromford *Derby 7*
    P *Ch Trust Fund Trust* **V** J WHEATLEY PRICE,
    NSM C J BAKER
MATSON (St Katherine) *Glouc 5* **P** *D&C* **R** H D BROAD,
    C R C PESTELL, **NSM** A D HAYMAN
MATTERDALE (not known) Greystoke, Matterdale,
    Mungrisdale, etc *Carl*
MATTERSEY (All Saints) Everton and Mattersey w
    Clayworth *S'well*
MATTINGLEY (not known) Heckfield w Mattingley and
    Rotherwick *Win*
MATTISHALL (All Saints) w Mattishall Burgh, Welborne and
    Yaxham *Nor 18* **P** *G&C Coll Cam and Bp (alt)*
    R D PEARSON, **C** I R BENTLEY
MATTISHALL BURGH (St Peter) Mattishall w Mattishall
    Burgh, Welborne etc *Nor*
MAUGHOLD (St Maughold) *S & M 4* **P** *The Crown*
    V D J GREEN, **NSM** E C B CORLETT
MAULDEN (St Mary) *St Alb 15* **P** *Bp* **R** D LEWTHWAITE
MAUNBY (St Michael) Ainderby Steeple w Yafforth and
    Kirby Wiske etc *Ripon*
MAUTBY (St Peter and St Paul) Filby, Thrigby, Mautby,
    Stokesby, Runham etc *Nor*
MAVESYN RIDWARE (St Nicholas) The Ridwares and
    Kings Bromley *Lich*
MAVIS ENDERBY (St Michael) Marden Hill Gp *Linc*
MAWDESLEY (St Peter) *Blackb 4* **P** *R Croston*
    R D J REYNOLDS
MAWGAN (St Mawgan) Cury and Gunwalloe w Mawgan
    Truro
MAWNAN (St Mawnan) (St Michael) *Truro 3* **P** *Bp*
    NSM D WILCOX
MAXEY (St Peter) Etton w Helpston and Maxey *Pet*
MAXSTOKE (St Michael and All Angels) *Birm 11* **P** *Lord*
    Leigh **V** R G BOLLARD
MAYBRIDGE (St Richard) *Chich 5* **P** *Bp*
    V R T E B WOODS, **NSM** K SMITH
MAYBUSH Redbridge (All Saints) Southn Maybush St Pet
    Win
MAYFIELD (Christ Church) *Lon 3* **P** *Bp*
    P-in-c D C L PRIOR, **Hon C** A M ANSELL
MAYFIELD (St Dunstan) *Chich 15* **P** *Keble Coll Ox*
    V G W HOLMES, **NSM** K L McCREADY
MAYFIELD (St John the Baptist) *Lich 20* **P** *Ch Soc Trust*
    P-in-c P E R HALL
MAYFORD (Emmanuel) Woking St Jo *Guildf*
MAYHILL (All Saints) Huntley and Longhope *Glouc*
MAYLAND (St Barnabas) (St Barnabas Family Centre)
    Chelmsf 11 **P** *Lord Fitzwalter and Bp (alt)*
    P-in-c M A COHEN
MEANWOOD (Holy Trinity) *Ripon 7* **P** *Bp*
    V R M WIGGEN
MEARE (Blessed Virgin Mary and All Saints) Glastonbury w
    Meare, W Pennard and Godney *B & W*
MEARS ASHBY (All Saints) and Hardwick and Sywell w
    Overstone *Pet 6* **P** *Duchy of Cornwall (2 turns),*
    Bracegirdle Trustees (1 turn),and Mrs C E Edmiston
    (1 turn) **R** G A FRIEND
MEASHAM (St Lawrence) *Leic 9* **P** *CPAS*
    V J N PEARSON

MEAVY (St Peter) Yelverton, Meavy, Sheepstor and Walkhampton *Ex*

MEDBOURNE (St Giles) Six Saints circa Holt *Leic*

MEDMENHAM (St Peter and St Paul) Hambleden Valley *Ox*

MEDOMSLEY (St Mary Magdalene) *Dur 8* **P** *Bp* **V** *Vacant* Ebchester (01207) 560289

MEDSTEAD (St Andrew) cum Wield *Win 2* **P** *The Crown* **R** T SMITH

MEERBROOK (St Matthew) Leek and Meerbrook *Lich*

MEESDEN (St Mary) Hormead, Wyddial, Anstey, Brent Pelham etc *St Alb*

MEETH (St Michael and All Angels) Hatherleigh, Meeth, Exbourne and Jacobstowe *Ex*

MEIR (Holy Trinity) *Lich 11* **P** *Bp* **P-in-c** G W WHITTY

MEIR HEATH (St Francis of Assisi) *Lich 17* **P** *Bp* **V** J W PAWSON

MEIR PARK (St Clare) Meir Heath *Lich*

MELBECKS (Holy Trinity) Swaledale *Ripon*

MELBOURN (All Saints) *Ely 8* **P** *D&C* **V** J K GREASLEY

MELBOURNE (St Michael) *Derby 15* **P** *Bp* **V** F ROSS, **NSM** W D COOPER

MELBOURNE (St Monica) Seaton Ross Gp of Par *York*

MELBURY (St Mary the Virgin) (St Osmund) *Sarum 1* **P** *Patr Bd* **TR** T R WEST, **TV** J E CURTIS, R N HUNGERFORD, **NSM** N E de CHAZAL

MELBURY ABBAS (St Thomas) Shaston *Sarum*

MELBURY BUBB (St Mary the Virgin) Melbury *Sarum*

MELBURY OSMUND (St Osmund) as above

MELCHBOURNE (St Mary Magdalene) The Stodden Churches *St Alb*

MELCOMBE HORSEY (St Andrew) Milton Abbas, Hilton w Cheselbourne etc *Sarum*

MELDON (St John the Baptist) Bolam w Whalton and Hartburn w Meldon *Newc*

MELDRETH (Holy Trinity) *Ely 8* **P** *D&C* **V** J K GREASLEY

MELKSHAM (St Barnabas) (St Michael and All Angels) *Sarum 17* **P** *DBP* **TR** M B G PAIN, **TV** C E SUGDEN, **NSM** K SUGDEN

MELKSHAM FOREST (St Andrew) Melksham *Sarum*

MELLING (St Thomas) Bickerstaffe and Melling *Liv*

MELLING (St Wilfrid) Tunstall w Melling and Leck *Blackb*

MELLIS (St Mary the Virgin) Thornhams Magna and Parva, Gislingham and Mellis *St E*

MELLOR (St Mary) *Blackb 2* **P** *V Blackb* **V** J P HUDSON

MELLOR (St Thomas) *Derby 6* **P** *Bp* **V** R M PHILLIPS

MELLS (St Andrew) w Buckland Dinham, Elm, Whatley, Vobster and Chantry *B & W 4* **P** *DBP (2 turns), Bp (1 turns)* **R** D OLIVE

MELMERBY (St John the Baptist) Skirwith, Ousby and Melmerby w Kirkland *Carl*

MELPLASH (Christ Church) Beaminster Area *Sarum*

MELSONBY (St James the Great) Forcett and Aldbrough and Melsonby *Ripon*

MELTHAM Christ the King (St Bartholomew) (St James) *Wakef 5* **P** *Almondbury w Farnley Tyas, and Simeon's Trustees (jt)* **V** A R VIGARS, **NSM** P ROLLS

MELTON (St Andrew) *St E 7* **P** *D&C Ely* **R** M SANDERS, **Hon C** H C SANDERS

MELTON, GREAT (All Saints) Hethersett w Canteloff w Lt and Gt Melton *Nor*

MELTON, HIGH (St James) Barnburgh w Melton on the Hill etc *Sheff*

MELTON, LITTLE (All Saints) Hethersett w Canteloff w Lt and Gt Melton *Nor*

MELTON, WEST (St Cuthbert) Brampton Bierlow *Sheff*

MELTON CONSTABLE (St Peter) Briston w Burgh Parva and Melton Constable *Nor*

MELTON MOWBRAY (St Mary) *Leic 3* **P** *Patr Bd* **TR** C A G JENKIN, **TV** A S HUNT, A C DEEGAN, **Hon C** S A BIRCH

MELTON ROSS (Ascension) w New Barnetby *Linc 6* **P** *Earl of Yarborough* **V** *Vacant*

MELVERLEY (St Peter) Kinnerley w Melverley and Knockin w Maesbrook *Lich*

MEMBURY (St John the Baptist) Yarcombe, Membury, Upottery and Cotleigh *Ex*

MENDHAM (All Saints) Fressingfield, Mendham, Metfield, Weybread etc *St E*

MENDLESHAM (St Mary) *St E 6* **P** *SMF* **V** P T GRAY

MENHENIOT (St Lalluwy and St Antoninus) *Truro 12* **P** *Ex Coll Ox* **Hon C** P C BELLENES

MENITH WOOD (Chapel) Teme Valley N *Worc*

MENSTON (St John the Divine) w Woodhead *Bradf 4* **P** *Bp* **V** J S WARD, **C** A G R WILSON

MENTMORE (St Mary the Virgin) Cheddington w Mentmore and Marsworth *Ox*

MEOLE BRACE (Holy Trinity) *Lich 26* **P** *Mrs D M Bather* **V** K T ROBERTS, **C** J H ROBINSON

MEOLS, GREAT (St John the Baptist) *Ches 8* **P** *Bp* **V** K J PRITCHARD

MEOLS, NORTH (St Cuthbert) *Liv 9* **P** *Personal Reps R F Hesketh Esq* **R** B J GERRARD

MEON, EAST (All Saints) *Portsm 5* **P** *Ld Chan* **V** P R WADSWORTH, **C** A D RICHARDS

MEON, WEST (St John the Evangelist) and Warnford *Portsm 5* **P** *Bp and DBP (alt)* **NSM** J R BARNETT, H G PRIDEAUX

MEONSTOKE (St Andrew) w Corhampton cum Exton *Portsm 1* **P** *Bp* **R** D E HENLEY

MEOPHAM (St John the Baptist) w Nurstead *Roch 1* **P** *D&C and Lt-Col F B Edmeades (jt)* **R** D L WILLIAMS

MEPAL (St Mary) Witcham w Mepal *Ely*

MEPPERSHALL (St Mary the Virgin) w Campton and Stondon *St Alb 22* **P** *St Jo Coll Cam (1 turn), Bp (2 turns)* **R** J H BARRALL

MERE (St Michael the Archangel) w West Knoyle and Maiden Bradley *Sarum 14* **P** *Bp* **V** W H V ELLIOTT

MERESIDE (St Wilfrid) Blackpool St Wilfrid *Blackb*

MEREVALE (St Mary the Virgin) Baxterley w Hurley and Wood End and Merevale etc *Birm*

MEREWORTH (St Lawrence) w West Peckham *Roch 7* **P** *Viscount Falmouth and D&C (alt)* **R** R N McCONACHIE

MERIDEN (St Laurence) *Cov 4* **P** *Chapter Cov Cathl* **R** M H DAWKINS

MERRINGTON (St John the Evangelist) *Dur 10* **P** *D&C* **P-in-c** N D BAKER

MERRIOTT (All Saints) w Hinton, Dinnington and Lopen *B & W 15* **P** *D&C Bris (2 turns), Bp (1 turn)* **R** J C KING

MERROW (St John the Evangelist) *Guildf 5* **P** *Earl of Onslow* **R** M D B LEWIS, **C** B J CUNNINGHAM, **NSM** D E C MATTHEWS

MERRY HILL (St Joseph) Penn Fields *Lich*

MERRYMEET (St Mary) Menheniot *Truro*

MERSEA, WEST (St Peter and St Paul) w East (St Edmund) *Chelmsf 17* **P** *Bp and The Crown (alt)* **P-in-c** R H ELPHICK, **NSM** J NEWHAM

MERSHAM (St John the Baptist) w Hinxhill *Cant 12* **P** *Abp* **P-in-c** J W TIPPING

MERSTHAM (St Katharine) (Epiphany) and Gatton *S'wark 25* **P** *Abp* **R** R J M GROSVENOR, **C** C WHEELER (nee MILLAR)

MERSTHAM, SOUTH (All Saints) *S'wark 25* **P** *Bp* **V** E CLAST

MERSTON (St Giles) N Mundham w Hunston and Merston *Chich*

MERTON (All Saints) Shebbear, Buckland Filleigh, Sheepwash etc *Ex*

MERTON (St James) *S'wark 12* **P** *Bp and V Merton St Mary (jt)* **V** I C DAVIES, **C** X SOOSAINAYAGAM

MERTON (St John the Divine) *S'wark 12* **P** *Bp and V Merton St Mary (jt)* **V** K I UPHILL

MERTON (St Mary) *S'wark 12* **P** *Bp* **V** T G LEARY, **NSM** D HAGGIE, M J HANCOCK

MERTON (St Peter) Caston w Griston, Merton, Thompson etc *Nor*

MERTON (St Swithun) Ambrosden w Mert and Piddington *Ox*

MESHAW (St John) Witheridge, Thelbridge, Creacombe, Meshaw etc *Ex*

MESSING (All Saints) Copford w Easthorpe and Messing w Inworth *Chelmsf*

MESSINGHAM (Holy Trinity) *Linc 4* **P** *Bp* **V** *Vacant* Scunthorpe (01724) 762823

MESTY CROFT (St Luke) Wednesbury St Paul Wood Green *Lich*

METFIELD (St John the Baptist) Fressingfield, Mendham, Metfield, Weybread etc *St E*

METHERINGHAM (St Wilfred) w Blankney and Dunston *Linc 18* **P** *Bp (2 turns), Br Field Products Ltd (1 turn)* **V** J H RICHARDSON

METHLEY (St Oswald) w Mickletown *Ripon 8* **P** *Bp (3 turns), Duchy of Lanc (1 turn)* **P-in-c** G R LURIE

METHWOLD (St George) *Ely 15* **P** *Ld Chan* **V** J B ROWSELL

METTINGHAM (All Saints) Wainford *St E*

METTON (St Andrew) Roughton and Felbrigg, Metton, Sustead etc *Nor*

MEVAGISSEY (St Peter) and St Ewe *Truro 1* **P** *Bp and Penrice Ho (St Austell) Ltd* **R** A WAKEFIELD

MEXBOROUGH (St John the Baptist) *Sheff 12* **P** *Adn York* **V** N P HOLMES, **C** D S BAILEY

MEYSEY HAMPTON (St Mary) w Marston Meysey and Castle Eaton *Glouc 13* **P** *Ch Soc Trust* **R** H BUSK

MICHAEL (St Michael and All Angels) *S & M 3* **P** *The Crown* **V** J L EVANS

MICHAELCHURCH ESCLEY (St Michael) Clodock and Longtown w Craswall, Llanveynoe etc *Heref*

MICHAELSTOW (St Michael) St Tudy w St Mabyn and Michaelstow *Truro*

MICHELDEVER (St Mary) and East Stratton, Woodmancote and Popham *Win 13* **P** *Exors Lord Northbrook (3 turns), Bp (2 turns)* **V** B R G FLENLEY

MICHELMERSH (Our Lady) and Timsbury and Farley Chamberlayne and Braishfield *Win 11* **P** *Bp* **R** D B KINGTON

MICKLEFIELD (St Mary the Virgin) w Aberford *York 6* **P** *Abp and Or Coll Ox (jt)* **V** D G MOORE, **P-in-c** D G MOORE

MICKLEGATE (Holy Trinity) and Bishophill Junior (St Mary) *York 8* **P** *D&C* **R** G S HIGGINSON

MICKLEHAM (St Michael) *Guildf 7* **P** *St Jo Foundn Sch* **P-in-c** J P HARKIN

MICKLEHURST (All Saints) *Ches 14* **P** *Bp* **V** D BOOTH

MICKLEOVER (All Saints) *Derby 10* **P** *MMCET* **V** A E HAVARD, **C** M K MADELEY

MICKLEOVER (St John) *Derby 10* **P** *Bp* **V** B M WILSON, **C** M A PRIDDIN

MICKLETON (St Lawrence) *Glouc 11* **P** *Ld Chan* **V** *Vacant* Mickleton (01386) 438279

MICKLEY (St George) *Newc 3* **P** *Bp* **V** J E SYMONS

MICKLEY (St John the Evangelist) Fountains Gp *Ripon*

MID MARSH Group, The *Linc 12* **P** *Rear Admiral G P D Hall, Bp, D&C, and Lord Deramore (by turn)* **R** P G FAULKNER

MIDDLE: *see also under substantive place names*

MIDDLE RASEN Group, The *Linc 5* **P** *Bp and DBP (jt)* **R** *Vacant* Market Rasen (01673) 842249

MIDDLEHAM (St Mary and St Alkelda) w Coverdale and East Witton *Ripon 4* **P** *Bp,* **R** *Craven-Smith-Milnes Esq, and W R Burdon Esq (jt)* **R** D WEYLES

MIDDLESBROUGH (All Saints) *York 19* **P** *Abp* **V** C D E WHEAT, **NSM** D P R MARTIN

MIDDLESBROUGH (Ascension) *York 19* **P** *Abp* **V** D G HODGSON, **C** R N LOCKE

MIDDLESBROUGH (Holy Trinity) N Ormesby *York*

MIDDLESBROUGH (St Agnes) *York 19* **P** *Abp* **P-in-c** J E VAUGHAN-WILSON

MIDDLESBROUGH (St Barnabas) Linthorpe *York*

MIDDLESBROUGH (St Chad) *York 19* **P** *Abp* **V** P F LANGFORD

MIDDLESBROUGH (St Columba w St Paul) *York 19* **P** *Abp* **P-in-c** S COOPER

MIDDLESBROUGH (St Cuthbert) *York 19* **P** *Abp* **P-in-c** M R NELSON, **NSM** S C CHALLENGER

MIDDLESBROUGH (St John the Evangelist) *York 19* **P** *Abp* **V** A CAMPBELL-WILSON

MIDDLESBROUGH (St Martin of Tours) *York 19* **P** *Abp* **V** P H BURMAN, **C** T L JONES

MIDDLESBROUGH (St Oswald) *York 19* **P** *Abp* **V** G J WOOD

MIDDLESBROUGH (St Thomas) *York 19* **P** *Abp* **V** H C HOPKINS

MIDDLESMOOR (St Chad) Upper Nidderdale *Ripon*

MIDDLESTOWN (St Luke) *Wakef 12* **P** *R Thornhill* **V** L J SHUTT

MIDDLETON (All Saints) Gt and Lt Henny w Middleton, Wickham St Paul etc *Chelmsf*

MIDDLETON (Holy Ghost) Kirkby Lonsdale *Carl*

MIDDLETON (Holy Trinity) Bitterley w Middleton, Stoke St Milborough etc *Heref*

MIDDLETON (Holy Trinity) *Heref 13* **P** *V Chirbury* **V** N D MINSHALL

MIDDLETON (Holy Trinity) Kelsale-cum-Carlton, Middleton-cum-Fordley etc *St E*

MIDDLETON (St Andrew) w Newton, Levisham and Lockton *York 21* **P** *Abp* **P-in-c** T A SMITH

MIDDLETON (St Cross) *Ripon 6* **P** *DBP* **V** M S HATTON

MIDDLETON (St George) (St Laurence) *Dur 12* **P** *Bp* **P-in-c** C LINGARD

MIDDLETON (St John the Baptist) *Birm 9* **P** *Bp* **P-in-c** D J LEE

MIDDLETON (St Leonard) (St Margaret) w Thornham St John *Man 18* **P** *Bp* **NSM** F JACKSON

MIDDLETON (St Mary the Virgin) *Ripon 6* **P** *V Rothwell* **V** J N O HORTON, **C** M O'BRIEN

MIDDLETON (St Mary) w East Winch *Nor 21* **P** *Ld Chan and W O Lancaster Esq (alt)* **V** P J BELL

MIDDLETON (St Michael and All Angels) Youlgreave, Middleton, Stanton-in-Peak etc *Derby*

MIDDLETON (St Nicholas) Felpham w Middleton *Chich*

MIDDLETON-BY-WIRKSWORTH (Holy Trinity) Wirksworth *Derby*

MIDDLETON CHENEY (All Saints) w Chacombe *Pet 1* **P** *BNC Ox (2 turns), Bp (1 turn)* **R** A VILLAGE

MIDDLETON-IN-CHIRBY (Holy Trinity) Middleton *Heref*

MIDDLETON-IN-TEESDALE (St Mary the Virgin) w Forest and Frith *Dur 11* **P** *Lord Barnard and The Crown (alt)* **R** G LINDEN

MIDDLETON JUNCTION (St Gabriel) *Man 18* **P** *Bp* **V** I B COOK

MIDDLETON ON LEVEN (St Cuthbert) Rudby in Cleveland w Middleton *York*

MIDDLETON-ON-SEA Conventional District *Chich 1* **C-in-c** P W NEWSAM

MIDDLETON-ON-THE-HILL (St Mary the Virgin) Kimbolton w Hamnish and Middleton-on-the-Hill *Heref*

MIDDLETON-ON-THE-WOLDS (St Andrew) Bainton w N Dalton, Middleton-on-the-Wolds etc *York*

MIDDLETON SCRIVEN (St John the Baptist) Billingsley w Sidbury, Middleton Scriven etc *Heref*

MIDDLETON STONEY (All Saints) Chesterton w Middleton Stoney and Wendlebury *Ox*

MIDDLETON TYAS (St Michael and All Angels) w Croft and Eryholme *Ripon 2* **P** *Prime Min and V Gilling (alt)* **R** *Vacant* Darlington (01325) 377562

MIDDLETOWN (St John the Baptist) Gt Wollaston *Heref*

MIDDLEWICH (St Michael and All Angels) w Byley *Ches 6* **P** *Bp* **V** E W COX

MIDDLEZOY (Holy Cross) and Othery and Moorlinch *B & W 5* **P** *Bp Worc (1 turn), Bp (2 turns)* **P-in-c** G WEYMONT

MIDGHAM (St Matthew) Woolhampton w Midgham and Beenham Valance *Ox*

MIDHOPE (St James) Penistone and Thurlstone *Wakef*

MIDHURST (St Mary Magdalene and St Denis) *Chich 10* **P** *Cowdray Trust* **V** A T CUNNINGTON

MIDSOMER NORTON (St John the Baptist) w Clandown *B & W 12* **P** *Ch Ch Ox* **V** C G CHIPLIN

MIDVILLE (St Peter) Stickney Gp *Linc*

MILBER (St Luke) *Ex 11* **P** *Bp* **V** J F BOARDMAN

MILBORNE PORT (St John the Evangelist) w Goathill *B & W 7* **P** *Mrs J E Smith (2 turns), Trustees (1 turn)* **V** B C B WHITWORTH

MILBORNE ST ANDREW (St Andrew) w Dewlish *Sarum 2* **P** *Rev J L Baillie* **V** *Vacant* Milborne St Andrew (0125887) 227

MILBORNE WICK (Mission Church) Milborne Port w Goathill *B & W*

MILBOURNE (Holy Saviour) Ponteland *Newc*

MILBURN (St Cuthbert) Long Marton w Dufton and w Milburn *Carl*

MILCOMBE (St Laurence) Bloxham w Milcombe and S Newington *Ox*

MILDEN (St Peter) Monks Eleigh w Chelsworth and Brent Eleigh etc *St E*

MILDENHALL (St John the Baptist) Marlborough *Sarum*

MILDENHALL (St Mary) *St E 11* **P** *Patr Bd (2 turns), Bp (1 turn)* **TR** D S MEIKLE, **TV** M G S WHITCOMBE, G S ANDERSON, D GARDNER, W O PANG, **C** N J LACEY, **NSM** P W TAMS

MILDMAY GROVE (St Jude and St Paul) *Lon 6* **P** *Islington Ch Trust* **C** F T PEARSON

MILE CROSS (St Catherine) Horsford and Horsham w Newton St Faith *Nor*

MILE CROSS (St Catherine) *Nor 2* **P** *Dr J P English, Canon G F Bridger, Rev K W Habershon, and Rev H Palmer (jt)* **V** D M SALWAY, **C** R A BETTS

MILE END Old Town (Holy Trinity) Bow H Trin and All Hallows *Lon*

MILE END Old Town (St Paul) Bow Common *Lon*

MILEHAM (St John the Baptist) Litcham w Kempston, E and W Lexham, Mileham etc *Nor*

MILES PLATTING (St Cuthbert) Man Apostles w Miles Platting *Man*

MILFORD (Holy Trinity) Belper Ch Ch and Milford *Derby*

MILFORD (St John the Evangelist) *Guildf 4* **P** *V Witley* **V** R J WELLS

MILFORD, SOUTH (St Mary the Virgin) Monk Fryston and S Milford *York*

MILFORD-ON-SEA (All Saints) *Win 10* **P** *Bp* **V** A M C DUNN, **Hon C** A RIDGE

MILKWALL (St Luke) Coleford w Staunton *Glouc*

MILL END (St Peter) and Heronsgate w West Hyde *St Alb 10* **P** *Bp and V Rickmansworth* **V** A A HORSLEY, **C** W B LISTER, **NSM** J LISTER (nee AISBITT)

MILL HILL (John Keble Church) *Lon 15* **P** *Bp*
  V O R OSMOND, **Hon C** R M HILLS, **NSM** P A JONES
MILL HILL (St Michael and All Angels) *Lon 15* **P** *Bp*
  V D F SHARPE, **NSM** R M HILLS
MILLAND (St Luke) Lynch w Iping Marsh and Milland *Chich*
MILLBROOK (All Saints) St John w Millbrook *Truro*
MILLBROOK (Christ the King) Barton Seagrave w Warkton *Pet*
MILLBROOK (Holy Trinity) *Win 12* **P** *Bp*
  R R N H HOLYHEAD
MILLBROOK Regents Park (St Clement) Millbrook *Win*
MILLBROOK (St James) *Ches 14* **P** *Bp, V Stalybridge St Paul, and Mrs E Bissill (jt)* **P-in-c** P N BROMILEY
MILLBROOK (St Michael and All Angels) Ampthill w Millbrook and Steppingley *St Alb*
MILLERS DALE (St Anne) Tideswell *Derby*
MILLFIELD (St Mark) *Dur 9* **P** *Bp* **V** M J JACKSON
MILLFIELD (St Mary) *Dur 9* **P** *The Crown*
  V B SKELTON
MILLHOUSES (Holy Trinity) *Sheff 2* **P** *Bp*
  V K E JONES, **NSM** I W DRAFFAN
MILLHOUSES (St Oswald) Sheff St Oswald *Sheff*
MILLINGTON (St Margaret) Pocklington and Owsthorpe and Kilnwick Percy etc *York*
MILLOM Holburn Hill (Mission) Millom *Carl*
MILLOM (Holy Trinity) (St George) *Carl 8* **P** *Bp and Trustees (jt)* **V** *Vacant* Cockermouth (01900) 825317
MILNROW (St James) *Man 20* **P** *TR Rochdale*
  V D BOWERS, **NSM** R WHYBORN, A CUNNINGTON
MILNTHORPE (St Thomas) Heversham and Milnthorpe *Carl*
MILSON (St George) Cleobury Mortimer w Hopton Wafers etc *Heref*
MILSTED (St Mary and the Holy Cross) Bredgar w Bicknor and Frinsted w Wormshill etc *Cant*
MILSTON (St Mary) Avon Valley *Sarum*
MILTON (All Saints) *Ely 6* **P** *K Coll Cam*
  R I M COWLEY, **C** D M OSBORN
MILTON (St Blaise) Steventon w Milton *Ox*
MILTON (St James) (St Andrew's Church Centre) (St Patrick) *Portsm 6* **P** *V Portsea St Mary* **V** *Vacant* Portsmouth (01705) 732786
MILTON (St John the Evangelist) Adderbury w Milton *Ox*
MILTON (St Mary Magdalene) *Win 8* **P** *V Milford*
  R A H BAILEY, **C** J HEARN, C J MURRAY
MILTON (St Peter) w St Jude *B & W 11* **P** *Ld Chan*
  V J N O WILLIAMS
MILTON (St Philip and St James) *Lich 13* **P** *Bp*
  V D M B WILMOT
MILTON (St Simon and St Jude) Gillingham *Sarum*
MILTON, GREAT (St Mary the Virgin) w LITTLE (St James) and Great Haseley *Ox 1* **P** *Bp and D&C Windsor (jt)* **R** N A BRYAN
MILTON, SOUTH (All Saints) Thurlestone w S Milton *Ex*
MILTON ABBAS (St James the Great), Hilton w Cheselbourne and Melcombe Horsey *Sarum 7* **P** *Bp (3 turns) and G A L F Pitt-Rivers Esq (1 turn)*
  R R S FERGUSON
MILTON ABBOT (St Constantine), Dunterton, Lamerton and Sydenham Demerel *Ex 25* **P** *Bp, J W Tremayne Esq, and Bedf Estates (jt)* **V** G J STANTON
MILTON BRYAN (St Peter) Woburn w Eversholt, Milton Bryan, Battlesden etc *St Alb*
MILTON CLEVEDON (St James) Evercreech w Chesterblade and Milton Clevedon *B & W*
MILTON COMBE (Holy Spirit) Buckland Monachorum *Ex*
MILTON DAMEREL (Holy Trinity) Holsworthy w Hollacombe and Milton Damerel *Ex*
MILTON ERNEST (All Saints) *St Alb 21* **P** *Bp*
  V C W GONIN
MILTON KEYNES (Christ the Cornerstone) *Ox 25* **P** *Bp*
  V D GOLDIE, **Chapl** M J BURNS, **NSM** W M CAREY
MILTON KEYNES VILLAGE (All Saints) Walton Milton Keynes *Ox*
MILTON LILBOURNE (St Peter) Pewsey TM *Sarum*
MILTON MALSOR (Holy Cross) Collingtree w Courteenhall and Milton Malsor *Pet*
MILTON NEXT GRAVESEND (Christ Church) *Roch 4* **P** *Bp* **V** J S KING, **Hon C** A P WIBROE, **NSM** D HITCHCOCK
MILTON NEXT GRAVESEND (St Peter and St Paul) Denton *Roch 4* **P** *Bp* **R** V J LAWRENCE
MILTON NEXT SITTINGBOURNE (Holy Trinity) *Cant 14* **P** *D&C* **V** W DRURY
MILTON REGIS (St Mary) Sittingbourne St Mary *Cant*

MILTON-UNDER-WYCHWOOD (St Simon and St Jude) Shipton-under-Wychwood w Milton-under-Wychwood *Ox*
MILVERTON (St Michael) w Halse and Fitzhead *B & W 19* **P** *Adn Taunton (4 turns), Bp and V Wiveliscombe (1 turn)* **R** A D NORRIS, **NSM** A NORRIS
MILVERTON, NEW (St Mark) *Cov 11* **P** *CPAS*
  V A MORT, **C** M RODHAM
MILVERTON, OLD (St James) Leamington Spa and Old Milverton *Cov*
MILWICH (All Saints) Fradswell, Gayton, Milwich and Weston *Lich*
MIMMS, NORTH N Mymms *St Alb*
MIMMS, SOUTH (Christ Church) *Lon 14* **P** *Ch Patr Trust* **V** M H McGOWAN, **C** I M CHAPMAN, **NSM** P W LIDDELOW
MINCHINHAMPTON (Holy Trinity) *Glouc 8* **P** *Bp*
  R D S YERBURGH, **Hon C** G P KNOTT, **NSM** P GRAHAM
MINEHEAD (St Andrew) (St Michael) (St Peter) *B & W 16* **P** *Lt-Col G W F Luttrell and Bp (jt)* **V** G J WRAYFORD, **C** D C IRESON
MINETY (St Leonard) Ashton Keynes, Leigh and Minety *Bris*
MININGSBY WITH EAST KIRKBY (St Nicholas) Marden Hill Gp *Linc*
MINLEY (St Andrew) *Guildf 1* **P** *Bp* **V** I M HANCOCK
MINNIS BAY (St Thomas) Birchington w Acol and Minnis Bay *Cant*
MINSKIP (Mission Room) Aldborough w Boroughbridge and Roecliffe *Ripon*
MINSTEAD (All Saints) Copythorne and Minstead *Win*
MINSTER (St Mary the Virgin) w Monkton *Cant 9* **P** *Abp* **V** *Vacant* Thanet (01843) 821250
MINSTER (St Merteriana) Boscastle w Davidstow *Truro*
MINSTER IN SHEPPEY (St Mary and St Sexburga) *Cant 14* **P** *Ch Patr Trust* **V** G H SPENCER, **C** E B DAVIES, **NSM** J G KNELL
MINSTER LOVELL (St Kenelm) and Brize Norton *Ox 8* **P** *Eton Coll and Ch Ch Ox (jt)* **V** A W D GABB-JONES
MINSTERLEY (Holy Trinity) *Heref 13* **P** *DBP and Bp (alt)* **P-in-c** W K ROWELL
MINSTERWORTH (St Peter) Churcham w Bulley and Minsterworth *Glouc*
MINTERNE MAGNA (St Andrew) Cerne Abbas w Godmanstone and Minterne Magna *Sarum*
MINTING (St Andrew) Bardney *Linc*
MIREHOUSE (St Andrew) *Carl 5* **P** *Bp* **V** M BARBER
MIRFIELD (St Mary) *Wakef 10* **P** *Bp* **V** M SQUIRES, **C** A I G SNOWDEN
MISERDEN (St Andrew) Bisley, Oakridge, Miserden and Edgeworth *Glouc*
MISSENDEN, GREAT (St Peter and St Paul) w Ballinger and Little Hampden *Ox 28* **P** *Bp* **V** D RYDINGS, **NSM** D M DERRICK
MISSENDEN, LITTLE (St John the Baptist) *Ox 28* **P** *Earl Howe* **V** D R HEMSLEY
MISSION (St John the Baptist) Bawtry w Austerfield and Misson *S'well*
MISTERTON (All Saints) and West Stockwith *S'well 1* **P** *D&C York and Bp (alt)* **V** M F B HARDY
MISTERTON (St Leonard) Haselbury Plucknett, Misterton and N Perrott *B & W*
MISTERTON (St Leonard) N w S Kilworth and Misterton *Leic*
MISTLEY (St Mary and St Michael) w Manningtree and Bradfield *Chelmsf 21* **P** *DBP and Bp (jt)* **R** P E PARKER
MITCHAM (Ascension) Pollards Hill *S'wark 12* **P** *Bp* **V** N J WORN
MITCHAM (Christ Church) *S'wark 12* **P** *Bp* **P-in-c** M J BULL
MITCHAM (St Barnabas) *S'wark 12* **P** *Bp* **V** A D KIRKWOOD
MITCHAM (St Mark) *S'wark 12* **P** *Bp* **V** A B RAMSAY
MITCHAM (St Olave) *S'wark 12* **P** *The Crown* **V** P G ENSOR
MITCHAM (St Peter and St Paul) *S'wark 12* **P** *Keble Coll Ox* **V** J M SHEPHERD, **C** S CARLSSON
MITCHELDEAN (St Michael and All Angels) Abenhall w Mitcheldean *Glouc*
MITFORD (St Mary Magdalene) *Newc 11* **P** *Brig E C Mitford* **V** D F MAYHEW
MITHIAN (St Peter) w Mount Hawke *Truro 6* **P** *Bp* **V** *Vacant* Porthtowan (01209) 890926
MITTON (All Hallows) Hurst Green and Mitton *Bradf*
MIXBURY (All Saints) Finmere w Mixbury, Cottisford, Hardwick etc *Ox*

MIXENDEN (Holy Nativity) *Wakef 4* **P** *Bp*
V R J BRADNUM
MOBBERLEY (St Wilfrid) *Ches 12* **P** *Bp* **R** M GRAHAM
MOCCAS (St Michael and All Angels) Cusop w Clifford,
Hardwicke, Bredwardine etc *Heref*
MODBURY (St George) *Ex 14* **P** *DBP* **V** J S COLE
MODDERSHALL (All Saints) Stone Ch Ch and Oulton *Lich*
MOGGERHANGER (St John the Evangelist) Northill w
Moggerhanger *St Alb*
MOIRA (St Hilda) Donisthorpe and Moira w Stretton-en-le-
Field *Leic*
MOLASH (St Peter) Chilham w Challock and Molash *Cant*
MOLDGREEN (Christ Church) *Wakef 1* **P** *R Kirkheaton*
V J HARRIS, **C** A J HUDSON
MOLESCROFT (St Leonard) Beverley Minster *York*
MOLESEY, EAST (St Mary) *Guildf 8* **P** *Bp*
P-in-c D J ADAMS
MOLESEY, EAST (St Paul) *Guildf 8* **P** *Bp*
P-in-c R L COTTON, **C** S J DAVIES
MOLESEY, WEST (St Peter) *Guildf 8* **P** *Rev W K Perry-
Gore* **V** W A J YEEND
MOLESWORTH (St Peter) Brington w Molesworth and Old
Weston *Ely*
MOLLAND (St Mary) Bishopsnympton, Rose Ash,
Mariansleigh etc *Ex*
MOLLINGTON (All Saints) Claydon w Mollington *Ox*
MOLTON, NORTH (All Saints) S Molton w Nymet St
George, High Bray etc *Ex*
MOLTON, SOUTH (St Mary Magdalene) w Nymet
St George, High Bray, Charles, Filleigh, East Buckland,
Warkleigh, Satterleigh, Chittlehamholt, Kingsnympton,
Romansleigh, North Molton, Twitchen and Chittlehampton
Ex 19 **P** *DBP* **TR** M J HOMEWOOD, **TV** G COWDRY,
S P GIRLING, J H BELL, **C** P STEPHENS
MONEWDEN (St Mary) Charsfield w Debach, Monewden,
Hoo etc *St E*
MONGEHAM, GREAT (St Martin) w Ripple and Sutton by
Dover *Cant 8* **P** *Abp* **R** A C STRATTA
MONK BRETTON (St Paul) *Wakef 7* **P** *V Royston*
V *Vacant* Barnsley (01226) 205338
MONK FRYSTON (St Wilfrid of Ripon) and South Milford
York 6 **P** *Ld Chan and Abp (alt)* **R** D G RICHARDSON
MONK SHERBORNE (All Saints) The Sherbornes w
Pamber *Win*
MONK SOHAM (St Peter) Worlingworth, Southolt,
Tannington, Bedfield etc *St E*
MONKEN HADLEY (St Mary the Virgin) *Lon 14*
P *N A Dove Esq* **R** J A M JENKINS
MONKHESLEDEN (St Mary w St John) Castle Eden w
Monkhesleden *Dur*
MONKHOPTON (St Peter) Upton Cressett w Monk Hopton
Heref
MONKLAND (All Saints) Leominster *Heref*
MONKLEIGH (St George) Landcross, Littleham, Monkleigh
etc *Ex*
MONKOKEHAMPTON (All Saints) *Ex 20* **P** *Bp* **R** *Vacant*
MONKS COPPENHALL (Christ Church) Crewe Ch Ch and
St Pet *Ches*
MONKS ELEIGH (St Peter) w Chelsworth and Brent Eleigh w
Milden *St E 10* **P** *Ld Chan (2 turns), M J Hawkins Esq
(1 turn), and Bp (1 turn)* **R** R A BIRD
MONKS HORTON (St Peter) Sellindge w Monks Horton
and Stowting etc *Cant*
MONKS KIRBY (St Editha) w Pailton and Stretton-under-
Fosse *Cov 6* **P** *Trin Coll Cam* **V** P S RUSSELL
MONKS RISBOROUGH (St Dunstan) *Ox 26* **P** *Bp*
P-in-c A F MEYNELL, **NSM** A A TAYLOR
MONKSEATON (St Mary) *Newc 8* **P** *Bp*
V J L HALLATT, **C** E R BURFITT, **Hon C** C G BELLAMY
MONKSEATON (St Peter) *Newc 8* **P** *Bp* **V** P J DUNLOP,
C P M BARON
MONKSILVER (All Saints) Stogumber w Nettlecombe and
Monksilver *B & W*
MONKTON (St Mary Magdalene) Minster w Monkton *Cant*
MONKTON (St Mary Magdalene) Honiton, Gittisham,
Combe Raleigh, Monkton etc *Ex*
MONKTON, WEST (St Augustine) *B & W 18* **P** *Bp*
R R SCHOFIELD
MONKTON COMBE (St Michael) Combe Down w
Monkton Combe and S Stoke *B & W*
**MONKTON FARLEIGH (St Peter), South Wraxall and
Winsley** *Sarum 17* **P** *D&C Bris (2 turns), Bp (1 turn)*
R D G SMITH, **NSM** M A CLARK
MONKTON WYLD (St Andrew) Marshwood Vale TM
Sarum
MONKWEARMOUTH (All Saints) *Dur 9* **P** *Bp* **V** *Vacant*
0191–565 6606

MONKWEARMOUTH (St Andrew) *Dur 9* **P** *Bp*
V M L BECK, **C** M WORTHINGTON, G M BECK
MONKWEARMOUTH (St Peter) *Dur 9* **P** *Bp*
P-in-c E G LLOYD
MONKWOOD (Mission Church) Bishop's Sutton and
Ropley and W Tisted *Win*
MONNINGTON-ON-WYE (St Mary) Letton w Staunton,
Byford, Mansel Gamage etc *Heref*
MONTACUTE (St Catherine of Alexandria) Odcombe,
Brympton, Lufton and Montacute *B & W*
MONTFORD (St Chad) Bicton, Montford w Shrawardine
and Fitz *Lich*
MONTON (St Paul) *Man 2* **P** *TR Eccles*
V V H MARKLAND
MONXTON (St Mary) Amport, Grateley, Monxton and
Quarley *Win*
MONYASH (St Leonard) Taddington, Chelmorton and
Flagg, and Monyash *Derby*
MOOR (St Thomas) Fladbury, Wyre Piddle and Moor *Worc*
MOOR ALLERTON (St John the Evangelist) (St Stephen)
Ripon 5 **P** *Patr Bd* **TR** J D W KING, **TV** P JACKSON,
C L C PEARSON
MOOR GRANGE (St Andrew) Hawksworth Wood *Ripon*
MOOR MILNER (Church Institute) Daresbury *Ches*
MOOR MONKTON (All Saints) Rufforth w Moor Monkton
and Hessay *York*
MOORBRIDGE LANE (St Luke) Stapleford *S'well*
MOORCOURT (St Mary) Pembridge w Moorcourt,
Shobdon, Staunton etc *Heref*
MOORDOWN (St John the Baptist) *Win 7* **P** *Bp*
V W A SWAIN
MOORENDS (St Wilfrith) *Sheff 11* **P** *Bp*
V K C NORTHOVER
MOORHOUSE (Chantry Chapel) Kneesall w Laxton and
Wellow *S'well*
MOORHOUSES (St Lawrence) Mareham-le-Fen and
Revesby *Linc*
MOORLAND Widecombe-in-the-Moor, Leusdon,
Princetown etc *Ex*
MOORLINCH (Blessed Virgin Mary) Middlezoy and Othery
and Moorlinch *B & W*
MOORSHOLM (St Mary) Boosbeck w Moorsholm *York*
MORBORNE (All Saints) Stilton w Denton and Caldecote
etc *Ely*
MORCHARD BISHOP (St Mary) N Creedy *Ex*
MORCOTT (St Mary the Virgin) w Glaston and Bisbrooke
Pet 14 **P** *Coutts & Co and Peterho Cam (alt)* **R** *Vacant*
Uppingham (01572) 822373
**MORDEN (Emmanuel Church Hall) (St George) (St Lawrence)
(St Martin)** *S'wark 12* **P** *Patr Bd* **TR** R F SKINNER,
TV C A WOOD, W MUNCEY, **C** J E G DASH
MORDEN (St Mary) Red Post *Sarum*
MORDIFORD (Holy Rood) Fownhope w Mordiford,
Brockhampton etc *Heref*
MORE (St Peter) Wentnor w Ratlinghope, Myndtown,
Norbury etc *Heref*
MOREBATH (St George) Bampton, Morebath, Clayhanger
and Petton *Ex*
MORECAMBE (St Barnabas) *Blackb 12* **P** *R Poulton-le-
Sands* **V** N L CUTTS
MORECAMBE (St Christopher) Bare *Blackb*
MORELEIGH (All Saints) Halwell w Moreleigh *Ex*
MORESBY (St Bridget) *Carl 5* **P** *Earl of Lonsdale*
R G D A THORBURN
MORESBY PARKS (Mission Church) Moresby *Carl*
MORESTEAD (not known) Twyford and Owslebury and
Morestead *Win*
MORETON (Christ Church) *Ches 8* **P** *Simeon's Trustees*
R R A WALTON, **C** E W McLEOD, A M TUCKER
MORETON (St Mary) Fyfield, Moreton w Bobbingworth
and Willingale etc *Chelmsf*
MORETON (St Mary) Bradeley, Church Eaton and Moreton
Lich
MORETON (St Nicholas) and Woodsford w Tincleton
Sarum 2 **P** *Hon Mrs M A Bartenk and Miss
M B F Frampton (alt)* **R** P D STEVENS
**MORETON, SOUTH (St John the Baptist) w NORTH (All
Saints), Aston Tirrold and Aston Upthorpe** *Ox 18*
P *Adn Berks, Hertf Coll Ox, and Magd Coll Ox (jt)*
R A F OTTER
MORETON CORBET (St Bartholomew) *Lich 28* **P** *Sir John
Corbet, Bt* **R** J E DAIMOND
MORETON HALL (Christ Church) Bury St Edmunds Ch
Ch *St E*
**MORETON-IN-MARSH (St David) w Batsford, Todenham
and Lower Lemington** *Glouc 15* **P** *Bp and Lord
Dulverton (jt)* **R** *Vacant* Moreton-in-Marsh (01608) 50389

MORETON JEFFRIES (St Peter and St Paul) Stoke Lacy, Moreton Jeffries w Much Cowarne etc *Heref*

MORETON MORRELL (Holy Cross) Newbold Pacey w Moreton Morrell *Cov*

MORETON-ON-LUGG (St Andrew) Wellington w Pipe-cum-Lyde and Moreton-on-Lugg *Heref*

MORETON PINKNEY (St Mary the Virgin) Weedon Lois w Plumpton and Moreton Pinkney etc *Pet*

MORETON SAY (St Margaret of Antioch) *Lich* 23
P *A E H Heber-Percy Esq* **P-in-c** G D PRICE,
C P J KNIGHT

MORETON VALENCE (St Stephen) Standish w Haresfield and Moreton Valence etc *Glouc*

MORETONHAMPSTEAD (St Andrew), North Bovey and Manaton *Ex* 11 **P** *Bp (3 turns), DBP (1 turn)*
P-in-c A R LEIGH

MORGAN'S VALE (St Birinus) Redlynch and Morgan's Vale *Sarum*

MORLAND (St Lawrence), Thrimby and Great Strickland
Carl 1 **P** *D&C* **P-in-c** K J COVE

MORLEY (St Botolph) High Oak *Nor*

MORLEY (St Matthew) *Derby 12* **P** *Bp*
P-in-c M A ROYLE

MORLEY (St Paul) Townend *Wakef 8* **P** *V Batley and V Morley St Peter (alt)* **V** I D JOHNSTONE

MORLEY (St Peter) High Oak *Nor*

MORLEY (St Peter) w Churwell *Wakef 8* **P** *Bp*
V, M G WHITTOCK, **C** J S ROBERTSHAW

MORNINGTHORPE (St John the Baptist) Hempnall *Nor*

MORPETH (St Aidan) (St James) (St Mary the Virgin)
Newc 11 **P** *Bp* **R** A S CRAIG, **C** G SOUTH, M L EVANS

MORSTON (All Saints) Stiffkey and Cockthorpe w Morston, Langham etc *Nor*

MORTEHOE (St Mary Magdalene) Ilfracombe, Lee, Woolacombe, Bittadon etc *Ex*

MORTIMER COMMON (St John) Stratfield Mortimer *Ox*

MORTIMER WEST END (St Saviour) w Padworth *Ox 12*
P *Englefield Estate Trust and Ld Chan (alt)*
P-in-c J A ELLIS

MORTLAKE (St Mary) w East Sheen *S'wark 16* **P** *Patr Bd*
TR B A SAUNDERS, **TV** J C ANSELL,
J P KENNINGTON, **C** D M J BARRINGTON,
Hon **C** P D KING

MORTOMLEY (St Saviour), High Green *Sheff 7* **P** *Bp*
V D G RHODES, **C** N A DAWSON, A MURRAY

MORTON (Holy Cross) and Stonebroom *Derby 1* **P** *Bp*
(2 turns), St Jo Coll Cam (1 turn) **R** I N PALLETT

MORTON (St Denis) Rolleston w Fiskerton, Morton and Upton *S'well*

MORTON (St John the Baptist) w Hacconby *Linc 13* **P** *Bp*
V *Vacant* Morton (01778) 570660

MORTON (St Luke) *Bradf 8* **P** *Bp* **V** A M E BROWN

MORTON (St Paul) *Linc 2* **P** *Bp* **V** B M DODDS

MORTON (St Philip and St James) *Lich 24* **P** *Ld Chan*
V T VILLIERS

MORTON BAGOT (Holy Trinity) Spernall, Morton Bagot and Oldberrow *Cov*

MORVAH (St Bridget of Sweden) Pendeen w Morvah *Truro*

MORVAL (St Wenna) Liskeard, St Keyne, St Pinnock, Morval etc *Truro*

MORVILLE (St Gregory) w Aston Eyre *Heref 9* **P** *DBP*
Hon **C** H J PATTERSON

MORWENSTOW (St John the Baptist) Kilkhampton w Morwenstow *Truro*

MOSBOROUGH (St Mark) *Sheff 1* **P** *Bp*
V R F BLACKBURN, **C** A J COOPER

MOSELEY (St Agnes) *Birm 8* **P** *V Moseley St Mary*
V D J NEW

MOSELEY (St Anne) *Birm 8* **P** *V Moseley St Mary*
V A T W REYNOLDS

MOSELEY (St Mary) *Birm 8* **P** *Bp* **V** H J OSBORNE,
C D L STAMPS, Hon **C** J G HASLAM, **NSM** J A GRIFFIN

MOSLEY COMMON (St John) *Man 13* **P** *Bp*
V A J LINDOP

MOSS BANK (Mission Church) Carr Mill *Liv*

MOSS SIDE (Christ Church) *Man 4* **P** *Trustees* **R** *Vacant*
0161–226 2476

MOSS SIDE (St James w St Clement) *Man 4* **P** *Bp*
R G A WHEALE, Hon **C** D M SEBER

MOSSER (St Philip) (Michael's Chapel) *Carl 6* **P** *Bp*
V C GODDARD

MOSSLEY (Holy Trinity) *Ches 11* **P** *R Astbury*
V S WATERS

MOSSLEY (St George) *Man 17* **P** *R Ashton-under-Lyne St Mich* **V** R J LINDSAY

MOSSLEY ESTATE (St Thomas Church) Bloxwich *Lich*

MOSSLEY HILL (St Barnabas) *Liv 4* **P** *Bp*
V K A ROWLANDS

MOSSLEY HILL (St Matthew and St James) *Liv 4*
P *Trustees* **V** D E WILLS, **C** A P J GALBRAITH

MOSSWOOD (St Barnabas) Cannock *Lich*

MOSTERTON (St Mary) Beaminster Area *Sarum*

MOSTON (St Chad) *Man 5* **P** *Bp* **R** G O'NEILL

MOSTON (St John) Ashley Lane *Man 5* **P** *Bp*
R C S FORD

MOSTON (St Luke) Lightbowne *Man*

MOSTON (St Mary) *Man 5* **P** *D&C* **R** D J LOW

MOTCOMBE (St Mary) Shaston *Sarum*

MOTSPUR PARK (Holy Cross) *S'wark 12* **P** *Bp*
V D G MIHILL

MOTTINGHAM (St Andrew) (St Alban Mission Church)
S'wark 1 **P** *Bp* **C** Y V CLARKE, **NSM** D WARREN

MOTTINGHAM (St Edward the Confessor) *S'wark 1* **P** *Bp*
P-in-c N J CALVER

MOTTISFONT (St Andrew) Broughton, Bossington, Houghton and Mottisfont *Win*

MOTTISTONE (St Peter and St Paul) Brighstone and Brooke w Mottistone *Portsm*

MOTTRAM IN LONGDENDALE (St Michael) *Ches 14*
P *Bp* **V** A J REES, **NSM** R L HILLS

MOULSECOOMB (St Andrew) *Chich 2* **P** *Bp*
TR C R LANSDALE, **TV** P R SEAMAN, D J BIGGS,
C C R LAWLOR

MOULSFORD (St John the Baptist) Streatley w Moulsford *Ox*

MOULSHAM (St John the Evangelist) *Chelmsf 9*
P *Provost* **V** J C HASSELL, **C** E SMITH

MOULSHAM (St Luke) *Chelmsf 9* **P** *Bp* **V** R E FARRELL

MOULSOE (Assumption of the Blessed Virgin Mary) Streatley w Moulsford *Ox*

MOULTON (All Saints) (Mission Room) *Linc 17* **P** *DBP*
V *Vacant* Holbeach (01406) 370791

MOULTON (Mission Church) Middleton Tyas w Croft and Eryholme *Ripon*

MOULTON (St James) Cowbit *Linc*

MOULTON (St Peter) Gazeley w Dalham, Moulton and Kentford *St E*

MOULTON (St Peter and St Paul) *Pet 4* **P** *Ch Soc Trust*
V P H BRECKWOLDT

MOULTON (St Stephen the Martyr) *Ches 6*
P *R Davenham* **V** J C ORRADINE

MOULTON, GREAT (St Michael) Bunwell, Carleton Rode, Tibenham, Gt Moulton etc *Nor*

MOUNT BURES (St John) Wormingford, Mt Bures and Lt Horkesley *Chelmsf*

MOUNT HAWKE (St John the Baptist) Mithian w Mt Hawke *Truro*

MOUNT PELLON (Christ Church) *Wakef 4* **P** *Bp*
V T J E MAYFIELD, **C** S GOTT

MOUNTFIELD (All Saints) Brightling, Dallington, Mountfield & Netherfield *Chich*

MOUNTNESSING (St Giles) Doddinghurst and Mountnessing *Chelmsf*

MOUNTSORREL (Christ Church) (St Peter) *Leic 7*
P *CPAS and Bp* **P-in-c** F BRODIE

MOW COP (St Luke's Mission Church) Odd Rode *Ches*

MOW COP (St Thomas) *Lich 16* **P** *Prime Min* **V** *Vacant*
Stoke-on-Trent (01782) 515077

MOWSLEY (St Nicholas) Husbands Bosworth w Mowsley and Knaptoft etc *Leic*

MOXLEY (All Saints) *Lich 7* **P** *Prime Min*
P-in-c I H MURRAY

MUCH: *see also under substantive place names*

MUCH BIRCH (St Mary and St Thomas a Becket) w Little Birch, Much Dewchurch, Llanwarne and Llandinabo
Heref 8 **P** *A W Twiston-Davies Esq (1 turn), Bp (3 turns), and Ld Chan (1 turn)* **P-in-c** A N JEVONS,
Hon **C** K B GARLICK

MUCHELNEY (St Peter and St Paul) Langport Area Chs *B & W*

MUCKLESTONE (St Mary) *Lich 12* **P** *Mrs F F Friend*
P-in-c M R H TURNER

MUDEFORD (All Saints) Christchurch *Win*

MUDFORD (Blessed Virgin Mary) Chilton Cantelo, Ashington, Mudford, Rimpton etc *B & W*

MUGGINTON (All Saints) and Kedleston *Derby 11* **P** *Major J W Chandos-Pole* **P-in-c** K JARDIN

MUGGLESWICK (All Saints) Blanchland w Hunstanworth and Edmundbyers etc *Newc*

MUKER (St Mary) Swaledale *Ripon*

MULBARTON (St Mary Magdalene) w Kenningham *Nor 7*
P *Mrs R M Watkinson* **P-in-c** J W STUBENBORD

MULLION (St Mellanus) *Truro 4* **P** *Bp* **P-in-c** I J BUTLER

MUMBY (St Thomas of Canterbury) Willoughby *Linc*

MUNCASTER (St Michael) Eskdale, Irton, Muncaster and Waberthwaite *Carl*

MUNDEN, LITTLE (All Saints) The Mundens w Sacombe *St Alb*

MUNDENS, The w Sacombe *St Alb 8* **P** *Ch Trust Fund Trust, K Coll Cam, and R M Abel Smith Esq (jt)* **R** A G MORTON

MUNDESLEY (All Saints) Trunch *Nor*

MUNDFORD (St Leonard) w Lynford *Nor 14* **P** *Ch Patr Trust* **P-in-c** G H WHEATLEY

MUNDHAM (St Peter) Brooke, Kirstead, Mundham w Seething and Thwaite *Nor*

MUNDHAM, NORTH (St Stephen) w Hunston and Merston *Chich 3* **P** *St Jo Coll Cam* **R** V C de R MALAN

MUNGRISDALE (St Kentigern) Greystoke, Matterdale, Mungrisdale, etc *Carl*

MUNSLEY (St Bartholomew) Tarrington w Stoke Edith, Aylton, Pixley etc *Heref*

MUNSLOW (St Michael) Diddlebury w Munslow, Holdgate and Tugford *Heref*

MUNSTER SQUARE (Christ Church) (St Mary Magdalene) *Lon 17* **P** *Bp* **V** *Vacant 0171–388 2166 or 3095*

MUNSTONE (Church Room) Holmer w Huntington *Heref*

MURCOTT (Mission Room) Islip w Charlton on Otmoor, Oddington, Noke etc *Ox*

MURROW (Corpus Christi) Southea w Murrow and Parson Drove *Ely*

MURSLEY (St Mary the Virgin) w Swanbourne and Little Horwood *Ox 26* **P** *Ch Soc Trust, Ch Patr Soc, and Hon J T Fremantle (by turn)* **R** J M KINCHIN-SMITH

MURSTON (All Saints) w Bapchild and Tonge *Cant 14* **P** *Abp and St Jo Coll Cam (jt)* **R** B A SHERSBY

MURTON (St James) Osbaldwick w Murton *York*

MURTON (St John the Baptist) Appleby *Carl*

MUSBURY (St Michael) Colyton, Southleigh, Offwell, Widworthy etc *Ex*

MUSBURY (St Thomas) *Blackb 1* **P** *The Crown* **V** S M AIKEN

MUSGRAVE (St Theobald) Brough w Stainmore, Musgrave and Warcop *Carl*

MUSKHAM, NORTH (St Wilfrid) and SOUTH (St Wilfrid) *S'well 3* **P** *Ld Chan* **NSM** A C ARMSTRONG, M B ARMSTRONG

MUSTON (All Saints) Hunmanby w Muston *York*

MUSTON (St John the Baptist) Bottesford and Muston *Leic*

MUSWELL HILL (St James) (St Matthew) *Lon 20* **P** *Bp and CPAS (jt)* **V** D A ROSS, **C** P G WILLIAMS, N H GREEN, **Hon C** P F WATSON, **NSM** H C HENDRY

MUTFORD (St Andrew) Carlton Colville w Mutford and Rushmere *Nor*

MYDDELTON SQUARE (St Mark) Clerkenwell H Redeemer and St Mark *Lon*

MYDDLE (St Peter) *Lich 28* **P** *Bp* **P-in-c** E A HADLEY

MYLAND (St Michael) Colchester St Mich Myland *Chelmsf*

MYLOR (St Mylor) w Flushing *Truro 3* **P** *Bp* **V** J C JAMES

MYLOR BRIDGE (All Saints) Mylor w Flushing *Truro*

MYMMS, NORTH (St Mary) (St Michael) *St Alb 7* **P** *Bp* **V** T W J RANSON, **C** G L LEGOOD

MYMMS, SOUTH (King Charles the Martyr) *St Alb 2* **P** *Bp Lon* **V** D M WILLIAMS, **NSM** G J RANDALL

MYMMS, SOUTH (St Giles) and Ridge *St Alb 2* **P** *DBP* **V** R E GAGE

MYNDTOWN (St John the Baptist) Wentnor w Ratlinghope, Myndtown, Norbury etc *Heref*

MYTHOLMROYD (St Michael) *Wakef 3* **P** *Bp* **V** D C HODGSON

MYTON ON SWALE (St Mary) Brafferton w Pilmoor, Myton on Swale etc *York*

NABB (Mission Church) Wrockwardine Wood *Lich*

NACKINGTON (St Mary) Petham and Waltham w Lower Hardres etc *Cant*

NACTON (St Martin) and Levington w Bucklesham and Foxhall *St E 2* **P** *DBP* **R** G L GRANT, **NSM** J S FOUNTAIN, D E N KING

NAFFERTON (All Saints) w Wansford *York 11* **P** *Abp* **V** J R BOOTH

NAILSEA (Christ Church) *B & W 13* **P** *R Nailsea H Trin* **V** A Q H WHEELER, **C** R H M LEGG

NAILSEA (Holy Trinity) *B & W 13* **P** *MMCET* **R** J T SIMONS, **C** J P ROWE, V POLLARD

NAILSTONE (All Saints) and Carlton w Shackerstone *Leic 13* **P** *The Crown and DBP (alt)* **R** W E QUINNEY

NAILSWORTH (St George) *Glouc 16* **P** *Bp* **V** J D STRONG

NANPANTAN (St Mary in Charnwood) Loughb Em *Leic*

NANPEAN (St George) St Stephen in Brannel *Truro*

NANSTALLION (St Stephen's Mission Room) Bodmin w Lanhydrock and Lanivet *Truro*

NANTWICH (St Mary) *Ches 15* **P** *Q H Crewe Esq and J C Crewe Esq (jt)* **R** J R PRICE, **C** R E REYNOLDS

NAPTON-ON-THE-HILL (St Lawrence), Lower Shuckburgh and Stockton *Cov 10* **P** *Ld Chan (2 turns), Sir Rupert Shuckburgh, Bt (1 turn), and New Coll Ox (2 turns)* **R** P L JACKSON

NARBOROUGH (All Saints) and Huncote *Leic 10* **P** *SMF* **R** N J BURTON

NARBOROUGH (All Saints) w Narford *Nor 21* **P** *Bp* **V** S R NAIRN

NARFORD (St Mary) Narborough w Narford *Nor*

NASEBY (All Saints) Clipston w Naseby and Haselbech w Kelmarsh *Pet*

NASH (All Saints) w Thornton, Beachampton and Thornborough *Ox 22* **P** *Mrs S Doulton (2 turns), Sir Ralph Verney, Bt (2 turns), and G & C Coll Cam (1 turn)* **R** A K PRING

NASH (St John the Baptist) Burford I *Heref*

NASSINGTON (St Mary the Virgin and All Saints) w Yarwell and Woodnewton *Pet 12* **P** *Lord Brassey and Bp (alt)* **V** R A LOVELESS

NATELY SCURES (St Swithun) Newnham w Nately Scures w Mapledurwell etc *Win*

NATLAND (St Mark) *Carl 9* **P** *V Kendal H Trin* **V** T PARK, **NSM** M P JAYNE

NAUGHTON (St Mary) Whatfield w Semer, Nedging and Naughton *St E*

NAUNTON (St Andrew) Upper and Lower Slaughter w Eyford and Naunton *Glouc*

NAUNTON BEAUCHAMP (St Bartholomew) Abberton, The Flyfords, Naunton Beauchamp etc *Worc*

NAVENBY (St Peter) Graffoe Gp *Linc*

NAVESTOCK (St Thomas) *Chelmsf 7* **P** *Bp* **P-in-c** R A L ROSE

NAWTON (St Hilda) Kirkdale *York*

NAYLAND (St James) w Wiston *St E 3* **P** *Ld Chan (2 turns) and DBP (1 turn)* **V** D A C STRANACK, **Hon C** D B WATLING

NAYLAND DRIVE (Church Centre) Clacton St Jas *Chelmsf*

NAZEING (All Saints) (St Giles) *Chelmsf 27* **P** *Ld Chan* **V** M D WEBSTER, **NSM** P A VOSS

NEASDEN (St Catherine w St Paul) *Lon 21* **P** *Bp and D&C St Paul's (jt)* **V** E E GAUNT

NEATISHEAD (St Peter), Barton Turf and Irstead *Nor 12* **P** *Bp* **P-in-c** M W SMITH, **Hon C** R S M MILLARD

NECHELLS (St Clement) Duddeston w Nechells *Birm*

NECTON (All Saints), Holme Hale w Pickenham, North and South *Nor* **P** *Major-Gen Robin Broke, Ch Soc Tr, MMCET and S Pickenham Estate Co Ltd (jt)* **I** P J TAYLOR, **C** A D HAMILTON

NEDGING (St Mary) Whatfield w Semer, Nedging and Naughton *St E*

NEEDHAM (St Peter) Redenhall, Harleston, Wortwell and Needham *Nor*

NEEDHAM MARKET (St John the Baptist) w Badley *St E 1* **P** *PCC* **V** R S STRINGER

NEEN SAVAGE (St Mary) Cleobury Mortimer w Hopton Wafers etc *Heref*

NEEN SOLLARS (All Saints) as above

NEENTON (All Saints) Ditton Priors w Neenton, Burwarton etc *Heref*

NEITHROP (St Paul) Banbury *Ox*

NELSON (St Bede) *Blackb 7* **P** *Bp* **V** M A BURGESS

NELSON (St Mary) Nelson in Lt Marsden *Blackb*

NELSON (St Philip) *Blackb 7* **P** *Bp* **V** S J R HARTLEY, **C** T J HOROBIN

NELSON IN LITTLE MARSDEN (St Mary) *Blackb 7* **P** *Trustees* *Vacant* Nelson (01282) 614919

NEMPNETT THRUBWELL (The Blessed Virgin Mary) Chew Stoke w Nempnett Thrubwell *B & W*

NENTHEAD (St John) Alston Team *Newc*

NESS Group, The *Linc 13* **P** *Burghley Ho Preservation Trust (1 turn), Ld Chan (1 turn), Bp abd DBP (2 turns)* **V** M J N HOWES

NESS, GREAT (St Andrew) Ruyton XI Towns w Gt and Lt Ness *Lich*

NESS, LITTLE (St Martin) as above

NESTON (St Mary and St Helen) *Ches 9* **P** *D&C* **V** A V SHUFFLEBOTHAM, **C** D V COOKSON

NESTON (St Phillip and St James) Gtr Corsham *Bris*

NESTON, LITTLE (St Michael and All Angels) Neston *Ches*

NETHER: *see also under substantive place names*

NETHER DENTON (St Cuthbert) Gilsland w Nether Denton *Carl*

NETHERAVON (All Saints) Avon Valley *Sarum*

NETHERBURY (St Mary) Beaminster Area *Sarum*

NETHEREXE (St John the Baptist) Stoke Canon, Poltimore w Huxham and Rewe etc *Ex*

NETHERFIELD (St George) w Colwick *S'well 11* **P** *DBP* **Hon C** K D WILLIAMS

NETHERFIELD (St John the Baptist) Brightling, Dallington, Mountfield & Netherfield *Chich*

NETHERHAMPTON (St Katherine) Wilton w Netherhampton and Fugglestone *Sarum*

NETHERLEY (Christ Church) Gateacre *Liv*

NETHERNE (St Luke) Merstham and Gatton *S'wark*

NETHERSEAL (St Peter) Nether and Over Seale *Derby*

NETHERTHONG (All Saints) Upper Holme Valley *Wakef*

NETHERTHORPE (St Bartholomew) Sheff St Bart *Sheff*

NETHERTHORPE (St Stephen) *Sheff 4* **P** *Ch Patr Trust and Sheff Ch Burgesses Trust (jt)* **V** N A CLEMAS

NETHERTON (All Souls) *Carl 7* **P** *Bp* **P-in-c** R BOWLZER

NETHERTON (St Andrew) Middlestown *Wakef*

NETHERTON (St Andrew) *Worc 9* **P** *V Dudley* **V** M G PRICE

NETHERTON (St Oswald) *Liv 1* **P** *Bp* **V** A J EDWARDS, **C** R L PEARSON

NETHERWITTON (St Giles) *Newc 11* **P** *Ld Chan* **V** W A GOFTON

NETLEY ABBEY Hound *Win*

NETLEY MARSH (St Matthew) Totton *Win*

NETTLEBED (St Bartholomew) w Bix and Highmore *Ox 6* **P** *Ch Patr Trust, Earl of Macclesfield, DBP, and R Rotherfield Greys (jt)* **R** B J WEAVER

NETTLECOMBE (Blessed Virgin Mary) Stogumber w Nettlecombe and Monksilver *B & W*

NETTLEDEN (Ashridge Chapel) Potten End w Nettleden *St Alb*

NETTLEDEN (St Lawrence) as above

NETTLEHAM (All Saints) *Linc 3* **P** *Bp* **P-in-c** G F SLEIGHT

NETTLESTEAD (St Mary) Gt and Lt Blakenham w Baylham and Nettlestead *St E*

NETTLESTEAD (St Mary the Virgin) E Peckham and Nettlestead *Roch*

NETTLETON (St John the Baptist) Swallow *Linc*

NETTLETON (St Mary) w Littleton Drew *Bris 9* **P** *Bp and Adn Swindon (alt)* **P-in-c** J N A BRADBURY, **P-in-c** A MADDOCK, **C** R V C LEWIS

NEVENDON (St Peter) Pitsea w Nevendon *Chelmsf*

NEVILLE'S CROSS (St John) Conventional District *Dur 2* **P** *Bp* **C-in-c** M F RUSK, **NSM** S C BARTON

NEW: *see also under substantive place names*

NEW BOROUGH and Leigh (St John the Evangelist) *Sarum 10* **P** *Ch Soc Trust* **V** R J A TULLOCH, **C** P W HUNTER

NEW BUILDINGS (Beacon Church) Sandford w Upton Hellions *Ex*

NEW FERRY (St Mark) *Ches 8* **P** *R Bebington* **V** D F WALKER

NEW HAW (All Saints) *Guildf 11* **P** *Bp* **V** G J TICKNER, **NSM** R A MILLER

NEW MILL (Christ Church) Upper Holme Valley *Wakef*

NEW MILLS (St George) (St James the Less) *Derby 6* **P** *V Glossop* **V** J H K NORTON, **C** K H BALL, **NSM** R J ANDERS

NEW SPRINGS (St John) *Liv 14* **P** *Bp* **P-in-c** J C SHARPLES

NEWALL GREEN (St Francis of Assisi) *Man 8* **P** *Bp* **P-in-c** P J DINES

NEWARK-UPON-TRENT (St Mary Magdalene) (St Augustine's Mission) (Christ Church) *S'well 3* **P** *The Crown* **TR** R A J HILL, **TV** G K KNOTT, **P** HUTCHINSON, **C** P S BAGSHAW, H J WILD

NEWBALD (St Nicholas) *York 14* **P** *Abp* **V** J WALKER

NEWBARNS (St Paul) w Hawcoat *Carl 8* **P** *DBP* **R** C C JENKIN, **C** M E DAY

NEWBIGGIN (St Edmund) Kirkby Thore w Temple Sowerby and Newbiggin *Carl*

NEWBIGGIN-BY-THE-SEA (St Bartholomew) Woodhorn w Newbiggin *Newc*

NEWBIGGIN HALL (St Wilfrid) Whorlton *Newc*

NEWBOLD (St John the Evangelist) and Dunston *Derby 5* **P** *V Chesterfield* **R** R J ROSS, **C** S I MITCHELL, A H HART, **NSM** P S RHODES

NEWBOLD (St Peter) Rochdale *Man*

NEWBOLD DE VERDUN (St James) and Kirkby Mallory *Leic 13* **P** *Bp and Trin Coll Ox (jt)* **R** C E FOX

NEWBOLD ON AVON (St Botolph) *Cov 6* **P** H A F W *Boughton Leigh Esq* **V** P M WILKINSON

NEWBOLD ON STOUR (St David) Tredington and Darlingscott w Newbold on Stour *Cov*

NEWBOLD PACEY (St George) w Moreton Morrell *Cov 8* **P** *Qu Coll Ox and Lt-Col J E Little (alt)* **V** J R WILLIAMS

NEWBOROUGH (All Saints) Hanbury w Newborough *Lich*

NEWBOROUGH (St Bartholomew) *Pet 13* **P** *The Crown* **V** K P FITZGIBBON

NEWBOTTLE (St James) King's Sutton and Newbottle and Charlton *Pet*

NEWBOTTLE (St Matthew) *Dur 6* **P** *Bp* **P-in-c** E WILKINSON

NEWBOURN (St Mary) Waldringfield w Hemley and Newbourn *St E*

NEWBROUGH (St Peter) Warden w Newbrough *Newc*

NEWBURGH (Christ Church) w Westhead *Liv 11* **P** *Bp and V Ormskirk (jt)* **V** N T B DEANE, **NSM** D M BURROWS

NEWBURN (St Michael and All Angels) *Newc 7* **P** M M C ET **V** R G BATEMAN, **C** A B BARTLETT

NEWBURY (St John the Evangelist) (St Nicholas and St Mary) *Ox 14* **P** *Bp* **TR** D C M COOK, **TV** F T BONHAM, B DAGNALL, M STRANGE, **C** S A WHITMORE, M A EASTIN, **NSM** J H G LEWIS, D S CASTLE

NEWBY (St Mark) *York 16* **P** *Abp* **V** M SPENCELEY

NEWCASTLE (Christ Church) (St Ann) *Newc 5* **P** *Bp* **V** A J A ROMANIS

NEWCASTLE (Epiphany) *Newc 5* **P** *Bp* **P-in-c** J E SADLER, **TV** M THOMPSON, J I COLLINSON

NEWCASTLE (St Andrew) (St Luke) *Newc 5* **P** *Bp and V Gosforth St Nic (jt)* **V** A W J MAGNESS

NEWCASTLE (St John the Evangelist) Clun w Bettws-y-Crwyn and Newc *Heref*

NEWCASTLE (St Philip) and St Augustine *Newc 7* **P** *Bp* **P-in-c** I G FALCONER

NEWCASTLE UNDER LYME (St George) *Lich 14* **P** *R Newc w Butterton* **P-in-c** K A L DENNIS

NEWCASTLE UNDER LYME (St Giles) w Butterton *Lich 14* **P** *Simeon's Trustees* **R** J G RIDYARD

NEWCASTLE UNDER LYME (St Paul) *Lich 14* **P** *Trustees* **V** M D HARDING

NEWCASTLE UPON TYNE Byker (St Anthony) Byker St Ant *Newc*

NEWCASTLE UPON TYNE Byker (St Martin) Byker St Martin *Newc*

NEWCASTLE UPON TYNE Byker (St Michael w St Lawrence) Byker St Mich w St Lawr *Newc*

NEWCASTLE UPON TYNE Byker (St Silas) Byker St Silas *Newc*

NEWCASTLE UPON TYNE Fenham (St James and St Basil) Fenham St Jas and St Basil *Newc*

NEWCASTLE UPON TYNE Heaton (St Gabriel) *Newc 6* **P** *Bp* **V** C M FUNWIN, **C** R L SIMPSON, **NSM** K BATTE, S E AULD

NEWCASTLE UPON TYNE High Elswick (St Paul) High Elswick St Paul *Newc*

NEWCASTLE UPON TYNE High Heaton (St Francis) *Newc 6* **P** *Bp* **V** R FINDLAYSON

NEWCASTLE UPON TYNE (Holy Cross) *Newc 7* **P** *Bp* **V** M J WEBB, **C** R HERON, **Hon C** P E DAVIES

NEWCASTLE UPON TYNE Jesmond Jesmond Clayton Memorial *Newc*

NEWCASTLE UPON TYNE Jesmond (Holy Trinity) Jesmond H Trin *Newc*

NEWCASTLE UPON TYNE Low Elswick (St Stephen) Low Elswick *Newc*

NEWCASTLE UPON TYNE Scotswood (St Margaret) Scotswood *Newc*

NEWCASTLE UPON TYNE (St Barnabas and St Jude) *Newc 5* **P** *V Jesmond Clayton Memorial and CPAS (alt)* **V** *Vacant* 0191–232 7837

NEWCASTLE UPON TYNE (St George) *Newc 5* **P** *Bp* **V** F R DEXTER, **C** J V J G WATSON

NEWCASTLE UPON TYNE (St Hilda) *Newc 5* **P** *Bp* **P-in-c** F R DEXTER

NEWCASTLE UPON TYNE (St John the Baptist) *Newc 5* **P** *V Newc* **P-in-c** P KENNEY

NEWCASTLE UPON TYNE (St Matthew w St Mary) *Newc 7* **P** *Bp* **P-in-c** I G FALCONER, **C** K L DUNN

NEWCASTLE UPON TYNE (St Thomas) Proprietary Chapel *Newc 5* **P** *Trustees of St Thos Chpl Charity* **C-in-c** I D HOUGHTON

NEWCASTLE UPON TYNE Walker (Christ Church) Walker *Newc*

NEWCASTLE UPON TYNE Walkergate (St Oswald) Byker St Mark and Walkergate St Oswald *Newc*

NEWCASTLE UPON TYNE, WEST Benwell Benwell Team *Newc*

NEWCHAPEL (St James the Apostle) *Lich 16* **P** *CPAS* **V** W E SLATER

NEWCHURCH (All Saints) *Portsm 7* **P** *Bp* **V** D H HEATLEY

NEWCHURCH (Christ Church) Hoar Cross w Newchurch *Lich*

NEWCHURCH (not known) *Liv 16* **P** *Bp* **R** A LITTON
NEWCHURCH (St Nicholas w St John) *Man 15* **P** *Bp*
R A TTOOMBS
NEWCHURCH (St Peter and St Paul) Dymchurch w
Burmarsh and Newchurch *Cant*
NEWCHURCH-IN-PENDLE (St Mary) Fence and
Newchurch-in-Pendle *Blackb*
NEWDIGATE (St Peter) *Guildf 7* **P** *Ld Chan*
R C J BLISSARD-BARNES
NEWENDEN (St Peter) Sandhurst w Newenden *Cant*
NEWENT (St Mary the Virgin) and Gorsley w Cliffords Mesne
Glouc 3 **P** *Bp* **P-in-c** R C SIMPSON, **C** P PHILLIPS,
NSM R G CHIVERS
NEWHALL (St John) *Derby 16* **P** *Bp* **V** I F R JARVIS
NEWHAVEN (St Michael) *Chich 18* **P** *Ch Patr Trust*
R N WESTON
NEWHEY (St Thomas) *Man 20* **P** *Bp* **V** S H TOMLINE
NEWICK (St Mary) *Chich 21* **P** *Ch Soc Trust and*
J H Cordle Esq (jt) **R** P P FRANCIS
NEWINGTON (St Christopher) St Laurence in the Isle of
Thanet *Cant*
NEWINGTON (St Giles) Dorchester *Ox*
NEWINGTON St John the Baptist w Dairycoates St Mary and
St Peter *York 15* **P** *Abp* **V** P A BURKITT,
NSM A CRAVEN
NEWINGTON (St Mary) *S'wark 8* **P** *Bp* **R** M A HART,
Hon C J WASH
NEWINGTON (St Mary the Virgin) w Hartlip and Stockbury
Cant 14 **P** *Abp* **V** *Vacant* Newington (01795) 844345
NEWINGTON (St Nicholas) Cheriton All So w Newington
Cant
NEWINGTON (St Paul) *S'wark 8* **P** *Bp* **V** G D SHAW
NEWINGTON, SOUTH (St Peter ad Vincula) Bloxham w
Milcombe and S Newington *Ox*
NEWLAND (All Saints) and Redbrook w Clearwell *Glouc 4*
P *Bp* **V** D J F ADDISON
NEWLAND (St Leonard), Guarlford and Madresfield
Worc 2 **P** *Exors Countess Beauchamp and Beauchamp*
Trustees (alt) **P-in-c** J H GREEN
NEWLANDS (not known) Thornthwaite cum Braithwaite
and Newlands *Carl*
NEWLAY LANE (St Margaret's Church Hall) Bramley
Ripon
NEWLYN (St Newlyn) *Truro 5* **P** *Bp* **P-in-c** W FISH
NEWLYN (St Peter) *Truro 5* **P** *Bp* **V** R L STRANGE
NEWMARKET (All Saints) *St E 11* **P** *Bp* **V** J C ROSS
NEWMARKET (St Mary the Virgin) w Exning St Agnes
St E 11 **P** *Bp and DBP (alt)* **R** G C SMITH
NEWNHAM (St Michael and All Angels) Badby w Newnham
and Charwelton w Fawsley etc *Pet*
NEWNHAM (St Nicholas) w Nately Scures w Mapledurwell w
Up Nateley w Greywell *Win 5* **P** *Bp, Qu Coll Ox, and*
Exors Lady Malmesbury (jt) **R** M R HAWES
NEWNHAM (St Peter and St Paul) Doddington, Newnham
and Wychling *Cant*
NEWNHAM (St Peter) w Awre and Blakeney *Glouc 3*
P *Haberdashers' Co and Bp (alt)* **V** G A J HUTTON
NEWNHAM (St Vincent) Ashwell w Hinxworth and
Newnham *St Alb*
NEWNTON, NORTH (St James) Swanborough *Sarum*
NEWPORT (St John the Baptist) *Portsm 8* **P** *Ch Patr*
Trust **V** A BROWN, **C** N I BOURNE
NEWPORT (St John the Baptist), Bishops Tawton and
Tawstock *Ex 15* **P** *Patr Bd* **TV** J C CARVOSSO,
P-in-c J P BENSON
NEWPORT (St Mary the Virgin) *Chelmsf 22* **P** *Bp*
V S SANDERSON
NEWPORT (St Nicholas) w Longford and Chetwynd *Lich 21*
P *Bp* **R** R T HIBBERT, **C** D J BABINGTON
NEWPORT (St Stephen) Howden TM *York*
NEWPORT (St Thomas) *Portsm 8* **P** *Bp* **V** *Vacant* Isle of
Wight (01983) 522733
NEWPORT PAGNELL (St Luke) w Lathbury and Moulsoe
Ox 27 **P** *Bp, Ch Ch Ox, and Lord Carrington (jt)*
R J H LEWIS, **C** J B RUSSELL, **Hon C** R C A LESLIE
NEWQUAY (St Michael) *Truro 7* **P** *Bp* **V** M H FISHER
NEWSHAM (St Bede) *Newc 1* **P** *Bp* **V** J R PRINGLE,
C J P HAGGER
NEWSHOLME (St John) Oakworth *Bradf*
NEWSOME (St John the Evangelist) and Armitage Bridge
Wakef 1 **P** *DBP, V Rashcliffe and Lockwood, and*
R Almondbury (jt) **V** I JACKSON
NEWSTEAD (St Mary the Virgin) Annesley Our Lady and
All SS *S'well*
NEWTIMBER (St John the Evangelist) Poynings w
Edburton, Newtimber and Pyecombe *Chich*
NEWTON and TOFT (St Michael) Middle Rasen Gp *Linc*
NEWTON (Church Hall) Blackwell *Derby*

NEWTON (Good Shepherd) Clifton upon Dunsmore and
Newton *Cov*
NEWTON (Mission Church) Embleton w Rennington and
Rock *Newc*
NEWTON (St Botolph) S Lafford *Linc*
NEWTON (St James) *Ely 7* **P** *Bp*
P-in-c N A WHITEHOUSE
NEWTON (St John the Baptist) Clodock and Longtown w
Craswall, Llanveynoe etc *Heref*
NEWTON (St Luke) Hatf *St Alb*
NEWTON (St Margaret) Lt Shelford w Newton *Ely*
NEWTON (St Michael and All Angels) *Ches 8* **P** *R W Kirby*
St Bridget **V** I A DAVENPORT
NEWTON (St Oswald) Gt Ayton w Easby and Newton in
Cleveland *York*
NEWTON (St Petrock) Shebbear, Buckland Filleigh,
Sheepwash etc *Ex*
NEWTON (St Stephen) Flowery Field *Ches 14* **P** *Bp*
P-in-c P J HIBBERT
NEWTON, NORTH (St Peter) w St Michaelchurch,
Thurloxton and Durston *B & W 14* **P** *Bp (3 turns),*
Sir Benjamin Slade, Bt (1 turn) **P-in-c** R RADCLIFFE
NEWTON, OLD (St Mary) w Stowupland *St E 6* **P** *Ch Patr*
Trust and DBP (alt) **V** *Vacant* Stowmarket (01449) 744551
NEWTON, SOUTH (St Andrew) Lower Wylye and Till
Valley *Sarum*
NEWTON, WEST (St Matthew) *Carl 7* **P** *Bp*
P-in-c P J SWAIN
NEWTON, WEST (St Peter and St Paul) Sandringham w W
Newton and Appleton w Wolferton w Babingley *Nor*
NEWTON ABBOT Highweek and Teigngrace *Ex*
NEWTON ABBOT (St Leonard) Wolborough w Newton
Abbot *Ex*
NEWTON ABBOT (St Michael) as above
NEWTON ABBOT (St Paul) as above
NEWTON ARLOSH (St John the Evangelist) Kirkbride w
Newton Arlosh *Carl*
NEWTON AYCLIFFE (St Clare) *Dur 14* **P** *Bp*
TR P A BALDWIN, **TV** C JAY, **C** N A CHAMBERLAIN,
NSM M FERGUSON
NEWTON BLOSSOMVILLE (St Nicolas) Lavendon w Cold
Brayfield, Clifton Reynes etc *Ox*
NEWTON BROMSWOLD (St Peter) Rushden w Newton
Bromswold *Pet*
NEWTON-BY-CASTLE-ACRE (All Saints) Castle Acre w
Newton, Rougham and Southacre *Nor*
NEWTON CAP (St Paul) Auckland St Andr and St Anne
Dur
NEWTON FERRERS (Holy Cross) w Revelstoke *Ex 21*
P *Bp and Comdr P E Yonge* **R** T R DEACON
NEWTON FLOTMAN (St Mary the Virgin) Swainsthorpe w
Newton Flotman *Nor*
NEWTON GREEN (All Saints) Assington w Newton Green
and Lt Cornard *St E*
NEWTON HALL (All Saints) *Dur 2* **P** *D&C*
P-in-c M J HARDY
NEWTON HALL (St James) Corbridge w Halton and
Newton Hall *Newc*
NEWTON HARCOURT (St Luke) Gt Glen, Stretton Magna
and Wistow etc *Leic*
NEWTON HEATH (All Saints) *Man 5* **P** *D&C*
R D G ATTFIELD
NEWTON HEATH (St Wilfrid and St Anne) *Man 5*
P *The Crown* **P-in-c** G N DOBSON
NEWTON IN MAKERFIELD (Emmanuel) *Liv 16* **P** *Bp*
R R BUSHELL
NEWTON IN MAKERFIELD (St Peter) *Liv 16* **P** *Lord*
Newton **V** G B KEEGAN
NEWTON IN MOTTRAM (St Mary) *Ches 14*
P *V Mottram* **P-in-c** P ENNION
NEWTON KYME (St Andrew) Tadcaster w Newton Kyme
York
NEWTON-LE-WILLOWS (All Saints) *Liv 16* **P** *Bp*
V D HALL
NEWTON LONGVILLE (St Faith) w Stoke Hammond and
Whaddon *Ox 26* **P** *Exors R J Dalziel Smith Esq, New Coll*
Ox, and Cam Univ (by turn) **R** A A WHALLEY
NEWTON ON OUSE (All Saints) Skelton w Shipton and
Newton on Ouse *York*
NEWTON-ON-RAWCLIFFE (St John) Middleton w
Newton, Levisham and Lockton *York*
NEWTON-ON-TRENT (St Peter) Saxilby Gp *Linc*
NEWTON POPPLEFORD (St Luke), Harpford and Colaton
Raleigh *Ex 7* **P** *Bp, I Aylesbeare, Farringdon, Clyst*
Honiton and Sowton, and DBP (jt) **V** T W BRIGHTON
NEWTON PURCELL (St Michael) Finmere w Mixbury,
Cottisford, Hardwick etc *Ox*

NEWTON REGIS (St Mary) w Seckington and Shuttington
Birm 12   **P** *Birm Dioc Trustees and Mrs E V G Inge-Innes-Lillingston (alt)*   **R**   S R MARRIOTT
NEWTON REIGNY (St John) Penrith w Newton Reigny and Plumpton Wall *Carl*
NEWTON SOLNEY (St Mary the Virgin) Bretby w Newton Solney *Derby*
NEWTON ST CYRES (St Cyres and St Julitta) Thorverton, Cadbury, Upton Pyne etc *Ex*
NEWTON ST LOE (Holy Trinity) Saltford w Corston and Newton St Loe *B & W*
NEWTON TONY (St Andrew) Bourne Valley *Sarum*
NEWTON TRACEY (St Thomas a Becket), Alverdiscott, Huntshaw, Yarnscombe and Horwood *Ex 20*   **P** *Bp, Ld Chan, and Lord Clinton (by turn)*   **P-in-c** R J P ACWORTH
NEWTON VALENCE (St Mary) and Selborne and East Tisted w Colemore *Win 2*   **P** *Bp, Earl of Selborne, and Sir James Scott (jt)*   **R**   J F W ANDERSON
NEWTOWN (Holy Spirit) Calbourne w Newtown *Portsm*
NEWTOWN (Holy Trinity) Soberton w Newtown *Portsm*
NEWTOWN (King Charles the Martyr) Loppington w Newtown *Lich*
NEWTOWN (St Mary the Virgin) Hungerford and Denford *Ox*
NEWTOWN (St Mary the Virgin and St John the Baptist) Burghclere w Newtown and Ecchinswell w Sydmonton *Win*
NEWTOWN (St Paul) Longnor, Quarnford and Sheen *Lich*
NEWTOWN LINFORD (All Saints) *Leic 12*
  P *Lord Deramore*   **P-in-c**   G W E C ASHBY
NIBLEY, NORTH (St Martin) Wotton-under-Edge w Ozleworth and N Nibley *Glouc*
NICHOLFOREST (St Nicholas) and Kirkandrews on Esk
Carl 2   **P** *Bp, Sir Charles Graham, Bt, and PCC (jt)*
  V   P J RIDLEY
NIDD (St Paul and St Margaret) *Ripon 1*   **P** *Viscount Mountgarret and R Knaresborough (alt)*   **V**   *Vacant* Harrogate (01423) 770060
NIDDERDALE, LOWER *Ripon 8*   **P** *Trustees K Bell Esq, DBP, and C J Dent Esq (jt)*   **R**   *Vacant* Boroughbridge (01423) 358662
NIDDERDALE, UPPER *Ripon 3*   **P** *D&C and V Masham and Healey (jt)*   **V**   P L DUNBAR
NINEBANKS (St Mark) Allendale w Whitfield *Newc*
NINEFIELDS (St Lawrence School Worship Centre) Waltham H Cross *Chelmsf*
NINFIELD (St Mary the Virgin) *Chich 14*   **P** *D&C Cant*
  R   P C CLEMENTS
NITON (St John the Baptist) *Portsm 7*   **P** *Qu Coll Ox*
  P-in-c   S E LLOYD,   **NSM**   J A WOOLLEY
NOAK HILL (St Thomas) Harold Hill St Geo *Chelmsf*
NOCTON (All Saints) Branston w Nocton and Potterhanworth *Linc*
NOEL PARK (St Mark) *Lon 19*   **P** *Bp*   **V**   R R ROBINSON
NOKE (St Giles) Islip w Charlton on Otmoor, Oddington, Noke etc *Ox*
NOMANS HEATH (St Mary the Virgin) *Lich 4*   **P** *Bp*
  V   *Vacant*
NONINGTON (St Mary the Virgin) w Wymynswold and Goodnestone w Chillenden and Knowlton *Cant 1*   **P** *Abp and Lord Fitzwalter (jt)*   **V**   P GOODSELL
NORBITON (St Peter) *S'wark 15*   **P** *V Kingston All SS*
  V   P A HOLMES,   **NSM**   C E HUMPHRIES
NORBURY (All Saints) Wentnor w Ratlinghope, Myndtown, Norbury etc *Heref*
NORBURY (St Mary and St Barlok) w Snelston *Derby 8*
  P *Mrs M F Stanton, L A Clowes Esq, and V Ashbourne (by turn)*   **R**   *Vacant*
NORBURY (St Oswald) *S'wark 23*   **P** *Bp*
  V   A G STUDDERT-KENNEDY,   **Hon C**   M K WATTS
NORBURY (St Peter) High Offley and Norbury *Lich*
NORBURY (St Philip) *S'wark 23*   **P** *Bp*
  V   P L WASHINGTON,   **Hon C**   C M KING
NORBURY (St Stephen) and Thornton Heath *S'wark 23*
  P *Bp*   **V**   F J M POLE
NORBURY (St Thomas) *Ches 16*   **P** *Lord Newton*
  V   W F M COLLINS,   **C**   M A FRENCH,   R H GREEN
NORDELPH (Holy Trinity) Wimbotsham w Stow Bardolph and Stow Bridge etc *Ely*
NORDEN (St Paul) w Ashworth *Man 20*   **P** *Bp*
  V   K N PROCTOR
NORFOLK PARK (St Leonard) Conventional District
Sheff 1   **C-in-c**   W N CRAFT
NORHAM (St Cuthbert) and Duddo *Newc 12*   **P** *D&C (1 turn), D&C Dur (2 turns)*   **V**   R THOMPSON
NORK (St Paul) *Guildf 9*   **P** *The Crown*   **V**   P J BROOKS
NORLAND (St Luke) Sowerby Bridge w Norland *Wakef*

NORLANDS (St James) Notting Dale St Clem w St Mark and St Jas *Lon*
NORLEY (St John the Evangelist) and Crowton *Ches 3*   **P** *Bp and V Weaverham (jt)*   **V**   R H N ROBB
NORMACOT (Holy Evangelists) *Lich 17*   **P** *DBP*
  P-in-c   H F HARPER
NORMANBY (St Andrew) Kirby Misperton w Normanby, Edston and Salton *York*
NORMANBY (St George) Eston w Normanby *York*
NORMANBY-LE-WOLD (St Peter) Walesby *Linc*
NORMANTON (All Saints) *Wakef 9*   **P** *Trin Coll Cam*
  C   T C DAVIS
NORMANTON (St Giles) *Derby 10*   **P** *CPAS*
  V   J C GRINHAM,   **C**   J G KELLY
NORMANTON, SOUTH (St Michael) *Derby 1*
  P *MMCET*   **R**   E E CHAMBERLAIN
NORMANTON-LE-HEATH (Holy Trinity) Packington w Normanton-le-Heath *Leic*
NORMANTON-ON-SOAR (St James) Sutton Bonington w Normanton-on-Soar *S'well*
NORMANTON-ON-TRENT (St Matthew) Sutton w Carlton and Normanton upon Trent etc *S'well*
NORRIS BANK (St Martin) *Man 3*   **R**   B LIPSCOMBE
NORRISTHORPE (All Souls) Heckmondwike *Wakef*
NORTH: *see also under substantive place names*
NORTH CAVE (All Saints) w Cliffe *York 14*
  P *P W J Carver Esq*   **V**   P N HAYWARD
NORTH-CHAPEL Parishes, The *Linc 10*
  P *Mrs W B Ashley, The Personal Reps of C L E Haigh-Esq, and Trustees (1 turn), and Duchy of Lanc (1 turn)*
  R   R K EMM
NORTH CHAPEL (St Michael) w Ebernoe *Chich 11*   **P** *Lord Egremont*   **R**   C G F KIRKHAM
NORTH COVE (St Botolph) Worlingham w Barnby and N Cove *St E*
NORTH END (Chapel of Ease) Burton Dassett *Cov*
NORTH END (St Francis) Portsea N End St Mark *Portsm*
NORTH END (St Nicholas) as above
NORTH HILL (St Torney) and Lewannick *Truro 9*
  P *Ld Chan and DBP (alt)*   **P-in-c**   B STAMFORD
NORTH SHIELDS (Christ Church) N Shields *Newc*
NORTH SHIELDS (St Augustine) (Christ Church) *Newc 5*
  P *Patr Bd*   **TR**   W N STOCK,   **TV**   D E CANT
NORTHALLERTON (All Saints) w Kirby Sigston *York 20*
  P *D&C Dur*   **V**   I J FOX,   **C**   W BARNES,   M K GORHAM
NORTHAM (St Margaret) w Westward Ho! and Appledore
Ex 17   **P** *DBP*   **TV**   R VARTY,   **P-in-c**   J T THOMPSON
NORTHAMPTON (All Saints w St Katherine) *Pet 4*   **P** *Bp*
  V   S H M GODFREY
NORTHAMPTON (Christ Church) *Pet 4*   **P** *Bp*   **V**   *Vacant* Northampton (01604) 33254
NORTHAMPTON (Emmanuel) *Pet 4*   **P** *DBP*
  TR   J F A M KNIGHT,   **C**   M A H JOHNSON
NORTHAMPTON (Holy Sepulchre w St Andrew and St Lawrence) *Pet 4*   **P** *Bp*   **V**   K E ANDERSON
NORTHAMPTON (Holy Trinity) *Pet 4*   **P** *Bp*   **V**   *Vacant* Northampton (01604) 711468
NORTHAMPTON (St Alban the Martyr) (Glorious Ascension) *Pet 4*   **P** *Bp*   **V**   G J STEELE,
  C   S J M READING
NORTHAMPTON (St Benedict) *Pet 7*   **P** *Bp*
  V   R D PRATT,   **C**   A SLATER
NORTHAMPTON (St David) Kingsthorpe w St Dav Northn *Pet*
NORTHAMPTON (St Giles) *Pet 4*   **P** *Simeon's Trustees*
  V   P A M GOMPERTZ,   **C**   H M CAW
NORTHAMPTON (St James) *Pet 4*   **P** *Bp*   **V**   J T SHORT
NORTHAMPTON (St Mary the Virgin) *Pet 4*   **P** *Bp*
  V   G I BURGON,   **C**   J L HUTCHINSON
NORTHAMPTON (St Matthew) *Pet 4*   **P** *DBP*
  V   J I MORTON,   **C**   L A W SWABY,   **Hon C**   M M CLARKE
NORTHAMPTON (St Michael and All Angels w St Edmund)
Pet 4   **P** *Bp*   **V**   W P K KENTIGERN-FOX,   **C**   M S VAYRO
NORTHAMPTON St Paul *Pet 4*   **P** *Bp*   **V**   S J EVANS,
Dss   D EVANS
NORTHAMPTON (St Peter) w Upton *Pet 4*   **P** *R Foundn of St Kath*   **R**   *Vacant* Northampton (01604) 714015
NORTHAW (St Thomas of Canterbury) *St Alb 6*
  P *Mrs K R Dore*   **V**   J N BATEMAN-CHAMPAIN,
  NSM   M K ROBINS,   **Hon Par Dn**   B L COOKE
NORTHBOROUGH (St Andrew) Peakirk w Glinton and Northborough *Pet*
NORTHBOURNE (St Augustine) Eastry and Northbourne w Tilmanstone etc *Cant*
NORTHCHURCH (St Mary) Berkhamsted St Mary *St Alb*
NORTHCOURT (Christ Church) Abingdon *Ox*

NORTHENDEN (St Wilfrid) *Man 8* **P** *Bp* **R** G S FORSTER
NORTHFIELD (St Laurence) *Birm 4* **P** *Keble Coll Ox*
R R I WARREN
NORTHFLEET (St Botolph) *Roch 4* **P** *The Crown*
V A C SMITH
NORTHGATE (St Elizabeth) Crawley *Chich*
NORTHIAM (St Mary) *Chich 20* **P** *MMCET* **R** D BOND
NORTHILL (St Mary the Virgin) w Moggerhanger
St Alb 17 **P** *Grocers' Co and Bp (alt)* **R** T D DESERT,
NSM J D LANE
NORTHINGTON (St John the Evangelist) The Candover
Valley *Win*
NORTHLEACH (St Peter and St Paul) w Hampnett and
Farmington *Glouc 14* **P** *Bp* **C** R A B MORRIS
NORTHLEIGH (St Giles) Colyton, Southleigh, Offwell,
Widworthy etc *Ex*
NORTHLEW (St Thomas of Canterbury) Okehampton w
Inwardleigh, Bratton Clovelly etc *Ex*
NORTHMOOR (St Denys) Lower Windrush *Ox*
NORTHMOOR GREEN (St Peter and St John) N Petherton
w Northmoor Green *B & W*
NORTHOLT (St Joseph) W End *Lon 22* **P** *DBP*
V D M BRADSHAW, **C** S BUTLER
NORTHOLT (St Mary) (St Hugh) (St Richard) *Lon 22*
P *BNC Ox* **R** P S WALKER, **NSM** M J WALKER
NORTHOLT PARK (St Barnabas) *Lon 22* **P** *Bp*
V P B DENTON, **C** A R CORSIE
NORTHORPE (St John the Baptist) Scotton w Northorpe
Linc
NORTHOWRAM (St Matthew) *Wakef 2* **P** *Bp*
V J L MARSHALL, **C** J M HOGGARD
NORTHREPPS (St Mary) Overstrand, Northrepps,
Sidestrand & Trimingham *Nor*
NORTHWICH (St Helen) Witton *Ches*
NORTHWICH (St Luke) (Holy Trinity) *Ches 6* **P** *Bp*
V R W CROOK
NORTHWOLD (St Andrew) *Ely 15* **P** *Bp* **R** J B ROWSELL
NORTHWOOD (Emmanuel) *Lon 23* **P** *Ch Trust Fund*
Trust **V** J A WALLIS, **C** M E BROWN, J R LIBBY,
J J WILSON, **NSM** P D O GREENE
NORTHWOOD (Holy Trinity) Hanley H Ev *Lich*
NORTHWOOD (Holy Trinity) *Lon 23* **P** *Trustees*
V P E FAINT, **C** D G ALEXANDER, O J FIELD
NORTHWOOD Pinner Road (St Edmund the
King) Northwood Hills St Edm *Lon*
NORTHWOOD (St John the Baptist) *Portsm 8* **P** *Bp*
R C B BURLAND
NORTHWOOD (St Mark) Kirkby *Liv*
NORTHWOOD GREEN (Mission Church) Westbury-on-
Severn w Flaxley and Blaisdon *Glouc*
NORTHWOOD HILLS (St Edmund the King) *Lon 23*
P *Bp* **V** P VANNOZZI
NORTON (All Saints) Stanton St Quintin, Hullavington,
Grittleton etc *Bris*
NORTON (All Saints) Brington w Whilton and Norton *Pet*
NORTON (St Andrew) Pakenham w Norton and Tostock
St E
NORTON (St Berteline and St Christopher) *Ches 3* **P** *DBP*
V R J GATES
NORTON (St Egwin) Harvington, Norton and Lenchwick
Worc
NORTON (St George) (St Nicholas) *St Alb 9* **P** *Bp*
V C F LILEY, **C** B KNIGHT
NORTON (St James) *Sheff 2* **P** *CCC Cam*
R M J MORGAN, **C** R B PARKER
NORTON (St James) Stoulton w Drake's Broughton and
Pirton etc *Worc*
NORTON (St Mary) *Cant 6* **P** *Ld Chan* **R** G H COLMAN
NORTON (St Mary) Twigworth, Down Hatherley, Norton,
The Leigh etc *Glouc*
NORTON (St Mary the Virgin) *Dur 16* **P** *Bp*
P-in-c S A D FERNS, **C** S J ATKINSON
NORTON (St Michael and All Angels) *Dur 16* **P** *V Norton*
St Mary **P-in-c** M G T GOBBETT
NORTON (St Peter) Norton *York*
NORTON, EAST (All Saints) Hallaton w Horninghold,
Allexton, Tugby etc *Leic*
NORTON, OVER (St James) Chipping Norton *Ox*
NORTON BAVANT (All Saints) Heytesbury and Sutton
Veny *Sarum*
NORTON BRIDGE (St Luke) Chebsey, Ellenhall and
Seighford-with-Creswell *Lich*
NORTON CANES (St James) *Lich 3* **P** *Bp* **R** *Vacant* Heath
Hayes (01543) 278969
NORTON CANON (St Nicholas) Weobley w Sarnesfield and
Norton Canon *Heref*
NORTON CUCKNEY (St Mary) *S'well 6* **P** *Lady Alexandra*
Cavendish Bentinck **V** *Vacant* Mansfield (01623) 842443

NORTON DISNEY (St Peter) Thurlby w Norton Disney
Linc
NORTON FITZWARREN (All Saints) *B & W 18*
P *MMCET* **R** D N STEVENSON
NORTON IN HALES (St Chad) Woore and Norton in Hales
Lich
NORTON IN THE MOORS (St Bartholomew) *Lich 13*
P *Lord Norton* **P-in-c** P S DAVIES
NORTON JUXTA MALTON (St Peter) *York 2* **P** *Abp*
V W C HEDLEY, **C** M D YEWDALL
NORTON JUXTA TWYCROSS (Holy Trinity) The Appleby
Gp *Leic*
NORTON-LE-CLAY (St John the Evangelist) Kirby-on-the-
Moor, Cundall w Norton-le-Clay etc *Ripon*
NORTON LEES (St Paul) Norton Woodseats St Paul *Sheff*
NORTON LINDSEY (Holy Trinity) Wolverton w Norton
Lindsey and Langley *Cov*
NORTON MALREWARD (Holy Trinity) *B & W 10* **P** *Bp*
R T K VIVIAN
NORTON MANDEVILLE (All Saints) High Ongar w
Norton Mandeville *Chelmsf*
NORTON ST PHILIP (St Philip and St James) w Hemington,
Hardington and Laverton *B & W 4* **P** *Bp and J B Owen-*
Jones Esq (alt) **R** J G WILLIAMS
NORTON SUB HAMDON (Blessed Virgin Mary) w West
Chinnock, Chiselborough and Middle Chinnock *B & W 6*
P *Bp* **R** B J DALTON
NORTON SUBCOURSE (St Mary) The Raveningham Gp
Nor
NORTON WOODSEATS (St Chad) *Sheff 2* **P** *Bp*
V E HUME
NORTON WOODSEATS (St Paul) *Sheff 2* **P** *R Norton*
V M P HIRONS
NORWELL (St Laurence), w Ossington, Cromwell and
Caunton *S'well 3* **P** *Bp, SMF, and Mrs P Goedhuis (jt)*
V R A WHITTAKER
NORWICH Heartsease (St Francis) *Nor 1* **P** *Bp*
P-in-c P L HOWARD
NORWICH (St Andrew) *Nor 1* **P** *DBF*
P-in-c R ALLINGTON-SMITH
NORWICH (St Augustine) Nor Over-the-Water *Nor*
NORWICH (St George) as above
NORWICH (St George) Tombland *Nor 1* **P** *Bp*
NSM J C MINNS
NORWICH (St Giles) *Nor 1* **P** *Ld Chan and Bp (alt)*
P-in-c D A ABRAHAM
NORWICH (St Helen) *Nor 1* **P** *Gt Hosp Nor*
P-in-c L WOOD
NORWICH (St Julian) Nor St Pet Parmentergate w St Jo *Nor*
NORWICH (St Mary in the Marsh) *Nor 1* **P** *D&C*
Hon C P W E CURRIE
NORWICH (St Mary Magdalene) Nor Over-the-Water *Nor*
NORWICH (St Peter Mancroft) (St John Maddermarket)
Nor 1 **P** *DBF* **R** D M SHARP, **C** R D SIMPER,
Hon C H R G COOKE, **NSM** R J M COLLIER
NORWICH St Peter Parmentergate w St John de Sepulchre
(St John) (St Julian) *Nor 1* **P** *Patr Bd* **P-in-c** M D SMITH
NORWICH (St Stephen) *Nor 1* **P** *D&C* **P-in-c** K G BEAKE
NORWICH Timberhill (St John) Nor St Pet Parmentergate w
St Jo *Nor*
NORWICH OVER-THE-WATER *Nor 1* **P** *Patr Bd*
TR R M S WOODHAM, **TV** A P WARD, H M WAKEMAN
NORWOOD (St Margaret) Upper Norwood All SS *S'wark*
NORWOOD (St Mary the Virgin) *Lon 23* **P** *SMF*
R M F GODDARD
NORWOOD, SOUTH (Holy Innocents) *S'wark 23* **P** *Bp*
V R D NEWMAN
NORWOOD, SOUTH (St Alban the Martyr) *S'wark 23*
P *Bp* **P-in-c** I S BROTHWOOD
NORWOOD, SOUTH (St Mark) *S'wark 23* **P** *Bp*
V P E THROWER
NORWOOD, UPPER (All Saints) *S'wark 23* **P** *V Croydon*
V A D MIDDLETON, **C** A J PRICE, **Hon C** V PARSONS
NORWOOD, UPPER (St John) *S'wark 23* **P** *Bp*
V D G MARTIN, **NSM** T L DAVIS
NORWOOD, WEST (St Luke) *S'wark 13* **P** *Abp*
V P H RONAYNE, **C** A R CHRISTIE, **Hon C** B ALLEN
NOTGROVE (St Bartholomew) Cold Aston w Notgrove and
Turkdean *Glouc*
NOTTING DALE (St Clement) (St Mark) and Norlands
(St James) *Lon 12* **P** *Bp* **V** H D J RAYMENT-PICKARD
NOTTING HILL (All Saints) (St Columb) *Lon 12* **P** *SMF*
V J K BROWNSELL, **NSM** R E DUGUID, D C CLUES
NOTTING HILL (St John) (St Peter) *Lon 12* **P** *Bp*
V H J STRINGER, **C** A J WATSON, **Hon C** D OONSLOW

NOTTING HILL (St Michael and All Angels) (Christ Church) (St Francis) Lon 12   **P** Trustees   **V** A B ANDREWS,   **C** R A BLOCK

NOTTINGHAM (All Saints) S'well 12   **P** Trustees   **V** D C WHITE, **Par Dn** E MATTHEWS-LOYDALL,   **C** J M PILGRIM

NOTTINGHAM (St Andrew) S'well 12   **P** Peache Trustees   **V** R M CLARK

NOTTINGHAM (St Ann w Emmanuel) S'well 12   **P** Trustees   **V** J P NEILL

NOTTINGHAM (St George w St John the Baptist) S'well 12   **P** Bp   **V** Vacant Nottingham (0115) 986 4881

NOTTINGHAM (St Jude) S'well 12   **P** CPAS   **V** S E DYAS,   **C** S D SILVESTER

NOTTINGHAM (St Mary the Virgin) and St Catharine S'well 12   **P** Bp   **V** J E M NEALE,   **C** S M CUMMING, **Hon C** J E LAMB

NOTTINGHAM (St Nicholas) S'well 12   **P** CPAS   **R** D J BETTS,   **C** S J HELLYER,   **NSM** J D BEALES

NOTTINGHAM (St Peter and St James) S'well 12   **P** Bp   **R** L J MORLEY,   J W HUCKLE,   **C** E M McLEAN

NOTTINGHAM (St Saviour) S'well 12   **P** CPAS   **V** J W BENTHAM,   **C** D A STEVENSON

NOTTINGHAM (St Stephen) Basford w Hyson Green S'well

NOWTON (St Peter) Hawstead and Nowton w Stanningfield etc St E

NUFFIELD (Holy Trinity) Ox 6   **P** MMCET   **R** J F SHEARER

NUN MONKTON (St Mary) Lower Nidderdale Ripon

NUNBURNHOLME (St James) and Warter York 7   **P** Abp and Marquis of Normanby (jt)   **R** K G SKIPPER

NUNEATON (St Mary) Cov 5   **P** V Nuneaton   **V** J T GRATY

NUNEATON (St Nicolas) Cov 5   **P** The Crown   **V** G J HARDWICK,   **C** C B POLLARD

NUNHEAD (St Antony) (St Silas) S'wark 6   **P** Bp   **V** A R C BROWNE

NUNNEY (All Saints) and Witham Friary, Marston Bigot, Wanstrow and Cloford B & W 4   **P** Bp, SMF, and C N Clarke Esq and Exors Duke of Somerset (jt)   **R** J K HODDER

NUNNINGTON (All Saints) Harome w Stonegrave, Nunnington and Pockley York

NUNTHORPE (St Mary's Church Hall) (St Mary the Virgin) York 22   **P** Abp   **V** T M THOMPSON,   **C** C M BURKE,   **NSM** P M HARRISON

NUNTON (St Andrew) Odstock w Nunton and Bodenham Sarum

NURSLING (St Boniface) (St John the Evangelist) and Rownhams Win 11   **P** Bp   **R** I D GARDNER

NURSTEAD (St Mildred) Meopham w Nurstead Roch

NUTBOURNE (St Wilfrid) Chidham Chich

NUTFIELD (St Peter and St Paul) S'wark 25   **P** Jes Coll Ox   **R** G I WILLIAMS

NUTFIELD, LOWER (Christ Church) S'wark 25   **P** Ch Patr Trust   **P-in-c** A E THOMPSON

NUTHALL (St Patrick) S'well 7   **P** Bp   **R** R PALIN

NUTHURST (St Andrew) Chich 8   **P** Bp Lon   **R** A G SAGE

NUTHURST (St Thomas) Packwood w Hockley Heath Birm

NUTLEY (St James the Less) Chich 21   **P** R Maresfield   **V** M T A BULMAN

NYMET (St George) S Molton w Nymet St George, High Bray etc Ex

NYMET ROWLAND (St Bartholomew) Lapford, Nymet Rowland and Coldridge Ex

NYMET TRACEY (St Bartholomew) Bow w Broad Nymet Ex

NYMPSFIELD (St Bartholomew) Uley w Owlpen and Nympsfield Glouc

NYNEHEAD (All Saints) Wellington and Distr B & W

OADBY (St Paul) (St Peter) Leic 5   **P** Bp   **TR** D H CLARK, **TV** R KANERIA,   **C** J D CURTIS, **Hon C** M J NOTLEY,   **NSM** G TURNOCK

OAKAMOOR (Holy Trinity) Alton w Bradley-le-Moors and Oakamoor w Cotton Lich

OAKDALE (St George) Sarum 8   **P** Bp   **TR** D K CALLARD, **TV** C G ROBINSON,   **C** J M BAILEY,   **NSM** D G BELLAIRS-COX

OAKE (St Bartholomew) Bradf w Oake, Hillfarrance and Heathfield B & W

OAKENGATES (Holy Trinity) Ketley and Oakengates Lich

OAKENSHAW (Church of the Good Shepherd) Willington and Sunnybrow Dur

OAKENSHAW (St Andrew) cum Woodlands Bradf 2   **P** Bp   **P-in-c** P G WALKER

OAKFIELD (St John) Portsm 7   **P** V St Helens   **V** H E WRIGHT

OAKFORD (St Peter) Washfield, Stoodleigh, Withleigh etc Ex

OAKHAM (All Saints) w Hambleton and Egleton and Braunston w Brooke Pet 14   **P** Dr E R Hanbury (1 turn), D&C Linc (2 turns)   **V** M W R COVINGTON,   **C** P J McKEE,   **NSM** E B WALKER,   B A NICHOLLS

OAKHANGER (St Luke's Mission Church) Alsager Ch Ch Ches

OAKHANGER (St Mary Magdalene) E and W Worldham, Hartley Mauditt w Kingsley etc Win

OAKHILL (All Saints) Ashwick w Oakhill and Binegar B & W

OAKHILL Eastwood View (shared church) Clifton St Jas Sheff

OAKINGTON (St Andrew) Ely 5   **P** Qu Coll Cam   **V** J C ALEXANDER

OAKLEY (St Mary) Worminghall w Ickford, Oakley and Shabbington Ox

OAKLEY (St Mary) Bromham w Oakley and Stagsden St Alb

OAKLEY (St Nicholas) N Hartismere St E

OAKLEY, EAST (St John) Church Oakley and Wootton St Lawrence Win

OAKLEY, GREAT (All Saints) w Wix Chelmsf 21   **P** Ch Patr Trust and St Jo Coll Cam (jt)   **P-in-c** P H WILLIAMS,   **NSM** P E H PALMER

OAKLEY, GREAT (St Michael) Corby SS Pet and Andr w Gt and Lt Oakley Pet

OAKLEY, LITTLE (St Peter) as above

OAKMOOR Bishopsnympton, Rose Ash, Mariansleigh etc Ex

OAKRIDGE (St Bartholomew) Bisley, Oakridge, Miserden and Edgeworth Glouc

OAKS IN CHARNWOOD (St James the Greater) and Copt Oak Leic 8   **P** DBP   **V** G A PADDOCK

OAKSEY (All Saints) Ashley, Crudwell, Hankerton, Long Newnton etc Bris

OAKWOOD (no dedication) Derby 9   **P** Bp and MMCET (jt)   **V** Vacant Derby (01332) 669213

OAKWOOD (St Thomas) Lon 18   **P** Bp   **V** J D TRIGG,   **C** N L SHARP

OAKWORTH (Christ Church) Bradf 8   **P** Bp   **V** D J SWALES

OARE (Blessed Virgin Mary) w Culbone B & W 16   **P** Bp   **P-in-c** A F I NOBLE

OARE (Holy Trinity) Swanborough Sarum

OARE (St Bartholomew) Chieveley w Winterbourne and Oare Ox

OARE (St Peter) The Brents and Davington w Oare and Luddenham Cant

OATLANDS (St Mary) Guildf 8   **P** Bp   **V** M ANKER,   **C** H WHITEHEAD

OBORNE (St Cuthbert) Queen Thorne Sarum

OCCOLD (St Michael) St E 16   **P** Lt-Comdr G C Marshall   **P-in-c** R H SMITH

OCKBROOK (All Saints) Derby 13   **P** Lt-Col T H Pares   **V** D M F NEWMAN,   **C** T M SUMPTER,   **NSM** J D BISHOP

OCKENDON, NORTH (St Mary Magdalene) Chelmsf 2   **P** Bp   **NSM** J E SKIPPER

OCKENDON, SOUTH (St Nicholas) Chelmsf 14   **P** Guild of All So   **P-in-c** R W SPRINGETT

OCKER HILL (St Mark) Lich 7   **P** Bp   **V** R A BRADBURY

OCKFORD RIDGE (St Mark) Godalming Guildf

OCKHAM (All Saints) w Hatchford Guildf 10   **P** Bp   **P-in-c** K A ELFORD

OCKLEY (St Margaret), Okewood and Forest Green Guildf 7   **P** Bp and J P M H Evelyn Esq (alt)   **R** C de F TICKNER

OCLE PYCHARD (St James the Great) Stoke Lacy, Moreton Jeffries w Much Cowarne etc Heref

ODCOMBE (St Peter and St Paul), Brympton, Lufton and Montacute B & W 6   **P** Ch Ch Ox (4 turns), C E B Clive-Ponsonby-Fane Esq (1 turn)   **R** J F JENKINS

ODD RODE (All Saints) Ches 11   **P** R Astbury   **R** R N WELBOURNE,   **C** P J CLARKE

ODDINGLEY (St James) Bowbrook S Worc

ODDINGTON (Holy Ascension) Broadwell, Evenlode, Oddington and Adlestrop Glouc

ODDINGTON (St Andrew) Islip w Charlton on Otmoor, Oddington, Noke etc Ox

ODDINGTON (St Nicholas) Broadwell, Evenlode, Oddington and Adlestrop Glouc

ODELL (All Saints) and Pavenham St Alb 21   **P** Lord Luke of Pavenham   **R** J T LIGHTOWLER,   **NSM** D R BANNARD-SMITH

ODIHAM (All Saints) Win 5   **P** Bp   **V** R C HUBBLE

ODSTOCK (St Mary) w Nunton and Bodenham Sarum 11   **P** Earl of Radnor   **P-in-c** R P HOLLINGSHURST

OFFCHURCH (St Gregory) *Cov 10* **P** *Bp*
P-in-c C M SIMPSON, **C** S A SIMPSON (nee RALPHS)
OFFENHAM (St Mary and St Milburgh) and Bretforton
Worc 1 **P** *Bp and D&C (alt)* **P-in-c** A J WRIGHT
OFFERTON (St Alban) (St John) *Ches 18* **P** *Bp*
V R E READ, **C** J E L ALEXANDER
OFFHAM (Old St Peter) Hamsey *Chich*
OFFHAM (St Michael) W Malling w Offham *Roch*
OFFLEY (St Mary Magdalene) King's Walden and Offley w
Lilley *St Alb*
OFFLEY, HIGH (St Mary the Virgin) and Norbury *Lich 12*
P *Bp* **R** D KNIGHT
OFFLEY HAY (Mission Church) Eccleshall *Lich*
OFFORD D'ARCY (All Saints) w Offord Cluny *Ely 12*
P *Ld Chan* **R** P J TAYLOR
OFFTON (St Mary) Somersham w Flowton and Offton w
Willisham *St E*
OFFWELL (St Mary the Virgin) Colyton, Southleigh,
Offwell, Widworthy etc *Ex*
OGBOURNE (St Andrew) Ridgeway *Sarum*
OGBOURNE (St George) as above
OGLEY HAY (St James) *Lich 1* **P** *Bp* **V** C N THOMAS,
C M P BRANSCOMBE
OGWELL (St Bartholomew) and Denbury *Ex 11* **P** *Bp and
SMF (jt)* **R** R G DAVIS
OKEFORD FITZPAINE (St Andrew) Childe Okeford,
Okeford Fitzpaine, Manston etc *Sarum*
**OKEHAMPTON (All Saints) (St James) w Inwardleigh;
Bratton Clovelly w Germansweek; Northlew w Ashbury; and
Bridestowe and Sourton** *Ex 12* **P** *Patr Bd*
TR R C CHAMBERLAIN, **TV** R W L VODEN,
C J G STONES, **Hon C** D K JAMESON
OKEWOOD (St John the Baptist) Ockley, Okewood and
Forest Green *Guildf*
OLD: *see also under substantive place names*
OLD FORD (St Paul w St Stephen) (St Mark) Victoria Park
Lon 7 **P** *Hyndman Trustees and CPAS (jt)*
P-in-c J OSBORNE
OLD HILL (Holy Trinity) *Worc 9* **P** *Ch Soc Trust*
V P D J SWANN
OLD LANE (Mission Church) Bloxwich *Lich*
OLD WIVES LEES (Mission Church) Chilham w Challock
and Molash *Cant*
OLDBERROW (St Mary) Spernall, Morton Bagot and
Oldberrow *Cov*
OLDBROOK (Community Church) Woughton *Ox*
OLDBURY *Birm 5* **P** *Bp* **P-in-c** R T ETHERIDGE
OLDBURY *Sarum 18* **P** *Bp, CPAS, Earl of Shelborne, and
E Money-Kyrle Esq (jt)* **P-in-c** J P R SAUNT
OLDBURY (St Nicholas) Bridgnorth, Tasley, Astley
Abbotts, Oldbury etc *Heref*
OLDBURY-ON-SEVERN (St Arilda) *Glouc 7* **P** *Ch Ch Ox*
P-in-c R W MARTIN
OLDBURY-ON-THE-HILL (St Arild) Boxwell, Leighterton,
Didmarton, Oldbury etc *Glouc*
OLDCOTES (St Mark's Mission Church) Langold *S'well*
OLDHAM Moorside (St Thomas) *Man 21* **P** *Trustees*
V J H GRAY
OLDHAM (St Ambrose) *Man 19* **P** *Bp* **V** B P H JAMES
OLDHAM (St Andrew) (St Mary w St Peter) *Man 19*
P *Patr Bd* **TR** J SYKES, **TV** C H RAZZALL
OLDHAM (St Barnabas) *Man 19* **P** *The Crown*
V F A CORBIN
OLDHAM (St Chad) Limeside *Man 19* **P** *Bp*
P-in-c N J HOWARD
OLDHAM (St James) *Man 19* **P** *R Prestwich St Mary*
V P PLUMPTON
OLDHAM (St Paul) *Man 19* **P** *Bp* **P-in-c** C MARSDEN,
C D J QUARMBY
OLDHAM (St Stephen and All Martyrs) Lower Moor
Man 19 **P** *Bp* **V** *Vacant 0161–678 9565*
OLDHURST (St Peter) Somersham w Pidley and Oldhurst
Ely
OLDLAND (St Anne) *Bris 2* **P** *Bp* **V** M H PERRY
OLDRIDGE (St Thomas) Tedburn St Mary, Whitestone,
Oldridge etc *Ex*
OLDSWINFORD (St Mary) Old Swinford Stourbridge *Worc*
OLIVER'S BATTERY (St Mark) Stanmore *Win*
OLLERTON (St Giles) (St Paulinus) w Boughton *S'well 6*
P *Ld Chan and Bp (alt)* **P-in-c** J M MASKELL,
C A A TOOBY
OLNEY (St Peter and St Paul) w Emberton *Ox 27* **P** *Bp*
R N P H POND, **C** A R NIXON, **Hon C** C M LOOKER
OLTON (St Margaret) *Birm 13* **P** *Bp and V Bickenhill (jt)*
V N S DODDS, **C** G H SAUNDERS
OLVESTON (St Mary of Malmesbury) *Bris 8* **P** *D&C*
P-in-c A D THORNE

OMBERSLEY (St Andrew) w Doverdale *Worc 8* **P** *Bp and
Lord Sandys (alt)* **P-in-c** S P KERR,
NSM R W WAGSTAFF
ONCHAN (St Peter) *S & M 2* **P** *The Crown*
V D BAGGALEY, **NSM** R HARPER
ONECOTE (St Luke) Ipstones w Berkhamsytch and Onecote
w Bradnop *Lich*
ONEHOUSE (St John the Baptist) Gt Finborough w
Onehouse and Harleston *St E*
ONGAR, HIGH (St Mary the Virgin) w Norton Mandeville
Chelmsf 28 **P** *Ch Soc Trust* **R** R J GRIFFITHS
ONIBURY (St Michael and All Angels) Culmington w
Onibury, Bromfield etc *Heref*
OPENSHAW (St Barnabas) *Man 1* **P** *Trustees*
R J WALLER
OPENSHAW, HIGHER (St Clement) *Man 1* **P** *Trustees*
R W NELSON
OPENWOODGATE (St Mark) Belper *Derby*
ORBY (All Saints) *Linc 8* **P** *Bp* **P-in-c** T STEELE
ORCHARD (Community Centre) Egglescliffe *Dur*
ORCHARD PORTMAN (St Michael) Staple Fitzpaine,
Orchard Portman, Thurlbear etc *B & W*
ORCHARD WAY (St Barnabas) Cheltenham St Mark *Glouc*
ORCHARDLEIGH (Blessed Virgin Mary) Beckington w
Standerwick, Berkley, Rodden etc *B & W*
ORCHESTON (St Mary) Tilshead, Orcheston and Chitterne
Sarum
ORCOP (St John the Baptist) St Weonards w Orcop,
Garway, Tretire etc *Heref*
ORDSALL (All Hallows) (St Alban) *S'well 5* **P** *Bp*
R A N EVANS, **C** S DIXON
ORE (Christ Church) *Chich 17* **P** *Simeon's Trustees*
V J G PANGBOURNE, **NSM** F ROWSON
ORE (St Barnabas) *Chich 17* **P** *Simeon's Trustees*
C C G SPENCER, **NSM** D K MOYNAGH
ORESTON (Church of the Good Shepherd) Plymstock *Ex*
ORFORD (St Andrew) *Liv 12* **P** *Bp* **V** J HILTON
**ORFORD (St Bartholomew) w Sudbourne, Chillesford, Butley
and Iken** *St E 7* **P** *Bp* **R** *Vacant Orford (01394) 450336*
ORFORD (St Margaret) *Liv 12* **P** *Bp* **V** M S FINLAY,
NSM J BROCKLEBANK
ORLESTONE (St Mary) w Snave and Ruckinge w Warehorne
Cant 12 **P** *Abp and Ld Chan (alt)* **P-in-c** R D KING
ORLETON (St George) w Brimfield *Heref 7* **P** *Bp* **R** *Vacant
Yarpole (01568) 780324*
ORLINGBURY (St Mary) Gt w Lt Harrowden and
Orlingbury *Pet*
ORMESBY (St Cuthbert) *York 19* **P** *Abp*
V R A SMAILES, **C** N M EDWARDS
**ORMESBY (St Margaret) w Scratby, Ormesby St Michael and
Rollesby** *Nor 6* **P** *Bp, D&C, DBP and R J H Tacon Esq
(jt)* **V** C W COUSINS
ORMESBY (St Michael) see above
ORMESBY, NORTH (Holy Trinity) *York 19* **P** *Abp*
P-in-c T J ROBINSON
ORMSBY Group, The SOUTH (St Leonard) *Linc 7*
P *A J Massingberd-Mundy Esq, Sir Thomas Ingilby, Bt, Mert
Coll Ox, Bp, and DBP (jt)* **R** R W B MASSINGBERD-
MUNDY
ORMSGILL (St Francis) Barrow St Matt *Carl*
ORMSIDE (St James) *Carl 1* **P** *Bp and D&C (jt)*
R P E P NORTON
ORMSKIRK (St Peter and St Paul) *Liv 11* **P** *Lord Derby*
V P M KIRBY, **C** J P LEFFLER
ORPINGTON (All Saints) *Roch 15* **P** *D&C*
V R R LUNNON, **C** K M PARRY, **NSM** M T SKINNER
ORPINGTON (Christ Church) *Roch 15* **P** *Ch Trust Fund
Trust, Bp, and V Orpington (jt)* **V** A C EAVES,
C J J FRAIS
ORPINGTON (St Andrew) *Roch 15* **P** *Bp* **V** J A GROVES
ORRELL (St Luke) *Liv 15* **P** *Bp* **V** C POPE
**ORSETT (St Giles and All Saints) and Bulphan and Horndon
on the Hill** *Chelmsf 14* **P** *Bp and D&C St Paul's (jt)*
R J A V FLORANCE, **NSM** J M WHITEHORN
ORSTON (St Mary) Whatton w Aslockton, Hawksworth,
Scarrington etc *S'well*
**ORTON (All Saints) and Tebay w Ravenstonedale and
Newbiggin-on-Lune** *Carl 1* **P** *Bp and Ravenstonedale
Trustees (1 turn), Resident Landowners (1 turn)*
R C R LEVEY
ORTON (St Giles) *Carl 1* **P** *MMCET* **R** *Vacant*
ORTON GOLDHAY (St John) Conventional District *Ely 13*
C-in-c F E G BRAMPTON
ORTON LONGUEVILLE (Holy Trinity) *Ely 13* **P** *Bp*
P-in-c M SOULSBY

ORTON MALBORNE (not known) Orton Longueville *Ely*

ORTON-ON-THE-HILL (St Edith of Polesworth) The Sheepy Gp *Leic*

ORTON WATERVILLE (St Mary) *Ely 13* **P** *Pemb Coll Cam* **P-in-c** G GOSWELL, **C** F E G BRAMPTON

ORWELL (St Andrew) *Ely 8* **P** *Bp and DBP (alt)*
R N A BRICE

OSBALDWICK (St Thomas) w Murton *York 4* **P** *Abp*
V R A STONE

OSBOURNBY (St Peter and St Paul) S Lafford *Linc*

OSCOTT, OLD (All Saints) Kingstanding St Mark *Birm*

OSENEY CRESCENT (St Luke) Kentish Town *Lon*

OSGATHORPE (St Mary the Virgin) Hathern, Long Whatton and Diseworth w Belton etc *Leic*

OSMASTON (St Martin) Brailsford w Shirley and Osmaston w Edlaston *Derby*

OSMINGTON (St Osmond) Preston w Sutton Poyntz and Osmington w Poxwell *Sarum*

OSMONDTHORPE (St Philip) *Ripon 8* **P** *Bp*
P-in-c P B STOODLEY

OSMOTHERLEY (St Peter) w Harlsey and Ingleby Arncliffe
York 20 **P** J B Barnard Esq (1 turn), Ld Chan (2 turns)
V A H DODD

OSMOTHERLY (St John) Ulverston St Mary w H Trin *Carl*

OSPRINGE (St Peter and St Paul) Eastling w Ospringe and Stalisfield w Otterden *Cant*

OSSETT (St Oswald's Mission Room) (Holy and Undivided Trinity) cum Gawthorpe *Wakef 10* **P** R Dewsbury
V M GREEN, **C** J P TAYLOR

OSSETT, SOUTH (Christ Church) *Wakef 10* **P** *Bp*
V F J MARSH, **C** M J CAREY, **NSM** R E RICHARDSON

OSSINGTON (Holy Rood) Norwell w Ossington, Cromwell and Caunton *S'well*

OSWALDKIRK (St Oswald) Ampleforth and Oswaldkirk and Gilling E *York*

OSWALDTWISTLE (Immanuel) (All Saints) *Blackb 1*
P *Trustees* **V** F PARR

OSWALDTWISTLE (St Paul) *Blackb 1* **P** *Trustees*
V M D RATCLIFFE

OSWESTRY (St Oswald) (Holy Trinity) *Lich 24* **P** *Earl of Powis* **V** D B CROWHURST, **C** T R K LAW,
T N THOROLD, **NSM** A B STRATFORD

OTFORD (St Bartholomew) *Roch 9* **P** *D&C Westmr*
V D W TOWNE

OTFORD LANE (Mission Hall) Knockholt w Halstead *Roch*

OTHAM (St Nicholas) w Langley *Cant 15* **P** *Abp and CPAS (jt)* **R** D A MUSTON, **NSM** D W BOND

OTHERY (St Michael) Middlezoy and Othery and Moorlinch *B & W*

OTLEY (All Saints) *Bradf 4* **P** *Bp* **V** I T RODLEY,
C K G DAVIES, M P SHORT

OTLEY (St Mary) Clopton w Otley, Swilland and Ashbocking *St E*

OTTER VALE Ottery St Mary, Alfington, W Hill, Tipton etc *Ex*

OTTERBOURNE (St Matthew) Compton and Otterbourne *Win*

OTTERBURN (St John the Evangelist) N Tyne and Redesdale Team *Newc*

OTTERFORD (St Leonard) Churchstanton, Buckland St Mary and Otterford *B & W*

OTTERHAM (St Denis) Boscastle w Davidstow *Truro*

OTTERINGTON, NORTH (St Michael and All Angels) The Thorntons and The Otteringtons *York*

OTTERINGTON, SOUTH (St Andrew) as above

OTTERSHAW (Christ Church) *Guildf 11* **P** *Bp*
V J W BATT

OTTERTON (St Michael) E Budleigh w Bicton and Otterton *Ex*

OTTERY ST MARY (St Mary the Virgin), Alfington, West Hill and Tipton St John w Venn Ottery *Ex 7* **P** *Patr Bd*
TR P J McGEE, **TV** P J NICKOLS-RAWLE,
C A M JORDAN

OTTRINGHAM (St Wilfrid) Keyingham w Ottringham, Halsham and Sunk Is *York*

OUGHTIBRIDGE (Ascension) *Sheff 7* **P** *V Wadsley*
V L M ATKINSON

OUGHTRINGTON (St Peter) *Ches 10* **P** *Bp*
R E M BURGESS

OULTON (St John the Evangelist) Stone Ch Ch and Oulton *Lich*

OULTON (St John) w Woodlesford *Ripon 8* **P** *Bp*
V W J HULSE

OULTON (St Michael) *Nor 9* **P** *Ch Soc Trust*
R A R PRITCHARD

OULTON (St Peter and St Paul) Saxthorpe w Corpusty, Blickling, Oulton etc *Nor*

OULTON BROAD (St Mark) (St Luke the Evangelist)
Nor 9 **P** *Simeon's Trustees* **V** W A STEWART,
C J M BEACH, **Hon C** J M STEWART

OUNDLE (St Peter) *Pet 12* **P** *Bp* **V** L R CADDICK,
NSM D M JARMY

OUSBY (St Luke) Skirwith, Ousby and Melmerby w Kirkland *Carl*

OUSDEN (St Peter) Wickhambrook w Lydgate, Ousden and Cowlinge *St E*

OUSEBURN, GREAT (St Mary) and LITTLE (Holy Trinity) w Marton-cum-Grafton *Ripon 3* **P** *Bp and St Jo Coll Cam (alt)* **V** S J TALBOTT, **NSM** M SAUNDERS

OUT RAWCLIFFE (St John the Evangelist) Hambleton w Out Rawcliffe *Blackb*

OUTLANE (St Mary Magdalene) Stainland *Wakef*

OUTWELL (St Clement) *Ely 19* **P** *Bp* **R** T J HEGGS

OUTWOOD (St John) *S'wark 24* **P** *Bp* **P-in-c** W G WOOD

OUTWOOD (St Mary Magdalene) *Wakef 12* **P** *V Stanley*
V J W BUTTERWORTH

OUTWOOD COMMON (St John the Divine) Billericay and Lt Burstead *Chelmsf*

OVAL WAY (All Saints) Chalfont St Peter *Ox*

OVENDEN (St George) *Wakef 4* **P** *V Halifax*
V S J L CROFT, **C** P F HINCKLEY

OVENDEN (St John the Evangelist) Bradshaw *Wakef*

OVER: *see also under substantive place names*

OVER (St Chad) *Ches 6* **P** *Bp* **V** J J E SUTTON,
C M SAVILLE

OVER (St John the Evangelist) *Ches 6* **P** *Lord Delamere and W R Cullimore Esq (jt)* **V** S F HAMILL-STEWART

OVER (St Mary) *Ely 5* **P** *Trin Coll Cam* **V** M WARRICK

OVERBURY (St Faith) w Teddington, Alstone and Little Washbourne w Beckford and Ashton under Hill *Worc 4*
P *D&C and MMCET (jt)* **V** J T W B JENKYNS,
NSM H M HUMPHREY

OVERCHURCH (St Mary) Upton (or Overchurch) *Ches*

OVERPOOL (St Francis) Ellesmere Port *Ches*

OVERSEAL (St Matthew) Nether and Over Seale *Derby*

OVERSTONE (St Nicholas) Mears Ashby and Hardwick and Sywell etc *Pet*

OVERSTRAND (St Martin), Northrepps, Sidestrand and Trimingham *Nor 22* **P** *Duchy of Lanc, DBP, and Bp (by turn)* **R** S HABGOOD

OVERTON (St Helen) *Blackb 12* **P** *V Lanc* **V** C BIRKET

OVERTON (St Mary) w Laverstoke and Freefolk *Win 6*
P *Bp* **R** N P CUMMING

OVERTON (St Michael and All Angels) Upper Kennett *Sarum*

OVING (All Saints) Schorne *Ox*

OVING (St Andrew) Tangmere and Oving *Chich*

OVINGDEAN (St Wulfran) *Chich 2* **P** *SMF*
P-in-c T S STRATFORD

OVINGHAM (St Mary the Virgin) *Newc 3* **P** *Bp*
V D L GOODACRE

OVINGTON (St John the Evangelist) Watton w Carbrooke and Ovington *Nor*

OVINGTON (St Mary) w Tilbury *Chelmsf 15*
P *M H Granger Esq* **R** *Vacant*

OVINGTON (St Peter) New Alresford w Ovington and Itchen Stoke *Win*

OWERMOIGNE (St Michael) Broadmayne, W Knighton, Owermoigne etc *Sarum*

OWERSBY, NORTH (St Martin) S Kelsey Gp *Linc*

OWLERTON (St John the Baptist) *Sheff 4* **P** *Ch Patr Trust* **NSM** G COCKAYNE

OWLPEN (Holy Cross) Uley w Owlpen and Nympsfield *Glouc*

OWLSMOOR (St George) *Ox 16* **P** *Bp* **V** *Vacant*
Crowthorne (01344) 771286

OWLSWICK (Chapel) Monks Risborough *Ox*

OWMBY Group, The (St Peter and St Paul) *Linc 3* **P** *Duchy of Lanc, Bp and D&C, and Major-Gen W M Hutton and Earl of Scarbrough (by turn)* **R** I R HOWITT

OWSLEBURY (St Andrew) Twyford and Owslebury and Morestead *Win*

OWSTON (All Saints) *Sheff 8* **P** *DBP* **V** R A C GRIEVE

OWSTON (St Andrew) Whatborough Gp of Par *Leic*

OWSTON (St Martin) *Linc 1* **P** *The Crown* **V** *Vacant*
Owston Ferry (0142772) 305

OWTHORNE (St Matthew) and Rimswell w Withernsea
York 13 **P** *Ld Chan and Abp (alt)* **V** P I ADDISON

OWTHORPE (St Margaret) *S'well 9* **P** *Trustees Sir Rupert Bromley* **P-in-c** G B BARRODALE

OWTON MANOR (St James) *Dur 13* **P** *Bp*
V P ANDERTON, **C** T D PIKE

OXBOROUGH (St John the Evangelist) w Foulden and Caldecote *Nor 14* **P** *G&C Coll Cam* **P-in-c** A C FOOTTIT

OXCLOSE (not known) *Dur 1* **P** *R Washington, TR Usworth, and V Fatfield (jt)* **P-in-c** K H DUNNE

OXENDON (St Helen) Arthingworth, Harrington w Oxendon and E Farndon *Pet*

OXENHALL (St Anne) Redmarley D'Abitot, Bromesberrow w Pauntley etc *Glouc*

OXENHOPE (St Mary the Virgin) *Bradf 8* **P** *Bp*
   V B GRAINGER

OXENTON Woolstone w Gotherington and Oxenton etc *Glouc*

OXFORD Canning Crescent (St Luke) Ox St Aldate *Ox*

OXFORD (St Aldate) *Ox 7* **P** *Simeon's Trustees*
   R D R MACINNES, **C** J S W CHORLTON,
   Hon C A R WINGFIELD-DIGBY, **NSM** J EDMONDS-SEAL,
   J SEARS, T BRADSHAW

OXFORD (St Andrew) *Ox 7* **P** *Trustees* **V** R F KEY,
   C D H JACKSON, **Hon C** E G H SAUNDERS,
   NSM S W HALL

OXFORD (St Barnabas and St Paul) *Ox 7* **P** *Keble Coll Ox*
   V E M WRIGHT, **NSM** D W MASON

OXFORD (St Clement) *Ox 4* **P** *Ox Ch Trust*
   R J B GILLINGHAM, **C** D A S MacLAREN,
   J L MACLAREN (nee ALEXANDER), **NSM** A BEETHAM,
   E J JOHNSON

OXFORD (St Ebbe w Holy Trinity and St Peter-le-Bailey)
   Ox 7 **P** *Ox Ch Trust* **R** D C M FLETCHER,
   C V E ROBERTS, D R A GIBB

OXFORD (St Giles) (St Philip) (St James) (St Margaret)
   Ox 7 **P** *St Jo Coll Ox* **V** J F P MORRISON-WELLS,
   NSM D R HOLMES, M SCREECH, A ASTON SMITH,
   A J E GREEN

OXFORD (St Mary Magdalene) *Ox 7* **P** *Ch Ch Ox*
   V H M WYBREW

OXFORD (St Mary the Virgin) (St Cross or Holywell)
   (St Peter in the East) *Ox 7* **P** *Or Coll Ox and Mert Coll*
   Ox (jt) **V** B W MOUNTFORD, **C** R H WATTS,
   D K WILLOWS, **Hon C** G L CARTER

OXFORD (St Matthew) *Ox 7* **P** *Ox Ch Trust*
   R J F SAMWAYS

OXFORD (St Michael at the North Gate w St Martin and All Saints) *Ox 7* **P** *Linc Coll Ox* **V** S J PIX

OXFORD (St Thomas the Martyr) (St Frideswide) and Binsey
   Ox 7 **P** *Ch Ch Ox* **V** R M SWEENEY,
   NSM R C de V MARTIN

OXHEY (All Saints) *St Alb 13* **P** *Bp* **V** A P DOUGLAS,
   C P I LEECH

OXHEY (St Matthew) *St Alb 13* **P** *DBP* **V** J ORME,
   C O MURPHY

OXHILL (St Lawrence) Tysoe w Oxhill and Whatcote *Cov*

OXLEY (Epiphany) *Lich 9* **P** *Bp* **V** G C FOWELL

OXNEAD (St Michael & all Angels) Buxton w Oxnead, Lammas and Brampton *Nor*

OXON and Shelton *Lich 26* **P** *V Shrewsbury SS Chad & Mary* **V** P F T FISHER

OXSHOTT (St Andrew) *Guildf 10* **P** *Bp* **V** J P CRESSWELL

OXSPRING (St Aidan) Penistone and Thurlstone *Wakef*

OXTED (St Mary) *S'wark 24* **P** *Bp* **R** G BENNETT,
   C A J HALE, **NSM** F A HARDING

OXTON (St Peter and St Paul) *S'well 15* **P** *Ld Chan, Bp, and Comdr M B P Francklin (by turn)* **V** M J BROCK

OXTON (St Saviour) *Ches 1* **P** *DBP* **V** A J POULTER,
   C M G REED, C M KEMP

PACKINGTON (Holy Rood) w Normanton-le-Heath *Leic 9*
   P *MMCET and The Crown (alt)* **V** H A BURTON

PACKWOOD (St Giles) w Hockley Heath *Birm 13* **P** *DBP and Bp (alt)* **V** P H ROE

PADBURY (St Mary the Virgin) Lenborough *Ox*

PADDINGTON (Emmanuel) Harrow Road *Lon 2*
   P *Hyndman Trustees* **V** M M H JONES

PADDINGTON (St David's Welsh Church) Extra-Parochial Place *Lon 2* **P-in-c** A P HAWKINS

PADDINGTON (St James) *Lon 2* **P** *Bp* **V** W G WILSON,
   C A J B MELDRUM

PADDINGTON (St John the Evangelist) (St Michael and All Angels) *Lon 2* **P** *DBP* **V** T J BIRCHARD,
   C J C TERRY, **Hon C** C D V RICHARDS

PADDINGTON (St Luke the Evangelist) W Kilburn St Luke w St Simon and St Jude *Lon*

PADDINGTON (St Mary) *Lon 2* **P** *Bp* **V** *Vacant* 0171-723 1968

PADDINGTON (St Mary Magdalene) *Lon 2* **P** *Keble Coll Ox* **V** R F BUSHAU

PADDINGTON (St Peter) *Lon 2* **P** *Ch Patr Trust*
   P-in-c G M BUCKLE, **NSM** F W WARD

PADDINGTON (St Saviour) *Lon 2* **P** *Bp*
   V G S BRADLEY, **C** W H BAYNES, **Hon C** M GIBSON,
   NSM F E BLACKMORE

PADDINGTON (St Stephen w St Luke) *Lon 2* **P** *Bp*
   P-in-c T A GILLUM

PADDINGTON GREEN (St Mary) Paddington St Mary *Lon*

PADDLESWORTH (St Oswald) Lyminge w Paddlesworth, Stanford w Postling etc *Cant*

PADDOCK WOOD (St Andrew) *Roch 10* **P** *D&C Cant*
   V D G St L WINTER, **C** S C TILLOTSON

PADGATE (Christ Church) *Liv 12* **P** *Patr Bd*
   TR N T MOFFATT, **TV** R C HARDCASTLE, M H MILLS

PADIHAM (St Leonard) (St Anne and St Elizabeth)
   Blackb 3 **P** *Bp* **V** J C DUXBURY

PADSTOW (St Petrock) *Truro 7*
   P *C R Prideaux Brune Esq* **V** M A BOXALL

PADWORTH (St John the Baptist) Mortimer W End w Padworth *Ox*

PAGANHILL (Holy Spirit) Whiteshill and Randwick *Glouc*

PAGHAM (St Thomas a Becket) *Chich 1* **P** *Abp*
   V J W MAYNARD

PAGLESHAM (St Peter) Canewdon w Paglesham *Chelmsf*

PAIGNTON (Christ Church) (School Room) *Ex 10* **P** *Peache Trustees* **V** R C ADAMS

PAIGNTON (St John the Baptist) (St Andrew) (St Boniface)
   Ex 10 **P** *DBP* **C** C H OSBORNE, S J STEPHENS

PAIGNTON (St Paul) Preston *Ex 10* **P** *Bp* **V** M J BURTON

PAILTON (St Denis) Monks Kirby w Pailton and Stretton-under-Fosse *Cov*

PAINSWICK (St Mary the Virgin) w Sheepscombe *Glouc 1*
   P *Ld Chan* **V** M R MILES, **NSM** M B COLE

PAKEFIELD (All Saints and St Margaret) *Nor 9* **P** *Ch Patr Trust* **R** R J K BAKER

PAKENHAM (St Mary) w Norton and Tostock *St E 9* **P** *Bp and Peterho Cam (jt)* **V** I HOOPER

PALGRAVE (St Peter) N Hartismere *St E*

PALLION (St Luke) *Dur 9* **P** *Bp* **V** *Vacant* 0191-565 6554

PALMARSH (Holy Cross) Hythe *Cant*

PALMERS GREEN (St John the Evangelist) *Lon 18*
   P *V Southgate Ch Ch* **V** R C KNOWLING, **C** G D ALLEN

PALTERTON (St Luke's Mission Room) E Scarsdale *Derby*

PAMBER (St Mary and St John the Baptist) The Sherbornes w Pamber *Win*

PAMBER HEATH (St Luke) Tadley St Pet *Win*

PAMPISFORD (St John the Baptist) *Ely 7*
   P *Mrs B A Killander* **V** *Vacant*

PANCRASWEEK (St Pancras) Pyworthy, Pancrasweek and Bridgerule *Ex*

PANFIELD (St Mary the Virgin) *Chelmsf 16* **P** *Bp*
   R *Vacant* Braintree (01376) 324615

PANGBOURNE (St James the Less) w Tidmarsh and Sulham
   Ox 12 **P** *Bp, Ch Soc Trust, and Mrs I E Moon (jt)*
   V J C HUTCHINSON

PANNAL (St Robert of Knaresborough) w Beckwithshaw
   Ripon 1 **P** *Bp and Peache Trustees (jt)*
   V M de la P BERESFORD-PEIRSE

PANSHANGER (United Church) Digswell and Panshanger *St Alb*

PAPCASTLE (Mission Church) Bridekirk *Carl*

PAPPLEWICK (St James) Linby w Papplewick *S'well*

PAPWORTH EVERARD (St Peter) *Ely 1* **P** *DBP*
   R P S DUFFETT

PAR (St Mary the Virgin) (Good Shepherd) *Truro 1* **P** *The Crown* **V** *Vacant* Par (01726) 812775

PARHAM (St Mary the Virgin) Campsea Ashe w Marlesford, Parham and Hacheston *St E*

PARHAM (St Peter) Amberley w N Stoke and Parham, Wiggonholt etc *Chich*

PARKEND (St Paul) Dean Forest St Paul *Glouc*

PARKESTON (St Paul) Dovercourt and Parkeston *Chelmsf*

PARKFIELD (Holy Trinity) Langley and Parkfield *Man*

PARKGATE (St Thomas) Neston *Ches*

PARKHAM (St James), Alwington, Buckland Brewer, Abbotsham, Hartland, Welcombe, Clovelly, Woolfardisworthy West and Buck Mills *Ex 17* **P** *Patr Bd (4 turns), Crown (1 turn)* **TR** W G BLAKEY,
   TV R D S SANDERS, D J FORD, **C** M WARD,
   Hon C J A WHEELER, **NSM** S R SANDERS

PARKLANDS (St Wilfrid) Conventional District *Chich 3*
   C-in-c K R WHELAN, **NSM** D A MORLING

PARKSTONE (Good Shepherd) Heatherlands St Jo *Sarum*

PARKSTONE (St Luke) *Sarum 8* **P** *Ch Trust Fund Trust*
   P-in-c J W DAVIES

PARKSTONE (St Peter) (St Osmund) w Branksea *Sarum 8*
   P *Patr Bd* **TR** N J C LLOYD, **TV** W M HETLING,
   C R H DAVEY, **Hon C** D J NEWMAN

PARKWOOD (Christ Church) Maidstone St Martin *Cant*

PARLAUNT ROAD (Christ the Worker) Langley Marish *Ox*

955

PARLEY, WEST (All Saints) (St Mark) *Sarum 10*
P P E E *Prideaux-Brune Esq* **R** A G WATTS,
C S E HUTTON
PARNDON, GREAT (St Mary) *Chelmsf 27* **P** *Bp*
R C P BURTON, **C** R J BULLOCK, J M RAGAN
PARNDON, LITTLE (St Mary) Harlow Town Centre w Lt
Parndon *Chelmsf*
PARR Blackbrook (St Paul) Parr *Liv*
PARR Derbyshire Hill (St Philip) as above
PARR (St Peter) (St Paul) (St Philip) *Liv 10* **P** *Patr Bd*
TR D A THOMPSON, **TV** P C CATON, C A GILBERT,
C D G GAVIN, P D RATTIGAN
PARR MOUNT (Holy Trinity) *Liv 10* **P** *V St Helens*
V C S WOODS, **NSM** R J G HOPKINS
PARRACOMBE (Christ Church) Lynton, Brendon,
Countisbury, Lynmouth etc *Ex*
PARTINGTON (St Mary) and Carrington *Ches 10* **P** *Bp and
V Bowdon (alt)* **V** I J HUTCHINGS,
C A Q GREENHOUGH
PARTNEY (St Nicholas) *Linc 7* **P** *DBP, Bp, Baroness
Willoughby de Eresby, and Mrs E M V Drake(by turn)*
R *Vacant* Spilsby (01790) 53570
PARTRIDGE GREEN (St Michael and All Angels) W
Grinstead *Chich*
PARWICH (St Peter) w Alsop en le Dale *Derby 8*
P D A G *Shields Esq* **V** *Vacant* Parwich (0133525) 226
PASSENHAM (St Guthlac) *Pet 5* **P** *MMCET*
R C J MURRAY
PASTON (All Saints) *Pet 13* **P** *Bp* **R** M J G TOMPKINS,
C G R DREWERY
PASTON (St Margaret) Trunch *Nor*
PATCHAM (All Saints) *Chich 2* **P** *MMCET*
V N E D MILMINE, **C** L L ABBOTT, A J M SPEAR,
C D REDKNAP
PATCHAM, SOUTH (Christ the King) *Chich 2* **P** *Bp*
V D H HUMPHREY
PATCHING (St John the Divine) Findon w Clapham and
Patching *Chich*
PATCHWAY (St Chad) *Bris 6* **P** *Trustees* **V** B E PENN,
C C D BLAKE
PATELEY BRIDGE (St Cuthbert) Upper Nidderdale *Ripon*
PATRICK (Holy Trinity) *S & M 3* **P** *Bp*
V B H PARTINGTON, **NSM** H G R SLADE
PATRICK BROMPTON (St Patrick) and Hunton *Ripon 4*
P *Bp* **V** D J CHRISTIE
PATRICROFT (Christ Church) *Man 2* **P** *Bp*
P-in-c N JONES
**PATRINGTON (St Patrick) w Hollym, Welwick and
Winestead** *York 13* **P** *DBP, Ld Chan, and CPAS
(by turn)* **R** I M WELLERY
PATRIXBOURNE (St Mary) w Bridge and Bekesbourne
Cant 1 **P** *Abp* **V** R GILBERT
PATTERDALE (St Patrick) *Carl 4* **P** *Trustees* **R** *Vacant*
Glenridding (017684) 82209
PATTINGHAM (St Chad) w Patshull *Lich 5* **P** *Bp and Lady
Kwiatkowska (jt)* **P-in-c** G BLOOMFIELD
**PATTISHALL (Holy Cross) w Cold Higham and Gayton w
Tiffield** *Pet 5* **P** *Bp, SS Coll Cam, and SMF (jt)*
R P J BROADBENT
PAUL (St Pol de Lion) *Truro 5* **P** *Ld Chan* **V** G HARPER
PAULERSPURY (St James the Apostle) Whittlebury w
Paulerspury *Pet*
PAULL (St Andrew and St Mary) Hedon w Paull *York*
PAULSGROVE (St Michael and All Angels) *Portsm 6*
P *Bp* **V** I W RUTHERFORD, **C** G J GILES
PAULTON (Holy Trinity) *B & W 12* **P** *Bp and R Chewton
Mendip (alt)* **V** R E INGLESBY
PAUNTLEY (St John the Evangelist) Redmarley D'Abitot,
Bromesberrow w Pauntley etc *Glouc*
PAVENHAM (St Peter) Odell and Pavenham *St Alb*
PAWLETT (St John the Baptist) Puriton and Pawlett *B & W*
PAXFORD (Mission Church) Blockley w Aston Magna and
Bourton on the Hill *Glouc*
PAXTON, GREAT (Holy Trinity) *Ely 12* **P** *D&C Linc*
V P J TAYLOR
PAXTON, LITTLE (St James) *Ely 12* **P** *D&C Linc*
V P G LEWIS
PAYHEMBURY (St Mary the Virgin) Broadhembury,
Payhembury and Plymtree *Ex*
PEACEHAVEN (Ascension) *Chich 18* **P** *Bp*
P-in-c D A HIDER, **C** A V BOWMAN
PEAK DALE (Holy Trinity) Wormhill, Peak Forest w Peak
Dale and Dove Holes *Derby*
PEAK FOREST (St Charles the King and Martyr) as above
PEAKIRK (St Pega) w Glinton and Northborough *Pet 13*
P *D&C R* *Vacant* Peterborough (01733) 252265
PEAR TREE (Jesus Chapel) Southn St Mary Extra *Win*
PEASE POTTAGE (Ascension) Slaugham *Chich*

PEASEDOWN ST JOHN (St John the Baptist) w Wellow
B & W 12 **P** *Bp and R H Horton-Fawkes Esq (jt)*
V H R L BONSEY
PEASEMORE (St Barnabas) Beedon and Peasemore w W
Ilsley and Farnborough *Ox*
PEASENHALL (St Michael) Yoxford and Peasenhall w
Sibton *St E*
PEASE'S WEST (St George) Crook *Dur*
PEASLAKE (St Mark) Shere *Guildf*
PEASLEY CROSS (Mission Hall) Parr Mt *Liv*
PEASMARSH (St Michael) Shalford *Guildf*
PEASMARSH (St Peter and St Paul) Beckley and Peasmarsh
Chich
PEATLING MAGNA (All Saints) Willoughby Waterleys,
Peatling Magna etc *Leic*
PEATLING PARVA (St Andrew) Gilmorton w Peatling
Parva and Kimcote etc *Leic*
PEBMARSH (St John the Baptist) Alphamstone w Lamarsh
and Pebmarsh *Chelmsf*
PEBWORTH (St Peter) w Dorsington and Honeybourne
Glouc 10 **P** *Bp* **R** T R C OVERTHROW
PECKHAM (St John w St Andrew) *S'wark 6* **P** *Bp*
V M S JOHNSON, **Hon C** J E LANE
PECKHAM (St Mary Magdalene) (St Paul) *S'wark 6*
P *Ch Patr Soc* **V** M F PAYNE, **C** K G A ANSAH
PECKHAM (St Saviour) *S'wark 7* **P** *Bp*
V W CHEATLEY, **NSM** D L HARTLEY
PECKHAM, EAST (Holy Trinity) and Nettlestead *Roch 7*
P *St Pet Coll Ox and D&C Cant (jt)* **P-in-c** A M LEIGH,
NSM R S LEIGH
PECKHAM, WEST (St Dunstan) Mereworth w W Peckham
Roch
PECKLETON (St Mary Magdalene) Desford and Peckleton
w Tooley *Leic*
PEDLINGE (Estate Chapel) Saltwood *Cant*
PEDMORE (St Peter) *Worc 12* **P** *Oldswinford Hosp*
R A L HAZLEWOOD
PEEL (St Paul) *Man 12* **P** *Patr Bd* **TR** P BRODY,
TV H BRUNYEE, **NSM** K HOPWOOD OWEN
PEEL GREEN (St Michael and All Angels and
St Catherine) Barton w Peel Green *Man*
PEGSWOOD (St Margaret) Bothal and Pegswood w
Longhirst *Newc*
PELDON (St Mary) w Great and Little Wigborough
Chelmsf 17 **P** *Ch Soc Trust and T Wheatley-Hubbard Esq*
P-in-c R H ELPHICK, **NSM** J NEWHAM
PELSALL (St Michael and All Angels) *Lich 6* **P** *Bp*
V P H BEARD, **C** D M PORTER, **NSM** A W BRYANT
PELTON (Holy Trinity) *Dur 9* **P** *R Chester le Street*
V W A TAYLOR
PELTON, WEST (St Paul) *Dur 1* **P** *Bp*
P-in-c R F BIANCHI
PELYNT (St Nun) *Truro 12* **P** *J B Kitson and Mrs S R
Parker (alt)* **V** A R INGLEBY, **Hon C** D A WOODS
PEMBERTON (St Francis of Assisi) Kitt Green *Liv 15*
P *R Wigan and Bp (jt)* **V** N P ANDERSON
PEMBERTON (St John) *Liv 15* **P** *R Wigan*
R J A SOUTHERN
PEMBERTON (St Mark) Newtown *Liv 15* **P** *Duke of
Sutherland, Bp, and R Pemberton St Jo (jt)* **V** D V ROUCH
**PEMBRIDGE (St Mary the Virgin) w Moorcourt, Shobdon,
Staunton-on-Arrow and Byton** *Heref 5* **P** *Ld Chan (1 turn),
J R Whitehead Esq and Miss R Whitehead (jt) (1 turn), and
DBP (2 turns)* **R** S HOLLINGHURST
PEMBURY (St Peter) *Roch 11* **P** *Ch Ch Ox*
V R H BRASIER
PEN SELWOOD (St Michael) *B & W 2* **P** *Bp*
R R J CLOETE
PENCOMBE (St John) Bredenbury w Grendon Bishop and
Wacton etc *Heref*
PENCOYD (St Denys) St Weonards w Orcop, Garway,
Tretire etc *Heref*
PENCOYS (St Andrew) Redruth w Lanner and Treleigh
Truro
PENDEEN (St John the Baptist) w Morvah *Truro 5*
P *R A H Aitken Esq and C W M Aitken Esq (jt)*
V A ROWELL, **NSM** J HARPER
PENDEFORD (St Paul) Tettenhall Regis *Lich*
PENDLEBURY (St Augustine) Swinton and Pendlebury
Man
PENDLEBURY (St John) *Man 6* **P** *Trustees* **V** C JONES,
C T P RYLEY
PENDLETON (All Saints) Sabden and Pendleton *Blackb*
PENDLETON (St Ambrose) *Man 6* **P** *Bp*
P-in-c A I SALMON
PENDLETON (St Thomas) w Charlestown *Man 6*
P *Patr Bd* **P-in-c** W S BRISON, **Hon C** J H FIFE,
D J H KEYTE

PENDOCK CROSS (Holy Redeemer) Berrow w Pendock, Eldersfield, Hollybush etc *Worc*

PENDOMER (St Roch) W Coker w Hardington Mandeville, E Chinnock etc *B & W*

PENGE (Christ Church w Holy Trinity) Anerley *Roch*

PENGE (St John the Evangelist) *Roch 12* **P** *Simeon's Trustees* **V** P R M VENABLES, **C** J E CRUTTER

PENGE (St Paul) *Roch 12* **P** *Ch Patr Trust* **V** D I CHARNOCK

PENGE LANE (Holy Trinity) *Roch 12* **P** *CPAS* **V** A R RUTHERFORD

PENHILL (St Peter) *Bris 10* **P** *Bp* **V** G S COLE

PENHURST (St Michael the Archangel) Ashburnham w Penhurst *Chich*

PENISTONE (St John the Baptist) and Thurlstone *Wakef 7* **P** *Bp* **TR** G W MIDGLEY, **C** H P JONES

PENKETH (St Paul) *Liv 13* **P** *Bp* **V** P W HOCKLEY

PENKHULL (St Thomas) *Lich 17* **P** *R Stoke-on-Trent* **V** I MAITIN

PENKRIDGE Team, The (St Michael and All Angels) *Lich 2* **P** *Patr Bd* **TR** G STATON, **TV** C L GILBERT, **C** C L CARTER (nee SMITH), P R CARTER

PENN (Holy Trinity) *Ox 20* **P** *Earl Howe* **NSM** J H PIERCE

PENN (St Bartholomew) (St Anne) *Lich 5* **P** *Bp* **V** G M F WILLIAMS, **C** M Y CLAYTON

PENN FIELDS St Philip (St Aidan) *Lich 5* **P** *Ch Trust Fund Trust* **V** W H NASH, **C** M J HUNTER

PENN STREET (Holy Trinity) *Ox 20* **P** *Earl Howe* **V** N J STOWE

PENNARD, EAST (All Saints) Ditcheat w E Pennard and Pylle *B & W*

PENNARD, WEST (St Nicholas) Glastonbury w Meare, W Pennard and Godney *B & W*

PENNINGTON (Christ Church) *Man 13* **P** *Trustees* **V** P W LEAKEY, **C** P ELLIS, **NSM** W G SPEDDING

PENNINGTON (St Mark) *Win 10* **P** *V Milford* **V** P H RENYARD

PENNINGTON (St Michael and the Holy Angels) w Lindal and Marton *Carl 8* **P** *Bp* **P-in-c** S D RUDKIN

PENNYCROSS (St Pancras) *Ex 22* **P** *CPAS* **V** T St J HAWKINS, **C** M J GRUBB

PENNYWELL (St Thomas) Sunderland Pennywell St Thos *Dur*

PENPONDS (Holy Trinity) *Truro 2* **P** *The Crown* **V** G J KEATING

PENRITH (Christ Church) (St Andrew) w Newton Reigny and Plumpton Wall *Carl 4* **P** *Bp* **TR** N W CARTER, **TV** H GRAINGER, C E FARRER

PENRUDDOCK (All Saints) Greystoke, Matterdale, Mungrisdale, etc *Carl*

PENSAX (St James the Great) Teme Valley N *Worc*

PENSBY (St Michael and All Angels) Barnston *Ches*

PENSHAW (All Saints) *Dur 6* **P** *Bp* **R** K WALKER, **C** D BODDY

PENSHURST (St John the Baptist) and Fordcombe *Roch 11* **P** *Viscount De L'Isle* **R** *Vacant* Penshurst (01892) 870316

PENSILVA (St John) St Ive and Pensilva w Quethiock *Truro*

PENSNETT (St Mark) *Worc 10* **P** *Bp* **V** J C STALLARD, **NSM** C A HATHORNE (nee MARSH)

PENTEWAN (All Saints) St Austell *Truro*

PENTLOW (St George and St Gregory), Foxearth, Liston and Borley *Chelmsf 15* **P** *K Foster Esq, Bp, and DBP (by turn)* **R** J T DAVIES

PENTNEY (St Mary Magdalene) w West Bilney *Nor 21* **P** *Bp* **V** S R NAIRN

PENTON MEWSEY (Holy Trinity) Hatherden w Tangley, Weyhill and Penton Mewsey *Win*

PENTONVILLE (St Silas w All Saints) (St James) *Lon 6* **P** *Bp* **V** A T J SALTER, **Hon C** D F PAULEY

PENTRICH (St Matthew) Swanwick and Pentrich *Derby*

PENTRIDGE (St Rumbold) Handley w Gussage St Andrew and Pentridge *Sarum*

PENWERRIS (St Michael and All Angels) (Holy Spirit) *Truro 3* **P** *V St Gluvias* **V** D S SMITH

PENWORTHAM (St Leonard) *Blackb 6* **P** *Bp* **V** T D WILBY

PENWORTHAM (St Mary) *Blackb 6* **P** *Miss A M Rawstorne* **V** D RAITT, **C** K L JUSTICE

PENZANCE (St John the Baptist) *Truro 5* **P** *Bp* **P-in-c** S M WRIST-KNUDSEN

PENZANCE (St Mary the Virgin) (St Paul) *Truro 5* **P** *Bp* **V** J F WHITLOCK

PEOPLETON (St Nicholas) and White Ladies Aston w Churchill and Spetchley and Upton Snodsbury and Broughton Hackett *Worc 4* **P** *Bp, Croom Estate Trustees, and Major*

R J G Berkley (1 turn), and Ld Chan (1 turn)* **R** H G PHILLIPS, **C** J E BAYLISS

PEOVER, NETHER (St Oswald) *Ches 12* **P** *Man Univ* **V** K M BURGHALL

PEOVER, OVER (St Lawrence) *Ches 12* **P** *DBP* **P-in-c** K M BURGHALL

PEPER HAROW (St Nicholas) Compton w Shackleford and Peper Harow *Guildf*

PEPLOW (The Epiphany) Hodnet w Weston under Redcastle *Lich*

PERIVALE (St Mary w St Nicholas) *Lon 22* **P** *Trustees* **P-in-c** D A CARPENTER

PERLETHORPE (St John the Evangelist) *S'well 6* **P** *Earl Manvers' Trustees* **V** *Vacant*

PERRANARWORTHAL (St Piran) St Stythians w Perranarworthal and Gwennap *Truro*

PERRANPORTH (St Michael's Mission Church) Perranzabuloe *Truro*

PERRANUTHNOE (St Michael and St Piran) St Hilary w Perranuthnoe *Truro*

PERRANZABULOE (St Piran) *Truro 6* **P** *D&C* **V** A J WRIGHT

PERROTT, NORTH (St Martin) Haselbury Plucknett, Misterton and N Perrott *B & W*

PERROTT, SOUTH (St Mary) Beaminster Area *Sarum*

PERRY BARR (St John the Evangelist) *Birm 3* **P** *Bp* **V** C S JONES

PERRY BEECHES (St Matthew) *Birm 3* **P** *St Martin's Trustees* **V** S P M MACKENZIE, **C** C G GRAHAM

PERRY COMMON (St Martin) *Birm 6* **P** *Bp* **V** J E M BARBER

PERRY GREEN (St Thomas) Much Hadham *St Alb*

PERRY HILL (St George) *S'wark 4* **P** *Bp and D&C (alt)* **V** W G GOLBOURNE

PERRY STREET (All Saints) *Roch 4* **P** *Bp* **V** P J MILLS, **C** A D WILLIAMS

PERSHORE (Holy Cross) w Pinvin, Wick and Birlingham *Worc 4* **P** *Patr Bd* **V** M A TRISTRAM, **C** A P DICKENS, **Hon C** B CHATWIN, **NSM** J WOOLLCOMBE

PERTENHALL (St Peter) The Stodden Churches *St Alb*

PETER TAVY (St Peter) *Ex 25* **P** *Guild of All So* **R** *Vacant*

PETERBOROUGH (All Saints) *Pet 13* **P** *Bp* **V** D J T MILLER

PETERBOROUGH (Christ the Carpenter) *Pet 13* **P** *Bp* **V** A P HOLFORD

PETERBOROUGH (Holy Spirit) Bretton *Pet 13* **P** *Bp* **V** P M HAWKINS, **C** B M SMITH

PETERBOROUGH (St Barnabas) *Pet 13* **P** *Bp* **P-in-c** M D DAVIES

PETERBOROUGH (St John the Baptist) (Mission Church) *Pet 13* **P** *Bp* **V** *Vacant* Peterborough (01733) 64899

PETERBOROUGH (St Jude) *Pet 13* **P** *Bp* **V** D G BOND

PETERBOROUGH (St Mark) *Pet 13* **P** *Bp* **V** C J PEARSON

PETERBOROUGH (St Mary) Boongate *Pet 13* **P** *D&C* **V** A P BROWN, **C** J GOULD, **NSM** C D MASON

PETERBOROUGH (St Paul) *Pet 13* **P** *Bp* **V** B SECKER

PETERCHURCH (St Peter) w Vowchurch, Turnastone and Dorstone *Heref 1* **P** *Bp (2 turns), Bp Birm (1 turn)* **R** A WILLIAMS, **NSM** F M HANCOCK, R S MURRIN

PETERLEE (St Cuthbert) *Dur 3* **P** *Bp* **V** K I WOODHOUSE, **C** A JOHNSTON

PETERSFIELD (St Peter) *Portsm 5* **P** *Bp* **V** C LOWSON, **C** D G BARTHOLOMEW

PETERSHAM (All Saints) (St Peter) *S'wark 16* **P** *Bp* **P-in-c** D L GAMBLE

PETERSMARLAND (St Peter) Shebbear, Buckland Filleigh, Sheepwash etc *Ex*

PETERSTOW (St Peter) Ross w Brampton Abbotts, Bridstow, Peterstow etc *Heref*

PETHAM (All Saints) and Waltham w Lower Hardres and Nackington w Upper Hardres and Stelling *Cant 2* **P** *Abp, St Jo Coll Ox, and Trustees Lord Tomlin (jt)* **P-in-c** R W BATEMAN, **C** P G COX

PETHERTON, NORTH (St Mary the Virgin) w Northmoor Green *B & W 14* **P** *Dr R Addy* **V** J T L STILL, **Hon C** N A F TOWNEND

PETHERTON, SOUTH (St Peter and St Paul) w the Seavingtons *B & W 15* **P** *D&C* **R** *Vacant* South Petherton (01460) 40377

PETHERWIN, NORTH (St Paternus) Egloskerry, N Petherwin, Tremaine and Tresmere *Truro*

PETHERWIN, SOUTH (St Paternus) Lezant w Lawhitton and S Petherwin w Trewen *Truro*

PETROCKSTOWE (St Petrock) Shebbear, Buckland Filleigh, Sheepwash etc *Ex*

PETT (St Mary and St Peter) Fairlight, Guestling and Pett *Chich*
PETT LEVEL (St Nicholas) as above
PETTAUGH (St Catherine) Helmingham w Framsden and Pettaugh w Winston *St E*
PETTISTREE (St Peter and St Paul) Wickham Market w Pettistree and Easton *St E*
PETTON (not known) w Cockshutt, Welshampton and Lyneal w Colemere *Lich 22* **P** *Bp, R K Mainwaring Esq, and Personal Reps Lord Brownlow (jt)* **R** J DURNELL
PETTON (St Petrock) Bampton, Morebath, Clayhanger and Petton *Ex*
PETTS WOOD (St Francis) *Roch 15* **P** *Bp* **V** J T GUNN
PETWORTH (St Mary) *Chich 11* **P** *Lord Egremont* **R** D S POLLARD
PEVENSEY (St Nicholas) (St Wilfred) *Chich 16* **P** *Bp* **P-in-c** A C H CHRISTIAN
PEWSEY Team Ministry, The (St John the Baptist) *Sarum 21* **P** *Patr Bd* **TR** C G FOX, **TV** D E TWISS
PHEASEY (St Chad) *Lich 6* **P** *DBP* **V** M J G BINNEY, **C** M R KINDER
PHILBEACH GARDENS (St Cuthbert) Earl's Court St Cuth w St Matthias *Lon*
PHILLACK (St Felicitas) w Gwithian and Gwinear *Truro 5* **P** *Wg Comdr T P D la Touche and Bp (alt)* **P-in-c** A T NEAL, **C** M A TREMBATH, C C McQUILLEN-WRIGHT, **NSM** A J HANCOCK, J B FOX
PHILLEIGH (St Philleigh) St Just in Roseland w Philleigh *Truro*
PICKENHAM, NORTH (St Andrew) Necton, Holme Hale w N and S Pickenham *Nor*
PICKENHAM, SOUTH (All Saints) as above
PICKERING (St Peter and St Paul) *York 21* **P** *Abp* **V** F J A HEWITT, **C** D J MATHER, **NSM** G P TAYLOR
PICKHILL (All Saints) Kirklington w Burneston and Wath and Pickhill *Ripon*
PICKWELL (All Saints) Burrough Hill Pars *Leic*
PICKWORTH (All Saints) Gt and Lt Casterton w Pickworth and Tickencote *Pet*
PICKWORTH (St Andrew) S Lafford *Linc*
PICTON (St Hilary) Kirklevington *York*
PIDDINGHOE (St John) Telscombe w Piddinghoe and Southease *Chich*
PIDDINGTON (St John the Baptist) Hardingstone and Horton and Piddington *Pet*
PIDDINGTON (St Nicholas) Ambrosden w Mert and Piddington *Ox*
PIDDLE, NORTH (St Michael) Abberton, The Flyfords, Naunton Beauchamp etc *Worc*
PIDDLEHINTON (St Mary the Virgin) see below
PIDDLETRENTHIDE (All Saints) w Plush, Alton Pancras and Piddlehinton *Sarum 2* **P** *Eton Coll, D&C, and D&C Win (by turn)* **P-in-c** R W B THOMSON
PIDLEY CUM FENTON (All Saints) Somersham w Pidley and Oldhurst *Ely*
PIERCEBRIDGE (St Mary) Coniscliffe *Dur*
PILHAM (All Saints) Corringham and Blyton Gp *Linc*
PILL (Christ Church) w Easton in Gordano and Portbury *B & W 13* **P** *Bp* **V** M R COCKING
PILLATON (St Modwen) Penkridge Team *Lich*
PILLATON (St Odolph) St Dominic, Landulph and St Mellion w Pillaton *Truro*
PILLERTON HERSEY (St Mary) Butlers Marston and the Pillertons w Ettington *Cov*
PILLEY (Mission Church) Tankersley *Sheff*
PILLEY (St Nicholas) Boldre w S Baddesley *Win*
PILLING (St John the Baptist) *Blackb 10* **P** *A F Mason-Hornby Esq and H D H Elletson Esq (alt)* **V** *Vacant* Blackpool (01253) 790231
PILNING (St Peter) w Compton Greenfield *Bris 8* **P** *Bp* **V** D B HARREX, **NSM** A J PARKER
PILSLEY (St Mary the Virgin) N Wingfield, Clay Cross and Pilsley *Derby*
PILTON (All Saints) Aldwincle w Thorpe Achurch, Pilton, Wadenhoe etc *Pet*
PILTON (St John the Baptist) w Croscombe, North Wootton and Dinder *B & W 8* **P** *Bp and Peache Trustees (jt)* **R** D R OSBORNE
PILTON (St Mary the Virgin) w Ashford *Ex 15* **P** *Ld Chan* **V** J C SPEAR, **NSM** D F GIBSON
PILTON (St Nicholas) Preston and Ridlington w Wing and Pilton *Pet*
PIMLICO Bourne Street (St Mary) Pimlico St Mary Graham Terrace *Lon*
PIMLICO (St Barnabas) *Lon 3* **P** *Bp* **P-in-c** O J HOLTH
PIMLICO (St Gabriel) *Lon 3* **P** *Bp* **V** D W SKEOCH, **NSM** W D PATTINSON

PIMLICO (St James the Less) Pimlico St Sav *Lon*
PIMLICO (St Mary) Graham Terrace *Lon 3* **P** *Trustees* **V** W S SCOTT, **Hon C** D PRIEST, P PILKINGTON
PIMLICO St Peter w Westminster (Christ Church) *Lon 3* **P** *Bp* **V** D B TILLYER, **C** W P KEYES, **NSM** A R CHIDWICK
Pimlico (St Saviour) *Lon 3* **P** *Bp* **P-in-c** R J ROGERS
PIMPERNE (St Peter), Stourpaine, Durweston and Bryanston *Sarum 7* **P** *DBP (2 turns), D&C (1 turn)* **R** G S M SQUAREY
PINCHBECK (St Mary) *Linc 17* **P** *Mrs B S Corley* **V** D R HILL
PINCHBECK, WEST (St Bartholomew) Surfleet *Linc*
PINHOE (St Michael and All Angels) (Hall) and Broadclyst *Ex 1* **P** *Patr Bd* **TR** A J MORTIMER, **NSM** M GENT
PINNER (St John the Baptist) *Lon 23* **P** *V Harrow* **V** D J TUCK, **C** I M McINTOSH, M F BOLLEY, D M BOURNE, **Hon C** M S NATTRASS, **NSM** I W MURRAY
PINVIN (St Nicholas) Pershore w Pinvin, Wick and Birlingham *Worc*
PINXTON (St Helen) (Church Hall) *Derby 1* **P** *Bp* **R** R J I PAGET
PIPE-CUM-LYDE (St Peter) Wellington w Pipe-cum-Lyde and Moreton-on-Lugg *Heref*
PIPEWELL (St Mary) Rothwell w Orton, Rushton w Glendon and Pipewell *Pet*
PIRBRIGHT (St Michael) *Guildf 12* **P** *Ld Chan* **V** R E N STREVENS
PIRNOUGH (All Hallows) Ditchingham, Hedenham and Broome *Nor*
PIRTON (St Mary) *St Alb 9* **P** *D&C Ely* **P-in-c** J M B POTIPHER
PIRTON (St Peter) Stoulton w Drake's Broughton and Pirton etc *Worc*
PISHILL (not known) Nettlebed w Bix and Highmore *Ox*
PITCHCOMBE (St John the Baptist) The Edge, Pitchcombe, Harescombe and Brookthorpe *Glouc*
PITCHFORD (St Michael and All Angels) Condover w Frodesley, Acton Burnell etc *Heref*
PITCOMBE (St Leonard) Bruton and Distr *B & W*
PITMINSTER (St Mary and St Andrew) w Corfe *B & W 18* **P** *DBP and M V Spurway Esq (alt)* **V** R L PARKER
PITNEY (St John the Baptist) Langport Area Chs *B & W*
PITSEA (St Gabriel) w Nevendon *Chelmsf 6* **P** *Bp* **R** L BLANEY
PITSFORD (All Saints) w Boughton *Pet 2* **P** *Bp* **R** S J TROTT
PITSMOOR (Christ Church) *Sheff 3* **P** *Ch Patr Trust and DBP (alt)* **V** D J H SPARKES
PITTINGTON (St Laurence) Sherburn w Pittington *Dur*
PITTON (St Peter) Alderbury Team *Sarum*
PITTVILLE (All Saints) Cheltenham All SS *Glouc*
PIXHAM (St Mary the Virgin) Dorking w Ranmore *Guildf*
PIXLEY (St Andrew) Tarrington w Stoke Edith, Aylton, Pixley etc *Heref*
PLAISTOW (Holy Trinity) Kirdford *Chich*
PLAISTOW (St Martin) (St Mary) (St Philip and St James) *Chelmsf 3* **P** *Patr Bd* **TV** C F TURNER, **C** R J MAGOR, **NSM** L C STEWARD
PLAISTOW (St Mary) *Roch 13* **P** *Bp* **V** P R HENWOOD, **NSM** E J DAVIS
PLAITFORD (St Peter) Bramshaw and Landford w Plaitford *Sarum*
PLALTS HEATH (St Edmund) Lenham w Boughton Malherbe *Cant*
PLAS NEWTON (St Michael) *Ches 2* **P** *Simeon's Trustees* **V** R J KITELEY
PLATT (St Mary the Virgin) *Roch 9* **P** *Bp* **V** D C FRANCIS
PLATT BRIDGE (St Nathaniel) *Liv 14* **P** *Bp* **V** M B DARBY
PLAXTOL (not known) *Roch 9* **P** *Bp* **R** M B HOBBS
PLAYDEN (St Michael) Rye *Chich*
PLAYFORD (St Mary) Gt and Lt Bealings w Playford and Culpho *St E*
PLEASLEY (St Michael) E Scarsdale *Derby*
PLEASLEY HILL (St Barnabas) *S'well 2* **P** *Bp* **V** A M SMYTHE
PLEASLEY VALE (St Chad) Mansf Woodhouse *S'well*
PLEMSTALL (St Peter) w Guilden Sutton *Ches 2* **P** *Capt P Egerton Warburton* **V** J A MALBON
PLESHEY (Holy Trinity) *Chelmsf 8* **P** *Bp* **P-in-c** J T HOWDEN
PLUCKLEY (St Mary) Egerton w Pluckley *Cant*
PLUCKLEY (St Nicholas) as above
PLUMBLAND (St Cuthbert) and Gilcrux *Carl 7* **P** *Bp and Exors E S C Curwen (jt)* **R** F L PRICE

PLUMPTON (All Saints) (St Michael and All Angels) w East
Chiltington cum Novington *Chich 18* **P** *Ld Chan*
 R G D BROSTER
PLUMPTON (St John the Baptist) Weedon Lois w Plumpton
and Moreton Pinkney etc *Pet*
PLUMPTON WALL (St John the Evangelist) Penrith w
Newton Reigny and Plumpton Wall *Carl*
PLUMSTEAD (Ascension) *S'wark 1* **P** *Bp*
 V C R WELHAM
PLUMSTEAD Shooters Hill (All Saints) *S'wark 1* **P** *CPAS*
 V H D OWEN, **Hon C** A L AYRES
PLUMSTEAD (St John the Baptist) w St James and St Paul
S'wark 1 **P** *Simeon's Trustees and CPAS (alt)*
 V P J ROGERS, **C** D J B HAZLEHURST
PLUMSTEAD (St Mark and St Margaret) *S'wark 1*
 P *DBP* **V** N E DAVIES
PLUMSTEAD (St Michael) Barningham w Matlaske w
Baconsthorpe etc *Nor*
PLUMSTEAD (St Nicholas) *S'wark 1* **P** *V Plumstead*
St Mark w St Marg **V** A G STEVENS
PLUMSTEAD, GREAT (St Mary) and LITTLE (St Gervase
and Protase) w Thorpe End and Witton *Nor 4* **P** *Bp and*
D&C (jt) **R** B W TOMLINSON
PLUMTREE (St Mary) *S'well 9* **P** *DBP*
 P-in-c P E GRIFFITHS, **NSM** D M GEE
PLUNGAR (St Helen) Barkestone w Plungar, Redmile and
Stathern *Leic*
PLYMOUTH Crownhill (Ascension) *Ex 23* **P** *Bp*
 P-in-c P HANCOCK
PLYMOUTH Emmanuel, Efford and Laira *Ex 24*
 P *Patr Bd* **TR** T J NOTTAGE, **TV** I J LOVETT,
J C WHITE, S J DOBSON, **C** J C OUGH, **NSM** P A WHITE
PLYMOUTH (St Andrew) and St Paul Stonehouse *Ex 24*
 P *Patr Bd* **TR** N H P McKINNEL, **TV** K F FREEMAN,
M T BAILEY, **C** R C H THOMAS, K F FREEMAN
PLYMOUTH (St Augustine) Plymouth Em, Efford and Laira
Ex
PLYMOUTH (St Gabriel) Peverell *Ex 24* **P** *Bp*
 V J J STARK, **NSM** L J HOWARTH
PLYMOUTH (St James the Less) Ham *Ex 22* **P** *Keble Coll*
Ox **V** T M S MORLEY
PLYMOUTH (St John the Evangelist) Sutton on Plym *Ex*
PLYMOUTH (St Jude) *Ex 24* **P** *Trustees*
 V S R DINSMORE, **C** D R DAVIS
PLYMOUTH (St Mary the Virgin) Plymouth Em, Efford and
Laira *Ex*
PLYMOUTH (St Matthias) Charles w St Matthias Plymouth
Ex
PLYMOUTH (St Peter) (All Saints) *Ex 22* **P** *Keble Coll*
Ox **V** S PHILPOTT, **C** W J JOHNSTONE
PLYMOUTH (St Simon) *Ex 24* **P** *St Simon Trustees*
 V J C STYLER
PLYMPTON (St Mary the Blessed Virgin) *Ex 23* **P** *Bp*
 V J F RICHARDS, **C** J M GIDDINGS, R W BECK,
 NSM M BRIMICOMBE
PLYMPTON (St Maurice) *Ex 23* **P** *D&C Windsor*
 R T E THOMAS
PLYMSTOCK (St Mary and All Saints) *Ex 24* **P** *D&C*
Windsor **V** P H W HAWKINS, **C** J J SPEAR, P R SEARLE
PLYMTREE (St John the Baptist) Broadhembury,
Payhembury and Plymtree *Ex*
POCKLEY (St John the Baptist) Harome w Stonegrave,
Nunnington and Pockley *York*
POCKLINGTON (All Saints) and Owsthorpe and Kilnwick
Percy w Great Givendale, Huggate and Millington *York 7*
 P *Abp* **R** R H K PROSSER
PODIMORE (St Peter) Ilchester w Northover, Limington,
Yeovilton etc *B & W*
PODINGTON (St Mary the Virgin) Wymington w Podington
St Alb
POINT CLEAR (Mission) St Osyth *Chelmsf*
POINTON (Christ Church) Sempringham w Pointon and
Birthorpe *Linc*
POKESDOWN (All Saints) *Win 7* **P** *V Christchurch*
 V B G APPS
POKESDOWN (St James) *Win 7* **P** *Bp*
 V A F J CHAMBERS, **NSM** P M SCHOLLAR
POLDENS, WEST *B & W 5* **P** *Bp* **V** A E D MURDOCH
POLEBROOK (All Saints) and Lutton w Hemington and
Luddington *Pet 12* **P** *Bp, Sir Stephen Hastings, and DBP*
(by turn) **R** I A LOVETT
POLEGATE (St John) (St Wilfred) *Chich 16* **P** *Bp*
 V D L N GUTSELL, **C** T L RINGLAND
POLESWORTH (St Editha) *Birm 12* **P** *Ld Chan*
 V D C BYFORD
POLING (St Nicholas) *Chich 1* **P** *Bp* **V** J E SLEGG
POLLINGTON (St John the Baptist) Gt Snaith *Sheff*

POLPERRO (St John the Baptist) Talland *Truro*
POLRUAN (St Saviour) Lanteglos by Fowey *Truro*
POLSTEAD (St Mary) *St E 3* **P** *St Jo Coll Ox*
 P-in-c G MARSDEN, D W FINCH
POLTIMORE (St Mary the Virgin) Stoke Canon, Poltimore
w Huxham and Rewe etc *Ex*
PONDERS END (St Matthew) *Lon 18* **P** *V Enfield*
 V B G RODFORD
PONDERSBRIDGE (St Thomas) Whittlesey and
Pondersbridge *Ely*
PONSANOOTH (St Michael and All Angels) Mabe *Truro*
PONSBOURNE (St Mary) Lt Berkhamsted and Bayford,
Essendon etc *St Alb*
PONSONBY (not known) Beckermet St Jo and St Bridget w
Ponsonby *Carl*
PONTEFRACT (All Saints) *Wakef 11* **P** *Bp* **V** *Vacant*
Pontefract (01977) 702286
PONTEFRACT (St Giles w St Mary) *Wakef 11* **P** *Bp*
 V G HIGGINS, **C** M C E BOOTES
PONTELAND (St Mary the Virgin) *Newc 7* **P** *Mert Coll*
Ox **C** J R SINCLAIR, **Hon C** P G WOLFENDEN,
C G THORNE
PONTESBURY First and Second Portions (St George)
Heref 13 **P** *St Chad's Coll Dur* **R** D H ROBERTS
PONTON, GREAT (Holy Cross) Colsterworth Gp *Linc*
PONTON, LITTLE (St Guthlac) as above
POOL (St Wilfrid) w Arthington *Ripon 1*
 P *C E W Sheepshanks Esq and V Otley (jt)* **V** D R H de la
HOYDE
POOLE (St James w St Paul) *Sarum 8* **P** *Ch Soc Trust and*
J H Cordle Esq (jt) **R** S C HOLBROOKE-JONES
POOLE KEYNES (St Michael and All Angels) Kemble,
Poole Keynes, Somerford Keynes etc *Glouc*
POOLEY BRIDGE (St Paul) Barton, Pooley Bridge and
Martindale *Carl*
POOLSBROOK (St Alban) Staveley and Barrow Hill *Derby*
POORTON, NORTH (St Mary Magdalene) Askerswell,
Loders and Powerstock *Sarum*
POPLAR (All Saints) *Lon 7* **P** *Patr Bd* **TR** A J WYNNE,
 TV J E I HAWKINS, **C** M J BROWN (nee PATTERSON)
POPPLETON, NETHER (St Everilda) w UPPER (All Saints)
York 1 **P** *Abp* **V** P W THOMAS, **Hon C** M C S FOSSETT
POPPLETON ROAD (Mission Room) York St Paul *York*
PORCHESTER (St James) *S'well 11* **P** *Bp*
 V R D A MORE, **C** C J RATTENBERRY
PORINGLAND (All Saints) *Nor 8* **P** *Bp, BNC Ox,*
J D Alston Esq, and G H Hastings Esq (3 turns) and DBP
(1 turn) **R** R B HEMS
PORLOCK (St Dubricius) w Stoke Pero *B & W 16*
 P *Ld Chan* **R** B E PRIORY
PORLOCK WEIR (St Nicholas) Porlock w Stoke Pero
B & W
PORT ERIN (St Catherine) Rushen *S & M*
PORT ISAAC (St Peter) St Endellion w Port Isaac and St
Kew *Truro*
PORT ST MARY (St Mary) Rushen *S & M*
PORTBURY (Blessed Virgin Mary) Pill w Easton in
Gordano and Portbury *B & W*
PORTCHESTER (St Mary) *Portsm 2*
 P *J R Thistlethwaite Esq* **V** M L S THOMAS,
 C S H HOLT, **Hon C** G S VARNHAM
PORTESHAM (St Peter) Abbotsbury, Portesham and
Langton Herring *Sarum*
PORTHILL (St Andrew) Wolstanton *Lich*
PORTHLEVEN (St Bartholomew) w Sithney *Truro 4* **P** *Bp*
 P-in-c P A A WALKER
PORTHPEAN (St Levan) St Austell *Truro*
PORTINSCALE (Mission) Crosthwaite Keswick *Carl*
PORTISHEAD (St Peter) *B & W 13* **P** *Mrs E Haigh*
 R A C TAYLOR, **C** W L ROBERTS
PORTKELLIS (St Christopher) Helston and Wendron *Truro*
PORTLAND (All Saints w St Peter) *Sarum 5* **P** *Bp*
 R D V GERRISH
PORTLAND (St John) *Sarum 5* **P** *Hyndman Trustees*
 P-in-c E LEWIS
PORTLEMOUTH, EAST (St Winwaloe Onocaus) Charleton
w Buckland Tout Saints etc *Ex*
PORTLOE (All Saints) Veryan w Ruan Lanihorne *Truro*
PORTMAN SQUARE (St Paul) Langham Place All So *Lon*
PORTON (St Nicholas) Bourne Valley *Sarum*
PORTREATH (St Mary) Illogan *Truro*
PORTSDOWN (Christ Church) *Portsm 4* **P** *Simeon's*
Trustees **V** J K HEWITT, **NSM** M MORGAN
PORTSEA (All Saints) *Portsm 6* **P** *V Portsea St Mary and*
Bp (jt) **V** L FOX, **NSM** M E TILLMAN

PORTSEA (Ascension) *Portsm 6* **P** *Bp* **NSM** M S R GOVER
PORTSEA North End (St Mark) *Portsm 6* **P** *V Portsea*
St Mary **V** J W BELL, **C** B T WILLIAMS, A G DAVIS
PORTSEA (St Alban) *Portsm 6* **P** *Bp* **NSM** C MACRAE
PORTSEA (St Cuthbert) *Portsm 6* **P** *Bp*
  V K M L H BANTING, **C** A C LEONARD, S MARTIN
PORTSEA (St George) *Portsm 6* **P** *Bp* **V** *Vacant*
PORTSEA (St Luke) *Portsm 6* **P** *Ch Patr Trust*
  V M J SMITHSON, **NSM** D H GIBSON
PORTSEA (St Mary) (St Faith and St Barnabas) (St Wilfrid)
  Portsm 6 **P** *Win Coll* **V** A R WRIGHT,
  C K R M BRISTOW, R C PEERS, D G BOURNE,
  NSM K H APPLEFORD, L C DENNESS
PORTSEA (St Saviour) *Portsm 6* **P** *Bp* **V** T KNIGHT,
  Hon C M C HALAHAN
PORTSLADE (Good Shepherd) *Chich 4* **P** *Bp*
  V P D CLEGG
PORTSLADE (St Nicolas) (St Andrew) *Chich 4* **P** *Bp*
  V R H RUSHFORTH
PORTSWOOD (Christ Church) *Win 12* **P** *Bp*
  V D C JAMES, **C** R D TURNBULL, **Hon C** J D BENWELL
PORTSWOOD (St Denys) *Win 12* **P** *Bp*
  P-in-c S FOULKES
POSBURY (St Francis Proprietary Chapel) Crediton and
  Shobrooke *Ex*
POSLINGFORD (St Mary) Clare w Poslingford, Cavendish
  etc *St E*
POSTBRIDGE (St Gabriel) Widecombe-in-the-Moor,
  Leusdon, Princetown etc *Ex*
POSTLING (St Mary and St Radegund) Lyminge w
  Paddlesworth, Stanford w Postling etc *Cant*
POSTWICK (All Saints) Brundall w Braydeston and
  Postwick *Nor*
POTT SHRIGLEY (St Christopher) *Ches 13* **P** *MMCET*
  V G H GREENHOUGH
POTTEN END (Holy Trinity) w Nettleden *St Alb 3* **P** *Bp*
  P-in-c J V M KIRKBY
POTTER HEIGHAM (St Nicholas) Ludham, Potter
  Heigham and Hickling *Nor*
POTTERHANWORTH (St Andrew) Branston w Nocton
  and Potterhanworth *Linc*
POTTERNE (St Mary the Virgin) w Worton and Marston
  Sarum 19 **P** *Bp* **V** P WILKINSON
POTTERNEWTON (St Martin) *Ripon 5* **P** *Trustees*
  V J R W SILLER, **C** N S ROBINSON, J TREETOPS,
  Par Dn D LEPPINGTON
POTTERS BAR (St Mary and All Saints) *St Alb 2* **P** *Bp*
  Lon **V** P J BEVAN, **C** A J DAVEY
POTTERS GREEN (St Philip Deacon) *Cov 1* **P** *Ld Chan*
  V W J ADAMSON
POTTERS MARSTON (St Mary) Barwell w Potters Marston
  and Stapleton *Leic*
POTTERSPURY (St Nicholas) w Furtho and Yardley Gobion
  and Cosgrove *Pet 5* **P** *D&C (2 turns), Jes Coll Ox*
  (1 turn) **V** M H CHAMPNEYS, **NSM** J ROBINSON
POTTO (St Mary) Whorlton w Carlton and Faceby *York*
POTTON (St Mary the Virgin) w Sutton and Cockayne Hatley
  St Alb 17 **P** *The Crown (3 turns), St Jo Coll Ox (1 turn)*
  R I WARTHUR, **NSM** D L SMITH
POUGHILL (St Michael and All Angels) N Creedy *Ex*
POUGHILL (St Olaf King and Martyr) *Truro 8* **P** *Ch Soc*
  Trust **V** L H KEENAN
POULNER (St John) Ringwood *Win*
POULSHOT (St Peter) Rowde and Poulshot *Sarum*
POULTON (St Luke) *Ches 7* **P** *Bp* **P-in-c** A J MAUNDER
POULTON (St Michael and All Angels) The Ampneys w
  Driffield and Poulton *Glouc*
POULTON LANCELYN (Holy Trinity) *Ches 8*
  P *R Bebington* **V** R J KIRKLAND
POULTON-LE-FYLDE (St Chad) *Blackb 13* **P** *DBP*
  V C H WILLIAMS, **C** A HOLLIDAY, I A HELLYER
POULTON-LE-SANDS (Holy Trinity) w Morecambe
  St Laurence *Blackb 12* **P** *V Lanc* **R** J A H CLEGG,
  C D J THOMPSON
POUND HILL (St Barnabas) Worth *Chich*
POUNDSBRIDGE (Chapel) Penshurst and Fordcombe *Roch*
POUNDSTOCK (St Winwaloe) Week St Mary w Poundstock
  and Whitstone *Truro*
POWDERHAM (St Clement Bishop and Martyr) Kenton,
  Mamhead, Powderham, Cofton and Starcross *Ex*
POWERSTOCK (St Mary the Virgin) Askerswell, Loders
  and Powerstock *Sarum*
POWICK (St Peter) Powyke *Worc*
POWYKE (St Peter) *Worc 2* **P** *Croome Estate Trustees*
  P-in-c J R ILSON

POYNINGS (Holy Trinity) w Edburton, Newtimber and
  Pyecombe *Chich 9* **P** *Ld Chan (1 turn), Bp and Abp*
  (1 turn) **P-in-c** D M WHITTOME
POYNTINGTON (All Saints) Queen Thorne *Sarum*
POYNTON (St George) *Ches 17* **P** *Bp*
  V J D THOMPSTONE, **C** P G BURROWS,
  NSM R J BROOKE
POYNTON, HIGHER (St Martin) Poynton *Ches*
PRATTS BOTTOM (All Souls) Green Street Green and
  Pratts Bottom *Roch*
PREES (St Chad) *Lich 28* **P** *Bp* **V** D J TITLEY
PREESALL (St Oswald) *Blackb 10* **P** *Bp* **V** E ANGUS,
  NSM M JENKINSON
PRENTON (St Stephen) *Ches 1* **P** *Bp* **V** L R LAWRENCE,
  C M D HOCKNULL, D C P MOORE, **NSM** W H HEAPS,
  E D O'NEILL
PRENTON DELL (St Alban) Prenton *Ches*
PRESCOT (St Mary) (St Paul) *Liv 10* **P** *K Coll Cam*
  V T M STEEL, **C** A SWIFT, **NSM** T FAGAN
PRESHUTE (St George) Marlborough *Sarum*
PRESTBURY (St Mary) (St Nicholas) *Glouc 11*
  P *Mrs F L Baghot de la Bere Aldendifer*
  C L A C MACLEAN, N M SETTERFIELD
PRESTBURY (St Peter) *Ches 13* **P** *C F Legh Esq*
  C J N CLARKE, **Hon C** R OTTLEY
PRESTEIGNE (St Andrew) w Discoed, Kinsham and Lingen
  Heref 5 **P** *Bp* **P-in-c** D R P HAYES
PRESTLEIGH (St James Mission Church) Shepton Mallet w
  Doulting *B & W*
PRESTOLEE (Holy Trinity) Ringley St Sav w H Trin
  Prestolee *Man*
PRESTON Acregate Lane (Mission) Preston St Matt *Blackb*
PRESTON (All Saints) *Blackb 14* **P** *Trustees*
  P-in-c F COOPER
PRESTON (All Saints) Siddington w Preston *Glouc*
PRESTON (All Saints) and Sproatley in Holderness *York 13*
  P *Abp* **R** S ROBINSON
PRESTON (Church of the Ascension) *Lon 21* **P** *Bp*
  V F C HUMPHRIES, **NSM** N D BIRD
PRESTON (Emmanuel) *Blackb 14* **P** *R Preston* **V** S HUNT
PRESTON (Good Shepherd) Brighton Gd Shep Preston
  Chich
PRESTON (St Alban) Brighton Resurr *Chich*
PRESTON (St Andrew) w Sutton Poyntz and Osmington w
  Poxwell *Sarum 5* **P** *Patr Bd* **TR** J K COOMBS,
  TV J S HOLLAND, **C** L C STOCK, P S THOMAS
PRESTON (St Augustine and St Saviour) Brighton St Aug
  and St Sav *Chich*
PRESTON (St Cuthbert) *Blackb 14* **P** *Bp* **V** D GASKELL
PRESTON (St John) (Christ the King Chapel) (St George) (St
  Saviour w St James) (St Stephen) *Blackb 14* **P** *Patr Bd*
  TV D BARTON, **P-in-c** R S LADDS, **C** J FRANCIS
PRESTON (St John the Baptist) *Glouc 3* **P** *Bp*
  P-in-c R HART
PRESTON (St John the Evangelist) *Chich 2* **P** *Bp*
  V F MITCHINSON
PRESTON (St Jude w St Paul) *Blackb 14* **P** *Bp and*
  V Preston St John **V** B J W ROBINSON
PRESTON (St Luke) (St Oswald) *Blackb 14* **P** *Bp and*
  Simeon's Trustees (jt) **V** M A MANLEY
PRESTON (St Mark) Ashton-on-Ribble St Mich w Preston
  St Mark *Blackb*
PRESTON (St Martin) King's Walden and Offley w Lilley
  St Alb
PRESTON (St Mary) *Blackb 14* **P** *Trustees*
  P-in-c B ROTHWELL
PRESTON (St Mary the Virgin) *St E 10* **P** *Em Coll Cam*
  P-in-c D M STIFF
PRESTON (St Matthew) (St Hilda) *Blackb 14* **P** *Bp*
  P-in-c P N TYERS
PRESTON (St Matthias) Brighton St Matthias *Chich*
PRESTON (St Mildred) Wingham w Elmstone and Preston w
  Stourmouth *Cant*
PRESTON (St Paul) Paignton St Paul Preston *Ex*
PRESTON (St Peter and St Paul) and Ridlington w Wing and
  Pilton *Pet 14* **P** *Bp, Baroness Willoughby de Eresby, and*
  DBP (jt) **R** A M S WILSON
PRESTON, EAST (St Mary) w Kingston *Chich 1* **P** *D&C*
  V *Vacant* Rustington (01903) 783318
PRESTON, GREAT (St Aidan) Kippax w Allerton Bywater
  Ripon
PRESTON BAGOT (All Saints) Claverdon w Preston Bagot
  Cov
PRESTON BISSET (St John the Baptist) Swan *Ox*
PRESTON BROOK (St Faith) Daresbury *Ches*
PRESTON CAPES (St Peter and St Paul) Badby w Newham
  and Charwelton w Fawsley etc *Pet*

PRESTON NEXT FAVERSHAM (St Catherine) w
Goodnestone and Graveney *Cant 6* **P** *Abp*
  V S C WILSON, **C** A A GOLD
PRESTON ON STOUR (St Mary) Ilmington w Stretton-on-
Fosse etc *Cov*
PRESTON ON TEES (All Saints) *Dur 16* **P** *Bp*
  V D T OSMAN, **C** J LINTERN
PRESTON-ON-WYE (St Lawrence) Madley w Tyberton,
Preston-on-Wye and Blakemere *Heref*
PRESTON PATRICK (St Patrick) Crosscrake and Preston
Patrick *Carl*
PRESTON PLUCKNETT (St James the Great) (St Peter)
B & W 7 **P** *Bp (2 turns), Mrs S W Rawlins (1 turn)*
  V A PERRIS, **C** J G EDWARDS
PRESTON UNDER SCARR (St Margaret) Wensley *Ripon*
PRESTON WEALDMOORS (St Lawrence) Edgmond w
Kynnersley and Preston Wealdmoors *Lich*
PRESTON WYNNE (Holy Trinity) Bodenham w Hope-
under-Dinmore, Felton etc *Heref*
PRESTONVILLE (St Luke) *Chich 2* **P** *Trustees*
  V C A M MARCH, **NSM** G B ROBERTS
PRESTWICH (St Gabriel) *Man 14* **P** *Bp*
  P-in-c P RICHARDSON
PRESTWICH (St Hilda) *Man 14* **P** *Trustees* **V** *Vacant*
0161–773 3378
PRESTWICH (St Margaret) (St George) *Man 14*
  P *R Prestwich St Mary the Virgin* **V** M ASHWORTH,
  Hon C M R ATKINSON
PRESTWICH (St Mary the Virgin) *Man 14* **P** *Trustees*
  R F BIBBY
PRESTWOLD (St Andrew) Wymeswold and Prestwold w
Hoton *Leic*
PRESTWOOD (Holy Trinity) and Great Hampden *Ox 28*
  P *Bp and Hon I H Hope-Morley (jt)* **R** J R WHITE,
  C C NICHOLSON
PRICKWILLOW (St Peter) *Ely 14* **P** *Bp*
  P-in-c F J KILNER, **C** A F PLEDGER
PRIDDY (St Lawrence) *B & W 1* **P** *Bp*
  V E A MACPHERSON
PRIESTWOOD (St Andrew) Bracknell *Ox*
PRIMROSE HILL (Holy Trinity) Lydney *Glouc*
PRIMROSE HILL (St Mary the Virgin) w Avenue Road
(St Paul) *Lon 16* **P** *Trustees* **V** J A OVENDEN,
  NSM C L VAN DER PUMP, S V WEBSTER
PRINCE ALBERT ROAD (St Mark) Regent's Park St Mark
Lon
PRINCE CONSORT ROAD (Holy Trinity) S Kensington H
Trin w All SS *Lon*
PRINCE'S PARK (St Paul) *Liv 4* **V** *Vacant*
PRINCES RISBOROUGH (St Mary) w Ilmer *Ox 21*
  P *Ld Chan* **R** N E GREEN, **C** B SMART,
  Hon C R E PEAKE, **NSM** A K PHILLIPS
PRINCETOWN (St Michael and All Saints) Widecombe-in-
the-Moor, Leusdon, Princetown etc *Ex*
PRIOR'S DEAN (not known) Greatham w Empshott and
Hawkley w Prior's Dean *Portsm*
PRIORS HARDWICK (St Mary the Virgin) w Priors Marston
and Wormleighton *Cov 10* **P** *Earl Spencer*
  P-in-c K J PHILLIPS
PRIORS LEE (St Peter) (St Georges) *Lich 27* **P** *Bp and*
V Shifnal (jt) **V** G L HANCOX
PRIORS MARSTON (St Leonard) Priors Hardwick, Priors
Marston and Wormleighton *Cov*
PRIORS PARK (Mission Hall) Tewkesbury w Walton
Cardiff *Glouc*
PRISTON (St Luke) Timsbury and Priston *B & W*
PRITTLEWELL (All Saints) Southend *Chelmsf*
PRITTLEWELL (St Luke) *Chelmsf 13* **P** *Bp*
  V D F C GIRLING
PRITTLEWELL (St Mary the Virgin) *Chelmsf 13* **P** *Bp*
  V R A MASON, **Hon C** A J MORLEY, **NSM** F M SMITH
PRITTLEWELL (St Peter) *Chelmsf 13* **P** *Bp*
  P-in-c G R STEEL, **NSM** S M WARING
PRITTLEWELL (St Stephen) *Chelmsf 13* **P** *Bp*
  P-in-c R A MASON
PROBUS (St Probus and St Grace), Ladock and Grampound w
Creed and St Erme *Truro 6* **P** *DBP* **TV** D H DIXON
PRUDHOE (St Mary Magdalene) *Newc 7* **P** *Dioc Soc*
  P-in-c D J ELKINGTON, **C** A A ELKINGTON
PUBLOW (All Saints) w Pensford, Compton Dando and
Chelwood *B & W 10* **P** *Bp* **R** J N COE
PUCKINGTON (St Andrew) Ilminster and District *B & W*
PUCKLECHURCH (St Thomas a Becket) and Abson *Bris 7*
  P *D&C* **V** I L WILLS
PUDDINGTON (St Thomas a Becket) N Creedy *Ex*

PUDDLETOWN (St Mary the Virgin) and Tolpuddle
Sarum 2 **P** *Trustees, Ch Ch Ox, and Viscount Rothermere*
(by turn) **P-in-c** J V WALTON
PUDLESTON (St Peter) Leominster *Heref*
PUDSEY (St Lawrence and St Paul) *Bradf 3* **P** *Bp and*
V Calverley (jt) **V** H M WIGLEY, **C** S M ROSSETER,
  K TROUT
PULBOROUGH (St Mary) *Chich 12* **P** *Lord Egremont*
  R K W DENFORD
PULFORD (St Mary the Virgin) Eccleston and Pulford *Ches*
PULHAM Market (St Mary Magdalene), Pulham St Mary
and Starston *Nor 10* **P** *The Crown (2 turns), Bp (1 turn)*
  R M E ELLSON
PULHAM (St Thomas a Beckett) Dungeon Hill *Sarum*
PULHAM ST MARY (St Mary the Virgin) Pulham Market,
Pulham St Mary and Starston *Nor*
PULLOXHILL (St James the Apostle) Silsoe, Pulloxhill and
Flitton *St Alb*
PULVERBATCH (St Edith) Longden and Annscroft w
Pulverbatch *Heref*
PUNCKNOWLE (St Mary the Blessed Virgin) Bride Valley
Sarum
PUNNETS TOWN (St Peter) Heathfield *Chich*
PURBROOK (St John the Baptist) *Portsm 4* **P** *Bp*
  V R I P COUTTS, **NSM** M M SHERWIN, B A MOSSE
PUREWELL (St John) Christchurch *Win*
PURFLEET (St Stephen) Aveley and Purfleet *Chelmsf*
PURITON (St Michael and All Angels) and Pawlett
B & W 14 **P** *Ld Chan (1 turn), D&C Windsor (2 turns)*
  V K G J WILLIAMS
PURLEIGH (All Saints), Cold Norton and Stow Maries
Chelmsf 11 **P** *Suttons Hosp, Or Coll Ox, and Bp (jt)*
  P-in-c D W COOLING, **NSM** M D COOLING
PURLEY (Christ Church) *S'wark 22* **P** *Bp*
  V C R TREFUSIS, **NSM** J N EMBERTON
PURLEY (St Barnabas) *S'wark 22* **P** *Bp* **V** A C WAIT
PURLEY (St Mark) Woodcote *S'wark 22* **P** *Bp*
  V P M SILLS, **C** H RHODES
PURLEY (St Mary the Virgin) *Ox 12* **P** *Ld Chan*
  R R B HOWELL, **C** B J BAILEY
PURLEY (St Swithun) *S'wark 22* **P** *Bp* **V** J K GREIG
PURLWELL (St Andrew) *Wakef 10* **P** *Bp*
  P-in-c K WILLIAMS
PURSE CAUNDLE (St Peter) The Caundles w Folke and
Holwell *Sarum*
PURSTON (St Thomas) cum South Featherstone *Wakef 11*
  P *Bp* **V** A S RAMSDEN
PURTON (St John) Sharpness w Purton and Brookend *Glouc*
PURTON (St Mary) *Bris 13* **P** *Bp* **V** B A FESSEY,
  NSM E G HALL
PUSEY (All Saints) *Ox 17* **P** *Bp* **R** C R RUDD
PUTFORD (St Stephen) *Ex 9* **P** *Bp* **V** H J ROCHE
PUTLEY (not known) Tarrington w Stoke Edith, Aylton,
Pixley etc *Heref*
PUTNEY (St Margaret) *S'wark 18* **P** *Bp*
  V A J R DRIVER, **NSM** R C BENSON, J M DRIVER (nee
  FRENCH)
PUTNEY (St Mary) (All Saints) *S'wark 18* **P** *D&C Worc*
  V J L DRAPER, **C** S M THEAKSTON, L T FRANCIS-
  DEHQANI, **Hon C** D PEACOCK, **NSM** T J E MARWOOD
PUTTENHAM (St John the Baptist) and Wanborough
Guildf 5 **P** *T I Perkins Esq and Ld Chan (alt)*
  P-in-c N S McGREGOR
PUTTENHAM (St Mary) Tring *St Alb*
PUXTON (St Saviour) Congresbury w Puxton and Hewish St
Ann *B & W*
PYE NEST (St James) King Cross *Wakef*
PYECOMBE (Transfiguration) Poynings w Edburton,
Newtimber and Pyecombe *Chich*
PYLLE (St Thomas a Becket) Ditcheat w E Pennard and
Pylle *B & W*
PYPE HAYES (St Mary the Virgin) *Birm 6* **P** *Trustees*
  V J F RYAN
PYRFORD (Church of the Good Shepherd) Wisley w
Pyrford *Guildf*
PYRFORD (St Nicolas) as above
PYRTON (St Mary) Watlington w Pyrton and Shirburn *Ox*
PYTCHLEY (All Saints) Isham w Pytchley *Pet*
PYWORTHY (St Swithun), Pancrasweek and Bridgerule
Ex 9 **P** *DBP* **P-in-c** R BURROW
QUADRING (St Margaret) Gosberton Clough and Quadring
Linc
QUAINTON (Holy Cross and St Mary) Schorne *Ox*
QUANTOXHEAD (Blessed Virgin Mary) (St Ethelreda)
B & W 17 **P** *Bp, Lady Gass, and Lt-Col W Luttrell (jt)*
  R J D A STEVENS, **NSM** P CUFF
QUARLEY (St Michael and All Angels) Amport, Grateley,
Monxton and Quarley *Win*

QUARNDON (St Paul) *Derby 11* **P** *Exors Viscount Scarsdale* **V** J D MORISON

QUARNFORD (St Paul) Longnor, Quarnford and Sheen *Lich*

QUARRENDON ESTATE (St Peter) Aylesbury w Bierton and Hulcott *Ox*

QUARRINGTON (St Botolph) w Old Sleaford *Linc 22* **P** *Bp* **R** D J MUSSON

QUARRY BANK (Christ Church) *Worc 10* **P** *The Crown* **V** T G CHAPMAN

QUARRY HILL (St Mary) Leeds City *Ripon*

QUATFORD (St Mary Magdalene) Bridgnorth, Tasley, Astley Abbotts, Oldbury etc *Heref*

QUATT (St Andrew) Alveley and Quatt *Heref*

QUEDGELEY (St James) Hardwicke, Quedgeley and Elmore w Longney *Glouc*

QUEEN CAMEL (St Barnabas) w West Camel, Corton Denham, Sparkford, Weston Bampfylde and Sutton Montis *B & W 3* **P** *Bp and DBP (2 turns), Ch Patr Trust, MMCET and Rev G Bennett (1 turn)* **R** *Vacant* Marston Magna (01935) 850326

QUEEN CHARLTON (St Margaret) Keynsham *B & W*

QUEEN THORNE *Sarum 4* **P** *Bp, Rev J M P Goodden, Major K S D Wingfield Digby, and MMCET (jt)* **P-in-c** A E H RUTTER

QUEENBOROUGH (Holy Trinity) *Cant 14* **P** *Abp* **V** R N MURCH

QUEENHILL (St Nicholas) Longdon, Castlemorton, Bushley, Queenhill etc *Worc*

QUEENSBURY (All Saints) *Lon 23* **P** *The Crown* **V** J N LUSCOMBE, **C** L HOLLAND

QUEENSBURY (Holy Trinity) *Bradf 2* **P** *Bp* **V** R G WOOD

QUENDON (not known) w Rickling and Wicken Bonhunt and Widdington *Chelmsf 22* **P** *Keble Coll Ox and Bp (alt)* **R** R J S BURN

QUENIBOROUGH (St Mary) Syston TM *Leic*

QUENINGTON (St Swithun) Coln St Aldwyns, Hatherop, Quenington etc *Glouc*

QUERNMORE (St Peter) Dolphinholme w Quernmore *Blackb*

QUETHIOCK (St Hugh) St Ive and Pensilva w Quethiock *Truro*

QUIDENHAM (St Andrew) *Nor 11* **P** *Ld Chan (1 turn), Patr Bd (3 turns)* **TR** M A SAVAGE, **C** P M KNIGHT

QUINTON and PRESTON DEANERY (St John the Baptist) Wootton w Quinton and Preston Deanery *Pet*

QUINTON (St Swithun) w Marston Sicca *Glouc 10* **P** *D&C Worc and Bp (jt)* **V** P WAKEFIELD, **NSM** J P M WILSON

QUINTON, THE (Christ Church) *Birm 2* **P** *Bp* **R** J R BARNETT, **C** N J BLANDFORD-BAKER

QUINTON ROAD WEST (St Boniface) *Birm 2* **P** *Bp* **V** W BROWN, **C** H L SAVAGE

QUORN (St Bartholomew) Quorndon *Leic*

QUORNDON (St Bartholomew) *Leic 7* **P** *Bp* **V** D H BOWLER, **NSM** M J MORRIS

QUY (St Mary) Stow w Quy *Ely*

RACKENFORD (All Saints) Washfield, Stoodleigh, Withleigh etc *Ex*

RACKHEATH (Holy Trinity) and Salhouse *Nor 4* **P** *Bp* **R** B V ROGERS, **Hon C** P A ROGERS

RACTON (St Peter) Compton, the Mardens, Stoughton and Racton *Chich*

RADBOURNE (St Andrew) Longford, Long Lane, Dalbury and Radbourne *Derby*

RADCLIFFE (St Andrew) Black Lane *Man 14* **P** *R Radcliffe St Mary* **V** P N W GRAYSHON

RADCLIFFE (St Mary) (St Thomas and St John) (St Philip Mission Church) *Man 14* **P** *Patr Bd* **TR** C H ELLIS, **TV** C E MANSLEY, **C** P D GULLY

RADCLIFFE-ON-TRENT (St Mary) and Shelford w Holme Pierrepont and Adbolton *S'well 8* **P** *DBP (2 turns), Ld Chan (1 turn)* **R** K H NEWCOMBE, **NSM** D E BENNETT

RADCLIVE (St John the Evangelist) Buckm w Radclive cum Chackmore *Ox*

RADDINGTON (St Michael) Wiveliscombe w Chipstable, Huish Champflower etc *B & W*

RADDON Thorverton, Cadbury, Upton Pyne etc *Ex*

RADFORD (All Souls) w Christ Church and St Michael *S'well 12* **P** *Bp* **V** D A JONES

RADFORD (St Nicholas) *Cov 2* **P** *Bp* **V** G HANDS, **Dss** M M OBEE

RADFORD (St Peter) *S'well 12* **P** *Bp* **V** J WALKER

RADFORD, NORTH (St Francis of Assisi) Cov St Fran N Radford *Cov*

RADFORD SEMELE (St Nicholas) and Ufton *Cov 10* **P** *Bp* **V** *Vacant* Leamington Spa (01926) 427374

RADIPOLE (Emmanuel) (St Adhelm) (St Ann) and Melcombe Regis *Sarum 5* **P** *Patr Bd* **TR** M P H STEAR, **TV** D N H MAKEPEACE, P W FINCH

RADLETT (Christ Church) (St John) *St Alb 1* **P** *V Aldenham* **V** G FELLOWS, **C** M J FLOWERDEW, **NSM** S M HALMSHAW

RADLEY (St James the Great) and Sunningwell *Ox 10* **P** *Radley Coll and DBP (by turn)* **R** *Vacant* Abingdon (01235) 554739

RADNAGE (St Mary) W Wycombe w Bledlow Ridge, Bradenham and Radnage *Ox*

RADNOR, OLD (St Stephen) Kington w Huntington, Old Radnor, Kinnerton etc *Heref*

RADSTOCK (St Nicholas) w Writhlington *B & W 12* **P** *Bp* **R** C P J TURNER

RADWAY (St Peter) Warmington w Shotteswell and Radway w Ratley *Cov*

RADWELL (All Saints) Stotfold and Radwell *St Alb*

RADWINTER (St Mary the Virgin) w Hempstead *Chelmsf 23* **P** *Keble Coll Ox* **R** B J MACDONALD-MILNE

RAGDALE (All Saints) Upper Wreake *Leic*

RAINFORD (All Saints) *Liv 11* **P** *V Prescot* **V** F R N MICHELL, **C** P MAKIN

RAINHAM (St Helen and St Giles) w Wennington *Chelmsf 2* **P** *MMCET* **R** T G LYNDS, **C** P H ANSELL, A LINDSAY

RAINHAM (St Margaret) *Roch 3* **P** *Bp* **V** B M M O'CONNOR, **C** A SPURR, E P I WESTBROOK (nee REED), **NSM** A V SHILLING

RAINHILL (St Ann) *Liv 13* **P** *Trustees* **V** T R EVANS, **C** E COLLISON

RAINOW (Holy Trinity) w Saltersford and Forest *Ches 13* **P** *Bp* **V** L LEWIS

RAINTON (not known) Baldersby w Dalton, Dishforth etc *York*

RAINTON, EAST (St Cuthbert) *Dur 6* **P** *D&C* **V** D GUEST

RAINTON, WEST (St Mary) *Dur 6* **P** *Bp* **R** D GUEST

RAINWORTH (St Simon and St Jude) *S'well 2* **P** *DBP* **V** J FERN, **C** P A CHAPMAN, J HEATH

RAITHBY (Holy Trinity) *Linc 7* **P** *Baroness Willoughby de Eresby* **R** G ROBSON

RAITHBY (St Peter) *Linc 12* **P** *Bp and Viscount Chaplain (alt)* **R** *Vacant*

RAME (St Germanus) Maker w Rame *Truro*

RAMPISHAM (St Michael and All Angels) Melbury *Sarum*

RAMPSIDE (St Michael) Aldingham and Dendron and Rampside *Carl*

RAMPTON (All Saints) *Ely 5* **R** E A HUBBARD

RAMPTON (All Saints) w Laneham, Treswell, Cottam and Stokeham *S'well 5* **P** *D&C York and The Crown (alt)* **R** M D DRURY

RAMSBOTTOM (St Andrew) *Man 10* **P** *Bp* **V** I M ROGERSON

RAMSBOTTOM (St John) (St Paul) *Man 10* **P** *Prime Min and Bp (alt)* **V** J ARCUS, **NSM** D ALTHAM

RAMSBURY (Holy Cross) Whitton *Sarum*

RAMSDALE (Christ Church) Baughurst, Ramsdell, Wolverton w Ewhurst etc *Win*

RAMSDEN (Church of Unity) Orpington All SS *Roch*

RAMSDEN (St James), Finstock and Fawler, Leafield w Wychwood and Wilcote *Ox 3* **P** *Bp, V Charlbury, and Sir Mark Norman, Bt (jt)* **R** B J FREETH

RAMSDEN BELLHOUSE (St Mary the Virgin) Ramsden Crays w Ramsden Bellhouse *Chelmsf*

RAMSDEN CRAYS w Ramsden Bellhouse *Chelmsf 6* **P** *Reformation Ch Trust* **NSM** J M ALLWRIGHT

RAMSDEN HEATH (St John) Downham w S Hanningfield *Chelmsf*

RAMSEY (St Michael) w Little Oakley and Wrabness *Chelmsf 21* **P** *Ld Chan* **V** S R NORTHFIELD

RAMSEY, NORTH (St Olave) Lezayre St Olave Ramsey *S & M*

RAMSEY, SOUTH (St Paul) *S & M 4* **P** *Bp* **V** P C ROBINSON

RAMSEY ST MARY'S (St Mary) The Ramseys and Upwood *Ely*

RAMSEYS (St Thomas a Becket) (St Mary) and Upwood, The *Ely 11* **P** *Patr Bd* **TR** R H ROLLETT, **TV** J R SIMPSON

RAMSGATE (Christ Church) *Cant 9* **P** *Ch Patr Trust* **V** S YOUNG

RAMSGATE (Holy Trinity) (St George) *Cant 9* **P** *Abp* **R** P A ADAMS

RAMSGATE (St Luke) *Cant 9* **P** *CPAS* **V** V G WILKINS, **NSM** J P BRENCHLEY, S GOLDING

RAMSGATE (St Mark) *Cant 9* **P** *CPAS* **V** *Vacant* Thanet (01843) 581042

RAMSGILL (St Mary) Upper Nidderdale *Ripon*

RAMSHOLT (All Saints) Alderton w Ramsholt and Bawdsey *St E*

RANBY (St German) Asterby Gp *Linc*

RANBY (St Martin) Babworth w Sutton-cum-Lound *S'well*

RAND (St Oswald) Wragby *Linc*

RANDWICK (St John the Baptist) Whiteshill and Randwick *Glouc*

RANGEMORE (All Saints) Dunstall w Rangemore and Tatenhill *Lich*

RANGEWORTHY (Holy Trinity) Wickwar w Rangeworthy *Glouc*

RANMOOR (St John the Evangelist) *Sheff 4* **P** *Trustees* **V** R M JARRATT, **Hon C** B C BROOKE

RANMORE (St Barnabas) Dorking w Ranmore *Guildf*

RANSKILL (St Barnabas) Scrooby *S'well*

RANTON (All Saints) Derrington, Haughton and Ranton *Lich*

RANWORTH (St Helen) w Panxworth and Woodbastwick *Nor 4* **P** *Bp and J Cator Esq (jt)* **V** P McFADYEN

RASHCLIFFE (St Stephen) and Lockwood *Wakef 5* **P** *R Almondbury and R Kirkheaton (jt)* **P-in-c** M J ARCHER

RASKELF (St Mary) Easingwold w Raskelf *York*

RASTRICK (St John the Divine) *Wakef 2* **P** *Bp* **V** S J TYNDALL

RASTRICK (St Matthew) *Wakef 2* **P** *V Halifax* **V** B FIRTH, **C** N D BEER

RATBY (St Philip and St James) w Groby *Leic 12* **P** *Patr Bd* **TR** A R LEIGHTON, **TV** M H HARDY, **NSM** S LEIGHTON, P SHERIDAN

RATCLIFFE CULEY (All Saints) The Sheepy Gp *Leic*

RATCLIFFE-ON-SOAR (Holy Trinity) Kingston and Ratcliffe-on-Soar *S'well*

RATCLIFFE ON THE WREAKE (St Botolph) Syston TM *Leic*

RATHMELL (Holy Trinity) Giggleswick and Rathmell w Wigglesworth *Bradf*

RATLEY (St Peter ad Vincula) Warmington w Shotteswell and Radway w Ratley *Cov*

RATLINGHOPE (St Margaret) Wentnor w Ratlinghope, Myndtown, Norbury etc *Heref*

RATTERY (Blessed Virgin Mary) S Brent and Rattery *Ex*

RATTLESDEN (St Nicholas) w Thorpe Morieux and Brettenham *St E 10* **P** *Bp (2 turns), Ld Chan (1 turn)* **R** R S EXCELL

RAUCEBY, NORTH (St Peter) Ancaster Wilsford Gp *Linc*

RAUGHTON HEAD (All Saints) w Gatesgill *Carl 3* **P** *DBP* **P-in-c** P KYBIRD, **NSM** H J CARTER

RAUNDS (St Peter) *Pet 10* **P** *Bp* **V** *Vacant* Wellingborough (01933) 625637

RAVENDALE Group, The *Linc 10* **P** *Ld Chan, Trustees of D Parkinson Settled Estates, and Bp (by turn)* **R** D J HAWKSBEE

RAVENDALE, EAST (St Martin) Ravendale Gp *Linc*

RAVENFIELD (St James) Bramley and Ravenfield w Hooton Roberts etc *Sheff*

RAVENGLASS (Mission Room) Eskdale, Irton, Muncaster and Waberthwaite *Carl*

RAVENHEAD (St John) Parr Mt *Liv*

RAVENHEAD (St John the Evangelist) *Liv 10* **P** *V St Helens* **V** E R DORAN, **C** M X THORPE

RAVENINGHAM Group, The (St Andrew) *Nor 8* **P** *Bp, Adn Nor Sir Nicholas Bacon Bt, Major C A Boycott, D&C, King's Coll Cam, and DBP (Jt)* **R** C POULARD, **C** M J TALBOT

RAVENSCAR (St Hilda) Scalby w Ravenscar and Staintondale *York*

RAVENSDEN (All Saints) Wilden w Colmworth and Ravensden *St Alb*

RAVENSHEAD (St Peter) *S'well 4* **P** *Bp* **V** G O SPEDDING

RAVENSTHORPE (St Denys) W Haddon w Winwick and Ravensthorpe *Pet*

RAVENSTHORPE (St Saviour) *Wakef 10* **P** *V Mirfield* **V** *Vacant* Dewsbury (01924) 465959

RAVENSTONE (All Saints) Gayhurst w Ravenstone, Stoke Goldington etc *Ox*

RAVENSTONE (St Michael and All Angels) and Swannington *Leic 8* **P** *Ld Chan and V Whitwick (alt)* **R** K C EMMETT

RAVENSTONEDALE (St Oswald) Orton and Tebay w Ravenstonedale etc *Carl*

RAWCLIFFE (St James) *Sheff 11* **P** *V Gt Snaith* **V** G HOLLINGSWORTH

RAWCLIFFE (St Mark) Clifton *York*

RAWCLIFFE BRIDGE (St Philip) Rawcliffe *Sheff*

RAWDON (St Peter) *Bradf 4* **P** *Bp and Trustees (jt)* **V** C M MORRIS, **C** K S TROMANS

RAWMARSH (St Mary the Virgin) w Parkgate *Sheff 6* **P** *Ld Chan* **R** M R H BELLAMY, **C** K WEST

RAWNSLEY (St Michael) Hednesford *Lich*

RAWRETH (St Nicholas) w Rettendon *Chelmsf 12* **P** *Ld Chan and Pemb Coll Cam (alt)* **R** A CORNISH

RAWTENSTALL (St Mary) *Man 15* **P** *CPAS* **V** G D PARKIN, **NSM** M V MURPHY

RAWTHORPE (St James) *Wakef 1* **P** *DBP* **V** R D BALDOCK

RAYDON (St Mary) Higham, Holton St Mary, Raydon and Stratford *St E*

RAYLEIGH (Holy Trinity) (St Michael) *Chelmsf 12* **P** *MMCET* **R** P F TAYLOR, **C** J A FISHER, D HILDRED, **NSM** J M HILL, I E LAWRENCE

RAYNE (All Saints) *Chelmsf 16* **P** *DBP* **R** *Vacant* Braintree (01376) 21938

RAYNES PARK (St Saviour) *S'wark 12* **P** *Bp* **V** G J BENTLEY

RAYNHAM, EAST (St Mary) South Raynham, E w W Raynham, Helhoughton, etc *Nor*

RAYNHAM, SOUTH (St Martin), East w West Raynham, Helhoughton, Weasenham and Wellingham *Nor 15* **P** *Bp, Marquess Townshend, and Viscount Coke (by turn)* **P-in-c** H C BRADBURY, V M SCOTT

REACH (St Ethelreda) Swaffham Bulbeck and Swaffham Prior w Reach *Ely*

READ IN WHALLEY (St John the Evangelist) *Blackb 8* **P** *V Whalley* **V** H A REID

READING (All Saints) *Ox 15* **P** *Bp* **V** *Vacant* Reading (01734) 572000

READING Greyfriars (St James) *Ox 15* **P** *Ch Trust Fund Trust* **C** J R WATTLEY

READING (Holy Trinity) *Ox 15* **P** *SMF* **C** M T COOMBE, **NSM** R H LUSTY

READING (St Agnes w St Paul) *Ox 15* **P** *Bp* **V** D I A BRAZELL, **C** E J BRAZELL, J P COLWILL

READING (St Barnabas) *Ox 15* **P** *Bp* **R** C F BOND, **NSM** G L FRENCH

READING (St Giles w St Saviour) *Ox 15* **P** *Bp* **R** M J G MELROSE, **C** V J A BULLOCK

READING (St John the Evangelist and St Stephen) *Ox 15* **P** *Simeon's Trustees* **V** A J BURDON, **C** P M BURDON, E MARQUEZ, **NSM** T R ASTIN

READING (St Luke) (St Bartholomew) *Ox 15* **P** *Bp and V Reading St Giles (alt)* **P-in-c** N A B DAVIES, **NSM** B D E BLACKMAN, C F PRATT, E M JACKSON

READING (St Mark) *Ox 15* **P** *Bp* **V** R G HAYNE

READING (St Mary the Virgin) (St Laurence) *Ox 15* **P** *Bp* **R** B SHENTON

READING (St Matthew) *Ox 15* **P** *Bp* **V** A J McCULLOCH

REAPSMOOR (St John) Longnor, Quarnford and Sheen *Lich*

REARSBY (St Michael and All Angels) Syston TM *Leic*

RECULVER (St Mary the Virgin) and Herne Bay St Bartholomew *Cant 7* **P** *Abp* **V** *Vacant* Canterbury (01227) 375154

RED HOUSE (St Cuthbert) Sunderland Red Ho *Dur*

RED POST *Sarum 7* **P** *Mrs V M Chattey, H W Plunkett-Ernle-Erle-Drax Esq, and Bp (by turn)* **V** H I M MADDOX

REDBOURN (St Mary) *St Alb 14* **P** *Earl of Verulam* **V** J G PEDLAR, **NSM** A D OSBORNE

REDBROOK (St Saviour) Newland and Redbrook w Clearwell *Glouc*

REDCAR (St Peter) *York 17* **P** *Trustees* **V** S N FISHER

REDCLIFFE BAY (St Nicholas) Portishead *B & W*

REDCLIFFE WAY (St Mary the Virgin) Bris St Mary Redcliffe w Temple etc *Bris*

REDDAL HILL (St Luke) *Worc 9* **P** *The Crown* **V** M F BAYNHAM

REDDISH (St Elisabeth) *Man 3* **P** *Bp* **R** N D HAWLEY, **C** J M PRESTWOOD

REDDISH, NORTH (St Agnes) *Man 3* **P** *The Crown* **R** M P N JEWITT

REDDITCH (St Stephen) *Worc 7* **P** *Bp* **V** D C SALT

REDDITCH, The Ridge: Redditch (St George), Headless Cross, Webheath and Crabbs Cross *Worc 7* **P** *Bp* **TR** B N HALFPENNY, **TV** A J SMITH, M HERBERT, M F BARTLETT

REDE (All Saints) Chedburgh w Depden, Rede and Hawkedon *St E*

REDENHALL (Assumption of the Blessed Virgin Mary), Harleston, Wortwell and Needham *Nor 10* **P** *Bp* **R** P MORRIS

REDFIELD (St Leonard) E Bris *Bris*
REDGRAVE cum Botesdale (St Mary) w Rickinghall *St E 16*
P P J H *Wilson Esq* R K W HOLDER
REDHILL (Christ Church) Wrington w Butcombe *B & W*
REDHILL (Holy Trinity) *S'wark 25* P *Simeon's Trustees*
V D P R SHACKLOCK, C S J BAILEY
REDHILL (St John the Evangelist) (Meadvale Hall)
S'wark 25 P *Bp* V T G A WOODERSON,
C C M E G TOURNAY
REDHILL (St Matthew) *S'wark 25* P *Bp* V P R WHITE,
NSM D T BRYANT
REDHORN *Sarum 19* P *Patr Bd* **TR** A BODY,
TV B J SMITH, NSM G D BAKER, M J C WHEELER
REDISHAM (St Peter) Wainford *St E*
REDLAND (not known) *Bris 6* P *Ch Trust Fund Trust*
V J M PERRIS, NSM J G CAINE (nee BALDWIN)
REDLINGFIELD (St Andrew) Stradbroke, Horham,
Athelington and Redlingfield *St E*
REDLYNCH (St Mary) and Morgan's Vale *Sarum 11*
P *DBF and V Downton (alt)* V R C LOWRIE
REDLYNCH (St Peter) Bruton and Distr *B & W*
REDMARLEY D'ABITOT (St Bartholomew) and
Bromesberrow w Pauntley, Upleadon and Oxenhall *Glouc 3*
P *Bp and Rev D J M Niblett (jt)* **P-in-c** T WILLIAMS,
Hon C W E W BARBER, NSM A W PERRY
REDMARSHALL (St Cuthbert) *Dur 16* P *The Crown*
R P S ATKINSON
REDMILE (St Peter) Barkestone w Plungar, Redmile and
Stathern *Leic*
REDMIRE (St Mary) Aysgarth and Bolton cum Redmire
Ripon
REDNAL (St Stephen the Martyr) *Birm 4* P *Bp*
V P W THOMAS
REDRUTH (St Andrew) (St Euny) w Lanner and Treleigh
Truro 2 P *DBP* **TR** R C BUSH, **TV** R SELLERS
REED (St Mary) Barkway, Reed and Buckland w Barley
St Alb
REEDHAM (St John the Baptist) w Cantley w Limpenhoe and
Southwood *Nor 4* P *Lt-Col E R F Gilbert (1 turn), Ch Soc*
Trust (2 turns) **P-in-c** R F GIBSON
REEPHAM (St Mary) and Hackford w Whitwell and
Kerdiston, Thurning w Wood Dalling and Salle *Nor 23*
P *Bp, CCC Cam, Pemb Coll Cam, Trin Coll Cam, and Ch*
Soc Trust(jt) R M D W PADDISON
REEPHAM (St Peter and St Paul) Fiskerton w Reepham
Linc
REGENT'S PARK (Christ Church) Munster Square Ch Ch
and St Mary Magd *Lon*
REGENT'S PARK (St Mark) *Lon 16* P *D&C St Paul's*
V T P N D JONES
REGIL (St James Mission Church) Winford w Felton
Common Hill *B & W*
REIGATE South Park (St Luke) Reigate St Luke S Park
S'wark
REIGATE (St Luke) South Park *S'wark 25* P *Bp*
V A J MAYER, NSM G TYLER
REIGATE (St Mark) *S'wark 25* P *Bp* V I H ROBERTSON
REIGATE (St Mary Magdalene) *S'wark 25* P *Trustees*
V R I THOMSON, C T D GILES, T J L ANDERSON,
Hon C M J H FOX, NSM D A HAGGAN, S M BROWN
REIGATE (St Philip) *S'wark 25* P *Bp* **P-in-c** J P SCOTT
REIGATE HEATH (not known) Reigate St Mary *S'wark*
REIGHTON (St Peter) w Speeton *York 10* P *Exors*
Sir Henry Strickland-Constable, Bt (3 turns), Abp (1 turn)
V *Vacant* Scarborough (01723) 891839
REKENDYKE (St Jude) *Dur 7* P *The Crown and D&C*
V A J BEALING, C P R BEALING
REMENHAM (St Nicholas) Henley on Thames w
Remenham *Ox*
REMPSTONE (All Saints) E and W Leake, Stanford-on-
Soar, Rempstone etc *S'well*
RENDCOMB (St Peter) *Glouc 12* P *Major M T N H Wills*
P-in-c P J SUDBURY
RENDHAM (St Michael) w Sweffling *St E 19* P *CPAS*
R *Vacant* Rendham (0172878) 495
RENDLESHAM (St Gregory the Great) Eyke w Bromeswell,
Rendlesham, Tunstall etc *St E*
RENHOLD (All Saints) *St Alb 16* P *MMCET*
P-in-c L R McDONALD
RENISHAW (St Matthew) Eckington w Handley and
Ridgeway *Derby*
RENNINGTON (All Saints) Embleton w Rennington and
Rock *Newc*
RENWICK (All Saints) Kirkoswald, Renwick and Ainstable
Carl
REPPS (St Peter) Martham and Repps with Bastwick,
Thurne etc *Nor*

REPTON (St Wystan) *Derby 16* P *Major F R D Burdett*
Fisher (1 turn), Exors H F Harpur-Crewe Esq (2 turns)
V J R P BARKER
RESTON, NORTH (St Edith) Wold-Marsh Gp *Linc*
RETFORD (St Saviour) *S'well 5* P *Simeon's Trustees*
V A C St J WALKER, C D J GRIFFITHS
RETFORD, EAST (St Swithin) *S'well 5* P *Bp* V J L OTTEY
RETFORD, WEST (St Michael) *S'well 5* P *Meynell*
Ch Trust R J L OTTEY
RETTENDON (All Saints) Rawreth w Rettendon *Chelmsf*
REVELSTOKE (St Peter) Newton Ferrers w Revelstoke *Ex*
REVESBY (St Lawrence) Mareham-le-Fen and Revesby *Linc*
REWE (St Mary the Virgin) Stoke Canon, Poltimore w
Huxham and Rewe etc *Ex*
REYDON (St Margaret) Blythburgh w Reydon *St E*
REYMERSTON (St Peter) w Cranworth, Letton, Southburgh,
Whinburgh and Westfield *Nor 18* P *Ch Soc Trust and*
MMCET (jt) R *Vacant*
RHODES (All Saints) (St Thomas) *Man 18* P *R Middleton*
V G D GARRETT
RHYDYCROESAU (Christ Church) *Lich 24* P *Bp*
R D B CROWHURST, C T R K LAW
RIBBESFORD (St Leonard) w Bewdley and Dowles *Worc 11*
P *E J Winnington-Ingram Esq* R A G ANDERSON,
NSM G D MORPHY, L E POCOCK
RIBBLETON (St Mary Magdalene) (St Anne's Church Centre)
(Ascension) *Blackb 14* P *Patr Bd* **TR** J W GODDARD,
C C R SCHAEFER, R MARSH, NSM T DE LACEY
RIBBY w Wrea (St Nicholas) *Blackb 11* P *V Kirkham*
V J WIXON
RIBCHESTER (St Wilfred) w Stidd *Blackb 14* P *Bp*
R A D HINDLEY
RIBSTON, LITTLE (St Helen) Spofforth w Kirk Deighton
Ripon
RIBY (St Edmund) Keelby w Riby and Aylesby *Linc*
RICCALL (St Mary) Barlby w Riccall *York*
RICHARDS CASTLE (All Saints) Ludlow, Ludford,
Ashford Carbonell etc *Heref*
RICHMOND (Holy Trinity and Christ Church) *S'wark 16*
P *CPAS* V D C CASSON, NSM J F HARTERINK
RICHMOND (St Luke) Kew St Phil and All SS w St Luke
S'wark
RICHMOND (St Mary Magdalene) (St Matthias) (St John the
Divine) *S'wark 16* P *K Coll Cam*
P-in-c M C J REINDORP, C W F WARREN,
J D S FRENCH, NSM H R SCOTT
RICHMOND (St Mary w Holy Trinity) w Hudswell *Ripon 2*
P *Bp* R C N H WHITE, C J G HAIGH
RICKERSCOTE (St Peter) *Lich 15* P *Bp and V Stafford*
St Paul (jt) V S J HOTCHEN
RICKINGHALL (St Mary) Redgrave cum Botesdale w
Rickinghall *St E*
RICKLING (All Saints) Quendon w Rickling & Wicken
Bonhunt & Widdington *Chelmsf*
RICKMANSWORTH (St Mary the Virgin) *St Alb 10* P *Bp*
V B L DRIVER, NSM A P L SHAW
RIDDINGS (Holy Spirit) Bottesford w Ashby *Linc*
RIDDINGS (St James) and Ironville *Derby 1* P *Wright*
Trustees and V Alfreton (jt) V P J A LEVERTON
RIDDLESDEN (St Mary the Virgin) *Bradf 8* P *Bp*
V G D N SMITH
RIDDLESDOWN (St James) *S'wark 22* P *Bp*
V R St L BROADBERRY, NSM J DAGLEISH,
D J ROWLAND
RIDDLESWORTH (St Peter) Garboldisham w Blo' Norton,
Riddlesworth etc *Nor*
RIDGE (St Margaret) S Mymms and Ridge *St Alb*
RIDGEWAY *Ox 19* P *DBP, CCC Ox, and Qu Coll Ox (jt)*
R A WADGE, NSM A P HOPWOOD
RIDGEWAY *Sarum 20* P *Patr Bd* **TR** N T POLLOCK,
TV R T JONES
RIDGEWAY (St John the Evangelist) Eckington w Handley
and Ridgeway *Derby*
RIDGEWELL (St Laurence) w Ashen, Birdbrook and Sturmer
Chelmsf 15 P *Duchy of Lanc, Bp, and DBP (by turn)*
R M D HEWITT
RIDGMONT (All Saints) Aspley Guise w Husborne Crawley
and Ridgmont *St Alb*
RIDING MILL (St James) *Newc 3* P *Viscount Allendale*
V M F FENWICK
RIDLEY (St Peter) *Roch 1* P *J R A B Scott Esq*
R L W G KEVIS, NSM E M R WALKER
RIDLINGTON (St Mary Magdalene and St
Andrew) Preston and Ridlington w Wing and Pilton *Pet*
RIDLINGTON (St Peter) Bacton w Edingthorpe w Witton
and Ridlington *Nor*

RIDWARES and Kings Bromley, The *Lich 1* **P** *Bp, Lord Leigh, and D&C (jt)* **R** F FINCH, **C** S FINN
RIEVAULX (St Mary) Helmsley *York*
RIGSBY (St James) Alford w Rigsby *Linc*
RIGTON, NORTH (St John) Kirkby Overblow *Ripon*
RILLINGTON (St Andrew) w Scampston, Wintringham and Thorpe Bassett *York 2* **P** *Major G R H Cholmley* **V** F B WILLIAMS
RIMPTON (The Blessed Virgin Mary) Chilton Cantelo, Ashington, Mudford, Rimpton etc *B & W*
RIMSWELL (St Mary) Owthorne and Rimswell w Withernsea *York*
RINGLAND (St Peter) Taverham w Ringland *Nor*
RINGLEY (St Saviour) (St Aidan) w Prestolee *Man 14* **P** *R Prestwich St Mary* **V** P F DAVEY, **NSM** D R JONES
RINGMER (St Mary the Virgin) *Chich 18* **P** *Abp* **V** H M MOSELEY, **NSM** J R LOWERSON
RINGMORE (All Hallows) Bigbury, Ringmore and Kingston *Ex*
RINGSFIELD (All Saints) Wainford *St E*
RINGSHALL (St Catherine) w Battisford, Barking w Darmsden and Great Bricett *St E 1* **P** *Bp, Ch Patr Trust, and J C W de la Bere Esq (jt)* **P-in-c** C A GRAY
RINGSTEAD (Nativity of the Blessed Virgin Mary) Denford w Ringstead *Pet*
RINGSTEAD (St Andrew) Hunstanton St Edm w Ringstead *Nor*
RINGWAY (All Saints) and St Mary *Ches 10* **P** *Bp* **V** B B GRIBBIN
RINGWOOD (St Peter and St Paul) *Win 8* **P** *K Coll Cam* **V** J R TURPIN
RINGWOULD (St Nicholas) w Kingsdown *Cant 8* **P** *R S C Monins Esq and Ch Patr Trust (jt)* **R** J A SILK
RIPE (St John the Baptist) Laughton w Ripe and Chalvington *Chich*
RIPLEY (All Saints) *Derby 12* **P** *Wright Trustees* **V** R P FULLER, **C** C J CARTER
RIPLEY (All Saints) *Ripon 3* **P** *Sir Thomas Ingilby, Bt* **P-in-c** S J BROWN
RIPLEY (St Mary) *Guildf 12* **P** *Bp* **V** C J ELSON
RIPON (Holy Trinity) *Ripon 3* **P** *Simeon's Trustees* **V** D MANN, **NSM** J A MONTGOMERY (nee YOUATT)
RIPON St Peter and St Wilfrid (Cathedral Church) *Ripon* **P** *The Crown* **V** *Vacant*
RIPPINGALE Group, The (St Andrew) *Linc 13* **P** *Baroness Willoughby de Eresby, Charterhouse, Bp, and St Jo Coll Dur (jt)* **R** *Vacant* Bourne (01778) 440380
RIPPLE (St Mary the Virgin) Gt Mongeham w Ripple and Sutton by Dover *Cant*
RIPPLE (St Mary), Earls Croome w Hill Croome and Strensham *Worc 5* **P** *Bp and Trustees of late Rev G Le S Amphlett (alt)* **R** C G HARDWICK
RIPPONDEN (St Bartholomew) *Wakef 4* **P** *Bp and V Halifax (jt)* **V** A G SWALLOW, **NSM** M JAMES
RISBY (St Giles) w Great Saxham, Little Saxham and Westley *St E 13* **P** *Ld Chan, Trustees Sir William Stirling, and DBP (by turn)* **R** C J ROGERS
RISE (All Saints) Sigglesthorne and Rise w Nunkeeling and Bewholme *York*
RISEHOLME (St Mary) Nettleham *Linc*
RISELEY (All Saints) w Bletsoe *St Alb 21* **P** *MMCET* **V** D J BOURNE
RISHTON (St Peter and St Paul) *Blackb 8* **P** *Trustees* **V** P A SMITH
RISHWORTH (St John) Ripponden *Wakef*
RISLEY (All Saints) *Derby 13* **P** *Bp* **P-in-c** I E GOODING
RISSINGTONS, The (St John the Baptist) (St Peter) *Glouc 15* **P** *C T R Wingfield Esq, Ld Chan, and DBP (by turn)* **P-in-c** S MOTH
RITCHINGS PARK (St Leonard) Iver *Ox*
RIVENHALL (St Mary the Virgin and All Saints) *Chelmsf 25* **P** *DBP* **R** N S COOPER
RIVER (St Peter and St Paul) *Cant 4* **P** *Abp* **R** P W A BOWERS, **NSM** L R CRUTTENDEN
RIVERHEAD (St Mary) w Dunton Green *Roch 8* **P** *R Sevenoaks and Bp (jt)* **V** G T CUNLIFFE
RIVERSIDE: Colnbrook, Datchet, Dorney, Eton, Eton Wick, Horton, Wraysbury *Ox 23* **P** *Patr Bd* **TR** W L KNIGHT, **TV** J A HARPER, P W ABRAHAMS, **C** P SWART-RUSSELL
RIVINGTON (not known) Horwich and Rivington *Man*
ROADE (St Mary the Virgin) and Ashton w Hartwell *Pet 5* **P** *Ld Chan and Bp (alt)* **V** *Vacant* Northampton (01604) 862284
ROADHEAD Kinkry Hill (Mission Room) Bewcastle, Stapleton and Kirklinton etc *Carl*

ROADWATER (St Luke) Old Cleeve, Leighland and Treborough *B & W*
ROBERTSBRIDGE (Mission Room) Salehurst *Chich*
ROBERTTOWN (All Saints) *Wakef 8* **P** *V Birstall* **P-in-c** N H S BERSWEDEN, **NSM** J A BERSWEDEN
ROBOROUGH Bickleigh (Roborough) and Shaugh Prior *Ex*
ROBOROUGH (St Peter) Beaford, Roborough and St Giles in the Wood *Ex*
ROBY (St Bartholomew) *Liv 2* **P** *Bp* **V** G S PEARSON, **C** M NORRIS
ROCESTER (St Michael) and Croxden w Hollington *Lich 20* **P** *Bp and Trustees (jt)* **V** J B HALL
ROCHDALE Deeplish (St Luke) *Man 20* **P** *Bp* **V** R F CUTLER
ROCHDALE (St Chad) (Good Shepherd) (St John the Divine) *Man 20* **P** *Bp* **TR** A SHACKLETON, **TV** G C DOBBS, J HARGREAVES, C A POWELL, D FINNEY, **NSM** I G KAY
ROCHDALE (St George w St Alban) *Man 20* **P** *Bp* **V** J B KELLY
ROCHE (St Gomonda of the Rock) and Withiel *Truro 1* **P** *Bp and DBP (jt)* **R** D J A POLLARD
ROCHESTER (St Justus) *Roch 5* **P** *Bp* **V** J G C LAWRENCE
ROCHESTER (St Margaret) (St Peter's Parish Centre) *Roch 5* **P** *Bp and D&C (jt)* **V** R THOMSON, **C** M ILYAS, **NSM** H DAUBNEY
ROCHESTER ROW (St Stephen) Westmr St Steph w St Jo *Lon*
ROCHFORD (St Andrew) *Chelmsf 12* **P** *Bp* **P-in-c** D J WILLIAMS
ROCHFORD (St Michael) Teme Valley S *Worc*
ROCK (St Peter and St Paul) Mamble w Bayton, Rock w Heightington etc *Worc*
ROCK (St Philip and St James) Embleton w Rennington and Rock *Newc*
ROCK FERRY (St Peter) *Ches 1* **P** *Bp* **V** R C TOAN
ROCKBEARE (St Mary w St Andrew) Aylesbeare, Rockbeare, Farringdon etc *Ex*
ROCKBOURNE (St Andrew) W Downland *Sarum*
ROCKCLIFFE (St Mary the Virgin) and Blackford *Carl 2* **P** *D&C* **V** R D A TANKARD
ROCKHAMPTON (St Oswald) Falfield w Rockhampton *Glouc*
ROCKINGHAM (St Leonard) Gretton w Rockingham and Caldecote *Pet*
ROCKLAND (All Saints) Lt w Gt Ellingham w Rockland *Nor*
ROCKLAND (St Peter) as above
ROCKLAND ST MARY (St Mary) with Hellington, Bramerton, Surlingham, Claxton, Carleton St Peter and Kirby Bedon w Whitlingham *Nor 8* **P** *Bp, Adn Nor, MMCET, and BNC Ox (jt)* **R** J A LEDWARD
RODBOROUGH (St Mary Magdalene) *Glouc 8* **P** *Bp* **R** S J RIGGS
RODBOURNE (Holy Rood) Gt Somerford, Lt Somerford, Seagry, Corston etc *Bris*
RODBOURNE CHENEY (St Mary) *Bris 10* **P** *Patr Bd* **TR** G W CREES, **TV** R W ADAMS, **C** M J GUILLEBAUD, **NSM** A J DEAN
RODDEN (All Saints) Beckington w Standerwick, Berkley, Rodden etc *B & W*
RODE, NORTH (St Michael) Bosley and N Rode w Wincle and Wildboarclough *Ches*
RODE HEATH (Good Shepherd) Odd Rode *Ches*
RODE MAJOR (Christ Church) *B & W 4* **P** *Bp* **R** M P CULVERWELL
RODHUISH (St Bartholomew) Dunster, Carhampton and Withycombe w Rodhuish *B & W*
RODING, HIGH (All Saints) Aythorpe w High and Leaden Roding *Chelmsf*
RODING, HIGH (Mission Hall) as above
RODINGTON (St George) Longdon-upon-Tern, Rodington, Uppington etc *Lich*
RODLEY (Ecumenical Centre) Bramley *Ripon*
RODLEY (Mission Church) Westbury-on-Severn w Flaxley and Blaisdon *Glouc*
RODMARTON (St Peter) Coates, Rodmarton and Sapperton etc *Glouc*
RODMELL (St Peter) Iford w Kingston and Rodmell *Chich*
RODMERSHAM (St Nicholas) Tunstall w Rodmersham *Cant*
RODNEY STOKE (St Leonard) w Draycott *B & W 1* **P** *Bp* **P-in-c** J C HALL
ROEHAMPTON (Holy Trinity) *S'wark 18* **P** *Bp* **C** A N TREDENNICK

ROFFEY (All Saints) Roughey (or Roffey) *Chich*

ROGATE (St Bartholomew) w Terwick and Trotton w Chithurst *Chich 10* **P** *Ld Chan* **R** *Vacant* Petersfield (01730) 821576

ROGERS LANE (St Andrew's Chapel) Stoke Poges *Ox*

ROKEBY (St Mary) Startforth and Bowes and Rokeby w Brignall *Ripon*

ROKER (St Aidan) Monkwearmouth All SS *Dur*

ROLLESBY (St George) w Burgh w Billockby w Ashby w Oby, Thurne and Clippesby *Nor 6* **P** *Bp, R J H Tacon Esq, and DBP (jt)* **R** *Vacant* Great Yarmouth (01493) 740323

ROLLESTON (Holy Trinity) w Fiskerton, Morton and Upton *S'well 15* **P** *Ld Chan* **P-in-c** A HEATON

ROLLESTON (St John the Baptist) Billesdon and Skeffington *Leic*

ROLLESTON (St Mary) *Lich 19* **P** *MMCET* **R** M D BIRT

ROLLRIGHT, GREAT (St Andrew) Hook Norton w Gt Rollright, Swerford etc *Ox*

ROLLRIGHT, LITTLE (St Phillip) Lt Compton w Chastleton, Cornwell etc *Ox*

ROLVENDEN (St Mary the Virgin) *Cant 11* **P** *Abp* **P-in-c** A E WILLIAMS

ROMALDKIRK (St Romald) w Laithkirk *Ripon 2* **P** *Bp and Earl of Strathmore's Trustees (alt)* **R** D DALTON

ROMANBY (St James) Northallerton w Kirby Sigston *York*

ROMANSLEIGH (St Rumon) S Molton w Nymet St George, High Bray etc *Ex*

ROMFORD (Ascension) Collier Row *Chelmsf 2* **P** *Trustees* **V** G P LAUT

ROMFORD (Good Shepherd) Collier Row *Chelmsf 2* **P** *CPAS* **V** R C SAMME, **C** P J COOK

ROMFORD (St Alban) *Chelmsf 2* **P** *Bp* **V** R S P HINGLEY

ROMFORD (St Andrew) St Agnes) *Chelmsf 2* **P** *New Coll Ox* **R** B J LEWIS, **C** P A KENNEDY

ROMFORD (St Edward the Confessor) *Chelmsf 2* **P** *New Coll Ox* **V** S J WAINE, **C** R HAGGIS, **NSM** G K ARBER

ROMFORD (St John the Divine) *Chelmsf 2* **P** *Bp* **V** G P LAW

ROMILEY (St Chad) Chadkirk *Ches*

ROMNEY, NEW (St Nicholas) w OLD (St Clement) and Midley *Cant 13* **P** *Abp* **P-in-c** J H COLEMAN, **NSM** M A GOOCH

ROMSEY (St Mary and St Ethelflaeda) *Win 11* **P** *Bp* **V** N C JONES, **C** D J SIMPSON, **NSM** D F WILLIAMS

ROMSLEY (St Kenelm) *Worc 9* **P** *R Halesowen* **R** M G CLARKE

ROOKERY, THE (St Saviour) Mow Cop *Lich*

ROOKHOPE (St John the Evangelist) Eastgate w Rookhope *Dur*

ROOS (All Saints) and Garton in Holderness w Tunstall, Grimston and Hilston *York 13* **P** *Abp (1 turn), SMF (2 turns)* **P-in-c** P MOATE

ROOSE (St Perran) Barrow St Geo w St Luke *Carl*

ROPLEY (St Peter) Bishop's Sutton and Ropley and W Tisted *Win*

ROPSLEY (St Peter) *Linc 14* **P** *Bp* **R** *Vacant* Ingoldsby (0147685) 255

ROSE ASH (St Peter) Bishopsnympton, Rose Ash, Mariansleigh etc *Ex*

ROSEDALE (St Lawrence) Lastingham w Appleton-le-Moors, Rosedale etc *York*

ROSHERVILLE (St Mark) *Roch 4* **P** *DBP* **V** P J DAVIES, **P-in-c** D G WILLEY

ROSLEY (Holy Trinity) Westward, Rosley-w-Woodside and Welton *Carl*

ROSLISTON (St Mary) Walton on Trent w Croxall etc *Derby*

ROSS (St Mary the Virgin) w Brampton Abbotts, Bridstow, Peterstow, Weston-under-Penyard, Hope Mansel and The Lea *Heref 8* **P** *DBP* **TR** R STIRRUP, **TV** T M ALBAN-JONES, R J WILLIAMSON, **C** E B SAVIGEAR

ROSSINGTON (St Michael) *Sheff 10* **P** *Bp* **R** M J SECCOMBE

ROSSINGTON, NEW (St Luke) *Sheff 10* **P** *Bp* **V** P F GASCOIGNE

ROSTHERNE (St Mary) w Bollington *Ches 12* **P** *C L S Cornwall-Legh Esq* **V** N D ROGERS

ROTHBURY (All Saints) *Newc 9* **P** *Duchy of Lanc* **R** L F T EDDERSHAW, **Hon C** A E TREWEEKS

ROTHERBY (All Saints) Upper Wreake *Leic*

ROTHERFIELD (St Denys) w Mark Cross *Chich 19* **P** *Bp, Adn Lewes and Hastings, and Ch Patr Trust (jt)* **P-in-c** D J CLEEVES

ROTHERFIELD GREYS (Holy Trinity) *Ox 6* **P** *R Rotherfield Greys St Nich* **V** D R B CARTER

ROTHERFIELD GREYS (St Nicholas) *Ox 6* **P** *Trin Coll Ox* **R** B G BUTLER-SMITH

ROTHERFIELD PEPPARD (All Saints) *Ox 6* **P** *Jes Coll Ox* **R** B G BUTLER-SMITH

ROTHERHAM (All Saints) *Sheff 6* **P** *Bp* **V** S G N BRINDLEY, **C** W MOORE, **NSM** M WATERS

ROTHERHITHE (Holy Trinity) *S'wark 5* **P** *R Rotherhithe St Mary* **V** P D MAURICE, **C** J WADSWORTH

ROTHERHITHE (St Katharine) Bermondsey St Kath w St Bart *S'wark*

ROTHERHITHE (St Mary) w All Saints *S'wark 5* **P** *Clare Coll Cam* **R** C E N RICHARDS, **Hon C** P J HINCHEY

ROTHERSTHORPE (St Peter and St Paul) Bugbrooke w Rothersthorpe *Pet*

ROTHERWICK (not known) Heckfield w Mattingley and Rotherwick *Win*

ROTHLEY (St Mary the Virgin and St John the Baptist) *Leic 6* **P** *MMCET* **V** N BAINES, **C** B CAMPBELL

ROTHWELL (Holy Trinity) *Ripon 8* **P** *Bp* **C** J N ASHWORTH, **NSM** G W SELLERS

ROTHWELL (Holy Trinity) w Orton and Rushton w Glendon and Pipwell *Pet 11* **P** *Hosp of Jes (1 turn), Bp (2 turns), J Hipwell Esq (1 turn),and Mert Coll Ox (1 turn)* **R** P R ROSE

ROTHWELL (St Mary the Virgin) Swallow *Linc*

ROTTINGDEAN (St Margaret) *Chich 2* **P** *Bp* **V** M P MORGAN

ROUGH CLOSE (St Matthew) Meir Heath *Lich*

ROUGH COMMON (St Gabriel) Harbledown *Cant*

ROUGH HAY (St Christopher) Darlaston St Lawr *Lich*

ROUGH HILLS (St Martin) *Lich 9* **P** *Bp* **V** J C OAKES

ROUGHAM (St Mary) Castle Acre w Newton, Rougham and Southacre *Nor*

ROUGHAM (St Mary), Beyton w Hessett and Rushbrooke *St E 10* **P** *MMCET, CPAS, Ld Chan, Mrs V J Clarke, and Bp (by turn)* **R** G H CLOTHIER

ROUGHEY (All Saints) *Chich 8* **P** *Bp* **V** A R REED

ROUGHTON (St Margaret) Thornton Gp *Linc*

ROUGHTON (St Mary) and Felbrigg, Metton, Sustead, Bessingham and Gunton w Hanworth *Nor 22* **P** *Bp and Exors G Whately (jt)* **R** K E A JAMES, **Hon C** E C BAILEY

ROUGHTOWN (St John the Baptist) *Man 17* **P** *Bp* **P-in-c** R A ANDERSON

ROUNDHAY (St Edmund) *Ripon 5* **P** *Bp* **C** J W DANIELS

ROUNDHAY (St John the Evangelist) *Ripon 5* **P** *DBF* **P-in-c** R G PLACE

ROUNDS GREEN (St James) *Birm 5* **P** *V Langley* **V** *Vacant* 0121–552 2822

ROUNDSHAW Conventional District *S'wark 25* **C-in-c** J B GOULD

ROUNDSWELL C D *Ex 15* **C-in-c** A C BING

ROUNDTHORN (St Matthew and St Aidan) *Man 19* **P** *Bp* **V** *Vacant* 0161–624 1007

ROUNTON, EAST (St Laurence) Rounton w Welbury *York*

ROUNTON, WEST (St Oswald) and East (St Laurence) w Welbury *York 20* **P** *Ld Chan* **P-in-c** B J MAYNE

ROUS LENCH (St Peter) Church Lench w Rous Lench and Abbots Morton *Worc*

ROUSHAM (St Leonard and St James) The Heyfords w Rousham and Somerton *Ox*

ROUTH (All Saints) *York 9* **P** *Ch Soc Trust and Reformation Ch Trust (jt)* **C** P R FORSTER

ROWANFIELD (Emmanuel) Cheltenham St Mark *Glouc*

ROWBERROW (St Michael and All Angels) Axbridge w Shipham and Rowberrow *B & W*

ROWDE (St Matthew) and Poulshot *Sarum 19* **P** *Bp and DBP (alt)* **R** *Vacant* Devizes (01380) 724413

ROWINGTON (St Lawrence) Hatton w Haseley, Rowington w Lowsonford etc *Cov*

ROWLAND LUBBOCK (Memorial Hall) E Horsley *Guildf*

ROWLANDS CASTLE (St John the Baptist) *Portsm 4* **P** *Bp* **R** N STUART-LEE

ROWLANDS GILL (St Barnabas) High Spen and Rowlands Gill *Dur*

ROWLEDGE (St James) *Guildf 3* **P** *Adn Surrey* **V** C J RICHARDSON

ROWLESTONE (St Peter) Ewyas Harold w Dulas, Kenderchurch etc *Heref*

ROWLEY (St Peter) w Skidby *York 9* **P** *Abp and Sir David Hildyard (jt)* **R** J M TRIGG, **NSM** H McCOUBREY

ROWLEY REGIS (St Giles) *Birm 5* **P** *Ld Chan* **V** J B NIGHTINGALE, **C** J BIRKETT

ROWNER (St Mary the Virgin) *Portsm 3* **P** *R J F Prideaux-Brune Esq* **R** C R GEORGE, **C** B D GOLDSMITH

ROWNEY GREEN (Mission Chapel) Alvechurch *Worc*

ROWSLEY (St Katherine) *Derby 2* **P** *Duke of Rutland* **V** *Vacant* Matlock (01629) 733296

ROWSTON (St Clement) Digby *Linc*
ROWTON (All Hallows) *Lich 29* **P** *Lord Barnard*
  V K D MINTY
ROXBOURNE (St Andrew) *Lon 23* **P** *Bp* **V** D J COCKBILL
ROXBY (St Mary) Winterton Gp *Linc*
ROXBY (St Nicholas) Hinderwell w Roxby *York*
ROXETH (Christ Church) *Lon 23* **P** *Patr Bd*
  TR B C COLLINS, **TV** J M WHITE, N T W TAYLOR,
  C P S MacKENZIE, H D KENDAL, C J PRICE,
  NSM V L BARON
ROXHOLME Leasingham *Linc*
ROXTON (St Mary Magdalene) w Great Barford *St Alb 17*
  P *Trin Coll Cam* **V** L G BLANCHARD
ROXWELL (St Michael and All Angels) *Chelmsf 8*
  P *New Coll Ox* **P-in-c** V W HYDON
ROYDON (All Saints) Grimston, Congham and Roydon *Nor*
ROYDON (St Peter) *Chelmsf 27* **P** *Earl Cowley*
  V P J COLLINS
ROYDON (St Remigius) *Nor 10* **P** *DBP*
  P-in-c W M C BESTELINK
ROYSTON (St John the Baptist) *St Alb 5* **P** *Bp*
  V L D HARMAN, **C** K M EMERY, **NSM** J H FIDLER
ROYSTON (St John the Baptist) *Wakef 7* **P** *Bp*
  V J L HUDSON, **C** J A BOOTH
ROYTON (St Anne) Longsight *Man 22* **P** *Bp*
  V D SHARPLES, **C** W E BRAVINER, **Hon C** P A CLARK
ROYTON (St Paul) *Man 22* **P** *R Prestwich St Mary*
  V Vacant 0161–624 2388
RUAN LANIHORNE (St Rumon) Veryan w Ruan
  Lanihorne *Truro*
RUAN MINOR (St Rumon) St Ruan w St Grade and
  Landewednack *Truro*
RUARDEAN (St John the Baptist) *Glouc 4* **P** *Bp*
  R C T DAVIES, **NSM** W J CAMMELL
RUBERY (St Chad) *Birm 4* **P** *The Crown* **V** J J J BARRETT
RUCKINGE (St Mary Magdalene) Orlestone w Snave and
  Ruckinge w Warehorne *Cant*
RUCKLAND (St Olave) S Ormsby Gp *Linc*
RUDBY IN CLEVELAND (All Saints) w Middleton *York 22*
  P *Abp* **V** D F LICKESS
RUDDINGTON (St Peter) *S'well 10* **P** *Simeon's Trustees*
  V F G HARRISON
RUDFORD (St Mary the Virgin) Highnam, Lassington,
  Rudford, Tibberton etc *Glouc*
RUDGWICK (Holy Trinity) *Chich 8* **P** *Ld Chan*
  V J D MORRIS
RUDHAM, EAST and WEST (St Mary), Houghton-next-
Harpley, Tattersett and Tatterford *Nor 16* **P** *Most Rev*
  G D Hand, Bp, Marquess of Cholmondeley, and Marquess
  Townshend (by turn) **R** V M SCOTT
RUDHEATH (Licensed Room) Witton *Ches*
RUDSTON (All Saints) Boynton and Kilham *York 10* **P** *Abp*
  (2 turns), Ld Chan (1 turn) **V** S V COPE
RUFFORD (St Mary the Virgin) *Blackb 6* **P** *Bp*
  R R E SWANN
RUFFORTH (All Saints) w Moor Monkton and Hessay
  York 1 **P** *MMCET and Abp (alt)* **R** J A RENDALL
RUGBY (St Andrew) (St George) (St John) (St Peter)
(St Philip) *Cov 6* **P** *Bp* **TR** E F CONDRY,
  TV A R STEVENS, E J SMITH,
  TV P M de la P BERESFORD, **NSM** P A MARTINDALE,
  D M CHARLES-EDWARDS, S E ENEVER
RUGBY (St Matthew) *Cov 6* **P** *Ch Trust Fund Trust*
  V M P SAXBY, **C** J M MORTIMER
RUGELEY (St Augustine) (Good Shepherd) *Lich 3*
  P *Patr Bd* **TR** M J NEWMAN, **TV** J BALL, R CHARLES
RUISHTON (St George) w Thornfalcon *B & W 18* **P** *Bp and*
  Dr W R Chisholm-Batten (alt) **V** D F GOODFIELD
RUISLIP (St Martin) *Lon 24* **P** *D&C Windsor*
  C P L de S HOMEWOOD
RUISLIP (St Mary) *Lon 24* **P** *Bp* **V** B G COPUS
RUISLIP MANOR (St Paul) *Lon 24* **P** *Bp* **V** A C BALL,
  C N A McINTOSH
RUMBURGH (St Michael and All Angels and St Felix) S
  Elmham and Ilketshall *St E*
RUNCORN (All Saints) *Ches 3* **P** *Ch Ch Ox*
  P-in-c J H A HAYES, **C** G P AYLETT, **NSM** N J AYLETT
RUNCORN (Holy Trinity) *Ches 3* **P** *Bp* **V** H W STRATTON
RUNCORN (St John the Evangelist) Weston *Ches 3* **P** *Bp*
  V J BRONNERT
RUNCORN (St Michael and All Angels) *Ches 3* **P** *Bp*
  P-in-c J H A HAYES
RUNCTON, NORTH (All Saints) W Winch w Setchey and
  N Runcton *Nor*
RUNCTON, SOUTH (St Andrew) Holme Runcton w S
  Runcton and Wallington *Ely*
RUNCTON HOLME (St James) as above
RUNHALL (All Saints) Barnham Broom *Nor*

RUNHAM (St Peter and St Paul) Filby, Thrigby, Mautby,
  Stokesby, Runham etc *Nor*
RUNNINGTON (St Peter and St Paul) Wellington and Distr
  B & W
RUNTON (Holy Trinity) Aylmerton w Runton *Nor*
RUNTON, EAST (St Andrew) as above
RUNWELL (St Mary) Wickford and Runwell *Chelmsf*
RUSCOMBE (St James the Great) and Twyford *Ox 16*
  P *Bp* **V** G R HAMBORG, **NSM** D FOOTE
RUSH GREEN (St Augustine) Romford *Chelmsf 2* **P** *Bp*
  V S SWIFT, **NSM** D HENDERSON
RUSHALL (Christ the King) (St Michael the Archangel)
  Lich 6 **P** *Sir Andrew Buchanan, Bt and*
  H C S Buchanan Esq (jt) **V** M J LEADBEATER,
  C K P SCOTT
RUSHALL (St Mary) Dickleburgh, Langmere, Shimpling,
  Thelveton etc *Nor*
RUSHALL (St Matthew) Uphavon w Rushall and Charlton
  Sarum
RUSHBROOKE (St Nicholas) Rougham, Beyton w Hessett
  and Rushbrooke *St E*
RUSHBURY (St Peter) *Heref 11* **P** *Bp Birm*
  R M BROMFIELD
RUSHDEN (St Mary) Sandon, Wallington and Rushden w
  Clothall *St Alb*
RUSHDEN (St Mary) (St Peter) (St Mark) w Newton
Bromswold *Pet 10* **P** *CPAS* **R** A SMITH,
  TV N P DENHAM, **C** A G KAYE, **NSM** E J TYE
RUSHEN Christ Church (Holy Trinity) *S & M 1*
  P *The Crown* **V** F H BIRD
RUSHFORD (St John the Evangelist) Garboldisham w Blo'
  Norton, Riddlesworth etc *Nor*
RUSHLAKE GREEN (Little St Mary) Warbleton and Bodle
  Street Green *Chich*
RUSHMERE (St Andrew) *St E 4* **P** *Bp*
  V R B THOMPSON, **C** M BROSNAN
RUSHMERE (St Michael) Carlton Colville w Mutford and
  Rushmere *Nor*
RUSHMOOR (St Francis) Churt *Guildf*
RUSHOCK (St Michael) Elmley Lovett w Hampton Lovett
  and Elmbridge etc *Worc*
RUSHOLME (Holy Trinity) *Man 4* **P** *CPAS* **R** A PORTER
RUSHTON (All Saints) Rothwell w Orton, Rushton w
  Glendon and Pipewell *Pet*
RUSHTON SPENCER Horton, Lonsdon and Rushton
  Spencer *Lich*
RUSKIN PARK (St Saviour) Herne Hill *S'wark*
RUSKINGTON (All Saints) *Linc 22* **P** *DBP* **R** D ASKEW
RUSLAND (St Paul) Colton w Satterthwaite and Rusland
  Carl
RUSPER (St Mary Magdalene) *Chich 8* **P** *Bp*
  P-in-c E A PASSINGHAM
RUSTHALL (St Paul) (St Paul's Mission Church) *Roch 11*
  P *R Speldhurst* **V** R E WHYTE, **C** J M J OUTEN (nee
  BAILEY)
RUSTINGTON (St Peter and St Paul) *Chich 1* **P** *Bp*
  V K L MASTERS, **C** M A LEPPARD
RUSTON, SOUTH Tunstead w Sco' Ruston *Nor*
RUSTON PARVA (St Nicholas) Burton Agnes w Harpham
  and Lowthorpe etc *York*
RUSWARP (St Bartholomew) Aislaby and Ruswarp *York*
RUYTON XI TOWNS (St John the Baptist) w Great Ness and
Little Ness *Lich 22* **P** *Bp and Guild of All So (jt) and*
  Ld Chan (alt) **V** R D BRADBURY
RYAL (All Saints) Stamfordham w Matfen *Newc*
RYARSH (St Martin) Birling, Addington, Ryarsh and
  Trottiscliffe *Roch*
RYBURGH, GREAT (St Andrew) and LITTLE w Gateley and
Testerton *Nor 16* **P** *Ch Coll Cam* **R** *Vacant* Great
  Ryburgh (0132878) 234
RYDAL (St Mary) *Carl 10* **P** *Bp* **P-in-c** M A KITCHENER
RYDE (All Saints) *Portsm 7* **P** *Bp* **P-in-c** D W DALE,
  NSM E W BUTCHER
RYDE (Holy Trinity) *Portsm 7* **P** *Bp* **V** M J SHEFFIELD,
  C D A GIBBONS, **NSM** T F SEAR, M D H JOHNSTON
RYDE (St James) Proprietary Chapel *Portsm 7* **P** *Ch Soc*
  Trust **C-in-c** B G C BAKER
RYE (St Mary the Virgin) *Chich 20* **P** *Patr Bd*
  TR M SHEPPARD, **TV** P CLARK, **NSM** M N HARPER
RYE HARBOUR (Holy Spirit) Rye *Chich*
RYE PARK (St Cuthbert) *St Alb 6* **P** *DBP* **V** H J SPANNER
RYECROFT (St Nicolas) Conventional District *Sheff 6*
  C-in-c S P PICKERING
RYEDALE, UPPER *York 18* **P** *Abp, Adn Cleveland,*
  R G Beckett Esq, and Exors Capt V M Wombwell (jt)
  R S M EAST
RYHALL (St John the Evangelist) w Essendine *Pet 8*
  P *Burghley Ho Preservation Trust* **P-in-c** R A PERRY

RYHILL (St James) *Wakef 9* **P** *Bp* **V** A W H ASHDOWN

RYHOPE (St Paul) *Dur 9* **P** *Bp* **V** G W FLETCHER,
NSM R N TEMPERLEY

RYLSTONE (St Peter) Burnsall w Rylstone *Bradf*

RYME INTRINSECA (St Hypolytus) Yetminster w Ryme
Intrinseca and High Stoy *Sarum*

RYPE (St John the Baptist) Laughton w Ripe and
Chalvington *Chich*

RYSTON (St Michael) w Roxham *Ely 16* **P** *Bp*
P-in-c J K ISAACS

RYTHER (All Saints) *York 6* **P** *Ld Chan*
P-in-c R E MESSER

RYTON (Holy Cross) w Hedgefield *Dur 5* **P** *Bp*
P-in-c T L JAMIESON, **NSM** K B POTTER

RYTON (Mission Chapel) Condover w Frodesley, Acton
Burnell etc *Heref*

RYTON (St Andrew) Beckbury, Badger, Kemberton, Ryton,
Stockton etc *Lich*

RYTON ON DUNSMORE (St Leonard) w Bubbenhall
Cov 6 **P** *Bp (1 turn), Provost & Chapter (2 turns)*
V J T SYKES

SABDEN (St Nicholas) and Pendleton-in-Whalley (All Saints)
Blackb 8 **P** *Bp and Trustees (jt)* **V** R NICHOLSON

SACKLETON (St George the Martyr) Street TM *York*

SACOMBE (St Catherine) The Mundens w Sacombe *St Alb*

SACRISTON (St Peter) and Kimblesworth *Dur 2* **P** *The
Crown* **P-in-c** N M JAY

SADBERGE (St Andrew) *Dur 12* **P** *Bp* **P-in-c** R J COOPER

SADDINGTON (St Helen) Kibworth and Smeeton Westerby
and Saddington *Leic*

SADDLEWORTH (St Chad) (Parochial Hall) *Man 21*
P *Bp* **V** C A E LAWRENCE, **NSM** G B ADAMS,
D RHODES

**SAFFRON WALDEN (St Mary) w Wendens Ambo and
Littlebury** *Chelmsf 23* **P** *Patr Bd* **TR** D P HARLOW,
TV S F C WILLIAMS, **C** L BOND, **NSM** J D RUSSELL-
SMITH

SAHAM TONEY (St George) Ashill w Saham Toney *Nor*

ST AGNES (St Agnes) *Truro 6* **P** *D&C* **V** M J ADAMS

ST ALBANS (Christ Church) *St Alb 11* **P** *Trustees*
V B UNDERWOOD

ST ALBANS (St Luke) *St Alb 11* **P** *DBP* **V** P G RICH,
Par Dn E G HARLOW

ST ALBANS (St Mary) Marshalswick *St Alb 11* **P** *Bp*
V R E PYKE

ST ALBANS (St Michael) *St Alb 11* **P** *Earl of Verulam*
V T M BEAUMONT

ST ALBANS (St Paul) *St Alb 11* **P** *V St Alb St Pet*
V A R HURLE, **C** L J BIGGS, **Hon C** G M ABBOTT,
NSM L M HURLE (nee POWNALL)

ST ALBANS (St Peter) *St Alb 11* **P** *The Crown*
V A H MEDFORTH, **C** V J LAMONT, S J W NORMAND

ST ALBANS (St Saviour) *St Alb 11* **P** *Bp* **V** B P MOORE

ST ALBANS (St Stephen) *St Alb 11* **P** *J N W Dudley Esq*
NSM L C HALL

ST ALLEN (St Alleyne) Kenwyn w St Allen *Truro*

ST ANNES-ON-THE-SEA (St Anne) Heyhouses on Sea
Blackb

ST ANNES-ON-THE-SEA (St Margaret) *Blackb 11* **P** *Bp*
V J H CATLEY, **NSM** M J THOMAS

ST ANNES-ON-THE-SEA (St Thomas) *Blackb 11*
P *J C Hilton Esq* **V** W FIELDING

ST ANTHONY-IN-MENEAGE (St Anthony) Manaccan w
St Anthony-in-Meneage and St Martin *Truro*

ST AUSTELL (Holy Trinity) *Truro 1* **P** *The Crown*
V A F MATTHEW, **C** R M ELKS, **Hon C** A SYKES

ST BEES (St Mary and St Bega) *Carl 5* **P** *Trustees*
V P R BRYAN

ST BLAZEY (St Blaise) *Truro 1* **P** *Bp* **V** F M BOWERS

ST BREOKE (St Breoke) and Egloshayle *Truro 10* **P** *Bp and
DBP (jt)* **P-in-c** B A ANDERSON

ST BREWARD (St Breward) Blisland w St Breward *Truro*

ST BRIAVELS (St Mary the Virgin) w Hewelsfield *Glouc 4*
P *D&C Heref* **P-in-c** P E PINKERTON

ST BURYAN (St Buriana), St Levan and Sennen *Truro 5*
P *Duchy of Cornwall* **R** A H BURLTON, **NSM** C M JAGO

ST CLEER (St Clarus) *Truro 12* **P** *Ld Chan*
V M A FRIGGENS

ST CLEMENT (St Clement) Truro St Paul and St Clem
Truro

ST CLETHER (St Clederus) Altarnon w Bolventor, Laneast
and St Clether *Truro*

ST COLAN (not known) St Columb Minor and St Colan
Truro

ST COLUMB MAJOR (St Columba) w St Wenn *Truro 7*
P *Bp* **R** R FLAW

ST COLUMB MINOR (St Columba) and St Colan *Truro 7*
P *Bp* **V** J F EDWARDS, **C** S L BRYAN, **NSM** P G DAVY

ST DAY (Holy Trinity) *Truro 2* **P** *D&C* **P-in-c** A S GOUGH

ST DECUMANS (St Decuman) *B & W 17* **P** *Bp*
V R M BARNETT

ST DENNIS (St Denys) *Truro 1* **P** *Bp* **P-in-c** T J RUSS

ST DEVEREUX (St Dubricius) Ewyas Harold w Dulas,
Kenderchurch etc *Heref*

**ST DOMINIC (St Dominica), Landulph and St Mellion w
Pillaton** *Truro 11* **P** *D&C and Trustees Major J Coryton,
Duchy of Cornwall, and SMF (by turn)* **R** R H EVERETT

ST EDMUNDS Anchorage Lane Conventional District
Sheff 8 **C-in-c** P G HARBORD

ST ENDELLION (St Endelienta) w Port Isaac and St Kew
Truro 10 **P** *Bp* **R** M G BARTLETT, **NSM** J POLLINGER

ST ENODER (St Enoder) *Truro 7* **P** *Bp*
P-in-c P A ROBSON

ST ENODOC (not known) St Minver *Truro*

ST ERME (St Hermes) Probus, Ladock and Grampound w
Creed and St Erme *Truro*

ST ERNEY (St Erney) Landrake w St Erney and Botus
Fleming *Truro*

ST ERTH (St Erth) *Truro 5* **P** *D&C* **V** A T NEAL,
C M A TREMBATH, C C McQUILLEN-WRIGHT

ST ERVAN (St Ervan) St Mawgan w St Ervan and St Eval
Truro

ST EVAL (St Uvelas) as above

ST EWE (All Saints) Mevagissey and St Ewe *Truro*

**ST GENNYS (St Gennys), Jacobstow w Warbstow and
Treneglos** *Truro 8* **P** *Bp and Earl of St Germains (jt)*
R P J RANDELL

ST GEORGE-IN-THE-EAST (St Mary) *Lon 7* **P** *Bp*
V J V SMITH

ST GEORGE-IN-THE-EAST w St Paul *Lon 7* **P** *Bp*
R G W CRAIG, **Hon C** M J W COOK

ST GEORGES (St George) Priors Lee and St Georges *Lich*

ST GERMANS (St Germans of Auxerre) *Truro 11* **P** *D&C
Windsor* **V** S COFFIN

ST GILES-IN-THE-FIELDS *Lon 3* **P** *Bp* **R** G C TAYLOR

ST GILES-IN-THE-HEATH (not known) Boyton,
N Tamerton, Werrington etc *Truro*

ST GILES IN THE WOOD (St Giles) Beaford, Roborough
and St Giles in the Wood *Ex*

ST GLUVIAS (St Gluvias) *Truro 3* **P** *Bp* **V** J HARRIS

ST GORAN (St Goranus) w St Michael Caerhays *Truro 1*
P *Bp* **NSM** L MASTERS

ST HELENS (St Helen) (Barton Street Mission) (St Andrew)
Liv 10 **P** *Trustees* **TR** C H B BYWORTH, **C** C R SMITH,
D J P MOORE

ST HELENS (St Helen) (St Catherine by the Green)
Portsm 7 **P** *Bp* **V** M L HILL-TOUT

ST HELENS (St Mark) *Liv 10* **P** *Trustees*
P-in-c J LABDON

ST HELENS (St Matthew) Thatto Heath *Liv 10* **P** *Bp*
V C L BRAY

ST HELIER (St Peter) (Bishop Andrewes Church) *S'wark 26*
P *Bp* **V** G J JENKINS, **C** P J DYKES

ST HILARY (St Hilary) w Perranuthnoe *Truro 5* **P** *D&C and
Mrs S R Parker (jt)* **R** *Vacant* Penzance (01736) 710294

ST IPPOLYTS (St Ippolyts) *St Alb 9* **P** *Bp*
P-in-c C J N MARTIN

ST ISSEY (St Issey) w St Petroc Minor *Truro 7* **P** *Keble Coll
Ox* **R** *Vacant* Rumford (01841) 540314

ST IVE (St Ive) and Pensilva w Quethiock *Truro 12* **P** *Bp
(1 turn), The Crown (2 turns)* **R** R J LUCAS

ST IVES (All Saints) *Ely 11* **P** *Guild of All So*
V J D MOORE

ST IVES (St Ia the Virgin) *Truro 5* **P** *V Lelant*
V A N COUCH

ST JOHN (St John the Baptist) w Millbrook *Truro 11* **P** *Bp
and Col Sir John Carew-Pole, Bt (alt)* **R** T W PILKINGTON

ST JOHN IN BEDWARDINE (St John the Baptist) *Worc 3*
P *D&C* **V** C PULLIN, **C** S P MOULT,
NSM J E K MOULT

ST JOHN IN WEARDALE (St John the Baptist) *Dur 15*
P *Bp* **V** D M SKELTON

ST JOHN LEE (St John of Beverley) *Newc 4* **P** *Viscount
Allendale* **R** W RIGBY

ST JOHN ON BETHNAL GREEN *Lon 7* **P** *Patr Bd*
TR N C GRIFFIN, **C** D A SHERRATT,
NSM R A VAUGHAN

ST JOHNS-IN-THE-VALE (St John) w Wythburn *Carl 6*
P *Bp and V Crosthwaite (alt)* **V** C G DARRALL

ST JOHN'S WOOD (St John) *Lon 4* **P** *Bp* **V** J SLATER,
C M D OAKLEY

ST JULIOT (St Julitta) Boscastle w Davidstow *Truro*

ST JUST IN PENWITH (St Just) *Truro 5* **P** *Ld Chan*
V S W LEACH

ST JUST IN ROSELAND (St Just) w Philleigh *Truro 6*
  P *A M J Galsworthy Esq and MMCET (jt)*
  R E R ANDREWS
ST KEVERNE (St Keverne) *Truro 4*   P *CPAS*
  V T M GOULDSTONE
ST KEW (St James the Great) St Endellion w Port Isaac and
  St Kew *Truro*
ST KEYNE (St Keyna) Liskeard, St Keyne, St Pinnock,
  Morval etc *Truro*
ST LAURENCE in the Isle of Thanet (St Laurence) *Cant 9*
  P *Patr Bd*   TR P J COTTON,   TV N D PERKINSON,
  C B P SHARP
ST LAWRENCE (Old Church) (St Lawrence) *Portsm 7*
  P *Bp*   NSM J A WOOLLEY
ST LAWRENCE (St Peter's Chapel) *Chelmsf 10*   P *Bp*
  R *Vacant*
ST LEONARD (St Leonard) Hawridge w Cholesbury and St
  Leonard *Ox*
ST LEONARDS and St Ives (All Saints) *Win 8*   P *Bp*
  V *Vacant* Ringwood (01425) 473406
ST LEONARDS (Christ Church and St Mary Magdalen)
  Chich 17   P *Bp and Trustees (jt)*   R R M HARPER,
  C D G LLOYD-JAMES,   NSM R G RALPH,   R L TREE
ST LEONARDS, UPPER (St John the Evangelist) *Chich 17*
  P *Trustees*   R R J H WILLIAMS
ST LEONARDS-ON-SEA (St Ethelburga) *Chich 17*
  P *Hyndman Trustees*   V B E CROSBY
ST LEONARDS-ON-SEA (St Leonard) *Chich 17*
  P *Hyndman Trustees*   R J B CROSS
ST LEONARDS-ON-SEA (St Matthew) Silverhill St Matt
  Chich
ST LEONARDS-ON-SEA (St Peter and St Paul) *Chich 17*
  P *Bp*   V A P-A BROWN
ST LEVAN (St Levan) St Buryan, St Levan and Sennen
  Truro
ST MABYN (St Mabena) St Tudy w St Mabyn and
  Michaelstow *Truro*
ST MARGARET'S (St Margaret) Clodock and Longtown w
  Craswall, Llanveynoe etc *Heref*
ST MARGARETS-AT-CLIFFE (St Margaret of Antioch) w
  Westcliffe and East Langdon w West Langdon *Cant 4*
  P *Abp*   V A M DURKIN
ST MARGARETS ON THAMES (All Souls) *Lon 11*   P *Bp*
  V *Vacant* 0181-892 4171
ST MARTHA-ON-THE-HILL (St Martha) Albury w St
  Martha *Guildf*
ST MARTIN (St Martin) w East and West Looe *Truro 12*
  P *Bp and Rev W M M Picken (jt)*   R N S FOX
ST MARTIN-IN-MENEAGE (St Martin) Manaccan w St
  Anthony-in-Meneage and St Martin *Truro*
ST MARTIN-IN-THE-FIELDS *Lon 3*   P *Bp*
  C B G SCHUNEMANN,   J S PRIDMORE,   NSM G LEE,
  W J RATCHFORD
ST MARTIN'S (St Martin) *Lich 24*   P *Lord Trevor*
  V W J WEBB
ST MARTIN'S (St Martin) Scilly Is *Truro*
ST MARY ABBOTS Kensington St Mary Abbots w St Geo
  Lon
ST MARY-AT-LATTON Harlow *Chelmsf 27*
  P *J L H Arkwright Esq*   V P J BEECH,   Hon C G R NEAVE
ST MARY BOURNE (St Peter) and Woodcott *Win 6*   P *Bp*
  V M A COPPEN
ST MARY CRAY and St Paul's (St Paulinus) *Cray Roch 15*
  P *Bp*   V J A THOMAS
ST MARY-LE-STRAND w St Clement Danes *Lon 3*
  P *Ld Chan and Burley Ho Preservation Trust (alt)*
  NSM G B McAVOY
ST MARYCHURCH (St Mary the Virgin) *Ex 10*   P *D&C*
  V K C MOSS,   C K JEFFRIES
ST MARYLEBONE (All Saints) *Lon 4*   P *Bp*
  V L A MOSES,   C P McGEARY,   Hon C J A YOUNGER
ST MARYLEBONE (All Souls) Langham Place All So *Lon*
ST MARYLEBONE (Annunciation) Bryanston Street *Lon 4*
  P *Bp*   V M W BURGESS
ST MARYLEBONE (Holy Trinity) (St Marylebone) *Lon 4*
  P *The Crown*   R J L CHATER,   Hon C R F McLAREN,
  C R OWEN
ST MARYLEBONE (St Cyprian) *Lon 4*   P *Bp*
  V P R HARDING,   C D WHITE
ST MARYLEBONE (St Mark) Hamilton Terrace *Lon 4*
  P *The Crown*   V D A R AIRD,   Hon C J PAPWORTH,
  R A DENNISTON
ST MARYLEBONE (St Mark w St Luke) Bryanston Square
  St Mary w St Marylebone St Mark *Lon*
ST MARYLEBONE (St Paul) *Lon 4*   P *Prime Min*
  R J P MAPLE,   C A R HACK
ST MARYLEBONE (St Peter) Langham Place All So *Lon*
ST MARY'S (St Mary) Scilly Is *Truro*

ST MARY'S BAY (All Saints) w St Mary-in-the-Marsh
  (St Mary the Virgin) and Ivychurch *Cant 13*   P *Abp*
  V J H COLEMAN,   Hon C A M CLARKE
ST MAWES (not known) St Just in Roseland w Philleigh
  Truro
ST MAWGAN (St Mawgan) w St Ervan and St Eval *Truro 7*
  P *D&C and Bp (alt)*   R J G SLEE,   C M L BARRETT,
  Hon C F T SURRIDGE
ST MELLION (St Melanus) St Dominic, Landulph and St
  Mellion w Pillaton *Truro*
ST MERRYN (St Merryn) *Truro 7*   P *Bp*
  NSM B B WOODMAN
ST MEWAN (St Mewan) *Truro 1*   P *A J M Galsworthy Esq*
  (2 turns), Penrice Ho (St Austell) Ltd(1 turn), and DBP
  (1 turn)   P-in-c D G ADAMS,   NSM M P CROWETT
ST MEWAN Sticker (St Mark's Mission Church) St Mewan
  Truro
ST MICHAEL PENKEVIL (St Michael) *Truro 6*   P *Viscount*
  Falmouth   R *Vacant* Truro (01872) 520431
ST MICHAEL ROCK (not known) St Minver *Truro*
ST MICHAELCHURCH (St Michael) N Newton w St
  Michaelchurch, Thurloxton etc *B & W*
ST MICHAELS ON WYRE (St Michael) *Blackb 10*
  P *R P Hornby Esq*   V K H GIBBONS
ST MINVER (St Menefreda) *Truro 10*   P *DBP*
  V P A FROWLEY
ST NECTAN (not known) Lostwithiel, St Winnow w St
  Nectan's Chpl etc *Truro*
ST NEOT (St Neot) and Warleggan *Truro 12*
  P *R G Grylls Esq (2 turns), DBP (1 turn)*   R H C T OLIVEY
ST NEOTS (St Mary) *Ely 12*   P *P W Rowley Esq*
  P-in-c R H W ARGUILE,   Hon C T R HENTHORNE
ST NEWLYN EAST (St Newlina) Newlyn St Newlyn *Truro*
ST NICHOLAS AT WADE (St Nicholas) w Sarre and Chislet
  w Hoath *Cant 7*   P *Abp*   P-in-c R R COLES,
  NSM R D PLANT
ST OSWALD IN LEE w Bingfield (St Mary) *Newc 2*   P *Bp*
  P-in-c C S PRICE
ST OSYTH (St Peter and St Paul) *Chelmsf 24*   P *Bp*
  V *Vacant* St Osyth (01255) 820348
ST PANCRAS (Holy Cross) (St Jude) (St Peter) *Lon 17*
  P *Bp*   C J A HAYWARD
ST PANCRAS (Holy Trinity w St Barnabas) Haverstock Hill
  H Trin w Kentish Town St Barn *Lon*
ST PANCRAS (Old Church) w Bedford New Town
  (St Matthew) *Lon 17*   P *D&C St Paul's*   V P DYSON
ST PANCRAS (St Pancras) (St James) (Christ Church)
  Lon 17   P *D&C St Paul's*   P-in-c B D CLOVER,
  C M G C YOUNG,   Hon C R I T JARRETT
ST PAUL'S CRAY (St Barnabas) *Roch 15*   P *CPAS*
  V G C DAY,   Hon C J E RAWLING
ST PAUL'S WALDEN (All Saints) *St Alb 9*   P *D&C*
  St Paul's   P-in-c A P WINTON
ST PETER in the Isle of Thanet (St Peter the Apostle)
  (St Andrew) *Cant 9*   P *Abp*   V N A S BURY,
  C M C BOWERS,   J A SAGE,   J F GANGA
ST PETER-UPON-CORNHILL St Pet Cornhill *Lon*
ST PETROC MINOR (not known) St Issey w St Petroc
  Minor *Truro*
ST PINNOCK (St Pinnock) Liskeard, St Keyne, St Pinnock,
  Morval etc *Truro*
ST RUAN w St Grade and Landewednack *Truro 4*   P *CPAS*
  and A F Vyvyan-Robinson (jt)   R G K BENNETT
ST SAMPSON (St Sampson) *Truro 1*   P *Bp*   R M J OATEY
ST STEPHEN BY LAUNCESTON *Truro 9*   P *D&C*
  V M L UREN
ST STEPHEN IN BRANNEL (not known) *Truro 1*   P *Capt*
  J D G Fortescue   R P L EUSTICE
ST STEPHENS (St Stephen) Saltash *Truro*
ST STYTHIANS w Perranarworthal and Gwennap *Truro 2*
  P *Viscount Falmouth (2 turns), D&C (1 turn)*
  V E J M HOGAN,   NSM I D T LITTLE
ST TEATH (St Teatha) *Truro 10*   P *Bp*   V *Vacant* Bodmin
  (01208) 850292
ST TUDY (St Tudy) w St Mabyn and Michaelstow *Truro 10*
  P *D&C Ox, Viscount Falmouth, and Duchy of Cornwall*
  (by turn)   R R J L WOOD
ST VEEP (St Cyricius) Lostwithiel, St Winnow w St Nectan's
  Chpl etc *Truro*
ST WENN (St Wenna) St Columb Major w St Wenn *Truro*
ST WEONARDS (St Weonard) w Orcop, Garway, Tretire,
  Michaelchurch, Pencoyd, Welsh Newton and Llanrothal
  Heref 8   P *Bp, D&C, and MMCET (jt)*   R S R ASHTON
ST WINNOW (St Winnow) Lostwithiel, St Winnow w St
  Nectan's Chpl etc *Truro*
SAINTBURY (St Nicholas) Willersey, Saintbury, Weston-
  sub-Edge etc *Glouc*

SALCOMBE (Holy Trinity) *Ex 7*   **P** *Keble Coll Ox*
V PRCABRAM
SALCOMBE REGIS (St Mary and St Peter) Sidmouth,
Woolbrook, Salcombe Regis, Sidbury etc *Ex*
SALCOT VIRLEY (St Mary the Virgin) Tollesbury w Salcot
Virley *Chelmsf*
SALE (St Anne) (St Francis's Church Hall) *Ches 10*   **P** *DBP*
V JSUTTON,   **C** RADICKSON,   AJMANNINGS
SALE (St Paul) *Ches 10*   **P** *Trustees*   **V** RSELWOOD
SALEBY (St Margaret) w Beesby and Maltby *Linc 8*   **P** *Bp*
and DBP   **P-in-c** AREADER-MOORE
SALEHURST (St Mary) *Chich 15*   **P** *Bp*
V JBLAMBOURNE
SALESBURY (St Peter) *Blackb 2*   **P** *V Blackb*
V JWHARTLEY
SALFORD Ordsall (St Clement) *Man 6*   **P** *Bp*
P-in-c DSCWYATT,   Hon **C** EFORRESTER
SALFORD (Sacred Trinity) *Man 6*   **P** *Exors Sir Josslyn
Gore-Booth, Bt*   **P-in-c** GBABB
SALFORD (St Ignatius and Stowell Memorial) *Man 6*   **P** *Bp*
R RKSBRACEGIRDLE
SALFORD (St Mary) Lt Compton w Chastleton, Cornwell
etc *Ox*
SALFORD (St Mary) Cranfield and Hulcote w Salford *St Alb*
SALFORD (St Paul w Christ Church) *Man 6*   **P** *The Crown
and Trustees (alt)*   **R** DSCWYATT,
Hon **C** BFBUCKLEY,   **NSM** PRSBOLTON
SALFORD (St Philip w St Stephen) *Man 6*   **P** *D&C*
R PDFOSTER
SALFORD PRIORS (St Matthew) *Cov 7*   **P** *Peache
Trustees*   **P-in-c** SRTASH
SALFORDS (Christ the King) *S'wark 25*   **P** *Bp*
V PCEDWARDS,   **NSM** PMHARTLEY,   FPLUMMER
SALHOUSE (All Saints) Rackheath and Salhouse *Nor*
SALING, GREAT (St James) Gt and Lt Bardfield w Gt and
Lt Saling *Chelmsf*
SALING, LITTLE (St Peter and St Paul) as above
SALISBURY (St Francis) *Sarum 15*   **P** *Bp*
V REDUNNINGS
SALISBURY (St Mark) *Sarum 15*   **P** *Bp*
P-in-c PJDHAWKSWORTH
SALISBURY (St Martin) *Sarum 15*   **P** *Bp*
P-in-c KROBINSON
SALISBURY (St Thomas and St Edmund) *Sarum 15*   **P** *Bp*
and D&C (alt)   **P-in-c** JCHATTON
SALKELD, GREAT (St Cuthbert) w Lazonby *Carl 4*   **P** *Bp*
P-in-c KREALE
SALLE (St Peter and St Paul) Reepham, Hackford w
Whitwell, Kerdiston etc *Nor*
SALT (St James the Great) and Sandon w Burston *Lich 15*
P *Keble Coll Ox and Personal Reps Earl of Harrowby (jt)*
NSM JECHALK
SALTASH (St Nicholas and St Faith) *Truro 11*   **P** *Patr Bd*
TR REBMAYNARD,   **TV** AJLING,   **NSM** WJONES
SALTBURN-BY-THE-SEA (Emmanuel) *York 17*   **P** *Abp,
Adn Cleveland, Marquis of Zetland, and M Jarratt Esq (jt)*
V IRPARKINSON
SALTBY (St Peter) High Framland Par *Leic*
SALTDEAN (St Nicholas) *Chich 2*   **P** *Bp*   **V** ADMAYES,
C RACLIFFORD
SALTER STREET (St Patrick) Tanworth St Patr Salter
Street *Birm*
SALTERHEBBLE (All Saints) *Wakef 4*   **P** *Ch Trust Fund
Trust*   **V** TJWILSON,   **C** KPARTINGTON,
NSM JCKFREEBORN
SALTERSFORD (St John the Baptist) Rainow w Saltersford
and Forest *Ches*
SALTFLEETBY (St Peter) *Linc 12*   **P** *Or Coll Ox, Bp, and
MMCET (jt)*   **P-in-c** DLUMB
**SALTFORD (Blessed Virgin Mary) w Corston and Newton St
Loe** *B & W 10*   **P** *DBP (2 turns), Duchy of Cornwall
(1 turn)*   **R** GRWHALL,   **NSM** CSHARE
SALTHOUSE (St Nicholas) Weybourne Gp *Nor*
SALTLEY (St Saviour) and Shaw, Alum Rock *Birm 10*   **P** *Bp
and Trustees (jt)*   **V** TEJONES
SALTNEY FERRY (St Matthew) Lache cum Saltney *Ches*
SALTON (St John of Beverley) Kirby Misperton w
Normanby, Edston and Salton *York*
SALTWOOD (St Peter and St Paul) *Cant 5*   **P** *Abp*
R RGHUMPHRISS
SALVINGTON (St Peter) Durrington *Chich*
SALWARPE (St Michael) and Hindlip w Martin Hussingtree
Worc 8   **P** *Bp, D&C, and Exors Lady Hindlip (by turn)*
R DEVINCE
SALWAY ASH (Holy Trinity) Beaminster Area *Sarum*
SAMBOURNE (Mission Church) Coughton *Cov*
SAMBROOK (St Luke) Cheswardine, Childs Ercall, Hales,
Hinstock etc *Lich*

SAMLESBURY (St Leonard the Less) Walton-le-Dale St
Leon w Samlesbury St Leon *Blackb*
SAMPFORD, GREAT (St Michael) The Sampfords *Chelmsf*
SAMPFORD, LITTLE (St Mary) as above
SAMPFORD ARUNDEL (Holy Cross) Wellington and
Distr *B & W*
SAMPFORD BRETT (St George) Bicknoller w Crowcombe
and Sampford Brett *B & W*
SAMPFORD COURTENAY (St Andrew) N Tawton,
Bondleigh, Sampford Courtenay etc *Ex*
**SAMPFORD PEVERELL (St John the Baptist), Uplowman,
Holcombe Rogus, Hockworthy, Burlescombe, Huntsham and
Halberton w Ash Thomas** *Ex 4*   **P** *Patr Bd*   **TR** BPETTY,
TV KGGALE
SAMPFORD SPINEY (St Mary) w Horrabridge *Ex 25*
P *D&C Windsor*   **R** CFURNESS
SAMPFORDS, The *Chelmsf 23*   **P** *New Coll Ox (1 turn),
Guild of All So (2 turns)*   **P-in-c** BJMACDONALD-MILNE
SANCREED (St Creden) *Truro 5*   **P** *D&C*   **V** SWLEACH
SANCTON (All Saints) *York 7*   **P** *Abp*   **V** JWALKER
SAND HILL (Church of the Good Shepherd) Farnborough
Guildf
SAND HUTTON (St Leonard) Thirsk *York*
SAND HUTTON (St Mary) *York 3*   **P** *Abp (2 turns), D&C
Dur (1 turn)*   **V** JWVALENTINE
SANDAL (St Catherine) *Wakef 9*   **P** *V Sandal Magna*
P-in-c MPCROFT,   **C** EMTURNER
SANDAL MAGNA (St Helen) *Wakef 9*   **P** *Peache Trustees*
V RGMARTIN
SANDBACH (St Mary) *Ches 11*   **P** *DBP*
V DWGSTOCKER,   **NSM** GAGAR
SANDBACH HEATH (St John the Evangelist) *Ches 11*
P *V Sandwich*   **V** EJGORDON
SANDBANKS (St Nicolas) Canford Cliffs and Sandbanks
Sarum
**SANDERSTEAD (All Saints) (St Anthony) (St Edmund the
King and Martyr)** *S'wark 22*   **P** *DBP*   **TR** CJSKILTON,
TV DSHEYWOOD,   PCGULVIN,   **C** JWBAKER
SANDERSTEAD (St Mary) *S'wark 22*   **P** *Bp*
V MWELFRED,   **NSM** MJJOHNSON
SANDFORD (All Saints) Burrington and Churchill *B & W*
SANDFORD (St Martin) Westcote Barton w Steeple Barton,
Duns Tew etc *Ox*
SANDFORD (St Martin) Wareham *Sarum*
SANDFORD (St Swithin) w Upton Hellions *Ex 2*   **P** *12 Govs
of Crediton Ch*   **R** *Vacant* Crediton (01363) 772530
SANDFORD-ON-THAMES (St Andrew) *Ox 4*   **P** *DBP*
P-in-c RCMORGAN
SANDFORD ORCAS (St Nicholas) Queen Thorne *Sarum*
SANDGATE (St Paul) w Folkestone (St George) *Cant 5*
P *Abp and Ld Chan (alt)*   **R** CENDAVIS,
C BELANGMAN,   **NSM** CBHILL,   GMARCH
SANDHURST (St Lawrence) Twigworth, Down Hatherley,
Norton, The Leigh etc *Glouc*
SANDHURST (St Michael and All Angels) *Ox 16*   **P** *Bp*
R ATLWILSON,   **C** RGHUGHES,   **NSM** JFKNOWLES
SANDHURST (St Nicholas) (Mission Church) w Newenden
Cant 11   **P** *Abp*   **R** RHDENGATE
SANDHURST, LOWER (St Mary) Sandhurst *Ox*
SANDIACRE (St Giles) *Derby 13*   **P** *Ld Chan*
R WBCOONEY
SANDIWAY (St John the Evangelist) *Ches 6*   **P** *Bp*
V JVGRIFFITH
SANDLEHEATH (St Aldhelm) Fordingbridge *Win*
SANDON (All Saints) Salt and Sandon w Burston *Lich*
SANDON (All Saints), Wallington and Rushden w Clothall
St Alb 5   **P** *Duchy of Lanc (1 turn), Marquess of Salisbury
(1 turn), and Bp (2 turns)*   **R** KWTWJOHNSON
SANDON (St Andrew) *Chelmsf 9*   **P** *Qu Coll Cam*
P-in-c HAMATTY
SANDOWN (Christ Church) *Portsm 7*   **P** *Ch Patr Trust*
V DMLOW
SANDOWN, LOWER (St John the Evangelist) *Portsm 7*
P *Bp*   **V** *Vacant*
SANDRIDGE (St Leonard) *St Alb 14*   **P** *Earl Spencer*
V PJNELSON
**SANDRINGHAM (St Mary Magdalene) w West Newton and
Appleton, Wolferton w Babingley and Flitcham** *Nor 17*
P *The Crown*   **R** GRHALL
SANDS (Church of the Good Shepherd) Seale *Guildf*
SANDS (St Mary and St George) High Wycombe *Ox*
SANDSEND (St Mary) Lythe w Ugthorpe *York*
SANDWICH (St Clement) *Cant 8*   **P** *Adn Cant*
R JMAROBERTS,   **NSM** RAGARDEN,   JCROBERTS
SANDY (St Swithun) *St Alb 17*   **P** *Lord Pym*
R EEJROWLAND
SANDY LANE (St Mary and St Nicholas) Bromham,
Chittoe and Sandy Lane *Sarum*

SANDYLANDS (St John) *Blackb 12* **P** *Bp* **V** J G REEVES
SANKEY, GREAT (St Mary) *Liv 13* **P** *Lord Lilford*
V G McKIBBIN
SANTAN (St Sanctain) *S & M 1* **P** *The Crown*
V G B CLAYTON
SANTON DOWNHAM (St Mary the Virgin) Brandon and
Santon Downham w Elveden *St E*
SAPCOTE (All Saints) and Sharnford w Wigston Parva
Leic 13 **P** *Ld Chan and DBP (alt)* **R** D W TYLDESLEY
SAPEY, UPPER (St Michael) Edvin Loach w Tedstone
Delamere etc *Heref*
SAPPERTON (St Kenelm) Coates, Rodmarton and
Sapperton etc *Glouc*
SAPPERTON (St Nicholas) w Braceby *Linc 14* **P** *Bp*
(1 turn), Sir Richard Welby, Bt (3 turns) **R** *Vacant*
SARISBURY (St Paul) *Portsm 2* **P** *V Titchfield*
V R H MOSELEY
SARK (St Peter) *Win 14* **P** *Le Seigneur de Sercq*
V P SIMPSON, **NSM** G L LEWORTHY
SARN (Holy Trinity) Churchstoke w Hyssington and Sarn
Heref
SARNESFIELD (St Mary) Weobley w Sarnesfield and
Norton Canon *Heref*
SARRATT (Holy Cross) *St Alb 10* **P** *Bp* **R** *Vacant*
Rickmansworth (01923) 264377
SATLEY (St Cuthbert) and Tow Law *Dur 15* **P** *Bp and Ld
Chan (alt)* **P-in-c** D A WRIGHT
SATTERLEIGH (St Peter) S Molton w Nymet St George,
High Bray etc *Ex*
SATTERTHWAITE (All Saints) Colton w Satterthwaite and
Rusland *Carl*
SAUGHALL, GREAT (All Saints) *Ches 9* **P** *Bp* **V** *Vacant*
Saughall (01244) 880213
SAUL (St James the Great) Frampton on Severn, Arlingham,
Saul etc *Glouc*
SAUNDERTON (St Mary and St Nicholas) Bledlow w
Saunderton and Horsenden *Ox*
SAUNTON (St Anne) Braunton *Ex*
SAUSTHORPE (St Andrew) Aswardby w Sausthorpe *Linc*
SAVERNAKE FOREST (St Katharine) Gt and Lt Bedwyn
and Savernake Forest *Sarum*
SAW MILLS (St Mary) Ambergate and Heage *Derby*
SAWBRIDGEWORTH (Great St Mary) *St Alb 4* **P** *Bp*
V *Vacant* Bishop's Stortford (01279) 723305
SAWLEY (All Saints) (St Mary) *Derby 13* **P** *D&C Lich*
R J R WARMAN, **C** J W B TOMLINSON
SAWLEY (St Michael) Fountains Gp *Ripon*
SAWREY (St Peter) Hawkshead and Low Wray w Sawrey
Carl
SAWSTON (St Mary) *Ely 7* **P** *SMF* **V** R L POWELL,
C S G FEARL
SAWTRY (All Saints) *Ely 13* **P** *Duke of Devonshire*
R J R SANSOM
SAXBY (St Helen) Owmby Gp *Linc*
SAXBY (St Peter) Waltham on the Wolds, Stonesby, Saxby
etc *Leic*
SAXBY ALL SAINTS (All Saints) *Linc 6*
P R H H *Barton Esq* **R** *Vacant*
SAXELBYE (St Peter) Ab Kettleby Gp *Leic*
SAXHAM, GREAT (St Andrew) Risby w Gt and Lt Saxham
and Westley *St E*
SAXHAM, LITTLE (St Nicholas) as above
SAXILBY Group, The (St Botolph) *Linc 2* **P** *Bp and DBP
(jt)* **P-in-c** R PROSSER
SAXLINGHAM (St Margaret) Gunthorpe w Bale w Field
Dalling, Saxlingham etc *Nor*
SAXLINGHAM NETHERGATE (St Mary) and Shotesham
Nor 5 **P** *Adn and Mrs M E Hicks (jt)* **P-in-c** I G BISHOP
SAXMUNDHAM (St John the Baptist) *St E 19* **P** *Exors
Mrs A H V Aldous* **R** A M R PLATT
SAXTEAD (All Saints) Framlingham w Saxtead *St E*
**SAXTHORPE (St Andrew) w Corpusty, Blickling, Oulton and
Heydon w Irmingland** *Nor 20* **P** *Pemb Coll Cam (1 turn),
MMCET and Bp (1 turn)* **P-in-c** K A HAWKES
SAXTON (All Saints) Sherburn in Elmet w Saxton *York*
SAYERS COMMON (Christ Church) Albourne w Sayers
Common and Twineham *Chich*
SCALBY (St Laurence) w Ravenscar and Staintondale
York 16 **P** *Abp (1 turn), D&C Nor (2 turns)*
V C N TUBBS
SCALDWELL (St Peter and St Paul) Walgrave w
Hannington and Wold and Scaldwell *Pet*
SCALEBY (All Saints) Irthington, Crosby-on-Eden and
Scaleby *Carl*
**SCALFORD (St Egelwin) w Goadby Marwood and Wycombe
and Chadwell, Eastwell and Eaton** *Leic 3* **P** *Ld Chan and
Bp (alt)* **R** L N KING

SCAMMONDEN, WEST (St Bartholomew) Barkisland w W
Scammonden *Wakef*
SCAMPSTON (St Martin) Rillington w Scampston,
Wintringham etc *York*
SCAMPTON (St John the Baptist) Aisthorpe w Scampton w
Thorpe le Fallows etc *Linc*
SCARBOROUGH (St Columba) *York 16* **P** *Abp*
V G R SOUTHEY
SCARBOROUGH (St James w Holy Trinity) *York 16* **P** *Abp
and CPAS (jt)* **V** R H MARTIN
SCARBOROUGH (St Luke) *York 16* **P** *Abp*
V M P CHAPPELL
SCARBOROUGH (St Mark) Newby *York*
SCARBOROUGH (St Martin) *York 16* **P** *Trustees*
V C J ARMSTRONG, **C** P C GRAY, **NSM** M SHIPLEY
**SCARBOROUGH (St Mary) w Christ Church and (Holy
Apostles)** *York 16* **P** *Abp* **V** R W JACKSON,
C B E KELLY, **Hon C** H S WATSON, **NSM** R C WALSER
(nee SHIELS)
SCARBOROUGH (St Saviour w All Saints) *York 16*
P *Abp* **V** A J MILLS
SCARCLIFFE (St Leonard) E Scarsdale *Derby*
SCARISBRICK (St Mark) (Good Shepherd) *Liv 11*
P *V Ormskirk* **V** A K GOODE
SCARLE, NORTH (All Saints) Swinderby *Linc*
SCARLE, SOUTH (St Helena) Collingham w S Scarle and
Besthorpe and Girton *S'well*
SCARNING (St Peter and St Paul) E Dereham and Scarning
Nor
SCARRINGTON (St John of Beverley) Whatton w
Aslockton, Hawksworth, Scarrington etc *S'well*
SCARSDALE, EAST *Derby 3* **P** *Patr Bd*
TR I E WINTERBOTTOM, **TV** G R BEVAN,
W J BLAKEMAN
SCARTHO (St Giles) *Linc 9* **P** *Jes Coll Ox*
R B A J PEARMAIN, **C** E A PALMER, C NORMAN,
NSM C L BOGGIS
SCAWBY (St Hibald), Redbourne and Hibaldstow *Linc 6*
P *Lt-Col R Sutton-Nelthorpe (2 turns), Bp (1 turn), and
Duke of St Alb (1 turn)* **V** P E COPPEN
SCAWTHORPE (St Luke) Doncaster St Leon and St Jude
Sheff
SCAWTON (St Mary) Upper Ryedale *York*
SCAYNES HILL (St Augustine) *Chich 6* **P** *Bp*
P-in-c G B MITCHELL
SCHOLES (St Philip) Barwick in Elmet *Ripon*
SCHOLES (St Philip and St James) *Wakef 8* **P** *Bp*
V *Vacant* Cleckheaton (01274) 873024
SCHORNE *Ox 24* **P** *Patr Bd (2 turns), Ld Chan (1 turn)*
TR T M THORP, **TV** I T WHITE, B G KYRIACOU
**SCILLY ISLANDS: St Mary's, St Agnes, St Martin's, Bryher
and Tresco** *Truro 6* **P** *Duchy of Cornwall*
TR M J PHILLIPS, **NSM** K D CAMPION
SCISSETT (St Augustine) High Hoyland, Scissett and
Clayton W *Wakef*
SCOFTON (St John the Evangelist) w Osberton *S'well 6*
P *G M T Foljambe Esq* **V** R E WHEATON
**SCOLE (St Andrew) w Brockdish, Billingford, Thorpe Abbots
and Thorpe Parva** *Nor 10* **P** *Bp, Ex Coll Ox, MMCET,
Adn Norfolk, and Exors Lady Mann (jt)* **R** *Vacant* Diss
(01379) 740250
SCOPWICK Group, The (Holy Cross) *Linc 18* **P** *Ld Chan*
P-in-c T R STOKES
SCORBOROUGH (St Leonard) Lockington and Lund and
Scorborough w Leconfield *York*
SCORTON (St Peter) *Blackb 10* **P** *V Lanc*
P-in-c R H BAKER
SCOT HAY (St Paul) Silverdale and Alsagers Bank *Lich*
SCOT WILLOUGHBY (St Andrew) S Lafford *Linc*
SCOTBY (All Saints) *Carl 2* **P** *Trustees* **V** F W BOVILL
SCOTFORTH (St Paul) *Blackb 12* **P** *Rt Rev J Nicholls*
V A CLITHEROW, **C** J HEIL
SCOTHERN (St Germain) Welton and Dunholme w
Scothern *Linc*
SCOTSWOOD (St Margaret) *Newc 7* **P** *Bp*
V N J HENSHALL
SCOTTER (St Peter) w East Ferry *Linc 4* **P** *Bp*
P-in-c O G FOLKARD, **NSM** L RADFORD, R I WATTS
SCOTTON (St Genewys) w Northorpe *Linc 4* **P** *Ld Chan*
P-in-c K A WINDSLOW, **NSM** W KEAST,
D L LANGFORD
SCOTTON (St Thomas) Farnham w Scotton, Staveley,
Copgrove etc *Ripon*
SCOTTOW (All Saints) Worstead, Westwick, Sloley,
Swanton Abbot etc *Nor*
SCOULTON (Holy Trinity) Hingham w Wood Rising w
Scoulton *Nor*

SCOUTHEAD (St Paul) Dobcross w Scouthead *Man*

SCRAMBLESBY (St Martin) Asterby Gp *Linc*

SCRAPTOFT (All Saints) *Leic 1* **P** *Dr M J A Sharp and Bp (jt)* **V** M E C DREW

SCRAYINGHAM (St Peter and St Paul) Stamford Bridge Gp of Par *York*

SCREDINGTON (St Andrew) Helpringham w Hale *Linc*

SCREMBY (St Peter and St Paul) Partney *Linc*

SCREMERSTON (St Peter) *Newc 12* **P** *Bp* **V** J W SHEWAN

SCREVETON (St Wilfrid) Car Colston w Screveton *S'well*

SCRIVELSBY (St Benedict) Thornton Gp *Linc*

SCROOBY (St Wilfrid) *S'well 5* **P** *Bp* **P-in-c** J J VAN DEN BERG

SCROPTON (St Paul) Marston on Dove w Scropton *Derby*

SCRUTON (St Radegund) Kirkby Fleetham w Langton on Swale and Scruton *Ripon*

SCULCOATES (St Paul) w Christ Church and St Silas *York 15* **P** *Abp* **V** *Vacant* Hull (01482) 224370

SCULTHORPE (St Mary and All Saints) N and S Creake w Waterden, Syderstone etc *Nor*

SCUNTHORPE (All Saints) *Linc 4* **P** *Bp* **V** M A BATTY

SCUNTHORPE (Resurrection) Berkeley *Linc 4* **P** *Bp* **P-in-c** A TOWELL

SEA MILLS (St Edyth) *Bris 8* **P** *Bp* **V** P R BAILEY, **NSM** D J A ADAMS

SEA PALLING (St Margaret) Happisburgh, Walcot, Hempstead w Eccles etc *Nor*

SEA VIEW (St Peter) *Portsm 7* **P** *Bp* **V** M L HILL-TOUT

SEABOROUGH (St John) Beaminster Area *Sarum*

SEABROOK (Mission Hall) Cheriton *Cant*

SEACOMBE (St Paul) *Ches 7* **P** *Trustees* **V** S F WALKER

SEACROFT (St James) (Church of the Ascension) (St Richard) *Ripon 8* **P** *DBF* **TR** A F BUNDOCK, **TV** P J LANGFORD, D E P WILKINSON, J SAXTON, **C** R BROOKE

SEAFORD (St Leonard) w Sutton *Chich 18* **P** *Ld Chan* **V** C H ATHERSTONE, **C** E J DAVIES, A W WEAVER

SEAFORTH (St Thomas) *Liv 1* **P** *Sir William Gladstone, Bt* **V** P A WINN

SEAGRAVE (All Saints) Sileby, Cossington and Seagrave *Leic*

SEAGRY (St Mary the Virgin) Gt Somerford, Lt Somerford, Seagry, Corston etc *Bris*

SEAHAM (St Mary the Virgin) w Seaham Harbour *Dur 3* **P** *Bp* **V** P JOBSON

SEAHAM, NEW (Christ Church) *Dur 3* **P** *Bp* **P-in-c** D A ROBERTS

SEAHAM HARBOUR (St John) Seaham w Seaham Harbour *Dur*

SEAL (St Lawrence) *Roch 8* **P** *Bp* **P-in-c** B P SIMMONS

SEAL (St Peter and St Paul) *Roch 8* **P** *DBP* **V** K C BLACKBURN

SEALE (St Lawrence) *Guildf 3* **P** *Adn Surrey* **P-in-c** N S McGREGOR

SEALE, NETHER (St Peter) and OVER (St Matthew) *Derby 16* **P** *Bp and C W Worthington (alt)* **R** J H LISTER

SEAMER (St Martin) w East Ayton *York 16* **P** *Abp* **V** J C MELLING

SEAMER IN CLEVELAND (St Martin) *York 22* **P** *Lord Egremont* **P-in-c** M D A DYKES

SEARBY (St Nicholas) w Owmby *Linc 5* **P** *D&C* **V** *Vacant*

SEASALTER (St Alphege Old Church) Whitstable *Cant*

SEASCALE (St Cuthbert) and Drigg *Carl 5* **P** *DBP* **V** W J P GRIME

SEATHWAITE (Holy Trinity) Broughton and Duddon *Carl*

SEATON (All Hallows) Lyddington w Stoke Dry and Seaton *Pet*

SEATON (St Gregory) *Ex 5* **P** *DBP* **V** N T SCHOFIELD

SEATON (St Paul) Camerton, Seaton and W Seaton *Carl*

SEATON, WEST (Holy Trinity) as above

SEATON CAREW (Holy Trinity) *Dur 13* **P** *Bp* **V** W WORLEY

SEATON HIRST (St John) (St Andrew) *Newc 11* **P** *Bp* **TR** P A G ETTERLEY, **TV** M J HILLS

SEATON ROSS Group of Parishes, The (St Edmund) *York 7* **P** *Ld Chan (1 turn), Abp and Schroder Exor & Trustee Co (2 turns)* **R** J V ANDREWS

SEATON SLUICE (St Paul) Delaval *Newc*

SEAVINGTON (St Michael and St Mary) S Petherton w the Seavingtons *B & W*

SEBERGHAM (St Mary) Caldbeck, Castle Sowerby and Sebergham *Carl*

SECKINGTON (All Saints) Newton Regis w Seckington and Shuttington *Birm*

SEDBERGH (St Andrew), Cautley and Garsdale *Bradf 6* **P** *Trin Coll Cam* **V** A W FELL, **NSM** F M I'ANSON

SEDGEBERROW (St Mary the Virgin) w Hinton-on-the-Green *Worc 1* **P** *D&C and Lasletts Charity (alt)* **P-in-c** H F GODDARD

SEDGEBROOK (St Lawrence) W w E Allington and Sedgebrook *Linc*

SEDGEFIELD (St Edmund) *Dur 14* **P** *Bp* **R** M Q KING, **C** J H LAWSON

SEDGEHILL (St Katherine) E Knoyle, Semley and Sedgehill *Sarum*

SEDGFORD (St Mary) Docking, The Birchams, Stanhoe and Sedgeford *Nor*

SEDGLEY (All Saints) *Worc 10* **P** *DBP* **TR** P G ASHBY, **TV** A K LANE, **C** I R PETRIE

SEDGLEY (St Mary the Virgin) *Worc 10* **P** *Bp and V Sedgley All SS (jt)* **V** S M MILLER, **HonC** J S WATTS

SEDLESCOMBE (St John the Baptist) w Whatlington *Chich 14* **P** *Ld Chan and Bp (alt)* **R** C I PRITCHARD

SEEND (Holy Cross) and Bulkington *Sarum 19* **P** *D&C (3 turns), Bp (1 turn)* **P-in-c** D C FROST

SEER GREEN (Holy Trinity) and Jordans *Ox 20* **P** *Bp* **P-in-c** J M STOKER

SEETHING (St Margaret) Brooke, Kirstead, Mundham w Seething and Thwaite *Nor*

SEFTON (St Helen) *Liv 5* **P** *Bp* **P-in-c** P J E CREAN

SEGHILL (Holy Trinity) *Newc 1* **P** *The Crown* **V** A MURRAY

SEIGHFORD (St Chad) Chebsey, Ellenhall and Seighford-with-Creswell *Lich*

SELATTYN (St Mary) Weston Rhyn and Selattyn *Lich*

SELBORNE (St Mary) Newton Valence, Selborne and E Tisted w Colemore *Win*

SELBY (St James the Apostle) *York 6* **P** *Simeon's Trustees* **V** D J WOOLLARD, **C** M J CUNDIFF

SELBY ABBEY (St Mary and St Germain) (St Richard) *York 6* **P** *Abp* **V** J A ROBERTSON, **C** C M DURNFORD

SELHAM (St James) Lurgashall, Lodsworth and Selham *Chich*

SELLACK (St Tysilio) How Caple w Sollarshope, Sellack etc *Heref*

SELLINDGE (St Mary the Virgin) w Monks Horton and Stowting and Lympne w West Hythe *Cant 12* **P** *Abp* **P-in-c** D R HANCOCK

SELLING (St Mary the Virgin) w Throwley and Sheldwich w Badlesmere and Leaveland *Cant 6* **P** *Abp and D&C (jt)* **R** J V H RUSSELL, **C** S M RAMSARAN (or COOPER), **Hon C** M JOHNSON

SELLY OAK (St Mary) *Birm 2* **P** *Bp* **V** C J ALDRIDGE

SELLY PARK (St Stephen) (St Wulstan) (St Stephen's Centre) *Birm 8* **P** *Trustees* **V** C J S TURNER, **C** P D SWAN, M I BENNETT

SELMESTON (St Mary) Berwick w Selmeston and Alciston *Chich*

SELSDON (St John) (St Francis) *S'wark 20* **P** *Bp* **TR** L A D WATSON, **TV** B A WELLS, **C** P J O'REILLY, **NSM** K HOLT, S MARTIN

SELSEY (St Peter) *Chich 3* **P** *Bp* **R** V R CASSAM

SELSIDE (St Thomas) Skelsmergh w Selside and Longsleddale *Carl*

SELSLEY (All Saints) Cainscross w Selsley *Glouc*

SELSTON (St Helen) *S'well 4* **P** *Wright Trustees* **V** J F JACKLIN, **C** C A K MAIDEN, **NSM** G E HILL

SELWORTHY (All Saints), Timberscombe, Wootton Courtenay and Luccombe *B & W 16* **P** *Bp* **R** P S C WALKER, **Hon C** M J DUVALL

SEMER (All Saints) Whatfield w Semer, Nedding and Naughton *St E*

SEMINGTON (St George) Steeple Ashton w Semington and Keevil *Sarum*

SEMLEY (St Leonard) E Knoyle, Semley and Sedgehill *Sarum*

SEMPRINGHAM (St Andrew) w Pointon and Birthorpe *Linc 21* **P** *The Crown* **P-in-c** C H WILSON

SEND (St Mary the Virgin) *Guildf 12* **P** *Bp* **NSM** G H CLAYTON

SENNEN (St Sennen) St Buryan, St Levan and Sennen *Truro*

SENNICOTTS (St Mary) Funtington and Sennicotts *Chich*

SESSAY (St Cuthbert) *York 20* **P** *Viscount Downe* **P-in-c** J H DAVIS

SETCHEY (St Mary) W Winch w Setchey and N Runcton *Nor*

SETMURTHY (St Barnabas) Bassenthwaite, Isel and Setmurthy *Carl*

SETTLE (Holy Ascension) *Bradf 5* **P** *Trustees* **V** S G RIDLEY

SETTRINGTON (All Saints) w North Grimston and Wharram *York 2* **P** *Abp and Lord Middleton (jt)* **R** *Vacant* North Grimston (01944) 768275

SEVENHAMPTON (St Andrew) w Charlton Abbotts and
Hawling w Whittington *Glouc 14* **P** *Bp, T W Bailey Esq,
E M Bailey Esq, MMCET, and Mrs J A Stringer (jt)*
V *Vacant* Cheltenham (01242) 820246
SEVENHAMPTON (St James) Highworth w Sevenhampton
and Inglesham etc *Bris*
SEVENOAKS (St John the Baptist) *Roch 8* **P** *Guild of
All So* **C** PEWAKELIN, **NSM** CJRDAWSON
SEVENOAKS (St Luke) Conventional District *Roch 8*
C-in-c RJMASON
SEVENOAKS (St Nicholas) *Roch 8* **P** *Trustees*
R OMTHOMSON, **C** RMARSDEN, MJSTANDEN,
Hon C NNHENSHAW, DGMILTON-THOMPSON,
NSM JWHICKMAN
SEVENOAKS WEALD (St George) *Roch 8* **P** *R Sevenoaks*
P-in-c LDRYDEN
SEVERN BEACH (St Nicholas) Pilning w Compton
Greenfield *Bris*
SEVERN STOKE (St Dennis) Kempsey and Severn Stoke w
Croome d'Abitot *Worc*
SEVINGTON (St Mary) *Cant 10* **P** *Ch Soc Trust*
P-in-c JWTIPPING
SEWARDS END (not known) Saffron Walden w Wendens
Ambo and Littlebury *Chelmsf*
SEWERBY (St John) Bridlington H Trin and Sewerby w
Marton *York*
SEWSTERN (Holy Trinity) Wymondham w Edmondthorpe,
Buckminster etc *Leic*
SHABBINGTON (St Mary Magdalene) Worminghall w
Ickford, Oakley and Shabbington *Ox*
SHACKERSTONE (St Peter) Nailstone and Carlton w
Shackerstone *Leic*
SHACKLEFORD (St Mary the Virgin) Compton w
Shackleford and Peper Harow *Guildf*
SHADFORTH (St Cuthbert) *Dur 2* **P** *D&C* **R** DJBELL,
C PTALLINSON
SHADINGFIELD (St John the Baptist) Hundred River *St E*
SHADOXHURST (St Peter and St Paul) Kingsnorth w
Shadoxhurst *Cant*
SHADWELL (St Paul) *Ripon 5* **P** *V Thorner* **V** *Vacant*
Leeds (0113) 273 7035
SHADWELL (St Paul) w Ratcliffe St James *Lon 7* **P** *Bp*
P-in-c RTSIMPSON
SHAFTESBURY (St James) Shaston *Sarum*
SHAFTESBURY (St Peter) as above
SHAFTON (St Hugh) Felkirk w Brierley *Wakef*
SHALBOURNE (St Michael and All Angels) Wexcombe
Sarum
SHALDEN (St Peter and St Paul) Bentworth and Shalden
and Lasham *Win*
SHALDON (St Nicholas) (St Peter) *Ex 10* **P** *SMF*
V ALMANHIRE
SHALFLEET (St Michael the Archangel) *Portsm 8*
P *Ld Chan* **V** *Vacant* Calbourne (0198378) 238
SHALFORD (St Andrew) Wethersfield w Shalford *Chelmsf*
SHALFORD (St Mary the Virgin) *Guildf 5* **P** *Ld Chan*
V DNHOBDEN, **NSM** JJSWANTON
SHALSTONE (St Edward the Confessor) Westbury w
Turweston, Shalstone and Biddlesden *Ox*
SHAMLEY GREEN (Christ Church) *Guildf 2* **P** *Bp*
V MCHUGHES
SHANGTON (St Nicholas) Gaulby *Leic*
SHANKLIN (St Blasius) *Portsm 7* **P** *Bp*
P-in-c AWSWANBOROUGH
SHANKLIN (St Saviour on the Cliff) *Portsm 7* **P** *Bp*
V *Vacant*
SHAP (St Michael) w Swindale and Bampton w Mardale
Carl 1 **P** *Earl of Lonsdale* **V** GGFIELD
SHAPWICK (Blessed Virgin Mary) w Ashcott and Burtle
B & W 5 **P** *Lord Vestey (2 turns), Bp (1 turn)*
V HLBAXTER
SHAPWICK (St Bartholomew) Sturminster Marshall,
Kingston Lacy and Shapwick *Sarum*
SHARD END (All Saints) *Birm 11* **P** *Keble Coll Ox*
V PJNICHOLAS
SHARDLOW (St James) Elvaston and Shardlow *Derby*
SHARESHILL (St Luke and St Mary the Virgin) *Lich 2*
P *Bp* **V** *Vacant* Wolverhampton (01902) 727579
SHARLSTON (St Luke) *Wakef 9* **P** *Bp* **V** RACHAPMAN
SHARNBROOK (St Peter) and Knotting w Souldrop
St Alb 21 **P** *Bp* **R** ROHUBBARD
SHARNFORD (St Helen) Sapcote and Sharnford w Wigston
Parva *Leic*
SHARPNESS (St Andrew) w Purton and Brookend *Glouc 2*
P *Bp* **V** DPMINCHEW
SHARRINGTON (All Saints) Gunthorpe w Bale w Field
Dalling, Saxlingham etc *Nor*

SHASTON *Sarum 6* **P** *Patr Bd* **TR** DDICKER,
TV DDBOTTERILL, TTAYLOR, **NSM** TJORCHARD
SHAUGH PRIOR (St Edward) Bickleigh (Roborough) and
Shaugh Prior *Ex*
SHAVINGTON (St Mark) Weston *Ches*
SHAW (Christchurch) Atworth w Shaw and Whitley *Sarum*
SHAW (Holy Trinity) *Man 22* **P** *R Prestwich St Mary*
V ANWILSON
SHAW (St Mary) cum Donnington *Ox 14* **P** *DBP*
R BTAYLOR
SHAW HILL (St Mary and St John) Saltley St Sav and Shaw
Hill SS Mary and Jo etc *Birm*
SHAWBURY (St Mary the Virgin) *Lich 28* **P** *Sir John
Corbet, Bt* **V** JEDAIMOND, **C** CJGROOCOCK
SHAWELL (All Saints) Swinford w Catthorpe, Shawell and
Stanford *Leic*
SHEARSBY (St Mary Magdalene) Arnesby w Shearsby and
Bruntingthorpe *Leic*
SHEBBEAR (St Michael), Buckland Filleigh, Sheepwash,
Langtree, Newton St Petrock, Petrockstowe, Petersmarland,
Merton and Huish *Ex 20* **P** *Ld Chan (1 turn), Patr Bd
(2 turns)* **TR** NGMEAD, **TV** CHANSON
SHEDFIELD (St John the Baptist) *Portsm 1* **P** *DBP*
V GBMORRELL, **Hon C** WTSMOORE,
NSM BRMcHUGH
SHEEN (St Luke) Longnor, Quarnford and Sheen *Lich*
SHEEN, EAST (All Saints) Mortlake w E Sheen *S'wark*
SHEEN, EAST (Christ Church) as above
SHEEPSCOMBE (St John the Evangelist) Painswick w
Sheepscombe *Glouc*
SHEEPSTOR (St Leonard) Yelverton, Meavy, Sheepstor and
Walkhampton *Ex*
SHEEPWASH (St Lawrence) Shebbear, Buckland Filleigh,
Sheepwash etc *Ex*
SHEEPY GROUP, The *Leic 13* **P** *Ld Chan, Pemb Coll Ox,
and MMCET (by turn)* **R** JRHAMBIDGE
SHEERING (St Mary the Virgin) Hatf Heath and Sheering
Chelmsf
SHEERNESS (Holy Trinity w St Paul) *Cant 14* **P** *V Minster-
in-Sheppey* **V** DWALKER
SHEERWATER (St Michael and All Angels) Woodham
Guildf
SHEET (St Mary Magdalene) *Portsm 5* **P** *Bp*
V PDINGRAMS, **NSM** CMPEEL
SHEFFIELD Abbeydale *Sheff 2* **P** *Ch Burgesses*
V RJHBEARD
SHEFFIELD Norwood (St Leonard) *Sheff 3* **P** *Bp*
V TWELLIS, **C** THCASWELL, AHMORGAN
SHEFFIELD Parson Cross (St Cecilia) *Sheff 3* **P** *Bp*
V AIDALTON
SHEFFIELD Sharrow (St Andrew) *Sheff 2* **P** *Trustees*
V NPAJOWETT, **C** CACOLLINS
SHEFFIELD (St Aidan w St Luke) Sheff Manor *Sheff*
SHEFFIELD (St Bartholomew) *Sheff 4* **P** *Ch Patr Trust and
Sheff Ch Burgesses Trust (jt)* **V** NHELM
SHEFFIELD (St Catherine of Siena) Richmond Road *Sheff 1*
P *The Crown* **V** HLOXLEY
SHEFFIELD (St Cuthbert) *Sheff 3* **P** *Ch Burgesses*
V BRTWOHIG
SHEFFIELD (St John the Evangelist) *Sheff 1*
P *Ch Burgesses* **V** CWKEMP, **C** BHICKS
SHEFFIELD (St Mark) Broomhill *Sheff 4* **P** *Ch Burgesses*
V AALKER, **Par Dn** JYTILLIER, **C** HAJOWETT
SHEFFIELD (St Mary) Bramhall Lane *Sheff 2*
P *Ch Burgesses and Provost (alt)* **V** JCSULLIVAN,
C MJBAYLEY
SHEFFIELD (St Matthew) Carver Street *Sheff 2* **P** *Bp*
V MWAKELY
SHEFFIELD (St Oswald) *Sheff 2* **P** *Ch Burgesses*
V JKMOORE
SHEFFIELD (St Paul) Wordsworth Avenue *Sheff 3* **P** *DBP*
V PTSTEVENS
SHEFFIELD (St Silas) Broomhall *Sheff 2* **P** *Ch Burgesses*
V MFHOLLAND
SHEFFIELD MANOR (St Swithun) *Sheff 1* **P** *Patr Bd*
TR RWBATKINSON, **TV** ARTEAL, CPARNESEN,
HJSMART
SHEFFIELD PARK (St John the Evangelist) Sheff St Jo
Sheff
SHEFFORD (St Michael) *St Alb 22* **P** *Adn Bedford,
R Clifton, and R Campton (jt)* **V** DRSMITH
SHEFFORD, GREAT (St Mary) Welford w Wickham and
Gt Shefford, Boxford etc *Ox*
SHEINTON (St Peter and St Paul) Wenlock *Heref*
SHELDON (St Giles) *Birm 11* **P** *KSD Wingfield
Digby Esq* **R** GWHERBERT, **C** SRPALMER,
NSM ABOULT

SHELDON (St James the Greater) Dunkeswell, Sheldon and Luppitt *Ex*

SHELDON (St Michael and All Angels) Ashford w Sheldon and Longstone *Derby*

SHELDWICH (St James) Selling w Throwley, Sheldwich w Badlesmere etc *Cant*

SHELF St Michael w Buttershaw St Aidan *Bradf 2* **P** *Bp*
TR D PEEL, **TV** J A HOLFORD, **C** J Y W RITCHIE

SHELFANGER (All Saints) Winfarthing w Shelfanger w Burston w Gissing etc *Nor*

SHELFORD (St Peter and St Paul) Radcliffe-on-Trent and Shelford etc *S'well*

SHELFORD, GREAT (St Mary) *Ely 7* **P** *Bp*
V C J HERBERT

SHELFORD, LITTLE (All Saints) w Newton *Ely 7* **P** *Bp*
R S G TAYLOR

SHELLAND (King Charles the Martyr) Buxhall w Shelland *St E*

SHELLEY (All Saints) Hadleigh w Layham and Shelley *St E*

SHELLEY (Emmanuel) and Shepley *Wakef 6*
P *V Kirkburton* **V** A HEZEL

SHELLEY (St Peter) Chipping Ongar w Shelley *Chelmsf*

SHELLINGFORD (St Faith) Uffington, Shellingford, Woolstone and Baulking *Ox*

SHELSLEY BEAUCHAMP (All Saints) Clifton-on-Teme, Lower Sapey and the Shelsleys *Worc*

SHELSLEY WALSH (St Andrew) as above

SHELTON (Christ Church) Oxon and Shelton *Lich*

SHELTON (St Mark) Hanley H Ev *Lich*

SHELTON (St Mary) Hempnall *Nor*

SHELTON (St Mary) The Stodden Churches *St Alb*

SHELTON (St Mary and All Saints) *S'well 3* **P** *Bp*
R G A FIRTH

SHELVE (All Saints) Hope w Shelve *Heref*

SHENFIELD (St Mary the Virgin) *Chelmsf 7*
P *R H Courage Esq* **R** P G BRETT

SHENINGTON (Holy Trinity) Horley w Hornton and Hanwell, Shenington etc *Ox*

SHENLEY (St Martin) *St Alb 1* **P** *DBP*
P-in-c C J TWYCROSS

SHENLEY (St Mary) Watling Valley *Ox*

SHENLEY GREEN (St David) *Birm 4* **P** *Bp*
V C J W JACKSON

SHENSTONE (St John the Baptist) *Lich 1* **P** *MMCET*
V B ANDREW, **NSM** J BASTON

SHENTON (St John the Evangelist) Market Bosworth, Cadeby w Sutton Cheney etc *Leic*

SHEPHERD'S BUSH (St Stephen) (St Thomas) *Lon 9*
P *Bp* **V** J H ASBRIDGE

SHEPLEY (St Paul) Shelley and Shepley *Wakef*

SHEPPERDINE (Chapel) Oldbury-on-Severn *Glouc*

SHEPPERTON (St Nicholas) *Lon 13* **P** *Bp* **R** C J SWIFT

SHEPRETH (All Saints) *Ely 8* **P** *Bp* **V** M W BAKER

SHEPSHED (St Botolph) *Leic 7* **P** *Lord Crawshaw*
V S J BOWRING

SHEPTON BEAUCHAMP (St Michael) Ilminster and District *B & W*

SHEPTON MALLET (St Peter and St Paul) w Doulting
B & W 8 **P** *Duchy of Cornwall and Bp (alt)*
R J S T WOOLMER, **C** M S PERSSON

SHEPTON MONTAGUE (St Peter) Bruton and Distr *B & W*

SHEPWELL GREEN (St Matthias) Willenhall St Giles *Lich*

SHERBORNE (Abbey Church of St Mary) (All Souls)
(St Paul) w Castleton and Lillington *Sarum 4*
P *Major K S D Wingfield Digby* **V** E J WOODS,
C J W S PATON, D LASHBROOKE

SHERBORNE (St Mary Magdalene), Windrush, the
Barringtons and Aldsworth *Glouc 14*
P *C T R Wingfield Esq, Ch Ch Ox, and DBP (by turn)*
P-in-c M SELWOOD

SHERBORNES (St Andrew) (Vyne Chapel) w Pamber, The
Win 4 **P** *Bp and Qu Coll Ox (jt)* **R** J N HAMILTON

SHERBOURNE (All Saints) Barford w Wasperton and Sherbourne *Cov*

SHERBURN (St Hilda) and West and East Heslerton w
Yedingham *York 2* **P** *D&C (2 turns), The Crown (2 turns),*
and Sir Stephen Hastings (1 turn) **P-in-c** D M B SHARPE,
NSM V D CLARKE

SHERBURN (St Mary) w Pittington *Dur 2* **P** *D&C*
V D J BELL, **C** P T ALLINSON, P E MARTIN

SHERBURN IN ELMET (All Saints) w Saxton *York 1*
P *Abp* **V** C I COATES, C V D CLARKE

SHERE (St James) *Guildf 2* **P** *Mrs H Bray*
R N B FARBRIDGE

SHEREFORD (St Nicholas) Toftrees w Shereford *Nor*

SHERFIELD ENGLISH (St Leonard) Awbridge w Sherfield English *Win*

SHERFIELD-ON-LODDON (St Leonard) and Stratfield Saye
w Hartley Wespall w Stratfield Turgis *Win 4* **P** *Bp, Duke of*
Wellington, and D&C Windsor (jt) **R** J N THOMAS

SHERFORD (St Martin) Stokenham w Sherford *Ex*

SHERIFF HUTTON (St Helen and the Holy Cross) and
Farlington *York 5* **P** *Abp (2 turns), DBP (1 turn)*
P-in-c D W D LEE

SHERIFFHALES (St Mary) Lilleshall and Sheriffhales *Lich*

SHERINGHAM (St Peter) *Nor 22* **P** *Bp*
P-in-c A C H LATHE

SHERINGHAM, UPPER (All Saints) Weybourne Gp *Nor*

SHERINGTON (St Laud) w Chicheley, North Crawley,
Astwood and Hardmead *Ox 27* **P** *Bp (2 turns), MMCET*
(1 turn), and Major J G B Chester (1 turn)
R M C STANTON-SARINGER

SHERMANBURY (St Giles) Henfield w Shermanbury and Woodmancote *Chich*

SHERNBOURNE (St Peter and St Paul) Dersingham w Anmer and Shernborne *Nor*

SHERRARDS GREEN (St Mary the Virgin) Gt Malvern Ch Ch *Worc*

SHERRINGTON (St Cosmo and St Damian) Ashton Gifford *Sarum*

SHERSTON MAGNA (Holy Cross), Easton Grey,
Luckington, Alderton and Foxley w Bremilham *Bris 12*
P *D&C, Bp, Adn Swindon and Lord Lilford (jt)*
V M H ROSS

SHERWOOD (St Martin) *S'well 13* **P** *Bp* **V** C GALE,
C P H REISS

SHERWOOD PARK (St Philip) Tunbridge Wells St Jas w St Phil *Roch*

SHEVINGTON (St Anne) *Blackb 4* **P** *R Standish*
V F A O D DAWSON

SHEVIOCK (Blessed Virgin Mary) Antony w Sheviock *Truro*

SHIFFORD (St Mary) Bampton w Clanfield *Ox*

SHIFNAL (St Andrew) *Lich 25* **P** *J Brook Esq* **V** *Vacant*
Telford (01952) 460625

SHILBOTEL (St James) Shilbottle *Newc*

SHILBOTTLE (St James) *Newc 9* **P** *Dioc Soc*
V R J GLOVER

SHILDON (St John) w Eldon *Dur 10* **P** *Bp (2 turns), The*
Crown (1 turn) **V** R CUTHBERTSON, **C** L POTTER

SHILDON, NEW (All Saints) *Dur 10* **P** *Bp*
V R V STAPLETON

SHILL VALLEY and Broadshire *Ox 8* **P** *J Heyworth Esq,*
Mrs P Allen, and Ch Ch Ox (1 turn), Ch Soc Tr,
F R Goodenough Esq, and D F Goodenough Esq (1 turn)
Hon C J M MOUNT

SHILLING OKEFORD (Holy Rood) *Sarum 6* **P** *DBP*
P-in-c M A TURNER

SHILLINGFORD (St George) Dunchideock and Shillingford St George w Ide *Ex*

SHILLINGSTONE (Holy Rood) Shilling Okeford *Sarum*

SHILLINGTON (All Saints) *St Alb 22* **P** *Bp*
V D MORGAN

SHILTON (Holy Rood) Shill Valley and Broadshire *Ox*

SHILTON (St Andrew) Bulkington w Shilton and Ansty *Cov*

SHIMPLINGTHORNE (St George) Lawshall w Shimplingthorne and Alpheton *St E*

SHINCLIFFE (St Mary the Virgin) *Dur 2* **P** *D&C*
R S M SANDHAM, **NSM** R D THOMSON

SHINEY ROW (St Oswald) *Dur 6* **P** *The Crown*
P-in-c K WALKER, **C** D BODDY

SHINFIELD (St Mary) *Ox 15* **P** *D&C Heref*
V S N H BAKER

SHINGAY Group of Parishes, The *Ely 8* **P** *Bp,*
Mrs E E Sclater, Ch Patr Trust, Down Coll Cam,
New CollOx, and Jes Coll Cam (jt) **V** *Vacant* Steeple
Morden (01763) 852747

SHIPBOURNE (St Giles) *Roch 10* **P** *E Cazalet Esq*
P-in-c M A PERRY

SHIPDHAM (All Saints) w East and West Bradenham
Nor 18 **P** *Bp* **R** *Vacant* Dereham (01362) 820234

SHIPHAM (St Leonard) Axbridge w Shipham and Rowberrow *B & W*

SHIPHAY COLLATON (St John the Baptist) *Ex 10* **P** *Bp*
V D A PINCHES

SHIPLAKE (St Peter and St Paul) w Dunsden *Ox 6*
P *D&C Windsor and DBP (jt)* **V** M R C PRICE

SHIPLEY (St Mary the Virgin) *Chich 8* **P** *C R Burrell Esq*
P-in-c D L POPE

SHIPLEY (St Paul) and Frizinghall St Margaret *Bradf 1*
P *Patr Bd* **TR** J R POOLE, **TV** P H BOOTH,
NSM K N MEDHURST

SHIPLEY (St Peter) *Bradf 1* **P** *TR Shipley St Paul and*
Frizinghall **V** C P EDMONDSON, **C** P O HART

SHIPPON (St Mary Magdalene) *Ox 10* **P** *Bp*
  V M A J GOODE
SHIPSTON-ON-STOUR (St Edmund) w Honington and
  Idlicote *Cov 9* **P** *Jes Coll Ox, D&C Worc, Bp (jt)*
  R A C DE SMET
SHIPTON (Holy Evangelist) Skelton w Shipton and Newton
  on Ouse *York*
SHIPTON (St James) Wenlock *Heref*
SHIPTON BELLINGER (St Peter) *Win 3* **P** *Bp*
  V A R H MACLEOD
SHIPTON GORGE (St Martin) Bride Valley *Sarum*
SHIPTON MOYNE (St John the Baptist) w Westonbirt and
  Lasborough *Glouc 16* **P** *Westonbirt Sch and DBP (jt)*
  NSM W I BARBOUR, J L BARBOUR
SHIPTON OLIFFE (St Oswald) Dowdeswell and
  Andoversford w the Shiptons etc *Glouc*
SHIPTON ON CHERWELL (Holy Cross) Yarnton w
  Begbroke and Shipton on Cherwell *Ox*
SHIPTON SOLLARS (St Mary) Dowdeswell and
  Andoversford w the Shiptons etc *Glouc*
SHIPTON-UNDER-WYCHWOOD (St Mary) w Milton-
  under-Wychwood, Fifield and Idbury *Ox 3* **P** *Bp*
  V G G B CANNING
SHIPTONTHORPE (All Saints) w Hayton *York 7* **P** *Abp*
  V K G SKIPPER
SHIREBROOK (Holy Trinity) E Scarsdale *Derby*
SHIREGREEN (St Hilda) *Sheff 3* **P** *Bp* **P-in-c** T W ELLIS
SHIREGREEN (St James and St Christopher) *Sheff 3*
  P *Provost* **P-in-c** A J P THOMPSON
SHIREHAMPTON (St Mary) *Bris 8* **P** *Bp*
  V F R SYMONS, **NSM** A W WHEELER
SHIREMOOR (St Mark) *Newc 8* **P** *Bp* **V** M C VINE,
  C A BRISCOE
SHIREOAKS (St Luke) *S'well 6* **P** *Bp*
  P-in-c M P D KENNARD
SHIRESHEAD (St James) *Blackb 12* **P** *V Cockerham*
  P-in-c T S EVANS
SHIRLAND (St Leonard) *Derby 1* **P** *Adn Chesterfield and*
  Trustees **R** D J MURDOCH
SHIRLEY (St George) *S'wark 20* **P** *Bp* **V** D J FROST,
  C G P REEVES, **Hon C** N N KIRKUP
SHIRLEY (St James) (St John) *Win 12* **P** *Ch Patr Trust*
  V P E IRWIN-CLARK, **C** E BUTT
SHIRLEY (St James the Great) (St John the Divine) (Christ
  the King) (St Luke) (St Mary Magdalene) *Birm 13*
  P *Patr Bd* **TR** M G B C CADDY, **TV** W K McMASTER,
  J G RICHARDS, **C** N I JONES
SHIRLEY (St John) *S'wark 20* **P** *Bp* **V** A H R QUINN,
  Hon C H G LEWIS, A C COLLIER
SHIRLEY (St Michael) Brailsford w Shirley and Osmaston w
  Edlaston *Derby*
SHIRLEY WARREN (St Jude) Southn St Jude *Win*
SHIRWELL (St Peter), Loxhore, Kentisbury, Arlington, East
  Down, Bratton Fleming, Challacombe and Stoke Rivers
  Ex 18 **P** *Patr Bd* **TR** J B H RICHARDS,
  TV R D SIMPSON, **Dss** E A SIMPSON
SHOBDON (St John the Evangelist) Pembridge w
  Moorcourt, Shobdon, Staunton etc *Heref*
SHOBNALL (St Aidan) *Lich 19* **P** *Bp*
  P-in-c D M MORRIS, **C** A R BAILEY
SHOBROOKE (St Swithin) Crediton and Shobrooke *Ex*
SHOCKLACH (St Edith) Tilston and Shocklach *Ches*
SHOEBURY, NORTH (St Mary the Virgin) *Chelmsf 13*
  P *Ld Chan* **V** S CARTER, **C** T M CODLING
SHOEBURY, SOUTH (St Andrew) (St Peter) *Chelmsf 13*
  P *Hyndman Trustees* **R** P A RAYNER, **C** M E MILLARD
SHOLDEN (St Nicholas) Deal St Leon and St Rich and
  Sholden *Cant*
SHOLING (St Francis of Assisi) (St Mary) *Win 12* **P** *Bp*
  V B J HAPTNELL, **C** H FIELDEN, K TAPLIN
SHOOTERS HILL (Christ Church) *S'wark 1* **P** *Bp*
  P-in-c R W JAMES
SHORE (St Barnabas) *Man 20* **P** *D&C V Vacant*
  Littleborough (01706) 78356
SHOREDITCH (St Leonard) and Hoxton St John the Baptist
  Lon 5 **P** *Patr Bd* **TR** P R TURP,
  TV W M MACNAUGHTON, **C** E P KAMRAN
SHOREHAM (St Giles) Kingston Buci *Chich*
SHOREHAM (St Peter and St Paul) *Roch 9* **P** *D&C*
  Westmr **V** B J SIMMONS
SHOREHAM, NEW (St Mary de Haura) *Chich 4* **P** *Bp*
  V K KINNAIRD
SHOREHAM, OLD (St Nicholas) *Chich 4* **P** *Bp*
  V K KINNAIRD
SHOREHAM BEACH (Good Shepherd) *Chich 4* **P** *Bp*
  V C BLAGG
SHORNE (St Peter and St Paul) *Roch 4* **P** *D&C*
  V P E LONGBOTTOM

SHORT HEATH (Holy Trinity) Willenhall H Trin *Lich*
SHORT HEATH (St Margaret) *Birm 6* **P** *Bp*
  V A E POWER
SHORTHAMPTON (All Saints) Charlbury w Shorthampton
  Ox
SHORTLANDS (All Saints' Community Church) Bromley
  SS Pet and Paul *Roch*
SHORTLANDS (St Mary) *Roch 12* **P** *Bp*
  V D S R REDMAN, **Hon C** P LEUNG,
  NSM J G MEDCALF
SHORTWOOD (All Saints) Nailsworth *Glouc*
SHORWELL (St Peter) w Kingston *Portsm 8* **P** *Bp*
  V J W RUSSELL
SHOSCOMBE (St Julian) Camerton w Dunkerton, Foxcote
  and Shoscombe *B & W*
SHOTESHAM (All Saints w St Mary) Saxlingham
  Nethergate and Shotesham *Nor*
SHOTLEY (St John) *Newc 3* **P** *Lord Crewe's Trustees*
  P-in-c T J ATKINS, **NSM** R VICKERS
SHOTLEY (St Mary) *St E 5* **P** *Bp* **R** R SPITTLE
SHOTTERMILL (St Stephen) *Guildf 4* **P** *Adn Surrey*
  V A C JONES
SHOTTERY (St Andrew) *Cov 8* **P** *Bp* **V** S A BEAKE,
  C S W FLETCHER
SHOTTESBROOKE (St John the Baptist) White Waltham w
  Shottesbrooke *Ox*
SHOTTESWELL (St Lawrence) Warmington w Shotteswell
  and Radway w Ratley *Cov*
SHOTTISHAM (St Margaret) w Sutton *St E 7* **P** *Bp*
  P-in-c M H INMAN
SHOTTLE (St Lawrence) Hazelwood *Derby*
SHOTTON (St Saviour) *Dur 3* **P** *Bp* **V** J F MASSHEDAR
SHOTWICK (St Michael) Burton and Shotwick *Ches*
SHOULDHAM (All Saints) *Ely 16* **P** *Bp*
  P-in-c G PARROTT
SHOULDHAM THORPE (St Mary) *Ely 16* **P** *Bp*
  P-in-c G PARROTT
SHRAWARDINE (St Mary) Bicton, Montford w
  Shrawardine and Fitz *Lich*
SHRAWLEY (St Mary), Witley, Astley and Abberley
  Worc 13 **P** *Bp and Guild of All So (jt)* **R** R P HEAPS,
  C D F GUTTERIDGE
SHRED (Mission Church) Slaithwaite w E Scammonden
  Wakef
SHREWSBURY (All Saints and St Michael) *Lich 26* **P** *Bp*
  V A W MARKS
SHREWSBURY (Holy Cross) (St Peter) *Lich 26* **P** *Bp*
  V F I ROSS
SHREWSBURY (Holy Trinity) (St Julian) *Lich 26* **P** *Bp and*
  Ch Patr Trust (jt) **V** P G FIRMIN
SHREWSBURY (St Alkmund) *Lich 26* **P** *Bp*
  P-in-c M POLLIT
SHREWSBURY (St Chad) w St Mary *Lich 26* **P** *Bp*
  V M POLLIT, **C** A J PRICE
SHREWSBURY (St George of Cappadocia) *Lich 26*
  P *V Shrewsbury St Chad* **V** R W D BIDDLE
SHREWSBURY (St Giles) w Sutton and Atcham *Lich 26*
  P *Bp and R L Burton Esq (jt)* **R** P J WILLIAMS
SHREWTON (St Mary) *Sarum 16* **P** *Ld Chan*
  V S M W TRICKETT
SHRIVENHAM (St Andrew) w Watchfield and Bourton
  Ox 17 **P** *Ld Chan* **V** T D RAWDON-MOGG,
  NSM E L GUTSELL
SHROPHAM (St Peter) Hockham w Shropham Gp of Par
  Nor
SHRUB END (All Saints) (St Cedd) *Chelmsf 17* **P** *Bp*
  V D E COWIE, **C** A COLEBROOKE
SHUCKBURGH, LOWER (St John the Baptist) Napton-on-
  the-Hill, Lower Shuckburgh etc *Cov*
SHUDY CAMPS (St Mary) *Ely 4* **P** *Bp*
  NSM M W B O'LOUGHLIN
SHURDINGTON (St Paul) Badgeworth w Shurdington
  Glouc
SHURLOCK ROW (All Saints) Waltham *Ox*
SHUSTOKE (St Cuthbert) The Whitacres and Shustoke *Birm*
SHUTE (St Michael) Kilmington w Shute *Ex*
SHUTFORD (St Martin) Broughton w N Newington and
  Shutford etc *Ox*
SHUTTINGTON (St Matthew) Newton Regis w Seckington
  and Shuttington *Birm*
SHUTTLEWOOD (St Laurence Mission Church) Bolsover
  Derby
SHUTTLEWORTH (St John) Ramsbottom St Jo and St Paul
  Man
SIBBERTOFT (St Helen) Welford w Sibbertoft and Marston
  Trussell *Pet*

SIBDON CARWOOD (St Michael) w Halford *Heref 11*
  P *Bp and R Holden (alt)* **V** *Vacant* Craven Arms (01588)
  673307
SIBERTSWOLD (St Andrew) Eythorne and Elvington w
  Waldershare etc *Cant*
SIBFORD (Holy Trinity) Epwell w Sibford, Swalcliffe and
  Tadmarton *Ox*
SIBLE HEDINGHAM (St Peter) w Castle Hedingham
  Chelmsf 20 **P** *Bp, and Hon T R Lindsay (alt)*
  R D N KELLY
SIBSEY (St Margaret) w Frithville *Linc 20* **P** *Ld Chan*
  V W G PAGE
SIBSON (St Botolph) The Sheepy Gp *Leic*
SIBTHORPE (St Peter) *S'well 3* **P** *Bp* **V** G A FIRTH
SIBTON (St Peter) Yoxford and Peasenhall w Sibton *St E*
SICKLINGHALL (St Peter's Mission Church) Kirkby
  Overblow *Ripon*
SID VALLEY Sidmouth, Woolbrook, Salcombe Regis,
  Sidbury etc *Ex*
SIDBURY (Holy Trinity) Billingsley w Sidbury, Middleton
  Scriven etc *Heref*
SIDBURY (St Giles and St Peter) Sidmouth, Woolbrook,
  Salcombe Regis, Sidbury etc *Ex*
SIDCUP (Christ Church) Longland *Roch 16* **P** *Ch Trust Fund*
  Trust **Hon C** H DYALL
SIDCUP (St Andrew) *Roch 16* **P** *Bp* **V** W ROBBINS,
  Hon C B W SHARPE
SIDCUP (St John the Evangelist) *Roch 16* **P** *D&C*
  Hon C B M VINCENT
SIDDAL (St Mark) *Wakef 4* **P** *Ch Trust Fund Trust*
  V H J R FEREDAY
SIDDINGTON (All Saints) Capesthorne w Siddington and
  Marton *Ches*
SIDDINGTON (St Peter) w Preston *Glouc 12* **P** *Ld Chan*
  and R T G Chester-Master Esq (alt) **R** H J MORRIS
SIDESTRAND (St Michael) Overstrand, Northrepps,
  Sidestrand & Trimingham *Nor*
SIDFORD (St Peter) Sidmouth, Woolbrook, Salcombe Regis,
  Sidbury etc *Ex*
SIDLESHAM (St Mary the Virgin) *Chich 3* **P** *Bp*
  P-in-c A K JENKINS
SIDLEY (All Saints) *Chich 14* **P** *R Bexhill*
  V N A TAYLOR, **NSM** S M TAYLOR
SIDLOW BRIDGE (Emmanuel) *S'wark 25* **P** *DBP*
  R W G CAMPEN
SIDMOUTH (All Saints) *Ex 7* **P** *CPAS*
  P-in-c J V MAPSON
SIDMOUTH (St Nicholas w St Giles), Woolbrook, Salcombe
  Regis, Sidbury w Sidford *Ex 7* **P** *Patr Bd*
  TV I C MORTER, J S LEE, **P-in-c** D H JAMES,
  NSM S W WILLINK
SIGGLESTHORNE (St Lawrence) and Rise w Nunkeeling and
  Bewholme *York 12* **P** *Prime Min and Ld Chan (alt)*
  R A MAKEL
SILCHESTER (St Mary) *Win 4* **P** *Duke of Wellington*
  R D C McKEEMAN
SILCHESTER COMMON (Mission Church) Silchester *Win*
SILEBY (St Mary), Cossington and Seagrave *Leic 6*
  P *Patr Bd* **TV** A S COSTERTON, **P-in-c** P A E SPRINGATE
SILK WILLOUGHBY (St Denis) *Linc 22* **P** *Sir Lyonel*
  Tollemache, Bt **P-in-c** D J MUSSON
SILKSTONE (All Saints) Hoylandswaine and Silkstone w
  Stainborough *Wakef*
SILKSTONE COMMON (Mission Room) as above
SILKSWORTH (St Matthew) *Dur 9* **P** *Bp*
  V S RYCROFT, **C** P L WALKER
SILLOTH (Christ Church) w Silloth St Paul *Carl 7*
  P *Simeon's Trustees (2 turns), V Holme Cultram St Mary*
  (1 turn) **V** M A HESLOP
SILSDEN (St James) *Bradf 8* **P** *Bp, Adn Craven, and*
  Trustees (jt) **V** J COOPER
SILSOE (St James), Pulloxhill and Flitton *St Alb 15* **P** *Ball*
  Coll Ox and Bp (alt) **V** B L NIXON
SILTON (St Nicholas) *Sarum 6* **P** *DBP* **R** *Vacant*
SILTON, NETHER (All Saints) Leake w Over and Nether
  Silton and Kepwick *York*
SILTON, OVER (St Mary) as above
SILVER END (St Francis) Rivenhall *Chelmsf*
SILVERDALE (St John) *Blackb 15* **P** *V Warton*
  V R MASHEDER
SILVERDALE (St Luke) and Alsagers Bank *Lich 14* **P** *Bp*
  and T H G Howard-Sneyd Esq (jt) **P-in-c** P G HOUGH,
  C P M JELF, **NSM** K R STABLES
SILVERHILL (St Matthew) *Chich 17* **P** *Simeon's Trustees*
  R R M COMBES
SILVERSTONE (St Michael) and Abthorpe w Slapton *Pet 5*
  P *The Crown, Leeson's Trustees, and T L Langton-*
  Lockton Esq (by turn) **P-in-c** B M SMITH

SILVERTON (St Mary), Butterleigh, Bickleigh and Cadeleigh
  Ex 8 **P** *Bp and Sir R V Carew* **R** *Vacant* Exeter (01392)
  860350
SILVINGTON (St Michael) Stottesdon w Farlow, Cleeton
  and Silvington *Heref*
SIMONBURN (St Mungo) Humshaugh w Simonburn and
  Wark *Newc*
SIMONSTONE (St Peter) Padiham *Blackb*
SIMPSON (St Thomas) Woughton *Ox*
SINFIN (St Stephen) *Derby 10* **P** *CPAS* **V** T F PRICE
SINFIN MOOR (not known) *Derby 10* **P** *Bp* **V** *Vacant*
  Derby (01332) 760016
SINGLETON (St Anne) w Weeton (St Michael) *Blackb 13*
  P *R Dumbreck and V Kirkham (jt)* **V** D WILLIAMS
SINGLETON (St Mary the Virgin) *Chich 13* **P** *Bp*
  R P M JENKINS
SINNINGTON (All Saints) *York 21* **P** *Simeon's Trustees*
  V *Vacant* Kirkbymoorside (01751) 31422
SISLAND (St Mary) Loddon, Sisland w Hales and
  Heckingham *Nor*
SISSINGHURST (Holy Trinity) w Frittenden *Cant 11*
  P *CPAS* **V** A E NORRIS
SITHNEY (St Sithney) Porthleven w Sithney *Truro*
SITTINGBOURNE (Holy Trinity) w Bobbing *Cant 14*
  P *Abp* **V** R A LOVE, **NSM** B D FOULGER,
  E J WILLIAMS
SITTINGBOURNE (St Mary) *Cant 14* **P** *Abp*
  P-in-c N M HALL (nee WANSTALL), **NSM** D W WEBB
SITTINGBOURNE (St Michael) *Cant 14* **P** *Abp*
  P-in-c C R MURRIE, **NSM** P R BECKINSALE
SIX HILLS (Mission) Old Dalby and Nether Broughton *Leic*
SIX MILE BOTTOM (St George) Lt Wilbraham *Ely*
SIX PILGRIMS, The *B & W 3* **P** *Ch Soc Trust, D&C, DBF,*
  and Bp (by turn) **R** *Vacant* Wheathill (0196324) 230
SIX SAINTS circa Holt: Bringhurst, Great Easton, Medbourne
  cum Holt, Stockerston and Blaston *Leic 4* **P** *D&C Pet and*
  Adn Leic (2 turns), St Jo Coll Cam (1 turn) **R** S R LONG
SIXHILLS (All Saints) Barkwith Gp *Linc*
SKEEBY (St Agatha's District Church) Easby w Brompton
  on Swale and Bolton on Swale *Ripon*
SKEFFINGTON (St Thomas a Beckett) Billesdon and
  Skeffington *Leic*
SKEFFLING (St Helen) Easington w Skeffling, Kilnsea and
  Holmpton *York*
SKEGBY (St Andrew) *S'well 4* **P** *Ld Chan*
  P-in-c J J FLETCHER, **NSM** L A CHURCH
SKEGNESS (St Clement) (St Matthew) and Winthorpe
  Linc 8 **P** *Earl of Scarbrough and Bp (alt)*
  P-in-c G J WICKSTEAD, **C** S C WITCOMBE, S A MOOR
SKELBROOKE (St Michael and All Angels) Burghwallis w
  Skelbrooke *Sheff*
SKELLINGTHORPE (St Lawrence) w Doddington *Linc 18*
  P *MMCET* **R** R G BILLINGHURST
SKELLOW (St Michael and All Angels) Owston *Sheff*
SKELMANTHORPE (St Aidan) *Wakef 6* **P** *Bp*
  P-in-c P D REYNOLDS
SKELMERSDALE (Church at the Centre) *Liv 11* **P** *Bp*
  V P A BARNETT
SKELMERSDALE (St Paul) *Liv 11* **P** *V Ormskirk*
  V G E GREENWOOD, **C** C J BROWN
SKELSMERGH (St John the Baptist) w Selside and
  Longsleddale *Carl 9* **P** *V Kendal H Trin and DBP (alt)*
  R R D J DEW
SKELTON (All Saints) w Upleatham *York 17* **P** *Abp*
  R T N EVANS
SKELTON (St Giles) w Shipton and Newton on Ouse *York 5*
  P *Abp* **P-in-c** M HARRISON
SKELTON (St Michael) and Hutton-in-the-Forest w Ivegill
  Carl 4 **P** *Bp, D&C, and CCC Ox (jt)* **R** B DAWSON
SKELTON-CUM-NEWBY (St Helen's Old Church) Kirby-
  on-the-Moor, Cundall w Norton-le-Clay etc *Ripon*
SKENDLEBY (St Peter and St Paul) Partney *Linc*
SKERNE (St Leonard) Hutton Cranswick w Skerne, Watton
  and Beswick *York*
SKERTON (St Chad) *Blackb 12* **P** *Bp* **V** T A G BILL,
  NSM F M EDWARDS
SKERTON (St Luke) *Blackb 12* **P** *Trustees* **V** A J FULLER
SKEYTON (All Saints) Felmingham, Skeyton, Colby,
  Banningham etc *Nor*
SKIDBY (St Michael) Rowley w Skidby *York*
SKILGATE (St John the Baptist) Brompton Regis w Upton
  and Skilgate *B & W*
SKILLINGTON (St James) Colsterworth Gp *Linc*
SKIPSEA (All Saints) w Ulrome and Barmston w Fraisthorpe
  York 10 **P** *Abp, Hon Susan Cunliffe-Lister and Exors*
  Dr W Kane (jt) **R** L TRENDER

SKIPTON (Christ Church) *Bradf 7* **P** *R Skipton H Trin*
V J E PEERS
SKIPTON (Holy Trinity) *Bradf 7* **P** *Ch Ch Ox*
R A P BOTWRIGHT, **C** R M WIGRAM
SKIPTON ON SWALE (St John) Baldersby w Dalton,
Dishforth etc *York*
SKIPWITH (St Helen) Bubwith w Skipwith *York*
SKIRBECK (Holy Trinity) *Linc 20* **P** *Trustees*
V B C OSBORNE, **C** S M SAMUELS, **NSM** J C COLE
SKIRBECK (St Nicholas) *Linc 20* **P** *DBP* **R** A F WAKELIN
SKIRBECK QUARTER (St Thomas) *Linc 20* **P** *DBP*
NSM M A BARSLEY
SKIRLAUGH (St Augustine) w Long Riston *York 12*
P *Abp* **V** D W PERRY
SKIRPENBECK (St Mary) Stamford Bridge Gp of Par *York*
**SKIRWITH (St John the Evangelist), Ousby and Melmerby w
Kirkland** *Carl 4* **P** *DBP and D&C (jt)*
P-in-c M H BURDEN
SLAD (Holy Trinity) Stroud and Uplands w Slad *Glouc*
SLADE GREEN (St Augustine) *Roch 14* **P** *Bp* **V** *Vacant*
Dartford (01322) 333970
SLAIDBURN (St Andrew) *Bradf 5* **P** *Ch Soc Trust*
P-in-c M R RUSSELL-SMITH
SLAITHWAITE (St James) w East Scammonden *Wakef 5*
P *V Huddersfield* **V** C R TOWNSEND
SLALEY (St Mary the Virgin) Healey and Slaley *Newc*
SLAPTON (Holy Cross) Ivinghoe w Pitstone and Slapton *Ox*
SLAPTON (St Botolph) Silverstone and Abthorpe w Slapton
Pet
SLAPTON (St James the Great) E Allington, Slapton and
Strete *Ex*
SLAUGHAM (St Mary) *Chich 6* **P** *M R Warren Esq*
R J E POSTILL, **NSM** J A WILSON
**SLAUGHTER, UPPER (St Peter) and LOWER (St Mary) w
Eyford and Naunton** *Glouc 15* **P** *F E B Witts Esq and Bp
(alt)* **P-in-c** J W S FIELDGATE
SLAUGHTERFORD (St Nicholas) Biddestone w
Slaughterford *Bris*
SLAWSTON (All Saints) Hallaton w Horninghold, Allexton,
Tugby etc *Leic*
SLEAFORD (St Denys) New Sleaford *Linc*
SLEAFORD, NEW (St Denys) *Linc 22* **P** *Bp*
V J S THOROLD, **Hon C** B W LEVICK,
NSM P G HARDING
**SLEDMERE (St Mary) and Cowlam w Fridaythorpe, Fimber
and Thixendale** *York 11* **P** *Abp and Sir T C M Sykes (jt)*
V D PICK
SLEEKBURN (St John) *Newc 1* **P** *D&C*
P-in-c P DAWSON
SLEIGHTS (St John) Eskdaleside w Ugglebarnby and
Sneaton *York*
SLIMBRIDGE (St John the Evangelist) *Glouc 2* **P** *Magd
Coll Ox* **R** E C CHARLESWORTH
SLINDON (St Chad) Eccleshall *Lich*
SLINDON (St Mary), Eartham and Madehurst *Chich 1*
P *Bp, D&C, and Mrs J Izard (jt)* **P-in-c** N M S WATERS,
NSM H J M COSSAR
SLINFOLD (St Peter) Itchingfield w Slinfold *Chich*
SLINGSBY (All Saints) Street TM *York*
SLIPTON (St John the Baptist) Lowick w Sudborough and
Slipton *Pet*
SLITTING MILL (St John the Baptist) Rugeley *Lich*
SLOANE STREET (Holy Trinity) Upper Chelsea H Trin w
St Jude *Lon*
SLOLEY (St Bartholomew) Worstead, Westwick, Sloley,
Swanton Abbot etc *Nor*
SLOUGH (St Paul) (Christ Church) *Ox 23* **P** *Trustees*
V G T KAYE, **NSM** A R CULLINGWORTH
SLOUGH, WEST *Ox 23* **P** *Patr Bd* **TV** F A WRIGHT,
P C FAULKNER, G A FINLAYSON, C J DYER
SLYNE (St Luke) w Hest *Blackb 15* **P** *Bp* **V** J B SELVEY
SMALL HEATH (St Aidan) (St Gregory) (St Oswald)
Birm 7 **P** *Patr Bd* **V** G A WILKINSON, **C** D K CHANDA
SMALLBRIDGE (St John the Baptist) and Wardle *Man 20*
P *Bp* **P-in-c** A J HOWELL
**SMALLBURGH (St Peter) w Dilham w Honing and
Crostwight** *Nor 12* **P** *Bp, T R Cubitt Esq, and
J C Wickman Esq (jt)* **P-in-c** B M LLEWELLYN
SMALLEY (St John the Baptist) *Derby 12* **P** *Bp*
P-in-c M A ROYLE
SMALLFIELD (Church Room) Burstow *S'wark*
SMALLHYTHE (St John the Baptist) Tenterden St Mildred
w Smallhythe *Cant*
SMALLTHORNE (St Saviour) *Lich 16* **P** *R Norton in the
Moors* **V** R J S GRIGSON
SMALLWOOD (St John the Baptist) Astbury and
Smallwood *Ches*

SMANNELL (Christ Church) w Enham Alamein *Win 3*
P *Bp* **R** D E C JARDINE
SMARDEN (St Michael) Biddenden and Smarden *Cant*
SMAWTHORPE St Michael *Wakef 11* **P** *Bp*
V E I CHETWYND
**SMEATON, GREAT (St Eloy) w Appleton Wiske and Birkby
and Danby Wiske w Hutton Bonville** *Ripon 2* **P** *MMCET
(2 turns), Abp York (1 turn)* **R** F SNOW
SMEETH (St Mary) Brabourne w Smeeth *Cant*
SMEETON WESTERBY (Christ Church) Kibworth and
Smeeton Westerby and Saddington *Leic*
SMETHCOTT (St Michael) Dorrington w Leebotwood,
Longnor, Stapleton etc *Heref*
SMETHWICK (Old Church) *Birm 5* **P** *Dorothy Parkes
Trustees* **V** M C W GORICK
**SMETHWICK (Resurrection) (St Alban) (St Stephen and St
Michael)** *Birm 5* **P** *Bp* **V** D RAYNER
SMETHWICK (St Matthew w St Chad) *Birm 5* **P** *Bp and
V Smethwick (alt)* **V** P E NICHOLSON
SMISBY (St James) Ticknall, Smisby and Stanton by Bridge
Derby
SMITHILLS HALL (Chapel) Halliwell St Pet *Man*
SMORRALL LANE (St Andrew) Bedworth *Cov*
SNAILBEACH (St Luke) Minsterley *Heref*
SNAILWELL (St Peter) *Ely 3* **P** *Mrs A Crawley*
P-in-c D J KIGHTLEY
SNAINTON (St Stephen) Brompton-by-Sawdon w Snainton,
Ebberston etc *York*
SNAITH (St Laurence Priory) Gt Snaith *Sheff*
**SNAITH, GREAT (Holy Trinity) (St John the Baptist)
(St Paul)** *Sheff 11* **P** *Bp* **TR** C ROBERTS,
TV J F HARDY
SNAPE (St John the Baptist) Sternfield w Benhall and Snape
St E
SNAPE CASTLE (Chapel of St Mary) W Tanfield and Well
w Snape and N Stainley *Ripon*
SNARESTONE (St Bartholomew) The Appleby Gp *Leic*
SNARFORD (St Lawrence) Wickenby Gp *Linc*
SNARGATE (St Dunstan) Appledore w Brookland,
Fairfield, Brenzett etc *Cant*
SNEAD (St Mary the Virgin) Wentnor w Ratlinghope,
Myndtown, Norbury etc *Heref*
SNEATON (St Hilda) Eskdaleside w Ugglebarnby and
Sneaton *York*
SNEINTON (St Christopher) w St Philip *S'well 12* **P** *CPAS
and Trustees (alt)* **V** I M BLAKE
SNEINTON (St Cyprian) *S'well 12* **P** *Bp* **V** W J GULL
SNEINTON (St Matthias) *S'well 12* **P** *Bp*
P-in-c R F B SMITH
SNEINTON (St Stephen) (St Alban) *S'well 12* **P** *SMF and
Bp (alt)* **V** D A HAILES
SNELLAND (All Saints) Wickenby Gp *Linc*
SNELSTON (St Peter) Norbury w Snelston *Derby*
SNETTISHAM (St Mary) w Ingoldisthorpe and Fring
Nor 17 **P** *Bp, CPAS, and D&C (jt)* **R** J D GRUNDY,
NSM J M T M GRUNDY
SNEYD (Holy Trinity) *Lich 16* **P** *Bp* **V** B L WILLIAMS
SNEYD GREEN (St Andrew) *Lich 16* **P** *Bp*
V B THOMPSON
SNIBSTON (St James) Hugglescote w Donington, Ellistown
and Snibston *Leic*
SNITTERBY (St Nicholas) Bishop Norton, Wadingham and
Snitterby *Linc*
SNITTERFIELD (St James the Great) w Bearley *Cov 7*
P *Bp and V Wootton Wawen* **V** R N TREW
SNODLAND (All Saints) (Christ Church) *Roch 1* **P** *Bp and
CPAS (jt)* **R** J E TIPP
**SNORING, GREAT (St Mary) w LITTLE (St Andrew) w
Kettlestone and Pensthorpe** *Nor 16* **P** *DBP (1 turn), St Jo
Coll Cam (2 turns)* **R** *Vacant* Thursford (01328) 878213
SNOWDEN HILL Chapel Farm (not known) Penistone and
Thurlstone *Wakef*
SNOWSHILL (St Barnabas) Childswyckham w Aston
Somerville, Buckland etc *Glouc*
SOBERTON (St Peter) w Newtown *Portsm 1* **P** *Bp*
V P J GARRATT
SOCKBURN (All Saints) Dinsdale w Sockburn *Dur*
SODBURY, LITTLE (St Adeline) Horton and Lt Sodbury
Glouc
SODBURY, OLD (St John the Baptist) Chipping Sodbury
and Old Sodbury *Glouc*
SOHAM (St Andrew) *Ely 3* **P** *Pemb Coll Cam*
V M G F SHEARS
SOHO (St Anne) (St Thomas) (St Peter) *Lon 3*
P *R Westmr St Jas* **P-in-c** F C STEVENS,
NSM S J MANLEY-COOPER
**SOLIHULL (Catherine de Barnes) (St Alphege) (St Helen) (St
Michael)** *Birm 13* **P** *Patr Bd* **TR** P E HAWKINS,

TV A S MONTGOMERIE, A T BULLOCK,
G L HODKINSON, **C** F J SMITH, **NSM** G M PEARSON
SOLLARS HOPE (St Michael) How Caple w Sollarshope,
Sellack etc *Heref*
SOMBORNE w Ashley *Win 11* **P** *Bp* **V** M J M NORTON
SOMERBY (All Saints) Burrough Hill Pars *Leic*
SOMERBY (St Margaret) N Wolds Gp *Linc*
SOMERBY, OLD (St Mary Magdalene) *Linc 14* **P** *Baroness
Willoughby de Eresby* **R** *Vacant*
SOMERCOTES and Grainthorpe w Conisholme *Linc 12*
P *Duchy of Lanc (2 turns), Magd Coll Cam and Bp (1 turn)*
R *Vacant* North Somercotes (0150785) 559
SOMERCOTES (St Thomas) *Derby 1* **P** *Bp*
P-in-c J B A COPE
SOMERCOTES, NORTH (St Mary) Somercotes and
Grainthorpe w Conisholme *Linc*
SOMERFORD (All Saints) Astbury and Smallwood *Ches*
SOMERFORD (St Mary) Christchurch *Win*
**SOMERFORD, GREAT (St Peter and St Paul), Little
Somerford, Seagry and Corston w Rodbourne** *Bris 12* **P** *Bp,
MMCET, and Ex Coll Ox (jt) (3 turns), Ld Chan
(2 turns)* **R** J E G OSWALD
SOMERFORD, LITTLE (St John the Baptist) Gt
Somerford, Lt Somerford, Seagry, Corston etc *Bris*
SOMERFORD KEYNES (All Saints) Kemble, Poole
Keynes, Somerford Keynes etc *Glouc*
**SOMERLEYTON (St Mary), Ashby, Fritton, Herringfleet,
Blundeston and Lound** *Nor 9* **P** *Lord Somerleyton and SMF
(jt)* **R** J B V RIVIERE
SOMERS TOWN (St Mary the Virgin) *Lon 17*
P *D&C St Paul's* **V** P DYSON, **C** T S P PHELAN
SOMERSAL HERBERT (St Peter) Sudbury and Somersal
Herbert *Derby*
SOMERSBY (St Margaret) S Ormsby Gp *Linc*
SOMERSHAM (St John the Baptist) w Pidley and Oldhurst
Ely 11 **P** *Bp* **R** D J EVANS
SOMERSHAM (St Mary) w Flowton and Offton w Willisham
St E 1 **P** *Bp and MMCET (jt)* **P-in-c** R J DEDMAN
SOMERTON (St James) The Heyfords w Rousham and
Somerton *Ox*
SOMERTON (St Margaret) Glem Valley United Benefice
St E
**SOMERTON (St Michael and All Angels) w Compton Dundon,
the Charltons and Kingsdon** *B & W 6* **P** *Bp Lon (1 turn), Bp
(2 turns), and DBP (1 turn)* **R** C A HADLEY,
C R O DAVIES
SOMERTON, WEST (St Mary) Winterton w E and W
Somerton and Horsey *Nor*
SOMPTING (St Mary the Virgin) (St Peter) *Chich 5*
P *OStJ* **V** J W RICHARDSON
SONNING (St Andrew) (St Patrick) *Ox 16* **P** *Bp*
V C H MORGAN, **Hon C** A C E SANDERS
SONNING COMMON (Christ the King) Kidmore End *Ox*
SOOKHOLME (St Augustine) Warsop *S'well*
SOOTHILL (St Luke) Hanging Heaton *Wakef*
SOPLEY (St Michael and All Angels) Burton and Sopley *Win*
SOPWORTH (St Mary the Virgin) Boxwell, Leighterton,
Didmarton, Oldbury etc *Glouc*
SOTHERTON (St Andrew) Uggeshall w Sotherton,
Wangford and Henham *St E*
SOTTERLEY (St Margaret) Hundred River *St E*
SOTWELL (St James) Brightwell w Sotwell *Ox*
SOUDLEY (St Michael) Cinderford St Jo *Glouc*
SOULBURY (All Saints) Stewkley w Soulbury and Drayton
Parslow *Ox*
SOULBY (St Luke) Kirkby Stephen w Mallerstang etc *Carl*
SOULDERN (Annunciation of the Blessed Virgin
Mary) Fritwell w Souldern and Ardley w Fewcott *Ox*
SOULDROP (All Saints) Sharnbrook and Knotting w
Souldrop *St Alb*
SOUNDWELL (St Stephen) *Bris 2* **P** *Bp*
V W R HARRISON
SOURTON (St Thomas of Canterbury) Okehampton w
Inwardleigh, Bratton Clovelly etc *Ex*
SOUTH: *see also under substantive place names*
SOUTH BANK (St John) *York 19* **P** *Abp* **V** M AISBITT
SOUTH CAVE (All Saints) and Ellerker w Broomfleet
York 14 **P** *CPAS and D&C Dur (jt)* **V** D C BAILEY,
C H A EDGERTON
SOUTH COVE (St Lawrence) Wrentham w Benacre,
Covehithe, Frostenden etc *St E*
SOUTH HILL (St Sampson) w Callington *Truro 11* **P** PCC
R R OAKES, **NSM** D N HATREY
SOUTH MOOR (St George) *Dur 8* **P** *Bp* **V** *Vacant* Stanley
(01207) 232564
SOUTH POOL (St Nicholas and St Cyriac) Charleton w
Buckland Tout Saints etc *Ex*
SOUTH SHIELDS (All Saints) *Dur 7* **P** *Patr Bd*
TR J D MILLER, **TV** R A SEARLE, **C** J R FOX

SOUTH SHIELDS (St Aidan) (St Stephen) *Dur 7* **P** *Bp and
D&C* **P-in-c** M T PEACH
SOUTH SHIELDS (St Hilda) w St Thomas *Dur 7* **P** *D&C*
V M T PEACH
SOUTH SHIELDS (St Oswin) *Dur 7* **P** *The Crown*
V G F FINN
SOUTH SHIELDS (St Simon) *Dur 7* **P** *The Crown*
V R F TOBIN
SOUTH SHORE (Holy Trinity) *Blackb 9* **P** J C Hilton Esq
V B DUNN, **C** P W ALLSOP, **NSM** D A BELL
SOUTH SHORE (St Peter) *Blackb 9* **P** *Bp*
P-in-c J BARKER
SOUTHACRE (St George) Castle Acre w Newton, Rougham
and Southacre *Nor*
SOUTHACRE (St George) as above
SOUTHALL (Christ the Redeemer) *Lon 22* **P** *Bp*
P-in-c N J ORCHARD
SOUTHALL (Emmanuel) Conventional District *Lon 22*
C-in-c L B SMILLIE
SOUTHALL (Holy Trinity) *Lon 22* **P** *Ch Patr Trust*
P-in-c D I BARNES
SOUTHALL (St George) *Lon 22* **P** *D&C St Paul's*
P-in-c D L E BRONNERT
SOUTHALL GREEN (St John) *Lon 22* **P** *Ch Patr Trust*
V D L E BRONNERT, **C** K B BEST, D J C BOOKLESS
SOUTHAM (Ascension) Bishop's Cleeve *Glouc*
SOUTHAM (St James) *Cov 10* **P** *The Crown* **R** *Vacant*
Southam (01926) 812413
SOUTHAMPTON City Centre (St Mary) (St Michael)
Win 12 **P** *Bp* **TR** R R WHEELER, **TV** S A ROBERTS,
J E PAXTON, V J ROCKALL, S W BARTON
SOUTHAMPTON Maybush (St Peter) *Win 12* **P** *Bp*
V N BOAKES, **C** E J WETHERELL, B L COX
SOUTHAMPTON (St Alban) Swaythling *Win*
SOUTHAMPTON (St Barnabas) *Win 12* **P** *Bp* **V** B J FRY
SOUTHAMPTON (St Mark) *Win 12* **P** *Ch Patr Trust*
V P D COOPER
SOUTHAMPTON (St Mary Extra) *Win 12* **P** *Bp*
V B P JAMES
SOUTHAMPTON Thornhill (St Christopher) *Win 12* **P** *Bp*
V G P ANNAS
SOUTHAMPTON Warren Avenue (St Jude) *Win 12* **P** *Bp*
V T MASLEN
SOUTHAMPTON Winkle Street (St Julian) Southn (City
Cen) *Win*
SOUTHBERGH (St Andrew) Reymerston w Cranworth,
Letton, Southburgh etc *Nor*
SOUTHBOROUGH (St Peter) (Christ Church) (St Matthew)
Roch 11 **P** CPAS **V** J C PORTHOUSE, **C** C B WICKS,
J A CASTLE
SOUTHBOROUGH (St Thomas) *Roch 11* **P** *Bp*
V R M SMITH
SOUTHBOURNE (All Saints) Pokesdown All SS *Win*
SOUTHBOURNE (St Christopher) *Win 7* **P** *Bp*
V J G BARKER
SOUTHBOURNE (St John the Evangelist) w West Thorney
Chich 13 **P** *Bp* **V** R W POIL, **NSM** M BAGGOTT
SOUTHBOURNE (St Katharine) (St Nicholas) *Win 7* **P** *Bp*
V *Vacant* Bournemouth (01202) 423986
SOUTHBROOM (St James) *Sarum 19* **P** *D&C*
V M A WARD, **C** R F TOOGOOD, **Hon C** T V F PAPE
SOUTHCHURCH (Christ Church) *Chelmsf 13* **P** *Bp*
V M J HARRIS
SOUTHCHURCH (Holy Trinity) *Chelmsf 13* **P** *Abp*
R M A BALLARD, **C** V G CATO (formerly LEGGETT)
SOUTHCOATES (St Aidan) Kingston upon Hull
Southcoates St Aid *York*
SOUTHCOURT (Good Shepherd) Walton H Trin *Ox*
SOUTHDENE (St Martin) Kirkby *Liv*
SOUTHEA (Emmanuel) w Murrow and Parson Drove *Ely 19*
P *Bp* **V** R J SEAMAN
SOUTHEASE (St Peter) Telscombe w Piddinghoe and
Southease *Chich*
**SOUTHEND (St John the Baptist) (St Mark) (All Saints) (St
Alban)** *Chelmsf 13* **P** *Bp and Patr Bd*
TR G R BENNETT, **TV** M G BLYTH
SOUTHEND (St Peter) Bradfield and Stanford Dingley *Ox*
SOUTHEND-ON-SEA (St Saviour) Westcliff *Chelmsf 13*
P *Bp, Adn Southend, and Churchwardens (jt)*
V J EWINGTON
SOUTHERY (St Mary) *Ely 16* **P** *Guild of All So*
R A G COCHRANE
SOUTHFIELDS (St Barnabas) *S'wark 18* **P** *Bp*
V D E EMMOTT
SOUTHFLEET (St Nicholas) *Roch 4* **P** CPAS
R C D GOBLE, **NSM** J C STONE
SOUTHGATE (Christ Church) *Lon 18*
P V Edmonton All SS **V** D M HOYLE, **C** R E M DOWLER

SOUTHGATE Local Ecumenical Project *St E 13*
  Min F SCAMMELL
SOUTHGATE (Shared Church) Grange *St Andr Ches*
SOUTHGATE (St Andrew) *Lon 18* **P** *Bp* **V** P STAYLOR,
  C E G GREER
SOUTHGATE (St Mary) *Chich 7* **P** *Patr Bd*
  TR A F HAWKER, **TV** M D S GREIG, L P R MEERING,
  J R J BURLEY, **C** R J SLIPPER
SOUTHGATE, NEW (St Paul) *Lon 14*
  P *V Southgate Ch Ch* **V** R M TAYLOR
SOUTHILL (All Saints) *St Alb 22* **P** *S C Whitbread Esq*
  P-in-c J K DIXON
SOUTHLAKE (St James's Church Centre) Woodley *Ox*
SOUTHLEIGH (St Lawrence) Colyton, Southleigh, Offwell,
  Widworthy etc *Ex*
SOUTHMEAD (St Stephen) *Bris 8* **P** *Bp* **V** R T BARKER,
  C T J DAPLYN, **NSM** D V EVANS (formerly SMITH)
SOUTHMINSTER (St Leonard) *Chelmsf 11* **P** *Govs*
  Charterhouse **V** J E BATEMAN
SOUTHOE (St Leonard) *Ely 12* **P** *Mert Coll Ox*
  R P G LEWIS
SOUTHOVER (St John the Baptist) *Chich 18* **P** *CPAS*
  R P J J MARKBY, **NSM** S L PANTER MARSHALL
SOUTHPORT (All Saints) (All Souls) *Liv 9* **P** *Trustees*
  V J E BASSETT, **NSM** D H MARSTON
SOUTHPORT (Christ Church) *Liv 9* **P** *Trustees*
  V S T REID, **C** D G BANNOCKS
SOUTHPORT (Emmanuel) *Liv 9* **P** *PCC* **V** M D WHYTE,
  C P C GREEN
SOUTHPORT (Holy Trinity) *Liv 9* **P** *Trustees*
  P-in-c R G GARNER
SOUTHPORT (St Luke) *Liv 9* **P** *V Southport H Trin*
  P-in-c I R SHACKLETON
SOUTHPORT (St Philip) (St Paul) *Liv 9* **P** *V Southport*
  Ch Ch and Trustees (jt) **V** J M BURGESS,
  C C G HOUGHTON
SOUTHPORT (St Simon and St Jude) *Liv 9* **P** *Trustees*
  V M J DUERDEN
SOUTHREPPS (St James) Trunch *Nor*
SOUTHREY (St John the Divine) Bardney *Linc*
SOUTHROP (St Peter) Coln St Aldwyns, Hatherop,
  Quenington etc *Glouc*
SOUTHSEA (Holy Spirit) *Portsm 6* **P** *Bp* **C** T L PESKETT
SOUTHSEA (St Jude) *Portsm 6* **P** *Trustees*
  V J V BYRNE, **C** S J HANCE, C A BELL, **NSM** G B HILL
SOUTHSEA (St Luke) Portsea St Luke *Portsm*
SOUTHSEA (St Peter) *Portsm 6* **P** *Bp* **V** *Vacant*
  Portsmouth (01705) 822786
SOUTHSEA (St Simon) *Portsm 6* **P** *Ch Patr Trust*
  V E A PRATT, **Hon C** P A LEWIS
SOUTHTOWN (St Mary) Gt Yarmouth *Nor*
SOUTHWARK (Christ Church) *S'wark 8* **P** *Marshall's*
  Charity **R** P B CHALLEN, **C** C E LATHAM,
  NSM A HURST
SOUTHWARK (Holy Trinity w St Matthew) *S'wark 8*
  P *Bp* **NSM** M BEATTIE
SOUTHWARK (St George the Martyr) (St Alphege) (St Jude)
  S'wark 8 **P** *Lon Corp (1 turn)*, *Ld Chan (4 turns)*,
  Walsingham Coll Trust Assn (1 turn) **R** A S LUCAS,
  C A D WEST
SOUTHWARK (St Hugh) Bermondsey St Hugh CD *S'wark*
SOUTHWATER (Holy Innocents) *Chich 8* **P** *V Horsham*
  V P MESSENGER
SOUTHWAY (Holy Spirit) *Ex 23* **P** *Ld Chan*
  V D M WOOD, **C** D J HOSKIN, **NSM** M J FAIRALL
SOUTHWELL (Holy Trinity) *S'well 15* **P** *CPAS*
  P-in-c M S TANNER
SOUTHWELL (St Andrew) Portland All SS w St Pet *Sarum*
SOUTHWICK (Holy Trinity) *Dur 9* **P** *D&C*
  P-in-c R DIXON
SOUTHWICK (St Columba) *Dur 9* **P** *Bp* **P-in-c** J R TROOP
SOUTHWICK (St James) w Boarhunt *Portsm 1*
  P-in-c H S GRIFFITHS
SOUTHWICK (St Mary the Virgin) Benefield and Southwick
  w Glapthorn *Pet*
SOUTHWICK (St Michael and All Angels) *Chich 4*
  P *Ld Chan* **R** C EVERETT-ALLEN, **C** J A LUSTED,
  Hon C H F McNEIGHT
SOUTHWICK (St Peter) *Chich 4* **P** *Bp* **P-in-c** G C CAREY
SOUTHWICK (St Thomas) N Bradley, Southwick and
  Heywood *Sarum*
SOUTHWOLD (St Edmund King and Martyr) *St E 15*
  P *Simeon's Trustees* **V** P E BUSTIN, **NSM** T HANDLEY
  MACMATH
SOUTHWOOD (Mission Church) Evercreech w Chesterblade
  and Milton Clevedon *B & W*
SOWERBY (St Mary) (St Peter) *Wakef 4* **P** *DBP*
  V J W MUIR

SOWERBY (St Oswald) *York 20* **P** *Abp* **V** J H DAVIS
SOWERBY BRIDGE (Christ Church) w Norland *Wakef 4*
  P *V Halifax* **V** P J JEFFERY
SOWTON (St Michael and All Angels) Aylesbeare,
  Rockbeare, Farringdon etc *Ex*
SPALDING (St John the Baptist) w Deeping St Nicholas
  Linc 17 **P** *Bp* **V** K A ALMOND
SPALDING (St Mary and St Nicholas) *Linc 17* **P** *Feoffees*
  V P G F NORWOOD, **C** H P JANSMA, A I McCORMICK
SPALDING (St Paul) *Linc 17* **P** *Bp and V Spalding (jt)*
  P-in-c D C MAYLOR
SPALDWICK (St James) w Barham and Woolley *Ely 10*
  P *Bp* **P-in-c** J ALFORD
SPARHAM (St Mary) Lyng, Sparham, Elsing and Bylaugh
  Nor
SPARKBROOK (Christ Church) *Birm 7* **P** *Aston Trustees*
  V S A HOLLOWAY
SPARKBROOK (Emmanuel) Sparkhill w Greet and
  Sparkbrook *Birm*
SPARKBROOK (St Agatha) w Balsall Heath St Barnabas
  Birm 7 **P** *Bp* **V** J A HERVE
SPARKFORD (St Mary Magdalene) Queen Camel w W
  Camel, Corton Denham etc *B & W*
SPARKHILL (St John the Evangelist) (St Bede and
  Emmanuel) w Greet St Bede and Sparkbrook *Birm 7*
  P *Dioc Trustees and Aston Trustees (alt)* **V** J A SELF,
  C T D HILL-BROWN
SPARKWELL (All Saints) *Ex 21* **P** *D&C Windsor*
  V F G DENMAN
SPARSHOLT (Holy Cross) Ridgeway *Ox*
SPARSHOLT (St Stephen) Crawley and Littleton and
  Sparsholt w Lainston *Win*
SPAXTON (St Margaret) w Goathurst, Enmore and Charlynch
  B & W 14 **P** *Bp, MMCET and Ch Trust Fund Trust (jt)*
  R R R EARNSHAW
SPEEN (St Mary the Virgin) Newbury *Ox*
SPEETON (St Leonard) Reighton w Speeton *York*
SPEKE (St Aidan) (All Saints) *Liv 4* **P** *Bp*
  TR M E PLUNKETT, **TV** J P NICHOLSON,
  J M WATERMAN
SPELDHURST (St Mary the Virgin) w Groombridge and
  Ashurst *Roch 11* **P** *DBP* **R** B C H FORTNUM,
  Hon C B E E MARSHALL
SPELSBURY (All Saints) Chadlington and Spelsbury, Ascott
  under Wychwood *Ox*
SPENCERS WOOD (St Michael and All Angels) Beech Hill,
  Grazeley and Spencers Wood *Ox*
SPENNITHORNE (St Michael) w Finghall and Hauxwell
  Ripon 4 **P** *R J Dalton Esq and M C A Wyvill Esq (alt)*
  R D W TORDOFF, **NSM** M G TORDOFF (nee PARKER)
SPENNYMOOR (St Paul) Whitworth w Spennymoor *Dur*
SPERNALL, Morton Bagot and Oldberrow *Cov 7* **P** *Mrs*
  J M Pinney and Bp (alt) **P-in-c** F J BALLINGER
SPETISBURY (St John the Baptist) w Charlton Marshall and
  Blandford St Mary *Sarum 7* **P** *Worc Coll Ox (1 turn), Bp*
  (2 turns) **R** D B PENNAL
SPEXHALL (St Peter) Halesworth w Linstead, Chediston,
  Holton etc *St E*
SPILSBY (St James) w Hundleby *Linc 7* **P** *Baroness*
  Willoughby de Eresby **V** G ROBSON, **C** I D McGRATH
SPITAL (St Agnes) New Windsor *Ox*
SPITAL (St Leonard's Mission Room) Chesterfield All SS
  Derby
SPITALFIELDS (Christ Church w All Saints) *Lon 7*
  P *MMCET* **R** P W BOWTELL
SPITALGATE (St John the Evangelist) Grantham *Linc*
SPITTAL (St John) *Newc 12* **P** *Bp and Mercers' Co (alt)*
  V J W SHEWAN
SPIXWORTH (St Peter) w Crostwick and Frettenham *Nor 2*
  P *Bp, Ch Soc Trust, and DBP (jt)* **R** A R GOOD
SPOFFORTH (All Saints) w Kirk Deighton *Ripon 1* **P** *Bp*
  R G JONES
SPONDON (St Werburgh) *Derby 9* **P** *Capt P J B Drury-*
  Lowe **V** R J ANDREWS, **C** P D MAYBURY
SPORLE (St Mary) Gt and Lt Dunham w Gt and Lt
  Fransham and Sporle *Nor*
SPOTLAND (St Clement) *Man 20* **P** *Bp*
  P-in-c B McNIVEN
SPRATTON (St Andrew) *Pet 2* **P** *Bp* **V** B LEE
SPREYTON (St Michael) *Ex 12* **P** *Bp* **V** C J L NAPIER
SPRIDLINGTON (St Hilary) Owmby Gp *Linc*
SPRIGG'S ALLEY (Mission Room) Chinnor w Emmington
  and Sydenham etc *Ox*
SPRING GROVE (St Mary) *Lon 11* **P** *Ch Patr Trust*
  V D G WILSON, **C** L P D ESSER
SPRING PARK (All Saints) *S'wark 20* **P** *Bp*
  V B L HAMMOND, **Hon C** B W HAMMOND

SPRINGFIELD (All Saints) *Chelmsf 8*
P *Air Cdre N S Paynter* R R J BROWN, NSM J MANN
SPRINGFIELD (Holy Trinity) *Chelmsf 8* P *Simeon's Trustees* V J K HAYWARD, C A K WILSON
SPRINGFIELD (St Christopher) *Birm 8* P *Trustees*
V S P CORBETT
SPRINGFIELD, EAST (Church of Our Saviour) (not known)
Chelmsf 8 P *Bp* P-in-c C E HOPKINSON
SPRINGFIELD, NORTH (St Augustine of Canterbury)
Chelmsf 8 P *Bp* P-in-c J D HAYWARD,
NSM P M A PEELING
SPRINGFIELDS (St Stephen) Wolv St Steph *Lich*
SPRINGHILL (St Peter) Birm St Pet *Birm*
SPRINGTHORPE (St George and St Laurence) Corringham and Blyton Gp *Linc*
SPRINGWELL (St Mary the Virgin) Sunderland St Mary and St Pet *Dur*
SPROATLEY (St Swithin) Preston and Sproatley in Holderness *York*
SPROTBROUGH (St Mary the Virgin) *Sheff 8* P *Bp*
R S J MATTHEWS
SPROUGHTON (All Saints) w Burstall *St E 5* P *D&C Cant*
(1 turn), Bp (2 turns) P-in-c R F PALLANT
SPROXTON (St Bartholomew) High Framland Par *Leic*
SPROXTON (St Chad) Helmsley *York*
SQUIRRELS HEATH (All Saints) *Chelmsf 2* P *Bp*
V A D C EVANS
SROWSTON (St Cuthbert) (St Mary and St Margaret) w Beeston *Nor 2* P *D&C* R M H STAGG
STADHAMPTON (St John the Baptist) Dorchester *Ox*
STAFFHURST WOOD (St Silvan) Limpsfield and Titsey *S'wark*
STAFFORD (Christ Church) (St Chad) (St Mary) *Lich 15*
P *Patr Bd* TR A G MURSELL, TV P M FREEMAN,
C J E McFARLANE, NSM M J FISHER
STAFFORD (St John the Baptist) and Tixall w Ingestre
Lich 15 P *Bp and Earl of Shrewsbury and Talbot (jt)*
V R M VAUGHAN, C M KELLOR
STAFFORD (St Paul) Forebridge *Lich 15* P *V Castle Ch*
V M R METCALF
STAFFORD, WEST (St Andrew) w Frome Billet *Sarum 2*
P *Brig S Floyer-Acland* P-in-c P C WHEATLEY
STAGSDEN (St Leonard) Bromham w Oakley and Stagsden *St Alb*
STAGSHAW CHAPEL (St Aidan) St Jo Lee *Newc*
STAINBY (St Peter) Witham Gp *Linc*
STAINCLIFFE (Christ Church) *Wakef 10* P *V Batley*
V C P MORTIMER
STAINCROSS (St John the Divine) *Wakef 7* P *Bp*
V *Vacant* Barnsley (01226) 382261
STAINDROP (St Mary) *Dur 11* P *Lord Barnard*
V D R JONES
STAINES (Christ Church) *Lon 13* P *Bp* V L O LINDO
STAINES (St Mary) (St Peter) *Lon 13* P *Ld Chan*
V M A M ST JOHN-CHANNELL, C N S VIGERS,
NSM P V K HOARE
STAINFIELD (St Andrew) Bardney *Linc*
STAINFORTH (St Mary) *Sheff 11* P *Bp* V C SMITH
STAINFORTH (St Peter) Langcliffe w Stainforth and Horton *Bradf*
STAINING (St Luke Mission Church) Blackpool St Mich *Blackb*
STAINLAND (St Andrew) *Wakef 2* P *V Halifax*
V S DANDO
STAINLEY, NORTH (St Mary the Virgin) W Tanfield and Well w Snape and N Stainley *Ripon*
STAINLEY, SOUTH (St Wilfrid) Markington w S Stainley and Bishop Thornton *Ripon*
STAINMORE (St Stephen) Brough w Stainmore, Musgrave and Warcop *Carl*
STAINTON (St Winifred) Tickhill w Stainton *Sheff*
STAINTON, GREAT (All Saints) Bishopton w Gt Stainton *Dur*
STAINTON BY LANGWORTH (St John the Baptist) Barlings *Linc*
STAINTON DALE (St John the Baptist) Scalby w Ravenscar and Staintondale *York*
STAINTON-IN-CLEVELAND (St Peter and St Paul)
York 22 P *Abp* V *Vacant* Middlesbrough (01642) 590423
STAINTON LE VALE (St Andrew) Walesby *Linc*
STAITHES (St Peter) Hinderwell w Roxby *York*
STAKEFORD (Holy Family) Choppington *Newc*
STALBRIDGE (St Mary) *Sarum 6* P *CCC Cam*
P-in-c M R GODSON
STALHAM (St Mary) and East Ruston w Brunstead *Nor 13*
P *Mrs S F Baker and DBP (alt)* V A C BILLETT
STALISFIELD (St Mary) Eastling w Ospringe and Stalisfield w Otterden *Cant*

STALLING BUSK (St Matthew) Askrigg w Stallingbusk *Ripon*
STALLINGBOROUGH (St Peter and St Paul) Healing and Stallingborough *Linc*
STALMINE (St James) *Blackb 10* P *V Lanc*
V T G MIDDLEDITCH
STALYBRIDGE (Holy Trinity and Christ Church) *Ches 14*
P *Trustees* V T G N GREEN, NSM M R CAVANAGH
STALYBRIDGE (St George) *Man 17* P *Lord Deramore and R Ashton-under-Lyne St Mich (jt)* V M J R TINKER,
NSM P BRIERLEY, D BROADBENT
STALYBRIDGE (St Paul) *Ches 14* P *Trustees*
V P L ROBINSON
STAMBOURNE (St Peter and St Thomas Becket) Toppesfield and Stambourne *Chelmsf*
STAMBRIDGE (St Mary and All Saints) *Chelmsf 12*
P *Ld Chan (1 turn), Govs Charterhouse (3 turns)*
P-in-c F W B KENNY
STAMFORD (All Saints) (St John the Baptist) *Linc 13*
P *Ld Chan and Burghley Ho Preservation Trust (alt)*
P-in-c N RUSSELL, Hon C D M BOND,
NSM R J MACKRILL
STAMFORD (Christ Church) *Linc 13* P *Bp* V D J SPICER
STAMFORD (St George) *Linc 13* P *Burghley Ho Preservation Trust* R K S SWITHINBANK
STAMFORD (St Mary) (St Martin) *Linc 13* P *Burghley Ho Preservation Trust* R N S D GIBSON
STAMFORD BRIDGE Group of Parishes, The (St John the Baptist) *York 7* P *Lord Egremont (2 turns), The Crown (1 turn), and Ld Chan (1 turn)* R J HARRISON
STAMFORD HILL (St Bartholomew) *Lon 19* P *The Crown*
V R N S LEECE
STAMFORD HILL (St Thomas) *Lon 19* P *R Hackney*
V E S MORROW
STAMFORDHAM (St Mary the Virgin) w Matfen *Newc 3*
P *Ld Chan* V R CAVAGAN
STANBRIDGE (St John the Baptist) Totternhoe, Stanbridge and Tilsworth *St Alb*
STANBURY (Mission Church) Haworth *Bradf*
STAND (All Saints) *Man 14* P *Earl of Wilton*
R R W WARNER, C D J FRENCH
STANDISH (St Nicholas) w Haresfield and Moreton Valence w Whitminster *Glouc 8* P *Bp and Col Sir Piers Bengough (jt)* V J A L B CATERER
STANDISH (St Wilfrid) *Blackb 4* P *Bp* R P K WARREN,
C E A SAVILLE
STANDLAKE (St Giles) Lower Windrush *Ox*
STANDON (All Saints) and Cotes Heath *Lich 12* P *Bp and V Eccleshall (jt)* R J H DEAKIN
STANDON (St Mary) *St Alb 4* P *Ch Fund Trust Fund*
V J L PELLEY
STANFIELD (St Margaret) Litcham w Kempston, E and W Lexham, Mileham etc *Nor*
STANFORD (All Saints) Lyminge w Paddlesworth, Stanford w Postling etc *Cant*
STANFORD (All Saints) *Nor 14* P *Bp* V *Vacant*
STANFORD (St Nicholas) Swinford w Catthorpe, Shawell and Stanford *Leic*
STANFORD BISHOP (St James) Acton Beauchamp and Evesbatch w Stanford Bishop *Heref*
STANFORD DINGLEY (St Denys) Bradfield and Stanford Dingley *Ox*
STANFORD IN THE VALE (St Denys) w Goosey and Hatford *Ox 17* P *D&C Westmr (3 turns), Simeon's Trustees (2 turns)* V M T WENHAM, C R S MARTIN
STANFORD-LE-HOPE (St Margaret) w Mucking
Chelmsf 14 P *MMCET* P-in-c J A K GUEST,
C M J LUNT, NSM L R SMITH
STANFORD-ON-SOAR (St John the Baptist) E and W Leake, Stanford-on-Soar, Rempstone etc *S'well*
STANFORD-ON-TEME (St Mary) Teme Valley N *Worc*
STANFORD RIVERS (St Margaret) Greensted-juxta-Ongar w Stanford Rivers *Chelmsf*
STANGROUND (St John the Baptist) (St Michael and All Angels) and Farcet *Ely 13* P *Em Coll Cam* TR D E S DE SILVA, TV I H FIRMSTONE
STANHOE (All Saints) Docking, The Birchams, Stanhoe and Sedgeford *Nor*
STANHOPE (St Thomas) w Frosterley *Dur 15* P *Bp and The Crown (alt)* R C N LOVELL
STANION (St Peter) Brigstock w Stanion *Pet*
STANLEY (All Saints) (St Andrew) *Derby 13* P *Bp*
P-in-c J C CLARKE
STANLEY (St Agnes) Endon w Stanley *Lich*
STANLEY (St Anne) *Liv 8* P *R W Derby* V M C DAVIES,
C G J CUFF
STANLEY (St Peter) *Wakef 12* P *Provost*
V W E HENDERSON

STANLEY (St Stephen) *Dur 8* **P** *Bp (2 turns), The Crown (1 turn)* **TR** R J WALLACE, **TV** D M BEATER, S T ROBSON

STANLEY (St Thomas) *Dur 15* **P** *R Brancepeth* **V** A FEATHERSTONE

STANLEY PONTLARGE (Chapel) Winchcombe, Gretton, Sudeley Manor etc *Glouc*

STANLEYS, The *Glouc 8* **P** *Mrs M J Hollings and Jes Coll Cam (jt)* **V** P L CHICKEN, **NSM** R M BRYANT

STANMER (not known) w Falmer *Chich 2* **P** *Bp* **P-in-c** A N ROBINSON

STANMORE (St Luke) *Win 13* **P** *Bp* **V** N P SEAL, **C** P B C SALISBURY

STANMORE, GREAT (St John the Evangelist) *Lon 23* **P** *R O Bernays Esq* **R** M H V BOWLES, **Hon C** C J E SPENCER

STANMORE, LITTLE (St Lawrence) *Lon 23* **P** *Bp* **R** P M REECE, **C** J C NEAL

STANNEY (St Andrew) Ellesmere Port *Ches*

STANNINGFIELD (St Nicholas) Hawstead and Nowton w Stanningfield etc *St E*

STANNINGLEY (St Thomas) *Ripon 6* **P** *V Leeds St Pet* **R** S C BROWN, **C** A T SHAW

STANNINGTON (Christ Church) *Sheff 4* **P** *Bp* **V** P W WEST, **C** N WILLIAMSON

STANNINGTON (St Mary the Virgin) *Newc 1* **P** *Bp* **V** K R WARD

STANSFIELD (All Saints) Denston w Stradishall and Stansfield *St E*

STANSTEAD (St James) Glem Valley United Benefice *St E*

STANSTEAD ABBOTS (St Andrew) *St Alb 8* **P** *Peache Trustees* **P-in-c** B F J GOODWIN, **NSM** J E KNIGHT

STANSTEAD ST MARGARET (St Mary the Virgin) Gt Amwell w St Marg *St Alb*

STANSTED (St Mary) w Fairseat and Vigo *Roch 9* **P** *Bp* **R** D G CLARK, C J L NOBLE

STANSTED (St Paul) (Christ Church) *Chich 13* **P** *Earl of Bessborough* **V** *Vacant*

STANSTED MOUNTFITCHET (St John) *Chelmsf 22* **P** *Bp* **V** R WALLACE, **NSM** B C WALLACE

STANTON (All Saints) (St John the Baptist) *St E 9* **P** *The Crown* **R** F T HOWARD

STANTON (St Gabriel) Marshwood Vale TM *Sarum*

STANTON (St Mary) Denstone w Ellastone and Stanton *Lich*

STANTON (St Mary and All Saints) Markfield *Leic*

STANTON (St Michael and All Angels) Toddington, Stanton, Didbrook w Hailes etc *Glouc*

STANTON BY BRIDGE (St Michael) Ticknall, Smisby and Stanton by Bridge *Derby*

STANTON-BY-DALE (St Michael and All Angels) w Dale Abbey *Derby 15* **P** *Bp* **R** I E GOODING

STANTON DREW (Blessed Virgin Mary) Bishop Sutton and Stanton Drew and Stowey *B & W*

STANTON FITZWARREN (St Leonard) Stratton St Margaret w S Marston etc *Bris*

STANTON HARCOURT (St Michael) Lower Windrush *Ox*

STANTON HILL (All Saints) Skegby *S'well*

STANTON-IN-PEAK (Holy Trinity) Youlgreave, Middleton, Stanton-in-Peak etc *Derby*

STANTON LACY (Hayton Bent Hall) Culmington w Onibury, Bromfield etc *Heref*

STANTON LACY (St Peter) as above

STANTON ON HINE HEATH (St Andrew) *Lich 28* **P** *Sir Alex Stanier, Bt* **V** J E DAIMOND

STANTON-ON-THE-WOLDS (All Saints) *S'well 9* **P** *Trustees of Sir Rupert Bromley* **P-in-c** T SISSON

STANTON PRIOR (St Lawrence) Farmborough, Marksbury and Stanton Prior *B & W*

STANTON ST BERNARD (All Saints) Swanborough *Sarum*

STANTON ST JOHN (St John the Baptist) Wheatley w Forest Hill and Stanton St John *Ox*

STANTON ST QUINTIN (St Quintin), Hullavington and Grittleton w Norton and Leigh Delamere *Bris 12* **P** *Bp, Eton Coll, and R W Neeld Esq (by turn)* **P-in-c** J W M MORGAN

STANTONBURY (Christ Church) and Willen *Ox 25* **P** *Patr Bd* **TR** J A PONTER, **TV** P F WORTHEN, R V PARRETT, H M BAKER, R WARD, **NSM** D B MILLS, J M APPLEBY

STANWAY (St Albright) (St Andrew) *Chelmsf 18* **P** *Magd Coll Ox* **V** H HEATH

STANWAY (St Peter) Toddington, Stanton, Didbrook w Hailes etc *Glouc*

STANWELL (St Mary the Virgin) *Lon 13* **P** *Ld Chan* **V** D C PEMBERTON, **NSM** H S L NICHOLSON

STANWICK (St Laurence) w Hargrave *Pet 10* **P** *Ld Chan (2 turns), F S Wier Esq (1 turn)* **P-in-c** E L WOOD

STANWIX (St Michael) *Carl 3* **P** *Bp* **V** C S SIMS, **C** D B LEAKE, W E SANDERS

STAPEHILL (All Saints) Hampreston *Sarum*

STAPENHILL (Immanuel) Conventional District *Derby 16* **Min** G D SIMMONS

STAPENHILL (St Peter) w Cauldwell *Derby 16* **P** *Ch Soc Trust* **V** E E LOBB, **C** S L SMALLWOOD

STAPLE (St James) Woodnesborough w Worth and Staple *Cant*

STAPLE FITZPAINE (St Peter) w Orchard Portman, Thurlbear and Stoke St Mary *B & W 18* **P** *Bp* **R** G COOKE

STAPLE TYE (St James) Gt Parndon *Chelmsf*

STAPLECROSS (St Mark) Ewhurst *Chich*

STAPLEFIELD COMMON (St Mark) *Chich 6* **P** *V Cuckfield* **V** *Vacant* Handcross (01444) 400241

STAPLEFORD (All Saints) Carlton-le-Moorland w Stapleford *Linc*

STAPLEFORD (St Andrew) *Ely 7* **P** *D&C* **P-in-c** K F M FISHER

STAPLEFORD (St Andrew's Mission Church) (St Helen) (St Luke) *S'well 7* **P** *CPAS* **V** C J HALL, **C** S M FALSHAW

STAPLEFORD (St Mary) Bramfield w Stapleford and Waterford *St Alb*

STAPLEFORD (St Mary) Lower Wylye and Till Valley *Sarum*

STAPLEFORD (St Mary Magdalene) Waltham on the Wolds, Stonesby, Saxby etc *Leic*

STAPLEFORD ABBOTTS (St Mary) Lambourne w Abridge and Stapleford Abbotts *Chelmsf*

STAPLEFORD TAWNEY (St Mary the Virgin) w Theydon Mount *Chelmsf 28* **P** *DBP* **P-in-c** P H W CHAPMAN

STAPLEGROVE (St John) *B & W 18* **P** *Bp* **R** N C VENNING

STAPLEHURST (All Saints) *Cant 11* **P** *St Jo Coll Cam* **R** B BARNES

STAPLETON (Holy Trinity) *Bris 7* **P** *Bp* **R** J A RISDON

STAPLETON (St John) Dorrington w Leebotwood, Longnor, Stapleton etc *Heref*

STAPLETON (St Martin) Barwell w Potters Marston and Stapleton *Leic*

STAPLETON (St Mary) Bewcastle, Stapleton and Kirklinton etc *Carl*

STARBECK (St Andrew) *Ripon 1* **P** *V Harrogate Ch Ch* **V** M B TAYLOR

STARCROSS (St Paul) Kenton, Mamhead, Powderham, Cofton and Starcross *Ex*

STARSTON (St Margaret) Pulham Market, Pulham St Mary and Starston *Nor*

STARTFORTH (Holy Trinity) and Bowes and Rokeby w Brignall *Ripon 2* **P** *Ld Chan (1 turn), Bp, Earl of Lonsdale and Lords of the Manor of Bowes (2 turns)* **V** G F DEAR

STATFOLD (St Matthew) Clifton Campville w Edingale *Lich*

STATHERN (St Guthlac) Barkestone w Plungar, Redmile and Stathern *Leic*

STAUGHTON, GREAT (St Andrew) *Ely 12* **P** *St Jo Coll Ox* **V** W N BROOK

STAUGHTON, LITTLE (All Saints) Keysoe w Bolnhurst and Lt Staughton *St Alb*

STAUNTON (All Saints) Coleford w Staunton *Glouc*

STAUNTON (St James) Hartpury w Corse and Staunton *Glouc*

STAUNTON (St Mary) w Flawborough *S'well 3* **P** *E G Staunton Esq* **R** *Vacant*

STAUNTON HAROLD (Holy Trinity) Breedon cum Isley Walton and Worthington *Leic*

STAUNTON ON ARROW (St Peter) Pembridge w Moorcourt, Shobdon, Staunton etc *Heref*

STAUNTON-ON-WYE (St Mary the Virgin) Letton w Staunton, Byford, Mansel Gamage etc *Heref*

STAVELEY (All Saints) Farnham w Scotton, Staveley, Copgrove etc *Ripon*

STAVELEY (St James), Ings and Kentmere *Carl 9* **P** *V Kendal H Trin* **V** G WATSON

STAVELEY (St John the Baptist) and Barrow Hill *Derby 3* **P** *Bp, Adn Chesterfield, and Duke of Devonshire (jt)* **TR** W A BUTT, **TV** J P HAYES

STAVELEY IN CARTMEL (St Mary) Leven Valley *Carl*

STAVERTON (St Catherine) w Boddington and Tredington w Stoke Orchard and Hardwicke *Glouc 11* **P** *Bp* **V** J B T HOMFRAY

STAVERTON (St Mary the Virgin) Daventry, Ashby St Ledgers, Braunston etc *Pet*

STAVERTON (St Paul) Hilperton w Whaddon and Staverton etc *Sarum*

STAVERTON (St Paul de Leon) Broadhempston, Woodland, Staverton etc *Ex*

STAWELL (St Francis) Middlezoy and Othery and
 Moorlinch *B & W*

STAWLEY (St Michael and All Angels) Wellington and Distr
 B & W

STEANE (St Peter) Farthinghoe w Hinton-in-the-Hedges w
 Steane *Pet*

STEART BAY (St Andrew) Cannington, Otterhampton,
 Combwich and Stockland *B & W*

STEBBING (St Mary the Virgin) w Lindsell *Chelmsf 19*
 P *Bp* **V** J SSUTTON, **NSM** S C BAZLINTON

STECHFORD (All Saints) (St Andrew) *Birm 10* **P** *St Pet*
 Coll Ox **P-in-c** G C FRANCIS, **C** G H P PETRICHER

STEDHAM (St James) w Iping *Chich 10* **P** *Bp*
 P-in-c R N WYATT

STEEP (All Saints) and Froxfield w Privett *Portsm 5*
 P *Ld Chan and Magd Coll Cam (alt)* **V** D M PINE,
 NSM J C GRACE

STEEPING, GREAT (All Saints) Firsby w Gt Steeping *Linc*

STEEPING, LITTLE (St Andrew) *Linc 7* **P** *Baroness*
 Willoughby de Eresby **R** G ROBSON

STEEPLE (St Lawrence and All Angels) *Chelmsf 11*
 P-in-c M A COHEN

STEEPLE (St Michael and All Angels) Corfe Castle, Church
 Knowle, Kimmeridge etc *Sarum*

STEEPLE ASHTON (St Mary the Virgin) w Semington and
 Keevil *Sarum 17* **P** *D&C Win (1 turn), Magd Coll Cam*
 (3 turns) **V** D M HART

STEEPLE ASTON (St Peter and St Paul) w North Aston and
 Tackley *Ox 9* **P** *BNC Ox, St Jo Coll Ox, and Exors Lt-Col*
 A D Taylor (jt) **R** M A H RODEN, **NSM** A M SHUKMAN

STEEPLE BARTON (St Mary) Westcote Barton w Steeple
 Barton, Duns Tew etc *Ox*

STEEPLE BUMPSTEAD (St Mary) and Helions Bumpstead
 Chelmsf 15 **P** *Ld Chan* **V** G R MANSFIELD

STEEPLE CLAYDON (St Michael) The Claydons *Ox*

STEEPLE LANGFORD (All Saints) Yarnbury *Sarum*

STEEPLE MORDEN (St Peter and St Paul) Shingay Gp of
 Par *Ely*

STEETLY (All Saints) Whitwell *Derby*

STEETON (St Stephen) *Bradf 8* **P** *V Kildwick*
 V K ROWEN, **C** E NICOL

STELLA (St Cuthbert) *Dur 5* **P** *Bp* **P-in-c** A OATES

STELLING (St Mary) Petham and Waltham w Lower
 Hardres etc *Cant*

STENIGOT (St Nicholas) Asterby Gp *Linc*

STEPNEY (St Dunstan and All Saints) *Lon 7* **P** *Bp*
 R C T J CHESSUN, **C** J A WEBBER, G D IRESON,
 A M M WILKINSON, **Hon C** G G WHITE

STEPPINGLEY (St Lawrence) Ampthill w Millbrook and
 Steppingley *St Alb*

STERNFIELD (St Mary Magdalene) w Benhall and Snape
 St E 19 **P** *Exors Mrs A H V Aldous, Mrs A C V Wentworth,*
 and Mrs M A Bertin (by turn) **R** N H BEVAN

STERT (St James) Redhorn *Sarum*

STETCHWORTH (St Peter) *Ely 4* **P** *Duke of Sutherland*
 P-in-c J S ASKEY

STEVENAGE (All Saints) Pin Green *St Alb 12* **P** *Bp*
 V C D FUTCHER, **C** M C HARRIS

STEVENAGE (Holy Trinity) *St Alb 12* **P** *Bp*
 V G H NEWTON, **C** H K DERHAM, **NSM** A MARINER

STEVENAGE (St Andrew and St George) *St Alb 12* **P** *Bp*
 R M BARNSLEY, **C** P J B HINDLE, D J SWAN

STEVENAGE (St Hugh) (St John) Chells *St Alb 12* **P** *Bp*
 V J D CAMPBELL, **C** B EBELING

STEVENAGE (St Mary) Sheppall w Aston *St Alb 12* **P** *Bp*
 V G B WHITE, **C** M EREAVIL, **NSM** A M GRIEVES

STEVENAGE (St Nicholas) *St Alb 12* **P** *Bp*
 V J R BAINBRIDGE

STEVENAGE (St Peter) Broadwater *St Alb 12* **P** *Bp*
 V D J BRENTNALL

STEVENTON (St Michael and All Angels) w Milton *Ox 10*
 P *Ch Ch Ox and D&C Westmr (jt)* **P-in-c** C J PATCHING

STEVENTON (St Nicholas) N Waltham and Steventon,
 Ashe and Deane *Win*

STEVINGTON (Church Room) (St Mary the Virgin)
 St Alb 21 **P** *Bp* **P-in-c** P N JEFFERY

STEWARDS LANE (St Thomas) Ditton St Mich *Liv*

STEWKLEY (St Michael and All Angels) w Soulbury and
 Drayton Parslow *Ox 26* **P** *Bp, Earl of Rosebery, and*
 MMCET (jt) **V** N J COTTON

STEWTON (St Andrew) Louth *Linc*

STEYNING (St Andrew) *Chich 12* **P** *MMCET* **V** *Vacant*
 Steyning (01903) 813256

STIBBARD (All Saints) Twyford, Guist, Bintree,
 Themelthorpe etc *Nor*

STIBBINGTON (St John the Baptist) *Ely 13* **P** *Sir Stephen*
 Hastings **P-in-c** P O POOLEY

STICKFORD (St Helen) Stickney Gp *Linc*

STICKLEPATH (St Mary) S Tawton and Belstone *Ex*

STICKLEPATH (St Paul) Barnstaple *Ex*

STICKNEY Group, The (St Luke) *Linc 7* **P** *DBP, Ld Chan,*
 and Bp (by turn) **V** J R WORSDALL

STIDD (St Saviour) Ribchester w Stidd *Blackb*

STIFFKEY (St John and St Mary) and Cockthorpe w Morston,
 Langham and Binham *Nor 19* **P** *Bp, Sir Euan Anstruther-*
 Gough-Calthorpe, Bt, and DBP (by turn) **R** R C WRIGHT

STIFFORD (St Cedd) (St Mary) *Chelmsf 14* **P** *Bp*
 R M B WOODMANSEY, **C** G E COLDHAM

STIFFORD, SOUTH (St Mary the Virgin) Grays Thurrock
 Chelmsf

STILLINGFLEET (St Helen) Escrick and Stillingfleet w
 Naburn *York*

STILLINGTON (St John) Grindon and Stillington *Dur*

STILLINGTON (St Nicholas) and Marton w Moxby *York 5*
 P *Abp* **V** *Vacant*

STILTON (St Mary Magdalene) w Denton and Caldectoe and
 Folksworth w Morborne and Haddon *Ely 13*
 P *Mrs H R Horne and Bp, Ld Chan (alt)* **R** R LONGFOOT

STINCHCOMBE (St Cyr) Cam w Stinchcombe *Glouc*

STINSFORD (St Michael) Charminster and Stinsford *Sarum*

STIRCHLEY (All Saints) Cen Telford *Lich*

STIRCHLEY (Ascension) *Birm 4* **P** *R Kings Norton*
 V D C BAKER, **NSM** M HARRIS (formerly PRATT)

STISTED (All Saints) w Bradwell-juxta-Coggeshall and
 Pattiswick *Chelmsf 16* **P** *Bp, Mrs D E G Keen, and Abp*
 (by turn) **P-in-c** J MARVELL

STITHIANS (St Stythians) St Stythians w Perranarworthal
 and Gwennap *Truro*

STIXWOULD (St Peter) Woodhall Spa Gp *Linc*

STOAK (St Lawrence) Ellesmere Port *Ches*

STOCK (St Barnabas) and Lydlinch *Sarum 6* **P** *G A L F Pitt-*
 Rivers Esq (2 turns), Col J L Yeatman (2 turns), and
 V Iwerne Minster (1 turn) **P-in-c** J C DAY

STOCK HARVARD (All Saints) *Chelmsf 9*
 P *Miss L C Harvard* **R** R A J BUCKINGHAM

STOCKBRIDGE (Old St Peter) (St Peter) and Longstock and
 Leckford *Win 11* **P** *Bp and St Jo Coll Ox (jt)*
 R P C AVES

STOCKBURY (St Mary Magdalene) Newington w Hartlip
 and Stockbury *Cant*

STOCKCROSS (St John) Welford w Wickham and Gt
 Shefford, Boxford etc *Ox*

STOCKERSTON (St Peter) Six Saints circa Holt *Leic*

STOCKING FARM (St Luke) *Leic 1* **P** *Bp* **V** M J SMITH

STOCKING PELHAM (St Mary) Braughing w Furneux
 Pelham and Stocking Pelham *St Alb*

STOCKINGFORD (St Paul) *Cov 5* **P** *V Nuneaton*
 P-in-c M F VINCENT, **C** V E W RUSHTON

STOCKLAND (St Mary Magdalene) Cannington,
 Otterhampton, Combwich and Stockland *B & W*

STOCKLAND (St Michael and All Angels) w Dalwood *Ex 5*
 P *DBP* **Hon C** J N C GIDDINGS

STOCKLAND GREEN (St Mark) *Birm 6* **P** *The Crown*
 P-in-c D E NEWSOME, **C** P A HINDS

STOCKLEIGH ENGLISH (St Mary the Virgin) N Creedy
 Ex

STOCKLEIGH POMEROY (St Mary the Virgin) as above

STOCKLINCH (St Mary Magdalene) Ilminster and District
 B & W

STOCKPORT South West (St George) (St Mark) *Ches 18*
 P *Patr Bd* **TR** J M ROFF, **TV** M J PARKER,
 S I D WHITE, **C** M R CHRISTIAN

STOCKPORT (St Augustine) Cheadle Heath *Ches*

STOCKPORT (St Mary) *Ches 18* **P** *G&C Coll Cam*
 R A M FAIRHURST, **NSM** H C BRIDGE, J BOWLES

STOCKPORT (St Matthew) *Ches 18* **P** *Bp*
 P-in-c S A FOSTER

STOCKPORT (St Saviour) *Ches 18* **P** *Trustees* **V** D F HAY

STOCKPORT (St Thomas) (St Peter) *Ches 18* **P** *Bp and*
 Ch Union (jt) **R** K D N KENRICK, **C** K R BROOKES

STOCKSBRIDGE (St Matthias) *Sheff 7* **P** *Bp*
 V D P PALMER

STOCKSFIELD (St John) Bywell St Pet *Newc*

STOCKTON (St Andrew) Teme Valley N *Worc*

STOCKTON (St Chad) *Dur 16* **P** *Bp*
 P-in-c J M PERKINS, **NSM** E WALKER

STOCKTON (St Chad) Beckbury, Badger, Kemberton,
 Ryton, Stockton etc *Lich*

STOCKTON (St John the Baptist) Yarnbury *Sarum*

STOCKTON (St Mark) *Dur 16* **P** *Bp* **NSM** J M THOMAS

STOCKTON (St Michael and All Angels) Napton-on-the-
 Hill, Lower Shuckburgh etc *Cov*

STOCKTON (St Michael and All Angels) Gillingham w
 Geldeston, Stockton, Ellingham etc *Nor*

STOCKTON HEATH (St Thomas) *Ches 4*
P *P G Greenall Esq* **V** T P F KENNY, **C** A G BROWN,
NSM D L MELLOR
STOCKTON-ON-TEES Green Vale (Holy Trinity)
Conventional District *Dur 16* **C-in-c** N E WATSON
STOCKTON-ON-TEES (St Chad) Stockton St Chad *Dur*
STOCKTON ON TEES (St James) *Dur 16* **P** *Bp*
V W T G GRIFFITHS
STOCKTON-ON-TEES (St John the Baptist) *Dur 16* **P** *Bp*
V S IRWIN
STOCKTON-ON-TEES (St Mark) Stockton St Mark *Dur*
STOCKTON-ON-TEES (St Paul) *Dur 16* **P** *The Crown*
V P M HOOD
STOCKTON-ON-TEES (St Peter) *Dur 16* **P** *Bp*
V M A WHITEHEAD, **C** D M DEWES, **NSM** M WATTS
STOCKTON-ON-TEES (St Thomas) *Dur 16* **P** *Bp*
V D J WHITTINGTON
STOCKTON-ON-THE-FOREST (Holy Trinity) w Holtby and
Warthill *York 4* **P** *Abp* **R** *Vacant* York (01904) 400337
STOCKWELL (St Michael) *S'wark 9* **P** *V Kennington
St Mark* **V** G S PARFITT
STOCKWELL GREEN (St Andrew) *S'wark 9* **P** *Abp, Bp,
and TR N Lambeth (jt)* **V** P R SIMMONDS
STOCKWITH, EAST (St Peter) *Linc 2* **P** *Ld Chan*
V M W PAGE-CHESTNEY, **NSM** S V PAGE-CHESTNEY
STOCKWITH, WEST (St Mary the Virgin) Misterton and W
Stockwith *S'well*
STOCKWOOD (Christ the Servant) Bris Ch the Servant
Stockwood *Bris*
STODDEN Churches, The *St Alb 21* **P** *MMCET and DBP
(alt)* **R** P C DELIGHT, **NSM** R L STOWE
STODMARSH (St Mary) Littlebourne and Ickham w
Wickhambreaux etc *Cant*
STODY (St Mary) Brinton, Briningham, Hunworth, Stody
etc *Nor*
STOGUMBER (Blessed Virgin Mary) w Nettlecombe and
Monksilver *B & W 17* **P** *D&C, and D&C Windsor (alt)*
R *Vacant* Stogumber (01984) 56221
STOGURSEY (St Andrew) w Fiddington *B & W 17* **P** *Eton
Coll and DBP (alt)* **R** A E APPLEGARTH
STOKE (St Mary and St Andrew) Colsterworth Gp *Linc*
STOKE (St Michael) Cov Caludon *Cov*
STOKE (St Peter and St Paul) Grain w Stoke *Roch*
STOKE, EAST (St Oswald) w Syerston *S'well 3* **P** *Bp*
R G A FIRTH
STOKE, NORTH (St Martin) Bath Weston All SS w N Stoke
and Langridge *B & W*
STOKE, NORTH (St Mary the Virgin) Langtree *Ox*
STOKE, SOUTH (St Andrew) Goring w S Stoke *Ox*
STOKE, SOUTH (St James the Great) Combe Down w
Monkton Combe and S Stoke *B & W*
STOKE, SOUTH (St Leonard) Arundel w Tortington and S
Stoke *Chich*
STOKE, WEST (St Andrew) *Chich 13* **P** *Bp*
R D A JOHNSON
STOKE ABBOTT (St Mary) Beaminster Area *Sarum*
STOKE ALBANY (St Botolph) w Wilbarston *Pet 9* **P** *Comdr
L M M Saunders-Watson* **R** F L SCUFFHAM
STOKE ALDERMOOR (St Catherine) Cov Caludon *Cov*
STOKE ASH (All Saints) Thorndon w Rishangles, Stoke
Ash, Thwaite etc *St E*
STOKE BARDOLPH (St Luke) Gedling *S'well*
STOKE BISHOP (St Mary Magdalene) *Bris 8* **P** *Bp*
V D J R RITCHIE, **NSM** C A FROUDE (nee WOOLCOCK)
STOKE BLISS (St Peter) Teme Valley S *Worc*
STOKE BRUERNE (St Mary the Virgin) w Grafton Regis and
Alderton *Pet 5* **P** *BNC Ox and Ld Chan (alt)* **R** *Vacant*
Roade (01604) 862352
STOKE BY CLARE (St John the Baptist) Clare w
Poslingford, Cavendish etc *St E*
STOKE BY NAYLAND (St Mary) w Leavenheath *St E 3*
P *Sir Joshua Rowley, Bt* **P-in-c** D W FINCH
STOKE CANON (St Mary Magdalene, Poltimore w Huxham
and Rewe w Netherexe *Ex 2* **P** *D&C, Lady Stucley, and Bp
(by turn)* **V** P D LAVIS
STOKE CHARITY (St Mary and St Michael) Wonston and
Stoke Charity w Hunton *Win*
STOKE CLIMSLAND (not known) *Truro 9* **P** *Duchy of
Cornwall* **R** T J FULLER
STOKE D'ABERNON (St Mary the Virgin) *Guildf 10*
P *K Coll Cam* **R** D C VINCENT
STOKE DAMEREL (St Andrew w St Luke) *Ex 22*
P *Trustees Lord St Levan* **R** G D CRYER
STOKE DOYLE (St Rumbold) Aldwincle w Thorpe
Achurch, Pilton, Wadenhoe etc *Pet*
STOKE DRY (St Andrew) Lyddington w Stoke Dry and
Seaton *Pet*

STOKE EDITH (St Mary) Tarrington w Stoke Edith,
Aylton, Pixley etc *Heref*
STOKE FERRY (All Saints) w Wretton *Ely 15* **P** *Ld Chan*
V A R BENNETT
STOKE FLEMING (St Peter) Blackawton and Stoke
Fleming *Ex*
STOKE GABRIEL (St Gabriel) and Collaton *Ex 13* **P** *Bp*
V R P PRANCE
STOKE GIFFORD (St Michael) *Bris 6* **P** *Bp*
TR D C R WIDDOWS, **TV** S J SMITH,
NSM G T D ANGEL, M G COATES
STOKE GOLDING (St Margaret) w Dadlington *Leic 13*
P *Bp* **P-in-c** C A R GASH
STOKE GOLDINGTON (St Peter) Gayhurst w Ravenstone,
Stoke Goldington etc *Ox*
STOKE HAMMOND (St Luke) Newton Longville w Stoke
Hammond and Whaddon *Ox*
STOKE HEATH (St Alban) Cov E *Cov*
STOKE HILL (St Peter) *Guildf 5* **P** *Bp* **V** D J FURNESS
STOKE HOLY CROSS (Holy Cross) w Dunston, Arminghall
and Caistor St Edmunds w Markshall *Nor 8*
P *D&C and Mrs D Pott (jt)* **R** D C BROOME
STOKE-IN-TEIGNHEAD (St Andrew) w Combe-in-Teignhead
and Haccombe *Ex 11* **P** *Sir Rivers Carew, Bt*
R R A SOUTHWOOD
STOKE LACY (St Peter and St Paul) and Moreton Jeffries w
Much Cowarne, Ocle Pychard and Ullingswick *Heref 2*
P *D&C, Bp Birm, P H G Morgan Esq, and Bp (by turn)*
P-in-c M R SMITH, **C** D PEARCE, E J BRYANT
STOKE LYNE (St Peter) Stratton Audley and Godington,
Fringford etc *Ox*
STOKE MANDEVILLE (St Mary the Virgin) Ellesborough,
The Kimbles and Stoke Mandeville *Ox*
STOKE NEWINGTON (St Andrew) *Lon 5* **P** *Bp*
V R K BALLANTINE
STOKE NEWINGTON St Faith (St Matthias) and All Saints
Lon 5 **P** *City Corp* **V** C A ROWE, **NSM** R A FARLEY
STOKE NEWINGTON (St John the
Evangelist) Brownswood Park *Lon*
STOKE NEWINGTON (St Mary) (Old Parish Church)
Lon 5 **P** *Bp* **R** A G SCOTT, **C** K J SCULLY
STOKE NEWINGTON (St Olave) *Lon 5* **P** *Ld Chan*
V P JAMESON
STOKE NEWINGTON COMMON (St Michael and All
Angels) *Lon 5* **P** *Bp* **P-in-c** N R EVANS
STOKE-NEXT-GUILDFORD (St John the Evangelist)
Guildf 5 **P** *Simeon's Trustees* **R** S R SIZER,
NSM D M WHITWAM
STOKE ORCHARD (St James the Great) Staverton w
Boddington and Tredington etc *Glouc*
STOKE PARK (St Peter) Ipswich St Mary at Stoke w St Pet,
Stoke Park *St E*
STOKE PERO (not known) Porlock w Stoke Pero *B & W*
STOKE POGES (St Giles) *Ox 23* **P** *Trustees Duke of Leeds
Trust* **V** C E HARRIS
STOKE PRIOR (St Luke) Leominster *Heref*
STOKE PRIOR (St Michael), Wychbold and Upton Warren
Worc 8 **P** *Bp and D&C (alt)* **R** D M WIGHT,
NSM S H WIGHT (nee JONES)
STOKE RIVERS (St Bartholomew) Shirwell, Loxhore,
Kentisbury, Arlington, etc *Ex*
STOKE ROW (St John the Evangelist) Langtree *Ox*
STOKE ST GREGORY (St Gregory) w Burrowbridge and
Lyng *B & W 18* **P** *D&C (2 turns), R O Meade-King Esq
(1 turn)* **V** C F E ROWLEY
STOKE ST MARY (St Mary) Staple Fitzpaine, Orchard
Portman, Thurlbear etc *B & W*
STOKE ST MICHAEL (St Michael) Leigh upon Mendip w
Stoke St Michael *B & W*
STOKE ST MILBOROUGH (St Milburgha) Bitterley w
Middleton, Stoke St Milborough etc *Heref*
STOKE SUB HAMDON (Blessed Virgin Mary) (All Saints
Mission Church) *B & W 6* **P** *Ch Patr Trust*
V H A HALLETT
STOKE TALMAGE (St Mary Magdalene) Tetsworth,
Adwell w S Weston, Lewknor etc *Ox*
STOKE TRISTER (St Andrew) Charlton Musgrove,
Cucklington and Stoke Trister *B & W*
STOKE UPON TERN (St Peter) Cheswardine, Childs Ercall,
Hales, Hinstock etc *Lich*
STOKE-UPON-TRENT (St Peter-ad-Vincula) (St Paul)
Lich 17 **P** *Bp* **TR** E C RUDDOCK, **TV** W H SMITH,
J A GORDON
STOKEHAM (St Peter) Rampton w Laneham, Treswell,
Cottam and Stokeham *S'well*
STOKENCHURCH (St Peter and St Paul) and Ibstone
Ox 29 **P** *Bp* **P-in-c** C J P CHADWICK

STOKENHAM (St Michael and All Angels) w Sherford
Ex 14 **P** *The Crown* **V** W A McCOUBREY

STOKESAY (St Christopher) (St John the Baptist) *Heref 11*
P *T P D La Touche Esq* **P-in-c** A N TOOP

STOKESBY (St Andrew) Filby, Thrigby, Mautby, Stokesby,
Runham etc *Nor*

STOKESLEY (St Peter and St Paul) *York 22* **P** *Abp*
R M D A DYKES, **C** D R WILLIAMS

STOLFORD (St Peter) Stogursey w Fiddington *B & W*

STON EASTON (Blessed Virgin Mary) Chewton Mendip w
Ston Easton, Litton etc *B & W*

STONDON (All Saints) Meppershall w Campton and
Stondon *St Alb*

STONDON MASSEY (St Peter and St Paul) Blackmore and
Stondon Massey *Chelmsf*

STONE (All Saints) w Woodford and Hill *Glouc 2*
P *Major R Jenner-Fust and V Berkeley (alt)*
V P C F WOOSTER

STONE (Christ Church) and Oulton-with-Moddershall
Lich 18 **P** *Simeon's Trustees* **V** D J WILLIAMS

STONE near Dartford (St Mary) *Roch 2* **P** *Bp*
R J A RANDALL

STONE (St John the Baptist) w Dinton and Hartwell *Ox 21*
P *Bp and Grocers' Co (jt)* **R** D J COOKE

STONE (St Mary the Virgin) Chaddesley Corbett and Stone
Worc

STONE (St Michael) w Aston (St Saviour) *Lich 18* **P** *Bp*
R *Vacant* Stone (01785) 812747

STONE CROSS (St Luke) w Langney, North *Chich 16*
P *Bp* **V** J M GRAVES

STONE-IN-OXNEY (St Mary the Virgin) Wittersham w
Stone-in-Oxney and Ebony *Cant*

STONE QUARRY (St Luke) E Grinstead St Swithun *Chich*

STONEBRIDGE (St Michael and All Angels) *Lon 21* **P** *Bp*
V R L SMITH, **C** F A DU-BOACHIE

STONEBROOM (St Peter) Morton and Stonebroom *Derby*

STONEFOLD (St John) Haslingden w Grane and Stonefold
Blackb

STONEGATE (St Peter) *Chich 19* **P** *E J B Hardcastle Esq*
and M H Reid Esq (jt) **P-in-c** M G P INSLEY,
C S W NUTH

STONEGRAVE (Holy Trinity) Harome w Stonegrave,
Nunnington and Pockley *York*

STONEHAM, NORTH (All Saints) *Win 9*
P *R H W Fleming Esq* **R** J E OWEN, **C** P G H DOORES,
J E PICKETT

STONEHAM, NORTH (St Nicholas) Valley Park *Win*

STONEHAM, SOUTH (St Mary) Swaythling *Win*

STONEHAM BASSETT, NORTH (St Michael) N Stoneham
Win

**STONEHAM BASSETT GREEN, NORTH (St
Christopher)** as above

STONEHOUSE (St Cyr) *Glouc 8* **P** *The Crown*
V J N K HARRIS

STONEHOUSE (St Paul) Plymouth St Andr and St Paul
Stonehouse *Ex*

STONELEIGH (St John the Baptist) *Guildf 9* **P** *Bp*
V D W RENSHAW

STONELEIGH (St Mary the Virgin) w Ashow and Baginton
Cov 4 **P** *Lord Leigh and Bp (jt)* **R** D E WEBSTER,
NSM E JOHNSON

STONESBY (St Peter) Waltham on the Wolds, Stonesby,
Saxby etc *Leic*

STONESFIELD (St James the Great) w Combe *Ox 9*
P *Duke of Marlborough* **R** G J H B van der WEEGEN

STONEY MIDDLETON (St Martin) Baslow w Curbar and
Stoney Middleton *Derby*

STONEY STANTON (St Michael) Croft and Stoney Stanton
Leic

STONEYCROFT (All Saints) *Liv 8* **P** *Bp* **V** W J STALKER

STONEYCROFT (St Paul) Liv St Paul Stoneycroft *Liv*

STONEYDELPH (St Martin in the Delph) Glascote and
Stonydelph *Lich*

STONHAM ASPAL (St Mary and St Lambert) Crowfield w
Stonham Aspal and Mickfield *St E*

STONHAM PARVA (St Mary) Creeting St Mary, Creeting
St Peter etc *St E*

STONNALL (St Peter) *Lich 1* **P** *V Shenstone*
P-in-c J R FAGAN

STONTON WYVILLE (St Denys) Church Langton w Tur
Langton, Thorpe Langton etc *Leic*

STONY STRATFORD (St Mary and St Giles) *Ox 25* **P** *Bp*
V C H J CAVELL-NORTHAM

STOODLEIGH (St Margaret) Washfield, Stoodleigh,
Withleigh etc *Ex*

STOPHAM (St Mary the Virgin) and Fittleworth *Chich 11*
P *D&C and Sir Brian Barttelot, Bt (jt)* **R** A I SMYTH

STOPSLEY (St Thomas) *St Alb 20* **P** *Bp* **V** *Vacant* Luton
(01582) 29194

STORRIDGE (St John the Baptist) Cradley w Mathon and
Storridge *Heref*

STORRINGTON (St Mary) *Chich 12* **P** *Keble Coll Ox*
R J M ACHESON, **NSM** M A JEWELL

STORTH (All Saints Mission) Arnside *Carl*

STOTFOLD (St Mary the Virgin) and Radwell *St Alb 22*
P *Bp* **R** S G PUGH

**STOTTESDON (St Mary) w Farlow, Cleeton St Mary and
Silvington** *Heref 9* **P** *Bp* **R** W J BROMLEY

STOUGHTON (Emmanuel) *Guildf 5* **P** *Simeon's Trustees*
V J F SALTER

STOUGHTON (St Mary) Compton, the Mardens, Stoughton
and Racton *Chich*

STOUGHTON (St Mary and All Saints) Thurnby w
Stoughton *Leic*

**STOULTON (St Edmund) w Drake's Broughton and Pirton
and Norton** *Worc 4* **P** *Earl of Cov, D&C, and Bp (jt)*
R I READ, **NSM** F L MIDDLEMISS

STOUR, EAST (Christ Church) Gillingham *Sarum*

STOUR, UPPER *Sarum 14* **P** *Exors H P R Hoare (1 turn),
Bp (2 turns), and Bourton Chpl Trustees (1 turn)*
R B C ATKINSON, **Hon C** P A RUNDLE

STOUR, WEST (St Mary) Gillingham *Sarum*

STOUR PROVOST (St Michael and All Angels) as above

STOUR ROW (All Saints) as above

STOUR VALLEY Group, The Clare w Poslingford,
Cavendish etc *St E*

STOURBRIDGE Norton (St Michael and All Angels)
Worc 12 **P** *Bp* **V** M J BEASLEY

STOURBRIDGE (St John the Evangelist) Old Swinford
Stourbridge *Worc*

STOURBRIDGE (St Mary) as above

STOURBRIDGE (St Thomas) *Worc 12* **P** *Bp*
V S HUTCHINSON, **NSM** C S MOORHOUSE

STOURPAINE (Holy Trinity) Pimperne, Stourpaine,
Durweston and Bryanston *Sarum*

**STOURPORT-ON-SEVERN (St Michael and All Angels) and
Wilden** *Worc 13* **P** *Earl of Bewdley and V Kidderminster St
Mary and All SS etc (jt)* **V** B GILBERT,
NSM S M DATSON

STOURTON (St Peter) Kinver and Enville *Lich*

STOURTON (St Peter) Upper Stour *Sarum*

STOURTON CAUNDLE (St Peter) The Caundles w Folke
and Holwell *Sarum*

STOVEN (St Margaret) Hundred River *St E*

STOW Group, The (St Mary the Virgin) *Linc 2* **P** *Bp and
DBP (jt)* **R** G S RICHARDSON

STOW w Quy *Ely 6* **P** *Bp* **P-in-c** R A MINTER

STOW, WEST (St Mary) Culford, W Stow and Wordwell w
Flempton etc *St E*

STOW BARDOLPH (Holy Trinity) Wimbotsham w Stow
Bardolph and Stow Bridge etc *Ely*

STOW BEDON (St Botolph) Caston w Griston, Merton,
Thompson etc *Nor*

STOW BRIDGE Mission (St Peter) Wimbotsham w Stow
Bardolph and Stow Bridge etc *Ely*

STOW LONGA (St Botolph) *Ely 10* **P** *Bp* **V** R A FROST

STOW MARIES (St Mary and St Margaret) Purleigh, Cold
Norton and Stow Maries *Chelmsf*

STOW ON THE WOLD (St Edward) *Glouc 15* **P** *DBP*
R R F ROTHERY

STOWE (Assumption of St Mary the Virgin) *Ox 22*
P *Stowe Sch* **P-in-c** R B JACKSON

STOWE (St Michael and All Angels) Bucknell w Chapel
Lawn, Llanfair Waterdine etc *Heref*

STOWE, UPPER (St James) Heyford w Stowe Nine
Churches *Pet*

STOWE BY CHARTLEY (St John the Baptist) Hixon w
Stowe-by-Chartley *Lich*

STOWE NINE CHURCHES (St Michael) Heyford w Stowe
Nine Churches *Pet*

STOWELL (St Leonard) Chedworth, Yanworth and Stowell,
Coln Rogers etc *Glouc*

STOWELL (St Mary Magdalene) Henstridge and Charlton
Horethorne w Stowell *B & W*

STOWEY (St Nicholas and Blessed Virgin Mary) Bishop
Sutton and Stanton Drew and Stowey *B & W*

STOWEY, NETHER (Blessed Virgin Mary) w Over Stowey
B & W 17 **P** *D&C Windsor and MMCET (alt)*
V P DENISON

STOWEY, OVER (St Peter and St Paul) Nether Stowey w
Over Stowey *B & W*

STOWFORD (St John) Marystowe, Coryton, Stowford,
Lewtrenchard etc *Ex*

STOWLANGTOFT (St George) Badwell Ash w Gt Ashfield, Stowlangtoft etc *St E*

STOWMARKET (St Peter and St Mary) *St E 6* **P** *Ch Patr Trust* **V** J R HARROLD, **NSM** R M STRETCH, D WEBB, R F GILBERT

STOWTING (St Mary the Virgin) Sellindge w Monks Horton and Stowting etc *Cant*

STOWUPLAND (Holy Trinity) Old Newton w Stowupland *St E*

STRADBROKE (All Saints) w Horham, Athelington and Redlingfield *St E 17* **P** *Bp (3 turns), Lt-Comdr G C Marshall (1 turn), and Dr G I Soden (1 turn)* **R** D J STREETER

STRADISHALL (St Margaret) Denston w Stradishall and Stansfield *St E*

STRADSETT (St Mary) Crimplesham w Stradsett *Ely*

STRAITS, THE (St Andrew) Sedgley All SS *Worc*

STRAMSHALL (St Michael and All Angels) *Lich 20* **P** *V Uttoxeter* **P-in-c** A G SADLER, **C** A O L HODGSON

STRANTON (All Saints) *Dur 13* **P** *St Jo Coll Dur* **V** S R TAYLOR, **C** S BUTLER (nee McVEIGH)

STRATFIELD MORTIMER (St Mary) *Ox 12* **P** *Eton Coll* **V** J A ELLIS, **NSM** C G LEA, M J OKE

STRATFIELD SAYE (St Mary) Sherfield-on-Loddon and Stratfield Saye etc *Win*

STRATFORD (St John the Evangelist and Christ Church) w Forest Gate St James *Chelmsf 3* **P** V W Ham **P-in-c** D A RICHARDS, **C** F WATKINS, M I HOLMDEN, Hon C J P RICHARDSON, **NSM** J V MEADWAY

STRATFORD NEW TOWN (St Paul) *Chelmsf 3* **P** *Ch Patr Trust* **V** *Vacant* 0181–534 3640

STRATFORD-ON-AVON (Holy Trinity) w Bishopton *Cov 8* **P** *Bp* **R** P L HOLLIDAY, **C** D J TURNER, M TURNER

STRATFORD ST MARY (St Mary) Higham, Holton St Mary, Raydon and Stratford *St E*

STRATFORD SUB CASTLE (St Lawrence) *Sarum 15* **P** *D&C* **P-in-c** B J HOPKINSON

STRATTON (St Andrew) and Launcells *Truro 8* **P** *Duchy of Cornwall and CPAS (alt)* **V** R N STRANACK

STRATTON (St Mary) (St Michael) and Wacton *Nor 5* **P** *G&C Coll Cam, DBP, and New Coll Ox (by turn)* **R** P L COLEY

STRATTON (St Mary the Virgin) Bradf Peverell, Stratton, Frampton etc *Sarum*

STRATTON (St Peter), North Cerney, Baunton and Bagendon *Glouc 12* **P** *R T G Chester Master Esq, Jes coll Ox, Univ Coll Ox (jt)* **R** H A S COCKS, **NSM** D H C LEESON, D R EADY

STRATTON, EAST (All Saints) Micheldever and E Stratton, Woodmancote etc *Win*

STRATTON, UPPER (St Philip) *Bris 12* **P** *Bp* **V** *Vacant* Swindon (01793) 723095

STRATTON AUDLEY (St Mary and St Edburga) and Godington, Fringford w Hethe and Stoke Lyne *Ox 2* **P** *Ch Ch Ox, Ld Chan, and CCC Ox (by turn)* **R** *Vacant* Bicester (01869) 277238

STRATTON ON THE FOSSE (St Vigor) Chilcompton w Downside and Stratton on the Fosse *B & W*

STRATTON ST MARGARET (St Margaret) w South Marston and Stanton Fitzwarren *Bris 12* **P** *Patr Bd* **TR** T D HAWKINGS, **TV** R J SNOW, **C** G A SARMEZEY, Hon C R J BURSTON

STRATTON STRAWLESS (St Margaret) Hevingham w Hainford and Stratton Strawless *Nor*

STREAT (not known) w Westmeston *Chich 9* **P** *Woodard Schs* **NSM** G R WALKER

STREATHAM (Christ Church) *S'wark 13* **P** *R Streatham St Leon* **V** C J IVORY, **C** H J N FULLERTON

STREATHAM Furzedown (St Paul) Streatham St Paul *S'wark*

STREATHAM (Immanuel) (St Andrew) *S'wark 13* **P** *Bp, Hyndman Trustees, and R Streatham St Leon (jt)* **C** J A CARROLL

STREATHAM (St Leonard) *S'wark 13* **P** *Bp* **R** J R WILCOX, Hon C L M WRIGHT

STREATHAM (St Paul) (St Andrew's Church Hall) *S'wark 17* **P** *Bp* **V** N A PARISH

STREATHAM (St Peter) *S'wark 13* **P** *St Steph Ho Ox* **V** A S WALKER, **C** C I PEARSON

STREATHAM (St Thomas) Telford Park St Thos *S'wark*

STREATHAM, WEST (St James) *S'wark 17* **P** *CPAS* **V** P I MOUNSTEPHEN

STREATHAM HILL (St Margaret the Queen) *S'wark 13* **P** *Bp* **V** G T WILLIAMS

STREATHAM PARK (St Alban) *S'wark 17* **P** *Ch Soc Trust* **V** M D MARSHALL, **C** B E STANNARD

STREATHAM VALE (Holy Redeemer) *S'wark 13* **P** *CPAS* **V** I H GILMOUR

STREATLEY (St Margaret) *St Alb 20* **P** *Bp* **V** R W WOOD, **C** P THORN

STREATLEY (St Mary) w Moulsford *Ox 18* **P** *Bp* **V** R J DAVISON, Hon C J P MACKNEY, **NSM** C L WINDEBANK

STREET (Holy Trinity) (Mission Church) w Walton *B & W 5* **P** *DBP* **R** F J GREED, **C** A R ELWOOD

STREET Team Ministry, The *York 3* **P** *Patr Bd* **TR** G S SIMPSON, **C** R E LONG

STREETLY (All Saints) *Lich 6* **P** *Bp* **V** P A R HAMMERSLEY, **C** G FRASER

STRELLEY (All Saints) Bilborough w Strelley *S'well*

STRENSALL (St Mary the Virgin) *York 5* **P** *Abp* **V** G C GALLEY

STRETE (St Michael) E Allington, Slapton and Strete *Ex*

STRETFORD (All Saints) *Man 7* **P** *Bp* **R** P K TOWNLEY

STRETFORD (St Bride) *Man 7* **P** *Trustees* **R** P J RAWLINGS, **NSM** V M ECCLES

STRETFORD (St Matthew) *Man 7* **P** *D&C* **R** H R ENTWISTLE, **NSM** B A DUNN

STRETFORD (St Peter) *Man 7* **P** *The Crown* **R** J S CROSS

STRETHALL (St Mary the Virgin) Heydon, Gt and Lt Chishill, Chrishall etc *Chelmsf*

STRETHAM (St James) w Thetford *Ely 14* **P** *Bp* **P-in-c** F J KILNER

STRETTON (St John) Penkridge Team *Lich*

STRETTON (St Mary) w Claymills *Lich 19* **P** *Baroness Gretton* **V** P D HOWARD

STRETTON (St Matthew) and Appleton Thorn *Ches 4* **P** *Mrs P F du Bois Grantham and Dr S P L du Bois Davidson (jt)* **V** R ROWLANDS

STRETTON (St Nicholas) Greetham and Thistleton w Stretton and Clipsham *Pet*

STRETTON, LITTLE (All Saints) Church Stretton *Heref*

STRETTON GRANDISON (St Laurence) Bosbury w Wellington Heath etc *Heref*

STRETTON MAGNA (St Giles) Gt Glen, Stretton Magna and Wistow etc *Leic*

STRETTON ON DUNSMORE (All Saints) Bourton w Frankton and Stretton on Dunsmore etc *Cov*

STRETTON ON DUNSMORE (Mission Church) as above

STRETTON ON FOSSE (St Peter) Ilmington w Stretton-on-Fosse etc *Cov*

STRETTON PARVA (St John the Baptist) Gaulby *Leic*

STRETTON SUGWAS (St Mary Magdalene) *Heref 4* **P** *DBP* **P-in-c** M A KELK

STRGGLETHORPE (St Michael) Brant Broughton and Beckingham *Linc*

STRICKLAND, GREAT (St Barnabas) Morland, Thrimby and Gt Strickland *Carl*

STRINES (St Paul) Marple All SS *Ches*

STRINGSTON (not known) Quantoxhead *B & W*

STRIXTON (St John) Wollaston and Strixton *Pet*

STROOD (St Francis) *Roch 6* **P** *Bp* **V** B R INGRAM

STROOD (St Nicholas) w St Mary *Roch 6* **P** *Bp and D&C (jt)* **V** A A MUSTOE

STROUD (Holy Trinity) (St Alban Mission Church) *Glouc 1* **P** *Bp* **P-in-c** D T MERRY, **C** S J EARLEY

STROUD (Mission Church) Steep and Froxfield w Privett *Portsm*

STROUD (St Laurence) and Uplands w Slad *Glouc 1* **P** *Bp* **V** B C E COKER, **C** J A NEWCOMBE

STROUD GREEN (Holy Trinity) *Lon 20* **P** *Bp* **V** B K LUNN, **C** W P WATERS

STROXTON (All Saints) Harlaxton *Linc*

STRUBBY (St Oswald) Wold-Marsh Gp *Linc*

STRUMPSHAW (St Peter) Burlingham St Edmund w Lingwood, Strumpshaw etc *Nor*

STUBBINGS (St James the Less) Hurley and Stubbings *Ox*

STUBBINS (St Philip) Edenfield and Stubbins *Man*

STUBBS CROSS (St Francis) Kingsnorth w Shadoxhurst *Cant*

STUBSHAW CROSS (St Luke) Ashton-in-Makerfield St Thos *Liv*

STUBTON (St Martin) Claypole *Linc*

STUDHAM (St Mary the Virgin) Kensworth, Studham and Whipsnade *St Alb*

STUDLAND (St Nicholas) Swanage and Studland *Sarum*

STUDLEY (Nativity of the Blessed Virgin Mary) *Cov 7* **P** *DBP* **P-in-c** R W DEIMEL, **C** T J HARMER

STUDLEY (St John the Evangelist) *Sarum 17* **P** *R Trowbridge St Jas* **P-in-c** P N BARNES

STUDLEY, HORTON-CUM (St Barnabas) Horton-cum-Studley *Ox*

STUKELEY, GREAT (St Bartholomew) w LITTLE (St Martin) *Ely 9* **P** *SMF and Bp (jt)* **P-in-c** A P LUDLOW

STUNTNEY (Holy Cross) *Ely 14* **P** *D&C*
P-in-c F J KILNER
STURMER (St Mary) Ridgewell w Ashen, Birdbrook and Sturmer *Chelmsf*
STURMINSTER MARSHALL (St Mary), Kingston Lacy and Shapwick *Sarum 10* **P** Eton Coll and Nat Trust *(alt)*
V I J MAYO
STURMINSTER NEWTON (St Mary) and Hinton St Mary *Sarum 6* **P** G A L F Pitt-Rivers Esq *(3 turns)*, *Col J L Yeatman (2 turns)*, and V Iwerne Minster *(1 turn)*
P-in-c J C DAY
STURRY (St Nicholas) w Fordwich and Westbere w Hersden *Cant 3* **P** Abp, Ld Chan, and St Aug Foundn Cant *(by turn)* **R** P J GAUSDEN
STURTON (St Hugh) Stow Gp *Linc*
STURTON, GREAT (All Saints) Hemingby *Linc*
STURTON-LE-STEEPLE (St Peter and St Paul) N Wheatley, W Burton, Bole, Saundby, Sturton etc *S'well*
STUSTON (All Saints) N Hartismere *St E*
STUTTON (St Aidan) Tadcaster w Newton Kyme *York*
STUTTON (St Peter) Brantham w Stutton *St E*
STYVECHALE (St James) *Cov 3* **P** Col A M H Gregory-Hood **V** J LEACH, **C** B R WILSON
SUCKLEY (St John the Baptist) Alfrick, Lulsley, Suckley, Leigh and Bransford *Worc*
SUDBOROUGH (All Saints) Lowick w Sudborough and Slipton *Pet*
SUDBOURNE (All Saints) Orford w Sudbourne, Chillesford, Butley and Iken *St E*
SUDBROOKE (St Edward) Barlings *Linc*
SUDBURY (All Saints) and Somersal Herbert *Derby 14* **P** Bp and DBP *(alt)* **P-in-c** D MILNER
SUDBURY (All Saints) w Ballingdon and Brundon *St E 12* **P** Simeon's Trustees **V** L F SIMPKINS
SUDBURY (St Andrew) *Lon 21* **P** Bp **V** *Vacant 0181-904 4016*
SUDBURY (St Gregory) St Peter and Chilton *St E 12* **P** Bp *(3 turns)*, Ch Soc Trust *(1 turn)* **P-in-c** L R PIZZEY
SUDDEN (St Aidan) Rochdale *Man*
SUDLEY MANOR (St Mary) Winchcombe, Gretton, Sudeley Manor etc *Glouc*
SUFFIELD (St Margaret) Felmingham, Skeyton, Colby, Banningham etc *Nor*
SUFFIELD PARK (St Martin) Cromer *Nor*
SUGLEY (Holy Saviour) *Newc 7* **P** Bp **V** B WALTON
SULBY (St Stephen's Chapel) Lezayre *S & M*
SULGRAVE (St James the Less) Culworth w Sulgrave and Thorpe Mandeville etc *Pet*
SULHAM (St Nicholas) Pangbourne w Tidmarsh and Sulham *Ox*
SULHAMSTEAD ABBOTS (St Mary) and Bannister w Ufton Nervet *Ox 12* **P** Qu Coll Ox and Or Coll Ox *(alt)*
R M WATTS
SULLINGTON (St Mary) and Thakeham w Warminghurst *Chich 12* **P** Bp and DBP *(alt)* **P-in-c** G JEFFERY
SUMMERFIELD (Christ Church) (Cavendish Road Hall) *Birm 2* **P** R Birm St Martin w Bordesley **V** J B KNIGHT
SUMMERFIELD (St John's Chapel) Hartlebury *Worc*
SUMMERSDALE (St Michael) Chich St Paul and St Pet *Chich*
SUMMERSTOWN (St Mary) *S'wark 17* **P** Ch Soc Trust
V R J RYAN
SUMMERTOWN (St Michael and All Angels) Wolvercote w Summertown *Ox*
SUNBURY, UPPER (St Saviour) *Lon 13* **P** V Sunbury
V A F P BROWN
SUNBURY-ON-THAMES (St Mary) *Lon 13*
P D&C St Paul's **V** J R DUDLEY, **C** G L WARREN
SUNDERLAND Pennywell (St Thomas) *Dur 9* **P** Bp
V M A MILLWARD, **C** D J STEPHENSON
SUNDERLAND Red House (St Cuthbert) *Dur 9* **P** D&C
V M BEBBINGTON
SUNDERLAND (St Chad) *Dur 9* **P** Bp **V** J D CHADD,
NSM J M M FRANCIS
SUNDERLAND (St Mary the Virgin) (St Peter) *Dur 9*
P Bp **V** K HUNT, **C** P J NORTH
SUNDERLAND (St Michael) *Dur 9* **P** Bp
TV I D HUNTER SMART, **NSM** W HALL
SUNDERLAND Town End Farm (St Bede) *Dur 9* **P** Bp
V J W POULTER
SUNDERLAND, NORTH (St Paul) *Newc 10* **P** Lord Crewe's Trustees **V** D G ROGERSON
SUNDERLAND POINT (Mission Church) Overton *Blackb*
SUNDON (St Mary) *St Alb 20* **P** L S PULLAN
SUNDRIDGE (St Mary) w Ide Hill *Roch 8* **P** Abp
R B E S GODFREY

SUNNINGDALE (Holy Trinity) *Ox 11* **P** Bp **V** M HILL
SUNNINGHILL (St Michael and All Angels) *Ox 11*
P St Jo Coll Cam **V** T W GUNTER, **NSM** G R PARISH
SUNNINGWELL (St Leonard) Radley and Sunningwell *Ox*
SUNNYSIDE (St Barnabas) E Grinstead St Swithun *Chich*
SUNNYSIDE (St Michael and All Angels) w Bourne End *St Alb 3* **P** CP AS **V** S P BREUKELMAN,
NSM R CLARKSON
SURBITON (St Andrew) (St Mark) *S'wark 15* **P** Bp
V D JACKSON, **TV** G N OWEN, **C** T D PAGE,
Hon C T BRAUN, **NSM** R H CROSSLAND
SURBITON (St Matthew) *S'wark 15* **P** R&S Ch Trust
V S A HONES, **C** H D UFFINDELL, A P C DOYE
SURBITON HILL (Christ Church) *S'wark 15* **P** Ch Soc Trust and Trustees *(jt)* **V** G WINTLE, **C** C M GREEN,
NSM D J BENDELL, M L GODIN
SURFLEET (St Lawrence) *Linc 17* **P** Bp and V Pinchbeck *(jt)* **V** *Vacant Surfleet (0177585) 230*
SURLINGHAM (St Mary) Rockland St Mary w Hellington, Bramerton etc *Nor*
SUSSEX GARDENS (St James) Paddington St Jas *Lon*
SUSTEAD (St Peter and St Paul) Roughton and Felbrigg, Metton, Sustead etc *Nor*
SUTCOMBE (St Andrew) *Ex 9* **P** Bp **R** H J ROCHE
SUTTERBY (not known) Langton w Sutterby *Linc*
SUTTERTON (St Mary) w Fosdyke and Algarkirk *Linc 21*
P Prime Min, Bp and DBP *(alt)* **P-in-c** H HALL,
NSM J F UDY
SUTTON (All Saints) Potton w Sutton and Cockayne Hatley *St Alb*
SUTTON (All Saints) Shottisham w Sutton *St E*
SUTTON (All Saints) w Shopland *Chelmsf 12* **P** SMF
P-in-c G A BISHTON
SUTTON (Christ Church) *S'wark 26* **P** R Sutton St Nic
C M S RANDALL
SUTTON (Mission Room) Felixkirk w Boltby *York*
SUTTON (St Andrew) *Ely 14* **P** D&C **NSM** M T COOPER
SUTTON (St Clement), Huttoft and Anderby *Linc 8*
P Bp *(2 turns)*, Magd Coll Cam *(1 turn)* **R** G J WILCOX
SUTTON (St George) (St Barnabas's Mission Church) *Ches 13* **P** Trustees **V** D S HARRISON
SUTTON (St James) *Ches 13* **P** Trustees
V C F EASTWOOD
SUTTON (St James) and Wawne (St Peter) *York 15*
P Patr Bd **TR** T W DOHERTY, **C** J H M DUMULLA
SUTTON (St John the Baptist) Barlavington, Burton w Coates, Sutton and Bignor *Chich*
SUTTON (St Mary) Calow and Sutton cum Duckmanton *Derby*
SUTTON (St Michael and All Angels) Castor w Sutton and Upton *Pet*
SUTTON (St Michael) w Ingham and Catfield *Nor 13* **P** Bp
R S WESTON
SUTTON (St Nicholas) *S'wark 26* **P** Hertf Coll Ox
C J A G POPP
SUTTON (St Nicholas) (All Saints) (St Michael and All Angels) *Liv 10* **P** Patr Bd **TR** J L HIGHAM,
TV A D J JEWELL, F E MYATT, S A MATHER
SUTTON (St Thomas) *Bradf 8* **P** Ch Ch Ox
P-in-c R HOWARD
SUTTON w Carlton and Normanton upon Trent and Marnham *S'well 3* **P** Bp **V** P M BISHOP
SUTTON, EAST (St Peter and St Paul) Sutton Valence w E Sutton and Chart Sutton *Cant*
SUTTON, GREAT (St John the Evangelist) *Ches 9*
P V Eastham **V** T J VIRTUE
SUTTON, NORTH Plymouth Em, Efford and Laira *Ex*
SUTTON AT HONE (St John the Baptist) *Roch 2* **P** D&C
V F E J WILLOUGHBY
SUTTON BASSETT (All Saints) Ashley w Weston by Welland and Sutton Bassett *Pet*
SUTTON BENGER (All Saints) Draycot *Bris*
SUTTON BONINGTON (St Michael) (St Anne) w Normanton-on-Soar *S'well 10* **P** Bp **P-in-c** C B PERKINS
SUTTON BRIDGE (St Matthew) *Linc 16* **P** Bp
P-in-c E J BANGAY (formerly REAST)
SUTTON BY DOVER (St Peter and St Paul) Gt Mongeham w Ripple and Sutton by Dover *Cant*
SUTTON CHENEY (St James) Market Bosworth, Cadeby w Sutton Cheney etc *Leic*
SUTTON COLDFIELD (Holy Trinity) *Birm 9* **P** Bp
R E G LONGMAN, **C** J L COOPER
SUTTON COLDFIELD (St Chad) *Birm 9* **P** Bp
V P A W WATTS
SUTTON COLDFIELD (St Columba) *Birm 9* **P** Bp
V R F JENKINS
SUTTON COURTENAY (All Saints) w Appleford *Ox 10*
P D&C Windsor **P-in-c** A L THOMAS

SUTTON-CUM-LOUND (St Bartholomew) Babworth w Sutton-cum-Lound *S'well*

SUTTON GREEN (All Souls) Woking St Pet *Guildf*

SUTTON HILL (Pastoral Centre) Madeley *Heref*

SUTTON IN ASHFIELD (St Mary Magdalene) *S'well 4* **P** *Bp*   **C**   L A de POMERAI,   **NSM**   D I M de POMERAI

SUTTON IN ASHFIELD (St Michael and All Angels) *S'well 4* **P** *Bp*   **P-in-c**   B G DUCKWORTH

SUTTON IN HOLDERNESS (St Michael) *York 15* **P** *Abp*   **V**   M P CHAFFEY

SUTTON LE MARSH (St Clement) Sutton, Huttoft and Anderby *Linc*

SUTTON MADDOCK (St Mary) Beckbury, Badger, Kemberton, Ryton, Stockton etc *Lich*

SUTTON MANDEVILLE (All Saints) Fovant, Sutton Mandeville and Teffont Evias etc *Sarum*

SUTTON MONTIS (Holy Trinity) Queen Camel w W Camel, Corton Denham etc *B & W*

SUTTON NEW TOWN (St Barnabas) *S'wark 26* **P** *Bp*   **V**   P A THOMPSON

SUTTON ON DERWENT (St Michael) Elvington w Sutton on Derwent and E Cottingwith *York*

SUTTON ON PLYM (St John the Evangelist) *Ex 24* **P** *Keble Coll Ox*   **V**   B R LAY

SUTTON-ON-SEA (St Clement) Sutton, Huttoft and Anderby *Linc*

SUTTON ON THE FOREST (All Hallows) *York 5* **P** *Ld Chan*   **P-in-c**   T A McCOULOUGH

SUTTON ON THE HILL (St Michael) Ch Broughton w Barton Blount, Boylestone etc *Derby*

SUTTON-ON-TRENT (All Saints) Sutton w Carlton and Normanton upon Trent etc *S'well*

SUTTON PARK (St Andrew) Sutton St Jas and Wawne *York*

SUTTON ST EDMUND (St Edmund) The Suttons w Tydd *Linc*

SUTTON ST JAMES (St James) as above

SUTTON ST MARY (otherwise known as Long Sutton) (St Mary) *Linc 16* **P** *Lady McGeoch*   **NSM**   R SPIVEY

SUTTON ST MICHAEL (St Michael) Sutton St Nicholas w Sutton St Michael *Heref*

SUTTON ST NICHOLAS Lutton w Gedney Drove End, Dawsmere *Linc*

SUTTON ST NICHOLAS (St Nicholas) w Sutton St Michael *Heref 4* **P** *Bp*   **R**   M A PAICE

SUTTON UNDER BRAILES (St Thomas a Becket) *Cov 9* **P** *Bp*   **R**   N J MORGAN,   **NSM**   J W ROLFE

SUTTON VALENCE (St Mary the Virgin) w East Sutton and Chart Sutton *Cant 15* **P** *Abp York*   **V**   D R BARKER

SUTTON VENY (St John the Evangelist) Heytesbury and Sutton Veny *Sarum*

SUTTON WALDRON (St Bartholomew) The Iwernes, Sutton Waldron and Fontmell Magna *Sarum*

SUTTONS w Tydd, The *Linc 16* **P** *Ld Chan (1 turn), V Long Sutton (2 turns)*   **V**   P V NOBLE

SWABY (St Nicholas) Wold-Marsh Gp *Linc*

SWADLINCOTE (Emmanuel) *Derby 16* **P** *V Gresley*   **V**   D J HORSFALL

SWAFFHAM (St Peter and St Paul) *Nor 14* **P** *Bp*   **V**   M P GREEN,   **C**   S F NUNNEY

SWAFFHAM BULBECK (St Mary) and Swaffham Prior w Reach *Ely 3* **P** *Bp and D&C (jt)*   **V**   M N HAWORTH

SWAFFHAM PRIOR (St Mary) Swaffham Bulbeck and Swaffham Prior w Reach *Ely*

SWAFIELD (St Nicholas) Trunch *Nor*

SWAINSTHORPE (St Peter) w Newton Flotman *Nor 7* **P** *Bp*   **P-in-c**   C J COLLISON

SWAINSWICK (Blessed Virgin Mary) Bath St Sav w Swainswick and Woolley *B & W*

SWALCLIFFE (St Peter and St Paul) Epwell w Sibford, Swalcliffe and Tadmarton *Ox*

SWALECLIFFE (St John the Baptist) Whitstable *Cant*

SWALEDALE *Ripon 2* **P** *Bp*   **V**   P S MIDWOOD

SWALLOW (Holy Trinity) *Linc 5* **P** *Rev J R H and Rev H C Thorold, DBP, Bp, and Earl of Yarborough (by turn)*   **R**   *Vacant* Swallow (01472) 371560

SWALLOWCLIFFE (St Peter) Tisbury *Sarum*

SWALLOWFIELD (All Saints) *Ox 15* **P** *D&C Heref*   **P-in-c**   P E BANNISTER

SWALWELL (Holy Trinity) *Dur 5* **P** *R Whickham*   **V**   J M H GIBSON

SWAN *Ox 24* **P** *Patr Bd*   **TR**   D W OWEN,   **TV**   D A HISCOCK

SWANAGE (All Saints) (St Mary the Virgin) and Studland *Sarum 9* **P** *Patr Bd*   **TR**   D J RACTLIFFE,   **TV**   W H N WATTS,   P G McAVOY

SWANBOROUGH *Sarum 9* **P** *Patr Bd*   **TR**   P J RIVETT,   **TV**   J D N GRAY

SWANBOURNE (St Swithun) Mursley w Swanbourne and Lt Horwood *Ox*

SWANLAND (St Barnabas) N Ferriby *York*

SWANLEY (St Mary) *Roch 2* **P** *Guild of All So*   **V**   M R BRUNDLE

SWANLEY (St Paul) *Roch 2* **P** *Merchant Taylors' Co*   **V**   A D PROCTER

SWANMORE (St Barnabas) *Portsm 1* **P** *DBP*   **V**   M R WELCH

SWANMORE (St Michael and All Angels) *Portsm 7* **P** *SMF*   **V**   M J SHEFFIELD,   **NSM**   T F SEAR, M D H JOHNSTON

SWANNINGTON (St George) Ravenstone and Swannington *Leic*

SWANNINGTON (St Margaret) Alderford w Attlebridge and Swannington *Nor*

SWANSCOMBE (St Peter and St Paul) *Roch 4* **P** *DBP*   **R**   T J MERCER

SWANTON ABBOT (St Michael) Worstead, Westwick, Sloley, Swanton Abbot etc *Nor*

SWANTON MORLEY (All Saints) w Beetley w East Bilney and Hoe *Nor 15* **P** *G&C Coll Cam, Ld Chan, and DBP (by turn)*   **R**   L A WILMAN

SWANTON NOVERS (St Edmund) Brinton, Briningham, Hunworth, Stody etc *Nor*

SWANWICK (St Andrew) and Pentrich *Derby 1* **P** *Wright Trustees and Duke of Devonshire (alt)*   **P-in-c**   D W ASHTON

SWANWICK (St Barnabas) Sarisbury *Portsm*

SWARBY (St Mary and All Saints) S Lafford *Linc*

SWARCLIFFE (St Luke) Seacroft *Ripon*

SWARDESTON (St Mary the Virgin) w East Carleton, Intwood, Keswick and Ketteringham *Nor 7* **P** *Bp, DBP, and Miss M B Unthank (jt)*   **R**   G M C JONES

SWARKESTONE (St James) Barrow-on-Trent w Twyford and Swarkestone *Derby*

SWARTHMORE (Mission Church) Pennington w Lindal and Marton *Carl*

SWATON (St Michael) Helpringham w Hale *Linc*

SWAVESEY (St Andrew) *Ely 5* **P** *Jes Coll Cam*   **V**   J D YULE,   **NSM**   A F JESSON

SWAY (St Luke) *Win 10* **P** *Bp*   **V**   J S WHITE

SWAYFIELD (St Nicholas) Corby Glen *Linc*

SWAYTHLING (St Mary South Stoneham w St Alban the Martyr) *Win 12* **P** *Bp and TR Southn City Cen (jt)*   **V**   J M MOORE,   **C**   M L RICHES

SWEFFLING (St Mary) Rendham w Sweffling *St E*

SWELL (St Catherine) Curry Rivel w Fivehead and Swell *B & W*

SWELL, LOWER (St Mary) Longborough, Sezincote, Condicote and the Swells *Glouc*

SWELL, UPPER (St Mary) as above

SWEPSTONE (St Peter) The Appleby Gp *Leic*

SWERFORD (St Mary) Hook Norton w Gt Rollright, Swerford etc *Ox*

SWETTENHAM (St Peter) Brereton w Swettenham *Ches*

SWILLAND (St Mary) Clopton w Otley, Swilland and Ashbocking *St E*

SWILLINGTON (St Mary) *Ripon 8* **P** *Bp* **R** *Vacant* Leeds (0113) 286 0172

SWIMBRIDGE (St James the Apostle) and West Buckland *Ex 18* **P** *Bp and Trustees Earl Fortescue (jt)*   **V**   P BOWERS

SWINBROOK (St Mary) Burford w Fulbrook, Taynton, Asthall etc *Ox*

SWINDERBY (All Saints) *Linc 18* **P** *Bp, Ld Chan, E M K Kirk Esq, and D&C (by turn)*   **V**   G C GOALBY

SWINDON (All Saints) (St Barnabas) *Bris 10* **P** *Bp*   **V**   P J BENNETT

SWINDON (Christ Church) (St Mary) *Bris 13* **P** *Ld Chan*   **V**   O C BARRACLOUGH,   **C**   J W F GOSLING,   J HOUSE

SWINDON Dorcan *Bris 12* **P** *Bp*   **TR**   B J DUCKETT,   **C**   I P S GOODING,   **NSM**   D N PARSONS

SWINDON New Town (St Mark) (St Adhelm) (St Luke) (St Saviour) *Bris 13* **P** *Patr Bd*   **TR**   L R HURRELL,   **TV**   P D ANDREWS,   J E POTTER,   **NSM**   A S PAGETT

SWINDON (St Andrew) (St John the Baptist) *Bris 13* **P** *Ld Chan*   **TR**   N J MONK,   **TV**   J FORTUNE-WOOD,   **C**   A C MACROW-WOOD

SWINDON (St Augustine) *Bris 10* **P** *Bp*   **V**   C DOBB

SWINDON (St John the Evangelist) *Lich 5* **P** *H Cooke Esq, A T Jenks Esq, and S King Esq (jt)*   **P-in-c**   S E ABLEWHITE

SWINDON (St Lawrence) w Uckington and Elmstone Hardwicke *Glouc 11* **P** *Bp*   **P-in-c**   B HUMPHREY

SWINDON (St Peter) Penhill *Bris*

SWINDON, WEST The Lydiards *Bris*

SWINE (St Mary) *York 12* **P** *W J A Wilberforce Esq and Baroness de Stempel (jt)*   **V**   *Vacant* Hull (01482) 815250

SWINEFLEET (St Margaret) The Marshland *Sheff*

SWINESHEAD (St Mary) *Linc 21* **P** *Bp* **V** *Vacant* Boston (01205) 820271

SWINESHEAD (St Nicholas) The Stodden Churches *St Alb*

SWINFORD (All Saints) w Catthorpe, Shawell and Stanford *Leic 11* **P** *DBP and Ld Chan (alt)* **V** P J C CLEMENTS

SWINFORD, OLD Stourbridge (St Mary) *Worc 12* **P** *Bp* **R** D O BELL, **C** L J WOOLHOUSE

SWINGFIELD (St Peter) Hawkinge w Acrise and Swingfield *Cant*

SWINHOPE (St Helen) Binbrook Gp *Linc*

SWINNOW (Christ the Saviour) Stanningley St Thos *Ripon*

SWINSTEAD (St Mary) Corby Glen *Linc*

SWINTON (Holy Rood) *Man 2* **P** TR Swinton and Pendlebury **V** M W DAGGETT

SWINTON (St Margaret) *Sheff 12* **P** *Sir Stephen Hastings* **V** M R JACKSON

SWINTON (St Peter) and Pendlebury *Man 2* **P** *Patr Bd* **TR** M R GRIFFITHS, **TV** D A DAVIES, **C** R T D PARKER, P B McEVITT

SWITHLAND (St Leonard) *Leic 7* **P** *Ld Chan* **P-in-c** R A HORTON

SWYNCOMBE (St Botolph) w Britwell Salome *Ox 1* **P** *Bp and Ld Chan (alt)* **R** J A FURNESS, **NSM** E R M HENDERSON

SWYNNERTON (St Mary) and Tittensor *Lich 18* **P** *Bp and Simeon's Trustees (jt)* **R** B J BREWER, **NSM** N M RUSSELL

SWYRE (Holy Trinity) Bride Valley *Sarum*

SYDE (St Mary) Brimpsfield, Cranham, Elkstone and Syde *Glouc*

SYDENHAM (All Saints) *S'wark 4* **P** *V Sydenham St Bart* **P-in-c** J O ARDLEY, **C** S M BURNETT

SYDENHAM (Holy Trinity) *S'wark 4* **P** *Simeon's Trustees* **V** R P DORMANDY, **C** M M JONES

SYDENHAM (St Bartholmew) *S'wark 4* **P** *Earl of Dartmouth* **V** M J KINGSTON, **NSM** C E ELVEY

SYDENHAM (St Mary) Chinnor w Emmington and Sydenham etc *Ox*

SYDENHAM (St Philip) *S'wark 4* **P** *V Sydenham St Bart* **V** P W TIERNAN

SYDENHAM, LOWER (St Michael and All Angels) Bell Green *S'wark 4* **P** *Bp* **P-in-c** J O ARDLEY, **C** S M BURNETT, **NSM** R W POTTIER

SYDENHAM DAMEREL (St Mary) Milton Abbot, Dunterton, Lamerton etc *Ex*

SYDERSTONE (St Mary) N and S Creake w Waterden, Syderstone etc *Nor*

SYDLING (St Nicholas) Bradf Peverell, Stratton, Frampton etc *Sarum*

SYERSTON (All Saints) E Stoke w Syerston *S'well*

SYKEHOUSE (Holy Trinity) Fishlake w Sykehouse, Kirk Bramwith, Fenwick etc *Sheff*

SYLEHAM (St Mary) Hoxne w Denham, Syleham and Wingfield *St E*

SYMONDS GREEN (Christ the King) Stevenage H Trin *St Alb*

SYMONDSBURY (St John the Baptist) and Chideock *Sarum 3* **P** *Bp* **P-in-c** R J FORBES

SYRESHAM (St James) Helmdon w Stuchbury and Radstone etc *Pet*

SYSTON (St Mary) Barkston and Hough Gp *Linc*

SYSTON Team Ministry, The (St Peter and St Paul) *Leic 6* **P** *Patr Bd* **TR** K R COURT, **TV** C A FLATTERS, J A HILLMAN, J S HOPEWELL, **C** N J HEALE

SYSTON (St Anne) Warmley, Syston and Bitton *Bris*

SYSTONBY (not known) Melton Mowbray *Leic*

SYWELL (St Peter and St Paul) Mears Ashby and Hardwick and Sywell etc *Pet*

TABLEY, OVER (St Paul) and High Legh *Ches 12* **P** *Bp and Mrs P H Langford-Brooke (1 turn), C L S Cornwall-Legh Esq (1 turn)* **V** *Vacant* Lymm (01925) 753612

TACKLEY (St Nicholas) Steeple Aston w N Aston and Tackley *Ox*

TACOLNESTON (All Saints) Wreningham *Nor*

TADCASTER (St Mary) w Newton Kyme *York 1* **P** *Abp* **V** R P BURTON, **C** B A GIBLIN

TADDINGTON (St Michael), Chelmorton and Flagg, and Monyash *Derby 4* **P** *V Bakewell* **V** T H COMLEY

TADDIPORT (St Mary Magdalene) Gt and Lt Torrington and Frithelstock *Ex*

TADLEY (St Peter) (St Paul) *Win 4* **P** *Bp* **R** J M NOCKELS

TADLEY, NORTH (St Mary) *Win 4* **P** *Bp* **V** B J NORRIS, **NSM** S G ARMSTRONG

TADLOW (St Giles) Shingay Gp of Par *Ely*

TADMARTON (St Nicholas) Epwell w Sibford, Swalcliffe and Tadmarton *Ox*

TADWORTH (Good Shepherd) *S'wark 25* **P** *V Kingswood St Andr* **V** R H McLEAN, **C** J F H GREEN

TAKELEY (Holy Trinity) w Little Canfield *Chelmsf 19* **P** *Bp and Ch Coll Cam* **P-in-c** F MILLAR

TALATON (St James the Apostle) Whimple, Talaton and Clyst St Lawr *Ex*

TALBOT VILLAGE (St Mark) *Sarum 8* **P** *Trustees* **V** C J F RUTLEDGE, **C** F A BAYES, **NSM** C H MEAD

TALKE O' THE HILL (St Martin) *Lich 14* **P** *V Audley* **R** J T PYE

TALKIN (not known) Hayton w Cumwhitton *Carl*

TALLAND (St Tallan) *Truro 12* **P** *DBP and W Gundry-Mills Esq (alt)* **V** J K P S ROBERTSHAW

TALLINGTON (St Laurence) Uffington Gp *Linc*

TAMERTON, NORTH (St Denis) Boyton, N Tamerton, Werrington etc *Truro*

TAMERTON FOLIOT (St Mary) *Ex 23* **P** *Ld Chan* **V** C W H GOODWINS

TAMWORTH (St Editha) *Lich 4* **P** *Bp* **V** J A WIDDAS, **C** N A DI CASTIGLIONE, D R W ROBBINS, **NSM** J READ

TANDRIDGE (St Peter) *S'wark 24* **P** *DBP* **P-in-c** A J HALE

TANFIELD (St Margaret of Antioch) *Dur 8* **P** *Bp* **V** R SHAW

TANFIELD, WEST (St Nicholas) and Well w Snape and North Stainley *Ripon 3* **P** *Bp and Mrs M E Bourne-Arton (alt)* **R** A C CARRUTHERS

TANGLEY (St Thomas of Canterbury) Hatherden w Tangley, Weyhill and Penton Mewsey *Win*

TANGMERE (St Andrew) and Oving *Chich 3* **P** *Bp and Duke of Richmond (jt)* **R** P M GILBERT

TANKERSLEY (St Peter) *Sheff 7* **P** *Sir Stephen Hastings* **P-in-c** K J E HALE

TANNINGTON (St Ethelbert) Worlingworth, Southolt, Tannington, Bedfield etc *St E*

TANSLEY (Holy Trinity), Dethick, Lea and Holloway *Derby 7* **P** *Bp, V Crich, and DBF (jt)* **P-in-c** R G LAWRENCE

TANSOR (St Mary) Warmington, Tansor, Cotterstock and Fotheringhay *Pet*

TANWORTH (St Mary Magdalene) *Birm 13* **P** *F D Muntz Esq* **V** M W TUNNICLIFFE, **Hon C** N I SANDERS

TANWORTH (St Patrick) Salter Street *Birm 13* **P** *V Tanworth* **V** C K RACE

TAPLOW (St Nicholas) Burnham w Dropmore, Hitcham and Taplow *Ox*

TARDEBIGGE (St Bartholomew) *Worc 7* **P** *Earl of Plymouth* **P-in-c** A WHITE

TARLETON (Holy Trinity) *Blackb 6* **P** *St Pet Coll Ox* **R** R W BUSSELL

TARLTON (St Osmund) Coates, Rodmarton and Sapperton etc *Glouc*

TARPORLEY (St Helen) *Ches 5* **P** *Bp (4 turns), D&C (1 turn), and Sir John Grey Regerton, Bt (1 turn)* **R** G L COOKSON

TARRANT GUNVILLE (St Mary) Tarrant Valley *Sarum*

TARRANT HINTON (St Mary) as above

TARRANT KEYNSTON (All Saints) as above

TARRANT MONKTON (All Saints) as above

TARRANT RUSHTON (St Mary) as above

TARRANT VALLEY *Sarum 7* **P** *Pemb Coll Cam (1 turn), Bp (2 turns), and Univ Coll Ox (1 turn)* **P-in-c** J J HAMILTON-BROWN

TARRING, WEST (St Andrew) *Chich 5* **P** *Abp* **R** W E JERVIS

TARRING NEVILLE (St Mary) Denton w S Heighton and Tarring Neville *Chich*

TARRINGTON (St Philip and St James) w Stoke Edith, Aylton, Pixley, Munsley, Putley and Yarkhill *Heref 6* **P** *A T Foley Esq, D&C, Hopton Trustees, H W Wiggin Esq, and J Hervey-Bathurst Esq (jt)* **R** J R SCARTH

TARVIN (St Andrew) *Ches 2* **P** *Bp* **V** D R HERBERT

TASBURGH (St Mary) w Tharston, Forncett and Flordon *Nor 5* **P** *M MCET, Bp, St Jo Coll Cam, and DBP (by turn)* **P-in-c** S G STEPHENSON

TASLEY (St Peter and St Paul) Bridgnorth, Tasley, Astley Abbotts, Oldbury etc *Heref*

TATENHILL (St Michael and All Angels) Dunstall w Rangemore and Tatenhill *Lich*

TATHAM (St James the Less) Wray w Tatham and Tatham Fells *Blackb*

TATHAM FELLS (Good Shepherd) as above

TATHWELL (St Vedast) Raithby *Linc*

TATSFIELD (St Mary) *S'wark 24* **P** *Bp* **P-in-c** C J CORKE

TATTENHALL (St Alban) and Handley *Ches 5* **P** *Bp and D&C (jt)* **R** G G TURNER

TATTENHAM CORNER (St Mark) and Burgh Heath
  Guildf 9 **P** *Bp* **V** G J CLIFTON-SMITH
TATTENHOE (St Giles) Watling Valley *Ox*
TATTERFORD (St Margaret) E and W Rudham,
  Houghton-next-Harpley etc *Nor*
TATTERSETT (All Saints and St Andrew) as above
TATTERSHALL (Holy Trinity) Coningsby w Tattershall
  Linc
TATTINGSTONE (St Mary) Bentley w Tattingstone *St E*
TATWORTH (St John the Evangelist) *B & W 15*
  P *V Chard* **V** R C P TERRELL
TAUNTON (All Saints) *B & W 18* **P** *Bp* **V** A J WRIGHT
TAUNTON (Holy Trinity) *B & W 18* **P** *Bp*
  V J B V LAURENCE
TAUNTON (St Andrew) *B & W 18* **P** *Bp* **V** R E FLOWER,
  C M J VENABLES, A R AAGAARD, **NSM** C F CRAGGS
TAUNTON (St James) *B & W 18* **P** *Simeon's Trustees*
  V A P BANNISTER
TAUNTON (St John the Evangelist) *B & W 18* **P** *Bp*
  P-in-c D ROBERTS
TAUNTON (St Mary Magdalene) *B & W 18* **P** *Ch Patr*
  Trust **V** N R MADDOCK, **C** A L SMITH
TAUNTON (St Peter) Lyngford *B & W 18* **P** *Bp*
  V T J GOSDEN, **C** E C BROWN, **NSM** P A SELF
TAVERHAM (St Edmund) w Ringland *Nor 2* **P** *Bp and*
  Major J M Mills (alt) **R** J E G CLARK, **C** A H CARR
TAVISTOCK (St Eustachius) and Gulworthy (St Paul) *Ex 25*
  P *Bp* **V** J E F RAWLINGS, **C** R WARING,
  NSM R WARING, J NELSON
TAW VALLEY Newport, Bishops Tawton and Tawstock *Ex*
TAWSTOCK (St Peter) as above
TAWTON, NORTH (St Peter), Bondleigh, Sampford
  Courtenay and Honeychurch *Ex 12* **P** *MMCET, K Coll*
  Cam, and D&C (jt) **R** M A BUTCHERS
TAWTON, SOUTH (St Andrew) and Belstone *Ex 12* **P** *D&C*
  Windsor and Bp (jt) **P-in-c** B WOOD
TAYNTON (St John the Evangelist) Burford w Fulbrook,
  Taynton, Asthall etc *Ox*
TAYNTON (St Laurence) Highnam, Lassington, Rudford,
  Tibberton etc *Glouc*
TEALBY (All Saints) Walesby *Linc*
TEAN, UPPER (Christ Church) *Lich 11* **P** *R Checkley*
  P-in-c R M JAMES
TEBAY (St James) Orton and Tebay w Ravenstonedale etc
  Carl
TEDBURN ST MARY (St Mary), Whitestone, Oldridge and
  Holcombe Burnell *Ex 6* **P** *Bp, Em Coll Cam, and*
  DBP (jt) **P-in-c** V D STANDING
TEDDINGTON (St Mark) and Hampton Wick (St John the
  Baptist) *Lon 11* **P** *Bp* **V** J P WARNER, **C** O C G HIGGS
TEDDINGTON (St Mary) (St Alban the Martyr) *Lon 10*
  P *Bp* **V** J M CLEAVER
TEDDINGTON (St Nicholas) Overbury w Teddington,
  Alstone etc *Worc*
TEDDINGTON (St Peter and St Paul) and Fulwell *Lon 10*
  P *Bp* **V** D H PALMER, **C** P A LOCK, P J W MURPHY,
  Hon C M L NICHOLAS
TEDSTONE DELAMERE (St James) Edvin Loach w
  Tedstone Delamere etc *Heref*
TEDSTONE WAFER (St Mary) as above
TEFFONT EVIAS (St Michael) Fovant, Sutton Mandeville
  and Teffont Evias etc *Sarum*
TEFFONT MAGNA (St Edward) as above
TEIGH (Holy Trinity) Whissendine and Market Overton
  Pet 14 **P** *Bp and Lady Gretton (alt)* **R** *Vacant*
  Whissendine (0166479) 333
TEIGNGRACE (St Peter and St Paul) Highweek and
  Teigngrace *Ex*
TEIGNMOUTH (St James) (St Michael the Archangel),
  Ideford w Luton, Ashcombe and Bishopsteignton *Ex 6*
  P *Patr Bd* **TR** P G LUFF, **C** N C LAW,
  Par Dn J W DEBENHAM, C M S LUFF
TELFORD, CENTRAL: Dawley, Lawley, Malinslee, Stirchley,
  Brookside and Hollinswood *Lich 27* **P** *Patr Bd (3 turns),*
  The Crown (1 turn) **TR** D M R WILLIAMS,
  TV P A CORNISH, P G FLAWLEY, **C** R E AVERY,
  NSM T E DAVIS
TELFORD PARK (St Thomas) S'wark 13 **P** *Trustees*
  V S A EVANS
TELLISFORD (All Saints) Rode Major *B & W*
TELSCOMBE (St Laurence) w Piddinghoe and Southease
  Chich 18 **P** *Gorham Trustees* **P-in-c** D A HIDER
TEME VALLEY NORTH: Knighton-on-Teme, Lindridge,
  Pensax, Menith Wood, Stanford-on-Teme and Stockton
  Worc 13 **P** *Bp and D&C (alt)* **R** R G SMITH
TEME VALLEY SOUTH: Eastham, Rochford, Stoke Bliss,
  Hanley Child, Hanley William and Kyre Wyard *Worc 13*
  P *Ld Chan, Bp, and Mrs V D Miles (by turn)* **R** M P LACK

TEMPLE (St Catherine) Blisland w St Breward *Truro*
TEMPLE BALSALL (St Mary) *Birm 13* **P** *Lady Leveson*
  Hosp **V** R H P WATSON WILLIAMS
TEMPLE BRUER (St John the Baptist) Graffoe Gp *Linc*
TEMPLE CLOUD (St Barnabas) Clutton w Cameley *B & W*
TEMPLE EWELL (St Peter and St Paul) w Lydden *Cant 4*
  P *Abp* **R** P CHRISTIAN
TEMPLE GRAFTON (St Andrew) w Binton *Cov 7* **P** *Dioc*
  Trustees **V** E F WILLIAMS
TEMPLE GUITING (St Mary) The Guitings, Cutsdean and
  Farmcote *Glouc*
TEMPLE HIRST (St John the Baptist) Haddlesey w
  Hambleton and Birkin *York*
TEMPLE NORMANTON (St James the Apostle) *Derby 5*
  P *Bp* **V** *Vacant*
TEMPLE SOWERBY (St James) Kirkby Thore w Temple
  Sowerby and Newbiggin *Carl*
TEMPLECOMBE (Blessed Virgin Mary) Abbas and
  Templecombe w Horsington *B & W*
TEMPLETON (St Margaret) Washfield, Stoodleigh,
  Withleigh etc *Ex*
TEMPSFORD (St Peter) Blunham w Tempsford and Lt
  Barford *St Alb*
TEN MILE BANK (St Mark) Hilgay *Ely*
TENBURY (St Mary) *Heref 12* **P** *Rev F J Evans*
  TR D S DORMOR, **TV** C V HUTT, **C** J GROVES
TENBURY (St Michael and All Angels) *Heref 12* **P** *St Mich*
  Coll **V** D S DORMOR, **NSM** J GRAY
TENDRING (St Edmund King and Martyr) and Little Bentley
  w Beaufort cum Moze *Chelmsf 24* **P** *Em Coll Cam, DBP,*
  and Ball Coll Ox (by turn) **R** C J A HARVEY
TENTERDEN (St Michael and All Angels) *Cant 11* **P** *Abp*
  P-in-c W H HOPKINSON
TENTERDEN (St Mildred) w Smallhythe *Cant 11* **P** *D&C*
  V D G TRUSTRAM
TERLING (All Saints) Fairstead w Terling and White Notley
  etc *Chelmsf*
TERRIERS (St Francis) *Ox 29* **P** *V High Wycombe*
  P-in-c A W DICKINSON, **NSM** M J WILLIAMS
TERRINGTON (All Saints) Bulmer w Dalby, Terrington
  and Welburn *York*
TERRINGTON ST CLEMENT (St Clement) *Ely 17*
  P *The Crown* **V** J F WILSON
TERRINGTON ST JOHN (St John) *Ely 17* **P** *The Crown*
  V C A BARBER
TERWICK (St Peter) Rogate w Terwick and Trotton w
  Chithurst *Chich*
TESTON (St Peter and St Paul) Wateringbury w Teston and
  W Farleigh *Roch*
TESTWOOD (St Winfrid) Totton *Win*
TETBURY (St Mary the Virgin) w Beverston *Glouc 16*
  P *Lt-Col J J B Pope (5 turns), The Crown (1 turn)*
  V J W HAWTHORNE, **NSM** P D STEARE
TETCOTT (Holy Cross) Ashwater, Halwill, Beaworthy,
  Clawton etc *Ex*
TETFORD (St Mary) S Ormsby Gp *Linc*
TETNEY (St Peter and St Paul) North-Chapel Parishes, The
  Linc
TETSWORTH (St Giles), Adwell w South Weston, Lewknor
  and Stoke Talmage w Wheatfield *Ox 1* **P** *Bp, Peache*
  Trustees, W R A Birch Reynardson Esq, Earl of Macclesfield,
  and Mrs D C H Mann (jt) **R** H B L BRIERLY,
  Dss M A BRIERLY
TETTENHALL REGIS (St Michael and All Angels) *Lich 5*
  P *Patr Bd* **TR** J D MAKEPEACE, **TV** G R HARPER,
  J J N QUIN, **C** D J DORMOR, **NSM** V A BARNSLEY
TETTENHALL WOOD (Christ Church) *Lich 5* **P** *Patr Bd*
  TR C R GOUGH, **TV** M A SMALLMAN, S H CARTER,
  C M L E LAST
TEVERSAL (St Katherine) *S'well 4* **P** *DBP*
  P-in-c A I TUCKER
TEVERSHAM (All Saints) *Ely 6* **P** *Bp*
  P-in-c C D BOULTON
TEW, GREAT (St Michael and All Angels) w LITTLE (St
  John the Evangelist) *Ox 3* **P** *Bp and J M Johnston Esq (jt)*
  V *Vacant* Great Tew (0160883) 293
TEWIN (St Peter) Datchworth w Tewin *St Alb*
TEWKESBURY (Holy Trinity) *Glouc 9* **P** *Ch Soc Trust*
  P-in-c P L SIBLEY
TEWKESBURY (St Mary the Virgin) w Walton Cardiff
  Glouc 9 **P** *Ld Chan* **V** M E TAVINOR, **C** P F QUINNELL
TEY, GREAT (St Barnabas) and Wakes Colne w Chappel
  Chelmsf 18 **P** *DBP, PCC Chappel and Bp (jt)*
  R J RICHARDSON
TEY, LITTLE (St James the Less) Marks Tey w Aldham and
  Lt Tey *Chelmsf*

TEYNHAM (St Mary) (Primary School Worship Centre) w Lynsted and Kingsdown *Cant 6* **P** *Adn Cant*
V G H COLMAN

THAKEHAM (St Mary) Sullington and Thakeham w Warminghurst *Chich*

THAME (All Saints) (St Mary the Virgin) w Towersey *Ox 1* **P** *Peache Trustees* **V** C C NEAL, **C** J G SIMMONS, C D STIRLING

THAMES DITTON (St Nicholas) *Guildf 8* **P** *K Coll Cam* **V** *Vacant* 0181-398 3446

THAMES VIEW (Christ Church) Barking St Marg w St Patr *Chelmsf*

THAMESMEAD (Church of the Cross) (St Paul's Ecumenical Centre) *S'wark 1* **P** *Bp* **TR** C M BYERS, **TV** N A McKINNON, J KOTHARE

THANINGTON (St Nicholas) (St Faith's Mission Church) *Cant 3* **P** *Abp* **P-in-c** T D HERBERT

THARSTON (St Mary) Tasburgh w Tharston, Forncett and Flordon *Nor*

THATCHAM (St Mary) *Ox 14* **P** *Patr Bd* **TR** P L SEAR, **TV** J M P HEDGES, **C** C DALE

THAXTED (St John the Baptist, Our Lady and St Laurence) *Chelmsf 23* **P** *Bp* **V** R N ROWE

THE: *see under substantive place name*

THEALE (Christ Church) Wedmore w Theale and Blackford *B & W*

THEALE (Holy Trinity) and Englefield *Ox 12* **P** *Magd Coll Ox and Englefield Est Trust (jt)* **R** D RICE

THEBERTON (St Peter) Kelsale-cum-Carlton, Middleton-cum-Fordley etc *St E*

THEDDINGWORTH (All Saints) Husbands Bosworth w Mowsley and Knaptoft etc *Leic*

THEDDLETHORPE (St Helen) *Linc 12* **P** *Baroness Willoughby de Eresby (2 turns), Bp (1 turn)* **P-in-c** D LUMB

THELBRIDGE (St David) Witheridge, Thelbridge, Creacombe, Meshaw etc *Ex*

THELNETHAM (St Nicholas) Hepworth, Hinderclay, Wattisfield and Thelnetham *St E*

THELVETON (St Andrew) Dickleburgh, Langmere, Shimpling, Thelveton etc *Nor*

THELWALL (All Saints) *Ches 4* **P** *Keble Coll Ox* **V** M L RIDLEY

THEMELTHORPE (St Andrew) Twyford, Guist, Bintree, Themelthorpe etc *Nor*

THENFORD (St Mary the Virgin) Greatworth and Marston St Lawrence etc *Pet*

THERFIELD (St Mary the Virgin) w Kelshall *St Alb 5* **P** *Ld Chan and D&C St Paul's (alt)* **R** *Vacant* Kelshall (01763) 287364

THETFORD (St Cuthbert) (St Peter) *Nor 11* **P** *Patr Bd* **TR** A D McGREGOR, **TV** M J M HUGHES, K WILSON, **Hon C** B R HOGWOOD

THETFORD, LITTLE (St George) Stretham w Thetford *Ely*

THEYDON BOIS (St Mary) *Chelmsf 26* **P** *M G E N Buxton Esq* **V** D DRISCOLL, **NSM** M CHAPMAN

THEYDON GARNON (All Saints) Epping Distr *Chelmsf*

THEYDON MOUNT (St Michael) Stapleford Tawney w Theydon Mt *Chelmsf*

THIMBLEBY (St Margaret) Thornton Gp *Linc*

THIRKLEBY (All Saints) w Kilburn and Bagby *York 20* **P** *Abp* **V** D G BILES

THIRSK (St Mary) *York 20* **P** *Abp* **TR** E R NORRIS, **TV** R M KIRKMAN, **C** H G SMART

THISTLETON (St Nicholas) Greetham and Thistleton w Stretton and Clipsham *Pet*

THIXENDALE (St Mary) Sledmere and Cowlam w Fridaythorpe, Fimer etc *York*

THOCKRINGTON (St Aidan) Chollerton w Birtley and Thockrington *Newc*

THOMPSON (St Martin) Caston w Griston, Merton, Thompson etc *Nor*

THONGSBRIDGE (St Andrew) Upper Holme Valley *Wakef*

THORESBY, NORTH (St Helen) North-Chapel Parishes, The *Linc*

THORESBY, SOUTH (St Andrew) Wold-Marsh Gp *Linc*

THORESWAY (St Mary) Swallow *Linc*

THORGANBY (All Saints) Binbrook Gp *Linc*

THORGANBY (St Helen) Wheldrake w Thorganby *York*

THORINGTON (St Peter) w Wenhaston, Bramfield and Walberswick *St E 15* **P** *Ld Chan (3 turns), Ch Patr Trust (1 turn), and Sir C N G Blois, Bt (1 turn)* **V** J M HUTCHINSON

THORLEY (St James the Great) *St Alb 4* **P** *Bp* **R** C P SLAUGHTER, **NSM** D HIRST

THORLEY (St Swithun) *Portsm 8* **P** *Bp* **V** *Vacant*

THORMANBY (St Mary Magdalene) Brafferton w Pilmoor, Myton on Swale etc *York*

THORNABY ON TEES (St Luke) (St Mark) (St Paul) (St Peter ad Vincula) *York 19* **P** *Abp* **TV** P HASTROP, **P-in-c** D HAWTHORN

THORNAGE (All Saints) Brinton, Briningham, Hunworth, Stody etc *Nor*

THORNBOROUGH (St Mary) Nash w Thornton, Beachampton and Thornborough *Ox*

THORNBURY (St Anna) Bredenbury w Grendon Bishop and Wacton etc *Heref*

THORNBURY (St Margaret) *Bradf 3* **P** *Vs Bradf, Calverley, and Laisterdyke (jt)* **V** J K DAY, **C** P A HEDGE

THORNBURY (St Mary) (St Paul) *Glouc 7* **P** *Ch Ch Ox* **V** M G P VOOGHT, **C** C R GORING

THORNBURY (St Peter) Black Torrington, Bradf w Cookbury etc *Ex*

THORNBY (St Helen) Cottesbrooke w Gt Creaton and Thornby *Pet*

THORNCOMBE (Blessed Virgin Mary) w Winsham and Cricket St Thomas *B & W 15* **P** *Bp Worc and C G S Eyre Esq (jt)* **V** B R SUTTON

THORNDON (All Saints) w Rishangles, Stoke Ash, Thwaite and Wetheringsett cum Brockford *St E 16* **P** *Bp, Capt F P Brooke-Popham, MMCET, and Ch Soc Trust (jt)* **R** *Vacant* Occold (0137971) 603

THORNE (St Nicholas) *Sheff 11* **P** *Bp* **V** P M BROWN, **C** K E TONES

THORNE COFFIN (St Andrew) Tintinhull w Chilthorne Domer, Yeovil Marsh etc *B & W*

THORNE ST MARGARET (St Margaret) Wellington and Distr *B & W*

THORNER (St Peter) *Ripon 8* **P** *Earl of Mexborough* **P-in-c** D R GRICE, **NSM** A B HAIGH

THORNES (St James) w Christ Church *Wakef 12* **P** *DBP* **P-in-c** C W DIXON

THORNEY (St Helen) Harby w Thorney and N and S Clifton *S'well*

THORNEY, WEST (St Nicholas) Southbourne w W Thorney *Chich*

THORNEY ABBEY (St Mary and St Botolph) *Ely 19* **P** *Bp* **P-in-c** A J MILTON

THORNEY CLOSE (St Peter) Sunderland St Mary and St Pet *Dur*

THORNEY HILL (All Saints) Bransgore *Win*

THORNEYBURN (St Aidan) N Tyne and Redesdale Team *Newc*

THORNFALCON (Holy Cross) Ruishton w Thornfalcon *B & W*

THORNFORD (St Mary Magdalene) Bradf Abbas and Thornford w Beer Hackett *Sarum*

THORNGUMBALD (St Mary) Burstwick w Thorngumbald *York*

THORNHAM (All Saints) Hunstanton St Mary w Ringstead Parva etc *Nor*

THORNHAM (St James) *Man 22* **P** *Bp* **V** *Vacant* Rochdale (01706) 45256

THORNHAM (St John) Middleton St Leon w Thornham St Jo *Man*

THORNHAM MAGNA (St Mary Magdalene) w Thornham Parva, Gislingham and Mellis *St E 16* **P** *Bp, Lord Henniker, and MMCET (jt)* **R** R W LEE

THORNHAM PARVA (St Mary) Thornhams Magna and Parva, Gislingham and Mellis *St E*

THORNHAUGH (St Andrew) Wittering w Thornhaugh and Wansford *Pet*

THORNHILL (Mission Church) Beckermet St Jo and St Bridget w Ponsonby *Carl*

THORNHILL (St Michael and All Angels) and Whitley Lower *Wakef 10* **P** *Lord Savile* **R** R W F HOWELL

THORNHILL LEES (Holy Innocents w St Mary) *Wakef 10* **P** *Bp* **V** J R ASHWORTH

THORNLEY (St Bartholomew) *Dur 1* **P** *Bp* **P-in-c** S WARD

THORNLEY (St Bartholomew) Wolsingham and Thornley *Dur*

THORNTHWAITE (St Mary the Virgin) cum Braithwaite and Newlands *Carl 6* **P** *V Crosthwaite and V Keswick St Jo (alt)* **P-in-c** C T MATTHEWS

THORNTHWAITE (St Saviour) Dacre w Hartwith and Darley w Thornthwaite *Ripon*

THORNTON Group, The (St Wilfrid) *Linc 11* **P** *R H Spurrier Esq, Bp, SMF, and Lt Col J L M Dymoke (2 turns), Ld Chan (1 turn)* **R** S W PEARCE

THORNTON (St Frideswyde) *Liv 5* **P** *R Sefton* **V** C RENWICK

THORNTON (St James) *Bradf 1* **P** *V Bradf* **V** S P HACKING, **Hon C** A HOLLIDAY

THORNTON (St Michael) Seaton Ross Gp of Par *York*
THORNTON (St Peter), Bagworth and Stanton *Leic 12*
P *MMCET* V A S COSTERTON
THORNTON, LITTLE (St John) *Blackb 13* P *Bp*
V P R F CLEMENCE
THORNTON CURTIS (St Laurence) Ulceby Gp *Linc*
THORNTON DALE (All Saints) and Ellerburne w Wilton
York 21 P *Mrs E M Morgan and Abp (alt)*
R J D S CLARK
THORNTON HEATH (St Jude w St Aidan) *S'wark 23*
P *Bp* V C H A GARRETT
THORNTON HEATH (St Paul) *S'wark 23* P *The Crown*
P-in-c G PADDICK
THORNTON HOUGH (All Saints) *Ches 9* P *Simeon's*
Trustees V J C CLARKE
THORNTON IN CRAVEN (St Mary) Broughton, Marton
and Thornton *Bradf*
THORNTON IN LONSDALE (St Oswald) w Burton in
Lonsdale *Bradf 6* P *Bp* V M J BAMFORTH
THORNTON LE BEANS (not known) The Thorntons and
The Otteringtons *York*
THORNTON LE FEN (St Peter) Brothertoft Gp *Linc*
THORNTON-LE-FYLDE (Christ Church) *Blackb 13*
P *Trustees* V J F FAIRCLOUGH, C P W BENNETT
THORNTON-LE-MOOR (All Saints) S Kelsey Gp *Linc*
THORNTON LE MOORS (St Mary) w Ince and Elton
Ches 3 P *Bp* V *Vacant* Helsby (01928) 724028
THORNTON LE STREET (St Leonard) The Thorntons and
The Otteringtons *York*
THORNTON RUST (Mission Room) Aysgarth and Bolton
cum Redmire *Ripon*
THORNTON STEWARD (St Oswald) Thornton Watlass w
Thornton Steward *Ripon*
THORNTON WATLASS (St Mary the Virgin) w Thornton
Steward *Ripon 4* P *Bp and D S Dodsworth Esq (jt)*
P-in-c D W EYLES, C S C WHITEHOUSE
THORNTONS and The Otteringtons, The *York 20* P *Ch Ch*
Ox, Linc Coll Ox, and Abp (by turn) R E W SPILLER
THOROTON (St Helena) Whatton w Aslockton,
Hawksworth, Scarrington etc *S'well*
THORP ARCH (All Saints) w Walton *York 1*
P *G H H Wheler Esq and G Lane Fox Esq (alt)*
P-in-c T ELBOURNE
THORPE (St Andrew) (Good Shepherd) *Nor 1* P *Trustees*
W J Birkbeck Esq R A J SNASDELL, C S J COLLIER,
Hon C W H MOORE
Thorpe (St Laurence) Farndon w Thorpe, Hawton and
Cotham *S'well*
THORPE (St Leonard) Fenny Bentley, Kniveton, Thorpe and
Tissington *Derby*
THORPE (St Mary) *Guildf 11* P *Keble Coll Ox*
V M J H ROTHWELL
THORPE (St Matthew) *Nor 1* P *R Thorpe St Andr*
C K J REEVE
THORPE (St Peter) Wainfleet Gp, The *Linc*
THORPE ABBOTS (All Saints) Scole, Brockdish, Billingford,
Thorpe Abbots etc *Nor*
THORPE ACHURCH (St John the Baptist) Aldwincle w
Thorpe Achurch, Pilton, Wadenhoe etc *Pet*
THORPE ARNOLD (St Mary the Virgin) Melton Mowbray
Leic
THORPE AUDIN (Mission Room) Badsworth *Wakef*
THORPE BASSETT (All Saints) Rillington w Scampston,
Wintringham etc *York*
THORPE BAY (St Augustine) *Chelmsf 13* P *Bp*
V E H BEAVAN, C M S PUDGE
THORPE CONSTANTINE (St Constantine) *Lich 4*
P *Mrs E V G Inge-Innes* R *Vacant*
THORPE EDGE (St John the Divine) *Bradf 3* P *Vs Bradf,*
Calverley, and Idle (jt) V C SPIVEY, C S C R PONSONBY
THORPE END (St David) Gt and Lt Plumstead w Thorpe
End and Witton *Nor*
THORPE EPISCOPI (St Andrew) Thorpe *Nor*
THORPE HAMLET (St Matthew) Thorpe St Matt *Nor*
THORPE HESLEY (Holy Trinity) *Sheff 6* P *Sir Stephen*
Hastings V A J LACEY
THORPE LANGTON (St Leonard) Church Langton w Tur
Langton, Thorpe Langton etc *Leic*
THORPE-LE-SOKEN (St Michael) *Chelmsf 24* P *Bp*
V P J CARTER
THORPE MALSOR (All Saints) Broughton w Loddington
and Cransley etc *Pet*
THORPE MANDEVILLE (St John the Baptist) Culworth w
Sulgrave and Thorpe Mandeville etc *Pet*
THORPE MARKET (St Margaret) Trunch *Nor*
THORPE MORIEUX (St Mary the Virgin) Rattlesden w
Thorpe Morieux and Brettenham *St E*

THORPE-NEXT-HADDISCOE (St Matthias) The
Raveningham Gp *Nor*
THORPE-ON-THE-HILL (St Michael) Swinderby *Linc*
THORPE SALVIN (St Peter) Harthill and Thorpe Salvin
Sheff
THORPE SATCHVILLE (St Michael and All
Angels) S Croxton Gp *Leic*
THORPE WILLOUGHBY (St Francis of Assisi) Brayton
York
THORRINGTON (St Mary Magdalene) Gt Bentley and
Frating w Thorrington *Chelmsf*
THORVERTON (St Thomas of Canterbury), Cadbury, Upton
Pyne, Brampford Speke and Newton St Cyres *Ex 2*
P *Ld Chan (1 turn), Patr Bd (3 turns)* TR L J YEO,
TV R E N WESTON
THRANDESTON (St Margaret) N Hartismere *St E*
THRAPSTON (St James) *Pet 10* P *Ld Chan* R D R BIRD
THREAPWOOD (St John) Malpas and Threapwood *Ches*
THRECKINGHAM (St Peter) S Lafford *Linc*
THREE LEGGED CROSS (All Saints) Verwood *Sarum*
THRELKELD (St Mary) *Carl 6* P *Trustees*
P-in-c C G DARRALL
THREXTON (All Saints) Gt and Lt Cressingham w
Threxton *Nor*
THRIGBY (St Mary) Filby, Thrigby, Mautby, Stokesby,
Runham etc *Nor*
THRIMBY (St Mary) Morland, Thrimby and Gt Strickland
Carl
THRINGSTONE (St Andrew) *Leic 8* P *Duchy of Lanc*
V B MATTHEWS
THRIPLOW (St George) *Ely 8* P *Bp* P-in-c J B MYNORS
THROCKING (Holy Trinity) Cottered w Broadfield and
Throcking *St Alb*
THROCKLEY (St Mary the Virgin) Newburn *Newc*
THROCKMORTON (Chapelry) Abberton, The Flyfords,
Naunton Beauchamp etc *Worc*
THROOP (St Paul) *Win 7* P *Ch Soc Trust*
V G E WALLACE
THROPTON (St Andrew) Rothbury *Newc*
THROWLEIGH (St Mary the Virgin) Chagford w Gidleigh
and Throwleigh *Ex*
THROWLEY (St Michael and All Angels) Selling w
Throwley, Sheldwich w Badlesmere etc *Cant*
THRUMPTON (All Saints) *S'well 10* P *G F Seymour Esq*
V A C SUTHERLAND, NSM J M GORICK
THRUSCROSS (no dedication) Dacre w Hartwith and
Darley w Thornthwaite *Ripon*
THRUSHELTON (St George) Marystowe, Coryton,
Stowford, Lewtrenchard etc *Ex*
THRUSSINGTON (Holy Trinity) Syston TM *Leic*
THRUXTON (St Bartholomew) Kingstone w Clehonger,
Eaton Bishop etc *Heref*
THRUXTON (St Peter and St Paul) Appleshaw, Kimpton,
Thruxton and Fyfield *Win*
THRYBERGH (St Leonard) *Sheff 6* P *J C M Fullerton Esq*
R B E LENG
THUNDERSLEY (St Michael and All Angels) (St Peter)
Chelmsf 10 P *Bp* R P J SANDBERG, C D L HUMPHREY
THUNDERSLEY, NEW (St George) *Chelmsf 10* P *Bp*
V J R D KEMP
THUNDRIDGE (St Mary) *St Alb 8* P *Bp*
V H J SHARMAN
THURCASTON (All Saints) w Cropston *Leic 12* P *Em Coll*
Cam R D F BREWIN
THURCROFT (St Simon and St Jude) *Sheff 5* P *Bp*
V J K BUTTERFIELD, NSM R GOMERSALL
THURGARTON (St Peter) w Hoveringham and Bleasby w
Halloughton *S'well 15* P *Ld Chan and Trin Coll Cam*
(alt) V A P de BERRY
THURGOLAND (Holy Trinity) Wortley w Thurgoland
Sheff
THURLASTON (All Saints) Enderby w Lubbesthorpe and
Thurlaston *Leic*
THURLASTON (St Edmund) Dunchurch *Cov*
THURLBY (St Firmin) Ness Gp *Linc*
THURLBY (St Germain) w Norton Disney *Linc 18* P *Bp and*
W R S Brown Esq (alt) P-in-c E I SLATER
THURLEIGH (St Peter) *St Alb 21* P *Bp* V C W GONIN
THURLESTONE (All Saints) w South Milton *Ex 14*
P *D&C* R P S STEPHENS
THURLOW, GREAT (All Saints) Haverhill w Withersfield,
the Wrattings etc *St E*
THURLOW, LITTLE (St Peter) as above
THURLOXTON (St Giles) N Newton w St Michaelchurch,
Thurloxton etc *B & W*
THURLSTONE (St Saviour) Penistone and Thurlstone
Wakef
THURLTON (All Saints) The Raveningham Gp *Nor*

THURMASTON (St Michael and All Angels) *Leic 6* **P** *Bp*
   V T R MARTIN, **C** D SHENTON
THURNBY (St Luke) w Stoughton *Leic 5* **P** *MMCET*
   V G W DUNSETH
THURNBY LODGE (Christ Church) *Leic 1* **P** *Bp*
   P-in-c P A TAILBY, **NSM** I M HILL
THURNE (St Edmund) Rollesby w Burgh w Billockby w
   Ashby w Oby etc *Nor*
THURNHAM (St Mary the Virgin) Bearsted w Thurnham
   Cant
THURNING (St Andrew) Reepham, Hackford w Whitwell,
   Kerdiston etc *Nor*
THURNING (St James the Great) Barnwell w Tichmarsh,
   Thurning and Clapton *Pet*
THURNSCOE (St Helen) *Sheff 12* **P** *Sir Stephen Hastings*
   R I A DAVIS
THURNSCOE (St Hilda) *Sheff 12* **P** *Bp*
   V M P THOMPSON
THURROCK, LITTLE (St John) *Chelmsf 14* **P** *Bp*
   V E N P TUFNELL, **C** C B REED
THURROCK, LITTLE (St Mary the Virgin) Grays
   Thurrock *Chelmsf*
THURROCK, WEST (Church Centre) as above
THURSBY (St Andrew) *Carl 3* **P** *D&C*
   P-in-c C J CROSSMAN
THURSFORD (St Andrew) Barney, Fulmodeston w
   Croxton, Hindringham etc *Nor*
THURSLEY (St Michael and All Angels) *Guildf 4*
   P *V Witley* **V** W D LANG
THURSTASTON (St Bartholomew) *Ches 8* **P** *D&C*
   R J B HARRIS
THURSTON (St Peter) *St E 9* **P** *Bp* **V** D M B MATHERS
THURSTONLAND (St Thomas) Upper Holme Valley
   Wakef
**THURTON (St Ethelbert) w Ashby Saint Mary, Bergh Apton
   w Yelverton and Framingham Pigot** *Nor 8* **P** *Bp and Major
   J H Thursby, Bp and MMCET, and Ld Chan (by turn)*
   R G E JESSUP
THUXTON (St Paul) Barnham Broom *Nor*
THWAITE (All Saints) Erpingham w Calthorpe, Ingworth,
   Aldborough etc *Nor*
THWAITE (St George) Thorndon w Rishangles, Stoke Ash,
   Thwaite etc *St E*
THWAITE (St Mary) Brooke, Kirstead, Mundham w
   Seething and Thwaite *Nor*
THWAITES (St Anne) Millom *Carl*
THWAITES BROW (St Barnabas) *Bradf 8* **P** *DBP*
   V P J ENDALL
THWING (All Saints) Langtoft w Foxholes, Butterwick,
   Cottam etc *York*
TIBBERTON (All Saints) w Bolas Magna and Waters Upton
   Lich 21 **P** *R Edgmond w Kynnersley etc, MMCET, and
   J B Davies Esq (jt)* **P-in-c** R F DABORN
TIBBERTON (Holy Trinity) Highnam, Lassington, Rudford,
   Tibberton etc *Glouc*
TIBBERTON (St Peter ad Vincula) Bowbrook S *Worc*
TIBENHAM (All Saints) Bunwell, Carleton Rode,
   Tibenham, Gt Moulton etc *Nor*
TIBSHELF (St John the Baptist) *Derby 1* **P** *MMCET*
   V E J ABLETT
TICEHURST (St Mary) and Flimwell *Chich 19* **P** *Bp,
   E J B Harcastle Esq, and A F Drewe Esq (jt)*
   V R J GOODCHILD
TICHBORNE (St Andrew) Cheriton w Tichborne and
   Beauworth *Win*
TICHMARSH (St Mary the Virgin) Barnwell w Tichmarsh,
   Thurning and Clapton *Pet*
TICKENCOTE (St Peter) Gt and Lt Casterton w Pickworth
   and Tickencote *Pet*
TICKENHAM (St Quiricus and St Julietta) *B & W 13*
   P *Ld Chan* **R** R W I GHEST
TICKHILL (St Mary) w Stainton *Sheff 10* **P** *Bp*
   V J A BOWERING
TICKNALL (St George), Smisby and Stanton by Bridge
   Derby 15 **P** *Bp and Exors H F Harpur-Crewe Esq (jt)*
   P-in-c R HILL
TICKTON (St Paul) Beverley Minster *York*
TIDCOMBE (St Michael) Wexcombe *Sarum*
TIDDINGTON (St Peter) Alveston *Cov*
TIDEBROOK (St John the Baptist) *Chich 19* **P** *V Wadhurst
   and V Mayfield (alt)* **V** M G P INSLEY
TIDEFORD (St Luke) St Germans *Truro*
TIDENHAM (St Mary) w Beachley and Lancaut *Glouc 4*
   P *Bp* **V** B R GREEN
TIDENHAM CHASE (St Michael and All Angels) Tidenham
   w Beachley and Lancaut *Glouc*
TIDESWELL (St John the Baptist) *Derby 4* **P** *D&C Lich*
   V M F H HULBERT, **NSM** E D MILROY

TIDMARSH (St Laurence) Pangbourne w Tidmarsh and
   Sulham *Ox*
TIDMINGTON (not known) Shipston-on-Stour w
   Honington and Idlicote *Cov*
TIDWORTH (Holy Trinity), Ludgershall and Faberstown
   Sarum 12 **P** *Ld Chan and DBP (alt)* **R** M J BRIDGER,
   C D JONES
TIFFIELD (St John the Baptist) Pattishall w Cold Higham
   and Gayton w Tiffield *Pet*
TILBROOK (All Saints) *Ely 10* **P** *SMF*
   P-in-c J HINDLEY, **NSM** B A BEARCROFT,
   J RAWLINSON
TILBURY, EAST (St Katherine) and West Tilbury and Linford
   Chelmsf 14 **P** *Ld Chan* **R** D J LOEWENDAHL
TILBURY DOCKS (St John the Baptist) *Chelmsf 14* **P** *Bp*
   V I R MOODY, **C** D J POWNEY
TILBURY JUXTA CLARE (St Margaret) Ovington w
   Tilbury *Chelmsf*
TILE CROSS (St Peter) *Birm 11* **P** *Bp* **V** N C FOSTER,
   NSM M MacLACHLAN (nee GRIFFITHS)
TILE HILL (St Oswald) *Cov 3* **P** *Bp* **V** B REGAN
TILEHURST (St Catherine of Siena) *Ox 15* **P** *Magd Coll
   Ox* **V** S W M HARTLEY
TILEHURST (St George) *Ox 15* **P** *Bp* **V** J J GILL
TILEHURST (St Mary Magdalen) *Ox 15* **P** *Bp*
   V R C W SMITH
TILEHURST (St Michael) *Ox 15* **P** *Magd Coll Ox*
   R F W DAWSON, **C** B SCOTT
TILFORD (All Saints) *Guildf 3* **P** *Bp* **P-in-c** D J INNES
TILGATE (Holy Trinity) Southgate *Chich*
TILLINGHAM (St Nicholas) *Chelmsf 11* **P** *D&C St Paul's*
   P-in-c I M FINN
TILLINGTON (All Hallows) *Chich 11* **P** *Lord Egremont*
   P-in-c C D BIDDELL
TILMANSTONE (St Andrew) Eastry and Northbourne w
   Tilmanstone etc *Cant*
TILNEY ALL SAINTS (All Saints) *Ely 17* **P** *Pemb Coll
   Cam* **V** C A BARBER
TILNEY ST LAWRENCE (St Lawrence) *Ely 17* **P** *Pemb
   Coll Cam* **V** *Vacant*
TILSHEAD (St Thomas a Becket), Orcheston and Chitterne
   Sarum 16 **P** *Bp (3 turns), D&C (1 turn)*
   P-in-c E H A HAYDEN
TILSTOCK (Christ Church), Edstaston and Whixall *Lich 28*
   P *V Prees, R Wem, and R Whitchurch (jt)*
   V A T BARTLAM
TILSTON (St Mary) and Shocklach *Ches 5* **P** *Bp*
   P-in-c J M HUNT
TILSTONE FEARNALL (St Jude) Bunbury and Tilstone
   Fearnall *Ches*
TILSWORTH (All Saints) Totternhoe, Stanbridge and
   Tilsworth *St Alb*
TILTON ON THE HILL (St Peter) Whatborough Gp of Par
   Leic
TILTY (St Mary the Virgin) Broxted w Chickney and Tilty
   etc *Chelmsf*
TIMBERLAND (St Andrew) Scopwick Gp *Linc*
TIMBERSCOMBE (St Petroc) Selworthy, Timberscombe,
   Wootton Courtenay etc *B & W*
TIMPERLEY (Christ Church) (St Andrew) (St Catherine)
   Ches 10 **P** *Trustees* **P** P W G BURWELL,
   C J V ANDERSON (nee FLAHERTY),
   Hon C M E HEPWORTH, **NSM** G M GILL
TIMSBURY (Blessed Virgin Mary) and Priston *B & W 9*
   P *Ball Coll Ox (3 turns), R W Lovegrove Esq (1 turn)*
   R C C BROWN
TIMSBURY (St Andrew) Michelmersh, Timsbury, Farley
   Chamberlayne etc *Win*
TIMWORTH (St Andrew) Fornham All SS and St Martin w
   Timworth *St E*
TINCLETON (St John the Evangelist) Moreton and
   Woodsford w Tincleton *Sarum*
TINDALE (Mission Church) Gilsland w Nether Denton *Carl*
TINGEWICK (St Mary Magdalen) Lenborough *Ox*
TINGRITH (St Nicholas) Westoning w Tingrith *St Alb*
TINSLEY (St Lawrence) *Sheff 1* **P** *Sir Stephen Hastings*
   P-in-c C T GIBSON
TINTAGEL (St Materiana) *Truro 10* **P** *D&C Windsor*
   P-in-c R THOMAS
**TINTINHULL (St Margaret) w Chilthorne Domer, Yeovil
   Marsh and Thorne Coffin** *B & W 6* **P** *Guild of All So*
   NSM A J YOUNG
TINTWISTLE (Christ Church) *Ches 14* **P** *Trustees*
   P-in-c J R WATTS
TINWELL (All Saints) Ketton w Tinwell *Pet*

TIPTOE (St Andrew) Hordle *Win*

TIPTON Great Bridge (St Luke) Tipton St Martin and St Paul *Lich*

TIPTON (St John) Ottery St Mary, Alfington, W Hill, Tipton etc *Ex*

TIPTON (St John the Evangelist) *Lich 7*   **P** *V W Bromwich St Jas*   **V**   J C GREATBATCH

TIPTON (St Mark) Ocker Hill *Lich*

TIPTON (St Martin) (St Paul) *Lich 7*   **P** *MMCET*
V   J H ALGAR

TIPTON (St Matthew) *Lich 7*   **P** *Simeon's Trustees*
V   M S PHILPS

TIPTREE (St Luke) Tolleshunt Knights w Tiptree and Gt Braxted *Chelmsf*

TIRLEY (St Michael) Hasfield w Tirley and Ashleworth *Glouc*

TISBURY (St John the Baptist) *Sarum 13*   **P** *Patr Bd* (3 turns), Ld Chan (1 turn)*   **TR**   C J MEYRICK,
C   G SOUTHGATE,   **NSM**   M A SHALLCROSS,   **R** WREN

TISMANS COMMON (St John the Baptist) Rudgwick *Chich*

TISSINGTON (St Mary) Fenny Bentley, Kniveton, Thorpe and Tissington *Derby*

TISTED, EAST w Colemore (St James) Newton Valence, Selborne and E Tisted w Colemore *Win*

TISTED, WEST (St Mary Magdalene) Bishop's Sutton and Ropley and W Tisted *Win*

TITCHFIELD (St Peter) *Portsm 2*   **P** *D&C Win*
V   J A MITCHELL-INNES

TITCHWELL (St Mary) Hunstanton St Mary w Ringstead Parva etc *Nor*

TITLEY (St Peter) Lyonshall w Titley, Almeley and Kinnersley *Heref*

TITTENSOR (St Luke) Swynnerton and Tittensor *Lich*

TITTLESHALL (St Mary) Litcham w Kempston, E and W Lexham, Mileham etc *Nor*

TIVERTON (St Andrew) *Ex 8*   **P** *Bp*
P-in-c   D M FLETCHER,   **Hon C**   B STRANGE

TIVERTON (St George) *Ex 8*   **P** *MMCET*   **V**   C G H DUNN

TIVERTON (St Paul) W Exe *Ex*

TIVERTON (St Peter) w Chevithorne *Ex 8*   **P** *Peache Trustees (3 turns), Ld Chan (1 turn)*   **P-in-c**   A R GIBSON,
NSM   D A LYDDON

TIVETSHALL (St Mary and St Margaret) Winfarthing w Shelfanger w Burston w Gissing etc *Nor*

TIVIDALE (St Michael the Archangel) (Holy Cross) (St Augustine) *Lich 7*   **P** *Bp*   **V**   D F MAWSON,
C   D E KENDRICK

TIVINGTON (St Leonard) Selworthy, Timberscombe, Wootton Courtenay etc *B & W*

TIXALL (St John the Baptist) Stafford St Jo and Tixall w Ingestre *Lich*

TIXOVER (St Luke) Easton on the Hill, Collyweston w Duddington etc *Pet*

TOCKENHAM (St Giles) Broad Town, Clyffe Pypard, Hilmarton etc *Sarum*

TOCKHOLES (St Stephen) Darwen St Cuth w Tockholes St Steph *Blackb*

TOCKWITH (Epiphany) and Bilton w Bickerton *York 1*
P *Abp and D&C (jt)*   **V**   D J TOMPKINS

TODBER (St Andrew) Gillingham *Sarum*

TODDINGTON (St Andrew), Stanton, Didbrook w Hailes and Stanway *Glouc 17*   **P** *DBP, Lord Neidpath, and Bp (by turn)*   **R**   M E BENNETT

TODDINGTON (St George of England) *St Alb 18*   **P** *Bp*
R   T A KNOX

TODENHAM (St Thomas of Canterbury) Moreton-in-Marsh w Batsford, Todenham etc *Glouc*

TODMORDEN (St Mary) (Christ Church) *Wakef 3*   **P** *Bp*
V   P N CALVERT

TODWICK (St Peter and St Paul) Aston cum Aughton w Swallownest, Todwick & Ulley *Sheff*

TOFT (St Andrew) w Caldecote and Childerley *Ely 1*
P *Ch Coll Cam*   **R**   D G DEBOYS,   **NSM**   A G WILMAN,
D A J WILMAN

TOFT (St John the Evangelist) Knutsford St Jo and Toft *Ches*

TOFT MONKS (St Margaret) The Raveningham Gp *Nor*

TOFT NEXT NEWTON (St Peter and St Paul) Middle Rasen Gp *Linc*

TOFTREES (All Saints) w Shereford *Nor 16*   **P** *Marquess Townshend*   **V** *Vacant*

TOFTS, WEST and Buckenham Parva *Nor 14*   **P** *Guild of All So*   **R** *Vacant*

TOKYNGTON (St Michael) *Lon 21*   **P** *Bp*   **V**   R J METIVIER

TOLLADINE (Christ Church) Worc St Barn w Ch Ch *Worc*

TOLLAND (St John the Baptist) Lydeard St Lawrence w Brompton Ralph etc *B & W*

TOLLARD ROYAL (St Peter ad Vincula) w Farnham, Gussage St Michael and Gussage All Saints, Ashmore and Chettle *Sarum 7*   **P** *Bp, Adn Dorset, Ch Soc Trust, A C L Sturge Esq, and J P C Bourke Esq (2 turns), Ld Chan (1 turn)*   **R**   G B BELL

TOLLER FRATRUM (St Basil) Melbury *Sarum*

TOLLER PORCORUM (St Andrew) Beaminster Area *Sarum*

TOLLER WHELME (St John) Melbury *Sarum*

TOLLERTON (St Michael) Alne *York*

TOLLERTON (St Peter) *S'well 9*   **P** *Ld Chan*
P-in-c   P E GRIFFITHS

TOLLESBURY (St Mary) w Salcot Virley *Chelmsf 25*   **P** *Bp (1 turn), Ex Coll Ox (3 turns)*   **V**   K M B LOVELL

TOLLESHUNT D'ARCY (St Nicholas) w Tolleshunt Major (St Nicholas) *Chelmsf 25*   **P** *Mrs E A Comerford and MMCET (jt)*   **P-in-c**   P R SOUTHERN

TOLLESHUNT KNIGHTS w Tiptree and Great Braxted *Chelmsf 25*   **P** *Bp (2 turns), Ld Chan (2 turns), and CCC Cam (1 turn)*   **R**   J A PRATT,   **C**   J M HENRY

TOLLINGTON (St Mark) *Lon 6*   **P** *Patr Bd*
TR   R S CAMPBELL,   **TV**   J O HUTCHINSON,
D E CLAYDEN,   **C**   D E SMITH,   W K DORGU

TOLPUDDLE (St John the Evangelist) Puddletown and Tolpuddle *Sarum*

TOLWORTH (Emmanuel) Surbiton Hill Ch Ch *S'wark*

TOLWORTH (St George) Surbiton St Matt *S'wark*

TONBRIDGE (St Peter and St Paul) (St Saviour) *Roch 10*
P *Mabledon Trust*   **V**   M A PERRY,   **C**   R E T FOXWELL,
J AUSTIN,   G E TOVAR,   **NSM**   B P ADAMS

TONBRIDGE (St Stephen) (St Eanswythe Mission Church) *Roch 10*   **P** *CPAS*   **V**   W D MACDOUGALL,
C   R J M BYRNE,   J C CHANDLER

TONG (St Bartholomew) *Lich 25*   **P** *Bp*   **V**   G FROST

TONG (St James) *Bradf 3*   **P** *CR*   **TR**   C G N DEY,
C   A CALLAN-TRAVIS

TONGE (St Giles) Murston w Bapchild and Tonge *Cant*

TONGE (St Michael) w Alkrington *Man 18*   **P** *R Middleton St Leon*   **V**   G F JOYCE,   **C**   P R HOLLEY

TONGE FOLD (St Chad) *Man 9*   **P** *Bp and Wm Hulme Trustees (alt)*   **V**   A J BUTTERWORTH

TONGE MOOR (St Augustine) (St Aidan) *Man 16*   **P** *Keble Coll Ox*   **V**   B J FINDLAY,   **C**   A R HEYES

TONGHAM (St Paul) *Guildf 1*   **P** *Adn Surrey*
V   P S J GARLAND

TONWELL (St Mary the Virgin) Bengeo *St Alb*

TOOT BALDON (St Lawrence) Dorchester *Ox*

TOOTING (All Saints) *S'wark 17*   **P** *Bp*   **V**   S J L KING

TOOTING (St Augustine) *S'wark 17*   **P** *Bp*   **V**   S J LOPEZ-FERREIRO

TOOTING GRAVENEY (St Nicholas) *S'wark 17*
P *MMCET*   **R**   J B HALL

TOOTING, UPPER (Holy Trinity) *S'wark 17*
P *R Streatham St Leon*   **V**   B M C BROGGIO,   **C**   P J ROSE-CASEMORE

TOPCLIFFE (St Columba) *York 20*   **P** *D&C*
C   E M BAXTER,   **NSM**   S R BAXTER

TOPCROFT (St Margaret) Hempnall *Nor*

TOPPESFIELD (St Margaret) and Stambourne *Chelmsf 20*
P *The Crown and Duchy of Lanc (alt)*
P-in-c   J M SUDDARDS

TOPSHAM (St Margaret) *Ex 1*   **P** *D&C*
V   R W C JEFFERY,   **NSM**   H A FULFORD

TORBRYAN (Holy Trinity) Ipplepen w Torbryan *Ex*

TORKSEY (St Peter) Stow Gp *Linc*

TORMARTON (St Mary Magdalene) Marshfield w Cold Ashton and Tormarton etc *Bris*

TORPENHOW (St Michael and All Angels) *Carl 7*   **P** *Bp*
V *Vacant* Low Ireby (019657) 295

TORPOINT (St James) *Truro 11*   **P** *R Antony* **V** *Vacant* Plymouth (01752) 812418

TORQUAY (St John) and Ellacombe *Ex 10*   **P** *Ch Patr Trust and Bp (jt)*   **P-in-c**   R W TAYLOR

TORQUAY (St Luke) *Ex 10*   **P** *D&C*   **P-in-c**   M J A BARR,
NSM   M E BARR (nee HAYTER)

TORQUAY (St Martin) Barton *Ex 10*   **P** *V St Marychurch*
V   G CHAPMAN,   **C**   P M J COOMBS

TORQUAY (St Mary Magdalene) Upton *Ex*

TORQUAY (St Matthias) (St Mark) (Holy Trinity) *Ex 10*
P *Ch Patr Trust, Bp and Torwood Trustees (jt)*
R   P J LARKIN,   **C**   A C EDMUNDS,   **Hon C**   J M PRINGLE,
NSM   P G H COOKE

TORRE (All Saints) *Ex 10*   **P** *Bp*   **V**   R I McDOWALL

TORRIDGE Shebbear, Buckland Filleigh, Sheepwash etc *Ex*

TORRINGTON, EAST (St Michael) Barkwith Gp *Linc*

TORRINGTON, GREAT (St Michael), Little Torrington and Frithelstock *Ex 20*   **P** *Ch Ch Ox (8 turns), Lord Clinton*

993

(1 turn), J de C Stevens-Guille Esq (1 turn)
V J D HUMMERSTONE
TORRINGTON, LITTLE (St Giles) Gt and Lt Torrington and Frithelstock *Ex*
TORRINGTON, WEST (St Michael) Barkwith Gp *Linc*
TORRISHOLME (Ascension) *Blackb 12* **P** *Bp*
V B H PITHERS, **C** A H MANSON-BRAILSFORD
TORTWORTH (St Leonard) Cromhall w Tortworth and Tytherington *Glouc*
TORVER (St Luke) *Carl 8* **P** *Peache Trustees*
P-in-c M H CANNON
TOSELAND (St Michael) Graveley w Papworth St Agnes w Yelling etc *Ely*
TOSSIDE (St Bartholomew) Long Preston w Tosside *Bradf*
TOSTOCK (St Andrew) Pakenham w Norton and Tostock *St E*
TOTHAM, GREAT (St Peter) *Chelmsf 25* **P** *Bp*
V M J HATCHETT
TOTHAM, LITTLE (All Saints) Goldhanger w Lt Totham *Chelmsf*
TOTLAND BAY (Christ Church) *Portsm 8* **P** *Ch Patr Trust* V J A YORKE
TOTLEY (All Saints) *Sheff 2* **P** *Bp* V J D BENSON
TOTNES (St Mary), Bridgetown and Berry Pomeroy and Dartington *Ex 13* **P** *Patr Bd* **TR** T R SMITH,
TV N J C PIGOTT, P WIMSETT, **NSM** R E YEO, J M YEO (nee HARRISON)
TOTON (St Peter) Attenborough *S'well*
TOTTENHAM (All Hallows) *Lon 19* **P** *D&C St Paul's*
V R B PEARSON
TOTTENHAM (Holy Trinity) *Lon 19* **P** *Bp*
P-in-c R A HAMILTON
TOTTENHAM (St Ann) Hanger Lane *Lon 19*
P *D&C St Paul's* **P-in-c** J M WOOD
TOTTENHAM (St Benet Fink) *Lon 19* **P** *D&C St Paul's*
V M A DAVENPORT
TOTTENHAM (St Mary) *Lon 19* **P** *Bp* **C** L J MILLER
TOTTENHAM (St Paul) *Lon 19*
P *V Tottenham All Hallows* **C** P J WILSON
TOTTENHAM (St Philip the Apostle) *Lon 19* **P** *Bp*
P-in-c K EVANS
TOTTENHILL (St Botolph) w Wormegay *Ely 16* **P** *Bp*
V J C W NOLAN
TOTTERIDGE (St Andrew) *St Alb 2* **P** *R Hatfield* V *Vacant*
0181–445 6787
TOTTERNHOE (St Giles), Stanbridge and Tilsworth
St Alb 18 **P** *Bp* V P C HOLLAND
TOTTINGTON (St Anne) *Man 10* **P** *R Bury St Mary*
Par Dn S G MARTIN
TOTTON *Win 10* **P** *Bp* **TR** P BAYES, **TV** J E HAIR,
A G RIVETT, D BROAD, **C** S A SMITH
TOW LAW (St Philip and St James) Satley and Tow Law *Dur*
TOWCESTER (St Lawrence) w Easton Neston *Pet 5* **P** *Bp and Lord Hesketh (alt)* **C** R N LEACH
TOWEDNACK (St Tewinock) *Truro 5* **P** *Bp*
P-in-c S W MIDDLETON-DANSKY
TOWER CHAPEL (St Nicholas) Whitehaven *Carl*
TOWERSEY (St Catherine) Thame w Towersey *Ox*
TOWN END FARM (St Bede) Sunderland Town End Farm *Dur*
TOWNSTAL (St Clement) Dartmouth *Ex*
TOXTETH (St Bede) Toxteth Park Ch Ch w St Bede *Liv*
TOXTETH (St Cyprian w Christ Church) *Liv 3* **P** *Simeon's Trustees* V D A LEWIS
TOXTETH (St Margaret) *Liv 6* **P** *St Chad's Coll Dur*
V R GALLAGHER
TOXTETH (St Philemon) (St Gabriel) St Cleopas *Liv 6*
P *Patr Bd* **TR** D C KIRKWOOD, **TV** P H JANVIER,
C G A F GRIFFIN, R V STOCK
TOXTETH PARK (Christ Church) (St Bede) *Liv 6*
P *Simeon's Trustees and Trustees (jt)* V M T RANDALL
TOXTETH PARK (St Agnes and St Pancras) *Liv 6*
P *St Chad's Coll Dur* V D H McKITTRICK
TOXTETH PARK (St Clement) *Liv 6* **P** *Trustees*
P-in-c F R CAIN
TOXTETH PARK (St Michael-in-the-Hamlet) (St Andrew)
Liv 6 *Simeon's Trustees* V S FORBES
TOYNTON, HIGH (St John the Baptist) *Linc 11* **P** *Bp*
V *Vacant*
TOYNTON ALL SAINTS (All Saints) Marden Hill Gp *Linc*
TOYNTON ST PETER (St Peter) as above
TOYS HILL (Hall) Hever, Four Elms and Mark Beech *Roch*
TRAFALGAR SQUARE (St Martin-in-the-Fields) St Martin-in-the-Fields *Lon*

TRAFFORD, OLD (St Bride) Stretford St Bride *Man*
TRAFFORD, OLD (St Hilda) *Man 7* **P** *The Crown*
R D G BARNETT
TRAFFORD, OLD (St John the Evangelist) *Man 7*
P *The Crown* **R** D I WHEELER, **C** M C HODSON
TRANMERE (St Catherine) *Ches 1* **P** *R Bebington*
V S R BECKLEY, **NSM** W H HEAPS, K THOMPSON
TRANMERE (St Paul w St Luke) *Ches 1* **P** *Bp*
V D J JOHNSON
TRANMERE PARK (St Peter's Hall) Guiseley w Esholt *Bradf*
TRAWDEN (St Mary the Virgin) *Blackb 7* **P** *Bp*
P-in-c R L ALLEN
TREALES (Christ Church) *Blackb 11* **P** *V Kirkham*
P-in-c P A L MADDOCK
TREBOROUGH (St Peter) Old Cleeve, Leighland and Treborough *B & W*
TREDINGTON (St Gregory) and Darlingscott w Newbold on Stour *Cov 9* **P** *Jes Coll Ox* **R** J P ELLIOTT
TREDINGTON (St John the Baptist) Staverton w Boddington and Tredington etc *Glouc*
TREETON (St Helen) Brinsworth w Catcliffe and Treeton *Sheff*
TREFONEN (All Saints) Llanyblodwel and Trefonen *Lich*
TREGADILLET (St Mary's Mission) Launceston *Truro*
TREGONY (not known) w St Cuby and Cornelly *Truro 6*
P *Bp* **R** C F P SHEPHERD
TREKNOW (Holy Family) Tintagel *Truro*
TRELEIGH (St Stephen) Redruth w Lanner and Treleigh *Truro*
TRELYSTAN (St Mary the Virgin) *Heref 13* **P** *Bp*
V P D HARRATT
TREMAINE (St Winwalo) Egloskerry, N Petherwin, Tremaine and Tresmere *Truro*
TRENDLEWOOD Nailsea H Trin *B & W*
TRENEGLOS (St Gregory) St Gennys, Jacobstow w Warbstow and Treneglos *Truro*
TRENT (St Andrew) Queen Thorne *Sarum*
TRENT VALE (St John the Evangelist) *Lich 17* **P** *R Stoke-on-Trent* V D W WATKIN
TRENTHAM (St Mary and All Saints) *Lich 18* **P** *Countess of Sutherland* V D MARSH, **C** R M GLADSTONE
TRENTISHOE (St Peter) *Ex 18* **P** *Bp* **R** *Vacant*
TRESCO (St Nicholas) Scilly Is *Truro*
TRESHAM (Chapel) Kingswood w Alderley and Hillesley *Glouc*
TRESLOTHAN (St John the Evangelist) *Truro 2* **P** *Mrs W A Pendarves* **NSM** D L HOLLINGDALE
TRESMERE (St Nicholas) Egloskerry, N Petherwin, Tremaine and Tresmere *Truro*
TRESWELL (St John the Baptist) Rampton w Laneham, Treswell, Cottam and Stokeham *S'well*
TRETHEVY (St Piran) Tintagel *Truro*
TRETIRE (St Mary) St Weonards w Orcop, Garway, Tretire etc *Heref*
TREVALGA (St Petroc) Boscastle w Davidstow *Truro*
TREVENSON (St Illogan) Illogan *Truro*
TREVERBYN (St Peter) *Truro 1* **P** *The Crown*
V J B SAUNDERS
TREVONE (St Saviour) Padstow *Truro*
TREWEN (St Michael) Lezant w Lawhitton and S Petherwin w Trewen *Truro*
TREYFORD CUM DIDLING (St Andrew) Harting w Elsted and Treyford cum Didling *Chich*
TRIMDON (St Mary Magdalene) *Dur 14* **P** *Miss S Moore*
V *Vacant* Wellfield (01429) 880430
TRIMDON GRANGE (St Alban) see below
TRIMDON STATION (St Alban) (St Paul) *Dur 14* **P** *Bp*
P-in-c G E GLOVER
TRIMINGHAM (St John the Baptist) Overstrand, Northrepps, Sidestrand & Trimingham *Nor*
TRIMLEY (St Martin) (St Mary the Virgin) *St E 2* **P** *Bp and Ld Chan (alt)* **R** C LEFFLER, **C** L J PAYNE
TRIMPLEY (Holy Trinity) Kidderminster St Mary and All SS w Trimpley etc *Worc*
TRING (St Martha) (St Peter and St Paul) (St Mary)
St Alb 3 **P** *Bp* **TR** J A S PAYNE COOK,
TV M M NATHANAEL, **Hon C** J E K RIDGWAY,
NSM E INALL
TROSTON (St Mary the Virgin) Blackbourne *St E*
TROTTISCLIFFE (St Peter and St Paul) Birling, Addington, Ryarsh and Trottiscliffe *Roch*
TROTTON (St George) Rogate w Terwick and Trotton w Chithurst *Chich*
TROUTBECK (Jesus Christ) *Carl 10* **P** *Bp*
P-in-c D R JACKSON
TROWBRIDGE (Holy Trinity) *Sarum 17* **P** *Patr Bd*
TV D J COOPER

TROWBRIDGE (St James) *Sarum 17* **P** *Ch Patr Trust*
R C F BROWN
TROWBRIDGE (St Thomas) and West Ashton *Sarum 17*
P *CPAS* **P-in-c** F SEARS, **Hon C** A S REYNOLDS,
NSM J DARLING
TROWELL (St Helen) *S'well 7* **P** *Lord Middleton*
R T HATTON, **Hon C** C E HART
TROWSE (St Andrew) Lakenham St Mark w Trowse *Nor*
TRULL (All Saints) w Angersleigh *B & W 18* **P** *DBP and*
M V Spurway Esq (jt) **R** R A HATHWAY
TRUMPINGTON (St Mary and St Michael) *Ely 2* **P** *Trin*
Coll Cam **V** N J THISTLETHWAITE
TRUNCH (St Botolph) *Nor 22* **P** *Duchy of Lanc (3 turns)*,
Patr Bd (1 turn) **TR** P B ALLAN,
TV E A CUNNINGTON, **C** B N CARLING,
Hon C P M FAWCETT, **NSM** R H MacPHEE
TRURO (St George the Martyr) (St John the Evangelist)
Truro 6 **P** *Prime Min and V Kenwyn St Cuby (alt)*
V D S R WILLS
TRURO (St Mary's Cathedral and Parish Church) *Truro 6*
P *The Crown* **R** D J SHEARLOCK, **C** I F FRITH
TRURO (St Paul) (St Clement) *Truro 6* **P** *Bp*
V P B STAPLES, **NSM** W C H STRIBLEY
TRUSHAM (St Michael and All Angels) Christow, Ashton,
Trusham and Bridford *Ex*
TRUSLEY (All Saints) Ch Broughton w Barton Blount,
Boylestone etc *Derby*
TRUSTHORPE (St Peter) Mablethorpe w Trusthorpe *Linc*
TRYSULL (All Saints) Wombourne w Trysull and
Bobbington *Lich*
TRYTHALL (Mission Church) Gulval *Truro*
TUBNEY (St Lawrence) Fyfield w Tubney and Kingston
Bagpuize *Ox*
TUCKHILL (Holy Innocents) Claverley w Tuckhill *Heref*
TUCKINGMILL (All Saints) *Truro 2* **P** *Bp* **V** B P LUCK
TUCKSWOOD (St Paul) *Nor 3* **P** *Bp* **V** *Vacant* Norwich
(01603) 53739
TUDDENHAM (St Martin) Westerfield and Tuddenham
St Martin w Witnesham *St E*
TUDDENHAM (St Mary) Mildenhall *St E*
TUDDENHAM, EAST (All Saints) Hockering, Honingham,
E and N Tuddenham *Nor*
TUDDENHAM, NORTH (St Mary the Virgin) as above
TUDELEY (All Saints) w Capel *Roch 10* **P** *Bp*
V S D RILEY
TUDHOE (St David) Croxdale and Tudhoe *Dur*
TUDHOE GRANGE (St Andrew) *Dur 10* **P** *Bp*
V N D BAKER
TUEBROOK (St John) W Derby (or Tuebrook) St Jo *Liv*
TUFFLEY (St Barnabas) *Glouc 5* **P** *Bp*
V C M R PEMBERTON, **C** M J ROBSON
TUFNELL PARK (St George and All Saints) *Lon 6*
P *Trustees and CPAS (jt)* **V** S F F PARKE,
C R MONTGOMERY
TUFTON (St Mary) Whitchurch w Tufton and Litchfield
Win
TUGBY (St Thomas a Becket) Hallaton w Horninghold,
Allexton, Tugby etc *Leic*
TUGFORD (St Catherine) Diddlebury w Munslow, Holdgate
and Tugford *Heref*
TULSE HILL (Holy Trinity and St Matthias) *S'wark 10*
P *Simeon's Trustees and Peache Trustees (jt)*
V J M SENTAMU, **Hon C** G E McWATT,
NSM M B POOLE, D J LUBBOCK
TUNBRIDGE WELLS (Holy Trinity w Christ Church)
Roch 11 **P** *Mabledon Trust and CPAS (jt)*
V J W BANNER
TUNBRIDGE WELLS (King Charles the Martyr) *Roch 11*
P *Trustees* **V** M J HANCOCK
TUNBRIDGE WELLS (St Barnabas) *Roch 11* **P** *Guild of*
All So **V** M S NICHOLLS
TUNBRIDGE WELLS (St James) w (St Philip) *Roch 11*
P *Patr Bd* **TR** N G NORGATE, **TV** D J ABBOTT,
C C J DOBSON
TUNBRIDGE WELLS (St John) *Roch 11* **P** *CPAS and*
V H Trin Tunbridge Wells (jt) **V** G R WALTER,
C M P WARREN
TUNBRIDGE WELLS (St Luke) *Roch 11* **P** *Five Trustees*
P-in-c J A WHEELER
TUNBRIDGE WELLS (St Mark) Broadwater Down
Roch 11 **P** *Bp Chich* **V** F R CUMBERLEGE,
C L A CURRELL
TUNBRIDGE WELLS (St Peter) Windmill Fields *Roch 11*
P *Trustees and CPAS (jt)* **V** P R PAYN
TUNSTALL (All Saints) Roos and Garton in Holderness w
Tunstall etc *York*
TUNSTALL (Christ Church) *Lich 16* **P** *Bp* **V** A D BUIK,
C M JEAVONS

TUNSTALL (Holy Trinity) Catterick *Ripon*
TUNSTALL (St John the Baptist) w Melling and Leck
Blackb 15 **P** *Bp, Lord Shuttleworth, Judge E S Temple, and*
Ripon Coll Cuddesdon (jt) **V** P A W COTTON
TUNSTALL (St John the Baptist) w Rodmersham *Cant 14*
P *D&C and G L Doubleday Esq (jt)* **R** D MATTHIAE
TUNSTALL (St Michael and All Angels) Eyke w
Bromeswell, Rendlesham, Tunstall etc *St E*
TUNSTEAD (Holy Trinity) *Man 15* **P** *Bp and Dioc*
Chan (jt) **V** E J ASHWORTH
TUNSTEAD (St Mary) w Sco' Ruston *Nor 12* **P** *Bp*
P-in-c A R LONG
TUNWORTH (All Saints) Herriard w Winslade and Long
Sutton etc *Win*
TUPSLEY (St Paul) w Hampton Bishop *Heref 3* **P** *Bp*
V J D REESE, **C** J E FOX (nee COULDRIDGE), A P LAW
TUPTON (St John) N Wingfield, Clay Cross and Pilsley
Derby
TUR LANGTON (St Andrew) Church Langton w Tur
Langton, Thorpe Langton etc *Leic*
TURKDEAN (All Saints) Cold Aston w Notgrove and
Turkdean *Glouc*
TURNASTONE (St Mary Magdalene) Peterchurch w
Vowchurch, Turnastone and Dorstone *Heref*
TURNDITCH (All Saints) *Derby 11* **P** *Bp* **V** *Vacant* Derby
(01332) 840161
TURNERS HILL (St Leonard) *Chich 7* **P** *Bp*
V J S LOXTON
TURNFORD (St Clement) Cheshunt *St Alb*
TURNHAM GREEN (Christ Church) *Lon 11* **P** *Bp*
P-in-c J E DAINTY
TURNWORTH (St Mary) Winterbourne Stickland and
Turnworth etc *Sarum*
TURTON (St Anne) (St James) *Man 16* **P** *Bp*
V J H DAULMAN
TURVEY (All Saints) *St Alb 21* **P** *Mrs P K C Hanbury*
R P N JEFFERY
TURVILLE (St Mary) Hambleden Valley *Ox*
TURWESTON (Assumption of the Blessed Virgin
Mary) Westbury w Turweston, Shalstone and Biddlesden
Ox
TUSHINGHAM (St Chad) and Whitewell (St Mary) *Ches 5*
P *MMCET* **R** P WINCHESTER
TUTBURY (St Mary the Virgin) *Lich 19* **P** *Duchy of Lanc*
V T J GANZ
TUTSHILL (St Luke) Tidenham w Beachley and Lancaut
Glouc
TUTTINGTON (St Peter and St Paul) Felmingham, Skeyton,
Colby, Banningham etc *Nor*
TUXFORD (St Nicholas) w Weston and Markham Clinton
S'well 3 **P** *Ld Chan and Bp (alt)* **V** J E MARTIN
TWEEDMOUTH (St Bartholomew) *Newc 12* **P** *D&C Dur*
V A S ADAMSON
TWERTON-ON-AVON Bath Twerton-on-Avon *B & W*
TWICKENHAM (All Hallows) *Lon 10* **P** *D&C St Paul's*
P-in-c G A BARBER
TWICKENHAM (All Saints) *Lon 10* **P** *Bp*
P-in-c P L BUSTIN
TWICKENHAM (St Mary the Virgin) *Lon 10*
P *D&C Windsor* **V** A GLYN-JONES, **C** A F STUART,
Hon C A F B ROGERS, D J ELLIOTT, N T VINCENT
TWICKENHAM, EAST (St Stephen) (St Paul) *Lon 10*
P *CPAS* **V** M G PEPPIATT, **C** D R McDOUGALL
TWICKENHAM COMMON (Holy Trinity) *Lon 10* **P** *Bp*
V D A WALTER
TWIGWORTH (St Matthew), Down Hatherley, Norton, The
Leigh, Evington and Sandhurst *Glouc 6* **P** *Bp (1 turn)*,
Ld Chan (2 turns), and D&C Bris (1 turn) **V** J O'BRIEN,
C J S MOESEL
TWINEHAM (St Peter) Albourne w Sayers Common and
Twineham *Chich*
TWINSTEAD (St John the Evangelist) Gt and Lt Henny w
Middleton, Wickham St Paul etc *Chelmsf*
TWITCHEN (St Peter) S Molton w Nymet St George, High
Bray etc *Ex*
TWO GATES (St Peter) Wilnecote *Lich*
TWO MILE ASH (not known) Watling Valley *Ox*
TWO MILE HILL (St Michael) *Bris 2* **P** *Prime Min*
V G A B KING-SMITH
TWYCROSS (St James) The Sheepy Gp *Leic*
TWYFORD (Assumption of the Blessed Virgin Mary) Swan
Ox
TWYFORD (St Andrew) Barrow-on-Trent w Twyford and
Swarkestone *Derby*
TWYFORD (St Andrew) S Croxton Gp *Leic*

TWYFORD (St Mary) and Owslebury and Morestead
Win 13 **P** *Em Coll Cam and Bp (alt)* **V** P V LIPPIETT,
  NSM J D MORRIS
TWYFORD (St Mary the Virgin) Ruscombe and Twyford
  Ox
**TWYFORD (St Nicholas), Guist, Bintree, Themelthorpe, Wood
  Norton and Stibbard** *Nor 23* **P** *Bp, and Mrs H M Cook (2
  turns), DBP (1 turn)* **R** A K GREENHOUGH
TWYNING (St Mary Magdalene) *Glouc 9* **P** *Ch Ch Ox*
  V *Vacant* Tewkesbury (01684) 292553
TWYWELL (St Nicholas) Cranford w Grafton Underwood
  and Twywell *Pet*
TYBERTON (St Mary) Madley w Tyberton, Preston-on-Wye
  and Blakemere *Heref*
TYDD (St Mary) The Suttons w Tydd *Linc*
TYDD ST GILES (St Giles) *Ely 19* **P** *Bp*
  P-in-c N A WHITEHOUSE
TYE GREEN (St Barnabas) Fairstead w Terling and White
  Notley etc *Chelmsf*
TYE GREEN (St Stephen) w St Andrew Netteswell
  Chelmsf 27 **P** *J L H Arkwright Esq* **P-in-c** A V WATSON
TYLDESLEY (St George) w Shakerley *Man 13* **P** *Bp*
  V R I McCALLA
TYLER HILL (St Francis) Hackington *Cant*
TYLERS GREEN (St Margaret) *Ox 29* **P** *Earl Howe*
  V M E HALL
TYLER'S HILL (St George) Gt Chesham *Ox*
TYNE, NORTH and Redesdale Team *Newc 2* **P** *Patr Bd*
  TR T R HARPER, **TV** B A McKAY, P ADAMSON
TYNEMOUTH Balkwell (St Peter) Balkwell *Newc*
TYNEMOUTH Cullercoats (St Paul) *Newc 8* **P** *Dioc Soc*
  V N BANKS, **NSM** D F TITTLEY
TYNEMOUTH Shiremoor (St Mark) Shiremoor *Newc*
TYNEMOUTH (St John Percy) *Newc 8* **P** *Dioc Soc*
  V C H HOPE
TYNEMOUTH PRIORY (Holy Saviour) *Newc 8* **P** *Dioc
  Soc* **V** R G FORD, **NSM** T C DUFF
TYNINGS LANE (St Mary's Mission Church) Aldridge *Lich*
TYRINGHAM (St Peter) Haversham w Lt Linford,
  Tyringham w Filgrave *Ox*
TYRLEY (Mission Room) Drayton in Hales *Lich*
TYSELEY (St Edmund) *Birm 7* **P** *The Crown* **V** P A EVENS
**TYSOE (Assumption of the Blessed Virgin Mary) w Oxhill and
  Whatcote** *Cov 9* **P** *Marquess of Northn and DBP (jt)*
  V D A KNIGHT
TYTHBY (Holy Trinity) Cropwell Bishop w Colston Bassett,
  Granby etc *S'well*
TYTHERINGTON (St James) Cromhall w Tortworth and
  Tytherington *Glouc*
TYTHERINGTON (St James) Heytesbury and Sutton Veny
  Sarum
TYTHERLEY, EAST (St Peter) Lockerley and E Dean w E
  and W Tytherley *Win*
TYTHERLEY, WEST (St Peter) as above
TYTHERTON KELLAWAYS (St Giles) Draycot *Bris*
TYTHERTON LUCAS (St Nicholas) Chippenham St Andr
  w Tytherton Lucas *Bris*
TYWARDREATH (St Andrew) w Tregaminion *Truro 1*
  P *DBP* **V** M J OATEY
UBLEY (St Bartholomew) Blagdon w Compton Martin and
  Ubley *B & W*
UCKFIELD (Holy Cross) (St Saviour) *Chich 21* **P** *Abp*
  R C J PETERS, **C** A J CARLILL, **Hon C** C G STABLES,
  NSM C HOWARTH, R C DALLING
UDIMORE (St Mary) Brede w Udimore *Chich*
UFFCULME (St Mary the Virgin) *Ex 4* **P** *Bp* **V** J P BIRD
UFFINGTON Group, The (St Michael and All Angels)
  Linc 13 **P** *Ld Chan (2 turns), Bp (2 turns), D&C
  (1 turn)* **R** T R SHEPHERD
UFFINGTON (Holy Trinity), Upton Magna and Withington
  Lich 29 **P** *J R de Q Quincey Esq* **R** C S COOKE
**UFFINGTON (St Mary), Shellingford, Woolstone and
  Baulking** *Ox 17* **P** *Bp (2 turns), J J Twynam Esq (1 turn)*
  R J GAWNE-CAIN
UFFORD (St Andrew) Barnack w Ufford and Bainton *Pet*
UFFORD (St Mary) w Bredfield and Hasketon *St E 7* **P** *Bp,
  Ld Chan, and Exors T E Bloise-Brooke Esq (by turn)*
  R P BOURNER
UFTON (St Michael and All Angels) Radford Semele and
  Ufton *Cov*
UGBOROUGH (St Peter) Ermington and Ugborough *Ex*
UGGESHALL (St Mary) w Sotherton, Wangford and Henham
  St E 15 **P** *Exors Earl of Stradbroke* **R** *Vacant* Wangford
  (0150278) 235
UGGLEBARNBY (All Saints) Eskdaleside w Ugglebarnby
  and Sneaton *York*
UGLEY (St Peter) Henham and Elsenham w Ugley *Chelmsf*
UGTHORPE (Christ Church) Lythe w Ugthorpe *York*

ULCEBY (All Saints) Willoughby *Linc*
ULCEBY Group, The (St Nicholas) *Linc 6* **P** *Ld Chan*
  V A R MARSDEN
ULCOMBE (All Saints) Harrietsham w Ulcombe *Cant*
ULDALE (St James) Bolton w Ireby and Uldale *Carl*
ULEY (St Giles) w Owlpen and Nympsfield *Glouc 2*
  P *Ld Chan* **R** C RAWLINSON, **Hon C** M D PAISH
ULGHAM (St John the Baptist) *Newc 11* **P** *Bp*
  NSM J WAIYAKI
ULLENHALL (St Mary the Virgin) Beaudesert and Henley-
  in-Arden w Ullenhall *Cov*
ULLESKELFE (St Saviour) Kirk Fenton w Kirkby Wharfe
  and Ulleskelfe *York*
ULLEY (Holy Trinity) Aston cum Aughton w Swallownest,
  Todwick & Ulley *Sheff*
ULLINGSWICK (St Luke) Stoke Lacy, Moreton Jeffries w
  Much Cowarne etc *Heref*
ULROME (St Andrew) Skipsea w Ulrome and Barmston w
  Fraisthorpe *York*
ULTING (All Saints) Hatf Peverel w Ulting *Chelmsf*
ULVERSTON (St Mary w Holy Trinity) (St Jude) *Carl 8*
  P *Peache Trustees* **R** J HOLDEN, **C** M A EDWARDS,
  NSM V CLARKE
UMBERLEIGH (Church of the Good Shepherd) S Molton w
  Nymet St George, High Bray etc *Ex*
UNDERBARROW (All Saints) *Carl 9* **P** *V Kendal H Trin*
  V *Vacant*
UNDERRIVER (St Margaret) *Roch 8* **P** *Bp*
  P-in-c B P SIMMONS
UNDERSKIDDAW (Parish Room) Crosthwaite Keswick
  Carl
UNDERWOOD (St Michael and All Angels) Brinsley w
  Underwood *S'well*
UNSTONE (St Mary) Dronfield w Holmesfield *Derby*
UNSWORTH (St George) *Man 10* **P** *R Prestwich St Mary*
  V R E MALLINSON
UP HATHERLEY (St Philip and St James) *Glouc 11*
  P *Ch Union* **V** J H HEIDT, **C** R NORTHING,
  C B THURSTON, **NSM** H R WOOD
UP MARDEN (St Michael) Compton, the Mardens,
  Stoughton and Racton *Chich*
UP NATELY (St Stephen) Newnham w Nately Scures w
  Mapledurwell etc *Win*
UP WALTHAM (St Mary the Virgin) *Chich 11* **P** *Lord
  Egremont* **R** *Vacant*
UPCHURCH (St Mary the Virgin) w Lower Halstow
  Cant 14 **P** *D&C* **V** J P LEFROY
UPHAM (All Saints) (Blessed Mary of Upham) *Portsm 1*
  P *Ld Chan* **R** S E WILKINSON
UPHAVON (St Mary the Virgin) w Rushall and Charlton
  Sarum 12 **P** *Mert Coll Ox, Ld Chan, and Ch Ch Ox
  (by turn)* **R** D G SLOGGETT
UPHILL (St Nicholas) (St Barnabas Mission Church)
  B & W 11 **P** *Patr Bd* **TR** D N MITCHELL,
  TV M J NORMAN, **C** S P PHILLIPSON-MASTERS
UPHOLLAND (St Thomas the Martyr) *Liv 11* **P** *Patr Bd*
  TR P D D BRADLEY, **TV** S W ELSTOB, **C** P S WRIGHT
UPLANDS (All Saints) Stroud and Uplands w Slad *Glouc*
UPLEADON (St Mary the Virgin) Redmarley D'Abitot,
  Bromesberrow w Pauntley etc *Glouc*
UPLOWMAN (St Peter) Sampford Peverell, Uplowman,
  Holcombe Rogus etc *Ex*
UPLYME (St Peter and St Paul) w Axmouth *Ex 5* **P** *CPAS
  and Hyndman Trustees (jt)* **R** F S WORTH
UPMINSTER (St Laurence) *Chelmsf 2* **P** *Rev H R Holden*
  R *Vacant* Upminster (01708) 220174
UPNOR (St Philip and St James) Frindsbury w Upnor *Roch*
UPOTTERY (St Mary the Virgin) Yarcombe, Membury,
  Upottery and Cotleigh *Ex*
UPPER: *see under substantive place names*
UPPERBY (St John the Baptist) *Carl 3* **P** *D&C*
  C A D CORDINER
UPPERTHONG (St John the Evangelist) Upper Holme
  Valley *Wakef*
**UPPINGHAM (St Peter and St Paul) w Ayston and Wardley w
  Belton** *Pet 14* **P** *Bp* **R** J I WILLETT
UPPINGTON (Holy Trinity) Longdon-upon-Tern,
  Rodington, Uppington etc *Lich*
UPSHIRE (St Thomas) Waltham H Cross *Chelmsf*
UPTON (All Saints) Lea Gp *Linc*
UPTON (Holy Ascension) *Ches 2* **P** *Duke of Westmr*
  V G H CONWAY, **NSM** G J WELCH
UPTON (St Dunstan) Lytchett Minster *Sarum*
UPTON (St James) Brompton Regis w Upton and Skilgate
  B & W
UPTON (St John the Baptist) Castor w Sutton and Upton
  Pet
UPTON (St Laurence) Upton cum Chalvey *Ox*

UPTON (St Margaret) S Walsham and Upton *Nor*
UPTON (St Margaret) and Copmanford *Ely 10*　**P** *Bp*
　NSM　I D M GIBSON
UPTON (St Mary) *Ches 8*　**P** *Simeon's Trustees*
　V　R J SHIMWELL,　**C**　C A BOYCE
UPTON (St Mary Magdalene) *Ex 10*　**P** *Simeon's Trustees
and Ch Patr Trust (alt)*　**R**　B J R GERRY
UPTON (St Mary the Virgin) Blewbury, Hagbourne and
　Upton *Ox*
UPTON (St Peter and St Paul) Rolleston w Fiskerton,
　Morton and Upton *S'well*
UPTON BISHOP (St John the Baptist) Linton w Upton
　Bishop and Aston Ingham *Heref*
UPTON CRESSETT w Monk Hopton *Heref 9*　**P** *DBP and
Miss E A Bird (alt)*　**Hon C**　H J PATTERSON
UPTON CROSS (St Paul) Linkinhorne *Truro*
UPTON CUM CHALVEY (St Mary) *Ox 23*　**P** *Bp*
　TR　R A FERGUSON,　**C**　C J BARLEY,　P M THOMAS
UPTON GREY (St Mary) Herriard w Winslade and Long
　Sutton etc *Win*
UPTON HELLIONS (St Mary the Virgin) Sandford w
　Upton Hellions *Ex*
UPTON LOVELL (St Augustine of Canterbury) Ashton
　Gifford *Sarum*
UPTON MAGNA (St Lucia) Uffington, Upton Magna and
　Withington *Lich*
UPTON NOBLE (St Mary Magdalene) Bruton and Distr
　B & W
UPTON PARK (St Alban) E Ham w Upton Park St Alb
　Chelmsf
UPTON PRIORY (Church of the Resurrection) *Ches 13*
　P *Bp*　**V**　D J SAMBELL,　**NSM**　U B GAMBLES
UPTON PYNE (Our Lady) Thorverton, Cadbury, Upton
　Pyne etc *Ex*
UPTON SCUDAMORE (St Mary the Virgin) Warminster St
　Denys, Upton Scudamore etc *Sarum*
UPTON SNODSBURY (St Kenelm) Peopleton and White
　Ladies Aston w Churchill etc *Worc*
UPTON ST LEONARDS (St Leonard) *Glouc 6*　**P** *Bp*
　P-in-c　E J PENNY,　**NSM**　D E PENNY
UPTON-UPON-SEVERN (St Peter and Paul) *Worc 5*
　P *Bp*　**R**　A R KING,　**NSM**　J A FRASER
UPTON WARREN (St Michael) Stoke Prior, Wychbold and
　Upton Warren *Worc*
UPWELL (Christ Church) *Ely 18*　**P** *R T Townley Esq*
　P-in-c　S TOOKE
UPWELL (St Peter) *Ely 19*　**P** *R T Townley Esq* **R** *Vacant*
　Wisbech (01945) 772213
UPWEY (St Laurence) Bincombe w Broadwey, Upwey and
　Buckland Ripers *Sarum*
UPWOOD (St Peter) The Ramseys and Upwood *Ely*
URCHFONT (St Michael and All Angels) Redhorn *Sarum*
URMSTON (St Clement) *Man 7*　**P** *Bp*　**V**　A M TILTMAN,
　C　P D ROLFE
URSWICK (St Mary the Virgin and St Michael) *Carl 8*
　P *Resident Landowners* **V** *Vacant*
USHAW MOOR (St Luke) Bearpark and Ushaw Moor *Dur*
USSELBY (St Margaret) S Kelsey Gp *Linc*
USWORTH (Holy Trinity) (St Michael and All Angels)
　Dur 1　**P** *Patr Bd*　**TV**　N S GOSSWINN,
　P-in-c　A MELTON
UTKINTON (St Paul) Tarporley *Ches*
UTLEY (St Mark) *Bradf 8*　**P** *Bp and R Keighley
St Andr (jt)*　**V**　W D JAMIESON,　**C**　D WALMSLEY,
　NSM　W GREEN
UTTERBY (St Andrew) Fotherby *Linc*
UTTOXETER (St Mary the Virgin) w Bramshall *Lich 20*
　P *D&C Windsor*　**P-in-c**　A G SADLER,　**C**　D F B BALDWIN
UXBRIDGE (St Andrew) (St Margaret) (St Peter) *Lon 24*
　P *Bp*　**TR**　J J WITCOMBE,　**TV**　S B ROBERTS,
　C　A M CUTTING,　A F SHEARD,　A J CHRISTIAN
VALLEY END (St Saviour) Chobham w Valley End *Guildf*
VALLEY PARK (St Francis) *Win 9*　**P** *Bp*
　V　P F HUTCHINSON
VANGE (All Saints) (St Chad) *Chelmsf 6*　**P** *MMCET*
　P-in-c　D A EATON,　**C**　S A ROBERTSON
VAUXHALL (St Peter) N Lambeth *S'wark*
VENN OTTERY (St Gregory) Ottery St Mary, Alfington, W
　Hill, Tipton etc *Ex*
VENTA Group, The Stoke H Cross w Dunston, Arminghall
　etc *Nor*
VENTNOR (Holy Trinity) *Portsm 7*　**P** *Bp*
　P-in-c　D H LAURIE
VENTNOR (St Alban) Godshill *Portsm*
VENTNOR (St Catherine) *Portsm 7*　**P** *Ch Patr Trust*
　P-in-c　D H LAURIE

VERNHAM DEAN (St Mary the Virgin) Hurstbourne
　Tarrant, Faccombe, Vernham Dean etc *Win*
VERWOOD (St Michael and All Angels) *Sarum 10*　**P** *Bp*
　V　A G GILL,　**C**　I K PROVOST
VERYAN (St Symphorian) w Ruan Lanihorne *Truro 6*
　P *D&C and DBP (jt)*　**R**　M B GEACH
VICTORIA DOCKS (Ascension) *Chelmsf 3*　**P** *Bp*
　P-in-c　R F H HOWARTH
VICTORIA DOCKS St Luke *Chelmsf 3*　**P** *Ld Chan*
　P-in-c　D P WADE,　**NSM**　J A GOSLING
VIGO (Village Hall) Stansted w Fairseat and Vigo *Roch*
VINEY HILL (All Saints) *Glouc 4*　**P** *Univ Coll Ox*
　P-in-c　G J HUTCHISON
VIRGINIA WATER (Christ Church) *Guildf 11*　**P** *Simeon's
Trustees*　**V**　D W VAIL
VIRGINSTOW (St Bridget) Boyton, N Tamerton,
　Werrington etc *Truro*
VOWCHURCH (St Bartholomew) Peterchurch w
　Vowchurch, Turnastone and Dorstone *Heref*
WABERTHWAITE (St John) Eskdale, Irton, Muncaster and
　Waberthwaite *Carl*
WACTON (All Saints) Stratton St Mary w Stratton St
　Michael etc *Nor*
**WADDESDON (St Michael and All Angels) w Over
Winchendon and Fleet Marston** *Ox 24*　**P** *Duke of
Marlborough*　**R**　C M HUTCHINGS
WADDINGHAM (St Mary and St Peter) Bishop Norton,
　Waddingham and Snitterby *Linc*
WADDINGTON (St Helen) *Bradf 5*　**P** *E C Parker Esq*
　V　A G BAILEY
WADDINGTON (St Michael) *Linc 18*　**P** *Linc Coll Ox*
　P-in-c　R J G PARKER,　**NSM**　S E KIDDLE
WADDON (St George) Croydon St Jo *S'wark*
WADENHOE (St Michael and All Angels) Aldwincle w
　Thorpe Achurch, Pilton, Wadenhoe etc *Pet*
WADHURST (St Peter and St Paul) *Chich 19*
　P *E J B Hardcastle Esq and M R Toynbee Esq (jt)*
　V　M G PINSLEY,　**C**　S W NUTH
WADINGHAM (St Mary and St Peter) Bishop Norton,
　Wadingham and Snitterby *Linc*
WADSHELF (Mission Room) Old Brampton and Loundsley
　Green *Derby*
WADSLEY (no dedication) *Sheff 4*　**P** *Ch Patr Trust*
　V　D B JEANS,　**C**　J E BRADLEY
WADWORTH (St John the Baptist) w Loversall *Sheff 10*
　P *V Doncaster and DBP (alt)*　**V**　R M HARVEY
WAINCLIFFE (St David) Beeston *Ripon*
WAINFLEET Group, The (All Saints) (St Mary) (St Michael)
　Linc 8　**P** *Ld Chan, Bp and T E Pitts Esq (alt)*
　R　P F COATES
WAINFORD *St E 14*　**P** *Bp, Mrs B I T Suckling, CPAS,
Magd Coll Cam, and Ch Soc Trust (jt)*　**R**　F GEORGE,
　NSM　R C B ALLEN,　J F W BUCHANAN,　N H SIMISTER
WAITHE (St Martin) North-Chapel Parishes, The *Linc*
WAKEFIELD Chantry Bridge (St Mary) Wakef St Andr and
　St Mary *Wakef*
WAKEFIELD (St Andrew and St Mary) (St Swithun)
　Wakef 12　**P** *Peache Trustees*　**V**　B S ELLIS
WAKEFIELD (St John the Baptist) *Wakef 12*　**P** *Provost*
　V　P M DOWLING,　**C**　W R S LAMB,
　Hon C　R B GRAINGER
WAKEFIELD (St Michael the Archangel) Westgate
　Common *Wakef*
WAKERING, GREAT (St Nicholas) w Foulness *Chelmsf 13*
　P *Bp*　**V**　B J SHANNON
WAKERING, LITTLE (St Mary the Virgin) Barling w Lt
　Wakering *Chelmsf*
WAKERLEY (St John the Baptist) Barrowden and Wakerley
　w S Luffenham *Pet*
WAKES COLNE (All Saints) Gt Tey and Wakes Colne w
　Chappel *Chelmsf*
WALBERSWICK (St Andrew) Thorington w Wenhaston,
　Bramfield & Walberswick *St E*
WALBERTON (St Mary) w Binsted *Chich 21*　**P** *Bp*
　V　M J SULLY
WALCOT (Bath Walcot) *B & W*
WALCOT (All Saints) Happisburgh, Walcot, Hempstead w
　Eccles etc *Nor*
WALCOT (St Nicholas) S Lafford *Linc*
WALCOT (St Oswald) Billinghay *Linc*
WALDEN, LITTLE (St John) Saffron Walden w Wendens
　Ambo and Littlebury *Chelmsf*
WALDERSLADE (St William) Chatham St Wm *Roch*
WALDINGFIELD, GREAT (St Lawrence) Acton w Gt
　Waldingfield *St E*
WALDINGFIELD, LITTLE (St Lawrence) Edwardstone w
　Groton and Lt Waldingfield *St E*
WALDITCH (St Mary) Bridport *Sarum*

WALDRINGFIELD (All Saints) w Hemley and Newbourn *St E 2* **P** *Canon T Waller and Rev A H N Waller, Ld Chan, and Sir Joshua Rowley, Bt (by turn)* **R** J P WALLER
WALDRON (All Saints) *Chich 15* **P** *Ex Coll Ox* **R** R W GREENLAND
WALES (St John the Baptist) *Sheff 5* **P** *Bp* **V** H J PATRICK
WALESBY (St Edmund) *S'well 3* **P** *DBP* **V** C C LEVY
WALESBY (St Mary and All Saints) *Linc 5* **P** *Bp, DBP, and W Drake Esq (jt)* **R** *Vacant* Tealby (01673) 838513
WALFORD (St Michael and All Angels) and Saint John, w Bishopswood, Goodrich, Marstow and Welsh Bicknor *Heref 8* **P** *Bp and Ld Chan (alt)* **R** P TARLING, **NSM** P B BARLOW
WALGRAVE (St Peter) w Hannington and Wold and Scaldwell *Pet 2* **P** *Bp (2 turns), BNC Ox (1 turn)* **R** D G THOMAS
WALHAM GREEN (St John) (St James) *Lon 9* **P** *Bp* **P-in-c** K D MOULE
WALKDEN (St Barnabas' Mission) see below
WALKDEN MOOR (St Paul) w Little Hulton *Man 12* **P** *Bp* **TR** A E BALLARD, **TV** A N BATEMAN, **C** A CUNNINGHAM
WALKER (Christ Church) *Newc 6* **P** *Bp* **V** R BEST, **C** J C HARDY
WALKERGATE (St Oswald) Byker St Mark and Walkergate St Oswald *Newc*
WALKERINGHAM (St Mary Magdalene) Beckingham w Walkeringham *S'well*
WALKERN (St Mary the Virgin) Benington w Walkern *St Alb*
WALKHAMPTON (St Mary the Virgin) Yelverton, Meavy, Sheepstor and Walkhampton *Ex*
WALKINGTON (All Hallows) Bishop Burton w Walkington *York*
WALKLEY (St Mary) *Sheff 4* **P** *Bp* **V** I K DUFFIELD
WALL (St George) St Oswald in Lee w Bingfield *Newc*
WALL (St John the Baptist) *Lich 1* **P** *R Lich SS Mary and Mich* **P-in-c** D A SMITH, **NSM** J G LISTER
WALLASEY (St Hilary) *Ches 7* **P** *Bp* **R** R ORTON
WALLASEY (St Nicholas) *Ches 7* **P** *Bp* **V** E J BENTLEY
WALLINGFORD (St Mary le More w All Hallows) (St Leonard) and St Peter w Crowmarsh Gifford and Newnham Murren *Ox 18* **P** *Bp* **TR** J MORLEY, **TV** S HAYTER, **Hon C** W P HEDGCOCK, **NSM** I S BECKWITH
WALLINGTON (Holy Trinity) (St Patrick) *S'wark 26* **P** *Ch Soc Trust* **V** D V LEWIS, **C** T M HUMPHREY, B E BROWN, J WATKINS
WALLINGTON (St Mary) Sandon, Wallington and Rushden w Clothall *St Alb*
WALLISDOWN (St Saviour) Talbot Village *Sarum*
WALLOP, NETHER (St Andrew) Over Wallop w Nether Wallop *Win*
WALLOP, OVER (St Peter) w Nether Wallop *Win 3* **P** *D&C York and Earl of Portsm (alt)* **P-in-c** A R GRAHAM
WALLSEND (St John the Evangelist) *Newc 8* **P** *Bp* **V** F WILSON
WALLSEND (St Luke) *Newc 8* **P** *Bp* **V** J G INGE, **C** S M B WELLS, **NSM** A J ELDER, S HAMIL
WALLSEND (St Peter) *Newc 8* **P** *Bp* **P-in-c** J ROSS, A A CLEMENTS
WALMER (St Mary) (St Saviour) (Blessed Virgin Mary) *Cant 8* **P** *Abp* **V** B A HAWKINS, **C** M K DAVIES, **NSM** S M LEE
WALMERSLEY (Christ Church) *Man 10* **P** *Trustees* **V** B STANNARD, **Hon C** M E MAYOH
WALMLEY (St John the Evangelist) *Birm 9* **P** *Trustess* **V** M B HARPER, **C** D A T MACGREGOR
WALMSLEY (Christ Church) *Man 16* **P** *V Bolton-le-Moors St Pet* **C** S C NEAL, **NSM** R E IDDON
WALNEY ISLAND (St Mary the Virgin) *Carl 8* **P** *V Dalton-in-Furness* **V** R J WILLIAMSON, **C** I GRAINGER
WALPOLE (St Mary the Virgin) Halesworth w Linstead, Chediston, Holton etc *St E*
WALPOLE ST PETER (St Peter and St Paul) w St Andrew *Ely 17* **P** *The Crown and DBP (alt)* **R** A R TREEN
WALSALL (Annunciation of Our Lady) Walsall St Gabr Fulbrook *Lich*
WALSALL (St Andrew) *Lich 6* **P** *Bp* **P-in-c** A P MITCHELL
WALSALL (St Gabriel) Fulbrook *Lich 6* **P** *Bp* **V** T R H COYNE, **NSM** W H POULTNEY
WALSALL (St Mary and All Saints) Palfrey *Lich 6* **P** *Bp* **P-in-c** N A M PUNZI, **C** F R MILLER
WALSALL (St Matthew) (St Luke) (St Martin) *Lich 6* **P** *Patr Bd* **TR** M B SANDERS, **TV** A G C SMITH, J E SHARPE, **C** P HOWELL-JONES

WALSALL St Paul *Lich 6* **P** *R Walsall* **V** J S DAVIS, **C** E M BARNES
WALSALL (St Peter) *Lich 6* **P** *R Walsall* **P-in-c** S R KIRBY
WALSALL THE PLECK (St John) and Bescot *Lich 6* **P** *V Walsall* **V** J REID
WALSALL WOOD (St John) *Lich 6* **P** *R Walsall* **V** M A RHODES
WALSDEN (St Peter) *Wakef 3* **P** *Bp* **P-in-c** G FRYER
WALSGRAVE ON SOWE (St Mary) *Cov 1* **P** *Ld Chan* **V** M TYLER, **NSM** F E TYLER (nee FOSTER)
WALSHAM, NORTH (St Nicholas) w Antingham *Nor 12* **P** *Bp* **V** M W SMITH, **C** R B STAINER, **NSM** V A WATTS
WALSHAM, SOUTH (St Laurence w St Mary) and Upton *Nor 4* **P** *Qu Coll Cam and Bp (jt)* **R** G A HENDY
WALSHAM LE WILLOWS (St Mary) and Finningham w Westhorpe *St E 9* **P** *R M Martineau Esq, DBP, and Ch Union (jt)* **R** *Vacant* Walsham-le-Willows (03598) 310
WALSHAW (Christ Church) *Man 10* **P** *Simeon's Trustees* **V** S FOSTER, **C** I J HALSALL
WALSINGHAM (St Mary and All Saints) (St Peter) and Houghton (St Giles) *Nor 16* **P** *J Gurney Esq* **P-in-c** K F HAYDON
WALSOKEN (All Saints) *Ely 19* **P** *DBP* **R** J DAVIS
WALTERSTONE (St Mary) Ewyas Harold w Dulas, Kenderchurch etc *Heref*
WALTHAM (All Saints) *Linc 10* **P** *The Crown* **P-in-c** I R SHELTON
WALTHAM (Holy Cross) *Chelmsf 26* **P** *Patr Bd* **TR** P J B HOBSON, **TV** J PEARCE, R A D ENEVER, **C** A J P GARROW
WALTHAM (St Bartholomew) Petham and Waltham w Lower Hardres etc *Cant*
WALTHAM (St Lawrence) *Ox 13* **P** *Lord Braybrooke* **V** P RADLEY
WALTHAM, GREAT (St Mary and St Lawrence) w Ford End *Chelmsf 8* **P** *Trin Coll Ox* **P-in-c** M T PROCTOR
WALTHAM, LITTLE (St Martin) *Chelmsf 8* **P** *Ex Coll Ox* **R** H ANSELL
WALTHAM, NEW (St Matthew) *Linc 10* **P** *The Crown* **V** *Vacant* Grimsby (01472) 827765
WALTHAM, NORTH (St Michael) and Steventon, Ashe and Deane *Win 6* **P** *DBP* **R** M S KENNING
WALTHAM ABBEY (Holy Cross) Waltham H Cross *Chelmsf*
WALTHAM CROSS (Christ Church) *St Alb 6* **P** *V Cheshunt* **V** M J BANISTER, **C** B V EAST
WALTHAM ON THE WOLDS (St Mary Magdalene), Stonesby, Saxby w Stapleford and Wyfordby *Leic 3* **P** *Duke of Rutland, Lady Gretton, and Sir Lyonel Tollemache, Bt (jt)* **R** J P STONE
WALTHAMSTOW (St Andrew) *Chelmsf 5* **P** *Bp* **V** M R J LAND
WALTHAMSTOW (St Barnabas and St James the Great) *Chelmsf 5* **P** *Bp* **V** A D COUCHMAN
WALTHAMSTOW (St Gabriel) *Chelmsf 5* **P** *Simeon's Trustees* **V** *Vacant* 0181–520 3411
WALTHAMSTOW (St John) *Chelmsf 5* **P** *TR Walthamstow* **P-in-c** A J BISHOP
WALTHAMSTOW (St Luke) *Chelmsf 5* **P** *Simeon's Trustees* **P-in-c** P R BUTLER, **C** J R ALLCOCK
WALTHAMSTOW (St Mary) (St Stephen) *Chelmsf 5* **P** *Patr Bd* **TV** R G V FOREMAN, **P-in-c** P R BUTLER, **C** R A MEAGER
WALTHAMSTOW (St Michael and All Angels) *Chelmsf 5* **P** *Bp* **P-in-c** J TETLOW
WALTHAMSTOW (St Peter-in-the-Forest) *Chelmsf 5* **P** *Bp* **V** K MELBOURNE, **C** L K NEWTON, **NSM** W S ROBINS, **Hon Par Dn** D E P PALK
WALTHAMSTOW (St Saviour) *Chelmsf 5* **P** *Bp* **V** P D D JAMES, **C** A G D CLAPP
WALTON (Holy Trinity) Street w Walton *B & W*
WALTON (Holy Trinity) *Ox 21* **P** *Patr Bd and DBP (jt)* **TV** N A HAND, R G HART, P D F HORNER, **C** S J REED
WALTON Milton Keynes *Ox 25* **P** *Patr Bd* **TR** D LUNN, **TV** D K MIELL
WALTON (not known) Gilmorton w Peatling Parva and Kimcote etc *Leic*
WALTON (St John) Brampton St Thos *Derby*
WALTON (St John the Evangelist) *Ches 4* **P** *P G Greenall Esq* **V** W J HIGHTON
WALTON (St Mary) Lanercost w Kirkcambeck and Walton *Carl*
WALTON (St Mary) (St Philip) *St E 2* **P** *Ch Trust Fund Trust* **P-in-c** G J ARCHER, **C** A L FOWLER, R G CORKE, **NSM** I W BARLEY, A C BARLEY, J K B FOWLER, B PERCY

WALTON (St Paul) Sandal St Helen *Wakef*
WALTON (St Peter) Thorp Arch w Walton *York*
WALTON (St Thomas) Baswich (or Berkswich) *Lich*
WALTON, EAST (St Mary) Gayton Gp of Par *Nor*
WALTON, HIGHER (All Saints) *Blackb 6*   **P** *V Blackb*
V   J HANNA
WALTON, WEST (St Mary) *Ely 17*   **P** *Ld Chan*
P-in-c   A R TREEN,   **NSM**   L D FYSH
WALTON BRECK (Christ Church) *Liv 7*   **P** *Simeon's*
Trustees   V   S B PIERCE
WALTON BRECK (Holy Trinity) *Liv 7*   **P** *Simeon's*
Trustees   V   C A PELL
WALTON D'EIVILLE (St James) *Cov 8*   **P** *Sir Richard*
Hamilton, Bt   **R**   N V HOWES
WALTON IN GORDANO (St Mary) E Clevedon and
Walton w Weston w Clapton *B & W*
WALTON IN GORDANO (St Paul) as above
WALTON-LE-DALE (St Leonard) w Samlesbury St Leonard
the Less *Blackb 6*   **P** *V Blackb St Mary and St Paul*
V   T TAYLOR
WALTON LE SOKEN (All Saints) (St George) *Chelmsf 24*
P *Bp*   V   G D A BENNET
WALTON LE WOLDS (St Mary) Barrow upon Soar w
Walton le Wolds *Leic*
WALTON-ON-THAMES (St Mary) *Guildf 8*   **P** *Bp*
V   T J SEDGLEY,   **C**   K W SCOTT,   M P STOKES
WALTON ON THE HILL (St John) *Liv 7*   **P** *Bp, Adn, and*
R Walton (jt)   V   S GROSSCURTH
WALTON ON THE HILL (St Luke) *Liv 7*   **P** *Bp*
V   H E ROSS
WALTON-ON-THE-HILL (St Mary) (St Aidan) *Liv 5*
P *Bp*   **TR**   P R TILLEY,   **TV**   G AMOS,   T H ALLEN,
C   P GARTSIDE,   K L F PITT
WALTON-ON-THE-HILL (St Peter) *Guildf 9*   **P** *Bp*
R   J S HARRIS
WALTON ON TRENT (St Lawrence) w Croxall and Coton in
the Elms w Rosliston *Derby 16*   **P** *Bp and*
D W H Neilson Esq (jt)   P-in-c   E J THOMPSON
WALWORTH (St Christopher) *S'wark*   **P** *Bp and Pemb Coll*
Miss   I   M DURRAN
WALWORTH (St John w the Lady Margaret) *S'wark 8*
P *Bp*   V   J F WALKER,   **Hon C**   E DAWSON
WALWORTH (St Peter) *S'wark 8*   **P** *Bp*   **TR**   G S MURRAY
WAMBROOK (Blessed Virgin Mary) Combe St Nicholas w
Wambrook *B & W*
WANBOROUGH (St Andrew) Lyddington and
Wanborough and Bishopstone etc *Bris*
WANBOROUGH (St Bartholomew) Puttenham and
Wanborough *Guildf*
WANDSWORTH (All Saints) (Holy Trinity) *S'wark 18*
P *Ch Soc Trust*   V   A G SIRMAN
WANDSWORTH Southfields (St Michael and All Angels)
S'wark 18   **P** *Ch Soc Trust*   V   D J CASIOT
WANDSWORTH (St Anne) *S'wark 18*   **P** *Bp*
V   M H CLARK,   **Hon C**   D M H REECE
WANDSWORTH (St Faith) *S'wark 18*   **P** *Bp*
V   C C M COWARD
WANDSWORTH (St Stephen) *S'wark 18*   **P** *CPAS*
V   G M VEVERS,   **Hon C**   J H FREEMAN
WANDSWORTH Wimbledon Park (St Paul) *S'wark 18*
P *Bp*   V   W A J ALLBERRY,   **C**   J M THOMAS,
NSM   G E D BONHAM-CARTER,   A J TOWNSEND
WANDSWORTH COMMON (St Mary Magdalene)
S'wark 17   **P** *Bp*   V   I KITTERINGHAM,
NSM   B STEWART
WANGFORD (St Peter) Uggeshall w Sotherton, Wangford
and Henham *St E*
WANLIP (Our Lady and St Nicholas) Birstall and Wanlip
Leic
WANSFORD (St Mary) Nafferton w Wansford *York*
WANSFORD (St Mary the Virgin) Wittering w Thornhaugh
and Wansford *Pet*
WANSTEAD (Holy Trinity) Hermon Hill *Chelmsf 4*   **P** *Bp*
V   A H ASHDOWN,   **Hon Par Dn**   D E P PALK
WANSTEAD (St Mary) (Christ Church) *Chelmsf 4*   **P** *Bp*
R   S F FOSTER,   **C**   J G JARMAN,   J BASKERVILLE
WANSTROW (Blessed Virgin Mary) Nunney and Witham
Friary, Marston Bigot etc *B & W*
WANTAGE (St Peter and St Paul) *Ox 19*   **P** *D&C Windsor*
V   J L SALTER,   **C**   C M SMITH
WANTAGE DOWNS *Ox 19*   **P** *Bp, CCC Ox, and*
C L Loyd Esq (jt)   **R**   E G ADLEY,   **NSM**   C J KING,
M G D ENDEAN,   D J PAGE
WANTISDEN (St John the Baptist) Eyke w Bromeswell,
Rendlesham, Tunstall etc *St E*
WAPLEY (St Peter) Yate New Town *Bris*

WAPPENBURY (St John the Baptist) w Weston under
Wetherley *Cov 10*   **P** *Bp*   P-in-c   P J CROOKS
WAPPENHAM (St Mary the Virgin) Weedon Lois w
Plumpton and Moreton Pinkney etc *Pet*
WARBLETON (St Mary) and Bodle Street Green *Chich 15*
P *Rev E S Haviland*   **R**   G FRANCE
WARBLINGTON (St Thomas a Becket) and Emsworth
Portsm 4   **P** *Bp and J H Norris Esq (alt)*
R   D J F PARTRIDGE,   **C**   J I OYET,   **NSM**   L H MORRIS
WARBOROUGH (St Lawrence) *Ox 1*   **P** *CCC Ox*   V   *Vacant*
Warborough (0186732) 8381
WARBOYS (St Mary Magdalene) w Broughton and Bury w
Wistow *Ely 11*   **P** *Bp and Ch Soc Trust (jt)*
R   S O LEEKE,   **C**   C HURST
WARBSTOW (St Werburgh) St Gennys, Jacobstow w
Warbstow and Treneglos *Truro*
WARBURTON (St Werburgh) *Ches 10*
P *Hon M L W Flower*   P-in-c   E M BURGESS
WARCOP (St Columba) Brough w Stainmore, Musgrave and
Warcop *Carl*
WARD END (Christ Church) Burney Lane *Birm*
WARD END (St Margaret) *Birm 10*   **P** *Aston Trustees*
V   R P BILLINGSLEY
WARDEN (St Michael and All Angels) w Newbrough *Newc 4*
P *Bp*   V   J W GLEDHILL
WARDEN, OLD (St Leonard) *St Alb 17*   **P** *R O Shuttleworth*
Trustees   V   P R CRESSALL
WARDINGTON (St Mary Magdalene) Cropredy w Gt
Bourton and Wardington *Ox*
WARDLE (St James the Apostle) Smallbridge and Wardle
Man
WARDLEWORTH (St Mary w St James) Rochdale *Man*
WARDLEY (All Saints) Swinton and Pendlebury *Man*
WARDLEY (St Botolph) Uppingham w Ayston and Wardley
w Belton *Pet*
WARDLOW (Good Shepherd) Ashford w Sheldon and
Longstone *Derby*
WARE (Christ Church) *St Alb 8*   **P** *CPAS*
V   D H WHEATON,   **C**   D A WILLIAMS
WARE (St Mary the Virgin) *St Alb 8*   **P** *Trin Coll Cam*
V   H E WILCOX,   **NSM**   M S E M BEAZLEY
WAREHAM (Lady St Mary) (St Martin) *Sarum 9*
P *Patr Bd*   **TR**   P G HARDMAN,   **TV**
A C ASHCROFT,   **C**   R C BARTLETT,   **NSM**   J CLEATON
WAREHORNE (St Matthew) Orlestone w Snave and
Ruckinge w Warehorne *Cant*
WARESIDE (Holy Trinity) Hunsdon w Widford and
Wareside *St Alb*
WARESLEY (St James) *Ely 12*   **P** *Pemb Coll Cam*
P-in-c   B CURRY
WARFIELD (St Michael the Archangel) *Ox 11*   **P** *DBP*
V   B H MEARDON,   **NSM**   A K BUSH
WARGRAVE (St Mary the Virgin) *Ox 16*   **P** *Lord Remnant*
V   J W RATINGS,   **NSM**   M D W PARTRIDGE
WARHAM (All Saints) Holkham w Egmere w Warham,
Wells and Wighton *Nor*
WARK (St Michael) Humshaugh w Simonburn and Wark
Newc
WARKLEIGH (St John) S Molton w Nymet St George, High
Bray etc *Ex*
WARKTON (St Edmund) Barton Seagrave w Warkton *Pet*
WARKWORTH (St Lawrence) and Acklington *Newc 9*   **P** *Bp*
and Trustees of the late Duke of Northd (alt)
NSM   J A RICHARDSON
WARKWORTH (St Mary the Virgin) Greatworth and
Marston St Lawrence etc *Pet*
WARLEGGAN (St Bartholomew) St Neot and Warleggan
Truro
WARLEY (St John the Evangelist) *Wakef 4*   **P** *V Halifax*
V   T L SWINHOE,   **NSM**   J S BRADBERRY,   P F MILLWARD
WARLEY, GREAT (Christ Church) *Chelmsf 7*   **P** *Bp*
P-in-c   A J PUGSLEY
WARLEY, GREAT (St Mary the Virgin) w Childerditch and
Ingrave *Chelmsf 7*   **P** *Hon G C D Jeffreys, MMCET and*
Ch Patr Trust (jt)   **NSM**   C J TRAVERS
WARLEY, LITTLE (St Peter) E and W Horndon w Lt
Warley *Chelmsf*
WARLEY WOODS (St Hilda) *Birm 5*   **P** *Bp*
V   M GRAHAM
WARLINGHAM (All Saints) w Chelsham and Farleigh
S'wark 19   **P** *Bp (3 turns), Mert Coll Ox (1 turn)*
P-in-c   R D W HAWKINS,   **C**   I A COUTTS,
S M SOKOLOWSKI (nee MAHON)
WARMFIELD (St Peter) *Wakef 9*   **P** *Oley Trustees Clare*
Coll Cam   V   *Vacant* Wakefield (01924) 893089

WARMINGHAM (St Leonard) Elworth and Warmingham *Ches*

WARMINGTON (St Mary the Blessed Virgin), Tansor w Cotterstock and Fotheringhay *Pet 12* **P** *Bp and D&C Linc (alt)* **V** *Vacant* Oundle (01832) 280263

WARMINGTON (St Michael) w Shotteswell and Radway w Ratley *Cov 8* **P** *Bp* **R** *R P PAUL*

WARMINSTER (Christ Church) *Sarum 14* **P** *R Warminster St Denys etc* **V** *F J WOODS*

WARMINSTER (St Denys), Upton Scudamore and Horningsham *Sarum 14* **P** *Qu Coll Ox (1 turn), Bp (2 turns)* **R** *R SHARPE*, **C** *G COGGINS*

WARMLEY (St Barnabas), Syston and Bitton *Bris 2* **P** *Bp* **R** *D G MITCHELL*, **C** *M P SIMPSON*, *J M CARPENTER*, **Hon C** *J E NORMAN*

WARMSWORTH (St Peter) *Sheff 10* **P** *Bp* **R** *Vacant* Doncaster (01302) 853324

WARMWELL (Holy Trinity) Broadmayne, W Knighton, Owermoigne etc *Sarum*

WARNBOROUGH, SOUTH (St Andrew) Herriard w Winslade and Long Sutton etc *Win*

WARNDON (St Nicholas) *Worc 6* **P** *Bp* **P-in-c** *P W HART*

WARNDON (St Wulstan) Worc St Wulstan *Worc*

WARNERS END (St Alban) Hemel Hempstead *St Alb*

WARNFORD (Our Lady) W Meon and Warnford *Portsm*

WARNHAM (St Margaret) *Chich 8* **P** *J C Lucas Esq* **V** *J R TAYLOR*

WARNINGLID (St Andrew) Slaugham *Chich*

WARREN PARK (St Clare) *Portsm 4* **P** *Bp* **V** *R C WHITE*, **NSM** *M S HARPER*

WARREN ROW (St Paul) Knowl Hill w Littlewick *Ox*

WARRINGTON (Holy Trinity) *Liv 12* **P** *R Warrington* **V** *I D ELLIOTT*

WARRINGTON (St Ann) *Liv 12* **P** *Simeon's Trustees* **V** *S R PARISH*

WARRINGTON (St Barnabas) Bank Quay *Liv 12* **P** *R Warrington and Bp (jt)* **V** *M RAYNOR*

WARRINGTON (St Elphin) (St John) *Liv 12* **P** *Lord Lilford* **R** *J O COLLING*, **C** *M D CHILCOTT*

WARSLOW (St Lawrence) Alstonfield, Butterton, Warslow w Elkstone etc *Lich*

WARSOP (St Peter and St Paul) *S'well 2* **P** *Trustees* **R** *C W BOWMAN*, **C** *P J STEAD*, **Hon C** *J V SHARPE*

WARTER (St James) Nunburnholme and Warter *York*

WARTHILL (St Mary) Stockton-on-the-Forest w Holtby and Warthill *York*

WARTLING (St Mary Magdalene) Herstmonceux and Wartling *Chich*

WARTNABY (St Michael) Ab Kettleby Gp *Leic*

WARTON (Holy Trinity) Austrey and Warton *Birm*

WARTON (St Oswald or Holy Trinity) w Yealand Conyers *Blackb 15* **P** *Bp* **V** *F BODDY*, **Hon C** *C R P ANSTEY*

WARTON (St Paul) *Blackb 11* **P** *Ch Ch Ox* **V** *G WORTHINGTON*

WARWICK (St Leonard) Wetheral w Warw *Carl*

WARWICK (St Mary) (St Nicholas) *Cov 11* **P** *Ld Chan and Patr Bd (alt)* **TR** *D C BRINDLEY*, **TV** *A A GORHAM*, *K M ROBERTS*, *G SANDERSON*

WARWICK (St Paul) *Cov 11* **P** *TR Warw* **V** *S W HEWITT*

WARWICK SQUARE (St Gabriel) Pimlico St Gabr *Lon*

WASDALE, NETHER (St Michael) Gosforth w Nether Wasdale and Wasdale Head *Carl*

WASDALE HEAD (not known) as above

WASH COMMON (St George) Newbury *Ox*

WASHBOURNE, GREAT (St Mary) Alderton, Gt Washbourne, Dumbleton etc *Glouc*

WASHFIELD (St Mary the Virgin), Stoodleigh, Withleigh, Calverleigh, Oakford, Templeton, Loxbeare, Rackenford, Cruwys Morchard and Cove *Ex 8* **P** *Patr Bd* **TR** *C H MEE*, **TV** *R C THORP*, **NSM** *J C W ROBERTS*

WASHFORD (St Mary) Old Cleeve, Leighland and Treborough *B & W*

WASHFORD PYNE (St Peter) N Creedy *Ex*

WASHINGBOROUGH (St John) w Heighington and Canwick *Linc 18* **P** *DBP and Mercers' Co (jt)* **R** *A C BELL*

WASHINGTON (Holy Trinity) *Dur 1* **P** *Bp* **P-in-c** *J G A ROBERTS*, **C** *A PATTMAN*

WASHINGTON (St Mary) Ashington, Washington and Wiston w Buncton *Chich*

WASHWOOD HEATH (St Mark) *Birm 10* **P** *V Saltley* **V** *R E CRANE*

WASING (St Nicholas) Aldermaston w Wasing and Brimpton *Ox*

WASKERLEY (St Andrew) Blanchland w Hunstanworth and Edmundbyers etc *Newc*

WASPERTON (St John the Baptist) Barford w Wasperton and Sherbourne *Cov*

WASS (St Thomas) Coxwold and Husthwaite *York*

WATCHET (Holy Cross Chapel) St Decumans *B & W*

WATCHET (St Decuman) as above

WATCHFIELD (St Thomas's Chapel) Shrivenham w Watchfield and Bourton *Ox*

WATER EATON (St Frideswide) *Ox 25* **P** *Bp* **V** *P A SMITH*

WATER NEWTON (St Remigius) *Ely 13* **P** *Keble Coll Ox* **P-in-c** *P O POOLEY*

WATER ORTON (St Peter and St Paul) *Birm 11* **P** *Patr Bd* **V** *S T MAYES*

WATER STRATFORD (St Giles) *Ox 22* **P** *DBP* **P-in-c** *J HUDSON*

WATERBEACH (St John) *Ely 6* **P** *Bp* **V** *D P E REINDORP*

WATERDEN (All Saints) N and S Creake w Waterden, Syderstone etc *Nor*

WATERFALL (St James and St Bartholomew) Calton, Cauldon, Grindon and Waterfall *Lich*

WATERFOOT (St James the Great) *Man 15* **P** *Trustees* **V** *Vacant* Rossendale (01706) 215959

WATERFORD (St Michael and All Angels) Bramfield w Stapleford and Waterford *St Alb*

WATERHEAD (Holy Trinity) *Man 21* **P** *The Crown* **V** *Vacant* 0161–624 4011

WATERHOUSES (St Paul) *Dur 2* **P** *R Brancepeth Esq* **P-in-c** *P R MURRAY*

WATERINGBURY (St John the Baptist) w Teston and West Farleigh *Roch 7* **P** *Peache Trustees and D&C (jt)* **P-in-c** *D V GOWER*

WATERLOO (Christ Church) (St Mary) *Liv 1* **P** *Trustees* **V** *R J HUTCHINSON*, **NSM** *D C M TAYLOR*

WATERLOO (St John) *Liv 1* **P** *Trustees* **P-in-c** *P W DEARNLEY*

WATERLOO (St John the Evangelist) (St Andrew) *S'wark 11* **P** *Abp and CPAS (jt)* **V** *C R TRUSS*, **C** *F J MAKAMBWE*

WATERLOOVILLE (St George the Martyr) *Portsm 4* **P** *Bp* **V** *M FERRIER*

WATERMILLOCK (All Saints) Greystoke, Matterdale, Mungrisdale, etc *Carl*

WATERMOOR (Holy Trinity) Cirencester *Glouc*

WATERPERRY (St Mary the Virgin) Holton and Waterperry w Albury and Waterstock *Ox*

WATERS UPTON (St Michael) Tibberton w Bolas Magna and Waters Upton *Lich*

WATERSTOCK (St Leonard) Holton and Waterperry w Albury and Waterstock *Ox*

WATERTHORPE (Emmanuel) Mosborough *Sheff*

WATFORD (Christ Church) (St Mark) *St Alb 13* **P** *Bp, V Watford, and Churchwardens (jt)* **V** *R C LEWIS*, **C** *A R BEEVER*

WATFORD (St Andrew) *St Alb 13* **P** *Bp and Churchwardens (jt)* **V** *G R WARREN*

WATFORD (St John) *St Alb 13* **P** *Bp* **V** *R SALTER*

WATFORD (St Luke) *St Alb 13* **P** *Bp, Adn St Alb, V Watford, and Ch Trust Fund Trust (jt)* **V** *J KIDDLE*

WATFORD (St Mary) *St Alb 13* **P** *Ch Trust Fund Trust* **V** *J M WOODGER*, **C** *D C WEAVER*, *D K DAWES*, **NSM** *A D MILTON*

WATFORD (St Michael and All Angels) *St Alb 13* **P** *Bp* **V** *J B BROWN*, **C** *W S D BURKE*

WATFORD (St Peter) *St Alb 13* **P** *Bp* **V** *C P COTTEE*

WATFORD (St Peter and St Paul) Long Buckby w Watford *Pet*

WATH (St Mary) Kirklington w Burneston and Wath and Pickhill *Ripon*

WATH BROW (Mission Church) Cleator Moor w Cleator *Carl*

WATH-UPON-DEARNE (All Saints) *Sheff 12* **P** *Ch Ch Ox* **C** *J M RICHARDS*

WATLING VALLEY, Milton Keynes (not known) *Ox 25* **P** *Patr Bd* **TR** *F G GODBER*, **TV** *S F MORRIS*, **C** *D YATES*, *S D GODDARD*

WATLINGTON (St Leonard) w Pyrton and Shirburn *Ox 1* **P** *Bp, Ch Ch Ox, and Earl of Macclesfield (by turn)* **V** *C I EVANS*, **C** *J M RUSSELL*

WATLINGTON (St Peter and St Paul) *Ely 16* **P** *Bp* **R** *J C W NOLAN*

WATTISFIELD (St Margaret) Hepworth, Hinderclay, Wattisfield and Thelnetham *St E*

WATTLESBOROUGH (St Margaret) Alberbury w Cardeston *Heref*

WATTON (St Mary) Hutton Cranswick w Skerne, Watton and Beswick *York*

WATTON (St Mary) w Carbrooke and Ovington *Nor 14*
P *Ld Chan (3 turns), Cam Univ (1 turn), and SMF
(2 turns)* **V** R J BOWETT
WATTON AT STONE (St Mary and St Andrew) *St Alb 12*
P *R M A Smith Esq* **P-in-c** B H GWINN
WAVENDON w WALTON Assumption (St Mary the
Virgin) Walton Milton Keynes *Ox*
WAVERTON (Christ Church) Bromfield w Waverton *Carl*
WAVERTON (St Peter) *Ches 5* **P** *Bp* **R** J M G DAVIES,
NSM E T DAVIES
WAVERTREE (Holy Trinity) *Liv 6* **P** *Bp*
R J EASTWOOD, **C** A W GOUGH, NSM L B BRUCE
WAVERTREE (St Bridget) *Liv 6* **P** *R Wavertree Holy Trin*
P-in-c W J SANDERS
WAVERTREE (St Mary) *Liv 6* **P** *Bp* **R** R H L WILLIAMS,
C P J PRIGG
WAVERTREE (St Thomas) *Liv 6* **P** *Simeon's Trustees*
V *Vacant* 0151–733 7804
WAWNE (St Peter) Sutton St Jas and Wawne *York*
WAXHAM, GREAT (St John) Happisburgh, Walcot,
Hempstead w Eccles etc *Nor*
WAYFORD (St Michael and All Angels) Crewkerne w
Wayford *B & W*
WEALD, NORTH Bassett (St Andrew) *Chelmsf 28* **P** *Bp*
V T C THORPE
WEALD, SOUTH (St Peter) *Chelmsf 7* **P** *Bp* **V** *Vacant*
Brentwood (01277) 212054
WEAR (St Luke) *Ex 3* **P** *V Topsham* **V** P J S CROCKETT
WEARE (St Gregory) Crook Peak *B & W*
WEARE GIFFARD (Holy Trinity) Landcross, Littleham,
Monkleigh etc *Ex*
WEASENHAM (All Saints) South Raynham, E w W
Raynham, Helhoughton, etc *Nor*
WEASENHAM (St Peter) as above
WEASTE (St Luke w All Saints) *Man 6* **P** *Bp and
V Eccles (jt)* **V** K M ARCHER
WEAVERHAM (St Mary the Virgin) *Ches 6* **P** *Bp*
V *Vacant* Weaverham (01606) 852110
WEAVERTHORPE (St Andrew) w Helperthorpe, Luttons
Ambo and Kirby Grindalythe *York 2* **P** *D&C (1 turn), Abp
(2 turns)* **V** B A ARMITAGE
WEBHEATH (St Philip) Redditch, The Ridge *Worc*
WEDDINGTON (St James) and Caldecote *Cov 5* **P** *Bp*
R A J ADAMS, **C** M CHATHAWAY
WEDMORE (St Mary) w Theale and Blackford *B & W 1*
P *Bp* **V** *Vacant* Wedmore (01934) 712254
WEDNESBURY (St Bartholomew) *Lich 7* **P** *Bp*
V D K BEEDON, NSM D MARSH
WEDNESBURY (St James and St John) *Lich 7* **P** *Trustees*
R I B COOK, **C** R M McINTYRE, NSM R C GILBERT
WEDNESBURY (St Paul) Wood Green *Lich 7* **P** *Bp*
V J D POINTS, **C** G E TOWLSON, D M HOLLINGTON
WEDNESFIELD (St Augustine and St Chad) *Lich 9*
P *Patr Bd* **TR** J D D PORTER, **TV** C W J STYLES,
C R DUNCAN, **C** V E DUNCAN
WEDNESFIELD (St Gregory) *Lich 9* **P** *Bp*
V D MELVILLE
WEDNESFIELD HEATH (Holy Trinity) *Lich 9* **P** *CPAS*
V S R J FRENCH
WEEDON (School Chapel) Schorne *Ox*
WEEDON BEC (St Peter and St Paul) w Everdon *Pet 3*
P *Bp* **V** D JACKS
WEEDON LOIS (St Mary and St Peter) w Plumpton and
Moreton Pinkney and Wappenham *Pet 1* **P** *Bp, Jes Coll
Ox, and Or Coll Ox (by turn)* **V** J W B PHILLIPS
WEEFORD (St Mary the Virgin) Whittington w Weeford
Lich
WEEK ST MARY (St Mary the Virgin) w Poundstock and
Whitstone *Truro 8* **P** *SS Coll Cam, Walsingham Coll, and
Guild of All So (jt)* **P-in-c** W I MEADS
WEEKE Win St Matt *Win*
WEEKLEY (St Mary the Virgin) Geddington w Weekley *Pet*
WEELEY (St Andrew) and Little Clacton *Chelmsf 24* **P** *Bp
and BNC Ox (alt)* **R** D M NEWMAN
WEETHLEY (St James) Alcester and Arrow w Oversley and
Weethley *Cov*
WEETING (St Mary) *Ely 15* **P** *G&C Coll Cam*
R A J ROWE
WEETON (St Barnabas) Kirkby Overblow *Ripon*
WEETON (St Michael) Singleton w Weeton *Blackb*
WEETSLADE (St Paul) *Newc 1* **P** *Bp* **V** H SCOTT
WELBORNE (All Saints) Mattishall w Mattishall Burgh,
Welborne etc *Nor*
WELBOURN (St Chad) *Linc 23* **P** *Hyndman Trustees*
R *Vacant*
WELBURN (St John the Evangelist) Bulmer w Dalby,
Terrington and Welburn *York*
WELBURY (St Leonard) Rounton w Welbury *York*

WELBY (not known) Melton Mowbray *Leic*
WELBY (St Bartholomew) Ancaster Wilsford Gp *Linc*
WELCOMBE (St Nectan) Parkham, Alwington, Buckland
Brewer etc *Ex*
WELDON (St Mary the Virgin) w Deene *Pet 9* **P** *DBP and
E Brudenell Esq (jt)* **R** T WITHERS GREEN
WELFORD (St Gregory) w Wickham and Great Shefford,
Boxford and Stockcross *Ox 14* **P** *Bp and BNC Ox (jt)*
R N C SANDS, **Hon C** S B APPLETON,
NSM T SHORTLAND
WELFORD (St Mary the Virgin) w Sibbertoft and Marston
Trussell *Pet 2* **P** *Bp* **V** R J CATTLE
WELFORD (St Peter) w Weston and Clifford Chambers
Glouc 10 **P** *DBP* **R** R D WYATT
WELHAM (St Andrew) Gt Bowden w Welham, Glooston
and Cranoe *Leic*
WELL (St Margaret) *Linc 8* **P** *J Reeve Esq*
P-in-c A READER-MOORE
WELL (St Michael) W Tanfield and Well w Snape and N
Stainley *Ripon*
WELL HILL (Mission) Chelsfield *Roch*
WELLAND (St James) Hanley Castle, Hanley Swan and
Welland *Worc*
WELLESBOURNE (St Peter) *Cov 8* **P** *Ld Chan*
V N V HOWES
WELLING (St John the Evangelist) *Roch 14* **P** *Bp*
V M G KICHENSIDE, **C** B W ROWLAND
WELLING (St Mary the Virgin) *S'wark 1* **P** *Bp*
V C E BLANKENSHIP, **C** L C GALE
WELLINGBOROUGH (All Hallows) *Pet 6* **P** *Exors Major
E C S Byng-Maddick* **V** I C HUNT, **C** N E FRY
WELLINGBOROUGH (All Saints) *Pet 6*
P *V Wellingborough* **V** P B WELCH
WELLINGBOROUGH (St Andrew) *Pet 6* **P** *Bp*
V J R WESTWOOD, NSM C J MOGRIDGE
WELLINGBOROUGH (St Barnabas) *Pet 6* **P** *Bp*
V D W WITCHELL, NSM M A TAYLOR
WELLINGBOROUGH (St Mark) *Pet 6* **P** *Bp*
V I R LOWELL
WELLINGBOROUGH (St Mary the Virgin) *Pet 6* **P** *Guild
of All So* **V** *Vacant* Wellingborough (01933) 225626
WELLINGHAM (St Andrew) South Raynham, E w W
Raynham, Helhoughton, etc *Nor*
WELLINGORE (All Saints) Graffoe Gp *Linc*
WELLINGTON (All Saints) (St John the Baptist) and District
B & W 19 **P** *Patr Bd* **TR** T W STOKES, **TV** R P LODGE,
L H COLTON, D P RANDELL, NSM C I BRIERLEY
WELLINGTON (All Saints) w Eyton (St Catherine) *Lich 27*
P *Ch Trust Fund Trust* **V** M E POTTER, **C** A C BROOM
WELLINGTON (Christ Church) *Lich 27* **P** *V Wellington w
Eyton* **P-in-c** M J CLARIDGE
WELLINGTON (St Margaret of Antioch) w Pipe-cum-Lyde
and Moreton-on-Lugg *Heref 4* **P** *Bp, Ch Union, and D&C
(by turn)* **P-in-c** C H DEE
WELLINGTON HEATH (Christ Church) Bosbury w
Wellington Heath etc *Heref*
WELLOW (St Julian the Hospitaller) Peasedown St John w
Wellow *B & W*
WELLOW (St Margaret) *Win 11* **P** *Bp* **V** G R BIGGS,
NSM N M HARRISON
WELLOW (St Swithun) Kneesall w Laxton and Wellow
S'well
WELLS (St Cuthbert) w Wookey Hole *B & W 8* **P** *D&C*
V C D TAYLOR
WELLS (St Thomas) w Horrington *B & W 8* **P** *D&C*
V C T TOOKEY, NSM A L BIRBECK
WELLS-NEXT-THE-SEA (St Nicholas) Holkham w Egmere
w Warham, Wells and Wighton *Nor*
WELNEY (St Mary) *Ely 18* **P** *Bp* **P-in-c** S TOOKE
WELSH BICKNOR (St Margaret) Walford and Saint John,
w Bishopswood etc *Heref*
WELSH FRANKTON (St Andrew) Ellesmere and Welsh
Frankton *Lich*
WELSH NEWTON (St Mary the Virgin) St Weonards w
Orcop, Garway, Tretire etc *Heref*
WELSH NEWTON COMMON (St Faith) as above
WELSHAMPTON (St Michael) Petton w Cockshutt,
Welshampton and Lyneal etc *Lich*
WELTON (St Helen) w Melton *York 15* **P** *DBP*
P-in-c A F RABLEN
WELTON (St James) Westward, Rosley-w-Woodside and
Welton *Carl*
WELTON (St Martin) Daventry, Ashby St Ledgers,
Braunston etc *Pet*
WELTON (St Mary) and Dunholme w Scothern *Linc 3* **P** *Bp
and DBP (jt)* **P-in-c** G S DARLISON, NSM K A GUY
WELTON-LE-MARSH (St Martin) w Gunby *Linc 8*
P *J M Montgomery-Massingberd Esq* **P-in-c** T STEELE

WELTON-LE-WOLD (St Martin) Louth *Linc*

WELWICK (St Mary) Patrington w Hollym, Welwick and Winestead *York*

WELWYN (St Mary the Virgin) (St Michael) w Ayot (St Peter) *St Alb 7*   **P** *All So Coll Ox*   **R** G R TRISTRAM, **C** B S PLEATHERS

WELWYN GARDEN CITY (St Francis of Assisi) *St Alb 7*   **P** *Bp*   **V** P A LOUIS,   **C** J A STOBART, **NSM** D M WEBSTER

WEM (St Peter and St Paul) *Lich 28*   **P** *Lord Barnard* **R** N MacGREGOR

WEMBDON (St George) *B & W 14*   **P** *Ch Soc Trust* **V** J S BARKS

WEMBLEY (St John the Evangelist) *Lon 21* **P** *Ch Patr Trust*   **P-in-c** D B WADLAND

WEMBLEY, NORTH (St Cuthbert) *Lon 21*   **P** *Bp* **P-in-c** M STEWART

WEMBLEY PARK (St Augustine) *Lon 21*   **P** *Bp* **C** J S FOULDS,   **NSM** A C BAYLEY

WEMBURY (St Werburgh) *Ex 21*   **P** *D&C Windsor* **V** T FREEMAN

WEMBWORTHY (St Michael) w Eggesford *Ex 16*   **P** *Bp and G A L Cruwys Esq (jt)*   **R** R A GRINSTED, **C** K A ELLIOTT

WENDENS AMBO (St Mary the Virgin) Saffron Walden w Wendens Ambo and Littlebury *Chelmsf*

WENDLEBURY (St Giles) Chesterton w Middleton Stoney and Wendlebury *Ox*

WENDLING (St Peter and St Paul) Gressenhall w Longham w Wendling etc *Nor*

WENDOVER (St Agnes's Chapel) (St Mary) *Ox 28* **P** *Ld Chan*   **NSM** B J ROBERTS,   H W HESLOP

WENDRON(St Wendron) Helston and Wendron *Truro*

WENDY (All Saints) Shingay Gp of Par *Ely*

WENHAM, GREAT (St John) Capel St Mary w Lt and Gt Wenham *St E*

WENHASTON (St Peter) Thorington w Wenhaston, Bramfield & Walberswick *St E*

WENLOCK *Heref 11*   **P** *Patr Bd*   **TR** R B DAVIES, **TV** W A BUCK,   M C CLUETT,   **NSM** C M HAYNES

WENLOCK, LITTLE (St Lawrence) Coalbrookdale, Iron-Bridge and Lt Wenlock *Heref*

WENLOCK, MUCH (Holy Trinity) Wenlock *Heref*

WENNINGTON (St Mary and St Peter) Rainham w Wennington *Chelmsf*

WENSLEY (Holy Trinity) *Ripon 4*   **P** *Lord Bolton* **R** *Vacant* Wensleydale (01969) 23736

WENTBRIDGE (St John) Darrington w Wentbridge *Wakef*

WENTNOR (St Michael and All Angels) w Ratlinghope, Myndtown, Norbury, More, Lydham and Snead *Heref 10* **P** *Ch Ch Ox (2 turns),Col A P Sykes (2 turns), and Lady More (1 turn)*   **R** R T FRANCE

WENTWORTH (Harley Mission Church) (Holy Trinity) *Sheff 12*   **P** *Sir Stephen Hastings*   **V** R J BUCKLEY

WENTWORTH (St Peter) Witchford w Wentworth *Ely*

WEOBLEY (St Peter and St Paul) w Sarnesfield and Norton Canon *Heref 5*   **P** *Bp (2 turns), R A Marshall Esq (1 turn)* **V** R A BIRT

WEOLEY CASTLE (St Gabriel) *Birm 2*   **P** *Bp* **V** M D CASTLE,   **C** D N MILLER

WEREHAM (St Margaret) *Ely 16*   **P** *Bp* **P-in-c** M TUCKER

WERNETH (St Paul) *Ches 16*   **P** *Trustees* **P-in-c** B S PERCIVAL

WERNETH (St Thomas) *Man 19*   **P** *Bp*   **V** J HUNTER

WERRINGTON (St John the Baptist w Emmanuel) *Pet 13* **P** *Bp*   **V** J B BATTMAN,   **C** D H JOHNSTON

WERRINGTON (St Martin of Tours) Boyton, N Tamerton, Werrington etc *Truro*

WERRINGTON (St Philip) *Lich 11*   **P** *V Caverswall* **V** J L HUMPHREYS

WESHAM (Christ Church) *Blackb 11*   **P** *V Kirkham* **V** A J WHYTE

WESSINGTON (Christ Church) S Wingfield and Wessington *Derby*

WEST: *see also under substantive place names*

WEST BAY (St John) Bridport *Sarum*

WEST DOWN (St Calixtus) Ilfracombe SS Phil and Jas w W Down *Ex*

WEST END (Holy Trinity) Bisley and W End *Guildf*

WEST END (St George) Esher *Guildf*

WEST END (St James) *Win 9*   **P** *Bp*   **V** J M PRESTON, **C** D S BENNETT

WEST END (St John the Evangelist) High Wycombe *Ox*

WEST GREEN (Christ Church w St Peter) *Lon 19*   **P** *Bp* **V** J T HAMBLIN

WEST GREEN (St Peter) Crawley *Chich*

WEST HEATH (St Anne) *Birm 4*   **P** *Bp*   **V** B GREEN, **C** S P MAYOSS-HURD

WEST HILL (St Michael the Archangel) Ottery St Mary, Alfington, W Hill, Tipton etc *Ex*

WEST MOORS (St Mary the Virgin) (St John the Evangelist) *Sarum 10*   **P** *Bp*   **V** I K CHISHOLM,   **C** R J H MAGILL

WEST ORCHARD (St Luke) Shaston *Sarum*

WEST RASEN (All Saints) Middle Rasen Gp *Linc*

WEST ROW (St Peter) Mildenhall *St E*

WESTACRE (All Saints) Gayton Gp of Par *Nor*

WESTBERE (All Saints) Sturry w Fordwich and Westbere w Hersden *Cant*

WESTBOROUGH (All Saints) Claypole *Linc*

WESTBOROUGH (St Clare) (St Francis) *Guildf 5*   **P** *Bp* **TR** H G MEIRION-JONES,   **TV** G P READ

WESTBOURNE Christ Church Conventional District *Win 7* **Min** B C RUFF

WESTBOURNE (St John the Baptist) *Chich 13*   **P** *Bp* **R** B J MARSHALL

WESTBROOK (St James) Hood Manor *Liv 12*   **P** *Bp, R Warrington, and V Gt Sankey (jt)*   **V** D W LONG

WESTBROOK (St Philip) Old Hall and Callands *Liv 12* **P** *Bp and R Warrington (jt)*   **V** L BENTLEY

WESTBURY (All Saints) *Sarum 14*   **P** *Bp*   **V** M J FLIGHT, **C** D K BELLAMY

WESTBURY (St Augustine) w Turweston, Shalstone and Biddlesden *Ox 22*   **P** *Bp, D&C Westmr, Mrs M L G Purefoy, and Exors Mrs E M Gordon (jt)*   **R** R LEIGH

WESTBURY (St Mary) *Heref 13*   **P** *Bp*   **P-in-c** C B BULL

WESTBURY-ON-SEVERN (St Peter and St Paul) w Flaxley and Blaisdon *Glouc 3*   **P** *Sir Thomas Crawley-Boevey Bt (1 turn), D&C Heref (2 turns),and Trustees late T Place Esq (1 turn)*   **V** D A COLBY,   **NSM** M WHITE

WESTBURY-ON-TRYM (Holy Trinity) *Bris 8*   **P** *SMF* **V** G M COLLINS,   **C** J C G BROMLEY

WESTBURY-ON-TRYM (St Alban) *Bris 8*   **P** *Bp* **V** J A H BOWES,   **NSM** C V CLARKE

WESTBURY PARK (St Alban) Westbury-on-Trym St Alb *Bris*

WESTBURY SUB MENDIP (St Lawrence) w Easton *B & W 1*   **P** *Bp*   **V** E A MACPHERSON

WESTCLIFF (Church of Reconciliation) Old Brumby *Linc*

WESTCLIFF (St Alban) Southend *Chelmsf*

WESTCLIFF (St Andrew) *Chelmsf 13*   **P** *Bp* **V** E R LITTLER

WESTCLIFF (St Cedd and the Saints of Essex) *Chelmsf 13* **P** *Bp*   **P-in-c** G R STEEL

WESTCLIFF (St Michael and All Angels) *Chelmsf 13*   **P** *Bp* **C** P A REILY

WESTCLIFF (St Paul) Prittlewell *Chelmsf*

WESTCLIFF (St Saviour) Southend St Sav Westcliff *Chelmsf*

WESTCLIFFE (St Peter) St Margarets-at-Cliffe w Westcliffe etc *Cant*

WESTCOMBE PARK (St George) *S'wark 1*   **P** *CPAS* **V** *Vacant* 0181–858 3006

WESTCOTE (St Mary the Virgin) w Icomb and Bledington *Glouc 15*   **P** *D&C Worc, Ch Ch Ox, and Bp (by turn)* **NSM** G R H SMITH

WESTCOTE BARTON (St Edward the Confessor) w Steeple Barton, Duns Tew and Sandford St Martin *Ox 9*   **P** *Duke of Marlborough, Exors Mrs Rittson-Thomas, DBP, D C D Webb Esq, and Bp (jt)*   **R** A W DAVIES

WESTCOTT (Holy Trinity) *Guildf 7*   **P** *Bp* **V** J D H WEYMAN

WESTCOTT (St Mary) Waddesdon w Over Winchendon and Fleet Marston *Ox*

WESTDENE (The Ascension) Patcham *Chich*

WESTERDALE (Christ Church) Ingleby Greenhow w Bilsdale Priory, Kildale etc *York*

WESTERFIELD (St Mary Magdalene) and Tuddenham w Witnesham *St E 4*   **P** *Bp, Peterho Cam, and DBP (alt)* **R** H LUNNEY,   **NSM** M J STONE

WESTERHAM (St Mary the Virgin) *Roch 8* **P** *J St A Warde Esq*   **V** P A BIRD

WESTERLEIGH (St James the Great) Yate New Town *Bris*

WESTERN DOWNLAND *Sarum 13*   **P** *Hyndman Trustees, Sir William van Straubenzee, and W J Purvis Esq (jt)* **R** M E RIDLEY

WESTFIELD (St Andrew) Reymerston w Cranworth, Letton, Southburgh etc *Nor*

WESTFIELD (St John the Baptist) *Chich 20*   **P** *Bp* **V** E N L FRANCE

WESTFIELD (St Mark) Woking St Pet *Guildf*

WESTFIELD (St Mary) *Carl 7*   **P** *Bp*   **V** A MITCHELL, **C** J E CROSSLEY

WESTFIELD (St Peter) *B & W 12*   **P** *Bp*   **V** J B THICKE, **NSM** D R BARGE

WESTGATE (St Andrew) *Dur 15*   **P** *Bp*   **V** D M SKELTON

WESTGATE (St James) *Cant 9*   **P** *Abp*   **V** J A CHEESEMAN

WESTGATE (St Martin) Torrisholme *Blackb*

WESTGATE COMMON (St Michael the Archangel)
Wakef 12 **P** *V Alverthorpe* **P-in-c** A S MACPHERSON
WESTGATE-ON-SEA (St Saviour) *Cant 9* **P** *Abp*
V S M EVANS
WESTHALL (St Andrew) Hundred River *St E*
WESTHAM (St Mary) *Chich 16* **P** *Duke of Devonshire*
V A C GINNO
WESTHAMPNETT (St Peter) W Hampnett *Chich*
WESTHEAD (St James) Newburgh w Westhead *Liv*
WESTHIDE (St Bartholomew) Withington w Westhide *Heref*
WESTHOPE (Mission Room) Canon Pyon w Kings Pyon
and Birley *Heref*
WESTHORPE (St Margaret) Walsham le Willows and
Finningham w Westhorpe *St E*
WESTHOUGHTON (St Bartholomew) *Man 11* **P** *Patr Bd*
TR S C TATTON-BROWN, **C** T P HUMPHRY,
Hon C G J SMETHURST
WESTHOUSES (St Saviour) Blackwell *Derby*
WESTLANDS (St Andrew) *Lich 14* **P** *Simeon's Trustees*
V W G H GARDINER
WESTLEIGH (St Paul) *Man 13* **P** *V Leigh St Mary*
V T D HARGREAVES-STEAD
WESTLEIGH (St Peter) *Ex 17* **P** *D&C* **V** G A SATTERLY
WESTLEIGH (St Peter) *Man 13* **P** *Bp, Dioc Chan, and
V Leigh St Mary (jt)* **V** R COOKE
WESTLETON (St Peter) w Dunwich *St E 19* **P** *Ch Patr
Trust (2 turns), Shadingfield Properties Ltd (1 turn)*
V R J GINN
WESTLEY (St Mary) Risby w Gt and Lt Saxham and
Westley *St E*
WESTLEY WATERLESS (St Mary the Less) *Ely 4* **P** *Exors
C L Thomas Esq* **P-in-c** J S ASKEY
WESTMEADS (St Michael and All Angels) Aldwick *Chich*
WESTMESTON (St Martin) Streat w Westmeston *Chich*
WESTMILL (St Mary the Virgin) Aspenden, Buntingford
and Westmill *St Alb*
WESTMINSTER Hanover Square (St George) Hanover
Square St Geo w St Mark *Lon*
WESTMINSTER (St James) Piccadilly *Lon 3* **P** *Bp
(2 turns), Ld Chan (1 turn)* **R** D St J REEVES,
C U S MONBERG, **Hon C** S B CATHIE,
NSM H W J VALENTINE
WESTMINSTER St James the Less *Lon 3* **P** *D&C Westmr*
V W J H CROSSLEY
WESTMINSTER (St Mary-le-Strand) St Mary-le-Strand w St
Clem Danes *Lon*
WESTMINSTER (St Matthew) *Lon 3* **P** *D&C Westmr*
P-in-c P A E CHESTER, **C** P C ATHERTON,
Hon C R E BALLARD
WESTMINSTER (St Stephen) w St John *Lon 3*
P *The Crown* **V** R C GODSALL, **C** J J WESTCOTT,
Hon C R MARSH
WESTOE, SOUTH (St Michael and All Angels) *Dur 7*
P *Bp* **V** J M HANCOCK
WESTON (All Saints) Bath Weston All SS w N Stoke and
Langridge *B & W*
WESTON (All Saints) *Ches 15* **P** *Bp* **P-in-c** W HODSON
WESTON (All Saints) Welford w Weston and Clifford
Chambers *Glouc*
WESTON (All Saints) *Guildf 8* **P** *Bp* **V** B M SHAND
WESTON (All Saints) Tuxford w Weston and Markham
Clinton *S'well*
WESTON (All Saints) w Denton *Bradf 4* **P** *Lt-Col
H V Dawson and C Wyvill Esq (jt)* **V** D E CREASER
WESTON (Holy Trinity) *St Alb 12* **P** *Mrs A M Pryor*
V E J POOLE
WESTON (Holy Trinity) *Win 12* **P** *Bp* **V** A L McPHERSON
WESTON (St Mary) Cowbit *Linc*
WESTON (St Peter) Hundred River *St E*
WESTON, OLD (St Swithun) Brington w Molesworth and
Old Weston *Ely*
WESTON, SOUTH (St Lawrence) Tetsworth, Adwell w S
Weston, Lewknor etc *Ox*
WESTON BAMPFLYDE (Holy Cross) Queen Camel w W
Camel, Corton Denham etc *B & W*
WESTON BEGGARD (St John the Baptist) Lugwardine w
Bartestree, Weston Beggard etc *Heref*
WESTON BY WELLAND (St Mary) Ashley w Weston by
Welland and Sutton Bassett *Pet*
WESTON COLVILLE (St Mary) *Ely 4* **P** *D&C*
NSM L R WICKHAM
WESTON COYNEY (St Andrew) Caverswall and Weston
Coyney w Dilhorne *Lich*
WESTON ESTATE CHURCH (not known) Otley *Bradf*
WESTON FAVELL (St Peter) *Pet 4* **P** *DBP*
R C W WAKE, **C** M M STRANGE, **NSM** G CRUMBOLD
WESTON HILLS (St John) Cowbit *Linc*

WESTON IN GORDANO (St Peter and St Paul) E Clevedon
and Walton w Weston w Clapton *B & W*
**WESTON LONGVILLE (All Saints) w Morton on the Hill w
Great w Little Witchingham** *Nor 23* **P** *J V Berney Esq
(1 turn), New Coll Ox (3 turns)* **R** J P P ILLINGWORTH
WESTON LULLINGFIELD (Holy Trinity) Baschurch and
Weston Lullingfield w Hordley *Lich*
WESTON MILL (St Philip) Devonport St Boniface and St
Phil *Ex*
WESTON-ON-THE-GREEN (St Mary) Kirtlington w
Bletchingdon, Weston etc *Ox*
WESTON-ON-TRENT (St Mary the Virgin) Aston-on-Trent
and Weston-on-Trent *Derby*
WESTON PATRICK (St Lawrence) Herriard w Winslade
and Long Sutton etc *Win*
WESTON POINT (Christ Church) Runcorn St Jo Weston
Ches
WESTON RHYN (St John) and Selattyn *Lich 24* **P** *Bp and
Mrs A F Hamilton-Hill (jt)* **R** N G COATSWORTH
WESTON-SUB-EDGE (St Lawrence) Willersey, Saintbury,
Weston-sub-Edge etc *Glouc*
**WESTON-SUPER-MARE Central Parishes (All Saints)
(Emmanuel) (St John the Baptist)** *B & W 11* **P** *Patr Bd*
TV P G CLARKE, E T PETTENGELL, **P-in-c** B IRONS
WESTON-SUPER-MARE (Christ Church) *B & W 11*
P *Trustees* **V** G W HOBDEN, **C** S M LEATHLEY
WESTON-SUPER-MARE (St Andrew) Bournville *B & W 11*
P *Bp* **V** H M WILLIAMS
WESTON-SUPER-MARE (St Paul) *B & W 11* **P** *Bp*
V P H DAVIES
WESTON TURVILLE (St Mary the Virgin) *Ox 28*
P *All So Coll Ox* **P-in-c** D N WALES, **NSM** N TAYLOR
WESTON-UNDER-LIZARD (St Andrew) Blymhill w
Weston-under-Lizard *Lich*
WESTON-UNDER-PENYARD (St Lawrence) Ross w
Brampton Abbotts, Bridstow, Peterstow etc *Heref*
WESTON UNDER REDCASTLE (St Luke) Hodnet w
Weston under Redcastle *Lich*
WESTON UNDER WETHERLEY (St Michael)
Wappenbury w Weston under Wetherley *Cov*
WESTON UNDERWOOD (St Laurence) Gayhurst w
Ravenstone, Stoke Goldington etc *Ox*
WESTON UPON TRENT (St Andrew) Fradswell, Gayton,
Milwich and Weston *Lich*
WESTON ZOYLAND (Blessed Virgin Mary) w Chedzoy
B & W 14 **P** *Bp* **V** *Vacant* Weston Zoyland (01278)
691251
WESTONBIRT (St Catherine) Shipton Moyne w Westonbirt
and Lasborough *Glouc*
WESTONING (St Mary Magdalene) w Tingrith *St Alb 15*
P *Ld Chan* **V** M J BETTIS
WESTOW (St Mary) Burythorpe, Acklam and Leavening w
Westow *York*
WESTWARD (St Hilda), Rosley-with-Woodside and Welton
Carl 3 **P** *D&C* **P-in-c** N L ROBINSON
WESTWARD HO! (Holy Trinity) Northam w Westward Ho!
and Appledore *Ex*
WESTWELL (St Mary) Shill Valley and Broadshire *Ox*
**WESTWELL (St Mary) w Hothfield and Eastwell w Boughton
Aluph** *Cant 10* **P** *Abp and Lord Hothfield (jt)*
V J F GLEADALL
WESTWICK (St Botolph) Worstead, Westwick, Sloley,
Swanton Abbot etc *Nor*
WESTWOOD Jacksdale (St Mary) Selston *S'well*
WESTWOOD (Mission Church) Golcar *Wakef*
WESTWOOD (St John the Baptist) *Cov 3* **P** *Bp*
V R D ALLON-SMITH
WESTWOOD (St Mary the Virgin) and Wingfield *Sarum 17*
P *D&C Bris, CPAS, and Bp (jt)* **R** R M LOWRIE
WESTWOOD (St Paul) Pinhoe and Broadclyst *Ex*
WESTWOOD, LOW (Christ Church) Ebchester *Dur*
WETHERAL (Holy Trinity and St Constantine) w Warwick
Carl 2 **P** *D&C* **P-in-c** C H COWPER, **NSM** P TIPLADY,
J M BLAKEMAN
WETHERBY (St James) *Ripon 1* **P** *Bp* **V** A M BARTON,
C C A JAMES
WETHERDEN (St Mary the Virgin) Haughley w Wetherden
St E
WETHERINGSETT (All Saints) Thorndon w Rishangles,
Stoke Ash, Thwaite etc *St E*
WETHERSFIELD (St Mary Magdalene) w Shalford
Chelmsf 16 **P** *Bp* **P-in-c** J F H SHEAD
WETLEY ROCKS (St John the Baptist) *Lich 13* **P** *Bp*
V D R WHITELEY
WETTENHALL (St David) Acton and Worleston, Church
Minshull and Wettenhall *Ches*
WETTON (St Margaret) Alstonfield, Butterton, Warslow w
Elkstone etc *Lich*

WETWANG (St Nicholas) and Garton-on-the-Wolds w Kirkburn *York* 11 **P** *Ld Chan* **V** R I JONES

WEXCOMBE *Sarum* 21 **P** *DBP* **TR** D M RYDER, **TV** S F EVERETT, N A LEIGH-HUNT, **NSM** A J DEBOO

WEXHAM (St Mary) *Ox* 26 **P** *Ld Chan* **R** G W FARMER

WEYBOURNE (All Saints), Upper Sheringham, Kelling, Salthouse, Bodham and East and West Beckham (The Weybourne Group) *Nor* 19 **P** *Bp* (2 turns), Sir Charles Mott-Radclyffe (1 turn), D&C (1 turn), and Lord Walpole (1 turn) **R** P J G BARNES-CLAY

WEYBREAD (St Andrew) Fressingfield, Mendham, Metfield, Weybread etc *St E*

WEYBRIDGE (St James) *Guildf* 8 **P** *Ld Chan* **R** S D BROOKES, **C** D W PECK

WEYHILL (St Michael and All Angels) Hatherden w Tangley, Weyhill and Penton Mewsey *Win*

WEYMOUTH (Holy Trinity) (St Nicholas) *Sarum* 5 **P** *Bp* **V** R H FRANKLIN, **C** R W HAWKINS, **NSM** R A WEAVER, R E MILVERTON

WEYMOUTH (St Edmund) *Sarum* 5 **P** *R Wyke Regis* **V** *Vacant* Weymouth (01305) 782408

WEYMOUTH (St John) Radipole and Melcombe Regis *Sarum*

WEYMOUTH (St Mary) as above

WEYMOUTH (St Paul) *Sarum* 5 **P** *Bp* **V** *Vacant* Weymouth (01305) 771217

WHADDON (St Margaret) Glouc St Geo w Whaddon *Glouc*

WHADDON (St Mary) *Ely* 8 **P** *D&C Windsor* **V** E DUCKETT

WHADDON (St Mary) Newton Longville w Stoke Hammond and Whaddon *Ox*

WHADDON (St Mary) Alderbury Team *Sarum*

WHADDON (St Mary the Virgin) Hilperton w Whaddon and Staverton etc *Sarum*

WHALEY BRIDGE (St James) *Ches* 16 **P** *Bp and Bp Derby* (alt) **R** D C SPEEDY

WHALEY THORNS (St Luke) E Scarsdale *Derby*

WHALLEY (St Mary and All Saints) *Blackb* 8 **P** *Hulme Trustees* **V** J M ACKROYD

WHALLEY RANGE (St Edmund) *Man* 4 **P** *Simeon's Trustees* **R** R J HORROCKS, **C** J A HORROCKS

WHALLEY RANGE (St Margaret) *Man* 4 **P** *Trustees* **R** R G BOULTER

WHALTON (St Mary Magdalene) Bolam w Whalton and Hartburn w Meldon *Newc*

WHAPLODE (St Mary) *Linc* 16 **P** *Ld Chan* **P-in-c** D A CARNEY

WHAPLODE DROVE (St John the Baptist) *Linc* 16 **P** *Feoffees* **P-in-c** J MONTAGUE

WHARNCLIFFE SIDE (not known) Oughtibridge *Sheff*

WHARRAM (St Mary) Settrington w N Grimston and Wharram *York*

WHARTON (Christ Church) *Ches* 6 **P** *R Davenham* **V** M A PICKLES

WHATBOROUGH Group of Parishes, The *Leic* 4 **P** *Bp* **V** H R BROAD

WHATCOTE (St Peter) Tysoe w Oxhill and Whatcote *Cov*

WHATFIELD (St Margaret) w Semer, Nedging and Naughton *St E* 3 **P** *Bp, Jes Coll Cam, and Reformation Ch Trust (jt)* **P-in-c** H J CRELLIN

WHATLEY (St George) Mells w Buckland Dinham, Elm, Whatley etc *B & W*

WHATLINGTON (St Mary Magdalene) Sedlescombe w Whatlington *Chich*

WHATSTANDWELL (Mission Room) Crich *Derby*

WHATTON (St John of Beverley) w Aslockton, Hawksworth, Scarrington, Orston and Thoroton *S'well* 8 **P** *Trustees* **V** D H BRIDGE-COLLYNS

WHEATACRE (All Saints) The Raveningham Gp *Nor*

WHEATCROFT (St Michael and All Angels) Scarborough St Martin *York*

WHEATFIELD (St Andrew) Tetsworth, Adwell w S Weston, Lewknor etc *Ox*

WHEATHAMPSTEAD (St Helen) *St Alb* 14 **P** *Bp* **R** T PURCHAS, **Hon C** C P A PURCHAS, **NSM** J HAZELWOOD

WHEATHILL (Holy Trinity) Ditton Priors w Neenton, Burwarton etc *Heref*

WHEATLEY (St Mary) Doncaster St Mary *Sheff*

WHEATLEY (St Mary the Virgin) w Forest Hill and Stanton St John *Ox* 1 **P** *Bp, Linc Coll Ox, and New Coll Ox* (by turns) **V** M T FARTHING, **NSM** J C H M LEE, A E BUTLER

WHEATLEY, NORTH (St Peter and St Paul) and West Burton w Bole and Saundby and Sturton w Littleborough *S'well* 5 **P** *Lord Middleton and G M T Foljambe Esq (alt)* **R** M W BRIGGS

WHEATLEY HILL (All Saints) *Dur* 3 **P** *Bp* **P-in-c** M J SHEARING

WHEATLEY HILLS (St Aidan) *Sheff* 9 **P** *Bp* **V** D J GOSS

WHEATLEY PARK (St Paul) *Sheff* 9 **P** *Bp* **V** G CREASEY

WHEATON ASTON (St Mary) Lapley w Wheaton Aston *Lich*

WHEELOCK (Christ Church) *Ches* 11 **P** *V Sandbach* **V** *Vacant* Crewe (01270) 762377

WHELDRAKE (St Helen) w Thorganby *York* 4 **P** *Abp and Sir Mervyn Dunnington-Jefferson (jt)* **R** D C W POST

WHELFORD (St Anne) Kempsford w Welford *Glouc*

WHELNETHAM, GREAT (St Thomas a Becket) and Little (St Mary) w Bradfield St George *St E* 10 **P** *Bp* **R** *Vacant* Sicklesmere (01284) 386332

WHELPLEY HILL (St Michael and All Angels) Gt Chesham *Ox*

WHENBY (St Martin) Bulmer w Dalby, Terrington and Welburn *York*

WHEPSTEAD (St Petronilla) Chevington w Hargrave and Whepstead w Brockley *St E*

WHERSTEAD (St Mary) *St E* 5 **P** *MMCET* **P-in-c** A B LEIGHTON

WHERWELL (St Peter and Holy Cross) Chilbolton cum Wherwell *Win*

WHETSTONE (St John the Apostle) *Lon* 14 **P** *Bp* **V** P J HENDERSON

WHETSTONE (St Peter) *Leic* 10 **P** *Bp* **P-in-c** V T GOODMAN

WHICHAM (St Mary) Bootle, Corney, Whicham and Whitbeck *Carl*

WHICHFORD (St Michael) Long Compton, Whichford and Barton-on-the-Heath *Cov*

WHICKHAM (St Mary the Virgin) *Dur* 5 **P** *Ld Chan* **P-in-c** D E BREED, **C** R A COLLINS

WHILTON (St Andrew) Brington w Whilton and Norton *Pet*

WHIMPLE (St Mary), Talaton and Clyst St Lawrence *Ex* 7 **P** *DBP, D&C and MMCET (jt)* **R** *Vacant* Whimple (01404) 822521

WHINBURGH (St Mary) Reymerston w Cranworth, Letton, Southburgh etc *Nor*

WHINMOOR (St Paul) Seacroft *Ripon*

WHINNEY HILL (St Peter) Thrybergh *Sheff*

WHIPPINGHAM (St Mildred) w East Cowes *Portsm* 8 **P** *Ld Chan* **P-in-c** S D CLEAVER, **NSM** G L LONG

WHIPSNADE (St Mary Magdalene) Kensworth, Studham and Whipsnade *St Alb*

WHIPTON (St Boniface) *Ex* 3 **P** *Bp* **V** C P BARRETT, **C** M M CAMERON

WHISSENDINE (St Andrew) Teigh w Whissendine and Market Overton *Pet*

WHISSONSETT (St Mary) Colkirk w Oxwick w Pattesley, Whissonsett etc *Nor*

WHISTON (St Mary Magdalene) *Sheff* 6 **P** *Bp* **R** G C M MILLS

WHISTON (St Mary the Virgin) *Pet* 7 **P** *Marquess of Northn* **R** D W JOHNSON

WHISTON (St Mildred) Foxt w Whiston *Lich*

WHISTON (St Nicholas) *Liv* 7 **P** *V Prescot* **V** G G AMEY

WHITACRE, NETHER (St Giles) The Whitacres and Shustoke *Birm*

WHITACRE, OVER (St Leonard) as above

WHITACRES and Shustoke, The *Birm* 11 **P** *S W Digby Esq* (1 turn), Bp (2 turns), and Ld Chan (1 turn) **R** J D WATERSTREET

WHITBECK (St Mary) Bootle, Corney, Whicham and Whitbeck *Carl*

WHITBOURNE (Bringsty Iron Church) Edvin Loach w Tedstone Delamere etc *Heref*

WHITBOURNE (St John the Baptist) as above

WHITBURN (no dedication) *Dur* 9 **P** *Bp* **R** K R SMITH, **C** J A DAY

WHITBY (St Hilda) (St John) (St Mary) *York* 23 **P** *Abp* **R** B A HOPKINSON, **C** G S ASKEY, P J MOGER

WHITBY (St Thomas) Ellesmere Port *Ches*

WHITBY ROAD (St Michael) W Slough *Ox*

WHITCHURCH (All Hallows) w Tufton and Litchfield *Win* 6 **P** *Bp* **V** M J GRYLLS

WHITCHURCH (St Alkmund) *Lich* 28 **P** *Bp* **R** R D JENKINS

WHITCHURCH (St Andrew) *Ex* 25 **P** *Bp* **V** S G MAY

WHITCHURCH (St Augustine) (St Nicholas) *Bris* 3 **P** *Bp* **V** R A D'V THORN, **C** S BAKER, **NSM** E A J CHIVERS

WHITCHURCH (St Dubricius) Llangarron w Llangrove, Whitchurch and Ganarew *Heref*

WHITCHURCH (St John the Evangelist) Schorne *Ox*

WHITCHURCH (St Lawrence) Lt Stanmore St Lawr *Lon*

WHITCHURCH (St Mary the Virgin) Ilmington w Stretton-on-Fosse etc *Cov*

WHITCHURCH (St Mary the Virgin) *Ox 6*   **P** *Bp*
  R   R M HUGHES

WHITCHURCH CANONICORUM (St Candida and Holy Cross) Marshwood Vale TM *Sarum*

WHITCHURCH HILL (St John the Baptist) Whitchurch St Mary *Ox*

WHITE COLNE (St Andrew) Earls Colne w White Colne and Colne Engaine *Chelmsf*

WHITE LADIES ASTON (St John) Peopleton and White Ladies Aston w Churchill etc *Worc*

WHITE NOTLEY (St Etheldreda) Fairstead w Terling and White Notley etc *Chelmsf*

WHITE RODING (St Martin) Abbess Roding, Beauchamp Roding and White Roding *Chelmsf*

WHITE WALTHAM (St Mary the Virgin) w Shottesbrooke *Ox 13*   **P** *Sir John Smith*   **R**   T E F COULSON

WHITE WELL (St Mary) St Paul's Walden *St Alb*

WHITECHAPEL (St James) w Admarsh-in-Bleasdale *Blackb 10*   **P** *Bp and V Lanc (alt)*   **V**   G CONNOR

WHITEGATE (St Mary) w Little Budworth *Ches 6*   **P** *Bp, Lord Delamere and W R Cullimore Esq (alt)*
  V   C P BURKETT

WHITEHAVEN (St James) *Carl 5*   **P** *Patr Bd*
  V   J H BAKER

WHITEHAWK (St Cuthman) *Chich 2*   **P** *Bp*
  P-in-c   J D WRIGHT

WHITEHILLS (St Mark) Kingsthorpe w St Dav Northn *Pet*

WHITEKINGTON (The Blessed Virgin Mary) Ilminster and District *B & W*

WHITELEAS (St Mary and St Martin) Horsley Hill S Shields *Dur*

WHITEPARISH (All Saints) Alderbury Team *Sarum*

WHITESHILL (St Paul) and Randwick *Glouc 1*   **P** *Bp*
  V   M F JEFFERY

WHITESTAUNTON (St Andrew) *B & W 15*   **P** *Gp Capt N W D Marwood-Elton*   **P-in-c**   P REGAN

WHITESTONE (St Catherine) Tedburn St Mary, Whitestone, Oldridge etc *Ex*

WHITESTONE PATHFINDER (St John the Evangelist) as above

WHITEWELL (St Mary) Tushingham and Whitewell *Ches*

WHITEWELL (St Michael) Chipping and Whitewell *Blackb*

WHITFIELD (Holy Trinity) Allendale w Whitfield *Newc*

WHITFIELD (St James) (St Luke) *Derby 6*   **P** *Bp*
  V   C COOPER

WHITFIELD (St John) Allendale w Whitfield *Newc*

WHITFIELD (St John the Evangelist) Helmdon w Stuchbury and Radstone etc *Pet*

WHITFIELD (St Peter) w Guston *Cant 4*   **P** *Abp and D&C (alt)*   **V**   J W PHILPOTT

WHITFORD (St Mary at the Cross) Kilmington w Shute *Ex*

WHITGIFT (St Mary Magdalene) The Marshland *Sheff*

WHITGREAVE (St John the Evangelist) Stafford *Lich*

WHITKIRK (St Mary) *Ripon 8*   **P** *Meynell Trustees*
  C   R G COOPER

WHITLEIGH (St Chad) *Ex 23*   **P** *Bp*   **V**   J M KIRKPATRICK

WHITLEY (Christ Church) *Ox 15*   **P** *Bp*   **V**   E A ESSERY,
  C   D M WEST

WHITLEY (St Helen) *Newc 4*   **P** *Bp* **V** *Vacant* Hexham (01434) 673379

WHITLEY (St James) *Cov 1*   **P** *Bp*
  P-in-c   M R PEATMAN,   **NSM**   D A PEATMAN (nee HUGHES)

WHITLEY, LOWER or NETHER (St Luke) Lt Leigh and Lower Whitley *Ches*

WHITLEY BRIDGE (All Saints) Kellington w Whitley *Wakef*

WHITLEY LOWER (St Mary and St Michael) Thornhill and Whitley Lower *Wakef*

WHITMINSTER (St Andrew) Standish w Haresfield and Moreton Valence etc *Glouc*

WHITMORE (St Mary and All Saints) Chapel Chorlton, Maer and Whitmore *Lich*

WHITNASH (St Margaret) *Cov 11*   **P** *Lord Leigh*
  R   A B GARDNER,   **C**   C A HOST

WHITNEY (St Peter and St Paul) Eardisley w Bollingham, Willersley, Brilley etc *Heref*

WHITSBURY (St Leonard) W Downland *Sarum*

WHITSTABLE (All Saints) *Cant 7*   **P** *DBP*
  TR   J S WOOD,   **TV**   D W FLEWKER,   J K BUTTERWORTH,
  S J CONEYS,   **C**   S J TURNER

WHITSTONE (St Anne) Week St Mary w Poundstock and Whitstone *Truro*

WHITTINGHAM (St Bartholomew) and Edlingham w Bolton Chapel *Newc 9*   **P** *D&C Carl and D&C Dur (alt)*
  V   J A FERGUSON

WHITTINGTON (Christ Church) *Ely 15*   **P** *Ch Patr Trust*
  V   A R BENNETT

WHITTINGTON (St Bartholomew) *Derby 5*   **P** *Bp*
  R   D C PICKERING

WHITTINGTON (St Bartholomew) Sevenhampton w Charlton Abbotts and Hawling etc *Glouc*

WHITTINGTON (St Giles) w Weeford *Lich 1*   **P** *Bp*
  V   J H MARTIN,   **Hon C**   C M J IBALL

WHITTINGTON (St John the Baptist) *Lich 24*   **P** *Mrs P Hamilton Hill*   **R**   D R NORTH

WHITTINGTON (St Michael the Archangel) w Arkholme and Gressingham *Blackb 15*   **P** *Ch Ch Ox, V Lanc, and V Melling (by turn)*   **V**   W G BOWNESS

WHITTINGTON (St Philip and St James) Worc SE *Worc*

WHITTINGTON, NEW (St Barnabas) *Derby 5*   **P** *Bp*
  V   J PINDER-PACKARD

WHITTLE-LE-WOODS (St John the Evangelist) *Blackb 4*
  P *V Leyland*   **V**   D M GILKES,   **C**   C A BELL

WHITTLEBURY (St Mary) w Paulerspury *Pet 5*
  P *The Crown and New Coll Ox (alt)*   **V**   E D HOUSTON

WHITTLESEY (St Andrew) (St Mary) and Pondersbridge *Ely 18*   **P** *Patr Bd*   **TR**   P H N COLLINS,
  C   A R M MARSHALL

WHITTLESFORD (St Mary and St Andrew) *Ely 7*
  P *Jes Coll Cam* **V** *Vacant* Cambridge (01223) 833382

WHITTON *Sarum 20*   **P** *Patr Bd*   **TV**   P R HYSON,
  R K HYATT,   **C**   P H C KINGMAN

WHITTON (St Augustine of Canterbury) *Lon 10*   **P** *Bp*
  V   R J COSH,   **NSM**   C S P DOUGLAS LANE

WHITTON (St John the Baptist) Alkborough *Linc*

WHITTON (St Mary) Burford II w Greete and Hope Bagot *Heref*

WHITTON (St Mary) (Ascension) and Thurleston w Akenham *St E 4*   **P** *Bp (2 turns), Exors G K Drury Esq (1 turn)*
  R   G G BAULCOMB,   **C**   A S F BENNETT

WHITTON (St Philip and St James) *Lon 10*
  P *V Twickenham St Mary*   **V**   J L VINCENT,
  NSM   M R THOMSETT

WHITTONSTALL (St Philip and St James) *Newc 3*
  P *D&C*   **P-in-c**   M F FENWICK

WHITWELL (St John the Evangelist) w Crambe, Flaxton, Foston and Huttons Ambo *York 3*   **P** *Abp and D&C Dur (jt)*   **R** *Vacant* Whitwell-on-the-Hill (0165381) 647

WHITWELL (St Lawrence) *Derby 3*   **P** *Bp*   **R** C A ROGERS

WHITWELL (St Mary) St Paul's Walden *St Alb*

WHITWELL (St Mary and St Rhadegunde) *Portsm 7*   **P** *Bp*
  V   S E LLOYD,   **NSM**   J A WOOLLEY

WHITWELL (St Michael and All Angels) Reepham, Hackford w Whitwell, Kerdiston etc *Nor*

WHITWELL (St Michael and All Angels) Empingham and Exton w Horn w Whitwell *Pet*

WHITWICK (St John the Baptist) *Leic 8*   **P** *Duchy of Lanc*
  V   P S LAWRIE

WHITWOOD (All Saints) *Wakef 11*   **P** *Bp*   **R**   C S BARTER

WHITWORTH (not known) Man Whitworth *Man*

WHITWORTH (not known) w Spennymoor *Dur 10*   **P** *D&C*
  P-in-c   J S BAIN,   **C**   M H J HAMPEL

WHITWORTH (St Bartholomew) *Man 20*   **P** *Keble Coll Ox*
  V   D H HUGHES

WHIXALL (St Mary) Tilstock, Edstaston and Whixall *Lich*

WHIXLEY (Ascension) w Green Hammerton *Ripon 3*   **P** *DBP and R Knaresborough (alt)*   **V**   C J DAVIDSON

WHORLTON (Holy Cross Old Church) w Carlton and Faceby *York 22*   **P** *Mrs H J F L Steel and Mrs K F L Davies (jt)*
  V   W J FORD

WHORLTON (St John the Evangelist) *Newc 7*   **P** *Bp*
  TR   S H CONNOLLY,   **TV**   M D TETLEY,   D J TULLY,
  NSM   M J SHIPTON (nee WILSON)

WHORLTON (St Mary) Barnard Castle w Whorlton *Dur*

WHYKE (St George) w Rumboldswhyke St Mary and Portfield All Saints *Chich 3*   **P** *Bp*   **R** *Vacant* Chichester (01243) 782535
  J BRECKNELL

WHYTELEAFE (St Luke) *S'wark 19*   **P** *Bp*
  P-in-c   J E SMITH

WIBTOFT (Assumption of Our Lady) Claybrooke cum Wibtoft and Frolesworth *Leic*

WICHENFORD (St Lawrence) Martley and Wichenford, Knightwick etc *Worc*

WICK (All Saints) Littlehampton and Wick *Chich*

WICK (St Bartholomew) w Doynton and Dyrham *Bris 2*
  P *Simeon's Trustees, Ld Chan, and M H W Blaythwayt Esq (by turn)*   **V**   P F YACOMENI

WICK (St Mary) Pershore w Pinvin, Wick and Birlingham *Worc*

WICK ST LAWRENCE (St Lawrence) Kewstoke w Wick St Lawrence *B & W*

WICKEN (St John the Evangelist) *Pet 5* **P** *Soc Merchant Venturers Bris* **P-in-c** E D HOUSTON

WICKEN (St Laurence) *Ely 3* **P** *Ch Patr Trust* **V** R F BELOE

WICKEN BONHUNT (St Margaret) Quendon w Rickling & Wicken Bonhunt & Widdington *Chelmsf*

WICKENBY Group, The (St Peter and St Laurence) *Linc 5* **P** *DBP, D&C York, Bp, and Charterhouse (by turn)* **R** *Vacant* Wickenby (01673) 885721

WICKERSLEY (St Alban) *Sheff 6* **P** *DBP* **R** R J DRAPER, **NSM** M J WHIPP

WICKFORD (St Andrew) (St Catherine) and Runwell *Chelmsf 6* **P** *Patr Bd* **TV** C A McCAFFERTY, **C** T F CLAY, **NSM** R V GOODWIN

WICKHAM (St Nicholas) *Portsm 1* **P** *Sir Richard Rashleigh Bt* **R** R A A HIRST

WICKHAM (St Paul and All Saints) Gt and Lt Henny w Middleton, Wickham St Paul etc *Chelmsf*

WICKHAM (St Swithun) Welford w Wickham and Gt Shefford, Boxford etc *Ox*

WICKHAM, EAST (St Michael) *S'wark 1* **P** *Provost and Chapter* **Hon C** C HEARD

WICKHAM, WEST (St Francis) *S'wark 20* **P** *Bp* **V** O N EVERSON

WICKHAM, WEST (St John) *S'wark 20* **P** *Bp* **V** J D B POOLE

WICKHAM, WEST (St Mary) *Ely 4* **P** *Bp* **P-in-c** W N C GIRARD

WICKHAM, WEST (St Mary of Nazareth) *S'wark 20* **P** *Bp* **V** F S MADGE

WICKHAM BISHOPS (St Bartholomew) w Little Braxted *Chelmsf 25* **P** *Bp (3 turns), CCC Cam (1 turn)* **R** C J SLY

WICKHAM MARKET (All Saints) w Pettistree and Easton *St E 18* **P** *Ch Trust Fund Trust, MMCET, and Ld Chan (by turn)* **V** G D R BELL

WICKHAM SKEITH (St Andrew) *St E 6* **P** *Ch Patr Trust* **P-in-c** P T GRAY

WICKHAMBREAUX (St Andrew) Littlebourne and Ickham w Wickhambreaux etc *Cant*

WICKHAMBROOK (All Saints) w Lydgate, Ousden and Cowlinge *St E 8* **P** *DBP, and Ld Chan (alt)* **R** E R CROUCHMAN

WICKHAMFORD (St John the Baptist) Badsey w Aldington and Wickhamford *Worc*

WICKHAMPTON (St Andrew) Freethorpe w Wickhampton, Halvergate etc *Nor*

WICKLEWOOD (All Saints) High Oak *Nor*

WICKMERE (St Andrew) w Little Barningham, Itteringham and Edgefield *Nor 20* **P** *Lord Walpole* **R** K A HAWKES

WICKWAR (Holy Trinity) w Rangeworthy *Glouc 7* **P** *Bp and Earl of Ducie (jt)* **R** D B SMALL

WIDCOMBE Bath Widcombe *B & W*

WIDDINGTON (St Mary) Quendon w Rickling & Wicken Bonhunt & Widdington *Chelmsf*

WIDDRINGTON (Holy Trinity) *Newc 11* **P** *Bp* **NSM** J WAIYAKI

WIDDRINGTON STATION (St Mary) Ulgham *Newc*

WIDECOMBE-IN-THE-MOOR (St Pancras), Leusdon, Princetown, Postbridge, Huccaby and Holne *Ex 11* **P** *Duchy of Cornwall (1 turn), Patr Bd (2 turns)* **TM** *Vacant*

WIDEMOUTH BAY (Our Lady and St Anne) Week St Mary w Poundstock and Whitstone *Truro*

WIDFORD (St John the Baptist) Hunsdon w Widford and Wareside *St Alb*

WIDFORD (St Mary) (Holy Spirit) *Chelmsf 9* **P** *CPAS* **R** N J HAY, **C** T C JONES

WIDFORD (St Oswald) Burford w Fulbrook, Taynton, Asthall etc *Ox*

WIDLEY w Wymering *Portsm 6* **P** *E G Nugee Esq* **V** *Vacant* Cosham (01705) 376307

WIDMER END (Good Shepherd) Hazlemere *Ox*

WIDMERPOOL (St Peter) Willoughby-on-the-Wolds w Wysall and Widmerpool *S'well*

WIDNES (St Ambrose) *Liv 13* **P** *Trustees* **V** P T JONES

WIDNES (St John) *Liv 13* **P** *Bp and V Farnworth (jt)* **V** D J GAIT

WIDNES (St Mary) *Liv 13* **P** *Bp* **V** *Vacant* 0151-424 4233

WIDNES (St Paul) *Liv 13* **P** *Bp* **P-in-c** A HODGE

WIDWORTHY (St Cuthbert) Colyton, Southleigh, Offwell, Widworthy etc *Ex*

WIELD (St James) Medstead cum Wield *Win*

WIGAN (All Saints) *Liv 14* **P** *Bp* **R** K M FORREST

WIGAN New Springs (St John) New Springs *Liv*

WIGAN (St Andrew) *Liv 15* **P** *R Wigan* **V** M R NICHOLLS

WIGAN (St Anne) *Liv 15* **P** *Bp* **V** R CRANKSHAW, **C** L McCLUSKEY

WIGAN (St Barnabas) Marsh Green *Liv 15* **P** *V Pemberton St Mark Newtown and Bp (jt)* **V** J WINNARD

WIGAN (St Catherine) *Liv 14* **P** *R Wigan* **V** J T CLEGG

WIGAN (St George) *Liv 14* **P** *R Wigan* **V** B C HARRISON

WIGAN (St James) (St Thomas) *Liv 15* **P** *R Wigan and Bp (jt)* **V** J A TAYLOR, **C** S E DRAPER

WIGAN (St Michael and All Angels) *Liv 15* **P** *R Wigan* **V** D G CLAWSON

WIGAN (St Stephen) *Liv 14* **P** *Bp* **P-in-c** E P TODD

WIGAN Whelley (St Stephen) Wigan St Steph *Liv*

WIGBOROUGH, GREAT (St Stephen) Peldon w Gt and Lt Wigborough *Chelmsf*

WIGBOROUGH, LITTLE (St Nicholas) as above

WIGGATON (St Edward the Confessor) Ottery St Mary, Alfington, W Hill, Tipton etc *Ex*

WIGGENHALL (St Mary Magdalen) *Ely 17* **P** *MMCET* **V** *Vacant*

WIGGENHALL ST GERMANS (St Mary the Virgin) and Islington St Mary *Ely 17* **P** *Ld Chan (2 turns), Bp (1 turn)* **V** *Vacant* St Germans (0155385) 371

WIGGINTON (St Bartholomew) *St Alb 3* **P** *Bp* **V** *Vacant* Tring (01442) 823273

WIGGINTON (St Giles) Hook Norton w Gt Rollright, Swerford etc *Ox*

WIGGINTON (St Leonard) (St James) *Lich 4* **P** *V Tamworth* **P-in-c** I R CARDINAL

WIGGINTON (St Mary and St Nicholas) Haxby w Wigginton *York*

WIGGLESWORTH (School) Giggleswick and Rathmell w Wigglesworth *Bradf*

WIGGONHOLT (not known) Amberley w N Stoke and Parham, Wiggonholt etc *Chich*

WIGHILL (All Saints) Healaugh w Wighill, Bilbrough and Askham Richard *York*

WIGHTON (All Saints) Holkham w Egmere w Warham, Wells and Wighton *Nor*

WIGMORE (St James the Apostle) Aymestrey and Leinthall Earles w Wigmore etc *Heref*

WIGMORE ABBEY *Heref 12* **P** *Guild of All So, D P H Lennox Esq, J W Watkins Esq, C C Hartley Esq, and Bp (jt)* **P-in-c** A TALBOT-PONSONBY, **NSM** G TALBOT-PONSONBY, D W G VICKERS

WIGSLEY Harby w Thorney and N and S Clifton *S'well*

WIGSTON, SOUTH (St Thomas) Glen Parva and S Wigston *Leic*

WIGSTON MAGNA (All Saints) (St Wistan) *Leic 5* **P** *Haberdashers' Co* **V** E J GREEN

WIGSTON PARVA (St Mary the Virgin) Sapcote and Sharnford w Wigston Parva *Leic*

WIGTOFT (St Peter and St Paul) Bicker and Wigtoft *Linc*

WIGTON (St Mary) *Carl 3* **P** *Bp* **V** G P RAVALDE, **C** R P BLACKETT

WIKE (School Room) Bardsey *Ripon*

WILBARSTON (All Saints) Stoke Albany w Wilbarston *Pet*

WILBERFOSS (St John the Baptist) Kexby w Wilberfoss *York*

WILBRAHAM, GREAT (St Nicholas) *Ely 6* **P** *DBP* **P-in-c** B E KERLEY, **C** J E ARMSTRONG

WILBRAHAM, LITTLE (St John) *Ely 6* **P** *CCC Cam* **P-in-c** B E KERLEY

WILBURTON (St Peter) *Ely 14* **P** *Adn Ely* **V** M P WADSWORTH

WILBURY (St Thomas) *St Alb 9* **P** *Bp* **V** D E DOWLING, **C** J N RAPLEY

WILBY (All Saints) Quidenham *Nor*

WILBY (St Mary the Virgin) Gt Doddington and Wilby *Pet*

WILBY (St Mary) w Brundish *St E 17* **P** *Dr F H C Marriott and Miss A W G Marriott (3 turns), Bp (1 turn)* **R** *Vacant* Stradbroke (01379) 84333

WILCOT (Holy Cross) Swanborough *Sarum*

WILCOTE (St Peter) Ramsden, Finstock and Fawler, Leafield etc *Ox*

WILDBOARCLOUGH (St Saviour) Bosley and N Rode w Wincle and Wildboarclough *Ches*

WILDEN (All Saints) Stourport-on-Severn and Wilden *Worc*

WILDEN (St Nicholas) w Colmworth and Ravensden *St Alb 21* **P** *Ld Chan, Bp, and DBP (by turn)* **R** J R ROGERS

WILFORD (St Wilfrid) *S'well 10* **P** *Lt Col Peter Clifton* **R** P NEWTON

WILFORD HILL (St Paul) *S'well 10* **P** *DBP* **V** G J PIGOTT, **Hon C** B M GRIFFITHS, **NSM** J H BATESON

WILKSBY (All Saints) Mareham-le-Fen and Revesby *Linc*

WILLAND (St Mary the Virgin) *Ex 4* **P** *CPAS* **R** K D AGNEW

WILLASTON (Christ Church) *Ches 9* **P** *DBF*
  V R W DENT
WILLASTON (St Luke) Wistaston *Ches*
WILLEN (St Mary Magdalen) Stantonbury and Willen *Ox*
WILLENHALL (Holy Trinity) *Lich 9* **P** *Patr Bd*
  TR E F BUXTON, **C** M I RHODES, T J LEYLAND,
  S A CHAPMAN
WILLENHALL (St Anne) *Lich 9* **P** *Mrs L Grant-Wilson*
  V C A St A RAMSAY
WILLENHALL (St Giles) *Lich 9* **P** *Trustees*
  V C R MARSHALL
WILLENHALL (St John the Divine) *Cov 1* **P** *V Cov H Trin*
  V T J COLLING
WILLENHALL (St Stephen) *Lich 9* **P** *Bp*
  V D R HARTLAND
WILLERBY (St Luke) Kirk Ella *York*
WILLERBY (St Peter) w Ganton and Folkton *York 16*
  P *M H Wrigley Esq, MMCET, and Rev G C Day (by turn)*
  R A A MACKENZIE
**WILLERSEY (St Peter), Saintbury, Weston-sub-Edge and
  Aston-sub-Edge** *Glouc 10* **P** *Gen Sir John Gibbon and
  Major G B Gibbon, Earl of Harrowby, and Bp (by turn)*
  R J M MASON
WILLESBOROUGH (Christ Church) (St Mary the Virgin)
  Cant 10 **P** *D&C* **R** M J McENERY, **C** C I GREEN
WILLESDEN (St Mark) Kensal Rise St Mark and St Martin
  Lon
WILLESDEN (St Martin) as above
WILLESDEN (St Mary) *Lon 21* **P** *D&C St Paul's*
  V I G BOOTH, **Hon C** J L McKENZIE
WILLESDEN (St Matthew) *Lon 21* **P** *Bp*
  P-in-c M D MOORHEAD, **C** K A ROBUS
WILLESDEN GREEN (St Andrew) (St Francis of Assisi)
  Lon 21 **P** *Bp* **V** P S ANDERSON, **C** R WARD
WILLEY (St Leonard) Churchover w Willey *Cov*
WILLIAN (All Saints) Letchworth St Paul w Willian *St Alb*
WILLINGALE (St Christopher) Fyfield, Moreton w
  Bobbingworth and Willingale etc *Chelmsf*
WILLINGDON (St Mary the Virgin) *Chich 16* **P** *D&C*
  V J R P ASHBY
WILLINGHAM (St Mary and All Saints) *Ely 5* **P** *Bp*
  R E A HUBBARD
WILLINGHAM, NORTH (St Thomas) Walesby *Linc*
WILLINGHAM, SOUTH (St Martin) Barkwith Gp *Linc*
WILLINGHAM BY STOW (St Helen) Stow Gp *Linc*
WILLINGTON (St Lawrence) Cople w Willington *St Alb*
WILLINGTON (St Michael) *Derby 16* **P** *CPAS*
  V C R WILSON
WILLINGTON (St Stephen) and Sunnybrow *Dur 15*
  P *R Brancepeth* **R** *Vacant* Bishop Auckland (01388) 746242
**WILLINGTON Team, The (Good Shepherd) (St Mary the
  Virgin) (St Paul)** *Newc 8* **P** *Prime Min* **TV** J H ADAMS,
  J M DOTCHIN, **C** B M HACKETT
WILLINGTON QUAY (St Paul) Willington Team *Newc*
WILLISHAM (St Mary) Somersham w Flowton and Offton
  w Willisham *St E*
WILLITON (St Peter) *B & W 17* **P** *V Watchet*
  V R J ALLEN
WILLOUGHBY (St Helen) *Linc 8* **P** *Baroness Willoughby
  de Eresby, Ball Coll Ox, and Bp (jt)* **R** D C ROBINSON
WILLOUGHBY (St Nicholas) Grandborough w Willoughby
  and Flecknoe *Cov*
**WILLOUGHBY-ON-THE-WOLDS (St Mary and All Saints)
  w Wysall and Widerpool** *S'well 9* **P** *MMCET*
  V J M PROTHERO
**WILLOUGHBY WATERLEYS (St Mary), Peatling Magna
  and Ashby Magna** *Leic 10* **P** *Bp* **R** P ETCHELLS
WILLOUGHTON (St Andrew) Glentworth Gp *Linc*
WILMCOTE (St Andrew) Aston Cantlow and Wilmcote w
  Billesley *Cov*
WILMINGTON (St Mary and St Peter) Arlington,
  Folkington and Wilmington *Chich*
WILMINGTON (St Michael) *Roch 2* **P** *D&C*
  V C F JOHNSON, **Hon C** P J IVESON
WILMSLOW (St Bartholomew) *Ches 12* **P** *Bp*
  R P J HUNT, **C** F H BARKER, **NSM** R A YATES,
  P M PULLAN, N J WALTHEW
WILNE (St Chad) and Draycott w Breaston *Derby 13* **P** *Bp*
  R G K G GRIFFITH
WILNECOTE (Holy Trinity) *Lich 4* **P** *V Tamworth*
  V A P HARPER, **C** R B READE, S M HEMSLEY
WILSDEN (St Matthew) Harden and Wilsden *Bradf*
WILSFORD (St Mary) Ancaster Wilsford Gp *Linc*
WILSFORD (St Michael) Woodford Valley *Sarum*
WILSFORD (St Nicholas) Redhorn *Sarum*
WILSHAMSTEAD (All Saints) and Houghton Conquest
  St Alb 19 **P** *St Jo Coll Cam and Bp (alt)*
  V D R PALMER, **NSM** R C WHITE

WILSHAW (St Mary) Meltham *Wakef*
WILSILL (St Michael and All Angels) Upper Nidderdale
  Ripon
WILSTHORPE (St Faith) Uffington Gp *Linc*
WILSTONE (St Cross) Tring *St Alb*
WILTON (St Cuthbert) *York 17* **P** *Abp* **V** R F ROWLING
WILTON (St George) *B & W 18* **P** *Mrs E C Cutbush*
  TR M D MOYNAGH, **TV** M D CLARK,
  Hon C R W COLWILL
WILTON (St George) Thornton Dale and Ellerburne w
  Wilton *York*
**WILTON (St Mary and St Nicholas) w Netherhampton and
  Fugglestone** *Sarum 16* **P** *Earl of Pembroke*
  R B R COOPER, **Hon C** S V COLLINS
WILTON PLACE (St Paul) *Lon 3* **P** *Bp*
  V A C C COURTAULD, **NSM** H C RUSCHMEYER,
  N DAWSON
WIMBISH (All Saints) Debden and Wimbish w Thunderley
  Chelmsf
WIMBLEDON (Emmanuel) Ridgway Proprietary Chapel
  S'wark 12 **Min** J J M FLETCHER, **C** G FYLES,
  Hon C D L JOHNSON, R J COEKIN
WIMBLEDON (St Luke) *S'wark 12* **P** *Simeon's Trustees*
  V D J WILES
**WIMBLEDON (St Mary) (St Matthew) (St Mark) (St John the
  Baptist)** *S'wark 12* **P** *Patr Bd* **TV** P J H DUNN,
  M J R FARR, **C** E A MORSE, **NSM** H A JOHNSON
WIMBLEDON, SOUTH (All Saints) *S'wark 12* **P** *Bp*
  V K J BALE, **Hon C** I P GREGORY
WIMBLEDON, SOUTH (Holy Trinity and St Peter)
  S'wark 12 **P** *Bp and TR Wimbledon St Mary (jt)*
  V D S GATLIFFE, **C** J M FRANCIS
WIMBLEDON, SOUTH (St Andrew) *S'wark 12* **P** *Bp*
  P-in-c A D WAKEFIELD
WIMBLEDON, WEST (Christ Church) *S'wark 12*
  P *TR Wimbledon* **V** C S M THOMSON
WIMBLEDON PARK Wimbledon St Luke *S'wark*
WIMBLINGTON (St Peter) *Ely 18* **P** *St Jo Coll Dur*
  P-in-c A L WAY
WIMBORNE (St Giles) Cranborne w Boveridge,
  Edmondsham etc *Sarum*
WIMBORNE (St John the Evangelist) New Boro and Leigh
  Sarum
WIMBORNE MINSTER (St Cuthberga) and Holt *Sarum 10*
  P *Patr Bd* **TR** D R PRICE, **C** G P HARRISON
**WIMBOTSHAM (St Mary) w Stow Bardolph and Stow Bridge
  w Nordelph** *Ely 16* **P** *Bp and R T Townley Esq (jt)*
  R R D TOMKINSON
WIMPOLE (St Andrew) *Ely 8* **P** *Bp* **R** N A BRICE
WINCANTON (St Peter and St Paul) *B & W 2* **P** *D&C*
  R R J CLOETE
WINCH, EAST (All Saints) Middleton w E Winch *Nor*
WINCH, WEST (St Mary) w Setchey and North Runcton
  Nor 21 **P** *H N D Gurney Esq (1 turn), Ld Chan (2 turns)*
  P-in-c P BROWN
WINCHAM (St Andrew) Lostock Gralam *Ches*
**WINCHCOMBE (St Peter), Gretton, Sudeley Manor and
  Stanley Pontlarge** *Glouc 17* **P** *Lady Ashcombe*
  V M J PAGE, **C** J E B KENCHINGTON (nee
  BALLANTYNE), **NSM** P M RAGBOURNE
WINCHELSEA (St Thomas) (St Richard) and Icklesham
  Chich 20 **P** *Bp and Guild of All So (jt)* **R** C G SCOTT,
  NSM G F PEGG
WINCHENDON, NETHER (St Nicholas) Long Crendon w
  Chearsley and Nether Winchendon *Ox*
WINCHENDON, OVER (St Mary Magdalene) Waddesdon
  w Over Winchendon and Fleet Marston *Ox*
**WINCHESTER (All Saints), Chilcomb (St Andrew), Chesil St
  Peter** *Win 13* **P** *Bp and Ld Chan (alt)* **R** C BASTON,
  Hon C T E HEMMING
WINCHESTER (Christ Church) *Win 13* **P** *Simeon's
  Trustees* **V** E S SHIRRAS, **C** J F A WILLIAMS, A JONES
WINCHESTER (Holy Trinity) Winnall *Win*
WINCHESTER (St Barnabas) *Win 13* **P** *Bp*
  V R C STONE, **NSM** W J WILSON
WINCHESTER (St Cross Hospital w St Faith) *Win 13*
  P *Bp* **V** S A OUTHWAITE
**WINCHESTER (St John the Baptist w St Martin
  Winnall)** Winnall *Win*
**WINCHESTER (St Lawrence and St Maurice) (St Swithun-
  upon-Kingsgate)** *Win 13* **P** *Ld Chan* **R** D V SCOTT,
  Hon C J M KERR, **NSM** N H de la MOUETTE
WINCHESTER St Matthew (St Paul's Mission Church)
  Win 13 **P** *Bp* **R** C N WRIGHT, **NSM** N W BIRKETT
WINCHESTER Stanmore (St Luke) Stanmore *Win*
WINCHESTER HYDE (St Bartholomew) *Win 13*
  P *Ld Chan* **V** G M ARMSTEAD, **NSM** J A FOREMAN

WINCHFIELD (St Mary the Virgin) Hartley Wintney, Elvetham, Winchfield etc *Win*

WINCHMORE HILL (Holy Trinity) *Lon 18* **P** *V Winchmore Hill St Paul* **V** C M GRAY

WINCHMORE HILL (St Andrew) Amersham *Ox*

WINCHMORE HILL (St Paul) *Lon 18* **P** *V Edmonton* **V** D J NASH, **C** P G KEARNS, C M MORTON

WINCLE (St Michael) Bosley and N Rode w Wincle and Wildboarclough *Ches*

WINCOBANK (St Thomas) Brightside w Wincobank *Sheff*

WINDERMERE (St Martin) *Carl 10* **P** *Bp and Trustees (jt)* **P-in-c** C M BUTT

WINDERMERE (St Mary) Applethwaite *Carl*

WINDHILL (Christ Church) *Bradf 1* **P** *Bp* **V** G PERCIVAL

WINDLESHAM (St John the Baptist) *Guildf 6* **P** *Ld Chan* **R** J A R PIERSSENE, **C** D G NEWSTEAD

WINDRUSH (St Peter) Sherborne, Windrush, the Barringtons etc *Glouc*

WINDSOR, NEW (Holy Trinity) (St John the Baptist w All Saints) *Ox 13* **P** *Ld Chan* **TR** J W G WHALE, **TV** A W H BUNCH, J G CRUICKSHANK

WINDSOR, OLD (St Luke's Mission Room) (St Peter and St Andrew) *Ox 13* **P** *Ld Chan* **V** J W STAPLES

WINESTEAD (St German) Patrington w Hollym, Welwick and Winestead *York*

WINFARTHING (St Mary) w Shelfanger w Burston w Gissing and Tivetshall *Nor 10* **P** *Ld Chan, Bp, and DBP (jt), Hertf Coll Ox (alt)* **R** D V WHALE

WINFORD (Blessed Virgin Mary and St Peter) w Felton Common Hill *B & W 10* **P** *Worc Coll Ox and Mrs H D Pullman (jt)* **R** J BOLTON

WINFORTON (St Michael and All Angels) Eardisley w Bollingham, Willersley, Brilley etc *Heref*

WINFRITH NEWBURGH (St Christopher) The Lulworths, Winfrith Newburgh and Chaldon *Sarum*

WING (St Peter and St Paul) Preston and Ridlington w Wing and Pilton *Pet*

WING w Grove (All Saints) *Ox 26* **P** *Bp* **V** B SAGAR

WINGATE GRANGE (Holy Trinity) *Dur 3* **P** *Bp* **V** P GRUNDY

WINGATES (St John the Evangelist) *Man 11* **P** *R Deane St Mary* **V** A J DOBB

WINGERWORTH (All Saints) *Derby 5* **P** *Bp* **R** S MILLINGTON, **Hon C** F H SHAW, **NSM** R E SMITH

WINGFIELD (St Andrew) Fressingfield, Mendham, Metfield, Weybread etc *St E*

WINGFIELD (St Mary) Westwood and Wingfield *Sarum*

WINGFIELD, NORTH (St Lawrence), Clay Cross and Pilsley *Derby 5* **P** *Bp* **TR** H L ORMEROD, **TV** B DALE, N S ATKINS, P G BYSOUTH

WINGFIELD, SOUTH (All Saints) and Wessington *Derby 1* **P** *Duke of Devonshire and V Crich (jt)* **V** W M RUMBALL

WINGHAM (St Mary the Virgin) w Elmstone and Preston w Stourmouth *Cant 1* **P** *Lord Fitzwalter and D&C (alt)* **V** P J BROWNBRIDGE

WINGRAVE (St Peter and St Paul) w Rowsham, Aston Abbotts and Cublington *Ox 26* **P** *Bp and Linc Coll Ox (jt)* **R** R O N WILLMOTT, **NSM** P R BINNS

WINKBURN (St John of Jerusalem) *S'well 15* **P** *Bp* **P-in-c** H H WILCOX

WINKFIELD (St Mary the Virgin) and Cranbourne *Ox 11* **P** *Bp* **V** S H BAYNES

WINKLEBURY (Good Shepherd) *Win 4* **P** M M CET **V** D T PERRETT, **NSM** R P BOWSKILL

WINKLEIGH (All Saints) *Ex 16* **P** *D&C* **V** P J NORMAN, **Hon C** G A HAMEY

WINKSLEY (St Cuthbert and St Oswald) Fountains Gp *Ripon*

WINLATON (St Paul) *Dur 5* **P** *Bp* **R** E JONES

WINMARLEIGH (St Luke) Cockerham w Winmarleigh and Glasson *Blackb*

WINNALL (Holy Trinity) (St John the Baptist w St Martin) *Win 13* **P** *Bp* **R** R J H TEARE

WINNERSH (St Mary the Virgin) Hurst *Ox*

WINSCOMBE (St James) *B & W 11* **P** *D&C* **V** I M HUBBARD, **NSM** C NELMES

WINSFORD (St Mary Magdalene) Exton and Winsford and Cutcombe w Luxborough *B & W*

WINSHAM (St Stephen) Thorncombe w Winsham and Cricket St Thomas *B & W*

WINSHILL (St Mark) *Derby 16* **P** *Lady H M Gretton and Baroness Gretton (jt)* **V** K C JONES

WINSLEY (St Nicholas) Monkton Farleigh, S Wraxall and Winsley *Sarum*

WINSLOW (St Laurence) w Great Horwood and Addington *Ox 24* **P** *Ld Chan (3 turns), New Coll Ox (2 turns), and DBP (1 turn)* **C** J M REES, **NSM** P A HOWARD

WINSON (St Michael) Bibury w Winson and Barnsley *Glouc*

WINSTER (Holy Trinity) *Carl 9* **P** *V Kendal H Trin* **V** K PARTINGTON

WINSTER (St John the Baptist) S Darley, Elton and Winster *Derby*

WINSTON (St Andrew) *Dur 11* **P** *Bp* **R** T J D OLLIER

WINSTON (St Andrew) Helmingham w Framsden and Pettaugh w Winston *St E*

WINSTONE (St Bartholomew) Daglingworth w the Duntisbournes and Winstone *Glouc*

WINTERBOURNE (St James) Chieveley w Winterbourne and Oare *Ox*

WINTERBOURNE (St Michael the Archangel) *Bris 7* **P** *St Jo Coll Ox* **R** E I BAILEY, **Hon C** W J DEIGHTON

WINTERBOURNE ABBAS (St Mary) The Winterbournes and Compton Valence *Sarum*

WINTERBOURNE BASSETT (St Katharine) Upper Kennett *Sarum*

WINTERBOURNE CLENSTON (St Nicholas) Winterbourne Stickland and Turnworth etc *Sarum*

WINTERBOURNE DOWN (All Saints) Frenchay and Winterbourne Down *Bris*

WINTERBOURNE EARLS (St Michael and All Angels) Bourne Valley *Sarum*

WINTERBOURNE GUNNER (St Mary) as above

WINTERBOURNE HOUGHTON (St Andrew) Winterbourne Stickland and Turnworth etc *Sarum*

WINTERBOURNE KINGSTON (St Nicholas) Red Post *Sarum*

WINTERBOURNE MONKTON (St Mary Magdalen) Upper Kennett *Sarum*

WINTERBOURNE MONKTON (St Simon and St Jude) Dorchester *Sarum*

WINTERBOURNE ST MARTIN (St Martin) The Winterbournes and Compton Valence *Sarum*

WINTERBOURNE STEEPLETON (St Michael) as above

WINTERBOURNE STICKLAND (St Mary) and Turnworth, Winterbourne Houghton, Winterbourne Whitechurch and Winterbourne Clenston *Sarum 7* **P** *Bp (3 turns), P D H Chichester Esq and Exors Mrs V P Railston (1 turn)* **R** R S GREEN, **NSM** A M F HALL

WINTERBOURNE STOKE (St Peter) Lower Wylye and Till Valley *Sarum*

WINTERBOURNE WHITECHURCH (St Mary) Winterbourne Stickland and Turnworth etc *Sarum*

WINTERBOURNE ZELSTONE (St Mary) Red Post *Sarum*

WINTERBOURNES and Compton Valence, The *Sarum 2* **P** *Adn Sherborne, Linc Coll Ox, and Sir Robert Williams, Bt (by turn)* **P-in-c** J R ADAMS

WINTERBURN (Chapel of Ease) Gargrave *Bradf*

WINTERINGHAM (All Saints) Alkborough *Linc*

WINTERSLOW (All Saints) (St John) *Sarum 11* **P** *St Jo Coll Ox* **R** C R F COHEN

WINTERTON Group, The (All Saints) *Linc 4* **P** *Lord St Oswald, Bp, and Capt J G G P Elwes (jt)* **V** D EDGAR

WINTERTON (Holy Trinity and All Saints) w East and West Somerton and Horsey *Nor 6* **P** *Bp, SMF, and D&C (jt)* **P-in-c** W D B WILLIAMS, **NSM** A T CADMORE

WINTHORPE (All Saints) *S'well 3* **P** *Keble Coll Ox* **P-in-c** J L SMITH

WINTHORPE (St Mary) Skegness and Winthorpe *Linc*

WINTON (St Mary Magdalene) *Man 2* **P** *Trustees* **V** D R SUTTON

WINTRINGHAM (St Peter) Rillington w Scampston, Wintringham etc *York*

WINWICK (All Saints) *Ely 10* **P** *Bp* **NSM** I D M GIBSON

WINWICK (St Michael and All Angels) W Haddon w Winwick and Ravensthorpe *Pet*

WINWICK (St Oswald) *Liv 16* **P** *Bp* **R** R G LEWIS

WIRKSWORTH (St Mary) *Derby 7* **P** *Bp* **TR** R S CANEY, **TV** M SMITH

WISBECH (St Augustine) *Ely 19* **P** *Bp* **V** R D BULL, **NSM** G G A WARING

WISBECH (St Peter and St Paul) *Ely 19* **P** *Bp* **V** W A L Z WALF, **C** J E PHILLIPS

WISBECH ST MARY (St Mary) *Ely 19* **P** *Bp* **P-in-c** F B H WOOLLEY, **C** P C OWEN-JONES

WISBOROUGH GREEN (St Peter ad Vincula) *Chich 11* **P** *Bp Lon* **V** D F PIKE

WISHAW (St Chad) *Birm 9* **P** *Bp* **P-in-c** D J LEE

WISHFORD, GREAT (St Giles) Lower Wylye and Till Valley *Sarum*

WISLEY (not known) w Pyrford *Guildf 12* **P** *Bp* **R** N J AIKEN, **C** P W MICKLETHWAITE, **NSM** K R CROOKS

WISSETT (St Andrew) Halesworth w Linstead, Chediston, Holton etc *St E*

WISSINGTON (St Mary the Virgin) Nayland w Wiston *St E*
WISTANSTOW (Holy Trinity) *Heref 11* **P** *Bp*
P-in-c G M SUMNER
WISTASTON (St Mary) *Ches 15* **P** *Trustees* **R** W J WHITE
WISTON (St Mary) Ashington, Washington and Wiston with Buncton *Chich*
WISTOW (All Saints) *York 6* **P** *Abp* **V** D J WOOLLARD, **NSM** M J CUNDIFF
WISTOW (St John the Baptist) Warboys w Broughton and Bury w Wistow *Ely*
WISTOW (St Wistan) Gt Glen, Stretton Magna and Wistow etc *Leic*
WITCHAM (St Martin) w Mepal *Ely 14* **P** *D&C* **NSM** M T COOPER
WITCHAMPTON (St Mary and St Cuthberga and All Saints) and Hinton Parva, Long Crichel w Moor Crichel *Sarum 10* **P** *Hon Mrs M A Marten* **P-in-c** G E WALTON
WITCHFORD (St Andrew) w Wentworth *Ely 14* **P** *D&C* **P-in-c** T AMBROSE
WITCHINGHAM GREAT (St Mary) Weston Longville w Morton and the Witchinghams *Nor*
WITCOMBE, GREAT (St Mary) *Glouc 6* **P** *M W Hicks Beach Esq* **C** W J BOON
WITHAM Group, The *Linc 14* **P** *Sir Lyonel Tollemache, Bt, Rev J R H and Rev H C Thorold, and Bp (jt)* **P-in-c** G P WILLIAMS
WITHAM (St Nicholas) *Chelmsf 25* **P** *Patr Bd* **TR** D SHERLOCK, **TV** B J MAPLEY, **C** K R PLAISTER
WITHAM, NORTH (St Mary) Witham Gp *Linc*
WITHAM, SOUTH (St John the Baptist) as above
WITHAM FRIARY (Blessed Virgin Mary and St John the Baptist and All Saints) Nunney and Witham Friary, Marston Bigot etc *B & W*
WITHAM-ON-THE-HILL (St Andrew) Edenham w Witham-on-the-Hill *Linc*
WITHCALL (St Martin) Raithby *Linc*
WITHERIDGE (St John the Baptist), Thelbridge, Creacombe, Meshaw, East and West Worlington *Ex 19* **P** *Bp, Exors Sir Denis Stucley, C M K Bruton Esq and MMCET (jt)* **P-in-c** V ROSS
WITHERLEY (St Peter) Higham-on-the-Hill w Fenny Drayton and Witherley *Leic*
WITHERNICK (St Alban) Aldbrough, Mappleton w Goxhill and Withernwick *York*
WITHERNSEA (St Nicholas) Owthorne and Rimswell w Withernsea *York*
WITHERSDALE (St Mary Magdalene) Fressingfield, Mendham, Metfield, Weybread etc *St E*
WITHERSFIELD (St Mary the Virgin) Haverhill w Withersfield, the Wrattings etc *St E*
WITHERSLACK (St Paul) *Carl 9* **P** *DBP* **V** K PARTINGTON
WITHIEL (St Clement) Roche and Withiel *Truro*
WITHIEL FLOREY (St Mary Magdalene) Brompton Regis w Upton and Skilgate *B & W*
WITHINGTON *Man 8* **P** *The Crown* **P-in-c** G R RAINES
WITHINGTON (St Crispin) *Man 4* **P** *Bp* **R** *Vacant* 0161–224 3452
WITHINGTON (St John the Baptist) Uffington, Upton Magna and Withington *Lich*
WITHINGTON (St Michael and All Angels) and Compton Abdale w Haselton *Glouc 14* **P** *Bp (2 turns), Ld Chan (1 turn)* **P-in-c** C D J G BURSLEM
WITHINGTON (St Paul) *Man 8* **P** *Trustees* **R** N W DAWSON
WITHINGTON (St Peter) w Westhide *Heref 4* **P** *Bp* **R** M A PAICE
WITHINGTON, LOWER (St Peter) Chelford w Lower Withington *Ches*
WITHLEIGH (St Catherine) Washfield, Stoodleigh, Withleigh etc *Ex*
WITHNELL (St Paul) Heapey St Barnabas and Withnell St Paul *Blackb*
WITHYBROOK (All Saints) Wolvey w Burton Hastings, Copston Magna etc *Cov*
WITHYCOMBE (St Nicholas) Dunster, Carhampton and Withycombe w Rodhuish *B & W*
WITHYCOMBE RALEIGH (All Saints) Withycombe Raleigh *Ex*
WITHYCOMBE RALEIGH (St John the Evangelist) (St John in the Wilderness) (All Saints) *Ex 1* **P** *Patr Bd* **TR** F A OSWIN, **TV** A H MACDONALD, J D H CLEMENTS
WITHYHAM (St John the Evangelist) *Chich 19* **P** *Guild of All So* **V** R L FEATHERSTONE
WITHYHAM (St Michael and All Angels) *Chich 19* **P** *Earl de la Warr* **R** *Vacant* Hartfield (01892) 770241
WITHYPOOL (St Andrew) Exford, Exmoor, Hawkridge and Withypool *B & W*

WITHYWOOD *Bris 1* **P** *Bp* **V** B E PEARCE, **C** D A PARRY
WITLEY (All Saints) *Guildf 4* **P** *Mrs C M Chandler and R D Chandler Esq (jt)* **V** I C S FENTON
WITLEY, GREAT (St Michael) Shrawley, Witley, Astley and Abberley *Worc*
WITLEY, LITTLE (St Michael) as above
WITNESHAM (St Mary) Westerfield and Tuddenham St Martin w Witnesham *St E*
WITNEY (St Mary the Virgin) (Holy Trinity) *Ox 8* **P** *Patr Bd* **TV** J M COLLINS, N J S PARRY, **C** G R ARTHUR, **Hon C** J H COOK
WITTENHAM, LITTLE (St Peter) Dorchester *Ox*
WITTERING (All Saints) w Thornhaugh and Wansford *Pet 8* **P** *Burghley Ho Preservation Trust (2 turns), Bp (1 turn)* **R** H R WATSON
WITTERING, EAST (St Anne) Earnley and E Wittering *Chich*
WITTERING, WEST (St Peter and St Paul) and Birdham w Itchenor *Chich 3* **P** *Bp* **R** J B WILLIAMS, **Hon C** C J HANKINS
WITTERSHAM (St John the Baptist) w Stone-in-Oxney and Ebony *Cant 13* **P** *Abp* **P-in-c** L J HAMMOND, **Hon C** M S WING
WITTON (St Helen) *Ches 6* **P** *Bp* **V** A A LONG, **C** P WAIN, **NSM** B R K PERKES
WITTON (St Margaret) Bacton w Edingthorpe w Witton and Ridlington *Nor*
WITTON (St Margaret) Gt and Lt Plumstead w Thorpe End and Witton *Nor*
WITTON (St Mark) *Blackb 2* **P** *V Blackb* **V** C L ALBIN
WITTON, EAST (St John the Evangelist) Middleham w Coverdale and E Witton *Ripon*
WITTON, NETHER (St Giles) Netherwitton *Newc*
WITTON, WEST (St Bartholomew) *Ripon 4* **P** *Lord Bolton* **V** *Vacant*
WITTON GILBERT (St Michael and All Angels) *Dur 2* **P** *D&C* **R** M J VAIZEY
WITTON LE WEAR (St Philip and St James) Hamsterley and Witton-le-Wear *Dur*
WITTON PARK (St Paul) *Dur 10* **P** *Bp* **V** N M J-W BEDDOW
WIVELISCOMBE (St Andrew) w Chipstable, Huish Champflower and Clatworthy *B & W 19* **P** *Bp and A H Trollope-Bellew Esq (jt)* **R** C J B MARSHALL, **C** G A OWEN, **NSM** S M GREEN
WIVELSFIELD (St Peter and St John the Baptist) *Chich 6* **P** *DBP* **V** S A FALLOWS
WIVENHOE (St Mary) *Chelmsf 17* **P** *Bp* **R** D G THOMAS
WIVETON (St Mary) Blakeney w Cley, Wiveton, Glandford etc *Nor*
WIX (St Mary the Virgin) Gt Oakley w Wix *Chelmsf*
WIXFORD (St Milburga) Exhall w Wixford *Cov*
WIXOE (St Leonard) Clare w Poslingford, Cavendish etc *St E*
WOBURN (St Mary) w Eversholt, Milton Bryan, Battlesden and Pottesgrove *St Alb 15* **P** *Bedf Estates Trustees* **V** P R MILLER
WOBURN SANDS (St Michael) *St Alb 15* **P** *Bp* **V** N JEFFERY
WOBURN SQUARE (Christ Church) Bloomsbury St Geo w Woburn Square Ch Ch *Lon*
WOKING (Christ Church) *Guildf 12* **P** *Ridley Hall Cam* **V** M F HERBERT, **C** J A HUGHMAN
WOKING (St John the Baptist) *Guildf 12* **P** *V Woking St Pet* **V** G P WILLIAMS, **C** P J PARTINGTON
WOKING (St Mary of Bethany) *Guildf 12* **P** *V Woking Ch Ch* **V** R DERBRIDGE, **Dss** A M HARRIS
WOKING (St Paul) *Guildf 12* **P** *Ridley Hall Cam* **V** S C PITTIS
WOKING (St Peter) *Guildf 12* **P** *Ch Soc Trust* **V** B J GRIMSTER
WOKINGHAM (All Saints) *Ox 16* **P** *Bp* **R** B C BAILEY, **Hon C** E R FIDDAMAN
WOKINGHAM (St Paul) *Ox 16* **P** *DBP* **P-in-c** R J STILLMAN, **C** P CHAPLIN, **NSM** R G HOLMES
WOKINGHAM (St Sebastian) *Ox 16* **P** *Bp* **V** D R BURDEN, **Hon C** A G POUNCE, **NSM** E C FUDGE
WOLBOROUGH (St Mary) w Newton Abbot *Ex 11* **P** *Earl of Devon* **P-in-c** A P G FRAMPTON-MORGAN, **NSM** A K CLARKE
WOLD (St Andrew) Walgrave w Hannington and Wold and Scaldwell *Pet*
WOLD-MARSH Group, The *Linc 8* **P** *Ld Chan (1 turn), Bp, D&C, and DBP (2 turns), and Duchy of Lanc (1 turn)* **P-in-c** M A PARSONS
WOLD NEWTON (All Saints) Binbrook Gp *Linc*

WOLD NEWTON (All Saints) Burton Fleming w Fordon, Grindale etc *York*

WOLDINGHAM (St Agatha) (St Paul) *S'wark 19* **P** *Bp*
P-in-c E B WOOD, **NSM** M C JOHNSON

WOLDS, NORTH Group *Linc 6* **P** *Bp, DBP, and D&C (jt)*
V *Vacant* Barnetby (01652) 688182

WOLFERLOW (St Andrew) Edvin Loach w Tedstone Delamere etc *Heref*

WOLFERTON (St Peter) Sandringham w W Newton and Appleton etc *Nor*

WOLFORD (St Michael and All Angels) w Burmington
Cov 9 **P** *Mert Coll Ox* **V** D C BROWN

WOLLASTON (St James) *Worc 12* **P** *Bp* **V** M J WILLOWS

WOLLASTON (St Mary) and Strixton *Pet 6* **P** *Bp*
V G S R COX

WOLLASTON, GREAT (All Saints) (St John the Baptist)
Heref 13 **P** *Bp* **P-in-c** C B BULL

WOLLATON (St Leonard) *S'well 14* **P** *Lord Middleton*
R D W S JAMES, **C** W D MILNER, **NSM** P D C BROWN

WOLLATON PARK (St Mary) *S'well 14* **P** *CPAS*
V G GREGORY, **C** P A WILLIAMS

WOLLESCOTE (St Andrew) *Worc 12* **P** *Bp*
V R A BROADBENT

WOLSINGHAM (St Mary and St Stephen) and Thornley
Dur 15 **P** *Bp* **R** R L WELSH

WOLSTANTON (St Margaret) *Lich 14* **P** *Bp*
TR K H MILLER, **TV** D M HARTLEY, G JOHNSON

WOLSTON (St Margaret) and Church Lawford *Cov 6*
P *DBP (2 turns), Bp (1 turn)* **V** P WATKINS,
C P A H SIMMONDS, **NSM** E M COWLEY

WOLVERCOTE (St Peter) w Summertown *Ox 7* **P** *Patr Bd*
TR A M GANN, **TV** D A E MICHAELS, **C** J M CONEY,
Hon **C** D S WIPPELL, **NSM** W L A PRYOR, G G WRIGHT

WOLVERHAMPTON Pond Lane (Mission Hall) Wolv St Luke *Lich*

WOLVERHAMPTON (St Andrew) *Lich 9* **P** *Bp*
V J L SMITH

WOLVERHAMPTON (St Chad) (St Mark's Centre)
(St Peter) *Lich 9* **P** *Patr Bd* **TR** J C B HALL-
MATTHEWS, **TV** K WILSON, D GHOSH, N POUNDE,
C D F TYNDALL, **NSM** R A COMMANDER

WOLVERHAMPTON (St John) *Lich 9* **P** *Bp*
P-in-c J R HOPCRAFT

WOLVERHAMPTON (St Jude) *Lich 9* **P** *CPAS*
V R E CARTER

WOLVERHAMPTON (St Luke) Blakenhall *Lich 9*
P *Trustees* **P-in-c** T G ANDERSON, **C** M A JONES

WOLVERHAMPTON (St Martin) Rough Hills *Lich*

WOLVERHAMPTON (St Matthew) *Lich 9* **P** *Baldwin Pugh
Trustees* **V** L P BEARD, **C** J C BRYAN

WOLVERHAMPTON (St Stephen) *Lich 9* **P** *Bp*
P-in-c J C OAKES, **C** G BUCKBY

WOLVERLEY (St John the Baptist) and Cookley *Worc 11*
P *D&C and Bp (jt)* **V** G SHILVOCK

WOLVERTON (Holy Trinity) (St George the Martyr)
Ox 25 **P** *Bp* **R** R G RHODES, **TV** J R HOLROYD

WOLVERTON (St Katherine) Baughurst, Ramsdell,
Wolverton w Ewhurst etc *Win*

WOLVERTON (St Mary the Virgin) w Norton Lindsey and
Langley *Cov 7* **P** *Bp* **R** *Vacant* Stratford-upon-Avon
(0789) 731278

WOLVEY (St John the Baptist) w Burton Hastings, Copston
Magna and Withybrook *Cov 5* **P** *Bp* **V** R J JAMES

WOLVISTON (St Peter) *Dur 16* **P** *D&C*
R G W R HARPER

WOMBOURNE (St Benedict) w Trysull and Bobbington
Lich 5 **P** *Patr Bd* **TV** W S FROST, C HUGHES

WOMBRIDGE (St Mary and St Leonard) *Lich 27*
V R W BAILEY

WOMBWELL (St Mary) *Sheff 12* **P** *Trin Coll Cam*
R E MITCHELL, **C** G S ROSE

WOMBWELL JUMP (St George) see above

WOMERSLEY (St Martin) and Kirk Smeaton *Wakef 11*
V *Vacant* Pontefract (01977) 620436

WONERSH (St John the Baptist) *Guildf 2* **P** *Selw Coll
Cam* **V** M K WILLIAMS, **C** P M C KETTLE,
NSM C V SOWTER

WONSTON (Holy Trinity) and Stoke Charity w Hunton
Win 13 **P** *Bp and D&C (jt)* **R** A JARDINE,
NSM R C CLARKSON

WONSTON, SOUTH (St Margaret) Wonston and Stoke
Charity w Hunton *Win*

WOOBURN (St Paul) *Ox 29* **P** *Bp* **V** R D S CAINK

WOOD DALLING (St Andrew) Reepham, Hackford w
Whitwell, Kerdiston etc *Nor*

WOOD DITTON (St Mary) w Saxon Street *Ely 4* **P** *Duke of
Sutherland* **V** A F HOMER

WOOD END (St Chad) *Cov 1* **P** *Ld Chan*
P-in-c M N A JONES

WOOD END (St Michael and All Angels) Baxterley w
Hurley and Wood End and Merevale etc *Birm*

WOOD GREEN (St Michael) w Bounds Green (St Gabriel)
(St Michael-at-Bowes) *Lon 19* **P** *Patr Bd*
TR J C BROADHURST, **TV** C J VIPERS, **C** J M W DAVIES

WOOD GREEN (St Paul) Wednesbury St Paul Wood Green
Lich

WOOD NORTON (All Saints) Twyford, Guist, Bintree,
Themelthorpe etc *Nor*

WOOD STREET (St Alban) Worplesdon *Guildf*

WOODBASTWICK (St Fabian and St Sebastian) Ranworth
w Panxworth and Woodbastwick *Nor*

WOODBERRY DOWN (St Olave) Stoke Newington St
Olave *Lon*

WOODBOROUGH (St Mary Magdalene) Swanborough
Sarum

WOODBOROUGH (St Swithun) *S'well 11* **P** *Bp*
V W G CALTHROP-OWEN

WOODBRIDGE (St John the Evangelist) *St E 7* **P** *Ch Patr
Trust* **P-in-c** R F WEBB

WOODBRIDGE (St Mary the Virgin) *St E 7* **P** *Bp*
R D J PITCHER, **C** J E WALLMAN

WOODBURY (Holy Cross) Axminster, Chardstock, Combe
Pyne and Rousdon *Ex*

WOODBURY (St Swithun) *Ex 1* **P** *D&C* **V** D J SHARE

WOODBURY SALTERTON (Holy Trinity) Clyst St Mary,
Clyst St George etc *Ex*

WOODCHESTER (St Mary) and Brimscombe *Glouc 8*
P *Simeon's Trustees* **R** D N GREEN

WOODCHURCH (All Saints) *Cant 10* **P** *Abp*
R S G FRANKLIN

WOODCHURCH (Holy Cross) *Ches 1* **P** *DBP*
R A D DEAN, **C** J D ADEY

WOODCOTE (St Leonard) Langtree *Ox*

WOODCOTE (St Peter) Lilleshall and Sheriffhales *Lich*

WOODCOTT (St James) St Mary Bourne and Woodcott *Win*

WOODDITTON (St Mary) Wood Ditton w Saxon Street *Ely*

WOODEATON (Holy Rood) Islip w Charlton on Otmoor,
Oddington, Noke etc *Ox*

WOODFORD (Christ Church) *Ches 12* **P** *Exors Lt-
Col Sir Walter Bromley-Davenport* **V** J H HALL

WOODFORD (St Barnabas) *Chelmsf 4* **P** *Bp* **V** A CROSS

WOODFORD (St Mary the Virgin) *Pet 10* **P** *DBP*
R *Vacant* Thrapston (01832) 732478

WOODFORD (St Mary w St Philip and St James)
Chelmsf 4 **P** *Bp* **R** S R BIRCHNALL

WOODFORD, SOUTH Hermon Hill (Holy
Trinity) Wanstead H Trin Hermon Hill *Chelmsf*

WOODFORD BRIDGE (St Paul) *Chelmsf 4*
P *R Woodford* **V** R C MATTHEWS, **NSM** I K MONKS

WOODFORD HALSE (St Mary the Virgin) w Eydon *Pet 1*
P *Ld Chan (2 turns), Bp (1 turn)* **V** J M COURTIE

WOODFORD VALLEY (All Saints) *Sarum 12* **P** *Bp*
V J L REYNOLDS

WOODFORD WELLS (All Saints) (St Andrew) *Chelmsf 4*
P *Trustees* **V** M J COLE, **C** L S RAYFIELD,
P G HARCOURT, **NSM** D J BLACKLEDGE

WOODGATE VALLEY Conventional District *Birm 2*
C-in-c E A H THOMAS

WOODGREEN (St Boniface) Hale w S Charford *Win*

WOODHALL (St James the Great) *Bradf 3* **P** *Bp*
V S BAILEY

WOODHALL, OLD Woodhall Spa Gp *Linc*

WOODHALL SPA Group *Linc 11* **P** *Bp and DBP (jt)*
R R I McMASTER

WOODHAM (All Saints) *Guildf 12* **P** *Bp*
V P G P FARRELL, **NSM** A J K MACKENZIE

WOODHAM (St Elizabeth of Hungary) Newton Aycliffe *Dur*

WOODHAM FERRERS (St Mary) and Bicknacre
Chelmsf 9 **P** *Lord Fitzwalter* **R** P R DOWMAN,
NSM M J COTTEE

WOODHAM FERRERS, SOUTH (Holy Trinity) (St Mary)
Chelmsf 9 **P** *Bp* **P-in-c** M L LANGAN, **C** K L HACKER
HUGHES

WOODHAM MORTIMER (St Margaret) w Hazeleigh
Chelmsf 11 **P** *Bp* **P-in-c** I D UNSTAN

WOODHAM WALTER (St Michael) *Chelmsf 11* **P** *Ch Soc
Trust* **R** *Vacant*

WOODHAY, EAST (St Martin) and Woolton Hill *Win 6*
P *Bp* **R** D J CARTER, **NSM** T E DOREY

WOODHAY, WEST (St Laurence) w Enborne, Hampstead
Marshall, Inkpen and Combe *Ox 14* **P** *Bp, D&C Windsor,
and J R Henderson Esq (jt)* **R** C C S NEILL,
C R J GODFREY

WOODHORN w Newbiggin *Newc 11* **P** *Bp* **V** J B HAY
WOODHOUSE (Christ Church) *Wakef 5* **P** *Bp*
   V S K M HENRY
WOODHOUSE (St Mark) and Wrangthorn *Ripon 7*
   P *DBP* **V** T G MUNRO, **C** H E MACE
WOODHOUSE (St Mary in the Elms) and Woodhouse Eaves
   Leic 7 **P** *DBP* **V** D M BUXTON
WOODHOUSE CLOSE (not known) Bishop Auckland
   Woodhouse Close CD *Dur*
WOODHOUSE EAVES (St Paul) Woodhouse and
   Woodhouse Eaves *Leic*
WOODHOUSE MILL (St James) Handsworth Woodhouse
   Sheff
WOODHOUSE PARK (Wm Temple Church) Wythenshawe
   Wm Temple Ch *Man*
WOODHOUSES (not known) Bardsley *Man*
WOODHOUSES (St John the Divine) Dunham Massey St
   Marg and St Mark *Ches*
WOODHURST (St John the Baptist) Bluntisham cum Earith
   w Colne and Woodhurst *Ely*
WOODINGDEAN (Holy Cross) *Chich 2* **P** *Bp* **TR** *Vacant*
   Brighton (01273) 681582
WOODKIRK (St Mary) W Ardsley *Wakef*
WOODLAND (St John the Baptist) Broadhempston,
   Woodland, Staverton etc *Ex*
WOODLAND (St John the Evangelist) Broughton and
   Duddon *Carl*
WOODLAND (St Mary) Lynesack *Dur*
WOODLANDS (All Saints) *Sheff 8* **P** *Bp* **V** M J GODFREY
WOODLANDS (Ascension) Cranborne w Boveridge,
   Edmondsham etc *Sarum*
WOODLANDS (Mission Chapel) W Meon and Warnford
   Portsm
WOODLANDS (St Katherine) *B & W 4* **P** *DBP*
   V J G PESCOD
WOODLANDS (St Mary) Kemsing w Woodlands *Roch*
WOODLANDS (St Stephen) Welford w Wickham and Gt
   Shefford, Boxford etc *Ox*
WOODLEIGH (St Mary the Virgin) and Loddiswell *Ex 14*
   P *D&C and MMCET (jt)* **C** R D WITHNELL
WOODLEY (St John the Evangelist) *Ox 15* **P** *DBP*
   TV P C ROBERTS, D R BYRNE, **C** C J VAN STRAATEN
WOODMANCOTE (Mission Church) Westbourne *Chich*
WOODMANCOTE (St James) Micheldever and E Stratton,
   Woodmancote etc *Win*
WOODMANCOTE (St Mark) Dursley *Glouc*
WOODMANCOTE (St Peter) Henfield w Shermanbury and
   Woodmancote *Chich*
WOODMANSEY (St Peter) Beverley Minster *York*
WOODMANSTERNE (St Peter) *S'wark 26* **P** *Ld Chan*
   R N A BARKER
WOODNESBOROUGH (St Mary the Blessed Virgin) w
   Worth and Staple *Cant 8* **P** *Abp* **V** E R ROUTH,
   Hon **C** D G WILLIS, **NSM** K I HAGGAR
WOODNEWTON (St Mary) Nassington w Yarwell and
   Woodnewton *Pet*
WOODPLUMPTON (St Anne) *Blackb 10* **P** *V St Michael's-*
   on-Wyre **P-in-c** I W FORBES
WOODRISING (St Nicholas) Hingham w Wood Rising w
   Scoulton *Nor*
WOODSETTS (St George) *Sheff 5* **P** *Bp* **V** P I RESON
WOODSFORD (St John the Baptist) Moreton and
   Woodsford w Tincleton *Sarum*
WOODSIDE (St Andrew) w East Hyde *St Alb 20* **P** *D&C*
   St Paul's **V** D R BOLSTER, **NSM** G N CRAPNELL
WOODSIDE (St James) *Ripon 7* **P** *Bp* **V** P Q TUDGE
WOODSIDE GREEN (St Andrew) Gt Hallingbury and Lt
   Hallingbury *Chelmsf*
WOODSIDE PARK (St Barnabas) *Lon 14* **P** *Ch Patr Trust*
   V J S H COLES, **C** G BOLAND
WOODSTOCK (St Mary Magdalene) Bladon w Woodstock
   Ox
WOODSTON (St Augustine of Canterbury) (Mission Church)
   Ely 13 **P** *Bp* **R** D G STEVENS
WOODTHORPE (St Mark) *S'well 11* **P** *Bp*
   V F W BRIDGER, **C** G R BOOTH, **NSM** R W BRIDGER
WOODTHORPE (St Peter) Staveley and Barrow Hill *Derby*
WOODTON (All Saints) Hempnall *Nor*
WOODVILLE (St Stephen) *Derby 16* **P** *Bp* **V** *Vacant*
   Burton-on-Trent (01283) 217278
WOOKEY (St Matthew) Coxley, Henton and Wookey *B & W*
WOOKEY HOLE (St Mary Magdalene) Wells St Cuth w
   Wookey Hole *B & W*
WOOL (Holy Rood) and East Stoke *Sarum 9* **P** *Bp (3 turns),*
   Keble Coll Ox (1 turn) **P-in-c** J P TOWNEND
WOOLACOMBE (St Sabinus) Ilfracombe, Lee,
   Woolacombe, Bittadon etc *Ex*

WOOLASTON (St Andrew) w Alvington and Aylburton
   Glouc 4 **P** *DBP and Ld Chan (by turn)* **R** L NEUDEGG,
   Hon **C** J M NEUDEGG
WOOLAVINGTON (Blessed Virgin Mary) w Cossington and
   Bawdrip *B & W 14* **P** *D&C Windsor and J A Church Esq*
   (alt) **V** N W STEEL
WOOLBEDING (All Hallows) *Chich 10* **P** *Cowdray Trust*
   R A T CUNNINGTON
WOOLBROOK (St Francis of Assisi) Sidmouth, Woolbrook,
   Salcombe Regis, Sidbury etc *Ex*
WOOLER (St Mary) Glendale Gp *Newc*
WOOLFARDISWORTHY (Holy Trinity) Parkham,
   Alwington, Buckland Brewer etc *Ex*
WOOLFARDISWORTHY EAST (St Mary) N Creedy *Ex*
WOOLFOLD (St James) *Man 10* **P** *R Bury St Mary*
   V *Vacant* 0161-764 6217
WOOLHAMPTON (St Peter) w Midgham and Beenham
   Valance *Ox 12* **P** *Bp, Keble Coll Ox, and CPAS (jt)*
   R *Vacant* Woolhampton (01734) 712264
WOOLHOPE (St George) Fownhope w Mordiford,
   Brockhampton etc *Heref*
WOOLLAND (not known) Hazelbury Bryan and the Hillside
   Par *Sarum*
WOOLLEY (All Saints) Bath St Sav w Swainswick and
   Woolley *B & W*
WOOLLEY (St Peter) *Wakef 9* **P** *Bp* **P-in-c** C OGLE
WOOLMER GREEN (St Michael) Welwyn w Ayot St Peter
   St Alb
WOOLPIT (Blessed Virgin Mary) w Drinkstone *St E 10*
   P *Bp and A Harvie-Clark Esq (alt)* **R** A G TAYLOR
WOOLSTASTON (St Michael and All Angels) Dorrington w
   Leebotwood, Longnor, Stapleton etc *Heref*
WOOLSTHORPE (St James) *Linc 19* **P** *Duke of Rutland*
   NSM S J HADLEY
WOOLSTON (Church of the Ascension) Padgate *Liv*
WOOLSTON (St Mark) *Win 12* **P** *Bp*
   V F P MATTHEWS, **NSM** A R BEVIS
WOOLSTONE (All Saints) Uffington, Shellingford,
   Woolstone and Baulking *Ox*
WOOLSTONE (not known) Woughton *Ox*
WOOLSTONE (St Martin) w Gotherington and Oxenton, and
   Kemerton *Glouc 9* **P** *DBP and Croome Estate*
   R J BUTLER
WOOLTON, MUCH (St Peter) *Liv 4* **P** *Bp*
   R J V ROBERTS, **C** J MARSDEN, T THOMAS
WOOLTON HILL (St Thomas) E Woodhay and Woolton
   Hill *Win*
WOOLVERSTONE (St Michael) Holbrook w Freston and
   Woolverstone *St E*
WOOLVERTON (St Lawrence) Rode Major *B & W*
WOOLWICH (St Mary and St Andrew) (St Michael and All
   Angels) *S'wark 1* **P** *Bp and Keble Coll Ox (jt)* **R** *Vacant*
   0181-854 2302 or 316 4338
WOOLWICH (St Thomas) *S'wark 1* **P** *Bp* **R** I M PAGE,
   Hon **C** J R W ACKLAND
WOOLWICH, NORTH (St John) w Silvertown *Chelmsf 3*
   P *Bp and Lon Corp (alt)* **P-in-c** R J A HAMER
WOONTON (Mission Room) Lyonshall w Titley, Almeley
   and Kinnersley *Heref*
WOORE (St Leonard) and Norton in Hales *Lich 23* **P** *Bp and*
   CPAS (jt) **P-in-c** P M JAMES
WOOSEHILL (Community Church) Bearwood *Ox*
WOOTTON Boars Hill (St Peter) *Ox 10* **P** *Bp*
   V P N CHALLENGER
WOOTTON (St Andrew) Ulceby Gp *Linc*
WOOTTON (St Edmund) *Portsm 8* **P** *DBP* **R** *Vacant* Isle
   of Wight (01983) 882213
WOOTTON (St George the Martyr) w Quinton and Preston
   Deanery *Pet 7* **P** *Ex Coll Ox and Bp (alt)* **R** D SCHOLEY
WOOTTON (St Martin) Elham w Denton and Wootton *Cant*
WOOTTON (St Mary the Virgin) *St Alb 19* **P** *MMCET*
   V C P STRONG, **NSM** R J ROBY
WOOTTON (St Mary) w Glympton and Kiddington *Ox 9*
   P *New Coll Ox (2 turns), Bp (1 turn), and Exors*
   E W Towler Esq (1 turn) **R** R J FARMAN,
   Hon Par Dn R FARMAN
WOOTTON, NORTH (All Saints) w SOUTH (St Mary)
   Nor 21 **P** *Ld Chan and G Howard Esq (alt)*
   R B R OAKE, **C** R L N HARRISON
WOOTTON, NORTH (St Peter) Pilton w Croscombe, N
   Wootton and Dinder *B & W*
WOOTTON BASSETT (St Bartholomew and All Saints)
   Sarum 18 **P** *DBP* **V** B J GARRATT
WOOTTON BRIDGE (St Mark) Wootton *Portsm*
WOOTTON COURTENAY (All Saints) Selworthy,
   Timberscombe, Wootton Courtenay etc *B & W*
WOOTTON FITZPAINE (not known) Marshwood Vale TM
   Sarum

WOOTTON RIVERS (St Andrew) Pewsey TM *Sarum*

WOOTTON ST LAWRENCE (St Lawrence) Church Oakley and Wootton St Lawrence *Win*

WOOTTON WAWEN (St Peter) *Cov 7* **P** *K Coll Cam* **P-in-c** L G MORTIMER

WORCESTER (St Andrew and All Saints w St Helen) Worc City St Paul and Old St Martin etc *Worc*

WORCESTER (St Barnabas) (Christ Church) *Worc 6* **P** *Bp* **TR** R G JONES, **TV** M J ROGERS, **C** C J SELBY

WORCESTER (St Clement) *Worc 6* **P** *D&C* **R** D A CHAPLIN

WORCESTER (St George w St Mary Magdalene) *Worc 6* **P** *Bp and V Claines (jt)* **V** S LOWE

WORCESTER (St John in Bedwardine) St Jo in Bedwardine *Worc*

WORCESTER (St Martin in the Cornmarket) Worc City St Paul and Old St Martin etc *Worc*

WORCESTER (St Michael) *Worc 3* **P** *Bp* **V** P R HOLZAPFEL

WORCESTER (St Stephen) Barbourne *Worc*

WORCESTER (St Wulstan) *Worc 6* **P** *Bp* **V** M J STRANGE, **Hon C** J W BAINBRIDGE

WORCESTER (St Wulstan) Warndon St Nic *Worc*

WORCESTER CITY (St Paul) (Old St Martin w St Swithun) (St Nicholas and All Saints) *Worc 6* **P** *Bp and D&C (jt)* **R** P D A COLLINS, **NSM** A M WHERRY

WORCESTER SOUTH EAST (St Martin w St Peter) (St Mark in the Cherry Orchard) (Holy Trinity w St Matthew) *Worc 6* **P** *Patr Bd* **TR** M A O LEWIS, **TV** N M WRIGHT, A J HAWKER, P E JONES, **NSM** S M SHARPLES

WORDSLEY (Holy Trinity) *Worc 10* **P** *Patr Bd* **TR** W M SMITH, **TV** R N LATHAM, D A PICKEN, **C** B J RUMBOLD, **NSM** G HODGSON

WORFIELD (St Peter) *Heref 9* **P** *J R S Greenshields Esq* **V** *Vacant* Worfield (01746) 716698

WORKINGTON (St John) *Carl 7* **P** *R Workington* **V** J M COOK

WORKINGTON (St Michael) *Carl 7* **P** *Exors E S C Curwen Esq* **R** T H M SAMPSON, **TV** H BROWN

WORKSOP (St Anne) *S'well 6* **P** *Bp* **V** F T BEECH

WORKSOP (St John the Evangelist) *S'well 6* **P** *CPAS* **V** G E JONES, **C** A R HUMPHRIES

WORKSOP (St Paul) *S'well 6* **P** *Bp* **V** *Vacant* Worksop (01909) 473289

WORKSOP PRIORY (St Mary and St Cuthbert) *S'well 6* **P** *St Steph Ho Ox* **V** A R WAGSTAFF, **C** K SMITH

WORLABY (St Clement) *Linc 6* **P** *DBP* **V** *Vacant* Saxby All SS 708

WORLDHAM, EAST (St Mary the Virgin) and WEST (St Nicholas), Hartley Mauditt w Kingsley and Oakhanger *Win 2* **P** *D&C and Bp (alt)* **V** P BRADFORD

WORLE (St Martin) (St Mark's Church Centre) *B & W 11* **P** *Ld Chan* **TR** N KENT, **TV** S S WILKINS, **C** P W TULLETT

WORLESTON (St Oswald) Acton and Worleston, Church Minshull and Wettenhall *Ches*

WORLINGHAM (All Saints) w Barnby and North Cove *St E 14* **P** *Ld Chan* **R** A A B JONES

WORLINGTON (All Saints) Mildenhall *St E*

WORLINGTON, EAST (St Mary) Witheridge, Thelbridge, Creacombe, Meshaw etc *Ex*

WORLINGTON, WEST (St Mary) as above

WORLINGWORTH (St Mary) w Southolt, Tannington, Bedfield and Monk Soham *St E 17* **P** *Lord Henniker, R C Rous Esq and Bp, and DBP (by turn)* **R** J D B MINCHER

WORMBRIDGE (St Peter) Ewyas Harold w Dulas, Kenderchurch etc *Heref*

WORMEGAY (St Michael and All Angels and Holy Cross) Tottenhill w Wormegay *Ely*

WORMHILL (St Margaret) and Peak Forest w Peak Dale and Dove Holes *Derby 4* **P** *Bp and Duke of Devonshire (jt)* **V** O J POST

WORMINGFORD (St Andrew), Mount Bures and Little Horkesley *Chelmsf 18* **P** *J J Tufnell Esq, Mrs F Reynolds, and Keble Coll Ox (jt)* **V** *Vacant* Bures (01787) 227398

WORMINGHALL (St Peter and St Paul) w Ickford, Oakley and Shabbington *Ox 21* **P** *Bp and Guild of All So (jt)* **NSM** E A MASON

WORMINGTON (St Katharine) Alderton, Gt Washbourne, Dumbleton etc *Glouc*

WORMLEIGHTON (St Peter) Priors Hardwick, Priors Marston and Wormleighton *Cov*

WORMLEY (Church Room) Broxbourne w Wormley *St Alb*

WORMLEY (St Laurence) as above

WORMSHILL (St Giles) Bredgar w Bicknor and Frinsted w Wormshill etc *Cant*

WORPLESDON (St Mary the Virgin) *Guildf 5* **P** *Eton Coll* **R** R P ROBINS, **C** H M WOODHEAD, **NSM** J BUSBY

WORSALL, HIGH AND LOW (All Saints) *York 22* **P** *Abp (3 turns), V Northallerton (1 turn)* **V** D MOORE

WORSBROUGH (St Mary) *Sheff 7* **P** *DBP* **V** *Vacant* Barnsley (01226) 203113

WORSBROUGH (St Thomas) (St James) *Sheff 7* **P** *Bp and The Crown (alt)* **V** D C GAY

WORSBROUGH COMMON (St Luke) *Sheff 7* **P** *Bp* **V** J TRICKETT

WORSLEY (St Mark) *Man 2* **P** *Bp* **TR** M R AINSWORTH, **TV** S D A KILLWICK

WORSLEY MESNES (not known) Wigan St Jas w St Thos *Liv*

WORSTEAD (St Mary), Westwick, Sloley, Swanton Abbot and Scottow *Nor 12* **P** *DBP, J T D Shaw Esq, D&C, and Bp (by turn)* **R** A R LONG

WORSTHORNE (St John the Evangelist) *Blackb 3* **P** *Trustees* **P-in-c** L LAYCOCK

WORTH (St Nicholas) *Chich 7* **P** *DBP* **TR** A PIPER, **TV** S W BARNES

WORTH (St Peter and St Paul) Woodnesborough w Worth and Staple *Cant*

WORTH MATRAVERS (St Aldhelm) Kingston, Langton Matravers and Worth Matravers *Sarum*

WORTH MATRAVERS (St Nicholas) as above

WORTHAM (St Mary the Virgin) N Hartismere *St E*

WORTHEN (All Saints) *Heref 13* **P** *New Coll Ox (8 turns), J J C Coldwell Esq (1 turn), I Chirbury (1 turn)* **R** N D MINSHALL

WORTHING Christ the King (Christ Church) (Holy Trinity) (St Matthew) (St Paul) *Chich 5* **P** *Patr Bd* **TR** G G GUINNESS, **TV** J A WILKINSON, V H J GILLETT, **C** P H SUDELL, **NSM** M E PARGETER

WORTHING (St Andrew) *Chich 5* **P** *Keble Coll Ox* **V** E J R CHOWN, **Hon C** E G OGDEN

WORTHING (St George) (Emmanuel) *Chich 5* **P** *Ch Soc Trust* **V** D E A MARROW

WORTHING (St Margaret) N Elmham w Billingford and Worthing *Nor*

WORTHING, WEST (St John the Divine) *Chich 5* **P** *Bp* **V** K WOOD

WORTHINGTON (St Matthew) Breedon cum Isley Walton and Worthington *Leic*

WORTING (St Thomas of Canterbury) *Win 4* **P** *MMCET* **R** C J M VAUGHAN

WORTLEY (St Leonard) w Thurgoland *Sheff 7* **P** *Dowager Countess of Wharncliffe and V Silkstone (jt)* **V** D WARNER

WORTLEY, NEW (St Mary's Parish Centre) St Bart Armley w St Mary New Wortley *Ripon*

WORTLEY DE LEEDS (St John the Evangelist) *Ripon 6* **P** *Trustees* **V** T G WARR

WORTON (Christ Church) Potterne w Worton and Marston *Sarum*

WORTON, NETHER (St James) Over w Nether Worton *Ox*

WORTON, OVER (Holy Trinity) w Nether Worton *Ox 5* **P** *Exors J B Schuster Esq* **R** *Vacant*

WOTTON (St John the Evangelist) and Holmbury St Mary *Guildf 7* **P** *Bp and J P M H Evelyn Esq (jt)* **R** P R FLEMING

WOTTON ST MARY WITHOUT (Holy Trinity) *Glouc 5* **P** *Bp* **V** P M NUNN, **NSM** A J FITCH

WOTTON-UNDER-EDGE (St Mary the Virgin) w Ozleworth and North Nibley *Glouc 2* **P** *Ch Ch Ox* **V** J A C MAY, **C** D M SHAW, **NSM** E M CHAPPELL

WOTTON UNDERWOOD (All Saints) Ludgershall w Wotton Underwood and Ashendon *Ox*

WOUGHTON *Ox 25* **P** *Patr Bd* **TR** F J BEVERIDGE, **TV** M A HOUSTON, **C** M J KIPPAX, **NSM** D J RUDIGER

WOUGHTON-ON-THE-GREEN (St Mary) Woughton *Ox*

WOULDHAM (All Saints) Burham and Wouldham *Roch*

WRABNESS (All Saints) Ramsey w Lt Oakley and Wrabness *Chelmsf*

WRAGBY (All Saints) *Linc 11* **P-in-c** P A McCULLOCK

WRAGBY (St Michael and Our Lady) Kinsley w Wragby *Wakef*

WRAMPLINGHAM (St Peter and St Paul) Barnham Broom *Nor*

WRANGBROOK (St Michael) Badsworth *Wakef*

WRANGLE (St Mary and St Nicholas) Old Leake w Wrangle *Linc*

WRANGTHORN (St Augustine of Hippo) Woodhouse and Wrangthorn *Ripon*

WRATTING, GREAT (St Mary) Haverhill w Withersfield, the Wrattings etc *St E*

YALDING

WRATTING, LITTLE (St Mary) as above
WRATTING, WEST (St Andrew) *Ely 4* **P** *D&C*
  NSM L R WICKHAM
WRAWBY (St Mary the Virgin) *Linc 6* **P** *Bp* **V** *Vacant*
  Brigg (01652) 657605
WRAXALL (All Saints) *B & W 13* **P** *Trustees*
  P-in-c A E PAYNE
WRAXALL (St Mary) Melbury *Sarum*
WRAXALL, NORTH (St James) Colerne w N Wraxall *Bris*
WRAXALL, SOUTH (St James) Monkton Farleigh, S
  Wraxall and Winsley *Sarum*
WRAY (Holy Trinity) w Tatham and Tatham Fells *Blackb 15*
  P *Bp, Trustees and PCCs (jt)* **V** R F JACKSON
WRAY, LOW (St Margaret) Hawkshead and Low Wray w
  Sawrey *Carl*
WRAYSBURY (St Andrew) Riverside *Ox*
WREAKE, UPPER *Leic 3* **P** *Bp and DBP (jt)*
  V G L SPENCER, **NSM** S T W GEARY
WREAY (St Mary) *Carl 3* **P** *D&C* **P-in-c** P KYBIRD,
  NSM H J CARTER
WRECCLESHAM (St Peter) *Guildf 3* **P** *Bp*
  V P H C DICKENS
WRENBURY (St Margaret) Baddiley and Wrenbury w
  Burleydam *Ches*
WRENINGHAM (All Saints) *Nor 7* **P** *Ld Chan (1 turn),*
  Patr Bd (4 turns) **TV** S G STEPHENSON,
  P-in-c J W STUBENBORD
WRENTHAM (St Nicholas) w Benacre, Covehithe, Frostenden,
  South Cove and Henstead *St E 15* **P** *Sir John Gooch, Bt*
  R C E HALLIWELL
WRENTHORPE (St Anne) *Wakef 12* **P** *Bp*
  V J K BUTTERWORTH
WRESSLE (St John of Beverly) Howden TM *York*
WRESTLINGWORTH (St Peter) Dunton w Wrestlingworth
  and Eyeworth *St Alb*
WRETHAM (St Ethelbert) Hockham w Shropham Gp of Par
  Nor
WRETTON (All Saints) Stoke Ferry w Wretton *Ely*
WRIBBENHALL (All Saints) *Worc 11* **P** *V Kidderminster*
  P-in-c H HUGHES
WRIGHTINGTON (St James the Great) *Blackb 4* **P** *Bp*
  V R TOWNLEY
WRINGTON (All Saints) w Butcombe *B & W 11* **P** *SMF*
  R N A HECTOR
WRITTLE (All Saints) w Highwood *Chelmsf 8*
  P *New Coll Ox* **V** R P LANE
WROCKWARDINE (St Peter) Longdon-upon-Tern,
  Rodington, Uppington etc *Lich*
WROCKWARDINE WOOD (Holy Trinity) *Lich 27* **P** *Bp*
  P-in-c C M CASE
WROOT (St Pancras) Epworth and Wroot *Linc*
WROSE (St Cuthbert) *Bradf 3* **P** *The Crown* **V** P N AYERS
WROTHAM (St George) *Roch 9* **P** *D&C* **R** *Vacant*
  Borough Green (01732) 882211
WROUGHTON (St John the Baptist) *Bris 13* **P** *Bp*
  R M A JOHNSON, **C** S A BULL
WROXALL (St John the Evangelist) *Portsm 7* **P** *Bp*
  V A TEDMAN
WROXALL (St Leonard) Hatton w Haseley, Rowington w
  Lowsonford etc *Cov*
WROXETER (St Mary) Buildwas and Leighton w Eaton
  Constantine etc *Lich*
WROXHAM (St Mary) w Hoveton St John w Hoveton St Peter
  and Belaugh *Nor 12* **P** *Bp* **R** A D PARSONS
WROXTON (All Saints) Broughton w N Newington and
  Shutford etc *Ox*
WYBERTON (St Leodegar) *Linc 21* **P** *DBP*
  R R H IRESON
WYBUNBURY (St Chad) w Doddington (St John) *Ches 15*
  P *Bp and Sir Evelyn Broughton, Bt (jt)* **V** P A CAMPBELL
WYCH, HIGH (St James) and Gilston w Eastwick *St Alb 4*
  P *V Sawbridgeworth (2 turns), P T S Bowlby Esq (1 turn)*
  R D C CLARKE
WYCHBOLD (St Mary de Wyche) Stoke Prior, Wychbold
  and Upton Warren *Worc*
WYCHE (All Saints) Lt Malvern, Malvern Wells and Wyche
  Worc
WYCHLING (St Margaret) Doddington, Newnham and
  Wychling *Cant*
WYCHNOR (St Leonard) *Lich 1* **P** *Personal Reps*
  W H Harrison Esq **V** S J MORRIS
WYCK RISSINGTON (St Laurence) The Rissingtons *Glouc*
WYCLIFFE (St Mary) Barningham w Hutton Magna and
  Wycliffe *Ripon*
WYCOMBE, HIGH (All Saints) (St Peter) *Ox 29*
  P *Patr Bd* **TR** F D HILLEBRAND, **TV** D J ROBERTSON,
  M H ATKINSON, L E PEPPER, R R J LAPWOOD,
  C J M WILKINSON, M J FULLER, S C WILLIAMS,

C E WILSON, B I de la T HARTLESS, **NSM** P VINEY,
M J PRAGNELL, C J WILLIAMS, V J BEAUMONT,
M H CLEMENTS
WYCOMBE, WEST (St Laurence) (St Paul) w Bledlow Ridge,
  Bradenham and Radnage *Ox 29* **P** *Bp, DBP, Peache*
  Trustees, and Sir Francis Dashwood (jt) **C** M J GILLHAM
  D B FOSTER, P A GILLHAM, E M DYKE,
  NSM A C WOODS
WYCOMBE AND CHADWELL (St Mary) Scalford w
  Goadby Marwood and Wycombe etc *Leic*
WYCOMBE LANE (St Mary) Wooburn *Ox*
WYCOMBE MARSH (St Anne) High Wycombe *Ox*
WYDDIAL (St Giles) Hormead, Wyddial, Anstey, Brent
  Pelham etc *St Alb*
WYE (St Gregory and St Martin) w Brook *Cant 2* **P** *Abp*
  P-in-c D STUART-SMITH
WYE, SOUTH Team Ministry *Heref* St Martin w St Fran (S
  Wye TM) *Heref*
WYESHAM (St James) Dixton *Heref*
WYFORDBY (St Mary) Waltham on the Wolds, Stonesby,
  Saxby etc *Leic*
WYKE *Win* St Matt *Win*
WYKE (Holy Trinity) Bruton and Distr *B & W*
WYKE (St Mark) *Guildf 5* **P** *Bp* **V** A W A KNOWLES
WYKE (St Mary the Virgin) *Bradf 2* **P** *Bp*
  P-in-c G H COLES, **C** P M HOLLINGS
WYKE REGIS (All Saints) *Sarum 5* **P** *D&C* **R** K A HUGO
WYKEHAM (All Saints) and Hutton Buscel *York 21*
  P *Viscount Downe and Sir Stephen Hastings (alt)*
  V E RICHARDS
WYKEHAM (St Nicholas) Wickham *Portsm*
WYKEN (Church of Risen Christ) Cov Caludon *Cov*
WYKEN (Holy Cross) as above
WYKEN (St Mary Magdalene) as above
WYLAM (St Oswin) *Newc 3* **P** *Bp* **V** R K BRYANT
WYLDE GREEN (Emmanuel) *Birm 9* **P** *Bp*
  V H J PITCHFORD
WYLYE (St Mary the Virgin) Yarnbury *Sarum*
WYMERING (St Peter and St Paul) Widley w Wymering
  Portsm
WYMESWOLD (St Mary) and Prestwold w Hoton *Leic 7*
  P *S J Packe-Drury-Lowe Esq and Bp (by turn)*
  V L ROBINSON
WYMINGTON (St Lawrence) w Podington *St Alb 21*
  P *R M Orlebar Esq (1 turn), DBP (3 turns)*
  R A R H WOODWARD
WYMONDHAM (St Mary and St Thomas) *Nor 7* **P** *Bp*
  V B L GANT, **C** S N WAKELY
WYMONDHAM (St Peter) w Edmondthorpe, Buckminster w
  Sewstern, Coston and Garthorpe *Leic 3* **P** *Ld Chan and*
  Sir Lyonel Tollemache, Bt (alt) **R** A R THREADGILL
WYMONDLEY, GREAT (St Mary the Virgin) and LITTLE
  (St Mary the Virgin) w Graveley and Chivesfield *St Alb 9*
  P *Bp and MMCET (jt)* **R** P J MADDEX
WYMYNSWOLD (St Margaret) Nonington w Wymynswold
  and Goodnestone etc *Cant*
WYNYARD PARK (Chapel) Grindon and Stillington *Dur*
WYRE PIDDLE (not known) Fladbury, Wyre Piddle and
  Moor *Worc*
WYRESDALE, OVER (Christ Church) *Blackb 12* **P** *Bp*
  V *Vacant* Lancaster (01524) 792393
WYRLEY, GREAT (St Mark) *Lich 3* **P** *R Cannock*
  V A F CREBER, **C** R BIDDLE
WYSALL (Holy Trinity) Willoughby-on-the-Wolds w Wysall
  and Widmerpool *S'well*
WYTHALL *Birm 4* **P** *R Kings Norton* **V** P M THOMSON
WYTHAM (All Saints) N Hinksey and Wytham *Ox*
WYTHBURN (not known) St Johns-in-the-Vale w Wythburn
  Carl
WYTHENSHAWE Lawton Moor (St Michael and All
  Angels) Lawton Moor *Man*
WYTHENSHAWE (St Martin) *Man 8* **P** *Bp*
  V P J DINES, **C** S G TALBOT
WYTHENSHAWE (St Richard of Chichester) *Man 8* **P** *Bp*
  V G A LAWSON
WYTHENSHAWE (William Temple Church) *Man 8* **P** *Bp*
  V H B EALES, **C** A PILKINGTON
WYTHER (Venerable Bede) *Ripon 6* **P** *Bp* **V** V E JOHNSON
WYTHOP (St Margaret) Cockermouth w Embleton and
  Wythop *Carl*
WYVERSTONE (St George) Bacton w Wyverstone and
  Cotton *St E*
WYVILL (St Catherine) Harlaxton *Linc*
YAFFORTH (All Saints) Ainderby Steeple w Yafforth and
  Kirby Wiske etc *Ripon*
YALDING (St Peter and St Paul) w Collier Street *Roch 7*
  P *Ld Chan* **V** J G K BATSON

YANWORTH (St Michael) Chedworth, Yanworth and Stowell, Coln Rogers etc *Glouc*
YAPHAM (St Martin) Barmby Moor w Allerthorpe, Fangfoss and Yapham *York*
YAPTON (St Mary) Clymping and Yapton w Ford *Chich*
YARCOMBE (St John the Baptist), Membury, Upottery and Cotleigh *Ex 5* **P** *The Crown (1 turn), Bp and D&C (1 turn)* **V** A J STONE
YARDLEY (St Cyprian) Hay Mill *Birm 10* **P** *Bp* **V** R E CHAMBERLAIN, **NSM** M ALDERSON
YARDLEY (St Edburgha) *Birm 10* **P** *St Pet Coll Ox* **V** F S COLLINS, **C** M R DORSETT, M E LEIGH
YARDLEY (St Lawrence) Ardeley *St Alb*
YARDLEY, SOUTH (St Michael and All Angels) *Birm 10* **P** *Bp* **V** K PUNSHON, **NSM** G R PIKE
YARDLEY GOBION (St Leonard) Potterspury, Furtho, Yardley Gobion and Cosgrove *Pet*
YARDLEY HASTINGS (St Andrew), Denton and Grendon w Castle Ashby *Pet 7* **P** *Bp and Marquess of Northn (alt)* **R** M R RYALL
YARDLEY WOOD (Christ Church) *Birm 8* **P** *Bp* **V** *Vacant* Birmingham (0121) 475 8329
YARKHILL (St John the Baptist) Tarrington w Stoke Edith, Aylton, Pixley etc *Heref*
YARLINGTON (Blessed Virgin Mary) Camelot Par *B & W*
YARM (St Mary Magdalene) *York 22* **P** *Abp* **R** D W SMITH, **NSM** P W ELLIOTT, M LOCKEY
YARMOUTH (St James) *Portsm 8* **P** *Keble Coll Ox* **R** *Vacant*
YARMOUTH, GREAT (St James) (St John) (St Nicholas) (St Paul) (St Luke) (St Mary) *Nor 6* **P** *Patr Bd* **TR** M S WOODS, **TV** M MAKOWER, P HUCKLE, **C** G M JESSOP, P T S KERLEY
YARNBURY *Sarum 16* **P** *Bp, CCC Ox, and D&C (by turn)* **R** B THOMAS
YARNFIELD (Mission Room St Barnabas) Swynnerton and Tittensor *Lich*
YARNSCOMBE (St Andrew) Newton Tracey, Alverdiscott, Huntshaw etc *Ex*
YARNTON (St Bartholomew) w Begbroke and Shipton on Cherwell *Ox 9* **P** *BNC Ox, Duke of Marlborough, and C Wolfson Trust (jt)* **R** E CRAIG
YARPOLE (St Leonard) Eye, Croft w Yarpole and Lucton *Heref*
YARWELL (St Mary Magdalene) Nassington w Yarwell and Woodnewton *Pet*
YATE New Town (St Mary) *Bris 7* **P** *Bp* **TR** C D SUTCH, **TV** D G BAINBRIDGE, K B JONES, **C** M CLACKER
YATELEY (St Peter) *Win 5* **P** *Bp* **V** N D BEAMER, **C** D J CHILLMAN, P FINDLEY, **NSM** B R LILLINGTON
YATESBURY (All Saints) Oldbury *Sarum*
YATTENDON (St Peter and St Paul) Hermitage and Hampstead Norreys, Cold Ash etc *Ox*
YATTON (All Saints) Much Marcle *Heref*
YATTON KEYNELL (St Margaret) *Bris 9* **P** *Bp* **P-in-c** J N A BRADBURY, **C** R V C LEWIS, **Hon C** G H EDWARDS
YATTON MOOR (Blessed Virgin Mary) *B & W 13* **P** *DBF* **TR** J L RUFFLE, **TV** J J CRUSE, C M HORSEMAN, **NSM** A J GAUNT (nee COTTELL)
YAVERLAND (St John the Baptist) Brading w Yaverland *Portsm*
YAXHAM (St Peter) Mattishall w Mattishall Burgh, Welborne etc *Nor*
YAXLEY (St Mary the Virgin) Eye w Braiseworth and Yaxley *St E*
YAXLEY (St Peter) *Ely 13* **P** *Ld Chan* **P-in-c** T J HEGGS, **NSM** G LIMBRICK
YEADON (St Andrew) *Bradf 4* **P** *Bp* **V** K C POTTER
YEADON (St John the Evangelist) *Bradf 4* **P** *R Guiseley w Esholt* **V** J F N ROBINSON
YEALMPTON (St Bartholomew) and Brixton *Ex 21* **P** *D&C Windsor and Bp (jt)* **V** M A WILKINSON
YEARSLEY (Holy Trinity) Crayke w Brandsby and Yearsley *York*
YEAVELEY (Holy Trinity) Alkmonton, Cubley, Marston, Montgomery etc *Derby*

YEDINGHAM (St John the Baptist) Sherburn and W and E Heslerton w Yedingham *York*
YELDEN (St Mary) The Stodden Churches *St Alb*
YELDHAM, GREAT (St Andrew) w LITTLE (St John the Baptist) *Chelmsf 15* **P** *Bp and Ld Chan (alt)* **P-in-c** J M SUDDARDS
YELFORD (St Nicholas and St Swithin) Lower Windrush *Ox*
YELLING (Holy Cross) Graveley w Papworth St Agnes w Yelling etc *Ely*
YELVERTOFT (All Saints) Crick and Yelvertoft w Clay Coton and Lilbourne *Pet*
YELVERTON (St Mary) Thurton *Nor*
YELVERTON (St Paul), Meavy, Sheepstor and Walkhampton *Ex 25* **P** *Patr Bd* **TR** R H TEBBS, **TV** M J LEVERTON, **NSM** J W M WEIR, M SALMON, N S SHUTT
YEOFORD CHAPEL (Holy Trinity) Crediton and Shobrooke *Ex*
YEOVIL (Holy Trinity) *B & W 7* **P** *The Crown* **V** J D BENNETT
YEOVIL (St Andrew) (St John the Baptist) w Kingston Pitney *B & W 7* **P** *Mrs S W Rawlins (3 turns), DBP (1 turn)* **C** H F THOMAS
YEOVIL (St Michael and All Angels) *B & W 7* **P** *Bp* **V** M D ELLIS, **C** N P A PNEMATICATOS
YEOVIL (St Peter) Preston Plucknett *B & W*
YEOVIL MARSH (All Saints) Tintinhull w Chilthorne Domer, Yeovil Marsh etc *B & W*
YETMINSTER (St Andrew) w Ryme Intrinseca and High Stoy *Sarum 4* **P** *Duchy of Cornwall (1 turn), Bp (3 turns)* **P-in-c** S R BATTY
YIEWSLEY (St Matthew) *Lon 24* **P** *V Hillingdon* **P-in-c** C R GOWER, **NSM** J CALDWELL
YOCKLETON (Holy Trinity) *Heref 13* **P** *Bp* **P-in-c** C B BULL
YORK Acomb (St Aidan) Acomb St Steph *York*
YORK (All Saints) Huntington *York*
YORK (All Saints) North Street *York 8* **P** *D&C* **P-in-c** E E S JONES
YORK (All Saints) Pavement w St Crux (St Martin) (St Helen) (St Denys) *York 8* **P** *Abp* **TR** D M PORTER, **TV** J A CORKER
YORK (Christ Church) Heworth *York*
YORK (Holy Trinity) as above
YORK (St Barnabas) *York 8* **P** *CPAS* **P-in-c** S R STANLEY
YORK (St Chad) *York 8* **P** *Abp* **V** D B EMMOTT
YORK (St Clement w St Mary) Bishophill Senior *York 8* **P** *Abp* **R** E E S JONES
YORK (St Edward the Confessor) Dringhouses *York*
YORK (St Hilda) *York 8* **P** *Abp* **V** C J MORGAN
YORK (St Lawrence w St Nicholas) *York 8* **P** *D&C* **V** P S THORNTON
YORK (St Luke) *York 8* **P** *Abp* **V** J McGRATH, **NSM** C W ANKERS, P J CUNNINGHAM
YORK (St Martin-cum-Gregory) Micklegate H Trin and Bishophill Junior St Mary *York*
YORK (St Mary) as above
YORK (St Michael-le-Belfrey) (St Cuthbert) *York 8* **P** *Abp* **V** D P WHITE, **NSM** W J ROBERTS
YORK (St Olave w St Giles) *York 8* **P** *Abp* **V** A C HODGE, **NSM** J L WAUGH
YORK (St Oswald) Fulford *York*
YORK (St Paul) Holgate Road *York 8* **P** *CPAS* **R** D R WOOLDRIDGE, **C** B HERITAGE, **NSM** K BURNETT-HALL
YORK (St Philip and St James) Clifton *York*
YORK (St Thomas w St Maurice) *York 8* **P** *Abp* **V** P WORDSWORTH
YORK (St Wulstan) Heworth *York*
YORKLEY, LOWER (St Luke's Church Centre) Dean Forest St Paul *Glouc*
YOULGREAVE (All Saints), Middleton, Stanton-in-Peak and Birchover *Derby 2* **P** *Duke of Devonshire and N B B Davie-Thornhill Esq (jt)* **V** R TAYLOR
YOXALL (St Peter) *Lich 1* **P** *Bp* **R** *Vacant* Yoxall (01543) 472528
YOXFORD (St Peter) and Peasenhall w Sibton *St E 19* **P** *Bp, Exors Lt Col J A Brooke and CPAS (jt) (alt)* **V** *Vacant* Yoxford (0172877) 712
ZEAL, SOUTH (St Mary) S Tawton and Belstone *Ex*
ZEAL MONACHORUM (St Peter) *Ex 2* **P** *DBP* **R** J C HALL, **Hon C** G SAUNDERS
ZEALS (St Martin) Upper Stour *Sarum*
ZENNOR (St Senera) *Truro 5* **P** *Bp* **P-in-c** S W MIDDLETON-DANSKY

CENTRAL LONDON CHURCHES

An index of parochial churches in central London postal districts. For details of clergy, patronage and deaneries consult the combined English benefice and church index. City and Guild churches are indexed together under London City and Guild respectively, in the preceding index.

Details of cathedrals and those extra-parochial churches and chapels which are Royal Peculiars, can be found in the relevant indexes.

E1 - Tower Hamlets
LONDON DOCKS Wapping Lane (St Peter)
SHADWELL The Highway (St Paul)
SPITALFIELDS Commercial Street (Christ Church w All Saints)
STEPNEY (St Dunstan and All Saints)
STEPNEY Cable Street (St Mary)
STEPNEY Canon Street Road (St George-in-the-East)
STEPNEY Dock Street (St Paul)

EC1 - City: North-West
CITY Holborn Viaduct (St Sepulchre without Newgate)
CITY Smithfield Gate (St Bartholomew the Less)
CITY West Smithfield (St Bartholomew the Great)
CLERKENWELL Clerkenwell Green (St James and St John)
CLERKENWELL Exmouth Market (Holy Redeemer)
FINSBURY King Square (St Clement)
HOLBORN Brooke Street (St Alban the Martyr)
MYDDELTON SQUARE (St Mark)

EC2 - City: North-East
CITY Coleman Street Lothbury (St Margaret)
CITY Fore Street Cripplegate (St Giles)
CITY Foster Lane (St Vedast)
CITY Soper Lane (St Mary le Bow)
CITY (St Botolph without Bishopgate)
GUILD Bow Lane (St Mary Aldermary)
GUILD Gresham Street (St Lawrence Jewry)
GUILD London Wall (All Hallows)
GUILD St Martin-le-Grand (St Botolph without Aldersgate)

EC3 - City: East
CITY Aldgate (St Botolph)
CITY Berkynchirche-by-the-Tower Byward Street (All Hallows)
CITY Bishopsgate (St Andrew Undershaft)
CITY Bishopsgate (St Helen)
CITY Clement's Lane Eastcheap (St Clement)
CITY Cornhill (St Michael)
CITY Cornhill (St Peter)
CITY Eastcheap (St Mary at Hill)
CITY Hart Street (St Olave)
CITY Lombard Street (St Edmund the King and Martyr)
CITY Lombard Street (St Mary Woolnoth)
CITY Lower Thames Street (St Magnus the Martyr)
GUILD Leadenhall Street (St Katharine Cree)
GUILD Rood Lane (St Margaret Pattens)

EC4 - City: West
CITY Fleet Street (St Bride)
CITY Garlickhythe Garlick Hill (St James)
CITY Queen Victoria Street (St Andrew-by-the-Wardrobe)
CITY Walbrook (St Stephen)
GUILD Abchurch Yard (St Mary Abchurch)
GUILD College Hill (St Michael Paternoster Royal)
GUILD Fleet Street (St Dunstan-in-the-West)
GUILD Holborn Circus (St Andrew)
GUILD Ludgate Hill (St Martin)
GUILD Paul's Wharf (St Benet)

N1 - Islington
BARNSBURY Thornhill Square (St Andrew)
CALEDONIAN ROAD (All Saints Hall)
CANONBURY Canonbury Road (St Stephen)
DE BEAUVOIR TOWN Northchurch Terrace (St Peter)
HOXTON Shepherdess Walk (Holy Trinity)

HOXTON (St John the Baptist)
ISLINGTON (St James the Apostle)
ISLINGTON Mildmay Grove (St Jude and St Paul)
ISLINGTON Upper Street (St Mary)
ISLINGTON (St Peter's Church Hall)
PENTONVILLE (St Silas w All Saints)
SHOREDITCH Hoxton Street (St Anne)
SHOREDITCH Hoxton (St Leonard)

NW1 - Camden Town
CAMDEN SQUARE (St Paul)
MUNSTER SQUARE Osnaburgh Street (St Mary Magdalene)
REGENT'S PARK Prince Albert Road (St Mark)
REGENT'S PARK Albany Street (Christ Church)
SOMERS TOWN Eversholt Street (St Mary the Virgin)
ST MARYLEBONE Clarence Gate (St Cyprian)
ST PANCRAS Pancras Road (Old Church)
ST PANCRAS Euston Road (St Pancras)

NW3 - Hampstead
HAMPSTEAD Belsize Park (St Peter)
HAMPSTEAD Downshire Hill (St John)
HAMPSTEAD Hampstead Square (Christ Church)
HAMPSTEAD Church Row (St John)
HAMPSTEAD Kidderpore Avenue (St Luke)
HAMPSTEAD Eton Road (St Saviour)
HAMPSTEAD Gospel Oak Savernake Road (All Hallows)
PRIMROSE HILL Primrose Hill Road (St Mary the Virgin)
ST PANCRAS Finchley Road (Holy Trinity w St Barnabas)

NW5 - Kentish Town
BROOKFIELD Highgate Rise (St Anne)
BROOKFIELD Dartmouth Park Road (St Mary)
CAMDEN TOWN Camden Road (St Michael)
KENTISH TOWN Lupton Street (St Benet and All Saints)
KENTISH TOWN Vicars Road (St Martin)
KENTISH TOWN Prince of Wales Road (St Silas-the-Martyr)
OSENEY CRESCENT (St Luke)

NW6 - Kilburn
BRONDESBURY Willesden Lane (Christ Church)
HAMPSTEAD Lyncroft Gardens (Emmanuel)
HAMPSTEAD West End Lane (St James)
KILBURN Kilburn Park Road (St Augustine)
KILBURN Priory Road (St Mary)

NW8 - St John's Wood
HAMILTON TERRACE (St Mark)
ST JOHN'S WOOD (St John)

SE1 - Bermondsey
BERMONDSEY Thorburn Square (St Anne)
BERMONDSEY Jamaica Road (St James w Christ Church)
BERMONDSEY Bermondsey Street (St Mary Magdalen w St Olave)
CAMBERWELL Avondale Square (St Philip)
SOUTHWARK Blackfriars Road (Christ Church)
SOUTHWARK New Kent Road (Holy Trinity w St Matthew)
SOUTHWARK Lancaster Street (St Alphege)
SOUTHWARK Borough High Street (St George the Martyr)
SOUTHWARK Tabard Street (St Hugh)
SOUTHWARK Borough High Street (St Jude)
WATERLOO Short Street (St Andrew)
WATERLOO Waterloo Road (St John the Evangelist)

CENTRAL LONDON CHURCHES

SE11 - Kennington
CAMBERWELL Wyndham Road (St Michael and All Angels)
KENNINGTON CROSS Kennington Cross (St Anselm)
KENNINGTON PARK St Agnes Place (St Agnes)
KENNINGTON Kennington Park Road (St Mark)
LAMBETH Lambeth Road (St Mary's Mission)
NEWINGTON Kennington Park Road (St Mary)
VAUXHALL Kennington Lane (St Peter)

SW1 - Westminster
BELGRAVIA Bourne Street (St Mary)
BELGRAVIA Eaton Square (St Peter)
BELGRAVIA Sloane Street (Holy Trinity)
BELGRAVIA Wilton Place (St Paul)
PIMLICO (St Saviour)
PIMLICO St Barnabas Street (St Barnabas)
PIMLICO Vauxhall Bridge Road (St James the Less)
PIMLICO Warwick Square (St Gabriel)
WESTMINSTER Chester Square (St Michael)
WESTMINSTER Great Peter Street (St Matthew)
WESTMINSTER Rochester Row (St Stephen)

SW3 - Chelsea
CHELSEA Christ Church Street (Christ Church)
CHELSEA Milner Street (St Simon Zelotes)
CHELSEA Old Church Street (All Saints)
CHELSEA Sydney Street (St Luke)
CHELSEA Walton Street (St Saviour)

SW5 - Earl's Court
EARL'S COURT Philbeach Gardens (St Cuthbert)
KENSINGTON Redcliffe Gardens (St Luke)
KENSINGTON, SOUTH Courtfield Gardens (St Jude)

SW6 - Fulham
FULHAM Church Gate (All Saints)
FULHAM Studdridge Street (Christ Church)
FULHAM Fulham Palace Road (St Clement)
FULHAM Parsons Green (St Dionis)
FULHAM Fulham Palace Road (St Etheldreda)
FULHAM Wandsworth Bridge Road (St Matthew)
FULHAM St Peter's Terrace (St Peter)
WALHAM GREEN (St John)

SW7 - South Kensington
BROMPTON (Holy Trinity)
KENSINGTON Gloucester Road (St Stephen)
KENSINGTON Prince Consort Road (Holy Trinity w All Saints)
KENSINGTON Queen's Gate (St Augustine)

SW8 - South Lambeth
BATTERSEA Patmore Street (St George w St Andrew)
BATTERSEA Queenstown Road (St Philip w St Bartholomew)
CLAPHAM Union Grove (Christ Church and St John)
LAMBETH, SOUTH Miles Street (St Anne and All Saints)
LAMBETH, SOUTH St Stephen's Terrace (St Stephen)

SW10 - West Brompton
BROMPTON, WEST The Boltons (St Mary)
CHELSEA World's End (St John)
CHELSEA (St John w St Andrew)

SW11 - Battersea
BATTERSEA Battersea Church Road (St Mary)
BATTERSEA Battersea Park Road (Christ Church and St Stephen)
BATTERSEA Plough Road (St Peter)
BATTERSEA St John's Hill (St Paul)
BATTERSEA PARK Battersea Park Road (St Saviour)
BATTERSEA PARK Prince of Wales Drive (All Saints)
CLAPHAM COMMON North Side (St Barnabas)
LAVENDER HILL (Ascension)
WANDSWORTH COMMON Cobham Close (St Michael)

W1 - West End
BRYANSTON SQUARE (St Mary)
BRYANSTON STREET (Annunciation)
GROSVENOR CHAPEL South Audley Street (no dedication)
HANOVER SQUARE (St George)
MARGARET STREET (All Saints)
MAYFAIR Down Street (Christ Church)
PICCADILLY (St James)
PORTMAN SQUARE Robert Adam Street (St Paul)
ST MARYLEBONE Langham Place (All Souls)
ST MARYLEBONE Marylebone Road (St Marylebone)
ST MARYLEBONE Old Marylebone Road (St Mark w St Luke)
ST MARYLEBONE Vere Street (St Peter)
SOHO Dean Street (St Anne)

WC1 - Bloomsbury
BLOOMSBURY WAY (St George)
HOLBORN Queen Square (St George the Martyr)
HOLBORN St Giles High Street (St Giles-in-the-Fields)
ST PANCRAS Cromer Street (Holy Cross)
WOBURN SQUARE (Christ Church)

W2 - Paddington
BAYSWATER St Petersburgh Place (St Matthew)
PADDINGTON GREEN (St Mary)
PADDINGTON Hyde Park Crescent (St John the Evangelist)
PADDINGTON Sussex Gardens (St James)
PADDINGTON Woodchester Street (St Mary Magdalene)
PADDINGTON Westbourne Park Road (St Stephen w St Luke)

WC2 - Holborn
COVENT GARDEN Bedford Street (St Paul)
TRAFALGAR SQUARE (St Martin-in-the-Fields)
WESTMINSTER (St Mary-le-Strand)

W6 - Hammersmith
FULHAM Margravine Road (St Alban)
FULHAM Lillie Road (St Augustine)
HAMMERSMITH Paddenswick Road (Holy Innocents)
HAMMERSMITH Glenthorne Road (St John the Evangelist)
HAMMERSMITH Queen Caroline Street (St Paul)
HAMMERSMITH Black Lion Lane (St Peter)

W8 - Kensington
KENSINGTON Earl's Court Road (St Philip)
KENSINGTON Victoria Road (Christ Church)
KENSINGTON Campden Hill (St George)
KENSINGTON Kensington High Street (St Mary Abbots)

W9 - Maida Hill
PADDINGTON Elgin Avenue Maida Vale (St Peter)
PADDINGTON Warwick Avenue Maida Vale (St Saviour)
PADDINGTON Fernhead Road (St Luke the Evangelist)

W10 - North Kensington
KENSAL GREEN Harrow Road (St John)
KENSINGTON Kensal Road (St Thomas)
KENSINGTON (St Helen)
LADBROKE GROVE (St Michael and All Angels)
NOTTING HILL Dalgarno Way (St Francis)

W11 - Notting Hill
KENSINGTON (St Clement)
NORLANDS Kensington (St James)
NOTTING HILL (All Saints)
NOTTING HILL (St John)
NOTTING HILL (St Peter)

W14 - West Kensington
HAMMERSMITH Rockley Road (St Simon)
HAMMERSMITH Sinclair Road (St Matthew)
KENSINGTON Addison Road (St Barnabas)
KENSINGTON Holland Road (St John the Baptist)
KENSINGTON, WEST Fulham Fields (St Andrew)
KENSINGTON, WEST Hammersmith Road (St Mary)

WELSH BENEFICES AND CHURCHES

An index of the benefices of the Church in Wales (shown in bold type) together with entries for churches and other licensed places of worship. Where the church name is the same as the benefice (or the first place name in the benefice), the church entry is omitted. Church dedications are indicated in brackets.

The benefice entry gives the full legal name, followed by the diocese, the deanery number (page 837), and the name(s) and appointment(s) of the clergy serving there (if there are none, the telephone number of the parsonage house is given). The following are the main abbreviations used; for others see the full list of abbreviations:-

C	Curate	**P-in-c**	Priest-in charge
C-in-c	Curate-in-charge	**Par Dn**	Parish Deacon
Dn-in-c	Deacon-in-charge	**R**	Rector
Dss	Deaconess	**TM**	Team Minister
Hon C	Honorary Curate	**TV**	Team Vicar
NSM	Non-stipendiary Minister	**V**	Vicar

ABBEY CWMHIR (St Mary the Virgin) Llanbadarn Fawr, Llandegley and Llanfihangel etc *S & B*

ABER-CUCH (St John) Maenordeifi and Capel Colman w Llanfihangel etc *St D*

ABER-ERCH (St Cawrdaf) Denio w Aber-erch *Ban*

ABERAERON (Holy Trinity) Henfynyw w Aberaeron and Llanddewi Aberarth *St D*

ABERAMAN (St Margaret) and Abercwmboi w Cwmaman *Llan 7* V R DONKIN, NSM B J JONES

ABERAVON (Holy Trinity) *Llan 8* V P R GOULD

ABERAVON (St Mary) (St Paul) *Llan 8* V S BARNES, C M A STARK

ABERBARGOED (St Peter) Bedwellty *Mon*

ABERCANAID (St Peter) *Llan 9* P-in-c G G FOSTER

ABERCARN *Mon 7* V N J HODGE

ABERCRAF (St David) and Callwen *S & B 7* V *Vacant* Abercrave (01639) 730640

ABERCWMBOI Aberaman and Abercwmboi w Cwmaman *Llan*

ABERCYNON (St Donat) (St Gwynno) *Llan 7* V N P JONES

ABERDARE (St Fagan) *Llan 7* V S J RYAN

ABERDARE (St John the Baptist) (St Elvan) (St Matthew) (St John the Evangelist) *Llan 7* V E K THOMAS, C C J AMOS, B TAYLOR

ABERDARON (St Hywyn) w Rhiw and Llanfaelrhys w Llangwnnadl and Penllech *Ban 11* R *Vacant*

ABERDYFI (St Peter) Llanegryn w Aberdyfi w Tywyn *Ban*

ABEREDW (St Cewydd) w Llandeilo Graban and Llanbadarn-y-Garreg w Crickadarn and Gwenddwr *S & B 2* V A C CHARTERS

ABERFFRAW (St Beuno) Trefdraeth w Aberffraw and Llangwyfan etc *Ban*

ABERGAVENNY (Holy Trinity) (Christ Church) *Mon 1* V R P MATTHEWS

ABERGAVENNY (St Mary) (Christchurch) w Llanwenarth Citra *Mon 1* V J H WINSTON, C M R E TOMLINSON, NSM D W F ROSSITER

ABERGELE (St Michael) (St David) *St As 6* V D J WELSH, NSM D WILLIAMS

ABERGORLECH (St David) Brechfa w Abergorlech etc *St D*

ABERGWILI (St David) w Llanfihangel-uwch-Gwili and Capel-y-Groes *St D 11* V J K DAVIES

ABERGWYNFI (St Thomas) Glyncorrwg w Afan Vale and Cymmer Afan *Llan*

ABERGWYNGREGYN (St Bodfan) Llanfairfechan w Abergwyngregyn *Ban*

ABERGYNOLWYN Llanegryn w Aberdyfi w Tywyn *Ban*

ABERHAFESP (St Gwynog) Newtown w Llanllwchaiarn w Aberhafesp *St As*

ABERKENFIG (St John) Penyfai w Tondu *Llan*

ABERKENFIG (St Theodore) St Brides Minor w Bettws *Llan*

ABERNANT (St Lucia) Tre-lech a'r Betws w Abernant and Llanwinio *St D*

ABERNANT (St Matthew) Aberdare St Jo *Llan*

ABERPERGWM (St Cadoc) and Blaengwrach *Llan 10* V R A ANGEL

ABERPORTH (St Cynwyl) w Tremain and Blaenporth *St D 6* R N R GRIFFIN

ABERSYCHEN (St Thomas) and Garndiffaith *Mon 10* V A W TYLER

ABERTILLERY (St Michael) *Mon 8* V D NICHOLSON, C T R PRESCOTT

ABERTYSSWG (St Paul) New Tredegar *Mon*

ABERYSKIR (St Mary and St Cynidr) Trallwng, Bettws Penpont w Aberyskir etc *S & B*

ABERYSTWYTH (St Michael) (Holy Trinity) (St Mary) (St Anne) *St D 10* R S R BELL, TV A T G JOHN, C H N L LATHAM, M J NEEDS, NSM C V JOHN, J WIGLEY

ACREFAIR (St Paul) Rhosymedre *St As*

AFAN VALE Glyncorrwg w Afan Vale and Cymmer Afan *Llan*

ALLTMAWR (St Mauritius) Builth and Llanddewi'r Cwm w Llangynog etc *S & B*

ALLTWEN (St John the Baptist) Cilybebyll *Llan*

AMBLESTON (St Mary) Spittal w Trefgarn and Ambleston w St Dogwells *St D*

AMLWCH (St Eleth) (St Peter) (St Gwenllwyfo) (St Eilian) *Ban 6* R *Vacant* Amlwch (01407) 830740

AMMANFORD (All Saints) Betws St Dav w Ammanford *St D*

AMMANFORD (St Michael) as above

AMROTH (St Elidyr) St Issell's and Amroth *St D*

ANGLE (St Mary) Castlemartin w Warren and Angle etc *St D*

ARDLEEN (Mission Church) Buttington and Pool Quay *St As*

ARTHOG (St Catherine) w Fairbourne w Llangelynnin w Rhoslefain *Ban 12* V A M HIRST

BAGILLT (St Mary) (St Peter) *St As 4* V B TAYLOR

BAGLAN (St Catherine) (St Baglan) *Llan 8* V D W LEWIS, C G H GREEN

BALA (Christ Church) Llancil w Bala and Frongoch and Llangower etc *St As*

BANGOR (Cathedral of St Deiniol) (St Mary) (Eglwys y Groes) (St James) (St David) (St Peter) *Ban 1* R A J HAWKINS, TV W ROBERTS, C K L SANDELLS-REES

BANGOR MONACHORUM (St Dunawd) and Worthenbury *St As 11* R P ROWENS

BANGOR TEIFI (St David) w Henllan and Llanfairorllwyn w Llangynllo *St D 7* R *Vacant* Velindre (01559) 370463

BARGOED (St Gwladys) and Deri w Brithdir *Llan 2* V P A COX, C D J MORTIMORE

BARMOUTH Llanaber w Caerdeon *Ban*

BARRY (All Saints) (St John w St Baruc) *Llan 6* R J G D OEPPEN, C G MILLAR

BARRY (St Paul) Merthyr Dyfan *Llan*

BASSALEG (St Basil) *Mon 6* V J T LEWIS, C V J PAYNE, O HARRIS

BATTLE (St Cynog) Brecon St Mary and Battle w Llanddew *S & B*

BEAUFORT (St Andrew) Ebbw Vale *Mon*

BEAUFORT (St David) as above

BEAUMARIS (St Mary and St Nicholas) (St Catherine) (St Seiriol) (St Cawrdaf) (St Michael) *Ban 5* R G M HUGHES

BEDDGELERT (St Mary) Penrhyndeudraeth w Llanfrothen w Beddgelert *Ban*

BEDLINOG (St Cadoc) Treharris w Bedlinog *Llan*

BEDLINOG (St Mary) as above

BEDWAS (St Barrwg) and Rudry *Mon 6* R R JEFFORD

BEDWELLTY (St Sannan) *Mon 7* V D J CARPENTER

BEGELLY (St Mary) w Ludchurch and Crunwere *St D 4* R *Vacant*

BEGUILDY (St Michael and All Angels) (St Peter) and Heyope *S & B 5* V G L J WARRINGTON

BENLLECH (St Andrew) Llanfair Mathafarn Eithaf w Llanbedrgoch *Ban*

BERRIEW (St Beuno) and Manafon *St As 10* V T W PRITCHARD

BERSE (Parish Church) and Southsea *St As 16* V R N PARRY

BETTISFIELD (St John the Baptist) Hanmer, Bronington, Bettisfield, Tallarn Green *St As*

BETTWS Trallwng, Bettws Penpont w Aberyskir etc *S & B*
BETTWS (St David) St Brides Minor w Bettws *Llan*
BETTWS (St David) *Mon 9* **V** PHVIVASH
BETTWS CHAPEL Llantillio Pertholey w Bettws Chpl etc *Mon*
BETTWS DISSERTH (St Mary) Llanelwedd w Llanfaredd w Llansantffraed etc *S & B*
BETTWS NEWYDD (not known) w Trostrey and Kemeys Commander and Llanfihangel Gobion w Llanfair Kilgeddin *Mon 5* **R** JRSTACEY
BETWS (Holy Trinity) Glasbury and Llowes w Clyro and Betws *S & B*
BETWS (St David) w Ammanford *St D 13*
V AFHERRICK, **C** BBARNES
BETWS BLEDRWS (St Bledrws or St Michael) *St D 9*
P-in-c DTWPRICE
BETWS CEDEWAIN (St Beuno) and Tregynon and Llanwyddelan *St As 7* **V** JRGUY
BETWS GARMON (St Garmon) Llanbeblig w Caernarfon and Betws Garmon etc *Ban*
BETWS GWERFUL GOCH (St Mary) Cerrigydrudion w Llanfihangel etc *St As*
BETWS IFAN (St John) w Bryngwyn *St D 6* **V** *Vacant*
BETWS LEUCU (St Lucia) Llangeitho and Blaenpennal w Betws Leucu etc *St D*
BETWS-Y-COED (St Mary) and Capel Curig w Penmachno w Dolwyddelan *Ban 2* **V** CJDPROBERT
BETWS-YN-RHOS (St Michael) Llanelian and Betws-yn-Rhos *St As*
BEULAH Llanwrtyd w Llanddulas in Tir Abad etc *S & B*
BIRCHGROVE (St John) Llansamlet *S & B*
BISHOPSTON (St Teilo) *S & B 8* **R** CGLEE
BISHTON (St Cadwaladr) *Mon 4* **R** PKWALKER
BISTRE (Emmanuel) (All Saints) (St Cecilia) *St As 14*
V JRKENNETT-ORPWOOD, **C** DTBLEWIS, **NSM** CRJAMES, PAWALKER
BLACKWOOD (St Margaret) *Mon 7* **V** DJONES
BLAEN-PORTH (St David) Aber-porth w Tre-main and Blaen-porth *St D*
BLAENAU FFESTINIOG (St David) Ffestiniog w Blaenau Ffestiniog *Ban*
BLAENAVON (St Peter) w Capel Newydd *Mon 10*
V PCJONES (formerly TITCOMBE)
BLAENCELYN (St David) Llangrannog w Llandysiliogogo w Penbryn *St D*
BLAENGARW (St James) Pontycymmer and Blaengarw *Llan*
BLAENGWRACH (St Mary) Aberpergwm and Blaengwrach *Llan*
BLAENLLECHAU (St Thomas) Ferndale w Maerdy *Llan*
BLAENPENNAL (St David) Llangeitho and Blaenpennal w Betws Leucu etc *St D*
BLAINA (St Peter) and Nantyglo *Mon 8* **R** MNPREVETT
BLEDDFA (St Mary Magdalene) Whitton and Pilleth and Cascob etc *S & B*
BLETHERSTON (St Mary) Llawhaden w Bletherston and Llanycefn *St D*
BODEDERN (St Edern) w Llechgynfarwy and Llechylched w Ceirchiog w Llanfihangel-yn-Nhywyn w Caergeiliog *Ban 3*
D-in-c CMEVANS
BODELYWDDAN (St Margaret) *St As 1* **R** RVBYLES
BODEWRYD (St Mary) Llanfechell w Bodewryd w Rhosbeirio etc *Ban*
BODFARI (St Stephen) Caerwys and Bodfari *St As*
BODFUAN (St Buan) Llanbedrog w Llannor w Llanfihangel etc *Ban*
BODWROG (St Twrog) Llandrygarn w Bodwrog and Heneglwys etc *Ban*
BONTDDU Llanaber w Caerdeon *Ban*
BONVILSTON (St Mary) St Nicholas w Bonvilston and St George-super-Ely *Llan*
BONYMAEN (St Margaret) Glantawe *S & B*
BORTH (St Matthew) and Eglwys-fach w Llangynfelyn *St D 10* **V** DEBFRANCIS
BORTH Y GEST Ynyscynhaearn w Penmorfa and Porthmadog *Ban*
BOSHERSTON (St Michael) St Petrox w Stackpole Elidor and Bosherston etc *St D*
BOTWNNOG (St Beuno) w Bryncroes (St Mary) *Ban 11*
R PDJAMES
BOUGHROOD (St Cynog) Llandefalle and Llyswen w Boughrood etc *S & B*
BOULSTON Slebech and Uzmaston w Boulston *St D*
BRAWDY (St David) Whitchurch w Solva and St Elvis w Brawdy etc *St D*
BRECHFA (St Teilo) w Abergorlech and Llanfihangel Rhos-y-corn *St D 14* **R** PHBTHOMAS

BRECON (Cathedral of St John the Evangelist) (St Mary) and Battle w Llanddew *S & B 1* **V** JHARRIS, **C** RMLLEWELLYN, MJBATCHELOR
BRECON (St David) w Llanspyddid and Llanilltyd *S & B 1*
V DETHOMAS
BRIDELL (St David) Cilgerran w Bridell and Llantwyd *St D*
BRIGHTON, NEW (St James) Mold *St As*
BRITHDIR (St David) Bargoed and Deri w Brithdir *Llan*
BRITHDIR (St Mark) Dolgellau w Llanfachreth and Brithdir etc *Ban*
BRITHDIR (St Mary) Llanrhaeadr-ym-Mochnant and Llanarmon etc *St As*
BRITON FERRY (St Clement) Llansawel w Briton Ferry *Llan*
BRONINGTON (Holy Trinity) Hanmer, Bronington, Bettisfield, Tallarn Green *St As*
BRONLLYS (St Mary) and Llanfilo w Llandefaelog Tre'graig *S & B 4* **V** PDIXON
BRONWYDD (St Celynnin) Llanpumsaint w Llanllawddog *St D*
BROUGHTON (St Mary) Hawarden *St As*
BROUGHTON (St Paul) (St Peter) *St As 16* **V** RGOWEN
BRYMBO (St Mary) *St As 16* **V** GRMATTHIAS
BRYN (St Tydfil) Llangynwyd w Maesteg *Llan*
BRYNAMAN (St Catherine) w Cwmllynfell *St D 13*
V ATEALE
BRYNCOEDIFOR (St Paul) Dolgellau w Llanfachreth and Brithdir etc *Ban*
BRYNEGLWYS (St Tysilio) *St As 12* **D-in-c** MCHARVEY
BRYNFORD (St Michael) Gorsedd w Brynford and Ysgeifiog *St As*
BRYNGWRAN Bodedern w Llechgynfarwy and Llechylched etc *Ban*
BRYNGWYN (St Mary) Betws Ifan w Bryngwyn *St D*
BRYNGWYN (St Michael) and Newchurch and Llanbedr Painscastle and Llanddewi Fach *S & B 4*
P-in-c JEJACKSON, **NSM** HJFISHER
BRYNGWYN (St Peter) Raglan w Llandenny and Bryngwyn *Mon*
BRYNMAWR (St Mary the Virgin) *S & B 3* **V** NJONES
BRYNNA Llanharan w Peterston-Montem *Llan*
BRYNYMAEN (Christ Church) w Trofarth *St As 6*
P-in-c JMWILLIAMS
BUCKHOLT Penallt and Trellech *Mon*
BUCKHOLT (St John the Baptist) Mon *Mon*
BUCKLEY (St Matthew) (Good Shepherd) *St As 14*
V JHAY
BUILTH (St Mary) and Llanddewi'r Cwm w Llangynog and Maesmynis and Llanynys and Alltmawr *S & B 2*
V ECJOHN, **C** HVPARSELL
BULWARK (St Christopher) Chepstow *Mon*
BURRY PORT (St Mary) and Pwll *St D 12*
V GDHARRIES, **NSM** EJWROBERTS
BURTON (St Mary) and Rosemarket *St D 5* **R** JHALE
BUTE TOWN (St Aidan) Pontlottyn w Fochriw *Llan*
BUTTINGTON (All Saints) and Pool Quay *St As 10*
V DHWILLIAMS
BWLCH (All Saints) Llangorse, Cathedine, Llanfihangel Talyllyn etc *S & B*
BWLCHGWYN (Christ Church) *St As 16* **V** EBWILLIAMS
BWLCHYCIBAU (Christ Church) Llanfyllin and Bwlchycibau *St As*
BYLCHAU (St Thomas) Henllan and Llannefydd and Bylchau *St As*
CADOXTON-JUXTA-BARRY (St Cadoc) (St Mary) *Llan 6*
R JMHUGHES
CADOXTON-JUXTA-NEATH (St Catwg) *Llan 10*
V *Vacant* Neath (01639) 644625
CAERAU (St Cynfelin) (St Peter) *Llan 8* **V** PADEROY-JONES, **NSM** CELASKEY
CAERAU w Ely (St David) (St Timothy) *Llan 3*
V JCBUTTIMORE
CAERDEON (St Philip) Llanaber w Caerdeon *Ban*
CAEREITHIN (St Teilo) *S & B 10* **V** TGMORRIS
CAERFALLWCH (St Paul) Halkyn w Caerfallwch w Rhesycae *St As*
CAERGEILIOG Bodedern w Llechgynfarwy and Llechylched etc *Ban*
CAERGYBI Holyhead w Rhoscolyn w Llanfair-yn-Neubwll *Ban*
CAERHUN (St Mary) w Llangelynnin w Llanbedr-y-Cennin *Ban 2* **V** WBYNON
CAERLEON (St Cadoc) *Mon 9* **V** AJEDWARDS, **C** MGHADDOCK
CAERLEON-ULTRA-PONTEM (Holy Spirit) Newport Ch Ch *Mon*
CAERNARFON (St Mary) Llanbeblig w Caernarfon and Betws Garmon etc *Ban*

CAERPHILLY (St Martin) (St Catherine) (St Andrew)
Llan 2 **R** M J SHORT, **C** I A JONES, D K WATERS
CAERSWS (St Mary) Llanwnnog and Caersws w Carno *Ban*
CAERWENT (St Stephen and St Tathan) w Dinham and Llanfair Discoed and Shirenewton w Newchurch *Mon 2*
V P W WOODMAN, **NSM** S J HOWELLS
CAERWYS (St Michael) and Bodfari *St As 2*
R J K MUSSON
CALDICOT (St Mary) *Mon 4* **V** P J S EDWARDS,
C J R CONNELL
CALLWEN (St John the Baptist) Abercraf and Callwen
S & B
CAMROSE (St Ishmael) and St Lawrence w Ford and Haycastle *St D 5* **V** B JONES
CANTON (St Catherine) *Llan 3* **V** A D HUNTER
CANTON (St John) *Llan 3* **R** *Vacant* Cardiff (01222) 29683
CANTON (St Luke) *Llan 3* **V** G F HORWOOD
CANTREF (St Mary) Llanfrynach and Cantref w Llanhamlach *S & B*
CAPEL (Dewi Sant) Llansadwrn w Llanwrda and Manordeilo *St D*
CAPEL BANGOR (Church) Llanbadarn Fawr w Capel Bangor and Goginan *St D*
CAPEL COELBREN (Capel Coelbren) *S & B 7* **V** *Vacant*
CAPEL COLMAN (St Colman) Maenordeifi and Capel Colman w Llanfihangel etc *St D*
CAPEL CURIG (St Michael) Betws-y-Coed and Capel Curig w Penmachno etc *Ban*
CAPEL CYNON (St Cynon) Llanarth and Capel Cynon w Talgarreg etc *St D*
CAPEL DEWI (St David) Llanllwni *St D*
CAPEL GARMON Llanrwst and Llanddoget and Capel Garmon *St As*
CAPEL IFAN (St John the Baptist) Pontyberem *St D*
CAPEL LLANILLTERN (St Ellteyrn) Llan w Capel Llanilltern *Llan*
CAPEL MAIR Llangeler *St D*
CAPEL NANTDDU Cefn Coed and Capel Nantddu w Vaynor etc *S & B*
CAPEL NEWYDD (St Paul) Blaenavon w Capel Newydd *Mon*
CAPEL TAFFECHAN Cefn Coed and Capel Nantddu w Vaynor etc *S & B*
CAPEL TYGWYDD Llandygwydd and Cenarth w Cilrhedyn etc *St D*
CAPEL-Y-FFIN (St Mary) Hay w Llanigon and Capel-y-Ffin *S & B*
CAPEL-Y-GROES Abergwili w Llanfihangel-uwch-Gwili etc *St D*
CARDIFF (Dewi Sant) *Llan 3* **V** A EDWARDS
CARDIFF (St Andrew and St Teilo) *Llan 3* **V** *Vacant* Cardiff (01222) 32407
CARDIFF (St John the Baptist) (St James the Great) (St Michael) *Llan 3* **V** M R ELLIS, **C** G P BIGMORE, A H STEVENS, **NSM** E J BURKE
CARDIFF (St Mary) (St Stephen) w Cardiff (St Dyfrig and St Samson) *Llan 3* **V** K J JORDAN, **C** G REEVES
CARDIGAN (St Mary) and Mwnt and Y Ferwig *St D 6*
V W H RICHARDS
CAREW (St Mary) Lamphey w Hodgeston and Carew *St D*
CARMARTHEN (St David) (Christ Church) *St D 11*
V T G JONES, **C** C HUGHES
CARMARTHEN (St Peter) (St John) *St D 11*
V A J R THOMAS, **C** J P LEWIS
CARMEL (Eglwys Fair) Gors-las *St D*
CARNHEDRYN Llanrhian w Llanhywel and Carnhedryn etc *St D*
CARNO (St John) Llanwnnog and Caersws w Carno *Ban*
CARROG (St Ffraid) Glyndyfrdwy and Llansantfraid Glyn Dyfrdwy *St As*
CASCOB (St Michael) Whitton and Pilleth and Cascob etc *S & B*
CASTELL DWYRAN (Church) Llanfallteg w Clunderwen and Castell Dwyran *St D*
CASTELLAN Maenordeifi and Capel Colman w Llanfihangel etc *St D*
CASTLE BYTHE Letterston w Llanfair Nant-y-Gof etc *St D*
CASTLE CAEREINION (St Garmon) Welshpool w Castle Caereinion *St As*
CASTLEMARTIN (St Michael and All Angels) w Warren and Angle and Rhoscrowther and Pwllcrochan *St D 1*
R A J TURNER
CATBROOK (St John the Baptist) Penallt and Trellech *Mon*
CATHEDINE (St Michael) Llangorse, Cathedine, Llanfihangel Talyllyn etc *S & B*

CEFN (St Mary) (All Saints) *St As 1* **R** R H GRIFFITHS
CEFN COED (St John the Baptist) and Capel Nantddu w Vaynor and Capel Taffechan *S & B 1* **V** B H JOHN
CEFN CRIBWR (St Colman) Kenfig Hill *Llan*
CEFN FOREST (St Thomas) Fleur-de-Lis *Mon*
CEFN HENGOED (St Anne) Gelligaer *Llan*
CEFN PENNAR (St Illtyd) Mountain Ash *Llan*
CEFNLLYS (St Michael) Llandrindod w Cefnllys and Disserth *S & B*
CEIRCHIOG (St David) Bodedern w Llechgynfarwy and Llechylched etc *Ban*
CELLAN (All Saints) Llanddewibrefi w Llanbadarn Odwyn and Cellan etc *St D*
CEMAES Llanfechell w Bodewryd w Rhosbeirio etc *Ban*
CEMAIS (St Tydecho) Mallwyd w Cemais and Llanymawddwy *Ban*
CENARTH (St Llawddog) Llandygwydd and Cenarth w Cilrhedyn etc *St D*
CERRIGCEINWEN (St Ceinwen) Llangefni w Tregaean and Llangristiolus etc *Ban*
CERRIGYDRUDION (St Mary Magdalene) w Llanfihangel Glyn Myfyr and Llangwm w Ysbyty Ifan and Pentrevoelas and Betws Gwerful Goch and Dinmael *St As 12*
D-in-c S BRUSH
CHEPSTOW (St Mary) *Mon 2* **V** J P HARRIS, **C** T G CLEMENT
CHERITON St Petrox w Stackpole Elidor and Bosherston etc *St D*
CHERITON (St Cadoc) Llanrhidian w Llanmadoc and Cheriton *S & B*
CHIRK (St Mary) *St As 13* **V** M B ROBERTS
CILCAIN (St Mary) and Nannerch and Rhyd-y-mwyn *St As 14* **R** R C PULLEN
CILCENNIN (Holy Trinity) Llanfihangel Ystrad and Cilcennin w Trefilan etc *St D*
CILFYNYDD (St Luke) *Llan 11* **P-in-c** C D CLARKE
CILGERRAN (St Llawddog) w Bridell and Llantwyd *St D 6*
R E L THOMAS
CILGWYN (St Mary) Newport w Cilgwyn and Dinas w Llanllawer *St D*
CILIAU AERON (St Michael) Llanerch Aeron w Ciliau Aeron and Dihewyd etc *St D*
CILRHEDYN Llandygwydd and Cenarth w Cilrhedyn etc *St D*
CILYBEBYLL (St John the Evangelist) *Llan 10*
R N R SANDFORD
CILYCWM (St Michael) and Ystrad-ffin w Rhandirmwyn Llanfair-ar-y-Bryn *St D 14* **V** J T WILLIAMS
CILYMAENLLWYD (St Philip and St James) Llandysilio w Egremont and Llanglydwen etc *St D*
CLARBESTON (St Martin of Tours) Wiston w Walton E and Clarbeston *St D*
CLOCAENOG (St Foddhyd) Llanfwrog and Clocaenog and Gyffylliog *St As*
CLUNDERWEN (St David) Llanfallteg w Clunderwen and Castell Dwyran *St D*
CLYDACH (St John the Evangelist) (St Mary) (St Michael) *S & B 7* **V** D H E MOSFORD, **C** S H LODWICK, **NSM** J M PHILLIPS
CLYDACH VALE (St Thomas) Tonypandy w Clydach Vale *Llan*
CLYDAU (St Clydai) Maenordeifi and Capel Colman w Llanfihangel etc *St D*
CLYNNOG FAWR (St Beuno) Llanaelhaearn w Clynnog Fawr *Ban*
CLYRO (St Michael and All Angels) Glasbury and Llowes w Clyro and Betws *S & B*
CLYTHA Llanddewi Rhydderch and Llangattock etc *Mon*
COCKETT (St Peter) Swansea St Pet *S & B*
COEDKERNEW Marshfield and Peterstone Wentloog etc *Mon*
COEDYPAEN (Christchurch) Llangybi and Coedypaen w Llanbadoc *Mon*
COETMOR (Church) Glanogwen *Ban*
COITY (St Mary) w Nolton *Llan 1* **R** D RICHARDS, **C** S J BARNES, P K McMULLEN
COLVA (St David) New Radnor and Llanfihangel Nantmelan etc *S & B*
COLWINSTON (St Michael) w Llandow and Llysworney *Llan 4* **R** R W A JONES
COLWYN (St Catherine) (St John the Baptist) *St As 6*
V D V GRIFFITH
COLWYN BAY (St Paul) (St Andrew) (St David) *St As 6*
V T G DAVIES
COMINS COCH Llanbadarn Fawr w Capel Bangor and Goginan *St D*
CONNAH'S QUAY (St Mark) (St David's Mission Church) *St As 14* **V** D P MORRIS, **C** K R SOUTHERTON

CONWY (St Mary and All Saints) w Gyffin *Ban 2*
  V   P R JONES
CORRIS (Holy Trinity) Pennal w Corris and Esgairgeiliog
Ban
CORWEN (St Mael and St Sulien) and Llangar w
  Gwyddelwern and Llawrybetws *St As 12* C H FENTON
COSHESTON (St Michael) Pemb Dock w Cosheston w Nash
  and Upton *St D*
COWBRIDGE (Holy Cross) *Llan 4* R R M E PATERSON,
  TM D Y L HELLARD, C V L PARKINSON
COYCHURCH (St Crallo) w Llangan and St Mary Hill
  Llan 1 R K ANDREWS
COYTREAHEN (St Thomas) Penyfai w Tondu *Llan*
CRAI (St Ilid) Llywel and Traean-glas w Llanulid *S & B*
CREGRINA (St David) Llanelwedd w Llanfaredd w
  Llansantffraed etc *S & B*
CRIBYN (St Silin) Llanfihangel Ystrad and Cilcennin w
  Trefilan etc *St D*
CRICCIETH (St Catherine) w Treflys *Ban 10*
  R F J S DAVIES
CRICKADARN (St Mary) Aberedw w Llandeilo Graban
  and Llanbadarn etc *S & B*
CRICKHOWELL (St Edmund) w Cwmdu and Tretower
  S & B 3 V J L VICKERY
CRIGGION (St Michael) Llandysilio and Penrhos and
  Llandrinio etc *St As*
CRINDAU (All Saints) Newport All SS *Mon*
CRINOW (St Teilo) Narberth w Mounton w Robeston
  Wathen and Crinow *St D*
CROESCEILIOG (St Mary) Cwmbran *Mon*
CROESERW (St Clare) Glyncorrwg w Afan Vale and
  Cymmer Afan *Llan*
CROSS HANDS (St Anne) Gors-las *St D*
CROSS INN (Holy Trinity) Llanllwchaearn and Llanina *St D*
CROSS KEYS (St Catherine) Risca *Mon*
CRUGYBYDDAR (St Peter) Beguildy and Heyope *S & B*
CRUMLIN (St Mary) Penmaen and Crumlin *Mon*
CRUNWERE (St Elidyr) Begelly w Ludchurch and Crunwere
  St D
CRYNANT (St Margaret) (Chapel of Ease) *Llan 10*
  V S F MINTY
CWM (St Mael and St Sulien) Dyserth and Trelawnyd and
  Cwm *St As*
CWM (St Paul) Ebbw Vale *Mon*
CWM-COCH (St Mark) Llandybie *St D*
CWMAMAN (Christ Church) *St D 13* V J L W WILLIAMS,
  NSM D J THOMAS
CWMAMAN (St Joseph) Aberaman and Abercwmboi w
  Cwmaman *Llan*
CWMANN (St James) Pencarreg and Llanycrwys *St D*
CWMAVON (St Michael) *Llan 8* V K W CHANT
CWMBACH (St Mary Magdalene) *Llan 7* V B H SHARP
CWMBACH LLECHRYD (St John the Divine) Newbridge-
  on-Wye and Llanfihangel Brynpabuan etc *S & B*
CWMBRAN (St Gabriel) *Mon 10* TV J S WILLIAMS,
  C WATKINS, NSM J M JENKINS, E J MARTIN
CWMBWRLA (St Luke) Swansea St Luke *S & B*
CWMCARN (St John the Evangelist) *Mon 7*
  V A DILWORTH
CWMCARVAN (St Clement) Dingestow and Llangovan w
  Penyclawdd etc *Mon*
CWMDARE (St Luke) Aberdare St Fagan *Llan*
CWMDDAUDDWR (St Winifred) (St Bride) w St Harmon's
  and Llanwrthwl *S & B 5* V D T HURLEY
CWMDU (St Michael the Archangel) Crickhowell w Cwmdu
  and Tretower *S & B*
CWMDUAD (St Alban) Cynwil Elfed and Newchurch *St D*
CWMFFRWD (St Anne) Llangynnwr and Cwmffrwd *St D*
CWMFFRWDOER (All Saints) Pontypool *Mon*
CWMLLYNFELL (St Margaret) Brynaman w Cwmllynfell
  St D
CWMPARC (St George) *Llan 12* V R E DAVIES
CWMTILLERY (St Paul) and Six Bells *Mon 8* V *Vacant*
CWMYOY (St Martin) Llanfihangel Crucorney w Oldcastle
  etc *Mon*
CWRT-HENRI (St Mary) Llangathen w Llanfihangel
  Cilfargen etc *St D*
CYDWELI (St Mary) (St Teilo) and Llandyfaelog *St D 12*
  V G J DAVIES
CYFFIG (St Cyffig) Whitland w Cyffig and Henllan Amgoed
  and Llan-gan *St D*
CYMAU (All Saints) Llanfynydd *St As*
CYMMER (St John the Evangelist) and Porth *Llan 12*
  V P M LEONARD, NSM M J MAUND
CYMMER AFAN (St John the Evangelist) Glyncorrwg w
  Afan Vale and Cymmer Afan *Llan*

CYNCOED (All Saints) (St Edeyrn) *Mon 6*
  R J C WOODWARD, TV S G WILLSON,
  M W SSERUNKUMA, TD J V MOLE
CYNWIL ELFED (St Cynwyl) and Newchurch *St D 11*
  V I D JOHN
CYNWYL GAEO (St Cynwyl) w Llansawel and Talley
  St D 14 V D R OLIVER
DAFEN (St Mich and All Angels) *St D* V *Vacant*
DALE (St James) and St Brides w Marloes *St D 5*
  V M BEYNON, NSM R D REED
DAROWEN (St Tudur) Penegoes and Darowen w Llanbryn-
  Mair *Ban*
DEFYNNOG (St Cynog) w Rhydybriw and Llandilo'r-fan
  S & B 1 V M P WILDING
DEGANWY (All Saints) Llanrhos *St As*
DENBIGH (St Mary) (St Marcella) (St David) and Nantglyn
  St As 2 R J H C DAVIES, C N H WILLIAMS
DENIO (St Peter) w Aber-erch *Ban 11*
  P-in-c M L WILLIAMS
DERI (St Peter) Bargoed and Deri w Brithdir *Llan*
DERWEN (St Mary) Llanfair, Derwen, Llanelidan and
  Efenechtyd *St As*
DEVAUDEN (St James) Itton and St Arvans w Penterry and
  Kilgwrrwg etc *Mon*
DIHEWYD (St Vitalis) Llanerch Aeron w Ciliau Aeron and
  Dihewyd etc *St D*
DINAS (Mission) and Penygraig w Williamstown *Llan 12*
  V S J BODYCOMBE
DINAS (St Brynach) Newport w Cilgwyn and Dinas w
  Llanllawer *St D*
DINGESTOW (St Dingad) and Llangovan w Penyclawdd and
  Tregaer and Cwmcarvan *Mon 3* V P M SCRIVEN
DINHAM Caerwent w Dinham and Llanfair Discoed etc
  Mon
DINMAEL (St Catherine) Cerrigydrudion w Llanfihangel etc
  St As
DISSERTH (St Cewydd) Llandrindod w Cefnllys and
  Disserth *S & B*
DOLBENMAEN (St Mary) w Llanystymdwy w Llangybi and
  Llanarmon *Ban 10* R W JONES
DOLFOR (St Paul) Kerry and Llanmerewig and Dolfor *St As*
DOLGARROG (St Mary) Caerhun w Llangelynnin w
  Llanbedr-y-Cennin *Ban*
DOLGELLAU (St Mary) w Llanfachreth and Brithdir and
  Bryncoedifor and Llanelltud *Ban 12* R C N COOPER
DOLWYDDELAN (St Gwyddelan) Betws-y-Coed and Capel
  Curig w Penmachno etc *Ban*
DOWLAIS (St John the Baptist) (Christ Church) *Llan 9*
  R S J MORGAN
DWYGYFYLCHI (St Gwynin) (St Seiriol) (St David) *Ban 2*
  V G B HUGHES
DYFFRYN Llanenddwyn w Llanddwywe, Llanbedr w
  Llandanwg *Ban*
DYFFRYN (St Matthew) *Llan 10* V T G SMITH
DYFFRYN HONDDU (St Cynog) Merthyr Cynog and
  Dyffryn Honddu etc *S & B*
DYSERTH (St Bridget) (St Michael) (St Mael and St Sulien)
  and Trelawnyd and Cwm *St As 1* V R W ROWLAND
EBBW VALE (Christchurch) (St John the Baptist) *Mon 8*
  R D J JONES, TV M J GILL, C L HARRISON
EDERN (St Edern) Nefyn w Pistyll w Tudweiliog w
  Llandudwen etc *Ban*
EFENECHTYD (St Michael) Llanfair, Derwen, Llanelidan
  and Efenechtyd *St As*
EGLWYS-FACH (St Michael) Borth and Eglwys-fach w
  Llangynfelyn *St D*
EGLWYS FAIR GLYN-TAF Whitland w Cyffig & Henllan
  Amgoed & Llan-gan *St D*
EGLWYS GYMYN (St Margaret) Pendine w Llanmiloe and
  Eglwys Gymyn w Marros *St D*
EGLWYS NEWYDD Ysbyty Cynfyn w Llantrisant and
  Eglwys Newydd *St D*
EGLWYS OEN DUW Llanwrtyd w Llanddulas in Tir Abad
  etc *S & B*
EGLWYSBREWIS (St Brewis) w St Athan w Gileston
  Llan 4 R J W BINNY
EGLWYSFACH Llansantffraid Glan Conway and
  Eglwysfach *St As*
EGLWYSILAN (St Ilan) *Llan 2* R J E PARKIN,
  C I D THACKER
EGLWYSRHOS (St Eleri and St Mary) Llanrhos *St As*
EGLWYSWEN (St Michael) Nevern and Y Beifil w
  Eglwyswrw and Meline etc *St D*
EGLWYSWRW (St Cristiolus) as above
EGREMONT Llandysilio w Egremont and Llanglydwen etc
  St D
ELERCH (St Peter) Penrhyn-coch and Elerch *St D*
ELY (St David) Caerau w Ely *Llan*

ELY (St Timothy) as above

ERBISTOCK (St Hilary) Overton and Erbistock and Penley *St As*

ERYRYS (St David) Treuddyn w Nercwys *St As*

ESCLUSHAM (Holy Trinity) *St As 16* V P H VARAH

ESGAIRGEILIOG Pennal w Corris and Esgairgeiliog *Ban*

EVANCOYD (St Peter) New Radnor and Llanfihangel Nantmelan etc *S & B*

EWENNY (St Michael) w St Brides Major *Llan 1* R M R PREECE

EYTON (St Deiniol) Ban Monachorum and Worthenbury *St As*

FAIRBOURNE (St Cynon) Arthog w Fairbourne w Llangelynnin w Rhoslefain *Ban*

FAIRHILL Cwmbran *Mon*

FAIRWATER (St Peter) *Llan 5* V M M DAVIES, NSM R L FORD

FAIRWATER (St Peter) Cwmbran *Mon*

FAWR Llandeilo and Taliaris *St D*

FELIN-FOEL (Holy Trinity) *St D 12* V A J MEATS

FELIN-GWM (St John) Llanegwad w Llanfynydd *St D*

FELINDRE (St Barnabas) Pen-boyr *St D*

FERNDALE (St Dunstan) (St Thomas) w Maerdy *Llan 12* V E E DAVIES, NSM S I DAVIES

FERRYSIDE (St Thomas) St Ishmael's w Llan-saint and Ferryside *St D*

FFESTINIOG (St Michael) w Blaenau Ffestiniog *Ban 7* V J N GILLIBRAND

FFYNNONGROYW (All Saints) Mostyn w Ffynnongroyw *St As*

FISHGUARD (St Mary) (St Nicholas) w Llanychar and Pontfaen w Morfil and Llanychlwydog *St D 3* V R M GRIFFITHS

FLEMINGSTON (St Michael) Cowbridge *Llan*

FLEUR-DE-LIS (St David) *Mon 7* V P M WINCHESTER, NSM D G BATE

FLINT (St Mary) (St Thomas) (St David) *St As 4* R G R JONES, C C N L POTTER, NSM M M GRAHAM

FOCHRIW (St Mary and St Andrew) Pontlottyn w Fochriw *Llan*

FORD (Church) Camrose and St Lawrence w Ford and Haycastle *St D*

FORDEN (St Michael) Montgomery and Forden and Llandyssil *St As*

FREYSTROP (St Justinian) Llangwm and Freystrop *St D*

FRON (Mission Church) Berriew and Manafon *St As*

FRONCYSYLLTE (St David) Chirk *St As*

FRONGOCH Llanycil w Bala and Frongoch and Llangower etc *St As*

FURNACE (Mission Church) Llanelli *St D*

GABALFA (St Mark) (Highfields Centre and Mynachdy Institute) *Llan 5* V W G R LEWIS, C I W JONES

GAERWEN Llanfihangel Ysgeifiog and Llanffinan etc *Ban*

GARNDIFFAITH (St John the Evangelist) Abersychen and Garndiffaith *Mon*

GARTHBEIBIO (St Tydecho) and Llanerfyl and Llangadfan *St As 8* R *Vacant*

GARTHBRENGY (St David) Merthyr Cynog and Dyffryn Honddu etc *S & B*

GARTHELI (St Gartheli) Llangeitho and Blaenpennal w Betws Leucu etc *St D*

GAUFRON (St David) Rhayader and Nantmel *S & B*

GELLIGAER (St Catwg) (St Margaret) (St Anne) *Llan 2* R *Vacant* Bargoed (01443) 830303

GILESTON (St Giles) Eglwysbrewis w St Athan w Gileston *Llan*

GILFACH GOCH (St Barnabas) Tonyrefail w Gilfach Goch *Llan*

GILVACH (St Margaret) Gelligaer *Llan*

GLADWESTRY (St Mary) New Radnor and Llanfihangel Nantmelan etc *S & B*

GLAIS (St Paul) Llansamlet *S & B*

GLAN ELY (Resurrection) *Llan 3* V R H MORGAN, C R E MOVERLEY

GLANAMAN (St Margaret) Cwmaman *St D*

GLANGWRYNE (Mission Church) Llangenni and Llanbedr Ystrad Yw w Patricio *S & B*

GLANOGWEN (Christ Church) *Ban 2* P-in-c I W JONES

GLANTAWE (St Margaret) (St Peter) *S & B 11* V H M LERVY

GLASBURY (St Peter) (All Saints) and Llowes w Clyro and Betws *S & B 4* V G M REED

GLASCOED (St Michael) Usk and Monkswood w Glascoed Chpl and Gwehelog *Mon*

GLASCOMBE (St David) Llanelwedd w Llanfaredd w Llansantffraed etc *S & B*

GLYN Brecon St David w Llanspyddid and Llanilltyd *S & B*

GLYNCOLLWNG Llanfeugan and Llanthetty and Glyncollwng etc *S & B*

GLYNCORRWG (St John the Baptist) (St Clare) (St Thomas) w Afan Vale and Cymmer Afan *Llan 8* R G J WAGGETT, TV J A P WALKER, C E M GREEN

GLYNDYFRDWY (St Thomas) and Llansantffraid Glyn Dyfrdwy *St As 12* V R S THOMAS

GLYNTAFF (St Mary) *Llan 11* V K D LERRY

GOETRE (St Peter) w Llanover *Mon 5* R C R F CALE

GOGINAN (Church) Llanbadarn Fawr w Capel Bangor and Goginan *St D*

GOLDCLIFFE (St Mary Magdalen) and Whiston and Nash *Mon 4* V K M DENISON

GOODWICK (St Peter) Llanwnda, Goodwick, w Manorowen and Llanstinan *St D*

GORS-LAS (St Lleian) *St D 13* V *Vacant* Cross Hands (01269) 842561

GORSEDD (St Paul) w Brynford and Ysgeifiog *St As 4* V J W K SOMERVILLE

GORSEINON (St Catherine) *S & B 9* V J I HOLDSWORTH, NSM W G G JAMES

GOVILON (Christchurch) w Llanfoist w Llanelen *Mon 1* R R T GREY

GOWERTON (St John the Evangelist) *S & B 9* V C J COLEBROOK

GRAIG (St John) *Llan 11* V C D CLARKE

GRANDSTON (St Catherine) Mathry w St Edren's and Grandston etc *St D*

GRANGETOWN (St Paul) *Llan 3* V L V DAVIES

GREENHILL Swansea St Matt w Greenhill *S & B*

GREENWAY (St Hilary) St Hilary Greenway *Mon*

GRESFORD (All Saints) *St As 16* V D GRIFFITHS

GRIFFITHSTOWN (St Hilda) *Mon 10* V C J WILCOX, C A F PYE

GROESWEN (St David) Pentyrch *Llan*

GRONANT (St Winifred) Llanasa *St As*

GROSMONT (St Nicholas) and Skenfrith and Llangattock Lingoed and Llanfair Chapel *Mon 1* R D K POPE

GUILSFIELD (St Aelhaiarn) *St As 10* R R A BIRD

GUMFRESTON (St Lawrence) Tenby *St D*

GWAENYSGOR Meliden and Gwaenysgor *St As*

GWAUN-CAE-GURWEN *St D 13* V J G M LADD

GWEHELOG Usk and Monkswood w Glascoed Chpl and Gwehelog *Mon*

GWENDDWR (St Dubricius) Aberedw w Llandeilo Graban and Llanbadarn etc *S & B*

GWENLLI (St Mark) Llanarth and Capel Cynon w Talgarreg etc *St D*

GWERNAFFIELD (Holy Trinity) and Llanferres *St As 14* V S CAWLEY, NSM J STEPHENS

GWERNAMYNYDD (St Mark) Mold *St As*

GWERNESNEY (St Michael) Llangwm Uchaf w Llangwm Isaf w Gwernesney etc *Mon*

GWERNFFRWD (St David) Llanyrnewydd *S & B*

GWERSYLLT (Holy Trinity) *St As 16* V R J PEARCE

GWYDDELWERN (St Beuno) Corwen and Llangar w Gwyddelwern and Llawrybetws *St As*

GWYNFE (All Saints) Llangadog and Gwynfe w Llanddeusant *St D*

GWYTHERIN (St Winifred) Llanfair Talhaearn and Llansannan etc *St As*

GYFFIN (St Benedict) Conwy w Gyffin *Ban*

GYFFYLLIOG (St Mary) Llanfwrog and Clocaenog and Gyffylliog *St As*

HAFOD (St John) Swansea St Mark and St Jo *S & B*

HAKIN (St Mary) Hubbertson *St D*

HALKYN (St Mary the Virgin) w Caerfallwch w Rhesycae *St As 4* R J GLOVER

HALTON (Mission Church) Chirk *St As*

HANMER (St Chad) and Bronington and Bettisfield and Tallarn Green *St As 11* V T J BLEWETT

HARLECH (St Tanwg) and Llanfair-juxta-Harlech w Llanfihangel-y-Traethau and Llandecwyn *Ban 7* V R E G HUGHES

HAROLDSTON ST ISSELLS (St Issell) Haverfordwest St Mary and St Thos w Haroldston *St D*

HAROLDSTON WEST (St Madog) Walton W w Talbenny and Haroldston W *St D*

HASGUARD Herbrandston and Hasguard w St Ishmael's *St D*

HAVERFORDWEST (St Martin) w Lambston *St D 5* V D J R LEAN

HAVERFORDWEST (St Mary) and St Thomas w Haroldston St Issells *St D 5* R D EVANS

HAWARDEN (St Deiniol) (Holy Spirit) *St As 14* R J B THELWELL, N BALL, P-in-c P J BILLINGHURST, C N R KING, NSM M QUINN

HAY (St Mary) (St John) w Llanigon and Capel-y-Ffin
S & B 4 **V** D E REES
HAYCASTLE (St Mary) Camrose and St Lawrence w Ford
and Haycastle *St D*
HENDY (St David) Llangennech and Hendy *St D*
HENEGLWYS (St Llwydian) Llandrygarn w Bodwrog and
Heneglwys etc *Ban*
HENFYNYW (St David) w Aberaeron and Llanddewi Aberarth
St D 8 **V** M L REES, **C** J W SMITH, **NSM** D W HEAL
HENLLAN (St David) Ban Teifi w Henllan and
Llanfairorllwyn etc *St D*
HENLLAN (St Sadwrn) and Llannefydd and Bylchau *St As 2*
R J P P WILLIAMS
HENLLAN AMGOED (St David) Whitland w Cyffig and
Henllan Amgoed and Llan-gan *St D*
HENLLYS (St Peter) Cwmbran *Mon*
HENRY'S MOAT (St Bernard) Maenclochog w Henry's
Moat and Mynachlogddu etc *St D*
HEOL-Y-CYW (St Paul) Llanilid w Pencoed *Llan*
HERBRANDSTON (St Mary) and Hasguard w St Ishmael's
St D 5 **R** D PARRY
HEYOPE (St David) Beguildy and Heyope *S & B*
HIGH CROSS (St Anne) Bassaleg *Mon*
HIRNANT (St Illog) Llanrhaeadr-ym-Mochnant and
Llanarmon etc *St As*
HIRWAUN (St Lleurwg) (St Winifred) *Llan 7*
V H M WILLIAMS, **C** H YAHAYA
HODGESTON (Church) Lamphey w Hodgeston and Carew
St D
HOLT (St Chad) *St As 16* **V** J T HUGHES
HOLYHEAD (St Cybi) (Morawelon) (St Ffraid) (St Gwenfaen)
w Rhoscolyn w Llanfair-yn-Neubwll *Ban 3* **R** J E NICE,
C C A LLEWELLYN, D H JAMES
HOLYWELL (St James) (Holy Trinity) *St As 4*
V J T EVANS, **NSM** P G TAYLOR
HOPE (Parish Church) *St As 14* **R** G L GRIFFITHS
HOWEY (St David) Llandrindod w Cefnllys and Disserth
S & B
HUBBERTSON (St David) (Holy Spirit) *St D 5*
R P BROWN, **C** P J BEMENT
HUNDLETON (St David) Monkton *St D*
ILSTON (St Illtyd) w Pennard *S & B 8* **V** D J WILKINSON
ISYCOED (St Paul) Marchwiel and Isycoed *St As*
ITTON (St Deiniol) and St Arvans w Penterry and Kilgwrrwg w
Devauden *Mon 2* **V** M J GOLLOP, **NSM** M E ZORAB
JAMESTON Manobier and St Florence w Redberth *St D*
JEFFREYSTON (St Jeffrey) w Reynoldston and East
Williamston and Loveston *St D 4* **R** N P DAVIES
JOHNSTON (St Peter) w Steynton *St D 5* **R** R A GORDON
JORDANSTON (St Cawrda) Mathry w St Edren's and
Grandston etc *St D*
KEMEYS COMMANDER (All Saints) Bettws Newydd w
Trostrey etc *Mon*
KEMEYS INFERIOR Tredunnoc and Llantrisant w
Llanhennock etc *Mon*
KENFIG Pyle w Kenfig *Llan*
KENFIG HILL (St Theodore) (St Colman) *Llan 8*
V G W JAMES
KERRY (St Michael) and Llanmerewig and Dolfor *St As 7*
V M J WALKER
KILGETTY Begelly w Ludchurch and Crunwere *St D*
KILGWRRWG (Holy Cross) Itton and St Arvans w Penterry
and Kilgwrrwg etc *Mon*
KILLAY (St Hilary) (St Martin) *S & B 6* **V** B H JONES,
C A J M MEREDITH
KILVEY (All Saints) Swansea St Thos and Kilvey *S & B*
KNELSTON Port Eynon w Rhosili and Llanddewi and
Knelston *S & B*
KNIGHTON (St Edward) and Norton *S & B 5*
V T J WILLIAMS, **NSM** K I WARRINGTON
LALESTON (St David) w Tythegston and Merthyr Mawr
Llan 1 **V** E J EVANS
LAMBSTON (St Ishmael) Haverfordwest St Martin w
Lambston *St D*
LAMPETER PONT STEFFAN (St Peter) w Silian *St D 9*
V W S T MORGAN
LAMPETER VELFREY (St Peter) and Llanddewi Velfrey
St D 15 **R** M G R MORRIS
LAMPHEY (St Faith and St Tyfei) w Hodgeston and Carew
St D 1 **V** G A DAVIES
LANDORE (St Paul) *S & B 10* **V** R J COSSLETT
LANGSTONE (not known) Bishton *Mon*
LANKNANSH (St Mary) Llantwit Major *Llan*
LAUGHARNE (St Martin) w Llansadwrnen and Llandawke
St D 15 **V** D B G DAVIES
LAVERNOCK (St Lawrence) Penarth w Lavernock *Llan*
LAWRENNY (St Caradog) Martletwy w Lawrenny and
Minwear etc *St D*

LECKWITH Llandough w Leckwith *Llan*
LETTERSTON (St Giles) w Llanfair Nant-y-Gof and
Puncheston w Little Newcastle and Castle Bythe *St D 3*
R R GRIFFITHS
LISVANE (St Denys) *Llan 2* **V** G E WILLIAMS
LISWERRY Newport St Andr *Mon*
LITTLE NEWCASTLE (St Peter) Letterston w Llanfair
Nant-y-Gof etc *St D*
LLAN-GAN Whitland w Cyffig and Henllan Amgoed and
Llan-gan *St D*
LLAN-LLWCH (St Mary) w Llangain and Llangynog
St D 11 **V** R I PROTHEROE
LLAN-NON (St Non) *St D 12* **V** *Vacant* Cross Hands
(01269) 841358
LLAN-SAINT (All Saints) St Ishmael's w Llan-saint and
Ferryside *St D*
LLAN-Y-BRI (Holy Trinity) Llansteffan and Llan-y-bri etc
St D
LLANABER (St Mary) (St John) (St David) w Caerdeon
Ban 7 **R** P W D FLAVELL
LLANAELHAEARN (St Aelhaiarn) w Clynnog Fawr *Ban 1*
R I THOMAS
LLANAFAN FAWR (St Afan) Newbridge-on-Wye and
Llanfihangel Brynpabuan etc *S & B*
LLANAFAN-Y-TRAWSCOED (St Afan) Llanfihangel w
Llanafan and Llanwnnws etc *St D*
LLANALLGO (St Gallo) Llaneugrad w Llanallgo and
Penrhosllugwy etc *Ban*
LLANANNO (St Anno) Llanbister and Llanbadarn Fynydd
w Llananno *S & B*
LLANARMON (St Garmon) Dolbenmaen w Llanystymdwy
w Llangybi etc *Ban*
LLANARMON DYFFRYN CEIRIOG (St
Garmon) Llansantffraid and Llanarmon and Pontfadog
St As
LLANARMON MYNYD (St Garmon) Llanrhaeadr-ym-
Mochnant and Llanarmon etc *St As*
LLANARMON YN IAL (St Garmon) Llandegla and
Llanarmon yn Ial *St As*
LLANARTH (St David) (St Teilo) and Capel Cynon w
Talgarreg and (St Mark) *St D 8* **C** L BOLTON
LLANARTH (St Teilo) Llanddewi Rhydderch and
Llangattock etc *Mon*
LLANARTHNE (St David) and Llanddarog *St D 11*
V H M THOMAS
LLANASA (St Asaph and St Cyndeyrn) (St Winifred) *St As 4*
V *Vacant* Prestatyn (01745) 853512
LLANBABO (St Pabo) Valley w Llanfachraeth *Ban*
LLANBADARN FAWR (St Padarn) and Llandegley and
Llanfihangel Rhydithon w Abbey Cwmhir *S & B 5*
R N D HALL
LLANBADARN FAWR (St Padarn) w Capel Bangor and
Goginan *St D 10* **V** R H WILLIAMS
LLANBADARN FYNYDD (St Padarn) Llanbister and
Llanbadarn Fynydd w Llananno *S & B*
LLANBADARN ODWYN (St Padarn) Llanddewibrefi w
Llanbadarn Odwyn and Cellan etc *St D*
LLANBADARN TREFEGLWYS (St
Padarn) Llansantffraed and Llanbadarn Trefeglwys etc
St D
LLANBADARN-Y-GARREG (St Padarn) Aberedw w
Llandeilo Graban and Llanbadarn etc *S & B*
LLANBADOC (St Madog) Llangybi and Coedypaen w
Llanbadoc *Mon*
LLANBADRIG (St Padrig) Llanfechell w Bodewryd w
Rhosbeirio etc *Ban*
LLANBEBLIG (St Peblig) w Caernarfon and Betws Garmon w
Waunfawr *Ban 1* **R** R F DONALDSON, **C** E OWEN
LLANBEDR (St Peter) Llanenddwyn w Llanddwywe,
Llanbedr w Llandanwg *Ban*
LLANBEDR DYFFRYN CLWYD (St Peter) Llangynhafal
and Llanbedr Dyffryn Clwyd *St As*
LLANBEDR PAINSCASTLE (St Peter) Bryngwyn and
Newchurch and Llanbedr etc *S & B*
LLANBEDR-Y-CENNIN (St Peter) Caerhun w
Llangelynnin w Llanbedr-y-Cennin *Ban*
LLANBEDR YSTRAD YW (St Peter) Llangenni and
Llanbedr Ystrad Yw w Patricio *S & B*
LLANBEDRGOCH (St Peter) Llanfair Mathafarn Eithaf w
Llanbedrgoch *Ban*
LLANBEDROG (St Pedrog) w Llannor w Llanfihangel
Bachellaeth w Bodfuan *Ban 11* **R** *Vacant* Pwllheli (01758)
740919
LLANBERIS (St Peris) (St Padarn) w Llanrug *Ban 1*
R P HUGHES
LLANBEULAN (St Peulan) w Llanfaelog and Tal-y-llyn
Ban 3 **R** T WYNNE

LLANBISTER (St Cynllo) and Llanbadarn Fynydd w Llananno
S & B 5 **V** V C HODGSON

LLANBLETHIAN (St Blethian) Cowbridge *Llan*

LLANBOIDY (St Brynach) Meidrim and Llanboidy and
Merthyr *St D*

LLANBRADACH (All Saints) Ystrad Mynach w
Llanbradach *Llan*

LLANBRYN-MAIR (St Mary) Penegoes and Darowen w
Llanbryn-Mair *Ban*

LLANCARFAN (St Cadoc) w Llantrithyd *Llan 4*
V M DAVIES

**LLANDAFF (Cathedral of St Peter and St Paul w St Dyfrig,
St Teilo and St Euddogwy) w Capel Llanilltern** *Llan 5*
V J ROGERS, **NSM** B-H KHOO

LLANDAFF North (All Saints) *Llan 5* **V** *Vacant* Cardiff
(01222) 564096

LLANDANWG Llanenddwyn w Llanddwywe, Llanbedr w
Llandanwg *Ban*

LLANDAVENNY Penhow, St Brides Netherwent w
Llandavenny etc *Mon*

LLANDAWKE (St Odoceus) Laugharne w Llansadwrnen
and Llandawke *St D*

LLANDDANIEL-FAB (St Deiniolfab) Llanfihangel
Ysgeifiog and Llanffinan etc *Ban*

LLANDDAROG (St Twrog) Llanarthne and Llanddarog
St D

LLANDDEINIOL (St Deiniol) Llanychaearn w Llanddeiniol
St D

LLANDDEINIOLEN (St Deiniol) Llanfair-is-gaer and
Llanddeiniolen *Ban*

LLANDDERFEL (St Derfel) Llandrillo and Llandderfel
St As

LLANDDEUSANT (St Marcellus and St Marcelluna) Valley
w Llanfachraeth *Ban*

LLANDDEW (St David) Brecon St Mary and Battle w
Llanddew *S & B*

LLANDDEWI Llanwrtyd w Llanddulas in Tir Abad etc
S & B

LLANDDEWI (St David) Port Eynon w Rhosili and
Llanddewi and Knelston *S & B*

LLANDDEWI ABERARTH (St David) Henfynyw w
Aberaeron and Llanddewi Aberarth *St D*

**LLANDDEWI BREFI (St David) w Llanbadarn Odwyn and
Cellan w Llanfair Clydogau and Llangybi** *St D 9*
V A W WILLIAMS

LLANDDEWI FACH (St David) Bryngwyn and Newchurch
and Llanbedr etc *S & B*

LLANDDEWI RHONDDA (St Barnabas) Pwllgwaun w
Llanddewi Rhondda *Llan*

LLANDDEWI RHONDDA (St David) as above

**LLANDDEWI RHYDDERCH (St David) and Llangattock-
juxta-Usk and Llanarth w Clytha and Llansantffraed**
Mon 1 **V** M S SADLER

LLANDDEWI YSTRADENNI (St David) *S & B 5* **V** *Vacant*

LLANDDEWI'R CWM (St David) Builth and Llanddewi'r
Cwm w Llangynog etc *S & B*

LLANDDOGET (St Doged) Llanrwst and Llanddoget and
Capel Garmon *St As*

LLANDDONA (St Dona) Llansadwrn w Llanddona and
Llaniestyn etc *Ban*

LLANDDOWROR (St Teilo) St Clears w Llangynin and
Llanddowror etc *St D*

LLANDDULAS (St Cynfryd) and Llysfaen *St As 6*
R J W M ROBERTS

LLANDDWYWE (St Ddwywe) Llanenddwyn w
Llanddwywe, Llanbedr w Llandanwg *Ban*

LLANDDYFNAN (St Ddyfnan) Llansadwrn w Llanddona
and Llaniestyn etc *Ban*

LLANDDYFNAN (St Deiniol) as above

LLANDECWYN (St Tecwyn) Harlech and Llanfair-juxta-
Harlech etc *Ban*

LLANDEFAELOG-FACH (St Maelog) Merthyr Cynog and
Dyffryn Honddu etc *S & B*

LLANDEFAELOG TRE'GRAIG Bronllys and Llanfilo w
Llandefaelog Tre'graig *S & B*

**LLANDEFALLE (St Matthew) and Llyswen w Boughrood and
Llanstephen w Talachddu** *S & B 4* **V** R M H JONES

LLANDEGFAN (St Tegfan) w Llandysilio *Ban 5*
V R JONES, **Hon C** P A G WESTLAKE

LLANDEGLA (St Tecla) and Llanarmon yn Ial *St As 3*
R C B HALL

LLANDEGLEY (St Tecla) Llanbadarn Fawr, Llandegley
and Llanfihangel etc *S & B*

LLANDEGVETH (St Tegfeth) Llanfrechfa and Llanddewi
Fach w Llandegveth *Mon*

LLANDEILO Maenclochog w Henry's Moat and
Mynachlogddu etc *St D*

LLANDEILO (St Teilo) and Taliaris *St D 14*
V W A STRANGE

LLANDEILO ABERCYWYN Llansteffan and Llan-y-bri etc
St D

LLANDEILO GRABAN (St Teilo) Aberedw w Llandeilo
Graban and Llanbadarn etc *S & B*

LLANDEILO TAL-Y-BONT (St Teilo) (St Michael)
S & B 9 **V** J P H WALTERS

LLANDELOY (St Teilo) Whitchurch w Solva and St Elvis w
Brawdy etc *St D*

LLANDENNY (St John the Apostle) Raglan w Llandenny
and Bryngwyn *Mon*

LLANDEUSSANT (St Simon and St Jude) Llangadog and
Gwynfe w Llanddeusant *St D*

LLANDEVAUD (St Peter) Penhow, St Brides Netherwent w
Llandavenny etc *Mon*

LLANDEWI FACH Llanfrechfa and Llanddewi Fach w
Llandegveth *Mon*

LLANDEWI SKIRRID (St David) Llantillio Pertholey w
Bettws Chpl etc *Mon*

LLANDEWI VELFREY (St David) Lamp Velfrey and
Llanddewi Velfrey *St D*

LLANDILO'R-FAN (St Teilo) Defynnog w Rhydybriw and
Llandilo'r-fan *S & B*

LLANDINAM (St Llonio) w Trefeglwys w Penstrowed *Ban 8*
V M G H B TUDOR

LLANDINGAT (St Dingad) w Myddfai *St D 14* **V** B T RICE

LLANDINORWIG (Christ Church) (St Mary) w Penisa'r-waen
Ban 1 **NSM** T ROBERTS

LLANDOGO (St Oudoceus) and Tintern *Mon 2*
R J E L WHITE

LLANDOUGH (St Dochdwy) w Leckwith *Llan 6*
R B M LODWICK

LLANDOUGH (St Dochwy) Cowbridge *Llan*

LLANDOVERY Llandingat w Myddfai *St D*

LLANDOW (Holy Trinity) Colwinston w Llandow and
Llysworney *Llan*

LLANDRILLO (St Trilio) (St Derfel) and Llandderfel
St As 15 **V** G W JONES

LLANDRILLO-YN-RHOS (St Trillo) (St George) *St As 6*
V E G PRICE, **C** J R MATTHIAS

**LLANDRINDOD (Holy Trinity) (Old Parish Church) w
Cefnllys and Disserth** *S & B 5* **R** G M H HUGHES,
NSM A TWEED

LLANDRINIO (St Trinio, St Peter and St Paul) Llandysilio
and Penrhos and Llandrinio etc *St As*

**LLANDRYGARN (St Trygarn) w Bodwrog and Heneglwys and
Trewalchmai** *Ban 4* **V** J F W JONES, **NSM** E D JERMAN

**LLANDUDNO (St George) (St Tudno) (Holy Trinity) (Our
Saviour)** *Ban 2* **R** P J COUSINS, **TV** J POWELL,
C M C PARRY

LLANDUDWEN (St Tudwen) Nefyn w Pistyll w Tudweiliog
w Llandudwen etc *Ban*

LLANDULAIS IN TIR ABAD (St David) Llanwrtyd w
Llanddulas in Tir Abad etc *S & B*

LLANDWROG (St Thomas) Llanwnda and Llandwrog *Ban*

LLANDWROG (St Twrog) as above

LLANDYBIE (St Tybie) *St D 13* **V** J H GRAVELL

LLANDYFAELOG (St Maelog) Cydweli and Llandyfaelog
St D

LLANDYFAN (Church) Llandybie *St D*

LLANDYFODWG (St Tyfodwg) *Llan 12* **P-in-c** E HASTEY

LLANDYFRIOG (St Tyfriog) Newc Emlyn w Llandyfriog
and Troed-yr-aur *St D*

LLANDYFRYDOG (St Tyfrydog) Llanerch-y-medd *Ban*

LLANDYGAI (St Tegai) (St Ann) w Tregarth *Ban 2*
V M PRICE-ROBERTS

LLANDYGWNNIN (St Gwyninin) Botwnnog w Bryncroes
Ban

**LLANDYGWYDD (St Tygwydd) (Capel Tygwydd) and
Cenarth w Cilrhedyn and Llangoedmor w Llechryd** *St D 7*
V D M MORRIS

LLANDYRNOG (St Tyrnog) (St Cwyfan) and Llangwyfan
St As 2 **R** J S DAVIES

LLANDYRY (Church) Pen-bre *St D*

LLANDYSILIO (St Tysilio) Llandegfan w Llandysilio *Ban*

**LLANDYSILIO (St Tysilio) (St Mary) and Penrhos and
Llandrinio w Criggion** *St As 10* **R** H G A JALLAND

**LLANDYSILIO (St Tysilio) w Egremont and Llanglydwen w
Cilymaenllwyd and Llanfyrnach** *St D 15* **V** *Vacant*
Clynderwen (01437) 563203

LLANDYSILIOGOGO (St Tysilio) Llangrannog w
Llandysiliogogo w Penbryn *St D*

LLANDYSSIL (St Tyssil) Montgomery and Forden and
Llandyssil *St As*

LLANDYSUL (St Tysul) *St D 7* **V** J H ROWLANDS

LLANEDEYRN (All Saints) Cyncoed *Mon*
LLANEDI (St Edith) w Tycroes and Saron *St D 13*
   V T J WILLIAMS
LLANEDWEN (St Edwen) Llanfihangel Ysgeifiog and
   Llanffinan etc *Ban*
LLANEGRYN (St Mary and St Egryn) w Aberdyfi w Tywyn
   Ban 12 **V** J M RILEY, **C** P A HOUSEMAN
LLANEGWAD (St Egwad) w Llanfynydd *St D 14*
   V P S JOHNES
LLANEILIAN (St Eilian) Amlwch *Ban*
LLANELEN (St Helen) Govilon w Llanfoist w Llanelen *Mon*
LLANELIAN (St Elian) and Betws-yn-Rhos *St As 6*
   R R H KENDRICK
LLANELIDAN (St Elidan) Llanfair, Derwen, Llanelidan and
   Efenechtyd *St As*
LLANELIEU (St Ellyw) Talgarth and Llanelieu *S & B*
LLANELLI (Christ Church) (St David) *St D 12*
   V D A WALKER
LLANELLI (St Elli) *S & B 3* **V** J R ELLIS, **NSM** J M ELLIS
LLANELLI (St Elli) (All Saints) (St Alban) *St D 12*
   V A R WILLIAMS, **C** K G TAYLOR, T J HEWITT
LLANELLI St Paul (St Peter) (St John) *St D 12*
   V M T DAVIES
LLANELLTUD (St Illtyd) Dolgellau w Llanfachreth and
   Brithdir etc *Ban*
LLANELWEDD (St Matthew) w Llanfaredd w Llansantffraed-
   in-Elwell w Bettws Disserth and Cregrina w Glascombe and
   Rhulen *S & B 2* **V** P A C PEARCEY
LLANENDDWYN (St Enddwyn) w Llanddwywe and Llanbedr
   w Llandanwg *Ban 7* **R** R A BEACON
LLANENGAN (St Engan) and Llangian *Ban 11*
   R W L JONES
LLANERCH AERON (St Non) w Ciliau Aeron and Dihewyd
   and Mydroilyn *St D 8* **R** E J EDMUNDS
LLANERCH-Y-MEDD (St Mair) (Eglwys Crist) *Ban 6*
   V *Vacant* Llannerchymedd (01248) 470585
LLANERFYL (St Erfyl) Garthbeibio and Llanerfyl and
   Llangadfan *St As*
LLANEUGRAD (St Eugrad) w Llanallgo and Penrhoslugwy w
   Llanfihangel Tre'r Beirdd *Ban 6* **R** *Vacant*
LLANFABON (St Mabon) (St John the Baptist) *Llan 2*
   R D S LEE
LLANFACHRETH (St Machreth) Dolgellau w Llanfachreth
   and Brithdir etc *Ban*
LLANFAELOG (St Maelog) Llanbeulan w Llanfaelog and
   Tal-y-llyn *Ban*
LLANFAELRHYS (St Maelrhys) Aberdaron etc *Ban*
LLANFAES Brecon St David w Llanspyddid and Llanilltyd
   S & B
LLANFAETHLU (St Maethlu) w Llanfwrog and Llanrhuddlad
   w Llanfair-yng-Nghornwy w Llanrhwydrus *Ban 3*
   R P H PRITCHARD
LLANFAGLAN (St Mary) Llanwnda and Llandwrog *Ban*
LLANFAIR (Church) Gwaun-cae-Gurwen *St D*
LLANFAIR (Church) Llandingat w Myddfai *St D*
LLANFAIR (St Mary) Grosmont and Skenfrith and
   Llangattock etc *Mon*
LLANFAIR-AR-Y-BRYN (St Mary) Cilycwm and Ystrad-
   ffin w Rhandir-mwyn etc *St D*
LLANFAIR CAEREINION (St Mary) w Llanllugan *St As 8*
   V P K D EVANS
LLANFAIR CLYDOGAU (St Mary) Llanddewibrefi w
   Llanbadarn Odwyn and Cellan etc *St D*
LLANFAIR DISCOED (St Mary) Caerwent w Dinham and
   Llanfair Discoed etc *Mon*
LLANFAIR DYFFRYN CLWYD (St Cynfarch and St Mary)
   (Jesus Chapel) and Derwen and Llanelidan and Efenechtyd
   St As 3 **V** G H TRIMBY
LLANFAIR-IS-GAER (St Mary) (Old Parish Church) and
   Llanddeiniolen *Ban 1* **V** G C OWEN
LLANFAIR-JUXTA-HARLECH (St Mary) Harlech and
   Llanfair-juxta-Harlech etc *Ban*
LLANFAIR KILGEDDIN Bettws Newydd w Trostrey etc
   Mon
LLANFAIR MATHAFARN EITHAF (St Mary) w
   Llanbedrgoch *Ban 5* **R** C S WILLIAMS, **NSM** L J PERRY
LLANFAIR NANT-GWYN (St Mary) Nevern and Y Beifil
   w Eglwyswrw and Meline etc *St D*
LLANFAIR NANT-Y-GOF (St Mary) Letterston w Llanfair
   Nant-y-Gof etc *St D*
LLANFAIR TALHAEARN (St Mary) and Llansannan w
   Llangernyw and Gwytherin *St As 6* **R** C A BILLINGTON
LLANFAIR-YN-NEUBWLL Holyhead w Rhoscolyn w
   Llanfair-yn-Neubwll *Ban*
LLANFAIR-YN-Y-CWMWD (St Mary) Newborough w
   Llangeinwen w Llangaffo etc *Ban*
LLANFAIR-YNG-NGHORNWY (St Mary) Llanfaethlu w
   Llanfwrog and Llanrhuddlad etc *Ban*

LLANFAIRFECHAN (St Mary) (Christ Church) w
   Abergwyngregyn *Ban 2* **R** E T JONES
LLANFAIRORLLWYN (St Mary) Ban Teifi w Henllan and
   Llanfairorllwyn etc *St D*
LLANFAIRPWLL (St Mary) w Penmynydd *Ban 5*
   R T O EVANS, **NSM** C HEBDEN
LLANFALLTEG (St Mallteg) w Clunderwen and Castell
   Dwyran *St D 15* **P-in-c** G R RENOWDEN
LLANFAREDD (St Mary) Llanelwedd w Llanfaredd w
   Llansantffraed etc *S & B*
LLANFECHAIN (St Garmon) Llansantffraid-yn-Mechain
   and Llanfechain *St As*
LLANFECHAN (St Afan) Llanganten and Llangammarch
   and Llanfechan etc *S & B*
LLANFECHELL (St Mechell) w Bodewryd w Rhosbeirio w
   Llanfflewin and Llanbadrig *Ban 6* **R** G W EDWARDS
LLANFERRES (St Berres) Gwernaffield and Llanferres
   St As
LLANFEUGAN (St Meugan) and Llanthetty and Glyncollwng
   w Llansantffraed-juxta-Usk *S & B 3* **V** W S P JACKSON
LLANFFINAN (St Ffinan) Llanfihangel Ysgeifiog and
   Llanffinan etc *Ban*
LLANFFLEWIN (St Fflewin) Llanfechell w Bodewryd w
   Rhosbeirio etc *Ban*
LLANFIHANGEL (St Michael) Llantwit Major *Llan*
LLANFIHANGEL ABERCYWYN (St Michael) St Clears w
   Llangynin and Llanddowror etc *St D*
LLANFIHANGEL ABERGWESSIN Llanwrtyd w
   Llanddulas in Tir Abad etc *S & B*
LLANFIHANGEL ABERYTHYCH (St
   Michael) Llangathen w Llanfihangel Cilfargen etc *St D*
LLANFIHANGEL-AR-ARTH (St Michael) *St D 7*
   V J H A JAMES
LLANFIHANGEL BACHELLAETH (St Buan) Llanbedrog
   w Llannor w Llanfihangel etc *Ban*
LLANFIHANGEL BRYNPABUAN (St Michael and All
   Angels) Newbridge-on-Wye and Llanfihangel Brynpabuan
   etc *S & B*
LLANFIHANGEL CILFARGEN Llangathen w
   Llanfihangel Cilfargen etc *St D*
LLANFIHANGEL CRUCORNEY (St Michael) w Oldcastle
   and Cwmyoy and Llanthony *Mon 1* **V** D W T DUNN
LLANFIHANGEL FECHAN (St Michael) Merthyr Cynog
   and Dyffryn Honddu etc *S & B*
LLANFIHANGEL GENAU'R-GLYN (St Michael) and
   Llangorwen *St D 10* **V** M H JOHN
LLANFIHANGEL GLYN MYFYR (St
   Michael) Cerrigydrudion w Llanfihangel etc *St As*
LLANFIHANGEL GOBION (St Michael) Bettws Newydd w
   Trostrey etc *Mon*
LLANFIHANGEL HELYGEN (St Michael) Llanllyr-yn-
   Rhos w Llanfihangel Helygen *S & B*
LLANFIHANGEL LLEDROD (St Michael) Llanilar w
   Rhostie and Llangwyryfon etc *St D*
LLANFIHANGEL NANTBRAN (St Michael) Trallwng,
   Bettws Penpont w Aberyskir etc *S & B*
LLANFIHANGEL NANTMELAN (St Michael) New
   Radnor and Llanfihangel Nantmelan etc *S & B*
LLANFIHANGEL PENBEDW Maenordeifi and Capel
   Colman w Llanfihangel etc *St D*
LLANFIHANGEL PONTYMOILE (St Michael) Mamhilad
   and Llanfihangel Pontymoile *Mon*
LLANFIHANGEL RHOS-Y-CORN (St Michael) Brechfa w
   Abergorlech etc *St D*
LLANFIHANGEL RHYDITHON (St Michael) Llanbadarn
   Fawr, Llandegley and Llanfihangel etc *S & B*
LLANFIHANGEL ROGIET Portskewett and Roggiett w
   Llanfihangel Rogiet *Mon*
LLANFIHANGEL TALYLLYN (St Michael) Llangorse,
   Cathedine, Llanfihangel Talyllyn etc *S & B*
LLANFIHANGEL-TOR-Y-MYNYDD (St
   Michael) Llanishen w Trellech Grange and Llanfihangel etc
   Mon
LLANFIHANGEL TRE'R BEIRDD (St
   Mihangel) Llaneugrad w Llanallgo and Penrhoslugwy etc
   Ban
LLANFIHANGEL-UWCH-GWILI (St Michael) Abergwili
   w Llanfihangel-uwch-Gwili etc *St D*
LLANFIHANGEL-Y-CREUDDYN (St Michael) w Llanafan-
   y-Trawscoed and Llanwnnws and Ysbyty Ystwyth *St D 10*
   V *Vacant*
LLANFIHANGEL-Y-PENNANT (St Michael) Llanegryn w
   Aberdyfi w Tywyn *Ban*
LLANFIHANGEL-Y-TRAETHAU (St Michael) Harlech
   and Llanfair-juxta-Harlech etc *Ban*
LLANFIHANGEL-YN-NHYWYN Bodedern w
   Llechgynfarwy and Llechylched etc *Ban*

LLANFIHANGEL-YNG-NGHWYNFA (St
  Michael) Llanwddyn and Llanfihangel and Llwydiarth
  St As
**LLANFIHANGEL YSGEIFIOG (St Michael) and Llanffinan
  w Llanidan and Llanddaniel-fab and Llanedwen** *Ban 4*
  NSM I JONES
LLANFIHANGEL-YSTERN-LLEWERN (St
  Michael) Rockfield and St Maughen's w Llangattock etc
  Mon
**LLANFIHANGEL YSTRAD (St Michael) and Cilcennin w
  Trefilan and Nantcwnlle** *St D 8* **V** D P DAVIES
LLANFILO (St Bilo) Bronllys and Llanfilo w Llandefaelog
  Tre'graig *S & B*
LLANFOIST (St Ffwyst) Govilon w Llanfoist w Llanelen
  Mon
LLANFOR (St Mor and St Deiniol) w Rhosygwaliau *St As 15*
  R *Vacant*
**LLANFRECHFA (All Saints) and Llanddewi Fach w
  Llandegveth** *Mon 10* **V** A SILVERTHORN
LLANFROTHEN (St Brothen) Penrhyndeudraeth w
  Llanfrothen w Beddgelert *Ban*
LLANFROTHEN (St Catherine) as above
LLANFRYNACH (St Brynach) Llandysilio w Egremont and
  Llanglydwen etc *St D*
LLANFRYNACH (St Brynach) Cowbridge *Llan*
LLANFRYNACH (St Brynach) and Cantref w Llanhamlach
  S & B 3 **V** P G R SIMS
LLANFUGAIL (St Migail) Valley w Llanfachraeth *Ban*
LLANFWROG (St Mwrog) Llanfaethlu w Llanfwrog and
  Llanrhuddlad etc *Ban*
**LLANFWROG (St Mwrog and St Mary) and Clocaenog and
  Gyffylliog** *St As 3* **R** J B DAVIES
LLANFYLLIN (St Myllin) and Bwlchycibau *St As 9*
  R P EN DAVID
LLANFYNYDD (St Egwad) Llanegwad w Llanfynydd *St D*
LLANFYNYDD (St Michael) (St Egwad) *St As 16*
  R A J POOLMAN
LLANGADFAN (St Cadfan) Garthbeibio and Llanerfyl and
  Llangadfan *St As*
LLANGADOG (St Cadog) and Gwynfe w Llanddeusant
  St D 14 **V** *Vacant* Llangadog (01550) 777061
LLANGADWALADR (St Cadwaladr) Llansilin w
  Llangadwaladr and Llangedwyn *St As*
LLANGADWALADR (St Cadwaladr) Trefdraeth w
  Aberffraw and Llangwyfan etc *Ban*
LLANGAFFO (St Caffo) Newborough w Llangeinwen w
  Llangaffo etc *Ban*
LLANGAIN (St Cain) Llan-llwch w Llangain and Llangynog
  St D
LLANGAMMARCH (St Cadmarch) Llanganten and
  Llangammarch and Llanfechan etc *S & B*
LLANGAN (St Canna) Coychurch w Llangan and St Mary
  Hill *Llan*
**LLANGANTEN (St Cannen) and Llangammarch and
  Llanfechan and Llanlleonfel** *S & B 2* **V** J P SMITH
LLANGAR (St John the Evangelist) Corwen & Llangar w
  Gwyddelwern and Llawrybetws *St As*
LLANGASTY TALYLLYN (St Gastyn) Llangorse,
  Cathedine, Llanfihangel Talyllyn etc *S & B*
**LLANGATHEN (St Cathen) w Llanfihangel Cilfargen and
  Llanfihangel Aberythych** *St D 14* **V** W R HUGHES
LLANGATTOCK (St Cattwg) and Llangynidr *S & B 3*
  V K RICHARDS, **NSM** A S ROBINSON
LLANGATTOCK-JUXTA-USK (St Cadoc) Llanddewi
  Rhydderch and Llangattock etc *Mon*
LLANGATTOCK LINGOED (St Cadoc) Grosmont and
  Skenfrith and Llangattock etc *Mon*
LLANGATTOCK-VIBON-AVEL (St Cadoc) Rockfield and
  St Maughen's w Llangattock etc *Mon*
LLANGEDWYN (St Cedwyn) Llansilin w Llangadwaladr
  and Llangedwyn *St As*
**LLANGEFNI (St Cyngar) w Tregaean and Llangristiolus w
  Cerrigceinwen** *Ban 4* **R** R J HUGHES
LLANGEINOR (St Ceinor) (St John the Baptist) *Llan 1*
  V C J SANDERSON
LLANGEINWEN (St Ceinwen) Newborough w Llangeinwen
  w Llangaffo etc *Ban*
**LLANGEITHO (St Ceitho) and Blaenpennal w Betws Leucu
  and Gartheli** *St D 9* **R** *Vacant* Llangeitho (0197423) 654
LLANGELER (St Celer) *St D 7* **V** *Vacant* Velindre (01559)
  370449
LLANGELYNNIN (St Celynin) Arthog w Fairbourne w
  Llangelynnin w Rhoslefain *Ban*
LLANGELYNNIN (St Celynnin) Caerhun w Llangelynnin w
  Llanbedr-y-Cennin *Ban*
LLANGENNECH (St Gwynog) and Hendy *St D 12*
  V B D WITT

LLANGENNI (St Cenau) and Llanbedr Ystrad Yw w Patricio
  S & B 3 **V** C J BLANCHARD, **NSM** R O MULLIS
LLANGENNITH (St Cenydd) Reynoldston w Penrice and
  Llangennith *S & B*
LLANGERNYW (St Digain) Llanfair Talhaearn and
  Llansannan etc *St As*
LLANGEVIEW (St David) Llangwm Uchaf w Llangwm Isaf
  w Gwernesney etc *Mon*
LLANGIAN (St Gian) Llanengan and Llangian *Ban*
LLANGIWG (St Ciwg) *S & B 7* **V** D T JENKINS
LLANGLYDWEN (St Cledwyn) Llandysilio w Egremont
  and Llanglydwen etc *St D*
LLANGOEDMOR (St Cynllo) Llandygwydd and Cenarth w
  Cilrhedyn etc *St D*
LLANGOLLEN (St Collen) (St John) w Trevor and Llantysilio
  St As 13 **V** W L JONES, **C** M JONES
LLANGOLMAN (St Colman) Maenclochog w Henry's Moat
  and Mynachlogddu etc *St D*
**LLANGORSE (St Paulinus), Cathedine, Llanfihangel Talyllyn,
  Llanywern and Llangasty Talyllyn** *S & B 4*
  V R T EDWARDS, **NSM** M J F WILLETT
LLANGORWEN (All Saints) Llanfihangel Genau'r-glyn and
  Llangorwen *St D*
LLANGOVAN (St Govan) Dingestow and Llangovan w
  Penyclawdd etc *Mon*
LLANGOWER (St Cywair) Llanycil w Bala and Frongoch
  and Llangower etc *St As*
**LLANGRANNOG (St Carannog) w Llandysiliogogo w
  Penbryn** *St D 8* **V** J C HARVEY
LLANGRISTIOLUS (St Cristiolus) Llangefni w Tregaean
  and Llangristiolus etc *Ban*
LLANGUNNOG Llanishen w Trellech Grange and
  Llanfihangel etc *Mon*
LLANGURIG (St Curig) Llanidloes w Llangurig *Ban*
LLANGWLLOG (St Cwyllog) Llanerch-y-medd *Ban*
LLANGWLLONG (St Anau) as above
LLANGWM Cerrigydrudion w Llanfihangel etc *St As*
LLANGWM (St Jerome) and Freystrop *St D 5*
  R W G HOOPER
LLANGWM ISAF (St John) Llangwm Uchaf w Llangwm
  Isaf w Gwernesney etc *Mon*
**LLANGWM UCHAF (St Jerome) w Llangwm Isaf w
  Gwernesney and Llangeview and Wolvesnewton** *Mon 5*
  V G ASTON
LLANGWNNADL (St Gwynhoedl) Aberdaron etc *Ban*
LLANGWYFAN Llandyrnog and Llangwyfan *St As*
LLANGWYFAN (St Cwyfan) Trefdraeth w Aberffraw and
  Llangwyfan etc *Ban*
LLANGWYFAN (St Cwyfan Old Church) as above
LLANGWYRYFON (St Ursula) Llanilar w Rhostie and
  Llangwyryfon etc *St D*
LLANGYBI (St Cybi) Dolbenmaen w Llanystymdwy w
  Llangybi etc *Ban*
LLANGYBI (St Cybi) Llanddewibrefi w Llanbadarn Odwyn
  and Cellan etc *St D*
LLANGYBI (St Cybi) and Coedypaen w Llanbadoc *Mon 5*
  R A E MORTON, **NSM** P A BRYANT
**LLANGYFELACH (St David and St Cyfelach) (St Teilo-on-
  the-Clase)** *S & B 7* **V** L HOPKINS, **NSM** P M L PHILLIPS
LLANGYNDEYRN (St Cyndeyrn) Pontyates and
  Llangyndeyrn *St D*
LLANGYNDIR (St Cynidr and St Mary) Llangattock and
  Llangynidr *S & B*
LLANGYNFELYN (St Cynfelyn) Borth and Eglwys-fach w
  Llangynfelyn *St D*
**LLANGYNHAFAL (St Cynhafal) and Llanbedr Dyffryn
  Clwyd** *St As 3* **R** P ROWEN
LLANGYNIN (St Cynin) St Clears w Llangynin and
  Llanddowror etc *St D*
LLANGYNLLO (St Cynllo) Ban Teifi w Henllan and
  Llanfairorllwyn etc *St D*
LLANGYNLLO (St Cynllo) Whitton and Pilleth and Cascob
  etc *S & B*
LLANGYNNWR (St Ceinwr) and Cwmffrwd *St D 11*
  V W D A GRIFFITHS
LLANGYNOG Builth and Llanddewi'r Cwm w Llangynog
  etc *S & B*
LLANGYNOG (St Cynog) Llan-llwch w Llangain and
  Llangynog *St D*
LLANGYNOG (St Cynog) (St Melangel) *St As 9*
  P-in-c P EN DAVID
**LLANGYNWYD (St Cynwyd) (St Stephen) (St Tydfil) w
  Maesteg** *Llan 8* **V** E B THOMAS, **NSM** G H J BALL
LLANGYNYW (St Cynyw) Meifod and Llangynyw *St As*
**LLANGYSTENNIN (St Cystenin) (St Michael) (St Katherine)
  (St Mary)** *St As 5* **R** T E MART
LLANHAMLACH (St Peter and St Illtyd) Llanfrynach and
  Cantref w Llanhamlach *S & B*

LLANHARAN (St Julius and St Aaron) w Peterston-super-Montem *Llan 1* V P N THOMPSON
LLANHARRY (St Illtud) *Llan 4* **P-in-c** J G WILLIAMS
LLANHENNOCK (St John) Tredunnoc and Llantrisant w Llanhennock etc *Mon*
LLANHILLETH (Christchurch) (St Mark) *Mon 8* V A J WAY
LLANHYWEL (St Hywel) Llanrhian w Llanhywel and Carnhedryn etc *St D*
LLANIDAN (St Nidan) Llanfihangel Ysgeifiog and Llanffinan etc *Ban*
LLANIDLOES (St Idloes) w Llangurig *Ban 8* V D J PARRY, NSM K FERGUSON
LLANIESTYN (St Iestyn) Llansadwrn w Llanddona and Llaniestyn etc *Ban*
LLANIESTYN (St Iestyn) Botwnnog w Bryncroes *Ban*
LLANIGON (St Eigon) Hay w Llanigon and Capel-y-Ffin *S & B*
LLANILAR (St Hilary) w Rhostie and Llangwyryfon w Llanfihangel Lledrod *St D 10* V E G JONES
LLANILID (St Illid and St Curig) w Pencoed *Llan 1* R E D EVANS
LLANILLTYD (St John) Brecon St David w Llanspyddid and Llanilltyd *S & B*
LLANINA (St Ina) Llanllwchaearn and Llanina *St D*
LLANISHEN (Christ Church) *Llan 2* V A W EVANS
LLANISHEN (St Dennis) w Trellech Grange and Llanfihangel Tor-y-Mynydd w Llangunnog and Llansoy *Mon 3* V G M DAVIES
LLANISHEN (St Isan) (St Faith) *Llan 2* V N G JONES
LLANLLAWDDOG (St Llawddog) Llanpumsaint w Llanllawddog *St D*
LLANLLAWER Newport w Cilgwyn and Dinas w Llanllawer *St D*
LLANLLECHID (St Llechid) (St Cross) *Ban 2* R D J DREDGE
LLANLLEONFEL (Parish Church) Llanganten and Llangammarch and Llanfechan etc *S & B*
LLANLLIBIO Valley w Llanfachraeth *Ban*
LLANLLOWELL (St Llywel) Tredunnoc and Llantrisant w Llanhennock etc *Mon*
LLANLLUGAN (St Mary) Llanfair Caereinion w Llanllugan *St As*
LLANLLWCHAEARN (St Llwchaiarn) and Llanina *St D 8* R R G DAVIES
LLANLLWCHAIARN (All Saints) Newtown w Llanllwchaiarn w Aberhafesp *St As*
LLANLLWCHAIARN (St Llwchaiarn) as above
LLANLLWNI (St Luke or St Llonio) *St D 9* **Dn-in-c** D BOWEN
LLANLLYFNI (St Rhedyw) (St John) (Christ Church) *Ban 1* R Vacant
LLANLLYR-YN-RHOS (St Llyr) w Llanfihangel Helygen *S & B 5* **P-in-c** D B JAMES
LLANMADOC (St Madoc) Llanrhidian w Llanmadoc and Cheriton *S & B*
LLANMAES (St Catwg) Llantwit Major *Llan*
LLANMARTIN (St Martin) Bishton *Mon*
LLANMEREWIG (St Llwchaiarn) Kerry and Llanmerewig and Dolfor *St As*
LLANMILOE (St Barbara) Pendine w Llanmiloe and Eglwys Gymyn w Marros *St D*
LLANNEFYDD (St Nefydd and St Mary) Henllan and Llannefydd and Bylchau *St As*
LLANNOR (Holy Cross) Llanbedrog w Llannor w Llanfihangel etc *Ban*
LLANOVER (St Bartholomew) Goetre w Llanover *Mon*
LLANPUMSAINT (Five Saints) w Llanllawddog *St D 11* V Vacant Llanpumsaint (0126784) 205
LLANRHAEADR-YM-MOCHNANT (St Dogfan) and Llanarmon Mynyd and Pennant and Hirnant *St As 9* **D-in-c** V E LEWIS
LLANRHAEADR-YNG-NGHINMEIRCH (St Dyfnog) and Prion *St As 2* V C W EVANS
LLANRHEITHAN (St Rheithan) Llanrhian w Llanhywel and Carnhedryn etc *St D*
LLANRHIAN (St Rhian) w Llanhywel and Carnhedryn w Llanrheithan *St D 3* V D R REES
LLANRHIDIAN (St Rhidian and St Illtyd) w Llanmadoc and Cheriton *S & B 8* V J W GRIFFIN
LLANRHOS (St Paul) *St As 5* V W D JENKINS, C M R BALKWILL, NSM J H ECCLES
LLANRHUDDLAD (St Rhuddlad) Llanfaethlu w Llanfwrog and Llanrhuddlad etc *Ban*
LLANRHWYDRUS as above
LLANRHYCHWYN (St Rhychwyn) Caerhun w Llangelynnin w Llanbedr-y-Cennin *Ban*
LLANRHYDD (St Meugan) Ruthin w Llanrhydd *St As*

LLANRHYSTUD (St Restitutis) Llansantffraed and Llanbadarn Trefeglwys etc *St D*
LLANRUG (St Gabriel) Llanberis w Llanrug *Ban*
LLANRUG (St Michael) as above
LLANRUMNEY (St Dyfrig) *Mon 6* V P VANN
LLANRWST (St Grwst) and Llanddoget and Capel Garmon *St As 5* R W R MORTIMER
LLANSADWRN (St Sadwrn) w Llanddona and Llaniestyn w Pentraeth w Llanddyfnan *Ban 5* R D PRYS
LLANSADWRN (St Sadwrn) w Llanwrda and Manordeilo *St D 14* V A J LEGG
LLANSADWRNEN (St Sadwrnen) Laugharne w Llansadwrnen and Llandawke *St D*
LLANSAMLET (St Samlet) (St John) (St Paul) *S & B 7* V C M DARVILL, C R P PITCHER, NSM T J WILLIAMS
LLANSANNAN (St Sannan) Llanfair Talhaearn and Llansannan etc *St As*
LLANSANNOR (St Senwyr) Cowbridge *Llan*
LLANSANTFFRAED (St Bridget) Llanddewi Rhydderch and Llangattock etc *Mon*
LLANSANTFFRAED (St Bridget) and Llanbadarn Trefeglwys w Llanrhystud *St D 8* V M S TAYLOR
LLANSANTFFRAED-IN-ELWELL (St Bridget) Llanelwedd w Llanfaredd w Llansantffraed etc *S & B*
LLANSANTFFRAED-JUXTA-USK (St Bride) Llanfeugan and Llanthetty and Glyncollwng etc *S & B*
LLANSANTFFRAID GLAN CONWAY (St Ffraid) (St Martin) and Eglwysfach *St As 5* R K HOWARD
LLANSANTFFRAID GLYN CEIRIOG (St Ffraid) and Llanarmon Dyffryn Ceiriog and Pontfadog *St As 13* **D-in-c** M V JONES
LLANSANTFFRAID-YN-MECHAIN (St Ffraid) and Llanfechain *St As 9* V L ROGERS
LLANSANTFRAID GLYN DYFRDWY (St Ffraid) Glyndyfrdwy and Llansantfraid Glyn Dyfrdwy *St As*
LLANSAWEL (St Mary) w Briton Ferry *Llan 10* V I D HAMER
LLANSAWEL (St Sawyl) Cynwyl Gaeo w Llansawel and Talley *St D*
LLANSILIN (St Silin) w Llangadwaladr and Llangedwyn *St As 9* V C F CARTER
LLANSOY (St Tysoi) Llanishen w Trellech Grange and Llanfihangel etc *Mon*
LLANSPYDDID (St Cattwg) Brecon St David w Llanspyddid and Llanilltyd *S & B*
LLANSTADWEL (St Tudwal) *St D 5* V M K LIKEMAN
LLANSTEFFAN (St Ystyffan) and Llan-y-bri and Llandeilo Abercywyn *St D 11* **D-in-c** S E JONES
LLANSTEPHEN (St Steffan) Llandefalle and Llyswen w Boughrood etc *S & B*
LLANSTINAN (St Justinian) Llanwnda, Goodwick, w Manorowen and Llanstinan *St D*
LLANTARNAM (St Michael) Cwmbran *Mon*
LLANTHETTY (St Tetti) Llanfeugan and Llanthetty and Glyncollwng etc *S & B*
LLANTHONY (St David) Llanfihangel Crucorney w Oldcastle etc *Mon*
LLANTILIO CROSSENNY (St Teilo) and Penrhos w Llanvetherine and Llanvapley *Mon 1* V C HAWES
LLANTILLIO PERTHOLEY (St Teilo) w Bettws Chapel and Llanddewi Skirrid *Mon 1* V M D VINE, NSM J M DRAPER
LLANTOOD Cilgerran w Bridell and Llantwyd *St D*
LLANTRISANT (Church) Ysbyty Cynfyn w Llantrisant and Eglwys Newydd *St D*
LLANTRISANT (St Afran, St Ieuan and St Sanan) Valley w Llanfachraeth *Ban*
LLANTRISANT (St Illtyd, St Gwynno and St Dyfodwg) (St Michael) (St David) *Llan 11* V E HUGHES, C A P BOOKLESS, NSM G A BLYTH
LLANTRISANT (St Peter, St Paul and St John) Tredunnoc and Llantrisant w Llanhennock etc *Mon*
LLANTRITHYD (St Illtyd) Llancarfan w Llantrithyd *Llan*
LLANTWIT (St Illtyd) Neath w Llantwit *Llan*
LLANTWIT FADRE (St Illtyd) (St Andrew) *Llan 11* V M K JONES, C H BUTLER
LLANTWIT MAJOR (St Illtud) (St Donat) *Llan 4* R D M JENKINS, TV P G MORRIS, M KOMOR, NSM D V GINN
LLANTWYD (St Illtud) Cilgerran w Bridell and Llantwyd *St D*
LLANTYSILIO (St Tysilio) Llangollen w Trevor and Llantysilio *St As*
LLANULID (St Ilid) Llywel and Traean-glas w Llanulid *S & B*

LLANUWCHLLYN (St Deiniol) Llanycil w Bala and Frongoch and Llangower etc *St As*

LLANVACHES (St Dyfrig) Penhow, St Brides Netherwent w Llandavenny etc *Mon*

LLANVAPLEY (St Mable) Llantilio Crossenny w Penrhos, Llanvetherine etc *Mon*

LLANVETHERINE (St James the Elder) as above

LLANWDDYN (St Wyddyn) and Llanfihangel-yng-Nghwynfa and Llwydiarth *St As 9* V SJTWYCROSS

LLANWELLWYFO (St Gwenllwyfo) Amlwch *Ban*

LLANWENARTH CITRA (St Peter) Abergavenny St Mary w Llanwenarth Citra *Mon*

LLANWENOG (St Gwenog) Llanybydder and Llanwenog w Llanwnnen *St D*

LLANWERN (St Mary) Bishton *Mon*

LLANWINIO (St Gwynio) Tre-lech a'r Betws w Abernant and Llanwinio *St D*

LLANWNDA (St Gwyndaf) and Goodwick (St Peter) w Manorowen and Llanstinan *St D 3* V SBTHATCHER

LLANWNDA (St Gwyndaf) (St Baglan Old Church) and Llandwrog *Ban 1* V DCBRYANT

LLANWNNEN (St Lucia) Llanybydder and Llanwenog w Llanwnnen *St D*

LLANWNNOG (St Gwynog) and Caersws w Carno *Ban 8* V DJCHAPMAN

LLANWNNWS (St Gwnnws) Llanfihangel w Llanafan and Llanwnnws etc *St D*

LLANWRDA (St Cwrdaf) Llansadwrn w Llanwrda and Manordeilo *St D*

LLANWRIN (St Ust and St Dyfrig) Machynlleth and Llanwrin *Ban*

LLANWRTHWL (St Gwrthwl) Cwmddauddwr w St Harmon's and Llanwrthwl *S & B*

LLANWRTYD (St James) (St David) w Llanddulas in Tir Abad and Eglwys Oen Duw and Llanfihangel Abergwessin and Llanddewi *S & B 2* V IBBESSANT

LLANWYDDELAN (St Gwyddelan) Betws Cedewain and Tregynon and Llanwyddelan *St As*

LLANWYNNO (St Gwynno) (Christ Church) *Llan 11* V PJBENNETT

LLANYBYDDER (St Peter) and Llanwenog w Llanwnnen *St D 9* V EDGRIFFITHS

LLANYCEFN (Church) Llawhaden w Bletherston and Llanycefn *St D*

LLANYCHAEARN (St Llwchaiarn) w Llanddeiniol *St D 10* V BJHJONES

LLANYCHAN (St Hychan) Llanynys w Llanychan *St As*

LLANYCHAR (Church) Fishguard w Llanychar and Pontfaen w Morfil etc *St D*

LLANYCHLWYDOG as above

LLANYCIL (St Beuno) w Bala and Frongoch and Llangower w Llanuwchllyn *St As 15* R GTHOMAS

LLANYCRWYS (St David) Pencarreg and Llanycrwys *St D*

LLANYMAWDDWY (St Tydecho) Mallywd w Cemais and Llanymawddwy *Ban*

LLANYNGHENEDL VALLEY (St Michael) Valley w Llanfachraeth *Ban*

LLANYNYS Builth and Llanddewi'r Cwm w Llangynog etc *S & B*

LLANYNYS (St Saeran) w Llanychan *St As 3* P-in-c DJWILLIAMS

LLANYRE Llanllyr-yn-Rhos w Llanfihangel Helygen *S & B*

LLANYRNEWYDD (St Gwynour) *S & B 8* V TEVANS

LLANYSTYMDWY (St John the Baptist) Dolbenmaen w Llanystymdwy w Llangybi etc *Ban*

LLANYWERN (St Mary the Virgin) Llangorse, Cathedine, Llanfihangel Talyllyn etc *S & B*

LLAWHADEN (St Aidan) w Bletherston and Llanycefn *St D 2* V ACLARK

LLAWRYBETWS (St James) Corwen & Llangar w Gwyddelwern and Llawrybetws *St As*

LLAY (St Martin) *St As 16* V DQBELLAMY

LLECHGYNFARWY (St Cynfarwy) Bodedern w Llechgynfarwy and Llechylched etc *Ban*

LLECHRYD (St Tydfil) Llandygwydd and Cenarth w Cilrhedyn etc *St D*

LLECHYLCHED (Holy Trinity) Bodedern w Llechgynfarwy and Llechylched etc *Ban*

LLOWES (St Meilig) Glasbury and Llowes w Clyro and Betws *S & B*

LLWYDCOED (St James) Aberdare St Fagan *Llan*

LLWYDIARTH (St Mary) Llanwddyn and Llanfihangel and Llwydiarth *St As*

LLWYNCELLYN (St Luke) Cymmer and Porth *Llan*

LLWYNDERW (Holy Cross) (Clyne Chapel) *S & B 6* V GEBENNETT, C DMGRIFFITHS

LLWYNGWRIL Arthog w Fairbourne w Llangelynnin w Rhoslefain *Ban*

LLWYNHENDY (St David) *St D* D-in-c AMGRAY

LLWYNYPIA Ystrad Rhondda w Ynyscynon *Llan*

LLYS-Y-FRAN (St Meilyr) New Moat w Llys-y-fran *St D*

LLYSDINAM Newbridge-on-Wye and Llanfihangel Brynpabuan etc *S & B*

LLYSFAEN (St Cynfran) Llanddulas and Llysfaen *St As*

LLYSWEN (St Gwendoline) Llandefalle and Llyswen w Boughrood etc *S & B*

LLYSWORNEY (St Tydfil) Colwinston w Llandow and Llysworney *Llan*

LLYWEL (St David) and Traean-glas w Llanulid *S & B 1* V DWDAVIES

LOUGHER (St Michael) (St David) (St Paul) *S & B 9* V DROBERTS, NSM NLWILLIAMS, KMORGAN

LOVESTON (St Leonard) Jeffreyston w Reynoldston and E Williamston etc *St D*

LUDCHURCH (St Elidyr) Begelly w Ludchurch and Crunwere *St D*

MACHEN (St Michael) (St John the Baptist) *Mon 6* R CFWARREN

MACHYNLLETH (St Peter) and Llanwrin *Ban 9* R EWROWLANDS

MAENCLOCHOG (St Mary) w Henry's Moat and Mynachlogddu and Llangolman w Llandeilo *St D 2* V MNHGRAINGER, NSM RHARPER

MAENORDEIFI (St David) (Old Parish Church) and Capel Colman w Llanfihangel Penbedw and Clydau w Penrhydd and Castellan *St D 6* Dn-in-c GWATKINS

MAENTWROG (St Twrog) w Trawsfynydd *Ban 7* R BEVANS

MAERDY (All Saints) Ferndale w Maerdy *Llan*

MAESGLAS and Duffryn *Mon* I ABWATERS

MAESMYNIS AND LLANYNYS (St David) Builth and Llanddewi'r Cwm w Llangynog etc *S & B*

MAESTEG (St David) Llangynwyd w Maesteg *Llan*

MAESTEG (St Michael) as above

MAESTEILO (St John) Llandeilo and Taliaris *St D*

MAESTIR (St Mary) Lamp Pont Steffan w Silian *St D*

MAGOR (St Mary) w Redwick and Undy *Mon 4* V BJPARFITT, C SGCARBY

MAINDEE Newport Maindee St Jo Ev *Mon*

MALLYWD (St Tydecho) w Cemais and Llanymawddwy *Ban 9* R GJVAUGHAN-JONES

MALPAS (St Mary) *Mon 9* V RMCAPPER

MAMHILAD (St Illtud) and Llanfihangel Pontymoile *Mon 5* NSM CHPEAD

MANAFON (St Michael) Berriew and Manafon *St As*

MANCOT (St Michael) Hawarden *St As*

MANOBIER (St James) and St Florence w Redberth *St D 1* V VFMILLGATE

MANORDEILO (St Paul) Llansadwrn w Llanwrda and Manordeilo *St D*

MANOROWEN (St Mary) Llanwnda, Goodwick, w Manorowen and Llanstinan *St D*

MANSELTON (St Michael and All Angels) *S & B 10* V THJONES

MARCHWIEL (St Marcella) and Isycoed *St As 11* R DASLIM

MARCROSS (Holy Trinity) Llantwit Major *Llan*

MARGAM (St Mary) (St David) *Llan 8* V DGBELCHER

MARLOES (St Peter) Dale and St Brides w Marloes *St D*

MARROS (St Lawrence) Pendine w Llanmiloe and Eglwys Gymyn w Marros *St D*

MARSHFIELD (St Mary) and Peterstone Wentloog and Coedkernew w St Bride's Wentloog *Mon 6* V TJGREEDY

MARTLETWY (St Marcellus) w Lawrenny and Minwear and Yerbeston w Templeton *St D 4* V MHROWLANDS

MATHERN (St Tewdric) and Mounton w St Pierre *Mon 2* V ARWILLIE

MATHRY (Holy Martyrs) w St Edren's and Grandston w St Nicholas and Jordanston *St D 3* V GOASSON

MATTHEWSTOWN (All Saints) Penrhiwceiber w Matthewstown and Ynysboeth *Llan*

MAUDLAM (St Mary Magdalene) Pyle w Kenfig *Llan*

MEIDRIM (St David) and Llanboidy and Merthyr *St D 15* V JGAINER

MEIFOD (St Tysilio and St Mary) and Llangynyw *St As 8* V GMORGAN

MELIDEN (St Melyd) (St Mary Magdalene) and Gwaenysgor *St As 1* V DPDHREES

MELINE (St Dogmael) Nevern and Y Beifil w Eglwyswrw and Meline etc *St D*

MENAI BRIDGE (St Mary) Llandegfan w Llandysilio *Ban*

MERLIN'S BRIDGE (St Mark) Haverfordwest St Mary and St Thos w Haroldston *St D*

MERTHYR (St Martin) Meidrim and Llanboidy and Merthyr *St D*

MERTHYR CYNOG (St Cynog) and Dyffryn Honddu w Garthbrengy w Llandefaelog-Fach and Llanfihangel Fechan *S & B 1* **V** T C JOHNS

MERTHYR DYFAN (St Dyfan and St Teilo) *Llan 6* **R** T A DOHERTY

MERTHYR MAWR (St Teilo) Laleston w Tythegston and Merthyr Mawr *Llan*

MERTHYR TYDFIL (Christ Church) (St Luke) *Llan 9* **V** S S MORGAN, **C** P S WEEDING

MERTHYR TYDFIL (St David) (St Tydfil's Well) *Llan 9* **R** M J MARSDEN

MERTHYR VALE (St Mary and Holy Innocents) Troedyrhiw w Merthyr Vale *Llan*

MICHAELSTON-LE-PIT (St Michael and All Angels) St Andrew's Major and Michaelston-le-Pit *Llan*

MICHAELSTON-SUPER-AVON Cwmavon *Llan*

MICHAELSTON-SUPER-ELY (St Michael) St Fagans w Michaelston-super-Ely *Llan*

MICHAELSTON-Y-FEDW (St Michael) St Mellons and Michaelston-y-Fedw *Mon*

MICHEL TROY (St Michael) Overmonnow w Wonastow and Michel Troy *Mon*

MILFORD HAVEN (St Katherine) (St Peter) (St Thomas a Becket) *St D 5* **V** J H M DAVIES

MINERA (St Mary) (St Tudfil) (St Andrew) (St David) *St As 16* **V** J G CANHAM

MINWEAR (St Womar) Martletwy w Lawrenny and Minwear etc *St D*

MISKIN (St John the Baptist) *Llan 7* **V** N C H BROWN

MOCHDRE (All Saints) *St As 7* **C** J WOOD

MOLD (St Mary) *St As 14* **V** C I DAY, **C** A F C KEULEMANS, P McLEAN

MONINGTON (St Nicholas) St Dogmael's w Moylgrove and Monington *St D*

MONKSWOOD (St Matthew) Usk and Monkswood w Glascoed Chpl and Gwehelog *Mon*

MONKTON (St Nicholas and St John) *St D 1* **V** R G LLOYD

MONMOUTH (St Mary the Virgin) *Mon 3* **V** J W C COUTTS, **Par Dn** U M P KROLL

MONTGOMERY (St Nicholas) and Forden and Llandyssil *St As 10* **R** B LETSON

MORFIL Fishguard w Llanychar and Pontfaen w Morfil etc *St D*

MORRISTON (St David) (St John) *S & B 7* **V** A J KNIGHT, **C** E A HARVEY-COOK

MOSTYN (Christ Church) w Ffynnongroyw *St As 4* **V** S D GREEN

MOUNTAIN ASH (St Margaret) (St Illtyd) *Llan 7* **V** D YEOMAN, **C** D J A BURTON

MOUNTON Narberth w Mounton w Robeston Wathen and Crinow *St D*

MOUNTON (St Andoenus) Mathern and Mounton w St Pierre *Mon*

MOYLGROVE (St Mynno, St David and St Andrew) St Dogmael's w Moylgrove and Monington *St D*

MWNT (Holy Cross) Cardigan and Mwnt and Y Ferwig *St D*

MYDDFAI (St Michael) Llandingat w Myddfai *St D*

MYDROILYN (Holy Trinity) Llanerch Aeron w Ciliau Aeron and Dihewyd etc *St D*

MYNACHLOGDDU (St Dogmael) Maenclochog w Henry's Moat and Mynachlogddu etc *St D*

MYNYDDISLWYN (St Tudor) *Mon 7* **TR** R J SUMMERS, **TV** A C EDWARDS, **TM** L A F C WATKINS

NANNERCH (St Michael) Cilcain and Nannerch and Rhyd-y-mwyn *St As*

NANTCWNLLE (St Cynllo) Llanfihangel Ystrad and Cilcennin w Trefilan etc *St D*

NANTGLYN (St James) Denbigh and Nantglyn *St As*

NANTMEL (St Cynllo) Rhayader and Nantmel *S & B*

NANTYGLO (Holy Trinity and St Anne) Blaina and Nantyglo *Mon*

NANTYMOEL SS Peter and Paul w Wyndham *Llan 1* **V** R G AUSTIN

NARBERTH (St Andrew) w Mounton w Robeston Wathen and Crinow *St D 4* **R** H A CHIPLIN

NASH (St Mary) Pemb Dock w Cosheston w Nash and Upton *St D*

NASH (St Mary) Goldcliffe and Whiston and Nash *Mon*

NEATH (St Thomas) (St David) (St Catherine) (St Peter and StPaul) w Llantwit *Llan 10* **R** W P THOMAS, **C** P M N GULLIDGE

NEBO (Dewi Sant) Llansantffraed and Llanbadarn Trefeglwys etc *St D*

NEFYN (St David) (St Mary) w Pistyll w Tudweiliog w Llandudwen w Edern *Ban 11* **V** E W THOMAS

NELSON (St John the Baptist) Llanfabon *Llan*

NERCWYS (St Mary) Treuddyn w Nercwys *St As*

NEVERN (St Brynach) and Y Beifil w Eglwyswrw and Meline and Eglwyswen and Llanfair Nant-gwyn *St D 6* **V** B LEWIS

NEW HEDGES (St Anne) Tenby *St D*

NEW MOAT (St Nicholas) w Llys-y-fran *St D 2* **NSM** R HARPER

NEW RADNOR (St Mary) and Llanfihangel Nantmelan and Evancoyd w Gladwestry and Colva *S & B 5* **V** G TURNER

NEW TREDEGAR (St Dingat) *Mon 7* **V** D J YOUNG

NEWBOROUGH (St Peter) w Llangeinwen w Llangaffo and Llanfair-yn-y-Cwmwd *Ban 4* **R** R L NEWALL

NEWBRIDGE (St Paul) (St Peter) *Mon 7* **V** T N COLEMAN

NEWBRIDGE-ON-WYE (All Saints) and Llanfihangel Brynpabuan w Cwmbach Llechryd and Llanafan Fawr *S & B 2* **V** B WOOLLASTON

NEWCASTLE (St Illtud) *Llan 1* **V** M D WITCOMBE, **NSM** O M PARRY

NEWCASTLE EMLYN (Holy Trinity) w Llandyfriog and Troed-yr-aur *St D 7* **C** E HOWELLS

NEWCHURCH (St Mary) Cynwil Elfed and Newchurch *St D*

NEWCHURCH (St Mary) Bryngwyn and Newchurch and Llanbedr etc *S & B*

NEWCHURCH (St Michael) Cynwil Elfed and Newchurch *St D*

NEWCHURCH (St Peter) as above

NEWCHURCH (St Peter) Caerwent w Dinham and Llanfair Discoed etc *Mon*

NEWMARKET Dyserth and Trelawnyd and Cwm *St As*

NEWPORT (All Saints) *Mon 9* **P-in-c** I S DOULL

NEWPORT (Cathedral of St Woolos) (St Martin) *Mon 9* **V** D G LEWIS

NEWPORT (Christ Church) *Mon 9* **V** R G HACKETT

NEWPORT (St Andrew) (St Philip) *Mon 9* **V** H J DAVIES

NEWPORT (St John Baptist) *Mon 9* **V** C D WESTBROOK

NEWPORT (St John the Evangelist) (St Mary) *Mon 9* **V** J D E DAVIES, **C** A C SULLY, **NSM** J K BEARDMORE

NEWPORT St Julian (St Julius and St Aaron) *Mon 9* **V** D R WILLIAMS, **C** J M HARRIS

NEWPORT (St Mark) *Mon 9* **V** K W SHARPE

NEWPORT (St Mary) w Cilgwyn and Dinas w Llanllawer *St D 6* **R** R C JONES, **NSM** P L DAVIES

NEWPORT (St Matthew) *Mon 9* **V** J P HARRIS, **C** M K R STALLARD

NEWPORT St Paul *Mon 9* **V** W E KELLY

NEWPORT (St Stephen) and Holy Trinity *Mon 9* **V** M R AINSCOUGH

NEWPORT (St Teilo) *Mon 9* **V** C J NICKLESS, **C** P MUSINDI, **NSM** I R GALT

NEWTON (St Peter) *S & B 6* **V** D THOMAS

NEWTON NORTH Slebech and Uzmaston w Boulston *St D*

NEWTON NOTTAGE (St John the Baptist) (All Saints) (St David) *Llan 8* **R** P R MASSON, **C** G N STARTIN, M D GABLE

NEWTOWN (St David) w Llanllwchaiarn w Aberhafesp *St As 7* **R** P B JONES, **NSM** A R MARSHALL, G K MARSHALL

NEYLAND (St Clement) Llanstadwel *St D*

NICHOLASTON (St Nicholas) Oxwich w Penmaen and Nicholaston *S & B*

NOLTON (St Madog) w Roch *St D 5* **R** A CRAVEN

NOLTON (St Mary) Coity w Nolton *Llan*

NORTHOP (St Eurgain and St Peter) (St Mary) *St As 14* **V** G L JONES

NORTON (Mission Church) Oystermouth *S & B*

NORTON (St Andrew) Knighton and Norton *S & B*

NOTTAGE (St David) Newton Nottage *Llan*

OAKWOOD (St John) Port Talbot St Agnes w Oakwood *Llan*

OAKWOOD (St Teilo) as above

OGMORE VALE (St John the Baptist) Llangeinor *Llan*

OLDCASTLE Llanfihangel Crucorney w Oldcastle etc *Mon*

OVERMONNOW (St Thomas) w Wonastow and Michel Troy *Mon 3* **V** J F GRAY

OVERTON (St Mary the Virgin) and Erbistock and Penley *St As 11* **R** P A CROWE

OXWICH (St Illtyd) w Penmaen and Nicholaston *S & B 8* **V** R H MORGAN

OYSTERMOUTH (All Saints) *S & B 6* **V** G H THOMAS, **C** I P CHARLESWORTH, **NSM** D J H WATKINS

PANTEG (St Mary) *Mon 10* **R** D G BRUNNING

PANTYFFRID (Mission Church) Berriew and Manafon *St As*

PATRICIO (St Issui the Martyr) Llangenni and Llanbedr Ystrad Yw w Patricio *S & B*

PEMBROKE (St Mary) (St Michael) (St Daniel) *St D 1* **V** C W BOWEN, **C** B W IRESON

PEMBROKE DOCK (St John) (St Patrick) (St Teilo) w
Cosheston w Nash and Upton *St D 1* **V** A THOMAS,
C W J JONES
PEN-BOYR (St Llawddog) *St D 7* **V** *Vacant* Velindre (01559)
370425
PEN-BRE (St Illtud) *St D 12* **V** V P ROBERTS
PENALLT (Old Church) and Trellech *Mon 3*
V J K C DENERLEY
PENALLY (St Nicholas) Tenby *St D*
PENARTH (All Saints) (St Peter) (St Luke) *Llan 6*
V F A G MUDGE, **C** R S EVANS
PENARTH (St Augustine) (Holy Nativity) w Lavernock
Llan 6 **R** N H COLLINS, **C** M N R BOWIE
PENBRYN (St Michael) Llangrannog w Llandysiliogogo w
Penbryn *St D*
PENCADER (St Mary) Llanfihangel-ar-arth *St D*
PENCARREG (St Patrick) and Llanycrwys *St D 9*
C-in-c B E MORRIS
PENCLAWDD Llanyrnewydd *S & B*
PENCOED (St David) Llanilid w Pencoed *Llan*
PENCOED (St Paul) as above
PENCOEDCAE (Mission) Graig *Llan*
PENDERYN (St Cynog) w Ystradfellte and Pontneathvaughan
S & B 1 **R** J H SCOTT
PENDINE (St Margaret) w Llanmiloe and Eglwys Gymyn w
Marros *St D 15* **R** K T LITTLER
PENDOYLAN (St Cadoc) and Welsh St Donats *Llan 5*
V E C R COUNSELL
PENEGOES (St Cadfarch) and Darowen w Llanbryn-Mair
Ban 9 **R** G ap GWILYM
PENHOW (St John the Baptist) and St Brides Netherwent w
Llandavenny and Llanvaches and Llandevaud *Mon 4*
V J HEALES
PENISA'R-WAEN (St Helen) Llandinorwig w Penisa'r-waen
Ban
PENLEY (St Mary Magdalene) Overton and Erbistock and
Penley *St As*
PENLLECH Aberdaron etc *Ban*
PENLLERGAER (St David) *S & B 9* **V** D R PAYNE
PENLLWYN (St Mary the Virgin) Mynyddislwyn *Mon*
PENLLYN (Chapel of Ease) Cowbridge *Llan*
PENMACHNO (St Tudclud) Betws-y-Coed and Capel Curig
w Penmachno etc *Ban*
PENMAEN (St David) and Crumlin *Mon 7* **V** R E HIGGINS
PENMAEN (St John the Baptist) Oxwich w Penmaen and
Nicholaston *S & B*
PENMARK (St Mary) w Porthkerry *Llan 6* **V** S C PARE
PENMORFA Ynyscynhaearn w Penmorfa and Porthmadog
Ban
PENMYNYDD (St Credifael) Llanfairpwll w Penmynydd
Ban
PENNAL (St Peter ad Vincula) w Corris and Esgairgeiliog
Ban 9 **R** G ap IORWERTH
PENNANT (St Thomas) Llanrhaeadr-ym-Mochnant and
Llanarmon etc *St As*
PENNANT MELANGELL (St Melangel) Llangynog *St As*
PENNARD (St Mary) Ilston w Pennard *S & B*
PENPONT (no dedication) Trallwng, Bettws Penpont w
Aberyskir etc *S & B*
PENRHIWCEIBER (St Winifred) w Matthewstown and
Ynysboeth *Llan 7* **V** G J FRANCIS
PENRHOS (Holy Trinity) Llandysilio and Penrhos and
Llandrinio etc *St As*
PENRHOS (St Cadoc) Llantilio Crossenny w Penrhos,
Llanvetherine etc *Mon*
PENRHOSLLUGWY (St Michael) Llaneugrad w Llanallgo
and Penrhosllugwy etc *Ban*
PENRHYDD Maenordeifi and Capel Colman w Llanfihangel
etc *St D*
PENRHYN-COCH (St John) and Elerch *St D 10*
P-in-c N FAIRLAMB
PENRHYNDEUDRAETH (Holy Trinity) w Llanfrothen w
Beddgelert *Ban 7* **V** J ASHLEY-ROBERTS
PENRHYNSIDE (St Sannan) Llanrhos *St As*
PENRHYNSIDE BAY (St David) as above
PENRICE (St Andrew) Reynoldston w Penrice and
Llangennith *S & B*
PENSARN (St David) Abergele *St As*
PENSTROWED (St Gwrhai) Llandinam w Trefeglwys w
Penstrowed *Ban*
PENTERRY (St Mary) Itton and St Arvans w Penterry and
Kilgwrrwg etc *Mon*
PENTIR (St Cedol) (St Elizabeth) *Ban 1*
P-in-c G W HEWITT
PENTRAETH (St Mary) Llansadwrn w Llanddona and
Llaniestyn etc *Ban*
PENTRE (St Peter) *Llan 12* **V** P H MORGANS

PENTRECHWYTH (St Peter) Glantawe *S & B*
PENTREFELIN Ynyscynhaearn w Penmorfa and
Porthmadog *Ban*
PENTREVOELAS (Parish Church) Cerrigydrudion w
Llanfihangel etc *St As*
PENTROBIN (St John) Hawarden *St As*
PENTWYN (St David) Cyncoed *Mon*
PENTWYN (St Mary) Penallt and Trellech *Mon*
PENTYRCH (St Cadwg) (St David) *Llan 5*
V G W A HOLCOMBE
PENYBONTFAWR Llanrhaeadr-ym-Mochnant and
Llanarmon etc *St As*
PENYCAE (St Thomas) *St As 16* **V** G PITT,
NSM B A PITT
PENYCLAWDD (St Martin) Dingestow and Llangovan w
Penyclawdd etc *Mon*
PENYDARREN (St John the Baptist) *Llan 9*
V M I WILLIAMS
PENYFAI (All Saints) w Tondu *Llan 1* **V** J F SEWARD
PENYFFORDD (Emmanuel) Hope *St As*
PENYGRAIG (St Barnabas) Dinas and Penygraig w
Williamstown *Llan*
PENYWAUN (St Winifred) Hirwaun *Llan*
PETERSTON-SUPER-ELY (St Peter) w St Brides-super-Ely
Llan 5 **R** R E YOUNG, **NSM** S P TOMS
PETERSTON-SUPER-MONTEM (St Peter) Llanharan w
Peterston-super-Montem *Llan*
PETERSTONE WENTLOOG (St Peter) Marshfield and
Peterstone Wentloog etc *Mon*
PILLETH (Our Lady of Pilleth) Whitton and Pilleth and
Cascob etc *S & B*
PISTYLL (St Beuno) Nefyn w Pistyll w Tudweiliog w
Llandudwen etc *Ban*
PLAS POWER (St Mary) Wrexham *St As*
PONT AMAN (St Thomas) Betws St Dav w Ammanford
St D
PONT DOLANOG (St John the Evangelist) Pont Robert and
Pont Dolanog *St As*
PONT-IETS Pontyates and Llangyndeyrn *St D*
PONT ROBERT (St John the Evangelist) and Pont Dolanog
St As 8 **C-in-c** J ROCK
PONTARDAWE (All Saints) Llangiwg *S & B*
PONTARDAWE (St Peter) as above
PONTARDDULAIS Llandeilo Tal-y-bont *S & B*
PONTARFYNACH Ysbyty Cynfyn w Llantrisant and
Eglwys Newydd *St D*
PONTARGOTHI (Holy Trinity) Llanegwad w Llanfynydd
St D
PONTBLYDDYN (Christ Church) *St As 14*
V C O BENNETT
PONTERWYD Ysbyty Cynfyn w Llantrisant and Eglwys
Newydd *St D*
PONTFADOG (St John) Llansantffraid and Llanarmon and
Pontfadog *St As*
PONTFAEN (St Brynach) Fishguard w Llanychar and
Pontfaen w Morfil etc *St D*
PONTLANIO Llanychaearn w Llanddeiniol *St D*
PONTLLANFRAITH (St Augustine) Mynyddislwyn *Mon*
PONTLLIW (St Anne) Penllergaer *S & B*
PONTLOTTYN (St Tyfaelog) (St Michael) (St Aidan) w
Fochriw *Llan 2* **V** M PERRY
PONTNEATHVAUGHAN (St John) Penderyn w
Ystradfellte and Pontneathvaughan *S & B*
PONTNEWYDD (Holy Trinity) *Mon 10* **V** D J DUNN
PONTNEWYNYDD (All Saints) Pontypool *Mon*
PONTRHYDFENDIGAID (St David) Tregaron w Ystrad
Meurig and Strata Florida *St D*
PONTSIAN (St John) Llandysul *St D*
PONTYATES (St Mary) and Llangyndeyrn *St D 12*
V D I DAVIES
PONTYBEREM (St John) *St D 12* **V** S R THOMAS
PONTYCLUN (St Paul) w Talygarn *Llan 4*
V A M REYNOLDS
PONTYCYMMER (St David) and Blaengarw *Llan 1*
V M H BOIT
PONTYGWAITH (St Mary Magdalene) Tylorstown w
Ynyshir *Llan*
PONTYMISTER (St Margaret) Risca *Mon*
PONTYPOOL (St James) (St Matthew) *Mon 10*
R B R PIPPEN, **TV** M L COX, R J MELLOWSHIP,
C J M T CARLYON (nee
ENGLAND)
PONTYPRIDD (St Catherine) (All Saints) (St David) (St
Matthew) *Llan 11* **V** J H S THOMAS, **C** N C H VARNON
POOL QUAY (St John the Evangelist) Buttington and Pool
Quay *St As*
PORT EYNON (St Cattwg) w Rhosili and Llanddewi and
Knelston *S & B 8* **V** D J MOSFORD

PORT TALBOT (St Agnes) w Oakwood *Llan 8* **V** S P KIRK
PORT TALBOT (St David) Margam *Llan*
PORT TALBOT (St Theodore) (Holy Cross) (St Peter)
Llan 8 **V** N LEA, **NSM** J S DUNN
PORTH Cymmer and Porth *Llan*
PORTH (St Paul) w Trealaw *Llan 12* **V** M J DAVIES
PORTHCAWL (All Saints) Newton Nottage *Llan*
PORTHKERRY (Rhoose Mission Church) Penmark w
Porthkerry *Llan*
PORTHKERRY (St Curig) as above
PORTHMADOG (St John) Ynyscynhaearn w Penmorfa and
Porthmadog *Ban*
PORTMADOC (St Cyngar) as above
PORTMADOC (St Mary) as above
**PORTSKEWETT (St Mary) and Roggiett w Llanfihangel
Rogiet** *Mon 4* **R** T H J PALMER
PRENDERGAST (St David) w Rudbaxton *St D 2*
R G D GWYTHER
PRESTATYN (Christ Church) (Church of Holy Spirit)
St As 1 **V** P C SOUTHERTON, **C** P T ALLSWORTH
PRINCES GATE (St Catherine) Lamp Velfrey and
Llanddewi Velfrey *St D*
PRION (St James) Llanrhaeadr-yng-Nghinmeirch and Prion
St As
PUNCHESTON (St Mary) Letterston w Llanfair Nant-y-Gof
etc *St D*
PUNCHSTON Fishguard w Llanychar and Pontfaen w
Morfil etc *St D*
PWLL (Holy Trinity) Burry Port and Pwll *St D*
PWLLCROCHAN Castlemartin w Warren and Angle etc
St D
PWLLGWAUN (St Mark) w Llanddewi Rhondda *Llan 11*
V M L CHIPLIN
PWLLHELI Denio w Aber-erch *Ban*
PYLE (St James) (St Mary Magdalene) w Kenfig *Llan 8*
V P G WHITE, **NSM** P G L JONES
QUAR, THE (St Tydfil's Well) Merthyr Tydfil St Dav *Llan*
QUEENSFERRY (St Andrew) Shotton *St As*
RADYR (St John the Baptist) (Christ Church) *Llan 5*
R W G BARLOW, **C** B JOHN
RAGLAN (St Cadoc) w Llandenny and Bryngwyn *Mon 5*
V S L GUEST
REDBERTH (Church) Manobier and St Florence w
Redberth *St D*
REDWICK (St Thomas) Magor w Redwick and Undy *Mon*
RESOLVEN (St David) w Tonna *Llan 10* **V** N HADFIELD,
NSM D O JONES
REYNOLDSTON (Church) Jeffreyston w Reynoldston and
E Williamston etc *St D*
REYNOLDSTON (St George) w Penrice and Llangennith
S & B 8 **R** P J WILLIAMS
RHANDIRMWYN (St Barnabas) Cilycwm and Ystrad-ffin
w Rhandir-mwyn etc *St D*
RHAYADER (St Clement) and Nantmel *S & B 5*
V L A MARSHALL
RHESYCAE (Christ Church) Halkyn w Caerfallwch w
Rhesycae *St As*
RHEWL (Church) Llanynys w Llanychan *St As*
RHIW (St Aelrhiw) Aberdaron etc *Ban*
RHIWLAS (Mission Church) Llansilin w Llangadwaladr and
Llangedwyn *St As*
RHIWLAS (St George) Pentir *Ban*
RHOS (St James) Llangeler *St D*
RHOSBEIRIO Llanfechell w Bodewryd w Rhosbeirio etc *Ban*
RHOSCOLYN Holyhead w Rhoscolyn w Llanfair-yn-
Neubwll *Ban*
RHOSCROWTHER (St Decumanus) Castlemartin w Warren
and Angle etc *St D*
RHOSDDU Wrexham *St As*
RHOSESEMOR Halkyn w Caerfallwch w Rhesycae *St As*
RHOSILI (St Mary the Virgin) Port Eynon w Rhosili and
Llanddewi and Knelston *S & B*
RHOSLEFAIN (St Mary) Arthog w Fairbourne w
Llangelynnin w Rhoslefain *Ban*
**RHOSLLANNERCHRUGOG (St John the Evangelist) (St
David) (St Mary)** *St As 16* **V** D J HART
RHOSNEIGR (Christ Church) Llanbeulan w Llanfaelog and
Tal-y-llyn *Ban*
RHOSROBIN (St Peter) Gwersyllt *St As*
RHOSTIE Llanilar w Rhostie and Llangwyryfon etc *St D*
RHOSTRYFAN (Mission Church) Llanwnda and Llandwrog
Ban
RHOSYGWALIAU (Holy Trinity) Llanfor w Rhosygwaliau
St As
RHOSYMEDRE (St John the Evangelist) *St As 13*
V R BAYLEY

RHUDDLAN (St Mary) *St As 1* **V** J G GRIFFITHS
RHULEN (St David) Llanelwedd w Llanfaredd w
Llansantffraed etc *S & B*
RHYD-Y-MWYN (St John the Evangelist) Cilcain and
Nannerch and Rhyd-y-mwyn *St As*
RHYDYBRIW (Capel Rhydybriw) Defynnog w Rhydybriw
and Llandilo'r-fan *S & B*
RHYDYFELIN (St Luke) *Llan 11* **V** C P SUTTON
RHYL (Holy Trinity) (St Thomas) (St John) (St Ann) *St As 1*
V H J LLOYD, **C** J D LOMAS
RHYMNEY (St David) *Mon 7* **V** T I GRIFFITHS
RISCA (St Mary) *Mon 6* **V** R E PAIN, **C** J C DOWDING,
NSM J A WELSH
ROATH (St German) *Llan 3* **V** J A GRIFFITHS,
NSM R L FANTHORPE
**ROATH (St Margaret) (St Anne) (St Edward) (St Philip) (St
Teilo's School)** *Llan 3* **V** P I REID
ROATH (St Martin) *Llan 3* **V** H G CLARKE,
NSM T G WATKIN
ROATH (St Saviour) *Llan 3* **V** A R ABJOHNS
ROBERTSTOWN (St John the Evangelist) Aberdare St Jo
Llan
ROBESTON WATHEN (Church) Narberth w Mounton w
Robeston Wathen and Crinow *St D*
ROBESTON WEST (St Andrew) Walwyn's Castle w
Robeston W *St D*
ROCH (St Mary) Nolton w Roch *St D*
**ROCKFIELD (St Cenedlon) and St Maughen's w Llangattock-
vibon-Avel and Llanfihangel-ystern-Llewern** *Mon 3*
V P M BOND
ROGERSTONE (St John the Baptist) Bassaleg *Mon*
ROGGIETT (St Mary) Portskewett and Roggiett w
Llanfihangel Rogiet *Mon*
ROSEMARKET (St Ishmael) Burton and Rosemarket *St D*
ROSSETT (Christ Church) *St As 16* **V** R A SUTER
RUABON (St Mary) (All Saints) *St As 13* **V** G C JONES
RUDBAXTON (St Michael) Prendergast w Rudbaxton *St D*
RUDRY (St James) Bedwas and Rudry *Mon*
RUMNEY (St Augustine) *Mon 6* **V** D A G HATHAWAY
RUTHIN (St Peter) w Llanrhydd *St As 3* **R** D J WILLIAMS
**ST ANDREW'S MAJOR (St Andrew) (St Peter) and
Michaelston-le-Pit** *Llan 6* **R** D H RHYDDERCH
ST ARVANS (St Arvan) Itton and St Arvans w Penterry and
Kilgwrrwg etc *Mon*
**ST ASAPH (Cathedral of St Asaph and St Cyndeyrn) and
Tremeirchion** *St As 1* **V** R H GRIFFITHS
ST ATHAN (St Tathan) Eglwysbrewis w St Athan w Gileston
Llan
ST BRIDES (St Bridget) Dale and St Brides w Marloes *St D*
ST BRIDES MAJOR (St Bridget) Ewenny w St Brides Major
Llan
ST BRIDES MINOR (St Bride) w Bettws *Llan 1*
R J F WARD
ST BRIDES NETHERWENT (St Bridget) Penhow, St Brides
Netherwent w Llandavenny etc *Mon*
ST BRIDES-SUPER-ELY (St Bride) Peterston-super-Ely w
St Brides-super-Ely *Llan*
ST BRIDE'S WENTLOOG Marshfield and Peterstone
Wentloog etc *Mon*
**ST CLEARS (St Mary Magdalen) w Llangynin and
Llanddowror and Llanfihangel Abercywyn** *St D 15*
V R THOMAS
ST DAVIDS (Cathedral of St David and St Andrew) *St D 3*
V J W EVANS
ST DOGMAEL'S (St Thomas) w Moylgrove and Monington
St D 6 **V** E R WILLIAMS
ST DOGWELLS (St Dogfael) Spittal w Trefgarn and
Ambleston w St Dogwells *St D*
ST EDREN'S Mathry w St Edren's and Grandston etc *St D*
ST ELVIS Whitchurch w Solva and St Elvis w Brawdy etc
St D
ST FAGANS (St Mary) w Michaelston-super-Ely *Llan 5*
R A R WINTLE
ST FLORENCE (St Florentius) Manobier and St Florence w
Redberth *St D*
ST GEORGE (St George) Towyn and St George *St As*
ST GEORGE-SUPER-ELY (St George) St Nicholas w
Bonvilston and St George-super-Ely *Llan*
ST HARMON'S (St Garmon) Cwmddauddwr w St Harmon's
and Llanwrthwl *S & B*
ST HILARY Greenway (St Hilary) *Mon 6* **V** T H WOOD
ST HILARY (St Hilary) Cowbridge *Llan*
ST ISHMAEL'S (St Ishmael) Herbrandston and Hasguard w
St Ishmael's *St D*
ST ISHMAEL'S (St Ishmael) w Llan-saint and Ferryside
St D 12 **V** R M JENKINS

ST ISSELL'S (St Issell) and Amroth *St D 4* **V** M BUTLER
ST LAWRENCE (St Lawrence) Camrose and St Lawrence w Ford and Haycastle *St D*
ST LYTHANS (St Bleiddian) Wenvoe and St Lythans *Llan*
ST MARY CHURCH (St Mary) Cowbridge *Llan*
ST MARY HILL (St Mary) Coychurch w Llangan and St Mary Hill *Llan*
ST MAUGHEN'S (St Meugan) Rockfield and St Maughen's w Llangattock etc *Mon*
ST MELLONS (St Mellon) and Michaelston-y-Fedw *Mon 6*
  V D KELLEN, **C** B RICHARDS, M I R DOWSETT, **NSM** G R DAVIES
ST NICHOLAS (St Nicholas) Mathry w St Edren's and Grandston etc *St D*
ST NICHOLAS (St Nicholas) w Bonvilston and St George-super-Ely *Llan 6* **R** E T WILSON
ST PETROX (St Pedrog) w Stackpole Elidor and Bosherston w St Twynnells *St D 1* **R** J H RICHARDS
ST PIERRE (St Peter) Mathern and Mounton w St Pierre *Mon*
ST THOMAS Haverfordwest St Mary and St Thos w Haroldston *St D*
ST TWYNNELLS (St Gwynog) St Petrox w Stackpole Elidor and Bosherston etc *Mon*
SANDFIELDS Aberavon H Trin *Llan*
SANDYCROFT (Holy Spirit) Hawarden *St As*
SANDYCROFT (St Francis) as above
SARON (St David) Llanedi w Tycroes and Saron *St D*
SEALAND (St Barth) Hawarden *St As*
SEBASTOPOL (St Oswald) Griffithstown *Mon*
SENGHENYDD (St Peter) Eglwysilan *Llan*
SEVEN SISTERS (St Mary) (St David) *Llan 10*
  V R I BLACKMORE
SHIRENEWTON (St Thomas a Becket) Caerwent w Dinham and Llanfair Discoed etc *Mon*
SHOTTON (St Ethelwold) *St As 14* **V** *Vacant* Hawarden (01244) 812183
SILIAN (St Sulien) Lamp Pont Steffan w Silian *St D*
SINAN (All Saints) Cefn *St As*
SIX BELLS (St John) Cwmtillery and Six Bells *Mon*
SKENFRITH (St Bride) Grosmont and Skenfrith and Llangattock etc *Mon*
SKETTY (St Paul) (Holy Trinity) *S & B 6*
  V R J WILLIAMS, **C** E M DOYLE, **NSM** S H JONES
SKEWEN (St John) (All Saints) (St Mary) *Llan 10*
  V P RAIKES, **C** I E DAVIES
SLEBECH (St John the Baptist Parish Centre) and Uzmaston w Boulston *St D 2* **V** W H WATKINS
SOLVA (St Aidan) Whitchurch w Solva and St Elvis w Brawdy etc *St D*
SOUTHERNDOWN (All Saints) Ewenny w St Brides Major *Llan*
SOUTHSEA (All Saints) Berse and Southsea *St As*
SOUTHSEA (St Alban) as above
SPITTAL (St Mary) w Trefgarn and Ambleston w St Dogwells *St D 2* **V** R D WHITE
STACKPOLE ELIDOR (St James and St Elidyr) St Petrox w Stackpole Elidor and Bosherston etc *St D*
STEYNTON (St Cewydd and St Peter) Johnston w Steynton *St D*
STRATA FLORIDA (St Mary) Tregaron w Ystrad Meurig and Strata Florida *St D*
SULLY (St John the Baptist) *Llan 6* **R** E B DOWDING
SWANSEA (Christ Church) *S & B 11* **V** E T HUNT
SWANSEA (St Barnabas) *S & B 11* **P-in-c** A E PIERCE
SWANSEA (St Gabriel) (St Augustine) *S & B 6*
  V E M WASTELL
SWANSEA (St James) *S & B 11* **V** A G HOWELLS, **C** G P NOYCE
SWANSEA (St Jude) *S & B 11* **V** D W WHITE
SWANSEA (St Luke) *S & B 10* **P-in-c** R J HANNEN
SWANSEA (St Mark) (St John) *S & B 10*
  Dn-in-c S J COLEMAN
SWANSEA (St Mary) (Holy Trinity) *S & B 11*
  V D E LEWIS, **C** A T R LEWIS, **NSM** P WARD
SWANSEA (St Matthew) w Greenhill *S & B 11*
  P-in-c L O WARD
SWANSEA (St Nicholas-on-the-Hill) *S & B 11*
  V D M GRIFFITHS, **NSM** L J TAYLOR
SWANSEA (St Peter) *S & B 10* **V** A G LEE, **C** S SARAPUK
SWANSEA (St Thomas) (St Stephen) and Kilvey *S & B 11*
  V P J GWYNN, **C** C D BROWN
TAI'RGWAITH (St David) Gwaun-cae-Gurwen *St D*
TAL-Y-LLYN (St David) Llanegryn w Aberdyfi w Tywyn *Ban*
TAL-Y-LLYN (St Mary) Llanbeulan w Llanfaelog and Tal-y-llyn *Ban*

TALACHDDU (St Mary) Llandefalle and Llyswen w Boughrood etc *S & B*
TALBENNY (St Mary) Walton W w Talbenny and Haroldston W *St D*
TALGARREG (St David) Llanarth and Capel Cynon w Talgarreg etc *St D*
TALGARTH (St Gwendoline) and Llanelieu *S & B 4*
  V D T WALTERS
TALIARIS (Holy Trinity) Llandeilo and Taliaris *St D*
TALLARN GREEN (St Mary Magdalene) Hanmer, Bronington, Bettisfield, Tallarn Green *St As*
TALLEY (St Michael) Cynwyl Gaeo w Llansawel and Talley *St D*
TALYBONT (St David) Llanfihangel Genau'r-glyn and Llangorwen *St D*
TALYGARN (St Anne) Pontyclun w Talygarn *Llan*
TALYLLYN Pennal w Corris and Esgairgeiliog *Ban*
TALYLLYN (St Mary) Llanegryn w Aberdyfi w Tywyn *Ban*
TEMPLETON (St John) Martletwy w Lawrenny and Minwear etc *St D*
TENBY (St Mary) (St Julian's Chapel) *St D 4*
  R C J HARVEY, **TV** S LEYSHON, **C** N CALE, **NSM** S M TEMPLE
TINTERN (St Michael) Llandogo and Tintern *Mon*
TIRABAD (St David) Llanwrtyd w Llanddulas in Tir Abad etc *S & B*
TIRTHIL (St Michael) Pontlottyn w Fochriw *Llan*
TON-YR-YWEN (School) Llanishen *Llan*
TONDU (St John) Penyfai w Tondu *Llan*
TONDU (St Thomas) as above
TONGWYNLAIS (St Michael) (St James) *Llan 5*
  V C B W SMITH
TONMAWR (St Teilo) Port Talbot St Agnes w Oakwood *Llan*
TONNA (St Anne) Resolven w Tonna *Llan*
TONPENTRE Ystradyfodwg *Llan*
TONYPANDY (St Andrew) w Clydach Vale *Llan 12*
  V N CAHILL
TONYREFAIL (St David) (St Alban) w Gilfach Goch *Llan 12* **V** E HASTEY
TOWNHILL Swansea St Nic *S & B*
TOWYN (St Mary) and St George *St As 1*
  V J W JAUNDRILL
TRAEAN-GLAS (St Mary) Llywel and Traean-glas w Llanulid *S & B*
TRALLWNG (St David) and Bettws, Penpont w Aberyskir and Llanfihangel Nantbran *S & B 1* **V** B M JONES
TRAWSFYNYDD (St Madryn) Maentwrog w Trawsfynydd *Ban*
TRE-GROES (St Ffraid) Llandysul *St D*
TRE-LECH A'R BETWS (St Teilo) w Abernant and Llanwinio *St D 11* **V** D E EVANS
TRE-MAIN (St Michael) Aber-porth w Tre-main and Blaen-porth *St D*
TREALAW (All Saints) Porth w Trealaw *Llan*
TREBANOS (St Michael) Clydach *S & B*
TREBOETH (St Alban) (Penlan Church) *S & B 10*
  V N J SHEARD, **NSM** R G JONES
TREDEGAR (St George) *Mon 7* **V** S M JOHN
TREDEGAR (St James) *Mon 7* **V** R R WEST, **NSM** J J WILKINS
TREDUNNOC (St Andrew) and Llantrisant w Llanhennock and Llanllowell *Mon 5* **V** R D WILLIAMS
TREFDRAETH (St Beuno) (Eglwys Crist y Brenin) w Aberffraw and Llangwyfan and Llangadwaladr *Ban 4*
  R J E T YENDALL
TREFEGLWYS (St Michael) Llandinam w Trefeglwys w Penstrowed *Ban*
TREFGARN (St Michael) Spittal w Trefgarn and Ambleston w St Dogwells *St D*
TREFILAN (St Hilary) Llanfihangel Ystrad and Cilcennin w Trefilan etc *St D*
TREFLYS (St Michael) Criccieth w Treflys *Ban*
TREFNANT (Holy Trinity) *St As 2* **R** W T CLACKEY
TREFOR (St George) Llanaelhaearn w Clynnog Fawr *Ban*
TREFRIW (St Mary) Caerhun w Llangelynnin w Llanbedr-y-Cennin *Ban*
TREGAEAN (St Caian) Llangefni w Tregaean and Llangristiolus etc *Ban*
TREGAER (St Mary) Dingestow and Llangovan w Penyclawdd etc *Mon*
TREGARON (St Caron) w Ystrad Meurig and Strata Florida *St D 9* **V** G R CALDERBANK
TREGARTH (St Mair) Llandygai w Tregarth *Ban*
TREGYNON (St Cynon) Betws Cedewain and Tregynon and Llanwyddelan *St As*

TREHARRIS (St Matthias) w Bedlinog *Llan 9*
  V A R BOYD-WILLIAMS
TREHERBERT (St Alban) (St Mary Communion Centre) w Treorchy *Llan 12* **V** C T REANEY
TRELAWNYD (St Michael) Dyserth and Trelawnyd and Cwm *St As*
TRELEWIS Treharris w Bedlinog *Llan*
TRELLECH (St Nicholas) Penallt and Trellech *Mon*
TRELLECH GRANGE (not known) Llanishen w Trellech Grange and Llanfihangel etc *Mon*
TREMADOC Ynyscynhaearn w Penmorfa and Porthmadog *Ban*
TREMEIRCHION (Corpus Christi) St As and Tremeirchion *St As*
TREORCHY (St Matthew) Treherbert w Treorchy *Llan*
TRETHOMAS (St Thomas) Bedwas and Rudry *Mon*
TRETOWER (St John the Evangelist) Crickhowell w Cwmdu and Tretower *S & B*
TREUDDYN (St Mary) w Nercwys *St As 14* **V** J B JONES
TREVETHIN (St Cadoc) Pontypool *Mon*
TREVETHIN (St John the Divine) as above
TREVOR (Church) Llangollen w Trevor and Llantysilio *St As*
TREWALCHMAI (St Morhaiarn) Llandrygarn w Bodwrog and Heneglwys etc *Ban*
TREWERN (Mission Church) Buttington and Pool Quay *St As*
TROED-YR-AUR (St Michael) Newc Emlyn w Llandyfriog and Troed-yr-aur *St D*
TROEDRHIWGARTH (St Mary the Virgin) *Llan 8*
  V D G MORRIS
TROEDYRHIW (St John) w Merthyr Vale *Llan 9*
  V *Vacant* Ynysowen (01443) 690249
TROFARTH (St John) Brynmaen w Trofarth *St As*
TROSTEY (St David) Bettws Newydd w Trostrey etc *Mon*
TUDWEILIOG (St Cwyfan) Nefyn w Pistyll w Tudweiliog w Llandudwen etc *Ban*
TUMBLE (Dewi Sant) Llan-non *St D*
TY SIGN (St David) Risca *Mon*
TYCOCH (All Souls) *S & B 6* **V** R BRITTON
TYCROES (St Edmund) Llanedi w Tycroes and Saron *St D*
TYLORSTOWN (Holy Trinity) (St Mary Magdalene) w Ynyshir *Llan 12* **V** R O LOWNDES
TYNANT (Mission Church) Maentwrog w Trawsfynydd *Ban*
TYTHEGSTON (St Tydwg) Laleston w Tythegston and Merthyr Mawr *Llan*
TYWYN (St Cadfan) Llanegryn w Aberdyfi w Tywyn *Ban*
TYWYN (St Matthew) as above
UNDY (St Mary) Magor w Redwick and Undy *Mon*
UPTON Pemb Dock w Cosheston w Nash and Upton *St D*
USK (St Mary) and Monkswood w Glascoed Chapel and Gwehelog *Mon 5* **V** R L DAVIES
UZMASTON (St Ismael) Slebech and Uzmaston w Boulston *St D*
VALLEY (St Michael) w Llanfachraeth (St Machraeth) *Ban 3* **R** T BONNET
VAYNOR (St Gwynno) Cefn Coed and Capel Nantddu w Vaynor etc *S & B*
WALTON EAST (St Mary) Wiston w Walton E and Clarbeston *St D*
WALTON WEST (All Saints) w Talbenny and Haroldston West *St D 5* **R** B D BO'MALLEY
WALWYN'S CASTLE (St James the Great) w Robeston West *St D 5* **R** D J LOWEN
WARREN Castlemartin w Warren and Angle etc *St D*
WATERSTON Llanstadwel *St D*
WATTSTOWN (St Thomas) Tylorstown w Ynyshir *Llan*
WAUNARLLWYDD (St Barnabas) *S & B 9* **V** P C FRENCH
WAUNFAWR (St John the Evangelist) Llanbeblig w Caernarfon and Betws Garmon etc *Ban*
WAUNFELIN (St John the Divine) Pontypool *Mon*
WAUNWEN (St Mark) Swansea St Mark and St Jo *S & B*
WELSH ST DONATS (St Donat) Pendoylan and Welsh St Donats *Llan*
WELSHPOOL (St Mary) (Christ Church) w Castle Caereinion *St As 10* **R** R L BROWN
WENVOE (St Mary) and St Lythans *Llan 6* **R** B T JOHNS
WHISTON (not known) Goldcliffe and Whiston and Nash *Mon*

WHITCHURCH (St David) w Solva and St Elvis w Brawdy and Llandeloy *St D 3* **V** R J E W REES
WHITCHURCH (St Mary) (St Thomas) (All Saints) *Llan 5*
  V F G TURNER, **C** E M LE GRICE, S F AMBANI, R L HEWETT, D J ADLINGTON
WHITEBROOK (Holy Trinity) Llandogo and Tintern *Mon*
WHITECHURCH IN KEMES Nevern and Y Beifil w Eglwyswrw and Meline etc *St D*
WHITFORD (St Mary and St Beuno) *St As 4*
  V R E KILGOUR
WHITLAND (St Mary) w Cyffig and Henllan Amgoed and Llan-gan *St D 15* **V** D E FAULKNER
WHITTON (St David) and Pilleth and Cascob w Llangynllo and Bleddfa *S & B 5* **V** A G LOAT
WICK (St James) Llantwit Major *Llan*
WILCRICK (St Mary) Bishton *Mon*
WILLIAMSTON, EAST (Church) Jeffreyston w Reynoldston and E Williamston etc *St D*
WILLIAMSTOWN (St Illtud) Dinas and Penygraig w Williamstown *Llan*
WISTON (St Mary Magdalene) w Walton East and Clarbeston *St D 2* **V** R JONES
WOLVESNEWTON (St Thomas a Becket) Llangwm Uchaf w Llangwm Isaf w Gwernesney etc *Mon*
WONASTOW (St Wonnow) Overmonnow w Wonastow and Michel Troy *Mon*
WORTHENBURY (St Deiniol) Ban Monachorum and Worthenbury *St As*
WREXHAM (St Giles' Parish Church) (St David) (St Mark) (St Mary) (All Saints) (St Margaret) (St James) (St John) *St As 16* **R** B SMITH, **TV** R EVANS, M K SNELLGROVE, M J BENNETT, **TD** S M HUYTON, **C** D J BLACK
WYNDHAM (St David) Nantymoel w Wyndham *Llan*
Y BEIFIL (St Andrew) Nevern and Y Beifil w Eglwyswrw and Meline etc *St D*
Y FERWIG (St Pedrog) Cardigan and Mwnt and Y Ferwig *St D*
YERBESTON Martletwy w Lawrenny and Minwear etc *St D*
YNYSBOETH Penrhiwceiber w Matthewstown and Ynysboeth *Llan*
YNYSCYNHAEARN (St Cynhaearn) (Mission Church) w Penmorfa and Porthmadog *Ban 10* **V** A J WILLIAMS, **C** A C BUCKLEY
YNYSCYNON (St Cynon) Ystrad Rhondda w Ynyscynon *Llan*
YNYSDDU (St Theodore) *Mon 7* **V** *Vacant* Blackwood (01495) 200257
YNYSHIR (St Anne) Tylorstown w Ynyshir *Llan*
YNYSHIR (St Thomas) as above
YNYSMEUDW (St Mary) Llangiwg *S & B*
YSBYTY CYNFYN (St John the Baptist) w Llantrisant and Eglwys Newydd *St D 10* **V** *Vacant* Ponterwyd (01970) 890663
YSBYTY YSTWYTH (St John the Baptist) Llanfihangel w Llanafan and Llanwnnws etc *St D*
YSFA (St Mark) Rhayader and Nantmel *S & B*
YSGEIFIOG (St Mary) Gorsedd w Brynford and Ysgeifiog *St As*
YSPYTY IFAN (St John the Baptist) Cerrigydrudion w Llanfihangel etc *St As*
YSTALYFERA (St David) *S & B 7* **V** *Vacant* Glantawe (01639) 842257
YSTRAD-FFIN (St Paulinus) Cilycwm and Ystrad-ffin w Rhandir-mwyn etc *St D*
YSTRAD MEURIG (St John the Baptist) Tregaron w Ystrad Meurig and Strata Florida *St D*
YSTRAD MYNACH (Holy Trinity) w Llanbradach *Llan 2*
  V M D BROOKS
YSTRAD RHONDDA (St Stephen) w Ynyscynon *Llan 12*
  V P S GALE
YSTRAD ROAD (St Illtyd) Swansea St Pet *S & B*
YSTRADFELLTE (St Mary) Penderyn w Ystradfellte and Pontneathvaughan *S & B*
YSTRADGYNLAIS (St Cynog) *S & B 7* **R** K EVANS, **NSM** J E PHILLIPS
YSTRADOWEN (St Owain) Cowbridge *Llan*
YSTRADYFODWG (St John the Baptist) *Llan 12*
  V P N COLEMAN

SCOTTISH INCUMBENCIES

An index of the incumbencies of the Scottish Episcopal Church. The incumbency entry gives the full legal name, followed by the diocese and the name(s) and appointment(s) of the clergy serving there (if there are none, the telephone number of the parsonage house is given). Church dedications are indicated in brackets. The following are the main abbreviations used; for others see the full list of abbreviations.

C	Curate	**NSM**	Non-stipendiary Minister
C-in-c	Curate-in-charge	**P-in-c**	Priest-in-charge
Dn-in-c	Deacon-in-charge	**Par Dn**	Parish Deacon
Dss	Deaconess	**R**	Rector
Hon C	Honorary Curate	**TM**	Team Minister

ABERCHIRDER (St Marnan) *Mor* **R** H M LOPDELL-BRADSHAW
ABERDEEN (Cathedral of St Andrew) *Ab*
  R W D WIGHTMAN, **NSM** R FINNIE, D J GORDON
ABERDEEN (St Clement) *Ab* **P-in-c** I D BARCROFT
ABERDEEN (St James) *Ab* **R** M C PATERNOSTER
ABERDEEN (St John the Evangelist) *Ab* **R** A B ALLAN,
  NSM R B EDWARDS
ABERDEEN (St Margaret of Scotland) *Ab* **R** A E NIMMO
ABERDEEN (St Mary) *Ab* **R** J D ALEXANDER
ABERDEEN (St Ninian) *Ab* **P-in-c** W D WIGHTMAN,
  NSM R FINNIE
ABERDEEN (St Peter) *Ab* **R** D N CALVIN-THOMAS
ABERDOUR (St Columba)—West Fife Team Ministry
  St And **R** *Vacant*
ABERFOYLE (St Mary) *St And* **R** A BUNNELL
ABERLOUR (St Margaret of Scotland) *Mor*
  R J M DUNCAN
ABOYNE (St Peter) *Ab* **P-in-c** C S GIBSON,
  NSM A F R FENNELL
AIRDRIE (St Paul) *Glas* **P-in-c** D S MUNGAVIN
ALEXANDRIA (St Mungo) *Glas* **R** *Vacant* Alexandria
  (01389) 52633
ALFORD (St Andrew) *Ab* **R** J WALKER,
  NSM J BURCHILL
ALLOA (St John the Evangelist) *St And*
  P-in-c A H D KNOCK, **NSM** D FINLAYSON, E FORGAN,
  S J HARRISON, R E MURRAY
ALYTH (St Ninian) *St And* **R** K W RATHBAND,
  NSM P S FERNANDO, D A CAMERON
ANNAN (St John the Evangelist) *Glas*
  P-in-c D J B FOSTEKEW
APPIN Portnacrois *Arg*
ARBROATH (St Mary) *Bre* **R** W F WARD
ARDBRECKNISH (St James) *Arg* **R** A M MACLEAN
ARDCHATTAN (Holy Spirit) *Arg* **R** A M MACLEAN
ARDROSSAN (St Andrew) *Glas* **R** S B SYMONS,
  NSM J JENKINS
ARPAFEELIE (St John the Evangelist) *Mor*
  R R F BURKITT
ARRAN, ISLE OF *Arg* **NSM** T A PRINGLE
AUCHENBLAE Drumtochty *Bre*
AUCHINDOIR (St Mary) *Ab* **NSM** J BURCHILL
AUCHMITHIE (St Peter) *Bre* **R** S FOX,
  NSM S G LETTON
AUCHTERARDER (St Kessog) *St And* **R** A C RUSSELL,
  NSM W B ROOTES
AYR (Holy Trinity) *Glas* **R** I JONES,
  C M P CALLAGHAN, **NSM** J A MASON
BAILLIESTON (St John) *Glas* **R** *Vacant*
BALERNO (St Mungo) *Edin* **R** M J H ROUND,
  NSM N F HALLAM
BALLACHULISH (St John) *Arg* **R** J R BETTELEY
BALLATER (St Kentigern) *Ab* **P-in-c** C S GIBSON,
  NSM A F R FENNELL
BANCHORY (St Ternan) *Ab* **R** R E ROYDEN
BANFF (St Andrew) *Ab* **R** R M HAINES, **C** J M PAISEY
BARROWFIELD (St John the Baptist) *Glas*
  NSM A W WINSPER
BATHGATE (St Columba) *Edin* **NSM** C CHAPLIN,
  P F KIRK
BEARSDEN (All Saints) *Glas* **R** K T ROACH
BELLS WYND Douglas *Glas*
BIELDSIDE (St Devenick) *Ab* **R** K D GORDON,
  NSM T A HART, **Dss** J E MACCORMACK
BIRNAM Dunkeld *St And*
BISHOPBRIGGS (St James-the-Less) *Glas*
  P-in-c S R PAISLEY
BLAIR ATHOLL Kilmaveonaig *St And*
BLAIRGOWRIE (St Catherine) *St And*
  R K W RATHBAND, **NSM** P S FERNANDO,
  D A CAMERON

BO'NESS (St Catharine) *Edin* **P-in-c** N D MacCALLUM
BRAEMAR (St Margaret) *Ab* **P-in-c** C S GIBSON,
  NSM A F R FENNELL
BRECHIN (St Andrew) *Bre* **R** S FOX, **NSM** S G LETTON
BRIDGE OF ALLAN (St Saviour) *St And*
  NSM D FINLAYSON
BRIDGE OF WEIR (St Mary) *Glas* **R** E G LINDSAY
BRIDGEND Islay *Arg*
BRORA (St Columba) *Mor* **P-in-c** A R GORDON
BROUGHTY FERRY (St Mary) *Bre* **R** R W BREADEN,
  C D McALISTER, **Hon C** A R TREW, H P DUFF
BUCKIE (All Saints) *Ab* **P-in-c** R M HAINES,
  C J M PAISEY
BUCKSBURN (St Machar) *Ab* **P-in-c** D HEDDLE
BURNSIDE Moffat *Glas*
BURNTISLAND (St Serf)—West Fife Team Ministry
  St And **C** K S NICHOLSON
BURRAVOE (St Colman) *Ab* **R** L S SMITH,
  NSM E H McNAB (nee LUMMIS)
CALLANDER (St Andrew) *St And* **R** A BUNNELL
CAMBUSLANG (St Cuthbert) *Glas* **R** A M BURN-MURDOCH, **NSM** M A DANSON
CAMPBELTOWN (St Kiaran) *Arg* **R** K V PAGAN
CARNOUSTIE (Holy Rood) *Bre* **R** D B MACKAY,
  Hon C J B HARDIE
CASTLE DOUGLAS (St Ninian) *Glas* **R** P P DANCE
CATTERLINE (St Philip) *Bre* **NSM** G H J PAISEY
CHALLOCH (All Saints) w Newton Stewart *Glas*
  P-in-c N E H NEWTON, **Hon C** D M MAIN, R C CUTLER
CHAPELHILL Cruden Bay *Ab*
CLARKSTON (St Aidan) *Glas* **P-in-c** D J NORWOOD,
  Hon C K R BREWIN, C CURTIS
CLERMISTON Edin Clermiston Em *Edin*
CLYDEBANK (St Columba) *Glas* **R** R J A HASLAM,
  C M N OXLEY, **NSM** G L NICOLL
COATBRIDGE (St John the Evangelist) *Glas*
  P-in-c D S MUNGAVIN
COLDSTREAM (St Mary and All Souls) *Edin*
  P-in-c G T C TAMS
COLINTON Edin St Cuth *Edin*
COMRIE (St Serf) *St And* **R** H G C LEE
COUPAR ANGUS (St Anne) *St And* **R** K W RATHBAND,
  NSM P S FERNANDO, D A CAMERON
COURTHILL Chapel Kishorn *Mor*
COVE BAY (St Mary) *Ab* **P-in-c** D N CALVIN-THOMAS
CRAIGHALL Ellon *Ab*
CRIEFF (St Columba) *St And* **R** H G C LEE
CROACHY Strathnairn St Paul *Mor*
CROMARTY (St Regulus) *Mor* **R** R F BURKITT
CRUDEN BAY (St James the Less) *Ab*
  R G H STRANRAER-MULL, **NSM** J F F SHEPHERD,
  G P WHALLEY, D E F FIRMIN, A L JAMES, R SPENCER,
  P A McKENZIE
CULLODEN (St Mary-in-the-Fields) *Mor*
  P-in-c A A SINCLAIR
CUMBERNAULD (Holy Name) *Glas* **P-in-c** D A COOK
CUMBRAE (Cathedral of The Isles and Collegiate Church of
  the Holy Spirit) *Arg* **P-in-c** D A GRAY
CUMINESTOWN (St Luke) *Ab* **R** R M HAINES,
  C J M PAISEY
CUPAR (St James the Great) *St And* **R** R G W NOCK,
  Par Dn M D HERVEY
DALBEATTIE (Christ Church) *Glas* **R** J F C WOODLEY
DALKEITH (St Mary) *Edin* **R** M A S GOODMAN,
  C D I McCOSH
DALMAHOY (St Mary) *Edin* **R** W L F MOUNSEY,
  NSM D A ROBERTSON
DALRY (St Peter) *Glas* **P-in-c** I BOFFEY
DINGWALL (St James the Great) *Mor*
  P-in-c M F HICKFORD
DOLLAR (St James the Great) *St And* **R** C P SHERLOCK,
  NSM D FINLAYSON, F A M LAWRY, H I SOGA

DORNOCH (St Finnbarr) *Mor*   **P-in-c** A R GORDON
DOUGLAS (Sancta Sophia) *Glas*   **R** B H C GORDON
DOUNE (St Modoc) *St And*   **NSM** S M COATES
DRUMLITHIE (St John the Baptist) *Bre*
  R M J R TURNER
DRUMTOCHTY (St Palladius) *Bre*   **R** M J R TURNER,
  NSM D P STEEL
DUFFTOWN (St Michael and All Angels) *Ab*
  C P J McCARTHY
DUMBARTON (St Augustine) *Glas*   **NSM** J M LOCOCK
DUMFRIES (St John the Evangelist) *Glas*
  R D W BAYNE,   **C** G A F HINCHCLIFFE
DUNBAR (St Anne) *Edin*   **R** I J PATON,   **NSM** J WOOD
DUNBLANE (St Mary) *St And*   **R** G TELLINI,
  NSM J W ALLAN
DUNDEE (Cathedral of St Paul) *Bre*   **R** M J BUNCE,
  NSM G J H PONT, G M GREIG
DUNDEE (St John the Baptist) *Bre*   **P-in-c** J J MORROW,
  NSM J P FORBES
DUNDEE (St Luke) *Bre*   **NSM** L STEVENSON
DUNDEE (St Margaret) *Bre*   **R** W J McAUSLAND,
  C P M BALFOUR
DUNDEE (St Martin) *Bre*   **P-in-c** D ELDER
DUNDEE (St Mary Magdalene) *Bre*   **R** D SHEPHERD,
  Hon C M T BONE
DUNDEE (St Ninian) *Bre*   **P-in-c** E M FAULKES
DUNDEE (St Salvador) *Bre*   **R** P J HARVIE
DUNFERMLINE (Holy Trinity)—West Fife Team Ministry
  St And   **R** D L REDWOOD,   **NSM** M KESTON,
  V A NELLIST,   E J COOK
DUNKELD (St Mary) w Birnam *St And*
  R R F PATERSON,   **NSM** I ATKINSON
DUNOON (Holy Trinity) *Arg*   **R** G A GUINNESS
DUNS (Christ Church) *Edin*   **R** C J MARTIN,
  Hon C A J TABRAHAM, M E JONES, G R W BURTON,
  NSM E S JONES
DUROR (St Adamnan) *Arg*   **R** D W DAY
EAST KILBRIDE (St Mark) *Glas*   **R** K G G GIBSON
EASTGATE Peebles *Edin*
EASTRIGGS (St John the Evangelist) *Glas*
  P-in-c J STEVENSON
EDINBURGH (Cathedral of St Mary) *Edin*
  R G J T FORBES,   **C** J CUTHBERT,   **NSM** R B HOGG,
  J M MILLARD, I RYRIE
EDINBURGH (Christ Church) *Edin*   **R** J A MEIN,
  TV D L COLLINGWOOD,   **Min** P D SKELTON,
  NSM R H PROCTER
EDINBURGH (Emmanuel) *Edin*   **P-in-c** P J WARREN
EDINBURGH (Good Shepherd) *Edin*   **R** D H RIMMER,
  NSM J E CHAPMAN (nee
  CRAVEN)
EDINBURGH (Holy Cross) *Edin*   **R** W D KORNAHRENS,
  NSM M F HARRISON
EDINBURGH (Old St Paul) *Edin*   **C** J P MASON,
  Hon C C S DAVIES-COLE, D A B JOWITT,
  NSM R G W STRONG, C NAISMITH
EDINBURGH (St Andrew and St Aidan) *Edin*
  R T G ENGH,   **NSM** I C McKENZIE
EDINBURGH (St Barnabas) *Edin*   **P-in-c** P D DIXON,
  NSM A C ANDERSON
EDINBURGH (St Columba) *Edin*   **R** A J FULLER,
  TV R O GOULD, J S RICHARDSON,   **NSM** S KILBEY
EDINBURGH (St Cuthbert) *Edin*   **R** M C GOLDSMITH
EDINBURGH (St David of Scotland) *Edin*
  P-in-c J N WYNN-EVANS
EDINBURGH (St Fillan) *Edin*   **R** F W TOMLINSON,
  NSM D EMERSON, D L COLLINGWOOD
EDINBURGH (St Hilda) *Edin*   **R** F W TOMLINSON,
  NSM D EMERSON, D L COLLINGWOOD
EDINBURGH (St James the Less) *Edin*   **R** A J BAIN,
  C S P C KYLE
EDINBURGH (St John the Evangelist) *Edin*
  R N CHAMBERLAIN,   **C** J F BURDETT,
  NSM P J BRAND, C A HUME
EDINBURGH (St Luke) Wester Hailes St Luke *Edin*
EDINBURGH (St Margaret of Scotland) *Edin*
  P-in-c A J BAIN,   **TV** A C MURPHY, M S NORTHCOTT,
  NSM C NAISMITH
EDINBURGH (St Mark) *Edin*   **R** T G ENGH,
  NSM S S COX, I C McKENZIE
EDINBURGH (St Martin of Tours) *Edin*
  R W J T BROCKIE,   **C** C T UPTON,   **NSM** D YEOMAN
EDINBURGH (St Michael and All Saints) *Edin*
  R K PEARSON,   **NSM** J E ROULSTON
EDINBURGH (St Ninian) *Edin*   **R** Vacant
EDINBURGH (St Paul and St George) *Edin*
  R M P MAUDSLEY

EDINBURGH (St Peter) *Edin*   **R** I D ZASS-OGILVIE,
  C I M POOBALAN
EDINBURGH (St Philip and St James) *Edin*   **R** K F SCOTT
EDINBURGH (St Salvador) *Edin*   **R** Vacant 0131–334 1808
EDINBURGH (St Thomas) Private Chapel *Edin*
  I M J PARKER,   **C** E N COOMBS
EDINBURGH (St Vincent) Private Chapel *Edin*
  Chapl M A CLARK
ELGIN (Holy Trinity) w Lossiemouth (St Margaret) *Mor*
  R G S BROWN,   **C** R E TAIT
ELIE AND EARLSFERRY (St Michael and All Angels)
  St And   **R** S G HALL
ELLON (St Mary on the Rock) *Ab*   **R** G H STRANRAER-
  MULL,   **NSM** J F F SHEPHERD, G P WHALLEY,
  D E F FIRMIN, A L JAMES, R SPENCER, P A McKENZIE
EORRAPAIDH (St Moluag) *Arg*   **R** S J G BENNIE,
  Hon C J R BULLAMORE
ERSKINE Renfrew *Glas*
EYEMOUTH (St Ebba) *Edin*   **R** Vacant Eyemouth (018907)
  50000
FALKIRK (Christ Church) *Edin*   **R** A D BRUNO
FASQUE (St Andrew) *Bre*   **R** M J R TURNER
FETTERCAIRN Fasque *Bre*
FOCHABERS Gordon Chapel *Mor*   **R** J M DUNCAN
FORFAR (St John the Evangelist) *St And*
  C E N RAMSAY,   **NSM** J M PRIOR
FORRES (St John the Evangelist) *Mor*   **R** R W FORREST
FORT WILLIAM (St Andrew) *Arg*   **R** J H J MACLEAY,
  NSM D N CLIFFORD
FORTROSE (St Andrew) *Mor*   **R** R F BURKITT
FRASERBURGH (St Peter) w New Pitsligo *Ab*
  R A O COUSLAND
FYVIE (All Saints) *Ab*   **R** A B MacGILLIVRAY
GALASHIELS (St Peter) *Edin*   **R** T D MORRIS,
  Hon C O L S DOVER
GALLOWGATE Aber St Marg *Ab*
GARTCOSH (St Andrew) *Glas*   **P-in-c** D S MUNGAVIN
GATEHOUSE OF FLEET (St Mary) *Glas*   **R** C M BROUN
GIRVAN (St John) *Glas*   **NSM** B H G COLLIE, J A MASON
GLASGOW (All Saints) *Glas*   **R** Vacant 0141–959 3730
GLASGOW (Cathedral of St Mary the Virgin) *Glas*
  R P B FRANCIS,   **C** M N OXLEY
GLASGOW (Good Shepherd and Ascension) *Glas*
  C S ROBERTSON,   **Hon C** S A MARSH
GLASGOW (Holy Cross) *Glas*   **NSM** D D KEEBLE
GLASGOW (St Bride) *Glas*   **R** G M M THOMSON,
  NSM I T DRAPER
GLASGOW (St Gabriel) *Glas*   **R** Vacant
GLASGOW (St George) *Glas*   **Hon C** S M P MAITLAND
GLASGOW (St Kentigern) *Glas*   **P-in-c** S P HOLLAND,
  Hon C J GRAHAM
GLASGOW (St Margaret) *Glas*   **R** N J PARKES,
  NSM K H MARSHALL
GLASGOW (St Matthew) *Glas*   **R** Vacant
GLASGOW (St Ninian) *Glas*   **R** D W J REID,
  C J B PENMAN,   **Hon C** R F GRAHAM
GLASGOW (St Oswald) *Glas*   **R** P J TAYLOR
GLASGOW (St Serf) *Glas*   **Min** K L MACAULAY
GLASGOW (St Silas) Private Chapel *Glas*
  Hon C M CLANCY
GLENCARSE (All Saints) *Bre*   **P-in-c** K E WRIGHT
GLENCOE (St Mary) *Arg*   **R** J R BETTELEY
GLENROTHES (St Luke the Evangelist) *St And*
  R H B FARQUHARSON,   **Par Dn** A M H ROBERTSON
GLENURQUHART (St Ninian) *Mor*   **NSM** J A HUTTON
GOUROCK (St Bartholomew) *Glas*   **C** J F LYON
GOVAN Glas St Gabr *Glas*
GRANGEMOUTH (St Mary) *Edin*   **R** N D MacCALLUM
GRANTOWN-ON-SPEY (St Columba) *Mor*
  P-in-c A WHEATLEY,   **Hon C** R K SHAW, E P MOSLEY
GREENOCK (St John the Evangelist) *Glas*   **R** C D LYON,
  NSM A G BOYD
GRETNA (All Saints) *Glas*   **P-in-c** J STEVENSON
GREYFRIARS Kircudbright *Glas*
GRULINE (St Columba) *Arg*   **P-in-c** D W DAY
GULLANE (St Adrian) *Edin*   **R** J C LINDSAY
HADDINGTON (Holy Trinity) *Edin*   **R** I J PATON,
  NSM J WOOD
HAMILTON (St Mary the Virgin) *Glas*
  R T C O MONTGOMERY
HARRIS, ISLE OF Leverburgh *Arg*
HAWICK (St Cuthbert) *Edin*   **R** S M PATERSON,
  NSM D K MAYBURY, D L MAYBURY
HAY DRIVE Edin St Andr and St Aid *Edin*
HELENSBURGH (St Michael and All Angels) *Glas*
  R A B LAING,   **NSM** A J MANN, B M THATCHER
HUNTLY (Christ Church) *Mor*   **R** H M LOPDELL-
  BRADSHAW

INNERLEITHEN (St Andrew) *Edin*   **P-in-c** G J SCOTT,
  NSM C B AITCHISON
INSCH (St Drostan) *Ab*   **R** A B MacGILLIVRAY
INVERARAY (All Saints) *Arg*   **R** *Vacant*
INVERBERVIE (St David) *Bre*   **P-in-c** I G STEWART
INVERGORDON (St Ninian) *Mor*   **R** C H CLAPSON,
  C C J PIPER
INVERGOWRIE (All Souls) *Bre*   **P-in-c** A W CUMMINS,
  NSM P M BALFOUR
INVERKEITHING (St Peter)—West Fife Team Ministry
  St And   **R** *Vacant*
INVERNESS (Cathedral of St Andrew) *Mor*
  R M E GRANT, **Hon C** J W L TAYLOR
INVERNESS (St John the Evangelist) *Mor*
  P-in-c A A SINCLAIR, **Hon C** E S STRANGE
INVERNESS (St Michael and All Angels) *Mor*
  R L A BLACK, **Hon C** D H BENNETT
INVERURIE (St Mary) *Ab*   **NSM** J BURCHILL
IONA (St Columba) *Arg*   **R** *Vacant*
IRVINE (St Andrew) Local Ecumenical Experiment *Glas*
  C-in-c S B SYMONS, **NSM** J JENKINS,
  A MONTGOMERIE
ISLAY (St Columba) *Arg*   **R** K V PAGAN
JEDBURGH (St John the Evangelist) *Edin*
  Hon C W J GROVER
JOHNSTONE (St John) *Glas*   **R** *Vacant* Johnstone (01505)
  20623
KEITH (Holy Trinity) *Mor*   **R** H M LOPDELL-BRADSHAW
KELSO (St Andrew) *Edin*   **P-in-c** D R H EDWARDSON
KEMNAY (St Anne) *Ab*   **NSM** J BURCHILL
KENTALLEN (St Moluag) *Arg*   **P-in-c** D W DAY
KESSOCK-TORE Arpafeelie *Mor*
KILLIN (St Fillan) *St And*   **R** C E J FRYER
KILMACOLM (St Fillan) *Glas*   **R** E G LINDSAY
KILMARNOCK (Holy Trinity) *Glas*   **R** K G STEPHEN,
  NSM J JENKINS
KILMARTIN (St Columba) *Arg*   **R** R F F FLATT
KILMAVEONAIG (St Adamnan) *St And*
  R R G DEVONSHIRE
KINCARDINE O'NEIL (Christ Church) *Ab*
  R R E ROYDEN
KINGHORN (St Mary and St Leonard) *St And*
  R J R LEIGH, **NSM** G N BENSON, M R FREEMAN
KINLOCH RANNOCH (All Saints) *St And*
  P-in-c J L L FAGERSON
KINLOCHLEVEN (St Paul) *Arg*   **P-in-c** D W DAY
KINLOCHMOIDART (St Finian) *Arg*   **P-in-c** D W DAY,
  NSM D N CLIFFORD
KINROSS (St Paul) *St And*   **R** A I WATT
KIRCUDBRIGHT (St Francis of Assisi) *Glas*
  R C M BROUN
KIRKCALDY (St Peter) *St And*   **R** J R LEIGH,
  NSM G N BENSON, M R FREEMAN
KIRKWALL (St Olaf) *Ab*   **R** J MORSON
KIRRIEMUIR (St Mary) *St And*   **C** E N RAMSAY,
  NSM D MACLEAN, J M PRIOR, P D WILLIAMS
KISHORN Chapel *Mor*   **R** *Vacant*
LADYBANK (St Mary) *St And*   **R** *Vacant*
LADYCROFT Balerno *Edin*
LANARK (Christ Church) *Glas*   **R** B H C GORDON
LANGHOLM (All Saints) *Glas*   **P-in-c** J STEVENSON
LARGS (St Columba) *Glas*   **R** G D DUNCAN,
  Hon C J POW
LASSWADE (St Leonard) *Edin*   **R** M A S GOODMAN,
  C D I McCOSH
LAURENCEKIRK (St Laurence) *Bre*   **R** M J R TURNER,
  NSM D P STEEL
LENZIE (St Cyprian) *Glas*   **R** K J SHAW
LERWICK (St Magnus) *Ab*   **R** L S SMITH,
  NSM E H McNAB (nee LUMMIS)
LEVEN (St Margaret) *St And*   **R** C D WHITE,
  NSM R T EVANS, T SHARPUS-JONES
LEVERBURGH *Arg*   **R** *Vacant*
LEWIS, ISLE OF Stornoway *Arg*
LINLITHGOW (St Peter) *Edin*   **R** *Vacant*
LIVINGSTON Local Ecumenical Project *Edin*
  TV P C J BURGESS, **Min** J M PORTEUS,
  NSM A M ARMSTRONG
LOCHALSH (St Donnan) *Mor*   **R** C R DORMER
LOCHBUIE (St Kilda) *Arg*   **P-in-c** D W DAY
LOCHEARNHEAD (St Angus) *St And*   **P-in-c** H G CLEE
LOCHGELLY (St Finnian)—West Fife Team Ministry
  St And   **R** *Vacant* Cowdenbeath (01383) 510002
LOCHGILPHEAD (Christ Church) *Arg*   **R** R F F FLATT
LOCKERBIE (All Saints) *Glas*   **P-in-c** D J B FOSTEKEW
LONGSIDE (St John) *Ab*   **C** I M THOMPSON
LOSSIEMOUTH (St Margaret) Elgin w Lossiemouth *Mor*

LUNAN HEAD (St Margaret) *St And*   **R** *Vacant*
MARYGATE Pittenweem *St And*
MAYBOLE (St Oswald) *Glas*   **NSM** J A MASON
MELROSE (Holy Trinity) *Edin*   **R** P A BURT,
  NSM D W WOOD
MILLPORT Cumbrae (or Millport) *Arg*
MILNGAVIE (St Andrew) *Glas*   **R** K T ROACH,
  C P G M FLETCHER
MOFFAT (St John the Evangelist) *Glas*
  Par Dn J M MARR, **Hon C** R J AMES, J K TOWERS
MONIFIETH (Holy Trinity) *Bre*   **R** R JONES
MONKSTOWN Ladybank *St And*
MONTROSE (St Mary and St Peter) *Bre*   **R** I G STEWART
MOTHERWELL (Holy Trinity) *Glas*   **R** M C REED
MUCHALLS (St Ternan) *Bre*   **Dn-in-c** K R A DALL,
  Par Dn J NELSON
MULL, ISLE OF Gruline *Arg*
MULL, ISLE OF Lochbuie *Arg*
MUSSELBURGH (St Peter) *Edin*   **Dn-in-c** J M JONES
MUTHILL (St James) *St And*   **R** A C RUSSELL,
  NSM W B ROOTES
NAIRN (St Columba) *Mor*   **R** *Vacant*
NETHER LOCHABER (St Bride) *Arg*   **R** *Vacant*
NEW GALLOWAY (St Margaret of Scotland) *Glas*
  P-in-c D JELLEY
NEW PITSLIGO (St John the Evangelist) Fraserburgh w
  New Pitsligo *Ab*
NEWBURGH (St Katherine) *St And*   **NSM** A P PEEBLES
NEWPORT-ON-TAY (St Mary) *St And*
  R J M RICHARDSON
NEWTON STEWART Challoch w Newton Stewart *Glas*
NORTH BALLACHULISH Onich *Arg*
NORTH BERWICK (St Baldred) *Edin*   **R** J C LINDSAY
OBAN (Cathedral of St John) *Arg*   **R** A M MACLEAN,
  NSM G ORPIN
OLD DEER (St Drostan) *Ab*   **C** I M THOMPSON
OLDMELDRUM (St Matthew) *Ab*   **R** A B MacGILLIVRAY
ONICH (St Bride) *Arg*   **R** J R BETTELEY
PAISLEY (Holy Trinity) *Glas*   **R** B A HUTTON
PAISLEY (St Barnabas) *Glas*   **R** B A HUTTON
PEEBLES (St Peter) *Edin*   **NSM** C B AITCHISON
PENICUIK (St James the Less) *Edin*   **R** J F A FARRANT,
  Hon C J PELHAM, **NSM** N F SUTTLE, F E McLEAN,
  M J FASS
PERTH (Cathedral of St Ninian) *St And*   **R** K G FRANZ,
  C R BANKER-PETERSEN, **NSM** R F SAUNDERS,
  J M HARRISON (nee HOLLINRAKE), M D ROBSON
PERTH (St John the Baptist) *St And*   **R** R C FYFFE,
  C D CAMPBELL, **Hon C** H L YOUNG, R H DARROCH,
  W F HARRIS
PETERHEAD (St Peter) *Ab*   **R** J H BOOKER
PINMORE *Glas*   **NSM** B H G COLLIE
PITLOCHRY (Holy Trinity) *St And*   **R** R G DEVONSHIRE
PITTENWEEM (St John the Evangelist) *St And*
  R S G HALL
POLTALLOCH Kilmartin *Arg*
POOLEWE (St Maelrubha) *Mor*   **R** C R DORMER,
  C E W PARK
PORT GLASGOW (St Mary the Virgin) *Glas*
  P-in-c S D N BARRETT
PORTNACROIS (Holy Cross) *Arg*   **P-in-c** D W DAY
PORTPATRICK (St Ninian) *Glas*   **R** *Vacant*
PORTREE (St Columba) *Arg*   **R** *Vacant*
PORTSOY (St John the Baptist) *Ab*   **P-in-c** R M HAINES,
  C J M PAISEY
PRESTONPANS (St Andrew) *Edin*   **P-in-c** J M JONES
PRESTWICK (St Ninian) *Glas*   **R** P D NOBLE
RENFREW (St Margaret) w Erskine *Glas*   **R** *Vacant* 0141–
  886 7858
ROSLIN (Collegiate Church of St Matthew) *Edin*
  P-in-c J DYER
ROSSLYN Chapel see above
ROTHESAY (St Paul) *Arg*   **R** *Vacant*
ROTHIEMURCHUS (St John the Baptist) *Mor*
  P-in-c A WHEATLEY, **Hon C** R K SHAW, E P MOSLEY
ST ANDREWS (All Saints) *St And*   **R** B A HARDY
ST ANDREWS (St Andrew) *St And*   **R** R A GILLIES,
  C P B ROBERTSON, **Hon C** G D WHITE,
  NSM D A BEADLE, J D MARTIN
ST FILLANS (Church of the Holy Spirit) *St And*   **R** *Vacant*
SANDYLOAN Gullane *Edin*
SELKIRK (St John the Evangelist) *Edin*   **R** W B ELLIOT,
  NSM E S JONES
SKYE, ISLE OF Portree *Arg*
SOUTH QUEENSFERRY (Priory Church St Mary of Mount
  Carmel) *Edin*   **P-in-c** D W McCARTHY,
  NSM A V SMITH

STANLEY (St Columba) *St And*   **NSM** R F SAUNDERS
STIRLING (Holy Trinity) *Edin*   **R** C JARMAN
STONEHAVEN (St James) *Bre*   **NSM** G H J PAISEY
STORNOWAY (St Peter) *Arg*   **R** S J G BENNIE,
  NSM J H DOWNIE
STRANRAER (St John the Evangelist) *Glas* **R** *Vacant*
STRATHNAIRN (St Paul) *Mor*   **R** M E GRANT,
  Hon C S A T MALLIN
STRATHPEFFER (St Anne) *Mor*   **P-in-c** M F HICKFORD
STRATHTAY (St Andrew) *St And*   **R** R F PATERSON
STRICHEN (All Saints) *Ab*   **C** I M THOMPSON
STROMNESS (St Mary) *Ab*   **R** J MORSON,
  Dss I St C COSBY
STRONTIAN *Arg*   **P-in-c** D W DAY,
  NSM D N CLIFFORD
TAIN (St Andrew) *Mor*   **P-in-c** M F HUNT
TARFSIDE (St Drostan) *Bre*   **R** S FOX,
  NSM S G LETTON
TAYPORT (St Margaret of Scotland) *St And*
  R J M RICHARDSON
TEINDHILLGREEN Duns *Edin*
THURSO (St Peter and Holy Rood) *Mor*
  P-in-c R MARTIN
TIGHNABRUAICH *Arg* **R** *Vacant*
TOFTS Dalry *Glas*

TORRY Aber St Pet *Ab*
TROON (St Ninian) *Glas*   **R** J A TRIMBLE
TURRIFF (St Congan) *Ab*   **R** R M HAINES,
  C J M PAISEY
UDDINGSTON (St Andrew) *Glas*   **R** A M BURN-
  MURDOCH, **NSM** M A DANSON
ULLAPOOL (St Mary the Virgin) *Mor*   **R** C R DORMER
West Coast Joint Congregations Moray *Mor*
  Hon C G J WILLEY
WEST FIFE Team Ministry—See ABERDOUR;
  BURNTISLAND; DUNFERMLINE; INVERKEITHING
  and LOCHGELLY *St And*   **TR** D L REDWOOD,
  C K S NICHOLSON, **NSM** M KESTON, V A NELLIST
WEST LINTON (St Mungo) *Edin*   **R** J F A FARRANT,
  Hon C J PELHAM, **NSM** F E McLEAN, M J FASS
WESTER HAILES (St Luke) *Edin*
  Miss P K R WHITEFIELD
WESTGATE Dunbar *Edin*
WESTHILL (Trinity) *Ab*   **P-in-c** I J FERGUSON
WHITERASHES (All Saints) *Ab*   **R** A B MacGILLIVRAY
WHITING BAY Is of Arran *Arg*
WICK (St John the Evangelist) *Mor*   **R** R MARTIN
WISHAW (St Andrew) *Glas*   **R** M C REED
WOODHEAD OF FETTERLETTER Fyvie *Ab*
YELL Burravoe *Ab*

IRISH BENEFICES AND CHURCHES

An index of the benefices of the Church of Ireland (shown in bold type), together with entries for churches and other licensed places of worship. Where the church name is the same as the benefice (or the first place name in the benefice), the church entry is omitted. Church dedications are indicated in brackets.

The benefice entry gives the full legal name, together with the diocese and the name(s) and appointment(s) of the clergy serving there (if there are none, the telephone number of the parsonage house is given). The following are the main abbreviations used; for others see the full list of abbreviations.

Bp's C	Bishop's Curate	**Hon C**	Honorary Curate
C	Curate	**I**	Incumbent (includes Rector or Vicar)
C-in-c	Curate-in-charge	**NSM**	Non-stipendiary Minister

AASLEAGH (St John the Baptist) Tuam w Cong and Aasleagh *T, K & A*
ABBEYLEIX (no dedication) w The Old Church, Ballyroan, Ballinakill, Killermogh, Aughmacart, Durrow and Attanagh *C & O* **I** PA HARVEY
ABBEYSTREWRY (no dedication) w Creagh, Tullagh, Castlehaven and Caheragh *C, C & R* **I** TR LESTER
ABINGDON (no dedication) Killaloe w Stradbally *L & K*
ACHILL (Holy Trinity) Aughaval w Achill, Knappagh, Dugort etc *T, K & A*
ACHONRY (Cathedral of St Crumnathy) w Tubbercurry and Killoran *T, K & A* **I** SF GILLMOR
ACTON (no dedication) w Drumbanagher *Arm* Bp's C MHARVEY
ADARE (St Nicholas) w Kilpeacon and Croom *L & K* **I** MJ BNUTTALL, NSM AMO'S FERGUSON
AGHABOG (no dedication) Ematris w Rockcorry, Aghabog and Aughnamullan *Clogh*
AGHADE (All Saints) Fenagh w Myshall, Aghade and Ardoyne *C & O*
AGHADERG (St Mellan) w Donaghmore and Scarva *D & D* **I** GN LITTLE
AGHADOE Killarney w Aghadoe and Muckross *L & K*
AGHADOWEY (St Guaire) w Kilrea *D & R* **I** JRD SLATER
AGHADOWN (Church Cross) Ballydehob w Aghadown *C, C & R*
AGHADOWN (St Matthew) as above
AGHADRUMSEE (no dedication) w Clogh and Drumsnatt *Clogh* **I** VE KILLE
AGHALEE (Holy Trinity) *D & D* **I** JA HARRON
AGHALURCHER (no dedication) w Tattykeeran, Cooneen and Mullaghfad *Clogh* **I** WT LONG
AGHANAGH (no dedication) Boyle and Elphin w Aghanagh, Kilbryan etc *K, E & A*
AGHANCON (no dedication) Shinrone w Aghancon etc *L & K*
AGHANLOO (St Lugha) Tamlaghtard w Aghanloo *D & R*
AGHAVEA (no dedication) *Clogh* **I** J McCLOUGHLIN
AGHAVILLY (St Mary) Arm St Mark w Aghavilly *Arm*
AGHAVOE (no dedication) Rathdowney w Castlefleming, Donaghmore etc *C & O*
AGHER (no dedication) Rathmolyon w Castlerickard, Rathcore and Agher *M & K*
AGHERTON (St John the Baptist) *Conn* **I** PW ROOKE
AGHOLD (no dedication) Tullow w Shillelagh, Aghold and Mullinacuff *C & O*
AGHOUR (St Lachtan) Kilkenny w Aghour and Kilmanagh *C & O*
AHASCRAGH Aughrim w Ballinasloe etc *L & K*
AHERLA Moviddy Union *C, C & R*
AHOGHILL (St Colmanell) w Portglenone *Conn* **I** WK MBREW
ALDERGROVE Killead w Gartree *Conn*
ALMORITIA (St Nicholas) Mullingar, Portnashangan, Moyliscar, Kilbixy etc *M & K*
ALTEDESERT (no dedication) Kildress w Altedesert *Arm*
ANNACLONE (Christ Church) Magherally w Annaclone *D & D*
ANNACREVY Powerscourt w Kilbride and Annacrevy *D & G*
ANNADUFF (St Ann) Kiltoghart w Drumshambo, Annaduff and Kilronan *K, E & A*
ANNAGH (St Andrew) w Drumaloor, Cloverhill, Drumgoon, Dernakesh, Ashfield and Killesherdoney *K, E & A* **I** WD JOHNSTON, C PD THORNBURY
ANNAGHMORE (St Francis) *Arm* **I** RJ N PORTEUS
ANNAHILT (Ascension) w Magherahamlet *D & D* **I** JR HOWARD
ANNALONG (no dedication) *D & D* **I** *Vacant*
ANNESTOWN Waterford w Killea, Drumcannon and Dunhill *C & O*

ANTRIM (All Saints) *Conn* **I** *Vacant*
ANTRIM (St Patrick) Conn w Antrim St Patr *Conn*
ARBOE (no dedication) Ballinderry w Tamlaght and Arboe *Arm*
ARDAGH (St Patrick) w Tashinny, Shrule and Kilcommick *K, E & A* Bp's C AW KINGSTON
ARDAMINE (St John the Evangelist) w Kiltennel, Glascarrig, Kilnamanagh, Kilmuckridge and Monamolin *C & O* **I** J JACOB
ARDARA (St Connall) w Glencolumbkille, Inniskeel, Glenties and Lettermacaward *D & R* **I** MS HARTE, NSM MC CLASSON
ARDCARNE (no dedication) Boyle and Elphin w Aghanagh, Kilbryan etc *K, E & A*
ARDCLINIS (St Mary) and Tickmacrevan w Layde and Cushendun *Conn* **I** KB de S SCOTT
ARDCOLM (no dedication) Wexford w Ardcolm and Killurin *C & O*
ARDEE (St Mary) Drogheda w Ardee, Collon and Termonfeckin *Arm*
ARDGLASS (St Nicholas) Lecale Gp *D & D*
ARDKEEN (Christ Church) Ballyhalbert w Ardkeen *D & D*
ARDMORE (no dedication) w Craigavon *D & D* **I** DM COLLINS
ARDMORE (St Paul) Youghal Union *C, C & R*
ARDNAGEEHY (no dedication) Fermoy Union *C, C & R*
ARDOYNE (Holy Trinity) Fenagh w Myshall, Aghade and Ardoyne *C & O*
ARDOYNE (Immanuel) Belf H Trin and Ardoyne *Conn*
ARDQUIN (no dedication) Ballyphilip w Ardquin *D & D*
ARDRAHAN Aughrim w Ballinasloe etc *L & K*
ARDSTRAW (St Eugene) w Baronscourt, Badoney Lower and Badoney Upper and Greenan *D & R* **I** WC McNEE
ARDTREA (St Andrew) w Desertcreat *Arm* **I** EP DUNDAS
ARKLOW (St Saviour) w Inch and Kilbride *D & G* **I** NJ W SHERWOOD
ARMAGH (Cathedral of St Patrick) *Arm* **I** H CASSIDY
ARMAGH (St Mark) w Aghavilly *Arm* **I** JW McKEGNEY, CG WYLIE, Bp's C CG WYLIE, C DC MATTHEWS
ARMAGHBREAGUE (no dedication) Keady w Armaghbreague and Derrynoose *Arm*
ARMOY (St Patrick) w Loughguile and Drumtullagh *Conn* **I** WE McCRORY
ARVAGH (no dedication) w Carrigallen, Gowna and Columbkille *K, E & A* **I** JRT WATSON
ASHFIELD (no dedication) Annagh w Drumgoon, Ashfield etc *K, E & A*
ASKEATON (St Mary) Rathkeale w Askeaton and Kilcornan *L & K*
ATHBOY (St James) w Ballivor and Killallon *M & K* **I** *Vacant*
ATHLONE (St Mary) w Benown, Kiltoom and Forgney *M & K* **I** IJ POWER
ATHY (St Michael) w Kilberry, Fontstown and Kilkea *D & G* **I** JL CRAMPTON
ATTANAGH Abbeyleix w Old Church, Ballyroan etc *C & O*
AUGHANUNSHIN Conwal Union w Gartan *D & R*
AUGHAVAL (no dedication) w Achill, Knappagh, Dugort, Castlebar and Turlough *T, K & A* **I** GL HASTINGS
AUGHAVAS (no dedication) Mohill w Farnaught, Aughavas, Oughteragh etc *K, E & A*
AUGHER (no dedication) w Newtownsaville and Eskrahoole *Clogh* **I** BM BOWER
AUGHMACART (St Tighernagh) Abbeyleix w Old Church, Ballyroan etc *C & O*
AUGHNACLIFFE Arvagh w Carrigallen, Gowna and Columbkille *K, E & A*
AUGHNACLOY Carnteel and Crilly *Arm*
AUGHNAMULLAN (Christ Church) Ematris w Rockcorry, Aghabog and Aughnamullan *Clogh*

AUGHRIM (Holy Trinity) w Ballinasloe, Clontuskert, Ahascragh, Woodlawn, Kilmacduagh and Ardrahan *L & K*   **I** T A SULLIVAN

AUGHRIM (St John the Evangelist) Castlemacadam w Ballinaclash, Aughrim etc *D & G*

BADONEY LOWER (St Patrick) Ardstraw w Baronscourt, Badoney Lower etc *D & R*

BADONEY UPPER (St Aichen) as above

BAGENALSTOWN Dunleckney w Nurney, Lorum and Kiltennel *C & O*

BAILIEBOROUGH (no dedication) w Knockbride, Shercock and Mullagh *K, E & A*   **NSM** A J LINDSAY

BALBRIGGAN (St George) Holmpatrick w Balbriggan and Kenure *D & G*

BALGRIFFIN (St Doulagh) Malahide w Balgriffin *D & G*

BALLAGHTOBIN (no dedication) Kells Union *C & O*

BALLEE (no dedication) Bright w Ballee and Killough *D & D*

BALLIGAN Ballywalter w Inishargie *D & D*

BALLINACLASH (no dedication) Castlemacadam w Ballinaclash, Aughrim etc *D & G*

BALLINADEE (no dedication) Bandon Union *C, C & R*

BALLINAFAD Boyle and Elphin w Aghanagh, Kilbryan etc *K, E & A*

BALLINALEA Mostrim w Granard, Clonbroney, Killoe etc *K, E & A*

BALLINALECK Cleenish w Mullaghdun *Clogh*

BALLINAMALLARD Magheracross *Clogh*

BALLINAMORE Mohill w Farnaught, Aughavas, Oughteragh etc *K, E & A*

BALLINASLOE (St John the Evangelist) Aughrim w Ballinasloe etc *L & K*

BALLINATONE Castlemacadam w Ballinaclash, Aughrim etc *D & G*

BALLINDERRY (no dedication) *Conn*   **I** E J HARRIS

BALLINDERRY (St John) w Tamlaght and Arboe *Arm*   **I** H J W MOORE

BALLINEEN Kinneigh Union *C, C & R*

BALLINGARRY (no dedication) Cloughjordan w Borrisokane etc *L & K*

BALLINLOUGH Roscommon w Donamon, Rathcline, Kilkeevin etc *K, E & A*

BALLINROBE (St Mary) Tuam w Cong and Aasleagh *T, K & A*

BALLINTEMPLE (no dedication) Kilmore w Ballintemple, Kildallon etc *K, E & A*

BALLINTEMPLE (St Mary) Cashel w Magorban, Tipperary, Clonbeg etc *C & O*

BALLINTOGHER Taunagh w Kilmactranny, Ballysumaghan etc *K, E & A*

BALLINTOY (no dedication) w Rathlin and Dunseverick *Conn*   **I** J N PATTERSON

BALLINTUBBERT (St Brigid) Stradbally w Ballintubbert, Coraclone etc *C & O*

BALLISODARE (Holy Trinity) w Collooney and Emlaghfad *T, K & A*   **I** R M STRATFORD

BALLIVOR Athboy w Ballivor and Killallon *M & K*

BALLNACARGY Mullingar, Portnashangan, Moyliscar, Kilbixy etc *M & K*

BALLYBAY (Christ Church) w Mucknoe and Clontibret *Clogh*   **I** G A KNOWD

BALLYBEEN (St Mary) *D & D*   **I** J M WHITE

BALLYBRACK Killiney Ballybrack *D & G*

BALLYBUNNION Tralee w Ballymacelligott, Kilnaughtin etc *L & K*

BALLYCANEW (no dedication) Gorey w Kilnahue, Leskinfere and Ballycanew *C & O*

BALLYCARNEY (no dedication) Ferns w Kilbride, Toombe, Kilcormack etc *C & O*

BALLYCARRY Kilroot and Templecorran *Conn*

BALLYCASTLE (Holy Trinity) Ramoan w Ballycastle and Culfeightrin *Conn*

BALLYCLARE Ballynure and Ballyeaston *Conn*

BALLYCLOG (St Patrick) Brackaville w Donaghendry and Ballyclog *Arm*

BALLYCLUG (St Patrick) Ballymena w Ballyclug *Conn*

BALLYCOMMON Geashill w Killeigh and Ballycommon *M & K*

BALLYCONNELL Swanlinbar w Tomregan, Kinawley, Drumlane etc *K, E & A*

BALLYCOTTON Youghal Union *C, C & R*

BALLYCULTER (Christ Church) Lecale Gp *D & D*

BALLYDEHOB (St Matthias) w Aghadown *C, C & R*   **I** P R DRAPER

BALLYEASTON (St John the Evangelist) Ballynure and Ballyeaston *Conn*

BALLYEGLISH (St Matthias) Desertlyn w Ballyeglish *Arm*

BALLYFIN (no dedication) Maryborough w Dysart Enos and Ballyfin *C & O*

BALLYGAWLEY (no dedication) Errigle Keerogue w Ballygawley and Killeshil *Arm*

BALLYHAISE Drung w Castleterra, Larah and Lavey etc *K, E & A*

BALLYHALBERT (St Andrew) w Ardkeen *D & D*   **I** *Vacant*

BALLYHOLME (St Columbanus) *D & D*   **I** A F ABERNETHY,   **C** W C S WRIGHT

BALLYHOOLEY (no dedication) Fermoy Union *C, C & R*

BALLYJAMESDUFF (no dedication) Lurgan etc w Ballymachugh, Kildrumferton etc *K, E & A*

BALLYKELLY Tamlaghtfinlagan w Myroe *D & R*

BALLYLESSON Drumbo *D & D*

BALLYMACARRETT (St Martin) *D & D*   **Bp's C** I R BETTS

BALLYMACARRETT (St Patrick) *D & D*   **I** D COE

BALLYMACASH (St Mark) *Conn*   **I** W G IRWIN,   **C** P G HEAK

BALLYMACELLIGOTT (no dedication) Tralee w Ballymacelligott, Kilnaughtin etc *L & K*

BALLYMACHUGH (St Paul) Lurgan etc w Ballymachugh, Kildrumferton etc *K, E & A*

BALLYMACKEY (St Michael) Nenagh *L & K*

BALLYMACORMACK (no dedication) Templemichael w Clongish, Clooncumber etc *K, E & A*

BALLYMAGLASSON Dunboyne w Kilcock, Maynooth, Moyglare etc *M & K*

BALLYMAHON Ardagh w Tashinny, Shrule and Kilcommick *K, E & A*

BALLYMARTLE (no dedication) Kinsale Union *C, C & R*

BALLYMASCANLAN (St Mary) w Creggan and Rathcor *Arm*   **I** G M KINGSTON

BALLYMENA (St Patrick) w Ballyclug *Conn*   **I** S GELLOYD,   **C** G E WITHERS,   T H PRIESTLY

BALLYMONEY Kinneigh Union *C, C & R*

BALLYMONEY (St Patrick) w Finvoy and Rasharkin *Conn*   **I** E R LAVERY,   **C** G M S WATSON

BALLYMORE Clondehorkey w Cashel *D & R*

BALLYMORE (St Mark) *Arm*   **I** S J BLACK

BALLYMORE EUSTACE (St John) Blessington w Kilbride, Ballymore Eustace etc *D & G*

BALLYMOTE Ballisodare w Collooney and Emlaghfad *T, K & A*

BALLYMOYER (St Luke) Newtownhamilton w Ballymoyer and Belleck *Arm*

BALLYNAFEIGH (St Jude) *D & D*   **I** W M MOORE,   **C** S GILCHRIST

BALLYNAHINCH Magheradroll *D & D*

BALLYNAKILL (All Saints) Abbeyleix w Old Church, Ballyroan etc *C & O*

BALLYNAKILL (St Thomas) Omey w Ballynakill, Errislannan and Roundstone *T, K & A*

BALLYNASCREEN Kilcronaghan w Draperstown and Sixtowns *D & R*

BALLYNURE (Ascension) Baltinglass w Ballynure etc *C & O*

BALLYNURE (Christ Church) and Ballyeaston *Conn*   **I** J F A BOND,   **NSM** F M BACH

BALLYPHILIP (no dedication) w Ardquin *D & D*   **I** S McCULLOUGH

BALLYRASHANE (St John the Baptist) w Kildollagh *Conn*   **I** N C SHORTT

BALLYROAN (no dedication) Abbeyleix w Old Church, Ballyroan etc *C & O*

BALLYSALLY (St Andrew) Coleraine *Conn*

BALLYSCULLION (no dedication) Drummaul w Duneane and Ballyscullion *Conn*

BALLYSCULLION (St Tida) *D & R*   **I** F J REILLY

BALLYSEEDY (no dedication) Tralee w Ballymacelligott, Kilnaughtin etc *L & K*

BALLYSHANNON Kilbarron w Rossnowlagh and Drumholm *D & R*

BALLYSILLAN Belf St Mark *Conn*

BALLYSUMAGHAN (no dedication) Taunagh w Kilmactranny, Ballysumaghan etc *K, E & A*

BALLYWALTER (Holy Trinity) w Inishargie *D & D*   **I** J R L BOWLEY

BALLYWARD Drumgath w Drumgooland and Clonduff *D & D*

BALLYWILLAN (Holy Trinity) *Conn*   **I** H HOPKINS

BALRATHBOYNE Kells w Balrathboyne, Moynalty etc *M & K*

BALTEAGH (St Canice) w Carrick *D & R*   **I** J J HEMPHILL

BALTIMORE Abbeystrewry Union *C, C & R*

BALTINGLASS (St Mary) w Ballynure, Stratford-on-Slaney and Rathvilly *C & O*   **I** M A McCULLAGH

BANAGHER (St Moresuis) Cumber Lower w Banagher *D & R*

BANAGHER (St Paul) Clonfert Gp of Par *L & K*

BANBRIDGE Seapatrick *D & D*

BANDON (St Peter) w Rathclaren, Innishannon, Ballinadee and Brinny *C, C & R* **I** M A J BURROWS, **C** O DONOHOE
BANGOR Primacy (Christ Church) *D & D* **C** I R GAMBLE
BANGOR (St Comgall) *D & D* **I** W R D McCREERY, **C** I R GAMBLE, C J CARSON
BANGOR ABBEY (Bangor Abbey) *D & D* **I** H LECKEY, **C** S A FIELDING, S D LOGAN
BANNOW (no dedication) Taghmon w Horetown and Bannow *C & O*
BANTRY Kilmocomogue Union *C, C & R*
BARONSCOURT (no dedication) Ardstraw w Baronscourt, Badoney Lower etc *D & R*
BARR (no dedication) Donacavey w Barr *Clogh*
BEARA (St Peter) *C, C & R* **I** *Vacant* Cork (21) 63036
BECTIVE Trim w Bective and Galtrim *M & K*
BELFAST (All Saints) *Conn* **I** C WEST, **NSM** R MOORE
BELFAST (Cathedral of St Anne) *Conn* **I** J SHEARER
BELFAST (Christ Church) *Conn* **I** S N M BAYLY
BELFAST (Holy Trinity) and Ardoyne *Conn* **C** C J ATKINSON
BELFAST Malone (St John) *Conn* **I** A E T HARPER
BELFAST (St Aidan) *Conn* **I** W R KELLY, **C** P REDFERN
BELFAST (St Andrew) *Conn* **NSM** S K HOUSTON
BELFAST (St Bartholomew) *Conn* **I** G B MOLLER
BELFAST (St Brendan) *D & D* **I** F McCREA
BELFAST (St Christopher) *D & D* **Bp's C** E M JOHNSTON
BELFAST (St Clement) *D & D* **I** J STEWART
BELFAST (St Donard) *D & D* **I** H N PEDLOW, **C** R T GILLIAN
BELFAST (St George) *Conn* **I** B STEWART, **NSM** G W ODLING-SMEE
BELFAST (St James) (St Silas) *Conn* **I** J O ROLSTON, **NSM** R MAXWELL
BELFAST (St Katharine) *Conn* **I** W J TAGGART
BELFAST (St Mark) *Conn* **I** L J MEDHURST
BELFAST (St Mary) (Holy Redeemer) *Conn* **I** J P WALKER, **C** D LOCKHART
BELFAST (St Mary Magdalene) *Conn* **Bp's C** A MALLON
BELFAST (St Matthew) *Conn* **I** G J O DUNSTAN, **C** D S McVEIGH
BELFAST (St Michael) *Conn* **I** N B DODDS
BELFAST (St Nicholas) *Conn* **I** F J RUSK
BELFAST (St Ninian) *Conn* **I** *Vacant*
BELFAST (St Paul) (St Barnabas) *Conn* **I** K M YOUNG
BELFAST (St Peter) *Conn* **I** S R McBRIDE
BELFAST (St Simon) (St Philip) *Conn* **I** W T HOEY
BELFAST (St Stephen) (St Luke) *Conn* **I** R H MOORE
BELFAST (St Thomas) *Conn* **I** W A LEWIS
BELFAST Upper Falls (St John the Baptist) *Conn* **I** E J COULTER
BELFAST Upper Malone (Epiphany) *Conn* **I** J I CARSON
BELFAST Whiterock (St Columba) *Conn* **Bp's C** C J McCOLLUM
BELLAGHY Ballyscullion *D & R*
BELLEEK (no dedication) Garrison w Slavin and Belleek *Clogh*
BELLEEK (St Luke) Newtownhamilton w Ballymoyer and Belleck *Arm*
BELLERENA Tamlaghtard w Aghanloo *D & R*
BELMONT (St Peter) Culmore w Muff and Belmont *D & R*
BELTURBET Annagh w Drumgoon, Ashfield etc *K, E & A*
BELVOIR (Transfiguration) *D & D* **I** T KEIGHTLEY
BENOWN (no dedication) Athlone w Benown, Kiltoom and Forgney *M & K*
BILBO (no dedication) Castlecomer w Colliery Ch, Mothel and Bilbo *C & O*
BILLIS (no dedication) Lurgan etc w Ballymachugh, Kildrumferton etc *K, E & A*
BILLY (no dedication) w Derrykeighan *Conn* **I** A A JOHNS
BIRR (St Brendan) w Eglish, Lorrha, Dorrha and Lockeen *L & K* **I** D L KEEGAN
BLACKLION Killinagh w Kiltyclogher and Innismagrath *K, E & A*
BLACKROCK (All Saints) Stillorgan w Blackrock *D & G*
BLACKROCK (St Michael) Douglas Union w Frankfield *C, C & R*
BLARNEY Carrigrohane Union *C, C & R*
BLESSINGTON (St Mary) w Kilbride, Ballymore Eustace and Holywood *D & G* **I** N K DUNNE
BOHO (no dedication) Devenish w Boho *Clogh*
BOOTERSTOWN Dub Booterstown *D & G*
BORNACOOLA Templemichael w Clongish, Clooncumber etc *K, E & A*
BORRIS Clonagoose Leighlin w Grange Sylvae, Shankill etc *C & O*
BORRIS Littleton Kilcooley w Littleon, Crohane and Fertagh *C & O*

BORRIS-IN-OSSORY (no dedication) Clonenagh w Offerlane, Borris-in-Ossory etc *C & O*
BORRISNAFARNEY (no dedication) Cloughjordan w Borrisokane etc *L & K*
BORRISOKANE (no dedication) as above
BOURNEY (St Burchin) Roscrea w Kyle, Bourney and Corbally *L & K*
BOVEVAGH (St Eugenius) Dungiven w Bovevagh *D & R*
BOYLE (no dedication) and Elphin w Aghanagh, Kilbryan, Ardcarne and Croghan *K, E & A* **I** *Vacant*
BRACKAVILLE (Holy Trinity) w Donaghendry and Ballyclog *Arm* **I** J T P TWOMEY
BRANTRY (Holy Trinity) Caledon w Brantry *Arm*
BRAY (Christ Church) *D & G* **I** D S G GODFREY, **NSM** C C WEST
BRIGHT (no dedication) w Ballee and Killough *D & D* **I** I P POULTON
BRIGOWN (St George) Fermoy Union *C, C & R*
BRINNY (no dedication) Bandon Union *C, C & R*
BROOKEBOROUGH Aghavea *Clogh*
BROOMHEDGE (St Matthew) *Conn* **I** P J GALBRAITH
BROUGHSHANE Skerry w Rathcavan and Newtowncrommelin *Conn*
BRUFF Kilmallock w Kilflynn, Kilfinane, Knockaney etc *L & K*
BRYANSFORD Castlewellan w Kilcoo *D & D*
BUNBEG Gweedore, Carrickfin and Templecrone *D & R*
BUNCLODY (St Mary) w Kildavin, Clonegal and Kilrush *C & O* **I** N J W WAUGH
BUNCRANA Fahan Lower and Upper *D & R*
BUNDORAN Cloonclare w Killasnett, Lurganboy and Drumlease *K, E & A*
BUSH Ballymascanlan w Creggan and Rathcor *Arm*
BUSHMILLS Dunluce *Conn*
CAHERAGH (St Mary) Abbeystrewry Union *C, C & R*
CAHERCONLISH (St Ailbe) Kilmallock w Kilflynn, Kilfinane, Knockaney etc *L & K*
CAHIR (St Paul) Clonmel w Innislounagh, Tullaghmelan etc *C & O*
CAIRNCASTLE (St Patrick) Kilwaughter w Cairncastle and Craigy Hill *Conn*
CALARY (no dedication) Newc w Newtownmountkennedy and Calary *D & G*
CALEDON (St John) w Brantry *Arm* **I** D B WILSON
CALRY (no dedication) *K, E & A* **Bp's C** D GRISCOME
CAMLOUGH (Christ the Redeemer) w Mullaglass *Arm* **I** R G HOEY
CAMP Dingle w Killiney and Kilgobbin *L & K*
CAMUS-JUXTA-BANN (St Mary) *D & R* **I** D BURNS
CAMUS-JUXTA-MOURNE (Christ Church) *D & R* **I** F W FAWCETT
CAPPAGH (St Eugene) w Lislimnaghan *D & R* **I** D J QUINN
CAPPOQUIN (St Anne) Lismore w Cappoquin, Kilwatermoy, Dungarvan etc *C & O*
CARBURY (no dedication) Clonsast w Rathangan, Thomastown etc *M & K*
CARLOW (St Mary) w Urglin and Staplestown *C & O* **I** G G DOWD
CARNALEA (St Gall) *D & D* **I** W P HOUSTON
CARNALWAY (St Patrick) Newbridge w Carnalway and Kilcullen *M & K*
CARNDONAGH Moville w Greencastle, Donagh, Cloncha etc *D & R*
CARNEW (All Saints) Crosspatrick Gp *C & O*
CARNLOUGH Ardclinis and Tickmacrevan w Layde and Cushendun *Conn*
CARNMONEY (Holy Evangelists) *Conn* **I** N P BAYLOR
CARNTEEL (St James) and Crilly *Arm* **I** G P BRIDLE
CARRICK (no dedication) Balteagh w Carrick *D & R*
CARRICK-ON-SHANNON Kiltoghart w Drumshambo, Annaduff and Kilronan *K, E & A*
CARRICKFERGUS (St Nicholas) *Conn* **I** J A McMASTER, **C** D P KERR, T A G McCANN
CARRICKFIN (St Andrew) Gweedore, Carrickfin and Templecrone *D & R*
CARRICKMACROSS (St Fin Barre) w Magheracloone *Clogh* **I** J L SUTCLIFFE
CARRIGALINE (St Mary) w Killanully and Monkstown *C, C & R* **I** A J HOUSTON
CARRIGALLEN (no dedication) Arvagh w Carrigallen, Gowna and Columbkille *K, E & A*
CARRIGANS Taughboyne, Craigadooish, Newtowncunningham etc *D & R*
CARRIGART Mevagh w Glenalla *D & R*
CARRIGROHANE (St Peter) w Garrycloyne, Inniscarra and Magourney *C, C & R* **I** H C MILLER
CARRIGTWOHILL (St David) Rathcooney Union *C, C & R*

CARROWDORE (Christ Church) w Millisle *D & D*   **I** *Vacant*
CARRYDUFF (St Ignatius) Killaney w Carryduff *D & D*
CASHEL (Cathedral of St John the Baptist) w Magorban, Tipperary, Clonbeg and Ballintemple *C & O*
  I PJKNOWLES, **NSM** BYFRYDAY
CASHEL (no dedication) Clondehorkey w Cashel *D & R*
CASTLEARCHDALE (St Patrick) Derryvullen N w Castlearchdale *Clogh*
CASTLEBAR (Christ Church) Aughaval w Achill, Knappagh, Dugort etc *T, K & A*
CASTLEBLAYNEY Ballybay w Mucknoe and Clontibret *Clogh*
CASTLECOMER (St Mary) w the Colliery Church, Mothel and Bilbo *C & O* **I** ADHORR
CASTLECONNELL Killaloe w Stradbally *L & K*
CASTLECONNOR (no dedication) Killala w Dunfeeny, Crossmolina, Kilmoremoy etc *T, K & A*
CASTLEDAWSON (Christ Church) *D & R* **I** RJSTEWART
CASTLEDERG Derg w Termonamongan *D & R*
CASTLEDERMOT (St James) Narraghmore w Timolin, Castledermot and Kinneagh *D & G*
CASTLEFLEMING (no dedication) Rathdowney w Castlefleming, Donaghmore etc *C & O*
CASTLEGREGORY Dingle w Killiney and Kilgobbin *L & K*
CASTLEHAVEN (no dedication) Abbeystrewry Union *C, C & R*
CASTLEKNOCK (St Brigid) and Mulhuddart, w Clonsilla *D & G* **I** WPCOLTON
CASTLELOST Mullingar, Portnashangan, Moyliscar, Kilbixy etc *M & K*
CASTLEMACADAM (Holy Trinity) w Ballinaclash, Aughrim and Macreddin *D & G* **I** GWBUTLER
CASTLEMAINE Kilcolman w Kiltallagh, Killorglin, Knockane etc *L & K*
CASTLEMARTYR (St Anne) Youghal Union *C, C & R*
CASTLEPOLLARD (St Michael) and Oldcastle w Loughcrew, Mount Nugent, Mayne and Drumcree *M & K*
  I GARMILNE
CASTLEREA Roscommon w Donamon, Rathcline, Kilkeevin etc *K, E & A*
CASTLERICKARD Rathmolyon w Castlerickard, Rathcore and Agher *M & K*
CASTLEROCK (Christ Church) w Dunboe and Fermoyle *D & R* **I** WBJOHNSTON
CASTLETERRA (no dedication) Drung w Castleterra, Larah and Lavey etc *K, E & A*
CASTLETOWN Killeshin w Cloydagh and Killabban *C & O*
CASTLETOWN Rathkeale w Askeaton and Kilcornan *L & K*
CASTLETOWN Kells w Balrathboyne, Moynalty etc *M & K*
CASTLETOWNBERE Beara *C, C & R*
CASTLETOWNROCHE (no dedication) Mallow Union *C, C & R*
CASTLETOWNSEND Abbeystrewry Union *C, C & R*
CASTLEVENTRY (no dedication) Ross Union *C, C & R*
CASTLEWELLAN (St Paul) w Kilcoo *D & D* **I** RFGREER
CAVAN Urney w Denn and Derryheen *K, E & A*
CELBRIDGE (Christ Church) w Straffan and Newcastle-Lyons *D & G* **I** DHBOYLAND
CHAPELIZOD (St Laurence) Dub Crumlin w Chapelizod *D & G*
CHARLEMONT (no dedication) Moy w Charlemont *Arm*
CLABBY (St Margaret) Tempo and Clabby *Clogh*
CLANABOGAN (no dedication) Edenderry w Clanabogan *D & R*
CLANE (St Michael and All Angels) w Donadea and Coolcarrigan *M & K* **I** DFRAZER
CLARA (St Brigid) w Liss, Moate and Clonmacnoise *M & K*
  NSM MMSGRAY-STACK
CLARE (no dedication) Loughgilly w Clare *Arm*
CLAUDY Cumber Upper w Learmount *D & R*
CLEENISH (no dedication) w Mullaghdun *Clogh*
  I WSWRIGHT
CLIFDEN Omey w Ballynakill, Errislannan and Roundstone *T, K & A*
CLOGH (Holy Trinity) Aghadrumsee w Clogh and Drumsnatt *Clogh*
CLOGHER (Cathedral of St Macartan) w Errigal Portclare *Clogh* **I** TRMOORE
CLOGHERNEY (St Partick) w Seskinore and Drumnakilly *Arm* **I** *Vacant*
CLONAGOOSE (St Moling) Leighlin w Grange Sylvae, Shankill etc *C & O*
CLONAKILTY Kilgariffe Union *C, C & R*
CLONALLON (no dedication) w Warrenpoint *D & D*
  I MDJMcCREADY
CLONARD Mullingar, Portnashangan, Moyliscar, Kilbixy etc *M & K*

CLONASLEE Mountmellick w Coolbanagher, Rosenallis etc *M & K*
CLONBEG (St Sedna) Cashel w Magorban, Tipperary, Clonbeg etc *C & O*
CLONBRONEY (St John) Mostrim w Granard, Clonbroney, Killoe etc *K, E & A*
CLONBULLOGUE Clonsast w Rathangan, Thomastown etc *M & K*
CLONCHA (no dedication) Moville w Greencastle, Donagh, Cloncha etc *D & R*
CLONDALKIN (St John) w Rathcoole *D & G*
  I JEMcCULLAGH, **NSM** OBOOTHMAN
CLONDEHORKEY (St John) w Cashel *D & R* **I** *Vacant*
CLONDEVADDOCK (Christ the Redeemer) w Portsalon and Leatbeg *D & R* **P-in-c** AHKERR
CLONDUFF (St John) Drumgath w Drumgooland and Clonduff *D & D*
CLONE (St Paul) Enniscorthy w Clone, Clonmore, Monart etc *C & O*
CLONEGAL (no dedication) Bunclody w Kildavin, Clonegal and Kilrush *C & O*
CLONEGAM (Holy Trinity) Fiddown w Clonegam, Guilcagh and Kilmeaden *C & O*
CLONENAGH (no dedication) w Offerlane, Borris-in-Ossory, Seirkieran and Roskelton *C & O* **I** HHJGRAY
CLONES (St Tighernach) w Killeevan *Clogh* **I** *Vacant*
CLONEYHURKE (no dedication) Portarlington w Cloneyhurke and Lea *M & K*
CLONFADFORAN Tullamore w Durrow, Newtownfertullagh, Rahan etc *M & K*
CLONFEACLE (St Patrick) w Derrygortreavy *Arm*
  I AJPARKHILL
CLONFERT (Cathedral of St Brendan) w Donanaughta, Banagher and Lickmolassy *L & K* **Bp's C** RWCARNEY
CLONGISH (St Paul) Templemichael w Clongish, Clooncumber etc *K, E & A*
CLONLARA Killaloe w Stradbally *L & K*
CLONLEIGH (St Lugadius) Raphoe w Raymochy and Clonleigh *D & R*
CLONMACNOISE (St Kieran) Clara w Liss, Moate and Clonmacnoise *M & K*
CLONMEL (St Mary) w Innislounagh, Tullaghmelan, Fethard, Kilvemnon and Cahir *C & O* **I** IJEKNOX
CLONMEL UNION (Christ Church) *C, C & R*
  I PJANDERSON
CLONMELLON Athboy w Ballivor and Killallon *M & K*
CLONMORE (St John) Enniscorthy w Clone, Clonmore, Monart etc *C & O*
CLONMORE (St John) Kiltegan w Hacketstown, Clonmore and Moyne *C & O*
CLONOE (St Michael) Tullaniskin w Clonoe *Arm*
CLONSAST (no dedication) w Rathangan, Thomastown, Monasteroris, Carbury and Rahan *M & K* **I** RWDEANE, **NSM** GWRRYAN
CLONSILLA (St Mary) Castleknock and Mulhuddart, w Clonsilla *D & G*
CLONTARF Dub Clontarf *D & G*
CLONTIBRET (St Colman) Ballybay w Mucknoe and Clontibret *Clogh*
CLONTUSKERT (St Matthew) Aughrim w Ballinasloe etc *L & K*
CLOONCLARE (no dedication) w Killasnett, Lurganboy and Drumlease *K, E & A* **Bp's C** CJSTEVENSON
CLOONCUMBER (no dedication) Templemichael w Clongish, Clooncumber etc *K, E & A*
CLOONEY (All Saints) w Strathfoyle *D & R*
  I JCDMAYES, **C** RCLOGUE
CLOUGH Craigs w Dunaghy and Killagan *Conn*
CLOUGHFERN (Ascension) *Conn* **I** JOMANN, **NSM** JMELSDON
CLOUGHJORDAN (St Kieran) w Borrisokane, Ballingary, Borrisnafarney and Templeharry *L & K*
  I SCDATKINSON
CLOUGHMILLS Craigs w Dunaghy and Killagan *Conn*
CLOVERHILL (St John) Annagh w Drumgoon, Ashfield etc *K, E & A*
CLOYDAGH (no dedication) Killeshin w Cloydagh and Killabban *C & O*
CLOYNE (Cathedral of St Colman) w Inch, Corkbeg, Midleton and Gurranekennefeake *C, C & R* **I** GPStJHILLIARD
COACHFORD Carrigrohane Union *C, C & R*
COALISLAND Brackaville w Donaghendry and Ballyclog *Arm*
COLAGHTY Lack *Clogh*
COLEBROOK Aghalurcher w Tattykeeran, Cooneen etc *Clogh*

COLERAINE Killowen *D & R*
COLERAINE (St Patrick) *Conn*   I K H CLARKE,
C M J ELLIOTT, D J BELL
COLIN (St Andrew) Derriaghy w Colin *Conn*
COLLIERY CHURCH, THE Castlecomer w Colliery Ch,
Mothel and Bilbo *C & O*
COLLON (no dedication) Drogheda w Ardee, Collon and
Termonfeckin *Arm*
COLLOONEY (St Paul) Ballisodare w Collooney and
Emlaghfad *T, K & A*
COLPE (St Columba) Julianstown and Colpe w Drogheda
and Duleek *M & K*
COLUMBKILLE (St Thomas) Arvagh w Carrigallen, Gowna
and Columbkille *K, E & A*
COMBER (St Mary) *D & D*   I J P O BARRY
COMERAGH Lismore w Cappoquin, Kilwatermoy,
Dungarvan etc *C & O*
CONARY (St Bartholomew) Dunganstown w Redcross and
Conary *D & G*
CONG (St Mary) Tuam w Cong and Aasleagh *T, K & A*
CONNOR (St Saviour) w Antrim St Patrick *Conn*
I S JONES
CONVOY (St Ninian) w Monellan and Donaghmore *D & R*
I M COMBER
CONWAL (no dedication) w Aughanunshin and Gartan
D & R   I W W MORTON
COOKSTOWN Derryloran *Arm*
COOLBANAGHER (St John) Mountmellick w
Coolbanagher, Rosenallis etc *M & K*
COOLCARRIGAN (no dedication) Clane w Donadea and
Coolcarrigan *M & K*
COOLKELLURE (St Edmund) Fanlobbus Union *C, C & R*
COOLOCK (St John) Raheny w Coolock *D & G*
COONEEN (no dedication) Aghalurcher w Tattykeeran,
Cooneen etc *Clogh*
COOTEHILL Annagh w Drumgoon, Ashfield etc *K, E & A*
CORACLONE (St Peter) Stradbally w Ballintubbert,
Coraclone etc *C & O*
CORBALLY (Christ Church) Roscrea w Kyle, Bourney and
Corbally *L & K*
CORK (Cathedral of St Fin Barre) (St Nicholas) *C, C & R*
I R L CLARKE, C M GRAHAM, NSM E W HUNTER
CORK (St Luke) w Shandon **(St Ann)** w St Mary *C, C & R*
I W J HEASLIP
CORKBEG (St Michael and All Angels) Cloyne Union
C, C & R
CORRAWALLEN (no dedication) Kilmore w Ballintemple,
Kildallon etc *K, E & A*
COURTMACSHERRY (St John the Evangelist) Kilgariffe
Union *C, C & R*
CRAIGADOOISH (no dedication) Taughboyne,
Craigadooish, Newtowncunningham etc *D & R*
CRAIGAVAD Glencraig *D & D*
CRAIGAVON (St Saviour) Ardmore w Craigavon *D & D*
CRAIGS (no dedication) w Dunaghy and Killagan *Conn*
I J C BUDD
CRAIGY HILL (All Saints) Kilwaughter w Cairncastle and
Craigy Hill *Conn*
CREAGH Abbeystrewry Union *C, C & R*
CREAGH Aughrim w Ballinasloe etc *L & K*
CRECORA Adare w Kilpeacon and Croom *L & K*
CREGAGH (St Finnian) *D & D*   I J N BATTYE,
C K HIGGINS
CREGGAN (no dedication) Ballymascanlan w Creggan and
Rathcor *Arm*
CRILLY (St George) Carnteel and Crilly *Arm*
CRINKEN (St James) *D & G*   I W E C STOREY
CROGHAN (Holy Trinity) Boyle and Elphin w Aghanagh,
Kilbryan etc *K, E & A*
CROHANE (no dedication) Kilcooley w Littleon, Crohane
and Fertagh *C & O*
CROM (Holy Trinity) Kinawley w Drumany and Crom
K, E & A
CROOKHAVEN (St Brendan) Kilmoe Union *C, C & R*
CROOM (no dedication) Adare w Kilpeacon and Croom
L & K
CROSSGAR Kilmore w Inch *D & D*
CROSSHAVEN Templebreedy w Tracton and Nohoval
C, C & R
CROSSMOLINA (no dedication) Killala w Dunfeeny,
Crossmolina, Kilmoremoy etc *T, K & A*
CROSSPATRICK Group (no dedication) w Kilcommon,
Kilpipe, Preban and Carnew, The *C & O*
I C CHALLENDER
CRUMLIN Dub Crumlin w Chapelizod *D & G*
CRUMLIN (St John) Glenavy w Tunny and Crumlin *Conn*

CRUMLIN ROAD Belf St Mary w H Redeemer *Conn*
CULDAFF (no dedication) Moville w Greencastle, Donagh,
Cloncha etc *D & R*
CULFEIGHTRIN (no dedication) Ramoan w Ballycastle
and Culfeightrin *Conn*
CULLYBACKEY Craigs w Dunaghy and Killagan *Conn*
CULMORE (Holy Trinity) w Muff and Belmont *D & R*
I C L MACONACHIE
CUMBER LOWER (Holy Trinity) w Banagher *D & R*
I Vacant
CUMBER UPPER (no dedication) w Learmount *D & R*
I J A MARTIN
CURRAGH (Garrison Church of St Paul) Kildare w
Kilmeague and Curragh *M & K*
CURRIN (St Andrew) w Drum and Newbliss *Clogh*
I T B GOLDING
CUSHENDALL Ardclinis and Tickmacrevan w Layde and
Cushendun *Conn*
CUSHENDUN (no dedication) as above
DALKEY (St Patrick) *D & G*   I R B ROUNTREE,
C T F BLENNERHASSETT
DARTREY Ematris w Rockcorry, Aghabog and
Aughnamullan *Clogh*
DELGANY (Christ Church) *D & G*   I D T MUIR
DENN (no dedication) Urney w Denn and Derryheen
K, E & A
DERG (no dedication) w Termonamongan *D & R*
I W P QUILL
DERNAKESH (Chapel of Ease) Annagh w Drumgoon,
Ashfield etc *K, E & A*
DERRALOSSARY Rathdrum w Glenealy, Derralossary and
Laragh *D & G*
DERRIAGHY (Christ Church) w Colin *Conn*
I G E GRAHAM
DERRYBRUSK (St Michael) Maguiresbridge w Derrybrusk
Clogh
DERRYGONNELLY Inishmacsaint *Clogh*
DERRYGORTREAVY (St Columba) Clonfeacle w
Derrygortreavy *Arm*
DERRYHEEN (no dedication) Urney w Denn and
Derryheen *K, E & A*
DERRYKIGHAN (St Colman) Billy w Derrykeighan *Conn*
DERRYLANE (no dedication) Killeshandra w Killegar and
Derrylane *K, E & A*
DERRYLIN Kinawley w Drumany and Crom *K, E & A*
DERRYLORAN (St Luran) *Arm*   I J M BARTON,
C J C WILSON, S R T BOYD
DERRYNOOSE (St John) Keady w Armaghbreague and
Derrynoose *Arm*
DERRYVOLGIE (St Columba) *Conn*   I C J POLLOCK
DERRYVULLEN NORTH (St Tighernach) w Castlearchdale
Clogh   I R C THOMPSON
DERRYVULLEN SOUTH (St Tighernach) w Garvary
Clogh   I J W STEWART
DERVOCK Billy w Derrykeighan *Conn*
DESERTCREAT (no dedication) Ardtrea w Desertcreat *Arm*
DESERTLYN (St John) w Ballyeglish *Arm*   I J CLYDE
DESERTMARTIN (St Conghall) w Termoneeny *D & R*
I K R KINGSTON
DESERTOGHILL (no dedication) Errigal w Garvagh *D & R*
DESERTSERGES (no dedication) Kinneigh Union *C, C & R*
DEVENISH (St Molaise) w Boho *Clogh*   I Vacant
DIAMOND (St Paul) Tartaraghan w Diamond *Arm*
DINGLE (St James) w Killiney and Kilgobbin *L & K*
I Vacant
DOAGH Kilbride *Conn*
DOLLINGSTOWN (St Saviour) Magheralin w Dollingstown
D & D
DONABATE (St Patrick) Swords w Donabate and
Killsallaghan *D & G*
DONACAVEY (no dedication) w Barr *Clogh*   I J HAY
DONADEA (St Peter) Clane w Donadea and Coolcarrigan
M & K
DONAGH (no dedication) Moville w Greencastle, Donagh,
Cloncha etc *D & R*
DONAGH (St Salvator) w Tyholland and Errigal Truagh
Clogh   I I F R PATTERSON
DONAGHADEE (no dedication) *D & D*
I L T C STEVENSON
DONAGHCLONEY (St Patrick) w Waringstown *D & D*
I J C MOORE
DONAGHEADY (St James) *D & R*   I F L GRAHAM
DONAGHENDRY (St Patrick) Brackaville w Donaghendry
and Ballyclog *Arm*
DONAGHMORE (no dedication) Rathdowney w
Castlefleming, Donaghmore etc *C & O*
DONAGHMORE (St Bartholomew) Aghaderg w
Donaghmore and Scarva *D & D*

DONAGHMORE (St Michael) w Upper Donaghmore *Arm*
  I R D LAWRENSON
DONAGHMORE (St Patrick) Convoy w Monellan and
  Donaghmore *D & R*
DONAGHPATRICK (St Patrick) Kells w Balrathboyne,
  Moynalty etc *M & K*
DONAMON (no dedication) Roscommon w Donamon,
  Rathcline, Kilkeevin etc *K, E & A*
DONANAUGHTA (St John the Baptist) Clonfert Gp of Par
  L & K
DONARD (no dedication) Donoughmore and Donard w
  Dunlavin *D & G*
**DONEGAL (no dedication) w Killymard, Lough Eske and
  Laghey** *D & R*   I T H TRIMBLE
DONEGORE (St John) Templepatrick w Donegore *Conn*
DONEMANA Donagheady *D & R*
DONERAILE (St Mary) Mallow Union *C, C & R*
DONNYBROOK (St Mary) Dub Irishtown w Donnybrook
  D & G
DONOUGHMORE (no dedication) and Donard w Dunlavin
  D & G   I S P SEMPLE
DORRHA (no dedication) Birr w Lorrha, Dorrha and
  Lockeen *L & K*
**DOUGLAS (St Luke) w Blackrock, Frankfield and
  Marmullane** *C, C & R*   I R E B WHITE,
  C A M WILKINSON, NSM A D KINGSTON
DOWN (Cathedral of the Holy and Undivided Trinity)
  D & D   I H LECKEY
DOWN (St Margaret) w Hollymount *D & D*
  I S M J DICKSON
DOWNPATRICK Down H Trin w Hollymount *D & D*
DOWNPATRICK Down Cathl *D & D*
DRAPERSTOWN (St Columb) Kilcronaghan w
  Draperstown and Sixtowns *D & R*
DREW MEMORIAL Belf St Simon w St Phil *Conn*
DRIMOLEAGUE (St Matthew) Fanlobbus Union *C, C & R*
DRINAGH (Christ Church) as above
**DROGHEDA (St Mary) Julianstown and Colpe w Drogheda
  and Duleek *M & K*
DROGHEDA (St Peter) w Ardee, Collon and Termonfeckin
  Arm I C J G BEVAN
DROMAHAIR Cloonclare w Killasnett, Lurganboy and
  Drumlease *K, E & A*
DROMARA (St John) w Garvaghy *D & D*   I P THOMPSON
DROMARD (Christ Church) Skreen w Kilmacshalgan and
  Dromard *T, K & A*
DROMOD (St Michael and All Angels) Kenmare w Sneem,
  Waterville etc *L & K*
DROMORE (Cathedral of Christ the Redeemer) *D & D*
  I W B NEILL
DROMORE (Holy Trinity) *Clogh*   I D W GAMBLE
DRUM (no dedication) Currin w Drum and Newbliss *Clogh*
DRUMACHOSE (Christ Church) *D & R*   I S McVEIGH,
  C A I GALLAGHER
DRUMALOOR (St Andrew) Annagh w Drumgoon, Ashfield
  etc *K, E & A*
DRUMANY (Christ Church) Kinawley w Drumany and
  Crom *K, E & A*
DRUMBANAGHER (St Mary) Acton w Drumbanagher
  Arm
DRUMBEG (St Patrick) *D & D*   I C W M COOPER
DRUMBO (Holy Trinity) *D & D*   I J C BELL
DRUMCANNON (Christ Church) Waterford w Killea,
  Drumcannon and Dunhill *C & O*
DRUMCAR Kilsaran w Drumcar, Dunleer and Dunany *Arm*
**DRUMCLAMPH (no dedication) w Lower Langfield and
  Upper Langfield** *D & R*   I F D CREIGHTON
**DRUMCLIFFE (St Columba) w Kilrush, Kilfenora, Kilfarboy,
  Kilnasoolagh, Shannon and Kilferagh** *L & K*
  I R CHANNA, NSM A W SHAW
DRUMCLIFFE (St Columba) w Lissadell and Munninane
  K, E & A   I I GALLAGHER
DRUMCONDRA Dub Drumcondra w N Strand *D & G*
DRUMCONRATH (St Peter) Kingscourt w Drumconrath,
  Syddan and Moybologue *M & K*
DRUMCREE (Ascension) *Arm*   I J A PICKERING
DRUMCREE (St John) Castlepollard and Oldcastle w
  Loughcrew etc *M & K*
DRUMGATH (St John) w Drumgooland and Clonduff
  D & D   I W A SEALE
DRUMGLASS (St Anne) w Moygashel *Arm*
  I F D SWANN, C G P McADAM
DRUMGOOLAND (no dedication) Drumgath w
  Drumgooland and Clonduff *D & D*
DRUMGOON (All Saints) Annagh w Drumgoon, Ashfield
  etc *K, E & A*
DRUMHOLM (no dedication) Kilbarron w Rossnowlagh
  and Drumholm *D & R*

DRUMINISKILL (Chapel of Ease) Killesher *K, E & A*
DRUMKEERAN Killinagh w Kiltyclogher and
  Innismagrath *K, E & A*
DRUMKEERAN (no dedication) w Templecarne and Muckross
  Clogh   I P F TIZZARD
DRUMLANE (no dedication) Annagh w Drumgoon,
  Ashfield etc *K, E & A*
DRUMLEASE (no dedication) Cloonclare w Killasnett,
  Lurganboy and Drumlease *K, E & A*
DRUMMAUL (St Brigid) w Duneane and Ballyscullion
  Conn   I J R WILSON
DRUMMULLY (no dedication) Galloon w Drummully
  Clogh
DRUMNAKILLY (Holy Trinity) Clogherney w Seskinore
  and Drumnakilly *Arm*
DRUMQUIN Drumclamph w Lower and Upper Langfield
  D & R
DRUMRAGH (St Columba) w Mountfield *D & R*
  I B McCARTHY, C J MOULD, J J MOULD
DRUMREILLY (no dedication) Mohill w Farnaught,
  Aughavas, Oughteragh etc *K, E & A*
DRUMSHAMBO (St John) Kiltoghart w Drumshambo,
  Annaduff and Kilronan *K, E & A*
DRUMSNATT (St Molua) Aghadrumsee w Clogh and
  Drumsnatt *Clogh*
DRUMTALLAGH (no dedication) Armoy w Loughguile
  and Drumtullagh *Conn*
**DRUNG (no dedication) w Castleterra, Larah and Lavey and
  Killoughter** *K, E & A*   I Vacant Cavan (49) 38204
DUBLIN Booterstown (St Philip and St James) *D & G*
  I S B FORDE
**DUBLIN (Christ Church Cathedral) Group: (St Andrew)
  (St Werburgh) (St Michan) St Paul and Grangegorman**
  D & G   I J T F PATERSON, Min W J STEWART,
  C R R J MORETON
DUBLIN Clontarf (St John the Baptist) *D & G*
  I T HASKINS, NSM M A GILBERT
DUBLIN Crumlin (St Mary) w Chapelizod *D & G*
  I W S LAING
DUBLIN Drumcondra (no dedication) w North Strand *D & G*
  I R K BROOKES
DUBLIN (Irish Church Missions) and St Thomas
  D & G , W J BRIDCUT
DUBLIN Irishtown (St Matthew) w Donnybrook *D & G*
  I R H BERTRAM, NSM J M GORDON
DUBLIN Mount Merrion (St Thomas) *D & G* I Vacant
DUBLIN Rathfarnham (no dedication) *D & G*
  I E C J WOODS, C A E TAYLOR
DUBLIN Rathmines (Holy Trinity) w Harold's Cross *D & G*
  I N G McENDOO
DUBLIN Sandford (no dedication) w Milltown *D & G*
  I R D HARMAN, NSM C E BAKER
DUBLIN Sandymount (St John the Evangelist) *D & G*
  P-in-c J M G CAREY, C G P IRVINE
DUBLIN Santry (St Pappan) w Glasnevin *D & G*
  I M D GARDNER
DUBLIN (St Ann) (St Stephen) *D & G* I C A EMPEY,
  C W H BLACK
DUBLIN (St Bartholomew) w Leeson Park Christ Church
  D & G   I J A McKAY
DUBLIN (St George and St Thomas), Finglas and Free Church
  D & G   Bp's C G E DYKE
**DUBLIN (St Patrick's Cathedral) Group: (St Catherine and St
  James) (St Audoen)** *D & G*   I M E STEWART,
  TV J W R CRAWFORD
DUBLIN Whitechurch (no dedication) *D & G*
  I A H N McKINLEY
DUBLIN (Zion Church) *D & G*   I W R J GOURLEY
DUGORT (St Thomas) Aughaval w Achill, Knappagh,
  Dugort etc *T, K & A*
DULEEK Julianstown and Colpe w Drogheda and Duleek
  M & K
DUN LAOGHAIRE (Christ Church) *D & G* I V G STACEY
DUNAGHY (St James) Craigs w Dunaghy and Killagan
  Conn
DUNANY Kilsaran w Drumcar, Dunleer and Dunany *Arm*
DUNBOE (St Paul) Castlerock w Dunboe and Fermoyle
  D & R
**DUNBOYNE Union (St Peter and St Paul) w Kilcock,
  Maynooth, Moyglare, Dunshaughlin and Ballymaglasson**
  M & K   I G L WILLIAMSON
DUNDALK (St Nicholas) w Heynestown *Arm*
  I M A J WILSON, C D A WORKMAN
DUNDELA (St Mark) *D & D*   I J N T CAMPBELL,
  C J R AUCHMUTY
DUNDONALD (St Elizabeth) *D & D*   I E CROOKS
DUNDRUM Cashel w Magorban, Tipperary, Clonbeg etc
  C & O

DUNDRUM (St Donard) Kilmegan w Maghera *D & D*

DUNEANE (no dedication) Drummaul w Duneane and Ballyscullion *Conn*

DUNFANAGHY (Holy Trinity), Raymunterdoney and Tullaghbegley *D & R*   **I**   F N WARREN

DUNFEENY (no dedication) Killala w Dunfeeny, Crossmolina, Kilmoremoy etc *T, K & A*

DUNGANNON Drumglass w Moygashel *Arm*

DUNGANSTOWN (St Kevin) w Redcross and Conary *D & G*   **I**   J R HEANEY

DUNGARVAN (St Mary) Lismore w Cappoquin, Kilwatermoy, Dungarvan etc *C & O*

DUNGIVEN (no dedication) w Bovevagh *D & R*   **I**   T R CONWAY

DUNGLOE Gweedore, Carrickfin and Templecrone *D & R*

DUNHILL (St John the Baptist) Waterford w Killea, Drumcannon and Dunhill *C & O*

DUNKERRIN (no dedication) Shinrone w Aghancon etc *L & K*

DUNLAVIN (St Nicholas) Donoughmore and Donard w Dunlavin *D & G*

DUNLECKNEY (St Mary) w Nurney, Lorum and Kiltennel *C & O*   **I**   C A FAULL

DUNLEER (no dedication) Kilsaran w Drumcar, Dunleer and Dunany *Arm*

DUNLUCE (St John the Baptist) *Conn*   **I**   S D HAZLETT

DUNMANWAY Fanlobbus Union *C, C & R*

DUNMORE EAST Waterford w Killea, Drumcannon and Dunhill *C & O*

DUNMURRY (St Colman) *Conn*   **I**   M J McCANN

DUNNALONG (St John) Leckpatrick w Dunnalong *D & R*

DUNSEVERICK (no dedication) Ballintoy w Rathlin and Dunseverick *Conn*

DUNSFORD (St Mary) Lecale Gp *D & D*

DUNSHAUGHLIN (St Seachnal) Dunboyne w Kilcock, Maynooth, Moyglare etc *M & K*

DURROW (St Columba) Tullamore w Durrow, Newtownfertullagh, Rahan etc *M & K*

DURROW (St Fintan) Abbeyleix w Old Church, Ballyroan etc *C & O*

DURRUS (St James the Apostle) Kilmocomogue Union *C, C & R*

DYSART ENOS (Holy Trinity) Maryborough w Dysart Enos and Ballyfin *C & O*

EASKEY (St Anne) Killala w Dunfeeny, Crossmolina, Kilmoremoy etc *T, K & A*

EDENDERRY Clonsast w Rathangan, Thomastown etc *M & K*

EDENDERRY (no dedication) w Clanabogan *D & R*   **I**   R W CLARKE

EDGEWORTHSTOWN Mostrim w Granard, Clonbroney, Killoe etc *K, E & A*

EGLANTINE (All Saints) *Conn*   **I**   C W BELL

EGLINTON Faughanvale *D & R*

EGLISH Birr w Lorrha, Dorrha and Lockeen *L & K*

EGLISH (Holy Trinity) w Killylea *Arm*   **I**   J M BATCHELOR

ELPHIN (no dedication) Boyle and Elphin w Aghanagh, Kilbryan etc *K, E & A*

EMATRIS (St John the Evangelist) w Rockcorry, Aghabog and Aughnamullan *Clogh*   **I**   J T A MERRY

EMLAGHFAD (no dedication) Ballisodare w Collooney and Emlaghfad *T, K & A*

ENNIS Drumcliffe w Kilnasoolagh *L & K*

ENNISCORTHY (St Mary) w Clone, Clonmore, Monart and Templescobin *C & O*   **I**   K S WILKINSON, **NSM** J DEACON

ENNISKEEN Kingscourt w Drumconrath, Syddan and Moybologue *M & K*

ENNISKERRY Powerscourt w Kilbride and Annacrevy *D & G*

ENNISKILLEN Rossory *Clogh*

ENNISKILLEN (Cathedral of St Macartin) *Clogh*   **I**   B J COURTNEY

ENNISNAG (St Peter) Kells Union *C & O*

ERRIGAL (St Paul) w Garvagh *D & R*   **I**   S SIMPSON

ERRIGAL PORTCLARE (no dedication) Clogh w Errigal Portclare *Clogh*

ERRIGAL TRUAGH (St Muadhan) Donagh w Tyholland and Errigal Truagh *Clogh*

ERRIGLE KEEROGUE (no dedication) w Ballygawley and Killeshil *Arm*   **I**   G J WHITEHEAD

ERRISLANNNAN (no dedication) Omey w Ballynakill, Errislannan and Roundstone *T, K & A*

ESKRAHOOLE (no dedication) Augher w Newtownsaville and Eskrahoole *Clogh*

EYRECOURT Clonfert Gp of Par *L & K*

FAHAN LOWER (Christ Church) and UPPER (St Mura) *D & R*   **Bp's C**   S D BARTON

FALLS, LOWER (St Luke) Belf St Steph w St Luke *Conn*

FALLS, UPPER Belf Upper Falls *Conn*

FANLOBBUS (St Mary) w Drimoleague, Drinagh and Coolkellure *C, C & R*   **I**   *Vacant*

FARNAUGHT (no dedication) Mohill w Farnaught, Aughavas, Oughteragh etc *K, E & A*

FAUGHANVALE (St Canice) *D & R*   **I**   C B LEEKE

FENAGH (All Saints) w Myshall, Aghade and Ardoyne *C & O*   **I**   *Vacant*

FERMOY (Christ Church) w Ballyhooley, Knockmourne, Ardnageehy and Brigown *C, C & R*   **I**   J L HAWORTH

FERMOYLE (no dedication) Castlerock w Dunboe and Fermoyle *D & R*

FERNS (Cathedral of St Edan) w Kilbride, Toombe, Kilcormack and Ballycarney *C & O*   **I**   L D A FORREST

FERRY, EAST Cloyne Union *C, C & R*

FERTAGH (no dedication) Kilcooley w Littleon, Crohane and Fertagh *C & O*

FETHARD (Holy Trinity) Clonmel w Innislounagh, Tullaghmelan etc *C & O*

FETHARD (St Mogue) New w Old Ross, Whitechurch, Fethard etc *C & O*

FIDDOWN (no dedication) w Clonegam, Guilcagh and Kilmeaden *C & O*   **I**   A L DAVIES

FINAGHY (St Polycarp) *Conn*   **I**   *Vacant* Belfast (01232) 629764

FINGLAS (St Canice) Dub St Geo and St Thos, Finglas and Free Ch *D & G*

FINNER (Christ Church) Killinagh w Kiltyclogher and Innismagrath *K, E & A*

FINTONA Donacavey w Barr *Clogh*

FINVOY (no dedication) Ballymoney w Finvoy and Rasharkin *Conn*

FIVEMILETOWN (St John) *Clogh*   **I**   R J RIDDEL

FLORENCECOURT Killesher *K, E & A*

FONTSTOWN (St John the Evangelist) Athy w Kilberry, Fontstown and Kilkea *D & G*

FORGNEY (St Munis) Athlone w Benown, Kiltoom and Forgney *M & K*

FOUNTAINS Lismore w Cappoquin, Kilwatermoy, Dungarvan etc *C & O*

FOXFORD Straid *T, K & A*

FOYNES Rathkeale w Askeaton and Kilcornan *L & K*

FRANKFIELD (Holy Trinity) Douglas Union w Frankfield *C, C & R*

FRENCH CHURCH Portarlington w Cloneyhurke and Lea *M & K*

FRENCHPARK Roscommon w Donamon, Rathcline, Kilkeevin etc *K, E & A*

GALLOON (St Comgall) w Drummully *Clogh*   **I**   A P S SYNNOTT

GALTRIM Trim w Bective and Galtrim *M & K*

GALWAY (St Nicholas) w Kilcummin *T, K & A*   **I**   R B MacCARTHY

GARRISON (no dedication) w Slavin and Belleek *Clogh*   **I**   V IRWIN

GARRYCLOYNE (no dedication) Carrigrohane Union *C, C & R*

GARTAN (St Columba) Conwal Union w Gartan *D & R*

GARTREE (no dedication) Killead w Gartree *Conn*

GARVAGH Errigal w Garvagh *D & R*

GARVAGHY (no dedication) Dromara w Garvaghy *D & D*

GARVARY (Holy Trinity) Derryvullen S w Garvary *Clogh*

GEASHILL (St Mary) w Killeigh and Ballycommon *M & K*   **I**   P H A LAWRENCE, **NSM** D HUTTON-BURY

GILFORD Tullylish *D & D*

GILFORD (St Paul) *D & D*   **I**   A P PATTERSON

GILNAHIRK (St Dorothea) *D & D*   **I**   T C KINAHAN

GLANDORE Ross Union *C, C & R*

GLANMIRE Rathcooney Union *C, C & R*

GLASCARRIG (no dedication) Ardamine w Kiltennel, Glascarrig etc *C & O*

GLASLOUGH Donagh w Tyholland and Errigal Truagh *Clogh*

GLASNEVIN (St Mobhi) Dub Santry w Glasnevin *D & G*

GLENAGEARY (St Paul) *D & G*   **I**   G C S LINNEY, **C**   G V WHARTON

GLENALLA (St Columbkille) Mevagh w Glenalla *D & R*

GLENARM Ardclinis and Tickmacrevan w Layde and Cushendun *Conn*

GLENAVY (St Aidan) w Tunny and Crumlin *Conn*   **I**   T WRIGHT

GLENBEIGH (St John) Kilcolman w Kiltallagh, Killorglin, Knockane etc *L & K*

GLENCAIRN Belf St Andr *Conn*

GLENCAR Cloonclare w Killasnett, Lurganboy and Drumlease *K, E & A*

GLENCOLUMBKILLE (St Columba) Ardara w
  Glencolumbkille, Inniskeel etc *D & R*
GLENCRAIG (Holy Trinity) *D & D*   **I** P S P HEWITT
GLENDERMOTT (no dedication) *D & R*   **I** R N MOORE,
  NSM H J K McLAUGHLIN
GLENEALY (no dedication) Rathdrum w Glenealy,
  Derralossary and Laragh *D & G*
GLENOE Glynn w Raloo *Conn*
GLENTIES (no dedication) Ardara w Glencolumbkille,
  Inniskeel etc *D & R*
GLENVILLE Fermoy Union *C, C & R*
GLYNN (St John) w Raloo *Conn*   **Bp's C** J A FAIR
GORESBRIDGE Leighlin w Grange Sylvae, Shankill etc
  C & O
**GOREY (Christ Church) w Kilnahue, Leskinfere and
  Ballycanew** *C & O*   **I** C W MULLEN,   **NSM** J F FORBES
GORTIN Ardstraw w Baronscourt, Badoney Lower etc
  D & R
GOWNA (no dedication) Arvagh w Carrigallen, Gowna and
  Columbkille *K, E & A*
GRACEFIELD (no dedication) Woodschapel w Gracefield
  Arm
GRANARD (St Patrick) Mostrim w Granard, Clonbroney,
  Killoe etc *K, E & A*
GRANGE (St Aidan) Loughgall w Grange *Arm*
GRANGE SYLVAE (St George) Leighlin w Grange Sylvae,
  Shankill etc *C & O*
GRANGEGORMAN (All Saints) Dub Ch Ch Cathl Gp
  D & G
GREENAN (no dedication) Ardstraw w Baronscourt,
  Badoney Lower etc *D & R*
GREENCASTLE (St Finian) Moville w Greencastle,
  Donagh, Cloncha etc *D & R*
GREENISLAND (Holy Name) *Conn*   **I** S H LOWRY
GREY ABBEY (St Saviour) w Kircubbin *D & D*
  I W A McMONAGLE
GREYSTONES (St Patrick) *D & G*   **I** E J SWANN
GROOMSPORT (no dedication) *D & D*   **I** J D TYNEY
GUILCAGH (St John the Evangelist) Fiddown w Clonegam,
  Guilcagh and Kilmeaden *C & O*
GURRANEKENNEFEAKE (no dedication) Cloyne Union
  C, C & R
GWEEDORE (St Patrick), Carrickfin and Templecrone
  D & R   **C** R P KELLY
HACKETSTOWN (St John the Baptist) Kiltegan w
  Hacketstown, Clonmore and Moyne *C & O*
HAROLD'S CROSS (no dedication) Dub Rathmines w
  Harold's Cross *D & G*
HELEN'S BAY (St John the Baptist) *D & D*   **I** R NESBITT
HEYNESTOWN (St Paul) Dundalk w Heynestown *Arm*
HIGHFIELD Belf Whiterock *Conn*
HILLSBOROUGH (St Malachi) *D & D*   **I** J F DINNEN
HILLTOWN Drumgath w Drumgooland and Clonduff
  D & D
HOLLYFORT Gorey w Kilnahue, Leskinfere and
  Ballycanew *C & O*
HOLLYMOUNT (no dedication) Down H Trin w
  Hollymount *D & D*
HOLMPATRICK (St Patrick) w Balbriggan and Kenure
  D & G   **I** R H WATTS
HOLYCROSS Templemore w Thurles and Kilfithmone
  C & O
HOLYWOOD (St Kevin) Blessington w Kilbride, Ballymore
  Eustace etc *D & G*
HOLYWOOD (St Philip and St James) *D & D*
  I J A MONROE,   **C** D I BLAKELY
HORETOWN (St James) Taghmon w Horetown and
  Bannow *C & O*
HORSELEAP Clara w Liss, Moate and Clonmacnoise *M & K*
HOWTH (St Mary) *D & G*   **I** C G HYLAND,
  NSM K E LONG
INCH Cloyne Union *C, C & R*
INCH (no dedication) Kilmore w Inch *D & D*
INCH (no dedication) Arklow w Inch and Kilbride *D & G*
INISHARGIE (St Andrew) Ballywalter w Inishargie *D & D*
INISHMACSAINT (St Ninnidh) *Clogh*   **I** *Vacant*
INISTIOGE (St Mary) Kells Union *C & O*
INNISCALTRA (St Caimin) Killaloe w Stradbally *L & K*
INNISCARRA (no dedication) Carrigrohane Union *C, C & R*
INNISHANNON (Christ Church) Bandon Union *C, C & R*
INNISKEEL (no dedication) Ardara w Glencolumbkille,
  Inniskeel etc *D & R*
INNISLOUNAGH (St Patrick) Clonmel w Innislounagh,
  Tullaghmelan etc *C & O*
INNISMAGRATH (no dedication) Killinagh w Kiltyclogher
  and Innismagrath *K, E & A*

INVER Larne and Inver *Conn*
**INVER (St John the Evangelist) w Mountcharles, Killaghtee
  and Killybegs** *D & R*   **I** A N STRINGER
INVER, Mountcharles and Killaghtee *D & R*   **I** *Vacant*
IRISHTOWN Dub Irishtown w Donnybrook *D & G*
IRVINESTOWN Derryvullen N w Castlearchdale *Clogh*
ISLANDMAGEE (St John) Whitehead w Islandmagee *Conn*
JOANMOUNT Belf H Trin and Ardoyne *Conn*
JOHNSTOWN Kilcooley w Littleon, Crohane and Fertagh
  C & O
JORDANSTOWN (St Patrick) *Conn*   **I** E J MOORE,
  C M A MALCOLM,   **NSM** I TEMPLETON (nee
  McCUTCHEON)
**JULIANSTOWN (St Mary) and Colpe w Drogheda and
  Duleek** *M & K*   **I** A J NELSON
KEADY (St Matthew) w Armaghbreague and Derrynoose
  Arm   **I** W G NEELY
**KELLS (St Columba) w Balrathboyne, Moynalty,
  Donaghpatrick and Castletown** *M & K*   **I** W J RITCHIE
**KELLS (St Mary) w Ballaghtobin, Kilmoganny, Ennisnag,
  Inistioge and Kilfane** *C & O*   **I** D L SANDES
KENAGH Ardagh w Tashinny, Shrule and Kilcommick
  K, E & A
KENMARE (St Patrick) w Sneem, Dromod and Valentia
  L & K   **P-in-c** R M CALDWELL
KENTSTOWN (St Mary) Navan w Kentstown, Tara, Slane,
  Painestown etc *M & K*
KENURE (no dedication) Holmpatrick w Balbriggan and
  Kenure *D & G*
KESH Magheraculmoney *Clogh*
KILBARRON (St Anne) w Rossnowlagh and Drumholm
  D & R   **I** D SKUCE
KILBERRY (no dedication) Athy w Kilberry, Fontstown
  and Kilkea *D & G*
KILBIXY (St Bigseach) Mullingar, Portnashangan,
  Moyliscar, Kilbixy etc *M & K*
KILBONANE (St Mark) Moviddy Union *C, C & R*
KILBRIDE (Holy Trinity) Ferns w Kilbride, Toombe,
  Kilcormack etc *C & O*
KILBRIDE (no dedication) Blessington w Kilbride,
  Ballymore Eustace etc *D & G*
KILBRIDE (St Bride) *Conn*   **I** C L HALL-THOMPSON
KILBRIDE (St Brigid) Arklow w Inch and Kilbride *D & G*
KILBRIDE BRAY (no dedication) Powerscourt w Kilbride
  and Annacrevy *D & G*
KILBRONEY (no dedication) *D & D*   **Bp's C** J H SIMS
KILBRYAN (no dedication) Boyle and Elphin w Aghanagh,
  Kilbryan etc *K, E & A*
KILCLEAGH Clara w Liss, Moate and Clonmacnoise *M & K*
KILCLIEF (no dedication) Lecale Gp *D & D*
KILCLUNEY (St John) Mullabrack w Markethill and
  Kilcluney *Arm*
KILCOCK Dunboyne w Kilcock, Maynooth, Moyglare etc
  M & K
**KILCOLMAN (no dedication) w Kiltallagh, Killorglin,
  Knockane and Glenbeigh** *L & K*   **I** M J D SHANNON,
  C J C STEPHENS
KILCOMMICK (no dedication) Ardagh w Tashinny, Shrule
  and Kilcommick *K, E & A*
KILCOMMON (no dedication) Crosspatrick Gp *C & O*
KILCOO (no dedication) Castlewellan w Kilcoo *D & D*
**KILCOOLEY (no dedication) w Littleton, Crohane and
  Fertagh** *C & O*   **I** *Vacant*
KILCOOLEY (St Columba) Ban Abbey *D & D*
KILCORMACK (St Cormac) Ferns w Kilbride, Toombe,
  Kilcormack etc *C & O*
KILCORNAN (no dedication) Rathkeale w Askeaton and
  Kilcornan *L & K*
KILCROHANE Kenmare w Sneem, Waterville etc *L & K*
**KILCRONAGHAN (no dedication) w Draperstown and
  Sixtowns** *D & R*   **I** S J CAMPBELL
KILCULLEN (St John) Newbridge w Carnalway and
  Kilcullen *M & K*
KILCUMMIN (no dedication) Galway w Kilcummin
  T, K & A
KILDALLON (no dedication) Kilmore w Ballintemple,
  Kildallon etc *K, E & A*
**KILDARE (Cathedral of St Brigid) w Kilmeague and Curragh
  Garrison Church** *M & K*   **I** *Vacant* Curragh (45) 41654
KILDARTON (no dedication) Lisnadill w Kildarton *Arm*
KILDAVIN (St Paul) Bunclody w Kildavin, Clonegal and
  Kilrush *C & O*
KILDOLLAGH (St Paul) Ballyrashane w Kildollagh *Conn*
KILDRESS (St Patrick) w Altedesert *Arm*   **I** B J A CRUISE
**KILDRUMFERTON (St Patrick), Ballymachugh and
  Ballyjamesduff** *K, E & A*   **I** R A CHALMERS

KILFANE (no dedication) Kells Union *C & O*

KILFARBOY (Christ Church) Drumcliffe w Kilnasoolagh *L & K*

KILFAUGHNABEG (Christ Church) Ross Union *C, C & R*

KILFENORA (Cathedral of St Fachan) Drumcliffe w Kilnasoolagh *L & K*

KILFERAGH (no dedication) as above

KILFINANE (St Andrew) Kilmallock w Kilflynn, Kilfinane, Knockaney etc *L & K*

KILFITHMONE (no dedication) Templemore w Thurles and Kilfithmone *C & O*

KILFLYNN (no dedication) Kilmallock w Kilflynn, Kilfinane, Knockaney etc *L & K*

KILGARIFFE (no dedication) w Kilmalooda, Kilnagross, Timoleague and Courtmacsherry *C, C & R* **I** *J R L CLARK*

KILGLASS (no dedication) Killala w Dunfeeny, Crossmolina, Kilmoremoy etc *T, K & A*

KILGLASS (St Anne) Mostrim w Granard, Clonbroney, Killoe etc *K, E & A*

KILGOBBIN (no dedication) Dingle w Killiney and Kilgobbin *L & K*

KILHORNE Annalong *D & D*

KILKEA (no dedication) Athy w Kilberry, Fontstown and Kilkea *D & G*

KILKEE Drumcliffe w Kilnasoolagh *L & K*

KILKEEL (Christ Church) *D & D* **I** *D A McCLAY*

KILKEEVIN (Holy Trinity) Roscommon w Donamon, Rathcline, Kilkeevin etc *K, E & A*

KILKENNY (Cathedral of St Canice) (St John), Aghour and Kilmanagh *C & O* **I** *N N LYNAS*

KILKENNY WEST Athlone w Benown, Kiltoom and Forgney *M & K*

KILL (no dedication) *D & G* **I** *Vacant*

KILL (St John) Naas w Kill and Rathmore *M & K*

KILL O' THE GRANGE Kill *D & G*

KILLABBAN (no dedication) Killeshin w Cloydagh and Killabban *C & O*

KILLADEAS (Priory Church) Trory w Killadeas *Clogh*

KILLAGAN (no dedication) Craigs w Dunaghy and Killagan *Conn*

KILLAGHTEE (St Peter) Inver w Mountcharles, Killaghtee and Killybegs *D & R*

KILLALA (Cathedral of St Patrick) w Dunfeeny, Crossmolina, Kilmoremoy, Castleconnor, Easkey and Kilglass *T, K & A* **I** *E G ARDIS,* **C** *P P HALLIDAY,* **NSM** *D T S CLEMENTS*

KILLALLON (St John) Athboy w Ballivor and Killallon *M & K*

KILLALOE (Cathedral of St Flannan) w Stradbally, Clonlara, Mountshannon, Abingdon and Tuomgraney *L & K* **I** *E C T PERDUE*

KILLANEY (St Andrew) w Carryduff *D & D* **I** *R FOX*

KILLANNE (St Anne) w Killegney, Rossdroit and Templeshanbo *C & O* **I** *A M JACKSON*

KILLANULLY Carrigaline Union *C, C & R*

KILLARGUE (no dedication) Killinagh w Kiltyclogher and Innismagrath *K, E & A*

KILLARNEY (St Mary) w Aghadoe and Muckross *L & K* **I** *B F B LOUGHEED*

KILLASHEE (St Paul) Templemichael w Clongish, Clooncumber etc *K, E & A*

KILLASNETT (no dedication) Cloonclare w Killasnett, Lurganboy and Drumlease *K, E & A*

KILLCONNELL Aughrim w Ballinasloe etc *L & K*

KILLEA (St Andrew) Waterford w Killea, Drumcannon and Dunhill *C & O*

KILLEA (St Fiach) Taughboyne, Craigadooish, Newtowncunningham etc *D & R*

KILLEAD (St Catherine) w Gartree *Conn* **I** *Vacant*

KILLEDMOND Dunleckney w Nurney, Lorum and Kiltennel *C & O*

KILLEEVAN (no dedication) Clones w Killeevan *Clogh*

KILLEGAR (no dedication) Killeshandra w Killegar and Derrylane *K, E & A*

KILLEGNEY (no dedication) Killanne w Killegney, Rossdroit and Templeshanbo *C & O*

KILLEIGH (no dedication) Geashill w Killeigh and Ballycommon *M & K*

KILLELAGH (no dedication) Maghera w Killelagh *D & R*

KILLENAULE (no dedication) Kilcooley w Littleon, Crohane and Fertagh *C & O*

KILLERMOGH (no dedication) Abbeyleix w Old Church, Ballyroan etc *C & O*

KILLERY Taunagh w Kilmactranny, Ballysumaghan etc *K, E & A*

KILLESHANDRA (no dedication) w Killegar and Derrylane *K, E & A* **I** *Vacant*

KILLESHER (St John) *K, E & A* **I** *J R SIDES*

KILLESHERDONEY (St Mark) Annagh w Drumgoon, Ashfield etc *K, E & A*

KILLESHIL (St Paul) Errigle Keerogue w Ballygawley and Killeshil *Arm*

KILLESHIN (no dedication) w Cloydagh and Killabban *C & O* **I** *G W CHAMBERS*

KILLESK (All Saints) New w Old Ross, Whitechurch, Fethard etc *C & O*

KILLETER Derg w Termonamongan *D & R*

KILLINAGH (no dedication) w Kiltyclogher and Innismagrath *K, E & A* **I** *R S P RICHEY*

KILLINCHY (no dedication) w Kilmood and Tullynakill *D & D* **I** *R R W DEVENNEY*

KILLINEY Ballybrack (no dedication) *D & G* **I** *Vacant* Dublin (1) 285–6180

KILLINEY (Holy Trinity) *D & G* **I** *C L PETERS*

KILLINEY (St Brendan) Dingle w Killiney and Kilgobbin *L & K*

KILLINICK (no dedication) Kilscoran w Killinick and Mulrankin *C & O*

KILLINKERE (no dedication) Lurgan etc w Ballymachugh, Kildrumferton etc *K, E & A*

KILLISKEY (no dedication) Wicklow w Killiskey *D & G*

KILLODIERNAN (no dedication) Nenagh *L & K*

KILLOE (St Catherine) Mostrim w Granard, Clonbroney, Killoe etc *K, E & A*

KILLORAN (no dedication) Achonry w Tubbercurry and Killoran *T, K & A*

KILLORGLIN (no dedication) Kilcolman w Kiltallagh, Killorglin, Knockane etc *L & K*

KILLOUGH (St Anne) Bright w Ballee and Killough *D & D*

KILLOUGHTER (no dedication) Drung w Castleterra, Larah and Lavey etc *K, E & A*

KILLOUGHY Tullamore w Durrow, Newtownfertullagh, Rahan etc *M & K*

KILLOWEN Kinneigh Union *C, C & R*

KILLOWEN (St John) *D & R* **I** *I H McDONALD,* **C** *K P WHITTAKER*

KILLSALLAGHAN (St David) Swords w Donabate and Killsallaghan *D & G*

KILLUCAN (St Etchen) Mullingar, Portnashangan, Moyliscar, Kilbixy etc *M & K*

KILLURIN (no dedication) Wexford w Ardcolm and Killurin *C & O*

KILLYBEGS (no dedication) Inver w Mountcharles, Killaghtee and Killybegs *D & R*

KILLYGARVAN (St Columb) Tullyaughnish w Kilmacrennan and Killygarvan *D & R*

KILLYLEA (St Mark) Eglish w Killylea *Arm*

KILLYLEAGH (St John the Evangelist) *D & D* **I** *R M McCONNELL*

KILLYMAN (St Andrew) *Arm* **I** *A S J WARKE*

KILLYMARD (no dedication) Donegal w Killymard, Lough Eske and Laghey *D & R*

KILMACABEA (no dedication) Ross Union *C, C & R*

KILMACDUAGH (no dedication) Aughrim w Ballinasloe etc *L & K*

KILMACRENNAN (St Finnian and St Mark) Tullyaughnish w Kilmacrennan and Killygarvan *D & R*

KILMACSHALGAN (St Mary) Skreen w Kilmacshalgan and Dromard *T, K & A*

KILMACTHOMAS (no dedication) Lismore w Cappoquin, Kilwatermoy, Dungarvan etc *C & O*

KILMACTRANNY (no dedication) Taunagh w Kilmactranny, Ballysumaghan etc *K, E & A*

KILMAKEE (St Hilda) *Conn* **I** *F G RUTLEDGE*

KILMALLOCK (St Peter and St Paul) w Kilflynn, Kilfinane, Knockaney, Bruff and Caherconlish *L & K* **I** *Vacant*

KILMALOODA (All Saints) Kilgariffe Union *C, C & R*

KILMANAGH (no dedication) Kilkenny w Aghour and Kilmanagh *C & O*

KILMEADEN (St Mary) Fiddown w Clonegam, Guilcagh and Kilmeaden *C & O*

KILMEAGUE (no dedication) Kildare w Kilmeague and Curragh *M & K*

KILMEEN (Christ Church) Kinneigh Union *C, C & R*

KILMEGAN (no dedication) w Maghera *D & D* **I** *B R RUSSELL*

KILMOCOMOGUE Union (no dedication) *C, C & R* **I** *P M WILLOUGHBY*

KILMOE (no dedication) w Teampol-na-mbocht, Schull and Crookhaven *C, C & R* **I** *N M CUMMINS*

KILMOGANNY (St Matthew) Kells Union *C & O*

KILMOOD (St Mary) Killinchy w Kilmood and Tullynakill *D & D*

KILMORE (Cathedral of St Fethlimidh) w Ballintemple, Kildallon, Newtowngore and Corrawallen *K, E & A*
I J C COMBE, **C** S JOHNSON, L D D SCOTT
KILMORE (Christ Church) w Inch *D & D*   I M F TAYLOR
KILMORE (no dedication) Monaghan w Tydavnet and Kilmore *Clogh*
KILMORE (no dedication) Kiltoghart w Drumshambo, Annaduff and Kilronan *K, E & A*
KILMORE (St Aidan) (St Saviour) *Arm*   I E T DUNDAS
KILMOREROY (St Michael) Killala w Dunfeeny, Crossmolina, Kilmoremoy etc *T, K & A*
KILMOYLEY Tralee w Ballymacelligott, Kilnaughtin etc *L & K*
KILMUCKRIDGE (no dedication) Ardamine w Kiltennel, Glascarrig etc *C & O*
KILMURRY (St Andrew) Moviddy Union *C, C & R*
KILNAGROSS (no dedication) Kilgariffe Union *C, C & R*
KILNAHUE (St John the Evangelist) Gorey w Kilnahue, Leskinfere and Ballycanew *C & O*
KILNALECK Lurgan etc w Ballymachugh, Kildrumferton etc *K, E & A*
KILNAMANAGH (St John) Ardamine w Kiltennel, Glascarrig etc *C & O*
KILNASOOLAGH (no dedication) Drumcliffe w Kilnasoolagh *L & K*
KILNAUGHTIN (St Brendan) Tralee w Ballymacelligott, Kilnaughtin etc *L & K*
KILPEACON (St Beacon) Adare w Kilpeacon and Croom *L & K*
KILPIPE (no dedication) Crosspatrick Gp *C & O*
KILREA (St Patrick) Aghadowey w Kilrea *D & R*
KILRONAN (St Thomas) Kiltoghart w Drumshambo, Annaduff and Kilronan *K, E & A*
KILROOT (St Colman) and Templecorran *Conn*
I R HENDERSON
KILROSSANTY (no dedication) Lismore w Cappoquin, Kilwatermoy, Dungarvan etc *C & O*
KILRUSH Drumcliffe w Kilnasoolagh *L & K*
KILRUSH (St Brigid) Bunclody w Kildavin, Clonegal and Kilrush *C & O*
KILSARAN (St Mary) w Drumcar, Dunleer and Dunany *Arm*   I A V G FLYNN
KILSCORAN (no dedication) w Killinick and Mulrankin *C & O*   I H J KEOGH
KILSKEERY (no dedication) w Trillick *Clogh*
I W J JOHNSTON
KILTALLAGH (St Carthage) Kilcolman w Kiltallagh, Killorglin, Knockane etc *L & K*
KILTEEVOGUE (St John) Stranorlar w Meenglas and Kilteevogue *D & R*
KILTEGAN (St Peter) w Hacketstown, Clonmore and Moyne *C & O*   I S A CROWTHER
KILTENNEL (no dedication) Ardamine w Kiltennel, Glascarrig etc *C & O*
KILTENNEL (St Peter) Dunleckney w Nurney, Lorum and Kiltennel *C & O*
KILTERNAN (St Kiernan) *D & G*   I D G MOYNAN
KILTINANLEA (no dedication) Killaloe w Stradbally *L & K*
KILTOGHART (St George) w Drumshambo, Anaduff and Kilronan *K, E & A*   I *Vacant*
KILTOOM Athlone w Benown, Kiltoom and Forgney *M & K*
KILTUBRIDE (St Brigid) Mohill w Farnaught, Aughavas, Oughteragh etc *K, E & A*
KILTULLAGH (no dedication) Roscommon w Donamon, Rathcline, Kilkeevin etc *K, E & A*
KILTYCLOGHER (no dedication) Killinagh w Kiltyclogher and Innismagrath *K, E & A*
KILVEMNON (St Hugh) Clonmel w Innislounagh, Tullaghmelan etc *C & O*
KILWARLIN UPPER (St John) w LOWER (St James) *D & D*   I J C T SKILLEN
KILWATERMOY (St Mary) Lismore w Cappoquin, Kilwatermoy, Dungarvan etc *C & O*
KILWAUGHTER (no dedication) w Cairncastle and Craigy Hill *Conn*   I R W JONES
KINAWLEY (Holy Trinity) w Drumany and Crom *K, E & A*
I G T W DAVISON
KINAWLEY (St Paul) Swanlinbar w Tomregan, Kinawley, Drumlane etc *K, E & A*
KINGSCOURT (St Ernan) w Drumconrath, Syddan and Moybologue *M & K*   I T G CORRIGAN
KINLOUGH Killinagh w Kiltyclogher and Innismagrath *K, E & A*
KINNEAGH (no dedication) Narraghmore w Timolin, Castledermot and Kinneagh *D & G*
KINNEIGH (St Bartholomew) w Ballymoney, Kilmeen, Desertserges, Killowen and Murragh *C, C & R*   I D COLE
KINNITTY (St Trinnian) Shinrone w Aghancon etc *L & K*

KINSALE (St Multose) w Runcurran, Ballymartle and Templetrine *C, C & R*   I D WILLIAMS
KIRCONRIOLA Ballymena w Ballyclug *Conn*
KIRCUBBIN (Holy Trinity) Grey Abbey w Kircubbin *D & D*
KNAPPAGH (St Thomas) Aughaval w Achill, Knappagh, Dugort etc *T, K & A*
KNOCK (St Columba) *D & D*   I G A McCAMLEY, **C** A J RUFLI
KNOCKANE (no dedication) Kilcolman w Kiltallagh, Killorglin, Knockane etc *L & K*
KNOCKANEY (St John) Kilmallock w Kilflynn, Kilfinane, Knockaney etc *L & K*
KNOCKBREDA (no dedication) *D & D*   I P F PATTERSON, **C** S S HEANEY
KNOCKBRIDE (no dedication) Bailieborough w Knockbride, Shercock and Mullagh *K, E & A*
KNOCKLOUGHRIM Desertmartin w Termoneeny *D & R*
KNOCKMOURNE (no dedication) Fermoy Union *C, C & R*
KNOCKNAGONEY (Annunciation) *D & D*
Bp's **C** D L BROWN
KNOCKNAMUCKLEY (St Matthias) *D & D*
I B T BLACOE
KNOCKNAREA (St Anne) Sligo w Knocknarea and Rosses Pt *K, E & A*
KYLE (no dedication) Roscrea w Kyle, Bourney and Corbally *L & K*
LACK (no dedication) *Clogh*   I R J JOHNSTON
LAGHEY (no dedication) Donegal w Killymard, Lough Eske and Laghey *D & R*
LAMBEG (no dedication) *Conn*   I K A McREYNOLDS
LANESBOROUGH Roscommon w Donamon, Rathcline, Kilkeevin etc *K, E & A*
LANGFIELD, LOWER (no dedication) Drumclamph w Lower and Upper Langfield *D & R*
LANGFIELD, UPPER (no dedication) as above
LARAGH (St John) Rathdrum w Glenealy, Derralossary and Laragh *D & G*
LARAH AND LAVEY (no dedication) Drung w Castleterra, Larah and Lavey etc *K, E & A*
LARNE AND INVER (St Cedma) *Conn*   I J A FAIR, **C** M R J G WALKER
LAVEY Drung w Castleterra, Larah and Lavey etc *K, E & A*
LAYDE (no dedication) Ardclinis and Tickmacrevan w Layde and Cushendun *Conn*
LEA (no dedication) Portarlington w Cloneyhurke and Lea *M & K*
LEAP Ross Union *C, C & R*
LEARMOUNT (no dedication) Cumber Upper w Learmount *D & R*
LEATBEG (no dedication) Clondevaddock w Portsalon and Leatbeg *D & R*
LECALE Group Down Cathl *D & D*
LECALE Group: Saul, Loughinisland, Ardglass, Dunsford, Ballyculter and Kilclief *D & D*   I J A B MAYNE, **C** G B FREEMAN
LECKPATRICK (St Patrick) w Dunnalong *D & R*
I D H J FERRY
LEESON PARK (Christ Church) Dub St Bart w Ch Ch Leeson Park *D & G*
LEIGHLIN (Cathedral of St Laserian) w Grange Sylvae, Shankill, Clonagoose and Gowran *C & O*
P-in-c C A FAULL, NSM D T BURNS
LEIXLIP (St Mary) Lucan w Leixlip *D & G*
LESKINFERE (no dedication) Gorey w Kilnahue, Leskinfere and Ballycanew *C & O*
LETTERKENNY Conwal Union w Gartan *D & R*
LETTERMACAWARD (no dedication) Ardara w Glencolumbkille, Inniskeel etc *D & R*
LICKMOLASSY Clonfert Gp of Par *L & K*
LIFFORD Raphoe w Raymochy and Clonleigh *D & R*
LIMAVADY Drumachose *D & R*
LIMAVADY Tamlaghtfinlagan w Myroe *D & R*
LIMERICK CITY (Cathedral of St Mary) (St Michael) *L & K*   I J M G SIRR, **C** S M NEILL
LISBELLAW (no dedication) *Clogh*   I E R G WEST
LISBURN (Christ Church) *Conn*   I S McCOMB
LISBURN (Christ Church Cathedral) *Conn*
I J T McCAMMON, **C** J HALES
LISBURN (St Paul) *Conn*   I K W COCHRANE, **C** P K McDOWELL
LISLIMNAGHAN (Holy Trinity) Cappagh w Lislimnaghan *D & R*
LISMORE (Cathedral of St Carthage) w Cappoquin, Kilwatermoy, Dungarvan, Kilrossanty, Stradbally and Kilmacthomas *C & O*   I C W WEEKES
LISNADILL (St John) w Kildarton *Arm*   I M C KENNEDY

LISNASKEA (Holy Trinity) *Clogh* I W L BENNETT
LISS (no dedication) Clara w Liss, Moate and Clonmacnoise *M & K*
LISSADELL (no dedication) Drumcliffe w Lissadell and Munninane *K, E & A*
LISSAN (no dedication) *Arm* I R H BOYD
LISTOWEL Tralee w Ballymacelligott, Kilnaughtin etc *L & K*
LITTLE ISLAND (St Lappan) Rathcooney Union *C, C & R*
LITTLETON (no dedication) Kilcooley w Littleon, Crohane and Fertagh *C & O*
LOCKEEN (no dedication) Birr w Lorrha, Dorrha and Lockeen *L & K*
LONDONDERRY Templemore *D & R*
LONDONDERRY (Christ Church) *D & R* I D S McLEAN
LONDONDERRY (St Augustine) *D & R* I C HOWE
LONGFORD Templemichael w Clongish, Clooncumber etc *K, E & A*
LORRHA (St Ruadhan) Birr w Lorrha, Dorrha and Lockeen *L & K*
LORUM (no dedication) Dunleckney w Nurney, Lorum and Kiltennel *C & O*
LOUGH ESKE (Christ Church) Donegal w Killymard, Lough Eske and Laghey *D & R*
LOUGHBRICKLAND Aghaderg w Donaghmore and Scarva *D & D*
LOUGHCREW Castlepollard and Oldcastle w Loughcrew etc *M & K*
LOUGHGALL (St Luke) w Grange *Arm* I I W ELLIS
LOUGHGILLY (St Patrick) w Clare *Arm* I J L WILSON
LOUGHGUILE (All Saints) Armoy w Loughguile and Drumtullagh *Conn*
LOUGHINISLAND (no dedication) Lecale Gp *D & D*
LUCAN (St Andrew) w Leixlip *D & G* I B A PIERCE
LUGGACURREN (Resurrection) Stradbally w Ballintubbert, Coraclone etc *C & O*
LURGAN (Christ the Redeemer) (St Andrew) *D & D* I K R GOOD, C T J CADDEN
LURGAN (no dedication) w Billis, Killinkere, Munterconnaught *K, E & A* I W D NELSON
LURGAN (St John the Evangelist) *D & D* I S G BOURKE
LURGANBOY (Chapel of Ease) Cloonclare w Killasnett, Lurganboy and Drumlease *K, E & A*
MACOSQUIN Camus-juxta-Bann *D & R*
MACREDDIN Castlemacadam w Ballinaclash, Aughrim etc *D & G*
MACROOM Moviddy Union *C, C & R*
MAGHERA (no dedication) Kilmegan w Maghera *D & D*
MAGHERA (St Lurach) w Killelagh *D & R* I T D ALLEN
MAGHERACLOONE (St Molua) Carrickmacross w Magheracloone *Clogh*
MAGHERACROSS (no dedication) *Clogh* I D P HOEY
MAGHERACULMONEY (St Mary) *Clogh* I W E McGIRR
MAGHERADROLL (no dedication) *D & D* I W W RUSSELL
MAGHERAFELT (St Swithin) *Arm* I T SCOTT
MAGHERAGALL (no dedication) *Conn* I G A CHEEVERS
MAGHERAHAMLET (no dedication) Annahilt w Magherahamlet *D & D*
MAGHERALIN (Holy and Undivided Trinity) w Dollingstown *D & D* I C R A EASTON
MAGHERALLY (St John the Evangelist) w Annaclone *D & D* I C R J RUDD
MAGORBAN (no dedication) Cashel w Magorban, Tipperary, Clonbeg etc *C & O*
MAGOURNEY Carrigrohane Union *C, C & R*
MAGUIRESBRIDGE (Christ Church) w Derrybrusk *Clogh* I P S WILSON
MALAHIDE (St Andrew) w Balgriffin *D & G* I N E C GAMBLE, NSM K H SHERWOOD
MALIN Moville w Greencastle, Donagh, Cloncha etc *D & R*
MALLOW (St James) w Doneraile and Castletownroche *C, C & R* Bp's C A G S WHITING
MALLUSK (St Brigid) *Conn* I I C BALLENTINE
MALONE Belf Malone St Jo *Conn*
MALONE, UPPER Belf Upper Malone (Epiphany) *Conn*
MANORCUNNINGHAM Raphoe w Raymochy and Clonleigh *D & R*
MANORHAMILTON Cloonclare w Killasnett, Lurganboy and Drumlease *K, E & A*
MARKETHILL (no dedication) Mullabrack w Markethill and Kilcluney *Arm*
MARMULLANE (St Mary) Douglas Union w Frankfield *C, C & R*
MARYBOROUGH (St Peter) w Dysart Enos and Ballyfin *C & O Vacant* Portlaoise (502) 21154

MAYNE Castlepollard and Oldcastle w Loughcrew etc *M & K*
MAYNOOTH (St Mary) Dunboyne w Kilcock, Maynooth, Moyglare etc *M & K*
MAYO (no dedication) Killeshin w Cloydagh and Killabban *C & O*
MEALIFFE Templemore w Thurles and Kilfithmone *C & O*
MEENGLASS (Ascension) Stranorlar w Meenglas and Kilteevogue *D & R*
MEVAGH (Holy Trinity) w Glenalla *D & R* I *Vacant*
MIDDLE CHURCH (no dedication) Ballinderry *Conn*
MIDDLETOWN (St John) Tynan w Middletown *Arm*
MIDLETON (St John the Baptist) Cloyne Union *C, C & R*
MILLISLE (St Patrick) Carrowdore w Millisle *D & D*
MILLTOWN Kilcolman w Kiltallagh, Killorglin, Knockane etc *L & K*
MILLTOWN (St Andrew) *Arm* I M E G MOORE
MILLTOWN (St Philip) Dub Sandford w Milltown *D & G*
MILLTOWN MALBAY Drumcliffe w Kilnasoolagh *L & K*
MITCHELSTOWN Fermoy Union *C, C & R*
MOATE (St Mary) Clara w Liss, Moate and Clonmacnoise *M & K*
MOHILL (St Mary) w Farnaught, Aughavas, Oughteragh, Kiltubride and Drumreilly *K, E & A* I C L B H MEISSNER
MOIRA (St John) *D & D* I T R WEST
MONAGHAN (St Patrick) w Tydavnet and Kilmore *Clogh* I *Vacant*
MONAMOLIN (St Molig) Ardamine w Kiltennel, Glascarrig etc *C & O*
MONART (St Peter) Enniscorthy w Clone, Clonmore, Monart etc *C & O*
MONASTEREVAN (St John the Evangelist) w Nurney and Rathdaire *M & K* I *Vacant* Monasterevan (45) 25411
MONASTERORIS (no dedication) Clonsast w Rathangan, Thomastown etc *M & K*
MONELLAN (no dedication) Convoy w Monellan and Donaghmore *D & R*
MONEYMORE Desertlyn w Ballyeglish *Arm*
MONEYREAGH (no dedication) Orangefield w Moneyreagh *D & D*
MONKSTOWN (Good Shepherd) *Conn* I A A McCARTNEY
MONKSTOWN (no dedication) *D & G* I K DALTON
MONKSTOWN (St John) Carrigaline Union *C, C & R*
MOSSLEY (Holy Spirit) *Conn* I N R CUTCLIFFE
MOSTRIM (St John) w Granard, Clonbroney, Killoe, Rathaspeck and Streete *K, E & A* I T G HUDSON
MOTHEL (no dedication) Castlecomer w Colliery Ch, Mothel and Bilbo *C & O*
MOUNT MERRION Dub Mt Merrion *D & G*
MOUNT MERRION (Pentecost) *D & D* I R C NEILL
MOUNT NUGENT (St Bride) Castlepollard and Oldcastle w Loughcrew etc *M & K*
MOUNTCHARLES (Christ Church) Inver w Mountcharles, Killaghtee and Killybegs *D & R*
MOUNTFIELD (no dedication) Drumragh w Mountfield *D & R*
MOUNTMELLICK (St Paul) w Coolbanagher, Rosenallis and Clonaslee *M & K* I R S J BOURKE
MOUNTRATH Clonenagh w Offerlane, Borris-in-Ossory etc *C & O*
MOUNTSHANNON Killaloe w Stradbally *L & K*
MOVIDDY (no dedication), Kilbonane, Kilmurry, Templemartin and Macroom *C, C & R* NSM J E FENNING
MOVILLA (no dedication) *D & D* I M WITHERS
MOVILLE (St Columb) w Greencastle, Donagh, Cloncha and Culdaff *D & R* I H GILMORE
MOY (St James) w Charlemont *Arm* I C W M ROLSTON
MOYBOLOGUE Kingscourt w Drumconrath, Syddan and Moybologue *M & K*
MOYDOW (no dedication) Ardagh w Tashinny, Shrule and Kilcommick *K, E & A*
MOYGASHEL (no dedication) Drumglass w Moygashel *Arm*
MOYGLARE (All Saints) Dunboyne w Kilcock, Maynooth, Moyglare etc *M & K*
MOYLISCAR Mullingar, Portnashangan, Moyliscar, Kilbixy etc *M & K*
MOYNALTY (St Mary) Kells w Balrathboyne, Moynalty etc *M & K*
MOYNE (St John) Kiltegan w Hacketstown, Clonmore and Moyne *C & O*
MOYNTAGHS Ardmore w Craigavon *D & D*
MOYRUS Omey w Ballynakill, Errislannan and Roundstone *T, K & A*
MUCKAMORE (St Jude) (St Matthias) *Conn* I B S CADDEN
MUCKNOE (St Maeldoid) Ballybay w Mucknoe and Clontibret *Clogh*

MUCKROSS (Holy Trinity) Killarney w Aghadoe and Muckross *L & K*

MUCKROSS (St John) Drumkeeran w Templecarne and Muckross *Clogh*

MUFF (no dedication) Culmore w Muff and Belmont *D & R*

MULHUDDART (St Thomas) Castleknock and Mulhuddart, w Clonsilla *D & G*

MULLABRACK (no dedication) w Markethill and Kilcluney *Arm* I W R FERGUSON, **NSM** N J HUGHES

MULLAGH (no dedication) Bailieborough w Knockbride, Shercock and Mullagh *K, E & A*

MULLAGHDUN (no dedication) Cleenish w Mullaghdun *Clogh*

MULLAGHFAD (All Saints) Aghalurcher w Tattykeeran, Cooneen etc *Clogh*

MULLAGLASS (St Luke) Camlough w Mullaglass *Arm*

MULLAVILLY (no dedication) *Arm* I B J HARPER

MULLINACUFF (no dedication) Tullow w Shillelagh, Aghold and Mullinacuff *C & O*

MULLINGAR (All Saints) w Portnashangan, Moyliscar, Kilbixy, Almoritia, Killucan, Clonard and Castlelost *M & K* I D P R CARMODY, C S ZIETSMAN

MULRANKIN (St David) Kilscoran w Killinick and Mulrankin *C & O*

MUNNINANE (St Kevin) Drumcliffe w Lissadell and Munninane *K, E & A*

MUNTERCONNAUGHT (no dedication) Lurgan etc w Ballymachugh, Kildrumferton etc *K, E & A*

MURRAGH (no dedication) Kinneigh Union *C, C & R*

MYROE (St John) Tamlaghtfinlagan w Myroe *D & R*

MYROSS Ross Union *C, C & R*

MYSHALL (Christ the Redeemer) Fenagh w Myshall, Aghade and Ardoyne *C & O*

NAAS (St David) w Kill and Rathmore *M & K* I M G WOODERSON

NARRAGHMORE (Holy Saviour) w Timolin, Castledermot and Kinneagh *D & G* I K V KENNERLEY

NAVAN (St Mary) w Kentstown, Tara, Slane, Painestown and Stackallen *M & K* I J D M CLARKE

NENAGH (St Mary) w Ballymackey, Templederry and Killodiernan *L & K* I P L TOWERS

NEWBLISS (no dedication) Currin w Drum and Newbliss *Clogh*

NEWBRIDGE (St Patrick) w Carnalway and Kilcullen *M & K* I W B HENEY

NEWCASTLE (no dedication) w Newtownmountkennedy and Calary *D & G* I M CLOSACK, C B J GO'ROURKE

NEWCASTLE (St John) *D & D* I M ELLIS

NEWCASTLE-LYONS (no dedication) Celbridge w Straffan and Newcastle-Lyons *D & G*

NEWCESTOWN Kinneigh Union *C, C & R*

NEWMARKET-ON-FERGUS Drumcliffe w Kilnasoolagh *L & K*

NEWRY (St Mary) (St Patrick) *D & D* I T H W DUNWOODY

NEWTOWNARDS (St Mark) *D & D* I K J SMYTH, C G CLUNIE, Hon C N L WHITE

NEWTOWNBARRY Bunclody w Kildavin, Clonegal and Kilrush *C & O*

NEWTOWNBUTLER Galloon w Drummully *Clogh*

NEWTOWNCROMMELIN (no dedication) Skerry w Rathcavan and Newtowncrommelin *Conn*

NEWTOWNCUNNINGHAM (All Saints) Taughboyne, Craigadooish, Newtowncunningham etc *D & R*

NEWTOWNFERTULLAGH Tullamore w Durrow, Newtownfertullagh, Rahan etc *M & K*

NEWTOWNFORBES Templemichael w Clongish, Clooncumber etc *K, E & A*

NEWTOWNGORE (no dedication) Kilmore w Ballintemple, Kildallon etc *K, E & A*

NEWTOWNHAMILTON (St John) w Ballymoyer and Belleck *Arm* I C F MOORE

NEWTOWNMOUNTKENNEDY (St Matthew) Newc w Newtownmountkennedy and Calary *D & G*

NEWTOWNSAVILLE (no dedication) Augher w Newtownsaville and Eskrahoole *Clogh*

NEWTOWNSTEWART Ardstraw w Baronscourt, Badoney Lower etc *D & R*

NOHOVAL (no dedication) Templebreedy w Tracton and Nohoval *C, C & R*

NURNEY (no dedication) Monasterevan w Nurney and Rathdaire *M & K*

NURNEY (St John) Dunleckney w Nurney, Lorum and Kiltennel *C & O*

OFFERLANE (no dedication) Clonenagh w Offerlane, Borris-in-Ossory etc *C & O*

OLD CHURCH, THE Abbeyleix w Old Church, Ballyroan etc *C & O*

OLD LEIGHLIN Leighlin w Grange Sylvae, Shankill etc *C & O*

OLDCASTLE (St Bride) Castlepollard and Oldcastle w Loughcrew etc *M & K*

OMAGH Drumragh w Mountfield *D & R*

OMEY (Christ Church) w Ballynakill, Errislannan and Roundstone *T, K & A* I C B WARREN

ORANGEFIELD (St John the Evangelist) w Moneyreagh *D & D* I W J R LAVERTY

OSSORY Kilcooley w Littleon, Crohane and Fertagh *C & O*

OUGHTERAGH (no dedication) Mohill w Farnaught, Aughavas, Oughteragh etc *K, E & A*

OUGHTERARD Galway w Kilcummin *T, K & A*

PACKANE Nenagh *L & K*

PAINESTOWN Navan w Kentstown, Tara, Slane, Painestown etc *M & K*

PALLASKENRY Rathkeale w Askeaton and Kilcornan *L & K*

PASSAGE WEST Douglas Union w Frankfield *C, C & R*

PAULSTOWN Leighlin w Grange Sylvae, Shankill etc *C & O*

PETTIGO Drumkeeran w Templecarne and Muckross *Clogh*

PILTOWN Fiddown w Clonegam, Guilcagh and Kilmeaden *C & O*

POMEROY (no dedication) *Arm* **NSM** W J A DAWSON

PORT LAOIS Maryborough w Dysart Enos and Ballyfin *C & O*

PORTADOWN (St Columba) *Arm* I W M ADAIR, C J M HARVEY

PORTADOWN (St Mark) *Arm* I W R TWADDELL, C D W ROBINSON, A MOORE

PORTAFERRY Ballyphilip w Ardquin *D & D*

PORTARLINGTON (St Paul) w Cloneyhurke and Lea *M & K* I J S PEOPLES

PORTGLENONE (no dedication) Ahoghill w Portglenone *Conn*

PORTLAW Fiddown w Clonegam, Guilcagh and Kilmeaden *C & O*

PORTNASHANGAN Mullingar, Portnashangan, Moyliscar, Kilbixy etc *M & K*

PORTRUSH Ballywillan *Conn*

PORTSALON (All Saints) Clondevaddock w Portsalon and Leatbeg *D & R*

PORTSTEWART Agherton *Conn*

PORTUMNA (Christ Church) Clonfert Gp of Par *L & K*

POWERSCOURT (St Patrick) w Kilbride and Annacrevy *D & G* I R D SMITH

PREBAN (St John) Crosspatrick Gp *C & O*

RAHAN Clonsast w Rathangan, Thomastown etc *M & K*

RAHAN (St Carthach) Tullamore w Durrow, Newtownfertullagh, Rahan etc *M & K*

RAHENY (All Saints) w Coolock *D & G* I J T CARROLL, C L J MACKEY

RALOO (no dedication) Glynn w Raloo *Conn*

RAMELTON Tullyaughnish w Kilmacrennan and Killygarvan *D & R*

RAMOAN (St James) w Ballycastle and Culfeightrin *Conn* I W A DUNCAN

RANDALSTOWN Drummaul w Duneane and Ballyscullion *Conn*

RAPHOE (Cathedral of St Eunan) w Raymochy and Clonleigh *D & R* I S R WHITE

RASHARKIN (St Andrew) Ballymoney w Finvoy and Rasharkin *Conn*

RATHANGAN (no dedication) Clonsast w Rathangan, Thomastown etc *M & K*

RATHASPECK (St Thomas) Mostrim w Granard, Clonbroney, Killoe etc *K, E & A*

RATHBARRON Achonry w Tubbercurry and Killoran *T, K & A*

RATHCAVAN (no dedication) Skerry w Rathcavan and Newtowncrommelin *Conn*

RATHCLAREN (Holy Trinity) Bandon Union *C, C & R*

RATHCLINE (no dedication) Roscommon w Donamon, Rathcline, Kilkeevin etc *K, E & A*

RATHCOOLE (no dedication) Clondalkin w Rathcoole *D & G*

RATHCOOLE (St Comgall) *Conn* I *Vacant*

RATHCOONEY (St Mary and All Saints) w Little Island and Carrigtwohill *C, C & R* I S F GLENFIELD

RATHCOR (no dedication) Ballymascanlan w Creggan and Rathcor *Arm*

RATHCORE (St Ultan) Rathmolyon w Castlerickard, Rathcore and Agher *M & K*

RATHDAIRE (Ascension) Monasterevan w Nurney and Rathdaire *M & K*

RATHDOWNEY (no dedication) w Castlefleming, Donaghmore, Rathsaran and Aghavoe *C & O* I J G MURRAY

RATHDRUM (St Saviour) w Glenealy, Derralossary and Laragh *D & G* **I** C N R HALLIDAY, **NSM** S A KINGSTON

RATHFARNHAM Dub Rathfarnham *D & G*

RATHFRILAND Drumgath w Drumgooland and Clonduff *D & D*

RATHGAR Dub Zion Ch *D & G*

RATHKEALE (Holy Trinity) w Askeaton, Foynes and Kilcornan *L & K* **NSM** R G GRAHAM

RATHLIN (St Thomas) Ballintoy w Rathlin and Dunseverick *Conn*

RATHMICHAEL (no dedication) *D & G* **I** F C APPELBE

RATHMINES Dub Rathmines w Harold's Cross *D & G*

RATHMOLYON (St Michael and All Angels) w Castlerickard, Rathcore and Agher *M & K* **I** *Vacant*

RATHMORE (St Columbkille) Naas w Kill and Rathmore *M & K*

RATHMULLAN Tullyaughnish w Kilmacrennan and Killygarvan *D & R*

RATHMULLAN (no dedication) w Tyrella *D & D* **I** C H QUINN

RATHOWEN Mostrim w Granard, Clonbroney, Killoe etc *K, E & A*

RATHSARAN (no dedication) Rathdowney w Castlefleming, Donaghmore etc *C & O*

RATHVILLY (St Mary) Baltinglass w Ballynure etc *C & O*

RAYMOCHY (no dedication) Raphoe w Raymochy and Clonleigh *D & R*

RAYMUNTERDONEY (St Paul) Dunfanaghy, Raymunterdoney and Tullaghbegley *D & R*

REDCROSS (Holy Trinity) Dunganstown w Redcross and Conary *D & G*

REDHILLS Drung w Castleterra, Larah and Lavey etc *K, E & A*

RICHHILL (St Matthew) *Arm* **I** M A ARMSTRONG

RIVERSTOWN Taunagh w Kilmactranny, Ballysumaghan etc *K, E & A*

ROCHFORT BRIDGE Mullingar, Portnashangan, Moyliscar, Kilbixy etc *M & K*

ROCKCORRY (no dedication) Ematris w Rockcorry, Aghabog and Aughnamullan *Clogh*

ROSCOMMON (St Colman) w Donamon, Rathcline, Kilkeevin, Kiltullagh and Tybohine *K, E & A* **P-in-c** R S JACKSON, **NSM** C LINDSAY

ROSCREA (St Cronan) w Kyle, Bourney and Corbally *L & K* **I** J A A CONDELL, **NSM** L W RUDDOCK

ROSENALLIS (St Brigid) Mountmellick w Coolbanagher, Rosenallis etc *M & K*

ROSKELTON (no dedication) Clonenagh w Offerlane, Borris-in-Ossory etc *C & O*

ROSS (Cathedral of St Fachtna) w Kilmacabea, Myross, Kilfaughnabeg and Castleventry *C, C & R* **I** R C A HENDERSON

ROSS, NEW (St Mary) w OLD (St Mary), Whitechurch, Fethard, Killesk and Tintern *C & O* **I** *Vacant* New Ross (51) 21391

ROSSCARBERY Ross Union *C, C & R*

ROSSDROIT (St Peter) Killanne w Killegney, Rossdroit and Templeshanbo *C & O*

ROSSES POINT (no dedication) Sligo w Knocknarea and Rosses Pt *K, E & A*

ROSSINVER (no dedication) Killinagh w Kiltyclogher and Innismagrath *K, E & A*

ROSSMIRE Lismore w Cappoquin, Kilwatermoy, Dungarvan etc *C & O*

ROSSNAKILL Clondevaddock w Portsalon and Leatbeg *D & R*

ROSSNOWLAGH (St John) Kilbarron w Rossnowlagh and Drumholm *D & R*

ROSSORY (no dedication) *Clogh* **I** C T PRINGLE, **NSM** F I NIXON

ROSTREVOR Kilbroney *D & D*

ROUNDSTONE (no dedication) Omey w Ballynakill, Errislannan and Roundstone *T, K & A*

RUNCURRAN Kinsale Union *C, C & R*

RUSHBROOKE Clonmel Union *C, C & R*

RUTLAND Carlow w Urglin and Staplestown *C & O*

RYNAGH Clonfert Gp of Par *L & K*

SAINTFIELD (no dedication) *D & D* **I** A S DELAMERE

SALLAGHY (no dedication) *Clogh* **Bp's C** W FENTON

SANDFORD Dub Sandford w Milltown *D & G*

SANDHILL Sligo w Knocknarea and Rosses Pt *K, E & A*

SANDYMOUNT Dub Sandymount *D & G*

SANTRY Dub Santry w Glasnevin *D & G*

SAUL (St Patrick) Lecale Gp *D & D*

SCARVA (St Matthew) Aghaderg w Donaghmore and Scarva *D & D*

SCHULL (Holy Trinity) Kilmoe Union *C, C & R*

SCOTSHOUSE Currin w Drum and Newbliss *Clogh*

SEAFORDE Lecale Gp *D & D*

SEAGOE (St Gobhan) *D & D* **I** D R CHILLINGWORTH, **C** K M POULTON, D HILLIARD

SEAPATRICK (Holy Trinity) (St Patrick) *D & D* **I** W J SCOTT, **C** B T STANLEY, **NSM** R M McCLEAN

SEIRKIERAN (St Kieran) Clonenagh w Offerlane, Borris-in-Ossory etc *C & O*

SESKINORE (no dedication) Clogherney w Seskinore and Drumnakilly *Arm*

SEYMOUR HILL Kilmakee *Conn*

SHANDON (St Ann) Cork St Luke Union *C, C & R*

SHANKILL Belf St Matt *Conn*

SHANKILL Lurgan Ch the Redeemer *D & D*

SHANKILL (St John) Leighlin w Grange Sylvae, Shankill etc *C & O*

SHANNON (Christ Church) Drumcliffe w Kilnasoolagh *L & K*

SHERCOCK (no dedication) Bailieborough w Knockbride, Shercock and Mullagh *K, E & A*

SHILLELAGH (no dedication) Tullow w Shillelagh, Aghold and Mullinacuff *C & O*

SHINRONE (St Mary) w Aghancon, Dunkerrin and Kinnitty *L & K* **I** R B HAYTHORNTHWAITE, **NSM** J J WHITE SPUNNER

SHRULE (no dedication) Ardagh w Tashinny, Shrule and Kilcommick *K, E & A*

SION MILLS (Good Shepherd) Urney w Sion Mills *D & R*

SIXMILECROSS (St Michael) w Termonmaguirke *Arm* **I** W R H DEVERELL

SIXTOWNS (St Anne) Kilcronaghan w Draperstown and Sixtowns *D & R*

SKERRIES Holmpatrick w Balbriggan and Kenure *D & G*

SKERRY (St Patrick) w Rathcavan and Newtowncrommelin *Conn* **I** J ROONEY

SKIBBEREEN Abbeystrewry Union *C, C & R*

SKREEN (no dedication) w Kilmacshalgan and Dromard *T, K & A* **Bp's C** A G MITCHELL

SLANE (St Patrick) Navan w Kentstown, Tara, Slane, Painestown etc *M & K*

SLAVIN (no dedication) Garrison w Slavin and Belleek *Clogh*

SLIGO (Cathedral of St Mary and St John the Baptist) w Knocknarea and Rosses Point *K, E & A* **I** S I McGEE

SNEEM (Transfiguration) Kenmare w Sneem, Waterville etc *L & K*

SPANISH POINT Drumcliffe w Kilnasoolagh *L & K*

STACKALLEN Navan w Kentstown, Tara, Slane, Painestown etc *M & K*

STAPLESTOWN (no dedication) Carlow w Urglin and Staplestown *C & O*

STEWARTSTOWN Brackaville w Donaghendry and Ballyclog *Arm*

STILLORGAN (St Brigid) w Blackrock *D & G* **I** M A GRAHAM

STONEYFORD (St John) *Conn* **Bp's C** G R SHAW

STORMONT (St Molua) *D & D* **I** W D HUMPHRIES

STRABANE Camus-juxta-Mourne *D & R*

STRADBALLY (All Saints) Stradbally w Stradbally *L & K*

STRADBALLY (St James) Lismore w Cappoquin, Kilwatermoy, Dungarvan etc *C & O*

STRADBALLY (St Patrick) w Ballintubbert, Coraclone, Timogue and Luggacurren *C & O* **I** W BEARE

STRAFFAN (no dedication) Celbridge w Straffan and Newcastle-Lyons *D & G*

STRAID (no dedication) *T, K & A* **I** *Vacant*

STRAND, NORTH (no dedication) Dub Drumcondra w N Strand *D & G*

STRANGFORD Lecale Gp *D & D*

STRANORLAR (no dedication) w Meenglas and Kilteevogue *D & R* **I** S IRVINE

STRATFORD-ON-SLANEY (St John the Baptist) Baltinglass w Ballynure etc *C & O*

STRATHFOYLE (no dedication) Clooney w Strathfoyle *D & R*

STREETE (no dedication) Mostrim w Granard, Clonbroney, Killoe etc *K, E & A*

SUMMER COVE Kinsale Union *C, C & R*

SWANLINBAR (St Augustine) w Tomregan, Kinawley, Drumlane and Templeport *K, E & A* **I** R G KEOGH

SWATRAGH Maghera w Killelagh *D & R*

SWORDS (St Columba) w Donabate and Killsallaghan *D & G* **I** W S BAIRD

SYDDAN (St David) Kingscourt w Drumconrath, Syddan and Moybologue *M & K*

SYDENHAM Belf St Brendan *D & D*

TAGHMON (St Munn) w Horetown and Bannow *C & O* **I** *Vacant*

TALLAGHT (St Maelruain) *D & G*   I   R G KINGSTON, NSM   A W YOUNG

TAMLAGHT Derryvullen S w Garvary *Clogh*

TAMLAGHT (St Luke) Ballinderry w Tamlaght and Arboe *Arm*

TAMLAGHT O'CRILLY UPPER (no dedication) w LOWER (no dedication) *D & R*   I   W A CAPPER

TAMLAGHTARD (St Gedanus) w Aghanloo *D & R*   I   *Vacant*

TAMLAGHTFINLAGAN (St Findlunganus) w Myroe *D & R*   I   H R GIVEN

TANEY (Christ Church) (St Nahi) *D & G*   I   W D SINNAMON,   C   P R CAMPION,   NSM   R C REED

TARA Navan w Kentstown, Tara, Slane, Painestown etc *M & K*

TARBERT Tralee w Ballymacelligott, Kilnaughtin etc *L & K*

TARTARAGHAN (St Paul) w Diamond *Arm*   I   W E C FLEMING

TASHINNY (no dedication) Ardagh w Tashinny, Shrule and Kilcommick *K, E & A*

TATTYKEERAN (no dedication) Aghalurcher w Tattykeeran, Cooneen etc *Clogh*

TAUGHBOYNE (St Baithan) w Craigadooish, Newtowncunningham and Killea *D & R*   I   D W T CROOKS

TAUNAGH (no dedication) w Kilmactranny, Ballysumaghan and Killery *K, E & A*   I   A MINION

TEAMPOL-NA-MBOCHT (Altar) Kilmoe Union *C, C & R*

TEMPLEBREEDY (Holy Trinity) w Tracton and Nohoval *C, C & R*   I   D W OXLEY

TEMPLECARNE (no dedication) Drumkeeran w Templecarne and Muckross *Clogh*

TEMPLECORRAN (St John) Kilroot and Templecorran *Conn*

TEMPLECRONE (St Crone) Gweedore, Carrickfin and Templecrone *D & R*

TEMPLEDERRY (no dedication) Nenagh *L & K*

TEMPLEHARRY (no dedication) Cloughjordan w Borrisokane etc *L & K*

TEMPLEMARTIN (St Martin) Moviddy Union *C, C & R*

TEMPLEMICHAEL (St John) w Clongish, Clooncumber, Killashee and Ballymacormack *K, E & A*   I   R S JACKSON

TEMPLEMORE Londonderry (Cathedral of St Columb) *D & R*   I   D CORR,   C   K G BARRY

TEMPLEMORE (St Mary) w Thurles and Kilfithmone *C & O*   C   T A SHERLOCK

TEMPLEPATRICK (St Patrick) w Donegore *Conn*   I   E H GOUGH

TEMPLEPORT (St Peter) Swanlinbar w Tomregan, Kinawley, Drumlane etc *K, E & A*

TEMPLESCOBIN (St Paul) Enniscorthy w Clone, Clonmore, Monart etc *C & O*

TEMPLESHANBO (St Colman) Killanne w Killegney, Rossdroit and Templeshanbo *C & O*

TEMPLETRINE (no dedication) Kinsale Union *C, C & R*

TEMPO (no dedication) and Clabby *Clogh*   I   D MORROW

TERMONAMONGAN (St Bestius) Derg w Termonamongan *D & R*

TERMONEENY (no dedication) Desertmartin w Termoneeny *D & R*

TERMONFECKIN (St Feckin) Drogheda w Ardee, Collon and Termonfeckin *Arm*

TERMONMAGUIRKE (St Columbkille) Sixmilecross w Termonmaguirke *Arm*

THOMASTOWN (no dedication) Clonsast w Rathangan, Thomastown etc *M & K*

THURLES (no dedication) Templemore w Thurles and Kilfithmone *C & O*

TICKMACREVAN (St Patrick) Ardclinis and Tickmacrevan w Layde and Cushendun *Conn*

TIMOGUE (St Mogue) Stradbally w Ballintubbert, Coraclone etc *C & O*

TIMOLEAGUE (Ascension) Kilgariffe Union *C, C & R*

TIMOLIN (St Mullin) Narraghmore w Timolin, Castledermot and Kinneagh *D & G*

TINTERN (St Mary) New w Old Ross, Whitechurch, Fethard etc *C & O*

TIPPERARY (St Mary) Cashel w Magorban, Tipperary, Clonbeg etc *C & O*

TOBERMORE Kilcronaghan w Draperstown and Sixtowns *D & R*

TOMREGAN (no dedication) Swanlinbar w Tomregan, Kinawley, Drumlane etc *K, E & A*

TOOMBE (St Catherine) Ferns w Kilbride, Toombe, Kilcormack etc *C & O*

TOOMNA (no dedication) Kiltoghart w Drumshambo, Annaduff and Kilronan *K, E & A*

TOORMORE Kilmoe Union *C, C & R*

TRACTON Templebreedy w Tracton and Nohoval *C, C & R*

TRALEE (St John the Evangelist) w Kilmoyley, Ballymacelligott, Ballyseedy, Kilnaughtin, Listowel and Ballybunnion *L & K*   I   R WARREN, NSM   H A P STEPHENS

TRAMORE Waterford w Killea, Drumcannon and Dunhill *C & O*

TRILLICK (Christ Church) Kilskeery w Trillick *Clogh*

TRIM (Cathedral of St Patrick) w Bective and Galtrim *M & K*   I   J A G BARRETT

TRORY (St Michael) w Killadeas *Clogh*   I   V E S McKEON

TUAM (Cathedral of St Mary) w Cong and Aasleagh *T, K & A*   I   A M A PREVITE

TUAMGRANEY (St Cronan) Killaloe w Stradbally *L & K*

TUBBERCURRY (St George) Achonry w Tubbercurry and Killoran *T, K & A*

TUBRID Drumkeeran w Templecarne and Muckross *Clogh*

TULLAGH (no dedication) Abbeystrewry Union *C, C & R*

TULLAGHBEGLEY (St Ann) Dunfanaghy, Raymunterdoney and Tullaghbegley *D & R*

TULLAGHMELAN (no dedication) Clonmel w Innislounagh, Tullaghmelan etc *C & O*

TULLAMORE (St Catherine) w Durrow, Newtownfertullagh, Rahan, Tyrellspass and Killoughy *M & K*   I   A J GRIMASON

TULLANISKIN (Holy Trinity) w Clonoe *Arm*   I   E M CULBERTSON

TULLOW (no dedication) *D & G*   I   K A KEARON

TULLOW (St Columba) w Shillelagh, Aghold and Mullinacuff *C & O*   I   *Vacant*

TULLYAUGHNISH (St Paul) w Kilmacrennan and Killygarvan *D & R*   I   W B A SMEATON

TULLYLISH (All Saints) *D & D*   I   D WILSON

TULLYNAKILL (no dedication) Killinchy w Kilmood and Tullynakill *D & D*

TUNNY (St Andrew) Glenavy w Tunny and Crumlin *Conn*

TURLOUGH (no dedication) Aughaval w Achill, Knappagh, Dugort etc *T, K & A*

TYBOHINE (no dedication) Roscommon w Donamon, Rathcline, Kilkeevin etc *K, E & A*

TYDAVNET (St Davnet) Monaghan w Tydavnet and Kilmore *Clogh*

TYHOLLAND (St Sillian) Donagh w Tyholland and Errigal Truagh *Clogh*

TYNAN (St Vindic) w Middletown *Arm*   I   *Vacant* Caledon (01861) 568619

TYRELLA (St John) Rathmullan w Tyrella *D & D*

TYRELLSPASS (St Sinian) Tullamore w Durrow, Newtownfertullagh, Rahan etc *M & K*

URGLIN (no dedication) Carlow w Urglin and Staplestown *C & O*

URNEY (Christ Church) w Sion Mills *D & R*   I   J I H STAFFORD

URNEY (no dedication) w Denn and Derryheen *K, E & A*   I   M R LIDWILL

VALENTIA (St John the Baptist) Kenmare w Sneem, Waterville etc *L & K*

VIRGINIA Lurgan etc w Ballymachugh, Kildrumferton etc *K, E & A*

WARINGSTOWN (Holy Trinity) Donaghcloney w Waringstown *D & D*

WARRENPOINT (no dedication) Clonallon w Warrenpoint *D & D*

WATERFORD (Christ Church Cathedral) w Killea, Drumcannon and Dunhill *C & O*   I   W B A NEILL,   C   A J NEVIN

WATERVILLE Kenmare w Sneem, Waterville etc *L & K*

WESTPORT Aughaval w Achill, Knappagh, Dugort etc *T, K & A*

WEXFORD (St Iberius) w Ardcolm and Killurin *C & O*   I   N T RUDDOCK,   NSM   I T EASTWOOD

WHITECHURCH Dub Whitechurch *D & G*

WHITECHURCH (no dedication) New w Old Ross, Whitechurch, Fethard etc *C & O*

WHITEGATE Cloyne Union *C, C & R*

WHITEHEAD (St Patrick) w Islandmagee *Conn*   I   K E RUDDOCK

WHITEHOUSE (St John) *Conn*   I   E J H SHEPHERD

WHITEROCK Belf Whiterock *Conn*

WICKLOW (no dedication) w Killiskey *D & G*   I   J P CLARKE

WILLOWFIELD (no dedication) *D & D*   I   N JARDINE,   C   G A HARRON

WOODLAWN (no dedication) Aughrim w Ballinasloe etc *L & K*

WOODSCHAPEL (St John) w Gracefield *Arm*   I   T S COULSON

YOUGHAL (St Mary's Collegiate) w Ardmore, Castlemartyr and Ballycotton *C, C & R*   I   P R THOMAS

ZION Dub Zion Ch *D & G*

CHAPLAINS OF THE DIOCESE OF GIBRALTAR IN EUROPE

Vicar General: Canon W G REID
14 Tufton Street, London SW1P 3QZ
0171-976 8001   Fax 976 8002

ARCHDEACONS
The Aegean and the Danube   S J B PEAKE
North West Europe   G G ALLEN
France   M P DRAPER
Gibraltar and Iberia   J K ROBINSON
Italy and Malta   E N DEVENPORT
Scandinavia   G A C BROWN
Switzerland   P J HAWKER

At chaplaincies with more than one chaplain the names are listed in order of seniority.

Austria
Vienna   S J B PEAKE

Belgium
Antwerp St Boniface   D W VAN LEEUWEN, P G MOONEY
Antwerp Seafarers' Centre   P G MOONEY
Brussels   N M WALKER
Charleroi   D W VAN LEEUWEN, C FILBERT-ULLMANN
Ghent   J C WALKER
Ostend w Knokke and Bruges   D E H MOLE
Tervuren w Liege   S J G SEAMER
Ypres   N A LLEWELLYN

Bulgaria
Sofia   C W NEWLANDS

Czech Republic
Prague   R A E KENT

Denmark
Copenhagen w Aarhus   D G PROSSER

Estonia
Tallinn   F A E CHADWICK

Finland
Helsinki w Tallin   F A E CHADWICK

France
Aquitaine (Bordeaux, Chancelade, Cognac, Limeuil, Monteton and Tocane)   *Vacant*
Beaulieu-sur-Mer   B B MATTHEWS
Biarritz   J M LIVINGSTONE
Boulogne-sur-Mer w Calais   D A RUDDLE
Cannes   A E MATHERS
Chantilly   J G V FOSTER, D M R FLACH
Dunkerque Missions to Seamen   A R W RIMMER
Fontainebleau   W A WILSON
Grenoble   J R BALL
Lille   W SCOTT
Lyon   J E PERRYMAN
Maison-Laffitte   O B EATON
Marseille w Aix-en-Provence   P N CASSIDY
Menton   A B WODEHOUSE
Nice w Vence   K J LETTS
Paris St George   M P DRAPER, M H HARRISON
Paris St Michael   A J WARBURTON, A W K BROWN
Pau   M F D CRIPPS
Rouen Missions to Seamen   C A B MARKE
St Raphael   T F UNSWORTH
Sophia Antipolis   R G L McALISTER
Strasbourg   A J L BARNETT, J L MURRAY
Toulouse   I L MORT
Versailles w Chevry (Gif-sur-Yvette)   D C MARSHALL, A MARSHALL

Germany
Berlin   J G TURNER
Bonn w Cologne   P M S CURRAN
Dusseldorf   J I BATTY
Frankfurt-am-Main   D W RATCLIFF
Freiburg-im-Breisgau   J R GIBBS
Hamburg   J K NEWSOME
Heidelberg   A G LENOX-CONYNGHAM, E C M K JONES
Leipzig   G M REAKES-WILLIAMS
Stuttgart   M S NAIDU
Wiesbaden   K E BELL

Gibraltar
Gibraltar   B W HORLOCK, M T COOMBE, D A S HOARE

Greece
Athens w Kifissia, Patras, Thessaloniki and Voulan   P K HARRISON, C E WETHERALL
Corfu   W ELLIOT

Hungary
Budapest   D MOSS

Italy
Florence w Siena   E N DEVENPORT
Milan w Genoa, Cadenabbia and Varese   T O MENDEL, M J GOUGH
Naples w Sorrento, Capri and Bari   M BULLOCK
Rome   G B EVANS
San Remo   B WARDROBE
Venice w Trieste   J R HARKINS

Latvia
Riga   G A C BROWN

Luxembourg
Luxembourg   C G POOLE

Malta
Sliema   R S MATHESON
Valetta   *Vacant*

Monaco
Monte Carlo   B W THOMAS

Morocco
Casablanca   P A LETFORD
Tangier   G S BEHEYDT

The Netherlands
Amsterdam w Den Helder and Heiloo   I L S WATSON, F J MACARTNEY

CHAPLAINS OF THE DIOCESE OF GIBRALTAR IN EUROPE

East Netherlands (Arnhem, Nijmegen and Twente)
  G G ALLEN
Eindhoven R A LENS VAN RIJN
Haarlem G G ALLEN
Hague, The I C WHITTLE, R W G DE MURALT
Pernis Missions to Seamen P W LEITCH
Rotterdam *Vacant*
Schiedam Missions to Seamen M K SPARROW
Utrecht w Amersfoort, Harderwijk and Zwolle T WHITFIELD
Voorschoten P J BOURNE

Norway

**Oslo w Bergen, Drammen, Kristiansand, Stavanger,
  Trondheim and Tonsberg** R LEWIS, L P FORD

Poland

Warsaw D H WILLIAMS

Portugal

Algarve P J W BLACKBURN, W G CHESHAM
Lisbon J K ROBSINSON
Madeira R L RAIKES
Porto (or Oporto) D WARD-BODDINGTON

Romania

Bucharest C W NEWLANDS

Russia

Moscow C R C COUSSMAKER

Serbia

Belgrade G T DOYLE

Spain

Barcelona R W SEWELL

Costa Blanca C M P JONES
Costa del Sol West M A HORSEY
Fuengirola T DEVAMANIKKAM
Ibiza C J M MAXWELL
Lanzarote J R JENKINS
Las Palmas E C FORD
Madrid R L HODSON
Malaga B P R PEGG
Menorca D JACKSON
Mojacar B A CRADDOCK
Nerja P M VELLACOTT
Palma de Mallorca W J HAWTHORNE
Playa de Las Americas, Tenerife R W THOMAS
Puerto de la Cruz, Tenerife C FOWLER
Puerto Pollensa, Mallorca C A C COOPER
Torrevieja D S MILLER

Sweden

Gothenburg w Halmstad, Jönköping and Uddevalla
  M D S COCKS
Stockholm w Gävle and Västerås G A C BROWN,
  J SSEMAKULA

Switzerland

Basle J R GIBBS
Berne w Neuchatel D C WOTHERSPOON
Geneva J K KIMBER
Lausanne L F STEEL
Lugano E A SIMMONDS
Montreux w Gstaad H C SASSER
Vevey w Château d'Oex and Villars D J FRANK
Zürich w Winterthur P J HAWKER, M J HAZELTON

Turkey

Ankara H F COCKSEDGE
Istanbul w Moda I W L SHERWOOD
Izmir (Smyrna) w Bornova J C WHITE

CHAPLAINS TO HER MAJESTY'S SERVICES

ROYAL NAVY

Chaplain of the Fleet and Archdeacon for the Royal Navy
(Director General of Naval Chaplaincy Services)
Ven M W BUCKS QHC
RN Chaplaincy Services, Room 203, Victory Building, HM Naval Base, Portsmouth PO1 3LS
Portsmouth (01705) 727903 Fax 727112

Chaplains RN

J P AMES	C A FRENCH	J O MORRIS
D BARLOW	S J GOLDING	I F NAYLOR
R D BAXENDALE	D H GOODBURN	R NURTON
S A R BEVERIDGE	J GREEN	M G POLL
K C BROMAGE	M J HARMAN	R L PYNE
M BROTHERTON	J A HEMPENSTALL	E D J-B RENFREY
R F BUCKLEY	J HILL	P J D S SCOTT
A M CALLON	R G HILLIARD	G J SMITH
B R CLARKE	C W W HOWARD	S P SPRINGETT
R COATES	M H JACKSON	S E STEPHENS
R C CUTLER	E W JONES	B F SWABEY
I EGLIN	N J KELLY	D W W THOMAS
G M ELMORE	T J LEWIS	W E WELDON
B D S FAIRBANK	C J LUCKRAFT	M L WISHART
W H FRANKLIN	A J F METTERS	N E WOODCOCK

ARMY

Chaplain-General to the Forces
Rev J HARKNESS CB, OBE, QHC
(The present Chaplain-General is a Church of Scotland Minister)

Deputy Chaplain-General and Archdeacon for the Army
Ven A DEAN QHC
Ministry of Defence (Army), Bagshot Park, Bagshot, Surrey GU19 5PL
Bagshot (01276) 471717 Fax 412834

Chaplains to the Forces

J G W ANDREWS	J R B GOUGH	M P MORTON
W G ASHTON	R L GREEN	E P MOSLEY
J L ASTON	S E GRIFFITH	R A OWEN
K P ATHERLEY	G F HADFIELD	W B PAINE
D G BAILEY	R J HALL	S P PARSELLE
T F BARNFATHER	M J HALSALL	D J PEACHELL
K D BELL	R W HAYTER	A G PHILLIPS
J BLACKBURN	A J HEAGERTY	K J PILLAR
J W BLAIR	D C HEAVER	R PLUCK
A J BOYD	R A HEMMINGS	J A H POLLARD
K M BRETEL	L T J HILLARY	D J M POLLOCK
C S T BRODDLE	J J HOLLIMAN	A H PRICE
A J BROWN	J P HOOLEY	J R PRICE
L H BRYAN	P A IRWIN	R M PRIEST
M A G BRYCE	H L JONES	S ROBBINS
R M BURT	M V JONES	J H E ROSKELLY
P J CABLE	K R JOYCE	P M RUTHERFORD
P M CARTER	P J A KENNEDY	P F A SPRINGFORD
J D S COATES	N A KNIGHTS JOHNSON	R W STEVENS
T A R COLE	R LANDALL	M R N STEVENSON
F COLLINS	C M LANGSTON	J H SYMONDS
J C D COOK	R A LOCKE	J TEE
N L COOK	J M LOVEDAY	A H THOMAS
A A COSLETT	R McALLEN	P THOMPSON
N N CROSSEY	R C McCARTNEY	D A TICKNER
A W CUMBERLIDGE	C MACDONALD	A J TOTTEN
V R DUNSTAN-MEADOWS	R A McDOWALL	P VICKERS
P A EAGLES	T R McKNIGHT	C J A WALKER
B ELLIOTT	D J MERCERON	S M M WALKER
S J FARMER	R M MITCHELL	D M T WALTERS
S A FRANKLIN	J W R MORRISON	R E WILLIAMS
C W GIBBS		C M WILSON

ROYAL AIR FORCE

Chaplain-in-Chief
Ven B H LUCAS CB, QHC

Assistant Chaplains-in-Chief
G B McAVOY MBE, QHC, P R TURNER QHC, A P BISHOP, A T R GOODE
Chaplaincy Services (RAF), HQ, Personnel and Training Command, RAF Innsworth, Gloucester GL3 1EZ
Gloucester (01452) 712612   Ext 5164   Fax 510828

Chaplains RAF

P J ABELL	N P HERON	D T OSBORN
R W BAILEY	R D HESKETH	C PARNELL-HOPKINSON
N B P BARRY	J C HETHERINGTON	R J PENTLAND
H W BEARN	A D HEWETT	M P ROEMMELE
J P M CHAFFEY	C E HEWITT	P SLADEN
L E D CLARK	J W G HUGHES	L E SPICER
S T COLLIS	S P IREDALE	J W K TAYLOR
I R COLSON	I A LAMBERT	I M THOMAS
E CORE	T R LEE	A J TURNER
J E COYNE	C W LONG	I S WARD
A J DAVIES	M F LOVELESS	R A P WARD
C W K DAVIES	D J McKAVANAGH	S J WARE
M J ELLIOTT	D S MACKENZIE	I J WESTON
A P R FLETCHER	A B McMULLON	A L WILLIS
A C GATRILL	K MADDY	J K WILSON
A J D GILBERT	R NOBLE	D WYNNE-JONES
I F GREENHALGH		

PRISON CHAPLAINS
HOME OFFICE PRISON SERVICE
(England and Wales)

Chaplain General of Prisons
Ven D FLEMING
Assistant Chaplain General (HQ)
T M JOHNS
HM Prison Service Chaplaincy, Abell House, John Islip Street, London SW1P 4LH
0171-217 5817   Fax 217 5090

Assistant Chaplains General
J R HARGREAVES,   R C PAYNE,   P J TAYLOR
HM Prison Service Chaplaincy, PO Box 349, Stafford ST16 3DL
Stafford (01785) 54421   Fax 227734

At institutions with more than one chaplain the names are listed in order of seniority.

PRISONS

Acklington   J M TRUMAN, S A JONES
Aldington   L WILLIAMS
Ashwell   J RIDLEY
Askham Grange   D H WATTS
Bedford   R A WILLCOX
Belmarsh   G HERRETT
Birmingham   B J GRACIE, P J WALKER
Blakenhurst   M L PALMER
Blantyre House   J H WAITE, J M BOURNE
Blundeston   R T COOK
Brinsford   P C ROBSON
Bristol   M PETERS, S J GILES
Brixton   G B K DODSWORTH, T G JACQUET
Buckley Hall   D W HIRST
Bullingdon   D G WAKEFIELD
Bullwood Hall   J R D KEMP
Camp Hill   R HIGGINBOTTOM
Canterbury   H J CROWIE
Cardiff   M J KIDDLE
Channings Wood   I G HALLIWELL, C V L CURD
Chelmsford   J K HAYWARD
Coldingley   G CLARKSON
Cookham Wood   J KING
Dartmoor   J D BIRD
Doncaster   J E BLAND
Dorchester   P F TURNBULL
Downview   P A NEWMAN
Drake Hall   C M WITHERS
Durham   E M DIXON, S A WATSON
Eastwood Park   R W MARTIN
Elmley   G WILLIAMS
Everthorpe   M R ESCRITT
Exeter   W H BIRDWOOD
Featherstone   A M BALL, K L WASSALL
Ford   B BARNES-CEENEY
Frankland   S BINDOFF
Full Sutton   I D GOMERSALL, M LOCKHART
Garth   P D AINSLEY
Gartree   M T PHILLIPS
Gloucester   A M LYNETT
Grendon and Spring Hill   K S POUND
Haslar   P A SUTTON
Haverigg   I C SMITH, J M SKINNER
Highdown   A R BODDY
Highpoint   J M N HUNT
Holloway   C BURGESS, M L KEARNS
Holme House   T A McCARTHY
Hull   C B DICK

Kingston (Portsmouth)   E H O'CONNOR
Kirkham   L S ROSE
Latchmere House   D L GAMBLE
Leeds   J M DIXON, J M LOWEN, J M STRIDE, J W THEOBALD, A P HARVEY
Leicester   M STARK
Lewes   D J H POWE
Leyhill   A K SWANN
Lincoln   A R DUCE, J L WELSH
Lindholme   P TARLETON
Liverpool   P A RENNIE, I R SHACKLETON, W F WEARN
Long Lartin   S BRACE
Maidstone   E GHINN
Manchester   N PROCTOR
Moorland   S C BONNEY
Morton Hall   M R RENNARD
Mount, The   J K CRICHTON
New Hall   M E SMITH
North Sea Camp   B R GRELLIER
Norwich   W A NOBLETT, E M TOLLER
Nottingham   J E FITZGERALD
Oxford   H D DUPREE
Parkhurst   B G ANDERSON
Pentonville   K R BROWN, W St C COLLINS
Preston   R P SPRATT, S E MASKREY, W DRAIN
Ranby   A HIRST
Reading   P D DERBYSHIRE
Rochester   D J BURTON, J G C LAWRENCE
Rudgate   S W P ROSHEUVEL
Send   G CLARKSON
Shepton Mallet   B W J MITFORD, M S PERSSON
Shrewsbury   R W D BIDDLE
Standford Hill   R T GREEN
Stocken   M C CRADDUCK
Styal   D J WOODLEY
Swansea   E T HUNT, M C JOHN
Thorp Arch   S W P ROSHEUVEL
Verne, The   J M BLOOMFIELD, E S MITCHELL
Wakefield   J LYNN
Wandsworth   P G W MEADEN, M REDFEARN
Wayland   P D STELL, J FELLINGHAM
Whatton   J PULMAN, J E FITZGERALD
Whitemoor   W J SALMON
Winchester   R J GUYMER
Woodhill   P GREEN
Wormwood Scrubs   P WESTWOOD, S EDWARDS, G E STEVENSON
Wymott   S RITCHIE

YOUNG OFFENDER INSTITUTIONS

Aylesbury A G MARLEY
Castington F A ELTRINGHAM
Deerbolt R ATTLEY
Dover B M W STARES
Erlestoke House G D BAKER, J P R SAUNT
Glen Parva H K DODHIA, J H J TEARNAN
Guys Marsh S C LISTON
Hatfield J M TOMLINSON
Hewell Grange R F LODGE
Hindley M J SMEATON, R N ARBERY
Hollesley Bay Colony A M CLARK, E A GILES

Huntercombe and Finnamore Wood E SUTHERLAND
Kirklevington Grange D MOORE
Lancaster Farms J W GEEN
Northallerton B J MAYNE
Onley G DARVILL, N D ADAMS
Portland M L STEER
Stoke Heath B K COOPER
Swinfen Hall J B ASTON, J R FAGAN
Thorn Cross D L MELLOR
Usk and Prescoed R L DAVIES
Wellingborough N C DENT
Werrington House J L HUMPHREYS

REMAND CENTRES

Brockhill R F LODGE
Low Newton E CUMMINGS
Pucklechurch I L WILLS, V I WOODS, S J GILES

Risley R GIBBARD
Wolds, The D O CASSWELL

CHANNEL ISLANDS

Jersey C I BUCKLEY

SCOTTISH PRISON SERVICE

Scottish Prison Service, Calton House, 5 Redheughs Rigg, Edinburgh E12 9HW
0131-556 8400   Fax 244 8774

Aberdeen J D ALEXANDER
Glasgow (Barlinnie) S D N BARRETT
Glenochil F A M LAWRY
Inverness A WHEATLEY

Perth M LAWRENSON
Polmont M C REED

NORTHERN IRELAND PRISON SERVICE

Northern Ireland Office, Dundonald House, Upper Newtownards Road, Belfast BT4 3SU
Belfast (01232) 520700   Fax 525327

Belfast N B DODDS
Belfast, Young Offender Centre J C BELL

Maghaberry J A HARRON
Maze, The W A MURPHY

IRISH PRISON SERVICE

Department of Justice, 72-76 St Stephen's Green, Dublin 2, Irish Republic
Dublin (1) 678 9711   Fax 676 4718

Arbour Hill W J BRIDCUT
Fort Mitchel C L HALL-THOMPSON

Limerick J M G SIRR
Mountjoy G E DYKE

WHOLE-TIME HOSPITAL CHAPLAINS
(England and Wales)

An index of whole-time hospital chaplains as defined by the Hospital Chaplaincies Council.

Secretary to the Hospital Chaplaincies Council
Rev R S CLARKE
Church House, Great Smith Street, London SW1P 3NZ
0171-222 9011   Fax 799 2714

At institutions with more than one chaplain the names are listed in order of seniority.

ADDENBROOKE'S Cambridge   C E HOUGH, I J P MORRIS
ALEXANDRA Redditch   B M JONES
ALL SAINTS Birmingham   D L HART
ANDOVER WAR MEMORIAL NHS TRUST   D F KING
ARROWE PARK Birkenhead   N P CHRISTENSEN
ASHWORTH   J C COSSINS
BARNSLEY DISTRICT GENERAL   M P YATES
BASINGSTOKE DISTRICT   P J GOOLD
BASSETLAW HOSPITAL AND COMMUNITY
   SERVICES NHS TRUST   A J COOPER
BEDFORD NHS TRUST   P N S GIBSON
BIRMINGHAM CHILDREN'S   K M RICKETTS,
   D MAWBEY
BIRMINGHAM MATERNITY   D MAWBEY
BOLTON GENERAL   N K GRAY, G F WEIR
BRADFORD ROYAL INFIRMARY   O A A O OLUMIDE
BRIGHTON GENERAL   G S JOHNSON
BRISTOL ROYAL HOSPITAL FOR SICK
   CHILDREN   H M A WILLIAMS
BRISTOL ROYAL INFIRMARY   R J YEOMANS
BROADGREEN Liverpool   A H P BAILLIE
BROADMOOR Crowthorne   T WALT
BROOK GENERAL London   M GODDARD
CAMDEN AND ISLINGTON COMMUNITY AND
   HEALTH SERVICES NHS TRUST   P W A WHELAN
CANTERBURY AND THANET COMMUNITY HEALTH
   CARE TRUST   E M SHEARCROFT
CARLTON HAYES   P F GREEN
CASTLE HILL Cottingham   P L DODD
CATERHAM LIFECARE NHS TRUST   R LAMONT
CENTRAL SHEFFIELD UNIVERSITY HOSPITALS NHS
   TRUST   D C F TUDOR, M J KELLAM
CHARING CROSS London   A H BORTHWICK, N SPICER
CHASE FARM Enfield   T M BARON
CHELSEA AND WESTMINSTER London   B P HUGHES
CHELTENHAM GENERAL   W B IRVINE
CHERRY KNOWLE Sunderland   C J WORSFOLD
CHESTER   E T DAVIES
CHURCHILL Oxford   S C BULLOCK
CITY HOSPITAL NHS TRUST (BIRMINGHAM)
   G DOWNS
CLAYBURY Woodford Bridge   M O PRITCHARD
COLCHESTER GENERAL   M W THOMPSON, R SMITH
CONQUEST Bexhill   D J JEFFREYS
DARLINGTON MEMORIAL   B SELMES
DERBY CITY   S TURNBULL
DERBYSHIRE ROYAL INFIRMARY   K J SKIPPON,
   M R COBB
DERRIFORD Plymouth   P S MACPHERSON, S F SEWELL
DEWSBURY DISTRICT   P L BENSON
DONCASTER ROYAL INFIRMARY AND MONTAGUE
   HOSPITAL NHS TRUST   C M FRETWELL
EALING GENERAL   P ROWNTREE
EAST HERTFORDSHIRE HOSPICE CARE   G G BROWN
EAST SURREY Redhill   N WALTER
EASTBOURNE DISTRICT GENERAL   J H KIMBERLEY
EPSOM HEALTHCARE NHS TRUST   C VALLINS
FARNBOROUGH Orpington   N J BUNKER
FAZAKERLEY Liverpool   S TRICKLEBANK
FREEMAN Newcastle upon Tyne   M MASTERMAN
FRIMLEY PARK   A W WARNER
FULBOURN Cambridge   J M LAW
FURNESS GENERAL   G GARBUTT
GEORGE ELIOT Nuneaton   E C POGMORE
GLENFIELD (NHS) TRUST Leicester   T H GIRLING
GLOUCESTERSHIRE ROYAL   D H GODWIN
GOOD HOPE DISTRICT GENERAL Sutton
   Coldfield   A T BALL
GREAT ORMOND STREET HOSPITAL FOR
   CHILDREN NHS TRUST   D R A BACON,
   R M PARTRIDGE
GREENWICH HEALTHCARE NHS TRUST
   C F A B J LE VAY

GRIMSBY DISTRICT GENERAL   H D TER BLANCHE,
   P RUSSELL
GUY'S London   C H N SMITH
HAINE Ramsgate   J M HALL
HALIFAX GENERAL   D A HUNTLEY
HAMMERSMITH London   E MORRIS
HARPERBURY Radlett   N HULME
HARROGATE DISTRICT AND GENERAL   R R WATSON
HARROW   A J ANDREWS
HARTLAND NHS TRUST East Birmingham   S R RESTALL
HEATHERWOOD East Berkshire   R A CHEEK
HELLESDON Norwich   I J BAILEY
HEMEL HEMPSTEAD GENERAL   C L SMITH
HEREFORD COUNTY   P A ROBERTS
HIGHCROFT Birmingham   J M MASON
HOMERTON London   D W HIZA
HOPE Salford   F N HOLMAN, A J ATKINS
HUDDERSFIELD NHS TRUST   J WESTON
IPSWICH   G T MELVIN, M W THORPE
JAMES PAGET Gorleston   W C SNOOK
JOHN RADCLIFFE Oxford   N P FENNEMORE
KENT AND CANTERBURY Canterbury   H D CONNOLL
KETTERING GENERAL AND ST MARY'S
   HOSPITALS   L S McCORMACK
KIDDERMINSTER GENERAL   P D BROTHWELL
KING'S HEALTHCARE NHS TRUST   S T MEYER,
   J M ALLFORD
KINGSTON   A GRIFFITHS
KINGSWAY   G MARTIN, J P RAFFAY
LANCASTER MOOR Lancaster   D V A BROWN
LEA CASTLE Kidderminster   P D BROTHWELL
LEEDS COMMUNITY AND MENTAL HEALTH
   SERVICES   R P WALFORD
LEEDS GENERAL INFIRMARY   D J RIVERS,
   A W S FURLONG
LEICESTER ROYAL INFIRMARY   C S RUSHFORTH,
   C E SOUTHALL
LEICESTERSHIRE HOSPICE   K G T COOK
LEWISHAM   A L SHAW
LINCOLN COUNTY GROUP   D X LOMAS
LITTLEMORE Oxford   F B STEVENSON
LUTON AND DUNSTABLE   J HEARN
MAIDSTONE   D A PORTER, N G STARTIN
MANCHESTER ROYAL INFIRMARY   A M RHODES,
   M W FOLLAND
MANOR Walsall   E J LEWIS, N L HIBBINS
MAUDSLEY London   M R SUTHERLAND
MAYDAY UNIVERSITY Thornton
   Heath   I G WOODROFFE, H A EVE, P L GIBBS
MEDWAY Gillingham   H J CONNELL
MERTON AND SUTTON COMMUNITY
   TRUST   H A SMITH
MIDDLESEX London   D J MASON, P KINSEY
MILTON KEYNES GENERAL   M R SAUNDERS
MONYHULL Birmingham   B J B EASTER
MUSGROVE PARK Taunton   P R HUXHAM
NAPSBURY St Albans   J D JOHNSON
NATIONAL HOSPITAL FOR NEUROLOGY AND
   NEUROSURGERY London   P W LEWIS
NEW CROSS Wolverhampton   D J JOHNSON
NEWCASTLE UPON TYNE GENERAL   M J SHIPTON
NEWHAM GENERAL   L C STEWARD
NORFOLK AND NORWICH   L A J WARD
NORTH DEVON DISTRICT Barnstaple   D F GIBSON,
   P D PILDITCH
NORTH MANCHESTER GENERAL   M R MORGAN
NORTH TEES HEALTH NHS TRUST Stockton-on-
   Tees   P O BENNISON
NORTH TYNESIDE   G M BASS
NORTHAMPTON GENERAL   R L INSTRELL
NORTHERN GENERAL Sheffield   D E R EQUEALL,
   L A SHIPTON
NORTHWICK PARK Harrow   A J ANDREWS

NOTTINGHAM CITY   M J KERRY, C BROWN, J MORTON
OLDCHURCH Romford   G LAKER
PEMBURY Tunbridge Wells   A P AYLING
PETERBOROUGH DISTRICT   J N CHUBB
PILGRIM Boston   M G JOHNSON
PINDERFIELDS GENERAL Wakefield   R W CRESSEY
POOLE GENERAL   E J LLOYD
PORTSMOUTH HOSPITALS NHS
   TRUST   R H MITCHELL
PRINCESS MARGARET Swindon   B M RICHARDS,
   A BUCKNALL
PRINCESS MARINA Northampton   C R GOODLEY
PRINCESS ROYAL Haywards Heath   L D POODHUN
PRINCESS ROYAL Telford   G A CROSSLEY
PRUDHOE Northumberland   M H WHEELWRIGHT
QUEEN ALEXANDRA Portsmouth   P R ELLMORE
QUEEN ELIZABETH Birmingham   J W WOODWARD,
   R G GLEESON, V J F COX
QUEEN ELIZABETH Gateshead   J R PERRY
QUEEN ELIZABETH II Welwyn Garden
   City   G N BUSTARD
QUEEN ELIZABETH King's Lynn   A L HAIG
QUEEN'S MEDICAL CENTRE Nottingham   C TURNER
RADCLIFFE INFIRMARY Oxford   A C McGOWAN
RAMPTON Retford   R A SIMMONS
ROYAL BERKSHIRE Reading   V MULLER, E M JACKSON
ROYAL BOURNEMOUTH GENERAL   K FELTHAM
ROYAL CORNWALL HOSPITAL TRUST
   Truro   D G HOLLANDS, J B SEWELL
ROYAL DEVON AND EXETER (WONFORD)
   Exeter   D J WALFORD
ROYAL EARLSWOOD Redhill   N J COPSEY
ROYAL FREE London   E S BRITT
ROYAL HALLAMSHIRE Sheffield   J A FRYER
ROYAL HAMPSHIRE COUNTY Winchester   N R FLOOD,
   R S CLARKE
ROYAL HULL HOSPITALS NHS TRUST   B S BOWES,
   M P PICKERING
ROYAL LIVERPOOL   S C PRATT
ROYAL LONDON Whitechapel   P J COWELL,
   F C CLARINGBULL
ROYAL MARSDEN London and Surrey   D F BROWN,
   J W SMITH
ROYAL OLDHAM   F D STUART
ROYAL SHREWSBURY   D W JOHNSON
ROYAL SOUTH HAMPSHIRE
   Southampton   G HANCOCKS
ROYAL SURREY COUNTY Guildford   R R WYNNE-
GREEN, R D C STEELE-PERKINS
ROYAL SUSSEX COUNTY Brighton   S C WALLS
ROYAL UNITED Bath   C M ROBERTS
ROYAL VICTORIA INFIRMARY Newcastle upon
   Tyne   A MAUDE, A J PATTERSON
ST ANDREW'S Northampton   J E CAMP
ST ANN'S Poole   K S TIMBRELL
ST BARNABAS' HOSPICE Worthing   J H McCORMACK
ST CHARLES' London   N J ROBERTS
ST CHRISTOPHER'S HOSPICE London   M C GARDNER
ST CLEMENT'S HOSPITAL AND ST ELIZABETH
   HOSPICE Ipswich   J C CASSELTON
ST EBBA'S Epsom   R N T MOORE
ST GEORGE'S Lincoln   J A GREEN
ST GEORGE'S London   I M AINSWORTH-SMITH,
   H A JOHNSON
ST GEORGE'S Stafford   G E O'BRIEN
ST HELEN'S AND KNOWSLEY HOSPITALS
   TRUST   G SPENCER
ST HELIER Carshalton   P W HOLLAND

ST HELIER GENERAL Jersey   M INMAN
ST JAMES'S UNIVERSITY Leeds   P R EVANS, M GASKELL
ST LAWRENCE'S Bodmin   R S MITCHELL
ST LUKE'S HOSPICE Sheffield   J SANKEY
ST MARTIN'S Canterbury   G W P WILTON
ST MARY'S Praed Street London   B A NEWTON
ST NICHOLAS Newcastle upon Tyne   F B ALLEN
ST RICHARD'S Chichester   C A ASHLEY
ST THOMAS' London   M J STEVENS, A M HARLEY
SALFORD MENTAL HEALTH SERVICES (NHS
   TRUST)   A R MIR, N BARNES
SALFORD ROYAL HOSPITALS NHS
   TRUST   M R ATKINSON
SALISBURY GENERAL INFIRMARY   C RENYARD
SHEFFIELD CHILDREN'S   M J KELLAM
SHOTLEY BRIDGE GENERAL Consett   K ALLISON
SOLIHULL DISTRICT   A M BOYD
SOUTH BIRMINGHAM ACUTE UNIT   D WRAPSON
SOUTH CLEVELAND Middlesbrough   P J CARRINGTON
SOUTH DERBYSHIRE MENTAL HEALTH NHS
   TRUST   J P RAFFAY
SOUTH WARWICKSHIRE Warwick   P S KNIGHT
SOUTH WESTERN London   W F BAZELY
SOUTHAMPTON COMMUNITY   A D MACDONALD
SOUTHEND   G L CROOK
SOUTHMEAD Bristol   D C DAVIES, H G WEBB
SOUTHAMPTON UNIVERSITY NHS
   TRUST   P W SPECK
SPRINGFIELD London   E W CARDEN
STAFFORD DISTRICT GENERAL   I S VAUGHAN
STANLEY ROYD Wakefield   C M GARTLAND
STOKE MANDEVILLE Aylesbury   D CRAWLEY,
   N TAYLOR
STOKE-ON-TRENT CITY GENERAL   D J HAWKINS
SUNDERLAND DISTRICT GENERAL   P H WEBB,
   C P A LOCKHART
TICKHILL ROAD Doncaster   J E PALIN
TOLWORTH Surbiton   G D KING
TOOTING BEC London   W F BAZELY
TORBAY Torquay   G S KENDALL, J M PRINGLE
TOWERS Humberstone   L J BUTLER
UNIVERSITY COLLEGE London   T MORLEY
UNIVERSITY Nottingham   D J STOTER, R D BENNETT,
   D R L WHITE, B J WOOD, J E SHEPHERD
WALSGRAVE Coventry   D H ROBINSON, A BEECH
WARLINGHAM PARK Croydon   A A WILSON
WARRINGTON DISTRICT GENERAL   P D MEARS
WATFORD GENERAL   M J CARTER
WELLS ROAD CENTRE Nottingham   G A BUCKLER
WEST CHESHIRE NHS TRUST   J A ROBERTS
WEST DORSET Dorchester   N D TOOTH
WEST MIDDLESEX UNIVERSITY
   Isleworth   P M BESTLEY
WEST PARK Epsom   D B A JOHNSON
WEXHAM PARK Slough   P J HARBORD, R A CHEEK
WHIPPS CROSS London   E J PORTEOUS
WHISTON Prescot   M THOMAS, G SPENCER
WHITTINGTON NHS TRUST   P W A WHELAN
WILLIAM HARVEY Ashford   V E PERRY
WINTERTON Sedgefield   W M GOLIGHTLY
WINWICK Warrington   P G HOUGHTON
WITHAM COURT ESMI UNIT Lincoln   D YOUNG
WITHINGTON Manchester   J F C PERRYMAN,
   J M AUSTERBERRY
WORCESTER ROYAL INFIRMARY   L R D RYDER,
   J M HUGHES
WYCOMBE GENERAL   M N FULLAGAR
YORK DISTRICT   G H WEBSTER

EDUCATIONAL CHAPLAINCIES

This index only lists deans and chaplains, and does not aim to provide a comprehensive list of clergy serving at educational institutions. At institutions with more than one entry the names are listed in order of seniority (or length of service at the institution if seniority is not known). Those institutions which do not currently have Anglican chaplains are not recorded.

General Synod Board of Education: Secretary Mr G Duncan
Church House, Great Smith Street, London SW1P 3NZ
0171–222 9011   Fax 799 2714

Universities

ANGLIA POLYTECHNIC   R H CADMAN, E M PERCY
ASTON   T F PYKE
BATH   V S ROBERTS, B CHAPMAN
BIRMINGHAM   A A GORHAM, H C BENSON
   See also   CENTRAL ENGLAND
BOURNEMOUTH   G H NUTTALL
BRADFORD   M R HARRISON
BRIGHTON   A W N S CANE, G T RIDEOUT
BRISTOL   A V I BERNERS-WILSON, C W BOWLER
   See also   WEST OF ENGLAND
BRUNEL   D I DADSWELL
CAMBRIDGE
   Christ's   M W PERCY
   Churchill   B D SPINKS
   Clare   N SAGOVSKY (Dean), J E E CHARMAN, J B WELLS
   Corpus Christi   R M PRYCE
   Downing   B R L KINSEY
   Emmanuel   J L CADDICK
   Gonville and Caius   J V M STURDY (Dean), J D McDONALD
   Jesus   T D JENKINS (Dean)
   King's   G L PATTISON (Dean), J McLUCKIE
   Magdalene   H E FINLAY
   Newnham   N W S CRANFIELD
   Pembroke   B WATCHORN (Dean)
   Peterhouse   G J WARD (Dean)
   Queens'   B L HEBBLETHWAITE (Dean), J M HOLMES
   St Catharine's   P J LANGHAM
   St John's   A A MACINTOSH (Dean), N I MOIR
   Selwyn   N W S CRANFIELD
   Trinity   A S BROWNE (Dean), A H STEVENS
   Trinity Hall   C M ELLIOTT (Dean), D A J WILMAN
   Wolfson   P A SPENCE
CENTRAL ENGLAND IN BIRMINGHAM   M HARRIS
CENTRAL LANCASHIRE   W E TURNER
CITY   L S A MARSH
COVENTRY   C R KENNEDY
DERBY   D A HESLOP
DURHAM
   Collingwood   B J H de la MARE
   Hatfield   D C GLOVER
   St Aidan's   R D THOMSON
   St Chad's   M P KENT, C W RYLAND
   St Hild and St Bede   R de la BAT SMIT
   St John's   N G EVANS
   St Mary's   M PARKER
   Trevelyan   K ANDERSON
   University   C YEATS
   Van Mildert   K ANDERSON
EAST ANGLIA   D J LLOYD
EAST LONDON   J P RICHARDSON
ESSEX   I M KENWAY
EXETER   J T LAW, D NIXON
GREENWICH   J P H JOHN, D J WALLER
HERTFORDSHIRE   W R de C M TAYLOR, G D BOOKER, S M HALMSHAW
HUDDERSFIELD   J T ALLISON
HULL   A BAILEY
HUMBERSIDE   D S SIMON, D G KENNEDY, J HOBBS
KEELE   G F COOKE
KENT   R W M BOWDER
KINGSTON   K V J HOPKINS, H D SHILSON-THOMAS
LANCASTER   B J W CAVE-BROWN-CAVE, T S EVANS

LEEDS   S J ROBINSON, C BARRETT
LEEDS METROPOLITAN   M P BENWELL   (chaplain designate)
LEICESTER   G TURNOCK
LIVERPOOL   M J CARTLEDGE, E M STOREY
LIVERPOOL JOHN MOORES   R E DICKINSON
LONDON   S G WILLIAMS, C R OWEN
   British Postgraduate Medical Foundation, The
      G L LEGOOD, J M KING
   Charing Cross and Westminster Medical School
      G L LEGOOD, J M KING
   Imperial College of Science, Technology and Medicine
      D G BANNOCKS
   King's   R A BURRIDGE (Dean), T F DITCHFIELD
   London Hospital Medical College, The   G L LEGOOD, J M KING
   London School of Economics and Political Science
      E J WALLER
   London School of Hygiene and Tropical Medicine, The
      G L LEGOOD, J M KING
   Queen Mary and Westfield   D PEEBLES, J KING
   Royal Free Hospital School of Medicine   G L LEGOOD, J M KING
   Royal Holloway and Bedford New   C J COCKSWORTH
   St Bartholomew's Hospital Medical College   G L LEGOOD, J M KING
   St George's Hospital Medical School   G L LEGOOD, J M KING
   School of Oriental and African Studies, The   S G WILLIAMS
   School of Pharmacy, The   C R OWEN
   United Medical and Dental Schools of Guy's and St Thomas's Hospitals   G L LEGOOD, J M KING
   University   S G WILLIAMS
   Wye   D STUART-SMITH
LONDON GUILDHALL   A J MARCETTI, A OSBORN
   See also CITY, EAST LONDON, GREENWICH, MIDDLESEX, NORTH LONDON, SOUTH BANK, THAMES VALLEY, WESTMINSTER
LOUGHBOROUGH   D A HART, S E FIELD
LUTON   R M LILLINGTON
MANCHESTER   A P JOHNSON, K S E OKEKE
MANCHESTER METROPOLITAN   A J SERVANT
MIDDLESEX   M EGGLETON, J M BEER
NEWCASTLE   R C MILLS
NORTHUMBRIA AT NEWCASTLE   I D HOUGHTON, D J WILSON
NORTH LONDON   B K SHIPSIDES
NOTTINGHAM   R G A RIEM
NOTTINGHAM TRENT   D F MYERS, D G CANTRELL
OXFORD
   All Souls   J McMANNERS
   Balliol   H D DUPREE
   Brasenose   G L CARTER
   Christ Church   J H DRURY (Dean), M G St A JACKSON
   Corpus Christi   J D MALTBY
   Exeter   D E MARSHALL
   Hertford   R M CHANTRY
   Jesus   A J MOORE
   Keble   J H DAVIES
   Lady Margaret Hall   A G DOIG
   Linacre   R C MORGAN
   Lincoln   R G GRIFFITH-JONES

Magdalen   J M W SEDGWICK (Dean)
Mansfield   F J L WINFIELD
Merton   M EVERITT
New   S R TUCKER (Dean)
Oriel   N J BIGGAR
Pembroke   J E PLATT
Queen's   P J M SOUTHWELL
St Edmund Hall   G HEGARTY
St Hilda's   B W MOUNTFORD
St Hugh's   L B FOSDIKE
St John's   T J GORRINGE
St Peter's   C M JONES
Somerville   R M CHANTRY
Trinity   T S M WILLIAMS
University   W G D SYKES
Wadham   R H WATTS
Worcester   A J E GREEN
OXFORD BROOKES   D G EVERETT
PLYMOUTH   R S WILLIAMS, C H BENSON, J E DICKER,
   D J STANTON

PORTSMOUTH   A J DORBER
READING   P J JENNER, H A N PLATTS
SALFORD   J H FIFE
SHEFFIELD   C A COLLINS
SHEFFIELD HALLAM   M R GOATER
SOUTHAMPTON   N J COATES
SOUTH BANK   R W MAYO
STAFFORDSHIRE   W G McNAMEE, A L HUGHES
SUNDERLAND   I D HUNTER SMART, C A DICK
SURREY   I St J FISHER
SUSSEX   G R P ASHENDEN, A N ROBINSON
TEESSIDE   C ROWLING
THAMES VALLEY   V A CORY
WARWICK   C M GREGORY
WEST OF ENGLAND   S A N DARLEY
WESTMINSTER   A CLARK
WOLVERHAMPTON   G WYNNE, H J PATTERSON
YORK   J C ROBERTSON

Colleges of Higher Education

This index only includes those establishments known to have Anglican chaplains. It is not intended to be a comprehensive list of all colleges of higher education.

BATH   G R W HALL
BISHOP GROSSETESTE Lincoln   R S EYRE
BOLTON INSTITUTE   C E VANN
BRITISH SCHOOL OF OSTEOPATHY   B SCHUNEMANN
CENTRAL SCHOOL OF SPEACH AND DRAMA
   London   J A OVENDEN
CHELTENHAM AND GLOUCESTER   G A POLLITT,
   F L STEWART-DARLING
CHESTER   S M STARKEY
GRIMSBY   J HOBBS
KING ALFRED'S Winchester   M A BARTON
NORWICH CITY   D K ALEXANDER
RIPON AND YORK ST JOHN   J G HOYLAND,
   D G PATON-WILLIAMS

ROEHAMPTON INSTITUTE   N JOHN
ROYAL ACADEMY OF MUSIC   C R OWEN
ROYAL AGRICULTURAL COLLEGE Cirencester
   R A BOWDEN
ROYAL AIR FORCE Cranwell   H W BEARN
ROYAL COLLEGE OF ART   D G BANNOCKS
ROYAL NAVAL Greenwich   G S HARCOURT
ROYAL NAVAL ENGINEERING   J P AMES
ST MARTIN'S Lancaster   M G SMITH
WEST LONDON INSTITUTE   D WILSON
WESTHILL Birmingham   K J R GODSELL
WORCESTER   M NOTT

Colleges of Further Education

This index only includes those establishments known to have Anglican chaplains. It is not intended to be a comprehensive list of all colleges of further education.

BASINGSTOKE COLLEGE OF TECHNOLOGY
   C M SAVAGE
BATH, CITY OF   A R HAWKINS
BILBOROUGH   E P BAILEY
BISHOP BURTON COLLEGE OF AGRICULTURE
   York   E A CULLING
BLACKBURN   J R CREE
BOLTON   C E VANN
BOSTON   A M PAVEY
BOURNEMOUTH AND POOLE   G H NUTTALL,
   J H S STEVEN, D H R JONES
BRACKNELL   D B TONKINSON
BRADFORD AND ILKLEY COMMUNITY
   M R HARRISON
CANNINGTON COLLEGE   P MARTIN
CITY OF BATH *See* BATH, CITY OF
CITY OF LIVERPOOL COMMUNITY *See* LIVERPOOL
   COMMUNITY, CITY OF
CITY OF WESTMINSTER *See* WESTMINSTER,
   CITY OF
CROYDON   C M KING
DAVENTRY TERTIARY   J W HARGREAVES
DUDLEY COLLEGE OF TECHNOLOGY   M BRAIN
DUNSTABLE   D W KESTERTON
ELMHURST BALLET Camberley   J H G CARTER
EVESHAM   L L BURN, J R N J BOMYER
FARNBOROUGH COLLEGE OF TECHNOLOGY
   P S J GARLAND
FRANKLIN SIXTH FORM   J L RHODES

GRIMSBY   J HOBBS
GUILDFORD COLLEGE OF TECHNOLOGY
   S A BAKER
HALESOWEN   M G CLARKE
HALTON   A HODGE
HARLOW   G R NEAVE
HAVERING   T D HULL
HEREFORD SIXTH FORM   A L LAW
HEREWARD   S F HARDWICK
HULL   R EVELEIGH, S J WALKER
KIRKLEY HALL   W A GOFTON
LEEDS COLLEGE OF BUILDING   S J BROWN
LIVERPOOL, CENTRAL   J S WILLIAMS
LIVERPOOL COMMUNITY, CITY OF   J S WILLIAMS
MANCHESTER COLLEGE OF ARTS AND
   TECHNOLOGY   S TURNER
MERRIST WOOD COLLEGE OF AGRICULTURE
   AND HORTICULTURE   R R ROBINS
NELSON AND COLNE   G S INGRAM
NEW COLLEGE Swindon   D ORMSTON
NORTH EAST WORCESTERSHIRE   D C HELMS,
   M HERBERT
NORTH HERTFORDSHIRE   D J COCKERELL
NORTH WEST LONDON   F B CAPIE
OAKLANDS   P A LOUIS
PENDLETON   A BUTLER
RICHMOND-UPON-THAMES   G A BARBER
ROYAL FOREST OF DEAN   D J F ADDISON
ST BRENDAN'S SIXTH FORM   P A WALL, J N HARRISON

ST MARK AND ST JOHN Plymouth D J CLARKE
SALFORD A CUNNINGHAM
SANDOWN P J PRIGG
SHUTTLEWORTH AGRICULTURAL Bedford
    J A TERRY
SOMERSET COLLEGE OF ARTS AND
    TECHNOLOGY D ROBERTS
SOMERSET COLLEGE OF AGRICULTURE AND
    HORTICULTURE Bridgwater P MARTIN

SOUTH MANCHESTER COMMUNITY D K PRYCE
SUFFOLK T W BROADBENT
TYNEMOUTH D E CANT
WEALD F D JAKEMAN
WESTMINSTER, CITY OF R D De BERRY
WEYMOUTH E LEWIS, M P H STEAR
WORCESTER TECHNICAL P D A COLLINS
WORCESTERSHIRE COLLEGE OF
    AGRICULTURE A J WILLIS

Schools

This index only includes those schools known to have Anglican chaplains. It is not intended to be comprehensive.

ABBERLEY HALL Worcester D F GUTTERIDGE
ABBEY GRANGE Leeds M C DOE
ABINGDON T P LEWIS, A MITRA
ACTON REYNALD Shrewsbury B T SWYNNERTON
AGNES STUART Leeds N P GEORGE
ALDENHAM Herts A M STEAD
ALICE OTTLEY Worcester P J WEDGWOOD
ALLEYN'S FOUNDATION Dulwich J H JONES,
    R M CATTLEY
ALL HALLOWS Rousdon J NEWTON
ARCHBISHOP TENISON GRAMMAR Kennington
    A J REID
ARDINGLY COLLEGE Haywards Heath K I GOSS
ARNOLD Blackpool B DUNN
BANCROFT Essex M J WALKER
BARNARD CASTLE Durham J A MOORE
BEARWOOD COLLEGE Wokingham D L LAWRENCE-
    MARCH
BEDFORD D M STEVENSON, I C BROWNE
BEDGBURY Kent N R GALLAGHER
BEECHWOOD PARK St Albans D J KERR
BENENDEN Kent P G M PRESTNEY
BENNETT MEMORIAL Tunbridge Wells C J S GILL,
    J CAPERON
BERKHAMSTED Hertfordshire P TAIT
BETHANY Kent C J ROOKWOOD
BIRKENHEAD Merseyside S J RIDLEY
BISHOP RAMSEY Pinner A V COLEMAN
BISHOP RAWSTORNE Preston R J BRUNSWICK
BISHOP'S STORTFORD COLLEGE B H TALBOTT
BISHOP WORDSWORTH Salisbury C M CUTHBERTSON
BLOXHAM Oxon D J DUNCANSON
BLUE COAT Birmingham J H D KENKINS
BLUE COAT Nottingham S KRZEMINSKI
BLUE COAT Reading N J BENNETT
BLUE COAT Walsall A J WILLIAMS
BLUNDELL'S Tiverton D H HAMER
BOX HILL Surrey J P HARKIN
BRADFIELD COLLEGE Berks D R MULLINER
BRAMCOTE Notts A N WOODSFORD
BRIGHTON COLLEGE A K BURTT
BRISTOL CATHEDRAL T J WHITE
BROMSGROVE Worcs S M AGNEW
BRUTON Somerset D PARSONS
BRYANSTON Dorset A J DAYNES, A J CLARKE,
    R E A ADAMSON
CANFORD Dorset C JERVIS
CAN SLADE Bolton D R EVANS
CASTERTON Carnforth G A GRUBB
CHAILEY HERITAGE Lewes T GALLETLY
CHARTERHOUSE Godalming S J HARKER, C J O'NEILL
CHELTENHAM COLLEGE G A POLLITT, N G LOWTON,
    P J STONE
CHELTENHAM LADIES' COLLEGE A D BARLOW,
    H R WOOD
CHRIST'S HOSPITAL Horsham G DOBBIE, K POWELL
CLERE Newbury D S CASTLE
CLIFTON COLLEGE Bristol P W DILL, J G W DICKIE
CRANBROOK Kent D COOK
CRANLEIGH Surrey N A T MENTON, A J KEEP
CROFT HOUSE Dorset M A TURNER
DAME ALLAN'S Newcastle J HAZELTON
DAUNTSEY'S Devizes D ROBINSON
DEAN CLOSE Cheltenham D G H YOUNG

DENSTONE COLLEGE Uttoxeter R M D ORAM
DERBY HIGH G O MARSHALL
DOVER COLLEGE Kent D J GILCHRIST
DOVER COLLEGE PREPARATORY C E N DAVIS
DUKE OF YORK'S ROYAL MILITARY Dover
    M A FORRESTER
DURHAM T J E FERNYHOUGH
EASTBOURNE COLLEGE R JOHNSON, C J COMYNS
ELIZABETH COLLEGE Guernsey G J BARRETT
ELLESMERE COLLEGE Shropshire J C VERNON
EMMANUEL Wandsworth E M HILL
EMSCOTE LAWN Warwick R C GARRATT
EPSOM COLLEGE Surrey S L GREEN, B R ROBERTS
ETON COLLEGE Windsor J S WITHERIDGE, D COOPER,
    C M JONES, T D MULLINS
EXETER I H BLYDE
EXETER CATHEDRAL G DAXTER
FELIXSTOWE COLLEGE C A C COOPER
FELSTED Essex C D GRIFFIN
FOREMARKE PREPARATORY N A BAILEY
FRAMLINGHAM COLLEGE Suffolk M C BOOKER,
    R J DIXON
GIGGLESWICK S B TAYLOR
GODOLPHIN Salisbury F C CARPENTER
GORDON'S Woking D H ROBINSON
GRENVILLE Bideford F F SIMON
GRESHAM'S Holt R N MYERSCOUGH
HABERDASHERS' ASKE'S Elstree D M LINDSAY
HAILYBURY COLLEGE Herts J S PULLEN,
    S M BEAUMONT
HALESOWEN COLLEGE M G CLARKE
HAMPTON Middx D C SWARBRIGG
HARLOW TERTIARY COLLEGE G R NEAVE
HARROW Middx J E POWER, P J E JACKSON
HAWTREYS Salisbury J ROUNDHILL
HEATHFIELD Ascot W B PUGH
HEREFORD CATHEDRAL G J MARSH, A C HUTCHINSON
HEREWARD COLLEGE Warks S F HARDWICK
HIGHGATE London P J J KNIGHT
HOLMEWOOD HOUSE Rochester C K CHANNER
HOLY TRINITY Crawley I W NATHANIEL
HURSTPIERPOINT COLLEGE W Sussex B A BOUCHER
HYMERS COLLEGE Hull J J PAGE
IAN RAMSAY Stockton N E WATSON
IPSWICH W WILSON, P M HAMLET
KESWICK Cumbria J T ROOKE
KIMBOLTON Huntingdon B A BEARCROFT,
    A P GOODCHILD
KING EDWARD Surrey R W E MILLINGTON
KING EDWARD'S Birmingham D H RAYNOR
KING EDWARD'S SIXTH FORM COLLEGE Worcs
    M C GOWDEY
KING EDWARD IV Norwich P W BUTCHER
KING'S Bruton W H M CAMERON
KING'S Canterbury J A THACKRAY
KING'S Ely T AMBROSE
KING'S Gloucester J B P J HADFIELD
KING'S Macclesfield R J CRAIG
KING'S Rochester P L F ALLSOP
KING'S PREPARATORY Rochester G J KIRK
KING'S Tynemouth W D MILLER
KING'S Worcester J CHARLES
KING'S COLLEGE Taunton A C SMITH
KING'S COLLEGE Wimbledon R G STEVENS

EDUCATIONAL CHAPLAINCIES

KINGHAM HILL Oxon R L M SHEPTON
LANCING COLLEGE W Sussex I M FORRESTER,
  J W HUNWICKE
LANGLEY Norwich D A J MacPHERSON
LATYMER Hammersmith G IBALL
LAXTON Peterborough A K THOMSON
LEEDS GRAMMAR M B HANSON
LIVERPOOL COLLEGE J R MACAULAY
LORD MAYOR TRELOAR COLLEGE Alton E B PRUEN
LORD WANDSWORTH COLLEGE Basingstoke B KEMP
LOUGHBOROUGH GRAMMAR A J S COX
LUCKLEY OAKFIELD Wokingham J WAKELING
MAGDALEN COLLEGE SCHOOL Oxford
  D J DUNNING, R C de V MARTIN
MALVERN COLLEGE S W LEWIS
MARLBOROUGH COLLEGE L F P GUNNER, D J DALES
MERCHANT TAYLORS' Crosby D A SMITH
MERCHANT TAYLORS' Northwood R D E BOLTON
MILLFIELD Somerset S F BLOXAM-ROSE, E C PHILLIPS-
  SMITH, W M MARSHALL
MILL HILL London P M HUNT
MILTON ABBEY Dorset C W MITCHELL-INNES
MOIRA HOUSE E Sussex G T RIDOUT
MONKTON COMBE Bath G P HERBERT
MORDON COLLEGE Blackheath R SAUNDERS
NEW HALL Essex R E TURNER
NORTH FORELAND LODGE Basingstoke R W POLITT
NORTHAMPTONSHIRE GRAMMAR S J TROTT
OAKHAM Leicester J N DARRALL
OLD SWINFORD HOSPITAL Worcester R H DARROCH
ORWELL PARK Ipswich G L GRANT
OSWESTRY A J B KEITH
OUNDLE Peterborough M G HONEYBALL, A K THOMSON,
  A C V ALDOUS
OXLEY PARKER Colchester J F BLORE
PANGBOURNE COLLEGE Berks J D R SPRIGGS
PIERREPONT Guildford J P WHITTAKER
PLYMOUTH COLLEGE A P ARNOLD
POCKLINGTON York M A SMITH
PORTSMOUTH GRAMMAR J M GRINDELL
PREBENDAL Chichester D NASON
PRESTFELDE Shrewsbury J J WADDINGTON-FEATHER
PURBECK Wareham A C ASHCROFT
QUAINTON HALL Harrow R H M FLETCHER
QUEEN ANNE'S Reading T P NICHOLSON
QUEEN ELIZABETH'S HOSPITAL Bristol R H CHUBB
QUEEN ETHELBURGA'S COLLEGE York S J TALBOTT
QUEEN MARGARET'S York G D HARRIS, R L OWEN
QUEEN MARY'S Ripon R B McFADDEN
RADLEY COLLEGE Oxon D S COULTON, P F BOYDEN
RANBY HOUSE Notts R F THEODOSIUS
REED'S Surrey B E CLOSE
REIGATE GRAMMAR M J H FOX
RENDCOMB Cirencester P J SUDBURY
REPTON Derby R L SHORT
RICHARD HUISH COLLEGE J T TYLER
RIDDLESWORTH HALL Norwich A V HEDGES
RISHWORTH W Yorkshire P FORD
RODNEY Notts D J BARTLETT
ROSSALL Fleetwood A D T RICHARDS
ROYAL GRAMMAR Lancaster J A HEMMINGS
ROYAL HOSPITAL Ipswich K S McCORMACK
ROYAL MASONIC FOR GIRLS Rickmansworth
  D F THOMPSON
ROYAL RUSSELL Croydon A H WOODHEAD
ROYAL Bath J KNOTT
ROYAL WOLVERHAMPTON P C ATKINSON
RUGBY Warks K LANYON JONES
ST AIDAN'S Harrogate W A WILBY
ST ALBANS E POLOMSKI
ST ALBANS FOR GIRLS M A McLEN
ST ANDREW'S Croydon P D HENDRY
ST AUBYN'S Tiverton I H BARHAM
ST AUGUSTINE'S Taunton D ROBERTS
ST BEDE'S Cambridge S C HOWARD
ST BEDE'S ECUMENUCAL Reigate J P SCOTT
ST BEES Cumbria P R BRYAN
ST BRANDON'S Bristol A J HALL
ST CATHERINE'S Bramley E M V BOUGHTON

ST DUNSTAN'S ABBEY Exeter G D CRYER
ST EDMUND'S Canterbury R H ELLIS
ST EDWARD'S Oxford D S WIPPELL, A D G WRIGHT
ST FELIX Suffolk H V EDWARDS, A K E SORENSEN
ST FRANCIS XAVIER N Yorkshire C N H WHITE
ST GEORGE'S Gravesend E M R WALKER
ST GEORGE'S Herts N P RICH
ST GEORGE'S CHOIR Windsor T J HARVEY
ST HILDA'S N Yorkshire J P PAYNE, B WILLIAMS
ST HILDA'S PRIORY N Yorkshire D R WISE
ST JAMES AND THE ABBEY Worcs C N H ATTWOOD
ST JOHN'S Leatherhead N GOSNELL
ST JOHN'S COLLEGE SCHOOL Cambridge
  O R SPENCER-THOMAS
ST LAWRENCE COLLEGE Ramsgate D D R BLACKWALL,
  S GOLDING, D J PEAT
ST MARGARET'S Exeter I H BLYDE
ST MARGARET'S Herts J C SYKES
ST MARGARET'S HIGH Liverpool K L MILLER
ST MARY'S Calne A G WOODS, M T B EVANS
ST MARY'S Cheshunt L S DRAKE
ST MARY'S Reigate D CLARKE
ST MARY'S Wantage R F CLAYTON-JONES
ST MARY AND ST ANNE Abbots Bromley D F COOMBES,
  J R HOUGHTON
ST MARY'S HALL Brighton D C PAIN
ST OLAVE'S Orpington H P C BROADBENT
ST OLAVE' York R HARGREAVES
ST PAUL'S Barnes A H MEAD, S E YOUNG
ST PAUL'S FOR GIRLS Hammersmith A FORD
ST PETER'S York S C HARVEY, L C CARBERRY
ST PETER'S COLLEGIATE Wolverhampton C CHAPMAN
ST PETER'S HIGH Exeter D JAMES, A J CLARKE
ST PIER'S HOSPITAL Lingfield D C EDWARDS
ST SWITHUN'S Winchester D C BINDON
SCARBOROUGH COLLEGE A J RICHARDSON
SEDBERGH Cumbria R G LAIRD
SEVENOAKS Kent N N HENSHAW, G A R SWANNELL
SHERBORNE Dorset C W M AITKEN, J DALY
SHIPLAKE COLLEGE Henley-on-Thames P V PARKER
SHREWSBURY G J WILLIAMS
SMALLWOOD MANOR Uttoxeter C J CANN
SOLIHULL W Midlands P H WRENN
STAMFORD Lincs M R RUFF
STANCLIFFE HALL Derbys M O DODD
STOCKPORT GRAMMAR M J PARKER, S I D WHITE
STOWE Bucks T M HASTIE-SMITH, R B JACKSON
SUMMER FIELDS Oxon B S A GADD
TALBOT HEATH Bournemouth K J RANDALL
TAUNTON G D EVANS
TONBRIDGE Kent J S BELL, T J E FERNEYHOUGH
TRENT Nottingham T R HAGGIS
TWYFORD Winchester W G B HOLLAND
UPPER CHINE Isle of Wight A SWANBOROUGH
UPPINGHAM Leics A J MEGAHEY
WARMINSTER D A GRIGOR, P N RAPSEY
WARWICK T H MORDECAI
WELBECK COLLEGE Notts F T BEECH
WELLINGBOROUGH B T LYONS
WELLINGTON Somerset J P HELLIER
WELLINGTON COLLEGE Berks D N OUTRAM
WELLS CATHEDRAL P S HOGG
WEST BUCKLAND Barnstaple A M KETTLE
WEST HEATH Sevenoaks G A R SWANNELL
WESTMINSTER R E BALLARD
WESTONBIRT Glos P DIXON
WEYDON Farnham J D A ADAMS
WHITGIFT Croydon K V G SMITH
WILSON'S Surrey D C JEFFERSON
WINCHESTER COLLEGE R G A FERGUSON, J D SMITH,
  N C A VON MALAISE
WINCHESTER HOUSE Northants R H DAVIS
WOODBRIDGE Suffolk M E PERCIVAL
WORKSOP COLLEGE C R FREY, P M KONIG
WREKIN Shropshire W L JONES
WROXALL ABBEY Warwick T J JOHNSON
WYCOMBE ABBEY High Wycombe R J WARDEN
WYCLIFFE COLLEGE Glos L D FYSH
YORK COLLEGE FOR GIRLS A C HODGE

THEOLOGICAL COLLEGES AND COURSES

This index includes the name of the principal or warden and the names of staff members who are Anglican clergy and whose appointments are at least half-time.

Theological Colleges

Church of Ireland Theological College Braemor Park, Dublin 14, Republic of Ireland
Tel: 00 353 1 4923506   Fax: 4923082
PRIN J R BARTLETT   VICE-PRIN W J MARSHALL
TUTORS/LECTS J J MARSDEN, T W GORDON,
J M YOUNG
College of the Resurrection Stocksbank Road, Mirfield, West Yorkshire WF14 0BW
Tel: (01924) 490441   Fax: 492738
PRIN D J LANE   VICE-PRIN G GUIVER CR
DIR STUDIES P ALLAN CR   TUTORS/LECTS
M SELBY, J GRIBBEN CR
Cranmer Hall St John's College, Durham DH1 3RJ
Tel: Durham (0191) 3743500   Fax: 3743573
PRIN *St John's* D V DAY[1]   WARDEN *Cranmer Hall*
J L PRITCHARD
DIR PAST STUDIES A M WHITE
TUTORS/LECTS M R VASEY, R N INNES
Oak Hill Theological College Chase Side, Southgate, London N14 4PS
Tel: (0181) 4490467   Fax: 441599
PRIN G F BRIDGER   VICE-PRIN
R W HEINZE   DEAN G M BUTTERWORTH
ACADEMIC REGISTRAR A BUTLER   TUTORS/LECTS
G M ABBOTT, R A HINES, P D A WESTON, M HANSEN,
H C HENDRY
The Queen's College at Birmingham Somerset Road, Edgbaston, Birmingham, B15 2QH
Tel: Birmingham (0121) 4541527   Fax: 4548171
PRIN P T FISHER   TUTORS D J BRYAN, A J JOYCE,
D J KENNEDY
Ridley Hall Cambridge, CB3 9HG
Tel: Cambridge (01223) 353040   Fax: 301287
PRIN G A CRAY   VICE-PRIN J S BEGBIE
DIR STUDIES M B THOMPSON
DIR PAST STUDIES A M E OSMASTON
Ripon College Cuddesdon Cuddesdon, Oxford OX44 9EX
Tel: Oxford (01865) 874427 or 874595 or 874404
PRIN J H GARTON   VICE-PRIN B CASTLE
TUTORS/LECTS A LE GRYS, M CHAPMAN
St Deiniol's Library Hawarden, Deeside, Clwyd CH5 3DF
Tel: Chester (01244) 532350
WARDEN P J JAGGER   SUB-WARDEN R F BUXTON
St John's College Bramcote, Nottingham NG9 3DS
Tel: Nottingham (0115) 925 1114   Fax: 9436438
PRIN J E GOLDINGAY   DIR STUDIES G A COOPER
TUTORS/LECTS J R BOWEN, A F CHATFIELD,
C E HART, J HENDERSON, D M MUIR, S J WALTON
St Michael and All Angels' College 54 Cardiff Road, Llandaff, Cardiff, CF5 2YJ
Tel: (01222) 563379
WARDEN J H L ROWLANDS   SUB-WARDEN
R M HARPER
DIR PAST STUDIES A JONES   TUTOR R A SPENCER
St Stephen's House 16 Marston Street, Oxford, OX4 1JX
Tel: Oxford (01865) 247874   Fax: 794338
PRIN *Vacant*   VICE-PRIN A BURNHAM
DIR STUDIES D G MOSS
Theological Institute of the Scottish Episcopal Church
21 Inverlieth Terrace, Edinburgh EH3 5NS
Tel: Edinburgh (0131) 343 2038   Fax: 315 3754
PRIN R A NIXON   DIR STUDIES
M T BONE   PASTORAL DIR I R JONES
ASST DIR G GOULDING, I PATON, M KESTON
Trinity College Stoke Hill, Bristol BS9 1JP
Tel: Bristol (0117) 968 2803
PRIN D K GILLETT   VICE-PRIN J NOLLAND
DIR STUDIES D J E ATTWOOD
TUTORS/LECTS P P JENSON, R H PESKETT,
P J ROBERTS, S M ROSE
Westcott House Jesus Lane, Cambridge CB5 8BP
Tel: Cambridge (01223) 350074   Fax: 301512
PRIN M G V ROBERTS   VICE-PRIN and DIR STUDIES
A K BERGQUIST
Wycliffe Hall 54 Banbury Road, Oxford OX2 6PW
Tel: Oxford (01865) 274200   Fax: 274215
PRIN R T FRANCE   VICE-PRIN W G CHALLIS
SEN TUTOR P J M SOUTHWELL
TUTORS/LECTS V M SINTON, G S TOMLIN,
D WENHAM, C J HEADLEY

Part-Time Courses

Carlisle Diocesan Training Institute Church House, West Walls, Carlisle, Cumbria CA3 8UE
Tel: Carlisle (01228) 22573
PRIN M S LANGLEY   TUTOR P J PIKE
East Anglian Ministerial Training Course EAMTC Office, Westcott House, Jesus Lane, Cambridge CB5 8BP
Tel: Cambridge (01223) 322633   Fax: 301512
PRIN J D TETLEY   VICE-PRIN J B MYNORS
DIR STUDIES A J TODD   TUTOR R KEELEY
East Midlands Ministry Training Course Department of Adult Education, The University, Nottingham, NG7 2RD
Tel: Nottingham (0115) 951 4854 or 951 4855
PRIN S F PARSONS   VICE-PRIN M J TAYLOR
North East Ordination Course Carter House, Pelaw Leazes Lane, Durham DH1 1TB
Tel: Durham (0191) 3848317   Fax: 3847529
PRIN T PITT   DIR STUDIES R JONES
DIR PRACTICAL THEOLOGY P JONES
Northern Ordination Course Luther King House, Brighton Grove, Rusholme, Manchester M14 5JP
Tel: Manchester (0161) 2256668   Fax: 2489201
PRIN M J WILLIAMS   DIR STUDIES
M M PARRY   DIR PAST STUDIES M TUNNICLIFFE
TUTORS C MCMULLEN, K CARVELEY
North Thames Ministerial Training Course Chase Side, Southgate, London N14 4PS
Tel: (0181) 3649442   Fax: 3648889
PRIN T M THORNTON   VICE-PRIN R A HINES
LONDON DIOCESAN CO-ORDINATOR R T SIMPSON
CHELMSFORD DIOCESAN CO-ORDINATOR
C J TRAVERS
St Albans and Oxford Ministry Course Church House, North Hinksey, Oxford OX2 0NB
Tel: Oxford (01865) 244566/790084
PRIN V N H STRUDWICK   ASSOC PRIN
G V GILLARD   DIR STUDIES S MOYISE[2]
The South East Institute for Theological Education Deanery Gate, The Precinct, Rochester, Kent ME1 1SJ and 27 Blackfriars Road, London SE1 8NY
Tel: (0171) 9284793
JOINT PRINCIPALS M J BADDELEY
A AMOS   COURSE TUTOR J GLEDHILL
SOUTHWARK   TUTOR G M HESKINS
Southern Training Scheme for Christian Ministry 19 The Close, Salisbury, SP1 2EE
Tel: Salisbury (01722) 412996
PRIN J J FULLER   VICE-PRIN M B CRAMERI
DIR STUDIES J CLARK
TUTOR A HALLIWELL
South West Ministry Training Course SWMTC Office, The Whisperings, Petherwin Gate, North Petherwin, Launceston, Cornwall PL15 8LW
Tel and Fax: (01566) 785545
PRIN D J P HEWLETT   TUTORS M CARTER,
G WATSON
West Midlands Ministerial Training Course The Queen's College, Somerset Road, Edgbaston, Birmingham B15 2QH
Tel: Birmingham (0121) 454 8597
PRIN C LE MOIGNAN[3]   TUTOR
C WORSLEY   TUTOR J L HUGHES
West of England Ministerial Training Course 7c College Green, Gloucester GL1 2LX
Tel and Fax: Gloucester (01452) 300494
PRIN R CLUTTERBUCK[4]   VICE-PRIN
J F JONES   DIR STUDIES M DAVIES[5]

Pre-Theological Training Courses

Aston Training Scheme Christ Church, Church Square, Oldbury, West Midlands B69 4DY
Tel: (0121) 5442227   Fax: 5528326
PRIN D R SPILLER   VICE-PRIN P HAMMERSLEY

[1] Mr Day is a lay person.
[2] Dr Moyise is a lay person.
[3] Dr Le Moignan is a Methodist minister.
[4] Dr Clutterbuck is a Methodist.
[5] Dr Davies is a Roman Catholic lay person.

BISHOPS OF ANGLICAN DIOCESES OVERSEAS

AUSTRALIA

PROVINCE OF NEW SOUTH WALES

Armidale
Peter Chiswell
Bishopscourt, PO Box 198,
Armidale, NSW 2350, Australia

Bathurst
Bruce W Wilson
Bishopscourt, PO Box 23,
Bathurst, NSW 2795, Australia

Canberra and
Goulburn
G V Browning
The Anglican Registry, GPO Box
1981, Canberra, ACT 2601
Australia

(Assistant)
Richard Randerson
address as above

Grafton
Bruce A Schultz
Bishopsholme, 37 Victoria Street,
Grafton, NSW 2460, Australia

Newcastle
Roger A Herft
Bishopscourt, Brown Street,
Newcastle, NSW 2300,
Australia

Riverina
Bruce Q Clark
Bishop's Lodge, Box 10, PO,
Narrandera, NSW 2700,
Australia

Sydney
(Archbishop)
R Harry Goodhew
Box Q190, Queen Victoria PO,
Sydney NSW 2000, Australia

(Assistants)
Ray Smith
(Liverpool-Bankstown)
c/o Box Q190, Queen Victoria PO Sydney,
NSW 2000, Australia

Paul W Barnett
(Bishop of North Sydney)
229 Fullers Road,
Chatswood, NSW 2067,
Australia

Dr Brian King
(Parramatta)
St John's Building,
191 Church Street, Parramatta,
NSW 2150, Australia

Peter R Watson
(South Sydney)
Box Q190, Queen Victoria PO,
Sydney NSW 2000, Australia

Dr Reginald J Piper,
(Wollongong)
74 Church Street,
Wollongong 2500, Australia

PROVINCE OF QUEENSLAND

Brisbane
(Archbishop)
Peter J Hollingworth
Bishopsbourne, Box 421,
GPO, Brisbane 4001,
Queensland, Australia

(Assistants)
John A Noble
St Martin's House, GPO Box 421,
Brisbane QLD 4001, Australia

Ron J C Williams
GPO Box 421, Brisbane, Australia

Clyde M Wood
PO Box 2600, Toowomba,
Queensland 4350, Australia

Carpentaria
Anthony F B Hall-Matthews
PO Box 180, Earlville,
Queensland 4871, Australia

North
Queensland
H John Lewis
Diocesan Registry, Box 1244,
Townsville, North Queensland 4810,
Australia

(Assistants)
Ian C Stuart
PO Box 110, Earlville,
Queensland 4870, Australia

Arthur A Malcolm
Bishop's House, 177 Smith Street,
Yarrabah, North Queensland 4871,
Australia

Northern
Territory
Richard F Appleby
Bishop's House, PO Box 39352,
Winnellie, NT 0820, Australia

Rockhampton
George A Hearn
Lis Escop, PO Box 116
Rockhampton, Queensland 4700
Australia

PROVINCE OF SOUTH AUSTRALIA

Adelaide
(Archbishop)
Ian G C George
Bishop's Court, 45 Palmer Place,
N Adelaide 5006, S Australia

(Assistant)
Stuart M Smith
GPO 2667, Adelaide 5001,
S Australia

The Murray
Graham H Walden
PO Box 394, Murray Bridge,
S Australia 5253

Willochra
David H McCall
Bishop's House, PO Box 96,
Gladstone, S Australia 5473

PROVINCE OF VICTORIA

Ballarat
David Silk
PO Box 89, Ballarat,
Victoria 3350, Australia

Bendigo
Vacant
PO Box 144, Bendigo,
Victoria 3550, Australia

Gippsland
Arthur Jones
PO Box 28, Sale,
Victoria 3850, Australia

Melbourne
(Archbishop
Primate)
Keith Rayner
Bishopscourt, 120 Clarendon St,
Melbourne 3002, Victoria,
Australia

(Assistants)
Andrew St John
(Bishop in Geelong)
The Bishop's House,
364 Shannon Ave, Newtown,
Victoria 3220, Australia

John W Wilson
St Paul's Cathedral Building,
Flinders Lane, Melbourne 3000,
Victoria, Australia

Andrew Curnow
(address as above)

James A Grant
(address as above)

John C Stewart
(address as above)

Wangaratta
Paul Richardson
PO Box 457, Wangaratta 3677,
Victoria, Australia

PROVINCE OF WESTERN AUSTRALIA

Bunbury
Hamish T Jamieson
Bishopscourt, PO Box 15, Bunbury,
6230 W Australia

North West
Australia
Anthony Howard Nicholls
PO Box 140, Geraldton,
W Australia 6530

(Assistant)
Bernard R Buckland
(Bishop for Kimberleys)
PO Box 158, Broome 6725,
W Australia

Perth
(Archbishop)
Peter F Carnley
GPO Box W2067, Perth 6001
W Australia

(Assistants)
Philip Huggins,
GPO Box W2067, Perth,
W Australia 6001

David O Murray
26 Queens Street, Freemantle,
W Australia 6160

Brian G Farran
(Goldfields Region)
PO Box 439, Kalgoorlie 6430
W Australia

DIOCESE OF TASMANIA

Tasmania
Phillip K Newell
GPO Box 7484, Hobart,
Tasmania 7001, Australia

(Assistant)
Ronald F Stone
address as above

BRAZIL

Brasilia	Almir Dos Santos Caixa Postal 00515, Cep 70359-970, Brasilia, DF, Brazil
Central Brazil	Sydney A Ruiz Av Rio Branco 277/907, Cinelandia, Rio de Janeiro RJ 20047-900, Brazil
Northern Brazil	Clovis E Rodrigues Caixa Postal 04704, Cep 51012-970, Recife, PE Brazil
Pelotas	Luiz O Prado Caixa Postal 791, Cep 96001-970, Pelotas, RS, Brazil
Sao Paulo (Primate)	Glauco Soares de Lima Rua Elias Zarzur 1239, 04736-002 Sao Paulo, SP Brazil
Southern Brazil	Claudio V S Gastal Caixa Postal 11504, Cep 91720-0150, Porto Alegre, RS, Brazil
South Western Brazil	Jubal Pereira Neves Caixa Postal 98, Cep 97001-970, Santa Maria, RS, Brazil

BURMA *see* MYANMAR

BURUNDI

Bujumbura	Pie Ntukamazina BP 1300, Bujumbura, Burundi
Buye	Samuel Ndayisenga Eglise Episcopale du Buye, BP 94, Ngozi, Burundi
Gitega	Jean Nduwayo BP 23, Gitega, Burundi
Matana (Archbishop)	Samuel Sindamuka BP 1300, Buja, Bujumbura, Burundi

CANADA

Primate of Canada	Michael G Peers 600 Jarvis Street, Toronto, ON M4Y 2J6, Canada

PROVINCE OF BRITISH COLUMBIA

British Columbia	R Barry Jenks Bishop's Close, 912 Vancouver Street, Victoria BC V8V 3V7, Canada
Caledonia	John E Hannen PO Box 278, Prince Rupert, BC V8J 3P6, Canada
Cariboo	James D Cruikshank 5-618 Tranquille Road, Kamloops, BC V2B 3H6, Canada
Kootenay (Archbishop) (Metropolitan of the Province of British Columbia)	David P Crawley 1876 Richter Street, Kelowna BC V1Y 2M9, Canada
New Westminster	Michael C Ingham Suite 302, 814 Richards Street, Vancouver, BC V6B 3A7, Canada
Yukon	Terrence O Buckle PO Box 4247, Whitehorse, Yukon, Y1A 3T3, Canada

PROVINCE OF CANADA

Central Newfoundland	Edward Marsh 34 Fraser Road, Gander, NF A1V 2E8, Canada
Eastern Newfoundland and Labrador	Donald F Harvey 19 King's Bridge Rd, St John's, NF A1C 3K4, Canada

Fredericton	George C Lemmon 115 Church Street, Fredericton, NB E3B 4C8, Canada
Montreal	Andrew Hutchinson 1444 Union Avenue, Montreal, PQ H3A 2B8, Canada
Nova Scotia	Arthur G Peters 5732 College Street, Halifax, NS B3H 1X3, Canada
(Suffragan)	Frederick J Hiltz (address as above)
Quebec	Bruce Stavert 31 rue des Jardins, Quebec, PQ G1R 4L6, Canada
Western Newfoundland (Archbishop) (Metropolitan of the Province of Canada)	S Stewart Payne 25 Main St, Corner Brook NF A2H 1C2, Canada

PROVINCE OF ONTARIO

Algoma	Ronald C Ferris PO Box 1168, 619 Wellington St E, Sault Ste Marie, ON P6A 5N7, Canada
Huron (Archbishop) (Metropolitan of the Province of Ontario)	Percy O'Driscoll 4-220 Dundas Street, London, ON N6A 1H3, Canada
(Suffragans)	C Robert Townshend (address as above)
	J Peck (address as above)
Moosonee	Caleb J Lawrence Box 841, Schumacher, ON P0N 1G0, Canada
Niagara	Walter G Asbil 67 Victoria Avenue S, Hamilton, ON L8N 2S8 Canada
Ontario	Dr Peter Mason The Diocesan Centre 90 Johnson Street, Kingston ON K7L 1XL, Canada
Ottawa	John A Baycroft 71 Bronson Avenue, Ottawa, ON K1R 6G6, Canada
Toronto	Terence Finlay 135 Adelaide Street East, Toronto, ON MSC 1L8, Canada
(Suffragans)	Douglas Blackwell 300 Dundas Street West, Whitby, ON L1N 2M5, Canada
	J Taylor Pryce Aurora Conference Centre 162 St John's Sideroad West, Aurora, ON L4G 3G8, Canada
	Michael H H Bedford-Jones St Paul's, L'Aoreaux, 3333 Finch Ave East, Scarborough, ON M1W 2R9, Canada
	Victoria Matthews PO Box 74510, Mississauga, ON L5H 4J6, Canada

PROVINCE OF RUPERT'S LAND

The Arctic	Christopher Williams PO Box 164, Iqaluit, NWT X0A 0H0, Canada
(Suffragan)	Vacant (address as above)
Athabasca	John R Clarke Box 6868, Peace River, AB T8S 1S6, Canada
Brandon	Malcolm A W Harding 341 13th Street, Brandon, MB R7A 4P8, Canada
Calgary (Archbishop) (Metropolitan of the Province of Rupert's Land)	John B Curtis 3015 Glencoe Road SW, Calgary, AB T2S 2L9, Canada

(Assistant)	Gary F Woolsey (address as above)
Edmonton	Kenneth L Genge 10033 84th Avenue, Edmonton, AB T6E 2G6, Canada
Keewatin	T W R Collings 915 Ottawa St Keewatin, ON P0X 1C0, Canada
(Suffragan)	Gordon W Beardy General Delivery, Big Trout Lake, ON P0V 1G0, Canada
Qu'Appelle	Eric Bays 1501 College Ave, Regina, SK S4P 1B8, Canada
Rupert's Land	Patrick V Lee 935 Nesbitt Bay, Winnipeg, MB R3T 1W6, Canada
Saskatchewan	J Anthony Burton Box 1088, Prince Albert, SK S6V 5S6, Canada
(Suffragan)	C J Arthurson Box 96, Lac La Ronge, Saskatchewan, S0J 1L0, Canada
Saskatoon	Thomas O Morgan PO Box 1965, Saskatoon SK S7K 3S5, Canada

CENTRAL AFRICA

Botswana (Archbishop)	Walter P K Makhulu PO Box 769, Gaborone, Botswana
Central Zambia	Clement W Hlanya-Shaba PO Box 70172, Ndola, Zambia
Central Zimbabwe	Jonathan Siyachitema PO Box 25, Gweru, Zimbabwe
Harare	R Peter Hatendi Bishop's Mount, PO UA7, Harare, Zimbabwe
Lake Malawi	Peter N Nyanja PO Box 30349, Lilongwe 3, Malawi
Lusaka	Stephen Mumba Bishop's Lodge, PO Box 30183 Lusaka, Zambia
Manicaland	Elijah M Masuko 115 Main St, Mutare, Zimbabwe
Matabeleland	Theophilus T Naledi PO Box 2422, Bulawayo, Zimbabwe
Northern Zambia	Bernard Malango PO Box 20173, Kitwe, Zambia
Southern Malawi	Nathaniel B Aipa PO Box Chilema, Zomba, Malawi

CEYLON (SRI LANKA)

Colombo	Kenneth M J Fernando Bishop's House 358/1 Bauddhaloka Mawatha, Colombo 7, Sri Lanka
Kurunagala	Andrew Kumarage Bishop's House, Kandy Road, Kurunagala, Sri Lanka

INDIAN OCEAN

Antananarivo (Archbishop)	Remi Rabenirina Eveche Anglican, Ambohimanoro, Antananarivo, Madagascar
Antsiranana	Keith J Benzies Eveche Anglican, BP 278, Antsiranana, Madagascar
Mahajanga	Jean-Claude Andrianjafimanana BP 169, Mahajanga 401, Madagascar
Mauritius	Rex Donat Bishop's House, Phoenix, Mauritius
Seychelles	French Chang-Him PO Box 44, Victoria, Mahe, Seychelles
Toamasina	Donald Westwood Smith Eveche Anglican, BP 531, Toamasina 501, Madagascar

JAPAN

Chubu	Samuel Wataru Hoyo 1-47 Yamawaki-cho, Showa-ku, Nagoya 466, Japan
Hokkaido	Augustine Hideaki Amagi Kita 15 jo, 20 Nishi 5-chome, Kita-ku, Sapporo 001, Japan
Kita Kanto (Archbishop)	James Takashi Yashiro 2-172 Sakuragi-cho, Omiya-shi 331, Japan
Kobe	John Junichiro Furumoto 5-11-1 Shimoyamate Dori, Chuo-ku, Kobe 650, Japan
Kyoto	Barnabas Mutsuji Moto Shimotachiuri-agaru, Karasumadori, Kamikyo-ku, Kyoto 602, Japan
Kyushu	Joseph Noriaki Iida 2-9-22 Kusagae, Chuo-ku, Fukuoka 810, Japan
Okinawa	Paul Saneaki Nakamura 101 Aza Yoshihara, Chatan-cho, Okinawa 90401, Japan
Osaka	Augustine Koichi Takano 2-1-8 Matsuzaki-cho Abeno-ku, Osaka 545, Japan
Tohoku	William Tatsuo Murakami 2-13-15 Kokubu-cho, Aoba-ku, Sendai 980, Japan
Tokyo	John Makoto Takeda 3-6-18 Shiba-koen, Minato-ku Tokyo 105, Japan
Yokohama	Raphael Shiro Kajiwara 14-57 Mitsusawa Shimo-cho Kanagawa-ku, Yokohama 221, Japan

JERUSALEM AND THE MIDDLE EAST

Cyprus and the Gulf (Bishop *in*)	Vacant 2 Grigori Afxentiou Street, PO Box 2075, Nicosia, Cyprus
Egypt (Bishop *in*)	Ghais A El-Malik Diocesan Office, PO Box 87 Zamalek, Cairo, Egypt
Iran (Bishop *in*)	Iraj Mottahedeh PO Box 135, Postal Code 81465 Isfahan, Iran
Jerusalem (Bishop *in*)(Primate)	Samir Kafity St George's Close, PO Box 1248 Jerusalem 91019, Israel

KENYA

Butere	Horace Etemesi PO Box 54, Butere, Kenya
Eldoret	Stephen Kewasis Nyorsok PO Box 3404, Eldoret, Kenya
Embu	Moses Njue PO Box 189, Embu, Kenya
Kajiado	Vacant PO Box 21, Kajido, Kenya
Katakwa	Eliud O Okiring PO Box 68, Amagoro, Kenya
Kirinyaga	David M Gitari PO Box 95, Kutus, Kenya
(Assistant)	Andrew Adano PO Box 51, Marsabit, Kenya
Kitui	Benjamin N P Nzimbi PO Box 282, Machakos, Kenya
Machakos	Vacant PO Box 282, Machakos, Kenya
Maseno North	Vacant PO Box 416, Kakamega, Kenya
Maseno South	Francis Mwayi-Abiero PO Box 114, Kisumu, Kenya
Maseno West	Joseph O Wasonga PO Box 793, Siaya, Kenya
Mombasa	Julius Robert PO Box 80072, Mombasa, Kenya
Mt Kenya Central	Julius Gatambo Guchuche PO Box 121, Murang'a, Kenya
Mt Kenya South	George M Njuguna PO Box 23031, Lower Kabete, Kenya
Mt Kenya West	Alfred Chipman PO Box 229, Nyeri, Kenya
Mumias	William Wesa PO Box 213, Mumias, Kenya
Nairobi	Vacant PO Box 40502, Nairobi, Kenya

Nambale	Josiah Were PO Box 4, Nambale, Kenya
Southern Nyanza	Haggai Nyang' PO Box 7, Homa Bay, Kenya
Taita Taveta	Samson Mwaluda PO Box 75, Voi, Kenya

KOREA

Pusan	Bundo Chae Hon Kim PO Box 103, Tongrae, Pusan, 607-061, Korea
Seoul	Matthew C Chung 3 Chong-dong, Chung-ku, Seoul 100-120, Korea
Taejon (Primate)	Paul Hwan Yoon PO Box 22, Taejon 300-600, Korea

MELANESIA

Central Melanesia (Archbishop)	Ellison L Pogo Archbishop's House, PO Box 19, Honiara, Solomon Islands
Hanuato'o	James Mason c/o PO Kirakira, Makira/Ulawa Province, Solomon Islands
Malaita	Vacant Bishop's House, PO Box 7, Auki, Malaita, Solomon Islands
North Vanuatu	Vacant
Temotu	Lazarus S Munamua Bishop's House, Luesalo, Lata, Santa Cruz, Solomon Islands
Vanuatu	Michael H Tavoa Bishop's House, PO Box 238, Luganville, Santo, Vanuatu
Ysabel	Walter Siba Bishop's House, PO Box 6, Buala, Jejevo, Santa Ysabel, Solomon Islands

MEXICO

Cuernavaca (Primate)	Jose G Saucedo Apartado Postal 192, Admon 4, CP 62431 Cuernavaca, Morelos, Mexico
(Co-Adjutor)	Martiniano Garcia-Montiel address as above
Mexico	Sergio Carranza-Gomez Ave San Jeronimo 117, Col S Angel, Deleg A Obregon 01000, Mexico DF
Northern Mexico	German Martinez-Marquez Acatlan Simon Bolivar 2005 Nte, Colonia Mitras Centro, 64460 Monterrey, NL, Mexico
South Eastern Mexico	Claro Huerta-Ramos Avenue de Las Americas, 73 Col Aguacatal 91130, Jalapa, Veracruz, Mexico
Western Mexico	Samuel Espinoza-Venegas Apartado 2-366, CP44280, 44100 Guadalajara, Jalisco, Mexico

MYANMAR (formerly BURMA)

Hpa-an	Daniel Hoi Kyin Bishopscourt, Cathedral of St Peter, Bishop Gone, Hpa-an, Kayin State, Myanmar
Mandalay	Andrew Hla Aung Bishopscourt, 22nd Street C Rd (between 85-86 Rd), Mandalay, Myanmar
Myitkyina	John Shan Lum Diocesan Office, Tha Kin Nat Pe Rd, Thida Ya, Myitkyina, Myanmar
Sittwe	Barnabas Theaung Hawi St John's Church, Paletwa, Sittwe, Myanmar
(Assistant)	U Aung Tha Tun address as above
Toungoo	Saw (John) Wilme Diocesan Office, Nat Shin Naung Road, Toungoo, Myanmar
Yangon (Archbishop)	Andrew Mya Han Bishopscourt, 140 Pyidaungsu Yeiktha Road, Dagon PO (11191), Yangon, Myanmar
(Assistant)	Joseph Than Pe address as above

NEW ZEALAND
(AOTEAROA, NEW ZEALAND
AND POLYNESIA)

Aotearoa	Whakahuihui Vercoe (Bishop to the Maoris) (34 Bennetts Road), PO Box 146, Rotorua, New Zealand
(Assistants)	Waiohau Rui Te Haara (Bishop in Tai Tokerau) PO Box 37-242, Auckland, New Zealand
	William Brown Turei (Bishop in Tai Rawhiti) PO Box 1128, Napier, New Zealand
	Muru Walters (Bishop in Te Upoko O Te Ika) 11 Hobson Street, Levin, New Zealand
Auckland	John Campbell Paterson PO Box 37-242, Parnell, Auckland, New Zealand
(Assistant)	Bruce MacGregor Moore PO Box 37-242, Parnell, Auckland New Zealand
Christchurch	David J Coles PO Box 8471, Riccarton Christchurch, New Zealand
Dunedin	Penelope A Jamieson PO Box 5445, Dunedin, New Zealand
Nelson	Derek L Eaton Bishopdale, PO Box 100, Nelson, New Zealand
Polynesia (Bishop in)	Jabez L Bryce Bishop's House, Box 35 GPO, Suva, Fiji Islands
(Assistant)	V M Hala'api'api address as above
Waiapu	Murray J Mills 8 Cameron Terrace, PO Box 227, Napier, Hawkes Bay, New Zealand
(Assistant)	George H Conner (Bishop in the Bay of Plenty) Bishop's House, 60 Judea Road, Tauranga, Aotearoa, New Zealand
Waikato	David J Moxon PO Box 21, Hamilton, Waikato, New Zealand
Wellington (Archbishop)	Brian N Davis PO Box 12-046, Bishopscourt, 28 Eccleston Hill, Wellington, New Zealand
(Assistants)	Thomas J Brown PO Box 12-046, Wellington New Zealand
	Brian R Carrell PO Box 422, Palmerston North, New Zealand

NIGERIA

Aba	Augustine Onyeyiriehukwu Iwuagwu Bishop's House, PO Box 212, Aba, Nigeria
Abuja	Peter J Akinola All Saints' Church, Bishop's House, Wuse, Abuja, Nigeria
Akoko	J O K Olowokure Bishopscourt, Lennon Hill PO Box 572, Ikare-Akoko Ondo State, Nigeria
Akure	Emmanuel B Gbonigi Bishopscourt, Alagbaka GRA, PO Box 1622, Akure, Nigeria
Asaba	Roland N C Nwosu Bishopscourt, Cable Point, PO Box 216, Asaba, Nigeria
Awka	Maxwell S Anikwenwa Bishopscourt, Ifite, Awkard, PO Box 130, Awka, Anambra State, Nigeria
Bauchi	E O Chukwuma Bishop's House, Bununu Road, New Gra, PO Box 2450, Bauchi, Nigeria
Benin	Peter Onekpe Bishopscourt, PO Box 82, Benin-City, Bendel State, Nigeria

Calabar	W G Ekprikpo Bishopscourt, PO Box 74, Calabar, Cross River State, Nigeria	Okigwe North	Alfred Nwaizuzu c/o PO Box 260, Nkwerre, Imo State, Nigeria
Egba	Matthew O Owadayo Bishopscourt, PO Box 267, Ibara, Abeokuta, Nigeria	Okigwe South	Bennett Okoro Ezeoke Nsu, PO Box 63, Nsu, Via Umuahia, Imo State, Nigeria
Egbado	Timothy I O Bolaji Bishopscourt, PO Box 8, Ilaro, Nigeria	Orlu	Samuel C N Ebo Bishopscourt, PO Box 260, Nkwerre, Imo State, Nigeria
Ekiti	Clement A Akinbola Bishopscourt, PO Box 12, Ado-Ekiti, Nigeria	Ondo	Samuel O Aderin Bishopscourt, College Road, PO Box 265, Ondo, Nigeria
Enugu	Gideon N Otubelu Bishop's House, Uwani, PO Box 418, Enugu, Nigeria	Osun	Seth Oni Fagbemi Bishopscourt, PO Box 285, Isale-Aro, Osogbo, Nigeria
Ibadan	Gideon Olajide Bishopscourt, PO Box 3075, Ibadan, Nigeria	Owerri	Benjamin Nwankiti Bishopscourt, Egbu, PO Box 31, Owerri, Imo State, Nigeria
Ife	Gabriel B Oloniyo Bishopscourt, Parakin Layout, Ile-Ife, Nigeria	Owo	Peter A Adebiyi Bishopscourt, PO Box 472, Owo, Ondo State, Nigeria
Ijebu	Abraham O Olowoyo PO Box 112, Ijebu-Ode, Nigeria	Sabongida Ora	Albert A Agbaje c/o PO Box 13 Sabongida Ora, Nigeria
Ijebu Remo	E O I Ogundana Bishopscourt, Ewusi Street, PO Box 522, Sagamu, Nigeria	Sokoto	Josiah Idowu-Fearon Bishop's Lodge, Dendo Road, PO Box 3489, Sokoto, Nigeria
Ikale-Ilaje	J Akin Omoyajowo Bishopscourt, Ikoya Road, Ilutitun, Osooro, Nigeria	Ukwa	Uju Obinya c/o PO Box 397, Aba, Nigeria
Ilesa	E A Ademowo Bishopscourt, Oke-Oye, PO Box 237, Ilesa, Nigeria	Umuahia	Ngochukwe U Ezuoke c/o St Stephen's Church, PO Box 96, Umuahia, Nigeria
Jos	Benjamin Argak Kwashi Bishopscourt, PO Box 6283, Jos, Nigeria	Uyo	Ebenezar E Nglass Bishopscourt, Uyo, Akwa Ibom State, Nigeria
Kaduna	Titus Ogbonyomi Bishopscourt, 4 Kanta Road, PO Box 72, Kaduna, Northern Nigeria	Warri	Nathaniel A Enuku Bishopscourt, PO Box 18, Ughelli, Nigeria
Kafanchan	William W Diya Bishopscourt, 5b Jemma'a Street PO Box 29, Kafanchan-Kaduna State, Nigeria	Yola	Chris O Efobi 10 Hong Road, PO Box 601, Yola-Gongola State, Nigeria
Kano	Benjamin O Omosebi Bishop's Court, 1B Stadium Road, PO Box 362, Kano, Nigeria	**PAPUA NEW GUINEA**	
Katsina	James S Kwasu Bishopscourt, PO Box 904, Katsina, Nigeria	Aipo Rongo	James Ayong PO Box 893, Mount Hagan, Western Highlands Province, Papua New Guinea
Kwara	Jeremiah O A Fabuluje Bishopscourt, Fate Road, PO Box 1884, Ilorin, Kwara State, Nigeria	Dogura	Tevita Talanoa PO Box 19, Dogura, via Alotau, MBP Papua New Guinea
Lagos (Archbishop)	Joseph A Adetiloye PO Box 13, Archbishop's Palace, 29 Marina, Lagos, Nigeria	New Guinea Islands	Vacant PO Box 159, Rabaul, ENBP, Papua New Guinea
Lokoja	George Bako Bishopscourt, PO Box 11, Lokoja, Nigeria	Popondota	Reuben Barago Tariambari PO Box 26, Popondetta, Oro Province, Papua New Guinea
Maiduguri	Emmanuel K Mani Bishopscourt, 1 Lake Chad Club Road, GRA, PO Box 1693, Maiduguri, Borno State, Nigeria	Port Moresby	Isaac Gadebo PO Box 6491, Boroko, NCD, Papua New Guinea
Makurdi	Nathaniel Nyom Bishopscourt, PO Box 1, Makurdi, Nigeria	**THE PHILIPPINES**	
Mbaise	Cyril Chukwka Anyanwu St Michael's Cathedral, Ife, Omo State, Nigeria	Prime Bishop and Metropolitan	Narciso Valentin Ticobay PO Box 10321, Broadway Centrum, 1112 Quezon City, Philippines
Minna	Nathaniel Yisa Bishopscourt, Dutsen Kura, PO Box 64, Minna, Nigeria	Central Philippines	Manuel C Lumpias Philippine Episcopal Church, PO Box 655, Manila 2800, Philippines
The Niger (Bishop on)	Jonathan Onyemelukwe Bishopscourt, PO Box 42, Onitsha, Nigeria	North Central Philippines	Joel A Pachao PO Box 137, 2600 Baguio City, Philippines
Niger Delta	Samuel O Elenwo Bishop's Lodge, PO Box 115, Port Harcourt, Nigeria	Northern Luzon	Ignacio C Soliba Bulanao, Tabuk, Kalinga-Apayao 1401, Philippines
Nsukka	Jonah Ilonuba St Paul's Cathedral, PO Box 16, Nsukka, Nigeria	Northern Philippines	Robert L O Longid Bontoc, Mountain Province 0601, Philippines
Oke-Osun	Abraham O Awoson Bishopscourt, PO Box 251, Gbongan, Osun State, Nigeria	Southern Philippines	James Buanda Manguramas PO Box 113, Cotabato City, 9301, Philippines

RWANDA

Butare	Venuste Mutiganda BP 225, Butare, Rwanda
Byumba	Onesphore Rwaje BP 17 Buyumba, Rwanda
Cyangugu	Daniel Nduhura c/o Avenue Pangi No 2, Muhumba Bukavu, Zaire
(Assistant)	Ken Barham Rosewood, Canadia Road, Battle, Sussex TN33 0LR, UK
Kibungo	Augustin Mvunabandi c/o EER, Gahini, BP 22, Kigali, Rwanda
Kigali	Jonathan Ruhumuliza PO Box 61, Kigali, Rwanda
Kigeme	Norman Kayumba PO Box 67, Gikongoro, Rwanda
(Assistant)	Alexis Bilindabagabo address as above
Shyira (Archbishop)	Augustin Nshamihigo c/o Diocese of Nairobi, PO Box 40502, Kenya
Shyogwe	Samuel Musubyimana address as above

SOUTHERN AFRICA

Bloemfontein	Thomas S Stanage Bishop's House 16 York Road, Bloemfontein 9301, South Africa
(Suffragan)	Elistan Patrick Glover address as above
Cape Town (Primate)	Desmond M Tutu Bishopscourt, Claremont 7700, South Africa
(Suffragans)	Mervyn Edwin Castle Bishopsholme, 18 Rue Ursula, Glenhaven, Bellville 7530, South Africa
	Alan G Quinlan Bishop's House, 77 Kildare Road, Newlands 7700, South Africa
	Edward Mackenzie 39 Paradise Road, Newlands 7700, South Africa
Christ the King	Peter J Lee PO Box 1653, Rosettenville 2130 South Africa
George	Derek G Damant PO Box 227, George 6530, South Africa
Grahamstown	David P Russell Bishopsbourne, PO Box 162, Grahamstown, 6140, South Africa
(Suffragan)	Anthony Thembinkosi Mdletshe address as above
Johannesburg	Duncan Buchanan Diocesan Office, PO Box 1131, Johannesburg 2000, South Africa
Kimberley and Kuruman	N Winston Ndungane PO Box 921, Kimberley 8300, South Africa
Klerksdorp	David C T Nkwe PO Box 548, Klerksdorp 2570, South Africa
Lebombo	Dinis Sengulane Caixa Postale 120, Maputo, Mozambique
Lesotho	Philip S Mokuku Bishop's House, PO Box MS 87, Maseru 100, Lesotho, Southern Africa
(Suffragan)	Andrew Duma address as above
Namibia	James H Kauluma PO Box 57, Windhoek, Namibia, South West Africa
(Suffragan)	Petrus Hilukiluah address as above
Natal	Michael Nuttall Bishop's House, 52 Roberts Road, Pietermaritzburg 3201, South Africa
(Suffragans)	Rubin Philip PO Box 4019, Durban 4900, South Africa
	Matthew M Makhaye PO Box 463, Ladysmith 3370, South Africa
Niassa	Paulino T Manhique Missao Anglicana de Messumba, CP 264, Lichinga, Niassa, Mozambique
Order of Ethiopia (Bishop of the)	Sigqibo Dwane PO Box 53014, Kenilworth 7745, South Africa
Port Elizabeth	Eric Pike 75 River Road, Walmer, Port Elizabeth 6065, South Africa
Pretoria	Richard A Kraft Bishop's House, 264 Celliers Street, PO Box 1032, Pretoria 0001, South Africa
(Suffragan)	Robin Briggs address as above
St Helena	John H Ruston Bishopsholme, St Helena Island, South Atlantic
St John's	Jacob Z Dlamini PO Box 163, Umtata, Transkei, Southern Africa
St Mark the Evangelist	Philip John Le Feuvre PO Box 643, Pietersburg 0700, South Africa
South Eastern Transvaal	David A Beetge PO Box 114, Springs 1560, South Africa
Swaziland	Lawrence B Zulu PO Box 118, Mbabane, Swaziland
Umzimvubu	Geoffrey Davies PO Box 644, Kokstad 4700, South Africa
Zululand	Peter Harker PO Box 147, Eshowe 3815, Zululand, Southern Africa

SOUTHERN CONE OF AMERICA

Argentina	David Leake Casilla de Correo 4293, Correo Centro, 1000 Buenos Aires, Argentina
Bolivia	Gregory Venables Casilla 9574, La Paz, Bolivia
Chile	Colin F Bazley Casilla de Correo 50675, Correo Central, Santiago, Chile
(Assistant)	Abelino Apeleo Casilla de Correo, 26-D Temuco, Chile
Northern Argentina (Primate)	Maurice Sinclair Casilla de Correo 187, CP 4400, Salta, Argentina
(Assistant)	Mario L Marino Casilla 19, CP 3636 Ingeniero Juarez, Formosa, Argentina
Paraguay	John Ellison Iglesia Anglicana Paraguya, Casilla de Correo 1124, Asuncion, Paraguay
Peru	Vacant Apartado 18-1032, Miraflores, Lima 18, Peru
Uruguay	Harold William Godfrey Casilla 6108, Montevideo, Uruguay

SUDAN

Bor	Nathaniel Garang c/o PO Box 52802, Nairobi, Kenya
(Suffragan)	Daniel Deng (Bishop of Renk Area) PO Box 65, Khartoum, Sudan
Juba (Archbishop)	Benjamin W Yugusuk c/o PO Box 110, Juba, Sudan
(Suffragans)	Michael S Lugor (Bishop of Rejaf Area) address as above
	Wilson Arop (Bishop of Torit Area) address as above

Kajo-Keji	Manasse B Dawidi c/o PO Box 52802, Nairobi, Kenya
Khartoum	Bulus Idris Tia PO Box 65, Omdurman, Sudan
(Suffragan)	Vacant (Bishop of Port Sudan Area) address as above
Malakal	Kedhekia Mabier c/o PO Box 65, Ondurman, Sudan
Maridi	Joseph Marona c/o PO Box 52802, Nairobi, Kenya
(Suffragan)	Levi Hassan (Bishop of Ibba Area) PO Box 110, Juba, Sudan
Mundri	Eluzai Munda c/o PO Box 110, Juba, Sudan
(Suffragan)	Ephraim A Natana (Bishop of Lui Area) address as above
Rumbek	Gabriel Roric Jur St Barnabas' Pro Cathedral, Rumbek, Sudan
(Suffragan)	Benjamin Mangar (Bishop of Yirol Area) PO Box 65, Omdurman, Sudan
Wau (Acting Bishop)	Gabriel Roric Jur PO Box 65, Omdurman, Sudan
(Suffragan)	Henry Riak Cuir PO Box 65, Omdurman, Sudan
Western Sudan	Kurkeil Mubarek Khamis PO Box 65, Omdurman, Sudan
(Suffragan)	Peter El Birish (Bishop of Kadugli Area) PO Box 65, Omdurman, Sudan
Yambio	Daniel Zindo PO Box 52802, Nairobi, Kenya
(Suffragan)	Benjamin J Ruate (Bishop of Ezzo Area) address as above
Yei	Seme L Solomona c/o PO Box 47429, Nairobi, Kenya

TANZANIA

Central Tanganyika	Godfrey Mdimi Mhogolo PO Box 15, Dodoma, Tanzania
(Assistant)	John Ball address as above
Dar es Salaam	Basil Sambano PO Box 25016, Ilala, Dar es Salaam, Tanzania
Kagera	Edwin A G Nyamubi PO Box 18, Ngara, Tanzania
Mara	Hilkia Omindo PO Box 131, Musoma, Tanzania
Masasi	Christopher B Sadiki Mtandi, Private Bag, PO Masasi, Masasi, Mtwara, Tanzania
Morogoro	Dudley Mageni PO Box 320, Morogoro, Tanzania
Mount Kilimanjaro	Simon Makundi PO Box 1057, Arusha, Tanzania
Mpwapwa	Simon Chiwanga PO Box 2, Mpwapwa, Tanzania
Rift Valley	Alpha Mohamed PO Box 82, Manyoni, Tanzania
Ruaha	Donald Mtetemela Box 1028, Iringa, Tanzania
Ruvuma	Stanford S Shauri PO Box 17, Liuli, Mbinga, Tanzanla
South-West Tanganyika	Charles J Mwaigoga PO Box 32, Njombe, Tanzania
Tabora	Francis Ntiruka, PO Box 1408, Tabora, Tanzania
Victoria Nyanza	John Changae PO Box 278, Mwanza, Tanzania
Western Tanganyika	Gerald Mpango PO Box 13, Kasulu, Tanzania
Zanzibar and Tanga (Archbishop)	John A Ramadhani PO Box 35, Korogwe, Tanzania

UGANDA

Bukedi	Nicodemus Okille PO Box 170, Tororo, Uganda
Bunyoro-Kitara	Wilson N Turumanya PO Box 20, Hoima, Uganda
Busoga	Cyprian Bamwoze PO Box 1658, Jinja, Uganda
Central Buganda	George Sinabulya PO Box 1200, Karoni-Gomba, Mpigi, Uganda
East Ankole	Elisha Kyamugambi PO Box 14, Mbarara, Ankole, Uganda
Kampala (Archbishop)	Livingstone Mpalanyi-Nkoyoyo PO Box 14123, Kampala, Uganda
(Assistant)	Lucas Gonahasa PO Box 335, Kampala, Uganda
Karamoja	Peter Lomongin c/o PO Box 1, Kampala, Uganda
Kigezi	William Rukirande PO Box 3, Kabale, Kigezi, Uganda
Kinkizi	John Ntegyereize PO Box 77, Karuhinda, Rukungiri, Uganda
Kitgum	Macleord Baker Ochola II PO Box 187, Kitgum, Uganda
Lango	Melchizedek Otim PO Box 6, Lira, Uganda
(Assistant)	William M Okodi address as above
Luwero	Mesusera Bugimbi PO Box 125, Luwero, Uganda
Madi and West Nile	Enoch Drati PO Box 370, Arua, Uganda
Mbale	Israel Koboyi Bishop's House, PO Box 473 Mhale, Uganda
Mityana	Wilson Mutebi PO Box 102, Mityana, Uganda
Muhabura	Ernest Shalita Church of Uganda, PO Box 22, Kisoro, Uganda
Mukono	Vacant PO Box 39, Mukono, Uganda
Namirembe	Samuel B Ssekkadde PO Box 14297, Kampala, Uganda
Nebbi	Henry Orombi PO Box 27, Nebbi, Uganda
North Kigezi	Vacant PO Box 23, Rukungiri, Uganda
North Mbale	Peter Mudonyi Bishop's House, PO Box 1293, Mbale, Uganda
Northern Uganda	Gideon Oboma PO Box 232, Gulu, Uganda
Ruwenzori	Eustace Kamanyire Bishop's House, PO Box 37, Fort Portal, Uganda
Soroti	Geresom Ilukor PO Box 107, Soroti, Uganda
South Ruwenzori	Zebidee K Masereka PO Box 142, Kasese, Uganda
West Ankole	Yoramu Bamunoba PO Box 140, Bushenyi, Uganda
West Buganda	Christopher D Senyonjo PO Box 242, Masaka, Uganda

UNITED STATES OF AMERICA

The roman numerals indicate to which of the nine provinces
of ECUSA the diocese belongs

Presiding Bishop	Edmond L Browning Episcopal Church Center, 815 Second Ave, New York, NY 10017 USA
Alabama (IV)	Robert O Miller Carpenter House, 521 N 20th St, Birmingham, AL 35203, USA
Alaska (VIII)	Steven Charleston Box 441, Fairbanks AK 99707, USA
Albany (II)	David S Ball 62 South Swan St, Albany, NY 12210, USA

Arizona (VIII)	Robert Reed Shahan 114 West Roosevelt St, Phoenix, AZ 85003, USA
Arkansas (VII)	Larry Maze Cathedral House, PO Box 164668, 300 West 17th St, Little Rock, AR 72216, USA
Atlanta (IV)	Frank Allan 2744 Peachtree Road, NW Atlanta, GA 30305, USA
Bethlehem (III)	J Mark Dyer 333 Wyandotte St, Bethlehem, PA 18015, USA
California (VIII)	William E Swing 1055 Taylor St, San Francisco, CA 94108, USA
(Assistants)	G R Millard 1812 Sandhill Road, 311, Palii Altu, CA 14304-2136, USA
	J R Wyatt 1204 Chelsa Way, Redwood City, CA 44061, USA
Central Ecuador (IX)	Jose Moreno Apartado 353-A, Quito, Ecuador
Central Florida (IV)	John W Howe PO Box 790, Winter Park, FL 32790, USA
(Assistant)	Reginald Hollis address as above
Central Gulf Coast (IV)	Charles Duvall 201 N Baylen Street Penacola FL 32591-3330, USA
Central New York (II)	David Joslin 310 Montgomery St, Suite 200, Syracuse, NY 13202-2093, USA
Central Pennsylvania (III)	Vacant 221 North Front St, Box 11937, Harrisburg, PA 17108-1937, USA
Chicago (V)	Frank T Griswold III 65 East Huron St, Chicago, IL 60611, USA
(Suffragan)	William Wiedrich address as above
Colombia (IX)	Bernardo Merino-Botero Apartado Aereo 52964, Bogota 2, Colombia, South America
Colorado (VI)	William J Winterrowd Box 18 M, Capitol Hill Station, Denver, CO 80218, USA
Connecticut (I)	Clarence N Coleridge 1335 Asylum Ave, Hartford, CT 06105, USA
Dallas (VII)	James H Stanton 1630 Garrett St, Dallas, TX 75206, USA
Delaware (III)	C Cabell Tennis 2020 Tatnall St, Wilmington, DE 19802, USA
Dominican Republic (IX)	Julio Cesar Holguin Apartado 764, Santo Domingo, Dominican Republic
East Carolina (IV)	Brice Sidney Sanders PO Box 1336, Kinston, NC 28501, USA
East Tennessee (IV)	Robert G Tharp PO Box 3807, Knoxville, TN 37927, USA
Eastern Oregon (VIII)	Rustin R Kimsey PO Box 620, The Dalles, Oregon 97058, USA
Easton (III)	Martin G Townsend Box 1027, Easton, MD 21601, USA
Eau Claire (V)	William C Wantland 510 South Farwell St, Eau Claire, WI 54701, USA
El Camino Real (VIII)	Richard L Shimpfy Box 1903, Monterey, CA 93940, USA
El Salvador (IX)	Martin Barhona 47 Avenida Sur, 723 Col. Flor Blanca, Apartado Postal (01) 274, San Salvador, El Salvador

Europe, Convocation of American Churches in	Jeffery William Rowthorn 23 Avenue George V, 75008 Paris, France
Florida (IV)	Stephen H Jecko 325 Market St, Jacksonville, FL 32202, USA
Fond du Lac (V)	Russell E Jacobus PO Box 149, Grafton Hall, 39 North Sophia St, Fond du Lac, WI 54935, USA
Fort Worth (VII)	Jack L Iker 6300 Ridlea Place 1100 Fort Worth, TX 76116, USA
Georgia (IV)	Henry Irving Loutitt Jr 611 E Bay St, Savannah, GA 31401, USA
Guatemala (IX)	Armando R Guerra-Soria Apartado 58a, Guatemala City Guatemala, Central America
Haiti (II)	Jean Zache Duracin Eglise Episcopale d'Haiti PO Box 1309, Port-au-Prince, Haiti
Hawaii (VIII)	Vacant Diocesan Office, 229 Queen Emma Sq, Honolulu HI 96813, USA
Honduras (IX)	Leo Frade Apartado Postal 586, San Pedro Sula, Honduras, Central America
Idaho (VIII)	John S Thornton PO Box 936, Boise, ID 83701, USA
Indianapolis (V)	Edward W Jones 1100 West 42nd St, Indianapolis, IN 46208, USA
Iowa (VI)	C Christopher Epting 225 37th St, Des Moines, IA 50312, USA
Kansas (VII)	William E Smalley Bethany Place, 833-35 Polk St, Topeka, KS 66612, USA
Kentucky (IV)	Edwin F Gulick 421 S 2nd St, Louisville, KY 40202, USA
Lexington (IV)	Don A Wimberley PO Box 610, Lexington, KY 40508, USA
Litoral Diocese of Ecuador (IX)	Alfredo Morante, Apartado 5250, Calle Bogota 1010, Bario Centenario, Guayaquil, Equador
Long Island (II)	Orris G Walker Jr 36 Cathedral Ave, Garden City, NY 11530, USA
Los Angeles (VIII)	Fred H Borsch 1220 West 4th St, Box 2164, Los Angeles, CA 90051, USA
(Suffragan)	Chester L Talton address as ahove
(Assistant)	John Krumm St Paul's Church, 1221 Wass St, Tustin, CA 92680, USA
Louisiana (IV)	James B Brown 1623 Seventh St, New Orleans, LA 70115-4111, USA
Maine (I)	Edward C Chalfont Loring House, 143 State St, Portland ME 04101, USA
Maryland (III)	Vacant 105 W Monument St, Baltimore, MD 21201, USA
(Suffragan)	Charles L Longest address as above
Massachusetts (I)	Thomas Shaw 138 Tremont Street, Boston, MA 02111, USA
(Suffragan)	Barbara Harris address as above
Michigan (V)	R Stewart Wood 4800 Woodward Ave, Detroit, MI 48201, USA
(Suffragan)	H Irving Mayson address as above
Milwaukee (V)	Roger J White 804 East Juneau Ave, Milwaukee WI 53202, USA

Minnesota (VI)	James L Jelinek 403 Oak Grove, Box 306, Minneapolis, MN 55403, USA
(Suffragan)	Sanford Z K Hampton address as above
Mississippi (IV)	Alfred C Marble Jr PO Box 1636, Jackson, MS 39205-1635, USA
Missouri (V)	Hayes H Rockwell 1210 Locust St, St Louis, MO 63103, USA
Montana (VI)	Charles I Jones 515 North Park Ave, Helena, MT 59601, USA
Navajoland Area Mission (VIII)	Steven Tsosie Plummer Box 720, Farmington, NM 87499, USA
Nebraska (VI)	James E Krotz 200 North 62nd St, Omaha, NB 68132, USA
Nevada (VIII)	Stewart C Zabriskie PO Box 6357, 2390 West 7th St, Reno, NV 89513, USA
New Hampshire (I)	Douglas E Theuner 63 Green St, Concord, NH 03301, USA
New Jersey (II)	Joe Morris Doss 808 West State St, Trenton, NJ 08618, USA
New York (II)	Richard F Grein Synod House, 1047 Amsterdam Ave, Cathedral Heights, New York, NY 10025, USA
(Suffragans)	Walter D Dennis address as above Catherine A Roskam address as above
(Assistant)	E Don Taylor address as above
Newark (II)	John S Spong 24 Rector St, Newark NJ 07102, USA
(Suffragan)	Jack McKelvey address as above
Nicaragua (IX)	Sturdie Downs Apartado 1207, Managua, Nicaragua
North Carolina (IV)	Robert W Estill PO Box 17025, 201 St Alban's Drive, Raleigh, NC 27619, USA
North Dakota (VI)	Andrew H Fairfield 2315 N University Drive, Fargo, ND 58102, USA
Northern California (VIII)	Jerry Lamb Box 161268,1318 27th Street, Sacramento, CA 95816, USA
Northern Indiana (V)	Francis C Gray Cathedral House, 117 N Lafayette Blvd, South Bend, IN 46601, USA
Northern Michigan (V)	Thomas Kreider Ray 131 E Ridge St, Marquette, MI 49855, USA
Northwest Texas (VII)	Sam B Hulsey PO Box 1067, Lubbock, TX 79408, USA
Northwestern Pennsylvania (III)	Robert D Rowley Jr 145 West 6th St, Erie, PA 16501, USA
Ohio (V)	J Clark Grew II 2230 Euclid Ave, Cleveland, OH 44115, USA
(Suffragan)	Arthur B Williams address as above
Oklahoma (VII)	Robert M Moody 519 NW 9th St, Box 1098, Oklahoma City, OK 73101, USA
Olympia (VIII)	Vincent W Warner Jr PO Box 12126, 1551 10th Ave E, Seattle, WA 98102, USA
Oregon (VIII)	Robert L Ladehoff PO Box 467 Lake Oswego, OR 97034, USA

Panama (IX)	Clarence W Hayes Box R, Balboa, Republic of Panama
Pennsylvania (III)	Allen L Bartlett 240 South Fourth Street, Philadelphia, PA 19106, USA
(Suffragan)	Franklin D Turner address as above
Pittsburg (III)	Alden M Hathaway 325 Oliver Ave, Pittsburgh, PA 15222, USA
Quincy (V)	Keith Ackerman 3601 N North St, Peoria, IL 61604, USA
Rhode Island (I)	Vacant 275 Main St, Providence, RI 02903, USA
Rio Grande (VII)	Terence Kelshaw 4304 Carlisle NE, Albuquerque, NM 87107, USA
Rochester (II)	William G Burrill 935 East Ave, Rochester, NY 14607, USA
San Diego (VIII)	Gethin B Hughes 2728 Sixth Ave, San Diego, CA 92103, USA
San Joaquin (IV)	John-David Schofield 4159 E Dakota Ave, Fresno, CA 93726, USA
South Carolina (IV)	Edward L Salmon 1020 King St, PO Drawer 2127, Charleston, SC 29403, USA
South Dakota (VI)	Creighton Robertson Box 517, Sioux Falls, South Dakota 57101, USA
Southeast Florida (IV)	Calvin O Schofield Jr 525 NE 15 St, Miami, FL 33132, USA
Southern Ohio (V)	Herbert Thompson 412 Sycamore St, Cincinnati, OH 45202, USA
(Suffragan)	Kenneth Price Jr address as above
Southern Virginia (III)	Frank H Vest 600 Talbot Hall Rd, Norfolk, VA 23505, USA
(Assistant)	O'Kelly Whitaker address as above
Southwest Florida (IV)	Roger Harris PO Drawer 491, St Petersburg, FL 33731, USA
Southwestern Virginia (III)	Arthur Heath Light 1000 First St SW, PO Box 2279, Roanoke, VA 24009, USA
Spokane (VIII)	Frank J Terry 245 E 13th Ave, Spokane, WA 99202, USA
Springfield (V)	Peter H Beckwith 821 S 2nd St, Springfield, IL 62704, USA
Taiwan (VIII)	John Chien 1-105-7 Hangchow, South Road, Taipei, Taiwan 10044, Republic of China
Tennessee (IV)	Bertram N Herlong 808 Board St, Nashville, TN 37203, USA
Texas (VII)	Maurice M Benitez 520 San Jacinto St, Houston, TX 77002, USA
(Suffragan)	William E Stirling address as above
Upper South Carolina (IV)	Dorsey F Henderson Box 1789, Columbia, SC 29202, USA
(Assistant)	W Franklin Carr address as above
Utah (VIII)	George E Bates 231 East First South St Salt Lake City, UT 84111, USA
Vermont (I)	Mary A McLeod The Bishop's House, Rock Point, Burlington, VT 05401, USA

Virgin Islands (II)	Vacant PO Box 7488, St Thomas, Virgin Islands, Vl 00801, USA
Virginia (III)	Peter Lee 110 W Franklin St, Richmond VA 23220, USA
(Suffragans)	F Clayton Matthews address as above David C Jones address as above
(Assistant)	Robert P Atkinson address as above
Washington (III)	Ronald H Haines Episcopal Church House, Mount St, Alban, Washington DC 20016, USA
(Suffragan)	Jane Holmes Dixon address as above
West Missouri (VII)	John C Buchanan PO Box 41326, Kansas City, MO 64141, USA
West Tennessee (IV)	James Coleman 692 Poplar Ave, Memphis, TN 38105, USA
West Texas (VII)	James Edward Folts PO Box 6885, San Antonio, TX 78209, USA
West Virginia (III)	John H Smith PO Box 5400, Charlestown, WV 25361, USA
Western Kansas (VII)	Vernon E Strickland Box 2507 (1508A East Iron), Salina, KS 67402-2507, USA
Western Louisiana (IV)	Robert J Hargrove Jr PO Box 4046, Alexandria LA 71301, USA
Western Massachusetts (I)	Robert S Denig 37 Chestnut St, Springfield, MA 01103, USA
Western Michigan (V)	Edward L Lee Jr The Cathedral, 2600 Vincent Ave, Kalamazoo, MI 49008, USA
Western New York (II)	David C Bowman 1114 Delaware Ave, Buffalo, NY 14209, USA
Western North Carolina (IV)	Robert H Johnson Box 368, In-the-Oaks, Black Mountain, NC 28711, USA
Wyoming (VI)	Bob G Jones 104 South Fourth St, Laramie, WY 82070, USA

WEST AFRICA

Accra	Francis W Thompson Bishopscourt, PO Box 8, Accra, Ghana
Bo	Samuel Sao Gbonda PO Box 21, Bo, Southern Province, Sierra Leone
Cape Coast	Kobina Quashie Bishopscourt, PO Box A233, Adiadel Estates, Cape Coast, Ghana
Freetown	Vacant Bishopscourt, PO Box 128, Freetown, Sierra Leone
Gambia	Solomon T Johnson Bishopscourt, PO Box 51, Banjul, The Gambia, West Africa
Guinea	Vacant PO Box 1187, Conakry, Guinea
Koforidua (Archbishop)	Robert Okine PO Box 980, Koforidua, Ghana
Kumasi	Edmund Yeboah Bishop's House, PO Box 144, Kumasi, Ghana
Liberia	Vacant PO Box 10-0277, 1000 Monrovia 10, Liberia
(Suffragan)	Edward Neufville address as above
Sekondi	Theophilus Annobil PO Box 85, Sekondi, Ghana

Sunyani/ Tamale	Joseph K Dadson Bishop's House, PO Box 110, Tamale NR, Ghana

WEST INDIES

Barbados	Rufus T Brome Mandeville House, St Michael, Barbados
Belize	Sylvestre Romero-Palma Bishopsthorpe, PO Box 535, Southern Foreshore, Belize City, Belize
Guyana	Randolph O George Austin House, Georgetown 1, Guyana
Jamaica	Neville W de Souza Church House 2 Caledonia Ave Kingston 5, Jamaica
(Suffragans)	William Murray (Bishop of Mandeville) PO Box 159, Mandeville, Jamaica
	Alfred Reid (Bishop of Montego Bay) PO Box 346, Montego Bay, St James, Jamaica
	Herman Spence (Bishop of Kingston) Church House, 2 Caledonia Ave, Kingston 5, Jamaica
Nassau and the Bahamas	Michael Eldon Addington House, PO Box N-7107, Nassau, Bahamas
(Co-Adjutor)	Drexel W Gomez PO Box N656, Nassau, Bahamas
North Eastern Caribbean and Aruba (Archbishop)	Orland U Lindsay Bishop's Lodge, PO Box 23, St John's, Antigua
(Suffragan)	Alfred E Jeffery address as above
Trinidad and Tobago	Rawle E Douglin Hayes Court, 21 Maraval Road, Port of Spain, Trinidad
Windward Islands	Sehon Goodridge PO Box 128, Bishop's House, Kingstown, St Vincent, West Indies

ZAIRE

Boga-Zaire (Archbishop)	P Byankya Njojo CAZ-Boga, PO Box 21285, Nairobi, Kenya
Bukavu	Fidele Balufuga Dirokpa CAZ-Bukavu, PO Box 53435, Nairobi, Kenya
(Assistant)	Peter Donald Dawson CAZ-Kindu, PO Box 53435, Nairobi, Kenya
Kisangani	Sylvestre Tibefa Mugera CAZ-Kisangani, PO Box 53435, Nairobi, Kenya
Nord Kivu	Methusela Munzenda Musubaho CAZ-Butembo, PO Box 21285, Nairobi, Kenya
Shaba	Emmanuel Kolini Mbona CAZ-Lubumbashi, c/o United Methodist Church, PO Box 22037, Kitwe, Zambia

EXTRA-PROVINCIAL DIOCESES

Bermuda (Canterbury)	Vacant Bishop's Lodge, PO Box 769, Hamilton HM CX, Bermuda
Costa Rica (Extra-Provincial to IX, USA)	Cornelius Wilson Apartado 2773, 1000 San Jose, Costa Rica
Cuba	Jorge Perera Hurtado Calle 6, No 273, Vedado, Habana 4, Cuba
§Hong Kong and Macao	Peter Kwong Bishop's House, 1 Lower Albert Road, Hong Kong

§ Also members of the Council of the Churches of East Asia

§Kuching (Canterbury) — John Leong Chee Yun
Bishop's House, PO Box 347, Kuching, 93704 Sarawak, East Malaysia

Lusitanian Church (Canterbury) — Fernando Soares
Rua de Elias Garcia 107-114,1, Dto, 4400 Vila Nova de Gala, Portugal

Puerto Rico (Extra-Provincial to IX, USA) — David Alvarez
Box C, Saint Just, PR 00750, Puerto Rico

§Sabah (Canterbury) — Yong Ping Chung
Rumah Bishop, Jalan Tangki, PO Box 10811, 88809 Kota Kinabalu, Sabah, E Malaysia

§Singapore (Canterbury) — Moses Tay (Chairman CCEA)
Bishopsbourne, 4 Bishopsgate, Singapore 1024

(Assistant) — John Tan
address as above

Spanish Reformed Episcopal Church (Canterbury) — Arturo S Galan
Calle Beneficencia 18, 28004, Madrid, Spain

Venezuela (Extra-Provincial to IX, USA) — Orlando Guerrero
Apartado 49-143, Avenue Caroni 100, Colinas de Bello Monte, Caracas 1042-A, Venezuela

§West Malaysia (Canterbury) — Lim Cheng Ean
Rumah Bishop, 14 Pesiaran Stonor, Kuala Lumpur 50450, West Malaysia

§ Also members of the Council of the Churches of East Asia

BISHOPS OF CHURCHES WHERE ANGLICANS HAVE UNITED WITH CHRISTIANS OF OTHER TRADITIONS

NORTH INDIA

Agra — Morris Andrews
Bishop's House, St Paul's Church, 4/116 Church Road, Civil Lines, Agra 282002, UP, India

Amritsar (Moderator) — Anand Chandu Lal
R B Prakash Chand Road, Opposite Police Lines, Amritsar 143 001, India

Andamans and Nicobar Islands — Edmund Matthew
Bishop's House, Post Box 19, Port Blair 744301, India

Barrackpore — Brojen Malakar
Bishop's Lodge, 86 Middle Road, Barrackpore 743101, W Bengal, India

Bhopal — Manohar B Singh
7 Old Sehore Rd, Indore 452001, MP, India

Bombay — Samuel B Joshua
St John's House, Duxbury Lane, Colaba, Bombay 400005, India

Calcutta — Dinesh C Gorai
Bishop's House, 51 Chowringhee, Calcutta 700-071, India

Chandigarh — Joel Vidyasagal Mal
Bishop's House, Mission Compound, Brown Road, Ludhiana 141008, Punjab, India

Chota Nagpur — Z James Terom
Bishop's Lodge, PO Box 1, Ranchi, 834001 Bihar, India

Cuttack (Deputy Moderator) — D K Mohanty
Bishop's House, Madhusudan Road, Cuttack 753001, Orissa, India

Delhi — Pritam Santram
Bishop's House, 1 Church Lane, New Delhi 11001, India

Durgapur — Onil Tirkey
Bishop's House, Darjeeling 734101,W Bengal, India

Eastern Himalayas — Gerald Andrews
Bishop's House, Darjeeling 734101,W Bengal, India

Gujarat — Paul Chauhan
Bishop's House, Ellis Bridge, Ahmedabad 38006, Gujarat State, India

Jabalpur — Sunil Cak
1033 Napier Town, Jabalpur, MP 482001, India

Kolhapur — MacDonald Claudius
Bishop's House, EP School Compound, Kolhapur 416003, Maharashtra, India

Lucknow — Arthur Raja Yasuf
Bishop's House, 25 Mahatma Gandhi Marg, Allahabad 211011, UP, India

Nagpur — Vinod Peter
Cathedral House, Nagpur 440001, Maharashtra, India

Nasik — George Ambatoo Ninan
Bishop's House, 1 Outram Rd, Tarakpur, Ahmednagar 414001, Maharashtra, India

North East India — Ernest Talibuddin
Bishop's Kuti, Shillong 1, 793 001 Meghalaya, India

Patna — Nedi M Bagh
Bishop's House, Christ Church Compound, Bhagalpur-812001, Bihar, India

Rajasthan — E C Anthony
63/R, Savitri Girls' College Road, Civil Lines, Ajmer 305006, Rajasthan, India

Sambalpur — Lingaram Tandy
Mission Compound, Balangir 767001, Orissa, India

SOUTH INDIA

Coimbatore (Bishop in) — William Moses
Bishop's House, Coimbatore, 641018, South India

Dornakal (Bishop in) — D Noah Samuel
Bishop's House, Dornakal SC Rly, Andhra Pradesh 5006381, South India

East Kerala (Bishop in) — K J Samuel
Bishop's House, Melukavumattom 686652, South India

Jaffna (Bishop in) — Subramaniam Jabanesan
Bishop's House, Vaddukoddai, Sri Lanka

Kanyakumari (Bishop in) — G Christadas
Bishop's House, Nagercoil 629001, Kanyakumari District, Tamilnadu, South India

Karimnagar (Bishop in) — Sanki John Theodore
Bishop's House, Mukarampura PO, Karimnagar 505002, Andhra Pradesh, South India

Karnataka Central (Bishop in) — Vacant
Bishop's House, Trinity Church, Bangalore 560008, South India

Karnataka North (Bishop in) (Moderator) — Vasant P Dandin
All Saints Church Compound, Dharwad 58008, Karnataka State, South India

Karnataka South (Bishop *in*)	D P Shettian Bishop's House, Balmatta Bangalore 575001 SK South India	Vellore (Bishop *in*)	R Trinity Bhaskeran Ashram Bungalow, Filterbed Road, Vellore, N Arcot Dt. 632001 South India

Krishna-Godavari (Bishop *in*)
T B D Prakasa Rao
Bishop Azariah High School Campus,
Vijayawada 520 010, AP,
South India

Madhya Kerala (Bishop *in*)
Sam Mathew
Bishop's House, Chetty St,
Kottayam 686001, Kerala State,
South India

Dhaka (Moderator)
Barnahas Dwijen Mondal
St Thomas's Church,
54 Johnson Road,
Dhaka 1100, Bangladesh

Madras (Bishop *in*)
Mazilimani Azariah
Bishop's House, Cathedral Road,
Madras 600086, South India

Kushtia
Michael S Baroi
Kushtia Diocesan Office,
94 N S Road, Thanapara, Kushtia,
Bangladesh

(Assistant)
Henry Thanaraj
Diocesan Office, Post Box 4914
Madras 600086, South India

Madurai-Ramnad
Vacant
Railway Colony, Madurai 625010,
Tamil Nadu, South India

Faisalabad
John Samuel
Bishop's House, PO Box 27,
Mission Road, Gojra, Faisalabad,
Pakistan

Medak
Peter Sugandhar
Bishop's House,
Cathedral Compound,
Medak 502110
AP, South India

Hyderabad
Bashir Jiwan
St Thomas Church, Jacob Road,
Hyderabad, Sind, Pakistan

Nandyal (Bishop *in*)
G T Abraham
Bishop's House, Nandyal,
RS 518502, Kurnool District,
Andhra Pradesh, South India

Karachi
Arne Rudvin
Bishop's House, Trinity Close,
Fatimah Jinnah Road, Karachi,
0405, Pakistan

North Kerala (Bishop *in*)
P G Kuruvilla
Diocesan Office, Shoranpur 679121
Kerala State, South India

Lahore
Alexander J Malik
Bishopsbourne, Cathedral Close
The Mall, Lahore 3, Pakistan

Rayalaseema (Bishop *in*)
Vacant
Bishop's House, Cuddapah 516001,
Cuddapah District 518502,
South India

Multan
Samuel D Chand
113 Qasim Rd, Multan Cantt,
Pakistan

South Kerala (Bishop *in*)
Samuel Amirtham
Bishop's House, CSI, LMS Compound,
Trivandrum 695001, Kerala State, South India

Peshawar
Mano Ramalshah
St John's Church, 1 Sir-Seyed Road,
Peshawar Cantonment,
North West Frontier Province, Pakistan

Tirunelveli (Bishop *in*)
Jason Dharmaraj
Bishopstowe, Box 18,
Tlrunelveli 627002,
South India

Raiwind (Deputy Moderator)
Samuel Azariah
15A Warris Road
Lahore 3, Pakistan

Trichy-Tanjore (Bishop *in*) (Deputy Moderator)
R Paulraj
PO Box 31, 8 Racquet Court Lane,
Tiruchirapalli 620001, South India

Sialkot (Moderator)
Samuel Pervez
Lal Kothi, Barah Patthar,
Sialkot 2, Pakistan

PROVINCIAL OFFICES

From which further information may be sought.

Anglican Communion Office Partnership House, 157 Waterloo Road, London SE1 8UT, UK.

Australia PO Box Q190, Queen Victoria PO, Sydney 2000, NSW, Australia.

Brazil Caixa Postal 11510, Cep 90841-970 Porto Alegre, RS Brazil.

Burundi BP 2098, Bujumbura, Burundi.

Canada 600 Jarvis St, Toronto, Ontario M4Y 2J6, Canada.

Central Africa PO Box 769, Gaborone, Botswana.

Ceylon 358/1 Bauddhaloka Mawatha, Colombo 7, Sri Lanka.

East Asia (Council of the Churches of East Asia) PO Box 655, Manila, Philippines.

England Church House, Great Smith Street, London SW1P 3NZ, UK.

Indian Ocean Box 44, Victoria, Mahe, Seychelles.

Ireland Church of Ireland House, Church Avenue, Rathmines, Dublin 6, Irish Republic.

Japan 65 Yarai-cho, Shinjuku-ku, Tokyo 162, Japan.

Jerusalem and the Middle East PO Box 87, Zamalek, Cairo, Egypt.

Kenya PO Box 40502, Nairobi, Kenya.

Korea 3 Chong-dong, Chung-ku, Seoul 100-120, Korea.

Melanesia PO Box 19, Honiara, Solomon Islands.

Mexico Apartado Postal 192, Admon 4, CP 62431, Cuernavaca, Morelos, Mexico.

Myanmar (formerly Burma) 140 Pyidaungsu-Yeiktha Road, Dagon PO (11191), Yangon, Myanmar.

New Zealand PO Box 885, Hastings, New Zealand.

Nigeria PO Box 78, Lagos, Nigeria.

Papua New Guinea Box 673, Lae, MP, Papua New Guinea.

Philippines c/o Prime Bishop of the Philippines, PO Box 10321, Broadway Centrum, 1112 Quezon City, Philippines.

Rwanda BP 2487, Kigali, Rwanda.

Scotland 21 Grosvenor Crescent, Edinburgh EH12 5EE, UK.

Southern Africa Bishopscourt, Claremont, 7700, South Africa.

South America Reconquista 522, 11000 Montevideo, Uruguay.

Sudan PO Box 110, Juba, Sudan.

Tanzania PO Box 899, Dodoma, Tanzania.

Uganda PO Box 14123, Kampala, Uganda.

USA 815 Second Ave, New York, NY 10017, USA.

Wales 39 Cathedral Rd, Cardiff, S Glamorgan CF1 9XF, UK.

West Africa PO Box 8, Accra, Ghana.

West Indies PO Box 23, St John's, Antigua, West Indies.

Zaire CAZ-Bunia, c/o PO Box 21285, Nairobi, Kenya.

South India CSI Centre, 5 Whites Road, Royapettah, Madras 600041, S India.

North India CN1, 16 Pandit Pant Marg, New Delhi 110001, India.

Pakistan c/o Cathedral Close, The Mall, Lahore 3, Pakistan.

Bangladesh St Thomas Church, 54 Johnson Road, Dhaka 1100, Bangladesh.

DIRECTORIES OF THE ANGLICAN PROVINCES

The following Provinces of the Anglican Communion are known to publish directories of their clergy. These may be ordered through Church House Bookshop, 31 Great Smith Street, London SW1P 3BN, which has information on the cost and availability of current and future editions.

Australia. *The Sydney Diocesan Year Book* contains lists of clergy in the various dioceses of Australia as well as more complete details of its own clergy. Published annually.
Sydney Diocesan Registry, Anglican Church of Australia, PO Box 0190, Queen Victoria Buildings, Sydney 2000, Australia.

Canada. *The Anglican Year Book.* Published annually.
Anglican Book Centre, 600 Jarvis Street, Toronto, Ontario, M4Y 2J6, Canada.

Ireland. *Church of Ireland Directory.* Published annually.
Styletype Publishing Co. (Ireland) Ltd., Sheldon House, 60 Pembroke Road, Dublin 4, Irish Republic.

Japan (in Japanese). *Seikokai Yearbook.* Published annually.
Nippon Sei Ko Kai Provincial Office, 4-21 Higashi 1-chome, Shibuya-Ku, Tokyo, Japan 150.

Jerusalem and the Middle East. *A Provincial Directory.* Published annually.
Provincial Office, Box 1248, 20 Nablus Road, Jerusalem.

New Zealand. *Clerical Directory.* Published annually.
Provincial Secretary, PO Box 2148, Rotorua, New Zealand.

Nigeria. *Nigeria Churchman's Year Book.*
Church House, 29 Marina, PO Box 78, Lagos, Nigeria.

Scotland. *Year Book and Directory of theScottish Episcopal Church.* Published annually.
Secretary General and Treasurer, 21 Grosvenor Crescent, Edinburgh EH12 5EE.

Southern Africa. *Clerical Directory.* Published annually.
Provincial Office, Bishopscourt, Claremont, 7700, South Africa.

Southern Cone of America. *Directorio Provincial.* Published every three years.
Casilla 50675, Santiago, Chile.

United States. *Episcopal Clerical Directory.* Published annually.
Church Hymnal Corporation, 800 Second Avenue, New York, NY 10017, USA.

West Africa. *West African Churchman's Calendar and Clerical Directory.* Published approximately every five years.
The Secretariat, Church of the Province of West Africa, Bishopscourt, PO Box 8, Accra, Ghana.

Diocesan lists are the source of information for the Churches of Brazil, Central Africa and Sri Lanka. In the West Indies, the Diocese of Jamaica publishes a Clerical Directory.

Close links with many overseas provinces are maintained by the United Society for the Propagation of the Gospel and by the Church Missionary Society, both at Partnership House, 157 Waterloo Road, London SE1 8XA (for USPG), and SE1 8UU (for CMS).

The Bible Churchmen's Missionary Society at 251 Lewisham Way, London SE4 1XF also has contacts with many provinces overseas.

The South American Missionary Society, serving not only that sub-continent but also the Iberian peninsula, is at Allen Gardiner House, Pembury Road, Tunbridge Wells, Kent TN2 3QU.

For the Provinces not listed above, information should be sought from the Provincial Secretary or from dioceses. Details of other Anglican missionary societies may be found in The *Church of England Year Book.*

ADDRESSES UNKNOWN

The following are clergy whose addresses are currently unknown. Full details are contained in the biographical section. We would be grateful for any information to help us complete our records in respect of these clergy.

ANDERSON, Mark Jonathan David. b 59. d 89. C Battersea Ch Ch and St Steph *S'wark* 92–93

BAKER, Brian Ernest Harry. b 38. d 76. V Staincliffe *Wakef* 89–93

BARTER, Very Rev Donald. b 34. d 69. Australia from 93

BARTLE, Alan. b 45. d 84. P-in-c Thorney Abbey *Ely* 93–95

BELL, Jeremy Aidan. b 46. d 82. Perm to Offic *Ex* from 83

BOXALL, David John. b 41. d 66. P-in-c Fletton *Ely* 90–94

BROADHEAD, Dr Alan John. b 38. d 66. USA from 71

BROWN, Bill. b 44. d 89. C Prittlewell *Chelmsf* 91–94

BURKE, Jonathan. b 53. d 82. R Bere Regis and Affpuddle w Turnerspuddle *Sarum* 85–92

BURROWS, Paul Anthony. b 55. d 79. USA from 85.

BUXTON, Edward Brian. b 41. d 66. Perm to Offic *Chelmsf* from 76

CLARK, Hugh Lockhart. b 44. d 72. R Clitheroe St Jas *Blackb* 89–92

COMBE, Edward Charles. b 40. d 89. USA from 94

COOPER, Colin Charles. b 40. d 66. USA from 94

CUTTELL, Jeffrey Charles. b 59. d 87. V Normanton *Wakef* 91–95

DAILEY, Douglas Grant. b 56. d 88. USA from 91

DALLY, Keith Richard. b 47. d 82. Ind Chapl *Chelmsf* 85–93; C Harold Hill St Geo 92–93

DANSKIN, William Campbell. b 35. d 80. R Challoch w Newton Stewart *Glas* 87–95

DAVIES, David Michael Cole. b 44. d 68. V Dafen and Llwynhendy *St D* 90–94

DAVIES, Ieuan. b 39. d 65. USA from 68

DAVIES, Thomas Neville James. b 27. d 56. CF 65–83

EDGE, Miss Renate Erika. b 50. d 88. Par Dn Leic H Apostles *Leic* 89–94.

ELLERY, Robert Martin. b 53. d 77. Perm to Offic *S'wark* 85–89

EVANS, Robert Charles. b 55. d 81. Chapl Rob Coll Cam 87–92

FORRYAN, Thomas Quested. b 64. d 90. C Aberavon *Llan* 93–94

FOSTER, Thomas Andrew Hayden. b 43. d 73. I New w Old Ross, Whitechurch, Fethard etc *C&O* 89–91

FOX, Norman Stanley. b 39. d 64. V Pensnett *Lich* 91–93

FROSTICK, Paul Andrew. b 52. d 77. V Bottisham and Lode etc *Ely* 90–94

GADD, Frederick Arthur. b 15. d 40. Canada from 57.

GATES, John Richard. b 47. d 73. V Cosby *Leic* 82–86

GIBBS, Prof Edmund. b 38. d 63. USA from 84

GOLDEN, Stephen Gerard. b 61. d 86. CF 90–94

GREENHALGH, Stephen. b 53. d 81. Chapl *RAF* 85–93

GREY, Edwin Charles. b 03. d 49. Perm to Offic *Glouc* 78–88

GUILLAN, Miss Barbara Doris. b 19. d 87. rtd 89

HANDLEY, Terence Anthony. b 55. d 87. V Stafford St Paul Forebridge 91–94

HEIDT, Michael Lewis. b 65. d 90. C Reading St Luke w St Bart *Ox* 90–94

HELLIWELL, Christopher John Guiscard. b 60. d 87. V Barton and Manfield w Cleasby *Ripon* 91–93

HEWITT, David John. b 40. d 68. V Chew Magna w Dundry *B&W* 88–93

HINGLEY, Christopher James Howard. b 48. d 80. Zimbabwe from 87

HOLDSWORTH, Ian Scott. b 52. d 81. P-in-c S Leigh *Ox* 84–89

HOWARD, David William. b 43. d 67. Jamaica from 72

HUGHES, Alan. b 34. d 60. USA from 76

HULETT, Mrs Janet Elizabeth Mary. b 48. d 91. NSM Broadwater St Mary *Chich* 91–95

HUMPHRIS, Richard. b 44. d 72. TV Kippax w Allerton Bywater *Ripon* 89–93

HUXLEY, William Thomas. b 31. d 63. R Kirby-le-Soken w Gt Holland *Chelmsf* 86–87

INGLEDEW, Peter David Gordon. b 48. d 78. Perm to Offic *Chich* from 93

IZZARD, Susan Amanda. b 59. d 87. C Handsworth St Jas *Birm* 89–91; Asst Chapl Qu Eliz Hosp Birm 90–91

JAMES, Gareth Hugh. b 40. d 66. rtd 93

KEEFER, John Samuel. b 46. d 72. Switzerland from 86

KING, Noel Quinton. b 22. d 50. Uganda from 55

KING, Tony Christopher. b 62. d 86. C Chingford SS Pet and Paul *Chelmsf* 92–93

LAWSON, David McKenzie. b 47. d 76. R Smithfield St Bart Gt *Lon* 91–93

LEONARD, Stanley Gwyn. b 15. d 41. Hon C Trevethin *Mon* 84–87

LITTLEWOOD, John Edward. b 50. d 75. Hon C Stoke Climsland *Truro* 89–91

LLOYD, Michael Francis. b 57. d 84. Chapl Ch Coll Cam 90–94

LUTHER, Stuart Frank. b 26. d 69. Hon C Romsey *Win* 72–90

MacQUAIDE, Arthur John Allan. b 13. d 38. rtd 80

MANTON, Paul Arthur. b 45. d 77. Ind Chapl *Lon* 80–87

MAPPLEBECKPALMER, Richard Warwick. b 32. d 58. USA from 88

MARTIN, Robin Hugh. b 35. d 58. rtd 93

MORRISON, John. b 18. d 76. Hon C Dundee St Martin *Bre* 82–92

MOUNTFORD, John. b 55. d 78. Australia 91–94

MUMFORD, Albert Edward. b 47. d 87. C Burbage w Aston Flamville *Leic* 91–94

MUMFORD, Dr David Bardwell. b 49. d 75. NSM Calverley *Bradf* 86–92

MYERS, Paul Henry. b 49. d 77. V Milton *Lich* 87–92

NEAL, Alan. b 27. d 84. R Annan *Glas* 86–94; R Lockerbie 86–94

NEALE, Alan James Robert. b 52. d 77. USA from 88

NELSON, Olive Margaret. b 21. dss 52. Rtd 82

NEWSON, John David. b 32. d 65. Lect Ch Ch Coll Cant 65–80

PALMER, Derek James. b 54. d 79. CF 83–92

PATON, Ian Fisher. b 13. d 38. Australia since 67

PEASTON, Canon Monroe. b 14. d 38. Rtd 84; USA from 84

PECK, Trevor Paul Owen. b 47. d 72. V Burgh le Marsh *Linc* 86–87; R Bratoft w Irby-in-the-Marsh 86–87

PHILIP, Peter Wells. b 35. d 67. New Zealand from 94

POWE, Roger Wayne. b 46. d 76. Asst Chapl Hurstpierpoint Coll Hassocks 81–90

PRATT, Basil David. b 38. d 67. CF 70–93

QUINN, Dr Frederick. d 94. USA from 95

RHODES, David Grant. b 43. d 72. Project Worker 'Faith in Leeds' from 94

RICHARDSON, Simon John. b 56. d 84. Sweden from 91

ROBINSON, David William Clough. b 40. d 67. Hon C Woodside Park St Barn *Lon* 78–85

SAYER, John Martin. b 35. d 61. USA from 78

SHIPLEY, Christopher John. b 44. d 73. Perm to Offic *York* 90–93

SIMONS, Mark Anselm. b 38. d 65. V Gt and Lt Driffield *York* 78–93

SKELTON, Melvyn Nicholas. b 38. d 64. Lic to Offic *St E* from 78

SMITH, Martin Lee. b 47. d 70. USA from 81

STAVELEY-WADHAM, Robert Andrew. b 43. d 81. Perm to Offic *Ely* from 88

STEPHENS-WILKINSON, Patricia Ann. b 45. d 89. NSM Machen *Mon* 89–93

SWALLOW, Robert Andrew. b 52. d 78. TV Fareham H Trin *Portsm* 90–92

THURSTON-SMITH, Trevor. b 59. d 86. C Horninglow *Lich* 87–91

TURRELL, Stephen John. b 35. d 83. NSM Addington *S'wark* 85–92

TYLER, Paul Graham Edward. b 58. d 83. V Esh *Dur* 89–92; V Hamsteels 89–92

VAN GORDER, Lloyd Franklin. b 11. d 73. Perm to Offic *Portsm* from 79

WAITE, Julian Henry. b 47. d 72. Chapl HM Pris Blantyre Ho from 90

WAKERELL, Richard Hinton. b 55. d 84. V Rickerscote *Lich* 93

WALLING, Mrs Caroline. b 47. d 86. Saudi Arabia from 94

WALLIS, Paul Justin. b 65. d 90. P-in-c Southsea St Pet *Portsm* 93–94

WANN, Canon Denis Francis. b 27. d 56. Australia from 95

WEDGWOOD GREENHOW, Stephen John Francis. b 57. d 84. USA from 87

WILBRAHAM, David. b 59. d 88. C St Helens St Helen *Liv* 91–93

WILTSHIRE, Robert Michael. b 50. d 89. NSM Droitwich Spa *Worc* from 89

WINSOR, Anthony Geoffrey. b 56. d 87. Barnardo's CANDL Project 88–89

ORDINATIONS TO THE DIACONATE
AT MICHAELMAS 1995

BARGE, David Robert. b 45. S Dios Minl Tr Scheme 92. **d** 95. NSM Westfield *B & W* from 95. *Westhill House, Wells Road, Radstock, Bath BA3 3SA* Mendip (01761) 433787

BARRETT, Mrs Rachel Jeanne Alexandra. b 56. Ex Univ BA78 PGCE79. SW Minl Tr Course 92. **d** 95. NSM Ex St Mark *Ex* from 95. *The Vicarage, 19 The Mede, Exeter EX4 8ED* Exeter (01392) 467552

BEADLE, Mrs Lorna. b 40. NE Ord Course DipHE95. **d** 95. C Ashington *Newc* from 95. *9 Arundel Square, Ashington, Northd NE63 8AW* Ashington (01670) 816467

BEETY, Arthur Edward. b 38. Sheff Univ BA60. Cant Sch of Min 92. **d** 95. NSM Cobham w Luddesdowne and Dode *Roch* from 95. *25 Golf Links Avenue, Gravesend, Kent DA11 7PA* Gravesend (01474) 534820

BLAKE, Mrs Margaret. b 48. Open Univ BA87. S'wark Ord Course 92. **d** 95. NSM Farnham *Guildf* from 95. *20 Willow Park, Ash, Aldershot, Hants GU12 6RD* Aldershot (01252) 25020

BOOYS, Mrs Susan Elizabeth (Sue). b 56. Bris Univ BA78 LMH Ox PGCE79. St Alb and Ox Min Course 92. **d** 95. *49 Faringdon Road, Stanford in the Vale, Faringdon, Oxon SN7 8NN* Stanford in the Vale (01367) 710251

BRIXTON, Miss Corinne Jayne. b 63. Ex Univ BSc84. Wycliffe Hall Ox BTh95. **d** 95. C Leytonstone St Jo *Chelmsf* from 95. *86 Mornington Road, Leytonstone, London E11 3DX* 0181-539 3935

BUCKLEY, John. b 42. **d** 95. C Macclesfield Team Par *Ches* from 95. *4 Harvest Road, Macclesfield, Cheshire SK10 2LH*

CHALKLEY, Andrew William Guy. b 64. **d** 95. C Liskeard, St Keyne, St Pinnock, Morval etc *Truro* from 95. *1 Maddever Crescent, Liskeard, Cornwall PL14 3PT* Liskeard (01579) 342136

CHAPMAN, Mrs Margaret. b 34. Univ Coll Lon BA72 Qu Mary Coll Lon MA74. E Anglian Minl Tr Course 94. **d** 95. NSM Theydon Bois *Chelmsf* from 95. *31 Loughton Way, Buckhurst Hill, Essex IG9 6AS* 0181-505 2188

EDEN, Grenville Mervyn. b 37. Bris Univ BA58 Lon Univ MPhil78. Ox Min Course 88. **d** 95. NSM Burnham w Dropmore, Hitcham and Taplow *Ox* from 95. *Langdale, Grays Park Road, Stoke Poges, Slough SL2 4JG* Slough (01753) 525962

EDWARDS, David John. b 60. Loughb Univ BA81 Homerton Coll Cam PGCE82. CA Tr Coll 86. **d** 95. C High Ongar w Norton Mandeville *Chelmsf* from 95. *101 Longfields, Ongar, Essex CM5 9DE* Ongar (01277) 362500

FENTON, Miss Penelope Ann (Penny). b 41. Leic Univ BSc64. Cant Sch of Min 92. **d** 95. NSM Eastling w Ospringe and Stalisfield w Otterden *Cant* from 95. *9 Brogdale Road, Faversham, Kent ME13 8SX* Faversham (01795) 536366

FORD (nee HARRISON-WATSON), Mrs Carole. b 44. Reading Univ BSc66 St Martin's Coll Lanc PGCE79. Carl Dioc Tr Inst 92. **d** 95. NSM Windermere *Carl* from 95. *Acre Lodge, Bridge Lane, Troutbeck, Windermere, Cumbria LA23 1LA* Windermere (015394) 42670

FRENCH, Michael John. b 37. W of England Minl Tr Course 92. **d** 95. NSM Cheltenham St Pet *Glouc* from 95. *8 Alexandria Walk, Cheltenham, Glos GL52 5LG* Cheltenham (01242) 236661

GAMBLE, Ronald George. b 41. Cant Sch of Min 92. **d** 95. NSM Loose *Cant* from 95. *18 Copper Tree Court, Maidstone, Kent ME19 9RW* Maidstone (01622) 747125

GARRETT, Ms Celia Joy. b 60. RGN91 RM85. Cant Sch of Min 92. **d** 95. NSM S Ashford St Fran *Cant* from 95. *St Francis House, Cryol Road, Ashford, Kent TN23 5AS* Ashford (01233) 625555

GAUNT (nee COTTELL), Mrs Avril Jane. b 50. SRN72 SCM74 Lon Univ DipNursing81. S Dios Minl Tr Scheme 92. **d** 95. NSM Yatton Moor *B & W* from 95. *The Chalet, Kenn Road, Kenn, Clevedon, Avon BS21 6TR* Clevedon (01275) 875992

GAVED, Kenneth John Drew. b 31. Local NSM Course 92. **d** 95. C W Wickham St Jo *S'wark* from 95. *42 Queensway, West Wickham, Kent BR4 9ER* 0181-462 4326

GLOVER, Judith Rosalind. b 53. NE Ord Course DipHE95. **d** 95. C Glendale Gp *Newc* from 95. *St Gregory's House, 20 Ryecroft Way, Wooler, Northd NE71 6BP* Wooler (01668) 281495

GODDARD, Giles William. b 62. Clare Coll Cam MA84. S'wark Ord Course 92. **d** 95. C N Dulwich St Faith *S'wark* from 95. *11 Hinckley Road, London SE15 4HZ* 0171-732 0879 Fax 403 3827

GOLDING, Neil Christopher. b 47. Warw Univ BA69. S'wark Ord Course 92. **d** 95. C Mitcham Ascension *S'wark* from 95. *44 Vale Road, Mitcham, Surrey CR4 1NN* 0181-679 9329

GRIFFITHS, Mrs Jean Rose. b 36. Avery Hill Coll TCert56. S'wark Ord Course 93. **d** 95. NSM Charlton St Luke w H Trin *S'wark* from 95; Asst Chapl HM Pris Brixton from 95. *90 Maryon Road, London SE7 8DJ* 0181-317 7467

HALE (nee McKAY), Mrs Margaret McLeish (Greta). b 37. RN76. W of England Minl Tr Course 92. **d** 95. NSM Bream *Glouc* from 95. *14 Meadow Walk, Sling, Coleford, Glos GL16 8LR* Dean (01594) 834919

HAMIL, Sheila. b 49. TCert71. NE Ord Course DipHE95. **d** 95. NSM Wallsend St Luke *Newc* from 95. *5 Kings Road South, Wallsend, Tyne & Wear NE28 7QT* 0191-263 2371

HARE, Christopher Sumner. b 49. Solicitor 73. W of England Minl Tr Course 92. **d** 95. NSM Saltford w Corston and Newton St Loe *B & W* from 95. *The Cottage, 84 Norman Road, Saltford, Bristol BS18 3BJ* Saltford (01225) 873510

HARRIS (nee LEE), Mrs Rebecca Susan. b 62. Man Univ BA85 S Glam Inst HE 86. Trin Coll Bris DipHE95. **d** 95. C Cirencester *Glouc* from 95. *51A Welldon Crescent, Harrow, Middx HA1 1QP* 0181-863 5721

HART, Mrs Gillian Mary (Gill). b 57. Sheff City Poly BA79. Carl Dioc Tr Inst 92. **d** 95. C Burgh-by-Sands and Kirkbampton w Kirkandrews etc *Carl* from 95. *192 Ireleth Road, Askam-in-Furness, Cumbria LA16 7DP* Dalton-in-Furness (01229) 465068

HOLDEN, Mark Noel. b 61. Collingwood Coll Dur BA82 Edin Univ CQSW85 Warw Univ TCert93. Qu Coll Birm 93. **d** 95. C Old Brumby *Linc* from 95. *32 Alvington Road, Scunthorpe, S Humberside DN16 2HD* Scunthorpe (01724) 840616

HOLMES, Brian. b 41. NE Ord Course DipHE95. **d** 95. NSM Darlington St Matt and St Luke *Dur* from 95. *24 Coniston Street, Darlington, Co Durham DL3 6DJ* Darlington (01325) 354669

HORNE, Dr Brian Edward. b 37. CEng68 MRAeS68 MIEE68 EurIng92 Lon Univ BSc62 PhD78. W of England Minl Tr Course 92. **d** 95. NSM Cheltenham St Mark *Glouc* from 95. *87A Rowanfield Road, Cheltenham, Glos GL51 8AF* Cheltenham (01242) 236786

HUGHES, Denis Charles. b 27. Local NSM Course 92. **d** 95. C S Merstham *S'wark* from 95; Asst Chapl E Surrey Hosp Redhill from 95. *1 South Close Green, Merstham, Redhill RH1 3DU* Merstham (01737) 642652

IVES, Raymond Charles. b 27. St Mark & St Jo Coll Lon CertEd50. Local NSM Course 92. **d** 95. C Croydon St Pet *S'wark* from 95. *60 Windermere Road, West Wickham, Kent BR4 9AW* 0181-777 4956

JENKINS, Alan David. b 60. Bris Poly BA83 Wolv Poly DipTM87 DipMP90. ASCAT DipApTh85 Wycliffe Hall Ox 93. **d** 95. C Tunbridge Wells St Jas w St Phil *Roch* from 95. *3 Andrews Close, Tunbridge Wells, Kent TN23 PA* Tunbridge Wells (01892) 531297

JOHNSON, Margaret Joan (Meg). b 41. S'wark Ord Course 92. **d** 95. NSM Sanderstead St Mary *S'wark* from 95. *117 Church Road, London SE19 2PR* 0181-653 5322

JOHNSTON, William Malcolm. b 48. St Alb and Ox Min Course 92. **d** 95. *59 Queensway, Banbury, Oxon OX16 9NF* Banbury (01295) 263542

KIMBER, Mrs Hazel Olive. b 33. Lon Univ CertEd73. Local NSM Course 92. **d** 95. C W Dulwich Em *S'wark* from 95. *18 Michaelston House, Kingswood Estate, London SE21 8PX* 0181-670 5298

LEE, Mrs Anne Louise. b 65. St Jo Coll Nottm BTh90 Wycliffe Hall Ox 94. **d** 95. C Wembley St Jo *Lon* from 95. *50 Fairfield Crescent, Edgware, Middx HA8 9AH* 0181-952 1342

LITJENS, Shan. b 55. **d** 95. C Fareham SS Pet and Paul *Portsm* from 95. *61 Oak Road, Fareham, Hants PO15 5HH*

LLOYD, William Geoffrey. b 48. Man Univ BA70. Oak Hill Th Coll 92. **d** 95. C Plaistow St Mary *Roch* from 95. *31 Fairfield Road, Bromley BR1 3QN* 0181-464 2181

McCARTHY, Miss Sandra Ellen. b 56. ARCM75 FRCO77 GRNCM78 Man Univ BMus77 Golds Coll Lon PGCE79. S'wark Ord Course 92. **d** 95. C Beckenham St Geo *Roch* from 95. *2 Durban Road, Beckenham, Kent BR3 4EZ* 0181-663 1706

McDERMOTT, Christopher Francis Patrick. b 54. Southeastern Coll USA BA84 Wheaton Coll Illinois MA87. E Anglian Minl Tr Course. **d** 95. C Gt Ilford SS Clem and Marg *Chelmsf* from 95. *25 Valentines Road, London IG1 4RZ* 0181 518 3982

MANNING, Adrian Peter. b 63. **d** 95. C Oxhey All SS *St Alb* from 95. *14 The Hoe, Watford WD1 5AY* 0181-420 1580

MARWOOD, Timothy John Edmonds (Tim). b 51. Whitelands Coll Lon CertEd72 Open Univ BA89 Lon Inst of Educn MA91. S'wark Ord Course 92. **d** 95. NSM Putney St Mary *S'wark* from 95. *54 Eversleigh Road, London SW11 5XA* 0171-223 0510

MERCER, Nicholas. b 49. **d** 95. C Northwood Hills St Edm *Lon* from 95. *London Bible College, Green Lane, Northwood, Middx HA6 2UW*

MOORE, Ms Arlene. b 64. Dundee Univ BSc87 Aber Coll of Educn PGCE90. CITC BTh95. **d** 95. C Portadown St Mark *Arm* from 95. *115 Brownstown Road, Portadown, Craigavon, Co Armagh BT62 3PZ* Portadown (01762) 335562

MUGRIDGE, Mrs Gloria Janet. b 45. R Holloway Coll Lon BA66 Bedf Coll Lon DSocStuds67. S Dios Minl Tr Scheme 90. **d** 95. NSM Dorchester *Sarum* from 95; Asst Chapl Weymouth Coll from 95. *63 Syward Close, Dorchester, Dorset DT1 2AN* Dorchester (01305) 269203

NELSON, Julie. b 52. St Aid Coll Dur BA73. SW Minl Tr Course 92. **d** 95. NSM Tavistock and Gulworthy *Ex* from 95. *21 Deer Park Road, Tavistock, Devon PL19 9HG* Tavistock (01822) 612736

NICHOLSON, Gary. b 62. BA91. Cranmer Hall Dur 91 NE Ord Course DipHE95. **d** 95. C Whitworth w Spennymoor *Dur* from 95. *14 Front Street, Helmington Row, Crook, Co Durham DL15 0RY* Crook (01388) 765266

NORMAN, Andrew Robert. b 63. Newc Poly DMS90 Univ Coll Ox BA84 Newc Poly 89 Selw Coll Cam BA94. Ridley Hall Cam CTM94. **d** 95. France *Eur* from 95. *St Michael's Church, 5 rue D'Aguesseau, Paris 75008, France* Paris (1) 47 42 70 88 Fax 47 42 70 11

OBIORA, Arthur Cuenyem. b 42. Local NSM Course 92. **d** 95. C Hatcham St Cath *S'wark* from 95. *15 Besson Street, London SE14 5AE* 0171-732 1065

PARKINSON, Nicholas John (Nick). b 46. FCCA75 Cranfield Inst of Tech MBA85. St Alb Minl Tr Scheme 92. **d** 95. NSM Woburn Sands *St Alb* from 95. *Thornbank House, 7 Church Road, Woburn Sands, Milton Keynes MK17 8TE* Milton Keynes (01908) 583397

PATCH, Simon John. b 63. Aus Nat Univ BA87. Chich Th Coll BTh95. **d** 95. C Ifield *Chich* from 95. *2 Lychgate Cottage, Ifield Street, Ifield, Crawley, W Sussex RH11 0NN*

PHILP (nee NOBLE), Mrs Ann Carol. b 42. Sarum Dioc Tr Coll CertEd63 Southn Univ MA(Ed)89 MIPD. S Dios Minl Tr Scheme. **d** 95. Chapl Sarum Cathl *Sarum* from 95; Dir Sarum Chr Centre from 95. *55 The Close, Salisbury SP1 2EL* Salisbury (01722) 323554 Fax as telephone

PRICE, Dr Roland Kendrick. b 41. Cam Univ MA64 Essex Univ PhD69. St Alb and Ox Min Course CBTS95. **d** 95. *19 Station Road, Cholsey, Oxon OX10 9PT* Cholsey (01491) 65199

RADCLIFFE, Eileen Rose (Rosie). b 54. Carl Dioc Tr Inst 92. **d** 95. C Lowther and Askham *Carl* from 95. *The Rectory, Lilac House, Lowther, Penrith, Cumbria CA10 2HH* Hackenthorpe (01931) 712277

RAINE, Alan. b 49. MIPD93. NE Ord Course DipHE95. **d** 95. NSM Jarrow *Dur* from 95. *49 Brixham Crescent, Jarrow, Tyne & Wear NE32 3SL* 0191-489 3042

RAWSON, Christopher Derek. b 39. Ox Min Course CBTS95. **d** 95. *Little May, Broadwell, Lechlade, Glos GL7 3QS* Filkins (01367) 860255

READ, Nicholas John (Nick). b 59. Keble Coll Ox BA81 MSc82 MA85. Ox Min Course 92. **d** 95. *54 The Green, Charlbury, Oxford OX7 3QB* Charlbury (01608) 811374

ROBINSON, Peter John Alan. b 61. St Jo Coll Cam BA83. St Jo Coll Dur BA92. **d** 95. C N Shields *Newc* from 95. *24 Cleveland Road, North Shields, Tyne & Wear NE29 0NG* 0191-258 0554

ROGERS, Mrs Pamela Rose. b 46. Keswick Hall Coll CertEd68. S Dios Minl Tr Scheme 92. **d** 95. C Axbridge w Shipham and Rowberrow *B & W* from 95. *28 Beech Road, Shipham, Winscombe, Avon BS25 1SB* Winscombe (01934) 842685

SAVILLE, Andrew. b 66. Worc Coll Ox BA88. Wycliffe Hall Ox DipTh MPhil. **d** 95. C Tonbridge SS Pet and Paul *Roch* from 95. *12 Salisbury Road, Tonbridge, Kent TN10 4PB* Tonbridge (01732) 357205

SEAMAN, Christopher Robin. b 34. Solicitor 62 St Jo Coll Ox BA58 MA74. Ox Min Course 92 St Alb and Ox Min Course 94. **d** 95. *6 Chaucer Court, Ewelme, Oxford OX10 6HW* Wallingford (01491) 834157

SEARLE, Dr John Francis. b 42. FRCA70 FRSM84 Lon Univ MB, BS66. SW Minl Tr Course 92. **d** 95. NSM Ex St Leon w H Trin *Ex* from 95. *8 Thornton Hill, Exeter EX4 4NS* Exeter (01392) 432153

SHACKELL, Daniel William. b 42. Local NSM Course 92. **d** 95. C Streatham St Leon *S'wark* from 95. *194 Crowborough Road, London SW17 9PF* 0181-767 4517

SHEPHERD, Thomas. b 52. SRN74 Man Univ BA79 Didsbury Coll Man PGCE83. N Ord Course 92. **d** 95. C Baguley *Man* from 95. *39 Dalebrook Road, Sale, Cheshire M33 3LD* 0161-905 1219

STODDART, Dr David Easton. b 36. MIMechE66 CEng66 FIMgt72 FIQA76 HND57 K Coll Dur BSc60 PhD66. W of England Minl Tr Course 92. **d** 95. NSM Stroud H Trin *Glouc* from 95. *Dunelm, Pinfarthings, Amberley, Stroud, Glos GL5 5JJ* Stroud (01453) 833028

SUTTON, Philip Frank. b 55. Lon Univ HND76. St Alb and Ox Min Course CBTS95. **d** 95. *19 Ashlong Road, Marston, Oxford OX3 0NH* Oxford (01865) 750904

SWANTON, John Joseph. b 61. Bradf and Ilkley Coll BA84 MCIH89 MRSH95. S Dios Minl Tr Scheme 92. **d** 95. NSM Shalford *Guildf* from 95. *43 The Moorings, Headley Road, Grayshott, Hindhead, Surrey GU26 6SD* Hindhead (01428) 607397

TYLER, Alison Ruth. b 51. Keele Univ BA74 Birm Univ DipSocWork78 CQSW78. S'wark Ord Course 93. **d** 95. NSM Hatcham St Cath *S'wark* from 95. *75 Erlanger Road, London SE14 5TQ* 0171-207 0756

URSELL, David John. b 45. R Agric Coll Cirencester NDA70 MRAC70. SW Minl Tr Course 92. **d** 95. NSM Dolton *Ex* from 95. *Aller Farm, Dolton, Winkleigh, Devon EX19 8PP* Dolton (01805) 4414

WALKLATE, Keith. b 46. FCIB MIEx FRSA. Ox Min Course 92. **d** 95. *Holly Tree House, 17 Old Glebe, Upper Tadmarton, Banbury, Oxon OX15 5TH* Swalcliffe (01295) 780273

WELLS, Jo Bailey. b 65. CCC Cam BA87 Minnesota Univ MA90 St Jo Coll Dur BA92. Cranmer Hall Dur BA92 DMinlStuds93. **d** 95. Chapl Clare Coll Cam from 95. *Clare College, Cambridge CB2 1TL* Cambridge (01223) 333229

WEST, Miss Caroline Elisabeth. b 61. RGN84. Wycliffe Hall Ox DipMin95. **d** 95. C Eastrop *Win* from 95. *19 Beaulieu Court, Riverdene, Basingstoke, Hants RG21 2DQ*

WILCOX, David Thomas Richard. b 42. **d** 95. C Bris St Mary Redcliffe w Temple etc *Bris* from 95. *2 Colston Parade, Redcliffe, Bristol BS1 6RA* Bristol (0117) 926 0587

CLERGY WHO HAVE DIED SINCE
THE LAST EDITION

A list of clergy who have died since 31 July 1993, when the compilation of the 1993/94 edition was completed. The month and year of death (if known) are recorded with each entry.

ADAMS, John Wrigley 10/93
AINGER, John Allen 10/93
AIRNE, Charles Clement Wallace 08/95
ALBIN, Hugh Oliver 02/95
ALDIS, Brian Cyril 11/94
ALEXANDER, Ernest William 09/93
ALFORD, John Richard 02/95
ALLDRED, Kenneth 07/95
ALLENBY, David Howard
  Nicholas 02/95
ALLISON, William Gordon 11/94
ANDREWS, Wilfrid Seymour 01/94
ARMITSTEAD, Geoffrey Arthur
  Dymoke 05/95
ARMSTRONG, James Irwin 10/94
ARNOTT, Arthur Frederick 05/94
ASH, Leslie Paul (Brother
  Timothy) 09/93
ASHTON, Patrick Thomas 04/94
ASHWORTH, James George
  Brooks 01/95
ASTON, Denys Gallen 11/94
ATKINSON, Kenneth 04/94
ATTERBURY, Ernest Harold 05/95
ATTFIELD, James Andrew 07/95
AUCKLAND, Clifford Aubrey 09/93
AUSTER, Neville Walter Lucas 07/95
AYRE, Henry George 03/95
AYRE, James 11/94
BAILEY, Alan George 11/94
BAKER, Donald Shearsmith 05/95
BALL, Harold Francis Noel 06/95
BALL, Marjorie 01/95
BARDSLEY, Cyril Booth 08/95
BARKER, Wallace Hamilton 04/94
BARROW, Michael David
  Johnstone 08/94
BARSLEY, Robin Cairns 09/93
BARTLETT, George 02/95
BASDEN, Maurice Edward 07/95
BATCUP, John Aubrey 03/95
BATES, Wilfred Abel 09/95
BATESON, Bernard Lionel 09/94
BATEY, George Thomas 09/94
BAULCH, John Francis 11/93
BAZIN, Lewis Charles John
  Wadsworth 10/94
BEAMISH, John William 12/94
BEASLEY, William Isaac (Brother
  Hilary) 12/93
BEAUMONT, Albert Edward 03/94
BEAVER, Maurice John 02/94
BEBB, John Edwin 10/93
BEECH, Michael John 02/95
BEENY, Reginald Charles Morris 12/94
BEGERNIE, Doreen Myrtle 01/95
BELL, Richard Alexander 09/93
BENNETT, Arthur 10/94
BENNETT, Peter Harry Edward 10/94
BENNETT, Stanley Gilbert 12/94
BENSTED, James de Carl
  Sowerby 08/94
BEVAN, Donald Keith 08/94
BEVAN, Kenneth Graham 12/93
BEVAN, Reginald Morgan 10/94
BEVAN, Trevor 02/95
BEYNON, David Griffith 01/94
BICKERSTAFF, John Austin
  Isaac 12/94
BICKERTON, David John
  Theodore 05/94
BIGGAR, Dennis Alfred 11/93
BINDER, Charles Louis Laurence 11/94
BISHOP, Clifford Leofric Purdy 09/94
BISHOP, John Albert 03/94
BLACKLAWS, Frederick William
  (Fred) 06/94
BLAKE, Richard Arthur (Francis) 09/95

BLANCH of Bishopthorpe, (Stuart
  Yarworth) 06/94
BLINSTON, John 05/94
BLISS, Leslie John 03/94
BOGGIS, Augustine Thomas
  Isaac 06/95
BOOLE, Robert Hugh Philip 02/95
BOOTH, Alexander John (Alex) 09/93
BOOTH, Joseph Arthur Paul 05/95
BOOTH, Raymond Lister 03/95
BOTTLEY, David Thomas 02/95
BOURNE, Charles Wittwer
  Wilfrid 12/93
BOWEN, Glyn 01/94
BOWEN, Howard Charles
  Campbell 06/95
BOWEN, Lawrence 09/94
BOWHILL, Allan Harold Leslie 07/95
BOWMAN, George Henry
  Lindsay 03/94
BOXLEY, John Edwin 04/94
BOYLE, Terence Robert (Terry) 03/94
BRABY, Peter 07/94
BRACK, Christopher Francis 09/93
BRADBROOKE, Edward 09/94
BRAMLEY, Charles Edward 04/95
BREE, Reginald Hooper 05/94
BRETT, Donald Angus Adair 03/94
BRIGGS, Herbert 01/94
BRIGGS, Ralph Irvin 02/95
BRINSMEAD, Keith 12/93
BROACKES, Ronald Reginald 10/93
BROADHEAD, Malcolm Keith 04/95
BROOKES, Albert 07/95
BROOKS, George Edward
  Thomas 07/95
BROOKS, Leslie Frederick 03/95
BROOMFIELD, Frederick Harry 07/94
BROWN, Denis Arthur Whitlock 12/94
BROWN, Ernest Frederick
  Leonard 05/94
BROWN, Howard Miles 03/94
BROWN, John 01/95
BROWN, John Simpson 10/94
BROWN, Laurence Ambrose 02/94
BROWN, Lawrence Richard 03/95
BROWN, Richard 03/94
BROWNING, George Henry 01/94
BRUNNER, William Thomas 12/94
BUCKMASTER, Cuthbert Harold
  Septimus 12/94
BULL, Albert Henry 11/94
BULLOCK, Florence Mabel
  Prudence 05/95
BURNESS, John Alfred 06/94
BURTON, Douglas Harry 11/94
BURTON, Philip 02/94
BURWELL, Peter William Gale 09/95
BUSTON, Dudley Graham 11/93
BUTCHER, Norman 11/94
BUTLER, John Kenneth 03/94
BUTLIN, Claude Charles Jack 02/95
CADMAN, Reginald Hugh 09/95
CAIN, Richard Douglas 01/95
CAMPBELL, Stuart 01/95
CANE, Peter Geoffrey 04/94
CANHAM, John Rowland
  Brindley 09/94
CANNING, Robert Kingswood 05/95
CARBERRY, Robin Linton 07/95
CARNES, Gerald Lambton 12/93
CARR, Bernard John Bedford 03/95
CARR, John Mabey 10/94
CASSON, Donald Trench 10/93
CASSON, Frank Alfred 03/94
CASTLEDINE, John 05/94
CATLING, Charles Skene 11/93
CAUDWELL, Cyril 10/94

CAWTHORNE, Henry Howarth 12/93
CHALLENGER, Cyril George 07/94
CHAMBERLAIN, Roy 02/94
CHAMBERS, Roland Arthur
  Blake 06/94
CHAMIER, Peter Lewis
  Deschamps 08/94
CHAPMAN, David 09/93
CHARLES, Jack William 06/94
CHARMAN, Arthur Ernest 09/93
CHARNLEY, John Trevor 03/94
CHEETHAM, Gilbert Stanley 03/95
CHEVERTON, David 07/95
CHIDZEY, Leonard Whitehead 03/94
CHIGNELL, Wilfred Rowland 01/94
CHILDS, Julie Mary 08/95
CHILDS, Stanley Herbert 06/95
CHIPPINGTON, George Ernest 01/95
CHIVERS, Thomas Harry (Tom) 07/94
CHURCH, Howard Joseph 03/95
CLARE, Arthur Hargreaves 03/94
CLAREY, Harry 03/95
CLARK, Douglas Austin 01/94
CLARK, Vivian George 09/93
CLARKE, Arthur 07/94
CLARKE, Leslie Reginald
  Minchin 01/95
CLARKE, Roland 04/94
CLARKE, Roy Langridge 08/95
CLATWORTHY, Thomas Donald
  Vaughan 09/93
CLIFT, John Wilfred 11/93
COLCHESTER, Halsey Sparrowe 01/95
COMERFORD, Peter Morris 02/95
CONWAY, Irvine Claude 11/93
COOKE, Alfred Hunt 03/95
COOKE, John 05/94
COOPER, Kenneth Roland (Ken) 07/95
COPELAND, Norman 01/95
COPNER, Thomas Herbert
  Woodward 03/95
CORDINGLEY, Francis Andre
  Annandale 07/95
CORNELL, Frederick William 08/95
CORNWELL, Reginald George 07/94
CORSER, Peter Robert Mosse 09/93
COTTINGHAM, Ronald
  Frederick 06/95
COTTRELL, Francis St John 11/94
COULTON-TORDOFF, Neville
  Stephen 03/95
COUND, David Bryan 02/94
COUPER, Donald George 10/94
COVENTRY, Frank 11/94
COX, Frank Allen 07/95
COX, Vernon James Frederick
  (Gideon) 07/95
COX, Wallace Francis 06/94
CRITTLE, Wilfrid 10/93
CROOK, John Michael 06/94
CROOKES, Richard John 04/95
CROOKS, John Robert Megaw 03/95
CROSS, Christopher Francis 10/93
CURTIS, Philip 11/94
d'AGUIAR, Carlos 05/94
DAMS, John Lockton 01/94
DANE, Henry Arthur 08/95
DARBY, Harold Richard 12/93
DARWIN, Oliver Maurice 02/95
DAUGHTRY, Norman 10/94
DAVID, Colin Mackie 12/93
DAVID, Edmund Watcyn Rees 02/94
DAVIDSON, George Morley 06/94
DAVIDSON, John Stuart 12/94
DAVIES, David Eldred 07/95
DAVIES, David Thomas 05/94
DAVIES, John Aubrey 07/95
DAVIES, Lawford Idwal 07/95

DAVIES, Oliver 05/94
DAVIES, Robert <u>Mark</u> 05/94
DAVIES, Roswell Morgan 06/95
DAVIES, William Kenneth (<u>Brother Edgar</u>) 04/95
DAVIES, Victor George 08/95
DAVIES, Vincent James 07/95
DAVIES, William Paul Seymour 10/94
DAWSON, George Alfred 01/94
DAWSON-WALKER, Eric Dawson 04/94
DAY, Philip Maurice 08/95
DAYBELL, Cecil John Richmond 08/94
DELEVINGNE, Gordon Gresswell 12/94
DENNIS, Peter Gwyn Morgan 04/94
DENNIS, Robert Ernest 11/94
DERBYSHIRE, Arnold Sydney 04/94
DILLISTONE, Frederick William 10/93
DINGLE, Geoffrey Philip Warren 05/95
DIXON, Aidan Geoffrey Wilson 03/94
DOBSON, Robert <u>Christopher</u> 04/94
DOBSON, Theodore Edward 12/93
DOE, William Frank 12/93
DONALD, Malcolm Collighan 01/94
DONNELLY, Arthur Ferguson 01/94
DOUGLASS, John Edward (<u>Jack</u>) 11/94
DOW, George <u>Francis</u> 01/95
DOWNING, Edward Nalder 12/94
DOWNS, Thomas Greaves 05/94
DREW, Emlyn Floyd 11/94
DRURY, Thomas Frank 11/93
DRY, John Malcolm 06/95
DUNCAN, Alexander Stewart 01/94
DUNFORD, Ernest Charles 04/94
DUNGAN, Victor Samuel 09/94
DURHAM, John Francis Langton 01/95
DUTTON, Arthur Mander 04/95
DYKES, Lawrence Gregson Fell 12/93
EARLE, Edward Ernest Maples 03/94
EASTEN, Edmund John Attlee 03/95
EASTWOOD, Dennis Townend 05/95
EDDLESTON, William 05/95
EDGINGTON, Harold James Figg 03/95
EDWARDS, David Forsyth 03/95
EDWARDS, David Idwal 04/94
EDWARDS, Ronald 08/95
ELLIOTT, Harry 09/93
ELLIOTT, Leslie Aidan 01/95
ELLIS, John George 10/94
ELLIS, Robert Charles Ross-Lewin 10/94
EMERSON, Donald Godfrey 03/94
EMRYS-JONES, John 09/94
EVA, Nigel James 04/95
EVANS, John 04/94
EVANS, John Daryll 02/95
EVANS, Richard Alan 12/93
EVASON, Andrew <u>Brian</u> 01/94
FACEY, Edward Lincoln 05/95
FARROW, Ronald (<u>Ron</u>) 07/95
FAVELL, John Walter Allen 06/94
FELSTEAD, Kenneth Walter Harry 02/94
FENTON, Albert George 09/93
FIFIELD, William Herbert 03/95
FINCH, Alfred John 11/93
FINCH, Richard <u>Michael</u> 10/94
FISHER, Ernest William 05/94
FLEMING, John Robert William 04/95
FLETCHER, Albert Reginald 11/93
FLITCROFT, John 02/94
FORD, Lionel Widdicombe 05/95
FORDHAM, James Charles Horace Adcock 12/93
FORTUNE, Eric Montague 05/94
FOSTER, John Anthony 06/95
FOWKES, Eric 02/95
FOWLE, Ian 07/95
FOX, Joseph William 09/94
FRANCIS, Roger 01/94
FRASER, John Keys 12/93
FREEMAN, William John 11/94
FREESTONE, Herbert Keith 01/95
FROGGATT, Alan 03/94
FROST, William Henry 12/94
FRY, Christopher David 12/94

FULLER, Colin Spencer 07/94
FURNIVALL, Charles Guy 08/94
GARBUTT, Arthur 08/95
GARDNER, Alfred 01/95
GARNER, Maurice Heath 12/93
GARRARD, Robert Ernest 05/95
GARRETT, William Edward Richard 03/95
GATER, William George Herbert 11/93
GATES, Peter Harvey 11/93
GEBBIE, John Hewitt 09/94
GILL, Mary Louise (<u>Sister Cecilia Mary</u>) 01/95
GITTINS, Thomas Raymond 03/95
GIVAN, Desmond George 01/94
GLASS, Edward Brown 06/95
GLASSWELL, Mark Errol 01/95
GODDARD, Christopher Robert Wynn 04/94
GODFREY, William Thomas 08/95
GODFREY-THOMAS, Cecil Stephens Godfrey 10/93
GOLLEDGE, Leonard 06/95
GOOK, Bernard William James 11/93
GORDON, Alan Rex 01/95
GOULDEN, Joseph Notley 01/94
GOULDING, Leonard William 09/94
GOW, William Masterton 06/95
GRAHAM, Geoffrey Noel 08/95
GRANGE, Tom Wilkinson 10/93
GRAY, Cyril Samuel 07/94
GRAY, George Samuel 11/93
GRAZEBROOK, Francis Michael 05/94
GREADY, Leslie 07/95
GREAVES, David Reginald 10/94
GREEN, Harry George 07/94
GREENSIDES, Leonard 11/93
GREENWAY, John Waller Harry Kelynge 11/94
GRESHAM, Eric Clifford 03/95
GRIFFITHS, Frederick Cyril Aubrey Comber 11/93
GRIFFITHS, Norman 10/94
GROSE, Reginald Ewart 09/94
GRUNEBERG, Alan Conrad 05/94
GUERNSEY, Hugh Crawford 05/95
GUINNESS, Robert Desmond 03/94
GUTHRIE, Arthur 11/93
GUY, Francis George 03/95
HABBERTON, Benjamin Walter 09/95
HACKETT, John 08/94
HADDELSEY, Charles Vincent Bernard 05/94
HADDEN, Geoffrey Paddock 08/95
HADDELSEY, Stephen Andrew 03/95
HADDOCK, Norman 05/94
HALL, Basil 10/94
HALL, Halsey Charles (<u>Charlie</u>) 02/94
HALSALL, James Campbell 03/94
HALSTEAD, Leonard 09/93
HAMILTON, O'Brien 03/95
HAMILTON, Stephen Heysham 03/95
HAMMER, Raymond Jack 01/94
HAMPTON, Cyril Herbert 04/95
HANCOCK, Michael 09/95
HAND, Charles 02/94
HARDING, Geoffrey Clarence 01/94
HARDING, Herbert <u>Collison</u> 11/94
HARDMAN, Edward Foster 02/94
HARDMAN, Harry 01/95
HARFIELD, William Charles 11/94
HARMAN, Leslie Wallace 07/95
HARMER, Gerald William Sinden 10/93
HARRINGTON, Graham Anthony 06/94
HARRISON, Alfred Tuke Priestman 08/95
HARRISON, Fred 03/95
HARTLEY, Cyril Seymour 12/94
HARTLEY, Peter Harold Trahair 02/94
HASTE, Rowland Herbert 12/93
HASTIE-SMITH, Ruthven Carruthers 12/93
HATTON, George Ockleston 06/94
HAUGHTON, Thomas George 01/95
HAYNES, Frederick Charles Ronald 04/94

HAYTHORNTHWAITE, William 08/94
HEADS, William Dobson 01/95
HEATLIE, James Welsh 11/93
HEAWOOD, Raymond Garth 03/95
HELLABY, Victor Richard Douglas 01/95
HENWOOD, John Henry 01/94
HEPWORTH, James Stanley 10/93
HESELTON, Peter Rodolphus 09/94
HESKETH, William Ritchie Harrison 11/94
HETHERINGTON, John Edward 07/94
HEYDON, Francis Garland William Woodard 03/94
HEYS, Sylvia 12/94
HICHENS, Thomas Sikes 10/94
HICK, Geoffrey Lockwood Allanson 05/95
HIGGINS, Leslie 02/94
HIGH, Gordon Maurice Verdun 03/94
HILL, Malcolm <u>John</u> 12/93
HILL, Richard Owen 05/95
HILLIARD, Dennis Robert Coote 01/95
HILLS-HARROP, George Douglas 07/95
HINCHLIFF, George Victor 02/94
HINDE, Richard Standish Elphinstone 02/95
HINES, Frank 11/94
HINKLEY, William Taylor 03/94
HOBBS, David Stanley 09/93
HODGES, Dudley Alban 10/94
HODGES, Eric Henry 10/93
HODGKINSON, John David 01/94
HODGSON, Robert Edward Stephen 11/94
HOLDEN, Hyla Rose 01/95
HOLDER, Frank 11/93
HOLMES, Charles Derek 01/95
HOLMES, Frederick William 09/94
HOOD, Kenneth Ernest 08/94
HOOPER, Charles German 03/95
HOPE, William 06/95
HOPKINS, Douglass 12/93
HOPKINS, Hugh Alexander Evan 11/94
HOPKINS, Thomas Edward 04/95
HORNE, Roger Harry 11/93
HORSLEY, Hugh Reginald 07/95
HOUGHTON, Bernard Frank 11/93
HOUNSOME, Allan George 11/94
HOWARD, Richard Leonard 04/95
HOWARD, Ronald Claude 06/95
HOWE, George Reginald 11/93
HOWELL, Kenneth Walter 09/95
HOYLE, Frederick James 02/94
HUDSON, Leslie William George 07/94
HUDSON, Wilfrid 01/94
HUGHES, Jack Griffiths 02/94
HUGHES, James Edmund Crowden 05/94
HUGHES, John George 08/94
HUMPHREYS, Owen Gwilym 07/94
HUMPHRIES, Reginald Norton 08/94
HUNT, Andrew Horton Colin 01/95
HUNT, William Warren 09/94
HUNTER, Robert Clifford 12/93
HURDLE, Thomas Vivian 10/94
HURLOW, Winston Gordon 09/93
HURST, George Herbert 06/94
HURST, Joseph Bennett 06/95
HUTCHINGS, Leslie Bloom 11/94
HUTCHINS, Charles Henry 11/94
HUTCHINSON, John Desmond 01/95
ILIFFE, Walter Richard 07/95
IRESON, Gordon Worley 03/94
ISAACSON, Cecil James 08/95
JACKSON, Cecil Thomas 12/93
JACKSON, John 06/95
JACOBS, Adrian John 11/93
JAMAL, Khalil Sany Shukry 09/93
JAMES, Alan Frederick 03/95
JARVIS, William Arthur Walter 05/94
JASPER, Arthur Thomas McLean 09/95
JEFFERY, Alfred Stephen 11/94
JENKINS, David Charles 09/94
JENKINS, Graham Llewelyn 03/94
JENKINS, Trefor Illtyd 09/94
JENKS, Patricia Anne (<u>Patsy</u>) 03/95

JOBLING, Raymond 04/95
JOHNSON, Alban Ernest
Mackenzie 05/95
JOHNSON, Hedley Wilson 10/93
JOHNSON, Robert Dunmore 01/94
JOHNSTON, David Charles 07/95
JOHNSTONE, Frederic St George
Harden 10/94
JONES, Albert 10/94
JONES, Daniel William Ellis 08/95
JONES, David Vernon 01/94
JONES, Edward Melville Royds
(Ted) 01/95
JONES, Gwyn Sproule 03/95
JONES, Jenkin Thomas Vivian 10/94
JONES, John Daniel 10/93
JONES, John Henry 05/95
JONES, Owain William 02/95
JONES, Richard 07/95
JONES, Thomas Glover 05/95
JONES, Wynne Martin Alban 01/94
JORDAN, Frederick William 07/95
JUDD, Jack Lewis 09/95
JUKES, Henry Augustus Lloyd 07/95
KAO, Peter 12/94
KAY, Thomas Kindon 01/94
KEABLE, Geoffrey 02/94
KENNABY, Noel Martin 01/94
KENNEN, Harry 07/95
KETTLE, Arthur John Clare 11/94
KILVERT, Robert Wynne (Bob) 10/93
KING, John Kenneth 09/93
KING, Leslie Richard 07/94
KING, Robert Victor 02/95
KINGSNORTH, John Sydney 10/93
KINGSTON, Walter Henry
Christopher 08/94
KINSELLA, Nigel John Andrew 10/93
KIRBY, Neville John 12/94
KIRKPATRICK, Robert 06/94
KIRKWOOD, Michael Robert
Russell 05/94
KNIGHT, John Boughton 02/94
LAIGHT, Frederick 06/95
LAMB, Philip James 04/94
LAMBURN, Roger George Patrick
(Robin) 10/93
LANGDON, Eric 08/95
LANHAM, Frederick James 07/94
LANKESTER, Joseph Posford 08/95
LARCOMBE, Leslie Duke 03/94
LATHAEN, William Alan 06/94
LAW, Geoffrey Arthur 09/95
LAWN, Geoffrey 02/95
LAWRENCE, Charles William 09/93
LAWSON, John Lawrence 04/95
LAWTON, George 10/93
LAWTON, John Arthur 04/95
LEANEY, Alfred Robert Clare 04/95
LEE, Kenneth 03/95
LEE, Leslie John 10/93
LEES, Jesse 04/95
LEONARD-WILLIAMS, David
Haigh 11/94
LEWIS, David Islwyn 02/95
LEWIS, Elvet 07/95
LEWIS, John 10/94
LEWIS, John Burrenston 12/93
LEWIS, Malcolm John 11/94
LEWIS, Philip Stacey 02/95
LEWIS, Richard Martin Lister 07/95
LEWIS, William George 09/95
LEWIS, William Herbert 03/94
LEWIS, William Meredith 06/94
LILLINGSTON-PRICE, Michael
Christopher 10/93
LISNEY, John Arthur Reginald 10/93
LITTLE, Richard Terence 09/94
LLEWELLYN, John Francis
Morgan 06/95
LLOYD, David Jones 10/94
LLOYD, James 10/93
LLOYD, Thomas Rees 01/95
LLOYD, Winston 12/94
LORD, Charles James 12/93
LORING, John Henry 06/95

LOVE, Hector William 11/93
LOVELESS, Kenneth Norman
Joseph 03/95
LOWTHER, Leslie Cyril 04/95
LOWTHER, Thomas 05/95
LUCAS, Harry McIntyre 03/95
LUMAN, Arthur Cecil Rowe 06/95
LUNT, Ronald Geoffrey 05/94
LYNCH, James Kenrick 09/94
LYON, John Richard George 02/95
McCLOGHRY, James 05/94
McCLURE, David Joseph 08/95
McCULLOCH, Donald 05/94
McCULLOCH, Robert Lewis 12/93
McDERMID, Richard Thomas
Wright 07/94
McELHINNEY, Samuel Herbert 02/95
MACGOWAN, John Boby 03/95
McGREEVY, Roy 08/95
McINTYRE, Robert Marshall 04/94
McKAY, Roy 11/93
McKEE, William Mulholland 04/95
McKIE, John David 03/94
McKINNEY, Wilson 03/95
MACKONOCHIE, Christopher 08/94
McLEAN, Douglas 04/95
MACMANAWAY, Launcelot 02/94
MacMILLAN, John Patrick 12/94
McQUINN, Wallace Steward 08/94
MADDEN, Sydney Richard
William 12/93
MADDOCK, Eric Rokeby 12/94
MADDOX, David Pugh 01/94
MADGE, Donald John 01/95
MALTBY, Keith Mason 11/94
MANDER, Ronald Charles Ridge 03/94
MANN, Brian Neville 08/94
MANN, Sydney 03/94
MAPPLEBECK, Anthony 09/94
MARRIOTT, David John 05/95
MARROW, Peter 02/94
MARSH, Ernest Henry 12/94
MARSHALL-EVANS, John 06/95
MARTIN, Albert Harold Morris
(Jimmy) 10/94
MARTIN, George Washington
Leslie 11/93
MARTIN-HARVEY, Martin 01/94
MASH, Neil Beresford 09/94
MASON, Ronald William 06/95
MASON, Walter Cecil 12/94
MATHIESON, Theodore 01/94
MATTHEWS, Charles 07/94
MATTHEWS, Hubert Samuel 06/94
MATTOCK, Donald Walter 08/95
MAUGHAM, James Reavley 10/94
MAY, Arthur Harry 06/95
MAY, Norman Gowen 09/94
MENTERN, Richard John 11/94
MILES, Frank Norman 06/94
MILES, Lawrence 10/93
MILLER, Norman Alfred Leslie 04/95
MINCHIN, Sidney Frederick 09/95
MOODY, Geoffrey Sidney 01/95
MOORE, Brian Birkett 11/93
MOORE, Ernest Roy 06/95
MOORE, Herbert Alexander
(Alec) 08/95
MOORE, Herbert Alfred Harold 04/94
MOORSE, Frank Robert 07/95
MORGAN, Evan Griffith 08/95
MORGAN, Evan Tom Parry 10/94
MORGAN, Gerallt 07/95
MORGAN, Robert Oscar Thomas 12/94
MORLEY, William Fenton 07/95
MORSON, John Basil 09/94
MORTIMER, Arthur James 06/95
MOSS, Arthur Robinson 08/95
MOSS, Barrie 03/95
MOSS, Francis Duncan 08/94
MOWLL, John Edward 09/95
MURPHY, Thomas 05/95
NEEP, Edwin Phipps 02/95
NEIGHBOUR, William 09/93
NESBITT, William Ralph 02/94
NESHAM, Robert Harold 04/95
NEWHAM, Raymond George 12/94
NEWMAN, Dennis Gerard 05/95

NEWSAM, Bernard Hugh 03/95
NICHOLAS, Gwynfryn Lloyd 06/95
NICHOLAS, William Ronald 11/93
NICHOLS, Matthew William
Hardwicke 09/95
NINHAM, Cecil Ronald 09/94
NOAKES, Harold Isaac 09/93
NOEL, Samuel Maurice 11/93
NOISE, Robin Allan 05/94
NORRIS, Edward Colston 11/93
NORRISS, Victor William 08/94
NORTH, George Lewis 09/95
NORWOOD, Christopher Leslie 01/95
NUTTALL, Robert 12/93
NYE, Charles Stanley 04/94
OAKES, Hugh Toft 07/95
OCCOMORE, Albert Ernest (Bill) 05/94
ODDIE, Samuel 11/93
OLDLAND, John Leyshon 05/95
OLIVER, Anthony Grant 07/94
O'NEIL, Thomas Arthur 05/95
ORME, John Theodore
Warrington 10/93
ORR, Nathaniel Blair 03/95
ORR, Reginald Henry Pache 09/94
OSBORN, Reginald Richardson 11/94
OWEN, George Charles 11/94
PACKER, James 10/93
PAGE, William Wilson 11/93
PAGE-WOOD, Ivan Thomas 12/93
PAINE, Ernest Liddell 08/94
PAISLEY, John Joseph 12/93
PALMER, Frank Reginald
Charles 10/93
PALMER, John Michael Joseph 06/94
PARK, Allan 01/95
PARKER, John William 07/94
PARKER, Reginald Boden 10/93
PARR, William George Hossack
Redmond 07/94
PARRY, Albert Evans 05/95
PARRY, William 06/94
PARSONS, Ernest Francis 06/94
PARSONS, Wilfred Herbert 08/95
PATTINSON, Kenneth Graham
(Ken) 10/93
PAULIN, James Marmaduke 12/93
PEACH, Sidney John Elias 06/94
PEACOCK, Hubert Henry Ernest 07/95
PEACOCK, Leslie John Frederick 01/94
PEACOCKE, Cuthbert Irvine 04/94
PECKOVER, Cecil Raymond 09/93
PEIRSON, Peter Kenneth 08/94
PEMBERTON, Thomas Warwick
Winstanley 04/94
PENWARDEN, Peter Herbert 03/95
PERRIN, Donald Barton Edward 08/94
PERRY, Harold George 05/94
PHENNA, Peter 05/95
PHILLIPS, Gordon Joshua 01/94
PHYALL, Albert Thomas 12/93
PICKARD, Francis William
James 10/93
PITCHES, Reginald Morgan 01/94
PLOWRIGHT, Ernest William 06/94
PONT, Philip Roy 01/95
POOLE, Arthur James 04/95
POSTON, Robert Charles 09/93
POTTS, Wilfred Mark Allinson 05/95
POWELL, Douglas Louis 04/94
POWELL, Edward 11/94
PRANCE, Frederick Charles Victor
(Fred) 09/94
PRECIOUS, John Robert (Bob) 12/94
PREECE, James Derick 02/94
PRESTON, John Martyn 06/95
PRICE, William Kenneth 07/95
PRICE, William Trevor 10/94
PRINCE, Hugh 01/95
PRITCHARD, Stephen Edward 12/93
PROCTOR, Cyril George Charles 12/93
PUNCHARD, Herbert Oliver 04/94
PURCELL, William Henry
Samuel 06/94
PYECROFT, Eric Stanley 11/93
RABY, Charles John 06/94
RADFORD, Maurice Frederick 07/94
RAMSAY, Jack 12/94

RANDALL, William Alfred (Bill) 09/95
RATHBONE, Norman Stanley 07/95
READING, Albert Edward 12/93
REDHEAD, Francis Edward 09/94
REED, Kathleen Jean Dorothy 12/93
REES, Hugh Lorimer Octavius 10/93
REES, John Tyssul 11/93
REEVES, Joseph Wilfred 09/94
RICHARDS, Brian Murley 02/95
RICHARDS, Derek Gordon 02/94
RICHARDS, Victor John Richard 05/94
RICHARDSON, Anne 04/95
RICHARDSON, Edward James
 Aubin 02/95
RIDGEWELL, Kenneth William 12/93
RIGBY, Ronald Robert Pierpoint 11/93
RINGWOOD, Arthur George 11/93
RITCHIE, John Brocket 10/94
RIVERS, Paul Tudor 06/94
ROBERTS, Arthur Clifford 04/95
ROBERTS, Derek Francis
 Madden 01/94
ROBERTS, Edward Thomas 04/95
ROBERTS, Francis Frederick
 Claudius 11/93
ROBERTS, Harold William 02/95
ROBERTS, Harry Benjamin 01/94
ROBERTS, John Haywood Boyd 09/93
ROBERTSON, Arthur Charles 01/95
ROBINSON, Peter Stanley 06/94
ROBSON, Andrew 04/95
RODGERS, Arthur Harold 11/93
ROE, George Henry Edward
 Talbot 05/94
ROEBUCK, Austin Vincent 11/94
ROGERS, David Eland 11/93
ROGERS, John Arnold 09/95
ROGERS, Philip Gordon 10/94
ROGERS, Vernon Donald 04/94
ROGERS, Vivian Francis Edward 02/94
ROLT, Eric Wilfrid 12/94
ROONEY, Leslie Francis 11/93
ROSE, John Spencer 09/93
ROSS, Philip James 12/93
ROUNTREE, Cecil John 05/95
ROWE, Everhard James 12/94
ROWE, Leslie Vernon 02/94
ROWLAND-SMITH, Albert 08/95
ROWLANDS, John Llewellyn 03/95
ROYLE, Edward 12/94
RUCK, William 08/94
RUDDOCK, Reginald Arthur 01/95
RUSBY, Frank Edward 01/94
RUTTER, William Ralph 12/93
RYAN, Michael Dennis George
 Conybeare 09/95
RYDER-JONES, William Henry 01/95
RYE, Peter Harry 07/94
ST JOHN, Ferdinand Richard
 John 08/94
SAMPSON, Frank 02/94
SANDERS, Raymond Joseph 02/94
SANDERSON, Howard Walter 05/95
SANDFORD, Edward Noel
 Teulon 07/94
SAYER, Cecil Albert 04/95
SCHAUFELBERGER, Johan
 Henry 04/95
SCOTT, John Gabriel 02/95
SCRIVEN, Stanley William 01/94
SCUPHOLME, Albert Cooper 02/95
SECRETT, Ian Russell 06/95
SENAR, Howard 11/94
SERGEL, Clement Stuart 11/94
SHAMASH, Albert Saul 06/95
SHARP, Bernard 12/94
SHARP, Nevill Maurice Granville 02/94
SHARPE, Robert Nelson 03/95
SHAW, Charles Edward 12/94
SHORTT, John Buckley 02/95
SIMPER, Allan Frederick 10/93
SIMPSON, Anthony Cyril 06/94
SIMPSON, Edward 01/94
SIMPSON, John Raymond 09/93
SINKER, Michael Roy 03/94
SKUSE, Frank Richard 05/94
SMART, Alfred Ernest 10/93
SMITH, Arthur Eric 05/94

SMITH, David Lloyd 07/94
SMITH, Howard Charles 12/93
SMITH, Jack Douglas 10/94
SMITH, Kenneth Harry 11/94
SMITH, Robert 04/95
SMITH, Willie Ernest 02/95
SMYTH, William Ernest 06/95
SNOW, William Harvey 10/94
SOBEY, Haydn Norman 12/94
SOLTAU, Bernard Alick 09/94
SOUTHCOMBE, Hector George 02/95
SPARLING, Arthur Cecil 09/93
SPEERS, John Stevenson 10/94
SPENCER, Christopher John
 Edward 09/95
SPENSER UNDERHILL,
 Mervyn 01/94
SPITTLE, Ralph Edward 02/95
SPRUYT, John Harry 01/94
STANBROOK, Harry 02/94
STANFORD, Ronald John 11/93
STARLING, Cyril James 10/94
STEEDMAN, Aubrey Wyld 12/93
STEER, Frederick Arthur 08/94
STEVENSON, James Jackson 02/95
STOCKWOOD, Arthur Mervyn 01/95
STONE, John Wesley 08/95
STOUT, Trevor 01/95
STOVES, Ernest 02/95
STRACHAN, Kenneth Archibald
 Gibson 10/94
STRINGER, James Philip 04/95
STUCKEY, Frederick Walter
 (Bill) 12/93
SUTCLIFFE, Geoffrey Alan 02/94
SWINBANK, Peter 11/94
SWINDELLS, Stephen Seel
 Sherwood 02/94
TALBOT, Richard Allen 09/93
TAYLOR, Francis Oswald 09/95
TEAGE, Alan Dixon 12/94
TEMPLE, Donald Hubert 12/94
THOMAS, Benjamin Lewis 02/94
THOMAS, Cyril 06/95
THOMAS, John Albert 09/93
THOMAS, John James Absalom 02/95
THOMAS, Melvyn 10/93
THOMAS, Michael Paul 01/95
THOMAS, Philip Edward 11/94
THOMAS, Vernon Douglas
 Ronald 03/95
THOMPSON, Alfred 03/95
THOMPSON, Arthur Hugh 11/93
THOMPSON, Michael Reginald 12/93
THOMPSON, William George 10/93
THORMAN, Peter 07/94
THORNHILL, Raymond 09/93
THORNTON, Stanley John 12/93
THORP, Robert Penfold 08/95
THROWER, George 08/94
TINDALL, Edward Frederick 11/94
TIPPER, David Allen 04/94
TIRRELL, Leslie Burditt 03/95
TOMLIN, Henry Alfred 10/94
TOMLINSON, Robert Herbert 12/93
TOMPKINS, James Charles
 Harrison 04/95
TONGE, David Theophilus 01/95
TOOBY, Derrick David Johnson 02/95
TOON, Norman 01/95
TOPLEY, John Ernest Wilmot 06/94
TRANTER, Paul Trevor William 08/94
TREDENNICK, John Edwin
 Foster 09/95
TRENGOVE, Harry Christopher 02/94
TRIPPASS, William Arthur 05/95
TRODDEN, Hugh 02/94
TROTTER, Donald McIntosh 05/94
TUCKER, Maurice Grahame 05/94
TUFTON, Colin Charles Guy 07/94
TURNBULL, Colin 01/94
TURNBULL, Eric Samuel 01/95
TURNER, John Arthur 06/94
TURTLE, Malcolm 01/94
TURVEY, Raymond Hilton 07/95
TUTE, John Armytage 01/95

TYLER, Frank Cecil 10/93
TYLER-WHITTLE, Michael
 Sidney 10/94
TUTE, John Armytage 01/95
UDALL, Geoffrey Sturt 03/94
UNWIN, Percival Alexander 07/95
UNWIN, Reginald Christopher 06/94
UPRICHARD, Horace Launcelot 02/94
UPTON, Robert de Courcy
 Everard 12/94
URCH, Harold Henry 10/93
VALENTINE, Robin James 11/93
VENTON, Bertram Ernest 10/93
VERITY, Cecil Beaumont 05/95
VERNON, Michael Helm 06/94
VERRELLS, Herbert Stuart 01/95
WADDINGTON, John Albert
 Henry 11/94
WAITE, Harry 10/94
WAKE, Hugh 10/93
WAKEFORD, Victor David 05/94
WALKER, John Thomas 01/95
WALKER, Victor John 06/94
WALLACE, Marjorie Emily 05/95
WALLER, Arthur Henry
 Naunton 01/95
WALSER, David 10/93
WALSH, Lionel Ernest 02/94
WALTERS, Egerton Edward
 Farrar 08/95
WALTON, John Sidney 09/93
WANSEY, John 05/95
WARD, Charles Leslie 03/94
WARD, George Henry 07/94
WARNES, Frank William 01/95
WARREN, Michael Meade King 04/94
WARRINGTON, Clement Egbert 12/93
WARRINGTON, William Leslie 04/95
WATERSON, Harold 03/95
WATSON, Edward Vincent Cornelius
 (Ned) 09/94
WATSON, Robert Bruce Scoular
 Jameson 12/94
WATSON, Robert Leslie 03/94
WATSON, Thomas Heys 06/95
WATTS, Ronald 06/95
WAY, Winfrid Hilary 05/94
WEBSTER, James George
 William 01/94
WEIGALL, Anthony Fitzroy 08/94
WELCH, Ivor Thomas Ronald 12/93
WEST, George Edward 09/94
WEST, James 01/95
WEST, Thomas 08/95
WESTMUCKETT, John Spencer 06/94
WHITE, Basil Rowntree 10/93
WHITE, Frederick Stanley 01/94
WHITE, John Bernard Valentine 10/94
WHITE, Richard 04/94
WHITE, Thomas Arthur 09/94
WHITTAKER, George Brian 04/95
WHITWORTH, Eric Watkinson 01/95
WICKHAM, Edward Ralph 09/94
WIGAN, Bernard John 10/94
WILCOCK, Christopher John 08/95
WILCOX, David 07/95
WILKES, Thomas Clement
 Broadbery 07/95
WILKINSON, David Reginald 03/94
WILKINSON, Edward Arthur
 Hewson 02/95
WILKINSON, Joseph Henry 02/95
WILKS, Basil Worsley 09/93
WILKS, Leslie Ronald 10/93
WILLIAMS, Charles Henry 11/93
WILLIAMS, Clifford Rex 11/94
WILLIAMS, David 04/95
WILLIAMS, David Griffith 05/95
WILLIAMS, Frederick John 09/95
WILLIAMS, Kenneth Hooper 05/94
WILLIAMS, Llewelyn Owen 07/94
WILLIAMS, Robert 08/94
WILLIAMS, William David
 Conwyl 04/95
WILLIAMSON, Frank 11/93
WILLIAMSON, Reginald 01/94
WILLIS, Donald 03/95
WILMUT, Ronald William 02/94

1084

WIMBUSH, Richard Knyvet 01/94
WITHINGTON, Harold 02/94
WOLFF, Curt Heinz 01/94
WOOD, Harold George 01/94
WOOD, Thomas Patrick
  Scarborough 03/94
WOODFORD, Frank 11/93
WOODWARD, Horace James
  (Jimmy) 05/95

WOODWORTH, Gerald Mark
  David 06/94
WOOLF, William John 11/94
WOOLFENDEN, Thomas 05/94
WOOLLEY, Cyril George 08/94
WOOLLEY, William Burrell 08/95
WORSLEY, Ronald Freeman 06/95
WORT, Ernest Winstone 01/95
WRIGHT, Evan Gilbert 11/94

WRIGHT, Frederick John (Fred) 12/94
WRIGHT, Leonard John 01/95
WYMAN, Arthur Howard 12/93
WYNNE, Edward 02/94
YARKER, Francis Bospidnick 12/93
YARNOLD, Grenville Dennis 11/94
YEOMANS, Ernest Harold 08/94
YOUELL, George 01/95
YOUNG, Malcolm Ryswinn 07/94

ENGLAND AND WALES

50 miles
80km

— Provincial boundary
— Diocesan boundary
...... County boundary
• Cathedral City

SCOTLAND

IRELAND

Northumberland
NEWCASTLE

Tyne & Wear

Cumbria
CARLISLE

DURHAM
Durham

Cleveland

RIPON

North Yorkshire

YORK

BRADFORD

BLACKBURN

Lancashire

West Yorkshire
WAKEFIELD

MANCHESTER
Greater Manchester

LIVERPOOL

Merseyside

South Yorkshire

SHEFFIELD

Humberside

LINCOLN

Lincolnshire

Nottinghamshire

SOUTHWELL

DERBY

Derbyshire

CHESTER
Cheshire

Isle of Man
SODOR & MAN

Clwyd
ST ASAPH

Gwynedd

1086

NORWICH
Norfolk

ST EDMUNDSBURY
& IPSWICH
Suffolk

Norwich

ELY
Cambridgeshire

ST ALBANS
Hertfordshire
Bedfordshire

CHELMSFORD
Essex

CANTERBURY
Kent

ROCHESTER

LONDON
Greater
London

SOUTHWARK

CHICHESTER
West Sussex
East Sussex

GUILDFORD
Surrey

PETERBOROUGH
Northamptonshire

LEICESTER
Leicestershire

COVENTRY
Warwickshire

West
Midlands
BIRMINGHAM

Buckinghamshire

OXFORD
Oxfordshire

Berkshire

WINCHESTER
Hampshire

PORTSMOUTH

LICHFIELD
Staffordshire

WORCESTER

GLOUCESTER
Gloucestershire

BRISTOL

Wiltshire

SALISBURY

HEREFORD
Shropshire

Hereford &
Worcester

Avon

BATH & WELLS
Somerset

Dorset

BANGOR

Powys

SWANSEA
&
BRECON

Gwent
MONMOUTH

LLANDAFF
Mid Glam
South
Glam

West Glam

EXETER
Devon

Dyfed

ST DAVIDS

Cornwall

TRURO

The Channel Islands are annexed
to the Diocese of Winchester

The Isles of Scilly are included
in the Diocese of Truro

SCOTLAND

0 10 20 30 40 50miles
0   20   40   60   80km

— Diocesan boundary
···· Regional boundary
● Location of Cathedral

MORAY

ROSS

and

CAITHNESS

ABERDEEN
and
ORKNEY

ABERDEEN
and
ORKNEY

Shetland
Islands

Inverness

Grampian

Highland

ARGYLL

ABERDEEN
and
ORKNEY

Aberdeen ●

and

ST ANDREWS

Tayside

DUNKELD

Oban ●

THE ISLES

and

Perth

Dundee

DUNBLANE

Fife

Central

Strathclyde

Glasgow ●

Edinburgh ●

Lothian

GLASGOW

and

EDINBURGH

Borders

GALLOWAY

Dumfries and Galloway

IRELAND

ENGLAND

IRELAND

0	10	20	30	40	50miles
0	20	40	60	80km	

DIOCESES IN PROVINCE OF ARMAGH

1. CONNOR
2. DERRY AND RAPHOE
3. DOWN AND DROMORE
4. ARMAGH
5. CLOGHER
6. KILMORE, ELPHIN AND ARDAGH
7. TUAM, KILLALA AND ACHONRY

PROVINCE OF ARMAGH

PROVINCE OF DUBLIN

Londonderry
Raphoe
Belfast
Lisburn
Dromore
Downpatrick
Clogher
Armagh
Enniskillen
Sligo
Killala
Kilmore
Trim
Tuam
Dublin
Clonfert
Kildare
Killaloe
Leighlin
Kilkenny
Ferns
Limerick
Cashel
Waterford
Lismore
Cork
Cloyne
Ross

Provincial Boundary
Diocesan Boundary
National Boundary
County Boundary
● Location of Cathedral

DIOCESES IN PROVINCE OF DUBLIN

8. MEATH AND KILDARE
9. DUBLIN AND GLENDALOUGH
10. CASHEL, WATERFORD, LISMORE, OSSORY, FERNS AND LEIGHLIN
11. LIMERICK, ARDFERT, AGHADOE, KILLALOE, KILFENORA CLONFERT, KILMACDUAGH AND EMLY
12. CORK, CLOYNE AND ROSS

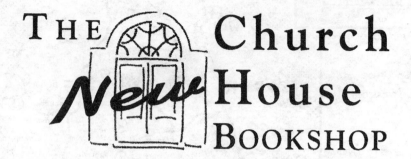